SCOTT

2005
STANDARD POSTAGE
STAMP CATALOGUE

ONE HUNDRED AND SIXTY-FIRST EDITION IN SIX VOLUMES

VOLUME 6
COUNTRIES OF THE WORLD
So-Z

EDITOR	James E. Kloetzel
ASSOCIATE EDITOR	William A. Jones
ASSISTANT EDITOR /NEW ISSUES & VALUING	Martin J. Frankevicz
VALUING ANALYST	Leonard J. Gellman
DESIGN MANAGER	Teresa M. Wenrick
IMAGE COORDINATOR	Nancy S. Martin
MARKETING/SALES DIRECTOR	William Fay
ADVERTISING	Renee Davis
CIRCULATION / PRODUCT PROMOTION MANAGER	Tim Wagner
EDITORIAL DIRECTOR/AMOS PRESS INC.	Michael Laurence

Released September 2004

Includes New Stamp Listings through the September 2004 *Scott Stamp Monthly* Catalogue Update

Copyright© 2004 by

Scott Publishing Co.

911 Vandemark Road, Sidney, OH 45365-0828

A division of AMOS PRESS, INC., publishers of *Scott Stamp Monthly, Linn's Stamp News, Coin World* and *Coin World's Coin Values.*

SCOTT PUBLISHING CO.

Specialty Series

Scott Publishing Co. produces album pages for more than 120 countries.
Scott Specialty pages are renowned for their quality and detail.
There are spaces for every major variety of postage stamp
within each country or specialty area.

Each space is identified by Scott number and many of the spaces are illustrated.
Pages are printed on one side only on chemically neutral paper
that will not harm your stamps.

Scott Specialty series pages are sold as page units only.
Binders and slipcases are sold separately.

For more information on the entire line of Scott products visit your favorite stamp dealer
or go online at:
www.amosadvantage.com

P.O. Box 828, Sidney OH 45365-0828
1-800-572-6885

AMOS
HOBBY PUBLISHING

Table of Contents

See Volume 1 for United States, United Nations and Countries of the World A-B.
See Volumes 2, 3 4, 5 for Countries of the World, C-Sl.

Volume 2: C-F
Volume 3: G-I
Volume 4: J-O
Volume 5: P-Sl

Scott Publishing Mission Statement

The Scott Publishing Team exists to serve the recreational,
educational and commercial hobby needs of stamp collectors and dealers.

We strive to set the industry standard for philatelic information and products by developing and
providing goods that help collectors identify, value, organize and present their collections.

Quality customer service is, and will continue to be, our highest priority.
We aspire toward achieving total customer satisfaction.

Copyright Notice

The contents of this book are owned exclusively by Scott Publishing Co. and all rights thereto are reserved under the Pan American and Universal Copyright Conventions.

Copyright @2004 by Scott Publishing Co., Sidney, OH. Printed in U.S.A.

COPYRIGHT NOTE

Permission is hereby given for the use of material in this book and covered by copyright if:

(a) The material is used in advertising matter, circulars or price lists for the purpose of offering stamps for sale or purchase at the prices listed therein; and

(b) Such use is incidental to the business of buying and selling stamps and is limited in scope and length, i.e., it does not cover a substantial portion of the total number of stamps issued by any country or of any special category of stamps of any country; and

(c) Such material is not used as part of any catalogue, stamp album or computerized or other system based upon the Scott catalogue numbers, or in any updated valuations of stamps not offered for sale or purchase; and

(d) Such use is not competitive with the business of the copyright owner; and

(e) Such use is for editorial purposes in publications in the form of articles or commentary, except for computer software or the serialization of books in such publications, for which separate written permission is required.

Any use of the material in this book which does not satisfy all the foregoing conditions is forbidden in any form unless permission in each instance is given in writing by the copyright owner.

Trademark Notice

The terms SCOTT, SCOTT'S, SCOTT CATALOGUE NUMBERING SYSTEM, SCOTT CATALOGUE NUMBER, SCOTT NUMBER and abbreviations thereof, are trademarks of Scott Publishing Co., used to identify its publications and its copyrighted system for identifying and classifying postage stamps for dealers and collectors. These trademarks are to be used only with the prior consent of Scott Publishing Co.

No part of this work may be reproduced in any form or by any means, electronic or mechanical, including photocopying, without permission in writing from Scott Publishing Co., P.O. Box 828, Sidney, OH 45365-0828.

ISBN 0-89487-337-7

Library of Congress Card No. 2-3301

You'll meet all kinds of interesting people inside the pages of *Scott Stamp Monthly!*

ENTERTAINING INFORMATIVE PROVOCATIVE

Every month you'll find:

- Entertaining and informative articles written by the hobby's leading authors and columnists.

- The very latest information on the world's new stamps in the Catalogue Update. Each month you get Scott numbers and photos for nearly 1,000 stamps.

- A magazine that serves an important function in the hobby, providing the latest information on new stamp issues, including illustrations and other details not available in other philatelic publications.

- Automatic enrollment into the Amos Advantage Program that can save you up to 50% off stamp supplies, accessories, supplements, books and catalogues!

12 Issues ONLY $29.95

NEW!

Scott Stamp Monthly now available online!
Go to: **www.scottonline.com**
to subscribe to our online edition!

Order online at:
www.amosadvantage.com
Call toll-free: 1-800-448-3611

write:
P.O. Box 828, Sidney, OH 45365-0828

(Offer valid only for U.S. subscribers. Canadian subscribers add $15.00 for postage. Foreign add $30.00 for postage.)

AMOS
HOBBY PUBLISHING

SCOTT

Scott Publishing Co.

SCOTT 911 VANDEMARK ROAD, SIDNEY, OHIO 45365   937-498-0802

Dear Scott Catalogue User:

Almost 200,000 value changes for the 2005 Standard catalogs!

There are almost 23,000 value changes in Volume 6 of the *2005 Scott Standard Postage Stamp Catalogue*, which covers countries of the world So-Z. The upward value trend that has been seen in the first five volumes continues as this year's Standard catalog reaches its final volume. Stamps of the Spanish area lead the way with more than 4,000 value changes, followed by Tonga, Uruguay, Switzerland, Syria, Venezuela and Sweden – each with more than a thousand changes.

The Volume 6 value changes bring the total for the 2005 Standard catalogs to more than 193,000. That's right – almost two hundred thousand value changes this year. Add to that approximately 12,000 new issues for this year (images and values). Then, we need to include the editorial changes that have been made – new major listings, new notes, improved explanations, additional values for never-hinged classic stamps, minor listings, dates of issue, and the myriad changes needed to assure consistency. Let's not forget the work that is still going on to complete the Scott stamp-scanning project. Many fresh images have been added in the Standard catalogs, leaving fewer than 3,000 images that still need to be replaced.

Western European currencies such as the euro, Swiss franc and British pound continue their strong performance, and this is reflected in many of the Volume 6 value changes. Classic and more modern stamps from strong-currency countries advance in value. And we continue to see considerable activity in the period between 1985-2000 because of the relative scarcity of modern material in today's stamp market. The huge volume of new issues that have been released in the last twenty years has made it virtually impossible for dealers to maintain comprehensive stocks of many stamps. This especially has put pressure on certain popular topical issues.

Where are the value changes in Volume 6?

There are more than 2,900 value changes for Spain proper and another 1,100 for the other Spanish areas in Volume 6. This sphere appears to be quite solid with most changes strongly upward. In classic Spain and up to the World War II period, the increases for unused material are usually in the range of 10-20 percent. A typical example is the 12-cuartos lilac stamp of 1850 picturing Queen Isabella II, Scott 2, which moves to $2,000 unused and $240 used this year, from $1,800 unused and $175 used last year. Values for back-of-the-book stamps of the same time period show the same 10-20 percent increases in value.

The stamps of Tonga have been thoroughly reviewed in the 2005 catalog, and more than 2,500 values have been upgraded. The stamp values show a very strong upward trend for issues from both the classic and more modern periods. Modern material is especially strong for sets with popular thematic content. The four-stamp set issued in 1989 featuring National Aviation, Scott 721-724, soars to $27.25 mint, never hinged and $23.50 used, from $8.90 both ways in 2004.

There are almost 3,400 value changes in the Latin American area, with the stamps of both Uruguay and Venezuela showing solid increases for 2005, usually in the range of 10-20 percent. The stamps of classic Uruguay for the first twenty years, including many minor varieties, lead the way. A good example is the inverted surcharge of the 5-centavos on 12-centavos blue coat-of-arms, Scott 24b, which climbs to $150 unused in 2005 from $45 last year. The stamps of modern Uruguay also demonstrate significant positive movement. The sheet of four issued in 1980 to celebrate the 50th anniversary of the Performing Arts Society, Scott 1060, advances in 2005 to $3 both mint, never-hinged and used, from $1.75 both ways last year.

For Venezuela, value changes begin with the stamps issued just prior to World War II and continue to the present. Upward changes are particularly strong for the period from the early 1980s to the early 1990s. Here, it is not unusual to see values double; however, there does not appear to be any particular collecting pattern to these changes. An example is the miniature sheet issued in 1986 to commemorate the 20th anniversary of the Children's Foundation, Scott 1376, which rises to $4 both mint, never hinged and used in this year's catalog, from $3 mint, never hinged and $1.25 used in 2004.

In Switzerland, the effect of the very strong Swiss franc on retail prices is clearly seen in most of the early material up to World War II. Values generally are strongly higher. The same is true for back-of-the-book values, which show the same 10-15 percent upward trend.

There are almost 1,500 value changes for Syria. It is interesting to note that these changes are split fairly evenly between stamps that were issued under French control and those issued after full Syrian independence. For the early stamps, French with surcharges for Syrian currency, the trend generally appears to be about 10-15 percent upward. Some increases are even more, such as the surcharged 6-stamp issue of 1920, Scott 25-30. This set advances to $313.45 both unused and used this year, from $244 both ways last year. For those stamps of the Syrian Arab Republic, issued between 1961-69, almost all mint, never-hinged stamps show a significant upward movement. This is true for both regular and air post stamps.

When we look at the stamps of Sweden, there are almost 1,100 value changes for 2005. For the early material and up to 1940, increases are usually in the range of 10-15 per cent. There are also scattered changes in modern issues, and they also show an upward trend. However, the strongest movement occurs in the back-of-the-book material, where the postage-due stamps lead the way. The first 11-stamp set of postage-dues, issued in 1874, Scott J1-J11, climbs to $1,172.75 in unused condition and $670.25 used in the 2005 catalog, from $908.50 unused and $516.50 used last year.

What about editorial changes for 2005?

Collectors of Spain should be happy to see some important editorial enhancements. The famous 1938 Submarine set of six stamps plus souvenir sheet, long excluded from the catalog, has now been added as Scott 605A-605G. These stamps were issued for use on a proposed submarine mail service between Barcelona and Mahon, Minorca. One voyage was made on this mail route, carrying 300 agency-prepared covers. These stamps, though they were sold at double face (which no doubt explains their previous exclusion from the Scott catalog), also were valid for ordinary mail. Values range from $5.50 for the lowest value unused or used, to $550 for the unused or used souvenir sheet. Values for the stamps never hinged are somewhat higher.

Also in Spain, the 1936-38 Revolutionary overprints issued by the Nationalist (Revolutionary) forces have been revised and expanded, with some new listings and new illustrations. Spain specialists will want to review this section carefully to see the many enhancements.

More than 100 new major numbers have been added for the 1934-43 issues of Tannu Tuva. These colorful stamps complete the Tannu Tuva listings, after which the area was incorporated into the Soviet Union, with Russian stamps being used from that point forward.

In Yemen, a new airmail major listing has been added for the 1975 75f surcharge on Yemen Scott C40, the 21b Revolution stamp.

Happy collecting,

James E. Kloetzel

James E. Kloetzel/Catalogue Editor

Acknowledgments

Our appreciation and gratitude go to the following individuals who have assisted us in preparing information included in this year's Scott Catalogues. Some helpers prefer anonymity. These individuals have generously shared their stamp knowledge with others through the medium of the Scott Catalogue.

Those who follow provided information that is in addition to the hundreds of dealer price lists and advertisements and scores of auction catalogues and realizations that were used in producing the catalogue values. It is from those noted here that we have been able to obtain information on items not normally seen in published lists and advertisements. Support from these people goes beyond data leading to catalogue values, for they also are key to editorial changes.

A special acknowledgment to Liane and Sergio Sismondo of The Classic Collector for their extraordinary assistance and knowledge sharing that has aided in the preparation of this year's Standard and Classic Specialized Catalogues.

A. R. Allison (Orange Free State Study Circle)
Arthur L.-F. Askins
Robert Ausubel (Great Britain Collectors Club)
Dr. H.U. Bantz (S. W. Africa Stamp Study Group)
John Barone (Stamptracks)
Jack Hagop Barsoumian (International Stamp Co.)
William Batty-Smith (Sarawak Specialists' Society)
Jules K. Beck (Latin American Philatelic Society)
Vladimir Berrio-Lemm (CEFIN_PANAMA)
Randall Brooksbank
Keith & Margie Brown
Mike Bush (Joseph V. Bush, Inc.)
Lawrence A. Bustillo (Suburban Stamp Inc.)
A. Bryan Camarda (University Stamp Co.)
Ronald Carlson
Tina & John Carlson (JET Stamps)
Joseph J. Cartafalsa
Richard A. Champagne
Albert F. Chang
Henry Chlanda
Richard E. Clever (Asia Philatelics)
Bob Coale
Laurie Conrad
Frank D. Correl
Andrew Cronin (Canadian Society of Russian Philately)
William T. Crowe (The Philatelic Foundation)
Tony Davis
Bob Dumaine (Sam Houston Duck Co.)
Esi Ebrani
Paul G. Eckman
Leon Finik (Loral Stamps)
Henry Fisher
Joseph E. Foley (Eire Philatelic Association)
Jeffrey M. Forster
Ernest E. Fricks (France & Colonies Philatelic Society)
Richard Friedberg
Michael A. Goldman (Regency Superior, Ltd.)
Daniel E. Grau
Fred F. Gregory
Erich E. Hamm (Philactica)
Alan Hanks
Jerone Hart (Aden & Somaliland Study Group)
John B. Head
Bruce Hecht (Bruce L. Hecht Co.)
Robert W. Hisey (Philatelic Society of Greater Southern Africa)
George W. Holschauer (Colonial Stamp Co.)
Philip J. Hughes (Croatian Philatelic Society)
Kalman V. Illyefalvi (Society for Hungarian Philately)
Michael Jaffe (Michael Jaffe Stamps, Inc.)
John I. Jamieson (Saskatoon Stamp Centre)
Peter C. Jeannopoulos
Stephen Joe (International Stamp Service)
Allan Katz (Ventura Stamp Company)
Stanford M. Katz
Lewis Kaufman
Patricia A. Kaufmann
Dr. James W. Kerr
Charles F. Kezbers
Dr. Thomas C. Kingsley
Juri Kirsimagi (Estonian Philatelic Society)
William V. Kriebel
Frederick P. Lawrence
John R. Lewis (The William Henry Stamp Co.)
Roberto Liera (AMEXFIL)
Ulf Lindahl (Ethiopian Philatelic Society)
William A. Litle

Gary B. Little (Luxembourg Collectors Club)
Pedro Llach (Filatelia Llach S.L.)
George Luzitano
Dennis Lynch
Marilyn R. Mattke
Dr. Hector R. Mena (Society for Costa Rica Collectors)
Mark S. Miller
Chuck Q. Moo
William E. Mooz
David Mordant (Postmark and Postal History Society of Southern Africa)
Gary M. Morris (Pacific Midwest Co.)
Bruce M. Moyer (Moyer Stamps & Collectibles)
Albert Olejnik
Victor Ostolaza
John E. Pearson (Pittwater Philatelic Service)
John Pedneault
Donald J. Peterson (International Philippine Philatelic Society)
Stanley M. Piller (Stanley M. Piller & Associates)
Virgil Pirvulescu
Todor Drumev Popov
Peter W. W. Powell
Stephen Radin (Albany Stamp Co.)
Ghassan D. Riachi
Omar Rodrigues
Eric Roberts
Michael Rogers (Michael Rogers, Inc.)
Jon W. Rose
Wilford H. Ross
Theodosios Sampson
Alex Schauss (Schauss Philatelics)
Jacques C. Schiff, Jr. (Jacques C. Schiff, Jr., Inc.)
Bernard Seckler (Fine Arts Philatelists)
Guy Shaw
Charles F. Shreve (Shreves Philatelic Galleries, Inc.)
Jeff Siddiqui (Pakistan Philatelic Study Circle)
Sergio & Liane Sismondo (The Classic Collector)
Christopher Smith
Jay Smith
Robert M. Spaulding (International Society for Japanese Philately)
Merle Spencer (The Stamp Gallery)
Richard Stark
Richard M. Stevens
Peter Thy (Philatelic Society for Greater Southern Africa)
Scott R. Trepel (Siegel Auction Galleries, Inc.)
Xavier Verbeck (American Belgian Philatelic Society)
Philip T. Wall
Daniel C. Warren
Richard A. Washburn
Giana Wayman (Asociacion Filatélica de Costa Rica)
William R. Weiss, Jr. (Weiss Auctions)
Ed Wener (Indigo)
Hans A. Westphal
Ken Whitby
Don White (Dunedin Stamp Centre)
John M. Wilson (Wilson Stamps)
Kirk Wolford (Kirk's Stamp Company)
Urmas Wompa
Robert F. Yacano (K-Line Philippines)
Ralph Yorio
Val Zabijaka
Dr. Michal Zika (Album)
Alfonso G. Zulueta, Jr.

Addresses, Telephone Numbers, Web Sites, E-Mail Addresses of General & Specialized Philatelic Societies

Collectors can contact the following groups for information about the philately of the areas within the scope of these societies, or inquire about membership in these groups. Aside from the general societies, we limit this list to groups that specialize in particular fields of philately, particular areas covered by the Scott Standard Postage Stamp Catalogue, and topical groups. Many more specialized philatelic society exist than those listed below. These addresses are updated yearly, and they are, to the best of our knowledge, correct and current. Groups should inform the editors of address changes whenever they occur. The editors also want to hear from other such specialized groups not listed.

Unless otherwise noted all website addresses begin with http://

American Philatelic Society
100 Match Factory Place
Bellefonte PA 16823-1367
Ph: (814) 933-3803
www.stamps.org
E-mail: apsinfo@stamps.org

American Stamp Dealers'
  Association
Joseph Savarese
3 School St.
Glen Cove NY 11542
Ph: (516) 759-7000
www.asdaonline.com
E-mail: asda@erols.com

International Society of Worldwide
  Stamp Collectors
Anthony Zollo
PO Box 150407
Lufkin TX 75915-0407
www.iswsc.org
E-mail: stamptmf@frontiernet.net

Junior Philatelists of America
Jennifer Arnold
PO Box 2625
Albany OR 97321
www.jpastamps.org
E-mail: exec.sec@jpastamps.org

Royal Philatelic Society
41 Devonshire Place
London, United Kingdom W1G 6JY
www.rpsl.org.uk
E-mail: secretary@rpsl.org.uk

Royal Philatelic Society of Canada
PO Box 929, Station Q
Toronto, ON, Canada M4T 2P1
Ph: (888) 285-4143
www.rpsc.org
E-mail: info@rpsc.org

Groups focusing on fields or aspects found in worldwide philately (some may cover U.S. area only)

American Air Mail Society
Stephen Reinhard
PO Box 110
Mineola NY 11501
www.americanairmailsociety.org
E-mail: sr1501@aol.com

American First Day Cover Society
Douglas Kelsey
PO Box 65960
Tucson AZ 85728-5960
Ph: (520) 321-0880
www.afdcs.org
E-mail: afdcs@aol.com

American Revenue Association
Eric Jackson
PO Box 728
Leesport PA 19533-0728
Ph: (610) 926-6200
www.revenuer.org
E-mail: eric@revenuer.com

American Topical Association
Ray E. Cartier
PO Box 57
Arlington TX 76004-0057
Ph: (817) 274-1181
americantopicalassn.org
E-mail: americantopical@msn.com

Errors, Freaks and Oddities
  Collectors Club
Jim McDevitt
955 S. Grove Blvd #65
Kingsland GA 31548-5263
Ph: (912) 729-1573
www.efoers.org
E-mail: cwouscg@aol.com

Fakes and Forgeries Study Group
Anthony Torres
107 Hoover Rd.
Rochester NY 14617-3611
E-mail: ajtorres@rochester.rr.com

First Issues Collectors Club
Kurt Streepy
P.O. Box 288
Clear Creek IN 47426-0288
www.firstissues.org
E-mail: orders@firstissues.org

International Philatelic Society of
  Joint Stamp Issues Collectors
Richard Zimmermann
124, Avenue Guy de Coubertin
Saint Remy Les Chevreuse, France
F-78470
perso.club-internet.fr/rzimmerm/
index.htm
E-mail: rzimmerm@club-internet.fr

National Duck Stamp Collectors
  Society
Anthony J. Monico
PO Box 43
Harleysville PA 19438-0043
www.hwcn.org/link/ndscs
E-mail: ndscs@hwcn.org

No Value Identified Club
Albert Sauvanet
Le Clos Royal B, Boulevard des Pas
Enchantes
St. Sebastien-sur Loire, France 44230
E-mail: alain.vailly@irin.univ_nantes.fr

The Perfins Club
Kurt Otternheimer
462 West Walnut St.
Long Beach NY 11561
Ph: (516) 431-3412
E-mail: oak462@juno.com

Post Mark Collectors Club
David Proulx
7629 Homestead Drive
Baldwinsville NY 13027
E-mail: stampdance@baldcom.net

Postal History Society
Kalman V. Illyefalvi
8207 Daren Court
Pikesville MD 21208-2211
Ph: (410) 653-0665

Precancel Stamp Society
Arthur Damm
176 Bent Pine Hill
North Wales PA 19454
Ph: (215) 368-6082
E-mail: sandamm@enter.net

United Postal Stationery Society
Cora Collins
PO Box 1792
Norfolk VA 23501-1792
www.upss.org
E-mail: poststat@juno.com

Groups focusing on U.S. area philately as covered in the Standard Catalogue

Canal Zone Study Group
Richard H. Salz
60 27th Ave.
San Francisco CA 94121

Carriers and Locals Society
John D. Bowman
232 Leaf Lane
Alabaster AL 35007
Ph: (205) 621-8449
www.pennypost.org
E-mail: johndbowman@charter.net

Confederate Stamp Alliance
Kevin Baker
3015 Fieldview Dr.
Murfreesboro TN 37128
www.csalliance.org
E-mail: kr.baker@comcast.net

Hawaiian Philatelic Society
Kay H. Hoke
PO Box 10115
Honolulu HI 96816-0115
Ph: (808) 521-5721
E-mail: bannan@pixi.com

Plate Number Coil Collectors Club
Frank Covey
16 Grandview Ave.
Macomb IL 61455
www.pnc3.org
president@pnc3.org

United Nations Philatelists
Blanton Clement, Jr.
P.O. Box 146
Morrisville PA 19067-0146
www.unpi.com
E-mail: bclemjr@yahoo.com

United States Stamp Society
Executive Secretary
PO Box 6634
Katy TX 77491-6631
www.usstamps.org
E-mail: webmaster@usstamps.org

U.S. Cancellation Club
Roger Rhoads
6160 Brownstone Ct.
Mentor OH 44060
www.geocities.com/athens/2088/
uscchome.htm
E-mail: rrrhoads@aol.com

U.S. Philatelic Classics Society
Mark D. Rogers
PO Box 80708
Austin TX 78708-0708
www.uspcs.org
E-mail: mrogers23@austin.rr.com

Groups focusing on philately of foreign countries or regions

Aden & Somaliland Study Group
Gary Brown
PO Box 106
Briar Hill, Victoria, Australia 3088
E-mail: garyjohn951@optushome.com.au

Albania Study Circle
Paul Eckman
PO Box 39880
Los Angeles CA 90039
E-mail: peckman797@earthlink.net

American Society of Polar
  Philatelists (Antarctic areas)
Alan Warren
PO Box 39
Exton PA 19341-0039
www.polarphilatelists.org
E-mail: alanwar@att.net

Andorran Philatelic Study Circle
D. Hope
17 Hawthorn Dr.
Stalybridge, Cheshire, United Kingdom
SK15 1UE
www.chy-an-piran.demon.co.uk/
E-mail: apsc@chy-an-piran.demon.co.uk

Australian States Study Circle
Ben Palmer
GPO 1751
Sydney, N.S.W., Australia 1043

Austria Philatelic Society
Ralph Schneider
PO Box 23049
Belleville IL 62223
Ph: (618) 277-6152
www.apsus.esmartweb.com
E-mail: rschneider39@charter.net

American Belgian Philatelic Society
Walter D. Handlin
1303 Bullens Lane.
Woodlin, PA 19094
groups.hamptonroads.com/ABPS
E-mail: wdhandlin1@comcast.net

Bechuanalands and Botswana
  Society
Neville Midwood
69 Porlock Lane
Furzton, Milton Keynes, United
Kingdom MK4 1JY
www.nevsoft.com
E-mail: bbsoc@nevsoft.com

Bermuda Collectors Society
Thomas J. McMahon
PO Box 1949
Stuart FL 34995
www.bermudacollectorssociety.org

Brazil Philatelic Association
William V. Kriebel
1923 ManningSt.
Philadelphia PA 19103-5728
Ph: (215) 735-3697
E-mail: kriebewv@drexel.edu

British Caribbean Philatelic Study
  Group
Dr. Reuben A. Ramkissoon
3011 White Oak Lane
Oak Brook IL 60523-2513
www.bcpsg.com
E-mail: rramkissoon@juno.com

British North America Philatelic
  Society (Canada & Provinces)
H. P. Jacobi
150 A St.
Surrey, B.C., Canada V4A 9W4
www.bnaps.org
E-mail: beaver@telus.net

British West Indies Study Circle
W. Clary Holt
PO Drawer 59
Burlington NC 27216
Ph: (336) 227-7461

Burma Philatelic Study Circle
A. Meech
7208 91st Ave.
Edmonton, AB, Canada T6B 0R8
E-mail: ameech@telusplanet.net

Ceylon Study Group
R. W. P. Frost
42 Lonsdale Road, Cannington
Bridgewater, Somerset, United
Kingdom TA5 2JS

Channel Islands Specialists Society
Miss S. Marshall
1 Grove Farm Drive, Leeds
West Yorks, LL16 6DD
United Kingdom

China Stamp Society
Paul H. Gault
PO Box 20711
Columbus OH 43220
www.chinastampsociety.org
E-mail: secretary@chinastampsociety.org

Colombia/Panama Philatelic Study
  Group (CORAPHIL)
PO Box 2245
El Cajon CA 92021
www.copaphil.org
E-mail: jimacross@cts.com

Society for Costa Rica Collectors
Dr. Hector R. Mena
PO Box 14831
Baton Rouge LA 70808
www.socorico.org
E-mail: hrmena@aol.com

Croatian Philatelic Society (Croatia
  & other Balkan areas)
Ekrem Spahich
502 Romero, PO Box 696
Fritch TX 79036-0696
Ph: (806) 857-0129
www.croatianmall.com/cps/
E-mail: ou812@arn.net

Cuban Philatelic Society of
  America
Ernesto Cuesta
PO Box 34434
Bethesda MD 20827
www.philat.com/cpsa

Cyprus Study Circle
Jim Wigmore
19 Riversmeet, Appledore
Bideford, N. Devon, United Kingdom
EX39 1RE
www.cyprusstudycircle.org/index.htm
E-mail: jameswigmore@aol.com

Society for Czechoslovak Philately
Peter Z. Kleskovic
27 Jay St.
Succasunna NJ 07876-1831
www.czechoslovakphilately.com

Danish West Indies Study Unit of
  the Scandinavian Collectors Club
John L. Dubois
Thermalogic Corp.
22 Kane Industrial Drive
Hudson MA 01749
Ph: (800) 343-4492
dwi.thlogic.com
E-mail: jld@thlogic.com

East Africa Study Circle
Ken Hewitt
16 Ashleigh Road
Solihull, United Kingdom B91 1AE
E-mail: EASC@ashleigh.me.uk

Egypt Study Circle
Mike Murphy
109 Chadwick Road
London, United Kingdom SE15 4PY
E-mail: egyptstudycircle@hotmail.com

Estonian Philatelic Society
Juri Kirsimagi
29 Clifford Ave.
Pelham NY 10803
Ph: (914) 738-3713

Ethiopian Philatelic Society
Ulf Lindahl
21 Westview Place
Riverside CT 06878
Ph: (203) 866-3540
members.home.net/fbheiser/
ethiopia5.htm
E-mail: ulindahl@optonline.net

Falkland Islands Philatelic Study
  Group
Carl J. Faulkner
Williams Inn, On-the-Green
Williamstown MA 01267-2620
Ph: (413) 458-9371

Faroe Islands Study Circle
Norman Hudson
28 Enfield Road
Ellesmere Port, Cheshire, United
Kingdom CH65 8BY
www.faroeislandssc.org.uk
E-mail: jntropics@hotmail.com

Former French Colonies Specialist
  Society
BP 628
75367 Paris Cedex 08, France
www.ifrance.com/colfra
E-mail: clubcolfra@aol.com

France & Colonies Philatelic
  Society
Walter Parshall
103 Spruce St.
Bloomfield NJ 07003-3514

Germany Philatelic Society
PO Box 779
Arnold MD 21012-4779
www.gps.nu
E-mail: germanyphilatelic@starpower.net

German Democratic Republic
  Study Group of the German
  Philatelic Society
Ken Lawrence
PO Box 210
Bellefonte PA 16823-0210
Ph: (814) 422-0625
E-mail: apsken@aol.com

Gibraltar Study Circle
www.abel.co.uk/~stirrups/GSC.HTM
E-mail: drstirrups@dundee.ac.uk

Great Britain Collectors Club
Parker A. Bailey, Jr.
PO Box 773
Merrimack NH 03054-0773
www.gbstamps.com/gbcc
E-mail: pbaileyjr@worldnet.att.net

Hellenic Philatelic Society of
  America (Greece and related
  areas)
Dr. Nicholas Asimakopulos
541 Cedar Hill Ave.
Wyckoff NJ 07481
Ph: (201) 447-6262
E-mail: nick1821@aol.com

International Society of Guatemala
  Collectors
Mrs. Mae Vignola
105 22nd Ave.
San Francisco CA 94121

Haiti Philatelic Society
Ubaldo Del Toro
5709 Marble Archway
Alexandria VA 22315
www.haitiphilately.org
E-mail: u007ubi@aol.com

Honduras Collectors Club
Jeff Brasor
PO Box 143383
Irving TX 75014

Hong Kong Stamp Society
Dr. An-Min Chung
3300 Darby Rd. Cottage 503
Haverford PA 19041-1064

Society for Hungarian Philately
Robert Morgan
2201 Roscomare Rd.
Los Angeles CA 90077-2222
www.hungarianphilately.org
E-mail: h.alan.hoover@hungarianphil
ately.org

India Study Circle
John Warren
PO Box 7326
Washington DC 20044
Ph: (202) 564-6876
www.indiastudycircle.org
E-mail: warren.john@epa.gov

Indian Ocean Study Circle
K. B. Fitton
50 Firlands
Weybridge, Surrey, United Kingdom
KT13 0HR
www.stampdomain.com/iosc
E-mail: keithfitton@intonet.co.uk

Society of Indo-China Philatelists
Norman S. Davis
PO Box 290406
Brooklyn NY 11229

Iran Philatelic Study Circle
Mehdi Esmaili
PO Box 750096
Forest Hills NY 11375
www.iranphilatelic.org
E-mail: m.esmaili@earthlink.net

Eire Philatelic Association (Ireland)
Myron G. Hill III
PO Box 1210
College Park MD 20741-1210
eirephilatelicassoc.org
E-mail: mhill@radix.net

Society of Israel Philatelists
Paul S. Aufrichtig
300 East 42nd St.
New York NY 10017

Italy and Colonies Study Circle
Andrew D'Anneo
1085 Dunweal Lane
Calistoga CA 94515
www.icsc.pwp.blueyonder.co.uk
E-mail: audanneo@napanet.net

International Society for Japanese
  Philately
Kenneth Kamholz
PO Box 1283
Haddonfield NJ 08033
www.isjp.org
E-mail: isjp@comcast.net

Korea Stamp Society
John E. Talmage
PO Box 6889
Oak Ridge TN 37831
www.pennfamily.org/KSS-USA
E-mail: jtalmage@usit.net

Latin American Philatelic Society
Jules K. Beck
30 1/2 Street #209
St. Louis Park MN 55426-3551

Latvian Philatelic Society
Aris Birze
569 Rougemount Dr.
Pickering, ON, Canada L1W 2C1

Liberian Philatelic Society
William Thomas Lockard
PO Box 106
Wellston OH 45692
Ph: (740) 384-2020
E-mail: tlockard@zoomnet.net

Liechtenstudy USA (Liechtenstein)
Ralph Schneider
PO Box 23049
Belleville IL 62223
Ph: (618) 277-6152
www.rschneiderstamps.com/Liechten
study.htm
E-mail: rsstamps@aol.com

Lithuania Philatelic Society
John Variakojis
3715 W. 68th St.
Chicago IL 60629
Ph: (773) 585-8649
www.filatelija.lt/lps/
E-mail: variakojis@earthlink.net

Luxembourg Collectors Club
Gary B. Little
3304 Plateau Dr.
Belmont CA 94002-1312
www.luxcentral.com/stamps/LCC
E-mail: lcc@luxcentral.com

Malaya Study Group
Keith Elliot
78 Howard Road
Bournemouth, United Kingdom BH8 9ED
home.freeuk.net/johnmorgan/msg.htm

Malta Study Circle
Alec Webster
50 Worcester Road
Sutton, Surrey, United Kingdom SM2 6QB
E-mail: alecwebster50@hotmail.com

Mexico-Elmhurst Philatelic Society International
David Pietsch
PO Box 50997
Irvine CA 92619-0997
E-mail: mepsi@msn.com

Society for Moroccan and Tunisian Philately
206, bld. Pereire
75017 Paris, France
members.aol.com/Jhaik5814
E-mail: splm206@aol.com

Nepal & Tibet Philatelic Study Group
Roger D. Skinner
1020 Covington Road
Los Altos CA 94024-5003
Ph: (650) 968-4163
fuchs-online.com/ntpsc/
E-mail: Hepper@terra.es

American Society of Netherlands Philately
Jan Enthoven
221 Coachlite Ct. S.
Onalaska WI 54650
Ph: (608) 781-8612
www.cs.cornell.edu/Info/People/aswin/NL/neth
E-mail: jenthoven@centurytel.net

New Zealand Society of Great Britain
Keith C. Collins
13 Briton Crescent
Sanderstead, Surrey, United Kingdom CR2 0JN
www.cs.stir.ac.uk/~rgc/nzsgb
E-mail: rgc@cs.stir.ac.uk

Nicaragua Study Group
Erick Rodriguez
11817 S.W. 11th St.
Miami FL 33184-2501
clubs.yahoo.com/clubs/nicaraguastudygroup
E-mail: nsgsec@yahoo.com

Society of Australasian Specialists/ Oceania
Henry Bateman
PO Box 4862
Monroe LA 71211-4862
Ph: (800) 571-0293 members.aol.com/stampsho/saso.html
E-mail: hbateman@jam.rr.com

Orange Free State Study Circle
J. R. Stroud
28 Oxford St.
Burnham-on-sea, Somerset, United Kingdom TA8 1LQ
www.ofssc.org
E-mail: jrstroud@classicfm.net

Pacific Islands Study Circle
John Ray
24 Woodvale Avenue
London, United Kingdom SE25 4AE
www.pisc.org.uk
E-mail: info@pisc.org.uk

Pakistan Philatelic Study Circle
Jeff Siddiqui
PO Box 7002
Lynnwood WA 98046
E-mail: jeffsiddiqui@msn.com

Centro de Filatelistas Independientes de Panama
Vladimir Berrio-Lemm
Apartado 0835-348
Panama, 10, Panama
E-mail: filatelia@cwpanama.net

Papuan Philatelic Society
Steven Zirinsky
PO Box 49, Ansonia Station
New York NY 10023
Ph: (718) 706-0616
E-mail: szirinsky@cs.com

International Philippine Philatelic Society
Robert F. Yacano
PO Box 100
Toast NC 27049
Ph: (336) 783-0768
E-mail: ryacano@tria.d.rr.com

Pitcairn Islands Study Group
Nelson A. L. Weller
2940 Wesleyan Lane
Winston-Salem NC 27106
Ph: (336) 724-6384
E-mail: nalweller@aol.com

Plebiscite-Memel-Saar Study Group of the German Philatelic Society
Clay Wallace
100 Lark Court
Alamo CA 94507
E-mail: clayw1@sbcglobal.net

Polonus Philatelic Society (Poland)
Arkadius Walinski
7414 Lincoln Ave. - D
Skokie IL 60076-3898
www.polonus.org

International Society for Portuguese Philately
Clyde Homen
1491 Bonnie View Rd.
Hollister CA 95023-5117
www.portugalstamps.com
E-mail: cjh1491@sbcglobal.net

Rhodesian Study Circle
William R. Wallace
PO Box 16381
San Francisco CA 94116
www.rhodesianstudycircle.org.uk
E-mail: bwall8rscr@earthlink.net

Canadian Society of Russian Philately
Andrew Cronin
PO Box 5722, Station A
Toronto, ON, Canada M5W 1P2
Ph: (905) 764-8968
www3.sympatico.ca/postrider/postrider
E-mail: postrider@sympatico.ca

Rossica Society of Russian Philately
Edward J. Laveroni
P.O. Box 320997
Los Gatos CA 95032-0116
www.rossica.org
E-mail: ed.laveroni@rossica.org

Ryukyu Philatelic Specialist Society
Carmine J. DiVincenzo
PO Box 381
Clayton CA 94517-0381

St. Helena, Ascension & Tristan Da Cunha Philatelic Society
Dr. Everett L. Parker
719 Moosehead Lake Rd.
Greenville ME 04441-9727
Ph: (207) 695-3163
ourworld.compuserve.com/homepages/ ST_HELENA_ASCEN_TDC
E-mail: eparker@midmaine.net

St. Pierre & Miquelon Philatelic Society
Jim Taylor
7704 Birch Bay Dr.
Blaine WA 98230
E-mail: jamestaylor@wavehome.com

Associated Collectors of El Salvador
Jeff Brasor
PO Box 143383
Irving TX 75014

Fellowship of Samoa Specialists
Jack R. Hughes
PO Box 1260
Boston MA 02117-1260
members.aol.com/tongaJan/foss.html

Sarawak Specialists' Society
Stu Leven
4031 Samson Way
San Jose CA 95124-3733
Ph: (408) 978-0193
www.britborneostamps.org.uk
E-mail: stulev@ix.netcom.com

Scandinavian Collectors Club
Donald B. Brent
PO Box 13196
El Cajon CA 92020
www.scc-online.org
E-mail: dbrent47@sprynet.com

Slovakia Stamp Society
Jack Benchik
PO Box 555
Notre Dame IN 46556

Philatelic Society for Greater Southern Africa
William C. Brooks VI
PO Box 4158
Cucamonga CA 91729-4158
Ph: (909) 484-2806
www.homestead.com/psgsa/index.html
E-mail: bbrooks@hss.co.sbcounty.gov

Spanish Philatelic Society
Robert H. Penn
1108 Walnut Drive
Danielsville PA 18038
Ph: (610) 767-6793

Sudan Study Group
Charles Hass
PO Box 3435
Nashua NH 03061-3435
Ph: (603) 888-4160
E-mail: hassstamps@aol.com

American Helvetia Philatelic Society (Switzerland, Liechtenstein)
Richard T. Hall
PO Box 15053
Asheville NC 28813-0053
www.swiss-stamps.org
E-mail: secretary@swiss-stamps.org

Tannu Tuva Collectors Society
Ken Simon
513 Sixth Ave. So.
Lake Worth FL 33460-4507
Ph: (561) 588-5954
www.seflin.org/tuva
E-mail: p00311 5b@pb.seflin.org

Society for Thai Philately
H. R. Blakeney
PO Box 25644
Oklahoma City OK 73125
E-mail: HRBlakeney@aol.com

Transvaal Study Circle
J. Woolgar
132 Dale Street
Chatham, Kent ME4 6QH, United Kingdom
www.transvaalsc.org

Ottoman and Near East Philatelic Society (Turkey and related areas)
Bob Stuchell
193 Valley Stream Lane
Wayne PA 19087
www.oneps.org
E-mail: president@oneps.org

Ukrainian Philatelic & Numismatic Society
George Slusarczuk
PO Box 303
Southfields NY 10975-0303
www.upns.org
E-mail: Yurko@warwick.net

Vatican Philatelic Society
Sal Quinonez
1 Aldersgate, Apt. 1002
Riverhead NY 11901-1830
Ph: (516) 727-6426

British Virgin Islands Philatelic Society
Roger Downing
PO Box 11156
St. Thomas VI 00801-1156
www.islandsun.com/FEATURES/bviphil9198.html
E-mail: issun@candwbvi.net

West Africa Study Circle
Dr. Peter Newroth
33-520 Marsett Place
Victoria, BC, Canada V8Z 7J1
www.wasc.org.uk/

Western Australia Study Group
Brian Pope
PO Box 423
Claremont, Western Australia, Australia 6910

Yugoslavia Study Group of the Croatian Philatelic Society
Michael Lenard
1514 North 3rd Ave.
Wausau WI 54401
Ph: (715) 675-2833
E-mail: mjlenard@aol.com

Topical Groups

Americana Unit
Dennis Dengel
17 Peckham Rd.
Poughkeepsie NY 12603-2018
www.americanaunit.org
E-mail: membership@americanaunit.org

Astronomy Study Unit
George Young
PO Box 632
Tewksbury MA 01876-0632
Ph: (978) 851-8283
www.fandm.edu/departments/
astronomy/miscell/astunit.html
E-mail: george-young@msn.com

Bicycle Stamp Club
Norman Batho
358 Iverson Place
East Windsor NJ 08520
Ph: (609) 448-9547
members.tripod.com/~bicyclestamps
E-mail: normbatho@worldnet.att.net

Biology Unit
Alan Hanks
34 Seaton Dr.
Aurora, ON, Canada L4G 2K1
Ph: (905) 727-6993

Bird Stamp Society
G. P. Horsman
9 Cowley Drive, Worthy Down
Winchester, Hants., United Kingdom
SO21 2OW
E-mail: rogerchapman@btinternet.com

Canadiana Study Unit
John Peebles
PO Box 3262, Station "A"
London, ON, Canada N6A 4K3
E-mail: john.peebles@sympatico.ca

Captain Cook Study Unit
Brian P. Sandford
173 Minuteman Dr.
Concord MA 01742-1923
www.captaincooksociety.com
E-mail:
USagent@captaincooksociety.com/

Casey Jones Railroad Unit
Bill Senkus
PO Box 4584
Walnut Creek CA 94596-4584
www.uqp.de/cjr/index.htm
E-mail: cjrru@att.net

Cats on Stamps Study Unit
Mary Ann Brown
3006 Wade Rd.
Durham NC 27705

Chemistry & Physics on Stamps
   Study Unit
Dr. Roland Hirsch
20458 Water Point Lane
Germantown MD 20874
www.cpossu.org
E-mail: rfhirsch@cpossu.org

Chess on Stamps Study Unit
Anne Kasonic
7625 County Road #153
Interlaken NY 14847
E-mail: akasonic@capital.net

Christmas Philatelic Club
Linda Lawrence
312 Northwood Drive
Lexington KY 40505
Ph: (859) 293-0151
www.hwcn.org/link/cpc
E-mail: stamplinda@aol.com

Christopher Columbus Philatelic
   Society
Donald R. Ager
PO Box 71
Hillsboro NH 03244-0071
Ph: (603) 464-5379
E-mail: meganddon@tds.net

Collectors of Religion on Stamps
Verna Shackleton
425 North Linwood Avenue #110
Appleton WI 54914
Ph: (920) 734-2417
www://my.vbe.com/~cmfourl/
coros1.htm
E-mail: corosec@sbcglobal.net

Dogs on Stamps Study Unit
Morris Raskin
202A Newport Rd.
Monroe Township NJ 08831
Ph: (609) 655-7411
www.dossu.org
E-mail: mraskin@cellurian.com

Earth's Physical Features Study
   Group
Fred Klein
515 Magdalena Ave.
Los Altos CA 94024
www.philately.com/society_news/
earths _physical.htm

Ebony Society of Philatelic Events
   and Reflections (African-
   American topicals)
Manuel Gilyard
800 Riverside Drive, Ste 4H
New York NY 10032-7412
www.esperstamps.org
E-mail: gilyardmani@aol.com

Embroidery, Stitchery, Textile Unit
Helen N. Cushman
1001 Genter St., Apt. 9H
La Jolla CA 92037
Ph: (619) 459-1194

Europa Study Unit
Donald W. Smith
PO Box 576
Johnstown PA 15907-0576
E-mail: eunity@aol.com or
donsmith65@msn.com

Fine & Performing Arts
Rachel S. Smith
8023 Mainsail Drive
Rohnert Park Ca 94928
E-mail: Rachel@nmc.org

Fire Service in Philately
Brian R. Engler, Sr.
726 1/2 W. Tilghman St.
Allentown PA 18102-2324
Ph: (610) 433-2782
E-mail: brenglersr@enter.net

Gay & Lesbian History on Stamps
   Club
Joe Petronie
PO Box 190842
Dallas TX 75219-0842
www.glhsc.org
E-mail: glhsc@aol.com

Gems, Minerals & Jewelry Study Unit
George Young
PO Box 632
Tewksbury MA 01876-0632
Ph: (978) 851-8283
www.rockhounds.com/rockshop/
gmjsuapp.txt
E-mail: george-young@msn.com

Graphics Philately Association
Mark Winnegrad
PO Box 380
Bronx NY 10462-0380

Journalists, Authors & Poets on Stamps
Ms. Lee Straayer
P.O. Box 6808
Champaign IL 61826
E-mail: lstraayer@dcbnet.com

Lighthouse Stamp Society
Dalene Thomas
8612 West Warren Lane
Lakewood CO 80227-2352
Ph: (303) 986-6620
www.lighthousestampsociety.org
E-mail: dalene1@wideopenwest.com

Lions International Stamp Club
John Bargus
304-2777 Barry Rd. RR 2
Mill Bay, BC, Canada V0R 2P0
Ph: (250) 743-5782

Mahatma Gandhi On Stamps
   Study Circle
Pramod Shivagunde
Pratik Clinic, Akluj
Solapur, Maharashtra, India 413101
E-mail: drnanda@bom6.vsnl.net.in

Mask Study Unit
Carolyn Weber
1220 Johnson Drive, Villa 104
Ventura CA 93003-0540
www.home.prcn.org/~pauld/ata/
units/masks.htm
E-mail: kencar@venturalink.net

Masonic Study Unit
Stanley R. Longenecker
930 Wood St.
Mount Joy PA 17552-1926
E-mail: natsco@usa.net

Mathematical Study Unit
Estelle Buccino
5615 Glenwood Rd.
Bethesda MD 20817-6727
Ph: (301) 718-8898
www.math.ttu.edu/msu/
E-mail: m.strauss@ttu.edu

Medical Subjects Unit
Dr. Frederick C. Skvara
PO Box 6228
Bridgewater NJ 08807
E-mail: fcskvara@bellatlantic.net

Mesoamerican Archeology Study
   Unit
Chris Moser
PO Box 1442
Riverside CA 92502
www.masu.homestead.com/info.html
E-mail:cmoser@ci.riverside.ca.us

Napoleonic Age Philatelists
Ken Berry
7513 Clayton Dr.
Oklahoma City OK 73132-5636
Ph: (405) 721-0044
E-mail: krb2@earthlink.net

Old World Archeological Study Unit
Eileen Meier
PO Box 369
Palmyra VA 22963
Ph: (434) 589-4222
www.owasu.org

Parachute Study Group
Bill Wickert
3348 Clubhouse Road
Virginia Beach VA 23452-5339
Ph: (757) 486-3614
E-mail: bw47psg@worldnet.att.net

Petroleum Philatelic Society
   International
Linda W. Corwin
5427 Pine Springs Court
Conroe TX 77304
Ph: (936) 441-0216
E-mail: corwin@pdq.net

Philatelic Computing Study Group
Robert de Violini
PO Box 5025
Oxnard CA 93031-5025
www.pcsg.org
E-mail: dviolini@adelphia.net

Philatelic Lepidopterists' Association
Alan Hanks
34 Seaton Dr.
Aurora, ON, Canada L4G 2K1
Ph: (905) 727-6933

Philatelic Music Circle
Cathleen Osborne
PO Box 1781
Sequim WA 98382
Ph: (360) 683-6373
www.stampshows.com/pmc.html

Rotary on Stamps Unit
Richard J. Dickson
PO Box 534
Irvington VA 22480
Ph: (804) 438-1178
E-mail: roshq@kaballero.com

Scouts on Stamps Society
   International
Carl Schauer
PO Box 526
Belen NM 87002
Ph: (505) 864-0098
www.sossi.org
E-mail: rfrank@sossi.org

Ships on Stamps Unit
Robert Stuckert
2750 Highway 21 East
Paint Lick KY 40461
Ph: (859) 925-4901
www.shipsonstamps.org

Space Unit
Carmine Torrisi
PO Box 780241
Maspeth NY 11378
Ph: (718) 386-7882
stargate.1usa.com/stamps/
E-mail: ctorrisi1@juno.com

Sports Philatelists International
Margaret Jones
5310 Lindenwood Ave.
St. Louis MO 63109-1758
www.sportstamps.org

Stamps on Stamps Collectors Club
Alf Jordan
156 West Elm Street
Yarmouth ME 04096
Ph: (650) 234-1136
www.stampsonstamps.org
E-mail: ajordan1@maine.rr.com

Windmill Study Unit
Walter J. Hollien
PO Box 346
Long Valley NJ 07853-0346
Ph: (908) 876-3672

Wine on Stamps Study Unit
James D. Crum
816 Kingsbury Ct.
Arroyo Grande CA 93420-4517
Ph: (805) 489-3559
E-mail: jdakcrum@aol.com

Women on Stamps Study Unit
Hugh Gottfried
2232 26th St.
Santa Monica CA 90405-1902
E-mail: hgottfried@adelphia.net

Zeppelin Collectors Club
Cheryl Ganz
PO Box A3843
Chicago IL 60690-3843

Expertizing Services

The following organizations will, for a fee, provide expert opinions about stamps submitted to them. Collectors should contact these organizations to find out about their fees and requirements before submitting philatelic material to them. The listing of these groups here is not intended as an endorsement by Scott Publishing Co.

General Expertizing Services

American Philatelic Expertizing
Service (a service of the
American Philatelic Society)
100 Match Factory Place
Bellefonte PA 16823-1367
Ph: (814) 237-3803
Fax: (814) 237-6128
www.stamps.org
E-mail: ambristo@stamps.org
Areas of Expertise: Worldwide

B. P. A. Expertising, Ltd.
PO Box 137
Leatherhead, Surrey, United Kingdom
KT22 0RG
E-mail: sec.bpa@tcom.co.uk
Areas of Expertise: British
Commonwealth, Great Britain,
Classics of Europe, South America and
the Far East

Philatelic Foundation
70 West 40th St., 15th Floor
New York NY 10018
Ph: (212) 221-6555
Fax: (212) 221-6208
www.philatelicfoundation.org
E-mail:philatelicfoundation@verizon.net
Areas of Expertise: U.S. & Worldwide

Professional Stamp Experts
PO Box 6170
Newport Beach CA 92658
Ph: (877) STAMP-88
Fax: (949) 833-7955
www.collectors.com/pse
E-mail: pseinfo@collectors.com
Areas of Expertise: Stamps and
covers of U.S., U.S. Possessions,
British Commonwealth

Royal Philatelic Society Expert
Committee
41 Devonshire Place
London, United Kingdom W1N 1PE
www.rpsl.org.uk/experts.html
E-mail: experts@rpsl.org.uk
Areas of Expertise: All

Expertizing Services Covering Specific Fields Or Countries

Canadian Society of Russian
Philately Expertizing Service
PO Box 5722, Station A
Toronto, ON, Canada M5W 1P2
Fax: (416)932-0853
Areas of Expertise: Russian areas

China Stamp Society Expertizing
Service
1050 West Blue Ridge Blvd
Kansas City MO 64145
Ph: (816) 942-6300
E-mail: hjmesq@aol.com
Areas of Expertise: China

Confederate Stamp Alliance
Authentication Service
c/o Patricia A. Kaufmann
10194 N. Old State Road
Lincoln DE 19960-9797
Ph: (302) 422-2656
Fax: (302) 424-1990
www.webuystamps.com/csaauth.htm
E-mail: trish@ce.net
Areas of Expertise: Confederate stamps
and postal history

Croatian Philatelic Society
Expertizing Service
PO Box 696
Fritch TX 79036-0696
Ph: (806) 857-0129
E-mail: ou812@arn.net
Areas of Expertise: Croatia and other
Balkan areas

Errors, Freaks and Oddities
Collectors
Club Expertizing Service
138 East Lakemont Dr.
Kingsland GA 31548
Ph: (912) 729-1573
Areas of Expertise: U.S. errors, freaks
and oddities

Estonian Philatelic Society
Expertizing Service
39 Clafford Lane
Melville NY 11747
Ph: (516) 421-2078
E-mail: esto4@aol.com
Areas of Expertise: Estonia

Hawaiian Philatelic Society
Expertizing Service
PO Box 10115
Honolulu HI 96816-0115
Areas of Expertise: Hawaii

Hong Kong Stamp Society
Expertizing Service
PO Box 206
Glenside PA 19038
Fax: (215) 576-6850
Areas of Expertise: Hong Kong

International Association of
Philatelics Experts
United States Associate members:

Paul Buchsbayew
119 W. 57th St.
New York NY 10019
Ph: (212) 977-7734
Fax: (212) 977-8653
Areas of Expertise: Russia, Soviet
Union

William T. Crowe
(see Philatelic Foundation)

John Lievsay
(see American Philatelic Expertizing
Service and Philatelic Foundation)
Areas of Expertise: France

Robert W. Lyman
P.O. Box 348
Irvington on Hudson NY 10533
Ph and Fax: (914) 591-6937
Areas of Expertise: British North
America, New Zealand

Robert Odenweller
P.O. Box 401
Bernardsville, NJ 07924-0401
Ph and Fax: (908) 766-5460
Areas of Expertise: New Zealand,
Samoa to 1900

Alex Rendon
P.O. Box 323
Massapequa NY 11762
Ph and Fax: (516) 795-0464
Areas of Expertise: Bolivia,
Colombia, Colombian States

Sergio Sismondo
10035 Carousel Center Dr.
Syracuse NY 13290-0001
Ph: (315) 422-2331
Fax: (315) 422-2956
Areas of Expertise: Cape of
Good Hope, Canada, British
North America

International Society for Japanese
Philately Expertizing Committee
32 King James Court
Staten Island NY 10308-2910
Ph: (718) 227-5229
Areas of Expertise: Japan and
related areas, except WWII Japanese
Occupation issues

International Society for
Portuguese Philately Expertizing
Service
PO Box 43146
Philadelphia PA 19129-3146
Ph: (215) 843-2106
Fax: (215) 843-2106
E-mail: s.s.washburne@worldnet.att
.net
Areas of Expertise: Portugal and
colonies

Mexico-Elmhurst Philatelic Society
International Expert Committee
PO Box 1133
West Covina CA 91793
Areas of Expertise: Mexico

Philatelic Society for Greater
Southern Africa Expert Panel
13955 W. 30th Ave.
Golden CO 80401
Areas of expertise: Entire South and
South West Africa area,
Bechuanalands, Basutoland, Swaziland

Ukrainian Philatelic & Numismatic
Society Expertizing Service
30552 Dell Lane
Warren MI 48092-1862
Ph: (810) 751-5754
Areas of Expertise: Ukraine, Western
Ukraine

V. G. Greene Philatelic Research
Foundation
P.O. Box 204, Station Q
Toronto, ON, Canada M4T 2M1
Ph: (416) 921-2073
Fax: (416) 921-1282
E-mail: vggfoundation@on.aibn.com
www.greenefoundation.ca
Areas of Expertise: British North
America

Information on Catalogue Values, Grade and Condition

Catalogue Value

The Scott Catalogue value is a retail value; that is, an amount you could expect to pay for a stamp in the grade of Very Fine with no faults. Any exceptions to the grade valued will be noted in the text. The general introduction on the following pages and the individual section introductions further explain the type of material that is valued. The value listed for any given stamp is a reference that reflects recent actual dealer selling prices for that item.

Dealer retail price lists, public auction results, published prices in advertising and individual solicitation of retail prices from dealers, collectors and specialty organizations have been used in establishing the values found in this catalogue. Scott Publishing Co. values stamps, but Scott is not a company engaged in the business of buying and selling stamps as a dealer.

Use this catalogue as a guide for buying and selling. The actual price you pay for a stamp may be higher or lower than the catalogue value because of many different factors, including the amount of personal service a dealer offers, or increased or decreased interest in the country or topic represented by a stamp or set. An item may occasionally be offered at a lower price as a "loss leader," or as part of a special sale. You also may obtain an item inexpensively at public auction because of little interest at that time or as part of a large lot.

Stamps that are of a lesser grade than Very Fine, or those with condition problems, generally trade at lower prices than those given in this catalogue. Stamps of exceptional quality in both grade and condition often command higher prices than those listed.

Values for pre-1900 unused issues are for stamps with approximately half or more of their original gum. Stamps with most or all of their original gum may be expected to sell for more, and stamps with less than half of their original gum may be expected to sell for somewhat less than the values listed. On rarer stamps, it may be expected that the original gum will be somewhat more disturbed than it will be on more common issues. Post-1900 unused issues are assumed to have full original gum. From breakpoints in most countries' listings, stamps are valued as never hinged, due to the wide availability of stamps in that condition. These notations are prominently placed in the listings and in the country information preceding the listings. Some countries also feature listings with dual values for hinged and never-hinged stamps.

Grade

A stamp's grade and condition are crucial to its value. The accompanying illustrations show examples of Very Fine stamps from different time periods, along with examples of stamps in Fine to Very Fine and Extremely Fine grades as points of reference.

FINE stamps (illustrations not shown) have designs that are quite off center, with the perforations on one or two sides very close to the design but not quite touching it. There is white space between the perforations and the design that is minimal but evident to the unaided eye. Imperforate stamps may have small margins, and earlier issues may show the design just touching one edge of the stamp design. Very early perforated issues normally will have the perforations slightly cutting into the design. Used stamps may have heavier than usual cancellations.

FINE-VERY FINE stamps will be somewhat off center on one side, or slightly off center on two sides. Imperforate stamps will have two margins of at least normal size, and the design will not touch any edge. For perforated stamps, the perfs are well clear of the design, but are still noticeably off center. *However, early issues of a country may be printed in such a way that the design naturally is very close to the edges. In these cases, the perforations may cut into the design very slightly.* Used stamps will not have a cancellation that detracts from the design.

VERY FINE stamps will be just slightly off center on one or two sides, but the design will be well clear of the edge. The stamp will present a nice, balanced appearance. Imperforate stamps will be well centered within normal-sized margins. *However, early issues of many countries may be printed in such a way that the perforations may touch the design on one or more sides. Where this is the case, a boxed note will be found defining the centering and margins of the stamps being valued.* Used stamps will have light or otherwise neat cancellations. This is the grade used to establish Scott Catalogue values.

EXTREMELY FINE stamps are close to being perfectly centered. Imperforate stamps will have even margins that are slightly larger than normal. Even the earliest perforated issues will have perforations clear of the design on all sides.

Scott Publishing Co. recognizes that there is no formally enforced grading scheme for postage stamps, and that the final price you pay or obtain for a stamp will be determined by individual agreement at the time of transaction.

Condition

Grade addresses only centering and (for used stamps) cancellation. *Condition* refers to factors other than grade that affect a stamp's desirability.

Factors that can increase the value of a stamp include exceptionally wide margins, particularly fresh color, the presence of selvage, and plate or die varieties. Unusual cancels on used stamps (particularly those of the 19th century) can greatly enhance their value as well.

Factors other than faults that decrease the value of a stamp include loss of original gum, regumming, a hinge remnant or foreign object adhering to the gum, natural inclusions, straight edges, and markings or notations applied by collectors or dealers.

Faults include missing pieces, tears, pin or other holes, surface scuffs, thin spots, creases, toning, short or pulled perforations, clipped perforations, oxidation or other forms of color changelings, soiling, stains, and such man-made changes as reperforations or the chemical removal or lightening of a cancellation.

Grading Illustrations

On the following two pages are illustrations of various stamps from countries appearing in this volume. These stamps are arranged by country, and they represent early or important issues that are often found in widely different grades in the marketplace. The editors believe the illustrations will prove useful in showing the margin size and centering that will be seen on the various issues.

In addition to the matters of margin size and centering, collectors are reminded that the very fine stamps valued in the Scott catalogues also will possess fresh color and intact perforations, and they will be free from defects.

Most examples shown are computer-manipulated images made from single digitized master illustrations.

Stamp Illustrations Used in the Catalogue

It is important to note that the stamp images used for identification purposes in this catalogue may not be indicative of the grade of stamp being valued. Refer to the written discussion of grades on this page and to the grading illustrations on the following two pages for grading information.

Fine-Very Fine →

SCOTT
CATALOGUES
VALUE
STAMPS IN
THIS GRADE

Very Fine →

Extremely Fine →

Fine-Very Fine →

SCOTT
CATALOGUES
VALUE
STAMPS IN
THIS GRADE

Very Fine →

Extremely Fine →

Fine-Very Fine

SCOTT
CATALOGUES
VALUE
STAMPS IN
THIS GRADE

Very Fine

Extremely Fine

Fine-Very Fine

SCOTT
CATALOGUES
VALUE
STAMPS IN
THIS GRADE

Very Fine

Extremely Fine

For purposes of helping to determine the gum condition and value of an unused stamp, Scott Publishing Co. presents the following chart which details different gum conditions and indicates how the conditions correlate with the Scott values for unused stamps. Used together, the Illustrated Grading Chart on the previous pages and this Illustrated Gum Chart should allow catalogue users to better understand the grade and gum condition of stamps valued in the Scott catalogues.

Gum Categories:	MINT N.H.	ORIGINAL GUM (O.G.)				NO GUM
	Mint Never Hinged *Free from any disturbance*	**Lightly Hinged** *Faint impression of a removed hinge over a small area*	**Hinge Mark or Remnant** *Prominent hinged spot with part or all of the hinge remaining*	**Large part o.g.** *Approximately half or more of the gum intact*	**Small part o.g.** *Approximately less than half of the gum intact*	**No gum** *Only if issued with gum*
Commonly Used Symbol:	★ ★	★	★	★	★	(★)
Pre-1900 Issues (Pre-1890 for U.S.)	*Very fine pre-1900 stamps in these categories trade at a premium over Scott value*			Scott Value for "Unused"		Scott "No Gum" listings for selected unused classic stamps
From 1900 to breakpoints for listings of never-hinged stamps	Scott "Never Hinged" listings for selected unused stamps	Scott Value for "Unused" (Actual value will be affected by the degree of hinging of the full o.g.)				
From breakpoints noted for many countries	Scott Value for "Unused"					

Never Hinged (NH; ★★): A never-hinged stamp will have full original gum that will have no hinge mark or disturbance. The presence of an expertizer's mark does not disqualify a stamp from this designation.

Original Gum (OG; ★): Pre-1900 stamps should have approximately half or more of their original gum. On rarer stamps, it may be expected that the original gum will be somewhat more disturbed that it will be on more common issues. Post-1900 stamps should have full original gum. Original gum will show some disturbance caused by a previous hinge(s) which may be present or entirely removed. The actual value of a post-1900 stamp will be affected by the degree of hinging of the full original gum.

Disturbed Original Gum: Gum showing noticeable effects of humidity, climate or hinging over more than half of the gum. The significance of gum disturbance in valuing a stamp in any of the Original Gum categories depends on the degree of disturbance, the rarity and normal gum condition of the issue and other variables affecting quality.

Regummed (RG; (★)): A regummed stamp is a stamp without gum that has had some type of gum privately applied at a time after it was issued. This normally is done to deceive collectors and/or dealers into thinking that the stamp has original gum and therefore has a higher value. A regummed stamp is considered the same as a stamp with none of its original gum for purposes of grading.

Understanding the Listings

On the opposite page is an enlarged "typical" listing from this catalogue. Below are detailed explanations of each of the highlighted parts of the listing.

1 Scott number — Scott catalogue numbers are used to identify specific items when buying, selling or trading stamps. Each listed postage stamp from every country has a unique Scott catalogue number. Therefore, Germany Scott 99, for example, can only refer to a single stamp. Although the Scott catalogue usually lists stamps in chronological order by date of issue, there are exceptions. When a country has issued a set of stamps over a period of time, those stamps within the set are kept together without regard to date of issue. This follows the normal collecting approach of keeping stamps in their natural sets.

When a country issues a set of stamps over a period of time, a group of consecutive catalogue numbers is reserved for the stamps in that set, as issued. If that group of numbers proves to be too few, capital-letter suffixes, such as "A" or "B," may be added to existing numbers to create enough catalogue numbers to cover all items in the set. A capital-letter suffix indicates a major Scott catalogue number listing. Scott uses a suffix letter only once. Therefore, a catalogue number listing with a capital-letter suffix will not also be found with the same letter (lower case) used as a minor-letter listing. If there is a Scott 16A in a set, for example, there will not also be a Scott 16a. However, a minor-letter "a" listing may be added to a major number containing an "A" suffix (Scott 16Aa, for example).

Suffix letters are cumulative. A minor "b" variety of Scott 16A would be Scott 16Ab, not Scott 16b.

There are times when a reserved block of Scott catalogue numbers is too large for a set, leaving some numbers unused. Such gaps in the numbering sequence also occur when the catalogue editors move an item's listing elsewhere or have removed it entirely from the catalogue. Scott does not attempt to account for every possible number, but rather attempts to assure that each stamp is assigned its own number.

Scott numbers designating regular postage normally are only numerals. Scott numbers for other types of stamps, such as air post, semipostal, postal tax, postage due, occupation and others have a prefix consisting of one or more capital letters or a combination of numerals and capital letters.

2 Illustration number — Illustration or design-type numbers are used to identify each catalogue illustration. For most sets, the lowest face-value stamp is shown. It then serves as an example of the basic design approach for other stamps not illustrated. Where more than one stamp use the same illustration number, but have differences in design, the design paragraph or the description line clearly indicates the design on each stamp not illustrated. Where there are both vertical and horizontal designs in a set, a single illustration may be used, with the exceptions noted in the design paragraph or description line.

When an illustration is followed by a lower-case letter in parentheses, such as "A2(b)," the trailing letter indicates which overprint or surcharge illustration applies.

Illustrations normally are 70 percent of the original size of the stamp. An effort has been made to note all illustrations not illustrated at that percentage. Virtually all souvenir sheet illustrations are reduced even more. Overprints and surcharges are shown at 100 percent of their original size if shown alone, but are 70 percent of original size if shown on stamps. In some cases, the illustration will be placed above the set, between listings or omitted completely. Overprint and surcharge illustrations are not placed in this catalogue for purposes of expertizing stamps.

3 Paper color — The color of a stamp's paper is noted in italic type when the paper used is not white.

4 Listing styles — There are two principal types of catalogue listings: major and minor.

Major listings are in a larger type style than minor listings. The catalogue number is a numeral that can be found with or without a capital-letter suffix, and with or without a prefix.

Minor listings are in a smaller type style and have a small-letter suffix or (if the listing immediately follows that of the major number) may show only the letter. These listings identify a variety of the major item. Examples include perforation, color, watermark or printing method differences, multiples (some souvenir sheets, booklet panes and se-tenant combinations), and singles of multiples.

Examples of major number listings include 16, 28A, B97, C13A, 10N5, and 10N6A. Examples of minor numbers are 16a and C13Ab.

5 Basic information about a stamp or set — Introducing each stamp issue is a small section (usually a line listing) of basic information about a stamp or set. This section normally includes the date of issue, method of printing, perforation, watermark and, sometimes, some additional information of note. *Printing method, perforation and watermark apply to the following sets until a change is noted.* Stamps created by overprinting or surcharging previous issues are assumed to have the same perforation, watermark and printing method as the original. Dates of issue are as precise as Scott is able to confirm and often reflect the dates on first-day covers, rather than the actual date of release.

6 Denomination — This normally refers to the face value of the stamp; that is, the cost of the unused stamp at the post office at the time of issue. When a denomination is shown in parentheses, it does not appear on the stamp. This includes the non-denominated stamps of the United States, Brazil and Great Britain, for example.

7 Color or other description — This area provides information to solidify identification of a stamp. In many recent cases, a description of the stamp design appears in this space, rather than a listing of colors.

8 Year of issue — In stamp sets that have been released in a period that spans more than a year, the number shown in parentheses is the year that stamp first appeared. Stamps without a date appeared during the first year of the issue. Dates are not always given for minor varieties.

9 Value unused and Value used — The Scott catalogue values are based on stamps that are in a grade of Very Fine unless stated otherwise. Unused values refer to items that have not seen postal, revenue or any other duty for which they were intended. Pre-1900 unused stamps that were issued with gum must have at least most of their original gum. Later issues are assumed to have full original gum. From breakpoints specified in most countries' listings, stamps are valued as never hinged. Stamps issued without gum are noted. Modern issues with PVA or other synthetic adhesives may appear ungummed. Self-adhesive stamps are valued as appearing undisturbed on their original backing paper. For a more detailed explanation of these values, please see the "Catalogue Value," "Condition" and "Understanding Valuing Notations" sections elsewhere in this introduction.

In some cases, where used stamps are more valuable than unused stamps, the value is for an example with a contemporaneous cancel, rather than a modern cancel or a smudge or other unclear marking. For those stamps that were released for postal and fiscal purposes, the used value represents a postally used stamp. Stamps with revenue cancels generally sell for less. Scott values for used self-adhesive stamps are for examples either on piece or off piece.

10 Changes in basic set information — Bold type is used to show any changes in the basic data given for a set of stamps. This includes perforation differences from one stamp to the next or a different paper, printing method or watermark.

11 Total value of a set — The total value of sets of three or more stamps issued after 1900 are shown. The set line also notes the range of Scott numbers and total number of stamps included in the grouping. The actual value of a set consisting predominantly of stamps having the minimum value of twenty cents may be less than the total value shown. Similarly, the actual value or catalogue value of se-tenant pairs or of blocks consisting of stamps having the minimum value of twenty cents may be less than the catalogue values of the component parts.

SCOTT NUMBER ①

ILLUS. NUMBER ②

PAPER COLOR ③

LISTING STYLES ④ MAJORS / MINORS

King George VI and Leopard – A6

King George VI A7

BASIC INFORMATION ON STAMP OR SET ⑤

DENOMINATION ⑥

COLOR OR OTHER DESCRIPTION ⑦

YEAR OF ISSUE ⑧

CATALOGUE VALUES ⑨ (UNUSED / USED)

CHANGES IN BASIC SET INFORMATION ⑩

TOTAL VALUE OF SET ⑪

1938-44 — **Engr.** — **Perf. 12½**

Scott	Illus.	Denom.	Description	Unused	Used
54	A6	½p	green	.20	1.00
54A	A6	½p	dk brown ('42)	.20	1.25
55	A6	1p	dark brown	.20	.25
55A	A6	1p	green ('42)	.20	.50
56	A6	1½p	dark carmine	.65	3.00
56A	A6	1½p	gray ('42)	.20	3.25
57	A6	2p	gray	1.25	.70
57A	A6	2p	dark car ('42)	.20	1.25
58	A6	3p	blue	.30	.35
59	A6	4p	rose lilac	1.25	.85
60	A6	6p	dark violet	1.75	.85
61	A6	9p	olive bister	1.75	1.75
62	A6	1sh	orange & blk	1.40	1.00

Typo.
Perf. 14
Chalky Paper

Scott	Illus.	Denom.	Description	Unused	Used
63	A7	2sh	ultra & dl vio, *bl*	5.50	6.50
64	A7	2sh6p	red & blk, *bl*	6.50	7.50
65	A7	5sh	red & grn, *yel*	22.50	12.50
a.			5sh dk red & dp grn, *yel* ('44)	50.00	37.50
66	A7	10sh	red & grn, *grn*	32.50	24.00

Wmk. 3

Scott	Illus.	Denom.	Description	Unused	Used
67	A7	£1	blk & vio, *red*	20.00	18.00
			Nos. 54-67 (18)	96.55	84.50
			Set, never hinged	150.00	

Catalogue Listing Policy

It is the intent of Scott Publishing Co. to list all postage stamps of the world in the *Scott Standard Postage Stamp Catalogue*. The only strict criteria for listing is that stamps be decreed legal for postage by the issuing country and that the issuing country actually have an operating postal system. Whether the primary intent of issuing a given stamp or set was for sale to postal patrons or to stamp collectors is not part of our listing criteria. Scott's role is to provide basic comprehensive postage stamp information. It is up to each stamp collector to choose which items to include in a collection.

It is Scott's objective to seek reasons why a stamp should be listed, rather than why it should not. Nevertheless, there are certain types of items that will not be listed. These include the following:

1. Unissued items that are not officially distributed or released by the issuing postal authority. If such items are officially issued at a later date by the country, they will be listed. Unissued items consist of those that have been printed and then held from sale for reasons such as change in government, errors found on stamps or something deemed objectionable about a stamp subject or design.

2. Stamps "issued" by non-existent postal entities or fantasy countries, such as Nagaland, Occusi-Ambeno, Staffa, Sedang, Torres Straits and others. Also, stamps "issued" in the names of legitimate, stamp-issuing countries that are not authorized by those countries.

3. Semi-official or unofficial items not required for postage. Examples include items issued by private agencies for their own express services. When such items are required for delivery, or are valid as prepayment of postage, they are listed.

4. Local stamps issued for local use only. Postage stamps issued by governments specifically for "domestic" use, such as Haiti Scott 219-228, or the United States non-denominated stamps, are not considered to be locals, since they are valid for postage throughout the country of origin.

5. Items not valid for postal use. For example, a few countries have issued souvenir sheets that are not valid for postage. This area also includes a number of worldwide charity labels (some denominated) that do not pay postage.

6. Intentional varieties, such as imperforate stamps that look like their perforated counterparts and are usually issued in very small quantities. Also, other egregiously exploitative issues such as stamps sold for far more than face value or stamps purposefully issued in artificially small quantities or only against advance orders. All of these kinds of items are usually controlled issues and/or are intended for speculation.

7. Items distributed by the issuing government only to a limited group, such as a stamp club, philatelic exhibition or a single stamp dealer, and later brought to market at inflated prices. These items normally will be included in a footnote.

The fact that a stamp has been used successfully as postage, even on international mail, is not in itself sufficient proof that it was legitimately issued. Numerous examples of so-called stamps from non-existent countries are known to have been used to post letters that have successfully passed through the international mail system.

There are certain items that are subject to interpretation. When a stamp falls outside our specifications, it may be listed along with a cautionary footnote.

A number of factors are considered in our approach to analyzing how a stamp is listed. The following list of factors is presented to share with you, the catalogue user, the complexity of the listing process.

Additional printings — "Additional printings" of a previously issued stamp may range from an item that is totally different to cases where it is impossible to differentiate from the original. At least a minor number (a small-letter suffix) is assigned if there is a distinct change in stamp shade, noticeably redrawn design, or a significantly different perforation measurement. A major number (numeral or numeral and capital-letter combination) is assigned if the editors feel the "additional printing" is sufficiently different from the original that it constitutes a different issue.

Commemoratives — Where practical, commemoratives with the same theme are placed in a set. For example, the U.S. Civil War Centennial set of 1961-65 and the Constitution Bicentennial series of 1989-90 appear as sets. Countries such as Japan and Korea issue such material on a regular basis, with an announced, or at least predictable, number of stamps known in advance. Occasionally, however, stamp sets that were released over a period of years have been separated. Appropriately placed footnotes will guide you to each set's continuation.

Definitive sets — Blocks of numbers generally have been reserved for definitive sets, based on previous experience with any given country. If a few more stamps were issued in a set than originally expected, they often have been inserted into the original set with a capital-letter suffix, such as U.S. Scott 1059A. If it appears that many more stamps than the originally allotted block will be released before the set is completed, a new block of numbers will be reserved, with the original one being closed off. In some cases, such as the U.S. Transportation and Great Americans series, several blocks of numbers exist. Appropriately placed footnotes will guide you to each set's continuation.

New country — Membership in the Universal Postal Union is not a consideration for listing status or order of placement within the catalogue. The index will tell you in what volume or page number the listings begin.

"No release date" items — The amount of information available for any given stamp issue varies greatly from country to country and even from time to time. Extremely comprehensive information about new stamps is available from some countries well before the stamps are released. By contrast some countries do not provide information about stamps or release dates. Most countries, however, fall between these extremes. A country may provide denominations or subjects of stamps from upcoming issues that are not issued as planned. Sometimes, philatelic agencies, those private firms hired to represent countries, add these later-issued items to sets well after the formal release date. This time period can range from weeks to years. If these items were officially released by the country, they will be added to the appropriate spot in the set. In many cases, the specific release date of a stamp or set of stamps may never be known.

Overprints — The color of an overprint is always noted if it is other than black. Where more than one color of ink has been used on overprints of a single set, the color used is noted. Early overprint and surcharge illustrations were altered to prevent their use by forgers.

Se-tenants — Connected stamps of differing features (se-tenants) will be listed in the format most commonly collected. This includes pairs, blocks or larger multiples. Se-tenant units are not always symmetrical. An example is Australia Scott 508, which is a block of seven stamps. If the stamps are primarily collected as a unit, the major number may be assigned to the multiple, with minors going to each component stamp. In cases where continuous-design or other unit se-tenants will receive significant postal use, each stamp is given a major Scott number listing. This includes issues from the United States, Canada, Germany and Great Britain, for example.

Special Notices

Classification of stamps

The *Scott Standard Postage Stamp Catalogue* lists stamps by country of issue. The next level of organization is a listing by section on the basis of the function of the stamps. The principal sections cover regular postage, semi-postal, air post, special delivery, registration, postage due and other categories. Except for regular postage, catalogue numbers for all sections include a prefix letter (or number-letter combination) denoting the class to which a given stamp belongs. When some countries issue sets containing stamps from more than one category, the catalogue will at times list all of the stamps in one category (such as air post stamps listed as part of a postage set).

The following is a listing of the most commonly used catalogue prefixes.

Prefix...	Category
C	Air Post
M	Military
P	Newspaper
N	Occupation - Regular Issues
O	Official
Q	Parcel Post
J	Postage Due
RA	Postal Tax
B	Semi-Postal
E	Special Delivery
MR	War Tax

Other prefixes used by more than one country include the following:

H	Acknowledgment of Receipt
I	Late Fee
CO	Air Post Official
CQ	Air Post Parcel Post
RAC	Air Post Postal Tax
CF	Air Post Registration
CB	Air Post Semi-Postal
CBO	Air Post Semi-Postal Official
CE	Air Post Special Delivery
EY	Authorized Delivery
S	Franchise
G	Insured Letter
GY	Marine Insurance
MC	Military Air Post
MQ	Military Parcel Post
NC	Occupation - Air Post
NO	Occupation - Official
NJ	Occupation - Postage Due
NRA	Occupation - Postal Tax
NB	Occupation - Semi-Postal
NE	Occupation - Special Delivery
QY	Parcel Post Authorized Delivery
AR	Postal-fiscal
RAJ	Postal Tax Due
RAB	Postal Tax Semi-Postal
F	Registration
EB	Semi-Postal Special Delivery
EO	Special Delivery Official
QE	Special Handling

New issue listings

Updates to this catalogue appear each month in the *Scott Stamp Monthly* magazine. Included in this update are additions to the listings of countries found in the *Scott Standard Postage Stamp Catalogue* and the *Specialized Catalogue of United States Stamps*, as well as corrections and updates to current editions of this catalogue.

From time to time there will be changes in the final listings of stamps from the *Scott Stamp Monthly* to the next edition of the catalogue. This occurs as more information about certain stamps or sets becomes available.

The catalogue update section of the *Scott Stamp Monthly* is the most timely presentation of this material available. Annual subscriptions to the *Scott Stamp Monthly* are available from Scott Publishing Co., Box 828, Sidney, OH 45365-0828.

Number additions, deletions & changes

A listing of catalogue number additions, deletions and changes from the previous edition of the catalogue appears in each volume. See Catalogue Number Additions, Deletions & Changes in the table of contents for the location of this list.

Understanding valuing notations

The *minimum catalogue value* of an individual stamp or set is 20 cents. This represents a portion of the cost incurred by a dealer when he prepares an individual stamp for resale. As a point of philatelic-economic fact, the lower the value shown for an item in this catalogue, the greater the percentage of that value is attributed to dealer mark up and profit margin. In many cases, such as the 20-cent minimum value, that price does not cover the labor or other costs involved with stocking it as an individual stamp. The sum of minimum values in a set does not properly represent the value of a complete set primarily composed of a number of minimum-value stamps, nor does the sum represent the actual value of a packet made up of minimum-value stamps. Thus a packet of 1,000 different common stamps — each of which has a catalogue value of 20-cents — normally sells for considerably less than 200 dollars!

The *absence of a retail value* for a stamp does not necessarily suggest that a stamp is scarce or rare. A dash in the value column means that the stamp is known in a stated form or variety, but information is either lacking or insufficient for purposes of establishing a usable catalogue value.

Stamp values in *italics* generally refer to items that are difficult to value accurately. For expensive items, such as those priced at $1,000 or higher, a value in italics indicates that the affected item trades very seldom. For inexpensive items, a value in italics represents a warning. One example is a "blocked" issue where the issuing postal administration may have controlled one stamp in a set in an attempt to make the whole set more valuable. Another example is an item that sold at an extreme multiple of face value in the marketplace at the time of its issue.

One type of warning to collectors that appears in the catalogue is illustrated by a stamp that is valued considerably higher in used condition than it is as unused. In this case, collectors are cautioned to be certain the used version has a genuine and contemporaneous cancellation. The type of cancellation on a stamp can be an important factor in determining its sale price. Catalogue values do not apply to fiscal, telegraph or non-contemporaneous postal cancels, unless otherwise noted.

Some countries have released back issues of stamps in canceled-to-order form, sometimes covering as much as a 10-year period. The Scott Catalogue values for used stamps reflect canceled-to-order material when such stamps are found to predominate in the marketplace for the issue involved. Notes frequently appear in the stamp listings to specify which items are valued as canceled-to-order, or if there is a premium for postally used examples.

Many countries sell canceled-to-order stamps at a marked reduction of face value. Countries that sell or have sold canceled-to-order stamps at *full* face value include Australia, Netherlands, France and Switzerland. It may be almost impossible to identify such stamps if the gum has been removed, because official government canceling devices are used. Postally used copies of these items on cover, however, are usually worth more than the canceled-to-order stamps with original gum.

Abbreviations

Scott Publishing Co. uses a consistent set of abbreviations throughout this catalogue to conserve space, while still providing necessary information.

COLOR ABBREVIATIONS

amb .amber	crim .crimson	ol .....olive
anil ..aniline	cr .....cream	olvn .olivine
ap ....apple	dk ....dark	org ...orange
aqua.aquamarine	dl ....dull	pck...peacock
az.....azure	dp ....deep	pnksh pinkish
bis....bister	db ....drab	Prus .Prussian
bl .....blue	emer emerald	pur...purple
bld ...blood	gldn .golden	redsh reddish
blk ...black	grysh grayish	res....reseda
bril ...brilliant	grn ...green	ros ...rosine
brn...brown	grnsh greenish	ryl ....royal
brnsh brownish	hel ...heliotrope	sal ....salmon
brnz .bronze	hn ....henna	saph .sapphire
brt....bright	ind ...indigo	scar ..scarlet
brnt..burnt	int ....intense	sep ...sepia
car ...carmine	lav....lavender	sien ..sienna
cer ...cerise	lem ...lemon	sil .....silver
chlky chalky	lil .....lilac	sl ......slate
cham chamois	lt ......light	stl ....steel
chnt .chestnut	mag..magenta	turq..turquoise
choc.chocolate	man ..manila	ultra.ultramarine
chr...chrome	mar ..maroon	Ven ..Venetian
cit ....citron	mv ...mauve	ver ...vermilion
cl .....claret	multi multicolored	vio ...violet
cob...cobalt	mlky milky	yel....yellow
cop...copper	myr ..myrtle	yelsh yellowish

When no color is given for an overprint or surcharge, black is the color used. Abbreviations for colors used for overprints and surcharges include: "(B)" or "(Blk)," black; "(Bl)," blue; "(R)," red; and "(G)," green.

Additional abbreviations in this catalogue are shown below:

Adm.............Administration
AFL.............American Federation of Labor
Anniv. ....Anniversary
APS.............American Philatelic Society
Assoc. ....Association
ASSR...........Autonomous Soviet Socialist Republic
b. ....Born
BEP.............Bureau of Engraving and Printing
Bicent. ....Bicentennial
Bklt.............Booklet
Brit. ....British
btwn............Between
Bur. ....Bureau
c. or ca........Circa
Cat..............Catalogue
Cent............Centennial, century, centenary
CIO.............Congress of Industrial Organizations
Conf............Conference
Cong. ....Congress
Cpl..............Corporal
CTO............Canceled to order
d. ....Died
Dbl. ....Double
EKU ....Earliest known use
Engr. ....Engraved
Exhib. ....Exhibition
Expo. ....Exposition
Fed. ....Federation
GB ....Great Britain
Gen.............General
GPO............General post office
Horiz. ....Horizontal
Imperf..........Imperforate
Impt............Imprint

Intl..............International
Invtd............Inverted
L..................Left
Lieut., lt. ......Lieutenant
Litho. ....Lithographed
LL ....Lower left
LR ....Lower right
mm ....Millimeter
Ms. ....Manuscript
Natl. ....National
No. ....Number
NY ....New York
NYC............New York City
Ovpt. ....Overprint
Ovptd. ....Overprinted
P.................Plate number
Perf.............Perforated, perforation
Phil. ....Philatelic
Photo. ....Photogravure
PO ....Post office
Pr. ....Pair
P.R. ....Puerto Rico
Prec. ....Precancel, precanceled
Pres.............President
PTT.............Post, Telephone and Telegraph
Rio ....Rio de Janeiro
Sgt. ....Sergeant
Soc..............Society
Souv.............Souvenir
SSR ....Soviet Socialist Republic, see ASSR
St. ....Saint, street
Surch. ....Surcharge
Typo............Typographed
UL ....Upper left
Unwmkd......Unwatermarked
UPU............Universal Postal Union
UR ....Upper Right
US...............United States
USPOD ....United States Post Office Department
USSR...........Union of Soviet Socialist Republics
Vert.............Vertical
VP................Vice president
Wmk...........Watermark
Wmkd..........Watermarked
WWI...........World War I
WWII..........World War II

Examination

Scott Publishing Co. will not comment upon the genuineness, grade or condition of stamps, because of the time and responsibility involved. Rather, there are several expertizing groups that undertake this work for both collectors and dealers. Neither will Scott Publishing Co. appraise or identify philatelic material. The company cannot take responsibility for unsolicited stamps or covers sent by individuals.

How to order from your dealer

When ordering stamps from a dealer, it is not necessary to write the full description of a stamp as listed in this catalogue. All you need is the name of the country, the Scott catalogue number and whether the desired item is unused or used. For example, "Japan Scott 422 unused" is sufficient to identify the unused stamp of Japan listed as "422 A206 5y brown."

Basic Stamp Information

A stamp collector's knowledge of the combined elements that make a given stamp issue unique determines his or her ability to identify stamps. These elements include paper, watermark, method of separation, printing, design and gum. On the following pages each of these important areas is briefly described.

Paper

Paper is an organic material composed of a compacted weave of cellulose fibers and generally formed into sheets. Paper used to print stamps may be manufactured in sheets, or it may have been part of a large roll (called a web) before being cut to size. The fibers most often used to create paper on which stamps are printed include bark, wood, straw and certain grasses. In many cases, linen or cotton rags have been added for greater strength and durability. Grinding, bleaching, cooking and rinsing these raw fibers reduces them to a slushy pulp, referred to by paper makers as "stuff." Sizing and, sometimes, coloring matter is added to the pulp to make different types of finished paper.

After the stuff is prepared, it is poured onto sieve-like frames that allow the water to run off, while retaining the matted pulp. As fibers fall onto the screen and are held by gravity, they form a natural weave that will later hold the paper together. If the screen has metal bits that are formed into letters or images attached, it leaves slightly thinned areas on the paper. These are called watermarks.

When the stuff is almost dry, it is passed under pressure through smooth or engraved rollers - dandy rolls - or placed between cloth in a press to be flattened and dried.

Stamp paper falls broadly into two types: wove and laid. The nature of the surface of the frame onto which the pulp is first deposited causes the differences in appearance between the two. If the surface is smooth and even, the paper will be of fairly uniform texture throughout. This is known as *wove paper*. Early papermaking machines poured the pulp onto a continuously circulating web of felt, but modern machines feed the pulp onto a cloth-like screen made of closely interwoven fine wires. This paper, when held to a light, will show little dots or points very close together. The proper name for this is "wire wove," but the type is still considered wove. Any U.S. or British stamp printed after 1880 will serve as an example of wire wove paper.

Closely spaced parallel wires, with cross wires at wider intervals, make up the frames used for what is known as *laid paper*. A greater thickness of the pulp will settle between the wires. The paper, when held to a light, will show alternate light and dark lines. The spacing and the thickness of the lines may vary, but on any one sheet of paper they are all alike. See Russia Scott 31-38 for examples of laid paper.

Batonne, from the French word meaning "a staff," is a term used if the lines in the paper are spaced quite far apart, like the printed ruling on a writing tablet. Batonne paper may be either wove or laid. If laid, fine laid lines can be seen between the batons.

Quadrille is the term used when the lines in the paper form little squares. *Oblong quadrille* is the term used when rectangles, rather than squares, are formed. See Mexico-Guadalajara Scott 35-37 for examples of oblong quadrille paper.

Paper also is classified as thick or thin, hard or soft, and by color if dye is added during manufacture. Such colors may include yellowish, greenish, bluish and reddish.

Brief explanations of other types of paper used for printing stamps, as well as examples, follow.

Pelure — Pelure paper is a very thin, hard and often brittle paper that is sometimes bluish or grayish in appearance. See Serbia Scott 169-170.

Native — This is a term applied to handmade papers used to produce some of the early stamps of the Indian states. Stamps printed on native paper may be expected to display various natural inclusions that are normal and do not negatively affect value. Japanese paper, originally made of mulberry fibers and rice flour, is part of this group. See Japan Scott 1-18.

Manila — This type of paper is often used to make stamped envelopes and wrappers. It is a coarse-textured stock, usually smooth on one side and rough on the other. A variety of colors of manila paper exist, but the most common range is yellowish-brown.

Silk — Introduced by the British in 1847 as a safeguard against counterfeiting, silk paper contains bits of colored silk thread scattered throughout. The density of these fibers varies greatly and can include as few as one fiber per stamp or hundreds. U.S. revenue Scott R152 is a good example of an easy-to-identify silk paper stamp.

Silk-thread paper has uninterrupted threads of colored silk arranged so that one or more threads run through the stamp or postal stationery. See Great Britain Scott 5-6 and Switzerland Scott 14-19.

Granite — Filled with minute cloth or colored paper fibers of various colors and lengths, granite paper should not be confused with either type of silk paper. Austria Scott 172-175 and a number of Swiss stamps are examples of granite paper.

Chalky — A chalk-like substance coats the surface of chalky paper to discourage the cleaning and reuse of canceled stamps, as well as to provide a smoother, more acceptable printing surface. Because the designs of stamps printed on chalky paper are imprinted on what is often a water-soluble coating, any attempt to remove a cancellation will destroy the stamp. *Do not soak these stamps in any fluid.* To remove a stamp printed on chalky paper from an envelope, wet the paper from underneath the stamp until the gum dissolves enough to release the stamp from the paper. See St. Kitts-Nevis Scott 89-90 for examples of stamps printed on this type of chalky paper.

India — Another name for this paper, originally introduced from China about 1750, is "China Paper." It is a thin, opaque paper often used for plate and die proofs by many countries.

Double — In philately, the term double paper has two distinct meanings. The first is a two-ply paper, usually a combination of a thick and a thin sheet, joined during manufacture. This type was used experimentally as a means to discourage the reuse of stamps.

The design is printed on the thin paper. Any attempt to remove a cancellation would destroy the design. U.S. Scott 158 and other Banknote-era stamps exist on this form of double paper.

The second type of double paper occurs on a rotary press, when the end of one paper roll, or web, is affixed to the next roll to save time feeding the paper through the press. Stamp designs are printed over the joined paper and, if overlooked by inspectors, may get into post office stocks.

Goldbeater's Skin — This type of paper was used for the 1866 issue of Prussia, and was a tough, translucent paper. The design was printed in reverse on the back of the stamp, and the gum applied over the printing. It is impossible to remove stamps printed on this type of paper from the paper to which they are affixed without destroying the design.

Ribbed — Ribbed paper has an uneven, corrugated surface made by passing the paper through ridged rollers. This type exists on some copies of U.S. Scott 156-165.

Various other substances, or substrates, have been used for stamp manufacture, including wood, aluminum, copper, silver and gold foil, plastic, and silk and cotton fabrics.

Wove   Laid   Granite

Quadrille   Oblong   Laid
Quadrille   Batonne

Watermarks

Watermarks are an integral part of some papers. They are formed in the process of paper manufacture. Watermarks consist of small designs, formed of wire or cut from metal and soldered to the surface of the mold or, sometimes, on the dandy roll. The designs may be in the form of crowns, stars, anchors, letters or other characters or symbols. These pieces of metal - known in the paper-making industry as "bits" - impress a design into the paper. The design sometimes may be seen by holding the stamp to the light. Some are more easily seen with a watermark detector. This important tool is a small black tray into which a stamp is placed face down and dampened with a fast-evaporating watermark detection fluid that brings up the watermark image in the form of dark lines against a lighter background. These dark lines are the thinner areas of the paper known as the watermark. Some watermarks are extremely difficult to locate, due to either a faint impression, watermark location or the color of the stamp. There also are electric watermark detectors that come with plastic filter disks of various colors. The disks neutralize the color of the stamp, permitting the watermark to be seen more easily.

Multiple watermarks of Crown Agents and Burma

Watermarks of Uruguay, Vatican City and Jamaica

WARNING: Some inks used in the photogravure process dissolve in watermark fluids (Please see the section on Soluble Printing Inks). Also, see "chalky paper."

Watermarks may be found normal, reversed, inverted, reversed and inverted, sideways or diagonal, as seen from the back of the stamp.

The relationship of watermark to stamp design depends on the position of the printing plates or how paper is fed through the press. On machine-made paper, watermarks normally are read from right to left. The design is repeated closely throughout the sheet in a "multiple-watermark design." In a "sheet watermark," the design appears only once on the sheet, but extends over many stamps. Individual stamps may carry only a small fraction or none of the watermark.

"Marginal watermarks" occur in the margins of sheets or panes of stamps. They occur on the outside border of paper (ostensibly outside the area where stamps are to be printed). A large row of letters may spell the name of the country or the manufacturer of the paper, or a border of lines may appear. Careless press feeding may cause parts of these letters and/or lines to show on stamps of the outer row of a pane.

Soluble Printing Inks

WARNING: Most stamp colors are permanent; that is, they are not seriously affected by short-term exposure to light or water. Many colors, especially of modern inks, fade from excessive exposure to light. There are stamps printed with inks that dissolve easily in water or in fluids used to detect watermarks. Use of these inks was intentional to prevent the removal of cancellations. Water affects all aniline inks, those on so-called safety paper and some photogravure printings - all such inks are known as *fugitive colors. Removal from paper of such stamps requires care and alternatives to traditional soaking.*

Separation

"Separation" is the general term used to describe methods used to separate stamps. The three standard forms currently in use are perforating, rouletting and die-cutting. These methods are done during the stamp production process, after printing. Sometimes these methods are done on-press or sometimes as a separate step. The earliest issues, such as the 1840 Penny Black of Great Britain (Scott 1), did not have any means provided for separation. It was expected the stamps would be cut apart with scissors or folded and torn. These are examples of imperforate stamps. Many stamps were first issued in imperforate formats and were later issued with perforations. Therefore, care must be observed in buying single imperforate stamps to be certain they were issued imperforate and are not perforated copies that have been altered by having the perforations trimmed away. Stamps issued imperforate usually are valued as singles. However, imperforate varieties of normally perforated stamps should be collected in pairs or larger pieces as indisputable evidence of their imperforate character.

PERFORATION

The chief style of separation of stamps, and the one that is in almost universal use today, is perforating. By this process, paper between the stamps is cut away in a line of holes, usually round, leaving little bridges of paper between the stamps to hold them together. Some types of perforation, such as hyphen-hole perfs, can be confused with roulettes, but a close visual inspection reveals that paper has been removed. The little perforation bridges, which project from the stamp when it is torn from the pane, are called the teeth of the perforation.

As the size of the perforation is sometimes the only way to differentiate between two otherwise identical stamps, it is necessary to be able to accurately measure and describe them. This is done with a perforation gauge, usually a ruler-like device that has dots or graduated lines to show how many perforations may be counted in the space of two centimeters. Two centimeters is the space universally adopted in which to measure perforations.

Perforation gauge

perce en arc   perce en lignes

perce en points   oblique roulette

perce en scie   perce serpentin

To measure a stamp, run it along the gauge until the dots on it fit exactly into the perforations of the stamp. If you are using a graduated-line perforation gauge, simply slide the stamp along the surface until the lines on the gauge perfectly project from the center of the bridges or holes. The number to the side of the line of dots or lines that fit the stamp's perforation is the measurement. For example, an "11" means that 11 perforations fit between two centimeters. The description of the stamp therefore is "perf. 11." If the gauge of the perforations on the top and bottom of a stamp differs from that on the sides, the result is what is known as *compound perforations.* In measuring compound perforations, the gauge at top and bottom is always given first, then the sides. Thus, a stamp that measures 11 at top and bottom and 10 1/2 at the sides is "perf. 11 x 10 1/2." See U.S. Scott 632-642 for examples of compound perforations.

Stamps also are known with perforations different on three or all four sides. Descriptions of such items are clockwise, beginning with the top of the stamp.

A perforation with small holes and teeth close together is a "fine perforation." One with large holes and teeth far apart is a "coarse perforation." Holes that are jagged, rather than clean-cut, are "rough perforations." *Blind perforations* are the slight impressions left by the perforating pins if they fail to puncture the paper. Multiples of stamps showing blind perforations may command a slight premium over normally perforated stamps.

The term *syncopated perfs* describes intentional irregularities in the perforations. The earliest form was used by the Netherlands from 1925-33, where holes were omitted to create distinctive patterns. Beginning in 1992, Great Britain has used an oval perforation to help prevent counterfeiting. Several other countries have started using the oval perfs or other syncopated perf patterns.

A new type of perforation, still primarily used for postal stationery, is known as microperfs. Microperfs are tiny perforations (in some cases hundreds of holes per two centimeters) that allows items to be intentionally separated very easily, while not accidentally breaking apart as easily as standard perforations. These are not currently measured or differentiated by size, as are standard perforations.

ROULETTING

In rouletting, the stamp paper is cut partly or wholly through, with no paper removed. In perforating, some paper is removed. Rouletting derives its name from the French roulette, a spur-like wheel. As the wheel is rolled over the paper, each point makes a small cut. The number of cuts made in a two-centimeter space determines the gauge of the roulette, just as the number of perforations in two centimeters determines the gauge of the perforation.

The shape and arrangement of the teeth on the wheels varies. Various roulette types generally carry French names:

Perce en lignes - rouletted in lines. The paper receives short, straight cuts in lines. This is the most common type of rouletting. See Mexico Scott 500.

Perce en points - pin-rouletted or pin-perfed. This differs from a small perforation because no paper is removed, although round, equidistant holes are pricked through the paper. See Mexico Scott 242-256.

Perce en arc and *perce en scie* - pierced in an arc or saw-toothed designs, forming half circles or small triangles. See Hanover (German States) Scott 25-29.

Perce en serpentin - serpentine roulettes. The cuts form a serpentine or wavy line. See Brunswick (German States) Scott 13-18.

Once again, no paper is removed by these processes, leaving the stamps easily separated, but closely attached.

DIE-CUTTING

The third major form of stamp separation is die-cutting. This is a method where a die in the pattern of separation is created that later cuts the stamp paper in a stroke motion. Although some standard stamps bear die-cut perforations, this process is primarily used for self-adhesive postage stamps. Die-cutting can appear in straight lines, such as U.S. Scott 2522, shapes, such as U.S. Scott 1551, or imitating the appearance of perforations, such as New Zealand Scott 935A and 935B.

Printing Processes

ENGRAVING (Intaglio, Line-engraving, Etching)

Master die — The initial operation in the process of line engraving is making the master die. The die is a small, flat block of softened steel upon which the stamp design is recess engraved in reverse.

Master die

Photographic reduction of the original art is made to the appropriate size. It then serves as a tracing guide for the initial outline of the design. The engraver lightly traces the design on the steel with his graver, then slowly works the design until it is completed. At various points during the engraving process, the engraver hand-inks the die and makes an impression to check his progress. These are known as progressive die proofs. After completion of the engraving, the die is hardened to withstand the stress and pressures of later transfer operations.

Transfer roll

Transfer roll — Next is production of the transfer roll that, as the name implies, is the medium used to transfer the subject from the master die to the printing plate. A blank roll of soft steel, mounted on a mandrel, is placed under the bearers of the transfer press to allow it to roll freely on its axis. The hardened die is placed on the bed of the press and the face of the transfer roll is applied to the die, under pressure. The bed or the roll is then rocked back and forth under increasing pressure, until the soft steel of the roll is forced into every engraved line of the die. The resulting impression on the roll is known as a "relief" or a "relief transfer." The engraved image is now positive in appearance and stands out from the steel. After the required number of reliefs are "rocked in," the soft steel transfer roll is hardened.

Different flaws may occur during the relief process. A defective relief may occur during the rocking in process because of a minute piece of foreign material lodging on the die, or some other cause. Imperfections in the steel of the transfer roll may result in a breaking away of parts of the design. This is known as a relief break, which will show up on finished stamps as small, unprinted areas. If a damaged relief remains in use, it will transfer a repeating defect to the plate. Deliberate alterations of reliefs sometimes occur. "Altered reliefs" designate these changed conditions.

Plate — The final step in pre-printing production is the making of the printing plate. A flat piece of soft steel replaces the die on the bed of the transfer press. One of the reliefs on the transfer roll is positioned over this soft steel. Position, or layout, dots determine the correct position on the plate. The dots have been lightly marked on

the plate in advance. After the correct position of the relief is determined, the design is rocked in by following the same method used in making the transfer roll. The difference is that this time the image is being transferred from the transfer roll, rather than to it. Once the design is entered on the plate, it appears in reverse and is recessed. There are as many transfers entered on the plate as there are subjects printed on the sheet of stamps. It is during this process that double and shifted transfers occur, as well as re-entries. These are the result of improperly entered images that have not been properly burnished out prior to rocking in a new image.

Modern siderography processes, such as those used by the U.S. Bureau of Engraving and Printing, involve an automated form of rocking designs in on preformed cylindrical printing sleeves. The same process also allows for easier removal and re-entry of worn images right on the sleeve.

Transferring the design to the plate

Following the entering of the required transfers on the plate, the position dots, layout dots and lines, scratches and other markings generally are burnished out. Added at this time by the siderographer are any required *guide lines, plate numbers* or other *marginal markings*. The plate is then hand-inked and a proof impression is taken. This is known as a plate proof. If the impression is approved, the plate is machined for fitting onto the press, is hardened and sent to the plate vault ready for use.

On press, the plate is inked and the surface is automatically wiped clean, leaving ink only in the recessed lines. Paper is then forced under pressure into the engraved recessed lines, thereby receiving the ink. Thus, the ink lines on engraved stamps are slightly raised, and slight depressions (debossing) occur on the back of the stamp. Prior to the advent of modern high-speed presses and more advanced ink formulations, paper had to be dampened before receiving the ink. This sometimes led to uneven shrinkage by the time the stamps were perforated, resulting in improperly perforated stamps, or misperfs. Newer presses use drier paper, thus both *wet* and *dry printings* exist on some stamps.

Rotary Press — Until 1914, only flat plates were used to print engraved stamps. Rotary press printing was introduced in 1914, and slowly spread. Some countries still use flat-plate printing.

After approval of the plate proof, older *rotary press plates* require additional machining. They are curved to fit the press cylinder. "Gripper slots" are cut into the back of each plate to receive the "grippers," which hold the plate securely on the press. The plate is then hardened. Stamps printed from these bent rotary press plates are longer or wider than the same stamps printed from flat-plate presses. The stretching of the plate during the curving process is what causes this distortion.

Re-entry — To execute a re-entry on a flat plate, the transfer roll is re-applied to the plate, often at some time after its first use on the press. Worn-out designs can be resharpened by carefully burnishing out the original image and re-entering it from the transfer roll. If the original impression has not been sufficiently removed and the transfer roll is not precisely in line with the remaining impression, the resulting double transfer will make the re-entry obvious. If the registration is true, a re-entry may be difficult or impossible to distinguish. Sometimes a stamp printed from a successful re-entry is identified by having a much sharper and clearer impression than its neighbors. With the advent of rotary presses, post-press re-entries were not possible. After a plate was curved for the rotary press, it was impossible to make a re-entry. This is because the plate had already been bent once (with the design distorted).

However, with the introduction of the previously mentioned modern-style siderography machines, entries are made to the preformed cylindrical printing sleeve. Such sleeves are dechromed and softened. This allows individual images to be burnished out and re-entered on the curved sleeve. The sleeve is then rechromed, resulting in longer press life.

Double Transfer — This is a description of the condition of a transfer on a plate that shows evidence of a duplication of all, or a portion of the design. It usually is the result of the changing of the registration between the transfer roll and the plate during the rocking in of the original entry. Double transfers also occur when only a portion of the design has been rocked in and improper positioning is noted. If the worker elected not to burnish out the partial or completed design, a strong double transfer will occur for part or all of the design.

It sometimes is necessary to remove the original transfer from a plate and repeat the process a second time. If the finished re-worked image shows traces of the original impression, attributable to incomplete burnishing, the result is a partial double transfer.

With the modern automatic machines mentioned previously, double transfers are all but impossible to create. Those partially doubled images on stamps printed from such sleeves are more than likely re-entries, rather than true double transfers.

Re-engraved — Alterations to a stamp design are sometimes necessary after some stamps have been printed. In some cases, either the original die or the actual printing plate may have its "temper" drawn (softened), and the design will be re-cut. The resulting impressions from such a re-engraved die or plate may differ slightly from the original issue, and are known as "re-engraved." If the alteration was made to the master die, all future printings will be consistently different from the original. If alterations were made to the printing plate, each altered stamp on the plate will be slightly different from each other, allowing specialists to reconstruct a complete printing plate.

Dropped Transfers — If an impression from the transfer roll has not been properly placed, a dropped transfer may occur. The final stamp image will appear obviously out of line with its neighbors.

Short Transfer — Sometimes a transfer roll is not rocked its entire length when entering a transfer onto a plate. As a result, the finished transfer on the plate fails to show the complete design, and the finished stamp will have an incomplete design printed. This is known as a "short transfer." U.S. Scott No. 8 is a good example of a short transfer.

TYPOGRAPHY (Letterpress, Surface Printing, Flexography, Dry Offset, High Etch)

Although the word "Typography" is obsolete as a term describing a printing method, it was the accepted term throughout the first century of postage stamps. Therefore, appropriate Scott listings in this catalogue refer to typographed stamps. The current term for this form of printing, however, is "letterpress."

As it relates to the production of postage stamps, letterpress printing is the reverse of engraving. Rather than having recessed areas trap the ink and deposit it on paper, only the raised areas of the design are inked. This is comparable to the type of printing seen by inking and using an ordinary rubber stamp. Letterpress includes all printing where the design is above the surface area, whether it is wood, metal or, in some instances, hardened rubber or polymer plastic.

For most letterpress-printed stamps, the engraved master is made in much the same manner as for engraved stamps. In this instance, however, an additional step is needed. The design is transferred to another surface before being transferred to the transfer roll. In this way, the transfer roll has a recessed stamp design, rather than one done in relief. This makes the printing areas on the final plate raised, or relief areas.

For less-detailed stamps of the 19th century, the area on the die not used as a printing surface was cut away, leaving the surface area raised. The original die was then reproduced by stereotyping or electrotyping. The resulting electrotypes were assembled in the required number and format of the desired sheet of stamps. The plate used in printing the stamps was an electroplate of these assembled electrotypes.

Once the final letterpress plates are created, ink is applied to the raised surface and the pressure of the press transfers the ink impression to the paper. In contrast to engraving, the fine lines of letterpress are impressed on the surface of the stamp, leaving a debossed surface. When viewed from the back (as on a typewritten page), the corresponding line work on the stamp will be raised slightly (embossed) above the surface.

PHOTOGRAVURE (Gravure, Rotogravure, Heliogravure)

In this process, the basic principles of photography are applied to a chemically sensitized metal plate, rather than photographic paper. The design is transferred photographically to the plate through a halftone, or dot-matrix screen, breaking the reproduction into tiny dots. The plate is treated chemically and the dots form depressions, called cells, of varying depths and diameters, depending on the degrees of shade in the design. Then, like engraving, ink is applied to the plate and the surface is wiped clean. This leaves ink in the tiny cells that is lifted out and deposited on the paper when it is pressed against the plate.

Gravure is most often used for multicolored stamps, generally using the three primary colors (red, yellow and blue) and black. By varying the dot matrix pattern and density of these colors, virtually any color can be reproduced. A typical full-color gravure stamp will be created from four printing cylinders (one for each color). The original multicolored image will have been photographically separated into its component colors.

Modern gravure printing may use computer-generated dot-matrix screens, and modern plates may be of various types including metal-coated plastic. The catalogue designation of Photogravure (or "Photo") covers any of these older and more modern gravure methods of printing.

For examples of the first photogravure stamps printed (1914), see Bavaria Scott 94-114.

LITHOGRAPHY (Offset Lithography, Stone Lithography, Dilitho, Planography, Collotype)

The principle that oil and water do not mix is the basis for lithography. The stamp design is drawn by hand or transferred from engraving to the surface of a lithographic stone or metal plate in a greasy (oily) substance. This oily substance holds the ink, which will later be transferred to the paper. The stone (or plate) is wet with an acid fluid, causing it to repel the printing ink in all areas not covered by the greasy substance.

Transfer paper is used to transfer the design from the original stone or plate. A series of duplicate transfers are grouped and, in turn, transferred to the final printing plate.

Photolithography — The application of photographic processes to lithography. This process allows greater flexibility of design, related to use of halftone screens combined with line work. Unlike photogravure or engraving, this process can allow large, solid areas to be printed.

Offset — A refinement of the lithographic process. A rubber-covered blanket cylinder takes the impression from the inked lithographic plate. From the "blanket" the impression is *offset* or transferred to the paper. Greater flexibility and speed are the principal reasons offset printing has largely displaced lithography. The term "lithography" covers both processes, and results are almost identical.

EMBOSSED (Relief) Printing

Embossing, not considered one of the four main printing types, is a method in which the design first is sunk into the metal of the die. Printing is done against a yielding platen, such as leather or linoleum. The platen is forced into the depression of the die, thus forming the design on the paper in relief. This process is often used for metallic inks.

Embossing may be done without color (see Sardinia Scott 4-6); with color printed around the embossed area (see Great Britain Scott 5 and most U.S. envelopes); and with color in exact registration with the embossed subject (see Canada Scott 656-657).

HOLOGRAMS

For objects to appear as holograms on stamps, a model exactly the same size as it is to appear on the hologram must be created. Rather than using photographic film to capture the image, holography records an image on a photoresist material. In processing, chemicals eat away at certain exposed areas, leaving a pattern of constructive and destructive interference. When the phororesist is developed, the result is a pattern of uneven ridges that acts as a mold. This mold is then coated with metal, and the resulting form is used to press copies in much the same way phonograph records are produced.

A typical reflective hologram used for stamps consists of a reproduction of the uneven patterns on a plastic film that is applied to a reflective background, usually a silver or gold foil. Light is reflected off the background through the film, making the pattern present on the film visible. Because of the uneven pattern of the film, the viewer will perceive the objects in their proper three-dimensional relationships with appropriate brightness.

The first hologram on a stamp was produced by Austria in 1988 (Scott 1441).

FOIL APPLICATION

A modern tecnique of applying color to stamps involves the application of metallic foil to the stamp paper. A pattern of foil is applied to the stamp paper by use of a stamping die. The foil usually is flat, but it may be textured. Canada Scott 1735 has three different foil applications in pearl, bronze and gold. The gold foil was textured using a chemical-etch copper embossing die. The printing of this stamp also involved two-color offset lithography plus embossing.

COMBINATION PRINTINGS

Sometimes two or even three printing methods are combined in producing stamps. In these cases, such as Austria Scott 933 or Canada 1735 (described in the preceding paragraph), the multiple-printing technique can be determined by studying the individual characteristics of each printing type. A few stamps, such as Singapore Scott 684-684A, combine as many as three of the four major printing types (lithography, engraving and typography). When this is done it often indicates the incorporation of security devices against counterfeiting.

INK COLORS

Inks or colored papers used in stamp printing often are of mineral origin, although there are numerous examples of organic-based pigments. As a general rule, organic-based pigments are far more subject to varieties and change than those of mineral-based origin.

The appearance of any given color on a stamp may be affected by many aspects, including printing variations, light, color of paper, aging and chemical alterations.

Numerous printing variations may be observed. Heavier pressure or inking will cause a more intense color, while slight interruptions in the ink feed or lighter impressions will cause a lighter appearance. Stamps printed in the same color by water-based and solvent-based inks can differ significantly in appearance. This affects several stamps in the U.S. Prominent Americans series. Hand-mixed ink formulas (primarily from the 19th century) produced under different conditions (humidity and temperature) account for notable color variations in early printings of the same stamp (see U.S. Scott 248-250, 279B, for example). Different sources of pigment can also result in significant differences in color.

Light exposure and aging are closely related in the way they affect stamp color. Both eventually break down the ink and fade colors, so that a carefully kept stamp may differ significantly in color from an identical copy that has been exposed to light. If stamps are exposed to light either intentionally or accidentally, their colors can be faded or completely changed in some cases.

Papers of different quality and consistency used for the same stamp printing may affect color appearance. Most pelure papers, for example, show a richer color when compared with wove or laid papers. See Russia Scott 181a, for an example of this effect.

The very nature of the printing processes can cause a variety of differences in shades or hues of the same stamp. Some of these shades are scarcer than others, and are of particular interest to the advanced collector.

Luminescence

All forms of tagged stamps fall under the general category of luminescence. Within this broad category is fluorescence, dealing with forms of tagging visible under longwave ultraviolet light, and phosphorescence, which deals with tagging visible only under shortwave light. Phosphorescence leaves an afterglow and fluorescence does not. These treated stamps show up in a range of different colors when exposed to UV light. The differing wavelengths of the light activates the tagging material, making it glow in various colors that usually serve different mail processing purposes.

Intentional tagging is a post-World War II phenomenon, brought about by the increased literacy rate and rapidly growing mail volume. It was one of several answers to the problem of the need for more automated mail processes. Early tagged stamps served the purpose of triggering machines to separate different types of mail. A natural outgrowth was to also use the signal to trigger machines that faced all envelopes the same way and canceled them.

Tagged stamps come in many different forms. Some tagged stamps have luminescent shapes or images imprinted on them as a form of security device. Others have blocks (United States), stripes, frames (South Africa and Canada), overall coatings (United States), bars (Great Britain and Canada) and many other types. Some types of tagging are even mixed in with the pigmented printing ink (Australia Scott 366, Netherlands Scott 478 and U.S. Scott 1359 and 2443).

The means of applying taggant to stamps differs as much as the intended purposes for the stamps. The most common form of tagging is a coating applied to the surface of the printed stamp. Since the taggant ink is frequently invisible except under UV light, it does not interfere with the appearance of the stamp. Another common application is the use of phosphored papers. In this case the paper itself either has a coating of taggant applied before the stamp is printed, has taggant applied during the papermaking process (incorporating it into the fibers), or has the taggant mixed into the coating of the paper. The latter method, among others, is currently in use in the United States.

Many countries now use tagging in various forms to either expedite mail handling or to serve as a printing security device against counterfeiting. Following the introduction of tagged stamps for public use in 1959 by Great Britain, other countries have steadily joined the parade. Among those are Germany (1961); Canada and Denmark (1962); United States, Australia, France and Switzerland (1963); Belgium and Japan (1966); Sweden and Norway (1967); Italy (1968); and Russia (1969). Since then, many other countries have begun using forms of tagging, including Brazil, China, Czechoslovakia, Hong Kong, Guatemala, Indonesia, Israel, Lithuania, Luxembourg, Netherlands, Penrhyn Islands, Portugal, St. Vincent, Singapore, South Africa, Spain and Sweden to name a few.

In some cases, including United States, Canada, Great Britain and Switzerland, stamps were released both with and without tagging. Many of these were released during each country's experimental period. Tagged and untagged versions are listed for the aforementioned countries and are noted in some other countries' listings. For at least a few stamps, the experimentally tagged version is worth far more than its untagged counterpart, such as the 1963 experimental tagged version of France Scott 1024.

In some cases, luminescent varieties of stamps were inadvertently created. Several Russian stamps, for example, sport highly fluorescent ink that was not intended as a form of tagging. Older stamps, such as early U.S. postage dues, can be positively identified by the use of UV light, since the organic ink used has become slightly fluorescent over time. Other stamps, such as Austria Scott 70a-82a (varnish bars) and Obock Scott 46-64 (printed quadrille lines), have become fluorescent over time.

Various fluorescent substances have been added to paper to make it appear brighter. These optical brightners, as they are known, greatly affect the appearance of the stamp under UV light. The brightest of these is known as Hi-Brite paper. These paper varieties are beyond the scope of the Scott Catalogue.

Shortwave UV light also is used extensively in expertizing, since each form of paper has its own fluorescent characteristics that are impossible to perfectly match. It is therefore a simple matter to detect filled thins, added perforation teeth and other alterations that involve the addition of paper. UV light also is used to examine stamps that have had cancels chemically removed and for other purposes as well.

Gum

The Illustrated Gum Chart in the first part of this introduction shows and defines various types of gum condition. Because gum condition has an important impact on the value of unused stamps, we recommend studying this chart and the accompanying text carefully.

The gum on the back of a stamp may be shiny, dull, smooth, rough, dark, white, colored or tinted. Most stamp gumming adhesives use gum arabic or dextrine as a base. Certain polymers such as polyvinyl alcohol (PVA) have been used extensively since World War II.

The *Scott Standard Postage Stamp Catalogue* does not list items by types of gum. The *Scott Specialized Catalogue of United States Stamps* does differentiate among some types of gum for certain issues.

Reprints of stamps may have gum differing from the original issues. In addition, some countries have used different gum formulas for different seasons. These adhesives have different properties that may become more apparent over time.

Many stamps have been issued without gum, and the catalogue will note this fact. See, for example, United States Scott 40-47. Sometimes, gum may have been removed to preserve the stamp. Germany Scott B68, for example, has a highly acidic gum that eventually destroys the stamps. This item is valued in the catalogue with gum removed.

Reprints and Reissues

These are impressions of stamps (usually obsolete) made from the original plates or stones. If they are valid for postage and reproduce obsolete issues (such as U.S. Scott 102-111), the stamps are *reissues*. If they are from current issues, they are designated as *second, third,* etc., *printing*. If designated for a particular purpose, they are called *special printings*.

When special printings are not valid for postage, but are made from original dies and plates by authorized persons, they are *official reprints. Private reprints* are made from the original plates and dies by private hands. An example of a private reprint is that of the 1871-1932 reprints made from the original die of the 1845 New Haven, Conn., postmaster's provisional. *Official reproductions* or imitations are made from new dies and plates by government authorization. Scott will list those reissues that are valid for postage if they differ significantly from the original printing.

The U.S. government made special printings of its first postage stamps in 1875. Produced were official imitations of the first two stamps (listed as Scott 3-4), reprints of the demonetized pre-1861 issues (Scott 40-47) and reissues of the 1861 stamps, the 1869 stamps and the then-current 1875 denominations. Even though the official imitations and the reprints were not valid for postage, Scott lists all of these U.S. special printings.

Most reprints or reissues differ slightly from the original stamp in some characteristic, such as gum, paper, perforation, color or watermark. Sometimes the details are followed so meticulously that only a student of that specific stamp is able to distinguish the reprint or reissue from the original.

Remainders and Canceled to Order

Some countries sell their stock of old stamps when a new issue replaces them. To avoid postal use, the *remainders* usually are canceled with a punch hole, a heavy line or bar, or a more-or-less regular-looking cancellation. The most famous merchant of remainders was Nicholas F. Seebeck. In the 1880s and 1890s, he arranged printing contracts between the Hamilton Bank Note Co., of which he was a director, and several Central and South American countries. The contracts provided that the plates and all remainders of the yearly issues became the property of Hamilton. Seebeck saw to it that ample stock remained. The "Seebecks," both remainders and reprints, were standard packet fillers for decades.

Some countries also issue stamps *canceled-to-order (CTO)*, either in sheets with original gum or stuck onto pieces of paper or envelopes and canceled. Such CTO items generally are worth less than postally used stamps. In cases where the CTO material is far more prevalent in the marketplace than postally used examples, the catalogue value relates to the CTO examples, with postally used examples noted as premium items. Most CTOs can be detected by the presence of gum. However, as the CTO practice goes back at least to 1885, the gum inevitably has been soaked off some stamps so they could pass as postally used. The normally applied postmarks usually differ slightly from standard postmarks, and specialists are able to tell the difference. When applied individually to envelopes by philatelically minded persons, CTO material is known as *favor canceled* and generally sells at large discounts.

Cinderellas and Facsimiles

Cinderella is a catch-all term used by stamp collectors to describe phantoms, fantasies, bogus items, municipal issues, exhibition seals, local revenues, transportation stamps, labels, poster stamps and many other types of items. Some cinderella collectors include in their collections local postage issues, telegraph stamps, essays and proofs, forgeries and counterfeits.

A *fantasy* is an adhesive created for a nonexistent stamp-issuing authority. Fantasy items range from imaginary countries (Occusi-Ambeno, Kingdom of Sedang, Principality of Trinidad or Torres Straits), to non-existent locals (Winans City Post), or nonexistent transportation lines (McRobish & Co.'s Acapulco-San Francisco Line).

On the other hand, if the entity exists and could have issued stamps (but did not) or was known to have issued other stamps, the items are considered *bogus* stamps. These would include the Mormon postage stamps of Utah, S. Allan Taylor's Guatemala and Paraguay inventions, the propaganda issues for the South Moluccas and the adhesives of the Page & Keyes local post of Boston.

Phantoms is another term for both fantasy and bogus issues.

Facsimiles are copies or imitations made to represent original stamps, but which do not pretend to be originals. A catalogue illustration is such a facsimile. Illustrations from the Moens catalogue of the last century were occasionally colored and passed off as stamps. Since the beginning of stamp collecting, facsimiles have been made for collectors as space fillers or for reference. They often carry the word "facsimile," "falsch" (German), "sanko" or "mozo" (Japanese), or "faux" (French) overprinted on the face or stamped on the back. Unfortunately, over the years a number of these items have had fake cancels applied over the facsimile notation and have been passed off as genuine.

Forgeries and Counterfeits

Forgeries and counterfeits have been with philately virtually from the beginning of stamp production. Over time, the terminology for the two has been used interchangeably. Although both forgeries and counterfeits are reproductions of stamps, the purposes behind their creation differ considerably.

Among specialists there is an increasing movement to more specifically define such items. Although there is no universally accepted terminology, we feel the following definitions most closely mirror the items and their purposes as they are currently defined.

Forgeries (also often referred to as *Counterfeits*) are reproductions of genuine stamps that have been created to defraud collectors. Such spurious items first appeared on the market around 1860, and most old-time collections contain one or more. Many are crude and easily spotted, but some can deceive experts.

An important supplier of these early philatelic forgeries was the Hamburg printer Gebruder Spiro. Many others with reputations in this craft included S. Allan Taylor, George Hussey, James Chute, George Forune, Benjamin & Sarpy, Julius Goldner, E. Oneglia and L.H. Mercier. Among the noted 20th-century forgers were Francois Fournier, Jean Sperati and the prolific Raoul DeThuin.

Forgeries may be complete replications, or they may be genuine stamps altered to resemble a scarcer (and more valuable) type. Most forgeries, particularly those of rare stamps, are worth only a small fraction of the value of a genuine example, but a few types, created by some of the most notable forgers, such as Sperati, can be worth as much or more than the genuine. Fraudulently produced copies are known of most classic rarities and many medium-priced stamps.

In addition to rare stamps, large numbers of common 19th- and early 20th-century stamps were forged to supply stamps to the early packet trade. Many can still be easily found. Few new philatelic forgeries have appeared in recent decades. Successful imitation of well-engraved work is virtually impossible. It has proven far easier to produce a fake by altering a genuine stamp than to duplicate a stamp completely.

Counterfeit (also often referred to as *Postal Counterfeit* or *Postal Forgery*) is the term generally applied to reproductions of stamps that have been created to defraud the government of revenue. Such items usually are created at the time a stamp is current and, in some cases, are hard to detect. Because most counterfeits are seized when the perpetrator is captured, postal counterfeits, particularly used on cover, are usually worth much more than a genuine example to spe-

cialists. The first postal counterfeit was of Spain's 4-cuarto carmine of 1854 (the real one is Scott 25). Apparently, the counterfeiters were not satisfied with their first version, which is now very scarce, and they soon created an engraved counterfeit, which is common. Postal counterfeits quickly followed in Austria, Naples, Sardinia and the Roman States. They have since been created in many other countries as well, including the United States.

An infamous counterfeit to defraud the government is the 1-shilling Great Britain "Stock Exchange" forgery of 1872, used on telegraph forms at the exchange that year. The stamp escaped detection until a stamp dealer noticed it in 1898.

Fakes

Fakes are genuine stamps altered in some way to make them more desirable. One student of this part of stamp collecting has estimated that by the 1950s more than 30,000 varieties of fakes were known. That number has grown greatly since then. The widespread existence of fakes makes it important for stamp collectors to study their philatelic holdings and use relevant literature. Likewise, collectors should buy from reputable dealers who guarantee their stamps and make full and prompt refunds should a purchased item be declared faked or altered by some mutually agreed-upon authority. Because fakes always have some genuine characteristics, it is not always possible to obtain unanimous agreement among experts regarding specific items. These students may change their opinions as philatelic knowledge increases. More than 80 percent of all fakes on the philatelic market today are regummed, reperforated (or perforated for the first time), or bear forged overprints, surcharges or cancellations.

Stamps can be chemically treated to alter or eliminate colors. For example, a pale rose stamp can be re-colored to resemble a blue shade of high market value. In other cases, treated stamps can be made to resemble missing color varieties. Designs may be changed by painting, or a stroke or a dot added or bleached out to turn an ordinary variety into a seemingly scarcer stamp. Part of a stamp can be bleached and reprinted in a different version, achieving an inverted center or frame. Margins can be added or repairs done so deceptively that the stamps move from the "repaired" into the "fake" category.

Fakers have not left the backs of the stamps untouched either. They may create false watermarks, add fake grills or press out genuine grills. A thin India paper proof may be glued onto a thicker backing to create the appearance an issued stamp, or a proof printed on cardboard may be shaved down and perforated to resemble a stamp. Silk threads are impressed into paper and stamps have been split so that a rare paper variety is added to an otherwise inexpensive stamp. The most common treatment to the back of a stamp, however, is regumming.

Some in the business of faking stamps have openly advertised foolproof application of "original gum" to stamps that lack it, although most publications now ban such ads from their pages. It is believed that very few early stamps have survived without being hinged. The large number of never-hinged examples of such earlier material offered for sale thus suggests the widespread extent of regumming activity. Regumming also may be used to hide repairs or thin spots. Dipping the stamp into watermark fluid, or examining it under long-wave ultraviolet light often will reveal these flaws.

Fakers also tamper with separations. Ingenious ways to add margins are known. Perforated wide-margin stamps may be falsely represented as imperforate when trimmed. Reperforating is commonly done to create scarce coil or perforation varieties, and to eliminate the naturally occurring straight-edge stamps found in sheet margin positions of many earlier issues. Custom has made straight-edged stamps less desirable. Fakers have obliged by perforating straight-edged stamps so that many are now uncommon, if not rare.

Another fertile field for the faker is that of overprints, surcharges and cancellations. The forging of rare surcharges or overprints began in the 1880s or 1890s. These forgeries are sometimes difficult to detect, but experts have identified almost all. Occasionally, overprints or cancellations are removed to create non-overprinted stamps or seemingly unused items. This is most commonly done by removing a manuscript cancel to make a stamp resemble an unused example. "SPECIMEN" overprints may be removed by scraping and repainting to create non-overprinted varieties. Fakers use inexpensive revenues or pen-canceled stamps to generate unused stamps for further faking by adding other markings. The quartz lamp or UV lamp and a high-powered magnifying glass help to easily detect removed cancellations.

The bigger problem, however, is the addition of overprints, surcharges or cancellations - many with such precision that they are very difficult to ascertain. Plating of the stamps or the overprint can be an important method of detection.

Fake postmarks may range from many spurious fancy cancellations to a host of markings applied to transatlantic covers, to adding normally appearing postmarks to definitives of some countries with stamps that are valued far higher used than unused. With the increased popularity of cover collecting, and the widespread interest in postal history, a fertile new field for fakers has come about. Some have tried to create entire covers. Others specialize in adding stamps, tied by fake cancellations, to genuine stampless covers, or replacing less expensive or damaged stamps with more valuable ones. Detailed study of postal rates in effect at the time a cover in question was mailed, including the analysis of each handstamp used during the period, ink analysis and similar techniques, usually will unmask the fraud.

Restoration and Repairs

Scott Publishing Co. bases its catalogue values on stamps that are free of defects and otherwise meet the standards set forth earlier in this introduction. Most stamp collectors desire to have the finest copy of an item possible. Even within given grading categories there are variances. This leads to a controversial practice that is not defined in any universal manner: stamp *restoration*.

There are broad differences of opinion about what is permissible when it comes to restoration. Carefully applying a soft eraser to a stamp or cover to remove light soiling is one form of restoration, as is washing a stamp in mild soap and water to clean it. These are fairly accepted forms of restoration. More severe forms of restoration include pressing out creases or removing stains caused by tape. To what degree each of these is acceptable is dependent upon the individual situation. Further along the spectrum is the freshening of a stamp's color by removing oxide build-up or the effects of wax paper left next to stamps shipped to the tropics.

At some point in this spectrum the concept of *repair* replaces that of restoration. Repairs include filling thin spots, mending tears by reweaving or adding a missing perforation tooth. Regumming stamps may have been acceptable as a restoration or repair technique many decades ago, but today it is considered a form of fakery.

Restored stamps may or may not sell at a discount, and it is possible that the value of individual restored items may be enhanced over that of their pre-restoration state. Specific situations dictate the resultant value of such an item. Repaired stamps sell at substantial discounts from the value of sound stamps.

Terminology

Booklets — Many countries have issued stamps in small booklets for the convenience of users. This idea continues to become increasingly popular in many countries. Booklets have been issued in many sizes and forms, often with advertising on the covers, the panes of stamps or on the interleaving.

The panes used in booklets may be printed from special plates or made from regular sheets. All panes from booklets issued by the United States and many from those of other countries contain stamps that are straight edged on the sides, but perforated between. Others are distinguished by orientation of watermark or other identifying features. Any stamp-like unit in the pane, either printed or blank, that is not a postage stamp, is considered to be a *label* in the catalogue listings.

Scott lists and values booklet panes. Modern complete booklets also are listed and valued. Individual booklet panes are listed only when they are not fashioned from existing sheet stamps and, therefore, are identifiable from their sheet stamp counterparts.

Panes usually do not have a used value assigned to them because there is little market activity for used booklet panes, even though many exist used and there is some demand for them.

Cancellations — The marks or obliterations put on stamps by postal authorities to show that they have performed service and to prevent their reuse are known as cancellations. If the marking is made with a pen, it is considered a "pen cancel." When the location of the post office appears in the marking, it is a "town cancellation." A "postmark" is technically any postal marking, but in practice the term generally is applied to a town cancellation with a date. When calling attention to a cause or celebration, the marking is known as a "slogan cancellation." Many other types and styles of cancellations exist, such as duplex, numerals, targets, fancy and others. See also "precancels," below.

Coil Stamps — These are stamps that are issued in rolls for use in dispensers, affixing and vending machines. Those coils of the United States, Canada, Sweden and some other countries are perforated horizontally or vertically only, with the outer edges imperforate. Coil stamps of some countries, such as Great Britain and Germany, are perforated on all four sides and may in some cases be distinguished from their sheet stamp counterparts by watermarks, counting numbers on the reverse or other means.

Covers — Entire envelopes, with or without adhesive postage stamps, that have passed through the mail and bear postal or other markings of philatelic interest are known as covers. Before the introduction of envelopes in about 1840, people folded letters and wrote the address on the outside. Some people covered their letters with an extra sheet of paper on the outside for the address, producing the term "cover." Used airletter sheets, stamped envelopes and other items of postal stationery also are considered covers.

Errors — Stamps that have some major, consistent, unintentional deviation from the normal are considered errors. Errors include, but are not limited to, missing or wrong colors, wrong paper, wrong watermarks, inverted centers or frames on multicolor printing, inverted or missing surcharges or overprints, double impressions, missing perforations and others. Factually wrong or misspelled information, if it appears on all examples of a stamp, are not considered errors in the true sense of the word. They are errors of design. Inconsistent or randomly appearing items, such as misperfs or color shifts, are classified as freaks.

Color-Omitted Errors — This term refers to stamps where a missing color is caused by the complete failure of the printing plate to deliver ink to the stamp paper or any other paper. Generally, this is caused by the printing plate not being engaged on the press or the ink station running dry of ink during printing.

Color-Missing Errors — This term refers to stamps where a color or colors were printed somewhere but do not appear on the finished stamp. There are four different classes of color-missing errors, and the catalog indicates with a two-letter code appended to each such listing what caused the color to be missing. These codes are used only for the United States' color-missing error listings.

FO = A *foldover* of the stamp sheet during printing may block ink from appearing on a stamp. Instead, the color will appear on the back of the foldover (where it might fall on the back of the selvage or perhaps on the back of another stamp.)

EP = A piece of *extraneous paper* falling across the plate or stamp paper will receive the printed ink. When the extraneous paper is removed, an unprinted portion of stamp paper remains and shows partially or totally missing colors.

CM = A misregistration of the printing plates during printing will result in a *color misregistration*, and such a misregistraion may result in a color not appearing on the finished stamp.

PS = A *perforation shift* after printing may remove a color from the finished stamp. Normally, this will occur on a row of stamps at the edge of the stamp pane.

Overprints and Surcharges — Overprinting involves applying wording or design elements over an already existing stamp. Overprints can be used to alter the place of use (such as "Canal Zone" on U.S. stamps), to adapt them for a special purpose ("Porto" on Denmark's 1913-20 regular issues for use as postage due stamps, Scott J1-J7) or to commemorate a special occasion (United States Scott 647-648).

A *surcharge* is a form of overprint that changes or restates the face value of a stamp or piece of postal stationery.

Surcharges and overprints may be handstamped, typeset or, occasionally, lithographed or engraved. A few hand-written overprints and surcharges are known.

Precancels — Stamps that are canceled before they are placed in the mail are known as precancels. Precanceling usually is done to expedite the handling of large mailings and generally allow the affected mail pieces to skip certain phases of mail handling.

In the United States, precancellations generally identified the point of origin; that is, the city and state. This information appeared across the face of the stamp, usually centered between parallel lines. More recently, bureau precancels retained the parallel lines, but the city and state designations were dropped. Recent coils have a service inscription that is present on the original printing plate. These show the mail service paid for by the stamp. Since these stamps are not intended to receive further cancellations when used as intended, they are considered precancels. Such items often do not have parallel lines as part of the precancellation.

In France, the abbreviation *Affranchts* in a semicircle together with the word *Postes* is the general form of precancel in use. Belgian precancellations usually appear in a box in which the name of the city appears. Netherlands precancels have the name of the city enclosed between concentric circles, sometimes called

a "lifesaver." Precancellations of other countries usually follow these patterns, but may be any arrangement of bars, boxes and city names.

Precancels are listed in the Scott catalogues only if the precancel changes the denomination (Belgium Scott 477-478); if the precanceled stamp is different from the non-precanceled version (such as untagged U.S. precancels); or if the stamp exists only precanceled (France Scott 1096-1099, U.S. Scott 2265).

Proofs and Essays — Proofs are impressions taken from an approved die, plate or stone in which the design and color are the same as the stamp issued to the public. Trial color proofs are impressions taken from approved dies, plates or stones in colors that vary from the final version. An essay is the impression of a design that differs in some way from the issued stamp. "Progressive die proofs" generally are considered to be essays.

Provisionals — These are stamps that are issued on short notice and intended for temporary use pending the arrival of regular issues. They usually are issued to meet such contingencies as changes in government or currency, shortage of necessary postage values or military occupation.

During the 1840s, postmasters in certain American cities issued stamps that were valid only at specific post offices. In 1861, postmasters of the Confederate States also issued stamps with limited validity. Both of these examples are known as "postmaster's provisionals."

Se-tenant — This term refers to an unsevered pair, strip or block of stamps that differ in design, denomination or overprint.

Unless the se-tenant item has a continuous design (see U.S. Scott 1451a, 1694a) the stamps do not have to be in the same order as shown in the catalogue (see U.S. Scott 2158a).

Specimens — The Universal Postal Union required member nations to send samples of all stamps they released into service to the International Bureau in Switzerland. Member nations of the UPU received these specimens as samples of what stamps were valid for postage. Many are overprinted, handstamped or initial-perforated "Specimen," "Canceled" or "Muestra." Some are marked with bars across the denominations (China-Taiwan), punched holes (Czechoslovakia) or back inscriptions (Mongolia).

Stamps distributed to government officials or for publicity purposes, and stamps submitted by private security printers for official approval, also may receive such defacements.

The previously described defacement markings prevent postal use, and all such items generally are known as "specimens."

Tete Beche — This term describes a pair of stamps in which one is upside down in relation to the other. Some of these are the result of intentional sheet arrangements, such as Morocco Scott B10-B11. Others occurred when one or more electrotypes accidentally were placed upside down on the plate, such as Colombia Scott 57a. Separation of the tete-beche stamps, of course, destroys the tete beche variety.

Currency Conversion

Country	Dollar	Pound	S Franc	Yen	HK $	Euro	Cdn $	Aus $
Australia	1.4445	2.5422	1.1144	0.0126	0.1852	1.7162	1.0389	-----
Canada	1.3904	2.4470	1.0727	0.0122	0.1782	1.6519	-----	0.9625
European Union	0.8417	1.4813	0.6494	0.0074	0.1079	-----	0.6054	0.5827
Hong Kong	7.8003	13.728	6.0178	0.0683	-----	9.2673	5.6101	5.4000
Japan	114.25	201.06	88.140	-----	14.646	135.73	82.168	79.091
Switzerland	1.2962	2.2812	-----	0.0113	0.1662	1.5400	0.9322	0.8973
United Kingdom	0.5682	-----	0.4384	0.0050	0.0728	0.6751	0.4087	0.3934
United States	-----	1.7599	0.7715	0.0088	0.1282	1.1881	0.7192	0.6923

Country	Currency	U.S. $ Equiv.
Solomon Islands	Australian dollar	.6527
Somalia	shilling	.0004
South Africa	rand	.1297
S. Georgia & S. Sandwich Isls.	British pound	1.6228
Spain	euro	1.1574
Sri Lanka	rupee	.0103
Sudan	pound	.0038
Surinam	guilder	.0004
Swaziland	emalangeni	.1307
Sweden	krona	.1263
Switzerland	franc	.7650
Syria	pound	.0217
Tajikistan	somoni	.3331
Tanzania	shilling	.0010
Thailand	baht	.0237
Timor	U.S. dollar	1.00
Togo	Community of French Africa (CFA) franc	.0018
Tokelau	New Zealand dollar	.5810
Tonga	pa'anga	.4670
Niuafo'ou	pa'anga	.4670
Trinidad & Tobago	dollar	.1630
Tristan da Cunha	British pound	1.6228
Tunisia	dinar	.7898
Turkey	lira	.0000006
Turk. Rep. of Northern Cyprus	lira	.000006
Turkmenistan	manat	.0002
Turks & Caicos Islands	U.S. dollar	1.00
Tuvalu	Australian dollar	.6527
Uganda	shilling	.0005
Ukraine	hryvnia	.1874
United Arab Emirates	dirham	.2723
Uruguay	peso	.0343
Uzbekistan	sum	.0011
Vanuatu	vatu	.0080
Vatican City	euro	1.1574
Venezuela	bolivar	.0006
Viet Nam	dong	.00006
Virgin Islands	U.S. dollar	1.00
Wallis & Futuna Islands	Community of French Pacific (CFP) franc	.0098
Yemen	rial	.0056
Yugoslavia	dinar	.0173
Zambia	kwacha	.0002
Zaire (Congo Dem. Rep.)	franc	.0024
Zimbabwe	dollar	.0012

Source: **Wall Street Journal** May 17, 2003. Figures reflect values as of May 14, 2004.

COMMON DESIGN TYPES

Pictured in this section are issues where one illustration has been used for a number of countries in the Catalogue. Not included in this section are over-printed stamps or those issues which are illustrated in each country.

EUROPA
Europa, 1956

The design symbolizing the cooperation among the six countries comprising the Coal and Steel Community is illustrated in each country.

Belgium	496-497
France	805-806
Germany	748-749
Italy	715-716
Luxembourg	318-320
Netherlands	368-369

Europa, 1958

"E" and Dove — CD1

European Postal Union at the service of European integration.

1958, Sept. 13

Belgium	527-528
France	889-890
Germany	790-791
Italy	750-751
Luxembourg	341-343
Netherlands	375-376
Saar	317-318

Europa, 1959

6-Link Enless Chain — CD2

1959, Sept. 19

Belgium	536-537
France	929-930
Germany	805-806
Italy	791-792
Luxembourg	354-355
Netherlands	379-380

Europa, 1960

19-Spoke Wheel CD3

First anniverary of the establishment of C.E.P.T. (Conference Europeenne des Admin-istrations des Postes et des Telecommunica-tions.) The spokes symbolize the 19 founding members of the Conference.

1960, Sept.

Belgium	553-554
Denmark	379
Finland	376-377
France	970-971
Germany	818-820
Great Britain	377-378
Greece	688
Iceland	327-328

Ireland	175-176
Italy	809-810
Luxembourg	374-375
Netherlands	385-386
Norway	387
Portugal	866-867
Spain	941-942
Sweden	562-563
Switzerland	400-401
Turkey	1493-1494

Europa, 1961

19 Doves Flying as One — CD4

The 19 doves represent the 19 members of the Conference of European Postal and Tele-communications Administrations C.E.P.T.

1961-62

Belgium	572-573
Cyprus	201-203
France	1005-1006
Germany	844-845
Great Britain	383-384
Greece	718-719
Iceland	340-341
Italy	845-846
Luxembourg	382-383
Netherlands	387-388
Spain	1010-1011
Switzerland	410-411
Turkey	1518-1520

Europa, 1962

Young Tree with 19 Leaves CD5

The 19 leaves represent the 19 original members of C.E.P.T.

1962-63

Belgium	582-583
Cyprus	219-221
France	1045-1046
Germany	852-853
Greece	739-740
Iceland	348-349
Ireland	184-185
Italy	860-861
Luxembourg	386-387
Netherlands	394-395
Norway	414-415
Switzerland	416-417
Turkey	1553-1555

Europa, 1963

Stylized Links, Symbolizing Unity — CD6

1963, Sept.

Belgium	598-599
Cyprus	229-231
Finland	419
France	1074-1075
Germany	867-868
Greece	768-769
Iceland	357-358
Ireland	188-189
Italy	880-881
Luxembourg	403-404
Netherlands	416-417
Norway	441-442
Switzerland	429
Turkey	1602-1603

Europa, 1964

Symbolic Daisy — CD7

5th anniversary of the establishment of C.E.P.T. The 22 petals of the flower symbolize the 22 members of the Conference.

1964, Sept.

Austria	738
Belgium	614-615
Cyprus	244-246
France	1109-1110
Germany	897-898
Greece	801-802
Iceland	367-368
Ireland	196-197
Italy	894-895
Luxembourg	411-412
Monaco	590-591
Netherlands	428-429
Norway	458
Portugal	931-933
Spain	1262-1263
Switzerland	438-439
Turkey	1628-1629

Europa, 1965

Leaves and "Fruit" CD8

1965

Belgium	636-637
Cyprus	262-264
Finland	437
France	1131-1132
Germany	934-935
Greece	833-834
Iceland	375-376
Ireland	204-205
Italy	915-916
Luxembourg	432-433
Monaco	616-617
Netherlands	438-439
Norway	475-476
Portugal	958-960
Switzerland	469
Turkey	1665-1666

Europa, 1966

Symbolic Sailboat — CD9

1966, Sept.

Andorra, French	172
Belgium	675-676
Cyprus	275-277
France	1163-1164
Germany	963-964
Greece	862-863
Iceland	384-385
Ireland	216-217
Italy	942-943
Liechtenstein	415
Luxembourg	440-441
Monaco	639-640
Netherlands	441-442
Norway	496-497
Portugal	980-982
Switzerland	477-478
Turkey	1718-1719

Europa, 1967

Cogwheels CD10

1967

Andorra, French	174-175
Belgium	688-689
Cyprus	297-299
France	1178-1179
Germany	969-970
Greece	891-892
Iceland	389-390
Ireland	232-233
Italy	951-952
Liechtenstein	420
Luxembourg	449-450
Monaco	669-670
Netherlands	444-447
Norway	504-505
Portugal	994-996
Spain	1465-1466
Switzerland	482
Turkey	B120-B121

Europa, 1968

Golden Key with C.E.P.T. Emblem CD11

1968

Andorra, French	182-183
Belgium	705-706
Cyprus	314-316
France	1209-1210
Germany	983-984
Greece	916-917
Iceland	395-396
Ireland	242-243
Italy	979-980
Liechtenstein	442
Luxembourg	466-467
Monaco	689-691
Netherlands	452-453
Portugal	1019-1021
San Marino	687
Spain	1526
Turkey	1775-1776

Europa, 1969

"EUROPA" and "CEPT" CD12

Tenth anniversary of C.E.P.T.

1969

Andorra, French	188-189
Austria	837
Belgium	718-719
Cyprus	326-328
Denmark	458
Finland	483
France	1245-1246
Germany	996-997
Great Britain	585
Greece	947-948
Iceland	406-407
Ireland	270-271
Italy	1000-1001
Liechtenstein	453
Luxembourg	474-475
Monaco	722-724
Netherlands	475-476
Norway	533-534
Portugal	1038-1040
San Marino	701-702
Spain	1567
Sweden	814-816

Switzerland................................500-501
Turkey......................................1799-1800
Vatican.....................................470-472
Yugoslavia...............................1003-1004

Europa, 1970

Interwoven Threads CD13

1970

Andorra, French 196-197
Belgium...................................741-742
Cyprus.....................................340-342
France......................................1271-1272
Germany..................................1018-1019
Greece..................................985, 987
Iceland.....................................420-421
Ireland......................................279-281
Italy..1013-1014
Liechtenstein 470
Luxembourg............................489-490
Monaco....................................768-770
Netherlands............................483-484
Portugal...................................1060-1062
San Marino..............................729-730
Spain.......................................1607
Switzerland..............................515-516
Turkey......................................1848-1849
Yugoslavia...............................1024-1025

Europa, 1971

"Fraternity, Cooperation, Common Effort" CD14

1971

Andorra, French 205-206
Belgium...................................803-804
Cyprus.....................................365-367
Finland.....................................504
France......................................1304
Germany..................................1064-1065
Greece.....................................1029-1030
Iceland.....................................429-430
Ireland......................................305-306
Italy..1038-1039
Liechtenstein 485
Luxembourg............................500-501
Malta..425-427
Monaco....................................797-799
Netherlands............................488-489
Portugal...................................1094-1096
San Marino..............................749-750
Spain 1675-1676
Switzerland..............................531-532
Turkey......................................1876-1877
Yugoslavia...............................1052-1053

Europa, 1972

Sparkles, Symbolic of Communications CD15

1972

Andorra, French 210-211
Andorra, Spanish 62
Belgium...................................825-826
Cyprus.....................................380-382
Finland.....................................512-513
France......................................1341
Germany..................................1089-1090
Greece.....................................1049-1050
Iceland.....................................439-440
Ireland......................................316-317
Italy..1065-1066
Liechtenstein 504
Luxembourg............................512-513
Malta..450-453
Monaco....................................831-832

Netherlands 494-495
Portugal 1141-1143
San Marino..............................771-772
Spain 1718
Switzerland..............................544-545
Turkey 1907-1908
Yugoslavia...............................1100-1101

Europa, 1973

Post Horn and Arrows CD16

1973

Andorra, French 219-320
Andorra, Spanish 76
Belgium...................................839-840
Cyprus.....................................396-398
Finland.....................................526
France......................................1367
Germany..................................1114-1115
Greece.....................................1090-1092
Iceland.....................................447-448
Ireland......................................329-330
Italy..1108-1109
Liechtenstein 528-529
Luxembourg............................523-524
Malta..469-471
Monaco....................................866-867
Netherlands............................504-505
Norway.....................................604-605
Portugal...................................1170-1172
San Marino..............................802-803
Spain 1753
Switzerland..............................580-581
Turkey 1935-1936
Yugoslavia...............................1138-1139

Europa, 2000

CD17

2000

Albania....................................2621-2622
Andorra, French 522
Andorra, Spanish 262
Armenia...................................610-611
Austria 1814
Azerbaijan...............................698-699
Belarus....................................350
Belgium...................................1818
Bosnia & Herzegovina (Moslem) 358
Bosnia & Herzegovina (Serb) ...111-112
Croatia.....................................428-429
Cyprus.....................................959
Czech Republic 3120
Denmark..................................1189
Estonia....................................394
Faroe Islands..........................376
Finland.....................................1129
Aland Islands..........................166
France......................................2771
Georgia....................................228-229
Germany..................................2086-2087
Gibraltar..................................837-840
Great Britain (Guernsey).........805-809
Great Britain (Jersey)..............935-936
Great Britain (Isle of Man) 883
Greece.....................................1959
Greenland...............................363
Hungary...................................3699-3700
Iceland.....................................910
Ireland......................................1230-1231
Italy 2349
Latvia.......................................504
Liechtenstein 1178
Lithuania.................................668
Luxembourg............................1035
Macedonia...............................187
Malta..1011-1012
Moldova...................................355
Monaco....................................2161-2162
Poland......................................3519
Portugal...................................2358
Portugal (Azores)....................455
Portugal (Madeira)..................208

Romania...................................4370
Russia......................................6589
San Marino..............................1480
Slovakia...................................355
Slovenia...................................424
Spain 3036
Sweden....................................2394
Switzerland..............................1074
Turkey......................................2762
Turkish Rep. of Northern Cyprus....500
Ukraine....................................379
Vatican City 1152

The Gibraltar stamps are similar to the stamp illustrated, but none have the design shown above. All other sets listed above include at least one stamp with the design shown, but some include stamps with entirely different designs. Bulgaria Nos. 4131-4132 and Yugoslavia Nos. 2485-2486 are Europa stamps with completely different designs.

PORTUGAL & COLONIES
Vasco da Gama

Fleet Departing CD20

Fleet Arriving at Calicut — CD21

Embarking at Rastello CD22

Muse of History CD23

San Gabriel, da Gama and Camoens CD24

Archangel Gabriel, the Patron Saint CD25

Flagship San Gabriel — CD26

Vasco da Gama — CD27

Fourth centenary of Vasco da Gama's discovery of the route to India.

1898

Azores 93-100
Macao.......................................67-74
Madeira.....................................37-44
Portugal....................................147-154
Port. Africa 1-8
Port. Congo...............................75-98
Port. India.................................189-196
St. Thomas & Prince Islands 170-193
Timor 45-52

Pombal
POSTAL TAX
POSTAL TAX DUES

Marquis de Pombal — CD28

Planning Reconstruction of Lisbon, 1755 — CD29

Pombal Monument, Lisbon — CD30

Sebastiao Jose de Carvalho e Mello, Marquis de Pombal (1699-1782), statesman, rebuilt Lisbon after earthquake of 1755. Tax was for the erection of Pombal monument. Obligatory on all mail on certain days throughout the year. Postal Tax Dues are inscribed "Multa."

1925

Angola RA1-RA3, RAJ1-RAJ3
Azores RA9-RA11, RAJ2-RAJ4
Cape Verde RA1-RA3, RAJ1-RAJ3
Macao.............. RA1-RA3, RAJ1-RAJ3
Madeira............. RA1-RA3, RAJ1-RAJ3
Mozambique..... RA1-RA3, RAJ1-RAJ3
Nyassa.............. RA1-RA3, RAJ1-RAJ3
Portugal RA11-RA13, RAJ2-RAJ4
Port. Guinea RA1-RA3, RAJ1-RAJ3
Port. India........ RA1-RA3, RAJ1-RAJ3
St. Thomas & Prince
Islands RA1-RA3, RAJ1-RAJ3
Timor RA1-RA3, RAJ1-RAJ3

Vasco da Gama CD34

Mousinho de Albuquerque CD35

Dam CD36

Prince Henry the Navigator CD37

Affonso de Albuquerque CD38

Plane over Globe CD39

1938-39

Angola 274-291, C1-C9
Cape Verde 234-251, C1-C9
Macao..........................289-305, C7-C15
Mozambique...............270-287, C1-C9
Port. Guinea 233-250. C1-C9
Port. India...................439-453, C1-C8
St. Thomas & Prince
Islands ... 302-319, 323-340, C1-C18
Timor 223-239, C1-C9

Lady of Fatima

Our Lady of the Rosary, Fatima, Portugal — CD40

1948-49

Angola	315-318
Cape Verde	266
Macao	336
Mozambique	325-328
Port. Guinea	271
Port. India	480
St. Thomas & Prince Islands	351
Timor	254

A souvenir sheet of 9 stamps was issued in 1951 to mark the extension of the 1950 Holy Year. The sheet contains: Angola No. 316, Cape Verde No. 266, Macao No. 336, Mozambique No. 325, Portuguese Guinea No. 271, Portuguese India Nos. 480, 485, St. Thomas & Prince Islands No. 351, Timor No. 254. The sheet also contains a portrait of Pope Pius XII and is inscribed "Encerramento do Ano Santo, Fatima 1951." It was sold for 11 escudos.

Holy Year

Church Bells and Dove CD41	Angel Holding Candelabra CD42

Holy Year, 1950.

1950-51

Angola	331-332
Cape Verde	268-269
Macao	339-340
Mozambique	330-331
Port. Guinea	273-274
Port. India	490-491, 496-503
St. Thomas & Prince Islands	353-354
Timor	258-259

A souvenir sheet of 8 stamps was issued in 1951 to mark the extension of the Holy Year. The sheet contains: Angola No. 331, Cape Verde No. 269, Macao No. 340, Mozambique No. 331, Portuguese Guinea No. 275, Portuguese India No. 490, St. Thomas & Prince Islands No. 354, Timor No. 258, some with colors changed. The sheet contains doves and is inscribed 'Encerramento do Ano Santo, Fatima 1951.' It was sold for 17 escudos.

Holy Year Conclusion

Our Lady of Fatima — CD43

Conclusion of Holy Year. Sheets contain alternate vertical rows of stamps and labels bearing quotation from Pope Pius XII, different for each colony.

1951

Angola	357
Cape Verde	270
Macao	352
Mozambique	356
Port. Guinea	275
Port. India	506
St. Thomas & Prince Islands	355
Timor	270

Medical Congress

CD44

First National Congress of Tropical Medicine, Lisbon, 1952. Each stamp has a different design.

1952

Angola	358
Cape Verde	287
Macao	364
Mozambique	359
Port. Guinea	276
Port. India	516
St. Thomas & Prince Islands	356
Timor	271

Postage Due Stamps

CD45

1952

Angola	J37-J42
Cape Verde	J31-J36
Macao	J53-J58
Mozambique	J51-J56
Port. Guinea	J40-J45
Port. India	J47-J52
St. Thomas & Prince Islands	J52-J57
Timor	J31-J36

Sao Paulo

Father Manuel de Nobrege and View of Sao Paulo — CD46

Founding of Sao Paulo, Brazil, 400th anniv.

1954

Angola	385
Cape Verde	297
Macao	382
Mozambique	395
Port. Guinea	291
Port. India	530
St. Thomas & Prince Islands	369
Timor	279

Tropical Medicine Congress

CD47

Sixth International Congress for Tropical Medicine and Malaria, Lisbon, Sept. 1958. Each stamp shows a different plant.

1958

Angola	409
Cape Verde	303
Macao	392
Mozambique	404
Port. Guinea	295
Port. India	569
St. Thomas & Prince Islands	371
Timor	289

Sports

CD48

Each stamp shows a different sport.

1962

Angola	433-438
Cape Verde	320-325
Macao	394-399
Mozambique	424-429
Port. Guinea	299-304
St. Thomas & Prince Islands	374-379
Timor	313-318

Anti-Malaria

Anopheles Funestus and Malaria Eradication Symbol — CD49

World Health Organization drive to eradicate malaria.

1962

Angola	439
Cape Verde	326
Macao	400
Mozambique	430
Port. Guinea	305
St. Thomas & Prince Islands	380
Timor	319

Airline Anniversary

Map of Africa, Super Constellation and Jet Liner — CD50

Tenth anniversary of Transportes Aereos Portugueses (TAP).

1963

Angola	490
Cape Verde	327
Mozambique	434
Port. Guinea	318
St. Thomas & Prince Islands	381

National Overseas Bank

Antonio Teixeira de Sousa — CD51

Centenary of the National Overseas Bank of Portugal.

1964, May 16

Angola	509
Cape Verde	328
Port. Guinea	319
St. Thomas & Prince Islands	382
Timor	320

ITU

ITU Emblem and the Archangel Gabriel — CD52

International Communications Union, Cent.

1965, May 17

Angola	511
Cape Verde	329
Macao	402
Mozambique	464
Port. Guinea	320
St. Thomas & Prince Islands	383
Timor	321

National Revolution

CD53

40th anniv. of the National Revolution. Different buildings on each stamp.

1966, May 28

Angola	525
Cape Verde	338
Macao	403
Mozambique	465
Port. Guinea	329
St. Thomas & Prince Islands	392
Timor	322

Navy Club

CD54

Centenary of Portugal's Navy Club. Each stamp has a different design.

1967, Jan. 31

Angola	527-528
Cape Verde	339-340
Macao	412-413
Mozambique	478-479
Port. Guinea	330-331
St. Thomas & Prince Islands	393-394
Timor	323-324

Admiral Coutinho

CD55

Centenary of the birth of Admiral Carlos Viegas Gago Coutinho (1869-1959), explorer and aviation pioneer. Each stamp has a different design.

1969, Feb. 17

Angola	547
Cape Verde	355
Macao	417
Mozambique	484
Port. Guinea	335
St. Thomas & Prince Islands	397
Timor	335

Administration Reform

Luiz Augusto Rebello da Silva — CD56

Centenary of the administration reforms of the overseas territories.

1969, Sept. 25

Angola	549
Cape Verde	357
Macao	419
Mozambique	491
Port. Guinea	337
St. Thomas & Prince Islands	399
Timor	338

Marshal Carmona

CD57

Birth centenary of Marshal Antonio Oscar Carmona de Fragoso (1869-1951), President of Portugal. Each stamp has a different design.

1970, Nov. 15

Angola	563
Cape Verde	359
Macao	422
Mozambique	493
Port. Guinea	340
St. Thomas & Prince Islands	403
Timor	341

Olympic Games

CD59

20th Olympic Games, Munich, Aug. 26-Sept. 11. Each stamp shows a different sport.

1972, June 20

Angola	569
Cape Verde	361
Macao	426
Mozambique	504
Port. Guinea	342
St. Thomas & Prince Islands	408
Timor	343

Lisbon-Rio de Janeiro Flight

CD60

50th anniversary of the Lisbon to Rio de Janeiro flight by Arturo de Sacadura and Coutinho, March 30-June 5, 1922. Each stamp shows a different stage of the flight.

1972, Sept. 20

Angola	570
Cape Verde	362
Macao	427
Mozambique	505
Port. Guinea	343
St. Thomas & Prince Islands	409
Timor	344

WMO Centenary

WMO Emblem — CD61

Centenary of international meterological cooperation.

1973, Dec. 15

Angola	571
Cape Verde	363
Macao	429
Mozambique	509
Port. Guinea	344
St. Thomas & Prince Islands	410
Timor	345

FRENCH COMMUNITY

Upper Volta can be found under Burkina Faso in Vol. 1
Madagascar can be found under Malagasy in Vol. 3
Colonial Exposition

People of French Empire CD70

Women's Heads CD71

France Showing Way to Civilization CD72

"Colonial Commerce" CD73

International Colonial Exposition, Paris.

1931

Cameroun	213-216
Chad	60-63
Dahomey	97-100
Fr. Guiana	152-155
Fr. Guinea	116-119
Fr. India	100-103
Fr. Polynesia	76-79
Fr. Sudan	102-105
Gabon	120-123
Guadeloupe	138-141
Indo-China	140-142
Ivory Coast	92-95
Madagascar	169-172
Martinique	129-132
Mauritania	65-68
Middle Congo	61-64
New Caledonia	176-179
Niger	73-76
Reunion	122-125
St. Pierre & Miquelon	132-135
Senegal	138-141
Somali Coast	135-138
Togo	254-257
Ubangi-Shari	82-85
Upper Volta	66-69
Wallis & Futuna Isls.	85-88

Paris International Exposition Colonial Arts Exposition

"Colonial Resources"
CD74   CD77

Overseas Commerce CD75

Exposition Building and Women CD76

"France and the Empire" CD78

Cultural Treasures of the Colonies CD79

Souvenir sheets contain one imperf. stamp.

1937

Cameroun	217-222A
Dahomey	101-107
Fr. Equatorial Africa	27-32, 73
Fr. Guiana	162-168
Fr. Guinea	120-126
Fr. India	104-110
Fr. Polynesia	117-123
Fr. Sudan	106-112
Guadeloupe	148-154
Indo-China	193-199
Inini	41
Ivory Coast	152-158
Kwangchowan	132
Madagascar	191-197
Martinique	179-185
Mauritania	69-75
New Caledonia	208-214
Niger	72-83
Reunion	167-173
St. Pierre & Miquelon	165-171
Senegal	172-178
Somali Coast	139-145
Togo	258-264
Wallis & Futuna Isls.	89

Curie

Pierre and Marie Curie CD80

40th anniversary of the discovery of radium. The surtax was for the benefit of the Intl. Union for the Control of Cancer.

1938

Cameroun	B1
Cuba	B1-B2
Dahomey	B2
France	B76
Fr. Equatorial Africa	B1
Fr. Guiana	B3
Fr. Guinea	B2
Fr. India	B6
Fr. Polynesia	B5
Fr. Sudan	B1
Guadeloupe	B3

Indo-China	B14
Ivory Coast	B2
Madagascar	B2
Martinique	B2
Mauritania	B3
New Caledonia	B4
Niger	B1
Reunion	B4
St. Pierre & Miquelon	B3
Senegal	B3
Somali Coast	B2
Togo	B1

Caillie

Rene Caille and Map of Northwestern Africa — CD81

Death centenary of Rene Caillie (1799-1838), French explorer. All three denominations exist with colony name omitted.

1939

Dahomey	108-110
Fr. Guinea	161-163
Fr. Sudan	113-115
Ivory Coast	160-162
Mauritania	109-111
Niger	84-86
Senegal	188-190
Togo	265-267

New York World's Fair

Natives and New York Skyline CD82

1939

Cameroun	223-224
Dahomey	111-112
Fr. Equatorial Africa	78-79
Fr. Guiana	169-170
Fr. Guinea	164-165
Fr. India	111-112
Fr. Polynesia	124-125
Fr. Sudan	116-117
Guadeloupe	155-156
Indo-China	203-204
Inini	42-43
Ivory Coast	163-164
Kwangchowan	121-122
Madagascar	209-210
Martinique	186-187
Mauritania	112-113
New Caledonia	215-216
Niger	87-88
Reunion	174-175
St. Pierre & Miquelon	205-206
Senegal	191-192
Somali Coast	179-180
Togo	268-269
Wallis & Futuna Isls.	90-91

French Revolution

Storming of the Bastille CD83

French Revolution, 150th anniv. The surtax was for the defense of the colonies.

1939

Cameroun	B2-B6
Dahomey	B3-B7
Fr. Equatorial Africa	B4-B8, CB1
Fr. Guiana	B4-B8, CB1
Fr. Guinea	B3-B7
Fr. India	B7-B11
Fr. Polynesia	B6-B10, CB1
Fr. Sudan	B2-B6
Guadeloupe	B4-B8
Indo-China	B15-B19, CB1
Inini	B1-B5
Ivory Coast	B3-B7

Kwangchowan B1-B5
Madagascar.......................B3-B7, CB1
Martinique.................................B3-B7
Mauritania..................................B4-B8
New Caledonia B5-B9, CB1
Niger..B2-B6
Reunion B5-B9, CB1
St. Pierre & Miquelon B4-B8
Senegal B4-B8, CB1
Somali Coast B3-B7
Togo...B2-B6
Wallis & Futuna Isls. B1-B5

Plane over
Coastal
Area
CD85

All five denominations exist with colony
name omitted.

1940

Dahomey C1-C5
Fr. Guinea C1-C5
Fr. Sudan...................................C1-C5
Ivory Coast C1-C5
Mauritania..................................C1-C5
Niger C1-C5
Senegal C12-C16
Togo..C1-C5

Defense of the Empire

Colonial
Infantryman — CD86

1941

Cameroun....................................B13B
Dahomey B13
Fr. Equatorial Africa B8B
Fr. Guiana B10
Fr. Guinea B13
Fr. India B13
Fr. Polynesia B12
Fr. Sudan B12
Guadeloupe B10
Indo-China B19B
Inini B7
Ivory Coast B13
Kwangchowan B7
Madagascar....................................B9
Martinique B9
Mauritania.....................................B14
New Caledonia B11
Niger B12
Reunion B11
St. Pierre & Miquelon B8B
Senegal B14
Somali Coast B9
Togo...B10B
Wallis & Futuna Isls. B7

Colonial Education Fund

CD86a

1942

Cameroun......................................CB3
Dahomey CB4
Fr. Equatorial Africa CB5
Fr. Guiana CB4
Fr. Guinea CB4

Fr. India CB3
Fr. Polynesia CB4
Fr. Sudan.....................................CB4
Guadeloupe CB3
Indo-China CB5
Inini CB3
Ivory Coast CB4
Kwangchowan CB4
Malagasy CB5
Martinique CB3
Mauritania....................................CB4
New Caledonia CB4
Niger CB4
Reunion CB4
St. Pierre & Miquelon....................CB3
Senegal CB5
Somali Coast CB3
Togo...CB3
Wallis & Futuna CB3

Cross of
Lorraine &
Four-motor
Plane
CD87

1941-5

Cameroun.................................. C1-C7
Fr. Equatorial Africa C17-C23
Fr. Guiana C9-C10
Fr. India C1-C6
Fr. Polynesia C3-C9
Fr. West Africa C1-C3
Guadeloupe C1-C2
Madagascar........................... C37-C43
Martinique C1-C2
New Caledonia C7-C13
Reunion C18-C24
St. Pierre & Miquelon C1-C7
Somali Coast C1-C7

Transport
Plane
CD88

Caravan
and Plane
CD89

1942

Dahomey C6-C13
Fr. Guinea C6-C13
Fr. Sudan................................ C6-C13
Ivory Coast C6-C13
Mauritania............................... C6-C13
Niger C6-C13
Senegal C17-C25
Togo....................................... C6-C13

Red Cross

Marianne
CD90

The surtax was for the French Red Cross
and national relief.

1944

Cameroun.................................... B28
Fr. Equatorial Africa B38
Fr. Guiana B12
Fr. India B14
Fr. Polynesia B13
Fr. West Africa B1
Guadeloupe B12
Madagascar................................ B15
Martinique B11
New Caledonia B13
Reunion B15
St. Pierre & Miquelon B13
Somali Coast B13

Wallis & Futuna Isls. B9

Eboue

CD91

Felix Eboue, first French colonial administrator to proclaim resistance to Germany after
French surrender in World War II.

1945

Cameroun...............................296-297
Fr. Equatorial Africa 156-157
Fr. Guiana 171-172
Fr. India 210-211
Fr. Polynesia 150-151
Fr. West Africa 15-16
Guadeloupe 187-188
Madagascar............................259-260
Martinique 196-197
New Caledonia 274-275
Reunion 238-239
St. Pierre & Miquelon 322-323
Somali Coast 238-239

Victory

Victory — CD92

European victory of the Allied Nations in
World War II.

1946, May 8

Cameroun C8
Fr. Equatorial Africa C24
Fr. Guiana C11
Fr. India C7
Fr. Polynesia C10
Fr. West Africa C4
Guadeloupe C3
Indo-China C19
Madagascar................................. C44
Martinique C3
New Caledonia C14
Reunion C25
St. Pierre & Miquelon C8
Somali Coast C8
Wallis & Futuna Isls. C1

Chad to Rhine

Leclerc's Departure from
Chad — CD93

Battle at Cufra Oasis — CD94

Tanks in Action, Mareth — CD95

Normandy Invasion — CD96

Entering Paris — CD97

Liberation of Strasbourg — CD98

"Chad to the Rhine" march, 1942-44, by
Gen. Jacques Leclerc's column, later French
2nd Armored Division.

1946, June 6

Cameroun................................. C9-C14
Fr. Equatorial Africa C25-C30
Fr. Guiana C12-C17
Fr. India C8-C13
Fr. Polynesia C11-C16
Fr. West Africa C5-C10
Guadeloupe C4-C9
Indo-China C20-C25
Madagascar......................... C45-C50
Martinique C4-C9
New Caledonia C15-C20
Reunion C26-C31
St. Pierre & Miquelon C9-C14
Somali Coast C9-C14
Wallis & Futuna Isls. C2-C7

UPU

French Colonials, Globe and
Plane — CD99

Universal Postal Union, 75th anniv.

1949, July 4

Cameroun....................................... C29
Fr. Equatorial Africa C34
Fr. India C17
Fr. Polynesia C20
Fr. West Africa C15
Indo-China C26
Madagascar.................................... C55
New Caledonia C24
St. Pierre & Miquelon C18
Somali Coast C18
Togo... C18
Wallis & Futuna Isls. C10

Tropical Medicine

Doctor Treating Infant CD100

The surtax was for charitable work.

1950

Cameroun	B29
Fr. Equatorial Africa	B39
Fr. India	B15
Fr. Polynesia	B14
Fr. West Africa	B3
Madagascar	B17
New Caledonia	B14
St. Pierre & Miquelon	B14
Somali Coast	B14
Togo	B11

Military Medal

Medal, Early Marine and Colonial Soldier — CD101

Centenary of the creation of the French Military Medal.

1952

Cameroun	332
Comoro Isls.	39
Fr. Equatorial Africa	186
Fr. India	233
Fr. Polynesia	179
Fr. West Africa	57
Madagascar	286
New Caledonia	295
St. Pierre & Miquelon	345
Somali Coast	267
Togo	327
Wallis & Futuna Isls.	149

Liberation

Allied Landing, Victory Sign and Cross of Lorraine — CD102

Liberation of France, 10th anniv.

1954, June 6

Cameroun	C32
Comoro Isls.	C4
Fr. Equatorial Africa	C38
Fr. India	C18
Fr. Polynesia	C22
Fr. West Africa	C17
Madagascar	C57
New Caledonia	C25
St. Pierre & Miquelon	C19
Somali Coast	C19
Togo	C19
Wallis & Futuna Isls.	C11

FIDES

Plowmen CD103

Efforts of FIDES, the Economic and Social Development Fund for Overseas Possessions

(Fonds d' Investissement pour le Developpement Economique et Social). Each stamp has a different design.

1956

Cameroun	326-329
Comoro Isls.	43
Fr. Polynesia	181
Fr. West Africa	65-72
Madagascar	292-295
New Caledonia	303
Somali Coast	268
Togo	331

Flower

CD104

Each stamp shows a different flower.

1958-9

Cameroun	333
Comoro Isls.	45
Fr. Equatorial Africa	200-201
Fr. Polynesia	192
Fr. So. & Antarctic Terr.	11
Fr. West Africa	79-83
Madagascar	301-302
New Caledonia	304-305
St. Pierre & Miquelon	357
Somali Coast	270
Togo	348-349
Wallis & Futuna Isls.	152

Human Rights

Sun, Dove and U.N. Emblem CD105

10th anniversary of the signing of the Universal Declaration of Human Rights.

1958

Comoro Isls.	44
Fr. Equatorial Africa	202
Fr. Polynesia	191
Fr. West Africa	85
Madagascar	300
New Caledonia	306
St. Pierre & Miquelon	356
Somali Coast	274
Wallis & Futuna Isls.	153

C.C.T.A.

CD106

Commission for Technical Cooperation in Africa south of the Sahara, 10th anniv.

1960

Cameroun	335
Cent. Africa	3
Chad	66
Congo, P.R.	90
Dahomey	138
Gabon	150
Ivory Coast	180
Madagascar	317
Mali	9
Mauritania	117
Niger	104
Upper Volta	89

Air Afrique, 1961

Modern and Ancient Africa, Map and Planes — CD107

Founding of Air Afrique (African Airlines).

1961-62

Cameroun	C37
Cent. Africa	C5
Chad	C7
Congo, P.R.	C5
Dahomey	C17
Gabon	C5
Ivory Coast	C18
Mauritania	C17
Niger	C22
Senegal	C31
Upper Volta	C4

Anti-Malaria

CD108

World Health Organization drive to eradicate malaria.

1962, Apr. 7

Cameroun	B36
Cent. Africa	B1
Chad	B1
Comoro Isls.	B1
Congo, P.R.	B3
Dahomey	B15
Gabon	B4
Ivory Coast	B15
Madagascar	B19
Mali	B1
Mauritania	B16
Niger	B14
Senegal	B16
Somali Coast	B15
Upper Volta	B1

Abidjan Games

CD109

Abidjan Games, Ivory Coast, Dec. 24-31, 1961. Each stamp shows a different sport.

1962

Chad	83-84
Cent. Africa	19-20
Congo, P.R.	103-104
Gabon	163-164, C6
Niger	109-111
Upper Volta	103-105

African and Malagasy Union

Flag of Union CD110

First anniversary of the Union.

1962, Sept. 8

Cameroun	373
Cent. Africa	21

Chad	85
Congo, P.R.	105
Dahomey	155
Gabon	165
Ivory Coast	198
Madagascar	332
Mauritania	170
Niger	112
Senegal	211
Upper Volta	106

Telstar

Telstar and Globe Showing Andover and Pleumeur-Bodou — CD111

First television connection of the United States and Europe through the Telstar satellite, July 11-12, 1962.

1962-63

Andorra, French	154
Comoro Isls.	C7
Fr. Polynesia	C29
Fr. So. & Antarctic Terr.	C5
New Caledonia	C33
Somali Coast	C31
St. Pierre & Miquelon	C26
Wallis & Futuna Isls.	C17

Freedom From Hunger

World Map and Wheat Emblem CD112

 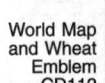

U.N. Food and Agriculture Organization's "Freedom from Hunger" campaign.

1963, Mar. 21

Cameroun	B37-B38
Cent. Africa	B2
Chad	B2
Congo, P.R.	B4
Dahomey	B16
Gabon	B5
Ivory Coast	B16
Madagascar	B21
Mauritania	B17
Niger	B15
Senegal	B17
Upper Volta	B2

Red Cross Centenary

CD113

Centenary of the International Red Cross.

1963, Sept. 2

Comoro Isls.	55
Fr. Polynesia	205
New Caledonia	328
St. Pierre & Miquelon	367
Somali Coast	297
Wallis & Futuna Isls.	165

African Postal Union, 1963

UAMPT
Emblem,
Radio Masts,
Plane and
Mail
CD114

Establishment of the African and Malagasy Posts and Telecommunications Union.

1963, Sept. 8

Cameroun	C47
Cent. Africa	C10
Chad	C9
Congo, P.R.	C13
Dahomey	C19
Gabon	C13
Ivory Coast	C25
Madagascar	C75
Mauritania	C22
Niger	C27
Rwanda	36
Senegal	C32
Upper Volta	C9

Air Afrique, 1963

Symbols of Flight — CD115

First anniversary of Air Afrique and inauguration of DC-8 service.

1963, Nov. 19

Cameroun	C48
Chad	C10
Congo, P.R.	C14
Gabon	C18
Ivory Coast	C26
Mauritania	C26
Niger	C35
Senegal	C33

Europafrica

Europe and Africa
Linked — CD116

Signing of an economic agreement between the European Economic Community and the African and Malagasy Union, Yaounde, Cameroun, July 20, 1963.

1963-64

Cameroun	402
Chad	C11
Cent. Africa	C12
Congo, P.R.	C16
Gabon	C19
Ivory Coast	217
Niger	C43
Upper Volta	C11

Human Rights

Scales of
Justice and
Globe
CD117

15th anniversary of the Universal Declaration of Human Rights.

1963, Dec. 10

Comoro Isls.	58
Fr. Polynesia	206
New Caledonia	329
St. Pierre & Miquelon	368
Somali Coast	300
Wallis & Futuna Isls.	166

PHILATEC

Stamp Album, Champs Elysees
Palace and Horses of Marly
CD118

Intl. Philatelic and Postal Techniques Exhibition, Paris, June 5-21, 1964.

1963-64

Comoro Isls.	60
France	1078
Fr. Polynesia	207
New Caledonia	341
St. Pierre & Miquelon	369
Somali Coast	301
Wallis & Futuna Isls.	167

Cooperation

CD119

Cooperation between France and the French-speaking countries of Africa and Madagascar.

1964

Cameroun	409-410
Cent. Africa	39
Chad	103
Congo, P.R.	121
Dahomey	193
France	1111
Gabon	175
Ivory Coast	221
Madagascar	360
Mauritania	181
Niger	143
Senegal	236
Togo	495

ITU

Telegraph,
Syncom Satellite
and ITU Emblem
CD120

Intl. Telecommunication Union, Cent.

1965, May 17

Comoro Isls.	C14
Fr. Polynesia	C33
Fr. So. & Antarctic Terr.	C8
New Caledonia	C40
New Hebrides	124-125
St. Pierre & Miquelon	C29
Somali Coast	C36
Wallis & Futuna Isls.	C20

French Satellite A-1

Diamant Rocket and Launching
Installation — CD121

Launching of France's first satellite, Nov. 26, 1965.

1965-66

Comoro Isls.	C15-C16
France	1137-1138
Fr. Polynesia	C40-C41
Fr. So. & Antarctic Terr.	C9-C10
New Caledonia	C44-C45
St. Pierre & Miquelon	C30-C31
Somali Coast	C39-C40
Wallis & Futuna Isls.	C22-C23

French Satellite D-1

D-1 Satellite in Orbit — CD122

Launching of the D-1 satellite at Hammaguir, Algeria, Feb. 17, 1966.

1966

Comoro Isls.	C17
France	1148
Fr. Polynesia	C42
Fr. So. & Antarctic Terr.	C11
New Caledonia	C46
St. Pierre & Miquelon	C32
Somali Coast	C49
Wallis & Futuna Isls.	C24

Air Afrique, 1966

Planes and Air Afrique
Emblem — CD123

Introduction of DC-8F planes by Air Afrique.

1966

Cameroun	C79
Cent. Africa	C35
Chad	C26
Congo, P.R.	C42
Dahomey	C42
Gabon	C47
Ivory Coast	C32
Mauritania	C57
Niger	C63
Senegal	C47
Togo	C54
Upper Volta	C31

African Postal Union, 1967

Telecommunications Symbols and Map
of Africa — CD124

Fifth anniversary of the establishment of the African and Malagasy Union of Posts and Telecommunications, UAMPT.

1967

Cameroun	C90
Cent. Africa	C46
Chad	C37
Congo, P.R.	C57
Dahomey	C61
Gabon	C58
Ivory Coast	C34
Madagascar	C85
Mauritania	C65
Niger	C75
Rwanda	C1-C3
Senegal	C60
Togo	C81
Upper Volta	C50

Monetary Union

Gold Token of the
Ashantis, 17-18th
Centuries — CD125

West African Monetary Union, 5th anniv.

1967, Nov. 4

Dahomey	244
Ivory Coast	259
Mauritania	238
Niger	204
Senegal	294
Togo	623
Upper Volta	181

WHO Anniversary

Sun,
Flowers
and WHO
Emblem
CD126

World Health Organization, 20th anniv.

1968, May 4

Afars & Issas	317
Comoro Isls.	73
Fr. Polynesia	241-242
Fr. So. & Antarctic Terr.	31
New Caledonia	367
St. Pierre & Miquelon	377
Wallis & Futuna Isls.	169

Human Rights Year

Human Rights
Flame — CD127

1968, Aug. 10

Afars & Issas	322-323

2nd PHILEXAFRIQUE

CD128

Opening of PHILEXAFRIQUE, Abidjan, Feb. 14. Each stamp shows a local scene and stamp.

1969, Feb. 14

Concorde

Concorde in Flight CD129

First flight of the prototype Concorde supersonic plane at Toulouse, Mar. 1, 1969.

1969

Development Bank

Bank Emblem — CD130

African Development Bank, fifth anniv.

1969

ILO

ILO Headquarters, Geneva, and Emblem — CD131

Intl. Labor Organization, 50th anniv.

1969-70

ASECNA

Map of Africa, Plane and Airport CD132

10th anniversary of the Agency for the Security of Aerial Navigation in Africa and Madagascar (ASECNA, Agence pour la Securite de la Navigation Aerienne en Afrique et a Madagascar).

1969-70

U.P.U. Headquarters

CD133

New Universal Postal Union headquarters, Bern, Switzerland.

1970

De Gaulle

CD134

First anniversary of the death of Charles de Gaulle, (1890-1970), President of France.

1971-72

African Postal Union, 1971

UAMPT Building, Brazzaville, Congo — CD135

10th anniversary of the establishment of the African and Malagasy Posts and Telecommunications Union, UAMPT. Each stamp has a different native design.

1971, Nov. 13

West African Monetary Union

African Couple, City, Village and Commemorative Coin — CD136

West African Monetary Union, 10th anniv.

1972, Nov. 2

African Postal Union, 1973

Telecommunications Symbols and Map of Africa — CD137

11th anniversary of the African and Malagasy Posts and Telecommunications Union (UAMPT).

1973, Sept. 12

Philexafrique II — Essen

CD138

CD139

Designs: Indigenous fauna, local and German stamps. Types CD138-CD139 printed horizontally and vertically se-tenant in sheets of 10 (2x5). Label between horizontal pairs alternately commemorates Philexafrique II, Libreville, Gabon, June 1978, and 2nd International Stamp Fair, Essen, Germany, Nov. 1-5.

1978-1979

BRITISH COMMONWEALTH OF NATIONS

The listings follow established trade practices when these issues are offered as units by dealers. The Peace issue, for example, includes only one stamp from the Indian state of Hyderabad. The U.P.U. issue includes the Egypt set. Pairs are included for those varieties issues with bilingual designs se-tenant.

Silver Jubilee

Windsor Castle and King George V CD301

Reign of King George V, 25th anniv.

1935

Gold Coast 108-111
Grenada............................124-127
Hong Kong 147-150
Jamaica.............................109-112
Kenya, Uganda, Tanganyika 42-45
Leeward Islands 96-99
Malta 184-187
Mauritius...........................204-207
Montserrat 85-88
Newfoundland 226-229
Nigeria 34-37
Northern Rhodesia 18-21
Nyasaland Protectorate............47-50
St. Helena 111-114
St. Kitts-Nevis 72-75
St. Lucia 91-94
St. Vincent.........................134-137
Seychelles 118-121
Sierra Leone 166-169
Solomon Islands....................60-63
Somaliland Protectorate..........77-80
Straits Settlements 213-216
Swaziland 20-23
Trinidad & Tobago 43-46
Turks & Caicos Islands 71-74
Virgin Islands........................69-72

The following have different designs but are included in the omnibus set:

Great Britain 226-229
Offices in Morocco 67-70, 226-229,
   422-425, 508-510
Australia 152-154
Canada 211-216
Cook Islands 98-100
India 142-148
Nauru..................................31-34
New Guinea 46-49
New Zealand 199-201
Niue 67-69
Papua 114-117
Samoa 163-165
South Africa.........................68-71
Southern Rhodesia 33-36
South-West Africa 121-124

202 stamps

Coronation

Queen
Elizabeth
and King
George VI
CD302

1937

Aden 13-15
Antigua................................81-83
Ascension.............................37-39
Bahamas 97-99
Barbados 190-192
Basutoland............................15-17
Bechuanaland Protectorate......121-123
Bermuda 115-117
British Guiana.....................227-229
British Honduras..................112-114
Cayman Islands......................97-99
Ceylon 275-277
Cyprus 140-142
Dominica.............................94-96
Falkland Islands 81-83
Fiji 114-116
Gambia 129-131
Gibraltar.............................104-106
Gilbert & Ellice Islands...............37-39
Gold Coast 112-114
Grenada............................128-130
Hong Kong 151-153
Jamaica.............................113-115
Kenya, Uganda, Tanganyika 60-62
Leeward Islands 100-102
Malta 188-190
Mauritius...........................208-210
Montserrat 89-91
Newfoundland 230-232
Nigeria 50-52
Northern Rhodesia 22-24
Nyasaland Protectorate............51-53
St. Helena 115-117
St. Kitts-Nevis 76-78
St. Lucia 107-109
St. Vincent.........................138-140
Seychelles 122-124
Sierra Leone 170-172
Solomon Islands....................64-66
Somaliland Protectorate..........81-83
Straits Settlements 235-237

Swaziland 24-26
Trinidad & Tobago 47-49
Turks & Caicos Islands 75-77
Virgin Islands........................73-75

The following have different designs but are included in the omnibus set:

Great Britain 234
Offices in Morocco 82, 439, 514
Canada 237
Cook Islands 109-111
Nauru..................................35-38
Newfoundland 233-243
New Guinea 48-51
New Zealand 223-225
Niue 70-72
Papua 118-121
South Africa.........................74-78
Southern Rhodesia 38-41
South-West Africa 125-132

249 stamps

Peace

King
George VI
and
Parliament
Buildings,
London
CD303

Return to peace at the close of World War II.

1945-46

Aden 28-29
Antigua................................96-97
Ascension.............................50-51
Bahamas 130-131
Barbados 207-208
Bermuda 131-132
British Guiana.....................242-243
British Honduras..................127-128
Cayman Islands..................112-113
Ceylon 293-294
Cyprus 156-157
Dominica...........................112-113
Falkland Islands 97-98
Falkland Islands Dep...........1L9-1L10
Fiji 137-138
Gambia 144-145
Gibraltar.............................119-120
Gilbert & Ellice Islands...............52-53
Gold Coast 128-129
Grenada............................143-144
Jamaica.............................136-137
Kenya, Uganda, Tanganyika 90-91
Leeward Islands 116-117
Malta 206-207
Mauritius...........................223-224
Montserrat 104-105
Nigeria 71-72
Northern Rhodesia 46-47
Nyasaland Protectorate............82-83
Pitcairn Island 9-10
St. Helena 128-129
St. Kitts-Nevis 91-92
St. Lucia 127-128
St. Vincent.........................152-153
Seychelles 149-150
Sierra Leone 186-187
Solomon Islands....................80-81
Somaliland Protectorate........108-109
Trinidad & Tobago 62-63
Turks & Caicos Islands 90-91
Virgin Islands........................88-89

The following have different designs but are included in the omnibus set:

Great Britain 264-265
   Offices in Morocco 523-524
Aden
   Kathiri State of Seiyun..............12-13
   Qu'aiti State of Shihr and Mukalla ....
  12-13
Australia 200-202
Basutoland............................29-31
Bechuanaland Protectorate......137-139
Burma..................................66-69
Cook Islands 127-130
Hong Kong 174-175
India 195-198
   Hyderabad 51
New Zealand 247-257
Niue 90-93
Pakistan-Bahawalpur.................O16
Samoa 191-194
South Africa.......................100-102
Southern Rhodesia 67-70

South-West Africa 153-155
Swaziland 38-40
Zanzibar............................222-223

164 stamps

Silver Wedding

King George VI and Queen
Elizabeth
CD304   CD305

1948-49

Aden 30-31
   Kathiri State of Seiyun..............14-15
   Qu'aiti State of Shihr and Mukalla ....
  14-15
Antigua................................98-99
Ascension.............................52-53
Bahamas 148-149
Barbados 210-211
Basutoland............................39-40
Bechuanaland Protectorate......147-148
Bermuda 133-134
British Guiana.....................244-245
British Honduras..................129-130
Cayman Islands..................116-117
Cyprus 158-159
Dominica...........................114-115
Falkland Islands 99-100
Falkland Islands Dep...........1L11-1L12
Fiji 139-140
Gambia 146-147
Gibraltar.............................121-122
Gilbert & Ellice Islands...............54-55
Gold Coast 142-143
Grenada............................145-146
Hong Kong 178-179
Jamaica.............................138-139
Kenya, Uganda, Tanganyika 92-93
Leeward Islands 118-119
Malaya
   Johore 128-129
   Kedah 55-56
   Kelantan 44-45
   Malacca 1-2
   Negri Sembilan 36-37
   Pahang 44-45
   Penang 1-2
   Perak 99-100
   Perlis 1-2
   Selangor 74-75
   Trengganu 47-48
Malta 223-224
Mauritius...........................229-230
Montserrat 106-107
Nigeria 73-74
North Borneo......................238-239
Northern Rhodesia 48-49
Nyasaland Protectorate............85-86
Pitcairn Island 11-12
St. Helena 130-131
St. Kitts-Nevis 93-94
St. Lucia 129-130
St. Vincent.........................154-155
Sarawak............................174-175
Seychelles 151-152
Sierra Leone 188-189
Singapore 21-22
Solomon Islands....................82-83
Somaliland Protectorate........110-111
Swaziland 48-49
Trinidad & Tobago 64-65
Turks & Caicos Islands 92-93
Virgin Islands........................90-91
Zanzibar............................224-225

The following have different designs but are included in the omnibus set:

Great Britain 267-268
   Offices in Morocco...., 93-94, 525-526
Bahrain 62-63
Kuwait 82-83
Oman 25-26
South Africa............................106
South-West Africa 159

138 stamps

U.P.U.

Mercury and Symbols of
Communications — CD306

Plane, Ship and
Hemispheres — CD307

Mercury
Scattering
Letters over
Globe
CD308

U.P.U.
Monument,
Bern
CD309

Universal Postal Union, 75th anniversary.

1949

Aden 32-35
   Kathiri State of Seiyun..............16-19
   Qu'aiti State of Shihr and Mukalla ....
  16-19
Antigua..............................100-103
Ascension.............................57-60
Bahamas 150-153
Barbados 212-215
Basutoland............................41-44
Bechuanaland Protectorate......149-152
Bermuda 138-141
British Guiana.....................246-249
British Honduras..................137-140
Brunei..................................79-82
Cayman Islands..................118-121
Cyprus 160-163
Dominica...........................116-119
Falkland Islands 103-106
Falkland Islands Dep...........1L14-1L17
Fiji 141-144
Gambia 148-151
Gibraltar.............................123-126
Gilbert & Ellice Islands...............56-59
Gold Coast 144-147
Grenada............................147-150
Hong Kong 180-183
Jamaica.............................142-145
Kenya, Uganda, Tanganyika 94-97
Leeward Islands 126-129
Malaya
   Johore 151-154
   Kedah 57-60
   Kelantan 46-49
   Malacca 18-21
   Negri Sembilan 59-62
   Pahang 46-49
   Penang 23-26
   Perak 101-104
   Perlis 3-6
   Selangor 76-79
   Trengganu 49-52
Malta 225-228
Mauritius...........................231-234
Montserrat 108-111
New Hebrides, British 62-65
New Hebrides, French 79-82
Nigeria 75-78
North Borneo......................240-243
Northern Rhodesia 50-53
Nyasaland Protectorate............87-90
Pitcairn Islands 13-16
St. Helena 132-135
St. Kitts-Nevis 95-98
St. Lucia 131-134
St. Vincent.........................170-173

The following have different designs but are included in the omnibus set:

319 stamps

University

Arms of
University
College
CD310

Alice, Princess
of Athlone
CD311

1948 opening of University College of the West Indies at Jamaica.

1951

28 stamps

Coronation

Queen Elizabeth
II — CD312

1953

The following have different designs but are included in the omnibus set:

106 stamps

Royal Visit 1953

Separate designs for each country for the visit of Queen Elizabeth II and the Duke of Edinburgh.

1953

13 stamps

West Indies Federation

Map of the
Caribbean
CD313

Federation of the West Indies, April 22, 1958.

1958

30 stamps

Freedom from Hunger

Protein Food
CD314

U.N. Food and Agricultural Organization's "Freedom from Hunger" campaign.

1963

37 stamps

Red Cross Centenary

Red Cross
and
Elizabeth
II
CD315

1963

70 stamps

Shakespeare

Shakespeare Memorial Theatre, Stratford-on-Avon — CD316

400th anniversary of the birth of William Shakespeare.

1964

12 stamps

ITU

ITU
Emblem
CD317

Intl. Telecommunication Union, cent.

1965

64 stamps

Intl. Cooperation Year

ICY Emblem CD318

1965

Antigua 155-156
Ascension 94-95
Bahamas 222-223
Basutoland.............................103-104
Bechuanaland Protectorate.....204-205
Bermuda 199-200
British Guiana.........................295-296
British Honduras.....................189-190
Brunei 118-119
Cayman Islands......................174-175
Dominica 187-188
Falkland Islands 156-157
Fiji 213-214
Gibraltar.................................169-170
Gilbert & Ellice Islands 104-105
Grenada 207-208
Hong Kong 223-224
Mauritius 293-294
Montserrat 176-177
New Hebrides, British 110-111
New Hebrides, French 126-127
Pitcairn Islands 54-55
St. Helena 182-183
St. Kitts-Nevis 165-166
St. Lucia 199-200
Seychelles 220-221
Solomon Islands 143-144
South Arabia 17-18
Swaziland 117-118
Tristan da Cunha 87-88
Turks & Caicos Islands 144-145
Virgin Islands 161-162

64 stamps

Churchill Memorial

Winston Churchill and St. Paul's, London, During Air Attack CD319

1966

Antigua 157-160
Ascension 96-99
Bahamas 224-227
Barbados 281-284
Basutoland.............................105-108
Bechuanaland Protectorate.....206-209
Bermuda 201-204
British Antarctic Territory 16-19
British Honduras.....................191-194
Brunei 120-123
Cayman Islands......................176-179
Dominica 189-192
Falkland Islands 158-161
Fiji 215-218
Gibraltar.................................171-174
Gilbert & Ellice Islands............106-109
Grenada 209-212
Hong Kong 225-228
Mauritius 295-298
Montserrat 178-181
New Hebrides, British 112-115
New Hebrides, French 128-131
Pitcairn Islands 56-59
St. Helena 184-187
St. Kitts-Nevis 167-170
St. Lucia 201-204
St. Vincent 241-244
Seychelles 222-225
Solomon Islands 145-148
South Arabia 19-22
Swaziland 119-122
Tristan da Cunha 89-92
Turks & Caicos Islands 146-149
Virgin Islands 163-166

136 stamps

Royal Visit, 1966

Queen Elizabeth II and Prince Philip CD320

Caribbean visit, Feb. 4 - Mar. 6, 1966.

1966

Antigua 161-162
Bahamas 228-229
Barbados 285-286
British Guiana.........................299-300
Cayman Islands......................180-181
Dominica 193-194
Grenada 213-214
Montserrat 182-183
St. Kitts-Nevis 171-172
St. Lucia 205-206
St. Vincent 245-246
Turks & Caicos Islands 150-151
Virgin Islands 167-168

26 stamps

World Cup Soccer

Soccer Player and Jules Rimet Cup CD321

World Cup Soccer Championship, Wembley, England, July 11-30.

1966

Antigua 163-164
Ascension 100-101
Bahamas 245-246
Bermuda 205-206
Brunei 124-125
Cayman Islands......................182-183
Dominica 195-196
Fiji 219-220
Gibraltar.................................175-176
Gilbert & Ellice Islands............125-126
Grenada 230-231
New Hebrides, British 116-117
New Hebrides, French 132-133
Pitcairn Islands 60-61
St. Helena 188-189
St. Kitts-Nevis 173-174
St. Lucia 207-208
Seychelles 226-227
Solomon Islands 167-168
South Arabia 23-24
Tristan da Cunha 93-94

42 stamps

WHO Headquarters

World Health Organization Headquarters, Geneva — CD322

1966

Antigua 165-166
Ascension 102-103
Bahamas 247-248
Brunei 126-127
Cayman Islands......................184-185
Dominica 197-198
Fiji 224-225
Gibraltar.................................180-181
Gilbert & Ellice Islands............127-128
Grenada 232-233
Hong Kong 229-230
Montserrat 184-185
New Hebrides, British 118-119
New Hebrides, French 134-135
Pitcairn Islands 62-63
St. Helena 190-191
St. Kitts-Nevis 177-178
St. Lucia 209-210

St. Vincent 247-248
Seychelles 228-229
Solomon Islands 169-170
South Arabia 25-26
Tristan da Cunha 99-100

46 stamps

UNESCO Anniversary

"Education" — CD323

"Science" (Wheat ears & flask enclosing globe). "Culture" (lyre & columns). 20th anniversary of the UNESCO.

1966-67

Antigua 183-185
Ascension 108-110
Bahamas 249-251
Barbados 287-289
Bermuda 207-209
Brunei 128-130
Cayman Islands......................186-188
Dominica 199-201
Gibraltar.................................183-185
Gilbert & Ellice Islands............129-131
Grenada 234-236
Hong Kong 231-233
Mauritius 299-301
Montserrat 186-188
New Hebrides, British 120-122
New Hebrides, French 136-138
Pitcairn Islands 64-66
St. Helena 192-194
St. Kitts-Nevis 179-181
St. Lucia 211-213
St. Vincent 249-251
Seychelles 230-232
Solomon Islands 171-173
South Arabia 27-29
Swaziland 123-125
Tristan da Cunha 101-103
Turks & Caicos Islands 155-157
Virgin Islands 176-178

84 stamps

Silver Wedding, 1972

Queen Elizabeth II and Prince Philip — CD324

Designs: borders differ for each country.

1972

Anguilla..................................161-162
Antigua 295-296
Ascension 164-165
Bahamas 344-345
Bermuda 296-297
British Antarctic Territory 43-44
British Honduras.....................306-307
British Indian Ocean Territory 48-49
Brunei 186-187
Cayman Islands......................304-305
Dominica 352-353
Falkland Islands 223-224
Fiji 328-329
Gibraltar.................................292-293
Gilbert & Ellice Islands............206-207
Grenada 466-467
Hong Kong 271-272
Montserrat 286-287
New Hebrides, British 169-170
Pitcairn Islands 127-128
St. Helena 271-272
St. Kitts-Nevis 257-258
St. Lucia 328-329
St.Vincent 344-345
Seychelles 309-310
Solomon Islands 248-249
South Georgia 35-36

Tristan da Cunha...................178-179
Turks & Caicos Islands 257-258
Virgin Islands 241-242

60 stamps

Princess Anne's Wedding

Princess Anne and Mark Phillips — CD325

Wedding of Princess Anne and Mark Phillips, Nov. 14, 1973.

1973

Anguilla..................................179-180
Ascension 177-178
Belize 325-326
Bermuda 302-303
British Antarctic Territory 60-61
Cayman Islands......................320-321
Falkland Islands 225-226
Gibraltar.................................305-306
Gilbert & Ellice Islands............216-217
Hong Kong 289-290
Montserrat 300-301
Pitcairn Island 135-136
St. Helena 277-278
St. Kitts-Nevis 274-275
St. Lucia 349-350
St. Vincent 358-359
St. Vincent Grenadines 1-2
Seychelles 311-312
Solomon Islands 259-260
South Georgia 37-38
Tristan da Cunha...................189-190
Turks & Caicos Islands 286-287
Virgin Islands 260-261

44 stamps

Elizabeth II Coronation Anniv.

CD326   CD327

CD328

Designs: Royal and local beasts in heraldic form and simulated stonework. Portrait of Elizabeth II by Peter Grugeon. 25th anniversary of coronation of Queen Elizabeth II.

1978

Ascension 229
Barbados 474
Belize 397
British Antarctic Territory 71
Cayman Islands 404
Christmas Island 87
Falkland Islands 275
Fiji 384
Gambia 380
Gilbert Islands 312
Mauritius 464
New Hebrides, British 258
St. Helena 317
St. Kitts-Nevis 354
Samoa 472

Queen Mother Elizabeth's 80th Birthday

CD330

Designs: Photographs of Queen Mother Elizabeth. Falkland Islands issued in sheets of 50; others in sheets of 9.

1980

Royal Wedding, 1981

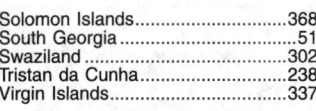

Prince Charles and Lady Diana — CD331

Wedding of Charles, Prince of Wales, and Lady Diana Spencer, St. Paul's Cathedral, London, July 29, 1981.

1981

Princess Diana

CD332

CD333

Designs: Photographs and portrait of Princess Diana, wedding or honeymoon photographs, royal residences, arms of issuing country. Portrait photograph by Clive Friend. Souvenir sheet margins show family tree, various people related to the princess. 21st birthday of Princess Diana of Wales, July 1.

1982

250th anniv. of first edition of Lloyd's List (shipping news publication) & of Lloyd's marine insurance.

CD335

Designs: First page of early edition of the list; historical ships, modern transportation or harbor scenes.

1984

Queen Mother 85th Birthday

CD336

Designs: Photographs tracing the life of the Queen Mother, Elizabeth. The high value in each set pictures the same photograph taken of the Queen Mother holding the infant Prince Henry.

1985

Queen Elizabeth II, 60th Birthday

CD337

1986, April 21

Royal Wedding

Marriage of Prince Andrew and Sarah Ferguson CD338

1986, July 23

Queen Elizabeth II, 60th Birthday

Queen Elizabeth II & Prince Philip, 1947 Wedding Portrait — CD339

Designs: Photographs tracing the life of Queen Elizabeth II.

1986

Royal Wedding, 1986

CD340

Designs: Photographs of Prince Andrew and Sarah Ferguson during courtship, engagement and marriage.

1986

Lloyds of London, 300th Anniv.

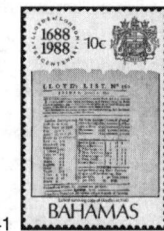

CD341

Designs: 17th century aspects of Lloyds, representations of each country's individual connections with Lloyds and publicized disasters insured by the organization.

1986

South Georgia 131-134
Trinidad & Tobago 484-487
Tristan da Cunha.....................439-442
Vanuatu 485-488
Zil Elwannyen Sesel................146-149

Moon Landing, 20th Anniv.

CD342

Designs: Equipment, crew photographs, spacecraft, official emblems and report profiles created for the Apollo Missions. Two stamps in each set are square in format rather than like the stamp shown; see individual country listings for more information.

1989

Ascension Is. 468-472
Bahamas 674-678
Belize.....................................916-920
Kiribati 517-521
Liberia 1125-1129
Nevis 586-590
St. Kitts..................................248-252
Samoa 760-764
Seychelles 676-680
Solomon Islands......................643-647
Vanuatu 507-511
Zil Elwannyen Sesel 154-158

Queen Mother, 90th Birthday

CD343   CD344

Designs: Portraits of Queen Elizabeth, the Queen Mother. See individual country listings for more information.

1990

Ascension Is. 491-492
Bahamas 698-699
Barbados 782-783
British Antarctic Territory 170-171
British Indian Ocean Territory 106-107
Cayman Islands........................622-623
Falkland Islands 524-525
Kenya 527-528
Kiribati 555-556
Liberia 1145-1146
Pitcairn Islands........................336-337
St. Helena 532-533
St. Lucia 969-970
Seychelles 710-711
Solomon Islands......................671-672
South Georgia 143-144
Swaziland 565-566
Tristan da Cunha 480-481
Zil Elwannyen Sesel 171-172

Queen Elizabeth II, 65th Birthday, and Prince Philip, 70th Birthday

CD345

CD346

Designs: Portraits of Queen Elizabeth II and Prince Philip differ for each country. Printed in sheets of 10 + 5 labels (3 different) between. Stamps alternate, producing 5 different triptychs.

1991

Ascension Is. 505-506
Bahamas 730-731
Belize.....................................969-970
Bermuda 617-618
Kiribati 571-572
Mauritius 733-734
Pitcairn Islands........................348-349
St. Helena 554-555
St. Kitts..................................318-319
Samoa 790-791
Seychelles 723-724
Solomon Islands......................688-689
South Georgia 149-150
Swaziland 586-587
Vanuatu 540-541
Zil Elwannyen Sesel 177-178

Royal Family Birthday, Anniversary

CD347

Queen Elizabeth II, 65th birthday, Charles and Diana, 10th wedding anniversary: Various photographs of Queen Elizabeth II, Prince Philip, Prince Charles, Princess Diana and their sons William and Henry.

1991

Antigua 1446-1455
Barbuda 1229-1238
Dominica..............................1328-1337
Gambia 1080-1089
Grenada 2006-2015
Grenada Grenadines............1331-1340
Guyana 2440-2451
Lesotho 871-875
Maldive Islands.....................1533-1542
Nevis 666-675
St. Vincent 1485-1494
St. Vincent Grenadines 769-778
Sierra Leone 1387-1396
Turks & Caicos Islands 913-922
Uganda 918-927

Queen Elizabeth II's Accession to the Throne, 40th Anniv.

CD348

CD349

Various photographs of Queen Elizabeth II with local Scenes.

1992 - CD348

Antigua 1513-1518
Barbuda 1306-1309
Dominica..............................1414-1419
Gambia 1172-1177
Grenada 2047-2052
Grenada Grenadines............1368-1373

Lesotho 881-885
Maldive Islands.....................1637-1642
Nevis 702-707
St. Vincent 1582-1587
St. Vincent Grenadines 829-834
Sierra Leone 1482-1487
Turks and Caicos Islands........978-987
Uganda 990-995
Virgin Islands..........................742-746

1992 - CD349

Ascension Islands 531-535
Bahamas 744-748
Bermuda 623-627
British Indian Ocean Territory 119-123
Cayman Islands........................648-652
Falkland Islands 549-553
Gibraltar 605-609
Hong Kong 619-623
Kenya 563-567
Kiribati 582-586
Pitcairn Islands........................362-366
St. Helena 570-574
St. Kitts..................................332-336
Samoa 805-809
Seychelles 734-738
Solomon Islands......................708-712
South Georgia 157-161
Tristan da Cunha 508-512
Vanuatu 555-559
Zambia 561-565
Zil Elwannyen Sesel 183-187

Royal Air Force, 75th Anniversary

CD350

1993

Ascension 557-561
Bahamas 771-775
Barbados 842-846
Belize..................................1003-1008
Bermuda 648-651
British Indian Ocean Territory 136-140
Falkland Is. 573-577
Fiji 687-691
Montserrat 830-834
St. Kitts..................................351-355

Royal Air Force, 80th Anniv.

Design CD350 Re-inscribed

1998

Ascension 697-701
Bahamas 907-911
British Indian Ocean Terr 198-202
Cayman Islands........................754-758
Fiji 814-818
Gibraltar 755-759
Samoa 957-961
Turks & Caicos Islands 1258-1265
Tuvalu 763-767
Virgin Islands...........................879-883

End of World War II, 50th Anniv.

CD351

CD352

1995

Ascension 613-617
Bahamas 824-828
Barbados 891-895
Belize..................................1047-1050
British Indian Ocean Territory 163-167
Cayman Islands........................704-708
Falkland Islands 634-638
Fiji 720-724
Kiribati 662-668
Liberia 1175-1179
Mauritius 803-805
St. Helena 646-654
St. Kitts..................................389-393
St. Lucia 1018-1022
Samoa 890-894
Solomon Islands......................799-803
South Georgia & S. Sandwich Is. ....
....198-200
Tristan da Cunha.....................562-566

UN, 50th Anniv.

CD353

1995

Bahamas 839-842
Barbados 901-904
Belize..................................1055-1058
Jamaica 847-851
Liberia 1187-1190
Mauritius 813-816
Pitcairn Islands........................436-439
St. Kitts..................................398-401
St. Lucia 1023-1026
Samoa 900-903
Tristan da Cunha.....................568-571
Virgin Islands...........................807-810

Queen Elizabeth, 70th Birthday

CD354

1996

Ascension 632-635
British Antarctic Territory 240-243
British Indian Ocean Territory 176-180
Falkland Islands 653-657
Pitcairn Islands........................446-449
St. Helena 672-676
Samoa 912-916
Tokelau 223-227
Tristan da Cunha.....................576-579
Virgin Islands...........................824-828

Diana, Princess of Wales (1961-97)

CD355

1998

Ascension	696
Bahamas	901A-902
Barbados	950
Belize	1091
Bermuda	753
Botswana	659-663
British Antarctic Territory	258
British Indian Ocean Terr.	197
Cayman Islands	752A-753
Falkland Islands	694
Fiji	819-820
Gibraltar	754
Kiribati	719A-720
Namibia	909
Niue	706
Norfolk Island	644-645
Papua New Guinea	937
Pitcairn Islands	487
St. Helena	711
St. Kitts	437A-438
Samoa	955A-956
Seycelles	802
Solomon Islands	866-867
South Georgia & S. Sandwich Islands	220
Tokelau	253
Tonga	980
Niuafo'ou	201
Tristan da Cunha	618
Tuvalu	762
Vanuatu	719
Virgin Islands	878

Wedding of Prince Edward and Sophie Rhys-Jones

CD356

1999

Ascension	729-730
Cayman Islands	775-776
Falkland Islands	729-730
Pitcairn Islands	505-506
St. Helena	733-734
Samoa	971-972
Tristan da Cunha	636-637
Virgin Islands	908-909

1st Manned Moon Landing, 30th Anniv.

CD357

1999

Ascension	731-735
Bahamas	942-946
Barbados	967-971
Bermuda	778
Cayman Islands	777-781

Fiji	853-857
Jamaica	889-893
Kirbati	746-750
Nauru	465-469
St. Kitts	460-464
Samoa	973-977
Solomon Islands	875-879
Tuvalu	800-804
Virgin Islands	910-914

Queen Mother's Century

CD358

1999

Ascension	736-740
Bahamas	951-955
Cayman Islands	782-786
Falkland Islands	734-738
Fiji	858-862
Norfolk Island	688-692
St. Helena	740-744
Samoa	978-982
Solomon Islands	880-884
South Georgia & South Sandwich Islands	231-235
Tristan da Cunha	638-642
Tuvalu	805-809

Prince William, 18th Birthday

CD359

2000

Ascension	755-759
Cayman Islands	797-801
Falkland Islands	762-766
Fiji	889-893
South Georgia and South Sandwich Islands	257-261
Tristan da Cunha	664-668
Virgin Islands	925-929

Reign of Queen Elizabeth II, 50th Anniv.

CD360

2002

Ascension	790-794
Bahamas	1033-1037
Barbados	1019-1023
Belize	1152-1156
Bermuda	822-826
British Antarctic Territory	307-311
British Indian Ocean Territory	239-243
Cayman Islands	844-848
Falkland Islands	804-808
Gibraltar	896-900
Jamaica	952-956
Nauru	491-495
Norfolk Island	758-762
Papua New Guinea	1019-1023
Pitcairn Islands	552
St. Helena	788-792
St. Lucia	1146-1150
Solomon Islands	931-935
South Georgia & So. Sandwich Is.	274-278
Swaziland	706-710
Tokelau	302-306
Tonga	1059

Niuafo'ou	239
Tristan da Cunha	706-710
Virgin Islands	967-971

Queen Mother Elizabeth (1900-2002)

CD361

2002

Ascension	799-801
Bahamas	1044-1046
Bermuda	834-836
British Antarctic Territory	312-314
British Indian Ocean Territory	245-247
Cayman Islands	857-861
Falkland Islands	812-816
Nauru	499-501
Pitcairn Islands	561-565
St. Helena	808-812
St. Lucia	1155-1159
Seychelles	830
Solomon Islands	945-947
South Georgia & So. Sandwich Isls.	281-285
Tokelau	312-314
Tristan da Cunha	715-717
Virgin Islands	979-983

Head of Queen Elizabeth II

CD362

2003

Ascension	822
Bermuda	865
British Antarctic Territory	322
British Indian Ocean Territory	261
Cayman Islands	878
Falkland Islands	828
St. Helena	820
South Georgia & South Sandwich Islands	294
Tristan da Cunha	731
Virgin Islands	1003

Coronation of Queen Elizabeth II, 50th Anniv.

CD363

2003

Ascension	823-825
Bahamas	1073-1075
Bermuda	866-868
British Antarctic Territory	323-325
British Indian Ocean Territory	262-264
Cayman Islands	879-881
Jamaica	970-972
Kiribati	825-827
Pitcairn Islands	577-581
St. Helena	821-823
St. Lucia	1171-1173
Tokelau	320-322
Tristan da Cunha	732-734
Virgin Islands	1004-1006

Prince William, 21st Birthday

CD364

2003

Ascension	826
British Indian Ocean Territory	265
Cayman Islands	882-884
Falkland Islands	829
South Georgia & South Sandwich Islands	295
Tokelau	323
Tristan da Cunha	735
Virgin Islands	1007-1009

British Commonwealth of Nations

Dominions, Colonies, Territories, Offices and Independent Members

Comprising stamps of the British Commonwealth and associated nations.

A strict observance of technicalities would bar some or all of the stamps listed under Burma, Ireland, Kuwait, Nepal, New Republic, Orange Free State, Samoa, South Africa, South-West Africa, Stellaland, Sudan, Swaziland, the two Transvaal Republics and others but these are included for the convenience of collectors.

1. Great Britain

Great Britain: Including England, Scotland, Wales and Northern Ireland.

2. The Dominions, Present and Past

AUSTRALIA

The Commonwealth of Australia was proclaimed on January 1, 1901. It consists of six former colonies as follows:

New South Wales	Victoria
Queensland	Tasmania
South Australia	Western Australia

Territories belonging to, or administered by Australia: Australian Antarctic Territory, Christmas Island, Cocos (Keeling) Islands, Nauru, New Guinea, Norfolk Island, Papua New Guinea.

CANADA

The Dominion of Canada was created by the British North America Act in 1867. The following provinces were former separate colonies and issued postage stamps:

British Columbia and	Newfoundland
Vancouver Island	Nova Scotia
New Brunswick	Prince Edward Island

FIJI

The colony of Fiji became an independent nation with dominion status on Oct. 10, 1970.

GHANA

This state came into existence Mar. 6, 1957, with dominion status. It consists of the former colony of the Gold Coast and the Trusteeship Territory of Togoland. Ghana became a republic July 1, 1960.

INDIA

The Republic of India was inaugurated on January 26, 1950. It succeeded the Dominion of India which was proclaimed August 15, 1947, when the former Empire of India was divided into Pakistan and the Union of India. The Republic is composed of about 40 predominantly Hindu states of three classes: governor's provinces, chief commissioner's provinces and princely states. India also has various territories, such as the Andaman and Nicobar Islands.

The old Empire of India was a federation of British India and the native states. The more important princely states were autonomous. Of the more than 700 Indian states, these 43 are familiar names to philatelists because of their postage stamps.

CONVENTION STATES

Chamba	Jhind
Faridkot	Nabha
Gwalior	Patiala

NATIVE FEUDATORY STATES

Alwar	Jammu
Bahawalpur	Jammu and Kashmir
Bamra	Jasdan
Barwani	Jhalawar
Bhopal	Jhind (1875-76)
Bhor	Kashmir
Bijawar	Kishangarh
Bundi	Las Bela
Bussahir	Morvi
Charkhari	Nandgaon
Cochin	Nowanuggur
Dhar	Orchha
Duttia	Poonch
Faridkot (1879-85)	Rajpeepla
Hyderabad	Sirmur
Idar	Soruth
Indore	Travancore
Jaipur	Wadhwan

NEW ZEALAND

Became a dominion on September 26, 1907. The following islands and territories are, or have been, administered by New Zealand:

Aitutaki	Ross Dependency
Cook Islands (Rarotonga)	Samoa (Western Samoa)
Niue	Tokelau Islands
Penrhyn	

PAKISTAN

The Republic of Pakistan was proclaimed March 23, 1956. It succeeded the Dominion which was proclaimed August 15, 1947. It is made up of all or part of several Moslem provinces and various districts of the former Empire of India, including Bahawalpur and Las Bela. Pakistan withdrew from the Commonwealth in 1972.

SOUTH AFRICA

Under the terms of the South African Act (1909) the self-governing colonies of Cape of Good Hope, Natal, Orange River Colony and Transvaal united on May 31, 1910, to form the Union of South Africa. It became an independent republic May 3, 1961.

Under the terms of the Treaty of Versailles, South-West Africa, formerly German South-West Africa, was mandated to the Union of South Africa.

SRI LANKA (CEYLON)

The Dominion of Ceylon was proclaimed February 4, 1948. The island had been a Crown Colony from 1802 until then. On May 22, 1972, Ceylon became the Republic of Sri Lanka.

3. Colonies, Past and Present; Controlled Territory and Independent Members of the Commonwealth

Aden	Bechuanaland
Aitutaki	Bechuanaland Prot.
Antigua	Belize
Ascension	Bermuda
Bahamas	Botswana
Bahrain	British Antarctic Territory
Bangladesh	British Central Africa
Barbados	British Columbia and
Barbuda	Vancouver Island
Basutoland	British East Africa
Batum	British Guiana

British Honduras
British Indian Ocean Territory
British New Guinea
British Solomon Islands
British Somaliland
Brunei
Burma
Bushire
Cameroons
Cape of Good Hope
Cayman Islands
Christmas Island
Cocos (Keeling) Islands
Cook Islands
Crete,
  British Administration
Cyprus
Dominica
East Africa & Uganda
  Protectorates
Egypt
Falkland Islands
Fiji
Gambia
German East Africa
Gibraltar
Gilbert Islands
Gilbert & Ellice Islands
Gold Coast
Grenada
Griqualand West
Guernsey
Guyana
Heligoland
Hong Kong
Indian Native States
  (see India)
Ionian Islands
Jamaica
Jersey

Kenya
Kenya, Uganda & Tanzania
Kuwait
Labuan
Lagos
Leeward Islands
Lesotho
Madagascar
Malawi
Malaya
  Federated Malay States
  Johore
  Kedah
  Kelantan
  Malacca
  Negri Sembilan
  Pahang
  Penang
  Perak
  Perlis
  Selangor
  Singapore
  Sungei Ujong
  Trengganu
Malaysia
Maldive Islands
Malta
Man, Isle of
Mauritius
Mesopotamia
Montserrat
Muscat
Namibia
Natal
Nauru
Nevis
New Britain
New Brunswick
Newfoundland
New Guinea

New Hebrides
New Republic
New South Wales
Niger Coast Protectorate
Nigeria
Niue
Norfolk Island
North Borneo
Northern Nigeria
Northern Rhodesia
North West Pacific Islands
Nova Scotia
Nyasaland Protectorate
Oman
Orange River Colony
Palestine
Papua New Guinea
Penrhyn Island
Pitcairn Islands
Prince Edward Island
Queensland
Rhodesia
Rhodesia & Nyasaland
Ross Dependency
Sabah
St. Christopher
St. Helena
St. Kitts
St. Kitts-Nevis-Anguilla
St. Lucia
St. Vincent
Samoa
Sarawak
Seychelles
Sierra Leone
Solomon Islands
Somaliland Protectorate
South Arabia
South Australia
South Georgia

Southern Nigeria
Southern Rhodesia
South-West Africa
Stellaland
Straits Settlements
Sudan
Swaziland
Tanganyika
Tanzania
Tasmania
Tobago
Togo
Tokelau Islands
Tonga
Transvaal
Trinidad
Trinidad and Tobago
Tristan da Cunha
Trucial States
Turks and Caicos
Turks Islands
Tuvalu
Uganda
United Arab Emirates
Victoria
Virgin Islands
Western Australia
Zambia
Zanzibar
Zululand

**POST OFFICES IN
FOREIGN COUNTRIES**
Africa
  East Africa Forces
  Middle East Forces
Bangkok
China
Morocco
Turkish Empire

COLLECT THE SCOTT WAY WITH

Specialty Series Pages

SCOTT ALBUMS FEATURE:

• High quality chemically neutral paper printed on one side. •

• All spaces identified by Scott numbers with either illustrations or descriptions. •

• All pages have matching borders. •

•Pages contain general postage issues, as well as complete back-of-the book materials. •

• Albums supplemented annually. •

For a complete list of Scott Specialty Series Pages available contact your local dealer,
or call Scott Publishing at 1-800-5SCOTT5 or write to P.O. Box 828, Sidney, OH 45365.

Colonies, Former Colonies, Offices, Territories Controlled by Parent States

Belgium
Belgian Congo
Ruanda-Urundi

Denmark
Danish West Indies
Faroe Islands
Greenland
Iceland

Finland
Aland Islands

France

COLONIES PAST AND PRESENT, CONTROLLED TERRITORIES
Afars & Issas, Territory of
Alaouites
Alexandretta
Algeria
Alsace & Lorraine
Anjouan
Annam & Tonkin
Benin
Cambodia (Khmer)
Cameroun
Castellorizo
Chad
Cilicia
Cochin China
Comoro Islands
Dahomey
Diego Suarez
Djibouti (Somali Coast)
Fezzan
French Congo
French Equatorial Africa
French Guiana
French Guinea
French India
French Morocco
French Polynesia (Oceania)
French Southern & Antarctic Territories
French Sudan
French West Africa
Gabon
Germany
Ghadames
Grand Comoro
Guadeloupe
Indo-China
Inini
Ivory Coast
Laos
Latakia
Lebanon
Madagascar
Martinique
Mauritania
Mayotte
Memel
Middle Congo
Moheli
New Caledonia
New Hebrides
Niger Territory
Nossi-Be

Obock
Reunion
Rouad, Ile
Ste.-Marie de Madagascar
St. Pierre & Miquelon
Senegal
Senegambia & Niger
Somali Coast
Syria
Tahiti
Togo
Tunisia
Ubangi-Shari
Upper Senegal & Niger
Upper Volta
Viet Nam
Wallis & Futuna Islands

POST OFFICES IN FOREIGN COUNTRIES
China
Crete
Egypt
Turkish Empire
Zanzibar

Germany

EARLY STATES
Baden
Bavaria
Bergedorf
Bremen
Brunswick
Hamburg
Hanover
Lubeck
Mecklenburg-Schwerin
Mecklenburg-Strelitz
Oldenburg
Prussia
Saxony
Schleswig-Holstein
Wurttemberg

FORMER COLONIES
Cameroun (Kamerun)
Caroline Islands
German East Africa
German New Guinea
German South-West Africa
Kiauchau
Mariana Islands
Marshall Islands
Samoa
Togo

Italy

EARLY STATES
Modena
Parma
Romagna
Roman States
Sardinia
Tuscany
Two Sicilies
  Naples
  Neapolitan Provinces
  Sicily

FORMER COLONIES, CONTROLLED TERRITORIES, OCCUPATION AREAS
Aegean Islands
Calimno (Calino)
Caso
Cos (Coo)
Karki (Carchi)
Leros (Lero)
Lipso
Nisiros (Nisiro)
Patmos (Patmo)
Piscopi
Rodi (Rhodes)
Scarpanto
Simi
Stampalia
Castellorizo
Corfu
Cyrenaica
Eritrea
Ethiopia (Abyssinia)
Fiume
Ionian Islands
  Cephalonia
  Ithaca
  Paxos
Italian East Africa
Libya
Oltre Giuba
Saseno
Somalia (Italian Somaliland)
Tripolitania

POST OFFICES IN FOREIGN COUNTRIES
"ESTERO"*
Austria
China
  Peking
  Tientsin
Crete
Tripoli
Turkish Empire
  Constantinople
  Durazzo
  Janina
Jerusalem
Salonika
Scutari
Smyrna
Valona
*Stamps overprinted "ESTERO" were used in various parts of the world.

Netherlands
Aruba
Netherlands Antilles (Curacao)
Netherlands Indies
Netherlands New Guinea
Surinam (Dutch Guiana)

Portugal

COLONIES PAST AND PRESENT, CONTROLLED TERRITORIES
Angola
Angra
Azores
Cape Verde
Funchal

Horta
Inhambane
Kionga
Lourenco Marques
Macao
Madeira
Mozambique
Mozambique Co.
Nyassa
Ponta Delgada
Portuguese Africa
Portuguese Congo
Portuguese Guinea
Portuguese India
Quelimane
St. Thomas & Prince Islands
Tete
Timor
Zambezia

Russia

ALLIED TERRITORIES AND REPUBLICS, OCCUPATION AREAS
Armenia
Aunus (Olonets)
Azerbaijan
Batum
Estonia
Far Eastern Republic
Georgia
Karelia
Latvia
Lithuania
North Ingermanland
Ostland
Russian Turkestan
Siberia
South Russia
Tannu Tuva
Transcaucasian Fed. Republics
Ukraine
Wenden (Livonia)
Western Ukraine

Spain

COLONIES PAST AND PRESENT, CONTROLLED TERRITORIES
Aguera, La
Cape Juby
Cuba
Elobey, Annobon & Corisco
Fernando Po
Ifni
Mariana Islands
Philippines
Puerto Rico
Rio de Oro
Rio Muni
Spanish Guinea
Spanish Morocco
Spanish Sahara
Spanish West Africa

POST OFFICES IN FOREIGN COUNTRIES
Morocco
Tangier
Tetuan

Dies of British Colonial Stamps

DIE A

DIE B

DIE I

DIE II

DIE A:
1. The lines in the groundwork vary in thickness and are not uniformly straight.
2. The seventh and eighth lines from the top, in the groundwork, converge where they meet the head.
3. There is a small dash in the upper part of the second jewel in the band of the crown.
4. The vertical color line in front of the throat stops at the sixth line of shading on the neck.

DIE B:
1. The lines in the groundwork are all thin and straight.
2. All the lines of the background are parallel.
3. There is no dash in the upper part of the second jewel in the band of the crown.
4. The vertical color line in front of the throat stops at the eighth line of shading on the neck.

DIE I:
1. The base of the crown is well below the level of the inner white line around the vignette.
2. The labels inscribed "POSTAGE" and "REVENUE" are cut square at the top.
3. There is a white "bud" on the outer side of the main stem of the curved ornaments in each lower corner.
4. The second (thick) line below the country name has the ends next to the crown cut diagonally.

DIE Ia.	DIE Ib.
1 as die II.	1 and 3 as die II.
2 and 3 as die I.	2 as die I.

DIE II:
1. The base of the crown is aligned with the underside of the white line around the vignette.
2. The labels curve inward at the top inner corners.
3. The "bud" has been removed from the outer curve of the ornaments in each corner.
4. The second line below the country name has the ends next to the crown cut vertically.

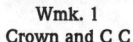
Wmk. 1
Crown and C C

Wmk. 2
Crown and C A

Wmk. 3
Multiple Crown
and C A

Wmk. 4
Multiple Crown
and Script C A

Wmk. 4a

Wmk. 314
St. Edward's Crown
and C A Multiple

Wmk. 373

Wmk. 384

British Colonial and Crown Agents Watermarks

Watermarks 1 to 4, 314, 373, and 384, common to many British territories, are illustrated here to avoid duplication.

The letters "CC" of Wmk. 1 identify the paper as having been made for the use of the Crown Colonies, while the letters "CA" of the others stand for "Crown Agents." Both Wmks. 1 and 2 were used on stamps printed by De La Rue & Co.

Wmk. 3 was adopted in 1904; Wmk. 4 in 1921; Wmk. 314 in 1957; Wmk. 373 in 1974; and Wmk. 384 in 1985.

In Wmk. 4a, a non-matching crown of the general St. Edwards type (bulging on both sides at top) was substituted for one of the Wmk. 4 crowns which fell off the dandy roll. The non-matching crown occurs in 1950-52 printings in a horizontal row of crowns on certain regular stamps of Johore and Seychelles, and on various postage due stamps of Barbados, Basutoland, British Guiana, Gold Coast, Grenada, Northern Rhodesia, St. Lucia, Swaziland and Trinidad and Tobago. A variation of Wmk. 4a, with the non-matching crown in a horizontal row of crown-CA-crown, occurs on regular stamps of Bahamas, St. Kitts-Nevis and Singapore.

Wmk. 314 was intentionally used sideways, starting in 1966. When a stamp was issued with Wmk. 314 both upright and sideways, the sideways varieties usually are listed also – with minor numbers. In many of the later issues, Wmk. 314 is slightly visible.

Wmk. 373 is usually only faintly visible.

Pronunciation Symbols

ə .... banana, collide, abut

'ə, ˌə .... humdrum, abut

ə .... immediately preceding \l\, \n\, \m\, \ŋ\, as in battle, mitten, eaten, and sometimes open \'ō-pᵊm\, lock and key \-ᵊŋ-\; immediately following \l\, \m\, \r\, as often in French table, prisme, titre

ər .... further, merger, bird

'ər- }
 } .... as in two different pronunciations
'ə-r } of hurry \'hər-ē, 'hə-rē\

a .... mat, map, mad, gag, snap, patch

ā .... day, fade, date, aorta, drape, cape

ä .... bother, cot, and, with most American speakers, father, cart

ȧ .... father as pronounced by speakers who do not rhyme it with bother; French patte

au̇ .... now, loud, out

b .... baby, rib

ch .... chin, nature \'nā-chər\

d .... did, adder

e .... bet, bed, peck

'ē, ˌē .... beat, nosebleed, evenly, easy

ē .... easy, mealy

f .... fifty, cuff

g .... go, big, gift

h .... hat, ahead

hw .... whale as pronounced by those who do not have the same pronunciation for both whale and wail

i .... tip, banish, active

ī .... site, side, buy, tripe

j .... job, gem, edge, join, judge

k .... kin, cook, ache

k̲ .... German ich, Buch; one pronunciation of loch

l .... lily, pool

m .... murmur, dim, nymph

n .... no, own

ⁿ .... indicates that a preceding vowel or diphthong is pronounced with the nasal passages open, as in French un bon vin blanc \œ̃ⁿ -bōⁿ -vaⁿ -bläⁿ\

ŋ .... sing \'siŋ\, singer \'siŋ-ər\, finger \'fiŋ-gər\, ink \'iŋk \

ō .... bone, know, beau

ȯ .... saw, all, gnaw, caught

œ .... French bœuf, German Hölle

œ̄ .... French feu, German Höhle

ȯi .... coin, destroy

p .... pepper, lip

r .... red, car, rarity

s .... source, less

sh .... as in shy, mission, machine, special (actually, this is a single sound, not two); with a hyphen between, two sounds as in grasshopper \'gras-ˌhä-pər\

t .... tie, attack, late, later, latter

th .... as in thin, ether (actually, this is a single sound, not two); with a hyphen between, two sounds as in knighthood \'nīt-ˌhu̇d\

t̲h̲ .... then, either, this (actually, this is a single sound, not two)

ü .... rule, youth, union \'yün-yən\, few \'fyü\

u̇ .... pull, wood, book, curable \'kyu̇r-ə-bəl\, fury \'fyu̇r-ē\

ue .... German füllen, hübsch

u̅e̅ .... French rue, German fühlen

v .... vivid, give

w .... we, away

y .... yard, young, cue \'kyü\, mute \'myüt\, union \'yün-yən\

ʸ .... indicates that during the articulation of the sound represented by the preceding character the front of the tongue has substantially the position it has for the articulation of the first sound of yard, as in French digne \dēnʸ\

z .... zone, raise

zh .... as in vision, azure \'a-zhər\ (actually, this is a single sound, not two); with a hyphen between, two sounds as in hogshead \'hȯgz-ˌhed, 'hägz-\

\ .... slant line used in pairs to mark the beginning and end of a transcription: \'pen\

ˈ .... mark preceding a syllable with primary (strongest) stress: \'pen-mən-ˌship\

ˌ .... mark preceding a syllable with secondary (medium) stress: \'pen-mən-ˌship\

- .... mark of syllable division

( ) .... indicate that what is symbolized between is present in some utterances but not in others: factory \'fak-t(ə-)rē\

÷ .... indicates that many regard as unacceptable the pronunciation variant immediately following: cupola \'kyü-pə-lə, ÷-ˌlō\

The system of pronunciation is used by permission from Merriam-Webster's Collegiate® Dictionary, Tenth Edition ©1993 by Merriam-Webster Inc., publisher of the Merriam-Webster® dictionaries.

SOLOMON ISLANDS

ˈsä-lə-mən ˈī-ləndz

British Solomon Islands

LOCATION — West Pacific Ocean, east of Papua
GOVT. — Independent state in British Commonwealth
AREA — 10,954 sq. mi.
POP. — 455,429 (1999 est.)
CAPITAL — Honiara

The Solomons include 10 large islands and four groups of small islands extending over an area of 375,000 square miles.

The British protectorate of British Solomon Islands changed its name to Solomon Islands in 1975 and achieved independence July 7, 1978.

12 Pence = 1 Shilling
20 Shillings = 1 Pound
100 Cents = 1 Dollar (1966)

Catalogue values for unused stamps in this country are for Never Hinged items, beginning with Scott 80 in the regular postage section and Scott B1 in the semi-postal section.

War Canoe — A1

Unwmk.

				Perf. 11
1907, Feb. 14		**Litho.**		
1	A1	½p ultra	10.50	16.00
2	A1	1p red	26.00	30.00
3	A1	2p dull blue	32.50	35.00
a.	Horiz. pair, imperf. btwn.		12,500.	
4	A1	2½p orange	37.50	47.50
a.	Vert. pair, imperf. btwn.		4,500.	
b.	Horiz. pair, imperf. btwn.		6,250.	4,750.
5	A1	5p yellow green	62.50	75.00
6	A1	6p chocolate	57.50	70.00
a.	Vertical pair, imperf. btwn.		4,250.	
7	A1	1sh violet	82.50	85.00
	Nos. 1-7 (7)		309.00	358.50

Imperf. between varieties should be accompanied by certificates of authenticity issued by competent authorities. Excellent counterfeits are plentiful.

War Canoe A2   George V A3

Wmk. Multiple Crown and CA (3)

			Engr.	**Perf. 14**
1908-11				
8	A2	½p green	1.75	1.10
9	A2	1p carmine	1.50	1.10
10	A2	2p gray	1.50	1.10
11	A2	2½p ultra	4.25	2.25
12	A2	4p red, yel ('11)	3.75	12.50
13	A2	5p olive green	10.50	8.00
14	A2	6p claret	11.50	7.50
15	A2	1sh black, green	9.75	8.00
16	A2	2sh vio, bl ('10)	45.00	62.50
17	A2	2sh6p red, bl ('10)	55.00	80.00
18	A2	5sh bl, yel ('10)	85.00	110.00
	Nos. 8-18 (11)		229.50	294.05

Inscribed "POSTAGE - POSTAGE"

				Typo.
1913-24				
19	A3	½p green	.95	4.00
20	A3	1p carmine	1.10	16.00
21	A3	3p violet, yel	1.00	4.75
a.	3p violet, orange buff		5.00	27.50
22	A3	11p dull violet & red	5.75	13.50

				Wmk. 4
23	A3	1½p scarlet ('24)	2.50	.70
	Nos. 19-23 (5)		11.30	38.95

Inscribed "POSTAGE - REVENUE"

				Wmk. 3
1914-23				
28	A3	½p green	.95	13.50
a.	½p yellow green ('17)		5.25	21.00
29	A3	1p carmine	1.75	1.50
a.	1p scarlet ('17)		5.50	7.50
30	A3	2p gray	3.50	10.50
31	A3	2½p ultra	2.25	5.75

Chalky Paper

32	A3	3p violet, yel ('23)	22.50	97.50
33	A3	4p blk & red, yel	2.25	3.00
34	A3	5p dull vio & ol grn	22.50	35.00
a.	5p brown purple & olive green		22.50	35.00
35	A3	6p dull vio & red vio	7.00	16.00
36	A3	1sh blk, green	5.50	8.00
a.	1sh blk, bl grn, ol back		8.50	27.50
37	A3	2sh dull vio & ultra, bl	8.00	11.50
38	A3	2sh6p blk & red, bl	11.00	22.50
39	A3	5sh grn & red, yel	32.50	55.00
a.	5sh green & red, orange buff		52.50	80.00
40	A3	10sh grn & red, grn	85.00	92.50
41	A3	£1 vio & blk, red	250.00	140.00
	Nos. 28-41 (14)		454.70	512.25

Inscribed "POSTAGE - REVENUE"

				Wmk. 4
1922-31				
43	A3	½p green	.40	4.00
44	A3	1p carmine ('23)	12.50	12.50
45	A3	1p violet ('27)	1.10	8.50
46	A3	2p gray ('23)	4.50	17.00
47	A3	3p ultra ('23)	.85	5.25

Chalky Paper

48	A3	4p blk & red, yel ('27)	4.00	26.00
49	A3	4½p red brn ('31)	3.50	22.50
50	A3	5p dull vio & ol grn	3.50	30.00
51	A3	6p dull vio & red vio	4.25	30.00
52	A3	1sh black, emer	3.25	14.00
53	A3	2sh dull vio & ultra, bl ('27)	9.25	42.50
54	A3	2sh6p blk & red, bl	8.50	45.00
55	A3	5sh grn & red, yel	30.00	62.50
56	A3	10sh grn & red, emer ('25)	100.00	110.00
	Nos. 43-56 (14)		185.60	429.75

No. 49 is on ordinary paper.

Common Design Types
pictured following the introduction.

Silver Jubilee Issue
Common Design Type

		Engr.	**Perf. 13½x14**
1935, May 6			
60	CD301	1½p car & dk bl	.90	.75
61	CD301	3p blue & brown	2.75	5.25
62	CD301	6p ol grn & lt bl	7.50	10.50
63	CD301	1sh brt vio & ind	6.50	8.75
	Nos. 60-63 (4)		17.65	25.25
	Set, never hinged		32.50	

Coronation Issue
Common Design Type

			Perf. 11x11½
1937, May 13			
64	CD302	1p dark purple	.25	.60
65	CD302	1½p dark carmine	.25	.50
66	CD302	3p deep ultra	.40	.40
	Nos. 64-66 (3)		.90	1.50
	Set, never hinged		1.25	

Spears and Shield — A4

Policeman and Chief — A5

Artificial Island, Malaita — A6

Canoe House, New Georgia A7

Roviana War Canoe — A8

View of Munda Point — A9

Meeting House, Reef Islands A10

Coconut Plantation A11

Breadfruit A12

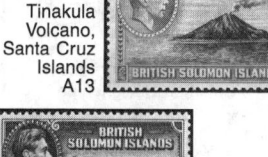

Tinakula Volcano, Santa Cruz Islands A13

Scrub Fowl — A14

Malaita Canoe — A15

Perf. 12½, 13½ (A7, A13, A14)

				Wmk. 4
1939-51				
67	A4	½p deep grn & ultra	.20	.90
68	A5	1p dk pur & choc	.20	.90
69	A6	1½p car & sl grn	.30	1.10
70	A7	2p blk & org brn	.35	1.40
a.	2p black & red brown ('43)		.35	1.60
	Never hinged		.70	
b.	Perf. 12 ('51)		.20	1.40
	Never hinged		.25	
71	A8	2½p ol grn & rose vio	.85	1.40
a.	Vert. pair, imperf. horiz.		10,500.	
72	A9	3p ultra & blk, perf. 13½	.55	1.10
a.	Perf. 12 ('51)		.75	2.25
	Never hinged		1.40	
73	A10	4½p dk brn & yel grn	3.25	12.00
74	A11	6p rose lil & dk pur	.30	.90
75	A12	1sh blk & grn	.70	.85
76	A13	2sh dp org & blk	4.25	4.50
a.	2sh dp org & vio blk ('43)		4.25	5.00
	Never hinged		5.50	
77	A14	2sh6p dull vio & blk	17.00	6.00
78	A15	5sh red & brt bl green	20.00	8.25
79	A10	10sh red lil & ol ('42)	4.50	9.50
	Nos. 67-79 (13)		52.45	48.80
	Set, never hinged		80.00	

Catalogue values for unused stamps in this section, from this point to the end of the section, are for Never Hinged items.

Peace Issue
Common Design Type

			Perf. 13½x14
1946, Oct. 15		**Wmk. 4**	**Engr.**
80	CD303	1½p carmine	.20	.70
81	CD303	3p deep blue	.20	.30

Silver Wedding Issue
Common Design Types

			Perf. 14x14½
1949, Mar. 14		**Photo.**	
82	CD304	2p black	.40	.40

Perf. 11½x11
Engr.; Name Typo.

83	CD305	10sh red violet	14.50	13.50

UPU Issue
Common Design Types
Engr.; Name Typo. on 3p and 5p

			Perf. 13½, 11x11½
1949, Oct. 10		**Wmk. 4**	
84	CD306	2p red brown	1.00	.85
85	CD307	3p indigo	2.40	.85
86	CD308	5p green	1.00	1.25
87	CD309	1sh slate	1.00	.85
	Nos. 84-87 (4)		5.40	3.80

Coronation Issue
Common Design Type

			Perf. 13½x13
1953, June 2		**Engr.**	
88	CD312	2p gray & black	.80	.50

Ysabel Canoe A16

Prow of Roviana Canoe — A17

Designs: 1p, Roviana canoe. 1½p, Artificial Island, Malaita. 2p, Canoe house. 3p, Malaita canoe. 5p, 1sh3p, Map. 6p, Trading schooner. 8p, 9p, Henderson Field, Guadalcanal. 1sh, Chart of Solomons and H.M.S. Swallow, recalling Capt. Philip Carteret's voyage of 1767. 2sh, Tinakula Volcano. 2sh6p, Meeting house, Reef Islands. 5sh, Alvaro de Mendana de Neyra and Caravel. 10sh, Constable and Chief. £1, Coat of Arms.

Perf. 11½x11, 11x11½, 12, 13

				Wmk. 4
1956-60			**Engr.**	
89	A16	½p lilac & orange	.20	.45
90	A16	1p red brn & ol grn	.20	.20
91	A16	1½p dk car & sl bl	.20	.50
92	A16	2p gray grn & choc	.20	.25
93	A17	2½p gray bl & blk	.40	.45
94	A16	3p dull red & grn	.40	.20
95	A16	5p blue & black	.20	.50
96	A16	6p bluish grn & blk	.35	.20
97	A16	8p black & ultra	.20	.20
98	A16	9p black & brt grn	2.25	.70
99	A17	1sh brn org & sl bl	.40	.45
100	A16	1sh3p blue & black	4.25	1.50
101	A17	2sh car rose & blk	9.00	1.50
102	A17	2sh6p rose lil & emer	5.25	.40
103	A16	5sh red brown	11.00	3.50
104	A17	10sh black brown	14.00	4.00
105	A16	£1 lt blue & blk	29.00	30.00
	Nos. 89-105 (17)		77.50	45.00

Issued: £1, 11/5/58; 9p, 1sh3p, 1/28/60; others, 3/1/56.

See Nos. 113-125.

Great
Frigate
Bird — A18

Perf. 13x12½

1961, Jan. 19   Litho.   Wmk. 314
106 A18 2p blue green &
                black   .20   .25
107 A18 3p rose red & black   .20   .20
108 A18 9p lilac & black   .25   .40
      Nos. 106-108 (3)   .65   .85

New constitution, brought into operation
Oct. 18, 1960. The watermark is sideways and
may be found facing both left and right.

Freedom from Hunger Issue
Common Design Type
1963, June 4   Photo.   Perf. 14x14½
109 CD314 1sh3p ultra   3.50 1.50

Red Cross Centenary Issue
Common Design Type
1963, Sept. 2   Litho.   Perf. 13
110 CD315 2p black & red   .40   .25
111 CD315 9p ultra & red   2.00 1.75

Types of 1956-60
Perf. 12, 13, 11½x11
1963-64   Engr.   Wmk. 314
113 A16 1p red brn & ol
                grn   .25   .25
114 A16 1½p dk car & sl bl   .25   .40
115 A16 2p gray grn &
                choc   .25   .20
117 A16 3p dull red & grn   .40   .20
119 A16 6p bluish grn &
                blk   .90   .40
121 A16 9p black & brt grn   .90   .40
123 A16 1sh3p blue & blk   1.10   .70
124 A16 2sh car rose & blk   2.50 4.25
125 A17 2sh6p rose lil & emer 9.00 9.00
      Nos. 113-125 (9)   15.55 15.80

Issued: 3p, 11/16; 6p, 9p, 1sh3p, 7/7/64; 1p,
1½p, 2p, 2sh, 2sh6p, 7/9/64.

ITU Issue
Common Design Type
Perf. 11x11½
1965, June 28   Litho.   Wmk. 314
126 CD317 2p ver & grnsh blue .35   .25
127 CD317 3p grnsh bl & ol bis .55   .40

Makira Food
Bowl — A19

Designs: 1p, 1sh, 1sh3p, Various orchids.
1½p, Scorpion shell. 2p, Papuan hornbill.
2½p, Ysabel shield. 3p, Rennellese club. 6p,
Moorish idol (fish). 9p, Great frigate bird. 2sh,
Sanford's sea eagle. 2sh6p, Malaita belt. 5sh,
Ornithoptera Victoreae (butterfly). 10sh, White
cockatoo. £1, Figurehead, western canoe.

Perf. 13x12½
1965, May 24   Litho.   Wmk. 314
Design Subject in Black
128 A19 ½p sl blue & lt bl   .20   .75
129 A19 1p orange & yel   .45   .30
130 A19 1½p blue & yel grn   .25   .45
131 A19 2p vio bl & lt bl   .35   .55
132 A19 2½p red brn & buff   .20   .40
133 A19 3p grn & lt grn   .20   .20
134 A19 6p brt car rose &
                org   .25   .70
135 A19 9p slate grn & buff   .30   .20
136 A19 1sh dp cl & rose   .85   .20
137 A19 1sh3p ver & buff   2.75 2.10
138 A19 2sh dp mag & lil   5.50 2.75
139 A19 2sh6p ol brn & buff   .70   .65
140 A19 5sh dk vio bl & lil   8.25 4.75
141 A19 10sh ol grn & yel   9.00 3.75
142 A19 £1 purple & red   8.25 4.75
      Nos. 128-142 (15)   37.50 22.50

For surcharges see Nos. 149-166.

Intl. Cooperation Year Issue
Common Design Type
1965, Oct. 25   Litho.   Perf. 14½
143 CD318 1p bl grn & cl   .20   .20
144 CD318 2sh6p lt violet &
                grn   1.10   .90

Churchill Memorial Issue
Common Design Type
1966, Jan. 24   Photo.   Perf. 14
145 CD319 2p multicolored   .25   .30
146 CD319 9p multicolored   .45   .30
147 CD319 1sh3p multicolored   .60   .30
148 CD319 2sh6p multicolored   .70   .85
      Nos. 145-148 (4)   2.00 1.75

Nos. 128-142 Surcharged with New
Value and Three Bars in Black or Red

Perf. 13x12½
1966-67   Litho.   Wmk. 314
149 A19 1c on ½p multi   .20   .20
150 A19 2c on 1p multi   .20   .20
151 A19 3c on 1½p multi   .20   .20
152 A19 4c on 2p multi   .20   .20
153 A19 6c on 6p multi   .20   .20
154 A19 6c on 2½p multi   .20   .20
155 A19 7c on 3p multi   .30   .30
156 A19 8c on 9p multi   .35   .35
  b.   "8" inverted   25.00 20.00
157 A19 10c on 1sh   .45   .45
158 A19 12c on 1sh3p multi   .45   .45
159 A19 13c on 1sh3p multi   .50   .50
160 A19 14c on 3p multi   .50   .50
161 A19 20c on 2sh multi   .85   .85
162 A19 25c on 2sh6p multi   1.10   1.10
163 A19 35c on 2sh multi   2.00   1.60
164 A19 50c on 5sh multi (R)   2.50   2.25
165 A19 $1 on 10sh multi   4.25   4.25
166 A19 $2 on £1 multi   8.75   8.75
      Nos. 149-166 (18)   23.20 22.55

The 12c, 14c, 35c have watermark sideways.
   Issued: 12c, 14c, 35c, 3/1/67; others,
2/14/66.

1966   Wmk. 314 Sideways
149a A19 1c on ½p   .20   .20
150a A19 2c on 1p   .20   .20
151a A19 3c on 1½p   .20   .20
152a A19 4c on 2p   .25   .25
153a A19 5c on 6p   .30   .30
154a A19 6c on 2½p   .35   .35
155a A19 7c on 3p   .40   .40
156a A19 8c on 9p   .45   .45
157a A19 10c on 1sh   .60   .60
159a A19 13c on 1sh3p   .75   .75
161a A19 20c on 2sh   1.25   1.25
162a A19 25c on 2sh6p   1.50   1.50
164a A19 50c on 5sh (R)   3.00   3.00
165a A19 $1 on 10sh   6.00   6.00
166a A19 $2 on £1   9.00   9.00
      Nos. 149a-166a (15)   24.45 24.45

World Cup Soccer Issue
Common Design Type
1966, July 1   Litho.   Perf. 14
167 CD321 8c multicolored   .30   .30
168 CD321 35c multicolored   1.10   1.10

WHO Headquarters Issue
Common Design Type
1966, Sept. 20   Litho.   Perf. 14
169 CD322 3c multicolored   .20   .20
170 CD322 50c multicolored   1.60   1.60

UNESCO Anniversary Issue
Common Design Type
1966, Dec. 1   Litho.   Perf. 14
171 CD323 3c "Education"   .40   .20
172 CD323 25c "Science"   .95   .40
173 CD323 $1 "Culture"   2.40   1.90
      Nos. 171-173 (3)   3.75   2.50

Henderson Field, Guadalcanal — A20

Design: 35c, US Marines landing, Red
Beach, Guadalcanal, 1942.

Perf. 14x14½
1967, Aug. 28   Photo.   Wmk. 314
174 A20 8c multi & silver   .20   .20
175 A20 35c multi & gold   .75   .75

Guadalcanal campaign in WW II, 25th anniv.

Mendana's Ship Off Puerta de la Cruz
(Honiara), Guadalcanal, 1568 — A21

Designs: 8c, Arrival of Missionaries. 35c,
Naval battle during World War II. $1, Honor
guard raising Union Jack during proclamation
of Protectorate.

1968, Feb. 2   Photo.   Perf. 14½
176 A21 3c pink & multi   .40   .20
177 A21 8c emerald & multi   .40   .20
178 A21 35c multicolored   .85   .20
179 A21 $1 blue & multi   1.10   2.25
      Nos. 176-179 (4)   2.75   2.85

400th anniv. of the discovery of the British
Solomon Islands by the Spanish navigator
Alvaro de Mendana de Neyra.

Vine Fishing
A22

Designs: 2c, Kite fishing. 3c, Platform fishing. 4c, Net fishing. 6c, Gold lip shell diving.
8c, Night fishing. 12c, Boat building. 14c,
Cocoa harvest. 15c, Road building. 20c, Geological survey by plane. 24c, Hauling timber.
35c, Copra. 45c, Harvesting rice. $1, Honiara
Port. $2, Map of the Islands, plane and route
of Internal Air Service.

Wmk. 314
1968, May 20   Photo.   Perf. 14½
180 A22 1c aqua, brn & blk   .20   .20
181 A22 2c lt yel grn, brn &
                blk   .20   .20
182 A22 3c brt grn, dk grn &
                blk   .20   .20
183 A22 4c brt rose lil, brn &
                blk   .20   .20
184 A22 6c multicolored   .30   .20
185 A22 8c dp ultra, org & blk .20   .20
186 A22 12c bister, red & blk .60   .35
187 A22 14c red org, brn & blk 1.75 2.25
188 A22 15c multicolored   .70   .70
189 A22 20c ultra, red & blk   3.50 2.25
190 A22 24c scarlet, yel & blk 1.75 2.50
191 A22 35c multicolored   1.75   .45
192 A22 45c yellow, red & blk 1.40   .45
193 A22 $1 vio bl, emer & blk 2.25 1.75
194 A22 $2 multicolored   5.00 4.00
      Nos. 180-194 (15)   20.00 16.00

Map of South Pacific and University
Degrees — A23

Perf. 12½x12
1969, Feb. 10   Litho.   Unwmk.
195 A23 3c multicolored   .20   .20
196 A23 12c multicolored   .25   .20
197 A23 35c multicolored   .55   .50
      Nos. 195-197 (3)   1.00   .90

Inauguration of the University of the South
Pacific in 1969, at the Royal New Zealand Air
Force Seaplane Station, Laucala Bay, Fiji.

Field Ball and
Games'
Emblem — A24

Stained Glass
Window with
Melanesian
Peace
Symbol — A25

Perf. 14½x14
1969, Aug. 13   Photo.   Wmk. 314
198 A24 3c shown   .20   .20
199 A24 8c Soccer   .20   .20
200 A24 14c Running   .35   .30
201 A24 45c Rugby   1.10   .95
      Nos. 198-201 (4)   1.85 1.65
  a. Souvenir sheet of 4, #198-201 5.50 5.50

3rd S. Pacific Games, Port Moresby, Aug.
13-23.
In No. 201a, shading was added below athlete's foot on 14c, and strengthened on 8c and
45c.

1969, Nov. 21   Photo.   Wmk. 314

Christmas: 8c, South Sea Islands scene
with palms and Star of Bethlehem.

202 A25 8c vio, grnsh bl & blk .20   .20
203 A25 35c black & multi   .60   .60

C. M. Woodford and Stamp of
1907 — A26

Designs: 7c, British Solomon Islands 1906
handstamp and cancellation, and New South
Wales No. 99. 18c, British Solomon Islands
No. 18 and 1913 Tulagi cancellation. 23c, New
General Post Office, Honiara.

1970, Apr. 15   Litho.   Perf. 13
204 A26 7c lilac rose & black .20   .20
205 A26 14c lt olive & black   .35   .35
206 A26 18c orange, yel & blk .45   .45
207 A26 23c multicolored   .65   .65
      Nos. 204-207 (4)   1.65 1.65

Issued to publicize the opening of the new
General Post Office in Honiara.

Map of
Solomon
Islands
A27

18c, British Solomon Islands coat of arms,
vert.

Perf. 14½x14, 14x14½
1970, June 15   Litho.   Wmk. 314
208 A27 18c multicolored   .55   .55
209 A27 35c multicolored   1.00 1.00

Adoption of the new 1970 Constitution.

Red Cross Headquarters,
Honiara — A28

35c, Map of British Solomon Islands showing Red Cross stations, wheelchair.

1970, Aug. 17   Perf. 14½x14
210 A28 3c multicolored   .20   .20
211 A28 35c multicolored   .95   .85

Centenary of British Red Cross Society.

Carved Angel and Southern Cross — A29

Reredos: Symbols of Trinity and Light at St. Luke's Church, Kia — A30

Perf. 14x13½, 13½x14
1970, Oct. 19   Litho.   Wmk. 314
212 A29 8c violet & bister brn   .25   .25
213 A30 45c multicolored   1.00 1.00

Christmas 1970.

Count de La Pérouse and "La Boussole" — A31

4c, Astrolabe, Polynesian reed map. 12c, Abel Tasman, sailing ship Heemskerk, 1643. 35c, Te Puki canoe, Santa Cruz.

1971, Jan. 28   Perf. 14½x14
214 A31 3c multicolored   1.00   .50
215 A31 4c multicolored   1.00   .50
216 A31 12c multicolored   1.25   .75
217 A31 35c multicolored   1.50 1.25
      Nos. 214-217 (4)   4.75 3.00

In honor of famous explorers and ships. See Nos. 228-231, 250-253.

Bishop Patteson, J. Atkin and S. Taroniara — A32

Designs: 4c, Last landing of the "Southern Cross" at Nukapu. 14c, Memorial for Bishop Patteson and map of Nukapu, vert. 45c, Ceremonial leaf tag (had been attached to Bishop's body), vert.

Perf. 14½x14, 14x14½
1971, Apr. 5   Litho.   Wmk. 314
218 A32 2c lt green & multi   .25   .25
219 A32 4c blue green & multi   .25   .25
220 A32 14c brt pink & multi   .25   .25
221 A32 45c brown & multi   .50   .50
      Nos. 218-221 (4)   1.25 1.25

Bishop John Coleridge Patteson (1827-71), head of the Melanesian mission.

Boxing, Games Emblem A33

8c, Soccer. 12c, Running. 35c, Spear fishing.

1971, Aug. 9   Perf. 14½x14
222 A33 3c orange & multi   .30   .30
223 A33 8c emerald & multi   .30   .30
224 A33 12c yellow & multi   .30   .30
225 A33 35c blue & multi   .50   .50
      Nos. 222-225 (4)   1.40 1.40

4th South Pacific Games, Papeete, French Polynesia, Sept. 8-19.

Melanesian Lectern (wood carving) — A34

Christmas: 45c, Stylized birds, painted by school girl Margarita Bara.

1971, Nov. 15   Litho.   Wmk. 314
226 A34 9c orange & multi   .20   .20
227 A34 45c blue & multi   1.10 1.10

Explorer Type of 1971

4c, Louis Antoine de Bougainville, La Boudeuse, 1776. 9c, Horizontal planisphere, 1574, ivory backstaff, 1695. 15c, Philip Carteret, H.M.S. Swallow, 1707. 45c, Small canoe of Malaita.

1972, Feb. 1   Perf. 14½
228 A31 4c brown & multi   .40   .25
229 A31 9c green & multi   .60   .25
230 A31 15c lt blue & multi   .75   .50
231 A31 45c blue & multi   2.25 2.25
      Nos. 228-231 (4)   4.00 3.25

Cupha Woodfordi A35

Designs: 1c, 2c, 3c, 4c, $2, Butterflies. 5c, 8c, 9c, 15c, $1. Fishes. 12c, 20c, 25c, 35c, 45c, Orchids. $5, Birds.

1972-73   Perf. 14
232 A35 1c shown   .20   .20
233 A35 2c Ornithoptera
              priamus   .20   .20
234 A35 3c Vindula sapor   .20   .20
235 A35 4c Papilio orssippus .20   .20
236 A35 5c Great trevally   .20   .20
237 A35 8c Little bonito   .35   .20
238 A35 9c Sapphire demoi-
              selle   .45   .30
239 A35 12c Costus speciosus 1.10 .45
240 A35 15c Orange anemone   1.10 .70
241 A35 20c Spathoglottis pli-
              cata   2.75 .85
242 A35 25c Ephemerantha
              comata   2.75 1.00
243 A35 35c Dendrobium
              cuthbertsonii   2.75 1.25
244 A35 45c Heliconia
              salomonica   2.25 1.75
245 A35 $1 Blue-finned trig-
              gerfish   2.75 3.50
246 A35 $2 Ornithoptera allot-
              ti   8.25 7.00
247 A35 $5 Great frigate bird 13.00 17.00
      Nos. 232-247 (16)   38.50 35.00

Issued: $5, 7/2/73; others, 7/2/72.
For overprints see Nos. 300-311.

Silver Wedding Issue, 1972
Common Design Type

Design: Queen Elizabeth II, Prince Philip, scroll and message drum on woven mat.

1972, Nov. 20   Photo.   Perf. 14x14½
248 CD324 8c car rose &
                  multi   .20   .20
249 CD324 45c olive & multi .50   .50

Explorer Type of 1971

Designs: 4c, Antoine R. J. d'Entrecasteaux and "The Recherche," 1791. 9c, Ship's hourglass, 17th century, and chronometer, 1761. 15c, Lieutenant Shortland and "The Alexander," 1788. 35c, Tomoko (war canoe).

Wmk. 314
1973, Mar. 9   Litho.   Perf. 14½
250 A31 4c blue & multi   .20   .20
251 A31 9c blue & multi   .55   .55
252 A31 15c blue & multi   1.00 1.00
253 A31 35c blue & multi   3.25 3.25
      Nos. 250-253 (4)   5.00 5.00

Pan Pipes A36

Musical Instruments: 9c, Castanets. 15c, Bamboo flute. 35c, Bauro gongs. 45c, Bamboo band.

1973, Oct. 1   Perf. 13½x14
254 A36 4c brick red & multi   .20   .20
255 A36 9c yellow bis & multi   .25   .25
256 A36 15c pink & multi   .40   .40
257 A36 35c blue green & multi .90   .90
258 A36 45c multicolored   1.25 1.25
      Nos. 254-258 (5)   3.00 3.00

Princess Anne's Wedding Issue
Common Design Type

1973, Nov. 14   Perf. 14
259 CD325 4c slate & multi   .30   .30
260 CD325 35c multicolored   .70   .70

Adoration of the Kings, by Jan Brueghel A37

Adoration of the Kings by: 22c, Peter Brueghel, vert. 45c, Botticelli.

1973, Nov. 26   Litho.   Perf. 14
Size: 39x25mm, 25x39mm
261 A37 8c pink & multi   .25   .25
262 A37 22c lilac & multi   .50   .50

Perf. 13½
Size: 47x35mm
263 A37 45c gray & multi   1.25 1.25
      Nos. 261-263 (3)   2.00 2.00

Christmas 1973.

Map of Solomon Islands — A38

1974, Feb. 18   Litho.   Perf. 13½
264 A38 4c blue & multi   .20   .20
265 A38 9c citron & multi   .25   .25
266 A38 15c violet gray & multi .45 .45
267 A38 35c emerald & multi 1.50 1.50
      Nos. 264-267 (4)   2.40 2.40

Visit of British Royal Family.

First Resident Commissioner Landing at Tulagi — A39

Designs: 9c, Marine radar and scanner unit, map of Islands. 15c, Islanders taken to "Blackbirder" ship. 45c, John F. Kennedy's P.T. 109 off Lumbari Island, 1943.

1974, May 15   Litho.   Perf. 14½
268 A39 4c multicolored   .20   .20
269 A39 9c multicolored   .45   .45
270 A39 15c multicolored   .60   .60
271 A39 45c multicolored   2.75 2.75
      Nos. 268-271 (4)   4.00 4.00

Ships and navigators.

Mailman, Map of Islands — A40

9c, Carrier pigeon, horiz. 15c, Angel Gabriel. 45c, Pegasus, horiz. Designs based on origami (folded paper) figures.

1974, Aug. 29   Wmk. 314   Perf. 14
272 A40 4c brt green & multi   .20   .20
273 A40 9c lemon & multi   .30   .20
274 A40 15c multicolored   .45   .35
275 A40 45c blue & multi   1.25 1.10
      Nos. 272-275 (4)   2.20 1.85

Centenary of Universal Postal Union.

Solomon Islands No. 208 A41

1974, Dec. 16   Litho.   Perf. 14½
276 A41 4c shown   .20   .20
277 A41 9c No. 107   .30   .30
278 A41 15c same   .50   .50
279 A41 45c like 4c   1.10 1.10
a.   Souvenir sheet of 4, #276-279 5.00 5.00
      Nos. 276-279 (4)   2.10 2.10

New Constitution, inaugurated Oct. 18, 1960.

Golden Whistler A42

Birds: 2c, River kingfisher. 3c, Red-throated fruit dove. 4c, Button quail. $2, Duchess lorikeet.

1975, Apr. 7   Wmk. 314   Perf. 14
280 A42 1c yellow grn & multi   .20   .20
281 A42 2c lt blue & multi   .20   .20
282 A42 3c brt pink & multi   .25   .25
283 A42 4c orange & multi   .35   .35
284 A42 $2 dp orange & multi 13.00 12.00
      Nos. 280-284 (5)   14.00 13.00

See Nos. 316-320, 323, 330-331. For overprints see Nos. 296-299.

Motor Vessel Walande A43

1975, May 29   Perf. 13½
285 A43 4c shown   .60   .20
286 A43 9c M. V. Melanesian   .80   .20
287 A43 15c Ship Marsina,
              house flag   1.10   .25
288 A43 45c S. S. Himalaya   2.00 1.50
      Nos. 285-288 (4)   4.50 2.15

Runner, 800-meters — A44

1975, Aug. 4   Litho.   Perf. 13½
289	A44	4c shown	.20	.20
290	A44	9c Long jump	.20	.20
291	A44	15c Javelin	.35	.35
292	A44	45c Soccer	1.00	1.00
a.		Souvenir sheet of 4, #289-292	5.00	5.00
		Nos. 289-292 (4)	1.75	1.75

5th South Pacific Games, Guam, Aug. 1-10.

Nativity and Candles A45

Christmas: 35c, Angels, shepherds and candles. 45c, Three Kings approaching Bethlehem, and candles.

1975, Oct. 13   Wmk. 373   Perf. 14
293	A45	15c multicolored	.35	.35
294	A45	35c multicolored	.80	.80
295	A45	45c multicolored	1.10	1.10
a.		Souvenir sheet of 3, #293-295	5.00	5.00
		Nos. 293-295 (3)	2.25	2.25

Nos. 236-245, 247, 280-284 Overprinted with Bar Obliterating "British" in Black or Silver

1975, Nov. 12   Litho.   Wmk. 314
296	A42	1c multicolored	.60	.20
297	A42	2c multicolored	1.10	.20
298	A42	3c multicolored	.80	.20
299	A42	4c multicolored	1.10	.20
300	A35	5c multicolored	.55	.20
301	A35	8c multicolored	.55	.40
302	A35	9c multicolored	.55	.40
303	A35	12c multicolored	1.75	.50
304	A35	15c multicolored	1.75	.70
305	A35	20c multicolored	2.25	.90
306	A35	25c multicolored	2.25	1.00
307	A35	35c multicolored	2.50	1.50
308	A35	45c multicolored	2.25	1.75
309	A42	$1 multicolored	1.75	3.50
310	A42	$2 multicolored	6.75	7.00
311	A35	$5 multicolored (S)	6.50	18.00
		Nos. 296-311 (16)	33.00	36.65

Ceremonial Food Bowl — A46

Artifacts: 15c, Barava, chief's money. 35c, Nguzu-nguzu, canoe protector spirit, vert. 45c, Nguzu-nguzu on canoe prow.

Wmk. 314
1976, Jan. 12   Litho.   Perf. 14
312	A46	4c scarlet & black	.20	.20
313	A46	15c lt violet & multi	.25	.25
314	A46	35c multicolored	.75	.75
315	A46	45c multicolored	.90	.90
		Nos. 312-315 (4)	2.10	2.10

Type of 1975 Inscribed "Solomon Islands" and

Golden Cowries A47

1c, Golden whistler. 2c, River kingfisher. 3c, Red-throated fruit dove. 4c, Button quail. 5c, Willie wagtail. 10c, Glory-of-the-sea cones. 12c, Rainbow lory. 15c, Pearly nautilus. 20c, Venus comb murex. 25c, Commercial trochus. 35c, Melon or baler shell. 45c, Orange spider conch. $1, Pacific triton. $2, Duchess lorikeet. $5, Great frigate bird.

1976   Wmk. 373   Perf. 14
316	A42	1c yel grn & multi	.20	.20
317	A42	2c lt blue & multi	.20	.20
318	A42	3c pink & multi	.20	.20
319	A42	4c orange & multi	.20	.20
320	A42	5c red brown & multi	.20	.20
321	A47	6c rose & multi	.20	.20
322	A47	10c multicolored	.25	.25
323	A47	12c yel grn & multi	.30	.30
324	A47	15c lilac & multi	.35	.35
325	A47	20c ultra & multi	.50	.50
326	A47	25c dull grn & multi	.60	.60
327	A47	35c bister & multi	.90	.90
328	A47	45c fawn & multi	1.10	1.10
329	A47	$1 olive & multi	2.50	2.50
330	A42	$2 multicolored	5.00	5.00
331	A42	$5 multicolored	12.00	12.00
		Nos. 316-331 (16)	24.70	24.70

Issue dates: $5, Dec. 6; others Mar. 8.

Coast Watchers, World War II A48

American Bicentennial: 20c, "Amagiri" ramming "P.T.109" and Lt. John F. Kennedy. 35c, Plane on Henderson Airfield. 45c, Map showing landing of US forces on Guadalcanal.

1976, May 24   Perf. 14
333	A48	6c black & multi	.40	.20
334	A48	20c black & multi	1.10	.55
335	A48	35c black & multi	1.50	.90
336	A48	45c black & multi	1.50	1.10
a.		Souvenir sheet of 4, #333-336	8.00	8.00
		Nos. 333-336 (4)	4.50	2.75

Alexander Graham Bell — A49

Designs: 20c, Radio-telephone and satellite. 35c, Ericsson's magneto telephone. 45c, Telephone, 1876, and stick telephone.

1976, July 26   Litho.   Perf. 14½x14
337	A49	6c lt ultra & multi	.20	.20
338	A49	20c multicolored	.45	.45
339	A49	35c orange & multi	.70	.70
340	A49	45c bister & multi	1.00	1.00
		Nos. 337-340 (4)	2.35	2.35

Centenary of first telephone call by Alexander Graham Bell, Mar. 10, 1876.

One-Eleven BAC — A50

Planes: 20c, Solair Britten Norman Islander. 35c, DC-3 Dakota. 45c, De Havilland DH50A.

1976, Sept. 13   Wmk. 373   Perf. 14
341	A50	6c black & multi	.20	.20
342	A50	20c black & multi	.65	.65
343	A50	35c black & multi	1.10	1.10
344	A50	45c black & multi	1.40	1.40
		Nos. 341-344 (4)	3.35	3.35

1st flight to Solomon Islands, 50th anniv.

Queen Receiving Lei, 1974 Visit — A51

Carved Wooden Figure — A52

35c, Communion plate, cup. 45c, Communion.

1977, Feb. 7   Litho.   Perf. 14x13½
345	A51	6c multicolored	.20	.20
346	A51	35c multicolored	.50	.50
347	A51	45c multicolored	.65	.65
		Nos. 345-347 (3)	1.35	1.35

25th anniv. of the reign of Elizabeth II.

1977, May 9   Perf. 14

Artifacts: 20c, Sea adaro or spirit. 35c, Shark-headed man. 45c, Seated man.
348	A52	6c yellow & multi	.25	.25
349	A52	20c blue & multi	.25	.25
350	A52	35c rose & multi	.55	.55
351	A52	45c multicolored	.70	.70
		Nos. 348-351 (4)	1.75	1.75

Man Spraying House, Anopheles Mosquito — A53

Designs: 20c, Taking blood samples. 35c, Microscope, map of Solomon Islands, Malaria Eradication Program emblem. 45c, Messenger delivering medicine to malaria patient.

1977, July 27   Litho.   Wmk. 373
352	A53	6c multicolored	.25	.25
353	A53	20c multicolored	.40	.40
354	A53	35c multicolored	.55	.55
355	A53	45c multicolored	.80	.80
		Nos. 352-355 (4)	2.00	2.00

Malaria eradication.

Adoration of the Shepherds — A54

Christmas: 20c, Nativity. 35c, Adoration of the Kings. 45c, Flight into Egypt.

Wmk. 373
1977, Sept. 12   Litho.   Perf. 14
356	A54	6c multicolored	.25	.25
357	A54	20c multicolored	.40	.40
358	A54	35c multicolored	.55	.55
359	A54	45c multicolored	.80	.80
		Nos. 356-359 (4)	2.00	2.00

Traditional Feather Money — A55

Designs: No. 361, New coins. No. 362, Banknotes. No. 363, Traditional shell money.

1977, Oct. 24   Litho.   Perf. 14x14½
360		6c brt green & multi	.20	.20
361		6c brt green & multi	.20	.20
a.	A55	Pair, #360-361	.30	.30
362		45c buff & multi	1.00	1.00
363		45c buff & multi	1.00	1.00
a.	A55	Pair, #362-363	2.00	2.00
		Nos. 360-363 (4)	2.40	2.40

New coinage.

Shortland Islands Figure — A56

Artifacts: 20c, Ceremonial shield. 35c, Santa Cruz ritual figure. 45c, Decorative combs.

1978, Jan. 11   Perf. 14
364	A56	6c multicolored	.20	.20
365	A56	20c multicolored	.45	.45
366	A56	35c multicolored	.80	.80
367	A56	45c multicolored	1.00	1.00
		Nos. 364-367 (4)	2.45	2.45

Elizabeth II Coronation Anniversary Issue
Common Design Types
Souvenir Sheet
Unwmk.

1978, Apr. 21   Litho.   Perf. 15
368		Sheet of 6	3.50	3.50
a.		CD326 45c King's dragon	.50	.50
b.		CD327 45c Elizabeth II	.50	.50
c.		CD328 45c Sandford eagle	.50	.50

No. 368 contains 2 se-tenant strips of Nos. 368a-368c, separated by horizontal gutter with commemorative and descriptive inscriptions and showing central part of coronation procession with coach.

National Flag — A57   Apostles by Dürer — A58

Independence: 15c, Governor General's flag. 35c, Cenotaph, Honiara, flags of U.S., Great Britain, New Zealand and Australia. 45c, Coat of Arms.

Wmk. 373
1978, July 7   Litho.   Perf. 14
369	A57	6c multicolored	.20	.20
370	A57	15c multicolored	.30	.30
371	A57	35c multicolored	.70	.70
372	A57	45c multicolored	.95	.95
		Nos. 369-372 (4)	2.15	2.15

1978, Oct. 4   Litho.   Perf. 14
373	A58	6c John	.20	.20
374	A58	20c Peter	.40	.40
375	A58	35c Paul	.70	.70
376	A58	45c Mark	.90	.90
		Nos. 373-376 (4)	2.20	2.20

Albrecht Dürer (1471-1528), German painter, 450th death anniversary.

Scouts Making Fire — A59

Designs: 20c, Camping. 35c, Solomon Islands Scouts. 45c, Canoeing.

1978, Nov. 15   Litho.   Perf. 14
377	A59	6c multicolored	.20	.20
378	A59	20c multicolored	.30	.30
379	A59	35c multicolored	.55	.55
380	A59	45c multicolored	.70	.70
		Nos. 377-380 (4)	1.75	1.75

50 years of Scouting in Solomon Islands.

Discovery A60

Designs: 18c, Capt. Cook, 1776, painting by Nathaniel Dance. 35c, Sextant. 45c, Capt. Cook after Flaxman / Wedgwood medallion.

Wmk. 373
1979, Jan. 16   Litho.   Perf. 11
381	A60	8c multicolored	.20	.20
382	A60	18c multicolored	.40	.40
383	A60	35c multicolored	.80	.80

Litho.; Embossed
384	A60	45c multicolored	1.00	1.00
		Nos. 381-384 (4)	2.40	2.40

Capt. Cook's voyages.

Fish Net Float A61

Artifacts: 20c, Armband made of shell money, vert. 35c, Ceremonial food bowl. 45c, Forehead ornament, vert.

1979, Mar. 21   Litho.   Perf. 14
385	A61	8c multicolored	.30	.30
386	A61	20c multicolored	.30	.30
387	A61	35c multicolored	.45	.45
388	A61	45c multicolored	.60	.60
		Nos. 385-388 (4)	1.65	1.65

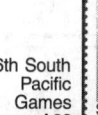

6th South Pacific Games A62

1979, June 4   Litho.   Wmk. 373
389	A62	8c Running	.20	.20
390	A62	20c Hurdles	.25	.25
391	A62	35c Soccer	.30	.30
392	A62	45c Swimming	.50	.50
		Nos. 389-392 (4)	1.25	1.25

Solomon Islands No. 14 — A63   Sea Snake — A64

Designs (Rowland Hill and): 20c, Great Britain No. 27. 35c, Solomon Islands No. 372. 45c, Solomon Islands No. 40.

1979, Aug. 16   Litho.   Perf. 14
393	A63	8c multicolored	.20	.20
394	A63	20c multicolored	.40	.40
395	A63	35c multicolored	.65	.65
		Nos. 393-395 (3)	1.25	1.25

Souvenir Sheet
396	A63	45c multicolored	1.25	1.25

Sir Rowland Hill (1795-1879), originator of penny postage.

Perf. 13½x13
1979-83   Litho.   Wmk. 373
397	A64	1c Sea snake	.20	.20
398	A64	3c Red-banded tree snake	.20	.20
399	A64	4c Whip snake	.20	.20
400	A64	6c Pacific boa	.20	.20
401	A64	8c Skink	.20	.20
402	A64	10c Gecko	.20	.20
403	A64	12c Monitor	.20	.20
404	A64	15c Angelhead	.25	.25
405	A64	20c Giant toad	.30	.30
406	A64	25c Marsh frog	.40	.40
407	A64	30c Horned frog	.50	.50
408	A64	35c Tree frog	.50	.50
408A	A64	40c Burrowing snake	.55	.55
409	A64	45c Guppy's snake	.65	.65
409A	A64	50c Tree gecko	.60	.60
410	A64	$1 Large skink	1.25	1.25
411	A64	$2 Guppy's frog	2.50	2.50
412	A64	$5 Estuarine crocodile	6.50	6.50
412A	A64	$10 Hawksbill turtle	13.00	13.00
		Nos. 397-412A (19)	28.40	28.40

Issued: $10, 9/20/82; 40c, 50c, 1/24/83; others, 9/1979 (undated).
Nos. 403, 406, 410, 412 reissued inscribed "1982." No. 407, "1983."

Madonna and Child, by Morando — A65

IYC Emblem and Madonna and Child: 20c, Bernardino Luini. 35c, Bellini. 50c, Raphael.

1979, Nov. 15   Perf. 14½
413	A65	4c multicolored	.20	.20
414	A65	20c multicolored	.25	.25
415	A65	35c multicolored	.40	.40
416	A65	50c multicolored	.65	.65
a.		Souvenir sheet of 4, #413-416	1.75	1.75
		Nos. 413-416 (4)	1.50	1.50

Christmas 1979, Intl. Year of the Child.

Curacoa and Crest A66

Ships and Crests: 20c, Herald, 1854. 35c, Royalist, 1889. 45c, Beagle, 1878.

Wmk. 373
1980, Jan. 23   Litho.   Perf. 14
417	A66	8c multicolored	.20	.20
418	A66	20c multicolored	.40	.40
419	A66	35c multicolored	.65	.65
420	A66	45c multicolored	.85	.85
		Nos. 417-420 (4)	2.10	2.10

See Nos. 435-438.

Steel Fishery Training Ship — A67

1980, Mar. 27   Litho.   Perf. 13½
421	A67	8c shown	.20	.20
422	A67	20c Fishery training ship	.25	.25
423	A67	45c Refrigerated carrier	.45	.40
424	A67	80c Research ship	.85	1.75
		Nos. 421-424 (4)	1.75	2.60

"Comliebank," Tulag Cancel — A68

1980, May 6   Litho.   Perf. 14½
425		Sheet of 4	2.00	2.00
a.		A68 45c shown	.50	.50
b.		A68 45c Douglas C-47	.50	.50
c.		A68 45c BAC 1-11, Honiara cancel	.50	.50
d.		A68 45c "Corabank," Auki cancel	.50	.50

London 1980 Intl. Stamp Exhib., May 6-14.

Queen Mother Elizabeth Birthday Issue
Common Design Type
Wmk. 373
1980, Aug. 4   Litho.   Perf. 14
426	CD330	45c multicolored	.50	.50

Angel with Trumpet — A69

Christmas: 20c, Angel with violin. 45c, Angel with trumpet. 80c, Angel with lute.

Wmk. 373
1980, Sept. 2   Litho.   Perf. 14½
427	A69	8c multicolored	.20	.20
428	A69	20c multicolored	.20	.20
429	A69	45c multicolored	.40	.40
430	A69	80c multicolored	.70	.70
		Nos. 427-430 (4)	1.50	1.50

Parthenos Sylvia — A70

Wmk. 373
1980, Nov. 12   Litho.   Perf. 13½
431	A70	8c shown	.40	.40
432	A70	20c Delias schoenbergi	.60	.60
433	A70	45c Jamides cephion	1.00	1.00
434	A70	80c Ornithoptera victoriae	1.50	1.50
		Nos. 431-434 (4)	3.50	3.50

See Nos. 461-464.

Ship & Crest Type of 1980
8c, Mounts Bay, 1959. 20c, Charybdis, 1970. 45c, Hydra, 1972-73. $1, Britannia, 1974.

1981, Jan. 14
435	A66	8c multicolored	.20	.20
436	A66	20c multicolored	.20	.20
437	A66	45c multicolored	.45	.45
438	A66	$1 multicolored	1.25	1.25
		Nos. 435-438 (4)	2.10	2.10

Maurelle's Map, 1742 — A71

Wmk. 373
1981, Mar. 23   Litho.   Perf. 14
439	A71	8c Francisco Maurelle, vert.	.20	.20
440	A71	10c shown	.20	.20
441	A71	45c La Princesa	.60	.60
442	A71	$1 Compass cards, vert.	1.00	1.00
		Nos. 439-442 (4)	2.00	2.00

Souvenir Sheet
443		Sheet of 4	1.60	1.60
a.		A71 25c any single	.35	.35

Bicent. of arrival of Francisco Antonio Maurelle and of charts of mapmaker Jean Nicholas Buache (1741-1825). No. 443 contains 4 44x28mm stamps, perf. 14½.

Women's Basketball — A72

Wmk. 373
1981, July 7   Litho.   Perf. 12
444	A72	8c shown	.20	.20
445	A72	10c Tennis	.20	.20
446	A72	25c Women's running	.35	.35
447	A72	30c Soccer	.35	.35
448	A72	45c Boxing	.50	.50
		Nos. 444-448 (5)	1.60	1.60

Souvenir Sheet
449	A72	$1 Emblem	1.25	1.25

Mini South Pacific Games, July.

Royal Wedding Issue
Common Design Type
1981, July 22   Perf. 13½x13
450	CD331	8c Bouquet	.20	.20
451	CD331	45c Charles	.30	.30
452	CD331	$1 Couple	1.00	1.00
		Nos. 450-452 (3)	1.50	1.50

For surcharge see No. B1.

Duke of Edinburgh's Awards, 25th Anniv. — A73

Wmk. 373
1981, Sept. 28   Litho.   Perf. 14
453	A73	8c Music	.25	.25
454	A73	25c Handicrafts	.25	.25
455	A73	45c Canoeing	.35	.35
456	A73	$1 Duke of Edinburgh	.90	.90
		Nos. 453-456 (4)	1.75	1.75

Holy Cross Cathedral, Honiara — A74

Christmas: 8c, 25c, Old churches, diff. 10c, St. Barnabas Anglican Cathedral, Honiara.

1981, Oct. 12
457	A74	8c multicolored	.30	.30
458	A74	10c multicolored	.30	.30
459	A74	25c multicolored	.40	.40
460	A74	$2 multicolored	1.50	1.50
		Nos. 457-460 (4)	2.50	2.50

Butterfly Type of 1980
Wmk. 373
1982, Jan. 5   Litho.   Perf. 13½
461	A70	10c Doleschallia bisaltide	.40	.40
462	A70	25c Papilio bridgei hecataeus	.70	.70

463	A70	35c Taenaris phorcas	.75	.75
464	A70	$1 Graphium sarpedon	2.40	2.40
		Nos. 461-464 (4)	4.25	4.25

Sanford's
Eagle — A75

1982, May 15   Litho.   Perf. 14

465	A75	12c Pair facing left	.45	.45
466	A75	12c Chick	.45	.45
467	A75	12c Mother feeding chicks	.45	.45
468	A75	12c Pair facing right	.45	.45
469	A75	12c Male flying	.45	.45
470	A75	12c Pair flying	.45	.45
		Nos. 465-470 (6)	2.70	2.70

Se-tenant in sheets of 24. The center horiz. row consists of 4 No. 470 + label. No block of 6 contains all 6 designs.

Princess Diana Issue
Common Design Type
Perf. 14½x14

1982, July 1   Litho.   Wmk. 373

471	CD333	12c Arms	.20	.20
472	CD333	40c Diana	.65	.65
473	CD333	50c Wedding	.90	.90
474	CD333	$1 Portrait	1.75	1.75
		Nos. 471-474 (4)	3.50	3.50

A76

1982, Oct. 11   Litho.   Perf. 14

475	A76	25c Running	.40	.40
476	A76	25c Boxing	.40	.40

Souvenir Sheet

477		Sheet of 3, #475-476, 477a	2.50	2.50
a.	A76	$1 Britannia facing left	1.50	1.50

12th Commonwealth Games, Brisbane, Australia, Sept. 30-Oct. 9.

1982, Oct. 11

478	A76	12c Royal couple	.25	.25
479	A76	12c Flags	.25	.25

Souvenir Sheet

480		Sheet of 3, #478-479, 480a	2.50	2.50
a.	A76	$1 Britannia facing right	1.50	1.50

Visit of Queen Elizabeth II and Prince Philip.

Scouting
Year
A78

Designs: Nos. 481, 485, Scout patroller. Nos. 482, 486, Brigade bugler. Nos. 483, 487, Baden-Powell. Nos. 484, 488, William Smith.

1982, Nov. 30

481	A78	12c dark blue & multi	.25	.25
482	A78	12c brown & multi	.25	.25
483	A78	25c dark blue & multi	.30	.30
484	A78	25c brown & multi	.30	.30
485	A78	35c green & multi	.30	.30
486	A78	35c red & multi	.30	.30
487	A78	50c green & multi	.50	.50
488	A78	50c red & multi	.50	.50
		Nos. 481-488 (8)	2.70	2.70

Turtles
A79

1983, Jan. 5   Perf. 14

489	A79	18c Leatherback	.30	.30
490	A79	35c Loggerhead	.55	.55
491	A79	45c Pacific Ridley	.70	.70
492	A79	50c Green	.80	.80
		Nos. 489-492 (4)	2.35	2.35

Commonwealth Day — A80

1983, Mar. 14

493	A80	12c Oliva vidum, conus generalis, murex tribulus	.20	.20
494	A80	35c Romu, kurila, kakadu, money belt	.55	.55
495	A80	45c Shells, bride necklaces	.70	.70
496	A80	50c Trochus niloticus, natural, polished	.75	.75
		Nos. 493-496 (4)	2.20	2.20

Manned Flight Bicentenary — A81

Wmk. 373

1983, June 30   Litho.   Perf. 14

497	A81	30c Montgolfiere, 1783	.40	.40
498	A81	35c Lockheed Hercules	.45	.45
499	A81	40c Wright Brothers' Flyer III, 1905	.50	.50
500	A81	45c Columbia space shuttle	.55	.55
501	A81	50c Beechcraft Baron-Solair	.65	.65
		Nos. 497-501 (5)	2.55	2.55

Christmas 1983 — A82

1983, Aug. 25

502	A82	12c Weto dance	.20	.20
503	A82	15c Custom wrestling	.20	.20
504	A82	18c Girl dancers	.25	.25
505	A82	20c Devil dancers	.30	.30
506	A82	25c Bamboo band	.35	.35
507	A82	35c Gilbertese dancers	.50	.50
508	A82	40c Pan pipers	.60	.60
509	A82	45c Afufu girl dancers	.65	.65
510	A82	50c Cross, flowers	.75	.75
a.		Souvenir sheet of 9, #502-510	3.75	3.75
		Nos. 502-510 (9)	3.80	3.80

Stamps in #510a do not have "Christmas 1983."
For overprints see Nos. 519-520.

World Communications Year — A83

Wmk. 373

1983, Dec. 19   Litho.   Perf. 14

511	A83	12c Telephone Exchange building	.20	.20
512	A83	18c Ham radio operator	.20	.20
513	A83	25c No. 11	.35	.35
514	A83	$1 No. 14	1.25	1.25
a.		Souvenir sheet of 1	1.50	1.50
		Nos. 511-514 (4)	2.00	2.00

No. 514a is inscribed "1908-1983." See No. 525 for sheet inscribed "1907-1984."

Local
Fungi — A84

1984, Jan. 30   Perf. 13½

515	A84	6c Calvatia gardneri	.20	.20
516	A84	18c Marasmiellus inoderma	.25	.25
517	A84	35c Pycnoporus sanguineus	.50	.50
518	A84	$2 Filoboletus manipularis	2.75	2.75
		Nos. 515-518 (4)	3.70	3.70

Type of No. 510 overprinted "VISIT OF POPE JOHN PAUL II May 9th, 1984"

1984, Apr. 16   Wmk. 373

519	A82	12c multicolored	.20	.20
520	A82	50c multicolored	.70	.70

Lloyd's List Issue
Common Design Type

1984, Apr. 21   Litho.   Perf. 14½x14

521	CD335	12c Olivebank, 1892	.20	.20
522	CD335	15c Tinhow, 1906	.20	.20
523	CD335	18c Oriana, Point Cruz	.25	.25
524	CD335	$1 Point Cruz view	1.40	1.40
		Nos. 521-524 (4)	2.05	2.05

WCY Type of 1983
Souvenir Sheet
Wmk. 373

1984, June 18   Litho.   Perf. 14

525	A83	$1 multicolored	1.40	1.40

UPU Congress. No. 514a is inscribed "1908-1983," No. 525 inscribed "1907-1984."

Asia-Pacific Broadcasting Union, 20th
Anniv. — A86

1984, July 2   Perf. 13½

526	A86	12c Village drums	.20	.20
527	A86	45c Radio City Guadalcanal	.60	.60
528	A86	60c Broadcasting studio	.80	.80
529	A86	$1 Broadcasting station	1.40	1.40
		Nos. 526-529 (4)	3.00	3.00

1984 Summer Olympics — A87

Perf. 13½x14

1984, Aug. 4   Litho.   Wmk. 373

530	A87	12c Flag, vert.	.20	.20
531	A87	25c Lawson Tama Stadium, Honiara	.45	.45
532	A87	50c Honiara Community Center	.85	.85
a.		Booklet pane, 2 ea #531-532	2.75	
533	A87	$1 Olympic Stadium	1.75	1.75
		Nos. 530-533 (4)	3.25	3.25

Souvenir Sheet

534	A87	95c Bronte Baths	4.50	4.50

Solomon Islds. first olympic participation. No. 534 available in booklet only. Margin shows swimmer A. Wickham (1886-1976).

Little Pied
Cormorant
(Ausipex '84)
A88

Wmk. 373

1984, Sept. 21   Litho.   Perf. 14½

535	A88	12c shown	.25	.25
536	A88	18c Australian grey duck	.35	.35
537	A88	35c Nankeen night-heron	.65	.65
538	A88	$1 Dollarbird	1.75	1.75
a.		Souvenir sheet of 4, #535-538	3.50	3.50
		Nos. 535-538 (4)	3.00	3.00

EXPO
'85,
Tsukuba,
Japan
A89

Designs: 12c, Japanese Memorial Shrine, Mt. Austen, Guadalcanal. 25c, Digital telephone exchange equipment. 45c, Soltai No. 7 fishing vessel. 85c, Coastal village.

Wmk. 373

1985, June 28   Litho.   Perf. 14

539	A89	12c multicolored	.20	.20
540	A89	25c multicolored	.35	.35
541	A89	45c multicolored	.60	.60
542	A89	85c multicolored	1.10	1.10
		Nos. 539-542 (4)	2.25	2.25

Queen Mother 85th Birthday
Common Design Type
Perf. 14½x14

1985, June 7   Litho.   Wmk. 384

543	CD336	12c VE Day, 1945	.20	.20
544	CD336	25c With Margaret	.30	.30
545	CD336	35c St. Patrick's Day celebration	.40	.40
546	CD336	$1 Holding Prince Henry	1.25	1.25
		Nos. 543-546 (4)	2.15	2.15

Souvenir Sheet

547	CD336	$1.50 In a gondola, Venice	2.00	2.00

For surcharge see No. B2.

Christmas — A90

1985, Aug. 30   Wmk. 373   Perf. 14½

548	A90	12c Titiana Village	.20	.20
549	A90	25c Sigana, Santa Isabel	.35	.35
550	A90	35c Artificial Island, Langa Lagoon	.45	.45
		Nos. 548-550 (3)	1.00	1.00

Intl. Youth Year — A91

12c, Girl Guide activities. 15c, Stop Polio Campaign. 25c, Relay runners, views of the islands. 35c, Relay runners, views of Australia. 45c, Saluting natl. flag, badges.

1985, Sept. 30			Perf. 14	
551	A91	12c multicolored	.55	.20
552	A91	15c multicolored	.60	.35
553	A91	25c multicolored	.80	.60
554	A91	35c multicolored	1.00	.70
555	A91	45c multicolored	1.10	.80
		Nos. 551-555 (5)	4.05	2.65

Girl Guides 75th anniv., 12c, 45c; IYY, others.

Souvenir Sheet

Audubon Birth Bicent. — A92

Bird illustration by Audubon.

1985, Nov. 25			Wmk. 384	
556	A92	Sheet of 3, 45c, 2 50c	6.50	6.50
a.		Portrait	1.75	1.75
b.		Osprey	2.25	2.25

Souvenir Sheet

Mini Hydro-Electric Project, Iriri Village — A93

Designs: 30c, Water-driven generator. 60c, Illuminated village house.

1986, Jan. 24			Perf. 14	
557	A93	Sheet of 2	3.00	3.00
a.		30c multicolored	1.00	1.00
b.		60c multicolored	1.75	1.75

Halley's Comet A94

Operation Raleigh, 1986: 18c, Construction of Red Cross Center, Gizo. 30c, Exploring rain forest. 60c, Observing Halley's Comet. $1, Ships Sir Walter Raleigh and Zebu.

Perf. 14½x14

1986, Mar. 27			Wmk. 373	
558	A94	18c multicolored	.70	.20
559	A94	30c multicolored	1.40	.40
560	A94	60c multicolored	2.00	1.25
561	A94	$1 multicolored	2.50	1.50
		Nos. 558-561 (4)	6.60	3.35

Queen Elizabeth II 60th Birthday
Common Design Type

Designs: 5c, Visiting Clydebank Town Hall with Prince Philip, 1947. 18c, At Queen Mother's 80th birthday, St. Paul's Cathedral, 1980. 22c, Walking among children of the islands, Pacific tour, 1982. 55c, 50th birthday, Windsor Castle, 1976. $2, Visiting Crown Agents' offices, 1983.

1986, Apr. 21		Wmk. 384	Perf. 14½	
562	CD337	5c scarlet, blk & sil	.20	.20
563	CD337	18c ultra & multi	.20	.20
564	CD337	22c green & multi	.20	.20
565	CD337	55c violet & multi	.50	.50
566	CD337	$2 rose vio & multi	1.90	1.90
		Nos. 562-566 (5)	3.00	3.00

Royal Wedding Issue, 1986
Common Design Type

Designs: 55c, Informal portrait. 60c, Andrew aboard royal navy vessel.

Wmk. 384

1986, July 23		Litho.	Perf. 14	
567	CD338	55c multicolored	.50	.50
568	CD338	60c multicolored	.60	.60

Souvenir Sheet

AMERIPEX '86 — A95

55c, US Memorial, Henderson Field, Guadalcanal. $1.65, Peace Corps emblem, Statue of Liberty, Pres. John F. Kennedy.

1986, May 22		Litho.	Perf. 13½	
569	A95	Sheet of 2	2.50	2.50
a.		55c multicolored	.60	.60
b.		$1.65 multicolored	1.75	1.75

Intl. Peace Year, Peace Corps 25th anniv. For surcharge see No. B3.

1987 America's Cup — A96

Previous winners, challengers, maps and club emblems: No. 570a, America, US, 1851. b, Magic, US, 1870. c, Madeleine, US, 1876. d, Mischief, US, 1881. e, Columbia, US, 1871. f, British Cup course, 1851. g, America II, US, 1987. h, America's Cup. i, Heart of America, US, 1987. j, French Kiss, France, 1987.
No. 571a, Puritan, US, 1885. b, Mayflower, US, 1886. c, Defender, US, 1895. d, Vigilant, US, 1893. e, Volunteer, US, 1887. f, America Cup course, Newport, 1930-1962. g, South Australia, Australia, 1987. h, KA14, Australia, 1987. i, New Zealand II, New Zealand, 1987. j, St. Francis IX, US, 1987.
No. 572a, Columbia, US, 1899. b, Columbia, US, 1901. c, Enterprise, US, 1930. d, Resolute, US, 1920. e, Reliance, US, 1903. f, America Cup course, 1964-1983. g, Kookaburra, Australia, 1987. h, Eagle, US, 1987. i, True North, Canada, 1987. j, Italia, Italy, 1987.
No. 573a, Rainbow, US, 1934. b, Ranger, US, 1937. c, Constellation, US, 1964. d, Weatherly, US, 1962. e, Columbia, US, 1958. f, Western Australia Cup course, 1987. g, Secret Cove, syndicate, 1987. h, Courageous III, US, 1987. i, France, France, 1987. j, Azzurra, Italy, 1987.

No. 574a, Intrepid, US, 1967. b, Intrepid, US, 1970. c, Freedom, US, 1980. d, Courageous, US, 1974. e, Courageous, US, 1977. f, Courageous, US, 1974. f, Australia II, Australia, 1983. g, Crusader, Great Britain, 1987. h, Sail America, US, 1987. i, Australia III, Australia, 1987. j, Royal Perth Yacht Club/America's Cup '87 emblem, 1987.

1986, Aug. 22		Litho.	Perf. 14½	
570		Strip of 10 + label	4.50	4.50
a.-d.	A96	18c any single	.20	.20
e.-f.	A96	30c any single	.25	.25
g.-j.	A96	$1 any single	.85	.85
571		Strip of 10 + label	4.50	4.50
a.-d.	A96	18c any single	.20	.20
e.-f.	A96	30c any single	.25	.25
g.-j.	A96	$1 any single	.85	.85
572		Strip of 10 + label	4.50	4.50
a.-d.	A96	18c any single	.20	.20
e.-f.	A96	30c any single	.25	.25
g.-j.	A96	$1 any single	.85	.85
573		Strip of 10 + label	4.50	4.50
a.-d.	A96	18c any single	.20	.20
e.-f.	A96	30c any single	.25	.25
g.-j.	A96	$1 any single	.85	.85
574		Strip of 10 + label	4.50	4.50
a.-d.	A96	18c any single	.20	.20
e.-f.	A96	30c any single	.25	.25
g.-j.	A96	$1 any single	.85	.85
		Nos. 570-574 (5)	22.50	22.50

Nos. 570-574 printed se-tenant with center labels picturing natl. arms, 1987 America's Cup emblem and trophy in sheets of 50.

Souvenir Sheet

1987, Feb. 4		Litho.	Perf. 14½	
575	A96	$5 Stars and Stripes, US, victor	5.25	5.25

Coral — A97

1987, Feb. 11		Litho.	Wmk. 384	
576	A97	18c Dendrophyllia gracilis	.50	.20
577	A97	45c Dendronephthya	.95	.50
578	A97	60c Clavularia	1.25	1.25
579	A97	$1.50 Melithaea squamata	2.75	2.75
		Nos. 576-579 (4)	5.45	4.70

Flowering Plants — A98

1987-88				
580	A98	1c Cassia fistula	.20	.20
581	A98	5c Allamanda cathartica	.20	.20
582	A98	10c Catharanthus roseus	.20	.20
583	A98	18c Mimosa pudica	.20	.20
584	A98	20c Hibiscus rosa-sinensis	.20	.20
585	A98	22c Clerodendrum thomsonae	.25	.25
586	A98	25c Bauhinia variegata	.30	.30
587	A98	28c Gloriosa rothschildiana	.30	.30
588	A98	30c Heliconia solomonensis	.35	.35
589	A98	40c Episcia hybrid	.45	.45
590	A98	45c Bougainvillea hybrid	.50	.50
591	A98	50c Alpinia purpurata	.60	.60
592	A98	55c Plumeria rubra	.60	.60
593	A98	60c Acacia farnesiana	.70	.70
594	A98	$1 Ipomea purpurea	1.10	1.10
595	A98	$2 Dianella ensifolia	2.25	2.25
596	A98	$5 Passiflora foetida	5.75	5.75
596A	A98	$10 Hemigraphis specie ('88)	9.00	9.00
		Nos. 580-596A (18)	23.15	23.15

Issue dates: $10, Mar. 1; others, May 12.

Mangrove Kingfisher — A99   Orchids — A100

Designs: a, Perched on root. b, Diving. c, Landing in water. d, Emerging with fish.

Perf. 14x14½

1987, July 15			Wmk. 373	
597		Strip of 4	11.00	11.00
a.-d.	A99	60c any single	2.50	2.50

No. 597 has a continuous design.

Perf. 13½x13

1987, Sept. 23			Wmk. 384	
598	A100	18c Dendrobium conanthum	1.00	.30
599	A100	30c Spathoglottis plicata	1.75	.35
600	A100	55c Dendrobium gouldii	2.10	.75
601	A100	$1.50 Dendrobium goldfinchii	4.50	3.75
		Nos. 598-601 (4)	9.35	5.15

Christmas 1987.

Transportation and Communications Decade — A101

Designs: 18c, Telecommunications link. 30c, Express mail service. 60c, Guadalcanal Road Improvement Project. $2, Beechcraft Queen Air, Henderson Airfield control tower.

Perf. 14x13½

1987, Oct. 31		Litho.	Unwmk.	
602	A101	18c multicolored	.25	.20
603	A101	30c multicolored	.60	.30
604	A101	60c multicolored	.65	.65
605	A101	$2 multicolored	2.75	2.75
		Nos. 602-605 (4)	4.25	3.90

Queen Victoria's Birdwing Butterfly — A102

Designs: No. 606a, Male. No. 606b, Larva. No. 606c, Pupa. No. 606d, Female.

1987, Nov. 25	Wmk. 384	Perf. 14½		
606		Strip of 4	15.00	15.00
a.-d.	A102	45c any single	3.25	3.25

Intl. Fund for Agricultural Development (IFAD), 10th Anniv. — A103

Natl. colors and: No. 607, Student, Natl. Agricultural Training Institute (NATI) farm and emblem (left stamp). No. 608, Students in working in NATI field and emblem (right stamp). No. 609, Flatbed truck transporting produce and emblem (left stamp). No. 610, Canoes, seagulls and emblem (right stamp).

Wmk. 384

1988, Feb. 12		Litho.		**Perf. 14½**
607		50c multicolored	.80	.80
608	120	61 multicolored	.80	.80
a.		A103 Pair, #607-608	1.60	1.60
609		$1 multicolored	1.00	1.00
610		$1 multicolored	1.00	1.00
a.		A103 Pair, #609-610	2.00	2.00
		Nos. 607-610 (4)	3.60	3.60

EXPO '88, Brisbane, Apr. 30-Oct. 30 — A104

Designs: 22c, Yacht in dry dock. 80c, Canoe. $1.50, Huts.

Perf. 13½x14

1988, Apr. 30				**Unwmk.**
611	A104	22c multicolored	.20	.20
612	A104	80c multicolored	.80	.80
613	A104	$1.50 multicolored	1.50	1.50
a.		Souv. sheet of 3, #611-613	2.50	2.50
b.		As "a," surcharged $3.50 in margin ('90)	12.00	12.00
		Nos. 611-613 (3)	2.50	2.50

National Independence, 10th Anniv. — A105

Perf. 13x13½

1988, July 7		Litho.		**Wmk. 373**
614	A105	22c *Capitana* in Estrella Bay	.90	.20
615	A105	55c Flag raising, 1893	1.10	.55
616	A105	80c Supreme Court	1.40	1.00
617	A105	$1 Traditional celebration	1.60	1.60
		Nos. 614-617 (4)	5.00	3.35

Australia Bicentennial — A106

Ships: 35c, M.V. *Papuan Chief.* 60c, M.V. *Nimos.* 70c, S.S. *Malaita.* $1.30, S.S. *Makambo.*

1988, July 30		**Wmk. 384**		**Perf. 14**
618	A106	35c multicolored	.85	.30
619	A106	60c multicolored	1.25	.45
620	A106	70c multicolored	1.40	.65
621	A106	$1.30 multicolored	1.50	1.50
a.		Souvenir sheet of 4, #618-621	3.75	3.75
		Nos. 618-621 (4)	5.00	2.90

A107   Orchids — A108

Wmk. 384

1988, Aug. 5		Litho.		**Perf. 14½**
622	A107	22c Archery	.65	.20
623	A107	55c Weight lifting	.90	.55
624	A107	70c Running	1.00	.70
625	A107	80c Boxing	1.25	.80
		Nos. 622-625 (4)	3.80	2.25

Souvenir Sheet
Wmk. 373

626	A107	$2 Olympic Stadium, horiz.	3.00	3.00

1988 Summer Olympics, Seoul.

Lloyds of London, 300th Anniv.
Common Design Type

Designs: 22c, King George V and Queen Mary at Lloyd's ground-breaking ceremony, 1925. 50c, *Forthbank,* horiz. 65c, Soltel Satellite Ground Station, horiz. $2, *Empress of China.*

1988, Oct. 31				**Perf. 14**
627	CD341	22c multicolored	.35	.20
628	CD341	50c multicolored	1.25	.40
629	CD341	65c multicolored	1.40	.60
630	CD341	$2 multicolored	3.25	2.00
		Nos. 627-630 (4)	6.25	3.20

Perf. 13½x13

1989, Jan. 20		Litho.		**Wmk. 373**
631	A108	22c *Bulbophyllum dennisii*	1.10	.25
632	A108	35c *Calanthe langei*	1.40	.50
633	A108	55c *Bulbophyllum blumei*	1.75	1.10
634	A108	$2 *Grammatophyllum speciosum*	3.50	3.50
		Nos. 631-634 (4)	7.75	5.35

Intl. Red Cross, 125th Anniv. — A109

Perf. 14x14½

1989, May 16				**Wmk. 384**
635		35c Disabled children	.50	.50
636		35c Children's Center minibus	.50	.50
a.		A109 Pair, #635-636	1.00	1.00
637		$1.50 Patient abed	1.75	1.75
638		$1.50 Physical therapy	1.75	1.75
a.		A109 Pair, #637-638	3.50	3.50
		Nos. 635-638 (4)	4.50	4.50

Sea Slugs A110

1989, June 30		**Wmk. 373**		**Perf. 14½**
639	A110	22c *Phyllidia varicosa*	.95	.25
640	A110	70c *Chromodoris bullocki*	2.40	1.50
641	A110	80c *Chromodoris leopardus*	2.40	1.60
642	A110	$1.50 *Phidiana indica*	3.00	3.00
		Nos. 639-642 (4)	8.75	6.35

Moon Landing, 20th Anniv.
Common Design Type

Apollo 16: 22c, Splashdown. 35c, Launch. 70c, Mission emblem. 80c, Ultraviolet color enhancement of Earth. $4, The Moon, as photographed during the *Apollo 11* mission.

1989, July 20		**Wmk. 384**		**Perf. 14**
Size of Nos. 644-645: 29x29mm				
643	CD342	22c multicolored	.60	.25
644	CD342	35c multicolored	.95	.50
645	CD342	70c multicolored	1.75	1.75
646	CD342	80c multicolored	1.90	1.90
		Nos. 643-646 (4)	5.20	4.40

Souvenir Sheet

647	CD342	$4 multicolored	5.00	5.00

Blowing Soap Bubbles A111

Children's games.

1989, Nov. 17				**Wmk. 384**
648	A111	5c Five stones catch, vert.	.20	.30
649	A111	67c shown	1.60	1.60
650	A111	73c Coconut shell empire	1.60	1.60
651	A111	$1 Seed wind sound, vert.	2.25	2.25
		Nos. 648-651 (4)	5.65	5.75

Souvenir Sheet
Wmk. 373

652	A111	$3 Baseball, softball, vert.	7.00	7.00

World Stamp Expo '89.

Christmas — A112

1989, Nov. 30				**Wmk. 384**
653	A112	18c Butterfly, fishermen	.50	.25
654	A112	25c Nativity	.70	.30
655	A112	45c Hospital ward	1.25	.45
656	A112	$1.50 Tug of war	3.00	3.00
		Nos. 653-656 (4)	5.45	4.00

Personal Ornaments A113

1990, Feb. 14		Litho.		**Wmk. 373**
657	A113	5c shown	.30	.40
658	A113	12c Necklace	.45	.30
659	A113	18c Islander, diff.	.50	.30
660	A113	$2 Head ornament	4.75	4.75
		Nos. 657-660 (4)	6.00	5.75

Cowrie Shells A114

1990, July 23				
666	A114	4c Spindle cowrie	.35	.50
667	A114	20c Map cowrie	.90	.35
668	A114	35c Sieve cowrie	1.25	.40
669	A114	50c Egg cowrie	1.75	1.75
670	A114	$1 Prince cowrie	2.75	2.75
		Nos. 666-670 (5)	7.00	5.75

Queen Mother, 90th Birthday
Common Design Types

25c, Queen Mother, 1987. $5, Inspecting damage to Buckingham Palace, 1940.

1990, Aug. 4		**Wmk. 384**		**Perf. 14x15**
671	CD343	25c multicolored	.75	.25
				Perf. 14½
672	CD344	$5 brown & blk	4.75	5.25

First Postage Stamp, 150th Anniv. A115

Designs: 35c, Postman, mail van. 45c, Solomon Islands Post Office. 50c, Solomon Islands No. 1. 55c, Young philatelist. 60c, Solomon Islands No. 20, Penny Black.

1990, Oct. 15		**Wmk. 373**		**Perf. 14**
673	A115	35c multicolored	.90	.45
674	A115	45c multicolored	1.00	.50
675	A115	50c multicolored	1.10	1.10
676	A115	55c multicolored	1.40	1.40
677	A115	60c multicolored	1.50	1.50
		Nos. 673-677 (5)	5.90	4.95

Birds A116

1990, Dec. 5				
678	A116	10c Purple swamphen	.75	.75
679	A116	25c Rufous brown pheasant dove	1.10	.50
680	A116	30c Superb fruit dove	1.40	.50
681	A116	45c Cardinal honey-eater	1.60	.70
682	A116	$2 Pigmy parrot	2.50	2.50
		Nos. 678-682 (5)	7.35	4.95

Birdpex '90, 20th Intl. Ornithological Congress, New Zealand.

Crop Pests — A117

				Perf. 14x13½
1991, Jan. 16		Litho.		**Wmk. 373**
683	A117	7c Sweet potato weevil	.50	.40
684	A117	25c Melon fly	.80	.30
685	A117	40c Taro beetle	1.10	.50
686	A117	90c Cocoa weevil borer	1.90	1.90
687	A117	$1.50 Rhinoceros beetle	2.10	2.10
		Nos. 683-687 (5)	6.40	5.20

Elizabeth & Philip, Birthdays
Common Design Types
Wmk. 384

1991, June 17		Litho.		**Perf. 14½**
688	CD346	90c multicolored	1.40	1.40
689	CD345	$2 multicolored	3.00	3.00
a.		Pair, #688-689 + label	4.50	4.50

No. 689a exists with two different labels.

Nutritional Foods — A118

1991, June 24		**Wmk. 373**		**Perf. 14**
690	A118	5c Coconut water	.20	.30
691	A118	25c Feed your child	1.25	1.25
692	A118	80c Mother's milk	1.50	1.50
693	A118	90c Local food	1.60	1.60
		Nos. 690-693 (4)	4.55	4.65

9th South Pacific Games — A119

Wmk. 384

1991, Aug. 8		Litho.		**Perf. 14**
694	A119	25c Volleyball	.60	.30
695	A119	40c Judo	.90	.60
696	A119	65c Squash	1.40	1.40
697	A119	90c Lawn bowling	1.90	1.90
		Nos. 694-697 (4)	4.80	4.20

Souvenir Sheet

698	A119	$2 Games emblem	4.00	4.00

Christmas — A120

Wmk. 373

				Perf. 14
1991, Oct. 28		**Litho.**		
699	A120	10c Food preparation	.30	.20
700	A120	25c Church service	.60	.20
701	A120	65c Feast	1.50	.90
702	A120	$2 Cricket match	3.50	3.50
a.		Souvenir sheet of 4, #699-702	7.00	7.00
		Nos. 699-702 (4)	5.90	4.80

Phila Nippon
'91 — A121

Tuna fishing: 5c, Yellowfin tuna. 30c, Boat for pole and line tuna fishing. 80c, Pole and line tuna fishing. $2, Arabushi processing. No. 707a, Food made from tuna, tori nanban. b, Aka miso soup.

Wmk. 384

				Perf. 14
1991, Nov. 16		**Litho.**		
703	A121	5c multicolored	.20	.20
704	A121	30c multicolored	.75	.45
705	A121	80c multicolored	1.25	1.25
706	A121	$2 multicolored	3.00	3.00
		Nos. 703-706 (4)	5.20	4.90

Souvenir Sheet

707	A121	80c Sheet of 2, #a.-b.	2.75	2.75

No. 707 contains two 28x45mm stamps.

Queen Elizabeth II's Accession to the Throne, 40th Anniv.
Common Design Type
Wmk. 384 (5c, 60c), 373

				Perf. 14
1992, Feb. 6		**Litho.**		
708	CD349	5c multicolored	.30	.40
709	CD349	20c multicolored	.60	.20
710	CD349	40c multicolored	.85	.30
711	CD349	60c multicolored	.90	.90
712	CD349	$5 multicolored	3.75	3.75
		Nos. 708-712 (5)	6.40	5.55

Alvaro Mendana de Niera (1541-1595), Discoveries in the Solomon Islands — A122

Granada '92: 10c, Thousand Ships Bay. 65c, Route to the Solomon Islands. 80c, Alvaro Mendana de Niera. $1, Graciosa Bay settlement. $5, Sailing ships.

Perf. 15x14½

				Wmk. 373
1992, Apr. 24		**Litho.**		
713	A122	10c multicolored	.40	.20
714	A122	65c multicolored	.95	.60
715	A122	80c multicolored	1.25	1.25
716	A122	$1 multicolored	1.60	1.60
717	A122	$5 multicolored	4.00	4.00
		Nos. 713-717 (5)	8.20	7.65

A123

A124

Perf. 14x13½

				Wmk. 373
1992, May 3		**Litho.**		
718	A123	25c Early portrait	.60	.35
719	A123	70c Wearing USMC fatigues	1.25	1.25
720	A123	90c Wearing uniform, cap	1.25	1.25
a.		Booklet pane, 2 ea #718, 720	3.75	
721	A123	$2 Statue	1.50	1.50
a.		Booklet pane, 2 ea #719, 721	5.50	
		Nos. 718-721 (4)	4.60	4.35

Souvenir Sheet

722	A123	$4 In dress uniform	6.50	6.50
a.		Booklet pane of 1	6.50	

Sergeant Major Jacob Vouza (1891-1984). One margin of Nos. 720a, 721a, and 722a is rouletted 8.

1992, May 22

World Columbian Stamp Expo '92, Chicago: 25c, Solomon Airlines domestic routes. 80c, Boeing 737-400 airplanes. $1.50, Solomon Airlines international routes. $5, Columbus and Santa Maria.

723	A124	25c multicolored	.70	.20
724	A124	80c multicolored	1.60	1.25
725	A124	$1.50 multicolored	2.25	2.25
726	A124	$5 multicolored	5.50	5.50
a.		Souvenir sheet of 4, #723-726	10.50	10.50
b.		As "a," ovptd. with Taipei '93 emblem in sheet margin	6.75	6.75
		Nos. 723-726 (4)	10.05	9.20

No. 726b issued Aug. 14, 1993.

Miniature Sheets

Battle of Guadalcanal, 50th Anniv. A125

Scenes from battle of Guadalcanal: No. 727a, Japanese landing at Esperance. b, US landings. c, Australian Navy cruiser. d, US Navy post office. e, Royal New Zealand Air Force PBY Catalina.

No. 728a, US Marine Wildcat fighters. b, Henderson Field under construction and attack. c, Heavy cruiser USS Quincy. d, Australian Navy heavy cruiser Canberra. e, US Marines land on Guadalcanal. f, Japanese aircraft carrier Ryujo. g, Japanese Zeke fighters attack US positions. h, Japanese bombers attack American beachhead. i, Japanese destroyers of Tokyo Express. j, Japanese heavy cruiser Chokai.

Wmk. 384

				Perf. 14
1992, Aug. 7		**Litho.**		
727	A125	30c Sheet of 5, #a.-e.	5.00	5.00
728	A125	80c Sheet of 10, #a.-j.	13.50	13.50

See No. 889.

Orchids A126

Perf. 14½x14

				Wmk. 373
1992, Dec. 14		**Litho.**		
729	A126	15c Dendrobium hybrid	.65	.25
730	A126	70c Vanda "Amy Laycock"	1.25	1.00
731	A126	95c Dendrobium mirbelianum	1.60	1.60
732	A126	$2.50 Dendrobium macrophyllum	2.50	2.50
		Nos. 729-732 (4)	6.00	5.35

See Nos. 752-755.

Crabs
A127

Wmk. 373

				Perf. 13
1993, Jan. 15		**Litho.**		
733	A127	5c Stalk-eyed ghost	.20	.20
734	A127	10c Red-spotted	.20	.20
735	A127	25c Flat	.20	.20
736	A127	30c Land hermit	.20	.20
737	A127	40c Grapsid	.25	.25
738	A127	45c Red & white painted	.25	.25
739	A127	55c Swift-footed	.30	.30
740	A127	60c Spanner	.35	.35
741	A127	70c Red hermit	.45	.45
742	A127	80c Red-eyed	.50	.50
743	A127	90c Rathbun red	.55	.55
744	A127	$1 Coconut	.60	.60
745	A127	$1.10 Red-spotted white	.65	.65
746	A127	$4 Ghost	2.25	2.25
a.		Souvenir sheet of 1, perf. 14	2.25	2.25
747	A127	$10 Mangrove fiddler	6.25	6.25
		Nos. 733-747 (15)	13.20	13.20

No. 746a for Hong Kong '97. Issued: #733-747, 1/15/93; #746a, 2/3/97.

World War II, 50th Anniv. A128

Designs: 30c, US War Memorial, Skyline Ridge. 80c, Country flags, Guadalcanal. 95c, Major General Alexander A. Vandegrift, map. $4, WWII Scouts, Gizo Islands.

Wmk. 373

				Perf. 14
1993, Apr. 19		**Litho.**		
748	A128	30c multicolored	.40	.25
749	A128	80c multicolored	1.10	1.10
750	A128	95c multicolored	1.25	1.25
751	A128	$4 multicolored	4.50	4.50
		Nos. 748-751 (4)	7.25	7.10

Orchid Type of 1992

Perf. 14½x14

				Wmk. 373
1993		**Litho.**		
752	A126	20c like #729	.40	.25
753	A126	85c like #730	1.10	1.10
754	A126	$1.15 like #731	1.40	1.40
755	A126	$3 like #732	4.00	4.00
		Nos. 752-755 (4)	6.90	6.75

Nos. 752, 755 are inscribed "World Orchid Conference." Nos. 753-754 are inscribed "Indopex '93 Exhibition."
Issued: #752, 755, 4/24; #753-754, 4/29.

Sinking of PT 109, 50th Anniv. A129

Designs: 30c, PT 109 about to be rammed. 50c, Native, Lt. John F. Kennedy. 95c, Message for help written on coconut, natives in canoe. $1.10, Kennedy, Navy and Marine Corps Medal. $5, PT 109.

Wmk. 373

				Perf. 13
1993, July 30		**Litho.**		
756	A129	30c multicolored	.50	.25
757	A129	50c multicolored	.60	.45
758	A129	95c multicolored	.80	.80
759	A129	$1.10 multicolored	1.10	1.10
		Nos. 756-759 (4)	3.00	2.60

Souvenir Sheet

Perf. 13x13½

760	A129	$5 multicolored	5.50	5.50

Nicobar Pigeon — A130

Wmk. 373

				Perf. 14
1993, Sept. 21		**Litho.**		
761	A130	30c shown	.30	.30
762	A130	50c One on ground	.50	.50
763	A130	65c Two on branches	.75	.70
764	A130	70c One on branch	1.00	1.00
765	A130	$1.10 One on berry branch	1.10	.90
766	A130	$3 Two in flight	2.50	2.50
		Nos. 761-766 (6)	6.15	5.90

World Wildlife Fund.

Dogs A131

Wmk. 373

				Perf. 14½
1994, Feb. 18		**Litho.**		
767	A131	30c Dachshund	.45	.25
768	A131	80c German shepherd	.90	.90
769	A131	95c Dobermann pinscher	1.10	1.10
770	A131	$1.10 Australian cattle dog	1.25	1.25
		Nos. 767-770 (4)	3.70	3.50

Souvenir Sheet

771	A131	$4 Boxer	6.50	6.50

Hong Kong '94.
No. 771 overprinted "19-25 Aug. Jakarta '95 Surcharge $2-00." was available only at the exhibition.

Dolphins A132

Wmk. 373

				Perf. 14
1994, May 9		**Litho.**		
772	A132	75c Striped	.85	.85
773	A132	85c Risso's	.95	.95
774	A132	$1.15 Common	1.25	1.25
775	A132	$2.50 Spinner	2.75	2.75
776	A132	$3 Bottlenose	3.00	3.00
		Nos. 772-776 (5)	8.80	8.80

Miniature Sheet

Butterflies A133

Designs: a, Vindula sapor. b, Papilio aegeus. c, Graphium hicetaon. d, Graphium mendana. e, PHILAKOREA '94 emblem. f, Graphium meeki. g, Danaus schenkii. h, Papilio ptolychus. i, Phaedyma fissizonata.

Wmk. 373

			Perf. 13½
1994, Aug. 16	**Litho.**		
777	A133	70c Sheet of 9, #a.-i.	5.50	5.50

For overprint see No. 842.

Intl. Year of the Family — A134

Designs: a, Girl writing letter in Brisbane, Australia, family reading letter on Santa Isabel, Solomon Islands. b, Boeing 737-400, Brisbane Intl. Airport, Australia. c, Boeing 737-400, Henderson Airfield, Guadalcanal, DHC 6-Twin Otter. d, Fera Airfield, Buala, Santa Isabel. e, Family.

1994, Aug. 18   *Perf. 13*
778 A134 $1.10 Strip of 5, #a.-e.   5.00 5.00
   f.   Sheet of 1, #778   5.00 5.00

Volcanoes of the Solomon Islands A135

Designs: 30c, Cook Island Volcano erupting under sea, 1967. 70c, Kavachi Volcano erupting from sea, 1977. 80c, Kavachi Volcano forming temporary island, 1978. 90c, Tinakulu Volcano, permanent island.
No. 783: a, Map of Solomon Island volcanoes. b, Diagram illustrating formation of volcanic island archipelago.

Wmk. 373
1994, Oct. 24   **Litho.**   *Perf. 14*
779 A135 30c multicolored   .40 .40
780 A135 70c multicolored   .70 .70
781 A135 80c multicolored   .80 .80
782 A135 90c multicolored   1.10 1.10
   Nos. 779-782 (4)   3.00 3.00
Souvenir Sheet
783 A135 $2 Sheet of 2, #a.-b.   3.50 3.50

La Perouse Expedition, 210th Anniv. A136

Designs: 30c, La Perouse, King Louis XVI. 80c, Map of Ile de La Perouse. 95c, L'Astrolabe. $1.10, La Boussole. $3, L'Astrolabe foundering on reef.

Wmk. 384
1994, Dec. 16   **Litho.**   *Perf. 14*
784 A136 30c multicolored   .50 .20
785 A136 80c multicolored   1.00 1.00
786 A136 95c multicolored   1.10 1.10
787 A136 $1.10 multicolored   1.25 1.25
788 A136 $3 multicolored   2.50 2.50
   Nos. 784-788 (5)   6.35 6.05

Visit South Pacific Year A137

30c, Tourists watching traditional dance, land hermit crab. 50c, Dendrobium rennellii, milkweed butterfly. 95c, Diver, moorish idol, fish. $1.15, Boats at shore, grapsid crab. $4, Flower, yellow-bibbed lorry.

Perf. 15x14½
1995, Feb. 17   **Litho.**   **Wmk. 373**
789 A137 30c multicolored   .25 .25
790 A137 50c multicolored   .65 .65
791 A137 95c multicolored   .75 .75
792 A137 $1.15 multicolored   .85 .85
   Nos. 789-792 (4)   2.50 2.50
Souvenir Sheet
793 A137 $4 multicolored   3.75 3.75

FAO, 50th Anniv. A138

1995, Apr. 5   *Perf. 12*
794 A138 70c Banana   .70 .70
795 A138 75c Paw paw   .70 .70
796 A138 95c Pomelo   .85 .85
797 A138 $2 Star fruit   2.00 2.00
   Nos. 794-797 (4)   4.25 4.25
Souvenir Sheet
798 A138 $3 Mango   2.50 2.50

End of World War II, 50th Anniv.
Common Design Types

Admirals, aircraft carriers: 95c, Vice Adm. Chuichi Nagumo, Akagi. $1, Rear Adm. Frank J. Fletcher, USS Yorktown. $2, Vice Adm. Robert L. Ghormley, USS Wasp. $3, Vice Adm. William F. Halsey, USS Enterprise. $5, Reverse of War Medal 1939-45.

1995, May 8   *Perf. 13½*
799 CD351 95c multicolored   1.10 1.10
800 CD351 $1 multicolored   1.10 1.10
801 CD351 $2 multicolored   1.90 1.90
802 CD351 $3 multicolored   2.75 2.75
   Nos. 799-802 (4)   6.85 6.85
Souvenir Sheet
Perf. 14
803 CD352 $5 multicolored   3.75 3.75

Orchids — A139

Designs: 45c, Calanthe triplicata. 75c, Dendrobium mohlianum. 85c, Flickingeria comata. $1.15, Dendrobium spectabile. $4, Coelogyne asperata.

Wmk. 373
1995, Sept. 1   **Litho.**   *Perf. 14*
804 A139 45c multicolored   .75 .30
805 A139 75c multicolored   .95 .75
806 A139 85c multicolored   .95 .95
807 A139 $1.15 multicolored   1.25 1.25
   Nos. 804-807 (4)   3.90 3.25
Souvenir Sheet
808 A139 $4 multicolored   3.75 3.75
   Singapore '95 (#808).

Christmas — A140

Designs: 90c, Start of canoe race. $1.05, Pan pipers, Christmas tree. $1.25, Picnic on beach. $1.45, Local church, nativity.

1995, Nov. 6   *Perf. 13x13½*
810 A140 90c multicolored   .75 .75
811 A140 $1.05 multicolored   .80 .80
812 A140 $1.25 multicolored   .90 .90
813 A140 $1.45 multicolored   1.10 1.10
   Nos. 810-813 (4)   3.55 3.55

Guglielmo Marconi (1847-1937), Radio, Cent. — A141

Designs: $1.05, Demonstration, Salisbury Plain, 1896. $1.20, Birth of maritime radio,

---

1900. $1.35, First ground air transmitter, Croydon, 1920. $1.45, Marconi visiting Japan on world tour, 1933-34.

Perf. 14½x14
1996, Feb. 28   **Litho.**   **Wmk. 373**
814 A141 $1.05 multicolored   .65 .65
815 A141 $1.20 multicolored   .75 .75
816 A141 $1.35 multicolored   .85 .85
817 A141 $1.45 multicolored   .95 .95
   Nos. 814-817 (4)   3.20 3.20

Lories A142

1996, Apr. 10   **Litho.**   *Perf. 14*
818 A142 75c Palm lorikeet   .50 .50
819 A142 $1.05 Duchess lorikeet   .70 .70
820 A142 $1.20 Yellow-bibbed lory   .85 .85
821 A142 $1.35 Cardinal lory   .95 .95
822 A142 $1.45 Meek's lorikeet   1.00 1.00
   Nos. 818-822 (5)   4.00 4.00
Souvenir Sheet
823 A142 $3 Rainbow lorikeet   1.90 1.90

CAPEX '96 — A143

Island scenes: 40c, Dug-out canoe. 90c, Man, bicycle. $1.20, Mobile Post Office bus. $1.45, "Tulagi Express."
$4, "Tepuke," traditional canoe from Temotu Province.

Wmk. 384
1996, June 8   **Litho.**   *Perf. 13*
824 A143 40c multicolored   .25 .25
825 A143 90c multicolored   .50 .50
826 A143 $1.20 multicolored   .70 .70
827 A143 $1.45 multicolored   .80 .80
   Nos. 824-827 (4)   2.25 2.25
Souvenir Sheet
828 A143 $4 multicolored   2.25 2.25

1996 Summer Olympic Games, Atlanta — A144

Olympic posters: 90c, Tokyo, 1964. $1.20, Los Angeles, 1932. $1.35, Paris, 1924. $2.50, London, 1908.

Wmk. 384
1996, June 30   **Litho.**   *Perf. 14*
829 A144 90c multicolored   .55 .55
830 A144 $1.20 multicolored   .70 .70
831 A144 $1.35 multicolored   .75 .75
832 A144 $2.50 multicolored   1.50 1.50
   Nos. 829-832 (4)   3.50 3.50

First Christian Mission, 150th Anniv. — A145

Designs: 40c, Suiesi, Makira Bay, 1846-47. 65c, Original sketches by Rev. L. Verguet, 1846, Surimahe. $1.35, Bishop Epalle's grave, Isabel, 1845. $1.45, Makira Mission, Jean Claude Colin, Marist founder.

Wmk. 373
1996, Sept. 12   **Litho.**   *Perf. 14*
833 A145 40c multicolored   .20 .20
834 A145 65c multicolored   .35 .35
835 A145 $1.35 multicolored   .75 .75
836 A145 $1.45 multicolored   .80 .80
   Nos. 833-836 (4)   2.10 2.10
Souvenir Sheet

Taipei '96 — A146

Illustration reduced.

1996, Oct. 21
837 A146 $1.50 Sandford's eagle   .85 .85

UNICEF, 50th Anniv. A147

Wmk. 373
1996, Nov. 21   **Litho.**   *Perf. 14½*
838 A147 40c Food   .20 .20
839 A147 $1.05 Recreation   .60 .60
840 A147 $1.35 Medicine   .75 .75
841 A147 $2.50 Education   1.40 1.40
   Nos. 838-841 (4)   2.95 2.95

No. 777 Ovptd. in Red with SINGPEX '97 Emblem
Wmk. 373
1997, Feb. 21   **Litho.**   *Perf. 13½*
842 A133 70c Sheet of 9, #a.-i.   3.50 3.50

Overprint is centered over entire sheet with each stamp containing portion of SINGPEX '97 emblem.
Overprint exists in black from a limited printing.

Northern Common Cuscus A148

15c, In tree. 60c, Eating berries. $2.50, In tree, climbing right. $3, Two in branches.

Wmk. 373
1997, Apr. 21   **Litho.**   *Perf. 12*
843 A148 15c multicolored   .20 .20
844 A148 60c multicolored   .30 .30
845 A148 $2.50 multicolored   1.10 1.10
846 A148 $3 multicolored   1.40 1.40
   Nos. 843-846 (4)   3.00 3.00

Whales — A149

a, Whale, calf, vert. b, Whale breaching.

Wmk. 373

1997, May 29   **Litho.**   *Perf. 14½*
847 A149 $2 Sheet of 2, #a.-b.   2.25 2.25
PACIFIC 97.

Queen Elizabeth II & Prince Philip, 50th Wedding Anniv. — A150

#848, Queen with two horses. #849, Prince. #850, Prince on polo pony. #851, Queen. #852, Queen, Prince at Royal Ascot.

1997, July 10   *Perf. 13*
848   $3 multicolored   1.75 1.75
849   $3 multicolored   1.75 1.75
  a.   A150 Pair, #848-849   3.50 3.50
850   $3 multicolored   1.75 1.75
851   $3 multicolored   1.75 1.75
  a.   A150 Pair, #850-851   3.50 3.50
  Nos. 848-851 (4)   7.00 7.00
Souvenir Sheet
852 A150 $3 multicolored   1.75 1.75

South Pacific Commission, 50th Anniv. — A151

Chelonia mydas: 50c, Laying eggs. 90c, Young turtles entering water. $1.50, Group swimming under water. $2, Two adults under water.

Wmk. 384

1997, Sept. 29   **Litho.**   *Perf. 14*
853 A151 50c multicolored   .30 .30
854 A151 90c multicolored   .50 .50
855 A151 $1.50 multicolored   .85 .85
856 A151 $2 multicolored   1.10 1.10
  Nos. 853-856 (4)   2.75 2.75

Christmas A152

Designs: $1.10, Oni mako. $1.40, Ysabel dancing women with bamboo sticks. $1.50, Pan pipers from Small Malaita. $1.70, Western bamboo band.
No. 861, vert.: a, Pachycephala pectoralis. b, Papilio aegeus, graphium meeki.

Wmk. 373

1997, Nov. 24   **Litho.**   *Perf. 13½*
857 A152 $1.10 multicolored   .60 .60
858 A152 $1.40 multicolored   .80 .80
859 A152 $1.50 multicolored   .85 .85
860 A152 $1.70 multicolored   .95 .95
  Nos. 857-860 (4)   3.20 3.20
Souvenir Sheet of 2
Perf. 14
861 A152 $1.50 #a.-b.   1.75 1.75
China Stamp Exhibition, Bangkok '97 (#861).
Issued: #857-860, 11/24; #861, 12/5.

Game Fish — A153

50c, Black marlin. $1.20, Shortbill swordfish. $1.40, Swordfish. $2, Indo-Pacific sailfish.

Perf. 14½
1998, Feb. 27   **Litho.**   **Unwmk.**
862 A153 50c multicolored   .20 .20
863 A153 $1.20 multicolored   .50 .50
864 A153 $1.40 multicolored   .60 .60
865 A153 $2 multicolored   .85 .85
  a.   Souv. sheet of 1, wmk. triangles   1.70 1.70
  Nos. 862-865 (4)   2.15 2.15
Singpex '98 (#865a). No. 865a issued 7/23 and sold for $3.

Diana, Princess of Wales (1961-97)
Common Design Type

$2, Wearing white dress (without hat). #867: a, Up close. b, Wearing white hat, dress. c, Wearing evening dress, black background. d, Taking flowers from children.

Perf. 14½x14
1998, Mar. 31   **Wmk. 373**
866 CD355 $2 multicolored   1.10 1.10
  Complete booklet, 10 #866   11.00
Sheet of 4
867 CD355 $2.50 #a.-d.   4.50 4.50
No. 867 sold for $10 + 50c, with surtax from international sales being donated to the Princess Diana Memorial Fund and surtax from national sales being donated to designated local charity.

Technical Cooperation Between Solomon Islands and Republic of China A154

Designs: 50c, Harvesting watermelons. $1.50, Harvesting rice.
No. 870: a, 80c, Growing cucumbers. b, $1.20, Growing tomatoes.

Wmk. 373

1998, May 29   **Litho.**   *Perf. 13*
868 A154 50c multicolored   .30 .30
869 A154 $1.50 multicolored   .80 .80
Souvenir Sheet
870 A154 Sheet of 2, #a.-b.   1.10 1.10

Melanesian Trade and Culture Show — A155

a, Group raising arms during traditional dance. b, Men with bows and arrow. c, Man smiling in front of water. d, Four men with poles in traditional dance. e, Masked man kneeling down with bow and arrow. f, Man in traditional garb, flowers. g, Group carrying poles. h, Man with spear and shield. i, Man in traditional garb, sun over water.

1998, July 3   *Perf. 13½*
871   Sheet of 9   4.50 4.50
  a.-c. A155 50c any single   .25 .25
  d.-f. A155 $1.20 any single   .50 .50
  g.-i. A155 $1.50 any single   .70 .70

Souvenir Sheet

New Natl. Parliament Building — A156

Illustration reduced.

1998, July 7
872 A156 $4 multicolored   2.25 2.25
Independence, 20th anniv.

Souvenir Sheet

Australia '99 World Stamp Expo — A157

Designs: a, HMS Endeavour, 1770. b, Los Reyes being careened at Guadalcanal, 1568.

1999, Mar. 19   *Perf. 13¼x13¾*
873 A157 $10 Sheet of 2, #a.-b.   4.00 4.00

PhilexFrance '99, World Philatelic Exhibition. A158

Marine Life: a, Beach. b, Great frigate bird. c, Coconut crab. d, Green turtle. e, Royal Spanish dancer nudibranch. f, Sun moon and stars butterflyfish. g, Striped Sweetlips. h, Saddle-back butterflyfish. i, Cuttlefish. j, Giant clam. k, Lionfish. l, Spiny lobster.

1999, July 2   *Perf. 13¼*
874 A158 $1 Sheet of 12, #a.-l.   4.75 4.75

1st Manned Moon Landing, 30th Anniv.
Common Design Type

Designs: 50c, Lift-off. $1.50, Lunar module above moon's surface. $2.50, Aldrin beside US flag. $3.40, Splashdown.
$4, Earth as seen from moon.

Perf. 14x13¾
1999, July 20   **Litho.**   **Wmk. 384**
875 CD357 50c multicolored   .20 .20
876 CD357 $1.50 multicolored   .60 .60
877 CD357 $2.50 multicolored   1.00 1.00
878 CD357 $3.40 multicolored   1.40 1.40
  Nos. 875-878 (4)   3.20 3.20
Souvenir Sheet
Perf. 14
879 CD357 $4 multicolored   1.60 1.60
  a.   Ovptd. in margin in red   1.90 1.90
No. 879 contains one circular stamp 40mm in diameter.
Issued 7/7/2000, overprint on No. 879a reads "WORLD STAMP EXPO - USA VALUE $5.00." Sold for $5.

Queen Mother's Century
Common Design Type

Queen Mother: $1, Inspecting bomb damage at Portsmouth, 1941. $1.50, At the Derby, 1983. $2.30, Receiving birthday wishes. $4.90, As colonel-in-chief of Royal Army Medical Corps.
$3, With King George VI, Winston Churchill, V-E Day, 1945.

1999, Aug. 16   *Perf. 13½*
880 CD358 $1 multicolored   .40 .40
881 CD358 $1.50 multicolored   .60 .60
882 CD358 $2.30 multicolored   .90 .90
883 CD358 $4.90 multicolored   1.90 1.90
  Nos. 880-883 (4)   3.80 3.80
Souvenir Sheet
884 CD358 $5 black   2.00 2.00

Ferrari Racing Cars A159

1999, Sept. 27   **Wmk. 373**   *Perf. 14*
885 A159 $1 212E   .40 .40
886 A159 $1.50 250TR   .60 .60
887 A159 $3.30 250LM   1.25 1.25
888 A159 $4.20 612 Can-Am   1.75 1.75
  Nos. 885-888 (4)   4.00 4.00

Guadalcanal Type of 1992

Designs: a, Flags at half staff. b, Cenotaph, Honiara. c, Solomon Peace Memorial Park. d, US War Memorial, Skyline Ridge. e, Reunion ship Ocean Pearl.

1999, Aug. 16   **Wmk. 384**
889 A125 30c Strip of 5, #a.-e, + label   .60 .60

Melanesian Mission, 150th Anniv. — A160

Christmas: a, $1, Bishop George Augustus Selwynd. b, $1, Bishop John Coleridge Patteson. c, $3.30, Text. d, $1.50, Stained glass. e, $1.50, Southern Cross.

1999, Nov. 12   **Unwmk.**
890 A160 Strip of 5, #a.-e.   3.25 3.25
See Norfolk Islands #693.

Millennium A161

Designs: Nos. 891, 893a, $1 Munda lighthouse, war canoe. Nos. 892, 893b, $4, Tulagi lighthouse, security boat.

2000, Apr. 27   *Perf. 13½x13¼*
891 A161 $1 multi   .40 .40
892 A161 $4 multi   1.60 1.60
Souvenir Sheet
893 A161 Sheet of 2, #a.-b.   2.00 2.00
Nos. 893a, 893b have red violet margins.

Souvenir Sheet

Commonwealth Youth Minister's Meeting — A162

Illustration reduced.

2000, May 22   Litho.   Perf. 13½x13¼
894   A162 $6 multi   2.25 2.25

Year of the Dragon A163

Dragon head facing: $1, Front. $3.90, Left.

2000, Nov. 13   Perf. 11¾x11½
Litho.   Unwmk.
895-896   A163   Set of 2   1.90 1.90
896a   Souvenir sheet, #895-896   1.90 1.90

East Rennell Island World Heritage Site A164

Map and: 50c, Rennell Island. $3.40, Lake Tegano. $4, Rennell shrikebill. $4.90, Endemic orchid.

2000, Nov. 30   Perf. 11¾x11½
Litho.
897-900   A164   Set of 4   5.00 5.00

2000 Summer Olympics and Olymphilex, Sydney — A165

Runners in: $1, 100-meter race. $4.50, 1500-meter race.

2000, Dec. 11   Perf. 14
901-902   A165   Set of 2   2.10 2.10
a.   Souvenir sheet, #901-902   2.10 2.10

Birds A166

Designs: 5c, Yellow-throated white eye. 20c, Purple swamphen. 50c, Blyth's hornbill. 80c, Yellow-faced myna. 90c, Blue-faced parrotfinch. $1, Crested tern. $2, Rainbow lorikeet. $3, Eclectus parrot. $4, Dwarf kingfisher. $10, Beach thick-knee. $20, Brahminy kite. $50, Superb fruit dove.

2001   Wmk. 373   Perf. 14¼x14½
903   A166   5c multi   .20   .20
904   A166   20c multi   .20   .20
905   A166   50c multi   .20   .20
906   A166   80c multi   .30   .30
907   A166   90c multi   .35   .35
908   A166 $1 multi   .40   .40
909   A166 $2 multi   .75   .75
910   A166 $3 multi   1.10   1.10
911   A166 $4 multi   1.50   1.50
912   A166 $10 multi   3.75   3.75

Size: 48x38mm
Perf. 13¾x13½
913   A166 $20 multi   7.50   7.50
913A   A166 $50 multi   18.00 18.00
       Nos. 903-913 (11)   16.25 16.25

Issued: Nos. 5c-$20, 2/1/01; $50, 6/1/01.

East Rennell Island Type of 2000 and

Hong Kong 2001 Stamp Exhibition A167

Snake color: $1.70, Yellow and brown. $2.30, Green and yellow.

2001, Feb. 1   Litho.   Perf. 11¾x11½
914-915   A167   Set of 2   1.50 1.50
Souvenir Sheet
916   A164 $5 Like #900   1.90 1.90

UN High Commissioner for Refugees, 50th Anniv. — A168

Designs: 50c, Refugees. $1, Food and medical supplies. $1.90, Shelter. $2.30, Education.

2001, July 28   Perf. 14¼
Litho.   Unwmk.
917-920   A168   Set of 4   2.10 2.10

Souvenir Sheet

New Year 2001 (Year of the Snake) — A168a

No. 920A: b, Red-banded tree snake. c, Whip snake. d, Pacific boa. e, Guppy's snake.
920A   A168a $1 Sheet of 4, #b-e   1.40 1.40

Reef Fish A169

Designs: 70c, Amphiprion chrysopterus. 90c, Amphiprion perideraion. $1, Premnas biaculeatus. $1.50, Amphiprion melanopus. $2.10, Amphiprion clarkii. $4.50, Dascyllus trimaculatus.

Wmk. 373
2001, Dec. 27   Litho.   Perf. 14
921-926   A169   Set of 6   3.75 3.75
926a   Souvenir sheet, #921-926   3.75 3.75

Worldwide Fund for Nature (WWF) A170

Various depictions of gray cuscus: $1, $1.70, $2.30, $5.

2002, Jan. 31
927-930   A170   Set of 4   3.50 3.50
a.   Horiz. strip of 4   3.50 3.50

Reign Of Queen Elizabeth II, 50th Anniv. Issue
Common Design Type

Designs: Nos. 931, 935a, $1, Princess Elizabeth with baby carriage, 1933. Nos. 932, 935b, $1.90, Wearing sunglasses. Nos. 933, 935c, $2.10, In 1955. Nos. 934, 935d, $2.30, Wearing hat. No. 935e, $10, 1955 portrait by Annigoni (38x50mm).

Perf. 14¼x14½, 13¾ (#935e)
2002, Feb. 6   Litho.   Wmk. 373
With Gold Frames
931-934   CD360   Set of 4   2.50 2.50

Souvenir Sheet
Without Gold Frames
935   CD360   Sheet of 5, #a-e   6.00 6.00

Methodist Mission, Cent. A172

Designs: $1, Typical old school building, Western Solomons. $1.70, Mrs. J. F. Goldie and companions. $2.10, Tandanya, first mission schooner. $2.30, Rev. J. F. Goldie and Solomon Islands chiefs. $5, Rev. Goldie and Sam Aqarao, vert.

2002, May 23   Unwmk.   Perf. 14¼
937-940   A172   Set of 4   2.25 2.25

Souvenir Sheet
941   A172 $5 multi   1.50 1.50

United We Stand — A173

Perf. 13½x13¼
2002, June 17   Unwmk.
942   A173 $2.10 multi   .60   .60

Souvenir Sheet

New Year 2002 (Year of the Horse) — A173a

No. 942A: b, Horse. c, Horse, horiz.

Perf. 13½x13¾, 13¾x13½
2002, July 7   Litho.
942A   A173a $4 Sheet of 2,
                      #a-b   2.40 2.40

No. 942 was printed in sheets of 4.

Cowrie Shells — A174

No. 943: a, $1, Sieve cowrie. b, $1, Kitten cowrie. c, $1, Stolid cowrie, eroded cowrie. d, $1.90, Tapering cowrie. e, $1.90, Tiger cowrie. f, $1.90, Lynx cowrie. g, $2.30, Map cowrie. h, $2.30, Pacific deer cowrie. i, $2.30, Tortoise cowrie.
$10, Golden cowrie.

Perf. 14¼x14½
2002, Aug. 2   Wmk. 373
943   A174   Sheet of 9, #a-i   4.25 4.25

Souvenir Sheet
944   A174 $10 multi   2.75 2.75

Phila Korea 2002 World Stamp Exhibition, Seoul.

Queen Mother Elizabeth (1900-2002)
Common Design Type

Designs: No. 945, $1, Without hat (sepia photograph). No. 946, $2.30, Wearing blue hat.
No. 947: a, $5, Wearing tiara (black and white photograph). b, $5, Wearing green blue hat.

Wmk. 373
2002, Aug. 5   Litho.   Perf. 14¼
With Purple Frames
945-946   CD361   Set of 2   .90   .90

Souvenir Sheet
Without Purple Frames
Perf. 14½x14¼
947   CD361   Sheet of 2, #a-b   2.75 2.75

Battle of Guadalcanal, 60th Anniv. — A175

US servicemen: $1, No. 952d, Coast Guard signalman First Class Douglas Munro. $1.90, No. 952b, Marine Corps Capt. Joe Foss. $2.10, No. 952c, Marine Corps Platoon Sergeant Mitchell Paige. $2.30, No. 952a, Navy Rear Admiral Norman Scott.

2002, Aug. 7   Unwmk.   Perf. 14
948-951   A175   Set of 4   2.00 2.00

Souvenir Sheet
952   A175 $5 Sheet of 4, #a-d   5.50 5.50

Christmas — A176

Paintings: $1, Christmas Night, by Lucas Cranach, the Elder. $2.10, Madonna and Child, by Giovanni Bellini. $2.30, Nativity, by Perugino, horiz. $5, Madonna and Child, by Simone Martini.

2002, Nov. 25   Litho.   Perf. 14
953-956   A176   Set of 4   2.75 2.75

New Year 2003 (Year of the Ram) A177

Perf. 14¼x14½
2003, Apr. 15   Litho.   Unwmk.
957   A177 $3 multi   .80   .80

Issued in sheets of 4.

U. S. Medals of Honor — A178

Designs: $1, Air Force Medal of Honor. $1.90, Navy Medal of Honor. $2.10, Army Medal of Honor. $2.30, Medal of Honor ribbon.

2003, June 6   Perf. 14
958-961   A178   Set of 4   2.00 2.00

Prince William, 21st Birthday — A179

No. 962: a, In gray suit. b, In red shirt. c, In black suit.
$15, In blue shirt.

2003, June 21
962 A179 $9 Sheet of 3, #a-c 7.25 7.25
Souvenir Sheet
963 A179 $15 multi 4.00 4.00

Solomon Islands - Republic of China Diplomatic Relations, 20th Anniv. A180

Designs: $1.50, Rice farmers. $2.10, Hospital.

2003, July 8 **Perf. 14¼**
964-965 A180 Set of 2 .95 .95

Coronation of Queen Elizabeth II, 50th Anniv. — A181

No. 966: a, Wearing tiara. b, Wearing green hat. c, Wearing blue hat.
$15, Wearing tiara, diff.

2003, June 2 **Litho.** **Perf. 14**
966 A181 $9 Sheet of 3, #a-c 7.25 7.25
Souvenir Sheet
967 A181 $15 multi 4.00 4.00

Powered Flight, Cent. — A182

No. 968: a, Boeing 747. b, Boeing 707. c, Lockheed Model 649. d, Boeing Model 247D. e, Fokker F.VII. f, Orville and Wilbur Wright. $15, Concorde.

2003, Dec. 17
968 A182 $4 Sheet of 6, #a-f 6.50 6.50
Souvenir Sheet
969 A182 $15 multi 4.00 4.00

SEMI-POSTAL STAMPS

Catalogue values for unused stamps in this section are for Never Hinged items.

No. 452 Overprinted in Red: "+ 50c SURCHARGE / CYCLONE RELIEF FUND / 1982"
Perf. 13½x13
1982, May 3 **Litho.** **Wmk. 373**
B1 CD331 $1 + 50c multi 2.25 2.25

Nos. 546 and 569 Surcharged "Cyclone Relief Fund 1986" and New Value in Scarlet
Perf. 14½x14
1986, Sept. 23 **Litho.** **Wmk. 384**
B2 CD336 $1 + 50c multi 1.50 1.50

Souvenir Sheet
Perf. 13½
B3 Sheet of 2 3.25 3.25
a. A95 55c + 25c multi .75 .75
b. A95 $1.65 + 75c multi 2.50 2.50

No. 840 Surcharged in Red

Wmk. 373
2003, Feb. 8 **Litho.** **Perf. 14½**
B4 A147 $1.35 +$3 multi 1.25 1.25
World AIDS Day.

No. 866 Surcharged in Red

Perf. 14½x14
2003, Mar. 17 **Wmk. 373**
B5 CD355 $2 +$5 multi 1.90 1.90
Surtax for Cyclones Zoe and Beni Relief Fund.

POSTAGE DUE STAMPS

D1

Perf. 12
1940, Sept. 1 **Typo.** **Wmk. 4**
J1 D1 1p emerald 4.00 5.50
J2 D1 2p dark red 4.25 5.50
J3 D1 3p chocolate 4.25 9.00
J4 D1 4p dark blue 6.50 9.00
J5 D1 5p deep green 7.25 17.50
J6 D1 6p brt red vio 7.25 14.00
J7 D1 1sh dull violet 9.00 24.00
J8 D1 1sh6p turq green 16.00 45.00
Nos. J1-J8 (8) 58.50 129.50
Set, never hinged 87.50

SOMALIA

sō-'mä-lē-ə

(Somali Democratic Republic)

(Italian Somaliland)

(Benadir)

LOCATION — Eastern Africa, bordering on the Indian Ocean and the Gulf of Aden
GOVT. — Probably none
AREA — 246,201 sq. mi.
POP. — 7,140,643 (1999 est.)
CAPITAL — Mogadishu

The former Italian colony which included the territory west of the Juba River became known as Oltre Giuba (Trans-Juba), was absorbed into Italian East Africa in 1936. Somalia stamps continued in use in Italian East Africa for several years. It was under British military administration from 1941-49. Italian trusteeship took effect in 1950, with a UN Advisory Council helping the administrator. On July 1, 1960, the former Italian colony merged with Somaliland Protectorate (British) to form the independent Republic of Somalia.

4 Besas = 1 Anna
16 Annas = 1 Rupee
100 Besas = 1 Rupee (1922)
100 Centesimi = 1 Lira (1905, 1925)
100 Centesimi = 1 Somalo (1950)
100 Centesimi = 1 Somali Shilling (1961)

Catalogue values for unused stamps in this country are for Never Hinged items, beginning with Scott 170 in the regular postage section, Scott B52 in the semi-postal section, Scott C17 in the airpost section, Scott CB11 in the airpost semi-postal section, Scott CE1 in the airpost special delivery section, Scott E8 in the special delivery section, Scott J55 in the postage due section, and Scott Q56 in the parcel post section.

Used values in italics are for postally used Italian Somalia stamps. CTO's or stamps with fake cancels sell for about the same as unused, hinged stamps.

Watermark

Wmk. 140 — Crown

Italian Somaliland

Elephant — A1   Lion — A2

Wmk. 140
1903, Oct. 12 **Typo.** **Perf. 14**
1 A1 1b brown 21.00 3.75
2 A1 2b blue green .70 1.90
3 A2 1a claret .70 3.25
4 A2 2a orange brown 1.40 6.50
5 A2 2½a blue .70 6.50
6 A2 5a orange 1.40 13.50
7 A2 10a lilac 1.40 13.50
Nos. 1-7 (7) 27.30 48.90
For surcharges see Nos. 8-27, 40-50, 70-77.

Surcharged
Centesimi 15

1905, Dec. 29
8 A2 15c on 5a orange 1,700. 350.00
9 A2 40c on 10a lilac 350.00 110.00

Surcharged

1906-07
10 A1 2c on 1b brown 4.75 7.25
11 A1 5c on 2b blue grn 4.75 4.75

Surcharged

12 A2 10c on 1a claret 4.75 4.75
13 A2 15c on 2a brn org ('06) 4.75 4.75
14 A2 25c on 2½a blue 4.75 4.75
15 A2 50c on 5a yellow 13.00 12.00

Surcharged

16 A2 1 l on 10a lilac 13.00 17.00
Nos. 10-16 (7) 49.75 55.25

Nos. 15 and 16 with bars over former Surcharge and

1916, Apr.
18 A2 5c on 50c on 5a yel 22.50 19.00
19 A2 20c on 1 l on 10a dl lil 4.00 13.00

No. 4 Surcharged

20 A2 20c on 2a org brn 10.50 4.75
Nos. 18-20 (3) 37.00 36.75

Nos. 11-16 Surcharged:

a   b

1922, Feb. 1
22 A1(a) 3b on 5c on 2b 6.50 10.50
23 A2(b) 6c on 10c on 1a 12.00 8.00
24 A2(b) 9b on 15c on 2a 12.00 10.50
25 A2(b) 15b on 25c on 2½a 13.00 8.00
26 A2(b) 30b on 50c on 5a 14.50 20.00
27 A2(b) 60b on 1 l on 10a 14.50 35.00
Nos. 22-27 (6) 72.50 92.00

Victory Issue

Italy Nos. 136-139
Surcharged

1922, Apr.

28	A64	3b on 5c olive grn	1.25	3.50
29	A64	6b on 10c red	1.25	3.50
30	A64	9b on 15c slate grn	1.25	4.75
31	A64	15b on 25c ultra	1.25	4.75
		Nos. 28-31 (4)	5.00	16.50

Nos. 10-16 Surcharged with Bars and

c　　　　　　　　　d

1923, July 1

40	A1	1b brown	5.75	14.50
41	A1(c)	2b on 2c on 1b	5.75	14.50
42	A1(c)	3b on 2c on 1b	5.75	8.50
43	A2(d)	5b on 50c on 5a	5.75	7.25
44	A1(c)	6b on 5c on 2b	10.00	7.25
45	A2(d)	18b on 10c on 1a	10.00	7.25
46	A2(d)	20b on 15c on 2a	11.00	7.25
47	A2(d)	25b on 15c on 2a	12.00	10.50
48	A2(d)	30b on 25c on 2½a	13.00	10.50
49	A2(d)	60b on 1 l on 10a	13.00	21.00
50	A2(d)	1r on 1 l on 10a	22.50	26.00
		Nos. 40-50 (11)	114.50	134.50

No. 40 is No. 10 with bars over the 1907 surcharge.

Propagation of the Faith Issue
Italy Nos. 143-146 Surcharged

1923, Oct. 24　　　　　Wmk. 140

51	A68	6b on 20c ol grn & brn org	3.00	13.00
52	A68	13b on 30c cl & brn org	3.00	13.00
53	A68	20b on 50c vio & brn org	2.25	14.50
54	A68	30b on 1 l bl & brn org	2.25	19.00
		Nos. 51-54 (4)	10.50	59.50

Fascisti Issue

Italy Nos. 159-164
Surcharged in Red or
Black

1923, Oct. 29　　Unwmk.　　Perf. 14

55	A69	3b on 10c dk grn (R)	3.50	4.75
56	A69	13b on 30c dk vio (R)	3.50	4.75
57	A69	20b on 50c brn car	3.50	6.00

Wmk. 140

58	A70	30b on 1 l blue	3.50	13.50
59	A70	1r on 2 l brown	3.50	16.00
60	A71	3r on 5 l blk & bl (R)	3.00	22.50
		Nos. 55-60 (6)	20.50	67.50

Manzoni Issue
Italy Nos. 165-170 Surcharged in Red

1924, Apr. 1

61	A72	6b on 10c brn red & blk	4.00	13.50
62	A72	9b on 15c bl grn & blk	4.00	13.50
63	A72	13b on 30c blk & sl	4.00	13.50
64	A72	20b on 50c org brn & blk	4.00	13.50

Surcharged

65	A72	30b on 1 l bl & blk	32.50	125.00
66	A72	3r on 5 l vio & blk	400.00	1,150.
		Nos. 61-66 (6)	448.50	1,329.

Victor Emmanuel Issue

Italy Nos. 175-177
Overprinted

1925-26　　Unwmk.　　Perf. 13½, 11

67	A78	60c brown car	.65	3.25
a.		Perf. 11	45.00	57.50
68	A78	1 l dk bl, perf 11	1.25	5.00
a.		Perf. 13½	4.50	17.50
69	A78	1.25 l dk blue ('26)	.65	8.00
a.		Perf. 11	275.00	300.00
		Nos. 67-69 (3)	2.55	16.25

Stamps of 1907-16 with Bars over Original Values

1926, Mar. 1　Wmk. 140　Perf. 14

70	A1	2c on 1b brown	17.00	21.00
71	A1	5c on 2b blue grn	10.00	12.00
72	A2	10c on 1a rose red	6.25	3.75
73	A2	15c on 2a org brn	6.25	5.25
74	A2	20c on 2a org brn	7.25	5.25
75	A2	25c on 2½a blue	7.25	8.00
76	A2	50c on 5a yellow	10.00	13.00
77	A2	1 l on 10a dull lil	17.00	17.50
		Nos. 70-77 (8)	81.00	85.75

Saint Francis of Assisi Issue

Italy Nos.
178-180
Overprinted

1926, Apr. 12　　　　　　Perf. 14

78	A79	20c gray green	1.25	5.25
79	A80	40c dark violet	1.25	5.25
80	A81	60c red brown	1.25	9.50

Italy Nos. 182 and Type of 1926
Overprinted in Red

Unwmk.　　　　　　Perf. 11

81	A82	1.25 l dark blue	1.25	11.00

Perf. 14

82	A83	5 l + 2.50 l ol grn	3.00	22.50
		Nos. 78-82 (5)	8.00	53.50

Italian Stamps of 1901-26 Overprinted

1926-30　　　　　　　Wmk. 140

83	A43	2c orange brown	1.40	2.00
84	A48	5c green	1.40	2.00
85	A48	10c claret	1.00	.30
86	A49	20c violet brown	1.00	1.10
87	A46	25c grn & pale grn	1.00	.80
88	A49	30c gray ('30)	7.50	11.00
89	A49	60c brown orange	2.10	3.00
90	A46	75c dk red & rose	60.00	11.00
91	A46	1 l brown & grn	2.10	.55
92	A46	1.25 l blue & ultra	5.50	1.40
93	A46	2 l dk grn & org	13.00	5.50
94	A46	2.50 l dk grn & org	13.00	7.50
95	A46	5 l blue & rose	35.00	16.00
96	A51	10 l gray grn & red	35.00	27.50
		Nos. 83-96 (14)	179.00	89.65

Volta Issue

Type of Italy, 1927,
Overprinted

1927, Oct. 10

97	A84	20c purple	3.50	14.50
98	A84	50c deep orange	5.75	9.00
a.		Double overprint	110.00	
99	A84	1.25 l brt blue	7.75	20.00
		Nos. 97-99 (3)	17.00	43.50

Italian Stamps of 1927-28 Overprinted in Black or Red

1928-30

100	A86	7½c lt brown	9.00	18.00
a.		Double overprint	175.00	
101	A85	50c brn & sl (R)	9.00	3.50
102	A86	50c brt violet ('30)	14.00	17.50

Perf. 11
Unwmk.

103	A85	1.75 l deep brown	35.00	8.25
		Nos. 100-103 (4)	67.00	47.25

Monte Cassino Issue

Types of Monte Cassino Issue of Italy
Overprinted in Red or Blue

1929, Oct. 14　Wmk. 140　Perf. 14

104	A96	20c dk green (R)	2.25	6.00
105	A96	25c red org (Bl)	2.25	6.00
106	A98	50c + 10c crim (Bl)	2.25	7.25
107	A98	75c + 15c ol brn (R)	2.25	7.25
108	A96	1.25 l + 25c dk vio (R)	4.75	12.00
109	A98	5 l + 1 l saph (R)	4.75	14.00

Overprinted in Red

Unwmk.

110	A100	10 l + 2 l gray brn	4.75	19.00
		Nos. 104-110 (7)	23.25	71.50

Royal Wedding Issue

Type of Italian Royal Wedding Stamps
of 1930 Overprinted

1930, Mar. 17　　　　　Wmk. 140

111	A101	20c yellow green	.70	2.10
112	A101	50c + 10c dp org	.50	3.00
113	A101	1.25 l + 25c rose red	.50	6.75
		Nos. 111-113 (3)	1.70	11.85

Ferrucci Issue

Types of Italian Stamps of 1930
Overprinted in Red or Blue

1930, July 26

114	A102	20c violet (R)	1.25	1.40
115	A103	25c dark green (R)	1.25	1.40
116	A103	50c black (R)	1.25	3.00
117	A103	1.25 l deep blue (R)	1.25	5.00
118	A104	5 l + 2 l dp car (bl)	3.00	9.50
		Nos. 114-118 (5)	8.00	20.30

Virgil Issue
Types of Italian Stamps of 1930
Overprinted in Red or Blue

1930, Dec. 4　Photo.　Wmk. 140

119	A106	15c violet blue	.60	3.00
120	A106	20c orange brown	.60	1.50
121	A106	25c dark green	.60	1.25
122	A106	30c lt brown	.60	1.50
123	A106	50c dull violet	.60	1.25
124	A106	75c rose red	.60	2.25
125	A106	1.25 l gray blue	.60	3.00

Engr.
Unwmk.

126	A106	5 l + 1.50 l dk vio	2.40	16.00
127	A106	10 l + 2.50 l ol brn	2.40	25.00
		Nos. 119-127 (9)	9.00	54.75

Saint Anthony of Padua Issue
Types of Italian Stamps of 1931
Overprinted in Blue or Red

1931, May 7　Photo.　Wmk. 140

129	A116	20c brown (Bl)	.80	4.75
130	A116	25c green (R)	.80	2.25
131	A118	30c gray brn (Bl)	.80	2.25
132	A118	50c dull vio (Bl)	.80	2.25
133	A120	1.25 l slate bl (R)	.80	4.75

Overprinted in Red or Black

Engr.　　　　　　　Unwmk.

134	A121	75c black (R)	.80	10.00
135	A122	5 l + 2.50 l dk brn (Bk)	2.25	25.00
		Nos. 129-135 (7)	7.05	51.25

Italy Nos. 218, 221
Overprinted in Red

1931 **Wmk. 140**
136 A94 25c dk green (R) 4.75 6.00
137 A95 50c purple (R) 6.00 1.50

Lighthouse at
Cape
Guardafui — A3

Tower at Mnara
Ciromo — A4

Governor's Palace
at Mogadishu — A5

Termite
Nest — A6

Ostrich — A7

Hippopotamus — A8

Greater
Kudu — A9

Lion — A10

1932 **Wmk. 140** **Photo.** **Perf. 12**
138 A3 5c deep brown 1.50 2.50
139 A3 7½c violet 2.10 6.25
140 A3 10c gray black 3.00 .25
141 A3 15c olive green 1.25 .70
142 A4 20c carmine 140.00 .20
143 A4 25c deep green 1.25 .25
144 A4 30c dark brown 10.00 .70
145 A5 35c dark blue 2.10 3.25
146 A5 50c violet 200.00 .25
147 A5 75c carmine 1.50 .40
148 A6 1.25 l dark blue 7.00 .35
149 A6 1.75 l red orange 3.00 .40
150 A6 2 l carmine 1.50 .30
151 A7 2.55 l indigo 11.00 27.50
152 A7 5 l carmine 6.25 2.50
153 A8 10 l violet 13.00 8.50
154 A9 20 l dark green 37.50 35.00
155 A10 30 l dark blue 37.50 50.00
  Nos. 138-155 (18) 479.45 139.30
  Set, never hinged 850.00

1934-37 **Perf. 14**
138a A3 5c deep brown .40 .30
139a A3 7½c violet .40 7.25
140a A3 10c gray black .40 .20
141a A3 15c olive green .40 1.25
142a A4 20c carmine .40 .20
143a A4 25c deep green .40 .20
144a A4 30c dark brown .85 .25
145a A5 35c dark blue 2.25 9.75
146a A5 50c violet 8.25 .20
147a A5 75c carmine 12.50 .25
148a A6 1.25 l dark blue 19.00 .50
149a A6 1.75 l red orange 47.50 6.25
150a A6 2 l carmine 19.00 .35
151a A7 2.55 l indigo 90.00 150.00
152a A7 5 l carmine 4.25 1.40
153a A8 10 l violet 75.00 14.50
154a A9 20 l dark green 7,000. 550.00

155a A10 Never hinged 8,750.
155a A10 25 l dark blue 450.00 160.00
  Nos. 138a-153a,155a (17) 731.00 352.85
  Set, never hinged 1,450.

Eleven denominations in the foregoing
series exist perf. 12x14 or 14x12.

Types of 1932
Issue
Overprinted in
Black or Red

1934, May **Perf. 14**
156 A3 10c brown (Bk) 3.50 6.50
157 A4 25c green 3.50 6.50
158 A5 50c dull vio (Bk) 2.40 6.50
159 A6 1.25 l blue 2.40 6.50
160 A7 5 l brown black 3.50 6.50
161 A8 10 l car rose (Bk) 3.50 9.00
162 A9 20 l dull blue 3.50 9.00
163 A10 25 l dark green 3.50 9.00
  Nos. 156-163 (8) 25.80 59.50
  Set, never hinged 52.50

Duke of the Abruzzi (Luigi Amadeo, 1873-1933).

Mother and
Child
A11

1934, Oct.
164 A11 5c ol grn & brn 2.00 6.50
165 A11 10c yel brn & blk 2.00 6.50
166 A11 20c scarlet & blk 2.00 5.25
167 A11 50c dk violet & brn 2.00 5.25
168 A11 60c org brn & blk 2.00 7.25
169 A11 1.25 l dk blue & grn 12.00 12.00
  Nos. 164-169,C1-C6 (12) 24.00 85.50
  Set, never hinged 47.50

Second Colonial Arts Exhibition, Naples.

> **Catalogue values for unused
> stamps in this section, from this
> point to the end of the section, are
> for Never Hinged items.**

Somalia

Tower at Mnara
Ciromo — A12

Governor's Palace,
Mogadishu — A13

Design: 5c, 20c, 60c, Ostrich.

Wmk. 277
1950, Mar. 24 **Photo.** **Perf. 14**
170 A12 1c gray black .20 .20
171 A12 5c carmine rose .20 .20
172 A13 6c violet .20 .20
173 A12 8c Prus green .20 .20
174 A13 10c dark green .20 .20
175 A12 20c blue green .20 .20
176 A12 35c red .20 .20
177 A13 55c brt blue .25 .20
178 A12 60c purple .30 .20
179 A12 65c brown .40 .20
180 A13 1s deep orange .65 .20
  Nos. 170-180,E8-E9 (13) 10.50 8.45

Council in
Session
A14

1951, Oct. 4
181 A14 20c dk green & brn 1.60 .25
182 A14 55c brown & violet 3.25 3.00
  Nos. 181-182,C27A-C27B (4) 7.30 7.25

Meeting of First Territorial Council.

Fair Emblem, Palm
Tree and
Minaret — A16

Mother and
Child — A17

1952, Sept. 14 **Wmk. 277** **Perf. 14**
185 A16 25c red & dk brown 1.25 1.75
186 A16 55c blue & dk brown 1.25 1.75
  Nos. 185-186,C28 (3) 3.50 5.50

1st Somali Fair, Mogadishu, Sept. 14-28.

1953, May 27
Center in Dark Brown
187 A17 5c rose violet .20 .20
188 A17 25c rose .20 .20
189 A17 50c blue .50 .75
  Nos. 187-189,C29 (4) 1.50 2.00

Anti-tuberculosis campaign.

Laborer at
Fair
Entrance
A18

1953, Sept. 28 **Unwmk.** **Perf. 11½**
190 A18 25c dk green & gray .20 .25
191 A18 60c blue & gray .30 .50
  Nos. 190-191,C30-C31 (4) 1.10 1.75

2nd Somali Fair, Mogadishu, 9/28-10/12.

Map and
Stamps
of 1903
A19

Perf. 13x13½
1953, Dec. 16 **Engr.** **Wmk. 277**
**"Stamps" in Brown and Rose
Carmine**
192 A19 25c deep magenta .20 .25
193 A19 35c dark green .20 .25
194 A19 60c orange .20 .25
  Nos. 192-194,C32-C33 (5) 1.20 1.75

50th anniv. of the 1st Somali postage
stamps.

Somalia
Brushwood
A20

Perf. 12½x13½
1954, June 1 **Photo.** **Unwmk.**
195 A20 25c dp blue & dk gray .20 .30
196 A20 60c orange brn & brown .20 .30
  Nos. 195-196,C37-C38 (4) 1.15 1.70

Convention of Nov. 11, 1953, with the Sovereign Military Order of Malta, providing for the
care of lepers.

Somali Flag
A21

Adenium
Somalense
A22

Perf. 13½x13
1954, Oct. 12 **Litho.** **Wmk. 277**
197 A21 25c blk, grn, bl, red & yel .20 .30

Adoption of a Somali flag. See No. C39.

1955, Feb. **Photo.** **Perf. 13**

Flowers: 5c, Haemanthus multiflorus martyn. 10c, Grinum scabrum. 25c, Poinciana
elata. 60c, Calatropis procera. 1s, Pancratium.
1.20s, Sesamothamnus bussernus.

198 A22 1c bl, dp rose & dk ol brn .20 .20
199 A22 5c bl, rose lil & grn .20 .20
200 A22 10c lilac & green .20 .20
201 A22 25c vio brn, yel & grn .30 .20
202 A22 60c blk, car & grn .20 .20
203 A22 1s red brn & grn .20 .25
204 A22 1.20s dk brn, vel & grn .20 .25
  Nos. 198-204,E10-E11 (9) 2.25 2.65

See #216-220. For overprint see #242.

Weaver at
Loom
A23

Design: 30c, Cattle fording stream.

Perf. 13½x14
1955, Sept. 24 **Wmk. 303**
205 A23 25c dark brown .20 .30
206 A23 30c dark green .20 .30
  Nos. 205-206,C46-C47 (4) .85 1.30

3rd Somali Fair, Mogadishu, Sept. 1955.

Casting
Ballots — A24

Arms of
Somalia — A25

1956, Apr. 30 **Perf. 14**
207 A24 5c brown & gray grn .20 .20
208 A24 10c brown & ol bis .20 .20
209 A24 25c brown & brn red .20 .20
  Nos. 207-209,C48-C49 (5) 1.00 1.00

Opening of the territory's first democratically
elected Legislative Assembly.

1957, May 6 **Wmk. 303** **Perf. 13½**
**Coat of Arms in Dull Yellow, Blue
and Black**
210 A25 5c lt red brown .20 .20
211 A25 25c carmine .20 .20
212 A25 60c bluish violet .20 .20
  Nos. 210-212,C50-C51 (5) 1.00 1.05

Issued in honor of the new coat of arms.

Dam at
Falcheiro
A26

10c, Juba River Bridge. 25c, Silos at Margherita.

1957, Sept. 28   Photo.   Perf. 14
213 A26 5c brown & purple   .20   .20
214 A26 10c bister & bl grn   .20   .20
215 A26 25c carmine & blue   .20   .20
  Nos. 213-215,C52-C53 (5)   1.00 1.20

Fourth Somali Fair and Film Festival.

Flower Type of 1955

Flowers: 1c, Adenium Somalense. 10c, Grinum scabrum. 15c, Adansonia digitata. 25c, Poinciana elata. 50c, Gloriosa virescens.

1956-59 Wmk. 303 Photo. Perf. 13
216 A22 1c bl, dp rose & dk ol brn .20 .20
217 A22 10c lil, grn & yel ('59)   .20 .20
218 A22 15c red, grn & yel ('58)   .20 .20
219 A22 25c dull lil, grn & yel ('59) .20 .20
220 A22 50c bl, grn, red & yel ('58) .20 .30
  Nos. 216-220 (5)   1.00 1.10

Fencer — A27

Soccer Player A28

Designs: 5c, Discus thrower. 6c, Motorcyclist. 8c, Fencer. 10c, Archer. 25c, Boxers.

1958, Apr. 28   Wmk. 303   Perf. 14
221 A27 2c violet   .20 .20
222 A28 4c green   .20 .20
223 A27 5c vermilion   .20 .20
224 A28 6c gray   .20 .20
225 A27 8c violet blue   .20 .20
226 A28 10c orange   .20 .20
227 A28 25c dark green   .20 .20
  Nos. 221-227,C54-C56 (10) 2.00 2.00

Book and Assembly Palace — A29

White Stork — A30

1959, June 19
228 A29 5c green & ultra   .20 .20
229 A29 25c ocher & ultra .20 .20
  Nos. 228-229,C59-C60 (4) .80 1.00

Opening of Somalia's Constituent Assembly. See No. C60a.

1959, Sept. 4   Photo.   Perf. 14
Birds: 10c, Saddle-billed stork. 15c, Sacred ibis. 25c, Pink-backed pelican.

230 A30 5c yellow, blk & red   .20 .20
231 A30 10c brown, red & yel   .20 .20
232 A30 15c orange & black   .20 .20
233 A30 25c dk car, blk & org   .20 .20
  Nos. 230-233,C61-C62 (6)   1.20 1.35

Incense Bush — A31

Arms of University Institute — A32

Design: 60c, Girl burning incense.

1959, Sept. 28   Wmk. 303
234 A31 20c orange & black   .20 .20
235 A31 60c blk, org & dk red   .20 .25
  Nos. 234-235,C63-C64 (4)   .90 1.20

5th Somali Fair, Mogadishu.

1960, Jan. 14   Photo.   Perf. 14
Designs: 50c, Map of Africa and arms, horiz. 80c, Arms of University Institute.

236 A32 5c brown & salmon   .20 .20
237 A32 50c lt vio bl, brn & blk .20 .20
238 A32 80c brt red & blk   .25 .25
  Nos. 236-238,C65-C66 (5)   1.25 1.25

Opening of the University Institute of Somalia.

Globe and Uprooted Oak Emblem A33

Palm — A34

Design: 60c, Like 10c but with inscription and emblem rearranged.

1960, Apr. 7   Perf. 14
239 A33 10c yel brn, grn & blk .20 .20
240 A33 60c dp bister & blk   .20 .20
241 A34 80c pink, grn & blk   .20 .20
  Nos. 239-241,C67 (4)   .85 .85

World Refugee Year, 7/1/59-6/30/60.

Republic

No. 217 Overprinted

Wmk. 303
1960, June 26   Photo.   Perf. 13
242 A22 10c lilac, grn & yel   6.00 6.50
  Nos. 242,C68-C69 (3)   22.50 18.00

Independence of British Somaliland, which became part of the Republic of Somalia.

Gazelle and Map of Africa — A36

25c, NYC skyline, UN Building and UN flag.

1960, July 1   Perf. 14
243 A36 5c lilac & brown   .20 .20
244 A36 25c blue   .20 .20
  Nos. 243-244,C70-C71 (4) 1.30 .90

Somalia independence.

Boy Drawing Giraffe A37

1960, Nov. 24
245 A37 10c shown   .20 .20
246 A37 15c Zebra   .20 .20
247 A37 25c Black rhinoceros .20 .20
  Nos. 245-247,C72 (4)   1.20 1.10

Olympic Torch, Somalia Flag — A38

Girl Harvesting Papaya — A39

10c, Runners, flag and Olympic rings.

1960   Wmk. 303   Perf. 14
248 A38 5c green & blue   .20 .20
249 A38 10c yellow & blue .20 .20
  Nos. 248-249,C73-C74 (4) .90 .90

17th Olympic Games, Rome, 8/25-9/11.

1961, July 5   Photo.
Girl harvesting: 10c, Durrah (sorghum). 20c, Cotton. 25c, Sesame. 40c, Sugar cane. 50c, Bananas. 75c, Peanuts, horiz. 80c, Grapefruit, horiz.

250 A39 5c multicolored   .20 .20
251 A39 10c multicolored   .20 .20
252 A39 20c multicolored   .20 .20
253 A39 25c multicolored   .20 .20
254 A39 40c multicolored   .20 .20
255 A39 50c multicolored   .20 .20
256 A39 75c multicolored   .20 .20
257 A39 80c multicolored   .30 .20
  Nos. 250-257 (8)   1.70 1.60

Shield, Bow and Quiver — A40

Pomacanthus Semicirculatus A41

Design: 45c, Pottery and incense jug.

1961, Sept. 28
258 A40 25c blk, car & ocher .20 .20
259 A40 45c blk, bl grn & ocher .20 .90
  Nos. 258-259,C82-C83 (4)   1.05 .90

6th Somali Fair, Mogadishu.

1962, Apr. 26   Photo.
Fish: 15c, Girl embroidering fish on cloth. 40c, Novaculichthys taeniourus.

260 A41 15c brown, blk & pink   .20 .20
261 A41 25c orange, blk & ultra .20 .20
262 A41 40c green, blk & rose   .25 .20
  Nos. 260-262,C84 (4)   1.55 1.20

Mosquito Trapped by Sprays A42

Design: 25c, Man with spray gun and malaria eradication emblem, vert.

1962, Oct. 25   Wmk. 303   Perf. 14
263 A42 10c orange red & grn   .20 .20
264 A42 25c rose lilac, brn & blk .20 .20
  Nos. 263-264,C85-C86 (4)   1.30 .90

WHO drive to eradicate malaria.

Police Auxiliary Woman A43

10c, Army auxiliary woman. 25c, Radio police car. 75c, First aid army auxiliary, vert.

1963, May 15   Wmk. 303   Perf. 14
265 A43 5c multicolored   .20 .20
266 A43 10c black & orange .20 .20
267 A43 25c multicolored   .20 .20
268 A43 75c multicolored   .25 .20
  Nos. 265-268,C87-C88 (6) 1.75 1.20

Women's auxiliary forces.

Carved Fork and Spoon and Wheat Emblem A44

1963, June 25   Photo.
269 A44 75c green & red brown .20 .20

FAO "Freedom from Hunger" campaign. See No. C89.

Pres. Aden Abdulla Osman — A45

1963, Sept. 15   Wmk. 303   Perf. 14
270 A45 25c bl, dk brn, org & lt bl .20 .20
  Nos. 270,C90-C91 (3)   1.25 .70

3rd anniv. of independence.

Dunes Theater A46

55c, African Merchants' and Artisans' Exhibit.

1963, Sept. 28   **Photo.**
271	A46	25c blue green	.20	.20
272	A46	55c carmine rose	.20	.20
		Nos. 271-272,C92 (3)	1.25	.80

7th Somali Fair, Mogadishu.

Somali Credit Bank Building A47

1964, May 16   **Wmk. 303**   *Perf. 14*
273	A47	60c indigo, red lil & yel	.30	.20
		Nos. 273,C93-C94 (3)	1.30	.70

10th anniv. of the Somali Credit Bank.

Running — A48

ITU Emblem and Map of Africa — A50

DC-3 A49

1964, Oct. 10   **Wmk. 303**   *Perf. 14*
274	A48	10c shown	.20	.20
275	A48	25c High jump	.20	.20
		Nos. 274-275,C95-C96 (4)	1.40	.90

18th Olympic Games, Tokyo, Oct. 10-25.

1964, Nov. 8   **Photo.**   *Perf. 14*

Design: 20c, Passengers leaving DC-3.
276	A49	5c dk blue & lil rose	.20	.20
277	A49	20c blue & orange	.30	.20
		Nos. 276-277,C97-C98 (4)	2.35	1.05

Establishment of Somali Air Lines.

1965, May 17   **Wmk. 303**   *Perf. 14*
278	A50	25c dp blue & dp org	.20	.20
		Nos. 278,C99-C100 (3)	1.40	.80

ITU centenary.

Tanning Industry A51

25c, Meat industry; cannery, cattle. 35c, Fishing industry; cannery, fishing boats.

1965, Sept. 28   **Photo.**   *Perf. 14*
279	A51	10c sepia & buff	.20	.20
280	A51	25c sepia & pink	.20	.20
281	A51	35c sepia & lt blue	.20	.20
		Nos. 279-281,C101-C102 (5)	1.75	1.05

8th Somali Fair, Mogadishu.

Hottentot Fig and Gazelle A52

Designs: 60c, African tulip and giraffes. 1sh, Ninfea and flamingos. 1.30sh, Pervincia and ostriches. 1.80sh, Bignonia and zebras.

1965, Nov. 1   **Wmk. 303**   *Perf. 14*
Flowers in Natural Colors
282	A52	20c blk & brt bl	.20	.20
283	A52	60c blk & dk gray	.20	.20
284	A52	1sh blk, sl grn & ol grn	.25	.20
285	A52	1.30sh blk & dp grn	.50	.20
286	A52	1.80sh blk & brt bl	.70	.25
		Nos. 282-286 (5)	1.85	1.05

Narina's Trogon A53

Birds: 35c, Bateleur eagle, vert. 50c, Vulture. 1.30sh, European roller. 2sh, Vulturine guinea fowl, vert.

1966, June 1   **Photo.**   **Wmk. 303**
287	A53	25c multicolored	.20	.20
288	A53	35c brt blue & multi	.20	.20
289	A53	50c multicolored	.20	.20
290	A53	1.30sh multicolored	.30	.20
291	A53	2sh multicolored	.50	.25
		Nos. 287-291 (5)	1.40	1.05

Globe and UN Emblem A54

UN emblem and: 1sh, Map of Africa. 1.50sh, Map of Somalia.

1966, Oct. 24   **Litho.**   *Perf. 13x12½*
292	A54	35c bl, pur & brt bl	.20	.20
293	A54	1sh brn, yel & brick red	.20	.20
294	A54	1.50sh grn, blk, bl & yel	.25	.25
		Nos. 292-294 (3)	.65	.65

21st anniversary of United Nations.

Woman Sitting on Crocodile A55

Paintings: 1sh, Woman and warrior. 1.50sh, Boy leading camel. 2sh, Women pounding grain.

Wmk. 303
1966, Dec. 1   **Photo.**   *Perf. 14*
295	A55	25c multicolored	.20	.20
296	A55	1sh multicolored	.20	.20
297	A55	1.50sh multicolored	.20	.20
298	A55	2sh multicolored	.25	.20
		Nos. 295-298 (4)	.85	.80

Somali art, exhibited in the Garesa Museum, Mogadishu.

UNESCO Emblem A56

1966, Dec. 20   **Wmk. 303**   *Perf. 14*
299	A56	35c blk, dk red & gray	.20	.20
300	A56	1sh blk, emer & yel	.20	.20
301	A56	1.80sh blk, ultra & red	.30	.25
		Nos. 299-301 (3)	.70	.65

UNESCO, 20th anniv.

Haggard's Oribi — A57   Dancers — A58

Gazelles: 60c, Long-snouted dik-dik. 1sh, Gerenuk. 1.80sh, Soemmering's gazelle.

1967, Feb. 20   **Photo.**   *Perf. 14*
302	A57	35c blk, ultra & bis	.20	.20
303	A57	60c blk, org & brn	.20	.20
304	A57	1sh blk, red & brn	.20	.20
305	A57	1.80sh blk, yel grn & brn	.90	.85
		Nos. 302-305 (4)	.90	.85

Unwmk.
1967, July 15   **Litho.**   *Perf. 13*

Designs: Various Folk Dances.
306	A58	25c multicolored	.20	.20
307	A58	1sh multicolored	.20	.20
308	A58	1.30sh multicolored	.20	.20
309	A58	2sh multicolored	.25	.25
		Nos. 306-309 (4)	.85	.85

Boy Scout Giving Scout Sign — A59

Designs: 50c, Boy Scouts with flags. 1sh, Boy Scout cooking and tent. 1.80sh, Jamboree emblem.

1967, Aug. 15
310	A59	35c multicolored	.20	.20
311	A59	50c multicolored	.20	.20
312	A59	1sh multicolored	.25	.20
313	A59	1.80sh multicolored	.50	.30
		Nos. 310-313 (4)	1.15	.90

12th Boy Scout World Jamboree, Farragut State Park, Idaho, Aug. 1-9.

Pres. Abdirascid Ali Scermarche and King Faisal — A60

Designs: 1sh, Clasped hands, flags of Somalia and Saudi Arabia.

Wmk. 303
1967, Sept. 21   **Photo.**   *Perf. 14*
314	A60	50c black & lt blue	.20	.20
315	A60	1sh multicolored	.20	.20
		Nos. 314-315,C103 (3)	.70	.60

Visit of King Faisal of Saudi Arabia.

Gaterin Gaterinus A61

Tropical Fish: 50c, Chaetodon semilarvatus. 1sh, Priacanthus hamrur. 1.80sh, Epinephelus summana.

1967, Nov. 15   **Litho.**   *Perf. 14*
316	A61	35c dk bl, yel & blk	.20	.20
317	A61	50c brt bl, ocher & blk	.20	.20
318	A61	1sh emer, org, brn & blk	.25	.20
319	A61	1.80sh pur, yel & blk	.50	.40
		Nos. 316-319 (4)	1.15	1.00

Physician Treating Infant A62   Waterbuck A64

Woman and Basket with Lemons A63

WHO, 20th anniv.: 1sh, Physician examining boy, and nurse. 1.80sh, Physician and nurse treating patient.

Wmk. 303
1968, Mar. 20   **Photo.**   *Perf. 14*
320	A62	35c blk, scar, bl & brn	.20	.20
321	A62	1sh blk, grn & brn	.20	.20
322	A62	1.80sh blk, org & brn	.30	.25
		Nos. 320-322 (3)	.70	.65

1968   **Litho.**   *Perf. 11½*

Designs: 10c, Oranges. 25c, Coconuts. 35c, Papayas. 40c, Limes. 50c, Grapefruit. 1sh, Bananas. 1.30sh, Cotton balls. 1.80sh, Speke's gazelle. 2sh, Lesser kudu. 5sh, Hunter's hartebeest. 10sh, Clark's gazelle (dibatag).
323	A63	5c lt blue & multi	.20	.20
324	A63	10c yellow & multi	.20	.20
325	A63	25c lt lilac & multi	.20	.20
326	A63	35c salmon & multi	.20	.20
327	A63	40c buff & multi	.20	.20
328	A63	50c multicolored	.20	.20
329	A63	1sh lt blue & multi	.20	.20
330	A63	1.30sh gray & multi	.25	.25
331	A64	1.50sh lt blue & multi	.20	.20
332	A64	1.80sh multicolored	.30	.25
333	A64	2sh pink & multi	.35	.25
334	A64	5sh multicolored	1.00	.80
335	A64	10sh multicolored	2.75	1.25
		Nos. 323-335 (13)	6.25	4.40

Issued: #323-330, 4/25; #331-335, 5/10.

Javelin — A65   Statuette — A66

Wmk. 303
1968, Oct. 12   **Photo.**   *Perf. 14*
336	A65	35c shown	.20	.20
337	A65	50c Running	.20	.20
338	A65	80c High jump	.20	.20
339	A65	1.50sh Basketball	.25	.20
a.		Souvenir sheet of 4, #336-339	.70	.60
		Nos. 336-339 (4)	.85	.80

19th Olympic Games, Mexico City, Oct. 12-27. No. 339a sold for 3.65sh.

Perf. 11½x12
1968, Dec. 1   **Litho.**   **Unwmk.**

Statuettes: 25c, Woman grinding grain. 35c, Woman potter. 2.80sh, Woman mat maker.
340	A66	25c rose lil, blk & brn	.20	.20
341	A66	35c brick red, blk & brn	.20	.20
342	A66	2.80sh green, blk & brn	.50	.35
		Nos. 340-342 (3)	.90	.75

Cornflower and Rhinoceros
A67

80c, Sunflower & elephant. 1sh, Oleander & antelopes. 1.80sh, Chrysanthemums & storks.

Perf. 13x12½
1969, Mar. 25   Litho.   Unwmk.
343 A67   40c red & multi   .20 .20
344 A67   80c violet & multi   .20 .20
345 A67   1sh blue & multi   .20 .20
346 A67   1.80sh yellow & multi   .30 .25
          Nos. 343-346 (4)   .90 .85

ILO Emblem and Blacksmiths — A68

Designs: 1sh, Oxdrawn plow. 1.80sh, Drawing water from well.

Wmk. 303
1969, May 10   Photo.   Perf. 14
347 A68   25c dk red, dp bis & blk .20 .20
348 A68   1sh car rose, brn & blk   .20 .20
349 A68   1.80sh multicolored   .30 .25
          Nos. 347-349 (3)   .70 .65

ILO, 50th anniversary.

Mahatma Gandhi — A69

Designs: 1.50sh, Gandhi, globe and hands releasing dove, horiz. 1.80sh, Gandhi seated.

Unwmk.
1969, Oct. 2   Photo.   Perf. 13
Size: 25x35½mm
350 A69   35c brown violet   .20 .20
Perf. 14½x14
Size: 37½x20mm
351 A69   1.50sh bister brn   .20 .20
Perf. 13
Size: 25x35½mm
352 A69   1.80sh olive gray   .25 .25
          Nos. 350-352 (3)   .65 .65

Mohandas K. Gandhi (1869-1948), leader in India's fight for independence.

1970
US Space Explorations. Set of seven. 60, 80c, 1, 1.50, 1.80, 2, 2.80sh. Souv. sheet, 14sh, issued Feb. 14. Nos. 7001-7008.

Nivprale Vevanes
A70

Butterflies: 50c, Leschenault. 1.50sh, Papilio (ornytoptera) aeacus. 2sh, Urania riphaeus.

Perf. 12½x13
1970, Mar. 25   Litho.   Unwmk.
353 A70   25c multicolored   .20 .20
354 A70   50c multicolored   .20 .20
355 A70   1.50sh orange & multi   .20 .20
356 A70   2sh yellow & multi   .30 .30
          Nos. 353-356 (4)   .90 .90

Somali Democratic Republic

Lenin Addressing Crowd — A71

Designs: 25c, Lenin walking with children. 1.80sh, Lenin in his study, horiz.

Perf. 12x12½, 12½x12
1970, Apr. 22   Litho.   Unwmk.
357 A71   25c multicolored   .20 .20
358 A71   1sh multicolored   .20 .20
359 A71   1.80sh multicolored   .25 .20
          Nos. 357-359 (3)   .65 .60

Lenin (1870-1924), Russian communist leader.

Bird Feeding Young
A72

35c, Monument & Battle of Dagahtur. 1sh, Arms of Somalia, UN emblem, vert. 2.80sh, Boy milking camel, & star, vert.

Perf. 14x13½, 13½x14
1970, July 28   Photo.   Wmk. 303
360 A72   25c blue & multi   .20 .20
361 A72   35c slate & multi   .20 .20
362 A72   1sh violet & multi   .20 .20
363 A72   2.80sh blue & multi   .65 .50
          Nos. 360-363 (4)   1.25 1.10

10th anniversary of independence.

"Agriculture" — A73

40c, Soldier and flag. 1sh, Hand on open book. 1.80sh, Grain, scales of justice and dove.

Perf. 14x13½
1970, Oct. 21   Photo.   Wmk. 303
364 A73   35c green & multi   .20 .20
365 A73   40c ultra & blk   .20 .20
366 A73   1sh red brown & blk   .20 .20
367 A73   1.80sh multicolored   .40 .25
          Nos. 364-367 (4)   1.00 .85

First anniversary of Oct. 21st Revolution.

Snake Strangling Black Man, Map of South Africa
A74

Design: 1.80sh, Concentration camp and symbols of justice holding scales.

Perf. 14x13½
1971, June 20   Photo.   Wmk. 303
368 A74   1.30sh multicolored   .30 .20
369 A74   1.80sh gray, red & blk   .45 .30

Against racial discrimination in South Africa.

Waves
A75

Design: 2.80sh, Waves and globe.

1971, June 30
370 A75   25c black & blue   .20 .20
371 A75   2.80sh blk, grn & bl   .60 .40

3rd World Telecommunications Day, May 17.

Map of Africa and Telecommunications System — A76

Design: 1.50sh, Map of Africa and telecommunications system, diff.

1971, July 25
372 A76   1sh blk, lt bl & grn   .20 .20
373 A76   1.50sh black & yellow   .30 .25

Pan-African Telecommunications system.

White Rhinoceros
A77

Wild Animals: 1sh, Cheetahs. 1.30sh, Zebras. 1.80sh, Lion attacking camel.

1971, Aug. 25
374 A77   35c ocher & multi   .20 .20
375 A77   1sh violet & multi   .25 .20
376 A77   1.30sh violet & multi   .45 .20
377 A77   1.80sh multicolored   .50 .25
          Nos. 374-377 (4)   1.40 .85

Headquarters, Mogadishu, Flag, Map of Africa — A78

Design: 1.30sh, Desert Fort.

1971, Oct. 18
378 A78   1.30sh blk & red org   .25 .25
379 A78   1.50sh blk, blue & yel   .30 .25

East and Central African Summit Conf.

Revolution Monument
A79

1sh, Field workers. 1.35sh, Building workers.

1971, Oct. 21
380 A79   10c black & blue   .20 .20
381 A79   1sh blk, yel brn & grn   .20 .20
382 A79   1.35sh blk, dp brn & yel .35 .20
          Nos. 380-382 (3)   .75 .60

2nd anniversary of 1969 revolution.

Vaccination of Cow — A80

1.80sh, Veterinarian vaccinating cow.

Perf. 14x13½
1971, Nov. 28   Photo.   Wmk. 303
383 A80   40c blk, red & bl   .40 .20
384 A80   1.80sh lt green & multi   .45 .35

Rinderpest campaign.

Postal Union Emblem, Dove and Letter
A81

1972, Jan. 25   Unwmk.
385 A81   1.50sh multicolored   .50 .45

10th anniv. of APU. See No. C108.

Children and UNICEF Emblem
A82

Design: 50c, Mother and child, vert.

1972, Mar. 30   Perf. 13x14, 14x13
386 A82   50c blk, bis brn & dk
             brn   .20 .20
387 A82   2.80sh lt blue & multi   .70 .50

UNICEF, 25th anniv. (in 1971).

Camel
A83

Designs: 10c, Cattle and cargo ship. 20c, Bull. 40c, Sheep. 1.70sh, Goat.

1972, Apr. 10   Perf. 14x13
388 A83   5c green & multi   .20 .20
389 A83   10c multicolored   .20 .20
390 A83   20c multicolored   .20 .20
391 A83   40c orange red & blk   .20 .20
392 A83   1.70sh dull grn & blk   .85 .45
          Nos. 388-392 (5)   1.65 1.25

Hands Holding Infant
A84

1sh, Youth Corps emblem, marchers with flags. 1.50sh, Woman, man, tent, tractor.

1972, Oct. 21   Photo.   Perf. 14x13½
393 A84   70c yellow & multi   .20 .20
394 A84   1sh red & multi   .25 .20
395 A84   1.50sh lt blue & multi   .35 .30
          Nos. 393-395 (3)   .80 .70

3rd anniversary of October 21 Revolution.

Folk Dance
A85

Folk Dances: 40c, Man and woman, vert. 1sh, Group dance, vert. 2sh, Two men and a woman.

1973 Photo. Perf. 14x13½, 13½x14
396 A85 5c dull blue & multi .20 .20
397 A85 40c brown & multi .20 .20
398 A85 1sh yellow & multi .25 .20
399 A85 2sh brick red & multi .45 .30
Nos. 396-399 (4) 1.10 .90

Hand Writing Somali Script A86

40c, Flame and "FAR SOMALI" inscription, vert. 1sh, Woman and sunburst with Somali script.

Perf. 13½x14, 14x13½
1973, Oct. 21 Photo.
400 A86 40c red & multi .20 .20
401 A86 1sh blue & multi .20 .20
402 A86 2sh yellow & multi .45 .30
Nos. 400-402 (3) .85 .70

Publicity for use of Somali script.

Map of Africa and Emblem — A87

Map of Africa with Target on Somalia — A88

1974, June 12 Perf. 13½x14
403 A87 40c multicolored .20 .20
404 A88 2sh multicolored .50 .30

OAU Meeting, Mogadishu.

Hurdler
A89

1sh, Runners. 1.40sh, Netball, vert.

1974, Aug. 1 Perf. 14x13, 13x14
405 A89 50c black & orange .20 .20
406 A89 1sh black & green .25 .20
407 A89 1.40sh black & olive .35 .25
Nos. 405-407 (3) .80 .65

Victory Pioneers — A90

Pioneers Helping Woman — A91

1974, Aug. 25 Photo. Perf. 13x14
408 A90 40c multicolored .20 .20
409 A91 2sh multicolored .40 .30

Victory Pioneers, founded Aug. 24, 1972, to defend Socialist Revolution.

Map of Arab Countries A92

Flags of Arab Countries A93

1974, Sept. 1 Perf. 14x13
410 A92 1.50sh multicolored .35 .20
411 A93 1.70sh multicolored .45 .25

Somalia's admission to the Arab League, Feb. 14, 1974.

Tank Tracks in Desert A94

Somalis Reading Books — A95

Perf. 14x13½, 13½x14
1974, Oct. 21 Litho.
412 A94 40c multicolored .20 .20
413 A95 2sh multicolored .50 .30

5th anniversary of the Oct. 21st Revolution.

Carrier Pigeons A96

Design: 3sh, Postrider.

1975, Feb. 15 Litho. Perf. 14x13½
414 A96 50c blue & multi .25 .20
415 A96 3sh multicolored 1.25 .45

UPU centenary (in 1974).

Africa A97

Design: 1.50sh, Carrier pigeons.

1975, Apr. 10
416 A97 1sh multicolored .30 .20
417 A97 1.50sh multicolored .50 .25

African Postal Union.

Somali Warrior — A98

Designs: Traditional costumes of Somali men (1sh, 10sh) and women (40c, 50c, 5sh).

1975, Oct. 27 Photo. Perf. 13½
418 A98 10c yellow & multi .20 .20
419 A98 40c lt blue & multi .20 .20
420 A98 50c multicolored .20 .20
421 A98 1sh green & multi .25 .20
422 A98 5sh claret & multi 1.25 .65
423 A98 10sh rose & multi 2.50 1.75
Nos. 418-423 (6) 4.60 3.20

Monument — A99

IWY Emblem A100

1975, Dec. 10 Litho. Perf. 13½x14
424 A99 50c blk & red org .20 .20
425 A100 2.30sh blk, pink & mag .50 .40

International Women's Year.

Abdulla Hassan Monument A101

Abdulla Hassan with Warriors — A102

1.50sh, Abdulla Hassan speaking to his men. 2.30sh, Attacking horsemen, horiz.

Perf. 14x13½, 13½x14
1976, Nov. 30 Photo.
426 A101 50c multicolored .20 .20
427 A102 60c multicolored .20 .20
428 A102 1.50sh multicolored .30 .25
429 A102 2.30sh multicolored .50 .35
Nos. 426-429 (4) 1.20 1.00

Sayid Mohammed Abdulla Hassan (1864-1920), poet and military leader.

Cypraea Gracilis A103

Sea Shells: 75c, Charonia bardayi. 1sh, Chlamys townsendi. 2sh, Cymatium ranzanii. 2.75sh, Conus argillaceus. 2.90sh, Strombus oldi.

1976, Dec. 15 Photo. Perf. 14x13½
430 A103 50c blue & multi .20 .20
431 A103 75c blue & multi .20 .20
432 A103 1sh blue & multi .25 .20
433 A103 2sh blue & multi .50 .30
434 A103 2.75sh blue & multi .75 .45
435 A103 2.90sh blue & multi .85 .45
a. Souvenir sheet of 6, #430-435 4.00 4.00
Nos. 430-435 (6) 2.75 1.80

No. 435a sold for 11sh.

Benin Head and Hunters — A104

Benin Head and: 75c, Handicrafts. 2sh, Dancers. 2.90sh, Musicians.

1977, Aug. 30 Photo. Perf. 14x13½
436 A104 50c multicolored .20 .20
437 A104 75c multicolored .20 .20
438 A104 2sh multicolored .45 .30
439 A104 2.90sh multicolored .60 .40
Nos. 436-439 (4) 1.45 1.10

2nd World Black and African Festival, FESTAC '77, Lagos, Nigeria, Jan. 15-Feb. 12.

Arms of Somalia A105

Designs: 75c, Somali flags, vert. 1.50sh, Pres. Mohammed Siad Barre and globe. 2sh, Arms over rising sun and flags, vert.

Perf. 13½x14, 14x13½
1977, Sept. 30 Photo.
440 A105 75c multicolored .20 .20
441 A105 1sh multicolored .20 .20
442 A105 1.50sh multicolored .25 .20
443 A105 2sh multicolored .45 .40
Nos. 440-443 (4) 1.10 1.00

Somali Socialist Revolutionary Party, established July 1, 1976.

Licaon Pictus A106

Protected Animals: 75c, Bush baby. 1sh, Somali ass. 1.50sh, Aardwolf. 2sh, Greater kudu. 3sh, Giraffe.

1977, Nov. 25 Photo. Perf. 14x13½
444 A106 50c multicolored .20 .20
445 A106 75c multicolored .20 .20
446 A106 1sh multicolored .25 .20
447 A106 1.50sh multicolored .35 .25

448	A106	2sh multicolored	.50	.35
449	A106	3sh multicolored	.70	.60
a.		Souvenir sheet of 6, #444-449	2.50	2.50
		Nos. 444-449 (6)	2.20	1.80

Leonardo da Vinci's Flying Machine A107

ICAO Emblem and: 1.50sh, Montgolfier's balloon. 2sh, Wright brothers' plane. 2.90sh, Somali Airlines turbojet.

1977, Dec. 23   Photo.   Perf. 14x13½

450	A107	1sh multicolored	.25	.20
451	A107	1.50sh multicolored	.35	.25
452	A107	2sh multicolored	.45	.40
453	A107	2.90sh multicolored	.70	.45
a.		Souvenir sheet of 4, #450-453	2.25	2.25
		Nos. 450-453 (4)	1.75	1.30

ICAO, 30th anniv. No. 453a sold for 10sh.

Dome of the Rock — A108

Lithographed and Engraved
1978, Apr. 30   Perf. 13x14

| 454 | A108 | 75c multicolored | .20 | .20 |
| 455 | A108 | 2sh multicolored | .45 | .35 |

Palestinian fighters and their families.

Stadium and Soccer Player — A109

Designs: 4.90sh, Stadium and goalkeeper. 5.50sh, Stadium and player.

1978, Aug. 5   Litho.   Perf. 14x13½

456	A109	1.50sh multicolored	.35	.35
457	A109	4.90sh multicolored	1.25	.90
458	A109	5.50sh multicolored	1.40	1.10
a.		Souvenir sheet of 3, #456-458	3.75	3.75
		Nos. 456-458 (3)	3.00	2.20

11th World Cup Soccer Championship, Argentina, June 1-25. No. 458a sold for 14sh.

Acacia Tortilis — A110

Trees: 50c, Ficus sycomorus, vert. 75c, Terminalia catapa, vert. 2.90sh, Baobab.

1978, Sept. 5   Photo.   Perf. 14

459	A110	40c multicolored	.20	.20
460	A110	50c multicolored	.20	.20
461	A110	75c multicolored	.20	.20
462	A110	2.90sh multicolored	.40	.40
		Nos. 459-462 (4)	1.00	1.00

Forest conservation.

Hibiscus — A111

Flowers of Somalia: 1sh, Cassia baccarinii. 1.50sh, Kigelia somalensis. 2.30sh, Dichrostachys glomerata.

1978, Dec. 15   Photo.   Perf. 13½x14

463	A111	50c multicolored	.20	.20
464	A111	1sh multicolored	.25	.20
465	A111	1.50sh multicolored	.30	.25
466	A111	2.30sh multicolored	.50	.35
a.		Souv. sheet, #463-466, perf. 14	2.50	2.50
		Nos. 463-466 (4)	1.25	1.00

Huri and Siganus Rivulatus A112

Fishery Development: 80c, Sail huri, gaterin gaterinus. 2.30sh, Fishing boats, hypacanthus amia. 2.50sh, Motorized fishing boat, mackerel.

1979, Sept. 1   Photo.   Perf. 14x13½

467	A112	75c multicolored	.20	.20
468	A112	80c multicolored	.20	.20
469	A112	2.30sh multicolored	.40	.40
470	A112	2.50sh multicolored	.45	.45
		Nos. 467-470 (4)	1.25	1.25

Sailing, IYC Emblem — A113

IYC Emblem, Children's Drawings: 50c, 90c, Schoolboy. 1.50sh, 2.50sh, Houses. 3sh, 4sh, Bird and flower. 1sh, as 75c.

1979, Sept. 10   Photo.   Perf. 13½x14

471	A113	50c multicolored	.20	.20
472	A113	90c multicolored	.20	.20
473	A113	1.50sh multicolored	.25	.25
474	A113	3sh multicolored	.50	.50
		Nos. 471-474 (4)	1.15	1.15

Souvenir Sheet of 4

| 474A | A113 | #b.-e. | 1.75 | 1.75 |

Intl. Year of the Child. No. 474A contains 90c, 1sh, 2.50sh, 4sh stamps and sold for 10sh.

University Students, Outdoor Classrooms — A114

Flower and: 50c, Housing construction. 75c, Children's recreation. 1sh, Doctor examining child, woman and man carrying grain and fish. 2.40sh, Woman and children carrying produce over dam. 3sh, Dish antenna.

1979, Nov. 30   Litho.   Perf. 14x13½

475	A114	20c multicolored	.20	.20
476	A114	50c multicolored	.20	.20
477	A114	75c multicolored	.20	.20
478	A114	1sh multicolored	.25	.20
479	A114	2.40sh multicolored	.60	.25
480	A114	3sh multicolored	.65	.30
		Nos. 475-480 (6)	2.10	1.35

Oct. 21 revolution, 10th anniversary.

Barbopsis Devecchii A115

Freshwater Fish: 90c, Phreatichthys andruzzii. 1sh, Uegitglanis zammaranoi. 2.50sh, Pardi's catfish.

1979, Dec. 12

481	A115	50c multicolored	.25	.20
482	A115	90c multicolored	.30	.20
483	A115	1sh multicolored	.35	.20
484	A115	2.50sh multicolored	1.00	.30
a.		Souvenir sheet of 4, #481-484	3.00	3.00
		Nos. 481-484 (4)	1.90	.90

No. 484a sold for 10sh.

Taleh Fortress, Congress Emblem — A116

1980, June 1   Photo.   Perf. 14x13½

| 485 | A116 | 2.25sh multicolored | .60 | .35 |
| 486 | A116 | 3.50sh multicolored | .90 | .55 |

1st International Congress of Somalian Studies, Mogadishu, July 6-13.

View of Marka — A117

1980, July 1   Litho.   Perf. 14

487	A117	75c shown	.20	.20
488	A117	1sh Gandershe + label	.25	.20
489	A117	2.30sh Afgooye + label	.65	.35
490	A117	3.50sh Muqdisho + label	1.00	.55
		Nos. 487-490 (4)	2.10	1.30

See Nos. 502-505, 527-530.

A118

1980, July 30   Photo.   Perf. 13½x14

491	A118	1sh Batis perkeo	.30	.20
492	A118	2.25sh Rynchostruthus socotranus louisae	.30	.35
493	A118	5sh Laniarius ruficeps	1.90	.80
a.		Souvenir sheet of 3, #491-493	2.75	1.25
		Nos. 491-493 (3)	2.50	1.35

A119

Perf. 13½x14, 14x13½
1981, Oct. 16   Litho.

494	A119	75c Globe, grain	.20	.20
495	A119	3.25sh Emblem, horiz.	.75	.50
496	A119	5.50sh like No. 494	1.50	.90
		Nos. 494-496 (3)	2.45	1.60

World Food Day.

13th World Telecommunications Day — A120

1981, Oct. 10   Perf. 13½x14

497	A120	1sh Shepherdess, sheep, dish antenna	.30	.20
498	A120	3sh Emblems	1.10	.50
499	A120	4.60sh like No. 498	1.10	.55
		Nos. 497-499 (3)	2.50	1.25

Hegira, 1500th Anniv. — A121

1982 World Cup — A122

1981, Oct.   Photo.   Perf. 13½x14

| 500 | A121 | 1.50sh multicolored | .30 | .20 |
| 501 | A121 | 3.80sh multicolored | .85 | .65 |

View Type of 1980

1982, May 31   Litho.   Perf. 13½x14

502	A117	2.25sh Balcad	.65	.35
503	A117	4sh Jowhar	1.25	.65
504	A117	5.50sh Golaleey	1.60	.90
505	A117	8.30sh Muqdisho	2.25	1.25
		Nos. 502-505 (4)	5.75	3.15

Nos. 502-505 each se-tenant with label showing regional map.

1982, June 13

Designs: Various soccer players.

506	A122	1sh multicolored	.35	.20
507	A122	1.50sh multicolored	.55	.25
508	A122	3.25sh multicolored	1.25	.55
a.		Souvenir sheet of 3, #506-508	2.25	1.00
		Nos. 506-508 (3)	2.15	1.00

ITU Plenipotentiaries Conference, Nairobi, Sept. — A123

1982, Oct. 15   Photo.   Perf. 14x13½

509	A123	75c green & multi	.20	.20
510	A123	3.25sh orange & multi	.85	.50
511	A123	5.50sh blue & multi	1.50	.90
		Nos. 509-511 (3)	2.55	1.60

Local Snakes — A124

2.80sh, Bitis arietans. 3.20sh, Psammophis punctulatus. 4.60sh, Rhamphiophis oxyrhynchus. 8.60sh, Sphalerosophis josephscorteccii.

1982, Dec. 20   Photo.   Perf. 14
512 A124 2.80sh multicolored .75 .40
513 A124 3.20sh multicolored .85 .50
514 A124 4.60sh multicolored 1.40 .65
  Nos. 512-514 (3) 3.00 1.55

Souvenir Sheet
515 A124 8.60sh multicolored 4.00 2.25

Somali
Woman — A125   A126

1982, Dec. 30   Perf. 14x13½
516 A125 1sh yel & multi .20 .20
517 A125 5.20sh lilac & multi .90 .85
518 A125 5.80sh org & multi .95 .90
519 A125 6.40sh blue & multi 1.10 1.00
520 A125 9.40sh lt brn & multi 1.60 1.50
521 A125 25sh green & multi 4.25 4.00
  Nos. 516-521 (6) 9.00 8.45

1983, July 20   Perf. 13½x14
522 A126 5.20sh multicolored .95 .65
523 A126 6.40sh multicolored 1.00 .85

World Communications Year.

2nd Intl. Congress of Somali Studies, Hamburg — A127

Various views of Hamburg.

1983, Aug. 1   Perf. 14
524 A127 5.20sh multicolored .85 .65
525 A127 6.40sh multicolored 1.00 .85

Military
Uniforms — A128

Designs: a, Air Force. b, Women's Auxiliary Corps. c, Border Police. d, People's Militia. e, Army Infantry. f, Custodial Corps. g, Police. h, Navy.

1983, Oct. 21   Litho.   Perf. 13½x14
526   Strip of 8 2.00
a.-h. A128 3.20sh, any single .25 .20

View Type of 1980

1983
527 A117 2.80sh Barawe .35 .20
528 A117 3.20sh Bur Hakaba .40 .20
529 A117 5.50sh Baydhabo .65 .30
530 A117 8.60sh Dooy Nuunaay 1.10 .50
  Nos. 527-530 (4) 2.50 1.20

Sea Shells
A129

1984, Feb. 15   Litho.   Perf. 14x13½
531 A129 2.80sh Volutocorbis
    rosavittoriae .25 .20
532 A129 3.20sh Phalium bi-
    tuberculosum .25 .20
533 A129 5.50sh Conus milneed-
    warsi .40 .30
  Nos. 531-533 (3) .90 .70

Souvenir Sheet
Perf. 14
534 A129 15sh Cypraea
    broderipi 1.25 .90

Olympics
1984 — A130

Riccione
Fair — A131

1984, Sept.   Litho.   Perf. 13½x14
535 A130 1.50sh Runners .20 .20
536 A130 3sh Discus .25 .20
537 A130 8sh Pole vaulting .65 .45
a.   Souvenir sheet of 3, #535-537 1.25 .90
  Nos. 535-537 (3) 1.10 .85

No. 537a sold for 15sh.

1984, Sept.   Litho.   Perf. 13½x14
538 A131 5.20sh multicolored .40 .30
539 A131 6.40sh multicolored .55 .40

Animals
A132

1984, Sept.   Litho.   Perf. 14x13½
540 A132 1sh Hystrix cristata .20 .20
541 A132 1.50sh Ichneumia albi-
    cauda .20 .20
542 A132 2sh Mungos mungo .20 .20
543 A132 4sh Mellivora capen-
    sis .40 .25
a.   Souvenir sheet of 4, #540-543 .90 .60
  Nos. 540-543 (4) 1.00 .85

No. 543a sold for 10sh.

Intl. Civil Aviation Org., 40th
Anniv. — A133

1984, Nov. 20   Litho.   Perf. 14
544 A133 3sh multicolored .20 .20
545 A133 6.40sh multicolored .25 .20

Souvenir Sheet
546   Sheet of 2 .35 .35
a.   A133 3sh like No. 544 .20 .20
b.   A133 6.40sh like No. 545 .25 .25

No. 546 contains 2 49½x46mm stamps.
Sold for 10sh.

Dove — A134

Constellations from the Book of Fixed Stars, by Abd al-Rahman al-Sufi.

1985, Aug. 10   Litho.   Perf. 13½x14
547 A134 4.30sh shown .45 .30
548 A134 11sh Bull 1.10 .80
549 A134 12.50sh Rams 1.25 .90
550 A134 13.80sh Archer 1.50 1.00
  Nos. 547-550 (4) 4.30 3.00

Architecture — A135

1985, Sept.   Litho.   Perf. 13½x14
551 A135 2sh Ras Kiambone
    + label .20 .20
552 A135 6.60sh Hannassa +
    label .55 .45
553 A135 10sh Mnarani + la-
    bel 1.50 1.10
554 A135 18.60sh as #551, diff.
    + label 2.75 1.75
  Nos. 551-554 (4) 5.00 3.50

See Nos. 572-575.

Lady
Somalia
Seated in
Posthorn
A136

1985, Oct.   Perf. 14x14½
555 A136 2sh multicolored .20 .20
556 A136 20sh multicolored 2.00 1.50
a.   Souvenir sheet of 2, #555-556,
    perf. 13½ 3.25 3.25

ITALIA '85, Rome. No. 556a sold for 30sh.

Bats
A137

1985, Dec. 25   Litho.   Perf. 14x13½
557 A137 2.50sh Triaenops per-
    sicus .20 .20
558 A137 4.50sh Cardioderma
    cor .20 .20
559 A137 16sh Tadarida con-
    dylura .55 .45
560 A137 18sh Coleura afra .65 .45
  Nos. 557-560 (4) 1.60 1.25

Souvenir Sheet
561   Sheet of 4 1.75 1.75
a.   A137 2.50sh like #552 .20 .20
b.   A137 4.50sh like #553 .20 .20
c.   A137 16sh like #554 .70 .70
d.   A137 18sh like #555 .80 .80

Nos. 561a-561d printed in continuous design. No. 561 sold for 50sh.

Economic Trade Agreement with
Kenya — A138

Design: Presidents Arap Moi and Barre, satellite communications.

1986, Feb. 15   Perf. 14
562 A138 9sh multi .30 .25
563 A138 14.50sh multi .50 .35

EUROFLORA
Flower Exhibition,
Genoa — A139

3rd Intl. Congress
on Somali
Studies — A140

1986, Apr. 25   Perf. 13½x14
564 A139 10sh Flower arrange-
    ment .35 .25
565 A139 15sh Arrangement, diff. .50 .40
a.   Souvenir sheet of 2, #564-565 1.25 1.25

No. 565a sold for 30sh.

1986, May 26
566 A140 11.35sh multi .40 .30
567 A140 20sh multi .70 .50

1986 World Cup Soccer
Championships, Mexico — A141

Various soccer plays.

1986, June Perf. 14x13½

568	A141	3.60sh multi	.20	.20
569	A141	4.80sh multi	.20	.20
570	A141	6.80sh multi	.25	.20
571	A141	22.60sh multi	.85	.55
a.		Souvenir sheet of 4, #568-571	1.75	1.75
		Nos. 568-571 (4)	1.50	1.15

No. 571a sold for 50sh.

Architecture Type of 1985

1986 Litho. Perf. 13½x14

572	A135	10sh Bulaxaar	.35	.30
573	A135	15sh Saylac	.50	.40
574	A135	20sh Saylac, diff.	.70	.55
575	A135	31sh Jasiiradaha Jawaay	1.10	.85
		Nos. 572-575 (4)	2.65	2.10

Nos. 572-575 each printed se-tenant with decorative label.

Red Crescent - Red Cross Rehabilitation Center, Mogadishu — A143

1987, May 8 Litho. Perf. 13½x13

576	A143	56sh multi	2.00 1.60

Souvenir Sheet

577	A143	56sh multi, diff.	2.25 2.25

No. 577 sold for 60sh. See Norway No. 908.

A144

A145

1987, Sept. 27 Litho. Perf. 13½x14

578	A144	20sh Running	.90	.70
579	A144	48sh Javelin	2.00	1.60
a.		Souvenir sheet of 2, #578-579	3.50	3.50

OLYMPHILEX '87, Rome. No. 579a sold for 75sh.

1987, Oct. 5 Photo. Perf. 13½x14½

580	A145	53sh multicolored	1.40	1.10
581	A145	72sh multicolored	1.90	1.40

Intl. Year of Shelter for the Homeless.

GEOSOM '87 — A146

A147

Maps: 10sh, 160,000,000 years ago. 20sh, 60,000,000 years ago. 40sh, 15,000,000 years ago. 50sh, Today.

1987, Nov. 24 Litho. Perf. 13½x14

582	A146	10sh multi	.25	.20
583	A146	20sh multi, diff.	.50	.40
584	A146	40sh multi, diff.	1.00	.75
585	A146	50sh multi, diff.	1.25	1.00
a.		Souv. sheet of 2, #583, 585	5.50	4.00
		Nos. 582-585 (4)	3.00	2.35

Symposium on the Geology of Somalia, Mogadishu, 11/24-12/1. #585a sold for 130sh.

1988, Dec. 31 Litho. Perf. 13½x14

586	A147	50sh multicolored	.50	.40
587	A147	168sh multicolored	1.60	1.20

World Health Organization, 40th anniv.

Wildlife A148

Perf. 13½x14, 14x13½

1989, Oct. 20 Litho.

588	A148	75sh Lepus somaliensis	.35	.30
589	A148	198sh Syncerus caffer	.90	.70
590	A148	200sh Papio hamadryas	.95	.70
591	A148	216sh Hippopotamus amphibius	1.00	.75
a.		Souvenir sheet of 2, #590-591	3.25	3.25
		Nos. 588-591 (4)	3.20	2.45

No. 591a contains 2 labels like #588-589. Sold for 700sh.

Somali Revolution, 20th Anniv. A149

Flowers, children's games: 70sh, Kick ball. 100sh, Swinging. 150sh, Teeter-totter. 300sh, Jumping rope, stick and hoop.

1989, Dec. 12 Litho. Perf. 14x13½

592	A149	70sh multicolored	1.40	1.10
593	A149	100sh multicolored	2.00	1.60
594	A149	150sh multicolored	3.00	2.40
595	A149	300sh multicolored	6.00	4.75
		Nos. 592-595 (4)	12.40	9.85

A150   A151

Liberation: Nos. 599-600, Dove breaking chains, horiz.

1991 Litho. Perf. 13½x14, 14x13½

596	A150	70sh lilac & multi	.65	.50
597	A150	100sh grn bl & multi	.90	.70
598	A150	150sh brt blue & multi	1.40	1.00
599	A150	150sh yellow & multi	1.40	1.00

600	A150	300sh yel grn & multi	2.75	2.00
601	A150	300sh yel grn & multi	2.75	2.00
		Nos. 596-601 (6)	9.85	7.20

Issued: Nos. 599-600, July 2; others, July 4.

No. 599 Ovptd. in Blue

1991 Litho. Perf. 14x13½

602	A150	150sh yellow & multi	1.40 1.00

1991 Litho. Perf. 14

Various minarets.

603	A151	30sh multicolored	.30	.30
604	A151	40sh multicolored	.45	.35
605	A151	50sh multicolored	.55	.40
606	A151	150sh multicolored	1.70	1.25
		Nos. 603-606 (4)	3.00	2.30

Relief efforts have demonstrated the breakdown of government services in Somalia. It is unclear which faction has control of the Postal Service, if any is operating. The status of Scott Nos. 607-638 will be reviewed once more information is available.

Gazelles A152

1992 Perf. 14x13½

Inscribed in Black

607	A152	500sh Two Speke's	2.50
608	A152	700sh One Speke's	3.50
609	A152	800sh One Soemmering's	4.50
610	A152	1000sh Two Soemmering's	5.50
		Nos. 607-610 (4)	16.00

World Wildlife Fund.

Without WWF Emblem
Inscribed in red lilac

611	A152	100sh like #607	.55
612	A152	200sh like #608	1.10
613	A152	300sh like #609	1.60
614	A152	400sh like #610	2.25

Inscribed in black

615	A152	1500sh Baboons	8.25
616	A152	2500sh Hippopotamus	13.00
617	A152	3000sh Giraffes	16.00
618	A152	5000sh Leopard	25.00
		Nos. 607-618 (12)	83.75

Nos. 607-618 are part of an expanding set. Numbers may change.
For overprints see No. 629-632.

Nos. 607-610 Ovptd. "PARTICIPANT / RIO 1992" in Orange

1992 Litho. Perf. 14x13½

629	A152	500sh on #607	2.75
630	A152	700sh on #608	3.75
631	A152	800sh on #609	4.50
632	A152	1000sh on #610	5.50
		Nos. 629-632 (4)	16.50

Discovery of America, 500th Anniv. A153

Designs: 100sh, Sighting land from crow's nest. 200sh, Three men pointing from ship. 300sh, Columbus in his cabin. 400sh, Claiming land. 2000sh, Building fort in New World.
No. 638: a, 800sh, like #634. b, 900sh, like #635. c, 1300sh, like #633.

1992

633	A153	100sh multicolored	.55
634	A153	200sh multicolored	1.10
635	A153	300sh multicolored	1.60
636	A153	400sh multicolored	2.25
637	A153	2000sh multicolored	11.00
		Nos. 633-637 (5)	16.50

Souvenir Sheet

638	A153	Sheet of 3, #a.-c.	16.50

Nos. 638a-638c do not have white border.
No. 638 exists imperf.

SEMI-POSTAL STAMPS

Italy Nos. B1-B4 Overprinted

1916 Wmk. 140 Perf. 14

B1	SP1	10c + 5c rose	3.50	11.50
B2	SP2	15c + 5c slate	12.50	15.00
B3	SP2	20c + 5c orange	3.50	12.50
B4	SP2	20c on 15c + 5c slate	12.50	25.00
		Nos. B1-B4 (4)	32.00	64.00

Holy Year Issue
Italy Nos. B20-B25 Surcharged in Black or Red

1925, June 1 Perf. 12

B5	SP4	6b + 3b on 20c + 10c	1.60	7.25
B6	SP4	13b + 6b on 30c + 15c	1.60	9.00
B7	SP4	15b + 8b on 50c + 25c	1.60	7.25
B8	SP4	18b + 9b on 60c + 30c	1.60	10.00
B9	SP8	30b + 15b on 1 l +50c (R)	1.60	13.50
B10	SP8	1r + 50b on 5 l +2.50 l (R)	1.60	20.00
		Nos. B5-B10 (6)	9.60	67.00

Colonial Institute Issue

"Peace" Substituting Spade for Sword — SP10

1926, June 1 Typo. Perf. 14

B11	SP10	5c + 5c brown	.35	2.50
B12	SP10	10c + 5c olive grn	.35	2.50
B13	SP10	20c + 5c blue grn	.35	2.50
B14	SP10	40c + 5c brown red	.35	2.50
B15	SP10	60c + 5c orange	.35	2.50
B16	SP10	1 l + 5c blue	.35	4.00
		Nos. B11-B16 (6)	2.10	16.50

The surtax was for the Italian Colonial Institute.

Types of Italian Semi-Postal Stamps of 1926 Overprinted

1927, Apr. 21 Unwmk. Perf. 11½

B17	SP10	40c + 20c dk brn & blk	1.10	10.00
B18	SP10	60c + 30c brn red & ol brn	1.10	10.00
B19	SP10	1.25 l + 60c dp bl & blk	1.25	19.00

B20 SP10 5 l + 2.50 l dk grn
& blk 1.75 *26.00*
Nos. B17-B24 (4) 5.20 *65.00*

The surtax was for the charitable work of the Voluntary Militia for Italian National Defense.

Allegory of Fascism and Victory — SP11

1928, Oct. 15   Wmk. 140   *Perf. 14*
B21 SP11 20c + 5c blue grn 1.10 *3.50*
B22 SP11 30c + 5c red 1.10 *3.50*
B23 SP11 50c + 10c purple 1.10 *5.25*
B24 SP11 1.25 l + 20c dk blue 1.10 *6.50*
Nos. B21-B24 (4) 4.40 *18.75*

46th anniv. of the Societa Africana d'Italia. The surtax aided that society.

Types of Italian Semi-Postal Stamps of 1928 Overprinted

1929, Mar. 4   Unwmk.   *Perf. 11*
B25 SP10 30c + 10c red & blk 1.90 *7.75*
B26 SP10 50c + 20c vio & blk 1.90 *7.75*
B27 SP10 1.25 l + 50c brn & bl 2.25 *11.00*
B28 SP10 5 l + 2 l ol grn &
blk 2.25 *20.00*
Nos. B25-B28 (4) 8.30 *46.50*

The surtax was for the charitable work of the Voluntary Militia for Italian National Defense.

Types of Italian Semi-Postal Stamps of 1926 Overprinted in Black or Red

1930, Oct. 20   *Perf. 14*
B29 SP10 30c + 10c dk grn
& bl grn (Bk) 8.00 *12.00*
B30 SP10 50c + 10c dk grn
& vio (R) 8.00 *14.00*
B31 SP10 1.25 l + 30c ol brn
& red brn
(R) 8.00 *20.00*
B32 SP10 5 l + 1.50 l ind &
grn (R) 27.50 *47.50*
Nos. B29-B32 (4) 51.50 *93.50*

The surtax was for the charitable work of the Voluntary Militia for Italian National Defense.

Irrigation Canal SP14

1930, Nov. 27   Photo.   Wmk. 140
B33 SP14 50c + 20c olive
brn 1.40 *6.50*
B34 SP14 1.25 l + 20c dp blue 1.40 *6.50*
B35 SP14 1.75 l + 20c green 1.40 *8.25*
B36 SP14 2.55 l + 50c purple 2.10 *13.00*
B37 SP14 5 l + 1 l dp car 2.10 *19.00*
Nos. B33-B37 (5) 8.40 *53.25*

25th anniv. of the Italian Colonial Agricultural Institute. The surtax was for the aid of that institution.

SP15

King Victor Emmanuel III — SP16

1935, Jan. 1
B38 SP15 5c + 5c blk
brn 1.10 *7.00*
B39 SP15 7½c + 7½c vio 1.10 *7.00*
B40 SP15 15c + 10c ol blk 1.10 *7.00*
B41 SP15 20c + 10c rose
red 1.10 *7.00*
B42 SP15 25c + 10c dp
grn 1.10 *7.00*
B43 SP15 30c + 10c brn 1.10 *7.00*
B44 SP15 50c + 10c pur 1.10 *7.00*
B45 SP15 75c + 15c rose
car 1.10 *7.00*
B46 SP15 1.25 l + 15c dp bl 1.10 *7.00*
B47 SP15 1.75 l + 25c red
org 1.10 *7.00*
B48 SP15 2.75 l + 25c gray 8.00 *24.00*
B49 SP15 5 l + 1 l dp cl 8.00 *24.00*
B50 SP15 10 l + 1.80 l red
brn 8.00 *24.00*
B51 SP16 25 l + 2.75 l brn
& red 72.50 *110.00*
Nos. B38-B51 (14) 107.50 *252.00*
Set, never hinged 210.00

Visit of King Victor Emmanuel III.

Catalogue values for unused stamps in this section, from this point to the end of the section, are for Never Hinged items.

Somalia

Nurse Holding Infant — SP17

1957, Nov. 30   Wmk. 303   *Perf. 14*
B52 SP17 10c + 10c red &
brn .20 .20
B53 SP17 25c + 10c grn &
brn .20 .20
Nos. B52-B53,CB11-CB12 (4) .85 .95

The surtax was for the fight against tuberculosis.

Republic

Refugees SP18

1964, Dec. 12   Photo.   *Perf. 14*
B54 SP18 25c + 10c vio bl & red .25 .20
Nos. B54,CB13-CB14 (3) 1.55 .70

The surtax was to help refugees.

Red Cross Nurse Feeding Child — SP19

Refugees SP20

Famine Relief: 80c+20c, Nomad in parched land, horiz. 2.40sh+10c, Family with fish and produce. 2.90sh+10c, Physician and Aid Society emblem, horiz.

1976, Dec. 10   *Perf. 13x14, 14x13*
B55 SP19 75c + 25c multi .25 .25
B56 SP19 80c + 20c multi .25 .25
B57 SP19 2.40sh + 10c multi .50 .50
B58 SP19 2.90sh + 10c multi .70 .70
Nos. B55-B58 (4) 1.70 1.70

1981, Dec. 15   Photo.   *Perf. 13½x14*
B59 SP20 2sh + 50c multi .70 .40
B60 SP20 6.80sh + 50c multi 2.00 .60
a. Souvenir sheet of 2, #B59-B60 4.00 1.60

TB Bacillus Centenary — SP31

1982, Dec. 30   Photo.   *Perf. 14*
B61 SP31 4.60sh + 60c multi 2.00 .85
B62 SP31 5.80sh + 60c multi 2.00 1.00

AIR POST STAMPS

View of Coast AP1

Cheetahs AP2

Wmk. 140
1934, Oct.   Photo.   *Perf. 14*
C1 AP1 25c sl bl & red org 2.00 *6.50*
C2 AP1 50c dk grn & blk 2.00 *5.25*
C3 AP1 75c brn & red org 2.00 *5.25*
a. Imperf.
C4 AP2 80c org brn & blk 2.00 *6.50*
C5 AP2 1 l scar & blk 2.00 *7.25*
C6 AP2 2 l dk bl & brn 2.00 *12.00*
Nos. C1-C6 (6) 12.00 *42.75*
Set, never hinged 24.00

2nd Colonial Arts Exhibition, Naples. For overprint see No. CO1.

Banana Tree and Airplane AP3

25c, 1.50 l, Banana tree, plane. 50c, 2 l, Plane over cotton field. 60c, 5 l, Plane over orchard. 75c, 10 l, Plane over field workers. 1 l, 3 l, Small girl watching plane.

1936   Photo.
C7 AP3 25c slate green .85 *1.75*
C8 AP3 50c brown .20 .20
C9 AP3 60c red orange 1.10 *3.25*
C10 AP3 75c orange brn .70 .95
C11 AP3 1 l deep blue .20 .20
C12 AP3 1.50 l purple .70 .40
C13 AP3 2 l slate blue 2.40 .65
C14 AP3 3 l copper red 7.25 3.00
C15 AP3 5 l yellow green 7.75 5.25
C16 AP3 10 l dp rose red 9.00 8.25
Nos. C7-C16 (10) 30.15 *23.90*
Set, never hinged 60.00

Catalogue values for unused stamps in this section, from this point to the end of the section, are for Never Hinged items.

Somalia

AP8

1950-51   Wmk. 277
C17 AP8 30c yellow brn .20 .30
C18 AP8 45c dk carmine .20 .30
C19 AP8 65c dk blue vio .20 .30
C20 AP8 70c dull blue .20 .30
C21 AP8 90c olive brn .20 .30
C22 AP8 1s lilac rose .20 .30
C23 AP8 1.35s violet .25 .70
C24 AP8 1.50s blue green .35 .60
C25 AP8 3s blue 2.50 2.50
C26 AP8 5s chocolate 3.00 3.00
C27 AP8 10s red org ('51) 3.25 2.50
Nos. C17-C27 (11) 10.55 11.10

Scene in Mogadishu AP8a

1951, Oct. 4
C27A AP8a 1s vio & Prus bl .85 *1.00*
C27B AP8a 1.50s ol grn & chnt
brn 1.60 *3.00*

First Territorial Council meeting.

Plane, Palm Tree and Minaret — AP9

Mother and Child — AP10

1952, Sept. 14
C28 AP9 1.20s ol bis & dp bl 1.00 *2.00*

1st Somali Fair, Mogadishu, Sept. 14-28.

1953, May 27
C29 AP10 1.20s dk grn & dk brn .60 .85

Somali anti-tuberculosis campaign.

Fair
Entrance
AP11

1953, Sept. 28   Unwmk.   Perf. 11½
C30 AP11 1.20s brn car & pink   .30 .50
C31 AP11 1.50s yel brn & buff   .30 .50
2nd Somali Fair, Mogadishu, Sept. 28-Oct. 12, 1953.

Plane
over
Map
and
Stamps
of 1903
AP12

Perf. 13x13½
1953, Dec. 16   Engr.   Wmk. 277
Early Stamps in Brn and Rose Car
C32 AP12 60c orange brown   .30 .50
C33 AP12 1s greenish black   .30 .50
1st Somali postage stamps, 5th anniv.

"UPU" among Constellations — AP13

Perf. 11½
1953, Dec. 16   Photo.   Unwmk.
C34 AP13 1.20s red & cream   .25 .35
C35 AP13 1.50s brown & cream   .30 .50
C36 AP13 2s green & lt blue   .30 .50
Nos. C34-C36 (3)   .85 1.35
UPU, 75th anniv. (in 1949).

Alexander   Somali
Island Juba   Flag — AP15
River — AP14

1954, June 1   Perf. 13½x12½
C37 AP14 1.20s dk grn & brn   .35 .50
C38 AP14 2s dk carmine & pur   .40 .60
See note after No. 196.

Perf. 13½x13
1954, Oct. 12   Litho.   Wmk. 277
C39 AP15 1.20s multicolored   .20 .30
Adoption of Somali flag.

Haggard's
Oribi — AP16

Designs: 45c, Phillip's dik-dik. 50c, Speke's gazelle. 75c, Gerenuk. 1.20s, Soemmering's gazelle. 1.50s, Waterbuck.

Wmk. 277
1955, Apr. 12   Photo.   Perf. 13½
Antelopes in Natural Colors
Size: 22x33mm
C40 AP16 35c gray grn & blk   .20 .50
C41 AP16 45c lilac & blk   1.60 .70
C42 AP16 50c rose lil & blk   .20 .50
C43 AP16 75c red   1.10 .50
C44 AP16 1.20s dk gray grn   1.10 1.40
C45 AP16 1.50s bright blue   1.60 2.40
Nos. C40-C45 (6)   5.80 6.00
See Nos. C57-C58.

Caravan at
Water Hole
AP17

Design: 1.20s, Village well.

Perf. 13½x14
1955, Sept. 24   Wmk. 303
C46 AP17 45c brown & orange   .20 .30
C47 AP17 1.20s sapphire & pink   .25 .40
3rd Somali Fair, Mogadishu, Sept. 1955.

Ballot Type of Regular Issue
1956, Apr. 30   Photo.   Perf. 14
C48 A24 60c brown & ultra   .20 .20
C49 A24 1.20s brown & org   .20 .20
Opening of the territory's first democratically elected Legislative Assembly.

Arms Type of Regular Issue
1957, May 6   Wmk. 303   Perf. 13½
Coat of Arms in Dull Yellow, Blue and Black
C50 A25 45c blue   .20 .20
C51 A25 1.20s bluish green   .20 .25
Issued in honor of the new coat of arms.

Type of Regular Issue, 1957 and

Oil Well — AP18

Design: 60c, Irrigation canal construction.

1957, Sept. 28   Perf. 14
C52 A26 60c blue & brown   .20 .30
C53 AP18 1.20s black & ver   .20 .30
Fourth Somali Fair and Film Festival.

Sport Type of Regular Issue
60c, Runner. 1.20s, Bicyclist. 1.50s, Basketball player.

1958, Apr. 28   Wmk. 303   Perf. 14
C54 A27 60c brown   .20 .20
C55 A27 1.20s blue   .20 .20
C56 A27 1.50s rose carmine   .20 .20
Nos. C54-C56 (3)   .60 .60

Animal Type of 1955
3s, Lesser kudu. 5s, Hunter's hartebeest.

1958-59   Photo.
Size: 20½x36½mm
C57 AP16 3s ocher & sepia   .60 .85
C58 AP16 5s gray, blk & yel ('59) .60 .85
See No. CE1.

Police
Bugler
AP19

1959, June 19   Photo.
C59 AP19 1.20s ocher & ultra   .20 .30
C60 AP19 1.50s olive grn & ultra .20 .30
a.   Souv. sheet of 4, #228-229,
C59-C60   1.25 1.75
Opening of the Constituent Assembly of Somalia.

Marabou
AP20

1959, Sept. 4   Wmk. 303
C61 AP20 1.20s shown   .20 .25
C62 AP20 2s Great egret   .20 .30

Incense
Shipment,
15th
Century
B.C.
AP21

Design: 2s, Incense burner and view of Mogadishu harbor.

1959, Sept. 28   Perf. 14
C63 AP21 1.20s red & blk   .20 .30
C64 AP21 2s blue, blk & org   .30 .45
5th Somali Fair, Mogadishu.

University
Institute
and Arms
AP22

Design: 1.20s, Front view of Institute.

1960, Jan. 14
C65 AP22 45c grn, blk & org brn .25 .25
C66 AP22 1.20s blue, ultra & blk .35 .35
Opening of the University Institute of Somalia.

Stork and
Uprooted Oak
Emblem — AP23

1960, Apr. 7   Wmk. 303   Perf. 14
C67 AP23 1.50s lt grn, bl & red .25 .25
World Refugee Year, 7/1/59-6/30/60.

Republic
#C42, C44 Overprinted Like #242
Wmk. 277
1960, June 26   Photo.   Perf. 13½
Antelopes in Natural Colors
C68 AP16 50c rose lil & blk   6.00 5.75
C69 AP16 1.20s dk gray grn   10.50 5.75
See note after No. 242.

Parliament
and Italian
Flag
AP25

1.80s, Somali flag and assembly building.

1960, July 1   Wmk. 303   Perf. 14
C70 AP25 1s org red, grn & red   .30 .30
C71 AP25 1.80s red org, ultra & blk .60 .60
Somalia's independence.

Animal Type of Regular Issue
1960, Nov. 24
C72 A37 3s Leopard   .60 .50

Olympic Games Type
45c, Runner, flag, Olympic rings. 1.80s, Long distance runner, flag, Olympic rings.

1960, Nov. 24
C73 A38 45c lilac & blue   .20 .20
C74 A38 1.80s org ver & bl   .30 .30
17th Olympic Games, Rome, 8/25-9/11.

Amauris
Fenestrata
and Jet
Plane
AP26

Various Butterflies.

1961, Sept. 9
C75 AP26 60c blue, brn & yel   .20 .20
C76 AP26 90c yel, blk & grn   .20 .20
C77 AP26 1s multicolored   1.60 .20
C78 AP26 1.80s org, blk & red   .40 .25
C79 AP26 3s multicolored   .50 .40
C80 AP26 5s ver, blk & brt bl   1.25 .70
C81 AP26 10s multicolored   2.50 1.25
Nos. C75-C81 (7)   6.65 3.20

Wooden
Headrest,
Comb and
Cap
AP27

Design: 1.80sh, Camel, metal sculpture.

1961, Sept. 28   Wmk. 303   Perf. 14
C82 AP27 1sh blk, ultra & ocher .25 .25
C83 AP27 1.80sh blk, yel & brn   .40 .30
6th Somali Fair, Mogadishu.

Fish Type
Fish: 2.70sh, Lutianus sebae.

1962, Apr. 26
C84 A41 2.70sh ultra, brn & rose
           brn   .90 .60

Mosquitoes and
Malaria
Eradication
Emblem — AP28

Police Auxiliary
Women — AP29

Wmk. 303
1962, Oct. 25   Photo.   Perf. 14
C85 AP28 1sh bis brn & blk   .30 .20
C86 AP28 1.80sh lt green & blk   .60 .30
WHO drive to eradicate malaria.

1963, May 15   Wmk. 303   Perf. 14

Women's Auxiliary Forces: 1.80sh, Army auxiliary women with flag.
C87 AP29   1sh dk bl, yel & org   .30 .20
C88 AP29   1.80sh multicolored   .60 .20

Freedom from Hunger Type

Design: 1sh, Sower and wheat.

1963, June 25
C89 A44 1sh dk brn, yel & bl   .40 .20

President Osman Type

1963, Sept. 15   Wmk. 303   Perf. 14
C90 A45   1sh multicolored   .55 .20
C91 A45   1.80sh multicolored   .50 .30

Somali Fair Type

Design: 1.80sh, Government Pavilion.

1963, Sept. 28   Photo.
C92 A46   1.80sh blue   .85 .40

Map of Somalia, Animals and Globe AP30

1.80sh, Somali Credit Bank emblem.

1964, May 16   Wmk. 303   Perf. 14
C93 AP30   1sh multicolored   .30 .20
C94 AP30   1.80sh blk, bl & yel   .70 .30

10th anniversary of Somali Credit Bank.

Olympic Type

1964, Oct. 10   Photo.
C95 A48   90c Diving   .40 .20
C96 A48   1.80sh Soccer   .60 .30

Elephants and DC-3 AP31

Design: 1.80sh, Plane over Mogadishu.

1964, Nov. 8   Photo.   Perf. 14
C97 AP31   1sh brown & green   .60 .25
C98 AP31   1.80sh black & blue   1.25 .40

Establishment of Somali Air Lines.

ITU Type

1965, May 17   Wmk. 303   Perf. 14
C99 A50   1sh dp grn & blk   .40 .20
C100 A50   1.80sh rose lil & brn   .80 .40

Somali Fair Type

Designs: 1.50sh, Sugar industry; harvesting sugar cane and refinery. 2sh, Dairy industry; bottling plant and milk cow.

1965, Sept. 28   Photo.   Perf. 14
C101 A51   1.50sh sepia & pale bl   .40 .20
C102 A51   2sh sepia & rose   .75 .25

Faisal Type

Design: 1.80sh, Ka'aba, Mecca, Pres. Abdirascid Ali Scermarche and King Faisal.

1967, Sept. 21   Wmk. 303   Perf. 14
C103 A60 1.80sh blk, dp rose & org .30 .20

Egret — AP32

Birds: 1sh, Southern carmine bee-eater. 1.30sh, Bruce's green pigeon. 1.80sh, Broad-tailed paradise whydah.

Perf. 11½

1968, Nov. 1   Unwmk.   Litho.
C104 AP32   35c blue & multi   .20 .20
C105 AP32   1sh green & multi   .20 .20
C106 AP32   1.30sh vio bl & multi   .25 .20
C107 AP32   1.80sh yellow & multi   .35 .25
Nos. C104-C107 (4)   1.00 .85

Somali Democratic Republic
Postal Union Type

1.30sh, Postal Union emblem and letter.

Perf. 14x13½

1972, Jan. 25   Photo.   Unwmk.
C108 A81   1.30sh multicolored   .40 .35

AIR POST SEMI-POSTAL STAMPS

King Victor Emmanuel III SPAP1

Wmk. 140

1934, Nov. 5   Photo.   Perf. 14
CB1 SPAP1 25c + 10c
    gray grn   2.40 3.50
CB2 SPAP1 50c + 10c brn   2.40 3.50
CB3 SPAP1 75c + 15c
    rose red   2.40 3.50
CB4 SPAP1 80c + 15c blk
    brn   2.40 3.50
CB5 SPAP1 1 l + 20c red
    brn   2.40 3.50
CB6 SPAP1 2 l + 20c brt
    bl   2.40 3.50
CB7 SPAP1 3 l + 25c pur   11.00 30.00
CB8 SPAP1 5 l + 25c org   11.00 30.00
CB9 SPAP1 10 l + 30c
    rose vio   11.00 30.00
CB10 SPAP1 25 l + 2 l dp
    grn   11.00 30.00
Nos. CB1-CB10 (10)   58.40 141.00
    Set, never hinged   125.00

65th birthday of King Victor Emmanuel III; non-stop flight from Rome to Mogadishu.
For overprint see No. CBO1.

> Catalogue values for unused stamps in this section, from this point to the end of the section, are for Never Hinged items.

Somalia
Type of Semi-Postal Stamps, 1957

1957, Nov. 30   Wmk. 303   Perf. 14
CB11 SP17   55c + 20c dk
    bl & brn   .20 .25
CB12 SP17 1.20s + 20c vio
    & brn   .25 .30

The surtax was for the fight against tuberculosis.

Type of Semi-Postal Issue, 1964

Designs: 75c+20c, Destroyed Somali village. 1.80sh+50c, Soldier aiding children, and map of Somalia, vert.

1964, Dec. 12   Photo.   Perf. 14
CB13 SP18   75c + 20c blk, org
    red & brn   .40 .20
CB14 SP18 1.80sh + 50c blk, ol
    bis & slate   .90 .30

AIR POST SPECIAL DELIVERY STAMP

> Catalogue value for the stamp in this section is for a Never Hinged item.

Antelopes APSD1

Wmk. 303

1958, Oct. 4   Photo.   Perf. 14
CE1 APSD1 1.70s org ver & blk   .60 .85

AIR POST OFFICIAL STAMP

No. C1 Overprinted

**11 NOV. 1934-XIII
SERVIZIO AEREO
SPECIALE**

Wmk. 140

1934, Nov. 11   Photo.   Perf. 14
CO1 AP1 25c sl bl & red
    org   1,200. 1,300.
    Never hinged   1,750.

Forgeries of this overprint exist.

AIR POST SEMI-POSTAL OFFICIAL STAMP

Type of Air Post Semi-Postal Stamps, 1934 Overprinted Crown and "SERVIZIO DI STATO" in Black

1934, Nov. 5   Wmk. 140   Perf. 14
CBO1 SPAP1 25 l + 2 l cop
    red   1,200. 1,500.
    Never hinged   1,500.

SPECIAL DELIVERY STAMPS

Italy No. E3 Surcharged

1923, July 16   Wmk. 140   Perf. 14
E1 SD1 30b on 60c dl red   16.00 11.50

Italy, Type of 1908 Special Delivery Stamp Surcharged

E2 SD2 60b on 1.20 l bl &
    red   24.00 22.50

"Italia" SD3

1924, June   Engr.   Unwmk.
E3 SD3 30b dk red & brn   6.25 6.50
E4 SD3 60b dk blue & red   9.25 11.50

Nos. E3-E4 Surcharged in Black or Red with Bars and

1926, Oct.
E5 SD3 70c on 30b (Bk)   7.00 8.50
E6 SD3 2.50 l on 60b (R)   8.50 10.00
a.   Imperf., pair   375.00

Same Surcharge on No. E3

1927   Perf. 11
E7 SD3 1.25 l on 30b   8.00 6.00
a.   Perf. 14   90.00 175.00
b.   Imperf., pair   375.00

> Catalogue values for unused stamps in this section, from this point to the end of the section, are for Never Hinged items.

Somalia

Bananas, Grant's Gazelles SD4

Wmk. 277

1950, Apr. 24   Photo.   Perf. 14
E8 SD4 40c blue green   3.00 2.25
E9 SD4 80c violet   4.50 4.00

Gardenias SD5

Design: 1s, Eryrhina melanocantha.

1955, Feb.   Perf. 13
E10 SD5 50c lilac & green   .25 .50
E11 SD5 1s bl, rose brn & grn   .50 .65

AUTHORIZED DELIVERY STAMP

Italy No. EY2 Overprinted in Black

1939   Wmk. 140   Perf. 14
EY1 AD2 10c brown   40.00 —

No. EY1 has yellowish gum. A 1941 printing in grayish brown, with white gum, was not issued. Value, 40 cents.

POSTAGE DUE STAMPS

Postage Due Stamps of Italy Overprinted

1906-08   Wmk. 140   Perf. 14
J1 D3   5c buff & magenta   4.25 16.00
J2 D3 10c buff & magenta   22.50 19.00
J3 D3 20c org & magenta   17.00 25.00
J4 D3 30c buff & magenta   14.00 29.00
J5 D3 40c buff & magenta   110.00 29.00
J6 D3 50c buff & magenta   29.00 32.50
J7 D3 60c buff & mag ('08)   26.00 32.50
J8 D3   1 l blue & magenta   525.00 125.00
J9 D3   2 l blue & magenta   475.00 125.00
J10 D3   5 l blue & magenta   475.00 140.00
J11 D3 10 l blue & magenta   82.50 125.00
Nos. J1-J11 (11)   1,780. 698.00

Postage Due Stamps of Italy Overprinted at Top of Stamps

1909-19
J12 D3   5c buff & magenta   3.00 9.50
J13 D3 10c buff & magenta   3.00 9.50
J14 D3 20c buff & magenta   5.00 12.50
J15 D3 30c buff & magenta   14.00 12.50

J16	D3	40c buff & magenta	14.00	16.00
J17	D3	50c buff & magenta	14.00	25.00
J18	D3	60c buff & mag ('19)	20.00	22.50
J19	D3	1 l blue & magenta	52.50	25.00
J20	D3	2 l blue & magenta	62.50	55.00
J21	D3	5 l blue & magenta	82.50	70.00
J22	D3	10 l blue & magenta	14.00	25.00
		Nos. J12-J22 (11)	284.50	282.50

Same with Overprint at Bottom of Stamps

1920

J12a	D3	5c buff & magenta	50.00	55.00
J13a	D3	10c buff & magenta	50.00	55.00
J14a	D3	20c buff & magenta	55.00	40.00
J15a	D3	30c buff & magenta	62.50	55.00
J16a	D3	40c buff & magenta	62.50	55.00
J17a	D3	50c buff & magenta	55.00	47.50
J18a	D3	60c buff & magenta	62.50	47.50
J19a	D3	1 l blue & magenta	62.50	70.00
J20a	D3	2 l blue & magenta	62.50	70.00
J21a	D3	5 l blue & magenta	62.50	87.50
		Nos. J12a-J21a (10)	585.00	567.50

D4

D5

1923, July 1

J23	D4	1b buff & black	.65	2.25
J24	D4	2b buff & black	.65	2.25
a.		Inverted numeral and ovpt.	62.50	
J25	D4	3b buff & black	.65	2.25
J26	D4	5b buff & black	1.25	2.25
J27	D4	10b buff & black	1.25	2.25
J28	D4	20b buff & black	1.25	2.25
J29	D4	40b buff & black	1.25	2.25
J30	D4	1r blue & black	1.90	13.00
		Nos. J23-J30 (8)	8.85	28.75

Type of Postage Due
Stamps of Italy
Overprinted

1926, Mar. 1

J31	D3	5c buff & black	10.50	11.50
J32	D3	10c buff & black	10.50	6.50
J33	D3	20c buff & black	10.50	11.50
J34	D3	30c buff & black	10.50	6.50
J35	D3	40c buff & black	10.50	6.50
J36	D3	50c buff & black	13.00	6.50
J37	D3	60c buff & black	13.00	6.50
J38	D3	1 l blue & black	22.50	11.50
J39	D3	2 l blue & black	32.50	11.50
J40	D3	5 l blue & black	35.00	17.00
J41	D3	10 l blue & black	35.00	22.50
		Nos. J31-J41 (11)	203.50	118.00

Numerals and Ovpt. Invtd.

J32a	D3	10c	90.00	
J33a	D3	20c	250.00	
J34a	D3	30c	90.00	
J35a	D3	40c	90.00	
J36a	D3	50c	90.00	
J37a	D3	60c	90.00	

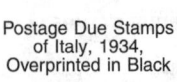
Postage Due Stamps
of Italy, 1934,
Overprinted in Black

1934, May 12

J42	D6	5c brown	.40	1.25
J43	D6	10c blue	.40	1.25
J44	D6	20c rose red	1.50	2.50
J45	D6	25c green	1.50	2.50
J46	D6	30c red orange	3.75	4.75
J47	D6	40c black brown	3.75	6.50
J48	D6	50c violet	7.75	1.75
J49	D6	60c black	10.50	14.00
J50	D7	1 l red orange	11.50	5.25
J51	D7	2 l green	22.50	14.00
J52	D7	5 l violet	26.00	26.00
J53	D7	10 l blue	26.00	29.00
J54	D7	20 l carmine	29.00	29.00
		Nos. J42-J54 (13)	144.55	137.75

Catalogue values for unused stamps in this section, from this point to the end of the section, are for Never Hinged items.

Somalia

1950   Wmk. 277   Photo.   Perf. 14

J55	D5	1c dark gray violet	.50	.50
J56	D5	2c deep blue	.50	.50
J57	D5	5c blue green	.50	.50
J58	D5	10c rose lilac	.50	.50

J59	D5	40c violet	2.50	2.50
J60	D5	1s dark brown	3.50	3.50
		Nos. J55-J60 (6)	8.00	8.00

PARCEL POST STAMPS

These stamps were used by affixing them to the way bill so that one half remained on it following the parcel, the other half staying on the receipt given the sender. Most used halves are right halves. Complete stamps were and are obtainable canceled, probably to order. Both unused and used values are for complete stamps.

Parcel Post Stamps
of Italy, 1914-17,
Overprinted

1917-19   Wmk. 140   Perf. 13½

Q1	PP2	5c brown	1.25	2.50
a.		Double overprint	150.00	
Q2	PP2	10c blue	1.25	2.50
Q3	PP2	20c black ('19)	65.00	40.00
Q4	PP2	25c red	3.25	6.00
a.		Double overprint	300.00	
Q5	PP2	50c orange	47.50	20.00
Q6	PP2	1 l lilac	14.00	14.00
Q7	PP2	2 l green	16.00	15.00
Q8	PP2	3 l bister	25.00	20.00
Q9	PP2	4 l slate	27.50	25.00
		Nos. Q1-Q9 (9)	200.75	145.00

Halves Used

Q1, Q4		.20
Q2		.20
Q3, Q5		2.75
Q6-Q7		.30
Q8		.50
Q9		1.25

Nos. Q5-Q9 were overprinted in 1922 with a slightly different type in which the final "A" of SOMALIA is directly over the final "A" of ITALIANA. They were not regularly issued. Value for set, $400.

Parcel Post Stamps
of Italy, 1914-17,
Overprinted

1923

Q10	PP2	25c red	22.50	25.00
Q11	PP2	50c orange	19.00	25.00
Q12	PP2	1 l violet	27.50	25.00
Q13	PP2	2 l green	27.50	25.00
Q14	PP2	3 l bister	47.50	25.00
Q15	PP2	4 l slate	47.50	25.00
		Nos. Q10-Q15 (6)	191.50	150.00

Halves Used

Q10		1.10
Q11, Q12		.30
Q13		.40
Q14		.85
Q15		1.60

Parcel Post Stamps of Italy, 1914-17,
Surcharged

1923

Q16	PP2	3b on 5c brown	3.25	2.50
Q17	PP2	5b on 5c brown	3.25	2.50
Q18	PP2	10b on 10c blue	4.00	3.25
Q19	PP2	25b on 25c red	5.00	4.00
Q20	PP2	50b on 50c org	1.00	7.25
Q21	PP2	1r on 1 l lilac	14.00	10.00
Q22	PP2	2r on 2 l green	18.00	14.00
Q23	PP2	3r on 3 l bister	20.00	20.00
Q24	PP2	4r on 4 l slate	25.00	25.00
		Nos. Q16-Q24 (9)	93.50	88.50

Halves Used

Q16-Q17		.20
Q18-Q19		.20
Q20-Q21		.30
Q22		.60
Q23		1.10
Q24		1.60

No. Q16 has the numeral "3" at the left also.

Parcel Post Stamps
of Italy, 1914-22
Overprinted

Somalia

PP1

1950   Wmk. 277   Photo.   Perf. 14

Q56	PP1	1c cerise	.20	.50
Q57	PP1	3c dark gray violet	.20	.50
Q58	PP1	5c rose lilac	.20	.50
Q59	PP1	10c red orange	.20	.50
Q60	PP1	20c dark brown	.20	.50
Q61	PP1	50c blue green	.30	.70

1926-31

Red Overprint

Q25	PP2	5c brown	8.75	10.00
Q26	PP2	10c blue	8.75	10.00
Q27	PP2	20c black	15.00	14.00
Q28	PP2	25c red	15.00	14.00
Q29	PP2	50c orange	15.00	14.00
Q30	PP2	1 l violet	15.00	14.00
Q31	PP2	2 l green	21.00	14.00
Q32	PP2	3 l yellow	7.00	10.00
Q33	PP2	4 l slate	7.00	10.00
Q34	PP2	10 l vio brn ('30)	8.75	14.00
Q35	PP2	12 l red brn ('31)	8.75	14.00
Q36	PP2	15 l olive ('31)	8.75	14.00
Q37	PP2	20 l dull vio ('31)	8.75	14.00
		Nos. Q25-Q37 (13)	147.50	166.00

Halves Used

Q25-Q26		.30
Q27-Q28, Q33		.70
Q29, Q34		.90
Q30-Q31		.50
Q32		.40
Q35-Q36		1.10
Q37		1.25

Nos. Q25-Q31 come with two types of overprint: I - The first "I" and last "A" of ITALIANA extend slightly on both sides of SOMALIA. II - Only the "I" extends. These seven stamps with type I overprint were not regularly issued, and Nos. Q27-Q31 (type I) sell for less than with type II overprint.

Black Overprint

Q38	PP2	10 l violet brown	25.00	7.25
Q39	PP2	12 l red brown	16.00	7.25
Q40	PP2	15 l olive	16.00	7.25
Q41	PP2	20 l dull brown	16.00	7.25
		Nos. Q38-Q41 (4)	73.00	29.00

Halves Used

Q38		.45
Q39-Q41		.30

Same Overprint on Parcel Post Stamps of Italy, 1927-38

1928-39

Black Overprint

Q42	PP3	25c red ('31)	17.50	25.00
Q43	PP3	30c ultra	.25	1.50
Q43A	PP3	50c orange	7,500.	3,000.
Q44	PP3	60c red	.25	1.50
Q45	PP3	1 l lilac ('31)	8.50	17.50
Q46	PP3	2 l green ('31)	8.50	17.50
Q47	PP3	3 l bister	.30	2.50
Q48	PP3	4 l gray black	.35	3.00
Q49	PP3	10 l rose lil ('34)	100.00	150.00
Q50	PP3	20 l lil brn ('34)	100.00	150.00
		Nos. Q42-Q43, Q44-Q50 (9)	235.65	368.50

Halves Used

Q42, Q50		1.00
Q43, Q44		.20
Q43A		40.00
Q45-Q48		.30
Q49		2.00

The 25c, 1 l and 2 l come with both types of overprint (see note below No. Q37). Both types were regularly issued. Values are for type I on 25c, type II on 1 l and 2 l.

Red Overprint

Q51	PP3	5c brown ('39)	13.00	
Q52	PP3	3 l bister ('30)	10.00	14.00
		Half stamp		.30
Q53	PP3	4 l gray black ('30)	10.00	14.00
		Half stamp		.30
		Nos. Q51-Q53 (3)	33.00	

Same Overprint in Black on Italy Nos. Q24-Q25

1940   Perf. 13

Q54	PP3	5c brown	.70	2.50
		Half stamp		.20
Q55	PP3	10c deep blue	1.00	3.00
		Half stamp		.20

Catalogue values for unused stamps in this section, from this point to the end of the section, are for Never Hinged items.

Q62	PP1	1s violet	1.25	3.00
Q63	PP1	2s brown	1.60	4.00
Q64	PP1	3s blue	1.75	4.50
		Nos. Q56-Q64 (9)	5.90	14.70

Halves Used

Q56-Q58		.20
Q59-Q60		.20
Q61		.30
Q62		.20
Q63		.30
Q64		.50

SOMALI COAST

sō-ˈmä-lē ˈkōst

(Djibouti)

LOCATION — Eastern Africa, bordering on the Gulf of Aden
GOVT. — French Overseas Territory
AREA — 8,500 sq. mi.
POP. — 86,000 (est. 1963)
CAPITAL — Djibouti (Jibuti)

The port of Obock, which issued postage stamps in 1892-1894, was included in the territory and began to use stamps of Somali Coast in 1902. See Obock in Vol. 4.

On Mar. 19, 1967, the territory changed its name to the French Territory of the Afars and Issas. The Republic of Djibouti was proclaimed June 27, 1977.

100 Centimes = 1 Franc

Catalogue values for unused stamps in this country are for Never Hinged items, beginning with Scott 224 in the regular postage section, Scott B13 in the semipostal section, Scott C1 in the airpost section, Scott CB1 in the airpost semi-postal section, and Scott J39 in the postage due section.

Navigation and Commerce
A1   A2

A3

Camel
and
Rider
A4

Obock Nos. 32-33, 35, 45 with Overprint or Surcharge Handstamped in Black, Blue or Red

1894   Unwmk.   Perf. 14x13½

1	A1	5c grn & red, grnsh (with bar)	110.00	100.00
a.		Without bar	850.00	600.00
2	A2	25c on 2c brn & bl, buff (Bl & Bk)	260.00	160.00
a.		"25" omitted	725.00	600.00
b.		"DJIBOUTI" omitted	725.00	600.00
c.		"DJIBOUTI" inverted	825.00	750.00
3	A3	50c on 1c blk & red, bl (R & Bl)	275.00	200.00
a.		"5" instead of "50"	1,200.	850.00
b.		"0" instead of "50"	1,200.	850.00

c.	"DJIBOUTI" omitted		1,200.	950.00

Imperf

4	A4	1fr on 5fr car	500.00	400.00
5	A4	5fr carmine	1,400.	1,000.

The overprint on No. 1 includes a bar to obliterate "OBOCK."
"DJIBOUTI" is in blue on No. 2, in red on No. 3.
Counterfeits exist of Nos. 4-5.

View of Djibouti, Somali Warriors — A5

French Gunboat A7

Crossing Desert (Size: 66mm wide, including simulated perfs.) — A8

Designs: 15c, 25c, 30c, 40c, 50c, 75c, Different views of Djibouti. 1fr, 2fr, Djibouti quay.

Imperf. (Simulated Perforations in Frame Color)

1894-1902 Typo.
Quadrille Lines Printed on Paper

6	A5	1c blk & claret	2.50	2.00
7	A5	2c claret & blk	2.50	2.00
8	A5	4c vio brn & bl	10.00	6.00
9	A5	5c bl grn & red	10.00	5.25
10	A5	5c grn & yel grn ('02)	7.25	6.00
11	A5	10c brown & grn	13.00	6.25
a.		Half used as 5c on cover ('01)		125.00
12	A5	15c violet & grn	13.00	6.25
13	A5	25c rose & blue	20.00	7.50
14	A5	30c gray brn & rose	13.00	7.50
a.		Half used as 15c on cover ('01)		400.00
15	A5	40c org & bl ('00)	42.50	30.00
16	A5	50c blue & rose	20.00	13.00
a.		Half used as 25c on cover ('01)		1,300.
17	A5	75c violet & org	37.50	27.50
18	A5	1fr ol grn & blk	17.00	13.00
19	A5	2fr gray brn & rose	72.50	57.50
20	A7	5fr rose & blue	150.00	100.00
21	A8	25fr rose & blue	725.00	750.00
22	A8	50fr blue & rose	500.00	500.00
		Nos. 6-20 (15)	430.75	289.75

High values are found with the overprint "S" (Specimen) erased and, usually, a cancellation added.
For surcharges see Nos. 24-27B.

A9

1899
Black Surcharge

23	A9	40c on 4c brn & bl	2,500.	22.50
a.		Double surcharge	4,750.	1,100.

Nos. 17-20 Surcharged

1902 Blue Surcharge

24	A5	0.05c on 75c	52.50	30.00
a.		Inverted surcharge	450.00	400.00
b.		Double surcharge	450.00	400.00
25	A5	0.10c on 1fr	60.00	42.50
a.		Inverted surcharge	425.00	325.00
b.		Double surcharge	350.00	325.00
26	A5	0.40c on 2fr	450.00	325.00
a.		Double surcharge	1,850.	1,500.

Black Surcharge

27	A7	0.75c on 5fr	425.00	325.00
a.		Inverted surcharge	2,250.	1,750.
c.		Double surcharge	2,250.	1,750.

Obock No. 57 Surcharged in Blue

27B	A7	0.05c on 75c gray lil & org	1,100.	800.00

A10

Nos. 15-16 Surcharged in Black

28	A10	5c on 40c	6.00	4.00
a.		Double surcharge	100.00	100.00
29	A10	10c on 50c	20.00	20.00
a.		Inverted surcharge	400.00	400.00
b.		Double surcharge	400.00	

Surcharged on Stamps of Obock

Group of Warriors A11

Black Surcharge

30	A11	5c on 30c bis & yel grn	11.00	8.00
a.		Inverted surcharge	190.00	190.00
b.		Double surcharge	175.00	160.00
c.		Triple surcharge		

A12

Red Surcharge

31	A12	10c on 25c blk & bl	11.00	9.25
a.		Inverted surcharge	200.00	200.00
b.		Double surcharge	225.00	225.00
c.		Triple surcharge	1,300.	1,300.

A13

Black Surcharge

32	A13	10c on 10fr org & red vio	27.50	22.50
a.		Double surcharge	190.00	175.00
b.		Triple surch., one invtd.	1,800.	1,700.

A14

Black Surcharge

33	A14	10c on 2fr dl vio & org	50.00	40.00
a.		"DJIBOUTI" inverted	200.00	175.00
b.		Large "0" in "10"	110.00	82.50
c.		Double surcharge	375.00	340.00

Same Surcharge on Obock No. 53 in Red

33D	A7	10c on 25c blk & bl	26,500.	18,000.

A14a

Black Surcharge on Obock Nos. 63-64

33E	A14a	5c on 25fr brn & bl	50.00	42.50
33F	A14a	10c on 50fr red vio & org	62.50	45.00
g.		"01" instead of "10"	160.00	150.00
h.		"CENTIMES" inverted	2,250.	2,250.
i.		Double surcharge	2,000.	1,700.

Tadjoura Mosque A15

Somalis on Camel A16

Warriors — A17

1902 Engr. Perf. 11½

34	A15	1c brn vio & org	.75	.75
35	A15	2c yel brn & yel grn	.90	.75
36	A15	4c bl & carmine	2.00	1.50
37	A15	5c bl grn & yel grn	2.00	1.00
38	A15	10c car & red org	5.25	3.25
39	A15	15c brn org & bl	5.25	3.25
40	A16	20c vio & green	11.50	6.00
41	A16	25c blue	17.00	10.50
a.		25c indigo & blue ('03)	20.00	11.00
42	A16	30c red & black	5.00	4.00
43	A16	40c orange & blue	11.50	7.25
44	A16	50c grn & red org	35.00	35.00
45	A16	75c orange & vio	6.50	4.00
46	A17	1fr red org & vio	20.00	12.50
47	A17	2fr yel grn & car	30.00	22.50
a.		Without names of designer and engraver at bottom	100.00	100.00
48	A17	5fr orange & blue	18.00	16.00
		Nos. 34-48 (15)	170.65	128.25

1903

49	A15	1c brn vio & blk	.75	.65
50	A15	2c yel brn & blk	1.10	.80
51	A15	4c lake & blk	1.50	1.25
a.		4c red & black	1.50	1.25
52	A15	5c bl grn & blk	3.25	2.25
53	A15	10c carmine & blk	6.50	2.50
54	A15	15c org brn & blk	14.50	7.50
55	A16	20c dl vio & blk	20.00	14.50
56	A16	25c ultra & blk	10.00	7.25
57	A16	40c orange & blk	7.25	7.25
58	A16	50c green & blk	18.00	11.00
59	A16	75c buff & blk	9.25	8.50
a.		75c brown orange & black	60.00	60.00
60	A17	1fr orange & blk	15.00	14.50
61	A17	2fr yel grn & blk	8.00	6.25
a.		Without names of designer and engraver at bottom	35.00	35.00

63	A17	5fr red org & blk	17.00	14.50
a.		5fr ocher & black	20.00	20.00
		Nos. 49-63 (14)	132.10	98.45

Imperforates, transposed colors and inverted centers exist in the 1902 and 1903 issues. Most of these were issued from Paris and some are said to have been fraudulently printed.

Tadjoura Mosque A18

Somalis on Camel — A19

Warriors — A20

1909 Typo. Perf. 14x13½

64	A18	1c maroon & brn	.65	.60
65	A18	2c vio & ol gray	.65	.60
66	A18	4c ol gray & bl	.85	.80
67	A18	5c grn & gray grn	1.10	.75
68	A18	10c car & ver	3.25	1.25
69	A18	20c blk & red brn	5.25	4.25
70	A19	25c bl & pale bl	4.00	2.50
71	A19	30c brn & scar	6.00	4.25
72	A19	35c vio & grn	7.25	4.50
73	A19	40c rose & vio	6.50	4.25
74	A19	45c brn & bl grn	6.50	4.25
75	A19	50c maroon & brn	6.50	5.25
76	A19	75c scarlet & grn	14.50	10.00
77	A20	1fr vio & brn	18.00	16.00
78	A20	2fr brn & rose	29.00	22.50
79	A20	5fr brn & bl grn	47.50	32.50
		Nos. 64-79 (16)	157.50	114.25

Drummer A21

Somali Girl A22

Djibouti-Addis Ababa Railroad Bridge — A23

1915-33 Perf. 13½x14
Chalky Paper

80	A21	1c brt vio & red brn	.20	.20
81	A21	2c ocher & ind	.20	.20
82	A21	4c dk brn & red	.20	.20
83	A21	5c yel grn & grn	.80	.75
84	A21	5c org & dl red ('22)	.45	.45
85	A22	10c car & dk red	1.25	.75
86	A22	10c ap grn & grn ('22)	.75	.75
87	A22	10c ver & grn ('25)	.20	.20
88	A22	15c brn vio & car	.65	.35
89	A22	20c org & blk brn	.20	.20
90	A22	20c dp grn & bl grn ('25)	.20	.20
91	A22	20c dk grn & red ('27)	.35	.35
92	A22	25c ultra & dl bl	.75	.45
93	A22	25c blk & bl grn ('22)	.80	.80
94	A22	30c blk & bl grn	1.60	1.25
95	A22	30c rose & red brn ('22)	1.00	1.00
96	A22	30c vio & ol grn ('25)	.20	.20
97	A22	30c grn & dl grn ('27)	.35	.35
98	A22	35c lt grn & dl rose	.45	.45
99	A22	40c bl & brn vio	.60	.45
100	A22	45c red brn & dk bl	.65	.65
101	A22	50c car rose & blk	8.00	5.25
102	A22	50c ultra & ind ('24)	.90	.90
103	A22	50c dk brn & red vio ('25)	.55	.55

104 A22	60c ol grn & red vio ('25)	.35	.20
105 A22	65c car rose & ol grn ('25)	.55	.35
106 A22	75c dl vio & choc	.55	.35
107 A22	75c ind & ultra ('25)	.45	.35
108 A22	75c brt vio & ol brn ('27)	1.25	.85
109 A22	85c vio brn & bl grn ('25)	.85	.75
110 A22	90c brn red & brt red ('30)	6.25	4.50
111 A23	1fr bis brn & red	1.25	.75
112 A23	1.10fr brn & ultra ('28)	3.25	3.25
113 A23	1.25fr dk bl & blk brn ('33)	7.25	6.00
114 A23	1.50fr bl & dk bl ('30)	1.00	.75
115 A23	1.75fr gray grn & lt red ('33)	6.25	4.00
116 A23	2fr bl vio & blk	2.25	1.75
117 A23	3fr red vio ('30)	8.25	5.75
118 A23	5fr rose red & blk	4.25	2.10
	Nos. 80-118 (39)	65.30	48.50

No. 99 is on ordinary paper.
For surcharges and overprints see Nos. 119-134, 183-193.

Nos. 83, 92
Surcharged in Green
or Blue

1922

119 A21	10c on 5c (G)	.45	.45
a.	Double surcharge	65.00	65.00
120 A22	50c on 25c (Bl)	.45	.45

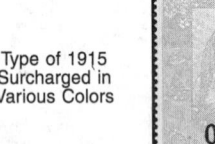

Type of 1915
Surcharged in
Various Colors

1922

121 A22	0,01c on 15c vio & rose (Bk)	.20	.20
122 A22	0,02c on 15c vio & rose (Bl)	.35	.35
123 A22	0,04c on 15c vio & rose (G)	.45	.45
124 A22	0,05c on 15c vio & rose (R)	.45	.45
	Nos. 121-124 (4)	1.45	1.45

Nos. 88, 99 and Type of 1915
Surcharged

60

1923-27

125 A22	60c on 75c ol grn & vio	.35	.35
126 A22	65c on 15c ('25)	1.40	1.40
127 A22	85c on 40c ('25)	1.10	1.10
128 A22	90c on 75c brn red & red ('27)	3.50	3.50
	Nos. 125-128 (4)	6.35	6.35

No. 118 and Type of 1915-17
Surcharged with New Value and Bars
in Black or Red

1924-27

129 A23	25c on 5fr	.80	.80
130 A23	1.25fr on 1fr dk bl & ultra (R) ('26)	.75	.75
131 A23	1.50fr on 1fr lt bl & dk bl ('27)	.80	.80
132 A23	3fr on 5fr ver & red vio ('27)	3.50	3.50
133 A23	10fr on 5fr brn red & ol brn ('27)	6.00	6.00
134 A23	20fr on 5fr gray grn & lil rose ('27)	10.00	10.00
	Nos. 129-134 (6)	21.85	21.85

Common Design Types
pictured following the introduction.

Colonial Exposition Issue
Common Design Types
Engr., Name of Country Typo. in Black

1931   Perf. 12½

135 CD70	40c deep green	4.00	4.00
136 CD71	50c violet	4.00	4.00
137 CD72	90c red orange	4.25	4.25
138 CD73	1.50fr dull blue	4.25	4.25
	Nos. 135-138 (4)	16.50	16.50

Paris International Exposition Issue
Common Design Types

1937   Engr.   Perf. 13

139 CD74	20c deep violet	1.25	1.25
140 CD75	30c dark green	1.25	1.25
141 CD76	40c carmine rose	1.25	1.25
142 CD77	50c dk brn & bl	1.25	1.25
143 CD78	90c red	1.40	1.40
144 CD79	1.50fr ultra	1.40	1.40
	Nos. 139-144 (6)	7.80	7.80

Colonial Arts Exhibition Issue
Souvenir Sheet
Common Design Type

1937   Imperf.

145 CD75	3fr dull violet	8.50	10.00

Mosque of Djibouti — A24   Somali Warriors — A25

Governor Léonce Lagarde — A26

View of Djibouti — A27

1938-40   Perf. 12x12½, 12½

146 A24	2c dull red vio	.20	.20
147 A24	3c slate grn	.20	.20
148 A24	4c dull red brn	.20	.20
149 A24	5c carmine	.20	.20
150 A24	10c blue gray	.20	.20
151 A24	15c slate black	.20	.20
152 A24	20c dark orange	.20	.20
153 A25	25c dark brown	.55	.45
154 A25	30c dark blue	.20	.20
155 A25	50c olive grn	.65	.55
156 A24	40c org brn ('40)	.20	.20
157 A24	45c dull grn ('40)	.20	.20
158 A25	50c red	.45	.35
159 A25	50c dull red vio	.65	.55
160 A25	60c black ('40)	.45	.45
161 A25	65c orange brown	.75	.65
162 A25	70c lt violet ('40)	1.00	1.00
163 A26	80c gray blk	1.60	1.25
164 A25	90c rose vio ('39)	1.10	1.10
165 A26	1fr carmine	2.25	1.50
166 A26	1fr black	.35	.35
167 A26	1.25fr magenta ('39)	.80	.80
168 A26	1.40fr pck bl ('40)	.85	.85
169 A26	1.50fr dull green	.65	.65
170 A26	1.60fr brn car ('40)	.85	.85
171 A26	1.75fr ultra	.85	.80
172 A26	2fr dk orange	.75	.60
173 A26	2.25fr ultra ('40)	1.10	1.10
174 A26	2.50fr org brn ('40)	1.60	1.60
175 A26	3fr dull violet	.75	.60
176 A27	5fr brn & pale cl	1.60	1.60
177 A27	10fr ind & pale bl	1.90	1.90
178 A27	20fr car lake & gray	1.90	1.90
	Nos. 146-178 (33)	25.40	23.45

For overprints and surcharge see Nos. 194-223.

New York World's Fair Issue
Common Design Type

1939   Engr.   Perf. 12½x12

179 CD82	1.25fr car lake	.85	.85
180 CD82	2.25fr ultra	.85	.85

Mosque of Djibouti
and Marshal
Pétain — A28

1941, Nov. 10   Engr.   Perf. 12x12½

181 A28	1fr yellow brown	.55
182 A28	2.50fr blue	.55

Nos. 181-182 were issued by the Vichy government in France, but were not placed on sale in Somali Coast.
For surcharges, see Nos. B11-B12.

Nos. 80-82, 84, 88,
91, 97, 103, 105,
114-115 Overprinted
in Black or Red

Perf. 13½x14, 14x13½
1943   Unwmk.

183 A21	1c	.90	.90
184 A21	2c	1.00	1.00
185 A21	4c	20.00	20.00
186 A21	5c	1.25	1.25
187 A22	15c	5.25	5.25
188 A22	20c	1.40	1.40
189 A22	30c	1.40	1.40
190 A22	50c	1.40	1.40
191 A22	65c	1.40	1.40
192 A23	1.50fr (R)	1.40	1.40
193 A23	1.75fr	8.00	8.00
	Nos. 183-193 (11)	43.40	43.40

Stamps of 1938-40 Overprinted in
Black or Red

On A24   On A25

On A26

On A27

1943   Perf. 12x12½, 12½

194 A24	2c dl red vio	1.50	1.50
195 A24	3c sl grn (R)	1.50	1.50
196 A24	4c dl red brn	1.50	1.50
197 A24	5c carmine	1.50	1.50
198 A24	10c bl gray (R)	.65	.65
199 A24	15c sl blk (R)	1.50	1.50
200 A24	20c dk org	1.50	1.50
201 A25	25c dk brn (R)	2.50	2.50
202 A25	30c dk bl (R)	.65	.65

---

203 A25	35c olive (R)	3.25	3.25
204 A24	40c brn org	.65	.65
205 A24	45c dl grn	3.00	3.00
206 A25	55c dl red vio (R)	1.50	1.50
207 A25	60c blk (R)	.65	.65
208 A25	70c lt vio (R)	.65	.65
a.	Inverted overprint	190.00	190.00
209 A26	80c gray blk (R)	.85	.85
210 A25	90c rose vio (R)	.65	.65
211 A26	1.25fr magenta	.85	.85
212 A26	1.40fr pck bl (R)	.65	.65
213 A26	1.50fr dl grn	1.50	1.50
214 A26	1.60fr brn car	.85	.85
215 A26	1.75fr ultra (R)	7.50	7.50
216 A26	2fr dk org	.90	.90
217 A26	2.25fr ultra	1.25	1.25
218 A26	2.50fr chestnut	1.25	1.25
219 A26	3fr dl vio (R)	1.25	1.25
220 A27	5fr brn & pale cl	8.00	8.00
221 A27	10fr ind & pale bl	125.00	125.00
222 A27	20fr car lake & gray	6.00	6.00

The space between overprint on Nos. 206 and 208 measures 10½mm.

No. 161 Surcharged
in Black

223 A25	50c on 65c org brn	.65	.65
	Nos. 194-223 (30)	179.65	179.65

> **Catalogue values for unused stamps in this section, from this point to the end of the section, are for Never Hinged items.**

Locomotive and Palms — A29

1943 Unwmk. Photo.   Perf. 14½x14

224 A29	5c royal blue	.20	.20
225 A29	10c pink	.20	.20
226 A29	25c emerald	.35	.35
227 A29	30c gray blk	.35	.35
228 A29	40c violet	.35	.35
229 A29	80c red brn	.35	.35
230 A29	1fr aqua	.35	.35
231 A29	1.50fr scarlet	.35	.35
232 A29	2fr brown	.35	.35
233 A29	2.50fr ultra	.55	.55
234 A29	4fr brt org	.80	.80
235 A29	5fr dp rose lil	.80	.80
236 A29	10fr lt ultra	.85	.85
237 A29	20fr green	1.00	1.00
	Nos. 224-237 (14)	6.85	6.85

For types A24-A26 without "RF," see Nos. 237A-237C.
For surcharges see Nos. 240-247.

Types of 1938-40 Without "RF"
1944, Apr. 3   Engr.   Perf. 12½

237A A24	40c org brn	.65
237B A25	50c red	.85
237C A26	1.50fr dull green	1.10
	Nos. 237A-237C (3)	2.60

Nos. 237A-237C were issued by the Vichy government in France, but were not placed on sale in Somali Coast.

Eboue Issue
Common Design Type
1945   Engr.   Perf. 13

238 CD91	2fr black	.55	.55
239 CD91	25fr Prus grn	1.10	1.10

Nos. 238 and 239 exist imperforate.

Nos. 224, 226 and 233 Surcharged
with New Values and Bars in Carmine
or Black

1945   Perf. 14½x14

240 A29	50c on 5c (C)	.45	.45
241 A29	60c on 5c (C)	.45	.45
242 A29	70c on 5c (C)	.45	.45
a.	Inverted surcharge	110.00	
243 A29	1.20fr on 5c (C)	.55	.55
244 A29	2.40fr on 25c	.65	.65
a.	Inverted surcharge	110.00	

245	A29	3fr on 25c	.65	.65
246	A29	4.50fr on 25c	.65	.65
a.		Inverted surcharge	110.00	
247	A29	15fr on 2.50fr (C)	1.00	1.00
		Nos. 240-247 (8)	4.85	4.75

Danakil Tent — A30

Khor-Angar Outpost A31

Obock-Tadjouran Road — A32

Somali Woman A33

Somali Village A34

Djibouti Mosque A35

1947	**Unwmk.**	**Photo.**	*Perf. 13*	
248	A30	10c vio bl & org	.20	.20
249	A30	30c ol brn & org	.20	.20
250	A30	40c dp plum & org	.20	.20
251	A31	50c bl grn & org	.20	.20
252	A31	60c choc & dp yel	.20	.20
253	A31	80c vio bl & org	.20	.20
254	A32	1fr bl & choc	.20	.20
255	A32	1.20fr bl grn & ol grn	.85	.65
256	A32	1.50fr org & vio bl	.35	.20
257	A33	2fr red lil & bl gray	.55	.45
258	A33	3fr dp bl & brn org	.85	.65
259	A33	3.60fr car rose & cop red	1.50	1.25
260	A34	4fr choc & bl gray	1.10	.85
261	A34	5fr org & choc	.65	.55
262	A34	6fr gray bl & int bl	1.10	.85
263	A34	10fr gray bl & red lil	1.25	.75
264	A35	15fr choc, gray bl & pink	1.25	.85
265	A35	20fr dk bl, gray bl & org	1.90	1.10
266	A35	25fr vio brn, lil rose & gray bl	4.00	2.50
		Nos. 248-266 (19)	16.75	11.85

Military Medal Issue
Common Design Type

1952	**Engraved and Typographed**		
267	CD101 15fr blk, grn, yel & dk pur	6.00	6.00

Imperforates
Most stamps of Somali Coast from 1956 onward exist imperforate in issued and trial colors, and also in small presentation sheets in issued colors.

FIDES Issue
Common Design Type and

Lighthouse, Ras-Bir — A36

15fr, Loading ship and map, Djibouti.

1956	**Unwmk.**	**Engr.**	*Perf. 13*	
268	CD103	15fr purple	1.50	1.00
269	A36	40fr dp ultra & gray	2.00	1.60

Flower Issue
Common Design Type
Design: 10fr, Haemanthus, horiz.

1958	**Photo.**	*Perf. 12½x12*	
270	CD104 10fr grn, red & yel	2.00	.85

Wart Hog — A37

40c, Cheetah. 50c, Gerenuk, vert.

1958	**Engr.**	*Perf. 13*	
271	A37	30c red brn & sepia	.35	.20
272	A37	40c brn & olive	.35	.20
273	A37	50c brn, grn & gray	.45	.20
		Nos. 271-273,C21 (4)	7.40	4.10

Human Rights Issue
Common Design Type

1958, Dec. 10		**Unwmk.**	
274	CD105 20fr brt pur & dk bl	1.50	1.50

Universal Declaration of Human Rights, 10th anniv.

Parrotfish A38

Designs: Various Tropical Fish.

1959	**Engr.**	*Perf. 13*	
275	A38	1fr brt bl, brn & red org	.45	.35
276	A38	2fr blk, lt bl, yel & grn	.45	.35
277	A38	3fr vio & blk brn	.45	.35
278	A38	4fr brt grnsh bl, org & lt brn	.65	.55
279	A38	5fr brt grnsh bl & blk	1.00	.75
280	A38	20fr brt bl, dl red brn & rose	2.00	1.50
281	A38	25fr red, grn & ultra	3.25	2.00
282	A38	60fr bl & dk grn	7.50	4.00
		Nos. 275-282 (8)	15.75	9.85

No. 276 is vertical.

Flamingo — A39

Birds: 15fr, Bee-eater, horiz. 30fr, Sacred ibis, horiz. 75fr, Pink-backed pelican.

1960	**Unwmk.**	*Perf. 13*	
283	A39	10fr bluish grn, bis & cl	2.00	.90
284	A39	15fr rose lil, grn & yel	2.75	1.00
285	A39	30fr bl, blk, org & brn	6.25	3.00
286	A39	75fr grn, sl grn & yel	9.00	5.50
		Nos. 283-286 (4)	20.00	10.40

Dragon Tree — A40

Klipspringer A41

Meleagrina Margaritifera A42

Designs: 4fr, Cony. 6fr, Large flatfish. 25fr, Fennecs. 40fr, Griffon vulture.

1962, Mar. 24		**Engr.**	*Perf. 13*	
287	A40	2fr grn, yel, org & brn	1.50	1.00
288	A40	4fr ocher & choc	1.50	1.10
289	A40	6fr brn, mar, grn & yel	3.25	2.00
290	A40	25fr red brn, ocher & grn	6.50	4.00
291	A40	40fr dk bl, brn & gray	9.25	5.50
292	A41	50fr bis, bl & lil	9.00	6.50
		Nos. 287-292 (6)	31.00	20.10

1962, Nov. 24			**Photo.**

Sea Shells: 10fr, Tridacna squamosa, horiz. 25fr, Strombus tricornis, horiz. 30fr, Trochus dentatus.

Shells in Natural Colors

293	A42	8fr red & blk	1.25	.75
294	A42	10fr car rose & blk	1.25	.90
295	A42	25fr dp bl & brn	3.25	1.25
296	A42	30fr rose lil & brn	3.25	1.60
		Nos. 293-296 (4)	9.00	4.50

See Nos. C28-C29.

Red Cross Centenary Issue
Common Design Type

1963, Sept. 2		**Engr.**	*Perf. 13*	
297	CD113 50fr org brn, gray & car	5.00	5.00

Astraea Coral — A43

Design: 6fr, Organ-pipe coral.

1963, Nov. 30		**Photo.**	*Perf. 13x13½*	
298	A43	5fr multi	1.60	1.10
299	A43	6fr multi	1.60	1.10

See Nos. C26-C27, C30.

Human Rights Issue
Common Design Type

1963, Dec. 20		**Engr.**	*Perf. 13*	
300	CD117 70fr dk brn & ultra	6.50	6.50

Philatec Issue
Common Design Type

1964, Apr. 7		**Unwmk.**	*Perf. 13*	
301	CD118 80fr dp lil rose, grn & brn	6.00	6.00

Houri (Somali Sailboats) A44

Design: 25fr, Sambouk (Somali sailboats).

1964, June 9			**Engr.**	
302	A44	15fr multi	1.25	.85
303	A44	25fr multi	2.00	1.25

View of Dadwayya and Map of Somali Coast A45

Design: 20fr, View of Tadjourah and map of Somali Coast.

1965, Oct. 20		**Engr.**	*Perf. 13*	
304	A45	6fr ultra, sl grn & red brn	.75	.55
305	A45	20fr ultra, org brn & brt grn	.85	.75

Senna — A46

1966		**Engr.**	*Perf. 13*	
306	A46	5fr shown	1.00	.65
307	A46	8fr Poinciana	1.00	.65
308	A46	25fr Aloe	1.25	1.00
		Nos. 306-308,C41 (4)	7.25	4.80

Desert Monitor A47

1967, May 8		**Engr.**	*Perf. 13*	
309	A47	20fr red brn, ocher & sepia	4.00	3.25

Stamps of Somali Coast were replaced in 1967 by those of the French Territory of the Afars and Issas.

SEMI-POSTAL STAMPS

Somali Girl — SP1

1915	**Unwmk.**	*Perf. 13½x14*	

Chalky Paper

B1	SP1	10c + 5c car & dk red	6.50	6.50

Curie Issue
Common Design Type

1938		**Engr.**	*Perf. 13*	
B2	CD80 1.75fr + 50c brt ultra	6.00	6.00

French Revolution Issue
Common Design Type

Photo., Name and Value Typo. in Black

1939				
B3	CD83	45c + 25c green	7.00	7.00
B4	CD83	70c + 30c brown	7.00	7.00
B5	CD83	90c + 35c red org	7.00	7.00
B6	CD83	1.25fr + 1fr rose pink	7.00	7.00
B7	CD83	2.25fr + 2fr blue	7.00	7.00
		Nos. B3-B7 (5)	35.00	35.00

Common Design Type and

Somali
Guard
SP2

Local Police — SP3

1941   Photo.   Perf. 13½
B8   SP2   1fr + 1fr red   1.00
B9   CD86 1.50fr + 3fr maroon   1.00
B10 SP3   2.50fr + 1fr blue   1.00
       Nos. B8-B10 (3)   3.00

Nos. B8-B10 were issued by the Vichy government in France, but were not placed on sale in Somali Coast.

Nos. 181-182
Surcharged in Black or Red

1944   Engr.   Perf. 12x12½
B11 50c + 1.50fr on 2.50fr deep
         blue (R)   .55
B12 + 2.50fr on 1fr green   .55
       Colonial Development Fund.

Nos. B11-B12 were issued by the Vichy government in France, but were not placed on sale in Somali Coast.

Catalogue values for unused stamps in this section, from this point to the end of the section, are for Never Hinged items.

Red Cross Issue
Common Design Type
Inscribed "Djibouti"

1944   Perf. 14½x14
B13 CD90 5fr + 20fr emerald   1.25 1.25
The surtax was for the French Red Cross and national relief.

Tropical Medicine Issue
Common Design Type

1950   Engr.   Perf. 13
B14 CD100 10fr + 2fr red brn &
                red   5.00 5.00
The surtax was for charitable work.

Anti-Malaria Issue
Common Design Type

1962, Apr. 7   Unwmk.   Perf. 13
B15 CD108 25fr + 5fr aqua   6.00 6.00

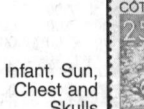

Infant, Sun,
Chest and
Skulls
SP4

1965, Dec. 10   Engr.   Perf. 13
B16 SP4 25fr + 5fr ocher, sl & brt
             grn   2.00 2.00
Campaign against tuberculosis.

AIR POST STAMPS

Catalogue values for unused stamps in this section are for Never Hinged items.

Common Design Type
Inscribed "Djibouti"

1941 Unwmk. Photo. Perf. 14½x14
C1   CD87 1fr dk orange   .65 .65
C2   CD87 1.50fr brt red   .65 .65
C3   CD87 5fr brown red   .85 .85
C4   CD87 10fr black   .90 .90
C5   CD87 25fr ultra   1.60 1.60
C6   CD87 50fr dark green   1.50 1.50
C7   CD87 100fr plum   2.25 2.25
       Nos. C1-C7 (7)   8.40 8.40

Obock & Djibouti

1943, June 21   Engr.   Perf. 13
C7A 1.50fr red brown   .55
C7B 4fr ultramarine   .55
50th Ann. of transfer of capital from Obock to Djibouti.
Nos. C7A-C7B were issued by the Vichy government in France, but were not placed on sale in Somali Coast.

Victory Issue
Common Design Type

1946   Perf. 12½
C8   CD92 8fr deep blue   1.00 1.00

Chad to Rhine Issue
Common Design Types

1946
C9   CD93 5fr gray black   1.25 1.25
C10 CD94 10fr dp orange   1.25 1.25
C11 CD95 15fr violet brn   1.25 1.25
C12 CD96 20fr brt violet   1.25 1.25
C13 CD97 25fr blue green   2.50 2.50
C14 CD98 50fr lt ultra   2.50 2.50
       Nos. C9-C14 (6)   10.00 10.00

Somali Gazing
Skyward — AP1

Frontier Post, Loyada — AP2

Governor's Mansion, Djibouti — AP3

Perf. 12½x13, 13x12½
1947   Photo.   Unwmk.
C15 AP1 50fr gray bl & choc   3.50 1.00
C16 AP2 100fr multicolored   4.50 2.25
C17 AP3 200fr multicolored   6.50 3.25
       Nos. C15-C17 (3)   14.50 6.50

UPU Issue
Common Design Type

1949   Engr.   Perf. 13
C18 CD99 30fr bl, dp bl, brn red
              & grn   7.25 7.25

Liberation Issue
Common Design Type

1954, June 6
C19 CD102 15fr indigo & purple 6.50 6.50

Somali Woman and Map of
Djibouti — AP4

1956, Feb. 20   Unwmk.
C20 AP4 500fr dk vio & rose
              vio   40.00 40.00

Mountain Reedbucks — AP5

1958, July 7   Engr.   Perf. 13
C21 AP5 100fr ultra, lt grn & dk
              red brn   6.25 3.50

Albert Bernard, Flag and
Troops — AP6

1960, Jan. 18
C22 AP6 55fr ultra, sepia & car 2.00 1.25
25th death anniv. of Administrator Albert Bernard at Moraito.

Great Bustard — AP7

1960, Oct. 24   Unwmk.   Perf. 13
C23 AP7 200fr brn, org & slate 18.00 12.50

Salt Dealers' Caravan at Assal
Lake — AP8

1962, Jan. 6   Engr.   Perf. 13
C24 AP8 500fr dk bl, red brn,
              pink & blk   20.00 12.50

Obock — AP9

1962, Mar. 11   Unwmk.   Perf. 13
C25 AP9 100fr blue & org brn   4.00 2.50
Centenary of the founding of Obock.

Rostellaria Magna — AP10

40fr, Millepore coral. 55fr, Brain coral. 100fr, Lambis bryonia (seashell). 200fr, Branch coral.

1962-63   Photo.   Perf. 13½x12½
C26 AP10 40fr multi ('63)   2.50 1.00
C27 AP10 55fr multi ('63)   4.00 2.50
C28 AP10 60fr multi   5.50 2.00
C29 AP10 100fr multi   8.00 4.00
C30 AP10 200fr multi ('63) 10.00 6.00
       Nos. C26-C30 (5)   30.00 15.50

Telstar Issue
Common Design Type

1963, Feb. 9   Engr.   Perf. 13
C31 CD111 20fr dp claret & dk
               grn   .75 .75

Zaroug (Somali Sailboats) — AP11

Designs: 50fr, Sambouk (boat) building. 300fr, Zeima sailboat.

1964-65   Engr.   Perf. 13
C32 AP11 50fr blue, ocher &
               choc   3.00 1.60
C33 AP11 85fr dk Prus grn,
               dk brn &
               mag   4.25 2.00
C34 AP11 300fr ultra, lt brn &
               bl grn ('65)   12.50 6.25
       Nos. C32-C34 (3)   19.75 9.85

Discus
Thrower — AP12

1964, Oct. 10   Engr.
C35 AP12 90fr rose lil, red brn &
               blk   8.50 6.50
18th Olympic Games, Tokyo, Oct. 10-25.

ITU Issue
Common Design Type

1965, May 17
C36 CD120 95fr lil rose, brt bl
               & lt brn   13.00 8.00

Camels in Ghoubet Kharab and Map of Somali Coast — AP13

1965		Engr.	Perf. 13	
C37	AP13	45fr Abbe Lake	2.25	1.25
C38	AP13	65fr shown	3.00	1.25

Issue dates: 45fr, Oct. 20; 65fr, July 16.

French Satellite A-1 Issue
Common Design Type

Designs: 25fr, Diamant rocket and launching installations. 30fr, A-1 satellite.

1966, Jan. 28		Engr.	Perf. 13	
C39	CD121	25fr redsh brn, ol brn & dl red	2.50	2.50
C40	CD121	30fr ol brn, dl red & redsh brn	2.50	2.50
a.		Strip of 2, #C39-C40 + label	9.00	9.00

Each sheet contains 16 triptychs (2x8).

Stapelia — AP14

1966		Engr.	Perf. 13	
C41	AP14	55fr sl grn, dl mag & emer	4.00	2.50

Feather Starfish and Coral — AP15

Fish: 25fr, Regal angelfish. 40fr, Pomocanthops filamentosus. 50fr, Amphiprion ephippium. 70fr, Squirrelfish. 80fr, Surgeonfish. 100fr, Pterois lunulatus.

1966		Photo.	Perf. 13	
C42	AP15	8fr multicolored	1.60	1.60
C43	AP15	25fr multicolored	3.25	3.25
C44	AP15	40fr multicolored	4.50	4.50
C45	AP15	50fr multicolored	6.25	6.25
C46	AP15	70fr multicolored	9.25	9.25
C47	AP15	80fr multicolored	12.00	12.00
C48	AP15	100fr multicolored	16.00	16.00
		Nos. C42-C48 (7)	52.85	52.85

French Satellite D-1 Issue
Common Design Type

1966, June 10		Engr.	Perf. 13	
C49	CD122	48fr dk brn, brt bl & grn	3.25	2.00

AIR POST SEMI-POSTAL STAMPS

Catalogue values for unused stamps in this section are for Never Hinged items.

SPAP1

Unwmk.

1942, June 22		Engr.	Perf. 13
CB1	SPAP1	1.50fr# 3.50fr green	.90
CB2	SPAP1	2fr + 6fr brown	.90

Native children's welfare fund.
Nos. CB1-CB2 were issued by the Vichy government in France, but were not placed on sale in Somali Coast

Colonial Education Fund
Common Design Type

1942, June 22			
CB3	CD86a	1.20fr + 1.80fr blue & red	1.25

No. CB3 was issued by the Vichy government in France, but was not placed on sale in Somali Coast.

Pharaoh Sacrificing before Horus and Hathor — SPAP2

Unwmk.

1964, Aug. 28		Engr.	Perf. 13	
CB4	SPAP2	25fr + 5fr multi	6.50	6.25

UNESCO world campaign to save historic monuments in Nubia.

POSTAGE DUE STAMPS

D1

1915		Unwmk. Typo. Chalky Paper	Perf. 14x13½	
J1	D1	5c deep ultra	.20	.20
J2	D1	10c brown red	.35	.35
J3	D1	15c black	.55	.55
J4	D1	20c purple	1.10	1.10
J5	D1	30c orange	1.10	1.10
J6	D1	50c maroon	2.25	2.25
J7	D1	60c green	3.25	3.25
J8	D1	1fr dark blue	3.50	3.50
		Nos. J1-J8 (8)	12.30	12.30

See Nos. J11-J20.

Type of 1915 Issue Surcharged

1927				
J9	D1	2fr on 1fr light red	6.00	6.00
J10	D1	3fr on 1fr lilac rose	6.00	6.00

Type of 1915

1938		Engr.	Perf. 12½x13	
J11	D1	5c light ultra	.20	.20
J12	D1	10c dark carmine	.20	.20
J13	D1	15c brown black	.20	.20
J14	D1	20c violet	.20	.20
J15	D1	30c orange yellow	.85	.85
J16	D1	50c brown	.55	.55
J17	D1	60c emerald	.85	.85
J18	D1	1fr indigo	1.75	1.75
J19	D1	2fr red	.80	.80
J20	D1	3fr dark brown	1.10	1.10
		Nos. J11-J20 (10)	6.70	6.70
		Set, never hinged	12.00	

Inscribed "Inst de Grav" below design.

Postage Due Stamps of 1915 Overprinted in Red or Black

1943		Unwmk.	Perf. 14x13½	
J21	D1	5c ultra (R)	.90	.90
J22	D1	10c brown red	.90	.90
J23	D1	15c black (R)	.90	.90
J24	D1	20c purple	.90	.90
J25	D1	30c orange	.90	.90
J26	D1	50c maroon	.90	.90
J27	D1	60c green	.90	.90
J28	D1	1fr dark blue (R)	5.75	5.75
		Nos. J21-J28 (8)	12.05	12.05
		Set, never hinged	18.00	

Postage Due Stamps of 1938 Overprinted in Red or Black

1943			Perf. 12½x13	
J29	D1	5c lt ultra (R)	.90	.90
J30	D1	10c dark car	.90	.90
J31	D1	15c brn blk (R)	.90	.90
J32	D1	20c violet	.90	.90
J33	D1	30c org yel	.90	.90
J34	D1	50c brown	.90	.90
J35	D1	60c emerald	.90	.90
J36	D1	1fr indigo (R)	.90	.90
J37	D1	2fr red	6.25	6.25
J38	D1	3fr dk brn (R)	7.25	7.25
		Nos. J29-J38 (10)	20.70	20.70
		Set, never hinged	40.00	

For type D1 without "RF," see Nos. J38A-J38E.

Type D1 Without "RF"
Engraved, Values Typo

1944, Apr. 3			
J38A	D1	30c org yel & lilac	.20
J38B	D1	50c yel brn & blk brn	.20
J38C	D1	60c grn & dk grn	.45
J38D	D1	2fr red & rose	.45
J38E	D1	3fr sepia & blk	.85
		Nos. J38A-J38E (5)	2.15

Nos. J38A-J38E were issued by the Vichy government in France, but were not placed on sale in Somali Coast.

Catalogue values for unused stamps in this section, from this point to the end of the section, are for Never Hinged items.

D2

1947		Photo.	Perf. 13½x13	
J39	D2	10c purple	.20	.20
J40	D2	30c brown	.20	.20
J41	D2	50c green	.35	.35
J42	D2	1fr deep orange	.35	.35
J43	D2	2fr lilac rose	.55	.55
J44	D2	3fr dk org brn	.55	.55
J45	D2	4fr blue	.75	.75
J46	D2	5fr orange red	.75	.75
J47	D2	10fr olive green	.75	.75
J48	D2	20fr blue violet	1.40	1.40
		Nos. J39-J48 (10)	5.85	5.85

SOMALILAND PROTECTORATE

sō-'mä-lē-,land
prə-'tek-t,ə-,rət

LOCATION — Eastern Africa, bordering on the Gulf of Aden
GOVT. — British Protectorate

AREA — 68,000 sq. mi.
POP. — 640,000 (estimated)
CAPITAL — Hargeisa

Formerly administered by the Indian Government, the territory was taken over by the British Foreign Office in 1898 and transferred to the Colonial Office in 1905.

Somaliland Protectorate became part of independent Somalia in 1960.

16 Annas = 1 Rupee
100 Cents = 1 Shilling (1951)

Catalogue values for unused stamps in this country are for Never Hinged items, beginning with Scott 108.

Stamps of India, 1882-1900, Overprinted at Top of Stamp

1903		Wmk. 39	Perf. 14	
1	A17	½a light green	2.50	4.25
2	A19	1a carmine rose	2.50	4.00
3	A21	2a violet	2.10	1.60
a.		Double overprint	725.00	
4	A28	2½a ultra	1.90	1.90
5	A22	3a brown orange	3.00	3.25
6	A23	4a olive green	3.25	3.00
7	A25	8a red violet	3.50	5.25
8	A26	12a brown, red	3.00	7.50
a.		Inverted overprint		1,200.
9	A29	1r car rose & grn	6.75	10.50
10	A30	2r yel brn & car rose	25.00	45.00
11	A30	3r green & brown	21.00	50.00
12	A30	5r violet & blue	35.00	57.50
		Wmk. Elephant's Head (38)		
13	A14	6a bister	4.50	4.75
		Nos. 1-13 (13)	114.00	198.50

Nos. 1-5 exist without the 2nd "I" of "BRITISH."

Same, but Overprinted at Bottom of Stamp

1903			Wmk. 39	
14	A28	2½a ultra	3.00	6.75
15	A26	12a violet, red	6.50	12.50
16	A29	1r car rose & grn	3.25	17.50
17	A30	2r yel brn & car rose	75.00	125.00
18	A30	3r green & brn	80.00	125.00
a.		Inverted overprint	600.00	
19	A30	5r violet & blue	75.00	110.00
		Wmk. 38		
20	A14	6a bister	6.00	5.75
		Nos. 14-20 (7)	248.75	402.50

Stamps of India, 1902-03, Ovptd.

1903			Wmk. 39	
21	A33	½a light green	2.50	.60
22	A34	1a car rose	1.40	.35
23	A35	2a violet	1.90	2.75
24	A37	3a brown orange	2.75	2.75
25	A38	4a olive green	1.60	4.50
26	A40	8a red violet	1.90	2.50
		Nos. 21-26 (6)	12.05	13.45

The above overprints vary in length, also in the relative positions of the letters. Nos. 21-23 exist without the second "I" of "British."

A1

King Edward VII — A2

1904		Wmk. 2		Typo.
27	A1	½a dl grn & grn	1.50	4.50
28	A1	1a carmine & blk	9.00	3.50
29	A1	2a red vio & dull vio	1.75	2.40
30	A1	2½a ultramarine	2.75	4.00
31	A1	3a gray grn & vio brn	1.75	2.75
32	A1	4a black & grn	1.75	5.00
33	A1	6a vio & gray grn	4.25	18.00
34	A1	8a pale blue & blk	3.50	5.75
35	A1	12a ocher & blk	6.50	11.50

Wmk. Crown and C C (1)

36	A2	1r gray grn	12.00	42.50
37	A2	2r red vio & dull vio	40.00	75.00
38	A2	3r blk & gray grn	40.00	85.00
39	A2	5r carmine & blk	40.00	85.00
		Nos. 27-39 (13)	164.75	344.90

1905				Wmk. 3
40	A1	½a dl grn & grn	1.40	8.00
41	A1	1a carmine & blk	10.50	1.75
42	A1	2a red vio & dull vio	7.75	9.00
43	A1	2½a ultramarine	3.25	10.50
44	A1	3a gray grn & vio brn	2.10	15.00
45	A1	4a black & gray grn	4.25	15.00
46	A1	6a violet & gray grn	3.25	25.00
47	A1	8a pale blue & blk	6.25	9.50
48	A1	12a ocher & black	6.75	10.50
		Nos. 40-48 (9)	45.50	104.25

Nos. 41, 42, 44-48 are on both ordinary and chalky paper.

1909				
49	A1	½a bluish green	24.00	27.50
50	A1	1a carmine	2.75	2.10

For overprints see Nos. O11-O16.

King George V
A3   A4

The ½, 1 and 2½a of type A3 are on ordinary paper, the other values of types A3 and A4 are on chalky paper.

1912-19				
51	A3	½a green	.70	9.25
52	A3	1a carmine	2.75	.60
53	A3	2a red vio & dull vio	3.75	16.00
54	A3	2½a ultramarine	1.10	9.75
55	A3	3a gray grn & vio brn	2.50	7.50
56	A3	4a blk & grn ('13)	2.75	11.50
57	A3	6a violet & green	2.75	5.75
58	A3	8a lt blue & blk	3.75	17.50
59	A3	12a ocher & blk	3.50	24.00
60	A4	1r dull grn & grn	12.00	18.00
61	A4	2r red vio & dull vio ('19)	20.00	75.00
62	A4	3r blk & gray grn ('19)	60.00	125.00
63	A4	5r car & blk ('19)	60.00	175.00
		Nos. 51-63 (13)	175.55	494.85

1921				Wmk. 4
64	A3	½a blue green	3.00	11.50
65	A3	1a scarlet	3.75	.80
66	A3	2a vio & dull vio	4.50	1.10
67	A3	2½a ultramarine	1.10	5.25
68	A3	3a gray grn & vio brown	2.75	8.50
69	A3	4a black & grn	2.75	8.50
70	A3	6a violet & grn	1.60	15.00
71	A3	8a lt blue & blk	2.10	6.25
72	A3	12a ocher & blk	9.00	17.50
73	A4	1r dull grn & grn	8.50	55.00
74	A4	2r vio & dull vio	25.00	55.00
75	A4	3r blk & gray grn	37.50	110.00
76	A4	5r scarlet & blk	70.00	190.00
		Nos. 64-76 (13)	171.55	484.40

Common Design Types
pictured following the introduction.

Silver Jubilee Issue
Common Design Type

1935, May 6	Engr.		Perf. 11x12	
77	CD301	1a car & dk blue	2.00	2.50
78	CD301	2a black & ultra	2.50	2.40
79	CD301	3a ultra & brown	2.00	10.50
80	CD301	1r brown vio & ind	6.50	10.50
		Nos. 77-80 (4)	13.00	25.90
		Set, never hinged	21.00	

Coronation Issue
Common Design Type

1937, May 13			Perf. 13½x14	
81	CD302	1a carmine	.20	.25
82	CD302	2a black	.35	1.60
83	CD302	3a bright ultra	.40	.60
		Nos. 81-83 (3)	.95	2.45
		Set, never hinged	1.40	

Blackhead Sheep — A5   Greater Kudu — A6

Map of Somaliland Protectorate
A7

1938, May 10	Wmk. 4		Perf. 12½	
84	A5	½a green	.25	5.50
85	A5	1a carmine	.25	1.60
86	A5	2a deep claret	1.10	1.90
87	A5	3a ultra	5.25	11.00
88	A6	4a dark brown	3.00	8.75
89	A6	6a purple	4.50	13.00
90	A6	8a gray black	1.00	13.50
91	A6	12a orange	4.25	16.00
92	A7	1r green	5.50	55.00
93	A7	2r rose violet	9.75	55.00
94	A7	3r ultramarine	12.00	32.50
95	A7	5r black	13.00	32.50
a.		Horiz. pair, imperf. btwn.	11,000.	
		Nos. 84-95 (12)	59.85	246.25
		Set, never hinged	100.00	

A8   A9

A10

1942, Apr. 22				
96	A8	½a green	.20	.35
97	A8	1a carmine	.20	.20
98	A8	2a deep claret	.30	.25
99	A8	3a ultramarine	1.10	.25
100	A9	4a dark brown	1.75	.25
101	A9	6a purple	1.75	.25
102	A9	8a gray	1.90	.25
103	A9	12a orange	1.90	.45
104	A10	1r green	.80	.60
105	A10	2r rose violet	.80	4.50
106	A10	3r ultra	1.40	8.50
107	A10	5r black	4.50	7.50
		Nos. 96-107 (12)	16.60	23.35
		Set, never hinged	27.50	

For surcharges see Nos. 116-126.

> **Catalogue values for unused stamps in this section, from this point to the end of the section, are for Never Hinged items.**

Peace Issue
Common Design Type
Perf. 13½x14

1946, Oct. 15	Wmk. 4			
108	CD303	1a carmine	.20	.20
a.		Perf. 13½	13.50	50.00
109	CD303	3a deep blue	.20	.20

Silver Wedding Issue
Common Design Types

1949, Jan. 28	Photo.		Perf. 14x14½	
110	CD304	1a scarlet	.20	.20

Engraved; Name Typographed
Perf. 11½x11

111	CD305	5r gray black	6.00	8.50

UPU Issue
Common Design Types
Surcharged in Black or Carmine with New Values in Annas
Engr.; Name Typo. on 3a, 6a

1949, Oct. 10		Perf. 13½, 11x11½		
112	CD306	1a on 10c rose car	.20	.20
113	CD307	3a on 30c ind (C)	1.10	.85
114	CD308	6a on 50c rose vio	.40	1.10
115	CD309	12a on 1sh red org	.40	.60
		Nos. 112-115 (4)	2.10	2.75

Nos. 96 and 98 to 107 Surcharged with New Value in Black or Carmine

1951, Apr. 2	Wmk. 4		Perf. 12½	
116	A8	5c on ½a green	.35	1.10
117	A8	10c on 2a deep claret	.35	.45
118	A8	15c on 3a ultramarine	1.50	1.10
119	A9	20c on 4a dark brown	2.00	.25
120	A9	30c on 6a purple	2.00	.60
121	A9	50c on 8a gray	2.25	.25
122	A9	70c on 12a red	4.00	4.00
123	A10	1sh on 1r green	1.10	.35
124	A10	2sh on 2r rose violet	5.50	14.00
125	A10	2sh on 3r ultra	6.25	5.25
126	A10	5sh on 5r black (C)	7.00	7.50
		Nos. 116-126 (11)	32.30	34.85

Coronation Issue
Common Design Type

1953, June 2	Engr.		Perf. 13½x13	
127	CD312	15c dark green & blk	.30	.20

Camel Carrying Somali House
A11   Askari Militiaman A12

Designs: 35c, 2sh, Rock Pigeon. 50c, 5sh, Martial eagle. 1sh, Blackhead sheep. 1sh30c, Tomb of Sheik Isaaq, Mait. 10sh, Taleh Fort.

1953-58		Engr.	Perf. 12½	
128	A11	5c gray	.20	.45
129	A12	10c red orange	1.50	.55
130	A11	15c blue green	.45	.60
131	A11	20c rose red	.45	.40
132	A12	30c lt chocolate	1.75	.40
133	A11	35c blue	2.75	1.75
134	A11	50c lil rose & brn	2.75	.55
135	A11	1sh grnsh blue	.40	.30
136	A11	1sh30c dark gray & ultra ('58)	6.75	3.00
137	A11	2sh violet & brn	19.50	5.00
138	A11	5sh emer & brn	19.50	6.00
139	A11	10sh rose lilac & brn	14.00	13.50
		Nos. 128-139 (12)	70.00	32.50

Nos. 131 and 135 Overprinted: "Opening of the Legislative Council 1957"

1957, May 21				
140	A11	20c rose red	.20	.20
141	A11	1sh greenish blue	.30	.30

Nos. 131 and 136 Overprinted: "Legislative Council Unofficial Majority, 1960"

1960, Apr. 5				
142	A11	20c rose red	.20	.20
143	A11	1sh30c dk gray & ultra	.30	.30

Changes in the Legislative Council.

Three stamps of Somalia were overprinted "Somaliland Independence 26 June 1960" and issued in Hargeisa on that day. Somaliland Protectorate became part of Somalia on July 1, 1960. These three stamps are listed in Vol. 5 as Somalia Nos. 242, C68-C69.

Stamps of Somaliland Protectorate were replaced by those of Somalia in 1960.

OFFICIAL STAMPS

Official Stamps of India, 1883-1900, Overprinted

1903, June 1	Wmk. 39		Perf. 14	
O1	A17	½a light green	7.50	55.00
O2	A19	1a carmine rose	17.50	9.25
O3	A21	2a violet	9.25	55.00
O4	A25	8a red violet	11.50	425.00
O5	A29	1r car rose & grn	11.50	625.00
		Nos. O1-O5 (5)	57.25	

India Nos. 61-63, 68, 49 Overprinted

1903				
O6	A33	½a green	.50	
O7	A34	1a carmine rose	.50	
O8	A35	2a violet	.80	
O9	A40	8a red violet	5.00	
O10	A29	1r car rose & grn	20.00	
		Nos. O6-O10 (5)	26.80	

Nos. O6-O10 were not regularly issued.

Regular Issue of 1904 Overprinted

1904		Wmk. Crown and C A (2)		
O11	A1	½a gray green	4.00	55.00
O12	A1	1a carmine & blk	3.75	8.00
O13	A1	2a red vio & dull vio	200.00	70.00
O14	A1	8a pale blue & blk	70.00	150.00
		Nos. O11-O14 (4)	277.75	283.00

Wmk. Crown and C C (1)

O15	A2	1r gray green	190.00	625.00

Same Overprint on No. 42

1905				Wmk. 3
O16	A1	2a red vio & dull vio	85.00	825.00

The period after "M" may be found missing on Nos. O11-O14 and O16.

SOUTH AFRICA

sauth 'a-fri-kə

LOCATION — Southern Africa
GOVT. — Republic
AREA — 472,730 sq. mi.
POP. — 43,426,386 (1999 est.)
CAPITAL — Pretoria (administrative); Cape Town (legislative); Bloemfontein (Judicial)

The union was formed on May 31, 1910, comprising the former British colonies of Cape of Good Hope, Natal, Transvaal and the Orange Free State, which became provinces. The union became a republic in 1961.

For previous listings, see individual headings.

12 Pence = 1 Shilling
20 Shillings = 1 Pound
100 Cents = 1 Rand (1961)

Catalogue values for unused stamps in this country are for Never Hinged items, beginning with Scott 74 in the regular postage section, Scott B1 in the semipostal section, Scott J30 in the postage due section, and Scott O21 in the officials section.

Watermarks

Wmk. 47 — Multiple Rosette

Wmk. 177 — Springbok's Head

Wmk. 201 — Multiple Springbok's Head

Wmk. 330 — Coat of Arms, Multiple

Wmk. 348 — RSA in Triangle, Multiple

Wmk. 359 — RSA in Triangle, Tete Beche

George V
A1   A2

1910   Engr.   Wmk. 47   Perf. 14
1   A1   2½p blue   3.00   1.75
Union Parliament opening, Nov. 4, 1910.

Type A2 stamps have very small margins at top and bottom. Values are for copies with perfs close to, or touching the frame.

1913-24	**Typo.**	**Wmk. 177**	
2	A2	½p green	1.50	.20
a.		Double impression	15,000.	
3	A2	1p scarlet	1.50	.20
4	A2	1½p org brn ('20)	.75	.20
a.		Tête beche pair	4.50	15.00
5	A2	2p dull violet	2.25	.20
6	A2	2½p ultra	5.50	1.60
7	A2	3p brn org & blk	13.00	.55
8	A2	3p ultra ('22)	4.75	1.60
9	A2	4p ol grn & org	11.00	.55
10	A2	6p violet & blk	9.50	.70
11	A2	1sh orange	20.00	.70
12	A2	1sh3p violet ('20)	17.50	11.00
13	A2	2sh6p green & cl	70.00	5.50
14	A2	5sh blue & claret	140.00	9.00
15	A2	10sh ol grn & blue	225.00	14.50
16	A2	£1 red & dp grn ('16)	850.00	450.00
a.		£1 lt red & gray green ('24)	1,100.	1,600.
		Nos. 2-16 (15)	1,372.	496.50

The ½p, 1p and 1½p have the words "Revenue" and "Inkomst" on the stamps. On other stamps of this type these words are replaced by short vertical lines.
All values exist in many shades. No. 4a exists with and without gutter between.
Unwatermarked copies of the 1p are the result of misplaced watermarks.
All values except the 2sh6p and £1 exist with watermark inverted.
For overprint see No. O1.

Coil Stamps
Perf. 14 Horizontally
17   A2   ½p green   9.25   1.90
18   A2   1p scarlet ('14)   11.50   6.25
19   A2   1½p org brown ('20)   17.00   27.50
20   A2   2p dull violet ('21)   18.00   9.00
Nos. 17-20 (4)   55.75   44.65

"Hope" — A3

Design: No. 22, inscribed SUIDAFRIKA.

1926   Engr.   Wmk. 201   Imperf.
21   A3   4p blue gray   2.00   1.40
22   A3   4p blue gray   2.00   1.40

Nos. 21 and 22 were privately rouletted and perforated, but such varieties were not officially made.
No. 21 (English inscription) was printed in a separate sheet from No. 22 (Afrikaans inscription).

English-Afrikaans Se-Tenant

Stamps with English inscriptions and with Afrikaans inscriptions were printed alternately in the same sheets, starting with No. 23. Major-number listings and values are for horizontal pairs (vertical pairs sell for about one-third less) of such stamps consisting of one English and one Afrikaans-inscribed stamp, unless otherwise described.
Values are for pairs with no fold marks between stamps and no perf separations.
Beware of pairs that have been rejoined.

Springbok A5

Jan van Riebeek's Ship, Drommedaris — A6

Orange Tree — A7

1926	**Typo.**	**Perf. 14½x14**	
23	A5	½p dk grn & blk, pair	3.00	3.50
a.		Single, English	.25	.20
b.		Single, Afrikaans	.25	.20
c.		Tete beche pair	1,500.	
d.		Center omitted	1,400.	
e.		Booklet pane of 6	190.00	
f.		As "e," perf. 14	300.00	
24	A6	1p car & blk, pair	3.00	3.00
a.		Single, English	.25	.20
b.		Single, Afrikaans	.25	.20
c.		Imperf., pair	1,350.	
d.		Tete beche pair	1,750.	
e.		Center omitted	275.00	
f.		Booklet pane of 6	160.00	
g.		As "f," perf. 14	250.00	
25	A7	6p org & grn, pair	42.50	47.50
a.		Single, English	3.00	2.25
b.		Single, Afrikaans	3.00	2.25
		Nos. 23-25 (3)	48.50	54.00

Nos. 23c and 24d are from uncut sheets printed for the perf. 14 booklet panes of 1928, Nos. 23f and 24g.
See Nos. 33-35, 42, 45-50, 59-61, 98-99. For overprints see Nos. O2-O4, O6-O9, O12-O15, O18, O21-O25, O30-O32, O42-O45, O48.

Government Buildings, Pretoria — A8

"Groote Schuur," Rhodes's Home — A9

Native Kraal — A10

Gnu — A11

Trekking — A12

Ox Wagon — A13

Cape Town and Table Mountain — A14

Perf. 14, 14x13½			
1927-28	**Engr.**	**Wmk. 201**	
26	A8	2p vio brn & gray, pair	13.50	26.00
a.		Single, English	2.10	1.40
b.		Single, Afrikaans	2.10	1.40
27	A9	3p red & blk, pair	24.00	37.50
a.		Single, English	2.10	1.40
b.		Single, Afrikaans	2.10	1.40
c.		Perf. 14x13½, pair	67.50	82.50
d.		As "c," single, English	3.25	2.75
e.		As "c," single, Afrikaans	3.25	2.75
28	A10	4p brown, pair ('28)	32.50	67.50
a.		Single, English	3.25	1.90
b.		Single, Afrikaans	3.25	1.90
29	A11	1sh dp bl & bis brn, pair	47.50	87.50
a.		Single, English	6.75	2.75
b.		Single, Afrikaans	6.75	2.75
30	A12	2sh6p brn & bl grn, pair	140.00	400.00
a.		Single, English	20.00	24.00
b.		Single, Afrikaans	20.00	24.00
c.		Perf. 14x13½, pair	475.00	675.00
d.		As "c," single, English	32.50	37.50
e.		As "c," single, Afrikaans	32.50	37.50
31	A13	5sh dp grn & blk, pair	275.00	650.00
a.		Single, English	30.00	40.00
b.		Single, Afrikaans	30.00	40.00
c.		Perf. 14x13½, pair	525.00	750.00
d.		As "c," single, English	47.50	52.50
e.		As "c," single, Afrikaans	47.50	52.50
32	A14	10sh ol brn & bl, pair	200.00	200.00
a.		Single, English	20.00	16.00
b.		Single, Afrikaans	20.00	16.00
c.		Perf. 14x13½, pair	275.00	375.00
d.		As "c," single, English	24.00	20.00
e.		As "c," single, Afrikaans	24.00	20.00
		Nos. 26-32 (7)	732.50	1,468.

See Nos. 36-41, 43-44, 53-54, 58, 62-66. For overprints see Nos. O5, O10-O111, O16-O17, O19-O20, O28, O33-O35, O39, O41, O49-O53.

Types of 1926-28 Redrawn "SUIDAFRIKA" (No Hyphen) on Afrikaans Stamps

The photogravure, unhyphenated stamps of 1930-45 are distinguished from the 1926-28 typographed or engraved stamps (also unhyphenated) by the following characteristics:
½p, 1p, 6p. Leg of "R" in AFRICA or AFRIKA ends in a straight line in the photogravure set; in a curved line in the typographed. No. 35 differs from No. 34, having 2mm space between POSSEEL—INKOMSTE instead of 1mm.
2p. A memorial statue has been added just above and leftward of the "2" in value tablet on Nos. 36-37 (photogravure).
3p. Top frame on No. 38 consists of 3 heavy lines. On No. 27 it has 3 heavy and 2 very thin lines.
4p. On Nos. 40-41 the background in upper corners is solid. On No. 28 it consists of horizontal and vertical lines. No. 41 has pretzel-shaped scroll endings at bottom. On No. 40 these scroll endings enclose a solid mass of color.
1sh. No. 43 has no fine shading lines projecting from the curved top of the left inner frame, as No. 29 has. On No. 43 the shading

of the last "A" of the country name partly covers the flower below it.

2sh6p. On No. 44 the shading below the country name is solid or shows signs of wear. On No. 30 it is composed of fine lines.

The engraved pictorials are much more finely executed and show details more clearly than the photogravure.

Perf. 15x14 (½p, 1p, 6p), 14

1930-45		Photo.		Wmk. 201
33	A5	½p bl grn & blk, pair	3.50	3.50
a.		Single, English	.20	.20
b.		Single, Afrikaans	.20	.20
c.		Tete-beche pair	1,250.	
d.		As "c," gutter between	1,750.	
e.		Booklet pane of 6	40.00	40.00
f.		Vert. pair, monolingual	5.00	5.00
34	A6	1p car & blk, pair	4.00	3.50
a.		Single, English	.20	.20
b.		Single, Afrikaans	.20	.20
c.		Center omitted	2,500.	
d.		Frame omitted	2,500.	
e.		Tete-beche pair	1,800.	
f.		As "e," gutter between	1,500.	
g.		Booklet pane of 6	16.00	16.00
35	A6	1p rose & blk, pair ('32)	35.00	4.50
a.		Single, English	1.00	.20
b.		Single, Afrikaans	1.00	.20
c.		Center omitted	750.00	
36	A8	2p vio & gray, pair ('31)	24.00	16.00
a.		Single, English	1.10	.40
b.		Single, Afrikaans	1.10	.40
c.		Frame omitted	1,000.	
d.		Tete-beche pair	6,500.	
e.		Booklet pane of 4	200.00	200.00
37	A8	2p vio & ind, pair ('38)	250.00	100.00
a.		Single, English	12.50	7.25
b.		Single, Afrikaans	12.50	7.25
38	A9	3p red & blk, pair ('31)	72.50	95.00
a.		Single, English	6.75	6.75
b.		Single, Afrikaans	6.75	6.75
39	A9	3p ultra & bl, pair ('33)	22.50	10.00
a.		Single, English	1.10	.80
b.		Single, Afrikaans	1.10	.80
c.		Center omitted	1,000.	
40	A10	4p redsh brn, pair ('32)	250.00	210.00
a.		Single, English	25.00	11.00
b.		Single, Afrikaans	25.00	11.00
41	A10	4p brn, pair ('36)	6.50	5.00
a.		Single, English	1.10	.45
b.		Single, Afrikaans	1.10	.45
42	A7	6p org & grn, pair ('31)	29.00	6.50
a.		Single, English	1.10	.45
b.		Single, Afrikaans	1.10	.45
43	A11	1sh dl bl & yel brn, pair	140.00	57.50
a.		Single, English	7.25	1.10
b.		Single, Afrikaans	7.25	1.10
c.		1sh dp bl & brn, pair ('32)	72.50	32.50
d.		As "c," single, English	5.25	.40
e.		As "c," single, Afrikaans	5.25	.40
44	A12	2sh 6p brn & bl, pair ('45)	29.00	19.00
a.		Single, English	1.75	.70
b.		Single, Afrikaans	1.75	.70
c.		2sh6p brn & sl grn ('36), pair	85.00	50.00
d.		As "c," single, English	10.00	4.00
e.		As "c," single, Afrikaans	10.00	4.00
f.		2sh6p choc & dp grn ('37), pair	75.00	40.00
g.		As "f," single, English	9.00	4.00
h.		As "f," single, Afrikaans	9.00	4.00
i.		2sh6p red brn & grn, pair ('32)	210.00	200.00
j.		As "i," single, English	17.00	6.50
k.		As "i," single, Afrikaans	17.00	6.50
		Nos. 33-44 (12)	866.00	530.50

No. 34 unwatermarked, or watermarked multiple clover leaf, is a proof.

Types of 1926-28 with "SUID-AFRIKA" Hyphenated on Afrikaans Stamps, and

Gold Mine — A15

Government Buildings, Pretoria — A16

Groote Schuur — A17

Groot Constantia — A18

½p. No. 45 shading in leaves and ornaments strengthened; 40 lines in center background. Size: 18½x22½mm.

No. 46 has 28 heavy horizontal shading lines in center background and similar thicker lines in frame. Top and bottom green bars are scored by a white horizontal line. Size: 18½x22½mm.

No. 47 is smaller, 18x22mm.

1p. No. 48, size 18½x22½mm.

No. 49, size 18x22mm.

No. 50. Size: 17½x21½mm.

2p. On Nos. 53-54, S's in SOUTH and POSTAGE are narrower than on Nos. 36-37.

6p. Die I, "SUID-AFRIKA" 16½mm. Shading in leaves framing oval very faint and broken. Size: 18½x22½mm.

Die II, "SUID-AFRIKA" 17mm. Leaves strongly shaded. Heavy lines of shading in background of tree. Size: 18½x22½mm.

Die III, "question mark" scrolls below top panel are cleanly defined without intrusion of background shading. Size: 18x22mm.

Nos. 45-67 were printed in many shades. Some denominations in some printings were partly or wholly screened. Except for No. 47, the screened stamps were issued after 1947.

5sh. No. 65. Type I, letters "U" and "A" in SOUTH AFRICA have projections. Size: 27x21½mm.

No. 66. Type II, letters "U" and "A" redrawn to eliminate projections. Size: 26½x21½mm.

Perf. 15x14 (½p, 1p, 6p), 14

1933-54		Photo.		Wmk. 201
45	A5	½p grn & gray, pair ('36)	4.00	.80
a.		Single, English	.25	.20
b.		Single, Afrikaans	.25	.20
c.		Bkt. pane of 6, marginal ads	25.00	25.00
d.		Perf. 13½x14 (coil), pair	30.00	47.50
e.		As "d," single, English	1.75	1.25
f.		As "d," single, Afrikaans	1.75	1.25
46	A5	½p grn & gray, redrawn, pair ('37)	4.00	.40
a.		Single, English	.20	.20
b.		Single, Afrikaans	.20	.20
c.		Booklet pane of 6	37.50	30.00
d.		Booklet pane of 2	8.00	1.00
e.		As "c," 4 blank margins	35.00	35.00
f.		Perf. 14½x14 (coil), pair	12.50	7.25
g.		As "f," single, English	2.25	.80
h.		As "f," single, Afrikaans	2.25	.80
47	A5	½p grn & gray, pair ('47)	1.25	.40
a.		Single, English	.20	.20
b.		Single, Afrikaans	.20	.20
c.		Bkt. pane of 6, marginal ads	4.00	3.50
d.		As "c," no horiz. margins	5.00	3.00
48	A6	1p car & gray, pair ('34)	1.10	.65
a.		Single, English	.20	.20
b.		Single, Afrikaans	.20	.20
c.		Booklet pane of 6	37.50	37.50
d.		Booklet pane of 2	3.00	1.25
e.		Perf. 14½x14 (coil), pair	30.00	52.50
f.		As "e," single, English	1.40	1.00
g.		As "e," single, Afrikaans	1.40	1.00
h.		Center omitted, pair	325.00	
j.		Bkt. pane of 6, marginal ads	27.50	27.50
k.		As "j," 4 blank margins	30.00	30.00
m.		Perf. 14½x14 (coil), pair	11.00	11.00
n.		As "m," single, English	1.40	1.40
p.		As "m," single, Afrikaans	1.40	1.40
49	A6	1p rose car & gray blk, pair ('40)	1.50	.30
a.		Single, English	.20	.20
b.		Single, Afrikaans	.20	.20
c.		Unwmkd., pair	325.00	325.00
d.		Booklet pane of 6	3.75	2.75
e.		Perf. 14½x14 (coil), pair	4.00	6.00
f.		As "e," single, English	1.40	.90
g.		As "e," single, Afrikaans	1.40	.90
h.		As "d," marginal ads	5.00	4.25
50	A6	1p car & blk, pair ('51)	.75	.20
a.		Single, English	.20	.20
b.		Single, Afrikaans	.20	.20
51	A15	1½p dk grn & gold, 27x21½mm, pair ('36)	2.00	1.40
a.		Single, English	.25	.20
b.		Single, Afrikaans	.25	.20
c.		Booklet pane of 4	9.00	8.00
d.		Center omitted, pair	1,000.	
52	A15	1½p sl grn & och, 22x18mm, pair ('41)	1.25	.25
a.		Single, English	.20	.20
b.		Single, Afrikaans	.20	.20
c.		Center omitted, pair	900.00	
d.		Booklet pane of 6	5.75	4.50
53	A8	2p bl vio & dl bl, pair ('38)	40.00	32.50
a.		Single, English	3.00	1.25
b.		Single, Afrikaans	3.00	1.25
54	A8	2p dl vio & gray, pair ('41)	24.00	45.00
a.		Single, English	.90	.50
b.		Single, Afrikaans	.90	.50

55	A16	2p pur & sl bl, 27x21½mm, pair ('45)	1.50	4.00
a.		Single, English	.20	.20
b.		Single, Afrikaans	.20	.20
56	A16	2p same, 21½ x 17¼mm, pair ('50)	1.00	4.50
a.		Single, English	.20	.20
b.		Single, Afrikaans	.20	.20
c.		Booklet pane of 6 ('51)	3.75	2.75
57	A17	3p ultra, pair ('40)	5.00	1.75
a.		Single, English	.20	.20
b.		Single, Afrikaans	.20	.20
c.		3p bl, pair ('49)	2.00	4.00
d.		As "c," single, English	.20	.20
e.		As "c," single, Afrikaans	.20	.20
58	A10	4p choc brn, pair ('52)	1.25	5.50
a.		Single, English	.20	.20
b.		Single, Afrikaans	.20	.20
59	A7	6p org & bl grn, I, pair ('37)	50.00	22.50
a.		Single, English	3.75	1.10
b.		Single, Afrikaans	3.75	1.10
60	A7	6p org & grn, II, pair ('38)	22.50	3.00
a.		Single, English	1.50	.25
b.		Single, Afrikaans	1.50	.25
61	A7	6p red org & bl grn, III ('50), pair	1.75	1.00
a.		Single, English	.20	.20
b.		Single, Afrikaans	.20	.20
c.		6p org & grn, III, pair ('46)	13.50	1.90
d.		As "c," single, English	1.00	.20
e.		As "c," single, Afrikaans	1.00	.20
62	A11	1sh chlky bl & lt brn ('50), pair	9.00	6.00
a.		As "f," single, English	.55	.20
b.		As "f," single, Afrikaans	.55	.20
c.		1sh lt bl & ol brn, pair ('39)	35.00	7.50
d.		As "c," single, English	1.00	.20
e.		As "c," single, Afrikaans	1.00	.20
f.		1sh vio bl & brnsh blk, pair	16.00	10.00
g.		Single, English	.50	.30
h.		Single, Afrikaans	.50	.30
63	A12	2sh6p brn & brt grn, pair ('49)	7.50	24.00
a.		Single, English	1.25	.75
b.		Single, Afrikaans	1.25	.75
64	A13	5sh grn & blk, I, pair	55.00	55.00
a.		Single, English	2.50	2.00
b.		Single, Afrikaans	2.50	2.00
65	A13	5sh bl grn & blk, I, pair ('49)	42.50	62.50
a.		Single, English	4.00	3.50
b.		Single, Afrikaans	4.00	3.50
66	A13	5sh grn & blk, II, pair ('54)	55.00	75.00
a.		Single, English	4.00	3.50
b.		Single, Afrikaans	4.00	3.50
67	A18	10sh ol blk & bl, pair ('39)	50.00	17.50
a.		Single, English	3.00	1.00
b.		Single, Afrikaans	3.00	1.00
		Nos. 45-67 (23)	381.85	364.15

See Nos. 98-99. For overprints see Nos. O26-O27, O29, O36-O38, O40, O46-O47, O54.

George V and Springboks — A19

1935, May 1		Wmk. 201		Perf. 15x14
68	A19	½p Prus grn & blk, pair	3.00	8.50
a.		Single, English top	.25	.25
b.		Single, Afrikaans top	.25	.25
69	A19	1p car rose & blk, pair	3.00	8.00
a.		Single, English top	.25	.25
b.		Single, Afrikaans top	.25	.25
70	A19	3p bl & dk bl, pair	14.00	45.00
a.		Single, English top	1.40	2.75
b.		Single, Afrikaans top	1.40	2.75
71	A19	6p org & grn, pair	30.00	72.50
a.		Single, English top	2.10	3.00
b.		Single, Afrikaans top	2.10	3.00
		Nos. 68-71 (4)	50.00	134.00
		Set, never hinged	100.00	

25th anniv. of the reign of George V.

English and Afrikaans inscriptions are transposed on alternate stamps. On the ½p, 3p and 6p with "SOUTH AFRICA" at top, "SILVER JUBILEUM" is at left of medallion, but on 1p with English at top, it is at the right.

Johannesburg International Philatelic Exhibition Issue
Souvenir Sheets

A20

A21

Black Overprint, "JIPEX 1936"

1936, Nov. 2				Perf. 15x14
72	A20	Sheet of 6 (½p)	5.00	9.50
73	A21	Sheet of 6 (1p)	4.00	6.50
		Set, never hinged	19.00	

Sheets made by overprinting booklet panes Nos. 45c and 48j. Sheets exist with and without horizontal perforations through right margin. Sheet size: 81x72½mm.

Catalogue values for unused stamps in this section, from this point to the end of the section, are for Never Hinged items.

George VI — A22

"KRONING SUID-AFRIKA" on alternate stamps.

1937, May 12				Perf. 14
74	A22	½p grn & ol blk, pair	.55	.40
a.		Single, English	.20	.20
b.		Single, Afrikaans	.20	.20
75	A22	1p car & ol blk, pair	.85	.40
a.		Single, English	.20	.20
b.		Single, Afrikaans	.20	.20
76	A22	1½p Prus grn & org, pair	.85	.70
a.		Single, English	.20	.20
b.		Single, Afrikaans	.20	.20
77	A22	3p bl & ultra, pair	1.75	2.00
a.		Single, English	.20	.20
b.		Single, Afrikaans	.20	.20
78	A22	1sh Prus bl & org brn, pair	5.00	3.50
a.		Single, English	.50	.25
b.		Single, Afrikaans	.50	.25
		Nos. 74-78 (5)	9.00	7.00

Coronation of George VI and Queen Elizabeth.

Wagon Wheel A23

Voortrekker Family A24

Alternate stamps inscribed "SOUTH AFRICA," "SUID-AFRIKA."

1938, Dec. 14   Perf. 15x14

79	A23	1p rose & slate, pair	7.00	5.50
a.		Single, English	.30	.30
b.		Single, Afrikaans	.30	.30
80	A24	1½p red brn & Prus bl, pair	8.00	6.50
a.		Single, English	.30	.35
b.		Single, Afrikaans	.30	.35

Issued to commemorate the Voortrekkers.

Infantry A25

Nurse and Ambulance A26

Airman and Spitfires (Flight Lt. Robert Kershaw) A27

Sailor A28

Women's Services A29

Artillery — A30   Welder — A31

Tank Corps A32

Signal Corps — A33

Bilingual inscriptions on 2p and 1sh.

Perf. 14 (2p, 4p, 6p), 15x14

1941-43   Photo.   Wmk. 201

81	A25	½p dp bl grn, pair	.90	.40
a.		Single, English	.20	.20
b.		Single, Afrikaans	.20	.20
82	A26	1p brt rose, pair	1.75	.70
a.		Single, English	.20	.20
b.		Single, Afrikaans	.20	.20
83	A27	1½p Prus grn, pair ('42)	1.10	.40
a.		Single, English	.20	.20
b.		Single, Afrikaans	.20	.20
84	A28	2p dk violet	.50	.20
85	A29	3p dp blue, pair	14.00	11.50
a.		Single, English	.50	.50
b.		Single, Afrikaans	.50	.50
86	A30	4p org brn, pair	12.25	8.75
a.		Single, English	.75	.60
b.		Single, Afrikaans	.75	.60
c.		4p red brown, pair	32.50	32.50

d.		As "c," single, English	1.50	1.00
e.		As "c," single, Afrikaans	1.50	1.00
87	A31	6p brt red org, pair	11.75	6.75
a.		Single, English	.50	.20
b.		Single, Afrikaans	.50	.20
88	A32	1sh dark brown	2.25	.50
89	A33	1sh3p dk ol brn, pair ('43)	10.00	6.00
a.		Single, English	.50	.30
b.		Single, Afrikaans	.50	.30
c.		1sh3p dark brown, pair	6.00	6.50
d.		As "c," single, English	.50	.30
e.		As "c," single, Afrikaans	.50	.30
		Nos. 81-89 (9)	54.50	35.20

Infantry-Nurse A34   A35

Airman-Sailor A36   A37

Women's Services — A38   Artillery — A39

Welder — A40   Tank Corps — A41

Bilingual inscriptions on 4p and 1sh.

Pairs: Perf. 14, Roul. 6½ btwn.
Strips of 3: Perf. 15x14, Roul. 6½ btwn.

1942-43   Photo.   Wmk. 201

90	A34	½p Horiz. strip of 3	.70	.55
a.		Single, English	.20	.20
b.		Single, Afrikaans	.20	.20
c.		As #90, imperf. between	350.00	
91	A35	1p Horiz. strip of 3 ('43)	.90	.60
a.		Single, English	.20	.20
b.		Single, Afrikaans	.20	.20
c.		As #91, imperf. between	350.00	
92	A36	1½p Horiz. pair	.70	.60
a.		Single, English	.20	.20
b.		Single, Afrikaans	.20	.20
c.		As #92, roul. 13	4.50	4.50
d.		As #92, imperf. btwn.	350.00	375.00
93	A37	2p Horiz. pair ('43)	.70	.50
a.		Single, English	.20	.20
b.		Single, Afrikaans	.20	.20
c.		As #93, imperf. btwn.	350.00	
94	A38	3p Vert strip of 3	5.50	8.50
a.		Single, English	.20	.20
b.		Single, Afrikaans	.20	.20
95	A39	4p Vert. strip of 3	16.00	9.00
a.		Single	.20	.20
96	A40	6p Horiz. pair	3.00	2.75
a.		Single, English	.20	.20
b.		Single, Afrikaans	.20	.20
97	A41	1sh Vert. pair	12.50	3.50
a.		Single	.20	.20
		Nos. 90-97 (8)	40.00	26.00

Because of the rouletting these are collected as pairs or strips of three, even on the bilingual stamps.

Types of 1926, Redrawn "SUID-AFRIKA" Hyphenated Coil Stamps

1943   Photo.   Perf. 15x14

98	A5	½p myrtle grn, vert. pair	1.25	3.00
a.		Single, English	.20	.20
b.		Single, Afrikaans	.20	.20
99	A6	1p rose pink, vert. pair	2.00	3.00
a.		Single, English	.20	.20
b.		Single, Afrikaans	.20	.20

"Victory" — A42

"Peace" — A43

Design: 3p, Profiles of couple ("Hope").

1945, Dec. 3   Photo.   Perf. 14

100	A42	1p rose pink & choc, pair	.25	.25
a.		Single, English	.20	.20
b.		Single, Afrikaans	.20	.20
101	A43	2p vio & sl bl, pair	.25	.25
a.		Single, English	.20	.20
b.		Single, Afrikaans	.20	.20
102	A43	3p ultra & dp ultra, pair	.35	.35
a.		Single, English	.20	.20
b.		Single, Afrikaans	.20	.20
		Nos. 100-102 (3)	.85	.85

World War II victory of the Allies.

George VI — A44

King George VI and Queen Elizabeth A45

Princesses Margaret Rose and Elizabeth A46

Perf. 15x14

1947, Feb. 17   Wmk. 201

103	A44	1p cer & gray, pair	.25	.25
a.		Single, English	.20	.20
b.		Single, Afrikaans	.20	.20
104	A45	2p purple, pair	.25	.25
a.		Single, English	.20	.20
b.		Single, Afrikaans	.20	.20
105	A46	3p dk blue, pair	.35	.35
a.		Single, English	.20	.20
b.		Single, Afrikaans	.20	.20
		Nos. 103-105 (3)	.85	.85

Visit of the British Royal Family, Mar.-Apr., 1947.

George VI, Elizabeth — A47   Gold Mine — A48

1948, Apr. 26   Photo.   Perf. 14

106	A47	3p dp chlky bl & sil, pair	.50	.50
a.		Single, English	.20	.20
b.		Single, Afrikaans	.20	.20

25th anniv. of the marriage of George VI and Queen Elizabeth.

Vertical Pairs Perf. 14 all around, Rouletted 6½ between

1948, Apr.

107	A48	1½p sl & och, vert. pair	1.25	2.00
a.		Single, English	.20	.20
b.		Single, Afrikaans	.20	.20

"Wanderer" in Port Natal A49

1949, May 2   Photo.   Perf. 15x14

108	A49	1½p red brown, pair	.45	.45
a.		Single, English	.20	.20
b.		Single, Afrikaans	.20	.20

Mercury and Globe — A50

1949, Oct. 1   Perf. 14x15

109	A50	½p dk green, pair	.50	.50
a.		Single, English	.20	.20
b.		Single, Afrikaans	.20	.20
110	A50	1½p dk red, pair	.75	.75
a.		Single, English	.20	.20
b.		Single, Afrikaans	.20	.20
111	A50	3p ultra, pair	1.25	1.25
a.		Single, English	.20	.20
b.		Single, Afrikaans	.20	.20
		Nos. 109-111 (3)	2.50	2.50

75th anniv. of the UPU.

Except for Nos. 216, 310-313, 518a, 669a this is the end of bi-lingual multiples in the postage section.

Voortrekkers en Route to Natal — A51

Voortrekker Monument, Pretoria A52

Voortrekkers Looking Toward Natal, and Open Bible — A53

1949, Dec. 1   Perf. 15x14

112	A51	1p magenta	.20	.20
113	A52	1½p dull green	.20	.20
114	A53	3p dark blue	.20	.20
		Nos. 112-114 (3)	.60	.60

Inauguration of the Voortrekker Monument at Pretoria.

Riebeeck's Seal and Dutch East India Company Monogram A54

Maria de la Quellerie — A55

2p, van Riebeeck's Ships. 4½p, Jan van Riebeeck. 1sh, Landing of van Riebeeck.

Perf. 15x14, 14x15

1952, Mar. 14   Wmk. 201

115	A54	½p dk brn & red vio	.20	.20
116	A55	1p dark green	.20	.20
117	A54	2p dark purple	.20	.20
118	A55	4½p dark blue	.20	.20
119	A54	1sh brown	.55	.50
		Nos. 115-119 (5)	1.35	1.30

300th anniv. of the landing of Jan van Riebeeck at the Cape of Good Hope.

Nos. 116-117 Overprinted "SATISE" (1p) and "SADIPU" (2p)

1952, Mar. 26
120 A55 1p dark green .30 .55
121 A54 2p dark purple .35 .70

South African Tercentenary Intl. Stamp Exhib., Cape Town, Mar. 26-Apr. 5, 1952.

Coronation Issue

Queen Elizabeth II — A97

1953, June 3 *Perf. 14x15*
192 A97 2p violet blue .20 .20

Cape Triangle of 1853 A98

1953, Sept. 1 *Perf. 15x14*
193 A98 1p red & dk brown .20 .20
194 A98 4p blue & indigo .25 .20

Cent. of the introduction of postage stamps in South Africa.

Merino Ram and Sheep — A99

1953, Oct. 1 *Perf. 14*
195 A99 4½p shown .35 .20
196 A99 1sh3p Springbok 1.25 .20
197 A99 1sh6p Aloes 1.00 .30
Nos. 195-197 (3) 2.60 .70

Arms of Orange Free State, Pen and Scroll A100

1954, Feb. 23 *Perf. 15x14*
198 A100 2p red org & dk brown .20 .20
199 A100 4½p gray & rose violet .25 .25

Orange Free State centenary.

Wart Hog A101

White Rhinoceros A102

Lion — A103

1954, Oct. 14 *Perf. 15x14*
200 A101 ½p shown .20 .20
201 A101 1p Gnu .20 .20
202 A101 1½p Leopard .20 .20
203 A101 2p Zebra .20 .20
Perf. 14
204 A102 3p shown .20 .20
205 A102 4p Elephant .40 .20
206 A102 4½p Hippopotamus .50 .20
207 A103 6p shown .45 .20

208 A102 1sh Kudu 2.75 .20
209 A103 1sh3p Springbok 1.75 .30
210 A102 1sh6p Gemsbok 1.60 .45
211 A102 2sh6p Nyala 3.75 .20
212 A102 5sh Giraffe 9.25 1.50
213 A102 10sh Sable antelope 14.00 3.25
Nos. 200-213 (14) 35.45 8.05

See Nos. 221-228, 241-244, 247, 250-253.

Paul Kruger — A104

Portrait: 6p, Martinus Wessels Pretorius.

Perf. 14x15
1955, Oct. 21 Photo. Wmk. 201
214 A104 3p slate green .25 .20
215 A104 6p brown violet .50 .25

Centenary of Pretoria.

Andries Pretorius, Church of the Vow and Flag of Natalia — A105

German Wagon and House — A106

1955, Dec. 1 *Perf. 14*
Inscribed alternately in English and Afrikaans.
216 A105 2p ultra & cer, pair .60 3.00
a. Single, English .20 .20
b. Single, Afrikaans .20 .20

Union Covenant Celebrations, Pietermaritzburg, Dec. 13-18, 1955.

1958, July 1 *Perf. 14*
218 A106 2p pale lilac & brown .20 .20

Cent. of the arrival of German settlers.

Seal of Academy A107

1959, May 1 Photo. Wmk. 201 *Perf. 15x14*
219 A107 3p brt blue & dk blue .20 .20
a. Dark blue omitted 1,800.

50th anniv. of the South African Academy of Science and Art, Pretoria.

Globe Showing Antarctica and South Africa — A108

Perf. 14x15
1959, Nov. 16 Wmk. 330
220 A108 3p blue grn, brn & org .20 .20

South African Natl. Antarctic Expedition.

Animal Types of 1954
1959-60 Wmk. 330 *Perf. 15x14*
221 A101 ½p Wart hog ('60) .30 1.75
222 A101 1p Gnu .20 .20
a. Redrawn .35 .20
Perf. 14
223 A102 3p White rhino .35 .20
224 A102 4p Elephant 1.00 .25
225 A103 6p Lion 1.90 .20
226 A102 1sh Kudu 2.75 .25
227 A102 2sh6p Nyala 8.50 6.00
228 A102 5sh Giraffe ('60) 18.00 26.00
Nos. 221-228 (8) 33.00 34.90

On No. 222a, the numeral "1" is centered above "S." On No. 222, "1" is slightly to right of "S."

Prime Ministers Botha, Smuts, Hertzog, Malan, Strydom and Verwoerd A109

Flag and Notes from National Anthem — A110

Pushing Wheel Uphill A111

6p, Arms of the Union and of four provinces. 1sh6p, Official Union festival emblem.

Perf. 14x15, 15x14
1960 Photo. Wmk. 330
235 A109 3p chocolate .20 .20
236 A110 4p lt blue & red org .25 .20
237 A110 6p yel grn, red & brn .35 .20
238 A111 1sh yel, dk bl & blk .70 .20
239 A111 1sh6p lt blue & blk 2.50 1.75
Nos. 235-239 (5) 4.00 2.55

50th anniv. of the founding of the Union. See Nos. 245-246, 248-249.

Map, Old and New Locomotives — A112

1960, May 2 *Perf. 15x14*
240 A112 1sh3p dark blue 3.25 1.25

Centenary of railways in South Africa.

Types of 1954 and 1960.
Designs: ½c, Wart hog. 1c, Gnu. 1½c, Leopard. 2c, Zebra. 2½c, Prime Ministers. 3½c, Flag and music notes. 5c, Lion. 7½c, Arms of Union and four provinces. 10c, Pushing wheel uphill. 12½c, Springbok. 20c, Gemsbok. 50c, Giraffe. 1r, Sable antelope.

Perf. 15x14, 14x15, 14 (A102, A103)
1961, Feb. 14 Photo. Wmk. 330
241 A101 ½c dk bluish grn .20 .20
242 A101 1c rose brown .20 .20
243 A101 1½c sepia .20 .20
244 A101 2c purple .20 .20
245 A109 2½c chocolate .25 .20
246 A110 3½c lt bl & red org .40 .20
247 A103 5c org & dk brn .50 .20
248 A110 7½c yel grn, red & brn .60 .25
249 A111 10c yel, dk bl & blk .70 .20

250 A103 12½c dull grn & dk brn 1.10 .60
251 A102 20c pink & dk brn 1.90 1.25
252 A102 50c org yel & blk brn 7.75 8.25
253 A102 1r blue & black 18.00 16.00
Nos. 241-253 (13) 32.00 28.00

Republic

Natal Pigmy Kingfisher A112a

Coral Tree Flower A112b

Pouring Gold A113

Groot Constantia A114

Designs: 1½c, Afrikander bull. 3c, Crimson-breasted shrike. 5c, Baobab tree. 7½c, Corn. 10c, Castle entrance, Cape Town. 12½c, Protea flower. 20c, Secretary bird. 50c, Cape Town, harbor. 1r, Bird of Paradise flower.
Two types of 2½c:
Type I - Lines of building faint.
Type II - Lines of building very strong; strong line between bottom of building and top of name panel.

Perf. 14x15, 15x14
1961, May 31 Photo. Wmk. 330
254 A112a ½c blue, mag & brn .20 .20
a. Perf. 14x13½ ('63) .20 .20
255 A112b 1c gray & red .20 .20
256 A112a 1½c brown carmine .20 .20
Perf. 14
257 A113 2c ultra & orange .20 .20
258 A114 2½c violet & grn (I) .30 .20
a. Type II .40 .20
259 A113 3c pink, dk bl & red .30 .20
260 A114 5c grnsh bl & yel .35 .20
261 A114 7½c emerald & brn .50 .20
a. Brown omitted
262 A114 10c emer & dk brn .75 .20
263 A114 12½c dk grn, red & yel 1.50 .20
a. Yellow omitted 600.00
264 A114 20c sal, sl bl & pink 4.00 .30
265 A113 50c ultra & blk 30.00 2.10
266 A113 1r blue, org & grn 22.50 2.10
Nos. 254-266 (13) 61.00 6.50

1961-63 Unwmk. *Perf. 15x14*
269 A112b 1c gray & red .25 .20
Perf. 14
270 A113 2c ultra & org ('63) 7.25 .35
271 A114 2½c violet & grn (II) .30 .20
272 A113 3c pink, dk bl & red .60 .20
273 A114 5c grnsh blue & yel .75 .20
274 A114 7½c emer & brn ('62) 1.10 .35
275 A114 10c green & dk brn 1.25 .50
276 A114 20c sal, sl bl & pink ('63) 17.50 4.75
277 A113 50c ultra & blk ('62) 26.00 5.25
Nos. 269-277 (9) 55.00 12.00

See Nos. 289-298, 317-322, 324, 326-338, 340-342, 376-377, 379-382, 383-385 and designs A135-A136.

Boeing 707 and Bleriot Monoplane A115

Folk Dancers A116

Perf. 14x15

1961, Dec. 1 Photo. Wmk. 330
280 A115 3c blue & red .50 .20
50th anniv. of South Africa's 1st air mail.

1962, Mar. 1
281 A116 2½c lt brn, choc & red org .30 .20
50th anniv. of folk dancing in South Africa.

"Chapman" Arriving in 1820 A117

Perf. 15x14

1962, Aug. 20 Photo. Wmk. 330
282 A117 2½c dp plum & bl grn .30 .20
283 A117 12½c choc & blue 2.75 1.50
Unveiling of the precinct stone of the British Settlers Monument at Grahamstown.

Red Disa Orchid, Castle Rock, Kirstenbosch Botanic Gardens — A118

1963, Mar. 14 **Perf. 14**
284 A118 2½c multicolored .35 .20
50th anniv. of the Kirstenbosch Botanic Gardens, Cape Town.

Centenary Emblem and Nurse — A119

12½c, Centenary emblem and globe, horiz.

1963, Aug. 30 Wmk. 348 **Perf. 14**
285 A119 2½c rose claret, blk & red .35 .20

Perf. 15x14
286 A119 12½c dk bl gray & red 3.50 1.60
a. Red Cross omitted 1,450.
Centenary of the International Red Cross.

Assembly Seat, Bunga Building, Umtata A120

Perf. 14½x14

1963, Dec. 11 Wmk. 348
287 A120 2½c dk brn & lt grn .30 .20
a. Light green omitted 1,600.
Transkei Legislative Assembly, 1st meeting.

Types of 1961

Perf. 15x14, 14x15

1963-67 Photo. Wmk. 348
Colors as Before
289 A112b 1c .20 .20
290 A112a 1½c ('67) 2.25 .85

Perf. 14
291 A113 2c ('64) .20 .20
292 A114 2½c (II) ('64) .50 .20
293 A114 5c ('66) 2.25 .20
294 A114 7½c ('66) 11.50 2.25
295 A114 10c ('64) 1.10 .20
296 A114 20c ('64) 4.50 .40
297 A113 50c ('66) 37.50 6.50
298 A113 1r ('64) 70.00 32.50
Nos. 289-298 (10) 130.00 43.50

Rugby Board Emblem, Springbok and Ball — A121

John Calvin — A122

Design: 12½c, Rugby player diving over goal line, horiz.

Perf. 14x15, 15x14

1964, May 8 Photo. Wmk. 348
301 A121 2½c dk green & brn .25 .20
302 A121 12½c yellow grn & blk 3.75 2.50
South African Rugby Board, 75th anniv.

1964, July 10 **Perf. 14**
303 A122 2½c choc, brt car & vio .35 .20
John Calvin (1509-64), French theologian and leader of the Reformation.

Nurse's Lamp — A123

Design: 12½c, Nurse holding lamp, horiz.

Perf. 14x15, 15x14

1964, Oct. 12 Photo. Wmk. 348
304 A123 2½c gold & ultra .25 .20
305 A123 12½c ultra & gold 2.75 2.75
a. Gold omitted 1,200.
South African Nursing Assoc., 50th anniv.

ITU Emblem and Satellites A124

Design: 12½c, ITU emblem, old and new communication equipment.

1965, May 17 **Perf. 15x14**
306 A124 2½c brt blue & org .30 .20
307 A124 12½c green & claret 3.00 2.50
Cent. of the ITU.

Pulpit, Groote Kerk, Cape Town — A125

Design: 12½c, Emblem of Dutch Reformed Church of South Africa, horiz.

Perf. 14x15, 15x14

1965, Oct. 21 Photo. Wmk. 348
308 A125 2½c dp brown & yel .25 .20
309 A125 12½c lt ultra, ocher & blk 3.00 2.75
Tercentenary of the Dutch Reformed Church in South Africa.

Diamond — A126

1966, May 31 **Perf. 14**
2½c, Flying bird, symbol of freedom & the future, horiz. 3c, Corn. 7½c, Table Mountain, horiz. Inscribed alternately in English & Afrikaans.
310 A126 1c blk, yel, dk & lt grn, pair .50 .50
a. Single, English .20 .20
b. Single, Afrikaans .20 .20
311 A126 2½c dk bl, ultra & yel grn, pair 1.25 1.25
a. Single, English .20 .20
b. Single, Afrikaans .20 .20

Perf. 14x15, 15x14
312 A126 3c red brn, red & yel, pair 2.50 2.50
a. Single, English .20 .20
b. Single, Afrikaans .20 .20
313 A126 7½c ultra, vio bl, och & blk, pair 7.00 7.00
a. Single, English .50 .40
b. Single, Afrikaans .50 .40
Nos. 310-313 (4) 11.25 11.25
5th anniversary of the Republic.
Nos. 310-313 with watermark 359 are reprints made for U.P.U. presentation booklets.

Hendrik F. Verwoerd and Union Buildings, Pretoria A127

Designs: 3c, Verwoerd's portrait, vert. 12½c, Verwoerd and map of South Africa.

Perf. 15x14, 14x15

1966, Dec. 6 Photo. Wmk. 348
314 A127 2½c grnsh blue & blk .20 .20
315 A127 3c yellow grn & blk .20 .20
316 A127 12½c dull blue & blk 1.40 1.25
Nos. 314-316 (3) 1.80 1.65
Dr. Verwoerd (1901-1966), Prime Minister.

Types of 1961 Redrawn and

Industry — A128

(Inscriptions in larger, bolder type)

½c, 1½c and 1r

On the 1r, the "N" of "VAN" is over the final "A" of "AFRIKA." On Nos. 266 and 298, the "N" is over "KA."

1c, 7½c and 12½c

2½c, 5c, 10c and 20c

2c, 3c and 50c (similar)

Perf. 14x15, 15x14

1964-68 Photo. Wmk. 348
Colors as Before
317 A112a ½c .20 .20
a. Imperf., pair 400.00
318 A112b 1c .30 .20

Perf. 14
319 A113 2c ('68) .30 .20
320 A114 2½c .35 .20
321 A113 3c .60 .20
322 A113 12½c 2.25 .20
323 A128 15c ('67) 5.00 .20
324 A113 1r 16.00 2.50
Nos. 317-324 (8) 25.00 3.90
See No. 339.

Redrawn Types of 1964-68

4c, Groot Constantia (like 2½c). 6c, Corn (like 7½c). 9c, Protea flower (like 12½c).

1967-71 Photo. Wmk. 359
326 A112a ½c .20 .20
327 A112b 1c .20 .20
328 A112a 1½c .20 .20
329 A113 2c ('68) 1.90 .20
330 A114 2½c .20 .20
331 A113 3c .20 .20
332 A114 4c ('71) .40 .20
333 A114 5c ('68) .20 .20
334 A114 6c ('71) 1.00 .20
335 A114 7½c 1.75 .20
336 A114 9c ('71) 1.25 .20
337 A114 10c ('68) 3.75 .25
338 A114 12½c ('70) 3.00 .55
339 A128 15c ('69) 6.00 .40
340 A114 20c ('68) 7.25 .55
341 A114 50c ('68) 8.00 .90
342 A113 1r ('68) 10.50 1.90
Nos. 326-342 (17) 46.00 6.75

Luminescence

Starting in 1969, South Africa began to add phosphorescent "frames" to its definitive stamps.
In 1971, stamps began to appear with the phosphorescent element throughout the paper.
Phosphorescent commemoratives include Nos. 357, 359 et cetera.

Martin Luther — A129

Door of Wittenberg Church — A130

Perf. 14x15
1967, Oct. 31 Litho. Wmk. 348
343 A129 2½c pink & black .20 .20
Wmk. 359
344 A130 12½c black & orange 2.25 2.00
450th anniversary of the Reformation.

Pres. J. J.
Fouché — A133

James B. M.
Hertzog
Statue — A134

Design: 12½c, Full-face portrait.

Perf. 14x15
1968, Apr. 10   Photo.   Wmk. 348
345 A133   2½c lt rose brn & dk
             brn   .30 .20
346 A133 12½c grysh bl & vio bl 2.50 2.25
           Wmk. 359
347 A133 12½c grysh bl & vio bl 2.75 2.25
           Nos. 345-347 (3)   5.55 4.70
Pres. Jacobus Johannes Fouché, inauguration.

Perf. 13½x14, 14x13½
1968, Sept. 21   Photo.   Wmk. 359
Designs: 2½c, Hertzog in 1902, with hat, horiz. 3c, Hertzog in 1924, horiz.
348 A134   2½c dk brn, lem & blk .20 .20
           Wmk. 348
349 A134   3c multicolored   .30 .20
350 A134 12½c org brn, org &
             blk   2.00 1.75
           Nos. 348-350 (3)   2.50 2.15
Unveiling of a monument in Bloemfontein honoring James Barry Munnik Hertzog (1866-1942), Boer general, prime minister of South Africa (1924-39).

Natal Pigmy
Kingfisher
A135

Kaffir Boom
Flower
A136

1969 Wmk. 359 Photo.   Perf. 14
351 A135 ½c blue & multi   .20 .20
   a.   Perf. 14x14½ (coil)   1.50 .20
352 A136 1c grysh brown & multi .20 .20
           See Nos. 374-375.

Springbok, Torch and
Rings — A137

1969, Mar. 15   Perf. 14x13½
353 A137 2½c olive, ind & red   .20 .20
354 A137 12½c bister, ind & red   1.60 1.40
South African Natl. Games, Bloemfontein, Mar. 15-Apr. 19.

Groote
Schuur
Hospital
and Dr.
Barnard
A138

Hands
Holding
Heart
A139

Perf. 13½x14
1969, July 7   Photo.   Wmk. 348
355 A138 2½c dp rose, pink & plum .20 .20
           Perf. 15x14
           Wmk. 359
356 A139 12½c dp bl & dp car   2.25 1.75
1st heart transplant operation (by Dr. Christiaan Barnard) and opening of the 47th South African Medical Cong., Pretoria.

Stagecoach of 1869 — A140

Transvaal
No. 1 — A141

Water Drop and
Flower — A142

Perf. 13½x14, 14x13½
1969, Oct. 6   Photo.   Wmk. 359
357 A140   2½c ocher, Prus bl &
              yel   .35 .20
358 A141 12½c sal, grn & gold   3.00 2.25
Centenary of South African postage stamps.

1970, Feb. 14   Perf. 14
Design: 3c, Waves, horiz.
359 A142 2½c brn, brt bl & grn   .20 .20
360 A142 3c pale gray, bl & ind   .35 .20
Issued to publicize the Water 70 campaign of the Department of Water Affairs.

Sower — A143

"BIBLIA"
A144

1970, Aug. 24   Photo.   Perf. 14
361 A143 2½c multicolored   .25 .20

Photo; Gold Impressed
362 A144 12½c ultra, blk & gold   2.60 2.25
150th anniv. of the South African Bible Soc.

Strijdom Tower,
Johannes G.
Strijdom — A145

Map of
Antarctica
A146

Perf. 14x13½, 13½x14
1971, May 22   Photo.   Wmk. 359
363 A145   5c blue, yel & blk   .40 .20
364 A146 12½c grnsh bl, vio bl &
              red   4.00 4.00
           Wmk. 330
365 A145   5c blue, yel & blk   2.00 .90
           Nos. 363-365 (3)   6.40 5.10
Intl. Stamp Exhib. (INTERSTEX), Cape Town, May 22-31. No. 364 also for the 10th anniv. of the Antarctic Treaty pledging peaceful uses of and scientific cooperation in Antarctica.

Landing of
British
Settlers,
1820, by
Thomas
Baines
A147

Martinus Steyn, Paul
Kruger, Unification
Monument — A148

1971, May 31   Wmk. 359
366 A147 2c magenta & rose red   .20 .20
367 A148 4c blue green & blk   .30 .20
10th anniv. of the Republic of South Africa.

Hendrik
Verwoerd
Dam
A149

1972, Mar. 4   Photo.   Perf. 14
           Size: 37x22mm
368 A149 4c shown   .25 .20
369 A149 5c Aerial view of dam .45 .20
           Size: 57x22mm
370 A149 10c Dam, reservoir and
             Verwoerd   1.50 .90
           Nos. 368-370 (3)   2.20 1.30
Inauguration of the Hendrik F. Verwoerd Dam of the Orange River Project.

Ram's Head and
Wool
Mark — A150

Lamb and Wool
Mark — A151

1972, May 15   Wmk. 359   Perf. 14
371 A150 4c blue & multi   .20 .20
372 A151 15c dull bl & dk bl   1.75 .40
South African wool industry. Issued in sheets of 100 with advertisements in margin. See Nos. 378-378A, 382A.

Cats — A152

Pylon — A153

1972, Sept. 19   Wmk. 359
373 A152 5c multicolored   1.00 .25
Centenary of the SPCA.

Redrawn Types of 1964-69 and Types
of 1972
**Perf. 14x15 (½c), 14 (1c, #382A),
12½**
1972-74		Photo.	Unwmk.	
374	A135	½c blue & multi	7.50	8.25
375	A136	1c grysh brn & red	.20	.20
376	A113	2c brt blue & org	.50	.20
377	A113	3c rose red & bluish black	.55	.65
378	A150	4c blue & multi	.85	.20
378A	A150	4c brown & multi	.40	.20
379	A114	5c grnsh bl & yel	1.00	.20
380	A114	6c emerald & brn	2.50	4.00
381	A114	9c dk grn, red & yel	2.25	.75
382	A114	10c emer & dk brn	2.50	.45
382A	A151	15c dull bl & dk bl	2.75	3.75
383	A114	20c sal, sl bl & pink	2.75	.60
384	A113	50c ultra & black	7.25	.75
385	A113	1r bl, org & grn	19.00	3.75
		Nos. 374-385 (14)	50.00	25.00
Issued: 2c, 1972; 6c, 15c, 1974: others, 1973.

1973, Feb. 1   Photo.   Perf. 12x12½
Designs: 4c, Electrical usage, pylon, power plant, horiz. 15c, Smokestacks.
           Size: 37½x20mm
386 A153 4c blue & multi   .25 .20
           Size: 20x27mm
           Perf. 12½
387 A153 5c blue & black   .35 .20
388 A153 15c ocher & multi   3.75 1.50
           Nos. 386-388 (3)   4.35 1.90
Electricity Supply Commission, 50th anniv.

Arms of
University
A154

Old University,
Cape Town
A156

New
University,
Pretoria
A155

1973, Apr. 2   Unwmk.   Perf. 12½
389 A154 4c blue & multi   .25 .20
           Perf. 12x12½
           Wmk. 359
390 A155 5c gold & multi   .35 .20
           Unwmk.   Perf. 12½
391 A156 15c gold & blk   3.25 1.65
Cent. of the Univ. of South Africa (UNISA).

Woltemade, Sailor and Horse — A157

Designs: 5c, Sinking ship in storm. 15c, "De Jonge Thomas" sinking.

1973, June 2   Photo.   Perf. 12x12½
392	A157	4c brown red, ol & blk	.25	.20
393	A157	5c olive, blk & citron	.45	.20
394	A157	15c brown, blk & ocher	5.50	4.50
		Nos. 392-394 (3)	6.20	4.90

Bicentenary of Wolraad Woltemade's heroism in saving 14 people from the ship "De Jonge Thomas" in Table Bay.

C. J. Langenhoven and Anthem — A158

4c, 5c, vert., Portrait and signature.

1973, Aug. 1   Perf. 12½
Size: 27x20mm
| 395 | A158 | 4c orange, blk & ultra | .50 | .20 |

Perf. 12½x12, 12x12½
Size: 21x38mm, 37x21mm
396	A158	5c orange, blk & ultra	.60	.20
397	A158	15c orange, blk & ultra	3.00	1.00
		Nos. 395-397 (3)	4.10	1.40

Cornelis Jacob Langenhoven (1873-1932), lawyer, writer, who worked for recognition of Afrikaans language.

World Map and Communications Network — A159

Perf. 12½
1973, Oct. 1   Photo.   Unwmk.
| 398 | A159 | 15c ultra & multi | 1.75 | 1.65 |
| a. | | Wmk. 359 | 2.50 | 2.25 |

International Telecommunications Day.

Restored Houses, Tulbagh — A160

Design: 5c, Church Street, Tulbagh.

1974, Mar. 14   Unwmk.   Perf. 12½
Size: 27x21mm
| 400 | A160 | 4c Prus green & multi | .25 | .20 |

Size: 57x20mm
| 401 | A160 | 5c ocher & multi | .45 | .20 |

Restoration of historic Church Street in Tulbagh after 1969 earthquake.

Burgerspond A161 — Prime Minister D. F. Malan A162

1974, Apr. 7   Photo.   Perf. 12½x12
| 402 | A161 | 9c multicolored | .80 | .55 |

Centenary of the first official coin struck in South Africa, 1874. The £1 gold coin shows portrait of Pres. Thomas Francois Burger.

1974, May 22   Photo.   Unwmk.
| 403 | A162 | 4c lt ultra & dk blue | .30 | .20 |

Centenary of the birth of Daniel F. Malan (1874-1959), prime minister of South Africa.

Congress Emblem A163

1974, June 13   Perf. 12x12½
| 404 | A163 | 15c silver & dk blue | 1.25 | .50 |

15th World Sugar Cong., Durban, 6/13-30.

"50" A164

1974, July 13   Photo.   Unwmk.
| 405 | A164 | 4c red & black | .35 | .20 |

50th anniversary of radio in South Africa.

Cultural Center, Grahamstown — A165

1974, July 13   Perf. 12x12½
| 406 | A165 | 5c red & black | .35 | .20 |

Natl. Monument to British settlers of 1820.

Natal No. 78, Transvaal No. 145, Cape of Good Hope No. 28 and Orange River Colony No. 4 — A166

1974, Oct. 9   Photo.   Perf. 12½
| 407 | A166 | 15c multicolored | 1.25 | .90 |

Centenary of Universal Postal Union.

Wild Iris — A167 — Cape Gannet — A168

Galjoen — A169

Bokmakierie (Shrike) — A170

Designs: 2c, Heather. 3c, Geranium. 4c, Calla lily. 7c, Zebrafish. 9c, Angelfish. 10c, Moorish idol. 14c, Roman fish. 15c, Greater double-collared sunbird. 20c, Yellow-billed hornbill. 25c, Barberton daisy. 50c, Blue cranes. 1r, Bateleur eagles.

Photo. and Engr.
1974, Nov. 11   Unwmk.   Perf. 12½
408	A167	1c pink & multi	.20	.20
409	A167	2c yellow & multi	.20	.20
410	A167	3c multicolored	.20	.20
411	A167	4c multicolored	.20	.20
412	A168	5c dull blue & multi	.20	.20
413	A169	6c multicolored	.25	.20
414	A169	7c lilac & multi	.30	.20
415	A169	9c buff & multi	.35	.20
416	A169	10c lt blue & multi	.40	.20
417	A169	14c salmon & multi	.60	.20
418	A168	15c gray & multi	.60	.20
419	A168	20c yellow & multi	.80	.30
420	A167	25c dk brown & multi	1.10	.35

Perf. 12x12½
421	A170	30c gray & multi	4.50	.75
422	A170	50c citron & multi	4.00	1.00
423	A170	1r multicolored	7.50	2.00
		Nos. 408-423 (16)	21.40	6.60

The coils that follow are two colors while the above sheet stamps are multicolored.

1974   Photo.   Perf. 12½
Coil Stamps
430	A167	1c pink & violet	.45	.30
431	A167	2c yellow & grn	.65	.25
432	A168	5c dull blue & blk	1.40	.70
433	A169	10c lt blue & indigo	9.50	5.75
		Nos. 430-433 (4)	12.00	7.00

See note on color that follows No. 423.

1975-76   Perf. 14
Same Designs
430a	A167	1c	.55	.25
431a	A167	2c ('76)	.45	.25
433a	A169	10c ('76)	5.00	5.50
		Nos. 430a-433a (3)	6.00	6.00

No. 430a has black control number on back of every fifth stamp.

Voortrekker Monument and Encampment — A171

1974, Dec. 6   Unwmk.   Perf. 12½
| 438 | A171 | 4c multicolored | .35 | .20 |

Voortrekker Monument, 25th anniversary.

Sasolburg Refinery A172

Perf. 12x12½, 12½
1975, Feb. 26   Litho.
| 439 | A172 | 15c red & multi | 1.25 | .90 |

25th anniversary of South Africa Coal, Oil and Gas Corp., Ltd. (SASOL).

Pres. Nicolaes Diederichs A173 — Jan C. Smuts A174

Litho. and Engr.
1975, Apr. 19   Perf. 12½x12
| 440 | A173 | 4c brown & gold | .20 | .20 |

Litho.
| 441 | A173 | 15c ultra & gold | .85 | .85 |

Installation of Dr. Nicolaes Diederichs as third State President.

Litho. and Engraved
1975, May 24
| 442 | A174 | 4c black | .30 | .20 |

Smuts (1870-1950), lawyer, gen., statesman.

Dutch East Indiaman, by Baines A175

Designs: Paintings by John Thomas Baines.

1975, June 18   Photo.   Perf. 12x12½
443	A175	5c gold & multi	.20	.20
444	A175	9c gold & multi	.30	.25
445	A175	15c gold & multi	.55	.45
446	A175	30c gold & multi	1.00	1.00
a.		Souvenir sheet of 4	3.50	3.50
		Nos. 443-446 (4)	2.05	1.90

John Thomas Baines (1820-75), painter. #446a contains 4 litho. stamps similar to #443-446.

Gideon Malherbe House, Paarl — A176

Photo. and Engr.
1975, Aug. 14   Perf. 12½
| 447 | A176 | 4c multicolored | .30 | .20 |

Society of Real Afrikanders (Genootskap of Regte Afrikaaners), cent.

Automatic Letter Sorting — A177

1975, Sept. 11   Photo.   Perf. 12½x12
| 448 | A177 | 4c brt blue & multi | .30 | .20 |

Postal automation.

Title Page, First Afrikaans Paper — A178 — Afrikaans Monument, Paarl — A179

1975, Oct. 10   Litho.   Perf. 12½x12
| 449 | A178 | 4c black & orange | .20 | .20 |
| 450 | A179 | 5c multicolored | .25 | .20 |

Inauguration of Afrikaans Language Monument.

Table Mountain — A180

1975, Nov. 13   Litho.   Perf. 12½
451	A180	15c shown	2.25	1.50
452	A180	15c Johannesburg	2.25	1.50
453	A180	15c Cape vineyards	2.25	1.50
454	A180	15c Lions, Kruger Natl. Park	2.25	1.50
a.		Block of 4, #451-454	9.00	9.00

Tourist publicity.

Satellites, Radar and Africa on Globe — A181

1975, Dec. 3   Litho.   Perf. 12½
455 A181 15c dk vio blue & multi   .60   .50
Satellite communications.

Lawn Bowler — A182

#457, Cricket batsman. #458, Polo player. #459, Golfer (Gary Player).

1976   Photo.   Perf. 12½x12
456 A182 15c green & blk   .60   .35
457 A182 15c yellow grn & blk   .60   .35
458 A182 15c olive & blk   .60   .35
459 A182 15c brt green & blk   .60   .35
  a. Miniature sheet of 4, #456-459   3.75   2.75
    Nos. 456-459 (4)   2.40   1.40

3rd World Bowling Championships, Zoo Lake Club, Johannesburg, Feb. 1976 (No. 456); cent. of cricket in South Africa (No. 457); intl. polo (No. 458); Gary Player, South African golf champion (No. 459).
Issue dates: #456, Feb. 18. #457, Mar. 12. #458, Aug. 16. #459, 459a, Dec. 2.

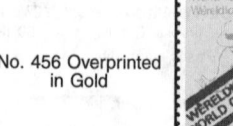

No. 456 Overprinted in Gold

1976, Apr. 6   Photo.   Perf. 12½x12
460 A182 15c green & black   .45   .45

Victory of South Africa in 3rd World Bowling championships.

Picnic under Baobab Tree A183

Paintings by Erich Mayer: 10c, Wagons at Foot of Blauberg, Transvaal. 15c, Hartbeessport Dam, near Pretorial. 20c, Street in Doornfontein.

1976, Apr. 20   Photo.   Perf. 12½x12½
461 A183 4c ocher & multi   .25   .20
462 A183 10c dk green & multi   .50   .45
463 A183 15c multicolored   .70   .60
464 A183 20c multicolored   1.10   1.00
  a. Souvenir sheet of 4, #461-464   3.50   3.50
    Nos. 461-464 (4)   2.55   2.25

Erich Mayer (1876-1960), painter. Artist's signature in horizontal gutter between 2 se-tenant pairs.

Wildlife Protection A184

1976, June 5   Litho.   Perf. 12x12½
465 A184 3c Cheetah   .25   .20
466 A184 10c Black rhinoceros   .55   .35
467 A184 15c Blesbok   1.10   .70
468 A184 20c Zebra   1.40   .95
    Nos. 465-468 (4)   3.30   2.20

All values exist on yellow toned paper. Value, twice that of stamps on white paper.

Emily Hobhouse, by Johan Hoekstra — A185

1976, June 8   Photo.   Perf. 12½x12
469 A185 4c multicolored   .25   .20
Emily Hobhouse (1860-1926), the "Angel of Mercy" during Anglo-Boer War.

S.S. Dunrobin Castle, 1876 A186

1976, Oct. 5   Litho.   Perf. 12x12½
470 A186 10c multicolored   .75   .30
Ocean Mail Service contract, centenary.

Family with Globe — A187

1976, Nov. 6   Photo.   Perf. 12½x12
471 A187 4c salmon & dull red   .25   .20
Family planning.

Wine Glasses A188

Jacob Daniel du Toit A189

1977, Feb. 14   Litho.   Perf. 12½x12
472 A188 15c multicolored   .50   .25
  a. Word "Die" omitted from left inscription   12.00   10.00
Quality of the Vintage Symposium, Cape Town, Feb. 14-21.

1977, Feb. 21   Photo.
473 A189 4c multicolored   .25   .20
Dr. Jacob Daniel du Toit (Totius; 1877-1953), theologian, educator, poet.

Transvaal Supreme Court A190

1977, May 18   Photo.   Perf. 12½x12
474 A190 4c red brown   .25   .20
Transvaal Supreme Court, centenary.

Sugarbush (Protea Repens) — A191

Photo. (1-5, 8, 10, 15, 20c); Litho. (others)

1977, May 27   Perf. 12½
475 A191 1c shown   .20   .20
476 A191 2c P. punctata   .20   .20
477 A191 3c P. neriifolia   .20   .20
478 A191 4c P. longifolia   .20   .20
479 A191 5c P. cynaroides   .20   .20
480 A191 6c P. canaliculata   .20   .20
481 A191 7c P. lorea   .20   .20
482 A191 8c P. mundii   .20   .20
483 A191 9c P. roupelliae   .20   .20
484 A191 10c P. aristata   .25   .20
485 A191 15c P. eximia   .25   .20
486 A191 20c P. magnifica   .25   .20
487 A191 25c P. grandiceps   .30   .20
488 A191 30c P. amplexicaulis   .45   .20
489 A191 50c Leucospermum cordifolium   .60   .30
490 A191 1r Paranomus reflexus   1.10   .65
491 A191 2r Orothamnus zeyheri   2.50   1.25
    Nos. 475-491 (17)   7.50   5.00

Perf. 14
477a A191 3c Litho.   .20   .20
479a A191 5c   .20   .20
480a A191 6c   .20   .20
481a A191 7c   .20   .20
482a A191 8c   .20   .20
483a A191 9c   .20   .20
484a A191 10c   .25   .20
486a A191 20c Litho.   .75   .30
487a A191 25c   .60   .30
488a A191 30c   .70   .25
489a A191 50c   1.25   .40
490a A191 1r   2.50   .80
491a A191 2r   4.75   1.50
    Nos. 477a-491a (13)   12.00   4.85

Perf. 14 Vertically
Photo.   Coil Stamps
492 A191 1c Silver tree   .20   .20
493 A191 2c Bottle brush   .20   .20
494 A191 5c Blushing bride   .20   .20
495 A191 10c Leucadendrom sessile   .20   .20
    Nos. 492-495 (4)   .80   .80

Some printings have control number on back of every fifth stamp.

Gymnastics — A192

1977, Aug. 15   Litho.   Perf. 12½x12
496 A192 15c multicolored   .40   .30
8th. Intl. Cong. of Physical Education and Sports for Girls and Women, Cape Town, Aug. 14-20.

World Map and "M" A193

1977, Sept. 15   Litho.   Perf. 12x12½
497 A193 15c multicolored   .40   .30
Introduction of international metric system.

Nuclear Power Plant and Uranium Atom A194

1977, Oct. 8
498 A194 15c multicolored   .40   .30
Uranium development.

Flag of South Africa A195

1977, Nov. 11
499 A195 5c multicolored   .20   .20
50th anniversary of national flag.

Walvis Bay, 1878 — A196

1978, Mar. 10   Litho.   Perf. 12½
500 A196 15c multicolored   .55   .40
Centenary of Walvis Bay annexation.

Dr. Andrew Murray — A197

1978, May 9   Perf. 12½x12
501 A197 4c multicolored   .20   .20
Dr. Andrew Murray, pioneer theologian, 150th birth anniversary.

Railroad Rail and ISCOR Emblem — A198

1978, June 5   Litho.   Perf. 12
502 A198 15c multicolored   .45   .40
50th anniversary of ISCOR (Iron and Steel Industrial Corporation).

Saldanha Bay — A199

Design: No. 504, Richard's Bay.

1978, July 21   Litho.   Perf. 12½
503 A199 15c multicolored   .55   .55
504 A199 15c multicolored   .55   .55
  a. Pair, #503-504   1.10   1.10
Opening of new harbors on east and west coasts of South Africa.

Landscape by Volschenk — A200

Designs: Landscapes by J. E. A. Volschenk.

1978, Aug. 21
505 A200 10c multicolored   .35   .35
506 A200 15c multicolored   .50   .50
507 A200 20c multicolored   .70   .70

B. J. Vorster — A201

1978, Oct. 10   Litho.   Perf. 12½x12
509 A201 4c maroon & gold   .20 .20
  a.   Perf. 14½x14   .75 .30

Perf. 14½x14
510 A201 15c violet & gold   .40 .30

Inauguration of Balthazar John Vorster as president of South Africa.

Golden Gate Highlands National Park — A202

Designs: 15c, Blyde River Canyon, Transvaal. 20c, Amphitheater, Natal National Park. 25c, Cango Caves, Cape Province.

1978, Nov. 13   Perf. 12½
511 A202 10c multicolored   .30 .30
512 A202 15c multicolored   .40 .40
513 A202 20c multicolored   .60 .60
514 A202 25c multicolored   .95 .95
       Nos. 511-514 (4)   2.25 2.25

Tourist publicity.

Tellurometer and Dr. I. R. Wadley — A203

1979, Feb. 12   Litho.   Perf. 12½
515 A203 15c multicolored   .30 .25

15th anniversary of the invention of the tellurometer (to measure radio distances).

South Africa No. C5 A204

1979, Mar. 30   Litho.   Perf. 14½x14
516 A204 15c multicolored   .35 .30

First stamp printed by South African Government Printer, 50th anniversary.

"Save Fuel" A205

Fuel Economy: No. 518, Language inscriptions reversed.

1979, Apr. 2   Photo.   Perf. 12x12½
517 A205 4c red & black   .20 .20
518 A205 4c red & black   .20 .20
  a.   Pair, #517-518   .25 .25

Battle of Isandlwana, by Melton Prior — A206

15c, Battle of Ulundi, by Louis Creswicke. 20c, Battle of Rorke's Drift, by Lt. Col. Crealock.

1979, May 25   Litho.   Perf. 14x13½
519 A206 4c red & black   .20 .20
520 A206 15c red & black   .40 .35
521 A206 20c red & black   .50 .40
  a.   Souv. sheet, #519-521 + label 3.00 3.00
       Nos. 519-521 (3)   1.10 .95

Centenary of Zulu War.

"Health Care and Service" — A207

1979, June 19   Litho.   Perf. 12½x12
522 A207 4c multicolored   .20 .20
  a.   Perf. 14¼x14   .25 .25

Health Year.

Boy and Girl Watching Candle — A208

1979, Sept. 13   Litho.   Perf. 14½x14
523 A208 4c multicolored   .20 .20

South African Christmas Stamp Fund, 50th anniversary.

Cape Town University, 150th Anniversary — A209

1979, Oct. 1   Litho.   Perf. 14x14½
524 A209 4c multicolored   .20 .20
  a.   Perf. 12x12½   .25 .25

Southern Sun Rose — A210

Designs: Roses.

1979, Oct. 4   Litho.   Perf. 14½x14
525 A210 4c multicolored   .20 .20
526 A210 15c multicolored   .35 .30
527 A210 20c multicolored   .45 .40
528 A210 25c multicolored   .65 .55
  a.   Souvenir sheet of 4, #525-528 2.25 2.25
       Nos. 525-528 (4)   1.65 1.45

Rosafari 1979, 4th World Rose Convention, Pretoria, October.

Stellenbosch University — A211

1979, Nov. 8
529 A211 4c shown   .20 .20
530 A211 15c Rhenish Church   .30 .25

Stellenbosch (oldest town in South Africa), 300th anniversary.

A212   A213

1979, Dec. 18   Photo.   Perf. 12½x12
531 A212 4c multicolored   .20 .20

Federation of Afrikaans Cultural Societies, 50th anniv.

1980, May 6   Litho.   Perf. 14½x14
Paintings by Pieter Wenning (1873-1921): 5c, Still Life with Sweet Peas. 25c, House in the Suburbs, Cape Town.
532 A213 5c multicolored   .20 .20
       Size: 45x37mm
533 A213 25c multicolored   .50 .35
  a.   Souvenir sheet of 2, #532-533 1.75 1.00

Great Star of Africa Diamond — A214

1980, May 12   Litho.   Perf. 14x14½
534 A214 15c shown   .45 .35
535 A214 20c Cullinan II diamond .55 .50

World Diamond Congress.

A215   A216

1980, Sept. 3   Litho.   Perf. 14½x14
536 A215 5c multicolored   .20 .20

Christian Louis Leipoldt (1880-1947), writer and physician.

1980, Oct. 9   Litho.
537 A216 5c multicolored   .20 .20

University of Pretoria, 50th anniv.

Marine With Ships, by Willem van de Velde — A217

Paintings: 10c, Firetail and Trainer, by George Stubbs. 15c, Lavinia, by Thomas Gainsborough, vert. 20c, Landscape, by Pieter Post.

1980, Nov. 3   Perf. 14½x14
538 A217 5c multicolored   .20 .20
539 A217 10c multicolored   .20 .20
540 A217 15c multicolored   .30 .25
541 A217 20c multicolored   .35 .30
  a.   Souvenir sheet of 4, #538-541 1.50 1.25
       Nos. 538-541 (4)   1.05 .95

Natl. Gallery, 50th anniv.

P.J. Joubert, Paul Kruger, M.W. Pretorius (First Leaders of Triumvirate Government) — A218

Design: 10c, Monument, flag of South African Republic, 1880, vert.

1980, Dec. 15   Perf. 14x14½ 14½x14
542 A218 5c multicolored   .20 .20
543 A218 10c multicolored   .20 .20

Paardekraal Monument (built on site of founding of triumverate government) centennial.

British Troops in Battle of Amajuba — A219

1981, Feb. 27   Litho.   Perf. 14x14½
544 A219 5c Boer snipers, vert.   .20 .20
545 A219 15c shown   .35 .30

Battle of Amajuba centenary (led to independence of Orange Free State).

Scene from Verdi's Aida A220

1981, May 23   Litho.   Perf. 14½x14
546 A220 20c Raka ballet scene   .35 .30
547 A220 25c shown   .45 .35
  a.   Souvenir sheet of 2, #546-547 1.00 .80

Opening of State Theater, Pretoria.

Pres. Marais   Deaf Girl
Viljoen — A221   Learning to
                        Speak — A222

508 A200 25c multicolored   .90 .90
  a.   Souvenir sheet of 4, #505-508 3.00 3.00
       Nos. 505-508 (4)   2.45 2.45

Jan Ernst Abraham Volschenk (1853-1936), first South African professional artist.

1981, May 30   *Perf. 14x14½*
Size: 57x21mm

548	A221	5c Former presidents	.20	.20
549	A221	15c shown	.30	.25

1981, June 12   *Perf. 14½x14*

550	A222	5c shown	.20	.20
551	A222	15c Man reading braille	.30	.25

Institute for the Deaf and Blind, Worcester, centenary.

Natl. Cancer Assn.
50th Anniv. — A223

1981, July 10

552	A223	5c multicolored	.20	.20

Calanthe
Natalensis
A224

Voortrekker
Movement, 50th
Anniv.
A225

1981, Sept. 11   Litho.

553	A224	5c shown	.20	.20
554	A224	15c Eulophia speciosa	.30	.25
555	A224	20c Disperis fanniniae	.40	.30
556	A224	25c Disa uniflora	.50	.40
a.		Souvenir sheet of 4, #553-556	2.50	2.25
		Nos. 553-556 (4)	1.40	1.15

10th World Orchid Conf., Durban, 9/11-17.

1981, Sept. 30   *Perf. 14x14½*

557	A225	5c multicolored	.20	.20

Scouting Year
A226

TB Bacillus
Centenary
A227

1982, Feb. 22   Litho.   *Perf. 14½x14*

558	A226	15c Baden-Powell	.30	.25

1982, Mar. 24   Litho.

559	A227	20c multicolored	.30	.25

Return of Simonstown Naval Base,
25th Anniv. — A228

1982, Apr. 2   *Perf. 14½x14*

560	A228	8c Submarine	.20	.20
561	A228	15c Strike craft	.25	.20
562	A228	20c Mine sweeper	.35	.30
563	A228	25c Harbor patrol boats	.45	.35
a.		Souvenir sheet of 4, #560-563	2.25	1.90
		Nos. 560-563 (4)	1.25	1.05

Old Provost,
Grahamstown
A229

Design: 2c, Tuynhuys, Kaapstad (Cape Town). 3c, Appelhof, Bloemfontein. 4c, Raadsaal, Pretoria. 5c, Die Kasteel, Kaapstad. 6c, Goewermentsgebou, Bloemfontein. 7c, Drostdy, Graaf-Reinet. 8c, Leeuwenhof, Cape Town. 9c, Libertas, Pretoria. 10c, City Hall, Pietermaritzburg. 11c, City Hall, Kimberley. 12c, City Hall, Port Elizabeth. 14c, Johannesburg City Hall. 15c, Hotel Milner, Matjesfontein. 16c, Durban City Hall. 20c, Post Office, Durban. 25c, Melrose House, Pretoria. 30c, Old Legislative Assembly Building, Pietermaritzburg. 50c, Raadsaal, Bloemfontein. 1r, Houses of Parliament, Cape Town. 2r, Uniegebou, Pretoria.
Coils have different designs.

1982-87   Litho.   *Perf. 14x14½*

564	A229	1c brown ('84)	.20	.20
565	A229	2c apple green	.20	.20
566	A229	2c green	.75	.20
567	A229	2c slate grn ('85)	.20	.20
568	A229	3c purple ('85)	1.25	.20
569	A229	4c olive grn ('85)	.20	.20
570	A229	5c carmine	.20	.20
571	A229	6c brt green	.20	.20
572	A229	7c gray green	.20	.20
573	A229	8c blue	.20	.20
574	A229	8c intense bl ('83)	.20	.20
575	A229	9c brt rose lilac	.20	.20
576	A229	10c lt red brown	.20	.20
577	A229	10c violet brn ('83)	.30	.20
578	A229	11c cerise ('84)	.25	.20
579	A229	12c dp ultra ('85)	.35	.20
580	A229	14c rose brn ('86)	.50	.20
581	A229	16c red ('87)	.60	.20
582	A229	20c vermilion	.25	.20
583	A229	20c black ('85)	.60	.20
584	A229	25c bister	.25	.20

Size: 45x27mm
Perf. 14½x14

586	A229	30c brown ('86)	1.50	.20
587	A229	50c Prus blue ('86)	2.25	.20
588	A229	1r violet blue ('86)	2.50	.20
589	A229	2r cerise ('85)	5.00	.20
		Nos. 564-589 (25)	18.55	5.00

For surcharge see No. B12.

Engr.

590	A229	1c dark brown	.20	.20
591	A229	2c slate grn ('83)	.20	.20
592	A229	3c violet	.20	.20
593	A229	4c olive green	.20	.20
594	A229	5c dark lake ('83)	.20	.20
595	A229	6c green blk ('84)	.20	.35
596	A229	15c blue	.20	.20
597	A229	20c black ('83)	.50	.20
598	A229	30c violet brown	.45	.25
599	A229	50c Prus blue	.70	.25
600	A229	1r violet blue	1.50	.20
601	A229	2r rose carmine	3.00	.30
		Nos. 590-601 (12)	7.55	2.75

In some cases there are slight design differences from litho. stamp.

Perf. 14 Horiz.

		Photo.	Coil Stamps	
602	A229	1c Residence, Swellendam	.20	.20
603	A229	2c City Hall, East London	.25	.20
604	A229	5c Rissik St. PO, Johannesburg	.30	.20
605	A229	10c Morgenster, Somerset West	.40	.20
		Nos. 602-605 (4)	1.15	.80

Bradysaurus
A230

Prehistoric Animals (Karoo Fossils).

1982, Dec. 1   Litho.   *Perf. 14x14½*

606	A230	8c shown	.30	.20
607	A230	15c Lystrosaurus	.60	.20
608	A230	20c Euparkeria	.80	.25

609	A230	25c Thrinaxodon	1.00	.35
a.		Souvenir sheet of 4, #606-609	3.00	3.00
		Nos. 606-609 (4)	2.70	1.00

Weather
Station,
Gough
Island
A231

1983, Jan. 19   Litho.

610	A231	8c shown	.20	.20
611	A231	20c Marion Isld. station	.30	.25
612	A231	25c Reading instruments	.40	.30
613	A231	40c Weather balloon, Antarctica	.65	.50
		Nos. 610-613 (4)	1.55	1.25

Steam Locomotives — A232

1983, Apr. 27   Litho.

614	A232	10c Class 82, 1952	.25	.20
615	A232	20c Class 16E, 1935	.45	.35
616	A232	25c Class 6H, 1901	.55	.45
617	A232	40c Class 15F, 1939	.95	.70
		Nos. 614-617 (4)	2.20	1.70

Soccer — A233

*Perf. 14½x14 (10c, 25c), 14x14½
(20c, 40c)*

1983, July 20   Litho.

618	A233	10c Rugby, vert.	.20	.20
619	A233	20c shown	.35	.25
620	A233	25c Sailing, vert.	.45	.30
621	A233	40c Equestrian	.65	.50
		Nos. 618-621 (4)	1.65	1.25

Plettenberg Bay — A234

1983, Oct. 12   Litho.   *Perf. 14½x14*

622	A234	10c shown	.20	.20
623	A234	20c Durban Beach	.30	.20
624	A234	25c West Coast beach	.40	.25
625	A234	40c Clifton beach scene	.65	.45
a.		Souvenir sheet of 4, #622-625	1.75	1.25
		Nos. 622-625 (4)	1.55	1.10

English Writers of
South Africa — A235

Designs: 10c, Thomas Pringle (1789-1834). 20c, Pauline Smith (1882-1959). 25c, Olive Schreiner (1855-1920). 40c, Percy FitzPatrick (1862-1931).

1984, Feb. 24   Litho.   *Perf. 14½x14*

626	A235	10c multicolored	.20	.20
627	A235	20c multicolored	.25	.20
628	A235	25c multicolored	.35	.25
629	A235	40c multicolored	.60	.35
		Nos. 626-629 (4)	1.40	1.00

Manganese — A236

1984, June 8   Litho.   *Perf. 14x14½*

630	A236	11c shown	.25	.20
631	A236	20c Chromium	.45	.25
632	A236	25c Vanadium	.60	.30
633	A236	30c Titanium	.70	.35
		Nos. 630-633 (4)	2.00	1.10

Bloukrans
River
Bridge
A237

1984, Aug. 24

634	A237	11c shown	.20	.20
635	A237	25c Durban 4-level Bridge Interchange	.45	.25
636	A237	30c Mfolozi Railroad Bridge	.55	.30
637	A237	45c Gouritz River Bridge	.80	.45
		Nos. 634-637 (4)	2.00	1.20

New Constitution
A238

Military Medals
A239

1984, Sept. 3   Litho.   *Perf. 14x14½*

638	A238	11c Preamble (English)	.30	.20
639	A238	11c Preamble (Afrikaans)	.30	.20
a.		Pair, #638-639	.60	.35
640	A238	25c Symbolic pillars, anthem	.65	.35
641	A238	30c Arms	.75	.40
		Nos. 638-641 (4)	2.00	1.15

1984, Nov. 9   *Perf. 14½x14*

642	A239	11c Pro Patria	.25	.20
643	A239	25c De Wet	.40	.25
644	A239	30c John Chard Decoration	.50	.30
645	A239	45c Honoris Crux	.70	.45
a.		Miniature sheet of 4, #642-645	2.00	1.25
		Nos. 642-645 (4)	1.80	1.20

Pres. Pieter
Willem Botha (b.
1916) — A240

1984, Nov. 2   Litho.   *Perf. 14x14½*

646	A240	11c multicolored	.20	.20
647	A240	25c multicolored	.40	.25

Frans David
Oerder,
Painter
(1867-1944)
A241

1985, Feb. 22   Litho.   *Perf. 14½x14*

648	A241	11c Reflections	.20	.20
649	A241	25c Ladies in a Garden	.40	.20
650	A241	30c Still-Life with Lobster	.50	.30

651 A241 50c Still-Life with Marigolds .80 .45
a. Souvenir sheet of 4, #648-651 2.00 2.00
Nos. 648-651 (4) 1.90 1.20

Cape
Parliament
Cent.
A242

1985, May 15 **Litho.**
652 A242 12c Parliament .20 .20
653 A242 25c Speaker's chair .35 .25
654 A242 30c The National Convention, by Ed-
ward Roworth .40 .30
655 A242 50c South African
arms .70 .40
Nos. 652-655 (4) 1.65 1.15

Indigenous
Flowers
A243

Cape Silver
A244

1985, Aug. 23 Litho. Perf. 14½x14
656 A243 12c Freesia .20 .20
657 A243 25c Nerine .65 .45
658 A243 30c Ixia .75 .50
659 A243 50c Gladiolus 1.40 .90
Nos. 656-659 (4) 3.00 2.05

1985, Nov. 5 Perf. 14½x14, 14x14½
660 A244 12c Sugar bowl, horiz. .20 .20
661 A244 25c Tea pot, horiz. .40 .20
662 A244 30c Goblet .45 .25
663 A244 50c Coffee pot .75 .40
Nos. 660-663 (4) 1.80 1.05

Blood
Transfusion
Services
A245

1986, Feb. 20 Perf. 14½x14
664 A245 12c Blood donation .20 .20
665 A245 20c Transfusion .35 .20
666 A245 25c Surgery .45 .20
667 A245 30c Emergency aid .55 .25
Nos. 664-667 (4) 1.55 .85

Republic of
South
Africa, 25th
Anniv.
A246

1986, May 30 Litho. Perf. 14x14½
668 A246 14c Text in Afrikaans .25 .20
669 A246 14c Text in English .25 .20
a. Pair, #668-669 .50 .50

Cultural Heritage — A247

Restoration projects: 14c, Drostdyhof, Free
Street, Graaff-Reinet, 19th cent. 20c, Pilgrim's
Rest, Eastern Transvaal, 1873. 25c, J.T.
Strapp and Son importers, c. 1893, Bethle-
hem. 30c, Palmdene, c. 1897,
Pietermaritzburg.

1986, Aug. 14
670 A247 14c multicolored .25 .20
671 A247 20c multicolored .35 .25
672 A247 25c multicolored .40 .30
673 A247 30c multicolored .50 .35
Nos. 670-673 (4) 1.50 1.10

Johannesburg, Cent. — A248

Discovery of Gold
in Roodepoort,
Cent. — A249

1986, Sept. 25 Perf. 14x14½
674 A248 14c Johannesburg,
1886 .25 .20
675 A249 20c Gold mine .35 .25
676 A248 25c Johannesburg,
1986 .40 .30
677 A249 30c Gold .50 .35
a. Souvenir sheet of 1 2.50 2.50
Nos. 674-677 (4) 1.50 1.10

No. 677a for Johannesburg stamp exhibition. Sold for 50c.

Pearl
Mountain — A250

Beetles — A251

1986, Nov. 20 Litho. Perf. 14x14½
678 A250 14c shown .25 .25
679 A250 20c The Column,
Drakensburg .35 .35
680 A250 25c Maltese Cross,
Cedarberg .45 .45
681 A250 30c Bourke's Luck
Potholes .55 .55
Nos. 678-681 (4) 1.60 1.60

1987, Mar. 6 Litho. Perf. 14x14½
690 A251 14c *Chaetodera regalis* .25 .25
691 A251 20c *Trichostetha fascicularis* .40 .40
692 A251 25c *Julodis viridipes* .50 .50
693 A251 30c *Ceroplesis militaris* .60 .60
Nos. 690-693 (4) 1.75 1.75

Petroglyphs
A252

1987, June 4 Perf. 14½x14
694 A252 16c Eland, Sebaaieni
Cave .30 .30
695 A252 20c Leaping lion,
Clocolan .40 .40
696 A252 25c Black wildebeest,
uMhlwazini Valley .50 .50
697 A252 30c San dance,
Floukraal .60 .60
Nos. 694-697 (4) 1.80 1.80

Paarl,
300th
Anniv.
A253

1987, Sept. 3
698 A253 16c Oude Pastorie .30 .30
699 A253 20c Winegrowing .40 .40
700 A253 25c Wagon-building .50 .50
701 A253 30c KWV Cathedral
Cellar .60 .60
Nos. 698-701 (4) 1.80 1.80

A souvenir sheet of one, No. 701, has decorative margin picturing emblem of the natl.
philatelic exhibition at Paarl, Sept. 16-19. Sold
for 50c.

Map, "The Bible" in 76
Languages — A254

Religious
Paintings by
Rembrandt
A255

Designs: 30c, *Belshazzar's Feast.* 50c, *St.
Matthew and the Angel,* vert.

Perf. 14x14½, 14½x14 (30c)
1987, Nov. 19
702 A254 16c shown .30 .30
703 A255 30c shown .60 .60
704 A255 50c multicolored 1.00 1.00
Nos. 702-704 (3) 1.90 1.90

Bible Society of South Africa.
A 40c stamp was prepared and sent to post
offices, but was not issued. Some were sold
contrary to the withdrawal order, and used
examples are known.
For surcharge see No. B13.

Discovery of
the Cape of
Good Hope
by
Bartolomeu
Dias — A256

Designs: 16c, Dias, astrolabe, Cape of
Good Hope. 30c, Kwaaihoek Memorial. 40c,
Caravels, 1488. 50c, Martellus Map, c. 1489.

1988, Feb. 3 Perf. 14½x14
706 A256 16c multicolored .30 .30
707 A256 30c multicolored .55 .55
708 A256 40c multicolored .75 .75
709 A256 50c multicolored .95 .95
Nos. 706-709 (4) 2.55 2.55

A souvenir sheet of one, No. 709, has decorative margin picturing emblem of the natl.
philatelic exhibition held at Pietermaritzburg,
Nov. 22-27. Sold for 70c.
For surcharge see No. B14.

French Huguenot
Settlement of the
Cape, 300th
Anniv. — A257

1988, Apr. 13 Perf. 14x14½
710 A257 16c Memorial, Frans-
chhoek .35 .35
711 A257 30c Map of France .60 .60
712 A257 40c French-Dutch Bible, 1672 .80 .80
713 A257 50c St. Bartholomew's
Day Massacre,
1572 1.00 1.00
Nos. 710-713 (4) 2.75 2.75

For surcharges see Nos. B15-B18.

Lighthouses
A258

1988, June 9 Perf. 14½x14
714 A258 16c Pelican Point, 1932 .30 .30
715 A258 30c Groenpunt, 1824 .55 .55
716 A258 40c Agulhas, 1849 .75 .75
717 A258 50c Umhlanga Rocks,
1954 .95 .95
a. Souvenir sheet of 4, #714-717 3.50 3.50
Nos. 714-717 (4) 2.55 2.55

"Standardised Mail"
"STANDARD POSTAGE"
Stamps inscribed thus were sold
for the amount shown in ( ) on date
of issue.

Succulents
A259

1988-93 Litho. Perf. 14x14½
735 A259 1c *Huernia
zebrina* .20 .20
736 A259 2c *Euphorbia
symmetrica* .20 .20
737 A259 5c *Lithops
dorotheae* .20 .20
738 A259 7c *Gibbaeum
newbrownii* .20 .20
739 A259 10c *Didymaotus
lapidiformis* .20 .20
740 A259 16c *Vanheerdea
divergens* .20 .20
741 A259 18c *Faucaria
tigrina* .20 .20
742 A259 20c *Conophytum
mundum* .20 .20
743 A259 21c *Gasteria arm-
strongii* .20 .20
744 A259 25c *Cheiridopsis
pecularis* .20 .20
745 A259 30c *Tavaresia bark-
lyi* .20 .20
a. Strip, 2 ea 1c, 2c, 5c, 7c, 30c 6.00
746 A259 35c *Dinteranthus
wilmotianus* .25 .20
747 A259 40c *Frithia pulchra* .30 .20
748 A259 (45c) *Stapelia
grandiflora* .30 .20
749 A259 50c *Lapidaria mar-
garetae* .35 .35
750 A259 90c *Dioscorea ele-
phantipes* .65 .40
751 A259 1r *Trichocaulon
cactiforme* .70 .55
752 A259 2r *Crassula
columnaris* 1.40 .75
753 A259 5r *Anacampseros
albissima* 5.25 2.00
Nos. 735-753 (19) 11.40 6.85

Coil Stamps
Photo.
Perf. 14 Horiz.
754 A259 1c *Adromischus
marianiae* 1.00 1.00
755 A259 2c *Titanopsis cal-
carea* .25 .25
756 A259 5c *Dactylopsis
digitata* .25 .25
757 A259 10c *Pleiospilos bo-
lusii* .50 .50
Nos. 754-757 (4) 2.00 2.00

Issued: 18c, 4/1/89; 5r, 3/1/90; 21c, 4/2/90;
#748, 4/1/93; others, 9/1/88.

Map and Settlers — A260

Exodus, Tapestry by W.H. Coetzer Studio — A261

Crossing the Drakensburg, Tapestry by Coetzer Studio (illustration reduced) — A262

Church of the Vow, Pietermaritzburg — A263

Perf. 14x14½, 14½x14 (50c)

1988, Nov. 21			**Litho.**	
758	A260	16c multicolored	.40	.25
759	A261	30c multicolored	.70	.45
760	A262	40c multicolored	.95	.60
761	A263	50c multicolored	1.10	.75
	Nos. 758-761 (4)		3.15	2.05

The Great Trek, 150th anniv.

Discovery of a Living Specimen of the Coelacanth, 50th Anniv. A264

Designs: 16c, *Latimeria chalumnae.* 30c, J. L. B. Smith, Margaret Courtenay-Latimer. 40c, Smith Institute of Ichthyology, Grahamstown. 50c, Fish, GEO two-man research submarine.

1989, Feb. 9			**Perf. 14½x14**	
762	A264	16c multicolored	.30	.30
763	A264	30c multicolored	.55	.55
764	A264	40c multicolored	.75	.75
765	A264	50c multicolored	.95	.95
a.	Souvenir sheet of 1		4.50	4.50
b.	Souvenir sheet of 2		.55	.55
	Nos. 762-765 (4)		2.55	2.55

No. 765a has decorative margin picturing emblem of the natl. philatelic exhibition WANDERERS 101, held Sept. 6-9. Sold for 1.50r.
No. 765b was issued 6/97, sold for 1r and is inscribed for Old Mutual Environmental Education Center in sheet margin.

Soil Conservation Campaign of the Natl. Grazing Strategy — A265

1989, May 3			**Perf. 14x14½**	
766	A265	18c Desertification	.35	.35
767	A265	30c Eroded gullies	.55	.55
768	A265	40c Barrage	.75	.75
769	A265	50c Verdant plain	.95	.95
	Nos. 766-769 (4)		2.60	2.60

Natl. Rugby Board, Cent. A266

Springboks, foreign team emblems, match scenes.

1989, June 22				
770	A266	18c France, 1980	.30	.25
771	A266	30c Australia, 1963	.55	.45
772	A266	40c New Zealand, 1937	.75	.60
773	A266	50c British Isles, 1896	.90	.75
	Nos. 770-773 (4)		2.50	2.05

Paintings by Jacob Hendrik Pierneef (1886-1957) A267

1989, Aug. 3			**Perf. 14½x14**	
774	A267	18c *Composition in Blue, 1928*	.30	.20
775	A267	30c *Zanzibar, 1926*	.55	.25
776	A267	40c *The Bushveld, 1949*	.75	.30
777	A267	50c *Cape Homestead, 1942*	.90	.40
a.	Souvenir sheet of 4, #774-777		2.75	2.75
	Nos. 774-777 (4)		2.50	1.15

Election of Pres. Frederik Willem de Klerk, Aug. 15 — A268

1989, Sept. 20			**Perf. 14x14½**	
778	A268	18c shown	.35	.20
779	A268	45c Portrait, diff.	.90	.50

Fossil Fuels, Nuclear and Thermal Power A269

18c, SOEKOR gas project, Mossel Bay. 30c, SASOL coal conversion plant. 40c, Koeberg nuclear power plant. 50c, ESKOM thermal power station.

1989, Oct. 19				
780	A269	18c multicolored	.25	.20
781	A269	30c multicolored	.45	.30
782	A269	40c multicolored	.55	.35
783	A269	50c multicolored	.75	.45
	Nos. 780-783 (4)		2.00	1.30

Cooperation in Southern Africa — A270

Maps and: 18c, Cahora Bassa hydroelectric power project. 30c, Railway network. 40c, Lesotho Highlands water project. 50c, Veterinary care.

1990, Feb. 15			**Perf. 14½x14**	
	Size of 18c, 40c: 68x26mm			
784	A270	18c multicolored	.30	.25
785	A270	30c multicolored	.55	.40
786	A270	40c multicolored	.70	.50
787	A270	50c multicolored	.90	.65
a.	Miniature sheet of 4, #784-787		2.50	2.50
	Nos. 784-787 (4)		2.45	1.80

Stamp Day — A271

Birds — A272

Stamps on stamps: a, Great Britain #1. b, Cape of Good Hope #2. c, Natal #4. d, Orange River Colony #10. e, Transvaal #3.

1990, May 12			**Litho.**	
788		Strip of 5	1.90	1.90
a.-e.	A271 21c any single		.35	.35

Penny Black, 150th anniv.

1990, Aug. 2	**Litho.**	**Perf. 14x14½**		

Designs: 21c, *Tauraco corythaix.* 35c, *Cossypha natalensis.* 40c, *Mirafra africana.* 50c, *Telophorus zeylonus.*

789	A272	21c multicolored	.40	.25
790	A272	35c multicolored	.65	.45
791	A272	40c multicolored	.75	.50
792	A272	50c multicolored	.95	.60
	Nos. 789-792 (4)		2.75	1.80

A souvenir sheet of 1 #792 was sold by the Philatelic Foundation of South Africa. Value $3.50.

Karoo Landscape, Near Britstown A273

Tourism: #794, Camps Bay, Cape Peninsula. #795, Giraffes, Kruger Natl. Park. #796, Boschendal homestead, Drakenstein.

1990, Nov. 1			**Perf. 14½x14**	
793	A273	50c multicolored	.60	.60
794	A273	50c multicolored	.60	.60
795	A273	50c multicolored	.60	.60
796	A273	50c multicolored	.60	.60
a.	Block of 4, #793-796		2.50	2.50

A274

A275

National Decorations: No. 797, Woltemade Cross for Bravery. No. 798, Order of the Southern Cross. No. 799, Order of the Star of South Africa. No. 800, Order for Meritorious Service. No. 801, Order of Good Hope.

1990, Dec. 6				
797	A274	21c multicolored	.30	.25
798	A274	21c multicolored	.30	.25
799	A274	21c multicolored	.30	.25
800	A274	21c multicolored	.30	.25
801	A274	21c multicolored	.30	.25
a.	Souv. sheet of 5, #797-801		1.50	1.50
b.	Strip of 5, #797-801		1.50	1.50

1991, Feb. 21			**Litho.**	

Animal Breeding: a, Boer horse. b, Bonsmara cattle. c, Dorper sheep. d, Ridgeback dog. e, Putterie racing pigeon.

802	A275	21c Strip of 5, #a.-e.	1.90	1.25

Achievements — A276

Designs: 25c, First heart transplant, vert. 40c, Matimba power plant. 50c, Dolos breakwater blocks. 60c, Western Deep Levels Gold Mine, world's deepest mine, vert.

Perf. 14½x14 (25c, 60c), 14x14½ (40c, 50c, #806a)

1991, May 30			**Litho.**	
803	A276	25c multicolored	.30	.20
804	A276	40c multicolored	.50	.25
805	A276	50c multicolored	.60	.30
806	A276	60c multicolored	.45	.35
a.	Souvenir sheet of 1		2.00	2.00
	Nos. 803-806 (4)		1.85	1.10

30th anniv. of Republic of South Africa.

1st Registration of Nurses & Midwives, Cent. — A277

1991, Aug. 15	**Litho.**	**Perf. 14x14½**		
807	A277	60c multicolored	.75	.75

Creation of South African Post Office Ltd. — A278

1991, Oct. 1			**Litho.**	
808		27c Post office	.30	.20
809		27c Telkom SA Ltd.	.30	.20
a.	A278 Pair, #808-809		.60	.60

South African Scientists A279

Designs: 27c, Sir Arnold Theiler (1867-1936), veterinarian. 45c, Sir Basil Schonland (1896-1972), physicist. 65c, Dr. Robert Broom (1866-1951), paleontologist. 85c, Dr. Alexander L. du Toit (1878-1948), geologist.

1991, Oct. 9			**Perf. 14½x14**	
810	A279	27c multicolored	.30	.20
811	A279	45c multicolored	.50	.35
812	A279	65c multicolored	.75	.40
813	A279	85c multicolored	.95	.50
	Nos. 810-813 (4)		2.50	1.40

Antarctic Treaty, 30th Anniv. A280

1991, Dec. 5 — Litho.

814 A280 27c SA Agulhas, penguins .35 .20
815 A280 65c Meteorological chart .90 .40

Conservation — A281

1992, Feb. 6 — Litho. Perf. 14x14½

816 A281 27c Prevent erosion .25 .20
817 A281 65c Water pollution .65 .40
818 A281 85c Air pollution .85 .50
Nos. 816-818 (3) 1.75 1.10

A souvenir sheet of 1 #817 was sold by Intersapa.

A282

A283

Designs depicting history of postal stones: No. 819, Sailing ships at Table Bay. No. 820, Sailors going ashore at Aguada de Saldanha. No. 821, Sailors discovering postal stone near Versse River. No. 822, Finding letters under postal stones. No. 823, Reading news from other mariners.

1992, May 9 — Litho. Perf. 14x14½

819 A282 35c multicolored .35 .30
820 A282 35c multicolored .35 .30
821 A282 35c multicolored .35 .30
822 A282 35c multicolored .35 .30
823 A282 35c multicolored .35 .30
a. Strip of 5, #819-823 1.90 1.90

Stamp Day.

Perf. 14½x14, 14x14½

1992, July 9 — Litho.

Antique Cape Furniture: No. 824, Queen Anne settee, c. 1750-70. No. 825, Stinkwood settee, c. 1800. No. 826, Canopy bed, c. 1800, vert. No. 827, Rocking cradle, 19th cent. No. 828, Waterbutt, c. 1800, vert. No. 829, Flemish style cabinet, c. 1700, vert. No. 830, Armoire, c. 1780-1790, vert. No. 831, Church chair, late 17th cent, vert. No. 832, Tub chair, c. 1770-1790, vert. No. 833, Bible desk, c. 1770, vert.

824 A283 35c multicolored .35 .30
825 A283 35c multicolored .35 .30
826 A283 35c multicolored .35 .30
827 A283 35c multicolored .35 .30
828 A283 35c multicolored .35 .30
829 A283 35c multicolored .35 .30
830 A283 35c multicolored .35 .30
831 A283 35c multicolored .35 .30
832 A283 35c multicolored .35 .30
833 A283 35c multicolored .35 .30
a. Miniature sheet of 10, #824-833 3.50

Sports A284

1992, July 24 — Perf. 14x14½

834 A284 35c Formula 1 Grand Prix .35 .30
835 A284 35c Soccer .35 .30
836 A284 55c Paris-le Cap Rally .55 .45
837 A284 70c Track .65 .55
838 A284 90c Rugby .85 .75
839 A284 1.05r Cricket 1.00 .85
a. Souvenir sheet of 6, #834-839 3.75 3.75
Nos. 834-839 (6) 3.75 3.20

A285

A286

1992, Oct. 8 — Litho. Perf. 14½x14

840 A285 35c Women's Monument .30 .30
841 A285 70c Sekupu Player .70 .55
842 A285 90c The Hunter .90 .75
843 A285 1.05r Postman Lehman 1.10 .85
a. Souvenir sheet of 4, #840-843 3.00 3.00
Nos. 840-843 (4) 3.00 2.45

Sculptures by Anton van Wouw (1862-1945). No. 843a sold for 3.30r.

1993, Jan. 28 — Litho.

South African Harbors.

844 A286 35c Walvis Bay .30 .25
845 A286 55c East London .50 .35
846 A286 70c Port Elizabeth .65 .45
847 A286 90c Cape Town .80 .60
848 A286 1.05r Durban 1.00 .70
a. Souv. sheet, #844-848 + label 3.25 3.25
Nos. 844-848 (5) 3.25 2.35

No. 848a sold for 3.90r.

A287

A288

Aircraft: a, Bristol Boxkite, 1907. b, Voisin, 1909. c, Bleriot XI, 1911. d, Paterson No. 2 biplane, 1913. e, Henri Farman F.27, 1915. f, BE2e, 1918. g, Vickers Vimy Silver Queen, 1920. h, SE-5a, 1921. i, Avro 504K, 1921. j, Armstrong-Whitworth Atalanta, 1930. k, DH66 Hercules, 1931. l, Westland Wapiti, 1931. m, Junkers F.13, 1932. n, Handley Page HP-42, 1933. o, Junkers Ju52/3m, 1934. p, Junkers Ju86, 1936. q, Hawker Hartbees, 1936. r, Short Empire flying boat Canopus, 1937. s, Miles Master II and Airspeed AS-10 Oxford, 1940. t, Harvard Mk IIa, 1942. u, Short Sunderland, 1945. v, Avro York, 1946. w, Douglas DC-7B, 1955. x, Sikorsky S-55C, 1956. y, Boeing 707-344, 1959.

1993, May 7 — Litho. Perf. 14x14½
Miniature Sheet of 25

849 A287 45c #a.-y. 10.00

A souvenir sheet containing #849a, 849y was sold by the Philatelic Foundation of South Africa.

1993-95 — Litho. Perf. 14x14½,

Endangered Fauna: 1c, Heleophryne rosei. 2c, Bradypodion taeniabronchum. 5c, Cordylus giganteus. 10c, Psammobates geometricus. 20c, Atelerix frontalis. 40c, Bunolagus monticularis. #856, Diceros bicornis. #856A, "Black Rhinocerous." 50c, Cercopithecus mitis. 55c, Proteles cristatus. 60c, Lycaon pictus. 70c, Hippotragus equinus. 75c, Poecilogale albinucha. 80c, Otis kori. 85c, Serinus citrinipectus. 90c, Spheniscus demersus. 1r, Grus carunculatus. 2r, Hirundo atrocaerulea. 5r, Polemaetus bellicosus. 10r, Terathopius ecaudatus.

Inscriptions in Latin

850 A288 1c multicolored .20 .20
851 A288 2c multicolored .20 .20
852 A288 5c multicolored .20 .20
853 A288 10c multicolored .20 .20

854 A288 20c multicolored .20 .20
a. Strip, 1c, 2 ea 2c, 20c .50
b. Strip, 20c, 2 ea 5c, 10c .50
c. Strip, 20c, 2 each 5c, 10c, perf. 14½ vert. .50
855 A288 40c multicolored .25 .20
856 A288 (45c) multicolored .30 .20
857 A288 50c multicolored .50 .20
a. Strip, #850, 852, 857, 2 #851, Perf. 14½ Vert. 1.00
858 A288 55c multicolored .30 .20
859 A288 60c multicolored .35 .20
860 A288 70c multicolored .40 .20
861 A288 75c multicolored .45 .20
862 A288 80c multicolored .50 .20
862A A288 85c multicolored .50 .30
863 A288 90c multicolored .55 .20
864 A288 1r multicolored .60 .20
865 A288 2r multicolored 1.25 .20
866 A288 5r multicolored 3.00 .50
867 A288 10r multicolored 6.00 1.50
Nos. 850-867 (19) 15.75 5.50

#857a exists with tab showing Reader's Digest emblem in either red or black; also in different order with emblem in blue.
Issued: #854b, 8/24/94; #854c, 10/94; #857a, 9/1/95; 85c, 10/2/95; others, 9/3/93.
See designs A336 and A343 (no frames).

Wildlife Type with English Inscriptions

Designs: 1c, Table Mountain ghost frog. 2c, Smith's dwarf chameleon. 10c, Geometric tortoise. 20c, Southern African hedgehog. 40c, Riverine rabbit. (45c), Black rhinoceros. 50c, Samango monkey. 60c, Cape hunting dog. 70c, Roan antelope. 90c, Jackass penguin. 1r, Wattled crane. 2r, Blue swallow. 5r, Martial eagle. 20r, Fish Eagle.

Perf. 14x14¼, 14 Vert. on 1 or 2 sides (1c, 2c, 10c, 55c), 13x14½ (#867F)

1996-98 — Litho.

867A A288 1c multicolored .20 .20
867B A288 2c multicolored .20 .20
867C A288 10c multicolored .20 .20
867D A288 20c multicolored .20 .20
867E A288 40c multicolored .20 .20
867F A288 (45c) multicolored .40 .25
n. Booklet pane of 10 3.00
Complete booklet, #867Fn 3.00
o. Souvenir sheet of 1 .55 .55
867G A288 50c multicolored .20 .20
867H A288 55c multicolored .50 .50
p. Strip of 5, 1c, 10c, 55c, 2 2c 1.00
867I A288 70c multicolored .25 .20
867J A288 90c multicolored .35 .20
867K A288 1r multicolored .35 .20
867L A288 2r multicolored .75 .20
867M A288 5r multicolored 1.75 .85

Perf. 14x14¼ Syncopated

867Q A288 20c multicolored .20 .20
867R A288 (45c) multicolored .50 .40
867S A288 50c multicolored .40 .25
867T A288 60c multicolored .25 .20
867U A288 1r multicolored 2.75 .25

Size: 34x25mm
Perf. 14¾ Syncopated

867V A288 20r multicolored 7.00 3.50

No. 867Fn is inscribed in sheet margin for ExpoScience Internationale '97, and sold for 1r.

No. 867Hp has tab showing Reader's Digest emblem and release date in either green or orange.
Issued: #867Hp, 8/1; #867F, 7/7/97.

First Postal Services in South Africa, 190th Anniv. A289

Designs: 45c, Dragoons, Cape Town-False Bay Route. 65c, Ox train, Cape Town-Stellenbosch. 85c, Khoi-Khoin runners. 1.05r, Post riders, Cape Town-eastern districts.

1993, Oct. 8 — Perf. 14x14½

868 A289 45c multicolored .30 .30
869 A289 65c multicolored .45 .40
870 A289 85c multicolored .55 .50
871 A289 1.05r multicolored .70 .65
Nos. 868-871 (4) 2.00 1.85

Tourism A290

a, Namaqualand. b, North Beach, Durban. c, Lion. d, Apple Express. e, Oryx gazella.

1993, Nov. 12 — Litho. Perf. 14½x14

872 A290 85c Strip of 5, #a.-e. 3.25 3.25

Export Fruits A291

1994, Jan. 28 — Litho. Perf. 14½x14

873 A291 85c Grapes .60 .50
874 A291 90c Apples .65 .55
875 A291 1.05r Plums .75 .60
876 A291 1.25r Oranges .95 .75
877 A291 1.40r Avocados 1.10 .85
Nos. 873-877 (5) 4.05 3.25

A souvenir sheet of 1 #873 was sold for 3r by the Philatelic Foundation of South Africa.

Peace and Goodwill — A292

Childrens' drawings: 45c, Smiling faces, by Nicole Davies. 70c, Dove flying toward olive tree, by Robynne Lawrie. 95c, Three girls, dove, scattered cartridge cases, by Batami Nothmann. 1.15r, Faces surrounding "peace," by Karen Uys.

1994, Apr. 8 — Litho. Perf. 14½x14

878 A292 45c multicolored .30 .25
879 A292 70c multicolored .45 .40
880 A292 95c multicolored .60 .55
881 A292 1.15r multicolored .70 .65
a. Souvenir sheet of 4 .55 .55
Nos. 878-881 (4) 2.05 1.85

No. 881a was issued 8/97, sold for 1.15r and is inscribed "Chernobyl's Children, a decade later 1986-1996" in margin.

Inauguration of Pres. Nelson Mandela — A293

Perf. 14x14½, 14½x14

1994, May 10 — Litho.

882 A293 45c shown .30 .25
883 A293 70c Anthems, horiz. .50 .40
884 A293 75c Flag, horiz. .70 .55
885 A293 1.15r Union Bldgs., horiz. .85 .65
Nos. 882-885 (4) 2.35 1.85

Tugboats — A294

1994, May 13 — Perf. 14½x14

886 A294 45c TS McEwen .30 .25
887 A294 70c Sir William Hoy .45 .40
888 A294 95c Sir Charles Elliott .60 .55
889 A294 1.15r Eland .75 .65
890 A294 1.35r Pioneer .85 .75
a. Souvenir sheet of 5, #886-890 3.25 3.25
Nos. 886-890 (5) 2.95 2.60

Our Family — A295

Children's paintings: a, Mother Hands Out Work (C1.5). b, My Friends and I at Play (C2.5). c, Family Life (C3.5). d, Sunday in Church (C4.5). e, I Visit My Brother in the Hospital (C5.5).

1994, July 10   Litho.   Perf. 14x14½
891 A295 45c Strip of 5, #a.-e.   1.50 1.50

Stamp Day — A296

1994, Sept. 30   Litho.   Perf. 14
892 A296 50c Bulk mail   .30   .30
893 A296 70c Proof of delivery   .40   .40
894 A296 95c Registered mail   .55   .55
895 A296 1.15r Express delivery   .65   .65
        Nos. 892-895 (4)   1.90 1.90

Heather — A297

Designs: a, Erica tenuifolia. b, Erica urnaviridis. c, Erica decora. d, Erica aristata. e, Erica dichrus.

1994, Nov. 18   Litho.   Perf. 14
896 A297 95c Strip of 5, #a.-e.   3.25 3.25

Tourism — A298

#897, Phacochoerus aethiopicus, Eastern, Transvaal Province. #898, Lost City, Sun City, North West Province. #899, Ceratotherium simum, KwaZulu/Natal Province. #900, Waterfront, Cape Town, Western Cape Province. #901, Adansonia digitata, Northern Transvaal Province. #902, Highland Route, Free State. #903, Augrabies Falls, Northern Cape Province. #904, Addo Elephant Natl. Park, Eastern Cape Province. #905, Union Buildings, Pretoria, Gauteng.
    Illustration reduced.

1995-97   Litho.   Perf. 14
897 A298 50c multicolored   .30   .30
898 A298 50c multicolored   .30   .30
899 A298 (60c) multicolored   .35   .35
900 A298 (60c) multicolored   .35   .35
901 A298 (60c) multicolored   .35   .35
  a.   #901 + label, perf. 14 on one
        side   .55   .55
  b.   Souvenir sheet of 1   .55   .55
902 A298 (60c) multicolored   .35   .35
903 A298 (60c) multicolored   .35   .35
904 A298 (60c) multicolored   .35   .35
905 A298 (60c) multicolored   .35   .35
  a.   Strip of 5, #901-905   1.75 1.75
        Nos. 897-905 (9)   3.05 3.05

#901a sold for 70c; #901b for 1.10r on date of issue.

Issued: #897, 1/18; #898, 2/15; #899, 4/28; #900, 5/12; #901-905, 6/30; #901a, 2/97; #901b 8/97.

South African Airforce, 75th Anniv. — A299

DeHavilland DH-9 biplane, Cheetah D fighter.

1995, Feb. 1   Litho.   Perf. 14
906 A299 50c multicolored   .30   .30

First Trans-Africa Flight, 75th Anniv. — A300

Vickers Vimy bomber Silver Queen, map of route.

1995, Feb. 1
907 A300 95c multicolored   .55   .55

South Africa, 1995 Rugby World Cup Champions A301

Designs: No. 908, Shown. No. 909, Player running with ball, vert. No. 910, Player holding trophy, vert. No. 911, Like #908, World Champions. No. 912, Scrum, two players.

1995   Litho.   Perf. 14
908 A301 (60c) multicolored   .30   .30
  a.   Perf. 14 horiz.   .30   .30
909 A301 (60c) multicolored   .30   .30
  a.   Souvenir sheet of 1   .50   .50
  b.   Perf. 14 vert.   .30   .30
  c.   Booklet pane, 5 each #908a,
        909b   3.00
        Complete booklet, #909c   3.00
  d.   Booklet pane, 10 #909b   3.00
        Complete booklet, #909d   3.00
910 A301 (60c) multicolored   .30   .30
911 A301 (60c) multicolored   .30   .30
        Size: 68x26mm
912 A301 1.15r multicolored   .55   .55
        Nos. 908-912 (5)   1.75 1.75

Issued: #910-911, 6/28; others 5/25.

CSIR (Council for Scientific and Industrial Research), 50th Anniv. A302

1995, June 15
913 A302 (60c) Purifying water   .35   .35

Marine Science in South Africa, Cent. A303

1995, Aug. 25   Litho.   Perf. 14
914 A303 (60c) Dr. JDF Gilchrist   .35   .35

Souvenir Sheet

Singapore '95 — A304

Illustration reduced.

1995, Sept. 1
915 A304 (60c) multicolored   .35   .35

Masakhane Campaign A305

1995   Perf. 14x14¼
916 A305 (60c) multicolored   .35   .35
  a.   Booklet pane of 10   3.50
        Complete booklet, No. 916a   3.50
        **Booklet Stamp
        Size: 29x20mm**
916B A305 (60c) multicolored
  c.   Booklet pane of 10
        Complete booklet, #916c

Issued: #916, 9/16; #916B, 12/1.

Visit of Pope John Paul II — A306   Mahatma Gandhi — A307

1995, Sept. 16   Perf. 14
917 A306 (60c) multicolored   .35   .35

1995, Oct. 2
Designs: (60c), 1906 Photograph. 1.40r, Ghandhi in later years.

918 A307 (60c) blue   .35   .35
  a.   Souvenir sheet of 1   .50   .50
919 A307 1.40r brown   .80   .80
  a.   Souvenir sheet of 1   .80   .80

No. 918a is inscribed in sheet margin for 50th anniv. of Congress Alliance for Democratic South Africa. Issued July 1997.
    Design on stamp in No. 919a extends to perforations.
    See India Nos. 1534-1535.

World Post Day — A308

1995
920 A308 (60c) multicolored   .35   .35
        **Size: 65x60mm
        Imperf**
921 A308 5r multicolored   3.00 3.00

Stampex '95.
Issued: (60c), 10/9; 5r, 10/19.

UN, 50th Anniv. A309

1995, Oct. 24   Litho.   Perf. 14
922 A309 (60c) multicolored   .35   .35

Souvenir Sheet

UNESCO, 50th Anniv. — A310

Illustration reduced.

1995, Oct. 24
923 A310 (60c) multicolored   .35   .35

Shells — A311   A312

1995, Nov. 24
924 A311 (60c) Afrivoluta priglei   .35   .35
925 A311 (60c) Lyria africana   .35   .35
926 A311 (60c) Marginella mosai-
                 ca   .35   .35
927 A311 (60c) Conus pictus   .35   .35
928 A311 (60c) Gypreaea fultoni   .35   .35
  a.   Strip of 5, #924-928   1.75 1.75

1996, Jan. 8   Litho.   Perf. 14
1996 African Cup of Nations Soccer Championships: Nos. 929-933, Various soccer plays, map of Africa. No. 934, Player in traditional uniform.

        Color of "RSA"
929 A312 (60c) blue   .35   .35
930 A312 (60c) yellow   .35   .35
931 A312 (60c) red   .35   .35
932 A312 (60c) gray   .35   .35
933 A312 (60c) green   .35   .35
  a.   Strip of 5, Nos. 929-933   1.75 1.75
        Souvenir Sheet
934 A312 (1.15r) multicolored   .65   .65

South African Victory in African Nations Soccer Championship A312a

1996, Feb. 8   Litho.   Perf. 14½x14
934A A312a (60c) multicolored   .30   .30

City of Bloemfontein, 150th Anniv. — A313

1996, Mar. 28 Litho. Perf. 14
935 A313 (60c) multicolored .30 .30

Souvenir Sheet

New Year 1996 (Year of the Rat) — A313a

Illustration reduced.

1996, May 18 Litho. Perf. 14
940D A313a 60c multicolored .25 .25

CHINA '96.

Man in a Donkey Cart, by Gerard Sekoto (1913-93) — A314

Paintings: #942, 2r, Song of the Pick. #943, 2r, Yellow Houses, Sophiatown, 1940, vert.

1996, June 1 Litho. Perf. 14
941 A314 1r multicolored .55 .55
942 A314 2r multicolored 1.10 1.10

Souvenir Sheet
943 A314 2r multicolored 1.10 1.10

Youth Day — A315

1996, June 8
944 A315 (60c) multicolored .30 .30

Comrades Marathon, 75th Anniv. — A316

1996, June 8 Litho. Perf. 14
945 A316 (60c) multicolored .30 .30

Souvenir Sheet

Parliament Building, Toronto — A316a

Illustration reduced.

1996, June 8 Litho. Perf. 14
945A A316a 2r multicolored .85 .85

CAPEX '96.

A317 A318

1996 Summer Olympic Games, Atlanta: No. 946: a, Cycling. b, Swimming. c, Boxing. d, Running. e, Pole vault.
1.40r, South African Olympic emblem.

1996, July 5 Litho. Perf. 14½x14
946 A317 (70c) Strip of 5, #a.-e. 1.75 1.75
Perf. 14
947 A317 1.40r multicolored .65 .65
No. 946 was issued in sheets of 10 stamps.

1996, Aug. 1 Litho. Perf. 14
Background color: a, Vermilion & multi. b, Deep blue & multi. c, Deep yellow & multi. d, Bright blue & multi. e, Red & multi.
948 Strip of 5 1.75 1.75
a.-e. A318 (70c) any single .35 .35
New Democratic Constitution.

South African Merchant Marine, 50th Anniv. — A319

Paintings of ships, by Peter Bilas: No. 949: a, Sea Pioneer. b, SA Winterberg. No. 950: a, Langloof. b, SA Vaal. 2r, Constantia.

1996, Aug. 5 Litho. Perf. 14
949 Pair .70 .70
a.-b. A319 (70c) any single .35 .35
950 Pair 1.40 1.40
a.-b. A319 1.40r any single .70 .70
Souvenir Sheet
950C A319 2r multicolored 1.00 1.00
No. 950C contains one 72x30mm stamp.

A320

A321

1996, Aug. 9 Litho. Perf. 14
951 A320 70c multicolored .35 .35
Natl. Women's Day.

1996, Oct. 9
952 A321 70c multicolored .35 .35
World Post Day.

Christmas — A322

1996, Oct. 9
953 A322 70c multicolored .35 .35
No. 953 exists in a privately produced souvenir, sold at 2r for charitable purposes.

Souvenir Sheet

Bloemfontein, 150th Natl. Stamp Show — A323

Illustration reduced.

1996, Oct. 9 Litho. Perf. 14½x14
954 A323 2r multicolored 1.00 1.00

South African Nobel Laureates, Death Cent. of Alfred Nobel — A324

a, Max Theiler, medicine, 1951. b, Albert Luthuli, peace, 1960. c, Alfred Nobel (1833-96). d, Allan Cormack, medicine, 1979. e, Aaron Klug, chemistry, 1982. f, Desmond Tutu, peace, 1984. g, Nadine Gordimer, literature, 1991. h, Symbol for Nobel Prizes 1901-96. i, Nelson R. Mandela, peace, 1993. j, F.W. de Klerk, peace, 1993.

1996, Nov. 4
955 A324 (70c) Sheet of 10, #a.- 3.50 3.50
j.
k. Souvenir sheet, #955c .40 .40

First Motor Car in South Africa, Cent. — A325

1997, Jan. 4 Litho. Perf. 14
956 A325 (70c) multicolored .35 .35

Souvenir Sheet

Hong Kong '97 — A326

Perf. 14 Syncopated
1997, Feb. 12 Litho.
957 A326 3r multicolored 1.60 1.60

Natl. Water Week and Water Day — A328

Save water for: No. 959, Farming. No. 960, Gardening. No. 961, Health. No. 962, Housing. No. 963, For all.

Perf. 14 Syncopated on 2 or 3 Sides
1997, Mar. 22 Litho.
Booklet Stamps
959 A328 (70c) multicolored .50 .50
960 A328 (70c) multicolored .50 .50
961 A328 (70c) multicolored .50 .50
962 A328 (70c) multicolored .50 .50
963 A328 (70c) multicolored .50 .50
a. Booklet pane, 2 each #959-963 5.00
Complete booklet 5.00

Perf. 14x14¼ on 2 or 3 Sides
1997, Mar. Litho.
Booklet Stamps
963B A328 (70c) Like #959 .50 .50
963C A328 (70c) Like #960 .50 .50
963D A328 (70c) Like #961 .50 .50
963E A328 (70c) Like #962 .50 .50
963F A328 (70c) Like #963 .50 .50
g. Bklt. pane, 2 ea #963B-963F 5.00
Complete booklet, #963Fg 5.00

South African Navy, 75th Anniv. — A329

Warships: No. 964, Strike craft SAS Kobie Coetsee. No. 965, Survey ship SAS Protea. No. 966, Mine counter-measures ship SAS Umkomaas. No. 967, Submarine Emily Hobhouse, anti-submarine frigate SAS President Pretorius.

1997, Apr. 1 Perf. 14 Syncopated
964 A329 (70c) multicolored .35 .35
965 A329 (70c) multicolored .35 .35
966 A329 (70c) multicolored .35 .35
967 A329 (70c) multicolored .35 .35
a. Block of 4, #964-967 1.40 1.40

First Democratic Elections, 5th Anniv. — A330

People voting, signs saying: No. 968, "Election Day, 27, April, 1994." No. 969, "Polling Station." No. 970, "Register Here." No. 971, "Vote Here." No. 972, "Ballot Box."

Perf. 14 Syncopated

1997, Apr. 26					**Litho.**
968	A330	(70c)	black & red	.50	.50
969	A330	(70c)	black & red	.50	.50
970	A330	(70c)	black & red	.50	.50
971	A330	(70c)	black & red	.50	.50
972	A330	(70c)	black & red	.50	.50
b.	Strip of 5, #968-972			2.50	2.50

Souvenir Sheet

New Year 1997 (Year of the
Ox) — A330a

Illustration reduced.

1997, May 2		**Litho.**		**Perf. 14**	
972A	A330a	4.50r multicolored		2.25	2.25

SAPDA '97.

A331   A332

Cultural Artifacts.

1997, May 18					**Perf. 14**
973	A331	(70c)	Zulu baskets	.35	.35
974	A331	(70c)	S. Sotho figure	.35	.35
975	A331	(70c)	S. Ndebele figure	.35	.35
976	A331	(70c)	Venda door	.35	.35
977	A331	(70c)	Tsonga medicine gourd	.35	.35
978	A331	(70c)	Wooden pot, N. cape	.35	.35
979	A331	(70c)	Khoi walking stick	.35	.35
980	A331	(70c)	Tswana knife handle	.35	.35
981	A331	(70c)	Xhosa pipe	.35	.35
982	A331	(70c)	Swazi vessel	.35	.35
a.	Sheet of 10, #973-982			3.50	3.50

1997, Dec.					**Perf. 14x15**
973a			Zulu baskets	.50	.50
974a			S. Sotho figure	.50	.50
975a			S. Ndebele figure	.50	.50
976a			Venda door	.50	.50
977a			Tsonga medicine gourd	.50	.50
978a			Wooden pot, N. cape	.50	.50
979a			Khoi walking stick	.50	.50
980a			Tswana knife handle	.50	.50
981a			Xhosa pipe	.50	.50
982a			Swazi vessel	.50	.50
982b			Bklt. pane, #973a-981a, 982b	5.00	
	Complete booklet, 2 #982c			10.00	

1997, June 5					**Perf. 14**
Birds.					
983	A332	(70c)	White-breasted cormorant	.35	.35
984	A332	(70c)	Hammerkop	.35	.35
985	A332	(70c)	Pied kingfisher	.35	.35
986	A332	(70c)	Purple heron	.35	.35
987	A332	(70c)	Black-headed heron	.35	.35
988	A332	(70c)	Darter	.35	.35
989	A332	(70c)	Green-backed heron	.35	.35
990	A332	(70c)	White-faced duck	.35	.35
a.	Souvenir sheet of 1			.55	.55
991	A332	(70c)	Saddle-billed stork	.35	.35
992	A332	(70c)	Water dikkop	.35	.35
a.	Sheet of 10, #983-992			3.50	3.50

No. 990a, issued 7/11/97, is inscribed in
sheet margin for JUNASS '97, and sold for 2r.

Grocott's, Muirhead & Gowie
Buildings, Grahamstown — A333

Illustration reduced.

1997, May 29		**Litho.**		**Perf. 14**	
993	A333	5r multicolored		3.00	3.00

PACIFIC 97.

Indigenous
Cattle
A335

Perf. 14½ Syncopated

1997, Aug. 10					
999	A335	(70c)	Nguni	.50	.50
1000	A335	(70c)	Bonsmara	.50	.50
1001	A335	(70c)	Afrikander	.50	.50
1002	A335	(70c)	Drakensberger	.50	.50
a.	Block of 4, #999-1002			2.00	2.00

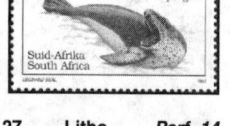

Antarctic
Wildlife
A336

1997, Aug. 27		**Litho.**		**Perf. 14**	
1003	A336	(70c)	Leopard seal	.40	.40
1004	A336	1.20r	Antarctic skua	.65	.65
1005	A336	1.70r	King penguin	.90	.90
	Nos. 1003-1005 (3)			1.95	1.95

Enoch Sontonga (1873-1905), Author
of Africa's Natl. Anthem — A337

Perf. 14 Syncopated

1997, Sept. 24					**Litho.**
1006	A337	(70c)	shown	.50	.50
1007	A337	(70c)	"Nkosi Sikelel iAfrika"	.50	.50
a.	Pair, #1006-1007			1.00	1.00

Heritage Day.

Souvenir Sheet

Cape Town '97 Natl. Stamp
Show — A338

1997, Oct. 8					**Perf. 14**
1008	A338	4.50r multicolored		2.25	2.25

Souvenir Sheet

World Post Day — A339

1997, Oct. 9				**Perf. 14 Syncopated**	
1009	A339	(70c)	multicolored	.70	.70

No. 1009 sold for 1r on day of issue.

SANTA (South
African Natl.
Tuberculosis Assoc.,
50th Anniv. — A340

Designs featuring former Christmas seals:
No. 1010, Bethlehem. No. 1011, Candles on
each side of Cross of Lorraine. No. 1012, Candles, angels, Cross. No. 1013, Cross, angel
kneeling. No. 1014, Santa carrying Cross. No.
1015, Madonna and Child, Cross. No. 1016,
Christmas trees. No. 1017, Magi. No. 1018,
Bell, stained glass window. No. 1019, Native
African kneeling, flag.

1997, Nov. 3				**Perf. 14 Syncopated**	
1010	A340	(70c)	multicolored	.50	.50
1011	A340	(70c)	multicolored	.50	.50
1012	A340	(70c)	multicolored	.50	.50
1013	A340	(70c)	multicolored	.50	.50
1014	A340	(70c)	multicolored	.50	.50
1015	A340	(70c)	multicolored	.50	.50
1016	A340	(70c)	multicolored	.50	.50
1017	A340	(70c)	multicolored	.50	.50
1018	A340	(70c)	multicolored	.50	.50
1019	A340	(70c)	multicolored	.50	.50
a.	Sheet of 10, #1010-1019			5.00	5.00

Souvenir Sheet

New Year 1998 (Year of the
Tiger) — A341

Illustration reduced.

1998, Jan. 28		**Litho.**		**Perf. 14x14½**	
1020	A341	5r multicolored		2.50	2.50

Natl. Sea
Rescue
Institute
A342

1998, Feb. 11				**Perf. 14 Syncopated**	
1021	A342	(70c)	multicolored	.50	.50

Fauna (no
frame) — A343

5c, Giant girdle-tailed lizard. 10c, Geometric
tortoise. 20c, Southern African hedgehog.
30c, Spotted hyena. 40c, Riverine rabbit. 50c,
Samango monkey. 60c, Cape hunting dog.
70c, Roan antelope. 80c, Kori bustard. 90c,
Jackass penguin. 1r, Wattled crane. #1032,
Impala. #1033, Waterbuck. #1034, Blue wilde-
beest. #1035, Eland. #1036, Kudu. #1037,
Black rhinoceros. #1038, White rhinoceros.
#1039, Buffalo. #1040, Lion. #1041, Leopard.
#1042, African elephant. #1044, Giraffe. 1.50r,
Tawny eagle, vert. 2r, Blue swallow. 2.30r,
Cape vulture, vert. 5r, Martial eagle. 10r,
Bataleur. 20r, Fish eagle.

Perf. 14x14¼, 14x14¼, 14¼x14 Syncopated (#1043), 14x14¼ Syncopated on 2 or 3 Sides (#1036B-1036F, 1042B-1042F)

1998-2000					**Litho.**
1021A	A343	5c multi		.20	.20
1022	A343	10c multi		.20	.20
1023	A343	20c multi		.20	.20
1024	A343	30c multi		.20	.20
1025	A343	40c multi		.20	.20
1026	A343	50c multi		.20	.20
1027	A343	60c multi		.20	.20
1028	A343	70c multi		.20	.20
1029	A343	80c multi		.30	.30
1030	A343	90c multi		.30	.30
1031	A343	1r multi		.30	.30
1032	A343	(1.10r) multi, vert.		.55	.55
1033	A343	(1.10r) multi, vert.		.55	.55
1034	A343	(1.10r) multi, vert.		.55	.55
1035	A343	(1.10r) multi, vert.		.55	.55
1036	A343	(1.10r) multi, vert.		.55	.55
a.	Strip of 5, #1032-1036			2.75	2.75
h.	Booklet pane, 2 each #1032-1036, "Standard" 5mm long			5.50	
	Booklet, #1036h			5.50	
1036B	A343	(1.10r) Like #1034		.35	.35
1036C	A343	(1.10r) Like #1035		.35	.35
1036D	A343	(1.10r) Like #1036		.35	.35
1036E	A343	(1.10r) Like #1032		.35	.35
1036F	A343	(1.10r) Like #1033		.35	.35
g.	Booklet pane, 2 each #1036B-1036F			3.50	
	Booklet, #1036Fg			3.50	
1037	A343	(1.10r) multi		.35	.35
a.	Booklet pane of 10			3.50	
	Complete bklt. #1037a			3.50	
1038	A343	(1.30r) multi		.45	.45
1039	A343	(1.30r) multi		.45	.45
1040	A343	(1.30r) multi		.45	.45
1041	A343	(1.30r) multi		.45	.45
1042	A343	(1.30r) multi		.45	.45
a.	Booklet pane, 2 ea #1038-1042			4.50	
	Complete bklt. #1042a			4.50	
1042B	A343	(1.30r) Like #1038		.45	.45
1042C	A343	(1.30r) Like #1039		.45	.45
1042D	A343	(1.30r) Like #1040		.45	.45
1042E	A343	(1.30r) Like #1041		.45	.45
1042F	A343	(1.30r) Like #1042		.45	.45
g.	Booklet pane, 2 each #1042B-1042F			4.50	
	Complete bklt. #1042Fg			4.50	
1043	A343	2r multi		.65	.65
1043A	A343	2r multi		.65	.65
1044	A343	3r multi		1.00	1.00
1045	A343	5r multi		1.75	1.75

Size: 20x38mm
Perf. 14¼x13¾

1045A	A343	1.50r multi		.50	.50
1045B	A343	2.30r multi		.75	.75

Size: 35x25mm
Perf. 14¼x14

1046	A343	10r multi		3.25	3.25
a.	Perf. 14¾			3.25	3.25

Perf. 14¾ Syncopated

1047	A343	20r multi		6.25	6.25
	Nos. 1021A-1047 (40)			26.65	26.65

Self-adhesive
Litho.
Die Cut Perf. 13x12¾

1048	A343	(1.10r) like #1033		.55	.55
1049	A343	(1.10r) like #1032		.55	.55
1050	A343	(1.10r) like #1036		.55	.55
1051	A343	(1.10r) like #1035		.55	.55
1052	A343	(1.10r) like #1034		.55	.55
a.	Strip of 5, #1048-1052			2.75	
h.	Booklet, 2 each #1048-1052			5.50	

Booklet Stamps
Self-Adhesive
Serpentine Die Cut 11x11¼

1052B	A343	(1.30r) Like #1035		.40	.40
1052C	A343	(1.30r) Like #1036		.40	.40
1052D	A343	(1.30r) Like #1032		.40	.40
1052E	A343	(1.30r) Like #1034		.40	.40

1052F A343 (1.30r) Like #1033 .40 .40
  g. Booklet pane, 2 each
    #1052B-1052F 4.00

Nos. 1038-1042F are inscribed "Airmail Postcard."

"Standard" on Nos. 1032-1036, 1036a is 5½mm long.

Nos. 1042B-1042F are booklet stamps. No. 1052Fg is a complete booklet. Nos. 1036B-1036F were issued in a booklet.

Issued: #1037, 1/98; 10c, 40c, 50c, 70c, 90c, 1r, 1/16/98; #1038-1042, 4/98; #1036B-1036F, 5/18/98; 3r, 6/24/98; 20c, 6/25/98; #1032-1036, 1048-1052, 5/18/98; 10r, 20r, 9/21/98; 1046a, 10/28/98; #1043A, 1/9/99; #1052B-1052F, 12/99; 1.50r, 2.30r, 6/5/00; 5c, 7/4/00.

Souvenir Sheet

Leopard — A344

Illustration reduced.

1998, May 1   **Perf. 14**
1053 A344 5r multicolored 2.50 2.50
SAPDA '98 Stamp Show, Johannesburg.

A345   A346

1998, June 8
1054 A345 (1.10r) multicolored .55 .55
1998 World Cup Soccer Championships, France. No. 1054 was issued in sheets of 10.

1998, June 28   **Perf. 14x14½**
Early South African History: #1055, Early stone age hand axe. #1056, Musuku. #1057, San rock engravings. #1058, Early iron age pots. #1059, Khoekhoe pot. #1060, Florisbad skull. #1061, San rock art. #1062, Mapungubwe gold. #1063, Lydenburg head. #1064, Taung child.
1055 A346 (1.10r) multicolored .40 .40
1056 A346 (1.10r) multicolored .40 .40
1057 A346 (1.10r) multicolored .40 .40
1058 A346 (1.10r) multicolored .40 .40
1059 A346 (1.10r) multicolored .40 .40
1060 A346 (1.10r) multicolored .40 .40
1061 A346 (1.10r) multicolored .40 .40
1062 A346 (1.10r) multicolored .40 .40
1063 A346 (1.10r) multicolored .40 .40
1064 A346 (1.10r) multicolored .40 .40
  a. Sheet of 10, #1055-1064 4.00 4.00
  a. Booklet, 2 #1064a 8.00

Raptors — A347

Designs: No. 1065, Pale chanting goshawk. No. 1066, Jackal buzzard. No. 1067, Lanner falcon. No. 1068, Bearded vulture. No. 1069, Black harrier. No. 1070, Cape vulture. No. 1071, Bateleur. No. 1072, Spotted eagle owl. No. 1073, White-headed vulture. No. 1074, African fish eagle.

1998, Aug. 16   **Perf. 14x15**
1065 A347 (1.10r) multicolored .40 .40
1066 A347 (1.10r) multicolored .40 .40
1067 A347 (1.10r) multicolored .40 .40
1068 A347 (1.10r) multicolored .40 .40
1069 A347 (1.10r) multicolored .40 .40
1070 A347 (1.10r) multicolored .40 .40
1071 A347 (1.10r) multicolored .40 .40
1072 A347 (1.10r) multicolored .40 .40
1073 A347 (1.10r) multicolored .40 .40
1074 A347 (1.10r) multicolored .40 .40
  a. Sheet of 10, #1065-1074 4.00 4.00
  b. Booklet pane, #1065-1074 4.00
    Complete booklet, 2 #1074b +
    2 prepaid postcards 9.75

Vert. and horiz. perforations extend to top, bottom and right edges of sheet on No. 1074a, but do not on No. 1074b.

Natl. Arbor Week A348

Trees: No. 1075, Baobab. No. 1076, Umbrella thorn. No. 1077, Shepherd's tree. No. 1078, Karee.

1998, Sept. 4   **Litho.**   **Perf. 13¾x14**
1075 A348 (1.10r) multi .40 .40
1076 A348 (1.10r) multi .40 .40
1077 A348 (1.10r) multi .40 .40
1078 A348 (1.10r) multi .40 .40
  a. Block of 4, #1075-1078 1.60 1.60

Christmas — A349

1998, Oct. 9   **Litho.**   **Perf. 14x15**
1079 A349 (1.10r) Angel .40 .40
1080 A349 (1.10r) Bell .40 .40
1081 A349 (1.10r) Package .40 .40
1082 A349 (1.10r) Christmas tree .40 .40
1083 A349 (1.10r) Star .40 .40
  a. Strip of 5, #1079-1083 2.00 2.00

Souvenir Sheet

World Post Day — A351

Illustration reduced.

1998, Oct. 9   **Litho.**   **Perf. 14x14½**
1089 A351 5r multicolored 1.75 1.75

Souvenir Sheet

ILSAPEX 1998, Midrand, South Africa — A352

Designs of unissued stamps created for 1927 definitive series in colors of: a, Red and green. b, Green and black.

1998, Oct. 20   **Litho.**   **Perf. 14½x14¼**
1090 A352 5r Sheet of 2, #a.-b. 3.50 3.50

Souvenir Sheet

Whales — A354

Illustration reduced.

1998, Oct. 23   **Litho.**   **Perf. 13½x14**
1095 A354 5r multicolored 1.75 1.75
See Namibia #919, Norfolk Island #665.

Souvenir Sheet

Clover SA Limited, 100th Anniv. — A354a

Illustration reduced.

1998, Nov. 15   **Litho.**   **Perf. 14¼x14**
1095A A354a (1.10r) multicolored .40 .40

Universal Declaration of Human Rights, 50th Anniv. — A355

1998, Dec. 9   **Perf. 14¼**
1096 A355 (1.10r) multicolored .40 .40

UPU, 125th Anniv. — A356

Designs: No. 1097, Dennis Royal Mail vehicle, 1913. No. 1098, Ford V8 Mail van, 1935. No. 1099, Mobile post office, 1937. No. 1100, Trojan post office van, 1927.

1999, Feb. 15   **Litho.**   **Perf. 13¾x14**
1097 A356 (1.10r) multi .35 .35
1098 A356 (1.10r) multi .35 .35
1099 A356 (1.10r) multi .35 .35
1100 A356 (1.10r) multi .35 .35
  a. Block of 4, #1097-1100 1.40 1.40

New Year 1999 (Year of the Rabbit) — A357

Illustration reduced.

1999, Feb. 16   **Litho.**   **Perf. 14x13½**
1101 A357 5r multicolored 1.75 1.75

Ships of the Southern Oceans — A358

1999, Mar. 19   **Litho.**   **Perf. 13¾x14**
1102 A358 (1.10r) Endeavour .35 .35
1103 A358 (1.10r) HMS Beagle .35 .35
1104 A358 (1.10r) Discovery .35 .35
1105 A358 (1.10r) Heemskerck .35 .35
  a. Block of 4, #1102-1105 1.40 1.40

Souvenir Sheet
Perf. 13¾
1106 A358   5r Lawhill, vert. 1.60 1.60
Australia 99 World Stamp Expo (No. 1106).

AIDS Awareness — A359

Perf. 14¼x14 on 3 sides
1999, Apr. 1
1107 A359 (1.20r) purple & multi .40 .40
1108 A359 (1.20r) green & multi .40 .40
  a. Booklet pane, 5 each #1107-
    1108 4.00
    Complete booklet, #1108a 4.00

Souvenir Sheets

IBRA '99, Nuremberg, Germany — A360

Illustration reduced.

1999, Apr. 27   **Perf. 14¼x14**
1109 A360 5r multi 1.60 1.60

SAPDA '99, Johannesburg — A361

Illustration reduced.

1999, Apr. 30   Perf. 13¾
1110 A361 5r multi   1.60 1.60

A362   A363

1999, May 1   Perf. 14x14¾
1111 A362 (1.20r) Nurse   .40 .40
1112 A362 (1.20r) Washerwoman   .40 .40
1113 A362 (1.20r) Lumberjack   .40 .40
1114 A362 (1.20r) Tree planter   .40 .40
1115 A362 (1.20r) Cook   .40 .40
1116 A362 (1.20r) Fisherman   .40 .40
1117 A362 (1.20r) Construction
                       worker   .40 .40
1118 A362 (1.20r) Miner   .40 .40
1119 A362 (1.20r) Mailman   .40 .40
1120 A362 (1.20r) Jackhammerer   .40 .40
   a.   Sheet of 10, #1111-1120   4.00 4.00

Labor Day.

1999, June 16   Perf. 14x14¼
1121 A363 (1.20r) multi   .40 .40

Inauguration of Pres. Thabo Mbeki.

Souvenir Sheet

Order of St. John, 900th
Anniv. — A364

Illustration reduced.

1999, June 23   Perf. 14x14¾
1122 A364 2r multi   .65 .65

Standard Bank
Arts Festival, 25th
Anniv. — A365

1999, June 29   Perf. 14x14¼
1123 A365 (1.20r) shown   .40 .40
1124 A365 (1.20r) Film   .40 .40
1125 A365 (1.20r) Music   .40 .40
1126 A365 (1.20r) Mask, diff.   .40 .40
1127 A365 (1.20r) Painter   .40 .40
   a.   Strip of 5, #1123-1127   2.00 2.00

Traditional
Wall
Art — A366

1999, Aug. 8   Perf. 13¼x13¾
1128 A366 (1.20r) North Ndebele .40 .40
1129 A366 (1.20r) South Ndebele .40 .40
1130 A366 (1.20r) Swazi   .40 .40
1131 A366 (1.20r) Venda   .40 .40
1132 A366 (1.20r) South Sotho   .40 .40
1133 A366 (1.20r) Xhosa   .40 .40
1134 A366 (1.20r) North Sotho   .40 .40

1135 A366 (1.20r) Tsonga   .40 .40
1136 A366 (1.20r) Zulu   .40 .40
1137 A366 (1.20r) Tswana   .40 .40
   a.   Sheet of 10, #1128-1137   4.00 4.00

Souvenir Sheet

China 1999 World Philatelic
Exhibition — A367

1999, Aug. 21   Perf. 14x13¼
1138 A367 5r multi   1.60 1.60

Souvenir Sheet

JOPEX '99 — A368

1999, Sept. 8 Litho. Perf. 14¼x14½
1139 A368 5r Strelitzia flower   1.60 1.60

Migratory
Animals — A369

1999, Oct. 4   Litho.   Perf. 14x14¾
1140 A369 (1.20r) Barn swallow   .40 .40
1141 A369 (1.20r) Great white
                       shark   .40 .40
1142 A369 (1.20r) Lesser kestrel .40 .40
1143 A369 (1.20r) Common
                       dolphin   .40 .40
1144 A369 (1.20r) European bee-
                       eater   .40 .40
1145 A369 (1.20r) Loggerhead
                       turtle   .40 .40
1146 A369 (1.20r) Curlew sandpi-
                       per   .40 .40
1147 A369 (1.20r) Wandering al-
                       batross   .40 .40
1148 A369 (1.20r) Springbok   .40 .40
1149 A369 (1.20r) Lesser flamin-
                       go   .40 .40
   a.   Sheet of 10, #1140-1149   4.00 4.00
          Complete booklet, 2 #1149a
          (stitched in) + 2 postal cards 9.50

Complete booklet sold for 29r.

Boer
War,
Cent.
A370

1999, Oct. 11   Litho.   Perf. 13¾
1150 A370 (1.20r) Boer men, wo-
                       man   .40 .40
1151 A370 (1.20r) Soldiers, ship .40 .40
   a.   Pair, #1150-1151   .80 .80
   b.   Booklet pane, #1150-1151,
            perf. 13¼x13¾ ('02)   .95

   Issued: No. 1151b, 5/31/02. See note after
No. 1282.

Millennium — A371

2000, Jan. 1   Litho.   Perf. 13¼x13¾
1152 A371 (1.20r) multi   .40 .40

Start of
National
Lottery
A372

2000, Mar. 2   Litho.   Perf. 13¼x13¾
1153 A372 (1.20r) multi   .40 .40

Family
Day — A373

2000, Apr. 5   Litho.   Perf. 13¼
1154 A373 (1.30r) multi   .40 .40

Souvenir Sheet

The Stamp Show 2000,
London — A374

Illustration reduced.

2000, May 20   Litho.   Perf. 13¼
1155 A374 4.60r multi   1.40 1.40

Frogs and
Toads — A375

No. 1156: a, Banded stream frog. b, Yellow-
striped reed frog. c, Natal leaf-folding frog. d,
Paradise toad. e, Table Mountain ghost frog. f,
Banded rubber frog. g, Dwarf grass frog. h,
Long-toed tree frog. i, Namaqua rain frog. j,
Bubbling kassina.
   4.60r, Forest tree frog.

Perf. 13¼x13¾
2000, June 23   Litho.
1156   Sheet of 10   4.00 4.00
   a.-j. A375 1.30r Any single   .40 .40
Souvenir Sheet
       Perf. 13¼
1157 A375 4.60r multi   1.40 1.40

   Junass 2000, Boksburg (No. 1157). No.
1157 contains one 48x30mm stamp.

Medicinal
Plants — A376

No. 1158: a, Stalked bulbine. b, Wild dagga.
c, Wild garlic. d, Pig's ear. e, Wild ginger.
No. 1159: a, Red paintbrush. b, Cancer
bush. c, Yellow star flower. d, Bitter aloe. e,
Sour fig.

2000, Aug. 1   Perf. 13¾x13¾
1158   Horiz. strip of 5   2.00 2.00
   a.-e. A376 1.30r Any single   .40 .40
1159   Horiz. strip of 5   3.75 3.75
   a.-e. A376 2.30r Any single   .70 .70

2000 Summer
Olympics,
Sydney — A377

Olympic rings and: 1.30r, Flagbearer. 1.50r,
Elena Meyer of South Africa and Derartu Tulu
of Ethiopia. 2.20r, Joshua Thugwane. 2.30r,
South African flag. 6.30r, Penny Heyns.

2000, Sept. 1   Perf. 13¼x13¾
1160-1164 A377 Set of 5   4.25 4.25

Intl. Year for
the Culture
of Peace
A378

2000, Sept. 19   Litho.   Perf. 13¼
1165 A378 1.30r multi   .40 .40

World Heritage Sites — A379

Designs: No. 1166, 1.30r, Robben Island.
No. 1167, 1.30r, Greater St. Lucia Wetland
Park. No. 1168, 1.30r, Sterkfontein Fossil
Hominid Complex.

2000, Sept. 22   Perf. 13¼x13¾
1166-1168 A379 Set of 3   1.25 1.25

World Post
Day — A380

2000   Litho.   Perf. 13¼x13

1169	A380	1.30r multi	.40	.40
a.		Perf. 13¾x13 + label	.45	.45

Issued: No. 1169, 10/9; No. 1169a, 11/8. No. 1169a was issued in sheets of 20 stamps + 20 different labels depicting characters on the MTN Gladiators 3 television show that sold for 35r.

Souvenir Sheet

Year of the Dragon — A381

2000, Oct. 9   Litho.   Perf. 13½x13

1170	A381	4.60r multi	1.40 1.40

Writers of the Boer War Era — A382

Medals and: 1.30r, Sol Plaatje, Johanna Brandt. 4.40r, Sir Arthur Conan Doyle, Sir Winston Churchill.

2000, Oct. 25   Litho.   Perf. 13¼x13¾

1171-1172	A382	Set of 2	1.75	1.75
a.		Booklet pane, #1171-1172	2.25	—

Issued: No. 1172a, 5/31/02. See note after No. 1282.

A383

Fish, Flowers, Butterflies and Birds — A384

Designs: 5c, Palette surgeonfish. 10c, Blue-banded surgeonfish. 20c, Royal angelfish. 30c, Emperor angelfish. 40c, Blackbar triggerfish. 50c, Coral rockcod. 60c, Powder-blue surgeonfish. 70c, Threadfin butterflyfish. 80c, Longhorn cowfish. 90c, Longnose butterflyfish. 1r, Coral beauty. Nos. 1184, 1200, 1205, 1210, 1215, 1219A, 1220, 1225, Botterblom, vert. Nos. 1185, 1201, 1206, 1211, 1216, 1219B, 1221, 1226, Blue marguerite, vert. Nos. 1186, 1202, 1207, 1212, 1217, 1219C, 1222, 1227, Karoo violet, vert. Nos. 1187, 1203, 1208, 1213, 1218, 1219D, 1223, 1228, Tree pelargonium, vert. Nos. 1188, 1204, 1209, 1214, 1219, 1219E, 1224, 1229, Black-eyed susy, vert. 1.40r, Gold-banded forester. 1.50r, Brenton blue. 1.60r, Yellow pansy butterfly. No. 1191, Silver-barred charaxes. No. 1231, Large-spotted acraea butterfly. 2r, Lilac-breasted roller, vert. 2.10r, Koppie charaxes butterfly. 2.30r, Citrus swallowtail. 2.50r, Common grass-yellow butterfly. 3r, Woodland kingfisher, vert. 5r, White-fronted bee-eater, vert. 6.30r, Green-banded swallowtail. 7r, Southern milkweed butterfly. 10r, African green pigeon, vert. 12.60r, False dotted-border. 14r, Lilac tip butterfly. 20r, Purple-crested lourie, vert.

Non-English country name inscriptions at top: Nos. 1200, 1204, 1207, 1217, 1219A, 1219E, 1220, 1224, 1227, Afrika Borwa. Nos. 1201, 1208, 1218, 1219B, 1221, 1228, Ningizimu Afrika. Nos. 1202, 1219C, 1222, Suid-Afrika. Nos. 1203, 1219D, 1223, Afrika Tshipembe. Nos. 1205, 1215, 1225, Afrika Dzonga. Nos. 1206, 1216, 1226, Afrika Sewula. Nos. 1209, 1219, 1229, Mzantsi Afrika.

Perf. 14½x14¾, 14¾x14½

2000, Nov. 15   Litho.

1173	A383	5c multi	.20	.20
a.		Perf. 13	.20	.20
1174	A383	10c multi	.20	.20
a.		Perf. 13	.20	.20
1175	A383	20c multi	.20	.20
a.		Perf. 13	.20	.20
1176	A383	30c multi	.20	.20
a.		Perf. 13	.20	.20
1177	A383	40c multi	.20	.20
a.		Perf. 13	.20	.20
1178	A383	50c multi	.20	.20
a.		Perf. 13	.20	.20
1179	A383	60c multi	.20	.20
a.		Perf. 13	.20	.20
1180	A383	70c multi	.20	.20
a.		Perf. 13	.20	.20
1181	A383	80c multi	.25	.25
a.		Perf. 13	.25	.25
1182	A383	90c multi	.30	.30
a.		Perf. 13	.25	.25
1183	A383	1r multi	.30	.30
a.		Perf. 13	.30	.30
1184	A383	1.30r multi	.40	.40
1185	A383	1.30r multi	.40	.40
1186	A383	1.30r multi	.40	.40
1187	A383	1.30r multi	.40	.40
1188	A383	1.30r multi	.40	.40
a.		Horiz. strip of 5, #1184-1188	2.00	2.00
1189	A383	1.40r multi	.45	.45
1190	A383	1.50r multi	.50	.50
1191	A383	1.90r multi	.60	.60
1192	A383	2r multi	.65	.65
a.		Perf. 13	.65	.65
1193	A383	2.30r multi	.70	.70
a.		Perf. 13	.95	.95
1194	A383	3r multi	.95	.95
a.		Perf. 13	.95	.95
1195	A383	5r multi	1.60	1.60
a.		Perf. 13	1.60	1.60
1196	A383	6.30r multi	2.00	2.00
1197	A383	10r multi	3.00	3.00
a.		Perf. 13 ('01)	3.00	3.00
1198	A383	12.60r multi	4.00	4.00
a.		Perf. 13 ('01)	4.50	4.50
1199	A383	20r multi	6.25	6.25
a.		Perf. 13	5.00	5.00

Issued: Nos. 1197a, 1199a, 10/1/01. No. 1179a, 10/1/01. Nos. 1178a, 1192a, 1194a, 1195a, 2002. No. 1173a, 4/2/03; No. 1174a, 5/22/03; Nos. 1175a, 1181a, 9/22/03; Nos. 1176a, 1182a, 1199a, 2/27/03; Nos. 1177a, 1180a, 1183a, 9/23/03.

Types of 2000
Die Cut Perf. 13x12½ on 2 or 3 Sides

2000, Nov. 15   Litho.

Booklet Stamps
Self-Adhesive

1200	A384	1.30r multi	.40	.40
1201	A384	1.30r multi	.40	.40
1202	A384	1.30r multi	.40	.40
1203	A384	1.30r multi	.40	.40
1204	A384	1.30r multi	.40	.40
1205	A384	1.30r multi	.40	.40
1206	A384	1.30r multi	.40	.40
1207	A384	1.30r multi	.40	.40
1208	A384	1.30r multi	.40	.40
1209	A384	1.30r multi	.40	.40
a.		Booklet, #1200-1209	4.00	

2001, May 16   Litho.   Perf. 13

1210	A383	1.40r multi	.45	.45
1211	A383	1.40r multi	.45	.45
1212	A383	1.40r multi	.45	.45
1213	A383	1.40r multi	.45	.45
1214	A383	1.40r multi	.45	.45
a.		Horiz. strip of 5, #1210-1214	2.25	2.25

Coil Stamps
Self-Adhesive
Serpentine Die Cut 13½

1215	A384	(1.40r) multi	.45	.45
1216	A384	(1.40r) multi	.45	.45
1217	A384	(1.40r) multi	.45	.45
1218	A384	(1.40r) multi	.45	.45
1219	A384	(1.40r) multi	.45	.45
1219A	A384	(1.40r) multi	.45	.45
1219B	A384	(1.40r) multi	.45	.45
1219C	A384	(1.40r) multi	.45	.45
1219D	A384	(1.40r) multi	.45	.45
1219E	A384	(1.40r) multi	.45	.45
f.		Strip of 10, #1215-1219E	4.50	

Booklet Stamps
Die Cut Perf. 13x12½ on 2 or 3 Sides

1220	A384	(1.40r) multi	.45	.45
1221	A384	(1.40r) multi	.45	.45
1222	A384	(1.40r) multi	.45	.45
1223	A384	(1.40r) multi	.45	.45
1224	A384	(1.40r) multi	.45	.45
1225	A384	(1.40r) multi	.45	.45
1226	A384	(1.40r) multi	.45	.45
1227	A384	(1.40r) multi	.45	.45
1228	A384	(1.40r) multi	.45	.45
1229	A384	(1.40r) multi	.45	.45
a.		Booklet, #1220-1229	4.50	
		Nos. 1173-1229 (62)	40.40	40.40

Type of 2000

2001, June 16   Litho.   Perf. 13

1230	A383	1.60r multi	.50	.50
1231	A383	1.90r multi	.60	.60
1232	A383	2.10r multi	.65	.65
1233	A383	2.50r multi	.80	.80
1234	A383	7r multi	2.25	2.25
1235	A383	14r multi	4.50	4.50
		Nos. 1230-1235 (6)	9.30	9.30

Myths and Legends — A385

Designs: 1.30r, The Rain Bull. 1.50r, The Treasure of the Grosvenor. 2.20r, Seven Magic Birds. 2.30r, The Hole in the Wall. 6.30r, Van Hunks and the Devil.

2001, Jan. 24   Litho.   Perf. 13¾

1236-1240	A385	Set of 5	4.25 4.25

Souvenir Sheet

Hong Kong 2001 Stamp Exhibition — A386

2001, Feb. 1   Perf. 14½x14

1241	A386	4.60r Tree snake	1.40	1.40

Sports Stars A387

Designs: No. 1242, 1.40r, Ernie Els, golfer. No. 1243, 1.40r, Terence Parkin, swimmer. No. 1244, 1.40r, Hezekiel Sepeng, runner. No. 1245, 1.40r, Rosina Magola, netball player. No. 1246, 1.40r, Francois Pienaar, rugby player. No. 1247, 1.40r, Zanele Situ, javelin thrower. No. 1248, 1.40r, Hestrie Cloete, high jumper. No. 1249, 1.40r, Lucas Radebe, soccer player. No. 1250, 1.40r, Vuyani Bungu, boxer. No. 1251, 1.40r, Jonty Rhodes, cricket player.

2001, Feb. 28   Perf. 13¾x14

1242-1251	A387	Set of 10	4.50	4.50
1251a		Sheet of 15 #1251 +15 labels, perf. 14½x14	6.50	

Labels on No. 1251a depict players from the 2000-01 South African World Cup Cricket team.

Kgalagadi Transfrontier Park — A388

Designs: 1.40r, Gemsboks, flags of South Africa and Botswana. 2.50r, Cheetahs. 2.90r, Sociable weaver birds. 3.60r, Meerkats.

2001, May 12   Litho.   Perf. 13x13¼

1252-1255	A388	Set of 4	3.25	3.25
1254a		Souvenir sheet, #1253-1254	1.75	1.75

See Botswana Nos. 714-717.

Campaign Against Child Abuse — A389

2001, May 16   Perf. 13¾

1256	A389	1.40r multi	.45	.45

Soweto Uprising, 25th Anniv. — A390

2001, June 16   Litho.   Perf. 13¾

1257	A390	1.40r multi	.45	.45

Bats — A391

No. 1258: a, Cape horseshoe bat. b, Welwitsch's hairy bat. c, Schreiber's long-fingered bat. d, Wahlberg's epauletted fruit bat. e, Short-eared trident bat. f, Common slit-faced bat. g, Egyptian fruit bat. h, Egyptian free-tailed bat, vert. i, De Winton's long-eared bat. j, Large-eared free-tailed bat.

Serpentine Die Cut 11¼
2001, June 22
Self-Adhesive

1258	A391	Sheet of 10, #a-j	4.50	4.50
a.-j.		1.40r Any single	.45	.45

Boer War, Cent. — A392

Designs: 1.40r, Rev. J. D. Kestell. 3r, Capt. Thomas Crean.

2001, Aug. 1   Perf. 13¼

1259-1260	A392	Set of 2	1.40	1.40
a.		Booklet pane, #1259-1260, perf. 13¼x13¾	1.75	

Issued: No. 1260a, 5/31/02. See note after No. 1282.

World Conference Against Racism, Durban — A393

No. 1262: a, Kgotlelelo le pharologantsho. b, Kubeketelelana kanye nekwehlukana. c, Verdraagsaamheid en diversiteit. d, U kondelelana na u fhambana. e, Kutlwisiso ka mefutafuta. f, Ku va ni mbilu yo leha ni kuhambana-hambana. g, Ibekezelelwano nehlukahlukano. h, Kgotlhelelo le pharologano. i, Ukubekezelelana nokungafani. j, Ukunyamezelana nokungafani.

2001, Aug. 1   **Perf. 13¾x13½**
1261 A393 2.10r shown   .65 .65
1262   Sheet of 10   4.50 4.50
a.-j. A393 1.40r Any single   .45 .45

See Brazil No. 2809.

Musical Instruments — A394

Designs: 1.40r, Concertina. 1.90r, Trumpet. 2.50r, Electric guitar. 3r, African drum. 7r, Cello.

Litho. with Foil Application
2001, Aug. 23   **Perf. 13¼x14**
1263-1267 A394 Set of 5   5.00 5.00

Christmas A395

Designs: 2r, Tree. 3r, Angel.

2001, Oct. 1   **Litho.**   **Perf. 13¼**
1268-1269 A395 Set of 2   1.60 1.60

Frame — A396

2001, Oct. 1   **Serpentine Die Cut**
Self-Adhesive
1270 A396 (1.40r) multi   .45 .45
a. Double-sided pane of 10 + 40
    labels   4.50

Volvo Round-the-World Yacht Race — A397

Designs: 1.40r, Yacht. 6r, Yacht, horiz.

2001, Oct. 23   **Perf. 13**
1271 A397 1.40r multi   .45 .45
Souvenir Sheet
Perf. 14x13¼
1272 A397 6r multi   1.90 1.90

No. 1272 contains one 40x30mm stamp.

2003 ICC Cricket World Cup, South Africa — A398

2001, Nov. 1   **Perf. 14x13¾**
1273 A398 (1.40r) multi   .45 .45

Souvenir Sheet

New Year 2002 (Year of the Horse) — A399

2001, Nov. 2   **Perf. 14x13¼**
1274 A399 6r multi   1.90 1.90

Marine Life — A400

No. 1275: a, Hammerhead shark. b, Loggerhead turtle, vert. c, Clown triggerfish, vert. d, Cape fur seal, vert. e, Bottlenosed dolphins. f, Crowned seahorse, vert. g, Blue-spotted ribbontail ray, vert. h, Moorish idol. i, Common octopus. j, Coral rock cod.

Serpentine Die Cut 12¾
2001, Nov. 2
Self-Adhesive
1275 A400 Sheet of 10   4.50 4.50
a.-j. (1.40r) Any single   .45 .45

Johannesburg World Summit on Sustainable Development — A401

Designs: Nos. 1276a, 1281c, Prosperity, vert. Nos. 1276b, 1281a, People, vert. Nos. 1276c, 1281b, Planet, vert. (1.50r), Water, sanitation and energy for all. No. 1278, Buildings, globe. No. 1279, Clean environment for health. (3.30r), Food security for all.
Sizes: Nos. 1276a-1276c, 22x32mm, Nos. 1281a-1281c, 21x26mm.

Perf. 13¾x13¼, 13¼x13 (#1277, 1279, 1280), 13¼x13¾ (#1278)
2002   **Litho.**
1276 A401 (1.40r) Strip of 3,
                      #a-c   1.40 1.40
1277 A401 (1.50r) multi   .50 .50
1278 A401   (3r)   multi   .95 .95
1279 A401   (3r)   multi   .95 .95
1280 A401 (3.30r) multi   1.00 1.00

Booklet Stamps
Self-Adhesive
Serpentine Die Cut on 2 or 3 Sides
1281 A401 (1.40r) Strip of 3,
                      #a-c   1.40 1.40
d. Booklet pane, 4 #1281a, 3
    #1281b-1281c   4.50 4.50
Nos. 1276-1281 (6)   6.20 6.20

Issued: Nos. 1276, 1278, 1281, 4/17. Nos. 1277, 1279, 1280, 8/25. No. 1279 is airmail.

Souvenir Sheet

End of Boer War, Cent. — A402

No. 1282: a, 1.50r, Army officer. b, 3.30r, Government official.

2002, May 31   **Perf. 13¼x13¾**
1282 A402   Sheet of 2, #a-b   1.50 1.50
c. Booklet pane, #1282   1.90   —
    Complete booklet, #1151b,
    1172a, 1260a, 1282c + 2
    postal cards   10.50

No. 1282c has rouletting between margin of No. 1282 and the booklet pane margin. Complete booklet sold for 45r.

African Union Summit A403

2002, June 25   **Perf. 13½**
1283 A403 1.50r multi   .50 .50
Values are for stamps with surrounding selvage.

Type of 2000

Designs: 1.80r, Emperor moth. 2.20r, Peach moth. 2.80r, Snouted tiger moth. 9r, False tiger moth. 16r, Moon moth.

2002, Sept. 20 **Litho.** **Perf. 13**
1284 A383 1.80r multi   .55 .55
1285 A383 2.20r multi   .70 .70
1286 A383 2.80r multi   .85 .85
1287 A383   9r multi   2.75 2.75
1288 A383 16r multi   5.00 5.00
Nos. 1284-1288 (5)   9.85 9.85

A404   A405

A406   A407

A408   A409

ICC Cricket World Cup

2002   **Perf. 12½x12¾**
1289 A404 (1.50r) multi   .50 .50
1290 A405 (1.50r) multi   .50 .50
1291 A407 (1.50r) multi   .50 .50
1292 A409 (1.50r) multi   .50 .50
1293 A406 (1.50r) multi   .50 .50
1294 A408 (1.50r) multi   .50 .50
Nos. 1289-1294 (6)   3.00 3.00

Issued: Nos. 1289, 1290, 9/23; 1292, 1294, 11/1; Nos. 1291, 1293, 12/21.

Souvenir Sheet

Steve Biko (1946-77), Anti-apartheid Leader — A410

2002, Oct. 9   **Perf. 14¾x14½**
1295 A410 4.75r multi   1.50 1.50
See note under No. 1321.

Souvenir Sheet

World Post Day — A411

2002, Oct. 9   **Perf. 13¼x13½**
1296 A411 4.75r multi   1.50 1.50

Christmas — A412

Stained glass patterns: 1.50r, 3r.

2002, Oct. 23   **Perf. 14x14¾**
1297-1298 A412 Set of 2   1.40 1.40

Souvenir Sheets

Sawfish — A413

Designs: No. 1299, 7r, Pristis pectinata. No. 1300, 7r, Pristis microdon.

2002, Oct. 23   *Perf. 13¾*
1299-1300 A413   Set of 2   4.50 4.50
JUNASS Philatelic Exhibition (#1299); Algoapex Philatelic Exhibition (#1300).

Souvenir Sheet

New Year 2003 (Year of the Ram) — A414

2002, Nov. 1   *Perf. 14½*
1301 A414   7r multi   2.25 2.25

AIDS Prevention — A415

No. 1302 — AIDS prevention ribbon and: a, Man with sunglasses, male symbol. b, Woman with open mouth. c, Woman with sunglasses, female symbol. d, Hand holding candle, "Stop." e, Woman, candle. f, Hand holding candle, "Be safe." g, Candle, hand pointing at ribbon. h, Open hand. i, Face in droplet. j, Open hand, pills.

Serpentine Die Cut 11¾
2002, Nov. 29   **Self-Adhesive**
1302   Booklet of 10   4.75 4.75
a.-j.   A415 (1.50r) Any single   .45 .45

Souvenir Sheet

Solar Eclipse of Dec. 4, 2002 — A416

2002, Dec. 4   *Perf. 14½*
1303 A416   4.75r multi   1.50 1.50

ICC Cricket World Cup — A417

No. 1304: a, Huts with windmill blades. b, Horseman. c, Cricket players with bats. d, Bus with people on roof. e, Mother and child. f, Double-decker bus.

2003, Feb. 28   *Perf. 14¼x13¾*
1304 A417 (1.50r) Sheet of 6, #a-
    f   2.75 2.75

Souvenir Sheet

Tembisile (Chris) Hani (1942-93), African National Congress Leader — A418

2003, Apr. 27   *Litho.*   *Perf. 14¾*
1305 A418 (1.65r) multi   .45 .45
    See note after No. 1321.

Life in Informal Settlements — A419

No. 1306: a, Women carrying water jugs on head. b, Man with guitar. c, Man with rake. d, Woman using sewing machine. e, Two children. f, Drink vendor. g, Shoemakers. h, Woman with green cap. i, Young woman with cap and tire. j, Woman with child.

2003, May 16   *Perf. 14x13¾*
1306 A419 (1.65r) Sheet of 10,
    #a-j   4.50 4.50

Souvenir Sheet

Africa Day — A420

2003, May 25   *Perf. 14¾*
1307 A420 11.70r multi   3.00 3.00

Souvenir Sheet

Oliver Reginald Tambo (1917-93), African National Congress President — A421

2003, May 29
1308 A421 (1.65r) multi   .45 .45
    See note after No. 1321.

Ballroom Dancing — A422

Designs: 1.65r, Salsa. 2.20r, Rumba. 2.80r, Waltz. 3.30r, Foxtrot. 3.80r, Tango.

2003, July 23   *Perf. 13¼x13¾*
1309-1313 A422   Set of 5   3.75 3.75

Dogs — A423

No. 1314: a, Africanis. b, Rhodesian Ridgeback. c, Boerboel. d, Basenji.

2003, Aug. 1   *Perf. 14½*
1314 A423 (1.65r) Sheet of 4, #a-
    d   1.90 1.90

Type of 2000

Designs: No. 1315, Botterblom, vert. No. 1316, Blue marguerite, vert. No. 1317, Karoo violet, vert. No. 1318, Tree pelargonium, vert. No. 1319, Black-eyed susy, vert.

2003, Sept. 15   *Litho.*   *Perf. 13*
1315 A383 (1.65r) multi   .45 .45
1316 A383 (1.65r) multi   .45 .45
1317 A383 (1.65r) multi   .45 .45
1318 A383 (1.65r) multi   .45 .45
1319 A383 (1.65r) multi   .45 .45
a.   Horiz. strip of 5, #1315-1319   2.25 2.25

Souvenir Sheet

Walter Max Ulyate Sisulu (1912-2003), African National Congress Deputy President — A424

2003, Sept. 24   *Perf. 14¾*
1320 A424 11.70r multi   3.50 3.50
    See note after No. 1321.

Souvenir Sheet

Robert Mangaliso Sobukwe (1924-1978), Pan Africanist Congress President — A425

2003, Sept. 24   *Perf. 14¾*
1321 A425 11.70r multi   3.50 3.50
    Nos. 1295, 1305, 1308, 1320 and 1321 were sold in, but unattached to, a commemorative booklet that sold for 60r.

Stamp of Fortune Television Show — A426

2003, Sept. 29   *Perf. 14¼x14*
1322 A426 (1.65r) multi   .50 .50

Engineering and Postal Communication — A427

No. 1323: a, Shongweni Dam (60x23mm). b, Kimberley Microwave Tower (30x47mm). c, Northern Cape Legislature Building (30x23mm). d, Durban Westville highway interchange (30x47mm). e, Postal truck on Community Bridge, Limpopo (30x23mm). f, Nelson Mandela Bridge, Johannesburg (60x23mm).

2003, Oct. 9   *Perf. 14x14¼*
1323 A427 (3.30r) Sheet of 6, #a-
    f   5.75 5.75
g.   Like No. 1323, with PIARC World Road Congress inscription in margin   5.75 5.75

Souvenir Sheet

South Africa - India Diplomatic Relations, 10th Anniv. — A428

2003, Oct. 16   *Perf. 14¾*
1324 A428 3.35r multi   .95 .95

Bid for Hosting 2010 World Cup Soccer Championships — A429

Emblem, soccer fan with painted face and: No. 1325, (3.80r), Map of Africa. No. 1326, (4.25r), Soccer players.

2003, Oct. 23
1325-1326 A429   Set of 2   2.40 2.40
    No. 1325 is airmail.

A431

Christmas — A432

No. 1328: a, Joseph, Mary on donkey. b, Angels. c, Magi. d, Madonna and Child. e, Dove.

2003, Nov. 3   Litho.   Perf. 14x14¼
1328   Horiz. strip of 5   2.40 2.40
a.-e.   A431 (1.65r) Any single   .45   .45
Perf. 14¾
1329   A432 3.80r shown   1.10 1.10

Elephants — A433

No. 1330: a, African elephants. b, Asian elephant.
Illustration reduced.

2003, Dec. 9   Perf. 14¼x14
1330   A433 3.35r Horiz. pair, #a-b 2.10 2.10

South Africa - Thailand diplomatic relations, 10th anniv. See Thailand No. 2105.

Powered Flight, Cent. — A434

No. 1331: a, Paterson Biplane. b, "Silver Queen" Vickers Vimy. c, Wapiti. d, De Havilland DH-9. e, Junkers Ju52/53. f, Sikorsky S-55 helicopter. g, Boeing 707. h, Rooivalk helicopter. i, SUNSAT Microsatellite. j, Mark Shuttleworth, first African in space, and Space Station.

2003, Dec. 17   Perf. 14¼x14
1331   A434 (1.65r) Sheet of 10,
        #a-j   5.00 5.00

Souvenir Sheet

New Year 2004 (Year of the Monkey) — A435

2004, Jan. 22   Perf. 13¾
1332   A435 11.70r multi   3.25 3.25

SEMI-POSTAL STAMPS

Catalogue values for unused stamps in this section are for Never Hinged items.

English-Afrikaans Se-Tenant
Stamps with English inscriptions and with Afrikaans inscriptions of Nos. B1-B11 were printed alternately in the same sheets. Major-number listings and values are for pairs consisting of one English and one Afrikaans-inscribed stamp.

Church of the Vow — SP1

Cradock's Pass — SP2

Voortrekker — SP3

Voortrekker Woman — SP4

1933-36 Photo. Wmk. 201 Perf. 14
B1 SP1 ½p + ½p grn & blk,
        pair ('36)   11.00 4.75
a.   Single, English   .55   .55
b.   Single, Afrikaans   .55   .55
B2 SP2 1p + ½p rose & blk,
        pair   7.25 3.75
a.   Single, English   .45   .35
b.   Single, Afrikaans   .45   .35
B3 SP3 2p + 1p dull vio &
        gray, pair   12.00 6.00
a.   Single, English   .55   .55
b.   Single, Afrikaans   .55   .55
B4 SP4 3p + 1½p dp blue &
        gray, pair   18.00 9.50
a.   Single, English   1.50 1.10
b.   Single, Afrikaans   1.50 1.10
        Nos. B1-B4 (4)   48.25 24.00

Issued to commemorate the Voortrekkers. Surtax went to the National Memorial Fund for a national Voortrekker monument.

Voortrekker Plowing — SP5

Crossing the Drakensberg — SP6

Signing Dingaan-Retief Treaty — SP7

Proposed Monument — SP8

1938, Dec. 14   Perf. 14
B5 SP5 ½p + ½p dl grn & ind,
        pair   5.50 5.25
a.   Single, English   .55   .45
b.   Single, Afrikaans   .55   .45
B6 SP6 1p + 1p rose & sl,
        pair   7.25 6.00
a.   Single, English   .65   .55
b.   Single, Afrikaans   .65   .55
        Perf. 15x14
B7 SP7 1½p + ½p Prus grn
        & choc, pair   17.50 10.50
a.   Single, English   1.10 1.10
b.   Single, Afrikaans   1.10 1.10
B8 SP8 3p + 3p chlky bl,
        pair   20.00 12.50
a.   Single, English   1.40 1.60
b.   Single, Afrikaans   1.40 1.60
        Nos. B5-B8 (4)   50.25 34.25

Voortrekker centenary. Surtax went to the Natl. Memorial Fund for a Voortrekker monument.

"The Old Vicarage," Huguenot Museum — SP9

Rising Sun and Cross — SP10

Huguenot Dwelling, Drakenstein Mountain Valley — SP11

1939, July 17   Photo.   Perf. 14
B9 SP9 ½p + ½p Prus grn &
        gray brn, pair   6.50 4.75
a.   Single, English   .50   .50
b.   Single, Afrikaans   .50   .50
B10 SP10 1p + 1p rose car &
        Prus grn, pair   6.25 6.00
a.   Single, English   .60   .60
b.   Single, Afrikaans   .60   .60
        Perf. 15x14
B11 SP11 1½p + 1½p, pair   16.00 9.00
a.   Single, English   .95   .95
b.   Single, Afrikaans   .95   .95
        Nos. B9-B11 (3)   28.75 19.75

250th anniv. of the landing of the Huguenots in South Africa. Surtax went to a fund to build a Huguenot memorial at Paarl.

No. 581 Surcharged in English or Afrikaans

a

b

c

d

1987, Nov. 16 Litho. Perf. 14x14½
B12   Pair   1.00 1.00
a.   A229(a) 16c +10c red   .50   .50
b.   A229(b) 16c +10c red   .50   .50
    Surcharge for flood relief.

No. 702 Surcharged in English or Afrikaans

1987, Dec. 1
B13   Pair   1.00 1.00
a.   A254(a) 16c +10c multicolored .50 .50
b.   A254(b) 16c +10c multicolored .50 .50

"+10c" is overprinted below text on Nos. B13a-B13b. Surcharge for flood relief.

No. 706 Surcharged in English or Afrikaans

1988, Mar. 1   Perf. 14½x14
B14   Pair   1.00 1.00
a.   A256(a) 16c +10c multicolored .50 .50
b.   A256(b) 16c +10c multicolored .50 .50
    Surcharge for flood relief.

Nos. 710-713 Surcharged in English or Afrikaans

1988, Apr. 13   Perf. 14x14½
B15   Pair   .85   .85
a.   A257(c) 16c +10c multicolored .40 .40
b.   A257(d) 16c +10c multicolored .40 .40
B16   Pair   1.60 1.60
a.   A257(c) 30c +10c multicolored .80 .80
b.   A257(d) 30c +10c multicolored .80 .80
B17   Pair   2.25 2.25
a.   A257(c) 40c +10c multicolored 1.10 1.10
b.   A257(d) 40c +10c multicolored 1.10 1.10
B18   Pair   2.75 2.75
a.   A257(c) 50c +10c multicolored 1.25 1.25
b.   A257(d) 50c +10c multicolored 1.25 1.25
        Nos. B12-B18 (7)   10.45 10.45

Surcharge for flood relief.
On Nos. B16a, B16b, the "+ 10" is in upper left corner.

AIR POST STAMPS

Mail Plane — AP1

Biplane in Flight — AP2

Unwmk.

1925, Feb. 26   Litho.   Perf. 12

C1	AP1	1p red	3.00	4.75
C2	AP1	3p ultramarine	10.00	13.00
C3	AP1	6p violet	17.50	24.00
C4	AP1	9p gray green	29.00	32.50
	Nos. C1-C4 (4)		59.50	74.25
	Set, never hinged		150.00	

Forgeries exist.

1929, Aug. 16   Typo.   Perf. 14x13½

C5	AP2	4p blue green	8.50	2.75
C6	AP2	1sh orange	27.50	21.00
	Set, never hinged		75.00	

> Catalogue values for unused stamps in this section, from this point to the end of the section, are for Never Hinged items.

"AIRMAIL POSTCARD" "AIRMAIL POSTCARD RATE"

Stamps inscribed thus were sold for the amount shown in ( ) on date of issue.

See Nos. 1038-1042F for stamps included with postage sets.

Endangered Fauna Type of 1993

1996, May 8   Litho.   Perf. 14x14½

C6A	A288	(1r) White rhinoceros	.50	.50
C6B	A288	(1r) Buffalo	.50	.50
C6C	A288	(1r) Lion	.50	.50
f.		Souvenir sheet of 1 + label	.55	.55
C6D	A288	(1r) Leopard	.50	.50
C6E	A288	(1r) African elephant	.50	.50
g.		Strip of 5, #936-940	2.50	
h.		Sheet of 10, 2 each #936-940	5.00	
i.		Booklet pane of 5, #936-940 + 5 labels	3.00	
		Complete booklet, #940c	3.00	

No. C6Cf is inscribed in sheet margin for Coach House, and sold for 1r.

Issued: #C6Cf, 2/97; #C6Ei, 7/27/97.

Inauguaration of Blue Train — AP3

Designs: No. C7, Double-headed Class 6E 1, electric locomotives, Cape Town to Beaufort West. No. C8, Double-headed Class 6E 1 electric locomotives, Hex River Valley. No. C9, 1960's Steam powered locomotives between Three Sisters and Huchinson. No. C10, Diesel locomotives, Modder River Bridge near Kimberly. No. C11, Diesel locomotives, Northern Transvaal.

1997, Aug. 1   Perf. 14 Syncopated

C7	AP3	(1r) multicolored	.60	.60
a.		Souv. sheet of 1, perf. 14	.60	.60
C8	AP3	(1r) multicolored	.60	.60
C9	AP3	(1r) multicolored	.60	.60
a.		Souvenir sheet of 1, perf. 14	.60	.60
C10	AP3	(1r) multicolored	.60	.60
C11	AP3	(1r) multicolored	.60	.60
a.		Strip of 5, #C7-C11	3.00	3.00

No. C7a is inscribed in sheet margin for The Cape Stamp Show and Harmers of London stamp auctioneers.

No. C9a was issued 11/97, sold for 1.30r and is inscribed for Eastgate Universal Stamps & Coins in sheet margin.

1998, Nov.   Litho.   Perf. 14¾x14

Booklet Stamps

C12	AP3	(1r) Like #C7	.60	.60
C13	AP3	(1r) Like #C8	.60	.60
C14	AP3	(1r) Like #C9	.60	.60
C15	AP3	(1r) Like #C10	.60	.60
C16	AP3	(1r) Like #C11	.60	.60
a.		Bklt. pane, 2 ea #C12-C16	6.00	
		Complete booklet, #C16a	6.00	
	Nos. C12-C16 (5)		3.00	3.00

Tourism AP4

Western Cape of South Africa: No. C7, Sandstone Cliffs. No. C8, Robben Island. No. C9, Pinehurst Homestead. No. C10, Waterfront, Capetown. No. C11, Boschendal Wine Estate.

1998, Sept. 28   Litho.   Perf. 14½x14

Booklet Stamps

C17	AP4	(1.30r) multicolored	.50	.50
C18	AP4	(1.30r) multicolored	.50	.50
C19	AP4	(1.30r) multicolored	.50	.50
C20	AP4	(1.30r) multicolored	.50	.50
C21	AP4	(1.30r) multicolored	.50	.50
a.		Bklt. pane, 2 ea #C17-C21 + label	5.00	
		Complete booklet, #C21a	5.00	
	Nos. C17-C21 (5)		2.50	2.50

Perf. 14¾x14 on 3 sides

1998, Sept. 28   Litho.

KwaZulu-Natal: No. C22, Drakensberge. No. C23, Zulu women and huts. No. C24, Rhinoceros and pelicans. No. C25, Rickshaw driver. No. C26, Indian dancers.

C22	AP4	(1.30r) multicolored	.50	.50
C23	AP4	(1.30r) multicolored	.50	.50
C24	AP4	(1.30r) multicolored	.50	.50
C25	AP4	(1.30r) multicolored	.50	.50
C26	AP4	(1.30r) multicolored	.50	.50
a.		Booklet pane, 2 ea #C22-C26	5.00	
		Complete booklet, #C26a	5.00	

Worldwide Fund for Nature AP5

1998, Oct. 23   Litho.   Perf. 14¾x14

C27	AP5	(1.30r) Cuvier's beaked whale	.45	.45
C28	AP5	(1.30r) Minke whale	.45	.45
C29	AP5	(1.30r) Bryde's whale	.45	.45
C30	AP5	(1.30r) Pygmy right whale	.45	.45
a.		Block of 4, #C27-C30	1.80	1.80
b.		Booklet pane, 3 each #C27-C28, 2 each #C29-C30	4.50	
		Complete booklet	4.50	
		Complete booklet, 2 #C30b + 2 postal cards	12.00	

No. C30b exists with and without perfs running through side and bottom pane margins.

Tourism Type of 1998

Mpumalanga and Northern Province: No. C31, Blyde River Canyon. No. C32, Lone Creek Falls. No. C33, Ndebele women. No. C34, Pilgrim's Rest historical town. No. C35, Elephants, Thulamela, Kruger National Park.

1999, Aug.   Litho.   Perf. 14¾x14

C31	AP4	(1.30r) multi	.40	.40
C32	AP4	(1.30r) multi	.40	.40
C33	AP4	(1.30r) multi	.40	.40
C34	AP4	(1.30r) multi	.40	.40
C35	AP4	(1.30r) multi	.40	.40
a.		Booklet pane, 2 each #C31-C35	4.00	
		Complete booklet, #C35a	4.00	

Big Game Animals — AP6

Designs: Nos. C36, C45, Elephant. Nos. C37, C44, Lion. Nos. C38, C43, Rhinoceros. Nos. C39, C42, Leopard. Nos. C40, C41, Buffalo.

Perf. 14¾x14½ on 3 or 4 Sides

2001, Apr. 25   Litho.

Booklet Stamps

C36	AP6	(1.90r) multi	.60	.60
C37	AP6	(1.90r) multi	.60	.60
C38	AP6	(1.90r) multi	.60	.60
C39	AP6	(1.90r) multi	.60	.60
C40	AP6	(1.90r) multi	.60	.60
a.		Booklet pane, 2 each #C36-C40	6.00	
		Booklet, 2 #C40a + 2 postal cards	12.00	

Self-Adhesive
Size: 30x24mm

Serpentine Die Cut 12x11½ on 2 or 3 Sides

C41	AP6	(1.90r) multi	.60	.60
C42	AP6	(1.90r) multi	.60	.60
C43	AP6	(1.90r) multi	.60	.60
C44	AP6	(1.90r) multi	.60	.60
C45	AP6	(1.90r) multi	.60	.60
a.		Booklet, 2 each #C41-C45	6.00	

Tourism — AP7

Designs: No. C46, (2.10r), Cango Caves. No. C47, (2.10r), Table Mountain. No. C48, (2.10r), West Coast. No. C49, (2.10r), Snow-covered mountains near Elliot. No. C50, (2.10r), Augrabies Waterfall. No. C51, (2.10r), Stellenbosch vineyard country. No. C52, (2.10r), Flowers, Namaqualand. No. C53, (2.10r), Tsitsikamma Forest. No. C54, (2.10r), Cape Mountain zebras. No. C55, (2.10r), Richtersveld Desert.

2001, Sept. 6   Litho.   Perf. 13¼x13¾

C46-C55	AP7	Set of 10	6.50	6.50

Pres. Nelson Mandela — AP8

Various photographs. Color of country name and size of stamps: a, Lilac, 31x48mm. b, Red and lilac, 50x38mm. c, Orange, 31x48mm. d, Orange, 31x31mm. e, Orange, 38x50mm. f, White, 38x50mm. g, White, 50x38mm. h, White, 31x48mm. i, Lilac, 38x50mm. j, Red, 31x31mm.

2001, Nov. 26   Perf. 14¾x14, 13¾

C56		Booklet	8.50	
a.-j.		AP8 (2.10r) Any booklet pane	.85	.85

No. C56 sold for 45r and included two postal cards.

Shaka (1785-1828), Zulu King — AP9

2003, Sept. 24   Litho.   Perf. 13x13¼

C57	AP9	(3.30r) multi	.95	.95

POSTAGE DUE STAMPS

D1

D2

Wmk. Springbok's Head (177)

1914-15   Typo.   Perf. 14

J1	D1	½p green & blk	.90	3.50
J2	D1	1p red & blk	.90	.20
J3	D1	2p vio & blk ('14)	4.50	.65
J4	D1	3p ultra & blk	.70	.65
J5	D1	5p brown & blk	1.75	15.00
J6	D1	6p gray & blk	8.75	15.00
J7	D1	1sh black & red	62.50	125.00
	Nos. J1-J7 (7)		80.00	160.00

1922   Unwmk.   Litho.   Rouletted 7-8

J8	D1	½p blue grn & blk	1.00	7.75
J9	D1	1p dull red & blk	1.10	.75
J10	D1	1½p yellow brn & blk	1.25	1.50
	Nos. J8-J10 (3)		3.35	10.00

1922-26   Perf. 14

J11	D1	½p blue grn & blk	.20	.20
J12	D1	1p rose & blk ('23)	.35	.20
J13	D1	1½p yel brn & blk ('24)	1.00	.80
J14	D1	2p vio & blk ('23)	.85	.40
a.		Imperf. pair	250.00	

J15	D1	3p blue & blk ('26)	5.00	5.00
J16	D1	6p gray & blue ('23)	10.00	5.00
	Nos. J11-J16 (6)		17.40	11.60

1927-28   Typo.

J17	D2	½p blue green & blk	.40	.40
J18	D2	1p rose & black	.40	.40
J19	D2	2p violet & black	.70	.60
J20	D2	3p ultra & black	6.50	6.50
J21	D2	6p gray & black	12.00	10.00
	Nos. J17-J21 (5)		20.00	18.00

Type of 1927-28 Redrawn

Perf. 15x14

1932-40   Photo.   Wmk. 201

J22	D2	½p blue grn & blk ('34)	1.00	1.25
J23	D2	1p rose car & blk ('34)	.95	.95
J24	D2	2p blk violet & blk	4.00	.30
a.		2p dark purple & black ('40)	11.00	.20
J25	D2	3p dp blue & blk	18.00	12.00
J26	D2	3p ultra & dk bl ('35)	3.50	.40
J27	D2	3p blue & dk bl ('40)	21.00	2.00
J28	D2	6p brn org & grn ('33)	18.00	6.00
J29	D2	6p red org & grn ('39)	8.50	2.00
	Nos. J22-J29 (8)		74.95	24.90

The ½p No. J22 photogravure has larger but thinner numeral and the "d" is taller and thinner than on No. J17.

The 1p No. J23 photogravure has numeral with parallel sides. The "d" is taller and thicker than on No. J18.

On Nos. J25 and J27 the numeral is followed by a large "d" with thick lines and a large round period below it.

Nos. J22, J24 and J25 have frame in photogravure, value typographed.

> Catalogue values for unused stamps in this section, from this point to the end of the section, are for Never Hinged items.

See "English-Afrikaans Se-tenant" note preceding No. 23.

D3

Horiz. strips of Three, Perf. 15x14 All Around, Rouletted 6½ Between

1943-44   Photo.   Wmk. 201

J30	D3	½p Prus green ('44)	8.50	22.50
a.		Single	.20	.20
J31	D3	1p brt carmine	9.50	5.25
a.		Single	.20	.20
J32	D3	2p dark purple	9.00	9.00
a.		Single	.20	.20
J33	D3	3p dark blue	55.00	62.50
a.		Single	.20	.20
	Nos. J30-J33 (4)		82.00	99.25

Catalogued as strips of 3 because of the perforations.

Type of 1932-38, Redrawn Thick Numerals, Capital "D"

1948-49   Perf. 15x14

J34	D2	½p blue green & blk	9.00	6.00
J35	D2	1p deep rose & blk	10.50	2.50
J36	D2	2p dk pur & blk ('49)	14.00	2.50
J37	D2	3p ultra & dk blue	12.00	9.00
J38	D2	6p dp org & grn ('49)	37.50	7.00
	Nos. J34-J38 (5)		83.00	27.00

Redrawn Type of 1948-49 Hyphen between Suid-Afrika

1950-58   Perf. 15x14

J40	D2	1p car rose & blk	1.10	.40
J41	D2	2p dk pur & blk ('51)	.75	.25
J42	D2	3p ultra & dk blue	5.75	2.25
J43	D2	4p emer & dk grn ('58)	13.00	10.00
J44	D2	6p dp org & grn ('52)	10.50	10.50
J45	D2	1sh brn red & dk brn ('58)	16.00	13.00
	Nos. J40-J45 (6)		47.10	36.40

D4

D5

Perf. 15x14
1961, Feb. 14   Photo.   Wmk. 330

J46	D4	1c cerise & blk	.20	2.50
J47	D4	2c purple & blk	.20	2.50
J48	D4	4c brt & dk green	1.100	6.00
J49	D4	5c chalky bl & slate	2.00	6.50
J50	D4	6c vermilion & dk grn	8.00	7.00
J51	D4	10c maroon & dk brn	8.50	10.00
		Nos. J46-J51 (6)	20.90	34.50

Republic
1961-69   **Perf. 15x14**

Afrikaans Inscription on Top and Left Side

J52	D5	1c cerise & blk	.40	.40
J53	D5	4c brt & dk green	3.50	2.50
J54	D5	6c vermilion & dk grn	7.00	6.00

English Inscription on Top and Left Side

J55	D5	1c cerise & blk ('62)	.25	3.00
J56	D5	2c purple & blk	.35	.35
J57	D5	4c brt & dk grn ('69)	10.00	14.00
J58	D5	5c chlky bl & dk bl	2.50	1.50
J59	D5	5c chlky bl & blk ('62)	2.25	9.00
J60	D5	10c maroon & blk	4.00	2.50
		Nos. J52-J60 (9)	29.75	40.25

1967-70   Photo.   Wmk. 359

Afrikaans Inscription on Top and Left Side

J61	D5	1c carmine rose & blk	.20	.20
J62	D5	2c brt purple & blk	.20	.20
a.		Perf. 14 ('71)	18.00	18.00
J63	D5	4c lt grn & blk ('71)	18.00	18.00
a.		4c bright & dark green ('70)	75.00	75.00
J64	D5	5c dk blue & blk	.60	.60
J65	D5	6c orange & dk grn	3.00	7.00
J66	D5	10c dk rose brown & blk	2.50	1.50

English Inscription on Top and Left Side

J67	D5	1c car rose & blk	.20	.20
J68	D5	2c brt purple & blk	.30	.30
a.		Perf. 14 ('71)	18.00	18.00
J69	D5	4c lt green & blk ('71)	20.00	18.00
a.		4c bright & dark green ('70)	25.00	20.00
b.		As "a", perf. 14 ('71)	42.50	42.50
J70	D5	5c dk blue & blk	.60	.60
J71	D5	6c orange & dk grn	3.00	7.00
J72	D5	10c dk rose brown & blk	2.50	1.50
		Nos. J61-J72 (12)	53.10	55.10

D6

1972, Mar. 22   **Perf. 14x13½**

J73	D6	1c brt yellow green	.40	1.25
J74	D6	2c orange	.60	2.25
J75	D6	4c dull purple	1.50	2.25
J76	D6	6c yellow	1.50	4.00
J77	D6	8c bright blue	2.50	4.00
J78	D6	10c rose red	4.50	6.25
		Nos. J73-J78 (6)	11.00	20.00

On the 2c, 6c and 10c "TO PAY" in first row at left.

OFFICIAL STAMPS

Type A2 stamps have very small margins at top and bottom. Values are for copies with perfs close to, or touching the frame.

Regular Issues Overprinted in Black

Periods in Overprint
On No. 5
1926   Wmk. 177   **Perf. 14**

O1	A2	2p dull violet	18.00	2.00

See "English-Afrikaans Se-tenant" note preceding No. 23.

On Nos. 23-25
Perf. 14½x14
Wmk. 201

O2	A5	½p dk grn & blk, pair	6.00	12.00
a.		Single, English	.75	1.25
b.		Single, Afrikaans	.75	1.25
O3	A6	1p car & blk, pair	4.00	7.00
a.		Single, English	.25	.50
b.		Single, Afrikaans	.25	.50
O4	A7	6p org & grn, pair	550.00	75.00
a.		Single, English	25.00	9.00
b.		Single, Afrikaans	25.00	9.00

Nos. 26 and 25 Overprinted (Reading Up)

b

No Periods in Overprint
1928-29   **Perf. 14, 14½x14**
Space between words 19mm

O5	A8	2p vio brn & gray, pair ('29)	3.50	10.00
a.		Single, English	.50	1.50
b.		Single, Afrikaans	.50	1.50
c.		Space 17½mm, pair	4.00	12.50
d.		As "c", single, English	.50	2.00
e.		As "c", single, Afrikaans	.50	2.00

Space between words 11½mm

O6	A7	6p org & grn, pair	18.00	25.00
a.		Single, English	2.00	2.75
b.		Single, Afrikaans	2.00	2.75

#23-25 Ovptd. type "b" Reading Down
Space between words 13½-14mm
1929   **Perf. 14½x14**

O7	A5	½p grn & blk, pair	2.00	2.75
a.		Single, English	.25	.30
b.		Single, Afrikaans	.25	.30
c.		Period after "OFFISIEEL" on English stamp	3.25	3.25
d.		Pair, "c" + normal ½p	30.00	30.00
e.		Period after "OFFISIEEL." on Afrikaans stamp	3.25	3.25
f.		Pair, "e" + normal ½p	35.00	35.00
O8	A6	1p car & blk, pair	2.50	3.50
a.		Single, English	.30	.40
b.		Single, Afrikaans	.30	.40
O9	A7	6p org & grn, pair	7.75	26.00
a.		Single, English	1.25	3.00
b.		Single, Afrikaans	1.25	3.00
c.		Period after "OFFISIEEL" on English stamp	8.00	10.00
d.		Pair, "c" + normal 6p	60.00	100.00
e.		Period after "OFFISIEEL." on Afrikaans stamp	9.00	12.00
f.		Pair, "e" + normal 6p	70.00	110.00
		Nos. O7-O9 (3)	12.25	32.25

#29-30 Ovptd. type "b" Reading Down
Space between words 17½-19mm
1931   Engr.   **Perf. 14, 14x13½**

O10	A11	1sh dp bl & bis brn, pair	30.00	85.00
a.		Single, English	3.00	9.00
b.		Single, Afrikaans	3.00	9.00
c.		Period after "OFFICIAL." on Afrikaans stamp	50.00	50.00
d.		Pair, "c" + normal 1sh	100.00	225.00
O11	A12	2sh6p brn & bl grn, pair	60.00	150.00
a.		Single, English	7.50	17.50
b.		Single, Afrikaans	7.50	17.50
c.		Period after "OFFICIAL." on Afrikaans stamp	72.50	72.50
d.		Pair, "c" + normal 2sh6p	275.00	475.00

Regular Issues of 1930-45 Overprinted type "b" Reading Down ("SUIDAFRIKA" on Afrikaans stamps)
Perf. 15x14 (½p, 1p, 6p), 14
1930-47   Photo.   Wmk. 201
Space between words 9½-12mm (Various spacings occur in same setting)

O12	A5	½p bl grn & blk (#33), pair ('31)	2.00	3.50
a.		Single, English	.20	.40
b.		Single, Afrikaans	.20	.40
c.		Period after "OFFISIEEL." on English stamp	3.50	4.00
d.		Pair, "c" + normal ½p	25.00	42.50
e.		Period after "OFFISIEEL." on Afrikaans stamp	3.25	3.50
f.		Pair, "e" + normal ½p	25.00	42.50

Space between words 12½-13½mm

O13	A5	½p bl grn & blk, pair (#33)	3.00	4.00
a.		Single, English	.25	.50
b.		Single, Afrikaans	.25	.50
O14	A6	1p car & blk, pair (#34)	3.50	3.50
a.		Single, English	.40	.50
b.		Single, Afrikaans	.40	.50
c.		Period after "OFFISIEEL." on English stamp	3.75	4.00
d.		Pair, "c" + normal 1p	25.00	32.50
e.		Period after "OFFISIEEL." on Afrikaans stamp	3.00	3.50
f.		Pair, "e" + normal 1p	25.00	32.50
O15	A6	1p rose & blk, pair (#35) ('33)	7.50	9.00
a.		Single, English	.75	1.00
b.		Single, Afrikaans	.75	1.00
c.		Double ovpt., pair	275.00	300.00
d.		As "c", single	45.00	45.00
			45.00	

Space between words 20½-22mm

O16	A8	2p vio & gray, pair (#36) ('31)	4.50	10.00
a.		Single, English	.60	1.25
b.		Single, Afrikaans	.60	1.25
O17	A8	2p vio & ind, pair (#37)	75.00	85.00
a.		Single, English	6.00	9.00
b.		Single, Afrikaans	6.00	9.00

Space between words 12½-13½mm

O18	A7	6p org & grn, pair (#42)	7.00	8.50
a.		Single, English	.75	.90
b.		Single, Afrikaans	.75	.90
c.		Period after "OFFISIEEL." on English stamp	6.50	6.50
d.		Pair, "c" + normal 6p	50.00	60.00
e.		Period after "OFFISIEEL." on Afrikaans stamp	5.50	5.50
f.		Pair, "e" + normal 6p	40.00	50.00

Space between words 21mm

O19	A11	1sh dp bl & brn, pair (#43c) ('32)	42.50	75.00
a.		Single, English	4.00	7.50
b.		Single, Afrikaans	4.00	7.50
c.		1sh dk bl & yel brn (#43), 19mm, pair	42.50	75.00
d.		As "c", single, English	3.00	7.50
e.		As "c", single, Afrikaans	3.00	7.50
f.		As "c", spaced 21mm, pair	42.50	65.00
g.		As "f", single, English	6.00	7.50
h.		As "f", single, Afrikaans	6.00	7.50

Space between words 17½-18½mm

O20	A12	2sh6p brn & sl grn (#44c) ('37), pair	65.00	100.00
a.		Single, English	10.00	12.50
b.		Single, Afrikaans	10.00	12.50
c.		Spaced 21mm, pair	45.00	70.00
d.		As "c", single, English	4.50	8.00
e.		As "c", single, Afrikaans	4.50	8.00
f.		2sh6p red brn & grn, pair (#44i) ('33)	50.00	90.00
g.		As "f", single, English	5.00	8.50
h.		As "f", single, Afrikaans	5.00	8.50
j.		2sh6p brn & bl, 19-20mm (#44) ('47), pair	30.00	60.00
k.		As "j", single, English	3.00	5.00
m.		As "j", single, Afrikaans	3.00	5.00
		Nos. O12-O20 (9)	210.00	298.50

> **Catalogue values for unused stamps in this section, from this point to the end of the section, are for Never Hinged items.**

Regular Issue of 1933-54 Overprinted type "b" Reading Down ("SUID-AFRIKA" Hyphenated)
1935-50   Photo.   **Perf. 15x14, 14**
Space between words given with each listing

O21	A5	½p grn & gray (#45), 12½-13mm, pair ('36)	3.25	15.00
a.		Single, English	.25	1.25
b.		Single, Afrikaans	.25	1.25
O22	A5	½p grn & gray, (#46), 11-13mm, pair ('38)	12.00	12.50
a.		Single, English	.50	1.00
b.		Single, Afrikaans	.50	1.00
O23	A5	½p grn & gray (#47), 11½mm, pair ('48)	1.25	5.00
a.		Single, English	.20	.70
b.		Single, Afrikaans	.20	.70
O24	A6	1p car & gray (#48), 11-13mm, pair	1.00	1.00
a.		Single, English	.20	.20
b.		Single, Afrikaans	.20	.20
O25	A6	1p rose car & gray blk (#49), 11½-12mm, pair ('41)	1.00	.50
a.		Single, English	.20	.20
b.		Single, Afrikaans	.20	.20
O26	A15	1½p dk grn & gold (#51), 19-21mm, pair ('37)	30.00	22.50
a.		Single, English	2.25	1.75
b.		Single, Afrikaans	2.25	1.75
O27	A15	1½p sl grn & och (#52), 16mm, pair ('44)	3.00	8.00
a.		Single, English	.30	.45
b.		Single, Afrikaans	.30	.45
c.		Ovpt. spaced 14-14½mm, pair	3.00	5.00
d.		As "c", single, English	.25	.80
e.		As "c", single, Afrikaans	.25	.80
O28	A8	2p bl vio & dl bl (#53), 20-21mm, pair ('39)	80.00	30.00
a.		Single, English	7.50	2.50
b.		Single, Afrikaans	7.50	2.50

O29	A16	2p pur & sl (#55), 19-21mm, pair ('48)	4.50	16.00
a.		Single, English	.25	1.50
b.		Single, Afrikaans	.25	1.50
O30	A7	6p org & bl grn, I (#59), 12-13mm, pair ('38)	80.00	40.00
a.		Single, English	6.50	3.75
b.		Single, Afrikaans	6.50	3.75
O31	A7	6p org & grn, II (#60), 12-13mm, pair ('39)	12.00	10.00
a.		Single, English	1.25	1.25
b.		Single, Afrikaans	1.25	1.25
O32	A7	6p org & grn III (#61), 11½-12mm, pair ('47)	5.50	8.00
a.		Single, English	.50	.90
b.		Single, Afrikaans	.50	.90
O33	A11	1sh lt bl & ol brn (#62c), 19-21mm, pair ('40)	65.00	27.50
a.		Single, English	4.50	2.00
b.		Single, Afrikaans	4.50	2.00
c.		"OFFICIAL" on both sides	500.00	
d.		"OFFISIEEL" on both sides	500.00	
e.		1sh chlky bl & lt brn (#62) ('50), pair	10.00	25.00
f.		As "e", single, English	.90	2.50
g.		As "e", single, Afrikaans	.90	2.50
h.		1sh vio bl & brnsh blk (#62f), 18-19mm, pair	65.00	27.50
j.		As "h", single, English	4.50	2.00
k.		As "h", single, Afrikaans	4.50	2.00
O34	A13	5sh grn & blk (#64) 19-20mm, pair	55.00	110.00
a.		Single, English	3.50	12.50
b.		Single, Afrikaans	3.50	12.50
O35	A13	5sh bl grn & blk (#65), 20mm, pair	40.00	110.00
a.		Single, English	3.50	12.50
b.		Single, Afrikaans	3.50	12.50
O36	A18	10sh ol blk & bl (#67), 19½-20mm, pair ('48)	85.00	175.00
a.		Single, English	7.50	22.50
b.		Single, Afrikaans	7.50	22.50
		Nos. O21-O36 (16)	478.50	591.00

Nos. 52 and 56 Overprinted type "b" Reading Up
Space between words 16mm
1949-50   **Size: 22x18mm**   **Perf. 14**

O37	A15	1½p sl grn & ocher, pair	35.00	40.00
a.		Single, English	2.25	3.50
b.		Single, Afrikaans	2.25	3.50

Size: 21½x17½mm

O38	A16	2p pur & sl bl, pair ('50)	1,500.	1,750.
a.		Single, English	125.	175.
b.		Single, Afrikaans	125.	175.

Nos. 64, 67 Overprinted

c

Space between words 18-19mm
1940   **Perf. 14**

O39	A13	5sh grn & blk, pair	85.00	100.00
a.		Single, English	3.00	10.00
b.		Single, Afrikaans	3.00	10.00
O40	A18	10sh ol brn & bl, pair	375.00	350.00
a.		Single, English	25.00	35.00
b.		Single, Afrikaans	25.00	35.00

No. 54 Overprinted type "c" Reading Up
Space between words 19mm
1945   **Perf. 14**

O41	A8	2p dl vio & gray, pair	8.00	22.50
a.		Single, English	.50	2.25
b.		Single, Afrikaans	.50	2.25

No. 47 Overprinted

OFFICIAL   OFFISIEEL

1947   **Perf. 15x14**

O42	A5	½p grn & gray, pair	22.50	20.00
a.		Single, English	1.00	2.00
b.		Single, Afrikaans	1.00	2.00

Stamps of 1937-54 Overprinted

1950-54   Perf. 15x14, 14
Space between words 10mm

O43	A5	½p grn & gray, pair (#47)	.90	1.50
a.		Single, English	.20	.20
b.		Single, Afrikaans	.20	.20
O44	A6	1p rose car & gray blk, pair (#49)	1.00	2.00
a.		Single, English	.20	.20
b.		Single, Afrikaans	.20	.20
O45	A6	1p car & blk, pair (#50)	1.00	1.50
a.		Single, English	.20	.20
b.		Single, Afrikaans	.20	.20

Space between words 14½mm

O46	A15	1½p sl grn & ocher, pair (#52)	1.50	3.00
a.		Single, English	.20	.35
b.		Single, Afrikaans	.20	.35
O47	A16	2p pur & sl bl, pair (#56)	1.00	2.00
a.		Single, English	.20	.20
b.		Single, Afrikaans	.20	.20
c.		Ovpt. reading up, pair		

Space between words 10mm

O48	A7	6p red org & bl grn, III, pair (#61c)	2.00	3.00
a.		Single, English	.35	.35
b.		Single, Afrikaans	.35	.35

Space between words 19mm

O49	A11	1sh chlky bl & lt brn, pair (#62)	6.75	15.00
a.		Single, English	.50	1.75
b.		Single, Afrikaans	.50	1.75
c.		1sh vio bl & brnsh blk (#62f), pair	140.00	150.00
d.		As "c," single, English	12.50	17.50
e.		As "c," single, Afrikaans	12.50	17.50
O50	A12	2sh6p brn & brt grn, pair (#63)	10.00	32.50
a.		Single, English	1.00	3.25
b.		Single, Afrikaans	1.00	3.25
O51	A13	5sh grn & blk, pair (#64)	175.00	90.00
a.		Single, English	2.00	9.00
b.		Single, Afrikaans	2.00	9.00
O52	A13	5sh bl grn & blk, I, pair (#65)	65.00	75.00
a.		Single, English	3.00	6.50
b.		Single, Afrikaans	3.00	6.50
O53	A13	5sh grn & blk, II, pair (#66)	80.00	80.00
a.		Single, English	4.00	9.00
b.		Single, Afrikaans	4.00	9.00
O54	A18	10sh ol blk & bl, pair (#67)	80.00	200.00
a.		Single, English	5.00	21.00
b.		Single, Afrikaans	5.00	21.00
		Nos. O43-O54 (12)	424.15	505.50

BOPHUTHATSWANA

ˌbō-ₔₚü-tät-ˈswä-nə

LOCATION — Noncontiguous enclaves, Republic of South Africa
GOVT. — Self-governing tribal homeland
AREA — 27,340 sq. mi.
POP. — 1,660,000 (1985)
CAPITAL — Mmabatho

Catalogue values for all unused stamps in this country are for Never Hinged items.

Independence from South Africa — A1

1977, Dec. 6   Perf. 12½   Litho.   Unwmk.

1	A1	4c Hands, dove released	.75	.75
2	A1	10c Leopard (state emblem)	1.50	1.10
3	A1	15c Coat of arms	3.00	2.25
4	A1	20c Flag	4.00	3.00
		Nos. 1-4 (4)	9.25	7.10

An imperf. souvenir sheet exists containing Nos. 1-4 printed in one color (blue). Not valid for postage.

Tribal Totems — A2

Designs: 1c, African buffalo (Malete, Hwaduba). 2c, Bush pig (Kolobeng). 3c, Chacma baboon (Hurutshe, Thlaro). 4c, Leopard (state emblem). 5c, Crocodile (Kwena-Fokeng). 6c, Savanna monkey (Kgatla). 7c, Lion (Taung). 8c, Spotted hyena (Phiring). 9c, Cape porcupine (Rokgodadi). 10c, Aardvark (Tlokwa). 15c, Fish (Tlhaping). 20c, Hunting dog (Tlhalerwa). 25c, Common duiker (Mfatlha). 30c, African elephant (Tlhako, Tloung). 50c, Python (Nogeng). 1r, Hippopotamus (Kubung). 2r, Greater kudu (Rolong).

1977, Dec. 6

5	A2	1c multicolored	.20	.20
6	A2	2c multicolored	.20	.20
7	A2	3c multicolored	.20	.20
8	A2	4c multicolored	5.00	2.40
9	A2	5c on 4c multi	1.40	.80
10	A2	6c multicolored	.25	.25
11	A2	7c multicolored	1.25	1.25
12	A2	8c multicolored	.35	.25
13	A2	9c multicolored	.45	.25
14	A2	10c multicolored	.35	.25
15	A2	15c multicolored	.45	.25
16	A2	20c multicolored	.45	.35
17	A2	25c multicolored	.50	.35
18	A2	30c multicolored	.60	.35
19	A2	50c multicolored	.85	.50
20	A2	1r multicolored	1.75	1.40
21	A2	2r multicolored	3.25	3.25
		Nos. 5-21 (17)	17.50	12.50

No. 9 was printed as a 4c stamp. Grass was printed over the 4c at upper right and 5c printed at upper left. Copies exist without the surcharge. No. 9A does not have the 4c.

Perf. 14

5a	A2	1c	.20	.20
6a	A2	2c	.20	.20
7a	A2	3c	.20	.20
8a	A2	4c	.20	.20
9A	A2	5c multicolored	.20	.20
11a	A2	7c	.20	.20
12a	A2	8c	.25	.25
14a	A2	10c	.25	.25
		Nos. 5a-14a (8)	1.70	1.70

World Hypertension Month — A3

1978, Apr. 7   Perf. 12x12½

22	A3	4c Avoid kidney infections	.60	.60
23	A3	10c Lower salt intake	1.00	1.00
24	A3	15c Overeating is dangerous	1.40	1.40
		Nos. 22-24 (3)	3.00	3.00

Road Safety A4

1978, July 12

25	A4	4c Don't drink and drive	.75	.45
26	A4	10c Keep children off roads	1.10	.65
27	A4	15c Pedestrians observe crossing signals	1.40	.80
28	A4	20c Observe stop signs	2.25	1.10
		Nos. 25-28 (4)	5.50	3.00

Cutting and Polishing Semi-precious Stones — A5

1978, Oct. 3

29	A5	4c Cutting slabs of travertine	.40	.20
30	A5	10c Polishing travertine	.75	.55
31	A5	15c Sorting stones	1.25	.75
32	A5	20c Factory at Taung	1.60	1.00
		Nos. 29-32 (4)	4.00	2.50

1st Airplane Flight, 75th Anniv. — A6

Illustration reduced.

1978, Dec. 1   Perf. 12½

33	A6	10c Wright Flyer	1.00	1.00
34	A6	15c Orville and Wilbur Wright	1.50	1.50

Pres. Lucas M. Mangope — A7

1978, Dec. 6

35	A7	4c Profile	.20	.20
36	A7	15c Portrait	.45	.45

Sorghum Beer Production A8

1979, Feb. 28   Perf. 14x14½

37	A8	4c Drying germinated wheat	.30	.30
38	A8	15c Cooking ground grain	.80	.80
39	A8	20c Straining the liquid	1.00	1.00
40	A8	25c Drinking beer	1.40	1.40
		Nos. 37-40 (4)	3.50	3.50

Tate-Knoetze Boxing Match — A9

1979, June 2

41	A9	15c John Tate	.90	.90
42	A9	15c Kallie Knoetze	.90	.90
a.		Pair, #41-42	2.00	2.00

Intl. Children's Year — A10

Illustrations by local youths: 4c, Boy dazzled by sun, from a folk tale, by Hendrick Sebapo. 15c, Africans and animal silhouettes, by Daisy Morapedi. 20c, Man in profile and landscape, by Peter Tladi. 25c, Old man, boy and mule, by Sebapo.

1979, June 7   Perf. 14½x14

43	A10	4c multicolored	.20	.20
44	A10	15c multicolored	.35	.35
45	A10	20c multicolored	.50	.50
46	A10	25c multicolored	.70	.70
		Nos. 43-46 (4)	1.75	1.75

Platinum Industry A11

Designs: 4c, Pouring molten metal. 15c, Platinum in industrial use. 20c, Telecommunications satellite in orbit. 25c, Jewelry.

1979, Aug. 15   Perf. 14x14½

47	A11	4c multicolored	.20	.20
48	A11	15c multicolored	.25	.25
49	A11	20c multicolored	.35	.35
50	A11	25c multicolored	.45	.45
		Nos. 47-50 (4)	1.25	1.25

Agriculture A12

1979, Oct. 25

51	A12	5c Cattle	.20	.20
52	A12	15c Picking cotton	.25	.25
53	A12	20c Researcher in corn field	.35	.35
54	A12	25c Fish in net	.45	.45
		Nos. 51-54 (4)	1.25	1.25

Stop Smoking Campaign A13   Edible Wild Fruit A14

1980, Mar. 5   Perf. 14½x14

55	A13	5c multicolored	.00	.25

1980, June 4

56	A14	5c Landolphia capensis	.20	.20
57	A14	10c Vangueria infausta	.25	.25
58	A14	15c Bequaertiodendron magalismontanum	.40	.40
59	A14	20c Sclerocarya caffra	.50	.50
		Nos. 56-59 (4)	1.35	1.35

Birds — A15

1980, Sept. 10

60	A15	5c Pied babbler	.20	.20
61	A15	10c Carmine bee-eater	.45	.45
62	A15	15c Shaft-tailed whydah	.70	.70
63	A15	20c Meyer's parrot	.90	.90
		Nos. 60-63 (4)	2.25	2.25

Sun City Tourist Attractions A16

1980, Dec. 5   Perf. 14x14½

64	A16	5c Hotel, casino, country club	.20	.20
65	A16	10c Golfer at Gary Player Country Club	.40	.40
66	A16	15c Casino interior	.60	.60
67	A16	20c Night club dancers	.80	.80
		Nos. 64-67 (4)	2.00	2.00

Intl. Year for the
Disabled — A17

1981, Jan. 30   Perf. 14½x14
68 A17 5c shown   .20 .20
69 A17 15c Blind boy   .25 .25
70 A17 20c Archer in wheelchair   .35 .35
71 A17 25c X-ray (tuberculosis)   .45 .45
      Nos. 68-71 (4)   1.25 1.25

Easter
A18

Bible quotes and: 5c, Lamb, sunset. 15c,
Bread. 20c, Man holding lamb. 25c, Wheat
field.

1981, Apr. 1   Perf. 14x14½
72 A18 5c multicolored   .20 .20
73 A18 15c multicolored   .30 .30
74 A18 20c multicolored   .45 .45
75 A18 25c multicolored   .55 .55
      Nos. 72-75 (4)   1.50 1.50

Telephones   Grasses
A19   A20

5c, Siemens & Halske wall telephone, 1885.
15c, Ericsson table model, 1895. 20c, Hasler
table model, 1900. 25c, Mix & Genest wall
model, 1904.

1981, July 31   Perf. 14½x14
76 A19 5c multicolored   .20 .20
77 A19 15c multicolored   .30 .30
78 A19 20c multicolored   .35 .35
79 A19 25c multicolored   .45 .45
      Nos. 76-79 (4)   1.30 1.30

1981, Nov. 25
80 A20 5c Themeda triandra   .20 .20
81 A20 15c Rhynchelytrum
            repens   .30 .30
82 A20 20c Eragrostis capensis   .35 .35
83 A20 25c Monocymbium cer-
            esiiforme   .45 .45
      Nos. 80-83 (4)   1.30 1.30

Boy Scouts,   Easter — A22
75th
Anniv. — A21

1982, Jan. 29
84 A21 5c Scout, 1982   .20 .20
85 A21 15c Mafeking Siege
            stamps   .35 .35
86 A21 20c Scout cadet, 1907   .45 .45
87 A21 25c Lord Baden-Powell   .55 .55
      Nos. 84-87 (4)   1.55 1.55

1982, Apr. 1
88 A22 15c John 12:1   .20 .20
89 A22 20c Matthew 21:1-2   .20 .20
90 A22 25c Mark 11:5-6   .50 .50
91 A22 30c Matthew 21:7   .60 .60
      Nos. 88-91 (4)   1.50 1.50

Table
Telephones — A23

1982, Sept. 3
92 A23 8c Ericsson, 1878   .20 .20
93 A23 15c Ericsson, 1885   .30 .30
94 A23 20c Ericsson, 1893   .35 .35
95 A23 25c Siemens & Halske,
            1898   .45 .45
      Nos. 92-95 (4)   1.30 1.30

Independence, 5th Anniv. — A24

8c, Old parliament building. 15c, New government offices. 20c, University, Mmabatho.
25c, Civic Center, Mmabatho.

1982, Dec. 6   Perf. 14x14½
96 A24 8c multicolored   .20 .20
97 A24 15c multicolored   .30 .30
98 A24 20c multicolored   .35 .35
99 A24 25c multicolored   .45 .45
      Nos. 96-99 (4)   1.30 1.30

Pilanesberg Nature Reserve — A25

1983, Jan. 5
100 A25 8c Ceratotherium
            simum   .25 .25
101 A25 20c Equus burchelli   .60 .60
102 A25 25c Hippotragus niger   .75 .75
103 A25 40c Alcelaphus caama   1.10 1.10
      Nos. 100-103 (4)   2.70 2.70

Easter
A26

1983, Mar. 30   Perf. 14½x14
104 A26 8c Matthew 21:7   .20 .20
105 A26 20c Mark 11:7   .35 .35
106 A26 25c Matthew 21:8   .40 .40
107 A26 40c Mark 11:9   .65 .65
      Nos. 104-107 (4)   1.60 1.60

Telephones   Birds of the
A27   Veld
                    A28

10c, ATM table model, c. 1920. 20c, A/S
Elektrisk wall model, c. 1900. 25c, Ericsson
wall model, c. 1900. 40c, Ericsson wall model,
c. 1900, diff.

1983, June 22
108 A27 10c multicolored   .20 .20
109 A27 20c multicolored   .35 .35
110 A27 25c multicolored   .45 .45
111 A27 40c multicolored   .70 .70
      Nos. 108-111 (4)   1.70 1.70

1983, Sept. 14
112 A28 10c Kori bustard   .25 .25
113 A28 20c Black korhaan   .55 .55
114 A28 25c Red-crested
            korhaan   .70 .70
115 A28 40c Stanley bustard   1.25 1.25
      Nos. 112-115 (4)   2.75 2.75

Grasses — A29

1984, Jan. 20
116 A29 10c Panicum maximum   .20 .20
117 A29 20c Hyparrhenia drege-
            ana   .30 .30
118 A29 25c Cenchrus ciliaris   .35 .35
119 A29 40c Urochloa brachyura   .55 .55
      Nos. 116-119 (4)   1.40 1.40

Easter
A30

1984, Mar. 23   Perf. 14½x14
120 A30 10c Mark 11:11   .20 .20
121 A30 20c Mark 11:15   .30 .30
122 A30 25c Matthew 21:19   .40 .40
123 A30 40c Matthew 21:19, diff.   .65 .65
      Nos. 120-123 (4)   1.55 1.55
      See Nos. 165-168, 173-176.

Mining
Industry
A31

1984, Apr. 2   Perf. 14½x14
124 A31 11c multicolored   .35 .35

Telephones — A32

11c, Shuchhardt table model, c. 1905. 20c,
Siemens wall model, c. 1925. 25c, Ericsson
table model, c. 1900. 30c, Oki table model, c.
1930.

1984, July 20
125 A32 11c multicolored   .20 .20
126 A32 20c multicolored   .30 .30
127 A32 25c multicolored   .40 .40
128 A32 30c multicolored   .45 .45
      Nos. 125-128 (4)   1.35 1.35

Lizards
A33

Designs: 11c, Yellow-throated plated lizard.
25c, Transvaal girdled lizard. 30c, Ocellated
sand lizard. 45c, Bibron's thick-toed gecko.

1984, Sept. 25   Perf. 14x14½
129 A33 11c multicolored   .20 .20
130 A33 25c multicolored   .40 .40
131 A33 30c multicolored   .50 .50
132 A33 45c multicolored   .75 .75
      Nos. 129-132 (4)   1.85 1.85

Child Health   Mafeking,
Care — A34   Cent. — A35

1985, Jan. 25
133 A34 11c Stop Polio   .20 .20
134 A34 25c Stop Measles   .40 .40
135 A34 30c Stop Diphtheria   .50 .50
136 A34 50c Stop Whooping
            Cough   .80 .80
      Nos. 133-136 (4)   1.90 1.90

1985, Mar. 11
Portraits: 11c, Montshiwa (1814-1896), chief
of the Barolong booRatshidi. 25c, Sir Charles
Warren (1840-1927), army commander who
established the Crown Colony and laid out the
town of Mafeking.

137 A35 11c multicolored   .20 .20
138 A35 25c multicolored   .35 .35

Industries
A36

Designs: 1c, Textile mill, Bophuthatswana.
2c, Sewing cloth sacks, Selosesha. 3c,
Ceramic tile production line. 4c, Processing
sheepskin. 5c, Manufacture of crossbows. 6c,
Automobile parts. 7c, Hosiery factory,
Babelegi. 8c, Specialized bicycle factory. 9c,
Lawn mower assembly line. 10c, Dress factory, Thaba Nchu. 12c, Automobile upholstery
factory. 14c, Milling industry, Mafeking. 15c,
Manufacturing of plastic bags. 16c,
Brickworks, Mmabatho. 18c, Manufacturing of
cutlery. 20c, Men's clothing factory. 25c, Chro-
mium plating baby carriage parts. 30c, Spray-
painting metal beds. 50c, Milk processing
plant. 1r, Printing works. 2r, Industrial complex, Babelegi.

1985-89   Perf. 14½x14
139 A36 1c multicolored   .20 .20
140 A36 2c multicolored   .20 .20
141 A36 3c multicolored   .20 .20
142 A36 4c multicolored   .20 .20
143 A36 5c multicolored   .20 .20
144 A36 6c multicolored   .20 .20
145 A36 7c multicolored   .20 .20
146 A36 8c multicolored   .20 .20
147 A36 9c multicolored   .20 .20
148 A36 10c multicolored   .20 .20
149 A36 12c multicolored   .25 .25
150 A36 14c multicolored   .30 .30
151 A36 15c multicolored   .35 .35
152 A36 16c multicolored   .35 .35
153 A36 18c multicolored   .40 .40
154 A36 20c multicolored   .45 .45
155 A36 25c multicolored   .60 .60
156 A36 30c multicolored   .70 .70
157 A36 50c multicolored   1.10 1.10
158 A36 1r multicolored   2.25 2.25
159 A36 2r multicolored   4.75 4.75
      Nos. 139-159 (21)   13.50 13.50

Issued: 1c-10c, 15c, 20c, 25c, 30c-2r,
10/25/85; 12c, 4/1/85; 14c, 4/1/86; 16c,
4/1/87; 18c, 7/3/89.

Easter Type of 1984

1985, Apr. 2
165 A30 12c Matthew 21:14   .20 .20
166 A30 25c Matthew 21:14, diff.   .35 .35
167 A30 30c Matthew 21:15   .40 .40
168 A30 50c Matthew 21:15-16   .70 .70
      Nos. 165-168 (4)   1.65 1.65

Tree Conservation
A37

1985, July 4 — Perf. 14x14½

169	A37	12c Fourea saligna	.20	.20
170	A37	25c Boscia albitrunca	.45	.45
171	A37	30c Erythrina lysistemon	.55	.55
172	A37	50c Bequaertiodendron magalismontanum	.90	.90
		Nos. 169-172 (4)	2.10	2.10

Easter Type of 1984

1986, Mar. 6 — Perf. 14½x14

173	A30	12c John 12:2	.20	.20
174	A30	20c John 12:3	.35	.35
175	A30	25c John 12:3, diff.	.45	.45
176	A30	30c Matthew 26:7	.55	.55
		Nos. 173-176 (4)	1.55	1.55

Paintings of Thaba Nchu in the Africana Museum, Johannesburg — A38

14c, Wesleyan Mission Station and Residence of Moroka, Chief of the Barolong, 1834, by Charles Davidson Bell. 20c, James Archbell's Congregation, 1834, by Bell. 25c, Mission Station at Thaba Nchu, 1850, by Thomas Baines (1822-75).

1986, May 15 — Perf. 14x14½

177	A38	14c multicolored	.20	.20
178	A38	20c multicolored	.25	.25
179	A38	25c multicolored	.35	.35
		Nos. 177-179 (3)	.80	.80

Incorporation of Thaba Nchu and Bophuthatswana, Oct. 1, 1983.
A souvenir sheet of one No. 179 has decorative margin continuing the painting and picturing the emblem of the philatelic exhibition held at Johannesburg, Oct. 6-11. Sold for 50c.

Temisano Development Projects A39

1986, Aug. 6 — Perf. 14½x14

180	A39	14c Agricultural production	.20	.20
181	A39	20c Community development	.35	.35
182	A39	25c Vocational training	.40	.40
183	A39	30c Secondary industries	.50	.50
		Nos. 180-183 (4)	1.45	1.45

BOP Airways, 5th Anniv. A40

1986, Oct. 16 — Perf. 14x14½

184	A40	14c Airline personnel, aircraft	.30	.30
185	A40	20c Passengers	.45	.45
186	A40	25c Mmabatho Intl. Airport	.60	.60
187	A40	30c Cessna Citation	.65	.65
		Nos. 184-187 (4)	2.00	2.00

Sports — A41

Wildflowers — A42

1987, Jan. 22

188	A41	14c Netball	.30	.30
189	A41	20c Tennis	.45	.45
190	A41	25c Soccer	.55	.55
191	A41	30c Running	.70	.70
		Nos. 188-191 (4)	2.00	2.00

1987, Apr. 23

192	A42	16c Berkheya zeyheri	.40	.40
193	A42	20c Plumbago auriculata	.50	.50
194	A42	25c Pterodiscus speciosus	.65	.65
195	A42	30c Gazania krebsiana	.75	.75
		Nos. 192-195 (4)	2.30	2.30

A souvenir sheet of one No. 194 has decorative black and white inscribed margin picturing the emblem of the natl. philatelic exhibition held at Paarl, Sept. 16-19. Sold for 70c.

Education — A43

Designs: 16c, E.M. Mokgoko Farmer Training Center, Ramatlabama. 20c, Main lecture block, University of Bophuthatswana, Mmabatho. 25c, Manpower Center. 30c, Hotel training school, Odi.

1987, Aug. 6 — Perf. 14½x14

196	A43	16c multicolored	.35	.35
197	A43	20c multicolored	.45	.45
198	A43	25c multicolored	.60	.60
199	A43	30c multicolored	.75	.75
		Nos. 196-199 (4)	2.15	2.15

Independence, 10th Anniv. — A44

Communications.

1987, Dec. 4

200	A44	16c Postal service	.25	.25
201	A44	30c Telephone	.45	.45
202	A44	40c Radio	.65	.65
203	A44	50c Television	.80	.80
		Nos. 200-203 (4)	2.15	2.15

Easter A45

1988, Mar. 31

204	A45	16c John 12:12-14	.25	.25
205	A45	30c Mark 14:10-11	.50	.50
206	A45	40c John 13:5	.70	.70
207	A45	50c John 13:26	.85	.85
		Nos. 204-207 (4)	2.30	2.30

Natl. Parks Board Activities — A46

1988, June 23 — Perf. 14½x14

208	A46	16c Environmental education	.40	.40
209	A46	30c Conservation	.80	.80
210	A46	40c Catering	1.10	1.10
211	A46	50c Tourism	1.40	1.40
		Nos. 208-211 (4)	3.70	3.70

A souvenir sheet of one No. 211 has black and white decorative margin picturing the emblem of the natl. philatelic exhibition held at Pietermaritzburg, Nov. 22-27. Sold for 70c.

Crops A47

1988, Sept. 15 — Perf. 14½x14

212	A47	16c Sunflowers	.35	.35
213	A47	30c Peanuts	.70	.70
214	A47	40c Cotton	1.00	1.00
215	A47	50c Cabbages	1.25	1.25
		Nos. 212-215 (4)	3.30	3.30

Dams — A48

1988, Nov. 17

216	A48	16c Ngotwane	.35	.35
217	A48	30c Groothoek	.65	.65
218	A48	40c Sehujwane	1.00	1.00
219	A48	50c Molatedi	1.10	1.10
		Nos. 216-219 (4)	3.10	3.10

Easter A49

1989, Mar. 9

220	A49	16c Mark 26:26	.35	.35
221	A49	30c Matthew 26:39	.65	.65
222	A49	40c Mark 14:45	1.00	1.00
223	A49	50c John 18:10	1.25	1.25
		Nos. 220-223 (4)	3.25	3.25

Children's Art — A50

Designs: 18c, "Rooster," by Thembi Atong. 30c, "Thatched Hut in Rural Setting," by Muhammad Mahri. 40c, "Modern World," by Tshepo Mashokwe. 50c, "Cityscape," by Miles Brown.

1989, May 11

224	A50	18c multicolored	.45	.45
225	A50	30c multicolored	.70	.70
226	A50	40c multicolored	.95	.95
227	A50	50c multicolored	1.25	1.25
		Nos. 224-227 (4)	3.35	3.35

Birds of Prey — A51

1989, Sept. 1 — Perf. 14x14½

228	A51	18c Elanus caeruleus	.60	.60
229	A51	30c Melierax canorus	1.00	1.00
230	A51	40c Falco naumanni	1.25	1.25
231	A51	50c Circaetus gallicus	1.65	1.65
a.		Souvenir sheet of 1	4.00	4.00
		Nos. 228-231 (4)	4.50	4.50

No. 231a has multicolored decorative margin picturing emblem of the WANDERERS 101 natl. philatelic exhibition held Sept. 6-9. Sold for 1.50r.

Traditional Thatched Dwellings A52

1989, Nov. 28 — Perf. 14½x14

232	A52	18c shown	.40	.40
233	A52	30c multi, diff.	.75	.75
234	A52	40c multi, diff.	.90	.90
235	A52	50c multi, diff.	1.10	1.10
		Nos. 232-235 (4)	3.15	3.15

Community Services A53

1990, Jan. 11

236	A53	18c Playground	.40	.40
237	A53	30c Immunization clinic	.65	.65
238	A53	40c Library	.95	.95
239	A53	50c Hospital	1.25	1.25
		Nos. 236-239 (4)	3.25	3.25

Wildlife (Small Mammals) A54

1990, Apr. 11 — Litho. — Perf. 14½x14

240	A54	21c Dendromus mystacalis	.55	.55
241	A54	30c Ictonyx striatus	.80	.80
242	A54	40c Elephantulus myurus	1.00	1.00
243	A54	50c Procavia capensis	1.25	1.25
a.		Souvenir sheet of 1	3.50	3.50
		Nos. 240-243 (4)	3.60	3.60

No. 243a has multicolored inscribed margin; text publicizes the natl. philatelic exhibition. Sold for 1.50r.

Sandgrouses — A55

1990, July 12 — Litho. — Perf. 14x14½

244	A55	21c Pterocles burchelli	.60	.60
245	A55	35c Pterocles bicinctus	1.10	1.10
246	A55	40c Pterocles namaqua	1.25	1.25
247	A55	50c Pterocles gutturalis	1.50	1.50
		Nos. 244-247 (4)	4.45	4.45

Bus Manufacturing — A56

a, Chassis welding. b, Mounting the engine. c, Body construction. d, Spray painting. e, Completed models and bare chassis.

1990, Aug. 3 — Perf. 14½x14

248		Strip of 5	3.00	3.00
a.-e.		A56 21c any single	.60	.60

Traditional Activities — A57

1990, Oct. 4   **Perf. 14x14½**
249	A57	21c Basketry	.45	.45
250	A57	35c Tanning	.75	.75
251	A57	40c Beer making	.85	.85
252	A57	50c Pottery making	1.10	1.10
		Nos. 249-252 (4)	3.15	3.15

Bophuthatswana Air Force, 10th Anniv. — A58

Helicopters: a, Alouette III. b, BK117. Airplanes: c, Pilatus Trainer PC-7. d, Pilatus Porter PC-6. e, Casa 212.

1990, Dec. 12   **Perf. 14½x14**
253		Strip of 5	6.00	6.00
a.-e.	A58	21c any single	1.00	1.00

Edible Wild Fruit — A59

1991, Jan. 24   Litho.   Perf. 14x14½
254	A59	21c Annona senegalensis	.45	.45
255	A59	35c Strychnos pungens	.75	.75
256	A59	40c Ficus sycomorus	.95	.95
257	A59	50c Dovyalis caffra	1.10	1.10
		Nos. 254-257 (4)	3.25	3.25

Easter A60

1991, Mar. 21   Litho.   Perf. 14½x14
258	A60	21c Mark 14:46	.55	.55
259	A60	35c Mark 14:53	.85	.85
260	A60	40c Mark 14:65	1.10	1.10
261	A60	50c Mark 14:67	1.25	1.25
		Nos. 258-261 (4)	3.75	3.75

Locomotives A61

1991, July 4   **Litho.**
Size: 72x25mm (25c, 50c)
262	A61	25c Class 6A	.60	.60
263	A61	40c Class 7A	1.00	1.00
264	A61	50c Class 6Z	1.25	1.25
265	A61	60c Class 8	1.65	1.65
		Nos. 262-265 (4)	4.50	4.50

A souvenir sheet of 1 #265 was sold by the Philatelic Foundation of South Africa. See Nos. 291-294.

Maps of Africa — A62

1991, Sept. 12   Litho.   Perf. 14x14½
266	A62	25c Caneiro chart, 1502	.50	.50
267	A62	40c Cantino chart, 1502	.85	.85
268	A62	50c Contarini map, 1506	1.10	1.10
269	A62	60c Waldseemuller map, 1507	1.40	1.40
		Nos. 266-269 (4)	3.85	3.85

Maps of Africa A63

1992, Jan. 9   Litho.   Perf. 14½x14
270	A63	27c Fracanzano, 1508	.45	.45
271	A63	45c Waldseemuller, 1513	.80	.80
272	A63	65c Waldseemuller, 1516	1.10	1.10
273	A63	85c Laurent Fries, 1522	1.40	1.40
		Nos. 270-273 (4)	3.75	3.75

Easter A64

1992, Apr. 1   **Litho.**
274	A64	27c Mark 15:1	.45	.45
275	A64	45c Mark 15:15	.80	.80
276	A64	65c Mark 15:17-18	1.10	1.10
277	A64	85c Mark 15:19	1.40	1.40
		Nos. 274-277 (4)	3.75	3.75

Acacia Trees — A65

1992, Sept. 17   **Litho.**
278	A65	35c Karroo	.45	.45
279	A65	70c Erioloba	.90	.90
280	A65	90c Tortilis	1.10	1.10
281	A65	1.05r Mellifera	1.25	1.25
		Nos. 278-281 (4)	3.70	3.70

A souvenir sheet of 1 #279 exists. Sold for 2.50r.

Lost City Hotel Complex, Sun City — A66

a, View from lake. b, Palace. c, Porte cochere. d, Lobby of Palace. e, Tusk bar.

1992, Nov. 19   Litho.   Perf. 14x14½
282		Strip of 5	3.25	3.25
a.-e.	A66	35c any single	.65	.65

Chickens A67

1993, Feb. 12   Litho.   Perf. 14½x14
283	A67	35c Light Sussex	.45	.45
284	A67	70c Rhode Island red	.90	.90
285	A67	90c Brown leghorn	1.25	1.25
286	A67	1.05r White leghorn	1.40	1.40
		Nos. 283-286 (4)	4.00	4.00

A souvenir shet of 1 #284 exists. Sold for 3r.

Easter A68

1993, Mar. 5
287	A68	35c Luke 23:25	.40	.40
288	A68	70c John 19:17	.80	.80
289	A68	90c Mark 15:21	1.10	1.10
290	A68	1.05r Mark 15:23	1.25	1.25
		Nos. 287-290 (4)	3.55	3.55

Trains Type of 1991

Designs: 45c, Mafeking locomotive shed, c. 1933, RR classes 10, 8, & 12. 65c, Locomotive No. 5. 85c, 1934 Royal visit, White Train, SAR Class 16B. 1.05r, SAR class 19D.

1993, June 18   **Litho.**
Size: 72x25mm (45c, 85c)
291	A61	45c multicolored	.50	.50
292	A61	65c multicolored	.75	.75
293	A61	85c multicolored	.95	.95
294	A61	1.05r multicolored	1.25	1.25
a.		Souvenir sheet of 4, #291-294	3.75	3.75
		Nos. 291-294 (4)	3.45	3.45

Maps of Africa A69

Name of cartographer, year published: 45c, Sebastian Munster, 1540. 65c, Jacopo Gastaldi, 1564. 85c, Gerardus Mercator the Younger, 1595. 1.05r, Abraham Ortelius, 1570.

1993, Aug. 20   **Litho.**
295	A69	45c multicolored	.50	.50
296	A69	65c multicolored	.75	.75
297	A69	85c multicolored	.95	.95
298	A69	1.05r multicolored	1.25	1.25
		Nos. 295-298 (4)	3.45	3.45

Easter A70

1994, Mar. 25   Litho.   Perf. 14½x14
299	A70	35c Luke 22:33	.35	.35
300	A70	65c Luke 23:35-36	.70	.70
301	A70	85c Luke 23:36	.90	.90
302	A70	1.05r Luke 23:38	1.00	1.00
		Nos. 299-302 (4)	2.95	2.95

Bophuthatswana ceased to exist 4/27/94.

CISKEI

ˈsis-ˌkī

LOCATION — Enclave, Republic of South Africa
GOVT. — Self-governing tribal homeland
AREA — 5,592 sq. mi.
POP. — 1,000,000
CAPITAL — Bisho

> Catalogue values for all unused stamps in this country are for Never Hinged Items.

Independence from South Africa — A1

Perf. 14x14½
1981, Dec. 4   Litho.   Unwmk.
1	A1	5c Pres. Sebe	.20	.20
2	A1	15c Coat of arms	.25	.25
3	A1	20c Flag	.30	.30
4	A1	25c Mace	.35	.35
		Nos. 1-4 (4)	1.10	1.10

An imperf. souvenir sheet exists containing Nos. 1-4 printed in one color (black). Not valid for postage.

Birds
A2   A3

1981-90   **Perf. 14½x14**
5	A2	1c Tauraco corythaix	.20	.20
6	A2	2c Motacilla capensis	.20	.20
7	A2	3c Centropus superciliosus	.20	.20
8	A2	4c Nectarinia famosa	.20	.20
9	A2	5c Anthropoides paradisea	.20	.20
10	A2	6c Onychognathus morio	.20	.20
11	A2	7c Ceryle maxima	.20	.20
12	A2	8c Bostrychia hagedash	.25	.20
13	A2	9c Cuculus clamosus	.25	.20
14	A2	10c Lybius torquatus	.25	.20
15	A2	11c Oriolus larvatus	.55	.20
16	A2	12c Alcedo cristata	.55	.20
17	A2	14c Upupa epops	.65	.20
18	A2	15c Haliaeetus vocifer	.25	.20
19	A2	16c Batis capensis	.65	.20
20	A3	18c Euplectes progne	1.00	.20
21	A2	20c Macronyx capensis	.35	.25
22	A2	21c Aplopelia larvata	3.25	.20
23	A2	25c Burhinus capensis	.40	.25
24	A2	30c Treron calva	.55	.35
25	A2	50c Poicephalus robustus	.90	.60
26	A2	1r Apaloderma narina	1.50	1.10
27	A2	2r Bubo capensis	3.25	2.25
		Nos. 5-27 (23)	16.00	8.20

Issued: 11c, 4/4/82; 12c, 4/1/85; 14c, 4/1/86; 16c, 4/1/87; 18c, 7/3/89; 21c, 7/3/90; others, 12/4/81.

Nursing A4

1982, Apr. 30   Perf. 14½x14, 14x14½
34	A4	8c Cecilia Makiwane, vert.	.20	.20
35	A4	15c Surgery, vert.	.25	.25
36	A4	20c Nurses pledge to serve	.35	.35
37	A4	25c Hospital care	.45	.45
		Nos. 34-37 (4)	1.25	1.25

Pineapple Industry A5

1982, Aug. 20   **Perf. 14x14½**
38	A5	8c Spraying	.20	.20
39	A5	15c Harvesting	.20	.20
40	A5	20c Transporting fruit to cannery	.20	.20
41	A5	30c Packing	.30	.30
		Nos. 38-41 (4)	.90	.90

Small Mammals A6

1982, Oct. 29

42	A6	8c *Lepus capensis*	.20	.20
43	A6	15c *Vulpes chama*	.30	.30
44	A6	20c *Xerus inaurus*	.35	.35
45	A6	25c *Felis caracal*	.40	.40
		Nos. 42-45 (4)	1.25	1.25

Trees — A7

1983, Feb. 2   **Perf. 14½x14**

46	A7	8c *Cussonia spicata*	.20	.20
47	A7	20c *Curtisia dentata*	.30	.30
48	A7	25c *Calodendrum capense*	.35	.35
49	A7	40c *Podocarpus falcatus*	.60	.60
		Nos. 46-49 (4)	1.45	1.45

1984, Jan. 6

50	A7	10c *Rhus chirindensis*	.20	.20
51	A7	20c *Phoenix reclinata*	.30	.30
52	A7	25c *Ptaeroxylon obliquum*	.35	.35
53	A7	40c *Apodytes dimidiata*	.60	.60
		Nos. 50-53 (4)	1.45	1.45

Sharks — A8

1983, Apr. 13   **Perf. 14x14½**

54	A8	8c Dusky	.20	.20
55	A8	20c Ragged-tooth	.40	.40

Size: 57x21mm

56	A8	25c Tiger	.50	.50
57	A8	30c Scalloped hammer-head	.60	.60
58	A8	40c Great white	.80	.80
		Nos. 54-58 (5)	2.50	2.50

Educational Institutions — A9

1983, July 6

59	A9	10c Lovedale	.20	.20
60	A9	20c Fort Hare	.20	.20
61	A9	25c Healdtown	.25	.25
62	A9	40c Lennox Sebe	.35	.35
		Nos. 59-62 (4)	1.00	1.00

Military Uniforms — A10

6th Foot, 1st Warwickshire Regiment, 1821-27 (No. 63): a, White drill uniform (D1.5). b, Light Company privates (D2.5). c, Grenadier Company sergeants (D3.5). d, Light Co. Officers (D4.5). e, Officer and field officer (D5.5).

Cape Mounted Rifles, 1827-35 (No. 64): a, Trooper and sergeant, 1830 (D1.5). b, Trooper and sergeant in full dress, 1835 (D2.5). c, Officers, 1830 (D3.5). d, Officers in full dress, 1827-34 (D4.5). e, Officers in full dress, 1834 (D5.5).

1983, Sept. 28   **Perf. 14½x14**

63		Strip of 5	1.50	1.50
a.-e.		A10 20c any single	.25	.25

1984, Oct. 26

64		Strip of 5	2.00	1.75
a.-e.		A10 25c any single	.40	.30

Sheets of 10 containing two strips of five.

Coastal Angling A11

Bait.

1984, Apr. 12   **Perf. 14x14½**

65	A11	11c Sand prawn	.20	.20
66	A11	20c Coral worm	.20	.20
67	A11	25c Bloodworm	.25	.25
68	A11	30c Red-bait	.35	.35
		Nos. 65-68 (4)	1.00	1.00

1985, Mar. 7

Game fish.

69	A11	11c *Lithognathus lithognathus*	.20	.20
70	A11	25c *Pachymetopon grande*	.55	.40
71	A11	30c *Argyrosomus hololepidotus*	.65	.45
72	A11	50c *Pomadasys commersonni*	1.00	.70
		Nos. 69-72 (4)	2.40	1.75

Migratory Birds and Maps — A12

1984, Aug. 17   **Perf. 14½x14**

73	A12	11c Banded sand martin	.25	.25
74	A12	25c House martin	.80	.80
75	A12	30c Greater striped swallow	.90	.90
76	A12	45c European swallow	1.25	1.25
		Nos. 73-76 (4)	3.20	3.20

Brownies A13

1985, May 3

77	A13	12c shown	.20	.20
78	A13	25c Rangers planting saplings	.35	.35
79	A13	30c Guide color guard	.40	.40
80	A13	50c Camping	.70	.70
		Nos. 77-80 (4)	1.65	1.65

Intl. Year of the Child, 75th anniv. of the Girl Guide movement.

Small Businesses A14

1985, Aug. 8   **Perf. 14x14½**

81	A14	12c Furniture	.20	.20
82	A14	25c Dress making	.30	.30
83	A14	30c Welding	.40	.40
84	A14	50c Basketry	.65	.65
		Nos. 81-84 (4)	1.55	1.55

Troop Ships — A15

1985, Nov. 15   **Perf. 14½x14**

85	A15	12c *Antelope*	.25	.25
86	A15	25c *Pilot*	.55	.55
87	A15	30c *Salisbury*	.60	.60
88	A15	50c *Olive Branch*	1.10	1.10
		Nos. 85-88 (4)	2.50	2.50

Miniature Sheet

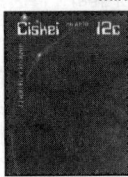

Halley's Comet — A16

Comet streaking through the solar system: a, A1.10. b, A2.10. c, A3.10. d, A4.10. e, A5.10. f, A6.10. g, A7.10. h, A8.10. i, A9.10. j, A10.10.
Illustration reduced.

1986, Mar. 20

89	A16	Sheet of 10	22.50	22.50
a.-j.		12c any single	2.25	2.25

Military Uniforms — A17

98th Foot Regiment: 14c, Fifer in winter. 20c, Private in summer. 25c, Grenadier Company sergeant in summer. 30c, Sergeant-major in winter.

1986, June 12

90	A17	14c multicolored	.25	.25
91	A17	20c multicolored	.35	.35
92	A17	25c multicolored	.45	.45
93	A17	30c multicolored	.50	.50
a.		Souvenir sheet of 1	3.50	3.50
		Nos. 90-93 (4)	1.55	1.55

No. 93a for the natl. philatelic exhibition held at Johannesberg, Oct. 6-11. Sold for 50c.

Bicycle Factory, Dimbaza A18

1986, Sept. 18

94	A18	14c Welding frames	.25	.25
95	A18	20c Painting	.35	.35
96	A18	25c Spoke installation	.40	.40
97	A18	30c Assembly	.50	.50
		Nos. 94-97 (4)	1.50	1.50

Independence, 5th Anniv. — A19

14c, Pres. Sebe. 20c, Natl. shrine, Ntaba kaNdoda. 25c, Legislative Assembly, Bisho. 30c, Automatic telephone exchange, Bisho.

1986, Dec. 4   **Perf. 14x14½**

98	A19	14c multicolored	.25	.25
99	A19	20c multicolored	.35	.35
100	A19	25c multicolored	.40	.40
101	A19	30c multicolored	.50	.50
		Nos. 98-101 (4)	1.50	1.50

Edible Mushrooms A20

1987, Mar. 19

102	A20	14c *Boletus edulis*	.30	.30
103	A20	20c *Macrolepiota zeyheri*	.45	.45
a.		Souvenir sheet of 1	3.50	3.50
104	A20	25c *Termitomyces*	.55	.55
105	A20	30c *Russula capensis*	.65	.65
		Nos. 102-105 (4)	1.95	1.95

No. 103a has fawn and black decorative margin picturing emblem of the natl. philatelic exhibition held at Paarl, Sept. 16-19. Sold for 50c.

Nkone Cattle A21

1987, June 18   **Perf. 14½x14**

106	A21	16c Cow and calf	.25	.25
107	A21	20c Cow	.35	.35
108	A21	25c Bull	.40	.40
109	A21	30c Herd	.50	.50
		Nos. 106-109 (4)	1.50	1.50

Toys — A22

Perf. 14x14½, 14½x14

1987, Sept. 17

110	A22	16c Windmill, vert.	.25	.25
111	A22	20c Rag doll, vert.	.35	.35
112	A22	25c Clay horse	.40	.40
113	A22	30c Wire vehicle	.50	.50
		Nos. 110-113 (4)	1.50	1.50

Folklore A23

Legend of Sikulume: 16c, Seven birds. 20c, Sikulume escapes cannibals. 25c, Fights sea monster. 30c, Elopes and is pursued by bride's father.

1987, Nov. 6   **Perf. 14½x14**

114	A23	16c multicolored	.25	.25
115	A23	20c multicolored	.35	.35
116	A23	25c multicolored	.40	.40
117	A23	30c multicolored	.50	.50
		Nos. 114-117 (4)	1.50	1.50

See Nos. 122, 139-142, 147-150.

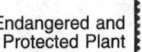

Endangered and Protected Plant Species — A24

1988, Mar. 17   **Perf. 14x14½**

118	A24	16c *Clivia nobilis*	.30	.30
119	A24	30c *Dierama pulcherrimum*	.60	.60
120	A24	40c *Moraea reticulata*	.75	.75

121	A24	50c	*Crinum campanu-latum*	.95	.95
a.			Souvenir sheet of 1	3.50	3.50
			Nos. 118-121 (4)	2.60	2.60

No. 121a margin pictures the emblem of the natl. philatelic exhibition held at Pietermaritzburg, Nov. 22-27. Sold for 1r.

Folklore Type of 1987
Miniature Sheet

Legend of Mbulukazi: a, Two wives (B1.10). b, Two doves appear to Numbakatali (B2.10). c, Birth of Mbulukazi and brother (B3.10). d, Mbulukazi and brother at river (B4.10). e, Chief's son announces marriage (B5.10). f, Chief's son presents wives Mbulukazi and Mahlunguluza with huts (B6.10). g, Mahlunguluza drowns Mbulukazi (B7.10). h, Ox tears down Mahlunguluza's hut (B8.10). i, Mbulukazi revived (B9.10). j, Chief's son embraces Mbulukazi, banishes Mahlunguluza (B10.10).

1988, Aug. 26
Size of Nos. 122a-122j: 36x20mm

| 122 | | Sheet of 10 | 3.75 | 3.75 |
| a.-j. | A23 16c any single | | .35 | .35 |

Citrus Farming A25

1988, Sept. 29

123	A25	16c	Nursery	.30	.30
124	A25	30c	Grafting	.60	.60
125	A25	40c	Picking fruit	.70	.70
126	A25	50c	Grading	.95	.95
			Nos. 123-126 (4)	2.55	2.55

Poisonous Mushrooms A26

1988, Dec. 1

127	A26	16c	*Amanita phalloides*	.40	.40
128	A26	30c	*Chlorophyllum molybdites*	.80	.80
129	A26	40c	*Amanita muscaria*	1.00	1.00
130	A26	50c	*Amanita pantherina*	1.25	1.25
			Nos. 127-130 (4)	3.45	3.45

Dams — A27

1989, Mar. 2   Perf. 14½x14

131	A27	16c	Kat River	.35	.35
132	A27	30c	Cata	.70	.70
133	A27	40c	Binfield Park	.90	.90
134	A27	50c	Sandile	1.00	1.00
			Nos. 131-134 (4)	2.95	2.95

Trout Hatcheries A28

Artificial fertilization: 18c, Obtaining eggs from trout. 30c, Fertilized ova, alevins. 40c, Rainbow trout at 5 weeks. 40c, Adult male rainbow trout.

1989, June 8

135	A28	18c	multicolored	.50	.50
136	A28	30c	multicolored	.75	.75
137	A28	40c	multicolored	1.10	1.10

138	A28	50c	multicolored	1.25	1.25
a.			Souvenir sheet of 1	4.00	4.00
			Nos. 135-138 (4)	3.60	3.60

No. 138a margin pictures emblem of the natl. philatelic exhibition WANDERERS 101, held Sept. 6-9. Sold for 1.50r.

Folklore Type of 1987

Legend of the Little Jackal and the Lion: 18c, Lion and Jackal hunt large eland. 30c, Jackal and offspring climbing to lair. 40c, Lion roaring, jackal under rock. 50c, Lion falling.

1989, Sept. 21

139	A23	18c	multicolored	.40	.40
140	A23	30c	multicolored	.70	.70
141	A23	40c	multicolored	.95	.95
142	A23	50c	multicolored	1.25	1.25
			Nos. 139-142 (4)	3.30	3.30

Early Transportation A29

1989, Dec. 7   Perf. 14x14½

143	A29	18c	Cape cart	.40	.40
144	A29	30c	Jubilee Spider	.70	.70
145	A29	40c	Transport wagon	.95	.95
146	A29	50c	Voortrekker wagon	1.25	1.25
			Nos. 143-146 (4)	3.30	3.30

Folklore Type of 1987

The Legend of Five Heads: 18c, Mpunzikazi presenting offering to Makanda Mahlanu, the 5-headed snake chief. 30c, Snake chief kills Mpunzikazi. 40c, Mpunzanyan presents offering to snake chief. 50c, Snake chief transformed into a man and marries Mpunzanyan.

1990, Mar. 15   Perf. 14½x14

147	A23	18c	multicolored	.40	.40
148	A23	30c	multicolored	.70	.70
149	A23	40c	multicolored	.95	.95
150	A23	50c	multicolored	1.25	1.25
			Nos. 147-150 (4)	3.30	3.30

Handmade Carpets — A30

1990, June 14 Litho. Perf. 14x14½

151	A30	21c	Hand weaving	.50	.50
152	A30	35c	Spinning	.80	.80
153	A30	40c	Dyeing yarn	.95	.95
154	A30	50c	Hand weaving, diff.	1.10	1.10
a.			Souvenir sheet of 1	3.50	3.50
			Nos. 151-154 (4)	3.35	3.35

No. 154a for the 150th anniv. of the Penny Black. Sold for 1.50r.

Plows — A31

1990, Sept. 6 Litho. Perf. 14½x14

155	A31	21c	Wooden beam, c. 1855	.35	.35
156	A31	35c	Triple disc, c. 1895	.60	.60
157	A31	40c	Reversible disc, c. 1895	.70	.70
158	A31	50c	"Het Volk", c. 1910	.85	.85
			Nos. 155-158 (4)	2.50	2.50

Prickly Pear — A32

1990, Nov. 29   Litho.

159	A32	21c	Vendor	.55	.55
160	A32	35c	Prickly pear bush	.90	.90
161	A32	40c	shown	1.00	1.00

| 162 | A32 | 50c | Flowering prickly pear | 1.25 | 1.25 |
| | | | Nos. 159-162 (4) | 3.70 | 3.70 |

Owls — A33

1991, Feb. 2 Litho. Perf. 14x14½

163	A33	21c	Marsh owl	.55	.55
164	A33	35c	Scops owl	.90	.90
165	A33	40c	Barn owl	1.10	1.10
166	A33	50c	Wood owl	1.25	1.25
a.			Miniature sheet of 1	3.75	3.75
			Nos. 163-166 (4)	3.80	3.80

First Letter From South Africa — A34

Designs: a, Map showing location of Sao Bras (Mossel Bay), 1500. b, Storm-damaged ship off Cabo Tormentoso, 1500. c, Pedro d'Ataide lands at Sao Bras, 1501. d, D'Ataide leaves letter in boot, 1501. e, Joao da Nova finds letter, 1501.

1991, May 11   Litho.

| 167 | A34 | 25c | Strip of 5, #a.-e. | 3.75 | 3.75 |

Inscriptions on #167a & 167b are reversed.

Solar System A35

1991, Aug. 1 Litho. Perf. 14½x14

168	A35	1c	Comet nucleus	.20	.20
169	A35	2c	Trojan asteroids	.20	.20
170	A35	5c	Meteoroid	.20	.20
171	A35	7c	Pluto	.20	.20
172	A35	10c	Neptune	.20	.20
173	A35	20c	Uranus	.20	.20
174	A35	25c	Saturn	.25	.25
175	A35	30c	Jupiter	.30	.30
176	A35	35c	Asteroid belt	.35	.35
177	A35	40c	Mars	.45	.45
178	A35	50c	Earth's moon	.55	.55
179	A35	60c	Earth	.65	.65
180	A35	1r	Venus	1.10	1.10
181	A35	2r	Mercury	2.40	2.40
182	A35	5r	Sun	5.50	5.50
a.			Min. sheet of 15, #168-182	16.00	16.00
			Nos. 168-182 (15)	12.75	12.75

Frontier Forts A36

Designs: 27c, Xhosa warrior, Fort Armstrong. 45c, Sir George Grey, Keiskamma Hoek Post. 65c, Chief Sandile, Fort Hare. 85c, Cavalryman, Cavalry Barracks, Peddie.

1991, Nov. 7 Litho. Perf. 14x14½

183	A36	27c	multicolored	.35	.35
184	A36	45c	multicolored	.65	.65
185	A36	65c	multicolored	.85	.85
186	A36	85c	multicolored	1.25	1.25
			Nos. 183-186 (4)	3.10	3.10

Cloud Formations — A37

1992, Mar. 19   Litho.

187	A37	27c	Cumulonimbus	.35	.35
188	A37	45c	Altocumulus	.65	.65
189	A37	65c	Cirrus	.85	.85
190	A37	85c	Cumulus	1.25	1.25
			Nos. 187-190 (4)	3.10	3.10

Satellites A38

1992, June 4 Litho. Perf. 14½x14½

191	A38	35c	Intelsat VI	.40	.40
192	A38	70c	GPS Navstar	.80	.80
193	A38	90c	Meteosat	1.00	1.00
194	A38	1.05r	Landsat VI	1.10	1.10
			Nos. 191-194 (4)	3.30	3.30

A souvenir sheet of one No. 192 exists. Sold for 2.50r.

Farm Implements A39

35c, John Deere universal disc-harrow, c. 1914. 70c, John Deere clod crusher & pulverizer, c. 1914. 90c, Self-dump hay rake, c. 1910. 1.05r, McCormick hay tedder, c. 1900.

1992, Aug. 20   Litho.

195	A39	35c	multicolored	.40	.40
196	A39	70c	multicolored	.80	.80
197	A39	90c	multicolored	1.00	1.00
198	A39	1.05r	multicolored	1.10	1.10
			Nos. 195-198 (4)	3.30	3.30

Hotels A40

Designs: 35c, Mpekweni Sun Marine Resort. 70c, Katberg Protea Hotel. 90c, Fish River Sun Hotel. 1.05r, Amatola Sun Hotel.

1992, Nov. 5   Litho.

199	A40	35c	multicolored	.40	.40
200	A40	70c	multicolored	.80	.80
201	A40	90c	multicolored	1.00	1.00
202	A40	1.05r	multicolored	1.10	1.10
			Nos. 199-202 (4)	3.30	3.30

Famous Explorers A41

Map of voyage, sailing ship, and explorer: 45c, San Gabriel, 1497-98, Vasco da Gama. 65c, Endeavour, 1768-71, James Cook. 85c, Victoria, 1519, Ferdinand Magellan. 90c, Golden Hinde, 1577-80, Sir Francis Drake. 1.05r, Heemskerck, 1642, Abel Tasman.

1993, May 19   Litho.

203	A41	45c	multicolored	.35	.35
204	A41	65c	multicolored	.60	.60
205	A41	70c	multicolored	.70	.70
206	A41	90c	multicolored	.75	.75
207	A41	1.05r	multicolored	.85	.85
			Nos. 203-207 (5)	3.25	3.25

Small Cage
Birds — A42

Designs: 45c, Serinus canarius domesticus.
65c, Melopsittacus undulatus. 85c, Agapornis
roseicollis. 90c, Nymphicus hollandicus. 1.05r,
Chloebia gouldiae.

1993, July 16   **Litho.**
208 A42 45c multicolored   .35 .35
209 A42 65c multicolored   .60 .60
210 A42 85c multicolored   .70 .70
211 A42 90c multicolored   .75 .75
212 A42 1.05r multicolored   .85 .85
     Nos. 208-212 (5)   3.25 3.25

A souvenir sheet of one No. 209 has inscription for National Philatelic Exhibition. Sold for
3r.

Churches
A43

45c, Goshen Mission Church. 65c, Kamas-
tone Mission Church. 85c, Richie Thompson
Memorial Church. 1.05r, Bryce Ross Memorial
Church.

1993, Sept. 17   **Litho.**
213 A43 45c black, buff & red   .50 .50
214 A43 65c black, blue & red   .70 .70
215 A43 85c black, tan & red   .95 .95
216 A43 1.05r blk, lt yel & red   1.25 1.25
     Nos. 213-216 (4)   3.40 3.40

Invader
Plants — A44

1993, Nov. 5   **Litho.**   **Perf. 14x14½**
217 A44 45c Opuntia aurantiaca   .50 .50
218 A44 65c Datura stramonium   .70 .70
219 A44 85c Sesbania punicea   .95 .95
220 A44 1.05r Nicotiana glauca   1.25 1.25
   a.   Souvenir sheet, #217-220   3.25 3.25
     Nos. 217-220 (4)   3.40 3.40

Shipwrecks
A45

1994, Feb. 18   **Litho.**   **Perf. 14½x14**
221 A45 45c SS Losna, 1921   .45 .45
222 A45 65c Catherine, 1846   .65 .65
223 A45 85c Bennebroek, 1713   .80 .80
224 A45 1.05r Sao Joao Bapista,
           1622   1.10 1.10
     Nos. 221-224 (4)   3.00 3.00

Roses
A46

1994, Apr. 15   **Litho.**   **Perf. 14½x14**
225 A46 45c Herman Steyn   .45 .45
226 A46 70c Esther
         Geldenhuys   .65 .65
227 A46 95c Margaret Was-
         serfall   .80 .80

---

228 A46 1.15r Prof. Fred Ziady   1.10 1.10
   a.   Souvenir sheet of 4, #225-228   3.00 3.00
     Nos. 225-228 (4)   3.00 3.00

Ciskei ceased to exist April 27, 1994.

TRANSKEI

ˌtranˌtsˈki

LOCATION — Enclave, East Cape
Province, Republic of South Africa
GOVT. — Self-governing tribal
homeland
AREA — 16,910 sq. mi.
POP. — 2,876,122 (1985)
CAPITAL — Umtata

Catalogue values for all unused
stamps in this country are for
Never Hinged items.

Independence from
South Africa — A1

     Perf. 12½
1976, Oct. 26   **Litho.**   **Unwmk.**
1 A1 4c Paramount Chief
         K.D. Matanzima   .50 .50
2 A1 10c Mace, flag   1.10 1.10
3 A1 15c Matanzima, diff.   1.90 1.90
4 A1 20c Coat of arms   2.50 2.50
     Nos. 1-4 (4)   6.00 6.00

An imperf. souvenir sheet exists containing
Nos. 1-4 printed in one color (black). Not valid
for postage.

Lubisi
Dam — A2

1976, Oct. 26   **Perf. 12x12½**
5 A2 1c shown   .20 .20
6 A2 2c Soil cultivation   .20 .20
7 A2 3c Threshing sor-
         ghum   .20 .20
8 A2 4c Transkei matron   3.00 .30
9 A2 5c Grinding corn   3.00 .30
10 A2 6c Cutting *Phormium
         tenax*   .25 .20
11 A2 7c Shepherd boy   .25 .20
12 A2 8c Felling timber   .25 .20
13 A2 9c Agricultural school   .30 .25
14 A2 10c Picking tea   .30 .25
15 A2 15c Wood gathering   .35 .25
16 A2 20c Weaving industry   .35 .20
17 A2 25c Improving cattle
         breeds   .45 .25
18 A2 30c Sledge transporta-
         tion   .75 .60
19 A2 50c Map, coat of arms   .65 .60
20 A2 1r Administrative
         Building, Umtata   1.25 1.25
21 A2 2r The Bunga, flag   2.25 2.10
     Nos. 5-21 (17)   14.00 7.50
     Perf. 14
5a A2 1c   .20 .20
6a A2 2c   .20 .20
7a A2 3c   .20 .20
8a A2 4c   .20 .20
9a A2 5c   .20 .20
10a A2 6c   .20 .20
12a A2 8c   .20 .20
13a A2 9c   .20 .20
14a A2 10c   .30 .30
15a A2 15c   .40 .40
16a A2 20c   .55 .55
17a A2 25c   .70 .70
18a A2 30c   .90 .90
19a A2 50c   1.40 1.40
     Nos. 5a-19a (14)   5.85 5.85

Transkei Airways Inaugural Flight,
Umtata-Johannesburg — A3

1977, Feb. 11
22 A3 4c Aircraft   .75 .75
23 A3 15c Aircraft, terminal   3.00 3.00

Artemesia affra — A4

Medicinal plants.

1977, May 16   **Perf. 12½x12**
24 A4 4c shown   .50 .50
25 A4 10c *Bulbine natalensis*   2.00 2.00
26 A4 15c *Melianthus major*   3.00 3.00
27 A4 20c *Cotyledon orbiculata*   4.25 4.25
     Nos. 24-27 (4)   9.75 9.75

1978, Sept. 25

Edible fruit.

28 A4 4c *Carissa bispinosa*   .20 .20
29 A4 10c *Dovyalis caffra*   .45 .45
30 A4 15c *Harpephyllum caffrum*   .65 .65
31 A4 20c *Syzygium cordatum*   .90 .90
     Nos. 28-31 (4)   2.20 2.20

1981, Apr. 15

Medicinal plants.

32 A4 5c *Leonotis leonurus*   .20 .20
33 A4 15c *Euphorbia bupleurifolia*   .30 .30
34 A4 20c *Pelargonium reniforme*   .40 .40
35 A4 25c *Hibiscus trionum*   .50 .50
     Nos. 32-35 (4)   1.40 1.40

Transkei
Radio, 1st
Anniv.
A5

1977, Oct. 26   **Perf. 12x12½**
36 A5 4c Disc jockey   .50 .50
37 A5 15c Announcer   1.25 1.25

"Help the Blind" — A6

1977, Nov. 18   **Perf. 12½x12**
38 A6 4c Basket weaver   .20 .20
39 A6 15c Reading Braille   .80 .80
40 A6 20c Spinning wool   1.00 1.00
     Nos. 38-40 (3)   2.00 2.00

1978, Nov. 30

"Care for Cripples."

41 A6 4c Leg brace on boy   .20 .20
42 A6 10c Man in wheelchair   .55 .55
43 A6 15c Nurse examining boy   .75 .75
     Nos. 41-43 (3)   1.50 1.50

Men's
Pipes
A7

1978, Mar. 1   **Perf. 12x12½**
44 A7 4c shown   .50 .50
45 A7 10c multi, diff.   .75 .75
46 A7 15c multi, diff.   1.25 1.25
47 A7 20c Woman's and witch
         doctor's pipes   1.50 1.50
     Nos. 44-47 (4)   4.00 4.00

Weaving
Industry
A8

1978, June 9
48 A8 4c Angora goat   .35 .35
49 A8 10c Spinning mohair   .80 .80
50 A8 15c Dyeing mohair   1.25 1.25
51 A8 20c Weaving mohair rug   1.60 1.60
     Nos. 48-51 (4)   4.00 4.00

Initiation Ceremony of Xhosa
Men — A9

1979, Jan. 30   **Perf. 12½**
52 A9 4c Chi Cha youth   .20 .20
53 A9 10c Youths in seclusion   .55 .55
54 A9 15c Umtshilo dance   .65 .65
55 A9 20c Leaving the Sutu   .85 .85
     Nos. 52-55 (4)   2.25 2.25

Chief   Water
Matanzima   Resources
A10   A11

1979, Feb. 20   **Perf. 14½x14**
56 A10 4c brn car & gold   .20 .20
57 A10 15c olive grn & gold   .40 .40

Inauguration of Matanzima, second state
president.

1979, Mar. 13   **Perf. 14½x14, 14x14½**
58 A11 4c Windmill   .20 .20
59 A11 10c Woman filling water
         jar   .40 .40
60 A11 15c Irrigation, Indwe Riv-
         er, horiz.   .60 .60
61 A11 20c Ncora dam, horiz.   .75 .75
     Nos. 58-61 (4)   1.95 1.95

Waterfalls   Child Healh
A12   Care
              A13

1979, Sept. 4
62 A12 4c Magwa Falls   .20 .20
63 A12 10c Bawa Falls   .30 .30
64 A12 15c Waterfall Bluff, horiz.   .45 .45
65 A12 20c Tsitsa Falls, horiz.   .60 .60
     Nos. 62-65 (4)   1.55 1.55

1979, Dec. 3   **Perf. 14½x14**
66 A13 5c Pre-natal nourish-
         ment   .20 .20
67 A13 15c Primary feeding   .45 .45
68 A13 20c Immunization   .65 .65
     Nos. 66-68 (3)   1.30 1.30

Fishing
Flies — A14

a, Durham ranger. b, Colonel Bates. c, Black gnat. d, Zug bug. e, March brown.

1980, Jan. 15   **Perf. 14x14½**
69	Strip of 5	2.50	2.50
a.-e.	A14 5c any single	.50	.50

1981, Jan. 15

Designs: a, Kent's lightning. b, Wickham's fancy. c, Jock Scott. d, Green highlander. e, Tan nymph.

70	Strip of 5	1.50	1.50
a.-e.	A14 10c any single	.30	.30

1982, Jan. 6

a, Royal coachman. b, Light spruce. c, Montana nymph. d, Butcher. e, Blue charm.

71	Strip of 5	1.50	1.50
a.-e.	A14 10c any single	.30	.30

1983, Mar. 2

Designs: a, Alexandra. b, Kent's marbled sedge. c, White marabou. d, Mayfly nymph. e, Silver Wilkinson.

72	Strip of 5	2.00	2.00
a.-e.	A14 20c any single	.40	.40

1984, Feb. 10

Designs: a, Silver gray. b, Ginger quill. c, Hardy's favorite. d, March brown nymph. e, Kent's spectrum Mohawk.

73	Strip of 5	2.50	2.50
a.-e.	A14 20c any single	.50	.50

Rotary Intl., 75th Anniv. — A15

Cycads — A16

1980, Feb. 22   **Perf. 14½x14**
74	A15 15c blk, ultra & gold	.40	.40

1980, Apr. 30
75	A16	5c	Encephalartos altensteinii	.20	.20
76	A16	10c	Encephalartos princeps	.25	.25
77	A16	15c	Encephalartos vilosus	.35	.35
78	A16	20c	Encephalartos friderici-guilielmi	.50	.50
			Nos. 75-78 (4)	1.30	1.30

Birds — A17

1980, July 30
79	A17	5c	Cuculus solitarius	.25	.25
80	A17	10c	Batis capensis	.55	.55
81	A17	15c	Balearica pavonina	.85	.85
82	A17	20c	Ploceus ocularius	1.10	1.10
			Nos. 79-82 (4)	2.75	2.75

Tourism — A18

1980, Oct. 26
83	A18	5c	Hole in the Wall	.20	.20
84	A18	10c	Port St. Johns	.30	.30
85	A18	15c	The Citadel	.40	.40
86	A18	20c	The Archway	.50	.50
			Nos. 83-86 (4)	1.40	1.40

Xhosa Women's Headdresses — A19

1981, Aug. 28
87	A19	5c	Eyamakhwenkwe	.20	.20
88	A19	15c	Eyabafana	.30	.30
89	A19	20c	Umfazana	.35	.35
90	A19	25c	Ixhegokazi	.45	.45
a.			Souvenir sheet of 4, #87-90	1.90	1.90
			Nos. 87-90 (4)	1.30	1.30

Independence, 5th Anniv. — A20

1981, Oct. 26   **Perf. 14x14½**
91	A20	5c	State House	.20	.20
92	A20	15c	University	.40	.40

Boy Scout Movement, 75th Anniv. A21   Great Medical Pioneers A22

1982, May 14   **Perf. 14½x14**
93	A21	8c	Salute	.20	.20
94	A21	10c	Planting tree	.20	.20
95	A21	20c	Rafting	.40	.40
96	A21	25c	Nature hike with dog	.50	.50
			Nos. 93-96 (4)	1.30	1.30

1982, Oct. 5
97	A22	15c	Hippocrates	.35	.35
98	A22	20c	Anton van Leeuwenhoek	.45	.45
99	A22	25c	William Harvey	.55	.55
100	A22	30c	Joseph Lister	.65	.65
			Nos. 97-100 (4)	2.00	2.00

1983, Aug. 17
101	A22	10c	Edward Jenner	.30	.30
102	A22	20c	Gregor Mendel	.65	.65
103	A22	25c	Louis Pasteur	.80	.80
104	A22	40c	Florence Nightingale	1.25	1.25
			Nos. 101-104 (4)	3.00	3.00

1984, Oct. 12
105	A22	11c	Nicholas of Cusa	.40	.40
106	A22	25c	William Morton	.90	.90
107	A22	30c	Wilhelm Roentgen	1.10	1.10
108	A22	45c	Karl Landsteiner	1.65	1.65
			Nos. 105-108 (4)	4.05	4.05

1985, Sept. 20
109	A22	12c	Andreas Vesalius	.45	.45
110	A22	25c	Marcello Malpighi	1.10	1.10
111	A22	30c	Francois Magendie	1.40	1.40
112	A22	50c	William Stewart Halsted	2.00	2.00
			Nos. 109-112 (4)	4.95	4.95
			Nos. 97-112 (16)	14.00	14.00

Umtata, Cent. A23

Architecture: 8c, City Hall. 15c, The Bunga. 20c, Botha Sigcau Building. 25c, Palace of Justice, Matanzima Building.

1982, Nov. 10   **Perf. 14x14½**
113	A23	8c	multicolored	.20	.20
114	A23	15c	multicolored	.20	.20
115	A23	20c	multicolored	.30	.30
116	A23	25c	multicolored	.40	.40
			Nos. 113-116 (4)	1.10	1.10

Wildcoast Holiday Resort, Mzamba A24

1983, May 25
117	A24	10c	Hotel complex	.20	.20
118	A24	20c	Beach scene	.35	.35
119	A24	25c	Casino	.45	.45
120	A24	40c	Carousel	.65	.65
			Nos. 117-120 (4)	1.65	1.65

Post Offices A25

1983, Nov. 9   **Perf. 14½x14**
121	A25	10c	Lady Frere	.20	.20
122	A25	20c	Idutywa	.30	.30
123	A25	25c	Lusikisiki	.40	.40
124	A25	40c	Cala	.60	.60
			Nos. 121-124 (4)	1.50	1.50

1984, May 11
125	A25	11c	Umzimkulu	.20	.20
126	A25	20c	Mount Fletcher	.30	.30
127	A25	25c	Qumbu	.40	.40
128	A25	30c	Umtata	.60	.60
			Nos. 125-128 (4)	1.50	1.50

Xhosa Lifestyle A26

1984-90
129	A26	1c	Amagqira	.20	.20
130	A26	2c	Horsemen	.20	.20
131	A26	3c	Mat maker	.20	.20
132	A26	4c	Xhosa dancers	.20	.20
133	A26	5c	Man, donkeys	.20	.20
134	A26	6c	Musicians	.20	.20
135	A26	7c	Fingo brides	.20	.20
136	A26	8c	Tasting beer	.20	.20
137	A26	9c	Thinning corn	.20	.20
138	A26	10c	Dance demonstration	.20	.20
139	A26	11c	Carrying water from the river	.20	.20
140	A26	12c	Meal preparation	.25	.25
141	A26	14c	Weeding	.25	.25
142	A26	15c	Stick fighting	.30	.30
143	A26	16c	Morning pasture	.30	.30
144	A26	20c	Abakhwetha dancers	.40	.40
145	A26	21c	Building initiation hut	.40	.40
146	A26	25c	Tribesmen singing	.45	.45
147	A26	30c	Matrons	.50	.50
148	A26	50c	Pipe maker	.95	.95
149	A26	1r	Intonjane women	1.90	1.90
150	A26	2r	Abakhwetha	4.00	4.00
			Nos. 129-150 (22)	11.90	11.90

Issued: 11c, 4/2/84; 12c, 4/1/85; 14c, 4/1/86; 16c, 4/1/87; 21c, 7/3/90; others, 7/6/84.

Soil Conservation A27

Designs: 11c, Erosion from over-grazing. 25c, Wall construction to collect sediment. 30c, Regeneration of vegetation. 50c, Cattle grazing on verdant plain.

1985, Feb. 7
155	A27	11c	shown	.20	.20
156	A27	25c	multicolored	.45	.45
157	A27	30c	multicolored	.50	.50
158	A27	50c	multicolored	.85	.85
			Nos. 155-158 (4)	2.00	2.00

Bridges A28

1985, Apr. 18
159	A28	12c	Tsitsa	.20	.20
160	A28	25c	White Kei	.45	.45
161	A28	30c	Mitchell	.50	.50
162	A28	50c	Umzimvubu	.85	.85
			Nos. 159-162 (4)	2.00	2.00

Match Industry — A29

1985, July 25   **Perf. 14½x14**
163	A29	12c	Peeling logs	.20	.20
164	A29	25c	Splint chopping	.45	.45
165	A29	30c	VPO machine	.50	.50
166	A29	50c	Filling boxes	.85	.85
			Nos. 163-166 (4)	2.00	2.00

Port St. Johns A30

Designs: 12c, Early street scene. 20c, Coaster Umzimvubu at the Old Jetty. 25c, Unloading corn from wagons at the Jetty. 30c, View of the town, 1890's.

1986, Feb. 6
167	A30	12c	multicolored	.20	.20
168	A30	20c	multicolored	.35	.35
169	A30	25c	multicolored	.45	.45
170	A30	30c	multicolored	.55	.55
a.			Souvenir sheet of 4, #167-170	2.50	2.50
			Nos. 167-170 (4)	1.55	1.55

Aloes — A31

1986, May 1
171	A31	14c	Aloe ferox	.20	.20
172	A31	20c	Aloe arborescens	.30	.30
173	A31	25c	Aloe maculata	.40	.40
174	A31	30c	Aloe ecklonis	.50	.50
a.			Souvenir sheet of 1	4.00	4.00
			Nos. 171-174 (4)	1.40	1.40

No. 174a margin pictures emblem of the natl. philatelic exhibition held at Johannesburg, Oct. 6-11. Sold for 50c.

Hydroelectric Power Stations A32

14c, First Falls, Umtata River. 20c, Second Falls, Umtata River. 25c, Ncora, Qumanco River. 30c, Collywobbles, Mbashe River.

1986, July 24
175	A32	14c	shown	.25	.25
176	A32	20c	multicolored	.35	.35
177	A32	25c	multicolored	.40	.40
178	A32	30c	multicolored	.50	.50
			Nos. 175-178 (4)	1.50	1.50

Independence, 10th Anniv. — A33

Designs: 14c, Prime Minister G. M. Matanzima. 20c, Technical College, Umtata. 25c, University of Transkei, Umtata. 30c, Palace of Justice, Umtata.

1986, Oct. 26
179	A33	14c multicolored	.20	.20
180	A33	20c multicolored	.30	.30
181	A33	25c multicolored	.35	.35
182	A33	30c multicolored	.40	.40
		Nos. 179-182 (4)	1.25	1.25

Transkei Airways, 10th Anniv. — A34

1987, Feb. 5
183	A34	14c shown	.30	.30
184	A34	20c Aircraft tail	.45	.45
185	A34	25c Nose, propellers	.55	.55
186	A34	30c Plane, control tower	.65	.65
		Nos. 183-186 (4)	1.95	1.95

Beadwork — A35

1987, May 22   *Perf. 14x14½*
187	A35	16c Pondo girl	.30	.30
188	A35	20c Bomvana woman	.40	.40
189	A35	25c Xessibe woman	.50	.50
a.		Souvenir sheet of 1	3.50	3.50
190	A35	30c Xhosa man	.65	.65
		Nos. 187-190 (4)	1.85	1.85

No. 189a has blue and black decorative margin picturing the emblem of the natl. philatelic exhibition held at Paarl, Sept. 16-19. Sold for 50c.

1987, Aug. 24
191	A36	16c *Latrodectus indistinctus*	.60	.60
192	A36	20c *Nephila pilipes fenestrata*	.75	.75
193	A36	25c *Lycosidae*	.95	.95
194	A36	30c *Argiope nigrovittata*	1.10	1.10
		Nos. 191-194 (4)	3.40	3.40

Spiders — A36

Domestic Animals A37

1987, Oct. 22
195	A37	16c Black pigs	.40	.40
196	A37	30c Goats	.75	.75
197	A37	40c Merino sheep	.95	.95
198	A37	50c Cattle	1.25	1.25
		Nos. 195-198 (4)	3.35	3.35

Seaweed — A38

1988, Feb. 18
199	A38	16c *Plocamium corallorhiza*	.40	.40
200	A38	30c *Gelidium amanzil*	.70	.70
201	A38	40c *Ecklonia biruncinata*	1.00	1.00
202	A38	50c *Halimeda cuneata*	1.25	1.25
		Nos. 199-202 (4)	3.35	3.35

Blanket Factory, Butterworth A39

1988, May 5   *Perf. 14½x14*
203	A39	16c Spinning machines	.40	.40
204	A39	30c Warping machine	.70	.70
205	A39	40c Weaving machine	1.00	1.00
206	A39	50c Raising the nap	1.25	1.25
		Nos. 203-206 (4)	3.35	3.35

Wreck of the *Grosvenor*, 1782 — A40

Designs: 16c, Ship, map. 30c, *The Wreck of the Grosvenor*, by R. Smirke. 40c, Dirk hilt, compass and coins salvaged. 50c, *African Hospitality*, by G. Morland.

1988, Aug. 4
207	A40	16c multicolored	.40	.40
208	A40	30c multicolored	.75	.75
209	A40	40c multicolored	1.00	1.00
210	A40	50c multicolored	1.25	1.25
a.		Souvenir sheet of 1	4.00	4.00
		Nos. 207-210 (4)	3.40	3.40

No. 210a margin pictures emblem of the natl. philatelic exhibition at Pietermaritzburg, Nov. 22-27. Sold for 1r.

Endangered Species A41

1988, Oct. 20
211	A41	16c *Felis nigripes*	.50	.50
212	A41	30c *Philantomba monticola*	.95	.95
213	A41	40c *Ourebia ourebi*	1.25	1.25
214	A41	50c *Lycaon pictus*	1.50	1.50
		Nos. 211-214 (4)	4.20	4.20

Locomotive, Trains and Bridges — A42

Designs: 16c, Class 14 CRB locomotive. 30c, CRB pulling train over Toleni-Halt Bridge. 40c, Train on the Great Kei River Bridge, vert. 50c, Train in the Kei Valley.

1989, Jan. 19   *Perf. 14x14½, 14½x14*
215	A42	16c multi	.45	.45
216	A42	30c multi	.85	.85
217	A42	40c multi	1.25	1.25
218	A42	50c multi, vert.	1.40	1.40
		Nos. 215-218 (4)	3.95	3.95

A souvenir sheet of one No. 218 has margin picturing the emblem of the natl. philatelic exhibition WANDERERS 101, held Sept. 6-9. Sold for 1.50r.

Basketry A43

1989, Apr. 20   *Perf. 14½x14*
219	A43	18c shown	.45	.45
220	A43	30c multi, diff.	.75	.75
221	A43	40c multi, diff.	.95	.95
222	A43	50c multi, diff.	1.25	1.25
		Nos. 219-222 (4)	3.40	3.40

Mackerel A44

1989, July 20
223	A44	18c shown	.50	.50
224	A44	30c Squid	.80	.80
225	A44	40c Brown mussel	1.00	1.00
226	A44	50c Rock lobster	1.40	1.40
		Nos. 223-226 (4)	3.70	3.70

Trees A45

1989, Oct. 5   *Perf. 14x14½*
227	A45	18c Broom cluster fig	.45	.45
228	A45	30c Natal fig	.75	.75
229	A45	40c Broad-leaved coral	.95	.95
230	A45	50c Cabbage tree	1.25	1.25
		Nos. 227-230 (4)	3.40	3.40

Fossils A46

1990, Jan. 18
231	A46	18c *Ginkgo koningensis*	.60	.60
232	A46	30c *Pseudoctenis spatulata*	1.10	1.10
233	A46	40c *Rissikia media*	1.40	1.40
234	A46	50c *Taeniopteris anavolans*	1.90	1.90
		Nos. 231-234 (4)	5.00	5.00

Great Medical Pioneers — A47

Diviners — A48

1990, Mar. 29   *Perf. 14x14½*
235	A47	18c Aretaeus	.60	.60
236	A47	30c Claude Bernard	1.00	1.00
237	A47	40c Oscar Minkowski	1.40	1.40
238	A47	50c Frederick Banting	1.75	1.75
		Nos. 235-238 (4)	4.75	4.75

1990, June 28 Litho. *Perf. 14x14½*
239	A48	21c Dancing to the Drum	.65	.65
240	A48	35c Lecturing Imichetywa	1.10	1.10
241	A48	40c Initiation ceremony	1.25	1.25
242	A48	50c Induction ceremony	1.50	1.50
a.		Souvenir sheet of 1	4.00	4.00
		Nos. 239-242 (4)	4.50	4.50

No. 242a for the 150th anniv. of the Penny Black. Sold for 1.50r.

Flowers — A49

Parasitic Plants — A50

1990, Sept. 20 Litho. *Perf. 14x14½*
243	A49	21c *Cyrtanthus obliquus*	.55	.55
244	A49	35c *Disa crassicornis*	.95	.95
245	A49	40c *Sandersonia aurantiaca*	1.10	1.10
246	A49	50c *Podranea ricasoliana*	1.25	1.25
		Nos. 243-246 (4)	3.85	3.85

1991, Jan. 10   Litho.
247	A50	21c *Harveya pulchra*	.60	.60
248	A50	35c *Harveya speciosa*	.95	.95
249	A50	40c *Alectra sessiliflora*	1.10	1.10
250	A50	50c *Hydnora africana*	1.40	1.40
		Nos. 247-250 (4)	4.05	4.05

Dolphins A51

1991, Apr. 4 Litho. *Perf. 14½x14*
251	A51	25c *Delphinus delphis*	.65	.65
252	A51	40c *Tursiops truncatus*	1.00	1.00
253	A51	50c *Sousa plumbea*	1.25	1.25
254	A51	60c *Grampus griseus*	1.50	1.50
		Nos. 251-254 (4)	4.40	4.40

Birds — A52

Medical Pioneers — A53

1991, June 20   Litho.
255	A52	25c *Balearica regulorum*	.70	.70
256	A52	40c *Gyps coprotheres*	1.10	1.10
257	A52	50c *Grus carunculata*	1.40	1.40
258	A52	60c *Neophron percnopterus*	1.60	1.60
a.		Souvenir sheet of 1	4.00	4.00
		Nos. 255-258 (4)	4.80	4.80

1991, Sept. 26 Litho. Perf. 14x14½

Developers of vaccines: 25c, Emil von Behring (1854-1917) and Shibasaburo Kitasato (1852-1931), diphtheria. 40c, Leon Albert Calmette (1863-1933) and Camille Guerin (1872-1961), tuberculosis. 50c, Jonas Salk (b. 1914), polio. 60c, John Franklin Enders (1897-1985), measles.

259	A53	25c multicolored	.55	.55
260	A53	40c multicolored	.95	.95
261	A53	50c multicolored	1.10	1.10
262	A53	60c multicolored	1.50	1.50
		Nos. 259-262 (4)	4.10	4.10

Orchids — A54

1992, Feb. 20   Litho.

263	A54	27c Eulophia speciosa	.40	.40
264	A54	45c Satyrium sphaero-carpum	.65	.65
265	A54	65c Disa scullyi	1.00	1.00
266	A54	85c Disa tysonii	1.25	1.25
		Nos. 263-266 (4)	3.30	3.30

Medical Pioneers A55

27c, Thomas Huckle Weller (b. 1915), developer of rubella vaccine. 45c, Ignaz Philipp Semmelweis (1818-65), diagnosed septicaemia. 65c, Sir James Young Simpson (1811-70), 1st to use chloroform in obstetrics. 85c, Rene Theophile Hyacinthe Laennec (1781-1826), inventor of stethoscope.

1992, Apr. 1   Litho.   Perf. 14½x14

267	A55	27c multicolored	.45	.45
268	A55	45c multicolored	.80	.80
269	A55	65c multicolored	1.10	1.10
270	A55	85c multicolored	1.40	1.40
		Nos. 267-270 (4)	3.75	3.75

Waterfowl — A56

1992, July 16   Litho.   Perf. 14x14½

271	A56	35c Anas erythrorhyncha	.45	.45
272	A56	35c Anas hottentota	.45	.45
a.		Pair, #271-272	.90	.90
273	A56	70c Oxyura punctata	.95	.95
274	A56	70c Thalassornis leuconotus	.95	.95
a.		Pair, #273-274	1.90	1.90
275	A56	90c Anas sparsa	1.25	1.25
276	A56	90c Alopochen aegyptiacus	1.25	1.25
a.		Pair, #275-276	2.50	2.50
277	A56	1.05r Anas smithi	1.25	1.25
278	A56	1.05r Anas capensis	1.25	1.25
a.		Pair, #277-278	2.75	2.75
		Nos. 271-278 (8)	7.80	7.80

A souvenir sheet of 1 #273 was sold by the Philatelic Foundation of South Africa.

Fossils A57

Designs: 35c, Pseudomelania sutherlandi. 70c, Gaudryceras denseplicatum. 90c, Neithea quinquecostata. 1.05r, Pugilina (Mayeria) acuticarinatus.

1992, Sept. 17   Litho.   Perf. 14½x14

279	A57	35c multicolored	.45	.45
280	A57	70c multicolored	.90	.90
281	A57	90c multicolored	1.25	1.25
282	A57	1.05r multicolored	1.40	1.40
		Nos. 279-282 (4)	4.00	4.00

Dogs — A58

1993, Feb. 12   Litho.

283	A58	35c Papillon	.45	.45
284	A58	70c Pekingese	.90	.90
285	A58	90c Chihuahua	1.25	1.25
286	A58	1.05r Dachshund	1.40	1.40
		Nos. 283-286 (4)	4.00	4.00

A souvenir sheet of one No. 284 exists. Soild for 3r.

Prehistoric Animals A59

1993, June 18   Litho.

287	A59	45c Fabrosaurus	.60	.60
288	A59	65c Diictodon	.85	.85
289	A59	85c Chasmatosaurus	1.10	1.10
290	A59	1.05r Rubidgea	1.40	1.40
		Nos. 287-290 (4)	3.95	3.95

Medical Pioneers A60

Designs: 45c, Sir Alexander Fleming (1881-1955), discovered penicillin and Lord Howard Walter Florey (1898-1968), purified penicillin for general use. 65c, Alexis Carrel (1873-1944), developed Carrel-Dakin fluid and method to suture blood vessels. 85c, James Lind (1716-1794), recommended citrus fruit to combat scurvy. 1.05r, Santiago Ramon y Cajal (1852-1934), established neuron as basic unit of nervous structure.

1993, Aug. 20   Litho.

291	A60	45c multicolored	.60	.60
292	A60	65c multicolored	.80	.80
293	A60	85c multicolored	1.00	1.00
294	A60	1.05r multicolored	1.25	1.25
		Nos. 291-294 (4)	3.65	3.65

Doves — A61

Designs: 45c, Streptopelia senegalensis. 65c, Turtur tympanistria. 85c, Turtur chalcospilos. 1.05r, Oena capensis.

1993, Oct. 15   Litho.   Perf. 14x14½

295	A61	45c multicolored	.60	.60
296	A61	65c multicolored	.85	.85
297	A61	85c multicolored	1.10	1.10
298	A61	1.05r multicolored	1.25	1.25
a.		Souvenir sheet of 4, #295-298	4.00	4.00
		Nos. 295-298 (4)	3.80	3.80

No. 298a sold for 3.50r.

Modern Shipwrecks A62

1994, Mar. 18   Litho.   Perf. 14½x14

299	A62	45c Clan Lindsay, 1898	.55	.55
300	A62	65c Horizon, 1967	.80	.80
301	A62	85c Oceanos, 1991	1.10	1.10
302	A62	1.05r Forresbank, 1958	1.25	1.25
		Nos. 299-302 (4)	3.70	3.70

A souvenir sheet of 1 #301 exists. Sold for 3r.

Transkei ceased to exist April 27, 1994.

VENDA

'ven-də

LOCATION — Enclave, Republic of South Africa
GOVT. — Self-governing tribal homeland
AREA — 4,040 sq. mi.
POP. — 343,480 (1980)
CAPITAL — Thohoyandou

Catalogue values for all unused stamps in this country are for Never Hinged items.

Independence from South Africa — A1

Designs: 4c, Mace, flag. 15c, Administrative buildings. 20c, P.R. Mphephu, paramount chief and president. 25c, Coat of arms.

Perf. 14½x14

1979, Sept. 13   Litho.   Unwmk.

1	A1	4c multicolored	.35	.35
2	A1	15c multicolored	.90	.90
3	A1	20c multicolored	1.25	1.25
4	A1	25c multicolored	1.75	1.75
		Nos. 1-4 (4)	4.25	4.25

Flowers — A2   Wood Carvings — A3

1979-85   Perf. 12½, 14 (11c, 12c)

5	A2	1c Tecomaria capensis	.20	.20
6	A2	2c Catophractes alexandri	.20	.20
7	A2	3c Triliceras longipedunculatum	.20	.20
8	A2	4c Dissotis princeps	.20	.20
9	A2	5c Gerbera jamesonii	1.75	.55
10	A2	6c Hibiscus mastersianus	.20	.20
11	A2	7c Nymphaea caerulaea	.20	.20
12	A2	8c Crinum lugardiae	.30	.20
13	A2	9c Xerophyta retinervis	.20	.20
14	A2	10c Hypoxis angustifolia	.25	.20
15	A2	11c Combretum microphyllum	.25	.20
16	A2	12c Clivia caulescens	.35	.20
17	A2	15c Pycnostachys urticifolia	.20	.20
18	A2	20c Zantedeschia jucunda	.20	.20
19	A2	25c Leonotis mollis	2.10	.80
20	A2	30c Littonia modesta	.35	.20
21	A2	50c Protea caffra	.55	.25
22	A2	1r Adenium multiflorum	.80	.45
23	A2	2r Strelitzia caudata	1.75	1.10
		Nos. 5-23 (19)	10.25	6.00

Issue dates: 11c, Apr. 2, 1984; 12c, Apr. 1, 1985; others, Sept. 13, 1979.

Perf. 14

5a	A2	1c	.20	.20
6a	A2	2c	.20	.20
7a	A2	3c	.20	.20
9a	A2	5c	.20	.20
12a	A2	8c	.20	.20
14a	A2	10c	.25	.20
19a	A2	25c	.70	.40
21a	A2	50c	1.50	.80
		Nos. 5a-21a (8)	3.45	2.40

1980, Feb. 13   Perf. 14½x14, 14x14½

Designs: 5c, Man with cup. 10c, Woman with corn, bowl and spoon. 15c, King Nebuchadnezzar, horiz. 20c, Python killing woman, horiz.

24	A3	5c multicolored	.20	.20
25	A3	10c multicolored	.35	.35
26	A3	15c multicolored	.50	.50
27	A3	20c multicolored	.70	.70
		Nos. 24-27 (4)	1.75	1.75

Tea Cultivation A4

1980, May 14   Perf. 14x14½

28	A4	5c Plants in nursery	.20	.20
29	A4	10c Harvest	.20	.20
30	A4	15c Withering	.40	.40
31	A4	20c Cut, twist, curl unit	.60	.60
		Nos. 28-31 (4)	1.40	1.40

Banana Industry A5

1980, Aug. 13

32	A5	5c Plants	.20	.20
33	A5	10c Cutting "hands"	.20	.20
34	A5	15c Sorting	.40	.40
35	A5	20c Packing	.60	.60
		Nos. 32-35 (4)	1.40	1.40

Butterflies A6   Sunbirds A7

1980, Nov. 13   Perf. 14½x14

36	A6	5c Precis tugela	.20	.20
37	A6	10c Charaxes bohemani	.25	.25
38	A6	15c Catacroptera cloanthe	.45	.45
39	A6	20c Papilio dardanus	.60	.60
		Nos. 36-39 (4)	1.50	1.50

1981, Feb. 16

40	A7	5c Anthreptes collaris	.20	.20
41	A7	15c Nectarinia mariquensis	.45	.45
42	A7	20c Nectarinia talatala	.60	.60
43	A7	25c Nectarinia senegalensis	.75	.75
		Nos. 40-43 (4)	2.00	2.00

Nwanedi Dam — A8

1981, May 6

44	A8	5c shown	.20	.20
45	A8	15c Mahovhohovho Falls	.20	.20
46	A8	20c Phiphidi Falls	.25	.25
47	A8	25c Lake Fundudzi	.35	.35
		Nos. 44-47 (4)	1.00	1.00

Orchids — A9

Musical Instruments — A10

1981, Sept. 11
48	A9	5c Cynorkis kassnerana	.20	.20
49	A9	15c Eulophia fridericii	.20	.20
50	A9	20c Bonatea densiflora	.25	.25
51	A9	25c Mystacidium brayboniae	.35	.35
a.		Souvenir sheet of 4, #48-51	1.50	1.50
		Nos. 48-51 (4)	1.00	1.00

1981, Nov. 13   *Perf. 14x14½*
52	A10	5c Mbila	.20	.20
53	A10	15c Phalaphala	.20	.20
54	A10	20c Tshizambi	.25	.25
55	A10	25c Ngoma	.35	.35
		Nos. 52-55 (4)	1.00	1.00

Sisal Cultivation A11

1982, Feb. 26
56	A11	5c Harvesting	.20	.20
57	A11	10c Drying	.20	.20
58	A11	20c Grading	.25	.25
59	A11	25c Baling	.35	.35
		Nos. 56-59 (4)	1.00	1.00

History of Writing — A12

Designs: 8c, Bison, petroglyph, Altamira, Spain. 15c, Animal, petroglyph, eastern California. 20c, Pictographic script on a Sumerian tablet. 25c, Bushman burial stone, Humansdorp, South Africa.

1982, June 15   *Perf. 14½x14*
60	A12	8c multicolored	.20	.20
61	A12	15c multicolored	.25	.25
62	A12	20c multicolored	.35	.35
63	A12	25c multicolored	.45	.45
		Nos. 60-63 (4)	1.25	1.25

1983, May 11   **Size: 21x37mm**

10c, Indus Valley script, 3000 B.C. 20c, Sumerian cuneiform, 2000 B.C. 25c, Egyptian hieroglyphics, 1300 B.C. 40c, Chinese handscroll, A.D. 1100.

64	A12	10c multicolored	.20	.20
65	A12	20c multicolored	.30	.30
66	A12	25c multicolored	.35	.35
67	A12	40c multicolored	.40	.40
		Nos. 64-67 (4)	1.25	1.25

1984, Feb. 17   *Perf. 14x14½*
Size: 37½x20½mm

Designs: 10c, Evolution of the cuneiform sign. 20c, Evolution of the Chinese character. 25c, Development of Cretan hieroglyphics. 40c, Development of Egyptian hieroglyphics.

68	A12	10c multicolored	.20	.20
69	A12	20c multicolored	.45	.45
70	A12	25c multicolored	.50	.50
71	A12	40c multicolored	.85	.85
		Nos. 68-71 (4)	2.00	2.00

1985, Mar. 21   *Perf. 14½x14*
Size: 34x24½mm

Designs: 11c, Southern Arabic characters. 25c, Phoenician characters. 30c, Aramaic characters. 50c, Canaanite characters.

72	A12	11c multicolored	.20	.20
73	A12	25c multicolored	.50	.50
74	A12	30c multicolored	.60	.60
75	A12	50c multicolored	1.00	1.00
		Nos. 72-75 (4)	2.30	2.30

1986, Apr. 10   *Perf. 14x14½*
Size: 24½x34mm
76	A12	14c Etruscan	.30	.30
77	A12	20c Greek	.45	.45
78	A12	25c Roman	.55	.55
79	A12	30c Cyrillic	.65	.65
		Nos. 76-79 (4)	1.95	1.95

1988, Apr. 28   *Perf. 14½x14*
Size: 34x26mm
80	A12	16c Chinese	.40	.40
81	A12	30c Hindi	.65	.65
82	A12	40c Russian	.90	.90
83	A12	50c Arabic	1.10	1.10
		Nos. 80-83 (4)	3.05	3.05
		Nos. 60-83 (24)	11.80	11.80

See Nos. 209-212.

Trees A13

1982, Sept. 17
84	A13	8c Euphorbia ingens	.20	.20
85	A13	15c Pterocarpus angolensis	.25	.25
86	A13	20c Ficus ingens	.35	.35
87	A13	25c Adansonia digitata	.45	.45
		Nos. 84-87 (4)	1.25	1.25

1983, Aug. 3
88	A13	10c Gardenia spatulifolia	.20	.20
89	A13	20c Hyphaene natalensis	.35	.35
90	A13	25c Albizia adianthifolia	.40	.40
91	A13	40c Sesamothamnus lugardii	.70	.70
		Nos. 88-91 (4)	1.65	1.65

1984, June 21
92	A13	11c Afzelia quanzensis	.20	.20
93	A13	20c Peltophorum africanum	.35	.35
94	A13	25c Gyrocarpus americanus	.45	.45
95	A13	30c Acacia sieberana	.55	.55
		Nos. 92-95 (4)	1.55	1.55
		Nos. 84-95 (12)	4.45	4.45

Frogs — A14

1982, Nov. 26   *Perf. 14x14½*
96	A14	8c Rana angolensis	.20	.20
97	A14	15c Chiromantis xerampelina	.35	.35
98	A14	20c Leptopelis	.45	.45
99	A14	25c Ptychadena anchietae	.60	.60
		Nos. 96-99 (4)	1.60	1.60

Migratory Birds and Maps — A15

1983, Feb. 16   *Perf. 14½x14*
100	A15	8c European bee-eater	.25	.25
101	A15	20c Steppe eagle	.60	.60
102	A15	25c Plum-colored starling	.75	.75
103	A15	40c White-bellied stork	1.25	1.25
		Nos. 100-103 (4)	2.85	2.85

Subtropical Fruit A16

1983, Oct. 26   *Perf. 14x14½*
104	A16	10c Avocado	.20	.20
105	A16	20c Mango	.25	.25
106	A16	25c Papaya	.30	.30
107	A16	40c Litchi	.55	.55
		Nos. 104-107 (4)	1.30	1.30

Migratory Birds — A17

1984, Apr. 26   *Perf. 14½x14*
108	A17	11c White stork	.30	.30
109	A17	20c Paradise flycatcher	.60	.60
110	A17	25c Yellow-billed kite	.75	.75
111	A17	30c Wood sandpiper	.90	.90
		Nos. 108-111 (4)	2.55	2.55

Independence, 5th Anniv. — A18

1984, Sept. 13   *Perf. 14½x14*
112	A18	11c Dzata Ruins	.20	.20
113	A18	25c Traditional hut	.40	.40
114	A18	30c Low-income housing	.45	.45
115	A18	45c Modern home	.70	.70
		Nos. 112-115 (4)	1.75	1.75

Songbirds A19   Food of the Veld A20

1985, Jan. 10
116	A19	11c Heuglin's robin	.30	.30
117	A19	25c Black-collared barbet	.65	.65
118	A19	30c Black-headed oriole	.80	.80
119	A19	50c Kurrichane thrush	1.25	1.25
		Nos. 116-119 (4)	3.00	3.00

1985, June 21   *Perf. 14x14½*
120	A20	12c Mimusops zeyheri	.25	.25
121	A20	25c Ziziphus mucronata	.55	.55
122	A20	30c Citrullus lanatus	.60	.60
123	A20	50c Berchemia discolor	1.10	1.10
		Nos. 120-123 (4)	2.50	2.50

See Nos. 173-176.

Ferns — A21

1985, Sept. 5   *Perf. 14½x14*
124	A21	12c Pellaea dura	.25	.25
125	A21	25c Actiniopteris radiata	.55	.55
126	A21	30c Adiantum hispidulum	.60	.60
127	A21	50c Polypodium polypodioides	1.10	1.10
		Nos. 124-127 (4)	2.50	2.50

Reptiles A22

1986-90   *Perf. 14x14½*
128	A22	1c Psammophylax tritaeniatus	.20	.20
129	A22	2c Pseudaspis cana	.20	.20
130	A22	3c Nucras taeniolata ornata	.20	.20
131	A22	4c Bitis arietans	.20	.20
132	A22	5c Mabuya capensis	.20	.20
133	A22	6c Naja haje annulifera	.20	.20
134	A22	7c Mabuya quinquetaeniata margaritifer	.20	.20
135	A22	8c Philothamnus semivariegatus	.20	.20
136	A22	9c Gerrhosaurus flavigularis	.20	.20
137	A22	10c Prosymna sundevallii lineata	.20	.20
138	A22	14c Platysaurus intermedius	.30	.30
139	A22	15c Lacerta rupicola	.30	.30
140	A22	16c Varanus niloticus	.35	.35
141	A22	18c Dendroaspis polylepis	.40	.40
142	A22	20c Afroedura transvaalica	.45	.45
143	A22	21c Chamaeleo dilepsis	.45	.45
144	A22	25c Elapsoidea sundevallii longicauda	.55	.55
145	A22	30c Pachydactylus tigrinus	.65	.65
146	A22	50c Mehelya capensis	1.10	1.10
147	A22	1r Cordylus warreni depressus	2.25	2.25
148	A22	2r Python sebae natalensis	4.50	4.50
		Nos. 128-148 (21)	13.30	13.30

Issued: 14c, 4/1/86; 16c, 4/1/87; 18c, 7/3/89; 21c, 8/3/90; others, 1/16/86.

Forestry A23

Designs: 14c, Planting pine seedlings. 20c, Felling and extracting saw timber. 25c, Unloading timber at sawmill. 30c, Construction workers using pre-cut lumber.

1986, June 26   *Perf. 14x14½*
153	A23	14c multicolored	.20	.20
154	A23	20c multicolored	.35	.35
155	A23	25c multicolored	.40	.40
156	A23	30c multicolored	.50	.50
		Nos. 153-156 (4)	1.45	1.45

FIVA World Classic Car Rally — A24

1986, Sept. 4   *Perf. 14½x14*
157	A24	14c 1910 Maxwell	.45	.45
158	A24	20c 1929 Bentley 4½ l	.65	.65
159	A24	25c 1933 Plymouth Coupe	.85	.85
160	A24	30c 1958 Mercedes Cabriolet	1.00	1.00
a.		Souvenir sheet of 1	5.00	5.00
		Nos. 157-160 (4)	2.95	2.95

No. 160a for the natl. philatelic exhibition held at Johannesburg, Oct. 6-11. Sold for 50c.

Waterfowl A25

Wood Carvings A26

1987, Jan. 8 Perf. 14x14½, 14½x14
161 A25 14c Sarkidiornis mela-
notos .65 .65
162 A25 20c Dendrocygna vidu-
ata .90 .90
163 A25 25c Plectropterus
gambensis 1.10 1.10
a. Souvenir sheet of 1 6.50 6.50
164 A25 40c Alopochen aegyptiacus 1.40 1.40
Nos. 161-164 (4) 4.05 4.05

Nos. 163-164 are horiz. No. 163a margin
pictures emblem of the natl. philatelic exhibition held at Paarl, Sept. 16-19. Sold for 50c.

1987, Apr. 9 Perf. 14½x14
165 A26 16c Iron Master .35 .35
166 A26 20c Distant Drums .40 .40
167 A26 25c Sunrise .55 .55
168 A26 30c Obedience .70 .70
Nos. 165-168 (4) 2.00 2.00

Freshwater
Fish — A27

1987, July 2 Perf. 14x14½
169 A27 16c Hydrocynus vittatus .70 .70
170 A27 20c Opsardium
zambezense .90 .90
171 A27 25c Oreochromis mossambicus 1.00 1.00
172 A27 30c Clarias gariepinus 1.25 1.25
Nos. 169-172 (4) 3.85 3.85

Food of the Veld Type

1987, Oct. 2
173 A20 16c Grewia occidentalis .35 .35
174 A20 30c Phoenix reclinata .70 .70
175 A20 40c Halleria lucida 1.00 1.00
176 A20 50c Cucumis africanus 1.25 1.25
Nos. 173-176 (4) 3.30 3.30

Coffee
Industry
A28

1988, Jan. 21 Perf. 14½x14
177 A28 16c Harvesting .40 .40
178 A28 30c Weighing .75 .75
179 A28 40c Sun drying 1.00 1.00
180 A28 50c Roasting 1.25 1.25
Nos. 177-180 (4) 3.40 3.40

Nurse's
Training
College,
Shayandima
A29

1988, Aug. 18
181 A29 16c shown .40 .40
182 A29 30c Microscopy .70 .70
183 A29 40c Anatomy lecture 1.00 1.00
184 A29 50c Clinical training 1.25 1.25
Nos. 181-184 (4) 3.35 3.35

Watercolors
by Kenneth
Thabo
A30

1988, Oct. 6
185 A30 16c Fetching Water .40 .40
186 A30 30c Grinding Maize .70 .70
187 A30 40c Offering Food 1.00 1.00
188 A30 50c Kindling the Fire 1.25 1.25
a. Souvenir sheet of 1 4.00 4.00
Nos. 185-188 (4) 3.35 3.35

No. 188a for the natl. philatelic exhibition
held at Pietermaritzburg, Nov. 22-27. Sold for
1.50r.
See Nos. 193-196.

Traditional
Kitchenware
A31

1989, Jan. 5
189 A31 16c Ndongwana .35 .35
190 A31 30c Ndilo .65 .65
191 A31 40c Mufaro .90 .90
192 A31 50c Muthatha 1.10 1.10
Nos. 189-192 (4) 3.00 3.00

Art Type of 1988

Traditional dances: watercolors by Kenneth
Thabo.

1989, Apr. 5
193 A30 18c Domba .35 .35
194 A30 30c Tshinzerere .65 .65
195 A30 40c Malende .90 .90
196 A30 50c Malombo 1.10 1.10
Nos. 193-196 (4) 3.00 3.00

Endangered Bird
Species — A32

1989, June 27
197 A32 18c Bucorvus
leadbeateri .60 .60
198 A32 30c Torgos tracheliotus 1.00 1.00
199 A32 40c Terathopius
ecaudatus 1.25 1.25
200 A32 50c Polemaetus bellicosus 1.65 1.65
a. Souvenir sheet of 1 4.00 4.00
Nos. 197-200 (4) 4.50 4.50

No. 200a for the natl. philatelic exhibition
WANDERERS 101, held Sept. 6-9. Sold for
1.50r.

Independence, 10th Anniv. — A33

1989, Sept. 13
201 A33 18c Pres. Ravele .35 .35
202 A33 30c Presidential office .65 .65
203 A33 40c Presidential residence .80 .80
204 A33 50c Thohoyandou Stadium 1.00 1.00
Nos. 201-204 (4) 2.80 2.80

Wildlife
Conservation,
Nwanedi Natl.
Park — A34

1990, Mar. 1
205 A34 18c Panthera leo .50 .50
206 A34 30c Equus burchelli .90 .90
207 A34 40c Acinonyx jubatus 1.10 1.10
208 A34 50c Ceratotherium
simum 1.40 1.40
a. Souvenir sheet of 1 3.75 3.75
Nos. 205-208 (4) 3.90 3.90

No. 208a for the natl. philatelic exhibition.
Sold for 1.50r.

History of Writing Type

Designs: 21c, Calligraphy. 30c, Musical
notation, Beethoven's Moonlight Sonata. 40c,
Computer characters. 50c, Black-and-white
television picture transmitted across interstel-
lar distances by the Arecibo radio telescope.

1990, May 23 Litho. Perf. 14½x14
209 A12 21c multicolored .55 .55
210 A12 30c multicolored .75 .75
211 A12 40c multicolored 1.00 1.00
212 A12 50c multicolored 1.40 1.40
Nos. 209-212 (4) 3.70 3.70

Aloe
Plants — A35

Butterflies — A36

1990, Aug. 23 Litho. Perf. 14½x14
213 A35 21c Aloe globuligemma .55 .55
214 A35 35c Aloe aculeata .90 .90
215 A35 40c Aloe lutescens 1.10 1.10
216 A35 50c Aloe angelica 1.25 1.25
Nos. 213-216 (4) 3.80 3.80

1990, Nov. 15 Perf. 14x14½
217 A36 21c Pseudacraea bois-
duvalii .70 .70
218 A36 35c Papilio nireus 1.25 1.25
219 A36 40c Charaxes jasius 1.40 1.40
220 A36 50c Aeropetes tulbaghia 1.65 1.65
Nos. 217-220 (4) 5.00 5.00

Birds
A37

1991, Mar. 7 Litho. Perf. 14½x14
221 A37 21c Batis capensis .65 .65
222 A37 35c Cossypha natalensis 1.00 1.00
223 A37 40c Anthreptes collaris 1.25 1.25
224 A37 50c Phyllastrephus
flavostriatus 1.50 1.50
Nos. 221-224 (4) 4.40 4.40

1991, June 6 Litho. Perf. 14½x14

Chinese inventions.

A38

225 A38 25c Paper made from
pulp .65 .65
226 A38 40c Magnetic compass 1.00 1.00
227 A38 50c Abacus 1.25 1.25

228 A38 60c Gunpowder 1.50 1.50
a. Souvenir sheet of 1 4.00 4.00
Nos. 225-228 (4) 4.40 4.40

Hotels
A39

1991, Aug. 29 Litho.
229 A39 25c Venda Sun .50 .50
230 A39 40c Mphephu Resort .85 .85
231 A39 50c Sagole Spa 1.00 1.00
232 A39 60c Luphephe-Nwanedi
Resort 1.40 1.40
Nos. 229-232 (4) 3.75 3.75

Trees
A40

1991, Nov. 21 Litho.
233 A40 27c Acacia
xanthophloea .45 .45
234 A40 45c Faurea saligna .80 .80
235 A40 65c Strelitzia caudata 1.10 1.10
236 A40 85c Kigelia africana 1.40 1.40
Nos. 233-236 (4) 3.75 3.75

Clothing
Factory
A41

1992, Mar. 5 Litho.
237 A41 27c Setting the web .35 .35
238 A41 45c Knitting a pattern .80 .80
239 A41 65c Using sewing machine 1.10 1.10
240 A41 85c Testing for flaws 1.40 1.40
Nos. 237-240 (4) 3.65 3.65

Bees
A42

1992, May 21 Litho.
241 A42 35c Honey bee .50 .50
242 A42 70c Carder bee 1.00 1.00
243 A42 90c Leafcutter bee 1.10 1.10
244 A42 1.05r Carpenter bee 1.40 1.40
Nos. 241-244 (4) 4.00 4.00

A souvenir sheet of 1 #242 was sold by the
Philatelic Foundation of South Africa.

Inventions
A43

Designs: 35c, Plow, Egypt 1259 B.C. 70c,
Wheel, Mesopotamia, 3200 B.C. 90c,
Brickmaking, Egypt, 3000 B.C. 1.05r, Sailing
ship, Egypt, 1600 B.C.

1992, Aug. 13
245 A43 35c multicolored .50 .50
246 A43 70c multicolored 1.00 1.00
247 A43 90c multicolored 1.10 1.10
248 A43 1.05r multicolored 1.40 1.40
Nos. 245-248 (4) 4.00 4.00

Crocodile
Farming
A44

1992, Oct. 15   **Litho.**
249 A44 35c Emerging from
                water   .50 .50
250 A44 70c Egg laying   1.00 1.00
251 A44 90c Hatchlings   1.10 1.10
252 A44 1.05r Maternal care   1.40 1.40
     Nos. 249-252 (4)   4.00 4.00

Domestic
Cats — A45

1993, Mar. 19   **Litho.**
253 A45 45c Burmese   .50 .50
254 A45 65c Tabby   1.00 1.00
255 A45 85c Siamese   1.10 1.10
256 A45 1.05r Persian   1.40 1.40
     Nos. 253-256 (4)   4.00 4.00

A souvenir sheet of one No. 254 has inscription for National Philatelic Exhibition. Sold for
3r.

Herons
A46

Designs: 45c, Butorides striatus. 65c, Nycticorax nycticorax. 85c, Ardea purpurea. 1.05r,
Ardea melanocephala.

1993, July 16 **Litho.** **Perf. 14½x14**
257 A46 45c multicolored   .60 .60
258 A46 65c multicolored   .90 .90
259 A46 85c multicolored   1.10 1.10
260 A46 1.05r multicolored   1.40 1.40
  a. Souvenir sheet of 4, #257-260 4.00 4.00
     Nos. 257-260 (4)   4.00 4.00

Shoe
Factory — A47

1993, Sept. 17 **Litho.** **Perf. 14x14½**
261 A47 45c Punching out sole
                lining   .60 .60
262 A47 65c Shaping heel   .90 .90
263 A47 85c Joining upper to
                inner sole   1.10 1.10
264 A47 1.05r Forming sole   1.40 1.40
     Nos. 261-264 (4)   4.00 4.00

Inventions
A48

1993, Nov. 5 **Litho.** **Perf. 14x14½**
265 A48 45c Axe   .60 .60
266 A48 65c Armor   .90 .90
267 A48 85c Arch   1.10 1.10
268 A48 1.05r Aqueduct   1.40 1.40
     Nos. 265-268 (4)   4.00 4.00

Dogs
A49

1994, Jan. 14 Litho. Perf. 14½x14
269 A49 45c Cocker spaniel   .60 .60
270 A49 65c Maltese   .90 .90
271 A49 85c Scottish terrier   1.10 1.10
272 A49 1.05r Miniature schnau-
                zer   1.40 1.40
     Nos. 269-272 (4)   4.00 4.00

A souvenir sheet of 1 #271 was sold for 3r
by the Philatelic Foundation of Southern Africa
and sold for 1.50r.

Monkeys
A50

Designs: 45c, Cercopithecus aethiops. 65c,
Galago moholi. 85c, Cercopithecus mitis.
1.05r, Otolemur crassicaudatus.

1994, Mar. 4 Litho. Perf. 14½x14
273 A50 45c multicolored   .55 .55
274 A50 65c multicolored   .85 .85
275 A50 85c multicolored   1.10 1.10
276 A50 1.05r multicolored   1.40 1.40
  a. Souvenir sheet of 4, #273-276 4.00 4.00
     Nos. 273-276 (4)   3.90 3.90

Starlings
A51

45c, Lamprotornis nitens. 70c, Cinnyricinclus leucogaster. 95c, Onychognathus morio.
1.15r, Creatophora cinerea.

1994, Apr. 29 Litho. Perf. 14½x14
277 A51 45c multicolored   .55 .55
278 A51 70c multicolored   .85 .85
279 A51 95c multicolored   1.10 1.10
280 A51 1.15r multicolored   1.40 1.40
     Nos. 277-280 (4)   3.90 3.90

Venda ceased to exist April 27, 1994.
The Venda postal service continued to oper-
ate until 1996.

———————————

SOUTH ARABIA

sauth ə-'rā-bē-ə

LOCATION — Southern Arabia
GOVT. — Federation; British
  dependency
AREA — 61,890 sq. mi.
POP. — 771,000 (est. 1966)
CAPITAL — Al Ittihad

The Federation of South Arabia was
established in 1959 and consists of 14
states including Aden colony and part
of Aden protectorate. When the Federation became independent, Nov. 30,
1967, it became the People's Republic
of Southern Yemen. See People's Democratic Republic of Yemen, Vol. 6.

100 Cents = 1 Shilling
1000 Fils = 1 Dinar (1965)

┌─────────────────────────────┐
│ **Catalogue values for all unused** │
│ **stamps in this country are for** │
│ **Never Hinged items.** │
└─────────────────────────────┘

Common Design Types
pictured following the introduction.

———————————

Red Cross Centenary Issue
Common Design Type
Wmk. 314
1963, Nov. 25 Litho. Perf. 13
1 CD315 15c black & red   .30 .30
2 CD315 1sh25c ultra & red   .80 .80

Arms of
Federation of
South
Arabia — A1

Flag of Federation — A2

Perf. 14½x14
1965, Apr. 1   Photo.   Unwmk.
3   A1   5f blue   .20 .20
4   A1   10f light violet blue   .20 .20
5   A1   15f blue green   .20 .20
6   A1   20f green   .20 .20
7   A1   25f orange brown   .20 .20
8   A1   30f lemon   .20 .20
9   A1   35f red brown   .20 .20
10 A1   50f rose red   .20 .20
11 A1   65f light yellow green   .20 .20
12 A1   75f rose carmine   .20 .20

Perf. 14½
**Flag in Black, Yellow, Green and
Blue**
13 A2   100f reddish brown   .25 .20
14 A2   250f dark blue   3.50 .60
15 A2   500f dark red   6.25 .50
16 A2   1d violet   10.50 5.00
     Nos. 3-16 (14)   22.50 8.30

Intl. Cooperation Year Issue
Common Design Type with Coat of
Arms Replacing Queen's Portrait
Wmk. 314
1965, Oct. 24   Litho.   Perf. 14½
17 CD318 5f blue grn & claret   .20 .20
18 CD318 65f lt violet & green   .80 .20

Churchill Memorial Issue
Common Design Type with Coat of
Arms Replacing Queen's Portrait
Unwmk.
1966, Jan. 24   Photo.   Perf. 14
**Design in Black, Gold and Carmine
Rose**
19 CD319 5f bright blue   .20 .20
20 CD319 10f green   .20 .20
21 CD319 65f brown   .60 .50
22 CD319 125f violet   1.25 .85
     Nos. 19-22 (4)   2.25 1.75

World Cup Soccer Issue
Common Design Type with Coat of
Arms Replacing Queen's Portrait
1966, July 1   Litho.   Perf. 14
23 CD321 10f multicolored   .60 .20
24 CD321 50f multicolored   1.40 .30

WHO Headquarters Issue
Common Design Type with Coat of
Arms Replacing Queen's Portrait
1966, Sept. 20   Litho.   Unwmk.
25 CD322 10f multicolored   .50 .20
26 CD322 75f multicolored   1.25 .40

UNESCO Anniversary Issue
Common Design Type with Coat of
Arms Replacing Queen's Portrait
1966, Dec. 15   Litho.   Perf. 14
27 CD323 10f "Education"   .30 .25
28 CD323 65f "Science"   1.50 1.25
29 CD323 125f "Culture"   3.25 4.00
     Nos. 27-29 (3)   5.05 5.50

ADVANTAGE STOCKSHEETS

Designed with the collector in mind, Advantage
stock sheets fit directly in your 2-post or 3-ring
National or Specialty album. For unprecedented
durability and flexibility choose Advantage
Stocksheets. Choose from 1 to 8 pockets.
Sheets are sold in packages of 10.

- Stock sheets match album pages in every
  respect, including border, size, and color.

- Punched and drilled to fit perfectly in binder.

- Available with 1 to 8 pockets.
  Ideal for storing minor varieties and
  collateral material. A great place to keep
  new issues until the next supplement is
  available.

- Provide the protection and durability of
  crystal clear acetate pockets on
  heavyweight pages.

NATIONAL BORDER

ITEM			RETAIL
AD11	1 Pocket	242mm	$15.99
AD12	2 Pockets	119mm	$15.99
AD13	3 Pockets	79mm	$15.99
AD14	4 Pockets	58mm	$15.99
AD15	5 Pockets	45mm	$15.99
AD16	6 Pockets	37mm	$15.99
AD17	7 Pockets	31mm	$15.99
AD18	8 Pockets	31mm	$15.99

SPECIALTY BORDER

AD21	1 Pocket	242mm	$15.99
AD22	2 Pockets	119mm	$15.99
AD23	3 Pockets	79mm	$15.99
AD24	4 Pockets	58mm	$15.99
AD25	5 Pockets	45mm	$15.99
AD26	6 Pockets	37mm	$15.99
AD27	7 Pockets	31mm	$15.99
AD28	8 Pockets	31mm S	$15.99

Available from your favorite stamp
dealer or direct from:

1-800-572-6885
P.O. Box 828,
Sidney OH 45365
www.amosadvantage.com

AMOS
HOBBY PUBLISHING

SOUTHERN NIGERIA

ˈsə-<u>th</u>ərn nī-ˈjir-ē-ə

LOCATION — In western Africa bordering on the Gulf of Guinea
GOVT. — British Crown Colony and Protectorate
AREA — 90,896 sq. mi.
POP. — 8,590,545
CAPITAL — Lagos

The Protectorate of Southern Nigeria, formed in 1900, absorbed in that year the Niger Coast Protectorate. In 1906 it united with Lagos and became the Colony and Protectorate of Southern Nigeria. An amalgamation was effected in 1914 between Northern and Southern Nigeria to form the Colony and Protectorate of Nigeria. See Nigeria, Northern Nigeria, Niger Coast Protectorate and Lagos.

12 Pence = 1 Shilling
20 Shillings = 1 Pound

Victoria   Edward VII
A1   A2

Wmk. Crown and C A (2)

1901, Mar.   **Typo.**   **Perf. 14**

1	A1	½p yel grn & blk	2.00	2.50
a.		½p yel grn & sepia ('02)	2.50	3.00
2	A1	1p car rose & blk	1.60	1.75
a.		1p carmine rose & sepia ('02)	2.50	2.00
3	A1	2p org brn & blk	3.75	4.25
4	A1	4p ol grn & blk	3.25	18.00
5	A1	6p red vio & blk	3.25	7.50
6	A1	1sh blk & gray grn	9.25	30.00
7	A1	2sh6p brn & blk	52.50	92.50
8	A1	5sh yellow & blk	55.00	110.00
9	A1	10sh vio & blk, yel	100.00	200.00
		Nos. 1-9 (9)	230.60	466.50

1903-04

10	A2	½p yel grn & blk	1.10	.35
11	A2	1p car rose & blk	1.50	.80
12	A2	2p org brn & blk	7.50	1.75
13	A2	2½p ultra & blk ('04)	2.25	.85
14	A2	4p ol grn & blk	3.25	6.25
15	A2	6p red vio & blk	4.50	9.25
16	A2	1sh blk & gray grn	35.00	22.50
17	A2	2sh6p brown & blk	30.00	70.00
18	A2	5sh yellow & blk	70.00	160.00
19	A2	10sh vio & blk, yel	35.00	100.00
20	A2	£1 pur & gray grn	375.00	750.00
		Nos. 10-20 (11)	565.10	1,121.

1904-07   **Wmk. 3**
Chalky Paper

21	A2	½p yel grn & blk	.60	.20
22	A2	1p carmine & blk	14.00	.25
23	A2	2p org brn & blk	3.00	.50
24	A2	2½p ultra & blk	1.10	1.10
24A	A2	3p vio & org brn ('07)	11.00	1.50
25	A2	4p ol grn & blk ('05)	16.00	29.00
26	A2	6p red vio & blk	13.50	4.00
27	A2	1sh blk & gray grn	3.75	4.00
28	A2	2sh6p brn & blk ('05)	27.50	20.00
29	A2	5sh yellow & blk	47.50	85.00
30	A2	10sh vio & blk, yel ('08)	110.00	200.00
31	A2	£1 pur & gray grn ('05)	175.00	210.00
		Nos. 21-31 (12)	422.95	555.55

#23 and 24 are on ordinary paper, #24A and 25 on chalky, and the other values on both papers.

1907-10
Ordinary Paper

32	A2	½p green ('08)	2.00	.25
33	A2	1p carmine	4.00	.70
34	A2	2p gray	3.00	.80
35	A2	2½p ultra	2.25	4.25

Chalky Paper

36	A2	3p violet, yel	2.25	.35
37	A2	4p scar & blk, yel	2.50	.90
38	A2	6p red vio & dl vio	29.00	3.75
39	A2	1sh black, green	8.00	.50

40	A2	2sh6p car & blk, bl	5.75	1.10
41	A2	5sh scar & grn, yel	45.00	55.00
42	A2	10sh red & grn, grn	75.00	110.00
43	A2	£1 blk & vio, red	210.00	250.00
		Nos. 32-43 (12)	388.75	427.60

1910   **Ordinary Paper**   **Redrawn**

44	A2	1p carmine	.85	.20

In the redrawn stamp the "1" of "1d" is not as thick as in No. 33 but the "d" is taller and broader.

King George V — A3

1912

45	A3	½p green	2.25	.20
46	A3	1p carmine	2.00	.20
47	A3	2p gray	.85	.95
48	A3	2½p ultra	3.25	3.25
49	A3	3p violet, yel	1.10	.35
50	A3	4p scar & blk, yel	1.50	2.40
51	A3	6p red vio & dl vio	1.50	1.50
52	A3	1sh black, green	3.25	.85
53	A3	2sh6p red & blk, bl	9.25	35.00
54	A3	5sh red & grn, yel	22.50	87.50
55	A3	10sh red & grn, grn	52.50	100.00
56	A3	£1 blk & vio, red	190.00	250.00
		Nos. 45-56 (12)	289.95	482.20

Stamps of Southern Nigeria were replaced in 1914 by those of Nigeria.

SOUTHERN RHODESIA

ˈsə-<u>th</u>ərn rō-ˈdē-zh͟ə

LOCATION — Southeastern Africa between Northern Rhodesia and Mozambique
GOVT. — British Colony
AREA — 150,333 sq. mi.
POP. — 4,010,000 (est. 1963)
CAPITAL — Salisbury

Prior to 1923 this territory was administered by the British South Africa Company. The colony was created in that year by the British Government at the request of the inhabitants. In 1953, Southern Rhodesia joined Northern Rhodesia and Nyasaland to form the Federation of Rhodesia and Nyasaland. When the Federation dissolved at the end of 1963, Southern Rhodesia again became an internally self-governing colony. See Rhodesia and Northern Rhodesia.

12 Pence = 1 Shilling
20 Shillings = 1 Pound

Catalogue values for unused stamps in this country are for Never Hinged items, beginning with Scott 56 in the regular postage section and Scott J1 in the postage due section.

King George V — A1

1924-30   **Unwmk.**   **Engr.**   **Perf. 14**

1	A1	½p dark green	2.00	.20
a.		Vert. pair, imperf. btwn.	800.00	925.00
b.		Horiz. pair, imperf. btwn.	800.00	925.00
c.		Horiz. pair, imperf. vert.	875.00	
2	A1	1p scarlet	1.90	.20
a.		Horiz. pair, imperf. btwn.	700.00	800.00
b.		Perf. 12½ (coil) ('30)	3.25	92.50
c.		Vert. pair, imperf. btwn.	1,150.	
d.		Vert. pair, imperf. horiz.	800.00	
3	A1	1½p bister brown	2.00	.90
a.		Horiz. pair, imperf. btwn.	8,750.	
b.		Vert. pair, imperf. btwn.	5,250.	
4	A1	2p vio blk & blk	2.50	.80
a.		Horiz. pair, imperf. btwn.	11,000.	
5	A1	3p deep blue	2.75	3.00
6	A1	4p org red & blk	3.00	3.25

7	A1	6p lilac & blk	2.25	4.00
a.		Horiz. pair, imperf. btwn.	35,000.	
8	A1	8p gray grn & vio	12.50	47.50
9	A1	10p rose red & bl	12.50	52.50
10	A1	1sh turq bl & blk	5.75	5.75
11	A1	1sh6p yellow & blk	22.50	37.50
12	A1	2sh brown & blk	20.00	20.00
13	A1	2sh6p blk brn & bl	35.00	70.00
14	A1	5sh bl grn & bl	70.00	140.00
		Nos. 1-14 (14)	194.65	385.60

Values for imperf between pairs are for stamps from the same pane. Stamps separated by wide margins are cross-gutter pairs and sell for much lower prices.

George V   Victoria Falls
A2   A3

1931-37   **Perf. 11½, 14 (1p)**

16	A2	½p dp green ('33)	.75	.20
a.		Bklt. pane of 6 ('32)	150.00	
b.		Perf. 12	.95	1.10
c.		Perf. 14 ('35)	1.90	.35
17	A2	1p scarlet ('35)	.60	.20
a.		Bklt. pane of 6 ('32)	150.00	
b.		Perf. 11½ ('33)	2.00	.20
c.		Perf. 12	1.10	.80
18	A2	1½p dp brown ('32)	3.00	.90
a.		Bklt. pane of 6 ('32)	600.00	
b.		Perf. 12 ('33)	62.50	47.50

Typo.   **Perf. 14½x14**

19	A3	2p blk brn & blk	4.50	1.75
20	A3	3p dark blue	11.50	12.50

Perf. 12, 11½ (2sh6p)
Engr.

21	A2	4p org red & blk	1.50	1.75
a.		Perf. 14 ('37)	37.50	55.00
b.		Perf. 11½ ('33)	20.00	5.75
22	A2	6p rose lilac & blk	2.50	3.50
a.		Perf. 14 ('36)	8.00	1.00
b.		Perf. 11½ ('33)	17.50	1.75
23	A2	8p green & violet	3.00	3.75
a.		Perf. 11½ ('34)	20.00	37.50
24	A2	9p gray grn & ver ('34)	7.00	10.50
25	A2	10p car & ultra	8.00	2.75
a.		Perf. 11½ ('33)	7.00	15.00
26	A2	1sh turq bl & blk ('36)	2.25	3.00
a.		Perf. 11½ ('33)	110.00	70.00
b.		Perf. 14 ('37)	110.00	160.00
27	A2	1sh6p ocher & blk	11.50	17.50
a.		Perf. 11½ ('36)	57.50	110.00
28	A2	2sh dk brn & blk	24.00	7.50
a.		Perf. 11½ ('33)	42.50	35.00
29	A2	2sh6p ol brn & ultra ('33)	32.50	35.00
a.		Perf. 12	37.50	40.00
30	A2	5sh bl grn & ultra	55.00	55.00
		Nos. 16-30 (15)	167.60	155.80

Victoria Falls — A4

1932, May   **Perf. 12½**

31	A4	2p dark brn & grn	4.50	1.10
32	A4	3p dark blue	4.75	2.10
a.		Vert. pair, imperf. horiz.	7,500.	9,250.
b.		Vert. pair, imperf. btwn.	17,500.	
		Set, never hinged	18.00	

See Nos. 37-37A.

Silver Jubilee Issue

Victoria Falls and George V
A5

1935, May 6   **Perf. 11x12**

33	A5	1p car rose & olive	2.75	1.50
34	A5	2p blk brn & lt grn	4.25	4.00
35	A5	3p blue & violet	5.50	9.50
36	A5	6p dp violet & blk	7.50	12.50
		Nos. 33-36 (4)	20.00	27.50
		Set, never hinged	37.50	

25th anniv. of the reign of George V.

"Postage and Revenue"
A6

1935-41   **Perf. 14**

37	A6	2p dk brn & grn ('41)	1.10	.25
b.		Perf. 12½	1.75	10.00
		Never hinged	3.00	
37A	A6	3p deep blue ('38)	1.75	.25
		Set, never hinged	5.25	

Queen Elizabeth, George VI — A7

1937, May 12   **Perf. 12½**

38	A7	1p carmine & gray grn	.60	.70
39	A7	2p brown & green	.65	1.75
40	A7	3p lt blue & violet	3.00	8.00
41	A7	6p red violet & blk	1.75	3.75
		Nos. 38-41 (4)	6.00	14.20
		Set, never hinged	9.00	

Coronation of George VI & Elizabeth.

King George VI — A8

1937, Nov. 25   **Perf. 14**

42	A8	½p yellow green	.35	.20
43	A8	1p red	.35	.20
44	A8	1½p red brown	.65	.35
45	A8	4p orange red	.85	.20
46	A8	6p dark gray	.85	.60
47	A8	8p blue green	1.25	2.25
48	A8	9p blue	1.25	.80
49	A8	10p violet	1.60	3.00
50	A8	1sh green & blk	1.25	.20
51	A8	1sh6p ocher & blk	7.25	2.50
52	A8	2sh brown & blk	10.50	.70
53	A8	2sh6p violet & blue	7.25	5.50
54	A8	5sh green & blue	16.00	2.75
		Nos. 42-54 (13)	49.40	19.25
		Set, never hinged	75.00	

Catalogue values for unused stamps in this section, from this point to the end of the section, are for Never Hinged items.

Seal of British South Africa Co. — A9

Fort Salisbury, 1890 — A10

Cecil John Rhodes — A11

Pioneer Fort and Mail Coach A12

Rhodes Makes Peace, 1896 — A13

Victoria Falls Bridge — A14

Sir Charles Coghlan — A15

Queen Victoria, George VI, Lobengula's Kraal and Government House A16

Unwmk.

1940, June 3   Engr.   Perf. 14

56	A9	½p dp grn & dull vio	.20	.40
57	A10	1p red & vio blue	.20	.20
58	A11	1½p cop brn & blk	.20	.50
59	A12	2p pur & brt grn	.50	.40
60	A13	3p dk blue & blk	.80	1.00
61	A14	4p brn & bl grn	.70	1.50
62	A15	6p sepia & dull grn	.80	1.40
63	A16	1sh dk bl & brt grn	1.10	1.40
		Nos. 56-63 (8)	4.50	6.80

50th anniv. of the founding of Southern Rhodesia by Cecil John Rhodes.

Pioneer — A17

1943, Nov. 1   Photo.   Wmk. 201

64	A17	2p Prus grn & choc	.20	.35

50th anniv. of Matabeleland under British control.

Princess Elizabeth and Princess Margaret Rose A18

King George VI and Queen Elizabeth A19

Unwmk.

1947, Apr. 1   Engr.   Perf. 14

65	A18	½p dk green & blk	.20	.20
66	A19	1p carmine & blk	.20	.20

Visit of the British Royal Family, Apr., 1947.

Victory Issue

Queen Elizabeth A20   George VI A21

Princess Elizabeth A22   Princess Margaret Rose A23

1947, May 8

67	A20	1p deep carmine	.20	.20
68	A21	2p slate black	.20	.20
69	A22	3p deep blue	.20	.20
70	A23	6p red orange	.40	.75
		Nos. 67-70 (4)	1.00	1.35

Victory of the Allied Nations in WW II.

Common Design Types pictured following the introduction.

UPU Issue
Common Design Types
Engr.; Name Typo.

1949, Oct. 10   Wmk. 4   Perf. 11x11½

71	CD307	2p slate black	.70	.50
72	CD308	3p slate blue	1.25	1.75

75th anniv. of the UPU.

Queen Victoria and King George VI A24

Unwmk.

1950, Sept. 12   Engr.   Perf. 14

73	A24	2p choc & blue grn	.45	.70

60th anniversary of Rhodesia.

Hospital, Doctor and Natives A25

Designs: 1p, African Scene. 2p, Native Houses, Modern City and Cecil Rhodes. 4½p, Dam and Natives. 1sh, Transportation.

1953, Apr. 15

74	A25	½p dk brown & blue	.20	.40
75	A25	1p blue grn & fawn	.20	.20
76	A25	2p vio & dk bl grn	.35	.20
77	A25	4½p dk bl & bl grn	1.50	2.25
78	A25	1sh chestnut & blk	2.00	.70
		Nos. 74-78 (5)	4.25	3.75

#77 is inscribed Matabeleland Diamond Jubilee.

Type of Nyasaland Prot., 1953

1953, May 30   Perf. 14x13½

79	A17	6p purple	.35	.35

Nos. 74-79 were issued to commemorate the Central African Cecil Rhodes Centenary Exhibition.

Coronation Issue

Elizabeth II — A26

1953, June 1   Perf. 12x12½

80	A26	2sh6p cerise	5.25	6.00

Sable Antelope A27   Rhodes' Grave A28

Flame Lily — A29

Designs: 1p, Tobacco planter. 3p, Farm Worker. 4½p, Victoria Falls. 6p, Baobab tree. 9p, Lion. 1sh, Zimbabwe ruins. 2sh, Birchenough Bridge. 2sh6p, Kariba Gorge. 5sh, Basket maker. 10sh, Balancing rocks. £1, Arms.

Perf. 14x13½, 13½x14

1953, Aug. 31
Portrait in Various Positions

81	A27	½p rose lake & dk ol grn	.20	.25
82	A27	1p choc & grn	.20	.20
83	A28	2p rose vio & org brn	.20	.20

Size: 28x22½mm

84	A29	3p car & sep	.45	.50
85	A29	4p gray, brn, car & grn	2.25	.20
86	A29	4½p ultra & blk	1.50	1.75
87	A28	6p aqua & olive	2.00	.20
88	A29	9p org brn & dp bl	3.00	1.50
89	A29	1sh grnsh bl & rose vio	.95	.20
90	A29	2sh red & rose vio	8.25	2.50
91	A29	2sh6p org brn & ol grn	6.00	3.00
92	A28	5s dk grn & org brn	13.00	7.00

Size: 37x27mm

93	A29	10sh ol grn & red brn	18.00	32.50
94	A29	£1 dk gray & car	29.00	32.50
		Nos. 81-94 (14)	85.00	82.50

Ansellia Orchid — A30

1964, Feb. 19   Photo.   Perf. 14½
Size: 23x19mm

95	A30	½p Corn	.20	1.00
96	A30	1p Cape buffalo	.20	.20
a.		Purple omitted	1,900.	
97	A30	2p Tobacco	.20	.20
98	A30	3p Kudu	.20	.20
99	A30	4p Oranges	.20	.20

Perf. 13½x13
Size: 27x23mm

100	A30	6p Flame lily	.20	.20
101	A30	9p shown	.80	.80
102	A30	1sh Emeralds	.75	.20
a.		Green omitted	2,100.	
103	A30	1sh3p Aloe	1.00	.20
104	A30	2sh Lake Kyle	1.50	1.00
105	A30	2sh6p Tiger fish	1.75	.80
a.		Red omitted	2,600.	
b.		Ultra omitted	5,750.	

Perf. 14½x14
Size: 32x27mm

106	A30	5sh Cattle	4.00	2.50
107	A30	10sh Guinea fowl	13.00	6.00
108	A30	£1 Arms	21.00	14.00
		Nos. 95-108 (14)	45.00	27.50

#95-108 with overprint "Independence 11th November 1965" are listed as Rhodesia #208-221.

Stamps of Southern Rhodesia were replaced in 1965 by those of Rhodesia (formerly Southern Rhodesia).

POSTAGE DUE STAMPS

Catalogue values for unused stamps in this section are for Never Hinged items.

Great Britain Postage Due Stamps of 1938-51 Overprinted in Black

1951   Wmk. 251   Perf. 14x14½

J1	D1	½p emerald	3.00	10.00
J2	D1	1p violet blue	2.75	2.75
J3	D1	2p black brown	3.00	1.60
J4	D1	3p violet	3.25	1.25
J5	D1	4p brt green	2.00	2.25
a.		4p slate green	150.00	300.00
J6	D1	1sh blue	3.25	2.00
		Nos. J1-J6 (6)	17.25	19.85

SOUTH GEORGIA

'sauth 'jor-jə

LOCATION — Island in South Atlantic Ocean, 1,100 mi. east of Tierra del Fuego
GOVT. — Dependency of Falkland Islands
AREA — 1,450 sq. mi.
POP. — Military and biological staff only.
CAPITAL — Grytviken Harbor (military garrison)

South Georgia remained a dependency of the Falkland Islands in 1962 when three other dependencies became Antarctic Territory, a separate colony. In 1985 South Georgia and the South Sandwich Islands became a separate colony. See Falkland Islands Dependencies Nos. 3L1-3L8.

12 Pence = 1 Shilling
20 Shillings = 1 Pound
100 Pence = 1 Pound (1971)

Catalogue values for all unused stamps in this country are for Never Hinged items.

Reindeer A1

Sperm Whale — A2

Designs: 1p, South Sandwich Islands map. 2½p, Penguins. 3p, Fur seals. 4p, Finback whale and ship. 5½p, Elephant seals. 6p,

Sooty albatross. 9p, Whaling ship. 1sh, Leopard seal. 2sh, Shackleton's cross. 2sh6p, Wandering albatross. 5sh, Elephant and fur seals. 10sh, Plankton and krill (shrimp). No. 15, Blue whale. No. 16, King penguins.

Wmk. 314 Upright

1963-69		**Engr.**		**Perf. 15**	
1	A1	½p dull red		.45	.90
a.		Perf. 14x15 ('67)		1.25	1.50
b.		Watermark sideways ('70)		1.50	3.75
2	A2	1p violet blue		.75	.90
3	A2	2p blue green		1.10	.90
4	A1	2½p black		5.00	2.25
5	A2	3p olive		2.50	.35
6	A1	4p green		4.50	.75
7	A1	5½p dull violet		2.25	.40
8	A2	6p orange		.70	.45
9	A1	9p blue		4.50	1.75
10	A1	1sh lilac		.70	.30
11	A1	2sh cit & lt blue		22.50	6.00
12	A1	2sh6p blue		22.50	4.00
13	A1	5sh ocher		20.00	4.00
14	A2	10sh rose claret		37.50	10.00
15	A1	£1 ultra		80.00	45.00
16	A2	£1 slate green		10.00	15.00
		Nos. 1-16 (16)		214.95	92.95
		Set, hinged		125.00	

Issued: No. 16, 12/1/69; others 7/10/63.

Stamps and Type of 1963 Surcharged with New Value (Decimal Currency) and 3 Bars

Wmk. 314 Upright; Sideways on ½p					
1971-72				**Perf. 15**	
17	A1	½p on ½p dull red		.85	.75
a.		Wmk. upright ('73)		2.75	2.75
18	A2	1p on 1p vio blue		1.00	.90
a.		Wmk. sideways ('76)		2.25	3.25
19	A1	1½p on 5½p dull vio		.75	.70
20	A2	2p on 2p blue grn		.60	.50
21	A1	2½p on 2½p black		.75	.70
22	A2	3p on 3p olive		.85	.75
23	A1	4p on 4p green		1.00	.90
24	A2	5p on 6p orange		1.40	1.25
25	A1	6p on 9p blue		.70	.55
26	A1	7½p on 1sh lilac		2.40	2.00
27	A1	10p on 2sh cit & lt bl		20.00	7.50
28	A1	15p on 2sh6p blue		17.50	9.00
29	A1	25p on 5sh ocher		13.00	7.50
30	A2	50p on 10sh rose claret, glazed paper ('72)		20.00	20.00
a.		Wmk. sideways ('76)		27.50	30.00
c.		Ordinary paper		47.50	25.00
		Nos. 17-30 (14)		80.80	53.00

Two types of surcharge are found on ½p, 1p, 1½p and 50p.

Issued: Nos. 17-29, 30b, 2/15/71. No. 30, 12/1/72. No. 30a, 3/9/76.

Wmk. 373 Sideways; Upright on 3p, 50p; Inverted on 1p, 5p					
1977					
17b	A1	½p on ½p dull red		1.60	1.60
18b	A2	1p on 1p vio blue		.90	.90
19b	A1	1½p on 5½p dl vio		1.00	1.00
21b	A1	2½p on 2½p black		11.00	3.25
22b	A2	3p on 3p olive		7.75	3.25
23b	A1	4p on 4p green		19.00	14.00
24b	A2	5p on 6p orange		2.75	2.75
26b	A1	7½p on 1sh lilac		1.90	8.25
27b	A1	10p on 2sh cit & lt bl		1.90	8.25
28b	A1	15p on 2sh6p blue		2.25	8.25
29b	A1	25p on 5sh ocher		1.90	8.25
30b	A2	50p on 10sh lil rose ('79)		1.90	8.25
		Nos. 17b-30b (12)		53.85	68.00

Ernest Shackleton and "Quest" — A3

1½p, "Endurance" in ice of Weddell Sea. 5p, Launching of sailboat "James Caird." 10p, Route of "James Caird" to South Georgia.

1972, Jan. 5		**Litho.**		**Perf. 13½**	
31	A3	1½p vio bl, blk & yel		1.20	1.75
32	A3	5p bl grn, blk & yel		1.40	2.25
33	A3	10p lt blue & blk		2.00	2.50
34	A3	20p multicolored		2.25	3.00
		Nos. 31-34 (4)		6.85	9.50

Sir Ernest Shackleton (1874-1922), explorer of Antarctica.

Common Design Types pictured following the introduction.

Silver Wedding Issue, 1972
Common Design Type

Design: Queen Elizabeth II, Prince Philip, elephant seal and king penguins.

1972, Nov. 20		**Photo.**		**Perf. 14x14½**	
35	CD324	5p slate grn & multi		.50	.50
36	CD324	10p violet & multi		1.00	1.00

Princess Anne's Wedding Issue
Common Design Type

1973, Dec. 1		**Litho.**		**Perf. 14**	
37	CD325	15p citron & multi		.20	.20
38	CD325	15p slate & multi		.60	.60

Churchill, Parliament and Big Ben — A4

Design: 25p, Churchill and battleship.

1974, Dec. 14		**Litho.**		**Perf. 14½**	
39	A4	15p vio blue & multi		1.25	1.25
40	A4	25p orange & multi		2.00	2.00
a.		Souvenir sheet of 2, #39-40		7.25	7.25

Sir Winston Churchill (1874-1965).

Capt. James Cook — A5

Cook's "Possession" — A6

Design: 16p, Possession Bay.

1975, Apr. 26				**Wmk. 314**	
41	A5	2p multicolored		2.25	1.00
42	A6	8p multicolored		3.50	1.75
43	A6	16p multicolored		3.75	2.50
		Nos. 41-43 (3)		9.50	5.25

Bicentenary of Capt. Cook's discovery of South Georgia.

"Discovery" and Biological Laboratory — A7

Designs: 8p, "William Scoresby" and Nansen-Pettersson water sampling bottles. 11p, "Discovery II" and plankton net. 25p, Biological station and krill (shrimp).

				Wmk. 373	
1976, Dec. 21		**Litho.**		**Perf. 14**	
44	A7	2p multicolored		.50	.35
45	A7	8p multicolored		1.25	1.25
46	A7	11p multicolored		1.50	1.40
47	A7	25p multicolored		3.75	2.50
		Nos. 44-47 (4)		7.00	5.50

25th anniversary of the biological investigations of the "Discovery."

Queen with Regalia and Westminster Abbey — A8

6p, Prince Philip visiting Shackleton Memorial, 1957. 33p, Queen in procession after coronation.

1977, Feb. 7				**Perf. 13½x14**	
48	A8	6p multicolored		.25	.25
49	A8	11p multicolored		.40	.40
50	A8	33p multicolored		1.25	1.25
		Nos. 48-50 (3)		1.90	1.90

25th anniv. of the reign of Elizabeth II.

Elizabeth II Coronation Anniversary Issue
Common Design Types
Souvenir Sheet
Unwmk.

1978, June 2		**Litho.**		**Perf. 15**	
51		Sheet of 6		3.00	3.50
a.		CD326 25p Panther of Henry VI		.60	.65
b.		CD327 25p Elizabeth II		.60	.65
c.		CD328 25p Fur seal		.60	.65

No. 51 contains 2 se-tenant strips of Nos. 51a-51c, separated by horizontal gutter with commemorative and descriptive inscriptions and showing central part of coronation procession with coach.

Resolution A9

Cook's voyages: 6p, Map of South Georgia and South Sandwich Islands with Cook's route. 11p, King penguin, drawing by Forster. 25p, Cook after Flaxman/Wedgwood medallion.

1979, Feb. 14		**Litho.**		**Perf. 11**	
52	A9	3p multicolored		1.25	1.00
53	A9	6p multicolored		1.25	.85
54	A9	11p multicolored		2.25	1.90
		Lithographed; Embossed			
55	A9	25p multicolored		2.50	2.25
		Nos. 52-55 (4)		7.25	6.00

SOUTH GEORGIA and SOUTH SANDWICH ISLANDS
Queen Elizabeth II 60th Birthday
Common Design Type

Designs: 10p, With King George and Queen Mary at christening of Prince Charles, 1948. 24p, Engagement of Prince Charles and Lady Diana, Buckingham Palace Music Room, 1981. 29p, Order of the British Empire, service at St. Paul's Cathedral, London, 1974. 45p, Banquet for Canadian Prime Minister Trudeau during the 1976 Olympics. 58p, Visiting Crown Agents' offices, 1983.

1986, Apr. 21		**Wmk. 384**		**Perf. 14½**	
101	CD337	10p multicolored		.25	.25
102	CD337	24p multicolored		.60	.60
103	CD337	29p multicolored		.75	.75
104	CD337	45p multicolored		1.10	1.10
105	CD337	58p multicolored		1.50	1.50
		Nos. 101-105 (5)		4.20	4.20

Wedding of Prince Andrew and Sarah Ferguson — A12

1986, Nov. 10		**Litho.**		**Perf. 14½**	
106	A12	17p Couple at Ascot		.80	1.10
107	A12	22p Wedding		.90	1.40
108	A12	29p Andrew, helicopter		1.60	1.60
		Nos. 106-108 (3)		3.30	4.10

Birds A13

1987, Apr. 24		**Litho.**		**Wmk. 384**	
109	A13	1p Dominican gull		.90	.90
110	A13	2p Blue-eyed cormorant		1.10	1.10
111	A13	3p Wattled sheathbill		1.25	1.25
112	A13	4p Brown skua		1.10	1.10
113	A13	5p Cape pigeon		1.10	1.10
114	A13	6p South Georgia diving petrel		1.10	1.10
115	A13	7p South Georgia pipit		1.25	1.25
116	A13	8p South Georgia pintail		1.25	1.25
117	A13	9p Fairy prion		1.25	1.25
118	A13	10p Chinstrap penguin		1.75	1.75
119	A13	20p Macaroni penguin		2.10	2.50
120	A13	25p Light-mantled sooty albatross		2.10	2.50
121	A13	50p Southern giant petrel		3.00	3.00
122	A13	£1 Wandering albatross		3.50	4.00
123	A13	£3 King penguin		9.50	10.50
		Nos. 109-123 (15)		32.25	34.55

3, 4, 7, 8, 20, 25, 50p and £3 vert.

Intl. Geophysical Year, 30th Anniv. — A14

1987, Dec. 5		**Litho.**		**Perf. 14½**	
124	A14	24p shown		.80	.80
125	A14	29p Grytviken Whaling Station		.90	.90
126	A14	58p Glaciologist		1.75	1.75
		Nos. 124-126 (3)		3.45	3.45

Sea Shells A15

1988, Feb. 26		**Wmk. 384**		**Perf. 14½**	
127	A15	10p Gaimardia trapesina		.60	.60
128	A15	24p Margarella tropidophoroides		1.40	1.40
129	A15	29p Trophon scotianus		1.60	1.60
130	A15	58p Chlanidota denseculpta		3.25	3.25
		Nos. 127-130 (4)		6.85	6.85

Lloyds of London, 300th Anniv.
Common Design Type

10p, Queen Mother at the official opening of the Lloyds Building, Lime Street, 1957. 24p, Lindblad Explorer, horiz. 29p, Leith Harbor whaling station, horiz. 58p, Whale oil tanker Horatio on fire.

1988, Sept. 17				**Perf. 14**	
131	CD341	10p multicolored		.40	.40
132	CD341	24p multicolored		.90	.90
133	CD341	29p multicolored		1.10	1.10
134	CD341	58p multicolored		2.50	2.50
		Nos. 131-134 (4)		4.90	4.90

Glacier Formations — A16

1989, July 31
135	A16	10p Glacier headwall	.50	.50
136	A16	24p Accumulation area	1.00	1.00
137	A16	29p Ablation area	1.25	1.25
138	A16	58p Calving front	2.50	2.50
		Nos. 135-138 (4)	5.25	5.25

Combined Services Expedition, 1964-65
A17

1989, Nov. 28 — Perf. 14x14½
139	A17	10p "Last ordeal" of the trek	.50	.50
140	A17	24p Survey of Royal Bay	1.10	1.10
141	A17	29p HMS *Protector*	1.25	1.25
142	A17	58p 1st Ascent of Mt. Paget	2.40	2.40
		Nos. 139-142 (4)	5.25	5.25

Queen Mother, 90th Birthday
Common Design Types
Designs: 26p, Queen Mother. £1, King, Queen & Air Raid Wardens, 1940.

Perf. 14x15
1990, Sept. 15 — Wmk. 384
143	CD343	26p multicolored	1.25	1.25

Perf. 14½
144	CD344	£1 blue & black	4.50	4.50

Shipwrecks
A18

1990, Dec. 22 — Litho. — Wmk. 384 — Perf. 14
145	A18	12p Brutus	.60	.50
146	A18	26p Bayard	1.25	1.00
147	A18	31p Karrakatta	1.50	1.50
148	A18	62p Louise	2.75	2.25
		Nos. 145-148 (4)	6.10	5.00

Elizabeth & Philip, Birthdays
Common Design Types
1991, July 2 — Perf. 14½
149	CD345	31p multicolored	1.50	1.50
150	CD346	31p multicolored	1.50	1.50
a.		Pair, #149-150 + label	6.00	6.00

No. 150a exists with two different labels.

Elephant Seals
A19

1991, Nov. 2 — Wmk. 373 — Perf. 14
151	A19	12p Two bulls	.80	.80
152	A19	26p One bull	1.60	1.60
153	A19	29p Using sand as sunscreen	1.60	1.60
154	A19	31p Bull, close up	1.60	1.60
155	A19	34p Harem on beach	2.00	2.00
156	A19	62p Cow and pup	3.25	3.25
		Nos. 151-156 (6)	10.85	10.85

Queen Elizabeth II's Accession to the Throne, 40th Anniv.
Common Design Type
1992, Feb. 6
157	CD349	7p multicolored	.25	.25
158	CD349	14p multicolored	.55	.55
159	CD349	29p multicolored	1.00	1.00
160	CD349	34p multicolored	1.25	1.25
161	CD349	68p multicolored	2.50	2.50
		Nos. 157-161 (5)	5.55	5.55

South Georgia Teal
A20

1992, Mar. 22 — Wmk. 384
162	A20	2p Adult, young	.20	.20
163	A20	6p Adult, nest of eggs	.55	.55
164	A20	12p Four swimming	1.25	1.25
165	A20	20p Adult, two chicks	2.00	2.00
		Nos. 162-165 (4)	4.00	4.00

World Wildlife Fund.

South Georgia Whaling Museum
A21

Designs: 15p, Abandoned factory, Grytviken. 31p, Whaler's lighter, bones. 36p, King Edward Cove. 72p, Museum Building.

Wmk. 373
1993, June 29 — Litho. — Perf. 13½
166-169	A21	Set of 4	7.50	7.50

Macaroni Penguins
A22

16p, Swimming underwater. 34p, Part of rookery. 39p, Two juveniles. 78p, Two adults.

Perf. 14x14½
1993, Dec. 10 — Litho. — Wmk. 373
170-173	A22	Set of 4	8.00	8.00

Ovptd. with Hong Kong '94 Emblem
1994, Feb. 18
174-177	A22		9.00	9.00

Whales and Dolphins
A23

Designs: 1p, Hourglass dolphin. 2p, Southern right whale dolphin. 5p, Long-finned pilot whale. 8p, Southern bottlenose whale. 9p, Killer whale. 10p, Minke whale. 20p, Sei whale. 25p, Humpback whale. 50p, Southern right whale. £1, Sperm whale. £3, Fin whale. £5, Blue whale.

Wmk. 373
1994, Jan. 24 — Litho. — Perf. 14
178	A23	1p multicolored	.45	.45
179	A23	2p multicolored	.65	.65
180	A23	5p multicolored	.90	.90
181	A23	8p multicolored	1.00	1.00
182	A23	9p multicolored	1.00	1.00
183	A23	10p multicolored	1.00	1.00
184	A23	20p multicolored	1.60	1.60
185	A23	25p multicolored	1.60	1.60
186	A23	50p multicolored	2.25	2.25
187	A23	£1 multicolored	4.00	4.00
188	A23	£3 multicolored	11.00	11.00
189	A23	£5 multicolored	18.00	18.00
		Nos. 178-189 (12)	43.45	43.45

Native Wildlife
A24

Wmk. 384
1994, Sept. 28 — Litho. — Perf. 14
190	A24	17p Bull elephant seals	.90	.90
191	A24	35p Fur seal, vert.	1.75	1.75
192	A24	40p Gray-headed albatrosses	2.00	2.00
193	A24	65p King penguins, vert.	3.00	3.00
		Nos. 190-193 (4)	7.65	7.65

Capt. C. A. Larsen's First Voyage to South Georgia
A25

1994, Dec. 1
194	A25	17p Map of Jason Harbor	.65	.65
195	A25	35p Castor, 1886	1.75	1.75
196	A25	40p Hertha, 1884	2.00	2.00
197	A25	65p Jason, 1881	3.25	3.25
		Nos. 194-197 (4)	7.65	7.65

End of World War II, 50th Anniv.
Common Design Types
#198, HMS Queen of Bermuda moored at Leith Harbor. #199, 4-inch gun, Hansen Point, four men of Norwegian Defense Force. £1, Reverse of War Medal 1939-45.

Wmk. 384
1995, May 8 — Litho. — Perf. 14
198	CD351	50p multicolored	2.00	2.00
199	CD351	50p multicolored	2.00	2.00
a.		Pair, #198-199	6.75	6.75

Souvenir Sheet
Wmk. 373
200	CD352	£1 multicolored	6.75	6.75

No. 199a is a continuous design.

Yachts — A26

Wmk. 373
1995, Nov. 16 — Litho. — Perf. 14½
201	A26	35p Damien II	1.75	1.75
202	A26	40p Curlew	2.25	2.25
203	A26	76p Mischief	3.75	3.75
		Nos. 201-203 (3)	7.75	7.75

Sir Ernest Shackleton's King Haakon Bay-Stromness Trek, 80th Anniv. — A27

Designs: 15p, Shackleton, Ridge 2493 Point of No Return. 20p, Frank Worsley, King Haakon Bay from Shackleton Gap. 30p, Map of Shackleton's route. 65p, Tom Crean, Manager's Villa, Stromness Whaling Station.

Wmk. 384
1996, May 20 — Litho. — Perf. 14
204	A27	15p multicolored	.75	.75
205	A27	20p multicolored	1.10	1.10
206	A27	30p multicolored	1.50	1.50
207	A27	65p multicolored	3.00	3.00
		Nos. 204-207 (4)	6.35	6.35

Chinstrap Penguins — A28

Perf. 14½x14
1996, Nov. 8 — Litho. — Wmk. 373
208	A28	17p Swimming	.90	.90
209	A28	35p Male, female	1.50	1.50
210	A28	40p Feeding chicks	1.75	1.75
211	A28	76p Feeding on krill	3.50	3.50
a.		Souvenir sheet of 1, perf. 14x14½	4.25	4.25
		Nos. 208-211 (4)	7.65	7.65

Return of Hong Kong to China (#211a).

Queen Elizabeth and Prince Philip, 50th Wedding Anniv. — A29

#212, Queen. #213, Prince driving team of horses. #214, Queen looking at horses. #215, Prince. #216, Princess Anne on horseback, Queen. #217, Prince, child on horseback. £1.50, Queen, Prince in open carriage, horiz.

Perf. 14½x14
1997, July 10 — Litho. — Wmk. 384
212		15p multicolored	1.00	1.00
213		15p multicolored	1.00	1.00
a.		A29 Pair, #212-213	2.25	2.25
214		17p multicolored	1.25	1.25
215		17p multicolored	1.25	1.25
a.		A29 Pair, #214-215	2.75	2.75
216		40p multicolored	2.50	2.50
217		40p multicolored	5.50	5.50
a.		A29 Pair, #216-217	2.50	2.50
		Nos. 212-217 (6)	12.50	12.50

Souvenir Sheet
218	A29	£1.50 multicolored	8.50	8.50

Flora and Fauna
A30

a, Reindeer. b, Antarctic tern. c, Gray-headed albatross. d, King penguin. e, Prickly burr. f, Fur seal.

Perf. 14½x14
1998, Mar. 16 — Litho. — Wmk. 373
219	A30	35p Sheet of 6, #a.-f.	9.50	9.50

Diana, Princess of Wales (1961-97)
Common Design Type
Designs: a, Looking left. b, In white evening dress. c, In red dress. d, In white.

1998, Mar. 31
220	CD355	35p Sheet of 4, #a.-d.	5.25	5.25

No. 220 sold for £1.40 + 20p, with surtax and 50% of the profits from the issue being donated to the Princess Diana Memorial Fund.

Tourism
A31

Designs: 30p, MS Explorer. 35p, Wandering albatross. 40p, Elephant seal. 65p, Post Office, King Edward Point.

Wmk. 373
1998, Sept. 28 — Litho. — Perf. 14½
221	A31	30p multicolored	1.50	1.50
222	A31	35p multicolored	1.75	1.75
223	A31	40p multicolored	1.90	1.90
224	A31	65p multicolored	3.25	3.25
		Nos. 221-224 (4)	8.40	8.40

Island Views A32

Designs: 9p, Grytviken and Sugartop Mountain. 17p, Old sealing ships, Grytviken. 35p, King Edward Point. 40p, Arrival at South Georgia. 65p, Church, Grytviken.

Wmk. 384

1999, Jan. 4		Litho.	Perf. 14	
225	A32	9p multicolored	.50	.50
226	A32	17p multicolored	1.00	1.00
227	A32	35p multicolored	1.90	1.90
228	A32	40p multicolored	2.10	2.10
229	A32	65p multicolored	3.50	3.50
		Nos. 225-229 (5)	9.00	9.00

Souvenir Sheet

Capt. James Cook's Ship HMS Resolution, 1773 — A33

Illustration reduced.

1999, Mar. 5			Perf. 13½	
230	A33	£1.50 multicolored	8.50	8.50

Australia '99, World Stamp Expo.

Queen Mother's Century
Common Design Type

Queen Mother: 25p, At air raid shelter, 1940. 30p, With Prince Edward, Lady Sarah Armstrong-Jones, Viscount Linley, 70th birthday. 35p, With Prince William, 94th birthday. 40p, As colonel-in-chief of Royal Anglian Regiment. £1, Funeral procession for Queen Victoria, portrait of Victoria.

Wmk. 384

1999, Aug. 18		Litho.	Perf. 13½	
231	CD358	25p multicolored	1.40	1.40
232	CD358	30p black	1.75	1.75
233	CD358	35p multicolored	2.00	2.00
234	CD358	40p multicolored	2.25	2.25
		Nos. 231-234 (4)	7.40	7.40

Souvenir Sheet

235	CD358	£1 black	8.00	8.00

Birds — A34

Designs: 1p, Chinstrap penguin, vert. 2p, White chinned petrel. 5p, Gray backed storm petrel, vert. 10p, South Georgia pipit, vert. 11p, Gray headed albatross. 30p, Blue petrel, vert. 35p, Black browed albatross. 40p, South Georgia diving petrel. 50p, Macaroni penguin, vert. £1, Light mantled sooty albatross. £3, South Georgia pintail. £5, King penguin, vert.

Wmk. 384

1999, Nov. 15		Litho.	Perf. 14	
236	A34	1p multicolored	.20	.20
237	A34	2p multicolored	.20	.20
238	A34	5p multicolored	.20	.20
239	A34	10p multicolored	.30	.30
240	A34	11p multicolored	.35	.35
241	A34	30p multicolored	.95	.95
242	A34	35p multicolored	1.10	1.10
243	A34	40p multicolored	1.25	1.25
244	A34	50p multicolored	1.60	1.60
245	A34	£1 multicolored	3.25	3.25
246	A34	£3 multicolored	10.00	10.00
247	A34	£5 multicolored	16.00	16.00
		Nos. 236-247 (12)	35.40	35.40

Millennium — A35

Perf. 14½x14¼				
1999, Dec. 18		Litho.	Wmk. 384	
248	A35	11p Sunrise	.60	.60
249	A35	11p Church	.60	.60
250	A35	11p Albatrosses	.60	.60
251	A35	35p Penguins	1.90	1.90
252	A35	35p Reindeer	1.90	1.90
253	A35	35p Sunset	1.90	1.90
		Nos. 248-253 (6)	7.50	7.50

Sir Ernest Shackleton (1874-1922), Polar Explorer — A36

Designs: 35p, Voyage across Scotia Sea, 1916. 40p, Shackleton, Thomas Crean and Frank Worsley crossing South Georgia. 65p, Shackleton's grave.

2000, Feb. 20		Wmk. 373	Perf. 14	
254	A36	35p multi	1.90	1.90
255	A36	40p multi	2.10	2.10
256	A36	65p multi	3.50	3.50
		Nos. 254-256 (3)	7.50	7.50

See British Antarctic Territory Nos. 285-287, Falkland Islands Nos. 758-760.

Prince William, 18th Birthday
Common Design Type

William: 25p, In suit, carrying bag, vert. 30p, With ski equipment, vert. 35p, Wearing suit and wearing sweater. 40p, In suit, waving. 50p, In beret, saluting.

Perf. 13¾x14¼, 14¼x13¾				
2000, June 21		Litho.	Wmk. 373	
Stamps With White Border				
257	CD359	25p multi	1.10	1.10
258	CD359	30p multi	1.25	1.25
259	CD359	35p multi	1.40	1.40
260	CD359	40p multi	1.90	1.90
		Nos. 257-260 (4)	5.65	5.65

Souvenir Sheet
Stamps Without White Border

Perf. 14¼				
261		Sheet of 5	7.50	7.50
a.	CD359	25p multi	.85	.85
b.	CD359	30p multi	1.00	1.00
c.	CD359	35p multi	1.10	1.10
d.	CD359	40p multi	1.40	1.40
e.	CD359	50p multi	1.75	1.75

King Penguins — A37

#262, 37p, Penguins at sea. #263, 37p, Adult & creche. #264, 43p, Advertisement walk & courtship. #265, 43p, Nesting.

Perf. 14¾x14				
2000, Oct. 16		Litho.	Wmk. 373	
262-265	A37	Set of 4	8.00	8.00

Royal Fleet Auxiliary Vessels A38

Designs: No. 266, 37p, RFA Sir Percivale. No. 267, 37p, RFA Tidespring. No. 268, 43p, RFA Diligence. No. 269, 43p, RFA Gold Rover.

Wmk. 373

2001, May 28		Litho.	Perf. 14	
266-269	A38	Set of 4	6.25	6.25

Marine Life — A39

Designs: 33p, Icefish. No. 271, 37p, Spiny back crab. No. 272, 37p, Krill, vert. 43p, Toothfish, vert.

Wmk. 373

2001, Oct. 22		Litho.	Perf. 13¾	
270-273	A39	Set of 4	5.50	5.50

Reign Of Queen Elizabeth II, 50th Anniv. Issue
Common Design Type

Designs: Nos. 274, 278a, 20p, With dog, 1952. Nos. 275, 278b, 37p, With Prince Philip, 1997. Nos. 276, 278c, 43p, Examining royal stamp collection, 1946. Nos. 277, 278d, 50p, Wearing blue hat, 1999. No. 278e, 50p, 1955 portrait by Annigoni (38x50mm).

Perf. 14¼x14½, 13¾ (#278e)				
2002, Feb. 6		Litho.	Wmk. 373	
With Gold Frames				
274-277	CD360	Set of 4	5.50	5.50

Souvenir Sheet
Without Gold Frames

278	CD360	Sheet of 5, #a-e	6.50	6.50

World Record Animals — A40

No. 279: a, 10p, Fin whale. b, 10p, Blue whale. c, 20p, Sperm whale. d, 37p, Leopard seal with mouth open. e, 37p, Leopard seal on ice. f, 43p, Elephant seal. £1.50, Elephant seal, diff.

2002, Mar. 2		Litho.	Perf. 13¾	
279	A40	Sheet of 6, #a-f	6.00	6.00

Souvenir Sheet

280	A40	£1.50 multi	5.50	5.50

Queen Mother Elizabeth (1900-2002)
Common Design Type

Designs: 22p, Wearing hat (black and white photograph). 40p, Wearing tiara. Nos. 283, 285a, 45p, Holding dog (black and white photograph). Nos. 284, 285b, 95p, Wearing white stole.

Perf. 14¼, 13¾x14¼ (#283-284)				
2002, Aug. 5		Litho.	Wmk. 373	
With Purple Frames				
281-284	CD361	Set of 4	7.50	7.50

Souvenir Sheet
Without Purple Frames

Perf. 14½x14¼				
285	CD361	Sheet of 2, #a-b	5.00	5.00

Antarctic Fur Seals — A41

Designs: No. 286, 40p, Seal in water. No. 287, 40p, Two seals on ice. No. 288, 45p, Six seals. No. 289, 45p, One seal.

Worldwide Fund for Nature (WWF) — A42

Gray-headed albatross: 40p, Adults at nesting ground. No. 291, 45p, Adult and chick (WWF emblem at LL). No. 292, 45p, Two adults (WWF emblem at UL). 70p, Bird's head.

Wmk. 373

2002, Oct. 25		Litho.	Perf. 13¾	
286-289	A41	Set of 4	5.25	5.25

Wmk. 373

2003, Jan. 6		Litho.	Perf. 14	
290-293	A42	Set of 4	7.50	7.50
293a		Strip of 4, #a-d	6.50	6.50

Head of Queen Elizabeth II
Common Design Type

Wmk. 373

2003, June 2		Litho.	Perf. 13¾	
294	CD362	£2 multi	7.50	7.50

Prince William, 21st Birthday
Common Design Type

No. 295: a, Color photograph at right. b, Color photograph at left.

Wmk. 373

2003, June 21		Litho.	Perf. 14¼	
295		Horiz. pair	4.50	4.50
a.-b.	CD364	70p Either single	2.25	2.25

History of South Georgia — A43

No. 296: a, HMS Sappho visits Grytviken, 1906. b, Norwegian reindeer introduced, 1911. c, Largest blue whale landed, 1912. d, Shackleton's island crossing, 1916. e, Shackleton Memorial Cross, 1922. f, Discovery investigations, 1925. g, First powered flight over South Georgia, 1938. h, Operation Tabarin, 1943. i, Duke of Edinburgh visits, 1957. j, Bird Island Research Station, 1958. k, Mt. Paget climbed, 1964. l, Liberation of the island, 1982. m, Royal charter and crest, 1985. n, Museum inaugurated, 1992. o, Applied fishery research, 2001. p, Grytviken remedial work, 2003.

Wmk. 373

2004, Feb. 6		Litho.	Perf. 13¼	
296	A43	40p Sheet of 16, #a-p	24.00	24.00

Royal Navy Ships A44

Designs: 10p, HMS Ajax. 25p, HMS Amazon. 45p, HMS Dartmouth. 50p, HMS Penelope. 70p, HMS St. Austell Bay. £1, HMS Plymouth.

Wmk. 373

2004, Apr. 26		Litho.	Perf. 14	
297-302	A44	Set of 6	11.00	11.00

SEMI-POSTAL STAMPS

Liberation of
South Georgia,
10th
Anniv. — SP1

Designs: 14p+6p, King Edward Point, Winter 1982. 29p+11p, Queen Elizabeth 2 in Cumberland Bay. 34p+16p, Royal Marines on South Sandwich Islands. 68p+32p, HMS Endurance and Wasp Helicopter.

Wmk. 384

1992, June 20	**Litho.**		**Perf. 14**	
B1	SP1 14p +6p multicolored		.90	.90
B2	SP1 29p +11p multicolored		1.50	1.50
B3	SP1 34p +16p multicolored		1.75	1.75
B4	SP1 68p +32p multicolored		3.75	3.75
a.	Souvenir sheet of 4, #B1-B4		9.00	9.00
	Nos. B1-B4 (4)		7.90	7.90

Surtax for Soldiers', Sailors' and Airmen's Families Association.

SOUTH KASAI

This part of a Congo province declared itself an autonomous state and in 1961 issued several series of stamps, some of which were overprints on Congo (ex-Belgian) stamps. Established nations did not recognize South Kasai as an independent state.

SOUTH MOLUCCAS
(Republik Maluku Selatan)

It appears that stamps of the so-called republic of South Moluccas were privately issued and had no postal use. Accordingly, they are not recognized as postage stamps.

SOUTH RUSSIA

sauth 'rəsh-ə

LOCATION — An area in southern Russia bordering on the Caspian and Black Seas.

A provisional government set up and maintained by General Denikin in opposition to the Bolshevik forces in Russia following the downfall of the Empire. The stamps were used in the field postal service established for carrying on communication between the various armies united in the revolt. These armies included the Don Cossacks, the Kuban Cossacks, and also the neighboring southern Russian people in favor of the counter-revolution against the Bolsheviks.

100 Kopecks = 1 Ruble

Values for used stamps are for CTO copies. Postally used specimens sell for considerably more.

Watermark

Wmk. 171 —
Diamonds

Don Government
(Novocherkassk)
Rostov Issue

Russian Stamps of 1909-17 Surcharged

1918	**Unwmk.**		**Perf. 14x14½**	
1	A14 25k on 1k dl org yel		1.75	1.90
a.	Inverted surcharge		25.00	40.00
2	A14 25k on 2k dl grn		.50	.60
a.	Inverted surcharge		20.00	35.00
3	A14 25k on 3k car		.50	.75
a.	Double surcharge		30.00	55.00
4	A15 25k on 4k car		2.50	3.50
a.	Inverted surcharge		20.00	35.00
5	A14 50k on 7k blue		5.00	6.50
	Imperf			
6	A14 25k on 1k orange		.50	1.25
a.	Inverted surcharge		20.00	35.00
7	A14 25k on 2k gray grn		7.50	12.50
8	A14 25k on 3k red		2.00	3.00
	Nos. 1-8 (8)		20.25	30.00

Counterfeits exist of Nos. 1-8.

Ermak, Cossack
Leader — A1

Inscription on Back

1919			**Perf. 11½**	
10	A1 20k green		35.00	85.00

This stamp was available for both postage and currency.

Novocherkassk Issue

Russian stamps with these surcharges are bogus.

Kuban Government
Ekaterinodar Issues
Russian Stamps of 1909-17
Surcharged:

d

e

f

g

h

i

1918-20	**Unwmk.**		**Perf. 14x14½**	
20	A14(d) 25k on 1k dl org yel		.40	.65
a.	Inverted surcharge		20.00	27.50
b.	Dbl. surch., one inverted		20.00	25.00
21	A14(d) 50k on 2k dl grn		5.00	6.00
a.	Inverted surcharge		20.00	27.50
b.	Double surcharge		15.00	20.00
c.	Dbl. surcharge inverted		10.50	20.00
22	A14(e) 70k on 5k dk cl		2.00	4.00
23	A14(f) 1r on 3k car		2.00	3.00
a.	Inverted surcharge		15.00	20.00
b.	Double surcharge		10.00	15.00
c.	Pair, one without surch.		10.00	15.00

24	A14(g) 1r on 3k car		.60	1.00
a.	Inverted surcharge		15.00	20.00
b.	Double surcharge		15.00	20.00
c.	Pair, one without surcharge		15.00	20.00
25	A15(h) 3r on 4k rose		10.00	15.00
b.	Inverted surcharge		35.00	50.00
c.	Double surcharge		35.00	60.00
d.	Dbl. surcharge inverted		35.00	60.00
26	A15(i) 10r on 4k rose		4.00	5.00
a.	10r on 4k carmine		8.00	13.00
b.	Inverted surcharge		35.00	55.00
27	A11(i) 10r on 15k red brn & dp bl		1.10	1.60
a.	Surchd. on face & back		15.00	15.00
b.	Dbl. surch., one inverted		35.00	60.00
28	A14(i) 25r on 3k car		2.25	2.00
a.	Inverted surcharge		10.00	20.00
29	A14(i) 25r on 7k bl		25.00	27.50
a.	Inverted surcharge		50.00	60.00
30	A11(i) 25r on 14k bl & car		50.00	65.00
a.	Inverted surcharge		65.00	70.00
31	A11(i) 25r on 25k dl grn & dk vio		25.00	47.50
a.	Inverted surcharge		50.00	70.00
	Nos. 20-31 (12)		127.35	178.25
	Imperf			
35	A14(d) 25d on 1k org		1.10	2.00
36	A14(d) 50k on 2k gray grn		.25	.35
a.	Inverted surcharge		25.00	25.00
b.	Double surcharge		25.00	25.00
c.	Pair, one without surch.		25.00	30.00
37	A14(e) 70k on 5k claret		2.10	3.25
38	A14(f) 1r on 3k red		1.25	2.00
a.	Inverted surcharge		20.00	20.00
b.	Double surcharge		10.00	15.00
c.	Pair, one without surch.		10.00	15.00
39	A14(g) 1r on 3k red		.50	.65
a.	Double surcharge		10.00	20.00
b.	Pair, one without surch.		10.00	20.00
c.	As "a," inverted		25.00	45.00
40	A11(i) 10r on 15k red brn & dp bl		3.75	4.75
41	A14(i) 25r on 3k red		5.25	7.00
a.	Inverted surcharge		40.00	
	Nos. 35-41 (7)		14.20	20.00

Russian Stamps of 1909-17
Surcharged

1919			**Perf. 14, 14½x15**	
45	A14 70k on 1k dl org yel		1.00	1.00
	Imperf			
46	A14 70k on 1k orange		1.00	1.50
a.	Inverted surcharge		15.00	20.00
b.	Double surch., one inverted		25.00	25.00

The 1k postal savings stamp with this surcharge inverted is a proof.
Counterfeits exist of Nos. 20-46.

Postal Savings Stamps Surcharged for Postal Use

A2

1919	**Wmk. 171**		**Perf. 14½x15**	
47	A2 10r on 1k red, buff		16.00	20.00
a.	Inverted surcharge		70.00	
48	A2 10r on 5k grn, buff		35.00	40.00
a.	Double surcharge		250.00	
49	A2 10r on 10k brn, buff		100.00	110.00
	Nos. 47-49 (3)		151.00	170.00

Counterfeits exist of Nos. 47-49.

Crimea
Russian Stamp of 1917 Surcharged   **35 коп.**

1919	**Unwmk.**		**Imperf.**	
51	A14 35k on 1k orange		.30	1.00
a.	Comma, instead of period in surcharge		1.00	

A3

Paper with Buff Network
Inscription on Back

1919			**Imperf.**	
52	A3 50k brown		35.00	75.00

Available for both postage and currency.

Russia Nos. 77, 82, 123, 73, 119
Surcharged

Nos. 53-57

Nos. 58-59

1920			**Perf. 14x14½**	
53	A14 5r on 5k dk claret		1.10	2.10
a.	Inverted surcharge		35.00	
b.			42.50	
54	A8 5r on 20k dl bl & dk car		1.10	2.10
a.	Inverted surcharge		20.00	
b.	Double surcharge		35.00	
c.	"5" omitted		20.00	
	Imperf			
55	A14 5r on 5k claret		1.10	2.10
a.	Inverted surcharge		15.00	

Same Surcharge on Stamp of
Denikin Issue, No. 64

57	A5 5r on 35k lt bl		10.00	13.00
a.	Double surcharge		75.00	
	Nos. 53-57 (4)		13.30	19.30

1920			**Perf. 14x14½**	
58	A14 100r on 1k dl org yel		3.75	
a.	"10" in place of "100"		50.00	
b.	Inverted surcharge		25.00	
c.	Double surcharge		50.00	
	Imperf			
59	A14 100r on 1k orange		2.75	

Nos. 53-57 were issued at Sevastopol during the occupation by General Wrangel's army. Nos. 58-59 were prepared but not used.

Denikin Issue

A5

St. George — A6

1919	**Unwmk.**		**Imperf.**	
61	A5 5k orange		.20	.25
62	A5 10k green		.20	.25
63	A5 15k red		.20	.35
64	A5 35k light blue		.20	.25
65	A5 70k dark blue		.20	.35
a.	Tête bêche pair		65.00	
66	A6 1r brown & red		.30	.50
67	A6 2r gray vio & yellow		.30	.75
68	A6 3r dl rose & green		.30	.75
69	A6 5r slate & violet		.75	1.10
70	A6 7r gray grn & rose		1.00	2.75
71	A6 10r red & gray		.75	2.00
	Nos. 61-71 (11)		4.40	9.30
	Perf. 11½			
68a	A6 3r dull rose & green		1.25	1.25
69a	A6 5r slate & violet		1.75	1.75
71a	A6 10r red & gray		1.40	1.60
	Nos. 68a-71a (3)		4.40	4.60

Nos. 61-71 were issued at Ekaterinodar and used in all parts of South Russia that were occupied by the People's Volunteer Army under Gen. Anton Ivanovich Denikin. The inscription on the stamps reads "United Russia."

Stamps of type A6 with rosettes instead of numerals in the small circles at the sides may be essays. Perforated copies of Nos. 61-67 and 70 are of private origin.

For surcharges see Russia, Offices in Turkish Empire Nos. 303-319.

SOUTH WEST AFRICA

sauth 'west 'a-fri-kə

(Namibia)

LOCATION — Southwestern Africa between Angola, Botswana and South Africa, bordering on the Atlantic Ocean

GOVT. — Administered by the Republic of South Africa under a mandate of the League of Nations

AREA — 318,261 sq. mi.

POP. — 1,039,800 (1982)

CAPITAL — Windhoek

Formerly a German possession, South West Africa was occupied by South African forces in 1915 and by the Treaty of Versailles was mandated to the Union of South Africa. On March 20, 1990 it became Namibia.

12 Pence = 1 Shilling
20 Shillings = 1 Pound
100 Cents = 1 Rand (1961)

Catalogue values for unused stamps in this country are for Never Hinged items, beginning with Scott 125 in the regular postage section, Scott B1 in the semipostal section, Scott J86 in the postage due section, and Scott O13 in the officials section.

Watermarks

Watermarks 177, 201, 330, 348 and 359 can be found at the beginning of South Africa.

Stamps of South Africa, Nos. 2-3, 5 and 9-16, Overprinted in English or Afrikaans alternately throughout the sheets.

Major-number listings and values of Nos. 1-40 and 85-93 are for pairs with both overprints.

Setting I

"South West" 14½mm wide
"Zuid-West" 13mm wide
Overprint Spaced 14mm

1923, Jan. 2			**Wmk. 177**	**Perf. 14**	
1	A2	½p green, pair		3.00	10.50
a.		Single, Dutch		1.10	1.10
2	A2	1p red, pair		3.75	10.50
a.		Single, Dutch		1.10	1.10
b.		Inverted overprint, pair		550.00	
c.		As "b," single, English		125.00	
d.		As "b," single, Dutch		125.00	
e.		"Af.rica"		175.00	210.00
f.		Double overprint, pair		1,000.	
g.		As "f," single, English		500.00	
h.		As "f," single, Dutch		500.00	
3	A2	2p dull vio, pair		4.75	14.00
a.		Single, Dutch		1.75	1.75
b.		Inverted overprint, pair		625.00	700.00
c.		As "b," single, English		110.00	
d.		As "b," single, Dutch		110.00	
4	A2	3p ultra, pair		8.50	19.00
a.		Single, Dutch		3.25	3.25
5	A2	4p ol grn & org, pair		15.00	52.50
a.		Single, Dutch		4.50	4.50
6	A2	6p vio & blk, pair		9.25	50.00
a.		Single, Dutch		4.75	4.75
7	A2	1sh orange, pair		27.50	55.00
a.		Single, Dutch		5.75	5.25
8	A2	1sh3p violet, pair		35.00	62.50
a.		Single, Dutch		6.50	6.50
b.		Inverted overprint, pair		375.00	

c.		As "b," single, English		45.00	
d.		As "b," single, Dutch		45.00	
9	A2	2sh6p grn & cl, pair		70.00	150.00
a.		Single, Dutch		22.50	22.50
10	A2	5sh blue & cl, pair		175.00	375.00
a.		Single, Dutch		57.50	57.50
11	A2	10sh ol grn & bl, pair		1,500.	2,900.
a.		Single, Dutch		475.00	500.00
12	A2	£1 red & dp grn, pair		800.00	2,000.
a.		Single, Dutch		300.00	300.00
		Nos. 1-12 (12)		2,651.	5,699.

Most values exist with "t" of "West" partly or totally missing. Vertical displacement in overprinting accounts for the copies with only one line of overprint.

For English from setting I "a," see note after No. 27.

Setting II

Words Same Width as Setting I
Overprint Spaced 9½-10mm

1923, Apr.					
13	A2	5sh blue & cl, pair		160.00	300.00
a.		Single, English		52.50	52.50
b.		Single, Dutch		52.50	52.50
c.		As #13, without period after "Afrika"		1,200.	1,300.
14	A2	10sh ol grn & bl, pair		575.00	1,000.
a.		Single, English		160.00	160.00
b.		Single, Dutch		160.00	160.00
c.		As #14, without period after "Afrika"		2,600.	3,250.
15	A2	£1 red & green, pair		1,150.	1,700.
a.		Single, English		225.00	225.00
b.		Single, Dutch		225.00	225.00
c.		As #15, without period after "Afrika"		6,000.	5,750.

Setting III

English as in Setting I
"Zuidwest" 11mm wide, No Hyphen
Overprint Spaced 14mm

1923-24					
16	A2	½p grn, pair ('24)		7.00	40.00
a.		Single, English		.30	4.25
b.		Single, Dutch		.30	4.25
17	A2	1p red, pair		6.25	10.50
a.		Single, English		.30	1.60
b.		Single, Dutch		.30	1.60
18	A2	2p dull vio, pair		6.25	10.50
a.		Single, English		.30	1.50
b.		Single, Dutch		.30	1.50
c.		Dbl. ovpt., pair		1,200.	
d.		As "c," single, English		90.00	
e.		As "c," single, Dutch		90.00	
19	A2	3p ultra, pair		5.75	11.50
a.		Single, English		.50	1.50
b.		Single, Dutch		.50	1.50
20	A2	4p ol grn & org, pair		7.00	24.00
a.		Single, English		.50	3.25
b.		Single, Dutch		.50	3.25
21	A2	6p vio & blk, pair		16.00	52.50
a.		Single, English		1.00	5.75
b.		Single, Dutch		1.00	5.75
22	A2	1sh orange, pair		16.00	52.50
a.		Single, English		1.00	5.75
b.		Single, Dutch		1.00	5.75
23	A2	1sh3p violet, pair		32.50	52.50
a.		Single, English		1.75	6.25
b.		Single, Dutch		1.75	6.25
24	A2	2sh6p grn & cl, pair		52.50	92.50
a.		Single, English		4.00	11.50
b.		Single, Dutch		4.00	11.50
25	A2	5sh blue & cl, pair		70.00	150.00
a.		Single, English		7.50	21.00
b.		Single, Dutch		7.50	21.00
26	A2	10sh ol grn & bl, pair		190.00	300.00
a.		Single, English		30.00	47.50
b.		Single, Dutch		30.00	47.50
27	A2	£1 red & green, pair		350.00	450.00
a.		Single, English		40.00	70.00
b.		Single, Dutch		40.00	70.00
		Nos. 16-27 (12)		759.25	1,246.

The English overprint of Setting III is the same as that of Setting I.

Setting IV

South West	Zuidwest
Africa.	Afrika.
g	h

"South West" 16mm wide
"Zuidwest" 12mm wide
Overprint Spaced 14mm

1924, July					
28	A2	2sh6p grn & cl, pair		92.50	175.00
a.		Single, English		13.00	32.50
b.		Single, Dutch		13.00	32.50

Setting VI

"South West" 16, 16½mm wide
"Zuidwest" 12½mm wide
Overprint Spaced 9½mm

1924, Dec.					
29	A2	½p green, pair		8.00	45.00
a.		Single, English		.35	5.75
b.		Single, Dutch		.35	5.75
30	A2	1p red, pair		3.75	11.50
a.		Single, English		.25	1.60
b.		Single, Dutch		.25	1.60
31	A2	2p dull vio, pair		5.75	25.00
a.		Single, English		.30	2.00
b.		Single, Dutch		.30	2.00
32	A2	3p ultra, pair		5.25	32.50
a.		Single, English		.45	3.25
b.		Single, Dutch		.45	3.25
33	A2	4p ol grn & org, pair		7.50	52.50
a.		Single, English		.50	4.50
b.		Single, Dutch		.50	4.50
34	A2	6p vio & blk, pair		10.50	55.00
a.		Single, English		.75	5.75
b.		Single, Dutch		.75	5.75
35	A2	1sh orange, pair		12.50	55.00
a.		Single, English		.75	5.75
b.		Single, Dutch		.75	5.75
36	A2	1sh3p violet, pair		17.50	55.00
a.		Single, English		.75	5.75
b.		Single, Dutch		.75	5.75
37	A2	2sh6p grn & cl, pair		32.50	80.00
a.		Single, English		3.00	11.50
b.		Single, Dutch		3.00	11.50
38	A2	5sh blue & cl, pair		47.50	110.00
a.		Single, English		6.00	16.00
b.		Single, Dutch		6.00	16.00
39	A2	10sh ol grn & bl, pair		75.00	150.00
a.		Single, English		10.00	22.50
b.		Single, Dutch		10.00	22.50
40	A2	£1 red & grn, pair		250.00	475.00
a.		Single, English		40.00	75.00
b.		Single, Dutch		40.00	75.00
		Nos. 29-40 (12)		475.75	1,146.

Setting VII
South Africa Nos. 21-22 Overprinted:

m

n

o

1926-27			**Wmk. 201**	**Imperf.**	
81	A3 (m)	4p blue gray		.85	3.50
82	A3 (n)	4p blue gray		.85	3.50
83	A3 (o)	4p blue gray ('27)		7.00	22.50
		Nos. 81-83 (3)		8.70	29.50

Nos. 81-83 were not officially perforated, but firms and individuals applied various forms of perforation and rouletting for their own convenience. Perf. 11 examples of Nos. 81-82 were made by John Meinert, Ltd., Windhoek, same values.

Setting VIII
South Africa Nos. 23-25 Overprinted Alternately with type "p" on English-inscribed Stamps and type "q" on Afrikaans-inscribed Stamps

"South West" 16½mm wide
"Suidwes" 11mm wide
Overprint Spaced 11½mm

1926			**Typo.**	**Perf. 14½x14**	
85	A5	½p dk grn & blk, pair		1.90	7.50
a.		Single, English		.35	1.00
b.		Single, Afrikaans		.35	1.00
c.		Afrikaans ovpt. on English stamp		.35	1.00
d.		English ovpt. on Afrikaans stamp		.35	1.00
e.		Pair, "c" + "d"		1.75	6.00
f.		As "e," without period after "Africa"		175.00	
86	A6	1p car & blk, pair		2.25	3.00
a.		Single, English		.35	.60
b.		Single, Afrikaans		.35	.60
c.		Afrikaans ovpt. on English stamp		.35	.60
d.		English ovpt. on Afrikaans stamp		.35	.60
e.		Pair, "c" + "d"		1.75	5.00
f.		As "e," without period after "Africa"		325.00	
87	A7	6p org & grn, pair		12.50	32.50
a.		Single, English		2.50	3.50
b.		Single, Afrikaans		2.50	3.50
c.		Afrikaans ovpt. on English stamp		2.00	3.50
d.		English ovpt. on Afrikaans stamp		2.00	3.50
e.		Pair, "c" + "d"		12.50	25.00
f.		As "e," without period after "Africa"		200.00	
		Nos. 85-87 (3)		16.65	43.00

For overprints see Nos. O1-O3.

Setting IX
South Africa Nos. 26-27, 29-32 Overprinted in Blue with types "p" and "q" Spaced 16mm

1927			**Engr.**	**Perf. 14**	
88	A8	2p vio brn & gray, pair		5.50	17.50
a.		Single, English		.25	2.00
b.		Single, Afrikaans		.25	2.00
89	A9	3p red & blk, pair		5.50	32.50
a.		Single, English		.50	3.00
b.		Single, Afrikaans		.50	3.00
90	A11	1sh dp bl & bis brn, pair		17.50	37.50
a.		Single, English		1.25	4.50
b.		Single, Afrikaans		1.25	4.50
91	A12	2sh6p brn & bl grn, pair		40.00	97.50
a.		Single, English		5.50	15.00
b.		Single, Afrikaans		5.50	15.00
92	A13	5sh dp grn & blk, pair		85.00	200.00
a.		Single, English		10.00	22.50
b.		Single, Afrikaans		10.00	22.50
93	A14	10sh ol brn & bl, pair		75.00	160.00
a.		Single, English		9.00	22.50
b.		Single, Afrikaans		9.00	22.50
		Nos. 88-93 (6)		228.50	545.00

South Africa Nos. 12 and 16a
Overprinted at Foot

1927	**Typo.**	**Wmk. 177**	
94	A2 1sh3p violet	1.40	7.50
a.	Without period after "A"	110.00	
95	A2 £1 lt red & gray grn	110.00	190.00
a.	Without period after "A"	1,750.	2,600.

South Africa Nos. 23-25 Overprinted
type "r" at Foot

1927	**Wmk. 201**	**Perf. 14½x14**	
96	A5 ½p green & blk, pair	2.25	7.50
a.	Single, English	.20	.90
b.	Single, Afrikaans	.20	.90
c.	As #96, without period after "A" on one stamp	47.50	85.00
97	A6 1p car & blk, pair	1.50	3.75
a.	Single, English	.20	.65
b.	Single, Afrikaans	.20	.65
c.	As #97, without period after "A" on one stamp	47.50	85.00
d.	Ovpt. at top, pair ('30)	2.00	16.00
e.	As "d," single, English	.35	1.90
f.	As "d," single, Afrikaans	.35	1.90
98	A7 6p org & grn, pair	13.00	26.00
a.	Single, English	1.25	3.25
b.	Single, Afrikaans	1.25	3.25
c.	As #98, without period after "A" on one stamp	125.00	
	Nos. 96-98 (3)	16.75	37.25

For overprints see Nos. O5-O7.

South Africa Nos. 26-32 Overprinted
type "r" at Top

1927-28	**Engr.**	**Perf. 14**	
99	A8 2p vio brn & gray, pair	10.50	27.50
a.	Single, English	1.00	1.75
b.	Single, Afrikaans	1.00	1.75
c.	As #99, without period after "A" on one stamp	85.00	125.00
d.	Double ovpt., one inverted	800.00	1,050.
100	A9 3p red & blk, pair	7.00	26.00
a.	Single, English	.50	3.75
b.	Single, Afrikaans	.50	3.75
c.	As #100, without period after "A" on one stamp	92.50	150.00
101	A10 4p brn, pair ('28)	17.50	45.00
a.	Single, English	1.25	8.00
b.	Single, Afrikaans	1.25	8.00
c.	As #101, without period after "A" on one stamp	97.50	150.00
102	A11 1sh dp bl & bis brn, pair	22.50	55.00
a.	Single, English	1.50	5.75
b.	Single, Afrikaans	1.50	5.75
c.	As #102, without period after "A" on one stamp	1,500.	
103	A12 2sh6p brn & bl grn, pair	47.50	97.50
a.	Single, English	6.00	14.00
b.	Single, Afrikaans	6.00	14.00
c.	As #103, without period after "A" on one stamp	190.00	325.00
104	A13 5sh dp grn & blk, pair	70.00	140.00
a.	Single, English	8.00	21.00
b.	Single, Afrikaans	8.00	21.00
c.	As #104, without period after "A" on one stamp	275.00	425.00
105	A14 10sh ol brn & bl, pair	110.00	225.00
a.	Single, English	20.00	32.50
b.	Single, Afrikaans	20.00	32.50
c.	As #105, without period after "A" on one stamp	375.00	625.00
	Nos. 99-105 (7)	285.00	616.00

For overprint see No. O8.

South Africa Nos. 33-34 Overprinted
type "r" at Foot

1930	**Photo.**	**Perf. 15x14**	
106	A5 ½p bl grn & blk, pair	9.25	32.50
a.	Single, English	.50	3.25
b.	Single, Afrikaans	.50	3.25
107	A6 1p car rose & blk, pair	7.50	30.00
a.	Single, English	.50	3.25
b.	Single, Afrikaans	.50	3.25

Kori
Bustard — A15

Cape
Cross — A16

Mail
Transport — A17

Bogenfels — A18

Windhoek — A19

Waterberg — A20

Lüderitz
Bay — A21

Bush
Scene — A22

Elands — A23

Zebras and
Brindled
Gnus — A24

Herero
Houses — A25

Welwitschia
Plant — A26

Okuwahakan
Falls — A27

		Perf. 14x13½		
1931-37		**Wmk. 201**		**Engr.**
108	A15	½p grn & blk, pair	2.75	3.00
a.	Single, English		.20	.20
b.	Single, Afrikaans		.20	.20
109	A16	1p red & ind, pair	2.75	3.00
a.	Single, English		.20	.20
b.	Single, Afrikaans		.20	.20
110	A17	1½p vio brn, pair ('37)	25.00	3.50
a.	Single, English		.20	.30
b.	Single, Afrikaans		.20	.30
111	A18	2p dk brn & dk bl, pair	.80	4.25
a.	Single, English		.20	.20
b.	Single, Afrikaans		.20	.20
112	A19	3p dp bl & gray blk, pair	.80	4.75
a.	Single, English		.20	.20
b.	Single, Afrikaans		.20	.20
113	A20	4p brn vio & grn, pair	2.10	8.00
a.	Single, English		.20	.25
b.	Single, Afrikaans		.20	.25
114	A21	6p ol brn & bl, pair	1.75	10.50
a.	Single, English		.20	.25
b.	Single, Afrikaans		.20	.25
115	A22	1sh bl & vio brn, pair	1.75	11.00
a.	Single, English		.20	.30
b.	Single, Afrikaans		.20	.30
116	A23	1sh3p ocher & pur, pair	8.75	12.50
a.	Single, English		.45	.60
b.	Single, Afrikaans		.45	.60
117	A24	2sh6p dk gray & rose, pair	22.50	27.50
a.	Single, English		1.25	2.00
b.	Single, Afrikaans		1.25	2.00
118	A25	5sh vio brn & ol grn, pair	19.00	45.00
a.	Single, English		1.25	3.25
b.	Single, Afrikaans		1.25	3.25
119	A26	10sh grn & brn, pair	52.50	57.50
a.	Single, English		4.50	7.00
b.	Single, Afrikaans		4.50	7.00
120	A27	20sh bl grn & mar, pair	85.00	95.00
a.	Single, English		12.50	12.50
b.	Single, Afrikaans		12.50	12.50
	Nos. 108-120 (13)		225.45	285.50

For overprints see Nos. O13-O27.

George V — A28

1935, May 6		**Perf. 14x13½**
121	A28 1p carmine & blk	.75	.30
122	A28 2p dk brown & blk	.75	.30
123	A28 3p blue & blk	10.00	21.00
124	A28 6p violet & blk	4.50	11.50
	Nos. 121-124 (4)	16.00	33.10
	Set, never hinged	30.00	

25th anniv. of the reign of George V.

Catalogue values for unused
stamps in this section, from this
point to the end of the section, are
for Never Hinged items.

Coronation Issue

Inscribed alternately in English and
Afrikaans

George VI — A29

1937, May 12	**Engr.**	**Perf. 13½x14**	
125	A29 ½p emer & blk, pair	.45	.25
a.	Single, English	.20	.20
b.	Single, Afrikaans	.20	.20
126	A29 1p car & blk, pair	.45	.25
a.	Single, English	.20	.20
b.	Single, Afrikaans	.20	.20
127	A29 1½p org & blk, pair	.45	.25
a.	Single, English	.20	.20
b.	Single, Afrikaans	.20	.20
128	A29 2p dk brn & blk, pair	.45	.30
a.	Single, English	.20	.20
b.	Single, Afrikaans	.20	.20
129	A29 3p brt bl & blk, pair	.55	.30
a.	Single, English	.20	.20
b.	Single, Afrikaans	.20	.20
130	A29 4p dk vio & blk, pair	.55	.35
a.	Single, English	.20	.20
b.	Single, Afrikaans	.20	.20

131	A29 6p yel & blk, pair	.55	2.75
a.	Single, English	.20	.30
b.	Single, Afrikaans	.20	.30
132	A29 1sh gray & blk, pair	2.00	3.25
a.	Single, English	.20	.75
b.	Single, Afrikaans	.20	.75
	Nos. 125-132 (8)	5.45	7.70

George VI & Queen Elizabeth coronation.

Voortrekker Issue

South Africa Nos. 79-80 Overprinted
type "r"

1938, Dec. 14	**Photo.**	**Perf. 15x14**	
133	A23 1p rose & sl, pair	10.00	8.25
a.	Single, English	1.00	1.25
b.	Single, Afrikaans	1.00	1.25
134	A24 1½p red brn & Prus bl, pair	12.50	10.00
a.	Single, English	1.50	1.50
b.	Single, Afrikaans	1.50	1.50

Issued to commemorate the Voortrekkers.

South Africa Nos. 81-89 Overprinted

	Perf. 14 (2p, 4p, 6p); 15x14		
1941-43		**Wmk. 201**	
135	A25 ½p dp blue grn, pair	1.25	1.90
a.	Single, English	.20	.20
b.	Single, Afrikaans	.20	.20
136	A26 1p brt rose, pair	1.50	1.75
a.	Single, English	.20	.20
b.	Single, Afrikaans	.20	.20
137	A27 1½p Prus grn, pair ('42)	2.50	2.75
a.	Single, English	.20	.20
b.	Single, Afrikaans	.20	.20
138	A28 2p dk violet	.60	.50
139	A29 3p dp blue, pair	12.50	7.50
a.	Single, English	.75	1.00
b.	Single, Afrikaans	.75	1.00
140	A30 4p brown, pair	5.00	7.50
a.	Single, English	.30	.75
b.	Single, Afrikaans	.30	.75
141	A31 6p brt red org, pair	2.75	3.50
a.	Single, English	.30	1.00
b.	Single, Afrikaans	.30	1.00
142	A32 1sh dk brown	1.00	.75
143	A33 1sh3p dk ol brn, pair ('43)	12.50	14.00
a.	Single, English	1.00	1.25
b.	Single, Afrikaans	1.00	1.25
	Nos. 135-143 (9)	39.60	40.15

South Africa Nos. 90-97 Overprinted

t u

Pairs or Strips of 3 Perf. 14 or
15x14 all around, Rouletted 6½ or
13 btwn.

1942-45		**Wmk. 201**	
144	A34(t) ½p dp grn, horiz. strip of 3	.75	.60
a.	Single, English	.20	.20
b.	Single, Afrikaans	.20	.20
c.	½p dp bl grn, horiz. strip of 3	1.50	2.25
d.	As "c," single, English	.20	.20
e.	As "c," single, Afrikaans	.20	.20
145	A35(t) 1p brt car, horiz. strip of 3	.75	.60
a.	Single, English	.20	.20
b.	Single, Afrikaans	.20	.20
c.	1p rose car, horiz. strip of 3	1.25	2.00
d.	As "c," single, English	.20	.20
e.	As "c," single, Afrikaans	.20	.20
146	A36(u) 1½p cop brn, horiz. pair	.75	.60
a.	Single, English	.20	.20
b.	Single, Afrikaans	.20	.20
147	A37(t) 2p dk vio, horiz. pair	.75	.75
a.	Single, English	.20	.20
b.	Single, Afrikaans	.20	.20
148	A38(t) 3p dp bl, vert. strip of 3	4.00	4.25
a.	Single, English	.20	.40
149	A39(t) 4p sl grn, vert. strip of 3	5.00	6.25
a.	Single	.20	.30
b.	As "c," single	50.00	
c.	Invtd. ovpt., strip of 3	500.00	300.00
150	A40(t) 6p brt red org, horiz. pair	2.75	1.60
a.	Single, English	.20	.30
b.	Single, Afrikaans	.20	.30

c.	Inverted overprint, pair	425.00		
d.	As "c," single, English	50.00	50.00	
e.	As "c," single, Afrikaans	50.00	50.00	
151	A41(u) 1sh dk brn, vert.			
	pair	12.00	11.00	
a.	Single	.75	1.50	
b.	As "c," single	70.00		
c.	Inverted overprint, pair	450.00	325.00	
152	A41(t) 1sh dk brn, vert.			
	pair	2.25	1.60	
a.	Single	.20	.30	
b.	As "c," single	45.00	40.00	
c.	Invtd. ovpt., vert. pair	375.00	275.00	
	Nos. 144-152 (9)	29.00	27.25	

Issue years: #144-145, 147-151, 1943; #152, 1944; #144c, 145c, 149c, 1945.

Peace Issue

South Africa Nos. 100-102 Overprinted
Type "w"

1945		**Wmk. 201**		*Perf. 14*
153	A42 1p rose pink &			
	choc, pair	.40	.40	
a.	Single, English	.20	.20	
b.	Single, Afrikaans	.20	.20	
c.	Inverted overprint, pair	240.00	240.00	
d.	As "c," single, English	37.50		
e.	As "c," single, Afrikaans	37.50		
154	A43 2p vio & sl bl, pair	.40	.40	
a.	Single, English	.20	.20	
b.	Single, Afrikaans	.20	.20	
155	A43 3p ultra & dp ultra,			
	pair	.85	.85	
a.	Single, English	.20	.20	
b.	Single, Afrikaans	.20	.20	
	Nos. 153-155 (3)	1.65	1.65	

WW II victory of the Allies.

Royal Visit Issue

South Africa Nos. 103-105 Overprinted

1947, Feb. 17			*Perf. 15x14*
156	A44 1p cerise & gray, pair	.30	.20
a.	Single, English	.20	.20
b.	Single, Afrikaans	.20	.20
157	A45 2p purple, pair	.30	.25
a.	Single, English	.20	.20
b.	Single, Afrikaans	.20	.20
158	A46 3p dk blue, pair	.35	.30
a.	Single, English	.20	.20
b.	Single, Afrikaans	.20	.20
	Nos. 156-158 (3)	.95	.75

Visit of the British Royal Family, Mar.-Apr., 1947.

South Africa No. 106 Overprinted

1948, Apr. 26			*Perf. 14*
159	A47 3p dp chalky bl & sil,		
	pair	1.25	.30
a.	Single, English	.20	.20
b.	Single, Afrikaans	.20	.20

25th anniv. of the marriage of George VI and Queen Elizabeth.

UPU Issue

South Africa Nos. 109-111 Overprinted
type "w" 13mm wide

1949, Oct. 1			*Perf. 14x15*
160	A50 ½p dk green, pair	1.10	1.50
a.	Single, English	.20	.25
b.	Single, Afrikaans	.20	.25
161	A50 1½p dk red, pair	1.10	1.50
a.	Single, English	.20	.25
b.	Single, Afrikaans	.20	.25
162	A50 3p ultra, pair	1.75	2.00
a.	Single, English	.20	.25
b.	Single, Afrikaans	.20	.25
	Nos. 160-162 (3)	3.95	5.00

75th anniv. of the UPU.

Except for Nos. 312-313, 423-428, this ends the bi-lingual multiples in the postage section.

Voortrekker Monument Issue

South Africa Nos. 112-114 Overprinted

1949, Dec. 1			*Perf. 15x14*
163	A51 1p magenta	.20	.20
164	A52 1½p dull green	.20	.20
165	A53 3p dark blue	.30	.30
	Nos. 163-165 (3)	.70	.70

Inauguration of the Voortrekker Monument at Pretoria.

South Africa Nos. 115-119 Overprinted

w

x

1952, Mar. 14			*Perf. 15x14, 14x15*
166	A54(w) ½p dk brown & red		
	vio	.40	.40
167	A55(x) 1p dark green	.40	.40
168	A54(w) 2p dark purple	.40	.40
169	A55(x) 4½p dark blue	1.00	1.00
170	A54(w) 1sh brown	2.00	2.00
	Nos. 166-170 (5)	4.20	4.20

300th anniv. of the landing of Jan van Riebeeck at the Cape of Good Hope.

Coronation Issue

Queen Elizabeth II and Flowers — A54

Various flowers.

1953, June 2		**Photo.**	*Perf. 14*
244	A54 1p carmine rose	.55	.30
245	A54 2p dark green	.55	.30
246	A54 4p deep magenta	1.10	.65
247	A54 6p deep blue	1.10	1.00
248	A54 1sh chestnut brown	1.60	1.25
	Nos. 244-248 (5)	4.90	3.50

Rock Painting of Two Bucks — A55

Rhinoceros Hunt — A56

Designs: 2p, "White Lady" (rock painting). 4p, Elephant and giraffe (rock painting). 4½p, Karakul lamb. 6p, Orambo blowing Kudu horn. 1sh, Ukuanjama woman. 1sh3p, Herero woman. 1sh6p, Ukuanjama girl. 2sh6p, Lioness. 5sh, Cape Oryx. 10sh, Elephant.

1954, Nov. 15		**Wmk. 201**	*Perf. 14*
249	A55 1p rose brown	.55	.20
250	A55 2p dk brown	.55	.20
251	A56 3p brown vio	1.10	.20
252	A55 4p olive gray	1.10	.20
253	A55 4½p blue vio	1.10	.20
254	A55 6p gray green	1.25	.40
255	A55 1sh magenta	2.10	.50
256	A55 1sh3p rose pink	4.00	1.00
257	A55 1sh6p dull purple	4.50	1.10
258	A55 2sh6p yel brown	8.50	2.50

259	A55 5sh blue	19.00	6.00	
260	A55 10sh dk green	30.00	12.50	
	Nos. 249-260 (12)	74.00	25.00	

1960		**Wmk. 330**	*Perf. 14*
261	A55 1p rose brown	1.00	.45
262	A55 2p dark brown	1.50	.60
263	A56 3p brown vio	2.00	1.25
264	A56 4p olive gray	4.50	5.00
265	A55 1sh6p dull purple	20.00	17.00
	Nos. 261-265 (5)	29.00	24.30

General Post Office, Windhoek — A57

Fishing Industry — A58

Designs: 1c, Finger Rock, Asab. 1½c, Monument, Mounted Soldier. 2c, Quivertree. 2½c, Administrator's residence. 3c, Swakopmund Lighthouse and flamingoes. 5c, Flamingo. 7½c, Christchurch. 10c, Diamonds. 12½c, Fort Namutoni. 15c, Hardap Dam. 20c, Topaz. 50c, Tourmaline. 1r, Heliodor.

1961-63		**Wmk. 330 Photo.**	*Perf. 14*
266	A57 ½c blue & brown	.40	.20
267	A58 1c pale lil & brn	.25	.20
268	A58 1½c sal & dk pur	.25	.20
269	A58 2c yel & green	4.50	.40
270	A57 2½c lt bl & red brn	.55	.20
271	A58 3c dp rose & vio bl	2.75	.50
272	A58 3½c blue grn & ind	.60	.20
273	A58 5c bluish gray &		
	red	5.50	.35
274	A58 7½c yellow & brn	.70	.70
275	A58 10c brt blue & yel	1.25	.20
276	A57 12½c yellow & ind	2.00	2.00
277	A57 15c dp brn & blue	8.50	3.25
278	A57 20c sal, brn & blk	4.25	.85
279	A58 50c org yel & Prus		
	grn	7.50	3.25
280	A58 1r brt blue, mar &		
	yel	11.00	7.50
	Nos. 266-280 (15)	50.00	20.00

Issued: 3c, 10/1/62; 15c, 3/16/63; others, 2/14/61.

1962-73			**Unwmk.**
281	A57 ½c blue & brn	.50	1.25
282	A58 1½c sal & dk pur		
	('63)	6.25	.25
283	A58 2c yellow & grn	10.50	3.00
284	A57 2½c lt bl & red brn		
	('64)	6.50	3.00
285	A58 3c dp rose & vio bl		
	('73)	1.00	1.00
286	A58 3½c bl grn & ind ('66)	10.50	4.50
287	A58 5c bluish gray & red	7.25	3.00
	Nos. 281-287 (7)	42.50	16.00

See Nos. 304-308, 314-328.

Hardap Dam and Development A59

Centenary Emblem and S.W.A. Map A60

1963, Mar. 16			**Wmk. 330**
294	A59 3c sepia green	.90	.90

Opening of Hardap Dam near Mariental.

1963, Aug. 30		**Unwmk.**	*Perf. 14*

Design: 15c, Emblem and globe.

295	A60 7½c blue, blk & red	5.75	3.50
296	A60 15c brn org, blk &		
	red	12.00	7.00

Centenary of the International Red Cross.

Assembly Hall — A61

John Calvin — A62

1964, May 14		**Photo.**	**Wmk. 330**
297	A61 3c salmon pink & vio bl	.90	.75

Issued to commemorate the opening of the new hall of the Legislative Assembly.

1964, Oct. 1		**Unwmk.**	*Perf. 14*
298	A62 2½c magenta & gold	.85	.55
299	A62 15c green & gold	4.50	3.50

John Calvin (1509-64), French theologian and leader of the Reformation.

Mail Runner, 1890 — A63

Kurt von François — A64

		Wmk. 348	
1965, Oct. 18		**Photo.**	*Perf. 14*
300	A63 3c red & deep brown	.45	.30
301	A64 15c green & deep brn	2.75	1.75

75th anniversary of Windhoek.

Dr. H. H. Vedder, Missionary, Educator and Senator, 90th Birthday — A65

1966, July 4			*Perf. 14*
302	A65 3c black & salmon	.40	.30
303	A65 15c black & light blue	2.50	2.25

Types of 1961-62

1966-67		**Wmk. 348 Photo.**	*Perf. 14*
		Chalky Paper	
304	A57 ½c lt blue & brn	11.00	3.00
304A	A58 1c pale lil & brn	.35	.20
305	A58 2c brt yel & dp grn	.35	.20
306	A57 2½c gray blue & red		
	brn	.50	.20
307	A58 3½c pale grn & vio bl	3.50	2.00
308	A58 7½c brt yel & brn	2.00	2.00
	Nos. 304-308 (6)	17.70	6.40

The watermark on Nos. 304, 305-308 is very faint, and these stamps can be distinguished by the shades and by the thick chalky paper. The watermark on No. 304A is clear. Issued: 2c, 2½c, 1966; others, 1967.

Camelthorn Tree — A66

Verwoerd A67

Swart A68

Design: 3c, Waves breaking against rock.

Perf. 14, 14x15 (15c)
1967, Jan. 6   Litho.   Wmk. 348
309	A66	2½c green & black	.30 .20
310	A67	3c brt blue & brown	.40 .20
311	A67	15c rose lilac & black	2.75 2.50
		Nos. 309-311 (3)	3.45 2.90

Dr. Hendrik F. Verwoerd (1901-1966), Prime Minister of South Africa.

Perf. 14x15
1968, Jan. 2   Photo.   Wmk. 359

15c, President and Mrs. C. R. Swart.

312		Strip of 3	3.75 3.75
a.	A68	3c Single, English	.55 .30
b.	A68	3c Single, Afrikaans	.55 .30
c.	A68	3c Single, German	.55 .30
313		Strip of 3	10.50 10.50
a.	A68	15c Single, English	3.00 2.50
b.	A68	15c Single, Afrikaans	3.00 2.50
c.	A68	15c Single, German	3.00 2.50

Charles Robberts Swart, 1st president of South Africa, (1961-67).

Types of 1961-62
Designs: 4c, like 2½c. 6c, Christchurch. 9c, Fort Namutoni.

1968-72   Wmk. 359   Photo.   Perf. 14
314	A57	½c blue & brown	1.00 .25
315	A57	½c blue & brn, redrawn ('70)	2.50 1.00
316	A58	1c pale lilac & brn ('70)	1.00 .25
317	A58	1½c salmon & dk pur	1.25 .35
318	A58	1½c sal & dk pur, redrawn ('71)	14.00 6.50
319	A58	2c yel & grn, redrawn ('70)	1.40 .35
320	A57	2½c lt bl & red brn ('70)	1.25 .25
321	A58	3c dp rose & vio bl ('70)	2.25 .30
322	A57	4c lt bl & red brn ('71)	5.50 .85
323	A58	5c bluish gray & red	2.25 .45
324	A58	6c yel & brn ('71)	10.50 3.50
325	A57	9c yel & ind ('71)	13.00 4.50
326	A58	10c brt bl & yel ('70)	5.75 1.05
327	A57	15c dp brn & bl ('72)	10.50 3.50
328	A58	20c org, brn & blk	9.50 2.00
		Nos. 314-328 (15)	81.65 25.70

Nos. 315, 318-319 are without inscription "Posgeld Incomste Postage Revenue" and the numerals have been enlarged. The ½c (#315), 2c and 10c were also issued as coils.

Water Type of South Africa, 1970
2½c, Water drop and flower. 3c, Waves, horiz.

1970, Feb. 14   Perf. 14
329	A142	2½c brown, brt bl & grn	.90 .65
330	A142	3c pale gray, bl & indigo	1.10 .80

Water '70 campaign of the South African Department of Water Affairs.

Bible Society Types of South Africa
Designs: 2½c, Sower, stained glass window. 12½c, "BIBLIA" and open book.

1970, Aug. 24   Photo.   Perf. 14
331	A143	2½c multicolored	1.10 .55

Photo.; Gold Impressed
332	A144	12½c ultra, blk & gold	11.00 8.00

South African Bible Soc., 150th anniv.

Stamp Exhibition Types of South Africa
Perf. 14x13½, 13½x14
1971, May 31   Photo.   Wmk. 359
333	A145	5c blue, yel & blk	4.00 3.25
334	A146	12½c grnsh bl, vio bl & red	47.50 27.50

Intl. Stamp Exhib. (INTERSTEX), Cape Town, May 22-31. No. 334 also for the 10th anniv. of the Antarctic Treaty pledging peaceful uses of and scientific cooperation in Antarctica.

Republic Anniversary Types of South Africa
1971, May 31   Perf. 14
335	A147	2c mag, rose red & buff	2.00 1.10
336	A148	4c blue green & black	3.50 1.40

10th anniv. of the Republic of South Africa.

Cat Type of South Africa
1972, Sept. 19   Perf. 14
337	A152	5c multicolored	2.25 1.40

Cent. of the SPCA.

Landscape, by Adolph Jentsch — A69

Designs: Various landscapes by Adolph Jentsch (1888-). 10c, 15c, vert.

1973, Apr. 28   Litho.   Perf. 11½x12½
338	A69	2c multicolored	.60 .60
339	A69	4c multicolored	1.40 1.40
340	A69	5c multicolored	1.75 1.75
341	A69	10c multicolored	3.75 3.75
342	A69	15c multicolored	5.50 5.50
		Nos. 338-342 (5)	13.00 13.00

Sarcocaulon Rigidum — A70   Pachypodium Namaqua-num — A71

Designs: 1c-50c, Various succulent plants. 1r, Welwitschia. 30c, 1r, horiz.

1973, Sept. 1   Litho.   Perf. 12½
Plants in Natural Colors
343	A70	1c light blue	.20 .20
344	A70	2c yellow	.20 .20
345	A70	3c salmon pink	.20 .20
346	A70	4c gray	.25 .20
347	A70	5c blue	.30 .20
348	A70	6c greenish gray	.40 .20
349	A70	7c bright yellow	.45 .20
350	A70	9c dull yellow	.50 .20
351	A70	10c blue green	.55 .20
352	A70	14c yellow green	.80 .40
353	A70	15c light brown	1.10 .40
354	A70	20c light olive	1.25 .45
355	A70	25c orange	1.60 .55

Perf. 12x12½, 12½x12
356	A71	30c dull yellow	2.00 .60
357	A71	50c light green	3.50 1.10
358	A71	1r blue green	7.00 2.25
		Nos. 343-358 (16)	20.30 7.55

1979   Same Designs   Perf. 14
344a	A70	2c	.20 .20
345a	A70	3c	.20 .20
347a	A70	5c	.30 .30
351a	A70	10c	.45 .45
356a	A70	30c	2.10 2.10
357a	A70	50c	2.00 2.00
		Nos. 344a-357a (6)	5.25 5.25

Coil Stamps
1973, Sept. 1   Photo.   Perf. 14
359	A70	1c brt pink & black	.20 .20
360	A70	2c yellow & black	.20 .20
361	A70	5c red & black	.30 .30

1978   Perf. 14 Vertically
361A	A70	1c brt pink & black	1.75 1.75
362	A70	2c yellow & black	.20 .20
362A	A70	5c red & black	.20 .20
		Nos. 359-362A (6)	2.85 2.85

See Nos. 423-428.

NOTE: coil stamps, Nos. 359-362A, are printed in two colors, sheet stamps are multicolored.

Chat-shrike — A72

Designs: Rare birds.

Perf. 12½x11½
1974, Feb. 13   Litho.
363	A72	4c shown	2.75 2.25
364	A72	5c Rosy-faced lovebirds	4.00 2.75
365	A72	10c Damara rockjumper	9.00 8.00
366	A72	15c Ruppell's parrot	16.00 12.50
		Nos. 363-366 (4)	31.75 25.50

Rock Carvings, Twyfelfontein A73   Mining A74

1974, Apr. 10   Litho.   Perf. 12½
367	A73	4c Giraffe & horse	1.60 .90
368	A73	5c Elephant	2.10 1.25

Perf. 12x12½
Size: 37x21½mm
369	A73	15c Deer, horiz.	10.00 5.50
		Nos. 367-369 (3)	13.70 7.65

1974, Sept. 30   Perf. 12½x11½
370	A74	10c Diamonds	4.75 2.00
371	A74	15c Diamond washing diagram	6.75 3.00

Map Showing Route, Covered Wagons A75

Perf. 11½x12
1974, Nov. 13   Unwmk.
372	A75	4c yellow & multi	1.25 .85

Centenary of "Thirstland Trek" from Transvaal through Kalahari Desert to Angola.

Peregrine Falcon — A76

Designs: Protected Birds of Prey.

1975, Mar. 19   Perf. 12½x11½
373	A76	4c shown	1.90 1.00
374	A76	5c Black eagle	2.50 1.50
375	A76	10c Martial eagle	5.50 2.75
376	A76	15c Egyptian vulture	7.50 4.25
		Nos. 373-376 (4)	17.40 9.25

Kolmanskop, Ghost Diamond Mining Town — A77

Designs: 9c, German steam traction engine, 1896. 15c, Old Fort, Windhoek and statue of Colonial German trooper on horseback.

1975, July 23   Litho.   Perf. 12x12½
377	A77	5c violet & multi	.35 .30
378	A77	9c ocher & multi	.75 .75
379	A77	15c yellow & multi	1.25 1.25
		Nos. 377-379 (3)	2.35 2.30

Historic monuments.

Swakopmund, by Otto Schröder — A78

Paintings by Otto Schröder (1913-75).

1975, Oct. 15   Litho.   Perf. 12x12½
380	A78	15c shown	1.25 1.25
381	A78	15c Luderitz	1.25 1.25
382	A78	15c Unloading freighters	1.25 1.25
383	A78	15c Ships at anchor, Walvis Bay	1.25 1.25
a.		Souvenir sheet of 4, #380-383	6.00 6.00
b.		Block of 4, #380-383	5.00 5.00

No. 383a has a horizontal gutter with black inscription on silver panel.

Elephants A79

Pre-historic Rock Paintings: 10c, Rhinoceros. 15c, Deer and hunter. 20c, Hunter with bow and arrow.

1976, Mar. 12   Litho.   Perf. 12x12½
384	A79	4c red brown & multi	.25 .20
385	A79	10c red brown & multi	.60 .60
386	A79	15c red brown & multi	.90 .90
387	A79	20c red brown & multi	1.50 1.50
a.		Souvenir sheet of 4, #384-387	3.75 3.75
		Nos. 384-387 (4)	3.25 3.20

Schloss Duwisib A80

Castles Built by German Settlers: 10c, Schwerinsburg. 20c, Heynitzburg.

1976, May 14   Litho.   Perf. 12x12½
388	A80	10c multicolored	.60 .60
389	A80	15c multicolored	.90 .90
390	A80	20c multicolored	1.25 1.25
		Nos. 388-390 (3)	2.75 2.75

Nature Protection A81

1976, July 16   Litho.   Perf. 11½x12½
391	A81	4c Daman	.45 .25
392	A81	10c Dik-diks	1.10 .65
393	A81	15c Tree squirrel	1.75 1.10
		Nos. 391-393 (3)	3.30 2.00

Augustineum Training Institute, Windhoek — A82

20c, Katutura State Hospital, Windhoek.

1976, Sept. 17   Litho.   Perf. 12x12½
394	A82	15c ocher & black	.60 .60
395	A82	20c citron & black	.80 .80

Owambo
Canal
System
A83

20c, Ruacana Dam and hydroelectric station.

1976, Nov. 19   Litho.   Perf. 12x12½
396 A83 15c multicolored   .60   .60
397 A83 20c multicolored   .80   .80

Water and electricity supply.

Sinking Ship off Namib Shore — A84

Designs: Namib Desert, various views.

1977, Mar. 29   Litho.   Perf. 12½
398 A84 4c multicolored   .20   .20
399 A84 10c multicolored   .50   .45
400 A84 15c multicolored   .75   .65
401 A84 20c multicolored   1.10   .95
      Nos. 398-401 (4)   2.55 2.25

Owambo
Kraal
A85

Designs: 10c, Giant grain baskets. 15c, Women pounding corn. 20c, Body painting.

1977, July 15   Litho.   Perf. 12x12½
402 A85 4c multicolored   .20   .20
403 A85 10c multicolored   .40   .40
404 A85 15c multicolored   .55   .55
405 A85 20c multicolored   .85   .85
      Nos. 402-405 (4)   2.00 2.00

Traditions of the Wambo people.

J. G. Strijdom Airport,
Windhoek — A86

1977, Aug. 22   Perf. 12½
406 A86 20c multicolored   .50   .50

Drostdy,
Lüderitz,
1910
A87

Historic Houses: 10c, Woermannhaus, Swakopmund, 1895. 15c, Neu-Heusis, Windhoek. 20c, Schmelenhaus, Bethanie, 1814.

1977, Nov. 4   Litho.   Perf. 12x12½
407 A87 5c multicolored   .20   .20
408 A87 10c multicolored   .40   .40
409 A87 15c multicolored   .60   .60
410 A87 20c multicolored   .80   .80
  a. Souvenir sheet of 4, #407-410 2.40 2.40
      Nos. 407-410 (4)   2.00 2.00

Side-winding
Adder — A88

Small Animals of the Namib Desert: 10c, Golden sand mole. 15c, Palmato gecko. 20c, Namaqua chameleon.

1978, Feb. 6   Litho.   Perf. 12½
411 A88 4c multicolored   .20   .20
412 A88 10c multicolored   .45   .45
413 A88 15c multicolored   .65   .65
414 A88 20c multicolored   .90   .90
      Nos. 411-414 (4)   2.20 2.20

Bushman
Hunter
Disguised
as Ostrich
A89

Bushmen: 10c, Woman carrying melons on back. 15c, Making fire. 20c, Family sitting in front of hut.

1978, Apr. 14   Litho.   Perf. 12x12½
415 A89 4c brown, buff & blk   .20   .20
416 A89 10c brown, buff & blk   .35   .35
417 A89 15c brown, buff & blk   .55   .55
418 A89 20c brown, buff & blk   .70   .70
      Nos. 415-418 (4)   1.80 1.80

Lutheran Church, Windhoek — A90

Designs: 10c, Lutheran Church, Swakopmund. 15c, Rhenish Mission Church, Otjimbingwe. 20c, Rhenish Mission Church, Keetmanshoop.

1978, June 16   Litho.   Perf. 12½
419 A90 4c ol bister & blk   .20   .20
420 A90 10c bister & blk   .35   .35
421 A90 15c pale red brn & blk   .55   .55
422 A90 20c blue gray & blk   .70   .70
  a. Souvenir sheet of 4, #419-422 1.90 1.90
      Nos. 419-422 (4)   1.80 1.80

Type of 1973 Inscribed in English,
German or Afrikaans:

a, UNIVERSAL / SUFFRAGE
b, ALLGEMEINES / WAHLRECHT
c, ALGEMENE / STEMREG

1978, Nov. 1   Litho.   Perf. 12½
423   Strip of 3   .25   .25
  a.-c. A70 4c any single   .20   .20
424   Strip of 3   .30   .30
  a.-c. A70 5c any single   .20   .20
425   Strip of 3   .60   .60
  a.-c. A70 10c any single   .20   .20
426   Strip of 3   .95   .95
  a.-c. A70 15c any single   .30   .30
427   Strip of 3   1.25 1.25
  a.-c. A70 20c any single   .40   .40
428   Strip of 3   1.60 1.60
  a.-c. A70 25c any single   .55   .55
      Nos. 423-428 (6)   4.95 4.95

General suffrage. Printed se-tenant with inscriptions alternating horizontally and vertically in sheets of 30 (3x10).

Greater
Flamingoes
A91

Water Birds: 15c, White-breasted cormorants. 20c, Chestnut-banded plovers. 25c, White pelicans.

1979, Apr. 5   Litho.   Perf. 14x14½
429 A91 4c multicolored   .20   .20
430 A91 15c multicolored   .45   .45
431 A91 20c multicolored   .60   .60
432 A91 25c multicolored   .75   .75
      Nos. 429-432 (4)   2.00 2.00

Silver
Topaz
A92

1979, Nov. 26   Litho.   Perf. 14x14½
433 A92 4c shown   .20   .20
434 A92 15c Aquamarine   .40   .40
435 A92 20c Malachite   .60   .60
436 A92 25c Amethyst   .70   .70
      Nos. 433-436 (4)   1.90 1.90

Killer
Whale — A93

1980, Mar. 25   Litho.   Perf. 14x14½
437 A93 4c shown   .30   .20

Size: 37½x21mm
438 A93 5c Humpback whale   .30   .20
439 A93 10c Southern right
            whale   .65   .45

Size: 57½x21mm
440 A93 15c Sperm whale, giant
            squid   1.10   .60
441 A93 20c Fin whale   1.50   .85

Size: 87½x21mm
442 A93 25c Blue whale, diver   1.60 1.00
  a. Souvenir sheet of 6, #437-442 6.25 6.25
      Nos. 437-442 (6)   5.45 3.30

Impala
A94

1980, June 25   Litho.   Perf. 14½x14
443 A94 5c shown   .20   .20
444 A94 10c Roan antelope   .30   .30
445 A94 15c Tsessebe   .45   .45
446 A94 20c Black-nosed impala   .60   .60
      Nos. 443-446 (4)   1.55 1.55

Cape Hunting
Dog — A95

1980-85   Litho.   Perf. 14½x14
447 A95 1c Black backed
            jackal   .20   .20
448 A95 2c shown   .20   .20
449 A95 3c Hyena   .20   .20
450 A95 4c Dorcas antelope   .20   .20
451 A95 5c Oryx   .20   .20
452 A95 6c Greater kudu   .20   .20

      Perf. 14x1414½
453 A95 7c Zebra, horiz.   .20   .20
454 A95 8c Porcupine,
            horiz.   .20   .20
455 A95 9c Honey badger,
            horiz.   .20   .20
456 A95 10c Cheetah, horiz.   .20   .20
456A A95 11c Blue wildebeest
            ('84)   .75   .20
456B A95 12c Syncerus caffer,
            horiz. ('85)   .45   .20
  c. Booklet pane of 10   4.50
457 A95 15c Hippopotamus,
            horiz.   .25   .25
458 A95 20c Taurotragus
            oryx, horiz.   .35   .35
459 A95 25c Rhinoceros,
            horiz.   .45   .45
460 A95 30c Lion, horiz.   .55   .55

      Perf. 14½x14
461 A95 50c Giraffe   .95   .95
462 A95 1r Leopard   1.75 1.75
463 A95 2r Elephant   3.50 3.50
      Nos. 447-463 (19)   11.00 10.20

Coil Stamps
1980, Oct. 1   Litho.   Perf. 14 Vert.
464 A95 1c Suricate suricate   .20   .20
465 A95 2c Guenon   .20   .20
466 A95 5c South African chac-
            ma   .60   .60
      Nos. 464-466 (3)   .60   .60
      See Nos. 556-557.

Von Bach Dam, Swakop River — A96

1980, Nov. 25   Litho.   Perf. 14x14½
467 A96 5c shown   .20   .20
468 A96 10c Swakoppoort Dam   .20   .20
469 A96 15c Naute Dam   .25   .25
470 A96 20c Hardap Dam   .35   .35
      Nos. 467-470 (4)   1.00 1.00

Water conservation in the desert.

Fish River Canyon — A97

Designs: Views of Fish River Canyon.

1981, Mar. 20   Litho.   Perf. 14½x14
471 A97 5c multicolored   .20   .20
472 A97 15c multicolored   .20   .20
473 A97 20c multicolored   .25   .25
474 A97 25c multicolored   .35   .35
      Nos. 471-474 (4)   1.00 1.00

Aloe Erinacea — A98

1981, Aug. 14
475 A98 5c shown   .20   .20
476 A98 15c Aloe viridiflora   .20   .20
477 A98 20c Aloe pearsonii   .30   .30
478 A98 25c Aloe littoralis   .35   .35
      Nos. 475-478 (4)   1.05 1.05

Paul Weiss-Haus Building, 1909,
Luderitz — A99

Designs: Historic buildings in Luderitz.

1981, Oct. 16
479 A99 5c shown   .20   .20
480 A99 15c Deutsche Afrika
            Bank, 1906   .25   .25
481 A99 20c Schroederhaus,
            1911   .35   .35
482 A99 25c Imperial P.O., 1908   .45   .45
  a. Souvenir sheet of 4, #479-482 1.40 1.40
      Nos. 479-482 (4)   1.25 1.25

Salt
Making
A100

1981, Dec. 4   Litho.   Perf. 14x14½
483 A100 5c Salt pan .20 .20
484 A100 15c Dumping and
            washing .20 .20
485 A100 20c Stockpiling .25 .25
486 A100 25c Loading .35 .35
    Nos. 483-486 (4) 1.00 1.00

Kalahari
Starred
Tortoise
A101

1982, Mar. 12
487 A101 5c shown .20 .20
488 A101 15c Leopard tortoise .25 .25
489 A101 20c Angulated tortoise .40 .40
490 A101 25c Speckled padloper .50 .50
    Nos. 487-490 (4) 1.35 1.35

Discoverers of South-West
Africa — A102

1982, May 28   Litho.   Perf. 14½x14
491 A102 15c Archbishop Olaus
            Magnus, sea
            monster .25 .25
492 A102 20c Bartolomeu Dias,
            ships, map .35 .35
493 A102 25c Caravel .45 .45
494 A102 30c Dias erecting
            cross, Angra das
            Voltas .55 .55
    Nos. 491-494 (4) 1.60 1.60

The
Needle,
Upper
Brandberg
A103

Designs: Mountain peaks.

1982, Aug. 3   Litho.   Perf. 14x14½
495 A103 6c Brandberg .20 .20
496 A103 15c Omatako twin
            peaks .20 .20
497 A103 20c shown .25 .25
498 A103 25c Spitzkuppe, Kara-
            kul sheep .35 .35
    Nos. 495-498 (4) 1.00 1.00

Traditional
Headdress,
Herero
Tribe — A104

1982, Oct. 15   Litho.   Perf. 14x14½
499 A104 6c shown .20 .20
500 A104 15c Himba .25 .25
501 A104 20c Ngandjera .35 .35
502 A104 25c Kwanyama .45 .45
    Nos. 499-502 (4) 1.25 1.25

See Nos. 524-527.

Fort
Vogelsang
A105

Bethany Chief Joseph
Fredericks — A106

Perf. 14x14½ (6c, 25c), 14½x14 (20c, 30-40c)
1983, Mar. 16
503 A105 6c shown .20 .20
504 A106 20c shown .30 .30
505 A105 25c Angra Pequena
            Bay .40 .40
506 A106 30c Explorer Heinrich
            Vogelsang .45 .45
507 A106 40c Adolf Luderitz
            (1834-1886) .65 .65
    Nos. 503-507 (5) 2.00 2.00

City of Luderitz centenary (1982).

Diamond
Field, 1908
A107

Ernest Oppenheimer
(1880-1957),
Diamond Industry
Leader — A108

Perf. 14x14½ (10-20c), 14½x14 (25-40c)
1983, June 8   Litho.
508 A107 10c shown .20 .20
509 A107 20c Field, diff. .40 .40
510 A108 25c shown .50 .50
511 A108 40c August Stauch,
            prospector .80 .80
    Nos. 508-511 (4) 1.90 1.90

75th anniv. of discovery of diamonds at
Luderitz.

Zebras Drinking, by J.J. van
Ellinckhuijzen (b. 1940) — A109

Paintings: 20c, Rossing Mountain, by Herman H.-J. Henckert (b. 1906). 25c, Stamped-
ing Buffalo, by Fritz Krampe (1913-1966). 40c,
Erongo Mountains, by Johann Blatt (1905-
1973).

1983, Sept. 1   Perf. 14x14½
512 A109 10c multicolored .20 .20
513 A109 20c multicolored .35 .35
514 A109 25c multicolored .45 .45
515 A109 40c multicolored .70 .70
    Nos. 512-515 (4) 1.70 1.70

Lobster
Industry
A110

1983, Nov. 23   Perf. 13½x14
516 A110 10c Lobsters .20 .20
517 A110 20c Dinghies .35 .35
518 A110 25c Raising trap .45 .45
519 A110 40c Packaging .70 .70
    Nos. 516-519 (4) 1.70 1.70

Historic Buildings,
Swakopmund — A111

1984, Mar. 8   Litho.   Perf. 14x13½
520 A111 10c Hohenzollern
            House .20 .20
521 A111 20c Railway Station .40 .40
522 A111 25c Imperial District
            Bureau .50 .50
523 A111 30c Ritterburg .60 .60
    Nos. 520-523 (4) 1.70 1.70

Headdress Type of 1982
1984, May 25   Litho.
524 A104 11c Kwambi .20 .20
525 A104 20c Bushman .40 .40
526 A104 25c Kwaluudhi .50 .50
527 A104 30c Mbukushu .60 .60
    Nos. 524-527 (4) 1.70 1.70

German Colonization
Centenary — A112

1984, Aug. 7   Litho.   Perf. 13½x14
528 A112 11c Map, flag .25 .25
529 A112 25c Flag raising .60 .60
530 A112 30c Land marker .70 .70
531 A112 45c Corvettes Elisa-
            beth & Leipzig 1.10 1.10
    Nos. 528-531 (4) 2.65 2.65

Spring
Flowers — A113

1984, Nov. 22   Litho.   Perf. 14½x14
532 A113 11c Sweet thorn .20 .20
533 A113 25c Camel thorn .50 .50
534 A113 30c Hook thorn .60 .60
535 A113 45c Candle-pod acacia .90 .90
    Nos. 532-535 (4) 2.20 2.20

Ostrich
A114

1985, Mar. 15
536 A114 11c Head of bird .25 .25
537 A114 25c Female nesting .70 .70
538 A114 30c Chick, eggs .80 .80
539 A114 50c Male mating dance 1.40 1.40
    Nos. 536-539 (4) 3.15 3.15

Historic Buildings, 1900-1912,
Windhoek — A115

1985, June 6
540 A115 12c Erkrath,
            Gathemann Build-
            ings, Kaiser
            Street .20 .20
541 A115 25c Gymnasium .35 .35

542 A115 30c Supreme Court .45 .45
543 A115 50c Railway Station .80 .80
    Nos. 540-543 (4) 1.80 1.80

600mm Narrow-gauge
Locomotives — A116

1985, Aug. 2
544 A116 12c Zwilling Schmal-
            spur, 1898 .35 .35
545 A116 25c Feldspur Side-Tank .70 .70
546 A116 30c 0-6-2 Side-Tank,
            1904 .80 .80
547 A116 50c Henschel hd Smal-
            spoor, 1912 1.50 1.50
    Nos. 544-547 (4) 3.35 3.35

Swakopmund-Tsumeb Railway line, 79th
anniv.

Endemic
Musical
Instruments
A117

1985, Oct. 17
548 A117 12c Lidumu-dumu .20 .20
549 A117 25c Ngoma .30 .30
550 A117 30c Okambulum
            bumbwa .35 .35
551 A117 50c Gwashi .60 .60
    Nos. 548-551 (4) 1.45 1.45

Diogo Cao,
Portuguese
Explorer,
1486 Visit to
SWA
A118

1986, Jan. 24   Perf. 14½x14
552 A118 12c Erecting padroes
            on shore .30 .30
553 A118 20c Cao coat of arms .55 .55
554 A118 25c Caravel .70 .70
555 A118 30c Portrait .90 .90
    Nos. 552-555 (4) 2.45 2.45

Wildlife Type of 1980
1986-87   Litho.   Perf. 14x14½
556 A95 14c Caracal, horiz. .80 .20
557 A95 16c Warthog, horiz. .50 .20

Issue dates: 14c, Apr. 1; 16c, Apr. 1, 1987.

Rock
Formations
A119

Designs: 14c, Granite bornhardt, Erongo.
20c, Vingerklip, Outjo. 25c, Aeolian sandstone, Kuiseb River. 30c, Columnar dolerite,
Twifelfontein.

1986, Apr. 24   Perf. 14½x14
566 A119 14c multicolored .25 .25
567 A119 20c multicolored .40 .40
568 A119 25c multicolored .50 .50
569 A119 30c multicolored .70 .70
    Nos. 566-569 (4) 1.85 1.85

Karakul Wool
(Swakara)
Industry — A120

1986, July 10   **Perf. 14x14½**
570	A120	14c Model	.35	.35
571	A120	20c Hand loom	.50	.50
572	A120	25c Sheep	.70	.70
573	A120	30c Rams	.80	.80
a.		Souvenir sheet of 1	3.00	3.00
		Nos. 570-573 (4)	2.35	2.35

No. 573a margin pictures design of No. 570 and Johannesburg stamp exhib. emblem. Sold for 50c to benefit stamp exhib.

Caprivi Strip — A121

1986, Nov. 6   **Litho.**   **Perf. 14½x14**
574	A121	14c Lake Liambezi	.35	.35
575	A121	20c Stock and crop farming	.55	.55
576	A121	25c Settlement	.70	.70
577	A121	30c Map	.90	.90
		Nos. 574-577 (4)	2.50	2.50

Paintings by Thomas Baines (1820-1875) A122

Designs: 14c, *Rhenish Mission Church at Gababis,* 1863. 20c, *Outspan in October,* 1861. 25c, *Outspan Under Oomahaama Tree,* 1862. 30c, *Swa-Kop River S.W. Africa,* 1861.

1987, Feb. 19   **Litho.**   **Perf. 14½x14**
578	A122	14c multicolored	.30	.30
579	A122	20c multicolored	.45	.45
580	A122	25c multicolored	.55	.55
a.		Souvenir sheet of 1	2.75	2.75
581	A122	30c multicolored	.70	.70
		Nos. 578-581 (4)	2.00	2.00

No. 580a for the natl. philatelic exhibition at Paarl, Sept. 16-19. Sold for 50c.

Insects A123

1987, May 7
582	A123	16c *Garreta nitens*	.45	.45
583	A123	20c *Alcimus stenurus*	.55	.55
584	A123	25c *Anthophora caerulea*	.70	.70
585	A123	30c *Hemiempusa capensis*	.80	.80
		Nos. 582-585 (4)	2.50	2.50

Resorts — A124

1987, July 23
586	A124	16c Okaukuejo, Etosha Natl. Park	.40	.40
587	A124	20c Daan Viljoen Game Park	.55	.55
588	A124	25c Ai-Ais Hot Springs	.65	.65
589	A124	30c Hardap, Mariental	.75	.75
		Nos. 586-589 (4)	2.35	2.35

Shipwrecks A125

1987, Oct. 15
590	A125	16c *Hope,* 1804	.40	.40
591	A125	30c *Tilly,* 1885	.90	.90
592	A125	40c *Eduard Bohlen,* 1909	1.10	1.10
593	A125	50c *Dunedin Star,* 1942	1.50	1.50
		Nos. 590-593 (4)	3.90	3.90

Discovery of the Cape of Good Hope by Bartolomeu Dias, 500th Anniv. — A126

1988, Jan. 7   **Perf. 14x14½**
594	A126	16c shown	.45	.45
595	A126	30c Caravel	.75	.75
596	A126	40c The Cantino Map, 1502	1.10	1.10
597	A126	50c King John II	1.40	1.40
		Nos. 594-597 (4)	3.70	3.70

Historic Sites A127

1988, Mar. 3   **Perf. 14½x14**
598	A127	16c Sossusvlei Clay Pans	.40	.40
599	A127	30c Sesriem Canyon	.65	.65
600	A127	40c Hoaruseb clay castles	.90	.90
601	A127	50c Hoba meteorite	1.50	1.50
		Nos. 598-601 (4)	3.45	3.45

Postal Service, Cent. A128

1988, July 7   **Perf. 14x14½**
602	A128	16c Otyimbingue P.O., 1888	.30	.30
603	A128	30c Windhoek P.O., 1904	.60	.60
604	A128	40c Mail runner, 1888	.80	.80
605	A128	50c Camel post, 1904	1.00	1.00
a.		Souvenir sheet of 1	2.75	2.75
		Nos. 602-605 (4)	2.70	2.70

No. 605a for the natl. philatelic exhibition held at Windhoek, July 7-9. Sold for 1r.

Birds — A129

1988, Nov. 3
606	A129	16c *Namibornis hereo*	.45	.45
607	A129	30c *Ammomanes grayi*	1.00	1.00
608	A129	40c *Eupodotis rueppellii*	1.10	1.10
609	A129	50c *Tockus monteiri*	1.60	1.60
		Nos. 606-609 (4)	4.15	4.15

Missionaries and Mission Stations — A130

16c, Carl Hahn (1818-95) & Gross-Barmen Mission. 30c, Johann Kronlein (1826-92) & Berseba Mission. 40c, Franz Kleinschmidt (1812-64) & Rehoboth Mission. 50c, Johann Schmelen (1777-1848) & Bethanien Mission.

1989, Feb. 16
610	A130	16c multicolored	.30	.30
611	A130	30c multicolored	.50	.50
612	A130	40c multicolored	.70	.70
613	A130	50c multicolored	.90	.90
		Nos. 610-613 (4)	2.40	2.40

Aviation Industry, 75th Anniv. A131

Maps and aircraft.

1989, May 18   **Perf. 14½x14**
614	A131	18c Beechcraft 1900, 1988	.30	.30
615	A131	30c Ryan Navion, 1948	.45	.45
616	A131	40c Junkers F13, 1930	.60	.60
617	A131	50c Pfalz Otto biplane, 1914	.80	.80
a.		Souvenir sheet of 1	3.00	3.00
		Nos. 614-617 (4)	2.15	2.15

No. 617a has decorative bright blue and black inscribed margin picturing emblem of natl. philatelic exhibition WANDERERS 101, held Sept. 6-9. Sold for 1.50r.

Namib Desert Sand Dunes — A132

1989, Aug. 14   **Perf. 14x14½**
Size of 30c, 50c: 31x21½mm
618	A132	18c Barchan dunes	.30	.30
619	A132	30c Star dunes	.55	.55
620	A132	40c Transverse dunes	.75	.75
621	A132	50c Crescent dunes	.90	.90
		Nos. 618-621 (4)	2.50	2.50

Suffrage, UN Resolution 435 — A133

1989, Aug. 24
622	A133	18c dull org & gray vio	.30	.30
623	A133	35c green & blue	.60	.60
624	A133	45c yellow & purple	.85	.85
625	A133	60c golden brn & gray grn	1.25	1.25
		Nos. 622-625 (4)	3.00	3.00

Minerals — A134

Mines A135

1989-90   **Perf. 14½x14**
626	A134	1c Gypsum	.20	.20
627	A134	2c Fluorite	.20	.20
628	A134	5c Mimetite	.20	.20
629	A134	7c Cuprite	.20	.20
630	A134	10c Azurite	.20	.20
631	A134	18c Boltwoodite	.30	.30
631A	A134	18c see footnote	14.00	8.00
632	A134	20c Dioptase	.30	.30
633	A135	25c Alluvial diamond field, Oranjemund	.35	.35
634	A135	30c Lead, copper & zinc mine, Tsumeb	.40	.40
635	A135	35c Zinc mine, Rosh Pinah	.50	.50
636	A134	40c Diamonds	.55	.55
637	A134	45c Wulfenite	.65	.65
638	A135	50c Tin mine, Uis	.70	.70
639	A135	1r Uranium mine, Rossing	1.50	1.50
640	A134	2r Gold	3.00	3.00
		Nos. 626-640 (16)	23.25	17.25

#631 has formula, $K(H_3O)(UO_2)(SiO4)$; #631A $K2(UO_2)2(SiO3)2(OH)2.5H_2O2$.
Issued: #631A, 10/25/90; others, 11/16/89. This set remained in use until Namibia issued a definitive set Jan. 2, 1991.

Flora — A136

1990, Feb. 1   **Perf. 14½x14**
641	A136	18c *Adenium boehmianum*	.45	.45
642	A136	35c *Adansonia digitata*	.85	.85
643	A136	45c *Kigelia africana*	1.10	1.10
644	A136	60c *Harpagophytum procumbens*	1.40	1.40
a.		Souvenir sheet of 1	2.50	2.50
		Nos. 641-644 (4)	3.80	3.80

No. 644a margin publicizes the natl. phil. exhib. Sold for 1.50r.

SEMI-POSTAL STAMPS

Catalogue values for unused stamps in this section are for Never Hinged items.

Voortrekker Monument Issue

South Africa Nos. B1-B4 Overprinted

1935-36   **Wmk. 201**   **Perf. 14**
B1	SP1	½p + ½p grn & blk, pair	3.00	6.25
a.		Single, English	.25	.85
b.		Single, Afrikaans	.25	.85
B2	SP2	1p + ½p rose & blk, pair	4.00	3.75
a.		Single, English	.30	.45
b.		Single, Afrikaans	.30	.45
B3	SP3	2p + 1p dl vio & gray, pair	13.00	7.00
a.		Single, English	.75	.90
b.		Single, Afrikaans	.75	.90
B4	SP4	3p + 1½p dp bl & gray, pair	25.00	37.50
a.		Single, English	1.50	4.50
b.		Single, Afrikaans	1.50	4.50
		Nos. B1-B4 (4)	45.00	54.50

Voortrekker Centenary Issue
South Africa Nos. B5-B8 Overprinted   **S.W.A.**

1938, Dec. 14   **Perf. 14**
B5	SP5	½p + ½p dl grn & indigo, pair	8.25	8.00
a.		Single, English	.75	1.25
b.		Single, Afrikaans	.75	1.25

    Perf. 15x14
B6	SP6	1p + 1p rose & sl, pair	17.00	10.00
a.		Single, English	.50	1.00
b.		Single, Afrikaans	.50	1.00
B7	SP7	1½p + 1½p Prus grn & choc, pair	22.50	14.50
a.		Single, English	1.25	2.50
b.		Single, Afrikaans	1.25	2.50
B8	SP8	3p + 3p chlky bl, pair	45.00	32.50
a.		Single, English	2.75	5.00
b.		Single, Afrikaans	2.75	5.00
		Nos. B5-B8 (4)	92.75	65.00

Same Overprint on South Africa Nos.
B9-B11

1939, July 17   *Perf. 14*

B9	SP9	½p + ½p Prus grn & gray brn, pair	6.75	5.00
a.		Single, English	.85	.85
b.		Single, Afrikaans	.85	.85
B10	SP10	1p + 1p rose car & Prus grn, pair	13.50	10.00
a.		Single, English	1.00	1.00
b.		Single, Afrikaans	1.00	1.00

Perf. 15x14

B11	SP11	1½p + 1½p rose vio, dk vio & Prus grn, pair	22.50	15.00
a.		Single, English	1.25	1.25
b.		Single, Afrikaans	1.25	1.25
		Nos. B9-B11 (3)	42.75	30.00

250th anniv. of the landing of the Huguenots in South Africa. Surtax went to a fund to build a Huguenot memorial at Paarl.

AIR POST STAMPS

South Africa
Nos. C5-C6
Overprinted

1930   **Unwmk.**   *Perf. 14x13½*

C1	AP2	4p blue green	8.00	32.50
a.		Without period after "A"	80.00	150.00
C2	AP2	1sh orange	12.50	57.50
a.		Without period after "A"	475.00	625.00

Overprinted

C3	AP2	4p blue green	1.50	7.00
a.		Double overprint	200.00	
b.		Inverted overprint	200.00	
c.		Small "I" in "AIR"	6.00	
C4	AP2	1sh orange	4.25	17.50
a.		Double overprint	575.00	

Monoplane over Windhoek — AP3

Biplane over Windhoek — AP4

Wmk. 201

1931, Mar. 5   **Engr.**   *Perf. 14*

C5	AP3	3p blue & dk brn, pair	30.00	35.00
a.		Single, English	2.00	3.00
b.		Single, Afrikaans	2.00	3.00
C6	AP4	10p brn vio & blk, pair	45.00	75.00
a.		Single, English	3.00	6.00
b.		Single, Afrikaans	3.00	6.00

POSTAGE DUE STAMPS

Postage Due Stamps of South Africa and Transvaal Overprinted like Regular Issues.
Setting I
On South Africa Nos. J11, J14

1923   **Unwmk.**   *Perf. 14*

J1	D1	½p blue grn & blk, pair	5.00	15.00
a.		Single, English	.35	4.00
b.		Single, Dutch	.35	4.00
c.		As #J1, without period after "Afrika"	100.00	
d.		Inverted ovpt., pair	325.00	

J2	D1	2p vio & blk, pair	3.00	20.00
a.		Single, English	.20	4.00
b.		Single, Dutch	.20	4.00
c.		As #J2, without period after "Afrika"	70.00	70.00

On South Africa Nos. J9-J10
Rouletted 7-8

J3	D1	1p dull red & blk,	7.00	12.00
a.		Single, English	.20	3.00
b.		Single, Dutch	.20	3.00
c.		As #J3, without period after "Afrika"	70.00	70.00
d.		Pair, imperf. between	825.00	
J4	D1	1½p yel brn & blk, pair	1.00	8.00
a.		Single, English	.20	1.75
b.		Single, Dutch	.20	1.75
c.		As #J4, without period after "Afrika"	42.50	42.50

On South Africa Nos. J3-J4, J6
Perf. 14
Wmk. 177

J5	D1	2p vio & blk, pair	17.00	27.50
a.		Single, English	1.75	7.50
b.		Single, Dutch	1.75	7.50
c.		As #J5, without period after "Afrika"	150.00	
J6	D1	3p ultra & blk, pair	9.00	27.50
a.		Single, English	.85	7.50
b.		Single, Dutch	.85	7.50
J7	D1	6p gray & blk, pair	24.00	40.00
a.		Single, English	2.50	12.50
b.		Single, Dutch	2.50	12.50
		Nos. J5-J7 (3)	50.00	95.00

On Transvaal Nos. J5-J6
Wmk. Multiple Crown and C A (3)

J8	D1	5p vio & blk, pair	4.00	27.50
a.		Single, English	.50	7.50
b.		Single, Dutch	.50	7.50
c.		As #J8, without period after "Afrika"	85.00	85.00
J9	D1	6p red brn & blk, pair	17.00	27.50
a.		Single, Dutch	1.75	7.50
c.		As #J9, without period after "Afrika"	140.00	

For No. J9 single in English see No. J17a and note after No. 27.
The "t" of "West" may be found partly or entirely missing on Nos. J1, J3-J6, J8-J9.

Setting II
On South Africa No. J9
Rouletted
Unwmk.

J10	D1	1p dull red & blk, pair	8,000.	
a.		Single, English	800.00	—
b.		Single, Dutch	800.00	—

On South Africa Nos. J3-J4
Perf. 14
Wmk. 177

J11	D1	2p vio & blk, pair	14.00	25.00
a.		Single, English	1.25	7.00
b.		Single, Dutch	1.25	7.00
c.		As #J11, without period after "Afrika"	110.00	125.00
J12	D1	3p ultra & blk, pair	7.00	20.00
a.		Single, English	.75	5.00
b.		Single, Dutch	.75	5.00
c.		As #J12, without period after "Afrika"	70.00	80.00

On Transvaal No. J5
Wmk. Multiple Crown and C A (3)

J13	D1	5p vio & blk, pair	75.00	140.00
a.		Single, English	15.00	
b.		Single, Dutch	15.00	

Setting III
On South Africa Nos. J11, J12, J9
Unwmk.

J14	D1	½p blue grn & blk, pair	7.00	17.50
a.		Single, English	.75	4.50
J15	D1	1p rose & blk, pair	8.00	20.00
a.		Single, English	.75	4.50
b.		Single, Dutch	.75	4.50

Rouletted 7

J16	D1	1p dull red & blk, pair	2.00	20.00

For Nos. J14 and J16 singles in English see Nos. J1a and J3a and note after No. 27.

On Transvaal No. J6
Perf. 14
Wmk. 3

J17	D1	6p red brown & blk, pair	17.00	60.00
a.		Single, English	1.75	17.50
b.		Single, Dutch	1.75	17.50

See note below No. 27.

Setting IV
On South Africa Nos. J11-J12, J16

1924   **Unwmk.**

J18	D1	½p blue grn & blk, pair	3.50	20.00
a.		Single, English	.45	5.00
b.		Single, Dutch	.45	5.00

J19	D1	1p rose & blk, pair	5.00	20.00
a.		Single, English	.60	5.00
b.		Single, Dutch	.60	5.00
J20	D1	6p gray & blk, pair	2.25	27.50
a.		Single, English	.30	8.00
b.		Single, Dutch	.30	8.00

On Transvaal No. J5
Wmk. Multiple Crown and C A (3)

J21	D1	5p violet & blk, pair	400.00	1,000.
a.		Single, English	100.00	
b.		Single, Dutch	100.00	

Setting V

i   j

"South West" 16mm wide
"Zuidwest" 12mm wide
Overprint Spaced 12mm
On South Africa Nos. J4, J11, J13

1924   **Unwmk.**

J22	D1	½p green & blk, pair	2.00	22.50
a.		Single, English	.25	6.50
b.		Single, Dutch	.25	6.50
J23	D1	1½p yel brown & blk	4.00	22.50
a.		Single, English	.50	6.50
b.		Single, Dutch	.50	6.50

Wmk. Springbok's Head (177)

J24	D1	3p ultra & black, pair	12.50	37.50
a.		Single, English	1.40	10.00
b.		Single, Dutch	1.40	10.00

On Transvaal No. J5
Wmk. Multiple Crown and C A (3)

J25	D1	5p violet & blk, pair	3.00	25.00
a.		Single, English	.40	7.50
b.		Single, Dutch	.40	7.50

Setting VI
On South Africa Nos. J4, J11-J16

1924, Dec.   **Unwmk.**

J26	D1	½p blue grn & blk, pair	5.00	25.00
a.		Single, English	.60	6.00
b.		Single, Dutch	.60	6.00
J27	D1	1p rose & blk, pair	1.50	7.50
a.		Single, English	.20	1.75
b.		Single, Dutch	.20	1.75
c.		As #J27, without period after "Africa"	87.50	
J28	D1	1½p yel brown & blk, pair	2.50	22.50
a.		Single, English	.30	5.50
b.		Single, Dutch	.30	5.50
c.		As #J28, without period after "Africa"	75.00	
J29	D1	2p vio & blk, pair	2.50	12.50
a.		Single, English	.30	3.00
b.		Single, Dutch	.30	3.00
c.		As #J29, without period after "Africa"	55.00	
J30	D1	3p bl & blk, pair	3.00	15.00
a.		Single, English	.75	3.50
b.		Single, Dutch	.75	3.50
c.		As #J30, without period after "Africa"	70.00	
J31	D1	6p gray & blk, pair	8.00	45.00
a.		Single, English	1.00	12.50
b.		Single, Dutch	1.00	12.50
c.		As #J31, without period after "Africa"	100.00	
		Nos. J26-J31 (6)	22.50	127.50

Wmk. Springbok's Head (177)

J32	D1	3p ultra & black, pair	6.00	35.00
a.		Single, English	.75	9.00
b.		Single, Dutch	.75	9.00

On Transvaal No. J5
Wmk. 3

J33	D1	5p violet & blk, pair	2.00	12.50
a.		Single, English	.25	3.00
b.		Single, Dutch	.25	3.00
c.		As #J33, without period after "Africa"	55.00	75.00

Setting VIII
On South Africa Nos. J18, J13-J16

1927   **Unwmk.**

J34	D2	1p rose & blk, pair	.90	9.00
a.		Single, English	.20	2.00
b.		Single, Afrikaans	.20	2.00
c.		As #J34, without period after "Africa"	10.50	17.50
J35	D1	1½p yel brown & blk, pair	.90	10.00
a.		Single, English	.20	2.50
b.		Single, Afrikaans	.20	2.50
c.		As #J35, without period after "Africa"	50.00	60.00
J36	D1	2p vio & blk, pair	2.50	12.50
a.		Single, English	.30	3.25
b.		Single, Afrikaans	.30	3.25
c.		As #J36, without period after "Africa"	50.00	60.00
J37	D1	3p bl & blk, pair	10.00	40.00
a.		Single, English	1.25	10.00
b.		Single, Afrikaans	1.25	10.00

c.		As #J37, without period after "Africa"	70.00	70.00
J38	D1	6p gray & blk, pair	7.50	27.50
a.		Single, English	1.00	8.00
b.		Single, Afrikaans	1.00	8.00
c.		As #J38, without period after "Africa"	100.00	115.00
		Nos. J34-J38 (5)	21.80	99.00

On Transvaal No. J5
Wmk. Multiple Crown and C A (3)

J39	D1	5p violet & blk, pair	16.00	75.00
a.		Single, English	1.75	20.00
b.		Single, Afrikaans	1.75	20.00

South Africa Nos. J15-J16   **S.W.A.**
Overprinted

1928   **Unwmk.**

J79	D1	3p blue & black	1.65	12.00
		Without period after "A"	30.00	35.00
J80	D1	6p gray & black	7.50	22.50
		Without period after "A"	125.00	

Same Overprint on South Africa Nos. J17-J21

J81	D2	½p blue grn & blk	.40	6.00
J82	D2	1p rose & black	.50	3.00
a.		Without period after "A"	40.00	45.00
J83	D2	2p violet & black	.65	3.75
a.		Without period after "A"	60.00	
J84	D2	3p ultra & black	1.50	17.50
J85	D2	6p gray & black	1.75	15.00
a.		Without period after "A"	40.00	55.00
		Nos. J81-J85 (5)	4.80	45.25

> Catalogue values for unused stamps in this section, from this point to the end of the section, are for Never Hinged items.

D3   D4

Wmk. 201

1931, Feb. 23   **Litho.**   *Perf. 12*
Size: 19x22mm

J86	D3	½p yel green & blk	.85	8.50
J87	D3	1p rose & black	.85	1.65
J88	D3	2p violet & black	.85	3.25
J89	D3	3p blue & black	3.25	18.00
J90	D3	6p gray & black	13.00	27.50
		Nos. J86-J90 (5)	18.80	58.90

Photo. (Frame) & Typo. (Center)

1959   *Perf. 14½x14*
Size: 17x21mm

J91	D3	1p rose & black	1.50	10.00
J92	D3	2p violet & black	1.50	10.00
J93	D3	3p blue & black	1.50	11.00
		Nos. J91-J93 (3)	4.50	31.00

1960   **Wmk. 330**
Size: 17x21mm

J94	D3	1p rose & black	3.50	4.00
J95	D3	3p blue & black	3.50	5.50

1961, Feb.   **Photo.**   *Perf. 14½x14*

J96	D4	1c green & black	.80	4.00
J97	D4	2c red & black	.80	4.00
J98	D4	4c lilac & black	.80	4.00
J99	D4	5c blue & black	1.25	4.75
J100	D4	6c emerald & black	1.50	6.75
J101	D4	10c yellow & black	3.00	8.50
		Nos. J96-J101 (6)	8.15	32.00

Type of South Africa, 1972

1972   **Wmk. 359**   *Perf. 14x13½*

J102	D6	1c bright green	.65	3.25
J103	D6	8c violet blue	2.50	6.00

OFFICIAL STAMPS

Nos. 85-87 (Setting VIII) Overprinted at top with type "c" on English-inscribed Stamps and type "d" on Afrikaans-inscribed Stamps

OFFICIAL   **OFFISIEEL**

c   d

Without Periods after Words

1927   Wmk. 201   Perf. 14½x14

O1	A5	½p dk green & blk, pair	75.00	175.00
a.		Single, English	9.00	25.00
b.		Single, Afrikaans	9.00	25.00
O2	A6	1p car & blk, pair	75.00	175.00
a.		Single, English	9.00	25.00
b.		Single, Afrikaans	9.00	25.00
O3	A7	6p org & grn, pair	90.00	175.00
a.		Single, English	9.50	25.00
b.		Single, Afrikaans	9.50	25.00

South Africa No. 5 Overprinted As Nos. 85-87 plus "c" and "d"

Perf. 14

Wmk. 177

O4	A2	2p dull violet	190.00	275.00
a.		Single, English	22.50	40.00
b.		Single, Afrikaans	22.50	40.00

Nos. 96-98 Overprinted like Nos. J79-J85 at foot, Overprinted Types "c" and "d" at Top

1929   Wmk. 201   Perf. 14½x14

O5	A5	½p green & blk, pair	.85	10.00
a.		Single, English	.20	2.50
b.		Single, Afrikaans	.20	2.50
O6	A6	1p car & blk, pair	1.00	11.00
a.		Single, English	.20	2.50
b.		Single, Afrikaans	.20	2.50
O7	A7	6p org & grn, pair	3.75	15.00
a.		Single, English	.75	3.50
b.		Single, Afrikaans	.75	3.50
		Nos. O5-O7 (3)	5.60	36.00

No. 99 Overprinted like Nos. J79-J85 at foot,
Overprinted at top

OFFICIAL.   OFFISIEEL.

With Periods after Words
Perf. 14

O8	A8	2p vio brn & gray, pair	2.50	17.00
a.		Single, English	.30	3.75
b.		Single, Afrikaans	.30	3.75
c.		Without period after "OFFICIAL"	5.00	30.00
d.		Pair, "c" + normal 2p	15.00	80.00
e.		Without period after "OFFISIEEL"	5.00	30.00
f.		Pair, "e" + normal 2p	15.00	80.00
g.		Pair, "c" + "e"	15.00	80.00

In each sheet of 120 stamps there were 12 No. O8c and 10 No. O8e.

South Africa Nos. 23-25 Overprinted

Without Periods after Words

1929   Wmk. 201   Perf. 14½x14

O9	A5	½p green & blk, pair	.60	11.00
a.		Single, English	.20	2.50
b.		Single, Afrikaans	.20	2.50
O10	A6	1p car & blk, pair	.70	11.00
a.		Single, English	.20	2.50
b.		Single, Afrikaans	.20	2.50
O11	A7	6p org & grn, pair	2.50	25.00
a.		Single, English	.30	6.00
b.		Single, Afrikaans	.30	6.00
		Nos. O9-O11 (3)	3.80	47.00

South Africa No. 26 Overprinted

With Periods after Words
Perf. 14

O12	A8	2p vio brn & gray, pair	1.00	15.00
a.		Single, English	.20	3.50
b.		Single, Afrikaans	.20	3.50
c.		Without period after "OFFICIAL"	3.50	35.00
d.		Pair, "c" + normal 2p	12.50	70.00

---

e.		Without period after "OFFISIEEL"	3.50	35.00
f.		Pair, "e" + normal 2p	12.50	70.00
g.		Pair, "c" + "e"	17.50	80.00

> **Catalogue values for unused stamps in this section, from this point to the end of the section, are for Never Hinged items.**

Nos. 108-109, 111 and 114 Overprinted in Red

OFFICIAL   OFFISIEEL

1931

O13	A15	½p green & blk, pair	8.50	15.00
a.		Single, English	1.00	3.50
b.		Single, Afrikaans	1.00	3.50
O14	A16	1p red & indigo, pair	.65	15.00
a.		Single, English	.20	3.50
b.		Single, Afrikaans	.20	3.50
O15	A18	2p dk brn & dk bl, pair	1.00	9.00
a.		Single, English	.20	2.00
b.		Single, Afrikaans	.20	2.00
O16	A21	6p ol brn & bl, pair	2.00	13.00
a.		Single, English	.25	3.00
b.		Single, Afrikaans	.25	3.00
		Nos. O13-O16 (4)	12.15	52.00

No. 110 Overprinted in Red

1938, July 1   Wmk. 201

O17	A17	1½p violet brn, pair	25.00	35.00
a.		Single, English	2.75	6.00
b.		Single, Afrikaans	2.75	6.00

Nos. 108-111, 114 Ovptd. in Red

1945-50   Wmk. 201   Perf. 14x13½

O18	A15	½p grn & blk, pair	8.00	21.00
a.		Single, English	1.00	4.25
b.		Single, Afrikaans	1.00	4.25
O19	A16	1p red & ind, pair ('50)	2.00	12.50
a.		Single, English	.25	3.00
b.		Single, Afrikaans	.25	3.00
O20	A17	1½p vio brn, pair	30.00	27.50
a.		Single, English	5.00	5.00
b.		Single, Afrikaans	5.00	5.00
O21	A18	2p dk brn & dk bl, pair ('47)	425.00	600.00
a.		Single, English	75.00	100.00
b.		Single, Afrikaans	75.00	100.00
O22	A21	6p ol brn & bl, pair	7.00	27.50
a.		Single, English	.80	5.00
b.		Single, Afrikaans	.80	5.00
		Nos. O18-O20, O22 (4)	47.00	88.50

Nos. 108-111, 114 Ovptd. in Red

1951-52

O23	A15	½p grn & blk, pair ('52)	11.00	15.00
a.		Single, English	1.25	4.00
b.		Single, Afrikaans	1.25	4.00
O24	A16	1p red & ind, pair	2.25	9.00
a.		Single, English	.30	1.75
b.		Single, Afrikaans	.30	1.75
c.		Ovpt. transposed, pair	50.00	82.50
d.		As "c," single, English ovpt.	10.00	
e.		As "c," single, Afrikaans ovpt.	10.00	
O25	A17	1½p violet brn, pair	22.50	22.50
a.		Single, English	3.00	5.00
b.		Single, Afrikaans	3.00	5.00
c.		Ovpt. transposed, pair	60.00	75.00
d.		As "c," single, English ovpt.	7.50	
e.		As "c," single, Afrikaans ovpt.	7.50	
O26	A18	2p dk brn & dk bl, pair	1.50	13.00
a.		Single, English	.20	3.50
b.		Single, Afrikaans	.20	3.50
c.		Ovpt. transposed, pair	32.50	90.00
d.		As "c," single, English ovpt.	4.50	
e.		As "c," single, Afrikaans ovpt.	4.50	
O27	A21	6p ol brn & blue, pair	2.75	30.00
a.		Single, English	.35	7.00
b.		Single, Afrikaans	.35	7.00
c.		Ovpt. transposed, pair	20.00	110.00
d.		As "c," single, English ovpt.	4.00	
e.		As "c," single, Afrikaans ovpt.	4.00	
		Nos. O23-O27 (5)	40.00	89.50

"Overprint transposed" means English inscription on Afrikaans stamp, or vice versa. Use of official stamps ceased in Jan. 1955.

ADVANTAGE STOCKSHEETS

Designed with the collector in mind, Advantage stock sheets fit directly in your 2-post or 3-ring National or Specialty album. For unprecedented durability and flexibility choose Advantage Stocksheets. Choose from 1 to 8 pockets.
Sheets are sold in packages of 10.

- Stock sheets match album pages in every respect, including border, size, and color.

- Punched and drilled to fit perfectly in binder.

- Available with 1 to 8 pockets. Ideal for storing minor varieties and collateral material. A great place to keep new issues until the next supplement is available.

- Provide the protection and durability of crystal clear acetate pockets on heavyweight pages.

NATIONAL BORDER

ITEM			RETAIL
AD11	1 Pocket	242mm	$15.99
AD12	2 Pockets	119mm	$15.99
AD13	3 Pockets	79mm	$15.99
AD14	4 Pockets	58mm	$15.99
AD15	5 Pockets	45mm	$15.99
AD16	6 Pockets	37mm	$15.99
AD17	7 Pockets	31mm	$15.99
AD18	8 Pockets	31mm	$15.99

SPECIALTY BORDER

AD21	1 Pocket	242mm	$15.99
AD22	2 Pockets	119mm	$15.99
AD23	3 Pockets	79mm	$15.99
AD24	4 Pockets	58mm	$15.99
AD25	5 Pockets	45mm	$15.99
AD26	6 Pockets	37mm	$15.99
AD27	7 Pockets	31mm	$15.99
AD28	8 Pockets	31mm S	$15.99

Available from your favorite stamp dealer or direct from:

1-800-572-6885
P.O. Box 828,
Sidney OH 45365
www.amosadvantage.com

AMOS
HOBBY PUBLISHING

SPAIN

'spän

LOCATION — Southwestern Europe, Iberian Peninsula
GOVT. — Monarchy
AREA — 194,884 sq. mi.
POP. — 39,167,744 (1999 est.)
CAPITAL — Madrid

Spain was a monarchy until about 1931, when a republic was established. After the Civil War (1936-39), the Spanish State of Gen. Francisco Franco was recognized. The monarchy was restored in 1975.

32 Maravedis = 8 Cuartos = 1 Real
1000 Milesimas = 100 Centimos = 1 Escudo (1866)
100 Milesimas = 1 Real
4 Reales = 1 Peseta
100 Centimos = 1 Peseta (1872)
100 Cents = 1 Euro (2002)

Catalogue values for unused stamps in this country are for Never Hinged items, beginning with Scott 909 in the regular postage section, Scott B139 in the semi-postal section, Scott C159 in the airpost section, and Scott E21 in the special delivery section.

Watermarks

Wmk. 104 — Loops

Wmk. 105 — Crossed Lines

Wmk. 116 — Crosses and Circles

Wmk. 178 — Castle

Stamps punched with a small round hole have done telegraph service. In this condition most of them sell for 20 cents to $20.
Stamps of 1854 to 1882 canceled with three parallel horizontal bars or two thin lines are remainders. Most of these are valued through No. 101.

For additional shades see the *Scott Classic Catalogue.*

Kingdom

Queen Isabella II
A1   A2

6 CUARTOS:
Type I — "T" and "O" of CUARTOS separated.
Type II — "T" and "O" joined.

Unwmk.
1850, Jan. 1   Litho.   *Imperf.*

1	A1	6c blk, thin paper (II)	350.00	13.00
a.		Thick paper (II)	400.00	20.00
b.		Thick paper (I)	400.00	16.00
c.		Thin paper (I)	400.00	22.50
2	A2	12c lilac	2,000.	240.00
a.		Thin paper	2,750.	250.00
3	A2	5r red	2,000.	240.00
4	A2	6r blue	2,600.	650.00
5	A2	10r green	3,650.	1,900.

Stamps of types A2, A3, A4, A6, A7a and A8 are inscribed "FRANCO" on the cuarto values and "CERTIFICADO," "CERTIFO" or "CERT DO" on the reales values.

A3   A4

1851, Jan. 1   Typo.
Thin Paper

6	A3	6c black	210.00	2.50
a.		Thick paper	400.00	10.00
7	A3	12c lilac	3,500.	150.00
8	A3	2r red	15,000.	9,000.
9	A3	5r rose	2,000.	210.00
a.		5r red brown (error)	12,000.	—
10	A3	6r blue	3,150.	850.00
a.		Cliche of 2r in plate of 6r	125,000.	100,000.
11	A3	10r green	2,250.	400.00

1852, Jan. 1
Thick Paper

12	A4	6c rose	300.00	2.25
a.		Thin paper	375.00	3.75
13	A4	12c lilac	1,600.	140.00
14	A4	2r pale red	13,000.	4,350.
15	A4	5r yellowish green	1,750.	95.00
16	A4	6r grnsh blue	2,850.	400.00

Arms of Madrid — A5

Isabella II — A6

1853, Jan. 1
Thin Paper

17	A5	1c bronze	2,000.	425.00
18	A5	3c bronze	11,500.	6,000.
19	A6	6c carmine rose	350.00	1.75
a.		Thick paper	475.00	11.00
b.		Thick bluish paper	700.00	16.00
20	A6	12c red violet	1,700.	95.00
21	A6	2r vermilion	9,000.	2,750.
22	A6	5r lt green	1,850.	95.00
23	A6	6r deep blue	2,500.	350.00

Nos. 17-18 were issued for use on Madrid city mail only. *They were reprinted on this white paper in duller colors.*

A7   A7a

Coat of Arms of Spain — A8

1854
Thin White Paper

24	A7	2c green	2,650.	400.00
c.		Thick paper	1,750.	425.00
25	A7a	4c carmine	325.00	1.75
a.		Thick paper	350.00	10.00
26	A8	6c carmine	275.00	1.40
27	A7a	1r indigo	2,700.	275.00
		Bar cancellation		12.00

28	A8	2r scarlet	1,300.	87.50
		Bar cancellation, #28 or 28a		5.50
c.		Thick paper	—	125.00
29	A8	5r green	1,250.	87.50
		Bar cancellation		8.50
30	A8	6r blue	2,100.	250.00
		Bar cancellation		12.50

See boxed note on bar cancellation before #1.

Thick Bluish Paper

31	A7	2c green	10,500.	1,600.
b.		Thin paper	8,500.	1,300.
32	A7a	4c carmine	325.00	4.50
c.		Thin paper	250.00	8.50
32A	A8	6c carmine	500.00	10.00
d.		Thin paper	—	55.00
33	A7a	1r pale blue		6,250.
		Bar cancellation		100.00
a.		Thin paper		6,000.
34	A8	2r dull red	4,000.	400.00
a.		Thin paper	4,000.	400.00

The 2c with watermark 104 is a proof.

Isabella II — A9

1855, Apr. 1   Wmk. 104
Blue Paper

36	A9	2c green	2,250.	95.00
a.		2c yellow green	2,350.	125.00
		Bar cancellation, #36 or 36a		6.00
37	A9	4c brown red	210.00	.55
a.		4c carmine	225.00	1.40
b.		4c lake	225.00	.90
		Bar cancellation, #37, 37a or 37b		1.50
38	A9	1r green blue	925.00	12.00
a.		1r blue	950.00	13.00
		Bar cancellation, #38 or 38a		3.00
b.		Cliché of 2r in plate of 1r	13,000.	2,000.
		Bar cancellation		500.00
39	A9	2r reddish violet	650.00	12.00
a.		2r deep violet	675.00	12.50
		Bar cancellation		2.25

1856, Jan. 1   Wmk. 105
Rough Yellowish Paper

40	A9	2c green	2,750.	200.00
		Bar cancellation		8.50
41	A9	4c rose	8.00	1.75
		Bar cancellation		1.50
42	A9	1r grnsh blue	2,750.	150.00
a.		1r dull blue	3,250.	175.00
		Bar cancellation, #42 or 42a		5.00
43	A9	2r brown violet	400.00	20.00
a.		2r dark reddish violet	425.00	30.00
		Bar cancellation, #43 or 43a		5.00

1856, Apr. 11   Unwmk.
White Smooth Paper

44	A9	2c blue green	425.00	35.00
a.		2c yellow green	450.00	37.50
		Bar cancellation, #44 or 44a		5.00
45	A9	4c rose	3.50	.30
a.		4c carmine	25.00	17.50
46	A9	1r blue	17.50	20.00
a.		1r pale greenish blue	19.00	22.50
		Bar cancellation, #46 or 46a		2.25
47	A9	2r brown lilac	55.00	20.00
a.		2r dull lilac	65.00	22.50
		Bar cancellation, #47 or 47a		4.75

Three types of No. 45.

1859

48	A9	12c dark orange	125.00	
		Bar cancellation		27.50

No. 48 was never put in use. *Reprints exist.*

A10   A11

1860-61
Tinted Paper

49	A10	2c green, *grn*	275.00	17.00
		Bar cancellation		2.00
50	A10	4c orange, *grn*	32.50	.60
51	A10	12c car, *buff*	275.00	11.00
		Bar cancellation		2.25
52	A10	19c brn, *buff* ('61)	2,400.	1,050.
53	A10	1r blue, *buff*	225.00	10.00
		Bar cancellation		2.00
54	A10	2r lilac, *lil*	300.00	8.75
		Bar cancellation		2.00

1862, July 16

55	A11	2c dp bl, *yel*	30.00	8.75
56	A11	4c dk brn, *redsh buff*	1.75	.50
a.		4c brown, *white*	17.50	5.00
57	A11	12c blue, *pnksh*	37.50	7.25
		Bar cancellation		2.25
58	A11	19c car, *lil*	160.00	190.00
a.		19c carmine, *white*	225.00	200.00
59	A11	1r brown, *yel*	50.00	17.00
		Bar cancellation		2.00
60	A11	2r green, *pnksh*	30.00	11.00
		Bar cancellation		2.25
		Nos. 55-60 (6)	309.25	234.50

A12   A13

1864, Jan. 1

61	A12	2c dk bl, *lil*	42.50	16.00
62	A12	4c rose, *redsh buff*	1.90	.60
a.		4c carmine, *reddish buff*	15.00	5.00
63	A12	12c green, *pnksh*	37.50	11.50
64	A12	19c violet, *pnksh*	160.00	160.00
65	A12	1r brown, *grn*	160.00	70.00
		Bar cancellation		
66	A12	2r bl, *pnksh*	37.50	11.50
		Bar cancellation		2.50
		Nos. 61-66 (6)	439.40	269.60

1865, Jan. 1   Litho.   *Imperf.*

67	A13	2c rose	225.00	27.50
68	A13	4c blue	2,400.	
69	A13	12c blue & rose	300.00	15.00
		Bar cancellation		3.25
a.		Frame inverted	13,500.	800.00
70	A13	19c brown & rose	1,150.	550.00
		Bar cancellation		55.00
71	A13	1r yellow grn	325.00	47.50
		Bar cancellation		5.75
72	A13	2r red lilac	325.00	27.50
		Bar cancellation		5.75
73	A13	2r rose	375.00	50.00
a.		2r salmon	325.00	60.00
		Bar cancellation, #73 or 73a		10.00

No. 68 is without gum and was never put into use.

IF YOU COLLECT SPAIN, UNITED STATES AND WORLDWIDE...
Early issues and Complete MINT SETS... ask for our FREE SALE CATALOGS AND MAIL AUCTIONS

FILATELIA LLACH,S.L.
"Stamp Dealers Since 1915"
489 Diagonal Avenue
08029 BARCELONA, SPAIN
Tel. +34-93-410 5000
Fax +34-93-4194728
E-mail:fillach@filateliallach.com
Website: www.filateliallach.com

A majority of the perforated stamps from 1865 to about 1950 are rather poorly centered. The very fine examples that are valued will be fairly well centered. Poorly centered stamps sell for less. Stamps of some issues are almost always badly centered, and our values will be for examples with fine centering. Such issues will be noted.

1865, Jan. 1   *Perf. 14*

74	A13	2c rose red	450.00	85.00
		Bar cancellation		7.00
75	A13	4c blue	27.50	.65
76	A13	12c blue & rose	450.00	47.50
		Bar cancellation		7.00
a.		Frame inverted	16,500.	1,650.
		As "a," bar cancel		550.00
77	A13	19c brown & rose	3,250.	1,750.
78	A13	1r yellow grn	1,300.	375.00
		Bar cancellation		15.00
79	A13	2r violet	1,000.	175.00
		Bar cancellation		14.00
80	A13	2r rose	1,100.	250.00
a.		2r salmon	1,100.	250.00
b.		2r dull orange	1,100.	250.00
				20.00

Values for Nos. 74-80 are for stamps with perforations touching the frame on at least one side.

A14

A14a

1866, Jan. 1

81	A14	2c rose	160.00	22.50
		Bar cancellation		2.75
82	A14	4c blue	32.50	.65
83	A14	12c orange	175.00	9.50
a.		12c orange yellow	275.00	19.00
84	A14	19c brown	825.00	325.00
		Bar cancellation		25.00
		Nos. 81-84 (4)	1,192.	357.65

1866

85	A14	10c green	225.00	19.050
		Bar cancellation		3.00
86	A14	20c lilac	140.00	15.00
		Bar cancellation		3.00
87	A14a	20c dull lilac	825.00	52.50
		Bar cancellation		2.25
		Nos. 85-87 (3)	1,190.	87.00

For the Type A14a 20c in green, see Cuba No. 25.

A15

A15a

A15b   A15c

1867-68

88	A15	2c yellow brown	375.00	37.50
89	A15a	4c blue	25.00	1.00
90	A15b	12c orange yellow	190.00	7.75
a.		12c dark orange	250.00	12.00
b.		12c red orange ('68)	850.00	42.50
91	A15c	19c rose	1,000.	425.00
		Bar cancellation		22.50

See Nos. 100-102. For overprints see Nos. 114a-115a, 124-128, 124a-128a, 124c-124c, 124e-126e.

A15d

A15e

92	A15d	10c blue green	250.00	22.50
		Bar cancellation		2.50
93	A15e	20c lilac	110.00	8.75
		Bar cancellation		2.50

For overprints see Nos. 116-117, 116a-117a, 116c-117c, 117d, 117e, 117f.

A16

A17

A18

A19

94	A16	5m green	42.50	17.00
		Bar cancellation		2.50
95	A17	10m brown	42.50	17.00
a.		Tête bêche pair	16,500.	
96	A18	25m blue & rose	225.00	25.00
a.		Frame inverted	14,500.	
		Bar cancellation		5.00
97	A18	50m bister brown	20.00	.75
		Nos. 94-97 (4)	330.00	59.75

See No. 98. For overprints see Nos. 118-122, 118a-122a, 120c-122c, 122d, 120e, 122e, 119f, 122f.

1868-69

98	A18	25m blue	250.00	15.00
		Bar cancellation		3.50
99	A19	50m violet	25.00	.60
100	A15b	100m brown	525.00	72.50
		Bar cancellation		2.50
101	A15c	200m green	190.00	14.00
		Bar cancellation		2.50
102	A15c	19c brown	2,250.	500.00

For overprints see Nos. 123, 123a, 123c, 123e.

Provisional Government

Excellent counterfeits exist of the provisional and provincial overprints.

For Madrid

Regular Issues Handstamped in Black

HABILITADO POR LA NACION.

1868-69

116	A15d	10c green	22.50	14.50
117	A15e	20c lilac	19.00	11.00
118	A16	5m green	14.50	5.00
119	A17	10m brown	15.00	5.00
120	A18	25m blue & rose	32.50	13.00
121	A18	25m blue	32.50	11.00
122	A18	50m bister brown	6.50	4.50
123	A19	50m violet	6.50	4.50
124	A15b	100m brown	65.00	26.00
125	A15c	200m green	22.50	8.25
126	A15b	12c orange	45.00	15.00
127	A15c	19c rose	300.00	125.00
128	A15c	19c brown	650.00	150.00
		Nos. 116-128 (13)	1,227.	392.75

Nos. 116-128 exist with handstamp in blue, a few in red. These sell for more.

For Andalusian Provinces

Regular Issues Handstamped Vertically in Blue

HABILITADO POR LA NACION.

114a	A15	2c brown	65.00	32.50
115a	A15a	4c blue	30.00	22.50
116a	A15d	10c green	32.50	13.00
117a	A15e	20c lilac	25.00	14.00
118a	A16	5m green	17.00	7.25
119a	A17	10m brown	11.50	5.00

120a	A18	25m blue & rose	37.50	13.00
b.		Frame inverted	22,000.	
121a	A18	25m blue	37.50	14.00
122a	A18	50m bister brown	8.25	5.00
123a	A19	50m violet	8.25	5.00
124a	A15b	100m brown	82.50	30.00
125a	A15c	200m green	27.50	11.00
126a	A15c	12c orange yel	30.00	12.00
127a	A15c	19c rose	375.00	190.00
128a	A15c	19c brown	700.00	250.00
		Nos. 114a-128a (15)	1,487.	624.25

For Valladolid Province

Regular Issues Handstamped in Black

HABILITADO POR LA NACION

(Two types of overprint)

116c	A15d	10c green	35.00	15.00
117c	A15e	20c lilac	32.50	16.00
120c	A18	25m blue & rose	50.00	13.00
121c	A18	25m blue	50.00	19.00
122c	A18	50m bister brown	13.00	8.25
123c	A19	50m violet	13.00	6.50
124c	A15b	100m brown	100.00	32.50
125c	A15c	200m green	32.50	13.00
126c	A15b	12c orange	35.00	11.50
127c	A15c	19c rose	325.00	160.00
128c	A15c	19c brown	850.00	210.00
		Nos. 116c-126c (9)	361.00	134.75

For Asturias Province

Regular Issues Handstamped in Black

Habilitado por la Junta Revolucionaria

117d	A15e	20c lilac	160.00	110.00
122d	A18	50m bister brown	175.00	110.00

For Teruel Province

Regular Issues Handstamped in Black

117e	A15e	20c lilac	65.00	50.00
120e	A18	25m blue & rose	82.50	50.00
122e	A18	50m bister brown	60.00	30.00
123e	A19	50m violet	60.00	30.00
124e	A15b	100m brown	140.00	65.00
125e	A15c	200m green	100.00	40.00
126e	A15c	12c orange	82.50	55.00
		Nos. 117e-126e (7)	590.00	320.00

For Salamanca Province

Regular Issues Handstamped in Blue

117f	A15e	20c lilac	65.00	50.00
119f	A17	10m brown	60.00	37.50
122f	A18	50m bister brown	65.00	45.00
		Nos. 117f-122f (3)	190.00	132.50

Duke de la Torre Regency

"España" — A20

1870, Jan. 1   *Typo.*

159	A20	1m brn lil, *buff*	6.50	6.50
		Bar cancellation		2.00
b.		1m brown lilac, *pinkish buff*	7.00	7.75
161	A20	2m blk, *pinkish*	7.75	8.00
a.		2m black, *buff*	8.75	9.00
163	A20	4m bister brn	15.00	12.00
164	A20	10m rose	17.00	6.00
		10m carmine	19.00	7.50
165	A20	25m lilac	52.50	6.50
		Bar cancellation		2.00
a.		25m gray lilac	55.00	6.50
b.		25m aniline violet	85.00	8.25
166	A20	50m ultra	10.00	.35
a.		50m dull blue	125.00	5.00
167	A20	100m red brown	29.00	5.25
		Bar cancellation		2.00
a.		100m claret	30.00	6.25
b.		100m orange brown	30.00	5.50
168	A20	200m pale brn	26.00	5.25
		Bar cancellation		2.00
169	A20	400m green	250.00	22.50
170	A20	1e600m dull lilac	1,250.	775.00
		Bar cancellation		22.50

171	A20	2e blue	1,100.	475.00
		Bar cancellation		27.50
172	A20	12c red brown	225.00	6.50
173	A20	19c yel grn	300.00	160.00

The 12c carmine rose and 12c blue on pink paper were never put into use. Value, $1,350.

Kingdom

A21

A22

King Amadeo
A23

A24

1872, Oct. 1   *Imperf.*

174	A21	¼c ultra	2.25	2.25
a.		Complete 1c (block of 4 ¼c)	82.50	75.00
b.		As "a," one cliche inverted	1,650.	1,600.

See No. 221A.

1872-73   *Perf. 14*

176	A22	2c gray lilac	17.50	7.75
a.		2c violet	27.50	17.00
b.		Imperf.		65.00
177	A22	5c green	125.00	60.00
a.		Imperf.		160.00
178	A23	5c rose ('73)	17.50	5.50
179	A23	6c blue	110.00	35.00
180	A23	10c brown lilac	350.00	225.00
181	A23	10c ultra ('73)	7.50	.50
182	A23	12c gray lilac	17.50	2.10
		Bar cancellation		2.00
183	A23	20c gray vio ('73)	140.00	82.50
		Bar cancellation		5.00
184	A23	25c brown	57.50	10.00
		Bar cancellation		2.00
185	A23	40c pale red brn	75.00	10.00
		Bar cancellation		2.00
186	A23	50c deep green	100.00	10.50
		Bar cancellation		2.00
187	A24	1p lilac	100.00	52.50
		Bar cancellation		2.00
188	A24	4p red brown	625.00	600.00
		Bar cancellation		6.00
189	A24	10p deep green	2,200.	2,300.
		Bar cancellation		225.00

First Republic

Mural Crown
A25

"España"
A26

1873, July 1   *Imperf.*

190	A25	¼c green	1.00	1.00
a.		Complete 1c (block of 4 ¼c)	37.50	19.00
		As "a," bar cancellation		2.00
d.		As "a," ultra (error)	190.00	160.00

1873, July 1   *Perf. 14*

191	A26	2c orange	13.00	6.00
192	A26	5c claret	29.00	6.00
		Bar cancellation		2.00
193	A26	10c green	6.50	.35
a.		Tête bêche pair		32,500.
194	A26	20c black	80.00	22.50
		Bar cancellation		3.50
195	A26	25c deep brown	27.50	6.00
		Bar cancellation		2.00
196	A26	40c brown vio	30.00	6.00
		Bar cancellation		2.00
197	A26	50c ultra	12.00	6.00
		Bar cancellation		2.00
198	A26	1p lilac	40.00	27.50
		Bar cancellation		2.00
199	A26	4p red brown	525.00	425.00
		Bar cancellation		12.50
200	A26	10p violet brn	1,750.	1,750.
		Bar cancellation		13.50

Only one example of No. 193a is known, and it is in a block of six stamps.

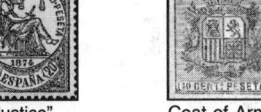

"Justice"
A27

Coat of Arms
A28

1874, July 1

201	A27	2c yellow	17.50	8.00
		Bar cancellation		2.00
202	A27	5c violet	27.50	9.50
		Bar cancellation		2.00
a.		5c red violet	27.50	9.50
203	A27	10c ultra	9.75	.35
a.		Imperf.	13.00	
204	A27	20c dark green	140.00	42.50
		Bar cancellation		3.75
205	A27	25c red brown	27.50	6.50
		Bar cancellation		2.00
a.		25c lilac (error)	300.00	
				27.50
b.		Imperf.		55.00
206	A27	40c violet	300.00	7.50
		Bar cancellation		2.00
a.		40c brown (error)	225.00	—
b.		Imperf.	175.00	
207	A27	50c yellow	87.50	7.00
		Bar cancellation		2.00
a.		Imperf.	110.00	
208	A27	1p yellow green	75.00	32.50
		Bar cancellation		2.00
a.		1p emerald	77.50	45.00
b.		Imperf.	140.00	
209	A27	4p rose	575.00	350.00
		Bar cancellation		7.50
a.		4p carmine	725.00	525.00
210	A27	10p black	2,500.	1,650.
		Bar cancellation		10.00

1874, Oct. 1

211	A28	10c red brown	22.50	.65
		Bar cancellation		1.50
a.		10c red brown	37.50	3.25
b.		Imperf.	82.50	

Kingdom

Nos. 212-221 are almost always badly centered and are often irregularly perforated. Values are for stamps with complete perforations and fine centering. Sound stamps with average centering are worth about 50% of these values. Stamps with very fine centering sell for more.

King Alfonso XII — A29

1875, Aug. 1
Blue Framed Numbers on Back, 1-100 on Each Sheet

212	A29	2c orange brown	22.50	11.00
a.		2c chocolate brown	30.00	15.00
b.		Imperf.	45.00	45.00
213	A29	5c lilac	77.50	13.00
a.		Imperf.	87.50	87.50
214	A29	10c blue	9.25	.40
		Bar cancellation		1.90
a.		Imperf.	22.50	22.50
215	A29	20c brown orange	300.00	140.00
216	A29	25c rose	65.00	8.00
		Bar cancellation		1.90
217	A29	40c deep brown	125.00	42.50
		Bar cancellation		4.50
a.		Imperf.	140.00	140.00
218	A29	50c gray lilac	190.00	42.50
		Bar cancellation		5.00
219	A29	1p black	190.00	90.00
		Bar cancellation		3.00
220	A29	4p dark green	525.00	525.00
221	A29	10p ultra	1,650.	1,750.

1876, June 1   Imperf.

221A	A21	¼c green	.25	.20
b.		Complete 1c (block 4 ¼c)	1.10	.30
c.		As "b," two ¼c sideways, one invtd.	110.00	110.00
d.		As "b," both upper ¼c invtd.	140.00	140.00
e.		As "b," upper left ¼c invtd.	1,000.	500.00
f.		As "b," both lower ¼c invtd.	140.00	140.00

No. 221Ac has one stamp upright, one inverted, one facing right and one facing left.

Nos. 222-230 are almost always badly centered. Values are for stamps with fine centering, fresh color and, in the case of mint stamps, full original gum. Sound stamps with average centering are worth about 50% of these values. Stamps with very fine centering sell for more.

King Alfonso XII
A30   A31

ONE PESETA:
Type I — Thin figures of value and "PESETA" in thick letters.
Type II — Thick figures of value and "PESETA" in thin letters.

Wmk. 178

1876, June 1   Engr.   Perf. 14

222	A30	5c yellow brown	14.00	3.75
223	A30	10c blue	3.75	.45
224	A30	20c bronze green	17.50	13.00
225	A30	25c brown	7.75	5.50
226	A30	40c black brown	75.00	100.00
227	A30	50c green	15.00	7.50
228	A30	1p dp blue, I	20.00	9.00
a.		1p ultra, II	27.50	13.00
229	A30	4p brown violet	47.50	55.00
230	A30	10p vermilion	125.00	125.00
		Nos. 222-230 (9)	325.50	319.20

Imperf

222a	A30	5c	11.00	
223a	A30	10c	5.50	
225a	A30	25c	12.00	
227a	A30	50c	17.00	
228b	A30	1p	25.00	
229a	A30	4p	87.50	
230a	A30	10p	190.00	

Two plates each were used for the 5c, 10c, 25c, 50c, 1p and 10p. The 1p plates are most easily distinguished.
The 20c value also exists imperf.

Unwmk.

1878, July 1   Typo.   Perf. 14

232	A31	2c mauve	32.50	11.00
a.		Imperf.	60.00	
233	A31	5c orange	45.00	14.00
234	A31	10c brown	7.75	.50
		Bar cancellation		2.50
235	A31	20c black	160.00	125.00
a.		Imperf.	275.00	
236	A31	25c olive bister	22.50	2.75
				4.75
237	A31	40c red brown	150.00	140.00
238	A31	50c blue green	87.50	11.00
				1.50
239	A31	1p gray	72.50	21.00
				1.50
240	A31	4p violet	190.00	125.00
241	A31	10p blue	375.00	350.00
a.		Imperf.	450.00	
		Nos. 232-241 (10)	1,142.	800.25

A32   A33

1879, May 1

242	A32	2c black	8.25	4.50
		Bar cancellation		3.00
243	A32	5c gray green	14.00	1.10
		Bar cancellation		2.50
244	A32	10c rose	13.00	.45
		Bar cancellation		1.50
245	A32	20c red brown	110.00	15.00
		Bar cancellation		2.00
246	A32	25c bluish gray	14.00	.45
		Bar cancellation		1.50
247	A32	40c brown	26.00	5.50
		Bar cancellation		2.00
248	A32	50c dull buff	100.00	5.00
		Bar cancellation		2.00
a.		50c yellow	190.00	7.00
249	A32	1p brt rose	125.00	2.25
		Bar cancellation		2.00
250	A32	4p lilac gray	600.00	32.50
		Bar cancellation		2.00
251	A32	10p olive bister	1,750.	190.00
		Bar cancellation		5.00

1882, Jan. 1

252	A33	15c salmon	7.75	.20
a.		15c reddish orange	27.50	.45
253	A33	30c red lilac	325.00	5.25
254	A33	75c gray lilac	225.00	4.75
a.		Imperf.	300.00	

Nos. 255-270 are usually poorly centered and often exhibit defective perforations. Values are for fine to very fine examples, well centered but not very fine, fresh and without perforation faults. Average copies sell for about half these values.

King Alfonso XIII
A34   A35

1889-99

255	A34	2c blue green	6.00	.45
256	A34	2c black ('99)	35.00	7.25
257	A34	5c blue	11.00	.20
258	A34	5c blue grn ('99)	125.00	1.40
259	A34	10c yellow brown	13.00	.20
260	A34	10c red ('99)	225.00	4.50
261	A34	15c violet brown	4.75	.20
262	A34	20c yellow green	45.00	4.75
263	A34	25c blue	17.50	.20
264	A34	30c olive gray	72.50	5.25
265	A34	40c brown	72.50	3.00
266	A34	50c rose	72.50	2.10
267	A34	75c orange	225.00	4.25
268	A34	1p dark violet	55.00	.45
a.		1p carmine rose (error)		350.00
269	A34	4p carmine rose	650.00	47.50
270	A34	10p orange red	1,050.	110.00

The 15c yellow, type A34 is an official stamp listed as No. O9.
Several values exist imperf.

Nos. 272-286 are almost always badly centered. Values are for stamps with fine centering, fresh color and, if unused, full original gum. Sound stamps with average centering sell for about half these values. Very fine copies sell for more.

Control Number on Back

1900-05		Engr.	Unwmk.
272	A35	2c bister brown	3.25	.20
273	A35	5c dark green	5.75	.20
274	A35	10c rose red	8.00	.20
275	A35	15c blue black	14.00	.20
276	A35	15c dull lilac ('02)	10.50	.20
277	A35	15c purple ('05)	5.75	.20
278	A35	20c grnsh black	32.50	2.75
279	A35	25c blue	5.25	.20
280	A35	30c deep green	32.50	.35
281	A35	40c olive bister	125.00	5.00
282	A35	40c rose ('05)	275.00	4.50
283	A35	50c slate blue	32.50	.55
284	A35	1p lake	30.00	.60
285	A35	4p dk violet	250.00	22.50
286	A35	10p brown orange	225.00	72.50
		Nos. 272-286 (15)	1,055.	110.15
		Set, never hinged	1,650.	

There are numerous shades and unissued colors for this issue.

Imperf

272a	A35	2c	57.50	
273a	A35	5c	25.00	
274a	A35	10c	25.00	
275a	A35	15c	110.00	
276a	A35	15c	22.50	
277a	A35	15c	17.00	
278a	A35	20c	90.00	
279a	A35	25c	17.00	
280b	A35	30c	110.00	
282a	A35	40c	275.00	
283a	A35	50c	125.00	
284a	A35	1p	57.50	
285a	A35	4p	225.00	
286a	A35	10p	190.00	

The 15c in red brown (value $700), 30c blue ($900), 1p olive ($800), 1p blue green ($750) and 1p dark violet ($750) were prepared but not issued.

Nos. 287-296 are almost always badly centered. Values are for stamps with fine centering, fresh color and, if unused, full original gum. Sound stamps with average centering sell for about half these values. Very fine copies sell for more.

Don
Quixote
Starts
Forth
A36

10c, Don Quixote attacks windmill. 15c, Meets country girls. 25c, Sancho Panza tossed in blanket. 30c, Don Quixote knighted. 40c, Tilting at sheep. 50c, On Wooden horse. 1p, Adventure with lions. 4p, In bullock cart, 10p, The Enchanted Lady.

Control Number on Back

1905, May 1				Typo.
287	A36	5c dark green	1.25	1.10
a.		Imperf.	55.00	
288	A36	10c orange red	2.25	1.75
289	A36	15c violet	2.25	1.75
a.		Imperf.	82.50	
290	A36	25c dark blue	5.75	3.25
291	A36	30c dk blue green	42.50	9.25
292	A36	40c bright rose	75.00	30.00
293	A36	50c slate	19.00	6.25
294	A36	1p rose red	250.00	80.00
295	A36	4p dk violet	110.00	80.00
296	A36	10p brown orange	160.00	125.00
		Nos. 287-296 (10)	668.00	338.35
		Set, never hinged	1,250.	

300th anniversary of the publication of Cervantes' "Don Quixote."
Counterfeits exist of Nos. 287-296.
For surcharges see Nos. 586-588, C91.

Six stamps picturing King Alfonso XIII and Queen Victoria Eugenia were put on sale Oct. 1, 1907, at the Madrid Industrial Exhibition. They were not valid for postage.

Alfonso
XIII — A46

A47

Blue Control Number on Back
Perf. 13x12½, 13, 13½x13, 14

1909-22				Engr.
297	A46	2c dark brown	.55	.55
a.		No control number	.55	.20
		Never hinged	1.00	
298	A46	5c green	1.25	.20
299	A46	10c carmine	1.75	.20
300	A46	15c violet	8.50	.20
301	A46	20c olive green	50.00	.90
302	A46	25c deep blue	4.75	.20
303	A46	30c blue green	8.50	.20
304	A46	40c rose	14.00	.65
305	A46	50c blue ('22)	11.50	.40
a.		50c slate blue	12.50	.40
		Never hinged	17.00	
306	A46	1p lake	30.00	.40
307	A46	4p deep violet	80.00	13.00
309	A46	10p orange	100.00	26.00
		Nos. 297-309 (12)	310.80	42.90
		Set, never hinged	600.00	

Nos. 297-309 exist imperforate. Value, unused $500.
The 5c exists in carmine; the 15c in blue (value $450); the 4p in lake (value $1,000). The 5c and 15c are unissued trial colors, privately perforated and back-numbered. The 4p lake is known only with perfin "B.H.A." (Banco Hispano-Americano). 100 copies of the 4p exist, most poorly centered.
See Nos. 310, 315-317. For overprints see Nos. C1-C5, C58-C61.
Counterfeits exist.

Control Number on Back in Red or Orange

1917				
310	A46	15c yellow ocher	3.50	.35
		Never hinged	6.00	
a.		Control number in blue	14.50	1.10

Control Number on Back in Blue

1918				
313	A46	40c light red	82.50	5.75
		Never hinged	150.00	

1920		Typo.	Imperf.
314	A47	1c blue green	.20	.20

Perf. 13x12½
Litho.

315	A46	2c bister	5.00	.20
316	A46	20c violet	42.50	.20
		Nos. 314-316 (3)	47.70	.60
		Set, never hinged	125.00	

Nos. 314-315 have no control number on back.
For overprints and surcharge see Nos. 358, 449, 457, 468, 10L1, 11LB1.

1921				Engr.
317	A46	20c violet	30.00	.20
		Never hinged	52.50	

Madrid Post Office — A48

1920, Oct. 1   Typo.   Perf. 13½
Center and Portrait in Black

| 318 | A48 | 1c blue green | .20 | .25 |
| 319 | A48 | 2c olive bister | .20 | .25 |

Control Number on Back

320	A48	5c green	.85	.90
321	A48	10c red	.85	.90
322	A48	15c yellow	1.40	1.10
323	A48	20c violet	1.60	1.50
324	A48	25c gray blue	2.25	2.50
325	A48	30c dark green	6.25	4.75
326	A48	40c rose	25.00	6.50
327	A48	50c brt blue	27.50	17.50
328	A48	1p brown red	27.50	14.50
329	A48	4p brown violet	85.00	60.00
330	A48	10p orange	175.00	125.00
		Nos. 318-330 (13)	353.60	235.65
		Set, never hinged	950.00	

Universal Postal Union Congress, Madrid, Oct. 10-Nov. 30.
Nos. 318-330 exist imperforate. Value, $2,500. stamps.

King Alfonso XIII
A49   A49a

FIFTEEN CENTIMOS:
Die I — Narrow "5."
Die II — Wide "5."

TWENTY FIVE CENTIMOS:
Die I — "25" is 2¾mm high. Vertical stroke of "5" is 1mm long.
Die II — "25" is 3mm high. Vertical stroke of "5" is 1½mm long.

Perf. 11 to 14, Compound

			1922-26	**Engr.**	**Unwmk.**
331	A49	2c olive green		.75	.20
a.		2c deep orange (error)		87.50	210.00
		Never hinged		110.00	

Control Number on Back

332	A49	5c red violet	3.50	.20
333	A49	5c claret	1.50	.20
334	A49	10c carmine	1.50	1.00
335	A49	10c yellow green	1.40	.20
a.		10c blue green ('23)	2.25	.20
		Never hinged	5.50	
336	A49	15c slate bl (I)	6.50	.20
a.		15c black green (II)	27.50	2.25
		Never hinged	50.00	
337	A49	20c violet	3.25	.20
338	A49	25c carmine (I)	3.25	.20
a.		25c rose red (II)	5.50	1.00
		Never hinged	11.00	
b.		25c lilac rose (error)	110.00	160.00
		Never hinged	190.00	
339	A49	30c black brn ('26)	12.00	.20
340	A49	40c deep blue	3.75	.20
341	A49	50c orange	16.00	.20
a.		50c orange red	77.50	1.90
		Never hinged	110.00	
342	A49a	1p blue black	15.00	.20
343	A49a	4p lake	70.00	3.50
344	A49a	10p brown	27.50	11.00
		Nos. 331-344 (14)	165.90	17.70
		Set, never hinged	350.00	

Nos. 331, 334, 336-344 exist imperf.
The 5c exists in vermilion (value $140); the 25c in dark blue (value $200). The 50c exists in red brown, the 4p in brown and 10p in lake; value, each $140. These five were not regularly issued.
For overprints see Nos. 359-370, 467.

"Santa Maria" and View of Seville A50

Herald of Barcelona — A51

Exposition Buildings — A52

King Alfonso XIII and View of Barcelona A53

1929, Feb. 15   Perf. 11

345	A50	1c grnsh blue	2.25	2.25
346	A51	2c pale yel grn	.25	.25
347	A52	5c rose lake	.45	.45

Control Number on Back

348	A53	10c green	.45	.45
349	A50	15c Prus blue	.75	.75
350	A51	20c purple	.50	.50
351	A50	25c brt rose	.50	.50
352	A52	30c black brn	3.75	4.25
353	A50	40c dark blue	7.00	7.25
354	A51	50c deep orange	3.75	4.25
355	A52	1p blue black	10.50	11.00
356	A53	4p deep rose	22.50	22.50
357	A53	10p brown	60.00	62.50
		Nos. 345-357,E2 (14)	130.15	136.90
		Set, never hinged	250.00	

Perf. 14

345a	A50	1c greenish blue	.70	.70
348a	A53	10c green	20.00	37.50
349a	A50	15c Prus blue	22.50	22.50
350a	A51	20c purple	26.00	37.50
351a	A50	25c bright rose	32.50	37.50
352a	A52	30c black brown	32.50	42.50
353a	A50	40c dark blue	70.00	90.00
354a	A51	50c deep orange	32.50	37.50
355a	A52	1p blue black	32.50	37.50
356a	A53	4p deep rose	25.00	25.00
357a	A53	10p brown	110.00	140.00
		Nos. 345a-357a,E2a (12)	433.20	535.70
		Set, never hinged	700.00	

Seville and Barcelona Exhibitions.
Nos. 345-357 exist imperf. Value $75 each. See note after No. 432.

Nos. 314, 331, 333, 335-344 Overprinted in Red or Blue

1929, June 10   Imperf.

| 358 | A47 | 1c blue green | .50 | .80 |

Perf. 13½x12½

359	A49	2c olive green	.50	.90
360	A49	5c claret (Bl)	.50	.90
361	A49	10c yellow green	.50	.90
362	A49	15c slate blue	.50	.90
363	A49	20c violet	.50	.90
364	A49	25c carmine (Bl)	.50	.90
365	A49	30c black brown	2.10	3.50
366	A49	40c deep blue	2.10	3.50
367	A49	50c orange (Bl)	2.10	3.50
368	A49a	1p blue black	10.00	17.50
369	A49a	4p lake (Bl)	10.00	19.00
370	A49a	10p brown (Bl)	35.00	65.00
		Nos. 358-370,E4 (14)	76.80	143.20
		Set, never hinged	150.00	

55th assembly of League of Nations at Madrid June 10-16. The stamps were available for postal use only on those days.
Nos. 359-370 values are for off-center copies. Well-centered stamps sell for about 4 times these values.

Exposition Building — A54

1930   Litho.   Perf. 11

371	A54	5c dk blue & salmon	5.50	5.00
372	A54	5c dk violet & blue	5.50	5.00
		Set, never hinged	19.00	

Barcelona Philatelic Congress and Exhibition. "C. F. y E. F." are the initials of "Congreso Filatelico y Exposicion Filatelica." For each admission ticket, costing 2.75 pesetas, the holder was allowed to buy one of each of these stamps.

A55

Locomotives A56

1930, May 10   Perf. 14

| 373 | A55 | 1c light blue | .50 | .60 |
| 374 | A55 | 2c apple green | .50 | .60 |

Control Number on Back

375	A55	5c lake	.50	.60
376	A55	10c yellow green	.50	.60
377	A55	15c bluish gray	.50	.60
378	A55	20c purple	.50	.60
379	A55	25c brt rose	.50	.60
380	A55	30c olive gray	1.60	1.40
381	A55	40c dark blue	1.60	1.50
382	A55	50c dk orange	3.50	4.50
383	A56	1p dark gray	4.25	5.00
384	A56	4p deep rose	77.50	60.00
385	A56	10p bister brn	300.00	300.00
		Nos. 373-385,C12-C17,E6 (20)	518.20	502.85
		Set, never hinged	1,100.	

11th Intl. Railway Congress, Madrid, 1930.
These stamps were on sale May 10-21, 1930, exclusively at the Palace of the Senate in Madrid and at the Barcelona and Seville expositions.

Francisco de Goya at Age 80
("1746 1828")   ("1828 1928")
A57   A59

"La Maja Desnuda" — A58

1930, June 15   Litho.   Perf. 12½
Inscribed "Correos Espana"

386	A57	1c yellow	.20	.20
387	A57	2c bister brn	.20	.20
388	A57	5c lilac rose	.20	.20
389	A57	10c green	.20	.20

Engr.

390	A57	15c lt blue	.20	.20
391	A57	20c brown violet	.20	.20
392	A57	25c red	.20	.20
393	A57	30c brown	4.25	4.25
394	A57	40c dark blue	4.25	4.25
395	A57	50c vermilion	4.25	4.25
396	A57	1p black	5.25	5.25
397	A58	1p dark violet	.75	.65
398	A58	4p slate gray	.55	.50
399	A58	10p red brown	10.50	8.00

Inscribed "1828 Goya 1928"
Litho.

| 400 | A59 | 2c olive green | .20 | .20 |
| 401 | A59 | 5c gray violet | .20 | .20 |

Engr.

402	A59	25c rose carmine	.25	.25
		Nos. 386-402,C18-C30,CE1,E7 (32)	46.60	44.05
		Set, never hinged	60.00	

To commemorate the death of Francisco de Goya y Lucientes, painter and engraver.
Nos. 386-399 were issued in connection with the Spanish-American Exposition at Seville.
Nos. 386-402 exist imperf. Values about 6 times those of perf. stamps.
See note after No. 432.

King Alfonso XIII — A61

Two types of the 40c:

Type I   Type II

1930   Perf. 11½, 12x11½

| 406 | A61 | 2c red brown | .20 | .20 |

Control Number on Back

407	A61	5c black brown	.65	.20
408	A61	10c green	3.00	.20
409	A61	15c slate green	10.00	.20
410	A61	20c dark violet	5.50	.20
411	A61	25c carmine	.65	.20
412	A61	30c brown lake	14.00	1.60
413	A61	40c dk blue (I)	19.00	1.00
a.		Type II	25.00	1.00
		Never hinged	45.00	
414	A61	50c orange	17.50	1.75
		Nos. 406-414 (9)	70.50	6.00
		Set, never hinged	190.00	

#406-414 exist imperf. Value for set, $350.
For overprints see #450-455, 458-466, 469-487.

Bow of "Santa Maria" — A63

Stern of "Santa Maria" — A64

"Santa Maria," "Niña," "Pinta" — A65

Columbus Leaving Palos — A66

Columbus Arriving in America — A67

1930, Sept. 29   Litho.   Perf. 12½

418	A63	1c olive gray	.20	.20
419	A64	2c olive green	.20	.20
420	A63	2c olive green	.20	.20
421	A63	5c red brown	.20	.20
422	A63	5c red brown	.20	.20
423	A64	10c blue green	.85	.70
424	A63	15c ultra	.85	.90
425	A64	20c violet	1.25	1.10

Engr.

426	A65	25c dark red	1.25	1.10
427	A66	30c bis brn, bl & blk brn	6.00	5.25
428	A65	40c ultra	5.50	5.75
429	A66	50c dk vio, bl & vio brn	7.75	5.75
430	A65	1p black	7.75	5.75
431	A67	4p blk & dk blue	8.75	6.50
432	A67	10p red brn & dk brn	35.00	32.50
		Nos. 418-432,E8 (16)	77.70	68.05
		Set, never hinged	140.00	

Christopher Columbus tribute.
Nos. 418 to 432 were privately produced. Their promoters presented a certain quantity of these labels to the Spanish Postal Authorities, who placed them on sale and allowed them to be used for three days, retaining the money obtained from the sale.
This note will also apply to Nos. 345-357, 386-402, 433-448, 557-571, B1-B105, C18-C57, C73-C87, CB1-CB5, CE1, E2, E7-E9, E15 and EB1.
Many so-called "errors" of color and perforation are known.
Nos. 418-432 exist imperf. Values about 5 times those of perf. stamps.
See Nos. 2671, B194.

Arms of Spain, Bolivia, Paraguay A68

Pavilion and Map of Central America — A69

Exhibition Pavilion of Ecuador — A70

Colombia Pavilion — A71

Dominican Republic Pavilion A72

Uruguay Pavilion A73

Argentina Pavilion A74

Chile Pavilion A75

Brazil Pavilion A76

Mexico Pavilion A77

Cuba Pavilion A78

Peru Pavilion A79

U.S. Pavilion A80

Exhibition Pavilion of Portugal — A81

King Alfonso XIII and Queen Victoria — A82

Unwmk.

1930, Oct. 10   Photo.   Perf. 14

433	A68	1c blue green	.20	.20
434	A69	2c bister brown	.20	.20
435	A70	5c olive brown	.20	.20
436	A71	10c dark green	.30	.30
437	A72	15c indigo	.30	.30
438	A73	20c violet	.30	.30
439	A74	25c car rose	.30	.30
440	A75	25c car rose	.30	.30
441	A76	30c rose lilac	1.50	1.50
442	A77	40c slate blue	.90	.90
443	A78	40c slate blue	.90	.90
444	A79	50c brown org	1.50	1.50
445	A80	1p ultra	2.25	2.25
446	A81	4p brown violet	30.00	27.50
447	A82	10p brown	2.10	2.10

Perf. 11, 14

Engr.

448	A82	10p orange brown	42.50	42.50
		Nos. 433-448,C50-C57,E9 (25)	100.90	94.05
		Set, never hinged	350.00	

Spanish-American Union Exhibition, Seville.
The note after No. 432 will also apply to Nos. 433-448. All values exist imperforate. Value $325.
Reprints of Nos. 433-448 have blurred colors, yellowish paper and an inferior, almost invisible gum. They sell for about $1 per set.

Revolutionary Issues
Madrid Issue

Regular Issues of 1920-30 Overprinted in Black, Green or Red

On No. 314

1931   Imperf.

449	A47	1c blue green	.20	.20

On Nos. 406-411
Perf. 11½

450	A61	2c red brown (G)	.30	.25
451	A61	5c black brn (R)	.40	.40
452	A61	10c green	.70	.70
453	A61	15c slate grn (R)	1.40	1.50
454	A61	20c dk violet (R)	1.40	1.50
455	A61	25c carmine (G)	1.90	2.25
		Nos. 449-455,E10 (8)	10.80	11.30
		Set, never hinged	19.00	

The status of Nos. 449-455, E10 has been questioned.

First Barcelona Issue

Regular Issues of 1920-30 Overprinted in Black or Red

On No. 314

1931   Imperf.

457	A47	1c blue green	.20	.20

On Nos. 406-414
Perf. 11½

458	A61	2c red brown	.20	.20
459	A61	5c black brown	.20	.20
460	A61	10c green	.55	.55
461	A61	15c slate grn (R)	.60	.60
462	A61	20c dk violet (R)	.60	.60
463	A61	25c carmine	.60	.60
464	A61	30c brown lake	4.50	4.50
465	A61	40c dk blue (R)	1.25	1.25
466	A61	50c orange	1.25	1.25

On Stamp of 1922-26

467	A49a	1p blue blk (R)	7.50	6.25
		Nos. 457-467,E11 (12)	22.45	21.20
		Set, never hinged	45.00	

Nos. 457-467 are known both with and without accent over "U."
The status of Nos. 457-467, E11 has been questioned.

Second Barcelona Issue

Regular Issues of 1920-30 Overprinted in Black or Red

On No. 314
Imperf

468	A47	1c blue green	.20	.20

On Nos. 406-414
Perf. 11½

469	A61	2c red brown	.20	.20
470	A61	5c black brown (R)	.20	.20
471	A61	10c green	.20	.20
472	A61	15c slate grn (R)	1.40	1.25
473	A61	20c dark violet (R)	.40	.45
474	A61	25c carmine	.40	.45
475	A61	30c brown lake	5.75	5.75
476	A61	40c dark blue (R)	1.25	1.25
477	A61	50c orange	4.50	3.50
		Nos. 468-477 (10)	14.50	13.45
		Set, never hinged	27.50	

The status of Nos. 469-477, C58-C61 has been questioned.

General Issue of the Republic
Nos. 406-414, 342 Overprinted in Blue or Red

1931, May 27

478	A61	2c red brown	.20	.20
479	A61	5c black brn (R)	.20	.20
480	A61	10c green (R)	.25	.20
481	A61	15c slate grn (R)	2.75	.20
482	A61	20c dk violet (R)	1.25	.75
483	A61	25c carmine	.40	.20
484	A61	30c brown lake	3.50	.75
485	A61	40c dk blue (R)	3.50	.45
486	A61	50c orange	6.00	.45
487	A49a	1p blue blk (R)	45.00	.75
		Nos. 478-487,E12 (11)	68.55	5.15
		Set, never hinged	150.00	

The setting contained 18 repetitions of "Republica Espanola" for each vertical row of 10 stamps. According to its sheet position, a stamp received different parts of the overprinted words.
Overprint position varieties include: reading down on 25c, 30c, 40c and 50c; double on 1p; double, both reading down, on 25c, 40c and 50c.

"Republica Espanola"
Stamps of various Spanish colonies overprinted "Republica Espanola" are listed with the colonies.

Fountain of Lions, The Alhambra, Granada A84

Interior of Mosque, Córdoba — A85

Alcántara Bridge and Alcazar, Toledo A86

Francisco García y Santos A87

Puerta del Sol, Madrid, on April 14, 1931 as Republic Was Proclaimed A88

Perf. 12½

1931, Oct. 10   Unwmk.   Engr.

491	A84	5c violet brown	.20	.25
492	A85	10c blue green	.30	.30
493	A86	15c dark violet	.30	.30
494	A85	25c deep red	.30	.30
495	A87	30c olive green	.30	.30
496	A84	40c indigo	1.00	1.00
497	A85	50c orange red	1.00	1.00
498	A86	1p black	1.90	2.10
499	A88	4p red violet	9.50	8.75
500	A88	10p red brown	30.00	30.00

Nos. 491-500,C62-C67,CO1-CO6 (22)   58.40 60.45
Set, never hinged   140.00

3rd Pan-American Postal Union Cong., Madrid.
Nos. 491-500 exist imperforate. Values about 5 times those of perforated stamps.
For overprints see Nos. O20-O29.

Symbolical of Montserrat Cut With a Saw — A89

Abbott Oliva and Monastery Workman — A90

"Black Virgin"
A91   A92

Montserrat Monastery — A93

1931, Dec. 9   Perf. 11, 14

501	A89	1c myrtle green	1.10	1.40
a.		Perf. 14	19.00	19.00
		Never hinged	37.50	

Control Number on Back

503	A89	5c black brown	.75	1.25
a.		Perf. 14	14.00	15.00
		Never hinged	27.50	
504	A89	10c yellow green	.85	1.25
a.		Perf. 14	14.00	17.00
		Never hinged	27.50	
505	A90	15c myrtle green	1.10	1.60
a.		Perf. 14	19.00	22.50
		Never hinged	37.50	
506	A91	20c dark violet	2.25	2.25
a.		Perf. 11	100.00	140.00
		Never hinged	190.00	
507	A92	25c lake	3.25	3.25
a.		Perf. 14	5.75	6.50
		Never hinged	11.50	
508	A91	30c deep red	35.00	32.50
a.		Perf. 14	37.50	37.50
		Never hinged	77.50	
509	A93	40c dull blue	20.00	17.50
a.		Perf. 11	140.00	160.00
		Never hinged	275.00	
510	A90	50c dark orange	45.00	42.50
a.		Perf. 14	62.50	72.50
		Never hinged	125.00	
511	A92	1p gray black	45.00	42.50
a.		Perf. 11	80.00	100.00
		Never hinged	160.00	
512	A93	4p lilac rose	450.00	450.00
a.		Perf. 14	475.00	825.00
		Never hinged	875.00	
513	A92	10p deep brown	350.00	300.00
a.		Perf. 14	725.00	875.00
		Never hinged	1,400.	

Nos. 501-511,C68-C72,E13 (17)   244.20 236.25
Set, never hinged   375.00
Nos. 501-513,C68-C72,E13 (19)   1,044. 986.25
Set, never hinged   1,900.

Commemorative of the building of the old Monastery at Montserrat, started in 1031, and of the image of the Black Virgin (said to have been carved by St. Luke) which was crowned by Pope Leo XIII in 1881.
Nos. 501-513 exist imperforate. Values about 3 times those of perforated stamps.
For surcharges see Nos. 589, C92-C96.

Francisco Pi y Margall — A95

Joaquín Costa — A96

Nicolás Salmerón A97

Pablo Iglesias A99

Emilio Castelar — A100

1931-32   Perf. 11½
Control Number on Back

516	A95	5c brnsh black	3.00	.30
517	A96	10c yellow green	7.25	.30
518	A97	15c slate green	4.75	.20
520	A99	25c lake	22.50	.70
b.		Imperf.	175.00	
		Never hinged	225.00	
521	A99	30c carmine rose	7.25	.20
c.		Imperf.	82.50	
		Never hinged	125.00	
522	A100	40c dark blue	42.50	4.50
523	A97	50c orange	52.50	7.75

Nos. 516-523 (7)   139.75 13.95
Set, never hinged   350.00

Without Control Number

516a	A95	5c brownish blk ('32)	4.50	.20
517a	A96	10c yel grn ('32)	4.00	.20
518a	A97	15c slate green ('32)	.60	.20
520a	A99	25c lake	32.50	.20
521a	A99	30c carmine rose	1.90	.20
522a	A100	40c dark blue ('32)	.20	.20
523a	A97	50c orange ('32)	26.00	.50

Nos. 516a-523a (7)   69.70 1.70
Set, never hinged   150.00

Without Control Number, Imperf.

516b	A95	5c	6.50	
517b	A96	10c	11.00	
518b	A97	15c	6.25	
520c	A99	25c	110.00	
521b	A99	30c	5.50	
522b	A100	40c	14.00	
523b	A97	50c	125.00	

Nos. 516b-523b (7)   278.25
Set, never hinged   550.00

See Nos. 532, 538, 550, 579, 579a.
For overprints and surcharges see Nos. 7LC12-7LC13, 7LC15-7LC16, 7LC18, 7LE4, 8LB6, 8LB9-8LB10, 9LC17-9LC18, 10L7, 10L10-10L12, 10L16-10L18, 10L22-10L23, 11L7, 11L10-11L12, 11LB8, 12L4, 12L8, 12L11-12L12, 13L8, 14L6, 14L10-14L12, 14L18, 14L22-14L24.

Blasco Ibáñez A103

Manuel Ruiz-Zorrilla A104

Without Control Number

1931-34   Perf. 11½

526	A103	2c red brown ('32)	.20	.20
528	A103	5c chocolate ('34)	.20	.20
532	A95	20c dark violet	.25	.20
534	A104	25c lake ('34)	.45	.20
538	A100	60c apple green ('32)	.20	.20

Nos. 526-538 (5)   1.30 1.00
Set, never hinged   2.50

Imperf

526a	A103	2c	14.00
528a	A103	5c	2.75
532a	A95	20c	6.25
534a	A104	25c	5.25
538a	A100	60c	6.25

Nos. 526a-538a (5)   34.50
Set, never hinged   70.00

For overprints and surcharges see Nos. 8LB3, 8LB7, 9LC3, 9LC8-9LC9, 9LC14, 10L6, 10L13, 11L4, 11L8, 11LB5, 11LB9, 12L5, 12L9, 13L5, 13L7, 14L3, 14L7, 14L15, 14L19.

Cliff Houses, Cuenca — A105

Alcázar of Segovia — A106

Gate of the Sun at Toledo — A107

1932-38   Perf. 10

539	A105	1p gray black ('38)	.20	.20
540	A106	4p magenta ('38)	.30	.40
541	A107	10p deep brn ('38)	.65	.70

Nos. 539-541 (3)   1.15 1.30
Set, never hinged   2.75

Imperf

539a	A105	1p	5.25	2.75
540a	A106	4p	9.00	6.50
541a	A107	10p	6.50	6.00

Nos. 539a-541a (3)   20.75 15.25
Set, never hinged   45.00

Perf. 11½

539b	A105	1p	.20	.20
540b	A106	4p	.70	.85
541b	A107	10p	1.90	3.00

Nos. 539b-541b (3)   2.80 4.05
Set, never hinged   5.00

For overprints and surcharge see Nos. 9LC19, 10L19, 13L9, 14L25, 14L27-14L28.

Numeral A108

Santiago Ramón y Cajal A109

1933   Unwmk.   Typo.   Imperf.

542	A108	1c blue green	.20	.20

Perf. 11½

543	A108	2c buff	.20	.20
a.		Perf. 13½x13	.65	.20
		Never hinged	1.40	
Set, never hinged			.65	

See Nos. 592-597. For surcharges and overprints see Nos. 590-590A, 634A-634D, 8LB1-8LB2, 9LC1-9LC2, 9LC4-9LC7, 9LC11-9LC12, 9LC20, 9LC26, 10L2-10L4, 11L1-11L2, 11LB2-11LB3, 12L1-12L2, 13L1-13L3, 14L1, 14L13.

1934   Engr.   Perf. 11½x11

545	A109	30c black brown	6.00	1.10
		Never hinged	14.00	
a.		Perf. 14	22.50	30.00
		Never hinged	42.50	
b.		Imperf.	32.50	
		Never hinged	55.00	

Type of 1931 and

Mariana Pineda A110

Concepción Arenal A111

Gumersindo de Azcarate A112

Gaspar Melchor de Jovellanos A113

1935

546	A110	10c green	.20	.20
547	A111	15c green	.20	.20
548	A112	30c carmine rose	7.25	.20
549	A113	30c rose red	.20	.20
550	A97	50c dark blue	1.00	.30

Nos. 546-550 (5)   8.85 1.10
Set, never hinged   20.00

Imperf

546a	A110	10c	1.60
547a	A111	15c	5.25
548a	A112	30c	26.00

549a	A113	30c		1.90
550a	A97	50c		225.00

Nos. 546a-550a (5) 259.75
Set, never hinged 500.00

Shades exist.
For overprints and surcharges see Nos. 7LE3, 8LB4-8LB5, 8LB8, 10L8-10L9, 10L14, 10L20-10L21, 11L5-11L6, 11L9, 11LB6-11LB7, 11LB10, 12L6-12L7, 12L10, 13L6, 14L4-14L5, 14L8, 14L16-14L17, 14L20.

Lope's Bookplate A116

Lope de Vega A117

Alcántara and Alcázar, Toledo A118

1935, Oct. 12   Perf. 11½x11, 11x11½

552	A116	15c myrtle green	5.75	.30
553	A117	30c rose red	2.50	.30
554	A117	50c dark blue	11.00	2.50
555	A118	1p blue black	21.00	1.60

Nos. 552-555 (4) 40.25 4.70
Set, never hinged 80.00

Imperf

552a	A116	15c	350.00
553a	A117	30c	9.00
554a	A117	50c	55.00
555a	A118	1p	45.00

Nos. 552a-555a (4) 459.00
Set, never hinged 850.00

Perf. 14

553b	A117	30c	6.50	14.50
554b	A117	50c	29.00	45.00
555b	A118	1p	32.50	50.00

Nos. 553b-555b (3) 68.00 109.50
Set, never hinged 150.00

Lope Felix de Vega Carpio (1562-1635), Spanish dramatist and poet.
For surcharge see No. 11LB11.

Map of Amazon by Bartolomeo Oliva, 16th Century A119

1935, Oct. 12   Perf. 11½

556	A119	30c rose red	1.90	.95
		Never hinged	3.75	
a.		Perf. 14	22.50	
		Never hinged	45.00	
b.		Imperf.	32.50	
		Never hinged	60.00	

Proposed Iglesias Amazon Expedition.

Miguel Moya — A120

Torcuato Luca de Tena — A121

José Francos Rodríguez A122

Alejandro Lerroux A123

Nazareth School and Rotary Press — A124

1936, Feb. 14   Photo.   Perf. 12½
Size: 22x26mm

557	A120	1c crimson	.20	.20
558	A121	2c orange brown	.20	.20
559	A122	5c black brown	.20	.20
560	A123	10c emerald	.20	.20

Size: 24x28½mm

561	A120	15c blue green	.20	.20
562	A121	20c violet	.20	.20
563	A122	25c red violet	.20	.20
564	A123	30c crimson	.20	.20

Size: 25½x30½mm

565	A120	40c orange	.50	.40
566	A121	50c yellow	.20	.20
567	A122	60c olive green	.50	.40
568	A123	1p gray black	.50	.40
569	A124	2p lt blue	6.50	3.25
570	A124	4p lilac rose	6.50	6.50
571	A124	10p red brown	17.00	15.00

Nos. 557-571,E15 (16) 33.55 28.05
Set, never hinged 47.50
Nos. 557-571,C73-C87,E15 (31) 61.25 46.90
Set, never hinged 90.00

Madrid Press Association, 40th anniversary.
Nos. 557-571 exist imperf. Values about 7 times those of perf. stamps.
See note after No. 432. See Nos. C73-C87.

Arms of Madrid — A125

1936, Apr. 2   Engr.   Imperf.

572	A125	10c brown black	42.50	42.50
573	A125	15c dark green	42.50	42.50

Set, never hinged 110.00

1st National Philatelic Exhibition which opened in Madrid, Apr. 2, 1936.
For overprints see Nos. C88-C89.

"Republica Espanola" A126

Gregorio Fernández A127

1936   Litho.   Perf. 11½, 13½x13

574	A126	2c orange brown	.20	.20
		Never hinged		.30

For surcharges & overprints see #591, 9LC24, 10L5, 11L3, 11LB4, 12L3, 13L4, 14L2, 14L14.

1936, Mar. 10   Engr.   Perf. 11½

576	A127	30c carmine	1.10	.85
		Never hinged	2.00	
a.		Perf. 14	9.00	8.25
		Never hinged	17.50	
b.		Imperf.	14.00	
		Never hinged	22.50	

Tercentenary of the death of Gregorio Fernandez, sculptor.
For overprints see Nos. 7LC20-7LC21.

Type of 1931 and

Pablo Iglesias
A128   A129

Velázquez A130

Fermín Salvoechea A131

1936-38   Perf. 11, 11½, 11½x11

577	A128	30c rose red	.20	.20
578	A129	30c car rose	1.10	.50
579	A100	40c car rose ('37)	1.10	.50
580	A129	45c carmine ('37)	.20	.20
581	A130	50c dark blue	.20	.20
582	A131	60c indigo ('37)	.75	.90
583	A131	60c dp orange ('38)	6.00	5.00

Nos. 577-583 (7) 9.55 7.50
Set, never hinged 24.00

Perf. 14

577a	A128	30c rose red		6.50
578a	A129	30c carmine rose		6.75
579a	A100	40c carmine rose		6.50
580a	A129	45c carmine		6.00
582a	A131	60c indigo		6.00
583a	A131	60c deep orange		9.50

Nos. 577a-583a (6) 41.25
Set, never hinged 82.50

Nos. 577-583 exist imperf. Value, set $70.
Set, never hinged, $140.
For overprints see Nos. C90, 7LC17, 7LC22-7LC23, 10L15, 14L21.

Statue of Liberty, Spanish and US Flags — A132

1938, June 1   Photo.   Perf. 11½

585	A132	1p multicolored	15.00	14.50
		Never hinged	26.00	
a.		Imperf., pair	75.00	50.00
		Never hinged	100.00	
b.		Horiz. pair, imperf. vert.	57.50	75.00
		Never hinged	85.00	
c.		Souvenir sheet of 1	25.00	30.00
		Never hinged	40.00	
d.		As "c," imperf.	250.00	225.00
		Never hinged	400.00	

150th anniv. of the U.S. Constitution.
For surcharge see No. C97.

No. 289 Surcharged in Black

1938   Perf. 14

586	A36	45c on 15c violet	14.00	14.00
		Never hinged	17.50	

7th anniversary of the Republic.
Values are for examples with perforations nearly touching the design on one or two sides.

No. 289 Surcharged in Black:

a

b

1938, May 1

587	A36	45c on 15c violet	3.00	3.00
588	A36	1p on 15c violet	5.25	5.25

Set, never hinged 11.00

Issued to commemorate Labor Day.
Values are for examples with perforations nearly touching the design on one or two sides.

No. 507 Surcharged in Black

1938, Nov. 10   Perf. 11½

589	A92	2.50p on 25c lake	.20	.20
		Never hinged	.20	
b.		Perf. 14	3.50	6.00
		Never hinged	6.00	

Types of 1933-36 Surcharged in Blue or Red

1938   Perf. 10, 11, 13½x13, 13x14

590	A108	45c on 1c grn (R)	.40	.25
b.		Imperf.	6.00	5.00
		Never hinged	10.00	
590A	A108	45c on 2c buff (Bl)	17.00	14.00
591	A126	45c on 2c org brn (Bl)	.20	.20
		Never hinged	.20	

Nos. 590-591 (3) 17.60 14.45
Set, never hinged 29.00

Numeral Type of 1933

1938-39   Litho.   Perf. 11½, 13
White or Gray Paper

592	A108	5c gray brown	.20	.20
593	A108	10c yellow green	.20	.20
594	A108	15c slate green	.20	.20
595	A108	20c vio, gray paper	.20	.20
596	A108	25c red violet	.20	.20
597	A108	30c scarlet	.20	.20

Nos. 592-597 (6) 1.20 1.20
Set, never hinged 1.40

"Republic" — A133

1938   Perf. 11½

598	A133	40c rose red	.20	.20
599	A133	45c car rose	.20	.20
a.		Printed on both sides	11.00	11.00
		Never hinged	27.50	
600	A133	50c ultra	.20	.20
601	A133	60c dp ultra	.50	.30

Nos. 598-601 (4) 1.10 .90
Set, never hinged 1.10

Nos. 598-601 exist imperf. Value for set $22.50.

Machine Gunners A134

Imprint: "Fournier Vitoria"
Perf. 10

658	A163	15c deep green	1.25 .20
659	A163	20c purple	8.25 1.25
660	A163	25c brown car	.60 .20
661	A163	30c deep red	3.75 .20
	Nos. 656-661 (6)		18.85 2.25
	Set, never hinged		55.00

Nos. 656-661 exist imperf.; value for set, $150 hinged, $225 never hinged. Part-perf. varieties exist.
For overprints see Nos. C98-C99.

Without Imprint
1938-50 **Perf. 11, 13½x13¼**

Two types of the 15 Centimos:
Type I — Medieval style numerals with diagonal line through "5."
Type II — Modern numerals. Narrower "5" without diagonal line.

662	A159	1c green, imperf.	.20 .20
663	A160	2c brn (18½x22mm; '40)	.20 .20
a.		2c bis brn (17½x21mm; '48)	.20
		Never hinged	.20
664	A161	5c gray brn ('39)	.20 .20
a.		Perf 13½x13¼ ('49)	.20
665	A161	10c dk carmine	.25 .20
a.		10c rose	.35 .20
		Never hinged	.75
b.		Perf 13½x13¼ ('49)	.20 .20
666	A161	15c dk green (I)	.90 .20
666A	A161	15c dk green (II)	.60 .20
	b.	Perf 13½x13¼ ('50)	.65 .20
		Never hinged	1.25
667	A162	70c dk blue ('39)	.75 .20
	Nos. 662-667 (7)		3.10 1.40
	Set, never hinged		4.25

1938, July 17 **Perf. 10**

668	A164	15c bl grn & lt grn	3.75 3.75
669	A164	25c rose red & rose	3.75 3.75
670	A164	30c bl & lt bl	2.10 2.50
671	A164	1p brown & yellow	82.50 80.00
	Nos. 668-671 (4)		92.10 90.00
	Set, never hinged		160.00

Second anniversary of the Civil War.
Nos. 678-681 exist imperforate. Value, set $725 hinged, $950 never hinged .

Isabella I
A165

Gen. Francisco Franco
A166

1938-39 **Litho.** **Perf. 10**

672	A165	20c brt violet ('39)	.50 .20
673	A165	25c brown carmine	5.25 .60
674	A165	30c rose red	.20 .20
675	A165	40c dull violet	.25 .20
676	A165	50c indigo ('39)	22.50 2.50
677	A165	1p deep blue	7.50 .90
	Nos. 672-677 (6)		36.20 4.60
	Set, never hinged		87.50

Nos. 672-677 exist imperforate. Value set, $225 hinged, $300 never hinged.

Imprint: "Sanchez Toda"
1939-40 **Perf. 10**

678	A166	20c brt violet	.30 .20
679	A166	25c rose lake	.30 .20
680	A166	30c rose carmine	.25 .20
681	A166	40c slate green	.20 .20
682	A166	45c vermilion ('40)	1.75 1.60
683	A166	50c indigo	.25 .20
684	A166	60c orange	2.75 2.50
685	A166	70c blue	.35 .20
686	A166	1p black	11.00 .20
687	A166	2p dark brown	16.00 1.10
688	A166	4p dark violet	87.50 16.00
689	A166	10p light brown	45.00 40.00
	Nos. 678-689 (12)		165.65 62.60
	Set, never hinged		240.00

#686-689 have value & "Pta." on 1 line while #702-705 have value & "Pta." on 2 lines.
Nos. 678-689 exist imperforate. Value set, $525 hinged, $650 never hinged.

Without Imprint
Perf. 9½x10¼

1939-47 **Litho.** **Unwmk.**

690	A166	5c dull brn vio	.40 .20
691	A166	10c brown orange	1.75 .60
692	A166	15c lt green	.45 .20
693	A166	20c brt violet ('40)	.40 .20
694	A166	25c dp claret ('40)	.40 .20
695	A166	30c blue ('40)	.40 .20

697	A166	40c Prus grn ('40)	.40 .20
a.		40c greenish black	.55 .20
		Never hinged	.65
698	A166	45c ultra ('41)	.45 .20
699	A166	50c indigo ('40)	.40 .20
a.		Perf. 11½ ('47)	30.00 3.00
		Never hinged	50.00
700	A166	60c dull org ('40)	.55 .20
701	A166	70c blue ('40)	.65 .20
702	A166	1p gray blk ('40)	5.50 .20
703	A166	2p dull brn ('41)	6.75 .20
704	A166	4p dull rose ('40)	25.00 .20
705	A166	10p lt brown ('40)	125.00 2.50
	Nos. 690-705 (15)		168.50 5.70
	Set, never hinged		275.00

Perf. 13x13¼

1949-53 **Litho.** **Unwmk.**

693a	A166	20c brt violet	.20 .20
694a	A166	25c dp claret	.20 .20
695a	A166	30c blue	.20 .20
696	A166	35c aqua ('51)	.20 .20
697b	A166	40c Prus grn ('50)	.20 .20
698a	A166	45c ultra ('52)	.20 .20
699b	A166	50c indigo	.20 .20
700a	A166	60c dull org	.20 .20
701a	A166	70c blue ('53)	13.00 .20
702a	A166	1p gray blk ('51)	8.25 .20
703a	A166	2p dull brn ('50)	3.25 .20
704a	A166	4p dull rose	5.00 .20
705a	A166	10p lt brown ('53)	1.10 .30
	Nos. 693a-705a (13)		31.95 2.70
	Set, never hinged		72.50

The 40c exists in three types, with variations in the value tablet: I. "CTS" does not touch bottom line. II. Light background in tablet. "CTS" touches bottom line. III. As type I, but with well defined lines of white and color around rectangle.
The 60c exists in two types: I. Top and left side of value tablet touch rest of design. II. Tablet separated from rest of design by white lines.
Five values exist with perf. 10: 5c, 10c, 45c, 4p and 10p.
The imperforate 10c dull claret, type A166, without imprint, is a postal tax stamp, RA14.

1944 **Redrawn**

706	A166	1p gray	45.00 .65
		Never hinged	90.00

"PTS" instead of "PTA" as No. 702.
Nos. 690-704 and 706 exist imperforate. Value, set $925.

The value reads "PTAS" instead of "PTS"

1944 **Unwmk.** **Perf. 9½x10½, 13**

709	A166	10p brown	12.00 .30
		Never hinged	17.50

General Franco — A167

St. John of the Cross — A168

1942-48 **Engr.** **Perf. 12½x13**

712	A167	40c chestnut	.40 .20
713	A167	75c dk bl, perf. 9½x10½ ('46)	3.50 .40
714	A167	90c dk green ('48)	.30 .20
a.		Perf. 9½x10½ ('47)	1.40 .20
715	A167	1.35p purple ('48)	.90 .20
a.		Perf. 9½x10½ ('46)	2.00 .40
	Nos. 712-715 (4)		5.10 1.00
	Set, never hinged		8.00

1942 **Litho.** **Perf. 9½x10½**

721	A168	20c violet	.50 .20
722	A168	40c salmon	1.10 .60
723	A168	75c ultra	1.40 1.75
	Nos. 721-723 (3)		3.00 2.55
	Set, never hinged		4.25

St. John of the Cross (1542-1591).
Nos. 721-723 exist imperforate. Value, $65 hinged, $80 never hinged.

Holy Year Issues

Statue in St. James Cathedral
A169

St. James of Compostela
A170

Incense Burner — A171

Carvings in St. James Cathedral
A172   A174

St. James — A173   St. James' Casket — A175

East Portal of Cathedral
A176

St. James Cathedral
A177

Perf. 9½x10½

1943, Oct. **Litho.** **Unwmk.**

724	A169	20c deep blue	.20 .20
725	A170	40c dk red brown	.45 .20
726	A171	75c deep blue	1.90 1.90

Nos. 725 and 727 exist imperforate. Value, $550.

1943-44 **Perf. 9½x10½, 10½x9½**

727	A172	20c rose red ('44)	.20 .20
728	A173	40c dull green	.45 .20
729	A174	75c dk blue ('44)	2.50 2.00

1944

730	A175	20c red violet	.20 .20
731	A176	40c dull brown	.65 .20
732	A177	75c bright blue	27.50 29.00
	Nos. 724-732 (9)		34.05 34.10
	Set, never hinged		65.00

Millenium of Castile Issues

Arms of Soria — A178

Arms of Castile — A179

Arms of Avila
A180

Fortress
A181

Arms of Segovia
A182

Arms of Fernan González
A183

Arms of Burgos
A185

Arms of Santander
A186

1944 **Litho.** **Perf. 9½x10½**

733	A178	20c violet	.20 .20
734	A179	40c dull brown	2.50 .45
735	A180	75c blue	2.50 2.75

1944

736	A181	20c rose violet	.20 .20
737	A182	40c dull brown	2.50 .45
738	A183	75c dull blue	2.40 2.50

1944

739	A180	20c red violet	.20 .20
740	A185	40c dull brown	1.90 .45
741	A186	75c blue	2.75 3.00
	Nos. 733-741 (9)		15.15 10.20
	Set, never hinged		24.00

Nos. 733, 738 and 741 exist imperforate. Value, $550. Value never hinged, $800.
No. 739 exists imperforate on grayish paper.

Francisco Gomez de Quevedo y Villegas (1580-1645), Writer — A187

1945, Sept. 8 **Engr.** **Perf. 10**

742	A187	40c dark brown	.65 .55
		Never hinged	1.10

Exists imperf. Value $70.

Type of Semi-Postal Stamp, 1940, Without Imprint at Lower Left and Right

1946, Jan. 1 **Litho.** **Perf. 11**

743	SP20	50c (40c + 10c) sl grn & rose vio	1.10 .25
		Never hinged	2.00

No. 743 was used as an ordinary postage stamp of 50c denomination.
Exists imperf. Value $70.

Elio Antonio de Nebrija — A188

University of Salamanca and Signature of Francisco de Vitoria — A189

1946, Oct. 12 **Engr.** **Perf. 9½x10**

744	A188	50c deep plum	.40 .30
745	A189	75c deep blue	.50 .45
	Nos. 744-745,C121 (3)		2.80 3.25
	Set, never hinged		4.75

Stamp Day and the Day of the Race, Oct. 12, 1946.
Nos. 744-745 and C121 exist imperforate. Value set, $160 inged, $240 never hinged.

Francisco de Goya
A190

Benito Jeronimo Feijoo y Montenegro
A191

1946, Oct 26
746 A190 25c deep plum .20 .20
747 A190 50c green .20 .20
748 A190 75c dark blue .60 .75
  Nos. 746-748 (3) 1.15
  Set, never hinged 1.00

Francisco de Goya, birth bicentenary.
Nos. 746-748 exist imperforate. Value set, $25 hinged, $32.50 never hinged.

1947, June 1   Unwmk.
749 A191 50c deep green .45 .35
  Never hinged .65

No. 749 exists imperforate. Value, $35.

Don Quixote
Reading
A192

"Don Quixote"
by Zuloaga
A193

1947, Oct. 9   Engr.   Perf. 9½x10½
750 A192 50c sepia .20 .25
751 A193 75c dark blue .35 .45
  Nos. 750-751,C122 (3) 4.55 4.70
  Set, never hinged 6.65

Stamp Day and the 400th anniv. of the birth of Miguel de Cervantes Saavedra.
Nos. 750-751 and C122 exist imperforate. Value set, $550 hinged, $650 never hinged.

General Franco
A194   A195

1948   Litho.   Perf. 12½x13
752 A194 15c green .20 .20
753 A195 50c rose violet .80 .20
  Set, never hinged 1.25

Nos. 752 and 753 exist imperforate. Value set, $400 hinged, $550 never hinged.
See Nos. 760-768, 780, 801-803. For surcharges see Nos. B137-B138.

Hernando
Cortez — A196

Mateo
Aleman — A197

1948, June 15   Engr.   Perf. 12½x13
754 A196 35c black .20 .20

Perf. 9½x10½
755 A197 70c dk violet brn 1.40 2.00
  a.   Perf. 12½x13 25.00 25.00
  Set, never hinged 2.25

No. 754 exists imperforate. Value set, $100 hinged, $125 never hinged.

Ferdinand III
(The
Saint) — A198

Grandson of
Adm. Ramon de
Bonifaz — A199

1948, Sept. 20 Litho. Perf. 12½x13
756 A198 25c rose violet .20 .20
757 A199 30c scarlet .20 .20
  Set, never hinged .50

700th anniversary of the Spanish navy and of the capture of Seville by Ferdinand the Saint.

José de
Salamanca y
Mayol — A200

Train Crossing
Pancorbo
Viaduct — A201

Perf. 12½x13, 13x12½
1948, Oct. 9   Unwmk.
758 A200 50c brown .50 .20
759 A201 5p deep green 1.40 .20
  Nos. 758-759,C125 (3) 3.40 1.90
  Set, never hinged 5.50

Centenary of Spanish railroads.

Franco Types of 1948

1948-49   Litho.   Perf. 12½x13
760 A194 5c brown .20 .20
761 A195 25c vermilion .20 .20
762 A195 35c blue green .20 .20
763 A194 40c red brown .55 .20
764 A195 45c car rose ('49) .30 .20
765 A194 50c bister .80 .20
766 A195 70c purple ('49) 1.50 .25
767 A195 75c dk vio blue 1.25 .25
768 A195 1p rose pink 4.00 .20
  Nos. 760-768 (9) 9.00 1.90
  Set, never hinged 13.00

No. 762 exists imperforate. Value, $400.

Symbols of
UPU
A202

1949, Oct. 9
769 A202 50c red brown .35 .20
770 A202 75c violet blue .35 .55
  Nos. 769-770,C126 (3) .90 1.20
  Set, never hinged 1.90

75th anniv. of the UPU.

St. John of
God — A203

Pedro Calderon
de la
Barca — A204

1950, Mar. 8   Engr.   Unwmk.
771 A203 1p dark violet 6.25 4.00
  Never hinged 11.50

400th anniversary of the death of St. John of God, humanitarian.

1950-53   Photo.   Perf. 12½

Designs: 10c Lope de Vega. 15c, Tirso de Molina. 20c, Juan Ruiz de Alarcon, dramatist. 50c, St. Antonio Maria Claret y Clara.

772 A204 5c brown ('51) .20 .20
773 A204 10c dp rose brn ('51) .20 .20
773A A204 15c dk sl grn ('53) .20 .20
774 A204 20c violet .20 .20

Perf. 12½x13
Engr.
775 A204 50c dk blue ('51) 2.50 1.50
  Nos. 772-775 (5) 3.30 2.30
  Set, never hinged 4.35

No. 774 exists imperforate. Value, $250.

Stamp of
1850 — A205

Queen Isabella
I — A206

1950, Oct. 12   Engr.   Imperf.
776 A205 50c purple 4.75 6.50
777 A205 75c ultra 4.75 6.50
778 A205 10p dk slate grn 85.00 87.50
779 A205 15p red 85.00 87.50
  Nos. 776-779,C127-C130 (8) 348.50 376.00
  Set, never hinged 550.00

Centenary of Spain's stamps.

Franco Type of 1948

1950   Litho.   Perf. 12½x13
780 A195 45c red .60 .20
  Never hinged .90

1951, Apr. 22   Photo.   Perf. 12½
781 A206 50c brown .50 .35
782 A206 75c blue .60 .35
783 A206 90c rose brown .35 .25
784 A206 1.50p orange 8.00 7.50
785 A206 2.80p olive grn 20.00 20.00
  Nos. 781-785 (5) 29.45 28.45
  Set, never hinged 52.50

500th anniversary of the birth of Queen Isabella I. See Nos. C132-C136.

Ferdinand, the
Catholic
A210

Maria Michaela
Dermaisiéres
A211

1952, May 10   Photo.   Perf. 13
787 A210 50c green .45 .30
788 A210 75c indigo 2.75 1.40
789 A210 90c rose brown .40 .35
790 A210 1.50p orange 7.75 8.00
791 A210 2.80p brown 15.00 16.00
  Nos. 787-791 (5) 26.35 26.05
  Set, never hinged 50.00

500th anniversary of the birth of Ferdinand the Catholic of Spain. See Nos. C139-C143.

1952, May 26   Perf. 12½x13
792 A211 90c claret .20 .20
  Never hinged .20

35th International Eucharistic Congress, Barcelona, 1952. See No. C137.

Dr. Santiago Ramon
y Cajal — A212

Portrait: 4.50p, Dr. Jaime Ferran y Clua.

1952, July 8   Photo.
793 A212 2p bright blue 13.50 .50
794 A212 4.50p red brown .50 .80
  Set, never hinged 22.50

Centenary of the births of Dr. Santiago Ramon y Cajal and Dr. Jaime Ferran y Clua.

University
Seal — A213

Luis de
Leon — A214

Cathedral
of
Salamanca
A215

1953, Oct. 12   Perf. 12½x13, 13x12½
795 A213 50c deep magenta .45 .30
796 A214 90c dark olive gray 1.65 2.00
797 A215 2p brown 11.00 3.25
  Nos. 795-797 (3) 13.10 5.55
  Set, never hinged 17.00

Stamp Day, 10/12/53, and 700th anniv. of the founding of the University of Salamanca.

The
Magdalene — A216

1954, Jan. 10   Perf. 12½x13
798 A216 1.25p deep magenta .20 .20
  Never hinged .20

José de Ribera, painter, 300th death anniv.

St. James of
Compostela
A217

St. James
Cathedral
A218

1954, Mar. 1
799 A217 50c dark brown .20 .20
800 A218 3p blue 27.50 2.50
  Set, never hinged 47.50

Holy year of Compostela, 1954.

Franco Types of 1948

1954   Litho.   Perf. 12½x13
801 A194 5c olive gray .20 .20
802 A195 30c deep green .20 .20
803 A194 80c dull car rose 1.65 .20
  Nos. 801-803 (3) 2.05 .60
  Set, never hinged 5.00

Virgin by Alonso
Cano — A219

Marcelino
Menendez y
Pelayo — A220

Virgins: 15c, Begoña. 25c, Of the Abandoned. 30c, Black. 50c, Of the Pillar. 60c, Covadonga. 80c, Kings'. 1p, Almudena. 2p, Africa. 3p, Guadalupe.

1954, July 18 Photo. Perf. 12½x13
804 A219 10c dk car rose .20 .20
805 A219 15c olive green .20 .20
806 A219 25c purple .20 .20
807 A219 30c brown .25 .20
808 A219 50c brown olive .55 .20
809 A219 60c gray .25 .20
810 A219 80c grnsh gray 2.50 .20
811 A219 1p lilac gray 2.50 .20

812 A219 2p red brown .75 .20
813 A219 3p bright blue .65 .65
Nos. 804-813 (10) 8.05 2.45
Set, never hinged 11.00

Issued to publicize the Marian Year.

1954, Oct. 12
814 A220 80c dk gray grn 5.75 .40
Never hinged 10.00

Stamp Day, October 12, 1954.

Gen. Franco — A221

Imprint: "F.N.M.T."

1954-56   Perf. 12½x13
815 A221 10c dk car lake .20 .20
816 A221 15c bister .20 .20
817 A221 20c dk ol grn ('55) .20 .20
818 A221 25c blue violet .20 .20
819 A221 30c brown .20 .20
820 A221 40c rose vio ('55) .20 .20
821 A221 50c dk brn olive .20 .20
822 A221 60c dk vio brown .20 .20
823 A221 70c dk green .20 .20
824 A221 80c dk blue grn .20 .20
825 A221 1p dp orange .20 .20
826 A221 1.40p lil rose ('56) .20 .20
827 A221 1.50p lt bl grn ('56) .20 .20
828 A221 1.80p emerald ('56) .20 .20
829 A221 2p red 13.00 1.25
830 A221 2p red lilac ('56) .20 .20
831 A221 3p Prus blue .20 .20
832 A221 5p dk red brn .20 .20
833 A221 6p dk gray ('56) .20 .20
834 A221 8p brt vio ('56) .20 .20
835 A221 10p yel grn ('55) .25 .20
Nos. 815-835 (21) 17.05 5.25
Set, never hinged 20.00

Coils: The 1.50p, No. 830, the 3p and the 6p were issued in coils in brighter tones (the 3p in 1974, others in 1973). Every fifth stamp has a black control number on the back.
See Nos. 937-938, 1852-1855.

St. Ignatius of Loyola — A222

St. Ignatius and Loyola Palace A223

Perf. 13x12½, 12½x13
1955, Oct. 12   Photo.   Unwmk.
836 A222 25c dull purple .20 .20
837 A223 60c bister .40 .30
838 A222 80c Prus green 1.65 .25
Nos. 836-838 (3) 2.25 .75
Set, never hinged 4.25

4th cent. of the death of St. Ignatius of Loyola, founder of the Jesuit Order, and Day of the Stamp.

Symbols of Telegraph and Radio Communication A224

St. Vincent Ferrer A225

1955, Dec. 8   Perf. 13x12½
839 A224 15c dk olive bis .30 .20
840 A224 80c Prus green 4.50 .25
841 A224 3p bright blue 8.50 1.25
Nos. 839-841 (3) 13.30 1.70
Set, never hinged 27.50

Spanish telegraph system centenary.

1955, Dec. 20   Perf. 13
842 A225 15c olive bister .40 .25
Never hinged .85

Canonization of St. Vincent Ferrer, 5th cent.

"Holy Family" by El Greco — A226

Marching Soldiers and Dove — A227

1955, Dec. 24   Perf. 13x12½
843 A226 80c dark green 3.75 .95
Never hinged 6.00

1956, July 17   Unwmk.
844 A227 15c olive bis & brn .20 .20
845 A227 50c lt ol grn & ol .50 .30
846 A227 80c mag & grnsh blk 4.25 .25
847 A227 3p ultra & dp blue 4.25 1.40
Nos. 844-847 (4) 9.20 2.15
Set, never hinged 19.00

20th anniversary of Civil War.

Ciudad de Toledo A228

1956, Aug. 3   Perf. 12½x13
848 A228 3p blue 3.50 2.00
Never hinged 5.75

Issued to publicize the voyage of the S. S. Ciudad de Toledo to Central and South America carrying the First Floating (Industrial) Exposition.

Black Virgin of Montserrat A229

Archangel Gabriel by Fra Angelico A230

Design: 60c, Monastery of Montserrat, mountains and crucifix.

1956, Sept. 11   Perf. 13x12½
849 A229 15c bister .20 .20
850 A229 60c violet black .20 .20
851 A229 80c blue green .35 .45
Nos. 849-851 (3) .75 .85
Set, never hinged .85

75th anniv. of the coronation of the Black Virgin of Montserrat.

1956, Oct. 12   Engr.
852 A230 80c dull green .90 .45
Never hinged 1.25

Stamp Day, Oct. 12.

Statistical Chart A231

1956, Nov. 3   Perf. 12½x13
853 A231 15c dk olive bis .35 .35
854 A231 80c green 3.50 .90
855 A231 1p red orange 3.50 .90
Nos. 853-855 (3) 7.35 2.15
Set, never hinged 10.00

Centenary of Spanish Statistics.

Hermitage and Monument A232

1956, Dec. 4
856 A232 80c dull blue grn 2.00 .25
Never hinged 5.50

20th anniversary of the nomination of Gen. Franco as chief of state and commander in chief of the army.

Hungarian Children A233

St. Marguerite Alacoque's Vision of Jesus A234

1956, Dec. 17   Perf. 13x12½
857 A233 10c brown lake .20 .20
858 A233 15c dk bister .20 .20
859 A233 50c olive gray .30 .20
860 A233 80c dk blue grn 2.25 .20
861 A233 1p red orange 2.50 .20
862 A233 3p brt blue 6.50 2.50
Nos. 857-862 (6) 11.95 3.50
Set, never hinged 20.00

Issued in sympathy to the children of Hungary.

1957, Oct. 12   Photo.   Unwmk.
863 A234 15c dk olive bis .20 .20
864 A234 60c violet blk .25 .20
865 A234 80c dk blue grn .35 .20
Nos. 863-865 (3) .80 .60
Set, never hinged 1.00

Centenary of the feast of the Sacred Heart of Jesus and for Stamp Day 1957.

Gonzalo de Cordoba — A235

1958, Feb. 28   Engr.   Perf. 13x12½
866 A235 1.80p yellow green .25 .20
Never hinged .35

Issued in honor of El Gran Capitan, 15th century military leader.

"The Parasol," by Goya — A236

"Wife of the Bookseller of Carretas Street" — A237

Goya Paintings: 50c, Duke of Fernan-Nunez. 60c, The Crockery Seller. 70c, Isabel Cobos de Porcel. 80c, Goya by Vicente Lopez. 1p, "El Pelele" (Carnival Doll). 1.80p, Goya's grandson Marianito. 2p, The Vintage. 3p, The Drinker.

1958, Mar. 24   Photo.   Perf. 13
Gold Frame
867 A236 15c bister .20 .20
868 A237 40c plum .20 .20
869 A237 50c olive gray .20 .20
870 A237 60c violet gray .20 .20
871 A237 70c dp yellow grn .20 .20
872 A237 80c dk slate grn .20 .20
873 A237 1p orange red .20 .20
874 A237 1.80p brt green .20 .20
875 A237 2p red lilac .40 .45
876 A236 3p brt blue .65 .85
Nos. 867-876 (10) 2.65 2.90
Set, never hinged 2.40

Issued to honor Francisco Jose de Goya and for the "Day of the Stamp," Mar. 24.
See Nos. 1111-1114. For other art types see A240a, A246a, A257, A272, A285a, A300, A310, A324, A340-A341, A360, A371 and footnote following No. 1606.

Exhibition Emblem and Globe — A238

1958, June 7   Perf. 13x12½
877 A238 80c car, dk brn & gray .55 .20
  a. Souvenir sheet, imperf. 20.00 20.00
878 A238 3p car, vio blk & bl 2.25 .90
  a. Souvenir sheet, imperf. 20.00 20.00
Set, never hinged 3.25
#877a-878a never hinged 55.00

No. 877a sold for 2p, No. 878a for 5p.
Universal and Intl. Exposition at Brussels.

Charles V — A239

Various Portraits of Charles V: 50c, 1.80p, with helmet. 70c, 2p, facing left. 80c, 3p, with beret.

1958, July 30   Photo.   Perf. 13
879 A239 15c buff & brown .20 .20
880 A239 50c lt grn & ol brn .20 .20
881 A239 70c gray, grn & blk .20 .20
882 A239 80c pale brn & Prus grn .20 .20
883 A239 1p bis & brick red .20 .20
884 A239 1.80p pale grn & brt grn .20 .20
885 A239 2p gray & lilac .30 .30
886 A239 3p pale brn & brt bl .85 .65
Nos. 879-886 (8) 2.35 2.15
Set, never hinged 3.25

400th anniv. of the death of Charles V (Carlos I of Spain.)

Escorial and Streamlined
Train — A240

Designs: 60c, 2p, Railroad bridge at
Despeñaperros, vert. 80c, 3p, Train and Castle
de La Mota.

1958, Sept. 29　　　　Perf. 12½x13
887	A240	15c dk olive bis	.20	.20
888	A240	60c dk purple	.20	.20
889	A240	80c dk blue grn	.20	.20
890	A240	1p red orange	.20	.20
891	A240	2p red lilac	.20	.20
892	A240	3p blue	.70	.40
	Nos. 887-892 (6)		1.70	1.40
	Set, never hinged		3.00	

Intl. Railroad Cong., Madrid, Sept. 28-Oct. 7.

Velazquez Self-
portrait
A240a

Velazquez Paintings: 15c, The Drinkers,
horiz. 40c, The Spinners. 50c, Surrender of
Breda. 60c, The Little Princesses. 70c, Prince
Balthazar. 1p, The Coronation of Our Lady.
1.80p, Aesop. 2p, Vulcan's Forge. 3p,
Menippus.

1959, Mar. 24　　Photo.　　Perf. 13
Gold Frame
893	A240a	15c dk brown	.20	.20
894	A240a	40c rose violet	.20	.20
895	A240a	50c olive	.20	.20
896	A240a	60c black brown	.20	.20
897	A240a	70c dp yellow grn	.20	.20
898	A240a	80c dk slate grn	.20	.20
899	A240a	1p orange red	.20	.20
900	A240a	1.80p emerald	.20	.20
901	A240a	2p red lilac	.20	.20
902	A240a	3p brt blue	.35	.45
	Nos. 867-876 (10)		2.65	2.90
	Set, never hinged		2.00	

Issued to honor Diego de Silva Velazquez
(1599-1660) and for Stamp Day, Mar. 24.
For other art types see A236-A237, A246a,
A257, A272, A285a, A300, A310, A324, A340-
A341, A360, A371 and footnote following No.
1606.

Civil War Memorial — A241

1959, Apr 1.　　Litho.　　Unwmk.
903	A241	80c yel grn & dk sl grn	.20	.20
	Never hinged			.30

Inauguration of the war memorial at the
monastery of the Holy Cross in the Valley of
the Fallen.

Louis XIV and Philip
IV — A242

1959, Oct. 24　Photo.　Perf. 13x12½
904	A242	1p gold & rose brn	.20	.20
	Never hinged			.30

300th anniv. of the signing of the Treaty of
the Pyrenees. Design shows the French-
Spanish meeting at Isle des Faisans in 1659,
as pictured in the Lebrun Tapestry, Versailles.

Monastery
of
Guadalupe
A243

80c, Monastery, different view. 1p, Portals.

1959, Nov. 16　Engr.　Perf. 12½x13
905	A243	15c lt red brown	.20	.20
906	A243	80c slate	.20	.20
907	A243	1p rose red	.20	.20
	Nos. 905-907 (3)		.60	.60
	Set, never hinged		.60	

Entrance of the Franciscan Brothers into
Guadalupe monastery, 50th anniv.

Holy Family, by
Goya — A244

1959, Dec. 10　Photo.　Perf. 13x12½
908	A244	1p orange brown	.20	.20
	Never hinged			.40

> **Catalogue values for unused
> stamps in this section, from this
> point to the end of the section, are
> for Never Hinged items.**

Lidian Bull
A245

Bullfighter, 19th
Century — A246

Designs: 20c, Rounding up bulls. 25c, Running with the bulls, Pamplona. 30c, Bull entering arena. 50c, Bullfighting with cape. 70c,
Bullfighting with banderillas. 80c, 1p, 1.40p,
1.50p, Fighting with muleta, various poses.
1.80p, Mounted bullfighter placing banderillas.

Perf. 12½x13, 13x12½
1960, Feb. 29　　Engr.　　Unwmk.
909	A245	15c sepia & bis	.20	.20
910	A245	20c vio & bl vio	.20	.20
911	A246	25c gray	.20	.20
912	A246	30c sepia & bister	.20	.20
913	A246	50c dull vio & sep	.20	.20
914	A246	70c sepia & sl grn	.20	.20
915	A246	80c blue grn & grn	.20	.20
916	A246	1p red & brn	.20	.20
917	A246	1.40p brown & lake	.20	.20
918	A246	1.50p grnsh bl & grn	.20	.20
919	A245	1.80p grn & dk grn	.20	.20
920	A246	5p brn & brn car	.55	.45
	Nos. 909-920,C159-C162 (16)		3.90	3.65

Murillo Self-portrait　　Christ of
A246a　　　　　　　　Lepanto
　　　　　　　　　　　A247

Murillo Paintings: 25c, The Good Shepherd.
40c, Rebecca and Eliezer. 50c, Virgin of the
Rosary. 70c, Immaculate Conception. 80c,
Children with Shell. 1.50p, Holy Family with
Bird, horiz. 2.50p, Children Playing Dice. 3p,
Children Eating. 5p, Children counting Money.

1960, Mar. 24　　Photo.　　Perf. 13
Gold Frame
921	A246a	25c dull violet	.20	.20
922	A246a	40c plum	.20	.20
923	A246a	50c olive gray	.20	.20
924	A246a	70c dp yel grn	.20	.20
925	A246a	80c deep green	.20	.20
926	A246a	1p violet brown	.20	.20
927	A246a	1.50p blue green	.20	.20
928	A246a	2.50p rose car	.20	.20
929	A246a	3p brt blue	1.25	.60
930	A246a	5p deep red brn	.35	.60
	Nos. 921-930 (10)		3.20	2.45

Issued to honor Bartolome Esteban Murillo
(1617-1682) and for Stamp Day, Mar. 24.
For other art types see A236-A237, A240a,
A257, A272, A285a, A300, A310, A324, A340-
A341, A360, A371 and footnote following No.
1606.

1960, Mar. 27　　　　Perf. 13x12½
80c, 2.50p, 10p, Holy Family Church,
Barcelona.
931	A247	70c brn car & grn	1.60	1.25
932	A247	80c blk & ol grn	1.60	1.25
933	A247	1p cl & brt red	1.60	1.25
934	A247	2.50p brt vio & gray vio	1.60	1.25
935	A247	5p sepia & bister	1.60	1.25
936	A247	10p sepia & bister	1.60	1.25
	Nos. 931-936,C163-C166 (10)		28.60	20.50

First International Congress of Philately,
Barcelona, March 26-Apr. 5. Nos. 931-936
could be bought at the exhibition upon presentation of 5p entrance ticket.

Franco Type of 1954-56
Imprint: "F.N.M.T.-B"

1960, Mar. 31　　　　　Perf. 13
937	A221	1p deep orange	1.40	.60
938	A221	5p dark red brown	1.40	.60

Printed and issued at the International Congress of Philately in Barcelona.

St. Juan de　　　　St. Vincent de
Ribera — A248　　　Paul — A249

1960, Aug. 16　　Photo.　　Perf. 13
939	A248	1p orange red	.20	.20
940	A248	2.50p lilac rose	.20	.20

Canonization of St. Juan de Ribera.

> **Common Design Types
> pictured following the introduction.**

Europa Issue, 1960
Common Design Type
1960, Sept. 19　　　　Perf. 12½x13
Size: 38½x21½mm
941	CD3	1p sl grn & ol bis	.90	.20
942	CD3	5p choc & salmon	.90	.60

1960, Sept. 27　Unwmk.　Perf. 13
943	A249	25c violet	.20	.20
944	A249	1p orange red	.40	.20

3rd centenary of the death of St. Vincent de
Paul.

Pedro
Menendez de　　　Runner — A251
Aviles — A250

70c, 2.50p, Hernando de Soto. 80c, 3p,
Ponce de Leon. 1p, 5p, Alvar Nunez Cabeza
de Vaca.

1960, Oct. 12　　　　Perf. 13x12½
945	A250	25c vio bl, *bl*	.20	.20
946	A250	70c slate grn, *pink*	.20	.20
947	A250	80c dk grn, *pale brn*	.20	.20
948	A250	1p org brn, *yel*	.20	.20
949	A250	2p dk car rose, *pink*	.30	.20
950	A250	2.50p lil rose, *buff*	.60	.20
951	A250	3p dk blue, *grnsh*	2.75	.50
952	A250	5p dk brown, *cit*	2.25	.85
	Nos. 945-952 (8)		6.70	2.55

Florida's discovery & colonization, 4th cent.

Perf. 13x12½, 12½x13
1960, Oct. 31　　　　　　Photo.
Sports: 40c, 2p, Bicycling, horiz. 70c, 2.50p,
Soccer, horiz. 80c, 3p, Athlete with rings. 1p,
5p, Hockey on roller skates, horiz.
953	A251	25c dk vio, brn & blk	.20	.20
954	A251	40c purple, org & blk	.20	.20
955	A251	70c brt green & red	.30	.20
956	A251	80c dp grn, car & blk	.25	.20
957	A251	1p red org, brt grn & blk	.55	.20
958	A251	1.50p Prus grn, brn & blk	.40	.20
959	A251	2p red lil, emer & blk	1.10	.20
960	A251	2.50p lil rose & green	.40	.20
961	A251	3p ultra, red & blk	.75	.20
962	A251	5p red brn, bl & blk	.75	.35
	Nos. 953-962,C167-C170 (14)		7.70	3.65

Isaac
Albeniz — A252

1960, Nov. 7　　　　　　Perf. 13
963	A252	25c dark gray	.20	.20
964	A252	1p orange red	.20	.20

Isaac Albeniz, composer, birth centenary.

Courtyard
of Samos
Monastery
A253

1p, Fountain, vert. 5p, Facade, vert.

Perf. 12½x13, 13x12½
1960, Nov. 21　　　　　　Engr.
965	A253	80c bl grn & Prus grn	.20	.20
966	A253	1p org brn & car rose	1.40	.20
967	A253	5p sepia & ocher	1.40	.45
	Nos. 965-967 (3)		3.00	.85

Issued in honor of the reconstructed Benedictine monastery at Samos, Lugo.

Adoration, by
Velazquez — A254

1960, Dec. 1　Photo.　Perf. 13x12½
968	A254	1p orange red	.30	.20

Flight into
Egypt by
Francisco
Bayeu
A255

1961, Jan. 23   **Perf. 12½x13**
969 A255 1p copper red   .25 .20
970 A255 5p dull red brown   .45 .30

World Refugee Year.

Leandro F. de   St. Peter by El
Moratin, by   Greco — A257
Goya — A256

1961, Feb. 13   **Perf. 13**
971 A256 1p henna brown   .20 .20
972 A256 1.50p dk blue green   .20 .20

Leandro Fernandez de Moratin (1760-
1828), poet and dramatist, 200th birth anniv.

1961, Mar. 24   **Perf. 13**
El Greco Paintings: 40c, Virgin Mary. 70c,
Head of Christ. 80c, Knight with Hand on
Chest. 1p, Self-portrait. 1.50p, Baptism of
Christ. 2.50p, Holy Trinity. 3p, Burial of Count
Orgaz. 5p, Christ Stripped of His Garments.
10p, St. Mauritius and the Theban Legion.

Gold Frame

973 A257 25c violet black   .20 .20
974 A257 40c lilac   .20 .20
975 A257 70c green   .25 .20
976 A257 80c Prus green   .25 .20
977 A257 1p chocolate   2.25 .20
978 A257 1.50p grnsh blue   .25 .20
979 A257 2.50p dk car rose   .45 .20
980 A257 3p bright blue   1.10 .45
981 A257 5p black brown   3.25 1.40
982 A257 10p purple   .55 .30
    Nos. 973-982 (10)   8.75 3.55

El Greco and Stamp Day, March 24.
For other art types see A236-A237, A240a,
A246a, A272, A285a, A300, A310, A324,
A340-A341, A360, A371 and footnote follow-
ing No. 1606.

Diego   Canceled
Velazquez — A258   Stamp — A259

Velazquez Paintings: 1p, Duke de Olivares.
2.50p, Infanta Margarita. 10p, Detail from The
Spinners, horiz.

Unwmk.
1961, Apr. 17   Engr.   Perf. 13
983 A258 80c dk blue & sl
              grn   1.90 .75
   a. Souvenir sheet   7.75 8.25
984 A258 1p brn red &
              choc   5.50 .75
   a. Souvenir sheet   7.75 8.25
985 A258 2.50p vio bl & bl   1.40 1.00
   a. Souvenir sheet   7.75 8.25
986 A258 10p grn & yel grn   6.25 2.50
   a. Souvenir sheet   7.75 8.25
    Nos. 983-986 (4)   15.05 5.00

300th anniversary (in 1960) of the death of
Velazquez, painter.
Each souvenir sheet contains one imperf.
stamp. The colors of the stamps have been
changed: 80c, red brown & slate; 1p, blue &
violet; 2.50p, green & blue; 10p, slate blue &
greenish blue. The sheets were sold at a
premium.

1961, May 6   Photo.   Perf. 13x12½
987 A259 25c gray & red   .20 .20
988 A259 1p orange & blk   1.10 .20
989 A259 10p olive grn & brn   1.10 .60
    Nos. 987-989 (3)   2.40 1.00

Issued for International Stamp Day.

Juan Vazquez   Flag, Angel and
de   Peace
Mella — A260   Doves — A261

1961, June 8   Unwmk.   Perf. 13
990 A260 1p henna brown   .45 .20
991 A260 2.30p red lilac   .20 .20

Birth centenary of Juan Vazquez de Mella y
Fanjul, politician and writer.

1961, July 10
Designs: 80c, Ships and Strait of Gibraltar.
1p, Alcazar and horseman. 1.50p, Ruins and
triumphal arch. 2p, Horseman over Ebro.
2.30p, Victory parade. 2.50p, Ship building.
3p, Steel industry. 5p, Map of Spanish irrigation dams and statue, horiz. 6p, Dama de
Elche statue and power station. 8p, Mining
development. 10p, General Franco.

992 A261 70c multicolored   .20 .20
993 A261 80c multicolored   .20 .20
994 A261 1p multicolored   .20 .20
995 A261 1.50p gold, pink & brn   .20 .20
996 A261 2p gold, gray & bl   .20 .20
997 A261 2.30p multicolored   .20 .20
998 A261 2.50p multicolored   .20 .20
999 A261 3p gold, red & dk
              gray   .35 .25
1000 A261 5p bl grn, ol gray
              & pink   2.25 1.10
1001 A261 6p multicolored   1.10 .75
1002 A261 8p gold, ol & sep   .70 .55
1003 A261 10p gold, gray &
              grn   .70 .55
    Nos. 992-1003 (12)   6.50 4.60

25th anniversary of national uprising.

Christ, San   Luis de Argote
Clemente, Tahull   y Gongora
A262   A263

Designs: 25c, Bas-relief, Compostela
Cathedral. 1p, Cloister of Silos. 2p, Virgin of
Irache.

1961, July 24   Unwmk.   Perf. 13
Gold Frame
1004 A262 25c blue violet   .40 .20
1005 A262 1p orange brown   .55 .20
1006 A262 2p deep plum   .75 .20
1007 A262 3p grnsh bl, sal &
              blk   .95 .40
    Nos. 1004-1007 (4)   2.65 1.00

Seventh Exposition of the Council of Europe
dedicated to Romanesque art, Barcelona-
Santiago de Compostela, July 10-Oct. 10.

1961, Aug. 10   Photo.   Perf. 13
1008 A263 25c violet black   .20 .20
1009 A263 1p henna brown   .50 .20

400th anniversary of the birth of Luis de
Argote y Gongora, poet.

Europa Issue, 1961
Common Design Type
1961, Sept. 18   Perf. 12½x13
Size: 37½x21½mm

1010 CD4 1p brt vermilion   .20 .20
1011 CD4 5p brown   .50 .30

Cathedral at   Sebastian de
Burgos   Belalcazar
A264   A265

1961, Oct. 1   Perf. 13
1012 A264 1p gold & olive green   .20 .20

25th anniversary of the nomination of Gen.
Francisco Franco as Head of State.

Builders of the New World

Portraits: 70c, 2.50p, Blas de Lezo. 80c, 3p,
Rodrigo de Bastidas. 1p, 5p, Nuflo de Chaves.

1961, Oct. 12   Photo.   Perf. 13x12½
1013 A265 25c indigo, grn   .20 .20
1014 A265 70c grn, cream   .20 .20
1015 A265 80c sl grn, pnksh   .20 .20
1016 A265 1p dk blue, sal   .60 .20
1017 A265 2p dk car, bluish   3.75 .20
1018 A265 2.50p lil, pale lil   .90 .45
1019 A265 3p blue, grysh   1.90 .80
1020 A265 5p brown, yel   2.00 .90
    Nos. 1013-1020 (8)   9.75 3.15

Issued to honor the discoverers and conquerors of Colombia and Bolivia.
See Nos. 1131-1138, 1187-1194, 1271-
1278, 1316-1323, 1377-1384, 1489-1496,
1548, 1550, 1587-1588, 1632-1633.

Patio of the Kings,
Escorial — A266

Views of Escorial: 80c, Patio. 1p, Garden of
the Monks and Escorial, horiz. 2.50p, Staircase. 5p, General view of Escorial, horiz. 6p,
Main altar.

Perf. 13x12½, 12½x13
1961, Oct. 31   Engr.   Unwmk.
1021 A266 70c bl grn & ol grn   .20 .20
1022 A266 80c Prus grn & ind   .20 .20
1023 A266 1p ocher & dk red   .55 .20
1024 A266 2.50p cl & dull vio   .55 .20
1025 A266 5p bister & dk brn   1.60 .70
1026 A266 6p sl bl & dull pur   2.25 1.50
    Nos. 1021-1026 (6)   5.35 3.00

Alfonso XII
Monument, Retiro
Park — A267

Church of St.
Mary,
Naranco — A268

Designs: 1p, King Philip II. 2p, Town hall,
horiz. 2.50p, Cibeles fountain, horiz. 3p, Alcala
gate, horiz. 5p, Cervantes memorial, Plaza de
Espagna.

Photogravure (25c, 2p, 5p)
Engraved (1p, 2.50p, 3p)
1961, Nov. 13   Unwmk.   Perf. 13
1027 A267 25c gray & dull pur   .20 .20
1028 A267 1p bis brn & gray   .30 .20
1029 A267 2p claret & gray   .30 .20
1030 A267 2.50p black & lilac   .25 .20
1031 A267 3p slate & ind   .60 .35

1032 A267 5p Prus grn &
              beige   1.10 .55
    Nos. 1027-1032 (6)   2.75 1.70

400th anniv. of Madrid as capital of Spain.

1961, Nov. 27
Designs: 1p, King Fruela I, founder of Oviedo. 2p, Cross of the Angels. 2.50p, King
Alfonso II. 3p, King Alfonso III. 5p, Apostles
from Oviedo Cathedral (sculpture).

1033 A268 25c pur & gray grn   .20 .20
1034 A268 1p bis brn & brn   .30 .20
1035 A268 2p dk brn & pale
              pur   .65 .20
1036 A268 2.50p claret & ind   .30 .20
1037 A268 3p slate & indigo   .65 .45
1038 A268 5p ol & ol grn   1.25 .55
    Nos. 1033-1038 (6)   3.35 1.80

1200th anniversary of the founding of Oviedo, capital of Asturia.

Nativity   "La Cierva"
Sculptured by   Autogiro — A270
José
Gines — A269

1961, Dec. 1   Photo.   Perf. 13x12½
1039 A269 1p dull purple   .30 .20

1961, Dec. 11   Unwmk.   Perf. 13
2p, Hydroplane "Plus Ultra.," horiz. 3p,
"Jesus del Gran Poder," plane of Madrid-
Manila flight, horiz. 5p, Bustard hunt by plane.
10p, Madonna of Loretto, patron saint of
Spanish airmen.

1040 A270 1p indigo & blue   .20 .20
1041 A270 2p grn, dl pur & blk   .20 .20
1042 A270 3p blk & ol grn   1.10 .35
1043 A270 5p dl pur, gray bl &
              blk   2.25 .90
1044 A270 10p blk, lt bl & ol gray   1.10 .60
    Nos. 1040-1044 (5)   4.85 2.25

50th anniversary of Spanish aviation.

Provincial Arms Issue

Alava — A271   Arms of
                     Spain — A271a

1962   Photo.   Perf. 13
1045 A271 5p Alava   .20 .20
1046 A271 5p Albacete   .20 .20
1047 A271 5p Alicante   .25 .20
1048 A271 5p Almeria   .25 .20
1049 A271 5p Avila   .25 .20
1050 A271 5p Badajoz   .20 .20
1051 A271 5p Baleares   .20 .20
1052 A271 5p Barcelona   .20 .20
1053 A271 5p Burgos   .65 .40
1054 A271 5p Caceres   .35 .25
1055 A271 5p Cadiz   .45 .35
1056 A271 5p Castellon de la
              Plana   3.50 1.50
    Nos. 1045-1056 (12)   6.70 4.10

1963
1057 A271 5p Ciudad Real   .45 .35
1058 A271 5p Cordoba   3.50 1.25
1059 A271 5p Coruña   .55 .35
1060 A271 5p Cuenca   .55 .35
1061 A271 5p Fernando Po   .80 .75
1062 A271 5p Gerona   .20 .20
1063 A271 5p Gran Canaria   .20 .20
1064 A271 5p Granada   .25 .25
1065 A271 5p Guadalajara   .55 .35
1066 A271 5p Guipuzcoa   .20 .20
1067 A271 5p Huelva   .20 .20
1068 A271 5p Huesca   .20 .20
    Nos. 1057-1068 (12)   7.65 4.65

1964
1069	A271	5p	Ifni	.20	.20
1070	A271	5p	Jaen	.20	.20
1071	A271	5p	Leon	.20	.20
1072	A271	5p	Lerida	.20	.20
1073	A271	5p	Logrono	.20	.20
1074	A271	5p	Lugo	.20	.20
1075	A271	5p	Madrid	.20	.20
1076	A271	5p	Malaga	.20	.20
1077	A271	5p	Murcia	.20	.20
1078	A271	5p	Navarra	.20	.20
1079	A271	5p	Orense	.20	.20
1080	A271	5p	Oviedo	.20	.20
		Nos. 1069-1080 (12)		2.40	2.40

1965
1081	A271	5p	Palencia	.20	.20
1082	A271	5p	Pontevedra	.20	.20
1083	A271	5p	Rio Muni	.20	.20
1084	A271	5p	Sahara	.20	.20
1085	A271	5p	Salamanca	.20	.20
1086	A271	5p	Santander	.20	.20
1087	A271	5p	Segovia	.20	.20
1088	A271	5p	Seville	.20	.20
1089	A271	5p	Soria	.20	.20
1090	A271	5p	Tarragona	.20	.20
1091	A271	5p	Tenerife	.20	.20
1092	A271	5p	Teruel	.20	.20
		Nos. 1081-1092 (12)		2.40	2.40

1966
1093	A271	5p	Toledo	.20	.20
1094	A271	5p	Valencia	.20	.20
1094A	A271	5p	Valladolid	.20	.20
1094B	A271	5p	Vizcaya	.20	.20
1094C	A271	5p	Zamora	.20	.20
1094D	A271	5p	Zaragoza	.20	.20
1094E	A271	5p	Ceuta	.20	.20
1094F	A271	5p	Melilla	.20	.20
1094G	A271a	10p	black	.20	.20
		Nos. 1093-1094G (9)		1.80	1.80
		Nos. 1045-1094G (57)		20.95	15.35

Zurbaran Self-
portrait
A272

Zurbaran Paintings: 25c, Martyr, horiz. 40c, Burial of St. Catherine. 70c, St. Casilda. 80c, Jesus crowning St. Joseph. 1.50p, St. Jerome. 2.50p, Virgin of Grace. 3p, The Apotheosis of St. Thomas Aquinas. 5p, The Virgin as a child. 10p, The Immaculate Virgin.

Unwmk.
1962, Mar. 24   Photo.   Perf. 13
Gold Frame
1095	A272	25c olive gray	.40	.20
1096	A272	40c purple	.40	.20
1097	A272	70c green	.50	.20
1098	A272	80c Prus green	.40	.20
1099	A272	1p chocolate	7.50	.20
1100	A272	1.50p brt blue grn	.90	.20
1101	A272	2.50p dk car rose	.90	.20
1102	A272	3p bright blue	1.00	.35
1103	A272	5p deep brown	2.50	.75
1104	A272	10p olive green	2.50	.75
		Nos. 1095-1104 (10)	17.00	3.25

Issued to honor Francisco de Zurbaran (1598-1664) and for Stamp Day, March 24.
For other art types see A236-A237, A240a, A246a, A257, A285a, A300, A310, A324, A340-A341, A360, A371 and footnote following No. 1606.

San Jose
Convent, Avila
A272a

St. Theresa (by
Velázquez?)
A273

Design: 1p, St. Theresa by Bernini.

1962, Apr. 10   Perf. 13
1105	A272a	25c bluish blk	.20	.20
1106	A272a	1p brown	.20	.20

Perf. 13x12½
1107	A273	3p bright blue	1.25	.40
		Nos. 1105-1107 (3)	1.65	.80

4th centenary of St. Theresa's reform of the Carmelite order.

Mercury — A274

1962, May 7
1108	A274	25c vio, rose & mag	.20	.20
1109	A274	1p brn, org & lt brn	.20	.20
1110	A274	10p dp grn, ol grn & brt grn	1.75	.80
		Nos. 1108-1110 (3)	2.15	1.20

International Stamp Day, May 7.

Painting Type of 1958

Rubens Paintings: 25c, Ferdinand of Austria. 1p, Self-portrait. 3p, Philip II. 10p, Duke of Lerma on horseback.

1962, May 28   Perf. 13
Gold Frame
Size: 25x30mm
1111	A237	25c violet black	.65	.30
1112	A237	1p chocolate	5.75	.30
1113	A237	3p blue	5.25	2.00

Perf. 13x12½
Size: 26x38mm
1114	A237	10p slate green	4.00	2.75
		Nos. 1111-1114 (4)	15.65	5.35

St. Benedict
A275

El Cid, Statue
by Cristobal
A276

Berruguete Sculptures: 80c, Apostle. 1p, St. Peter. 2p, St. Christopher carrying Christ Child. 3p, Ecce Homo (Christ). 10p, St. Sebastian.

1962, July 9   Perf. 13x12½
1115	A275	25c lt blue & plum	.20	.20
1116	A275	80c sal & ol gray	.30	.20
1117	A275	1p gray & red	.40	.20
1118	A275	2p gray & magenta	3.25	.20
1119	A275	3p brn pink & dk bl	1.25	.85
1120	A275	10p rose & brown	1.25	.50
		Nos. 1115-1120 (6)	6.65	2.15

Alonso Berruguete (1486-1561), architect, sculptor and painter.

Perf. 13x12½, 12½x13
1962, July 30   Engr.

2p, Equestrian statue by Anna Huntington. 3p, El Cid's treasure chest, horiz. 10p, Oath-taking ceremony at Santa Gadea, horiz.
1121	A276	1p lt green & gray	.25	.20
1122	A276	2p brown & choc	1.40	.20
1123	A276	3p blue & sl grn	4.25	1.10
1124	A276	10p lt grn & sl grn	2.75	.60
		Nos. 1121-1124 (4)	8.65	2.10

El Cid Campeador (Rodrigo Diaz de Vivar, 1040-99), Spain's national hero.

Europa Issue, 1962

Bee and Honeycomb — A277

1962, Sept. 13   Photo.   Perf. 12½x13
1125	A277	1p deep rose	.25	.20
1126	A277	5p dull green	1.25	.45

Discus Thrower
A278

UPAE Emblem
A279

80c, Runner. 1p, Hurdler. 3p, Sprinter at start.

1962, Oct. 7   Perf. 13x12½
1127	A278	25c pale pink & vio blk	.20	.20
1128	A278	80c pale yel & dk grn	.25	.20
1129	A278	1p pale rose & brn	.20	.20
1130	A278	3p pale bl & dk grn	.25	.30
		Nos. 1127-1130 (4)	.90	.90

Second Spanish-American Games, Madrid, Oct. 7-12.

Builders of the New World
Portrait Type of 1961

Portraits: 25c, 2p, Alonso de Mendoza. 70c, 2.50p, Jiménez de Quesada. 80c, 3p, Juan de Garay. 1p, 5p, Pedro de la Gasca.

1962, Oct. 12   Unwmk.
1131	A265	25c rose lil, gray	.20	.20
1132	A265	70c grn, pale pink	1.00	.20
1133	A265	80c dk grn, pale yel	.70	.20
1134	A265	1p red brn, gray	1.40	.20
1135	A265	2p car, lt bl	3.25	.20
1136	A265	2.50p dk vio,pnksh	.70	.25
1137	A265	3p dp bl, pale pink	7.00	1.25
1138	A265	5p brn, pale yel	3.50	1.50
		Nos. 1131-1138 (8)	17.75	4.00

1962, Oct. 20   Engr.   Perf. 13
1139	A279	1p sepia & green	.20	.20

50th anniv. of the founding of the Postal Union of the Americas and Spain, UPAE.

The Annunciation,
by Murillo — A280

Holy Family by
Pedro de
Mena — A281

Mysteries of the Rosary: 70c, The Visitation, Correa. 80c, Nativity, Murillo. 1p, The Presentation, Pedro de Campaña. 1.50p, The Finding in the Temple, (unknown painter). 2p, The Agony in the Garden, Gianquinto. 2.50p, The Scourging at the Pillar, Alonso Cano. 3p, The Crowning with Thorns, Tiepolo. 5p, Carrying of the Cross, El Greco. 8p, The Crucifixion, Murillo. 10p, The Resurrection, Murillo.

1962, Oct. 26
1140	A280	25c lilac & brown	.20	.20
1141	A280	70c grn & dk bl grn	.20	.20
1142	A280	80c ol & dk bl grn	.20	.20
1143	A280	1p green & gray	4.00	.70
1144	A280	1.50p green & dk bl	.20	.20
1145	A280	2p brown & violet	1.10	.50
1146	A280	2.50p dk brn & rose claret	.40	.20
1147	A280	3p lilac & gray	.40	.20
1148	A280	5p brn & dk car	.60	.35
1149	A280	8p vio brn & blk	.60	.20
1150	A280	10p grn & yel grn	.95	.25
		Nos. 1140-1150,C171-C174 (15)	11.45	4.40

1962, Dec. 6   Photo.   Perf. 13x12½
1151	A281	1p olive gray	.35	.20

Malaria
Eradication
Emblem
A282

1962, Dec. 21   Perf. 12½x13
1152	A282	1p blk, yel grn & yel	.20	.20

WHO drive to eradicate malaria.

Pope John
XXIII and
St. Peter's,
Rome
A283

1962, Dec. 29   Engr.
1153	A283	1p dp plum & blk	.25	.20

Vatican II, the 21st Ecumenical Council of the Roman Catholic Church. See No. 1199.

St. Paul, by El
Greco
A284

Courtyard,
Poblet
Monastery
A285

1963, Jan. 25   Perf. 13
1154	A284	1p brn, blk & olive	.30	.20

St. Paul's visit to Spain, 1,900th anniv.

Perf. 12½x13, 13x12½
1963, Feb. 25   Unwmk.

Designs: 1p, Royal sepulcher. 3p, View of monastery, horiz. 5p, Gothic arch.
1155	A285	25c choc & slate grn	.20	.20
1156	A285	1p org ver & rose car	.35	.20
1157	A285	3p vio bl & dk bl	1.10	.20
1158	A285	5p brown & ocher	2.40	.90
		Nos. 1155-1158 (4)	4.05	1.50

Issued in honor of the Cistercian monastery of Santa Maria de Poblet.

José de Ribera,
Self-portrait
A285a

Coach
A286

Ribera Paintings: 25c, Archimedes. 40c, Jacob's Flock. 70c, Triumph of Bacchus. 80c, St. Christopher. 1.50p, St. Andrew. 2.50p, St. John the Baptist. 3p, St. Onofre. 5p, St. Peter. 10p, The Immaculate Virgin.

Unwmk.
1963, Mar. 24   Photo.   Perf. 13
Gold Frame
1159	A285a	25c violet	.35	.20
1160	A285a	40c red lilac	.40	.20
1161	A285a	70c green	1.00	.20
1162	A285a	80c dark green	1.00	.20
1163	A285a	1p brown	1.00	.20
1164	A285a	1.50p blue green	1.00	.20
1165	A285a	2.50p car rose	2.75	.20
1166	A285a	3p dark blue	3.00	.50
1167	A285a	5p olive	10.50	2.25
1168	A285a	10p dull red brn	4.00	1.40
		Nos. 1159-1168 (10)	25.00	5.55

Issued to honor José de Ribera (1588-1652) and for Stamp Day, Mar. 24.

For other art types see A236-A237, A240a, A246a, A257, A272, A300, A310, A324, A340-A341, A360, A371 and footnote following No. 1606.

1963, May 3   **Perf. 13x12½**
1169 A286 1p multicolored   .20 .20
First Intl. Postal Conference, Paris, 1863.

Globe
A287

1963, May 8   **Perf. 12½x13**
1170 A287 25c multicolored   .20 .20
1171 A287 1p multicolored   .20 .20
1172 A287 10p multicolored   1.10 .65
   Nos. 1170-1172 (3)   1.50 1.05

Issued for International Stamp Day, 1963.

"Give us this Day our Daily Bread..." A288

1963, June 1   **Unwmk.**
1173 A288 1p multicolored   .20 .20
FAO "Freedom from Hunger" campaign.

"Pillars of Hercules" and Globes — A289

Seal of Council of San Sebastian A290

Designs: 80c, Fleet of Columbus. 1p, Columbus and compass rose.

1963, June 4   **Perf. 13**
1174 A289 25c multicolored   .20 .20
1175 A289 80c brn, lt grn & gold   .20 .20
1176 A289 1p sl grn, sepia & gold   .25 .20
   Nos. 1174-1176 (3)   .65 .60

Cong. of Institutions of Spanish Culture, June 5-15.

1963, June 27   **Photo.**
80c, Burning of city, 1813. 1p, View, 1836.

1177 A290 25c vio, grn & blk   .20 .20
1178 A290 80c dk brn, gray & red   .20 .20
1179 A290 1p dk grn, grn & ol   .30 .20
   Nos. 1177-1179 (3)   .70 .60

Rebuilding of San Sebastian, 150th anniv.

Europa Issue, 1963

Our Lady of Europe — A291

1963, Sept. 16   Engr.   Perf. 13x12½
1180 A291 1p bis brn & choc   .20 .20
1181 A291 5p bluish grn & blk   .60 .45

Arms of Order of Mercy — A292

King James I — A293

Designs: 1p, Our Lady of Mercy. 1.50p, St. Pedro Nolasco. 3p, St. Raimundo de Penafort.

1963, Sept. 24   Photo.   Perf. 13
1182 A292 25c blk, car rose & gold   .20 .20

Engr.
1183 A293 80c sepia & green   .20 .20
1184 A293 1p gray vio & brn vio   .20 .20
1185 A293 1.50p dull bl & blk   .20 .20
1186 A293 3p gray & black   .20 .20
   Nos. 1182-1186 (5)   1.00 1.00

Coronation of Our Lady of Mercy, 75th anniv.

Builders of the New World
Portrait Type of 1961

25c, 2p, Father Junipero Serra. 70c, 2.50p, Vasco Nuñez de Balboa. 80c, 3p, José de Galvez. 1p, 5p, Diego Garcia de Paredes.

1963, Oct. 12   **Perf. 13x12½**
1187 A265 25c vio bl, bl   .20 .20
1188 A265 70c grn, pale rose   .20 .20
1189 A265 80c dk grn, yel   .50 .20
1190 A265 1p dk bl, pale rose   .60 .20
1191 A265 2p magenta, lt bl   1.75 .20
1192 A265 2.50p vio bl, dl rose   1.10 .20
1193 A265 3p brt bl, pink   2.40 1.00
1194 A265 5p brown, yel   3.00 2.25
   Nos. 1187-1194 (8)   9.75 4.45

The Good Samaritan — A294

1963, Oct. 28   **Unwmk.**
1195 A294 1p gold, pur & brt car   .20 .20
Centenary of International Red Cross.

Holy Family by Alonso Berruguete (1486-1561) A295

Father Raymond Lully A296

1963, Dec. 2   Photo.   Perf. 13x12½
1196 A295 1p dark green   .20 .20
Christmas 1963. See No. 1279.

1963, Dec. 5   **Engr.**
Portrait: 1.50p, Cardinal Luis Antonio de Belluga (1662-1743).

1197 A296 1p dk violet & blk   .20 .20
1198 A296 1.50p sepia & dull vio   .20 .20
   Nos. 1197-1198,C175-C176 (4)   3.40 1.35

Papal Type of 1962

Design: 1p, Pope Paul VI and St. Peter's, Rome.

1963, Dec. 30   **Perf. 12½x13**
1199 A283 1p dk green & blk   .20 .20

Second session of Vatican II, the 21st Ecumenical Council of the Roman Catholic Church.

Alcazar, Segovia A297

Dragon Caves, Majorca — A298

Tourism: 40c, Potes, Santander. 50c, Leon Cathedral. No. 1202, Crypt of San Isidro at Leon. No. 1203, Costa Brava. 80c, Christ of the Lanterns, Cordova. No. 1206, Court of Lions, Alhambra, Granada. No. 1208, Interior of La Mezquita, Cordova. 1.50p, View of Gerona.

1964   **Engr.**   **Perf. 13**
1200 A297 40c sepia & blue   .20 .20
1201 A298 50c gray & sepia   .20 .20
1202 A297 70c ind & dk bl grn   .20 .20
1203 A298 70c violet & brown   .20 .20
1204 A298 80c dp ultra & blk   .20 .20
1205 A297 1p vio bl & pur   .20 .20
1206 A297 1p rose red & dl pur   .20 .20
1207 A298 1p dk green & blk   .20 .20
1208 A298 1p brn vio & rose   .20 .20
1209 A297 1.50p gray grn, brn & blk   .20 .20
   Nos. 1200-1209 (10)   2.00 2.00

See Nos. 1280-1289.

Santa Maria de Huerta Monastery A299

Joaquin Sorolla, Self-portrait A300

Designs: 1p, Great Hall. 5p, View of monastery with apse, horiz.

1964, Feb. 24   Perf. 13x12½, 12½x13
1212 A299 1p gray grn & grn   .20 .20
1213 A299 2p grnsh blue & sepia   .25 .20
1214 A299 5p dark blue   1.50 .75
   Nos. 1212-1214 (3)   1.95 1.15

Santa Maria Monastery, Huerta, 8th cent.

1964, Mar. 24   Photo.   Perf. 13
Sorolla Paintings: 25c, The Jug (woman and child). 40c, Oxen and Driver, horiz. 70c, Man and Woman from La Mancha. 80c, Fisher Woman of Valencia. 1p, Self-portrait. 1.50p, Round up, horiz. 2.50p, Fishermen, horiz. 3p, Children at the Beach, horiz. 5p, Unloading the Boat. 10p, Man and Woman on Horseback, Valencia.

Gold Frame
1215 A300 25c violet   .20 .20
1216 A300 40c purple   .20 .20
1217 A300 70c dp yellow grn   .20 .20
1218 A300 80c bluish grn   .20 .20
1219 A300 1p brown   .20 .20
1220 A300 1.50p Prus blue   .20 .20
1221 A300 2.50p dk car rose   .20 .20
1222 A300 3p violet blue   .45 .45

1223 A300 5p chocolate   1.40 1.00
1224 A300 10p deep green   .65 .35
   Nos. 1215-1224 (10)   3.90 3.20

Issued to honor Joaquin Sorolla y Bastida (1863-1923) and for Stamp Day, March 24.

For other art types see A236-A237, A240a, A246a, A257, A272, A285a, A310, A324, A340-A341, A360, A371 and footnote following No. 1606.

"Peace" A301

"Sport" — A302

Designs: 40c, Radio and television. 50c, New apartments. 70c, Agriculture. 80c, Reforestation. 1p, Economic development. 1.50p, Modern architecture. 2p, Transportation. 2.50p, Hydroelectric development. 3p, Electrification. 5p, Scientific achievements. 6p, Buildings, tourism. 10p, Generalissimo Franco.

1964, Apr. 1
1225 A301 25c blk, emer & gold   .20 .20
1226 A302 30c blk, bl & sal pink   .20 .20
1227 A301 40c gold & blk   .20 .20
1228 A302 50c multicolored   .20 .20
1229 A301 70c multicolored   .20 .20
1230 A301 80c multicolored   .20 .20
1231 A302 1p multicolored   .25 .20
1232 A301 1.50p multicolored   .20 .20
1233 A301 2p multicolored   .20 .20
1234 A302 2.50p multicolored   .20 .20
1235 A301 3p gold, blk & red   .90 .90
1236 A302 5p gold, grn & red   .30 .30
1237 A301 6p multicolored   .45 .45
1238 A302 10p multicolored   .55 .55
   Nos. 1225-1238 (14)   4.25 4.20

Issued to commemorate 25 years of peace.

Bullfight and Unisphere A303

Stamp of 1850 and Modern Stamps A304

Designs: 1p, Spanish pavilion, horiz. 2.50p, La Mota castle, Medina de Campo. 5p, Spanish dancer. 50p, Jai alai.

Perf. 12½x13, 13x12½
1964, Apr. 23   **Engr.**
1239 A303 1p bl grn & yel grn   .20 .20
1240 A303 1.50p carmine & brn   .20 .20
1241 A303 2.50p dk bl & sl grn   .20 .20
1242 A303 5p car & dk car rose   .30 .30
1243 A303 50p vio bl & dk bl   .85 .40
   Nos. 1239-1243 (5)   1.75 1.30

New York World's Fair, 1964-65.

1964, May 6   **Perf. 13x12½**
1244 A304 25c dk car rose & dl pur   .20 .20
1245 A304 1p yel grn & dk bl   .20 .20
1246 A304 10p orange & rose red   .40 .35
   Nos. 1244-1246 (3)   .80 .75

Issued for International Stamp Day, 1964.

Virgin of Hope — A305

Santa Maria — A306

1964, May 31   Photo.   Perf. 13x12½

1247	A305	1p dark green	.20	.20

Canonical coronation of the Virgin of Hope (La Macarena) in St. Gil's Church, Seville, May 31.

1964, July 16   Perf. 13

Designs (ships): 15c, 13th cent. ship of King Alfonso X, from medieval manuscript, vert. 25c, Carrack, from 15th cent. engraving, vert. 50c, Galley. 70c, Galleon. 80c, Xebec. 1p, Warship, Santisima Trinidad, vert. 1.50p, 18th cent. corvette, Atrevida, vert. 2p, Steamer, Isabel II. 2.50p, Frigate, Numancia, Spain's 1st armored ship. 3p, Destroyer. 5p, Submarine of Isaac Peral. 6p, Cruiser, Baleares. 10p, Training ship, Juan Sebastian Elcano.

1248	A306	15c dp rose & vio blk	.20	.20
1249	A306	25c org yel & gray grn	.20	.20
1250	A306	40c ultra & dk bl	.20	.20
1251	A306	50c slate grn & dk bl	.20	.20
1252	A306	70c vio & dk bl	.20	.20
1253	A306	80c dl bl grn & ultra	.20	.20
1254	A306	1p org & vio brn	.20	.20
1255	A306	1.50p car & sepia	.20	.20
1256	A306	2p blk & slate grn	.75	.20
1257	A306	2.50p rose car & dl vio	.20	.20
1258	A306	3p sepia & indigo	.20	.20
1259	A306	5p dk bl, lt grn & vio	.90	.90
1260	A306	6p lt green & vio	.80	.80
1261	A306	10p org yel & rose red	.35	.20
		Nos. 1248-1261 (14)	4.80	4.10

Issued to honor the Spanish Navy.

Europa Issue, 1964
Common Design Type

1964, Sept. 14   Photo.   Perf. 12½x13
Size: 21½x39mm

1262	CD7	1p bis, red & grn	.35	.20
1263	CD7	5p brt bl, mag & grn	1.25	1.10

Madonna of Alcazar — A307

Shot Put — A308

1964, Oct. 9   Photo.   Perf. 13

1264	A307	25c bister & brn	.20	.20
1265	A307	1p gray & indigo	.20	.20

Reconquest of Jerez de la Frontera, 700th anniv.

1964, Oct. 10
Gold Olympic Rings

1266	A308	25c shown	.20	.20
1267	A308	80c Broad jump	.20	.20
1268	A308	1p Slalom	.20	.20
1269	A308	3p Judo	.20	.20
1270	A308	5p Discus	.20	.20
		Nos. 1266-1270 (5)	1.00	1.00

1964 Olympic Games.

Builders of the New World
Portrait Type of 1961

25c, 2p, Diego de Almagro. 70c, 2.50p, Francisco de Toledo. 80c, 3p, Archbishop Toribio de Mogrovejo. 1p, 5p, Francisco Pizarro.

1964, Oct. 12   Perf. 13x12½

1271	A265	25c pale grn & vio	.20	.20
1272	A265	70c pink & ol gray	.20	.20
1273	A265	80c buff & Prus grn	.30	.20
1274	A265	1p buff & gray vio	.30	.20
1275	A265	2p pale bl & ol gray	.30	.20
1276	A265	2.50p pale grn & cl	.25	.20
1277	A265	3p gray & dk bl	3.00	1.00
1278	A265	5p yellow & brown	1.75	1.25
		Nos. 1271-1278 (8)	6.30	3.45

Christmas Type of 1963

Nativity by Francisco de Zurbaran (1598-1664).

1964, Dec. 4   Photo.

1279	A295	1p olive black	.20	.20

Tourism Types of 1964

Designs: 25c, Columbus monument, Barcelona. 30s, Facade of Santa Maria, Burgos. 50c, Santa Maria la Blanca (medieval synagogue), Toledo. 70c, Bridge, Zamora. 80c, La Giralda (tower) and Cathedral of Seville. 1p, Boat and nets in Cudillero harbor. No. 1286, Cathedral of Burgos, interior. No. 1287, View of Mogrovejo, Santander. 3p, Bridge, Cambados, Pontevedra. 6p, Silk merchants' hall (Lonja), Valencia, interior.

1965   Engr.   Perf. 13

1280	A298	25c dk blue & blk	.20	.20
1281	A298	30c dull grn & sep	.20	.20
1282	A298	50c cl & rose car	.20	.20
1283	A297	70c vio bl & ind	.20	.20
1284	A298	80c rose cl & dk pur	.20	.20
1285	A298	1p dp cl, car & blk	.20	.20
1286	A298	2.50p brn vio & bis	.20	.20
1287	A297	2.50p dull bl & gray	.20	.20
1288	A298	3p rose car & dk brn	.20	.20
1289	A298	6p slate & black	.20	.20
		Nos. 1280-1289 (10)	2.00	2.00

Alfonso X, the Wise (1232-84) A309

Julio Romero de Torres, Self-portrait A310

25c, Juan Donoso-Cortes (1809-53). 2.50p, Gaspar M. Jovellanos (1744-1810). 5p, St. Dominic de Guzman (1170-1221).

1965, Feb. 25   Engr.   Perf. 13x12½

1292	A309	25c slate bl & blk	.20	.20
1293	A309	70c blue & indigo	.20	.20
1294	A309	2.50p slate grn & sep	.20	.20
1295	A309	5p dull grn & sl grn	.25	.25
		Nos. 1292-1295 (4)	.85	.85

1965, Mar. 24   Photo.   Perf. 13

De Torres Paintings: 25c, Girl with Jar. 40c, "The Song" (girl with guitar). 70c, Madonna of the Lanterns. 80c, Girl with guitar. 1.50p, "The Poem of Cordova" (pensive woman). 2.50p, Martha and Mary. 3p, "The Poem of Cordova" (two women holding statue of angel). 5p, Girl with the Charcoal. 10p, Back of woman's head.

Gold Frame

1296	A310	25c dull purple	.20	.20
1297	A310	40c purple	.20	.20
1298	A310	70c olive green	.20	.20
1299	A310	80c slate green	.20	.20
1300	A310	1p dk red brn	.20	.20
1301	A310	1.50p blue green	.20	.20
1302	A310	2.50p lilac rose	.20	.20
1303	A310	3p dark blue	.35	.25
1304	A310	5p brown	.35	.25
1305	A310	10p slate green	.50	.30
		Nos. 1296-1305 (10)	2.60	2.20

Issued to honor Julio Romero de Torres (1880-1930) and for Stamp Day, March 24. For other art types see A236-A237, A240a, A246a, A257, A272, A285a, A300, A324, A340-A341, A360, A371 and footnote following No. 1606.

Bull and Symbolic Stamps — A311

1965, May 6   Perf. 13x12½

1306	A311	25c multicolored	.20	.20
1307	A311	1p orange & multi	.20	.20
1308	A311	10p multicolored	.50	.30
		Nos. 1306-1308 (3)	.90	.70

Issued for International Stamp Day, 1965.

ITU Emblem, Old and New Communication Equipment — A312

1965, May 17   Perf. 12½x13

1309	A312	1p salmon, blk & red	.20	.20

International Telecommunication Union, cent.

Pilgrim — A313

Explorer, Royal Flag of Spain and Ships — A314

Design: 2p, Pilgrim (profile).

1965, July 25   Photo.   Perf. 13

1310	A313	1p multicolored	.20	.20
1311	A313	2p multicolored	.20	.20

Issued to commemorate the Holy Year of St. James of Compostela, patron saint of Spain.

1965, Aug. 28   Perf. 13x12½

1312	A314	3p red, blk & yel	.20	.20

400th anniv. of the settlement of Florida, and the 1st permanent European settlement in the continental US, St. Augustine, Fla. See US No. 1271.

St. Benedict — A315

Sports Palace, Madrid — A316

Europa Issue, 1965

1965, Sept. 27   Engr.   Perf. 13x12½

1313	A315	1p yel grn & sl grn	.20	.20
1314	A315	5p lilac & violet	.50	.30

1965, Oct. 9   Photo.   Perf. 13

1315	A316	1p gray, gold & dk brn	.20	.20

Issued to commemorate the meeting of the International Olympic Committee in Madrid.

Builders of the New World
Portrait Type of 1961

25c, 2p, Don Fadrique de Toledo. 70c, 2.50p, Father José de Anchieta. 80c, 3p, Francisco de Orellana. 1p, 5p, St. Luis Beltran.

1965, Oct. 12   Photo.   Perf. 13x12½

1316	A265	25c pale grn & dp pur	.20	.20
1317	A265	70c pink & brown	.20	.20
1318	A265	80c cream & Prus grn	.20	.20
1319	A265	1p buff & dk vio	.20	.20
1320	A265	2p lt bl & dk ol grn	.20	.20
1321	A265	2.50p lt blue & pur	.20	.20
1322	A265	3p gray & dk bl	1.00	.35
1323	A265	5p yellow & brn	1.00	.20
		Nos. 1316-1323 (8)	3.20	1.85

Chamber of Charles V, Yuste Monastery A317

Stamp of 1865 (No. 78) A318

Yuste Monastery: 1p, Courtyard, horiz. 5p, View of monastery, horiz.

Perf. 12½x13, 13x12½

1324	A317	1p bl gray & blk	.20	.20
1325	A317	2p red brn & brn blk	.20	.20
1326	A317	5p grayish bl & grn	.25	.25
		Nos. 1324-1326 (3)	.65	.65

Monastery of Yuste, Estremadura.

1965, Nov. 22   Perf. 13x12½

Designs: 1p, Stamp of 1865 (No. 77). 5p, Stamp of 1865 (No. 80).

1327	A318	80c blk & yel grn	.20	.20
1328	A318	1p plum, brn & rose	.20	.20
1329	A318	5p sepia & org brn	.20	.20
		Nos. 1327-1329 (3)	.60	.60

Cent. of the 1st Spanish perforated postage stamps.

Nativity A319

1965, Dec. 1   Photo.   Perf. 12½x13

1330	A319	1p bright green	.20	.20

Virgin of Peace, Antipolo A320

Globe and Four Beasts of Apocalypse A321

Design: 3p, Father Andres de Urdaneta.

1965, Dec. 3   *Perf. 13x12½*
1331 A320 1p pale sal & ol brn   .20 .20
1332 A320 3p gray & dp blue   .20 .20
Christianization of the Philippines, 400th anniv.

1965, Dec. 29   **Photo.**   *Perf. 13x12½*
1333 A321 1p grnsh bl, yel & brn   .20 .20
Vatican II, the 21st Ecumenical Council of the Roman Catholic Church, 10/11/62-12/8/65.

Adm. Alvaro de Bazan (1526-88) A322

Exhibition Emblem; Type Block "P" A323

2p, Daza de Valdes, scientist, 17th cent.

1966, Feb. 26   **Engr.**   *Perf. 13x12½*
1334 A322 25c dull blue & gray   .20 .20
1335 A322 2p magenta & violet   .20 .20
See Nos. C177-C178.

1966, Mar. 4   **Photo.**   *Perf. 13*
1336 A323 1p red, grn & vio bl   .20 .20
Graphic Arts and Advertising Packaging Exhibition "Graphispack," Barcelona, 3/4-13.

José Maria Sert, Self-portrait A324

Santa Maria Church, Guernica — A325

Sert Paintings: 25c, The Magic Ball. 40c, Evocation of Toledo, horiz. 70c, Christ on the Cross. 80c, Parachutists. 1.50p, "Audacity." 2.50p, "Justice." 3p, Jacob Wrestling with the Angel. 5p, "The Five Continents." 10p, Sts. Peter and Paul.

1966, Mar. 24
      Gold Frame
1337 A324 25c dk purple   .20 .20
1338 A324 40c dp magenta   .20 .20
1339 A324 70c green   .20 .20
1340 A324 80c dk ol grn   .20 .20
1341 A324 1p claret brn   .20 .20
1342 A324 1.50p dull blue   .20 .20
1343 A324 2.50p dk red   .20 .20
1344 A324 3p deep blue   .20 .20
1345 A324 5p sepia   .20 .20
1346 A324 10p grnsh blk   .20 .20
   Nos. 1337-1346 (10)   2.00 2.00
Issued to honor José Maria Sert (1876-1945) and for Stamp Day, Mar. 24.
For other art types see A236-A237, A240a, A246a, A257, A272, A285a, A300, A310, A340-A341, A360, A371 and footnote following No. 1606.

1966, Apr. 28   **Photo.**   *Perf. 13*
Designs: 1p, Arms of Guernica and Luno. 3p, Tree of Guernica.
1347 A325 80c bl, sepia & grn   .20 .20
1348 A325 1p yel grn & multi   .20 .20
1349 A325 3p bl, grn & vio brn   .20 .20
   Nos. 1347-1349 (3)   .60 .60
Founding of Guernica and Luno, 6th cent.

Cover with Stamp of 1850 (#1) A326

Designs (covers): 1p, 5r (#3). 10p, 10r (#5).

1966, May 6   *Perf. 12½x13*
1350 A326 25c rose vio, blk & red   .20 .20
1351 A326 1p red brn, org & blk   .20 .20
1352 A326 10p ol grn, grn & org   .25 .20
   Nos. 1350-1352 (3)   .65 .60
Issued for International Stamp Day, 1966.

Bohi Valley — A327

Torla, Huesca A328

Tourism: 40c, Portal of Sigena Monastery, Huesca. 50c, Santo Domingo Church, Soria. 80c, Torre del Oro, Seville. 1p, Palm and view, Pico de Teyde, Santa Cruz de Tenerife. 1.50p, Monastery of Guadalupe, Caceres. 2p, Alcala de Henares University. 3p, Seo Cathedral, Lerida. 10p, Courtyard of St. Gregorio, Valladolid.

1966   **Engr.**   *Perf. 13*
1353 A327 10c gray grn & bl grn   .20 .20
1354 A328 15c gray grn & brn   .20 .20
1355 A327 40c bis brn & brn   .20 .20
1356 A327 50c car rose & dp cl   .20 .20
1357 A327 80c lilac & rose vio   .20 .20
1358 A327 1p vio bl & bl grn   .20 .20
1359 A328 1.50p dk bl & blk   .20 .20
1360 A328 2p sl bl & sepia   .20 .20
1361 A328 3p ultra & blk   .20 .20
1362 A327 10p brt bl & grnsh bl   .20 .20
   Nos. 1353-1362 (10)   2.00 2.00

Tree and Globe A329

1966, June 6   **Photo.**   *Perf. 12½x13*
1363 A329 1p brn & dk grn   .20 .20
6th Intl. Forestry Cong., Madrid, June 6-18.

Navy Emblem — A330

1966, July 1   **Photo.**   *Perf. 13*
1364 A330 1p gray & dk bl   .20 .20
Naval Week, Barcelona, July 1-8.

Guadamur Castle — A331

Castles: 25c, Alcazar, Segovia. 40c, La Mota. 50c, Olite. 70c, Monteagudo. 80c, Butron, vert. 1p, Manzanares. 3p, Almansa, vert.

1966, Aug. 13   **Engr.**   *Perf. 13*
1365 A331 10c grysh bl & sep   .20 .20
1366 A331 25c violet & purple   .20 .20
1367 A331 40c grnsh bl & bl grn   .20 .20
1368 A331 50c grnsh bl & ultra   .20 .20
1369 A331 70c vio bl & ind   .20 .20
1370 A331 80c vio & sl grn   .20 .20
1371 A331 1p ol bis & gray   .20 .20
1372 A331 3p rose & red lil   .20 .20
   Nos. 1365-1372 (8)   1.60 1.60

Don Quixote, Dulcinea and Aldonza Lorenzo — A332

1966, Sept. 5   **Photo.**   *Perf. 13*
1373 A332 1.50p sal, lt grn & blk   .20 .20
4th World Congress of Psychiatry, Madrid.

Europa Issue, 1966

The Rape of Europa A333

1966, Sept. 28   **Photo.**   *Perf. 12½x13*
1374 A333 1p multicolored   .20 .20
1375 A333 5p multicolored   .25 .20

Don Quixote and Sancho Panza on Clavileno A334

Title Page of "Dotrina Christiana" A335

1966, Oct. 9   *Perf. 13x12½*
1376 A334 1.50p sl bl, red brn & dk brn   .20 .20
17th Cong. of the Intl. Astronautical Federation.

Builders of the New World
Types of 1961 and A335

30c, Antonio de Mendoza. 1p, José A. Manso de Velasco. 1.20p, Coins of Lima, 1699. 1.50p, Manuel de Castro y Padilla. 3p, Portal of Oruro Convent, Bolivia. 3.50p, Manuel de Amat. 6p, Inca courier, El Chasqui.

1966, Oct. 12
1377 A265 30c pale pink & brn   .20 .20
1378 A335 50c pale bis & brn   .20 .20
1379 A265 1p gray & vio   .20 .20
1380 A335 1.20p gray & slate   .20 .20
1381 A265 1.50p pale grn & dp grn   .20 .20
1382 A335 3p pale gray & dp bl   .20 .20
1383 A265 3.50p pale lil & pur   .25 .25
1384 A265 6p buff & sepia   .20 .20
   Nos. 1377-1384 (8)   1.65 1.65

Ramon del Valle Inclan — A336

Portraits: 3p, Carlos Arniches. 6p, Jacinto Benavente y Martinez.

1966, Nov. 7   **Photo.**   *Perf. 13*
1385 A336 1.50p blk & green   .20 .20
1386 A336 3p blk & gray vio   .20 .20
1387 A336 6p blk & slate   .20 .20
   Nos. 1385-1387 (3)   .60 .60
Issued to honor Spanish writers. See design A355.

Carthusian Monastery, Jerez A337

St. Mary Carthusian Monastery: 1p, Portal, vert. 5p, Entrance gate.

    Perf. 13x12½, 12½x13
1966, Nov. 24   **Engr.**
1388 A337 1p grnsh bl & sl bl   .20 .20
1389 A337 2p green & yel grn   .20 .20
1390 A337 5p lilac & claret   .20 .20
   Nos. 1388-1390 (3)   .60 .60

Nativity, Sculpture by Pedro Duque Cornejo A338

1966, Dec. 5   **Photo.**   *Perf. 12½x13*
1391 A338 1.50p multicolored   .20 .20

Regional Costumes Issue

Woman from Alava — A339

1967   **Photo.**   *Perf. 13*
1392 A339 6p shown   .20 .20
1393 A339 6p Albacete   .20 .20
1394 A339 6p Alicante   .20 .20
1395 A339 6p Almeria   .20 .20
1396 A339 6p Avila   .20 .20
1397 A339 6p Badajoz   .20 .20
1398 A339 6p Baleares   .20 .20
1399 A339 6p Barcelona   .20 .20
1400 A339 6p Burgos   .20 .20
1401 A339 6p Caceres   .20 .20
1402 A339 6p Cadiz   .20 .20
1403 A339 6p Castellon de la Plana   .20 .20
   Nos. 1392-1403 (12)   2.40 2.40

1968
1404 A339 6p Ciudad Real   .20 .20
1405 A339 6p Cordoba   .20 .20
1406 A339 6p Coruna   .20 .20
1407 A339 6p Cuenca   .20 .20
1408 A339 6p Fernando Po   .20 .20
1409 A339 6p Gerona   .20 .20
1410 A339 6p Gran Canaria, Las Palmas   .20 .20
1411 A339 6p Granada   .20 .20
1412 A339 6p Guadalajara   .20 .20
1413 A339 6p Guipuzcoa   .20 .20
1414 A339 6p Huelva   .20 .20
1415 A339 6p Huesca   .20 .20
   Nos. 1404-1415 (12)   2.40 2.40

1969
1416 A339 6p Ifni   .20 .20
1417 A339 6p Jaen   .20 .20
1418 A339 6p Leon   .20 .20
1419 A339 6p Lerida   .20 .20
1420 A339 6p Logroño   .20 .20
1421 A339 6p Lugo   .20 .20

1422	A339	6p Madrid	.20	.20
1423	A339	6p Malaga	.20	.20
1424	A339	6p Murcia	.20	.20
1425	A339	6p Navarra	.20	.20
1426	A339	6p Orense	.20	.20
1427	A339	6p Oviedo	.20	.20
	Nos. 1416-1427 (12)		2.40	2.40

1970

1428	A339	6p Palencia	.20	.20
1429	A339	6p Pontevedra	.20	.20
1430	A339	6p Sahara	.20	.20
1431	A339	6p Salamanca	.20	.20
1432	A339	6p Santa Cruz de Tenerife	.20	.20
1433	A339	6p Santander	.20	.20
1434	A339	6p Segovia	.20	.20
1435	A339	6p Seville	.20	.20
1436	A339	6p Soria	.20	.20
1437	A339	6p Tarragona	.20	.20
1438	A339	6p Teruel	.20	.20
1439	A339	6p Toledo	.20	.20
	Nos. 1428-1439 (12)		2.40	2.40

1971

1440	A339	6p Valencia	.20	.20
1441	A339	8p Valladolid	.20	.20
1442	A339	8p Vizcaya	.20	.20
1443	A339	8p Zamora	.20	.20
1444	A339	8p Zaragoza	.20	.20
	Nos. 1440-1444 (5)		1.00	1.00
	Nos. 1392-1444 (53)		10.60	10.60

Archers
A340

Ornament — A341

50c, Boar hunt. 1.20p, Bison. 1.50p, Hands. 2p, Warrior. 2.50p, Deer. 3.50p, Archers. 4p, Hunters & gazelle. 6p, Hunters & deer herd.

1967, Mar. 27   Photo.   Perf. 13
Gold Frame

1449	A340	40c ocher & car rose	.20	.20
1450	A340	50c gray & dk red	.20	.20
1451	A341	1p ocher & org ver	.20	.20
1452	A340	1.20p gray & rose brn	.20	.20
1453	A340	1.50p gray & red	.20	.20
1454	A341	2p lt brn & dk car rose	.20	.20
1455	A341	2.50p sky bl & rose brn	.20	.20
1456	A340	3.50p yellow & blk	.20	.20
1457	A341	4p citron & red	.20	.20
1458	A341	6p olive & red	.20	.20
	Nos. 1449-1458 (10)		2.00	2.00

Issued for Stamp Day, 1967. The designs are from paleolithic and mesolithic wall paintings found in Spanish caves.

For other art types see A236-A237, A240a, A246a, A257, A272, A285a, A300, A310, A324, A360, A371 and footnote following No. 1606.

Palma Cathedral and Conference Emblem — A342

1967, Mar. 28
1459 A342 1.50p brt blue grn   .20   .20
Issued to publicize the Congress of the Interparliamentary Union, Palma de Mallorca.

W. K. Röntgen, X-ray Tube and Atom — A343

1967, Apr. 3   Photo.   Perf. 13
1460 A343 1.50p green   .20   .20
7th Cong. of Latin Radiologists and 1st Cong. of European Radiologists, Barcelona, Apr. 2-8.

Averroes (1120-1198), Physician and Philosopher — A344

Portraits: 3.50p, José de Acosta (1539-1600), Jesuit, historian, poet. 4p, Moses ben Maimonides (1135-1204), Jewish philosopher and physician. 25p, Andres Laguna, 16th century physician.

1967, Apr. 6   Engr.   Perf. 13x12½

1461	A344	1.20p lil & dl vio	.20	.20
1462	A344	3.50p mag & dl pur	.20	.20
1463	A344	4p brn & sep	.20	.20
1464	A344	25p dl bl & blk	.25	.20
	Nos. 1461-1464 (4)		.85	.80

Europa Issue, 1967
Common Design Type

1967, May 2   Photo.   Perf. 13
Size: 25x31mm

1465	CD10	1.50p sl grn, red brn & dl red	.20	.20
1466	CD10	6p vio, brt bl & brn	.20	.20

Exhibition Building and Fountain, Valencia — A345

1967, May 3
1467 A345 1.50p gray grn   .20   .20
International Fair at Valencia, 50th anniv.

Numeral Postmark No. 3 of 1850 — A346

Guardian Angel Over Indigent Sleeper — A347

Designs: 1.50p, No. 2, 12c stamp of 1850 with crowned M postmark of Madrid. 6p, No. 4, 6r stamp of 1850 with 1r postmark.

1967, May 6

1468	A346	40c brn org, dl bl & blk	.20	.20
1469	A346	1.50p brn, grn & blk	.20	.20
1470	A346	6p bl, red & blk	.20	.20
	Nos. 1468-1470 (3)		.60	.60

Intl. Stamp Day, 1967. See #1527-1528.

1967, May 16   Perf. 13

1471	A347	1.50p bl, blk, brn & red	.20	.20

Issued for National Caritas Day to honor Caritas, Catholic welfare organization.

Betanzos Church, Coruña — A348

International Tourist Year Emblem A349

Tourism: 1p, Tower of St. Miguel Church, Palencia. 1.50p, Human pyramid (Castellers). 2.50p, Columbus monument, Huelva. 5p, The Enchanted City, Cuenca. 6p, Church of Our Lady, Sanlucar, Cadiz.

1967, July 26   Engr.   Perf. 13

1472	A348	10c ultra & blk	.20	.20
1473	A348	1p dl bl & blk	.20	.20
1474	A348	1.50p lt brn & blk	.20	.20
1475	A348	2.50p grnsh bl & dk bl	.20	.20
1476	A349	3.50p dl pur & dk bl	.20	.20
1477	A348	5p yel grn & dk grn	.20	.20
1478	A348	6p red lil & dl lil	.20	.20
	Nos. 1472-1478 (7)		1.40	1.40

Balsareny Castle — A350

Castles: 1p, Jarandilla. 1.50p, Almodovar. 2p, Ponferrada, vert. 2.50p, Peniscola. 5p, Coca. 6p, Loarre. 10p, Belmonte.

1967, Aug. 11   Engr.

1479	A350	50c gray & lt brn	.20	.20
1480	A350	1p bl gray & dl pur	.20	.20
1481	A350	1.50p bl gray & sage grn	.20	.20
1482	A350	2p brick red & bis brn	.20	.20
1483	A350	2.50p grnsh bl & sep	.20	.20
1484	A350	5p rose vio & vio bl	.20	.20
1485	A350	6p bis brn & gray brn	.20	.20
1486	A350	10p aqua & slate	.20	.20
	Nos. 1479-1486 (8)		1.60	1.60

Globe, Snowflake and Thermometer A351

Galleon, Map of Americas, Spain and Philippines A352

1967, Aug. 30   Photo.
1487 A351 1.50p bright blue   .20   .20
12th Intl. Refrigeration Cong., Madrid, Sept. 4-8.

1967, Oct. 10   Photo.   Perf. 13
1488 A352 1.50p red lilac   .20   .20
4th Congress of Spanish, Portuguese, American & Philippine Municipalities, Barcelona, Oct. 6-12.

Builders of the New World
Type of 1961 and

Nootka Settlement A353

Designs: 40c, Francisco de la Bodega. 50c, Old map of Nootka coast, vert. 1p, Francisco Antonio Mourelle. 1.50p, Esteban José Martinez. 3p, Old maps of coast of Northern California. 3.50p, Cayetano Valdes. 6p, Ships, San Elias, Alaska.

1967, Oct. 12

1489	A265	40c pink & grnsh gray	.20	.20
1490	A353	50c dk brn	.20	.20
1491	A265	1p pale bl & red lil	.20	.20
1492	A353	1.20p dk ol grn	.20	.20
1493	A353	1.50p pale pink & bl grn	.20	.20
1494	A353	3p buff & vio blk	.20	.20
1495	A265	3.50p pale pink & bl	.25	.25
1496	A353	6p red brn, *bluish*	.20	.20
	Nos. 1489-1496 (8)		1.65	1.65

Issued to honor the explorers of the Northwest coast of North America.

Roman Statue and Gate A354

José Bethencourt A355

Designs: 3.50p, Ancient plower with ox team, horiz. 6p, Roman coins of Caceres.

1967, Oct. 31   Photo.   Perf. 13

1497	A354	1.50p multi	.20	.20
1498	A354	3.50p multi	.20	.20
1499	A354	6p multi	.20	.20
	Nos. 1497-1499 (3)		.60	.60

Founding of Caceres by the Romans, 2000th anniv.

1967, Nov. 15

1.50p, Enrique Granados (composer). 3.50p, Ruben Dario (poet). 6p, St. Ildefonso.

1500	A355	1.20p gray & red brn	.20	.20
1501	A355	1.50p blk & grn	.20	.20
1502	A355	3.50p brn & pur	.20	.20
1503	A355	6p blk & slate	.20	.20
	Nos. 1500-1503 (4)		.80	.80

Issued to honor famous Spanish men. See design A336.

Santa Maria de
Veruela
Monastery
A356

St. José Receiving
Last Unction, by
Goya
A357

Designs: 3.50p, Aerial view of monastery,
horiz. 6p, Inside view, horiz.

1967, Nov. 24   Engr.   Perf. 13
1504 A356 1.50p ultra & ind   .20 .20
1505 A356 3.50p grn & blk   .20 .20
1506 A356 6p rose vio & bis
            brn   .20 .20
    Nos. 1504-1506 (3)   .60 .60

1967, Nov. 27   Photo.
1507 A357 1.50p multi   .20 .20

200th anniversary of the canonization of St.
José de Calasanz (1556-1648), founder of the
first Christian Schools in Rome.

Nativity, by
Francisco
Salzillo — A358

1967, Dec. 5
1508 A358 1.50p multi   .20 .20

Christmas, 1967.

Slalom
A359

3.50p, Bobsled, vert. 6p, Ice hockey.

1968, Feb. 6   Photo.   Perf. 13
1509 A359 1.50p multi   .20 .20
1510 A359 3.50p multi   .20 .20
1511 A359 6p multi   .20 .20
    Nos. 1509-1511 (3)   .60 .60

Issued to commemorate the 10th Winter
Olympic Games, Grenoble, France, Feb. 6-18.

Mariano Fortuny,
Self-portrait
A360

Fortuny Paintings: 40c, The Vicariate, horiz.
50c, "Fantasy" (pianist). 1p, "Idyll" (piper and
sheep). 1.20p, The Print Collector, horiz. 2p,
Old Man in the Sun. 2.50p, Calabrian Man.
3.50p, Lady with Fan. 4p, Battle of Tetuan,
1860. 6p, Queen Christina in Carriage, horiz.

1968, Mar. 25   Photo.   Perf. 13
Gold Frame
1512 A360 · 40c dp red lil   .20 .20
1513 A360 50c dk bl grn   .20 .20
1514 A360   1p brown   .20 .20
1515 A360 1.20p dp vio   .20 .20
1516 A360 1.50p dp grn   .20 .20
1517 A360   2p org brn   .20 .20
1518 A360 2.50p car rose   .20 .20
1519 A360 3.50p dk red brn   .20 .20
1520 A360   4p dk ol   .20 .20
1521 A360   6p brt bl   .20 .20
    Nos. 1512-1521 (10)   2.00 2.00

Issued to honor Mariano Fortuny y Carbo
(1838-74), and for Stamp Day.
For other art types see A236-A237, A240a,
A246a, A257, A272, A285a, A300, A310,

A324, A340-A341, A371 and footnote following No. 1606.

Beatriz
Galindo
A361

Famous Women: 1.50p, Agustina de Aragon. 3.50p, Maria Pacheco. 6p, Rosalia de
Castro.

1968, Apr. 8   Engr.   Perf. 12½x13
1522 A361 1.20p yel brn & blk   .20 .20
1523 A361 1.50p bl grn & dk bl   .20 .20
1524 A361 3.50p lt vio & dk vio .20 .20
1525 A361 6p gray bl & blk   .20 .20
    Nos. 1522-1525 (4)   .80 .80

Europa Issue, 1968
Common Design Type
1968, Apr. 29   Photo.   Perf. 13
Size: 38x22mm
1526 CD11 3.50p brt bl, gold &
            brn   .20 .20

Spain No. 1 with
Galicia Puebla
Postmark — A362

Map of León and
Seal — A363

Stamp Day: 3.50p, Spain No. 4 with Serena
postmark.

1968, May 6   Photo.   Perf. 13
1527 A362 1.50p blk, bl & ocher .20 .20
1528 A362 3.50p bl, dk grn & blk .20 .20

See Nos. 1568-1569, 1608, 1677, 1754.

Perf. 13x12½, 12½x13
1968, June 15   Photo.

Designs: 1.50p, Roman legionary. 3.50p,
Emperor Galba coin, horiz.
Size: 25x38½mm
1529 A363 1p lil, red brn & yel .20 .20
Size: 25x47½mm
1530 A363 1.50p brn, dk brn &
            buff   .20 .20
Size: 37½x26mm
1531 A363 3.50p ocher & sl grn   .25 .25
    Nos. 1529-1531 (3)   .65 .65

1900th anniversary of the founding of León
by the Roman Legion VII Gemina.

Human Rights
Emblem
A364

Benavente Palace,
Baeza
A365

1968, June 25   Photo.   Perf. 13x12½
1532 A364 3.50p bl, red & grn   .20 .20

International Human Rights Year, 1968.

1968, July 15   Engr.   Perf. 13
Tourism: 1.20p, View of Salamanca with
Tormes River Bridge, horiz. 1.50p, Statuary
group from St. Vincent's Church, Avila (The
Adoration of the Magi). 2p, Tomb of Martin
Vazquez de Arce, Cathedral of Sigüenza,
horiz. 3.50p, Portal of St. Mary's Church,
Sangüesa, Navarre.
1533 A365 50c dp rose & brn   .20 .20
1534 A365 1.20p emer & sl grn   .20 .20
1535 A365 1.50p dp grn & ind   .20 .20
1536 A365   2p lil rose & blk   .20 .20
1537 A365 3.50p brt lil & rose lil .20 .20
    Nos. 1533-1537 (5)   1.00 1.00

Escalona
Castle,
Toledo — A366

Castles: 1.20p, Fuensaldaña, Valladolid.
1.50p, Peñafiel, Valladolid. 2.50p, Vil-
lasobroso, Pontevedra. 6p, Frias, Burgos,
vert.

1968, July 29   Engr.   Perf. 13
1538 A366 40c dk bl & sepia   .20 .20
1539 A366 1.20p vio brn & vio
            blk   .20 .20
1540 A366 1.50p ol & blk   .20 .20
1541 A366 2.50p ol grn & blk   .20 .20
1542 A366 6p vio bl & bl grn   .20 .20
    Nos. 1538-1542 (5)   1.00 1.00

Rifle
Shooting
A367

Designs: 1.50p, Horse jumping. 3.50p,
Bicycling. 6p, Sailing, vert.

Perf. 12½x13, 13x12½
1968, Sept. 24   Photo.
1543 A367   1p multi   .20 .20
1544 A367 1.50p multi   .20 .20
1545 A367 3.50p multi   .20 .20
1546 A367 6p multi   .20 .20
    Nos. 1543-1546 (4)   .80 .80

19th Olympic Games, Mexico City, 10/12-27.

Builders of the New World
Type of 1961 and

Map of Capuchin
Missions along
Orinoco River,
1732 — A368

1p, Diego de Losada. 1.50p, Losada family
coat of arms. 3.50p, Diego de Henares. 6p,
Map of Caracas, drawn by Diego de Henares,
1578, horiz.

1968, Oct. 12   Photo.   Perf. 13
1547 A368 40c grnsh bl, bluish .20 .20
1548 A265   1p red lil, gray   .20 .20
1549 A368 1.50p sl, pale rose   .20 .20
1550 A265 3.50p dk bl, pnksh   .20 .20
1551 A368 6p dk ol bis   .20 .20
    Nos. 1547-1551 (5)   1.00 1.00

Christianization of Venezuela and the founding of Caracas.

St. Maria del Parral
Monastery,
Segovia — A369

3.50p, Monastery, inside view. 6p, Madonna
& Child, statue from main altar.

1968, Nov. 25   Engr.   Perf. 13
1552 A369 1.50p gray bl & rose
            vio   .20 .20
1553 A369 3.50p brn & red brn   .20 .20
1554 A369 6p rose claret &
            brn   .20 .20
    Nos. 1552-1554 (3)   .60 .60

Nativity, by
Federico Fiori da
Urbino — A370

Alonso Cano by
Velázquez
A371

1968, Dec. 2   Photo.   Perf. 13x12½
1555 A370 1.50p gold & multi   .20 .20

Christmas, 1968.

1969, Mar. 24   Photo.   Perf. 13
Cano Paintings: 40c, St. Agnes. 50c, St.
John. 1p, Jesus and Angel. 2p, Holy Family.
2.50p, Circumcision of Jesus. 3p, Jesus and
the Samaritan Woman. 3.50p, Madonna and
Child. 4p, Sts. John Capistrano and Bernardino, horiz. 6p, Vision of St. John the Baptist.

Gold Frame
1556 A371 40c deep plum   .20 .20
1557 A371 50c green   .20 .20
1558 A371   1p sepia   .20 .20
1559 A371 1.50p slate grn   .20 .20
1560 A371   2p red brown   .20 .20
1561 A371 2.50p dp red lil   .20 .20
1562 A371   3p ultra   .20 .20
1563 A371 3.50p dk rose brn   .20 .20
1564 A371   4p dull lilac   .20 .20
1565 A371   6p slate blue   .20 .20
    Nos. 1556-1565 (10)   2.00 2.00

Alonso Cano (1601-1667), and Stamp Day.
For other art types see A236-A237, A240a,
A246a, A257, A272, A285a, A300, A310,
A324, A340-A341, A360 and footnote follow-
ing No. 1606.

DNA
(Genetic
Code)
Molecule
and Chart
A372

1969, Apr. 7   Photo.   Perf. 13
1566 A372 1.50p gray & multi   .20 .20

Issued to publicize the 6th European Congress of Biochemistry, Madrid, Apr. 7-11.

Europa Issue, 1969
Common Design Type
1969, Apr. 28
Size: 38x22mm
1567 CD12 3.50p multi   .20 .20

Stamp Day Type of 1968

1.50p, Spain #6 with crowned M postmark.
3.50p, Spain #11 with Corvera postmark.

1969, May 6   Photo.   Perf. 13
1568 A362 1.50p blk, red & grn   .20 .20
1569 A362 3.50p grn, bl & red   .20 .20

Issued for Stamp Day, 1969.

Spectrum
A373

1969, May 26
1570 A373 1.50p blk & multi   .20   .20

Issued to publicize the 15th International Spectroscopy Colloquium, Madrid, May 26-30.

World Map, Red Crescent, Cross, Lion and Sun Emblems
A374

1969, May 30
1571 A374 1.50p multi   .20   .20

League of Red Cross Societies, 50th anniv.

Last Supper, Finial from Lugo Cathedral — A375

1969, June 4
1572 A375 1.50p grn, brn & blk   .20   .20

300th anniversary of the dedication of Galicia Province to the reign of Jesus.

Turegano Castle, Segovia
A376

Father Junipero Serra — A377

Castles: 1.50p, Villalonso, Zamora. 2.50p, Velez Blanco, Almeria. 3.50p, Castilnovo, Segovia. 6p, Torrelobaton, Valladolid.

1969, June 24   Engr.   Perf. 13
1573 A376   1p dl grn & sl   .20   .20
1574 A376 1.50p bluish lil & dk bl   .20   .20
1575 A376 2.50p bl vio & bluish lil   .20   .20
1576 A376 3.50p red brn & ol grn   .20   .20
1577 A376   6p gray grn & dl brn   .20   .20
    Nos. 1573-1577 (5)   1.00   1.00

1969, July 16   Photo.   Perf. 13
1578 A377 1.50p multi   .20   .20

Bicentenary of San Diego, Calif.

Rock of Gibraltar — A378

Dama de Elche — A379

2p, View of Gibraltar across the Bay of Algeciras.

1969, July 18
1579 A378 1.50p bl grn   .20   .20
1580 A378   2p brt rose lil   .20   .20

1969, July 23   Engr.   Perf. 13
Tourism: 1.50p, Alcañiz Castle, Teruel, horiz. 3p, Murcia Cathedral. 6p, St. Maria de la Redonda, Logrono.

1581 A379 1.50p dl grn & blk   .20   .20
1582 A379   3p yel grn & bl grn   .20   .20
1583 A379 3.50p gray bl & dk bl   .20   .20
1584 A379   6p yel grn & vio blk   .20   .20
    Nos. 1581-1584 (4)   .80   .80

Builders of the New World
Type of 1961 and

Santo Domingo Church, Santiago, Chile — A380

1.50p, Casa de Moneda de Chile, horiz. 2p, Ambrosio O'Higgins. 3.50p, Pedro de Valdivia. 6p, First large bridge over Mapocho River, horiz.

1969, Oct. 12   Photo.   Perf. 13
1585 A380 40c lt bl & dk red brn   .20   .20
1586 A380 1.50p pale rose & dk vio   .20   .20
1587 A265   2p pale pink & ol   .20   .20
1588 A265 3.50p pale yel & dk Prus grn   .35   .30
1589 A380   6p pale yel & blk brn   .25   .20
    Nos. 1585-1589 (5)   1.20   1.10

Exploration and development of Chile. See Nos. 1630-1631, 1634.

Adoration of the Magi, by Juan Bautista Mayno — A381

Christmas: 2p, Nativity, bas-relief from altar of Cathedral of Gerona.

1969, Nov. 3
1590 A381 1.50p multi   .20   .20
1591 A381   2p multi   .20   .20

Tomb of Alfonso VIII and Wife, Las Huelgas Monastery, Burgos — A382

Designs: 1.50p, Las Huelgas Monastery. 6p, Inside view, vert.

1969, Nov. 22   Engr.
1592 A382 1.50p lt bl grn & indigo   .20   .20
1593 A382 3.50p ultra & vio bl   .40   .35
1594 A382   6p olive & yel grn   .20   .20
    Nos. 1592-1594 (3)   .85   .75
    See Nos. 1639-1641.

St. Juan de Avila, by El Greco — A383

St. Stephen, by Luis de Morales — A384

Design: 50p, Bishop Rodrigo Ximenez de Rada, Juan de Borgona mural.

1970, Feb. 25   Engr.   Perf. 13
1595 A383 25p pale pur & ind   4.00   .20
1596 A383 50p brn org & brn   1.60   .20

1970, Mar. 24   Photo.   Perf. 13
Morales Paintings: 1p, Annunciation. 1.50p, Madonna and Child with St. John. 2p, Madonna and Child. 3p, Presentation at the Temple. 3.50p, St. Jerome. 4p, St. John de Ribera. 5p, Ecce Homo. 6p, Pieta. 10p, St. Francis of Assisi.

1597 A384 50c gold & multi   .20   .20
1598 A384   1p gold & multi   .20   .20
1599 A384 1.50p gold & multi   .20   .20
1600 A384   2p gold & multi   .20   .20
1601 A384   3p gold & multi   .20   .20
1602 A384 3.50p gold & multi   .20   .20
1603 A384   4p gold & multi   .20   .20
1604 A384   5p gold & multi   .20   .20
1605 A384   6p gold & multi   .20   .20
1606 A384   10p gold & multi   .20   .20
    Nos. 1597-1606 (10)   2.00   2.00

Issued to honor Luis de Morales, "El Divino" (1509-1586), and for Stamp Day.
For other art types see A397, A410, A431, A448, A473, A501, A522, A538, A558 and footnote following No. 876.

Europa Issue, 1970
Common Design Type
1970, May 4   Photo.   Perf. 13x12½
Size: 37½x22mm
1607 CD13 3.50p brt bl & gold   .20   .20

Stamp Day Type of 1968
Stamp Day: 2p, Spain No. 51 with "Ferro Carril de Langreo" postmark.

1970, May 4   Perf. 13x12½
1608 A362 2p dl red, grn & blk   .20   .20

Barcelona Fair Building
A385

1970, May 27   Perf. 13
1609 A385 15p multi   .25   .20

Barcelona Trade Fair, 50th anniversary.

Miguel Primo de Rivera — A386

1970, June 6   Photo.   Perf. 13
1610 A386 2p buff, brn & ol grn   .20   .20

Gen. Miguel Primo de Rivera (1870-1930), Spanish dictator, 1923-1930.

Valencia de Don Juan Castle — A387

Castles: 1.20p, Monterrey. 3.50p, Mombeltran. 6p, Sadaba. 10p, Bellver.

1970, June 24   Engr.
1611 A387   1p blk & dl bl   .35   .20
1612 A387 1.20p lt grnsh bl & vio   .20   .20
1613 A387 3.50p pale grn & brn   .20   .20
1614 A387   6p sep & dl pur   .20   .20
1615 A387   10p fawn & sepia   .80   .20
    Nos. 1611-1615 (5)   1.75   1.00

Alcazaba Castle, Almeria
A388

Tourism: 1p, Malaga Cathedral. 1.50p, St. Mary of the Assumption, Lequemo, vert. 2p, Cloister of St. Francis of Orense. 3.50p, Market (Lonja), Zaragoza, vert. 5p, The Gate of Vitoria, vert.

1970, July 23   Engr.   Perf. 13
1616 A388 50c bluish gray & dl pur   .20   .20
1617 A388   1p red brn & ocher   .20   .20
1618 A388 1.50p bluish gray & sl grn   .20   .20
1619 A388   2p sl & dk bl   .40   .20
1620 A388 3.50p pur & vio bl   .20   .20
1621 A388   5p gray grn & red brn   .80   .20
    Nos. 1616-1621 (6)   2.00   1.20

Tailor, from Book Published in Madrid, 1589
A389

1970, Aug. 18   Photo.   Perf. 13
1622 A389 2p mag, brn & dl vio   .20   .20

14th Intl. Tailoring Congress, Madrid.

Diver and Map of Europe
A390

1970, Aug. 25
1623 A390 2p grn & brt bl   .20   .20

12th European Championships in Swimming, Diving and Water Polo, Barcelona.

Concha Espina — A391

1p, Guillen de Castro. 1.50p, Juan Ramon Jimenez. 2p, Gustavo Adolfo Becquer. 2.50p, Miguel de Unamuno. 3.50p, José M. Gabriel y Galan.

1970, Sept. 21   Photo.   Perf. 13x12½
1624 A391 50c brn, vio bl & pale rose   .20   .20
1625 A391   1p sl grn, dp rose lil & gray   .20   .20
1626 A391 1.50p dk bl, brt grn & gray   .20   .20
1627 A391   2p grn, dk ol & buff   .20   .20
1628 A391 2.50p pur, rose lake & buff   .20   .20

1629 A391 3.50p brn, dk red & gray .20 .20
Nos. 1624-1629 (6) 1.20 1.20

Issued to honor Spanish writers.

Builders of the New World
Portrait Type of 1961 and Building Type of 1969

40c, Ecala House, Queretaro, Mexico. 1.50p, Mexico Cathedral, horiz. 2p, Vasco de Quiroga. 3.50p, Brother Juan de Zumarraga. 6p, Cathedral Towers, Morelia, Mexico.

1970, Oct. 12   Photo.   Perf. 13
1630 A380 40c lt bl & ol gray .20 .20
1631 A380 1.50p lt bl & brn .20 .20
1632 A265 2p buff & dk vio .50 .20
1633 A265 3.50p pale grn & dk grn .20 .20
1634 A380 6p pale pink & Prus bl .25 .20
Nos. 1630-1634 (5) 1.35 1.00

Exploration and development of Mexico.

Map of Western Mediterranean — A392

1970, Oct. 20   Photo.   Perf. 13
1635 A392 2p multi .20 .20

Geographical and Statistical Institute, cent.

Adoration of the Shepherds, by El Greco — A393

Christmas: 2p, Adoration of the Shepherds, by Murillo.

1970, Oct. 30
1636 A393 1.50p multi .20 .20
1637 A393 2p multi .20 .20

UN Emblem and Headquarters — A394

1970, Nov. 3
1638 A394 8p multi .20 .20

25th anniversary of the United Nations.

Monastery Type of 1969

Ripoll Monastery: 2p, Portal. 3.50p, View of monastery. 5p, Inside court.

1970, Nov. 12   Engr.
1639 A382 2p vio & pur .45 .20
1640 A382 3.50p org & mar .20 .20
1641 A382 5p Prus grn & yel grn .90 .20
Nos. 1639-1641 (3) 1.55 .60

Map with Main European Pilgrimage Routes — A395

Cathedral of St. David, Wales A396

#1643, Map of main pilgrimage routes. #1644, St. Bridget statue, Vadstena, Sweden. #1645, Santiago Cathedral. #1646, Tower of St. Jacques, Paris. #1647, Pilgrim before entering Santiago de Compostela. #1648, St. James statue, Pistoia, Italy. #1649, Lugo Cathedral. 2.50p, Villafranca del Bierzo church. #1652, Astorga Cathedral. 3.50p, San Marcos de León. #1654, Charlemagne, bas-relief, Aachen Cathedral, Germany. #1655, San Tirso de Sahagun. 5p, San Martín de Fromista. 6p, Bas-relief, King's Hospital, Burgos. 7p, Portal of Santo Domingo de la Calzada. 7.50p, Cloister, Najera. 8p, Puente de la Reina (Christ on the Cross and portal). 9p, Santa Maria de Eunate. 10p, Cross of Roncesvalles.

1971   Engr.   Perf. 13
1642 A395 50c grnsh bl & sep .20 .20
1643 A396 50c bl & dl vio .20 .20
1644 A395 1p brn & sl grn .20 .20
1645 A395 1p grn & sl grn .20 .20
1646 A395 1.50p dl grn & dp plum .25 .20
1647 A396 1.50p vio bl & lil .25 .20
1648 A395 2p dk pur & blk .25 .20
1649 A395 2p sl grn & dk bl .80 .20
1650 A396 2.50p vio brn & dl vio .20 .20
1651 A396 3p ultra & dk bl .25 .20
1652 A396 3p dl red & rose lil .40 .20
1653 A396 3.50p dp org & gray grn .20 .20
1654 A396 4p ol grn .35 .20
1655 A396 4p grnsh bl & brn .20 .20
1656 A396 5p lt grn & blk .35 .20
1657 A396 6p lt ultra .20 .20
1658 A395 7p lil & dl vio .45 .20
1659 A396 7.50p car lake & dl vio .20 .20
1660 A395 8p grn & vio blk .25 .25
1661 A396 9p grn & vio .25 .25
1662 A395 10p grn & brn .40 .20
Nos. 1642-1662 (21) 6.00 4.30

Holy Year of Compostela, 1971.

Ignacio Zuloaga, Self-portrait A397

Amadeo Vives, Composer A398

Zuloaga Paintings: 50c, "My Uncle Daniel." 1p, View of Segovia, horiz. 1.50p, Countess of Alba. 3p, Juan Belmonte. 4p, Countess of Noailles. 5p, Pablo Uranga. 8p, Cobblers' Houses at Lerma, horiz.

1971, Mar. 24   Photo.   Perf. 13
1663 A397 50c gold & multi .20 .20
1664 A397 1p gold & multi .20 .20
1665 A397 1.50p gold & multi .20 .20
1666 A397 2p gold & multi .20 .20
1667 A397 3p gold & multi .20 .20
1668 A397 4p gold & multi .20 .20
1669 A397 5p gold & multi .20 .20
1670 A397 8p gold & multi .20 .20
Nos. 1663-1670 (8) 1.60 1.60

Ignacio Zuloaga (1870-1945). Stamp Day. For other art types see A384, A410, A431, A448, A473, A501, A522, A538, A558 and footnote following No. 876.

1971, Apr. 20

2p, St. Teresa of Avila. 8p, Benito Perez Galdos, writer. 15p, Ramon Menendez Pidal, writer.

1671 A398 1p multicolored .20 .20
1672 A398 2p multicolored .20 .20
1673 A398 8p multicolored .20 .20
1674 A398 15p multicolored .20 .20
Nos. 1671-1674 (4) .80 .80

Europa Issue, 1971
Common Design Type

1971, Apr. 29   Photo.   Perf. 13
Size: 37x26mm
1675 CD14 2p lt bl, brn & vio bl .50 .20
1676 CD14 8p lt grn, dk brn & dk grn .35 .35

Stamp Day Type of 1968

Spain No. 1 with blue "A" cancellation.

1971, May 6
1677 A362 2p black, bl & olive .20 .20

Gymnast — A399

Design: 2p, Gymnast on bar.

1971, May 14
1678 A399 1p ocher & multi .20 .20
1679 A399 2p lt blue & multi .20 .20

9th European Gymnastic Championships for Men, Madrid, May 14-15.

Great Bustard A400

Designs: 2p, Pardine lynx. 3p, Brown bear. 5p, Red-legged partridge, vert. 8p, Spanish ibex, vert.

1971, May 24
1680 A400 1p multicolored .20 .20
1681 A400 2p multicolored .20 .20
1682 A400 3p multicolored .20 .20
1683 A400 5p multicolored .35 .25
1684 A400 8p multicolored .35 .35
Nos. 1680-1684 (5) 1.30 1.20

Legionnaires — A401

2p, Legionnaires on dress parade. 5p, Memorial service. 8p, Desert fighter and tank column.

1971, June 21   Photo.   Perf. 13
1685 A401 1p multicolored .20 .20
1686 A401 2p multicolored .20 .20
1687 A401 5p multicolored .20 .20
1688 A401 8p multicolored .30 .30
Nos. 1685-1688 (4) .90 .90

50th anniversary of the Legion, a voluntary military organization.

UNICEF Emblem, Children of Various Races — A402

1971, Sept. 10
1689 A402 8p multicolored .20 .20

25th anniv. of UNICEF.

Don Juan of Austria, Fleet Commander A403

Hockey Players, Hockey League and Games Emblems — A404

Designs: 5p, Battle of Lepanto, horiz. 8p, Holy League banner in Cathedral.

1971, Oct. 7   Engr.   Perf. 13
1690 A403 2p sepia & slate grn .40 .20
1691 A403 5p chocolate .75 .20
1692 A403 8p rose car & vio bl .60 .60
Nos. 1690-1692 (3) 1.75 1.00

400th anniversary of the Battle of Lepanto against the Turks.

1971, Oct. 15   Photo.
1693 A404 5p multicolored .50 .20

First World Hockey Cup, Barcelona, Oct. 15-24.

De Havilland DH-9 over Seville A405

Design: 15p, Boeing 747 over Plaza de la Cibeles, Madrid.

1971, Oct. 25
1694 A405 2p multicolored .25 .20
1695 A405 15p multicolored .25 .20

50th anniversary of Spanish air mail service.

Nativity, Avia Altarpiece A406

Emilia Pardo Bazan — A407

Christmas: 8p, Nativity, Sagas altarpiece.

1971, Nov. 4   **Perf. 12½x13**
1696 A406 2p multicolored   .20 .20
1697 A406 8p multicolored   .20 .20

1972, Jan. 27   **Engr.**   **Perf. 13**
Portraits: 25p, José de Espronceda. 50p, King Fernan Gonzalez.

1698 A407 15p brown & slate grn   .20 .20
1699 A407 25p lt grn & slate grn   .25 .20
1700 A407 50p claret & dp brn   .55 .20
    Nos. 1698-1700 (3)   1.00 .60

Honoring Emilia Pardo Bazan (1852-1921), novelist (15p); José de Espronceda (1808-1842), poet (25p); Fernan Gonzalez (910-970), first King of Castile (50p).

Figure Skating — A408

Don Quixote Title Page, 1605 — A409

Design: 2p, Ski jump and Sapporo Olympic emblem, horiz.

1972, Feb. 10   **Photo.**
1701 A408 2p gray & multi   .35 .20
1702 A408 15p blue & multi   .20 .20

11th Winter Olympic Games, Sapporo, Japan, Feb. 3-13.

1972, Feb. 24   **Engr.**   **Perf. 13x12½**
1703 A409 2p brown & claret   .20 .20

International Book Year 1972.

A410

A411

Gutierrez Solana Paintings: 1p, Clowns, horiz. 2p, José Gutierrez Solana with wife and child. 3p, Balladier. 4p, Fisherman. 5p, Mask makers. 7p, The book collector. 10p, Merchant marine captain. 15p, Afterdinner speaker, horiz.

1972, Mar. 24   **Photo.**   **Perf. 13**
1704 A410 1p gold & multi   .20 .20
1705 A410 2p gold & multi   .35 .20
1706 A410 3p gold & multi   .40 .20
1707 A410 4p gold & multi   .20 .20
1708 A410 5p gold & multi   1.25 .35
1709 A410 7p gold & multi   .55 .20
1710 A410 10p gold & multi   .55 .20
1711 A410 15p gold & multi   .55 .25
    Nos. 1704-1711 (8)   4.05 1.80

José Gutierrez Solana (1886-1945). Stamp Day 1972.
For other art types see A384, A397, A431, A448, A473, A501, A522, A538, A558 and footnote following No. 876.

1972, Apr. 21
1712 A411 1p Fir   .20 .20
1713 A411 2p Strawberry tree   .35 .20
1714 A411 3p Cluster pine   .40 .20

1715 A411 5p Evergreen oak   .55 .20
1716 A411 8p Juniper   .35 .30
    Nos. 1712-1716 (5)   1.85 1.10

Europeans Interlocking A412

Pre-stamp Cordoba Postmark (1824-42) A413

Europa, 1972
Common Design Type and Type A412
1972, May 2
1717 A412 2p dull grn & ocher   1.60 .20
    Size: 25x38mm
1718 CD15 8p multicolored   .60 .45

1972, May 6   **Perf. 12½x13**
1719 A413 2p dull yel, blk & car   .20 .20
    Stamp Day 1972.

Santa Catalina Castle, Jaen — A414

Castles: 1p, Sajazarra, Rioja, vert. 3p, Biar, Alicante. 5p, San Servando, Toledo. 10p, Pedraza, Segovia.

1972, June 22   **Engr.**   **Perf. 13**
1720 A414 1p dull bl grn & brn   .40 .35
1721 A414 2p gray olive & grn   .75 .20
1722 A414 3p rose car & red
             brn   .75 .20
1723 A414 5p vio bl & dull grn   .75 .20
1724 A414 10p slate & lilac   2.25 .20
    Nos. 1720-1724 (5)   4.90 1.15

Weight Lifting, Olympic Emblems — A415

1972, Aug. 26   **Photo.**   **Perf. 13**
1725 A415 1p Olympic emblems,
           fencing, horiz.   .20 .20
1726 A415 2p shown   .25 .20
1727 A415 5p Sculling   .20 .20
1728 A415 8p Pole vaulting   .25 .25
    Nos. 1725-1728 (4)   .90 .85

20th Olympic Games, Munich, 8/26-9/11.

Egyptian Mongoose A416

1972, Sept. 14
1729 A416 1p Aquatic mole, vert.   .20 .20
1730 A416 2p Chamois   .20 .20
1731 A416 3p Wolf   .25 .20
1732 A416 5p shown   .50 .20
1733 A416 7p Spotted genet   .40 .20
    Nos. 1729-1733 (5)   1.55 1.00

Brigadier M.A. de Ustariz — A417

San Juan, 1870 A418

1972, Oct. 12   **Photo.**   **Perf. 13**
1734 A417 1p shown   .20 .25
1735 A418 2p shown   .25 .20
1736 A418 5p San Juan, 1625   .40 .20
1737 A418 8p Map of Plaza and
           Bay, 1792   .40 .30
    Nos. 1734-1737 (4)   1.25 .95

450th anniversary of San Juan.

St. Tomas Monastery, Avila — A419

8p, Inside view. 15p, Cloister, horiz.

1972, Oct. 26   **Engr.**
1738 A419 2p Prus bl & gray
           grn   .80 .20
1739 A419 8p gray & claret   .65 .30
1740 A419 15p violet & red lil   .50 .20
    Nos. 1738-1740 (3)   1.95 .70

Teatro del Liceo, Barcelona A420

1972, Nov. 7   **Perf. 12½x13**
1741 A420 8p ultra & sepia   .25 .20

125th anniversary of the Gran Teatro del Liceo in Barcelona.

Annunciation — A421

Christmas: 8p, Angel and shepherds. Designs are from Romanesque murals in the Collegiate Basilica of San Isidro, Leon.

1972, Nov. 14   **Photo.**   **Perf. 13**
1742 A421 2p gold & multi   .20 .20
1743 A421 8p gold & multi   .20 .20

Juan de Herrera and Escorial A422

Great Spanish Architects: 10p, Juan de Villanueva and Prado. 15p, Ventura Rodriguez and Apollo Fountain.

1973, Jan. 29   **Engr.**   **Perf. 12½x13**
1744 A422 8p sepia & slate grn   .50 .20
1745 A422 10p blk brn & bluish
           blk   1.60 .20
1746 A422 15p brt green & indigo   .40 .20
    Nos. 1744-1746 (3)   2.50 .60

Myrica Faya — A423

Europa, Roman Mosaic — A424

Designs: Flora of Canary Islands.

1973, Mar. 21   **Photo.**   **Perf. 13**
1747 A423 1p Apollonias
           canariensis,
           horiz.   .20 .20
1748 A423 2p shown   .55 .20
1749 A423 4p Palms   .20 .20
1750 A423 5p Holly   .55 .20
1751 A423 15p Dracaena draco   .30 .20
    Nos. 1747-1751 (5)   1.80 1.00

Europa Issue
Common Design Type and A424
1973, Apr. 30   **Photo.**   **Perf. 13**
1752 A424 2p multicolored   .45 .20
    Size: 37x26mm
1753 CD16 8p lt blue, blk & red   .40 .25

Stamp Day Type of 1968
Stamp Day: 2p, Spain No. 23 with red Madrid, 1853, cancellation.

1973, May 5
1754 A362 2p black, blue & red   .20 .20

Iznajar Dam on Genil River — A425

1973, June 9   **Photo.**   **Perf. 12½x13**
1755 A425 8p multicolored   .20 .20

11th Congress of the International Commission on High Dams, Madrid, June 11-15.

Oñate University, Guipuzcoa A426

Designs: 2p, Plaza del Campo and fountain, Lugo. 3p, Plaza de Llerena and fountain, Badajoz, vert. 5p, House of Columbus, Las Palmas. 8p, Windmills, La Mancha.

1973, June 11   **Engr.**   **Perf. 13**
1756 A426 1p gray & sepia   .20 .20
1757 A426 2p brt grn & sl grn   .55 .20
1758 A426 3p dk brn & org brn   .55 .20
1759 A426 5p dk gray & vio blk   1.40 .20
1760 A426 8p dk gray & car   .60 .20
    Nos. 1756-1760 (5)   3.30 1.00

Azure-winged Magpie — A427

Knight, Holy
Fraternity of
Castile,
1488 — A428

Birds: 1p, Black-bellied sand grouse, horiz.
2p, Black stork, horiz. 7p, Imperial eagle,
horiz. 15p, Red-crested pochard.

1973, July 3   Photo.   Perf. 13

1761	A427	1p multicolored	.20	.20
1762	A427	2p multicolored	.35	.20
1763	A427	5p multicolored	.50	.40
1764	A427	7p multicolored	.60	.20
1765	A427	15p multicolored	.25	.25
		Nos. 1761-1765 (5)	1.90	1.25

1973, July 17

Uniforms: 2p, Knight, Castile, 1493, horiz.
3p, Harquebusier, 1534. 7p, Mounted rifleman, 1560. 8p, Infantry sergeants, 1567.

1766	A428	1p multicolored	.20	.20
1767	A428	2p multicolored	.45	.20
1768	A428	3p multicolored	.45	.20
1769	A428	7p multicolored	.35	.20
1770	A428	8p multicolored	.35	.25
		Nos. 1766-1770 (5)	1.80	1.05

See Nos. 1794-1798, 1824-1828, 1869-
1873, 1902-1906, 1989-1993, 2020-2024,
2051-2055, 2078-2082.

Fish in Net
A429

1973, Sept. 12   Photo.   Perf. 13
1771 A429 2p multicolored   .20 .20
6th Intl. Fishing Exhibition, Vigo, Sept. 12-19.

Conference Hall — A430

1973, Sept. 14
1772 A430 8p multicolored   .20 .20
Plenipotentiary Conf. of the Intl. Telecommunications Union, Torremolinos, Sept. 1973.

Vicente López,
Self-portrait
A431

Stamp Day (Paintings by Vicente López y
Portaña (1772-1850)): 1p, King Ferdinand VII.
3p, Señora de Carvallo. 4p, Marshal Cas-
telldosrrius. 5p, Queen Isabella II. 7p, Francisco Goya. 10p, Maria Amalia de Sajonia.
15p, The organist Felix López.

1973, Sept. 29   Photo.   Perf. 13

1773	A431	1p gold & multi	.20	.20
1774	A431	2p gold & multi	.25	.20
1775	A431	3p gold & multi	.25	.20
1776	A431	4p gold & multi	.20	.20
1777	A431	5p gold & multi	.20	.20
1778	A431	7p gold & multi	.20	.20
1779	A431	10p gold & multi	.25	.20
1780	A431	15p gold & multi	.25	.20
		Nos. 1773-1780 (8)	1.80	1.60

For other art types see A384, A397, A410,
A448, A473, A501, A522, A538, A558 and
footnote following No. 876.

Leon
Cathedral,
Nicaragua
A432

Designs: 2p, Subtiava Church. 5p, Portal of
Governor's House, vert. 8p, Rio San Juan
Castle.

1973, Oct. 12

1781	A432	1p multicolored	.20	.20
1782	A432	2p multicolored	.30	.20
1783	A432	5p multicolored	.50	.25
1784	A432	8p multicolored	.50	.20
		Nos. 1781-1784 (4)	1.50	.85

Hispanic-American buildings in Nicaragua.

Pope Gregory XI
and Pedro
Fernandez
Pecha — A433

1973, Oct. 26
1785 A433 2p multicolored   .20 .20
600th anniversary of the founding of the
Order of the Hermites of St. Jerome by Pedro
Fernandez Pecha.

St. Domingo de
Silos Monastery
A434

Nativity, Column
Capital, Silos
Church
A435

Designs: 8p, Cloister walk, horiz. 15p, Three
saints, sculpture.

Perf. 13x12½, 12½x13

1973, Oct. 26   Engr.

1786	A434	2p brn & rose mag	.45	.20
1787	A434	8p dk blue & purple	.20	.20
1788	A434	15p Prus grn & indigo	.25	.20
		Nos. 1786-1788 (3)	.90	.60

St. Domingo de Silos Monastery, Burgos.

1973, Nov. 6   Photo.   Perf. 13

Christmas: 8p, Adoration of the Kings,
Butrera Church, horiz.

1789	A435	2p multicolored	.20	.20
1790	A435	8p multicolored	.20	.20

Map of
Spain and
Americas
with Dates
of First
Printings
A436

500 years of Spanish Printing: 7p, Teacher
and Pupils, woodcut from "Libros de los Sue-
nos," Valencia, 1474, vert. 15p, Title page
from "Los Sinodales," Segovia, 1472.

1973, Dec. 11   Engr.   Perf. 13

1791	A436	1p ind & slate grn	.30	.20
1792	A436	7p violet bl & purple	.20	.20
1793	A436	15p purple & black	.25	.20
		Nos. 1791-1793 (3)	.75	.60

Uniform Type of 1973

Uniforms: 1p, Harquebusier on horseback,
1603. 2p, Harquebusiers, 1632. 3p, Cuiras-
sier, 1635. 5p, Mounted drummer of the
Dragoons, 1677. 9p, Two Musketeers, 1694.

1974, Jan. 5   Photo.   Perf. 13

1794	A428	1p multicolored	.20	.20
1795	A428	2p multicolored	.50	.20
1796	A428	3p multicolored	.70	.20
1797	A428	5p multicolored	.90	.20
1798	A428	9p multicolored	.25	.25
		Nos. 1794-1798 (5)	2.55	1.10

Nautical Chart of
Western Europe
and North
Africa — A437

1974, Jan. 26
1799 A437 2p multicolored   .20 .20
50th anniv. of the Superior Geographical
Council of Spain. The chart is from a 14th
cent. Catalan atlas.

M. Biada
and Steam
Engine
A438

1974, Apr. 2   Photo.   Perf. 13
1800 A438 2p multicolored   .20 .20
Barcelona-Mataro Railroad, 125th anniv.

Young
Collector,
Album,
Magnifier
A439

Exhibition Emblem — A440

Design: 8p, Emblem, globe and arrows.

1974, Apr. 4   Perf. 13
1801 A439 2p lilac rose & multi   .20 .20

Perf. 12½

1802	A440	5p buff, blk & dull bl	.35	.30
1803	A440	8p dull green & multi	.30	.25
		Nos. 1801-1803 (3)	.85	.75

Espana 75, International Philatelic Exhibition, Madrid, Apr. 4-13, 1975.

Woman with
Offering — A441

Europa: 8p, Woman from Baza, painted
sculpture.

1974, Apr. 29   Photo.   Perf. 13

1804	A441	2p multicolored	.50	.20
1805	A441	8p multicolored	.25	.25

No. 28 and
1854
Seville
Cancel
A442

1974, May 6
1806 A442 2p black, blue & red   .20 .20
World Stamp Day.

Father
Jaime
Balmes
A443

Designs: 10p, Father Pedro Poveda. 15p,
Jorge Juan y Santacilla.

1974, May 28   Engr.   Perf. 13

1807	A443	8p blue gray & sepia	.20	.20
1808	A443	10p red brn & dk brn	.60	.20
1809	A443	15p brown & slate	.20	.20
		Nos. 1807-1809 (3)	1.00	.60

Famous Spaniards: Jaime Balmes (1810-
1848), mathematician; death centenary of
Pedro Poveda, pedagogue; Don Jorge Juan
(1712-1773), explorer and writer.

Templeto, by
Bramante,
Rome — A444

1974, June 4   Photo.
1810 A444 5p multicolored   .20 .20
Cent. of the Spanish Academy of Fine Arts,
Rome.

Aqueduct,
Segovia
A445

Designs: 2p, Tajo Bridge, Alcantara. 3p,
Marcus Valerius Martial lecturing. 4p, Triumphal Arch, Tarragona, vert. 5p, Theater,
Merida. 7p, Bishop Ossius of Cordoba preaching. 8p, Tribunal Arch, Talavera Forum, vert.
9p, Emperor Trajan, vert.

1974, June 25   Engr.

1811	A445	1p brown & black	.20	.20
1812	A445	2p gray grn & sepia	.30	.20
1813	A445	3p lt & dk brown	.20	.20
1814	A445	4p green & indigo	.20	.20
1815	A445	5p gray bl & choc	.20	.20
1816	A445	7p gray grn & lilac	.20	.20
1817	A445	8p dk brown & green	.20	.20
1818	A445	9p brt red lil & cl	.20	.20
		Nos. 1811-1818 (8)	1.70	1.60

Roman architecture and history in Spain.

Greek
Tortoise
A446

Reptiles: 2p, Common chameleon. 5p, Wall
gecko. 7p, Emerald lizard. 15p, Blunt-nosed
viper.

1974, July 3   Photo.

1819	A446	1p multicolored	.20	.20
1820	A446	2p multicolored	.30	.20
1821	A446	5p multicolored	.60	.20
1822	A446	7p multicolored	.40	.25
1823	A446	15p multicolored	.20	.20
		Nos. 1819-1823 (5)	1.70	1.35

Uniform Type of 1973

Uniforms: 1p, Hussar and horse, 1705. 2p, Artillery officers, 1710. 3p, Piper and drummer, Granada Regiment, 1734. 7p, Mounted standard-bearer, Numancia Dragoons, 1737. 8p, Standard-bearer and soldier, Zamora Regiment, 1739.

1974, July 17

1824	A428	1p multicolored	.20	.20
1825	A428	2p multicolored	.40	.20
1826	A428	3p multicolored	.40	.20
1827	A428	7p multicolored	.30	.20
1828	A428	8p multicolored	.20	.20
		Nos. 1824-1828 (5)	1.50	1.00

Life Saving A447

1974, Sept. 5 Photo. *Perf. 13*

1829	A447	2p multicolored	.20	.20

18th World Life Saving Championships, Barcelona, Sept. 1974.

Eduardo Rosales, by Federico Madrazo — A448

Stamp Day (Eduardo Rosales, 1836-73, Paintings): 1p, Tobias and the Angel. 3p, The Last Will of Isabella the Catholic. 4p, Nena (little girl). 5p, Presentation of John of Austria to Charles I. 7p, The First Step. 10p, St. John the Evangelist. 15p, St. Matthew.

1974, Sept. 29 Photo. *Perf. 13*

1830	A448	1p gold & multi	.20	.20
1831	A448	2p gold & multi	.20	.20
1832	A448	3p gold & multi, horiz.	.20	.20
1833	A448	4p gold & multi	.20	.20
1834	A448	5p gold & multi, horiz.	.20	.20
1835	A448	7p gold & multi, horiz.	.20	.20
1836	A448	10p gold & multi	.30	.20
1837	A448	15p gold & multi	.20	.20
		Nos. 1830-1837 (8)	1.70	1.60

For other art types see A384, A397, A410, A431, A473, A501, A522, A538, A558 and footnote following No. 876.

"International Mail" — A449

UPU Monument, Bern — A450

1974, Oct. 9

1838	A449	2p dark blue & multi	.20	.20
1839	A450	8p red & multi	.20	.20

Centenary of Universal Postal Union.

Sobremonte House, Cordoba, Argentina — A451

Ruins of San Ignacio de Mini, 18th Century — A452

The Gaucho Martin Fierro — A453

Design: 2p, Municipal Council Building, Buenos Aires, 1829.

1974, Oct. 12

1840	A451	1p multicolored	.20	.20
1841	A451	2p multicolored	.40	.20
1842	A452	5p multicolored	.30	.20
1843	A453	10p multicolored	.25	.20
		Nos. 1840-1843 (4)	1.15	.80

Cultural ties with Latin America.

Nativity, Valdavia Church A454

Adoration of the Kings, Valcobero Church — A455

1974 Photo. *Perf. 13*

1844	A454	2p multicolored	.20	.20
1845	A455	3p lt blue & multi	.20	.20
1846	A455	8p olive & multi	.20	.20
		Nos. 1844-1846 (3)	.60	.60

Christmas 1974.
Issue dates: 2p, 8p, Nov. 4; 3p, Dec. 2.

Teucriun Lanigerum A456

Flowers: 2p, Hypericum ericoides. 4p, Thymus longiflorus. 5p, Anthyllis onobrychioides. 8p, Helianthemun paniculatum.

1974, Nov. 8

1847	A456	1p multicolored	.20	.20
1848	A456	2p multicolored	.20	.20
1849	A456	4p multicolored	.20	.20
1850	A456	5p multicolored	.25	.20
1851	A456	8p multicolored	.20	.20
		Nos. 1847-1851 (5)	1.05	1.00

Franco Type of 1954-56
Imprint: "F.N.M.T."

1974-75 Photo. *Perf. 12½x13*

1852	A221	4p rose car ('75)	.20	.20
1853	A221	7p brt ultra	.20	.20
1854	A221	12p blue green	.20	.20
1855	A221	20p rose carmine	.25	.20
		Nos. 1852-1855 (4)	.85	.80

Leyre Monastery A457

8p, Column and bas-relief, vert. 15p, Crypt.

1974, Dec. 10 Engr. *Perf. 12½x13*

1862	A457	2p slate grn & bl gray	.45	.20
1863	A457	8p carmine	.20	.20
1864	A457	15p grnsh black	.35	.20
		Nos. 1862-1864 (3)	1.00	.60

Leyre Monastery, Navarre.

Spain Nos. 1 and 1802 — A458

Mail Coach, 1850 A459

Designs: 8p, Mail ship of Indian Service. 10p, Chapel of St. Mark.

Perf. 12½x13, 13x12½

1975, Jan. 2 Engr.

1865	A458	2p slate blue	.35	.30
1866	A459	3p olive & brown	.45	.40
1867	A459	8p lilac & slate bl	1.00	.50
1868	A458	10p brn & slate grn	.50	.40
		Nos. 1865-1868 (4)	2.30	1.60

125th anniversary of Spanish postage stamps.

Uniform Type of 1973

1p, Sergeant and grenadier, Toledo Regiment, 1750. 2p, Royal Artillery, 1762. 3p, Queen's Regiment, 1763. 5p, Fusiliers, Vitoria Regiment, 1766. 10p, Dragoon, Sagunto Regiment, 1775.

1975, Jan. 7 Photo. *Perf. 13*

1869	A428	1p multicolored	.20	.20
1870	A428	2p multicolored	.20	.20
1871	A428	3p multicolored	1.60	.25
1872	A428	5p multicolored	.50	.20
1873	A428	10p multicolored	1.40	.25
		Nos. 1869-1873 (5)	3.90	1.10

Antonio Gaudi A460

Designs: 10p, Antonio Palacios and Casa Guell, Barcelona. 15p, Secundino Zuazo.

1975, Feb. 25 Engr. *Perf. 13*

1874	A460	8p green & black	.20	.20
1875	A460	10p carmine & dp claret	.40	.20
1876	A460	15p brown & black	.20	.20
		Nos. 1874-1876 (3)	.80	.60

Contemporary Spanish architects.

Souvenir Sheets

Spanish Goldsmiths' Works — A461

Designs: 2p, Agate box, 9th cent. 3p, Votive crown of Recesvinto. 8p, Cover of Evangelistary, Roncesvalles Collegiate Church, 12th cent. 10p, Chalice of Infanta Donna Urraca, 11th cent. 12p, Processional monstrance, St. Domingo de Silos, 16th cent. 15p, Sword of Boabdil, 15th cent. 25p, Sword and head of Charles V (Carlos I of Spain). 50p, Earring and bracelet from Aliseda, 6th-4th centuries B.C. 3p, 10p, 12p, 25p vertical (No. 1878).

1975, Apr. 4 Engr. *Perf. 13*

1877	A461	Sheet of 4	8.00	8.00
a.		2p gray & Prussian blue	2.00	2.00
b.		8p brown & Prus blue	2.00	2.00
c.		15p gray & dark carmine	2.00	2.00
d.		50p dark carmine & gray	2.00	2.00
1878	A461	Sheet of 4	8.00	8.00
a.		3p slate green & gray	2.00	2.00
b.		10p sepia & slate	2.00	2.00
c.		12p gray & bluish black	2.00	2.00
d.		25p sepia & bluish black	2.00	2.00

Espana 75 Intl. Phil. Exhib., Madrid, 4/4-13.

Pomegranates A462

Woman Gathering Honey, Arana Cave — A463

1975, Apr. 21 Photo.

1879	A462	1p Almonds, nuts and blossoms, horiz.	.20	.20
1880	A462	2p shown	.25	.20
1881	A462	3p Oranges	.25	.20
1882	A462	4p Chestnuts	.20	.20
1883	A462	5p Apples	.20	.20
		Nos. 1879-1883 (5)	1.10	1.00

1975, Apr. 28 Photo. *Perf. 13*

Europa: 12p, Horse, wall painting from Tito Bustillo Cave, horiz.

1884	A463	3p brown & multi	.25	.20
1885	A463	12p brown & multi	.35	.20

Pre-stamp León Cancellation A464

1975, May 6 *Perf. 12½x13*

1886	A464	3p multicolored	.20	.20

World Stamp Day.

World Tourism Organization Emblem — A465

1975, May 12   Photo.   Perf. 13
1887 A465 3p dark blue   .20 .20
First General Assembly of the World Tourism Organization, Madrid, May 1975.

Fair Emblem, Agricultural Symbols — A466

1975, May 14
1888 A466 3p multicolored   .20 .20
25th Agricultural Fair.

Equality Between Men and Women A467

1975, June 3
1889 A467 3p multicolored   .20 .20
International Women's Year.

Virgin of Cabeza Sanctuary A468

1975, June 18   Photo.   Perf. 13
1890 A468 3p multicolored   .20 .20
Virgin of Cabeza Sanctuary, site of siege during Civil War, 1937.

Cervantes' Prison Cell, Argamasilla de Alba — A469

Tourism: 2p, Bridge of St. Martin, Toledo. 3p, Church of St. Peter, Tarrasa. 4p, Arch, Alhambra, Granada, vert. 5p, Street, Mijas, Malaga, vert. 7p, Church of St. Mary, Tarrasa, vert.

1975, June 25   Engr.   Perf. 13
1891 A469 1p purple & black   .20 .20
1892 A469 2p red brn & brn   .20 .20
1893 A469 3p slate & sepia   .20 .20
1894 A469 4p orange & claret   .20 .20
1895 A469 5p slate grn & indigo   .20 .20
1896 A469 7p violet bl & indigo   .40 .20
       Nos. 1891-1896 (6)   1.40 1.20

Salamander — A470

1975, July 9   Photo.   Perf. 13
1897 A470 1p shown   .20 .20
1898 A470 2p Newt   .25 .20
1899 A470 3p Tree toad   .25 .20
1900 A470 6p Midwife toad   .20 .20
1901 A470 7p Leaf frog   .20 .20
       Nos. 1897-1901 (5)   1.10 1.00

Uniform Type of 1973

1p, Cavalry officer, 1788. 2p, Fusilier, Asturias Regiment, 1789. 3p, Infantry Colonel, 1802. 4p, Artillery standard-bearer, 1803. 7p, Sapper, 1809.

1975, July 17
1902 A428 1p multicolored   .20 .20
1903 A428 2p multicolored   .50 .20
1904 A428 3p multicolored   .20 .20
1905 A428 4p multicolored   .20 .20
1906 A428 7p multicolored   .20 .20
       Nos. 1902-1906 (5)   1.30 1.00

Infant and Children Playing A471

1975, Sept. 9   Photo.   Perf. 13
1907 A471 3p multicolored   .20 .20
"Defend Life."

Scroll and Emblem A472

1975, Sept. 25
1908 A472 3p multicolored   .20 .20
13th International Congress of Latin Notaries, Barcelona, Sept. 26-Oct. 4.

Blessing of the Birds A473

Scenes from Apocalypse: 2p, Angel at River of Life. 3p, Angel Guarding Gate of Paradise. 4p, Fox carrying cock. 6p, Daniel with wild bulls. 7p, The Last Judgment. 10p, Four horsemen of the Apocalypse. 12p, Bird holding snake.

1975, Sept. 29
1909 A473 1p gold & multi   .20 .20
1910 A473 2p gold & multi, vert.   .20 .20
1911 A473 3p gold & multi, vert.   .20 .20
1912 A473 4p gold & multi   .20 .20
1913 A473 6p gold & multi   .20 .20
1914 A473 7p gold & multi, vert.   .25 .25
1915 A473 10p gold & multi, vert. .20 .20
1916 A473 12p gold & multi, vert. .20 .20
       Nos. 1909-1916 (8)   1.65 1.65
Millenium Gerona Cathedral.
For other art types see A384, A397, A410, A431, A448, A501, A522, A538, A558 and footnote following No. 876.

Symbols of Industry A474

1975, Oct. 7   Engr.   Perf. 13
1917 A474 3p violet & lilac   .20 .20
Spanish industrialization.

Pioneers' Covered Wagon A475

Designs: 1p, El Cabildo, meeting house of 1st Uruguayan Government. 3p, Fort St. Theresa over River Plate. 8p, Montevideo Cathedral, vert.

1975, Oct. 12   Photo.
1918 A475 1p multicolored   .20 .20
1919 A475 2p multicolored   .20 .20
1920 A475 3p multicolored   .25 .20
1921 A475 8p multicolored   .20 .20
       Nos. 1918-1921 (4)   .85 .80
Cultural ties with Latin America; sesquicentennial of Uruguay's independence.

Ruined Columns, San Juan de la Peña — A476

Madonna, Mosaic, Navarra Cathedral — A477

3p, Monastery, horiz. 8p, Cloister, horiz.

Perf. 13x12½, 12½x13
1975, Oct. 28   Engr.
1922 A476 3p slate grn & brn   .30 .20
1923 A476 8p violet & brt lil   .20 .20
1924 A476 10p dp magenta & car   .25 .20
       Nos. 1922-1924 (3)   .75 .60
San Juan de la Pena Monastery.

1975, Nov. 4   Photo.   Perf. 13
Christmas: 12p, Flight into Egypt, carved capital, Navarra Cathedral, horiz.
1925 A477 3p multicolored   .20 .20
1926 A477 12p multicolored   .20 .20

King Juan Carlos I — A478

Queen Sofia and King — A479

Designs: No. 1928, Queen Sofia.

1975, Dec. 29 Photo. Perf. 13x12½
1927 A478 3p multicolored   .20 .20
1928 A478 3p multicolored   .20 .20

Perf. 12½
1929 A479 3p multicolored   .20 .20
1930 A479 12p multicolored   .20 .20
       Nos. 1927-1930 (4)   .80 .80
King Juan Carlos I, accession to the throne.

Pilgrim Virgin, Pontevedra A480

Mountains and Center Emblem A481

1976, Jan. 2   Engr.   Perf. 13
1931 A480 3p rose & brown   .20 .20
Holy Year of St. James of Compostela, patron saint of Spain.

1976, Feb. 10   Photo.
1932 A481 6p multicolored   .20 .20
Catalunya Excursion Center, centenary.

Cosme Damian Churruca — A482

Navigators: 12p, Luis de Requesens. 50p, Juan Sebastian Elcano, horiz.

1976, Mar. 1   Engr.   Perf. 13
1933 A482 7p vio brn & grnsh blk 1.50 .25
1934 A482 12p lt blue & violet   .20 .20
1935 A482 50p dp brn & gray ol   .55 .20
       Nos. 1933-1935 (3)   2.25 .65

A. G. Bell, Radar and Telephone A483

1976, Mar. 10   Photo.
1936 A483 3p multicolored   .20 .20
Centenary of first telephone call by Alexander Graham Bell, March 10, 1876.

"Watch at Street Crossings" A484

Road Safety: 3p, "Don't pass when in doubt," vert. 5p, "Wear seat belts."

1976, Apr. 6   Photo.   Perf. 13
1937 A484 1p orange & multi   .20 .20
1938 A484 3p gray & multi   .35 .20
1939 A484 5p lilac & multi   .20 .20
       Nos. 1937-1939 (3)   .75 .60

St. George, Alcoy Cathedral A485

1976, Apr. 23
1940 A485 3p multicolored   .20 .20
7th centenary of the apparition of St. George in Alcoy.

Talavera
Pottery
A486

Europa: 12p, Lace making.

1976, May 3   Photo.   Perf. 13
1941 A486 3p multicolored   .70 .20
1942 A486 12p multicolored   .85 .30

17th Conference of European Postal and
Telecommunications Administrations.

6r Stamp of 1851
with Coruna
Cancel — A487

1976, May 6
1943 A487 3p blue, org & blk   .20 .20

World Stamp Day.

Coin of
Caesar
Augustus
A488

7p, Map of Roman camp on banks of Ebro,
and coin. 25p, Orpheus, mosaic from Roman
era, vert.

1976, May 26   Engr.   Perf. 13
1944 A488 3p dk brn & mar   1.90 .20
1945 A488 7p dk brown & blue   1.00 .30
1946 A488 25p brown & black   .50 .20
     Nos. 1944-1946 (3)   3.40 .70

Founding of Saragossa, 2000th anniv.

Spanish-made Rifle, 1757 — A489

Designs (Bicentennial Emblem and): 3p,
Bernardo de Galvez, Spanish governor. 5p,
Dollar bank note, Richmond, 1861. 12p, Span-
ish capture of Pensacola from English.

1976, May 29
1947 A489 1p dk brn & vio bl   .20 .20
1948 A489 3p sl grn & dk brn   .90 .20
1949 A489 5p dk brn & sl grn   .40 .20
1950 A489 12p sl grn & dk brn   .40 .30
     Nos. 1947-1950 (4)   1.90 .90

American Bicentennial.

Old
Customs
House,
Cadiz
A490

Customs   Houses: 3p, Madrid. 7p,
Barcelona.

1976, June 9
1951 A490 1p black & maroon   .20 .20
1952 A490 3p sepia & green   .55 .20
1953 A490 7p red brn & vio brn 1.10 .35
     Nos. 1951-1953 (3)   1.85 .75

Postal Savings
Box with
Symbols — A491

Railroad Post
Office — A492

Rural
Mailman in
Winter
A493

Postal Service: 10p, Automatic letter sorting
machine.

1976, June 16   Photo.
1954 A491 1p multicolored   .20 .20
1955 A492 3p multicolored   .35 .20
1956 A493 6p multicolored   .20 .20
1957 A493 10p multicolored   .25 .20
     Nos. 1954-1957 (4)   1.00 .80

King and
Queen,
Map of
Americas
A494

1976, June 25
1958 A494 12p multicolored   .25 .20

Visit of King Juan Carlos I and Queen Sofia
to the Americas, June 1976.

San Marcos,
León — A495

Greco-Roman
Wrestling — A496

Tourism (Famous Hotels): 2p, Las Cañadas,
Tenerife. 3p, Portal of R. R. Catolicos, Santi-
ago, vert. 4p, Cruz de Tejeda, Las Palmas. 7p,
Gredos, Avila. 12p, La Arruzafa, Cordoba.

1976, June 30   Engr.   Perf. 13
1959 A495 1p slate & sepia   .20 .20
1960 A495 2p green & indigo   .65 .20
1961 A495 3p brn & red brn   .45 .20
1962 A495 4p sepia & slate   .25 .20
1963 A495 7p slate & sepia   .85 .35
1964 A495 12p rose brn & pur   1.00 .25
     Nos. 1959-1964 (6)   3.40 1.40

1976, July 9   Photo.
   Montreal Olympic Emblem and: 1p, Men's
rowing, horiz. 2p, Boxing, horiz. 12p,
Basketball.

1965 A496 1p multicolored   .20 .20
1966 A496 2p lilac & multi   .35 .20
1967 A496 3p multicolored   .25 .20
1968 A496 12p multicolored   .25 .20
     Nos. 1965-1968 (4)   1.05 .80

21st Olympic Games, Montreal, Canada,
July 17-Aug. 1.

King Juan Carlos
I — A497

1976-77   Photo.   Perf. 13
1969 A497 10c orange ('77)   .20 .20
1970 A497 25c apple grn ('77)   .20 .20
1971 A497 30c dp blue ('77)   .20 .20
1972 A497 50c purple ('77)   .20 .20
1973 A497 1p emerald ('77)   .20 .20
1974 A497 1.50p scarlet   .20 .20
1975 A497 2p dp blue   .20 .20
1976 A497 3p dp green   .20 .20
1977 A497 4p blue grn ('77)   .20 .20
1978 A497 5p dp car rose   .20 .20
1979 A497 6p brt green ('77)   .20 .20
1980 A497 7p olive   .20 .20
1982 A497 8p brt blue ('77)   .20 .20
1983 A497 10p lilac rose ('77)   .20 .20
1984 A497 12p golden brown   .25 .20
1985 A497 15p vio blue ('77)   .30 .20
1986 A497 20p brt red lil ('77) .35 .20
     Nos. 1969-1986 (17)   3.70 3.40

Nos. 1979, 1983 also issued as coils with
number on back of every fifth stamp.
See Nos. 2185-2194.

Uniform Type of 1973

Uniforms: 1p, Trumpeter, Alcantara Regiment, 1815. 2p, Sapper, 1821. 3p, Engineer in
dress uniform, 1825. 7p, Artillery infantry,
1828. 25p, Infantry riflemen, 1830.

1976, July 17
1989 A428 1p multicolored   .20 .20
1990 A428 2p multicolored   .80 .20
1991 A428 3p multicolored   .30 .20
1992 A428 7p multicolored   .25 .25
1993 A428 25p multicolored   .30 .20
     Nos. 1989-1993 (5)   1.85 1.05

Blood Donors
A498

Mosaic,
Batitales
A499

1976, Sept. 7   Engr.   Perf. 13
1994 A498 3p carmine & black   .20 .20

Give blood, save a life!

1976, Sept. 22
Designs: 3p, Lugo city wall. 7p, Obverse
and reverse of Roman 1st Legion coin.

1995 A499 1p black & purple   .20 .20
1996 A499 3p black & dp brn   .25 .20
1997 A499 7p green & magenta   .45 .20
     Nos. 1995-1997 (3)   .90 .60

2000th anniversary of Lugo City.

Parliament,
Madrid
A500

1976, Sept. 23
1998 A500 12p green & sepia   .20 .20

63rd Conference of Inter-parliamentary
Union, Madrid.

Still Life, by L. E.
Menendez — A501

St. Christopher
Carrying Christ
Child — A502

Luis Eugenio Menendez Paintings: 2p,
Peaches and jar. 3p, Pears, melon and barrel.
4p, Brace of pigeons and basket. 6p, Sea
bream and oranges, horiz. 7p, Water melon
and bread, horiz. 10p, Figs, bread and jug,
horiz. 12p, Various fruits, horiz.

1976, Sept. 29   Photo.   Perf. 13
1999 A501 1p gold & multi   .20 .20
2000 A501 2p gold & multi   .20 .20
2001 A501 3p gold & multi   .20 .20
2002 A501 4p gold & multi   .20 .20
2003 A501 6p gold & multi   .20 .20
2004 A501 7p gold & multi   .30 .25
2005 A501 10p gold & multi   .25 .20
2006 A501 12p gold & multi   .30 .25
     Nos. 1999-2006 (8)   1.85 1.70

Luis Eugenio Menendez (1716-1780).
Stamp Day 1976.
For other art types see A384, A397, A410,
A431, A448, A473, A522, A538, A558 and
footnote following No. 876.

1976, Oct. 8
Christmas: 3p, Nativity, horiz. Both designs
after painted wood carvings.

2007 A502 3p multicolored   .75 .20
2008 A502 12p multicolored   1.50 .50

Nicoya Church,
Costa
Rica — A503

Juan Vazquez de
Coronado — A504

Designs: 3p, Orosi Mission, Costa Rica,
horiz. 12p, Tomas de Acosta.

1976, Oct. 12
2009 A503 1p multicolored   .20 .20
2010 A504 2p multicolored   .25 .20
2011 A503 3p multicolored   .20 .20
2012 A504 12p multicolored   .25 .20
     Nos. 2009-2012 (4)   .90 .80

Spain's link with Costa Rica.

Map of South and Central America, Santa Maria, King and Queen
A505

1976, Oct. 12
2013 A505 12p multicolored .20 .20
Visit of King Juan Carlos I and Queen Sofia to Latin America.

St. Peter of Alcantara Monastery
A506

Tomb of Peter of Alcantara
A507

St. Peter of Alcantara
A508

1976, Oct. 29   Engr.   Perf. 13
2014 A506 3p dp brown & sepia .30 .20
2015 A507 7p dk purple & blk .20 .20
2016 A508 20p brown & dk brown .30 .20
Nos. 2014-2016 (3) .80 .60
St. Peter of Alcantara (1499-1562), Franciscan reformer.

Hand Releasing Doves
A509

1976, Nov. 23   Litho.   Perf. 13
2017 A509 3p multicolored .20 .20
11th Philatelic Exhibition of the National Association of the Handicapped.

Casals and Cello
A510

Design: 5p, Manuel de Falla and Fire Dance from El Amor Brujo.

1976, Dec. 29   Engr.   Perf. 13
2018 A510 3p black & vio bl .20 .20
2019 A510 5p slate grn & car .20 .20
Birth centenaries of Pablo Casals (1876-1973), cellist and composer, and of Manuel de Falla (1876-1946), composer.

Uniform Type of 1973

Uniforms: 1p, Outrider, Calatrava Lancers, 1844. 2p, Sapper, 1850. 3p, Corporal, Light Infantry, 1861. 4p, Drum Major, 1861. 20p, Artillery Captain, Mounted, 1862.

1977, Jan. 5   Photo.   Perf. 13
2020 A428 1p multicolored .20 .20
2021 A428 2p multicolored .35 .20
2022 A428 3p multicolored .20 .20
2023 A428 4p multicolored .20 .20
2024 A428 20p multicolored .25 .20
Nos. 2020-2024 (5) 1.20 1.00

King James I
A511

1977, Feb. 10   Engr.   Perf. 13
2025 A511 4p purple & ocher .20 .20
James I, El Conquistador (1208-1276), King of Aragon, 700th death anniversary.

Jacinto Verdaguer — A512

Portraits: 7p, Miguel Servet. 12p, Pablo Sarasate. 50p, Francisco Tarrega.

1977, Feb. 22
2026 A512 5p purple & dk red .25 .20
2027 A512 7p olive & slate grn .20 .20
2028 A512 12p dk blue & bl grn .20 .20
2029 A512 50p lt green & brown .55 .20
Nos. 2026-2029 (4) 1.20 .80
Honoring Jacinto Verdaguer (1845-1902), Catalan poet; Miguel Servet (1511-1553), physician and theologian; Pablo Sarasate (1844-1908), violinist and composer; Francisco Tarrega (1854-1909), creator of modern Spanish guitar music.

Marquis de Penaflorida — A513

1977, Feb. 24   Engr.   Perf. 13
2030 A513 4p dull green & brn .20 .20
Bicentenary of the Economic Society of the Friends of the Land (agricultural improvements).

Trout
A514

1977, Mar. 8   Photo.
2031 A514 1p Salmon, vert. .20 .20
2032 A514 2p shown .20 .20
2033 A514 3p Eel .20 .20
2034 A514 4p Carp .20 .20
2035 A514 6p Barbel .20 .20
Nos. 2031-2035 (5) 1.00 1.00

Slalom
A515

1977, Mar. 24   Engr.   Perf. 13
2036 A515 5p multicolored .20 .20
World Ski Championships, Granada, Sierra Nevada, Mar. 24-27.

La Cuadra, 1900
A516

Spanish Pioneer Automobiles: 4p, Hispano Suiza, 1916. 5p, Elizalde, 1915. 7p, Abadal, 1914.

1977, Apr. 23   Photo.   Perf. 13
2037 A516 2p multicolored .20 .20
2038 A516 4p multicolored .20 .20
2039 A516 5p multicolored .20 .20
2040 A516 7p multicolored .20 .20
Nos. 2037-2040 (4) .80 .80

Ordesa National Park
A517

Europa: 3p, Tree in Doñana National Park.

1977, May 2   Litho.
2041 A517 3p multicolored .20 .20
2042 A517 12p multicolored .25 .20

Plaza Mayor, Spanish Stamps, Tongs
A518

1977, May 7   Engr.   Perf. 13
2043 A518 3p multicolored .20 .20
50th anniversary of Philatelic Market on Plaza Mayor, Madrid.

Enrique de Osso, St. Theresa and Book
A519

1977, June 7   Photo.   Perf. 13
2044 A519 8p multicolored .20 .20
Centenary of the founding by Enrique de Osso of the Society of St. Theresa of Jesus.

Toledo Gate, Ciudad Real — A520

Tourism: 2p, Roman aqueduct, Almuñecar. 3p, Cathedral, Jaen, vert. 4p, Ronda Gorge,

Malaga, vert. 7p, Ampudia Castle, Palencia. 12p, Bisagra Gate, Toledo.

1977, June 24   Engr.   Perf. 13
2045 A520 1p orange & brown .20 .20
2046 A520 2p sepia & slate .20 .20
2047 A520 3p violet & purple .20 .20
2048 A520 4p brt & dk green .20 .20
2049 A520 7p brown & black .20 .20
2050 A520 12p vio & org brn .20 .20
Nos. 2045-2050 (6) 1.20 1.20

Uniform Type of 1973

Uniforms: 1p, Military Administration official, 1875. 2p, Cavalry lancers, 1883. 3p, General Staff Commander, 1884. 7p, Trumpeter, Divisional Artillery, 1887. 25p, Medical Corps official, 1895.

1977, July 16   Photo.
2051 A428 1p multicolored .20 .20
2052 A428 2p multicolored .20 .20
2053 A428 3p multicolored .20 .20
2054 A428 7p multicolored .20 .20
2055 A428 25p multicolored .30 .20
Nos. 2051-2055 (5) 1.10 1.00

A521

A522

St. Emilian Cuculatus and earliest known Catalan manuscript.

1977, Sept. 9   Engr.   Perf. 13
2056 A521 5p violet, grn & brn .20 .20
Millennium of Catalan language.

1977, Sept. 29   Photo.   Perf. 13
Federico Madrazo (1815-94) Portraits: 1p, The Boy Florez. 2p, Duke of San Miguel. 3p, Senora Coronado. 4p, Campoamor. 6p, Marquesa de Montelo. 7p, Rivadeneyra. 10p, Countess of Vilches. 15p, Senora Gomez de Avellaneda.

2057 A522 1p gold & multi .20 .20
2058 A522 2p gold & multi .20 .20
2059 A522 3p gold & multi .20 .20
2060 A522 4p gold & multi .20 .20
2061 A522 6p gold & multi .20 .20
2062 A522 7p gold & multi .20 .20
2063 A522 10p gold & multi .20 .20
2064 A522 15p gold & multi .20 .20
Nos. 2057-2064 (8) 1.60 1.60
For other art types see A384, A397, A410, A431, A448, A473, A501, A538, A558 and footnote following No. 876.

Sailing Ship and Mail Routes, 18th Century — A523

1977, Oct. 7   Engr.
2065 A523 15p black, brn & grn .30 .30
ESPAMER '77 Philatelic Exhibition, Barcelona, Oct. 7-13, and for the Bicentenary for regular mail routes to the Indies (Central and South America). No. 2065 issued in sheets of 8 stamps and 8 labels showing exhibition emblem.

Church of St. Francis, Guatemala City A524

Designs (Guatemala City): 3p, Modern buildings. 7p, Government Palace. 12p, Columbus Square and monument.

1977, Oct. 12   Photo.   Perf. 13
2066 A524 1p multicolored   .20 .20
2067 A524 3p multicolored   .20 .20
2068 A524 7p multicolored   .20 .20
2069 A524 12p multicolored   .20 .20
       Nos. 2066-2069 (4)   .80 .80

Spain's link with Guatemala.

San Pedro Monastery, Cardeña A525

Designs: 7p, Cloister. 20p, Tomb of El Cid and Dona Gimena.

1977, Oct. 28   Engr.
2070 A525 3p vio blue & slate   .20 .20
2071 A525 7p brown & maroon   .20 .20
2072 A525 20p green & slate   .25 .20
       Nos. 2070-2072 (3)   .65 .60

San Pedro Monastery, Cardena, Bugos.

Adoration of the Kings A526

Christmas: 12p, Flight into Egypt, vert. Designs from Romanesque paintings in Jaca Cathedral Museum.

1977, Nov. 3   Photo.
2073 A526 5p multicolored   .20 .20
2074 A526 12p multicolored   .20 .20

Old and New Iberia Planes A527

1977, Nov. 3
2075 A527 12p multicolored   .20 .20
IBERIA, Spanish Airlines, 50th anniversary.

Felipe de Borbon, Prince of Asturias — A528

Judo, Games Emblem — A529

1977, Dec. 22   Photo.   Perf. 13
2076 A528 5p multicolored   .20 .20

Felipe de Borbon, Spanish crown prince.

1977, Dec. 29
2077 A529 3p multicolored   .20 .20

10th World Judo Championships, Taiwan.

Uniform Type of 1973

Uniforms: 1p, Flag bearer, 1908. 2p, Lieutenant Colonel, Hussar, 1909. 3p, Mounted artillery lieutenant, 1912. 5p, Engineers' captain, 1921. 12p, Captain General, 1925.

1978, Jan. 5
2078 A428 1p multicolored   .20 .20
2079 A428 2p multicolored   .20 .20
2080 A428 3p multicolored   .20 .20
2081 A428 5p multicolored   .20 .20
2082 A428 12p multicolored   .20 .20
       Nos. 2078-2082 (5)   1.00 1.00

Hilarión Eslava and Score A530

8p, José Clara and sculpture. 25p, Pio Baroja and farm. 50p, Antonio Machado Ruiz and castle.

1978, Feb. 20   Engr.   Perf. 13
2083 A530 5p black & dk pur   .20 .20
2084 A530 8p blue grn & blk   .20 .20
2085 A530 25p yel grn & blk   .30 .20
2086 A530 50p dk pur & dk brn   .55 .20
       Nos. 2083-2086 (4)   1.25 .80

Miguel Hilarión Eslava (1807-1878), composer; José Clara, sculptor; Pio Baroja (1872-1956), author and physician; Antonio Machado Ruiz (1875-1939), poet and playwright.

Burial of Christ, by de Juni — A531

Detail from Burial of Christ — A532

Designs: No. 2089, Juan de Juni. No. 2090, Rape of Sabine Women, by Rubens. No. 2091, Rape (detail) and Rubens portrait. No. 2092, Rubens signature and palette. No. 2093, Judgment of Paris, by Titian. No. 2094, Judgment and Titian portrait. No. 2095, Initial "TF" and palette.

1978, Mar. 28   Engr.   Perf. 12½x13
2087 A532 3p multicolored   .20 .20
2088 A531 3p multicolored   .20 .20
2089 A532 3p multicolored   .20 .20
   a.   Strip of 3, #2087-2089   .25 .25
2090 A532 5p multicolored   .20 .20
2091 A531 5p multicolored   .20 .20
2092 A532 5p multicolored   .20 .20
   a.   Strip of 3, #2090-2092   .25 .25
2093 A532 8p multicolored   .20 .20
2094 A531 8p multicolored   .20 .20
2095 A532 8p multicolored   .20 .20
   a.   Strip of 3, #2093-2095   .25 .25

Juan de Juni (1507-77), sculptor, (3p); Peter Paul Rubens (1577-1640), painter, (5p); Titian (1477-1576), painter, (8p).

Edelweiss in Pyrenees — A533

Designs: 5p, Fish and duck, wetlands. 7p, Forest, and forest destroyed by fire. 12p, Waves, oil rig, tanker and city. 20p, Sea gulls and seals, vert.

1978, Apr. 4   Photo.   Perf. 13
2096 A533 3p multicolored   .20 .20
2097 A533 5p multicolored   .20 .20
2098 A533 7p multicolored   .20 .20
2099 A533 12p multicolored   .20 .20
2100 A533 20p multicolored   .25 .20
       Nos. 2096-2100 (5)   1.05 1.00

Protection of the environment.

Palace of Charles V, Granada A534

Europa: 12p, The Lonja, Seville.

1978, May 2   Engr.   Perf. 13
2101 A534 5p dull grn & sl grn   .20 .20
2102 A534 12p dull grn & car rose .20 .20

"España" — A535

1978, May 5   Photo.   Perf. 12½
2103 A535 12p multicolored   .20 .20

Spain's admission to the Council of Europe.

Symbols and Emblems of Postal Service A536

1978, June 27   Engr.   Perf. 13
2104 A536 5p slate green   .20 .20

Stamp Day.

Map of Las Palmas, 16th Century A537

5p, Hermitage of Columbus Church, vert. 12p, View of Las Palmas, 16th century.

1978, June 23   Photo.
2105 A537 3p multicolored   .20 .20
2106 A537 5p multicolored   .20 .20
2107 A537 12p multicolored   .20 .20
       Nos. 2105-2107 (3)   .60 .60

Founding of Las Palmas, 500th anniv.

Pablo Picasso, Self-portrait A538

Picasso Paintings: 3p, Señora Canals. 8p, Jaime Sabartes. 10p, End of the Act (actress). 12p, Science and Charity (woman patient, doctor, nurse and child), horiz. 15p, "Las Mennas" (blue period), horiz. 20p, The Sparrows. 25p, The Painter and his Model, horiz.

1978, Sept. 29   Photo.   Perf. 13
2108 A538 3p gold & multi   .20 .20
2109 A538 5p gold & multi   .20 .20
2110 A538 8p gold & multi   .20 .20
2111 A538 10p gold & multi   .20 .20
2112 A538 12p gold & multi   .20 .20
2113 A538 15p gold & multi   .20 .20
2114 A538 20p gold & multi   .25 .20
2115 A538 25p gold & multi   .30 .20
       Nos. 2108-2115 (8)   1.75 1.60

Pablo Picasso (1881-1973). Stamp Day 1978.
A 7p stamp like No. 2111 was not issued.
For other art types see A384, A397, A410, A431, A448, A473, A501, A522, A558 and footnote following No. 876.

José de San Martin A539

Design: 12p, Simon Bolivar.

1978, Oct. 12   Engr.   Perf. 13
2116 A539 7p sepia & car   .20 .20
2117 A539 12p violet & car   .20 .20

José de San Martin (1778-1850) and Simon Bolivar (1783-1830), South American liberators.

Flight into Egypt, Capital from St. Mary de Nieva A540

Christmas: 12p, Annunciation, capital from St. Mary de Nieva.

1978, Nov. 3   Photo.   Perf. 13
2118 A540 5p multicolored   .20 .20
2119 A540 12p multicolored   .20 .20

Mexican Calendar Stone A541

Designs (King Juan Carlos I, Queen Sofia and): No. 2121, Machu Picchu. No. 2122, Calchaqui jars from Tucuman and Angalgala.

1978
2120 A541 5p multicolored   .20 .20
2121 A541 5p multicolored   .20 .20
2122 A541 5p multicolored   .20 .20
       Nos. 2120-2122 (3)   .60 .60

Royal visits to Mexico, Peru and Argentina.
Issued: #2120 (Mexico), Nov. 17; #2121 (Peru), Nov. 22; #2122 (Argentina), Nov. 26.

King Philip
V — A542

Rulers of Spain: No. 2124, Louis I. 8p, Ferdinand VI. 10p, Carlos III. 12p, Carlos IV. 15p, Ferdinand VII. 20p, Isabella II. 25p, Alfonso XII. 50p, Alfonso XIII. 100p, Juan Carlos I.

1978, Nov. 22   Engr.   Perf. 13
2123	A542	5p dk blue & rose red	.20	.20
2124	A542	5p olive & dull grn	.20	.20
2125	A542	8p vio bl & red brn	.20	.20
2126	A542	10p blue grn & blk	.20	.20
2127	A542	12p brown & mar	.20	.20
2128	A542	15p black & indigo	.20	.20
2129	A542	20p olive & indigo	.25	.20
2130	A542	25p ultra & vio brn	.30	.20
2131	A542	50p vermilion & brn	.55	.25
2132	A542	100p ultra & vio blk	1.10	.35
	Nos. 2123-2132 (10)		3.40	2.20

Spanish Flag, Preamble to
Constitution, Parliament — A543

1978, Dec.   Photo.   Perf. 13
2133 A543 5p multicolored   .20 .20
Proclamation of New Constitution.

Illuminated Pages from Bible and
Codex — A544

1978, Dec. 27
2134 A544 5p multicolored   .20 .20
Millennium of the consecration of the Basilica of Santa Maria de Ripoll.

Car and Drop of
Oil — A545

Designs: 8p, Insulated house and thermometer. 10p, Hand pulling plug.

1979, Jan. 24   Photo.   Perf. 13
2135	A545	5p multicolored	.20	.20
2136	A545	8p multicolored	.20	.20
2137	A545	10p multicolored	.20	.20
	Nos. 2135-2137 (3)		.60	.60

Energy conservation.

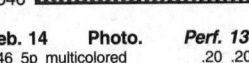

De La
Salle,
Students
A546

1979, Feb. 14   Photo.   Perf. 13
2138 A546 5p multicolored   .20 .20
Institute of Christian Brothers, founded by Jean-Baptiste de la Salle, centenary.

Jorge
Manrique — A547

Portraits: 8p, Fernan Caballero (pen name of Cecilia Böhl de Faber). 10p, Francisco Villaespesa. 20p, Gregorio Marañon.

1979, Feb. 28   Engr.
2139	A547	5p green & brown	.20	.20
2140	A547	8p dark red & blue	.20	.20
2141	A547	10p brown & purple	.20	.20
2142	A547	20p green & olive	.25	.20
	Nos. 2139-2142 (4)		.85	.80

Jorge Manrique, poet, 500th death anniversary; Fernan Caballero, Francisco Villaespesa, and Gregorio Marañon, writers, birth centenaries.

Running
and
Jumping
A548

Sport for All: 8p, Children kicking ball and skipping rope, jogging and bicycling. 10p, Family jogging, and dog.

1979, Mar. 14   Photo.   Perf. 13
2143	A548	5p multicolored	.20	.20
2144	A548	8p multicolored	.20	.20
2145	A548	10p multicolored	.20	.20
	Nos. 2143-2145 (3)		.60	.60

Children in
Library
A549

1979, Apr. 27   Photo.   Perf. 13
2146 A549 5p multicolored   .20 .20
International Year of the Child.

Manuel Ysasi (1810-1855) Postal
Reformer — A550

Europa: 5p, Mounted messenger and postilion, 1761 engraving, vert.

1979, Apr. 30   Engr.
2147	A550	5p brown & sepia	.20	.20
2148	A550	12p red brn & sl grn	.20	.20

Radar and
Satellite
A551

5p, Symbolic people and cables, vert.

1979, May 17   Photo.   Perf. 13
2149	A551	5p multicolored	.20	.20
2150	A551	8p multicolored	.20	.20

World Telecommunications Day, May 17.

Bulgaria No. 1, Sofia Opera House,
Housing Development — A552

1979, May 18
2151 A552 12p multicolored   .20 .20
Philaserdica '79, International Philatelic Exhibition, Sofia, Bulgaria, May 18-27.

Tank, Jet
and
Destroyer
A553

1979, May 25
2152 A553 5p multicolored   .20 .20
Armed Forces Day.

Messenger Handing Letter to
King — A554

1979, June 15   Litho. & Engr.
2153 A554 5p multicolored   .20 .20
Stamp Day 1979.

Daroca Gate,
Zaragoza — A555

Architecture: 8p, Gerona Cathedral. 10p, Interior, Carthusian Monastery Church, Granada. 20p, Portal, Palace of the Marques de Dos Aguas, Valencia.

1979, June 27   Engr.
2154	A555	5p vio bl & lilac brn	.20	.20
2155	A555	8p dk blue & sepia	.20	.20
2156	A555	10p black & green	.20	.20
2157	A555	20p brown & sepia	.25	.20
	Nos. 2154-2157 (4)		.85	.80

Turkey
Sponge
A556

Fauna: 7p, Crayfish. 8p, Scorpion. 20p, Starfish. 25p, Sea anemone.

1979, July 11   Photo.   Perf. 13
2158	A556	5p multicolored	.20	.20
2159	A556	7p multicolored	.20	.20
2160	A556	8p multicolored	.20	.20
2161	A556	20p multicolored	.25	.20
2162	A556	25p multicolored	.30	.20
	Nos. 2158-2162 (5)		1.15	1.00

Gen.
Antonio
Gutierrez
and Battle
A557

1979, Aug.   Engr.
2163 A557 5p multicolored   .20 .20
Naval defense of Tenerife, 18th century.

A558

A559

Juan de Juanes Paintings: 8p, Immaculate Conception. 10p, Holy Family. 15p, Ecce Homo. 20p, St. Stephen in the Synagogue. 25p, The Last Supper, horiz. 50p, Adoration of the Mystic Lamb, horiz.

1979, Sept. 28   Photo.   Perf. 13x13½
2164	A558	8p multicolored	.20	.20
2165	A558	10p multicolored	.20	.20
2166	A558	15p multicolored	.20	.20
2167	A558	20p multicolored	.25	.20
2168	A558	25p multicolored	.30	.20
2169	A558	50p multicolored	.55	.20
	Nos. 2164-2169 (6)		1.70	1.20

For other art types see A384, A397, A410, A431, A448, A473, A501, A522, A538 and footnote following No. 876.

1979, Oct. 3   Photo.   Perf. 13x13½
Zaragoza Cathedral, Mother and Child statue.
2170 A559 5p multicolored   .20 .20
8th Mariology and 15th International Marianist Congresses, Zaragoza, Oct. 3-12.

Felipe de
Borbon,
Hospital
A560

1979, Oct.   Perf. 13½x13
2171 A560 5p multicolored   .20 .20
Hospital of the Child Jesus, centenary.

St. Bartholomew College,
Bogota — A561

Hispanidad 79: 12p, University of St. Mark, Lima, coat of arms.

1979, Oct. 12   Engr.   Perf. 13
2172	A561	7p multicolored	.20	.20
2173	A561	12p multicolored	.20	.20

Clasped Hands, Badge, Governor's Palace A562

Design: No. 2175, Statute book, vert.

Lithographed and Engraved
1979, Oct. 27   *Perf. 13*
2174 A562 8p multicolored   .20 .20
2175 A562 8p multicolored   .20 .20
Catalonian and Basque autonomy statute.

Type A54, Barcelona Coat of Arms A563

Photogravure and Engraved
1979, Nov. 6   *Perf. 13½x13*
2176 A563 5p multicolored   .20 .20
Barcelona Philatelic Congress and Exhibition, 50th anniversary.

Nativity, Capital from St. Peter the Elder A564

Christmas 1979: 19p, Flight into Egypt, column from St. Peter the Elder, Huesca.

1979, Nov. 14   **Photo.**
2177 A564 8p multicolored   .20 .20
2178 A564 19p multicolored   .25 .20

Carlos I, Coat of Arms A565

Kings of the House of Austria (Hapsburg Dynasty): 20p, Philip II. 25p, Philip III. 50c, Philip IV. 100p, Carlos II.

1979, Nov. 22   **Engr.**   *Perf. 13*
2179 A565 15p sl grn & dk bl   .20 .20
2180 A565 20p dk blue & mag   .25 .20
2181 A565 25p violet & yel bis   .30 .20
2182 A565 50p brown & sl grn   .55 .20
2183 A565 100p magenta & brn   1.10 .30
       Nos. 2179-2183 (5)   2.40 1.10

2nd International Olive Oil Year — A566

1979, Dec. 4   **Photo.**   *Perf. 13½x13*
2184 A566 8p multicolored   .20 .20

King Juan Carlos I Type of 1976
1980-84   **Photo.**   *Perf. 13*
2185 A497 13p dk red brn ('81)   .25 .20
2186 A497 14p red orange ('82)   .25 .20
2187 A497 16p sepia   .30 .20
2188 A497 17p bluish gray ('84)   .25 .20
2189 A497 19p orange   .35 .20
2190 A497 30p dk green ('81)   .40 .20
2191 A497 50p org ver ('81)   .90 .20
2192 A497 60p blue ('81)   .80 .20
2193 A497 75p brt yel grn ('81)   1.00 .30
2194 A497 85p gray ('81)   1.25 .45
       Nos. 2185-2194 (10)   5.75 2.35
No. 2186 also issued as coil with number on back of every fifth stamp.

Train and People A567

1980, Feb. 20   **Engr.**   *Perf. 13½*
2200 A567 3p shown   .20 .20
2201 A567 4p Bus   .20 .20
2202 A567 5p Subway   .20 .20
       Nos. 2200-2202 (3)   .60 .60
Public transportation.

Steel Export A568

1980, Mar. 15   **Photo.**   *Perf. 13½x13*
2203 A568 5p shown   .20 .20
2204 A568 8p Ships   .20 .20
2205 A568 13p Shoes   .20 .20
2206 A568 19p Machinery   .25 .20
2207 A568 25p Technology   .30 .20
       Nos. 2203-2207 (5)   1.15 1.00

Federico Garcia Lorca (1899-1936) — A569

Europa: 19p, José Ortega y Gasset (1883-1955), philosopher and statesman.

1980, Apr. 28   **Engr.**   *Perf. 13½*
2208 A569 8p violet & ol grn   .20 .20
2209 A569 19p brown & dk grn   .25 .20

Armed Forces Day A570

1980, May 24   **Photo.**   *Perf. 13½x13*
2210 A570 8p multicolored   .20 .20

Soccer Players A571

1980, May 23
2211 A571 8p shown   .20 .20
2212 A571 19p Soccer ball, flags   .25 .20
World Soccer Cup 1982.

Bourbon Arms, Ministry of Finance A572

1980, June 9   **Engr.**   *Perf. 13½*
2213 A572 8p dark brown   .20 .20
Public Finances in Bourbon Spain Exhibition.

Helen Keller, Sign Language A573

1980, June 27
2214 A573 19p dk yel grn & rose lake   .25 .20
Helen Keller (1880-1968), deaf mute writer and lecturer.

Mounted Postman, 12th Century Panel, Barcelona — A574

Lithographed and Engraved
1980, June 28   *Perf. 13x12½*
2215 A574 8p multicolored   .20 .20
Stamp Day.

King Alfonso and Count of Maceda at 1930 National Exhibition A575

1980, July 1   **Photo.**   *Perf. 13½*
2216 A575 8p multicolored   .20 .20
1st Natl. Stamp Exhibition, Barcelona, 50th anniv.

A576

A577

Altar of the Virgin, La Palma Cathedral.

1980, July 12   **Engr.**   *Perf. 13*
2217 A576 8p black & brown   .20 .20
Appearance of the Virgin of the Snow at La Palma, 300th anniversary.

1980, Aug. 9   **Engr.**   *Perf. 13*
2218 A577 100p slate & sepia   1.10 .20
Ramon Perez de Ayala (1881-1962), novelist and diplomat.

Souvenir Sheet

La Atlantida Ruins, Mexican Bonampak Musicians — A578

Designs: b, Sun Gate, Tiahuanaco; Roman arch, Medinaceli. c, Alonso de Ercilla, Garcilaso de la Vega; title pages from La Arauca and Commentario Reales. d, Virgin of Quito, Virgin of Seafarers.

1980, Oct. 3   **Engr.**   *Perf. 13*
2219 A578 Sheet of 4 + 2 labels 2.25 2.25
   a. 25p multicolored   .30 .30
   b. 25p multicolored   .30 .30
   c. 50p multicolored   .55 .45
   d. 100p multicolored   1.10 .85
ESPAMER '80 Stamp Exhib., Madrid, Oct. 3-12.

400th Anniversary of Buenos Aires — A579

1980, Oct. 24
2220 A579 19p multicolored   .25 .20

Miniature Sheet

The Creation, Tapestry, Gerona Cathedral — A580

1980, Nov.   **Litho.**   *Perf. 13½x13*
2221 A580 Sheet of 6   2.50 2.00
   a.-c. 25p, any single   .25 .20
   d.-f. 50p, any single   .55 .25

Conference Building, Flags of Participants A581

Holy Family Church of Santa Maria, Cuina — A582

1980, Nov. 11   **Photo.**   *Perf. 13½*
2222 A581 22p multicolored   .25 .20

1980, Nov. 12

Christmas 1980, 22p, Adoration of the Kings, portal, Church of Santa Maria, Cuina, horiz.

| 2223 A582 | 10p multicolored | .20 | .20 |
| 2224 A582 | 22p multicolored | .25 | .20 |

Pedro Vives and His Airplane A583

Designs: Aviation pioneers.

1980, Dec. 10

2225 A583	5p shown	.20	.20
2226 A583	10p Benito Loygorri	.20	.20
2227 A583	15p Alfonso De Orle- ans	.20	.20
2228 A583	22p Alfredo Kindelan	.25	.20
Nos. 2225-2228 (4)		.85	.80

Winter University Games A584

1981, Mar. 4   Perf. 13½x13
| 2229 A584 | 30p multicolored | .35 | .20 |

Picasso's Birth Centenary Emblem, by Joan Miro — A585

1981, Mar. 27   Perf. 13
| 2230 A585 | 100p multicolored | 1.00 | .25 |

Pablo Picasso (1881-1973).

Galician Autonomy — A586

1981, Mar. 27   Photo.   Perf. 13
| 2231 A586 | 12p multicolored | .20 | .20 |

Homage to the Press A587

1981, Apr. 8   Photo.   Perf. 13½x13
| 2232 A587 | 12p multicolored | .20 | .20 |

International Year of the Disabled — A588

1981, Apr. 29   Litho.
| 2233 A588 | 30p multicolored | .35 | .20 |

Soccer Players A589

1981, May 2   Photo.
| 2234 A589 | 12p Soccer players, diff., vert. | .20 | .20 |
| 2235 A589 | 30p shown | .35 | .20 |

1982 World Cup Soccer.

Europa Issue 1981

La Jota Folkdance A590

1981, May 4   Engr.
| 2236 A590 | 12p shown | .20 | .20 |
| 2237 A590 | 30p Virgin of Rocio pro- cession | .35 | .20 |

Armed Forces Day — A591

Gabriel Miro (1879-1930), Writer — A592

1981, May 29   Photo.   Perf. 13x13½
| 2238 A591 | 12p multicolored | .20 | .20 |

1981, June 17   Engr.

Famous Men: 12p, Francisco de Quevedo (1580-1645), writer. 30p, St. Benedict (480-543), patron saint of Europe.

2239 A592	6p purple & dk grn	.20	.20
2240 A592	12p brown & purple	.20	.20
2241 A592	30p dk green & brown	.35	.20
Nos. 2239-2241 (3)		.75	.60

Mail Messenger, 14th Cent., Woodcut A593

Photogravure and Engraved
1981, June 19   Perf. 12½x13
| 2242 A593 | 12p multicolored | .20 | .20 |

Stamp Day.

Map of Balearic Islands, Diego Homem's Atlas, 1563 — A594

1981, July 8   Photo.   Perf. 13x12½
| 2243 A594 | 7p shown | .20 | .20 |
| 2244 A594 | 12p Canary Islds., Prunes map, 1563 | .20 | .20 |

Kings Alfonso XII and Juan Carlos, Advocates Arms A595

1981, July 27   Engr.   Perf. 13½x13
| 2245 A595 | 50p multicolored | .55 | .20 |

Chamber of Advocates of State (Public Prosecutor) centenary.

King Sancius VI of Navarre with City Charter, 12th Cent. Miniature A596

1981, Aug. 5   Photo.   Perf. 12½x13
| 2246 A596 | 12p multicolored | .20 | .20 |

Vitoria, 800th anniv.

Exports A597

1981, Sept. 30   Photo.   Perf. 13½x13
2247 A597	6p Fruit	.20	.20
2248 A597	12p Wine	.20	.20
2249 A597	30p Vehicles	.35	.20
Nos. 2247-2249 (3)		.75	.60

Congress Palace, Buenos Aires A598

1981, Oct. 12   Engr.   Perf. 13½x13
| 2250 A598 | 12p dk bl & car rose | .20 | .20 |

ESPAMER '81 Intl. Stamp Exhibition, Buenos Aires, Nov. 13-22.

World Food Day A599

1981, Oct. 16
| 2251 A599 | 30p multicolored | .35 | .20 |

Souvenir Sheet

Guernica, by Pablo Picasso (1881-1973) — A600

1981, Oct. 25   Photo.
| 2252 A600 | 200p multicolored | 2.25 | 2.25 |

Control number comes in two types.

A601

A602

Christmas 1981: 12p, Adoration of the Kings, Cervera de Pisuerga, Palencia. 30p, Nativity, Paredes de Nava.

1981, Nov. 18   Litho.   Perf. 13
| 2253 A601 | 12p shown | .20 | .20 |
| 2254 A601 | 30p multicolored | .35 | .20 |

1981, Oct. 21   Engr.   Perf. 13x12½

King Juan Carlos I.

2268 A602	100p brown	1.25	.20
2269 A602	200p dark green	2.60	.20
2270 A602	500p dark blue	6.25	.55
Nos. 2268-2270 (3)		10.10	.95

Postal Museum, Madrid A603

1981, Nov. 30   Engr.   Perf. 13
| 2273 A603 | 7p Telegrapher | .20 | .20 |
| 2274 A603 | 12p Coach | .20 | .20 |

Souvenir Sheet

2275		Sheet of 4	1.90 1.90
c.		A603 50p Emblem	.55 .50
d.		A603 100p Cap, posthorn, pouch	1.10 1.00

No. 2275 also contains Nos. 2273, 2274.

Royal Mint Building, Seville A604

1981, Dec. 4   **Engr.**   *Perf. 13*
2276 A604 12p black & brown   .20 .20

Spanish Administration of the Bourbons in the Indies.

A605

A606

12p, Iparraguirre (1820-81). 30p, Juan Ramon Jimenez (1881-1958), writer. 50p, Pedro Calderon (1600-81), playwright.

1981-82
2277	A605 12p black & dk bl	.20	.20
2278	A605 30p dk bl & dk grn	.35	.20
2279	A605 50p black & violet	.55	.20
	Nos. 2277-2279 (3)	1.10	.60

Issued: 12p, 12/16; 30p, 50p, 3/10/82.

1982, Feb. 24   **Photo.**
2280 A606 14p Poster by Joan Miro .20 .20
2281 A606 33p Cup, emblem   .40 .20

Espana '82 World Cup Soccer.

A607   A608

1982, Mar. 10   **Engr.**
2282 A607 30p grn & dk grn   .35 .20

Andres Bello (1782-1865), writer.

1982, Mar. 31   **Photo.**   *Perf. 13*
2283 A608 14p St. John of Compostelo   .20 .20

Holy Year of Compostelo.

A609-A610

Operetta composers and scenes from their works: #2284, Manuel Fernandez Caballero (1835-1906). #2285, Gigantes and Cabezudos. #2286, Amadeo Vives Roig (1871-1932). #2287, Dona Francisquita. #2288, Tomas Breton Hernandez (1850-1923). #2289, Verbena of Paloma.

Lithographed and Engraved

1982, Apr. 28   *Perf. 13*
2284	A609 3p multicolored	.20	.20
2285	A610 3p multicolored	.20	.20
a.	Pair, #2284-2285	.20	.20
2286	A609 6p multicolored	.20	.20
2287	A610 6p multicolored	.20	.20
a.	Pair, #2284-2285	.20	.20
2288	A609 8p multicolored	.20	.20
2289	A610 8p multicolored	.20	.20
a.	Pair, #2284-2285	.25	.20

See Nos. 2319-2324, 2378-2383.

Europa 1982 — A611

1982, May 3   **Engr.**   *Perf. 12½*
2290 A611 14p Unification, 1512   .20 .20
2291 A611 33p Discovery of New
                World, 1492   .40 .20

Armed Forces Day — A612

1982, May 28   **Photo.**   *Perf. 13*
2292 A612 14p multicolored   .20 .20

1982 World Cup A613

Designs: Soccer players.

1982, June 13   *Perf. 13*
2293 A613 14p multicolored   .20 .20
2294 A613 33p multicolored   .40 .20

Souvenir Sheets

2295		Sheets of 4, #2293-2294, 9p, 100p, each	1.75 1.75
a.		A613 9p Captains' handshake	.20 .20
b.		A613 100p Player holding cup	1.10 1.10

#2295 has two types of margin, each showing 7 arms of the 14 host cities. One sheet has 3 blue coats of arms, the other has 2.

Stamp Day — A614

1982, July 16   **Litho.**   *Perf. 12½*
2296 A614 14p Map, postal code   .20 .20

Organ Transplants A615

1982, July 28   **Photo.**   *Perf. 13*
2297 A615 14p Symbolic organs   .20 .20

Storks and Express Train — A616

Locomotive, 1850 — A617

Perf. 12½, 13 (A617)
1982, Sept. 27   **Photo.**
2298	A616 9p shown	.20	.20
2299	A617 14p shown	.20	.20
2300	A617 33p Santa Fe locomotive	.40	.20
	Nos. 2298-2300 (3)	.80	.60

23rd Intl. Railways Congress, Malaga.

ESPAMER '82 Intl. Stamp Exhibition, San Juan, Oct. 12-17 A618

1982, Oct. 12   **Engr.**   *Perf. 13½x13*
2301 A618 33p dk blue & pur   .40 .20

St. Teresa of Avila (1515-1582) — A619

1982, Oct. 15
2302 A619 33p Statue by Gregorio
                Hernandez   .40 .20

Visit of Pope John Paul II, Oct. 31-Nov. 9 — A620

1982, Oct. 31   **Engr.**   *Perf. 12½*
2303 A620 14p multicolored   .20 .20

Water Wheel, Alcantarilla A621

Landscapes and Monuments: 6p, Bank of Spain, 19th cent., horiz. 9p, Crucifixion. 14p, St. Martin's Tower, Teruel. 33p, St. Andrew's Gate, Zamora.

1982, Nov. 5   *Perf. 13x12½, 12½x13*
2304	A621 4p gray & dk blue	.20	.20
2305	A621 6p dk blue & gray	.20	.20
2306	A621 9p brt blue & vio	.20	.20
2307	A621 14p brt blue & vio	.20	.20
2308	A621 33p claret & brown	.40	.20
	Nos. 2304-2308 (5)	1.20	1.00

Christmas 1982 A622

1982, Nov. 17   **Photo.**   *Perf. 13½*
2309 A622 14p Nativity, wood carving, by Gil de Siloe .20 .20
2310 A622 33p Flight into Egypt   .40 .20

Pablo Gargallo, Sculptor, Birth Centenary A623

Salesian Fathers in Spain, Centenary A624

1982, Dec. 9   **Engr.**   *Perf. 13*
2311 A623 14p blue & dk grn   .20 .20

1982, Dec. 16   **Photo.**   *Perf. 12½x13*
2312 A624 14p multicolored   .20 .20

Arms of King Juan Carlos I A625

1983, Feb. 9   **Photo.**   *Perf. 12½*
2313 A625 14p multicolored   .20 .20

Andalusia Autonomy Statute A626

1983　　**Litho.**　　*Perf. 13½*
2314 A626 14p shown 　.25 .20
2315 A626 14p Cantabria 　.25 .20

Issued: #2314, Feb. 28; #2315, Mar. 15.

State
Security
Forces
A627

1983, Mar. 23　　　**Photo.**
2316 A627 9p Natl. Police Force 　.20 .20
2317 A627 14p Civil Guard 　.20 .20
2318 A627 33p Superior Police
Corps 　.40 .20

Operetta Type of 1982

Designs: #2319, Scene from La Parranda. Francisco Alonso Lopez (1887-1948). #2320, Francisco Alonso Lopez (1887-1948). #2321, Jacinto Guerrero y Torres (1895-1951). #2322, Scene from La Rosa del Azafran. #2323, Jesus de Guridi Bidaola (1886-1961). #2324, Scene from El Caserio.

Lithographed and Engraved

1983, Apr. 22　　　*Perf. 13*
2319 A610 4p multicolored 　.20 .20
2320 A609 4p multicolored 　.20 .20
　a.　Pair, #2319-2320 　.20 .20
2321 A609 6p multicolored 　.20 .20
2322 A610 6p multicolored 　.20 .20
　a.　Pair, #2321-2322 　.25 .25
2323 A609 9p multicolored 　.20 .20
2324 A610 9p multicolored 　.20 .20
　a.　Pair, #2323-2324 　.35 .35

Europa 1983 — A628

Designs: 16p, Scene from Don Quixote, by Miguel Cervantes. 38p, L. Torres Quevaedo's Niagara Spanish aerocar.

1983, May 5　**Engr.**　*Perf. 13x12½*
Granite Paper
2325 A628 16p dk grn & brn red 　.20 .20
2326 A628 38p brown 　.45 .20

Francisco Salzillo
Alvarez (1707-83),
Painter — A629

World
Communications
Year — A630

Designs: 38p, Antonio Soler Ramos (1729-1783), composer. 50p, Joaquin Turina Perez (1882-1949), composer. 100p, St. Isidro Labrador (1082-1170), patron saint of Madrid.

1983, May 14　　　*Perf. 13*
2327 A629 16p purple & dk grn 　.20 .20
2328 A629 38p blue & brown 　.45 .20
2329 A629 50p bl grn & dk brn 　.55 .20
2330 A629 100p red brn & pur 　1.10 .25
　Nos. 2327-2330 (4) 　2.30 .85

1983, May 17　　**Photo.**　*Perf. 13*
2331 A630 38p multicolored 　.45 .20

Rioja Autonomous Region — A631

Lithographed and Engraved

1983, May 25　　　*Perf. 13*
2332 A631 16p multicolored 　.25 .20

Armed Forces
Day — A632

1983, May 26　　**Photo.**
2333 A632 16p multicolored 　.20 .20

Intl.
Canine
Exhibition,
Madrid,
June 1984
A633

Lithographed and Engraved

1983, June 8　　　*Perf. 13½*
2334 A633 10p Pointer 　.20 .20
2335 A633 16p Mastiff 　.20 .20
2336 A633 26p Iberian hound 　.35 .25
2337 A633 38p Navarro pointer 　.50 .20
　Nos. 2334-2337 (4) 　1.25 .85

Discovery of Tungsten
Bicentenary — A634

Scouting
Year
A635

400th
Anniv. of
University
of
Zaragoza
A636

1983, June 22　　**Photo.**　*Perf. 13*
2338 A634 16p Elhuyar brothers 　.20 .20
2339 A635 38p multicolored 　.45 .20
2340 A636 50p multicolored 　.60 .20
　Nos. 2338-2340 (3) 　1.25 .60

Murcia Autonomous Region — A637

Photogravure and Engraved

1983, July 8　　　*Perf. 13½*
2341 A637 16p Arms 　.25 .20

Asturias Autonomous Region — A638

Lithographed and Engraved

1983, Sept. 8　　　*Perf. 13*
2342 A638 14p Victory Cross,
Covadonga Basili-
ca 　.25 .20

Intl. Institute of Statistics, 44th
Congress, Madrid, Sept. 12-22
A639

1983, Sept. 12　**Photo.**　*Perf. 13*
2343 A639 38p Institute building 　.45 .20

Stamp Day — A640

Lithographed and Engraved

1983, Oct. 8　　　*Perf. 13x12½*
2344 A640 16p Roman mail cart 　.35 .30

No. 2344 se-tenant with label publicizing ESPANA '84 Philatelic Exhibition, April 27-May 6, 1984.

Valencia
Autonomy
Statute,
1st Anniv.
A641

1983, Oct. 10　　　*Perf. 13*
2345 A641 16p multicolored 　.25 .20

View of Seville, 16th cent. — A642

1983, Oct. 12　**Engr.**　*Perf. 12½x13*
2346 A642 38p multicolored 　.45 .20

Spanish-American trade in 17th century.

Stained-glass
Windows
A643

Designs: 10p King, Leon Cathedral. 16p, Epiphany, Gerona Cathedral. 38p, Apostle Santiago, Royal Hospital Chapel, Santiago.

Lithographed and Engraved

1983, Oct. 28　　　*Perf. 12½x13*
2347 A643 10p multicolored 　.20 .20
2348 A643 16p multicolored 　.25 .20
2349 A643 38p multicolored 　.45 .20
　Nos. 2347-2349 (3) 　.90 .60

Church at Llivia,
Gerona — A644

Designs: 6p, Temple, Santa Maria del Mar, Barcelona. 16p, Cathedral, Ceuta. 38p, Gate of the Santiago Bridge, Melilla. 50p, Charity Hospital, Seville.

1983, Nov. 9　**Engr.**　*Perf. 13x12½*
2350 A644 3p dk bl gray & grn 　.20 .20
2351 A644 6p dark blue gray 　.20 .20
2352 A644 16p red brn & dull vio 　.20 .20
2353 A644 38p bis brn & rose
car 　.45 .25
2354 A644 50p brown & org red 　.55 .20
　Nos. 2350-2354 (5) 　1.60 1.05

Christmas
1983 — A645

Indalecio Prieto
(1883-1962),
Patriot — A646

1983, Nov. 23　**Photo.**　*Perf. 13x13½*
2355 A645 16p The Nativity,
Tortosa 　.20 .20
2356 A645 38p The Adoration, Vich 　.45 .20

1983, Dec. 14　**Engr.**　*Perf. 13*
2357 A646 16p red brn & blk 　.20 .20

Industrial
Accident
Prevention
A647

1984, Jan. 25　**Photo.**　*Perf. 13½*
2358 A647 7p Construction worker 　.20 .20
2359 A647 10p Fire 　.20 .20
2360 A647 16p Electrical plug, pli-
ers 　.20 .20
　Nos. 2358-2360 (3) 　.60 .60

Extremadura
Statute of
Autonomy, First
Anniv. — A648

Lithographed and Engraved

1984, Feb. 25　　　*Perf. 13*
2361 A648 16p multicolored 　.25 .20

1500th Anniv. of City of Burgos A649

1984, Mar. 1   **Engr.**
2362 A649 16p multicolored   .20 .20

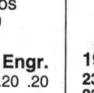

Carnivals A650

1984   **Photo.**   **Perf. 13½x13**
2363 A650 16p Santa Cruz de Tenerife   .25 .20
2364 A650 16p Valencia Fallas   .25 .20
     Issued: #2363, Mar. 5; #2364, Mar. 16.

Man and the Biosphere A651

1984, Apr. 11
2365 A651 38p da Vinci's Study of Man   .45 .25

Aragon Statute of Autonomy, 2nd Anniv. A652

Lithographed and Engraved
1984, Apr. 23   **Perf. 13x13½**
2366 A652 16p Map   .25 .20

Juan Carlos — A653

Souvenir Sheet

Espana '84 (Spanish Royal Family): b, Sofia of Greece. c, Cristina de Borbon. d, Prince of Asturias Felipe de Borbon. e, Elene de Borbon.

1984, Apr. 27   **Perf. 12½x13**
2367 A653   Sheet of 5   3.25 3.25
a.-e.   38p, any single   .65 .65

Congress Emblem — A654

1984, May 3   **Engr.**   **Perf. 13x13½**
2368 A654 38p purple & red   .45 .20
     World Philatelic Federation, 53rd Congress, Madrid, May 7-9.

Europa (1959-84) A655

1984, May 5
2369 A655 16p orange   .20 .20
2370 A655 38p dark blue   .45 .25

Armed Forces Day A656

Design: 17p, Monument to Hunters Regiment of Caceres, by Mariano Benlliure.

1984, May 19   **Photo.**   **Perf. 13½x13**
2371 A656 17p multicolored   .25 .20

Canary Islds. Statute of Autonomy — A657

Castilla-La Mancha Statute of Autonomy — A658

Lithographed and Engraved
1984, May 29   **Perf. 13**
2372 A657 16p Arms, map   .25 .20

1984, May 31   **Perf. 13**
2373 A658 17p Arms   .25 .20

King Alfonso X (1252-84) A659

Design: 38p, Ignacio Barroquer (1884-1965), ophthalmologist

1984, June 20   **Engr.**   **Perf. 13**
2374 A659 16p multicolored   .25 .20
2375 A659 38p multicolored   .45 .20

Balearic Islands Statute of Autonomy — A660

1984, June 29   **Litho. & Engr.**
2376 A660 17p multicolored   .25 .20

Feast of San Fermin of Pamplona A661

1984, July 5   **Photo.**
2377 A661 17p Bull runners   .25 .20

Operetta Type of 1982

#2378, El Nino Judio. #2379, Pablo Luna (1880-1942). #2380, Ruperto Chapi (1851-1909). #2381, La Revoltosa. #2382, La Reina Mora. #2383, Jose Serrano (1873-1941).

Lithographed and Engraved
1984, July 20   **Perf. 13**
2378 A610   6p multicolored   .20 .20
2379 A609   6p multicolored   .20 .20
a.   Pair, #2378-2379   .20 .20
2380 A609   7p multicolored   .20 .20
2381 A610   7p multicolored   .20 .20
a.   Pair, #2380-2381   .20 .20
2382 A610 10p multicolored   .20 .20
2383 A609 10p multicolored   .20 .20
a.   Pair, #2382-2383   .30 .30

1984 Summer Olympics A662

Greek or Roman sculptures.

1984, July 27   **Photo.**
2384 A662 1p Chariot race   .20 .20
2385 A662 2p Diving, vert.   .20 .20
2386 A662 5p Wrestling   .20 .20
2387 A662 8p Discus, vert.   .20 .20
     Nos. 2384-2387 (4)   .80 .80

Navarra Statute of Autonomy A663

Lithographed and Engraved
1984, Aug. 16   **Perf. 13**
2388 A663 17p multicolored   .25 .20

Intl. Bicycling Championship, Barcelona, Aug. 27-Sept. 2 — A664

1984, Aug. 27   **Photo.**
2389 A664 17p multicolored   .20 .20

Castilla and Leon Statute of Autonomy A665

1984, Sept. 5   **Litho. & Engr.**
2390 A665 17p multicolored   .25 .20

Jerez Vintage Feast — A666

1984, Sept. 20   **Photo.**   **Perf. 13**
2391 A666 17p Women picking grapes   .25 .20

Journey to the Holy Land by Sister Egeria, 1600th Anniv. — A667

1984, Sept. 26
2392 A667 40p Map, Sister Egeria .45 .25

Stamp Day — A668

1984, Oct. 5   **Litho. & Engr.**
2393 A668 17p Arab postrider   .20 .20

Father Junipero Serra (1713-84), Mission Founder in California A669

1984, Oct. 12   **Engr.**   **Perf. 13**
2394 A669 40p Map, Serra, mission .45 .20

Christmas 1984 A670

1984, Nov. 21   **Photo.**
2395 A670 17p Nativity   .20 .20
2396 A670 40p Adoration of the Kings, vert.   .45 .20

Madrid Autonomy Statue A671

1984, Nov. 28   **Litho. & Engr.**
2397 A671 17p Arms, buildings   .25 .20

Andean Pact, 15th Anniv. A672

Condor, Flags of Bolivia, Colombia, Ecuador, Peru and Venezuela.

1985, Jan. 16   **Photo.**   *Perf. 13*
2398 A672 17p multicolored   .20 .20

The Virgin of Louvain, by Jan Gossaert (c. 1478-1536) A673

Santa Cruz College, Valladolid University, 500th Anniv. — A674

1985, Jan. 21   *Perf. 13½*
2399 A673 40p multicolored   .45 .20
EUROPALIA '85. See Belgium No. 1185.

1985, Feb. 20   **Litho. & Engr.**
2400 A674 17p Main gateway   .20 .20

OLYMPHILEX '85, Lausanne, Switz. — A675

1985, Mar. 18   **Photo.**
2401 A675 40p multicolored   .45 .20

ESPAMER '85, Cuba A676

1985, Mar. 20   **Engr.**
2402 A676 40p Cathedral, Havana   .45 .25

Fairs A677

Perf. 13½, 13½x14 (#2405)
1985   **Photo.**
2403 A677 17p Seville   .25 .20
2404 A677 17p Alcoy   .25 .20
2405 A677 17p Arriondas-Ribadesella   .25 .20
2406 A677 18p Toledo, vert.   .25 .20
   Nos. 2403-2406 (4)   1.00 .80
Issued: #2403, Apr. 16; #2404, Apr. 22; #2405, Aug. 2; #2406, June 6.

Intl. Youth Year — A678

1985, Apr. 17   **Engr.**   *Perf. 13½*
2407 A678 17p blk, hn brn & dk grn .20 .20

Europa '85 A680

Designs: 18p, Antonio de Cabezon (1510-1566), organist and composer, court Musician to Felipe II. 45p, Natl. Youth Orchestra.

1985, May 3   **Engr.**
2408 A680 18p dk bl, dk red & blk, buff   .25 .20
2409 A680 45p ol grn, dk red & blk, buff   .50 .25

Armed Forces Day A681

1985, May 24   **Photo.**
2410 A681 18p multicolored   .25 .20

Natl. Flag Bicent. — A682

#2411, Arms of King Carlos III, text of 1785 Decree, sailing ship Santisima Trinidad. #2412, Natl. arms, Article No. 4 from 1978 Constitution, lion ornament from Chamber of Deputies Building.

Lithographed and Engraved
1985, May 28   *Perf. 13x13½*
2411   18p multicolored   .25 .20
2412   18p multicolored   .25 .20
  a. A682 Pair, #2411-2412   .45 .45

Intl. Environment Day — A683

1985, June 5   **Photo.**
2413 A683 17p multicolored   .20 .20

Juan Carlos — A684

1985-92   **Photo.**   *Perf. 14*
2414 A684 10c indigo   .20 .20
2415 A684 50c lt blue green   .20 .20
2416 A684 1p brt blue   .20 .20
2417 A684 2p dark green   .20 .20
2418 A684 3p chestnut brn   .20 .20
2419 A684 4p olive green   .20 .20
2420 A684 5p brt rose lilac   .20 .20
2421 A684 6p brown black   .20 .20
2422 A684 7p brt violet   .20 .20
2423 A684 7p apple grn   .20 .20
2424 A684 8p gray black   .20 .20
2425 A684 10p lake   .20 .20
2426 A684 12p red   .20 .20
2427 A684 13p Prus blue   .20 .20
2428 A684 15p emerald   .20 .20
2429 A684 17p yellow bis   .20 .20
2430 A684 18p brt grnsh bl   .25 .20
2431 A684 19p violet brn   .25 .20
  a. Booklet pane of 6   1.50
2432 A684 20p brt pink   .25 .20
2433 A684 25p olive green   .30 .20
2434 A684 27p deep rose lil   .35 .20
2435 A684 30p ultra   .35 .20
2436 A684 45p brt green   .50 .20
2437 A684 50p violet blue   .55 .20
2438 A684 55p black brown   .60 .20
2439 A684 60p dark orange   .65 .20
2440 A684 75p deep rose lil   .80 .30
  Nos. 2414-2440 (27)   8.05 5.55
Issued: 1p, 5p, 8p, 12p, 18p, 45p, 6/12; #2422, 17p, 7/16; #2423, 1/86; 2p, 3p, 4p, 10p, 4/3/86; 19p, 9/27/86; 6p, 20p, 30p, 1/26/87; 50p, 60p, 75p, 4/24/89; 10c, 50c, 13p, 15p, 5/16/89; 25p, 55p, 12/14/90; 27p, 2/92.

Astrophysical Observatory Opening, La Palma, Canary Islands — A685

1985, June 25   **Photo.**   *Perf. 14*
2441 A685 45p multicolored   .50 .20

European Music Year — A686

Designs: 12p, Ataulfo Argenta, conductor. 17p, Tomas Luis de Victoria, composer. 45p, Fernando Sor, composer.

Litho. & Engr.
1985, June 26   *Perf. 13*
2442 A686 12p multicolored   .20 .20
2443 A686 17p multicolored   .25 .20
2444 A686 45p multicolored   .50 .20
  Nos. 2442-2444 (3)   .95 .60

Bernal Diaz del Castillo (1492-1585), Historian — A687

Famous men: 12p, Esteban Terradas (1883-1950), mathematician. 17p, Vicente Aleixandre (1898-1984), 1977 Nobel laureate in literature. 45p, Leon Felipe Camino (1884-1968), poet.

1985, July 24   **Engr.**   *Perf. 13½*
2445 A687 7p dk red, blk & dk grn, buff   .20 .20
2446 A687 12p brt ver, dk bl & blk, buff   .20 .20
2447 A687 17p blk, dk grn & dk red, buff   .25 .20
2448 A687 45p bis, blk & dk grn, buff   .55 .20
  Nos. 2445-2448 (4)   1.20 .80

Monastic Mail Delivery, 1122 — A688

Lithographed and Engraved
1985, Sept. 27   *Perf. 13*
2449 A688 17p multicolored   .25 .20
Stamp Day 1985.

12th Rhythmic Gymnastics World Championships, Valladolid — A689

1985, Oct. 9   **Photo.**   *Perf. 13x13½*
2450 A689 17p Ribbon exercise   .20 .20
2451 A689 45p Hoop exercise   .50 .25

Souvenir Sheet

Prado Museum, La Alcachofa Fountain — A690

Lithographed and Engraved
1985, Oct. 18   *Perf. 13*
2452 A690 17p multicolored   .50 .50
EXFILNA '85, Madrid, Oct. 18-27.

Virgin and Child, Seville Cathedral A691

Stained glass windows: 12p, Monk, by Peter Boniface, Toledo Cathedral. 17p, King Henry II of Castile, Alcazar of Segovia.

1985, Oct. 24   *Perf. 12½x13*
2453 A691 7p multicolored   .20 .20
2454 A691 12p multicolored   .20 .20
2455 A691 17p multicolored   .20 .20
  Nos. 2453-2455 (3)   .60 .60

Christmas 1985 A692

14th-15th century paintings in the Episcopal Museum, Vich: 17p, Nativity, Guimera Altarpiece retable, 14th cent., by Ramon de Mur. 45p, Epiphany, from an embroidered frontal, 15th cent.

1985, Nov. 27　　Photo.　　Perf. 13½
2456　A692　17p multicolored　　.20　.20
2457　A692　45p multicolored　　.50　.20

Birds — A693

1985, Dec. 4　　　　　　Litho. & Engr.
2458　A693　6p Sylvia cantillans　.20　.20
2459　A693　7p Monticola saxa-
　　　　　　　　tilis　　　　　　.20　.20
2460　A693　12p Sturnus unicolor　.25　.20
2461　A693　17p Panurus
　　　　　　　　biarmicus　　　.35　.20
　　Nos. 2458-2461 (4)　　　1.00　.80

Wildlife conservation.

Count of Penaflorida (1729-
1785) — A694

1985, Dec. 11　　Engr.　　Perf. 13½
2462　A694　17p dark blue　　　.20　.20

Francisco Javier de Munibe e Idiaguez,
founded Natl. Economic Society of Friends in
1765.

Government Palace, Madrid, and
Accession Agreement Text — A695

17p, Map and flags of EEC countries. 30p,
Hall of Columns, Royal Palace. 45p, Member
flags.

1986, Jan. 7.　　Litho.　　Perf. 13½x13
2463　A695　7p multicolored　　.20　.20
2464　A695　17p multicolored　　.20　.20
2465　A695　30p multicolored　　.35　.20
2466　A695　45p multicolored　　.60　.20
　a.　Bkt. pane of 4, #2463-2466　3.25
　　Nos. 2463-2466 (4)　　　1.35　.80

Admission of Spain and Portugal to European Economic Community. See Portugal
Nos. 1661-1662.

Tourism — A696

Historic sites: 12p, Inner courtyard, La Lupi-
ana Monastery, Guadalajara. 35p, Balcony of
Europe, Nerja.

1986, Jan. 20　Engr.　　Perf. 13x12½
2467　A696　12p dk rose, brn & gray
　　　　　　　　brn　　　　　.20　.20
2468　A696　35p brt blue & sep　.45　.20

2nd World Conference on Merino
Sheep — A697

1986, Jan. 27　　Photo.　　Perf. 13½
2469　A697　45p multicolored　　.50　.25

Masquerade, 19th Cent., by F.
Hohenleiter — A698

1986, Feb. 5
2470　A698　17p multicolored　　.25　.20

Cadiz Carnival.

Intl. Peace Year — A699

Lithographed and Engraved
1986, Feb. 12　　　　Perf. 13x13½
2471　A699　45p multicolored　　.50　.25

Festival of
Religious
Music,
Cuenca
A700

1986, Mar. 26　　Photo.　　Perf. 13½
2472　A700　17p multicolored　　.25　.20

Chamber of Commerce, Cent. — A701

Painting detail: Swearing in of the Regent,
Queen Maria Christina, Before the Spanish
Parliament, 1886, by Francisco Jover and Joa-
quin Sorolla y Bastida, Senate Palace, Madrid.

1986, Apr. 9　　Engr.　　Perf. 13½
2473　A701　17p sage grn & grnsh
　　　　　　　　blk　　　　　.20　.20

Emigration of
Spaniards — A702

1986, Apr. 22　　　　　　　Photo.
2474　A702　45p multicolored　　.50　.25

Europa 1986 — A703

Lithographed and Engraved
1986, May 5　　　　Perf. 13x13½
2475　A703　17p Youth feeding birds　.25　.20
2476　A703　45p Girl watering tree　.55　.25

Our Lady
of the Dew
Festival,
Almonte
A704

1986, May 14　　Photo.　　Perf. 13½x13
2477　A704　17p multicolored　　.25　.20

Army Day
A705

Captains-General Building, Canary Islands.

1986, May 16　　Engr.　　Perf. 13½
2478　A705　17p pale yel brn, sep &
　　　　　　　　red　　　　　.20　.20

Rodrigo City
Cathedral
A706

Design: 35p, Calella Lighthouse.

1986, June 16　　　　Perf. 12½x13½
2479　A706　12p blue & black　　.20　.20
2480　A706　35p multicolored　　.55　.20

10th World Basketball Championships,
July 5-20 — A707

1986, July 4　　Photo.　　Perf. 12½
2481　A707　45p multicolored　　.50　.20

Famous
Men — A708

Mystery of the
Virgin's Death
Festival
Elche — A709

Designs: 7p, Francisco Loscos Bernal
(1823-1886), botanist. 11p, Salvador Espriu
(1913-1985), author. 17p, Jose Martinez Ruiz
(Azorin, 1873-1967), artist. 45p, Jose Vitori-
ano Gonzalez (Juan Gris, 1887-1927), painter.

1986, July 16　　Engr.　　Perf. 13
2482　A708　7p olive grn & bl　.20　.20
2483　A708　11p brt rose & blk　.20　.20
2484　A708　17p dk brn vio & blk　.20　.20
2485　A708　45p org, red vio & blk　.50　.20
　　Nos. 2482-2485 (4)　　　1.10　.85

1986, Aug. 11　Photo.　　Perf. 13x13½
2486　A709　17p Angels carrying
　　　　　　　　soul　　　　　.25　.20

5th World Swimming, Water Polo,
Diving and Synchronized Swimming
Championships — A710

1986, Aug. 13　　Engr.　　Perf. 13½
2487　A710　45p multicolored　　.50　.25

10th World Pelota
Championships — A711

1986, Sept. 12
2488　A711　17p multicolored　　.25　.20

Stamp Day — A712

Messenger, The Husband's Return, Song
63, TI1 Codex, 1979 edition, Spanish Royal
Academy.

1986, Sept. 27　Litho.　　Perf. 13x12½
2489　A712　17p multicolored　　.20　.20

Souvenir Sheet

EXFILNA '86, Cordova, Oct. 9-
18 — A713

1986, Oct. 7　　　　　Litho. & Engr.
2490　A713　17p Man, Cordova
　　　　　　　　"Mosque"　　.25　.25

Discovery of America, 500th Anniv. (in 1992) — A714

Men and text: 7p, Aristotle, text from De Cielo et Mundo. 12p, Seneca, text from Medea. 17p, San Isidoro, text from Etimologias. 30p, Pedro de Ailly, text from Imago Mundi. 35p, Mayan, prophesy from Libros de Chilam Balam. 45p, European, prophesy from Libros de Chilam Balam.

Lithographed and Engraved
1986, Oct. 15   *Perf. 13x13½*
2491	A714	7p multicolored	.20 .20
2492	A714	12p multicolored	.20 .20
2493	A714	17p multicolored	.20 .20
2494	A714	30p multicolored	.35 .20
2495	A714	35p multicolored	.40 .20
2496	A714	45p multicolored	.50 .20
a.		Bklt. pane of 6, #2491-2496	1.90
		Nos. 2491-2496 (6)	1.85 1.20

Caspar de Portola y Rovira (1717-1786), Pioneer of California — A715

1986, Nov. 6   *Perf. 13½*
2497   A715 22p multicolored   .25 .20

Christmas A716

Wood carving details: 19p, The Holy Family, by Diego de Siloe (c. 1495-1563), Natl. Sculpture Museum, Valladolid, vert. 48p, Nativity, Toledo Cathedral altarpiece, by Felipe de Borgona (c. 1475-1543).

1986, Nov. 19   Photo.   *Perf. 13½*
2498	A716	19p multicolored	.25 .20
2499	A716	48p multicolored	.55 .20

Spanish-Islamic Cultural Heritage — A717

Famous men: 7p, Abd Al Rahman II (792-852), 4th independent emir of Cordoba. 12p, Ibn Hazm (994-1064), scholar. 17p, Al-Zarqali (1061-1100), astronomer. 45p, Alfonso VII, scholar, Toledo School of Translators.

1986, Dec. 3   Engr.
2500	A717	7p org red & dk red brn	.20 .20
2501	A717	12p brn blk & red org	.20 .20
2502	A717	17p black & dk blue	.25 .20
2503	A717	45p green & black	.50 .20
		Nos. 2500-2503 (4)	1.15 .80

Alfonso R. Castelao (1886-1950), Artist, Writer — A718

Lithographed and Engraved
1986, Dec. 11   *Perf. 13x13½*
2504   A718 32p El Buen Cura, 1917   .40 .20

Globe, Chateau de la Muette A719

1987, Jan. 14   *Perf. 14*
2505   A719 48p multicolored   .55 .20

Organization for Economic Cooperation and Development, OECD, 25th anniv.

EXPO '92, Seville A720

1987, Jan. 21   Photo.
2506	A720	19p Geometric shapes	.35 .20
2507	A720	48p Earth, Moon's surface	.95 .20

See Nos. 2540-2541, 2550-2551.

Portrait of Vitoria, by Vera Fajardo A721

1987, Feb. 11   Engr.
2508   A721 48p dark rose brown   .55 .20

Francisco de Vitoria (c. 1486-1546), theologian, teacher and a founder of intl. law.

Marine Corps, 450th Anniv. A722

Design: 18th Cent. 74-gun man-of-war, period standard bearer, corps insignia.

1987, Feb. 25
2509   A722 19p multicolored   .25 .20

Deusto University, Cent. — A723

1987, Feb. 26   Engr.   *Perf. 14x13½*
2510   A723 19p blk, hn brn & dk grn   .25 .20

UN Child Survival Campaign A724

1987, Mar. 4   *Perf. 13½x14*
2511   A724 19p red brown & blk   .25 .20

Constitution of Cadiz, 175th Anniv. — A725

Nos. 2512a-2512c in a continuous design: The Promulgation of 1812, by Salvador Viniegra. No. 2512d, Anniv. emblem.

1987, Mar. 18   Litho.   *Perf. 13½*
2512		Strip of 4	1.10 1.00
a.-d.	A725	25p, any single	.30 .20

Ceramicware A726

Designs: 7p, Pharmaceutical jar, 15th cent., Manises of Valencia. 14p, Abstract figurine, 20th cent., Sargadelos of Galicia. 19p, Neoclassical lidded urn, 18th cent., Buen Retiro of Madrid. 32p, Water jar, 20th cent., Salvatierra of Extremadura. 40p, Pitcher, 18th cent., Talavera of Toledo. 48p, Pitcher, 18th-19th cent., Granada of Andalucia.

Lithographed and Engraved
1987, Mar. 20   *Perf. 12½x13*
2513		Block of 6 + 3 labels	1.75 1.75
a.	A726	7p multicolored	.20 .20
b.	A726	14p multicolored	.20 .20
c.	A726	19p multicolored	.25 .20
d.	A726	32p multicolored	.40 .25
e.	A726	40p multicolored	.45 .25
f.	A726	48p multicolored	.55 .25

See No. 2552.

Passion Week in Zamora and Seville A727

Paintings: 19p, The Amanecer Procession, by Gallego Marquina, vert. 48p, Jesus Carrying the Cross, by Martinez Montanes, and the Gate of Forgiveness, Seville Cathedral.

1987, Apr. 13   Photo.   *Perf. 14x13½*
2514	A727	19p multicolored	.25 .20
2515	A727	48p multicolored	.55 .20

Tourism A728

14p, Rock of Ifach, Calpe. 19p, Nave of Santa Marina d'Ozo Church, Pontevedra, before restoration. 40p, Sonanes Palace, Villacarriedo. 48p, Monastery of St. Joan de les Abadesses, Gerona, vert.

1987   Engr.   *Perf. 12½x13*
2515A	A728	14p dp bl & sage grn	.20 .20
2516	A728	19p dp grn & grnsh blk	.25 .20
2516A	A728	40p dp claret	.45 .20
2517	A728	48p black	.55 .20
		Nos. 2515A-2517 (4)	1.45 .80

Issued: 19p, 48p, 4/21; 14p, 40p, 6/10.

Europa 1987 A729

Modern architecture: 19p, Bilbao Bank, Madrid, designed by Saenz de Oiza, vert. 48p, Natl. Museum of Roman Art, Merida, designed by Rafael Moneo.

Lithographed and Engraved
1987, May 4   *Perf. 14x13½*
2518	A729	19p multicolored	.25 .20
2519	A729	48p multicolored	.55 .20

Horse Fair, Jerez de La Frontera A730

1987, May 6   Photo.   *Perf. 13½x14*
2520   A730 19p multicolored   .25 .20

Ramon Carande (1887-1986), Historian — A731

1987, May 29   Engr.
2521   A731 40p blk & dk vio brn   .45 .20

Postal Code Inauguration — A732

1987, June 1   Litho.   *Perf. 14*
2522   A732 19p multicolored   .25 .20

Eibar Weaponry School, 75th Anniv. A733

1987, July 2   Litho.   *Perf. 14*
2523   A733 20p multicolored   .25 .20

1992 Summer Olympics, Barcelona A734

1987, July 15   Photo.
2524	A734	32p Casa de Battlo masonry	.40 .20
2525	A734	65p Athletes	.75 .20

25th Folk Festival of the Pyrenees, Jaca — A735

1987, July 22
2526 A735 50p multicolored .55 .20

Monturiol and Submarine Designs A736

1987, Sept. 9 Engr. Perf. 13½x14
2527 A736 20p black brown .25 .20

Narcis Monturiol (d. 1887), builder of the submarine Ictineos.

Stamp Day — A737

Illuminated codex from *Constitutiones Jacobi II Regis Majoricum*, 14th cent., King Albert I Royal Library, Brussels.

Litho. & Engr.
1987, Sept. 16 Perf. 13
2528 A737 20p multicolored .25 .20
Postal service of Mallorca under James II.

ESPAMER '87 — A738

Designs: 8p, Handstamped letter that traveled from La Coruna to Havana, Cuba, 18th cent. 12p, La Coruna Harbor, 19th cent., engraving. 20p, Illustration of Havana harbor from *Viaje Alrededor da La Isla de Cuba*, by Francisco Mialche, 18th cent. 50p, West Indies packets.

1987, Oct. 2 Litho. & Engr. Perf. 13
2529 A738 Sheet of 4 3.25 3.25
  a.   8p blk, brt blue & red .30 .30
  b.   12p brt blue, red & blk .45 .45
  c.   20p blk, brt blue & red .75 .75
  d.   50p blk, brt blue & red 1.75 1.75

No. 2529 printed se-tenant (rouletted between) with ESPAMER entrance ticket. Sold for 180p. Size: 150x83mm (including ticket).

Souvenir Sheet

EXFILNA '87, Gerona, Oct. 24-Nov. 1 — A739

Greek statue, Emporion, Olympic torchbearer.

1987, Oct. 24 Photo. Perf. 13x12½
2530 A739 20p multicolored .25 .25

Discovery of America, 500th Anniv. (in 1992) — A740

Ships and: 14p, Amerigo Vespucci (1454-1512), Italian navigator. 20p, Ferdinand and Isabella. 32p, Friar Juan Perez, Queen's confessor. 40p, Juan de la Cosa (c. 1460-1510), master of the Santa Maria, cartographer who made first map of the New World. 50p, Christopher Columbus. 65p, Vicente Yanez Pinzon (c. 1460-1523) and Martin Alonso Pinzon (c. 1441-1493), brothers, navigators and ship owners, accompanied Columbus on voyage.

Litho. & Engr.
1987, Oct. 30 Perf. 13
2531 A740 14p multicolored .20 .20
2532 A740 20p multicolored .25 .20
2533 A740 32p multicolored .40 .20
2534 A740 40p multicolored .45 .20
2535 A740 50p multicolored .55 .20
2536 A740 65p multicolored .75 .30
  a.   Bklt. pane of 6, #2531-2536 3.00
     Nos. 2531-2536 (6) 2.60 1.30

Christmas — A741

Self-portrait, Sculpture by Victorio Macho (1887-1966) A742

1987, Nov. 17 Photo. Perf. 14x13½
2537 A741 20p Ornaments .25 .20
2538 A741 50p Zambomba, tambourine .55 .20

1987, Dec. 23 Engr.
2539 A742 50p brown black .55 .20

EXPO '92 Type of 1987
1987, Dec. 29 Photo. Perf. 13½x14
2540 A720 20p like No. 2506 .30 .20
2541 A720 50p like No. 2507 .55 .20

HRH Sofia and Juan Carlos, 50th Birth Annivs. — A743

1987, Jan. 5 Perf. 13x13½
2542 A743 20p Sofia .25 .20
2543 A743 20p Juan Carlos .25 .20
  a.   Pair, #2542-2543 + label .50 .50

Clara Campoamor (b. 1888), Suffragette — A744

1988, Feb. 12 Photo. Perf. 14
2544 A744 20p multicolored .25 .20

1988 Winter Olympics, Calgary — A745

1988, Feb. 15 Perf. 14
2545 A745 45p Speed skater .50 .20

Passion Week in Valladolid and Malaga — A746

1988, Mar. 30 Photo. Perf. 14
Designs: 20p, Valladolid Cathedral and 17th cent. statue of Christ at the column by Gregorio Fernandez. 50p, Christ carrying the cross along Malaga procession route.

2546 A746 20p multicolored .25 .20
2547 A746 50p multicolored .55 .20

Tourism A747

1988, Apr. 7
2548 A747 18p Paella pan, ingredients .25 .20
2549 A747 45p Covadonga Natl. Park .50 .20

EXPO '92 Type of 1987
Era of Discoveries: 8p, Road to globe, rays of light, vert. 45p, Compass rose, globe.

1988, Apr. 12
2550 A720 8p multicolored .20 .20
2551 A720 45p multicolored .50 .20

Art Type of 1987
Glassware: a, Chalice, Valencia, 18th cent. b, Cadalso de los Vidrios, Madrid, 18th cent. c, Candy dish, La Granja de San Ildefonso, 18th cent. d, Castril double-handled jar, Andalucia, 18th cent. e, Jug, Catalina, 17th cent. f, Bottle, Baleares, 20th cent.

Litho. & Engr.
1988, Apr. 13 Perf. 12½x13
2552 Block of 6 + 6 labels 1.50 1.50
  a.-f. A726 20p any single .25 .20

Stamp Day 1988 — A748

Francis of Taxis, postmaster by royal appointment (1505) in charge of establishing communications between Spain, France, Germany, Rome, Naples.

1988, Apr. 29 Engr. Perf. 12½x13
2553 A748 20p dk violet & dk brn .25 .20

General Workers' Union (UGT), Cent. A749

Emblem and Pablo Iglesias, union pioneer.

1988, May 1 Photo. Perf. 14
2554 A749 20p multicolored .25 .20

Europa 1988 — A750

Transport and communication: 20p, Locomotive made in Spain and operated in Cuba, 1837. 50p, Spanish telegraph in the Philippines linking Plaza de Manila and Bagumbayan Camp, 1818.

1988, May 5 Engr. Perf. 13
2555 A750 20p black & dk red .25 .20
2556 A750 50p black & dk grn .55 .20

Jean Monnet (1888-1979), Economist A751

1988, May 9 Perf. 14x13½
2557 A751 45p blue black .50 .20

Universal Exposition, Barcelona, Cent. A752

1988, May 31 Photo. Perf. 13½x14
2558 A752 50p multicolored .55 .20

Intl. Music and Dance Festival, Granada — A753

1988, June 1   **Perf. 14x13½**
2559 A753 50p multicolored   .55   .20

World Expo '88, Brisbane, Australia A754

1988, June 14   **Perf. 13½x14**
2560 A754 50p Bull   .55   .20

Coronation of the Virgin of Hope — A755

1988, June 18   **Perf. 14x13½**
2561 A755 20p multicolored   .25   .20
   Holy Week in Malaga.

Souvenir Sheet

EXFILNA '88, June 25-July 3, Madrid — A756

1988, June 25   **Perf. 13x12½**
2562 A756 20p Ciudadela Fortress floor plan   .25   .25

Tourism A757

1988, July 11   **Engr.**   **Perf. 13½x14**
2563 A757 18p Cantabrian Coast storehouse   .25   .20
2564 A757 45p Dulzaina (wind instrument)   .50   .20

28th World Roller Hockey Championships, La Coruna — A758

1988, Sept. 7   **Photo.**   **Perf. 13½x14**
2565 A758 20p multicolored   .25   .20

1st World Cong. of Spanish Regional Shelters — A759

1988 Summer Olympics, Seoul — A760

1988, Sept. 9   **Perf. 14**
2566 A759 20p multicolored   .25   .20

1988, Sept. 10   **Litho.**
2567 A760 50p Yachting   .55   .20

Catalonia Millennium — A761

1988, Sept. 21   **Photo.**   **Perf. 12½**
2568 A761 20p multicolored   .25   .20

1st Call to Session of the Leon Court, 800th Anniv. — A762

   Illumination & seal of Alfonso IX, King of Leon.

1988, Sept. 26   **Photo.**   **Perf. 12½x13**
2569 A762 20p multicolored   .25   .20

Federation of Spanish Philatelic Societies, 25th Anniv. A763

1988, Sept. 27   **Perf. 14x13½**
2570 A763 20p multicolored   .25   .20

1992 Summer Olympics, Barcelona A764

1988, Oct. 3   **Photo.**   **Perf. 14**
2571 A764 8p multicolored   .20   .20
   See Nos. B139-B141.

A765

A766

   Design: Castle in Valencia and royal seal of James I, 13th cent.

1988, Oct. 7   **Perf. 14x13½**
2572 A765 20p multicolored   .25   .20
   Reconquest of Valencia by King James I, 750th anniv.

1988, Oct. 10   **Perf. 13x13½**
2573 A766 20p multicolored   .25   .20
   Civil Law, cent.

Discovery of America (in 1992), 500th Anniv. — A767

   Conquerors, explorers and symbols: No. 2574, Hernando Cortez, conqueror of Mexico, and serpent Quetzalcoatl. No. 2575, Vasco Nunez de Balboa, discoverer of the Pacific Ocean, and sun setting over sea. No. 2576, Francisco Pizarro, conqueror of Peru, and llama. No. 2577, Portuguese navigator Ferdinand Magellan, Juan de Elcano (c. 1476-1526) and globe symbolizing circumnavigation of the world. No. 2578, Alvar Nunez Cabeza de Vaca (c. 1490-1560), explorer, and sunrise. No. 2579, Andres de Urdaneta (1498-1568), and symbol of the west-to-east route between the Philippines and America that he discovered.

1988, Oct. 13   **Engr.**   **Perf. 13x13½**
2574 A767 10p multicolored   .20   .20
2575 A767 10p multicolored   .20   .20
2576 A767 20p multicolored   .25   .20
2577 A767 20p multicolored   .25   .20
2578 A767 50p multicolored   .55   .20
2579 A767 50p multicolored   .55   .20
   a.   Bklt. pane of 6, #2574-2579   2.00
     Nos. 2574-2579 (6)   2.00 1.20

Henry III of Castile, 1st Prince of Asturias — A768

1988, Oct. 26   **Photo.**   **Perf. 13**
2580 A768 20p multicolored   .25   .20
   1st Bestowal of the title Prince of Asturias, 600th anniv., guaranteeing that the throne would continue to be inherited according to primogeniture.

Christmas — A769

1988, Nov. 24   **Photo.**   **Perf. 14**
2581 A769 20p Snowflakes   .25   .20
2582 A769 50p Shepherd, horiz.   .55   .20

Sites and Cities Appearing on the UNESCO World Heritage List — A770

1988, Dec. 1   **Engr.**   **Perf. 12½x13**
2583 A770 18p Mosque of Cordoba, vert.   .25   .20
2584 A770 20p Burgos Cathedral, vert.   .30   .20
2585 A770 45p El Escorial Monastery   .55   .20
2586 A770 50p The Alhambra, Granada   .65   .20
     Nos. 2583-2586 (4)   1.75   .80

Natl. Constitution, 10th Anniv. — A771

1988, Dec. 7   **Photo.**   **Perf. 14**
2587 A771 20p multicolored   .25   .20

Souvenir Sheet

Charles III (1759-1788) and the Enlightenment — A772

1988, Dec. 14   **Engr.**   **Perf. 13x12½**
2588 A772 45p black & dk grn   .55   .55

Natl. Organization for the Blind, 50th Anniv. — A773

1988, Dec. 27   **Photo.**   **Perf. 14**
2589 A773 20p multicolored   .25   .20

Fr. Luis de
Granada (1504-
1588)
A774

1988, Dec. 31
2590 A774 20p multicolored .25 .20

1992
Summer
Olympics,
Barcelona
A775

1989, Jan. 3
2591 A775 20p multicolored .25 .20

Stamp
Collecting — A776

1989, Jan. 3
2592 A776 20p multicolored .25 .20

French
Revolution,
Bicent. — A777

1989, Jan. 24   Photo.   Perf. 13
2593 A777 45p multicolored .50 .20

Maria de
Maeztu (b.
1882),
Educator
A778

1989, Feb. 7   Photo.   Perf. 14x13½
2594 A778 20p multicolored .25 .20

Postal
Service,
Cent.
A779

Litho. & Engr.
1989, Mar. 11   Perf. 13½x14
2595 A779 20p Uniform, 1889 .25 .20

Stamp
Day — A780

Design: Intl. postal treaty negotiated with
France and Italy by Franz von Taxis, 1601.

1989, Apr. 4   Engr.   Perf. 13
2596 A780 20p black .25 .20

A781

1989, Apr. 22   Perf. 14x13½
2597 A781 20p black .25 .20
    Casa del Cordon, Burgos.

1989, May 5   Photo.   Perf. 13x13½
    Europa: Children's toys.
2598 A782 40p shown .45 .20
2599 A782 50p Top .55 .20

A782

Spain's
Presidency
of the
European
Economic
Community
A783

1989, May 9   Perf. 13½x14
2600 A783 45p multicolored .50 .20

Souvenir Sheet

Holy Family with St. Anne, by El
Greco — A784

1989, May 20   Litho.   Perf. 14x13½
2601 A784 20p multicolored .25 .25
    EXFILNA '89. Exists imperf in different
colors.

Gabriela Mistral
(1889-1957),
Chilean Poet
Awarded 1945
Nobel Prize for
Literature — A785

Litho. & Engr.
1989, June 1   Perf. 14x13½
2602 A785 50p multicolored .60 .20

European Parliament 3rd
Elections — A786

1989, June 12   Photo.   Perf. 13x13½
2603 A786 45p multicolored .50 .20

Lace
A787

Lace produced in: a, Catalonia. b, Andalusia. c, Extremadura. d, Canary Isls. e, Castile-
La Mancha. f, Galicia.

Litho. & Engr.
1989, June 20   Perf. 13x12½
2604   Block of 6 + 3 labels 1.40 1.40
    a.-f. A787 20p any single .25 .20
    Three center labels printed in a continuous
design and picture lace-making.

Pope John Paul II at the Intl. Catholic
Youth Forum, Santiago — A788

1989, Aug. 19   Engr.   Perf. 13x12½
2605 A788 50p myrtle grn, dk red
        brn & blk .55 .20

Athletics
World Cup,
Barcelona
A789

1989, Sept. 1   Photo.   Perf. 13½x14
2606 A789 50p multicolored .55 .20

A790

Type A34 — A791

Litho. & Engr.
1989, Sept. 19   Perf. 14x13½
2607 A790 50p multicolored .55 .20
    Charlie Chaplin (1889-1977), English come-
dian and actor.

1989, Oct. 2   Photo.   Perf. 14x13½
2608 A791 50p gray, ver & blk .55 .20
    Cent. of the 1st Alfonso XIII issue.

A792

A793

Fr. Andres Manjon (d. 1923), teacher.

1989, Oct. 13
2609 A792 20p multicolored .25 .20
    Founding of the Ave Maria Schools by Fr.
Manjon, cent.

1989, Nov. 7   Litho. & Engr.
    UPAE emblem and "Irrigating Corn Field in
November, 17th Cent.," an illustration from the
New Chronicle and Good Government, by
Guaman Poma de Ayala.
2610 A793 50p multicolored .55 .20
    America issue.

Christmas
A794

Perf. 14x13½, 13½x14
1989, Nov. 29   Photo.
2611 A794 20p Star, "NAVIdAd
        89," vert. .25 .20
2612 A794 45p shown .50 .20

Sites on the UNESCO World Heritage
List — A795

Litho. & Engr.
1989, Dec. 5   Perf. 13x12½
2613 A795 20p Altamira Caverns .25 .20
2614 A795 20p Santiago de
        Compostela .25 .20

2615 A795 20p Roman aqueduct,
Segovia   .25 .20
2616 A795 20p Guell Park and
palace, Mila
House   .25 .20
   Nos. 2613-2616 (4) 1.00 .80

Souvenir Sheet

Sites on the World Heritage
List — A796

Royal palaces: a, El Escorial. b, Aranjuez. c,
Summer palace, La Granja, San Ildefonso. e,
Madrid.

1989, Dec. 20   Engr.   Perf. 13x13½
2617   Sheet of 4   2.00 2.00
  a.-d. A796 45p any single   .30 .30

Illustration by
Daniel Garcia
Perez, Winner of
the 2nd Youth
Stamp Design
Contest — A797

1990, Jan. 29   Photo.   Perf. 14x13½
2618 A797 20p multicolored   .25 .20
  1992 Summer Olympics, Barcelona.

A798

A799

1990, Feb. 2
2619 A798 20p multicolored   .25 .20
  World Cycle Cross Championship, Getzu.

1990, Feb. 12   Engr.
2620 A799 20p dark purple   .25 .20
  Victoria Kent (1897-1987), prisons directer,
reformer.

Honorary Postman Rafael Alvarez
Sereix and Cancel — A800

Litho. & Engr.
1990, Apr. 18   Perf. 13
2621 A800 20p sepia, buff & dull
grn   .25 .20
  Stamp Day.

Europa
1990
A801

Post offices.

Perf. 13½x14, 14x13½
1990, May 4   Photo.
2622 A801 20p Vitoria   .25 .20
2623 A801 50p Malaga, vert.   .55 .20

Intl. Telecommunications Union, 125th
Anniv. — A802

1990, May 17   Perf. 13½x14
2624 A802 8p multicolored   .20 .20

Wrought
Iron — A803

Designs: a, 15th Cent. door knocker. b, 16th
cent. lyre-shaped door knocker. c, 17th Cent.
pistol. d, 17th-18th Cent. door knocker. e, 19th
Cent. lock. f, Fire iron.

Litho. & Engr.
1990, May 18   Perf. 12½
2625   Block of 6 + 3 labels   1.40 1.40
  a.-f. A803 20p any single   .25 .20
  Nos. 2625a-2625f printed se-tenant in a
continuous design. Three labels continue the
design and contain text or picture a forge.

Souvenir Sheet

Patio de La Infanta, Zaporta Palace,
Zaragoza — A804

Illustration reduced.

1990, May 25   Engr.   Perf. 14x13½
2626 A804 20p red brown   .25 .25
  EXFILNA '90.

Charity, by
Lopez
Alonso — A805

1990, June 19   Litho.   Perf. 13½x13
2627 A805 8p multicolored   .20 .20
  Daughters of Charity in Spain, bicentennial.

Jose Padilla, Composer, Birth
Centenary — A806

1990, June 19   Photo.   Perf. 13x12½
2628 A806 20p multicolored   .30 .20

Town of Estella, 900th Anniv. — A807

1990, June 19   Litho. & Engr.
2629 A807 45p multicolored   .60 .20

Novel, "Tirant lo
Blanch," 500th
Anniv. — A808

1990, June 19   Perf. 12½x13
2630 A808 50p multicolored   .65 .20

Souvenir Sheet

Crypt, Palencia Cathedral — A809

Illustration reduced.

1990, June 22   Engr.   Perf. 13½x14
2631 A809 20p red brown   .25 .25
  Topical philatelic exposition.

A810

A811

1990, Aug. 27   Photo.   Perf. 14x13½
2632 A810 50p multicolored   .55 .20
  17th Intl. Congress of Historical Sciences.

Litho. & Engr.
1990, Nov. 14   Perf. 14
  America Issue: UPAE emblem and Car-
ribean fauna.
2633 A811 50p multicolored   .55 .20

A812

A813

Christmas: Scenes from the film "Cosmic
Poem" by Jose Antonio Sistiaga.

1990, Nov. 22   Photo.
2634 A812 25p multicolored   .30 .20
2635 A812 45p multi, horiz.   .50 .20

Litho. & Engr.
1990, Nov. 28   Perf. 13
  Tapestries in Monastary of San Lorenzo: a,
The Crucifixion by Jan van Roome and Ber-
nard van Orley. b, Flamenco Soldiers by Philip
Wouvermans. c, Shipwreck of the Telemac by
Miguel Angel Houasse. d, Flowers by Fran-
cisco Goya.

2636   Sheet of 4   1.00 1.00
  a.-d. A813 20p any single   .25 .20

European Tourism
Year — A814

1990, Dec. 1   Photo.   Perf. 14
2637 A814 45p multicolored   .50 .20

World Heritage List — A815

Designs: No. 2638, Church of San Vicente, Avila. No. 2639, Tower of San Pedro, Teruel, vert. No. 2640, Church of San Miguel de Lillo, Oviedo, vert. No. 2641, Tower of Bujaco, Caceres.

Litho. & Engr.

1990, Dec. 10			**Perf. 13**	
2638	A815	20p multicolored	.30	.20
2639	A815	20p multicolored	.30	.20
2640	A815	20p multicolored	.30	.20
2641	A815	20p multicolored	.30	.20
	Nos. 2638-2641 (4)		1.20	.80

Natl. Orchestra of Spain A816

1990, Dec. 20   Photo.   Perf. 13½x14
2642 A816 25p grn, yel grn & blk   .30   .20

Maria Moliner (1900-1981), Spanish Linguist — A817

1991, Jan. 21   Photo.   Perf. 14x13½
2643 A817 25p multicolored   .35   .20

Souvenir Sheet

Santa Fe, 500th Anniv. — A818

Illustration reduced.

Litho. & Engr.
1991, Apr. 19   Perf. 13½x14
2644 A818 25p brown & purple   .35   .35

World Philatelic Exhibition, Granada '92.

Child's Drawing — A819

1991, Apr. 12   Photo.   Perf. 14x13½
2645 A819 25p Olympic rings, sailboats   .35   .20

Juan de Tassis y Peralta (1582-1622), Postal Reformer A820

1991, Apr. 26   Engr.   Perf. 12½
2646 A820 25p black   .35   .20

Stamp Day.

Souvenir Sheet

Porcelain and Ceramics — A821

a, Apothecary jar, 17th cent. b, Figurine, 18th cent. c, Vase, 19th cent. d, Plate, 19th cent.

1991, May 3   Litho. & Engr.   Perf. 13
2647 A821 25p Sheet of 4, #a.-d.   1.25 1.25
  a.-d. Any single   .30   .25

See No. 2692.

Europa A822

1991, May 28   Litho.   Perf. 13½x14
2648 A822 25p INTA-NASA ground station   .35   .20
2649 A822 45p Olympus I satellite   .55   .20

St. John of the Cross (1651-1695), Mystic — A823

Anniversaries: No. 2651, Fr. Luis de Leon (1527-1591), Augustinian writer, vert. No. 2652, Abd Al Rahman III (891-961), Moslem caliph, vert. No. 2653, St. Ignatius of Loyola (1451-1556), founder of Society of Jesus, vert.

Perf. 13½x14, 14x13½

1991, June 6			**Litho.**	
2650	A823	15p multicolored	.20	.20
2651	A823	15p multicolored	.20	.20
2652	A823	25p multicolored	.35	.20
2653	A823	25p multicolored	.35	.20
	Nos. 2650-2653 (4)		1.10	.80

Antique Furniture A824

Designs: a, Wedge top armoire, 18th cent. b, Hutch cabinet, c. 19th cent. c, Ladder-back cane chair, c. 19th cent. d, Baby cradle, 19th cent. e, Round-top trunk, c. 19th cent. f, Ornate chest, c. 18th cent.

Litho. & Engr.
1991, Sept. 9   Perf. 12½x13
2654   Block of 6 + 3 labels   1.90 1.90
  a.-f. A824 25p any single   .30   .20

Orfeo Catala (Catalan Choral Society), Cent. — A825

Intl. Fishing Exposition, Vigo — A826

1991, Sept. 6   Litho.   Perf. 14x13½
2655 A825 25p multicolored   .35   .20

1991, Sept. 10
2656 A826 55p multicolored   .65   .20

America Issue — A827

Christmas — A828

Litho. & Engr.
1991, Nov. 4   Perf. 14x13½
2657 A827 55p Nocturlabe   .65   .20

1991, Nov. 22   Photo.   Perf. 14x13½

25p, The Nativity, illustration from 17th cent. book. 45p, The Birth of Christ, 16th cent. icon.

2658 A828 25p multicolored   .35   .20
2659 A828 45p multicolored   .55   .20

Souvenir Sheet

The Meadowlands of St. Isidro by Goya — A829

Litho. & Engr.
1991, Dec. 12   Perf. 13½x14
2660 A829 25p multicolored   .35   .35

EXFILNA '91, Madrid.

Sites on UNESCO World Heritage List — A830

#2661, Giralda bell tower, Seville Cathedral. #2662, Alcantara Gate, Toledo, vert. #2663, Casa de las Conchas, Salamanca, vert. #2664, Garajonay Natl. Park, Gomera, Canary Islands.

Perf. 12½x13, 13x12½

1991, Dec. 16			**Engr.**	
2661	A830	25p brown & blue	.40	.20
2662	A830	25p red brn & brn	.40	.20
2663	A830	25p red brn & blk	.40	.20
2664	A830	25p violet & dk grn	.40	.20
	Nos. 2661-2664 (4)		1.60	.80

See Nos. 2756, 2830.

Carlos Ibanez de Ibero (1825-1891), Cartographer A831

Antarctic Treaty, Research Ship A52 — A832

1991, Dec. 27   Litho.   Perf. 14x13½
2665 A831 25p multicolored   .35   .20
2666 A832 55p multicolored   .65   .20

Margarita Xirgu (1889-1969), Actress — A833

1992, Jan. 20   Perf. 14
2667 A833 25p lake & gold   .35   .20

Child's Drawing A834

1992, Feb. 14 **Perf. 13½x14**
2668 A834 25p multicolored .35 .20
EXPO 92.

Pedro Rodriguez Campomanes (1723-1802), Historian, Postal Administrator — A835

1992, Feb. 21 **Perf. 13x12½**
2669 A835 27p multicolored .45 .20

Expo '92, Seville A836

1992, Feb. 28 **Perf. 13½x14**
2670 A836 27p gray, blk & brn .40 .20

Columbus Types of 1930
Souvenir Sheet
1992, Apr. 24 **Engr.** **Perf. 14**
2671 Sheet of 2 6.00 6.00
a. A65 250p black 3.00 2.50
b. A67 250p brown 3.00 2.50

Intl. Philatelic Exhibition, Granada '92.

Miniature Sheets

Expo '92, Seville A837

#2672: a, Expo '92 World Trade Center. b, Aerial tram. c, Avenue 4. d, Barqueta Gate. e, Nature pavilion. f, Biosphere. g, Alamillo Bridge. h, Press center. i, 15th Century pavilion. j, Expo harbor. k, Tourist train. l, One day entrance ticket.
#2673: a, Cartuja Monastery. b, Arena. c, Monorail train. d, Europe Avenue. e, Discovery pavilion. f, Auditorium. g, Avenue 1. h, Plaza of the Future. i, Gate to Italy's exhibit. j, Terminal. k, Expo theater. l, Expo Mascot, Curro.

1992, Apr. 21 Litho. Perf. 13½x14
2672 A837 Sheet of 12 + 4 labels 3.50 3.50
a.-l. 17p any single .35 .25
2673 A837 Sheet of 12 + 4 labels 5.50 5.50
a.-l. 27p any single .50 .30

See No. B195.

1992 Paralympics, Barcelona — A838

1992, Apr. 22 **Photo.** **Perf. 14**
2674 A838 27p multicolored .40 .20

Discovery of America, 500th Anniv. A839

Europa: 17p, Preparation Before Departing from Palos, by R. Espejo. 45p, Globe, ships, and buildings at La Rabida.

1992, May 5 **Photo.** **Perf. 14**
2675 A839 17p multicolored .25 .20
2676 A839 45p multicolored .60 .20

Souvenir Sheets

Voyages of Columbus — A840

#2677, Columbus in sight of land. #2678, Landing of Columbus. #2679, Columbus soliciting aid from Isabella. #2680, Columbus welcomed at Barcelona. #2681, Columbus presenting natives. #2682, Columbus.
Borders on Nos. 2677-2682 are lithographed. Nos. 2677-2682 are similar in design to US Nos. 230-231, 234-235, 237, 245.

Litho. & Engr.
1992, May 22 **Perf. 14**
2677 A840 60p blue 1.10 1.10
2678 A840 60p brown violet 1.10 1.10
2679 A840 60p chocolate 1.10 1.10
2680 A840 60p purple 1.10 1.10
2681 A840 60p black brown 1.10 1.10
2682 A840 60p black 1.10 1.10
Nos. 2677-2682 (6) 6.60 6.60

See US Nos. 2624-2629, Italy Nos. 1883-1888 and Portugal Nos. 1918-1923.

1992 Winter & Summer Olympics, Albertville & Barcelona A841

1992, June 19 **Photo.** **Perf. 14**
2683 A841 45p multicolored .60 .20

A842 A843

1992, June 5 **Photo.** **Perf. 14x13½**
2684 A842 27p blue & yellow .40 .20
World Environment Day.

1992, Oct. 29 **Litho.** **Perf. 14x13½**
2685 A843 17p multicolored .25 .20
Juan Luis Vives (1492-1540), Philosopher.

Pamplona Choir, Cent. A844

1992, Oct. 29 **Perf. 13½x14**
2686 A844 27p multicolored .35 .20

Unified Europe — A845

1992, Nov. 4 **Photo.** **Perf. 14x13½**
2687 A845 45p multicolored .60 .20

Christmas A846

1992, Nov. 5 **Perf. 13½x14**
2688 A846 27p multicolored .40 .20

1992 Special Olympics, Madrid A847

1992, Sept. 7 **Photo.** **Perf. 13½x14**
2689 A847 27p brown & blue .35 .20

Souvenir Sheet

St. Paul's Church, Valladolid — A848

Litho. & Engr.
1992, Oct. 9 **Perf. 14x13½**
2690 A848 27p multicolored .35 .35
Exfilna '92, Natl. Philatelic Exhibition, Valladolid.

Discovery of America, 500th Anniv. A849

1992, Oct. 15 **Perf. 13½x140**
2691 A849 60p dk brn, lt brn & bis .75 .20

Natl. Heritage Type of 1991
Miniature Sheet
Codices: a, Veitia, 18th cent. b, Trujillo of Peru, 18th cent. c, The Chess Book, 13th cent. d, General History of New Spain, 16th cent.

Litho. & Engr.
1992, Dec. 10 **Perf. 13**
2692 A821 27p Sheet of 4, #a.-d. 1.40 1.40

Road Safety A850

Environmental Protection A851

Health and Sanitation — A852

1993 **Photo.** **Perf. 14x13½**
2693 A850 17p green & red .35 .20
2694 A851 28p green & blue .40 .20
2695 A852 65p blue & green .90 .20
Nos. 2693-2695 (3) 1.65 .60

Issued: 17p, 4/20; 28p, 1/4; 65p, 2/12.

Maria Zambrano (1904-1991), Writer — A854

1993, Jan. 18 **Photo.** **Perf. 14**
2697 A854 45p buff, lil rose & brn .65 .25

Andres Segovia (1893-1987), Guitarist — A855

1993, Feb. 19 **Engr.** **Perf. 14x13½**
2698 A855 65p black & brown .90 .25

1908 Mailbox, Madrid Postal Museum A856

Litho. & Engr.
1993, Mar. 12 **Perf. 13½x14**
2699 A856 28p multicolored .45 .20
Stamp Day.

Mushrooms — A857

1993, Mar. 18 **Photo.** **Perf. 14**
2700 A857 17p Amanita caesarea .35 .20
2701 A857 17p Lepiota procera .35 .20
2702 A857 28p Lactarius sanguifluus .40 .20
2703 A857 28p Russula cyanoxantha .40 .20
Nos. 2700-2703 (4) 1.50 .80

See Nos. 2759-2762.

Souvenir Sheet

Holy Week Celebration — A858

1993, Apr. 2   Litho.   Perf. 14x13½
2704 A858 100p multicolored   1.40 1.40

Exfilna '93, Alcaniz. Margin of No. 2704 is Litho. & Engr.

Fusees, by Joan Miro A859

Europa: 65p, La Bague d'Aurore, by Miro, vert.

Perf. 13½x14, 14x13½
1993, May 5   Litho.
2705 A859 45p blue & black   .60 .20
Litho. & Engr.
2706 A859 65p multicolored   .90 .20

Year of St. James A860

Designs: 17p, Transfer of St. James' body by boat. 28p, Discovery of tomb of St. James. 45p, St. James on horseback.

1993, May 13 Photo.   Perf. 13½x14
2707 A860 17p multicolored   .35 .20
2708 A860 28p multicolored   .40 .20
2709 A860 45p multicolored   .60 .25
      Nos. 2707-2709 (3)   1.35 .65

World Telecommunications Day — A861

1993, May 17
2710 A861 28p multicolored   .40 .20

Compostela '93 — A862

Stylized designs: 28p, Pilgrims paying homage to Saint James. 100p, Pilgrim under star tree while on way to Santiago de Compostela, vert.

1993, May 18 Photo.   Perf. 13½x14
2711 A862 28p multicolored   .45 .20
Souvenir Sheet
Perf. 14x13½
2712 A862 100p multicolored   1.40 1.40

World Environment Day — A863

1993, June 4   Litho.   Perf. 14x13½
2713 A863 28p multicolored   .40 .20

King Juan Carlos
A864   A864a

1993-98   Photo.   Perf. 14x13½
A864 Gold and:
2714 A864   1p prussian bl   .20   .20
2715 A864   2p green   .20   .20
2716 A864 10p magenta   .20   .20
2717 A864 15p green   .20   .20
2718 A864 16p brn lake   .20   .20
2719 A864 17p yel org   .25   .20
2720 A864 18p grn bl   .20   .20
2721 A864 19p brown   .25   .20
2722 A864 20p lil rose   .25   .20
2723 A864 21p dark grn   .25   .20
2724 A864 28p vio brn   .35   .20
2725 A864 29p olive   .40   .20
2726 A864 30p ultramarine   .40   .20
2727 A864 32p green   .45   .20
2728 A864 35p red   .40   .25
2729 A864 45p bluish grn   .55   .20
2730 A864 55p sepia   .75   .20
   a.   Block of 4, #2715, 2720,
        2725, 2730 + 2 labels   1.50 .30
2731 A864 60p org brn   .90   .50
   a.   Block of 4, #2716, 2721,
        2726, 2731 + 2 labels   1.75 .95
2732 A864 65p red org   .75   .20
   a.   Block of 4, #2719, 2724,
        2729, 2732 + 2 labels   1.75 1.75
2733 A864 70p vermilion   .80   .45
Engr.
2734 A864a 100p brown   1.25   .30
2735 A864a 200p green   2.75   .60
2736 A864a 300p maroon   4.00   .90
2737 A864a 500p blue   6.75 1.50
2738 A864a 1000p vio blk   14.00 3.25
   Nos. 2714-2738 (25)   36.70 11.15

Issued: 17p, 28p, 45p, 65p, 5/21/93; 1p, 18p, 29p, 1/31/94; 19p, 30p, 1994; 19p, 30p, 1/3/95; 10p, 60p, 6/5/95; 1000p, 11/24/95; 100p, 200p, 300p, 500p, 12/12/96; 21p, 32p, 1/27/97; 2p, 16p, 5/19/97; 15p, 3/6/98; 35p, 2/13/98; 70p, 1/30/98. 20p, 11/20/00.

Don Juan de Borbon (1913-1993), Count of Barcelona — A865

1993, June 20 Photo.   Perf. 14x13½
2744 A865 28p multicolored   .35 .20

Igualada-Martorell Railway, Cent. — A866

1993, July 4   Engr.   Perf. 13½x14
2745 A866 45p black & green   .60 .20

Natl. Mint (F.N.M.T.), Cent. A867

1993, Sept. 13
2746 A867 65p dark blue   .90 .20

Explorers A868

Designs: 45p, Alejandro Malaspina (1754-1809), Italian explorer of South America. 65p, Jose Celestino Mutis (1732-1808), Spanish naturalist in the Americas, vert.

Perf. 13½x14, 14x13½
1993, Sept 20   Litho.
2747 A868 45p multicolored   .60 .20
2748 A868 65p multicolored   .90 .20

Ciconia Nigra A869

Endangered birds: No. 2750, Gypaetus barbatus (Quebrantahuesos).

Litho. & Engr.
1993, Oct. 11   Perf. 13½x14
2749 A869 65p pink & black   .90 .20
2750 A869 65p orange & black   .90 .20

Child's Painting — A870

1993, Oct. 2   Litho.   Perf. 14x13½
2751 A870 45p multicolored   .60 .20

European Year of the Elderly A871

1993, Oct. 29   Photo.   Perf. 14
2752 A871 45p multicolored   .60 .20

A872

Christmas — A873

Perf. 13½x14, 14x13½
1993, Nov. 23   Photo.
2753 A872 17p multicolored   .25 .20
Litho., Photo. & Engr.
2754 A873 28p multicolored   .40 .20

Jorge Guillen (1893-1984), Poet — A874

1993, Nov. 29   Engr.   Perf. 14x13½
2755 A874 28p green   .40 .20

UNESCO World Heritage Type of 1991

Design: 50p, Monastery of Santa Maria of Poblet, Tarragona.

1993, Dec. 3   Engr.   Perf. 13x12½
2756 A830 50p multicolored   .65 .20

Spanish Film Industry A875

29p, Luis Bunuel (1900-83), director. 55p, Segundo de Chomon (1871-1929), film pioneer.

1994, Jan. 28   Photo.   Perf. 14
2757 A875 29p multicolored   .40 .20
2758 A875 55p multicolored   .75 .20

Mushroom Type of 1993

1994, Feb. 18   Photo.   Perf. 14
2759 A857 18p Boletus satanas   .20 .20
2760 A857 18p Boletus edulis   .20 .20
2761 A857 29p Amanita phal-
             loides   .35 .20
2762 A857 29p Lactarius delici-
             osus   .35 .20
   Nos. 2759-2762 (4)   1.10 .80

Minerals A876

a, Cinnabar. b, Sphalerite. c, Pyrite. d, Galena.

1994, Feb. 25
2763 A876 29p Block of 4, #a.-d.,
             + 2 labels   1.40 1.40

Barrister's Mailbox A877

Litho. & Engr.
1994, Mar. 9   Perf. 13½x14
2764 A877 29p light & dark brn   .35 .20
             Stamp Day.

ILO, 75th Anniv. A878

1994, Apr. 7   Photo.   Perf. 13½x14
2765 A878 65p multicolored   .85   .20

Art of Salvador Dali (1904-89) A879

Paintings: #2766, Retrato de Gala. #2767, Poesia de America. #2768, El Gran Masturbador. #2769, Port Alguer. #2770, Self portrait. #2771, Cesta del Pan. #2172, El Enigma Sin Fin. #2173, Galatea de las Esferas.

1994, Apr. 22   Perf. 13½x14, 14x13½
2766 A879 18p multi   .20   .20
2767 A879 18p multi, vert.   .20   .20
2768 A879 29p multi   .35   .20
2769 A879 29p multi, vert.   .35   .20
2770 A879 55p multi, vert.   .70   .20
2771 A879 55p multi   .70   .20
2772 A879 65p multi   .85   .20
2773 A879 65p multi, vert.   .85   .20
    Nos. 2766-2773 (8)   4.20   1.60

Josep Pla (1897-1981), Writer — A880

1994, Apr. 23   Engr.   Perf. 13½x14
2774 A880 65p dark grn & lake   .85   .20

A881

A882

A883

Painting: Martyrdom of St. Andrew, by Rubens.

1994, Apr. 29   Photo.   Perf. 14
2775 A881 55p multicolored   .70   .20
Carlos de Amberes Foundation, 400th anniv.

1994, May 3   Photo.
2776 A882 18p multicolored   .20   .20
Litho., Photo. & Engr.
2777 A883 29p multicolored   .35   .20
Santa Cruz de Tenerife, 400th anniv. (#2776). Complutense University of Madrid, 700th Anniv. (#2777).

Europa A884

Designs: 55p, Severo Ochoa (1905-93), 1959 Nobel Laureate in Medicine. 65p, Miguel Angel Catalan (1894-1957), physicist.

1994, May 5   Litho. & Engr.
2778 A884 55p multicolored   .70   .20
2779 A884 65p multicolored   .85   .20

Spanish Literature A885

Novels by Camilo Jose Cela: 18p, The Family of Pascual Duarte. 29p, Journey to Alcarria.

1994, May 11   Photo.
2780 A885 18p multicolored   .20   .20
2781 A885 29p multicolored   .35   .20

King Sancho Ramirez, 900th Death Anniv. — A886

Treaty of Tordesillas, 500th Anniv. — A887

Design: 55p, Natl. Archives, Simancas.

Litho. & Engr.
1994, June 7   Perf. 14
2782 A886 18p multicolored   .20   .20
2783 A887 29p multicolored   .35   .20
2784 A887 55p multicolored   .70   .20
    Nos. 2782-2784 (3)   1.25   .60

Souvenir Sheet

Cathedral of St. Anne, Las Palmas, Grand Canary Island — A888

Illustration reduced.

1994, July 1   Perf. 13½x14
2785 A888 100p multicolored   1.25   1.25
Exfilna '94, Natl. Philatelic Exhibition, Grand Canary Island.

Yachts — A889

1994, July 15   Photo.   Perf. 14x13½
2786 A889 16p Giralda   .20   .20
2787 A889 29p Saltillo   .35   .20

Roman City of Augusta Emerita (Merida), Badajoz — A890

Litho. & Engr.
1994, Sept. 8   Perf. 13
2788 A890 55p lake, brn & buff   .70   .20
UNESCO World Heritage list.

Museum of Cards, Alava — A891

Antique cards: 18p, Horse of Spades. 29p, Jack of Diamonds. 55p, King of Hearts. 65p, War god, Mars, of Diamonds.

1994, Sept. 20   Photo.   Perf. 14x13½
2789 A891 18p multicolored   .20   .20
2790 A891 29p multicolored   .35   .20
2791 A891 55p multicolored   .70   .20
2792 A891 65p multicolored   .90   .20
    Nos. 2789-2792 (4)   2.15   .80

Postal Transportation — A892

1994, Oct. 11   Litho.   Perf. 13½
2793 A892 65p DC-8   .90   .20

Public Transit — A893

Civil Guard A894

1994, Oct. 17   Photo.   Perf. 14x13½
2794 A893 18p multicolored   .20   .20
Perf. 13½x14
2795 A894 29p multicolored   .40   .20

Western European Union A895

1994, Oct. 21   Perf. 13½x14
2796 A895 55p multicolored   .75   .20

Olympic Venues A896

Designs: a, Track. b, Skiing. c, Equestrian. d, Wrestling. e, Archery. f, Cycling. g, Soccer. h, Field hockey. i, Swimming. j, Sailing.

1994, Oct. 27
2797   Block of 10 + 10 labels 4.25   4.25
    a.-j. A896 29p any single   .40   .40
Labels inscribed with names of Spanish gold medalists and Intl. Olympic Committee cent.
See Nos. 2822, 2850.

Christmas — A897

1994, Nov. 18   Perf. 14x13½
2798 A897 29p multicolored   .40   .20

Spanish Motion Pictures A898

Designs: 30p, Belle Epoque, by Fernando Trueba. 60p Volver A Empezar (Begin the Beguine), by Jose Luis Garci.

1995, Jan. 20   Photo.   Perf. 14
2799 A898 30p multicolored   .40   .20
2800 A898 60p multicolored   .85   .20

City of Logrono, 900th Anniv. A899

1995, Jan. 25
2801 A899 30p multicolored   .40   .20

Souvenir Sheet

SIERRA NEVADA '95, Granada — A900

Illustration reduced.

1995, Jan. 30
2802 A900 130p White star flower 1.75 1.75

World Alpine Skiing Championships.

Mushrooms — A901

1995, Feb. 9 Photo. Perf. 13½x14
2803 A901 19p Coprinus comatus .25 .20
2804 A901 30p Dermocybe cinnamomea .40 .20

Minerals
A902

Designs: a, Dolomite. b, Technical School for Mining Engineers, Madrid. c, Aragonite.

1995, Feb. 24
2805 Strip of 3 1.25 1.25
a.-c. A902 30p any single .40 .20

Stamp Day
A903

1995, Mar. 9 Engr.
2806 A903 30p Bronze lion's head .40 .20

Alejandro Goicoechea Omar, TALGO Train — A904

Design: 60p, Young Omar, early train.

1995, Mar. 17 Photo. Perf. 14
2807 A904 30p multicolored .40 .20
2808 A904 60p multicolored .85 .20

A905 A906

1995, Apr. 6
2809 A905 60p multicolored .85 .20

Nature conservation in Europe.

Litho. & Engr.
1995, Apr. 7 Perf. 14
18th Century Sailing Ships: 19p, San Juan Nepomuceno. 30p, San Telmo.
2810 A906 19p multicolored .25 .20
2811 A906 30p multicolored .40 .20

Nos. 2810-2811 printed in miniature sheets of 4.

Lebaniego Celebration Year — A907

60p, Mountains, St. Toribio Monastery.

1995, Apr. 21 Photo. Perf. 12½
2812 A907 30p multicolored .40 .20
2813 A907 60p multicolored .85 .20

Spanish Literature
A908

Designs: 19p, El Nino Yuntero, by Miguel Hernandez (1910-42). 30p, Juanita la Larga, by Juan Valera (1824-1905), vert.

Litho. & Engr.
1995, Apr. 27 Perf. 14
2814 A908 19p multicolored .25 .20
Engr.
2815 A908 30p green & blue .40 .20

Jose Marti (1853-95), Cuban Writer
A909

1995, Apr. 28 Photo.
2816 A909 60p multicolored .85 .20

Spanish Cartoon Characters
A910

1995, May 4 Photo. Perf. 14
2817 A910 30p Captain Trueno .45 .20
2818 A910 60p Carpanta, vert. .90 .20

See Nos. 2854-2855.

Europa
A911

1995, May 5
2819 A911 60p multicolored .90 .20

Motion Pictures, Cent.
A912

19p, Auguste and Louis Lumiere, early camera.

1995, May 12 Engr. Perf. 14
2820 A912 19p brownish black .25 .20

Press Assoc. of Madrid, Cent.
A913

1995, May 12 Litho.
2821 A913 30p multicolored .45 .20

Olympic Venue Type of 1994

Designs: a, Track. b, Basketball. c, Boxing. d, Soccer. e, Gymnastics. f, Equestrian. g, Field hockey. h, Canoeing. i, Polo. j, Two-man rowing. k, Tennis. l, Shooting. m, Sailing. n, Water polo.

1995, June 2 Photo. Perf. 14
2822 Block of 14 + 6 labels 6.25 6.25
a.-n. A896 30p any single .45 .20

Labels are inscribed with names of Spanish silver medallists.

UN, 50th Anniv.
A914

FAO, 50th Anniv. — A915

World Tourism Organization, 20th Anniv. — A916

1995, June 26
2823 A914 60p multicolored .90 .20
2824 A915 60p multicolored .90 .20
2825 A916 60p multicolored .90 .20
Nos. 2823-2825 (3) 2.70 .60

A917

1995, July 1
2826 A917 60p multicolored .90 .20

Spanish Presidentcy of the European Community Council of Ministers.

A918

1995, Sept. 4 Photo. Perf. 14
2827 A918 60p multicolored .90 .20

4th World Conference on Women, Beijing.

Souvenir Sheet

17th Intl. Conference of Cartography, Barcelona — A919

Illustration reduced.

1995, Sept. 5
2828 A919 130p multicolored 2.00 2.00

Santiago de Compostela University, 500th Anniv. — A920

1995, Sept. 15
2829 A920 30p multicolored .45 .20

UNESCO World Heritage Type of 1991 and

A921

#2830, Royal Monastery of Santa Maria de Guadalupe, vert. #2831, Map of Santiago de Compostela's 9th cent. route through northern Spain.

1995, Sept. 29 Engr. Perf. 12½
2830 A830 60p dark brown .90 .20
Photo. & Engr.
2831 A921 60p multicolored .90 .20

Ecological Protection System, Lagunas Machegas
A922

Ducks: 60p, Anade real, pato colorado.

1995, Oct. 11 Photo. Perf. 14
2832 A922 60p multicolored .90 .20

America Issue.

Souvenir Sheet

EXFILNA '95, Nat. Philatelic Exhibition, Malaga — A923

Illustration reduced.

Litho. & Engr.
1995, Oct. 6 Perf. 14x13½
2833 A923 130p dark green 2.00 2.00

Archaeology — A924

#2834, Cave of Menga, Antequera, Malaga. #2835, Ruins of Torralba, Minorca.

1995, Oct. 20   Photo.
2834 A924 30p multicolored   .45   .20
2835 A924 30p multicolored   .45   .20

Souvenir Sheet

The Contemporary Poets, by Antonio Maria Esquivel (1806-57) — A925

Group of poets: a, Seated at left. b, One reading from paper. c, Four standing. d, Standing, seated at right.
Illustration reduced.

1995, Oct. 27
2836   A925 Sheet of 4   2.50 2.50
   a.   19p multicolored   .25   .25
   b.   30p multicolored   .45   .45
   c.-d.   60p any single   .90   .90

Christmas
A926

Design: 30p, Capital sculpture of "Adoration of the Magi," Collegiate Church of San Martin de Elines, Cantabria.

1995, Nov. 17   Photo.   Perf. 14
2837 A926 30p multicolored   .45   .20

Espamer '96, Aviation & Space Philatelic Exhibitions, Seville — A927

#2838, Sevilla-Plaza de Armas Railway Station. #2839, Lorenzo Galindez de Carvajal, Master Courier, King Fernando's Court, vert.

1995, Dec. 20   Photo.   Perf. 13
2838 A927 60p multicolored   .90   .20
2839 A927 60p multicolored   .90   .20

Spanish Motion Pictures, Cent. A928

Designs: 30p, Scene from first Spanish motion picture, "Salida de los Fieles del Pilar de Zaragoza." 60p, Poster for 1952 motion picture, "Bienvenido, Mister Marshall."

1996, Jan. 30   Photo.   Perf. 14
2840 A928 30p multicolored   .45   .20
2841 A928 60p multicolored   .90   .20

Spanish Mining — A929

Designs: 30p, Miner's lamp from Museum of Mining and Industry, mine shaft. 60p, Fluorite.

1996, Feb. 7
2842 A929 30p multicolored   .45   .20
2843 A929 60p multicolored   .90   .20

Madrid-Irun Visual Telegraph Line, 150th Anniv. — A930

1996, Mar. 8   Engr.   Perf. 14
2844 A930 60p lake & gray grn   .90   .20
Stamp Day.

Barcelona, 10th Anniv. of Urban Transformation — A931

1996, Mar. 22
2845 A931 30p multicolored   .45   .20

Endangered Wildlife — A932

1996, Mar. 27   Photo.
2846 A932 30p Ursus arctos   .45   .20

18th Cent. Sailing Ship Type of 1995
Designs: 30p, King Phillip. 60p, Catalán.

Litho. & Engr.
1996, Apr. 19   Perf. 14x13½
2847 A906 30p multicolored   .45   .20
2848 A906 60p multicolored   .90   .20
Nos. 2847-2848 printed in miniature sheets of 4.

Madrid Bar Assoc., 400th Anniv. A933

1996, Apr. 23   Photo.   Perf. 14
2849 A933 19p multicolored   .25   .20

Olympic Venue Type of 1994
Symbols of Olympic venues, bronze ribbon: a, like #2797a. b, like #2822c. c, like #2797b. d, like 2797h. e, like #2797i. f, like 2822h. g, like #2822k. h, like #2822 l. i, like #2797j.

1996, Apr. 26   Photo.   Perf. 14
2850   Block of 9 + 6 labels   4.00 4.00
  a.-i.   A896 30p Any single   .45   .20
Labels are inscribed with names of Spanish bronze medalists.

Souvenir Sheets

A934

Royal Family — A935

Espamer '96 Philatelic Exhibition, World Aviation and Space Exposition: No. 2851a, Map of Seville-Larache Air Route, 1921. b, Zeppelin cover, Seville, 1930. c, Rocket launch. d, Hispano HA 200 SAETA aircraft. Illustration reduced (A935).

1996, May 4
2851   Sheet of 4   5.75 5.75
  a.-d.   A934 100p any single   1.40 1.40
2852 A935 400p multicolored   5.75 5.75

Carmen Amaya, Flamenco Dancer — A936

1996, May 6   Perf. 14x13½
2853 A936 60p multicolored   .90   .20
Europa.

Cartoon Characters Type of 1995
1996, May 10   Perf. 14x13½, 13½x14
2854 A910 19p El Jabato, vert.   .25   .20
2855 A910 30p El Reporter
            Tribulete   .45   .20

Paintings by Francisco de Goya Y Lucientes (1746-1828) — A937

19p, Gen. Don Antonio Ricardos, vert. 30p, Dairymaid of Bordeaux, vert. 60p, Boys with a Mastiff. 130p, The 3rd of May, 1808.

1996, May 31   Photo.   Perf. 14x13½
2856 A937 19p multicolored   .25   .20
2857 A937 30p multicolored   .45   .20

Perf. 13½x14
2858 A937 60p multicolored   .85   .20
2859 A937 130p multicolored   1.75 .40
   Nos. 2856-2859 (4)   3.30 1.00

Philatelic Service, 50th Anniv. A938

1996, June 4   Perf. 13½x14
2860 A938 30p multicolored   .40   .20

Popular Personalities — A939

Designs: 19p, José Monge Cruz, singer, vert. 30p, Lola Flores, movie star.

Perf. 14x13½, 13½x14
1996, June 14
2861 A939 19p multicolored   .25   .20
2862 A939 30p multicolored   .45   .20

Lanuza Central Market, Zaragoza A940

1996, July 5   Photo.   Perf. 13½x14
2863 A940 30p multicolored   .45   .20
19th Intl. Congress of Architects, Barcelona.

Gerardo Diego (1896-1987), Poet — A941

Joaquín Costa (1846-1911), Lawyer, Teacher — A942

1996, Sept. 13   Engr.
2864 A941 19p red, black & vio   .25   .20
Litho. & Engr.
2865 A942 30p multicolored   .45   .20

UNICEF, 50th Anniv. — A943

1996, Sept. 13   Photo.
2866 A943 60p blue, black & red   .90   .20

Archaeological Finds — A944

Designs: No. 2867, Naveta Des Tudons, tomb, 2000-1500BC. No. 2868, Cabezo de Alcala, reamains of Roman temple, 54-49BC.

1996, Sept. 27   Photo.
2867 A944 30p multicolored   .45   .20
2868 A944 30p multicolored   .45   .20

Souvenir Sheet

Exfilna '96, Natl. Philatelic Exhibition, Vitoria-Gasteiz — A945

Painting of Vitoria-Gasteiz, capital of Alava Province, by Ignacio Diaz Ruiz de Olano (1860-1937). Illustration reduced.

1996, Oct. 11 Engr. Perf. 14x13½
2869 A945 130p rose carmine 1.75 1.75
Sheet margin is litho.

America Issue — A946

Traditional costume of Charro Region, Salamanca.

1996, Oct. 15 Photo. Perf. 14
2870 A946 60p multicolored .85 .20

Sites on UNESCO World Heritage List — A947

Designs: 19p, Albaicin, old Muslim quarter, Granada, vert. 30p, Gateway to Tiberiades Square, statue of Maimonides. 60p, Deer, De Donana Natl. Park, Huelva province, vert.

Perf. 12½x13, 13x12½
1996, Oct. 25 Engr.
2871 A947 19p dark blue violet .25 .20
2872 A947 30p deep claret .40 .20
2873 A947 60p dark blue .85 .20
Nos. 2871-2873 (3) 1.50 .60

Spanish Literature A948

Designs: 30p, "La Regenta," by Leopoldo Garcia-Alas Ureña (1852-1901), vert. 60p, Don Juan Tenorio, by José Zorrilla Moral (1817-93).

Perf. 14x13½, 13½x14
1996, Nov. 13 Engr.
2874 A948 30p bl, dep mag & dp vio .40 .20
2875 A948 60p dp blue & dp brn .80 .20

Christmas — A949

Birth of Christ, by Fernando Gallego.

1996, Nov. 22 Photo. Perf. 14
2876 A949 30p multicolored .40 .20

Souvenir Sheet

Official Map of Spain and Its Provinces — A950

Illustration reduced.

1996, Dec. 5
2877 A950 130p multicolored 1.75 1.75

A951

Endangered species.

1997, Jan. 30 Photo. Perf. 14x13½
2878 A951 32p Genetta genetta .45 .20
See Nos. 2928, 2978-2980.

A952

1997, Feb. 28 Photo. Perf. 14x13½
2879 A952 32p multicolored .40 .20
Juvenia '97, Natl. Juvenile Philatelic Exhibition.

Stamp Day A953

1997, Mar. 7 Engr. Perf. 14
2880 A953 65p Antique letter box .80 .20

Spanish Motion Pictures — A954

1997, Mar. 12 Photo.
2881 A954 21p "Trip to Nowhere" .25 .20
2882 A954 32p "The South" .40 .20

World Day of Water — A955

19th Cent. Sailing Ships — A956

1997, Mar. 22 Perf. 14x13½
2883 A955 65p multicolored .80 .20

1997, Apr. 16 Litho. & Engr.
2884 A956 21p Frigate Asturias .25 .20
2885 A956 32p Spanish Brigantine .40 .20
Nos. 2884-2885 were each issued in sheets of 4.

Bilbao School of Engineering, Cent., — A957

194p, Atocha Station, High-Speed Spanish Train (AVE), 5th Anniv.

1997, Apr. 22 Photo. Perf. 14x13½
2886 A957 32p multicolored .40 .20
2887 A957 194p multicolored 2.50 .70

Dr. Josep Trueta (1897-1977), Orthopedic Surgeon — A958

1997, Apr. 30 Perf. 14
2888 A958 32p multicolored .40 .20

Stories and Legends — A959

Europa: Princess, Prince, gnome, castle.

1997, May 5 Photo. Perf. 14x13½
2889 A959 65p multicolored .80 .20

Fictional Characters A960

Designs: 21p, "El Lazarillo de Tormes," vert. 32p, "El Séneca," by José María Pemán.

1997, May 8 Engr. Perf. 14
2890 A960 21p green & black .25 .20
2891 A960 32p black & blue .40 .20

Anxel Fole (1903-86), Poet, Writer A961

1997, May 17 Photo.
2892 A961 65p multicolored .80 .20

Comics A962

1997, May 30
2893 A962 21p The Ulysses Family .25 .20
2894 A962 32p The Masked Warrior .40 .20

Popular Personalities — A963

32p, Manuel Rodríguez Sánchez (Manolete) (1917-47), bullfighter. 65p, Charlie Rivel (Josep Andreu i Lasserre) (1896-1983), circus clown.

1997, June 5 Photo. Perf. 14
2895 A963 32p multicolored .40 .20
2896 A963 65p multicolored .80 .20

A964

A965

"The Age of Man" Cultural Exhibition: a, 21p, Painting, "The Annunciation," from Church of Nuestra Señora de la Peña, Agreda. b, 32p, Cathedral of El Burgo de Osma. c, 65p, Miniature from Codex titled "Commontary on the Apocalypse," by Beasus of Liebana, 786AD. d, 140p, Statue of Santo Domingo de Silos.

1997, June 13 Perf. 13
2897 A964 Sheet of 4, #a.-d. 3.00 3.00

1997, June 24 Perf. 14
2898 A965 65p multicolored .80 .20
30th European Men's Basketball Championships.

NATO Summit, Madrid — A966

1997, July 8   **Perf. 13**
2899 A966 65p multicolored   .80   .20

A967

A968

Design: Natl. monument to honor grape harvesting, Requena.

1997, July 11   **Litho.**   **Perf. 14**
2900 A967 32p multicolored   .40   .20

1997, July 24   **Photo.**
Anniversaries: 21p, Don Antonio Canovas del Castillo (1828-97), politician. 32p, Roman colony of Elche, 2000th anniv. 65p, Naval defense of Tenerife, bicent.

2901 A968 21p multicolored   .25   .20
2902 A968 32p multicolored   .40   .20
2903 A968 65p multicolored   .80   .25
     Nos. 2901-2903 (3)   1.45   .65

Peace in Basque Region — A969

Spanish Artists — A970

1997, July 30   **Photo.**   **Perf. 14**
2904 A969 32p multicolored   .35   .20

1997, Sept. 12
Designs: 32p, Mariano Benlliure Gil (1862-1947), sculptor. 65p, Photograph of Remero Vasco, by José Ortíz Echagüe (1886-1980).

2905 A970 32p multicolored   .35   .20
2906 A970 65p black & beige   .75   .20

VIGO '97, World Exposition on Fisheries A971

1997, Sept. 17   **Litho.**
2907 A971 32p multicolored   .35   .20

Anniversaries — A972

21p, City of Melilla, 500th anniv., vert. 32p, Declaration of St. Pascual Baylon as patron saint of World Eucharistic Congress, cent., vert. 65p, Ausias March (1397-1459), writer.

1997, Sept. 24   **Photo.**
2908 A972 21p multicolored   .20   .20
2909 A972 32p multicolored   .35   .20
     Engr.
2910 A972 65p multicolored   .75   .20
     Nos. 2908-2910 (3)   1.30   .60

Sites on UNESCO World Heritage List — A973

Churches in Oviedo: 21p, San Julian de los Prados. 32p, Santa Cristina de Lena.

1997, Sept. 26   **Engr.**   **Perf. 13**
2911 A973 21p multicolored   .20   .20
2912 A973 32p multicolored   .35   .20

29th Intl. Congress of Transport and Communications Museums, Madrid — A974

1997, Oct. 1   **Litho.**   **Perf. 14x13½**
2913 A974 140p multicolored   1.75   .65

Souvenir Sheet

Monument to Don Pelayo, Revillagigedo Palace, Gijón — A975

Illustration reduced.

1997, Oct. 4   **Litho. & Engr.**   **Perf. 14**
2914 A975 140p multicolored   1.75   1.75

Exfilna '97, Natl. Stamp Exhibition, Gijón, Asturias

Opening of Royal Theater, Madrid — A976

Designs: 21p, Miguel Fleta (1897-1938), opera singer. 32p, Outside view of theater.

1997, Oct. 11   **Engr.**   **Perf. 14x13½**
2915 A976 21p violet brown   .25   .20
2916 A976 32p gray brown   .40   .20

America Issue — A977

Foundation of St. Cristobal de La Laguna, 500th Anniv. — A978

1997, Oct. 10   **Photo.**
2917 A977 65p Postman   .80   .30

1997, Oct. 17   **Litho. & Engr.**
2918 A978 32p multicolored   .40   .20

6th World Conference on Down Syndrome, Madrid — A979

1997, Oct. 23   **Photo.**   **Perf. 13½x14**
2919 A979 65p blue & yellow   .80   .30

Veterinary College, Cordoba, 150th Anniv. A980

1997, Nov. 14   **Engr.**   **Perf. 14**
2920 A980 21p green & blue   .25   .20

Christmas — A981

Painting, Adoration of the Kings, by Pedro Berruguete.

1997, Nov. 20   **Photo.**
2921 A981 32p multicolored   .40   .20

Jewish Heritage in Spain A982

Designs: 21p, Porta Nova, Ourense. No. 2923, Women's Gallery, Cordoba Synagogue. No. 2924, Jewish quarter, Caceres, 15th cent. 65p, Jewish Museum, Girona.

1997, Nov. 28   **Engr.**   **Perf. 13½x14**
2922 A982 21p black & brown   .25   .20
2923 A982 32p black & violet   .40   .20
2924 A982 32p black & brown   .40   .20
2925 A982 65p black & violet   .80   .30
   a.   Strip of 4, #2922-2925   1.90   .75
     See Nos. 2969-2972.

Spanish Sports Accomplishments — A983

1997, Dec. 5   **Photo.**
2926 A983 32p multicolored   .40   .20

XACOBEO 99 — A984

1998, Jan. 12   **Photo.**   **Perf. 14x13½**
2927 A984 35p blk, org & gray   .45   .25

Endangered Species Type of 1997

1998, Feb. 5
2928 A951 35p Lynx pardina   .45   .25

Bilbao Athletic Club, Cent. A986

1998, Feb. 10   **Perf. 13½x14**
2929 A986 35p multicolored   .45   .25

Comic Book Characters A987

Designs: 35p, Mortadelo and Filemón, by Ibáñez, vert. 70p, Zipi & Zape, by Escobar.

Perf. 14x13½, 13½x14
1998, Feb. 26   **Photo.**
2930 A987 35p multicolored   .45   .25
2931 A987 70p multicolored   .90   .45
     See Nos. 2998-2999.

Gredos State Hotel A988

1998, Mar. 12   **Photo.**   **Perf. 13½x14**
2932 A988 35p multicolored   .45   .25

Self-Government Statutes for Melilla and Ceuta — A989

1998, Mar. 16 *Perf. 13½x14, 14x13½*
2933 A989 150p Melilla 1.90 1.00
2934 A989 150p Ceuta, vert. 1.90 1.00

"Generation of '98" Authors — A990

Design: Azorín (José Martinez Ruiz) (1873-1967), Pío Baroja (1872-1956), Miguel de Unamuno (1864-1936), Ramiro de Maetzu (1874-1936), Antonio Machado (1875-1939), Ramon Valle Inclán (1866-1936).

1998, Apr. 3 **Photo.** *Perf. 14*
2935 A990 70p multicolored .90 .45

A991

A992

Design: Pedro Abarca de Bolea, Count of Aranda (1719-98), soldier, politician.

1998, Apr. 17
2936 A991 35p multicolored .45 .25

1998, Apr. 29 **Engr.** *Perf. 14x13½*
Literary characters from: 35p, Fernando de Rojas' "Le Celestina." 70p, Benito Perez Galdos' "Fortunata and Jacinta."
2937 A992 35p multicolored .45 .25
2938 A992 70p multicolored .90 .45

Ships A993

1998, Apr. 30 **Litho.** *Perf. 14*
2939 A993 35p Embarcación real .45 .25
2940 A993 70p Jabeque tajo .90 .45

Popular Festivals — A994

1998, May 5 **Photo.**
2941 A994 70p Bonfire of St. John .90 .45
Europa.

College of Medicine, Madrid, Cent. A995

Dr. D. Carlos Jiménez Díaz (1898-1967).

1998, May 18 *Perf. 13½x14*
2942 A995 35p multicolored .45 .25

Popular Personalities — A996

35p, Félix Rodríguez de la Fuente (b. 1928), wildlife activist. 70p, Alfonso Aragón Bermúdez ("Fofó") (1923-76), circus comic, vert.

1998, May 28 *Perf. 13½x14, 14x13½*
2943 A996 35p multicolored .45 .25
2944 A996 70p multicolored .90 .45

A997

A998

Design: King Philip II (1527-98).

1998, June 1 **Photo.** *Perf. 14x13½*
2945 A997 35p multicolored .45 .25

1998, June 2 **Litho. & Engr.**
Fedrico Garcia Lorca (1898-1936), poet, dramatist.
2946 A998 35p multicolored .45 .25

Spanish Stamp Engravers A999

35p, Antonio Manso (1934-93), Spain #2129. 70p, J.L.L. Sánchez Toda (1901-), Spain #546.

1998, June 5 *Perf. 14*
2947 A999 35p multicolored .45 .25
2948 A999 70p multicolored .90 .45

Philippine Independence, Cent. — A1000

Design: Spanish flag, Basilica of Cebu, Holy Child of Cebu, Philippine flag.

1998, June 12 Photo. *Perf. 13½x14*
2949 A1000 70p multicolored .95 .50
See Philippines No. 2539.

Sculpture, "Foster Brothers," by Aniceto Marinas (1866-1953) A1000a

1998, July 10 **Photo.** *Perf. 14*
2949A A1000a 35p multi .50 .25

Expo '98, Lisbon A1001

1998, Sept. 4
2950 A1001 70p multicolored .95 .50

Letter Writing — A1002

Scenes from "Don Quixote" - #2951: a, "En un lugas de la Mancha." b, "Llenósele la fanta-sía." c, "Armado caballero." d, "La del alba sería." e, "Le molió como cibera." f, "El donoso escrutinio." g, "Has de saber, amigo Sancho." h, "Los gigantes." i, "Viole bajar y subir con tanta gracia." j, "El escuadrón de ovejas." k, "Los galeotes." l, "Los cueros."
No. 2952: a, "El encantamiento." b, "Oh princesa del toboso." c, "El caballero de los espejos." d, "El leon." e, "La cueva de montesi-nos." f, "Clavileño." g, "Sancho gobernador." h, "Doña Rodríguez." i, "Compañero mío." j, "Parecioles espaciosísimo." k, "El caballero de la blanca luna." l, "La vuelta a casa."

1998, Sept. 25 *Perf. 13*
2951 Sheet of 12 3.25 3.25
a.-l. A1002 20p any single .25 .20
2952 Sheet of 12 3.25 3.25
a.-l. A1002 20p any single .25 .20
See #3016, 3053-3954, 3121, 3175.

20th Intl. Conference on Data Protection, Santiago de Compostela — A1003

1998, Sept. 16 **Litho.** *Perf. 14*
2953 A1003 70p multicolored .90 .45

Souvenir Sheet

EXFILNA '98 Natl. Philatelic Exhibition — A1004

Litho. & Engr.
1998, Sept. 18 *Perf. 14*
2954 A1004 150p Cathedral of Barcelona 2.00 2.00

UNESCO World Heritage Sites — A1005

Designs: 35p, Walled city of Cuenca. 70p, Silk Exchange, Valencia.

1998, Sept. 19 **Engr.** *Perf. 13*
2955 A1005 35p blue & brown .45 .25
2956 A1005 70p red & brown .90 .45

Angel Ganivet (1865-98), Writer A1006

1998, Oct. 6 **Engr.** *Perf. 14*
2957 A1006 35p brown & purple .50 .25

A1007

A1008

1998, Oct. 6
2958 A1007 70p multicolored 1.00 .50
The Giralda of Seville, 800th Anniv.

1998, Oct. 8 **Engr.** *Perf. 14*
2959 A1008 35p brn & yel grn .50 .25
Aga Khan Architecture Award, Alhambra of Granada.

Stamp Day
A1009

1998, Oct. 9 **Photo.**
2960 A1009 70p multicolored 1.00 .50

María Guerrero (1867-1928), Theater Actress — A1010

1998, Oct. 13
2961 A1010 70p multicolored 1.00 .50
America Issue.

Spanish Railroads, 150th Anniv. A1011

1998, Oct. 28 **Engr.**
2962 A1011 35p multicolored .50 .25

Juan Carlos I Antarctic Base A1012

1998, Nov. 6 **Photo.**
2963 A1012 35p multicolored .50 .25

A1013

Christmas (Works of art): 35p, Chestnut Seller, by Rafael Seco. 70p, Marriage of the Virgin and St. Joseph, Cathedral of Oviedo.

1998, Nov. 13
2964 A1013 35p multicolored .50 .25
2965 A1013 70p multicolored 1.00 .50

Souvenir Sheet

A1014

1998, Nov. 11 **Photo.** **Perf. 14**
The Cathedral of San Salvador, Zaragoza (Details from Altarpiece: a, Holding cross, angel. b, Holy family.
2966 A1014 35p Sheet of 2, a.-b. 1.00 1.00

Founding of New Mexico, 400th Anniv. A1015

Designs: 35p, Expedition of Juan de Oñate. 70p, Early map of Nueva Espana (Mexico) and Nuevo Mexico.

1998, Nov. 20
2967 A1015 35p multicolored .50 .25
2968 A1015 70p multicolored 1.00 .50

Jewish Heritage in Spain Type of 1997
Designs: No. 2969, Bust of Benjamin de Tudela, Tudela Commune, Navarre. No. 2970, Residence, Hervás Community, Cáceres. No. 2971, Courtyard, Corpus Christi Church, Segovia. No. 2972, Santa Maria la Blanca Synagogue, Toledo.

1998, Nov. 23 **Engr.**
2969 A982 35p dp blue & dp ol .50 .25
2970 A982 35p dp blue & dp cl .50 .25
2971 A982 70p dp blue & dp ol 1.00 .50
2972 A982 70p dp blue & dp cl 1.00 .50
  a. Strip of 4, #2969-2972 3.00 3.00
Nos. 2969, 2971 have Star of David. Nos. 2970, 2972 have menorah.

UNESCO Biosphere Reserve, Minorca A1016

1998, Dec. 2 **Photo.**
2973 A1016 35p multicolored .50 .25

Spanish Olympic Academy, 30th Anniv. A1017

1998, Dec. 9
2974 A1017 70p Bust of Plato, amphora 1.00 .50

Universal Declaration of Human Rights, 50th Anniv.
A1018 A1019
Designs: 35p, Angel Sanz Briz (1910-80), Spanish ambassador. 70p, Fingerprints.

1998, Dec. 10
2975 A1018 35p multicolored .50 .25
2976 A1019 70p multicolored 1.00 .50

Carthusian Horses — A1020

Designs: a, 100p, Mare standing with colt. b, 185p, Two with heads together. c, 35p, Adult standing in grass. d, 150p, Adult standing in flowers. e, 20p, Colt lying down, mare eating grass. f, 70p, Head of adult, silhouette.

1998, Dec. 29
2977 A1020 Block of 6, #a.-f. 7.75 7.75
España 2000, Intl. Philatelic Exhibition.
Issued in sheets of two blocks, the lower one in a different order. Two of the devices shown on the coat of arms appear on each block at the intersection of the perfs. On the top block the crown is on a.-b., d.-e., while the "H" is on b.-c., e.-f. On the bottom block the location of these devices is reversed, giving all the stamps in the sheet a slightly different design.
See #3019, 3052.

Endangered Fauna Type of 1997
Designs: 35p, Gallotia simonyi machadoi (lizard), horiz. 70p Pandion haliaetus (raptor). 100p, Puffinus puffinus (bird), horiz.

1999, Jan. 28 **Photo.** **Perf. 14**
2978 A951 35p multicolored .50 .25
2979 A951 70p multicolored 1.00 .50
2980 A951 100p multicolored 1.40 .70
  Nos. 2978-2980 (3) 2.90 1.45

Xacobeo '99 A1021

Designs: 35p, Stone cross of Paradela, vert. 70p, Sculpture of St. James, door on Church of St. James, Sangüesa. 100p, Stone cross, Cizur Bridge, Pamplona, vert. 185p, Jurisdictional stone pillar, Boadilla del Camino, vert.

Litho. & Engr.
1999, Feb. 22 **Perf. 13¾**
2981 A1021 35p multicolored .45 .25
2982 A1021 70p multicolored .90 .45
2983 A1021 100p multicolored 1.25 .65
2984 A1021 185p multicolored 2.25 1.10
  Nos. 2981-2984 (4) 4.85 2.45

Barcelona Soccer Club, Cent. — A1022

1999, Mar. 11 **Photo.** **Perf. 14**
2985 A1022 35p multicolored .45 .25

Juvenia '99, Natl. Junior Philatelic Exhibition A1023

1999, Mar. 12 **Litho.** **Perf. 14**
2986 A1023 35p multicolored .50 .25

Spanish Police Force, 175th Anniv. A1024

1999, Mar. 26
2987 A1024 35p multicolored .50 .25

Souvenir Sheet

Palace of Alfonso I el Batallador, Zaragoza — A1025

Illustration reduced.

Litho. & Engr.
1999, Apr. 9 **Perf. 14x13½**
2988 A1025 185p multicolored 2.50 2.50
Exfilna '99, Zaragoza.

Spanish Amateur Radio Union, 50th Anniv. A1026

1999, Apr. 16 **Photo.** **Perf. 14**
2989 A1026 70p multicolored .95 .50

7th World Track & Field Championships, Seville — A1027

1999, Apr. 30 **Photo.** **Perf. 14x13½**
2990 A1027 70p multicolored .90 .45

Monfragüe Nature Park A1028

Litho. & Engr.
1999, May 5 **Perf. 13½x14**
2991 A1028 70p multicolored .90 .45
Europa.

Barcelona Subway System, 75th Anniv. A1029

1999, May 7 **Photo.** **Perf. 14**
2992 A1029 70p multicolored .90 .45

Spanish Art — A1030

Designs: 35p, Portrait of King Solomon. 70p, Artifact from cathedral, Palencia.

1999, May 14
2993 A1030 35p multicolored .45 .25
2994 A1030 70p multicolored .90 .45

Introduction of the Euro — A1031

Design: a, European Union flag.
Maps: b, Germany. c, Austria. d, Belgium e, Spain. f, Finland. g, France. h, Netherlands. i, Ireland. j, Italy. k, Luxembourg. l, Portugal.

1999, May 28 *Perf. 13½x14*
2995 A1031 166p Sheet of 12,
#a.-l. 25.00 25.00

Denomination is shown in both pesetas and euros. Each stamp shows the equivilent of 1 euro in the currency of the represented country.

Royal Recreation Club of Huelva A1032

1999, June 7
2996 A1032 35p multicolored .45 .25

Souvenir Sheet

Palma '99, Natl. Topical Philatelic Exhibition — A1033

Illustration reduced.

1999, June 18 *Perf. 14x13½*
2997 A1033 185p multicolored 2.50 2.50

Comic Book Character Type

35p, Dona Urraca, by Jorge, vert. 70p, El Coyote, by José Mallorquí Figuerola, vert.

1999, June 11 Photo. *Perf. 13¾*
2998 A987 35p multicolored .45 .25
2999 A987 70p multicolored .90 .45

Defense of Las Palmas de Gran Canaria, 400th Anniv. A1034

1999, June 25 Litho. & Engr.
3000 A1034 70p multicolored .90 .45

A1035

A1036

1999, July 2 Photo. *Perf. 13¾*
3001 A1035 35p multicolored .45 .25
San Pedro de Villanueva Benedictine Monastery.

1999, July 12
3002 A1036 35p multicolored .45 .25
Village of Balmaseda, 800th anniv.

Carlos Buigas (b. 1898), Graphic Designer A1037

1999, July 12
3003 A1037 70p multicolored .90 .45

General Society of Authors and Editors, Cent. — A1038

1999, July 12
3004 A1038 70p multicolored .90 .45

Spanish Mining Institute, 150th Anniv. A1039

1999, July 12
3005 A1039 150p multicolored 1.90 .95

El Cid (Rodrigo Diaz de Vivar) (1040-99) A1040

1999, July 16 Photo. *Perf. 13¾*
3006 A1040 35p multicolored .45 .25

Paintings by Jose Vela Zanetti (1913-99) A1041

70p, "Winter." 150p, "The Harvest."

1999, Sept. 10 Photo. *Perf. 13¾*
3007 A1041 70p multi .90 .45
3008 A1041 150p multi, vert. 1.90 .95

Diego Velazquez (1599-1660), Painter — A1042

Paintings: 35p, Sebastián de Morra. 70p, Sibyl.

1999, Sept. 24
3009 A1042 35p multicolored .45 .25
3010 A1042 70p multicolored .90 .45

Intl. Year of Older Persons A1043

1999, Sept. 30
3011 A1043 35p multicolored .45 .25

Oix Castle, Lower Pyrenees A1044

1999, Oct. 1 Engr. *Perf. 13½x14*
3012 A1044 70p blue & vio brn .90 .45

World Heritage Sites — A1045

Designs: 35p, San Millán de Yuso Monastery. 70p, San Millán de Suso Monastery.

1999, Oct. 8 *Perf. 13x12½*
3013 A1045 35p multicolored .45 .25
3014 A1045 70p multicolored .90 .45

UPU, 125th Anniv. A1046

1999, Oct. 9 Photo. *Perf. 13¾*
3015 A1046 70p multicolored .90 .45

Letter Writing Type of 1998

Designs: a, "Cumplimos 150 años." b, "Recorremos el mundo." c, "Llegamos juntos." d, "Escríbeme." e, "Ama la lectura." f, "Vive la naturaleza." g, "Te mostramos el patrimonio." h, "Te acercamos a la pintura." i, "Jugamos contigo." j, "Sentimos la musica." k, "Y además nos coleccionan." l, "Os esperamos."

1999, Oct. 13 Photo. *Perf. 13x12½*
3016 Sheet of 12 3.00 3.00
a.-l. A1002 20p any single .25 .20

America Issue, A new Millennium Without Arms — A1047

1999, Oct. 15 *Perf. 13¾*
3017 A1047 70p multicolored .90 .45

Intl. Congress of Money Museums, Madrid — A1048

1999, Oct. 18 Engr. *Perf. 13x12½*
3018 A1048 70p blue & brown .90 .45

Carthusian Horse Type of 1998

Designs: a, 185p, White horse, six men. b, 70p, Espana Intl. Philatelic Exhibition emblem. c, 100p, Two white horses. d, 150p, Two white horses, one with leg raised. e, 35p, Emblem, exhibition dates. f, 20p, Horse, handler.

1999, Nov. 3 Photo. *Perf. 13¾*
3019 A1020 Block of 6, #a.-f. 7.25 7.25
See footnote following No. 2977.

Christmas A1049

35p, Adoration of the Magi, Toledo Cathedral retable. 70p, Child, statue, candles.

1999, Nov. 5
3020 A1049 35p multi, vert. .45 .25
3021 A1049 70p multi .90 .45

Spanish Postage Stamps, 150th Anniv. A1050

a, King Juan Carlos, altered 12c design A2. b, King, altered 6c design A1. c, King, altered 5r design A2. d, King, altered 6r design A2. e, 150th anniv. emblem, altered 6c design A1. f, King, altered 10r design A2. g, King, coat of arms.

Litho. & Engr.
2000, Jan. 3 *Perf. 13¾x14*
3022 Sheet of 12 5.25 5.25
a.-g. A1050 35p any single .45 .25
#3022 contains 2 ea #3022a-3022d, 3022f, 1 ea #3022e, 3022g.

Endangered Butterflies — A1051

Designs: 35p, Parnassius apollo. 70p, Agriades zullichi.

2000, Jan. 31   Photo.   Perf. 13¾
3023 A1051 35p multi   .45 .25
3024 A1051 70p multi   .85 .45

First Printing at Montserrat Monastery, 500th Anniv. — A1052

2000, Feb. 4   Photo.   Perf. 13¾
3025 A1052 35p multi   .45 .25

Holy Roman Emperor Charles V (1500-58) A1053

2000, Feb. 24   Perf. 12¾x13
3026 A1053 35p shown   .45 .25
3027 A1053 70p At age 40   .85 .45

Souvenir Sheet
Perf. 13¼x12¾
3028 A1053 150p In armor   1.75 1.75
    No. 3028 contains one 40x49mm stamp.
    See Belgium Nos. 1791-1793.

"Age of Man" Exhibition, Astorga — A1054

Designs: 70p, Carving of the Virgin Mary. 100p, Cross, Arab perfume bottle.

2000, Mar. 24   Photo.   Perf. 14x13¾
3029 A1054 70p multi   .75 .40
3030 A1054 100p multi   1.10 .55

Ferdinand of Aragon Inn, Sos A1055

2000, Apr. 7   Perf. 13¾x14
3031 A1055 35p multi   .40 .20

University Anniversaries — A1056

35p, Lleida, 700th anniv. 70p, Valencia, 500th anniv. (in 1999).

2000, Apr. 12   Engr.   Perf. 13¾x14
3032 A1056 35p red lil & brown   .40 .20
3033 A1056 70p blue & choc   .75 .40

A1057

A1058

2000, Apr. 28   Photo.   Perf. 14x13¾
3034 A1057 35p multi   .40 .20
    Royal Barcelona Sports Club, soccer team, cent.

2000, May 4
3035 A1058 35p multi   .40 .20
    María de las Mercedes de Borbón y Orleáns (1910-2000), mother of King Juan Carlos.

Europa Issue
Common Design Type
2000, May 9
3036 CD17 70p multi   .75 .40

Royal Academy of Medicine, Seville, 300th Anniv. A1060

Julio Rey Pastor (1888-1962), Mathematician — A1061

Pharmacy College of Granada, 150th Anniv. — A1062

Valencia, City of Arts and Sciences A1063

2000, May 25   Perf. 13¾x14, 14x13¾
3037 A1060 35p multi   .40 .20
3038 A1061 70p multi   .75 .40
3039 A1062 100p multi   1.10 .55
3040 A1063 185p multi   2.00 1.00
    Nos. 3037-3040 (4)   4.25 2.15
    Intl. Mathematics Year (No. 3038).

Comic Strips A1064

Designs: 35p, Las Hermanas Gilda, by Manuel Vázquez. 70p, Roberto Alcázar y Pedrín, by Eduardo Vañó, vert.

2000, May 26   Perf. 13¾x14, 14x13¾
3041 A1064 35p multi   .40 .20
3042 A1064 70p multi   .75 .40

Guggenheim Museum, Bilbao — A1065

2000, June 2   Photo.   Perf. 13¾x14
3043 A1065 70p multi   .75 .40
    Bilbao, 700th anniv.

Angel From Prayer in the Garden, Sculpture by Francisco Salzillo (1707-73) A1066

2000, June 9   Photo.   Perf. 14x13¼
3044 A1066 70p multi   .75 .40

Souvenir Sheet

Fountains of San Francisco, Aviles — A1067

Illustration reduced.

Litho. & Engr.
2000, June 16   Perf. 14x13¾
3045 A1067 185p multi   1.90 .95
    Exfilna 2000 Philatelic Exhibition, Aviles.

Trees A1068

Designs: 70p, Pinus sylvestris. 150p, Quercus ilex (encina).

Perf. 12¾x12½
2000, June 19   Photo.
3046-3047 A1068 Set of 2   2.25 1.10

Local Festivals A1069

Designs: 35p, Fire Walking Festival, San Pedro Manrique. 70p, Chivalry Festival of San Juan, Ciudadela.

2000, June 23   Perf. 13¾x14
3048-3049 A1069 Set of 2   1.10 .55

Josemaria Escrivá de Balaguer (1902-75), Founder of Opus Dei. A1070

Litho. & Engr.
2000, June 26   Perf. 13¾x14
3050 A1070 70p black & orange   .75 .40

Souvenir Sheet

World Map of Juan de la Cosa, 500th Anniv. — A1071

2000, July 14   Photo.   Perf. 13¾x14
3051 A1071 150p multi   1.60 .80

Carthusian Horses Type of 1998

No. 3052: a, 20p, Head of horse, five horses. b, 35p, White horse, sun partially obscured by clouds. c, 70p, Horse's head, two horses galloping. d, 100p, Heads of two horses. e, 150p, Horse's head, horse in lilac. f, 185p, Horse with bridle.

2000, July 28
3052 A1020 Block of 6, #a-f   5.75 5.75
    See note following No. 2977.

Letter Writing Type of 1998

No. 3053: a, Atapuerca Man, 800,000 B.C. b, Cave paintings of Altamira, 12,000 B.C. c, Phoenecians, 1100 B.C. d, Tartessians, 800 B.C. e, Iberians and Celts, 500 B.C. f, Lady of Elche, Iberian statue, 480 B.C. g, Carthaginians, 237 B.C. h, Roman Spain, 197 B.C. i, Viriathus, Lusitanian war leader against Romans, 147 B.C. j, Siege of Numantia, 133 B.C. k, Segovia aqueduct, A.D. 50. l, Vandals, Suebis, and Alanis, 409.

No. 3054: a, Visigoths, 415. b, Conversion of Recared to Catholicism, 589. c, Arabs, 711. d, Victory over Arabs by Asturian King, Pelayo, 722. e, Discovery of alleged tomb of St. James, 813. f, Collapse of the caliphate, 1031. g, Death of El Cid, 1099. h, Alfonso VIII's victory at Las Navas de Tolosa, 1212. i, Alfonso X (the Wise) becomes King, 1252. j, Trastámara Dynasty, 1369. k, Spanish Inquisition, 1478. l, Union of Aragon and Castile, 1479.

2000, Sept. 22   Perf. 13x12¾
3053   Sheet of 12   2.50 2.50
    a.-l. A1002 20p Any single   .20 .20
3054   Sheet of 12   2.50 2.50
    a.-l. A1002 20p Any single   .20 .20

World Heritage Sites — A1072

Designs: 35p, Las Médulas. 70p, Pyrénées - Mt. Perdido, vert. 150p, Catalan Music Palace, Barcelona.

Perf. 13x12¾(35p), 12¾
2000, Sept. 21   Litho. (35p), Engr.
3055-3057 A1072 Set of 3   2.75 1.40

Souvenir Sheets

España 2000 Intl. Philatelic
Exhibition — A1073

Designs: No. 3058, Hand of Julio Iglesias, singer. No. 3059, Signature of Alejandro Sanz, singer. No. 3060, Signature of Antonio Banderas, movie star. No. 3061, Mannequin, signature of Jesús del Pozo, fashion designer. No. 3062, Signature of Miguel Induráin, cyclist. No. 3063, Soccer ball, signature of Raúl González, soccer player. No. 3064, Hands of Joaquín Cortés, dancer. No. 3065, Feet of Sara Baras, dancer. No. 3066, Emblem of TVE 1 television network. No. 3067, Radio and antenna. No. 3068, Newspaper mastheads.

Illustration reduced.

Perf. 13 (round stamps), 13¾x14
2000   Photo.
3058-3068 A1073 200p Set of
11   32.50 32.50
  150th anniv. of Spanish stamps, #3066.
  Nos. 3060-3061, 3064-3068 each contain one 41x28mm rectangular stamp.
  Exist imperf.
  Issued: #3058-3059, 10/6; #3060, 10/7; #3061, 10/8; #3062-3063, 10/9; #3064-3065, 10/10; #3066, 10/11; #3067, 10/12; #3068, 10/13.

Alfredo Kraus
(1927-99),
Operatic
Tenor — A1074

2000, Oct. 27   Perf. 14x13¾
3069 A1074 70p multi   1.00 .40

America Issue,
Fight Against
AIDS — A1075

2000, Oct. 19   Photo.   Perf. 14x13¾
3070 A1075 70p multi   1.00 .40

Christmas
A1076

Designs: 35p, Nativity scene. 70p, Birth of Christ, by Conrad von Soest.

2000, Nov. 9   Perf. 12¾
3071-3072 A1076 Set of 2   1.50 .55
  See Germany No. B878-B879.

Santa María la
Real Church,
Aranda de
Duero — A1077

2000, Nov. 10   Engr.   Perf. 14x13¾
3073 A1077 35p brown   .50 .25

Spanish
Literature
A1078

Designs: 35p, Entre Naranjos, by Vicente Blasco Ibáñez. 70p, La Venganza de Don Mendo, by Pedro Muñoz Seca. 100p, El Alcalde Zalamea, by Pedro Calderón de la Barca.

Photo., Engr. (100p)
2000, Nov. 17   Perf. 13¾x14
3074-3076 A1078   Set of 3   3.00 1.10

Commercial
Agents College,
75th
Anniv. — A1079

2001, Jan. 8   Photo.   Perf. 14x13¾
3077 A1079 40p multi   .60 .25

Fire
Fighters — A1080

2001, Jan. 19
3078 A1080 75p multi   1.10 .45

Infantry
College,
Toledo,
150th
Anniv.
A1081

2001, Feb. 16   Perf. 13¾x14
3079 A1081 120p multi   1.75 .65

Intl. Campaign
Against Domestic
Violence — A1082

2001, Feb. 22   Perf. 14x13¾
3080 A1082 155p multi   2.25 .85

First
Spanish
Mail Box,
Mayorga
A1083

2001, Mar. 2   Engr.   Perf. 13¾x14
3081 A1083 155p black   2.25 .85
  Stamp Day.

Juvenia
2001, Natl.
Youth
Philatelic
Exhibition
A1084

2001, Mar. 9   Photo.
3082 A1084 120p multi   1.75 .70

Inn Type of 2000
2001, Mar. 16   Perf. 14x13¾
3083 A1055 40p Placencia Inn,
           vert.   .60 .20

Famous
People
A1085

Designs: 40p, Joaquín Rodrigo (1901-99), musician. 75p, Rafael Alberti (1902-99), writer.

2001, Mar. 22   Engr.   Perf. 13¾x14
3084-3085 A1085   Set of 2   1.75 .60

Castles
A1086

Designs: 40p, Zuda, Tortosa, vert. 75p, Cid, Jadraque. 155p, San Fernando, Figueres. 260p, Montesquiu, Montesquiu.

2001, Apr. 20   Perf. 14x13¾, 13¾x14
3086-3089 A1086   Set of 4   8.00 3.00

Book
Day — A1087

2001, Apr. 23   Photo.   Perf. 14x13¾
3090 A1087 40p multi   .60 .20

Souvenir Sheet

First Flights, 75th Anniv. — A1088

No. 3091: a, 40p, Spain-Argentina. b, 75p, Spain-Philippines. c, 155p, Spain-Equatorial Guinea. d, 260p, Commemorative flight.

2001, Apr. 26   Perf. 13¾x14
3091 A1088   Sheet of 4, #a-d 8.00 3.00

Grand Theater,
Liceu — A1089

2001, Apr. 27   Perf. 14x13¾
3092 A1089 120p multi   1.75 .65

King Juan
Carlos — A1091

2001   Photo.   Perf. 12¾x13¼
3093 A1091 5p sil & lil rose   .20 .20
3094 A1091 40p sil & yel grn   .60 .25
3095 A1091 75p sil & bl vio   1.10 .40
3096 A1091 100psil & lt red brn 1.50 .55
  Nos. 3093-3096 (4)   3.40 1.40
  Issued: 40p, 5/4; 5p, 75p, 6/28; 100p, 7/15.

Europa — A1092

2001, May 9   Photo.   Perf. 14x13¾
3097 A1092 75p multi   .80 .40

Architecture
A1093

Designs: 40p, San Martiño Church, Noia. 75p, Santa Maria Cathedral, Tui. 155p, Villaconcha dovecote, Frechilla.

Engr., Photo. (75p)
2001, May 17   Perf. 14x13¾
3098-3100 A1093   Set of 3   4.00 1.50

Luarca
Harbor
A1094

2001, May 26   Photo.   Perf. 13¾x14
3101 A1094 40p multi   .60 .25

Cardinal Rodrigo de Castro (1523-
1600) — A1095

2001, June 1
3102 A1095 40p multi   .60 .25

Leopoldo Alas, "Clarín," (1852-1901), Writer — A1096

2001, June 13
3103 A1096 75p multi   1.10 .40

Trees A1097

Designs: 40p, Olive. 75p, Beech.

2001, June 22   *Perf. 12¾*
3104-3105 A1097 Set of 2   1.75 .60

King's Soccer Cup, 25th Anniv. A1098

2001, July 6   Litho.   *Perf. 13¾x14*
3106 A1098 40p multi   .60 .25
Issued in sheets of 8 + 4 labels.

Local Festivals A1099

Designs: 40p, Cipotegato, Tarazona. 120p, Giants of Pí, Barcelona, vert.

Perf. 13¾x14, 14x13¾
2001, July 10   Photo.
3107-3108 A1099 Set of 2   2.40 .80

Baltasar Gracian (1601-58), Writer A1100

2001, July 13   *Perf. 13¾x14*
3109 A1100 120p multi   1.75 .60

"Age of Man" Exhibition — A1101

Designs: 120p, Our Lady of La Calva. 155p, Cathedral dome, Zamora.

2001, July 20   Engr.   *Perf. 14x13¾*
3110-3111 A1101 Set of 2   4.00 1.50

Grandparent's Day — A1102

Siervas de Jesús de la Caridad A1103

Perf. 14x13¾, 13¾x14
2001, July 26   Photo.
3112 A1102 40p multi   .60 .25
3113 A1103 75p multi   1.10 .40

Salamanca, European City of Culture — A1104

Illustration reduced.

2001, Sept. 5   Photo.   *Perf. 13x13¼*
3114 A1104 75p multi   1.10 .40

Covadonga Basilica, Cent. of Consecration — A1105

2001, Sept. 7   *Perf. 13¾x14*
3115 A1105 40p multi   .60 .25

Emblem of Privatized Postal System A1106

2001, Sept. 15
3116 A1106 40p multi   .60 .25

Souvenir Sheet

Exfilna 2001 Natl. Philatelic Exhibition, Vigo — A1107

Engr. (Litho. Margin)
2001, Sept. 21
3117 A1107 260p multi   4.00 4.00

St. Dominic of Silos (c. 1000-73) — A1108

Litho. & Engr.
2001, Oct. 4   *Perf. 14x13¾*
3118 A1108 40p multi   .60 .25
a.   Souvenir sheet of 1 with margin like stamp design   .60 .60
b.   Souvenir sheet of 1 with margin differing   .60 .60

Year of Dialogue Among Civilizations A1109

2001, Oct. 9   Photo.
3119 A1109 120p multi   1.75 .70
Stamp Day.

Posidonia Oceanica, Ses Salines Nature Reserve A1110

2001, Oct. 15   *Perf. 13¾x14*
3120 A1110 155p multi   2.25 .85
America issue — UNESCO World Heritage Sites.

Letter Writing Type of 1998
No. 3121: a, Christopher Columbus, 1492. b, Treaty of Tordesillas, 1494. c, Election of King Charles I as Holy Roman Emperor Charles V, 1519. d, Conquest of Mexico by Hernán Cortés, 1519. e, Circumnavigation by Juan Sebastián Elcano, 1522. f, Campaign against Incas by Francisco Pizarro, 1532. g, Ascension to throne of King Philip II, 1556. h, Start of construction of El Escoríal Monastery, 1563. i, Battle of Lepanto, 1571. j, Saints John of the Cross, Teresa of Jesus and painter El Greco, 1580. k, First play by Lope de Vega, 1593. l, Ascension to throne of King Philip III, 1598.

2001, Oct. 19   *Perf. 13x12½*
3121   Sheet of 12   4.50 4.50
a.-l. A1002 25p Any single   .40 .20

Souvenir Sheet

Bullfighter Curro Romero — A1111

2001, Oct. 25   *Perf. 14x13¾*
3122 A1111 260p multi   4.00 4.00

Christmas A1112

Designs: 40p, Virgin With Child, by Alfredo Roldan. 75p, Adoration of the Shepherds, by José Ribera.

2001, Nov. 8   *Perf. 12¾*
3123-3124 A1112 Set of 2   1.75 .60
a.   Souvenir sheet, # 3123-3124, Germany #B895-B896, litho., perf. 13¼   5.50 5.50
See Germany No. B896a.

Score of "El Sombrero de Tres Picos," by Manuel de Falla (1876-1946) — A1113

2001, Nov. 14   Photo.   *Perf. 13¾x14*
3125 A1113 75p multi   1.10 .40

Comic Strips A1114

Designs: 40p, Cartoon by Josep Coll i Coll. 75p, Rompetechos, by Francisco Ibañez.

2001, Nov. 20
3126-3127 A1114 Set of 2   1.75 .60

Carlos Cano (1946-2000), Singer — A1115

2001, Nov. 23   *Perf. 14x13¾*
3128 A1115 40p black   .60 .25

Intl. Volunteer Day for Economic and Social Development A1116

2001, Nov. 27
3129 A1116 120p multi   1.75 .70

World Heritage Sites — A1117

No. 3130: a, Catalan Romanesque Churches of the Vall de Boí. b, The Mystery of Elx (Elche). c, Hospital de Sant Pau, Barcelona. d, San Cristóbal de La Laguna. e, Archaeological Site of Atapuerca. f, Palmeral of Elche. g, Monuments of Oviedo. h, Roman Walls of Lugo. i, Rock Art of the Mediterranean Basin. j, Ibiza, Biodiversity and Culture. k, Archaeological Ensemble of Tarraco. l, University and Historic Precinct of Alcalá de Henares.

2001, Nov. 30   *Perf. 12¾*
3130   Sheet of 12   7.00 7.00
a.-l. A1117 40p Any single   .60 .25

Souvenir Sheet

Ministry of Development, 150th
Anniv. — A1118

No. 3131 — Maps showing: a, 40p, Automated postal centers. b, 75p, Ports. c, 120p,
High-speed train lines. d, 155p, Airports. e,
260p, Highways.

2001, Dec. 11
3131 A1118 Sheet of 5, #a-e, +
         label   9.75 9.75

Souvenir Sheet

King Juan Carlos, 25th Anniv. of
Reign — A1119

No. 3132: a, 40p, Crown Prince Felipe. b,
40p, Princess Elena (patterned dress). c, 40p,
Royal arms. d, 40p, Princess Cristina (black
dress). e, 75p, King Juan Carlos. f, 75p,
Queen Sofia. g, 260p, Royal palace, Madrid
(49x28mm).

2001, Dec. 14   *Perf. 12¾x13¼*
3132 A1119 Sheet of 7, #a-g   8.50 8.50

100 Cents = 1 Euro (€)
King Juan Carlos Type of 2001 With
Euro Denominations Only

2002, Jan. 2   Photo.   Perf. 13¾x14
3133 A1091 1c sil & black   .20 .20
3134 A1091 5c sil & brt blue   .20 .20
3135 A1091 10c sil & gray blue .20 .20
3136 A1091 25c sil & claret   .60 .20
3137 A1091 50c sil & gray   1.25 .35
3138 A1091 75c sil & red lil 1.90 .55

Perf. 12¾x13¼

3139 A1091 €1 sil & green   2.50 .75
3140 A1091 €2 sil & ver   5.00 1.50
        Nos. 3133-3140 (8)   11.85 3.95

Spain's
Presidency
of
European
Union
A1120

Color of star at UR: 25c, Orange. 50c,
White.

2002, Jan. 2   Photo.   Perf. 13¾x14
3141-3142 A1120 Set of 2   1.90 .65

Trees
A1121

Designs: 50c, Savin (sabina). 75c, Elm
(olmo).

2002, Jan. 25   *Perf. 12¾*
3143-3144 A1121 Set of 2   3.00 1.10

A1122   A1123

A1124   A1125

A1126   A1127

A1128   A1129
Flowers
Die Cut Perf. 13
2002, Feb. 20   **Litho.**
Self-Adhesive
3145   Booklet of 8   5.00
  a. A1122 25c multi   .60 .25
  b. A1123 25c multi   .60 .25
  c. A1124 25c multi   .60 .25
  d. A1125 25c multi   .60 .25
  e. A1126 25c multi   .60 .25
  f. A1127 25c multi   .60 .25
  g. A1128 25c multi   .60 .25
  h. A1129 25c multi   .60 .25

España
2002 Youth
Philatelic
Exhibition,
Salamanca
A1130

Designs: 50c, Exhibition emblem.
€1.80, Emblem and New Cathedral, vert.

2002, Feb. 22   Photo.   Perf. 13¾x14
3146 A1130 50c multi   1.25 .45
Souvenir Sheet
Perf. 14x13¾
3147 A1130 €1.80 multi   4.50 4.50
         See No. 3183.

Father Francisco
Piquer, Founder of
Pawn Brokerage
A1131

2002, Feb. 25   Litho.   Perf. 14x13¾
3148 A1131 25c multi   .60 .25
Caja Madrid Savings Bank, 300th anniv.

Real Madrid
Soccer
Team, Cent.
A1132

2002, Feb. 25   *Perf. 13¾x14*
3149 A1132 75c yel & gray 1.90 .65

Souvenir Sheet

Tarazona Town Hall Portico — A1133

2002, Feb. 26
3150 A1133 €2.10 multi   5.25 5.25
         Philaiberia '02, Tarazona.

Alejandro Mon
(1801-82),
Politician — A1134

2002, Feb. 27   *Perf. 14x13¾*
3151 A1134 25c multi   .60 .25

Retirement of
Peseta
Currency — A1135

2002, Feb. 28   **Litho.**
3152 A1135 25c multi   .60 .25

Sil Canyons,
Ribiera
Sacra — A1136

Cabo de
Gata Natl.
Park
A1137

2002, Mar. 8   Perf. 14x13¾, 13¾x14
3153 A1136 75c multi   1.90 .65
3154 A1137 €2.10 multi   5.25 2.75

Zaragoza Military
Academy, 75th
Anniv. — A1138

2002, Mar. 15   *Perf. 14x13¾*
3155 A1138 25c multi   .60 .25

Real Unión Soccer
Team,
Cent. — A1139

2002, Mar. 22
3156 A1139 50c multi   1.25 .45

Stamp Day
A1140

2002, Mar. 25   *Perf. 13¾x14*
3157 A1140 25c multi   .60 .25

Castle Type of 2001
Designs: 25c, Banyeres de Mariola. 50c,
Soutomaior. 75c, Cataларo.

2002, Apr. 8   Engr.   Perf. 13¾x14
3158-3160 A1086 Set of 3   3.75 1.40

Tudela,
1200th
Anniv.
A1141

2002, Apr. 12   **Photo.**
3161 A1141 75c multi   1.90 .70

Monastery
of Sant
Cugat,
1000th
Anniv.
A1142

2002, Apr. 12
3162 A1142 €1.80 multi   4.50 2.25

Luis
Cernuda
(1902-63),
Poet
A1143

2002, May 8
3163 A1143 50c multi   .90 .45

Dr. Federico Rubio (1827-1902) — A1144

2002, May 8
3164 A1144 50c multi   1.25   .45

Europa A1145

2002, May 9
3165 A1145 50c multi   1.25   .45

Reincorporation of Menorca to Spanish Crown, Bicent. — A1146

2002, May 10
3166 A1146 50c multi   1.25   .45

World Equestrian Games — A1147

No. 3167: a, Carriage driving. b, Endurance (Raid). c, Dressage (Doma). d, Reining. e, Vaulting (Volteo). f, Jumping (Saltos). g, Three-day event (Completo). Illustration reduced.

2002, May 11   **Perf. 12¾x13¼**
3167   Sheet of 7 + 2 labels 9.50 9.50
a.-e. A1147 25c Any single   .60   .25
f.   A1147 75c multi   1.90   .70
g.   A1147 €1.80 multi   4.50 2.25

Dolores Peinado (1819-94), Character From Folk Song "La Dolores" A1148

2002, May 31   **Perf. 13¾x14**
3168 A1148 50c multi   1.25   .50

Souvenir Sheet

Exfilna 2002 Natl. Philatelic Exhibition, Salamanca — A1149

No. 3169 — Plaza Mayor, Salamanca: a, 25c, West facade. b, 25c, City Hall. c, 25c, Royal Pavilion. d, €1.80, Aerial view.

Engr. (#a-c), Litho. (#d, margin)
2002, July 7   **Perf. 13¾x14**
3169 A1149 Sheet of 4, #a-d 6.25 6.25

Iberian Airlines, 75th Anniv. A1150

Airplanes: 25c, Rohrbach R-VIII Roland. 50c, Boeing 747.

2002, June 10 Photo. Perf. 13¾x14
3170-3171 A1150 Set of 2   1.90   .75

Wine Producing Regions — A1151

Grapes and map of: 25c, Rias Baixas region. 50c, Rioja region. 75c, Manzanilla — Sanlúcar de Barrameda region.

2002   **Perf. 14x13¼**
3172-3174 A1151 Set of 3 3.75 1.50
Issued: 25c, 7/27; 50c, 75c, 9/20.

Letter Writing Type of 1998

No. 3175: a, Publication of *Don Quixote*, by Miguel de Cervantes, 1605. b, Accession to throne of King Philip IV and rise in power of Conde-Duque de Olivares, 1621. c, Rivalry of poets Francisco de Quevedo and Luis de Góngora, 1620. d, Painting of "Las Meninas" by Diego Velázquez, 1656. e, Accession to throne of King Charles II, 1665. f, Accession to throne of King Philip V, 1701. g, Accesstion to throne of Kign Ferdinand VI, 1746. h, Accession to throne of King Charles III, 1759. i, Squillaci Riots, 1766. j, Gaspar Melchor de Jovellanos, 1787. k, Accession to throne of King Charles IV, 1788. l, Appointment of Manuel de Godoy as prime minister, 1792.

2002, Sept. 27   **Perf. 12¾**
3175   Sheet of 12   3.00 3.00
a.-l. A1002 10c Any single .25   .20

Expiatory Temple of the Holy Family, by Architect Antonio Gaudí (1852-1926) A1152

2002, Sept. 27 Litho. Perf. 14x13¾
3176 A1152 50c blue & black 1.25 .50

A1153

A1154

A1155

A1156

A1157

A1158

A1159

Paintings With Musical Instruments by Goyo Domínguez A1160

2002, Sept. 30   Die Cut Perf. 13
Self-Adhesive
3177   Booklet pane of 8   5.00
a. A1153 25c multi   .60   .25
b. A1154 25c multi   .60   .25
c. A1155 25c multi   .60   .25
d. A1156 25c multi   .60   .25
e. A1157 25c multi   .60   .25
f. A1158 25c multi   .60   .25
g. A1159 25c multi   .60   .25
h. A1160 25c multi   .60   .25

America Issue — Youth, Education and Literacy A1161

2002, Oct. 14 Photo. Perf. 13¾x14
3178 A1161 75c multi   1.90   .75

Almanzor (Muhammad ibn Abu Amir al-Mansur, c. 938-1002), Caliph of Córdoba — A1162

2002, Oct. 25
3179 A1162 75c multi   1.90   .75

Dijous Bó Fair, Mallorca — A1163

2002, Nov. 4   **Perf. 14x13¾**
3180 A1163 75c multi   1.90   .75

UNESCO World Heritage Sites — A1164

No. 3181 — Architectural details of: a, Aranjuez. b, Santa Maria Church, Calatayud. c, San Martin Church, Teruel. d, Santa Maria Church, Tobed. e, Santa Tecla Church, Cervera de la Cañada. f, San Pablo Church, Zaragoza.

2002, Nov. 8
3181 A1164 Sheet of 7, #a-
            d, f, 2 #e, + 5
            labels   19.00 19.00
a.-b. 25c Either single .60   .25
c.   50c multi   1.25   .50
d.   75c multi   1.90   .75
e.   €1.80 multi   4.50 2.25
f.   €2.10 multi   5.25 2.75

The two examples of No. 3181e are tete-beche in the sheet.

Inn Type of 2000
2002, Nov. 15   **Perf. 13¾x14**
3182 A1055 25c Alcañiz Inn   .60   .25

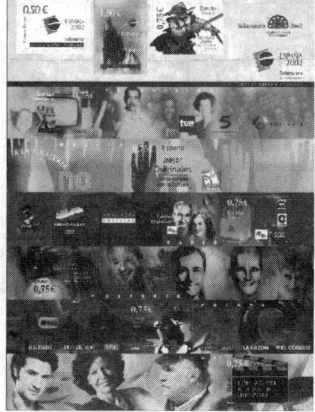

España 2002 Youth Philatelic Exhibition, Salamanca — A1165

Designs: No. 3183a, 50c, Like #3146. Nos. 3183b, 3190, 75c, Character from comic Strip "El Capitan Alatriste," by Arturo Pérez-Reverte. Nos. 3183c, 3185, 75c, Television and names of television shows. Nos. 3183d, 3189, 75c, Hand and compact disc. Nos. 3183e, 3187, 75c, Radio, musical notes and logos of Spanish radio stations. Nos. 3183f, 3188, 75c, Skier, race car, soccer ball, bicyclist and names of Spanish sports stars. Nos. 3183g, 3186, 75c, Photojournalist. Nos. 3183h, 3184, 75c, Clapboard and names of Spanish film personalities. No. 3183i, €1.80, Like #3147, vert.

2002   **Die Cut Perf. 13**
Litho.
Self-Adhesive (#3183)
3183 A1165 Sheet of 9   19.00 19.00
a.   50c multi   1.25   .50
b.-h. 75c Any single   1.90   .75
i.   €1.80 multi   4.50 2.25
Souvenir Sheets
Perf. 13¾x14
3184-3190 A1165 Set of 7 11.50 11.50

Issued: No. 3183, 11/17; No. 3184, 11/18; No. 3185, 11/19; No. 3186, 11/20; No. 3187, 11/21; No. 3188, 11/22; No. 3189, 11/23; No. 3190, 11/24.

No. 3183 exists with at least three different pictures on backing paper.

San Jorge Church,
Alcoy — A1166

Litho. & Engr.

2002, Nov. 25   *Perf. 14x13¾*
3191 A1166 75c multi   1.90   .75

Compludo
Forge,
León
A1167

2002, Nov. 27   *Perf. 13¾x14*
3192 A1167 50c multi   1.25   .50

Souvenir Sheet

Stained Glass Window, Santa Maria
Cathedral, Vitoria-Gasteiz — A1168

2002, Nov. 27   *Perf. 14x13¾*
3193 A1168 50c multi   1.25   .50

Crucifix, Hío   Christmas
A1169   A1170

2002, Nov. 29
3194 A1169 25c multi   .60   .25

2002, Nov. 29   Photo.

Designs: 25c, Adoration of the Magi, from
church altarpiece, Calzadilla de los Barros.
50c, Maternity, by Goyo Dominguez.
3195-3196 A1170 Set of 2   1.90   .75

Opening of
Somport
Tunnel
A1171

2003, Jan. 17 Photo. *Perf. 13¾x14*
3197 A1171 51c multi   1.10   .55

Traditional Dress
from Ansó
Valley — A1172

2003, Jan. 20   *Perf. 14x13¾*
3198 A1172 76c multi   1.75   .85

World Leprosy
Day, 50th
Anniv. — A1173

2003, Jan. 21
3199 A1173 26c multi   .55   .30

Pedro Rodríguez
de Campomanes
(1723-1802),
Jurist — A1174

2003, Feb. 14
3200 A1174 26c multi   .55   .30

Juvenia
2003 Natl.
Youth
Philatelic
Exhibition,
Benissa
A1175

2003, Feb. 21   *Perf. 13¾x14*
3201 A1175 51c multi   1.10   .55

Práxedes Mateo Sagasta (1825-1903),
Politician — A1176

2003, Mar. 11
3202 A1176 26c multi   .55   .30

ABC
Newspaper,
Cent.
A1177

2003, Mar. 17
3203 A1177 €2.15 multi   4.50 2.25

Nobel Prize Winners For Physiology or
Medicine From Spain — A1178

No. 3204: a, Santiago Ramón y Cajal, 1906.
b, Severo Ochoa, 1959.

Illustration reduced.

Litho. & Engr.

2003, Mar. 20   *Perf. 13x12¾*
3204 A1178 Horiz. pair   3.25 3.25
  a.   51c multi   1.25   .55
  b.   76c multi   1.90   .80

See Sweden No. 2460.

School of Civil Engineering, Madrid,
Bicent. — A1179

Designs: 26c, Tui Bridge.
No. 3206: a, Estrecho de Puentes Dam. b,
El Musel Port.

2003, Mar. 21 Photo. *Perf. 13¾x14*
3205 A1179 26c multi   .55   .30
Souvenir Sheet
3206   Sheet of 3, #3205,
              3206a, 3206b   3.25 1.75
  a.   A1179 51c multi   1.10   .55
  b.   A1179 76c multi   1.60   .80

La Verdad
Newspaper,
Cent.
A1180

2003, Mar. 26
3207 A1180 26c multi   .55   .30

Paintings by
Chico Montilla
A1181

No. 3208: a, La Hoz de Priego. b, Fields of
Gold. c, Desfiladero de los Tornos. d, Campos
de Pastrana. e, Campos de Armilla. f, Nenúfar.
g, De qué Color es el Vento? h, Flores
Tempranas.

Die Cut Perf. 13
2003, Mar. 28   Litho.
Self-Adhesive
3208   Booklet pane of 8   4.50
a.-h. A1181 26c Any single   .55   .30

Ramón
José
Sender
(1901-82),
Writer
A1182

Litho. & Engr.
2003, Mar. 31   *Perf. 13½x14*
3209 A1182 €2.15 multi   4.75 2.40

Rural
Schools
A1183

2003, Apr. 3 Photo. *Perf. 13¾x14*
3210 A1183 26c multi   .55   .30

Souvenir Sheet

EXFILNA 2003 Natl. Philatelic
Exhibition, Granada — A1184

Litho. (margin) & Engr. (stamp)
2003, Apr. 7
3211 A1184 €2.15 multi   4.75 2.40

Aviles,
1000th
Anniv.
A1185

2003, Apr. 11   Photo.
3212 A1185 51c multi   1.10   .55

Stamp Day
A1186

2003, Apr. 11
3213 A1186 €1.85 multi   4.00 2.00

Europa
A1187

2003, Apr. 24
3214 A1187 76c multi   1.75   .85

Atlético de Madrid
Soccer Team,
Cent. — A1188

2003, Apr. 25   *Perf. 14x13¾*
3215 A1188 26c red & blue   .60   .30

Roman
Theater,
Zaragoza
A1189

2003, May 5   *Perf. 13¾x14*
3216 A1189 €1.85 multi   4.25 2.10

European Year of the Disabled A1190

2003, May 8   Photo. & Embossed
3217 A1190 76c multi   1.75   .85

Castles A1191

Designs: 26c, San Felipe Castle, Ferrol. 51c, Cuellar Castle, Segovia. 76c, Montilla Castle, Córdoba.

2003, May 17   Engr.   Perf. 13¾x14
3218-3220 A1191   Set of 3   3.75 1.90

Battles of Ceriñola and Garellano, 500th anniv. (No. 3220).

World Swimming Championships, Barcelona — A1192

2003, May 23   Photo.   Perf. 14x13¾
3221 A1192   Sheet of 5 + label   13.00 6.50
a.   26c Breaststroke   .60   .30
b.   51c Diving   1.25   .60
c.   76c Synchronized swimming   1.75   .85
d.   €1.85 Freestyle   4.25 2.10
e.   €2.15 Water polo   5.00 2.50

Max Aub (1903-72), Writer — A1193

2003, June 2   Engr.
3222 A1193 76c black & red   1.75   .85

Sabadell Soccer Team, Cent. — A1194

2003, June 4   Photo.
3223 A1194 76c multi   1.75   .85

Juan Bravo Murillo (1803-73), Prime Minister — A1195

2003, June 9
3224 A1195 51c multi   1.25   .60

Diario de Cadiz Newspaper, 136th Anniv. — A1196

2003, June 16
3225 A1196 26c multi   .60   .30

Souvenir Sheet

Royal Automobile Club of Spain, Cent. — A1197

2003, June 27   Perf. 13¾x14
3226 A1197   Sheet of 4   7.75 4.00
a.   26c 1967 Dodge Dart Bar-
       reiros   .60   .30
b.   51c 1957-73 Seat 600   1.10   .55
c.   76c 1907 Hispano-Suiza 20/30
       HP   1.75   .85
d.   €1.85 1953 Pegaso Z-102
       Berlinetta   4.25 2.10

Chilean Postage Stamps, 150th Anniv. — A1198

2003, July 1   Photo.   Perf. 14x13¾
3227 A1198 76c Chile Type A1   1.75   .85

El Diario Montañés Newspaper, Cent. — A1199

2003, July 4
3228 A1199 26c multi   .60   .30

Santa Catalina Inn, Jaén — A1200

Illustration reduced.

2003, July 9   Perf. 13x13¼
3229 A1200 76c multi + label   1.75   .85

Diario de Navarra Newspaper, Cent. — A1201

2003, July 11   Perf. 13¾x14
3230 A1201 26c multi   .60   .30

Seu Vella, Lleida, 800th Anniv. A1202

2003, July 22   Engr.   Perf. 13¾x14
3231 A1202 €1.85 pur & brn blk   4.25 2.10

El Adelanto de Salamanca Newspaper, 120th Anniv. — A1203

2003, July 24   Photo.   Perf. 14x13¾
3232 A1203 26c multi   .60   .30

A1204   A1205

A1206   A1207

A1208   A1209

A1210   A1211

Paintings by Alfredo Roldán
A1210   A1211

Die Cut Perf. 13
2003, July 28   Litho.
Self-Adhesive
3233   Booklet pane of 8   5.00
a.   A1204 A multi   .60   .30
b.   A1205 A multi   .60   .30
c.   A1206 A multi   .60   .30
d.   A1207 A multi   .60   .30
e.   A1208 A multi   .60   .30
f.   A1209 A multi   .60   .30
g.   A1210 A multi   .60   .30
h.   A1211 A multi   .60   .30

Nos. 3233a-3233g each sold for 26c on day of issue.

El Correo Gallego Newspaper, 125th Anniv. — A1212

2003, Aug. 1   Photo.   Perf. 13¾x14
3234 A1212 26c multi   .60   .30

El Comercio de Gijón Newspaper, 125th Anniv. — A1213

2003, Sept. 2
3235 A1213 26c multi   .60   .30

Holy Cross of Caravaca A1214

2003, Sept. 4   Perf. 14x13¾
3236 A1214 76c multi   1.75   .85

Holy Year 2003.

World Sailing Championships, Gulf of Cádiz — A1215

2003, Sept. 9   Perf. 13¾x14
3237 A1215 76c multi   1.75   .85

Wine of Penedés Region — A1216

Wine of Montilla-Moriles Region — A1217

Wine of Valdepeñas Region — A1218

Wine of Bierzo Region — A1219

2003   **Perf. 14x13¾**
3238	A1216	26c multi	.60	.30
3239	A1217	51c multi	1.25	.60
3240	A1218	76c multi	1.75	.90
3241	A1219	€1.85 multi	4.50	2.25
	Nos. 3238-3241 (4)		8.10	4.05

Issued: 26c, 10/30; others, 9/22.

Academy of Military Engineering, Bicent. — A1220

2003, Sept. 24   **Perf. 13¾x14**
3242	A1220	51c multi	1.25	.60

Souvenir Sheet

Santa María Cathedral, León, 700th Anniv — A1221

2003, Sept. 26   **Litho. & Engr.**
3243	A1221	76c multi	1.75	.90

Souvenir Sheet

Royal Geographical Society, Cent. — A1222

2003, Oct. 1
3244	A1222	€1.85 multi	4.50	2.25

Trees — A1223

Designs: 26c, Ficus macrophylla. 51c, Quercus rober.

2003, Oct. 3   **Photo.**   **Perf. 14x13¾**
3245-3246	A1223	Set of 2	1.90	.95

School of Aeronautical Engineering, Madrid, 75th Anniv. — A1224

2003, Oct. 6   **Perf. 13¾x14**
3247	A1224	51c multi	1.25	.60

America Issue - Rail Transport A1225

2003, Oct. 14
3248	A1225	76c multi	1.75	.90

El Viejo y el Pájaro, by Luis Seoane — A1226

2003, Oct. 17   **Perf. 14x13¾**
3249	A1226	€1.85 multi	4.50	2.25

El Correo de Andalucia Newspaper, Cent. — A1227

Faro de Vigo Newspaper, 150th Anniv. — A1228

La Voz de Galicia Newspaper, 121st Anniv. — A1229

2003, Nov. 3   **Perf. 13¾x14**
3250	A1227	26c multi	.60	.30
3251	A1228	26c multi	.60	.30
3252	A1229	26c multi	.60	.30
	Nos. 3250-3252 (3)		1.80	.90

Camilo José Cela (1916-2002), 1989 Nobel Laureate in Literature A1230

2003, Nov. 10   **Perf. 14x13¾**
3253	A1230	26c multi	.65	.30

Parade of the Magi — A1231

Nativity, by Raquel Fariñas — A1232

2003, Nov. 10
3254	A1231	26c multi	.65	.30
3255	A1232	51c multi	1.25	.60
	Christmas.			

España 2004 Intl. Philatelic Exhibition A1233

Designs: 76c, Exhibition emblem. €1.85, Exhibition venue, Valencia.

2003, Nov. 14   **Perf. 13¾x14**
3256	A1233	76c multi	1.90	.95

Souvenir Sheet
3257	A1233	€1.85 multi	4.50	2.25

Organos de Montoro A1234

2003, Nov. 17
3258	A1234	51c multi	1.25	.60

Souvenir Sheet

Completion of National Geological Map — A1235

2003, Nov. 24
3259	A1235	26c multi	.65	.30

Souvenir Sheets

Constitution, 25th Anniv. — A1236

Various photos or paintings with inscriptions in lower left corner of: No. 3260, 26c, RCM-FNMT. No. 3261, 26c, Miguel Torner. No. 3262, 26c, R. Seco. No. 3263, 26c, Araceli Alarcón. No. 3264, 26c, Galicia. No. 3265, 26c, Fesanpe. No. 3266, 26c, J. Carrero. No. 3267, 26c, J. Carrero, vert. No. 3268, 26c, Goyo Domínguez, vert. No. 3269, 26c, Juan Bautista Nieto, vert.

2003, Dec. 5   **Perf. 13¾x14, 14x13¾**
3260-3269	A1236	Set of 10	6.50	3.25

Powered Flight, Cent. A1237

2003, Dec. 17   **Engr.**   **Perf. 13¾x14**
3270	A1237	76c blue & brown	1.90	.95

King Juan Carlos Type of 2001 With Euro Denominations Only

2004, Jan. 2   **Photo.**   **Perf. 12¾x13¼**
3271	A1091	2c sil & brt pink	.20	.20
3272	A1091	27c sil & blue	.70	.35
3273	A1091	52c sil & bister brn	1.25	.65
3274	A1091	77c sil & dull grn	1.90	.95
	Nos. 3271-3274 (4)		4.05	2.15

Roman Art of Jaca — A1238

No. 3275: a, Grate. b, Huesca Cathedral Bible page. c, Painting of two apostles. d, Cloister, Monastery of San Juan de la Peña. e, Coins. f, Capital, Church of Santiago de Jaca. g, Detail of sarcophagus of Doña Sancha. h, Wooden carved crucifix.

Serpentine Die Cut 13

2004, Jan. 16   Litho.

Self-Adhesive

3275	Booklet pane of 8		5.50
a.-h.	A1238 A Any single	.65	.35

Nos. 3275a-3275h each sold for 27c on day of issue.

Souvenir Sheets

Paintings of Women Reading by Fabio Hurtado — A1239

No. 3276: a, 27c, Woman reading book in rowboat. b, 52c, Woman with head on hand reading book. c, 77c, Woman reading newspaper.
No. 3277: a, 27c, Woman with legs crossed reading book. b, 52c. Woman on back reading book. c, 77c, Woman with black hat reading book.

2004, Jan. 23   **Photo.**   **Perf. 13¾x14**

Sheets of 3, #a-c, + label

3276-3277	A1239	Set of 2	7.75	4.00

Campaign Against Cancer A1240

2004, Feb. 2

3278	A1240 27c multi	.70	.35

"La Terrona" Oak Tree, Zarza de Montánchez A1241

2004, Feb. 6   **Perf. 14x13¾**

3279	A1241 52c multi	1.40	.70

World Rowing Championships, Banyoles — A1242

2004, Feb. 9   **Perf. 13¾x14**

3280	A1242 77c multi	1.90	.95

School Letter Writing Campaign — A1243

No. 3281 - Scenes from comic strip Trazo de Tiza, by Miguelanxo Prado: a, Woman on cliff. b, Sailboat. c, Woman near injured gull. d, Aerial view of lighthouse.

2004, Feb. 10

3281	A1243 27c Sheet of 4, #a- d, + 12 labels	2.75	1.40

Souvenir Sheet

Santa María de Carracedo Monastery, Bierzo — A1244

2004, Mar. 8   **Perf. 14x13¾**

3282	A1244 €1.90 multi	4.75	2.40

36th Chess Olympiad A1245

2004, Mar. 18   **Perf. 13¾x14**

3283	A1245 77c multi	1.90	.95

Clocks — A1246

No. 3284: a, 27c, Clock with Muse Calliope, 19th cent. b, 52c, Clock with Cupid, 18th cent. c, 77c, Clock with Empress María Luisa, child and harp, 19th cent. d, €1.90, Clock with Venus and Cupid, 18th cent.

Perf. 13¼x12¾

2004, Mar. 31   **Litho. & Engr.**

3284	A1246 Sheet of 4, #a-d	8.50	4.25

SEMI-POSTAL STAMPS

Red Cross Issue

Princesses María Cristina and Beatrice SP1

Queen as a Nurse — SP2   Queen Victoria Eugénia — SP3

Prince of Asturias — SP4   King Alfonso XIII — SP5

Perf. 12½

1926, Sept. 15   **Unwmk.**   **Engr.**

B1	SP1	1c black	1.90	1.90
B2	SP2	2c ultra	1.90	1.90
B3	SP3	5c violet brn	4.25	3.25
B4	SP4	10c green	3.50	3.25
B5	SP1	15c indigo	1.40	1.25
B6	SP4	20c dull violet	1.40	1.25
a.		20c violet brown (error)	500.00	325.00
B7	SP5	25c rose red	.25	.25
B8	SP1	30c blue green	32.50	32.50
B9	SP3	40c dark blue	19.00	17.50
B10	SP2	50c red orange	19.00	17.00
B11	SP4	1p slate	1.40	.90
B12	SP3	4p magenta	1.10	.65
B13	SP5	10p brown	1.10	.90
		Nos. B1-B13,EB1 (14)	97.45	91.25
		Set, never hinged	160.00	

The 20c was printed in violet brown for use in the colonies (Cape Juby, Spanish Guinea, Spanish Morocco and Spanish Sahara). No. B6a, the missing overprint error, is listed here because it is not known to which colony it belongs.

For overprints see Nos. B19-B46.

Airplane and Map of Madrid-Manila Flight — SP6

1926, Sept. 15

B14	SP6	15c dp ultra & org	.30	.30
B15	SP6	20c car & yel grn	.30	.30
B16	SP6	30c dk brn & ultra	.30	.30
B17	SP6	40c dk grn & brn org	.30	.30
B18	SP6	4p magenta & yel	82.50	82.50
		Nos. B14-B18,CB1-CB5 (10)	91.20	91.20
		Set, never hinged	150.00	

Madrid to Manila flight of Captains Eduardo G. Gallarza and Joaquim Loriga y Taboada.

Nos. B1-B18, CB1-CB5 and EB1 were used for regular postage on Sept. 15, 16, 17, 1926. Subsequently the unsold stamps were given to the Spanish Red Cross Society, by which they were sold uncanceled but they then had no franking power.

For overprints see Nos. B47-B53.

Coronation Silver Jubilee Issue

Red Cross Stamps of 1926 Overprinted "ALFONSO XIII," Dates and Ornaments in Various Colors

1927, May 27

B19	SP1	1c black (R)	4.50	4.00
B20	SP2	2c ultra (Bl)	7.75	7.75
B21	SP3	5c vio brn (R)	1.90	1.90
a.		Double overprint	37.50	
B22	SP4	10c green (Bl)	55.00	55.00
B23	SP1	15c indigo (R)	1.60	1.60
B24	SP4	20c dull vio (Bl)	3.00	3.00
B25	SP5	25c rose red (Bl)	.45	.45
B26	SP1	30c blue grn (Bl)	.85	.85
B27	SP3	40c dk blue (R)	.85	.85
B28	SP2	50c red org (Bl)	.85	.85
B29	SP4	1p slate (R)	1.60	1.60
B30	SP3	4p magenta (R)	8.25	8.25
B31	SP5	10p brown (G)	32.50	32.50
		Nos. B19-B31 (13)	119.10	118.60
		Set, never hinged	200.00	

Same with Additional Surcharges of New Values

B32	SP2	3c on 2c (G)	9.50	9.50
B33	SP2	4c on 2c (Bk)	9.50	9.50
B34	SP5	10c on 25c (Bk)	.55	.55
B35	SP5	25c on 25c (Bl)	.55	.55
B36	SP2	55c on 2c (R)	1.00	1.00
B37	SP4	55c on 10c (Bk)	55.00	55.00
B38	SP4	55c on 20c (Bk)	55.00	55.00
B39	SP1	75c on 15c (R)	.70	.70
B40	SP1	75c on 30c (R)	140.00	140.00
B41	SP3	80c on 25c (R)	52.50	50.00
B42	SP4	2p on 40c (R)	1.00	1.00
B43	SP4	2p on 1p (R)	1.00	1.00
B44	SP2	5p on 50c (R)	1.90	1.90
B45	SP3	5p on 4p (Bk)	3.25	3.25
B46	SP5	10p on 10p (G)	27.50	27.50
		Nos. B32-B46 (15)	358.95	356.45
		Set, never hinged	550.00	

Nos. B14-B18 Overprinted

B47	SP6	15c (Br)	.40	.40
a.		Double overprint	30.00	
B48	SP6	20c (Bl)	.40	.40
a.		Brown overprint (error)	65.00	
b.		Inverted overprint	30.00	
B50	SP6	30c (R)	.40	.40
a.		Blue overprint (error)	65.00	
b.		Double overprint	30.00	
B52	SP6	40c (Br)	.40	.40
a.		Inverted overprint	30.00	
b.		Double ovpt. (Bl + Br)	95.00	
B53	SP6	4p (Bl)	95.00	95.00
a.		Inverted overprint	160.00	

Semi-Postal Special Delivery Stamp

Overprinted "ALFONSO XIII," Dates and Ornaments in Violet

B54	SPSD1 20c	5.50	5.50
	Nos. B47-B54 (6)	102.10	102.10

Nos. CB1-CB5 Overprinted in Various Colors

B55	SPAP1	5c (R)	1.90	1.60
a.		Inverted overprint	30.00	
B56	SPAP1	10c (R)	2.25	2.25
a.		Inverted overprint	30.00	
B57	SPAP1	25c (Bl)	.40	.40
B58	SPAP1	50c (Bl)	.40	.40
a.		Double ovpt., one invtd.	72.50	
B59	SPAP1	1p (R)	2.50	2.50
a.		Inverted overprint	95.00	

Same with Additional Surcharges of New Values

B60	SPAP1	75c on 5c (R)	4.50	3.25
a.		Inverted surcharge	30.00	
B61	SPAP1	75c on 10c (R)	17.00	13.00
a.		Inverted surcharge	30.00	
B62	SPAP1	75c on 25c (Bl)	32.50	27.50
a.		Double surcharge	55.00	
B63	SPAP1	75c on 50c (Bl)	15.00	13.00
		Nos. B55-B63 (9)	76.45	63.90
		Set, never hinged	190.00	

Nos. B54-B63 were available for ordinary postage.

Stamps of Spanish Offices in Morocco and Spanish Colonies, 1926 (Spain Types SP3, SP5) Surcharged in Various Colors with New Values and

On Spanish Morocco

B64	SP3	55c on 4p bis (Bl)	17.50	17.50
B65	SP5	80c on 10p vio (Br)	17.50	17.50

On Spanish Tangier

B66	SP5	1p on 10p vio	90.00	90.00
B67	SP3	4p bis (G)	32.50	32.50

On Cape Juby

B68	SP5	5p on 4p bis (R)	57.50	57.50
B69	SP5	10p on 4p bis vio (R)	32.50	32.50

On Spanish Guinea

B70	SP5	1p on 10p vio (Bl)	17.50	17.50
B71	SP3	2p on 10p vio (G)	17.50	17.50

On Spanish Sahara

B72	SP5	80c on 10p vio (R)	27.50	27.50
B73	SP3	2p on 4p bis (G)	17.50	17.50
Nos. B64-B73 (10)			327.50	327.50
Set, never hinged			600.00	

Nos. B64-B73 were available for postage in Spain only.

Nos. B19-B73 were for the 25th year of the reign of King Alfonso XIII.

Counterfeits of Nos. B64-B73 abound.

Catacombs Restoration Issues

Pope Pius XI and King Alfonso XIII SP7

1928, Dec. 23   Engr.   Perf. 12½
Santiago Issue

B74	SP7	2c violet & blk	.25	.25
B75	SP7	2c lake & blk	.30	.30
B76	SP7	3c bl blk & vio	.25	.25
B77	SP7	3c dl bl & vio	.30	.30
B78	SP7	5c ol grn & vio	.65	.65
B79	SP7	10c yel grn & blk	1.10	1.10
B80	SP7	15c bl grn & vio	3.75	3.75
B81	SP7	25c dp rose & vio	3.75	3.75
B82	SP7	40c ultra & blk	.25	.25
B83	SP7	55c ol brn & vio	.25	.25
B84	SP7	80c red & blk	.25	.25
B85	SP7	1p gray blk & vio	.25	.25
B86	SP7	2p red brn & blk	5.25	5.25
B87	SP7	3p pale rose & vio	5.25	5.25
B88	SP7	4p vio brn & blk	5.25	5.25
B89	SP7	5p grnsh blk & vio	5.25	5.25

Toledo Issue

B90	SP7	2c bl blk & car	.25	.25
B91	SP7	2c ultra & car	.30	.30
B92	SP7	3c bis brn & ul-tra	.25	.25
B93	SP7	3c ol grn & ultra	.30	.30
B94	SP7	5c red vio & car	.65	.65
B95	SP7	10c yel grn & ul-tra	1.10	1.10
B96	SP7	15c slate bl & car	3.75	3.75
B97	SP7	25c red brn & ul-tra	3.75	3.75
B98	SP7	40c ultra & car	.25	.25
B99	SP7	55c dk brn & ultra	.25	.25
B100	SP7	80c black & car	.25	.25
B101	SP7	1p yellow & car	.25	.25
B102	SP7	2p dk gray & ul-tra	5.25	5.25
B103	SP7	3p violet & car	5.25	5.25
B104	SP7	4p vio brn & car	5.25	5.25
B105	SP7	5p bister & ultra	5.25	5.25
Nos. B74-B105 (32)			64.70	64.70
Set, never hinged			100.00	

Nos. B74-B105 replaced regular stamps from Dec. 23, 1928 to Jan. 6, 1929. The proceeds from their sale were given to a fund to restore the catacombs of Saint Damasus and Saint Praetextatus at Rome.

Nos. B74-B105 exist imperforate. Value set, $325 hinged, $375 never hinged.

Issues of the Republic

SP13

1938, Apr. 15   Perf. 11½

B106	SP13	45c + 2p bl & grnsh bl	.75	.65
a.		Imperf., pair	12.50	12.50
b.		Souv. sheet of 1	22.50	22.50
c.		Souv. sheet of 1, imperf.	525.00	525.00
		Never hinged	700.00	

Surtax for the defenders of Madrid.

For overprint and surcharge see Nos. B108, CB6.

Nurse and Orderly Carrying Wounded Soldier — SP14

1938, June 1   Engr.   Perf. 10

B107	SP14	45c + 5p cop red	.55	.55
a.		Imperf., pair	200.00	

For surcharge see No. CB7.

No. B106 Overprinted in Black

1938, Nov. 7   Perf. 11½

B108	SP13	45c + 2p	3.25	3.25
		Never hinged	5.00	

Defense of Madrid, 2nd anniversary. A similar but larger overprint was applied to cover blocks of four. Value never hinged, $30.

Values for souvenir sheets of 1937-38 are for copies with some faults. Undamaged sheets are very hard to find.

Spanish State
Souvenir Sheets

Alcazar, Toledo SP15

Design: No. B108C, A patio of Alcazar after Civil War fighting.

1937   Unwmk.   Photo.   Perf. 11½
Control Numbers on Back

B108A	SP15	2p org brn	19.00	19.00
b.		Imperf.	400.00	400.00
B108C	SP15	2p dark green	19.00	19.00
d.		Imperf.	400.00	400.00
		Set, never hinged	82.50	
		Set, B108Ab, B108Cd, never hinged	950.00	

Nos. B108A-B108C sold for 4p each.

SP16

Designs: 20c, Covadongas Cathedral. 30c, Palma Cathedral, Majorca. 50c, Alcazar of Segovia. 1p, Leon Cathedral.

1938   Unwmk.   Photo.   Perf. 12½
Control Numbers on Back

B108E	SP16	Sheet of 4	37.50	37.50
f.		20c dull violet	5.00	5.00
g.		30c rose red	5.00	5.00
h.		50c bright blue	5.00	5.00
i.		1p greenish gray	5.00	5.00
j.		Imperf. sheet	65.00	65.00
		Never hinged	100.00	

Each sheet sold for 4p.

SP17

Designs, alternating in sheet: Flag bearer. Battleship "Admiral Cervera." Soldiers in trenches. Moorish guard.

1938, July 1   Unwmk.   Perf. 13
Control Numbers on Back

B108K	SP17	Sheet of 20	32.50	32.50
		Never hinged	42.50	
l.		Imperf. sheet	150.00	150.00
		Never hinged	210.00	

Sheet measures 175x132mm. Consists of five vertical rows of four 2c violet, 3c deep blue, 5c olive gray, 10c deep green and 30c red orange, with each denomination appearing in two different designs. Marginal inscription: "Homenaje al Ejercito y a la Marina" (Honoring the Army and Navy). Sold for 4p, or double face value.

Souvenir Sheets

Don Juan of Austria — SP18

Battle of Lepanto SP19

Perf. 12½
1938, Dec. 15   Unwmk.   Engr.
Control Numbers on Back

B108M	SP18	30c dk car	22.50	22.50
B108N	SP19	50c blue black	22.50	22.50
Nos. B108M-B108N (2)			45.00	45.00
		Set, never hinged	77.50	

Imperf

B108O	SP18	30c black vio	550.00	550.00
B108P	SP19	50c dk sl grn	550.00	550.00
Nos. B108O-B108P (2)			1,100.	1,100.
		Set, never hinged	1,300.	

Victory over the Turks in the Battle of Lepanto, 1571.

Nos. B108M-B108P contain one stamp. The dates "1571-1938" appear in the lower sheet margin. Size: 89x74mm. Sold for 10p a pair.

LOCAL CHARITY STAMPS
Hundreds of different charity stamps were issued by local organizations and cities during the Civil War, 1936-39. Some had limited franking value, but most were simply charity labels. They are of three kinds: 1. Local semipostals. 2. Obligatory surtax stamps. 3. Propaganda or charity labels.

Ruins of Belchite SP20

Miracle of Calanda — SP21

Designs: 10c+5c, 70c+20c, Ruins of Belchite. 15c+10c, 80c+20c, The Rosary. 20c+10c, 1.50p+50c, El Pilar Cathedral. 25c+10c, 1p+30c, Mother Raffols praying. 40c+10c, 2.50p+50c, The Little Chamber. 45c+15c, 1.40p+40c, Oath of the Besieged. 10p+4p, The Apparition.

Perf. 10½, 11½x10½, 11½
1940, Jan. 29   Litho.   Unwmk.
Design SP20

B109	10c + 5c dp bl & vio brn		.20	.20
B110	15c + 10c rose vio & dk grn		.25	.25
B111	20c + 10c vio & dp bl		.25	.25
B112	25c + 10c dp rose & vio brn		.25	.25
B113	40c + 10c sl grn & rose vio		.20	.20
B114	45c + 15c vio & dp rose		.30	.30
B115	70c + 20c multi		.30	.30
B116	80c + 20c dp rose & vio		.40	.40
B117	1p + 30c dk sl grn & pur		.40	.40
B118	1.40p + 40c pur & gray blk		32.50	32.50
B119	1.50p + 50c lt bl & brn vio		.50	.50
B120	2.50p + 50c choc & bl		.50	.50

Design SP21

B121	4p + 1p rose lil & sl grn		11.00	11.00
B122	10p + 4p ultra & chnt		160.00	160.00
Nos. B109-B122,CB8-CB17,EB2 (25)			444.35	444.25
	Set, never hinged		700.00	

19th centenary of the Virgin of the Pillar. The surtax was used to help restore the Cathedral at Zaragoza, damaged during the Civil War.

No. B121 exists in violet & slate green, No. B122 in ultramarine & brown violet. Value, $42.50 each.

Nos. B109-B122 exist imperf. Value, $750. See No. 743, CB8-CB17.

General Franco — SP23

Knight and Lorraine Cross — SP24

1940, Dec. 23   Unwmk.   _Perf. 10_
B123 SP23 20c + 5c dk grn & red   .65 .65
B124 SP23 40c + 10c dk bl & red   .90 .40
Set, never hinged   3.00

The surtax was for the tuberculosis fund.
See Nos. RA15, RAC1.

Stamps of 10c denomination, types
SP23 to SP28, are postal tax issues.

1941, Dec. 23
B125 SP24 20c + 5c bl vio & red   .50 .30
B126 SP24 40c + 10c sl grn &
                    red   .50 .25
Set, never hinged   1.25

The surtax was used to fight tuberculosis.
See Nos. RA16, RAC2.

Cross of Lorraine
SP25   SP26

1942, Dec. 23   Litho.
B127 SP25 20c + 5c pale brn &
                    rose red   1.40 1.25
B128 SP25 40c + 10c lt bluish
                    grn & rose red .80 .45
Set, never hinged   3.25

The surtax was used to fight tuberculosis.
See Nos. RA17, RAC3.

1943, Dec. 23   Photo.   _Perf. 11½_
B129 SP26 20c + 5c dl sl grn
                    & dl red   3.25 1.40
B130 SP26 40c + 10c brt bl &
                    dl red   2.00 1.10
Set, never hinged   10.00

The surtax was used to fight tuberculosis.
See Nos. RA18, RAC4.

Dragon   St. George
Slaying — SP27   Slaying the
                     Dragon — SP28

Perf. 9½x10

1944, Dec. 23   Unwmk.
B131 SP27 20c + 5c sl grn &
                    red   .25 .25
B132 SP27 40c + 10c dl vio &
                    red   .50 .50
B133 SP27 80c + 10c ultra &
                    rose   7.75 7.75
        Nos. B131-B133 (3)   8.50 8.50
Set, never hinged   13.00

The surtax was used to fight tuberculosis.
See Nos. RA19, RAC5.

1945, Dec. 23
Lorraine Cross in Red
B134 SP28 20c + 5c dl gray
                    grn   .25 .20
B135 SP28 40c + 10c vio   .30 .20
B136 SP28 80c + 10c ultra   8.00 7.50
        Nos. B134-B136 (3)   8.55 7.90
Set, never hinged   12.50

The surtax was used to fight tuberculosis.
See Nos. RA20, RAC6.

Nos. 753 and 768
Surcharged in Blue

1950, Oct. 23
B137 A195 50c + 10c   32.50 32.50
    a. "Caudillo" 14¾mm wide 95.00 97.50

B138 A195 1p + 10c   32.50 32.50
    a. "Caudillo" 14¾mm wide 95.00 97.50
Set, never hinged   100.00
    a   #B137a-B138a, never
                hinged   225.00

Visit of General Franco to Canary Islands.
First printing, brighter colors and pale blue
surcharge, was issued in Canary Islands.
Value, $200 hinged, $250 never hinged, $200
used. Second printing was issued in Madrid
Feb. 22, 1951. See No. CB18.

> **Catalogue values for unused
> stamps in this section, from this
> point to the end of the section, are
> for Never Hinged items.**

1992
Summer
Olympics,
Barcelona '92
SP29

1988, Oct. 3   Photo.   _Perf. 14_
B139 SP29 20p +5p Track and
                    field   .35 .35
B140 SP29 45p +5p Badminton   .60 .60
B141 SP29 50p +5p Basketball   .70 .70
        Nos. B139-B141 (3)   1.65 1.65

See Nos. B146-B152, B163-B168, B177-
B179, B184-B186, B191-B193.

EXPO '92,
Seville — SP30

Globes and sites of previous exhibitions: No.
B142, Crystal Palace, London, 1851. No.
B143, Eiffel Tower, Paris, 1889. No. B144,
"The Atom," Brussels, 1958. No. B145, Monu-
ment, Osaka, 1970.

1989, Feb. 9   Photo.   _Perf. 14x13½_
B142 SP30 8p +5p multi   .20 .20
B143 SP30 8p +5p multi   .20 .20
B144 SP30 20p +5p multi   .30 .30
B145 SP30 20p +5p multi   .30 .30
        Nos. B142-B145 (4)   1.00 1.00

1992 Summer Olympics Type of 1988
1989, Mar. 7   Photo.   _Perf. 14_
B146 SP29 8p +5p Handball   .25 .25
B147 SP29 18p +5p Boxing   .35 .35
B148 SP29 20p +5p Cycling   .35 .35
B149 SP29 45p +5p Equestrian   .60 .60
        Nos. B146-B149 (4)   1.55 1.55

1989, Oct. 3   Photo.   _Perf. 13½x14_
B150 SP29 18p +5p Fencing   .65 .65
B151 SP29 20p +5p Soccer   .65 .65
B152 SP29 45p +5p Pommel
                    horse   1.25 1.25
        Nos. B150-B152 (3)   2.55 2.55

500th Anniv. Emblem and Produce or
Fauna Indigenous to the
Americas — SP31

1989, Oct. 16 Litho. _Perf. 13x13½_
B153 SP31 8p +5p Cocoa   .20 .20
B154 SP31 8p +5p Corn   .20 .20
B155 SP31 20p +5p Tomato   .30 .30
B156 SP31 20p +5p Horse   .30 .30
B157 SP31 50p +5p Potato   .60 .60
B158 SP31 50p +5p Turkey   .60 .60
    a. Bkt. pane of 6, #B153-B158 2.25
        Nos. B153-B158 (6)   2.20 2.20

Discovery of America, 500th anniv.

EXPO '92,
Seville
SP32

Curro, the character trademark, and symbols of development in Spain.

1990, Feb. 22   Photo.   _Perf. 14_
B159 SP32 8p +5p multi   .20 .20
B160 SP32 20p +5p multi, diff.   .30 .30
B161 SP32 45p +5p multi, diff.   .60 .60
B162 SP32 50p +5p multi, diff.   .70 .70
        Nos. B159-B162 (4)   1.80 1.80

1992 Summer Olympics Type of 1988
1990, Mar. 7   Photo.   _Perf. 13½x14_
B163 SP29 18p +5p Weight lifting .30 .30
B164 SP29 20p +5p Field hockey   .30 .30
B165 SP29 45p +5p Judo   .55 .55
        Nos. B163-B165 (3)   1.15 1.15

1990, Oct. 3   Photo.   _Perf. 13½x14_
B166 SP29 8p +5p Wrestling   .20 .20
B167 SP29 18p +5p Swimming   .40 .40
B168 SP29 20p +5p Baseball   .50 .50
        Nos. B166-B168 (3)   1.10 1.10

Discovery of America, 500th Anniv. (in
1992) — SP33

Drawings of sailing ships.

1990, Oct. 15   Litho.   _Perf. 13_
B169 SP33 8p +5p "Viajes-A"   .20 .20
B170 SP33 8p +5p "Viajes-B"   .20 .20
B171 SP33 20p +5p "Viajes-C"   .30 .30
B172 SP33 20p +5p "Viajes-D"   .30 .30
    a. Bkt. pane of 4, #B169-B172 1.00
        Nos. B169-B172 (4)   1.00 1.00

Expo '92,
Seville
SP34

Designs: 15p+5p, La Cartuja, Monastery of
Santa Maria de las Cuevas. 25p+5p, Amphi-
theater. 45p+5p, La Cartuja Bridge. 55p+5p,
La Bargueta Bridge.

Litho. & Engr.
1991, Feb. 12   _Perf. 14_
B173 SP34 15p +5p multi   .30 .30
B174 SP34 25p +5p multi   .40 .40
B175 SP34 45p +5p multi   .65 .65
B176 SP34 55p +5p multi   .80 .80
        Nos. B173-B176 (4)   2.15 2.15

Summer Olympics Type of 1988
1991, Mar. 7   Litho.   _Perf. 13½x14_
B177 SP29 15p + 5p Five ath-
                    letes   .30 .30
B178 SP29 25p + 5p Kayaking   .40 .40
B179 SP29 45p + 5p Rowing   .65 .65
        Nos. B177-B179 (3)   1.35 1.35

Madrid,
European
City of
Culture,
1992
SP35

Designs: 15p+5p, Fountain of Apollo.
25p+5p, Statue of Alvaro de Bazan. 45p+5p,
Bank of Spain. 55p+5p, St. Isidore's Institute.

1991, July 29   Photo.   _Perf. 13½x14_
B180 SP35 15p + 5p multi   .30 .30
B181 SP35 25p + 5p multi   .40 .40
B182 SP35 45p + 5p multi   .60 .60
B183 SP35 55p + 5p multi   .75 .75
        Nos. B180-B183 (4)   2.05 2.05

1992 Summer Olympics Type of 1988
1991, Oct. 3   Litho.   _Perf. 14_
B184 SP29 15p +5p Tennis   .45 .45
B185 SP29 25p +5p Table tennis .60 .60
B186 SP29 55p +5p Shooting   1.25 1.25
        Nos. B184-B186 (3)   2.30 2.30

Discovery of America, 500th Anniv.,
1992 — SP36

15p+5p, Garcilaso Gomez Suarez de Figueroa, the Inca, poet. 25p+5p, Pope Alexander
VI. 45p+5p, Luis de Santangel, banker.
55p+5p, Friar Toribio de Paredes, monk.

1991, Oct. 15   Photo.   _Perf. 13x13½_
B187 SP36 15p +5p multi   .30 .30
B188 SP36 25p +5p multi   .40 .40
B189 SP36 45p +5p multi   .60 .60
B190 SP36 55p +5p multi   .75 .75
    a. Bkt. pane of 4, #B187-B190 2.00
        Nos. B187-B190 (4)   2.05 2.05

1992 Summer Olympics Type of 1988
1992, Mar. 6   Photo.   _Perf. 13½x14_
B191 SP29 15p +5p Archery   .40 .40
B192 SP29 25p +5p Sailing   .55 .55
B193 SP29 55p +5p Volleyball   1.10 1.10
        Nos. B191-B193 (3)   2.05 2.05

Columbus Type of 1930
Souvenir Sheet
1992, Mar. 31   Engr.   _Perf. 14_
B194   Sheet of 3   1.00 1.00
    a. A65 17p +5p dark red   .30 .30
    b. A65 17p +5p ultramarine .30 .30
    c. A65 17p +5p black   .30 .30

Discovery of America, 500th anniv.

Expo '92 Type
Design: No. B195, Seville, 16th cent.

1992, Apr. 21   Litho.   _Perf. 13½x14_
Souvenir Sheet
B195 A837 17p +5p multi   .35 .35

1992 Summer
Olympics,
Barcelona — SP37

Perf. 14x13½, 13½x14
1992, July 16   Photo.
B196 SP37 17p +5p Mascot
                    COBI   .40 .40
B197 SP37 17p +5p Hand hold-
                    ing torch, horiz. .40 .40
B198 SP37 17p +5p "25 Jul"   .40 .40
        Nos. B196-B198 (3)   1.20 1.20

1992
Summer
Olympics,
Barcelona
SP38

Designs: a, Olympic Stadium. b, San Jordi
Sports Palace. c, INEF Sports University.

1992, July 25   _Perf. 13½x14_
B199 SP38 27p +5p Triptych,
                    #a.-c.   1.40 1.40

1992 Summer Olympics, Barcelona
SP39   SP40

#B200, Olympic mascot as stamp collector.
#B201, Sagrada Family Church, Barcelona.

1992, July 29   Photo.   Perf. 14x13½
B200 SP39 17p +5p multi   .35   .35
B201 SP40 17p +5p multi   .35   .35

Olymphilex '92 (#B201).

Madrid, European
City of
Culture — SP41

#B202, Municipal Museum. #B203, Royal
Theater. #B204, The Prado Museum. #B205,
Queen Sofia Natl. Center for the Arts.

1992, Nov. 24   Photo.   Perf. 14x13½
B202 SP41 17p +5p multi   .35   .30
B203 SP41 17p +5p multi   .35   .30
B204 SP41 17p +5p multi   .35   .30
B205 SP41 17p +5p multi   .35   .30
    Nos. B202-B205 (4)   1.40   1.20

AIR POST STAMPS

Regular Issue of 1909-
10 Overprinted in Red
or Black

Perf. 13x12½, 14
1920, Apr. 4   Unwmk.
C1 A46 5c green (R)   1.10   .70
  a. Imperf., pair   95.00   95.00
  b. Double overprint   32.50   32.50
  c. Inverted overprint   82.50   82.50
  d. Double ovpt., one invtd. 32.50 27.50
  e. Triple overprint   32.50   27.50
C2 A46 10c car (Bk)   1.40   .90
  a. Imperf., pair   95.00   95.00
  b. Double overprint   32.50   32.50
  d. Double ovpt., one invtd. 32.50 27.50
C3 A46 25c dp blue (R)   2.25   1.25
  a. Inverted overprint   82.50   82.50
  b. Double overprint   32.50   32.50
C4 A46 50c sl blue (R)   10.00   4.50
  a. Imperf., pair   95.00   95.00
C5 A46 1p lake (Bk)   32.50   17.00
  a. Imperf., pair   350.00 350.00
    Nos. C1-C5 (5)   47.25   24.35
    Set, never hinged   87.50

Dangerous counterfeits are plentiful.
A 30c green was authorized, but not issued.
Value, $550.
For overprints see Nos. C58-C61.

"Spirit of St.
Louis" over Coast
of Europe — AP1

Plane and
Congress
Seal — AP2

Seville-Barcelona Exposition Issue
Control Numbers on Back
1929, Feb. 15   Engr.   Perf. 11
C6 AP1 5c brown   5.00   5.00
C7 AP1 10c rose   5.00   5.00
C8 AP1 25c dark blue   5.50   5.50
C9 AP1 50c purple   5.75   5.75
C10 AP1 1p green   30.00   25.00
C11 AP1 4p black   21.00   20.00
    Nos. C6-C11 (6)   72.25   66.25
    Set, never hinged   150.00

Nos. C6 to C11 exist imperforate. Value,
$575.

The so-called errors of color of Nos.
C10, C18-C21, C23-C24, C28-C31,
C37, C40, C42, C44, C46, C48, C50,
C52, C55, C62-C67 are believed to
have been irregularly produced.

Railway Congress Issue
Control Numbers on Back
1930, May 10   Litho.   Perf. 14
C12 AP2 5c bister brn   4.75   4.75
C13 AP2 10c rose   4.75   4.75
C14 AP2 25c dark blue   4.75   4.75
C15 AP2 50c purple   12.00   12.00
  a. Vert. pair, imperf. between 300.00
      Never hinged   600.00
C16 AP2 1p yellow green   25.00   25.00
C17 AP2 4p black   25.00   25.00
    Nos. C12-C17 (6)   76.25   76.25
    Set, never hinged   150.00

The note after No. 385 will apply here also.
Dangerous counterfeits exist.

Goya Issue

Fantasy of
Flight
AP3

Asmodeus and
Cleofas — AP4

Fantasy of
Flight
AP5

Fantasy of
Flight — AP6

1930, June 15   Engr.   Perf. 12½
C18 AP3 5c brn red & yel   .20   .20
C19 AP3 15c blk & red org   .20   .20
C20 AP3 25c brn car & dp red .20   .20
C21 AP4 5c ol grn & grnsh
                bl   .20   .20
C22 AP4 10c sl grn & yel grn .20   .20
C23 AP4 20c ultra & rose red .20   .20
C24 AP4 40c vio bl & lt bl   .30   .30
C25 AP5 30c brown & vio   .30   .30
C26 AP5 50c ver & grn   .30   .30
C27 AP5 4p brn car & blk   2.10   2.10
C28 AP6 1p vio brn & vio   .30   .30
C29 AP6 4p bl blk & sl grn 2.10   2.10
C30 AP6 10p blk brn & bis brn 7.75 7.75
    Nos. C18-C30,CE1 (14)   14.55 14.55
    Set, never hinged   22.50

Exist imperf. Value, set $150.

Christopher Columbus Issue

La Rábida Monastery — AP7

Martín Alonso
Pinzón — AP8

Vicente Yanez
Pinzón — AP9

Columbus in His Cabin — AP10

1930, Sept. 29   Litho.
C31 AP7 5c lt red brn   .25   .20
C32 AP7 5c olive bister   .25   .20
C33 AP7 10c blue green   .25   .20
C34 AP7 15c dark violet   .25   .20
C35 AP7 20c ultra   .25   .20
                Engr.
C36 AP8 25c carmine rose   .25   .20
C37 AP9 30c dp red brn   1.75   1.75
C38 AP8 40c indigo   1.75   1.75
C39 AP9 50c orange   1.75   1.75
C40 AP8 1p dull violet   1.75   1.75
C41 AP10 4p olive green   1.75   1.75
C42 AP10 10p light brown   10.00 11.00
    Nos. C31-C42 (12)   20.25 20.95
    Set, never hinged   30.00

Exist imperf. Value, set $190.

Spanish-American Issue

AP11

Columbus
AP12

Columbus
and Pinzón
Brothers
AP13

1930, Sept. 29   Litho.
C43 AP11 5c lt red   .20   .20

C44 AP11 10c dull green   .20   .20
                Engr.
C45 AP12 25c scarlet   .20   .20
C46 AP12 50c slate gray   2.25   1.90
C47 AP12 1p fawn   2.25   1.90
C48 AP13 4p slate blue   2.25   1.90
C49 AP13 10p brown violet   10.00   9.25
    Nos. C43-C49 (7)   17.35 15.55
    Set, never hinged   27.50

Exist imperf. Value, set $160.

Spanish-American Exhibition Issue

Santos-Dumont and First Flight of His
Airplane — AP14

Teodoro
Fels and
His
Airplane
AP15

Dagoberto Godoy and Pass over
Andes — AP16

Sacadura
Cabral
and Gago
Coutinho
and Their
Airplane
AP17

Sidar of Mexico
and Map of
South
America — AP18

Ignacio Jiménez
and Francisco
Iglesias — AP19

Charles A.
Lindbergh,
Statue of
Liberty,
Spirit of
St. Louis
and Cat
AP20

Santa
Maria,
Plane and
Torre del
Oro,
Seville
AP21

1930, Oct. 10   Photo.   Perf. 14

C50	AP14	5c gray black	.65	.45
C51	AP15	10c dk olive grn	.65	.45
C52	AP16	25c ultra	.65	.45
C53	AP17	50c blue gray	1.40	1.10
C54	AP18	50c black	1.40	1.10
C55	AP19	1p car lake	3.00	2.25
a.		1p brown violet	87.50	55.00
		Never hinged	125.00	
C56	AP20	1p deep green	3.00	2.25
C57	AP21	4p slate blue	6.00	4.50
		Nos. C50-C57 (8)	16.75	12.55
		Set, never hinged	60.00	

Exist imperf. Value, set $110.
Note after No. 432 also applies to Nos. C31-C57.

Reprints of Nos. C50-C57 have blurred impressions, yellowish paper. Value: one-tenth of originals.

Nos. C1-C4
Overprinted in Red or
Black

1931   Perf. 13x12½

C58	A46	5c green (R)	11.00	10.00
C59	A46	10c carmine (Bk)	11.00	10.00
C60	A46	25c deep blue (R)	15.00	14.50
C61	A46	50c slate blue (R)	30.00	22.50
		Nos. C58-C61 (4)	67.00	57.00
		Set, never hinged	140.00	

Counterfeits of overprint exist.
The status of Nos. C58-C61 has been questioned.

Plane
and
Royal
Palace,
Madrid
AP22

Madrid
Post
Office
and
Cibeles
Fountain
AP23

Plane
over
Calle de
Alcalá,
Madrid
AP24

1931, Oct. 10   Engr.   Perf. 12

C62	AP22	5c brown violet	.20	.30
C63	AP22	10c deep green	.20	.30
C64	AP22	25c dull red	.20	.30
C65	AP23	50c deep blue	.40	.45
C66	AP23	1p deep violet	.60	.55
C67	AP24	4p black	7.75	10.00
		Nos. C62-C67 (6)	9.35	11.90
		Set, never hinged	13.00	

3rd Pan-American Postal Union Congress, Madrid.
Exist imperf. Value, set $45.
For overprints see Nos. CO1-CO6.

Montserrat Issue

Plane over
Montserrat
Pass — AP25

1931, Dec. 9   Perf. 11½
Control Number on Back

C68	AP25	5c black brown	.50	.50
C69	AP25	10c yellow green	2.25	2.25
C70	AP25	25c deep rose	9.00	9.00

C71	AP25	50c orange	32.50	32.50
C72	AP25	1p gray black	22.50	22.50
		Nos. C68-C72 (5)	66.75	66.75
		Set, never hinged	85.00	

Perf. 14

C68a	AP25	5c	6.75	13.00
C69a	AP25	10c	37.50	40.00
C70a	AP25	25c	67.50	67.50
C71a	AP25	50c	67.50	67.50
C72f	AP25	1p	67.50	67.50
		Nos. C68a-C72f (5)	246.75	255.50
		Set, never hinged	275.00	

900th anniv. of Montserrat Monastery.
Nos. C68-C72 exist imperf. Value, $525.

Autogiro over
Seville — AP26

1935-39   Perf. 11½

C72A	AP26	2p gray blue	20.00	4.50
g.		Imperf., pair	250.00	

Re-engraved

C72B	AP26	2p dk blue ('38)	.65	.25
c.		Imperf., pair	20.00	
d.		Perf. 10 ('39)	1.50	1.10
		Set, #C72A-C72B, never hinged	42.50	

The sky has heavy horizontal lines of shading. Entire design is more heavily shaded than No. C72A.
No. C72B exists privately perforated 14. Value, $9 unused, $9 used.
For overprints see Nos. 7LC14, 7LC19, 14L26.

Eagle and Newspapers — AP27

Press Building,
Madrid — AP28

Don Quixote and Sancho Panza Flying
on the Wooden Horse — AP29

Design: 15c, 30c, 50c, 1p, Autogiro over House of Nazareth.

1936, Mar. 11   Photo.   Perf. 12½

C73	AP27	1c rose car	.20	.20
C74	AP28	2c dark brown	.20	.20
C75	AP27	5c black brown	.20	.20
C76	AP28	10c dk yellow grn	.20	.20
C77	AP28	15c Prus blue	.20	.20
C78	AP27	20c violet	.20	.20
C79	AP28	25c magenta	.20	.20
C80	AP28	30c red orange	.20	.20
C81	AP27	40c orange	.50	.20
C82	AP28	50c light blue	.30	.20
C83	AP28	60c olive green	.65	.40
C84	AP28	1p brnsh black	.65	.45
C85	AP29	2p brt ultra	5.00	2.25
C86	AP29	4p lilac rose	5.00	2.75
C87	AP29	10p violet brown	14.00	11.00
		Nos. C73-C87 (15)	27.70	18.85
		Set, never hinged	37.50	

Madrid Press Association, 40th anniv.
Exist imperf. Value, set $250 hinged and $325 never hinged.
See note after No. 432.

Types of Regular
Postage of 1936
Overprinted in
Blue or Red

1936   Imperf.

C88	A125	10c dk red (Bl)	150.00	150.00
C89	A125	15c dk blue (R)	150.00	150.00
		Set, never hinged	450.00	

1st National Philatelic Exhibition which opened in Madrid, Apr. 2, 1936.

No. 577 Overprinted in
Black

1936, Aug. 1   Perf. 11½

C90	A128	30c rose red	3.00	3.75
		Never hinged	6.00	
b.		Imperf., pair	140.00	

Issued in commemoration of the flight of aviators Antonio Arnaiz and Juan Calvo from Manila to Spain.
Counterfeit overprints exist.
Exists privately perforated 14. Value, $50 unused, $50 used.

No. 288 Surcharged in Black

1938, Apr. 13   Perf. 14

C91	A36	2.50p on 10c	72.50	72.50
		Never hinged	125.00	

7th anniversary of the Republic.
Values are for examples with perforations nearly touching the design on one or two sides.

No. 507 Surcharged in Various Colors

1938, Aug.   Perf. 11½

C92	A92	50c on 25c (Bk)	25.00	25.00
C93	A92	1p on 25c (G)	1.90	1.40
C94	A92	1.25p on 25c (R)	1.90	1.40
C95	A92	1.50p on 25c (Bl)	1.90	1.40
C96	A92	2p on 25c (Bk & R)	35.00	30.00
		Nos. C92-C96 (5)	65.70	59.20
		Set, never hinged	100.00	

No. 585 Surcharged

1938, June 1   Perf. 11

C97	A132	5p on 1p multi	210.00	210.00
		Never hinged	325.00	
a.		Imperf., pair	450.00	450.00
b.		Inverted surcharge	300.00	300.00
c.		Souvenir sheet	7775.00	7775.00
		Never hinged	1,150.	
d.		Souvenir sheet, imperf.	5,000.	5,000.
e.		Double surcharge	375.00	375.00

Surcharge differs from above illustration.

Counterfeit overprints exist.

Type of 1938-39
Overprinted in Red or
Carmine

1938, May   Perf. 10, 10½

C98	A163	50c indigo (R)	.70	.55
C99	A163	1p dk blue (C)	3.00	.70
		Set, never hinged	4.50	

Exist imperf. Value, each $80.
Copies without overprint are proofs.

Juan de
la Cierva
and his
Autogiro
over
Madrid
AP30

1939, Jan.   Unwmk.   Litho.   Perf. 11

C100	AP30	20c red orange	.60	.40
C101	AP30	25c dk carmine	.45	.20
C102	AP30	35c brt violet	.65	.40
C103	AP30	50c dk brown	.65	.25
C105	AP30	1p blue	.65	.25
C107	AP30	2p green	3.25	1.75
C108	AP30	4p dull blue	5.00	2.75
		Nos. C100-C108 (7)	11.25	6.00
		Set, never hinged	19.00	

Exist imperf. Value, set $325.

1941-47   Perf. 10

C109	AP30	20c dk red orange	.20	.20
C110	AP30	25c redsh brown	.20	.20
C111	AP30	35c lilac rose	1.60	.50
C112	AP30	50c brown		.45
C113	AP30	1p chalky blue	1.40	.20
C114	AP30	2p lt gray grn	1.60	.20
C115	AP30	4p gray blue	5.00	.30
C116	AP30	10p brt purple ('47)	3.75	.65
		Nos. C109-C116 (8)	14.20	2.45
		Set, never hinged	26.00	

Issued in honor of Juan de la Cierva (1895-1936), inventor of the autogiro.
Nos. C109-C115 exist imperf. Value, set $300.
The overprint "EXPOSICION NACIONAL DE FILATELIA 1948 SAN SEBASTIAN" multiple, in parallel horizontal lines, on Nos. C109 to C113 and other airmail stamps, was privately applied.

Correo Aéreo   *Correo Aéreo*

Nos. 625-634, 660, 676 and 677 with either of these overprints have not been established as issues of the Spanish government.

Mariano
Pardo de
Figueroa
(Dr.
Thebussem)
AP31

1944, Oct. 12   Engr.   Perf. 10

C117	AP31	5p brt ultra	15.00	13.00
		Never hinged	21.00	

"Stamp Day" and "Day of the Race," Oct. 12, 1944. Valid for franking air mail correspondence one day only.

Mail
Coach,
Plane and
Count of
St. Louis
AP32

1945, Oct. 12　　　Unwmk.
C118 AP32 10p yellow green　17.50　19.00
　　Never hinged　　　　　25.00

"Stamp Day" and "Day of the Race," Oct. 12, 1945, and to honor Luis José Sartorius, Count of St. Louis, who issued the decree for Spain's 1st postage stamps. No. C118 was valid for franking air mail correspondence one day only.

C118 exists imperf. Value, $800.

Maj. Joaquin Garcia Morato AP33

1945, Nov. 27
C119 AP33 10p deep claret　13.50　5.00
　　Never hinged　　　　30.00

C119 exists imperf. Value, $275 hinged, $400 never hinged.

Capt. Carlos Haya Gonzalez AP34

Bartolomé de las Casas AP35

1945, Dec. 14
C120 AP34 4p red　　　　5.50　4.50
　　Never hinged　　　　11.50

C120 exists imperf. Value, $375 hinged and $450 never hinged.

1946, Oct. 12　　Perf. 11½x11
C121 AP35 5.50p green　1.90　2.50
　　Never hinged　　　3.00

Stamp Day and Day of the Race. Exists imperf. Value $16.

Don Quixote and Sancho Panza Astride Clavileno AP36

1947, Oct. 9　　　　Perf. 10
C122 AP36 5.50p purple　4.00　4.00
　　Never hinged　　　6.00

Stamp Day and the 400th anniversary of the birth of Miguel de Cervantes Saavedra. C122 exists imperf. Value, $500.

Manuel de Falla — AP37

Ignacio Zuloaga — AP38

1947, Dec. 1　　Perf. 9½x10½
Control Number on Back
C123 AP37 25p dk vio brn　27.50　15.00
C124 AP38 50p dk carmine　110.00　40.00
　　Set, never hinged　　　225.00

For overprint see No. CB18. C124 exists imperf. Value, $850.

Train and Plane — AP39

1948, Oct. 9　Litho.　Perf. 13x12½
C125 AP39 2p scarlet　1.50　1.50
　　Never hinged　　　2.25

Cent. of Spanish railroads and Stamp Day.

UPU Type of Regular Issue with Pedestal and Propeller Added
1949, Oct. 9　　　Perf. 12½x13
C126 A202 4p dk olive green　.20　.45
　　Never hinged　　　　.40

Stamp Day and the 75th anniv. of the UPU.

Stamp of 1850 AP40

Map of Western Hemisphere AP41

1950, Oct. 12　Engr.　Imperf.
C127 AP40　1p rose brn　4.50　6.50
C128 AP40 2.50p brown org　4.50　6.50
C129 AP40　20p dark blue　80.00　87.50
C130 AP40　25p green　80.00　87.50
　Nos. C127-C130 (4)　169.00 188.00
　Set, never hinged　　290.00

Centenary of Spanish postage stamps.

1951, Apr. 16　Photo.　Perf. 12½
C131 AP41 1p blue　4.50　2.25
　　Never hinged　　6.25

6th Congress of the Postal Union of the Americas and Spain.

Isabella I AP42

1951, Oct. 12　Engr.　Perf. 13
C132 AP42　60c dk gray grn　6.50　.40
C133 AP42　90c orange　.80　.35
C134 AP42 1.30p plum　5.00　4.00
C135 AP42 1.90p sepia　4.50　4.00
C136 AP42 2.30p dk blue　2.75　2.75
　Nos. C132-C136 (5)　19.55 11.70
　Set, never hinged　　27.50

Stamp Day and 500th anniv. of the birth of Queen Isabella I.

"The Eucharist" by Tiepolo — AP43

St. Francis Xavier — AP44

1952, May 26　Photo.　Perf. 12½x13
C137 AP43 1p gray green　3.00　.60
　　Never hinged　　　3.50

35th International Encharistic Congress, Barcelona, 1952.

1952, July 3　　　　Engr.
C138 AP44 2p deep blue　30.00　14.00
　　Never hinged　　　50.00

400th anniv. of the death of St. Francis Xavier.

Ferdinand the Catholic and Columbus Presenting Natives AP45

1952, Oct. 12
C139 AP45　60c dull green　.25　.20
C140 AP45　90c orange　.25　.20
C141 AP45 1.30p plum　.45　.30
C142 AP45 1.90p sepia　2.00　2.00
C143 AP45 2.30p deep blue　10.00　9.50
　Nos. C139-C143 (5)　12.95 12.20
　Set, never hinged　　17.50

500th anniversary of the birth of Ferdinand the Catholic and to publicize Stamp Day.

Joaquin Sorolla y Bastida AP46

Miguel Lopez de Legazpi AP47

1953, Oct. 9　　　Perf. 13x12½
C144 AP46 50p dark violet　300.00 22.50
　　Never hinged　　　675.00

Issued to honor Joaquin Sorolla y Bastida (1863-1923), impressionist painter.

1953, Nov. 5
C145 AP47 25p gray black　57.50 27.50
　　Never hinged　　　125.00

Spanish-Philippine Postal Convention of 1951.

Leonardo Torres Quevedo (1852-1939), Mathematician and Inventor — AP48

Perf. 13x12½
1955, Sept. 6　Engr.　Unwmk.
C146 AP48 50p bluish gray & blk　5.00　.90
　　Never hinged　　　11.00

Plane and Caravel AP49

1955-56　　Photo.　Perf. 12½x13
C147 AP49　20c gray grn ('56)　.20　.20
C148 AP49　25c gray violet　.20　.20
C149 AP49　50c ol gray ('56)　.20　.20
C150 AP49　1p red orange　.20　.20
C151 AP49 1.10p emer ('56)　.20　.20
C152 AP49 1.40p rose car　.20　.20
C153 AP49　3p brt blue ('56)　.20　.20
C154 AP49 4.80p yellow　.20　.20
C155 AP49　5p redsh brown　1.50　.20
C156 AP49　7p lilac ('56)　.45　.20
C157 AP49　10p lt ol grn ('56)　.50　.25
　Nos. C147-C157 (11)　4.05　2.25
　Set, never hinged　　4.00

Mariano Fortuny y Carbo (1838-1874), Painter — AP50

1956, Jan. 10　Engr.　Perf. 13x12½
C158 AP50 25p grnsh black　14.00　.90
　　Never hinged　　　30.00

> **Catalogue values for unused stamps in this section, from this point to the end of the section, are for Never Hinged items.**

Bullfight Type of Regular Issue
25c, Small town arena. 50c, Fighting with cape. 1p, Dedication of the bull. 5p, Bull ring.

Perf. 13x12½, 12½x13
1960, Feb. 29　Engr.　Unwmk.
C159 A246 25c brn car & dl lil　.20　.20
C160 A245 50c blue　.20　.20
C161 A246　1p red & dull red　.20　.20
C162 A245　5p red lilac & vio　.55　.40
　Nos. C159-C162 (4)　1.15　1.00

Jai Alai AP51

1960, Mar. 27　Photo.　Perf. 12½x13
C163 AP51　1p brt red & dk
　　　　brn　4.75　3.25
C164 AP51　5p dull brn &
　　　　mag　4.75　3.25
C165 AP51　6p vio blk & mag　4.75　3.25
C166 AP51　10p grn, mag & dk
　　　　brn　4.75　3.25
　Nos. C163-C166 (4)　19.00 13.00

1st Intl. Cong. of Philately, Barcelona, Mar. 26-Apr. 5. Nos. C163-C166 could be bought at the exhibition upon presentation of 5p entrance ticket.

Sport Type of Regular Issue
Sports: 1.25p, 6p, Steeplechase, horiz. 1.50p, 10p, Basque ball game.

Perf. 12½x13, 13x12½
1960, Oct. 31　　　　Unwmk.
C167 A251 1.25p choc & car　.30　.20
C168 A251 1.50p pur, brn & blk　.30　.20
C169 A251　6p vio blk & car　.95　.55
C170 A251　10p ol grn, red &
　　　　blk　1.25　.55
　Nos. C167-C170 (4)　2.80　1.50

Rosary Type of Regular Issue
Mysteries of the Rosary: 25c, The Ascension, Bayeu. 1p, The Descent of the Holy Ghost, El Greco. 5p, The Assumption, Mateo Cerezo. 10p, The Coronation of the Virgin Mary, El Greco.

1962, Oct. 26　Engr.　Perf. 13
C171 A280 25c vio & dl gray vio　.25　.20
C172 A280　1p olive & brown　.35　.20
C173 A280　5p brn & rose cl　.60　.25
C174 A280　10p bluish grn & yel
　　　　grn　1.40　.50
　Nos. C171-C174 (4)　2.60　1.15

Recaredo I, Visigothic King, 586-601 — AP52

Portrait: 50p, Francisco Cardinal Jimenez de Cisneros (1436-1517).

1963, Dec. 5　Engr.　Perf. 13x12½
C175 AP52 25p dull purple　1.10　.40
C176 AP52 50p green & black　1.90　.55

1966, Feb. 26
Portraits: 25p, Seneca (4 B.C.-65 A.D.). 50p, Pope St. Damasus I (304?-384).

C177 AP52 25p yel grn & dk grn　1.75　.20
C178 AP52 50p sky bl & gray bl　2.75　.55

Plaza de Espana, Seville AP53

1981, Nov. 26   Engr.   Perf. 13
C179 AP53 13p shown   .20 .20
C180 AP53 20p Rande River   .25 .20
              Bridge,
              Pontevedra

St. Thomas, by El Greco — AP54

1982, July 7   Photo.   Perf. 13
C181 AP54 13p Sts. Andrew and   .20 .20
              Francis
C182 AP54 20p shown   .20 .20

Bowling AP55

1983, Apr. 13   Photo.   Perf. 13
C183 AP55 13p Bicycling, vert.   .20 .20
C184 AP55 20p shown   .20 .20

AIR POST SEMI-POSTAL STAMPS

Red Cross Issue

Ramon Franco's Plane Plus Ultra SPAP1

Perf. 12½, 13
1926, Sept. 15   Engr.   Unwmk.
CB1 SPAP1 5c black & vio   1.40 1.40
CB2 SPAP1 10c ultra & blk   3.00 3.00
CB3 SPAP1 25c carmine & blk   .30 .30
CB4 SPAP1 50c red org & blk   .30 .30
CB5 SPAP1 1p black & green   2.50 2.50
      Nos. CB1-CB5 (5)   7.50 7.50

For overprints and surcharges see Nos. B55-B63.

No. B106 Surcharged in Black

1938, Apr. 15   Perf. 11½
CB6 SP13 45c + 2p + 5p   250.00 225.00
      Never hinged   375.00
  a. Imperf., pair   900.00 900.00
  b. Souvenir sheet of 1   4,000. 4,500.
  c. Souvenir sheet, imperf.   5,500. 6,000.
  d. Souv. sheet, surch. invtd.   5,750. 5,750.

The surtax was used to benefit the defenders of Madrid.

This issue has been extensively counterfeited.

No. B107 Surcharged

1938, June 1   Perf. 10
CB7 SP14 45c + 5p + 3p   10.00 9.75
      Never hinged   17.50

Monument SPAP2

Dome Fresco by Goya, Cathedral of Zaragoza SPAP3

#CB9, CB14, Caravel Santa Maria. #CB10, CB12, The Ascension. #CB13, The Coronation. #CB17, Bombardment of Cathedral of Zaragoza.

Perf. 10½, 11½x10½, 11½
1940, Jan. 29   Litho.   Unwmk.
Bicolored
CB8   SPAP2 25c + 5c   .25 .25
CB9   SPAP2 50c + 5c   .25 .25
CB10 SPAP2 65c + 15c   .25 .25
CB11 SPAP2 70c + 15c   .25 .25
CB12 SPAP2 90c + 20c   .25 .25
CB13 SPAP2 1.20p + 30c   .25 .25
CB14 SPAP2 1.40p + 40c   .25 .25
CB15 SPAP2 2p + 50c   .40 .40
CB16 SPAP3 4p + 1p sl   9.75 9.75
              grn &
              rose lil
CB17 SPAP3 10p + 4p
              chnt &
              ultra   225.00 225.00
      Nos. CB8-CB17 (10)   236.90 236.90
      Set, never hinged   325.00

19th centenary of the Pillar Virgin. The surtax was used to help restore the Cathedral at Zaragoza, damaged during the Civil War.

No. CB16 exists in slate green & violet, No. CB17 in red violet & ultramarine. Value, $32.50 each.

Exist imperf. Value, set $350.

No. C123 Surcharged in Black

1950-51   Perf. 9½x10½
Control Number on Back
CB18 AP37 25p + 10c   250.00 225.00
      Never hinged   500.00
  a. Without control number   2,900. 1,250.
      Without control number,
      never hinged   4,750.

Visit of Gen. Franco to the Canary Islands, Oct., 1950.

The control number was printed on the gum, and regummed copies of No. CB18 are frequently offered as No. CB18a.

Counterfeit surcharges exist.

Issued: #CB18a, 10/23/50; #CB18 2/22/51.

AIR POST SPECIAL DELIVERY STAMP

Goya Commemorative Issue

Type of Air Post Stamp of 1930 Overprinted

1930   Unwmk.   Perf. 12½
CE1 AP4 20c bl blk & lt brn
              (Bk)   .20 .20
      Never hinged   .25
  a. Blue overprint   15.00 7.75
      Never hinged   21.00
  b. Overprint omitted   15.00 22.50
      Never hinged   22.50

See note after No. 432.

AIR POST OFFICIAL STAMPS

Pan-American Postal Union Congress Issue
Types of Air Post Stamps of 1931 Overprinted in Red or Blue

1931   Unwmk.   Perf. 12
CO1 AP22 5c red brown (R)   .20 .20
CO2 AP22 10c blue grn (Bl)   .20 .20
CO3 AP22 25c rose (Bl)   .20 .20
CO4 AP23 50c lt blue (R)   .20 .20
CO5 AP23 1p violet (R)   .20 .20
CO6 AP24 4p gray blk (R)   3.25 3.25
      Nos. CO1-CO6 (6)   4.25 4.25
      Set, never hinged   5.75

Shades exist.
Exist imperf. Value, set $22.50.

SPECIAL DELIVERY STAMPS

Pegasus and Coat of Arms — SD1

1905-25   Unwmk.   Typo.   Perf. 14
Control Number on Back
E1 SD1 20c deep red   40.00 .30
  a. 20c rose red, litho. ('25)   35.00 .30
  b. Imperf., pair   275.00
  c. As "a," imperf., pair   275.00

Gazelle SD2

Pegasus — SD3

1929   Engr.   Perf. 11
Control Number on Back
E2 SD2 20c dull red   17.50 20.00
      Never hinged   32.50
  a. Perf. 14   29.00 32.50
      Never hinged   50.00

Seville and Barcelona Exhibitions. See note after No. 432.

1929-32   Perf. 13½x12½, 11½
Control Number on Back
E3 SD3 20c red   19.00 3.75
      Never hinged   37.50
  a. Imperf., pair   375.00
  b. Without control number, perf.
      11½ ('32)   55.00 1.40
      Never hinged   87.50
  c. As "b," imperf., pair   875.00

No. E3 Overprinted like Nos. 358-370
E4 SD3 20c red (BI)   12.00 25.00
      Never hinged   22.50

League of Nations 55th assembly.
For overprints see Nos. E5, E10-E12.

No. E3 Overprinted in Blue

1930   Perf. 13½x12½, 11½
E5 SD3 20c red   12.00 .65
      Never hinged   30.00

Railway Congress Issue

Electric Locomotive — SD4

1930, May 10   Litho.   Perf. 14
Control Number on Back
E6 SD4 20c brown orange   50.00 50.00
      Never hinged   87.50

See note after No. 385.

Goya Issue

Type of Regular Issue of 1930 Overprinted

1930   Perf. 12½
E7 A57 20c lilac rose   .20 .30
      Never hinged   .40

Christopher Columbus Issue
Type of Regular Issue of 1930 Overprinted

1930 Sept. 29
E8 A64 20c brown violet   1.75 1.75
      Never hinged   2.75

See note after No. 432.

Spanish-American Exhibition Issue

View of Seville Exhibition — SD5

1930, Oct. 10   Photo.   Perf. 14
E9   SD5 20c orange   .40   .25
         Never hinged   .55

See note after No. 432.

Madrid Issue

No. E5 Overprinted in
Green

1931   Perf. 11½
E10 SD3 20c red   4.50   4.50
         Never hinged   6.50

The status of No. E10 has been questioned.

Barcelona Issue

No. E3 Overprinted

E11 SD3 20c red   5.00   5.00
         Never hinged   10.00

No. E11 also exists with accent over "U."
The status of No. E11 has been questioned.

No. E3 Overprinted in
Blue

E12 SD3 20c red   5.50   1.00
         Never hinged   17.00

Montserrat Issue

Pegasus — SD6

1931   Engr.   Perf. 11
Control Number on Back
E13 SD6 20c vermilion   22.50 22.50
         Never hinged   32.50
  a.   Perf. 14   55.00 60.00

SD7

1934   Perf. 10
E14 SD7 20c vermilion   .20   .20
         Never hinged   .20
  a.   Imperf., pair   32.50

For overprints see #10LE1, 11LE1-11LE4,
14LE1.

Newsboy — SD8

Pegasus
SD9

1936   Photo.   Perf. 12½
E15 SD8 20c rose carmine   .25   .30
         Never hinged   .40

Madrid Press Association, 40th anniv.
See note after No. 432.

Spanish State

1937-38 Unwmk. Litho.   Perf. 11
**With imprint "Hija. de B Fournier-
Burgos"**
E16 SD9 20c violet brn   7.75   4.50
         Never hinged   10.00
  a.   Imperf., pair   77.50

Without Imprint
E17 SD9 20c dk vio brn ('38)   1.50   .30
         Never hinged   2.50
  a.   Imperf., pair   50.00

No. 645 Overprinted in
Black

1937
E18 A162 20c dark violet   11.00 11.00
         Never hinged   13.00

Pegasus
SD10

1939-42   Perf. 10½
Imprint: "SANCHEZ TODA"
E19 SD10 25c carmine   4.50   .70
         Never hinged   5.75
  a.   Imperf., pair   50.00

Without Imprint
Perf. 10
E20 SD10 25c carmine ('42)   .20   .20
         Never hinged   .30

┌─────────────────────────────────────┐
│ Catalogue values for unused   │
│ stamps in this section, from this   │
│ point to the end of the section, are │
│ for Never Hinged items.   │
└─────────────────────────────────────┘

"Flight"
SD11

Centaur — SD12

Perf. 12½x13, 13x12½
1956, Feb. 12   Photo.   Unwmk.
E21 SD11 2p scarlet   .20   .20
E22 SD12 4p black & magenta   .20   .20

1965-66
E23 SD11 3p dp car   .20   .20
E24 SD11 5p dp org ('66)   .20   .20
E25 SD12 6.50p dk vio & rose
                    brn ('66)   .20   .20
      Nos. E21-E25 (5)   1.00   1.00

Chariot
SD13

Mail Circling
Globe — SD14

1971, June 1   Photo.   Perf. 13
E26 SD13 10p red & yel grn   .20   .20
E27 SD14 15p red, bl & blk   .20   .20

Communications — SD15

1993, Apr. 20 Photo. Perf. 14x13½
E28 SD15 180p red & yellow   2.50   .35

SEMI-POSTAL SPECIAL DELIVERY STAMPS

Red Cross Issue

Royal Family
Group
SPSD1

1926 Unwmk. Engr. Perf. 12½, 13
EB1 SPSD1 20c red vio & vio
                     brn   8.75   8.75
         Never hinged   15.00

See notes after Nos. 432 and B18.
For overprint see No. B54.

Motorcyclist
and
Zaragoza
Cathedral
SPSD2

1940   Litho.   Perf. 11½
EB2 SPSD2 25c + 5c rose red &
                     buff   .40   .30

19th cent. of the Pillar Virgin. The surtax
was used to help restore the Cathedral at
Zaragoza, damaged during the Civil War.

DELIVERY TAX STAMPS

D1

1931   Unwmk.   Litho.   Perf. 11½
ER1 D1 5c black   7.25   .20
         Never hinged   11.00

For overprints see Nos. ER2-ER3, 7LE5-
7LE6.

No. ER1 Overprinted in
Red

1931
ER2 D1 5c black   1.25   1.40
         Never hinged   2.10

No. ER2 also exists with accent over "U."

No. ER1 Overprinted in
Red

ER3 D1 5c black   3.00   3.00
         Never hinged   5.00

These stamps were originally issued for
Postage Due purpose but were later used as
regular postage stamps.

WAR TAX STAMPS

These stamps did not pay postage
but represented a fiscal tax on mail matter in addition to the postal fees. Their
use was obligatory.

Coat of Arms
WT1   WT2

Unwmk.
1874, Jan. 1   Typo.   Perf. 14
MR1 WT1 5c black   8.25   .95
  a.   Imperf. pair   14.00
MR2 WT1 10c pale blue   10.50   1.60
  a.   Imperf. pair   57.50

1875, Jan. 1
MR3 WT2 5c green   5.25   .60
  a.   Imperf., pair   27.50
MR4 WT2 10c lilac   11.00   2.75
  a.   Imperf., pair   55.00

King Alfonso XII
WT3   WT4

1876, June 1
MR5 WT3 5c pale green   6.25   1.00
MR6 WT3 10c blue   6.25   1.00
  a.   Cliche of 5c in plate of
           10c   125.00
MR7 WT3 25c black   45.00 17.00
MR8 WT3 1p lilac   475.00 110.00
MR9 WT3 5p rose   700.00 300.00

Nos. MR5-MR9 exist imperforate. Value,
$1,100.

1877, Sept. 1
MR10	WT4	15c claret	27.50 1.00
a.		Imperf., pair	100.00
MR11	WT4	50c yellow	700.00 110.00

WT5 WT6

1879
MR12	WT5	5c blue	37.50
MR13	WT5	10c rose	22.50
MR14	WT5	15c violet	14.00
MR15	WT5	25c brown	22.50
MR16	WT5	50c olive green	14.00
MR17	WT5	1p bister	22.50
MR18	WT5	5p gray	82.50
	Nos. MR12-MR18 (7)		215.50

Nos. MR12-MR18 were never placed in use.
Nos. MR17 and MR18 exist imperf. Value, $225.

Inscribed "1897 A 1898"
1897 *Perf. 14*
MR19	WT6	5c green	3.00 1.90
MR20	WT6	10c green	3.00 1.90
MR21	WT6	15c green	375.00 175.00
MR22	WT6	20c green	7.50 3.00

Nos. MR19-MR22 exist imperf. Value for set $825.

Inscribed "1898-99"
1898
MR23	WT6	5c black	2.25 1.75
MR24	WT6	10c black	2.25 1.75
MR25	WT6	15c black	45.00 9.50
MR26	WT6	20c black	3.50 3.00
	Nos. MR23-MR26 (4)		53.00 16.00

Nos. MR23-MR26 exist imperf. Value about $275 a pair.

King Alfonso
XIII — WT7

1898
MR27	WT7	5c black	7.50 .60
a.		Imperf., pair	77.50

OFFICIAL STAMPS

Coat of Arms
O1 O2

1854, July 1 **Typo.** *Imperf.*
O1	O1	½o blk, *yellow*	2.10 2.75
O2	O1	1o blk, *rose*	2.75 3.25
a.		1o black, *blue*	29.00
O3	O1	4o blk, *green*	7.50 9.25
O4	O1	1 l blk, *blue*	52.50 60.00
	Nos. O1-O4 (4)		64.85 75.25

1855-63
O5	O2	½o blk, *yellow*	1.50 1.75
a.		½o black, *green* ('63)	1.75 1.90
O6	O2	1o blk, *rose*	1.50 1.75
a.		1o black, *salmon rose*	3.25 1.90
O7	O2	4o blk, *green*	3.25 1.90
a.		4o black, *yellow green*	8.75 1.90
O8	O2	1 l blk, *gray blue*	14.50 17.50
	Nos. O5-O8 (4)		20.75 22.90

The "value indication" on Nos. O1-O8 actually is the weight of the mail in onzas (ounces, "o") and libras (pounds, "l") for which they were valid.

Type of Regular Issue of 1889
1895 *Perf. 14*
O9	A34	15c yellow	10.00 6.00
a.		Imperf., pair	250.00

Coat of Arms — O5

1896-98
O10	O5	rose	5.25 1.75
a.		Imperf., pair	87.50
O11	O5	dk blue ('98)	17.50 6.00

Cervantes Issue

Chamber of
Deputies
O6

Statue of
Cervantes — O7

Cervantes — O9

National
Library
O8

1916, Apr. 22 **Engr.** *Perf. 12*
For the Senate
O12	O6	green & blk	1.10 .90
O13	O7	brown & blk	1.10 .90
O14	O8	carmine & blk	1.10 .90
O15	O9	brown & blk	1.10 .90

For the Chamber of Deputies
O16	O6	violet & blk	1.10 .90
O17	O7	carmine & blk	1.10 .90
O18	O8	green & blk	1.10 .90
O19	O9	violet & blk	1.10 .90
	Nos. O12-O19 (8)		8.80 7.20

Exist imperf. Value set of pairs, $110.
Exist with centers inverted. Value for set, $87.50.

Pan-American Postal Union Congress Issue

Types of
Regular Issue
of 1931
Overprinted in
Red or Blue

1931 *Perf. 12½*
O20	A84	5c dk brown (R)	.40 .20
O21	A85	10c brt green (Bl)	.40 .20
O22	A86	15c dull violet (R)	.40 .20
O23	A85	25c deep rose (Bl)	.40 .20
O24	A87	30c olive green (Bl)	.40 .20
O25	A84	40c ultra (R)	.55 .50
O26	A85	50c deep orange (Bl)	.55 .50
O27	A86	1p blue black (R)	.55 .50

O28	A88	4p magenta (Bl)	12.50 12.50
O29	A88	10p lt brown (R)	22.50 22.50
	Nos. O20-O29 (10)		38.65 37.50
	Set, never hinged		55.00

Nos. O22-O29 exist imperf. Values about 3 times those quoted.

POSTAL TAX STAMPS

PT5 PT6

Perf. 10½x11½
1937, Dec. 23 **Litho.**
RA11	PT5	10c blk, pale bl & red	7.25 4.50
	Never hinged		19.00
a.	Imperf. pair		72.50
	Never hinged		100.00

The tax was for the tuberculosis fund.

1938, Dec. 23 *Perf. 11½*
RA12	PT6	10c multicolored	4.50 1.75
	Never hinged		10.00
a.	Imperf. pair		45.00
	Never hinged		50.00

The tax was for the tuberculosis fund.

"Spain"
Holding
Wreath of
Peace
over
Marching
Soldiers
PT7

1939, July 18 *Perf. 11*
RA13	PT7	10c blue	.20 .20
	Never hinged		.25
a.	Imperf. pair		65.00
	Never hinged		82.50

Type of Regular Issue, 1939
Without Imprint
Unwmk.
1939, Dec. 23 **Litho.** *Imperf.*
RA14	A166	10c dull claret	.20 .20
	Never hinged		.25

Tuberculosis Fund Issues
Types of Corresponding Semi-Postal Stamps
1940, Dec. 23 *Perf. 10*
RA15	SP23	10c violet & red	.20 .20
	Never hinged		.25

1941, Dec. 23
RA16	SP24	10c black & red	.20 .20
	Never hinged		.25

1942, Dec. 23
RA17	SP25	10c dl sal & rose red	.20 .20
	Never hinged		.25

1943, Dec. 23 **Photo.** *Perf. 11*
RA18	SP26	10c purple & dl red	.30 .25
	Never hinged		.50

Perf. 9½x10
1944, Dec. 23 **Litho.** **Unwmk.**
RA19	SP27	10c salmon & rose	.20 .20
	Never hinged		.25

1945, Dec. 23
RA20	SP28	10c salmon & car	.20 .20
	Never hinged		.25

Mother and
Child — PT8

1946, Dec. 22 **Litho.** *Perf. 9½x10½*
RA21	PT8	5c violet & red	.20 .20
RA22	PT8	10c green & red	.20 .20
	Set, never hinged		.40

See No. RAC7.

Lorraine Cross Tuberculosis
PT9 Sanatorium
 PT10

Perf. 9½x10½
1947, Dec. 22 **Unwmk.**
RA23	PT9	5c dk brown & red	.20 .20
RA24	PT10	10c vio bl & red	.20 .20
	Set, never hinged		.40

See No. RAC8.

Aesculapius "El Cid"
PT11 PT11a

Photogravure; Cross Engraved
1948, Dec. 22 **Unwmk.** *Perf. 12½*
RA25	PT11	5c brown & car	.20 .20
RA26	PT11	10c dp green & car	.20 .20
	Set, never hinged		.40

The tax on Nos. RA15-RA26 was used to fight tuberculosis. See Nos. RAB1, RAC9.

1949, Feb. 1 **Litho.** *Perf. 10½x9½*
RA27	PT11a	5c violet	.20 .20
	ever hinged		.25

The tax aided displaced children. Valid for ordinary postage after Dec. 24, 1949.

Tuberculosis Fund Issues

Galleon and Pine Branch and
Lorraine Candle — PT13
Cross — PT12

Photogravure; Cross Engraved
1949, Dec. 22 *Perf. 12½*
RA28	PT12	5c violet & red	.20 .20
RA29	PT12	10c yel grn & red	.20 .20
	Set, never hinged		.40

See Nos. RAB2, RAC10.

1950, Dec. 22
Cross in Carmine
RA30	PT13	5c rose violet	.20 .20
RA31	PT13	10c deep green	.20 .20
	Set, never hinged		.35

See Nos. RAB3, RAC11.

Children at Nurse and Baby
Seashore PT15
PT14

1951, Oct. 1
Cross in Carmine
RA32 PT14 5c rose brown .20 .20
RA33 PT14 10c dull green .35 .20
Set, never hinged .75

See No. RAC12.

1953, Oct. 1
Cross in Carmine
RA34 PT15 5c carmine lake .30 .20
RA35 PT15 10c gray blue .80 .20
Set, never hinged 2.25

The tax on RA28-RA35 was used to fight tuberculosis. See No. RAC13.

POSTAL TAX SEMI-POSTAL STAMPS

Types of Corresponding Postal Tax Stamps

Photogravure; Cross Engraved
1948 Unwmk. Perf. 12½
RAB1 PT11 50c + 10c red brn & car .80 .75
Never hinged 1.25

1949
RAB2 PT12 50c + 10c dk ol bis & red .50 .25
Never hinged .80

1950
RAB3 PT13 50c + 10c brn & car 1.25 1.25
Never hinged 2.25

The surtax on Nos. RAB1-RAB3 was used to fight tuberculosis. Combines domestic letter rate and tax obligatory Dec. 22-Jan. 3.

POSTAL TAX AIR POST STAMPS

Tuberculosis Fund Issues
Franco Type of Semi-Postal Stamps

Unwmk.
1940, Dec. 23 Litho. Perf. 10
RAC1 SP23 10c bright pink & red .90 .90
Never hinged 2.50

Knight and Lorraine Cross — PTAP2

1941, Dec. 23
RAC2 PTAP2 10c blue & red .25 .25
Never hinged .50

Lorraine Cross and Doves PTAP3

1942, Dec. 23
RAC3 PTAP3 10c dl sal & rose .80 .50
Never hinged 1.25

Cross of Lorraine — PTAP4

Tuberculosis Sanatorium PTAP5

1943, Dec. 23 Photo. Perf. 11
RAC4 PTAP4 10c vio & dl red .90 1.00
Never hinged 1.60

1944, Dec. 23 Litho. Perf. 10x9½
RAC5 PTAP5 25c salmon & rose 3.75 3.75
Never hinged 5.50

Lorraine Cross and Eagle — PTAP6

1945, Dec. 23 Perf. 10
RAC6 PTAP6 25c red & car 1.40 1.25
Never hinged 1.75

Eagle — PTAP7

1946, Dec. 22
RAC7 PTAP7 25c red & car .20 .20
Never hinged .40

Tuberculosis Sanatorium PTAP8

1947, Dec. 22 Perf. 11½
RAC8 PTAP8 25c red vio .20 .20
Never hinged .40

Photogravure; Cross Engraved
1948, Dec. 22 Perf. 12½
RAC9 PTAP9 25c ultra & car .30 .25
Never hinged .60

Plane over Sanatorium PTAP9

Bell and Lorraine Cross PTAP10

Dove and Flowers PTAP11

1949, Dec. 22
RAC10 PTAP10 25c maroon & red .20 .20
Never hinged .25

1950, Dec. 22
RAC11 PTAP11 25c dk bl & car .30 .30
Never hinged .60

Mother and Child PTAP12

Tobias and Archangel PTAP13

1951, Oct. 1
RAC12 PTAP12 25c brn & car .50 .20
Never hinged .80

1953, Oct. 1
RAC13 PTAP13 25c brn & car 3.50 5.50
Never hinged 6.50

FRANCHISE STAMPS

F1

F2

1869 Unwmk. Litho. Imperf.
S1 F1 blue 47.50 35.00
a. Tête bêche pair 125.00 110.00

The franchise of No. S1 was granted to Diego Castell to use in distributing his publications on Spanish postal history.

1881
S2 F2 black, buff 32.50 14.00

The franchise of No. S2 was granted to Antonio Fernandez Duro for his book, "Resena histórico-descriptiva de los sellos correos de Espana."

Reprints of No. S2 have been made on carmine, blue, gray, fawn and yellow paper.

CARLIST STAMPS

From the beginning of the Civil War (April 21, 1872) until separate stamps were issued on July 1, 1873, stamps of France were used on all mail from the provinces under Carlist rule.

King Carlos VII — A1

Tilde on N — A1a

Unwmk.
1873, July 1 Litho. Imperf.
X1 A1 1r blue 500.00
X2 A1a 1r blue 450.00 300.00

These stamps were reprinted three times in 1881 and once in 1887. The originals have 23 white lines and dots in the lower right spandrel. They are thin and of even width and spacing. The first reprint has 17 to 20 lines in the spandrel, most of them thick and of irregular width and length. The second and third reprints have 21 very thin lines, the second from the bottom being almost invisible. In the fourth reprint the lower right spandrel is an almost solid spot of color.

Originals of type A1 have the curved line above "ESPANA" broken at the left of the "E." All reprints of this type have the curved line continuous.

The reprints exist in various shades of blue, rose, red, violet and black.

King Carlos VII A2

A3

A4

A5

1874
X3 A2 1r violet 240.00 240.00
X4 A3 16m rose 4.75 72.50
X5 A4 ½r rose 100.00 100.00

Nos. X3 and X6-X7 were for use in the Basque Provinces and Navarra; No. X4 in Catalonia, and No. X5 in Valencia.

Two types of No. X5, alternating in each sheet.

No. X4 with favor cancellation (lozenge of dots) sells for same price as unused.

1875
White Paper
X6 A5 50c green 8.00 82.50
a. 50c blue green 25.00 100.00
b. Bluish paper 50.00
X7 A5 1r brown 8.00 82.50
a. Bluish paper 50.00

Fake cancellations exist on Nos. X1-X7.

REVOLUTIONARY OVERPRINTS

Issued by the Nationalist (Revolutionary) Forces

Many districts or cities made use of the stamps of the Republic overprinted in various forms. Most such overprinting was authorized by military or postal officials but some were without official sanction. These overprints were applied in patriotic celebration and partly as a protection from the use of unoverprinted stamps seized or stolen by soldiers.

BURGOS AIR POST STAMPS

RAP1

Revenue Stamps Overprinted in Red, Blue or Black

1936, Dec. 1 Unwmk. Perf. 11½
Control Number on Face of Stamp
7LC1 RAP1 25c gray grn & blk (R) 42.50 42.50
a. Blue overprint 42.50 42.50
7LC2 RAP1 1.50p bl & blk (R) 5.50 5.50
7LC3 RAP1 3p rose & blk (Bl) 5.50 5.50
Nos. 7LC1-7LC3 (3) 53.50 53.50
Set, never hinged 85.00

RAP2

RAP4

Perf. 13½
Blue Control Number on Back

7LC4	RAP2	15c green (R)	3.75	3.75
7LC5	RAP2	25c blue (R)	27.50	27.50
	Set, never hinged		40.00	

Perf. 11½
Without Control Number
Overprint in Black

7LC6	RAP4	1.50p dk blue	6.50	6.50
7LC7	RAP4	3p carmine	6.50	6.50
	Set, never hinged		19.00	

RAP5   RAP6

Overprint in Black
Perf. 13½, 11½

| 7LC8 | RAP5 | 1.20p green | 25.00 | 25.00 |
| | Never hinged | | 32.50 | |

Perf. 14
Control Number on Back

7LC9	RAP6	1.20p green	25.00	25.00
7LC10	RAP6	2.40p green	25.00	25.00
	Set #7LC9-7LC10, never hinged		62.50	

No. 7LC9 is inscribed "CLASE 8a."

RAP7

1937   Unwmk.   Perf. 11½
Control Number on Back

| 7LC11 | RAP7 | 25c ultra (R) | 210.00 | 210.00 |

Stamps of Spain, 1931-
36, Overprinted in Red
or Black (10p)

Perf. 11, 11½, 11x11½
1937   Unwmk.
Overprint 13mm high

7LC12	A100	40c blue	1.10	1.10
a.	Ovpt. 15mm high		1.10	1.10
7LC13	A97	50c dark blue	1.40	1.40
a.	Ovpt. 15mm high		1.40	1.40
7LC14	A130	50c dark blue	1.75	1.75
a.	Ovpt. 15mm high		1.75	1.75
7LC15	A100	60c apple green	2.50	2.50
a.	Ovpt. 15mm high		2.50	2.50
7LC16	AP26	2p gray blue	32.50	32.50
a.	Ovpt. 15mm high		32.50	32.50
7LC17	A49a	10p brown	82.50	82.50
a.	Ovpt. 15mm high		82.50	82.50
	Nos. 7LC12-7LC17 (6)		121.75	121.75

Issue dates: Nos. 7LC12-7LC17, 4/1. Nos.
7LC12a-7LC17a, 5/1.

Spain Nos. 576, 578 and 541b
overprinted in Blue or Black

Nos. 7LC18,   Nos. 7LC20,
7LC19   7LC21

Perfs as on Basic Stamps
1937, May

7LC18	A127	30c carmine (Bk)	1.40	1.40
7LC19	A127	30c carmine (Bl)	.70	.70
7LC20	A129	30c car rose (Bk)	1.40	1.40

7LC21	A129	30c car rose (Bl)	.70	.70
7LC22	A107	10p dp brn (Bk)	11.00	11.00
	Nos. 7LC18-7LC22 (5)		15.20	15.20

Spain Nos. 539b and 540b, the 1p and 4p
values, were prepared with this overprint in
January, 1938, but were not issued. Value,
each $4.50.

BURGOS ISSUE SPECIAL DELIVERY STAMPS

Pair of Spain No. 546 Overprinted in
Black

1936   Unwmk.   Perf. 11½x11

7LE3	A110	20c (10c+10c) emer	4.50	4.50
	Never hinged		8.25	
a.	Overprint inverted		14.00	

Type of Regular Stamp
of 1931 Overprinted in
Red

| 7LE4 | A95 | 20c dark violet | 10.00 | 10.00 |

Type of Delivery Tax Stamp of 1931
Overprinted in Red on four 5c stamps

Perf. 11½

| 7LE5 | D1 | 20c black | 8.75 | 8.00 |
| | Never hinged | | 12.00 | |

Same Overprinted in Red on four 5c
stamps

| 7LE6 | D1 | 20c black | 30.00 | 25.00 |
| | Never hinged | | 45.00 | |

SD1

1936   Unwmk.   Perf. 11½

7LE7	SD1	20c green & blk	7.25	5.50
7LE8	SD1	20c green & red	7.25	5.50
	Set, never hinged		22.50	

Nos. 7LE7-7LE8 exist with control number
on back. Value $42.50 each.

CADIZ ISSUE SEMI-POSTAL STAMPS

Stamps of Spain, 1931-
36, Surcharged in Black
or Red

1936   Unwmk.   Imperf.

| 8LB1 | A108 | 1c + 5c blue grn | .20 | .20 |

Perf. 11½x11, 11½

8LB2	A108	2c + 5c orange brn	.20	.20
8LB3	A103	5c + 5c choc (R)	.45	.45
8LB4	A110	10c + 5c green	.45	.45
8LB5	A111	15c + 5c Prus grn (R)	2.75	2.75
8LB6	A95	20c + 5c dk vio (R)	3.25	3.25
8LB7	A104	25c + 5c lake	2.50	2.50
8LB8	A113	30c + 5c rose red	1.40	1.40
8LB9	A100	40c + 5c dk blue (R)	3.25	3.25
8LB10	A97	50c + 5c dk blue	6.50	6.50
	Nos. 8LB1-8LB10 (10)		20.95	20.95

CANARY ISLANDS AIR POST STAMPS

**Issued for Use via the Lufthansa
Service**

Stamps of Spain, 1932-
34, Surcharged in Blue

1936, Oct. 27   Unwmk.   Imperf.

| 9LC1 | A108 | 50c on 1c bl grn | 27.50 | 17.50 |

Perf. 11½x11

9LC2	A108	80c on 2c buff	14.50	6.50
9LC3	A103	1.25p on 5c choc	30.00	17.50
	Nos. 9LC1-9LC3 (3)		72.00	41.50
	Set, never hinged		82.50	

The date July 18, 1936, in the overprints of
Nos. 9LC1-9LC22 marks the beginning of the
Franco insurrection.

Spain Nos. 542, 543,
528 and 641
Surcharged in Black,
Red or Green

The surcharge on Nos. 9LC4 and 9LC6
exists in two types: Type I, 2½-3mm space
between numerals and "Cts.". Type II, 1½-
2mm space between numerals and "Cts."

1936-37   Imperf.

9LC4	A108	50c on 1c bl (I)	4.50	2.75
a.	Overprint type II		11.00	7.75
9LC5	A108	50c on 1c bl grn (R) ('37)	4.50	2.75

Perf. 11, 11½x11

9LC6	A108	80c on 2c buff (I)	2.25	1.60
a.	Overprint type II		5.50	3.25
9LC7	A108	80c on 2c buff (R)	3.25	1.60
9LC8	A103	1.25 Pts on 5c choc (R)	6.25	4.50
9LC9	A103	Pts 1.25 on 5c choc (R) ('37)	17.00	11.00
9LC10	A161	1.25p on 5c brn (G) ('37)	3.25	1.40
	Nos. 9LC4-9LC10 (7)		41.00	25.60
	Set, never hinged		60.00	

Issued: Nos. 9LC4, 9LC6, 11/28/36; No.
9LC8, 1/7/37; Nos. 9LC4a, 9LC6a, 9LC9,
2/12/37; Nos. 9LC5, 9LC7, 9LC10, 3/2/37.

Spain Nos. 542, 543
and 641 Surcharged in
Blue

1937, Mar. 31   Imperf.

The surcharge on Nos. 9LC11-9LC13 exists
in two types: Type I, 18mm tall. Type II, 20mm
tall.

| 9LC11 | A108 | 50c on 1c bl grn (I) | 11.00 | 5.50 |
| a. | Overprint type II | | 4.50 | 2.25 |

Perf. 11

9LC12	A108	80c on 2c buff (I)	11.00	4.50
a.	Overprint type II		2.75	1.10
9LC13	A161	1.25p on 5c brown (I)	3.25	1.10
	Nos. 9LC11-9LC13 (3)		25.25	11.10
	Set, never hinged		37.50	

Type II overprints issued 4/17/37.

Stamps of Spain, 1931-
1936, Surcharged in
Blue or Red (#9LC17,
9LC19)

The surcharge on Nos. 9LC15 and 9LC18
exists in two types: Type I, 2mm space
between "+" and denomination. Type II, "+"
abuts surcharged denomination. Other values
are Type I.

1937

9LC14	A104	25c + 50c lake	45.00	10.00
9LC15	A162	30c + 80c rose	16.00	7.75
a.	Overprint type II		16.00	7.75
9LC16	A162	30c + 1.25p rose	20.00	8.25
9LC17	A97	50c + 1.25p dp bl	26.00	11.00
9LC18	A100	60c + 80c ap grn	21.00	8.75
a.	Overprint type II		22.50	10.00
9LC19	A105	1p + 1.25p bl blk	65.00	22.50
	Nos. 9LC14-9LC19 (6)		193.00	68.25
	Set, never hinged		250.00	

The surcharge represents the airmail rate
and the basic stamp the postage rate.
Issued: 9LC15a, 9LC18a, 4/15. 9LC14-
9LC19, 5/5.

Spain Nos. 542, 624
and 641 Surcharged in
Black

1937, May 25   Unwmk.   Imperf.

| 9LC20 | A108 | 50c on 1c bl grn | 7.75 | 4.50 |

Perf. 11½, 11½x11

9LC21	A143	80c on 2c org brn	6.50	2.25
9LC22	A161	1.25p on 5c gray brn	6.50	2.25
	Nos. 9LC20-9LC22 (3)		20.75	9.00
	Set, never hinged		27.50	

Stamps and Type of
Spain, 1933-36,
Surcharged in Black

1937, July   Perf. 13½x13, 11, 11½

9LC23	A143	50c on 2c org brn	3.25	2.25
9LC24	A126	80c on 2c org brn	250.00	140.00
9LC25	A161	80c on 5c gray brn	3.25	2.25
9LC26	A108	1.25p on 1c bl grn	3.75	2.25
9LC27	A161	2.50p on 10c grn	14.50	8.75

Spain Nos. 647, 650
and 652 Surcharged in
Black or Red

Perf. 11

| 9LC28 | A162 | 30c + 80c rose | 2.75 | 1.40 |
| 9LC29 | A162 | 50c + 1.25p dk bl (R) | 9.50 | 5.00 |

9LC30 A162 1p + 1.25p bl
        (R)   14.50   8.75
Nos. 9LC23-9LC30 (8)   301.50 170.65
Set, never hinged   375.00

See note after No. 9LC19.

AP1

Perf. 14x13½
1937, July 16   **Wmk. 116**
Surcharge in Various Colors
9LC31 AP1   50c on 5c ultra
        (Br)   2.75   2.50
9LC32 AP1   80c on 5c ultra
        (G)   1.90   1.75
9LC33 AP1 1.25p on 5c ultra
        (V)   2.25   2.25
Nos. 9LC31-9LC33 (3)   6.90   6.50
Set, never hinged   10.00

Spain Nos. 641, 643
and 640 Surcharged
in Green or Orange

1937, Oct. 29   **Unwmk.**   **Perf. 11**
9LC34 A161   50c on 5c (G)   8.50   3.75
9LC35 A161   80c on 10c (O)   5.25   2.75
9LC36 A160 1.25p on 2c (G)   9.50   7.25
Nos. 9LC34-9LC36 (3)   23.25 13.75
Set, never hinged   32.50

Spain Nos. 638, 640
and 643 Surcharged in
Red, Blue or Violet

1937, Dec. 23   **Imperf.**
9LC37 A159   50c on 1c (R)   9.50   4.50
Perf. 11, 11x11½
9LC38 A160   80c on 2c (Bl)   3.75   2.75
9LC39 A161 1.25p on 10c (V)   8.50   3.50
Nos. 9LC37-9LC39 (3)   21.75 10.75
Set, never hinged   32.50

Spain Nos. 647, 650 to
652 Surcharged in
Black, Green or Brown

1937, Dec. 29
9LC40 A162 30c + 30c rose   4.50   3.75
9LC41 A162 50c + 2.50p dk
         bl (G)   29.00 21.00
9LC42 A162 60c + 2.30p yel
               29.00 21.00
9LC43 A162   1p + 5p bl (Br)   35.00 21.00
Nos. 9LC40-9LC43 (4)   97.50 66.75
Set, never hinged   110.00

See note after No. 9LC19.

Stamps of Spain, 1936,
Surcharged in Black,
Green, Blue or Red

1938, Feb. 2   **Perf. 11, 11½, 11x11½**
9LC44 A160   50c on 2c brn   5.00   3.75
9LC45 A161   80c on 5c brn
        (G)   3.75   3.25
9LC46 A162   80c on 30c rose
        (Bl)   4.50   2.50
9LC47 A161 1.25p on 10c grn
        (Bl)   4.50   3.25
9LC48 A162 1.25p on 50c dk
         bl (R)   4.50   2.75
Nos. 9LC44-9LC48 (5)   22.25 15.50
Set, never hinged   27.50

Spain Nos. 645, 646
and 649 Surcharged in
Brown, Green or Violet

1938, Feb. 14
9LC51 A162 2.50p on 20c
        (Br)   50.00 25.00
9LC52 A162   5p on 25c
        (G)   50.00 25.00
9LC53 A162   10p on 40c (V)   50.00 25.00
Nos. 9LC51-9LC53 (3)   150.00 75.00
Set, never hinged   175.00

MALAGA ISSUE

Stamps of 1920-36
Overprinted in Black or
Red

1937   **Unwmk.**   **Imperf.**
10L1 A47   1c blue green   .20   .20
10L2 A108 1c blue green   .20   .20
10L3 A108 1c lt green (R)   .20   .20
Perf. 13½, 13½x13, 11, 11½x11
10L4 A108   2c orange brn   14.50 14.50
10L5 A126   2c orange brn   .20   .20
10L6 A103   5c chocolate (R)   .20   .20
10L7 A96   10c yellow green   12.00 12.00
10L8 A110   10c emerald   .30   .30
10L9 A111   15c Prus grn (R)   .55   .55
10L10 A97   15c blue grn (R)   .55   .55
10L11 A95   20c dk violet (R)   .50   .50
10L12 A99   25c lake   1.50   1.50
10L13 A104   25c lake   .50   .50
10L14 A113   30c carmine   .50   .50
10L15 A129   30c carmine rose   2.50   2.50
10L16 A100   40c blue (R)   .45   .45
10L17 A97   50c dk blue (R)   2.50   2.50
10L18 A100   60c apple green   1.40   1.40
10L19 A105   1p black (R)   2.75   2.75
Nos. 10L1-10L19 (19)   41.50 41.50

Stamps of 1932-35 Overprinted in Red
or Black in panes of 25, reading down.
"8.2.37" and "¡Arriba Espana!" form the
lower half of all overprints. The upper
half varies.

   Overprint a (1st and 2nd rows): "MALAGA
AGRADECIDA A TRANQUILLO-BIANCHI"
   Overprint b (3rd row): "MALAGA A SU SAL-
VADOR QUEIPO DE LLANO"
   Overprint c (4th and 5th rows): "MALAGA A
SU CAUDILLO FRANCO"
   Values are for vertical strips of 3 containing
examples of each overprint type.

1937   **Perf. 11½**
10L20 A111 15c Prus grn (R)   5.50   5.50
   a.   15c single stamp, ovpt. a   .85   .85
   b.   15c single stamp, ovpt. b   1.60   1.60
   c.   15c single stamp, ovpt. c   .85   .85
10L21 A113 30c rose red (Bk)   5.50   5.50
   a.   30c single stamp, ovpt. a   .85   .85
   b.   30c single stamp, ovpt. b   1.60   1.60
   c.   30c single stamp, ovpt. c   .85   .85
10L22 A97 50c dk blue (R)   8.75   8.75
   a.   50c single stamp, ovpt. a   1.60   1.60
   b.   50c single stamp, ovpt. b   3.25   3.25
   c.   50c single stamp, ovpt. c   1.60   1.60
10L23 A100 60c apple grn (Bk)   11.00 11.00
   a.   60c single stamp, ovpt. a   1.60   1.60
   b.   60c single stamp, ovpt. b   3.25   3.25
   c.   60c single stamp, ovpt. c   1.60   1.60
Nos. 10L20-10L23 (4)   30.75 30.75

SPECIAL DELIVERY STAMP

Overprinted like Nos. 10L1-10L19 on
Type of Special Delivery Stamp of
1934

1937   **Perf. 10**
10LE1 SD7 20c rose red (Bk)   .45   .45

ORENSE ISSUE

Stamps of 1931-36
Overprinted in Red,
Blue or Black

1936   **Imperf.**
11L1 A108   1c blue grn (Bl)   .45   .45
   a.   Red overprint   1.10   1.10
Perf. 11½, 13½x13
11L2 A108   2c org brn (Bk)   3.50   3.25
11L3 A126   2c org brn (Bk)   .65   .65
11L4 A103   5c brown (R)   1.50   1.50
11L5 A110   10c lt green (Bl)   2.25   2.25
   a.   Red overprint   11.00 11.00
11L6 A111   15c Prus grn (R)   3.25   3.25
11L7 A95   20c violet (Bl)   3.25   3.25
11L8 A104   25c lake (Bk)   3.75   3.75
11L9 A113   30c rose red (Bl)   2.75   2.75
   a.   Black overprint   5.50   5.50
11L10 A100   40c blue (R)   3.75   3.75
   a.   Imperf, pair   50.00
11L11 A97   50c dark blue (R)   6.50   6.50
11L12 A100   60c apple grn (Bk)   4.75   4.75
   a.   Red overprint   17.00 17.00
   b.   As "a," Imperf, pair   50.00
Nos. 11L1-11L12 (12)   36.35 36.10

SEMI-POSTAL STAMPS

Stamps of Spain, 1931-
36, Surcharged in Blue
on front and on back of
stamp

1936-37   **Unwmk.**   **Imperf.**
11LB1 A47   1c + 5c bl
         grn   2.25   2.25
11LB2 A108   1c + 5c
         green   .40   .40
Perf. 13½x13, 11½, 11½x11
11LB3 A108   2c + 5c org
         brn   .45   .45
11LB4 A126   2c + 5c red
         brn   .45   .45
11LB5 A103   5c + 5c choc   .65   .65
11LB6 A110   10c + 5c emer   .65   .65
11LB7 A111   15c + 5c Prus
         grn   .95   .95
11LB8 A95   20c + 5c vio-
         let   .65   .65
11LB9 A104   25c + 5c lake   .95   .95
11LB10 A113   30c + 5c rose
         red   2.75   2.75
11LB11 A117   30c + 5c rose
         red   42.50 42.50
11LB12 A100   60c + 5c apple grn   190.00 190.00
Nos. 11LB1-11LB12 (12)   242.65 242.65

SPECIAL DELIVERY STAMPS

Type of Special Delivery Stamp
of 1934 Overprinted "!VIVA ESPANA!"
in Blue or Black

1936   **Perf. 10**
11LE1 SD7 20c rose red (Bl)   1.90   1.90
11LE2 SD7 20c rose red (Bk)   4.25   4.25
Same with Surcharge "+ 5 cts."
11LE3 SD7 20c + 5c rose red   1.00   1.00
**Same Surcharge, Overprint
Repeated at Right**
11LE4 SD7 20c + 5c rose red   1.10   1.10
Nos. 11LE1-11LE4 (4)   8.25   8.25

SAN SEBASTIAN ISSUE

For Use in Province of Guipuzcoa

Stamps of 1931-36
Overprinted in Red or
Blue

1937   **Unwmk.**   **Imperf.**
12L1 A108   1c bl grn (R)   .65   .65
Perf. 11, 13½
12L2 A108   2c buff (Bl)   1.00   1.50
12L3 A126   2c org brn (Bl)   2.10   2.10
12L4 A95   5c chocolate (R)   5.00   5.00
12L5 A103   5c chocolate (R)   1.75   1.75
12L6 A110   10c emerald (R)   1.75   1.75
12L7 A111   15c Prus grn (R)   2.10   2.10
12L8 A95   20c dk violet (R)   2.75   2.75
12L9 A104   25c car lake (Bl)   2.75   2.75
12L10 A113   30c rose red (Bl)   2.75   2.75
12L11 A100   40c blue (R)   5.50   5.50
12L12 A97   50c dark blue (R)   5.50   5.50
Nos. 12L1-12L12 (12)   33.60 34.10

SANTA CRUZ DE TENERIFE ISSUE

Stamps of Spain, 1931-
36 Overprinted in Black
or Red

1936   **Unwmk.**   **Imperf.**
13L1 A108   1c bl grn (R)   .75   .75
13L2 A108   1c bl grn (Bk)   2.75   2.75
Perf. 11, 13½
13L3 A108   2c buff (Bk)   5.50   5.50
13L4 A126   2c org brn (Bk)   .95   .95
13L5 A103   5c choc (R)   3.00   3.00
13L6 A110   10c green (R)   3.00   3.00
13L7 A104   25c lake (R)   11.00 11.00
13L8 A100   40c dk blue (R)   3.25   3.25
13L9 A107   10p dp brn (R)   225.00 225.00
Nos. 13L1-13L9 (9)   255.20 255.20

Many forgeries of #13L9 exist.

SEVILLE ISSUE

Stamps of Spain, 1931-
36, Overprinted in Black
or Red

1936   **Imperf.**
14L1 A108   1c blue grn (Bk)   .25   .25
Perf. 13½x13, 11, 11½x11
14L2 A126   2c org brn (Bk)   .30   .30
14L3 A103   5c chocolate (R)   .40   .40
14L4 A110   10c emerald (Bk)   .50   .50
14L5 A111   15c Prus grn (R)   1.25   1.25
14L6 A95   20c violet (R)   1.25   1.25
14L7 A104   25c lake (Bk)   1.25   1.25
14L8 A113   30c carmine (Bk)   1.25   1.25
14L9 A128   30c rose red (Bk)   7.50   7.50
14L10 A100   40c blue (R)   5.00   5.00
14L11 A97   50c dk blue (R)   5.00   5.00
14L12 A100   60c apple grn (Bk)   6.00   6.00
Nos. 14L1-14L12 (12)   29.95 29.95

Stamps of Spain, 1931-
36, Handstamped in
Black

1936   **Imperf**
14L13 A108   1c blue grn   .25   .25
Perf. 13½x13, 11, 11x11½, 11½x11
14L14 A126   2c orange brn   .40   .40
14L15 A103   5c chocolate   .40   .40
14L16 A110   10c emerald   .40   .40
14L17 A111   15c Prus green   .50   .50
14L18 A95   20c violet   .50   .50
14L19 A104   25c lake   .50   .50
14L20 A113   30c carmine   .50   .50
14L21 A128   30c rose red   2.75   2.75
14L22 A100   40c blue   .95   .95
14L23 A97   50c dk blue   2.75   2.75
14L24 A100   60c apple grn   .90   .90
14L25 A105   1p black   2.75   2.75
14L26 AP26   2p gray blue   12.00 12.00
14L27 A106   4p magenta   6.50   6.50
14L28 A107   10p deep brown   9.50   9.50
Nos. 14L13-14L28,14LE1 (17)   42.00 42.00

The date "Julio-1936" in the overprints of
Nos. 14L1-14L28 and 14LE1 marks the beginning of the Franco insurrection.

SPECIAL DELIVERY STAMP

Overprinted like Nos. 14L13-14L25 on
Type of Special Delivery Stamp of
1934

1936   **Perf. 10**
14LE1 SD7 20c rose red   1.75   1.75

SPANISH GUINEA

'spa-nish 'gi-nē

LOCATION — In western Africa, bordering on the Gulf of Guinea
GOVT. — Spanish Colony
AREA — 10,852 sq. mi.
POP. — 212,000 (est. 1957)
CAPITAL — Santa Isabel

Spanish Guinea 1-84 were issued for and used only in the continental area later called Rio Muni. From 1909 to 1960, Spanish Guinea also included Fernando Po, Elobey, Annobon and Corisco.
Fernando Po and Rio Muni united in 1968 to become the Republic of Equatorial Guinea.

100 Centimos = 1 Peseta

Catalogue values for unused stamps in this country are for Never Hinged items, beginning with Scott 319 in the regular postage section, Scott B13 in the semipostal section, and Scott C13 in the airpost section.

King Alfonso XIII
A1   A2

1902   **Unwmk.**   **Typo.**   *Perf. 14*
Blue Control Numbers on Back

1	A1	5c dark green	10.00	5.75
2	A1	10c indigo	10.00	5.75
3	A1	25c claret	75.00	42.50
4	A1	50c deep brown	75.00	42.50
5	A1	75c violet	75.00	42.50
6	A1	1p carmine rose	110.00	42.50
7	A1	2p olive green	140.00	92.50
8	A1	5p dull red	225.00	160.00
		Nos. 1-8 (8)	720.00	434.00
		Set, never hinged	1,100.	

Exists imperf, value set $1,500.

Revenue Stamps Surcharged

1903   *Imperf.*
Blue or Black Control Numbers on Back

8A	10c on 25c blk (R)		525.00	190.00
8B	10c on 50c org (Bl)		110.00	32.50
8D	10c on 1p 25c car (Bk)		725.00	325.00
8F	10c on 2p cl (Bk)		775.00	500.00
g.	Blue surcharge		1,200.	725.00
8H	10c on 2p 50c red brn (Bl)		1,150.	625.00
8J	10c on 5p ol blk (R)		1,400	425.00

Nos. 8A-8J are surcharged on stamps inscribed "Posesiones Espanolas de Africa Occidental" and "1903," with arms at left.

This surcharge was also applied to revenue stamps of 10, 15, 25, 50, 75 and 100 pesetas and in other colors.
See Nos. 98-101C.

1903   **Typo.**   *Perf. 14*
Blue Control Numbers on Back

9	A2	¼c black	1.10	.75
10	A2	½c blue green	1.10	.75
11	A2	1c claret	1.10	.65
12	A2	2c dark olive	1.10	.65
13	A2	3c dark brown	1.10	.65
14	A2	4c vermilion	1.10	.65
15	A2	5c black brown	1.10	.65
16	A2	10c red brown	1.75	.65
17	A2	15c dark blue	6.25	5.75
18	A2	25c orange buff	6.25	5.75
19	A2	50c carmine lake	11.50	12.50
20	A2	75c violet	16.00	12.50
21	A2	1p blue green	25.00	20.00
22	A2	2p dark green	25.00	20.00
23	A2	3p scarlet	70.00	26.00
24	A2	4p dull blue	82.50	45.00

25	A2	5p dark violet	150.00	65.00
26	A2	10p carmine rose	225.00	90.00
		Nos. 9-26 (18)	626.95	308.00
		Set, never hinged	1,100.	

1905

Same, Dated "1905"
Blue Control Numbers on Back

27	A2	1c black	.20	.20
28	A2	2c blue grn	.20	.20
29	A2	3c claret	.20	.20
30	A2	4c bronze grn	.20	.20
31	A2	5c dark brown	.20	.20
32	A2	10c red	1.10	.65
33	A2	15c black brown	3.25	2.25
34	A2	25c chocolate	3.25	2.25
35	A2	50c dark blue	7.25	5.25
36	A2	75c orange buff	7.75	5.25
37	A2	1p carmine rose	7.75	5.25
38	A2	2p violet	19.00	11.00
39	A2	3p blue green	50.00	22.50
40	A2	4p dark green	50.00	32.50
40A	A2	5p vermilion	80.00	35.00
41	A2	10p dull blue	140.00	110.00
		Nos. 27-41 (16)	370.35	232.90
		Set, never hinged	575.00	

Stamps of Elobey, 1905, Overprinted in Violet or Blue

1906

42	A1	1c rose	3.25	1.90
43	A1	2c deep violet	3.25	1.90
44	A1	3c black	3.25	1.90
45	A1	4c orange red	3.25	1.90
46	A1	5c deep green	3.25	1.90
47	A1	10c blue green	7.25	4.25
48	A1	15c violet	12.50	7.50
49	A1	25c rose lake	12.50	7.50
50	A1	50c orange buff	17.50	10.50
51	A1	75c dark blue	21.00	12.00
52	A1	1p red brown	37.50	21.00
53	A1	2p black brown	55.00	32.50
54	A1	3p vermilion	77.50	45.00
55	A1	4p dark brown	350.00	210.00
56	A1	5p bronze green	350.00	210.00
57	A1	10p claret	1,400.	850.00
		Nos. 42-54 (13)	257.00	149.75

King Alfonso XIII
A3   A4

1907   **Typo.**
Blue Control Numbers on Back

58	A3	1c dark green	.55	.20
59	A3	2c dull blue	.55	.20
60	A3	3c violet	.55	.20
61	A3	4c yellow grn	.55	.20
62	A3	5c carmine lake	.55	.20
63	A3	10c orange	3.00	1.00
64	A3	15c brown	2.25	.65
65	A3	25c dark blue	2.25	.65
66	A3	50c black brown	2.25	.65
67	A3	75c blue green	2.25	.65
68	A3	1p red	4.25	1.10
69	A3	2p dark brown	7.25	5.00
70	A3	3p olive gray	7.25	5.00
71	A3	4p maroon	9.25	5.00
72	A3	5p green	9.75	7.50
73	A3	10p red violet	15.00	9.75
		Nos. 58-73 (16)	67.50	37.95
		Set, never hinged	100.00	

Issue of 1907 Surcharged in Black or Red

1908-09

74	A3	05c on 1c dk grn (R)	3.25	1.60
75	A3	05c on 2c blue (R)	3.25	1.60
76	A3	05c on 3c violet	3.25	1.60
77	A3	05c on 4c yel grn	3.25	1.60
78	A3	05c on 10c orange	3.25	1.60
a.	Red surcharge		6.50	3.00
84	A3	15c on 10c orange	17.00	10.00
		Nos. 74-84 (6)	33.25	18.00

Many stamps of this issue are found with the surcharge inverted, sideways, double and in both black and red. Other stamps of the 1907 issue are known with this surcharge but are not believed to have been put in use. Value, each $17.

1909   **Typo.**   *Perf. 14½*
Blue Control Numbers on Back

85	A4	1c orange brown	.20	.20
86	A4	2c rose	.20	.20
87	A4	5c dark green	1.00	.20
88	A4	10c vermilion	.30	.20
89	A4	15c dark brown	.30	.20
90	A4	20c violet	.55	.25
91	A4	25c dull blue	.55	.25
92	A4	30c chocolate	.65	.20
93	A4	40c lake	.40	.20
94	A4	50c dark violet	.40	.20
95	A4	1p blue green	11.00	5.50
96	A4	4p orange	2.75	3.25
97	A4	10p red	2.75	3.25
		Nos. 85-97 (13)	21.05	14.10
		Set, never hinged	32.50	

For overprints see Nos. 102-114.

Revenue Stamps Surcharged like Nos. 8A-8J in Black

1909   *Imperf.*
With or Without Control Numbers on Back

98		10c on 50c bl grn	80.00	52.50
a.	Red or violet surcharge		100.00	72.50
99		10c on 1p 25c violet	100.00	72.50
100		10c on 2p dk brn	550.00	325.00
100A		10c on 5p dk vio	550.00	325.00
101		10c on 25p red brn	725.00	525.00
101A		10c on 50p brn lil	2,500.	1,450.
101B		10c on 75p carmine	2,500.	1,450.
101C		10c on 100p orange	2,500.	1,450.

Nos. 98-101C are surcharged on undated stamps, arms centered. Stamps inscribed: "Territorios Espanoles del Africa Occidental." Basic revenue stamps similar to Rio de Oro type A3.

Stamps of 1909 Overprinted with Handstamp in Black, Blue, Green or Red

1911

102	A4	1c orange brn (Bl)	.25	.20
103	A4	2c rose (G)	.25	.20
104	A4	5c dk green (R)	1.25	.20
105	A4	10c vermilion	.70	.30
106	A4	15c dk brown (R)	1.25	.50
107	A4	20c violet	1.50	.70
108	A4	25c dull blue (R)	1.75	1.60
109	A4	30c choc (Bl)	2.50	2.25
110	A4	40c lake (Bl)	2.75	2.25
111	A4	50c dark violet	4.50	3.25
112	A4	1p blue grn (R)	37.50	27.50
113	A4	4p orange (R)	19.00	15.00
114	A4	10p red (G)	25.00	27.50
		Nos. 102-114 (13)	98.20	81.45
		Set, never hinged	150.00	

The date "1911" is missing from the overprint on the first stamp in each row, or ten times in each sheet of 100 stamps. This variety occurs on all stamps of the series. Value, set $400.

King Alfonso XIII
A5   A6

1912   **Typo.**   *Perf. 13½*
Blue Control Numbers on Back

115	A5	1c black	.20	.20
116	A5	2c dark brown	.20	.20
117	A5	5c deep green	.20	.20
118	A5	10c red	.20	.20
119	A5	15c claret	.20	.20
120	A5	20c red	.30	.20
121	A5	25c dull blue	.20	.20
122	A5	30c lake	2.50	1.90
123	A5	40c car rose	1.60	.75
124	A5	50c brown org	1.40	.25
125	A5	1p dark violet	1.60	.95
126	A5	4p lilac	3.75	1.90
127	A5	10p blue green	7.75	7.00
		Nos. 115-127 (13)	20.10	13.65
		Set, never hinged	32.50	

For overprints and surcharges see Nos. 141-157.

1914   *Perf. 13*
Blue Control Numbers on Back

128	A6	1c dull violet	.20	.20
129	A6	2c car rose	.20	.20
130	A6	5c deep green	.20	.20
131	A6	10c vermilion	.20	.20

132	A6	15c dark violet	.20	.20
133	A6	20c dark brown	.70	.40
134	A6	25c dark blue	.30	.20
135	A6	30c brown orange	1.10	.40
136	A6	40c blue green	1.10	.40
137	A6	50c dp claret	.55	.25
138	A6	1p vermilion	1.25	1.50
139	A6	4p maroon	5.00	3.25
140	A6	10p olive black	5.50	6.00
		Nos. 128-140 (13)	16.50	13.40
		Set, never hinged	25.00	

Stamps with these or similar overprints are unauthorized and fraudulent.

Stamps of 1912 Overprinted

1917   *Perf. 13½*

141	A5	1c black	90.00	60.00
142	A5	2c dark brown	90.00	60.00
143	A5	5c deep green	.25	.20
144	A5	10c red	.25	.20
145	A5	15c claret	.25	.20
146	A5	20c red	.25	.20
147	A5	25c dull blue	.25	.20
148	A5	30c lake	.25	.20
149	A5	40c carmine rose	.50	.25
150	A5	50c brown orange	.25	.20
151	A5	1p dark violet	.50	.25
152	A5	4p lilac	6.25	3.00
153	A5	10p blue green	6.25	3.00
		Nos. 141-153 (13)	195.20	127.90
		Set, never hinged	225.00	

Nos. 143-153 exist with overprint double, inverted, in dark blue, reading "9117" and in pairs one without overprint.

Stamps of 1917 Surcharged

1918

154	A5	5c on 40c car rose	27.50	11.00
155	A5	10c on 4p lilac	27.50	11.00
156	A5	15c on 20c red	50.00	19.00
157	A5	25c on 1p bl grn	50.00	19.00
a.	"52" for "25"		375.00	325.00
		Nos. 154-157 (4)	155.00	60.00
		Set, never hinged	225.00	

The varieties "Gents" and "Censt" occur on Nos. 154-157. Values 50 percent more.

King Alfonso XIII
A7   A8

1919   **Typo.**   *Perf. 13*
Blue Control Numbers on Back

158	A7	1c lilac	.85	.25
159	A7	2c rose	.85	.25
160	A7	5c vermilion	.85	.25
161	A7	10c violet	1.40	.25
162	A7	15c brown	1.40	.40
163	A7	20c blue	1.40	.65
164	A7	25c green	1.40	.65
a.	25c blue (error)		52.50	
165	A7	30c orange	1.75	.65
166	A7	40c orange	3.75	.65
167	A7	50c red	3.75	.65
168	A7	1p light green	3.75	2.25
169	A7	4p claret	8.25	8.50
170	A7	10p brown	17.00	16.00
		Nos. 158-170 (13)	46.40	31.40
		Set, never hinged	60.00	

1920
Blue Control Numbers on Back
171	A8	1c brown	.20	.20
172	A8	2c dull rose	.20	.20
173	A8	5c gray green	.20	.20
174	A8	10c dull rose	.20	.20
175	A8	15c orange	.20	.20
176	A8	20c yellow	.20	.20
177	A8	25c dull blue	.75	.20
178	A8	30c greenish blue	27.50	17.50
179	A8	40c lt brown	1.25	.20
180	A8	50c lilac	1.40	.20
181	A8	1p light red	1.40	.20
182	A8	4p bright rose	4.50	4.50
183	A8	10p gray lilac	6.50	8.75
		Nos. 171-183 (13)	44.50	32.75
		Set, never hinged	65.00	

A9

Nipa House — A10

1922
Blue Control Numbers on Back
184	A9	1c dark brown	.50	.20
185	A9	2c claret	.50	.20
186	A9	5c blue green	.50	.20
187	A9	10c pale red	3.50	.95
188	A9	15c orange	.50	.20
189	A9	20c lilac	2.25	.85
190	A9	25c dark blue	3.75	1.00
191	A9	30c violet	3.50	1.10
192	A9	40c turq blue	2.50	.55
193	A9	50c deep rose	2.50	.55
194	A9	1p myrtle green	2.50	.55
195	A9	4p red brown	10.50	10.50
196	A9	10p yellow	21.00	20.00
		Nos. 184-196 (13)	54.00	36.85
		Set, never hinged	77.50	

1924
Blue Control Numbers on Back
197	A10	5c choc & bl	.20	.20
198	A10	10c gray grn & bl	.20	.20
199	A10	15c rose & blk	.20	.20
200	A10	20c violet & blk	.20	.20
201	A10	25c org red & blk	.40	.25
202	A10	30c orange & blk	.40	.20
203	A10	40c dl bl & blk	.40	.20
204	A10	50c claret & blk	.40	.20
205	A10	60c red brn & blk	.40	.20
206	A10	1p dk vio & blk	1.60	.20
a.		Center inverted	275.00	125.00
207	A10	4p brt bl & blk	3.75	2.25
208	A10	10p bl grn & blk	8.75	4.50
		Nos. 197-208 (12)	16.90	8.80
		Set, never hinged	22.50	

Seville-Barcelona Issue of Spain, 1929, Overprinted in Red or Blue

1929   *Perf. 11*
209	A52	5c rose lake	.25	.30
210	A53	10c green (R)	.25	.30
211	A50	15c Prus bl (R)	.25	.30
212	A51	20c purple (R)	.25	.30
213	A50	25c brt rose	.25	.30
214	A52	30c black brn	.25	.30
215	A53	40c dk blue (R)	.45	.45
216	A51	50c dp orange	.45	.45
217	A52	1p blue blk (R)	7.75	4.50
218	A53	4p deep rose	16.00	8.75
219	A53	10p brown	30.00	17.00
		Nos. 209-219 (11)	56.15	32.95
		Set, never hinged	87.50	

Porter A11

Drummers A12

King Alfonso XIII and Queen Victoria — A13

1931   Engr.   *Perf. 14*
220	A11	1c blue green	.20	.20
221	A11	2c red brown	.20	.20

Blue Control Numbers on Back
222	A11	5c brown black	.20	.20
223	A11	10c light green	.20	.20
224	A11	15c dark green	.20	.20
225	A11	20c deep violet	.20	.20
226	A12	25c carmine	.20	.20
227	A12	30c lake	.30	.20
228	A12	40c dark blue	.75	.55
229	A12	50c red orange	1.60	1.10
230	A13	80c blue violet	2.75	1.60
231	A13	1p black	5.00	4.50
232	A13	4p violet rose	32.50	17.00
233	A13	5p dark brown	14.50	12.00
		Nos. 220-233 (14)	58.80	38.35
		Set, never hinged	97.50	

Exist imperf. Value for set, $300.
See Nos. 262-271. For overprints and surcharges see Nos. 234-277, 282-283, 298.

REPUBLICA

Stamps of 1931 Overprinted

ESPAÑOLA

1931
234	A11	1c blue green	.20	.20
235	A11	2c red brown	.20	.20
236	A11	5c brown black	.20	.20
237	A11	10c light green	.20	.20
238	A11	15c dark green	.20	.20
239	A11	20c deep violet	.20	.20
240	A12	25c carmine	.20	.20
241	A12	30c lake	.40	.20
242	A12	40c dark blue	1.40	.45
243	A12	50c red orange	9.75	5.50
244	A13	80c blue violet	3.00	1.60
245	A13	1p black	10.00	3.50
246	A13	4p violet rose	17.50	10.50
247	A13	5p dark brown	17.50	10.50
		Nos. 234-247 (14)	60.95	33.65
		Set, never hinged	90.00	

Stamps of 1931 Overprinted in Red or Blue

1933
248	A11	1c blue grn (R)	.20	.20
249	A11	2c red brown (Bl)	.20	.20
250	A11	5c brown blk (R)	.20	.20
251	A11	10c lt green (Bl)	.20	.20
252	A11	15c dk green (R)	.20	.20
253	A11	20c dp violet (Bl)	.40	.20
254	A12	25c carmine (Bl)	.40	.20
255	A12	30c lake (Bl)	.45	.20
256	A12	40c dk blue (R)	2.75	.70
257	A12	50c red orange (Bl)	17.00	3.50
258	A12	80c blue vio (R)	5.50	3.00
259	A13	1p black (R)	19.00	3.25
260	A13	4p violet rose (Bl)	35.00	15.00
261	A13	5p dk brown (Bl)	35.00	15.00
		Nos. 248-261 (14)	116.50	42.05
		Set, never hinged	160.00	

Types of 1931
Without Control Number

1934-35   Engr.   *Perf. 10*
262	A11	1c blue green ('35)	8.25	.20
263	A11	2c red brown ('35)	8.25	.20
264	A11	5c brown blk	1.50	.20
265	A11	10c light green	1.50	.20
266	A11	15c dark green	2.75	.20
267	A12	30c rose red	3.25	.20
268	A12	50c indigo ('35)	7.25	.70
		Nos. 262-268 (7)	32.75	1.90
		Set, never hinged	47.50	

Types of 1931

1941   Litho.   Unwmk.
269	A11	5c olive gray	2.10	.20
270	A11	20c violet	2.10	.20
271	A12	40c gray green	.85	.20
		Nos. 269-271 (3)	5.05	.60
		Set, never hinged	6.25	

Stamps of 1931-33 Surcharged in Black

a   b

1936-37   *Perf. 10, 14*
272	A12	30c on 40c (#228)	3.75	2.25
273	A12	30c on 40c (#242)	15.00	3.50
274	A12	30c on 40c (#256)	57.50	17.50
		Nos. 272-274 (3)	76.25	23.25
		Set, never hinged	110.00	

The surcharge on Nos. 272-274 exists in two types, differing in the "3" which is scarcer in italic.

No. 268 Surcharged Type "b" in Red
275	A12	1p on 50c indigo	22.50
276	A12	4p on 50c indigo	72.50
277	A12	5p on 50c indigo	42.50
		Nos. 275-277 (3)	137.50

Nos. 275-277 were not issued.

Stamps of Spain, 1936, Overprinted in Black or Carmine

1938   *Perf. 11*
278	A161	10c gray green	1.50	.45
279	A162	15c gray black (C)	1.50	.45
280	A162	20c dark violet	3.50	1.40
281	A162	25c brown lake	3.50	1.40
		Nos. 278-281 (4)	10.00	3.70
		Set, never hinged	13.00	

Stamps of 1931-33, Surcharged in Black

1939
282	A13	40c on 80c (#244)	11.00	7.25
283	A13	40c on 80c (#258)	11.00	4.50
		Set, never hinged	30.00	

A14   A15

Revenue Stamps Surcharged in Black

1940-41   *Perf. 11½*
284	A14	5c on 35c pale grn	5.75	1.90
285	A14	25c on 60c org brn	5.75	2.25
286	A14	50c on 75c blk brn	8.00	2.50
		Nos. 284-286 (3)	19.50	6.65

Red Surcharge
287	A15	10c on 75c blk brn	8.00	2.50
288	A15	15c on 1.50p lt vio	5.75	2.25
289	A15	25c on 60c org brn	10.00	3.25
		Nos. 287-289 (3)	23.75	8.00

A16   A17

Black or Carmine Surcharge
Perf. 11
290	A16	1p on 17p deep red	45.00	13.50
291	A17	1p on 40p yel grn (C)	11.00	3.50

See No. C1.

A18   A19

Black Surcharge
Perf. 11, 13x12½
292	A18	5c carmine	5.50	1.40
293	A19	1p yellow	87.50	32.50

A20   General Francisco Franco — A21

Black Surcharge
294	A20	1p on 15c gray grn	9.50	3.25

1940   *Perf. 11½, 13½*
295	A21	5c olive brown	2.50	.40
296	A21	40c blue	3.75	.40
297	A21	50c green	4.50	.40
a.		50c greenish gray	19.00	7.25
		Nos. 295-297 (3)	10.75	1.20
		Set, never hinged	20.00	

Nos. 295-297 exist imperf. Value $45.

No. 270 Surcharged in Black

1942
298	A11	3p on 20c vio	8.75	1.25

Spain, Nos. 702 and 704 Overprinted in Carmine or Black

1942   *Perf. 9½x10½*
299	A166	1p gray blk (C)	.45	.20
300	A166	4p dl rose (Bk)	6.50	.65

The overprint on No. 299 exists in two types: Spacing between lines of 2mm, and spacing of 3mm. The 3mm spacing sells for about twice as much.

For surcharges and overprint see #302-303, C3.

Spain, No. 703 Overprinted in Carmine

1943
301	A166	2p dull brown	.85	.20

Nos. 299 and 301 Surcharged in Green   Habilitado para quince cts.

1949   Unwmk.   *Perf. 9½x10½*
302	A166	5c (cinco) on 1p gray blk	.25	.20
303	A166	15c (cinco) on 2p dl brn	.25	.20

The two types of No. 299, described in footnote, also exist on No. 302.

Men Poling
Canoe
A22

1949, Oct. 9   Litho.   Perf. 12½x13
304 A22 4p dk vio   .85 .65
   Never hinged   1.25
   UPU, 75th anniversary.

San Carlos
Bay — A23

Designs: Various Views

1949-50   Perf. 12½x13
305 A23 2c brown   .20 .20
306 A23 5c rose vio   .20 .20
307 A23 10c Prussian bl   .20 .20
308 A23 15c dp ol gray   .25 .20
309 A23 25c red brown   .25 .20
309A A23 30c brt yel ('50) .20 .20
310 A23 40c olive gray   .20 .20
311 A23 45c rose lake   .20 .20
312 A23 50c brn orange   .20 .20
312A A23 75c ultra ('50)   .20 .20
313 A23 90c dl bl grn   .25 .20
314 A23 1p gray   .90 .20
315 A23 1.35p violet   3.50 1.00
316 A23 2p sepia   9.50 2.00
317 A23 5p lilac rose   13.00 5.00
318 A23 10p light brn   52.50 20.00
   Nos. 305-318 (16)   81.75 30.40
   Set, never hinged   125.00

> Catalogue values for unused
> stamps in this section, from this
> point to the end of the section, are
> for Never Hinged items.

Surveyor
A24

1951, Dec. 5
319 A24 50c orange   .25 .20
320 A24 5p indigo   6.25 1.25
   Intl. Conference of West Africans, 1951.

Drummer
A25

1952, Mar. 10
321 A25 5c red brown   .20 .20
322 A25 50c olive gray   .20 .20
323 A25 5p violet   2.25 .20
   Nos. 321-323 (3)   2.65 .60

Musician
A26

Design: 60c, Musician facing right.

1953, July 1   Photo.
324 A26 15c sepia   .20 .20
325 A26 60c brown   .20 .20
   Nos. 324-325,B25-B26 (4) .80 .80

Woman and   Drummer
Dove   A28
A27

1953, Sept. 5   Perf. 13x12½
326 A27 5c orange   .20 .20
327 A27 10c brt lilac rose .20 .20
328 A27 60c brown   .20 .20
329 A28 1p dull purple   .85 .20
330 A28 1.90p greenish blk 2.25 .30
   Nos. 326-330 (5)   3.70 1.10

Tragocephala
Nobilis — A29

Butterfly: 60c, Papilio antimachus.

1953, Nov. 23
331 A29 15c dark green   .20 .20
332 A29 60c brown   .25 .20
   Nos. 331-332,B27-B28 (4) .85 .80
   Colonial Stamp Day.

Hunter
A30

Design: 60c, Hunter and elephant.

1954, June 10   Perf. 12½x13
333 A30 15c dark gray green .20 .20
334 A30 60c dark brown   .30 .20
   Nos. 333-334,B29-B30 (4) .90 .80

Swimming
Turtle
A31

1954, Nov. 23
335 A31 15c shown   .20 .20
336 A31 60c Shark   .30 .20
   Nos. 335-336,B31-B32 (4) .90 .80
   Colonial Stamp Day.

Manuel
Iradier y
Bulfy, Birth
Cent. (in
1954)
A32

1955, Jan. 18
337 A32 60c orange brown   .20 .20
338 A32 1p dark violet   2.75 .30

Priest Saying
Mass — A33

1955, June 1   Photo.   Perf. 13x12½
339 A33 50c olive gray   .20 .20
   Nos. 339,B33-B34 (3) .60 .60
   Centenary of the establishment of an Apostolic Prefecture at Fernando Po.

Palace of
Pardo
A34

1955, July 18   Perf. 12½x13
340 A34 5c ol brn   .20 .20
341 A34 15c brn lake   .20 .20
342 A34 80c Prus grn   .20 .20
   Nos. 340-342 (3)   .60 .60
   Treaty of Pardo, 1778.

Red-eared   Orchid — A36
Guenons — A35

1955, Nov. 23   Perf. 13x12½
343 A35 70c gray grn & bl .30 .20
   Nos. 343,B35-B36 (3) .70 .60
   Colonial Stamp Day.

1956, June 1   Unwmk.
Flower: 50c, Strophantus Kombe.
344 A36 20c bluish green   .20 .20
345 A36 50c brown   .20 .20
   Nos. 344-345,B37-B38 (4) .80 .80
   See Nos. 360-361, B53-B54.

Arms of Santa   African Gray
Isabel — A37   Parrot — A38

1956, Nov. 23   Perf. 13x12½
346 A37 70c light olive green .20 .20
   Nos. 346,B39-B40 (3) .60 .60
   Colonial Stamp Day.

1957, June 1   Photo.
347 A38 70c olive green   .20 .20
   Nos. 347,B41-B42 (3) .60 .60

Elephants
A39

Design: 70c, Elephant, vert.

Perf. 12½x13, 13x12½
1957, Nov. 23
348 A39 20c blue green   .20 .20
349 A39 70c emerald   .20 .20
   Nos. 348-349,B43-B44 (4) .80 .80
   Colonial Stamp Day.

Boxing
A40

Basketball   Preaching
A41   Missionary
                    A42

Various Sports: 15c, 2.30p, Jumping. 80c,
3p, Runner at finish line.

1958, Apr. 10   Photo.   Unwmk.
350 A40 5c violet brn   .20 .20
351 A41 10c orange brn   .20 .20
352 A40 15c brown   .20 .20
353 A41 80c green   .20 .20
354 A40 1p orange red   .20 .20
355 A41 2p rose lilac   .20 .20
356 A40 2.30p dl violet   .35 .20
357 A41 3p brt blue   .35 .20
   Nos. 350-357 (8)   1.90 1.60

1958, June 1   Perf. 13x12½
Design: 70c, Crucifix and missal.
358 A42 20c blue green   .20 .20
359 A42 70c green   .20 .20
   Nos. 358-359,B48-B49 (4) .80 .80
   Catholic missions in Spanish Guinea, 75th
anniv.

Type of 1956 Inscribed: "Pro-Infancia
1959"

1959, June 1   Perf. 13x12½
360 A36 20c Castor bean   .20 .20
361 A36 70c Digitalis   .20 .20
   Nos. 360-361,B53-B54 (4) .80 .80
   Promoting child welfare.
   Stamps of Spanish Guinea were succeeded
by those of Fernando Po and Rio Muni in
1960.

SEMI-POSTAL STAMPS

Red Cross Issue
Types of Semi-Postal Stamps of
Spain, 1926, Overprinted in Black or
Blue

GUINEA ESPAÑOLA

1926   Unwmk.   Perf. 12½, 13
B1   SP3 5c black brown   9.50 6.25
B2   SP4 10c dark green   9.50 6.25
B3   SP1 15c dark vio (Bl) 2.10 1.40
B4   SP4 20c violet brown   2.10 1.40
B5   SP5 25c deep carmine   2.10 1.40
B6   SP1 30c olive green   2.10 1.40
B7   SP3 40c ultra   .45 .20
B8   SP2 50c red brown   .45 .20
B9   SP5 60c myrtle green   .45 .20
B10 SP4 1p vermilion   .45 .20
B11 SP3 4p bister   1.75 1.25
B12 SP5 10p light violet   6.25 4.25
   Nos. B1-B12 (12)   37.20 24.40
   Set, never hinged   52.50

   See Spain No. B6a for No. B4 without overprint. For surcharges see Spain Nos. B70-
B71.

> Catalogue values for unused
> stamps in this section, from this
> point to the end of the section, are
> for Never Hinged items.

Allegory — SP1

Leopard — SP2

1950, Dec. 1   Photo.   Perf. 13x12½
B13 SP1 50c + 10c ultra   .25   .20
B14 SP1 1p + 25c dk grn   10.00 3.50
B15 SP1 6.50p + 1.65p dp org   2.50 1.60
   Nos. B13-B15 (3)   12.75 5.30

The surtax was to help the native population.

1951, Nov. 23
B16 SP2 5c + 5c brown   .20   .20
B17 SP2 10c + 5c red orange   .20   .20
B18 SP2 60c + 15c olive brn   .30   .20
   Nos. B16-B18 (3)   .70   .60

Colonial Stamp Day, Nov. 23.

Love Lily — SP3

Brown-cheeked Hornbill — SP4

1952, June 1
B19 SP3 5c + 5c brown   .20   .20
B20 SP3 50c + 10c gray   .20   .20
B21 SP3 2p + 30c blue   1.25   .90
   Nos. B19-B21 (3)   1.65 1.30

The surtax was to help the native population.

1952, Nov. 23   Perf. 12½
B22 SP4 5c + 5c brown   .20   .20
B23 SP4 10c + 5c brown car   .20   .20
B24 SP4 60c + 15c dk green   .40   .25
   Nos. B22-B24 (3)   .80   .65

Colonial Stamp Day, Nov. 23.

Music Type of Regular Issue
1953, July 1   Perf. 12½x13
B25 A26 5c + 5c like #324   .20   .20
B26 A26 10c + 5c like #325   .20   .20

The surtax was to help the native population.

Insect Type of Regular Issue
1953, Nov. 23   Perf. 13x12½
B27 A29 5c + 5c like #331   .20   .20
B28 A29 10c + 5c like #3332   .20   .20

Hunter Type of Regular Issue
1954, June 10   Perf. 12½x13
B29 A30 5c + 5c like #333   .20   .20
B30 A30 10c + 5c like #334   .20   .20

The surtax was to help the native population.

Type of Regular Issue
1954, Nov. 23
B31 A31 5c + 5c like #335   .20   .20
B32 A31 10c + 5c like #336   .20   .20

Type of Regular Issue and

Baptism — SP5

Perf. 13x12½
1955, June 1   Photo.   Unwmk.
B33 A33 10c + 5c like #339   .20   .20
B34 SP5 25c + 10c shown   .20   .20

Type of Regular Issue and

Red-eared Guenons SP6

Perf. 13x12½, 12½x13
1955, Nov. 23
B35 A35 5c + 5c like #343   .20   .20
B36 SP6 15c + 5c shown   .20   .20

Flower Type of Regular Issue
1956, June 1   Perf. 13x12½
B37 A36 5c + 5c like #344   .20   .20
B38 A36 15c + 5c like #345   .20   .20

The tax was for native welfare work.

Type of Regular Issue and

Drummers and Arms of Bata SP7

Perf. 13x12½, 12½x13
1956, Nov. 23
B39 A37 5c + 5c like #346   .20   .20
B40 SP7 15c + 5c shown   .20   .20

Type of Regular Issue and

African Gray Parrot SP8

Perf. 13x12½, 12½x13
1957, June 1   Photo.   Unwmk.
B41 A38 5c + 5c like #347   .20   .20
B42 SP8 15c + 5c shown   .20   .20

The surtax was for child welfare.

Type of Regular Issue, 1957
Perf. 12½x13, 13x12½
1957, Nov. 23
B43 A39 10c + 5c like #348   .20   .20
B44 A39 15c + 5c like #349   .20   .20

Pigeons and Arms of Valencia and Santa Isabel SP9

1958, Mar. 6   Perf. 12½x13
B45 SP9 10c + 5c org brn   .20   .20
B46 SP9 15c + 10c bister   .20   .20
B47 SP9 50c + 10c ol gray   .20   .20
   Nos. B45-B47 (3)   .60   .60

The surtax was to aid the victims of the Valencia flood, Oct., 1957.

Type of Regular Issue, 1958
1958, June 1   Photo.   Perf. 13x12½
B48 A42 10c + 5c like #358   .20   .20
B49 A42 15c + 5c like #359   .20   .20

The surtax was to help the native population.

Butterflies SP10

Early Bicycle SP11

Stamp Day: Various butterflies.

1958, Nov. 23   Unwmk.
B50 SP10 10c + 5c brown red   .20   .20
B51 SP10 25c + 10c brt pur   .20   .20
B52 SP10 50c + 10c gray olive   .20   .20
   Nos. B50-B52 (3)   .60   .60

Type of Regular Issue 1956 Inscribed: "Pro-Infancia 1959"
1959, June 1   Photo.   Perf. 13x12½
B53 A36 10c + 5c like #361   .20   .20
B54 A36 15c + 5c like #360   .20   .20

The surtax was for child welfare.

1959, Nov. 23

Designs: 20c+5c, Bicycle race. 50c+20c, Bicyclist winning race.
B55 SP11 10c + 5c lt rose brn   .20   .20
B56 SP11 20c + 5c turq blue   .20   .20
B57 SP11 50c + 20c olive gray   .20   .20
   Nos. B55-B57 (3)   .60   .60

Stamp Day.

AIR POST STAMPS

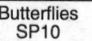
AP1

Revenue Stamp Surcharged "Habilitado para / Correo Aéreo / Intercolonial / Una Peseta"
   Type I - "Correo Aereo," 20½mm.
   Type II - "Correo Aereo," 22mm.

1941   Unwmk.   Perf. 11
C1 AP1 1p on 17p dp red, I   30.00 6.50
 a.   Type II   40.00 9.25

Spain No. C113
Overprinted in **Golfo de Guinea.** Red

1942, June 23
C2 AP30 1p chalky blue   1.60   .25

No. 300 Overprinted in Green
**Correo Aéreo
Viaje Ministerial
10-19 Enero 1948**

1948, Jan. 15   Perf. 10½x9½
C3 A166 4p dull rose   7.50 2.25
   Never hinged   12.00

The overprint exists in two types: I - The numeral 1's are lower case L's. II - The numeral 1's are actual ones.

Count of Argelejo and Frigate Catalina at Fernando Po, 1778
AP2

1949, Nov. 23   Photo.   Perf. 12½x13
C4 AP2 5p dark slate green   .85   .65
   Never hinged   1.25

Stamp Day, Nov. 23, 1949.

Manuel Iradier and Native Products — AP3

Woman Holding Dove — AP5

Benito Rapids AP4

1950, Nov. 23   Unwmk.   Perf. 12½
C5 AP3 5p dk brn   2.10   .85
   Never hinged   3.00

Stamp Day, Nov. 23, 1950.

1951, Mar. 1   Litho.   Perf. 12½x13
Various views.
C6 AP4 25c ocher   .20   .20
C7 AP4 50c lilac rose   .20   .20
C8 AP4 1p green   .20   .20
C9 AP4 2p bright blue   .20   .20
C10 AP4 3.25p rose lilac   .45   .20
C11 AP4 5p gray brown   3.75 1.60
C12 AP4 10p rose red   15.00 6.00
   Nos. C6-C12 (7)   20.00 8.60
   Set, never hinged   32.50

> **Catalogue values for unused stamps in this section, from this point to the end of the section, are for Never Hinged items.**

1951, Apr. 22   Engr.   Perf. 10
C13 AP5 5p dark blue   19.00 2.50

500th birth anniv. of Queen Isabella I.

Ferdinand the Catholic — AP6

Soccer Players — AP7

1952, July 18   Photo.   Perf. 13x12½
C14 AP6 5p red brown   25.00 6.00

500th birth anniv. of Ferdinand the Catholic of Spain.

1955-56   Unwmk.
C15 AP7 25c blue vio ('56)   .20   .20
C16 AP7 50c olive ('56)   .20   .20
C17 AP7 1.50p brown ('56)   .85   .20
C18 AP7 4p rose car ('56)   2.75   .35
C19 AP7 10p yellow grn   1.50   .35
   Nos. C15-C19 (5)   5.50 1.30

Planes and Arm Holding Spear — AP8

1957, Sept. 19   Perf. 13x12½
C20 AP8 25p bister & sepia   6.75   .75

30th anniv. of the Atlantida Squadron flight to Spanish Guinea.

SPECIAL DELIVERY STAMP

View of
Fernando
Po — SD1

Perf. 12½x13

1951, Mar. 1	Litho.	Unwmk.	
E1	SD1 25c rose carmine	.20	.20
	Never hinged		.25

STOCKSHEETS

HAGNER STYLE STOCK SHEETS

Hagner-style stock pages offer convenience and flexibility. Pages are produced on thick, archival-quality paper with acetate pockets glued from the bottom of each pocket. They're ideal for the topical collector who may require various page styles to store a complete collection.

- Black background makes beautiful stamp presentation.
- Pockets use pull away/snap back principle.
- Made from archival-quality heavyweight paper that offers unprecedented protection and clarity.
- Multi-hole punch fits most binder types.
- Available in 9 different page formats.
  8½" x 11" size accomodates every size stamp.

Sold in packages of 10.
Available with pockets on one side or both sides.
"D" in item number denotes two-sided page.

1 POCKET
242 mm

Item	Retail
S1	$10.99
S1D	$15.99

2 POCKET
119 mm

Item	Retail
S2	$10.99
S2D	$15.99

3 POCKET
79 mm

Item	Retail
S3	$10.99
S3D	$15.99

4 POCKET
58 mm

Item	Retail
S4	$10.99
S4D	$15.99

5 POCKET
45 mm

Item	Retail
S5	$10.99
S5D	$15.99

6 POCKET
37 mm

Item	Retail
S6	$10.99
S6D	$15.99

7 POCKET
31 mm

Item	Retail
S7	$10.99
S7D	$15.99

8 POCKET
27 mm

Item	Retail
S8	$10.99
S8D	$15.99

MULTI-POCKETS
36 mm
67 mm
139 mm

Item	Retail
S9	$10.99
S9D	$15.99

SCOTT

1-800-572-6885
P.O. Box 828, Sidney OH 45365-0828
www.amosadvantage.com

AMOS
HOBBY PUBLISHING

Publishers of *Coin World*, *Linn's Stamp News*
and *Scott Publishing Co.*

SPANISH MOROCCO

'spa-nish mə-'rä-ˌkō

LOCATION — Northwest coast of Africa
GOVT. — Spanish Protectorate
AREA — 17,398 sq. mi. (approx.)
POP. — 1,010,117 (1950)
CAPITAL — Tetuán

Spanish Morocco was a Spanish Protectorate until 1956 when it, along with the French and Tangier zones of Morocco, became the independent country, Morocco.

100 Centimos = 1 Peseta

Catalogue values for unused stamps in this country are for Never Hinged items, beginning with Scott 280 in the regular postage section, Scott B27 in the semipostal section, Scott C24 in the airpost section, and Scott E11 in special delivery section.

Spanish Offices in Morocco

Spain No. 221A
Overprinted in Carmine

1903-09   **Unwmk.**   **Imperf.**

1	A21	¼c blue green	.50	.20
a.		Complete 1c (block 4 ¼c)	1.90	1.25

See Nos. 26, 39, 52, Tetuan 1, 7.

Stamps of Spain Overprinted in Carmine or Blue

a

On Stamps of 1900
Perf. 14

2	A35	2c bister brown	1.10	1.00
3	A35	5c green	1.25	.55
4	A35	10c rose red (Bl)	1.50	.25
5	A35	15c brt violet	2.10	.15
6	A35	20c grnsh black	8.25	2.50
7	A35	25c blue	.65	.60
8	A35	30c blue green	2.00	2.50
9	A35	40c rose (Bl)	8.75	4.25
10	A35	50c slate grn	5.00	4.00
11	A35	1p lake (Bl)	10.00	5.75
12	A35	4p dull violet	27.50	10.00
13	A35	10p brown org (Bl)	27.50	25.00
		Nos. 1-13 (13)	99.10	57.15
		Set, never hinged	140.00	

Many varieties of overprint exist. Nos. 7-13 exist imperf. Value, $500.
See Tetuan Nos. 2-6, 8-15.

On Stamps of 1909-10

1909-10   **Perf. 13x12½, 14**

14	A46	2c dark brown	.55	.20
15	A46	5c green	2.75	.20
16	A46	10c carmine (Bl)	3.25	.20
17	A46	15c violet	7.50	.45
18	A46	20c olive green	19.00	.95
19	A46	25c deep blue	65.00	
20	A46	30c blue green	6.00	.45
21	A46	40c rose (Bl)	6.00	.45
22	A46	50c slate blue	10.50	10.00
23	A46	1p lake (Bl)	25.00	21.00
24	A46	4p deep violet	65.00	
25	A46	10p orange (Bl)	65.00	
		Nos. 14-18,20,23 (9)	80.55	33.90
		Set, never hinged	110.00	
		Nos. 14-25 (12)	275.55	

The stamps overprinted "Correo Espanol Marruecos" were used in all Morocco until the year 1914. After the issue of special stamps for the Protectorate the "Correo Espanol" stamps were continued in use solely in the city of Tangier.
Many varieties of overprint exist.
Nos. 19, 24 and 25 were not regularly issued.
See Nos. 27-38, 40-51, 53-67, 75-76, 78.

Spanish Morocco

Spain No. 221A
Overprinted in Carmine

1914   **Imperf.**

26	A21	¼c green	.20	.20
a.		Complete 1c (block 4 ¼c)	1.25	.90

Stamps of Spain 1909-10 Overprinted in Carmine or Blue

Perf. 13x12½, 14

27	A46	2c dark brown (C)	.20	.20
28	A46	5c green (C)	.20	.20
29	A46	10c carmine (Bl)	.20	.20
30	A46	15c violet (C)	1.10	.75
31	A46	20c olive grn (C)	2.10	1.50
32	A46	25c deep blue (C)	2.10	1.10
33	A46	30c blue grn (C)	4.25	2.10
34	A46	40c rose (Bl)	9.75	3.00
35	A46	50c slate blue (C)	5.00	2.10
36	A46	1p lake (Bl)	5.00	3.00
37	A46	4p dp violet (C)	25.00	21.00
38	A46	10p orange (Bl)	37.50	27.50
		Nos. 26-38,E1 (14)	96.10	64.60
		Set, never hinged	140.00	

Many varieties of overprint exist, including inverted.
#27-38 exist imperf. Value for set, $525.

Stamps of Spain 1876 and 1909-10 Overprinted in Red or Blue

1915   **Imperf.**

39	A21	¼c blue grn (R)	.20	.20
a.		Complete 1c (block 4 ¼c)	1.25	.95

Perf. 13x12½, 14

40	A46	2c dk brown (R)	.20	.20
41	A46	5c green (R)	.25	.25
42	A46	10c carmine (Bl)	.25	.25
43	A46	15c violet (R)	.25	.25
44	A46	20c olive grn (R)	.95	.25
45	A46	25c deep blue (R)	.95	.40
46	A46	30c blue grn (R)	1.10	.45
47	A46	40c rose (Bl)	3.00	.45
48	A46	50c slate blue (R)	5.00	.40
49	A46	1p lake (Bl)	5.00	.45
50	A46	4p deep violet (R)	32.50	21.00
51	A46	10p orange (Bl)	47.50	22.50
		Nos. 39-51,E2 (14)	99.40	48.50
		Set, never hinged	140.00	

One stamp in the setting on Nos. 39-51 has the first "R" of "PROTECTORADO" inverted. Many other varieties of overprint exist, including double and inverted.
Nos. 40-51 exist imperf. Value, set $650.

Stamps of Spain 1877 and 1909-10 Overprinted in Red or Blue

b

1916-18   **Imperf.**

52	A21	¼c blue grn (R)	1.10	.20
a.		Complete 1c (block 4 ¼c)	1.75	1.25

Perf. 13x12½, 14

53	A46	2c dk brown (R)	1.10	.20
54	A46	5c green (R)	5.00	.20
55	A46	10c carmine (Bl)	5.50	.20
56	A46	15c violet (R)	140.00	
57	A46	20c olive grn (R)	140.00	
58	A46	25c dp blue (R)	19.00	3.00
59	A46	30c blue grn (R)	25.00	20.00
60	A46	40c rose (Bl)	26.00	.45
61	A46	50c slate blue (R)	12.00	.20
62	A46	1p lake (Bl)	30.00	2.10
63	A46	4p dp violet (R)	50.00	29.00
64	A46	10p orange (Bl)	100.00	65.00
		Nos. 52-55,58-64 (11)	274.70	120.55
		Set, never hinged	400.00	
		Nos. 52-64 (13)	554.70	
		Set, never hinged	1,000.	

Nos. 56-57 were not regularly issued.
Varieties of overprint, including double and inverted, exist for several denominations.
The 5c exists in olive brown. Value $525.

Same Overprint on Spain No. 310
1920

65	A46	15c ocher (Bl)	5.50	.30

Exists imperf.; also with overprint inverted.

Nos. 44, 46 Perforated through the middle and each half Surcharged "10 céntimos" in Red
1920

66	A46	10c on half of 20c	5.00	1.90
67	A46	15c on half of 30c	11.00	7.25

No. E2 Divided and Surcharged in Black

68	SD1	10c on half of 20c	12.00	7.75
a.		"10/cts." surcharge added	110.00	45.00
		Nos. 66-68 (3)	28.00	16.90

Values of Nos. 66-68 are for pairs, both halves of the stamp. Varieties were probably made deliberately.

"Justice" — A1

Revenue Stamps Perforated through the Middle and each half Surcharged with New Value in Red or Green

1920   **Perf. 11½**

69	A1	5c on 5p lt bl	9.50	1.90
70	A1	5c on 10p green	.40	.20
71	A1	10c on 25p dk grn	.40	.20
a.		Inverted surcharge	11.00	10.00
72	A1	10c on 50p indigo	.45	.30
73	A1	15c on 100p red (G)	.45	.30
74	A1	15c on 500p cl (G)	12.50	6.50
		Nos. 69-74 (6)	23.70	9.40
		Set, never hinged	30.00	

Values of Nos. 69-74 are for pairs, both halves of the stamp.

Stamps of Spain 1917-20 Overprinted Type "a" in Blue or Red

1921-24   **Perf. 13**

75	A46	15c ocher (Bl)	1.25	.20
76	A46	20c violet (R)	1.90	.20

Stamps of Spain 1920-21 Overprinted Type "b" in Red
Imperf

77	A47	1c blue green	1.40	.20

Engr.
Perf. 13

78	A46	20c violet	10.00	.20

See No. 92.

Stamps of Spain, 1922 Overprinted Type "a" in Red or Blue

1923-28   **Perf. 13½x12½**

79	A49	2c olive green (R)	3.50	.20
80	A49	5c red violet (Bl)	3.50	.20
81	A49	10c yellow green (R)	4.25	.20
82	A49	20c violet (R)	6.00	.90
		Nos. 79-82 (4)	17.25	1.50

Same Overprinted Type "b"

1923-25

83	A49	2c olive green (R)	.65	.20
84	A49	5c red violet (Bl)	.65	.20
85	A49	10c yellow grn (R)	2.75	.20
86	A49	15c blue (R)	2.75	.20
87	A49	20c violet (R)	6.00	.20
88	A49	25c carmine (Bl)	12.00	1.40
89	A49	40c deep blue (R)	12.50	4.50
90	A49	50c orange (Bl)	32.50	7.75
91	A49a	1p blue black (R)	50.00	4.50
		Nos. 83-91,E3 (10)	128.05	27.40
		Set, never hinged	190.00	

Spain No. 314 Overprinted Type "a" in Red

1927   **Imperf.**

92	A47	1c blue green	.20	.20

Mosque of Alcazarquivir
A2

Moorish Gateway at Larache
A3

Well at Alhucemas
A4

View of Xauen — A5

View of Tetuan — A6

1928-32   **Engr.**   **Perf. 14, 14½**

93	A2	1c red ("Cs")	.20	.20
94	A2	1c car rose ("Ct") ('32)	.30	.30
95	A2	2c dark violet	.20	.20
96	A2	5c deep blue	.20	.20
97	A2	10c dark green	.20	.20
98	A2	15c orange brown	.40	.20
99	A3	20c olive green	.40	.20
100	A3	25c copper red	.40	.20
102	A3	30c black brown	1.50	.20
103	A3	40c dull blue	1.90	.20
104	A3	50c brown violet	4.00	.20
105	A4	1p yellow green	6.00	.15
106	A5	2.50p red violet	19.00	7.50
107	A6	4p ultra	15.00	4.50
		Nos. 93-107,E4 (15)	53.20	15.95
		Set, never hinged	65.00	

For surcharges see Nos. 164-167.

Seville-Barcelona Issue of Spain, 1929, Overprinted in Red or Blue

PROTECTORADO
MARRUECOS

1929   **Perf. 11, 14**

108	A50	1c greenish blue	.25	.25
109	A51	2c pale yel grn	.25	.25
110	A52	5c rose lake (Bl)	.25	.25
111	A53	10c green	.25	.25
112	A50	15c Prussian blue	.25	.25
113	A51	20c purple	.25	.25
114	A50	25c bright rose (Bl)	.25	.25
115	A52	30c black brown (bl)	.65	.55
116	A53	40c dark blue	.65	.55
117	A51	50c deep orange (Bl)	.65	.55
118	A52	1p blue black	5.25	4.25
119	A53	4p deep rose (Bl)	12.00	9.75
120	A53	10p brown (Bl)	26.00	21.00
		Nos. 108-120 (13)	46.95	38.40
		Set, never hinged	62.50	

See Nos. L1-L11.

Stamps of Spain, 1922-31, Overprinted Type "a" in Black, Blue or Red

1929-34   **Perf. 11½, 13x12½**

121	A49	5c claret (Bk)	3.25	.20
122	A61	10c green (R)	2.75	.40
123	A61	15c slate grn (R)	97.50	1.00
124	A61	20c violet (R)	2.75	.45
125	A61	30c brown lake (Bl)	3.00	1.00
126	A61	40c dark blue (R)	11.00	5.00
127	A49	50c orange (Bl)	27.50	4.75
128	A49a	10p brown (R)	2.75	4.25
		Nos. 121-128 (8)	150.50	17.05
		Set, never hinged	210.00	

Stamps of Spain, 1922-26, overprinted diagonally as above, and with no control number, or with "A000,000" on back, were not issued but were presented to the delegates at the 1929 UPU Congress in London.

Stamps of Spain 1931-32, Overprinted in Black **MARRUECOS**

1933-34 | | | *Imperf.*
130 A108 1c blue green | .20 | .20

Perf. 11½

131	A108	2c buff	.20	.20
132	A95	5c brnsh black	.20	.20
133	A96	10c yellow green	.20	.20
134	A97	15c slate green	.20	.20
135	A95	20c dark violet	.20	.20
136	A104	25c lake	.20	.20
137	A99	30c carmine rose	50.00	5.00
138	A100	40c dark blue	.50	.20
139	A97	50c orange	.95	.20
140	A100	60c apple green	.95	.20
141	A105	1p blue black	.95	.40
142	A106	4p magenta	2.10	2.10
143	A107	10p deep brown	3.00	4.75
	Nos. 130-143,E7 (15)		61.10	14.45
	Set, never hinged		82.50	

Street Scene in Tangier — A7

View of Xauen A8

Gate in Town Wall, Arzila — A9

Street Scene in Tangier A10

Mosque of Alcazarquivir A11

Caliph and His Guard A12

View of Tangier A13

Green Control Numbers Printed on Gum

1933-35		**Photo.**	**Perf. 14, 13½**	
144	A7	1c brt rose	.20	.20
145	A8	2c green ('35)	.20	.20
146	A9	5c magenta ('35)	.20	.20
147	A10	10c dark green	.20	.20
148	A11	15c yellow ('35)	1.60	.20
149	A7	20c slate green	.60	.20
150	A12	25c crimson ('35)	16.00	.20
151	A10	30c red brown	4.25	.20
152	A13	40c deep blue	7.50	.20
153	A13	50c red orange	22.50	3.75
154	A8	1p slate blk ('35)	10.00	.20
155	A9	2.50p brown ('35)	17.50	3.75
156	A11	4p yel grn ('35)	17.50	3.75
157	A12	5p black ('35)	22.50	4.00
	Nos. 144-157,E5 (15)		121.75	17.20
	Set, never hinged		175.00	

For surcharge see No. CB1.

Mosque — A14

Landscape A15

Green Control Numbers Printed on Gum

1935				
158	A14	25c violet	.85	.20
159	A15	30c crimson	12.00	.20
160	A14	40c orange	6.00	.20
161	A15	50c bright blue	6.00	.20
162	A14	60c dk blue green	6.00	.20
163	A15	2p brown lake	30.00	4.25
	Nos. 158-163 (6)		60.85	5.25
	Set, never hinged		80.00	

See No. 174.

Regular Issue and Special Delivery Stamp of 1928, Surcharged in Blue, Green or Red with New Values and Ornaments

1936				
164	A6	1c on 4p ultra (Bl)	.20	.20
165	A5	2c on 2.50p red vio (G)	.20	.20
166	A3	5c on 25c cop red (R)	.20	.20
167	A4	10c on 1p yel grn (G)	6.25	3.50
168	SD2	15c on 20c blk (Bl)	.475	1.75
	Nos. 164-168 (5)		11.60	5.85
	Set, never hinged		15.00	

Caliph and Viziers — A16

View of Bokoia A17

View of Alcazarquivir — A18

Sidi Saida Mosque A19

Caliph and Procession A20

Without Control Numbers

1937		**Photo.**	**Perf. 13½**	
169	A16	1c green	.20	.20
170	A17	2c red violet	.20	.20
171	A18	5c orange	.20	.20
172	A16	15c violet	.20	.20
173	A19	30c red	.50	.20
a.	Souvenir sheet of 4, #170-173		17.00	10.00

174	A14	1p ultra	5.00	.20
a.	Souv. sheet of 4, #169-171, 174		17.00	10.00
175	A20	10p brown	45.00	15.00
	Nos. 169-175 (7)		51.30	16.20
	Set, never hinged		60.00	

Nos. 173a, 174a for 1st year of the Spanish Civil War.

Nos. 173a, 174a were privately overprinted "TANGER" in black on each stamp in the sheet for "use" in the International City of Tangier, and "GUINEA" for "use" in Spanish Guinea.

Harkeno Rifleman — A21

Troops Marching A22

Designs: 2c, Legionnaires. 5c, Cavalryman leading his mount. 10c, Moroccan phalanx. 15c, Legion flag-bearer. 20c, Colonial soldier. 25c, Ifni sharpshooters. 30c, Mounted trumpeters. 40c, Cape Juby Dromedary Corps. 50c, Regular infantry. 60c, Caliphate guards. 1p, Orderly on guard. 2p, Sentry. 2.50p, Regular cavalry. 4p, Orderly.

1937			**Perf. 13½**	
176	A21	1c dull blue	.20	.20
177	A21	2c orange brn	.20	.20
178	A21	5c cerise	.20	.20
179	A21	10c emerald	.20	.20
180	A21	15c brt blue	.20	.20
181	A21	20c red brown	.20	.20
182	A21	25c magenta	.20	.20
183	A21	30c red orange	.20	.20
184	A21	40c orange	.20	.20
185	A21	50c ultra	.20	.20
186	A21	60c yellow grn	.20	.20
187	A21	1p blue violet	.20	.20
188	A21	2p Prus blue	6.50	3.50
189	A21	2.50p gray black	6.50	3.50
190	A21	4p dark brown	6.50	3.50
191	A22	10p black	6.50	3.50
	Nos. 176-191,E6 (17)		28.60	16.60
	Set, never hinged		45.00	

First Year of Spanish Civil War.
Exists imperf. Value, set $200.
For overprints see Nos. 214-229.

Spanish Quarter — A25

Designs: 10c, Moroccan quarter. 15c, Street scene, Larache. 20c, Tetuan.

1939	**Unwmk.**	**Photo.**	**Perf. 13½**	
194	A25	5c orange	.20	.20
195	A25	10c brt blue grn	.20	.20
196	A25	15c golden brown	.40	.20
197	A25	20c brt ultra	.40	.20
	Nos. 194-197 (4)		1.20	.80

Postman — A26

Mail Box — A27

Landscape A28

Street Scene, Alcazarquivir A29

View of Xauen — A30

Sentry Guarding Palace at Sat — A31

The Chieftain — A32

Market Place, Larache — A33

Tetuán — A34

Ancient Gateway at Xauen — A35

Scene in Alcazarquivir A36

Post Office A37

Spanish War Veterans — A38

Victory Flag Bearers — A39

Cavalry — A40

Day of Court — A41

1940 Unwmk. Photo. Perf. 11½x11

198	A26	1c dark brown	.20	.20
199	A27	2c olive grn	.20	.20
200	A28	5c dk blue	.20	.20
201	A29	10c dk red lilac	.20	.20
202	A30	15c dk green	.20	.20
203	A31	20c purple	.20	.20
204	A32	25c black brown	.20	.20
205	A33	30c brt green	.20	.20
206	A34	40c slate green	1.40	.20
207	A35	45c orange ver	.55	.20
208	A36	50c brown orange	.55	.20
209	A37	70c sapphire	.55	.20
210	A38	1p indigo & brn	1.50	.20
211	A39	2.50p choc & dk grn	7.75	1.90
212	A40	5p dk cerise & sep	1.50	.20
213	A41	10p dk ol grn & brn org	14.50	3.25
		Nos. 198-213,E8 (17)	30.15	8.15
		Set, never hinged	50.00	

"ZONA" printed in black on back.
Exists imperf. Value, set $250.

Stamps of 1937 Overprinted in Various Colors

1940 Unwmk. Perf. 13½

214	A21	1c dull blue (Bk)	.55	.55
215	A21	2c org brn (Bk)	.55	.55
216	A21	5c cerise (Bk)	.55	.55
217	A21	10c emerald (Bk)	.55	.55
218	A21	15c brt blue (Bk)	.55	.55
219	A21	20c red brn (Bk)	.55	.55
220	A21	25c mag (Bk)	.55	.55
221	A21	30c red org (V)	.55	.55
222	A21	40c orange (V)	1.00	1.00
223	A21	50c ultra (Bk)	1.00	1.00
224	A21	60c yel grn (Bk)	1.00	1.00
225	A21	1p blue vio (V)	1.00	1.00
226	A21	2p Prus bl (Bl)	32.50	32.50
227	A21	2.50p gray blk (V)	32.50	32.50
228	A21	4p dk brn (Bl)	32.50	32.50
229	A22	10p black (R)	32.50	29.00
		Nos. 214-229,E10 (17)	145.65	142.15
		Set, never hinged	225.00	

4th anniversary of Spanish Civil War.

Larache A42

Alcazarquivir A43

Market Place, Larache — A44

Tangier
A45   A46

1941 Unwmk. Photo. Perf. 10½

230	A42	5c dk brn & brn	.20	.20
231	A43	10c dp rose & ver	.20	.20
232	A44	15c sl grn & yel grn	.20	.20
233	A45	20c vio bl & dp bl	.40	.20
234	A46	40c dp plum & claret	1.00	.20
		Nos. 230-234 (5)	2.00	1.00

Exists imperf. Value, set $100.

1943 Perf. 12x12½

234A	A43	5c dark blue	.20	.20
235	A44	40c dull violet brn	17.00	.20

Plowing A47

Harvesting A48

Returning from Work A49

Transporting Wheat — A50

Vegetable Garden A51

Picking Oranges A52

Goat Herd — A53

1944 Unwmk. Photo. Perf. 12½

236	A47	1c choc & lt bl	.20	.20
237	A48	2c sl grn & lt grn	.20	.20
238	A49	5c choc & grnsh blk	.20	.20
239	A50	10c brt ultra & red org	.20	.20
240	A51	15c sl grn & lt grn	.20	.20
241	A52	20c dp cl & blk	.20	.20
242	A53	25c lt bl & choc	.20	.20
243	A47	30c yel grn & brt ultra	.20	.20
244	A48	40c choc & red vio	.20	.20
245	A49	50c brt ultra & red brn	.45	.20
246	A50	75c yel grn & brt ultra	.50	.20
247	A51	1p brt ultra & choc	.50	.20
248	A52	2.50p blk & brt ultra	4.00	1.60
249	A53	10p sal & gray blk	8.50	3.25
		Nos. 236-249 (14)	15.75	7.25
		Set, never hinged	22.00	

Exists imperf. Value, set $100.

Potters A54

Dyers A55

Blacksmiths A56

Cobblers A57

Weavers A58

Metal Workers A59

1946 Unwmk. Litho. Perf. 10½x10

250	A54	1c purple & brn	.20	.20
251	A55	2c dk Prus grn & vio blk	.20	.20
252	A54	10c dp org & vio bl	.20	.20
253	A54	15c dk bl & bl grn	.20	.20
254	A54	25c yel grn & ultra	.20	.20
255	A56	40c dk bl & brn, perf. 12½	.20	.20
256	A55	45c black & rose	.50	.20
257	A57	1p dk Prus grn & dp bl	.60	.20
258	A58	2.50p dp org & gray	1.75	.65
259	A59	10p dk bl & gray	3.00	1.50
		Nos. 250-259 (10)	7.05	3.75
		Set, never hinged	8.00	

Control letter "Z" in circle in black on back.
Exists imperf. Value, set $80.

A60

Sanitorium — A61

1946, Sept. 1 Perf. 11½x10½, 10½

260	A60	10c crim & bl grn	.20	.20
261	A61	25c crimson & brn	.20	.20
		Nos. 260-261,B14-B16 (5)	1.50	1.05

Issued to aid anti-tuberculosis work.

A62   A63

1947 Perf. 10

262	A62	10c carmine & blue	.20	.20
263	A63	25c red & chocolate	.20	.20
		Nos. 262-263,B17-B19 (5)	1.50	1.30

Issued to aid anti-tuberculosis work.

Commerce by Railroad A64

Commerce by Truck A65

Urban Market A66

Country Market A67

Caravan A68

Maritime Commerce A69

1948 Litho. Perf. 10, 10x10½

264	A64	2c purple & brn	.20	.20
265	A65	5c dp cl & vio	.20	.20
266	A66	15c brt ultra & bl grn	.20	.20
267	A67	25c blk & Prus grn	.20	.20
268	A65	35c brt ultra & gray blk	.20	.20
269	A68	50c red & violet	.20	.20
270	A66	70c dk gray grn & ultra	.20	.20
271	A67	90c cer & dk gray grn	.20	.20
272	A68	1p brt ultra & vio	.60	.20
273	A64	2.50p vio brn & sl grn	1.50	.45
274	A69	10p blk & dp ultra	2.75	1.25
		Nos. 264-274 (11)	6.45	3.50
		Set, never hinged	7.50	

Exists imperf. Value, set $80.

Emblem of Tuberculosis
Association
A70   A71

Design: 25c, Plane over sanatorium.

1948, Oct. 1   **Perf. 10**
275 A70 10c car & green   .20   .20
276 A70 25c car & grnsh gray   1.40   .60
    Nos. 275-276,B20-B23 (6)   22.15 8.40

        See No. B39.

1949

10c, Road of Health. 25c, Minaret and Palm.

Black Control Number on Back

277 A71 5c car & green   .20   .20
278 A71 10c car & dk vio   .20   .20
279 A71 25c car & black   .60   .25
    Nos. 277-279,B25-B26 (5)   2.00   1.10

Catalogue values for unused stamps in this section, from this point to the end of the section, are for Never Hinged items.

Mail Transport,   Herald — A73
1890 — A72

Designs: 5c, 50c, 90c, Mail transport, 1890.
10c, 45c, 1p, Mail transport, 1906. 15c, 1.50p,
Mail transport, 1913. 35c, 75c, 5p, Mail transport, 1914. 10p, Mail transport, 1918.

1950   **Litho.**   **Perf. 10½**
280 A72 5c choc & vio bl   .20   .20
281 A72 10c deep bl & sep   .20   .20
282 A72 15c grnsh blk & em-
            er   .20   .20
283 A72 35c pur & gray blk   .20   .20
284 A72 45c dp car & rose lil   .20   .20
285 A72 50c emer & dk brn   .20   .20
286 A72 75c dk vio bl & bl   .20   .20
287 A72 90c grnsh blk &
            rose car   .20   .20
288 A72 1p blk brn & gray   .20   .20
289 A72 1.50p carmine & blue   .70   .20
290 A72 5p black & vio brn   1.25   .20
291 A72 10p purple & blue   26.00 10.00
    Nos. 280-291,E11 (13)   53.75 21.20

UPU, 75th anniv. (in 1949).
Nos. 280-291 exist imperf. Value $350.

1950   **Unwmk.**   **Perf. 10**
Frame and Device in Carmine
Black Control Number on Back

292 A73 5c gray black   .20   .20
293 A73 10c Old fort   .20   .20
294 A73 25c Sanatorium   .50   .30
    Nos. 292-294,B27-B28 (5)   1.60   1.20

                         Boar Hunt
                         A74

10c, 1p, Hunters and hounds. 50c, Boar
hunt. 5p, Fishermen. 10p, Moorish fishing
boat.

1950, Dec. 30   **Perf. 10½x10**
Black Control Number on Back

295 A74 5c dk brn & rose vio   .20   .20
296 A74 10c carmine & gray   .20   .20
297 A74 50c green & sepia   .20   .20
298 A74 1p bl vio & claret   .40   .20

---

299 A74 5p dp claret & bl vio .65   .25
300 A74 10p grnsh blk & dp cl 1.90   .40
    Nos. 295-300 (6)   3.55   1.45

Emblem — A75   Worship — A77

Armed
Attack
A76

10c, Patients expressing gratitude. 25c,
Plane in the Clouds.

        Dated "1951"

1951   **Perf. 12**
Frame and Device in Carmine
Black Control Number on Back

301 A75 5c green   .20   .20
302 A75 10c blue violet   .20   .20
303 A75 25c gray black   .75   .30
    Nos. 301-303,B29-B32 (7)   11.15 5.00

Issued to aid anti-tuberculosis work.

1952   **Perf. 11**

Designs: 10c, Horses on parade. 15c, Holiday procession. 20c, Road to market. 25c,
"Brother-hoods." 35c, "Offering." 45c, Soldiers.
50c, On the rooftop. 75c, Teahouse. 90c, Wedding. 1p, Pilgrimage. 5p, Storyteller. 10p, Market corner.

Black Control Number on Back

304 A76 5c dk blue & brn   .20   .20
305 A76 10c dk brn & lil rose   .20   .20
306 A76 15c black & emer   .20   .20
307 A76 20c ol grn & red vio   .20   .20
308 A76 25c red & lt blue   .20   .20
309 A76 35c olive & orange   .20   .20
310 A76 45c red & rose red   .20   .20
311 A76 50c rose car & gray grn .20   .20
312 A76 75c purple & ultra   .20   .20
313 A76 90c dk bl & rose vio   .20   .20
314 A76 1p dk bl & red brn   .20   .20
315 A76 5p red & blue   1.40   .25
316 A76 10p dk grn & gray blk 2.00   .40
    Nos. 304-316,E12 (14)   5.80   3.05

1952, Oct. 1   **Dated "1952"**

10c, Distributing alms. 25c, Prickly pear.

Black Control Number on Back

317 A77 5c car & dk ol grn   .20   .20
318 A77 10c car & dk brown   .20   .20
319 A77 25c car & dp blue   .35   .20
    Nos. 317-319,B33-B37 (8)   7.50   3.80

Semi-Postal Types of 1948-49 Dated
            "1953"

1953   **Litho.**   **Perf. 10**
Black Control Number on Back

320 SP7 5c shown   .20   .20
321 SP9 10c like #B26   .20   .20
322 SP7 25c like #B23   .85   .35
    Nos. 320-322,B38-B42 (8)   13.65 5.35

Issued to aid anti-tuberculosis work.

                         A78

1953, Nov. 15
Black Control Number on Back

323 A78 5c red   .20   .20
324 A78 10c gray green   .20   .20

Mountain   Zauia — A80
Women — A79

50c and 2.50p, Water carrier. 90c and 2p,
Mountaineers and donkey. 1p and 4.50p,
Moorish women and child. 10p, Mounted
dignitary.

1953, Dec. 15   **Photo.**
Black Control Number on Back

334 A79 35c grn & rose vio   .20   .20
335 A79 50c red & green   .20   .20
336 A79 90c dk bl & org   .20   .20
337 A79 1p dk brn & grn   .20   .20
338 A79 1.25p dk grn & car rose .20   .20
339 A79 2p dk rose vio & bl   .20   .20
340 A79 2.50p black & orange   .50   .25
341 A79 4.50p brt car rose & dk
            grn   2.00   .35
342 A79 10p green & black   2.50   .65
    Nos. 334-342,E13 (10)   6.40   2.65

25th anniv. of Spanish Morocco's first definitive postage stamps.

1954, Nov. 1   **Dated "1954"**

10c, "The Family." 25c, Plane, Spanish
coast.

Black Control Number on Back

343 A80 5c car & bl grn   .20   .20
344 A80 10c car & dk brn   .20   .20
345 A80 25c car & blue   .20   .20
    Nos. 343-345,B43-B45 (6)   6.95   4.40

Queen's   Honor
Gate — A81   Guard — A82

1955   **Litho.**   **Perf. 11**
Black Control Number on Back
Frames in Black

346 A81 15c shown   .20   .20
347 A81 25c Saida   .20   .20
348 A81 80c like #346   .20   .20
349 A81 1p like #347   .20   .20
350 A81 15p Ceuta   2.50   .65
    Nos. 346-350,E14 (6)   3.50   1.65

                Perf. 13x12½
1955, Nov. 8   **Photo.**   **Unwmk.**

Designs: 25c, 80c, 3p, Caliph Moulay Hassan ben el-Medi. 30c, 1p, 5p, Caliph and procession. 15p, Coat of arms.

351 A82 15c ol brn & ol   .20   .20
352 A82 25c lil & dp rose   .20   .20
353 A82 30c brn blk & Prus
            grn   .20   .20
354 A82 70c Prus grn & yel grn .20   .20
355 A82 80c ol & ol brn   .20   .20
356 A82 1p dk bl & redsh brn   .20   .20
357 A82 1.80p black & bl vio   .20   .20
358 A82 3p blue & gray   .20   .20
359 A82 5p dk grn & brn   1.10   .45

                Engr.

360 A82 15p red brn & yel grn 2.50   1.65
    Nos. 351-360 (10)   5.20   3.70

30th anniv. of accession to throne by Caliph
Moulay Hassan ben el-Medi ben Ismail.
Succeeding issues, released under the
Kingdom, are listed under Morocco.

SEMI-POSTAL STAMPS

Types of Semi-Postal Stamps of
Spain, 1926, Overprinted in Black or
Blue

1926   **Unwmk.**   **Perf. 12½, 13**
B1 SP1 1c orange   7.00   4.50
B2 SP2 2c rose   10.00   8.25
B3 SP3 5c black brn   3.50   3.00
B4 SP4 10c dark grn   3.50   3.00
B5 SP1 15c dk violet (Bl) .65 .55
B6 SP2 20c violet brn   .65   .55
B7 SP5 25c deep carmine .65   .55
B8 SP3 30c olive grn   .65   .55
B9 SP3 40c ultra   .20   .20
B10 SP2 50c red brown   .20   .20
B11 SP4 1p vermilion   .20   .20
B12 SP3 4p bister   .65   .55
B13 SP5 10p light violet 2.75 2.25
    Nos. B1-B13,EB1 (14) 33.10 26.45
    Set, never hinged   52.50

See Spain No. B6a for No. B6 without overprint. For surcharges see Spain Nos. B64-
B65.

Tuberculosis Fund Issues

SP1   SP2

                         SP3

        Perf. 10½, 11½x10½
1946, Sept. 1   **Litho.**   **Unwmk.**
B14 SP1 25c + 5c crim & rose vio .20 .20
B15 SP2 50c + 10c crim & blue   .25 .20
B16 SP3 90c + 10c crim & gray
            brn   .65 .25
    Nos. B14-B16 (3)   1.10 .65

Medical   Nurse and
Center — SP4   Children — SP5

"Protection"   Herald
SP6   SP7

1947   *Perf. 10*
B17   SP4   25c + 5c red & violet   .20   .20
B18   SP5   50c + 10c red & blue   .25   .20
B19   SP6   90c + 10c red & sepia   .65   .50
     Nos. B17-B19 (3)   1.10   .90

1948, Oct. 1
   Designs: No. B21, Protection. No. B22,
Sun bath. No. B23, Plane over Ben Karrich.
B20   SP7   50c + 10c car & dk
           vio   .20   .20
B21   SP7   90c + 10c car & dk
           gray   1.10   .40
B22   SP7   2.50p + 50c car & brn   7.75   2.75
B23   SP7   5p + 1p car & vio bl   11.50   4.25
     Nos. B20-B23 (4)   20.55   7.60

       See Nos. 320, 322.

Moulay Hassan   Flag — SP9
ben el-Medi ben
Ismail — SP8

1949, May 15
B24   SP8   50c + 10c lilac rose   .25   .20
   Wedding of the Caliph at Tetuan, June 5.

Tuberculosis Fund Issues
   Design: No. B26, Fight with dragon.

1949
    Black Control Numbers on Back
B25   SP9   50c + 10 car & brown   .25   .20
B26   SP9   90c + 10 car & grnsh
          gray   .75   .25
       See No. 321.

| Catalogue values for unused |
| stamps in this section, from this |
| point to the end of the section, are |
| for Never Hinged items. |

Crowd at   Warrior — SP11
Fountain of
Life — SP10

   90c+10c, Mohammedan hermit's tomb.

1950, Oct. 1   Litho.   *Perf. 10*
   Black Control Numbers on Back
     Frame and Cross in Carmine
B27   SP10   50 + 10c dk brown   .20   .20
B28   SP10   90 + 10c dk green   .50   .30

1951   Unwmk.   *Perf. 12*
   Designs: 90c+10c, Fort. 1p+5p, Port of
Salvation. 1.10p+25c, Road to market.

    Black Control Numbers on Back
B29   SP11   50c + 10c car &
           brn   .20   .20
B30   SP11   90c + 10c car & bl   .30   .20
B31   SP11   1p + 5p car &
           gray   6.00   2.50
B32   SP11   1.10p + 25p car &
           gray   3.50   1.40
     Nos. B29-B32 (4)   10.00   4.30
       See No. B40.

Pilgrimage   Armed
SP12   Horseman in
              Action
              SP13

   Designs: 60c+25c, Palmettos. 90c+10c,
Fort. 1.10p+25c, Agave. 5p+2p, Warrior.

1952   *Perf. 11*
   Black Control Numbers on Back
B33   SP12   50 + 10c car & gray   .20   .20
B34   SP12   60 + 25c car & dk
           grn   .65   .35
B35   SP12   90 + 10c car & vio
           brn   .65   .35
B36   SP12   1.10p + 25p car & pur   1.50   .70
B37   SP12   5p + 2p car & gray   3.75   1.60
     Nos. B33-B37 (5)   6.75   3.20

1953   *Perf. 10*
   #B39, As #276. #B41c, Plane & clouds.

   Black Control Numbers on Back
B38   SP13   50c + 10c car & vio   .20   .20
B39   A70   60c + 25c car &
           brn   1.90   .65
B40   SP11   90c + 10c car & blk   .55   .25
B41   SP13   1.10p + 25c car & vio
           brn   2.75   1.00
B42   A73   5p + 2p car & bl   7.00   2.50
     Nos. B38-B42 (5)   12.40   4.60

Stork — SP14

   50c+10c, Father & Child. 5p+2p, Tomb.

1954   **Photo.**
   Black Control Numbers on Back
B43   SP14   5c + 5c car & rose
           vio   .20   .20
B44   SP14   50c + 10c car & gray
           grn   .65   .35
B45   SP14   5p + 2p car & gray   5.50   3.25
     Nos. B43-B45 (3)   6.35   3.80

AIR POST STAMPS

Mosque de Baja and
Plane — AP1

         View of
         Tetuán and
         Plane
         AP2

   10c, Stork of Alcazar. 25c, Shore scene,
plane. 40c, Desert tribesmen watching plane.
75c, View of shoreline at Larache. 1p, Arab
mailman, plane above. 1.50p, Arab farmers,
stork. 2p, Plane at twilight. 3p, Shadow of
plane over city.

1938   Unwmk.   Photo.   *Perf. 13½*
C1   AP1   5c red brown   .20   .20
C2   AP1   10c emerald   .20   .20
C3   AP1   25c crimson   .20   .20
C4   AP1   40c dull blue   1.60   .50

C5   AP2   50c cerise   .20   .20
C6   AP2   75c ultra   .20   .20
C7   AP1   1p dark brown   .20   .20
C8   AP1   1.50p purple   .55   .30
C9   AP1   2p brown lake   .30
C10   AP1   3p gray black   1.40   .20
     Nos. C1-C10 (10)   5.05   2.40

    Exist imperf. Value, set $140.
    For surcharge see No. C32.

Landscape,   Mosque,
Ketama — AP3   Tangier — AP4

Velez — AP5   Sanjurjo — AP6

Strait of Gibraltar
     AP7   AP8

1942   *Perf. 12½*
C11   AP3   5c deep blue   .20   .20
C12   AP4   10c orange brn   .20   .20
C13   AP5   15c grnsh black   .20   .20
C14   AP6   90c dark rose   .20   .20
C15   AP7   5p black   1.10   .75
     Nos. C11-C15 (5)   1.90   1.55

    Exist imperf. Value, set $45.

1949   Litho.   *Perf. 10*
   Designs: 5c, 1.75p, Strait of Gibraltar. 10c,
20c, 3p, Market day. 30c, 4p, Kebira Fortress.
6.50p, Airmail arrival. 8p, Horseman.

C16   AP8   5c vio brn & brt grn   .20   .20
C17   AP8   10c blk & rose lil   .20   .20
C18   AP8   30c dk vio bl & grnsh
           gray   .20   .20
C19   AP8   1.75p car & bl vio   .20   .20
C20   AP8   3p dk blue & gray   .20   .20
C21   AP8   4p grnsh blk & car
           rose   .25   .20
C22   AP8   6.50p brt grn & brn   .85   .20
C23   AP8   8p rose lil & bl vio   1.40   .40
     Nos. C16-C23 (8)   3.50   1.80

    Exist imperf. Value, set $80.

| Catalogue values for unused |
| stamps in this section, from this |
| point to the end of the section, are |
| for Never Hinged items. |

         Road to Tetuan — AP9

   Designs: 4p, Arrival of mail from Spain. 8p,
Greeting plane. 16p, Shadow of plane.

1952   *Perf. 11*
   Black Frames and Inscriptions
   Black Control Numbers on Back
C24   AP9   2p brt blue   .20   .20
C25   AP9   4p scarlet   .25   .20
C26   AP9   8p dk olive green   .40   .20
C27   AP9   16p violet brown   2.00   .85
     Nos. C24-C27 (4)   2.85   1.45

   Part of the proceeds was used toward the
establishment of a postal museum at Tetuan.

      Plane over
      Boat — AP10

   Designs: 60c, Mosques, Sidi Saidi. 1.10p,
Plowing. 4.50p, Fortress, Xauen.

1953   *Perf. 10*
C28   AP10   35c dp bl & car rose   .20   .20
C29   AP10   60c dk car & sl grn   .20   .20
C30   AP10   1.10p dp blue & blk   .20   .20
C31   AP10   4.50p dk car & dk brn   .85   .30
     Nos. C28-C31 (4)   1.45   .90

    Exist imperf. Value, set $75.

   No. C6 Surcharged with New Value in
              Black

          Type I

          Type II

1953   *Perf. 13½*
C32   AP2   50c on 75c ultra (I)   .45   .20
   a.   50c on 75c ultra (II)   .45   .20
   b.   Vert. gutter pair, types I and II   2.50

   Sheets of 2 panes, 25 stamps each, with
gutter between. Upper pane surcharged type I,
lower type II.

AIR POST SEMI-POSTAL STAMPS

    No. 150 Surcharged in Black
         18-7-36

     ═ **0'25 + 2'00** ═

1936   Unwmk.   *Perf. 14*
CB1   A12   25c + 2p on 25c   10.00   4.50
   a.   Bars at right omitted   32.50   32.50
   b.   Blue surcharge   22.50   11.50

    25c was for postage, 2p for air post.

   Nos. C1-C10 surcharged "Lucha
Antituberculosa," a Lorraine cross and
surtax are stated to be bogus.

Crowd at
Palace — SPAP1

1949, May 15   Unwmk.   Perf. 10
CB2 SPAP1 1p + 10c gray black   .70 .30
Wedding of the Caliph at Tetuan, June 5.

SPECIAL DELIVERY STAMPS

Special Delivery Stamp of Spain
Overprinted in Blue

1914   Unwmk.   Perf. 14
E1 SD1 20c red   3.50 1.75

Special Delivery
Stamp of Spain   PROTECTORADO
Overprinted in Blue   ESPAÑOL
EN MARRUECOS

1915
E2 SD1 20c red   2.25 1.40
For bisected surcharge see No. 68.

Special Delivery Stamp of Spain
Overprinted in Blue

1923
E3 SD1 20c red   8.25 8.25

Mounted
Courier
SD2

1928   Engr.   Perf. 14, 14½
E4 SD2 20c black   3.50 1.40
For surcharge see No. 168.

Moorish   Mounted
Postman — SD3   Courier — SD4

1935   Photo.   Perf. 14
Green Control Number on Back
E5 SD3 20c vermilion   1.00 .20
See No. E9.

1937   Perf. 13½
E6 SD4 20c bright carmine   .20 .20
1st Year of the Spanish Civil War.

For surcharge see No. E10.

Spain No. E14 Overprinted in Black

1938   Perf. 10
E7 SD7 20c vermilion   1.25 .20

Arab Postman   Airmail 1935
SD5   SD6

1940   Photo.   Perf. 11½x11
E8 SD5 25c scarlet   .25 .20
"ZONA" printed on back in black.

Type of 1935

1940   Litho.   Perf. 10
E9 SD3 20c black brown   1.40
No. E9 was prepared but not issued.

No. E6 Surcharged
with New Value, Bars
and

1940   Perf. 13½
E10 SD4 25c on 20c brt car   7.25 7.25
4th anniversary of Spanish Civil War.

> **Catalogue values for unused
> stamps in this section, from this
> point to the end of the section, are
> for Never Hinged items.**

1950   Unwmk.   Litho.   Perf. 10½
E11 SD6 25c carmine & gray   24.00 9.00
UPU, 75th anniv. (in 1949).

Moorish
Postrider
SD7

1952   Perf. 11
Black Control Number on Back
E12 SD7 25c car & rose car   .20 .20

Rider with   Gate of
Special Delivery   Tangier — SD9
Mail — SD8

1953   Photo.   Perf. 10
Black Control Number on Back
E13 SD8 25c dk bl & car rose   .20 .20
25th anniv. of Spanish Morocco's first definitive postage stamps.

1955   Litho.   Perf. 11
Black Control Number on Back
E14 SD9 2p violet & black   .20 .20

SEMI-POSTAL SPECIAL DELIVERY STAMP

Type of Semi-Postal Special Delivery
Stamp of Spain, 1926, Overprinted like
#B1-B13
1926   Unwmk.   Perf. 12½, 13
EB1 SPSD1 20c ultra & black   2.50 2.10

POSTAL TAX STAMPS

General Francisco
Franco — PT1

1937-39 Unwmk. Photo. Perf. 12½
RA1 PT1 10c sepia   .45 .20
  a.   Sheet of 4, imperf.   2.75 1.60
RA2 PT1 10c copper brn ('38)   .45 .20
  a.   Sheet of 4, imperf.   2.75 1.60
RA3 PT1 10c blue ('39)   .45 .20
  a.   Sheet of 4, imperf.   2.75 1.60
   Nos. RA1-RA3 (3)   1.35 .60
Set, never hinged   1.75
Set, RA1a-RA3a   10.50
The tax was used for the disabled soldiers in
North Africa.

Soldiers
PT2

1941   Litho.   Perf. 13½
RA4 PT2 10c brt grn   3.50 .20
RA5 PT2 10c rose pink   3.50 .20
RA6 PT2 10c henna brn   3.50 .20
RA7 PT2 10c ultra   3.50 .20
   Nos. RA4-RA7 (4)   14.00 .80
Set, never hinged   22.50
The tax was used for the disabled soldiers in
North Africa.
Exist imperf. Value, set $40.

General Francisco
Franco — PT3

1943   Photo.   Perf. 10
RA8 PT3 10c chalky blue   6.25 .20
RA9 PT3 10c slate blue   6.25 .20
RA10 PT3 10c dl gray brn   6.25 .20
RA11 PT3 10c blue violet   6.25 .20
   Nos. RA8-RA11 (4)   25.00 .80
Set, never hinged   35.00
Exists imperf. Value, set $87.50.

1944   Perf. 12
RA12 PT3 10c dp mag & brn   5.50 .20
RA13 PT3 10c dp org & dk grn   5.50 .20
Set, never hinged   14.50
Exists imperf. Value, set $37.50.

1946   Litho.
RA14 PT3 10c ultra & brown   6.00 .20
RA15 PT3 10c gray blk & rose lil   6.00 .20
Set, never hinged   16.00
Exists imperf. Value, set $37.50.

TANGIER

For the International City of Tangier
Seville-Barcelona Issue of Spain,
1929, Overprinted in Blue or Red
TANGER

1929   Perf. 11
L1 A52 5c rose lake   .25 .25
L2 A53 10c green (R)   .25 .25
L3 A50 15c Prus blue (R)   .25 .25
L4 A51 20c purple (R)   .25 .25
L5 A50 25c brt rose   .25 .25
L6 A53 30c black brn   .25 .25
L7 A53 40c dk blue (R)   .65 .65
L8 A51 50c deep org   .65 .65
L9 A53 1p blue blk (R)   7.00 7.00
L10 A53 4p deep rose   19.00 19.00
L11 A53 10p brown   27.50 27.50
   Nos. L1-L11 (11)   56.30 56.30
Never hinged   87.50

> Overprints of 1937-39
> The following overprints on stamps
> of Spain exist in black or in red:
> "TANGER" vertically on Nos. 517-
> 518, 522-523, 528, 532, 534, 539-
> 543, 549.
> "Correo Espanol Tanger" horizon-
> tally or vertically in three lines on
> Nos. 540, 592-597 (gray paper), 598-
> 601.
> "Tanger" horizontally on Nos. 539-
> 541, 592-601.
> "Correo Tanger" horizontally in two
> lines on five consular stamps.

Woman — A1   Palm Tree — A2

Man — A3   Old Map of
Tangier — A4

Tangier   Moroccan
Street — A5   Women — A6

Head of Moor — A7

**Perf. 9½x10½, 12½x13 (1c, 2c, 10c,
20c)**
1948-51   Photo.   Unwmk.
L12 A1 1c blue grn ('51)   .20 .20
L13 A1 2c red org ('51)   .20 .20
Engr.
L14 A2 5c vio brn ('49)   .20 .20
L15 A3 10c deep blue ('51)   .20 .20
L16 A3 20c gray ('51)   .20 .20
L17 A3 25c green ('51)   .20 .20
L18 A4 30c dk slate grn   .30 .20
L19 A5 45c car rose   .30 .20
L20 A6 50c dp claret   .30 .20
L21 A7 75c deep blue   .60 .20
L22 A7 90c green   .50 .20
L23 A4 1.35p org ver   1.90 .30

L24	A6	2p purple	3.50	.30
L25	A5	10p dk grnsh bl ('49)	4.75	.55
		Nos. L12-L25,LE1 (15)	14.10	3.65
		Never hinged	22.50	

Nos. L18-L25, LE1 exist imperf. Value, set $275.

TANGIER SEMI-POSTAL STAMPS

Types of Semi-Postal Stamps of Spain, 1926, Overprinted

CORREO ESPAÑOL
TANGER

1926   **Perf. 12½, 13**

LB1	SP1	1c orange	6.50	6.50
LB2	SP2	2c rose	6.50	6.50
LB3	SP3	5c black brn	3.25	3.25
LB4	SP4	10c dk green	3.25	3.25
LB5	SP1	15c dk violet	1.25	1.25
LB6	SP4	20c violet brn	1.25	1.25
LB7	SP5	25c dp carmine	1.25	1.25
LB8	SP1	30c olive grn	1.25	1.25
LB9	SP2	40c ultra	.25	.25
LB10	SP2	50c red brn	.25	.25
LB11	SP4	1p vermilion	.60	.60
LB12	SP3	4p bister	.60	.60
LB13	SP5	10p lt violet	3.00	3.00
		Nos. LB1-LB13,LEB1 (14)	32.45	32.45
		Never hinged	50.00	

For overprints & surcharges see Spain Nos. B66-B67.

TANGIER AIR POST STAMPS

Overprints of 1939
The following overprints on stamps of Spain exist in black or in red:
"Correo Aereo Tanger" in two lines on Nos. 539-541, 596 (gray paper), 600, C72B.
"Via Aerea Tanger" in three lines on Nos. 539-540, 592-597 (gray paper), 599, 601, E14.
"Correo Aereo Tanger" in three lines on four consular stamps.
"Correo Espanol Tanger" in three lines on No. C72B.
"Tanger" on No. C72B.

Plane over Shore — AP1

Twin-Engine Plane — AP2

Passenger Plane in Flight — AP3

Perf. 11x11½, 11½

1949-50		**Engr.**	**Unwmk.**	
LC1	AP1	20c violet brn ('50)	.25	.20
LC2	AP2	25c bright red	.25	.20
LC3	AP3	35c dull green	.25	.20
LC4	AP1	1p violet ('50)	.80	.40
LC5	AP2	2p deep blue	1.50	.45
LC6	AP3	10p brown violet	2.75	1.00
		Nos. LC1-LC6 (6)	5.80	2.05
		Never hinged	8.50	

Nos. LC1, LC4-LC6 exist imperf. Value $50 each.

TANGIER SPECIAL DELIVERY STAMP

Arab Postrider — SD1

1949   **Unwmk.**   **Engr.**   **Perf. 13**

LE1	SD1	25c red	.75	.30
		Never hinged	1.25	

TANGIER SEMI-POSTAL SPECIAL DELIVERY STAMP

Types of Semi-Postal Special Delivery Stamp of Spain, 1926, Overprinted like #LB1-LB13

1926   **Unwmk.**   **Perf. 12½, 13**

LEB1	SPSD1	20c ultra & black	3.25	3.25
		Never hinged	5.50	

TETUAN

Stamps of Spanish Offices in Morocco, 1903-09, Handstamped in Black, Blue or Violet

1908   **Unwmk.**   **Imperf.**

1	A21	¼c blue green	13.00	10.00
		Perf. 14		
2	A35	2c bister brown	140.00	60.00
3	A35	5c green	125.00	35.00
4	A35	10c rose red	125.00	35.00
5	A35	20c grnsh black	275.00	125.00
6	A35	25c blue	92.50	35.00
		Nos. 1-6 (6)	770.50	300.00

Same Handstamp On Stamps of Spain, 1876 and 1900-05, in Black, Blue or Violet

1908   **Imperf.**

7	A21	¼c deep green	7.50	3.25
		Perf. 14		
8	A35	2c bister brn	37.50	13.00
9	A35	5c dark green	50.00	22.50
10	A35	10c rose red	47.50	22.50
11	A35	15c purple	47.50	25.00
12	A35	20c grnsh black	140.00	110.00
13	A35	25c blue	72.50	35.00
14	A35	30c blue green	160.00	60.00
15	A35	40c olive bister	210.00	110.00
		Nos. 7-15 (9)	772.50	401.25

Counterfeits of this overprint are plentiful.

SPANISH SAHARA

'spa-nish sə-'har-ə

(Spanish Western Sahara)

LOCATION — Northwest Africa, bordering on the Atlantic
GOVT. — Spanish possession
AREA — 102,703 sq. mi.
POP. — 76,425 (1970)
CAPITAL — Aaiún

Spanish Sahara is a subdivision of Spanish West Africa. It includes the colony of Rio de Oro and the territory of Saguiet el Hamra. Spanish Sahara was formerly known as Spanish Western Sahara, which superseded the older title of Rio de Oro.

In 1976, Spanish Sahara was divided between Morocco and Mauritania.

100 Centimos = 1 Peseta

> **Catalogue values for unused stamps in this country are for Never Hinged items, beginning with Scott 51 in the regular postage section, Scott B13 in the semipostal section, Scott C8 in the airpost section, and Scott E1 in the special delivery section.**

Tuareg and Camel — A1

1924 **Unwmk.** **Typo.** **Perf. 13**
Control Number on Back

1	A1	5c blue green	2.10	.70
2	A1	10c gray green	2.10	.70
3	A1	15c turq blue	2.10	.70
4	A1	20c dark violet	2.10	1.00
5	A1	25c red	2.10	1.00
6	A1	30c red brown	2.10	1.00
7	A1	40c dark blue	2.10	1.00
8	A1	50c orange	2.10	1.00
9	A1	60c violet	2.10	1.00
10	A1	1p rose	11.00	5.50
11	A1	4p chocolate	50.00	27.50
12	A1	10p claret	125.00	85.00
		Nos. 1-12 (12)	204.90	126.10
		Set, never hinged	275.00	

#1-12 were for use in La Aguera & Rio de Oro.

An unissued set of 10, similar to Nos. 3-12, exists perf. 10 or imperf, and no control number except on 50c. The set also exists perf 14. Value, $225.

For overprints see Nos. 24-35.

Seville-Barcelona Issue of Spain, 1929 Overprinted in Blue or Red

1929   **Perf. 11**

13	A52	5c rose lake	.25	.25
14	A53	10c green (R)	.25	.25
15	A50	15c Prus blue (R)	.25	.25
16	A51	20c purple (R)	.25	.25
17	A50	25c bright rose	.25	.25
18	A52	30c black brown	.25	.25
19	A53	40c dark blue (R)	.45	.40
20	A51	50c deep orange	.45	.40
21	A52	1p blue black (R)	2.25	1.60
22	A53	4p deep rose	17.00	14.00
23	A53	10p brown	32.50	27.50
		Nos. 13-23 (11)	54.15	45.40
		Set, never hinged	75.00	

Stamps of 1924 Overprinted in Red or Blue

1931   **Perf. 13**

24	A1	5c blue grn (R)	.70	.55
25	A1	10c gray grn (R)	.70	.55
26	A1	15c turq blue (R)	.70	.55
27	A1	20c dark violet (R)	.70	.55
28	A1	25c red	.75	.55
29	A1	30c red brown	.75	.55
30	A1	40c dark blue (R)	3.50	1.90
31	A1	50c orange	3.50	1.90
32	A1	60c violet	3.50	1.90
33	A1	1p rose	3.50	1.90
34	A1	4p chocolate	37.50	19.00
35	A1	10p claret	72.50	42.50
		Nos. 24-35 (12)	128.30	71.25
		Set, never hinged	160.00	

The stamps of the 1931 issue exist with the overprint reading upward, downward or horizontally. Some values also exist with double

overprint, double overprint, one inverted and diagonal overprint.

Stamps of Spain, 1936-40, Overprinted in Carmine or Blue

1941-46   **Unwmk.**   **Imperf.**

36	A159	1c green	1.50	1.50
		Perf. 10 to 11		
37	A160	2c org brn (Bl)	1.50	1.50
38	A161	5c gray brown	.45	.45
39	A161	10c dk car (Bl)	1.50	1.50
40	A161	15c dark green	.45	.45
41	A166	20c bright violet	.45	.45
42	A166	25c deep claret	1.10	.90
43	A166	30c light blue	1.10	1.10
44	A166	40c Prus grn	.45	.45
45	A166	50c indigo	14.00	1.25
46	A166	70c blue	9.00	1.90
47	A166	1p gray black	17.50	2.75
48	A166	2p dull brown	100.00	60.00
49	A166	4p dull rose (Bl)	250.00	160.00
50	A166	10p lt brown	775.00	250.00
		Nos. 36-50 (15)	1,174.	484.20
		Set, never hinged	1,500.	

Counterfeit overprints exist.

> **Catalogue values for unused stamps in this section, from this point to the end of the section, are for Never Hinged items.**

Dorcas Gazelles — A2

Designs: 2c, 20c, 45c, 3p, Caravan. 5c, 75c, 10p, Camel troops.

1943   **Unwmk.**   **Perf. 12½**

51	A2	1c brown & lil rose	.20	.20
52	A2	2c yel grn & sl bl	.20	.20
53	A2	5c magenta & vio	.20	.20
54	A2	15c slate grn & grn	.20	.20
55	A2	20c violet & red brn	.20	.20
56	A2	40c rose vio & vio	.20	.20
57	A2	45c brn vio & red	.30	.20
58	A2	75c indigo & blue	.30	.20
59	A2	1p red & brown	1.10	.70
60	A2	3p bl vio & sl grn	2.25	1.40
61	A2	10p black brn & blk	32.50	19.00
		Nos. 51-61,E1 (12)	38.75	23.45

Nos. 51-61, E1 exist imperf. Value for set, $80.

Gen. Franco and Desert Scene A5

1951   **Photo.**   **Perf. 12½x13**

62	A5	50c deep orange	.20	.20
63	A5	1p chocolate	.30	.25
64	A5	5p blue green	29.00	11.00
		Nos. 62-64 (3)	29.50	11.45

Visit of Gen. Francisco Franco, 1950.

Allegorical Figure and Globe — A6

Woman Musician — A7

1953, Mar. 2   *Perf. 13x12½*
65 A6 5c red orange   .20 .20
66 A6 35c dk slate green   .20 .20
67 A6 60c brown   .20 .20
    Nos. 65-67 (3)   .60 .60
75th anniv. of the founding of the Royal Geographical Society.

1953, June 1
Design: 60c, Man musician.
68 A7 15c olive gray   .20 .20
69 A7 60c brown   .20 .20
    Nos. 68-69,B25-B26 (4)   .80 .80

Orange Scorpionfish — A8

Fish: 60c, Banded sargo.

1953, Nov. 23   *Perf. 12½x13*
70 A8 15c dk olive green   .20 .20
71 A8 60c orange   .20 .20
    Nos. 70-71,B27-B28 (4)   .80 .80
Colonial Stamp Day.

Hurdlers A9

Runner — A10

1954, June 1   *Perf. 12½x13, 13x12½*
72 A9   15c gray green   .20 .20
73 A10 60c brown   .20 .20
    Nos. 72-73,B29-B30 (4)   .80 .80

Atlantic Flyingfish A11

1954, Nov. 23   *Perf. 12½x13*
74 A11 15c shown   .20 .20
75 A11 60c Gilthead   .20 .20
    Nos. 74-75,B31-B32 (4)   .80 .80
Colonial Stamp Day.

Emilio Bonelli A12

1955, June 1   Photo.   Unwmk.
76 A12 50c olive gray   .20 .20
    Nos. 76,B33-B34 (3)   .60 .60
Birth cent. of Emilio Bonelli, explorer.

Scimitar-horned Oryx — A13

1955, Nov. 23
77 A13 70c green   .20 .20
    Nos. 77,B35-B36 (3)   .60 .60
Colonial Stamp Day.

Antirrhinum Romosissimum A14

Design: 50c, Sesiviun portulacastrum.

1956, June 1   *Perf. 13x12½*
78 A14 20c bluish green   .20 .20
79 A14 50c brown   .20 .20
    Nos. 78-79,B37-B38 (4)   .80 .80

Arms of Aaiun and Camel Rider A15

1956, Nov. 23   *Perf. 12½x13*
80 A15 70c olive grn & sepia   .20 .20
    Nos. 80,B39-B40 (3)   .60 .60
Colonial Stamp Day.

Dromedaries A16

Golden Eagle A17

15c, 80c, Ostrich. 50c, 1.80p, Mountain gazelle.

1957, Apr. 10   *Perf. 13x12½*
81 A16 5c purple   .20 .20
82 A16 15c bister   .20 .20
83 A16 50c dark olive   .20 .20
84 A16 70c yellow green   .65 .20
85 A16 80c blue green   .65 .20
86 A16 1.80p lilac rose   .65 .20
    Nos. 81-86 (6)   2.55 1.20

1957, June 1   Photo.   Unwmk.
87 A17 70c dark green   .20 .20
    Nos. 87,B41-B42 (3)   .60 .60

Striped Hyena — A18

Design: 70c, Striped Hyena, horiz.

Perf. 13x12½, 12½x13
1957, Nov. 23
88 A18 20c slate green   .20 .20
89 A18 70c yellowish green   .20 .20
    Nos. 88-89,B43-B44 (4)   .80 .80
Stamp Day.

Don Quixote and the Lion A19

Cervantes A20

Gray Heron A21

1958, June 1   *Perf. 12½x13, 13x12½*
90 A19 20c bister brn & grn   .20 .20
91 A20 70c dk grn & yel grn   .20 .20
    Nos. 90-91,B48-B49 (4)   .80 .80

Cervantes Type of 1958
Designs: 20c, Actor as "Peribanez," by Lope de Vega. 70c, Lope de Vega.

1959, June   Photo.   *Perf. 13x12½*
92 A20 20c lt green & brn   .20 .20
93 A20 70c yel grn & slate grn   .20 .20
    Nos. 92-93,B53-B54 (4)   .80 .80
Promoting child welfare.

1959, Oct. 15   *Perf. 13x12½*
Birds: 50c, 1.50p, 5p, Sparrowhawk. 75c, 2p, 10p, Sea gull.
94   A21 25c dull violet   .20 .20
95   A21 50c dark olive   .20 .20
96   A21 75c dark brown   .20 .20
97   A21 1p red orange   .20 .20
98   A21 1.50p brt green   .20 .20
99   A21 2p brt red lilac   .80 .20
100 A21 3p blue   .80 .20
101 A21 5p red brown   1.40 .20
102 A21 10p olive green   8.00 3.75
     Nos. 94-102 (9)   12.00 5.35

Scene from "The Pilferer Don Pablos" by Quevedo — A22

Francisco Gomez de Quevedo A23

1960, June   *Perf. 13x12½, 12½x13*
103 A22 35c slate green   .20 .20
104 A23 80c Prussian green   .20 .20
     Nos. 103-104,B58-B59 (4)   .80 .80
Francisco Gomez de Quevedo, writer.

Houbara Bustard — A24

Map of Spanish Sahara — A25

Gen. Franco and Camel Rider A26

Design: 50c, 1p, 2p, 5p, Doves.

1961, Apr. 18   Photo.   *Perf. 13x12½*
105 A24 25c blue violet   .20 .20
106 A24 50c olive gray   .20 .20
107 A24 75c brown violet   .20 .20
108 A24 1p orange ver   .20 .20

109 A24 1.50p blue green   .20 .20
110 A24 2p magenta   .70 .20
111 A24 3p dark blue   .85 .20
112 A24 5p red brown   1.00 .30
113 A24 10p olive   2.75 1.40
     Nos. 105-113 (9)   6.30 3.10

1961, Oct. 1   *Perf. 13x12½, 12½x13*
Design: 70c, Chapel of Aaiun.
114 A25 25c gray violet   .20 .20
115 A26 50c olive brown   .20 .20
116 A25 70c brt green   .20 .20
117 A26 1p red orange   .20 .20
     Nos. 114-117 (4)   .80 .80
25th anniv. of the nomination of Gen. Francisco Franco as Chief of State.

Neurada Procumbres A27

Clock Fish A28

50c, 1.50p, 10p, Anabasis articulata, flower. 70c, 2p, Euphorbia resinifera, cactus.

1962, Feb. 26   *Perf. 13x12½*
118 A27 25c black violet   .20 .20
119 A27 50c dark brown   .20 .20
120 A27 70c brt green   .20 .20
121 A27 1p orange ver   .20 .20
122 A27 1.50p blue green   .30 .20
123 A27 2p red lilac   1.00 .20
124 A27 3p slate   1.75 .25
125 A27 10p olive   4.00 1.40
     Nos. 118-125 (8)   7.85 2.85

Perf. 13x12½, 12½x13
1962, July 10   Photo.
Design: 50c, Avia fish, horiz.
126 A28 25c violet black   .20 .20
127 A28 50c dark green   .20 .20
128 A28 1p orange brown   .20 .20
     Nos. 126-128 (3)   .60 .60

Goats A29

Stamp Day: 35c, Sheep.

1962, Nov. 23   *Perf. 12½x13*
129 A29 15c yellow green   .20 .20
130 A29 35c magenta   .20 .20
131 A29 1p orange brown   .20 .20
     Nos. 129-131 (3)   .60 .60

Seville Cathedral Tower — A30

1963, Jan. 29   *Perf. 13x12½*
132 A30 50c olive   .20 .20
133 A30 1p brown orange   .20 .20
Issued to help Seville flood victims.

Camel Riders — A31

Hands Releasing Dove and Arms — A32

Design: 50c, Tuareg and camel.

1963, June 1   **Unwmk.**
134 A31 25c deep violet   .20 .20
135 A31 50c gray   .20 .20
136 A31 1p orange red   .20 .20
     Nos. 134-136 (3)   .60 .60
     Issued for child welfare.

1963, July 12
137 A32 50c Prussian green   .20 .20
138 A32 1p orange brown   .20 .20

     Issued for Barcelona flood relief.

John Dory A33

Fish: 50c, Plain bonito, vert.

Perf. 12½x13, 13x12½
1964, Mar. 6   **Photo.**
139 A33 25c purple   .20 .20
140 A33 50c olive green   .20 .20
141 A33 1p brown red   .20 .20
     Nos. 139-141 (3)   .60 .60
     Issued for Stamp Day 1963.

Moth and Flowers A34

Design: 50c, Two moths, vert.

Perf. 12½x13, 13x12½
1964, June 1   **Unwmk.**
142 A34 25c dull violet   .20 .20
143 A34 50c brown black   .20 .20
144 A34 1p orange red   .20 .20
     Nos. 142-144 (3)   .60 .60
     Issued for child welfare.

Camel Rider and Microphone A35

Squirrel A36

Designs: 50c, 1.50p, 3p, Boy with flute and camels. 70c, 2p, 10p, Woman with drum.

1964, Sept.   Photo.   Perf. 13x12½
145 A35 25c dull purple   .20 .20
146 A35 50c olive   .20 .20
147 A35 70c green   .20 .20
148 A35 1p dull red brn   .20 .20
149 A35 1.50p bright green   .20 .20
150 A35 2p Prus green   .20 .20
151 A35 3p dark blue   .20 .20
152 A35 10p carmine lake   1.25 .60
     Nos. 145-152 (8)   2.70 2.00

1964, Nov. 23   **Unwmk.**
     Stamp Day: 1p, Squirrel's head, horiz.
153 A36 50c olive gray   .20 .20
154 A36 1p brown carmine   .20 .20
155 A36 1.50p green   .20 .20
     Nos. 153-155 (3)   .60 .60

Tuareg Girl — A37

Wellhead and Camel Rider — A38

25 Years of Peace: 1p, Physician examining patient, horiz.

Perf. 13x12½, 12½x13
1965, Feb. 22   **Photo.**
156 A37 50c black brown   .20 .20
157 A38 1p dark red   .20 .20
158 A38 1.50p deep blue   .20 .20
     Nos. 156-158 (3)   .60 .60

Anthia Sexmaculata — A39

1p, 3p, Blepharopsis mendica, vert.

Perf. 12½x13, 13x12½
1965, June 1   **Unwmk.**
159 A39 50c slate blue   .20 .20
160 A39 1p blue green   .20 .20
161 A39 1.50p brown   .20 .20
162 A39 3p dark blue   .90 .50
     Nos. 159-162 (4)   1.50 1.10
     Issued for child welfare.

Basketball A40

Arms and Camels A41

1965, Nov. 23   **Perf. 13x12½**
163 A40 50c rose claret   .20 .20
164 A41 1p deep magenta   .20 .20
165 A40 1.50p slate blue   .20 .20
     Nos. 163-165 (3)   .60 .60
     Issued for Stamp Day.

Ship "Rio de Oro" A42

Design: 1.50p, S.S. Fuerte Ventura.

1966, June 1 Photo.   Perf. 12½x13
166 A42 50c olive   .20 .20
167 A42 1p dark red brown   .20 .20
168 A42 1.50p blue green   .20 .20
     Nos. 166-168 (3)   .60 .60
     Issued for child welfare.

Ocean Sunfish — A43

A44

Designs: 10c, 1.50p, Bigeye tuna, horiz.

1966, Nov. 23   Photo.   Perf. 13
169 A43 10c bl gray & cit   .20 .20
170 A43 40c slate & pink   .20 .20
171 A43 1.50p brown & olive   .20 .20
172 A43 4p rose vio & gray   .80 .80
     Nos. 169-172 (4)
     Issued for Stamp Day.

1967, June 1   Photo.   Perf. 13
     Designs: 40c, 4p, Flower and leaves.
173 A44 10c blk, ocher & gray grn   .20 .20
174 A44 40c emerald & lilac   .20 .20
175 A44 1.50p dk grn & yel grn   .20 .20
176 A44 4p brt blue & org   .20 .20
     Nos. 173-176 (4)   .80 .80
     Issued for child welfare.

Aaiun Harbor A45

Design: 4p, Villa Cisneros Harbor.

1967, Sept. 28 Photo.   Perf. 12½x13
177 A45 1.50p brt bl & red brn   .20 .20
178 A45 4p brt bl & bis brn   .20 .20
     Modernization of harbor installations.

Ruddy Sheldrake A46

Stamp Day: 1.50p, Flamingo, vert. 3.50p, Rufous bush robin.

1967, Nov. 23   Photo.   Perf. 13
179 A46 1p bister brn & grn   .20 .20
180 A46 1.50p brt rose & gray   .20 .20
181 A46 3.50p brn red & sep   .25 .20
     Nos. 179-181 (3)   .65 .60

Scorpio — A47

Mailman — A48

Zodiac Issue
1.50p, Aries. 2.50p, Virgo.

1968, Apr. 25   Photo.   Perf. 13
182 A47 1p brt mag, *lt yel*   .20 .20
183 A47 1.50p brown, *pink*   .20 .20
184 A47 2.50p dk vio, *yel*   .25 .20
     Nos. 182-184 (3)   .65 .60
     Issued for child welfare.

1968, Nov.   Photo.   Perf. 13x12½
     Stamp Day: 1p, Post horn, pigeon, letter and Spain No. 1. 1.50p, Letter, canceller and various stamps of Spain and Ifni.
185 A48 1p dp lil rose & dk bl   .20 .20
186 A48 1.50p green & sl grn   .20 .20
187 A48 2.50p dp org & dk bl   .20 .20
     Nos. 185-187 (3)   .60 .60

Dorcas Gazelle — A49

Designs: 1.50p, Doe and fawn. 2.50p, Gazelle and camel. 6p, Leaping gazelle.

1969, June 1   Photo.   Perf. 13
188 A49 1p gldn brn & blk   .20 .20
189 A49 1.50p gldn brn & blk   .20 .20
190 A49 2.50p gldn brn & blk   .20 .20
191 A49 6p gldn brn & blk   .30 .25
     Nos. 188-191 (4)   .90 .85

Child welfare. See Nos. 196-199, 209-212.

Woman Playing Drum — A50

Stamp Day: 1.50p, Man with flute. 2p, Drum and camel rider, horiz. 25p, Flute, horiz.

1969, Nov. 23   Photo.   Perf. 13
192 A50 50c brn red & lt ol   .20 .20
193 A50 1.50p dk bl grn & grnsh gray .20 .20
194 A50 2p indigo & bis brn   .20 .20
195 A50 25p brn & lt bl grn   .80 .25
     Nos. 192-195 (4)   1.40 .85

Animal Type of 1969
Fennec: 50c, Sitting. 2p, Running. 2.50p, Head. 6p, Vixen and pups.

1970, June 1   Photo.   Perf. 13
196 A49 50c dp bister & blk   .20 .20
197 A49 2p org brn & blk   .20 .20
198 A49 2.50p dp bister & blk   .20 .20
199 A49 6p dp bister & blk   .30 .30
     Nos. 196-199 (4)   .90 .80
     Issued for child welfare.

Grammodes Boisdeffrei — A51

Designs: 1p, like 50c. 2p, 5p, Danaus chrysippus. 8p, Celerio euphorbiae.

1970, Nov. 23   Photo.   Perf. 12½
200 A51 50c red & multi   .20 .20
201 A51 1p carmine & multi   .20 .20
202 A51 2p green & multi   .20 .20

203 A51 5p Prus bl & multi   .25 .20
204 A51 8p dk blue & multi   .30 .30
    Nos. 200-204 (5)   1.15 1.10
Issued for Stamp Day. See Nos. 233-234.

Gazelle, Arms of   Smara
Aaiun — A52   Mosque — A53

Designs: 2p, Inn, horiz. 5p, Assembly
building, Aaiun, horiz.

Perf. 12½x13, 13x12½
1971, June 1   **Photo.**
205 A52 1p multicolored   .20 .20
206 A53 2p gray grn & ol   .20 .20
207 A53 5p lt bl & lt red brn   .20 .20
208 A53 25p lt bl & grnsh gray   .75 .30
    Nos. 205-208 (4)   1.35 .90
Issued for child welfare.

Animal Type of 1969

Birds: 1.50p, 2p, Trumpeter bullfinch. 5p,
Cream-colored courser. 10p, Lanner (falcon).

1971, Nov. 23 **Photo.** **Perf. 12½**
209 A49 1.50p black & multi   .20 .20
210 A49 2p blue & multi   .20 .20
211 A49 5p green & multi   .20 .20
212 A49 24p black & multi   .70 .30
    Nos. 209-212 (4)   1.30 .90
Stamp Day.

Saharan
Woman — A55

Tuareg
Woman — A56

1.50p, 2p, Saharan man. 8p, 10p, Man's
head. 12p, Woman. 15p, Soldier. 24p, Dancer.

1972, Feb. 18 **Photo.** **Perf. 13**
213 A55 1p blue, pink & brn   .20 .20
214 A55 1.50p brn, lil & blk   .20 .20
215 A55 2p green, buff & sep   .20 .20
216 A55 5p green, pur & vio
              brn   .20 .20
217 A55 8p black, lt grn & vio   .20 .20
218 A55 10p black, gray & Prus
              bl   .25 .20
219 A55 12p multicolored   .30 .25
220 A55 15p multicolored   .40 .35
221 A55 24p multicolored   .85 .50
    Nos. 213-221 (9)   2.80 2.30

1972, June 1 **Photo.** **Perf. 13**
222 A56 8p shown   .25 .20
223 A56 12p Tuareg man   .35 .20
Child welfare.

Mother and
Child — A57

1972, Nov. 23 **Photo.** **Perf. 13**
224 A57 4p shown   .20 .20
225 A57 15p Saharan man   .40 .20
Stamp Day. See No. 229.

Dunes
A58

Design: 7p, Old Market and Gate, Aaiun.

1973, June 1 **Photo.** **Perf. 13**
226 A58 2p multicolored   .20 .20
227 A58 7p multicolored   .20 .20
Child welfare.

Type of 1972 and

View of
Villa
Cisneros
A59

1973, Nov. 23 **Photo.** **Perf. 13**
228 A59 2p shown   .20 .20
229 A57 7p Tuareg man   .20 .20
Stamp Day.

UPU Monument,
Bern — A60

1974, May **Photo.** **Perf. 13**
230 A60 15p multicolored   .45 .20
Centenary of the Universal Postal Union.

1974, May

2p, Court and Minaret, Villa Cisneros
Mosque.

Gate, Smara
Mosque — A61

231 A61 1p multicolored   .20 .20
232 A61 2p multicolored   .20 .20
Child welfare.

Animal Type of 1970

1974, Nov. **Photo.** **Perf. 13**
233 A51 2p Desert eagle owl   .20 .20
234 A51 5p Lappet-faced vulture   .20 .20
Stamp Day.

Espana 75
Emblem, Spain
No. 1084 — A63

Old Man — A65

Children
A64

1975, Apr. 4 **Photo.** **Perf. 13**
235 A63 8p olive, blk & bl   .20 .20
Espana 75 Intl. Phil. Exhib., Madrid, 4/4-13.

1975 **Photo.** **Perf. 13**
236 A64 1.50p shown   .20 .20
237 A64 3p Children's village   .20 .20
Child welfare.

1975, Nov. 7 **Photo.** **Perf. 13**
238 A65 3p blk, lt grn & mar   .20 .20

SEMI-POSTAL STAMPS

Red Cross Issue
Types of Semi-Postal Stamps of
Spain, 1926, Overprinted

SAHARA ESPAÑOL

1926 **Unwmk.** **Perf. 12½, 13**
B1   SP3 5c black brown   8.00 8.00
B2   SP4 10c dark green   8.00 8.00
B3   SP1 15c dark violet   2.50 2.50
B4   SP4 20c violet brown   2.50 2.50
B5   SP5 25c deep carmine   2.50 2.50
B6   SP1 30c olive green   2.50 2.50
B7   SP3 40c ultra   .20 .20
B8   SP2 50c red brown   .20 .20
B9   SP5 60c myrtle green   .20 .20
B10 SP4 1p vermilion   .20 .20
B11 SP3 4p bister   2.50 1.90
B12 SP5 10p light violet   6.50 5.50
    Nos. B1-B12 (12)   35.80 34.20
    Set, never hinged   47.50

See Spain No. B6a for No. B4 without overprint. For surcharges see Spain #B72-B73.

**Catalogue values for unused
stamps in this section, from this
point to the end of the section, are
for Never Hinged items.**

Shepherd and
Lamb — SP1

Dromedary and
Calf — SP2

1950, Oct. 20 **Photo.** **Perf. 13x12½**
B13 SP1 50c + 10c brown   .20 .20
B14 SP1 1p + 25c rose brn   9.75 5.50
B15 SP1 6.50p + 1.65p dk
              gray grn   5.50 1.60
    Nos. B13-B15 (3)   15.45 7.30
The surtax was for child welfare.

1951, Nov. 23
B16 SP2 5c + 5c brown   .20 .20
B17 SP2 10c + 5 red org   .20 .20
B18 SP2 60c + 15c olive brn   .30 .20
    Nos. B16-B18 (3)   .70 .60
Colonial Stamp Day, Nov. 23.

Child and
Protector
SP3

Ostrich
SP4

1952, June 1
B19 SP3 5c + 5c brown   .20 .20
B20 SP3 50c + 10c gray   .20 .20
B21 SP3 2p + 30c blue   1.40 .95
    Nos. B19-B21 (3)   1.80 1.35
The surtax was for child welfare.

1952, Nov. 23 **Perf. 12½**
B22 SP4 5c + 5c brown   .20 .20
B23 SP4 10c + 5c brn car   .20 .20
B24 SP4 60c + 15c dk grn   .30 .20
    Nos. B22-B24 (3)   .70 .60
Colonial Stamp Day, Nov. 23.

Musician Type of Regular Issue
1953, June 1 **Perf. 13x12½**
B25 A7 5c + 5c like #68   .20 .20
B26 A7 10c + 5c like #69   .20 .20
The surtax was for child welfare.

Fish Type of Regular Issue
1953, Nov. 23 **Perf. 12½x13**
B27 A8 5c + 5c like #70   .20 .20
B28 A8 10c + 5c like #71   .20 .20

Athlete Types of Regular Issue
1954, June 1 **Perf. 12½x13, 13x12½**
B29 A9 5c + 5c brn org   .20 .20
B30 A10 10c + 5c purple   .20 .20
The surtax was to help the native population.

Fish Type of Regular Issue
1954, Nov. 23 **Perf. 12½x13**
B31 A11 5c + 5c like #74   .20 .20
B32 A11 10c + 5c like #75   .20 .20

Type of Regular Issue and

Emilio
Bonelli
SP5

1955, June 1 **Photo.** **Unwmk.**
B33 A12 10c + 5c red vio   .20 .20
B34 SP5 25c + 10c violet   .20 .20
The surtax was for child welfare.

Antelope Type of Regular Issue
15c+5c, Head of scimitar-horned oryx.

1955, Nov. 23 **Perf. 12½x13**
B35 A13 5c + 5c org brn   .20 .20
B36 A13 15c + 5c olive bister   .20 .20

Flower Type of Regular Issue
1956, June 1 **Perf. 13x12½**
B37 A14 5c + 5c like #78   .20 .20
B38 A14 15c + 5c like #79   .20 .20
The tax was for the children.

Aaiun Type of Regular Issue and

Arms of Villa Cisneros and Man — SP6

Perf. 12½x13, 13x12½

1956, Nov. 23   **Unwmk.**
| B39 | A15 | 5c + 5c pur & blk | .20 | .20 |
| B40 | SP6 | 15c + 5c bis & grn | .20 | .20 |

Eagle Type of Regular Issue

15c+5c, Lesser spotted eagle in flight.

1957, June 1   **Perf. 13x12½**
| B41 | A17 | 5c + 5c red brown | .20 | .20 |
| B42 | A17 | 15c + 5c golden brn | .20 | .20 |

The surtax was for child welfare.

Hyena Type of Regular Issue

Perf. 13x12½, 12½x13

1957, Nov. 23
| B43 | A18 | 10c + 5c like #88 | .20 | .20 |
| B44 | A18 | 15c + 5c like #89 | .20 | .20 |

Stork and Arms of Valencia and Aaiun SP7

1958, Mar. 6   **Photo.**   **Perf. 12½x13**
B45	SP7	10c + 5c org brn	.20	.20
B46	SP7	15c + 10c bister	.20	.20
B47	SP7	50c + 10c brn olive	.20	.20
		Nos. B45-B47 (3)	.60	.60

The surtax was to aid the victims of the Valencia flood, Oct. 1957.

Cervantes Type of Regular Issue

15c+5c, Don Quixote & Sancho Panza.

1958, June 1   **Perf. 13x12½**
| B48 | A20 | 10c + 5c hn brn & chnt brn | .20 | .20 |
| B49 | A20 | 15c + 5c dp org & slate grn | .20 | .20 |

The surtax was for child welfare.

Hoopoe Lark — SP8   Mailman — SP9

25c+10c, Hoopoe larks, horiz. 50c+10c, Bird.

Perf. 13x12½, 12½x13

1958, Nov. 23   **Photo.**   **Unwmk.**
B50	SP8	10c + 5c brn red	.20	.20
B51	SP8	25c + 10c brt pur	.20	.20
B52	SP8	50c + 10c olive	.20	.20
		Nos. B50-B52 (3)	.60	.60

Cervantes Type of Regular Issue

10c+5c, Lope de Vega. 15c+5c, Actress from "Star of Seville," by Lope de Vega.

1959, June   **Perf. 13x12½**
| B53 | A20 | 10c + 5c org brn & ol gray | .20 | .20 |
| B54 | A20 | 15c + 5c dp ocher & choc | .20 | .20 |

The surtax was for child welfare.

1959, Nov. 23   **Photo.**

Stamp Day: 20c+5c, Mailman. 50c+20c, Mailman on camel.
B55	SP9	10c + 5c rose & brn	.20	.20
B56	SP9	20c + 5c lt grn & brn	.20	.20
B57	SP9	50c + 20c ol gray & slate	.20	.20
		Nos. B55-B57 (3)	.60	.60

Quevedo Type of Regular Issue

Designs: 10c+5c, Francisco Gomez de Quevedo. 15c+5c, Winged wheel and hourglass, symbolic of "Hora de Todas."

1960, June 1   **Perf. 12½x13, 13x12½**
| B58 | A23 | 10c + 5c maroon | .20 | .20 |
| B59 | A22 | 15c + 5c bister brown | .20 | .20 |

The surtax was for child welfare.

Leopard SP10   Alonso Fernandez de Lugo SP11

Stamp Day: 20c+5c, Desert fox. 30c+10c, Eagle and leopard. 50c+20c, Sand fox.

1960, Nov. 23   **Photo.**   **Perf. 13x12½**
B60	SP10	10c + 5c rose lilac	.20	.20
B61	SP10	20c + 5c dk slate grn	.20	.20
B62	SP10	30c + 10c chocolate	.20	.20
B63	SP10	50c + 20c olive gray	.20	.20
		Nos. B60-B63 (4)	.80	.80

Animal Type of 1961 inscribed: "Pro-Infancia 1961"

Designs: Various Mountain Gazelles.

1961, June 21   **Unwmk.**
B64	SP10	10c + 5c rose brn	.20	.20
B65	SP10	25c + 10c gray vio	.20	.20
B66	SP10	80c + 20c dk grn	.20	.20
		Nos. B64-B66 (3)	.60	.60

The surtax was for child welfare.

1961, Nov. 23   **Perf. 13x12½**

Stamp Day: #B68, B70, Diego de Herrera.
B67	SP11	10c + 5c org red	.20	.20
B68	SP11	25c + 10c dk pur	.20	.20
B69	SP11	30c + 10c dk red brn	.20	.20
B70	SP11	1p + 10c red org	.20	.20
		Nos. B67-B70 (4)	.80	.80

AIR POST STAMPS

In 1942, seven air post stamps of Spain, Nos. C100-C108, were overprinted "SAHARA ESPANOL", but satisfactory information regarding their status is not available.

Catalogue values for unused stamps in this section are for Never Hinged items.

Ostriches — AP1   Desert Scene — AP2

1943   **Unwmk.**   **Litho.**   **Perf. 12½**
C8	AP1	5c cer & vio brn	.20	.20
C9	AP2	25c yel grn & ol grn	.20	.20
C10	AP1	50c ind & turq grn	.20	.20
C11	AP2	1p pur & grnsh bl	.20	.20
C12	AP1	1.40p gray grn & bl	.20	.20

C13	AP2	2p mag & org brn	1.50	1.10
C14	AP1	5p brown & purple	2.10	1.10
C15	AP2	6p brt bl & gray grn	37.50	19.00
		Nos. C8-C15 (8)	42.10	22.20

Nos. C8-C15 exist imperf. Value of set $87.50.

Diego Garcia de Herrera AP3

1950, Nov. 23   **Photo.**
| C16 | AP3 | 5p rose violet | 2.25 | 1.00 |

Stamp Day.

Woman Holding Dove — AP4

1951, Apr. 22   **Engr.**   **Perf. 10**
| C17 | AP4 | 5p deep green | 22.50 | 6.50 |

500th birth anniv. of Queen Isabella I. No. C17 is valued in the grade of fine.

Helmet and Trappings AP5   Plane and Camel Rider AP6

1952, July 18   **Photo.**   **Perf. 13x12½**
| C18 | AP5 | 5p brown | 27.50 | 6.50 |

500th birth anniv. of Ferdinand the Catholic, of Spain.

1961, May 16   **Unwmk.**
| C19 | AP6 | 25p gray brown | 2.50 | .80 |

SPECIAL DELIVERY STAMPS

Catalogue value for unused stamps in this section are for Never Hinged items.

Type A2 Inscribed "URGENTE"

1943   **Unwmk.**   **Perf. 12½**
| E1 | A2 | 25c Camel troops | 1.10 | .75 |

Messenger on Motorcycle — SD1

Unwmk.
1971, Sept. 6   **Photo.**   **Perf. 13**
| E2 | SD1 | 10p bright rose & olive | .50 | .30 |

SPANISH WEST AFRICA

'spa-nish 'west 'a-fri-kə

LOCATION — Northwest Africa bordering on the Atlantic Ocean
GOVT. — Spanish administration
AREA — 117,000 sq. mi.
POP. — 95,000 (1950)
CAPITAL — Sidi Ifni

Spanish West Africa was the major political division of Spanish areas in northwest Africa. It included Spanish Sahara (Rio de Oro and Saguiet el Hamra) Ifni and, for administrative purposes, Southern Morocco. Separate stamp issues have been used for Rio de Oro, Ifni and La Aguera.

Catalogue values for all unused stamps in this country are for Never Hinged items.

Native — A1

Perf. 13x12½
1949, Oct.   **Litho.**   **Unwmk.**
| 1 | A1 | 4p dark gray green | 1.90 | .90 |

UPU, 75th anniversary.

Nomad Camp A2

5c, 30c, 75c, 2p, Tinzgarrentz Oasis. 10c, 40c, 90c, 5p, Desert well. 15c, 45c, 1p, Caravan.

1950, June 5   **Perf. 12½x13**
2	A2	2c brown	.20	.20
3	A2	5c rose violet	.20	.20
4	A2	10c Prussian blue	.20	.20
5	A2	15c deep olive gray	.20	.20
6	A2	25c red brown	.20	.20
7	A2	30c bright yellow	.20	.20
8	A2	40c olive gray	.20	.20
9	A2	45c rose lake	.20	.20
10	A2	50c brown orange	.20	.20
11	A2	75c ultramarine	.20	.20
12	A2	90c dull blue grn	.20	.20
13	A2	1p gray	.20	.20
14	A2	1.35p violet	.55	.45
15	A2	2p sepia	1.10	.90
16	A2	5p lilac rose	10.50	3.00
17	A2	10p light brown	25.00	19.00
		Nos. 2-17 (16)	39.55	25.75

AIR POST STAMPS

Isabella the Catholic, Queen of Castile — AP1

Perf. 13x12½
1949, Nov. 23   **Photo.**   **Unwmk.**
| C1 | AP1 | 5p yellow brown | 1.60 | .90 |

Stamp Day, Nov. 23, 1949.

Desert
Camp
AP2

Designs: Various Desert Scenes.

			Perf. 12½x13	
1951, Mar. 1		**Litho.**		
C2	AP2	25c ocher	.20	.20
C3	AP2	50c lilac rose	.20	.20
C4	AP2	1p green	.25	.20
C5	AP2	2p bright blue	.55	.20
C6	AP2	3.25p rose lilac	1.10	.75
C7	AP2	5p gray brown	11.50	2.75
C8	AP2	10p rose red	22.50	17.50
	Nos. C2-C8 (7)		36.30	21.80

SPECIAL DELIVERY STAMP

Tilimenzo
Pass and
Franco
SD1

	Perf. 12½x13	
1951, Mar. 1	**Litho.**	**Unwmk.**
E1 SD1 25c rose carmine	.30	.25

STOCKSHEETS

HAGNER STYLE STOCK SHEETS

Hagner-style stock pages offer convenience and flexibility. Pages are produced on thick, archival-quality paper with acetate pockets glued from the bottom of each pocket. They're ideal for the topical collector who may require various page styles to store a complete collection.

- Black background makes beautiful stamp presentation.
- Pockets use pull away/snap back principle.
- Made from archival-quality heavyweight paper that offers unprecedented protection and clarity.
- Multi-hole punch fits most binder types.
- Available in 9 different page formats. 8½" x 11" size accomodates every size stamp.

Sold in packages of 10.
Available with pockets on one side or both sides.
"D" in item number denotes two-sided page.

1 POCKET — 242 mm

Item	Retail
S1	$10.99
S1D	$15.99

2 POCKET — 119 mm

Item	Retail
S2	$10.99
S2D	$15.99

3 POCKET — 79 mm

Item	Retail
S3	$10.99
S3D	$15.99

4 POCKET — 58 mm

Item	Retail
S4	$10.99
S4D	$15.99

5 POCKET — 45 mm

Item	Retail
S5	$10.99
S5D	$15.99

6 POCKET — 37 mm

Item	Retail
S6	$10.99
S6D	$15.99

7 POCKET — 31 mm

Item	Retail
S7	$10.99
S7D	$15.99

8 POCKET — 27 mm

Item	Retail
S8	$10.99
S8D	$15.99

MULTI-POCKETS — 36 mm / 67 mm / 139 mm

Item	Retail
S9	$10.99
S9D	$15.99

1-800-572-6885
P.O. Box 828, Sidney OH 45365-0828
www.amosadvantage.com

AMOS
HOBBY PUBLISHING

Publishers of *Coin World, Linn's Stamp News*
and *Scott Publishing Co.*

SRI LANKA

„srē 'läη-kə

LOCATION — Indian Ocean south of India
GOVT. — Democratic Socialist Republic
AREA — 26,244 sq. mi.
POP. — 19,144,875 (1999 est.)
CAPITAL — Colombo

Sri Lanka was named Ceylon until May 22, 1972. Issues inscribed "Ceylon" are listed under that name in Volume 2.

100 Cents = 1 Rupee

Catalogue values for all unused stamps in this country are for Never Hinged items.

Watermark

Wmk. 385 — CARTOR

Wmk. 233 — "Harrison & Sons, London" in Script

Wmk. 388 — Multiple "SPM"

Lotus and Sunrise over Adam's Peak — A162

1972, May 22   Litho.   Perf. 13½x13
470 A162 15c blue & multi   .35   .35
Inauguration of Ceylon as Republic of Sri Lanka.

A162a

Overprinted "1972" in Red

1972, May 26   Perf. 14x13½
471 A162a 5c orange brn & multi   .35   .35
World Fellowship of Buddhists, Sri Lanka, May 22-28.
Supposedly not issued without overprint, copies sell for 25-cents.

Book Year Emblem, Oil Lamp — A163

1972, Sept. 8   Photo.   Perf. 13
472 A163 20c yellow & dk brn   .25   .25
International Book Year 1972.

Imperial Angelfish A164

Tropical Fish: 3c, Green chromide. 30c, Skipjack bonito. 2r, Black ruby barbs.

Perf. 14x13½
1972, Oct. 12   Litho.   Unwmk.
473 A164   2c ultra & multi   .20   .65
474 A164   3c dp orange & multi   .20   .65
475 A164   30c brt green & multi   1.75   .35
476 A164   2r dp green & multi   5.00   5.00
     Nos. 473-476 (4)   7.15   6.65
3rd Session of Indian Ocean Fisheries Commission, Colombo, Oct. 9-14.

Bandaranaike Memorial Hall — A165

1973, May 17   Litho.   Perf. 14
477 A165 15c lt ultra & vio blue   .30   .30
Opening of Bandaranaike Memorial International Conference Hall.

Women Holding Lotus A166

Rock and Temple Paintings: 35c, King giving away his children, Degaldoruwa Temple, near Kandy, 18th cent. 50c, Prince and gravedigger, Polonaruwa, 12th cent. 90c, Holy man holding lotus, Polonaruwa, 12th cent. Design of 1.55r is from Sigiriya, 5th cent.

1973, Sept. 3   Perf. 13½x14
478 A166   35c lt gray & multi   .35   .20
479 A166   50c gray & multi   .40   .20
480 A166   90c slate & multi   .60   .60
481 A166   1.55r brown & multi   .75   1.00
   a.   Souvenir sheet of 4, #478-481   3.25   3.25
     Nos. 478-481 (4)   2.10   2.00
For surcharges see Nos. 538-540.

Bandaranaike Conference Hall — A167

1974, Sept. 6   Litho.   Perf. 14
482 A167 85c multicolored   .35   .35
20th Commonwealth Parliamentary Conference, Sri Lanka, Sept. 1-15.

S.W.R.D. Bandaranaike A168

"UPU," "100" and UPU Emblem A170

1974, Sept. 25   Photo.   Perf. 14½
486 A168 15c ultra & multi   .20   .20
For surcharge see No. 541.

1974, Oct. 9   Litho.   Perf. 13
490 A170 50c multicolored   .85   .70

Parliament, Colombo A171

1975, Apr. 1   Litho.   Perf. 13½
491 A171 1r multicolored   .30   .30
Interparliamentary Union, Spring Meeting at Bandaranaike Memorial International Conference Hall, Sri Lanka, Mar. 31-Apr. 5.

Ponnambalam Ramanathan A172   D. J. Wimalasurendra A173

1975, Sept. 4   Litho.   Perf. 13½
492 A172 75c multicolored   .30   .30
Sir Ponnambalam Ramanathan (1851-1930), lawyer and educator.

1975, Sept. 17
493 A173 75c ultra & blue blk   .35   .35
Devapura Jayasena Wimalasurendra (1874-1953), engineer and irrigation specialist.

Map, Mrs. Bandaranaike, Dove — A174

1975, Dec. 22   Litho.   Perf. 13½
494 A174 1.15r blue & multi   1.75   1.25
International Women's Year 1975.

Rhododendron Zeylanicum A175

Flowers: 50c, Exacum trinerve. 75c, Daffodil orchid. 10r, Wormia triquetra.

1976, Jan. 1   Litho.   Perf. 1[?]
495 A175   25c blue & multi   .20   .2[0]
496 A175   50c ocher & multi   .20   .2[0]
497 A175   75c black & multi   .25   .2[5]
498 A175   10r black & multi   3.50   3.5[0]
   a.   Souvenir sheet of 4, #495-498   12.50   12.5[0]
     Nos. 495-498 (4)   4.15   4.1[5]

Mahaveli-ganga Sluice — A176

1976, Jan. 8   Litho.   Perf. 13x12½
499 A176 85c lt blue, lt grn & lil   .30   .50
Mahaveli-ganga River diversion.

Radar Station — A177

1976, May 6   Litho.   Perf. 14
500 A177 1r blue & multi   .70   .70
Opening of Satellite Earth Station, Padukka.

Prince Siddhartha as White Elephant and Sleeping Queen — A178

Birth of Buddha: 10c, King consulting astrologers. 1.50r, King entertaining astrologers at banquet. 2r, Queen taken in procession to her parents. 2.25r, Flag bearers, musicians in procession. 5r, Queen giving birth to Prince Siddhartha, the Buddha. Designs taken from 18th cent. wall paintings in Dambawa Vihara Temple.

1976, May 7   Litho.   Perf. 13½
501 A178   5c blue & multi   .20   .40
502 A178   10c blue & multi   .20   .40
503 A178   1.50r blue & multi   .70   .55
504 A178   2r blue & multi   .80   .60
505 A178   2.25r blue & multi   .85   1.10
506 A178   5r blue & multi   1.25   1.90
   a.   Souvenir sheet of 6, #501-506   11.50   11.50
     Nos. 501-506 (6)   4.00   4.95

Blue Sapphire A179

Gems of Sri Lanka: 1.15r, Cat's-eye. 2r, Star sapphire. 5r, Ruby.

1976, June 16   Perf. 12x12½
507 A179   60c multicolored   4.50   .35
508 A179   1.15r multicolored   7.25   1.75
509 A179   2r multicolored   7.75   3.75
510 A179   5r multicolored   10.50   10.50
   a.   Souv. sheet of 4, #507-510   42.50   35.00
     Nos. 507-510 (4)   30.00   16.35

Prime Minister
Sirimavo
Bandaranaike
A180

Statue of
Liberty
A181

1976, Aug. 3 Photo. *Perf. 14¼x14½*
511 A180 1.15r pink & multi .35 .35
512 A180 2r pink & multi .60 .60

5th Summit Conference of Non-aligned
Countries, Colombo, Aug. 9-19.

1976, Nov. 29 Litho. *Perf. 14*
513 A181 2.25r lt blue & indigo .75 1.00

American Bicentennial.

A. G. Bell,
Telephone and
Telephone Line
A182

Maitreya
Bodhisattva
A183

1976, Dec. 21 Litho. *Perf. 13x13½*
514 A182 1r orange & multi .50 .30

Centenary of first telephone call by Alexander Graham Bell, Mar. 10, 1876.

1977, Jan. 1 Litho. *Perf. 12½x13*
Bronze Statues: 1r, Sundara Murti Swami,
11th century. 5r, Goddess Tara.
515 A183 50c multicolored .30 .20
516 A183 1r multicolored .35 .35
517 A183 5r multicolored 2.25 2.25
  Nos. 515-517 (3) 2.90 2.80

Colombo Museum, centenary.

Kandyan Crown,
1737-1815
A184

2r, Kandyan throne and footstool, 1693-
1815.

1977, Jan. 18
518 A184 1r multicolored .45 .45
519 A184 2r multicolored .85 1.00

Rahula
Thero — A185

Brass
Lamps — A186

No. 521, Ponnambalam Arunachalam.

1977 Litho. *Perf. 13½*
520 A185 1r multicolored .70 .70
521 A185 1r multicolored .30 .30

Sri Rahula Thero, 15th cent. poet and
scholar, and Sir Ponnambalam Arunachalam
(1851-1930), 1st president of Ceylon University Assoc., member of Congress.
Issue dates: #520, Feb. 23; #521, Mar. 10.

1977, Apr. 7 *Perf. 13*
Handicrafts: 25c, Jewelry box and jewelry.
50c, Caparisoned ivory elephant. 5r, Sinhala
wooden mask.
522 A186 20c multicolored .20 .20
523 A186 25c multicolored .20 .20
524 A186 50c multicolored .35 .25
525 A186 5r multicolored 2.50 2.75
  a. Souvenir sheet of 4, #522-525 4.50 4.75
  Nos. 522-525 (4) 3.25 3.40

Mohammed
Cassim Siddi
Lebbe — A187

1977, June 11 Litho. *Perf. 13*
526 A187 1r multicolored .35 .50

Lebbe (1838-98), lawyer, educator and
Moslem journalist.

Girl Guide
A188

1977, Dec. 13 Litho. *Perf. 15*
527 A188 75c multicolored .85 .35

60th anniversary of Sri Lanka Girl Guides.

Parliament and
Wheel of
Life — A189

Runners — A190

1978, Feb. 4 Photo. *Perf. 12x12½*
528 A189 15c green & gold .20 .20

J.R. Jayewardene, first elected president,
assumption of office.
See Nos. 559, 611-611A, 847. For
surcharges see Nos. 542, 572, 698A-698B.

1978, Apr. 27 Litho. *Perf. 15*
529 A190 15c multicolored .30 .35

National Youth Service Council.
For surcharge see No. 543.

Bodhisattva
in Royal
Attire in
Lotus
Position
A191

Vesak Festival: 50c, Bodhisattva without
royal attire cutting off his hair with sword. Both
designs from rock carvings in Borobudur Temple, Java.

1978, May 16 *Perf. 13*
530 A191 15c multicolored 1.00 .30
531 A191 50c multicolored 1.25 1.25

Veera Puran
Appu and his
Flag — A192

Birdwing
Butterfly — A193

1978, Aug. 8 Litho. *Perf. 13*
532 A192 15c multicolored .30 .20

Veera Puran Appu (1848-1908), revolutionist, 130th birth anniversary.

1978, Nov. 28 Litho. *Perf. 14x13½*
Butterflies: 50c, Tamil lacewing. 5r, Blue
oakleaf. 10r, Blue mormon.
534 A193 25c multicolored .60 .20
535 A193 50c multicolored 1.10 .20
536 A193 5r multicolored 1.90 1.25
537 A193 10r multicolored 1.90 2.00
  a. Souvenir sheet of 4, #534-537 15.00 12.50
  Nos. 534-537 (4) 5.50 3.65

Nos. 478, 480-481 Surcharged with
New Value and Bar

1978 Litho. *Perf. 13½x14*
538 A166 5c on 90c multi 2.00 2.25
539 A166 10c on 35c multi .50 .50
540 A166 1r on 1.55r multi 1.25 .50
  Nos. 538-540 (3) 3.75 3.25

Nos. 486, 528 Surcharged with New
Value and 2 Bars; No. 529 with New
Value on Pink Panel
Perf. 14½, 12x12½, 15

1979, Jan. Litho.; Engr.
541 A168 25c on 15c multi 4.25 4.25
542 A189 25c on 15c multi 4.25 4.25
543 A190 25c on 15c multi 4.25 4.25
  Nos. 541-543 (3) 12.75 12.75

Ceylon No. 390 Overprinted Vertically
"SRI LANKA" in Green and
Surcharged in Black

1979, Mar. 22 Photo. *Perf. 11½*
Granite Paper
544 A118 15c on 10c brt green 2.40 1.75

Arrival of Sacred
Tooth — A194

Wrestlers — A195

Wall Paintings from Kelaniya Temple: 25c,
Prince Danta and Princess Hema Mala bringing Sacred Tooth from Kalinga, 4th century
A.D. 1r, Princess Theri Sanghamitta bringing,
by ship, the bodhi tree branch, 3rd century
B.C. 10r, King Kirti offering fan of authority to
supreme patriarch, 18th century.

1979, May 3 Litho. *Perf. 13½*
546 A194 25c multicolored .20 .20
547 A194 1r multicolored .20 .20
548 A194 10r multicolored 1.10 1.25
  a. Souvenir sheet of 3, #546-548 2.40 2.50
  Nos. 546-548 (3) 1.50 1.65

2523rd Vesak Festival, May 11.

1979, May 18 Litho. *Perf. 14*
Design: 50r, Dancer. Woodcarvings from
Embekke Temple.
549 A195 20r multicolored 1.90 1.25
550 A195 50r multicolored 3.00 2.75

Piyadasa Sirisena
A196

Dudley S.
Senanayake
A197

1979, May 22 *Perf. 13x13½*
551 A196 1.25r deep green .35 .35

Piyadasa Sirisena (1875-1946), patriot,
journalist, novelist and poet.

1979, June 19 Photo.
552 A197 1.25r deep green .20 .20

27th death anniversary of Prime Minister
Dudley S. Senanayake.

Mother
Feeding Child,
IYC Emblem
A198

Designs: 3r, Faces and IYC emblem. 5r,
Children with rope and ball, IYC emblem.

1979, July 31 Litho. *Perf. 12½*
553 A198 5c multicolored .20 .20
554 A198 3r multicolored .30 .60
555 A198 5r multicolored .40 .65
  Nos. 553-555 (3) .90 1.45

International Year of the Child.

Ceylon No. 2,
Rowland
Hill — A199

Airlanka
Emblem — A200

1979, Aug. 27 Litho. *Perf. 13½*
556 A199 3r multicolored .35 .50

Sir Rowland Hill (1795-1879), originator of
penny postage.

1979, Sept. 1 Litho. *Perf. 12½*
557 A200 3r red, dk grn & blk .85 1.00

Airlanka National Airline, inaugural flight,
Colombo-Bangkok.

Coconut
Palm — A201

1979, Oct. 9 Litho. *Perf. 13½*
558 A201 2r multicolored .70 .80

Asian and Pacific Coconut Community, 10th
anniversary.

No. 528 Redrawn Without Date
1979, Oct. 9 Photo. *Perf. 13*
Size: 20x24mm
559 A189 25c green & gold .35 .20

Family in Cogwheel, Parliament A202

1979, Oct. Litho. *Perf. 13½*
560 A202 2r multicolored .60 .75
Intl. Conf. of Parliamentarians on Population & Development, Colombo, Aug. 28-Sept. 1.

Swami Vipulananda (1892-1947), Philosopher & Theologian — A203

1979, Nov. 18 *Perf. 12½*
561 A203 1.25r multicolored .30 .30

Text and Crescent A204

1979, Nov. 22
562 A204 3.75r multicolored .50 .80
Hegira (pilgrimage year).

Institute Emblem A205

Blue Magpie A206

1979, Nov. 29 *Perf. 13*
563 A205 15c multicolored .30 .35
Ayurveda Medical Institute, 50th anniversary.

1979, Dec. 13 Litho. *Perf. 14*
564 A206 10c shown .20 .40
565 A206 15c Lorikeet .75 .20
566 A206 75c Arrenga .20 .20
567 A206 1r Spurfowl .20 .20
568 A206 5r Yellow-fronted barbet .60 1.00
569 A206 10r Yellow-eared bulbul .75 1.00
a. Souvenir sheet of 6, #564-569 6.25 6.25
Nos. 564-569 (6) 2.70 3.00
For surcharge see No. 1062B.

Rotary Emblem, Map of Sri Lanka A207

1979, Dec. 27 Litho. *Perf. 14½*
570 A207 1.50r multicolored .95 1.10
Rotary International, 75th anniversary.

A. Ratnayake, Educator and Pres. of Senate — A208

1980, Jan. 7 Photo. *Perf. 14x13½*
571 A208 1.25r slate green .25 .25

No. 559 Surcharged
1980, Mar. 17 Photo. *Perf. 13*
572 A189 35c on 25c multi .20 .20
One position has ".33" instead of ".35."

Leaf, Wheel, Fan (Buddhist Symbols) A209

1980, Mar. 25 Photo. *Perf. 13½x14*
573 A209 10c Steeple .30 .60
574 A209 35c shown .30 .25
All Ceylon Buddhist Cong., 60th anniv.

Col. Henry Olcott, Buddhist Emblem — A210

Journey of Patachara, Temple Painting — A211

1980, May 17 Litho. *Perf. 14*
575 A210 2r multicolored .75 1.00
Col. Henry S. Olcott (1832-1907), American theosophist and Buddhist lecturer, centenary of arrival in Sri Lanka.

1980, May 23 *Perf. 13½x14*
Vesak Festival (Paintings, life of Buddha): 1.60r, Patachara crossing river.
576 A211 35c multicolored .25 .20
577 A211 1.60r multicolored .95 1.25

George E. De Silva — A212

1980, June 8 *Perf. 13x13½*
578 A212 1.60r multicolored .25 .25
George E. de Silva (1879-1950), politician.

Siva Temples, Polonnaruwa — A213

1980, Aug. 25 Litho. *Perf. 13½*
579 A213 35c shown .20 .25
580 A213 35c Cave Temples, Dambulla .20 .25
581 A213 35c Sacred Tooth Temple, Kandy .20 .25
582 A213 1.60r Abhayagiri Hill .30 .60
583 A213 1.60r Jetavanarama Hill .30 .60

584 A213 1.60r Sigiri .30 .60
a. Souvenir sheet of 6, #579-584 2.50 2.00
Nos. 579-584 (6) 1.50 2.55
UNESCO "Cultural Triangle" Project.

Department of Cooperative Development, 50th Anniversary A214

1980, Oct. 1 Litho. *Perf. 13½*
585 A214 20c multicolored .20 .25

Women's Movement Emblem A215

1980, Oct. 16 Photo. *Perf. 14x13½*
586 A215 35c multicolored .20 .30
Mahila Samiti (Rural Women's Movement), 50th anniversary.

Nativity — A216

1980, Nov. 20 Litho. *Perf. 13½*
587 A216 35c shown .20 .20
588 A216 3.75r Three kings .50 .75
a. Souvenir sheet of 2, #587-588 .75 .85
Christmas 1980/Year of the family.

Colombo Public Library Opening A217

1980, Dec. 17 *Perf. 12x12½*
589 A217 35c multicolored .20 .20

Peacock Banner A218

Designs: Ancient flags.
1980, Dec. 18 *Perf. 13*
590 A218 10c shown .20 .20
591 A218 25c Elephant banner .20 .20
592 A218 1.60r Sinhalese royal flag .25 .25
593 A218 20r Kings Civil Standard 1.25 1.75
a. Souvenir sheet of 4, #590-593 2.00 2.25
Nos. 590-593 (4) 1.90 2.40

Fishing Cat — A219

1981, Feb. 10 Litho. *Perf. 14*
594 A219 2.50r on 1.60r, shown .50 .20
595 A219 3r on 1.50r, Golden palm cat .50 .25
596 A219 4r on 2r, Mouse deer .50 .45
597 A219 5r on 3.75r, Rusty-spotted cat .60 .60
a. Souvenir sheet of 4, #594-597 2.40 2.50
Nos. 594-597 (4) 2.10 1.50
See #728-730A, 928. For surcharge see #731.

Population and Housing Census — A220

1981, Mar. 2 Litho. *Perf. 12½x12*
598 A220 50c multicolored .50 .60

Ceylon Light Infantry Centenary A221

The Death of Buddha, Carved Panel, 1st Cent. — A222

1981, Apr. 1 Litho. *Perf. 12*
599 A221 2r multicolored 1.25 1.25

1981, May 5 *Perf. 13x13½*
600 A222 35c shown .20 .20
601 A222 50c Silk banner .20 .20
602 A222 7r Statuette .75 1.75
a. Souvenir sheet of 3, #600-602 5.00 5.00
Nos. 600-602 (3) 1.15 2.15
Vesak Festival.

St. John Baptist de la Salle A223

1981, May 15 Litho. *Perf. 12½x12*
603 A223 2r multicolored 1.25 1.40
De la Salle Brothers Order, 300th anniv.

Polwatte Sri Buddadatta A224

Intl. Year of the
Disabled — A225

Famous Men: No. 605, Mohottiwatte Guna-
nanda, Buddhist leader. No. 606, Gnanapra
Kasar, Catholic missionary. No. 607, Al-Haj
T.B. Jayah, Muslim teacher. No. 608, James
Peiris. No. 609, N.M. Perera, founded first
Marxist Party in Sri Lanka, 1935.

1981	Photo.	Perf. 12	
604	A224 50c olive bister	.50	.60
605	A224 50c dull red brown	.50	.60
606	A224 50c lilac	.50	.60
607	A224 50c gray green	.50	.55
608	A224 50c brown	.60	.55
609	A224 50c crimson rose	.50	.60
	Nos. 604-609 (6)	3.10	3.50

Issued: #604-606, 5/22; #607, 5/31; #609,
6/6; #608, 12/20.
See #623-624, 640-642, 646, 672-676, 713-
717.

1981, June 19	Litho.	Perf. 12x12½	
610	A225 2r multicolored	1.00	1.10

No. 528 Redrawn with Denomination
in Upper Right Corner

1981-83	Photo.	Perf. 13	
	Size: 20x24mm		
611	A189 50c green & gold	2.75	.20
611A	A189 60c green & gold	9.00	1.25

Issued: 50c, June 6; 60c, Dec. 30, 1983.
For surcharges see Nos. 698A-698B.

Hand
Putting
Ballot in
Box
A226

	Perf. 12½x12, 12x12½		
1981, July 7		Litho.	
612	A226 50c shown	.20	.20
613	A226 7r Ballot box on map, vert.	1.25	1.50

Universal Franchise, 50th anniv.

Rhys
Davids
(Society
Founder)
A227

1981, July 14		Perf. 12½x12	
614	A227 35c multicolored	.70	.25

All Ceylon
Buddhist
Students'
Federation,
25th Anniv.
A228

1981, July 21	Litho.	Perf. 13½	
615	A228 2r multicolored	.70	.70

Family
Planning — A229

7th World
Acupuncture
Cong. — A230

1981, Sept. 25			
616	A229 50c multicolored	.50	.60

1981, Oct. 20	Litho.	Perf. 12x12½	
617	A230 2r multicolored	2.50	2.75

Visit of
Queen
Elizabeth
II, Oct.
A231

Designs: Flags of Gt. Britain and Sri Lanka.

1981, Oct. 21		Perf. 14	
618	A231 50c multicolored	.35	.25
619	A231 5r multicolored	1.25	1.50
a.	Souvenir sheet of 2, #618-619	2.75	3.00

Forest
Conservation
A232

1981, Nov. 27		Perf. 13½x13	
620	A232 35c Forest	.20	.20
621	A232 50c Tree planting	.25	.25
622	A232 5r Jack tree	1.75	2.00
a.	Souvenir sheet of 3, #620-622, perf. 14x13	2.25	3.00
	Nos. 620-622 (3)	2.20	2.45

Famous Men Type of 1981

Designs: No. 623, F.R. Senanayaka (1882-
1926), lawyer and politician. No. 624, Philip
Gunawardhane, politician, 10th death anniv.

1982	Litho.	Perf. 14	
623	A224 50c brown	.60	.70
624	A224 50c bright rose	.60	.70

Issue dates: #623, Jan. 1; #624, Jan. 11.

Dept. of Inland
Revenue, 50th
Anniv.
A233

Natl. Television
Inauguration
A234

1982, Feb. 9	Litho.	Perf. 14	
625	A233 50c multicolored	.60	.75

1982, Feb. 15			
626	A234 2.50r multicolored	2.40	2.50

Sesquicentennial
of Cricket
Introduction and
Centenary of Sri
Lanka vs.
England
Match — A235

1982, Feb. 17			
627	A235 2.50r multicolored	5.50	5.50

Osbeckia
Wightiana
A236

1982, Apr. 1		Perf. 12	
628	A236 35c shown	.20	.20
629	A236 2r Mesua nagassari-	.30	.25
630	A236 7r Rhodomyrtus to- mentosa	.75	.85
631	A236 20r Phaius tancarvil- leae	2.10	2.25
a.	Souvenir sheet of 4, #628-631	8.50	9.00
	Nos. 628-631 (4)	3.35	3.55

Food and
Nutrition
Planning
A237

World Hindu
Conference
A238

1982, Apr. 6	Litho.	Perf. 13	
632	A237 50c multicolored	1.10	1.10

1982, Apr. 21		Perf. 14x14½	
633	A238 50c multicolored	1.00	1.10

Vesak
Festival
1982
A239

Scenes from Jataka Story (Pre-incarnation
of Buddha), Cloth Painting, 3rd cent. B.C.,
Hanguranketa Temple (King Vessantara and):
35c, Giving away white elephant. 50c, Royal
Family in Vankagiri Forest. 2.50r, Giving away
his children to a Brahmin. 5r, Royal family in
chariot.

1982, Apr. 23		Perf. 14	
634	A239 35c multicolored	.65	.20
635	A239 50c multicolored	.80	.20
636	A239 2.50r multicolored	2.75	2.50
637	A239 5r multicolored	3.75	3.50
a.	Souvenir sheet of 4, #634-637	9.50	9.50
	Nos. 634-637 (4)	7.95	6.40

New
Parliament
Building
Opening
A240

1982, Apr. 29			
638	A240 50c multicolored	.90	.90

Scouting
Year
A241

1982, May 24	Litho.	Perf. 12½x12	
639	A241 50c multicolored	2.25	2.00

Famous Men Type of 1981

1982		Perf. 12x12½	
640	A224 50c C.W.W. Kannan- gara	.95	1.00
641	A224 50c G.P. Malalasekara	.95	1.00
642	A224 50c John Kotelawala	.95	1.00
	Nos. 640-642 (3)	2.85	3.00

Issued: #640, 5/22; #641, 5/26; #642, 6/8.

World Buddhist Leaders
Conference — A242

1982, June 10		Perf. 12½x12	
643	A242 50c multicolored	1.00	1.10

World Environment Day — A243

1982, June 5			
644	A243 50c multicolored	1.90	1.25

YMCA Centenary — A244

1982, June 24	Photo.	Perf. 11½	
645	A244 2.50r multicolored	3.75	3.75

Famous Men Type of 1981

1982, June 14	Litho.	Perf. 12x12½	
646	A224 50c Waitialingam Duraiswamy	.90	1.00

Weliwita
Saranankara
Sangharaja
A245

1982, July 5			
647	A245 50c orange & black	.90	1.00

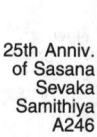

25th Anniv. of Sasana Sevaka Samithiya A246

1982, Aug. 8
648 A246 50c multicolored   .90 1.00

TB Bacillus Centenary A247

1982, Sept. 21
649 A247 50c Koch, microscope, bacillus   2.25 1.50

Eye Donation Society — A248

1982, Nov. 16   Litho.   Perf. 12x12½
650 A248 2.50r Emblems, map   3.25 3.50

125th Anniv. of Ceylon Postage Stamps — A249

1982, Dec. 1   Litho.   Perf. 13½
651 A249 50c Ceylon #5, 302   .50 .50
652 A249 2.50r Ceylon #12, #611   1.40 1.60
   a. Souv. sheet, #651-652, perf. 12   3.25 3.25
     Natl. Stamp Exhibition.

Sir Oliver Goonetilleke A250

1982, Dec. 17   Litho.   Perf. 12x12½
653 A250 50c black & brown   .65 .75

25th Anniv. of Sarvodaya Social Movement A251

1983, Jan. 1   Perf. 13½
654 A251 50c multicolored   .90 .90

55th Anniv. of Amateur Radio Society A252

1983, Jan. 17
655 A252 2.50r multicolored   3.75 4.00

Customs Cooperation Council and First Intl. Customs Day — A253

1983, Jan. 26   Litho.   Perf. 12
656 A253 50c orange & multi   .50 .40
657 A253 5r green & multi   3.50 3.75

Bottlenose Dolphin A254

1983, Feb. 22   Perf. 14½x14
658 A254 50c shown   .75 .20
659 A254 2r Dugongs   1.25 .75
660 A254 2.50r Humpback whale   3.50 2.00
661 A254 10r Great sperm whale   8.00 6.00
   Nos. 658-661 (4)   13.50 8.95

Ceylon Shipping Corp. A255

1983, Mar. 1   Perf. 12x12½
662 A255 50c Container ship   .30 .20
663 A255 2.50r Liner services map   1.10 .65
664 A255 5r Conventional ship   1.60 1.50
665 A255 20r Oil tanker   2.50 3.00
   Nos. 662-665 (4)   5.50 5.35

Intl. Women's Day — A256

1983, Mar. 8   Perf. 13½
666 A256 50c Woman, flag   .25 .20
667 A256 5r Woman, map   .90 1.25

Commonwealth Day — A257

1983, Mar. 14
668 A257 50c Waterfall   .20 .20
669 A257 2.50r Tea picking   .20 .20
670 A257 5r Harvesting   .25 .50
671 A257 20r Cultural pageant   .75 1.25
   Nos. 668-671 (4)   1.40 2.15

Famous Men Type of 1981
1983   Litho.   Perf. 12
672 A224 50c Henry W. Amarasuriya   .30 .50
   Size: 29x40mm
673 A224 50c Charles A. Lorenz   .30 .50
674 A224 50c Simon G. Perera   .30 .50
675 A224 50c Nordeen H.M. Abdul Cader   .30 .50
676 A224 50c C.W. Tamotherampillai   .80 .90
   Nos. 672-676 (5)   2.00 2.90

   No. 676 shows Tamotherampillai looking towards the right of the stamp. A version that was to be issued May 22, showed someone labeled C. W. Tamotherampillai looking straight ahead.
   Issued: No. 676, Oct. 1; others, May 22.

25th Anniv. of Lions Club A258

1983, May 7   Litho.   Perf. 14
677 A258 2.50r multicolored   3.75 2.50

Vesak Festival 1983 — A259

   Various Colombo murals.

1983, May 13   Perf. 12½x12
678 A259 35c multicolored   .20 .20
679 A259 50c multicolored   .20 .20
680 A259 5r multicolored   .65 .95
681 A259 10r multicolored   1.00 1.25
   a. Souvenir sheet of 4, #678-681   2.25 2.50
   Nos. 678-681 (4)   2.05 2.40

125th Anniv. of Telecommunication Service — A260

1983, May 17   Perf. 12x12½
682 A260 2r shown   .80 .60
683 A260 10r World Communications Year   2.50 3.00

Gam Udawa Village Re-awakening Movement — A261

1983, June 23   Litho.   Perf. 12x12½
684 A261 50c Family   .20 .25
685 A261 5r Village   .60 1.00

Cattle Transport A262

1983, Aug. 1   Litho.   Perf. 12
686 A262 35c shown   .20 .20
687 A262 2r Train   1.90 1.50
688 A262 2.50r Cattle cart   .90 1.00
689 A262 5r Model T Ford   2.00 2.25
   Nos. 686-689 (4)   5.00 4.95

Sir Tikiri Banda Panabokke, 20th Death Anniv. — A263

1983, Sept. 2   Litho.   Perf. 13½x14
690 A263 50c dark red   .90 .90

Ceylon Wood Pigeon A264

1983, Dec. 1   Litho.   Perf. 14½
691 A264 25c shown   .45 .60
692 A264 35c Ceylon white-eye   .50 .50
693 A264 2r Dusky-blue flycatcher   .55 .40
694 A264 20r Ceylon coucal   .80 1.00
   a. Souvenir sheet of 4, #691-694   4.00 4.50
   Nos. 691-694 (4)   2.30 2.50
   See No. 877. For surcharge see No. 780A.

Christmas, Stone Carvings — A265

1983, Dec. 5   Litho.   Perf. 12½x13
695 A265 50c multicolored   .20 .20
696 A265 5r ultra & bister   .35 .50
   a. Souv. sheet, #695-696+label   .75 1.25

A266

A267

1983, Nov. 25   Litho.   Perf. 14x15
697 A266 50c brown   .90 .90
   Rev. Pelene Thero (1878-1955), Buddhist leader.

1983   Litho.   Perf. 13½
698 A267 50c Ahamed Orabi Al-Misri   .90 .90

#611 Surcharged with Four Bars, #611A with Three Bars and New Denomination in Black or Green

1983-85		Photo.	Perf. 13	
698A	A189	60c on 50c ('83)	3.00	1.75

Size: 20x24mm

| 698B | A189 | 75c on 60c (G) ('85) | .20 | .20 |

Ovpt. on No. 698A also exists with two bars. Value, $3.75.
Issue dates: both Dec. 1.

World Food Day (Oct. 16) A268

1984, Jan. 2			Perf. 12½x12	
699	A268	3r Rice paddy	.40	.75

Colombo Tea Auctions Centenary A269

1984, Jan. 31				
700	A269	1r Auction House	.25	.20
701	A269	2r Emblem	.45	.45
702	A269	5r Tea picker	1.10	1.25
703	A269	10r Auction	2.25	2.50
		Nos. 700-703 (4)	4.05	4.40

Mahapola Anniversary (Educational System) — A270

1984, Feb. 10			Perf. 12	
704	A270	60c Students	.20	.20
705	A270	1r Classroom	.20	.20
706	A270	5.50r Student in library, lab	.35	.75
707	A270	6r Emblem	.40	.75
		Nos. 704-707 (4)	1.15	1.90

Vesak Festival 1984 A271

Wooden Casket Paintings, Temple Godapitiya Rajamaha Vihara, Akuressa: Scenes from Daham Sonda Jathaka legend.

1984, Apr. 27			Litho.	Perf. 14	
708	A271	35c multicolored		.25	.25
709	A271	60c multicolored		.50	.25
710	A271	5r multicolored		1.50	1.60
711	A271	10r multicolored		1.75	2.00
a.		Souv. sheet of 4, #708-711, perf. 13x13½		2.50	2.50
		Nos. 708-711 (4)		4.00	4.05

Lions Club Intl., District 306A — A272

1984, May 5		Litho.	Perf. 14x14½	
712	A272	60c multicolored	1.60	1.00

Famous Men Type of 1981

Designs: No. 713, K. Balasingham, lawyer. No. 714, Mohamed Macan Markar (1879-1952), Muslim politician. No. 715, W. Arthur de Silva (d. 1942), industrialist. No. 716, Tissa Mahanayake Thero (1826-1907), Buddhist educator. No. 717, G.P. Wickremarachchi, medical pioneer.

1984, May 22		Litho.	Perf. 12x12½	
713	A224	60c brown	.30	.50
714	A224	60c green	.30	.50
715	A224	60c orange red	.30	.50
716	A224	60c bister	.30	.50
717	A224	60c yellow green	.30	.50
		Nos. 713-717 (5)	1.50	2.50

Public Service Mutual Provident Assoc. Centenary A273

1984, June 16			Perf. 13x13½	
718	A273	4.60r Emblem	.55	1.25

Village Re-awakening Movement A274

1984, June 23			Perf. 12x12½	
719	A274	60c "One Million Houses"	.50	.50

Asia-Pacific Broadcasting Union, 20th Anniv. — A275

1984, June 30			Perf. 12½x12	
720	A275	7r Map	2.75	2.75

For surcharge see No. 776.

Cultural Pageant A276

Procession: a, Drummers, elephant. b, Torch bearers, 3 elephants (green or red masks). c, Torch bearers, 3 elephants (orange or yellow masks). d, Dancers. Continuous design.

1984, Aug. 11		Litho.	Perf. 12½x12	
721		Strip of 4	4.75	4.75
a.-d.	A276	4.60r any single	1.10	1.10
e.		Souvenir sheet of 4	5.00	5.50

Orchid Circle of Sri Lanka, 50th Anniversary A277

1984, Aug. 31			Perf. 14	
722	A277	60c Vanda memoria	1.10	1.00
723	A277	4.60r Acanthephippium bicolor	2.50	2.75
724	A277	5r Vanda Tessellata	1.50	2.00
725	A277	10r Anoectochillus setaceus	4.50	4.50
a.		Souvenir sheet of 4, #722-725	12.50	12.50
		Nos. 722-725 (4)	9.60	10.25

Wildlife Type of 1981

1982-89		Litho.	Perf. 14	
728	A219	2.50r Felis viverrina	.30	.25
729	A219	3r Paradoxurus zeylonensis	4.25	4.25
730	A219	4r Tragulus meminna	.30	.30
730A	A219	5r Felis rubiginosa ('89)	.40	.30
		Nos. 728-730A (4)	5.25	5.10

No. 729 has brown inscriptions. See No. 928 for black inscriptions.
No. 728 is unwatermarked.
Issued: 2.50r, 6/1/83; 3r, 6/21/83; 4r, 11/16/82; 5r, 12/1/89.

No. 728 Surcharged in Brown

1985, Dec. 1		Litho.	Perf. 14	
731	A219	5.75r on 2.50r multi	3.50	1.50

The Observer Newspaper, 150th Anniv. A280

1984, Aug. 31		Litho.	Perf. 13x13½	
732	A280	4.60r Publisher, Colombo	2.10	2.25

Natl. School Games — A281

1984, Oct. 5			Perf. 13½x13	
733	A281	60c blue, gray & blk	2.50	2.00

D. S. Senanayake (1884-1952), Prime Minister — A282

1984, Oct. 20			Perf. 14½x14	
734	A282	35c Irrigated field	.20	.20
735	A282	60c Statue	.20	.20
736	A282	4.60r Reservoir	.30	.35
737	A282	6r Parliament House, Colombo	.40	.45
		Nos. 734-737 (4)	1.10	1.20

World Food Program — A284

Baari Arabic College, Weligama, Cent. — A285

1984, Dec. 10		Litho.	Perf. 13x13½	
738	A284	7r Globe, Sri Lankans working field	1.90	1.25

1984, Dec. 24			Perf. 13x12½	
739	A285	4.60r dull bl grn & blk	1.25	1.50

Intl. Youth Year — A286

World Religion Day — A287

1985, Jan. 1			Perf. 12½x13	
740	A286	4.60r multicolored	.80	.60
741	A286	20r multicolored	2.50	2.50

For surcharge see No. 790.

1985, Jan. 20			Perf. 12	

Design: Emblems of World religions.

742	A287	4.60r multicolored	1.60	1.75

Royal College, Colombo, 150th Anniv. — A288

Mahapola Scholarship Program for Development & Education, 5th Anniv. — A289

1985, Jan. 29			Perf. 13x12½	
743	A288	60c College crest	.20	.25
744	A288	7r Campus	1.40	1.60

1985, Feb. 7			Perf. 14	
745	A289	60c Diplomas, freighter, office buildings	1.00	1.00

Wariyapola Sri Sumangala Thero, Leader of the 1818 Great Uva Rebellion — A290

1985, Mar. 2			Perf. 13x13½	
746	A290	60c brown & yellow	.70	.80

Victoria Project A291

Perf. 12½x12, 12x12½

1985, Apr. 12				Litho.	
747	A291	60c Victoria Dam		.90	.50
748	A291	7r Dam, map, vert.		5.25	5.25

Vesak Festival 1985 — A292

Natl. Heroes — A293

Designs: 35c, Frontispiece of the Buddhist Annual golden jubilee issue. 60c, Women worshiping at temple, Vesak Poya Holiday cent. 6r, Bauddha Mandiraya, Colombo. 9r, Buddhist flag cent.

1985, Apr. 26   *Perf. 13x12½*
749 A292 35c multicolored .20 .20
750 A292 60c multicolored .20 .20
751 A292 6r multicolored .50 .60
752 A292 9r multicolored .75 .80
    a. Souvenir sheet of 4, #749-752 6.25 6.25
      Nos. 749-752 (4) 1.65 1.80

1985, May 22   *Perf. 13x12½*
#753,753, Waskaduwe Sri Subhuthi Thero (1835-1917), Pali scholar, philologist responsible for the Sinhala dictionary. #754, Rev. Fr. Peter A. Pillai (1904-64), educational & social reformer. #755, Dr. Senarath Paranavitane (c. 1900-72), epigraphist. #756, A.M. Wapche Marikar (1829-1925), educational reformer, architect.

Pale Yellow Orange and
753 A293 60c tan .25 .30
754 A293 60c brt rose lilac .25 .30
755 A293 60c brown .25 .30
756 A293 60c emerald .25 .30
      Nos. 753-756 (4) 1.00 1.20

Gam Udawa — Yovur Udanaya Village Reformation Movement A294

1985, June 23   *Perf. 13½x13*
757 A294 60c multicolored 1.25 1.25

Colombo Young Poets Assoc., 50th Anniv. — A295

1985, June 25   *Perf. 14*
758 A295 60c Emblem .50 .50

Kothmale Project Commission — A296

1985, Aug. 24
759 A296 60c Dam, lake .75 .25
760 A296 6r Hydro-electric power station 3.25 3.50

A297

A298

Child Survival: 35c, Mother breastfeeding. 60c, Infant, oral inoculant. 6r, Weighing toddler. 9r, Infant, intravenous inoculant.

1985, Sept. 1   **Wmk. 385**   *Perf. 13½*
761 A297 35c multicolored .35 .20
762 A297 60c multicolored .50 .30
763 A297 6r multicolored 2.25 2.50

764 A297 9r multicolored 2.75 3.00
    a. Souvenir sheet of 4, #761-764 6.00 6.00
      Nos. 761-764 (4) 5.85 6.00

1985, Sept. 2   **Unwmk.**   *Perf. 14*
765 A298 7r Womb, infant 4.75 4.75
10th Asian & Oceanic Congress of Obstetrics & Gynecology.

World Tourism Org., 10th Anniv. A299

1985, Sept. 27   **Litho.**   *Perf. 14*
766 A299 1r Conch shell horn .25 .20
767 A299 6r Parliament complex .95 .95
768 A299 7r Tea plantation 1.10 1.10
769 A299 10r Buddhist monastery, Ruwanveliseya 1.60 1.75
    a. Souv. sheet of 4, #766-769, perf. 13½ 7.00 7.00
      Nos. 766-769 (4) 3.90 4.00

Land Development Ordinance, 50th Anniv. — A300

Sinhal Translation, Koran — A301

1985, Oct. 15   *Perf. 14x15*
770 A300 4.60r Deeds presentation 3.00 3.25

1985, Oct. 17   **Wmk. 385**   *Perf. 13½*
771 A301 60c violet & gold 1.25 1.00

Christmas — A302

1985, Nov. 5   *Perf. 12*
772 A302 60c Our Lady of Matara .35 .20
773 A302 9r Our Lady of Madhu 1.75 2.00
    a. Souvenir sheet of 2, #772-773 8.00 8.50

SAARC 1st Summit, Dec. 7-8 A303

1985, Dec. 8   *Perf. 14½x14*
774 A303 60c shown 3.25 3.75
775 A303 5.50r Flags on UN emblem 3.25 3.25

No. 720 Surcharged in Intense Blue
1986, Jan. 20   *Perf. 12½x12*
776 A275 1r on 7r Map 7.00 3.00

Viceroy Special Train A304

1986, Feb. 2   *Perf. 12½x13*
777 A304 1r multicolored 1.25 1.50
Colombo-Kandy line inauguration.

Students A305

1986, Feb. 14   *Perf. 14*
778 A305 75c multicolored .65 .65
Mahapola Scholarship Program for development and education, 6th anniv.

Don Richard Wijewardene (1886-1950), Newspaper Publisher — A306   Welitara Gnanatillake Mahanayake Thero (1858-1941), Scientist — A307

1986, Feb. 23   *Perf. 14x15*
779 A306 75c sage grn & brn .30 .40

1986, Feb. 26   **Wmk. 385**   *Perf. 13½*
780 A307 75c multicolored .85 .90

No. 692 Surcharged
1986, Mar. 10   **Litho.**   *Perf. 14½*
780A A264 7r on 35c 5.25 1.50

Natl. Red Cross Society, 50th Anniv. A308

1986, Mar. 31   *Perf. 12½x13*
781 A308 75c multicolored 2.75 2.25

Halley's Comet A309

1986, Apr. 5   *Perf. 12½*
782 A309 50c Comet is not an omen .20 .20
783 A309 75c Constellations .20 .20
784 A309 6.50r Trajectory diagrams .25 .90
785 A309 8.50r Edmond Halley .35 1.25
    a. Souvenir sheet of 4, #782-785, perf. 12½x13 6.00 7.00
      Nos. 782-785 (4) 1.00 2.55

Sinhalese and Tamil New Year — A310

Designs: 50c, Woman lighting lamp. 75c, Woman, holiday foods. 6.50r, Women celebrating around table. 8.50r, Food preparation, feast, anointment ritual.

1986, Apr. 10
786 A310 50c multicolored .20 .20
787 A310 75c multicolored .20 .20
788 A310 6.50r multicolored .30 .80
789 A310 8.50r multicolored .50 1.00
    a. Souvenir sheet of 4, #786-789, perf. 13x12½ 4.25 4.75
      Nos. 786-789 (4) 1.20 2.20

No. 740 Surcharged
1986, Apr. 29   *Perf. 12½x13*
790 A286 1r on 4.60r multi 4.50 3.25

Vesak Festival A311

Jathaka Story frescoes from the house Samudragiri Vihara, Mirissa, recounting the life of Siddhartha (583-463 B.C.): 50c, King Kurudhamma Jathakaya gives elephant to the brahman. 75c, Vasavarthi heaven. 5r, Sujatha's milk rice offering. 10d, Thapassu and Bhalluka's parched corn and honey offering.

1986, May 16
791 A311 50c multicolored .20 .20
792 A311 75c multicolored .20 .20
793 A311 5d multicolored .50 1.25
794 A311 10d multicolored .60 1.75
      Nos. 791-794 (4) 1.50 3.40

Natl. Heroes — A312

Natl. Cooperative Movement, 75th Anniv. — A313

#795, Kalukondayave Sri Prajnasekhara Mahanayaka Thero (1895-1977), theologian. #796, Brahmachari Walisinghe Harischandra (1876-1913), historian, social reformer. #797, Martin Wickramasinghe (1890-1970), author. #798, Ganapathipillai Gangaser Ponnambalam (1901-72), diplomat. #799, Aboobucker Mohammed Abdul Azeez (1911-73), scholar.

1986, May 22   *Perf. 13x12½*
795 A312 75c multicolored .20 .45
796 A312 75c multicolored .20 .45
797 A312 75c multicolored .20 .45
798 A312 75c multicolored .20 .45
799 A312 75c multicolored .20 .45
      Nos. 795-799 (5) 1.00 2.25

1986, June 23
800 A313 1r multicolored 1.50 1.75

Gam Udawa, Intl. Year of Housing A314

1986, June 23   *Perf. 13½x13*
801 A314 75c multicolored   1.90 1.90

Arthur V. Dias — A315

1986, July 31   *Perf. 14x15*
802 A315 1r multicolored   1.90 2.00

World Wildlife Fund A316

Elephants: a, Adult with tusks. b, Adult, calf. c, Adult, d, Family in river.

1986, Aug. 5   *Perf. 15x14*
803   Strip of 4   40.00 30.00
a.-d. A316 5r any single   9.00 7.50

2nd Indo-Pacific Congress on Legal Medicine and Forensic Sciences — A317

1986, Aug. 14   *Perf. 13½x13*
804 A317 8.50r multicolored   3.50 3.50

Submarine Cable — A318

1986, Sept. 8   *Perf. 13½x14*
805 A318 5.75r Handset, map   5.00 3.50
South-East Asia, Middle East, Western Europe Submarine Cable System.

Dag Hammarskjold Award — A320

Second Natl. School Games, Sept. 22-27 — A321

1986, Sept. 20   Litho.   *Perf. 13x12½*
808 A320 2r multicolored   .80 .80

1986, Sept. 22   *Perf. 12*
809 A321 1r multicolored   3.50 2.00

Natl. Surveyor's Institute, 60th Anniv. — A322

1986, Sept. 27   *Perf. 13½x13*
810 A322 75c multicolored   .70 .80

Ananda College, Cent. A323

College crest and: 75c, College. 5r, Athletic field. 5.75r, Founders Migettuwatte Gunananda, Hikkaduwe Sumangala and Col. H.S. Olcott, Buddhist flag and College, 1886, 1986. 6r, Crest on flag.

1986, Nov. 1   *Perf. 12*
811 A323   75c multicolored   .20 .20
812 A323   5r multicolored   .30 .40
813 A323 5.75r multicolored   .35 .40
814 A323   6r multicolored   .45 .55
   Nos. 811-814 (4)   1.30 1.55

Wildlife Conservation — A324

1986, Nov. 11
815 A324 35c Mangrove habitat   .55 .25
816 A324 50c Rhizophora apiculata   .65 .35
817 A324 75c Germinating flower   .75 .35
818 A324   6r Fiddler crab   5.25 5.50
   Nos. 815-818 (4)   7.20 6.45

Preservation of mangrove habitats.

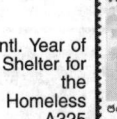

Intl. Year of Shelter for the Homeless A325

1987, Jan. 1   Litho.   *Perf. 13x13½*
819 A325 75c multicolored   2.40 .75

A.I. Thero, 19th Cent. Theologian A326

Proctor John De Silva (b. 1854), Lawyer and Playwright A327

1987, Jan. 29   *Perf. 12*
820 A326 5.75r multicolored   3.75 1.10

1987, Jan. 31
821 A327 5.75r multicolored   .85 .85

Mahapola Educational Plan, 7th Anniv. — A328

1987, Feb. 6
822 A328 75c multicolored   .85 .85

Dr. R.L. Brohier, Historian — A329

1987, Feb. 14
823 A329 5.75r multicolored   3.25 1.50

Sri Lanka Tire Corp., 25th Anniv. A330

1987, Mar. 23   *Perf. 14*
824 A330 5.75r multicolored   .70 .70

Sri Lanka Medical Assoc., Cent. A331

1987, Mar. 24   *Perf. 13x13½*
825 A331 5.75r multicolored   3.00 3.25

Farmers' Pension and Social Security Plan — A332

AGRO MAHAWELI '87 Agricultural Exposition A333

1987, Mar. 29   *Perf. 14*
826 A332 75c multicolored   .75 .80

1987, Apr. 2   *Perf. 12*
827 A333 75c multicolored   .50 .50

Child Immunization Program — A334

1987, Apr. 7   *Perf. 13½*
828 A334 1r multicolored   3.25 .50
World Health Day.

Sinhalese and Tamil New Year — A335

1987, Apr. 9   *Perf. 12*
829 A335 75c Three girls, swing   .20 .20
830 A335   5r Lamp, women   .60 .60

Vesak Festival Lanterns A336

1987, May 4   *Perf. 12*
831 A336 50c Lotus   .20 .20
832 A336 75c Octagonal   .20 .20
833 A336   5r Star   .40 .40
834 A336 10r Gok   .60 .60
a.   Souvenir sheet of 4, #831-834   1.50 1.50
   Nos. 831-834 (4)   1.40 1.40

Natl. Olympic Committee, 50th Anniv. — A337

1987, May 8   *Perf. 13½*
835 A337 10r multicolored   3.25 1.25

Birds
A338

1987, May 18   **Perf. 14**
836 A338 50c Layard's parakeet   .65   .20
837 A338 1r Legge's
               flowerpecker   .95   .20
838 A338 5r Sri Lanka white-
               headed starling   1.40   1.50
839 A338 10r Sri Lanka rufous
               babbler   1.75   1.90
   a. Souvenir sheet of 4, #836-839   6.50   6.50
       Nos. 836-839 (4)   4.75   3.80

   #839 exists dated "1990."

Natl.
Heroes — A339

   #840, Heenatiyana Sri Dhammaloka Thero,
20th cent. theologian. #841, P. de S.
Kularatne, educator. #842, M.C. Abdul
Rahuman, politician.

1987, May 22   **Perf. 12**
840 A339 75c multicolored   .50   .35
841 A339 75c multicolored   .50   .35
842 A339 75c multicolored   .50   .35
       Nos. 840-842 (3)   1.50   1.05

Gam
Udawa
A340

1987, June 23
843 A340 75c multicolored   .35   .35
   Village reformation movement.

Natl.
Forestry
Agency,
Cent.
A341

1987, June 25
844 A341 75c Mesua nagassari-
               um   .25   .25
845 A341 5r Elephants in forest   1.75   1.75

Founder
H.S. Olcott
and
College
A342

1987, June 30
846 A342 75c multicolored   2.40   .40
   Dharmaraja College, cent.

   No. 528 Redrawn with Denomination
in Upper Right Corner
1987, July 1   Photo.   Perf. 13x13½
          Size: 20x24mm
847 A189 75c green & gold   .20   .20

Youth
Services
Emblem
A343

1987, July 15   Litho.   Perf. 12
848 A343 75c multicolored   .30   .30
   Natl. Youth Services Act, 20th anniv.

Mahaweli
Games — A344

Ceylon Bible
Society, 175th
Anniv. — A345

1987, Sept. 5   Litho.   Perf. 12
849 A344 75c multicolored   3.50   1.75

1987, Oct. 2
850 A345 5.75r multicolored   .70   .70

Kandy Friend-in-Need Society, 150th
Anniv. — A346

1987, Nov. 4   **Perf. 13½x13**
851 A346 75c multicolored   .30   .30

Christmas   Sir Ernest de Silva
1987 — A347   (1887-1957),
                   Banker,
                   Philatelist — A348

1987, Nov. 25   Litho.   Perf. 12
852 A347 75c Mother and Child   .20   .20
853 A347 10r Infant, star, dove   .40   .40
   a. Souvenir sheet of 2, #852-853   1.40   1.50

1987, Nov. 25   **Perf. 13x13½**
854 A348 75c multicolored   .25   .25

1st Convocation
Ceremony at
Buddhist and Pali
University — A349

Missionary Work
of Fr. Joseph Vaz
(1651-1711),
300th
Anniv. — A350

1987, Dec. 14   **Perf. 12**
855 A349 75c yel, lake & org yel   .25   .25

1987, Dec. 15
856 A350 75c multicolored   .25   .25

Buddhist
Publication Soc.,
Kandy, 30th
Anniv. — A351

   Design: Wheel of Life, dagaba (temple
cupola) and Bo (Tree of Life) leaf.

1988, Jan. 1   Litho.   Perf. 12
857 A351 75c multicolored   .30   .30

Mahapola
Dharmayatra,
5th Anniv.
A352

1988, Jan. 4   **Perf. 13½x13**
858 A352 75c multicolored   .50   .50

Ceylon Arts Soc.,
Cent. — A353

1988, Jan. 8   **Perf. 12**
859 A353 75c multicolored   .85   .75

Opening of
the Natl.
Youth Center,
Maharagama
A354

1988, Jan. 31   **Perf. 13½x13**
860 A354 1r multicolored   3.50   .50

Natl.
Independence,
40th
Anniv. — A355

Mahapola
Movement, 8th
Anniv. — A356

1988, Feb. 4   **Perf. 12**
861 A355 75c shown   .20   .20
862 A355 8.50r Heraldic lion, "40"   .90   .90

1988, Feb. 11
863 A356 75c Youth Education
               Services   .25   .25

Transportation Board, 30th
Anniv. — A357

1988, Feb. 19
864 A357 5.75r multicolored   .70   .70

Weligama Sri
Sumangala Maha
Nayake Thero
(1825-1905),
Buddhist Monk,
Sanskrit
Scholar — A358

1988, Mar. 13
865 A358 75c multicolored   .25   .25

Artillery
Regiment,
Cent.
A359

1988, Apr. 20
866 A359 5.75r multicolored   3.00   .90

Chevalier I.X.
Pereira (1888-
1951),
Politician — A360

1988, Apr. 26   Litho.   Perf. 12
867 A360 5.75r multicolored   .35   .35

Vesak
Festival
A361

   Paintings in Suriyagoda Sri Naren-
draramaya Viharaya temple, Kandy District:
50c, Buddha inviting deities and brahmas to
be born into the world as Buddhists. 75c, Buddha walking seven steps on seven lotus flowers, followers paying homage.

1988, May 13 — *Perf. 12½x12*
868 A361 50c multicolored .30 .30
869 A361 75c multicolored .30 .30
   a. Souvenir sheet of 2, #868-869 .90 .90

Natl. Heroes — A362

Designs: No. 870, Rev.-Father Ferdinand Bonnel (1873-1945), Jesuit priest who founded St. Michael's College, Batticaloa. No. 871, Sir Razik Fareed (1893-1984), political and social reformer. No. 872, W.F. Gunawardhana (b. 1861), founder of the Oriental Studies Soc. No. 873, Edward Alexander Nugawela (1898-1972), politician. No. 874, Sir Edwin Arthur Lewis Wijeyewardene (b. 1887), first Ceylonese chief justice, attorney general.

1988, May 22 — *Perf. 12x12½*
870 A362 75c multicolored .20 .20
871 A362 75c multicolored .20 .20
872 A362 75c multicolored .20 .20
873 A362 75c multicolored .20 .20
874 A362 75c multicolored .20 .20
   Nos. 870-874 (5) 1.00 1.00

Gam Udawa, 10th Anniv. A363

1988, June 23 — *Litho.* *Perf. 12*
875 A363 75c multicolored .25 .25

Village reformation movement.

Maliyadeva College, Cent. — A364

1988, June 30 — *Perf. 13½x13*
876 A364 75c multicolored .25 .25

Bird Type of 1983

1988, Sept. 28 — *Litho.* *Perf. 14½*
877 A264 7r like No. 692 .35 .35

Mohamed J.M. Lafir (1929-1980), World Amateur Billiards Champion — A365

1988, July 5 — *Litho.* *Perf. 12½x12*
878 A365 5.75r multicolored .35 .35

Australia Bicentennial — A366

1988, July 19 — *Litho.* *Perf. 12*
879 A366 8.50r multicolored .60 .60

A367

A368

1988, Aug. 11 — *Perf. 12x12½*
880 A367 75c multicolored .20 .20

Gunaratna Maha Nayake Thero (1752-1832), Buddhist and Sinhalese language scholar.

1988, Sept. 3 — *Perf. 12*
881 A368 75c multicolored .20 .20

Mahaweli games.

1988 Summer Olympics, Seoul — A369

WHO, 40th Anniv. — A370

1988, Sept. 6 — *Perf. 12x12½*
882 A369 75c Running .20 .20
883 A369 1r Swimming .20 .20
884 A369 5.75r Boxing .45 .45
885 A369 8.50r Handshake, map, emblems .75 .75
   a. Souvenir sheet of 4, #882-885 2.10 2.25
   Nos. 882-885 (4) 1.60 1.60

1988, Sept. 12 — *Perf. 12*
886 A370 75c multicolored .35 .35

3rd Natl. School Games, Sept. 20-25 A371

1988, Sept. 20
887 A371 1r multicolored 2.10 .40

Mahatma Gandhi — A372

1988, Oct. 2 — *Perf. 12*
888 A372 75c multicolored .85 .35

Transportation and Communication Decade, 1978-88 — A373

Modes of transportation and: 75c, Globe. 5.75r, Communication tower.

1988, Oct. 24 — *Litho.* *Perf. 12½x12*
889 A373 75c multicolored .30 .20
890 A373 5.75r multicolored 1.25 .90

Randenigala Project — A374

1988, Oct. 31 — *Perf. 12*
891 A374 75c Woman, dam, power station .20 .20
892 A374 5.75r Hydrelectric dam .45 .45

Some copies were distributed at the time the set was originally planned to be issued in 1986.

A375

Christmas — A376

1988, Nov. 17 — *Litho.* *Perf. 13½*
893 A375 75c multicolored .35 .35

Opening of Gramodaya Folk Art Center.

1988, Nov. 25 — *Perf. 12x12½*
894 A376 75c shown .20 .20
895 A376 8.50r Shepherds see star .70 .70
   a. Souvenir sheet of 2, #894-895 1.60 1.60

A377

Waterfalls — A378

1988, Dec. 28 — *Perf. 12*
896 A377 75c multicolored .20 .20

E.W. Adikaram (1905-85), educator.

1989, Aug. 11 — *Litho.* *Perf. 12*
897 A378 75c Dunhinda .20 .20
898 A378 1r Rawana .20 .20
899 A378 5.75r Laxapana .90 .90
900 A378 8.50r Diyaluma 1.10 1.10
   Nos. 897-900 (4) 2.40 2.40

Free Distribution of School Text Books, 10th Anniv. A379

1989, Jan. 23 — *Litho.* *Perf. 13½x13*
901 A379 75c multicolored .20 .20

Poets — A380

1989, Jan. 27 — *Perf. 13*
902 A380 75c Wimalaratne Kumaragama .20 .20
903 A380 75c G.H. Perera .20 .20
904 A380 75c Sagara Palansuriya .20 .20
905 A380 75c P.B. Alwis Perera .20 .20
   Nos. 902-905 (4) .80 .80

Mahapola Educational Plan, 8th Anniv. — A381

1989, Feb. — *Perf. 13½*
906 A381 75c multicolored .20 .20

Chamber of Commerce, 150th Anniv. — A382

1989, Mar. 25 — *Litho.* *Perf. 12*
907 A382 75c multicolored .20 .20

AGRO
Mahaweli
A383

1989, Sept. 2   Litho.   Perf. 12
908 A383 75c multicolored   .20 .20

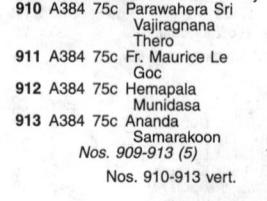

Famous
Men
A384

1989, May 22
909 A384 75c Simon Casie Chitty   .20 .20
910 A384 75c Parawahera Sri
                Vajiragnana
                Thero   .20 .20
911 A384 75c Fr. Maurice Le
                Goc   .20 .20
912 A384 75c Hemapala
                Munidasa   .20 .20
913 A384 75c Ananda
                Samarakoon   .20 .20
       Nos. 909-913 (5)   1.00 1.00
            Nos. 910-913 vert.

Hartley College,
150th Anniv. (in
1988) — A385

1989, June 5
914 A385 75c multicolored   .20 .20

Vesak
Festival
A386

Various paintings in Medawala Viharaya,
Harispattuwa.

1989, May 15   Litho.   Perf. 12½x12
915 A386 50c multicolored   .20 .20
916 A386 75c multicolored   .20 .20
917 A386 5r multicolored   .40 .40
918 A386 5.75r multicolored   .50 .50
   a.   Souvenir sheet of 4, #915-918   1.90 1.90
          Nos. 915-918 (4)   1.30 1.30

For surcharge see No. 953A.

Pres. Premadasa's Declaration
Establishing the Ministry of Buddha
Sasana — A387

1989, June 18   Litho.   Perf. 12½x12
919 A387 75c multicolored   .25 .25

Gam
Udawa,
11th
Anniv.
A388

1989, June 23
920 A388 75c multicolored   .25 .25

Village reformation movement.

French
Revolution,
Bicent.
A389

1989, Aug. 26   Litho.   Perf. 13½x13
921 A389 8.50r rose & deep blue 1.10 1.10

Bank of
Ceylon, 50th
Anniv.
A390

1989, Aug. 31
922 A390 75c Old, new head-
                quarters   .20 .20
923 A390 5r Emblem, flowers   .50 .50

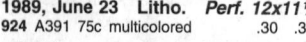

Jana Saviya
Grants
A391

1989, June 23   Litho.   Perf. 12x11½
924 A391 75c multicolored   .30 .30

Development program to eliminate poverty
and improve the standard of living through
education and by providing food, health care,
shelter and clothing.
   See No. 953. For surcharge see No. 955.

Baptist
Mission,
177th
Anniv.
A392

1989, Aug. 19   Perf. 12½x12
925 A392 5.75r James Chater,
                church, 1812   .35 .35

State Literary
Festival — A393

Wilhelm
Geiger — A394

1989, Sept. 22   Perf. 12x11½
926 A393 75c multicolored   .20 .20

1989, Sept. 30   Perf. 13x13½
927 A394 75c multicolored   .20 .20

Wilhelm Geiger (1856-1943), German philologist who studied Sinhalese.

Wildlife Type of 1981
1989, Oct. 11   Perf. 14
928 A219 3r like No. 595   1.40 .35

No. 928 has black inscriptions and is dated
"1989." See No. 729 for brown inscriptions.

Famous
Lawyers — A395

Sir Cyril de
Zoysa — A396

1989, Oct. 16   Perf. 12x11½
929 A395 75c H.V. Perera (1890-
                1969)   .20 .20
930 A395 75c Sir Ivor Jennings
                (1903-1965)   .20 .20

1989, Oct. 26   Perf. 13x13½
931 A396 75c multicolored   .25 .25

Sir Cyril de Zoysa (1896-1978), key figure in
the Buddhist cultural reformation.

Asia-Pacific
Telecommunity,
10th
Anniv. — A397

1989, Nov. 1   Perf. 12x12½
932 A397 5.75r multicolored   .50 .50

Sri
Sucharitha
Viyaparaya
Oratory
Children's
Soc., 50th
Anniv.
A398

1989, Nov. 9   Perf. 13
933 A398 75c multicolored   .50 .50

1st Moon
Landing, 20th
Anniv. — A399

Christmas — A400

1989, Nov. 10   Perf. 12x12½
934 A399 75c Apollo 11 liftoff,
                crew   .20 .20
935 A399 1r Astronaut de-
                scending ladder   .20 .20
936 A399 2r Astronaut on lu-
                nar surface   .40 .40
937 A399 5.75r Lunar surface,
                view of Earth   .70 .70
   a.   Souvenir sheet of 4, #934-937   2.40 2.40
          Nos. 934-937 (4)   1.50 1.50

1989, Nov. 21   Perf. 13½
938 A400 75c Adoration of the
                Shepherds   .20 .20
939 A400 8.50r Adoration of the
                Magi   .60 .60
   a.   Souvenir sheet of 2, #938-939   1.40 1.50

Devananda
Nayake
Thero — A401

1989, Nov. 25   Perf. 12x11½
940 A401 75c multicolored   .35 .35

Devananda Nayake Thero (1921-1983),
religious scholar, educator, reformer.

Rev. William
Ault, College
and Crest
A402

1989, Nov. 29   Perf. 11½x12
941 A402 75c multicolored   .25 .25

Batticaloa Methodist Central College, 175th
anniv.

Nuwara
Eliya Golf
Club, Cent.
A403

1989, Dec. 8   Perf. 14x13½
942 A403 75c shown   2.25 .30
943 A403 8.50r Course, golf
                house   6.50 3.50

Raja — A404

1989, Dec. 12 **Perf. 13x13½**
944 A404 75c multicolored 4.00 .75
Raja (1913-1988), the royal tusker of the Sri Dalada Maligawa that carried the relic casket in the Kandy Esala Procession.

Gampaha Wickamarachchi Ayurveda Medical College, 60th Anniv. — A405

1989, Dec. 14 **Perf. 13½x13**
945 A405 75c Founder, institute .35 .35

Udunuwara Sri Sarananda Mahanayake Thero (1867-1947), Educator — A406

1989, Dec. 20 **Perf. 12x12½**
946 A406 75c multicolored .20 .20

Railway Dept., 125th Anniv. A407

1989, Dec. 27 **Perf. 11½x12, 13 (3r)**
947 A407 75c Train, viaduct .50 .25
948 A407 2r Train, light signal, Maradana Station .90 .40
949 A407 3r Steam locomotive, semaphore signal 1.10 .45
950 A407 7r 1st train in Sri Lanka 1.40 .65
Nos. 947-950 (4) 3.90 1.75

A408

A409

1989, Dec. 28 **Perf. 13x13½**
951 A408 75c multicolored 1.50 .35
Thomas Cooray (1901-88), 1st native Sri Lankan Cardinal.

1990, Jan. 14 **Perf. 12x12½**
952 A409 1r multicolored 1.90 .30
Justin Wijayawardena (1904-82), educator, politician.

Jana Saviya Grants Type of 1989
1990, Jan. 31 Litho. **Perf. 12x11½**
953 A391 1r multicolored .20 .20

No. 918 Surcharged

.25

1990, Feb. 16 Litho. **Perf. 12½x12**
953A A386 25c on 5.75r multi .90 .25

Induruwe Uttarananda Mahanayake Thero — A411

1990, Mar. 15 Litho. **Perf. 12**
954 A411 1r multicolored 1.60 1.10

No. 924 Surcharged **1.00**

1990, Mar. 22 Litho. **Perf. 12x11½**
955 A391 1r on 75c multi 1.10 1.00

Silver Jubilee of Laksala A413

Traditional handicrafts.

1990, Apr. 2 Litho. **Perf. 12**
956 A413 1r Drums .20 .20
957 A413 2r Silverware .20 .20
958 A413 3r Lacquerware .30 .25
959 A413 8r Dumbara mats .75 .65
Nos. 956-959 (4) 1.45 1.30

Vesak Festival A414

Various paintings in Wewurukannala Buduraja Maha Viharaya.

1990, May 2 **Perf. 12½x12**
960 A414 75c multicolored .20 .20
961 A414 1r multicolored .20 .20
962 A414 2r multicolored .20 .20

963 A414 8r multicolored .40 .40
a. Souvenir sheet of 4, #960-963 1.60 1.60
Nos. 960-963 (4) 1.00 1.00

A415

Famous Men — A416

1990, May 22 **Perf. 12**
964 A415 1r Rev. T.M.F. Long .40 .15
Size: 25x39mm
Perf. 12x12½
965 A416 1r D.P.A. Wijewardene .40 .20
966 A416 1r L.T.P. Manjusri .40 .20
967 A416 1r M.D. Ratnasuriya .40 .20
Nos. 964-967 (4) 1.60 .75

Gam Udawa Program, 12th Anniv. A417

1990, June 23 **Perf. 12½x12**
968 A417 1r multicolored 2.25 .50

Dept. of Archaeology, Cent. — A418

1r, Gold reliquary from Delivala Temple, c. 200 B.C. 2r, Statuette of Ganesha (the Elephant God) from Polonnaruwa. 3r, Terrace of the Bodhi-tree at Isurumuni Vihara. 8r, Stone seat with inscription of King Nissankamalle, 12th cent. A.D.

1990, July 7 **Perf. 12**
969 A418 1r black & orange .25 .20
970 A418 2r black & gray .40 .20
971 A418 3r black, yel grn & gold .55 .25
972 A418 8r black & gold 1.10 1.00
Nos. 969-972 (4) 2.30 1.65

Sri Lanka Tennis Assoc., 75th Anniv. A419

1990, Aug. 14 **Perf. 13½**
973 A419 1r Player ready to volley .80 .80
974 A419 1r Player receiving volley .80 .80
a. Pair, #973-974 1.60 1.60
975 A419 8r Men players 2.75 2.75
976 A419 8r Women players 2.75 2.75
a. Pair, #975-976 5.50 5.50
Nos. 973-976 (4) 7.10 7.10

Fish — A420

1990, Sept. 14 **Perf. 11½**
977 A420 25c Spotted loach .20 .20
978 A420 2r Ornate paradise fish .45 .20
979 A420 8r Mountain labeo 1.10 1.10
980 A420 20r Cherry barb 2.25 2.25
a. Souvenir sheet of 4, #977-980 4.75 5.00
Nos. 977-980 (4) 4.00 3.75

A421

A422

1990, Dec. 26 **Perf. 12**
981 A421 1r Letter box, 1904 .65 .20
982 A421 2r Mail runner, 1815 1.25 .40
983 A421 5r Mail coach, 1832 2.10 2.10
984 A421 10r Nuwara-Eliya Post Office, 1894 3.25 3.25
Nos. 981-984 (4) 7.25 5.95
Sri Lanka Postal Service, 175th anniv.

1990, Oct. 28 Litho. **Perf. 12**
985 A422 1r multicolored 4.25 1.25
Rukmani Devi (1923-78), actress.

Christmas A423

1990, Nov. 28 **Perf. 13**
986 A423 1r Mary, Joseph at inn .30 .20
987 A423 10r Adoration of the Magi 2.40 2.50
a. Souv. sheet of 2, #986-987, perf. 12 3.50 3.50

World AIDS Day A424

1990, Nov. 30
988 A424 1r multicolored .75 .20
989 A424 8r AIDS Virus 3.25 3.25

A425

A426

1990, Dec. 8   *Perf. 12*
990   A425   1r multicolored   2.25   .90
     Dharmapala College, 50th anniv.

1990, Dec. 14   **Litho.**   *Perf. 12*
991   A426   1r olive green & brown   2.25   .90
     Peri Sunderam (b. 1890), political & social reformer.

Ceylon Institute of Chemistry, 50th anniv. — A427

1991, Jan. 25   **Litho.**   *Perf. 12*
992   A427   1r multicolored   2.75   .90

Vesak Festival
A428

Various scenes from Buddha's life.

1991, May 17   **Litho.**   *Perf. 12*
993   A428   75c multicolored   .30   .20
994   A428   1r multicolored   .30   .20
995   A428   2r multicolored   .60   .35
996   A428   11r multicolored   2.75   3.00
   a.   Souvenir sheet of 4, #993-996   4.50   4.50
     Nos. 993-996 (4)   3.95   3.75

A429

A430

1991, May 31   *Perf. 12*
997   A429   1r multicolored   1.25   .85
     Mahabodhi Society, cent.

1991, May 22   **Litho.**   *Perf. 12x12½*
     Famous men.
998   A430   1r Narada Thero   .55   .45
999   A430   1r Sir Muttu
           Coomaraswamy   .55   .45
1000   A430   1r Dr. Andreas Nell   .55   .45
1001   A430   1r W.A. Silva   .55   .45
     Nos. 998-1001 (4)   2.20   1.80

Gam Udawa, 13th Anniv.
A431

1991, June 23   **Litho.**   *Perf. 12½*
1002   A431   1r multicolored   2.25   .85

Henpitagedera Gnanaseeha Nayake Thero (1909-1981), Religious Leader — A432

1991, Aug. 1
1003   A432   1r multicolored   2.25   .85

Colombo Plan, 40th Anniv.
A433

1991, July 1   **Litho.**   *Perf. 12*
1004   A433   1r multicolored   2.25   .85

Survey Dept., 190th Anniv.
A434

1991, Aug. 2   *Perf. 12½*
1005   A434   1r multicolored   2.25   .85

Police Service, 125th Anniv.
A435

1991, Sept. 3   **Litho.**   *Perf. 12½*
1006   A435   1r multicolored   1.60   .60

6th SAARC Summit
A436

1991, Dec. 21   **Litho.**   *Perf. 12½*
1007   A436   1r shown   .20   .20
1008   A436   8r Flags encircling bldg.   .60   .50

Kingswood College, Cent. — A437

1991, Oct. 26   *Perf. 12½x12*
1009   A437   1r multicolored   .80   .40

Christmas — A439

1991, Nov. 19   **Litho.**   *Perf. 12½*
1014   A439   1r The Annunciation   .20   .20
1015   A439   10r Nativity scene   .80   1.25
   a.   Sheet of 2, #1014-1015   1.75   1.90

A440

1991, Nov. 23
     Telecommunications: 1r, Early telephone network. 2r, Switchboard operations. 8r, Satellite transmitters, cable network. 10r, Telephone, fiber optic cable, computer, cordless telephone, FAX machine.

1016   A440   1r multicolored   .25   .20
1017   A440   2r multicolored   .30   .20
1018   A440   8r multicolored   .70   .90
1019   A440   10r multicolored   .85   .90
     Nos. 1016-1019 (4)   2.10   2.20

5th South Asian Federation Games
A441

1991, Dec. 22   *Perf. 14*
1020   A441   1r Mascot   .30   .20
1021   A441   2r Emblem   .55   .25
1022   A441   4r Stadium, Colombo   1.00   1.00
1023   A441   11r Globe and flags   2.10   2.25
     Nos. 1020-1023 (4)   3.95   3.70

Year of Exports
A442

1992, Jan. 13   **Litho.**   *Perf. 11½x12*
1024   A442   1r multicolored   2.00   .85

Mahinda College, Cent.
A443

1992, Mar. 2   **Litho.**   *Perf. 11½x12*
1025   A443   1r multicolored   .25   .25

General Ranjan Wijeratne (1931-1991)
A444

1992, Mar. 2   **Litho.**   *Perf. 12x12½*
1026   A444   1r multicolored   .25   .20

Tea Production, 125th Anniv.
A445

     Field of tea and: 1r, Tea picker. 2r, Family, cup and glass of tea. 5r, Package of tea. 10r, James Taylor.

1992, Feb. 12   *Perf. 13½*
1027   A445   1r multicolored   .50   .20
1028   A445   2r multicolored   .85   .25
1029   A445   5r multicolored   2.40   2.40
1030   A445   10r multicolored   3.00   3.25
     Nos. 1027-1030 (4)   6.75   6.10

Newstead College, 175th Anniv. (in 1991)
A446

1992, Mar. 13   **Litho.**   *Perf. 11½x12*
1031   A446   1r multicolored   .25   .25
     Dated 1991.

Mahapola Scholarship Fund, 11th Anniv. — A447

1992, Mar. 30   *Perf. 12*
1032   A447   1r multicolored   .25   .25

Vesak Festival
A448

     Mural paintings from Kottimbulwala Rajamaha Vihara: 75c, Dukula and Parika retiring to forest. 1r, Sama and parents living in forest. 8r, Sama directing blind parents to hermitage. 11r, Sama's parents approach wounded son.

1992, May 5   **Litho.**   *Perf. 11½x12*
1033   A448   75c multicolored   .20   .20
1034   A448   1r multicolored   .20   .20
1035   A448   8r multicolored   1.00   1.10
1036   A448   11r multicolored   1.25   1.40
   a.   Souvenir sheet, #1033-1036   3.00   3.25
     Nos. 1033-1036 (4)   2.65   2.90

A449

A450

National Heroes: No. 1037, Wadeebhasinha Dewamottawe Amarawansa Thero. No. 1038, R. A. Mirando. No. 1039, Gate Mudaliyar N. Canaganayagam. No. 1040, I.L.M. Abdul Azeez.

1992, May 22   *Perf. 14*
1037 A449 1r multicolored   .20   .20
1038 A449 1r multicolored   .20   .20
1039 A449 1r multicolored   .20   .20
1040 A449 1r multicolored   .20   .20
    Nos. 1037-1040 (4)   .80   .80

1992, June 14   **Litho.**   *Perf. 12x12½*
1041 A450 1r multicolored   .25   .25
Introduction of Buddhism on Sri Lanka by Anubudu Mihindu Jayanthi, 2300th anniv.

Gam Udawa, 14th Anniv. A451

1992, June 23   *Perf. 12*
1042 A451 1r multicolored   .20   .20

Postal Excellence Service Awards A452

Designs: 1r, Award presentation, postal work. 10r, Award of excellence medals, No. 1043 canceled on envelope.

1992, July 11   *Perf. 14*
1043 A452 1r multicolored   .30   .25
1044 A452 10r multicolored   3.00   3.00

A453

A454

Masks of Sri Lanka.

1992, Aug. 19   **Litho.**   *Perf. 13*
1045 A453 1r Narilata   .20   .20
1046 A453 2r Mudali   .25   .20
1047 A453 5r Queen   .45   .50
1048 A453 10r King   .80   .90
   a.   Souvenir sheet, #1045-1048   2.00   2.25
    Nos. 1045-1048 (4)   1.70   1.80

1992, Sept. 15   **Litho.**   *Perf. 14*
1049 A454 1r Running   .25   .20
1050 A454 11r Rifle shooting   1.60   1.75
1051 A454 13r Swimming   2.10   2.25
1052 A454 15r Weight lifting   2.25   2.50
   a.   Souvenir sheet, #1049-1052   6.75   7.00
    Nos. 1049-1052 (4)   6.20   6.70

1992 Summer Olympics, Barcelona.

Cricket in Sri Lanka, 160th Anniv. A455

1992, Sept. 8   **Litho.**   *Perf. 13*
1053 A455 5r multicolored   3.25   2.75

Vijaya Kumaratunga, Entertainer and Political Leader, Birth Anniv. — A456

1992, Oct. 9
1054 A456 1r multicolored   .35   .30

Al-Bahjathul Ibraheemiyyah Arabic College, Cent. — A457

1992, Oct. 24   *Perf. 12*
1055 A457 1r multicolored   .35   .30

A458

Christmas A459

1992, Oct. 25   **Litho.**   *Perf. 12x11½*
1056 A458 1r multicolored   1.00   .50
Dutch Reformed Church in Sri Lanka, 350th anniv.

1992, Nov. 17   **Litho.**   *Perf. 12x11½*
1057 A459 1r Holy Family   .20   .20
1058 A459 9r Church, family   .80   .90
   a.   Souvenir sheet, #1057-1058   1.60   1.75

Discovery of America, 500th Anniv. A460

Designs: 1r, Ships at sea, Aug. 1492. 11r, First landing in the Americas, Oct. 1492. 13r, Santa Maria aground, Dec. 1492. 15r, Return to Spain, Apr. 1493.

1992, Dec. 1   *Perf. 14*
1059 A460 1r multicolored   .50   .20
1060 A460 11r multicolored   1.25   1.25
1061 A460 13r multicolored   1.50   1.60
1062 A460 15r multicolored   1.50   1.75
   a.   Souvenir sheet, #1059-1062   5.50   5.75
    Nos. 1059-1062 (4)   4.75   4.80

No. 564 Surcharged   **2.00** ▬

1992, Dec. 1   **Litho.**   *Perf. 14*
1062B A206 2r on 10c multi   1.25   .75

Dambagasare Sri Sumedhankara Maha Nayake Thero (1892-1984), Buddhist Monk — A461

1992, Dec. 10   **Litho.**   *Perf. 12*
1063 A461 1r multicolored   .20   .20

University Education in Sri Lanka A462

1992, Dec. 12   **Litho.**   *Perf. 12*
1064 A462 1r multicolored   .20   .20
No. 1064 was not available until Dec. 1993.

University of Colombo, 50th Anniv. (in 1992) A463

1993, Mar. 23   **Litho.**   *Perf. 13*
1065 A463 1r multicolored   .30   .30

Zahira College, Cent. A464

1993, Apr. 7
1066 A464 1r multicolored   .60   .30

Vesak Festival — A465

Designs based on verses from the Dhammapada (sermons of Buddha): 75c, Magandiya being presented to Buddha. 1r,

---

Kisa Gotami carrying dead child. 3r, Patachara, dead family members. 10r, Conversion of Angulimala, the murderer.

1993, Apr. 30   *Perf. 12x12½*
1067 A465 75c multicolored   .20   .20
1068 A465 1r multicolored   .20   .20
1069 A465 3r multicolored   .50   .60
1070 A465 10r multicolored   1.10   1.25
   a.   Souvenir sheet, #1067-1070   2.10   2.10
    Nos. 1067-1070 (4)   2.00   2.25

A466

A467

1993, May 10   *Perf. 12*
1071 A466 1r Guide, tent, emblem   .50   .25
1072 A466 5r Activities, map   1.75   1.75
Girl Guides in Sri Lanka, 75th Anniv. (in 1992).

1993, May 22   *Perf. 14*
National Heroes: No. 1073, Yagirala Sri Pagnananda Maha Nayaka Thero. No. 1074, C.P. De Silva. No. 1075, Wilmot A. Perera. No. 1076, N.D.H. Abdul Caffoor.

1073 A467 1r multicolored   .25   .20
1074 A467 1r multicolored   .25   .20
1075 A467 1r multicolored   .25   .20
1076 A467 1r multicolored   .25   .20
    Nos. 1073-1076 (4)   1.00   .80

Gam Udawa, 15th Anniv. A468

1993, June 23   **Litho.**   *Perf. 12½*
1077 A468 1r multicolored   .85   .40

Co-operative Consumer Service, 50th Anniv. — A469

1993, July 3   *Perf. 13*
1078 A469 1r multicolored   .85   .40

Birds A470

Designs: 3r, Ashy-headed laughing thrush. 4r, Ceylon brown-capped babbler. 5r, Red-faced malkoha. 10r, Ceylon hill-mynah.

1993, July 14   *Perf. 12½x12*
1079 A470 3r multicolored   .30   .20
1080 A470 4r multicolored   .30   .20
1081 A470 5r multicolored   .40   .35

1082 A470 10r multicolored .75 .80
   a. Souvenir sheet, #1079-1082 2.75 3.00
   Nos. 1079-1082 (4) 1.75 1.55

Talawila
Church,
150th
Anniv.
A471

1993, July 26 *Perf. 13*
1083 A471 1r multicolored .85 .40

Postal Excellence
Service
Awards — A472

1993, Aug. 22
1084 A472 1r multicolored .70 .35

Technical
Education
in Sri
Lanka,
Cent.
A473

1993, Dec. 17
1085 A473 1r multicolored .70 .35

Musaeus College,
Cent. — A474

1993, Nov. 15
1086 A474 1r multicolored 1.50 .40

Christmas
A475

Designs: 1r, Presentation of infant Jesus in
Temple of Jerusalem. 17r, Boy Jesus in
Temple.

1993, Nov. 30 Litho. *Perf. 14x13½*
1087 A475 1r multicolored .20 .20
1088 A475 17r multicolored .80 .90
   a. Souvenir sheet, #1087-1088 1.25 1.40

Youth and Health — A476

1993, Dec. 16 *Perf. 14*
1089 A476 1r multicolored .35 .30

Old Boy's Assoc.,
Trinity College,
Kandy,
Cent. — A478

1994, Feb. 11 Litho. *Perf. 12½*
1091 A478 1r multicolored .35 .30

St.
Thomas
College,
Matara,
150th
Anniv.
A479

1994, Mar. 10 Litho. *Perf. 13*
1092 A479 1r multicolored .35 .30

St.
Joseph's
College,
125th
Anniv.
A480

1994, Apr. 4 Litho. *Perf. 12½*
1093 A480 1r multicolored .35 .30

Siyambalangamuwe Sri Gunaratana
Thero — A481

1994, Apr. 2 Litho. *Perf. 13*
1094 A481 1r multicolored 1.25 .30

ILO, 75th
Anniv. — A482

1994, May. 12
1095 A482 1r multicolored .80 .40

Vesak
Festival
A483

Designs show actions by Bodhisatva in four
of ten perfections: 1r, Dana, displaying gener-
osity. 2r, Sila, morality. 5r, Nekkhamma,
ascetic surrounded by worshippers. 17r,
Panna, wisdom dispensed by Bodhisatva to
others.

1994, May 7 Litho. *Perf. 12½*
1096 A483 1r multicolored .20 .20
1097 A483 2r multicolored .70 .40
1098 A483 5r multicolored .80 .80
1099 A483 17r multicolored 1.75 1.90
   a. Souvenir sheet, #1096-1099 4.00 4.25
   Nos. 1096-1099 (4) 3.45 3.30

Famous
People
A484

Designs: No. 1100, Pres. Ranasinghe
Premadasa. No. 1101, Ven. Mihiripanne
Dhammaratana Thero. No. 1102, E. Per-
iyathambipillai, poet. No. 1103, Dr. Colvin R.
De Silva, politician.

1994, May 22 Litho. *Perf. 14*
1100 A484 1r multicolored .25 .20
1101 A484 1r multicolored .25 .20
1102 A484 1r multicolored .25 .20
1103 A484 1r multicolored .25 .20
   Nos. 1100-1103 (4) 1.00 .80

World
Conference
of Intl.
Federation
of Social
Workers,
Colombo
A485

1994, July 9 Litho. *Perf. 12½*
1104 A485 8r blue, lt blue & blk 1.10 1.10

Bellanwila Sri Somaratana Nayake
Thero — A486

1994, Aug. 2 Litho. *Perf. 12½*
1105 A486 1r multicolored .70 .40

Infotel
Lanka '94
A487

1994, Sept. 8
1106 A487 10r multicolored 1.60 1.75

Intl. Year of
Indigenous
People — A488

Designs: 1r, Veddah man making bow. 17r,
Veddah man seated by rock art paintings.

1994, Sept. 12 Litho. *Perf. 12*
1107 A488 1r multicolored .20 .20
1108 A488 17r multicolored 3.00 3.00

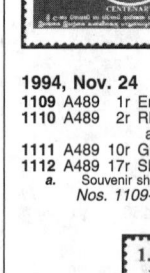

Natl.
Wildlife &
Nature
Protection
Society,
Cent.
A489

1994, Nov. 24 Litho. *Perf. 12½*
1109 A489 1r Emblem .20 .20
1110 A489 2r Rhino-horned lizard .45 .25
1111 A489 10r Giant squirrel 1.25 1.25
1112 A489 17r Sloth bear 1.75 2.00
   a. Souvenir sheet, #1109-1112 4.00 4.25
   Nos. 1109-1112 (4) 3.65 3.70

Gam
Udawa,
16th Anniv.
A490

1994, Sept. Litho. *Perf. 13*
1113 A490 1r multicolored .25 .20

A491   A492

1994, Oct. 11 Litho. *Perf. 12½*
1114 A491 1r multicolored .70 .40
Double entry bookkeeping, 500th anniv.

1995, Feb. 22 *Perf. 14*
1115 A492 1r Water lily .25 .20

Richmond
College
Old Boys
Assoc.,
Cent.
A493

1994 *Perf. 12½*
1116 A493 1r multicolored .20 .20

ICAO, 50th
Anniv.
A494

1994, Dec. 7 Litho. *Perf. 13*
1117 A494 10r multicolored 2.00 2.00

Christmas
A495

Designs: 1r, Nativity. 17r, Jesus growing up,
at home with Joseph and Mary.

1994, Dec. 8 Litho. Perf. 13
1118 A495 1r multicolored   .20 .20
1119 A495 17r multicolored 1.50 1.60
  a. Souvenir sheet, #1118-1119 1.90 2.10

Assoc. for Advancement of Science, 50th Anniv. — A496

1994, Dec. 19 Litho. Perf. 13
1120 A496 1r multicolored 1.00 .40

Orchid Circle of Ceylon, 60th Anniv. — A498

Orchids: 50c, Dendrobium maccarthiae. 1r, Cottonia peduncularis. 5r, Bulbophyllum wightii. 17r, Habenaria crinifera.

1994, Dec. 27 Litho. Perf. 13
1122 A498 50c multicolored .20 .20
1123 A498 1r multicolored   .20 .20
1124 A498 5r multicolored   .45 .40
1125 A498 17r multicolored 1.00 1.10
  a. Souvenir sheet, #1122-1125 3.25 3.50
  Nos. 1122-1125 (4) 1.85 1.90

Visit of Pope John Paul II, Beatification of Fr. Joseph Vaz — A499

1995, Jan. 20
1126 A499 1r multicolored 1.60 .35

St. Joseph's College, Colombo, Cent. A500

1995, Mar. 2 Litho. Perf. 13
1127 A500 1r multicolored .25 .20

Royal Asiatic Society of Sri Lanka, 150th Anniv. — A501

1995, Apr. 4
1128 A501 1r multicolored .70 .35

Sirimavo Bandaranaike, World's First Woman Prime Minister — A502

1995, Apr. 17 Litho. Perf. 12
1129 A502 2r multicolored .50 .30

A503

A504

Vesak Festival (Designs show actions by a Bodhisatva in four of ten perfections): 1r, Endeavor, standing on shore. 2r, Forebearance, one holding another. 10r, Veracity, two people listening to truths. 17r, Resolution, man holding hoe.

1995, May 5 Perf. 12x12½
1130 A503 1r multicolored   .20 .20
1131 A503 2r multicolored   .20 .20
1132 A503 10r multicolored .70 .75
1133 A503 17r multicolored 1.25 1.40
  a. Souvenir sheet, #1130-1133 2.75 3.00
  Nos. 1130-1133 (4) 2.35 2.55

1995, June 3 Perf. 11
1134 A504 2r M. C. Abdul Cader .70 .45

St. Aloysius College, Galle, Cent. A506

1995, June 21 Litho. Perf. 12½x12
1136 A506 2r multicolored .90 .45

T.B. Ilangaratna (1913-92), Politician A507

1995, July 7 Litho. Perf. 13
1137 A507 2r multicolored .90 .45

Dhamma School, Cent. A508

1995, Aug. 3
1138 A508 2r multicolored .90 .45

General Post Office, Colombo, Cent. A509

1995, Aug. 22 Litho. Perf. 13½
1139 A509 1r multicolored .45 .20

Help the Elderly — A510

1995, Oct. 1 Litho. Perf. 14x13½
1140 A510 2r multicolored .90 .45

41st Commonwealth Parliamentary Conference — A511

1995, Oct. 9 Litho. Perf. 14x13½
1141 A511 2r multicolored .90 .45

UN, 50th Anniv. — A512

World Thrift Day — A513

1995, Oct. 24 Perf. 13½x14
1142 A512 2r multicolored .90 .55

1995, Oct. 15
1143 A513 2r multicolored .90 .45

Christmas A514

Designs: 2r, Arms of Colombo and Kurunegla, Persian cross from Anuradhapura, Christian church. 20r, Clasping arms, nativity scene.

1995, Nov. 10 Litho. Perf. 13
1144 A514 2r multicolored   .20 .20
1145 A514 20r multicolored 1.40 1.50
  a. Souvenir sheet, #1144-1145 1.60 1.75

A515   A516

1995, Dec. 8
1146 A515 2r multicolored 1.00 .50

SAARC, 10th anniv.

1996, Jan. 22 Litho. Perf. 12
1147 A516 50c Little Basses   .20 .20
1148 A516 75c Great Basses   .20 .20
1149 A516 2r Devinuwara   .25 .20
1149A A516 2.50r like #1149 .25 .25
1150 A516 20r Galle   1.10 1.25
  a. Souv. sheet, #1147-1149,
      1150 2.25 2.50
  Nos. 1147-1150 (5) 2.00 2.10

Lighthouses of Sri Lanka.
For surcharges see Nos. 1191-1193.

Vincent High School, Batticaloa, 175th Anniv. — A517

1996, Jan. 17 Litho. Perf. 13
1151 A517 2r multicolored .90 .45

Handicrafts A518

1996, Mar. 13 Perf. 12
1152 A518 25c Traditional
           sesath   .20 .20
1153 A518 8.50r Pottery   .35 .30
1154 A518 10.50r Mats   .45 .50
1155 A518 17r Lace   .65 .75
  a. Souvenir sheet, #1152-1155 1.75 1.90
  Nos. 1152-1155 (4) 1.65 1.75

For surcharges see Nos. 1189-1190.

A519

A520

1996, Mar. 21
1156 A519 2r multicolored .70 .45

Chundikuli Girls' College, Jaffna, cent.

1996, Apr. 30 Litho. Perf. 12

Vesak Festival: 1r, Capa cradling her son, teasing her husband. 2r, Dantika, mahout, elephant. 5r, Subha holding her eye in her hand, man of low morals. 10r, Punna explaining purification by water to Brahmin.

1157 A520 1r multicolored   .20 .20
1158 A520 2r multicolored   .20 .20
1159 A520 5r multicolored   .20 .20
1160 A520 10r multicolored .40 .40
  a. Souvenir sheet, #1157-1160 1.60 1.75
  Nos. 1157-1160 (4) 1.00 1.00

1996 Summer Olympic Games, Atlanta A521

1996, July 22   Litho.   Perf. 13½
1161	A521	1r Diving, vert.	.20	.20
1162	A521	2r Volleyball, vert.	.55	.20
1163	A521	5r Shooting	.80	.75
1164	A521	17r Running	1.40	1.60
		Nos. 1161-1164 (4)	2.95	2.75

Sri Lanka, 1996 World Cup Cricket
Champions — A522

1996, Aug. 18
1165	A522	2r Bowler	.40	.20
1166	A522	10.50r Wicketkeeper	.70	.70
1167	A522	17r Batsman	1.10	1.25
1168	A522	20r Trophy	1.25	1.40
a.		Souvenir sheet, #1165-1168	4.00	4.25
		Nos. 1165-1168 (4)	3.45	3.55

No. 1168a contains two se-tenant pairs.

Jaffna
Central
College,
180th
Anniv.
A523

1996, Sept. 7   Litho.   Perf. 13½
1169	A523	2r multicolored	.85	.45

A524

1996, Nov. 4   Litho.   Perf. 13½x14
1170	A524	2r multicolored	.85	.55

UNESCO, 50th anniv.

1996, Dec. 2   Perf. 13½x13

Christmas (Scenes of parables from murals, Trinity College Chapel): 2r, Washing of the feet. 17r, Good Samaritan.

1171	A525	2r multicolored	.20	.20
1172	A525	17r multicolored	.80	.90
a.		Souvenir sheet, #1171-1172	1.00	1.10

A525

UNICEF, 50th
Anniv. — A526

Swami
Vivekananda
A527

1996, Dec. 12   Litho.   Perf. 13½x14
1173	A526	5r multicolored	.55	.60

1997, Jan. 15   Perf. 13½x13
1174	A527	2.50r multicolored	.55	.50

Personalities
A528

Vesak
Festival — A529

Designs: No. 1175, Lt. Gen. Denzil Kobbekaduwa. No. 1176, Ven. Welivitiye Serata Thero. No. 1177, Dr. S.A. Wickremasinghe.

1997, Apr. 4   Litho.   Perf. 13½x13
1175	A528	2r multicolored	.40	.30
1176	A528	2r multicolored	.40	.30
1177	A528	2r multicolored	.40	.30
		Nos. 1175-1177 (3)	1.20	.90

1997, May 7   Perf. 12x12½

Cemeteries, monuments to the dead: 1r, Thuparama. 2.50r, Ruwanvalisaya. 3r, Abhayagiri Dagaba. 17r, Jetavana Dagaba.

1178	A529	1r multicolored	.20	.20
1179	A529	2.50r multicolored	.20	.20
1180	A529	3r multicolored	.20	.20
1181	A529	17r multicolored	.50	.50
a.		Souvenir Sheet of 4, #1178-1181	.95	.95
		Nos. 1178-1181 (4)	1.10	1.10

D.J. Kumarage,
Birth
Cent. — A530

1997, Apr. 4   Litho.   Perf. 13½x14
1182	A530	2.50r multicolored	.70	.45

Medicinal
Herbs — A531

2.40r, Munronia pinnata. 14r, Rauvolfia serpentina.

1997, July 22   Litho.   Perf. 13½x14
1183	A531	2.50r multicolored	.20	.20
1184	A531	14r multicolored	.80	.90

Tourism
A532

1997, Sept. 11   Perf. 12
1185	A532	20r multicolored	1.10	1.10

St.
Servatius
College,
Matara,
Cent.
A533

1997, Nov. 1   Perf. 12½x12
1186	A533	2.50r multicolored	.50	.25

Mahagama
Sekera — A534

1997, Apr. 4   Litho.   Perf. 13½x13
1187	A534	2r multicolored	.30	.25

Asterisks obliterate portions of Mahagama Sekera's name.

Sri Jayawardenapura Vidalaya, Kotte,
175th Anniv. — A535

1997, Jan. 28   Perf. 12½
1188	A535	2.50r multicolored	.25	.20

Nos. 1153-1154 Surcharged

1997, May 6   Litho.   Perf. 12
1189	A518	1r on 8.50r, #1153	2.50	.30
1190	A518	11r on 10.50r, #1154 (a)	2.25	2.25
a.		Surcharge type b	2.25	2.25

Surcharge Type a on #1190 is 2½mm high. Type b surcharge is 3mm high.

No. 1149 Surcharged

c   d

e

1997, Feb. 12   Litho.   Perf. 12
1191	A516(c)	2.50r on 2r	3.00	3.00
1192	A516(d)	2.50r on 2r	3.00	3.00
1193	A516(e)	2.50r on 2r	3.00	3.00
		Nos. 1191-1193 (3)	9.00	9.00

A number has been reserved additional surcharge on No. 1149.

Reptiles
A537

2.50r, Lyre head lizard. 5r, Boie's roughside. 17r, Common Lanka skink. 20r, Great forest gecko.

1997, Oct. 18   Litho.   Perf. 12
1195	A537	2.50r multicolored	.20	.20
1196	A537	5r multicolored	.20	.20
1197	A537	17r multicolored	.50	.50
1198	A537	20r multicolored	.60	.60
a.		Souvenir sheet, #1195-1198	2.25	2.25
		Nos. 1195-1198 (4)	1.50	1.50

A538

Christmas: 2.50r, Holy Family. 20r, Adoration of the Magi.

1997, Nov. 20   Perf. 12½x13
1199	A538	2.50r multicolored	.20	.20
1200	A538	20r multicolored	.70	.70
a.		Souvenir sheet, #1199-1200	1.00	1.00

1997, Nov. 11   Litho.   Perf. 12½

Personalities: #1201, Hegoda Sri Indasara Thero (1932-87), religious leader. #1202, Abdul Aziz (d. 1990), politician. #1203, Subramaniam Vithiananthan (b. 1924), teacher, writer. #1204, Vivienne Goonewardene (1916-96), politician.

1201	A539	2.50r multicolored	.20	.20
1202	A539	2.50r multicolored	.20	.20
1203	A539	2.50r multicolored	.20	.20
1204	A539	2.50r multicolored	.20	.20
a.		Block of 4, #1201-1204	.70	.70

Young
Men's
Buddhist
Assoc.,
Colombo,
Cent.
A540

1998, Jan. 1   Litho.   Perf. 12½
1205	A540	2.50r multicolored	.25	.20

A539

Traditional Jewelry and Crafts — A541

Designs: 2.50r, Chunam box. 5r, Necklace of agate. 10r, Bangle and hairpin. 17r, Sigiri earrings.

1998, Apr. 24   Litho.   Perf. 13½
1206	A541	2.50r multicolored	.20	.20
1207	A541	5r multicolored	.20	.20
1208	A541	10r multicolored	.40	.40
1209	A541	17r multicolored	.70	.70
a.		Souvenir sheet, #1206-1209	1.90	2.00

Independence, 50th Anniv. — A542

Natl. flag and: 2r, People holding up arms, letters and symbols. No. 1211, Ceylon #300. No. 1212, People standing, images of industry and technology. 5r, People playing musical instruments, book, pen, television, musical instruments. 10r, People holding up items, symbols of religion, government.

Perf. 13, 13½ (#1211)
1998, Feb. 4   Litho.
1210	A542	2r multicolored	.20	.20
1211	A542	2.50r multicolored	.20	.20
1212	A542	2.50r multicolored	.20	.20
1213	A542	5r multicolored	.20	.20
1214	A542	10r multicolored	.40	.40
		Nos. 1210-1214 (5)	1.20	1.20

No. 1211 is 28x38mm.

William Gopallawa, 1st President A543

1998   Litho.   Perf. 13½
1215	A543	2.50r multicolored	.25	.20

5th Natl. Scout Jamboree A544

Designs: 2.50r, Scouts holding flag, emblem, campground. 17r, Campground, flag, emblems, scout saluting.

1998, Feb. 18
1216	A544	2.50r multicolored	.45	.20
1217	A544	17r multicolored	2.00	2.00

World Health Organization, 50th Anniv. — A545

1998, Apr. 7   Litho.   Perf. 13x12½
1218	A545	2.50r multicolored	.25	.20

St. John's College, Jaffna, 175th Anniv. — A546

1998, May 7   Litho.   Perf. 14½x14
1219	A546	2.50r multicolored	.25	.20

Elephas Maximus Ceylonensis — A547

Designs: 2.50r, Wading in lake. 10r, Female, calf. 17r, Three standing in plains. 50r, Large bull.

1998, May 28   Perf. 13
1220	A547	2.50r multicolored	.40	.20
1221	A547	10r multicolored	.75	.50
1222	A547	17r multicolored	1.00	1.10
1223	A547	50r multicolored	1.75	2.00
a.		Souvenir sheet, #1220-1223	4.50	4.50
		Nos. 1220-1223 (4)	3.90	3.80

Vesak Festival — A548

Kelaniya Rajamaha Vihara paintings: 1r, Waterfalls, tree. 2.50r, Procession of people, elephant with rider. 4r, Looking at mother with newborn baby. 17r, Presenting child for ceremony, laying stone.

1998, Apr. 30   Litho.   Perf. 12½
1224	A548	1r multicolored	.20	.20
1225	A548	2.50r multicolored	.20	.20
1226	A548	4r multicolored	.20	.20
1227	A548	17r multicolored	.60	.60
a.		Souvenir sheet, #1224-1228	1.10	1.10
		Nos. 1224-1227 (4)	1.20	1.20

SAARC Summit, Colombo — A549

1998   Litho.   Perf. 14½x14
1228	A549	2.50r multicolored	.25	.20

1998, Year of Information Technology A550

1998   Litho.   Perf. 13½
1229	A550	2.50r multicolored	.25	.20

Personalities A551

#1230, Ven. Pannakitti Nayake Thero. #1231, Sir Nicholas Attygalle. #1232, Dr. Samuel Fisk Green. #1233, Prof. Ediriweera Sarachchandra.

1998   Perf. 13
1230	A551	2.50r multicolored	.25	.20
1231	A551	2.50r multicolored	.25	.20
1232	A551	2.50r multicolored	.25	.20
1233	A551	2.50r multicolored	.25	.20
		Nos. 1230-1233 (4)	1.00	.80

Meteorological Dept., 50th Anniv. — A552

1998   Litho.   Perf. 14x13½
1234	A552	2.50r multicolored	.45	.20

26th Forum of South Asia, Africa & Middle East Lions Clubs Intl. — A553

1998, Nov. 20   Litho.   Perf. 14x14½
1235	A553	2.50r multicolored	.25	.20

Christmas A554

1998, Dec. 10   Perf. 13½x14
1236	A554	2.50r Nativity	.20	.20
1237	A554	20r Annunciation	.55	.55
a.		Souvenir sheet, #1236-1237	1.10	1.10

A555

Kandyan Dancer — A556

S.W.R.D. Bandaranaike, Birth Cent.: No. 1238, Wearing white scarf. No. 1239, Wearing blue scarf.

1999, Jan. 8   Litho.   Perf. 12
1238	A555	3.50r multicolored	.20	.20
1239	A555	3.50r multicolored	.20	.20
a.		Souvenir sheet, #1238-1239, perf. 12½	.25	.25

1999, Feb. 3   Photo.   Perf. 12
1240	A556	1r brown	.20	.20
1241	A556	2r green blue	.20	.20
1242	A556	3r plum	.20	.20
1243	A556	3.50r blue	.20	.20
1244	A556	4r dark red	.20	.20

Size: 21x26mm
1245	A556	5r green	.20	.20
1246	A556	10r violet	.30	.25
1247	A556	13.50r bright red	.40	.35
1248	A556	17r blue green	.50	.40
1249	A556	20r olive bister	.60	.50
		Nos. 1240-1249 (10)	3.00	2.70

Telecommunications, 50th Anniv. — A557

Portraits of Sir Arthur C. Clarke, diagrams of Orbital Concept: a, Rocket launch, satellites, space shuttle. b, Satellites, earth from outer space, space capsule.

1999, Feb. 10   Litho.   Perf. 12
1250	A557	3.50r Pair, #a.-b.	.30	.30

Dated 1998.

Salvation Army, 116th Anniv. A558

1999, Apr. 28   Litho.   Perf. 11¾x12
1251	A558	3.50r multicolored	.30	.25

British Council, 50th Anniv. — A559

1999, May 20   Perf. 12
1252	A559	3.50r multicolored	.30	.25

Sumithrayo Organization Suicide Hot Line, 25th Anniv. — A560

1999, June 14   Perf. 12½
1253	A560	3.50r multicolored	.25	.20

Vesak Festival — A561

Designs: 2r, Flowers. 3.50r, Leaf, wheel. 13.50r, Nut, flower. 17r, Young people with traditional lanterns.

Unwmk.

1999, May 25		**Litho.**	**Perf. 12**	
1254	A561	2r multicolored	.20	.20
1255	A561	3.50r multicolored	.20	.20
1256	A561	13.50r multicolored	.30	.30
1257	A561	17r multicolored	.40	.40
	Nos. 1254-1257 (4)		1.10	1.10

Souvenir Sheet
Wmk. 388
Perf. 12½

1258	Sheet of 4	1.10	1.10
a.	A561 2r like #1254	.20	.20
b.	A561 3.50r like #1255	.20	.20
c.	A561 13.50r like #1256	.30	.30
d.	A561 17r like #1257	.40	.40

Independent Television Network, 20th Anniv. — A562

1999, June 5	**Unwmk.**	**Perf. 12¾**	
1259	A562 3.50r multicolored	.25	.20

Vidyodaya Pirivena, 125th Anniv. A563

Perf. 12¾

1999, Sept. 17	**Litho.**	**Unwmk.**	
1260	A563 3.50r multicolored	.25	.20

Sri Lankan Cinema, 50th Anniv. — A564

1999, Sept. 17		**Litho.**	**Perf. 12¾**	
1261	A564	3.50r Handaya, 1979	.20	.20
1262	A564	4r Nidhanaya, 1972	.20	.20
1263	A564	10r Gam Peraliya, 1963	.20	.20
1264	A564	17r Kadawunu Poronduwa, 1947	.30	.30
a.	Souvenir sheet, #1261-1264		.80	.80
	Nos. 1261-1264 (4)		.90	.90

Bhakthi Prabodanaya Magazine, Cent. — A565

1999, Sept.	**Litho.**	**Perf. 12x12¼**
1265 A565 3.50r multicolored	.25	.20

Hector Kobbekaduwa, Politician — A566

Perf. 12¾x12½

1999, Sept. 19	**Wmk. 388**	**Litho.**
1266 A566 3.50r multicolored	.20	.20

National Army, 50th Anniv. — A567

1999, Oct. 10	**Unwmk.**	**Perf. 12¾**
1267 A567 3.50r multicolored	.20	.20

Convention on the Rights of the Child, 10th Anniv. — A568

1999, Nov. 20	**Perf. 12¾x12½**	
1268 A568 3.50r multicolored	.20	.20

A569

1999, Nov. 26	**Perf. 12¾**	
1269 A569 3.50r multicolored	.20	.20

Balangoda Ananda Maitreya Mahanyake Thero (b. 1895), Buddhist priest.

1999, Dec. 12	**Perf. 12¾**	

A570

Paintings.

1270	A570	3.50r By David Paynter	.20	.20
1271	A570	4r By Justin Daraniyagala	.20	.20
1272	A570	17r By Ivan Peries	.45	.45
1273	A570	20r By Solias Mendis	.55	.55
a.	Souvenir sheet of 4, #1270-1273		1.25	1.25
	Nos. 1270-1273 (4)		1.40	1.40

Athletic Accomplishments — A571

Designs: 1r, Kumar Anandan's swim across Palk Strait. 3.50r, World champions in cricket. 13.50r, International fame in track and field.

1999			**Perf. 12¾**	
1274	A571	1r multicolored	.20	.20
1275	A571	3.50r multicolored	.20	.20
1276	A571	13.50r multicolored	.35	.35
	Nos. 1274-1276 (3)		.75	.75

Natl. Commission for UNESCO, 50th Anniv. — A572

Perf. 12¾x12½

1999, Nov. 16	**Litho.**	**Wmk. 388**
1277 A572 13.50r multi	.40	.40

Christmas A573

1999, Nov. 30		**Perf. 12½x12¾**	
1278	A573 3.50r shown	.20	.20
1279	A573 20r Magi	.55	.55
a.	Souvenir sheet, #1278-1279	.75	.75

Famous People — A574

Designs: No. 1280, Dr. Pandithamani S. Kanapathipillai, Tamil scholar. No. 1281, Sunil Santha, musician. No. 1282, Dr. Al Haj Badi-udin Mahmud, Education minister.

1999, Dec. 3			**Perf. 12¾x12½**	
1280	A574	3.50r multi	.20	.20
1281	A574	3.50r multi	.20	.20
1282	A574	3.50r multi	.20	.20
	Nos. 1280-1282 (3)		.60	.60

No. 1149A Surcharged

1999, Dec. 3	**Litho.**	**Perf. 12**
1282A A516 2r on 2.50r multi		

Butterflies — A575

Designs: 3.50r, Striped albatross. 13.50r, Ceylon tiger. 17r, Three-spot grass yellow. 20r, Great orange tip.

Perf. 12x11¾

1999, Dec. 30			**Unwmk.**	
Granite Paper				
1283	A575	3.50r multi	.20	.20
1284	A575	13.50r multi	.40	.40
1285	A575	17r multi	.50	.50
1286	A575	20r multi	.55	.55
a.	Souvenir sheet, #1283-1286		1.75	1.75
	Nos. 1283-1286 (4)		1.65	1.65

Corals A576

1999, Dec. 30			**Perf. 11¾x12**	
Granite Paper				
1287	A576	3.50r Boulder	.20	.20
1288	A576	13.50r Blue-tipped	.40	.40
1289	A576	14r Brain-boulder	.40	.40
1290	A576	22r Elkhorn	.65	.65
a.	Souvenir sheet, #1287-1290		1.75	1.75
	Nos. 1287-1290 (4)		1.65	1.65

Auditor General's Department, Bicent. — A576a

Perf. 12½x12¾

1999, Dec.	**Litho.**	**Unwmk.**
1290B A576a 3.50r multi	.20	.20

Year 2000 — A577

Satellite and: 10r, Birds, religious symbols. No. 1292, Scales, girl, Red Cross, computer. No. 1293, airplane, satellite dish, man at computer. No. 1294, Hands, symbols of women's equality, crippled and blind.

2000, Jan. 1			**Perf. 11¾**	
Granite Paper				
1291	A577	10r multi	.25	.25
1292	A577	100r multi	3.00	3.00
1293	A577	100r multi	3.00	3.00
1294	A577	100r multi	3.00	3.00
a.	Souvenir sheet, #1291-1294		9.25	9.25
	Nos. 1291-1294 (4)		9.25	9.25

Kurunagala Diocese, 50th Anniv. A578

Unwmk.

2000, Feb. 2	**Litho.**	**Perf. 12**
1295 A578 13.50r multi		.40	.40

Wesley College, Colombo, 125th Anniv. A579

2000, Mar. 2   *Perf. 11¾x12*
1296   A579   3.50r multi   .20   .20

Panadura Pinwatte Saddharmakara Vidyayathana Pirivena, Cent. — A580

2000, Mar. 12
1297   A580   3.50r multi   .20   .20
block>

Vesak Festival — A581

2r, Arrival of Jaya Sri Maha Bodhi sapling. 3.50r, King Devanampiyatissa carrying sapling on his head. 10r, Venerating sapling. 13.50r, Royal tree planting, Anuradhapura.

2000, Apr. 28 Litho.   *Perf. 12¾x12½*
1298-1301   A581   Set of 4   .85   .85
1301a   Souvenir sheet, #1298-1301   .85   .85

Sri Lanka Bar Association, 25th Anniv. (in 1999) — A582

2000, June 10   *Perf. 12*
1302   A582   3.50r multi   .20   .20

Co-operative Wholesale Establishment, 50th Anniv. — A583

2000, July 1   *Perf. 12¾*
1303   A583   3.50r multi   .20   .20

No. 979 Surcharged

2000, July 21 Litho.   *Perf. 11½*
1303A   A420   50c on 8r multi   —   —

St. Patrick's College, Jaffna, 150th Anniv. A584

2000, July 21
1304   A584   3.50r multi   .20   .20

Survey Dept., 200th Anniv. A585

2000, Aug. 2
1305   A585   3.50r multi   .20   .20

Central Bank of Sri Lanka, 50th Anniv. — A586

2000, Aug. 27   *Perf. 13¼*
1306   A586   3.50r multi   .20   .20

Dr. Maria Montessori (1870-1952), Educator — A587

2000, Aug. 31   *Perf. 11¾*
1307   A587   3.50r multi   .20   .20

2000 Summer Olympics, Sydney — A588

Sydney Olympic Games emblem and: a, Hurdler, map. b, Shooter, runners. c, Runners. d, Hurdlers, swimmer.

2000, Sept. 7
1308   A588   10r Horiz. strip of 4,   1.00   1.00
             #a-d
e.   Souvenir sheet, #1308   1.00   1.00

All Ceylon Young Men's Muslim Association Conference, 50th Anniv. — A589

2000, Sept. 16
1309   A589   3.50r multi   .20   .20

Hotel Industry, 25th Anniv. A590

2000, Sept. 18   *Perf. 12¾*
1310   A590   10r multi   .25   .25

Immigration and Emigration Dept., 50th Anniv. A591

2000, Oct. 2   *Perf. 11¾*
1311   A591   3.50r multi   .20   .20

Traditional Dancer — A592

Perf. 13½x13 Syncopated
2000, Oct. 5   Litho.
1312   A592   50r multi   1.25   1.25
1313   A592   100r multi   2.50   2.50
1314   A592   200r multi   5.00   5.00
    Nos. 1312-1314 (3)   8.75   8.75

All-Ceylon Buddhist Congress Natl. Awards Ceremony A593

2000, Aug. 27 Litho.   *Perf. 12¾*
1315   A593   3.50r multi   .20   .20

Saumiyamoorthy Thondaman, Government Minister — A594

2000, Oct. 30
1316   A594   3.50r multi   .20   .20

Famous People — A595

Designs: No. 1317, 3.50r, Most Ven. Baddegama Siri Piyaratana Nayake Thero, educator. No. 1318, 3.50r, Aluthgamage Simon de Silva (1874-1920), writer. No. 1319, 3.50r, Desigar Ramanujam (1907-68), politician.

Perf. 12x12¼ (#1317), 12¾x12½
2000, Nov. 14
1317-1319   A595   Set of 3   .25   .25

Christmas A596

Designs: 2r, Joseph, Mary, donkey. 17r, Holy family.

2000, Nov. 23   *Perf. 12¾x12½*
1320-1321   A596   Set of 2   .45   .45
1321a   Souvenir sheet, #1320-
          1321, perf. 12   .45   .45

Lalith Athulathmudali (1936-93), Politician — A597

2000, Nov. 30   *Perf. 12½x12¾*
1322   A597   3.50r multi   .20   .20

Medicina Alternativa Medical Society, 38th Anniv. A598

2000, Dec. 1   *Perf. 12¾*
1323   A598   13.50r multi   .35   .35

Ladies' College, Cent. — A599

2000, Dec. 7
1324   A599   3.50r multi   .20   .20

Navy, 50th Anniv. A600

2000, Dec. 9
1325   A600   3.50r multi   .20   .20

Peliyagoda Vidyalankara Pirivena, 125th Anniv. — A601

2000, Dec. 30   *Perf. 12x12¼*
1326   A601   3.50r multi   .20   .20

Bishop's College, 125th Anniv. A602

2001, Jan. 19   **Litho.**
1327 A602 3.50r multi   .20   .20

St. Thomas' College, 150th Anniv. A603

2001, Feb. 3   **Perf. 12¾**
1328 A603 3.50r multi   .20   .20

Lanka Mahila Samiti Women's Training Society, 70th Anniv. A604

2001, Feb. 15
1329 A604 3.50r multi   .20   .20

Air Force, 50th Anniv. A605

2001, Mar. 9
1330 A605 3.50r multi   .20   .20

St. Lawrence's School, Cent. A606

2001, Mar. 15
1331 A606 3.50r multi   .20   .20

Bernard Soysa (1914-97), Politician — A607

2001, Mar. 20   **Perf. 12¾**
1332 A607 3.50r multi   .20   .20

Vesak Festival — A608

Designs: 2r, Sri Nagadeepa Chaithya, Jaffna. 3.50r, Muthiyangana Chaithya, Badulla. 13.50r, Kirivehera, Kataragama. 17r, Sri Dalada Maligawa, Kandy.

2001, Apr. 7   **Litho.**   **Perf. 13½x13¾**
1333 A608   2r multi   .20   .20
    a.   Perf. 14¼   .20   .20

Perf. 14¼
1334 A608   3.50r multi   .20   .20
    a.   Perf. 13½x13¾   .20   .20
1335 A608   13.50r multi   .30   .30
1336 A608   17r multi   .40   .40
    a.   Souvenir sheet, #1333a, 1334-
       1336   .90   .90

Hansa Jataka, by George Keyt (1901-93) — A609

Illustration reduced.

2001, Apr. 24   **Perf. 13¼**
1337 A609 13.50r multi   .30   .30

Coins A610

Designs: 3.50r, Kahavanu gold coin, 9th cent. 13.50r, Vijayabahu I silver coin, 1055-1111. 17r, Sethu copper coin, 13th-14th cent. 20r, Buddha Jayanthi 5r commemorative silver coin, 1957.

Perf. 13¾x13½, 14¼ (17r)
2001, June 18
1338 A610   3.50r multi   .20   .20
1339 A610   13.50r multi   .35   .35
1340 A610   17r multi   .40   .40
    a.   Perf. 13¾x13½x14¼x13½   .40   .40
1341 A610   20r multi   .45   .45
    a.   Perf. 13¾x13½x14¼x13½   .45   .45
    b.   Souvenir sheet, #1338-1339,
       1340a, 1341a   1.40   1.40

Colombo Plan, 50th Anniv. — A611

2001, July 2   **Perf. 13½x13¾**
1342 A611 10r multi   .25   .25

US-Sri Lankan Diplomatic Relations, 150th Anniv. A612

2001, July 3   **Perf. 12¾**
1343 A612 10r multi   .25   .25

Lance Corporal Gamini Kularatne (1966-91), Military Hero — A613

2001, July 14   **Perf. 13¾x13½**
1344 A613 3.50r multi   .20   .20

Prince and Princess of Wales College, Moratuwa, 125th Anniv. A614

2001, Sept. 14   **Perf. 13¼**
1345 A614 3.50r multi   .20   .20

Year of Dialogue Among Civilizations A615

2001, Oct. 9   **Perf. 13x13½**
1346 A615 10r multi   .25   .25

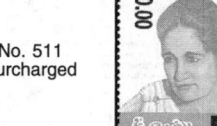

No. 511 Surcharged

2001, July 9   Photo.   Perf. 14¼x14½
1347 A180   5r on 1.15r multi   —   —
1348 A180   10r on 1.15r multi   —   —
An additional surcharge was released in this set. The editors would like to examine it.

13th Meeting of Parties to the Montreal Protocol — A616

2001, Oct. 18   Litho.   Perf. 13x13¼
1349 A616 13.50r multi   .35   .35

Ramakrishna Mission Students' Home, Batticaloa, 75th Anniv. — A617

2001, Oct. 19   **Perf. 12¾**
1350 A617 3.50r multi   .20   .20

Drummer — A618

Drummer from: 1r, 2r, 3r, 3.50r, Daul. 4r, 5r, 10r, Kandy. 13.50r, 17r, 20r, Low country.

2001, Nov. 8   Litho.   Perf. 12½x13¼
1351 A618   1r rose   .20   .20
1352 A618   2r emerald   .20   .20
1353 A618   3r fawn   .20   .20
1354 A618   3.50r dark blue   .20   .20
Size: 23x28mm
Perf. 13¼x12½
1355 A618   4r pink   .20   .20
1356 A618   5r orange   .20   .20
1357 A618   10r violet   .25   .25
1358 A618   13.50r dull purple   .35   .35
1359 A618   17r yel orange   .40   .40
1360 A618   20r Prus blue   .50   .50
    Nos. 1351-1360 (10)   2.70   2.70

S.W.R.D. Bandaranaike Natl. Memorial Foundation, 25th Anniv. — A619

2001, Nov. 27   **Perf. 13¾x13¼**
1361 A619 3.50r multi   .20   .20

Christmas A620

Designs: 3.50r, Jesus and children. 17r, The Annunciation.

2001, Nov. 28   **Perf. 13**
1362-1363 A620   Set of 2   .50   .50
    1363a   Souvenir sheet, #1362-
       1363   .50   .50

Frogs A621

Designs: 3.50r, Conical wart pygmy tree frog. 13.50r, Sharp-snout saddle tree frog. 17r, Round-snout pygmy tree frog. 20r, Sri Lanka wood frog.

2001, Dec. 3   **Perf. 13¼x13**
1364-1367 A621   Set of 4   1.25   1.25
    1367a   Souvenir sheet, #1364-
       1367   1.25   1.25

St. Bridget's Convent, Cent. A622

2002, Feb. 1
1368 A622 3.50r multi   .20   .20

Ceylon Government Gazette, 200th Anniv. — A623

2002, Mar. 15   Litho.   Perf. 13¾x14
1369 A623 3.50r multi   .20   .20

Stamps of the following designs were available in the philatelic marketplace but were said by Sri Lankan postal authorities to have never been released by them.

D. S. Senanayake (1884-1952), Prime Minister — A624

2002, Mar. 22   *Perf. 14x13¾*
1370 A624 3.50r multi   .20   .20

Gamini Dissanayake (1942-94), Assassinated Government Minister — A625

2002, Mar. 27   *Perf. 13¾x14*
1371 A625 3.50r multi   .20   .20

Lester James Peries (b. 1919), Film Director A626

2002, Apr. 5   *Perf. 13¼x13*
1372 A626 3.50r multi   .20   .20

Natural Beauty of Sri Lanka — A627

Designs: 5r, Sinharaja Forest Reserve. 10r, Horton Plains National Park. 13.50r, Knuckles Range. 20r, Rumassala Cliff and Bonavista Coral Reef.

2002, Apr. 10   *Perf. 13x13¼*
1373-1376 A627   Set of 4   1.10   1.10

Pres. Ranasinghe Premadasa (1924-93) A628

2002, Apr. 29   *Perf. 13¾x14*
1377 A628 4.50r multi   .20   .20

Sri Lanka - Japan Diplomatic Relations, 50th Anniv. — A629

2002, Apr. 29   *Perf. 14x13¾*
1378 A629 16.50r multi   .35   .35

Vesak Festival A630

Dambulla Raja Maha Vihara rock paintings: 3r, Queen Mahamaya's dream. 4.50r, Birth of Prince Siddhartha. 16.50r, Siddhartha's exhibition of archery talents. 23r, Ordination of Prince Siddhartha.

2002, May 17   *Perf. 13¾x14*
1379-1382 A630   Set of 4   1.00   1.00
1382a   Souvenir sheet, #1379-
1382   1.00   1.00

Most Venerable Madihe Pannasiha Maha Nayaka Thera, Religious Leader, 90th Birthday — A631

2002, June 23   *Perf. 14x13¾*
1383 A631 4.50r multi   .20   .20

Sri Lanka Oriental Studies Society, Cent. A632

2002, July 24   *Perf. 13¾x14*
1384 A632 4.50r multi   .20   .20

Rifai Thareeq Association, 125th Anniv. — A633

2002, July 26
1385 A633 4.50r multi   .20   .20

14th Asian Track and Field Championships, Colombo — A634

Designs: 4.50r, Discus thrower. 16.50r, Sprinter. 23r, Hurdler. 26r, Long jumper.

2002, Aug. 8
1386-1389 A634   Set of 4   1.50   1.50

National Museum, 125th Anniv. — A635

No. 1390: a, Carved lion (sitting). b, Carved lion (standing with head turned). Illustration reduced.

2002, Aug. 27
1390 A635 4.50r Horiz. pair, #a-b   .20   .20

Woman's Hand Holding Flower — A636

2002, Aug. 28   *Perf. 14x13¾*
1391 A636 10r multi   .20   .20
Tourism promotion.

Dr. A. C. S. Hameed (1929-99), Government Minister — A637

2002, Sept. 3
1392 A637 4.50r multi   .20   .20

Freemasons' Hall, Colombo, Cent. — A638

2002, Sept. 5   *Perf. 13¾x14*
1393 A638 4.50r multi   .20   .20

Holy Cross College, Kalutara, Cent. A639

2002, Sept. 13
1394 A639 4.50r multi   .20   .20

German Dharmaduta Society, 50th Anniv. — A640

2002, Sept. 21   *Perf. 14x13¾*
1395 A640 4.50r multi   .20   .20

Intl. Children's Day — A641

2002, Oct. 1
1396 A641 4.50r multi   .20   .20

Dr. M. C. M. Kaleel (1899-1995), Government Minister — A642

2002, Oct. 18
1397 A642 4.50r green   .20   .20

Dr. Wijayananda Dahanayake (1902-97), Prime Minister — A644

2002, Oct. 22   Litho.   *Perf. 14x13¾*
1399 A644 4.50r brown   .20   .20

Sri Lanka - Netherlands Relations, 400th Anniv. — A645

2002, Nov. 22   *Perf. 13¾x14*
1400 A645 16.50r multi   .35   .35

Christmas — A646

Designs: 4.50r, Madonna and Child. 26r, Holy Family.

2002, Dec. 15   *Perf. 13x13¼*
1401-1402 A646   Set of 2   .65   .65
1402a   Souvenir sheet, #1401-
1402   .65   .65

Sri Lanka - China Rubber and Rice Pact, 50th Anniv. A647

2002, Dec. 20   *Perf. 13¾x14*
1403 A647 4.50r multi   .20   .20

Kopay Christian College, 150th Anniv. A648

2002, Dec. 28
1404 A648 4.50r multi .20 .20

No. 925 Surcharged

2002 ?　　Litho.　　Perf. 12½x12
1405 A392 25c on 5.75r multi .20 .20

No. 1354 Surcharged

2002 ?　　Litho.　　Perf. 12½x13¼
1406 A618 4.50r on 3.50r dk bl .20 .20

Teachers' College, Maharagama, Cent. — A649

2003, Jan. 21　　Perf. 13¾x14
1407 A649 4.50r multi .20 .20

Holy Family Convent, Bambalapitiya, Cent. — A650

2003, Feb. 3　　Perf. 14x13¾
1408 A650 4.50r multi .20 .20

Drummer Type of 2001 and

No. 1359 Surcharged

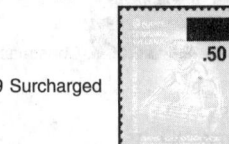

Drummer from: 16.50r, Low country.

**　　Perf. 13¼x12½**
2003, Feb. 17　　　　　　Litho.
1409 A618 50c on 5r org yel .20 .20
1410 A618 16.50r purple .35 .35

M. D. Banda (1914-74), Government Minister — A651

2003, Mar. 14　　Perf. 13¾x14
1411 A651 4.50r multi .20 .20

Balagalle Saraswati Maha Pirivena, Cent. A652

2003, Apr. 3
1412 A652 4.50r multi .20 .20

D. B. Welagedara, Politician — A653

2003, Apr. 22　　Perf. 14x13¾
1413 A653 4.50r multi .20 .20

Vesak Festival — A654

Designs: 2.50r, Paying obeisance to parents. 3r, Dhamma school. 4.50r, Going on alms round. 23r, Meditation.

2003, Apr. 26
1414-1417 A654　　Set of 4　　.70 .70
1417a　　Souvenir sheet, #1414-
　　　　1417　　.70 .70

Dagoba Construction Features — A655

Designs: 4.50r, Stupa. 16.50r, Guard stone, horiz. (58x28mm). 50r, Moonstone, horiz.

2003, Apr. 28　Perf. 13x13¼, 13¼x13
1418-1420 A655　　Set of 3　　1.50 1.50
1420a　　Souvenir sheet, #1418-
　　　　1420　　1.50 1.50

Second World Hindu Conference, Colombo — A656

2003, May 2　　Perf. 14x13¾
1421 A656 4.50r multi .20 .20

International Nursing Day — A657

2003, May 12　　Perf. 13¾x14
1422 A657 4.50r multi .20 .20

Sirimavo Bandaranaike Memorial Exhibition Center — A658

2003, May 17　　Perf. 13¼x12
1423 A658 4.50r multi .20 .20

Al-Haj H. S. Ismail (1901-73), Parliament Speaker — A659

2003, May 18　　Perf. 14x13¾
1424 A659 4.50r multi .20 .20

Board of Investment, 25th Anniv. — A660

2003, May 21　　Perf. 13¾x12
1425 A660 4.50r multi .20 .20

World Biodiversity Day — A661

Designs: 4r, Pidurutalagal Mountain Range. 4.50r, Seven Maidens Mountain Range. 16.50r, Kirigalpoththa Mountain. 23r, Ritigala Mountain.

2003, May 22　　Perf. 13¾x12
1426-1429 A661　　Set of 4　　1.00 1.00

Saralankara College, Gonapinuwala, Cent. — A662

2003, June 6　　Perf. 13¾x14
1430 A662 4.50r multi .20 .20

A663　　　　　A664

First Arab settlement, Beruwala: 4.50r, Masjidul Abrar. 23r, Masjidul Abrar, horiz. (57x22mm).

**　　Perf. 14x13¾, 13¼x12 (23r)**
2003, June 8
1431-1432 A663　　Set of 2　　.60 .60

2003, June 23　　Perf. 14x13¾
1433 A664 4.50r multi .20 .20

Anti-narcotics Week.

Syamopali Maha Nikaya, 250th Anniv. A665

Designs: No. 1434, 4.50r, Asgiri Maha Viharaya. No. 1435, 4.50r, Malwathu Maha Viharaya.

2003, July 13　　Perf. 13¾x14
1434-1435 A665　　Set of 2　　.20 .20

Lanka Philex Intl. Stamp Exhibition, Colombo — A666

2003, July 31　　Perf. 13¼x12
1436 A666 16.50r multi .35 .35
a.　　Souvenir sheet of 1 .35 .35

Dr. Ananda Tissa de Alwis, Government Minister — A667

2003, Aug. 21　　Perf. 13¾x14
1437 A667 4.50r multi .20 .20

Panadura Controversy, 130th Anniv. — A668

2003, Aug. 24　　Perf. 14x13¾
1438 A668 4.50r multi .20 .20

Venerable Haldanduwana Dhammarakkitha Thero — A669

2003, Sept. 3　　　　Litho.
1439 A669 4.50r multi .20 .20

Ragama Walpola Poson Maha Perahara, 75th Anniv. A670

2003, Sept. 10 **Perf. 13¾x14**
1440 A670 4.50r multi .20 .20

M. H. M. Ashraff (1948-2000), Government Minister — A671

2003, Sept. 18 **Perf. 14x13¾**
1441 A671 4.50r multi .20 .20

Sisters of the Holy Angels, Cent. A672

2003, Sept. 27 **Perf. 13¾x14**
1442 A672 4.50r multi .20 .20

Birds — A673

No. 1443: a, Black-necked stork. b, Purple swamphen. c, Gray heron. d, White-throated kingfisher. e, Black-crowned night heron. f, Scarlet minivet. g, White-rumped shama. h, Malabar trogon. i, Asian paradise flycatcher. j, Little green bee-eater. k, Brown wood owl. l, Crested serpent eagle. m, Crested goshawk. n, Jungle owlet. o, Rufous-bellied eagle. p, Black-headed munia. q, Pompadour green pigeon. r, Plum-headed parakeet. s, Coppersmith barbet. t, Emerald dove. u, Blue-faced malkoha. v, Scimitar babbler. w, Painted francolin. x, Red-backed woodpecker. y, Malabar pied hornbill.

2003, Sept. 27 **Perf. 14x13¾**
1443 A673 4.50r Sheet of 25, #a-y 2.40 2.40

World Habitat Day — A674

2003, Oct. 6 **Perf. 13**
1444 A674 4.50r multi .20 .20

World Post Day A675

2003, Oct. 9 **Perf. 14x13¾**
1445 A675 23r multi .50 .50

Blue Sapphire A676

2003, Oct. 21 **Perf. 12x13½**
1446 A676 4.50r multi .20 .20

Ponificate of Pope John Paul II, 25th Anniv. — A677

2003, Oct. 22 **Perf. 13**
1447 A677 4.50r multi .20 .20

Deepavali Festival — A678

2003, Oct. 23
1448 A678 4.50r multi .20 .20

Pinnawala Elephant Orphanage A679

Designs: 4.50r, Two adult and two young elephants. 16.50r, Elephants and caretaker. 23r, Two adult elephants. 26r, Elephants in water.

2003, July 13 Litho. Perf. 13½x13
1449-1452 A679 Set of 4 1.50 1.50
1452a Souvenir sheet, #1449-1452 1.50 1.50

Waterfalls — A680

Designs: 2.50r, Ramboda. 4.50r, Saint Clair. 23r, Bopath Ella. 50r, Devon.

2003, Nov. 11 **Perf. 14x13¾**
1453-1456 A680 Set of 4 1.75 1.75

Ukku Banda Wanninayake (1905-73), Finance Minister — A681

2003, Nov. 23 **Perf. 13**
1457 A681 4.50r multi .20 .20

Christmas A682

Designs: 4.50r, Church. 16.50r, Shepherds and angel, vert.

2003, Nov. 30
1458-1459 A682 Set of 2 .45 .45

Pandith W. D. Amaradeva, Musician, 76th Birthday — A683

2003, Dec. 5
1460 A683 4.50r multi .20 .20

Gangarama Seemamalakaya — A684

2003, Dec. 20
1461 A684 4.50r multi .20 .20

Daham Pahana, Sri Pushparamaya, Malegoda — A685

2003, Dec. 31
1462 A685 4.50r multi .20 .20

Shazuliyathul Fassiya Tharika — A686

2004, Jan. 6
1463 A686 18r multi .40 .40

Chavakachcheri Hindu College, Cent. — A687

2004, Jan. 30 **Perf. 12x13½**
1464 A687 4.50r multi .20 .20

Royal-Thomian Cricket Match, 125th Anniv. — A688

2004, Jan. 30 **Perf. 13**
1465 A688 4.50r multi .20 .20

POSTAL-FISCAL STAMP

The editors believe that seven additional revenues stamps were authorized for postal use during 1979-98 and would like to examine them.

National Coat of Arms — PF1

Perf. 14½x14
1984 **Engr.** **Wmk. 233**
AR6 PF1 50r vermilion 1.00 1.50
AR7 PF1 100r deep claret 2.00 3.00

A lithographed 500r value exists but was not authorized for postal use.

STELLALAND

'ste-lə-ˌland

LOCATION — South Africa
GOVT. — Republic
AREA — 5,000 sq. mi. (approx.)
CAPITAL — Vryburg

This short-lived republic was set up by the Boers in an effort to annex territory ruled by the Bechuana chiefs. Great Britain refused to recognize it and in 1885 sent an expeditionary force which ended the political career of the country.

Stellaland was annexed by Great Britain in 1885 and became a part of British Bechuanaland.

12 Pence = 1 Shilling

Coat of Arms
A1   A2

1884, Feb.   Unwmk.   Typo.   Perf. 12

1	A1	1p red	210.00	375.00
a.		Horiz. pair, imperf. vert.	4,250.	
b.		Vert. pair, imperf. horiz.	4,250.	
2	A1	3p orange	24.00	375.00
a.		Horiz. pair, imperf. vert.	750.00	
b.		Vert. pair, imperf. horiz.	1,400.	
3	A1	4p gray	24.00	400.00
a.		Horiz. pair, imperf. vert.	750.00	
4	A1	6p lilac	24.00	325.00
a.		Horiz. pair, imperf. vert.	1,100.	
b.		Vert. pair, imperf. horiz.	1,300.	
5	A1	1sh green	50.00	700.00
		Nos. 1-5 (5)	332.00	2,175.

Imperf. varieties are believed to be proofs.

No. 3 Handstamped "Twee" in Blackish Violet

1885

6	A2	2p on 4p gray	3,750.

The status of No. 6 has long been questioned.

STRAITS SETTLEMENTS

'strāts 'se-təl-mənt

LOCATION — Malay Peninsula in southeastern Asia
GOVT. — British Colony
AREA — 1,356 sq. mi.
POP. — 1,435,895 (estimated)
CAPITAL — Singapore

The colony comprised the settlements of Malacca, Singapore and Penang, which were incorporated under one government in 1826 and the administration transferred from India to the Secretary of State for the Colonies in 1867.

The colony was dissolved in 1946 when Singapore became a separate crown colony. Malacca and Penang were incorporated into the Malayan Union, which became the Federation of Malaya in 1948.

Stamps of India were used in Malacca, Penang and Singapore, 1854-67.

See Malaya for stamps of the Federated Malay States, the Federation of Malaya, Johore, Kedah, Kelantan, Malacca, Negri Sembilan, Pahang, Penang, Perak, Perlis, Selangor, Sungei Ujong and Trengganu.

100 Cents = 1 Dollar

Stamps of India Surcharged in Red, Blue, Black Violet or Green:

     24 CENTS
Nos. 1-7   Nos. 8-9

1867, Sept. 1   Wmk. 38   Perf. 14

1	A7	1½c on ½a bl (R)	97.50	225.00
2	A7	2c on 1a brn (R)	125.00	92.50
3	A7	3c on 1a brn (Bl)	140.00	97.50
4	A7	4c on 1a brn (Bk)	275.00	300.00
5	A7	6c on 2a yel (V)	625.00	275.00
6	A7	8c on 2a yel (G)	200.00	50.00
7	A9	12c on 4a grn (R)	1,050.	350.00
a.		Double surcharge	2,250.	
8	A7	24c on 8a rose (Bl)	425.00	92.50
9	A7	32c on 2a yel (Bk)	375.00	100.00

Manuscript Surcharge, Pen Bar Across "THREE HALF" of No. 1

9A	A7	2(c) on 1½c on ½a	10,500.	5,000.

Values for Nos. 1-9A are for stamps with perforations touching the frame line on one or two sides. Used values for Nos. 1-9 are for stamps with company chops in addition to postal cancellations.

A2   A3

A4   A5

1867-72   Typo.   Wmk. 1   Perf. 14

10	A2	2c bister brown	29.00	4.50
11	A2	4c rose	45.00	7.50
12	A2	6c violet	87.50	16.00
13	A3	8c yellow	150.00	9.75
a.		8c orange	150.00	11.00
14	A3	12c blue	110.00	7.50
15	A3	24c green	110.00	5.75
16	A4	30c claret ('72)	225.00	12.50
17	A5	32c pale red	500.00	75.00
18	A5	96c olive gray	300.00	45.00
		Nos. 10-18 (9)	1,556.	183.50

Corner ornaments of types A2, A3 and A5 differ for each value.

See Nos. 19, 40-44, 48-50, 52-57. For surcharges see Nos. 20-35, 58-59, 61-66, 73-82, 91. For overprints see Malaya, Johore No. 1, Perak Nos. 1, O1-O2, Selangor Nos. 1-2, Sungei Ujong Nos. 2-3.

See the *Scott Classic Catalogue* for other shades.

Stamps of Straits Settlements, 1867-82, overprinted "B" are listed under Bangkok.

1871   Perf. 12½

19	A5	96c olive gray	2,300.	275.00

Stamps of 1867-72 Surcharged:

1879, May   Perf. 14

20	A3	5c on 8c yellow	100.00	160.00
a.		No period after "CENTS"	800.00	875.00
21	A5	7c on 32c pale red	110.00	100.00
a.		No period after "CENTS"	1,050.	1,150.

No. 16 Surcharged:

    10
         g

10 10 10 10
 j   *k*   *m*   *h*

1880

22	A4(e)	10c on 30c	175.00	57.50
23	A4(f)	10c on 30c	550.00	125.00
24	A4(g)	10c on 30c	190.00	57.00
25	A4(h)	10c on 30c		
25A	A4(j)	10c on 30c	3,750.	925.00
25B	A4(k)	10c on 30c	3,750.	925.00
25C	A4(m)	10c on 30c	3,750.	925.00

Surcharges e & f and g, h, j & m are virtually identical. These must have an expert certificate identifying them. Values can be suspect because of misidentifications.

Unused examples are valued without gum.

With Additional Surcharge   *cents.*

26	A4(e)	10c on 30c	325.00	75.00
27	A4(f)	10c on 30c	4,500.	700.00
27A	A4(g)	10c on 30c	2,100.	300.00
28	A4(h)	10c on 30c	8,000.	1,250.
28A	A4(j)	10c on 30c	8,000.	1,250.
28B	A4(k)	10c on 30c	8,000.	1,250.
28C	A4(m)	10c on 30c	8,000.	1,250.

Unused examples are valued without gum.

No. 13 Surcharged:

1880

29	A3(n)	5c on 8c yellow	110.00	150.00
30	A3(o)	5c on 8c yellow	425.00	525.00
31	A3(p)	5c on 8c yellow	125.00	160.00

No. 11 Surcharged   **5 cents.**

1882, Jan.

32	A2	5c on 4c rose	275.00	300.00

Nos. 12, 14a, 16 Surcharged

 10 cents.

1880-81

33	A2	10c on 6c violet ('81)	62.50	7.25
a.		Double surcharge	2,100.	
34	A3	10c on 12c blue ('81)	70.00	19.00
35	A4	10c on 30c claret	400.00	97.50
		Nos. 33-35 (3)	532.50	123.75

A6   A7

1882, Jan.   Typo.   Perf. 14

38	A6	5c violet brown	87.50	97.50
39	A7	10c slate	400.00	75.00

See Nos. 45-47, 51. For surcharges see Nos. 60, 67-72, 89-92.

1882-99   Wmk. Crown and C A (2)

40	A2	2c bister brown	225.00	45.00
41	A2	2c car rose ('83)	7.00	.95
a.		2c rose	40.00	3.75
42	A2	4c rose	110.00	5.75
43	A2	4c car rose ('99)	5.25	1.50
44	A2	4c bister brn ('83)	25.00	1.50
45	A6	5c ultra ('83)	12.50	1.10
46	A6	5c brown ('94)	5.25	1.10
47	A6	5c magenta ('99)	2.75	2.40
48	A2	6c violet	2.25	3.75
49	A3	8c orange	3.50	1.10
50	A3	8c ultra ('94)	5.25	.60

51	A7	10c slate	5.25	1.50
52	A3	12c vio brn ('83)	75.00	11.50
53	A3	12c claret ('94)	11.50	9.75
54	A3	24c blue grn ('83)	5.00	4.50
a.		24c yellow green ('84)	80.00	7.00
55	A4	30c claret ('91)	9.75	10.50
56	A5	32c red org ('87)	8.00	3.00
57	A5	96c olive gray ('88)	87.50	52.50
		Nos. 40-57 (18)	605.75	158.00

For overprints see Malaya, Perak #O3-O9, Selangor #3-4, Sungei Ujong #6-7, 11.

Preceding Issues Surcharged

Surcharged Vertically

TWO CENTS

1883-84   Wmk. 2, 1

58	A3	2c on 8c orange	110.00	75.00
a.		Double surcharge	2,600.	1,100.
59	A5	2c on 32c pale red	625.00	200.00
a.		Double surcharge		
60	A6	2c on 5c ultra ('84)	125.00	140.00
a.		Pair, one without surcharge		
b.		Double surcharge		
		Nos. 58-60 (3)	860.00	415.00

Five types of surcharge on No. 58, two types on No. 59 and three types on No. 60.

2 Cents.

Surcharged in Black

1883   Wmk. 2

61	A2	2c on 4c rose	85.00	97.50
b.		"s" of "Cents." inverted	1,250.	1,350.

                Wmk. 1

62	A3	2c on 12c blue	275.00	140.00
a.		"s" of "Cents." inverted	3,500.	1,900.

Surcharged in Black or Blue   **8 Cents**

1884

63	A3	8c on 12c blue	375.00	140.00

                Wmk. 2

64	A3	8c on 12c vio brn	325.00	140.00

With Additional Surcharge Handstamped in Red

8

65	A3	8c on 8c on 12c vio brn (R + Bk)	275.00	300.00
66	A3	8c on 8c on 12c vio brn (R + Bl)	7,000.	

Surcharged in Black or Red   **4 Cents**

1884

67	A6	4c on 5c ultra (Bk)	3,250.	4,000.
68	A6	4c on 5c ultra (R)	110.00	100.00

No. 68 Surcharged in Red   **4**

69	A6	4c on 4c on 5c ultra		10,000.

No. 69 may be a trial printing. "Usage" seems to been restricted to less than 10 letters known sent from the Postmaster General to his wife.

Surcharged in Black   **3 CENTS**

1885-87

70	A6	3c on 5c ultra	125.00	275.00
a.		Double surcharge	2,300.	

Surcharged in Black

3 cents

71	A6	3c on 5c vio brn ('86)	210.00	225.00

Surcharged

2 Cents

72	A6	2c on 5c ultra ('87)	25.00	70.00
a.		Double surcharge	1,150.	1,050.
b.		"C" omitted	2,900.	

In the surcharged issues of 1883 to 1887, Nos. 59, 62, 63 and 71 are on stamps watermarked Crown and C C, the others are watermarked Crown and C A.

Surcharged

THREE CENTS

1885-94   Wmk. Crown and C A (2)

73	A5	3c on 32c magenta	1.50	1.10
74	A5	3c on 32c rose ('94)	3.75	.85
a.		Without surcharge	3,000.	

No. 74a value is for copy with perfs touching frame line.

Surcharged

10 CENTS

1891

75	A3	10c on 24c green	3.50	1.50
a.		Narrow "0" in "10"	32.50	32.50

Surcharged

THIRTY CENTS

76	A5	30c on 32c red orange	8.00	4.25

Surcharged

ONE CENT

1892

77	A2	1c on 2c rose	2.25	4.25
78	A2	1c on 4c bister brn	5.75	6.25
a.		Double surcharge	1,150.	
79	A2	1c on 6c violet	1.60	5.50
a.		Dbl. surch., one invtd.	1,350.	1,250.
80	A3	1c on 8c orange	1.25	1.50
81	A3	1c on 12c vio brown	5.75	10.50
		Nos. 77-81 (5)	16.60	28.00

Surcharged

ONE CENT

82	A3	1c on 8c gray green	1.10	1.75

Queen Victoria — A13

1892-99   Typo.

83	A13	1c gray green	3.50	.80
84	A13	3c car rose ('95)	12.50	.55
85	A13	3c brown ('99)	6.25	.70
86	A13	25c dk vio & grn	26.00	7.50
87	A13	50c ol grn & car	22.50	3.00
88	A13	$5 org & car ('98)	550.00	300.00
		Nos. 83-88 (6)	620.75	312.55

Denomination of $5, is in color on plain tablet.

Stamps of 1883-94 Surcharged

4 cents.

1899

89	A6	4c on 5c ultra	3.75	15.00
a.		Double surcharge		1,400.
90	A6	4c on 5c brown	3.25	5.50
91	A3	4c on 8c brt blue	1.50	3.25
b.		Double surcharge	1,100.	975.00
		Nos. 89-91 (3)	8.50	23.75

Type of 1882 Issue Surcharged

FOUR CENTS

92	A6	4c on 5c rose	.85	.40
a.		Without surcharge	29,000.	

King Edward VII — A14

Numerals of 5c, 8c, 10c, 30c, $1 and $5, type A14, are in color on plain tablet.

1902   Wmk. 2   Typo.

93	A14	1c green	3.00	3.50
94	A14	3c vio & org	4.00	.25
95	A14	4c violet, red	5.50	.35
96	A14	5c violet	6.25	.95
97	A14	8c violet, blue	4.00	.30
98	A14	10c vio & blk, yel	27.50	1.75
99	A14	25c violet & grn	12.50	7.00
100	A14	30c gray & car rose	21.00	9.25
101	A14	50c grn & car rose	22.50	22.50
102	A14	$1 green & blk	25.00	75.00
103	A14	$2 violet & blk	75.00	80.00
104	A14	$5 grn & brn org	225.00	190.00
104A	A14	$100 dl vio & grn, yel	10,500.	
		Nos. 93-104 (12)	431.25	390.85

High values of the 1902 and 1904 issues with revenue cancellations are of minimal value. No. 104A is inscribed "Postage & Revenue" but the limit of weight probably precluded its use postally.
See Nos. 113, 115-128B, 133.

A15   A16

A17   A18

1903-04

105	A15	1c gray green	1.75	9.25
106	A16	3c dull violet	12.50	5.25
107	A17	4c violet, red	5.00	.35
108	A18	8c violet, blue	55.00	1.50
		Nos. 105-108 (4)	74.25	16.35

See Nos. 109-112, 114, 129-132, 134.

1904-11   Wmk. 3

Chalky Paper

109	A15	1c gray green	3.25	.20
110	A16	3c dull violet	2.75	.35
111	A17	4c violet, red	9.75	.85
112	A17	4c dull vio ('08)	6.25	.20
113	A14	5c violet ('06)	11.00	2.75
114	A18	8c violet, bl	24.00	1.75
115	A14	10c vio & blk, yel	8.00	.90
116	A14	10c vio, yel ('08)	7.50	1.10
117	A14	25c vio & grn	35.00	24.00
118	A14	25c violet ('09)	15.00	8.00
119	A14	30c gray & car rose	55.00	3.00
120	A14	30c vio & org ('09)	45.00	4.50
121	A14	50c grn & car rose	35.00	17.50
122	A14	50c blk, grn ('10)	5.75	5.50
123	A14	$1 green & blk	52.50	21.00
124	A14	$1 blk & red, bl ('11)	16.00	5.75
125	A14	$2 violet & blk	110.00	97.50
		Revenue cancel		12.00
126	A14	$2 grn & red, yel ('09)	27.50	27.50
127	A14	$5 grn & brn org	210.00	160.00
128	A14	$5 grn & red, grn ('10)	125.00	85.00
		Revenue cancel		5.00
128A	A14	$25 green & blk	1,600.	1,600.
		Revenue cancel		55.00
128B	A14	$100 dl vio & grn, yel	11,500.	
		Revenue cancel		200.00
		Nos. 109-128 (20)	804.25	467.35

Nos. 125, 128A and 128B are on chalky paper, the other values are on both ordinary and chalky. The note about No. 104A will apply to No. 128B.

1906-11

Ordinary Paper

129	A15	1c blue grn ('10)	26.00	1.25
130	A16	3c carmine ('08)	3.25	.20
131	A17	4c carmine ('07)	6.25	3.00
132	A17	4c lake ('11)	2.25	.95
133	A14	5c orange ('09)	3.25	2.25
134	A18	8c ultra ('06)	4.00	.60
		Nos. 129-134 (6)	45.00	8.25

Stamps of Labuan 1902-03, Overprinted or Surcharged in Red or Black

a   b

STRAITS SETTLEMENTS.

FOUR CENTS.

c

Perf. 12½ to 16 and Compound

1907   Unwmk.

134A	A38(a)	1c violet & blk	70.00	200.00
135	A38(a)	2c grn & blk	200.00	350.00
136	A38(a)	3c brn & blk	22.50	97.50
137	A38(c)	4c on 12c yel & blk	2.75	7.00
a.		No period after "CENTS"	350.00	—
138	A38(c)	4c on 16c org brn & grn (Bk)	5.00	9.25
a.		With additional name in red	750.00	800.00
139	A38(c)	4c on 18c bis & blk	3.25	7.50
a.		No period after "CENTS"	300.00	—
b.		"FOUR CENTS." & bar double	8,000.	
140	A38(a)	8c org & blk	3.25	9.25
141	A38(b)	10c sl bl & brn	8.00	8.00
a.		No period after "Settlements"	360.00	

142	A38(a)	25c grnsh bl & grn	16.00	45.00
143	A38(a)	50c gray lil & vio	17.50	80.00
144	A38(a)	$1 org & red brn	52.50	125.00
		Nos. 134A-144 (11)	400.75	938.50

A19   A20

1908-11   Typo.   Wmk. 3   Perf. 14

Chalky Paper

145	A19	$25 bl & vio, bl ('11)	1,500.	1,150.
146	A19	$500 violet & org	85,000.	
		Revenue cancel		275.

No. 146 is inscribed "Postage-Revenue" but was probably used only for revenue.
Excellent forgeries of No. 146 exist.

1910

Chalky Paper

147	A20	21c maroon & vio	7.50	40.00
148	A20	45c black, green	3.00	4.50

King George V

A21   A22

A23   A24

A25   A26

Die I (Type A24).

For description of dies I and II see back of this section of the Catalogue.
The 25c, 50c and $2 denominations of type A24 show the numeral on horizontally-lined tablet.

1912-18   Chalky Paper   Wmk. 3

149	A21	1c green	7.00	1.50
150	A21	1c black ('18)	1.50	1.10
151	A25	2c dp green ('18)	1.10	.60
152	A22	3c scarlet	1.50	.40
a.		3c carmine	2.25	1.00
153	A23	4c gray violet	.90	.40
154	A23	4c scarlet ('18)	2.75	.20
a.		Booklet pane of 1		
b.		Booklet pane of 12		
c.		4c carmine ('18)	2.75	.20
155	A24	5c orange	2.00	.60
156	A25	6c claret ('18)	2.00	.60
157	A25	8c ultra	2.00	.90
158	A24	10c violet, yel	1.75	.60
159	A24	10c ultra ('18)	4.50	.60
160	A26	21c maroon & vio	5.50	11.00
161	A24	25c vio & red vio	12.50	9.75
162	A24	30c vio & org ('14)	9.25	2.25
163	A26	45c blk, bl grn, ol back ('14)	3.75	22.50
a.		45c black, emerald ('17)	3.75	15.00
164	A24	50c black, grn ('14)	6.50	3.25
a.		50c blk, bl grn, olive back	21.00	8.50
b.		50c black, emerald	14.00	11.00
c.		Die II	3.50	4.50
165	A24	$1 blk & red, bl ('14)	10.50	9.75
166	A24	$2 grn & red, yel ('15)	12.50	50.00
167	A24	$5 grn & red, grn ('15)	92.50	70.00
a.		$5 grn & red, bl grn, ol back	160.00	97.50
b.		$5 grn & red, emer ('15)	200.00	110.00
c.		Die II	110.00	75.00
		Nos. 149-167 (19)	180.00	186.00

The 1c, 3c, 5c and 8c are on ordinary paper.

Surface-colored Paper

168	A24	10c violet, yel	1.75	1.10
169	A26	45c black, grn ('14)	7.50	21.00
170	A24	$2 grn & red, yel ('14)	8.50	50.00
171	A24	$5 grn & red, grn	85.00	50.00
		Nos. 168-171 (4)	102.75	122.10

See Nos. 179-201. For surcharges see Nos. B1-B2.

A27

1915

172	A27	$25 bl & vio, bl	1,250.	500.00
		Revenue cancel		5.75
173	A27	$100 red & blk, bl	5,500.	
		Revenue cancel		90.00
174	A27	$500 org & dl vio	42,500.	
		Revenue cancel		200.00

Although Nos. 173 and 174 were available for postage, it is probable that they were used only for fiscal purposes.
See Nos. 202-204.

Die II (Type A24)
1921-32   Wmk. 4
Ordinary Paper

179	A21	1c black	.60	.20
180	A25	2c green	.60	.20
181	A25	2c brown	8.00	3.00
182	A22	3c green	1.75	.90
183	A23	4c scarlet	2.25	4.75
184	A23	4c dp violet ('25)	.70	.20
185	A23	4c orange ('29)	1.10	.20
186	A24	5c orange ('23)	2.75	1.50
a.		Die I	1.75	.20
187	A24	5c dk brown ('32)	3.25	.20
a.		Die I ('32)	5.75	.20
188	A24	6c claret	2.25	.25
189	A25	6c scarlet ('27)	3.00	.20
a.		6c rose red ('25)	22.50	11.00
190	A24	10c ultra (I)	2.00	3.00

Chalky Paper

191	A24	10c vio, yel ('27)	2.25	.35
a.		Die I ('25)	3.00	7.50
192	A25	12c ultra	1.10	.20
193	A26	21c mar & vio	7.00	55.00
194	A24	25c vio & red vio	5.75	2.00
a.		Die I	32.50	80.00
195	A24	30c violet & org	2.25	1.50
a.		Die I	26.00	40.00
196	A26	35c orange & vio	14.00	7.00
197	A26	35c vio & car ('31)	11.50	8.00
198	A24	50c blk, emerald	2.00	.45
199	A24	$1 blk & red, bl	7.00	.75
200	A24	$2 grn & red, yel	11.50	9.25
201	A24	$5 grn & red, grn	97.50	37.50
202	A27	$25 bl & vio, bl	750.00	140.00
203	A27	$100 red & blk, bl	450.00	1,900.
204	A27	$500 org & dl vio	35,000.	
		Nos. 179-201 (23)	190.10	136.60

No. 192 is on ordinary paper.
Nos. 203 and 204 were probably used only for fiscal purposes.

Stamps of 1912-21 Overprinted in Black:

"MALAYA-BORNEO EXHIBITION," in Three Lines
1922   Wmk. 3

151d	A25	2c deep green	32.50	85.00
154d	A23	4c scarlet	8.50	26.00
155d	A24	5c orange	5.75	22.50
157d	A25	8c ultra	2.00	8.50
161d	A24	25c vio & red vio	4.25	35.00
163d	A26	45c blk, bl grn, ol back	4.25	30.00
165d	A24	$1 blk & red, bl	210.00	800.00
166d	A24	$2 grn & red, yel	32.50	125.00
167d	A24	$5 grn & red, grn	275.00	450.00

Wmk. 4

179d	A21	1c black	3.25	14.00
180d	A25	2c green	2.75	16.00
183d	A23	4c scarlet	3.50	30.00
186d	A24	5c orange (II)	3.00	45.00
190d	A24	10c ultra	3.00	29.00
199d	A24	$1 blk & red, bl	24.00	140.00
		Nos. 151d-199d (15)	614.25	1,856.

Industrial fair at Singapore, Mar. 31-Apr. 15, 1922.

Common Design Types
pictured following the introduction.

Silver Jubilee Issue
Common Design Type
1935, May 6   Engr.   Perf. 11x12

213	CD301	5c black & ultra	2.50	.35
214	CD301	8c indigo & green	2.50	3.50
215	CD301	12c ultra & brown	2.50	4.25
216	CD301	25c brown vio & ind	3.00	5.75
		Nos. 213-216 (4)	10.50	13.85
		Set, never hinged	15.00	

George V A28	George VI A29

1936-37   Typo.   Perf. 14
Chalky Paper

217	A28	1c black ('37)	.85	.20
218	A28	2c green	.85	.80
220	A28	4c orange brn	1.75	.80
221	A28	5c brown	.65	.35
222	A28	6c rose red	1.10	1.25
223	A28	8c gray	1.10	.80
224	A28	10c dull vio	1.25	.70
225	A28	12c ultra	1.75	3.00
226	A28	25c rose red & vio	1.10	.60
227	A28	30c org & dk vio	1.10	3.50
229	A28	40c dk vio & car	1.10	2.75
230	A28	50c blk, emerald	4.00	1.40
232	A28	$1 red & blk, blue	16.00	1.90
233	A28	$2 rose red & gray grn	30.00	11.50
234	A28	$5 grn & red, grn ('37)	60.00	11.50
		Nos. 217-234 (15)	122.60	41.05
		Set, never hinged	210.00	

Coronation Issue
Common Design Type
1937, May 12   Engr.   Perf. 13½x14

235	CD302	4c deep orange	.20	.20
236	CD302	8c gray black	.30	.20
237	CD302	12c bright ultra	.50	.65
		Nos. 235-237 (3)	1.00	1.05
		Set, never hinged	1.75	

Two Dies

Die I. Printed in two operations. Lines of background touch outside of central oval. Foliage of palms touches outer frame line. Palm frond in front of King's eye has two points.

Die II. Printed from a single plate. Lines of background separated from central oval by a white line. Foliage of palms does not touch outer frame line. Palm frond in front of King's eye has one point.

1937-41   Typo.   Perf. 14

238	A29	1c black (I)	2.75	.20
239	A29	2c green (I)	9.00	.25
c.		Die II ('38)	35.00	.45
239A	A29	2c brown org ('41) (II)	1.25	5.00
239B	A29	3c green ('41) (II)	2.25	3.00
240	A29	4c brown org (I)	8.00	.25
a.		Die II ('38)	50.00	.25
241	A29	5c brown (I)	10.00	.35
a.		Die II ('39)	27.50	.20
242	A29	6c rose red ('38) (I)	5.50	.50
243	A29	8c gray ('38) (I)	19.00	.25
244	A29	10c dull vio (I)	4.00	.20
245	A29	12c ultra ('38) (I)	8.00	.35
245A	A29	15c ultra ('41) (II)	3.25	6.25
246	A29	25c rose red & vio (I)	40.00	1.10
247	A29	30c org & vio (I)	25.00	2.00
248	A29	40c dk vio & rose red (I)	10.00	2.25
249	A29	50c blk, emer ('38) (I)	10.00	.45
250	A29	$1 red & blk, bl ('38) (I)	15.00	.40
251	A29	$2 rose red & gray grn ('38) (I)	30.00	4.25
252	A29	$5 grn & red, grn ('38) (I)	25.00	4.50
		Nos. 238-252 (18)	228.00	31.55
		Set, never hinged	375.00	

For overprints see #256-271, N1-N29 and Malaya, Malacca #N1-N14, Penang #N1-N26.

Stamps and Type of 1937-41 Overprinted in Red or Black

1945-48

256	A29	1c black (R)	.20	.20
257	A29	2c brown org (II)	.25	.20
a.		Die I ('46)	7.50	3.75
258	A29	3c green	.25	.25
259	A29	5c brown	.75	.60
260	A29	6c gray	.25	.20
261	A29	8c rose red	.25	.20
262	A29	10c dull vio (I)	.30	.20
a.		10c claret (II) ('48)	10.00	1.00
263	A29	12c ultra	1.75	3.25
264	A29	15c ultra (Bk)	2.25	4.75
265	A29	15c ultra (R)	.25	.25
266	A29	25c rose red & vio	1.40	.25
a.		Double overprint	400.00	
267	A29	50c blk, emer (R)	.60	.20
268	A29	$1 rose red & blk	2.00	.25
269	A29	$2 rose red & gray grn	2.50	.65
270	A29	$5 grn & red, grn	72.50	72.50
271	A29	$5 brn org & vio	3.75	2.75
		Nos. 256-271 (16)	89.25	86.65
		Set, never hinged	125.00	

The letters "B M A" are initials of "British Military Administration".
An 8c gray with BMA overprint was prepared but not issued. Value $5.
The 6c gray, 8c rose red and $5 brown orange & violet exist without BMA overprint, but were issued only with it.
No. 262a does not exist without overprint. No. 262 exists in at least three shades.

SEMI-POSTAL STAMPS

Nos. 152-153 Surcharged

1917   Wmk. 3   Perf. 14

B1	A22	3c + 2c scarlet	2.75	29.00
a.		No period after "C"	325.00	575.00
B2	A23	4c + 2c gray violet	3.50	29.00
a.		No period after "C"	350.00	575.00

POSTAGE DUE STAMPS

D1

1924-26   Typo.   Wmk. 4   Perf. 14

J1	D1	1c violet	5.75	7.50
J2	D1	2c black	3.75	1.50
J3	D1	4c green ('26)	2.25	5.50
J4	D1	8c red	5.25	.60
J5	D1	10c orange	7.00	.95
J6	D1	12c ultramarine	8.00	.75
		Nos. J1-J6 (6)	32.00	16.80
		Set never hinged	50.00	

OCCUPATION STAMPS

Issued Under Japanese Occupation
Straits Settlements Nos. 238, 239A, 239B, 243 and 245A Handstamped in Red

1942, Mar. 16   Wmk. 4   Perf. 14

N1	A29	1c black	10.50	20.00
N2	A29	2c brown orange	10.50	15.00
N3	A29	3c green	40.00	80.00
N4	A29	8c gray	18.00	21.00
N5	A29	15c ultra	12.00	17.50
		Nos. N1-N5 (5)	91.00	153.50
		Set never hinged	140.00	

Other denominations with this handstamp are believed to be proofs.
The handstamp reads: "Seal of Post Office of Malayan Military Department."

Stamps of Straits Settlements, 1937-41, Handstamped in Red, Black, Violet or Brown

1942, Apr. 3

N6	A29	1c black	4.00	4.00
N6A	A29	2c green (V)	500.00	500.00
N7	A29	2c brown org	4.00	3.50
N8	A29	3c green	4.00	3.50
N9	A29	5c brown	30.00	30.00
N10	A29	6c gray	4.00	3.50
N11	A29	10c dull violet	45.00	45.00
N12	A29	12c ultra	90.00	90.00
N13	A29	15c ultra	4.50	4.00
N14	A29	30c orange & vio	350.00	350.00
N15	A29	40c dk vio & rose red	100.00	125.00
N16	A29	50c blk, emerald	60.00	60.00
N17	A29	$1 red & blk, bl	80.00	80.00
N18	A29	$2 rose red & gray grn	140.00	150.00
N19	A29	$5 grn & red, grn	200.00	165.00

Nos. N6-N7, N9, N11-N12, N15-N19 with red handstamp were used in Sumatra. The 2c green with red handstamp was not regularly issued.

Straits Settlements Nos. 239A, 239B, 243 and 245A Overprinted in Black

1942

N20	A29	2c brown orange	1.25	6.00
a.		Inverted overprint	7.25	21.00
b.		Dbl. ovpt., one invtd.	35.00	70.00
N21	A29	3c green	37.50	75.00
N22	A29	8c gray	3.50	2.75
a.		Inverted overprint	10.50	32.50
N23	A29	15c ultra	9.00	9.25
		Nos. N20-N23 (4)	51.25	93.00
		Set never hinged	77.50	

Straits Settlements Nos. 239A and 243 Overprinted in Black

1942, Nov. 3

N24	A29	2c brown orange	17.50	25.00
a.		Inverted overprint	225.00	225.00
N25	A29	8c gray	12.50	20.00
a.		Inverted overprint	225.00	225.00

Agricultural-Horticultural Exhibition held at Kuala Lumpur, Selangor, Nov. 1-2, 1942. Sold only at a temporary post office at the exhibition.

Straits Settlements Nos. 243, 245 and 248 Overprinted in Black or Red

1943

N26	A29	8c gray (Bk)	1.10	.60
a.		Inverted overprint	35.00	62.50

N27	A29	8c gray (R)	1.50	3.00
N28	A29	12c ultramarine	.95	10.50
N29	A29	40c dk vio & rose red	1.10	4.50
		Nos. N26-N29 (4)	4.65	18.60
		Set never hinged	7.00	

The Japanese characters read: "Japanese Postal Service."

SUDAN

sü-'dan

LOCATION — Northeastern Africa, south of Egypt
GOVT. — Republic
AREA — 967,500 sq. mi.
POP. — 27,953,000 (1997 est.)
CAPITAL — Khartoum

10 Milliemes = 1 Piaster
100 Piasters = 1 Egyptian Pound
Dinar (1992)

Catalogue values for unused stamps in this country are for Never Hinged items, beginning with Scott 79 in the regular postage section, Scott C35 in the air post section, Scott CO1 in the air post official section, Scott J12 in the postage due section, and Scott O28 in the officials section.

Watermarks

Wmk. 71 — Rosette

Wmk. 179 — Multiple Crescent and Star

Wmk. 214 — Multiple S G

Wmk. 334 — Rectangles

Wmk. 345 — Rhinoceros

Egyptian Stamps of 1884-93 Overprinted in Black

1897, Mar. 1   Wmk. 119   Perf. 14

1	A18	1m brown	2.00	2.00
a.		Inverted overprint	275.00	
2	A19	2m green	2.00	2.25
3	A21	3m orange	1.25	1.75
4	A22	5m carmine rose	1.75	1.50
a.		Inverted overprint	275.00	
5	A14	1p ultra	7.50	10.00
6	A15	2p orange brown	50.00	15.00
7	A16	5p gray	42.50	17.50
a.		Double overprint	4,500	
8	A22	10p violet	30.00	40.00
		Nos. 1-8 (8)	137.00	82.00

Counterfeits of Nos. 1-8 are plentiful.

Camel Post — A1

1898, Mar. 1   Typo.   Wmk. 71

9	A1	1m rose & brn	.75	1.25
10	A1	2m brown & grn	2.00	1.75
11	A1	3m green & vio	2.10	2.00
12	A1	5m black & rose	1.75	.75
13	A1	1p yel brn & ultra	5.25	3.50
14	A1	2p ultra & blk	22.50	6.75
15	A1	5p grn & org brn	27.50	16.00
16	A1	10p dp vio & blk	25.00	2.50
		Nos. 9-16 (8)	86.85	34.50

See Nos. 17-27, 43-50. For overprints see Nos. C3, MO1-MO15, O1-O9, O17-O24. For surcharges see Nos. 28, 62, C16.

1902-21   Wmk. 179

17	A1	1m car rose & brn ('05)	1.25	.50
18	A1	2m brown & grn	1.75	.20
19	A1	3m grn & vio ('03)	2.40	.30
20	A1	4m ol brn & bl ('07)	1.60	2.50
21	A1	4m brn & red ('07)	1.60	.80
22	A1	5m blk & rose red ('03)	2.00	.20
23	A1	1p brn & ultra ('03)	2.40	.30
24	A1	2p ultra & blk ('08)	25.00	3.00
25	A1	2p org & vio brn ('21)	4.00	10.00
26	A1	5p grn & org brn ('08)	22.50	.35
27	A1	10p dp vio & blk ('11)	22.50	4.00
		Nos. 17-27 (11)	87.00	21.15

No. 15 Surcharged in Black

1903, Sept.   Wmk. 71

| 28 | A1 | 5m on 5p | 7.00 | 10.00 |
| a. | | Inverted surcharge | 275.00 | 260.00 |

A2

1921-22   Typo.   Wmk. 179

29	A2	1m orange & blk ('22)	.90	4.00
30	A2	2m dk brn & org ('22)	10.00	12.00
31	A2	3m green & vio ('22)	2.75	10.00
32	A2	4m brown & grn ('22)	6.75	4.00
33	A2	5m blk & ol brn ('22)	2.50	.20
34	A2	10m black & car ('22)	3.50	.20
35	A2	15m org brn & ultra	3.00	1.00
		Nos. 29-35 (7)	29.40	31.40

See Nos. 36-42. For overprints see Nos. C1-C2, O10-O16.
For surcharges see Nos. 60-61.

1927-40   Wmk. 214

36	A2	1m org yel & blk	.60	.20
37	A2	2m dk brn & org	.50	.20
38	A2	3m green & violet	.60	.20
39	A2	4m brown & green	.50	.20

40	A2	5m blk & ol brn	.50	.20
a.		Booklet pane of 4		
41	A2	10m black & car	1.50	.20
42	A2	15m org brn & ultra	1.50	.20
43	A1	2p orange & vio brn	1.50	.20
44	A1	3p dk bl & red brn ('40)	2.50	.20
45	A1	4p black & ultra ('36)	3.00	.20
46	A1	5p dk grn & org brn	1.25	.20
47	A1	6p blk & pale bl ('36)	5.00	1.00
48	A1	8p blk & pck grn ('36)	6.50	2.50
49	A1	10p dp vio & blk	3.00	.20
50	A1	20p bl & lt bl ('35)	3.00	.20
		Nos. 36-50 (15)	31.45	6.10

Charles George Gordon — A3

Gordon Memorial College A4

Memorial Service at Khartoum — A5

1935, Jan. 1   Engr.   Perf. 13½x14

51	A3	5m deep green	.50	.20
52	A3	10m brown	.60	.20
53	A3	13m ultra	2.00	7.50
54	A3	15m carmine	1.50	.20
55	A4	2p deep blue	1.50	.20
56	A4	5p orange	1.75	.35
57	A4	10p dull violet	7.00	7.25
58	A5	20p black	30.00	40.00
59	A5	50p red brown	75.00	85.00
		Nos. 51-59 (9)	119.85	140.90

50th anniv. of the death of Gen. Charles George ("Chinese") Gordon (1833-85).

No. 41 Surcharged in Black

Wmk. Multiple S G (214)
1940, Feb. 25   Typo.   Perf. 14

| 60 | A2 | 5m on 10m black & car | .50 | .50 |

Nos. 40 and 48 Surcharged in Black

a

b

1940-41

| 61 | A2(a) | 4½p on 5m ('41) | 55.00 | 4.50 |
| 62 | A1(b) | 4½p on 8p | 45.00 | 7.50 |

Sudan Landscape A6

1941   Perf. 13½, 14x13½
Litho.   Unwmk.
Size: 21½x17½mm

63	A6	1m orange & slate bl	1.10	4.00
64	A6	2m chocolate & org	1.10	4.00
65	A6	3m grn & rose vio	1.10	.20
66	A6	4m choc & bl grn	.55	.50
67	A6	5m indigo & ol bis	.20	.20
68	A6	10m indigo & rose pink	5.50	2.00
69	A6	15m chestnut & ultra	.75	.20

Size: 29x25mm

71	A6	2p orange & claret	4.00	.60
72	A6	3p dk blue & fawn	.75	.20
73	A6	4p blk & brt ultra	.90	.20
74	A6	5p dk grn & brn org	3.50	8.50
75	A6	6p ind & turq bl	13.00	.40
76	A6	8p black & green	10.00	.50
77	A6	10p rose vio & gray	40.00	.75
78	A6	20p dk & lt blue	35.00	30.00
		Nos. 63-78 (15)	117.45	52.25
		Set, never hinged	175.00	

Catalogue values for unused stamps in this section, from this point to the end of the section, are for Never Hinged items.

Types of 1898-1940 with Changed Arabic Wording Below Camel

A7

A8

EGYPT
AND
SUDAN
FOR SPECIALISTS

Please offer me Egypt and Sudan.
I'm eager to buy collections, classics (especially blocks and covers), essays, proofs, all varieties, rare postmarks, postal stationery, interpostal seals, & etc., and all related publications.

If you collect Egypt or Sudan, ask for my latest pricelist and please tell me about your collection & needs. **What may I offer you? Thank you.**

PETER R. FELTUS
P.O. Box 5339
Berkeley, CA 94705
Tel: (510) 658-9627

Wmk. 214

1948, Jan. 1		**Typo.**		**Perf. 14**
79	A7	1m dk orange & blk	.35	3.00
80	A7	2m chocolate & org	.75	4.00
81	A7	3m green & rose lilac	.25	3.50
82	A7	4m choc & sl grn	.50	.25
83	A7	5m black & ol brn	5.00	1.75
84	A7	10m black & car	5.00	.20
a.		Center inverted	—	
85	A7	15m org brn & ultra	4.00	.20
86	A8	2p org yel & vio brn	7.50	2.00
87	A8	3p dk bl & red brn	6.00	.25
88	A8	4p black & ultra	4.00	1.50
89	A8	5p dk grn & org	4.00	1.50
90	A8	6p blk & pale bl	4.00	3.00
91	A8	8p blk & peacock grn	4.00	3.00
92	A8	10p dp rose lil & blk	10.00	3.50
93	A8	20p dk blue & blue	4.50	.20
a.		Perf. 13	55.00	175.00
94	A8	50p ultra & carmine	7.00	2.25
		Nos. 79-94 (16)	67.85	30.15

Arabic inscription, types A7 and A8: "Berid es-Sudan"; types A1 and A2; "Postai-Sudaniye."
For overprints see Nos. O28-O43.

Stamp of 1898 — A9

1948, Oct. 1				**Perf. 12½x13**
95	A9	2p dull blue & gray blk		.40 .20

50th anniv. of Sudan's 1st postage stamp.

A10

1948, Dec. 19				**Perf. 13**
96	A10	10m black & carmine		.30 .20
97	A10	5p dk green & orange		.65 .65

Legislative Assembly opening, Dec., 1948.

Nubian Ibex — A11

Cotton Picking — A12

Camel Post — A13

Designs: 2m, Shoebill. 3m, Giraffe. 4m, Baggara girl. 5m, Shilluk warrior. 10m, Hadendowa. 15m, Sudan policeman. 3p, Ambatch canoe. 3½p, Nuba wrestlers. 4p, Weaving. 5p, Saluka farming. 6p, Gum tapping. 8p, Darfur chief. 10p, Stack laboratory. 20p, Nile lechwe.

1951, Sept. 1		**Typo.**		**Perf. 14**
Center in Black (#98-104)				
98	A11	1m orange	1.00	1.00
99	A11	2m ultra	1.50	.75
100	A11	3m dark green	5.50	2.50
101	A11	4m emerald	1.25	3.00
102	A11	5m plum	2.00	.20
103	A11	10m light blue	.25	.20
104	A11	15m dp orange brn	3.00	.20

			Perf. 13	
105	A12	2p lt blue & dk blue	.25	.20
106	A12	3p vio blue & brn	6.00	.20
107	A12	3½p brown & bl grn	1.75	.20
108	A12	4p black & dp blue	1.00	.20
109	A12	5p emer & org brn	.40	.20
110	A12	6p black & blue	7.00	2.25
111	A12	8p brown & dp bl	12.00	2.25
112	A12	10p green & black	1.25	.20
113	A12	20p black & blue grn	4.00	1.50
114	A12	50p black & carmine	12.00	1.50
		Nos. 98-114 (17)	60.15	16.55

See #159. For overprints see #O44-O61, O75.

Camel Post — A14

1954, Jan. 9				**Perf. 12½x13**
115	A14	15m emerald & brn org	.45	.85
116	A14	3p black & blue	.50	1.40
117	A14	5p red violet & blk	.75	1.00
		Nos. 115-117 (3)	1.70	3.25

Self-government in the Sudan.
A quantity of these sets inscribed "1953" was sold in London. They were not valid for postage. Value, set $15.

Independent Republic

Map of Sudan and Sun — A15   Rhinoceros Carrying Globe — A16

Wmk. 214

1956, Sept. 15		**Engr.**		**Perf. 14**
118	A15	15m rose lilac & org	.50	.80
119	A15	3p dk blue & org	.50	1.25
120	A15	5p green & org	.50	.95
		Nos. 118-120 (3)	1.50	3.00

Independence Day, Jan. 1, 1956.

1958, Aug. 2				
Center in Orange				
121	A16	15m plum	.40	.20
122	A16	3p blue	.65	.35
123	A16	5p green	.95	.60
		Nos. 121-123 (3)	2.00	1.15

APU Cong., Khartoum, Aug. 2, 1958.

Soldier, Farmer and Map of Nile — A17

Lithographed and Engraved

1959, Nov. 17		**Unwmk.**		**Perf. 14**
124	A17	15m brown, yel & ultra	.20	.20
125	A17	3p multicolored	.55	.30
126	A17	55m multicolored	.70	.40
		Nos. 124-126 (3)	1.45	.90

Sudanese army revolution, 1st anniv.

Arab League Center A17a

			Perf. 13x13½	
1960, Mar. 22		**Photo.**		**Wmk. 328**
127	A17a	15m dull green & blk	.25	.20

Opening of the Arab League Center and the Arab Postal Museum in Cairo.

Uprooted Oak Emblem, Refugee Man and Child — A18

Wmk. 214

1960, Apr. 7		**Litho.**		**Perf. 14**
128	A18	15m black, buff & ultra	.20	.20
129	A18	55m black, beige & org	.60	.50

World Refugee Year, 7/1/59-6/30/60.

Soccer Player — A19

Forest — A20

1960, Aug. 25		**Wmk. 214**		**Perf. 14**
130	A19	15m ultra, blk & yel	.20	.20
131	A19	3p yellow, blk & grn	.50	.45
132	A19	55m emerald, blk & yel	.75	.60
		Nos. 130-132 (3)	1.45	1.25

17th Olympic Games, Rome, 8/25-9/11.

1960, Sept. 6				
133	A20	15m multicolored	.20	.20
134	A20	3p multicolored	.40	.20
135	A20	55m multicolored	.65	.35
		Nos. 133-135 (3)	1.25	.75

5th World Forestry Cong., Seattle, WA, Aug. 29-Sept. 10.

King Tirhaqah, 689-663 B.C. — A21   Girl with Book — A22

Unwmk.

1961, Mar. 1		**Engr.**		**Perf. 14**
136	A21	15m yellow grn & brown	.20	.20
137	A21	3p salmon & violet	.45	.30
138	A21	55m lt blue & red brown	.75	.40
		Nos. 136-138 (3)	1.40	.90

Save historic monuments in Nubia.
An imperf. souvenir sheet exists, not sold at post offices, containing one each of Nos. 136-138. Size: 154x97mm. The sheet was not issued for postal purposes and cancellation requests are declined. Value $8.

1961, Nov. 17		**Litho.**		**Wmk. 214**
139	A22	15m violet, claret & pink	.20	.20
140	A22	3p orange, blk & blue	.45	.30
141	A22	55m gray grn, blk & och	.60	.40
		Nos. 139-141 (3)	1.25	.90

50 years of girls' education in the Sudan.

Malaria Eradication Emblem — A23   Arab League Building, Cairo — A24

1962, Apr. 7		**Unwmk.**		**Perf. 14**
142	A23	15m black, pur & blue	.40	.20
143	A23	55m dk brown & green	.55	.50

WHO drive to eradicate malaria.

1962, Apr. 22		**Photo.**		**Perf. 13½x13**
144	A24	15m deep orange	.30	.20
145	A24	55m blue green	.50	.40

Arab League Week, Mar. 22-28.

Type of 1951 and

Palace of the Republic, Khartoum — A25   Cotton Picker — A26

Designs: 15m, Straw cover. 35m, 4p, Wild animals. 55m, 6p, Cattle. 8p, Date palms. 10p, Sailboat. 20p, Bohein Temple, 1500 B.C. 50p, Sennar Dam. £1, Camel Post (A13 redrawn).

		Perf. 14½x14, 14x14½		
1962, Oct. 1		**Litho.**		**Wmk. 345**
Size: 23x19mm, 19x23mm				
146	A25	5m blue	.20	.20
147	A26	10m blue & lilac	.20	.20
148	A25	15m multicolored	.20	.20
149	A25	2p lt purple	.20	.20
150	A26	3p bl grn, red brn & brn	.35	.20
151	A26	35m yel grn, brn & org brn	.65	.20
152	A25	4p red, lt bl & lil	.65	.20
153	A25	55m gray & yel ol	.65	.20
154	A25	6p brown & lt blue	.85	.20
155	A25	8p green	.85	.20

		Perf. 14x14½, 13x13½, 14x13½, 13½x14		
Size: 24½x30mm, 30x24½mm				
156	A26	10p lt bl, red brn & blk	.95	.40
157	A25	20p gray ol & yel grn	2.25	.75
158	A25	50p dk gray, ol & bl	5.50	1.25
		Engr.		
159	A13	£1 green & brn org	10.50	5.00
		Nos. 146-159 (14)	24.00	9.40

The frame of No. 159 has been altered with Arabic inscription on top and English at bottom.
See Nos. 420, 427-428. For surcharge and overprints see Nos. 430, O62-O74, O92, O99-O100.

1975-79				**Unwmk.**
Perfs, Sizes and Printing Methods as Before				
146a	A25	5m ('76)	.20	.20
147a	A26	10m ('76)	.20	.20
148a	A25	15m	.20	.20
149a	A25	2p	.20	.20
150a	A26	3p ('76)	.20	.20
151a	A26	35m	.20	.20
152a	A26	4p	.20	.20
153a	A25	55m ('79)	.25	.20
154a	A25	6p	.25	.20
155a	A25	8p ('77)	.35	.20
156a	A26	10p	.40	.20
157a	A25	20p	1.00	.40
158a	A25	50p	2.50	.60
159a	A13	£1		
		Nos. 146a-158a (13)	6.15	3.20

Corn and Millet — A27

Centenary Emblem and Medals — A28

1963, Mar. 21   Litho.   Wmk. 345
160 A27 15m. emerald, gray & brn   .25 .20
161 A27 55m violet, lt & dk blue   .60 .30

FAO "Freedom from Hunger" campaign.

1963, Oct. 1   Perf. 14
162 A28 15m blk, red, gray & gold   .30 .20
163 A28 55m grn, gray, red & gold   .75 .40

Centenary of the International Red Cross.

Melchior — A29

Khashm El Girba Dam — A30

Designs: 30m, St. Joseph seated, with cross and manuscript, horiz. 55m, Archangel with cross. Designs from frescoes in excavated Faras Church.

1964, Mar. 8   Litho.   Perf. 14
164 A29 15m multicolored   .25 .20
165 A29 30m red brn, blk & brn   .40 .30
166 A29 55m red brn, blk & brn   1.10 .75
       Nos. 164-166 (3)   1.75 1.25

UNESCO world campaign to save historic monuments in Nubia.

Perf. 14x14½, 14½x14
1964, Apr. 22   Wmk. 345
New York World's Fair, 1964-65: 3p, Pavilion. 55m, Illustrated map of Sudan, vert.

167 A30 15m lt vio bl & vio brn   .20 .20
168 A30   3p multicolored   .20 .20
169 A30 55m multicolored   .55 .25
       Nos. 167-169 (3)   .95 .65

Eleanor Roosevelt and People Breaking Chains — A31

Arab Postal Union Emblem — A32

1964, Dec. 10   Perf. 14
170 A31 15m grnsh blue & blk   .20 .20
171 A31   3p violet & black   .35 .20
172 A31 55m orange brn & blk   .50 .30
       Nos. 170-172 (3)   1.05 .70

Eleanor Roosevelt (1884-1962), on the 16th anniv. of the Universal Declaration of Human Rights.

1964, Dec. 30   Litho.
173 A32 15m brick red, blk & gold   .20 .20
174 A32   3p gray green, blk & gold   .35 .20
175 A32 55m violet, blk & gold   .50 .30
       Nos. 173-175 (3)   1.05 .70

10th anniv. of the Permanent Office of the Arab Postal Union.

ITU Emblem, Old and New Communication Equipment — A33

1965, May 17   Wmk. 345   Perf. 13½
176 A33 15m brown & gold   .20 .20
177 A33   3p black & gold   .35 .20
178 A33 55m green & gold   .50 .30
       Nos. 176-178 (3)   1.05 .70

Cent. of the ITU.

"Gurashi" and Revolutionists — A34

1965, Nov. 10   Litho.   Perf. 12
179 A34 15m deep ocher & black   .20 .20
180 A34   3p bright red & black   .35 .20
181 A34 55m dark gray & black   .50 .30
       Nos. 179-181 (3)   1.05 .70

1st anniv. of the October 21st Revolution and to honor "Gurashi," one of its heroes.

ICY Emblem — A35

El Siddig el Mahdi — A36

Perf. 14½x14
1965, Dec. 10   Litho.   Wmk. 345
182 A35 15m violet & blk   .20 .20
183 A35   3p yellow green & blk   .35 .20
184 A35 55m vermilion & blk   .50 .30
       Nos. 182-184 (3)   1.05 .70

International Cooperation Year, 1965.

1966, Jan. 1   Perf. 13
185 A36 15m lt blue & vio blue   .40 .20
186 A36   3p orange & brown   .60 .25
187 A36 55m gray & red brown   1.25 .65
       Nos. 185-187 (3)   2.25 1.10

El Siddig el Mahdi (1911-61), imam of Ansar region and political leader.

Mubarak Zaroug A37

1966, Jan. 1   Litho.
188 A37 15m pink & lt olive grn   .35 .20
189 A37   3p brt olive grn & dk grn   .60 .35
190 A37 55m orange brn & dk brn   1.25 .60
       Nos. 188-190 (3)   2.20 1.15

Issued in memory of Mubarak Zaroug (1917-65), lawyer and political leader.

WHO Headquarters, Geneva — A38

1966, June 11   Photo.   Perf. 11½x11
191 A38 15m blue   .20 .20
192 A38   3p magenta   .30 .20
193 A38 55m brown   .50 .25
       Nos. 191-193 (3)   1.00 .65

Inauguration of WHO Headquarters, Geneva.

Map of Sudan and Crests of Upper Nile, Blue Nile and Kassala Provinces — A39

Designs: 3p, Map of Sudan and crests of Equatoria, Kordofan and Khartoum Provinces. 55m, Map of Sudan and crests of Bahr El Gazal, Darfur and Northern Provinces.

1967, Apr. 1   Litho.   Perf. 14
194 A39 15m org, pur & lt blue grn   .20 .20
195 A39   3p dp org, vio & lt blue   .35 .30
196 A39 55m yel, dp claret & yel grn   1.25 .60
       Nos. 194-196 (3)   1.80 1.10

Month of the South.

Giraffe and ITY Emblem — A40

Clasped Hands and Arab League Emblem — A41

Perf. 12½x13
1967, Aug. 15   Litho.   Wmk. 345
197 A40 15m multicolored   .30 .20
198 A40   3p multicolored   .70 .40
199 A40 55m multicolored   1.00 .40
       Nos. 197-199 (3)   2.00 1.00

International Tourist Year 1967.

Perf. 11x11½
1967, Aug. 29   Photo.   Unwmk.
200 A41 15m orange & ultra   .30 .20
201 A41   3p brown org & emer   .40 .35
202 A41 55m lemon & violet   .75 .70
       Nos. 200-202 (3)   1.45 1.25

Arab League Summit Conference.

Emblem of Palestine Liberation Organization — A42

1967, Aug. 29   Perf. 11½x11
203 A42 15m olive, car & yel   .20 .20
204 A42   3p green, car & yel   .25 .20
205 A42 55m brt green, car & yel   .45 .30
       Nos. 203-205 (3)   .90 .75

Palestine Liberation Organization.

Abdullahi el Fadil el Mahdi A43

Perf. 11½x11
1968, Feb. 15   Photo.   Unwmk.
206 A43 15m ultra & brt purple   .40 .20
207 A43   3p dp ultra & brt grn   .60 .30
208 A43 55m orange & green   1.25 .55
       Nos. 206-208 (3)   2.25 1.05

Issued in memory of Abdullahi el Fadil el Mahdi (1892-1966), political leader.

Mohammed Nur el Din — A44

1968, Feb. 15
209 A44 15m sl blue & apple grn   .40 .20
210 A44   3p blue & olive   .60 .30
211 A44 55m blue & violet blue   1.25 .55
       Nos. 209-211 (3)   2.25 1.05

Issued in memory of Mohammed Nur el Din (1898-1964), political leader.

Ahmed Yousif Hashim A45

Perf. 11½x11
1968, Mar. 5   Photo.   Unwmk.
212 A45 15m green & brown   .40 .20
213 A45   3p brt blue & sepia   .60 .30
214 A45 55m indigo & violet   1.25 .55
       Nos. 212-214 (3)   2.25 1.05

Ahmed Yousif Hashim (1906-1958), journalist.

Mohammed Ahmed el Mardi (1905-1966), Political Leader — A46

Perf. 11x11½
1968, Mar. 5   Photo.   Unwmk.
215 A46 15m Prus bl & vio bl   .40 .20
216 A46   3p ultra, och & dl rose   .60 .30
217 A46 55m dk blue & brown   1.25 .55
       Nos. 215-217 (3)   2.25 1.05

DC-3 A47

20th anniv. of Sudan Airways: 2p, De Havilland Dove. 3p, Fokker Friendship. 55m, De Havilland Comet 4C.

1968, Dec. 15   Litho.   Perf. 13½x13
218 A47 15m multicolored   .30 .20
219 A47   2p multicolored   .30 .20
220 A47   3p multicolored   .40 .20
221 A47 55m multicolored   .50 .30
       Nos. 218-221 (4)   1.50 .90

African Development Bank Emblem
(right) — A48

Wmk. Rectangles (334)

1969, Dec. 20   Photo.   Perf. 13
222	A48	2p black, gray & gold	.30	.20
223	A48	4p dark red & gold	.30	.20
224	A48	65m green & gold	.50	.25
		Nos. 222-224 (3)	1.10	.65

5th anniv. of the African Development Bank.

ILO Emblem
A49

1969, Dec. 27   Litho.   Perf. 14
225	A49	2p blue, blk & pink	.30	.20
226	A49	4p yellow, blk & silver	.30	.20
227	A49	65m green, blk & lilac	.50	.25
		Nos. 225-227 (3)	1.10	.65

50th anniv. of the ILO.

Citizens
A50

1970, May 25   Perf. 11½x11
228	A50	2p multicolored	
228A	A50	4p multicolored	
228B	A50	65m multicolored	
	Set, 228-228B	75.00	—

First anniv. of May 25th Revolution.
This set was withdrawn on day of issue;
1721 sets of the 2p, 4p and 65m stamps in
same design were sold through the Philatelic
service. A few copies of No. 228 were sold at
Post offices. Nos. 229-231 were issued in
October to replace this set.

Citizens
A51

1970, Oct. 21   Photo.   Perf. 11½x11
229	A51	2p brown, olive & red	.20	.20
230	A51	4p lt blue, olive & red	.40	.20
231	A51	65m olive, dk blue & red	.55	.25
		Nos. 229-231 (3)	1.15	.65

1st anniv. of the May 25th Revolution.

Map and
Flags of
UAR, Libya,
Sudan
A52

1971, Jan. 2   Unwmk.   Perf. 11½
232	A52	2p lt green, car & blk	.30	.20

Signing of the Charter of Tripoli affirming the
unity of UAR, Libya and the Sudan, Dec. 27,
1970.

Education Year
Emblem — A53   Emblem — A54

1971, May 2   Photo.   Perf. 11x11½
233	A53	2p blue, blk & brn	.30	.20
234	A53	4p carmine, blk & brn	.30	.20
235	A53	65m vio brn, blk & brn	.50	.25
		Nos. 233-235 (3)	1.10	.65

International Education Year.

1971, Nov. 10   Perf. 11x11½
236	A54	2p yellow, grn & blk	.30	.20
237	A54	4p blue, grn & blk	.35	.30
238	A54	10½p gray, grn & blk	.90	.75
		Nos. 236-238 (3)	1.45	1.25

2nd anniversary of May 25th Revolution.

Arab League
and Sudanese   UN
Emblems — A55   Emblem — A56

1972, Feb. 10   Photo.   Perf. 11x11½
239	A55	2p yellow, grn & blk	.20	.20
240	A55	4p orange, bl & blk	.40	.20
241	A55	10½p orange, brn & blk	.80	.45
		Nos. 239-241 (3)	1.40	.85

25th anniv. (in 1971) of the Arab League.

1972, Mar. 12   Photo.   Perf. 11x11½
242	A56	2p emer, rose red & org	.20	.20
243	A56	4p ultra, rose red & org	.40	.20
244	A56	10½p blk, rose red & org	.80	.55
		Nos. 242-244 (3)	1.40	.95

25th anniv. (in 1970) of the UN.

Emblems
and
Measure
A57

1972, Apr. 22   Photo.   Perf. 11½x11
245	A57	2p multicolored	.20	.20
246	A57	4p lt blue & multi	.45	.20
247	A57	10½p pink & multi	1.00	.60
		Nos. 245-247 (3)	1.65	1.00

World Standards Day, Oct. 14, 1970.

Pres.
Nimeiry
and Arms
of Sudan
A58

1972, May 2   Litho.   Perf. 13x13½
248	A58	2p vio bl, blk & gold	.20	.20
249	A58	4p dp org, blk & gold	.40	.20
250	A58	10½p ol grn, blk & gold	.80	.55
		Nos. 248-250 (3)	1.40	.95

Election of Gaafar al-Nimeiry as President,
Oct. 1971.

Arms of
Sudan
and
Congress
Emblem
A59

1972, Oct. 15   Photo.   Perf. 11½x11
251	A59	2p blue & multi	.20	.20
252	A59	4p multicolored	.25	.20
253	A59	10½p lt olive & multi	.75	.30
		Nos. 251-253 (3)	1.20	.70

Founding Congress of the Sudanese Socialist Union.

Letter and
African
Postal
Union
Emblem
A60

1972, Dec. 16
254	A60	2p yellow & multi	.20	.20
255	A60	4p multicolored	.25	.20
256	A60	10½p blue & multi	.90	.40
		Nos. 254-256 (3)	1.35	.80

10th anniv. (in 1971) of the APU.

Emblems of
Sudanese
Provinces
A61

Designs: 4p, Governing Council of Sudan.
10½p, Heraldic eagle and Unity emblem, vert.

1973, Jan. 1   Litho.   Perf. 13
257	A61	2p gold & multi	.20	.20
258	A61	4p dk red brn & blk	.25	.20
259	A61	10½p silver, org & grn	.90	.40
		Nos. 257-259 (3)	1.35	.80

National Unity Day, March 3, 1972.

Emperor Haile
Selassie — A62

1973, June 25   Unwmk.   Perf. 13
260	A62	2p tan & multi	.20	.20
261	A62	4p silver & multi	.60	.25
262	A62	10½p gold & multi	1.25	.45
		Nos. 260-262 (3)	2.05	.90

80th birthday of Haile Selassie, Emperor of
Ethiopia.

Nasser
and
Crowd
A63

1973, July 15   Photo.   Perf. 11½x11
263	A63	2p black	.20	.20
264	A63	4p pale green & blk	.25	.20
265	A63	10½p lilac & blk	.70	.40
		Nos. 263-265 (3)	1.15	.80

Gamal Abdel Nasser (1918-70), President
of Egypt.

UN and FAO Emblems, Portal and
Map of Resettlement Project — A64

1973, Dec. 30   Litho.   Perf. 13
266	A64	2p multicolored	.20	.20
267	A64	4p multicolored	.25	.20
268	A64	10½p multicolored	.90	.45
		Nos. 266-268 (3)	1.35	.85

World Food Program, 10th anniversary.

Scout Emblem,
Knotted Rope
and Stave — A65

1974, Jan. 15
269	A65	2p multicolored	.30	.20
270	A65	4p multicolored	.50	.20
271	A65	10½p multicolored	1.10	.50
		Nos. 269-271 (3)	1.90	.90

24th World Boy Scout Conference.

INTERPOL
Emblem
A66

1974, Feb. 16   Litho.   Perf. 13x13½
272	A66	2p orange & multi	.30	.20
273	A66	4p gray & multi	.40	.20
274	A66	10½p lt blue & multi	.75	.40
		Nos. 272-274 (3)	1.45	.80

50th anniv. of Intl. Criminal Police Organ.

K.S.M.
Building
A67

1974, July 1   Litho.   Perf. 13x13½
275	A67	2p lilac rose & multi	.20	.20
276	A67	4p lt green & multi	.40	.20
277	A67	10½p vermilion & multi	.90	.40
		Nos. 275-277 (3)	1.50	.80

50th anniversary of the Faculty of Medicine,
University of Khartoum.

African Postal
Union and UPU
Emblems — A68

4p, Letters, Arab Postal Union and UPU
emblems. 10½p, Letters, UPU and African
Postal Union emblems.

1974, Sept. 9   Litho.   Perf. 13½
278	A68	2p multicolored	.20	.20
279	A68	4p lt blue & multi	.20	.20
280	A68	10½p lilac & multi	.80	.40
		Nos. 278-280 (3)	1.20	.80

Centenary of Universal Postal Union.

Ali Abdel Latif, Abdel Fadil Elmaz, Revolutionary Flag and Nile — A69

1975, July 26   Litho.   Perf. 14x13½
281 A69   2½p green & vio blue   .25   .20
282 A69   4p rose & vio blue   .50   .20
283 A69   10½p sepia & vio blue   .90   .40
   Nos. 281-283 (3)   1.65   .80

50th anniversary of 1924 revolution. Portraits show political and military leaders of the revolution.

ADB Emblem with Map of Africa A70

1975, July 26
284 A70   2½p multicolored   .25   .20
285 A70   4p multicolored   .45   .20
286 A70   10½p multicolored   .90   .40
   Nos. 284-286 (3)   1.60   .80

African Development Bank, 10th anniv.

Radar Station and Camel Rider — A71

1976, Feb. 2   Litho.   Perf. 13½x14
287 A71   2½p lt green & multi   .20   .20
288 A71   4p lilac & multi   .25   .20
289 A71   10½p vio blue & multi   .75   .40
   Nos. 287-289 (3)   1.20   .80

Umm Haraz Satellite Station.

IWY Emblem, Flag and Woman A72

1976, May 10   Litho.   Perf. 14x13½
290 A72   2½p multicolored   .20   .20
291 A72   4p multicolored   .30   .20
292 A72   10½p dk blue & multi   .80   .40
   Nos. 290-292 (3)   1.30   .80

International Women's Year 1975.

Arms of Sudan, Olympic Rings, Track — A73

1976, July 17   Litho.   Perf. 13½x14
293 A73   2½p green & multi   .45   .20
294 A73   4p green & multi   .50   .20
295 A73   10½p green & multi   1.25   .55
   Nos. 293-295 (3)   2.20   1.00

21st Olympic Games, Montreal, Canada, July 17-Aug. 1.

Education, Engineering, Forestry, Agriculture and Defense — A74

1977, July 20   Litho.   Perf. 13½x14
296 A74   2½p multicolored   .20   .20
297 A74   4p multicolored   .25   .20
298 A74   10½p multicolored   .75   .40
   Nos. 296-298 (3)   1.20   .80

5th anniversary of national unity.

Archbishop Capucci — A75

1977, Oct. 22   Photo.   Perf. 11x11½
299 A75   2½p black   .50   .20
300 A75   4p black & green   1.00   .40
301 A75   10½p black & red   1.25   .60
   Nos. 299-301 (3)   2.75   1.20

Palestinian Archbishop Hilarion Capucci, jailed by Israel in 1974.

Fair Emblem, Sudanese Flag A76

Perf. 11½x 11
1978, Jan. 19   Photo.   Wmk. 342
302 A76   3p multicolored   .20   .20
303 A76   4p multicolored   .35   .20
304 A76   10½p multicolored   .60   .40
   Nos. 302-304 (3)   1.15   .80

International Khartoum Fair, Jan. 19-27.

APU Emblem A77

1978, Mar. 8   Litho.   Perf. 14x13½
305 A77   3p black, car & sil   .25   .20
306 A77   4p dk green, blk & sil   .30   .20
307 A77   10½p ultra, blk & sil   .75   .40
   Nos. 305-307 (3)   1.30   .80

APU, 25th anniv. (in 1977).

Jinnah and Sudanese Flag A78

1978, May 6   Litho.   Perf. 13
308 A78   3p multicolored   .20   .20
309 A78   4p multicolored   .40   .20
310 A78   10½p multicolored   .65   .40
   Nos. 308-310 (3)   1.25   .80

Mohammed Ali Jinnah (1876-1948), first Governor General of Pakistan.

Desert A79

1978, May 6   Perf. 14x13½
311 A79   3p multicolored   .20   .20
312 A79   4p multicolored   .40   .20
313 A79   10½p multicolored   .90   .45
   Nos. 311-313 (3)   1.50   .85

UN Desertification Conference.

Lion God Apedemek, African Unity Emblems — A80

1978, July 18   Litho.   Perf. 13½x14
314 A80   3p multicolored   .20   .20
315 A80   4p multicolored   .25   .20
316 A80   10½p multicolored   .65   .35
   Nos. 314-316 (3)   1.10   .75

15th African Summit Conference, Khartoum, July 18-21.

A81

1979, Oct. 1   Litho.   Perf. 13½x14
317 A81   3½p multicolored   .20   .20
318 A81   6p multicolored   .40   .20
319 A81   13p multicolored   .65   .35
   Nos. 317-319 (3)   1.25   .75

May Revolution, 10th Anniversary.

A82

1980, Jan. 19   Litho.   Perf. 13½x14
320 A82   4½p orange & black   .20   .20
321 A82   8p olive green & blk   .55   .20
322 A82   15½p blue & black   1.10   .45
   Nos. 320-322 (3)   1.85   .85

UNESCO emblem, children holding globe.

IYC Emblem, Hands Protecting Child A83

1980, Mar. 15   Perf. 14x13½
323 A83   4½p multicolored   .20   .20
324 A83   8p multicolored   .45   .30
325 A83   15½p multicolored   .80   .45
   Nos. 323-325 (3)   1.45   .95

International Year of the Child (1979).

25th Anniv. of Independence — A84

1982, Mar. 4   Photo.   Perf. 11½
326 A84   60m multicolored   .20   .20
327 A84   120m multicolored   .50   .30
328 A84   250m multicolored   1.10   .75
   Nos. 326-328 (3)   1.80   1.25

World Food Day, Oct. 16, 1981 A85

1983, Jan. 15   Photo.   Perf. 11½
329 A85   60m Emblem on map, reaching hands   .20   .20
330 A85   120m Produce   .50   .20
331 A85   250m Map, grain   1.00   .50
   Nos. 329-331 (3)   1.70   .90

A86

A87

1984, Feb. 20   Litho.   Perf. 13½
332 A86   10p pink & silver   .20   .20
333 A86   25p lt blue & silver   .60   .40
334 A86   40p green & silver   1.10   .65
   Nos. 332-334 (3)   1.90   1.25

25th Anniv. of Economic Commission for Africa (1983).

1984, June 16   Litho.   Perf. 14
335 A87   10p multicolored   .20   .20
336 A87   25p multicolored   .60   .40
337 A87   40p multicolored   1.00   .55
   Nos. 335-337 (3)   1.80   1.15

Cent. of Shaykan Battle, Kordofan (1983).

Olympic Week A88

1984, Dec. 1   Litho.   Perf. 14
338 A88 10p multicolored   .20   .20
339 A88 25p multicolored   .70   .35
340 A88 40p multicolored   1.10   .60
  Nos. 338-340 (3)   2.00   1.15

Sudan-Egypt Integration Charter, 2nd Anniv. — A89

Bakht Erruda, Teacher Training Institute — A90

1985, Mar. 16   Photo.   Perf. 13½x13
341 A89 10p multicolored   .20   .20
342 A89 25p multicolored   .60   .40
343 A89 40p multicolored   1.10   .60
  Nos. 341-343 (3)   1.90   1.20

1985, Apr. 1
344 A90 10p multicolored   .20   .20
345 A90 25p multicolored   .30   .20
346 A90 40p multicolored   .50   .40
  Nos. 344-346 (3)   1.00   .80

April 6 Uprising, 1st Anniv. A91

1986, Apr. 1   Litho.   Perf. 14
347 A91   5p multicolored   .20   .20
348 A91 25p multicolored   .60   .40
349 A91 40p multicolored   1.10   .60
  Nos. 347-349 (3)   1.90   1.20

World Food Day 1986 A92

Perf. 13x13½, 13½x13 (30p), 14 (50p)

1988, Jan. 1   Litho.
350 A92   25p Net fishermen   .45   .20
351 A92   30p Two fish, vert. .45   .20
352 A92   50p Globe   .60   .40
353 A92   75p Stylized fish on wave 1.00 .50
354 A92 300p Fish in sea   3.75   1.50
  Nos. 350-354 (5)   6.25   2.80

Souvenir Sheet
Imperf
354A A92 75p like 25p   1.50   1.50

Child Survival — A93

Perf. 14, Imperf. (No. 357)

1988, Mar. 15   Litho.
355 A93   50p Breast-feeding, vert. .50 .20
356 A93   75p Oral rehydration 1.00 .40
357 A93   75p like 50p, vert. 1.25   1.25
358 A93 100p Oral vaccine   1.25   .50
359 A93 150p Growth monitoring 1.50   .85
  Nos. 355-359 (5)   5.50   3.20

No. 357 issued without gum. Size: 63x84mm.

Red Crescent in Sudan, 30th Anniv. (in 1987) — A94

World Food Day, Oct. 16, 1987, and the Small Farmer — A95

Designs: 100p, Crescent, candle. 150p, Crescent, stylized figure of a man.

1988, Oct. 31   Litho.   Perf. 14
360 A94   40p org yel, blk & dk red .45 .20
361 A94 100p blk, blue grn & dk red 1.00 .50
362 A94 150p blk, brt blue & dk red 1.40 .85
  Nos. 360-362 (3)   2.85   1.55
  Nos. 361-362 horiz.

1988, Oct. 31   Perf. 13x13½, 13½x13

FAO emblem and: 40p, Early farming tools, horiz. 100p, Ox-drawn plow. 150p, Crude public water supply.

363 A95   40p multicolored   .45   .20
364 A95 100p shown   1.00   .50
365 A95 150p multicolored   1.40   .75
  Nos. 363-365 (3)   2.85   1.45

Khartoum Bank, 75th Anniv. A96

Designs: 40p, Anniv. emblem. 100p, Spheres, emblem, medallion on ribbon. 150p, Text, emblem.

1988, Oct. 31   Perf. 14
366 A96   40p multicolored   .45   .20
367 A96 100p multicolored   1.00   .50
368 A96 150p multicolored   1.50   .75
  Nos. 366-368 (3)   2.95   1.45

Declaration of Palestinian State, 1st Anniv. — A97

#370, 372, 374, Crowd of demonstrators.

1989, Dec. 10   Litho.   Perf. 14
369 A97 100p yellow grn & multi .95 .60
370 A97 100p buff & multi   .95   .60
371 A97 150p lt vio & multi 1.40   .95
372 A97 150p lt blue & multi 1.40   .95
373 A97 200p pink & multi   1.90   1.25
374 A97 200p lt green & multi 1.90 1.25
  Nos. 369-374 (6)   8.50   5.60

Palestinian Uprising (Nos. 370, 372, 374).

African Development Bank, 25th Anniv. — A99

1989, Dec. 28   Perf. 13x13½
375 A99 100p yel grn, blk & sil .95 .60
376 A99 150p blue, blk & sil 1.40   .95
377 A99 200p plum, blk & sil 1.90   1.25
  Nos. 375-377 (3)   4.25   2.80

Independence, 33rd Anniv. (in 1989) — A100

1990, Jan. 22   Litho.   Perf. 13½x13
378 A100   50p blue & yellow   .35   .20
379 A100 100p deep claret & yel .75 .45
380 A100 150p brt rose & yel 1.00   .70
381 A100 200p dp rose lil & yel 1.40 .90
  Nos. 378-381 (4)   3.50   2.25

Mammals A101

1990, Feb. 20   Perf. 13x13½
382 A101   25p Leopard   .30   .20
383 A101   50p Elephant   .50   .20

Perf. 14
384 A101   75p Giraffe, vert. .75   .35
385 A101 100p White rhinoceros 1.00   .45
386 A101 125p Addax, vert.   1.25   .60
  Nos. 382-386 (5)   3.80   1.80

No. 385 inscribed "Rino."

Birds — A102

1990, Mar. 25   Perf. 13½x13
387 A102   25p Zande hornbill .30   .20
388 A102   50p Marabou stork   .75   .20
389 A102   75p Buff-crested bustard 1.10 .45
390 A102 100p Saddle-bill   1.50   .55

Perf. 14
391 A102 150p Bald-headed ibis 2.00 .75
  Nos. 387-391 (5)   5.65   2.15

Traditional Dances A103

Perf. 13x13½, 13½x13
1990, May 10   Litho.
392 A103   25p Mardoum   .20   .20
393 A103   50p Zandi, vert.   .45   .25
394 A103   75p Kambala, vert. .60   .45
395 A103 100p Nubian, vert.   .75   .60
396 A103 125p Sword   .85   .75
  Nos. 392-396 (5)   2.85   2.25

Natl. Salvation Revolution, 1st Anniv. — A104

1991, Apr. 14   Litho.   Perf. 13
399 A104 150p multicolored   1.00   .70
400 A104 200p multicolored   1.40   .90
401 A104 250p multicolored   1.75   1.10
402 A104   £5 multicolored   3.50   2.25
403 A104 £10 multicolored   7.00   4.50
  Nos. 399-403 (5)   14.65   9.45

For surcharge see No. 438.

Type of 1962 and:

Shoebill A105

Camel Postman A109

1991, July 1   Perf. 13½x13
404 A105   25p shown   .20   .20
405 A105   50p Sunflower   .35   .20
406 A105   75p Gum Arabic   .50   .35
407 A105 100p Cotton   .70   .45
408 A105 125p Crowned crane .90   .60

Size: 30x24mm
Perf. 14x14½, 13½x14
409 A105 150p Kenana Sugar Co., horiz. 1.00 .70
410 A105 175p Secretary bird 1.25   .80
411 A105   £2 Atbara cement factory, horiz. 1.40 .90

Size: 26x37mm
Perf. 14
412 A105 250p King Taharqa statue 1.75 1.10
413 A105   £3 Republican palace 2.10 1.40

Size: 24x30mm
Perf. 13½x14
414 A105   £4 Hug jar   2.75   1.90
415 A105   £5 Gabana coffee pot 3.50 2.25

Size: 36x27mm
Litho. & Engr.
Perf. 14
Wmk. 334
416 A109   £8 Pterois volitans, horiz. 5.50 3.75
417 A109 £10 Animal wealth, horiz. 7.00 4.50
418 A109 £15 Nubian ibex   10.50   6.75
419 A109 £20 shown   14.00   9.00
  Nos. 404-419 (16)   53.40 34.85

1992   Litho.   Unwmk.   Perf. 14½x14
420 A25   25p Cattle   .20   .20

1990   Unwmk.   Perf. 14x13½
427 A25   £5 Bohein Temple   3.50   2.25

Perf. 13½x14
428 A26 £10 Sailboat   7.00   4.50

This is an expanding set. Numbers will change if necessary.

See Nos. O76-O100. For surcharges see Nos. 430, 436-437, 438A-443, 451, O104-O111.

No. 156a Handstamp Surcharged in
Blue Violet

1990, Sept. *Perf. 13½x14*
430 A26 £1 on 10p #156a — 2.00
Surcharge on No. 430 is often incomplete.

Pan-African
Rinderpest
Campaign
A114

Perf. 13½x13
1991, July 27 Litho. Unwmk.
431 A114 £1 black & brt grn .70 .45
432 A114 £2 dp violet & emer 1.40 .90
433 A114 £5 orange & blue grn 3.50 2.25
Nos. 431-433 (3) 5.60 3.60

Nos. 404, 407, 411, 413-414
Surcharged in Black or Blue Violet

Nos. 406, 409, 420 Surcharged

Nos. 405, 416 Surcharged

5d   No. 409 Surcharged
in Black

No. 406   No. 412
Surcharged in   Surcharged in Red
Black

35d

No. 408 Surcharged

1992?-97
Perfs. & Printing Methods as Before
436 A105 1d on 100p
 #407 (Blk) 3.75 2.50
437 A105 2d on £2 #411 7.25 4.75
438 A104 2.50d on 25p #404 9.00 5.75
438A A105 2.50d on 25p #420 2.50 1.75
439 A105 3d on £3 #413 11.00 7.00
440 A105 4d on £4 #414 14.50 9.50
441 A105 5d on 50p #405 2.75 .90
443 A105 7.50d on 75p #406 7.50 5.00
446 A105 1.50d on 150p
 #409 1.50 1.00
447 A105 15d on 150p
 #409 — —
448 A105 25d on 75p #406 — —
449 A105 25d on 250p
 #412 — —
451 A105 35d on £8 #416 4.75 1.60
a. Inverted surcharge — —
452 A105 100d on 125p
 #408 5.75 5.75
 Nos. 436-452 (11) 70.25 45.50
This is an expanding set. Numbers will change if necessary.

Intl. Human
Rights
Day — A115

Fung Sultanate,
5th Cent. — A116

Designs: £5, Chain links, rainbow of colors,
horiz. 750p, Trellis, rose, inscription.

1993, Dec. 20 Litho. Perf. 14
454 A115 £4 multicolored .75 .50
455 A115 £5 multicolored 1.00 .65
456 A115 750p multicolored 1.50 1.00
 Nos. 454-456 (3) 3.25 2.15

1993, Dec. 20
Designs: £5, Inscription on tablet. 750p,
Inscription in circle, helmet, horiz.
457 A116 £4 multicolored .80 .50
458 A116 £5 multicolored 1.00 .65
459 A116 750p multicolored 1.50 1.00
 Nos. 457-459 (3) 3.30 2.15

Wild
Ass — A117

A118

1994, July 15 Litho. Perf. 14½
460 A117 4d With young .45 .20
461 A117 8d Standing .85 .30
462 A117 10d Running 1.10 .40
463 A117 15d Up close 1.60 .55
 Nos. 460-463 (4) 4.00 1.45

1994, Aug. 1 Litho. Perf. 14
464 A118 5d vermilion & multi .25 .20
465 A118 7d green & multi .40 .25
466 A118 15d gray & multi .85 .55
 Nos. 464-466 (3) 1.50 1.00
Intl. Olympic Committee, cent.

A119   A120

1994, Dec. 7 Litho. Perf. 13½
467 A119 5d lilac & multi .25 .20
468 A119 7d brown & multi .35 .20
469 A119 15d blue & multi .80 .50
 Nos. 467-469 (3) 1.40 .90
ICAO, 50th anniv.

1995, July 15 Litho. Perf. 14
1994 World Cup Soccer Championships,
US: 4d, Goalie, green vest. 5d, Like 4d, blue
vest. 7d, Player about to kick ball, green shirt.
8d, Like 7d, brown shirt. 10d, Player, long-
sleeved shirt. 15d, Player, yellow shirt. 20d,
Player, magenta & blue background. 25d,
Player, white shirt & pants. 35d, Like 20d, blue
& green background.
75d, Goalie, orange shirt, horiz. 100d,
Player kicking ball, horiz.
470 A120 4d multicolored .20 .20
471 A120 5d multicolored .20 .20
472 A120 7d multicolored .25 .20
473 A120 8d multicolored .30 .20
474 A120 10d multicolored .40 .25
475 A120 15d multicolored .60 .40
476 A120 20d multicolored .75 .50
477 A120 25d multicolored .95 .60
478 A120 35d multicolored 1.25 .80
 Nos. 470-478 (9) 4.90 3.35
Souvenir Sheets
479 A120 75d multicolored 5.50 3.75
480 A120 100d multicolored 7.50 5.00

A121

A122

1995, Dec. 16 Litho. Perf. 13½
481 A121 15d apple grn & blk 1.25 .80
482 A121 25d blue & black 2.00 1.25
483 A121 30d purple & black 2.40 1.60
 Nos. 481-483 (3) 5.65 3.65
Arab League, 50th anniv.

1996, May 4 Litho. Perf. 13½
484 A122 15d orange & multi .30 .20
485 A122 25d apple grn & multi .50 .35
486 A122 30d purple & multi .60 .60
 Nos. 484-486 (3) 1.40 1.15
Common Market for East and South Africa
(COMESA).

A123   A124

1997, Jan. 22 Photo. Perf. 13½
487 A123 25d black & violet .35 .20
488 A123 35d black & red brown .50 .35
489 A123 50d black & brown .70 .45
 Nos. 487-489 (3) 1.55 1.00
Abdel Rahman el Mahdi (1885-1959).

1997, June 1 Photo. Perf. 13½x13
490 A124 5d multicolored .20 .20
Waiting For Peace.

A125   A126

1997, Oct. 15 Photo. Perf. 13½
491 A125 25d lilac & multi 1.10 .75
492 A125 35d apple grn & multi 1.50 1.00
493 A125 50d green, black & sil 2.25 1.50
 Nos. 491-493 (3) 4.85 3.25
Police Commanders, Arab Security Conference, 25th anniv.

1997, Nov. 1
Al-Shaykh Qaribulla's Mosque:Various
views of mosque.
494 A126 25d blue & multi 1.10 .75
495 A126 35d yellow & multi 1.50 1.00
496 A126 50d buff & multi, vert. 2.25 1.50
 Nos. 494-496 (3) 4.85 3.25

A127   A128

1998, Jan. 18 Litho. Perf. 13½
497 A127 25d multicolored .30 .20
498 A127 35d violet & multi .45 .30
499 A127 50d multicolored .65 .40
 Nos. 497-499 (3) 1.40 .90
Pan African Postal Union, 18th anniv.

1998, Jan. 25 Perf. 13½x13, 13x13½
Sudanese Archeology: No. 500, Kerma pottery, 2500 BC. No. 501, Fresco, Faras church,
11th cent. No. 502, Close-up of fresco, Faras
Church, 11th cent. 60d, C Group pottery, 2000
BC. No. 504, Meroe pottery, 4000 BC. No.
505, Tomb of Natakamani Meroitic king, 1st
cent. BC, vert. 100d, C Group pottery, 2000
BC, diff.
500 A128 50d multicolored .65 .40
501 A128 50d multicolored .65 .40
502 A128 50d multicolored .65 .40
503 A128 60d multicolored .75 .50
504 A128 75d multicolored .95 .65
505 A128 75d multicolored .95 .65
506 A128 100d multicolored 1.25 .85
 Nos. 500-506 (7) 5.85 3.85

A129

A130

1998, Mar. 1 Perf. 13x13½
507 A129 100d Ruins, Camel
 Post rider 1.25 .85
First Sudanese Postage Stamp, cent.

1999, May 15 Litho. Perf. 13¼x13½
508 A130 75d multicolored 2.25 1.50
509 A130 100d green & multi 3.00 2.00
510 A130 150d blue & multi 4.50 3.00
Nos. 508-510 (3) 9.75 6.50

Battle of Kerreri, cent.

American Bombing of Elshifa
Pharmaceuticals Factory, Aug. 20,
1998 — A131

75d, Bomb damage. 100d, Company
emblem, falling bombs. 150d, Casualties.

Perf. 13¾x13½, 13¾x13¼
1999, July 1 Litho.
511 A131 75d multi 1.75 1.75
512 A131 100d multi, vert. 2.25 2.25
513 A131 150d multi 3.50 3.50
Nos. 511-513 (3) 7.50 7.50

A132   A133

Perf. 13¼x13½, 13½x13¼
1999, Oct. 20 Litho.
514 A132 75d shown 2.40 2.40
515 A133 100d shown 3.00 3.00
516 A132 150d 7 people 4.75 4.75
Nos. 514-516 (3) 10.15 10.15

Intl. Year of the Elderly.

SOS Children's Villages, 50th
Anniv. — A134

1999, Oct. 31 Perf. 13½x13¼
517 A134 75d brn & multi 2.40 2.40
518 A134 100d grn & multi 3.00 3.00
519 A134 150d blue & multi 4.75 4.75
Nos. 517-519 (3) 10.15 10.15

UPU, 125th Anniv.
(in 1999) — A134a

2000, Mar. 1 Litho. Perf. 13½x13¼
Denomination Color
519A A134a 75d red 3.50 3.50
519B A134a 100d violet 4.75 4.75
519C A134a 150d black 7.00 7.00
Nos. 519A-519C (3) 15.25 15.25

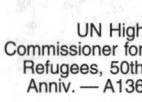

UN High
Commissioner for
Refugees, 50th
Anniv. — A136

Frame color: 100d, Green. 150d, Red. 200d,
Violet.

Perf. 13¼x13½
2001, Aug. 15 Litho.
523-525 A136 Set of 3 —

Al-Zubair
Prize for
Innovation
and
Scientific
Excellence
A137

Frame color: 100d, Yellow. 150d, Red. 200d,
Green.

2002, Feb. 14 Perf. 13¼
526-528 A137 Set of 3 —

Association for the
Promotion of
Scientific
Innovation — A138

Frame color: 100d, Black. 150d, Red. 200d,
Green.

2002, Feb. 14
529-531 A138 Set of 3 —

Guinea
Worm
Eradication
Campaign
A140

Designs: 100d, Infested foot, campaign
emblem. 150d, Campaign emblem. 200d,
Child, campaign emblem.

2002, Mar. 3 Litho. Perf. 13¼
535-537 A140 Set of 3 —

Sudanese postal officials have
declared as illegal the following items:
Sheets of six stamps depicting Pope
John Paul II (2 different)
Miniature sheet of two stamps depict-
ing Pope John Paul II (2 different).

Association of African Banknote and
Security Document Printers 11th
Annual Conference — A142

Conference emblem and: 100d, Association
emblem, circular design. 150d, Banknote
rosettes. 200d, Archaeological ruins.

2003, May 10 Litho. Perf. 13½x13¼
541-543 A142 Set of 3 6.25 6.25

Mango — A143   Nile Perch — A144

Cattle — A145   Soldiers — A146

Muhammad
Ahmad (Al-
Mahdi, 1844-85),
Religious
Leader — A147

Butterflyfish — A148

Temple of Amun
Ra — A149

Baobab
Tree — A150

Doum Palm
Tree — A151

Sheep — A152

Grapefruit
A153

Oil Rigs
A154

Tomb of Sheikh El-
Mursi
A155

Camel Postman
A156

Perf. 13½x13¼, 13¼x13½
2003, July 15
544 A143 50d multi .70 .70
545 A144 50d multi .70 .70
546 A145 75d multi 1.00 1.00
547 A146 100d multi 1.40 1.40
548 A147 100d multi 1.40 1.40
549 A148 125d multi 1.75 1.75
550 A149 150d multi 2.10 2.10
551 A150 150d multi 2.10 2.10
552 A151 150d multi 2.10 2.10
553 A152 150d multi 2.10 2.10
554 A153 200d multi 2.75 2.75
555 A154 200d multi 2.75 2.75
556 A155 300d multi 4.25 4.25
557 A156 500d multi 7.00 7.00
a. Souvenir sheet, #544-557, imperf. 32.50 32.50
Nos. 544-557 (14) 32.10 32.10

Parliament, 50th Anniv. — A157

Panel colors: 100d, Lilac. 200d, Yellow
orange. 250d, Pink.

2004, Jan. 5 Perf. 13½x13¼
558-560 A157 Set of 3 6.25 6.25

General Secretariat for Council of
Ministers, 50th Anniv. — A158

Panel colors: 100d, Light blue. 200d, Yellow.
250d, Pink.

2004, Jan. 8
561-563 A158 Set of 3 6.25 6.25

Rural Women's Innovation — A159

Panel colors: 100d, Light blue. 200d, Yellow.
250d, Lilac.

2004, Jan. 26
564-566 A159 Set of 3 6.25 6.25

AIR POST STAMPS

Nos. 40-41, 43 Overprinted in Black

Nos. C1-C2   No. C3

1931 Wmk. 214 Perf. 11½x12½, 14
C1 A2 5m blk & olive brown .60 1.00
C2 A2 10m blk & carmine 1.00 4.00
C3 A1 2p org & vio brown 1.00 3.50
Nos. C1-C3 (3) 2.60 8.50

Statue of
Gen.
C. G. Gordon
AP3

1931-35 Engr. Perf. 14
C4 AP3 3m dk brn & grn
('33) 3.00 6.00
C5 AP3 5m grn & blk 1.10 .20
C6 AP3 10m car rose & blk 1.10 .25
C7 AP3 15m dk brn & brn .45 .20
C8 AP3 2p org & blk .40 .20
C9 AP3 2½p bl & red vio
('33) 3.25 .20
C10 AP3 3p gray & blk .65 .20
C11 AP3 3½p dl vio & blk 1.50 .90
C12 AP3 4½p gray & brn 11.00 16.00
C13 AP3 5p ultra & blk 1.10 .35
C14 AP3 7½p pck grn & dk
grn ('35) 10.00 6.00
C15 AP3 10p peacock bl &
sep ('35) 10.00 .75
Nos. C4-C15 (12) 43.55 31.25

See Nos. C23-C30. For surcharges see
Nos. C17-C22, C31-C34.

No. 43 Surcharged
in Black

1932, July 18 Typo.
C16 A1 2½p on 2p 1.75 4.00

Nos. C6, C4-
C5, C12
Surcharged

1935	Engr.	Perf. 14	
C17	AP3 15m on 10m	.45	.20
a.	Double surcharge	600.00	775.00
b.	Arabic characters omitted	650.00	
C18	AP3 2½p on 3m	.95	6.00
a.	"½" 2¼mm high instead of 3mm	2.50	20.00
b.	Second Arabic character of surcharge omitted	55.00	125.00
C19	AP3 2½p on 5m	.50	1.75
a.	"½" 2¼mm high instead of 3mm	1.50	9.00
b.	Second Arabic character of surcharge omitted	30.00	60.00
c.	Inverted surcharge	800.00	900.00
d.	As "a,"Inverted	3,750.	
e.	As "b," inverted	1,500.	1,600.
C20	AP3 3p on 4½p	2.00	50.00
C21	AP3 7½p on 4½p	6.50	45.00
	"7¼" instead of "7½"		
C22	AP3 10p on 4½p	6.50	45.00
	Nos. C17-C22 (6)	16.90	107.95

Type of 1931-35

1936-37		Perf. 11½x12½	
C23	AP3 15m dk brn & brn ('37)	4.00	.20
C24	AP3 2p org & blk ('37)	5.00	15.00
C25	AP3 2½p bl & red vio	3.00	.20
C26	AP3 3p gray & blk ('37)	1.00	.40
C27	AP3 3½p dl vio & blk ('37)	2.50	12.00
C28	AP3 5p ultra & blk ('37)	4.00	.40
C29	AP3 7½p pck grn & dk grn ('37)	4.50	10.00
C30	AP3 10p pck bl & sep ('37)	4.50	20.00
	Nos. C23-C30 (8)	28.50	58.20

Nos. C25, C11, C14 and C15
Surcharged as in 1935

1938	Wmk. 214	Perf. 11½x12½, 14	
C31	AP3 5m on 2½p	1.00	.25
C32	AP3 3p on 3½p	15.00	30.00
a.	On No. C27	400.00	500.00
C33	AP3 3p on 7½p	6.00	6.00
a.	On No. C29	400.00	500.00
C34	AP3 5p on 10p	1.00	5.00
a.	On No. C30	400.00	500.00
	Nos. C31-C34 (4)	23.00	41.25

Catalogue values for unused
stamps in this section, from this
point to the end of the section, are
for Never Hinged items.

Bridge Over
Blue Nile,
Khartoum
AP4

Designs: 2½p, Kassala Jebel. 3p, Water
wheel. 3½p, Port Sudan. 4p, Gordon Memorial College. 4½p, Nile post boat. 6p, Suakin.
20p, General Post Office, Khartoum.

1950, July 1	Engr.	Perf. 12	
C35	AP4 2p dk bl grn & blk	5.00	.65
C36	AP4 2½p red org & bl	.40	.85
C37	AP4 3p dp bl & plum	2.75	.35
C38	AP4 3½p chnt & choc	.90	2.10
C39	AP4 4p bl & brn	.90	1.50
C40	AP4 4½p ultra & blk	2.50	3.00
C41	AP4 6p car & blk	2.00	1.75
C42	AP4 20p plum & blk	2.00	3.25
	Nos. C35-C42 (8)	16.45	13.45

For overprints see Nos. CO1-CO8.

AIR POST OFFICIAL

Catalogue values for unused
stamps in this section are for
Never Hinged items.

Nos. C35 to
C42
Overprinted
in Carmine
or Black

1950, July 1	Wmk. 214	Perf. 12	
CO1	AP4 2p dk bl grn & blk (C)	13.00	2.50
CO2	AP4 2½p red org & bl	1.40	1.50
CO3	AP4 3p dp bl & plum	.75	1.00
CO4	AP4 3½p chnt & choc	.75	5.50
CO5	AP4 4p bl & brn	.75	4.75
CO6	AP4 4½p ultra & blk (C)	3.50	13.00
CO7	AP4 6p car & blk (C)	.95	3.75
CO8	AP4 20p plum & blk (C)	4.75	11.00
	Nos. CO1-CO8 (8)	25.85	43.00

POSTAGE DUE STAMPS

Postage Due Stamps
of Egypt, 1889,
Overprinted in Black

1897	Wmk. 119	Perf. 14	
J1	D3 2m green	1.50	5.00
J2	D3 4m maroon	1.50	5.00
J3	D3 1p ultra	10.00	4.00
J4	D3 2p orange	10.00	8.50
	Nos. J1-J4 (4)	23.00	22.50

Steamboat on Nile
River — D1

1901	Typo.	Wmk. 179	
J5	D1 2m orange brn & blk	.70	.50
J6	D1 4m blue green & brn	2.00	1.00
J7	D1 10m blue vio & blue grn	4.00	3.50
J8	D1 20m car rose & ultra	3.75	3.75
	Nos. J5-J8 (4)	10.45	8.75

1927-30	Wmk. Multiple S G (214)		
J9	D1 2m org brn & blk ('30)	2.50	2.50
J10	D1 4m blue grn & brn	1.00	.75
J11	D1 10m violet & blue grn	1.50	1.60
	Nos. J9-J11 (3)	5.00	4.85

Catalogue values for unused
stamps in this section, from this
point to the end of the section, are
for Never Hinged items.

Redrawn

Bottom inscription
altered — D2

1948, Jan. 1			
J12	D2 2m dp orange & blk	1.00	21.00
J13	D2 4m blue grn & choc	2.25	21.00
J14	D2 10m rose lil & bl grn	17.00	13.00
a.	Wmk. 345 ('73)		
J15	D2 20m brt car rose & ultra	18.00	24.00
a.	Wmk. 345 ('73)		
	Nos. J12-J15 (4)	38.25	79.00

ARMY OFFICIALS

Regular Issues of 1898 and 1902-08
Overprinted in Black:

Nos. MO1, MO3 and MO2, MO4

1905	Wmk. 71	Perf. 14	
MO1	A1 1m rose & brown	125.00	125.00
a.	Pair, #MO1 and #MO2	3,250.	1,750.
b.		2,750.	
MO2	A1 1m rose & brown	1,800.	1,800.
	Wmk. 179		
MO3	A1 1m car rose & brn	3.00	2.00
a.	"OFFICIAL"	45.00	30.00
b.	Inverted overprint	70.00	60.00
MO4	A1 1m car rose & brn	475.00	24.00
a.	Inverted overprint	350.00	375.00

Regular Issues of
1902-11
Overprinted in
Black

1906-11			
MO5	A1 1m car rose & brn	1.25	.30
a.	"Army" and "Service" 14mm apart	275.00	200.00
b.	Inverted overprint	425.00	450.00
c.	Pair, one without ovpt.		3,750.
d.	Double overprint		800.00
e.	"Service" omitted		3,750.
MO6	A1 2m brn & grn	10.00	.95
a.	Pair, one without ovpt.	2,500.	
b.	"Army" omitted	3,000.	
MO7	A1 3m green & violet	16.00	.40
a.	"Army" omitted	2,000.	
MO8	A1 5m blk & rose red	1.40	.20
a.	Inverted overprint	225.00	
b.	Double overprint	225.00	225.00
c.	Double ovpt., one invtd.	875.00	400.00
MO9	A1 1p yel brn & ultra	12.00	.40
a.	"Army" omitted	2,000.	2,000.
MO10	A1 2p ultra & blk ('09)	45.00	12.50
a.	Double overprint		
MO11	A1 5p grn & org brn ('08)	100.00	60.00
MO12	A1 10p dp vio & blk ('11)	500.00	600.00
	Nos. MO5-MO12 (8)	685.65	674.75

Same Overprint On Regular Issue of
1898
Wmk. 71

MO13	A1 2p ultra & black	60.00	10.00
a.	Inverted overprint		
MO14	A1 5p grn & org brn	95.00	175.00
MO15	A1 10p dp vio & blk	140.00	375.00

There are two types of this overprint which
may be distinguished by the size and shape of
the "y."

OFFICIAL STAMPS

Regular Issue of
1898 Overprinted
in Black

1902-06	Wmk. 71	Perf. 14	
O1	A1 1m rose & brown	2.00	7.50
a.	Inverted overprint	275.00	400.00
b.	Round periods	7.50	30.00
c.	Double overprint	550.00	
d.	Oval "O" in overprint	90.00	
e.	As "d," inverted overprint	5,000.	
O2	A1 10p dp vio & blk ('06)	13.00	20.00

Same Ovpt. on Stamps of 1902-11

1903-12	Wmk. 179		
O3	A1 1m car rose & brn ('04)	.45	.20
a.	Double overprint		
O4	A1 3m grn & vio ('04)	2.25	.20
a.	Double overprint		
O5	A1 5m blk & rose red	2.25	.20
O6	A1 1p yel brn & ultra	2.25	.20
O7	A1 2p ultra & blk	20.00	.20
O8	A1 5p grn & org brn	1.75	.20
O9	A1 10p dp vio & blk	3.75	47.50
	Nos. O3-O9 (7)	32.70	48.75

Regular Issue of 1927-
40 Overprinted in Black

Perf. 14, 13½x 14			
1936-46	Wmk. 214		
O10	A2 1m dk org & int blk ('46)	.75	3.50
O11	A2 2m dk brn & dk org ('45)	.25	.20
O12	A2 3m green & vio ('37)	1.25	.20
O13	A2 4m brown & green	1.60	.20
O14	A2 5m blk & ol brn ('40)	.35	.20
O15	A2 10m blk & car ('46)	.35	.20
O16	A2 15m org brn & ultra ('37)	3.00	.20

O17	A1 2p org & vio brn ('37)	5.00	.20
O18	A1 3p dk bl & red brn ('46)	2.75	.50
O19	A1 4p blk & ultra ('46)	12.50	1.00
O20	A1 5p dk grn & org brn	6.75	.20
O21	A1 6p blk & pale bl ('46)	4.00	2.00
O22	A1 8p blk & pck grn ('46)	2.75	9.00
O23	A1 10p dp vio & blk ('37)	15.00	2.50
O24	A1 20p bl & lt bl ('46)	13.00	20.00
	Nos. O10-O24 (15)	69.30	29.10

Catalogue values for unused
stamps in this section, from this
point to the end of the section, are
for Never Hinged items.

#79-85 Overprinted Like #O10-O16

1948, Jan. 1			
O28	A7 1m dk org & blk	.25	1.50
O29	A7 2m choc & org	1.00	.20
O30	A7 3m grn & rose lil	1.75	3.00
O31	A7 4m choc & sl grn	1.75	1.00
O32	A7 5m blk & ol brn	1.75	.20
O33	A7 10m blk & car	1.50	.35
O34	A7 15m org brn & ultra	1.75	.20

Nos. 86-94 Overprinted Like Nos.
O17-O24

O35	A8 2p org yel & vio brn	1.75	.20
O36	A8 3p dk bl & red brn	1.75	.20
O37	A8 4p blk & ultra	1.75	.20
a.	Perf. 13	14.00	16.00
O38	A8 5p dk grn & org	2.25	.20
O39	A8 6p blk & pale bl	1.75	.20
O40	A8 8p blk & pck grn	1.75	1.25
O41	A8 10p dp rose lil & blk	2.50	.20
O42	A8 20p dk bl & bl	3.75	1.00
a.	Perf. 13		
O43	A8 50p ultra & car	55.00	25.00
	Nos. O28-O43 (16)	82.00	34.90

Nos. 98-104 Overprinted Liked Nos.
O10-O16 in Red

1951, Sept. 1	Wmk. 214	Perf. 14	
Center in Black			
O44	A11 1m orange	.20	.20
O45	A11 2m ultra	.20	.20
O46	A11 3m dk grn	.60	.60
O47	A11 4m emerald	.20	.20
O48	A11 5m plum	.20	.20
O49	A11 10m light blue	.20	.20
O50	A11 15m dp org brn	.20	.20

Nos. 105-114 Overprinted Like Nos.
O17-O24 in Black or Red
Perf. 13

O51	A12 2p lt bl & dk bl	.20	.20
a.	Inverted overprint	350.00	
O52	A12 3p vio bl & brn	.60	.20
O53	A12 3½p brn & bl grn	.80	.40
O54	A12 4p blk & dp bl	.80	.20
O55	A12 5p emer & org brn	.85	.20
O56	A12 6p blk & bl	1.00	.35
O57	A12 8p brn & dp bl	1.40	.35
O58	A12 10p grn & blk (R)	1.75	.20
O59	A12 20p blk & bl grn	2.75	1.25
a.	Inverted overprint		700.00
O60	A13 50p blk & car	8.50	4.00
	Nos. O44-O60 (17)	20.45	9.30

No. 112 Overprinted Like Nos. O17-
O24 in Black

1958			
O61	A12 10p green & black	.65	.20

Nos. 146-159
Overprinted

Perf. 14½x14, 14x14½

1962, Oct. 1   Litho.   Wmk. 345
Size: 23x19mm, 19x23mm

O62	A25	5m blue	.20	.20
O63	A26	10m blue & lilac	.20	.20
O64	A25	15m yel, vio, org & brn	.20	.20
O65	A26	2p lt pur	.25	.20
O66	A26	3p bl grn, red brn & brn	.35	.20
O67	A26	35m yel grn, brn & org brn	.40	.20
O68	A26	4p red, lt bl & lil	.45	.25
O69	A25	55m gray & yel ol	.75	.45
O70	A25	6p brn & lt bl	.85	.45
O71	A25	8p green	1.10	.55

Size: 24½x30mm, 30x24½mm

O72	A26	10p lt bl, red brn & blk	1.50	.65
O73	A25	20p gray ol & yel grn	3.00	1.40
a.		Perf. 13½x12½	2.75	1.90
O74	A25	50p dk gray, ol & bl	7.50	3.50
a.		Perf. 13½x14	6.50	3.25

Engr.

O75	A13	£1 grn & brn org	19.00	12.50
		Nos. O62-O75 (14)	35.75	20.95

The overprint measures 12x4½mm on Nos. O62-O71; 16x6mm on Nos. O72-O75.

1975-79   Unwmk.
Same Perfs., Sizes and Printing Methods as Before

O62a	A25	5m	.20	.20
O63a	A26	10m ('76)	.20	.20
O64a	A25	15m	.20	.20
O65a	A26	2p	.20	.20
O66a	A26	3p	.35	.25
O67a	A26	35m	.40	.25
O68a	A26	4p	.45	.25
O69a	A25	55m	.75	.45
O70a	A25	6p ('76)	.80	.45
O71a	A25	8p	1.10	.55
O72a	A26	10p	1.50	.70
O73b	A25	20p	2.50	1.25
O74b	A25	50p	2.50	1.25
O75a	A13	£1 ('79)	19.00	12.50
		Nos. O62a-O75a (14)	30.15	18.70

Nos. 404-419
Overprinted

Perf. 13½x13

1991, July 1   Litho.   Unwmk.

O76	A105	25p on #404	.20	.20
O77	A105	50p on #405	.20	.20
O78	A105	75p on #406	.35	.20
O79	A105	100p on #407	.45	.30
O80	A105	125p on #408	.55	.35

Size: 30x24mm
Perf. 14x14½, 13½x14

O81	A105	150p on #409	.65	.40
O82	A105	175p on #410	.80	.50
O83	A105	£2 on #411	.90	.60

Size: 26x37mm
Perf. 14

O84	A105	250p on #412	1.10	.70
O85	A105	£3 on #413	1.35	.90

Size: 24x30mm
Perf. 13½x14

O86	A105	£4 on #414	1.75	1.10
O87	A105	£5 on #415	2.20	1.40

Size: 36x27mm
Perf. 14   Wmk. 334

O88	A105	£8 on #416	3.50	2.25
O89	A105	£10 on #417	4.40	5.00
O90	A105	£15 on #418	6.60	4.25
O91	A105	£20 on #419	8.80	5.75
		Nos. O76-O91 (16)	33.80	24.10

For surcharges see Nos. O104-O111.

Nos. 420, 427-428
Overprinted

1992   Litho.   Unwmk.   Perf. 14½

O92	A25	25p on #420	.25	.20

Perf. 14x13½, 13½x14

O99	A25	£5 on #427	2.50	1.75
O100	A25	£10 on #428	5.25	3.50
		Nos. O92-O100 (3)	8.00	5.45

Nos. O79, O81, O83, O85-O87
Surcharged in Blue Violet or Black

		Perf. 13½x13		
1993?		**Litho.**	**Unwmk.**	
O104	A105	1d on 100p #O79	1.00	.65
		Perf. 13½x14		
O105	A105	1.50d on 150p #O81	1.50	1.00
O107	A105	2d on £2 #O83	2.00	1.25
		Perf. 14		
O109	A105	3d on £3 #O85	3.00	2.00
		Perf. 14½x14		
O110	A105	4d on £4 #O86	4.00	2.75
		Perf. 13½x14		
O111	A105	5d on £5 #O87 (Blk)	5.00	3.25
		Perf. 14		
		Size: 36x27mm		
O112	A109	35d on £8 #O88	14.50	14.50
		Nos. O104-O112 (7)	31.00	25.40

Coat of Arms — O1

2003		**Litho.**	**Perf. 13½x13½**	
O113	O1	50d multi	.50	.50
O114	O1	100d multi	.95	.95
O115	O1	200d multi	1.90	1.90
O116	O1	300d multi	3.00	3.00
		Nos. O113-O116 (4)	6.35	6.35

SURINAM

ˈsur-ə-ˌnam

(Dutch Guiana)

LOCATION — On the northeast coast of South America, bordering on the Atlantic Ocean
GOVT. — Republic
AREA — 63,234 sq. mi.
POP. — 431,156 (1999 est.)
CAPITAL — Paramaribo

The Dutch colony of Surinam became an integral part of the Kingdom of the Netherlands under the Constitution of 1954. It became an independent state November 25, 1975.

100 Cents = 1 Gulden (Florin)

> Catalogue values for unused stamps in this country are for Never Hinged items, beginning with Scott 168 in the regular postage section, Scott B34 in the semi-postal section, Scott C23 in the airpost section, Scott CB1 in the airpost semi-postal section, and Scott J33 in the postage due section.

Watermark

Wmk. 202 — Circles

King William III — A1   Numeral of Value — A2

Perf. 11½, 11½x12, 12½x12, 13½, 14

1873-89		**Typo.**	**Unwmk.**	
		Without Gum		
1	A1	1c lil gray ('85)	2.10	2.40
2	A1	2c yellow ('85)	1.40	1.40
3	A1	2½c rose	1.40	1.40
4	A1	3c green	17.50	15.00
5	A1	5c dull violet	15.00	4.75
6	A1	10c bister	3.25	2.25
7	A1	12½c sl bl ('85)	17.00	6.75
8	A1	15c gray ('89)	20.00	6.75
9	A1	20c green ('89)	30.00	27.50
10	A1	25c grnsh blue	70.00	8.00
11	A1	25c ultra	240.00	20.00
12	A1	30c red brn ('88)	30.00	32.50
13	A1	40c dk brn ('89)	27.50	26.00
14	A1	50c brown org	26.00	17.00
15	A1	1g red brn & gray ('89)	42.50	42.50
16	A1	2.50g grn & org ('79)	65.00	57.50
		Nos. 1-16 (16)	608.65	271.70
		Perf. 14, Small Holes		
3b	A1	2½c rose	10.00	11.50
4b	A1	3c green	18.00	24.00
5b	A1	5c dull violet	18.00	15.00
6b	A1	10c bister	17.00	20.00
11b	A1	25c ultra	225.00	60.00
14b	A1	50c brown org	47.50	40.00
		Nos. 3b-14b (6)	335.50	170.50

The paper of Nos. 3-6, 11 and 14 sometimes has an accidental bluish tinge of varying strength. During its manufacture a chemical whitener (bluing agent) was added in varying quantities. No particular printing was made on bluish paper.
"Small hole" varieties have the spaces between the holes wider than the diameter of the holes.
For surcharges see Nos. 23, 31-35, 39-42.

1890			*Perf. 11½x11, 12½*	
17	A2	1c gray	1.60	1.10
18	A2	2c yellow brn	2.50	2.00
19	A2	2½c carmine	2.00	1.60
20	A2	3c green	4.75	3.25
21	A2	5c ultra	21.00	1.10
		Nos. 17-21 (5)	31.85	9.05

For surcharges see Nos. 63-64.

A3

1892, Aug. 11			*Perf. 10½*	
		Without Gum		
22	A3	2½c black & org	1.50	1.00
a.		First and fifth vertical words have fancy "F"	22.50	14.00
b.		Imperf.	2.00	
c.		As "a," imperf.	27.50	

No. 14 Surcharged in Black

$2\frac{1}{2}$

CENT.

1892, Aug. 1			*Perf. 14*	
23	A1	2½c on 50c	210.00	10.00
a.		Perf. 12½x12	300.00	9.00
b.		Perf. 11½x12	350.00	12.50
c.		Double surcharge	300.00	225.00
d.		Perf. 14, small holes	225.00	12.50

Nos. 23-23c were issued without gum.

Queen Wilhelmina — A5

1892-93		**Typo.**	*Perf. 12½*	
25	A5	10c bister	35.00	2.75
26	A5	12½c rose lilac	40.00	4.75
27	A5	15c gray	3.25	2.75
28	A5	20c green	3.75	2.75
29	A5	25c blue	8.25	4.75
30	A5	30c red brown	4.75	4.00
		Nos. 25-30 (6)	95.00	21.25

For surcharges see Nos. 65-66.

Nos. 7-12 Surcharged

1898		*Perf. 11½x12, 12½x12, 13½*		
		Without Gum		
31	A1	10c on 12½c sl bl	22.50	3.25
32	A1	10c on 15c gray	52.50	45.00
33	A1	10c on 20c green	4.25	4.25
34	A1	10c on 25c grnsh bl	9.00	5.25
c.		Perf. 11½x12	10.00	10.00
34A	A1	10c on 25c ultra	475.00	425.00
b.		Perf. 11½x12	550.00	475.00
35	A1	10c on 30c red brn	4.25	4.25
a.		Double surcharge	275.00	

Dangerous counterfeits exist.

Netherlands Nos. 80, 83-84
Surcharged

50 Cᵀ   SURINAME
No. 36   Nos. 37-38

1900, Jan. 8			*Perf. 12½*	
		Without Gum		
36	A11	50c on 50c	18.00	6.25
		Engr.		
		Perf. 11½x11		
37	A12	100c on 1g dk grn	17.50	10.50
38	A12	2.50g on 2½g brn lil	15.00	9.75
		Nos. 36-38 (3)	50.50	26.50

For surcharge see No. 67.

Nos. 13-16 Surcharged

		Perf. 11½, 11½x12, 12½x12, 14		
1900				**Typo.**
		Without Gum		
39	A1	25c on 40c	3.25	2.40
40	A1	25c on 50c	3.25	2.40
a.		Perf. 14, small holes	110.00	125.00
b.		Perf. 11½x12	3.75	3.75
41	A1	50c on 1g	27.50	24.00
42	A1	50c on 2.50g	110.00	125.00
		Nos. 39-42 (4)	144.00	153.80

Counterfeits of No. 42 exist.

A9

Queen Wilhelmina
A10   A11

1902-08		Typo.	Perf. 12½	
44	A9	½c violet	.75	.65
45	A9	1c olive grn	1.50	1.00
46	A9	2c yellow brn	8.25	3.25
47	A9	2½c blue grn	3.75	.35
48	A9	3c orange	6.00	4.00
49	A9	5c red	6.00	.35
50	A9	7½c gray ('08)	13.00	6.00
51	A10	10c slate	8.50	.70
52	A10	12½c deep blue	3.25	.35
53	A10	15c dp brown	22.50	7.75
54	A10	20c olive grn	21.00	4.00
55	A10	22½c brn & ol grn	17.50	9.75
56	A10	25c violet	14.50	1.00
57	A10	30c orange brn	35.00	11.00
58	A10	50c lake brown	27.50	6.75

Engr.
Perf. 11

59	A11	1g violet	45.00	13.50
60	A11	2½g slate blue	42.50	50.00
	Nos. 44-60 (17)		276.50	120.40

Nos. 44-58, and possibly 59-60, were partially issued without gum.

A12

1909 Typeset *Serrate Roulette 13½*
Without Gum

61	A12	5c red	8.50	7.00
a.	Tête bêche pair		140.00	125.00

Perf. 11½x10½

62	A12	5c red	10.00	8.50
a.	Tête bêche pair		90.00	92.50

Nos. 17-18, 29-30, 38 Surcharged in Red

Nos. 63-64   Nos. 65-66

No. 67

30 cent

1911, July 15   Typo.   Perf. 12½
Without Gum

63	A2	½c on 1c	1.50	.95
64	A2	½c on 2c	8.50	6.75
65	A5	15c on 25c	65.00	50.00
66	A5	20c on 30c	9.25	6.75

Engr.
Perf. 11½x11

67	A12	30c on 2.50g on 2½g	110.00	100.00
	Nos. 63-67 (5)		194.25	164.45

A13

1912, July   Typeset   Perf. 11½
Without Gum

70	A13	½c lilac	.85	.85
a.	Horiz. pair, imperf. btwn.		200.00	
71	A13	2½c dk green	.85	.85
72	A13	5c pale red	6.75	6.75
a.	Vert. pair, imperf. btwn.		240.00	
73	A13	12½c deep blue	8.25	8.25
	Nos. 70-73 (4)		16.70	16.70

Numeral of
Value — A14

Queen Wilhelmina
A15   A16

1913-31		Typo.	Perf. 12½	
74	A14	½c violet	.35	.25
75	A14	1c olive green	.35	.20
76	A14	1½c blue, perf 11½ ('21)	.35	.20
a.	Perf. 12½ ('32)		1.00	.75
77	A14	2c yellow brn	1.40	1.00
78	A14	2½c green	.80	.20
79	A14	3c yellow	.70	.55
80	A14	3c green ('26)	2.75	2.25
81	A14	4c chlky bl ('26)	7.00	4.25
82	A14	5c rose	1.40	.20
83	A14	5c green ('22)	1.75	.90
84	A14	5c lilac ('26)	1.40	.20
85	A14	6c bister ('26)	2.50	2.25
86	A14	6c red org ('31)	1.90	.45
87	A14	7½c drab	.90	.35
a.	Perf. 11x11½		1.25	.55
88	A14	7½c orange ('27)	1.25	.35
89	A14	7½c yellow ('31)	7.75	7.75
90	A14	10c violet ('22)	4.25	4.25
91	A14	10c rose ('26)	3.50	.50
92	A15	10c car rose	1.25	.55
93	A15	12½c blue	1.60	.55
94	A15	12½c red ('22)	1.75	1.90
95	A15	15c olive grn	.50	.60
96	A15	15c lt blue ('26)	6.50	4.00
97	A15	20c green	3.00	2.75
98	A15	20c blue ('22)	2.00	1.75
99	A15	20c ol grn ('26)	3.00	2.50
100	A15	22½c orange	2.25	2.25
101	A15	25c red violet	3.50	.35
102	A15	30c slate	4.25	1.00
103	A15	32½c vio & org ('22)	12.50	15.00
104	A15	35c sl & red ('26)	4.25	4.25

Perf. 11, 11½, 11½x11, 12½
Engr.

105	A16	50c green	3.50	.75
a.	Perf. 12½ ('32)		12.00	1.40
106	A16	1g brown	4.75	.45
a.	Perf. 12½ ('32)		13.00	.85
107	A16	1½g dp vio ('26)	30.00	30.00
108	A16	2½g carmine	25.00	22.50
a.	Perf. 11½x11		30.00	27.50
	Nos. 74-108 (35)		149.90	117.25

All stamps issued before 1919 were without gum.
Early printings of Nos. 74-104 had water soluble ink.
For surcharges see Nos. 116-120, 139.

Queen
Wilhelmina — A17

1923, Oct. 5   Perf. 11, 11x11½, 11½

109	A17	5c green	.90	.60
110	A17	10c car rose	1.50	1.25
111	A17	20c indigo	3.00	2.50
112	A17	50c brown org	16.00	17.50
113	A17	1g brown vio	22.50	15.00
114	A17	2½g gray blk	65.00	175.00
115	A17	5g brown	87.50	210.00
	Nos. 109-115 (7)		196.40	421.85

25th anniv. of the assumption of the government of the Netherlands by Queen Wilhelmina, at age 18.
Values for Nos. 114-115 used are for copies clearly dated before July 15, 1924.

Nos. 83, 93-94, 98 Surcharged in
Black or Red:

j

k

m

1925, Dec. 19   Typo.   Perf. 12½

116	A14	3c on 5c green	1.10	1.10
117	A15	10c on 12½c red	2.25	2.25
118	A15	15c on 12½c blue (R)	1.50	1.50
119	A15	15c on 20c blue	1.50	1.50
	Nos. 116-119 (4)		6.35	6.35

No. 100 Surcharged in
Blue

1926, Jan. 1

120	A15	12½c on 22½c org	21.00	21.00

Postage Due Stamps Nos. J14 and
J29 Surcharged in Blue or Black:

o   p

121	D2(o)	12½c on 40c (Bl)	3.25	3.25
122	D2(p)	12½c on 40c (Bk)	24.00	24.00
	Nos. 120-122 (3)		48.25	48.25

No. 121 issued without gum.

Queen
Wilhelmina — A21

1927-30		Engr.	Perf. 11½	
123	A21	10c carmine	.75	.35
124	A21	12½c red orange	1.50	1.60
125	A21	15c dark blue	1.75	.50
126	A21	20c indigo	1.75	.70
127	A21	21c dk brown ('30)	17.00	17.00
128	A21	22½c brown ('28)	6.75	8.25
129	A21	25c dk violet	2.50	.60
130	A21	30c dk green	2.50	.95
131	A21	35c black brown	2.50	2.50
	Nos. 123-131 (9)		37.00	32.45

Types of Netherlands
Marine Insurance
Stamps Inscribed
"SURINAME" and
Surcharged

1927, Oct. 26

132	MI1	3c on 15c dk grn	.55	.55
133	MI1	10c on 60c car rose	.55	.55
134	MI1	12½c on 75c gray brn	.55	.55
135	MI2	15c on 1.50 dk blue	2.25	2.25
136	MI2	25c on 2.25g org brn	5.75	5.75
137	MI3	30c on 4½g black	7.25	5.75
138	MI3	50c on 7½g red	5.75	5.75
	Nos. 132-138 (7)		22.65	21.15

Nos. 135-137 have "FRANKEERZEGEL" in small capitals in one line. Nos. 135 and 136 have a heavy bar across the top of the stamp.

No. 88 Surcharged

1930, Mar. 1   Typo.   Perf. 12½

139	A14	6c on 7½c orange	1.75	.90

Prince William I
(Portrait by Van
Key) — A22

1933, Apr. 24   Photo.

141	A22	6c deep orange	5.25	1.50

400th birth anniv. of Prince William I, Count of Nassau and Prince of Orange, frequently referred to as William the Silent.

Van   Queen
Walbeeck's   Wilhelmina
Ship   A24
A23

1936-41		Litho.	Perf. 13½x12½	
142	A23	½c yellow brn	.25	.25
143	A23	1c lt yellow grn	.35	.20
144	A23	1½c brt blue	.45	.35
145	A23	2c black brown	.50	.25
146	A23	2½c green	.25	.20
a.	Perf. 13 ('41)		7.75	2.75
147	A23	3c dark ultra	.50	.35
148	A23	4c orange	.50	.60
149	A23	5c gray	.50	.25
150	A23	6c red	2.00	1.60
151	A23	7½c red violet	.25	.20
a.	7½c plum, perf. 13 ('41)		2.40	.25

Engr.
Perf. 14, 12½
Size: 20x30mm

152	A24	10c vermilion	.70	.20
a.	Perf. 12½ ('39)		47.50	9.25
153	A24	12½c dull green	2.75	1.00
154	A24	15c dark blue	1.00	.50
155	A24	20c yellow org	1.75	.50
156	A24	21c dk gray	2.75	2.50
a.	Perf. 12½ ('39)		3.00	3.00
157	A24	25c brown lake	1.90	.85
158	A24	30c brown vio	3.00	.85
159	A24	35c olive brown	3.25	3.25

Perf. 12½x14
Size: 22x33mm

160	A24	50c dull yel grn	3.25	1.60
161	A24	1g dull blue	6.00	1.90
162	A24	1.50g black brown	17.00	13.50
163	A24	2.50g rose lake	10.00	6.75
	Nos. 142-163 (22)		58.90	37.60

For surcharges see Nos. 181-183, B37-B40.

Queen
Wilhelmina — A25

Perf. 12½x12
1938, Aug. 30   Photo.   Wmk. 202
164	A25	2c dull purple	.35	.25
165	A25	7½c red orange	.85	.80
166	A25	15c royal blue	2.10	2.00
		Nos. 164-166 (3)	3.30	3.05

Reign of Queen Wilhelmina, 40th anniv.

> Catalogue values for unused stamps in this section, from this point to the end of the section, are for Never Hinged items.

Van Walbeeck's Ship — A26

Queen Wilhelmina — A27

1941   Unwmk.   Typo.   Perf. 12
168	A26	1c lt yellow grn	.60	.20
169	A26	2c black brown	1.40	1.40

Type A26 is similar to type A23 except for the white side frame lines which extend to the base.
For surcharges see No. 180.

1941-46   Photo.   Perf. 13½x12½
Size: 18x22½mm
174	A27	12½c royal blue ('46)	.25	.20

Perf. 12½
175	A27	15c ultra	17.50	6.50

Royal Family — A28

1943, Nov. 2   Engr.   Perf. 13½x13
176	A28	2½c deep orange	.25	.35
177	A28	7½c red	.25	.20
178	A28	15c black	1.75	1.50
179	A28	40c deep blue	2.25	1.75
		Nos. 176-179 (4)	4.50	3.80

Birth of Princess Margriet Francisca of the Netherlands.

Nos. 168, 151, 152 Surcharged with New Values and Bars in Black
1945   Unwmk.   Perf. 13, 14, 12
180	A26	½c on 1c	.20	.20
181	A23	2½c on 7½c	1.60	1.75
182	A24	5c on 10c	.55	.40
183	A24	7½c on 10c	.65	.40
a.		Double surcharge	175.00	190.00
		Nos. 180-183 (4)	3.00	2.75

Bauxite Mine, Moengo — A29

Queen Wilhelmina
A30   A31

Designs: 1½c, Bush Negroes on Cottica River near Moengo. 2c, Waterfall in interior. 2½c, Road scene, Coronie District. 3c, Surinam River near Berg en Dahl Plantation. 4c, Government Square, Paramaribo. 5c, Mining

---

gold. 6c, Street in Paramaribo. 7½c, Sugar cane train.

1945, Nov. 5   Engr.   Perf. 12
184	A29	1c rose carmine	.25	.25
185	A29	1½c rose lake	1.00	1.00
186	A29	2c violet	.45	.35
187	A29	2½c olive brn	.45	.35
188	A29	3c dull green	1.00	.55
189	A29	4c brown	1.00	.60
190	A29	5c blue	1.00	.25
191	A29	6c olive	1.75	1.25
192	A29	7½c deep orange	.65	.30
193	A30	10c blue	1.25	.20
194	A30	15c brown	1.60	.20
195	A30	20c dull green	2.50	.20
196	A30	22½c gray	3.00	.70
197	A30	25c carmine	7.75	3.50
198	A30	30c olive green	7.75	.45
199	A30	35c brt blue grn	13.00	5.75
200	A30	40c rose lake	7.50	.25
201	A30	50c red orange	7.50	.25
202	A30	60c violet	7.50	.65
203	A31	1g red brown	9.50	.30
204	A31	1.50g lilac	8.00	.65
205	A31	2.50g olive brn	16.00	.75
206	A31	5g rose carmine	35.00	10.00
207	A31	10g red brown	60.00	15.00
		Nos. 184-207 (24)	195.40	43.80

For surcharges see #240, B41-B46, CB2-CB3.

Nos. 151 and 152 Surcharged with New Value and Bar in Blue or Black
1947   Perf. 13½x12½, 14
209	A23	1½(c) on 7½c (Bl)	.20	.20
a.		Double surcharge	200.00	
210	A24	2½c on 10c (Bk)	.90	.30

Numeral   Queen
A32   Wilhelmina
A33

Perf. 12½x13½
1948, July 21   Unwmk.   Photo.
211	A32	1c dark red	.20	.20
212	A32	1½c plum	.20	.20
213	A32	2c purple	.20	.20
214	A32	2½c olive grn	1.10	.20
215	A32	3c dark green	.20	.20
216	A32	4c red brown	.20	.20

Perf. 13½x12½
217	A33	5c deep blue	.35	.20
218	A33	6c dark olive	.85	.65
219	A33	7½c scarlet	.35	.20
220	A33	10c blue	.50	.20
221	A33	12½c dark blue	1.00	.90
222	A33	15c henna brown	1.40	.35
223	A33	17½c dk vio brn	1.50	1.10
224	A33	20c dk blue grn	1.25	.20
225	A33	22½c slate blue	1.25	.60
226	A33	25c crimson	1.25	.25
227	A33	27½c car lake	1.25	.20
228	A33	30c olive green	1.50	.20
229	A33	37½c olive brn	2.50	1.75
230	A33	40c lilac rose	1.75	.25
231	A33	50c red orange	1.75	.25
232	A33	60c purple	2.00	.35
233	A33	70c black	2.25	.60
		Nos. 211-233 (23)	24.80	9.45

See Nos. 241-242.

Wilhelmina - Juliana
A34   A35

1948, Aug. 30   Engr.   Perf. 12½x14
234	A34	7½c vermilion	.65	.65
235	A34	12½c deep blue	.65	.65

Reign of Queen Wilhelmina, 50th anniv.

Perf. 14x13
1948, Sept. 10   Wmk. 202   Photo.
236	A35	7½c deep orange	2.75	2.75
237	A35	12½c ultra	2.75	2.75

Investiture of Queen Juliana, Sept. 6, 1948.
For surcharges see Nos. B53-B54.

Post Horns
Entwined — A36

1949, Oct. 1   Unwmk.   Perf. 11½x12
238	A36	7½c brown red	5.25	2.75
239	A36	27½c dull blue	5.25	2.00

UPU, 75th anniversary.

No. 192 Surcharged with New Value, Square and Bar in Black
1950, Aug. 9   Perf. 12
240	A29	1c on 7½c dp org	.60	.60

Numeral Type of 1948
1951, Apr. 5   Perf. 12½x13½
241	A32	5c deep blue	1.10	.20
242	A32	7½c deep orange	2.75	1.50

A37

Queen Juliana — A38

1951, Apr. 5   Perf. 13½x13
243	A37	10c blue	.35	.20
244	A37	15c henna brn	.80	.20
245	A37	20c dk blue grn	2.00	.20
246	A37	25c crimson	1.25	.30
247	A37	27½c carmine lake	1.25	.45
248	A37	30c olive green	1.25	.30
249	A37	35c olive brown	1.50	1.25
250	A37	40c lilac rose	1.60	.30
251	A37	50c red orange	2.00	.35

Engr.
Perf. 12½x12
252	A38	1g red brown	21.00	.25
		Nos. 243-252 (10)	33.00	3.55

For surcharge see No. 271.

Shooting Fish   Fisherman
A39   A40

Designs: 5c, Bauxite mining. 6c, Log raft. 7½c, Plowing with Water Buffalo. 10c, Woman picking fruit. 12½c, Armored catfish. 15c, Macaw. 17½c, Armadillo. 20c, Poling canoe. 25c, Common iguana.

1953-55   Photo.   Perf. 14x13, 13x14
253	A39	2c olive green	.20	.20
254	A40	2½c blue green	.25	.20
255	A40	5c gray	.30	.20
256	A40	6c bright blue	1.50	1.00
257	A40	7½c purple	.20	.20
258	A40	10c bright red	.20	.20
259	A40	12½c dk gray blue	1.75	1.10
260	A40	15c crimson	.60	.20
261	A40	17½c red brown	2.75	1.60
262	A40	20c Prus green	.50	.20
263	A40	25c olive green	2.50	.65
a.		Min. sheet of 4, #259-261, 263	35.00	35.00
		Nos. 253-263 (11)	10.75	5.75

Issued: 2c, 7½c, 10c, 20c, 5/9/53; #263a, 2/14/55;.others, 12/1/54.

Queen Juliana — A41

Harvesting Bananas — A46

1954, Dec. 15   Perf. 13½
264	A41	7½c dark red brown	.65	.65

Charter of the Kingdom, adopted Dec. 15, 1954.

1955, May 12   Perf. 14x13
Designs: 7½c, Pounding rice. 10c, Preparing cassava. 15c, Fishing.
265	A46	2c dark green	1.25	1.25
266	A46	7½c dull yellow	2.25	2.00
267	A46	10c orange brown	2.25	2.00
268	A46	15c ultra	2.25	2.00
		Nos. 265-268 (4)	8.00	7.25

4th anniv. of the establishment of the Caribbean Tourist Assoc.

Globe and   Flags and Map
Mercury's Rod   of Caribbean
A47   A48

1955, Sept. 19   Unwmk.   Perf. 13x12
269	A47	5c bright ultra	.35	.30

Paramaribo Trade Fair, Oct. 1955.

1956, Dec. 6   Litho.   Perf. 13x14
270	A48	10c lt blue & red	.30	.25

10th anniv. of Caribbean Commission.

No. 247 Surcharged

1958, Nov. 11   Photo.   Perf. 13½x13
271	A37	8c on 27½c car lake	.20	.20

Queen   Symbolic
Juliana — A49   Flowers — A50

Perf. 12½x12

1959, Oct. 15   Unwmk.   Litho.
272	A49	1g magenta	1.25 .20
273	A49	1.50g olive bister	2.00 .50
274	A49	2.50g dk carmine	2.75 .30
275	A49	5g dull blue	5.75 .30
		Nos. 272-275 (4)	11.75 1.30

1959, Dec. 15   Photo.   Perf. 12½x13
276	A50	20c multicolored	2.50 1.50

5th anniv. of the constitution. Flowers in design symbolize Netherlands, Surinam and Netherlands Antilles.

Charles Lindbergh's Plane — A51

10c, De Snip plane. 15c, Cessna 170B. 20c, Super Constellation. 40c, Boeing 707 Jet.

1960, Mar. 12   Perf. 12½
277	A51	8c chalky blue	.90 1.00
278	A51	10c bright green	1.25 1.50
279	A51	15c rose red	1.25 1.50
280	A51	20c pale violet	1.50 1.75
281	A51	40c light brown	2.25 2.00
		Nos. 277-281 (5)	7.15 8.25

Inauguration of Zanderij Airport, Mar. 12. Nos. 277-281 show 25 years of Surinam's civil aviation.

Flag of Surinam and Map — A52

Arms of Surinam — A53

1960, July 1   Litho.   Perf. 12½x13
282	A52	10c multicolored	.50 .50

Perf. 13x12½
283	A53	15c multicolored	.50 .50

Day of Freedom, July 1.

Bananas — A54

Finance Building — A55

1961, Mar. 1   Litho.   Perf. 13½
284	A54	1c shown	.20 .20
285	A54	2c Citrus fruit	.20 .20
286	A54	3c Cacao	.20 .20
287	A54	4c Sugar cane	.20 .20
288	A54	5c Coffee	.20 .20
289	A54	6c Coconuts	.20 .20
290	A54	8c Rice	.20 .20
		Nos. 284-290 (7)	1.40 1.40

1961   Perf. 13½x14, 14x13½

Buildings: 15c, Court of Justice. 20c, Concordia Lodge (Masons). 25c, Neve Shalom Synagogue, Paramaribo, horiz. 30c, Old Dutch lock in New Amsterdam. 35c, Government office, horiz. 40c, Governor's palace, horiz. 50c, Legislative Council, horiz. 60c, Old Dutch Reformed Church, horiz. 70c, Zeelandia Fortress, horiz.

291	A55	10c multi	.20 .20
292	A55	15c multi	.20 .20
293	A55	20c multi	.25 .25
294	A55	25c multi	.50 .50
295	A55	30c multi	1.25 1.25
296	A55	35c multi	1.25 1.25
297	A55	40c multi	.65 .65
298	A55	50c multi	.65 .65
299	A55	60c multi	.75 .75
300	A55	70c multi	.90 .90
		Nos. 291-300 (10)	6.60 6.60

Issued: 10c, 20c, 25c, 50c, 70c, 4/1; others, 5/15.

Dag Hammarskjold (1905-1961) A56

1962, Jan. 2   Litho.   Perf. 11½, 12½
301	A56	10c brt blue & blk	.20 .20
302	A56	20c lilac & blk	.20 .20

Dag Hammarskjold, Secretary General of the United Nations, 1953-61.
Sheets of both perfs. exist either with or without extension of perforations through the margins.

A56a

A57

1962, Feb. 1   Photo.   Perf. 14x13
303	A56a	20c olive green	.25 .25

Silver wedding anniversary of Queen Juliana and Prince Bernhard.

1962, May 2   Litho.   Perf. 13x14

Malaria eradication emblem.
304	A57	8c bright red	.20 .20
305	A57	10c blue	.20 .20

WHO drive to eradicate malaria.

Stoelmans Guesthouse — A58

Design: 15c, Torarica Hotel.

1962, July 4   Perf. 14x13½
306	A58	10c multicolored	.30 .30
307	A58	15c multicolored	.30 .30

Opening of the Torarica Hotel in Paramaribo and Stoelmans Guesthouse on Stoelman Island.

Deaconess Residence and Recreation Area — A59

Design: 20c, Deaconess Hospital.

1962, Nov. 30
308	A59	10c multicolored	.30 .30
309	A59	20c multicolored	.30 .30

Hands Holding Wheat Emblem A60

20c, Farmer harvesting & wheat emblem, vert.

Perf. 14x13, 13x14
1963, Mar. 21   Photo.
310	A60	10c deep carmine	.20 .20
311	A60	20c dark blue	.20 .20

FAO "Freedom from Hunger" campaign.

Broken Chain — A61

1963, June 28   Litho.   Perf. 14x13
312	A61	10c red & blk	.20 .20
313	A61	20c green & blk	.20 .20

Centenary of emancipation of the slaves.

Prince William of Orange Landing at Scheveningen A61a

Faja Lobbi Wreath A62

1963, Nov. 21   Photo.   Perf. 13½x14
Size: 26x26mm
314	A61a	10c dull bl, blk & brn	.20 .20

Founding of the Kingdom of the Netherlands, 150th anniv.

1964, Dec. 15   Litho.   Perf. 12½x13
315	A62	25c multicolored	.25 .25

Charter of the Kingdom of the Netherlands, 10th anniv.

Abraham Lincoln (1809-1865) — A63

1965, Apr. 14   Litho.   Perf. 12½x13
316	A63	25c olive bister & brn	.20 .20

ICY Emblem A64

1965, May 26   Perf. 13x12½
317	A64	10c orange & blue	.20 .20
318	A64	15c red & violet bl	.20 .20

International Cooperation Year.

Bauxite Mine, Moengo A65

Red-breasted Blackbird — A66

Designs: 15c, Alum Pottery Works, Paranam. 20c, Hydroelectric plant, Afobaka. 25c, Aluminum smeltery, Paranam.

1965, Oct. 9   Photo.   Unwmk.
319	A65	10c ocher	.20 .20
320	A65	15c dark green	.20 .20
321	A65	20c dark blue	.20 .20
322	A65	25c carmine	.20 .20
		Nos. 319-322 (4)	.80 .80

Opening of the Brokopondo Power Station.

1966, Feb. 16   Litho.   Perf. 13x14

2c, Great kiskadee. 3c, Silver-beaked tanager. 4c, Ruddy ground dove. 5c, Blue-gray tanager. 6c, Glittering-throated emerald (hummingbird). 8c, Turquoise tanager. 10c, Pale-breasted robin.

323	A66	1c brt grn, blk & red	.20 .20
324	A66	2c lt ultra, yel & brn	.20 .20
325	A66	3c multi	.20 .20
326	A66	4c lt ol grn, red brn & blk	.20 .20
327	A66	5c org, ultra & blk	.20 .20
328	A66	6c multi	.20 .20
329	A66	8c gray, vio bl & blk	.20 .20
330	A66	10c multi	.20 .20
		Nos. 323-330 (8)	1.60 1.60

Central Hospital A67

Design: 15c, Hospital, side view.

1966, Mar. 9   Litho.   Perf. 13x12½
331	A67	10c multi	.20 .20
332	A67	15c multi	.20 .20

Opening of Central Hospital, Paramaribo.

Father Petrus Donders — A68

Designs: 10c, Church and parsonage, Batavia. 15c, Msgr. Joannes B. Swinkels. 25c, Cathedral, Paramaribo.

1966, Mar. 26   Photo.   Perf. 12½x13
333	A68	4c org brn & blk	.20 .20
334	A68	10c rose brn & blk	.20 .20
335	A68	15c yel brn & blk	.20 .20
336	A68	25c lt vio & blk	.20 .20
		Nos. 333-336 (4)	.80 .80

Centenary of the Redemptorist Mission in Surinam (Congregation of the Most Holy Redeemer).

100-Year-Old
Tree — A69

1966, May 9   Litho.   Perf. 13x12½
337 A69 25c grn, dp org & blk   .20 .20
338 A69 30c red org, grn & blk   .20 .20
　Centenary of the Surinam Parliament.

Television
Transmitter, Eye and
Globe — A70

1966, Oct. 20   Litho.   Perf. 12½x13
339 A70 25c dk bl & ver   .20 .20
340 A70 30c brn & ver   .20 .20
　Inauguration of television service.

Bauxite
Industry,
1916 — A71

　Design: 25c, Bauxite industry, 1966.

1966, Dec. 19   Litho.   Perf. 13x12½
341 A71 20c yel, org & blk   .20 .20
342 A71 25c org, bl & blk   .20 .20
　50th anniversary of bauxite industry.

Central
Bank,
Paramaribo
A72

　Design: 25c, Central Bank, different view.

1967, Apr. 1   Litho.   Perf. 13x12½
343 A72 10c dp yel & blk   .20 .20
344 A72 25c lil & blk   .20 .20
　Central Bank of Surinam, 10th anniv.

Amelia
Earhart,
Lockheed
Electra and
Paramaribo
A73

1967, June 3   Photo.   Perf. 13x12½
345 A73 20c yel & dk car   .20 .20
346 A73 25c yel & grn   .20 .20
　30th anniv. of Amelia Earhart's visit to Surinam, June 3-4, 1937.

Siva Nataraja, God of
Dance, and
Ballerina's
Foot — A74

　Design: 25c, Drummer's mask "Bashi Lele,"
and scroll of violin.

1967, June 21   Litho.   Perf. 12½x13
347 A74 10c yel grn & bl   .20 .20
348 A74 25c yel grn & brn   .20 .20
　20th anniv. of the Surinam Cultural Center
Foundation.

New Amsterdam, 1660 (New York
City) — A75

　Designs after 17th Century Engravings: 10c,
Fort Zeelandia, Paramaribo, 1670. 25c, Breda
Castle, Netherlands, 1667.

1967, July 31   Litho.   Perf. 13½x13
349 A75 10c yel, blk & bl   .20 .20
350 A75 20c red brn, yel & blk .20 .20
351 A75 25c bl grn, yel & blk   .20 .20
　　Nos. 349-351 (3)   .60 .60
　300th anniv. of the Treaty of Breda between
Britain, France and the Netherlands.

WHO
Emblem
A76

1968, Apr. 7   Litho.   Perf. 13x12½
352 A76 10c magenta & dk bl   .20 .20
353 A76 25c bl & dk pur   .30 .30
　WHO, 20th anniversary.

Chandelier
and
Christian
Symbols
A77

　15c, like 10c, reversed. Brass chandelier
from the Reformed Church, Paramaribo.

1968, May 29   Litho.   Perf. 13x12½
354 A77 10c dark blue   .20 .20
355 A77 25c dp yel grn   .30 .30
　Reformed Church of Paramaribo, 300th
anniv.

Missionary
Store,
1768 — A78

　Designs: 25c, Main Church and store, Paramaribo, 1868. 30c, C. Kersten & Co., 1968.

1968, June 29   Litho.   Perf. 13x12½
356 A78 10c yel & blk   .20 .20
357 A78 25c lt grnsh bl & blk .20 .20
358 A78 30c lilac rose & blk   .20 .20
　　Nos. 356-358 (3)   .60 .60
　200th anniv. of C. Kersten & Co., which is
partially owned by the Evangelical Brotherhood Missionary Society.

Joden Savanne
Synagogue
A79

Mahatma
Gandhi
A81

Spectacled
Caiman
A80

　Designs: 20c, Map of Joden Savanne and
Surinam River. 30c, Gravestone, 1733. The
Hebrew inscriptions are quotations from the
Bible: 20c, Joshua 24:2; 25c, Isaiah 56:7; 30c,
Genesis 31:52.

1968, Aug. 28   Perf. 12½x13
359 A79 20c multi   .30 .30
360 A79 25c multi   .35 .35
361 A79 30c multi   .35 .35
　　Nos. 359-361 (3)   1.00 1.00
　Founding of the first synagogue in the Western Hemisphere in 1685 in Joden Savanne,
Surinam.

Perf. 13x12½, 12½x13
1969, Aug. 20   Litho.
　20c, Squirrel monkey, vert. 25c, Armadillo.

362 A80 10c grn & multi   .50 .40
363 A80 20c bl gray & multi .50 .40
364 A80 25c vio & multi   .50 .40
　　Nos. 362-364 (3)   1.50 1.20

1969, Oct. 2   Litho.   Perf. 12½x13
365 A81 25c red & blk   .25 .25
　Mohandas K. Gandhi (1869-1948), leader in
India's fight for independence.

ILO Emblem
A82

1969, Oct. 29   Litho.   Perf. 13x12½
366 A82 10c brt bl grn & blk .20 .20
367 A82 25c red & blk   .25 .25
　ILO, 50th anniversary.

Queen Juliana
and Rising
Sun — A82a

1969, Dec. 15   Photo.   Perf. 14x13
368 A82a 25c blue & multi   .30 .30
　15th anniv. of the Charter of the Kingdom of
the Netherlands. Phosphorescent paper.

"1950-1970"
A83

1970, Apr. 3   Litho.   Perf. 13x12½
369 A83 10c brn, grn & org   .20 .20
370 A83 25c emer, dk bl & org .25 .25
　20th anniv. of secondary education in
Surinam.

Inauguration of UPU Headquarters,
Bern — A84

　Design: 25c, UPU Headquarters, sideview
and UPU emblem.

1970, May 20   Litho.   Perf. 13x12½
371 A84 10c sky bl & dk pur   .20 .20
372 A84 25c red & blk   .30 .30

"UNO"
A85

Plane over
Paramaribo
A86

1970, June 26   Litho.   Perf. 12½x13
373 A85 10c ocher & yel   .20 .20
374 A85 25c dp bl & ultra   .30 .30
　25th anniversary of the United Nations.

1970, July 15
　Designs: 20c, Plane over map of Totness,
25c, Plane over Nieuw-Nickerie.

375 A86 10c bl, vio bl & gray   .25 .25
376 A86 20c yel, red & gray   .25 .25
377 A86 25c pink, dk red & gray .25 .25
　　Nos. 375-377 (3)   .75 .75
　40th anniv. of domestic airmail service.

Plan of Soccer
Field and
Ball — A87

Morse
Key — A89

Cocoi Heron
A88

　Plan of soccer field with ball in different
positions.

1970, Oct. 1
378 A87 4c yel, red brn & blk   .20 .20
379 A87 10c pale lem, red brn &
　　　　　blk   .20 .20
380 A87 15c lt yel grn, red brn &
　　　　　blk   .20 .20
381 A87 25c lt grn, red brn & blk .30 .30
　　Nos. 378-381 (4)   .90 .90
　50th anniv. of the Soccer Assoc. of Surinam.

1971, Feb. 14   Litho.   Perf. 13x12½
　Birds in Flight: 20c, Flamingo. 25c, Scarlet
macaw.

382 A88 15c gray & multi   .65 .40
383 A88 20c ultra & multi   .65 .40
384 A88 25c pale grn & multi   .65 .40
　　Nos. 382-384 (3)   1.95 1.20
　25th anniversary of regular air service
between the Netherlands, Surinam and
Netherlands Antilles.

1971, May 17   Photo.   Perf. 12½x13
　Designs: 20c, Telephone. 25c, Lunar landing module, telescope.

385 A89 15c light green & multi .35 .30
386 A89 20c blue & multi   .40 .40
387 A89 25c lilac & multi   .50 .45
　　Nos. 385-387 (3)   1.25 1.15
　3rd World Telecommunications Day.

Prince Bernhard, Fokker F27, Boeing 747B — A89a

Map of Surinam, Population Chart — A90

1971, June 29   Photo.   Perf. 13x14
388 A89a 25c multi   .60 .50
60th birthday of Prince Bernhard.

1971, July 31   Litho.   Perf. 12½x13
Design: 30c, Map of Surinam and individual representing population.

389 A90 15c gray bl, blk & ver   .20 .20
390 A90 30c ver, gray bl & blk   .25 .25
50th anniv. of the first census; introduction of civil registration in Surinam.

William Mogge's Map of Surinam A91

1971, Oct. 27   Perf. 11½x11
391 A91 30c dull yel & dk brn   .45 .50
300th anniv. of the first map of Surinam.

Map of Albina A92

August Kappler — A93

Drop of Water — A94

20c, View of Albina from Maroni River.

1971, Dec. 13   Perf. 13x12½, 12½x13
392 A92 15c sapphire & blk   .30 .30
393 A92 20c brt grn & blk   .35 .35
394 A93 25c yel & blk   .35 .35
     Nos. 392-394 (3)   1.00 1.00
125th anniv. of the founding of Albina by August Kappler (1815-1887).

1972, Feb. 2   Perf. 12½x13
Design: 30c, Faucet and water tower.
395 A94 15c vio & blk   .30 .30
396 A94 30c bl & blk   .40 .40
Surinam water works, 40th anniversary.

Air Mail Envelope A95

1972, Aug. 2   Litho.   Perf. 13x12½
397 A95 15c red & blue   .20 .20
398 A95 30c blue & red   .25 .25
Arrival of the 1st airmail in Surinam, carried by Capt. Dutertre from French Guiana, 50th anniv.

Giant Tree — A96

Hindu Woman in Rice Field — A97

Designs: 20c, Wood transport by air lift. 30c, Hands tending seedling.

1972, Dec. 20   Photo.   Perf. 12½x13
399 A96 15c yel & dk brn   .20 .20
400 A96 20c bl & dp brn   .20 .20
401 A96 30c brt grn & dp brn   .40 .40
     Nos. 399-401 (3)   .80 .80
Surinam Forestry Commission, 25th anniv.

1973, June 5   Litho.   Perf. 13½x14
25c, J. F. A. Cateau van Rosevelt with map of Surinam, ship "Lalla Rookh." 30c, Symbolic bird, flower, sun, flag, factories.

402 A97 15c purple & yel   .25 .25
403 A97 25c maroon & gray   .25 .20
404 A97 30c yel & light blue   .30 .30
     Nos. 402-404 (3)   .80 .75
1st immigrants from India, cent.

Queen Juliana, Surinam and House of Orange Colors A97a

Engr. & Photo.
1973, Sept. 4   Perf. 12½x12
405 A97a 30c sil, blk & org   .55 .55
25th anniversary of reign of Queen Juliana.

INTERPOL Emblem — A98

Mailman — A99

Design: 30c, INTERPOL emblem, Surinam visa handstamp.

1973, Nov. 7   Litho.   Perf. 14x14½
406 A98 15c vio bl & multi   .20 .20
407 A98 30c lt bl, lil & blk   .30 .30
50th anniv. of Intl. Criminal Police Org.

1973, Dec. 12   Litho.   Perf. 12½x13
15c, Pigeons carrying Letters. 30c, Map of Surinam, plane, ship, train and truck.

408 A99 15c lt yel grn & bl   .20 .20
409 A99 25c sal, blk & bl   .25 .25
410 A99 30c ver & multi   .40 .40
     Nos. 408-410 (3)   .85 .85
Centenary of stamps of Surinam.

Patient and Blood Transfusion A100

30c, Cross section of tissue and oscilloscope.

1974, June 1   Litho.   Perf. 14½x14
411 A100 15c red brn & multi   .20 .20
412 A100 30c lemon & multi   .25 .25
75th anniversary of the Medical College.

Crop Dusting A101

1974, July 17   Litho.   Perf. 13½
413 A101 15c shown   .20 .20
414 A101 30c Fertilizer plant   .25 .25
Foundation for Development of Mechanical Agriculture in Surinam, 25th anniv.

Old Title Page — A102

1974, July 31   Perf. 14x14½
415 A102 15c multicolored   .20 .20
416 A102 30c multicolored   .25 .25
"Weekly Wednesday Surinam Newspaper," bicent. 1st editor was Beeldsnijder Matroos.

Paramaribo Main Post Office A103

Design: 30c, Post Office, different view.

1974, Sept. 11   Litho.   Perf. 14½x14
417 A103 15c brown & blk   .20 .20
418 A103 30c blue & blk   .30 .30
Centenary of Universal Postal Union.

Gold Panner A104

Design: 30c, Modern excavator.

1975, Feb. 5   Litho.   Perf. 13x12½
419 A104 15c brown & olive bis   .20 .20
420 A104 30c vermilion & maroon   .25 .25
Centenary of prospecting policy granting concessions for winning of raw materials.

Symbolic Design A105

1975, June 25   Litho.   Perf. 13x12½
421 A105 15c green & multi   .30 .30
422 A105 25c blue & multi   .35 .35
423 A105 30c red & multi   .35 .35
     Nos. 421-423 (3)   1.00 1.00
Cent. of Intl. Meter Convention, Paris, 1875.

Hands Holding Saw — A106

Designs: 50c, Book with notes and letter "a." 75c, Hands holding ball.

1975, Nov. 25   Litho.   Perf. 13½x14
424 A106 25c yellow, red & brn   .25 .25
425 A106 50c yellow, red & pur   .50 .50
426 A106 75c dk bl, org & emer   .75 .75
     Nos. 424-426 (3)   1.50 1.50
Independence. Sheets of 10 (5x2) with ornamental margins.

Oncidium Lanceanum A107

Central Bank, Paramaribo A109

Orchids: 2c, Epidendrum stenopetalum. 3c, Brassia lanceana. 4c, Epidendrum ibaguense. 5c, Epidendrum fragrans.

1975-76   Litho.   Perf. 14½x13½
427 A107 1c multicolored   .20 .20
428 A107 2c multicolored   .20 .20
429 A107 3c multicolored   .20 .20
430 A107 4c multicolored   .20 .20
431 A107 5c multicolored   .20 .20

Perf. 14x13½
436 A109 1g rose lil & blk   .90 .20
437 A109 1½g brn, dp org & blk   1.40 .20
438 A109 2½g red brn, org red
                & blk   2.25 .20
439 A109 5g grn, yel grn &
                blk   4.50 .20
440 A109 10g dk vio bl & blk   10.00 .20
     Nos. 427-431,436-440 (10)   20.05 2.30
Issued: #436-439, Nov. 25, 1975; #427-431, Feb. 18, 1976; #440, May 5, 1976.
For surcharges see Nos. 772-774, 810.

Flag of Surinam — A110

Design: 35c, Coat of Arms.

1976, Mar. 3   Perf. 14x13½
445 A110 25c emerald & multi   .35 .35
446 A110 35c red orange & multi   .45 .45
Sheets of 12 (6x2) with ornamental margins.

Pomacanthus Semicirculatus — A111

Fish: 2c, Adioryx diadema. 3c, Pogonoculius zebra. 4c, Balistes vetula. 5c, Myripristis jacobus.

1976, June 2   Litho.   Perf. 12½x13
447 A111 1c multicolored   .20 .20
448 A111 2c multicolored   .20 .20
449 A111 3c multicolored   .20 .20

450	A111	4c multicolored	.20 .20
451	A111	5c multicolored	.25 .20

Nos. 427-431,C55-C57 (8)   6.50 3.85

See #471-475, 504-508, C72-C74, C85-C87.

19th Century Switchboard and
Telephone — A112

35c, Satellite, globe and 1976 telephone.

1976, Aug. 5   Litho.   Perf. 13½x14
452	A112	20c yellow & multi	.20 .20
453	A112	35c ultra & multi	.40 .40

Centenary of first telephone call by Alexander Graham Bell, Mar. 10, 1876.

The Story of Anansi Tori, by A.
Baag — A113

Designs: 30c, "Surinam Now" (young people), by R. Chang. 35c, Lamentation, by Nola Hatterman, vert. 50c, Chess Players, by Q. Jan Telting.

Perf. 13½x14, 14x13½
1976, Sept. 29   Photo.
454	A113	20c multicolored	.25 .25
455	A113	30c multicolored	.40 .35
456	A113	35c multicolored	.45 .40
457	A113	50c multicolored	.65 .60

Nos. 454-457 (4)   1.75 1.60

Paintings by Surinam artists.

Franklin's Divided Snake Poster,
1754 — A114

1976, Nov. 10   Litho.   Perf. 13½x14
458	A114	20c green & blk	.25 .25
459	A114	60c orange & blk	.75 .75

American Bicentennial.

Ionopsis
Utricularioides
A115

Surinam
Costume
A116

Orchids: 30c, Rodriguezia secunda. 35c, Oncidium pusillum. 55c, Sobralia sessilis. 60c, Octomeria surinamensis.

1977, Jan. 19   Litho.   Perf. 14½x13½
460	A115	20c vermilion & multi	.25 .20
461	A115	30c ultra & multi	.40 .25
462	A115	35c magenta & multi	.40 .30
463	A115	55c yellow & multi	.60 .50
464	A115	60c green & multi	.60 .55

Nos. 460-464 (5)   2.25 1.80

1977, Mar. 2   Litho.   Perf. 14x13½
Various Surinamese women's costumes.
465	A116	10c brt blue & multi	.20 .20
466	A116	15c green & multi	.20 .20
467	A116	25c violet & multi	.25 .25
468	A116	60c orange & multi	.45 .45
469	A116	75c ultra & multi	.60 .60
470	A116	1g yellow & multi	.80 .80

Nos. 465-470 (6)   2.50 2.50

Fish Type of 1976

Tropical Fish: 1c, Liopropoma carmabi. 2c, Holacanthus ciliaris. 3c, Opistognathus aurifrons. 4c, Anisotremus virginicus. 5c, Gramma loreto.

1977, June 8   Litho.   Perf. 13x13½
471	A111	1c multicolored	.20 .20
472	A111	2c multicolored	.20 .20
473	A111	3c multicolored	.20 .20
474	A111	4c multicolored	.20 .20
475	A111	5c multicolored	.20 .20

Nos. 471-475,C72-C74 (8)   3.55 2.90

Edison's Phonograph, 1877 — A117

Design: 60c, Modern turntable.

1977, Aug. 24   Litho.   Perf. 13½x14
476	A117	20c multicolored	.20 .20
477	A117	60c multicolored	.45 .45

Invention of the phonograph, cent.

Packet
Curacao,
1827
A118

Designs: 15c, Hellevoetsluis Harbor and postmark, 1827. 30c, Sea chart and technical details of packet Curacao. 35c, Logbook and compass rose. 60c, Map of Paramaribo harbor and 1852 postmark. 95c, Modern liner Stuyvesant.

1977, Sept. 28   Litho.   Perf. 14x13½
478	A118	5c grnsh bl & dk bl	.20 .20
479	A118	15c orange & mar	.20 .20
480	A118	30c lt brn & blk	.20 .20
481	A118	35c olive & blk	.20 .20
482	A118	60c lilac & blk	.25 .25
483	A118	95c yel grn & dk grn	.40 .40

Nos. 478-483 (6)   1.45 1.45

Regular steamer connection between the Netherlands and Surinam, 150th anniversary.

Passiflora
Quad-rangularis
A119

Javanese
Costume
A120

Flowers: 30c, Centropogon surinamensis. 55c, Gloxinia perennis. 60c, Hydrocleis nymphoides. 75c, Clusia grandiflora.

1978, Feb. 8   Litho.   Perf. 13x14
484	A119	20c multicolored	.20 .20
485	A119	30c multicolored	.20 .20
486	A119	55c multicolored	.30 .25
487	A119	60c multicolored	.35 .30
488	A119	75c multicolored	.40 .35

Nos. 484-488 (5)   1.45 1.30

1978, Mar. 1   Litho.   Perf. 13x14
People of Surinam, Costumes: 20c, Forest black. 35c, Chinese. 60c, Creole. 75c, Aborigine Indian. 1g, Hindustani.
489	A120	10c multicolored	.20 .20
490	A120	20c multicolored	.20 .20
491	A120	35c multicolored	.20 .20
492	A120	60c multicolored	.30 .25
493	A120	75c multicolored	.35 .30
494	A120	1g multicolored	.55 .50

Nos. 489-494 (6)   1.80 1.65

Air Post Stamps
of 1972
Surcharged

1977, Nov. 15   Litho.   Perf. 13½x14
495	AP6	1c on 25c #C44	.20 .20
496	AP6	4c on 15c #C42	.20 .20
497	AP6	4c on 30c #C45	.20 .20
498	AP6	5c on 40c #C47	.25 .20
499	AP6	10c on 75c #C54	.30 .20

Nos. 495-499 (5)   1.15 1.00

"Luchtpost" obliterated with 2 bars.

Old Municipal
Church
A121

Johannes
King — A122

Designs: 55c, New Municipal Church. 60c, Johannes Raillard.

1978, May 31   Litho.   Perf. 14x13
500	A121	10c blue, blk & gray	.20 .20
501	A122	20c gray & blk	.20 .20
502	A121	55c rose lil & blk	.30 .30
503	A122	60c orange & blk	.35 .35

Nos. 500-503 (4)   1.05 1.05

Evangelical Brothers Community Church, Paramaribo, bicentenary.

Tropical Fish Type of 1976

Tropical Fish: 1c, Nannacara Anomala. 2c, Leporinus fasciatus. 3c, Pristella riddlei. 4c, Nannostomus beckfordi. 5c, Rivulus agilae.

1978, June 21   Litho.   Perf. 12½x13½
504	A111	1c multicolored	.20 .20
505	A111	2c multicolored	.20 .20
506	A111	3c multicolored	.20 .20
507	A111	4c multicolored	.20 .20
508	A111	5c multicolored	.20 .20

Nos. 504-508,C85-C87 (8)   3.55 2.75

Souvenir Sheet

Commewijne
River
Development
A124

Development: 60c, Map of Surinam and dam. 95c, Planes and world map.

1978, Oct. 18   Litho.   Perf. 14x13
509		Sheet of 3	1.10 1.10
a.		A124 20c multi	.20 .20
b.		A124 60c multi	.35 .35
c.		A124 95c multi	.50 .50

Coconuts
A125

Wright Brothers' Flyer 1
A126

1978-85   Litho.   Perf. 13½x13
510	A125	5c shown	.20 .20
a.		Bklt. pane, 4 #510, 3 #511, 5 #515 ('80)	2.00
511	A125	10c Oranges	.20 .20
512	A125	15c Papayas	.20 .20
a.		Bklt. pane, 5 #512, 6 #514 + label ('79)	2.00
513	A125	20c Bananas	.20 .20
514	A125	25c Soursop	.20 .20
514A	A125	30c Cocoa beans ('85)	.55 .55
b.		Bklt. pane, 6 #514A, 1 #513 = label ('85)	3.25 3.25
515	A125	35c Watermelon	.30 .30

Nos. 510-515 (7)   1.85 1.85

Perf. 13x14, 14x13
1978, Dec. 13   Litho.
Designs: 20c, Daedalus and Icarus, vert. 95c, DC 8. 125c, Concorde.
516	A126	20c multicolored	.20 .20
517	A126	60c multicolored	.45 .45
518	A126	95c multicolored	.65 .65
519	A126	125c multicolored	.85 .85

Nos. 516-519 (4)   2.15 2.15

75th anniversary of 1st powered flight.

Rodriguezia
Candida
A127

Javanese
Dancer
A128

Flowers: 20c, Stanhopea grandiflora. 35c, Scuticaria steelei. 60c, Bollea violacea.

1979, Feb. 7   Litho.   Perf. 13x14
520	A127	10c multicolored	.20 .20
521	A127	20c multicolored	.20 .20
522	A127	35c multicolored	.30 .25
523	A127	60c multicolored	.45 .35

Nos. 520-523 (4)   1.15 1.00

1979, Feb. 28
Dancing Costumes: 10c, Forest Negro. 15c, Chinese. 20c, Creole. 25c, Aborigine Indian. 35c, Hindustani.
524	A128	5c multicolored	.20 .20
525	A128	10c multicolored	.20 .20
526	A128	15c multicolored	.20 .20
527	A128	20c multicolored	.20 .20
528	A128	25c multicolored	.20 .20
529	A128	35c multicolored	.25 .25

Nos. 524-529 (6)   1.25 1.25

Equetus
Pulchellus
A129

Tropical Fish: 2c, Apogon binotatus. 3c, Anisotremus virginicus. 5c, Bodianus rufus. 35c, Microspathodon chrysurus.

1979, May 30   Photo.   Perf. 14x13
530	A129	1c multicolored	.20 .20
531	A129	2c multicolored	.20 .20
532	A129	3c multicolored	.20 .20
533	A129	5c multicolored	.20 .20
534	A129	35c multicolored	.30 .25

Nos. 530-534,C89-C91 (8)   2.50 2.20

See Nos. 557-561, C92-C94.

Javanese
Wooden
Head — A130

Folkart: 35c, Head ornament, Indian. 60c, Horse's head, Javanese.

1979, Aug. 29   Litho.   Perf. 14x13
535	A130	20c multicolored	.20 .20
536	A130	35c multicolored	.30 .30
537	A130	60c multicolored	.50 .50

Nos. 535-537 (3)   1.00 1.00

Sir Rowland Hill
A131

Javanese Girl's
Costume
A133

SOS Emblem,
House
A132

1979, Oct. 3   Litho.   Perf. 13x14
538 A131 1g yellow & olive   .70 .60
Sir Rowland Hill (1795-1879), originator of penny postage.

1979, Oct. 3   Perf. 13x14
Design: 60c, SOS emblem and buildings.
539 A132 20c multicolored   .20 .20
540 A132 60c multicolored   .40 .40
Intl. Year of the Child; SOS Children's Villages, 30th anniv.

1980, Feb. 6   Photo.   Perf. 13x14
541 A133 10c Javanese girl   .20 .20
542 A133 15c Forest Black boy   .20 .20
543 A133 25c Chinese girl   .20 .20
544 A133 60c Creole girl   .40 .35
545 A133 90c Indian girl   .60 .50
546 A133 1g Hindustani boy   .65 .55
    Nos. 541-546 (6)   2.25 2.00

Rotary Intl.,
75th
Anniversary
A134

20c, Handshake, Rotary emblem, vert.

Perf. 13x14, 14x13
1980, Feb. 23   Litho.
547 A134 20c ultra & yellow   .20 .20
548 A134 60c ultra & yellow   .50 .40

Rowland
Hill — A135

Weight
Lifting — A136

1980, May 6   Litho.   Perf. 13x14
549 A135 50c Mailcoach   .30 .30
550 A135 1g shown   .60 .60
a.   Souvenir sheet   .75 .75
551 A135 2g People mailing letters   1.25 1.00
    Nos. 549-551 (3)   2.15 1.90

London 1980 Intl. Stamp Exhibition, May 6-14. No. 550a contains No. 550 in changed colors. Blue and black margin shows designs of Nos. 549, 551, London 1980 emblem. (No. 550 in lilac rose and multicolored; stamps of No. 550a in light green and multicolored).

1980, June 17
552 A136 20c shown   .20 .20
553 A136 30c Diving   .25 .25
554 A136 50c Gymnast   .30 .30
555 A136 75c Basketball   .50 .50
556 A136 150c Running   1.00 1.00
a.   Souvenir sheet of 3, #554-556   2.00 2.00
    Nos. 552-556 (5)   2.25 2.25

22nd Summer Olympic Games, Moscow, July 19-Aug. 3.

Fish Type of 1979

Tropical Fish: 10c, Osteoglossum bicirrhosum. 15c, Colossoma species. 25c,

Hemigrammus pulcher. 30c, Petitella georgiae. 45c, Copeina guttata.

1980, Sept. 10   Photo.   Perf. 14x13
557 A129 10c multicolored   .20 .20
558 A129 15c multicolored   .20 .20
559 A129 25c multicolored   .20 .20
560 A129 30c multicolored   .20 .20
561 A129 45c multicolored   .30 .30
    Nos. 557-561,C92-C94 (8)   2.65 2.30

Open Hands
(Reflection)
A137

Passiflora
Laurifolia
A138

Souvenir Sheet
1980, Nov. 19   Litho.   Perf. 13x14
562   Sheet of 3   2.50 2.50
a.   A137 50c shown   .25 .25
b.   A137 1g Shaking hands (cooperation)   .45 .45
c.   A137 2g Victory sign   .90 .90
    5th anniv. of independence.

1981, Jan. 14   Litho.   Perf. 13x14
Designs: Flower paintings by Maria Sibylle Merian (1647-1717).
563 A138 20c shown   .20 .20
564 A138 30c Aphelandra pectinata   .25 .25
565 A138 60c Caesalpinia pulcherrima   .50 .50
566 A138 75c Hibiscus mutabilis   .60 .60
567 A138 1.25g Hippeastrum puniceum   1.10 1.10
    Nos. 563-567 (5)   2.65 2.65

Renovation of
the Economic
Order — A139

1981, Feb. 25   Perf. 14x13
568 A139 30c shown   .20 .20
569 A139 60c Educational Order   .35 .35
570 A139 75c Social Order   .40 .40
571 A139 1g Political Order   .55 .55
a.   Souvenir sheet of 2, #569, 571   2.00 2.00
    Nos. 568-571 (4)   1.50 1.50

Government renovation.

Miniature Sheet

Youths — A140

1981, Apr. 29   Litho.   Perf. 14x13½
572 A140   Sheet of 2   1.75 1.75
a.   1g shown   .75 .75
b.   1.50g Youths, diff.   .75 .75

Youth and its future. Entire sheet in continuous design.

Souvenir Sheet

No. 424,
Exhibition
Hall — A141

1981, May 22   Litho.   Perf. 13½x14
573   Sheet of 3   2.50 2.50
a.   A141 50c shown   .35 .40
b.   A141 1g Penny Black   .70 .75
c.   A141 2g Austria #5   1.40 1.50
WIPA '81 Intl. Philatelic Exhibition, Vienna, May 22-31.

Leptodactylus
Pentadactylus
A142

1981, June 24   Photo.   Perf. 14x13
574 A142 40c Phyllomedusa hypochondrialis   .60 .30
575 A142 50c shown   .75 .40
576 A142 60c Hyla boans   .90 .50
    Nos. 574-576,C95-C97 (6)   6.60 3.60

Child Wearing
Earphones
A143

1981, Sept. 16   Litho.   Perf. 14x13
580 A143 50c shown   .40 .40
581 A143 100c Child reading Braille   .80 .80
582 A143 150c Woman in wheelchair   1.25 1.25
    Nos. 580-582 (3)   2.45 2.45

Intl. Year of the Disabled.

Planter's
House on
Parakreek
River — A144

Designs: Illustrations from Voyage to Surinam, by P.I. Benoit.

1981, Oct. 21   Photo.   Perf. 14x13
583 A144 20c shown   .20 .20
584 A144 30c Sarameca St., Paramaribo   .25 .25
585 A144 75c Negro Hamlet, Paramaribo   .60 .60
586 A144 1g Fish Market, Paramaribo   .80 .80
a.   Miniature sheet of 1, perf 13½x13   1.25 1.10
587 A144 1.25g Blaauwe Berg Cascade   1.00 1.00
    Nos. 583-587 (5)   2.85 2.85

Research and
Peaceful Uses
of Space
A145

1982, Jan. 13   Litho.
588 A145 35c Satellites   .35 .35
589 A145 65c Columbia space shuttle   .65 .65
590 A145 1g Apollo-Soyuz   1.00 1.00
    Nos. 588-590 (3)   2.00 2.00

Caretta
Caretta
A146

1982, Feb. 17   Photo.   Perf. 14x13
591 A146 5c shown   .20 .20
592 A146 10c Chelonia mydas   .20 .20
593 A146 20c Dermochelys coriacea   .30 .20
594 A146 25c Eretmochelys imbricata   .40 .25
595 A146 35c Lepidochelys olivacea   .50 .30
    Nos. 591-595,C98-C100 (8)   5.85 4.00

25th Anniv. of
Lions Intl. in
Surinam
A147

1982, May 7   Litho.
596 A147 35c multicolored   .40 .40
597 A147 70c multicolored   .75 .75

A148

A149

1982, May 18   Litho.   Perf. 13x14
598 A148 35c Helping the sick   .50 .50
599 A148 65c Birthplace, map   1.00 1.00
a.   Souvenir sheet   1.00 1.00

Beatification of Father Petrus Donders, May 23.

1982, June 9   Litho.   Perf. 13x14
600 A149 50c Stamp designing   .40 .40
601 A149 100c Printing   .85 .85
602 A149 150c Collecting   1.25 1.25
a.   Souvenir sheet of 3, #600-602   2.50 2.50
    Nos. 600-602 (3)   2.50 2.50

PHILEXFRANCE '82 Stamp Exhibition, Paris, June 11-21. Nos. 600-602 in continuous design.

TB Bacillus
Centenary
A150

1982, Sept. 15   Litho.   Perf. 14x13
603 A150 35c Text   .35 .35
604 A150 65c Microscope   .75 .75
605 A150 150c Bacillus   1.90 1.90
    Nos. 603-605 (3)   3.00 3.00

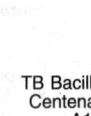

Marienburg
Sugar Co.
Centenary
A151

1982, Oct. 20
606 A151 35c Mill   .30 .30
607 A151 65c Gathering cane   .60 .60
608 A151 100c Rail transport   .95 .95
609 A151 150c Gears   1.50 1.50
    Nos. 606-609 (4)   3.35 3.35

A152

Inga
Edulis — A153

EBG Missionaries, 250th Anniv. in Caribbean: 35c, Municipal Church, horiz. 65c, St. Thomas Monastery, horiz. 150c, Johan Leonhardt Dober (1706-1766).

Perf. 14x13, 13x14
1982, Dec. 13   Litho.
610 A152 35c multicolored   .30 .30
611 A152 65c multicolored   .55 .55
612 A152 150c multicolored   1.50 1.50
    Nos. 610-612 (3)   2.35 2.35

1983, Jan. 12

Flower Paintings by Maria Sibylle Merian (1647-1717). Nos. 613-618 horiz.

613	A153	1c Erythrina fusca	.20	.20
614	A153	2c Ipomoea acuminata	.20	.20
615	A153	3c Heliconia psittacorum	.20	.20
616	A153	5c Ipomoea	.20	.20
617	A153	10c Herba non denominata	.20	.20
618	A153	15c Anacardium occidentale	.30	.30
619	A153	20c shown	.40	.35
620	A153	25c Abelmoschus moschatus	.55	.50
621	A153	30c Argemone mexicana	.70	.65
622	A153	35c Costus arabicus	.75	.70
623	A153	45c Muellera frutescens	1.00	.90
624	A153	65c Punica granatum	1.50	1.40
		Nos. 613-624 (12)	6.20	5.80

Scouting Year — A154

500th Birth Anniv. of Raphael — A155

1983, Feb. 22   Litho.   Perf. 13x14

625	A154	40c Anniv. emblem	.65	.65
626	A154	65c Baden-Powell	1.00	1.00
627	A154	70c Tent, campfire	1.10	1.10
628	A154	80c Ax in log	1.25	1.25
		Nos. 625-628 (4)	4.00	4.00

1983, Apr. 13   Photo.

Crayon sketches.

629	A155	5c multicolored	.20	.20
630	A155	10c multicolored	.20	.20
631	A155	40c multicolored	.50	.50
632	A155	65c multicolored	.75	.75
633	A155	70c multicolored	.80	.80
634	A155	80c multicolored	1.00	1.00
		Nos. 629-634 (6)	3.45	3.45

1982 Coins and Banknotes A156

1983, June 1   Litho.   Perf. 14x13

635	A156	5c 1-cent coin	.20	.20
636	A156	10c 5-cent coin	.20	.20
637	A156	40c 10-cent coin	.50	.50
638	A156	65c 25-cent coin	.75	.75
639	A156	70c 1g note	.80	.80
640	A156	80c 2.50g note	1.00	1.00
		Nos. 635-640 (6)	3.45	3.45

For surcharge & overprints see Nos. 751, J59-J60.

25th Anniv. of Dept. of Construction A157

Manned Ballooning, 200th Anniv. A159

Local Butterflies A158

1983, June 15   Litho.   Perf. 13x14

641	A157	25c Map	.30	.30
642	A157	50c Map, bulldozers	.60	.60

Perf. 13x14, 14x13

1983, Sept. 14   Litho.

Drawings by Maria Sibylle Merian (1647-1717). Nos. 643-648 vert.

643	A158	1c Papile anchisiades esper	.20	.20
644	A158	2c Urania leilus	.20	.20
645	A158	3c Morpho deidamia	.20	.20
646	A158	5c Thysania aguippina	.20	.20
647	A158	10c Morpho sp.	.25	.20
648	A158	15c Metamorpha dido	.35	.25
649	A158	20c Morpho menelaus	.45	.30
650	A158	25c Manduca rustica	.65	.40
651	A158	30c Rothschildia sp.	.75	.50
652	A158	35c Catopsilia ebule	.90	.60
653	A158	45c Pailio androgeos	1.25	.80
654	A148	65c Eumorpha vitis	1.75	1.25
		Nos. 643-654 (12)	7.15	5.10

1983, Oct. 19   Litho.   Perf. 13x14

Designs: 5c, 1783, sheep, cock and duck. 10c, first manned flight, d'Arlandes and Pilatre de Rozier. 40c, first hydrogen balloon, Jacques Charles. 65c, 1870, Paris flight, minister Gambetta. 70c, Double Eagle II, transatlantic flight. 80c, Intl. Balloon Festival, Albuquerque.

655	A159	5c multicolored	.20	.20
656	A159	10c multicolored	.20	.20
657	A159	40c multicolored	.65	.65
658	A159	65c multicolored	1.00	1.00
659	A159	70c multicolored	1.10	1.10
660	A159	80c multicolored	1.25	1.25
		Nos. 655-660 (6)	4.40	4.40

Martin Luther, 500th Birth Anniv. — A160

1983, Dec. 7   Litho.

661	A160	25c Portrait	.30	.25
662	A160	50c Engraving	.60	.55

Local Flowers A161

Local Seashells A162

1984, Jan. 11   Litho.

663	A161	5c Catasetum discolor	.20	.20
664	A161	10c Menadenium labiosum	.20	.20
665	A161	40c Comparettia falcata	.65	.60
666	A161	50c Rodriquezia decora	1.00	.90
667	A161	70c Oncidium papilio	1.10	1.00
668	A161	75c Epidendrum porpax	1.25	1.10
		Nos. 663-668 (6)	4.40	4.00

1984, Feb. 22   Litho.

669	A162	40c Arca zebra	.95	.65
670	A162	65c Trachycardium egmontianum	1.60	1.10
671	A162	70c Tellina radiata	1.60	1.10
672	A162	80c Vermicularia knorrii	2.00	1.25
		Nos. 669-672 (4)	6.15	4.10

Intl. Civil Aviation Org., 40th Anniv. A163

1984, May 16   Litho.   Perf. 14x13

673	A163	35c Sea plane	.40	.40
674	A163	65c Surinam Airways jet	.90	.90

A164   A165

Greek Art and Artifacts: Ancient Games.

1984, June 13   Perf. 13x14

675	A164	2c Running	.20	.20
676	A164	3c Javelin, discus, long jump	.20	.20
677	A164	5c Massage	.20	.20
678	A164	10c Ointment massage	.20	.20
679	A164	15c Wrestling	.20	.20
680	A164	20c Boxing	.20	.20
681	A164	30c Horse racing	.35	.35
682	A164	35c Chariot racing	.40	.40
683	A164	45c Temple of Olympia	.50	.50
684	A164	50c Crypt entrance	.60	.60
685	A164	65c Olympia Stadium	.80	.80
686	A164	75c Zeus (bust)	.85	.85
a.		Min. sheet of 3, #675, 682, 686	1.50	1.50
		Nos. 675-686 (12)	4.70	4.70

1984 Summer Olympics.
For overprint see No. 843.

1984, Sept. 18   Litho.   Perf. 13x14

687	A165	50c Ball, net	.80	.75
688	A165	90c Ball in net	1.40	1.25

Intl. Council of Military Sports basketball championship.

World Chess Championship, Moscow — A166

1984, Oct. 10   Litho.   Perf. 14x13

689	A166	10c Red Square	.20	.20
690	A166	15c Knight, king, pawn	.20	.20
691	A166	30c Kasparov	.35	.35
692	A166	50c Board	.60	.60
693	A166	75c Karpov	.80	.80
a.		Souv. sheet of 3 (30c, 50c, 75c), perf 13½x13	2.00	2.00
694	A166	90c Game	1.10	1.10
		Nos. 689-694 (6)	3.45	3.45

For overprints see Nos. 742, 796.

World Food Day, Oct. 16 — A167

1984, Oct. 10

695	A167	50c Children receiving milk	.60	.60
696	A167	90c Food	1.00	1.00

A168   A169

Cacti.

1985, Jan. 9   Litho.   Perf. 13x14

697	A168	5c Leaf	.20	.20
698	A168	10c Melon	.20	.20
699	A168	30c Pillar	.45	.45
700	A168	50c Fig	.70	.70
701	A168	75c Nightqueen	1.10	1.10
702	A168	90c Segment	1.25	1.25
		Nos. 697-702 (6)	3.90	3.90

1985, Feb. 22

Independence, 5th Anniv.: 5c, Star, red stripe from national flag. 30c, Unified labor.

50c, Perpetual flowering plant. 75c, Growth of agriculture. 90c, Peace dove and plant.

703	A169	5c multicolored	.20	.20
704	A169	30c multicolored	.40	.40
705	A169	50c multicolored	.65	.65
a.		Min. sheet of 3, 2 #703, #705	.85	
706	A169	75c multicolored	1.00	1.00
707	A169	90c multicolored	1.25	1.25
		Nos. 703-707 (5)	3.50	3.50

Chamber of Commerce and Industry, 75th Anniv. A170

UN Emblem, Natl. Coat of Arms — A171

1985, Apr. 17   Litho.   Perf. 14x13

708	A170	50c Chamber emblem	.50	.50
709	A170	90c Chamber, factories	.90	.90

1985, Apr. 29   Litho.   Perf. 13x14

710	A171	50c multicolored	.50	.50
711	A171	90c multicolored	.90	.90

UN, 40th anniv.

Trains — A172

1985, June 5   Litho.   Perf. 13½

712	A172	5c No. 192	.20	.20
713	A172	5c Monaco, No. J50	.20	.20
a.		Pair, #712-713	.20	.20
714	A172	10c Locomotive "Dam"	.20	.20
715	A172	10c Diesel locomotive	.20	.20
a.		Pair, #714-715	.30	.30
716	A172	20c Steam locomotive "No. 3737"	.25	.25
717	A172	20c Netherlands locomotive "IC III"	.25	.25
a.		Pair, #716-717	.50	.50
718	A172	30c Stephenson's locomotive "Rocket"	.40	.40
719	A172	30c French Railways high-speed TGV	.40	.40
a.		Pair, #716-717	.80	.80
720	A172	50c Stephenson's locomotive "Adler"	.65	.65
721	A172	50c French Railways commuter train	.65	.65
a.		Pair, #720-721	1.30	1.30
722	A172	75c Locomotive "General"	1.00	1.00
723	A172	75c Japanese bullet train "Shinkansen"	1.00	1.00
a.		Pair, #722-723	2.00	2.00
		Nos. 712-723 (12)	5.40	5.40

For surcharges see Nos. 749-750, 808-809, 928-929.

Birds — A173

1985-95   Litho.   Perf. 14x13

724	A173	10c Toucan	.20	.20
725	A173	1g American purple fowl	.90	.90
a.		Miniature sheet of 1	1.90	1.90
726	A173	1.50g Tiger bird	1.50	1.50
727	A173	2.50g Red ibis	2.50	2.50
728	A173	5g Guyana red cockerel	4.50	4.50
729	A173	10g Harpy eagle	9.00	9.00
730	A173	15g Parrot	18.00	18.00
731	A173	20g Owl	28.00	28.00
732	A173	1300g Rose lepelaar	25.00	25.00

733	A173	1780g Toucan	7.25	7.25
734	A173	2225g Hummingbird	9.00	9.00
735	A173	2995g Hoatzin	12.50	12.50
		Nos. 724-735 (12)	118.35	118.35

Nos. 724, 730 inscribed 1990.
Issued: 1g, 1.50g, 2.50g, 8/21; #725a, 5g, 1/2/86; 10g, 10/1/86; 10c, 15g, 1/30/91; 25g, 1/20/93; 1300g, 3/31/94; 1780g, 2225g, 2995g, 9/6/95.
See #1040, 1053-1055, 1108-1111, 1136-1138, 1160, 1194-1195, 1220-1221. For surcharges & overprint see #963-964, J63.

Mailboxes — A174

1985, Oct. 2   Litho.   Perf. 13x14

736	A174	15c Germany, 1900	.20	.20
737	A174	30c France, 1900	.30	.30
738	A174	50c England, 1932	.50	.50
739	A174	90c Netherlands, 1850	.90	.90
		Nos. 736-739 (4)	1.90	1.90

Natl. Independence, 10th Anniv. — A175

1985, Nov. 22

740	A175	50c Agriculture	.50	.50
741	A175	90c Industry	.90	.90
a.		Miniature sheet of 2, #740-741	1.40	1.40

No. 691
Ovptd. in Red

1985, Nov. 22   Litho.   Perf. 14x13

742	A166	30c multi	1.50	1.50

Orchids, World Wildlife Fund — A177

1986, Feb. 19   Litho.   Perf. 14x13

743	A177	5c Epidendrum ciliare	.20	.20
744	A177	15c Cycnoches chlorochilon	.50	.50
745	A177	30c Epidendrum anceps	1.00	1.00
746	A177	50c Epidendrum vespa	1.60	1.60
		Nos. 743-746 (4)	3.30	3.30

Halley's Comet A178

Designs: 50c, The Bayeux Tapestry, c. 1092, France. 110c, Halley's Comet.

1986, Mar. 5   Litho.   Perf. 14x13

747	A178	50c multi	.50	.50
748	A178	110c multi	1.00	1.00

Nos. 720-721 Surcharged in Red

1986, May 28   Litho.   Perf. 13½

749	A172	15c on 50c #720	.50	.50
750	A172	15c on 50c #721	.50	.50
a.		Pair, #749-750	1.00	1.00

No. 639
Surcharged

1986, June 25   Litho.

751	A156	30c on 70c multi	1.00	1.00

Finance Building, Paramaribo, 150th anniv.

Surinam Shipping Co., 50th Anniv. A179

1986, Sept. 1   Litho.   Perf. 14x13

752	A179	50c Emblem	.50	.50
753	A179	110c Freighter Saramacca	1.10	1.10

Monkeys A180

1987, Jan. 7   Litho.

755	A180	35c Alouatta	.40	.40
756	A180	60c Aotus	.65	.65
757	A180	110c Saimiri	1.25	1.25
758	A180	120c Cacajao	1.40	1.40
		Nos. 755-758 (4)	3.70	3.70

Esperanto, Cent. — A181

1987, Feb. 4   Litho.

759	A181	60c shown	.60	.60
760	A181	110 World map, doves	1.25	1.25
761	A181	120c L.L. Zamenhof	1.40	1.40
		Nos. 759-761 (3)	3.25	3.25

10th Pan-American Games, Indianapolis, July 23 — A182

Forestry Commission, 40th Anniv. — A183

1987, June 3   Litho.   Perf. 13x14

763	A182	90c Soccer	.85	.85
764	A182	110c Swimming	1.10	1.10
765	A182	150c Basketball	1.40	1.40
		Nos. 763-765 (3)	3.35	3.35

1987, July 21   Litho.   Perf. 13x14

766	A183	90c Emblem	1.00	1.00
767	A183	120c Logging	1.25	1.25
768	A183	150c Parrot in virgin forest	1.60	1.60
		Nos. 766-768 (3)	3.85	3.85

Intl. Year of Shelter for the Homeless A184

1987, Sept. 2   Litho.   Perf. 14x13

769	A184	90c Distressed boy, encampment	.85	.85
770	A184	120c Man, ghetto	1.25	1.25

Founders Catherine and William Booth — A185

1987, Sept. 2   Litho.   Perf. 14x13

771	A185	150c multi	1.40	1.40

Salvation Army in the Caribbean, cent.

Nos. 436-438
Surcharged

1986, Dec. 29   Litho.   Perf. 13½x13

772	A109	35c on 1g	1.50	1.50
773	A109	50c on 1.50g	2.25	2.25
774	A109	60c on 2.50g	2.75	2.75
		Nos. 772-774 (3)	6.50	6.50

Fruits — A186

1987, Oct. 14   Litho.   Perf. 13x13½

775	A186	10c Bananas	.20	.20
776	A186	15c Cacao	.20	.20
777	A186	20c Pineapple	.20	.20
778	A186	25c Papaya	.30	.30
779	A186	35c Oranges	.40	.40
		Nos. 775-779 (5)	1.30	1.30

Aircraft and Aircraft on Stamps — A187

1987, Oct. 14   Litho.   Perf. 13½

784	A187	25c Degen, 1808	.25	.25
785	A187	25c Ultra Light	.25	.25
a.		Pair, #784-785	.50	.50
786	A187	35c J.C.H. Ellehammer, 1906	.35	.35
787	A187	35c Concorde jet	.35	.35
a.		Pair, #786-787	.70	.70
788	A187	60c Fokker F7, 1924	.60	.60
789	A187	60c Fokker F28 jet	.60	.60
a.		Pair, #788-789	1.25	1.25
790	A187	90c Spin Fokker, 1910	.85	.85
791	A187	90c DC-10	.85	.85
a.		Pair, #790-791	1.75	1.75
792	A187	110c Orion, 1932	1.10	1.10
793	A187	110c Boeing 747	1.10	1.10
a.		Pair, #792-793	2.25	2.25
794	A187	120c No. 346	1.25	1.25
795	A187	120c No. 518	1.25	1.25
a.		Pair, #794-795	2.50	2.50
		Nos. 784-795 (12)	8.80	8.70

No. 693a Overprinted "3e match sevilla 1987" on Stamps in 3 or 4 Lines and with Bar and "sevilla 1987" in Sheet Margin

1987, Nov. 2   Litho.   Perf. 13½x13
Souvenir Sheet

796		Sheet of 3	19.00	
a.		A166 30c Kasparov	3.50	
b.		A166 50c Board	6.00	
c.		A166 75c Karpov	9.00	

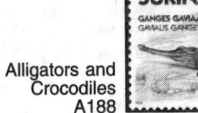

Alligators and Crocodiles A188

1988, Jan. 20   Litho.   Perf. 14x13

797	A188	50c Gavialis gangeticus	.50	.50
798	A188	60c Crocodylus niloticus	.65	.65

799	A188	90c Melanosuchus niger	.95	.95
800	A188	110c Mississippi alligator	1.25	1.25
		Nos. 797-800 (4)	3.35	3.35

Traditional Wedding Costumes — A189

1988, Feb. 24   Litho.   Perf. 13x14

801	A189	35c Javanese	.35	.35
802	A189	60c Bushman	.60	.60
803	A189	80c Chinese	.80	.80
804	A189	110c Creole	1.10	1.10
805	A189	120c Indian	1.25	1.25
806	A189	130c Hindustan	1.40	1.40
		Nos. 801-806 (6)	5.50	5.50

Nos. 722-723 and 440 Surcharged in Black or Silver

Perf. 13½x13, 13½

808	A172	60c on 75c #722	3.50	
809	A172	60c on 75c #723	3.50	
a.		Pair, #808-809	7.00	
810	A109	125c on 10g #440 (S)	7.50	
		Nos. 808-810 (3)	14.50	

1988, Mar. 23   Litho.

1988 Summer Olympics, Seoul — A190

Abolition of Slavery, 125th Anniv. — A191

1988, May 4   Litho.   Perf. 13x14

812	A190	90c Relay	.85	.85
813	A190	110c Soccer	1.10	1.10
814	A190	120c Pole vault	1.25	1.25
a.		Souvenir sheet of 3, #812-814	3.25	3.25
815	A190	250c Women's tennis	2.50	2.50
		Nos. 812-815 (4)	5.70	5.70

1988, June 29   Litho.

816	A191	50c Abaisa Monument	.60	.60
817	A191	110c Kwakoe Monument	1.25	1.25
818	A191	120c Home of Anton de Kom	1.40	1.40
		Nos. 816-818 (3)	3.25	3.25

See Netherlands Antilles Nos. 597-598.

Intl. Fund for Agricultural Development (IFAD), 10th Anniv. A192

1988, Sept. 21   Perf. 14x13
819 A192 105c Crop harvest   1.25 1.25
820 A192 110c Net fishing   1.25 1.25
821 A192 125c Agricultural re-
             search   1.40 1.40
    Nos. 819-821 (3)   3.90 3.90

FILACEPT '88, The
Netherlands, Oct.
18-23 — A193

1988, Oct. 18   Litho.   Perf. 13x14
822 A193 120c Egypt #49   1.10 1.10
823 A193 150c Netherlands #334   1.40 1.40
824 A193 250c Surinam #238   2.40 2.40
    Nos. 822-824 (3)   4.90 4.90

Souvenir Sheet
**Same Types, Colors Changed (120c,
150c)**
825   Sheet of 3   5.00 5.00
  a. A193 120c Egypt Type A23 (4m
             green)   1.10 1.10
  b. A193 150c Netherlands Type
             A81 (10c red brown)   1.40 1.40
  c. A193 250c Surinam No. 239   2.40 2.40

Stylized
Butterfly
Stroke
A194

1988, Nov. 1   Litho.   Perf. 14x13
826 A194 110c multi   1.25 1.25

Anthony Nesty, swimmer and 1st Olympic
gold medalist from Surinam.

Otters
A195

1989, Jan. 18   Litho.   Perf. 14x13
827 A195 10c Otter   .20   .20
828 A195 20c Two on land   .20   .20
829 A195 25c Two crossing log   .25   .25
830 A195 30c Fishing   .35   .35
    Nos. 827-830,C107 (5)   3.00 3.00

Classic and Modern
Automobiles — A196

1989, June 7   Litho.   Perf. 13½
           Design A196
831   25c 1930 Mercedes
            Tourenwagen   .25   .25
832   25c 1985 Mercedes-
            Benz 300E   .25   .25
  a. Pair, #831-832   .50   .50
833   60c 1897 Daimler   .60   .60
834   60c 1986 Jaguar Sover-
            eign   .60   .60
  a. Pair, #833-834   1.20 1.20
835   90c 1898 Renault Voi-
            turette   .90   .90
836   90c 1989 Renault 25TX   .90   .90
  a. Pair, #835-836   1.80 1.80
837   105c 1927 Volvo Jacob   1.00 1.00
838   105c 1989 Volvo 440   1.00 1.00
  a. Pair, #837-838   2.10 2.10
839   110c Left half of Monaco
            #484   1.10 1.10
840   110c Right half of Mona-
            co #484   1.10 1.10
  a. Pair, #839-840   2.25 2.25
841   120c 1936 Toyota AA   1.25 1.25
842   120c 1988 Toyota Corolla
            sedan   1.25 1.25
  a. Pair, #841-842   2.50 2.50
    Nos. 831-842 (12)   10.20 10.20

No. 686a Ovptd. "PHILEXFRANCE
7t/m 17 juli 1989" on Margin, with
Exhibition Emblem on Stamps in Gold
1989, July 7   Litho.   Perf. 13x14
           Miniature Sheet
843   Sheet of 3   1.50 1.50
  a. A164 2c on No. 675   .20   .20
  b. A164 35c on No. 682   .40   .40
  c. A164 75c on No. 686   .95   .95

PHILEXFRANCE '89.

Photography,
150th Anniv.
A197

1989, Sept. 6   Litho.   Perf. 14x13
844 A197 60c Joseph Niepce   .70   .70
845 A197 110c Daguerreotype
             camera   1.25 1.25
846 A197 120c Louis Daguerre   1.40 1.40
    Nos. 844-846 (3)   3.35 3.35

America
Issue — A198

UPAE emblem and pre-Columbian amulets.

1989, Oct. 12   Litho.   Perf. 13x14
847 A198 60c Amazon or Jade
             Stones   .70   .70
848 A198 110c Bisque fertility
             statue   1.25 1.25

The White
House,
Washington,
DC, and
Stamps on
Stamps
A199

Perf. 13x14, 14x13
1989, Nov. 17   Litho.
849 A199 110c No. 445, vert.   1.25 1.25
850 A199 150c US No. 990   1.75 1.75
851 A199 250c No. 459   2.75 2.75
  a. Souv. sheet, #849-851, perf
          13x14, 14   5.75 5.75
    Nos. 849-851 (3)   5.75 5.75

World Stamp Expo '89 and 20th UPU Congress, Washington, DC.

UNESCO Intl.   Arya Dewaker
Literacy   Temple, 60th
Year — A200   Anniv. — A201

1990, Jan. 19   Photo.   Perf. 13x14
852 A200 60c shown   .75   .75
853 A200 110c Emblems   1.40 1.40
854 A200 120c Emblems, youth
             reading   1.50 1.50
    Nos. 852-854 (3)   3.65 3.65

1990, Feb. 14   Litho.
855 A201 60c dk red brn, blk &
             red   .75   .75
856 A201 110c vio blue & blk   1.40 1.40
857 A201 200c emer grn & blk   2.50 2.50
    Nos. 855-857 (3)   4.65 4.65

A202   A203

1990, May 4
858 A202 110c Surinam #C1   1.25 1.25
859 A202 200c Great Britain #1   2.25 2.25
860 A202 250c Great Britain
             #208   2.75 2.75
  a. Souvenir sheet of 3, #858-860 6.75 6.75
    Nos. 858-860 (3)   6.25 6.25

Penny Black, 150th anniv. Stamps World
London '90.

1990, Aug. 9
861 A203 60c Couple carrying
             baskets   .70   .70
862 A203 110c Woman carrying
             bundle   1.25 1.25
863 A203 120c Man carrying
             baskets   1.40 1.40
    Nos. 861-863 (3)   3.35 3.35

Javanese Immigration, cent.

Flowers — A204

1990, Sept. 5   Perf. 13½
864 A204 25c Punica
              granatum   .30   .30
865 A204 25c Passiflora
              laurifolia   .30   .30
  a. Pair, #864-865   .55   .55
866 A204 35c Hippeastrum
              puniceum   .40   .40
867 A204 35c Ipomaea
              batatas   .40   .40
  a. Pair, #866-867   .80   .80
868 A204 60c Hibiscus
              syriacus   .70   .70
869 A204 60c Jasminum of-
              ficinale   .70   .70
  a. Pair, #868-869   1.40 1.40
870 A204 105c Musa serapion-
              is   1.25 1.25
871 A204 105c Hibiscus
              mutabilis   1.25 1.25
  a. Pair, #870-871   2.50 2.50
872 A204 110c Plumiria rubra   1.25 1.25
873 A204 110c Hibiscus diver-
              sifolius   1.25 1.25
  a. Pair, #872-873   2.50 2.50
874 A204 120c Bixa orellana   1.40 1.40
875 A204 120c Ceasalpinia
              pulcherima   1.40 1.40
  a. Pair, #874-875   2.80 2.80
    Nos. 864-875 (12)   10.60 10.60

America
Issue — A205

1990, Oct. 10   Litho.   Perf. 14x13
876 A205 60c bluish grn & blk   .65   .65
877 A205 110c brn & blk   1.25 1.25

Organization
of American
States,
Cent. — A206

1990, Oct. 10
878 A206 110c multicolored   1.25 1.25

Independence, 15th
Anniv. — A207

1990, Nov. 21   Litho.   Perf. 13x14
879 A207 10c shown   .20   .20
880 A207 60c Passion flower   .75   .75
881 A207 110c Dove with olive
             branch   1.30 1.30
    Nos. 879-881 (3)   2.25 2.25

Architecture
A208

Buildings: 35c, Waterfront warehouse. 60c,
Upper class residence. 75c, Labor inspection
building. 105c, Plantation supervisor's residence. 110c, Ministry of Labor. 200c, Small
residences.

1991, May 15   Litho.   Perf. 14x13
882 A208 35c multicolored   .45   .45
883 A208 60c multicolored   .80   .80
884 A208 75c multicolored   1.00 1.00
885 A208 105c multicolored   1.40 1.40
886 A208 110c multicolored   1.50 1.50
887 A208 200c multicolored   2.75 2.75
    Nos. 882-887 (6)   7.90 7.90

Puma
Concolor
A209

Various pictures of pumas.

Perf. 13x14, 14x13
1991, Sept. 12   Litho.
892 A209 10c multi, vert.   .20   .20
893 A209 20c multi, vert.   .25   .25
894 A209 25c multi, vert.   .35   .35
895 A209 30c multi, vert.   .45   .45
896 A209 125c multi   1.75 1.75
897 A209 500c multi   6.25 6.25
    Nos. 892-897 (6)   9.25 9.25

Nos. 896-897 are airmail.

Discovery of America, 500th Anniv. (in
1991) — A210

Diagram showing Columbus' route: 60c,
Western Atlantic and Caribbean Sea. 110c,
Eastern Atlantic.

1991, Oct. 11   Perf. 13x14
898   60c lt bl, red & blk   .80   .80
899   110c lt bl, red & blk   1.40 1.40
  a. Pair, #898-899   2.25 2.25

UPAEP. No. 899a has continous design.

Snakes — A211

#900, Corallus enydris. #901, Corallus
caninus. #902, Lachesis muta. #903, Boa constrictor. #904, Micrurus surinamensis. #905,
Crotalus durissus. #906, Eunectes murinus.
#907, Clelia cloelia. #908, Epicrates cenchris.

#909, Chironius carinatus. #910, Oxybelis
argentieus. #911, Spilotes pullatus.

1991, Nov. 14   *Perf. 13½*
900	A211	25c multicolored	.30	.30
901	A211	25c multicolored	.30	.30
a.		Pair, #900-901	.60	.60
902	A211	35c multicolored	.40	.40
903	A211	35c multicolored	.40	.40
a.		Pair, #902-903	.80	.80
904	A211	60c multicolored	.70	.70
905	A211	60c multicolored	.70	.70
a.		Pair, #904-905	1.40	1.40
906	A211	75c multicolored	.85	.85
907	A211	75c multicolored	.85	.85
a.		Pair, #906-907	1.70	1.70
908	A211	110c multicolored	1.25	1.25
909	A211	110c multicolored	1.25	1.25
a.		Pair, #908-909	2.50	2.50
910	A211	200c multicolored	2.25	2.25
911	A211	200c multicolored	2.25	2.25
a.		Pair, #910-911	4.50	4.50
		Nos. 900-911 (12)	11.50	11.50

Orchids — A212

A213

Designs: 50c, Cycnoches haagii. 60c,
Lycaste cristata. 75c, Galeandra dives, horiz.
125c, Vanilla mexicana. 150c, Cyrtopodium
glutiniferum. 250c, Gongora quinquenervis.

1992, Feb. 12   *Perf. 13x14, 14x13*
912	A212	50c multicolored	.55	.55
913	A212	60c multicolored	.70	.70
914	A212	75c multicolored	.85	.85
915	A212	125c multicolored	1.40	1.40
916	A212	150c multicolored	1.70	1.70
917	A212	250c multicolored	2.80	2.80
		Nos. 912-917 (6)	8.00	8.00

Souvenir Sheet

Designs: a, 75c, #847. b, 125c, #848. c,
150c, #898. d. 250c, #899.

1992, Mar. 24   *Litho.*   *Perf. 13x13½*
918	A213	Sheet of 4, #a.-d.	7.00	7.00

Granada '92, Intl. Philatelic Exibition.

1992 Summer
Olympics,
Barcelona — A214

1992, Apr. 8   *Litho.*   *Perf. 13x14*
919	A214	35c Basketball	.40	.40
920	A214	60c Volleyball	.70	.70
921	A214	75c Running	.85	.85
922	A214	125c Soccer	1.40	1.40
923	A214	150c Cycling	1.70	1.70
924	A214	250c Swimming	2.80	2.80
a.		Souvenir sheet of 3, #921, 922, 924, perf 13x13½	5.00	5.00
		Nos. 919-924 (6)	7.85	7.85

YWCA, 50th
Anniv.
A215

1992, June 12   *Litho.*   *Perf. 14x13*
925	A215	60c red brown & multi	.70	.70
926	A215	250c purple & multi	2.75	2.75

Expulsion of
Jews from
Spain, 500th
Anniv.
A216

1992, Aug. 17
927	A216	250c multicolored	2.75	2.75

Nos. 712-713 Surcharged

1992, Aug. 17   *Perf. 13½*
928	A172	1c on 5c multi	.20	.20
929	A172	1c on 5c multi	.20	.20
a.		Pair, #928-929	.20	.20

A217   A218

1992, Sept. 15   *Perf. 13x14*
930	A217	60c green & multi	.70	.70
931	A217	250c pink & multi	2.75	2.75

Jan E. Matzeliger (1852-1889), inventor of
shoe lasting machine.

1992, Oct. 12
932	A218	60c blue grn & multi	.70	.70
933	A218	250c dp org & multi	2.75	2.75

Discovery of America, 500th anniv.

Christmas — A219

Various abstract designs.

1992, Nov. 15
934	A219	10c multicolored	.20	.20
935	A219	60c multicolored	.70	.70
936	A219	250c multicolored	2.75	2.75
937	A219	400c multicolored	4.50	4.50
		Nos. 934-937 (4)	8.15	8.15

Medicinal
Plants
A220

Designs: 50c, Costus arabicus, vert. 75c,
Quassia amara, vert. 125c, Combretum
rotundifolium. 500c, Bixa orellana.

         Perf. 13x14, 14x13

1993, Feb. 3   *Litho.*
938	A220	50c multicolored	.45	.45
939	A220	75c multicolored	.65	.65
940	A220	125c multicolored	1.10	1.10
941	A220	500c multicolored	4.25	4.25
		Nos. 938-941 (4)	6.45	6.45

Beetles and Grasshoppers — A221

Designs: No. 942, Macrodontia cervicornis.
No. 943, Acrididae. No. 944, Curculionidae.
No. 945, Acrididae, diff. No. 946, Euchroma
gigantea. No. 947, Tettigonidae. No. 948, Tettigonidae. No. 949, Phanaeus festivus. No.
950, Gryllidae. No. 951, Phanaeus lancifer.
No. 952, Tettigonidae. No. 953, Batus
barbicornis.

1993, June 30   *Litho.*   *Perf. 13½*
942	A221	25c multicolored	.30	.30
943	A221	25c multicolored	.30	.30
a.		Pair, #942-943	.55	.55
944	A221	35c multicolored	.40	.40
945	A221	35c multicolored	.40	.40
a.		Pair, #944-945	.80	.80
946	A221	50c multicolored	.55	.55
947	A221	50c multicolored	.55	.55
a.		Pair, #946-947	1.10	1.10
948	A221	100c multicolored	1.10	1.10
949	A221	100c multicolored	1.10	1.10
a.		Pair, #948-949	2.25	2.25
950	A221	175c multicolored	2.00	2.00
951	A221	175c multicolored	2.00	2.00
a.		Pair, #950-951	4.00	4.00
952	A221	220c multicolored	2.50	2.50
953	A221	220c multicolored	2.50	2.50
a.		Pair, #952-953	5.00	5.00
		Nos. 942-953 (12)	13.70	13.70

A222

A223

#956b, 250c, like #955. #956c, 500c, like
#956.

1993, July 30   *Perf. 13x14*
954	A222	50c Brazil No. 3	.55	.55
955	A222	250c Brazil No. 2	2.75	2.75
956	A222	500c Brazil No. 1	5.75	5.75
		Nos. 954-956 (3)	9.05	9.05

Souvenir Sheet
956A	A222	Sheet of 2, #b.-c.	8.50	8.50

1st Brazilian postage stamps, 150th Anniv.
Brasiliana '93 (#956A).
Nos. 956b-956c have purple border.

1993, Oct. 12   *Perf. 14x13*
957	A223	50g brown & multi		
958	A223	100g green & multi		

America issue: Paleosuchus palpebrosus.

Christmas
Angels — A224

25g, African angel with drum. 45g, Asian
angel holding lamp. 50g, Oriental angel holding lantern. 150g, American Indian angel holding wand.

1993, Nov. 15   *Litho.*   *Perf. 13x14*
959	A224	25g multicolored	.40	.40
960	A224	45g multicolored	.75	.75
961	A224	50g multicolored	.80	.80
962	A224	150g multicolored	2.50	2.50
		Nos. 959-962 (4)	4.45	4.45

The foreign exchange rate of the
Surinam florin was allowed to float
freely against foreign currencies on Oct.
19, 1994. The florin's value against the
dollar has fluctuated dramatically.
Stamps may sell for values significantly
different from those quoted in the Scott
listings.

Nos. 729-730
Surcharged

1993   *Litho.*   *Perf. 14x13*
963	A173	5g on 10g Harpy eagle	.20	.20
964	A173	5g on 15g Parrot	4.50	4.50

Surcharges differ slightly. Issued: #963,
12/16. #964, 12/28.

Traditional Musical
Instruments — A225

1994, Feb. 16   *Litho.*   *Perf. 13x14*
965	A225	25g Indian drum	1.25	1.25
966	A225	50g Bosland Creooise drum	2.25	2.25
967	A225	75g Tambourine	3.50	3.50
968	A225	100g Hindu drum	4.75	4.75
		Nos. 965-968 (4)	11.75	11.75

Environmental
Protection
A226

1994, June 8   *Litho.*   *Perf. 14x13*
969	A226	50g Smoke stacks	1.75	1.75
970	A226	350g Dying fish	12.50	12.50

Intl. Olympic
Committee,
Cent. — A227

1994, July 4   *Litho.*   *Perf. 14x13*
971	A227	250g multicolored	7.75	7.75

1994 World Cup
Soccer
Championships,
US — A228

1994, July 4   *Perf. 13x14*
972	A228	100g Goalkeeper's hands	3.00	3.00
973	A228	250g Soccer shoe	7.75	7.75
974	A228	300g Goal	9.00	9.00
a.		Souvenir sheet of 2, #973-974	17.00	17.00
		Nos. 972-974 (3)	19.75	19.75

Butterflies — A229

1994, Sept. 7   Litho.   Perf. 13½

975	A229	25g Dulcedo	.70	.70
976	A229	25g Ithomia	.70	.70
a.		Pair, #975-976	1.40	1.40
977	A229	30g Danaus	.75	.75
978	A229	30g Danaus, diff.	.75	.75
a.		Pair, #977-978	1.50	1.50
979	A229	45g Echenais	1.10	1.10
980	A229	45g Bithijs	1.10	1.10
a.		Pair, #979-980	2.20	2.20
981	A229	75g Junonia evarette	1.90	1.90
982	A229	75g Anartia ja-trophae	1.90	1.90
a.		Pair, #981-982	3.80	3.80
983	A229	250g Heliconius	6.25	6.25
984	A229	250g Heliconius era-to	6.25	6.25
a.		Pair, #983-984	12.50	12.50
985	A229	300g Eurytides	7.75	7.75
986	A229	300g Parides	7.75	7.75
a.		Pair, #985-986	15.50	15.50
		Nos. 975-986 (12)	36.90	36.90

For surcharges see #1088-1091.

FEPAPOST '94 — A230

1994, Oct. 1   Litho.   Perf. 14x13

987	A230	250g Netherlands #B148	6.25	6.25
988	A230	300g #168	7.75	7.75
a.		Souvenir sheet of 2, #987-988, perf. 13½x13	14.00	14.00

America Issue A231

Post vehicles: 50g, Airplane, canoe. 400g, Van, donkey cart.

1994, Oct. 12   Litho.   Perf. 13½

989	A231	50g multicolored	1.25	1.25
990	A231	400g multicolored	10.50	10.50

A232   A233

Christmas: (A), Angel in sky. 250g, Mother reading to children. 625g, Woman kneeling in prayer.

1994, Nov. 22   Perf. 13x14

991	A232	(A) multicolored	.50	.50
992	A232	250g multicolored	1.40	1.40
993	A232	625g multicolored	3.50	3.50
		Nos. 991-993 (3)	5.40	5.40

No. 991 sold for 37g on day of issue.

1995, Jan. 31

994	A233	375g shown	2.25	2.25
995	A233	650g Volleyballs	3.75	3.75
a.		Souvenir sheet, #994-995	6.00	6.00

Volleyball, cent.

Medicinal Plants — A234

Designs: No. 998, Stachytarpheta jamaicense. No. 999, Ruellia tuberosa. No. 1000, Peperomia pellucida. No. 1001, Ocimum sanctum. No. 1002, Phyllanthus amarus. No. 1003, Portulaca oleracea. No. 1004, Wulffia

baccata. No. 1005, Sesamum indicum. No. 1006, Ascelepias curassavica. No. 1007, Heliotropium indicum. No. 1008, Wedelia trilobata. No. 1009, Lantana camara.

1995, Mar. 31   Litho.   Perf. 13½

998	A234	30g multicolored	.25	.25
999	A234	30g multicolored	.25	.25
a.		Pair, #998-999	.45	.45
1000	A234	50g multicolored	.35	.35
1001	A234	50g multicolored	.35	.35
a.		Pair, #1000-1001	.70	.70
1002	A234	75g multicolored	.55	.55
1003	A234	75g multicolored	.55	.55
a.		Pair, #1002-1003	1.10	1.10
1004	A234	250g multicolored	1.75	1.75
1005	A234	250g multicolored	1.75	1.75
a.		Pair, #1004-1005	3.50	3.50
1006	A234	500g multicolored	3.50	3.50
1007	A234	500g multicolored	3.50	3.50
a.		Pair, #1006-1007	7.00	7.00
1008	A234	600g multicolored	4.25	4.25
1009	A234	600g multicolored	4.25	4.25
a.		Pair, #1008-1009	8.50	8.50
		Nos. 998-1009 (12)	21.30	21.30

World Wildlife Fund — A235

25g, Herpailurus yaguarondi. 30g, same up close. 50g, Leopardus tigrinus. 100g, same up close. 1000g, Leopardus wiedi. 1200g, same up close.

1995, May 31   Perf. 14x13

1010	A235	25g multicolored	.40	.30
1011	A235	30g multicolored	.40	.30
1012	A235	50g multicolored	.40	.30
1013	A235	100g multicolored	1.25	.75
1014	A235	1000g multicolored	4.50	4.50
1015	A235	1200g multicolored	5.50	5.50
		Nos. 1010-1015 (6)	12.45	11.65

Nos. 1014-1015 are airmail and do not contain WWF emblem.

UN, 50th Anniv. — A236

1995, June 26   Litho.   Perf. 13x14

1016	A236	135g green & multi	.65	.65
1017	A236	740g blue & multi	3.50	3.50

Surinam Police Force, Cent. — A237

1995, June 21   Perf. 14x13

1018	A237	875g multicolored	8.00	8.00

Nilom Junior Chamber, 25th Anniv. A238

1995, Sept. 6   Litho.   Perf. 14x13

1019	A238	700g multicolored	2.00	2.00

Environmental Protction A239

1995, Oct. 12

1020	A239	135f multicolored	.60	.60
1021	A239	1500f multicolored	6.50	6.50

America issue.

A240   A241

Christmas: 70g, Shepherds, star. 135g, Flight into Egypt. 295g, Magi. 1000g, Nativity, horiz.

1995, Nov. 15   Perf. 13x14, 14x13

1022	A240	70g multicolored	.30	.30
1023	A240	135g multicolored	.60	.60
1024	A240	295g multicolored	1.25	1.25
1025	A240	1000g multicolored	4.50	4.50
a.		Souvenir sheet of 1		
		Nos. 1022-1025 (4)	6.65	6.65

For surcharges see #1065A-1065B.

1995, Dec. 5   Perf. 13x14

Paintings of Jesters, by Corneille.

1026	A241	135f With bird	.60	.60
1027	A241	615f With cat	2.75	2.75

Orchids — A242

#1028, Cyrtopodium cristatum. #1029, Epidendrum cristatum. #1030, Otostylis lepida. #1031, Cochleanthes guianensis. #1032, Rudolfiella aurantiaca. #1033, Catasetum longifolium. #1034, Maxillaria splendens. #1035, Encyclia granitica. #1036, Catasetum macrocarpum. #1037, Brassia caudata. #1038, Vanilla grandiflora. #1039, Maxillaria rufescens.

1996, Feb. 29   Litho.   Perf. 13½

1028	A242	10g multicolored	.20	.20
1029	A242	10g multicolored	.20	.20
a.		Pair, #1028-1029	.20	.20
1030	A242	75g multicolored	.35	.35
1031	A242	75g multicolored	.35	.35
a.		Pair, #1030-1031	.70	.70
1032	A242	135g multicolored	.65	.65
1033	A242	135g multicolored	.65	.65
a.		Pair, #1032-1033	1.30	1.30
1034	A242	250g multicolored	1.25	1.25
1035	A242	250g multicolored	1.25	1.25
a.		Pair, #1034-1035	2.50	2.50
1036	A242	300g multicolored	1.50	1.50
1037	A242	300g multicolored	1.50	1.50
a.		Pair, #1036-1037	3.00	3.00
1038	A242	750g multicolored	3.75	3.75
1039	A242	750g multicolored	3.75	3.75
a.		Pair, #1038-1039	7.50	7.50
		Nos. 1028-1039 (12)	15.40	15.40

Bird Type of 1985

1996, Apr. 16   Litho.   Perf. 14x13

1040	A173	2000f Kraagpapegaai	8.75	8.75

Ecotourism A243

Designs: No. 1041, Traditional huts. No. 1042, Butterfly in rain forest. No. 1043, Two natives. No. 1044, Native woman.

Perf. 13½x13 on 3 Sides

1996, Apr. 30   Litho.

Booklet Stamps

1041	A243	70g multicolored	.30	.30
1042	A243	70g multicolored	.30	.30
1043	A243	135g multicolored	.60	.60
1044	A243	135g multicolored	.60	.60
a.		Booklet pane of 4, #1041-1044	1.80	
		Complete booklet, #1044a	1.80	

Radio, Cent. — A244

135g, First wireless radio communication device, vert. 615g, Guglielmo Marconi.

Perf. 13x14, 14x13

1996, May 17   Litho.

1045	A244	135g multicolored	.60	.60
1046	A244	615g multicolored	2.75	2.75

1996 Summer Olympic Games, Atlanta — A245

Olymphilex '96, Atlanta — A245a

Stamp on stamp: b, 135f, #678. c, 865f, #683.

Illustration A254a reduced.

1996, June 27   Litho.   Perf. 13x14

1047	A245	70g Basketball	.40	.40
1048	A245	135g Athletics	.75	.75
1049	A245	195g Badmin-ton	1.10	1.10
1050	A245	200g Swim-ming	1.25	1.25
1051	A245	900g Cycling	5.50	5.50
1052	A245	1000g Hurdles	6.00	6.00
		Nos. 1047-1052 (6)	15.00	15.00

Souvenir Sheet

1052A	A245a	Sheet of 2, #b.-c.	6.00	6.00

Bird Type of 1985

Designs: 75f, Fisman. 160f, Fremusu-aka. 1765f, Roodpoot honingzuiger.

1996, Oct. 2   Litho.   Perf. 14x13

1053	A173	75f multicolored	.45	.45
1054	A173	160f multicolored	1.00	1.00
1055	A173	1765f multicolored	11.00	11.00
		Nos. 1053-1055 (3)	12.45	12.45

A246

Women's Traditional Costumes: Various styles.

1996, Oct. 9   Litho.   Perf. 13x14

1056		135f multicolored	.80	.80
1057		990f multicolored	6.00	6.00
a.	A246	Pair, #1056-1057	6.70	6.70

America issue.

A247

1996, Oct. 30   Litho.   Perf. 13x14

Christmas: Various stylized designs of Madonna and Child.

1058	A247	10f multicolored	.20	.20
1059	A247	45f multicolored	.45	.45
1060	A247	135f multicolored	.80	.80
1061	A247	285f multicolored	1.75	1.75

1062	A247 750f multicolored		4.50	4.50
a.	Souvenir sheet, #1062		4.50	4.50
	Nos. 1058-1062 (5)		7.70	7.70

A248   A249

Youth Care: Paintings, by Jan Telting: 135f, Brown dog, child. 865f, White dog, child.

1996, Dec. 4   **Litho.**   **Perf. 13x14**

1063	A248 135f multicolored		.80	.80
1064	A248 865f multicolored		5.25	5.25

1996, Dec. 13

City of Albina, 150th Anniv.: August Kappler (1815-87), founder.

1065	A249 875f multicolored		5.25	5.25

Nos. 1024, 1025 Surcharged in Black or Silver

Methods and perfs as before

1996, Dec. 16

1065A	A240 (125g) on 295g		1.40	1.40
1065B	A240 (125g) on 1000g			
		(S)	1.40	1.40

SURALCO (Surinam Aluminum Co.) — A250

10f, Opening of aluminum smelter, Paranam, 1965. 70f, Drilling blasting holes for ore exploration, Moengo, 1947. 130f, Workers' housing, Moengo, 1919. 150f, Dust-free loading of alumina, Paranam dock, 1995. 160f, Constructing dam, power station, 1960. 730f, Schooner Moengo, 1922.

Perf. 13½x13 on 2 or 3 Sides

1996, Dec. 18

Booklet Stamps

1066	A250 10f multicolored		.20	.20
1067	A250 70f multicolored		.45	.45
1068	A250 130f multicolored		.80	.80
1069	A250 150f multicolored		.90	.90
1070	A250 160f multicolored		1.00	1.00
1071	A250 730f multicolored		4.50	4.50
a.	Booklet pane, #1066-1071 + label		7.75	
	Complete booklet, #1071a		7.75	

Heinrich von Stephan (1831-97) — A251

1997, Jan. 31   **Litho.**   **Perf. 13x14**

1072	A251 275f brown & multi		1.75	1.75
1073	A251 475f dk blue & multi		2.75	2.75

Fauna — A252

#1074, Cebus nigrivittatus. #1075, Cebus apella. #1076, Saguinus midas. #1077, Ateles paniscus. #1078, Ateles geoffroyi panamensis. #1079, Ateles geoffroyi frontatus. #1080, Cacajao calvus. #1081, Lagothrix flavicauda. #1082, Saguinus bicolor. #1083, Saguinus oedipus. #1084, Alouatta seniculus. #1085, Saimiri sciureus.

1997, Feb. 12   **Litho.**   **Perf. 13½**

1074	A252 25f multicolored		.20	.20
1075	A252 25f multicolored		.20	.20
a.	Pair, #1074-1075		.30	.30
1076	A252 75f multicolored		.45	.45
1077	A252 75f multicolored		.45	.45
a.	Pair, #1076-1077		.90	.90
1078	A252 100f multicolored		.60	.60
1079	A252 100f multicolored		.60	.60
a.	Pair, #1078-1079		1.20	1.20
1080	A252 275f multicolored		1.60	1.60
1081	A252 275f multicolored		1.60	1.60
a.	Pair, #1080-1081		3.20	3.20
1082	A252 300f multicolored		1.75	1.75
1083	A252 300f multicolored		1.75	1.75
a.	Pair, #1082-1083		3.50	3.50
1084	A252 725f multicolored		4.50	4.50
1085	A252 725f multicolored		4.50	4.50
a.	Pair, #1084-1085		9.00	9.00
	Nos. 1074-1085 (12)		18.20	18.20

Retracing and Completion of Amelia Earhart's Trans-Global Flight by Linda Finch — A253

1997, Mar. 30   **Litho.**   **Perf. 14x13**

1086	A253 275f multicolored		1.75	1.75

Surinam Museum, 50th Anniv. A254

1997, Apr. 3

1087	A254 625f multicolored		3.75	3.75

Nos. 983-986 Surcharged in Black or Silver

1996-97   **Litho.**   **Perf. 13½**

1088	A229 50f on 250g #983		1.40	1.40
1089	A229 50f on 250g #984		1.40	1.40
a.	Pair, #1088-1089		2.80	2.80
1090	A229 100f on 300g #985			
		(S)	2.75	2.75
1091	A229 100f on 300g #986			
		(S)	2.75	2.75
a.	Pair, #1090-1091		5.50	5.50
	Nos. 1088-1091 (4)		8.30	8.30

Issued; #1089a, 11/1; #1091a, 1/1/97.

Orchids — A255

Designs: 25f, Selenipedium steyermarkii. 50f, Phragmipedium schlimii. 75f, Criosantes

arietina. 200f, Cypripedium margaritaceum. 775f, Paphiopedilum gratrixianum.

1997, Apr. 3   **Litho.**   **Perf. 13x14**

1092	A255 25f multicolored		.20	.20
1093	A255 50f multicolored		.30	.30
1094	A255 75f multicolored		.45	.45
1095	A255 200f multicolored		1.25	1.25
1096	A255 775f multicolored		4.75	4.75
	Nos. 1092-1096 (5)		6.95	6.95

Souvenir Sheet

PACIFIC 97, San Francisco — A256

Illustration reduced.

1997, May 29   **Litho.**   **Perf. 13½x13**

1097	A256 675f #458-459		4.00	4.00

A257   A258

Mosques: 50f, Great Mosque, Isfahan, Iran. 125f, Dome of the Rock, Jerusalem. 175f, Madrasa of Ulugh beg, Samarkand. 225f, Taj Mahal, Agra, India. 275f, Kaiser St. Mosque, Paramaribo. 325f, Sülcjamiye, Istanbul.

1997, July 7   **Perf. 13x14**

Background Color

1098	A257 50f pink		.30	.30
1099	A257 125f olive		.75	.75
1100	A257 175f blue		1.00	1.00
1101	A257 225f purple		1.40	1.40
1102	A257 275f green		1.75	1.75
1103	A257 325f brown		1.75	1.75
a.	Souvenir sheet of 1		2.00	2.00
	Nos. 1098-1103 (6)		7.20	7.20

Perf. 13x13½ on 3 Sides

1997, Aug. 16   **Litho.**

State Oil Co. Refinery, Saramacca: 50f, Pumping station. 125f, Derrick, butterfly. #1106, Storage tanks. #1107, Gauge, testing mechanism.

Booklet Stamps

1104	A258 50f multicolored		.25	.25
1105	A258 125f multicolored		.75	.75
1106	A258 275f multicolored		1.75	1.75
1107	A258 275f multicolored		1.75	1.75
a.	Booklet pane, #1104-1107		4.50	
	Complete booklet, #1107a		4.50	

Bird Type of 1985

1997, Sept. 17   **Litho.**   **Perf. 14x13**

1108	A173 50f Krabu-owrukuku		.30	.30
1109	A173 125f Mangrodoifi		.75	.75
1110	A173 275f Peprefowru		1.75	1.75
1111	A173 3150f Kroonvink		19.00	19.00
	Nos. 1108-1111 (4)		21.80	21.80

A259   A260

Child Care: 50f, Right side of boy's face. 100f, Left side of boy's face. 175f, Right side of girl's face. 225f, Left side of girl's face. 350f, 675f, Boy's face upside down, girl's face.

1997, Dec. 4   **Litho.**   **Perf. 13x14**

1112	A259 50f multicolored		.30	.30
1113	A259 100f multicolored		.60	.60
1114	A259 175f multicolored		1.00	1.00
1115	A259 225f multicolored		1.40	1.40
1116	A259 350f multicolored		2.10	2.10
	Nos. 1112-1116 (5)		5.40	5.40

Souvenir Sheet

1117	A259 675f multicolored		4.00	4.00

1997, Dec. 4

Christmas: 125f, Madonna and Child. 225f, Children looking at baby. 450f, Angel. 675f, Children singing, horiz.

1118	A260 125f multicolored		.75	.75
1119	A260 225f multicolored		1.40	1.40
1120	A260 450f multicolored		2.75	2.75
	Nos. 1118-1120 (3)		4.90	4.90

Souvenir Sheet

1121	A260 675f multicolored		4.00	4.00

America Issue — A261

Designs: 170f, Postal worker, motorcycle. 230f, Postal worker carrying package.

1997, Dec. 10   **Litho.**   **Perf. 13x14**

1122	170f multicolored		1.00	1.00
1123	230f multicolored		1.40	1.40
a.	A261 Pair, #1122-1123		2.40	2.40

Moths & Butterflies — A262

1998, Jan. 26   **Perf. 13½**

1124	A262 50f Alcandor		.30	.30
1125	A262 50f Achilles		.30	.30
a.	Pair, #1124-1125		.60	.60
1126	A262 75f Alphenor		.45	.45
1127	A262 75f Ceres		.45	.45
a.	Pair, #1126-1127		.90	.90
1128	A262 100f Cecropia		.60	.60
1129	A262 100f Helenor		.60	.60
a.	Pair, #1128-1129		1.20	1.20
1130	A262 175f Promothea		1.00	1.00
1131	A262 175f Cassiae		1.00	1.00
a.	Pair, #1130-1131		2.00	2.00
1132	A262 275f Ino		1.75	1.75
1133	A262 275f Phidippus		1.75	1.75
a.	Pair, #1132-1133		3.50	3.50
1134	A262 725f Palamedes		4.50	4.50
1135	A262 725f Helenor, diff.		4.50	4.50
a.	Pair, #1134-1135		9.00	9.00
	Nos. 1124-1135 (12)		17.20	17.20

Bird Type of 1985

1998, Mar. 12   **Perf. 14x13, 13x14**

1136	A173 50f Marjrietje		.30	.30
1137	A173 225f Aka		1.40	1.40
1138	A173 2425f Timmerman, vert.		14.50	14.50
	Nos. 1136-1138 (3)		16.20	16.20

Hindustani Immigration, 125th Anniv. A263

Designs: 175f, Painting showing first immigrants from boat, "Lala Rooch." 200f, Statue of Baba and Mai, first immigrants from India.

1998, June 4   **Litho.**   **Perf. 14x13**

1139	A263 175f multicolored		1.00	1.00
1140	A263 200f multicolored		1.25	1.25

Temples A264

Designs: 50f, Sri Lanka. 75f, Golden Pagoda, Burma, vert. 275f, Swayambhunath, Nepal, vert. 325f, Borobudur, Indonesia. 400f, Wat Phra Kaew, Thailand, vert. 450f, Peking Temple, China, vert. 675f, Statue, Borobudur, Indonesia, vert.

Perf. 13½x12½, 12½x13½

1998, June 4
1141	A264	50f	multicolored	.30	.30
1142	A264	75f	multicolored	.45	.45
1143	A264	275f	multicolored	1.60	1.60
1144	A264	325f	multicolored	1.90	1.90
1145	A264	400f	multicolored	2.25	2.50
1146	A264	450f	multicolored	2.75	2.75
	Nos. 1141-1146 (6)			9.25	9.50

Souvenir Sheet
1147	A264	675f	multicolored	4.00	4.00

No. 1147 is a continuous design.

Ferry Boat A265

1998, Oct. 31   Perf. 13½x14
1148	A265	275f	blue & multi	1.60	1.60
1149	A265	400f	sepia & multi	2.50	2.50

America Issue — A266

Outstanding women: 400f, Sophie Redmond (1907-55). 1000f, Grace Ruth Schneiders-Howard (1869-1968).

1998, Oct. 8   Litho.   Perf. 13x14
1150	A266	400f	multicolored	2.40	2.40
1151	A266	1000f	multicolored	6.00	6.00

World Stamp Exhibition, The Hague, Netherlands A267

Designs: 400f, #245, portions of #174, #141. 800f, #174, portions of #245, #141. 2400f, #141, portions of #245, #174.

1998, Oct.   Litho.   Perf. 14x13
1152	A267	400f	multicolored	2.40	2.40
1153	A267	800f	multicolored	4.75	4.75

Souvenir Sheet
1154	A267	2400f	multicolored	14.50	14.50

A268   A269

Christmas: Various nativity scenes.

1998, Nov. 1   Perf. 13x14
1155	A268	50f	multicolored	.20	.20
1156	A268	325f	multicolored	1.10	1.10
1157	A268	400f	multicolored	1.25	1.25
1158	A268	1225f	multicolored	4.00	4.00
	Nos. 1155-1158 (4)			6.55	6.55

Souvenir Sheet
1159	A268	1400f	multicolored	4.50	4.50

Bird Type of 1985

1998, Nov. 16   Litho.   Perf. 14x13
1160	A173	3800f	Butarides striatus	12.50	12.50

1998, Dec. 4   Litho.   Perf. 13x14
1161	A269	400f	Mother, child, foods	1.25	1.25
1162	A269	1000f	Mother, child, flower	3.25	3.25

World Health Organization, 50th anniv.

Child Care — A270

1998, Dec. 4   Litho.   Perf. 14x13
1163	A270	375f	shown	1.25	1.25
1164	A270	400f	Flying kite, diff.	1.25	1.25
1165	A270	1225f	Holding kite	4.00	4.00
	Nos. 1163-1165 (3)			6.50	6.50

Heliconia — A271

#1166, Caribaea kawauchi. #1167, Pastazae. #1168, Rostrata. #1169, Sexy pink. #1170, Collinsiana. #1171, Wagneriana. #1172, Bihai-nappi. #1173, Jaded forest. #1174, Golden torch. #1175, Latispatha-red yellow gyro. #1176, Sexy pink, diff. #1177, Nappi yellow.

1999, Jan. 27   Litho.   Perf. 13½
1166	A271	50f	multicolored	.20	.20
1167	A271	50f	multicolored	.20	.20
a.			Pair, #1166-1167	.30	.30
1168	A271	200f	multicolored	.65	.65
1169	A271	200f	multicolored	.65	.65
a.			Pair, #1168-1169	1.25	1.25
1170	A271	300f	multicolored	1.00	1.00
1171	A271	300f	multicolored	1.00	1.00
a.			Pair, #1170-1171	2.00	2.00
1172	A271	400f	multicolored	1.25	1.25
1173	A271	400f	multicolored	1.25	1.25
a.			Pair, 1172-1173	2.50	2.50
1174	A271	750f	multicolored	2.50	2.50
1175	A271	750f	multicolored	2.50	2.50
a.			Pair, #1174-1175	5.00	5.00
1176	A271	1300f	multicolored	4.25	4.25
1177	A271	1300f	multicolored	4.25	4.25
a.			Pair, #1176-1177	8.50	8.50
	Nos. 1166-1177 (12)			19.70	19.70

Old Plantation Houses A272

1999, Mar. 17   Litho.   Perf. 14x13
1178	A272	75f	Katwijk	.25	.25
1179	A272	300f	Sorgvliet	1.00	1.00
1180	A272	400f	Peperpot	1.25	1.25
1181	A272	2225f	Spieringshoek	7.25	7.25
	Nos. 1178-1181 (4)			9.75	9.75

Endangered Species — A273

1999, June 30   Litho.   Perf. 13x14
1182	A273	75f	Flamingo	.25	.25
1183	A273	375f	Orangutan	1.25	1.25
1184	A273	450f	Elephant	1.50	1.50
1185	A273	500f	Whale	1.60	1.60
1186	A273	850f	Frog	2.75	2.75
1187	A273	900f	Rhinoceros	3.00	3.00
1188	A273	1600f	Giant panda	5.25	5.25
1189	A273	7250f	Tiger	24.00	24.00
	Nos. 1182-1189 (8)			39.60	39.60

Coppename Bridge A274

1999, June 30   Perf. 14x13
1190	A274	850f	black & green	2.75	2.75
1191	A274	2250f	black & blue	7.25	7.25

A275   A276

1999, July 9   Perf. 13x14
1192	A275	850f	multicolored	2.75	2.75
1193	A276	2650f	multicolored	8.75	8.75
a.			Souvenir sheet, #1192-1193, perf. 13x13½	11.50	11.50

Surinam Conservation Foundation, 30th anniv. (No. 1192), Central Surinam Nature Preserve, 1st anniv. (No. 1193).

Bird Type of 1985-95

1999, Aug. 21   Perf. 14x13
1194	A173	1000f	Blauwtje	3.25	3.25
1195	A173	5500f	Kepanki	17.50	17.50

A277

1999, Oct. 9   Perf. 13x14
1196	A277	950f	Earth	3.00	3.00
1197	A277	1000f	Saturn	3.25	3.25

UPU, 125th anniv.

A278

1999, Oct. 9
1198		1000f	Gun	3.25	3.25
1199		2250f	Flower	7.25	7.25
a.			A278 Pair, #1198-1199	10.50	10.50

America issue, A New Millennium Without Arms.

Christmas — A279

1999, Nov. 3   Perf. 13x14
1200	A279	500f	Star, stable	1.60	1.60
1201	A279	850f	Christmas tree	2.75	2.75
1202	A279	900f	Angel	3.00	3.00
1203	A279	1000f	Candle	3.25	3.25
	Nos. 1200-1203 (4)			10.60	10.60

Souvenir Sheet
1204	A279	2275f	Mother and child	7.25	7.25

Children's Pictures A280

1999, Dec. 3   Litho.   Perf. 14x13
1205	A280	1100f	multi	3.50	3.50
1206	A280	1400f	multi, diff.	4.50	4.50
1207	A280	1600f	multi, diff.	5.00	5.00
a.			Souvenir sheet of 1	5.00	5.00
	Nos. 1205-1207 (3)			13.00	13.00

Children's Drawings A281

2000, Jan. 3   Litho.   Perf. 14x13
1208	A281	1000f	By Tahirih van Kanten	3.25	3.25
1209	A281	2500f	By Tirsa Braaf	8.00	8.00

See No. 1224.

Traffic Signs — A282

2000   Perf. 13x14
1210	A282	2000f	Turn right	6.50	6.50
1211	A282	2000f	No passing	6.50	6.50
1212	A282	2000f	Sharp turns	6.50	6.50
1213	A282	2000f	Traffic circle	6.50	6.50
	Nos. 1210-1213 (4)			26.00	26.00

Issued: #1210, 1/3; #1211, 4/3; #1212, 5/18. #1213, 9/29.

Fruits A283

No. 1214, 50f: a, Citrullus vulgaris. b, Carica papaya.
No. 1215, 175f: a, Mangifera indica. b, Garcinia mangostana.
No. 1216, 200f: a, Musa nana. b, Citrus paradisi.
No. 1217, 250f: a, Punika granatum. b, Ananas comosus.
No. 1218, 325f: a, Cocos nucifera. b, Passiflora quadrangularis.
No. 1219, 5000f: a, Citrus sinensis. b, Persea gratissima.

2000, Feb. 29   Litho.   Perf. 13¼
Pairs, #a-b
1214-1219	A283		Set of 6	13.50	13.50

No. 1219 is airmail.

Bird Type of 1985

Designs: 1100f, Dendrocygna autumnalis. 4425f, Ceryle torquata.

2000, Apr. 3   Perf. 14x13
1220	A173	1100f	multi	1.25	1.25
1221	A173	4425f	multi	5.00	5.00

Surinam River Bridge A284

Lettering in: 1100f, Red. 1700f, Blue.

2000, May 18
1222-1223	A284		Set of 2	3.00	3.00

Children's Drawings Type
Souvenir Sheet
2000   *Perf. 13¼x13*
1224 A281 3575f #1208, 1209   4.00 4.00

World Stamp Expo 2000, Anaheim, Stampin' the Future children's stamp design contest.

2000 Summer Olympic, Sydney A285

No. 1225, 1100f: a, Soccer. b, Track and field.
No. 1226, 3900f: a, Tennis. b, Swimming.
No. 1227: a, Soccer, diff. b, Swimming, diff.

2000, Aug. 8   Litho.   Perf. 13¼
Pairs, #a-b
1225-1226 A285   Set of 2   10.50 10.50
Souvenir Sheet
1227 A285 2500f Sheet of 2,
               #a-b   5.25 5.25

America Issue, Fight Against AIDS — A286

No. 1228: a, 1100f, Foot with condom stamping out AIDS, horiz. b, 6400f, People holding condoms.

2000   *Perf. 13x14*
1228 A286   Pair, #a-b   7.75 7.75

25th Anniv. of International Agencies Ltd. as Philatelic and Numismatic Agent — A287

Designs: 125f, Paper money. 5900f, Stamps.

2000, Nov. 24
1229-1230 A287   Set of 2   5.00 5.00
1230a   Souvenir sheet, #1229-
               1230   5.00 5.00

Children — A288

Child: 1100f, Walking. 3900f, Breastfeeding. 2000f, With umbilical cord, horiz.

2000, Dec. 5   *Perf. 13x14*
1231-1232 A288   Set of 2   4.50 4.50
Souvenir Sheet
Perf. 14x13
1233 A288 2000f multi   1.75 1.75

Fight Against Poverty A289

Country name in: 1100f, Green. 4900f, Red.

2000   *Perf. 14x13*
1234-1235 A289   Set of 2   4.50 4.50

Christmas — A290

Designs: 1100f, Star of Bethlehem. 3900f, Madonna and Child. 3000f, Magi with gifts, horiz.

2000   *Perf. 13x14*
1236-1237 A290   Set of 2   4.50 4.50
Souvenir Sheet
Perf. 14x13
1238 A290 3000f multi   2.60 2.60

No. 945a Surcharged

Methods and Perfs as Before
2000 (?)
1238A   Pair   1.90 1.90
  b. A221 1000f on 25c No. 942   .95 .95
  c. A221 1000f on 25c No. 943   .95 .95
1239   Pair   5.00 5.00
  a. A221 3100f on 35c No. 944 2.50 2.50
  b. A221 3100f on 35c No. 945 2.50 2.50

Birds A291

No. 1240, 50f: a, Rood zwart vink tagara. b, Tyarman.
No. 1241, 175f: a, Sabaku. b, Kolibrie.
No. 1242, 200f: a, Aka. b, Timmerman.
No. 1243, 250f: a, Paarskeel cotinga. b, Zwarte kraag donfowru.
No. 1244, 825f: a, Kees. b, Stonkuyake.
No. 1245, 7500f: a, Guyanese rood cotinga. b, Butabuta.

2001, Jan. 31   Litho.   Perf. 13¼
Pairs, #a-b
1240-1245 A291   Set of 6   15.00 15.00
No. 1245 is airmail.

Traffic Signs Type of 2000
2001   Litho.   Perf. 13x14
1246 A282 2000f No parking   1.90 1.90
1247 A282 4000f Drawbridge   3.75 3.75
1248 A282 4000f Tractor, No en-
               try   3.75 3.75
Issued: 2000f, 3/8; No. 1247, 4/25; No. 1248, 9/12.

UN Women's Human Rights Campaign A292

Youth Philately A293

Designs: 1400f, Female and male symbols. 4600f, Woman.

2001, Mar. 15   Litho.   Perf. 13x14
1249-1250 A292   Set of 2   5.50 5.50

2001, Apr. 25
Children's art by: 650f, Bhoelai Surender Kumar. 5350f, Sharon Cameron.
1251-1252 A293   Set of 2   5.50 5.50

Bird Type of 1985
Designs: 4500f, Charadrius collaris. 9000f, Bubo virginianus.

2001, May 10   *Perf. 14x13*
1253 A173 4500f multi   4.25 4.25
1254 A173 9000f multi   8.25 8.25

Fruit — A294

Designs: 150f, Sapotille. 200f, Noni vrucht. 800fr, Baby bananas. 1200f, Mope. 1700f, Pommerak.

2001, July 20 Litho. Perf. 12¾x13½
1255-1259 A294   Set of 5   3.75 3.75

America Issue — A295

Paramaribo buildings: Nos. 1260a, 1261a, 1700f, Bishop's house. Nos. 1260b, 1261b, 7300f, Presidential palace. Illustration reduced.

2001, Sept. 12   Litho.   Perf. 14x13
Country Name in Red
1260 A295   Pair, #a-b   8.25 8.25
Souvenir Sheet
Country Name in Green
Perf. 13¼x13
1261 A295   Sheet of 2, #a-b   8.25 8.25

Stamp Day — A296

Designs: No. 1262a, 3750f, #648 (green background). No. 1262b, 5250f, #29 (red background).
No. 1263a, 3750f, #648 (red background). No. 1263b, 5250f, #29 (orange background).

2001, Oct. 19   *Perf. 14x13*
1262 A296   Pair, #a-b   8.25 8.25
Souvenir Sheet
Perf. 13x13¼
1263 A296   Sheet of 2, #a-b   8.25 8.25

Christmas A297

Children's Sports — A298

2001, Nov. 2   *Perf. 13¼*
1264 A297 1700f blue & multi   1.50 1.50
Perf. 14x13
1265 A298 5000f red & multi   4.50 4.50
Souvenir Sheet
Perf. 13¼x13
1266 Sheet of 2   6.00 6.00
  a. A297 1700f green & multi   1.50 1.50
  b. A298 5000f blue & multi   4.50 4.50

No. 947a Surcharged in Gold

2001, Dec. 7   Litho.   Perf. 13½
1266C   Pair   4.50 4.50
  d. A221 2500f on 50c No. 946 2.25 2.25
  e. A221 2500f on 50c No. 947 2.25 2.25

Traffic Signs Type of 2000
2001-02   *Perf. 13x14*
1267 A282 4000f Pedestrian
               crossing   3.75 3.75
1268 A282 4000f Yield   3.75 3.75
Issued: No. 1267, 12/7/01; No. 1268, 2/13/02.

Parrots A299

No. 1269, 150f: a, Deroptyus accitrinus. b, Amazona achrocephala.
No. 1270, 200f: a, Ara manilata. b, Amazona dufresniana.
No. 1271, 800f: a, Ara severa. b, Pionites melanocephala.
No. 1272, 1200f: a, Ara nobilis. b, Pionus fiscus.
No. 1273, 1700f: a, Ara chloroptera. b, Pionopsitta caicca.
No. 1274, 5325f: a, Ara macao. b, Amazona farinosa.

2002, Jan. 9   *Perf. 13¼*
Pairs, #a-b
1269-1274 A299   Set of 6   17.50 17.50
No. 1274 is airmail.

Traffic Signs Type of 2000
2002, Apr. 17   Litho.   Perf. 13x14
1275 A282 4000f U turn   3.75 3.75

Traffic Signs Type of 2000

2002-03   **Litho.**   **Perf. 12¾x14**
1276 A282 4000f Pedestrian
    path   3.75   3.75
1277 A282 4000f Train cross-
    ing without
    barriers   3.75   3.75
1278 A282 4000f Motorcycles   3.75   3.75
    Nos. 1276-1278 (3)   11.25 11.25
    Issued: No. 1276, 6/19/02; No. 1277, 9/20/02; No. 1278, 2/13/03.

Costumes   Birds
A300   A301

Costumes of: Nos. 1279a, 1279c, 1279e, 1279g, 1279i, 1279k, Various men. Nos. 1279b, 1279d, 1279f, 1279h, 1279j, 1279l, Various women.

2002, May 15   **Perf. 12¾x13¼**
1279   Horiz. strip of 12   17.00 17.00
  a.-b. A300 150f Either single   .20   .20
  c.-d. A300 200f Either single   .20   .20
  e.-f. A300 800f Either single   .75   .75
  g.-h. A300 1200f Either single   1.10   1.10
  i.-j. A300 1700f Either single   1.60   1.60
  k.-l. A300 4950f Either single   4.50   4.50

2002, June 19   **Perf. 12¾x14**
1280 A301 5000f Royal flycatcher   4.75   4.75
1281 A301 8500f Swampufowru   7.75   7.75

Amphilex 2002 Intl. Stamp Exhibition,
Amsterdam — A302

No. 1282: a, 1700f, Netherlands #244 (yellow background). b, 6800f, Netherlands #103 (maroon background).
No. 1283: a, 1700f, Like No. 1282a (maroon background). b, 6800f, Like No. 1282b (yellow background).
Illustration reduced.

2002, Aug. 30   **Perf. 13¼x12¾**
1282 A302   Horiz. pair, #a-b   7.75   7.75
Souvenir Sheet
1283 A302   Sheet of 2, #a-b   7.75   7.75

Souvenir Sheet
No. 1230a Overprinted in Gold

America Issue - Youth, Education and
Literacy — A303

2002, Aug. 30   **Litho.**   **Perf. 13x14**
1284 A287   Sheet of 2   5.75   5.75
  a. 250f on 125f #1229   .25   .25
  b. 5900f #1230 overprinted   5.50   5.50

No. 1285 — Letters, numbers and: a, 1700f, Stylized head and question mark. b, 7300f, "X" in signature box.

2002, Sept. 20   **Perf. 13¼x12¾**
1285 A303   Horiz. pair, #a-b   8.25   8.25

Christmas
A304

Designs: No. 1286, 1700f, Unclothed Santa Claus and clothing (light blue background). No. 1287, 5000f, Christmas tree, decorations and gifts (green background).
No. 1288: a, 1700f, Like No. 1286 (yellow background). b, 5000f, Like No. 1287 (blue background).

2002, Nov. 6
1286-1287 A304   Set of 2   6.25   6.25
Souvenir Sheet
1288 A304   Sheet of 2, #a-b   6.25   6.25

Nos. 949a, 953a Surcharged Like No. 1266C in Gold or Silver

2002 ?   **Litho.**   **Perf. 13½**
1289   Pair   4.75   4.75
  a. A221 2500f on 100c #948   2.25   2.25
  b. A221 2500f on 100c #949   2.25   2.25
1290   Pair   7.00   7.00
  a. A221 3750f on 220c #952 (S)   3.50   3.50
  b. A221 3750f on 220c #953 (S)   3.50   3.50

Birds — A305

No. 1291: a, Falco deiroleucus. b, Lophornis ornatus. c, Touit purpurata. d, Thanlurania furcata. e, Myrmeciza ferruginea. f, Pteroglossus aracari. g, Cotinga cotinga. h, Granatellus pelzelni. i, Euphonia musica. j, Pitangus lictor. k, Cacicus haemorrhous. l, Columba speciosa.

2003, Jan. 9   **Perf. 13¼x14**
1291   Block of 12   17.00 17.00
  a.-b. A305 150f Either single   .20   .20
  c.-d. A305 200f Either single   .20   .20
  e.-f. A305 800f Either single   .75   .75
  g.-h. A305 1200f Either single   1.10   1.10
  i.-j. A305 1700f Either single   1.60   1.60
  k.-l. A305 4950f Either single   4.50   4.50

No. 951a Surcharged in Silver Like No. 1266C

2002, Dec. 30   **Litho.**   **Perf. 13½**
1292   Pair   5.00   5.00
  a. A221 2750f on 175c #950   2.50   2.50
  b. A221 2750f on 175c #951   2.50   2.50

Dolls — A306

No. 1293: a, A. M. 352/1030. b, S&H 1079, 1892. c, Jumeau, 1895 (denomination in white). d, Jumeau, 1895 (denomination in red). e, A. M. 390, 1900. f, Minerva, 1900. g, K&R 126, 1905. h, K&R, 1905. i, Handwerck, 1905. j, SFBJ, 1907. k, A. M. 980, 1920. l, K&R, 1910.

2003, May 12   **Perf. 13½x14**
1293   Block of 12   9.75   9.75
  a.-l. A306 1000f Any single   .80   .80

A307   A308

Designs: 150f, Izaak Enschedé. 800f, Old building of Johann Enschedé Printers, horiz.

1700f, Surinam #7. 3850f, First Surinam banknote printed by Enschedé, horiz.
7500f, Like 150f.

Perf. 12¾x13½, 13½x12¾
2003, June 3
1294-1297 A307   Set of 4   5.25   5.25
Souvenir Sheet
1298 A307 7500f multi   6.00   6.00
   Johann Enschedé and Sons, printers, 300th anniv.

2003, Sept. 3   **Perf. 12¾x14**
   Birds: 5400f, Anthracothorax viridigula. 6600f, Campephilus melanoleucos.
1299 A308 5400f multi   4.25   4.25
1300 A308 6600f multi   5.25   5.25

Traffic Signs Type of 2000

2003, Sept. 3   **Litho.**   **Perf. 12¾x14**
1303 A282 4000f 10% grade   3.25   3.25

Christmas — A310

Designs: 1700f, Children, dog, toy horse. 5300f, Woman holding candle.

2003, Nov. 6   **Litho.**   **Perf. 12¾x14**
1306 A310 1700f multi   1.40   1.40
1307 A310 5300f multi   4.25   4.25
  a. Horiz. pair, #1306-1307 + central label   5.75   5.75
  b. Souvenir sheet, #1306-1307   5.75   5.75

Powered Flight, Cent.
A311

Designs: 1700f, Santos-Dumont 14bis, first European flight, 1906. 5300f, Replica of 1903 aircraft by Richard Pearse, New Zealand.

2003, Dec. 13   **Perf. 14x12¾**
1308 A311 1700f multi   1.40   1.40
1309 A311 5300f multi   4.25   4.25
  a. Souvenir sheet, #1308-1309   5.75   5.75

Butterflies
A312

No. 1310: a, Anartia amathea. b, Vanessa carye. c, Papilio demetrius. d, Precis octavia. e, Papilio blumei. f, Papilio aritodemus ponceanus. g, Zerynthia rumina. h, Parides gundlachianus. i, Ornithoptera priamus. j, Lyropteryx apollonia. k, Agrias narcissus. l, Elzunia bonplandii.

2004, Jan. 12   **Perf. 12¾x14**
1310   Block of 12   22.00 22.00
  a.-b. A312 150f Either single   .20   .20
  c.-d. A312 200f Either single   .20   .20
  e.-f. A312 800f Either single   .65   .65
  g.-h. A312 1200f Either single   .95   .95
  i.-j. A312 1700f Either single   1.40   1.40
  k.-l. A312 L Either single   7.50   7.50
Nos. 1310k-1310l sold for 9500f on day of issue.

SEMI-POSTAL STAMPS

SP1   SP2

Green Cross — SP3

Perf. 12½
1927, Aug. 1   **Unwmk.**   **Photo.**
B1 SP1 2c (+ 2c) bl blk & grn   1.00   .90
B2 SP2 5c (+ 3c) vio & grn   1.00   .90
B3 SP3 10c (+ 3c) ver & grn   1.75   1.50
  Nos. B1-B3 (3)   3.75   3.30
  Set, never hinged   7.25

   Surtax was given to the Green Cross Society, which promotes public health services.

Nurse and   Good Samaritan
Patient   SP5
SP4

1928, Dec. 1   **Perf. 11½**
B4 SP4 1½c (+ 1½c) ultra   4.50   4.50
B5 SP4 2c (+ 2c) bl grn   4.50   4.50
B6 SP4 5c (+ 3c) vio   4.50   4.50
B7 SP4 7½c (+ 2½c) ver   4.50   4.50
  Nos. B4-B7 (4)   18.00 18.00
  Set, never hinged   57.50

   The surtax on these stamps was for a fund to combat indigenous diseases.

1929, Dec. 1   **Perf. 12½**
B8 SP5 1½c (+ 1½c) grn   5.75   5.75
B9 SP5 2c (+ 2c) scar   5.75   5.75
B10 SP5 5c (+ 3c) ultra   5.75   5.75
B11 SP5 6c (+ 4c) blk   5.75   5.75
  Nos. B8-B11 (4)   23.00 23.00
  Set, never hinged   65.00

   Surtax for the Green Cross Society.

Surinam Mother and
Child — SP6

1931, Dec. 14
B12 SP6 1½c (+ 1½c) blk   4.00   4.00
B13 SP6 2c (+ 2c) car rose   4.00   4.00
B14 SP6 5c (+ 3c) ultra   4.00   4.00
B15 SP6 6c (+ 4c) dp grn   4.00   4.00
  Nos. B12-B15 (4)   16.00 16.00
  Set, never hinged   45.00

The surtax was for Child Welfare Societies.

Designs Symbolical of the Creed
of the Moravians
SP7   SP8

1935, Aug. 1   **Perf. 13x14**
B16 SP7 1c (+ ½c) dk brn   2.00   2.00
B17 SP7 2c (+ 1c) dp ultra   2.00   2.00
B18 SP8 3c (+ 1½c) grn   2.40   2.40
B19 SP8 4c (+ 2c) red org   2.40   2.40
B20 SP8 5c (+ 2½c) blk brn   2.75   2.75
B21 SP7 10c (+ 5c) car   2.75   2.75
  Nos. B16-B21 (6)   14.30 14.30
  Set, never hinged   55.00

   200th anniv. of the founding of the Moravian Mission in Surinam.

Surinam Child — SP9

1936, Dec. 14   *Perf. 12½*
B22	SP9	2c (+ 1c) dk grn	2.00	2.00
B23	SP9	3c (+ 1½c) dk bl	2.00	2.00
B24	SP9	5c (+ 2½c) brn blk	2.75	2.75
B25	SP9	10c (+ 5c) lake	2.75	2.75
	Nos. B22-B25 (4)		9.50	9.50
	Set, never hinged		22.50	

Surtax for baby food and the Green Cross Society.

"Emancipation" SP10

Surinam Girl SP11

1938, June 1   Litho.   *Perf. 12½x12*
B26	SP10	2½c (+ 2c) dk bl grn	1.60	1.25

Photo.
B27	SP11	3c (+ 2c) vio blk	1.60	1.25
B28	SP11	5c (+ 3c) dk brn	1.75	1.50
B29	SP11	7½c (+ 5c) indigo	1.75	1.50
	Nos. B26-B29 (4)		6.70	5.50
	Set, never hinged		13.00	

75th anniv. of the abolition of slavery in Surinam. Surtax to Slavery Remembrance Committee.

Creole Woman — SP12

Javanese Woman — SP13

Hindustani Woman — SP14

American Indian Woman — SP15

1940, Jan. 8   Engr.   *Perf. 13x14*
B30	SP12	2½c (+ 2c) dk grn	1.75	1.75
B31	SP13	3c (+ 2c) red org	1.75	1.75
B32	SP14	5c (+ 3c) dp bl	1.75	1.75
B33	SP15	7½c (+ 5c) henna brn	1.75	1.75
	Nos. B30-B33 (4)		7.00	7.00
	Set, never hinged		11.00	

Surtax to leper care and baby food.

> **Catalogue values for unused stamps in this section, from this point to the end of the section, are for Never Hinged items.**

Netherlands Coat of Arms and Inscription, "Netherlands Shall Rise Again" — SP16

1941, Aug. 30   Litho.   *Perf. 12½*
B34	SP16	7½c + 7½c dp org, ultra & blk	2.50	2.00
B35	SP16	15c + 15c scar, ultra & blk	2.50	2.00
B36	SP16	1g + 1g gray & ultra	17.50	15.00
	Nos. B34-B36 (3)		22.50	19.00

The surtax was used to buy fighters for Dutch pilots in the Royal Air Force of Great Britain.

Nos. 145, 169, 146, 151 Surcharged in Red:

1942, Jan. 2
B37	A23	2c + 2c blk brn, I	1.60	1.60
a.		Type II	1.60	1.60
B38	A26	2c + 2c blk brn, I	40.00	32.50
a.		Type II	40.00	32.50
B39	A23	2½c + 2c green, I	1.60	1.60
a.		Type II	1.60	1.60
B40	A23	7½c + 5c red vio, III	1.60	1.60
a.		Type IV	6.00	6.00
b.		Type V	15.00	15.00
	Nos. B37-B40,CB1 (5)		47.30	39.80

The surtax was for the Red Cross.

In type III, the "c" may be "large," as illustrated, or "small," as in type II. Value is the same.

The distinctive feature of type IV is the pointed ending of the lower part of the "5."

Types of Regular Issue of 1945 Surcharged in Black

5 CENT VOOR HET NATIONAAL STEUNFONDS

Unwmk.

1945, July 23   Engr.   *Perf. 12*
B41	A29	7½c + 5c dp org	2.75	1.90
B42	A30	15c + 10c brn	2.25	1.90
B43	A30	20c + 15c dl grn	2.25	1.90
B44	A30	22½c + 20c gray	2.25	1.90
B45	A30	40c + 35c rose lake	2.25	1.90
B46	A30	60c + 50c vio	2.25	1.90
	Nos. B41-B46 (6)		14.00	11.40

Surtax for the National Welfare Fund.

Star — SP17

Marie Curie — SP18

1947, Dec. 16   Photo.   *Perf. 13½x13*
B47	SP17	7½c + 12½c red org	2.25	1.75
B48	SP17	12½c + 37½c blue	2.25	1.75
	Nos. B47-B48,CB4-CB5 (4)		9.00	7.00

The surtax was used to combat leprosy.

1950, May 15   *Perf. 14x13*

7½c+22½c, 27½c+12½c, Wm. Roentgen.
B49	SP18	7½c + 7½c	10.00	6.00
B50	SP18	7½c + 22½c	10.00	6.00
B51	SP18	27½c + 12½c	10.00	6.00
B52	SP18	27½c + 97½c	10.00	6.00
	Nos. B49-B52 (4)		40.00	24.00

The surtax was used to combat cancer.

Nos. 236-237 Surcharged in Black (#B53) or Red (#B54)

1953, Feb. 18   **Wmk. 202**
B53	A35	12½c + 7½c on 7½c	2.00	1.90
B54	A35	20c + 10c on 12½c	2.00	1.90

The surtax was for flood relief in the Netherlands.

Stadium, Paramaribo — SP19

1953, Aug. 29   Unwmk.   *Perf. 13½*
B55	SP19	10c + 5c claret	7.00	5.00
B56	SP19	15c + 7½c brn	7.00	5.00
B57	SP19	30c + 15c dk grn	7.00	5.00
	Nos. B55-B57 (3)		21.00	15.00

Opening of the new stadium.

Surinam Children — SP20

Doves — SP21

1954, Nov. 1   *Perf. 13x14*
B58	SP20	7½c + 3c sepia	3.75	3.00
B59	SP20	10c + 5c bl grn	3.75	3.00
B60	SP20	15c + 7½c red brn	3.75	3.00
B61	SP20	30c + 15c blue	3.75	3.00
	Nos. B58-B61 (4)		15.00	12.00

Surtax for the youth center of the Moravian Church.

1955, May 5   *Perf. 14x13*
B62	SP21	7½c + 3½c brt red	2.75	3.00
B63	SP21	15c + 8c ultra	2.75	3.00

The Netherlands' liberation, 10th anniv.

Queen Juliana and Prince Bernhard SP22

1955, Oct. 27   **Unwmk.**
B64	SP22	7½c + 2½c dk olive	.55	.55

Royal visit to Surinam, 1955. Surtax for the Royal present.

Theater, 1837 — SP23

Designs: 10c+5c, Theater and car, circa 1920. 15c+7½c, Theater and car, circa 1958. 20c+10c, Theater interior.

1958, Feb. 15   Litho.   *Perf. 13x12½*
B65	SP23	7½c + 3c lt bl & blk	.45	.45
B66	SP23	10c + 5c rose lil & blk	.45	.45
B67	SP23	15c + 7½c lt grn & blk	.45	.45
B68	SP23	20c + 10c org & blk	.45	.45
	Nos. B65-B68 (4)		1.80	1.80

120th anniv. of the "Thalia" theatrical society.

Carved Eating Utensils and Map of South America SP24

Native Art (Map of So. America and): 10c+5c, Feather headgear. 15c+7c, Clay pottery. 20c+10c, Carved wooden stool.

1960, Jan. 15
B69	SP24	8c + 4c multi	.90	.90
B70	SP24	10c + 5c salmon, red & bl	.90	.90
B71	SP24	15c + 7c red org, grn & sepia	.90	.90
B72	SP24	20c + 10c lt bl, ultra & bis	.90	.90
	Nos. B69-B72 (4)		3.60	3.60

SP25   SP26

Design: Uprooted Oak emblem of WRY.

1960, Apr. 7   *Perf. 13x14*
B73	SP25	8c + 4c choc & grn	.20	.20
B74	SP25	10c + 5c vio bl & grn	.20	.20

World Refugee Year, July 1, 1959-June 30, 1960. The surtax was for aid to refugees.

1960, Aug. 10   Litho.   *Perf. 14x13*
B75	SP26	8c + 4c Shot put	.55	.55
B76	SP26	10c + 5c Basketball	.55	.55
B77	SP26	15c + 7c Runner	.85	.85
B78	SP26	20c + 10c Swimmer	.85	.85
B79	SP26	40c + 20c Soccer	.85	.85
	Nos. B75-B79 (5)		3.65	3.65

17th Olympic Games, Rome, 8/25-9/11. Surtax for Olympic Committee.

Girl Scout Signaling SP27

Designs: 10c+3c, Scout Saluting, vert. 15c+4c, Brownies around toadstool. 20c+5c, Scouts around campfire, vert. 25c+6c, Scouts cooking outdoors.

Perf. 14x13, 13x14

1961, Aug. 19   Litho.

Multicolored Designs
B80	SP27	8c + 2c blue	.30	.30
B81	SP27	10c + 3c lilac	.35	.35
B82	SP27	15c + 4c yellow	.35	.35
B83	SP27	20c + 5c brn red	.40	.40
B84	SP27	25c + 6c aqua	.40	.40
	Nos. B80-B84 (5)		1.80	1.80

Caribbean Girl Scout Jamborette. Surtax for various charities.

Hibiscus SP28

Flowers: 10c+5c, Caesalpinia pulcherrima. 15c+6c, Heliconia psittacorum. 20c+10c, Lochnera rosea. 25c+12c, Ixora macrothyrsa.

1962, Mar. 7   Photo.   *Perf. 14x13*

Cross in Red
B85	SP28	8c + 4c dk ol & scar	.32	.30
B86	SP28	10c + 5c dk bl & org	.32	.30
B87	SP28	15c + 6c multi	.32	.30
B88	SP28	20c + 10c multi	.32	.30

B89 SP28 25c + 12c dk bl grn,
red & yel   .32 .30
Nos. B85-B89 (5)   1.60 1.50

The surtax was for the Red Cross.

Hands
Protecting
Duck — SP29

American Indian
Girl — SP30

1962, Dec. 15   Litho.   Perf. 13x14

B90 SP29 2c + 1c shown   .20 .20
B91 SP29 8c + 2c Dog   .20 .20
B92 SP29 10c + 3c Donkey   .20 .20
B93 SP29 15c + 4c Horse   .25 .25
Nos. B90-B93 (4)   .85 .85

The surtax was for the Organization for
Animal Protection.

1963, Oct. 30   Photo.   Unwmk.

Girls: 10c+4c, Negro. 15c+10c, East Indian.
20c+10c, Indonesian. 40c+20c, Caucasian.

B94 SP30 8c + 3c Prus grn   .20 .20
B95 SP30 10c + 4c red brn   .20 .20
   a. Min. sheet, 2 each #B94-B95   1.25 1.25
B96 SP30 15c + 10c dp blue   .25 .25
B97 SP30 20c + 10c brn red   .25 .25
B98 SP30 40c + 20c red vio   .35 .35
Nos. B94-B98 (5)   1.25 1.25

The surtax was for Child Welfare.

X-15
SP31

Designs: 8c+4c, Flag of the Aeronautical
and Astronautical Foundation. 10c+5c,
20c+10c, Agena B Ranger rocket.

1964, Apr. 15   Perf. 13x12½

B99 SP31 3c + 2c blk & rose
lake   .20 .20
B100 SP31 8c + 4c blk, ultra &
lt ultra   .20 .20
B101 SP31 10c + 5c blk & grn   .20 .20
B102 SP31 15c + 7c blk & yel
brn   .20 .20
B103 SP31 20c + 10c blk & vio   .20 .20
Nos. B99-B103 (5)   1.00 1.00

Surtax for the Aeronautical and Astronautical Foundation of Surinam.

Stylized Campfire
amid Trees — SP32

Girls Skipping
Rope — SP33

1964, July 29   Litho.   Perf. 13x14

B104 SP32 3c + 1c brn ol, yel bis
& lem   .20 .20
B105 SP32 8c + 4c bluish blk, vio
bl & yel bis   .20 .20
B106 SP32 10c + 5c dk red, red &
yel bis   .20 .20
B107 SP32 20c + 10c grnsh blk, ol
grn & yel bis   .20 .20
Nos. B104-B107 (4)   .80 .80

Jamborette at Paramaribo, Aug. 20-30,
marking the 40th anniv. of the Surinam Boy
Scout Association.
Surtax for various charities.

1964, Nov. 30   Photo.   Perf. 14x13

10c+4c, Children on swings. 15c+9c, Girl on
scooter. 20c+10c, Boy rolling hoop.

B108 SP33 8c + 3c dk blue   .20 .20
B109 SP33 10c + 4c red   .20 .20
   a. Min. sheet, 2 each #B108-B109   .55 .55
B110 SP33 15c + 9c olive grn   .20 .20
B111 SP33 20c + 10c magenta   .20 .20
Nos. B108-B111 (4)   .80 .80

Issued for Child Welfare.

Mother and
Child — SP34

Designs: 4c+2c, Pregnant woman. 15c+7c,
Child. 25c+12c, Old man.

1965, Feb. 27   Photo.   Perf. 13x14

B112 SP34 4c + 2c green   .20 .20
B113 SP34 10c + 5c brn & grn   .20 .20
B114 SP34 15c + 7c Prus bl & grn   .20 .20
B115 SP34 25c + 12c brt pur & grn   .20 .20
Nos. B112-B115 (4)   .80 .80

50th anniv. of the Green Cross Assoc.
which promotes public health services.

Girl with
Leopard and
Spider
SP35

Designs: 10c+5c, Boy with monkey and spider. 15c+7c, Girl with tortoise and spider.
25c+10c, Boy with rabbit and spider.

Perf. 13x12½

1965, Nov. 26   Litho.   Unwmk.

B116 SP35 4c + 4c lt grn & blk   .20 .20
B117 SP35 10c + 5c ocher & blk   .20 .20
B118 SP35 15c + 7c dp org & blk   .55 .55
   a. Min. sheet, 2 each #B116, B118   .55 .55
B119 SP35 25c + 10c lt ultra & blk   .20 .20
Nos. B116-B119 (4)   .80 .80

Issued for Child Welfare.

"Help them to
a safe haven"
SP35a

1966, Jan. 31   Photo.   Perf. 14x13

B120 SP35a 10c + 5c blk & grn   .20 .20
B121 SP35a 25c + 10c blk & rose
brn   .20 .20
   a. Min. sheet of 3, 2 #B120, B121   .45 .45

The surtax was for the Intergovernmental
Committee for European Migration (ICEM).
The message on the stamps was given and
signed by Queen Juliana.

Mary
Magdalene,
Disciples and
"Round Table"
Emblem
SP36

"New Year's
Eve" Boys with
Bamboo Gun
SP37

Mary Magdalene (John 20:18), and Service
Club Emblems: 15c+8c, Toastmasters Intl.
20c+10c, Junior Chamber, Surinam. 25c+12c,
Rotary Intl. 30c+15c, Lions Intl.

1966, Apr. 13   Photo.   Perf. 12½x13

B122 SP36 10c + 5c dp crim, blk
& gold   .20 .20
B123 SP36 15c + 8c dp vio, blk
& bl   .20 .20
B124 SP36 20c + 10c yel org, blk
& ultra   .20 .20
B125 SP36 25c + 12c grn, blk &
gold   .20 .20
B126 SP36 30c + 15c ultra, blk &
gold   .20 .20
Nos. B122-B126 (5)   1.00 1.00

Easter charities.

1966, Nov. 25   Litho.   Perf. 12½x13

Designs: 15c+8c, "The End of Lent," boys
pouring paint over each other. 20c+10c, "Liberation Day," parading children. 25c+12c,
"Queen's Birthday," children on hobbyhorses.
30c+15c, "Christmas," Children decorating
room with star.

B127 SP37 10c + 5c multi   .20 .20
B128 SP37 15c + 8c multi   .20 .20
B129 SP37 20c + 10c multi   .20 .20
   a. Min. sheet of 3, 2 #B127,
B129   .35 .35
B130 SP37 25c + 12c multi   .20 .20
B131 SP37 30c + 15c multi   .20 .20
Nos. B127-B131 (5)   1.00 1.00

Child welfare.

Good
Samaritan
Giving His Coat
SP38

Children Stilt-
walking
SP39

The Good Samaritan: 15c+8c, Dressing the
wounds. 20c+10c, Feeding the poor man.
25c+12c, Poor man riding Samaritan's horse.
30c+15c, Samaritan taking poor man to the
inn.

1967, Mar. 22

B132 SP38 10c + 5c yellow & blk   .20 .20
B133 SP38 15c + 8c lt blue & blk   .20 .20
B134 SP38 20c + 10c buff & blk   .20 .20
B135 SP38 25c + 12c pale rose
& blk   .20 .20
B136 SP38 30c + 15c grn & blk   .20 .20
Nos. B132-B136 (5)   1.00 1.00

Easter charities.

1967, Nov. 21   Litho.   Perf. 12½x13

Children's Games: 15c+8c, Boys playing
with marbles. 20c+10c, Girl playing dibs (five
stones). 25c+12c, Boy making kite. 30c+15c,
Girls play-cooking.

B137 SP39 10c + 5c multi   .20 .20
B138 SP39 15c + 8c multi   .20 .20
B139 SP39 20c + 10c multi   .20 .20
   a. Min. sheet, #B139, 2 #B137   .45 .45
B140 SP39 25c + 12c multi   .20 .20
B141 SP39 30c + 15c multi   .20 .20
Nos. B137-B141 (5)   1.00 1.00

Child welfare.

Cross, Ash
Wednesday
SP40

Hopscotch
SP41

Easter Symbols: 15c+8c, Palms, Palm Sunday. 20c+10c, Bread and Wine, Maundy
Thursday. 25c+12c, Cross, Good Friday.
30c+15c, Chrismon, Easter Sunday.

1968, Mar. 27   Litho.   Perf. 12½x13

B142 SP40 10c + 5c lilac & gray   .20 .20
B143 SP40 15c + 8c brick red &
grn   .20 .20
B144 SP40 20c + 10c yellow &
dk grn   .20 .20
B145 SP40 25c + 12c gray & blk   .20 .20

B146 SP40 30c + 15c brt yel &
brn   .20 .20
Nos. B142-B146 (5)   1.00 1.00

Easter charities.

1968, Nov. 22   Litho.   Perf. 12½x13

15c+8c, Balancing pyramid. 20c+10c,
Handball. 25c+12c, Handicraft. 30c+15c, Tug-
of-war.

B147 SP41 10c + 5c fawn & blk   .20 .20
B148 SP41 15c + 8c lt ultra & blk   .20 .20
B149 SP41 20c + 10c pink & blk   .20 .20
   a. Min. sheet, #B149, 2 #B147   .50 .50
B150 SP41 25c + 12c yel grn & blk   .25 .25
B151 SP41 30c + 15c bluish lil & blk   .30 .30
Nos. B147-B151 (5)   1.15 1.15

Child welfare.

Globe with Map
of South
America
SP42

Pillow Fight
SP43

1969, Apr. 2   Litho.   Perf. 12½x13

B152 SP42 10c + 5c bl & lt bl   .25 .25
B153 SP42 15c + 8c sl grn & yel   .25 .25
B154 SP42 20c + 10c sl grn &
gray grn   .25 .25
B155 SP42 25c + 12c brn & bis   .25 .25
B156 SP42 30c + 15c vio & gray   .25 .25
Nos. B152-B156 (5)   1.25 1.25

Easter charities.

1969, Nov. 21   Litho.   Perf. 12½x13

15c+8c, Eating contest. 20c+10c, Pole
climbing. 25c+12c, Sack race. 30c+15c,
Obstacle race.

B157 SP43 10c + 5c lt ultra &
mag   .20 .20
B158 SP43 15c + 8c yel & brn   .25 .25
B159 SP43 20c + 10c gray & dp
bl   .20 .20
   a. Min. sheet, #B159, 2 B157   .80 .80
B160 SP43 25c + 12c pink & brt
bl   .25 .25
B161 SP43 30c + 15c emer &
brn   .25 .25
Nos. B157-B161 (5)   1.15 1.15

Child welfare.

Butterfly
SP44

Ludwig van
Beethoven,
1786
SP45

Designs: 10c+5c, Flower. 20c+10c, Flying
bird. 25c+12c, Sun. 30c+15c, Star.

1970, Mar. 25   Litho.   Perf. 12½x13

B162 SP44 10c + 5c multi   .50 .50
B163 SP44 15c + 8c multi   .50 .50
B164 SP44 20c + 10c multi   .50 .50
B165 SP44 25c + 12c multi   .50 .50
B166 SP44 30c + 15c multi   .50 .50
Nos. B162-B166 (5)   2.50 2.50

Easter.

1970, Nov. 25   Litho.   Perf. 12½x13

Various Portraits of Beethoven: 15c+8c, In
1804. 20c+10c, In 1812. 25c+12c, In 1814.
30c+15c, In 1827 (death mask).

Portrait and Inscription in Gray and Ocher

B167	SP45	10c + 5c green	.50	.50
B168	SP45	15c + 8c scarlet	.50	.50
B169	SP45	20c + 10c blue	.50	.50
a.		Min. sheet, #B169, 2 #B167	1.60	1.60
B170	SP45	25c + 12c red org	.50	.50
B171	SP45	30c + 15c purple	.50	.50
		Nos. B167-B171 (5)	2.50	2.50

Ludwig van Beethoven (1770-1827), composer. The surtax was for child welfare.

Donkey and Palm — SP46

Leapfrog, by Peter Brueghel — SP47

Easter: 15c+8c, Cock. 20c+10c, Lamb of God. 25c+12c, Cross and Crown of Thorns. 30c+15c, Sun.

1971, Apr. 7   Litho.   Perf. 12½x13

B172	SP46	10c + 5c multi	.50	.50
B173	SP46	15c + 8c blue & multi	.50	.50
B174	SP46	20c + 10c multi	.50	.50
B175	SP46	25c + 12c multi	.50	.50
B176	SP46	30c + 15c multi	.50	.50
		Nos. B172-B176 (5)	2.50	2.50

Easter charities.

1971, Nov. 24   Photo.   Perf. 13x14

Children's Games, by Peter Brueghel: 15c+8c, Girl strewing flowers. 20c+10c, Spinning the hoop. 25c+12c, Ball players. 30c+15c, Stilt walker.

B177	SP47	10c + 5c multi	.60	.60
B178	SP47	15c + 8c multi	.60	.60
B179	SP47	20c + 10c multi	.60	.60
a.		Min. sheet, #B179, 2 #B177	2.00	2.00
B180	SP47	25c + 12c multi	.60	.60
B181	SP47	30c + 15c multi	.60	.60
		Nos. B177-B181 (5)	3.00	3.00

Child welfare.

Easter Candle — SP48   Toys — SP49

Easter: 15c+8c, Christ teaching Apostles, and crosses. 20c+10c, Cup and folded hands. 25c+12c, Fish in net. 30c+15c, Judas' bag of silver.

1972, Mar. 29   Litho.   Perf. 12½x13

B182	SP48	10c + 5c multi	.45	.45
B183	SP48	15c + 8c multi	.45	.45
B184	SP48	20c + 10c multi	.45	.45
B185	SP48	25c + 12c multi	.45	.45
B186	SP48	30c + 15c multi	.45	.45
		Nos. B182-B186 (5)	2.25	2.25

Easter charities.

1972, Nov. 29   Litho.   Perf. 12½x13

Designs: 15c+8c, Abacus and clock. 20c+10c, Pythagorean theorem. 25c+12c, Model of molecule. 30c+15c, Monkey wrench and drill. Each design represents a different stage of education.

B187	SP49	10c + 5c multi	.50	.50
B188	SP49	15c + 8c multi	.50	.50
B189	SP49	20c + 10c multi	.50	.50
a.		Min. sheet, #B189, 2 #B187	1.50	1.50
B190	SP49	25c + 12c multi	.50	.50
B191	SP49	30c + 15c multi	.50	.50
		Nos. B187-B191 (5)	2.50	2.50

Child welfare.

Jesus Calming the Waves — SP50

Easter: 15c+8c, The washing of the feet. 20c+10c, Jesus carrying Cross. 25c+12c, Cross and "ELI, ELI, LAMA SABACHTHANI?" 30c+15c, on the road to Emmaus.

1973, Apr. 4   Litho.   Perf. 12½x13

B192	SP50	10c + 5c multi	.45	.45
B193	SP50	15c + 8c multi	.45	.45
B194	SP50	20c + 10c multi	.45	.45
B195	SP50	25c + 12c multi	.45	.45
B196	SP50	30c + 15c multi	.45	.45
		Nos. B192-B196 (5)	2.25	2.25

Easter charities.

Red Cross and Florence Nightingale SP51

1973, Oct. 3   Litho.   Perf. 14½x14

B197	SP51	30c + 10c multi	.90	.90

30th anniversary of Surinam Red Cross.

Flower SP52   Bitterwood SP53

1973, Nov. 28   Litho.   Perf. 14x14½

B198	SP52	10c + 5c shown	.25	.25
B199	SP52	15c + 8c Tree	.45	.45
B200	SP52	20c + 10c Dog	.40	.40
a.		Min. sheet, #B200, 2 #B198	1.25	1.25
B201	SP52	25c + 12c House	.60	.60
B202	SP52	30c + 15c Girl	.60	.60
		Nos. B198-B202 (5)	2.30	2.30

Child welfare.

1974, Apr. 3   Litho.   Perf. 14x14½

Tropical Flowers: 15c+8c, Passion flower. 20c+10c, Wild angelica. 25c+12c, Candlestick senna. 30c+15c, Blood flower.

B203	SP53	10c + 5c multi	.45	.45
B204	SP53	15c + 8c multi	.45	.45
B205	SP53	20c + 10c multi	.45	.45
B206	SP53	25c + 12c multi	.45	.45
B207	SP53	30c + 15c multi	.45	.45
		Nos. B203-B207 (5)	2.25	2.25

Easter charities.

Boy Scout, Tent and Trees — SP54

Designs: 15c+8c, 5th Caribbean Jamboree emblem. 20c+10c, Scouts and emblem.

1974, Aug. 21   Litho.   Perf. 14x14½

B208	SP54	5c + 5c multi	.40	.40
B209	SP54	10c + 8c multi	.40	.40
B210	SP54	20c + 10c multi	.40	.40
		Nos. B208-B210 (3)	1.20	1.20

50th anniversary of Surinam Boy Scouts.

Fruit — SP55

Designs: 15c+8c, Children, birds and nest (security). 20c+10c, Flower, mother and child (protection). 25c+12c, Child and corn (good food). 30c+15c, Dancing children (child care).

1974, Nov. 27   Litho.   Perf. 14½x14

B211	SP55	10c + 5c multi	.25	.25
B212	SP55	15c + 8c multi	.35	.35
B213	SP55	20c + 10c multi	.35	.35
a.		Min. sheet, #B213, 2 #B211	1.00	1.00
B214	SP55	25c + 12c multi	.55	.55
B215	SP55	30c + 15c multi	.60	.60
		Nos. B211-B215 (5)	2.10	2.10

Child welfare.

The Good Shepherd SP56   Woman and IWY Emblem SP57

Designs: 20c+10c, Peter's denial. 30c+15c, The Women at the Tomb. 35c+20c, Jesus showing His wounds to Thomas.

1975, Mar. 26   Litho.   Perf. 12½x13

B216	SP56	15c + 5c yel grn & grn	.45	.45
B217	SP56	20c + 10c org & dk bl	.60	.60
B218	SP56	30c + 15c yel & red	.60	.60
B219	SP56	35c + 20c bl & pur	.60	.60
		Nos. B216-B219 (4)	2.25	2.25

Easter charities.

1975, May 14   Litho.   Perf. 12½x13

B220	SP57	15c + 5c multi	.65	.65
B221	SP57	30c + 15c multi	.65	.65

International Women's Year.

Carib Indian Water Jug — SP58   Feeding the Hungry — SP59

Designs: 20c+10c, 35c+20c, Indian arrow head, diff. 30c+15c, Wayana board with animal figures.

1975, Nov. 12   Litho.   Perf. 12½x13

B222	SP58	15c + 5c multi	.20	.20
B223	SP58	20c + 10c multi	.55	.55
a.		Min. sheet, #B223, 2 #B222	1.50	1.50
B224	SP58	30c + 15c multi	.90	.90
B225	SP58	35c + 20c multi	.90	.90
		Nos. B222-B225 (4)	2.55	2.55

Child welfare.

Perf. 14½x13½

1976, Apr. 14   Photo.

Paintings: 25c+15c, Visiting the Sick. 30c+15c, Clothing the Naked. 35c+15c, Burying the Dead. 50c+25c, Giving Water to the Thirsty. Designs after panels in Alkmaar Church, 1504.

B226	SP59	20c + 10c multi	.40	.40
B227	SP59	25c + 15c multi	.50	.50
B228	SP59	30c + 15c multi	.65	.65
a.		Souv. sheet, #B228, 2 #B226	2.00	2.00
B229	SP59	35c + 15c multi	.65	.65
B230	SP59	50c + 25c multi	1.00	1.00
		Nos. B226-B230 (5)	3.20	3.20

Easter.

Pekingese and Boy's Head — SP60

25c+10c, German shepherd. 30c+15c, Dachshund. 35c+15c, Retriever. 50c+25c, Terrier.

1976   Litho.   Perf. 13½

B231	SP60	20c + 10c multi	.75	.50
B232	SP60	25c + 10c multi	1.00	.70
B233	SP60	30c + 15c multi	1.25	.80
a.		Min. sheet, #B233, 2 #B231	2.50	2.00
B234	SP60	35c + 15c multi	1.25	.85
B235	SP60	50c + 25c multi	2.00	1.25
		Nos. B231-B235 (5)	6.25	4.10

Surtax was for child welfare.

St. Veronica's Veil — SP61   Descent from the Cross — SP62

Easter: Religious scenes, side panels, front and back, from triptych by Jan Mostaert (1473-1555).

1977, Apr. 6   Litho.   Perf. 13½x14

B236	SP61	20c + 10c multi	.25	.25
B237	SP61	25c + 15c multi	.35	.35
B238	SP61	30c + 15c multi	.40	.40
B239	SP62	35c + 15c multi	.45	.45
B240	SP61	50c + 25c multi	.55	.55
		Nos. B236-B240 (5)	2.00	2.00

Dog and Girl's Head — SP63   Crosses, Luke 23:43 — SP64

Child's Head and: 25c+15c, Monkey. 30c+15c, Rabbit. 35c+15c, Cat. 50c+25c, Parrot.

1977, Nov. 23   Litho.   Perf. 13x14

B241	SP63	20c + 10c multi	.25	.25
B242	SP63	25c + 15c multi	.30	.30
B243	SP63	30c + 15c multi	.35	.35
a.		Min. sheet, #B243, 2 #B241	.90	.90
B244	SP63	35c + 15c multi	.40	.40
B245	SP63	50c + 25c multi	.55	.55
		Nos. B241-B245 (5)	1.85	1.85

Surtax was for child welfare.

1978, Mar. 22   Litho.   Perf. 12½x14

Easter: 25c+15c, Serpent and Cross, John 3:14. 30c+15c, Lamb and blood, Exodus 12:13. 35c+15c, Passover plate, chalice and bread. 60c+30c, Cross and solar eclipse.

B246	SP64	20c + 10c multi	.25	.25
B247	SP64	25c + 15c multi	.35	.35
B248	SP64	30c + 15c multi	.40	.40
B249	SP64	35c + 15c multi	.45	.45
B250	SP64	60c + 30c multi	.90	.90
		Nos. B246-B250 (5)	2.35	2.35

Child's Head and White Cat — SP65

Church, Cross and
Chalice — SP66

Child's head and cats in various positions.

1978, Nov. 22   Litho.   Perf. 14x13
B251 SP65 20c + 10c multi   .25   .25
B252 SP65 25c + 15c multi   .40   .30
B253 SP65 30c + 15c multi   .45   .35
 a.   Min. sheet, #B253, 2 #B251   .90   .90
B254 SP65 35c + 15c multi   .50   .40
B255 SP65 60c + 30c multi   .85   .70
     Nos. B251-B255 (5)   2.45 2.00

Surtax was for child welfare.

1979, Apr. 11   Litho.   Perf. 13x14

Easter: Cross, chalice and various
churches.

B256 SP66 20c + 10c multi   .20   .20
B257 SP66 30c + 15c multi   .30   .30
B258 SP66 35c + 15c multi   .40   .40
B259 SP66 40c + 20c multi   .45   .45
B260 SP66 60c + 30c multi   .65   .65
     Nos. B256-B260 (5)   2.00 2.00

Boy, Bird, Red
Cross, Blood
Transfusion
Bottle — SP67

1979, Nov. 21   Litho.   Perf. 13x14
B261 SP67 20c + 10c multi   .20   .20
B262 SP67 30c + 15c multi   .30   .30
B263 SP67 35c + 15c multi   .40   .40
 a.   Min. sheet, #B263, 2 #B261   1.25 1.25
B264 SP67 40c + 20c multi   .45   .45
B265 SP67 60c + 30c multi   .65   .65
     Nos. B261-B265 (5)   2.00 2.00

Surtax was for child welfare.

Cross — SP68   Anansi — SP69

Easter: Various symbols.

1980, Mar. 26   Litho.   Perf. 13x14
B266 SP68 20c + 10c multi   .25   .25
B267 SP68 30c + 15c multi   .35   .35
B268 SP68 40c + 20c multi   .45   .45
B269 SP68 50c + 25c multi   .55   .55
B270 SP68 60c + 30c multi   .65   .65
     Nos. B266-B270 (5)   2.25 2.25

1980, Nov. 5   Litho.   Perf. 13x14

Characters from Anansi and His Creditors.

B271 SP69 20c + 10c shown   .25   .25
B272 SP69 25c + 15c Ba Tigri   .35   .35
B273 SP69 30c + 15c
            Kakafowroe   .40   .40
B274 SP69 35c + 15c Ontiman   .45   .45
B275 SP69 60c + 30c Mat
            Kalaka   .80   .80
 a.   Min. sheet, #B275, 2 #B271   1.40 1.40
     Nos. B271-B275 (5)   2.25 2.25

Surtax was for child welfare.

Woman
Reading
SP70

1980, Dec. 10   Perf. 14x13
B276 SP70 25c + 10c shown   .30   .30
B277 SP70 50c + 15c Gardening   .55   .55
B278 SP70 75c + 20c With
            grandchildren   .80   .80
     Nos. B276-B278 (3)   1.65 1.65

Surtax was for the elderly.

Crucifixion   Indian Girl
SP71   SP72

Easter: Scenes from the Passion of Christ.

1981, Apr. 8   Litho.   Perf. 13x14
B279 SP71 20c + 10c multi   .25   .25
B280 SP71 30c + 15c multi   .40   .40
B281 SP71 50c + 25c multi   .70   .70
B282 SP71 60c + 30c multi   .75   .75
B283 SP71 75c + 35c multi   .90   .90
     Nos. B279-B283 (5)   3.00 3.00

Surtax was for the elderly.

1981, Nov. 26   Litho.
B284 SP72 20c + 10c shown   .25   .25
B285 SP72 30c + 15c Black   .45   .45
B286 SP72 50c + 25c Hindustani   .75   .75
B287 SP72 60c + 30c Javanese   .80   .80
B288 SP72 75c + 35c Chinese   .90   .90
 a.   Souv. sheet, #B288, 2 #B285   2.50 2.50
     Nos. B284-B288 (5)   3.15 3.15

Surtax was for child welfare.

Easter   Man Pushing
SP73   Wheelbarrow
                    SP74

Designs: Stained-glass windows, Sts. Peter
and Paul Church, Paramaribo.

1982, Apr. 7   Litho.   Perf. 13x14
B289 SP73 20c + 10c multi   .30   .30
B290 SP73 35c + 15c multi   .55   .55
B291 SP73 50c + 25c multi   .80   .80
B292 SP73 65c + 30c multi   .85   .85
B293 SP73 75c + 35c multi   1.00 1.00
     Nos. B289-B293 (5)   3.50 3.50

1982, Nov. 17   Litho.

Children's Drawings of City Cleaning
Activities.

B294 SP74 20c + 10c multi   .30   .30
B295 SP74 35c + 15c multi   .55   .55
B296 SP74 50c + 25c multi   .80   .80
B297 SP74 65c + 30c multi   .85   .85
B298 SP74 75c + 35c multi   1.00 1.00
 a.   Souv. sheet, #B298, 2 #B295   2.25 2.25
     Nos. B294-B298 (5)   3.50 3.50

Surtax was for child welfare.

Easter — SP75   Pitcher — SP76

Mosaic Symbols.

1983, Mar. 23   Litho.   Perf. 13x14
B299 SP75 10c + 5c Dove   .20   .20
B300 SP75 15c + 5c Bread   .25   .25
B301 SP75 25c + 10c Fish   .45   .45
B302 SP75 50c + 25c Eye   1.00 1.00
B303 SP75 65c + 30c Wine cup   1.10 1.10
     Nos. B299-B303 (5)   3.00 3.00

1983, Nov. 16   Litho.   Perf. 13x14
B304 SP76 10c + 5c shown   .20   .20
B305 SP76 15c + 5c Headdress   .20   .20
B306 SP76 25c + 10c Medicine
            rattle   .35   .35
B307 SP76 50c + 25c Sieve   .90   .90
B308 SP76 65c + 30c Basket   1.00 1.00
 a.   Min. sheet, #B305, B306,
            B308   1.75 1.75
     Nos. B304-B308 (5)   2.65 2.65

Easter — SP77   SP78

1984, Apr. 4   Litho.   Perf. 13x14
B309 SP77 10c + 5c Cross, rose   .20   .20
B310 SP77 15c + 15c Cemetery   .20   .20
B311 SP77 25c + 10c Candles   .35   .35
B312 SP77 50c + 25c Cross,
            crown of thorns   .90   .90
B313 SP77 65c + 30c Candle   1.00 1.00
     Nos. B309-B313 (5)   2.65 2.65

1984, Aug. 15   Litho.

Boy Scouts in Surinam, 60th Anniv.:
30c+10c, 8th Caribbean Jamboree emblem.
35c+10c, Salute. 50c+10c, Gardening.
90c+10c, Campfire in map of Surinam. Surtax
was for Boy Scouts.

B314 SP78 30c + 10c multi   .45   .45
B315 SP78 35c + 10c multi   .55   .55
B316 SP78 50c + 10c multi   .65   .65
B317 SP78 90c + 10c multi   1.10 1.10
     Nos. B314-B317 (4)   2.75 2.75

Children's   Easter — SP80
Games — SP79

1984, Nov. 14   Litho.   Perf. 13x14
B318 SP79 5c + 5c Kites   .20   .20
B319 SP79 10c + 5c Kites, diff.   .20   .20
B320 SP79 30c + 10c Pingi-
            pingi-kasi   .45   .45
B321 SP79 50c + 25c Cricket   .90   .90
 a.   Souv. sheet of 3, #B319-B321 1.60 1.60
B322 SP79 90c + 30c Peroen,
            peroen   1.40 1.40
     Nos. B318-B322 (5)   3.15 3.15

Surtax was for child welfare.

1985, Mar. 27   Litho.   Perf. 12½x14
B323 SP80 5c + 5c multi   .20   .20
B324 SP80 10c + 5c multi   .20   .20
B325 SP80 30c + 15c multi   .45   .45
B326 SP80 50c + 25c multi   .75   .75
B327 SP80 90c + 30c multi   1.25 1.25
     Nos. B323-B327 (5)   2.85 2.85

Surtax for child welfare.

Map, Emblem   Literacy
SP81   SP82

1985, Oct. 22   Litho.   Perf. 13x14
B328 SP81 30c + 10c shown   .40   .40
B329 SP81 50c + 10c Crucifix,
            missionaries   .60   .60
B330 SP81 90c + 20c Scroll   1.00 1.00
     Nos. B328-B330 (3)   2.00 2.00

Evangelical Brotherhood Mission in Surinam, 250th anniv. Surtax for mission medical
and social work.

1985, Nov. 6
B331 SP82 5c + 5c Boy reading   .20   .20
B332 SP82 10c + 5c Learning al-
            phabet   .20   .20
B333 SP82 30c + 10c Writing   .35   .35
B334 SP82 50c + 25c Girl read-
            ing   .75   .75
 a.   Min. sheet of 3, #B332-B334   1.40 1.40
B335 SP82 90c + 30c Studying   1.25 1.25
     Nos. B331-B335 (5)   2.75 2.75

Surtax for child welfare.

Easter — SP83   Sts. Peter and
                     Paul Cathedral,
                     Cent. — SP84

1986, Mar. 19   Litho.   Perf. 13x14
B336 SP83 5c + 5c multi   .20   .20
B337 SP83 10c + 5c multi   .20   .20
B338 SP83 30c + 15c multi   .45   .45
B339 SP83 50c + 25c multi   .75   .75
B340 SP83 90c + 30c multi   1.10 1.10
     Nos. B336-B340 (5)   2.70 2.70

1986, May 28   Litho.
B341 SP84 30c + 10c Exterior   .45   .45
B342 SP84 50c + 10c Saints,
            bas-relief   .65   .65
B343 SP84 110c + 30c Baptismal
            font   1.65 1.65
     Nos. B341-B343 (3)   2.75 2.75

Ancient Order
of Foresters
Court Charity,
Cent. — SP85

1986, July 29   Litho.   Perf. 14x13
B344 SP85 50c + 20c Foresters
            emblem   .75   .75
B345 SP85 110c + 30c Court
            building   1.65 1.65

Youth
Activities
SP86

1986, Nov. 5   Litho.   Perf. 14x13
B346 SP86 5c + 5c Hopscotch   .20   .20
B347 SP86 10c + 5c Ballet   .20   .20
B348 SP86 30c + 10c Mobile li-
            brary   .40   .40
B349 SP86 50c + 25c Crafts   .70   .70
 a.   Min. sheet of 3, #B347-B349   1.40 1.40
B350 SP86 110c + 30c Educa-
            tion   1.50 1.50
     Nos. B346-B350 (5)   3.00 3.00

Surtax for Children's Charities.

Easter — SP87   Natl. Girl Guides
                     Movement, 40th
                     Anniv. — SP88

Stations of the cross.

1987, Apr. 8   Litho.   Perf. 13x14
B351 SP87 5c + 5c Crucifixion   .20   .20
B352 SP87 10c + 5c Christ on
            cross   .20   .20
B353 SP87 35c + 15c Descent
            from cross   .50   .50
B354 SP87 60c + 30c Funeral
            procession   .85   .85

B355 SP87 110c + 50c Entomb-
ment 1.50 1.50
Nos. B351-B355 (5) 3.25 3.25

Surtax for annual Easter Charity programs.

1987, May 7 **Litho.**

Designs: 15c+10c, Mushroom, Brownie's emblem. 60c+10c, Clover, Guides' emblem. 110c+10c, Campfire, Rangers' emblem. 120c+10c, Ivy, Captain's emblem.

B356 SP88 15c + 10c multi .35 .35
B357 SP88 60c + 10c multi .75 .75
B358 SP88 110c + 10c multi 1.40 1.40
B359 SP88 120c + 10c multi 1.50 1.50
Nos. B356-B359 (4) 4.00 4.00

Surtax for the Surinam Girl Guides.

Caribbean Manari — SP89

Easter — SP90

1987, Nov. 4 **Litho.** **Perf. 13x14**
B360 SP89 50c + 25c Herring bone .80 .80
B361 SP89 60c + 30c Tortoise-back .90 .90
B362 SP89 110c + 50c Whirlpool (squares) 1.60 1.60
a. Min. sheet of 2, #B360, B362 2.50 2.50
Nos. B360-B362 (3) 3.30 3.30

Surtax to benefit child welfare organizations.

1988, Mar. 23 **Perf. 13x13½**
B363 SP90 50c + 25c multi .65 .65
B364 SP90 60c + 30c multi .85 .85
B365 SP90 110c + 50c multi 1.60 1.60
Nos. B363-B365 (3) 3.10 3.10

Surtax for annual Easter Charity programs.

Intl. Red Cross and Red Crescent Organizations, 125th Anniv. — SP91

#B367, Anniv. & blood donation emblems.

1988, Oct. 26 **Litho.** **Perf. 13x14**
B366 SP91 60c + 30c multi 1.00 1.00
B367 SP91 120c + 60c multi 2.00 2.00

Children's Drawings SP92

1988, Dec. 5 **Litho.** **Perf. 14x13**
B368 SP92 50c + 25c Man and animal .70 .70
B369 SP92 60c + 30c Children and nature .80 .80
B370 SP92 110c + 50c Stop drugs 1.50 1.50
a. Souv. sheet of 3, #B368-B370, perf 13½x13 3.25 3.25
Nos. B368-B370 (3) 3.00 3.00

Surtax to benefit children's charities.

Easter 1989 — SP93

Details from Hungarian altarpieces: 60c+30c, Scenes of the Passion, by M.S., 1506. 105c+50c, Crucifixion, by Tamas of Koszvar, 1427. 110c+55c, Miracles, by Tamas of Koszvar, 1427.

1989, Mar. 21 **Litho.** **Perf. 13½**
Size: No. B372, 28½x36½mm
B371 SP93 60c + 30c multi 1.00 1.00
B372 SP93 105c + 50c multi 1.75 1.75
B373 SP93 110c + 55c multi 1.90 1.90
Nos. B371-B373 (3) 4.65 4.65

Surtax for annual East Charity programs.

Children's Drawings SP94

No. B374, Helping each other. No. B375, Child and nature. No. B376, In the school bus.

1989, Dec. 6 **Litho.** **Perf. 14x13**
B374 SP94 60c +30c multi 1.10 1.10
B375 SP94 105c +50c multi 1.90 1.90
B376 SP94 110c +55c multi 2.00 2.00
a. Souv. sheet of 2, #B374, B376 3.25 3.25
Nos. B374-B376 (3) 5.00 5.00

Surtax for children's charities.

Easter — SP95

Designs: No. B377, Mother holding Christ child. No. B378, Christ, follower. No. B379, Mary holding martyred Christ.

1990, Mar. 28 **Litho.** **Perf. 13x14**
B377 SP95 60c +30c multi 1.00 1.00
B378 SP95 105c +50c multi 1.75 1.75
B379 SP95 110c +55c multi 1.90 1.90
Nos. B377-B379 (3) 4.65 4.65

Children's Drawings SP96

1990, Dec. 4 **Litho.** **Perf. 14x13**
B380 SP96 60c +30c Children, hammock 1.25 1.25
B381 SP96 105c +50c Child, animal, palm tree 2.00 2.00
B382 SP96 110c +55c Child, bird in tree 2.25 2.25
a. Souv. sheet of 2, #B380, B382, perf. 13½x13 3.00 3.00
Nos. B380-B382 (3) 5.50 5.50

SP97 SP98

Easter: 60c+30c, Christ carrying cross. 105c+50c, The Crucifixion. 110c+55c, Woman cradling Christ's body.

1991, Mar. 20 **Litho.** **Perf. 13x14**
B383 SP97 60c +30c multi 1.10 1.10
B384 SP97 105c +50c multi 1.25 1.25
B385 SP97 110c +55c multi 2.00 2.00
a. Souv. sheet of 2, #B383, B385 3.25 3.25
Nos. B383-B385 (3) 4.35 4.35

1991, Dec. 4 **Litho.** **Perf. 13x14**
Children's Drawings: 60c+30c, Child in wheelchair. 105c+50c, Child beside trees. 110c+55c, Children playing outdoors.
B386 SP98 60c +30c multi 1.00 1.00
B387 SP98 105c +50c multi 1.75 1.75
B388 SP98 110c +55c multi 1.90 1.90
a. Souv. sheet of 2, #B386, B388 3.00 3.00
Nos. B386-B388 (3) 4.65 4.65

SP99 SP100

Easter: 60c+30c, Crucifixion. 105c+50c, Taking away body of Christ. 110c+55c, Resurrection.

1992, Mar. 18
B389 SP99 60c +30c multi 1.00 1.00
B390 SP99 105c +50c multi 1.75 1.75
B391 SP99 110c +55c multi 1.90 1.90
Nos. B389-B391 (3) 4.65 4.65

1992, Dec. 3 **Litho.** **Perf. 13x14**
Children's Drawings: 60c + 30c, Child as tree. 105c + 50c, Face as tree. 110c, + 55c, Boy and girl hanging from tree.
B392 SP100 60c +30c multi 1.00 1.00
B393 SP100 105c +50c multi 1.75 1.75
B394 SP100 110c +55c multi 1.90 1.90
a. Souv. sheet, #B392, B394 3.00 3.00
Nos. B392-B394 (3) 4.65 4.65

Surtax for Child Welfare.

SP101 SP102

Easter: 60c+30c, Message from Christ. 110c+50c, Crucifixion. 125c+60c, Resurrection.

1993, Mar. 31 **Litho.** **Perf. 13x14**
B395 SP101 60c +30c multi 1.10 1.10
B396 SP101 110c +50c multi 1.75 1.75
B397 SP101 125c +60c multi 2.10 2.10
Nos. B395-B397 (3) 4.95 4.95

1993, Dec. 3
Children Playing Hopscotch: 25c+10c, 2 children. 35c+10c, 3 children. 50c+25c, 8 children. 75c+25c, 7 children.
B398 SP102 25c + 10c grn & multi .80 .80
B399 SP102 35c +10c bl & multi 1.00 1.00
B400 SP102 50c +25c grn & multi 1.75 1.75
a. Souvenir sheet of 2, #B399-B400 3.75 3.75
B401 SP102 75c +25c bl & multi 2.25 2.25
Nos. B398-B401 (4) 5.80 5.80

Surtax for Child Welfare.
Stamps in No. B400a do not have the 1993 date in lower left corner.

AIR POST STAMPS

Allegory of Flight — AP1

Perf. 12½
1930, Sept. 3 **Unwmk.** **Engr.**
C1 AP1 10c dull red 3.00 .40
C2 AP1 15c ultra 3.00 .60
C3 AP1 20c dull green .20 .20
C4 AP1 40c orange .20 .30

C5 AP1 60c brown violet .45 .35
C6 AP1 1g gray black 1.25 1.40
C7 AP1 1½g deep brown 1.40 1.50
Nos. C1-C7 (7) 9.50 4.75

Vlucht
Nos. C1-C7 Do. X
Overprinted in Black or Red
1931

1931, Aug. 8
C8 AP1 10c red (Bk) 17.50 14.00
a. Double overprint 425.00
C9 AP1 15c ultra (Bk) 17.50 14.00
C10 AP1 20c dull grn (R) 17.50 14.00
C11 AP1 40c orange (Bk) 26.00 21.00
a. Double overprint 425.00
C12 AP1 60c brn vio (R) 55.00 47.50
C13 AP1 1g gray blk (R) 65.00 57.50
C14 AP1 1½g deep brn (Bk) 65.00 60.00
Nos. C8-C14 (7) 263.50 228.00

The variety with period omitted after "Do" occurs twice on each sheet.
Warning: The red overprint may dissolve in water.

Type of 1930
Thick Paper
1941, Sept. 25 **Litho.** **Perf. 13**
C15 AP1 20c lt green 1.00 .75
C16 AP1 40c lt orange 6.00 4.25
C17 AP1 2½g yellow 6.00 10.00
C18 AP1 5g blue green 250.00 275.00
C19 AP1 10g lt bister 14.00 42.50
Nos. C15-C19 (5) 277.00 332.50

The lines of shading on Nos. C15 and C16 are not as heavy as on Nos. C3 and C4. For surcharges see Nos. C24-C25.

Type of 1930
Redrawn
1941 **Engr.** **Perf. 12**
C20 AP1 10c light red 1.25 .30
C21 AP1 60c dl brn vio .75 .40
C22 AP1 1g black 16.00 19.00
Nos. C20-C22 (3) 18.00 19.70

Redrawn stamps have three horizontal lines through post horn and many minor variations. For surcharges see Nos. C23, CB1.

> **Catalogue values for unused stamps in this section, from this point to the end of the section, are for Never Hinged items.**

Nos. C21, C17, C19 Surcharged with New Values and Bars in Carmine
1945, Mar. 12 **Perf. 13, 12**
C23 AP1 22½c on 60c .35 .55
a. Inverted surcharge 250.00 250.00
C24 AP1 1g on 2½g 12.00 12.00
C25 AP1 5g on 10g 17.50 18.00
Nos. C23-C25 (3) 29.85 30.55

Women of Netherlands and Surinam — AP2
Globe and Winged Post Horn — AP3

Perf. 12x12½
1949, May 10 **Photo.** **Unwmk.**
C26 AP2 27½c henna brown 5.75 2.75

Valid only on first flight of Paramaribo-Amsterdam service.

1954, Sept. 25 **Perf. 13½x12½**
C27 AP3 15c dp ultra & ultra 1.10 1.00

Establishment of airmail service in Surinam, 25th anniv.

Redstone Mercury Rocket and Comdr. Alan B. Shepard, Jr. — AP4

15c, Cosmonaut Gagarin in capsule and globe.

1961, July 3   **Litho.**   *Perf. 12*
C28	AP4	15c multicolored	.85	.85
C29	AP4	20c multicolored	.85	.85

"Man in Space," Major Yuri A. Gagarin, USSR, and Comdr. Alan B. Shepard, Jr., US. Printed in sheets of 12 (4x3) with ornamental borders and inscriptions. Two printings differ in shades and selvage perforations.

Water Tower — AP5

Eucyane Bicolor — AP6

Designs: 15c, 65c, Brewery. 20c, Boat on lake. 25c, 75c, Wood industry. 30c, Bauxite mine. 35c, 50c, Poelepantje bridge. 40c, Ship in harbor. 45c, Wharf.

1965, July 31   **Photo.**   *Perf. 14x13½*
Size: 25x18mm
C30	AP5	10c olive grn	.20	.20
C31	AP5	15c ocher	.20	.20
C32	AP5	20c slate grn	.20	.20
C33	AP5	25c violet blue	.20	.20
C34	AP5	30c blue green	.20	.20
C35	AP5	35c red orange	.25	.25
C36	AP5	40c orange	.25	.25
C37	AP5	45c dk carmine	.25	.25
C38	AP5	50c vermilion	.25	.25
C39	AP5	55c emerald	.25	.25
C40	AP5	65c bister	.30	.30
C41	AP5	75c blue	.30	.30
		Nos. C30-C41 (12)	2.85	2.85

See Nos. C75-C82.

1972, July 26   **Litho.**   *Perf. 13½x14*
C42	AP6	15c shown	.20	.20
C43	AP6	20c Helicopis cupido	.25	.20
C44	AP6	25c Papilio thoas thoas	.25	.20
C45	AP6	30c Urania leilus	.30	.20
C46	AP6	35c Stalachtis calliope	.30	.40
C47	AP6	40c Stalachtis phlegia	.35	.30
C48	AP6	45c Victorina steneles	.45	.20
C49	AP6	50c Papilio neophilus	.50	.20
C50	AP6	55c Anartia amathea	.60	.50
C51	AP6	60c Adelpha cytherea	.65	.95
C52	AP6	65c Heliconius doris metharmina	.65	.65
C53	AP6	70c Nessaea obrinus	.75	.75
C54	AP6	75c Ageronia feronia	.75	.60
		Nos. C42-C54 (13)	6.00	5.50

Surinam butterflies. Valid for regular postage also. For surcharges, see Nos. 495-499. #C42, C45 exist perf 14 with redrawn design.

Fish Type of 1976

Fish: 35c, Chaetodon unimaculatus. 60c, Centropyge loriculus. 95c, Caetodon collare.

1976, June 2   **Litho.**   *Perf. 12½x13*
C55	A111	35c multicolored	1.00	.55
C56	A111	60c multicolored	1.75	.90
C57	A111	95c multicolored	2.75	1.40
		Nos. C55-C57 (3)	5.50	2.85

Black-headed Sugarbird AP7

Birds of Surinam: 20c, Leistes militaris. 30c, Paradise tangara. 40c, Whippoorwill. 45c, Hemitraupis flavicollis. 50c, White-tailed goldthroated hummingbird. 55c, Saberwing. 60c, Blackcap parrot, vert. 65c, Toucan, vert. 70c, Manakin, vert. 75c, Collared parrot, vert. 80c, Cayenne cotinga, vert. 85c, Trogon, vert. 95c, Black-striped tropical tree owl, vert.

1977   **Litho.**   *Perf. 14x13, 13x14*
C58	AP7	20c multi	.25	.20
C59	AP7	25c multi	.30	.20
C60	AP7	30c multi	.35	.20
a.		Min. sheet of 4, 2 each #C59-C60, perf. 13½x14	2.50	1.50
C61	AP7	40c multi	.55	.35
C62	AP7	45c multi	.55	.35
C63	AP7	50c multi	.65	.40

C64	AP7	55c multi	.75	.45
C65	AP7	60c multi	.80	.50
C66	AP7	65c multi	.85	.55
C67	AP7	70c multi	.95	.55
C68	AP7	75c multi	1.00	.65
C69	AP7	80c multi	1.00	.65
C70	AP7	85c multi	1.10	.75
C71	AP7	95c multi	1.40	.90
		Nos. C58-C71 (14)	10.50	6.70

A souv. sheet of 4 with same stamps and perf. as No. C60a has marginal inscription "Amphilex 77" with magnifier over No. 424. Sold in folder at phil. exhib. in Amsterdam May 26-June 5, 1977.

Issued: 25c, 30c, 50c, 60c, 75c, 80c, 95c, Apr. 27; #C60a, May 26; others, Aug. 24.

See Nos. C88, C101. For surcharges and overprints see Nos. C102-C105, C108-C111, J58, J62.

Tropical Fish Type of 1976

60c, Chaetodon striatus. 90c, Bodianus pulchellus. 120c, Centropyge argi.

1977, June 8   **Litho.**   *Perf. 13x13½*
C72	A111	60c multi	.50	.40
C73	A111	90c multi	.80	.60
C74	A111	120c multi	1.25	.90
		Nos. C72-C74 (3)	2.55	1.90

Type of 1965 Redrawn

Designs: 5c, Brewery. 10c, Water tower. 20c, Boat on lake. 25c, Wood industry. 30c, Bauxite mine. 35c, Poelepantje bridge. 40c, Ship in harbor. 60c, Wharf.

1976-78   **Photo.**   *Perf. 12½x13½*
Size: 22x18mm
C75	AP5	5c ocher	.20	.20
a.		Bklt. pane, 4 #C75, 3 #C82 + label	2.50	
C76	AP5	10c olive green	.55	.55
a.		Bklt. pane, 1 #C76, 4 #C80 + label	2.75	
C77	AP5	20c slate green	.20	.20
a.		Bklt. pane, 2 ea #C77-C79	2.75	
b.		Bklt. pane, 6 #C77, 2 #C81	2.50	
C78	AP5	25c vio bl	.55	.55
C79	AP5	30c bl grn	.65	.65
C80	AP5	35c red org	.55	.55
C81	AP5	40c org	.90	.90
C82	AP5	60c dk car	.75	.75
		Nos. C75-C82 (8)	4.35	4.35

Nos. C75-C82 issued in booklets only. Nos. C75a and C77b have inscribed selvage the size of 4 stamps; Nos. C76a and C77a the size of 6 stamps.

Issued: 10c-35c, 12/8; 5c, 40c, 60c, #C77b, 1/11/78.

Tropical Fish Type of 1976

60c, Astyanax species. 90c, Corydoras wotroi. 120c, Gasteropelecus sternicla.

1978, June 21   **Litho.**   *Perf. 13x13½*
C85	A111	60c multi	.50	.40
C86	A111	90c multi	.95	.60
C87	A111	120c multi	1.10	.75
		Nos. C85-C87 (3)	2.55	1.75

Bird Type of 1977

Design: 5g, Crested curassow, vert.

1979, Jan. 10   **Engr.**   *Perf. 13x13½*
C88	AP7	5g violet	6.00	3.00

Tropical Fish Type of 1979

60c, Cantherinus macrocerus. 90c, Holocenthrus rufus. 120c, Holacanthus tricolor.

1979, May 30   **Photo.**   *Perf. 14x13*
C89	A129	60c multi	.30	.25
C90	A129	90c multi	.45	.35
C91	A129	120c multi	.65	.55
		Nos. C89-C91 (3)	1.40	1.15

Tropical Fish Type of 1979

60c, Symphysodon discus. 75c, Aeqidens curviceps. 90c, Catoprion mento.

1980, Sept. 10   **Photo.**   *Perf. 14x13*
C92	A129	60c multi	.40	.30
C93	A129	75c multi	.55	.40
C94	A129	90c multi	.60	.50
		Nos. C92-C94 (3)	1.55	1.20

Frog Type of 1981

1981, June 24   *Perf. 13x14*
C95	A142	75c Phyllomedusa burmeisteri, vert.	1.10	.60
C96	A142	1g Dendrobates tinctorius, vert.	1.50	.80
C97	A142	1.25g Bufo guttatus, vert.	1.75	1.00
		Nos. C95-C97 (3)	4.35	2.40

Turtle Type of 1982

1982, Feb. 17   **Photo.**   *Perf. 14x13*
C98	A146	65c Platemys platycephala	1.00	.65
C99	A146	75c Phrynops gibba	1.25	.80
C100	A146	125c Rhinoclemys punctularia	2.00	1.40
		Nos. C98-C100 (3)	4.25	2.85

Bird Type of 1977

1985, Jan. 9   **Litho.**   *Perf. 13x14*
C101	AP7	90c Venezuelan Amazon, vert.	2.50	2.50

For overprint see No. J61.

No. C60 Surcharged

1986, Oct. 1   **Litho.**   *Perf. 14x13*
C102	AP7	15c on 30c multi	2.50	2.50

Nos. C70-C71 and C67 Surcharged

1987, Mar.   **Litho.**   *Perf. 13x14*
C103	AP7	10c on 85c No. C70	1.50	1.50
C104	AP7	10c on 95c No. C71	1.50	1.50
C105	AP7	25c on 70c No. C67	4.00	4.00
		Nos. C103-C105 (3)	7.00	7.00

Otter Type of 1989

1989, Jan. 18   **Litho.**   *Perf. 13x14*
C107	A195	185c Otters, vert.	2.00	2.00

No. C63 Surcharged

1993, Jan. 20   **Litho.**   *Perf. 14x13*
C108	AP7	35c on 50c multi	.40	.40

Nos. C62, C64-C65 Surcharged

1994, Apr. 11   *Perf. 14x13, 13x14*
C109	AP7	( ) on 60c #C65		
C110	AP7	( ) on 45c #C62		
C111	AP7	( ) on 55c #C64		
		Nos. C109-C111 (3)	1.75	1.75

The face value of Nos. C109-C111 fluctuates with postal rate changes. Face values on day of issue were: No. C109, 2.50f; No. C110, 10f; No. C111, 25f. No. C109 paid the additional 5 grams letter rate to the Netherlands. No. C110 paid the basic rate to North and South America and the Caribbean. No. C111 paid the basic 10-gram letter rate to the Netherlands.
Size and location of surcharge varies.

AIR POST SEMI-POSTAL STAMPS

> **Catalogue values for unused stamps in this section are for Never Hinged items.**

No. C20 Surchd. in Red like No. B40.
Unwmk.
1942, Jan. 2   **Engr.**   *Perf. 12*
CB1	AP1	10c + 5c lt red, III	2.50	2.50
a.		Type IV	4.25	5.25
b.		Type V	11.50	14.00

The surtax was for the Red Cross. See note on types III and IV below No. B40.

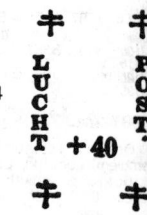

Nos. 193 and 194 Surcharged in Carmine

1946, Feb. 24   *Perf. 12*
CB2	A30	10c + 40c blue	1.00	1.00
CB3	A30	15c + 60c brown	1.00	1.00

The surtax was for the Red Cross.

Star Type of Semi-Postals
Perf. 13½x12½
1947, Dec. 16   **Photo.**
CB4	SP17	22½c + 27½c gray	2.25	1.75
CB5	SP17	27½c + 47½c grn	2.25	1.75

POSTAGE DUE STAMPS

D1   D2

Type I - 34 loops. "T" of "BETALEN" over center of loop; top branch of "E" of "TE" shorter than lower branch.
Type II - 33 loops. "T" of "BETALEN" over space between two loops.
Type III - 32 loops. "T" of "BETALEN" slightly to the left of center of loop; top branch of first "E" of "BETALEN" shorter than lower branch.
Type IV - 37 loops and letters of "PORT" larger than in the other 3 types.

Value in Black
Perf. 12½x12
1886-88		**Typo.**	**Unwmk.**	
		Type III		
J1	D1	2½c lilac	3.00	3.00
J2	D1	5c lilac	9.00	9.00
J3	D1	10c lilac	100.00	65.00
J4	D1	20c lilac	9.00	9.00
J5	D1	25c lilac	12.50	12.50
J6	D1	30c lilac ('88)	2.50	2.50
J7	D1	40c lilac	6.00	6.00
J8	D1	50c lilac ('88)	3.00	3.00
		Nos. J1-J8 (8)	145.00	110.00
		Type I		
J1a	D1	2½c	6.00	6.00
J2a	D1	5c	11.00	11.00
J3a	D1	10c	125.00	90.00
J4a	D1	20c	22.50	22.50
J5a	D1	25c	19.00	19.00
J6a	D1	30c	22.50	22.50
J7a	D1	40c	12.50	12.50
J8a	D1	50c	4.00	4.00
		Nos. J1a-J8a (8)	222.50	187.50
		Type II		
J1b	D1	2½c	5.00	5.00
J2b	D1	5c	10.00	10.00
J3b	D1	10c	1,250.	1,250.
J4b	D1	20c	9.00	9.00
J5b	D1	25c	300.00	300.00
J6b	D1	30c	75.00	75.00
J7b	D1	40c	350.00	350.00
J8b	D1	50c	5.00	5.00
		Type IV		
J3c	D1	10c	350.00	250.00
J5c	D1	25c	160.00	150.00
J7c	D1	40c	150.00	150.00
		Nos. J3c-J7c (3)	660.00	550.00

Nos. J1-J16 were issued without gum. For surcharges see Nos. J15-J16.

1892-96		**Value in Black**	*Perf. 12½*	
		Type III		
J9	D2	2½c lilac	.40	.40
J10	D2	5c lilac	1.25	1.00
J11	D2	10c lilac	24.00	22.50
J12	D2	20c lilac	2.50	2.25
J13	D2	25c lilac	10.00	10.00
		Type I		
J9a	D2	2½c	.40	.40
J10a	D2	5c	2.00	2.00
J11a	D2	10c	24.00	20.00
J12a	D2	20c	5.00	5.00
J13a	D2	25c	13.00	12.50
J14	D2	40c ('96)	3.25	4.50

Type II

J9b	D2	2½c	.80	.80
J10b	D2	5c	3.00	3.00
J11b	D2	10c	40.00	42.50
J12b	D2	10c	90.00	90.00
J13b	D2	25c	100.00	100.00

For surcharges see Nos. 121-122.

Stamps of 1888 Surcharged in Red

1911, July 15

J15	D1	10c on 30c lil (III)	80.00	80.00
a.		10c on 30c lilac (I)	200.00	225.00
b.		10c on 30c lilac (II)	1,800.	1,800.
J16	D1	10c on 50c lil (III)	110.00	110.00
a.		10c on 50c lilac (I)	115.00	115.00
b.		10c on 50c lilac (II)	115.00	115.00

D3

Type I
Value in Color of Stamp

1913-31   Perf. 12½, 13½x12½

J17	D2	½c lilac ('30)	.20	.20
J18	D2	1c lilac ('31)	.20	.25
J19	D2	2c lilac ('31)	.20	.20
J20	D2	2½c lilac	.20	.20
J21	D2	5c lilac	.20	.20
J22	D2	10c lilac	.20	.20
J23	D2	12c lilac ('31)	.20	.20
J24	D2	12½c lilac ('22)	.20	.20
J25	D2	15c lilac ('26)	.35	.30
J26	D2	20c lilac	.55	.30
J27	D2	25c lilac	.30	.20
J28	D2	30c lilac ('26)	.30	.40
J29	D2	40c lilac	9.25	9.00
J30	D2	50c lilac ('26)	.85	.75
J31	D2	75c lilac ('26)	1.00	1.00
J32	D3	1g lilac ('26)	1.10	1.00
		Nos. J17-J32 (16)	15.30	14.60

Catalogue values for unused stamps in this section, from this point to the end of the section, are for Never Hinged items.

D4

1945   Litho.   Perf. 12

J33	D4	1c light brown violet	.20	.30
J34	D4	5c light brown violet	3.00	2.50
J35	D4	25c light brown violet	7.00	.50
		Nos. J33-J35 (3)	10.20	3.30

D5   D6

Perf. 13½x12½

1950   Unwmk.   Photo.

J36	D5	1c purple	1.75	1.50
J37	D5	2c purple	2.75	1.40
J38	D5	2½c purple	2.25	1.50
J39	D5	5c purple	3.25	.30
J40	D5	10c purple	1.75	.30
J41	D5	15c purple	4.50	2.00
J42	D5	20c purple	1.50	2.75
J43	D5	25c purple	9.00	.20
J44	D5	50c purple	15.00	1.10
J45	D5	75c purple	37.50	30.00
J46	D5	1g purple	14.00	5.50
		Nos. J36-J46 (11)	93.25	46.55

1956

J47	D6	1c purple	.20	.20
J48	D6	2c purple	.35	.30
J49	D6	2½c purple	.35	.30
J50	D6	5c purple	.35	.30
J51	D6	10c purple	.50	.50
J52	D6	15c purple	.50	.50
J53	D6	20c purple	.50	.50
J54	D6	25c purple	.55	.30
J55	D6	50c purple	1.50	.35

J56	D6	75c purple	2.00	1.10
J57	D6	1g purple	2.75	.90
		Nos. J47-J57 (11)	9.40	5.05

Stamps of 1977-1985 Overprinted "TE BETALEN"

Perf. 13x14, 14x13

1987, July   Litho.

J58	AP7	65c No. C66	2.00	2.00
J59	A156	65c No. 638	2.00	2.00
J60	A156	80c No. 640	2.50	2.50
J61	AP7	90c No. C101	2.75	2.75
J62	AP7	95c No. C71	3.00	3.00
J63	A173	1g No. 725	3.25	3.25
		Nos. J58-J63 (6)	15.50	15.50

SWAZILAND

ˈswä-zē-ˌland

LOCATION — Southeast Africa bordered by the Transvaal and Zululand in South Africa and by Mozambique
GOVT. — Constitutional monarchy
AREA — 6,705 sq. mi.
POP. — 985,335 (1999 est.)
CAPITAL — Mbabane

An independent state in the 19th century, Swaziland was administered by Transvaal from 1894 to 1906, when the administration was transferred to the British High Commissioner for South Africa. In 1934 Swaziland and Bechuanaland Protectorate came under the administration of the British High Commissioner for Basutoland. The issuing of individual postage stamps had been resumed in 1933. Internal self-government was introduced in 1967. Independence was proclaimed September 6, 1968.

12 Pence = 1 Shilling
20 Shillings = 1 Pound
100 Cents = 1 Rand (1961)
100 Cents = 1 Emalangeni (1975)

Catalogue values for unused stamps in this country are for Never Hinged items, beginning with Scott 38 in the regular postage section and Scott J1 in the postage due section.

Coat of   George V — A2
Arms — A1

Black Overprint

1889   Unwmk.   Perf. 12½, 12½x12

1	A1	½p gray	10.50	21.00
a.		Inverted overprint	925.00	725.00
b.		"Swazielan"	1,250.	800.00
c.		As "b," inverted overprint		4,250.
2	A1	1p rose	20.00	19.00
a.		Inverted overprint	800.00	750.00
3	A1	2p olive bister	20.00	18.00
a.		Inverted overprint	800.00	525.00
b.		"Swazielan"	550.00	475.00
c.		Perf. 12½x12	100.00	24.00
4	A1	6p gray blue	22.50	45.00
5	A1	1sh green	12.50	16.00
a.		Inverted overprint	700.00	525.00
6	A1	2sh6p yellow	275.00	300.00
7	A1	5sh slate	175.00	225.00
a.		Inverted overprint	1,900.	2,100.
b.		"Swazielan"	5,250.	
c.		As "b," inverted overprint	5,750	
8	A1	10sh lt brown	5,000.	3,750.

1892   Red Overprint

9	A1	½p gray	8.50	19.00
a.		Inverted overprint	575.00	
b.		Double overprint	525.00	525.00

Beware of counterfeits.
Reprints have a period after "Swaziland."

Stamps of Swaziland were replaced by those of Transvaal in 1895. Swaziland issues were resumed in 1933.

Perf. 14

1933, Jan. 2   Engr.   Wmk. 4

10	A2	½p green	.35	.35
11	A2	1p carmine	.35	.25
12	A2	2p lt brown	.35	.50
13	A2	3p ultra	.50	3.00
14	A2	4p orange	3.25	3.50
15	A2	6p rose violet	1.50	1.10
16	A2	1sh olive green	1.75	3.25
17	A2	2sh6p violet	17.50	25.00
18	A2	5sh gray	35.00	57.50
19	A2	10sh black brown	92.50	125.00
		Nos. 10-19 (10)	153.05	219.45

Common Design Types pictured following the introduction.

Silver Jubilee Issue
Common Design Type

1935, May 4   Perf. 11x12

20	CD301	1p carmine & blue	.60	1.75
21	CD301	2p black & ultra	.60	1.50
22	CD301	3p ultra & brown	.65	5.75
23	CD301	6p brown, vio & ind	.75	1.75
		Nos. 20-23 (4)	2.60	10.75
		Set, never hinged	5.00	

Coronation Issue
Common Design Type

1937, May 12   Perf. 11x11½

24	CD302	1p dark carmine	.35	.55
25	CD302	2p brown	.35	.20
26	CD302	3p deep ultra	.35	.55
		Nos. 24-26 (3)	1.05	1.30
		Set, never hinged	1.60	

George VI — A3

1938, Apr. 1   Perf. 13, 13x13½

27	A3	½p green	.25	1.50
28	A3	1p rose carmine	.80	1.50
29	A3	1½p light blue	.30	.85
a.		Perf. 14 ('42)	1.40	1.00
		Never hinged	3.25	
30	A3	2p brown	.30	.45
31	A3	3p ultra	2.75	2.00
32	A3	4p red orange	.40	1.60
33	A3	6p rose violet	3.50	1.75
34	A3	1sh olive green	.95	.75
35	A3	2sh6p dark violet	10.50	2.75
36	A3	5sh gray	20.00	15.00
37	A3	10sh black brown	4.75	6.50
		Nos. 27-37 (11)	44.50	34.65
		Set, never hinged	57.50	

Catalogue values for unused stamps in this section, from this point to the end of the section, are for Never Hinged items.

Peace Issue

South Africa, Nos. 100-102 Overprinted

Basic stamps inscribed alternately in English and Afrikaans.

1945, Dec. 3   Wmk. 201   Perf. 14

38	A42	1p rose pink & choc, pair	.50	.60
a.		Single, English	.20	.20
b.		Single, Afrikaans	.20	.20
39	A43	2p vio & sl blue, pair	.50	.60
a.		Single, English	.20	.25
b.		Single, Afrikaans	.20	.20
40	A43	3p ultra & dp ultra, pair	.50	1.25
a.		Single, English	.20	.25
b.		Single, Afrikaans	.20	.25
		Nos. 38-40 (3)	1.50	2.45

World War II victory of the Allies.

Royal Visit Issue
Type of Basutoland, 1947
Perf. 12½

1947, Feb. 17   Wmk. 4   Engr.

44	A3	1p red	.20	.20
45	A4	2p green	.20	.20
46	A5	3p ultramarine	.20	.20
47	A6	1sh dark violet	.80	.80
		Nos. 44-47 (4)		

Visit of the British Royal Family, 3/25/47.

Silver Wedding Issue
Common Design Types

1948, Dec. 1   Photo.   Perf. 14x14½

48	CD304	1½p bright ultra	.20	.20

Perf. 11½x11

Engraved; Name Typographed

49	CD305	10sh violet brown	50.00	30.00

UPU Issue
Common Design Types
Engr.; Name Typo. on 3p, 6p
Perf. 13½, 11x11½

1949, Oct. 10   Wmk. 4

50	CD306	1½p blue	.35	.20
51	CD307	3p indigo	.65	.65
52	CD308	6p red lilac	.85	.65
53	CD309	1sh olive	.95	.65
		Nos. 50-53 (4)	2.80	2.15

Coronation Issue
Common Design Type

1953, June 3   Engr.   Perf. 13½x13

54	CD312	2p yellow brown & blk	.20	.20

Asbestos Mine — A4

Married Woman — A5

1p, 2sh 6p, Highveld view. 3p, 1sh 3p, Courting couple. 4½p, 5sh, Warrior. 6p, £1, Kudu. 1sh, Asbestos mine. 10sh, Married woman.

Perf. 13x13½, 13½x13

1956, July 2   Engr.   Wmk. 4
Center in Black, except Nos. 63-64

55	A4	½p orange	.20	.20
56	A4	1p emerald	.20	.20
57	A5	2p redsh brown	.35	.20
58	A5	3p rose red	.25	.20
59	A5	4½p ultra	.70	.20
60	A5	6p magenta	.45	.20
61	A5	1sh gray olive	.35	.20
62	A5	1sh3p brown	1.25	7.50
63	A4	2sh6p car & brt grn	1.25	1.10
64	A5	5sh blue gray & vio	8.00	2.00
65	A5	10sh dull violet	17.00	6.50
66	A5	£1 turquoise	40.00	25.00
		Nos. 55-66 (12)	70.00	43.50

Nos. 55-61 and 63-66 Surcharged with New Value

2½c 2½c 4c 4c
I   II   I   II

5c 5c 25c 25c
I   II   I   II

50c 50c 50c
I   II

R1 R1 R1 R2 R2
I   II   III   I   II

1961

67	A4	½c on ½p	2.75	2.00
a.		Inverted surcharge	500.00	
68	A4	1c on 1p	.20	.20
a.		"1c" at center	27.50	
b.		Double surcharge	500.00	
69	A5	2c on 2p	.20	.20
70	A5	2½c on 2p	.20	.20
71	A5	2½c on 3p (I)	.20	.20
a.		Type II	.20	.25

72	A5	3½c on 2p	.20	.20
73	A5	4c on 4½p (II)	.20	.20
a.		Type I	.20	
74	A5	5c on 6p (II)	.20	.20
a.		Type I	.20	
75	A4	10c on 1sh	21.00	5.50
a.		Double surcharge	550.00	
76	A4	25c on 2sh6p (I)	.30	.90
a.		Type II, "25c" centered	1.25	.60
b.		Type II, "25c" at lower left	190.00	225.00
77	A5	50c on 5sh (I)	.30	1.10
a.		Type II	6.00	2.50
b.		Type III	375.00	450.00
78	A5	1r on 10sh (I)	1.75	1.50
a.		Type II	3.50	3.50
b.		Type III	55.00	60.00
79	A5	2r on £1 (II, "R2" at middle left)	8.00	4.75
a.		Type I	10.00	
b.		Type II, "R2" at center bottom	27.50	45.00
		Nos. 67-79 (13)	35.50	17.15

The type II "25c" surcharge is nearly centered in the sky on No. 76a, and is at lower left touching the value tablet on No. 76b.

Surcharge types are numbered chronologically.

For surcharges see Nos. J3-J6.

Types of 1956

½c, 10c, Asbestos mine. 1c, 25c, Highveld view. 2c, 1r, Married woman. 2½c, 12½c, Courting couple. 4c, 50c, Warrior. 5c, 2r, Kudu.

Perf. 13x13½, 13½x13

			Wmk. 4	
1961		**Engr.**		
Center in Black, except Nos. 88-89				
80	A4	½c orange	.20	.70
81	A4	1c emerald	.20	.20
82	A5	2c redsh brown	.20	2.10
83	A5	2½c rose red	.20	.20
84	A5	4c ultra	.20	.90
85	A5	5c magenta	.40	.20
86	A4	10c gray olive	.20	.20
87	A5	12½c brown	1.50	.40
88	A4	25c car & brt green	2.50	2.75
89	A5	50c blue gray & vio	2.75	1.40
90	A5	1r dull violet	5.25	8.75
91	A5	2r turquoise	11.50	10.50
		Nos. 80-91 (12)	25.10	28.30

Swazi Shields — A6

Train and Railroad Map — A7

Designs: 1c, Battle axe. 2c, Forestry. 2½c, Ceremonial headdress. 3½c, Musical instrument. 4c, Irrigation. 5c, Widow bird. 7½c, Rock paintings. 10c, Secretary bird. 12½c, Pink arum lily. 15c, Married woman. 20c, Malaria control. 25c, Swazi warrior. 50c, Ground hornbill, horiz. 1r, Aloes. 2r, Msinsi (flame tree), horiz.

Perf. 12½x14, 14x12½

			Wmk. 314	
1962, Apr. 24		**Photo.**		
92	A6	½c ocher, blk & brn	.20	.20
93	A6	1c gray & orange	.20	.60
94	A6	2c lt yel grn, dk grn & blk	.20	.20
95	A6	2½c vermilion & blk	.20	.20
96	A6	3½c gray & emerald	.20	.60
97	A6	4c aqua & black	.20	.20
98	A6	5c orange red & blk	.55	.20
99	A6	7½c dull ocher & brn	.55	.35
100	A6	10c lt blue & black	1.10	.20
101	A6	12½c lt olive & dp car	1.10	1.90
102	A6	15c red lilac & blk	1.50	1.00
103	A6	20c emerald & blk	.45	1.25
104	A6	25c ultra & blk	.55	1.00
105	A6	50c rose red & dk brn	8.75	3.75
106	A6	1r bister & emer	3.25	2.50
107	A6	2r ultra & scar	13.50	8.75
		Nos. 92-107 (16)	32.50	22.90

For surcharge & overprints see #138, 143-159.

Freedom from Hunger Issue
Common Design Type

			Perf. 14x14½	
1963, June 4				
108	CD314	15c lilac	.45	.45

Red Cross Centenary Issue
Common Design Type

			Perf. 13	
1963, Sept. 2		**Litho.**		
109	CD315	2½c black & red	.20	.20
110	CD315	15c ultra & red	.65	.65

Perf. 11½x12

			Wmk. 314	
1964, Nov. 5		**Engr.**		
111	A7	2½c purple & brt grn	.40	.20
112	A7	3½c dk olive & blue	.50	.65
113	A7	15c dk brown & orange	.70	.65
114	A7	25c dk blue & yellow	.90	.75
		Nos. 111-114 (4)	2.50	2.25

Opening of the Swaziland Railroad linking Ka Dake with Lourenco Marques.

ITU Issue
Common Design Type

			Perf. 11x11½	
1965, May 17		**Litho.**	**Wmk. 314**	
115	CD317	2½c blue & bister	.20	.20
116	CD317	15c red lil & rose red	.50	.50

Intl. Cooperation Year Issue
Common Design Type

			Perf. 14½	
1965, Oct. 25				
117	CD318	½c bl grn & claret	.20	.20
118	CD318	15c lt violet & grn	.50	.50

Churchill Memorial Issue
Common Design Type

			Perf. 14	
1966, Jan. 24		**Photo.**		
Design in Black, Gold and Carmine Rose				
119	CD319	½c brt blue	.20	.50
120	CD319	2½c green	.30	.20
121	CD319	15c brown	.50	.40
122	CD319	25c violet	.75	.80
		Nos. 119-122 (4)	1.75	1.90

UNESCO Anniversary Issue
Common Design Type

			Perf. 14	
1966, Dec. 1		**Litho.**		
123	CD323	2½c "Education"	.20	.20
124	CD323	7½c "Science"	.30	.30
125	CD323	15c "Culture"	.65	.65
		Nos. 123-125 (3)	1.15	1.15

King Sobhuza II and Map of Swaziland — A8

Design: 7½c, 25c, King Sobhuza II, vert.

Perf. 14½x14, 14x14½

			Wmk. 314	
1967, Apr. 25		**Photo.**		
126	A8	2½c multicolored	.20	.20
127	A8	7½c multicolored	.20	.20
128	A8	15c multicolored	.20	.20
129	A8	25c multicolored	.30	.30
		Nos. 126-129 (4)	.90	.90

Attainment of internal self-government.

King Sobhuza II, University Buildings and Graduates — A9

Perf. 14x14½

			Unwmk.	
1967, Sept. 1		**Photo.**		
130	A9	2½c yel, sepia & dp bl	.20	.20
131	A9	7½c blue, sepia & dp bl	.20	.20
132	A9	15c dl rose, sepia & dp bl	.20	.20
133	A9	25c lt vio, sepia & dp bl	.30	.30
		Nos. 130-133 (4)	.90	.90

1st conferment of degrees by the University of Botswana, Lesotho and Swaziland at Roma, Lesotho.

Swazi Reed Dance (Umhlanga) — A10

Designs: 3c, 15c, Feast of the First Fruits, Incwala (bull, sun and king), horiz.

Perf. 14½x14, 14x14½

			Wmk. 314	
1968, Jan. 5		**Photo.**		
134	A10	3c red, blk & silver	.20	.20
135	A10	10c brown, blk, org & sil	.20	.20
136	A10	15c red, blk & gold	.20	.20
137	A10	25c brown, blk, org & gold	.30	.30
		Nos. 134-137 (4)	.90	.90

No. 98 Surcharged with New Value

			Perf. 12½x14	
1968, May 1				
138	A6	3c on 5c org red & blk	.25	.20

Independent Kingdom

Plowing and King Sobhuza II — A11

Designs: 4½c, Cable lift carrying asbestos. 17½c, Worker cutting sugar cane. 25c, Iron ore mining and map showing Swaziland railroad.

Perf. 14x12½

			Wmk. 314	
1968, Sept. 6		**Photo.**		
139	A11	3c gold & multi	.20	.20
140	A11	4½c gold & multi	.20	.20
141	A11	17½c gold & multi	.20	.20
142	A11	25c slate & gold	.50	.50
a.		Strip of 4, #139-142	2.50	2.50
		Nos. 139-142 (4)	1.10	1.10

Swaziland's independence.

Nos. 139-142 printed in sheets of 50. No. 142a printed in sheets of 20 (4x5).

Nos. 92-107	**INDEPENDENCE**
Overprinted; No. 96 Surcharged	**1968**

			Perf. 12½x14, 14x12½	
1968, Sept. 6				
143	A6	½c ocher, blk & brn	.20	.20
144	A6	1c gray & orange	.20	.20
145	A6	2c multicolored	.20	.20
146	A6	2½c vermilion & blk	.80	1.50
147	A6	3c on 2½c #146	.20	.20
148	A6	3½c gray & emerald	.20	.20
149	A6	4c aqua & black	.20	.20
150	A6	5c org red & blk	3.75	.20
151	A6	7½c dull ocher & brn	.60	.20
152	A6	10c lt blue & blk	4.00	.20
153	A6	12½c lt olive & dp car	.35	.60
154	A6	15c red lilac & blk	.35	.75
155	A6	20c emerald & blk	1.00	1.60
156	A6	25c ultra & blk	.45	.75
157	A6	50c rose red & dk brn	7.50	4.50
a.		Wmk. sideways	3.00	3.00
158	A6	1r bister & emerald	2.75	4.50
159	A6	2r ultra & scarlet	5.25	9.00
a.		Wmk. sideways	5.00	5.00
		Nos. 143-159 (17)	28.00	25.00

Caracal (African Lynx) — A12

 (see below)

Waterbuck — A12a

1c, Cape porcupine. 2c, Crocodile. 3c, Lion. 3½c, African elephants. 5c, Bush pig. 7½c, Impalas. 10c, Chacma baboon. 12½c, Ratel (honey badger). 15c, Leopard. 20c, Blue wildebeest (brindled gnu). 25c, White (square-lipped) rhinoceros. 50c, Burchell's zebra. 2r, Giraffe.

Perf. 13x12½, 12½x13

			Wmk. 314	
1969, Aug. 1		**Litho.**		
Size: 30½x21½mm				
160	A12	½c multicolored	.20	.20
161	A12	1c multicolored	.20	.20
162	A12	2c multicolored	.20	.20
Size: 35x25mm				
163	A12	3c multicolored	.20	.20
a.		Wmk. upright ('75)	.65	.45

164	A12	3½c multicolored	.20	.20
Size: 30½x21½mm, 21½x30½mm				
165	A12	5c multicolored	.30	.20
166	A12	7½c multicolored	.40	.20
167	A12	10c multicolored	.60	.20
168	A12	12½c multicolored	.65	2.50
169	A12	15c multicolored	.70	.65
170	A12	20c multicolored	.85	.50
171	A12	25c multicolored	1.10	1.00
172	A12	50c multicolored	1.90	2.75
173	A12a	1r multicolored	4.50	5.50
174	A12a	2r multicolored	9.50	10.00
		Nos. 160-174 (15)	21.50	25.00

See #228-229. For surcharges see #259-260.

King Sobhuza II and Flags — A13

Designs: 7½c, 25c, UN emblem, UN Headquarters, NY, and King Sobhuza II.

Perf. 13½

			Wmk. 314	
1969, Sept. 24		**Litho.**		
175	A13	3c dp blue & multi	.20	.20
176	A13	7½c pink & multi	.20	.20
177	A13	12½c yellow & multi	.25	.25
178	A13	25c lt blue & multi	.35	.35
		Nos. 175-178 (4)	1.00	1.00

1st anniv. of admission to the UN.

Walking Racer, Shield and King — A14

Bauhinia Galpinii and King — A15

Designs: 7½c, Runner. 12½c, Hurdler. 25c, Parade of Swaziland team with flag bearer.

Perf. 14x14½

			Wmk. 314	
1970, July 16		**Litho.**		
179	A14	3c red org & multi	.20	.20
180	A14	7½c yellow & multi	.20	.20
181	A14	12½c lt blue & multi	.25	.25
182	A14	25c multicolored	.40	.40
		Nos. 179-182 (4)	1.05	1.05

Issued to publicize the 9th Commonwealth Games, Edinburgh, July 16-25.

Perf. 14x14½

			Wmk. 314	
1971, Feb. 1		**Litho.**		

Flowers of Swaziland: 10c, Crocosmia aurea. 15c, Gloriosa superba. 25c, Watsonia densiflora.

183	A15	3c bister & multi	.35	.20
184	A15	10c pale salmon & multi	.35	.20
185	A15	15c pale green & multi	.55	.25
186	A15	25c multicolored	.75	.60
		Nos. 183-186 (4)	2.00	1.25

King Sobhuza II — A16

Designs (King Sobhuza II): 3½c, In 1971. 7½c, In tribal costume at gathering of chiefs (Incwala). 25c, Opening Swazi parliament.

1971, Dec. 22				
187	A16	3c blue & multi	.20	.20
188	A16	3½c gold, blk, bl & brn	.20	.20
189	A16	7½c gold & multi	.20	.20
190	A16	25c lilac & multi	.30	.20
		Nos. 187-190 (4)	.90	.90

50th anniv. of the reign of Sobhuza II.

UNICEF Emblem, King Sobhuza II — A17

1972, Apr. 17   Perf. 14½x14
191 A17 15c violet & black   .20   .20
192 A17 25c olive & black   .50   .60

25th anniv. (in 1971) of UNICEF.

Traditional Reed Dancers — A18

**   Perf. 13½x14**
1972, Sept. 11   Wmk. 314
193 A18 3½c shown   .20   .20
194 A18 7½c Swazi beehive hut .25   .25
195 A18 15c Ezulwini Valley   .50   .50
196 A18 25c Usutu River fishing .80 .80
          Nos. 193-196 (4)   1.75 1.75

Tourist publicity.

Mosquito Control A19

1973, May 21   Litho.   Perf. 14½
197 A19 3½c shown   .25   .20
198 A19 7½c Anti-malaria vaccination .75 .50

25th anniv. of WHO.

Mpaka Coal Mines — A20

7½c, Oxen pulling plow. 15c, Weir over Komati River. 25c, Experimental rice plantation.

**   Perf. 13½x14**
1973, June 21   Wmk. 314
199 A20 3½c multicolored   .20   .20
200 A20 7½c multicolored   .20   .20
201 A20 15c multicolored   .35   .25
202 A20 25c multicolored   .60   .50
          Nos. 199-202 (4)   1.35 1.15

Development of natural resources.

Swaziland Coat of Arms — A21

10c, King Sobhuza II in dress uniform. 15c, Parliament. 25c, National Somhlolo Stadium.

1973, Sept. 7   Litho.   Perf. 14
203 A21 3c brick red & black   .20   .20
204 A21 10c dull orange & multi .20 .20
205 A21 15c blue & multi   .35   .50
206 A21 25c yellow & multi   .45 1.00
          Nos. 203-206 (4)   1.20 1.90

5th anniversary of independence.

Botswana, Lesotho, Swaziland Flags and Cap — A22

12½c, Kwaluseni Campus. 15c, Map of Africa & location of Botswana, Lesotho & Swaziland. 25c, Shield of University.

1974, Mar. 29   Litho.   Perf. 14
207 A22 7½c orange & multi   .20   .20
208 A22 12½c emerald & multi   .20   .20
209 A22 15c yellow & multi   .25   .25
210 A22 25c ultra & multi   .35   .35
          Nos. 207-210 (4)   1.00 1.00

10th anniversary of the University of Botswana, Lesotho and Swaziland.

Sobhuza as Student at Lovedale College, South Africa — A23

1974, July 22   Litho.   Perf. 13x11
211 A23 3c shown   .20   .20
212 A23 9c Sobhuza as middle-aged man .20 .20
213 A23 25c As old man   .60   .60
          Nos. 211-213 (3)   1.00 1.00

75th birthday of King Sobhuza II.

Mail Carried by Overhead Cable A24

1974, Oct. 9   Perf. 14
214 A24 4c Post Office, Lobamba .20 .20
215 A24 10c Mbabane temporary P.O., 1902 .20 .20
216 A24 15c shown   .40   .40
217 A24 25c Mule-drawn mail coach .50 .50
          Nos. 214-217 (4)   1.30 1.30

Centenary of Universal Postal Union.

**Animal Type of 1969
"E" instead of "R"**

Designs as before.

1975, Jan. 2   Litho.   Perf. 12½x13
228 A12a 1e multicolored   1.50 1.50
229 A12a 2e multicolored   3.50 3.50

Girl's Umcwasho Ceremony — A26

Swazi youth: 10c, Butimba, hunting ceremony. 15c, Lusekwane, ceremony of preparation, horiz. 25c, Gcina Regiment marching with flags.

1975, Mar. 20   Wmk. 314   Perf. 14
232 A26 3c lt green & multi   .20   .20
233 A26 10c lt violet & multi .20   .20
234 A26 15c brown org & multi .30   .30
235 A26 25c yellow & multi   .50   .50
          Nos. 232-235 (4)   1.20 1.20

Matsapa Airport Control Tower A27

5c, Fire brigade car and staff. 15c, Douglas C-47 Dakota. 25c, Hawker Siddeley 748.

1975, Aug. 18   Litho.   Perf. 14½
236 A27 4c multicolored   .25   .20
237 A27 5c multicolored   .65   .30
238 A27 15c multicolored   1.60   .30
239 A27 25c multicolored   2.25 2.00
          Nos. 236-239 (4)   4.75 3.75

10th anniversary of internal air service.

Women in Service — A28

Green Pigeon — A29

4c, Elephant with IWY emblem, horiz. 5c, Queen Labotsibeni, grandmother of King Sobhuza II, horiz. 15c, Handicrafts women.

**   Wmk. 373**
1975, Dec. 22   Litho.   Perf. 14
240 A28 4c ultra, blk & gray   .20   .20
241 A28 5c bister & multi   .20   .20
242 A28 15c multicolored   .30   .30
243 A28 25c multicolored   .40   .55
          Nos. 240-243 (4)   1.10 1.25

International Women's Year 1975.

1976, Jan. 2   Wmk. 373   Perf. 14

Birds: 1c, Black-headed oriole, horiz. 3c, Melba finch, horiz. 4c, Plum-colored starling. 5c, Black-headed heron. 6c, Stonechat. 7c, Chorister robin. 10c, Gorgeous bush shrike. 15c, Black-collared barbet. 20c, Gray heron. 25c, Giant kingfisher. 30c, Black eagle. 50c, Red bishop. 1e, Pin-tailed whydah. 2e, Lilac-breasted roller, horiz.

244 A29 1c orange & multi   .75   .75
245 A29 2c lilac & multi   .85   .85
246 A29 3c yel grn & multi   1.10 1.10
247 A29 4c gray blue & multi   .85   .85
248 A29 5c orange & multi   .95   .95
249 A29 6c orange & multi   1.60 1.60
250 A29 7c orange & multi   1.50 1.50
251 A29 10c slate & multi   1.60 1.60
252 A29 15c lt green & multi 2.40 2.40
253 A29 20c ocher & multi   3.50 3.50
254 A29 25c orange & multi   3.75 3.75
255 A29 30c orange & multi   3.75 3.75
256 A29 50c sepia & multi   2.40 2.40
257 A29 1e vermilion & multi 2.75 2.75
258 A29 2e lt blue & multi   4.75 4.75
          Nos. 244-258 (15)   32.50 32.50

Nos. 166 and 168 Surcharged in Ultramarine or Brown

1976   Wmk. 314   Perf. 13x12½
259 A12 3c on 7½c multi (U)   1.00 1.25
260 A12 6c on 12½c multi (B) 1.50 1.50

Denomination at lower left on No. 260.

Blindness from Malnutrition — A30

Designs (WHO Emblem and): 10c, Retina, "Operation prevents blindness." 20c, Blind

eye, "Blindness from trachoma." 25c, Medicine and syringe, "Medicine and rehabilitation."

**   Wmk. 373**
1976, June 15   Litho.   Perf. 14
261 A30 5c multicolored   .20   .20
262 A30 10c multicolored   .30   .20
263 A30 20c multicolored   .60   .55
264 A30 25c multicolored   .65   .65
          Nos. 261-264 (4)   1.75 1.60

World Health Day: Foresight prevents blindness.

Marathon Runner — A31

Soccer — A32

Designs (Olympic Rings and): 6c, Boxing. 20c, Soccer. 25c, Olympic torch and flame.

1976, July 17   Litho.   Wmk. 373
265 A31 5c lt blue & multi   .20   .20
266 A31 6c olive & multi   .20   .20
267 A31 20c lt violet & multi .35   .35
268 A31 25c dull orange & multi .45 .45
          Nos. 265-268 (4)   1.20 1.20

21st Olympic Games, Montreal, Canada, July 17-Aug. 1.

1976, Sept. 13   Litho.   Perf. 14½

Designs: 5c, Player heading ball. 20c, Goalkeeper catching ball. 25c, Player kicking ball.

269 A32 4c blue & multi   .20   .20
270 A32 5c olive & multi   .20   .20
271 A32 20c red & multi   .35   .35
272 A32 25c multicolored   .50   .50
          Nos. 269-272 (4)   1.25 1.25

FIFA membership for Swaziland in 1976 (Federation Internationale de Football Associations).

A. G. Bell and 1976 Telephone — A33

Designs (A. G. Bell and Telephone): 5c, 1895. 10c, 1876. 15c, 1877. 20c, 1905.

1976, Nov. 22   Perf. 14
273 A33 4c multicolored   .20   .20
274 A33 5c multicolored   .20   .20
275 A33 10c multicolored   .20   .20
276 A33 15c multicolored   .30   .30
277 A33 20c multicolored   .40   .40
          Nos. 273-277 (5)   1.30 1.30

Centenary of first telephone call by Alexander Graham Bell, Mar. 10, 1876.

Elizabeth II and Sobhuza II — A34

Designs: 25c, Queen's coach at Admiralty Arch. 50c, Queen seated in coach.

1977, Feb. 7   Perf. 13½
278 A34 20c silver & multi   .25   .25
279 A34 25c silver & multi   .30   .30
280 A34 50c silver & multi   .65   .65
          Nos. 278-280 (3)   1.20 1.20

25th anniv. of the reign of Elizabeth II.

Matsapa College
A35

10c, Men's & Women's uniforms & jeep. 20c, Police badge. 25c, Dog handler & dog.

1977, May 2		**Litho.**	**Perf. 14**	
281	A35	5c multi	.20	.20
282	A35	10c multi	.20	.20
283	A35	20c multi, vert.	.45	.45
284	A35	25c multi	.55	.55
		Nos. 281-284 (4)	1.40	1.40

50 years of police training in Swaziland.

Various Animals
A36

Rock Paintings: 10c, 20c, Groups of men. 15c, Cattle and herdsman.

		Perf. 14x14½		
1977, Aug. 8			**Wmk. 373**	
285	A36	5c multicolored	.20	.20
286	A36	10c multicolored	.35	.35
287	A36	15c multicolored	.55	.55
288	A36	20c multicolored	.75	.75
a.		Souvenir sheet of 4, #285-288	3.00	3.00
		Nos. 285-288 (4)	1.85	1.85

Rock paintings from Highveld area, c. 1700-1850.

Evergreens, Timber, Map of Highveld — A37

Designs: 10c, Pineapple and map of Middleveld. 15c, Map of Lowveld, orange and lemon. 20c, Map of Lubombo and grazing cattle. No. 293, Map of Swaziland and produce, vert.: UL, Evergreens; UR, Orange and lemon; LL, Pineapple; LR, Cattle.

1977, Oct. 17		**Litho.**	**Perf. 13½**	
289	A37	5c multicolored	.20	.20
290	A37	10c multicolored	.40	.40
291	A37	15c multicolored	.60	.60
292	A37	20c multicolored	.85	.85
		Nos. 289-292 (4)	2.05	2.05

Souvenir Sheet

293		Sheet of 4	2.00	2.00
a.-d.		A37 25c single stamp	.45	.45

Nos. 293a-293d are vertical.

Cussonia Spicata Thunb. — A38

Trees: 10c, Sclerocarya birrea. 20c, Pterocarpus angolensis. 25c, Erythrina lysistemon.

1978, Jan. 12		**Litho.**	**Wmk. 373**	
294	A38	5c multicolored	.20	.20
295	A38	10c multicolored	.25	.25
296	A38	20c multicolored	.50	.50
297	A38	25c multicolored	.60	.60
		Nos. 294-297 (4)	1.55	1.55

Rural Electrification, Lobamba — A39

Hydroelectric Power: 10c, Edwaleni Power Station. 20c, Switchgear, Maguduza Power Station. 25c, Hydroturbine hall, Edwaleni.

1978, Mar. 6		**Litho.**	**Perf. 13½**	
298	A39	5c black & ocher	.20	.20
299	A39	10c black & yel grn	.20	.20
300	A39	20c black & blue	.30	.30
301	A39	25c black & rose mag	.45	.45
		Nos. 298-301 (4)	1.15	1.15

Elizabeth II Coronation Anniversary Issue
Souvenir Sheet
Common Design Types

1978, Apr. 21		**Unwmk.**	**Perf. 15**	
302		Sheet of 6	2.00	2.00
a.	CD326	25c Queen's lion	.35	.35
b.	CD327	25c Elizabeth II	.35	.35
c.	CD328	25c African Elephant	.35	.35

No. 302 contains 2 se-tenant strips of Nos. 302a-302c, separated by horizontal gutter with commemorative and descriptive inscriptions and showing central part of coronation procession with coach.

Clay Pots
A40

Handicrafts: 10c, Basketwork. 20c, Wooden utensils. 30c, Wooden pot with lid.

		Wmk. 373		
1978, June 26		**Litho.**	**Perf. 13½**	
303	A40	5c multicolored	.20	.20
304	A40	10c multicolored	.20	.20
305	A40	20c multicolored	.30	.30
306	A40	30c multicolored	.50	.50
		Nos. 303-306 (4)	1.20	1.20

See Nos. 317-320.

Defense Force
A41

Designs: 6c, King's Regiment. 10c, Tinkabi tractor and ox-drawn plow. 15c, Laying water pipe. 25c, Adult literacy class. 50c, Fire engine and ambulance.

1978, Sept. 6		**Litho.**	**Perf. 14**	
307	A41	4c multicolored	.20	.20
308	A41	6c multicolored	.20	.20
309	A41	10c multicolored	.20	.20
310	A41	15c multicolored	.20	.20
311	A41	25c multicolored	.35	.35
312	A41	50c multicolored	.70	.70
		Nos. 307-312 (6)	1.85	1.85

10th anniversary of independence.

Angel Appearing to the Shepherds — A42

Christmas: 10c, Adoration of the Kings. 15c, Angel warning Joseph in a dream. 25c, Flight into Egypt.

1978, Dec. 12		**Litho.**	**Perf. 14**	
313	A42	5c multicolored	.20	.20
314	A42	10c multicolored	.20	.20
315	A42	15c multicolored	.25	.25
316	A42	25c multicolored	.45	.45
		Nos. 313-316 (4)	1.10	1.10

Handicrafts Type of 1978

1979, Jan. 10			**Perf. 13½**	
317	A40	5c Sisal bowls	.20	.20
318	A40	15c Clay pots	.30	.30
319	A40	20c Basketwork	.35	.35
320	A40	30c Hide shield	.55	.55
		Nos. 317-320 (4)	1.40	1.40

Prospecting at Phophonyane
A43

15c, Early 3-stamp battery mill. 25c, Cyanide tanks at Piggs Peak. 50c, Pouring off molten gold.

		Wmk. 373		
1979, Mar. 27		**Litho.**	**Perf. 14**	
321	A43	5c blue & gold	.20	.20
322	A43	15c brown & gold	.30	.30
323	A43	25c green & gold	.50	.50
324	A43	50c red & gold	1.10	1.10
		Nos. 321-324 (4)	2.10	2.10

Centenary of discovery of gold in Swaziland.

Girls at Piano, 1892, by Renoir
A44

Paintings by Renoir: 15c, Madame Charpentier and her Children, 1878. 25c, Girls Picking Flowers, 1889. 50c, Girl with Watering Can, 1876.

1979, May 8			**Perf. 13½**	
325	A44	5c multicolored	.20	.20
326	A44	15c multicolored	.25	.25
327	A44	25c multicolored	.40	.40
328	A44	50c multicolored	.80	.80
a.		Souvenir sheet of 4, #325-328	1.90	1.90
		Nos. 325-328 (4)	1.65	1.65

International Year of the Child.

Swaziland No. 40 and Rowland Hill — A45

Rowland Hill and: 10c, Swaziland #18. 25c, Swaziland #142. 50c, Swaziland #105.

1979, July 17		**Litho.**	**Perf. 14½**	
329	A45	10c multicolored	.20	.20
330	A45	20c multicolored	.30	.30
331	A45	25c multicolored	.35	.35
		Nos. 329-331 (3)	.85	.85

Souvenir Sheet

332	A45	50c multicolored	.80	.80

Sir Rowland Hill (1795-1879), originator of penny postage.

5c Cupro-Nickel Coin — A46

Coins: 10c, King Sobhuza II and sorghum. 20c, King and elephant head. 50c, Coat of arms. 1e, Mother and son.

Big Bend Post Office
A47

15c, Mount Ntondozi microwave station vert. 20c, Swaziland #53. 50c, Swaziland #217.

1979, Sept. 6		**Litho.**	**Wmk. 373**	
333	A46	5c multicolored	.20	.20
334	A46	10c multicolored	.20	.20
335	A46	20c multicolored	.25	.25
336	A46	50c multicolored	.55	.55
337	A46	1e multicolored	1.10	1.10
		Nos. 333-337 (5)	2.30	2.30

1979, Nov. 22				
338	A47	5c multicolored	.20	.20
339	A47	15c multicolored	.20	.20
340	A47	20c multicolored	.25	.25
341	A47	50c multicolored	.55	.55
		Nos. 338-341 (4)	1.20	1.20

25th anniv. of Post and Telecommunications service (5c, 15c); 10th anniv. of UPU membership (20c, 50c).

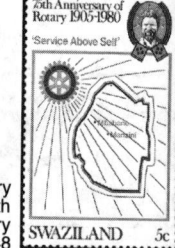

Rotary International, 75th Anniversary
A48

		Wmk. 373		
1980, Feb. 23		**Litho.**	**Perf. 14**	
342	A48	5c shown	.20	.20
343	A48	15c Hospital equipment	.25	.25
344	A48	50c Rotary principles	.90	.90
345	A48	1e Headquarters, Evanston, IL	1.75	1.75
		Nos. 342-345 (4)	3.10	3.10

Eucomis Autumnalis — A49

Flowers: 1c, Brunsvigia radulosa. 2c, Aloe suprafoliata. 3c, Haemanthus magificus. 4c, Aloe marlothii. 5c, Dicoma zeyheri. 6c, Aloe kniphofioides. 7c, Cyrtanthus bicolor. 15c, Leucospermum gerrardii. 20c, Haemanthus multiflorus. 30c, Acridocarpus natalitius. 50c, Adenium swazicum. 1e, Protea simplex. 2e, Calodendrum capense. 5e, Gladiolus ecklonii. All vert. except. 15c, 20c, 30c, 50c.

1980, Apr. 28		**Unwmk.**	**Perf. 13½**	
346	A49	1c multicolored	.20	.20
347	A49	2c multicolored	.20	.20
348	A49	3c multicolored	.20	.20
349	A49	4c multicolored	.20	.20
350	A49	5c multicolored	.20	.20
351	A49	6c multicolored	.20	.20
352	A49	7c multicolored	.20	.20
353	A49	10c multicolored	.20	.20
354	A49	15c multicolored	.30	.30
355	A49	20c multicolored	.40	.40
356	A49	30c multicolored	.55	.55
357	A49	50c multicolored	.70	.70

		Size: 22x37½mm		
358	A49	1e multicolored	1.40	1.40
359	A49	2e multicolored	3.00	3.00
360	A49	5e multicolored	7.00	7.00
		Nos. 346-360 (15)	14.95	14.95

No. 348a does not have a date inscription below design.
For surcharges see Nos. 465-470.

1983			**Perf. 12**	
346a	A49	1c	.20	.20
347a	A49	2c	.20	.20
348a	A49	3c	2.00	2.00
349a	A49	4c	.20	.20
350a	A49	5c	3.00	2.00
351a	A49	6c	.20	.20

353a	A49	10c	.20 .20
355a	A49	20c	.45 .45
	Nos. 346a-355a (8)		6.45 5.45

Inscribed 1983. Nos. 348a, 350a do not have a date inscription below design.

Mail Runner, London 1980 Emblem A50

1980, May 6   Wmk. 373   Perf. 14
361 A50 10c shown .20 .20
362 A50 20c Mail truck .25 .25
363 A50 25c Mail sorting .30 .30
364 A50 50c Mail ropeway .60 .60
Nos. 361-364 (4) 1.35 1.35

London 80 Intl. Stamp Exhib., May 6-14.

Yellow Fish A51

1980, Aug. 25   Litho.   Perf. 14
365 A51 5c shown .20 .20
366 A51 10c Silver barbel .20 .20
367 A51 15c Tigerfish .30 .30
368 A51 30c Squeaker fish .55 .55
369 A51 1e Bream 1.90 1.90
Nos. 365-369 (5) 3.15 3.15

Oribi Antelope A52

1980, Oct. 1   Litho.   Perf. 14
370 A52 5c shown .20 .20
371 A52 10c Nile crocodile, vert. .20 .20
372 A52 50c Pangolin .85 .85
373 A52 1e Leopard, vert. 1.75 1.75
Nos. 370-373 (4) 3.00 3.00

Bus A53

1981, Jan. 5   Litho.   Perf. 14½
374 A53 5c shown .20 .20
375 A53 25c Jet .50 .50
376 A53 30c Truck .55 .55
377 A53 1e Train 1.90 1.90
Nos. 374-377 (4) 3.15 3.15

Mantenga Falls — A54

1981, Apr. 16   Litho.   Perf. 14
378 A54 5c shown .20 .20
379 A54 15c Mananga Yacht Club .25 .25
380 A54 30c White rhinoceri, Mliwane Game Sanctuary .50 .50
381 A54 1e Gambling 1.65 1.65
Nos. 378-381 (4) 2.60 2.60

Royal Wedding Issue
Common Design Type
Wmk. 373

1981, July 21   Litho.   Perf. 14
382 CD331 10c Bouquet .20 .20
383 CD331 25c Charles .40 .40
384 CD331 1e Couple 1.50 1.50
Nos. 382-384 (3) 2.10 2.10

Installation of King Sobhuza II, 1921 A55

60th Anniv. of King Sobhuza II's Reign (King and): 10c, Visit of Royal Family, 1947. 15c, Coronation of Queen Elizabeth II, 1953. 25c, Independence ceremony, 1968. 30c, Early portrait. 1e, Parliament buildings.

Wmk. 373
1981, Aug. 24   Perf. 14½
385 A55 5c multicolored .20 .20
386 A55 10c multicolored .20 .20
387 A55 15c multicolored .25 .25
388 A55 25c multicolored .40 .40
389 A55 30c multicolored .50 .50
390 A55 1e multicolored 1.60 1.60
Nos. 385-390 (6) 3.15 3.15

Duke of Edinburgh's Awards, 25th Anniv. — A56   Intl. Year of the Disabled — A57

1981, Nov. 5   Litho.   Perf. 14
391 A56 5c Basketball .20 .20
392 A56 20c Compass reading .35 .35
393 A56 50c Square .90 .90
394 A56 1e Duke of Edinburgh 1.75 1.75
Nos. 391-394 (4) 3.20 3.20

1981, Dec. 7   Perf. 14x14½, 14½x14
395 A57 5c Men learning carpentry, horiz. .20 .20
396 A57 15c Boy learning Braille .30 .30
397 A57 25c Carpentry, diff. .50 .50
398 A57 1e Driving, horiz. 2.00 2.00
Nos. 395-398 (4) 3.00 3.00

Papilio Demodocus — A58

1982, Jan. 6   Litho.   Perf. 14
399 A58 5c shown .20 .20
400 A58 10c Charaxes candiope .35 .35
401 A58 50c Papilio nireus 1.75 1.75
402 A58 1e Eurema desjardinsii 3.50 3.50
Nos. 399-402 (4) 5.80 5.80

A59   A60

1982, Apr. 27   Litho.   Perf. 14
403 A59 5c Non-smoker, flowers .20 .20
404 A59 10c Smoker, non-smoker .25 .25

First Intl. Conference on Smoking and Health, Apr. 25-29

Perf. 13½x13
1982, June 16   Litho.   Wmk. 373
a, Female fishing owl. b, Pair. c, Owl in nest, egg. d, Adult and young owls. e, Male.
405 Strip of 5, multi 110.00 35.00
a.-e. A60 35c, any single 20.00 10.00

Princess Diana Issue
Common Design Type

1982, July 1   Perf. 14½
406 CD333 5c Arms .20 .20
407 CD333 20c Diana .35 .35
408 CD333 50c Wedding .90 .90
409 CD333 1e Portrait 1.75 1.75
Nos. 406-409 (4) 3.20 3.20

Sugar Industry A61

1982, Sept. 1   Litho.
410 A61 5c Planting sugar cane .20 .20
411 A61 20c Harvesting cane .45 .45
412 A61 30c Mhlume Mills .65 .65
413 A61 1e Rail transport 2.25 2.25
Nos. 410-413 (4) 3.55 3.55

Baphalali Red Cross Society A62

1982, Nov. 9   Perf. 14
414 A62 5c Immunization .20 .20
415 A62 20c Red Cross Juniors .35 .35
416 A62 50c Disaster relief .90 .90
417 A62 1e Red Cross founder Henry Dunant 1.75 1.75
Nos. 414-417 (4) 3.20 3.20

Scouting Year — A63

Perf. 14½x14
1982, Dec. 6   Litho.   Wmk. 373
418 A63 5c Reciting promise .20 .20
419 A63 10c Hiking .25 .25
420 A63 25c Community development .65 .65
421 A63 75c Baden-Powell 1.90 1.90
Nos. 418-421 (4) 3.00 3.00

Souvenir Sheet
422 A63 1e Emblem 3.00 3.00

A64   Beaded Vulture — A65

1983, Mar. 14   Litho.   Perf. 14
423 A64 6c Satellite view .20 .20
424 A64 10c King Sobhuza II, flag .20 .20
425 A64 50c Beehive huts, horiz. 1.00 1.00
426 A64 1e Spraying sugar crop, horiz. 2.00 2.00
Nos. 423-426 (4) 3.40 3.40

Commonwealth Day.

Perf. 13½x13
1983, May 16   Litho.   Wmk. 373
Designs: a, Male. b, Pair. c, Nest, egg. d, Female at nest. e, Adult, fledgeling.
427 Strip of 5 6.00 6.00
a.-e. A65 35c, any single 1.10 1.10

Soccer Tour of Swaziland 1983 — A66

1983, Aug. 20   Litho.   Perf. 14x13½
428 A66 75c Natl. team 1.40 1.40
429 A66 75c Tottenham Hotspur, vert. 1.40 1.40
430 A66 75c Manchester United 1.40 1.40
Nos. 428-430 (3) 4.20 4.20

Manned Flight Bicentenary A67

1983, Sept. 22   Litho.   Perf. 14
431 A67 5c Montgolfiere, 1783, .20 .20
432 A67 10c Wright brothers' plane .20 .20
433 A67 25c Royal Swazi Fokker Fellowship .40 .40
434 A67 50c Bell X-1 jet .85 .85
Nos. 431-434 (4) 1.65 1.65

Souvenir Sheet
435 A67 1e Columbia space shuttle take-off, vert. 2.00 2.00

Alfred Nobel, 100th Birth Anniv. A68

1983, Oct. 21
436 A68 6c Albert Schweitzer .20 .20
437 A68 10c Dag Hammarskjold .30 .30
438 A68 50c Albert Einstein 1.00 1.00
439 A68 1e shown 2.00 2.00
Nos. 436-439 (4) 3.50 3.40

World Food Program A69

1983, Nov. 29
440 A69 6c Maize .20 .20
441 A69 10c Rice .30 .30
442 A69 50c Cattle .85 .85
443 A69 1e Tractor 1.75 1.75
Nos. 440-443 (4) 3.10 3.10

Women's College A70

Wmk. 373
1984, Mar. 12   Litho.   Perf. 14
444 A70 5c shown .20 .20
445 A70 15c Technical training school .30 .30
446 A70 50c University .90 .90
447 A70 1e Primary school 1.75 1.75
Nos. 444-447 (4) 3.15 3.15

Bald Ibis — A71

Designs: a, Male. b, Male, female. c, Nest, egg. d, Female at nest. e, Adult, fledgeling.

1984, May 18   Litho.   Perf. 13½x13
448   Strip of 5   5.50 5.50
a.-e.   A71 35c, any single   1.00 1.00

1984 UPU Congress — A72

Mail Coaches.

1984, June 15   Litho.   Perf. 14½
449 A72 7c Mule-drawn coach   .20   .20
450 A72 15c Oxen-drawn post
                wagon   .30   .30
451 A72 50c Mule-drawn, diff.   .90   .90
452 A72 1e Bristol-London   1.75 1.75
        Nos. 449-452 (4)   3.15 3.15

1984 Summer Olympics A73

1984, July 28   Perf. 14
453 A73 7c Running   .20   .20
454 A73 10c Swimming   .20   .20
455 A73 50c Shooting   .85   .85
456 A73 1e Boxing   1.75 1.75
a.   Souvenir sheet of 4, #453-456 3.50 3.50
        Nos. 453-456 (4)   3.00 3.00

Local Fungi A74

1984, Sept. 19   Litho.   Perf. 14
457 A74 10c Suillus bovinus   .20   .20
458 A74 15c Langermannia gi-
                gantea, vert.   .30   .30
459 A74 50c Coriolus versicolor,
                vert.   .90   .90
460 A74 1e Boletus edulis   1.75 1.75
        Nos. 457-460 (4)   3.15 3.15

20th Anniv. of Swazi Railways A75

1984, Nov. 5   Litho.   Wmk. 373
461 A75 10c Opening ceremony   .20   .20
462 A75 25c Type 15A locomo-
                tive, Siweni Ex-
                change Yard   .50   .50
463 A75 30c Container loading,
                Matsapha Station   .60   .60
464 A75 1e No. 268, Alto Tunnel 2.00 2.00
a.   Souvenir sheet of 4, #461-464 3.50 3.50
        Nos. 461-464 (4)   3.30 3.30

Nos. 346a, 346-349, 351-352 Surcharged

1984, Dec. 15   Perf. 12
465 A49 10c on 4c #349   .20   .20
a.   Perf. 13½   50.00 50.00

Perf. 13½, 12 (#469)
466 A49 15c on 7c #352   .20   .20
467 A49 20c on 3c #348   .20   .20
a.   Perf 12   —

468 A49 25c on 6c #351   .20   .20
469 A49 30c on 1c #346a   .25   .25
470 A49 30c on 2c #347   .25   .25
        Nos. 465-470 (6)   1.30 1.30

Rotary Intl., 80th Anniv. A76

1985, Feb. 23   Wmk. 373   Perf. 14
471 A76 10c Rotary emblem,
                world map   .20   .20
472 A76 15c Training scholar-
                ships   .20   .20
473 A76 50c Two children   .60   .60
474 A76 1e Nurse, children   1.25 1.25
        Nos. 471-474 (4)   2.25 2.25

Life Cycle of the Ground Hornbill — A77

Audubon birth bicentenary.

1985, May 15   Wmk. 373
475   Strip of 5   3.00 3.00
a.-e.   A77 25c, any single   .55   .55

Queen Mother 85th Birthday
Common Design Type

Perf. 14½x14

1985, June 7   Litho.   Wmk. 384
476 CD336 10c Visit to South Af-
                rica, 1947   .20   .20
477 CD336 15c With Elizabeth II
                and Margaret   .20   .20
478 CD336 50c 75th birthday cel-
                ebration   .50   .50
479 CD336 1e Holding Prince
                Henry   1.10 1.10
        Nos. 476-479 (4)   2.00 2.00

Souvenir Sheet
480 CD336 2e Greeting Prince
                Andrew   2.00 2.00

Classic Automobiles — A78

Wmk. 373
1985, Sept. 16   Litho.   Perf. 14
481 A78 10c Buick Tourer   .20   .20
482 A78 15c Four-cylinder Rover .20   .20
483 A78 50c De Dion Bouton   .45   .45
484 A78 1e Ford Model-T   .90   .90
        Nos. 481-484 (4)   1.75 1.75

Intl. Youth Year A79

1985, Dec. 2
485 A79 10c Bridge-building   .20   .20
486 A79 20c Girl Guides camping .20   .20
487 A79 50c Recreation   .45   .45
488 A79 1e Guides collecting
                branches   .90   .90
        Nos. 485-488 (4)   1.75 1.75

Girl Guide Movement, 20c, 1e. IYY, 10c, 50c.

Halley's Comet A80

1986, Feb. 27   Wmk. 384   Perf. 14½
489 A80 1.50e multicolored   1.50 1.50

Queen Elizabeth II 60th Birthday
Common Design Type

10c, Princess Anne's christening, 1950. 30c, Wedding of Prince Charles and Lady Diana, 1981. 45c, With George VI, the Duchess of York and Sobhuza II at Nhlangano, 1947. 1e, At Windsor Polo Ground, 1984. 2e, Visiting Crown Agents' offices, 1983.

1986, Apr. 21   Perf. 14x14½
490 CD337 10c scar, blk & sil   .20   .20
491 CD337 30c ultra & multi   .30   .30
492 CD337 45c green, blk & sil   .45   .45
493 CD337 1e violet & multi   .95   .95
494 CD337 2e rose vio & multi   2.00 2.00
        Nos. 490-494 (5)   3.90 3.90

For overprints see Nos. 527-530.

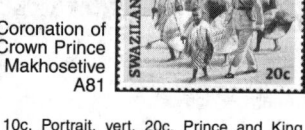

Coronation of Crown Prince Makhosetive A81

10c, Portrait, vert. 20c, Prince and King Sobhuza II at an Incwala ceremony. 25c, Prince at primary school. 30c, At school in England. 40c, Escorted from Matsapha Airport by Guard of Honor. 2e, Dancing the Simemo.

1986, Apr. 25   Perf. 14½
495 A81 10c multicolored   .20   .20
496 A81 20c multicolored   .25   .25
497 A81 25c multicolored   .30   .30
498 A81 30c multicolored   .35   .35
499 A81 40c multicolored   .45   .45
500 A81 2e multicolored   2.25 2.25
        Nos. 495-500 (6)   3.80 3.80

Assoc. of Round Tables in Central Africa, 50th Anniv. — A82

Club emblems.

Wmk. 384
1986, Oct. 4   Litho.   Perf. 14
501 A82 15c Orbis   .20   .20
502 A82 25c Ehlanzeni 51   .25   .25
503 A82 55c Mbabane 30   .50   .50
504 A82 70c Bulembu 54   .60   .60
505 A82 2e Manzini 44   1.75 1.75
        Nos. 501-505 (5)   3.30 3.30

Butterflies — A83

Unwmk.
1987, Mar. 17   Litho.   Perf. 14
506 A83 10c Yellow pansy   .20   .20
507 A83 15c Guineafowl   .20   .20
508 A83 20c Red forest
                charaxes   .20   .20
509 A83 25c Paradise skipper   .25   .25
510 A83 30c Broad-bordered
                acraea   .30   .30
511 A83 35c Veined swallow-
                tail   .35   .35
512 A83 45c Large striped
                swordtail   .40   .40
513 A83 50c Eyed pansy   .45   .45
514 A83 55c Zebra white   .50   .50

515 A83 70c Gaudy commo-
                dore   .60   .60
516 A83 1e Common dotted
                border   .90   .90
517 A83 5e Queen purple tip   4.25 4.25
518 A83 10e Natal barred blue   8.50 8.50
        Nos. 506-518 (13)   17.10 17.10

See Nos. 600-611. For surcharges see Nos. 574-577. Compare with design A101.

White Rhinoceros A84

1987, July 1   Wmk. 384   Perf. 14½
519 A84 15c Two adults   1.25   .75
520 A84 25c Adult, calf   2.00 1.25
521 A84 45c Adult walking   5.00 3.50
522 A84 70c Adult in mud   6.00 4.00
        Nos. 519-522 (4)   14.25 9.50

World Wildlife Fund.

Flowers — A85

1987, Oct. 19   Litho.   Perf. 14½
523 A85 15c Blue moon   .20   .20
524 A85 35c Danse de feu   .35   .35
525 A85 55c Odin   .55   .55
526 A85 2e Lilium davidii   2.00 2.00
        Nos. 523-526 (4)   3.10 3.10

Nos. 491-494 Ovptd. "40TH WEDDING ANNIVERSARY" in Silver

Perf. 14x14½

1987, Dec. 9   Litho.   Wmk. 384
527 CD337 30c ultra & multi   .30   .30
528 CD337 45c green, blk & sil   .45   .45
529 CD337 1e violet & multi   1.00 1.00
530 CD337 2e rose vio & multi   2.00 2.00
        Nos. 527-530 (4)   3.75 3.75

Insects A86

Wmk. 384
1988, Mar. 14   Perf. 14
531 A86 15c Zabalius aridus   .20   .20
532 A86 55c Callidea bohemani   .60   .60
533 A86 1e Phymateus viridipes 1.00 1.00
534 A86 2e Nomadacris
                septemfasciata   2.00 2.00
        Nos. 531-534 (4)   3.80 3.80

1988 Summer Olympics, Seoul A87

1988, Aug. 22   Litho.   Wmk. 384
535 A87 15c Flag-bearer, stadi-
                um   .20   .20
536 A87 35c Tae kwon do   .40   .40
537 A87 1e Boxing   1.00 1.00
538 A87 2e Tennis   2.00 2.00
        Nos. 535-538 (4)   3.60 3.60

Intl. Tennis Federation, 75th anniv. (2e).

Small
Mammals
A88

Wmk. 384
1989, Jan. 16   Litho.   *Perf. 14*

539	A88	35c Green monkey	.40	.40
540	A88	55c Rock dassie	.60	.60
541	A88	1e Zorilla	1.00	1.00
542	A88	2e African wildcat	2.00	2.00
		Nos. 539-542 (4)	4.00	4.00

Intl. Red Cross and Red Crescent
Organizations, 125th Anniv. — A89

Wmk. 373
1989, Sept. 21   Litho.   *Perf. 12*

543	A89	15c David Hynd	.20	.20
544	A89	60c First aid	.60	.60
545	A89	1e Sigombeni Clinic	1.00	1.00
546	A89	2e Relief work	2.00	2.00
		Nos. 543-546 (4)	3.80	3.80

21st Birthday
of King
Mswati III
A90

King Mswati III: 15c, With Prince of Wales,
1987. 60c, With Pope John Paul II, 1988. 1e,
Introduction to the nation while crown prince.
2e, With queen mother.

**   *Perf. 14½x14***
1989, Nov. 15   Unwmk.

547	A90	15c multicolored	.20	.20
548	A90	60c multicolored	.55	.55
549	A90	1e multicolored	.95	.95
550	A90	2e multicolored	1.90	1.90
		Nos. 547-550 (4)	3.60	3.60

African
Development
Bank, 25th
Anniv. — A91

15c, Manzini-Mahamba Road. 60c,
Mbabane microwave radio link. 1e, Mbabane
Government Hospital. 2e, Ezulwini Power
Switching Station.

**   *Perf. 14x14½***
1989, Dec. 18   Wmk. 384

551	A91	15c multicolored	.20	.20
552	A91	60c multicolored	.40	.40
553	A91	1e multicolored	.70	.70
554	A91	2e multicolored	1.40	1.40
		Nos. 551-554 (4)	2.70	2.70

Stamp
World
London
'90 — A92

Wmk. 384
1990, May 3   Litho.   *Perf. 12½*

555	A92	15c Intl. priority mail	.20	.20
556	A92	60c Facsimile service	.45	.45
557	A92	1e Post office	.75	.75
558	A92	2e Ezulwini Earth Sat-
ellite Station	1.50	1.50
		Nos. 555-558 (4)	2.90	2.90

Souvenir Sheet

559	A92	2e Mail runner	1.50	1.50

150th anniv. of the Penny Black.

Queen Mother, 90th Birthday
Common Design Types
1990, Aug. 4 Wmk. 384 *Perf. 14x15*

565	CD343	75c Queen Mother	.40	.40

**   *Perf. 14½***

566	CD344	4e King, Queen vis-
iting Hatfield
House	2.25	2.25

Intl.
Literacy
Year
A94

Wmk. 373
1990, Sept. 21   Litho.   *Perf. 14*

567	A94	15c shown	.20	.20
568	A94	75c Outdoor class	.60	.60
569	A94	1e Modern instruction	.70	.70
570	A94	2e Receiving diploma	1.50	1.50
		Nos. 567-570 (4)	3.00	3.00

UN Development
Program, 40th
Anniv. — A95

**   *Perf. 13½x14***
1990, Dec. 10   Litho.   Wmk. 373

571	A95	60c Rural water supply	.45	.45
572	A95	1e Seed production	.75	.75
573	A95	2e Low cost housing	1.50	1.50
		Nos. 571-573 (3)	2.70	2.70

Nos. 509-510, 512, 514 Surcharged

Unwmk.
1990, Dec. 17   Litho.   *Perf. 14*

574	A83	10c on 25c multi	.20	.20
575	A83	15c on 30c multi	.25	.25
575A	A83	15c on 45c multi	50.00	30.00
576	A83	20c on 45c multi	.35	.35
577	A83	40c on 55c multi	.70	.70

National
Heritage
A96

**   *Perf. 14x14½***
1991, Feb. 11   Wmk. 233

578	A96	15c Lobamba Hot
Spring	.20	.20
579	A96	60c Sibebe Rock	.45	.45
580	A96	1e Jolobela Falls	.75	.75
581	A96	2e Mantjolo Sacred
Pool	1.50	1.50
		Nos. 578-581 (4)	2.90	2.90

Souvenir Sheet
**   *Perf. 14***

581A	A96	2e Usushwana River	1.50	1.50

Coronation
of King
Mswati III,
5th Anniv.
A97

**   *Perf. 14x13½***
1991, Apr. 24   Litho.   Wmk. 373

582	A97	15c King making radio
address	.20	.20
583	A97	75c Butimba royal hunt	.55	.55
584	A97	1e King, schoolmates,
1986	.75	.75
585	A97	2e King opening parlia-
ment	1.50	1.50
		Nos. 582-585 (4)	3.00	3.00

Elizabeth & Philip, Birthdays
Common Design Types
Wmk. 384
1991, June 17   *Perf. 14½*

586	CD346	1e multicolored	.75	.75
587	CD345	2e multicolored	1.50	1.50
a.		Pair, #586-587 + label	2.25	2.25

Flowers — A98   Christmas — A99

1991, Sept. 30   Wmk. 373   *Perf. 14*

588	A98	15c Xerophyta retinervis	.20	.20
589	A98	75c Bauhinia galpinii	.55	.55
590	A98	1e Dombeya
rotundifolia	.75	.75
591	A98	2e Kigelia africana	1.50	1.50
		Nos. 588-591 (4)	3.00	3.00

Wmk. 373
1991, Dec. 18   Litho.   *Perf. 13½*

592	A99	20c Santa Claus, chil-
dren	.20	.20
593	A99	70c Carolers	.55	.55
594	A99	1e Priest reading Bible	.75	.75
595	A99	2e Nativity Scene	1.50	1.50
		Nos. 592-595 (4)	3.00	3.00

Reptiles
A100

1992, Feb. 25

596	A100	20c Lubombo flat lizard	.20	.20
597	A100	70c Natal hinged tor-
toise	.55	.55
598	A100	1e Swazi thick-toed
gecko	.75	.75
599	A100	2e Nile monitor	1.50	1.50
		Nos. 596-599 (4)	3.00	3.00

Butterflies
A101

1992-2000   Litho.   *Perf. 14*

600	A101	5c Red tip	.20	.20
601	A101	10c like #506	.20	.20
602	A101	15c like #507	.20	.20
603	A101	20c like #508	.20	.20
604	A101	25c like #509	.20	.20
605	A101	30c like #510	.20	.20
606	A101	35c like #512	.30	.30
607	A101	45c like #512	.35	.35
608	A101	50c like #513	.40	.40
609	A101	55c like #514	.45	.45
610	A101	70c like #515	.50	.50
611	A101	1e like #516	.80	.80
612	A101	5e Like #517	—	—
		Nos. 600-612 (12)	4.00	4.00

Issued: Nos. 600-611, 8/26/92. No. 612,
2000.
Nos. 600-611 dated 1991. No. 612 dated
2000.
Nos. 600-612 have different portrait of King
Mswati III from Nos. 506-517.

A102   A103

Designs: 20c, Missionaries with royal family.
1e, Pioneer missionaries.

1992, Dec. 16   Litho.   *Perf. 13½x14*

614	A102	20c multicolored	.20	.20
615	A102	1e multicolored	.75	.75

Evangelical Alliance Mission in Swaziland,
cent.

1993, Mar. 18   Litho.   *Perf. 13½x14*

Cooking Utensils: 20c, Calabashes. 70c,
Contemporary pottery for cooking. 1e,
Wooden bowls. 2e, Quern for grinding seeds.

616	A103	20c multicolored	.20	.20
617	A103	70c multicolored	.50	.50
618	A103	1e multicolored	.70	.70
619	A103	2e multicolored	1.40	1.40
		Nos. 616-619 (4)	2.80	2.80

A104   A105

King Mswati, 25th Birthday: 25c, King
Mswati as baby with mother. 40c, King Mswati
III addressing PTA meeting. 1e, King Sobhuza
II receiving Instrument of Independence, 1968.
2e, King Mswati III delivering first speech on
Coronation Day, 1986.

1993, Sept. 6   Litho.   *Perf. 13½x14*

620	A104	25c multicolored	.20	.20
621	A104	40c multicolored	.25	.25
622	A104	1e multicolored	.55	.55
623	A104	2e multicolored	1.25	1.25
		Nos. 620-623 (4)	2.25	2.25

Independence, 25th anniv.

1993, Nov. 25   *Perf. 13½*

Common Waxbill

624	A105	25c Male & female	.20	.20
625	A105	40c Nest & eggs	.25	.25
626	A105	1e Incubating	.60	.60
627	A105	2e Feeding nestlings	1.25	1.25
		Nos. 624-627 (4)	2.30	2.30

A106   A107

1994, Feb. 22   Litho.   *Perf. 13½*

628	A106	25c Education	.20	.20
629	A106	40c Rural services	.20	.20
630	A106	1e Swazi culture	.60	.60
631	A106	2e People to people	1.25	1.25
		Nos. 628-631 (4)	2.25	2.25

US Peace Corps, 25th anniv.

1994, Sept. 15   *Perf. 13½x14*

Mushrooms.

632	A107	30c Horse mushroom	.20	.20
633	A107	40c Penny bun bolete	.20	.20
634	A107	1e Rusulla verdigris	.50	.50
635	A107	2e Honey fungus	1.10	1.10
		Nos. 632-635 (4)	2.00	2.00

ICAO, 50th Anniv. A108

1994, Nov. 30   Litho.   Perf. 14
636 A108 30c Natl. airline .20 .20
637 A108 40c Control tower .20 .20
638 A108 1e Air rescue service .50 .50
639 A108 2e Air traffic control 1.10 1.10
　　Nos. 636-639 (4) 2.00 2.00

A109　　　　　A110

Traditional handicrafts.

1995, Apr. 7   Litho.   Perf. 13½
640 A109 35c Wooden bowls .20 .20
641 A109 50c Chicken nests .30 .30
642 A109 1e Leather crafts .55 .55
643 A109 2e Wood carvings 1.10 1.10
　　Nos. 640-643 (4) 2.15 2.15

1995, June 5   Litho.   Perf. 13½
FAO, 50th anniv.: 35c, Corn harvest. 50c, Planting vegetables. 1e, Herd of cattle. 2e, Sorghum harvest.
644 A110 35c multicolored .20 .20
645 A110 50c multicolored .30 .30
646 A110 1e multicolored .55 .55
647 A110 2e multicolored 1.10 1.10
　　Nos. 644-647 (4) 2.15 2.15

Lourie A111

1995, Sept. 27   Litho.   Perf. 13½x13
648 A111 35c Knysna lourie .20 .20
649 A111 50c Lourie in flight .30 .30
650 A111 1e Purple crested lourie .55 .55
651 A111 2e Gray lourie 1.10 1.10
　　Nos. 648-651 (4) 2.15 2.15

Reptiles A112

1996, Jan. 17   Litho.   Perf. 13½x13
652 A112 35c Chameleon .20 .20
653 A112 50c Rock monitor .25 .25
654 A112 1e African python .55 .55
655 A112 2e Tree agama 1.00 1.00
　　Nos. 652-655 (4) 2.00 2.00

Trees — A113

1996, Apr. 23   Litho.   Perf. 13
656 A113 40c Waterberry .20 .20
657 A113 60c Sycamore fig .35 .35
658 A113 1e Stem fruit .60 .60
659 A113 2e Wild medlar 1.10 1.10
　　Nos. 656-659 (4) 2.25 2.25

Local Landmarks A114

Designs: 40c, First church, Mahamba Methodist. 60c, Colonial Secretariat, Mbabane. 1e, King Sobhuza II Memorial Monument. 2e, First High Court Building, Hlatikulu.

1996, Aug. 26   Litho.   Perf. 13½x13
660 A114 40c multicolored .20 .20
661 A114 60c multicolored .30 .30
662 A114 1e multicolored .60 .60
663 A114 2e multicolored 1.10 1.10
　　Nos. 660-663 (4) 2.20 2.20

UNICEF, 50th Anniv. A115

Designs: 40c, Basic education for all. 60c, Universal child immunization, vert. 1e, No more polio, vert. 2e, Children first, vert.

1996, Dec. 31   Litho.   Perf. 13½x14
664 A115 40c multicolored .20 .20

Perf. 14x13½
665 A115 60c multicolored .30 .30
666 A115 1e multicolored .45 .45
667 A115 2e multicolored .90 .90
　　Nos. 664-667 (4) 1.85 1.85

Wild Animals A116

50c, Klipspringer, vert. 70c, Gray duiker, vert. 1e, Antbear. 2e, Cape clawless otter.

Perf. 14x13½, 13½x14
1997, Sept. 22   Litho.
668 A116 50c multicolored .25 .25
669 A116 70c multicolored .35 .35
670 A116 1e multicolored .45 .45
671 A116 2e multicolored .95 .95
　　Nos. 668-671 (4) 2.00 2.00

Traditional Costumes — A117

1997, Dec. 1   Litho.   Perf. 13x13½
672 A117 50c Umgaco .20 .20
673 A117 70c Sigeja .30 .30
674 A117 1e Umdada .40 .40
675 A117 2e Ligcebesha .85 .85
　　Nos. 672-675 (4) 1.75 1.75

Toads and Frogs A118

1998, June 1   Litho.   Perf. 14
676 A118 55c Olive toad .20 .20
677 A118 75c African bullfrog .25 .25
678 A118 1e Water lily frog .35 .35
679 A118 2e Bushveld rain frog .95 .95
　　Nos. 676-679 (4) 1.75 1.75

Independence, 30th Anniv., King Mswati III, 30th Birthday — A119

55c, King Sobhuza II Memorial Park. 75c, King Mswati III taking oath. 1e, King Mswati III delivering 1st speech. 2e, King Sobhuza II receiving instrument of independence.

Perf. 13½x14, 14x13½
1998, Sept. 3   Litho.
680 A119 55c multicolored .20 .20
681 A119 75c multicolored .25 .25
682 A119 1e multicolored .35 .35
683 A119 2e multicolored .65 .65
　　Nos. 680-683 (4) 1.45 1.45

Traditional Utensils — A120

1999, May 17   Litho.   Perf. 13¾x13¼
684 A120 60c Grinding stone .20 .20
685 A120 75c Stirring sticks .25 .25
686 A120 80c Clay pot .25 .25
687 A120 95c Swazi spoons .30 .30
688 A120 1.75e Beer cup .60 .60
689 A120 2.40e Mortar and pestle .80 .80
　　Nos. 684-689 (6) 2.40 2.40

UPU, 125th Anniv. A121

Perf. 13¾x13½
1999, Oct. 9   Litho.   Unwmk.
690 A121 60c Internet service, vert. .20 .20
691 A121 80c Cellular phone service, vert. .25 .25

Perf. 13½x13¾
692 A121 1e Intl. mail exchange .35 .35
693 A121 2.40e Training school .80 .80
　　Nos. 690-693 (4) 1.60 1.60

Wildlife A122

Designs: 65c, Lion, vert. 90c, Leopard. 1.50e, Rhinoceros. 2.50e, Buffalo, vert.

Perf. 13½x13¼, 13¼x13½
2000, July 3   Litho.   Unwmk.
694 A122 65c multi .20 .20
695 A122 90c multi .25 .25
696 A122 1.50e multi .45 .45
697 A122 2.50e multi .75 .75
　　Nos. 694-697 (4) 1.65 1.65

Worldwide Fund for Nature (WWF) — A123

Designs: 65c, Oribi with young. 90c, Oribi. 1.50e, Klipspringers. 2.50e, Klipspringers, diff.

Wmk. 373
2001, Feb. 1   Litho.   Perf. 1
698-701 A123 Set of 4 1.40 1.4
701a　　　Sheet, 4 each #698-701 5.75 5.7

Environmental Protection — A124

Designs: 70c, Fighting forest fires. 95c, Tree planting. 2.05e Construction of Maguga Dam. 2.80e, Building embankment.

2001, July 30   Litho.   Perf. 1·
702-705 A124 Set of 4 1.60 1.6·

Reign Of Queen Elizabeth II, 50th Anniv. Issue
Common Design Type

Designs: Nos. 706, 710a, 70c, Princess Elizabeth, Princess Anne, Princes Philip and Charles, 1947. Nos. 707, 710b, 95c, Wearing purple hat. Nos. 708, 710c, 2.05e, Wearing crown. Nos. 709, 710d, 2.80e, Wearing yellow hat, 2001. No. 710e, 22.50e, 1955 portrait by Annigoni (38x50mm).

Perf. 14¼x14½, 13¾ (#710e)
2002, Feb. 6   Litho.   Wmk. 373
With Gold Frames
706-709 CD360 Set of 4 1.10 1.10

Souvenir Sheet
Without Gold Frames
710 CD360 Sheet of 5, #a-e 5.25 5.25

Tourism A125

Designs: 75c, Swazi chalets. 1e, King Mswati III facing lions, vert. 2.05e, Crocodile. 2.80e, Ostriches.

Perf. 13¼x13¾, 13¾x13¼
2002, Dec. 23   Litho.
711-714 A125 Set of 4 1.60 1.60

Musical Instruments — A126

Designs: 80c, Mouth organ, vert. 1.05e, Rattles. 2.35e, Kudu horn trumpet. 2.80e, Chordphone, vert.

2003, Aug. 12   Litho.   Perf. 14
715-718 A126 Set of 4 1.90 1.90

AIDS Prevention — A127

Designs: 85c, Community home-based care. 1.10e, Know your HIV status. 2.45e, Testing blood samples, vert. 3.35e, Unsterilized instruments can transmit HIV and AIDS, vert.

Perf. 13¼x13¾, 13¾x13¼
2004, Mar. 9   Litho.
719-722 A127 Set of 4 2.40 2.40

POSTAGE DUE STAMPS

Catalogue values for unused stamps in this section are for Never Hinged items.

D1   D2

1933   Typo.   Wmk. 4   Perf. 14

J1	D1 1p carmine rose	.30	2.00
a.	Wmk. 4a (error)	100.00	
J2	D1 2p violet	2.25	8.50

No. 57 Surcharged

I   II

1961   Engr.   Perf. 13½x13

J3	A5 (2d) on 2p, type I	10.00	12.00
a.	Type II	.40	
J4	A5 1c on 2p, type I	2.00	3.25
a.	Type II	1.50	1.50
J5	A5 2c on 2p, type I	2.00	3.25
a.	Type II	1.10	1.10
J6	A5 5c on 2p, type I	2.00	3.25
a.	Type II	1.75	1.75
	Nos. J3-J6 (4)	16.00	21.75
	Nos. J3a-J6a (4)	4.75	
	Nos. J4a-J6a (3)		4.35

No. J3a was surcharged after decimal currency was introduced.

Type of 1933

1961   Typo.   Perf. 14

J7	D1 1c carmine rose	.20	.20
J8	D1 2c violet	.30	.30
J9	D1 5c green	.75	1.00
	Nos. J7-J9 (3)	1.25	1.50

Wmk. 314

1971, Feb. 1   Litho.   Perf. 11½

J10	D2 1c carmine rose	.30	.35
J11	D2 2c dull purple	.40	.50
J12	D2 5c green	.70	.80
	Nos. J10-J12 (3)	1.40	1.65

1977, Jan. 17   Wmk. 373

J10a	D2 1c carmine rose	.30	.30
J11a	D2 2c dull purple	.40	.40
J12a	D2 5c green	.70	.70
	Nos. J10a-J12a (3)	1.40	1.40

1978-91   Perf. 15x14

Size: 17½x21mm

J13	D2 1c carmine lake	.20	.20
J14	D2 2c purple	.20	.20
J15	D2 5c green	.20	.20
J16	D2 10c sky blue	.20	.20
J17	D2 25c brown	.30	.20
	Nos. J13-J17 (5)	1.10	1.00

Nos. J14-J15 reissued dated 1991.
Issued: 1c-5c, 4/20; 10c-25c, 7/17/91.

SCOTTMOUNTS

For stamp presentation unequaled in beauty and clarity, insist on ScottMounts. Made of 100% inert polystyrol foil, ScottMounts protect your stamps from the harmful effects of dust and moisture. Available in your choice of clear or black backs, ScottMounts are center-split across the back for easy insertion of stamps and feature crystal clear mount faces. Double layers of gum assure stay-put bonding on the album page. Discover the quality and value ScottMounts have to offer.

ScottMounts are available from your favorite stamp dealer or direct from:

Discover the quality and value ScottMounts have to offer.

For a complete list of ScottMount sizes call or write Scott Publishing Co.

SCOTT

Scott Publishing Co.
1-800-572-6885
P.O. Box 828 Sidney OH 45365-0828
www.amosadvantage.com

AMOS
HOBBY PUBLISHING

Publishers of:
Coin World, Linn's Stamp News and Scott Publishing Co.

SWEDEN

'swē-dən

LOCATION — Northern Europe, occupying the eastern half of the Scandinavian Peninsula
GOVT. — Constitutional Monarchy
AREA — 173,341 sq. mi.
POP. — 8,911,296 (1999 est.)
CAPITAL — Stockholm

48 skilling banco = 1 riksdaler banco
(until 1858)
100 öre = 1 riksdaler (1858 to 1874)
100 öre = 1 krona (since 1874)

Catalogue values for unused stamps in this country are for Never Hinged items, beginning with Scott 358 in the regular postage section, and Scott B37 in the semi-postal section.

Watermarks

Wmk. 180 — Crown

Wmk. 307 — Crown and 1955

Wmk. 181 — Wavy Lines

Port Payé
Post Suède

SWEDEN
and other
NORDIC COUNTRIES

You are welcome to try filling your wants from Scandinavia's biggest stamp stock.
Ask for our 142 page illustrated price list $10. U.S. postpaid.
Free with orders.

● ● ●

Satisfaction Guaranteed
Please visit us at
www.gummesson.se

Rolf Gummesson AB
(Since 1939)
Kungsgatan 55
111 22 Stockholm, Sweden
e-mail: rolf@gummesson.se

We accept VISA, MasterCard, Euro Card and American Express

ASDA member since 1948.

Values for unused stamps are for examples with original gum as defined in the catalogue introduction except Nos. 1-5, including reprints, and LX1 which are valued without gum.

Coat of Arms
A1   A2

1855		Unwmk. Typo.	Perf. 14
1	A1	3s blue		
		green	6,750.	2,750.
a.		3s orange (error)		3,000,000.
2	A1	4s lt blue	1,250.	70.00
a.		4s gray blue	5,400.	275.00
3	A1	6s gray	8,000.	975.00
a.		6s gray brown	—	2,250.
b.		Imperf.		
4	A1	8s orange	4,250.	550.00
a.		8s yellow orange	4,250.	450.00
b.		8s lemon yellow		1,200.
c.		Imperf.		
5	A1	24s dull red	6,500.	1,500.

Nos. 1-5 were reprinted two or three times perf. 14, once perf. 13. Value of the lowest cost perf. 14 reprints, $375 each. Perf. 13, $325 each.
The reprints were made after Nos. 1-5 were withdrawn, but before being demonitized. Used copies are known.

1858-61			Perf. 14
6	A2	5o green	160.00	18.00
a.		5o deep green	575.00	140.00
7	A2	9o violet	350.00	225.00
a.		9o lilac	450.00	275.00
8	A2	12o blue	175.00	1.90
9	A2	12o ultra ('61)	310.00	12.50
10	A2	24o orange	400.00	27.50
a.		24o yellow	400.00	35.00
11	A2	30o brown	400.00	27.50
a.		30o red brown	450.00	45.00
12	A2	50o rose	500.00	80.00
a.		50o carmine	550.00	92.50
		Nos. 6-12 (7)	2,295.	392.40

Nos. 6 and 8 exist with double impressions. No. 8 is known printed on both sides. No. 11 exists imperf.
Nos. 6-8, 10-12 were reprinted in 1885, perf. 13. Value $100 each. Also reprinted in 1963, perf. 13½, with lines in stamp color crossing denominations, and affixed to book page. Value $12.50 each.

Lion and Arms
A3   A4

1862-69				
13	A3	3o bister brown	150.00	13.50
a.		Printed on both sides		2,300.
14	A4	17o red violet ('66)	600.00	160.00
15	A4	17o gray ('69)	650.00	650.00
16	A4	20o vermilion ('66)	225.00	16.00
		Nos. 13-16 (4)	1,625.	839.50

Nos. 13-15 were reprinted in 1885, perf. 13. Values $65, $100 and $65, respectively.

Numeral of Value — A5   Coat of Arms — A6

1872-77			Perf. 14
17	A5	3o bister brown	60.00	8.00
18	A5	4o gray ('76)	425.00	125.00
19	A5	5o blue green	310.00	4.50
a.		5o emerald	500.00	55.00
20	A5	6o violet	325.00	40.00
a.		6o dark violet	325.00	40.00
21	A5	6o gray ('74)	900.00	87.50
22	A5	12o blue	160.00	1.00
23	A5	20o vermilion	800.00	7.00
a.		20o dull org yel ('75)	3,500.	35.00
b.		Double impression, dull yel & ver ('76)	3,250.	45.00
24	A5	24o orange	700.00	35.00
a.		24o yellow	700.00	35.00
25	A5	30o pale brown	600.00	9.25
a.		30o black brown	600.00	11.50

26	A5	50o rose	650.00	40.00
a.		50o carmine	700.00	40.00
27	A6	1rd bister & blue	800.00	75.00
a.		1rd bister & ultra	800.00	75.00
		Nos. 17-27 (11)	5,730.	432.25

1877-79			Perf. 13
28	A5	3o yellow brown	60.00	5.00
29	A5	4o gray ('79)	190.00	3.50
30	A5	5o dark green	125.00	1.00
31	A5	6o lilac	140.00	4.00
a.		6o red lilac	150.00	4.50
32	A5	12o blue	26.00	.80
33	A5	20o vermilion	225.00	1.00
a.		"TRETIO" instead of "TJUGO" ('79)	8,250.	5,250.
34	A5	24o orange ('78)	55.00	25.00
a.		24o yellow	125.00	26.00
35	A5	30o pale brown	350.00	1.90
a.		30o black brown	400.00	2.50
36	A5	50o carmine ('78)	260.00	7.00
37	A6	1rd bister & blue	1,850.	400.00
38	A6	1k bister & bl ('78)	500.00	16.00
		Nos. 28-36,38 (10)	1,931.	65.20

Imperf., Pairs

28a	A5	3o		750.00
29a	A5	4o		750.00
30a	A5	5o		750.00
31b	A5	6o		750.00
32a	A5	12o		750.00
33b	A5	20o		750.00
34b	A5	24o		750.00
35b	A5	30o		1,500.
36a	A5	50o		750.00
38a	A6	1k		750.00

See Nos. 40-44, 46-49. For surcharges see Nos. B1-B10, B22-B31.
No. 37 has been reprinted in yellow brown and dark blue; perforated 13. Value, $325.

King Oscar II — A7

1885			Typo.
39	A7	10o dull rose	190.00	.65
a.		Imperf., pair		2,000.

Numeral Type with Post Horn on Back

1886-91			
40	A5	2o orange ('91)	2.10	6.00
a.		Period before "FRIMARKE"	11.00	22.50
b.		Imperf., pair	725.00	
41	A5	3o yellow brn ('87)	11.00	21.00
42	A5	4o gray	25.00	1.40
43	A5	5o green	55.00	.65
44	A5	6o red lilac ('88)	27.50	55.00
a.		6o violet	30.00	55.00
45	A7	10o pink	77.50	.25
a.		10o rose	77.50	.25
b.		Imperf.		2,500.
46	A5	20o vermilion	100.00	.65
47	A5	30o pale brown	175.00	1.50
48	A5	50o rose	150.00	3.75
49	A6	1k bister & dk bl	82.50	2.50
a.		Imperf., pair	600.00	
		Nos. 40-49 (10)	705.60	92.70

Nos. 32, 34 with Blue Surcharge

1889, Oct. 1				
50	A5	10o on 12o blue	3.25	4.50
51	A5	10o on 24o orange	11.00	37.50

King Oscar II
A10   A11

1891-1904		Typo.	Perf. 13
52	A9	1o brown & ultra ('92)	1.40	.65
53	A9	2o brown & yellow org	3.25	.30
54	A9	3o brown & orange ('92)	.55	1.50

Wmk. 180

A9

55	A9	4o carmine & ultra ('92)	4.75	.30

Engr.

56	A10	5o yellow green	2.75	.20
a.		5o blue green	11.50	.20
d.		5o brown (error)	5,500.	
e.		Booklet pane of 6	72.50	
57	A10	8o red violet ('03)	3.25	1.10
58	A10	10o carmine	4.50	.20
c.		Booklet pane of 6	82.50	
59	A10	15o red brown ('96)	22.50	.30
60	A10	20o blue	22.50	.30
61	A10	25o red orange ('96)	27.50	.40
62	A10	30o brown	50.00	.30
63	A10	50o slate	80.00	.65
64	A10	50o olive gray ('04)	80.00	.65
65	A11	1k car & sl ('00)	140.00	1.90
		Nos. 52-65 (14)	442.95	8.75

Imperf., Pairs

52a	A9	1o	82.50
53a	A9	2o	275.00
54a	A9	3o	275.00
55a	A9	4o	250.00
56b	A10	5o No. 56	82.50
c.		No. 56a	300.00
57a	A10	8o	325.00
58a	A10	10o	52.50
59a	A10	15o	375.00
60a	A10	20o	140.00
61a	A10	25o	475.00
62a	A10	30o	450.00
63a	A10	50o	525.00
64a	A10	50o	375.00
65a	A11	1k	525.00

No. 56d may be a proof.
See Nos. 75-76.

Stockholm Post Office — A12

1903, Oct. 26				
66	A12	5k blue	225.00	25.00
a.		Imperf., pair	1,900.	

Opening of the new General Post Office at Stockholm.
For surcharge see No. B11.

Arms — A13   Gustaf V — A14

Perf. 13, 13x13½

1910-14		Typo.	Wmk. 180
67	A13	1o black ('11)	.65	1.50
68	A13	2o orange	1.75	3.50
69	A13	4o violet	2.50	1.10

Engr.

70	A14	5o green ('11)	14.00	29.00
71	A14	10o carmine	9.50	.50
72	A14	1k black, yel ('11)	87.50	.50
73	A14	5k claret, yel ('14)	1.75	3.00
		Nos. 67-73 (7)	117.65	39.10

See #77-98. For surcharges see #99-104, Q1-Q2.

1911			Unwmk.
75	A10	20o blue	20.00	14.00
76	A10	25o red orange	25.00	3.50

1910-19				
77	A14	5o green ('11)	1.90	.20
a.		Booklet pane of 10	225.00	
b.		Booklet pane of 4	125.00	
78	A14	7o gray grn ('18)	.20	.20
a.		Booklet pane of 10	8.75	
79	A14	8o magenta ('12)	.20	.20
80	A14	10o carmine ('10)	1.90	.20
a.		Booklet pane of 10	225.00	
b.		Booklet pane of 4	125.00	
81	A14	12o rose lake ('18)	.25	.20
a.		Booklet pane of 10	6.50	
82	A14	15o red brown ('11)	6.50	.20
a.		Booklet pane of 10	325.00	
83	A14	20o deep blue ('11)	9.50	.20
a.		Booklet pane of 10	350.00	
84	A14	25o orange red ('11)	.25	.20
85	A14	27o pale blue ('18)	.40	.90
86	A14	30o claret brn ('11)	20.00	.20
87	A14	35o dk violet ('11)	17.00	.20
88	A14	40o olive green ('17)	32.50	.20
89	A14	50o gray ('12)	57.50	.20
90	A14	55o pale blue ('18)	1,550.	4,250.

King Oscar II

90	A14	65o pale ol grn ('18)	.65 1.60
91	A14	80o black ('18)	1,550. 4,250.
92	A14	90o gray green ('18)	.60 .55
93	A14	1k black, yel ('19)	92.50 .30

Nos. 77-89,91,93-94 (16)   241.85   5.75

Excellent forgeries of Nos. 90 and 92 exist.

1911-19   Typo.   Wmk. 181   Perf. 13

95	A13	1o black	.20 .20
96	A13	2o orange	.20 .20
97	A13	3o pale brown ('19)	.20 .20
98	A13	4o pale violet	.20 .20

Nos. 95-98 (4)   .80   .80

Remainders of Nos. 95-98 received various private overprints, mostly as publicity for stamp exhibitions. They were not postally valid.

Unwatermarked Stamps with Watermarks

Stamps of these and later issues through the UPU Congress issue of 1924, are frequently found with watermark showing parts of the words "Kungl Postverket" in double-lined capitals. This watermark is normally located in the margins of the sheets of unwatermarked paper or paper watermarked wavy lines or crown.

Nos. 80, 84, 91, 90, 92 Surcharge:

a   b

1918   Unwmk.

99	A14(a)	7o on 10o	.20 .20
100	A14(b)	12o on 25o	1.90 .40
a.		Inverted surcharge	300.00 350.00
101	A14(a)	12o on 65o	.85 1.40
102	A14(a)	27o on 55o	.75 1.60
103	A14(a)	27o on 65o	1.40 3.50
104	A14(a)	27o on 80o	.85 1.60

Nos. 99-104 (6)   5.95   8.70

Arms A15   Heraldic Lion Supporting Arms of Sweden A16

Two types each of 5o green, 5o copper red and 10o violet, type A16.

Perf. 10 Vertically
1920-25   Engr.   Unwmk.

115	A15	3o copper red	.20 .20
116	A16	5o green	3.75 .25
117	A16	5o cop red ('21)	6.25 .25
118	A16	10o green ('21)	21.00 .30
a.		Tête bêche pair	1,550. 2,500.
119	A16	10o violet ('25)	5.25 .20
120	A16	25o orange ('21)	13.00 .25
121	A16	30o brown	.45 .20

Wmk. 181

122	A16	5o green	1.10 .90
123	A16	5o cop red ('21)	8.25 .55
124	A16	10o green ('21)	2.50 .85
125	A16	30o brown	8.25 14.00

Nos. 115-125 (11)   70.00   17.95

Coil Stamps

Unless part of a booklet pane any stamp perforated only horizontally or vertically is a coil stamp.

1920-26   Unwmk.   Perf. 10

126	A16	5o green	3.50 .50
a.		Booklet pane of 10	55.00
127	A16	10o green ('21)	11.50 3.50
a.		Booklet pane of 10	125.00
128	A16	10o violet ('25)	6.50 .85
a.		Booklet pane of 10	72.50
129	A16	30o brown	32.50 3.25

Wmk. 181

130	A16	5o green	11.50 20.00
131	A16	10o green ('21)	45.00 70.00
a.		Booklet pane of 10	325.00

Perf. 13 Vertically
Unwmk.

132	A16	5o green ('25)	14.00 7.75
133	A16	5o cop red ('21)	425.00 140.00
134	A16	10o violet ('26)	25.00 32.50

Wmk. 181

135	A16	5o green ('25)	1.60 4.50
136	A16	5o copper red ('22)	1.90 5.50
137	A16	10o green ('24)	9.00 22.50
138	A16	10o violet ('25)	8.00 17.50

Nos. 126-138 (13)   595.00   328.35

The paper used for the earlier printings of types A16, A17, A18, A18a and A20 is usually tinted by the color of the stamp. Printings of 1934 and later are on white paper in slightly different shades.

King Gustaf V — A17

1920-21   Unwmk.   Perf. 10 Vertically

139	A17	10o rose	27.50 .25
140	A17	15o claret	.30 .25
141	A17	20o blue	35.00 .25

Perf. 10

142	A17	10o rose	12.50 5.50
143	A17	20o blue ('21)	29.00 8.25
a.		Booklet pane of 10	325.00

Nos. 139-143 (5)   104.30   14.50

Wmk. 181

144	A17	20o blue	4,000.

Crown and Post Horn
A18   A18a

See note after No. 138 regarding paper. There are 2 types of the 35, 40, 45 and 60o.

1920-34   Unwmk.   Perf. 10 Vert.

145	A18	35o yellow ('22)	42.50 .60
146	A18	40o olive green	32.50 .75
147	A18	45o brown ('22)	1.25 .55
148	A18	60o claret	19.00 .20
149	A18	70o red brn ('22)	.60 2.50
150	A18	80o deep green	.40 .25
151	A18	85o myrtle grn ('29)	3.75 .40
152	A18	90o lt blue ('25)	55.00 .20
153	A18a	1kr dp org ('21)	7.75 .25
154	A18	110o ultra	.50 .30
155	A18	115o red brn ('29)	9.00 .40
156	A18	120o gray blk ('25)	62.50 .50
157	A18	120o lil rose ('33)	14.00 .45
158	A18	140o gray black	.90 .30
159	A18	145o brt grn ('30)	8.50 .55

Wmk. 181

160	A18	35o yellow ('23)	60.00 6.25
161	A18	60o red violet	95.00 110.00
162	A18	80o blue green	8.25 12.00
163	A18	110o ultra	3.50 3.75

Nos. 145-163 (19)   424.90   140.20

The value for #147 is for the 2nd type, issued in 1925.

Gustavus Adolphus A19   King Gustaf V A20

Perf. 10 Vertically
1920, July 28   Unwmk.

164	A19	20o deep blue	2.25 .40

Wmk. 181

165	A19	20o blue	150.00 19.00

Unwmk.
Perf. 10

166	A19	20o blue	6.25 1.90
a.		Booklet pane of 10	87.50

Nos. 164-166 (3)   158.50   21.30

Tercentenary of Swedish post which first ran between Stockholm and Hamburg.

1921-36   Unwmk.   Perf. 10 Vert.

See note after No. 138 regarding paper. There are two types each of the 15o rose and 40o olive green.

167	A20	15o violet ('22)	17.00 .20
168	A20	15o rose ('25)	5.50 .25
169	A20	15o brown ('36)	4.75 .30
170	A20	20o violet	.20 .20
171	A20	20o rose ('22)	22.50 .50
172	A20	20o orange ('25)	.20 .30
174	A20	25o rose red ('22)	.55 1.50
175	A20	25o dk bl ('25)	17.00 .20
176	A20	25o dk ultra ('34)	17.00 .50
177	A20	25o yel org ('36)	32.50 .30
178	A20	30o blue ('23)	19.00 .30
179	A20	30o brown ('36)	22.50 .20
180	A20	30o lt ultra ('36)	6.00 .55
181	A20	35o red vio ('30)	21.00 .40
182	A20	40o blue	.45 .60
183	A20	40o ol grn ('29)	42.50 1.10
184	A20	45o brown ('29)	5.00 .40
185	A20	50o gray	1.75 .20
186	A20	85o myrtle grn ('25)	17.00 1.50
187	A20	115o brn red ('25)	11.00 1.50
188	A20	145o apple grn ('25)	8.25 1.50

Nos. 167-188 (21)   271.65   12.50

Wmk. 181

189	A20	15o violet ('22)	2,650. 775.00
189A	A20	20o violet	4,500.

1922-36   Unwmk.   Perf. 10

190	A20	15o violet	17.50 .55
a.		Booklet pane of 10	325.00
191	A20	15o rose red ('25)	22.50 .75
a.		Booklet pane of 10	350.00
192	A20	15o brown ('36)	5.75 .95
a.		Booklet pane of 10	82.50
193	A20	20o violet ('22)	.50 1.50
a.		Booklet pane of 10	8.25

Nos. 190-193 (4)   46.25   3.75

Gustavus Vasa — A21

1921, June   Perf. 10 Vertically

194	A21	20o violet	12.50 22.50
195	A21	110o ultra	55.00 7.50
196	A21	140o gray black	30.00 7.50

Nos. 194-196 (3)   97.50   37.50

400th anniversary of Gustavus Vasa's war of independence from the Danes.

Universal Postal Union Congress

Composite View of Stockholm's Skyline A22

King Gustaf V — A23

1924, July 4   Unwmk.   Perf. 10

197	A22	5o red brown	1.60 3.25
198	A22	10o green	1.60 3.25
199	A22	15o dk violet	1.60 2.50
200	A22	20o rose red	12.50 17.00
201	A22	25o dp orange	15.00 21.00
202	A22	30o deep blue	14.50 21.00
a.		30o greenish blue	87.50 125.00
203	A22	35o black	19.00 26.00
204	A22	40o olive green	29.00 32.50
205	A22	45o deep brown	32.50 32.50
206	A22	50o gray	32.50 32.50
207	A22	60o violet brn	47.50 55.00
208	A22	80o myrtle grn	35.00 35.00
209	A23	1k green	57.50 87.50
210	A23	2k rose red	140.00 250.00
211	A23	5k deep blue	300.00 450.00

Wmk. 181

212	A22	10o green	26.00 55.00

Nos. 197-212 (16)   765.80   1,124.
Set, never hinged   1,200.

Postrider Watching Airplane A24

Carrier Pigeon and Globe — A25

1924, Aug. 16   Engr.   Unwmk.

213	A24	5o red brown	2.75 3.75
214	A24	10o green	2.75 5.75
215	A24	15o dk violet	3.00 3.00
216	A24	20o rose red	21.00 32.50
217	A24	25o deep orange	26.00 32.50
218	A24	30o deep blue	26.00 32.50
a.		30o greenish blue	90.00 52.50

Sweden and Scandinavia
• Free Catalog   • Stamps
• Postal History   • Literature
• Want Lists Filled   • Albums
• New Issue Service

www.JaySmith.com

Jay Smith

P.O. Box 650-X829
Snow Camp, NC 27349
email:info-x829@JaySmith.com

CALL TOLL FREE
1-800-447-8267
(U.S. and CANADA)
or 336-376-9991
FAX 336-376-6750

• The Scandinavia Specialist Since 1973 •

219 A24 35o black ... 32.50 47.50
220 A24 40o olive green ... 32.50 32.50
221 A24 45o deep brown ... 37.50 35.00
222 A24 50o gray ... 50.00 62.50
223 A24 60o violet brown ... 50.00 77.50
224 A24 80o myrtle green ... 37.50 35.00
225 A25 1k green ... 75.00 87.50
226 A25 2k rose red ... 140.00 75.00
227 A25 5k deep blue ... 275.00 210.00

Wmk. 181

228 A24 10o dark green ... 22.50 *60.00*
　　Nos. 213-228 (16) ... 834.00 832.50
　　Set, never hinged ... 1,450.

Universal Postal Union issue.

Royal Palace at
Stockholm
A26

1931, Nov. 26　Unwmk.　Perf. 10
229 A26 5k dark green ... 110.00 1.10
　　Never hinged ... 300.00
a.　Booklet pane of 10 ... 1,900.

Death of
Gustavus
Adolphus — A27

1932, Nov. 1
230 A27 10o dark violet ... 2.50 5.50
a.　Booklet pane of 10 ... 37.50
231 A27 15o dark red ... 4.50 1.90
a.　Booklet pane of 10 ... 57.50

Perf. 10 Vertically
232 A27 10o dark violet ... 1.90 .20
233 A27 15o dark red ... 2.50 .20
234 A27 25o dark blue ... 6.00 .95
235 A27 90o dark green ... 22.50 2.25
　　Nos. 230-235 (6) ... 39.90 11.00
　　Set, never hinged ... 80.00

300th anniv. of the death of King Gustavus Adolphus II who was killed on the battlefield of Lützen, Nov. 6, 1632.

Catching Sunlight in
Bowl — A28

1933, Dec. 6　　　　Perf. 10
236 A28 5o green ... 2.50 1.50
a.　Booklet pane of 10 ... 42.50

There are two types of No. 236.

Perf. 10 Vertically
237 A28 5o green ... 2.50 .20

Perf. 13 Vertically
238 A28 5o green ... 3.50 7.25
　　Nos. 236-238 (3) ... 8.50 8.95
　　Set, never hinged ... 17.50

Swedish Postal Savings Bank, 50th anniv.

The Old Law
Courts — A29

The "Four
Estates" and
Arms of
Engelbrekt
A34

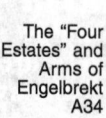

Designs: 10o, Stock exchange. 15o, Parish church (Storkyrkan). 25o, House of the Nobility. 35o, House of Parliament.

1935, Jan. 10　　　　Perf. 10
239 A29 5o green ... 2.25 1.40
a.　Booklet pane of 10 ... 50.00
240 A29 10o dull violet ... 4.25 *5.75*
a.　Booklet pane of 10 ... 50.00

---

241 A29 15o carmine ... 4.75 1.10
a.　Booklet pane of 10 ... 75.00

Perf. 10 Vertically
242 A29 5o green ... 1.25 .20
243 A29 10o dull violet ... 5.75 .20
244 A29 15o carmine ... 2.25 .20
245 A29 25o ultra ... 6.00 .60
246 A29 35o deep claret ... 12.00 2.25
247 A34 60o deep claret ... 17.50 2.50
　　Nos. 239-247 (9) ... 56.00 14.20
　　Set, never hinged ... 110.00

500th anniv. of the Swedish Parliament.

Chancellor Axel
Oxenstierna
A35

Post
Runner — A36

Mounted
Courier — A37

Old Sailing
Packet — A38

Mail Paddle
Steamship
A39

Mail
Coach — A40

1855 Stamp
Model — A41

Mail Train — A42

Postmaster
General A. W.
Roos — A43

Mail Truck and
Trailer — A44

Modern Swedish
Liner — A45

Junkers Plane
with
Pontoons — A46

1936, Feb. 20　Engr.　Perf. 10
248 A35 5o green ... 1.75 .85
a.　Booklet pane of 18 ... 72.50
249 A36 10o dk violet ... 2.10 2.75
a.　Booklet pane of 18 ... 95.00
250 A37 15o dk carmine ... 3.00 .55
a.　Booklet pane of 18 ... 250.00

Perf. 10 Vertically
251 A35 5o green ... 1.75 .20
252 A36 10o dk violet ... 1.75 .20
253 A37 15o dk carmine ... 3.25 .20
254 A38 20o lt blue ... 8.25 5.00
255 A39 25o lt ultra ... 5.25 .50
256 A40 30o yellow brn ... 17.50 3.25
257 A41 35o plum ... 5.50 1.25
258 A42 40o olive grn ... 5.75 2.75
259 A43 45o myrtle grn ... 7.75 1.50
260 A44 50o gray ... 22.50 2.75
261 A45 60o maroon ... 29.00 .70
262 A46 1k deep blue ... 8.25 8.50
　　Nos. 248-262 (15) ... 123.35 30.95
　　Set, never hinged ... 300.00

300th anniv. of the Swedish Postal Service. See Nos. 946-950, B55-B56.

Airplane
over
Bromma
Airport
A47

Emanuel
Swedenborg — A48

1936, May 23　　　Perf. 10 Vert.
263 A47 50o ultra ... 5.50 7.75
　　Never hinged ... 10.50

Opening of Bromma Airport near Stockholm.

Swedish Booklets

Before 1940, booklets were handmade and usually held two panes of 10 stamps (2x5). About every third booklet contained one row of stamps with straight edges at right or left side. Setenant pairs may be obtained with one stamp perforated on 4 sides and one perforated on 3 sides.

Starting in 1940, booklet stamps have one or more straight edges.

1938, Jan. 29　　　Perf. 12½
264 A48 10o violet ... 1.50 .25
a.　Perf. on 3 sides ... 10.00 2.75
　　Never hinged ... 17.00
b.　Booklet pane of 10 ... 22.50

Perf. 12½ Vertically
266 A48 10o violet ... 1.10 .20
267 A48 100o green ... 3.75 1.40
　　Nos. 264-267 (3) ... 6.35 1.85
　　Set, never hinged ... 12.00

250th anniv. of the birth of Swedenborg, scientist, philosopher and religious writer.

Johann Printz
and Indian
Chief — A49

"Kalmar Nyckel"
Sailing from
Gothenburg
A50

Symbolizing the
Settlement of
New
Sweden — A51

Holy Trinity
Church,
Wilmington,
Del. — A52

Queen
Christina — A53

1938, Apr. 8　　　Perf. 12½ Vert
268 A49 5o green ... .65 .20
269 A50 15o brown ... .90 .20
270 A51 20o red ... 1.60 .70
271 A52 30o ultra ... 5.25 .85
272 A53 60o brown lake ... 8.25 .25

Perf. 12½
273 A49 5o green ... 1.60 1.00
a.　Perf. on 3 sides ... 10.00 7.50
　　Never hinged ... 17.00
a.　Booklet pane of 18 ... 62.50
274 A50 15o brown ... 2.75 .70
a.　Perf. on 3 sides ... 17.00 4.75
　　Never hinged ... 26.00
b.　Booklet pane of 18 ... 100.00
　　Nos. 268-274 (7) ... 21.00 3.95
　　Set, never hinged ... 32.50

Tercentenary of the Swedish settlement at Wilmington, Del. See No. B54.

King Gustaf V — A54

1938, June 16　　　Perf. 12½ Vert.
275 A54 5o green ... .65 .20
276 A54 15(o) brown ... .75 .20
277 A54 30(o) ultra ... 17.50 .75

Perf. 12½
278 A54 5o green ... 1.40 .25
a.　Perf. on 3 sides ... 13.00 5.50
　　Never hinged ... 22.50
b.　Booklet pane of 10 ... 32.50
279 A54 15(o) brown ... 1.90 .30
a.　Perf. on 3 sides ... 20.00 1.40
　　Never hinged ... 32.50
b.　Booklet pane of 10 ... 37.50
　　Nos. 275-279 (5) ... 22.20 1.70
　　Set, never hinged ... 29.00

80th birthday of King Gustaf V.

King Gustaf
V — A55

Three
Crowns — A56

1939　　　　　　Perf. 12½ Vertically
280 A55 10o violet ... .65 .20
281 A55 20o carmine ... 2.25 .40
282 A56 60o lake ... .65 .20
283 A56 85o dk green ... .30 .20
284 A56 90o peacock blue ... .30 .20
285 A56 1k orange ... .30 .20
286 A56 1.15k henna brn ... .30 .20
287 A56 1.20k brt rose vio ... 1.60 .20
288 A56 1.45k lt yel grn ... 2.25 .20

Perf. 12½
289 A55 10o violet ... 1.60 3.00
a.　Perf. on 3 sides ... 47.50 65.00
　　Never hinged ... 77.50

b. Bklt. pane of 10, perf. on 4
sides 27.50
Nos. 280-289 (10) 10.20 5.50
Set, never hinged 17.50

See Nos. 394-398, 416-417, 425-426, 431,
439-441, 473, 588-591, 656-664.

Per Henrik Ling — A57

1939, Feb. 25 *Perf. 12½ Vert.*
290 A57 5o green .20 .20
291 A57 25(o) brown 1.10 .30
Perf. 12½
292 A57 5o green .90 .40
a. Perf. on 3 sides 14.00 3.75
Never hinged 29.00
b. Booklet pane of 10 22.50
Nos. 290-292 (3) 2.20 .90
Set, never hinged 3.50

Centenary of the death of P. H. Ling, father
of Swedish gymnastics.

J. J. Berzelius — A58   Carl von Linné — A59

Perf. 12½ Vertically
1939, June 2 Engr.
293 A58 10o violet 3.75 .20
294 A59 15o fawn .20 .20
295 A59 30o ultra 11.50 .45
296 A59 50o gray 13.00 1.00
Perf. 12½
297 A58 10o violet 2.10 .55
a. Perf. on 3 sides 72.50 19.00
Never hinged 125.00
b. Booklet pane of 10 50.00
298 A59 15o fawn 3.00 .20
a. Perf. on 3 sides 11.50 .45
Never hinged 19.00
c. As "a," bklt. pane of 20 450.00
Nos. 293-298 (6) 33.55 2.60
Set, never hinged 47.50

200th anniv. of the founding of the Royal
Academy of Science at Stockholm.

King Gustaf V — A60

Type A55 Re-engraved
1939-46 *Perf. 12½*
299 A60 5o dp green ('46) .20 .20
b. Perf. on 3 sides ('41) .40 .20
Never hinged .50
c. As "b," bklt. pane of 20 12.00
300 A60 10(o) violet ('46) .20 .20
a. Bklt. pane of 10, perf. on 4
sides 35.00
Never hinged 2.25
e. Perf. on 3 sides 2.25 .20
i. As "c," booklet pane of 20 50.00
300D A60 15(o) chestnut ('46) .20 .20
f. Perf. on 3 sides ('45) .40 .20
Never hinged .65
j. As "f," booklet pane of 20 7.75
300G A60 20(o) red ('42) .30 .20
h. Booklet pane of 20 6.50
Nos. 299-300G (4) .90 .80
Set, never hinged 1.40

No. 300 differs slightly from the original due
to deeper engraving. No. 300G was issued
only in booklets; all copies have one straight
edge.
Nos. 299, 300, 300D exist in booklet panes
of 20 made from sheets of stamps. These can
be collected as booklets.

1940-42 *Perf. 12½ Vertically*
301 A60 5o dp green ('41) .25 .20
302 A60 10(o) violet .20 .20
302A A60 15(o) chestnut ('42) .20 .20
303 A60 20(o) red .20 .20
304 A60 25(o) orange 1.00 .20
305 A60 30(o) ultra .40 .20
306 A60 35(o) red vio ('41) .60 .20
307 A60 40(o) olive grn .60 .20

308 A60 45(o) dk brown .60 .20
309 A60 50(o) gray blk ('41) 3.25 .20
Nos. 301-309 (10) 7.30 2.00
Set, never hinged 11.50

Numerals measure 4½mm high. Less shading around head gives a lighter effect. Horizontal lines only as background for "SVERIGE."
See Nos. 391-393, 399.

Carl Michael   Tobias Sergel
Bellman — A61   A62

1940, Feb. 4 Engr. *Perf. 12½ Vert.*
310 A61 5o green .20 .20
311 A61 35(o) rose red .60 .25
Perf. 12½
312 A61 5o green 1.25 .50
a. Perf. on 3 sides 10.00 .55
Never hinged 21.00
b. Booklet pane of 10 22.50
c. As "a," bklt. pane of 20 425.00
Nos. 310-312 (3) 2.05 .95
Set, never hinged 3.00

Bellman (1740-95), lyric poet.

1940, Sept. 5 *Perf. 12½ on 3 Sides*
313 A62 15o lt brown 7.50 .25
a. Booklet pane of 20 275.00
Perf. 12½ Vertically
314 A62 15o lt brown 3.25 .20
315 A62 50o gray black 17.00 1.00
Nos. 313-315 (3) 27.75 1.45
Set, never hinged 47.50

Bicentenary of birth of Johan Tobias von
Sergel (1740-1814), sculptor.

Reformers   View of
Presenting Bible to   Skansen
Gustavus Vasa   A64
A63

1941, May 11 *Perf. 12½ on 3 Sides*
316 A63 15o brown 2.75 .45
a. Booklet pane of 18 90.00
Perf. 12½ Vertically
317 A63 15o brown .20 .20
318 A63 90o ultra 19.00 .85
Nos. 316-318 (3) 21.95 1.50
Set, never hinged 35.00

400th anniv. of the 1st authorized version of
the Bible in Swedish.

1941, June 18 *Perf. 12½ on 3 Sides*
319 A64 10o violet 2.00 .55
a. Booklet pane of 20 85.00
Perf. 12½ Vertically
320 A64 10o violet 3.00 .20
321 A64 60o red lilac 8.00 .45
Nos. 319-321 (3) 13.00 1.20
Set, never hinged 21.00

50th anniv. of Skansen, an open air extension of the Nordic Museum.

Royal Palace at   Artur Hazelius
Stockholm   A66
A65

1941 *Perf. 12½ on 3 Sides*
322 A65 5k blue 1.50 .20
Never hinged 2.50
a. Perf. on 4 sides 29.00 .95
Never hinged 47.50
b. Bklt. pane of 20, perf. 3 sides 45.00
c. Bklt. pane of 10, perf. 4 sides 550.00

For coil stamp see No. 537.

1941, Aug. 30 *Perf. 12½ on 3 Sides*
323 A66 5o lt green 2.50 .55
a. Booklet pane of 20 100.00
Perf. 12½ Vertically
324 A66 5o lt green .20 .20
325 A66 1k lt orange 6.00 3.25
Nos. 323-325 (3) 8.70 4.00
Set, never hinged 16.00

Issued to honor Artur Hazelius, founder of
Skansen, Nordic museum.

St. Bridget of
Sweden — A67

Perf. 12½ on 3 Sides
1941, Oct. 7 Engr.
326 A67 15o deep brown 1.90 .40
a. Booklet pane of 18 60.00
Perf. 12½ Horiz.
327 A67 15o deep brown .20 .20
328 A67 1.20k red vio 21.00 9.00
Nos. 326-328 (3) 23.10 9.60
Set, never hinged 37.50

King Gustavus
III — A68

K. G. Tessin,
Architect — A69

1942, June 29 *Perf. 12½ on 3 Sides*
329 A68 20o red 1.25 .35
a. Booklet pane of 20 45.00
Perf. 12½ Vertically
330 A68 20o red .60 .20
331 A69 40o olive green 14.00 1.10
Nos. 329-331 (3) 15.85 1.65
Set, never hinged 26.00

Sesquicentennial of the Swedish National
Museum, Stockholm.

Torsten Rudenschold and Nils
Mansson — A70

1942, July 1 *Perf. 12½ Horiz.*
332 A70 10o magenta .25 .40
a. Booklet pane of 10 4.50
Perf. 12½ Vertically
333 A70 10o magenta .25 .35
334 A70 90o light blue 2.50 6.00
Nos. 332-334 (3) 3.00 6.75
Set, never hinged 5.00

Swedish Public School System, 100th anniv.

Carl Wilhelm   King Gustaf V
Scheele   A72
A71

1942, Dec. 9 *Perf. 12½ on 3 Sides*
335 A71 5o green 1.50 .80
a. Booklet pane of 20 55.00
Perf. 12½ Vertically
336 A71 5o green .20 .20
337 A71 60o deep magenta 6.00 .35
Nos. 335-337 (3) 7.70 1.35
Set, never hinged 13.00

200th anniv. of the birth of Carl Wilhelm
Scheele, chemist.

Perf. 12½ Horizontally
1943, June 16
338 A72 20o red .60 .35
339 A72 30o ultra .90 2.50
340 A72 60o brt red vio .90 3.25
Perf. 12½ on 3 Sides
341 A72 20o red 3.00 .85
a. Booklet pane of 20 140.00
Nos. 338-341 (4) 5.40 6.95
Set, never hinged 10.00

85th birthday of King Gustaf V, June 16.

Rifle   Oscar
Federation   Montelius
Emblem   A74
A73

1943, July 22 *Perf. 12½ Vert.*
342 A73 10o rose violet .20 .20
343 A73 90o dp ultra 3.00 .35
Perf. 12½ on 3 Sides
344 A73 10o rose violet .40 .40
a. Booklet pane of 20 11.00
Nos. 342-344 (3) 3.60 .95
Set, never hinged 5.50

50th anniversary of the Swedish Voluntary
Rifle Associations.

1943, Sept. 9 Engr. *Perf. 12½ Vert.*
345 A74 5o green .20 .20
346 A74 1.20k brt red vio 6.00 2.50
Perf. 12½ on 3 Sides
347 A74 5o green .55 .40
a. Booklet pane of 20 19.00
Nos. 345-347 (3) 6.75 3.10
Set, never hinged 10.50

Montelius (1843-1921), archaeologist.

Johan Mansson's
Chart of Baltic,
1644 — A75

Perf. 12½ on 3 Sides
1944, Apr. 15 Engr. Unwmk.
348 A75 5o green .60 .80
a. Booklet pane of 20 25.00
Perf. 12½ Vertically
349 A75 5o green .20 .20
350 A75 60o lake 3.00 .55
Nos. 348-350 (3) 3.80 1.55
Set, never hinged 6.00

1st Swedish Marine Chart, tercentenary.

"The Lion of   Clas Fleming
Smaland"   A77
A76

30o, "Kung Karl." 40o, "Gustaf V." 90o,
Stern of "Amphion," Flagship of Gustavus III.

1944, Oct. 13 *Perf. 12½ Vert.*
351 A76 10o purple .35 .35
352 A77 20o red .30 .20
353 A76 30o blue .50 .80
354 A76 40o olive green .60 1.25
355 A76 90o gray black 6.00 2.25
Perf. 12½ on 3 Sides
356 A76 10o purple .60 1.50
a. Booklet pane of 20 24.00

357 A77 20o red   2.25 .35
  a. Booklet pane of 20   90.00
    Nos. 351-357 (7)   10.60 6.70
    Set, never hinged   17.00

Issued to honor the Swedish Fleet and mark the tercentenary of the Swedish naval victory at Femern, 1644.
See Nos. B53, B57-B58.

> Catalogue values for unused stamps in this section, from this point to the end of the section, are for Never Hinged items.

Red
Cross — A81

Torch and
Quill
Pen — A82

1945, Feb. 27   *Perf. 12½ Vert.*
358 A81 20o red   .60 .20
    Perf. 12½ on 3 Sides
359 A81 20o red   2.50 .40
  a. Booklet pane of 20   65.00

Swedish Red Cross Society, 80th anniv.

1945, May 29   *Perf. 12½ Vert.*
360 A82 5o green   .20 .20
361 A82 60o carmine rose   5.50 .35
    Perf. 12½ on 3 Sides
362 A82 5o green   .35 .35
  a. Booklet pane of 20   7.75
    Nos. 360-362 (3)   6.05 .90

Tercentenary of Swedish press.

Rydberg
A83

Oak Tree
A84

1945, Sept. 21   *Perf. 12½ Vert.*
363 A83 20o red   .35 .20
364 A83 90o blue   5.50 .35
    Perf. 12½ on 3 Sides
365 A83 20o red   1.25 .35
  a. Booklet pane of 20   30.00
    Nos. 363-365 (3)   7.10 .90

Viktor Rydberg (1828-95), author.

1945, Oct. 27   *Perf. 12½ Vert.*
366 A84 10o violet   .25 .25
367 A84 40o olive   1.40 1.10
    Perf. 12½ on 3 Sides
368 A84 10o violet   .40 .55
  a. Booklet pane of 20   10.00
    Nos. 366-368 (3)   2.05 1.90

125th anniv. of the Savings Bank movement.

Angel and Lund
Cathedral
A85

View of Lund
Cathedral
A86

    Perf. 12½ Vertically
1946, May 28   Unwmk.
369 A85 15o orange brn   .70 .45
370 A86 20o red   .20 .20
371 A85 90o ultra   7.50 .65
    Perf. 12½ on 3 Sides
372 A85 15o orange brn   .60 .90
  a. Booklet pane of 20   18.00
373 A86 20o red   2.25 .35
  a. Booklet pane of 20   45.00
    Nos. 369-373 (5)   11.25 2.55

Lund Cathedral, 800th anniversary.

Mare and
Colt — A87

Esaias
Tegner — A88

1946, June 8   *Perf. 12½ Vert.*
374 A87 5o green   .20 .20
375 A87 60o carmine rose   5.50 .25
    Perf. 12½ on 3 Sides
376 A87 5o green   .30 .35
  a. Booklet pane of 20   6.50
    Nos. 374-376 (3)   6.00 .80

Centenary of Swedish agricultural shows.

    Perf. 12½ Vertically
1946, Nov. 2   Engr.   Unwmk.
377 A88 10o deep violet   .20 .20
378 A88 40o dk olive grn   1.75 .55
    Perf. 12½ on 3 Sides
379 A88 10o dp violet   .25 .20
  a. Booklet pane of 20   6.00
    Nos. 377-379 (3)   2.20 .95

Esaias Tegner (1782-1846), poet.

Nobel — A89

Geijer — A90

1946, Dec. 10   *Perf. 12½ Vert.*
380 A89 20o red   .80 .20
381 A89 30o ultra   2.25 .45
    Perf. 12½ on 3 Sides
382 A89 20o red   1.90 .45
  a. Booklet pane of 20   40.00
    Nos. 380-382 (3)   4.95 1.10

50th anniversary of the death of Alfred Nobel, inventor and philanthropist.

1947, Apr. 23   *Perf. 12½ Vert.*
383 A90 5o dk yellow grn   .25 .20
384 A90 90o ultra   4.25 .25
    Perf. 12½ on 3 Sides
385 A90 5o dk yellow grn   .30 .35
  a. Booklet pane of 20   7.00
    Nos. 383-385 (3)   4.80 .80

Centenary of the death of Erik Gustaf Geijer, historian, philosopher and poet.

King Gustaf
V — A91

1947, Dec. 8 Engr.   *Perf. 12½ Horiz.*
386 A91 10o deep violet   .20 .20
387 A91 20o red   .20 .20
388 A91 60o red violet   1.40 1.25
    Perf. 12½ on 3 Sides
389 A91 10o deep violet   .20 .30
  a. Booklet pane of 20   3.00
390 A91 20o red   .25 .30
  a. Booklet pane of 20   7.50
    Nos. 386-390 (5)   2.25 2.25

40th anniv. of the reign of King Gustaf V.

King and 3-Crown Types of 1939
1948   Unwmk.   *Perf. 12½ Vertically*
391 A60 5o orange   .25 .20
392 A60 10o green   .30 .20
393 A60 25o violet   1.50 .20
394 A56 55o orange brown   1.40 .20
395 A56 80o olive green   .80 .20
396 A56 1.10k violet   7.00 .20
397 A56 1.40k dk blue green   .80 .20
398 A56 1.75k brt grnsh blue   12.50 6.75
    Perf. 12½ on 3 Sides
399 A60 10o green   .25 .20
  a. Booklet pane of 20   6.00
    Nos. 391-399 (9)   24.80 8.35

Plowman,
Early and
Modern
Buildings
A92

Gustaf VI
Adolf (Letters
in color)
A97

Christopher
Polhem
A98

1948, Apr. 26   *Perf. 12½ Vert.*
400 A92 15o orange brown   .25 .20
401 A92 30o ultra   .50 .45
402 A92 1k orange   1.50 .85
    Perf. 12½ on 3 Sides
403 A92 15o orange brown   .35 .35
  a. Booklet pane of 20   8.50
    Nos. 400-403 (4)   2.60 1.85

Centenary of the Swedish pioneers' settlement in the United States.

1949, Jan. 22   *Perf. 12½ Vert.*
404 A93 20o red   .45 .20
405 A93 30o blue   .80 .65
406 A93 80o olive green   2.75 .45
    Perf. 12½ on 3 Sides
407 A93 20o red   .80 .25
  a. Booklet pane of 20   16.00
    Nos. 404-407 (4)   4.80 1.55

Birth centenary of August Strindberg (1849-1912), author and playwright.

Girl and Boy
Gymnasts — A94

    Perf. 12½ Horiz.
1949, July 27   Engr.
408 A94 5o ultra   .20 .35
409 A94 15o brown   .35 .20
    Perf. 12½ on 3 Sides
410 A94 15o brown   .45 .55
  a. Booklet pane of 20   9.00
    Nos. 408-410 (3)   1.00 1.10

2nd Lingiad or World Gymnastics Festival, Stockholm, July-August 1949.

A95

Symbols of
UPU — A96

1949, Oct. 9   *Perf. 12½ Vert.*
411 A95 10o green   .25 .20
412 A95 20o red   .30 .20
    Perf. 12½ Horizontally
413 A96 30o lt blue   .40 .65
    Perf. 12½ on 3 sides
414 A95 10o green   .20 .20
  a. Booklet pane of 20   3.50
415 A95 20o red   .20 .20
  a. Booklet pane of 20   4.00
    Nos. 411-415 (5)   1.35 1.45

75th anniv. of the formation of the UPU.

Three-Crown Type of 1939
    Perf. 12½ Vertically
1949, Nov. 11   Unwmk.
416 A56 65o lt yellow grn   .75 .20
417 A56 70o peacock blue   4.00 1.25

1951, June 6   *Perf. 12½ Ver*
    Without Imprint
418 A97 10o dull green   .25 .2
419 A97 15o chestnut brown   .35 .2
420 A97 20o carmine rose   .35 .2
421 A97 25o gray   .65 .2
422 A97 30o ultra   .45 .2
    Perf. 12½ on 3 sides
423 A97 10o dull green   .30 .2
  a. Booklet pane of 20   6.00
424 A97 25o gray   .50 .2
  a. Booklet pane of 20   12.00
    Nos. 418-424 (7)   2.85 1.4

See Nos. 435-438, 442-443, 456-461, 50
505-509, 515-517.

Three-Crown Type of 1939
1951, June 1   *Perf. 12½ Ver*
425 A56 85o orange brown   5.75 1.5
426 A56 1.70k red   1.25 .2

1951, Aug. 30   *Perf. 12½ Ver*
427 A98 25o gray   1.25 .2
428 A98 45o brown   .40 .3
    Perf. 12½ on 3 sides
429 A98 25o gray   .35 .3
  a. Booklet pane of 20   9.00
    Nos. 427-429 (3)   2.00 .8

200th anniversary of the death of Christe
pher Polhem, engineer and technician.

Numeral
(Lettering in
color)
A99

Olaus Petri
Preaching
A100

Type A99 and 3-Crown Type of 193
1951, Nov.   Engr.   *Perf. 12½ Ver*
430 A99 5o rose carmine   .25 .2
431 A56 1.50k red violet   1.60 1.2

For other stamps similar to type A99, se
type A115a, Nos. 503-504, 513-514, 570, 580
666-667.

1952, Apr. 19   *Perf. 12½ Horiz*
432 A100 25o gray black   .25 .2
433 A100 1.40k brown   2.50 .6
    Perf. 12½ on 3 sides
434 A100 25o gray black   1.60 2.4
  a. Booklet pane of 20   50.00
    Nos. 432-434 (3)   4.35 3.2

Olaus Petri (1493-1552), Lutheran clergy
man, historian and Bible translator.

**King and 3-Crown Types of 1951
and 1939**
1952   *Perf. 12½ Vertically*
    Without Imprint
435 A97 20o gray   .30 .20
436 A97 25o car rose   1.25 .20
437 A97 30o dk brown   .50 .30
438 A97 40o blue   1.00 .25
439 A56 50o gray   1.75 .20
440 A56 75o orange brown   2.75 .80
441 A56 2k red violet   .90 .20
    Perf. 12½ on 3 sides
442 A97 20o gray   .55 .25
  a. Booklet pane of 20   15.00
443 A97 25o carmine rose   1.25 .25
  a. Booklet pane of 20   27.50
    Nos. 435-443 (9)   10.25 2.6

Ski Jump
A101

Ice Hockey
A102

40o, Woman throwing slingball. 1.40kr,
Wrestlers.

Perf. 12½ Vert. (V), Horiz. (H)
1953, May 27
444	A101	10o green (V)	.50	.20
445	A102	15o brown (H)	.50	.90
446	A102	40o deep blue (H)	1.25	1.50
447	A101	1.40k red violet (V)	4.00	1.25

Perf. 12½ on 3 sides
448	A101	10o green	.75	.90
a.		Booklet pane of 20	17.50	
		Nos. 444-448 (5)	7.00	4.75

50th anniv. of Swedish Athletic Association.

Old Stockholm
A103

Original and
Present Seals of
Stockholm
A104

1953, June 17   **Perf. 12½ Vert.**
449	A103	25o blue	.25	.20
450	A104	1.70k red	2.75	.65

Perf. 12½ on 3 sides
451	A103	25o blue	.60	.30
a.		Booklet pane of 20	17.50	
		Nos. 449-451 (3)	3.60	1.15

700th anniv. of the founding of Stockholm.

"Telephone" — A105

1953, Nov. 2   **Perf. 12½ Horiz.**
452	A105	25o shown	.25	.20
453	A105	40o "Radio"	1.00	1.40
454	A105	60o "Telegraph"	2.50	2.50

Perf. 12½ on 3 sides
455	A105	25o shown	.50	.40
a.		Booklet pane of 20	20.00	
		Nos. 452-455 (4)	4.25	4.50

Centenary of the foundation of the Swedish Telegraph Service.

King Type of 1951
1954   **Perf. 12½ Vertically**
Without Imprint
456	A97	10o dark brown	.20	.20
457	A97	25o ultra	.25	.20
458	A97	30o red	7.50	.20
459	A97	40o olive green	.60	.20

Perf. 12½ on 3 sides
460	A97	10o dark brown	.25	
a.		Booklet pane of 10	9.00	
b.		Booklet pane of 20	7.50	
461	A97	25o ultra	.25	.20
a.		Booklet pane of 4	14.00	
b.		Booklet pane of 8	100.00	
c.		Booklet pane of 20	10.00	
		Nos. 456-461 (6)	9.05	1.20

The booklet pane of 4 contains two copies of No. 461 which are perforated on two adjoining sides.

Skier
A106

Anna Maria
Lenngren
A107

1954, Feb. 13   **Perf. 12½ Vert.**
462	A106	20o shown	.50	.35
463	A106	1k Girl skier	8.50	1.10

Perf. 12½ on 3 sides
464	A106	20o shown	1.10	1.75
a.		Booklet pane of 20	35.00	
		Nos. 462-464 (3)	10.10	3.20

World Ski Championship Matches, 1954.

1954, June 18   **Perf. 12½ Horiz.**
465	A107	20o gray	.25	.20
466	A107	65o dark brown	4.75	3.25

Perf. 12½ on 3 sides
467	A107	20o gray	1.25	1.60
a.		Booklet pane of 20	35.00	
		Nos. 465-467 (3)	6.25	5.05

200th anniversary of the birth of Anna Maria Lenngren, author.

Rock Carvings
A108

Coat of Arms
A109

1954, Nov. 8   **Perf. 12½ Vert.**
468	A108	50o gray	.25	.20
469	A108	60o dp carmine	.35	.20
470	A108	65o dk olive grn	1.25	.20
471	A108	75o dk brown	2.00	.20
472	A108	90o dk blue	.60	.20
		Nos. 468-472 (5)	4.45	1.00

See Nos. 510-512, 655.

Three-Crown Type of 1939
1954, Dec. 10   **Perf. 12½ Vert.**
473	A56	2.10k dp ultra	7.50	.20

1955, May 16   **Perf. 12½ Vert.**
474	A109	25o blue	.20	.20
475	A109	40o green	1.25	.25

Perf. 12½ on 3 sides
476	A109	25o blue	.20	.20
a.		Booklet pane of 4	9.00	
b.		Booklet pane of 20	4.00	
		Nos. 474-476 (3)	1.65	.65

Centenary of Sweden's 1st postage stamps.
The booklet pane of 4 contains two copies of No. 476 which are perforated on two adjoining sides.

Crown and
Flag — A110

A111

Perf. 12½
1955, June 6   **Unwmk.**   **Litho.**
477	A110	10o green, bl & yel	.20	.20
478	A110	15o lake, bl & yel	.30	.30

National Flag Day.

Wmk. 307
1955, July 1   **Typo.**   **Perf. 13**
479	A111	3o yellow green	2.25	5.00
480	A111	4o blue	2.25	5.00
481	A111	6o gray	2.25	5.00
482	A111	8o orange yellow	2.25	5.00
483	A111	24o salmon	2.25	5.00
		Nos. 479-483 (5)	11.25	25.00

Cent. of the 1st Swedish postage stamps. Nos. 479-483 were printed in sheets of nine. They were sold in complete sets at the Stockholmia Philatelic Exhibition, July 1-10, 1955. A set cost 45 ore (face value) plus 2k (entrance fee).

Per Atterbom
A112

Greek Horseman
A113

Perf. 12½ Horizontally
1955, July 21   **Engr.**   **Unwmk.**
484	A112	20o dark blue	.25	.20
485	A112	1.40k sepia	3.25	.65

Perf. 12½ on 3 sides
486	A112	20o dark blue	1.25	1.40
a.		Booklet pane of 20	35.00	
		Nos. 484-486 (3)	4.75	2.25

Cent. of the death of Per Daniel Amadeus Atterbom, poet.

1956, Apr. 16   **Perf. 12½ Vert.**
487	A113	20o carmine	.50	.30
488	A113	25o ultra	.50	.20
489	A113	40o gray green	2.25	2.10

Perf. 12½ on 3 sides
490	A113	20o carmine	.40	.55
a.		Booklet pane of 20	10.00	
491	A113	25o ultra	.40	.20
a.		Booklet pane of 20	10.00	
		Nos. 487-491 (5)	4.05	3.35

Issued to publicize the Olympic Equestrian Competitions, Stockholm, June 10-17, 1956.

Northern Countries Issue

Whooper
Swans — A113a

Perf. 12½ Vertically
1956, Oct. 30   **Engr.**   **Unwmk.**
492	A113a	25o rose red	.20	.20
493	A113a	40o ultra	.75	.55

See footnote after Norway No. 354.

Railroad
Builders — A114

Designs: 25o, First Swedish locomotive and passenger car. 40o, Express train crossing Arsta bridge.

1956, Dec. 1   **Perf. 12½ Vert.**
494	A114	10o olive green	.50	.20
495	A114	25o ultra	.25	.20
496	A114	40o orange	2.50	2.75

Perf. 12½ on 3 sides
497	A114	10o olive green	.45	.35
a.		Booklet pane of 20	11.00	
498	A114	25o ultra	.75	.45
a.		Booklet pane of 20	18.00	
		Nos. 494-498 (5)	4.45	3.95

Centenary of Swedish railroads.

Ship in Distress
and
Lifeboat — A115

Perf. 12½ Vertically
1957, June 1   **Engr.**   **Unwmk.**
499	A115	30o blue	3.75	.20
500	A115	1.40k deep rose	4.50	1.25

Perf. 12½ on 3 sides
501	A115	30o blue	1.60	1.25
a.		Booklet pane of 20	45.00	
		Nos. 499-501 (3)	9.85	2.70

Swedish Life Saving Society, 50th anniv.

King Type of 1951
1957, June 1   **Perf. 12½ Vert.**
Without Imprint
502	A97	25o dark brown	1.10	1.40

Re-engraved Types of 1951 and 1954 with Imprint, and

Numeral (Letters in white) — A115a

1957-64   **Perf. 12½ Vertically**
503	A115a	5o red ('61)	.20	.20
a.		5o dark red	.20	.20
504	A115a	10o blue ('61)	.20	.20
a.		10o dark blue	.30	.25

505	A97	15o dark red	.30	.20
506	A97	20o gray	.25	.20
507	A97	25o brown	.60	.20
508	A97	30o blue	.45	.20
509	A97	40o olive green	1.25	.20
510	A108	55o vermilion	1.25	.20
511	A108	70o orange	.60	.20
512	A108	80o yellow green	.80	.20

Perf. 12½ on 3 sides
513	A115a	5o red ('61)	.20	.20
a.		Bklt. pane of 20 ('64)	2.00	
b.		5o dark red	5.00	1.00
c.		Bklt. pane, 5 #513b, 5 #515	22.50	
514	A115a	10o blue ('61)	.20	.20
a.		10o dark blue	20.00	2.50
b.		Bklt. pane, #514a, 3 #517	37.50	
515	A97	15o dark red	.60	.20
a.		Bklt. pane of 20	12.00	
516	A97	20o gray	1.00	.60
a.		Bklt. pane of 20	30.00	
517	A97	30o blue	.75	.20
a.		Bklt. pane of 20	35.00	
		Nos. 503-517 (15)	8.65	3.40

In the redrawn Numeral type A99, "Sverige, ore" and the "g" tail flourishes are white instead of in color.
Booklet pane including #513 is listed as #581b.
The booklet pane of 4, No. 514b, contains two copies of No. 517 which are imperf. on two adjoining sides. No. 514a was issued only in booklet pane No. 514b.
See Nos. 570, 580, 580a, 581b, 584b, 586b-586c, 666-667, 668a, 669b-669c.

Helicopter Mail
Service — A116

Perf. 12½ Vertically
1958, Feb. 10   **Engr.**   **Unwmk.**
518	A116	30o blue	.20	.20
519	A116	1.40k brown	4.25	1.00

Perf. 12½ on 3 sides
520	A116	30o blue	.80	.55
a.		Booklet pane of 20	20.00	
		Nos. 518-520 (3)	5.25	1.75

10th anniversary of helicopter mail service to the Stockholm archipelago, Feb. 10.

Modern and 17th
Century
Vessels — A117

1958, Feb. 10   **Perf. 12½ Vert.**
521	A117	15o dark red	.30	.25
522	A117	40o gray olive	3.25	3.25

Perf. 12½ on 3 sides
523	A117	15o dark red	.50	.50
a.		Booklet pane of 20	12.00	
		Nos. 521-523 (3)	4.05	4.00

3 centuries of transatlantic mail service.

Soccer
Player — A118

1958, May 8   **Perf. 12½ Vert.**
524	A118	15o vermilion	.50	.20
525	A118	20o yellow green	.50	.20
526	A118	1.20k dark blue	1.25	.90

Perf. 12½ on 3 sides
527	A118	15o vermilion	.45	.45
a.		Booklet pane of 20	9.00	
528	A118	20o yellow green	.45	.65
a.		Booklet pane of 20	12.00	
		Nos. 524-528 (5)	3.15	2.40

Issued to publicize the 6th World Soccer Championships, Stockholm, June 8-29.

Bessemer Converter
A119

Selma Lagerlof
A120

Perf. 12½ Horizontally

1958, June 18	Engr.	Unwmk.	
529	A119 30o gray blue	.25	.20
530	A119 1.70k dull red brown	3.00	.80

Perf. 12½ on 3 sides

531	A119 30o gray blue	.55	.55
a.	Booklet pane of 20	15.00	
	Nos. 529-531 (3)	3.80	1.55

Centenary of the first successful Bessemer blow in Sweden, July 18, 1858.

1958, Nov. 20		Perf. 12½ Horiz.
532	A120 20o dark red	.20 .30
533	A120 30o blue	.20 .20
534	A120 80o olive green	.75 .90

Perf. 12½ on 3 Sides

535	A120 20o dark red	.50	.75
a.	Booklet pane of 20	13.00	
536	A120 30o blue	.50	.60
a.	Booklet pane of 20	16.00	
	Nos. 532-536 (5)	2.15	2.75

Selma Lagerlof, writer, birth cent.

Palace Type of 1941

1958, Sept. 17		Perf. 12½ Vert.
537	A65 5k blue	2.75 .20

Electric Power Line — A121

Hydroelectric Plant and Dam — A122

Perf. 12½ Horiz. (H), Vert. (V)

1959, Jan. 20		Unwmk.
538	A121 30o ultra (H)	.35 .20
539	A122 90o carmine rose (V)	3.25 2.40

Perf. 12½ on 3 sides

540	A121 30o ultra	.50	.50
a.	Booklet pane of 20	14.00	
	Nos. 538-540 (3)	4.10	3.10

50th anniv. of the establishment of the State Power Board.

Verner von Heidenstam
A123

Forest
A124

Perf. 12½ Horizontally

1959, July 6	Engr.	Unwmk.
541	A123 15o rose carmine	.75 .20
542	A123 1k slate	3.00 .90

Perf. 12½ on 3 Sides

543	A123 15o rose carmine	.50	.85
a.	Booklet pane of 20	13.00	
	Nos. 541-543 (3)	4.25	1.95

Verner von Heidenstam, poet, birth cent.

1959, Sept. 4	Perf. 12½ Horiz.

Design: 1.40k, Felling tree.

| 544 | A124 30o green | 1.00 .20 |
| 545 | A124 1.40k brown red | 3.50 .60 |

Perf. 12½ on 3 sides

546	A124 30o green	.90	1.10
a.	Booklet pane of 20	25.00	
	Nos. 544-546 (3)	5.40	1.90

Administration of crown lands and forests, cent.

Svante Arrhenius
A125

Anders Zorn
A126

Perf. 12½ Horizontally

1959, Dec. 10	Engr.	Unwmk.
547	A125 15o dull red brown	.25 .20
548	A125 1.70k dark blue	3.50 .45

Perf. 12½ on 3 sides

549	A125 15o dull red brown	.45	.50
a.	Booklet pane of 20	10.00	
	Nos. 547-549 (3)	4.20	1.15

Arrhenius (1859-1927), chemist and physicist.

1960, Feb. 18	Perf. 12½ Horiz.
550	A126 30o gray	.25 .20
551	A126 80o sepia	3.00 2.00

Perf. 12½ on 3 sides

552	A126 30o gray	1.40	.50
a.	Booklet pane of 20	35.00	
	Nos. 550-552 (3)	4.65	2.70

Zorn (1860-1920), painter and sculptor.

Uprooted Oak Emblem
A127

People of Various Races, WRY Emblem
A128

Perf. 12½ Vert. (V), Horiz. (H)

1960, Apr. 7	Engr.	Unwmk.
553	A127 20o red brown (V)	.20 .20
554	A128 40o purple (H)	.30 .30

Perf. 12½ on 3 sides

555	A127 20o red brown	.40	.40
a.	Booklet pane of 20	10.00	
	Nos. 553-555 (3)	.90	.90

World Refugee Year, 7/1/59-6/30/60.

Target Shooting
A129

Gustaf Froding
A130

Design: 90o, Parade of riflemen.

1960, June 30	Perf. 12½ Vert.
556	A129 15o rose carmine	.25 .20
557	A129 90o grnsh blue	2.50 2.00

Perf. 12½ on 3 sides

558	A129 15o rose carmine	.35	.40
a.	Booklet pane of 20	9.00	
	Nos. 556-558 (3)	3.10	2.60

Centenary of the founding of the Voluntary Shooting Organization.

1960, Aug. 22	Perf. 12½ Horiz.
559	A130 30o red brown	.25 .20
560	A130 1.40k slate green	2.50 .30

Perf. 12½ on 3 sides

561	A130 30o red brown	.35	.35
a.	Booklet pane of 20	10.00	
	Nos. 559-561 (3)	3.10	.85

Gustaf Froding (1860-1911), poet.

Common Design Types pictured following the introduction.

Europa Issue, 1960
Common Design Type

1960, Sept. 19		Perf. 12½ Vert.

Size: 27x21mm

| 562 | CD3 40o blue | .20 .20 |
| 563 | CD3 1k red | .80 .30 |

Hjalmar Branting (1860-1925), Labor Party Leader and Prime Minister — A131

Perf. 12½ Horiz.

1960, Nov. 23		Engr.
564	A131 15o rose carmine	.20 .20
565	A131 1.70k slate blue	3.00 .40

Perf. 12½ on 3 sides

566	A131 15o rose carmine	.45	.60
a.	Booklet pane of 20	6.00	
	Nos. 564-566 (3)	3.65	1.20

SAS Issue

DC-8 Airliner — A131a

Perf. 12½ Vertically

1961, Feb. 24		Unwmk.
567	A131a 40o blue	.30 .20

Perf. 12½ on 3 sides

| 568 | A131a 40o blue | .75 | 1.10 |
| a. | Booklet pane of 10 | 12.50 | |

Scandinavian Airlines System, SAS, 10th anniv.

Numeral Type of 1957, Three-Crown Type of 1939 and

Gustaf VI Adolf (Letters, numerals in white)
A132

Rune Stone, Oland, 11th Century
A133

1961-65		Perf. 12½ Vert.
570	A115a 15o green ('62)	.30 .20
571	A132 15o red	.35 .20
572	A132 20o gray	.35 .20
573	A132 25o brown	.35 .20
574	A132 30o ultra	1.50 .20
575	A132 30o lilac ('62)	.55 .20
576	A132 35o lilac	.55 .20
577	A132 35o ultra ('62)	1.10 .20
578	A132 40o emerald	1.00 .20
579	A132 50o gray grn ('62)	.65 .20

Perf. 12½ on 3 sides

580	A132 15o grn ('65)	.30	.20
a.	Bklt. pane, 2 each #514, 580, 583	2.25	
581	A132 15o red	.25	.20
a.	Bklt. pane of 20	5.00	
b.	Bklt. pane, 5 #513, 5 #581	2.50	
582	A132 20o gray	1.25	.75
a.	Bklt. pane of 20	27.50	
583	A132 25o brown ('62)	.35	.20
a.	Bklt. pane of 20	15.00	
b.	Bklt. pane of 4	2.25	
584	A132 30o ultra	.65	.20
a.	Bklt. pane of 20	15.00	
b.	Bklt. pane, #514 + 3 #584	4.00	
585	A132 30o lilac ('64)	.65	.50
a.	Bklt. pane of 20	14.00	
586	A132 35o ultra ('62)	.55	.20
a.	Bklt. pane of 20	12.50	
b.	Bklt. pane, 3 #514, 2 #586 + blank label	5.00	
c.	As "b," inscribed label	3.50	

Perf. 12½ Vertically

588	A56 1.05k Prus grn ('62)	1.10	.30
589	A56 1.50k brown ('62)	.80	.20
590	A56 2.15k dk sl grn ('62)	4.00	.55
591	A56 2.50k emerald	.85	.20

Perf. 12½ on 3 sides

592	A133 10k dl red brn	20.00	.50
a.	Bklt. pane of 10 ('68)	250.00	
b.	Bklt. pane of 20	850.00	
	Nos. 570-592 (22)	37.45	6.10

Booklet panes of 4, 5 or 6 (Nos. 580a, 583b, 584b, 586b, 586c) contain two stamps which are imperf. on two adjoining sides.

Combination panes (Nos. 580a, 581b, 584b, 586b, 586c) come in different arrangements of the denominations.

The label of No. 586c is inscribed "ett brev / betyder / sa / mycket" ("a letter means so much"). The label inscription "nord 63 / 5-13 oktober / GOTEBORG" was privately applied to No. 586b by the Gothenburg Philatelic Society to raise funds for Nord 63 Philatelic Exhibition in Gothenburg. The pane was sold for the equivalent of $1 US, 5 times face value.

See Nos. 648-654A, 666a, 668-672F.

K.-G. Pilo, Self-portrait
A134

Jonas Alstromer
A135

1961, Apr. 17		Perf. 12½ Horiz.
594	A134 30o brown	.20 .20
595	A134 1.40k Prus blue	3.25 1.00

Perf. 12½ on 3 sides

596	A134 30o brown	1.00	.40
a.	Booklet pane of 20	30.00	
	Nos. 594-596 (3)	4.45	1.60

Karl-Gustaf Pilo (1711-1793), painter. Self-portrait from "The Coronation of Gustavus III."

1961, June 2		Perf. 12½ Vert.
597	A135 15o dull claret	.20 .20
598	A135 90o grnsh blue	1.00 2.00

Perf. 12½ on 3 sides

599	A135 15o dull claret	.25	.40
a.	Booklet pane of 20	7.00	
	Nos. 597-599 (3)	1.45	2.60

200th anniversary of the birth of Jonas Alstromer, pioneer of agriculture and industry.

17th Century Printer and Student in Library — A136

Perf. 12½ Vert.

1961, Sept. 22		Engr.
600	A136 20o dark red	.25 .20
601	A136 1k blue	6.00 1.00

Perf. 12½ on 3 sides

602	A136 20o dark red	.30	.50
a.	Booklet pane of 20	9.00	
	Nos. 600-602 (3)	6.55	1.70

300th anniversary of the regulation requiring copies of all Swedish printed works to be deposited in the Royal Library.

Roentgen, Prudhomme, von Behring, van't Hoff — A137

1961, Dec. 9		Perf. 12½ Vertically
603	A137 20o vermilion	.20 .20
604	A137 40o blue	.20 .20
605	A137 50o green	.50 .20

Perf. 12½ on 3 sides

606	A137 20o vermilion	.25	.20
a.	Booklet pane of 20	6.00	
	Nos. 603-606 (4)	1.15	.80

Winners of the 1901 Nobel Prize; Wilhelm K. Roentgen, Rene Sully Prudhomme, Emil von Behring, Jacob van't Hoff.

See Nos. 617-619, 673-676, 689-692, 710-713, 769-772, 804-807.

A138

A139

Footsteps and postmen's badges.

1962, Jan. 29   Engr.   Perf. 12½ Vert.
607 A138 30o lilac   .20   .20
608 A138 1.70k rose red   3.25   .40

Perf. 12½ on 3 sides
609 A138 30o lilac   .40   .40
a.   Booklet pane of 20   11.00
     Nos. 607-609 (3)   3.85   1.00

Local mail delivery service in Sweden, cent.

1962, Mar. 21   Perf. 12½ Horiz.
Voting Tool (Budkavle), Codex of Law and
Gavel
610 A139 30o dark blue   .25   .20
611 A139 2k red   4.00   .35

Perf. 12½ on 3 sides
612 A139 30o dark blue   .40   .40
a.   Booklet pane of 20   10.50
     Nos. 610-612 (3)   4.65   .95

Centenary of the municipal reform laws.

St. George,
Great Church,
Stockholm
A140

Skokloster Castle
A141

Perf. 12½ Horiz. (H), Vert. (V)
1962, Sept. 24
613 A140 20o rose lake (H)   .25   .20
614 A141 50o dk slate grn (V)   .35   .30

Perf. 12½ on 3 sides
615 A140 20o rose lake   .20   .25
a.   Booklet pane of 20   6.00
616 A141 50o dk slate grn   .80   1.00
a.   Booklet pane of 10   9.00
     Nos. 613-616 (4)   1.60   1.75

Nobel Prize Winners Type of 1961
Designs: 25o, Theodor Mommsen and Sir
Ronald Ross. 50o, Hermann Emil Fischer,
Pieter Zeeman and Hendrik Antoon Lorentz.

1962, Dec. 10   Perf. 12½ Vert.
617 A137 25o dark red   .25   .30
618 A137 50o blue   .30   .40

Perf. 12½ on 3 sides
619 A142 25o dark red   .35   .65
a.   Booklet pane of 20   10.00
     Nos. 617-619 (3)   .90   1.35

Winners of the 1902 Nobel Prize.

Ice Hockey — A143

1963, Feb. 15   Perf. 12½ Horiz.
620 A143 25o green   .20   .20
621 A143 1.70k violet bl   3.00   .60

Perf. 12½ on 3 sides
622 A143 25o green   .25   .40
a.   Booklet pane of 20   7.00
     Nos. 620-622 (3)   3.45   1.20

1963 Ice Hockey World Championships.

Wheat Emblem
and Stylized
Hands — A144

1963, Mar. 21   Perf. 12½ Vertically
623 A144 35o lilac rose   .20   .20
624 A144 50o violet   .25   .25

Perf. 12½ on 3 sides
625 A144 35o lilac rose   .25   .25
a.   Booklet pane of 20   6.00
     Nos. 623-625 (3)   .70   .70

FAO "Freedom from Hunger" campaign.

Engineering and
Industry
Symbols — A145

1963, May 27   Perf. 12½ Vertically
626 A145 50o gray   .50   .25
627 A145 1.05k orange   2.50   2.50

Perf. 12½ on 3 sides
628 A145 50o gray   2.25   2.50
a.   Booklet pane of 10   27.50
     Nos. 626-628 (3)   5.25   5.25

Gregoire
François Du
Reitz — A146

Perf. 12½ Vertically
1963, Sept. 16   Engr.   Unwmk.
629 A146 25o brown   .30   .35
630 A146 35o dark blue   .20   .20
631 A146 2k dark red   3.00   .55

Perf. 12½ on 3 sides
632 A146 25o brown   .50   .75
a.   Booklet pane of 20   16.00
633 A146 35o dark blue   .40   .25
a.   Booklet pane of 20   10.00
     Nos. 629-633 (5)   4.40   2.10

300th anniversary of the Swedish Board of
Health. Dr. Du Rietz (1607-1682) was first
president of the "Collegium Medicorum," forerunner of the Board of Health.

Hammarby,
Home of Carl
von Linné
(Linnaeus)
A147

1963, Oct. 25   Perf. 12½ Vert.
634 A147 20o orange red   .20   .20
635 A147 50o yellow grn   .30   .25

Perf. 12½ on 3 sides
636 A147 20o orange red   .30   .35
a.   Booklet pane of 20   6.00
     Nos. 634-636 (3)   .80   .80

Nobel Prize Winners Type of 1961
Designs: 25o, Svante Arrhenius, Niels Fin-
sen, Bjornstjerne Bjornson. 50o, Antoine
Henri Becquerel, Pierre and Marie Curie.

Perf. 12½ Vertically
1963, Dec. 10   Engr.   Unwmk.
637 A137 25o gray olive   .60   .50
638 A137 50o chocolate   .40   .35

Perf. 12½ on 3 sides
639 A137 25o gray olive   .50   .80
a.   Booklet pane of 20   16.00
     Nos. 637-639 (3)   1.50   1.65

Winners of the 1903 Nobel Prize.

A149

A150

"The Assumption of Elijah."

1964, Feb. 3   Perf. 12½ Horiz.
640 A149 35o lt ultra   .50   .20
641 A149 1.05k dull red   3.50   3.50

Perf. 12½ on 3 sides
642 A149 35o lt ultra   .35   .35
a.   Booklet pane of 20   10.00
     Nos. 640-642 (3)   4.35   4.05

Erik Axel Karlfeldt (1864-1931), poet.

1964, June 12   Perf. 12½ Horiz.
Seal of Archbishop Stephen.
643 A150 40o slate green   .25   .25
644 A150 60o orange brown   .25   .35

Perf. 12½ Vertically
645 A150 40o slate green   .25   .25
a.   Booklet pane of 10   2.25
646 A150 60o orange brown   .30   .35
a.   Booklet pane of 10   3.25
     Nos. 643-646 (4)   1.05   1.20

800th anniv. of the Archbishopric of Uppsala.

Types of Regular Issues, 1939-61, and

Post
Horns — A151

Ship Grave, Skane
(Bronze
Age) — A152

1964-71   Engr.   Perf. 12½ Vert.
647 A151 20o sl bl & org
                 yel ('65)   .20   .20
648 A132 35o gray   .50   .20
649 A132 40o ultra   .60   .20
650 A132 45o orange   .60   .20
651 A132 45o violet bl ('67)   .60   .20
652 A132 50o green ('68)   .40   .20
652A A132 55o dark red
                 ('69)   .40   .20
653 A132 60o rose car   .50   .60
653A A132 65o dull grn ('71)   .80   .20
654 A132 70o lil rose ('67)   .50   .20
654A A132 85o dp cl ('71)   .80   .30
655 A132 95o violet   2.75   3.25
656 A56   1.20k lt blue   3.00   3.00
657 A56   1.80k dk blue ('67)   1.10   .50
658 A56   1.85k blue ('67)   3.00   1.00
659 A56   2k dp car ('69)   .40   .20
660 A56   2.30k choc ('65)   5.25   .20
661 A56   2.55k red   1.90   2.40
662 A56   2.80k red ('67)   .75   .20
663 A56   2.85k orange ('65)   2.75   4.00
664 A56   3k brt ultra   1.00   .20
665 A152 3.50k grnsh gray
                 ('66)   1.00   .20

Perf. 12½ on 3 sides
666 A115a 10o brown   .20   .25
a.   Bklt. pane, 2 each #666,
     667, 583   3.00
667 A115a 15o brown   .30   .55
668 A132 30o rose red ('66)   .70   .75
a.   Bklt. pane, 2 each #513,
     580, 668   1.00
b.   Perf. on 3 sides   1.10   1.10
No. 668 is perf. on 2 adjoining sides.
669 A132 40o ultra   .20   .20
a.   Bklt. pane of 20   16.00
b.   Bklt. pane, 2 ea #514, 669   1.50
c.   Bklt. pane, 2 each #513-
     514, 580, 668b-669   4.00
670 A132 45o org ('67)   .55   .20
a.   Bklt. pane of 20   12.50
671 A132 45o vio bl ('67)   .70   .20
a.   Bklt. pane of 20   14.00
672 A132 50o green ('69)   .50   .60
a.   Bklt. pane of 10   3.75
672B A132 55o dk red ('69)   .50   .20
c.   Bklt. pane of 10   3.75
672D A132 65o dull grn ('71)   .85   .50
e.   Bklt. pane of 10   7.50
672F A132 85o dp cl ('71)   .70   1.00
g.   Bklt. pane of 10   7.00
     Nos. 647-672F (32)   34.00 22.30

Some combination booklet panes of 4, 6 or
10 contain two stamps which are imperf. on
two adjoining sides. Combination panes come

---

in different arrangements of the
denominations.

Fluorescent Paper
Starting in 1967, fluorescent paper
was used in printing both definitive and
commemorative issues. Its use was
gradually eliminated starting in 1976.
Numerous definitives and a few commemoratives were printed on both ordinary and fluorescent paper.

Nobel Prize Winners Type of 1961
30o, José Echegaray y Eizaguirre, Frédéric
Mistral and John William Strutt, Lord Rayleigh.
40o, Sir William Ramsey and Ivan Petrovich
Pavlov.

Perf. 12½ Vertically
1964, Dec. 10   Engr.
673 A137 30o blue   .35   .35
674 A137 40o red   .55   .25

Perf. 12½ on 3 Sides
675 A137 30o blue   .45   .60
a.   Booklet pane of 20   12.00
676 A137 40o red   .65   .30
a.   Booklet pane of 20   18.00
     Nos. 673-676 (4)   2.00   1.50

Winners of the 1904 Nobel Prize.

Visby Town
Wall
A154

Antenna
A155

1965, Apr. 5   Perf. 12½ Horiz.
677 A154 30o dk car rose   .30   .20
678 A154 2k brt ultra   3.50   .25

Perf. 12½ on 3 Sides
679 A154 30o dk car rose   .25   .20
a.   Booklet pane of 20   7.00
     Nos. 677-679 (3)   4.05   .80

1965, May 17   Perf. 12½ Horiz.
680 A155 60o lilac   .35   .25
681 A155 1.40k bluish blk   2.25   1.25

Perf. 12½ on 3 Sides
682 A155 60o lilac   .90   1.25
a.   Booklet pane of 10   12.50
     Nos. 680-682 (3)   3.50   2.75

Centenary of the ITU.

Prince Eugen — A156

1965, July 5   Perf. 12½ Horiz.
683 A156 40o black   .20   .20
684 A156 1k brown   2.10   .30

Perf. 12½ on 3 Sides
685 A156 40o black   .25   .25
a.   Booklet pane of 20   7.00
     Nos. 683-685 (3)   2.55   .75

Prince Eugen (1865-1947), painter and
patron of the arts.

Fredrika Bremer
(1801-65),
Novelist — A157

Perf. 12½ Vertically
1965, Oct. 25   Engr.
686 A157 25o violet   .20   .20
687 A157 3k gray green   4.75   .35

Perf. 12½ on 3 Sides
688 A157 25o violet   .25   .20
a.   Booklet pane of 20   5.00
     Nos. 686-688 (3)   5.20   .75

Nobel Prize Winners Type of 1961

30o, Philipp von Lenard, Adolf von Baeyer. 40o, Robert Koch, Henryk Sienkiewicz.

Perf. 12½ Vertically

1965, Dec. 10   **Unwmk.**
689 A137 30o ultra   .35   .35
690 A137 40o dark red   .40   .25

Perf. 12½ on 3 Sides

691 A137 30o ultra   .45   .55
  a.   Booklet pane of 20   11.00
692 A137 40o dark red   .85   .25
  a.   Booklet pane of 20   22.50
      Nos. 689-692 (4)   2.05 1.40

Winners of the 1905 Nobel Prize.

Nathan Soderblom   Speed Skater
A158   A159

1966, Jan. 15   **Perf. 12½ Horiz.**
693 A158 60o brown   .35   .20
694 A158 80o green   .85   .20

Perf. 12½ on 3 Sides

695 A158 60o brown   .55   .75
  a.   Booklet pane of 10   7.00
      Nos. 693-695 (3)   1.75 1.15

Nathan Soderblom (1866-1931), Protestant theologian, who worked for the union of Christian churches and received 1930 Nobel Peace Prize.

1966, Feb. 18   **Perf. 12½ on 3 Sides**   **Engr.**
696 A159 5o rose red   .20   .20
697 A159 25o slate green   .20   .20
698 A159 40o dark blue   .25   .55
  a.   Bklt. pane, 4 ea #696-697, 2
      #698   2.25
      Nos. 696-698 (3)   .65   .95

World Speed Skating Championships for Men, Gothenburg, Feb. 18-20, and 75th anniversary of World Skating Championships.

National Museum, Staircase, 1866 — A160   Baron Louis Gerhard De Geer — A161

1966, Mar. 26   **Perf. 12½ Vert.**
699 A160 30o violet   .20   .20
  a.   Booklet pane of 10   2.50
700 A160 2.30k olive green   .80 1.00
  a.   Booklet pane of 10   9.00

National Gallery, Blasieholmen, Stockholm, cent. The design is from an 1866 woodcut showing the inauguration of the Museum.

1966, May 12   **Perf. 12½ Vertically**
701 A161 40o dark blue   .25   .20
702 A161 3k brown carmine   3.50   .65

Perf. 12½ on 3 Sides

703 A161 40o dark blue   .25   .35
  a.   Booklet pane of 20   8.00
      Nos. 701-703 (3)   4.00 1.20

Cent. of the reform of the Representative Assembly under the leadership of Minister of Justice (1858-70) Baron Louis Gerhard De Geer (1818-96).

Stage, Drottningholm Court Theater — A162   Almqvist and Wild Rose — A163

Perf. 12½ on 3 Sides

1966, June 15   **Engr.**
Salmon Paper
704 A162 5o vermilion   .20   .20
705 A162 25o olive bister   .20   .20
706 A162 40o dark purple   .40   .55
  a.   Bkt. pane, 4 ea #704-705, 2
      #706   2.00
      Nos. 704-706 (3)   .80   .95

Drottningholm Court Theater, 200th anniv.

Perf. 12½ Horizontally

1966, Sept. 26   **Engr.**
707 A163 25o magenta   .25   .20
708 A163 1k green   2.25   .30

Perf. 12½ on 3 Sides

709 A163 25o magenta   .20   .20
  a.   Booklet pane of 20   5.50
      Nos. 707-709 (3)   2.70   .70

Carl Jonas Love Almqvist (1793-1866), writer and poet.

Nobel Prize Winner Type of 1961

Designs: 30o, Joseph John Thomson and Giosue Carducci. 40o, Henri Moissan, Camillo Golgi and Santiago Ramon y Cajal.

Perf. 12½ Vertically

1966, Dec. 10   **Engr.**
710 A137 30o rose lake   .35   .20
711 A137 40o dark green   .35   .20

Perf. 12½ on 3 Sides

712 A137 30o rose lake   .35   .40
  a.   Booklet pane of 20   9.00
713 A137 40o dark green   .45   .45
  a.   Booklet pane of 20   12.00
      Nos. 710-713 (4)   1.50 1.25

Winners of the 1906 Nobel Prize.

Field Ball Player A164   EFTA Emblem A165

1967, Jan. 12   **Perf. 12½ Horiz.**
714 A164 45o dk violet blue   .20   .20
715 A164 2.70k dp rose lilac   2.75 1.10

Perf. 12½ on 3 Sides

716 A164 45o dk violet blue   .25   .25
  a.   Booklet pane of 20   6.00
      Nos. 714-716 (3)   3.20 1.30

World Field Ball Championships, Jan. 12-21.

1967, Feb. 15   **Perf. 12½ Horiz.**
717 A165 70o orange   .40   .30

Perf. 12½ on 3 Sides

718 A165 70o orange   1.10 1.10
  a.   Booklet pane of 10   15.00

European Free Trade Association. Tariffs were abolished Dec. 31, 1966, among EFTA members: Austria, Denmark, Finland, Great Britain, Norway, Portugal, Sweden, Switzerland.

"The Fjeld," by Sixten Lundbohm A166   Lion Fortress, Gothenburg A167

Uppsala Cathedral A168   Gripsholm Castle A169

1967   **Engr.**   **Perf. 12½ Vert.**
719 A166 35o dl bl & blk brn   .20   .20

Perf. 12½ Horiz.

720 A167 3.70k violet   1.25   .20
721 A168 4.50k dull red   1.40   .20

Perf. 12½ Vert.

722 A169 7k vio bl & rose red   2.00   .40

Perf. 12½ on 3 Sides

723 A166 35o dl bl & blk brn   .20   .20
  a.   Booklet pane of 10   2.50
      Nos. 719-723 (5)   5.05 1.20

Issued: #719, 721, 723, 3/15; #720, 2/15; #722, 4/11.

Table Tennis — A170

1967, Apr. 11   **Perf. 12½ Horiz.**
724 A170 35o bright magenta   .20   .20
725 A170 90o greenish blue   .90   .40

Perf. 12½ on 3 Sides

726 A170 35o bright magenta   .25   .25
  a.   Booklet pane of 20   6.00
      Nos. 724-726 (3)   1.35   .85

World Table Tennis Championships, Stockholm.

Man with Axe and Fettered Beast — A171   Double Mortise Corner — A172

Designs: 15o, Man fighting two bears. 30o, Warrior disguised as wolf pursuing enemy. 35o, Two warriors with swords and lances. The designs are taken from 6th century bronze plates (1¾in. x 2½in.) used to decorate helmets; now in Swedish Museum of National Antiquities.

1967, May 17   **Perf. 12½ on 3 Sides**   **Engr.**
727 A171 10o dk brown & dp bl   .20 .20
728 A171 15o dp blue & dk brn   .20 .20
729 A171 30o brt pink & dk brn   .20 .20
730 A171 35o dk brown & brt pink   .20 .20
  a.   Bkt. pane, 4 #727, 2 ea #728-730   1.75
      Nos. 727-730 (4)   .80 .80

Lithographed and Photogravure

1967, June 16   **Perf. 12½**
731 A172 10o olive & multi   .20 .20
732 A172 35o dk blue multi   .20 .20
  a.   Bkt. pane, 6 #731, 4 #732   1.75

Issued to honor generations of Finnish settlers in Sweden.

Right-hand Driving as Seen Through Windshield — A173

1967, Sept. 2   **Engr.**   **Perf. 12½ Vert.**
733 A173 35o dp bl, ocher & blk   .20   .25
734 A173 45o yel grn, ocher & blk   .20   .20

Perf. 12½ Horiz.

735 A173 35o dp bl, ocher & blk   .20   .25
  a.   Booklet pane of 10   2.50
736 A173 45o yel grn, ocher & blk   .20   .20
  a.   Booklet pane of 10   2.50
      Nos. 733-736 (4)   .80   .90

Issued to publicize the introduction of right-hand driving in Sweden, Sept. 3, 1967.

Postrider A174   The Prodigal Son, 13th cent., Rada Church A174a

Griffin A174b   Rocky Isles in Bloom, by Harald Lindberg A175

Dalsland Canal — A176

Log roller — A176a

Gothenburg Harbor — A176b

Horse-drawn timber sled — A176c

Nils Holgersson Riding Wild Goose — A176d

Windmills, Olana Island — A176e

Steamer Storskar and Royal Palace, Stockholm A176f

Elk — A177

Roe deer — A177a

Dancing cranes — A177b

Mail Coach, by Eigil Schwab A177c

Illustration from Lapponia, by Johannes Schefferus — A177d

Blood-money Coins and Old Map of Sweden A177e

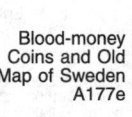
Great Seal, 1439 (St. Erik with Banner and Shield) — A177f

10o, Merchant vessel in Oresund, 1661. 20o, St. Stephen as a boy tending horses, medallion from Dädesio Church. #742, Lion, from Grodinge tapestry, 15th cent. 2.55k, Seal of Magnus Ladulas, 1285 (King Magnus Birgersson on throne with lily scepter and orb). 3k, Seal of Duke Erik Magnusson, 1306 (Duke on horseback with standard of Folkunga dynasty). 6k, Gustavus Vasa's silver daler.

1967-72		**Perf. 12½ Horiz. or Vert.**	
737	A174	5o red & blk	.20 .20
738	A174	10o blue & blk	.20 .20
739	A174a	15o sl grn, *grnsh* ('71)	.20 .20
740	A174	20o sep, *buff* ('70)	.20 .20
741	A174b	25o bis & blk ('71)	.20 .20
742	A174b	25o blk & bis ('71)	.20 .20
a.		Pair, #741-742	.40 .40
743	A175	30o ultra & ver	.20 .20
744	A176	40o blk, dk grn & ultra ('68)	.20 .20
745	A176a	45o bl & brn blk ('70)	.20 .20
746	A176b	55o bl & vio, vert. ('71)	.20 .20
747	A176c	60o black brn ('71)	.20 .20
747A	A176d	65o brt blue ('71)	.20 .20
748	A176e	75o slate grn ('71)	.20 .20
749	A176f	80o blue & blk ('71)	.25 .20
750	A177	90o sep & bl gray	.30 .20
750A	A177a	95o sepia ('72)	.20 .20
751	A177b	1k slate grn ('68)	.40 .20
751A	A177c	1.20k multi ('71)	.30 .20
751B	A177d	1.40k lt bl & red ('72)	.40 .20
752	A177f	2.55k brt blue ('70)	.65 .50
753	A177f	3k dk gray bl ('70)	.60 .20
754	A177e	4k black ('71)	1.00 .46
755	A177f	5k Prus grn ('70)	1.00 .20
755A	A177e	6k indigo ('72)	1.25 .20
		Perf. 12½ on 3 Sides	
756	A174	5o red & blk	.20 .20
a.		Booklet pane of 20	.60
757	A174	10o bl & blk ('69)	.20 .20
a.		Booklet pane of 20	1.90
758	A175	30o ultra & ver	.20 .20
a.		Booklet pane of 10	2.40
759	A176	40o blk, dk grn & ultra ('68)	.20 .20
a.		Booklet pane of 10	2.00

760	A176a	45o bl & brn blk ('70)	.20 .20
a.		Booklet pane of 10	1.60
761	A176b	55o bl & vio, perf. 12½ horiz. ('71)	.20 .20
a.		Booklet pane of 10	2.00
762	A176d	65o brt blue ('71)	.20 .20
a.		Booklet pane of 10	1.90
763	A176e	75o slate grn ('72)	.50 .20
a.		Booklet pane of 10	5.50
764	A177	90o sepia & bl gray	.90 .75
a.		Booklet pane of 10	7.25
		Nos. 737-764 (33)	11.75 7.45

King Gustaf VI Adolf — A178

Perf. 12½ Horiz.

1967, Nov. 11			**Engr.**
765	A178	45o lt ultra	.25 .20
766	A178	70o green	.30 .20
		Perf. 12½ on 3 Sides	
767	A178	45o lt ultra	.25 .25
a.		Booklet pane of 20	4.50
768	A178	70o green	.55 .65
a.		Booklet pane of 10	6.50
		Nos. 765-768 (4)	1.35 1.30

85th birthday of King Gustaf VI Adolf.

Nobel Prize Winners Type of 1961

35o, Eduard Buchner (Chemistry), Albert A. Michelson (Physics). 45o, Charles L. A. Laveran (Medicine), Rudyard Kipling (Literature).

1967, Dec. 9		**Perf. 12½ Vert.**	
769	A137	35o vermilion	.50 .40
770	A137	45o dark blue	.40 .20
		Perf. 12½ on 3 Sides	
771	A142	35o vermilion	.60 .85
a.		Booklet pane of 10	7.50
772	A142	45o dark blue	.40 .40
a.		Booklet pane of 10	6.50
		Nos. 769-772 (4)	1.90 1.85

Winners of the 1907 Nobel Prize.

Franz Berwald, Violin and His Music — A179

1968, Apr. 3		**Perf. 12½ Horiz.**	
773	A179	35o black & red	.30 .20
774	A179	2k blk, vio bl & org yel	3.00 .65
		Perf. 12½ on 3 Sides	
775	A179	35o black & red	.35 .40
a.		Booklet pane of 10	4.00
		Nos. 773-775 (3)	3.65 1.25

Franz Berwald (1796-1868), composer. Design includes opening bar of overture to his opera, "The Queen of Golconda."

National Bank Seal — A180

Perf. 12½ Vertically

1968, May 15			**Engr.**
776	A180	45o dull blue	.25 .20
777	A180	70o black, *pink*	.25 .30
		Perf. 12½ on 3 Sides	
778	A180	45o dull blue	.35 .40
a.		Booklet pane of 10	4.00
779	A180	70o black, *pink*	.50 .65
a.		Booklet pane of 10	6.50
		Nos. 776-779 (4)	1.35 1.55

300th anniv. of the National Bank of Sweden. Nos. 777, 779 are on non-fluorescent paper.

Seal of Lund University — A181

Butterfly Orchid — A182

1968, June 4		**Perf. 12½ on 3 sides**	
780	A181	10o deep blue	.20 .20
781	A181	35o red	.30 .40
a.		Bklt. pane, 6 #780, 4 #781	2.25

300th anniversary of University of Lund.

1968, June 4

Nordic Wild Flowers: No. 783, Wood anemone. No. 784, Dog rose. No. 785, Prune Cherry. No. 786, Lily of the valley.

782	A182	45o slate green	.60 .30
783	A182	45o gray green	.60 .30
784	A182	45o sl grn & rose car	.60 .30
785	A182	45o gray green	.60 .30
786	A182	45o slate green	.60 .30
a.		Bklt. pane, 2 each #782-786	11.00
		Nos. 782-786 (5)	3.00 1.50

World Council of Churches' Emblem A183

Electron Orbits A184

1968, July 4		**Perf. 12½ Horiz.**	
787	A183	70o plum	.30 .30
788	A183	90o Prus green	.80 .35
		Perf. 12½ on 3 Sides	
789	A183	70o plum	.50 .85
a.		Booklet pane of 10	7.50
		Nos. 787-789 (3)	1.60 1.50

4th General Assembly of the World Council of Churches, Uppsala, July 4-19.

		Perf. 12½ Horizontally	
1968, Aug. 9			**Engr.**
790	A184	45o rose carmine	.35 .20
791	A184	2k dark blue	2.75 .30
		Perf. 12½ on 3 Sides	
792	A184	45o rose carmine	.40 .40
a.		Booklet pane of 10	5.00
		Nos. 790-792 (3)	3.50 .90

Establishment of the 1st 3 People's Colleges, cent.

"Orienteer" Finding Way through Forest — A185

"Fingerkrok" by Axel Petersson — A186

		Perf. 12½ Horizontally	
1968, Sept. 5			**Engr.**
793	A185	40o violet & red brn	.25 .30
794	A185	2.80k green & violet	3.00 3.00
		Perf. 12½ on 3 Sides	
795	A185	40o violet & red brn	.40 .55
a.		Booklet pane of 10	5.00
		Nos. 793-795 (3)	3.65 3.85

Issued to publicize the World Championships in Orienteering, Linkoping, Sept. 28-29.

		Perf. 12½ on 3 Sides	
1968, Oct. 28			**Engr.**
796	A186	5o green	.20 .20
797	A186	25o sepia	1.40 1.10
798	A186	45o blk brn & red brn	.20 .25
a.		Bklt. pane, 3 #796, 2 #797, 3 #798	3.00
		Nos. 796-798 (3)	1.80 1.55

Axel Petersson, called "Doderhultarn" (1868-1925), sculptor.

Black-backed Gull — A187

Designs: No. 799, Varying hare. No. 801, Red fox. No. 802, Hooded crows harassing golden eagle. No. 803, Weasel.

		Perf. 12½ on 3 Sides	
1968, Nov. 9			**Engr.**
799	A187	30o blue	.45 .70
800	A187	30o black	.45 .70
801	A187	30o dark brown	.45 .70
802	A187	30o black	.45 .70
803	A187	30o blue	.45 .70
a.		Bklt. pane, 2 each #799-803	4.50
		Nos. 799-803 (5)	2.25 3.50

See Nos. 873-877.

Nobel Prize Winners Type of 1961

35o, Elie Metchnikoff, Paul Ehrlich, Ernest Rutherford. 45o, Gabriel Lippmann, Rudolf Eucken.

1968, Dec. 10		**Perf. 12½ Vertically**	
804	A137	35o maroon	.45 .40
805	A137	45o dark green	.35 .20
		Perf. 12½ on 3 Sides	
806	A137	35o maroon	.50 1.00
a.		Booklet pane of 10	6.00
807	A137	45o dark green	.35 .35
a.		Booklet pane of 10	5.00
		Nos. 804-807 (4)	1.65 1.95

Nordic Cooperation Issue

Five Ancient Ships — A187a

1969, Feb. 28		**Engr. Perf. 12½ Vert.**	
808	A187a	45o dark gray	.35 .25
809	A187a	70o blue	.45 .75
		Perf. 12½ on 3 Sides	
810	A187a	45o dark gray	.40 .75
a.		Booklet pane of 10	11.00
		Nos. 808-810 (3)	1.20 1.75

See footnote after Norway No. 524.

Worker, by Albin Amelin — A188

		Perf. 12½ Horiz.	
1969, Mar. 31			**Engr.**
811	A188	55o dk carmine rose	.20 .20
812	A188	70o dk blue	.60 .60
		Perf. 12½ on 3 Sides	
813	A188	55o dk carmine rose	.25 .20
a.		Booklet pane of 10	4.00
		Nos. 811-813 (3)	1.05 1.00

50th anniv. of the ILO.

Europa Issue, 1969
Common Design Type

1969, Apr. 28		**Photo. Perf. 14 Vert.**	
		Size: 27x22mm	
814	CD12	70o orange & multi	1.25 .40
815	CD12	1k vio blue & multi	1.25 .20
		Perf. 14 on 3 Sides	
816	CD12	70o orange & multi	2.00 2.25
a.		Booklet pane of 10	20.00
		Nos. 814-816 (3)	4.50 2.85

Not fluorescent.

Albert Engstrom
with Owl, Self-
portrait
A189

1969, May 12 Engr. Perf. 12½ Vert.
817 A189 35o black brown   .20 .20
818 A189 55o blue gray   .30 .20
     Perf. 12½ on 3 Sides
819 A189 35o black brown   .35 .45
 a.   Booklet pane of 10   3.50
820 A189 55o blue gray   .30 .30
 a.   Booklet pane of 10   3.00
       Nos. 817-820 (4)   1.15 1.15

Albert Engstrom (1869-1940), cartoonist.

Souvenir Sheet

Paintings by Ivan Agueli — A190

1969, June 6   Litho.   Perf. 13½
821 A190   Sheet of 6   2.10 3.25
 a.   45o Landscape   .30   .40
 b.   45o Still life   .30   .40
 c.   45o Near East town   .30   .40
 d.   55o Young woman   .30   .40
 e.   55o Sunny landscape   .30   .40
 f.   55o Street at night   .30   .40

Ivan Agueli (1869-1917), painter. Size:
#821a-821c,   35x28mm.   #821d-821e,
28x44mm. #821f, 48x44mm. Not fluorescent.

Tjorn Bridges — A191

Designs: 15o, 30o, Various bridges.

Perf. 12½ on 3 Sides
1969, Sept. 3   **Engr.**
       Size: 20x19mm
       Bluish Paper
822 A191 15o deep blue   1.10 .45
823 A191 30o dk grn & blk   1.10 .45
       Size: 41x19mm
824 A191 55o blk & dp bl   1.10 .45
 a.   Bkt. pane, 2 each #822-824 8.00
       Nos. 822-824 (3)   3.30 1.35

Tjorn highway bridges connecting the
Islands of Orust and Tjorn in the Gothenburg
Archipelago with the mainland.

Man's Head,
Woodcarving — A192

Warship Wasa, 1628 — A193

Designs: No. 826, Crowned lion. No. 827,
Great Swedish coat of arms. No. 828, Lion,
front view. No. 829, Man's head (different from
No. 825).

1969, Sept. 3   Perf. 12½ on 3 Sides
825 A192 55o dark red   .30 .20
826 A192 55o brown   .30 .20
827 A193 55o dark blue   .45 .45

---

828 A192 55o brown   .30 .20
829 A192 55o dark red   .30 .20
830 A193 55o dark blue   .45 .45
 a.   Bkt. pane, #827, #830, 2 each
       #825-826, 828-829   4.50
       Nos. 825-830 (6)   2.10 1.70

Salvaging in 1961 of the warship Wasa,
sunk on her maiden voyage, Aug. 10, 1628.

Soderberg   Bo Bergman
A194   A195

Perf. 12½ Horiz.
1969, Oct. 13   **Engr.**
831 A194 45o brown, buff   .25 .25
     Perf. 12½ Vert.
832 A195 55o green, grnsh   .25 .25
     Perf. 12½ on 3 Sides
833 A194 45o brown, buff   .25 .45
 a.   Booklet pane of 10   4.00
834 A195 55o green, grnsh   .25 .20
 a.   Booklet pane of 10   4.00
       Nos. 831-834 (4)   1.00 1.10

Hjalmar Soderberg (1869-1941), writer; Bo
Bergman (1869-1967), poet.

Lever Light, Lightship, Landsort and
Svenska Lighthouses — A196

Perf. 12½ Vert.
1969, Nov. 17   **Photo.**
835 A196 30o gray, blk & pink   .25 .20
836 A196 55o lt bl, blk & brn   .25 .20

300th anniversary of Swedish lighthouses.

Pelle's New
Suit — A197

The Adventures
of Nils — A198

Swedish Fairy Tales: No. 839, Pippi Longstocking (little girl, horse and monkey). No.
840, Vill-Vallareman (boy blowing horn). No.
841, Kattresan (child riding on back of cat).

Perf. 12½ on 3 Sides
1969, Nov. 17   **Engr.**
837 A197 35o org, red & dk brn 1.25 1.40
838 A198 35o dark brown   1.25 1.40
839 A197 35o org, red & dk brn 1.25 1.40
840 A198 35o dark brown   1.25 1.40
841 A197 35o org, red & dk brn 1.25 1.40
 a.   Bkt. pane, 2 each #837-841 20.00
       Nos. 837-841 (5)   6.25 7.00

Issued for use in Christmas cards.

Dr. Emil T.
Kocher and
Wilhelm
Ostwald — A199

55o, Selma Lagerlof, open book. 70o,
Guglielmo Marconi, Carl Ferdinand Braun.

1969, Dec. 10   Perf. 12½ Vert.
842 A199 45o dull green   .70 .35
843 A199 55o blk, pale sal   .60 .20
844 A199 70o black   .60 1.00

Perf. 12½ on 3 Sides
845 A199 45o dull green   .40 .40
 a.   Booklet pane of 10   5.00
846 A199 55o blk, pale sal   .40 .30
 a.   Booklet pane of 10   4.50
       Nos. 842-846 (5)   2.70 2.25

Winners of the 1909 Nobel Prize.

Weather Vane,   Door with Iron
Soderala   Fittings,
Church   Bjorksta
A200   Church,
                    Vastmanland
                    A201

Swedish Art Forgings: 10o, like 5o, facing
right. 30o, Memorial cross, Ekshärad church-
yard, Varmland.

Perf. 12½ on 3 sides
1970, Feb. 9   **Engr.**
847 A200 5o slate grn & brn   .25 .20
848 A200 10o slate grn & brn   .25 .20
849 A200 30o blk & slate grn   .25 .20
     Perf. 12½ Vert.
850 A201 55o brn & slate grn   .25 .20
 a.   Bkt. pane, 2 each #847-850 2.00 2.75
       Nos. 847-850 (4)   1.00 .80

Ljusman
River
Rapids
A202

1970, May 11 Engr. Perf. 12½ Vert.
851 A202 55o black & multi   .25 .20
852 A202 70o black & multi   .50 .40

European Nature Conservation Year, 1970.

Skiing — A203

"Around the Arctic Circle": No. 853, View of
Kiruna. No. 855, Boat on mountain lake in
Stora Sjofellet National Park. No. 856, Reindeer herd and herdsman. No. 857, Rocket
probe under northern lights.

Perf. 12½ Horiz.
1970, June 5   **Engr.**
853 A203 45o sepia   .40 .65
854 A203 45o violet blue   .40 .65
855 A203 45o dull green   .40 .65
856 A203 45o sepia   .40 .65
857 A203 45o violet blue   .40 .65
 a.   Bkt. pane, 2 each #853-857 4.50
       Nos. 853-857 (5)   2.00 3.25

China Palace, Drottningholm Park,
1769 — A204

Perf. 12½ Vert.
1970, Aug. 28   **Photo.**
858 A204 2k yel, grn & pink   1.10 .20

Glimmingehus, Skane
Province, 15th
Century — A205

Perf. 12½ Horiz.
1970, Aug. 28   **Engr**
859 A205 55o gray green   .20 .2
     Perf. 12½ on 3 Sides
860 A205 55o gray green   .30 .2
 a.   Booklet pane of 10   2.50

Timber Industry   Miner
A206   A208

Shipping Industry — A207

Designs: No. 863, Heavy industry (propeller). No. 864, Hydroelectric power (dam and
diesel). No. 865, Mining (freight train and
mine). No. 866, Technical research.

Perf. 12½ on 3 sides
1970, Sept. 28   **Engr**
861 A206 70o indigo & lt brn   2.00 2.2
862 A207 70o ind, lt brn & dp
           plum   2.00 2.2
863 A206 70o ind & dp plum   2.00 2.2
864 A207 70o ind & dp plum   2.00 2.2
865 A207 70o ind & dp plum   2.00 2.2
866 A206 70o dp plum & lt brn 2.00 2.2
 a.   Booklet pane of 6, #861-866 12.00 15.0
867 A208 1k black, buff   .35 .2
 a.   Booklet pane of 10   3.00
     Perf. 12½ Vertically
868 A208 1k black, buff   .30 .3
       Nos. 861-868 (8)   12.65 14.0

Swedish trade and industry.

"Love,
Not
War"
A209

Design: 70o, Four-leaf clovers symbolizing
efforts for equality and brotherhood.

Engraved and Lithographed
1970, Oct. 24   Perf. 12½ Horiz
869 A209 55o rose red, yel & blk .20 .20
 a.   Booklet pane of 4   1.00
870 A209 70o emerald, yel & blk   .30 .3
 a.   Booklet pane of 4   1.00
     Perf. 12½ Vert.
871 A209 55o rose red, yel & blk .20 .20
872 A209 70o emerald, yel & blk   .30 .3
       Nos. 869-872 (4)   1.00 1.0

25th anniversary of the United Nations.

Bird Type of 1968

Birds: No. 873, Blackbird. No. 874, Grea
titmouse. No. 875, Bullfinch. No. 876, Green
finch. No. 877, Blue titmouse.

Perf. 12½ on 3 Sides
1970, Nov. 20   **Photo**
873 A187 30o blue grn & multi   .70 .70
874 A187 30o bister & multi   .70 .70
875 A187 30o blue & multi   .70 .70
876 A187 30o pink & multi   .70 .70
877 A187 30o org & multi   .70 .7
 a.   Bkt. pane, 2 each #873-877 7.25 11.0
       Nos. 873-877 (5)   3.50 3.5

Paul Johann
Ludwig Heyse
A210

Kerstin
Hesselgren
A211

Designs: 55o, Otto Wallach and Johannes
Diderik van der Waals. 70o, Albrecht Kossel.

Perf. 12½ Horiz.

				Engr.
1970, Dec. 10				
678	A210	45o violet	.80	.35
679	A210	55o slate blue	.50	.20
680	A210	70o gray	.80	.90

Perf. 12½ on 3 Sides

681	A210	45o violet	.60	.75
a.	Booklet pane of 10		6.50	
682	A210	55o slate blue	.55	.25
a.	Booklet pane of 10		6.50	
	Nos. 678-682 (5)		3.25	2.45

Winners of the 1910 Nobel Prize.

Perf. 12½ Horiz.

				Engr.
1971, Feb. 19				
683	A211	45o dp claret, gray	.30	.25
684	A211	1k dp brn, buff	.40	.20

Perf. 12½ on 3 Sides

685	A211	45o dp claret, gray	.30	.45
a.	Booklet pane of 10		3.25	
	Nos. 683-685 (3)		1.00	.90

50th anniv. of woman suffrage; Kerstin Hesselgren, was 1st woman member of Swedish
Upper House.

Terns in Flight
A212

Abstract Music,
by Ingvar
Lidholm
A213

1971, Mar. 26		**Perf. 13½ Vert.**		
686	A212	40o dark red	.25	.30
687	A212	55o violet blue	.55	.20

Perf. 12½ on 3 Sides

688	A212	55o violet blue	.40	.20
a.	Booklet pane of 10		3.75	
	Nos. 686-688 (3)		1.20	1.00

Joint northern campaign for the benefit of
refugees.

Perf. 12½ Horiz.

				Engr.
1971, Aug. 27				
689	A213	55o deep lilac	.20	.20
690	A213	85o green	.30	.20

Perf. 12½ on 3 Sides

691	A213	55o deep lilac	.20	.30
a.	Booklet pane of 10		2.00	
	Nos. 689-691 (3)		.70	.70

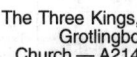

The Three Kings,
Grotlingbo
Church — A214

Flight
into
Egypt,
Stanga
Church
A215

Designs: 10o, Adam and Eve, Gammelgarn
Church. 55o, Saint on horseback and Samson
with the lion, Hogrän Church.

Perf. 12½ on 3 Sides

				Engr.
1971, Sept. 28				
692	A214	5o violet & brn	.50	.30
693	A214	10o violet & sl grn	.50	.30

Perf. 12½ Horiz.

894	A215	55o slate grn & brn	.50	.30
895	A215	65o brown & vio blk	.20	.20
a.	Bklt. pane, #892-894, 2 #895		2.00	2.75
	Nos. 892-895 (4)		1.70	1.10

Art of medieval stonemasons in Gotland.

Toddler and
Automobile
Wheel — A216

1971, Oct. 20		**Perf. 12½ Vert.**		
896	A216	35o black & red	.20	.30
897	A216	65o dp blue & multi	.35	.20

Perf. 12½ on 3 Sides

898	A216	65o dp blue & multi	.40	.25
a.	Booklet pane of 10		5.75	
	Nos. 896-898 (3)		.95	.75

Publicity for road safety.

King Gustavus
Vasa's Sword, c.
1500 — A217

Swedish Crown Regalia: No. 900, Scepter.
No. 901, Crown. No. 902, Orb (Scepter, crown
and orb were made in 1561 for Erik XIV). No.
903, Karl IX's anointing horn, 1606.

Perf. 12½ on 3 Sides

				Engr.
1971, Oct. 20				
899	A217	65o lt blue & multi	.35	.25
900	A217	65o lt ol grn & multi	.35	.25
901	A217	65o dk blue & multi	.35	.25
902	A217	65o lt ol grn & multi	.35	.25
903	A217	65o lt blue & multi	.35	.25
a.	Bklt. pane, 2 each #899-903		4.50	7.00
	Nos. 899-903 (5)		1.75	1.25

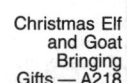

Christmas Elf
and Goat
Bringing
Gifts — A218

Christmas Customs (Old Prints): No. 905,
Christmas market. No. 906, Dancing children
and father playing fiddle. No. 907, Ice-skating
on frozen waterways in Stockholm. No. 908,
Sleigh ride to church.

1971, Nov. 10				
904	A218	35o deep carmine	1.25	1.00
905	A218	35o violet blue	1.25	1.00
906	A218	35o violet brown	1.25	1.00
907	A218	35o violet blue	1.25	1.00
908	A218	35o slate green	1.25	1.00
a.	Bklt. pane, 2 each #904-908		12.50	13.00
	Nos. 904-908 (5)		6.25	5.00

Maurice
Maeterlinck
A219

Women Athletes
A220

Designs: 65o, Wilhelm Wien and Allvar Gull-
strand. 85o, Marie Sklodovska Curie.

1971, Dec. 10		**Perf. 12½ Horiz.**		
909	A219	55o orange	.55	.45
910	A219	65o green	.55	.20
911	A219	85o dk carmine	.55	.50

Perf. 12½ on 3 Sides

912	A219	55o orange	.60	.80
a.	Booklet pane of 10		6.00	
913	A219	65o green	.55	.35
a.	Booklet pane of 10		6.00	
	Nos. 909-913 (5)		2.80	2.30

Winners of the 1911 Nobel Prize.

1972, Feb. 23		**Perf. 12½ on 3 Sides**		
914	A220	55o Fencing	.60	.75
915	A220	55o Diving	.60	.75
916	A220	55o Gymnastics	.60	.75
917	A220	55o Tennis	.60	.75
918	A220	55o Figure skating	.60	.75
a.	Bklt. pane, 2 each #914-918		6.25	9.00
	Nos. 914-918 (5)		3.00	3.75

Lars Johan
Hierta, by
Christian
Eriksson — A221

Frans Michael
Franzen, by
Soderberg and
Hultstrom — A222

Hugo Alfven, by
Carl
Milles — A223

Georg Stiernhielm,
by David K.
Ehrenstrahl — A224

**Photo., Perf 12½ Horiz. (35, 85o);
Engr., Perf. 12½ Vert. (50, 65o)**

1972 Feb. 23				
919	A221	35o multicolored	.20	.25
920	A222	55o violet	.20	.20
921	A223	65o bluish black	.20	.20
922	A224	85o multicolored	.30	.45
	Nos. 919-922 (4)		.90	1.10

Hierta (1801-72), journalist. Franzen (1772-
1847), poet. Alfven (1872-1960), composer.
Stiernhielm (1598-1672), poet, writer,
scientist.

Lifting
Molten
Glass
A225

Swedish Glassmaking: No. 924, Glass
blower. No. 925, Decorating vase. No. 926,
Annealing vase. No. 927, Polishing jug.

Perf. 12½ Horiz.

				Engr.
1972, Mar. 22				
923	A225	65o black	.70	.55
924	A225	65o violet blue	.70	.55
925	A225	65o carmine	.70	.55
926	A225	65o black	.70	.55
927	A225	65o violet blue	.70	.55
a.	Bklt. pane, 2 each #923-927		7.00	
	Nos. 923-927 (5)		3.50	2.75

Horses and Ruin of Borgholm
Castle — A226

Designs: No. 929, Oland Island Bridge. No.
930, Kalmar Castle. No. 931, Salmon fishing.
No. 932, Schooner Falken, Karlskrona.

1972, May 8		**Perf. 12½ Horiz.**		
928	A226	55o chocolate	.45	.45
929	A226	55o dk violet blue	.45	.45
930	A226	55o chocolate	.45	.45
931	A226	55o blue green	.45	.45
932	A226	55o dk violet blue	.45	.45
a.	Bklt. pane, 2 each #928-932		3.00	
	Nos. 928-932 (5)		2.25	2.25

Tourist attractions in Southeast Sweden.

"Only one Earth" Environment
Emblem — A227

"Spring," Bror
Hjorth — A228

1972, June 5	**Engr.**	**Perf. 12½ Vert.**		
933	A227	65o blue & carmine	.30	.20

Perf. 12½ Horiz.

934	A227	65o blue & carmine	.30	.30
a.	Booklet pane of 10		2.50	

Perf. 12½ Vert.

935	A228	85o brown & multi	.30	.30
a.	Booklet pane of 4		1.00	
	Nos. 933-935 (3)		.90	.80

UN Conference on Human Environment,
Stockholm, June 5-16.

Junkers JU52 — A229

Historic Planes: 5o, Junkers F13. 25o,
Friedrichshafen FF49. 75o, Douglas DC-3.

1972, Sept. 8		**Perf. 12½ on 3 Sides**		
Size: 20x19mm				
936	A229	5o lilac	.20	.20
Size: 44x19mm				
937	A229	15o blue	.35	.35
938	A229	25o blue	.35	.35
939	A229	75o gray green	.30	.20
a.	Bklt. pane, #937-938, 2 ea #936, 939		1.40	1.75
	Nos. 936-939 (4)		1.20	1.10

Stockholm from the South, by Johan
Fredrik Martin — A230

Amphion
Figurehead, by
Per
Ljung — A231

Lady with Veil, by
Alexander
Roslin — A232

#941, Anchor Forge, by Pehr Hillestrom.
#943, Quadriga, by Johan Tobias von Sergel.
#945, (Queen) Sofia Magdalena, by Carl Gus-
taf Pilo.

1972, Oct. 7	**Engr.**	**Perf. 12½ Horiz.**		
940	A230	75o greenish black	.30	.35
941	A230	75o dark brown	.30	.35

Perf. 12½ on 3 Sides

942	A231	75o dark carmine	.30	.45
943	A231	75o dark carmine	.30	.45

Perf. 12½ on 2 Sides

944	A232	75o dk brn, blk & dk car	.30	.45
945	A232	75o dk brn, blk & dk car	.30	.45
a.		Booklet pane of 6, #940-945	2.00	2.75

18th century Swedish art.

Types of 1936
Imprint: "1972"

1972, Oct. 7　　Perf. 12½ on 3 Sides

946	A36	10o dark carmine	.35	.40
947	A37	15o yellow green	.35	.40
948	A42	40o deep blue	.35	.40
949	A44	50o deep claret	.35	.40
950	A45	60o deep blue	.35	.40
a.		Bkt. pane, 2 each #946-950	2.50	4.50
		Nos. 946-950 (5)	1.75	2.00

Olle Hjortzberg (1872-1959), stamp designer. Booklet sold for 5k of which 1.50k was for Stockholmia 74, Intl. Phil. Exhib., Sept. 21-29, 1973.

Santa Claus — A233

St. Lucia Singers A234

Perf. 14 on 3 Sides

1972, Nov. 6　　　　　　　Photo.

951	A233	45o Candles	.25	.25
952	A233	45o shown	.25	.25
a.		Bkt. pane, 5 each #951-952	2.50	

Perf. 12½ Vert.

953	A234	75o gray & multi	.35	.20
		Nos. 951-953 (3)	.85	.70

Christmas 1972 (children's drawings).

Horse — A235

Viking Ship — A236

Willows, by Peter A. Persson A237

Trosa, by Reinhold Ljunggren A238

Spring Birches, by Oskar Bergman A239

King Gustaf VI Adolf — A240

Perf. 12½ Horiz. or Vert.

1972-73　　　　　　　　　Engr.

954	A235	5o maroon ('73)	.20	.20
955	A236	10o dk blue ('73)	.20	.20
956	A237	40o sepia ('73)	.20	.20
957	A238	50o blk & brn ('73)	.20	.20

958	A239	55o yel grn ('73)	.20	.20
959	A240	75o indigo	.20	.20
960	A240	1k dp carmine	.30	.20

1973　　　　　　Perf. 12½ on 3 Sides

961	A235	5o maroon	.20	.20
a.		Booklet pane of 20	.50	
962	A236	10o dark blue	.20	.20
a.		Booklet pane of 20	.60	
963	A240	75o indigo	.30	.20
a.		Booklet pane of 10	2.50	
		Nos. 954-963 (10)	2.20	2.00

King Gustaf VI Adolf — A245

Chinese Objects — A246

Designs: No. 983, King opening Parliament. No. 984, Etruscan vase and dish. No. 985, King with flowers.

1972, Nov. 11　　　　　Perf. 12½ Vert.

981	A245	75o violet blue	1.25	2.40
982	A246	75o slate green	1.25	2.40
983	A245	75o maroon	1.25	2.40
984	A246	75o violet blue	1.25	2.40
985	A245	75o slate green	1.25	2.40
a.		Bkt. pane of 5, #981-985	5.75	12.00

90th birthday of King Gustaf VI Adolf. Booklet sold for 4.75k of which 1k was for the King Gustaf VI Adolf Foundation for Swedish Cultural Activities.

Paul Sabatier and Victor Grignard — A247

Dr. Alexis Carrel — A248

75o, Nils Gustaf Dalen. 1k, Gerhart Hauptmann.

1972, Dec. 8　Engr.　Perf. 12½ Vert.

986	A247	60o olive bister	.50	.35

Perf. 12½ Horiz.

987	A248	65o dark blue	.60	.35
988	A248	75o violet	.90	.20
989	A248	1k redsh brown	.90	.25
		Nos. 986-989 (4)	2.90	1.15

Winners of the 1912 Nobel Prize.

Mail Coach, 1923 — A249

Design: 70o, Postal autobus, 1972.

Perf. 12½ on 3 Sides

1973, Jan. 18　　　　　　　　Engr.

990	A249	60o black, yellow	.30	.25
a.		Booklet pane of 10	1.50	

Perf. 12½ Vert.

991	A249	70o blue, orange & grn	.30	.25

Tintomara, by Lars Johan Werle — A250

Orpheus and Eurydice, by Christoph W. Gluck — A251

1973, Jan. 18　　　　Perf. 12½ Horiz.

992	A250	75o green	.20	.20

Booklet Stamp

993	A251	1k red lilac	.30	.25
a.		Booklet pane of 5	1.50	

Bicentenary of the Royal Theater in Stockholm. The 75o shows a stage setting by Bo-Ruben Hedwall for Tintomara, a new opera, performed for the bicentenary celebration. The 1k shows painting by Pehr Hillestrom of Orpheus and Eurydice, which was first opera performed in Royal Theater.

Vaasa Ski Race, Dalecarlia — A252

Designs: No. 995, "Going to Church in Mora" (church boats), by Anders Zorn. No. 996, Church stables, Rättvik. No. 997, Falun copper mine. No. 998, Midsummer Dance, by Bengt Nordenberg.

1973, Mar. 2　　　　Perf. 12½ Horiz.

994	A252	65o slate green	.30	.40
995	A252	65o slate green	.30	.40
996	A252	65o black	.30	.40
997	A252	65o slate green	.30	.40
998	A252	65o claret	.30	.40
a.		Bkt. pane, 2 each #994-998	3.00	
		Nos. 994-998 (5)	1.50	2.00

Tourist attractions in Dalecarlia.

Worker, Confederation Emblem — A253

1973, Apr. 26　　　　　Perf. 12½ Vert.

999	A253	75o dark carmine	.20	.20
1000	A253	1.40k slate blue	.40	.20

75th anniversary of the Swedish Confederation of Trade Unions (LO).

Observer Reading Temperature A254

Design: No. 1002, Clouds, photographed by US weather satellite.

1973, May 24　Engr.　Perf. 12½ Vert.

1001	A254	65o slate green	.75	.35
1002	A254	65o black & ultra	.75	.35
a.		Pair, #1001-1002	1.50	2.00

Cent. of the Swedish Weather Organization and of Intl. Meteorological Cooperation.

Nordic Cooperation Issue 1973

Nordic House, Reykjavik A254a

1973, June 26　　　　　Perf. 12½ Vert.

1003	A254a	75o multicolored	.35	.20
1004	A254a	1k multicolored	.45	.20

A century of postal cooperation among Denmark, Finland, Iceland, Norway and Sweden and in connection with the Nordic Postal Conference, Reykjavik, Iceland.

Carl Peter Thunberg (1743-1828) — A255

Swedish Explorers: No. 1006, Anders Sparrman (1748-1820) and Polynesian double canoe. No. 1007, Nils Adolf Erik Nordenskjold (1832-1901) and ship in pack ice. No. 1008, Salomon August Andrée (1854-1897) and balloon on snow field. No. 1009, Sven Hedin (1865-1952) and camel riders.

1973, Sept. 22　　　　Perf. 12½ Horiz.

1005	A255	1k sl grn, bl & brn	.75	.90
1006	A255	1k bl, sl grn & brn	.75	.90
1007	A255	1k bl, sl grn & brn	.75	.90
1008	A255	1k black & multi	.75	.90
1009	A255	1k black & multi	.75	.90
a.		Bkt. pane of 5, #1005-1009	4.00	5.50

Plower with Ox Team A256

Designs: No. 1011, Woman working flax brake. No. 1012, Farm couple planting potatoes. No. 1013, Women baking bread. No. 1014, Man with horse-drawn sower.

1973, Oct. 24　　　　Perf. 12½ Horiz.

1010	A256	75o grnsh black	1.00	.25
1011	A256	75o red brown	1.00	.25
1012	A256	75o grnsh black	1.00	.25
1013	A256	75o plum	1.00	.25
1014	A256	75o red brown	1.00	.25
a.		Bkt. pane, 2 ea #1010-1014	10.00	
		Nos. 1010-1014 (5)	5.00	1.25

Centenary of Nordic Museum, Stockholm.

Gray Seal — A257

King Gustaf VI Adolf — A258

Protected Animals: 20o, Peregrine falcon. 25o, Lynx. 55o, Otter. 65o, Wolf. 75o, White-tailed sea eagle.

1973, Oct. 24　Perf. 12½ on 3 Sides

1015	A257	10o slate green	.20	.20
1016	A257	20o violet	.20	.20
1017	A257	25o Prus green	.20	.20
1018	A257	55o Prus green	.20	.20
1019	A257	65o violet	.20	.20
1020	A257	75o slate green	.35	.35
a.		Bkt. pane, 2 each #1015-1020	2.50	2.00
		Nos. 1015-1020 (6)	1.35	1.35

1973, Oct. 24　　　　　Perf. 12½ Vert.

1021	A258	75o dk violet blue	.20	.20
1022	A258	1k purple	.30	.20

King Gustaf VI Adolf (1882-1973).

The Three Kings A259

Charles XIV John A260

The Goosegirl, by Josephson A261

#1024, Merry country dance. #1026, Basket with stylized Dalecarlian gourd plant.

Perf. 14 Horiz.

1973, Nov. 12			Photo.
1023	A259	45o multicolored	.35	.30
1024	A259	45o multicolored	.35	.30
a.		Bklt. pane, 5 each #1023-1024	2.75	

Coil Stamps

1025	A260	45o multicolored	1.40	.20
1026	A260	75o multicolored	1.40	.20
a.		Pair, #1025-1026	2.75	3.25
		Nos. 1023-1026 (4)	3.50	1.00

Christmas 1973. Designs are from Swedish peasant paintings.

Perf. 12½ Horiz.

1973, Nov. 12			Engr.
1027	A261	10k multicolored	2.50	.25

Ernst Josephson (1851-1906), painter.

Alfred Werner and Heike Kamerlingh-Onnes
A262

Charles Robert Richet
A263

Design: 1.40k, Rabindranath Tagore.

1973, Dec. 10	Engr.	Perf. 12½ Vert.
1028	A262	75o dark violet	.45	.20

Perf. 12½ Horiz.

1029	A263	1k dark brown	.55	.30
1030	A263	1.40k green	.65	.20
		Nos. 1028-1030 (3)	1.65	.70

Winners of 1913 Nobel Prize.

Ski Jump
A264

Skiing: No. 1032, Cross-country race. No. 1033, Relay race. No. 1034, Slalom. No. 1035, Women's cross-country race.

Perf. 12½ Horiz.

1974, Jan. 23			Engr.
1031	A264	65o slate green	.45	.55
1032	A264	65o violet blue	.45	.55
1033	A264	65o slate green	.45	.55
1034	A264	65o dk carmine	.45	.55
1035	A264	65o violet blue	.45	.55
a.		Bklt. pane, 2 each #1031-1035	4.50	
		Nos. 1031-1035 (5)	2.25	2.75

Drawing of First Industrial Digester
A265

Hans Järta and Quotation from 1809 — A266

Samuel Owen and 19th Century Factory
A267

1974, Mar. 5	Engr.	Perf. 12½ Vert.
1036	A265	45o sepia	.20	.20
1037	A266	60o green	.20	.30
1038	A267	75o dull red	.20	.20
		Nos. 1036-1038 (3)	.60	.70

Centenary of sulphite pulp process (45o); Hans Järta (1774-1847), statesman responsible for the Instrument of Government Act of 1809 (60o); Samuel Owen (1774-1854), English-born industrialist who introduced new production methods (75o).

Stora Sjofallet (Great Falls) — A268

Street in Ystad — A269

1974, Apr. 2			Perf. 12½ Horiz.
1039	A268	35o blue grn & blk	.20	.20

Perf. 12½ on 3 Sides

1040	A269	75o dull claret	.20	.20
a.		Booklet pane of 10	2.00	

UPU Type of 1924 A270

1974	Engr.	Perf. 12½ on 3 Sides
1041	A270	20o green	.20	.30
1042	A270	25o ultra	.20	.30
1043	A270	30o dark brown	.20	.30
1044	A270	35o dark red	.20	.30
a.		Bklt. pane, 2 each #1041-1044	1.00	
		Nos. 1041-1044 (4)	.80	1.20

Miniature Sheets

Perf. 12½

1045		Sheet of 4	1.00	1.75
a.		A270 20o ocher, single stamp	.30	.45
1046		Sheet of 4	1.00	1.75
a.		A270 25o dk vio, single stamp	.30	.45
1047		Sheet of 4	1.00	1.75
a.		A270 30o dk red, single stamp	.30	.45
1048		Sheet of 4	1.00	1.75
a.		A270 35o yel grn, single stamp	.30	.45

Stockholmia 74 philatelic exhibition, Stockholm, Sept. 21-29. Booklet sold for 3k with surtax going toward financing the exhibition.
Nos. 1045-1048 sold during exhibition in folder with 5k entrance ticket.
Issued: #1041-1044, 4/2; #1045-1048, 9/21.

"Man in Storm," by Bror Marklund — A271

Europa: 1k, Sculpture by Picasso, Lake Vanern, Kristinehamm.

Perf. 12½ Horiz.

1974, Apr. 29			Engr.
1049	A271	75o violet brown	1.10	.20
1050	A271	1k slate green	1.25	.20

King Carl XVI Gustaf — A272

1974-78	Engr.	Perf. 12½ Vert.
1068	A272	75o slate grn	.20	.20
1069	A272	90o brt blue ('75)	.20	.20
1070	A272	1k maroon	.35	.20

1071	A272	1.10k rose red ('75)	.35	.20
1072	A272	1.30k green ('76)	.40	.20
1073	A272	1.40k violet bl ('77)	.30	.20
1074	A272	1.50k red lilac ('80)	.30	.20
1075	A272	1.70k orange ('78)	.40	.20
1076	A272	2k dk brown ('80)	.40	.20

Perf. 12½ on 3 Sides

1077	A272	75o slate green	.20	.20
a.		Booklet pane of 10	2.00	
1078	A272	90o brt blue ('75)	.20	.20
a.		Booklet pane of 10	2.00	
1079	A272	1k maroon ('76)	.35	.20
a.		Booklet pane of 10	2.50	
1080	A272	1.10k rose red ('77)	.35	.20
a.		Booklet pane of 10	2.50	
1081	A272	1.30k green ('78)	.30	.20
a.		Booklet pane of 10	3.00	
1082	A272	1.50k red lilac ('80)	.30	.20
a.		Booklet pane of 10	3.00	
		Nos. 1068-1082 (15)	4.60	3.00

A273

Central Post Office, Stockholm
A274

Mailman, Northernmost Rural Delivery Route — A275

Perf. 12½ on 3 Sides

1974, June 7			Engr.
1084	A273	75o violet brown	.70	.30
1085	A274	75o violet brown	.70	.30
a.		Bklt. pane, 5 ea #1084-1085	5.75	

Perf. 12½ Vert.

1086	A275	1k slate green	.35	.20
		Nos. 1084-1086 (3)	1.75	.80

Centenary of Universal Postal Union.

Regatta
A276

Scenes from Sweden's West Coast: No. 1088, Vinga Lighthouse. No. 1089, Varberg Fortress. No. 1090, Seine fishing. No. 1091, Fishing village Mollosund.

1974, June 7			Perf. 12½ Horiz.
1087	A276	65o crimson	.40	.40
1088	A276	65o blue	.40	.40
1089	A276	65o dk olive green	.40	.40
1090	A276	65o slate green	.40	.40
1091	A276	65o brown	.40	.40
a.		Bklt. pane, 2 each #1087-1091	3.00	
		Nos. 1087-1091 (5)	2.00	2.00

Mr. Simmons, by Axel Fridell — A277

Thread and Spool — A278

Perf. 12½ on 3 Sides

1974, Aug. 28			Engr.
1092	A277	45o black	.25	.20
a.		Booklet pane of 10	1.75	

Perf. 12½ Horiz.

1093	A277	1.40k deep claret	.35	.20

Swedish Publicists' Club, centenary.

1974, Aug. 28			Perf. 12½ Horiz.

#1095, Sewing machines (abstract).

1094	A278	85o deep violet	.20	.30
1095	A278	85o black & org	.25	.30
a.		Pair, #1094-1095	.50	.60

Swedish textile and clothing industries.

Tugs in Stockholm Harbor — A279

#1096, Tanker. #1097, Liner "Snow Storm." #1098, Ice breakers Tor and Atle. #1099, Skane Train Ferry, Trelleborg-Sassnitz.

1974, Nov. 16			Perf. 12½ Horiz.
1096	A279	1k dark blue	.50	.65
1097	A279	1k dark blue	.50	.65
1098	A279	1k dark blue	.50	.65
1099	A279	1k dark blue	.50	.65
1100	A279	1k dark blue	.50	.65
a.		Bklt. pane of 5, #1096-1100	2.50	4.00

Swedish shipping industry.

Miniature Sheet

Quilt from Skepptuna Church — A280

Deer, Quilt from Hog Church — A281

Designs are from woolen quilts, 15th-16th centuries. Motifs shown on No. 1101 are stylized deer, griffins, lions, unicorn and horses.

1974, Nov. 16	Photo.	Perf. 14
1101	A280	Sheet of 10	8.50	10.00
a.-j.		45o, single stamp	.85	.70

Perf. 13 Horiz.

1102	A281	75o bl blk, red & yel	.20	.20

Max von Laue — A282

Designs: 70o, Theodore William Richards. 1k, Robert Bárány.

1974, Dec. 10	Engr.	Perf. 12½ Vert.
1103	A282	65o rose red	.35	.20
1104	A282	70o slate	.35	.30
1105	A282	1k indigo	.75	.20
		Nos. 1103-1105 (3)	1.45	.70

Winners of 1914 Nobel Prize.

A283

No. 1106, Sven Jerring's children's program. No. 1107, Televising parliamentary debate.

1974, Dec. 10		Perf. 12½ Vert.
1106		75o dk blue & brn	.65	.20
1107		75o brown & dk bl	.65	.20
a.	A283	Pair, #1106-1107	1.25	2.00

Swedish Broadcasting Corp., 50th anniv.

Account Holder's Envelope A285

Photogravure and Engraved
1975, Jan. 21   **Perf. 14 Vert.**
1108 A285 1.40k ocher & blk   .35 .35
Swedish Postal Giro Office, 50th anniv.

Male and Female Architects, New Parliament A286

Jenny Lind (1820-87), by J. O. Sodermark A287

1975, Mar. 25 Engr. Perf. 12½ Vert.
1109 A286 75o slate green   .20 .20
Perf. 12½ Horiz.
1110 A287 1k claret   .50 .20
Perf. 12½ on 3 Sides
1111 A286 75o slate green   .25 .20
  a.   Booklet pane of 10   2.00
    Nos. 1109-1111 (3)   .95 .60
International Women's Year 1975.

Horseman, Helmet Decoration A288

"Gold Men" A289

Designs: 15o, Scabbard and hilt. 20o, Shield buckle. 55o, Iron helmet.

1975, Mar. 25 Perf. 12½ on 3 sides
1112 A288 10o dull red   .20 .20
1113 A288 15o slate green   .20 .20
1114 A288 20o violet   .20 .20
1115 A288 55o violet brown   .20 .20
  a.   Bklt. pane, 2 each #1112-1115   .60 .75
Perf. 12½ Horiz.
1116 A289 25o deep yellow   .20 .20
    Nos. 1112-1116 (5)   1.00 1.00

Treasures from tombs of the Vendel period (550-800 A.D.), and "gold men" (25o) from Eketorp II excavations (400-700 A.D.).

Europa Issue 1975

New Year's Eve at Skansen, by Eric Hallstrom — A290

Inferno, by August Strindberg — A291

Perf. 12½ Vert.
1975, Apr. 28   **Photo.**
1117 A290 90o multi   .75 .20
Perf. 12½ Horiz.
1118 A291 1.10k multi   .75 .20

Capercaillie A292

Rok Stone, 9th Century A293

1975, May 20 Engr. Perf. 12½ Vert.
1119 A292 170o indigo   .45 .20
Perf. 12½ Horiz.
1120 A293 2k deep claret   .45 .20

Metric Tape Measure — A294

Folke Filbyter Statue, by Milles — A296

Hernqvist by Per Krafft the Younger — A295

1975, May 20   **Perf. 12½ Vert.**
1121 A294 55o deep blue   .25 .30
1122 A295 70o yel brn & dk brn   .20 .20
Perf. 12½ Horiz.
1123 A296 75o violet   .25 .20
    Nos. 1121-1123 (3)   .70 .70

Cent. of Intl. Meter Convention, Paris, 1875; bicent. of Swedish veterinary medicine, founded by Peter Hernqvist (1726-1808); Carl Milles (1875-1955), sculptor.

Officers' Mess, Rommehed, 1798 — A297

No. 1124, Skelleftea Church Village, 17th cent. No. 1125, Foundry and furnace, Engelsberg, 18th cent. No. 1126, Gunpowder Tower, Visby. No. 1127, Falun Mine pithead gear, 1852.

1975, June 13   **Perf. 12½ Horiz.**
1124 A297 75o black   .20 .50
1125 A297 75o dk carmine   .20 .50
1126 A297 75o black   .20 .50
1127 A297 75o dk carmine   .20 .50
1128 A297 75o violet blue   .20 .50
  a.   Bklt. pane, 2 each #1124-1128   2.00
    Nos. 1124-1128 (5)   1.00 2.50
European Architectural Heritage Year 1975.

Rescue at Sea: Helicopter over Ice-covered Tanker — A298

Designs: No. 1129, Fire fighters: firemen fighting fire. No. 1130, Customs narcotics service: trained dogs checking cargo. No. 1131, Police: Officer talking to boy on bridge. No. 1132, Hospital Service: patient arriving by ambulance.

1975, Aug. 27   **Perf. 12½ Horiz.**
1129 A298 90o dk car rose   .30 .30
1130 A298 90o dk bl   .30 .30
1131 A298 90o dk car rose   .30 .30
1132 A298 90o dk bl   .30 .30
1133 A298 90o green   .30 .30
  a.   Bklt. pane, 2 each #1129-1133   3.00
    Nos. 1129-1133 (5)   1.50 1.50
Public service organizations watching, guarding, helping.

"Fryckstad" A299

"Gotland" A300

Design: 90o, "Prins August."

1975, Aug. 27 Perf. 12½ on 3 Sides
Size: 20x19mm
1134 A299 5o green   .20 .20
1135 A300 5o dark blue   .20 .20
Size: 45x19mm
1136 A299 90o slate green   .45 .20
  a.   Bklt. pane, 2 each #1134-1136   1.50 2.00
    Nos. 1134-1136 (3)   .85 .60

Scouts — A301

1975, Oct. 11 Photo. Perf. 14 Vert.
1137 90o Around campfire   .50 .20
1138 90o In canoes   .50 .20
  a.   A301 Pair, #1137-1138   1.00 1.50

Nordjamb 75, 14th World Boy Scout Jamboree, Lillehammer, Norway, July 29-Aug. 7.

Hedgehog A303

Old Man Playing Key Fiddle — A304

Romeo and Juliet Ballet — A305

1975, Oct. 11 Engr. Perf. 12½ Vert.
1139 A303 55o black   .20 .20
1140 A304 75o dk red   .30 .20
Perf. 12½ Horiz.
1141 A305 7k blue green   1.75 .20
Perf. 12½ on 3 Sides
1142 A303 55o black   .20 .20
  a.   Booklet pane of 10   1.50
    Nos. 1139-1142 (4)   2.45 .80

Virgin Mary, 12th Cent. Statue — A306

Chariot of the Sun, from 12th Cent. Altar — A307

Mourning Mary, c. 1280 — A308

Jesse at Foot of Genealogical Tree, c. 1510 — A309

Christmas: #1145, Nativity, from 12th cent. gilt-copper altar. #1148, like #1147.

Perf. 14 Horiz.
1975, Nov. 11   **Photo.**
1143 A306 55o multi   .20 .20
Perf. 12½ on 3 Sides
1144 A307 55o gold & multi   .20 .20
1145 A307 55o gold & multi   .20 .20
  a.   Bklt. pane, 5 each #1144-1145   2.00
Perf. 12½ Horiz.
Engr.
1146 A308 90o brown   .35 .20
Perf. 12½ on 3 Sides
1147 A309 90o red   .60 .20
1148 A309 90o blue   .60 .20
  a.   Bklt. pane, 5 ea #1147-1148   6.00
    Nos. 1143-1148 (6)   2.15 1.20

No. 1145a was issued with top row of 5 either No. 1144 or No. 1145.

William H. and William L. Bragg — A310

Designs: 90o, Richard Willstätter. 1.10k, Romain Rolland.

1975, Dec. 10 Engr. Perf. 12½ Vert.
1149 A310 75o claret   .20 .30
1150 A310 90o violet blue   .20 .20
1151 A310 1.10k slate green   .40 .30
    Nos. 1149-1151 (3)   .80 .80
Winners of 1915 Nobel Prize.

Cave of the Winds, by Eric Grate — A311

1976, Jan. 27   **Perf. 12½ Vert.**
1152 A311 1.90k slate green   .50 .20
The sculpture by Eric Grate (b. 1896) stands in front of the Town Hall of Vasteras.

Razor-billed Auks and Black Guillemot A312

Bobbin Lace Maker from Vadstena A313

1976, Mar. 10 Engr. Perf. 12½ Vert.
1153 A312 85o dark blue   .20 .20
Perf. 12½ Horiz.
1154 A313 1k claret brn   .25 .20
Perf. 12½ on 3 Sides
1155 A312 85o dk bl   .20 .30
  a.   Booklet pane of 10   2.00
1156 A313 1k claret brn   .30 .20
  a.   Booklet pane of 10   3.00
    Nos. 1153-1156 (4)   .95 .90

Old and New Telephones, Relays — A314

1976, Mar. 10   **Perf. 12½ Vert.**
1157 A314 1.30k brt violet   .35 .20
1158 A314 3.40k red   .90 .40
Centenary of first telephone call by Alexander Graham Bell, March 10, 1876.

Europa Issue 1976

Lapp Elk Horn Spoon — A315   Tile Stove — A316

Perf. 14½ Horiz.
1976, May 3   **Photo.**
1159 A315 1k multi   .65 .20
1160 A316 1.30k multi   .65 .30

Wheat and Cornflower Seeds — A317

Viable and Nonviable Seedlings A318

1976, May 3 Engr.   **Perf. 12½ Vert.**
1161 A317 65o brown   .20 .20
1162 A318 65o choc & grn   .20 .20
a. Pair, #1161-1162   .40 .60
Swedish seed testing centenary.

King Carl XVI Gustaf and Queen Silvia — A319

Perf. 12½ Vert.
1976, June 19   **Engr.**
1163 A319 1k rose car   .30 .20
1164 A319 1.30k slate grn   .40 .20
Perf. 12½ on 3 Sides
1165 A319 1k rose car   .30 .20
a. Booklet pane of 10   3.00
Nos. 1163-1165 (3)   1.00 .60
Wedding of King Carl XVI Gustaf and Silvia Sommerlath.

View from Ringkallen, by Helmer Osslund — A320

Views in Angermanland Province: No. 1167, Tugboat pulling timber. No. 1168, Haydrying racks. No. 1169, Granvagsnipan slope, Angerman River. No. 1170, Seine fishing.

1976, June 19   **Perf. 12½ Horiz.**
1166 A320 85o slate grn   .30 .40
1167 A320 85o vio bl   .30 .40
1168 A320 85o dp brn   .30 .40
1169 A320 85o vio bl   .30 .40
1170 A320 85o brn red   .30 .40
a. Bklt. pane, 2 each #1166-1170   3.00
Nos. 1166-1170 (5)   1.50 2.00

Roman Cross and Ship's Wheel — A321

1976, June 19   **Perf. 12½ Horiz.**
1171 A321 85o brt bl & bl   .25 .25
Swedish Seamen's Church, centenary.

Torgny Segerstedt and 1917 Page of Gothenburg Journal — A322

1976, June 19   **Perf. 12½ Vert.**
1172 A322 1.90k brn & blk   .55 .30
Torgny Segerstedt (1876-1945), editor in chief of the Gothenburg Journal of Commerce and Shipping, birth centenary.

Coiled Snake, Bronze Buckle — A323   Pilgrim's Badge, Adoration of the Magi — A324

Drinking Horn, 14th Century — A325   Chimney Sweep — A326

Girl's Head, by Bror Hjorth, 1922 — A327

Perf. 12½ Horiz., Vert. (30o)
1976, Sept. 8   **Engr.**
1173 A323 15o bister   .20 .20
1174 A324 20o green   .20 .20
1175 A325 30o dk rose brn   .20 .20
1176 A326 90o indigo   .25 .20
1177 A327 9k yel grn & sl grn   2.50 .25
Nos. 1173-1177 (5)   3.35 1.05

Inventors A328

#1178, John Ericsson (1803-1889), ship propeller and "Monitor". #1179, Helge Palmcrantz (1842-80) & reaper. #1180, Lars Magnus Ericsson (1846-1926) & switchboard. #1181, Sven Wingquist (1876-1953) & ball bearing. #1182, Gustaf de Laval (1845-1913) & milk separator.

1976, Oct. 9 Engr.   **Perf. 12½ Horiz.**
1178 A328 1.30k multi   .50 .65
1179 A328 1.30k multi   .50 .65
1180 A328 1.30k multi   .50 .65
1181 A328 1.30k multi   .50 .65
1182 A328 1.30k multi   .50 .65
a. Bklt. pane of 5, #1178-1182   3.75
Swedish inventors and their technological inventions.

Hands and Cogwheels A329

1976, Oct. 9   **Perf. 12½ Vert.**
1183 A329 85o org & dk vio   .25 .20
1184 A329 1k yel grn & brn   .35 .20
Industrial safety.

Verner von Heidenstam, Lake Vattern — A330

1976, Nov. 17   **Perf. 12½ Vert.**
1185 A330 1k yellow green   .30 .20
1186 A330 1.30k blue   .45 .45
Verner von Heidenstam (1859-1940), Swedish poet, 1916 Nobel Prize winner.

Archangel Michael A331   Virgin Mary Visiting St. Elizabeth A332

Christmas: No. 1189, like No. 1187. No. 1190, St. Nicholas saving 3 children. No. 1191, like No. 1188. No. 1192, Illuminated page, prayer to Virgin Mary. 65o, stamps are from Flemish prayer book, c. 1500. 1k stamps are from Austrian prayer book, late 15th century.

Perf. 12½ Horiz.
1976, Nov. 17   **Photo.**
1187 A331 65o blue & multi   .20 .20
1188 A332 1k gold & multi   .25 .20
Perf. 12½ on 3 Sides
1189 A331 65o blue & multi   .20 .30
1190 A331 65o blue & multi   .20 .30
a. Bklt. pane, 5 each #1189-1190   1.50
Perf. 12½ Vert.
1191 A332 1k gold & multi   .25 .20
1192 A332 1k gold & multi   .25 .20
a. Bklt. pane, 5 each #1191-1192   2.50
Nos. 1187-1192 (6)   1.35 1.40

Five Water Lilies — A333

Photogravure and Engraved
1977, Feb. 2   **Perf. 12½ Horiz.**
1193 A333 1k brt grn & multi   .35 .20
1194 A333 1.30k ultra & multi   .35 .40
Nordic countries cooperation for protection of the environment and 25th Session of Nordic Council, Helsinki, Feb. 19.

Tailor — A334

1977, Feb. 24   **Perf. 12½ Vert.**
1195 A334 2.10k red brn   .55 .20

Longdistance Skating — A335

Perf. 12½ Horiz.
1977, Mar. 24   **Engr.**
1196 A335 95o shown   .25 .35
1197 A335 95o Swimming   .25 .35
1198 A335 95o Bicycling   .25 .35
1199 A335 95o Jogging   .25 .35
1200 A335 95o Badminton   .25 .35
a. Bklt. pane, 2 each #1196-1200   2.50
Nos. 1196-1200 (5)   1.25 1.75
Physical fitness.

Politeness, by "OA," 1905 — A336

1977, Mar. 24 Perf. 12½ on 3 Sides
1201 A336 75o black   .25 .20
a. Booklet pane of 10   2.50
Perf. 12½ Horiz.
1202 A336 3.80k red   1.00 .45
Oskar Andersson (1877-1906), cartoonist.

Calle Schewen A337

No. 1204, Seagull. No. 1205, Dancers and accordionist. No. 1206, Fishermen in boat. No. 1207, Tree on shore at sunset.
Designs are illustrations for poem The Calle Schewen Waltz, by Evert Taube, and include bars of music of this song.

1977, May 2 Engr.   **Perf. 12½ Horiz.**
1203 A337 95o slate grn   .25 .35
1204 A337 95o vio bl   .25 .35
1205 A337 95o grn & blk   .25 .35
1206 A337 95o dark blue   .25 .35
1207 A337 95o red   .25 .35
a. Bklt. pane, 2 each #1203-1207   2.50
Nos. 1203-1207 (5)   1.25 1.75
Tourist publicity for Roslagen (archipelago) and to honor Evert Taube (1890-1976), poet.

Gustavianum, Uppsala University A338

1977, May 2 Photo.   **Perf. 12½ Vert.**
1208 A338 1.10k multi   .35 .20
Perf. 12½ on 3 Sides
1209 A338 1.10k multi   .35 .20
a. Booklet pane of 10   3.50
Uppsala University, 500th anniversary.

Europa Issue 1977

Forest in Snow A339

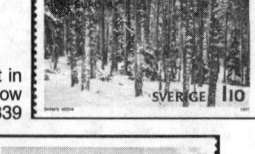

Rapadalen Valley — A340

1977, May 2   **Perf. 12½ Vert.**
1210	A339	1.10k multi	.90 .20
1211	A340	1.40k multi	.90 .60

Owl — A341

Cast-iron Stove Decoration — A342

Gotland Ponies A343

1977, Sept. 8   **Engr.**   **Perf. 12½ Vert.**
1212	A341	45o dk slate grn	.25 .20

Perf. 12½ Horiz.
1213	A342	70o dk vio bl	.25 .20

Booklet Stamp
1214	A343	1.40k brown	.40 .30
a.		Booklet pane of 5	2.00
		Nos. 1212-1214 (3)	.90 .70

Wild Berries — A344

Perf. 14 on 3 Sides
1977, Sept. 8   **Photo.**
1215	A344	75o Blackberry	.20 .35
1216	A344	75o Cranberry	.20 .35
1217	A344	75o Raspberry	.20 .35
1218	A344	75o Whortleberry	.20 .35
1219	A344	75o Alpine strawberry	.20 .35
a.		Bklt. pane, 2 each #1215-1219	2.00 3.50
		Nos. 1215-1219 (5)	1.00 1.75

Horse-drawn Trolley — A345

Designs: Public transportation.

1977, Oct. 8   **Engr.**   **Perf. 12½ Horiz.**
1220	A345	1.10k shown	.30 .35
1221	A345	1.10k Electric trolley	.30 .35
1222	A345	1.10k Ferry	.30 .35
1223	A345	1.10k Tandem bus	.30 .35
1224	A345	1.10k Subway	.30 .35
a.		Bklt. pane of 5, #1220-1224	1.50 2.50

Putting up Sheaf for the Birds — A346   Preparing Dried Soaked Fish — A347

Traditional Christmas Preparations: No. 1227, Children baking ginger snaps. No. 1228, Bringing in Yule tree. No. 1229, Making straw goat. No. 1230, Candle dipping.

Perf. 12½ Horiz.
1977, Nov. 17   **Engr.**
1225	A346	75o violet	.20 .20
1226	A347	1.10k yel grn	.30 .20

Perf. 12½ on 3 Sides
1227	A346	75o ocher	.20 .20
1228	A346	75o slate grn	.20 .20
a.		Bklt. pane, 5 each #1227-1228	1.50
1229	A347	1.10k dk red	.30 .20
1230	A347	1.10k dk bl	.30 .20
a.		Bklt. pane, 5 each #1229-1230	2.50
		Nos. 1225-1230 (6)	1.50 1.20

Christmas 1977.

Henrik Pontoppidan, Karl Adolph Gjellerup A348

Design: 1.40k, Charles Glover Barkla.

1977, Nov. 17   **Perf. 12½ Vert.**
1231	A348	1.10k red brn	.30 .20
1232	A348	1.40k yel grn	.40 .50

1917 Nobel Prize winners: Henrik Pontoppidan (1857-1943) and Karl Adolph Gjellerup (1857-1919), Danish writers; Charles Glover Barkla (1877-1944), English X-ray pioneer.

Space Without Affiliation, by Arne Jones — A349   Brown Bear — A350

1978, Jan. 25   **Perf. 12½ Horiz.**
1233	A349	2.50k vio bl	.65 .20

1978, Apr. 11   **Perf. 12½ Horiz.**
1234	A350	1.15k dark brown	.30 .20

Europa Issue 1978

Orebro Castle — A351   Arch and Stairs — A352

1978, Apr. 11   **Perf. 12½ Vert.**
1235	A351	1.30k slate green	.80 .20

Perf. 12½ Horiz.
1236	A352	1.70k dull red	.90 .55

Pentecostal Preacher and Congregation A353

Free Churches: No. 1238, Swedish Missionary Society. No. 1239, Evangelical

National Missionary Society. No. 1240, Baptist Society. No. 1241, Salvation Army.

1978, Apr. 11   **Perf. 12½ on 3 sides**
1237	A353	90o purple	.20 .30
1238	A353	90o slate	.20 .30
1239	A353	90o violet	.20 .30
1240	A353	90o slate	.20 .30
1241	A353	90o purple	.20 .30
a.		Bklt. pane, 2 each #1237-1241	2.00
		Nos. 1237-1241 (5)	1.00 1.50

Independent Christian Associations.

Brosarp Hills — A354

Grindstone Production A355

Red Limestone Cliff — A356

Designs: No. 1243, Avocets. No. 1245, Linnaea borealis (Linné's favorite flower.) No. 1247, Linné with Lapp drum, wearing Lapp clothes and Dutch doctor's hat.

Perf. 12½ Horiz.
1978, May 23   **Engr.**
1242	A354	1.30k gray green	.35 .30
1243	A354	1.30k violet blue	.35 .30

Perf. 12½ on 3 Sides
1244	A355	1.30k violet brown	.35 .40
1245	A355	1.30k brown red	.35 .40

Perf. 12½ on 2 Sides
1246	A356	1.30k violet blue	.35 .40
1247	A356	1.30k violet brown	.35 .40
a.		Bklt. pane of 6, #1242-1247	2.10

Travels of Carl von Linné (1707-1778), botanist.

Cranes, Lake Hornborgasjon — A357

Designs: No. 1248, Gliding School, Alleberg. No. 1250, Skara Church, Lacko Island. No. 1251, Ancient rock tomb, Luttra. No. 1252, Cloth merchants, sculpture by Nils Sjogren.

1978, May 23   **Perf. 12½ Horiz.**
1248	A357	1.15k dull green	.30 .30
1249	A357	1.15k maroon	.30 .30
1250	A357	1.15k violet blue	.30 .30
1251	A357	1.15k dk gray grn	.30 .30
1252	A357	1.15k brn & gray grn	.30 .30
a.		Bklt. pane, 2 each #1284-1252	3.00
		Nos. 1248-1252 (5)	1.50 1.50

Tourist publicity for Vastergotland.

Laurel and Scroll — A358

1978, May 23   **Perf. 12½ Vert.**
1253	A358	2.50k gray & sl grn	.65 .20

Stockholm University, centenary.

Homecoming, by Carl Kylberg — A359

Nude, by Karl Isakson A360   Self-portrait, by Ivar Arosenius A361

1978, Sept. 5   **Engr.**   **Perf. 12½ Vert.**
1254	A359	90o multicolored	.30 .25

Perf. 12½ Horiz.
1255	A360	1.15k multi	.30 .30
1256	A361	4.50k multi	1.25 .40
		Nos. 1254-1256 (3)	1.85 .95

Swedish painters: Carl Kylberg (1878-1952); Karl Isakson (1878-1922); Ivar Arosenius (1878-1909).

North Arrow (Compass Rose), Map, 1769 — A362

1978, Sept. 5   **Perf. 12½ Horiz.**
1257	A362	10k lilac	2.75 .20

Coronation Coach, 1699 — A363

1978, Oct. 7   **Engr.**   **Perf. 12½ Horiz.**
1258	A363	1.70k dk red, *yel*	.45 .40
a.		Booklet pane of 5	2.25

Orange Russula — A364

Designs: Edible mushrooms.

1978, Oct. 7   **Perf. 12½ on 3 Sides**
1259	A364	1.15k shown	.30 .35
1260	A364	1.15k Lycoperdon perlatum	.30 .35
1261	A364	1.15k Macrolepiota procera	.30 .35
1262	A364	1.15k Cantharellus cibarius	.30 .35
1263	A364	1.15k Boletus edulis	.30 .35
1264	A364	1.15k Ramaria botrytis	.30 .35
a.		Bklt. pane of 6, #1259-1264	2.00

Toy Ferris Wheel — A365   Rider Drawing Water Cart — A366

Toys: No. 1266, Teddy bear. No. 1267, Dalecarlian wooden horse. No. 1268, Doll. No. 1269, Spinning tops.

Perf. 12½ Horiz.

1978, Nov. 14   **Engr.**
1265	A365	90o dk red & grn	.20	.20
1266	A365	1.30k brt ultra	.35	.20

Perf. 12½ on 3 Sides
Photo.
1267	A365	90o multicolored	.20	.20
1268	A365	90o multicolored	.20	.20
a.		Bklt. pane, 5 each #1267-1268	2.00	
1269	A366	1.30k multicolored	.35	.20
1270	A366	1.30k multicolored	.35	.20
a.		Bklt. pane, 5 each #1269-1270	2.50	
		Nos. 1265-1270 (6)	1.65	1.20

Christmas 1978.

Fritz Haber — A367

Design: 1.70k, Max Planck.

1978, Nov. 14   Engr.   Perf. 12½ Vert.
1271	A367	1.30k dark brown	.30	.20
1272	A367	1.70k dark violet bl	.45	.50

1918 Nobel Prize winners: Fritz Haber (1868-1934), German chemist; Max Planck (1858-1947), German physicist. See #1310-1312, 1341-1344, 1387-1389.

Bandy — A368

1979, Jan. 25   Engr.   Perf. 12½ Vert.
1273	A368	1.05k violet blue	.30	.20
1274	A368	2.50k orange	.65	.20

Child Wearing Gas Mask in Heavy Traffic — A369

1979, Mar. 13   Perf. 12½ Vert.
1275	A369	1.70k dark blue	.45	.50

International Year of the Child.

Drill-weave Tapestry, c. 1855-1860 A370

Carrier Pigeon, Hand with Quill A371

1979, Mar. 13   Perf. 12½ Horiz.
1276	A370	4k gray & red	1.10	.20

Perf. 14x14½ on 3 Sides
1979, Apr. 2   **Photo.**
1277	A371	(1k) ultra & yel	.90	.20
a.		Booklet pane of 20	18.00	

Price of booklet 20k.

DISCOUNT BOOKLETS

Every Swedish household received during Apr. 1979, 2 coupons for the purchase of 2 discount booklets, #1277a. The stamps were for use on post cards and letters within Sweden. The stamps are inscribed "INRIKES POST."

The program continued with numerous changes. The Inscription changed to "PRIVATPOST" in 1981, the same year that denominations were added. At some point the stamps could also be used to Denmark, Norway, Finland and Iceland. In 1991 the discount value of the stamps ended July, 1.

The last stamps inscribed "PRIVAT POST" were issued in 1993.

Mail Service by Boat, Grisslehamn to Echero A372

Europa: 1.70k, Hand on telegraph.

1979, May 7   Engr.   Perf. 12½ Vert.
1278	A372	1.30k slate grn & blk	1.10	.20
1279	A372	1.70k ocher & blk	1.10	.75

Woodcutter, Winter — A373

Designs: No. 1281, Sowing, spring. No. 1282, Grazing cattle, summer. No. 1283, Harvester, summer. No. 1284, Plowing, autumn.

1979, May 7   Perf. 12½ Horiz.
1280	A373	1.30k multicolored	.30	.20
1281	A373	1.30k sl grn & dk brn	.30	.20
1282	A373	1.30k dk brn & sl grn	.30	.20
1283	A373	1.30k sl grn & ocher	.30	.20
1284	A373	1.30k multicolored	.30	.20
a.		Bklt. pane, 2 each #1280-1284	3.00	
		Nos. 1280-1284 (5)	1.50	1.00

Tourist Steamer Juno — A374

Roller Bridge, Hajstorp — A375

Sailing Ship — A376

Gota Canal: No. 1286, Borenshult Lock. No. 1288, Hand-drawn gate. No. 1290, Rowboat in Forsvik lock.

1979, May 7   Perf. 12½ Horiz.
1285	A374	1.15k violet blue	.30	.35
1286	A374	1.15k slate green	.30	.35

Perf. 12½ on 3 Sides
1287	A375	1.15k dull purple	.30	.35
1288	A375	1.15k carmine	.30	.35

Perf. 12½ on 2 Sides
1289	A376	1.15k violet blue	.30	.35
1290	A376	1.15k slate green	.30	.35
a.		Bklt. pane of 6, #1285-1290	2.00	
		Nos. 1285-1290 (6)	1.80	2.10

Strikers and Sawmill A377

Temperance Movement Banner — A378

Jons Jacob Berzelius A379

Johan Olof Wallin A380

1979, Sept. 6   Engr.   Perf. 12½ Vert.
1291	A377	90o car & dp brn	.20	.25

Perf. 12½ Horiz.
Litho.
1292	A378	1.30k multi	.35	.20

Engr.
1293	A379	1.70k brown & grn	.45	.40
1294	A380	4.50k slate blue	1.25	.30
		Nos. 1291-1294 (4)	2.25	1.15

Centenaries of Sundsvall strike and Swedish Temperance Movement; birth bicentennials of Jons Jacob Berzelius (1779-1848), physician and chemist; Johan Olof Wallin (1779-1839), Archbishop and poet.

Dragonfly A381

Green Spotted Toad A383

Pike A382

1979, Sept. 6   Perf. 12½ Horiz.
1295	A381	60o violet	.40	.35

Perf. 12½ Vert.
1296	A382	65o gray	.50	.30
1297	A383	80o olive green	.50	.35
		Nos. 1295-1297 (3)	1.40	1.00

Swedish Rococo — A384

Designs: 90o, Potpourri pot. 1.15k, Portrait, by Johan Henrik Scheffel. 1.30k, Silver coffeepot. 1.70k, Bust of Carl Johan Cronstedt.

Souvenir Sheet
Engraved and Photogravure
1979, Oct. 6   Perf. 12x12½
1298	A384	Sheet of 4	2.40	2.40
a.-d.		Any single	.40	.40

No. 1298 sold for 6k; surtax was for philately.

Herrings, Age Determination — A386

Sea Research: No. 1300, Acoustic survey of sea bottom. No. 1301, Water bloom of algae in Baltic Sea. No. 1302, Computer map of herring distribution in South Baltic Sea. No. 1303, Research ship Argos.

1979, Oct. 6   Engr.   Perf. 12½ Horiz.
1299	A386	1.70k multicolored	.40	.50
1300	A386	1.70k sepia	.40	.50
1301	A386	1.70k multicolored	.40	.50
1302	A386	1.70k sepia	.40	.50
1303	A386	1.70k multicolored	.40	.50
a.		Bklt. pane of 5, #1299-1303	2.00	2.75

Brooch from Jamtland A387

Ljusdal Costume A388

Christmas (Costumes and Jewelry from): #1305, Pendant, Smaland. #1307, Osteraker. #1308, Goinge. #1309, Mora.

Perf. 12½ Horiz.
1979, Nov. 15   **Engr.**
1304	A387	90o dk Prus blue	.30	.20
1305	A387	1.30k dull red	.35	.20

Perf. 12½ on 3 Sides
Photo.
Size: 22x27mm
1306	A388	90o multicolored	.30	.20
1307	A388	90o multicolored	.30	.20
a.		Bklt. pane, 5 each #1306-1307	2.50	

Perf. 12½ Vert.
Size: 26x44mm
1308	A388	1.30k multicolored	.35	.20
1309	A388	1.30k multicolored	.35	.20
a.		Bklt. pane, 5 each #1308-1309	3.50	
		Nos. 1304-1309 (6)	1.95	1.20

Nobel Prize Winner Type of 1978

1919 Winners: 1.30k, Jules Bordet (1870-1961), Belgian bacteriologist. 1.70k, Johannes Stark (1874-1957), German physicist. 2.50k, Carl Spitteler (1845-1924), Swiss poet.

1979, Nov. 15   Engr.   Perf. 12½ Vert.
1310	A367	1.30k lilac	.30	.20
1311	A367	1.70k ultra	.45	.70
1312	A367	2.50k olive green	.65	.20
		Nos. 1310-1312 (3)	1.40	1.10

Wind Power — A389

Renewable Energy Sources: No. 1314, Biodegradable material. No. 1315, Solar energy. No. 1316, Geothermal energy. No. 1317, Hydro power.

1980, Jan. 29   Perf. 12½ on 3 sides
1313	A389	1.15k dark blue	.30	.35
1314	A389	1.15k dk grn & bis	.30	.35
1315	A389	1.15k yellow orange	.30	.35
1316	A389	1.15k dark green	.30	.35
1317	A389	1.15k dk bl & dk grn	.30	.35
a.		Bklt. pane, 2 each #1313-1317	3.00	4.50
		Nos. 1313-1317 (5)	1.50	1.75

Crown Princess Victoria and King Carl XVI Gustaf — A390

1980, Feb. 26   Perf. 12½ on 3 sides
1318 A390 1.30k brt blue   .30   .20
 a.   Booklet pane of 10   3.00

Perf. 12½ Vert.
1319 A390 1.30k brt blue   .40   .20
1320 A390 1.70k carmine rose   .60   .40
  Nos. 1318-1320 (3)   1.30   .80

Child Holding Adult's Hand — A391

Hand Holding Cane — A392

1980, Apr. 22   Perf. 12½ Horiz.
1321 A391 1.40k red brown   .30   .20
1322 A392 1.60k slate green   .40   .20

Parents' insurance system; care for the elderly.

Squirrel — A393

Perf. 15 on 3 Sides
1980, May 12   Photo.
1323 A393 (1k) ultra & yellow   .90   .20
 a.   Booklet pane of 20   18.00

See note after No. 1277.

Elise Ottesen-Jensen (1886-1973), Journalist A394

Europa: 1.70k, Joe Hill (1879-1915), member of American Workers' Movement and poet.

1980, June 4 Engr.   Perf. 12½ Vert.
1324 A394 1.30k green   .70   .20
1325 A394 1.70k red   .80   .80

Banga Farm, Alfta, Halsingland Province — A395

Tourism (Halsingland Province): No. 1327, Iron Works, Iggesund. No. 1328, Blaxas Ridge, Forsa. No. 1329, Tybling farm, Tyby. No. 1330, Sunds Canal, Hudiksvall.

1980, June 4   Perf. 12½ Horiz.
1326 A395 1.15k red   .30   .40
1327 A395 1.15k dark blue   .30   .40
1328 A395 1.15k dark green   .30   .40
1329 A395 1.15k chocolate   .30   .40
1330 A395 1.15k dark blue   .30   .40
 a.   Bklt. pane of 2 each #1326-1330 3.00
  Nos. 1326-1330 (5)   1.50   2.00

Chair, Scania, 1831 — A396

Cradle, North Bothnia, 19th Century — A397

Perf. 12½ Horiz.
1980, Sept. 9   Engr.
1331 A396 1.50k grnsh blue   .40   .20

Perf. 12½ Vert.
1332 A397 2k dk red brown   .65   .30

Norden 80.

Scene from "Diagonal Symphony," 1924 — A398

1980, Sept. 9   Perf. 12½ Horiz.
1333 A398 3k dark blue   .80   .20

Viking Eggeling (1880-1925), artist and film maker.

Souvenir Sheet

Gustaf Erikson's Carriage — A399

Swedish Automobile History: 90o, Gustaf Erikson's carriage. 1.15k, Vabis, 1909. 1.30k, Thulin, 1923. 1.40k, Scania, 1903. 1.50k, Tidaholm, 1917. 1.70k, Volvo, 1927.

Photogravure and Engraved
1980, Oct. 11   Perf. 12½
1334 A399 Sheet of 6   3.25   3.50
 a.-f. Any single   .65   .65

No. 1334 sold for 9k.

Bamse the Bear — A401

Farmer Kronblom — A402

Christmas 1980 (Comic Strip Characters): No. 1336, Mandel Karlsson, vert. No. 1337, Adamson, vert.

1980, Oct. 11 Engr. Perf. 12½ Vert.
1335 A401 1.15k multicolored   .45   .20

Perf. 12½ on 3 sides
Photo.
1336 A401 1.15k multicolored   .40   .20
 a.   Booklet pane of 10   4.00

Perf. 12½ Horiz.
Engr.
1337 A401 1.50k black   .40   .20

Photo.
1338 A402 1.50k multicolored   .30   .20
 a.   Booklet pane of 10   3.00
  Nos. 1335-1338 (4)   1.55   .80

Angel Blowing Horn A403

Necken, by Ernst Josephson A404

Perf. on 3 Sides
1980, Nov. 18   Engr.
1339 A403 1.25k multicolored   .35   .20
 a.   Booklet pane of 12   4.00

Christmas 1980.

1980, Nov. 18   Perf. 12½ Horiz.
1340 A404 8k multicolored   2.10   .20

Nobel Prize Winner Type of 1978

1920 Winners: #1341, Knut Hamsun (1859-1953), Norwegian writer. #1342, August Krogh (1874-1949), Danish Physiologist, #1343, Charles-Edouard Guillaume (1861-1938), French physicist. #1344, Walther Nernst (1864-1941), German chemist.

1980, Nov. 18   Perf. 13 on 3 Sides
1341 A367 1.40k dk blue gray   .40   .30
1342 A367 1.40k red   .40   .30
 a.   Bklt. pane, 5 each #1341-1342 4.00
1343 A367 2k green   .55   .55
1344 A367 2k brown   .55   .55
 a.   Bklt. pane, 5 each #1343-1344 5.50
  Nos. 1341-1344 (4)   1.90   1.70

Ernst Wigforss (1881-1977), Politician & Writer A405

Freya (Fertility Goddess) A406

1981, Jan. 29 Engr. Perf. 12½ Vert.
1345 A405 5k rose carmine   1.40   .30

1981, Jan. 29   Perf. 12½ on 3 Sides

Norse Mythological Characters: 10o, Thor (thunder god). 15o, Heimdall (rainbow god). 50o, Frey (god of peace, fertility, weather). 1k, Odin.

1346 A406 10o blue black   .20   .20
1347 A406 15o dk carmine   .20   .20
1348 A406 50o dk carmine   .20   .20
1349 A406 75o deep green   .20   .20
1350 A406 1k blue black   .25   .20
 a.   Bklt. pane, 2 each #1346-1350 2.10
  Nos. 1346-1350 (5)   1.05   1.00

Gyrfalcon A407

1981, Feb. 26 Engr. Perf. 12½ Vert.
1351 A407 50k multicolored   13.50   .75
 a.   Booklet pane of 4   55.00

Troll Chasing Boy — A408

Europa: 2k, Lady of the Woods.

1981, Apr. 28   Engr.
1352 A408 1.50k dk blue & red   .70   .20
1353 A408 2k dk green & red   .80   .30

Intl. Year of the Disabled — A409

1981, Apr. 28
1354 A409 1.50k dk green   .40   .20
1355 A409 3.50k purple   .95   .40

Arms of Oster-gotland Province A410

Sail Boat, Bohuslan A411

Perf. 14½ on 3 Sides
1981, May 18   Photo.
1356 A410 1.40k shown   .90   .20
1357 A410 1.40k Jamtland   .90   .20
1358 A410 1.40k Dalarna   .90   .20
1359 A410 1.40k Bohuslan   .90   .20
 a.   Bklt. pane, 5 each #1356-1359 18.00
  Nos. 1356-1359 (4)   3.60   .80

See note after No. 1277. See Nos. 1403-1406, 1456-1459, 1492-1495, 1534-1537, 1592-1595.

Perf. 12½ on 3 Sides
1981, May 26   Engr.
1360 A411 1.65k shown   .45   .45
1361 A411 1.65k Blekinge   .45   .45
1362 A411 1.65k Norrbotten   .45   .45
1363 A411 1.65k Halsingland   .45   .45
1364 A411 1.65k Gotland   .45   .45
1365 A411 1.65k Skane   .45   .45
 a.   Bklt. pane of 6, #1360-1365 2.75 3.50

King Carl XVI Gustaf A412

Queen Silvia A413

1981-84   Perf. 12½ Vert.
1366 A412 1.65k dark green   .45   .20
1367 A413 1.75k dark red   .45   .35
1368 A412 1.80k dark blue   .50   .20
1369 A412 1.90k red ('84)   .50   .20
1370 A412 2.40k violet brn   .65   .40
1371 A413 2.40k grnsh black ('84) .65 .70
1372 A412 2.70k brt lilac   .75   .40
1373 A413 3.20k red   .85   .45
  Nos. 1366-1373 (8)   4.80   2.90

Day and Night — A414

Scene from Par Lagerkvist's Autobiography Guest of Reality — A415

Perf. 12½ on 3 Sides
1981, Sept. 9   Engr.
1376 A414 1.65k dark blue   .45   .20
 a.   Booklet pane of 10   4.50

1981, Sept. 9   Perf. 12½ Horiz.
1377 A415 1.50k dark green   .40   .20

Conductor Sixten Ehrling and Opera
Singer Birgit Nilsson — A416

Bjorn Borg,   Baker's Sign
Tennis Player   A418
A417

Designs: No. 1378, Electric locomotive.
No. 1379, Trucks. No. 1381, Oil rig. No. 1383,
Ingemar Stenmark, skier.

Perf. 12½ on 2 (Type A416) or 3
(Type A417) sides

1981, Sept. 9			
1378	A416	2.40k rose carmine	.65 .50
1379	A416	2.40k red	.65 .50
1380	A416	2.40k rose lilac	.65 .50
1381	A416	2.40k deep violet	.65 .50
1382	A417	2.40k dark blue	.65 .60
1383	A417	2.40k dark blue	.65 .60
a.		Bklt. pane of 6, #1378-1383	4.00 4.00

1981, Sept. 9			**Perf. 12½ Vert.**
1384	A418	2.30k shown	.90 .20
1385	A418	2.30k Pewter shop	
		sign	.90 .20
a.		Pair, #1384-1385	1.90 1.90

A419

Swedish Films: a, Olof Ahs in The Coach-
man. b, Ingrid Bergman and Gosta Ekman in
Intermezzo. c, Greta Garbo in The Gosta
Berling Saga, d, Stig Jarrel and Alf Kjellin in
Persecution. e, Kari Sylwan and Harriet
Andersson in Cries and Whispers

Photogravure and Engraved

1981, Oct. 10			**Perf. 13½**
1386	A419	Sheet of 5	3.50 3.50
a.-e.		Any single	.55 .60

No. 1386 sold for 10k.

Nobel Prize Winner Type of 1978

1921 Winners: 1.35k, Albert Einstein (1879-
1955), German physicist. 1.65k, Anatole
France (1844-1924), French writer. 2.70k,
Frederick Soddy (1877-1956), British chemist.

1981, Nov. 24	Engr.		**Perf. 12½ Vert.**
1387	A367	1.35k red	.35 .30
1388	A367	1.65k green	.45 .20
1389	A367	2.70k blue	.75 .75
		Nos. 1387-1389 (3)	1.55 1.25

Christmas
1981 — A421

Designs: Wooden birds.

1981, Nov. 24		**Perf. 12½ on 3 Sides**
1390	A421	1.40k red	.40 .20
1391	A421	1.40k green	.40 .20
a.		Bklt. pane, 5 each #1390-1391	4.00

Knight on
Horseback,
by John
Bauer
A422

John Bauer (1882-1918), Fairytale Illustra-
tor: No. 1393, "What a Miserable Little Pale-
face, said the Troll Mother." No. 1394, Marsh
Princess. No. 1395, Now the Dusk of the
Night is already Upon Us.

Perf. 12x12½ on 3 sides

1982, Feb. 16			Engr.
1392	A422	1.65k multicolored	.50 .40
1393	A422	1.65k multicolored	.50 .40
1394	A422	1.65k multicolored	.50 .40
1395	A422	1.65k multicolored	.50 .40
a.		Bklt. pane of 4, #1392-1395	2.00

Impossible
Figures — A423

Designs: Geometric figures.

1982, Feb. 16			**Perf. 12½ Horiz.**
1396	A423	25o violet brown	.20 .20
1397	A423	50o brown olive	.20 .20
1398	A423	75o dark blue	.25 .20
		Nos. 1396-1398 (3)	.65 .60

Newspaper   Graziella, by
Distributor, by   Carl Larsson
Svenolov Ehren   A425
A424

1982, Feb. 16			
1399	A424	1.35k deep violet	.50 .20
1400	A425	5k violet brown	1.50 .20

Europa Issue 1982

Land
Reform,
19th
Cent.
A426

Anders Celsius
(1701-1744),
Inventor of
Temperature
Scale — A427

1982, Apr. 26	Engr.		**Perf. 12½ Vert.**
1401	A426	1.65k dk olive grn	2.00 .20

Perf. 12½ on 3 Sides

1402	A427	2.40k dark green	1.00 .65
a.		Booklet pane of 6	5.00

Provincial Arms Type of 1981
Perf. 14 on 3 Sides

1982, Apr. 26			Photo.
1403	A410	1.40k Dalsland	.95 .20
1404	A410	1.40k Oland	.95 .20
1405	A410	1.40k Vastmanland	.95 .20
1406	A410	1.40k Halsingland	.95 .20
a.		Bklt. pane, 5 each #1403-1406	19.00
		Nos. 1403-1406 (4)	3.80 .80

See note after No. 1277.

Elin Wagner (1882-
1949), Writer — A428

Perf. 12½ Horiz.

1982, June 3			Engr.
1407	A428	1.35k Sketch by Siri	
		Derkert	.50 .35

Burgher
House — A429

Embroidered Lace
Ribbon, 19th
Cent. — A430

1982, June 3		**Perf. 12½ Vert.**
1408	A429	1.65k brown	.55 .20

Perf. 12½ Horiz.

1409	A430	2.70k bister	.90 .60

Cent. of Museum of Cultural History, Lund.

1982 Intl.
Buoyage
System
A431

Designs: Various buoy signals.

1982, June 3			**Perf. 13 Horiz.**
1410	A431	1.65k shown	.60 .30
1411	A431	1.65k Ferry	.60 .30
1412	A431	1.65k Six sailboats	.60 .30
1413	A431	1.65k One-globed	
		buoy	.60 .30
1414	A431	1.65k Two-globed	
		buoy	.60 .30
a.		Bklt. pane, 2 each #1410-1414	6.00
		Nos. 1410-1414 (5)	3.00 1.50

Vietnamese Workers in
Sweden — A432

Living Together: Swedish emigration and
immigration.

1982, Aug. 26	Engr.	**Perf. 13 Horiz.**	
1415	A432	1.65k Leaving Swe-	
		den, 1880	.50 .25
1416	A432	1.65k shown	.50 .25
1417	A432	1.65k Local voting	
		right	.50 .25
1418	A432	1.65k Girls	.50 .25
a.		Bklt. pane, 2 each #1415-1418	4.00
		Nos. 1415-1418 (4)	2.00 1.00

Wild
Orchids — A433

Photogravure and Engraved

1982, Oct. 9			**Perf. 12x13**

Wild Orchids: 1.65k (No. 1419a), Orchis
mascula. 1.65k (No. 1419d), Cypripedium
calcéolus. 2.40k, Epipactis palustris. 2.70k,
Dactylorhiza sambucina.

1419	A433	Sheet of 4	4.50 4.50
a.-d.		Any single	1.10 1.00

Sold for 10k for benefit of stamp collecting.

Christmas
1982 — A434

Stained-glass Windows, Church at Lye, Gotland, 14th cent.

Perf. 13 on 3 Sides

1982, Nov. 24			Photo.
1420	A434	1.40k Angel	.45 .40
1421	A434	1.40k Child in the	
		Temple	.45 .40
1422	A434	1.40k Adoration of the	
		Kings	.45 .40
1423	A434	1.40k Tidings to the	
		Shepherds	.45 .40
1424	A434	1.40k Birth of Christ	.45 .40
a.		Bklt. pane, 2 each #1420-1424	4.50
		Nos. 1420-1424 (5)	2.25 2.00

Signature, Atomic Model — A435

Nobel Prizewinners in Physics (Quantum
Mechanics): No. 1425, Niels Bohr, Denmark,
1922. No. 1426, Erwin Schrodinger, Austria,
1933. No. 1427, Louis de Broglie, France,
1929. No. 1428, Paul Dirac, England, 1933. No.
1429, Werner Heisenberg, Germany, 1932.

1982, Nov. 24	Engr.	**Perf. 13 Horiz.**	
1425	A435	2.40k multi	.80 .75
1426	A435	2.40k multi	.80 .75
1427	A435	2.40k multi	.80 .75
1428	A435	2.40k multi	.80 .75
1429	A435	2.40k multi	.80 .75
a.		Bklt. pane of 5, #1425-1429	4.00
		Nos. 1425-1429 (5)	4.00 3.75

Fruit   Games
A436   A436a

Crown and   King Carl XVI
Posthorn   Gustaf
A436b   A436c

Queen Silvia   Games
A436d   A436e

1983-85		Engr.	**Perf. 12½ Vert.**
1430	A436	5o Horse chest-	
		nut	.20 .20
1431	A436	10o Norway maple	.20 .20
1432	A436	15o Dogrose	.20 .20
1433	A436	20o Sloe	.20 .20
1434	A436a	50o Fox and	
		cheese	.20 .20
1435	A436a	60o Dominoes	.20 .20
1436	A436a	70o Ludo	.20 .20
1437	A436a	80o Chinese	
		checkers	.20 .20
1438	A436a	90o Backgammon	.20 .20
1439	A436b	1.60k deep blue	.40 .20
1440	A436c	2k black	.40 .20
1441	A436b	2.50k bister	.50 .20
1442	A436c	2.70k dull red brn	.70 .45

Perf. 12½ Horiz.

1443	A436e	3k Chess	.60 .20

Perf. 12½ Vert.

1444	A436d	3.20k brt blue	1.00	.75
1445	A436b	4k dp car	.80	.20
		Nos. 1430-1445 (16)	6.20	4.00

Issued: #1430-1433, 2/10/83; #1434-1438, 1443, 10/12/85; #1439-1442, 1444-1445, 1/24/85.

See Nos. 1567-1580, 1783.

Peace Movement Centenary
A437

1983, Feb. 10

1446	A437	1.35k blue	.30	.30

Nils Ferlin (1898-1961), Poet — A438

1983, Feb. 10

1447	A438	6k dk grn	1.25	.20

500th Anniv. of Printing in Sweden A439

1983, Feb. 10   *Perf. 13 Horiz.*

1448	A439	1.65k Lead type	.45	.35
1449	A439	1.65k Dialogus Creaturarum, 1483	.45	.35
1450	A439	1.65k Carolus XII Bible, 1703	.45	.35
1451	A439	1.65k ABC Books, 1760s	.45	.35
1452	A439	1.65k Laser photo composition	.45	.35
a.		Bklt. pane, 2 each #1448-1452	4.50	
		Nos. 1448-1452 (5)	2.25	1.75

Sweden-US Relations Bicentenary — A440

1983, Mar. 24

1453	A440	2.70k Ben Franklin, Swedish Arms	.80	.65
a.		Booklet pane of 5	4.00	

See US No. 2036.

Nordic Cooperation Issue — A441

Perf. 12½ Horiz.

1983, Mar. 24   Engr.
Size: 21x27mm

1454	A441	1.65k Bicycling	.60	.20

Perf. 13 Vert.

1455	A441	2.40k Sailing	.90	.65

Provincial Arms Type of 1981

1983, Apr. 25   Photo.   *Perf. 14½x14*

1456	A410	1.60k Vastergotland	.90	.20
1457	A410	1.60k Medelpad	.90	.20
1458	A410	1.60k Gotland	.90	.20
1459	A410	1.60k Gastrikland	.90	.20
a.		Bklt. pane, 5 each #1456-1459	19.00	
		Nos. 1456-1459 (4)	3.60	.80

See note after No. 1277.

Europa — A442

Perf. 12½ Horiz.

1983, Apr. 25   Engr.

1460	A442	1.65k Swedish Ballet Co.	1.25	.20
1461	A442	2.70k Sliding-jaw wrench	1.25	1.00

A443

Designs: 1k, 3k, 10-ore King Oscar II definitive essays, 1884. 2k, No. 39. 4k, No. 58.

1983, May 25   *Perf. 12½*

1462	A443	1k blue	.25	.35
1463	A443	2k red	.55	.55
1464	A443	3k blue	.95	.85
1465	A443	4k green	1.25	1.00
a.		Bklt. pane of 4, #1462-1465	3.00	

STOCKHOLMIA Intl. Stamp Exhibition, Aug. 28-Sept. 7, 1986.

Red Cross — A444   Greater Karlso — A445

1983, Aug. 24   *Perf. 12½ Horiz.*

1466	A444	1.50k red	.55	.20
1467	A445	1.60k dk blue	.55	.20

Planorbis Snail — A446   Arctic Fox — A447

1983, Aug. 24   *Perf. 12½ on 3 Sides*

1468	A446	1.80k green	.50	.20
a.		Booklet pane of 10	5.00	

Perf. 12½ Horiz.

1469	A447	2.10k grnsh blk	.65	.20

See Nos. 1488-1489, 1526-1527, 1623-1626, 1678-1680, 1762-1763.

Hjalmar Bergman (1883-1931), Writer — A448

1983, Aug. 24   *Perf. 13 Horiz.*

1470	A448	1.80k Portrait	.60	.20
1471	A448	1.80k Jac the Clown illustration by Nisse Skoog	.60	.20
a.		Pair, #1470-1471	1.50	.80

View of Helgeandsholmen, Stockholm, by Franz Hogenberg, 1580 — A449

1983, Aug. 24   *Perf. 12½ Vert.*

1472	A449	2.70k dl pur & dk bl	.95	.50

A450

Photogravure and Engraved

1983, Oct. 1   *Perf. 13½*

1473	A450	Sheet of 5	4.50	4.50
a.		1.80k Wilhelm Stenhammar, pianist	.75	.75
b.		1.80k Aniara (opera)	.75	.75
c.		1.80k Lars Gullin, jazz saxophonist	.75	.75
d.		1.80k ABBA, pop music group	.75	.75
e.		2.70k Hins Anders, violinist	.75	.75

Sold for 11.50k.

Christmas 1983 — A452

Postcard designs: No. 1474, Christmas Gnomes around the tree. No. 1475, on straw goats. No. 1476, Folk children, Christmas porridge and gingerbread. No. 1477, Gnomes carrying Christmas gifts on a pole.

Perf. 12½ on 3 sides

1983, Nov. 22   Photo.

1474	A452	1.60k multi	.45	.30
1475	A452	1.60k multi	.45	.30
1476	A452	1.60k multi	.45	.30
1477	A452	1.60k multi	.45	.30
a.		Bklt. pane, 3 each #1474-1477	5.50	
		Nos. 1474-1477 (4)	1.80	1.20

Chemistry, Nobel Prize Winners — A453

Designs: No. 1478, Arne Tiselius (1902-1971), Electrophoresis Studies. No. 1479, George De Hevsy (1885-1966), Radioactive isotope tracers. No. 1480 Svante Arrenius (1859-1927), Theory of Electrolytic Dissociation. No. 1481, Theodor Svedberg (1884-1971), Colloid Studies. No. 1482, Hans Von Euler-Chelpin (1873-1964). Enzyme and Vitamin Structures.

Photogravure and Engraved

1983, Nov. 22   *Perf. 12½ Horiz.*

1478	A453	2.70k slate	.80	.75
1479	A453	2.70k dp bl vio	.80	.75
1480	A453	2.70k red lilac	.80	.75
1481	A453	2.70k blue blk	.80	.75
1482	A453	2.70k grnsh blk	.80	.75
a.		Bklt. pane of 5, #1478-1482	4.00	

Postal Savings Centenary — A454

Design: 100o, Three crowns.

1984, Feb. 9   Engr.   *Perf. 12½ Vert.*

1483	A454	100o orange	.35	.20
1484	A454	1.60k purple	.55	.30
1485	A454	1.80k pink	.65	.20
		Nos. 1483-1485 (3)	1.55	.70

Europa 1984 A455

Symbolic bridge of communications exchange.

1984, Feb. 9   *Perf. 12½ Horiz.*

1486	A455	1.80k red	.40	.20
a.		Booklet pane of 10	4.00	

Perf. 13 Vert.

1487	A455	2.70k dp ultra	1.60	.80

Conservation Type of 1983 and

Angelica — A457

1984, Mar. 27   *Perf. 12½ on 3 Sides*

1488	A447	1.90k Lemmings	.60	.20
1489	A447	1.90k Musk ox	.60	.20
a.		Bklt. pane, 5 each #1488-1489	6.00	

Perf. 12½ Horiz.

1490	A457	2k shown	.70	.20
1491	A457	2.25k Alpine birch	.80	.50
		Nos. 1488-1491 (4)	2.70	1.10

Provincial Arms Type of 1981

1984, Apr. 24   Photo.   *Perf. 14½x14*

1492	A410	1.60k Sodermanland	.95	.20
1493	A410	1.60k Blekinge	.95	.20
1494	A410	1.60k Vasterbotten	.95	.20
1495	A410	1.60k Skane	.95	.20
a.		Bklt. pane, 5 ea #1492-1495	19.00	
		Nos. 1492-1495 (4)	3.80	.80

See note after No. 1277.

A459

Swedish Patent System Centenary: No. 1496, Paraffin stove, F.W. Lindquist, 1892. No. 1497, Industrial robot ASEA-IRB 6. No. 1498, Fan suction vacuum cleaner, Axel Wennergren, 1912. No. 1499, Inboard-outboard motor, AQ-200, No. 1500, SLIC integrated electronic circuit. No. 1501, Tetrahedron container, 1948, 1951.

Perf. 12½ on 3 Sides

1984, June 6   Engr.

1496	A458	2.70k red	.80	.80
1497	A458	2.70k sepia	.80	.80
1498	A458	2.70k green	.80	.80
1499	A458	2.70k green	.80	.80
1500	A458	2.70k sepia	.80	.80
1501	A458	2.70k blue	.80	.80
a.		Bklt. pane of 6, #1496-1501	5.00	

Lithographed and Engraved

1984, June 6   *Perf. 12½*

Stockholmia '86 (Famous Letters): 1k, Erik XIV's marriage proposal to Queen Elizabeth I, 1561. 2k, Erik Dahlbergh to Sten Bielke, 1684.

A458 image:
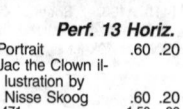

3k, Feather letter, 1834. 4k, August Strindberg to Harriet Bosse, 1905.

1502	A459	1k multi	.35	.45
1503	A459	2k multi	.60	.55
1504	A459	3k multi	.80	.80
1505	A459	4k multi	1.10	1.10
a.	Bklt. pane of 4, #1502-1505		3.00	

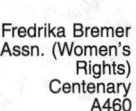

Fredrika Bremer Assn. (Women's Rights) Centenary A460

Perf. 12½ Vert.

1984, Aug. 28   Engr.

1506	A460	1.50k pink	.50	.20
1507	A460	6.50k red	2.00	.60

Medieval Towns A461

Engravings by E. Dahlbergh or M. Karl.

1984, Aug. 28   **Perf. 12½x13**

1508	A461	1.90k Jonkoping	.50	.50
1509	A461	1.90k Karlstad	.50	.50
1510	A461	1.90k Gavle	.50	.50
1511	A461	1.90k Sigtuna	.50	.50
1512	A461	1.90k Norrkoping	.50	.50
1513	A461	1.90k Vadstena	.50	.50
a.	Bklt. pane of 6, #1508-1513		3.25	

Viking Satellite, 1985 A462

1984, Oct. 13   **Perf. 12½ Vert.**

1514	A462	1.90k Satellite	.60	.30
1515	A462	3.20k Receiving station	1.00	.75

Souvenir Sheet

Swedish Aviation History — A463

Designs: a, Thulin D Two-Seater, 1915. b, SAAB-90 Scandia, 1946. c, Carl Gustaf Cederstrom (1867-1918, "The Flying Baron"), Bleriot, 1910. d, Tomten, 1927. e, Carl Nyberg's Flugan, 1900.

1984, Oct. 13   **Perf. 12½**

1516	A463	Sheet of 5	4.50	4.00
a.-d.	1.90k, any single		.85	.75
e.	2.70k, multi		1.10	1.00

Sold for 12k.

Christmas 1984 — A465

Birds.

Lithographed and Engraved

1984, Nov. 29   **Perf. 12½ on 3 Sides**

1517	A465	1.60k Coccothraustes coccothraustes	.55	.35
1518	A465	1.60k Bombycilla garrulus	.55	.35
1519	A465	1.60k Dendrocopos major	.55	.35
1520	A465	1.60k Sitta europaea	.55	.35
a.	Bklt. pane, 3 each #1517-1520		7.00	
	Nos. 1517-1520 (4)		2.20	1.40

Inner Ear A466

Nobel Prize Winners in Physiology or Medicine: No. 1521, Georg von Bekesy, 1961, hearing. No. 1522, John Eccles, Alan Hodgkin & Andrew Huxley, 1963, Nerve cell activation. No. 1523, Julius Axelrod, Bernard Katz & Ulf von Euler, 1970, nerve cell storage and release. No. 1524, Roger Sperry, Hubel, Wiesel, 1981, brain functions. No. 1525, David Hubel, Torsten Wiesel, 1981, Visual information processing.

Perf. 12½ Horiz.

1984, Nov. 29   Engr.

1521	A466	2.70k shown	1.00	.85
1522	A466	2.70k Nerve, arrows	1.00	.85
1523	A466	2.70k Nerve (front, side)	1.00	.85
1524	A466	2.70k Brain halves	1.00	.85
1525	A466	2.70k Eye	1.00	.85
a.	Bklt. pane of 5, #1521-1525		5.00	

Conservation Type of 1983 and

A467

Perf. 13 on 3 Sides

1985, Mar. 14   Engr.

1526	A447	2k Muscardinus avellanarius	.55	.20
1527	A447	2k Salvelinus salvelinus	.55	.20
a.	Bklt. pane, 5 each #1526-1527		5.50	

World Wildlife Fund.

Perf. 12½ Horiz.

1528	A467	2.20k Nigritella nigra	.60	.20
1529	A467	3.50k Nymphaea alba	1.10	.20
	Nos. 1526-1529 (4)		2.80	.80

World Table Tennis Championships A468

1985, Mar. 14   **Perf. 12½ Vert.**

1530	A468	2.70k Jan-Ove Waldner, Sweden	1.00	.45
1531	A468	3.20k Cai Zhenhua, China	1.25	.65

Clavichord — A469

Key Harp — A470

1985, Apr. 24   **Perf. 13 Vert.**

1532	A469	2k bluish blk, buff	2.40	.20

Perf. 13 on 3 Sides

1533	A470	2.70k dl red brn, buff	.85	.60
a.	Booklet pane of 6		4.25	

Europa 1985.

Provincial Arms Type of 1981
Perf. 14½x14 on 3 Sides

1985, Apr. 24   Photo.

1534	A410	1.80k Narke	.60	.20
1535	A410	1.80k Angermanland	.60	.20
1536	A410	1.80k Varmland	.60	.20

1537	A410	1.80k Smaland	.60	.20
a.	Bklt. pane, 5 ea #1534-1537		13.00	
	Nos. 1534-1537 (4)		2.40	.80

See note after No. 1277.

St. Cnut's Land Grant to Lund Cathedral, 900th Anniv. — A471

Seal of St. Cnut and: No. 1538, Lund Cathedral. No. 1539, City of Helsingdorg.

Perf. 12½ on 3 Sides

1985, May 21   Engr.

1538	A471	2k bluish blk & blk	.60	.20
1539	A471	2k blk & dk red	.60	.20
a.	Bklt. pane, 5 each, #1538-1539		6.00	

See Denmark Nos. 777-778.

Stockholmia '86 — A472

Paintings of old Stockholm: No. 1540, A View of Slussen, by Sigrid Hjerten (1919). No. 1541, Skeppsholmen, Winter, by Gosta Adrian-Nilsson (1919). No. 1542, A Summer's Night by the Riddarholmen, by Hilding Linnquist (1945). No. 1543, Klara Church Tower, by Otte Skold (1927).

Lithographed and Engraved

1985, May 21   **Perf. 12½**

1540	A472	2k multi	.55	.55
1541	A472	2k multi	.55	.55
1542	A472	3k multi	.90	.85
1543	A472	4k multi	1.25	1.00
a.	Bklt. pane of 4, #1540-1543		3.50	

Swedish Touring Club Cent. — A473

#1544, Touring Club Syl Station (c. 1920). #1545, Af Chapman Hostel, Stockholm.

1985, May 21   Engr.   **Perf. 12½ Vert.**

1544		2k blk & dp bl	.65	.25

Size: 58x23mm

1545		2k dp bl & blk	.65	.25
a.	A473 Pair, #1544-1545		1.30	.80

Trade Signs — A474

Perf. 12½ on 3 Sides

1985, Aug. 28   Engr.

1546	A474	10o Music Shop, Slottsgatan	.20	.20
1547	A474	20o Furrier, Stockholm	.20	.20
1548	A474	20o Coppersmith, Landskrona	.20	.20
1549	A474	50o Haberdasher, Stockholm	.20	.20
1550	A474	2k Shoemaker, Norrkoping	.70	.20
a.	Bklt. pane, #1546-1549, 2 #1550		1.75	
	Nos. 1546-1550 (5)		1.50	1.00

The Dying Spartan Hero, Otryades, 1779, by Johan Tobias Sergel — A475

Baron Carl Frederik Adelcrantz, Academy Pres., 1754, by Alexander Roslin (1718-1793) — A476

1985, Aug. 28   **Perf. 12½ Vert.**

1551	A475	2k slate blue	.70	.30

Perf. 12½ Horiz.

1552	A476	7k dk red brn	2.50	.45

Royal Academy of Fine Arts, 250th anniv.

Intl. Youth Year — A477

Children's drawings: 2k, Participation, by Marina Karlsson. 2.70k, Development, by Madeleine Andersson. 3.20k, Peace, by Charlotta Ankar.

Lithographed and Engraved

1985, Oct. 12   **Perf. 12½x13**

1553	A477	Sheet of 3	3.00	3.25
b.	2k multi		.90	1.00
c.	2.70k multi		.90	1.00
	3.20k multi		.90	1.00

Sold for 10k.

Prime Minister Per Albin Hansson (1885-1946) — A478

Birger Sjoberg (1885-1929), Journalist, Novelist, Poet — A479

1985, Oct. 12   Engr.   **Perf. 12½ Vert.**

1556	A478	1.60k black & red	.55	.35

Perf. 12½ Horiz.

1557	A479	4k dk blue grn	1.25	.35

Christmas 1985 — A480

15th cent. religious paintings by Albertus Pictor.

Perf. 13x12½ on 3 Sides

1985, Nov. 21   Engr.

1558	A480	1.80k Annunciation	.60	.40
1559	A480	1.80k Birth of Christ	.60	.40
1560	A480	1.80k Adoration of the Magi	.60	.40
1561	A480	1.80k Mary as the Apocalyptic Virgin	.60	.40
a.	Bklt. pane, 3 each #1558-1561		7.25	
	Nos. 1558-1561 (4)		2.40	1.60

Nobel Laureates in Literature — A481

Authors: No. 1562, William Faulkner (1897-1962), 1949, Southern United States. No. 1563, Halldor Kiljan Laxness (b.1902), 1955, Iceland. No. 1564, Miguel Angel Asturias (1899-1974), 1967, Guatemala. No. 1565, Yasunari Kawabata (1899-1972), 1968, Japan. No. 1566, Patrick White (b. 1912), 1973, Australia.

Lithographed and Engraved

1985, Nov. 21		Perf. 13 Horiz.	
1562	A481	2.70k myr grn	.90	.80
1563	A481	2.70k dp brn, chlky bl & myr grn	.90	.80
1564	A481	2.70k myr grn & tan	.90	.80
1565	A481	2.70k chlky bl & myr grn	.90	.80
1566	A481	2.70k chlky bl & ocher	.90	.80
a.		Blkt. pane of 5, #1562-1566	4.50	

Types of 1983-85
Engr., Litho. (1.80k, 3.20k, 6k)

1986-89			Perf. 12½ Vert.	
1567	A436b	1.70k dk violet	.55	.20
1568	A436b	1.80k brt violet	.55	.20
1569	A436c	2.10k dk blue	.55	.20
1570	A436c	2.20k int blue	.65	.20
1571	A436c	2.30k dk ol grn	.80	.20
1572	A436b	2.80k emerald	.90	.50
1573	A436c	2.90k dk green	.90	.60
1574	A436c	3.10k dk brown	.95	.65
1575	A436b	3.20k yellow brn	.90	.75
1576	A436d	3.30k dk rose brn	1.10	.65
1577	A436d	3.40k dk red	.90	.45
1578	A436d	3.60k green	1.00	.60
1579	A436d	3.90k violet blue	1.65	.75
1580	A436b	6k blue green	2.00	.35
		Nos. 1567-1580 (14)	13.40	6.30

Issued: 2.10, 2.90, 3.40k, 1/23'; 1.70, 2.80k, 2/20; 1.80, 3.10, 3.20, 3.60, 6k, 1/27/87; 2.20k, 1/29/88; 2.30, 3.30, 3.90k, 4/20/89. See No. 1796.

Waterbirds A484

Perf. 13 on 2 or 3 Sides

1986, Jan. 23			Engr.	
1582	A484	2.10k Eider	.55	.20
1583	A484	2.10k Smaspov	.55	.20
a.		Blkt. pane, 5 each #1582-1583	5.50	
1584	A484	2.30k Storlom	.75	.20
		Nos. 1582-1584 (3)	1.85	.60

STOCKHOLMIA '86 — A485

Lithographed and Engraved

1986, Jan. 23			Perf. 13	
1585	A485	2k #33a, cancel	.80	.70
1586	A485	2k Stamp engraver	.80	.70
1587	A485	3k #268, 271, US #836	1.25	1.10
1588	A485	4k Boy soaking stamps	1.50	1.40
a.		Blkt. pane of 4, #1585-1588	4.50	

See US Nos. 2198-2201a.

Swedish PO, 350th Anniv. A486

Sundial A487

Lithographed and Engraved

1986, Feb. 20		Perf. 13x12½	
1589	A486	2.10k org yel & dk bl	.55	.20
a.		Bkkt. pane of 8	4.50	

1986, Feb. 20	Engr.	Perf. 13 Horiz.	

No. 1591, Motto of the Swedish Academy.

1590	A487	1.70k dk bl & lake, gray	.55	.50
1591	A487	1.70k grn & dk red, gray	.55	.50
a.		Pair, #1590-1591	1.25	1.25

Royal Swedish Academy of Letters, History and Antiquities, and Swedish Academy, bicents.

Provincial Arms Type of 1981
Perf. 15x14½ on 3 Sides

1986, Apr. 23			Photo.	
1592	A410	1.90k Harjedalen	.95	.20
1593	A410	1.90k Uppland	.95	.20
1594	A410	1.90k Halland	.95	.20
1595	A410	1.90k Lapland	.95	.20
a.		Bkkt. pane, 5 each #1592-1595	19.00	
		Nos. 1592-1595 (4)	3.80	.80

See note after No. 1277.

King Carl XVI Gustaf — A488

Royal Cipher — A489

40th birthday: No. 1598, King presenting Nobel Prize for literature to Czeslaw Milosz, 1980. No. 1600, Royal family at Soldien palace.

Lithographed and Engraved

1986, Apr. 23		Perf. 12 on 3 Sides	
1596	A488	2.10k grnsh blk & pale grn	.60	.30
1597	A489	2.10k dk bl, pink & gold	.60	.30
1598	A488	2.10k dk bl & pale bl	.60	.30
1599	A489	2.10k dk bl, pale grn & gold	.60	.30
1600	A488	2.10k blk & pale pink	.60	.30
a.		Bkkt. pane, 2 each #1596-1600	6.00	
		Nos. 1596-1600 (5)	3.00	1.50

Olof Palme (1927-1986), Prime Minister — A490

Perf. 13 on 3 Sides

1986, Apr. 11			Engr.	
1601	A490	2.10k dk lilac rose	.85	.85
1602	A490	2.90k grnsh black	1.10	1.10
a.		Bkkt. pane, 5 ea #1601-1602	10.00	

Nordic Cooperation Issue — A491

Sister towns.

1986, May 27	Engr.	Perf. 13 Vert.	
1603	A491	2.10k Uppsala	.70	.20
1604	A491	2.90k Eskilstuna	1.00	.65

Europa 1986 — A492

1986, May 27		Perf. 13 Horiz.	
1605	A492	2.10k Automotive pollutants	1.75	.20

Perf. 13 on 3 Sides

| 1606 | A492 | 2.90k Industrial pollutants | 1.10 | .60 |
| a. | | Booklet pane of 6 | 5.00 | |

STOCKHOLMIA '86 — A493

Designs: No. 1607, Mail handling terminal, Tomteboda, 1986. No. 1608, Railroad mail car, 19th cent. No. 1609, Post Office, 18th cent. No. 1610, Postman, 17th cent.

Lithographed and Engraved

1986, Aug. 29			Perf. 13	
1607	A493	2.10k multi	1.50	3.00
1608	A493	2.10k multi	1.50	3.00
1609	A493	2.90k multi	1.50	3.00
1610	A493	2.90k multi	1.50	3.00
a.		Bkkt. pane of 4, #1607-1610	6.00	12.50

Bkkt. sold for 40k, including 30k ticket to STOCKHOLMIA '86.

Souvenir Sheet

World Class Athletes in Track and Field — A494

Designs: a, Ann-Louise Skoglund, 400-meter hurdle, 1982. b, Dag Wennlund, 1986, and Eric Lemming, c. 1900, javelin. c, Standing high jumper and Patrik Sjoberg, high jump, 1985. d, Anders Garderud, 300-meter steeplechase record-holder.

1986, Oct. 18	Engr.	Perf. 12½	
1611	A494	Sheet of 4	3.75	3.75
a.-d.		2.10k, any single	.85	.85

No. 1611 sold for 11k to benefit philatelic organizations.

Intl. Peace Year — A495

Amnesty Intl., 25th Anniv. — A496

1986, Oct. 18		Perf. 13 Vert.	
1612	A495	3.40k bluish blk & emer grn	1.10	1.00
1613	A496	3.40k dk red & bluish blk	1.10	1.00
a.		Pair, #1612-1613	2.50	2.25

Christmas — A497

Winter village scenes.

Perf. 13x12½ on 3 Sides

1986, Nov. 25		Litho. & Engr.	
1614	1.90k Postal van	.65	.35
1615	1.90k Postman on bicycle	.65	.35
1616	1.90k Children, sled	.65	.35
1617	1.90k Child mailing letter	.65	.35
a.	A497 Block of 4, #1614-1617	2.75	2.50
b.	Bkkt. pane of 12, 3 #1617a	8.50	

Nobel Peace Prize Laureates — A498

#1618, Bertha von Suttner, 1905. #1619, Carl von Ossietzky, 1935. No. 1608, Albert Luthuli, 1960. #1621, Martin Luther King, Jr., 1964. #1622, Mother Teresa, 1979.

1986, Nov. 25		Engr.	Perf. 13 Horiz.	
1618	A498	2.90k brt bl, blk & hn brn	1.00	.85
1619	A498	2.90k blk & hn brn	1.00	.85
1620	A498	2.90k brt bl, blk & brn blk	1.00	.85
1621	A498	2.90k brn blk & hn brn	1.00	.85
1622	A498	2.90k blk, brt bl & hn brn	1.00	.85
a.		Bkkt. pane of 5, #1618-1622	5.00	

Conservation Type of 1983
Perf. 13 on 3 Sides

1987, Mar. 10			Engr.	
1623	A447	2.10k Parnassius mnemosyne	.60	.20
1624	A447	2.10k Gentianella campestris	.60	.20
a.		Booklet pane, 5 ea #1623-1624	6.00	

Perf. 13 Horiz.

1625	A447	2.50k Osmoderma eremita	.85	.20
1626	A447	4.20k Arnica montana	1.40	.20
		Nos. 1623-1626 (4)	3.45	.80

Swedish Aviation Industry A500

1987, Mar. 10		Perf. 13 Vert.	
1627	A500	25k Saab SF340	6.75	.60

Europa 1987 — A501

Nos. 1628-1629, City Library, Asplund. No. 1630, Lewerentz Marcus Church.

1987, May 14	Engr.	Perf. 13 Vert.	
1628	A501	2.10k int blk & grn	1.25	.25

Perf. 13 on 3 Sides

1629	A501	3.10k emer grn & red brn	.80	.70
1630	A501	3.10k emer grn & sep	.80	.70
a.		Bkkt. pane, 3 each #1629-1630	6.00	
		Nos. 1628-1630 (3)	2.85	1.65

Illustrations from Children's Novels by Astrid Lindgren (b. 1907) — A502

Perf. 13x12½ on 3 Sides

1987, May 14			**Litho. & Engr.**	
1631	A502	1.90k Karlsson Pa Taket	1.10	.25
1632	A502	1.90k Barnen and Bullerbyn	1.10	.25
1633	A502	1.90k Madicken	1.10	.25
1634	A502	1.90k Mio, Min Mio	1.10	.25
1635	A502	1.90k Nils Karlsson-Pyssling	1.10	.25
1636	A502	1.90k Emil and Lonneberga	1.10	.25
1637	A502	1.90k Ronja Rovardotter	1.10	.25
1638	A502	1.90k Pippi Longstocking	1.10	.25
1639	A502	1.90k Broderna Lejonhjarta	1.10	.25
1640	A502	1.90k Lotta Pa Brakmakargatan	1.10	.25
a.		Bklt. pane, 2 ea #1631-1640	22.00	
		Nos. 1631-1640 (10)	11.00	2.50

See note after No. 1277.

Medieval Towns — A503

#1641, Hans Brask, Bishop of Linkoping, 16th cent. #1642, Nykopingshus Castle.

1987, May 14		**Engr.**	**Perf. 12½ Vert.**	
1641	A503	2.10k blk, dk vio & yel bis	.70	.35
1642	A503	2.10k dk vio, blk & yel bis	.70	.35
a.		Pair, #1641-1642	1.40	1.40

Swedes in the Service of Mankind A504

Designs: No. 1643, Raoul Wallenberg, Swedish diplomat in Budapest during World War II. No. 1644, Dag Hammarskjold (1905-1961), UN secretary-general. No. 1645, Folke Bernadotte af Wisborg (1895-1948), organizer of the Red Cross operation that saved thousands from Nazi death camps.

Perf. 12½ Horiz.

1987, Aug. 10			**Engr.**	
1643	A504	3.10k blue	.90	.85
1644	A504	3.10k green	.90	.85
1645	A504	3.10k brown violet	.90	.85
a.		Bklt. pane, 2 each #1643-1645	6.00	
		Nos. 1643-1645 (3)	2.70	2.55

Gripsholm Castle, 450th Anniv. — A505

Paintings from the Royal Castle Collection, Gripsholm: No. 1646, King Gustav I Vasa (d. 1560), artist unknown. No. 1647, Blue Tiger, 1673, favorite horse of King Charles XI, by D.K. Ehrenstrahl. No. 1648, Hedvig Charlotta Nordenflycht (1718-1763), poet, by Kopia J.H. Scheffel. No. 1649, Gripsholm Castle Outer Courtyard, 17th Cent., 19th cent. lithograph by C.J. Billmark.

1987, Aug. 10		**Perf. 13 Vert.**		
1646	A505	2.10k multi	.60	.35
1647	A505	2.10k multi	.60	.35
1648	A505	2.10k multi	.60	.35

1649	A505	2.10k multi	.60	.35
a.		Bklt. pane of 8, 2 strips of #1646-1649 with gutter btwn.	5.25	
		Nos. 1646-1649 (4)	2.40	1.40

Botanical Gardens A506

Designs: No. 1650, Victoria cruziana (water lily), Victoria House, Bergian Garden, c. 1790, Stockholm University. No. 1651, Layout of baroque palace garden, by Carl Harleman (1700-1753), Uppsala University. No. 1652, White anemones, rock garden, Gothenberg Botanical Gardens, 1923. No. 1653, Tulip tree blossoms, Academy Garden, c. 1860, Lund University.

1987, Oct. 10		**Engr.**	**Perf. 13 Vert.**	
1650	A506	2.10k multi	.60	.35
1651	A506	2.10k multi	.60	.35
1652	A506	2.10k multi	.60	.35
1653	A506	2.10k multi	.60	.35
a.		Bklt. pane, 2 each #1650-1653 with gutter between	5.25	
		Nos. 1650-1653 (4)	2.40	1.40

The Circus in Sweden, Bicent. — A507

Litho. & Engr.

1987, Oct. 10			**Perf. 13**	
1654	A507	2.10k Juggler, clown	.85	.85
1655	A507	2.10k High wire	.85	.85
1656	A507	2.10k Equestrian	.85	.85
a.		Bklt. pane of 3, #1654-1656	2.55	

Stamp Day. Sold for 8k.

Christmas A508

Customs: No. 1657, Putting porridge in the stable for the gray Christmas elf. No. 1658, Watering horses at a north-running stream on Boxing Day. No. 1659, Sled-race home from church on Christmas Day. No. 1660, Hanging out sheaves of wheat to foretell a good harvest.

Perf. 13 on 3 Sides

1987, Nov. 25			**Litho.**	
1657	A508	2k multi	.50	.30
1658	A508	2k multi	.50	.30
1659	A508	2k multi	.50	.30
1660	A508	2k multi	.50	.30
a.		Bklt. pane, 3 each #1657-1660	6.50	
		Nos. 1657-1660 (4)	2.00	1.20

Nobel Prize Winners in Physics A509

Space and diagram or formula: No. 1661, Antony Hewish, Great Britain, 1974. No. 1662, Subrahmanyan Chandrasekhar, US, 1983. No. 1663, William Fowler, US, 1983. No. 1664, Arno Penzias and Robert Wilson, US, 1978. No. 1665, Martin Ryle, Great Britain, 1974.

1987, Nov. 25		**Engr.**	**Perf. 13**	
1661	A509	2.90k dark blue	.85	.85
1662	A509	2.90k blk	.85	.85
1663	A509	2.90k dark blue	.85	.85

1664	A509	2.90k dark blue	.85	.85
1665	A509	2.90k blk	.85	.85
a.		Bklt. pane of 5, #1661-1665	4.25	

Inland Boats A510

1988, Jan. 29		**Engr.**	**Perf. 13**	
1666	A510	3.10k Skiff, Lake Hjalmaren	.60	.70
1667	A510	3.10k Village boat, Lake Vattern	.60	.70
1668	A510	3.10k Rowboat, Byske	.60	.70
1669	A510	3.10k Flat-bottomed rowboat, Asnen	.60	.70
1670	A510	3.10k Ice boat, Lake Vanern	.60	.70
1671	A510	3.10k Church boat, Lake Locknesjon	.60	.70
a.		Bklt. pane of 6, #1666-1671	5.00	

A511

A512

Settling of New Sweden, 350th Anniv. — A513

Designs: No. 1672, 17th Cent. European settlers negotiating with American Indians, map of New Sweden, the Swedish ships *Kalmar Nyckel* and *Fogel Grip*, based on an 18th cent. illustration from a Swedish book about the American Colonies. No. 1673, Bishop Hill and painter Olof Krans. No. 1674, Carl Sandburg (1878-1967), author, and Jenny Lind (1820-1887), opera singer known as the "Swedish Nightingale." No. 1675, Charles Lindbergh (1902-1974), and *The Spirit of St. Louis*. No. 1676, American astronaut with Swedish Hasselblad camera on the Moon. No. 1677, Swedish players in National Hockey League.

Litho. & Engr., Engr. (#1674-1675)

1988, Mar. 29		**Perf. 13x12½ Horiz**		
1672	A511	3.60k multi	1.00	.95
1673	A511	3.60k multi	1.00	.95

Perf. 13x12½ on 3 Sides

1674	A512	3.60k brn	1.00	.95
1675	A512	3.60k dk bl & brn	1.00	.95

Perf. 13x12½ on 2

1676	A513	3.60k dk bl & yel	1.00	.95
1677	A513	3.60k dk red, dk bl & blk	1.00	.95
a.		Bklt. pane of 6, #1672-1677	6.00	

See US No. C117 and Finland No. 768.

Conservation Type of 1983

Species Inhabiting Coastal Waters

Perf. 13 on 3 Sides

1988, Mar. 29			**Engr.**	
1678	A447	2.20k Haliaetus albicilla	.55	.20
1679	A447	2.20k Halichoerus grypus	.55	.20
a.		Bklt. pane, 5 #1678, 5 #1679	5.50	

Perf. 13 Horiz.

1680	A446	4.40k Anguilla anguilla	1.45	.25
		Nos. 1678-1680 (3)	2.55	.65

Midsummer Celebration A515

Skara Township Millennium A516

Perf. 12½ on 3 Sides

1988, May 17			**Litho. & Engr.**	
1681	A515	2k Wildflowers in meadow	.95	.25
1682	A515	2k Rowing	.95	.25
1683	A515	2k Children making wreaths	.95	.25
1684	A515	2k Raising maypole	.95	.25
1685	A515	2k Fiddlers	.95	.25
1686	A515	2k Ferry	.95	.25
1687	A515	2k Dancing	.95	.25
1688	A515	2k Accordion player	.95	.25
1689	A515	2k Maypole, residence	.95	.25
1690	A515	2k Bouquet of flowers	.95	.25
a.		Bklt. pane, 2 ea #1681-1690	19.00	
		Nos. 1681-1690 (10)	9.50	2.50

See note after No. 1277.

1988, May 17			**Perf. 13 Horiz.**	

Design: Detail from Creation, a Skara Cathedral stained-glass window by Bo Beskow, 20th cent.

1691	A516	2.20k multi	.80	.40

Stora Mining Co., 700th Anniv. — A517

Royal Dramatic Theater, Stockholm, Founded by King Gustav III in 1788 — A518

1988, May 17			**Engr.**	
1692	A517	4.40k Mine, 18th cent.	1.65	.45

1988, May 17

Design: Scene fron *The Queen's Diamond Ornament*, about the murder of King Gustav III at the Royal Opera in 1792.

1693	A518	8k grn, red & blk	2.75	.90

Self-portrait, 1923, by Nils Dardel (1888-1943) A519

Paintings: No. 1695, *Old Age Home in Autumn*, c. 1930, by Vera Nilsson (1888-1979). No. 1696, *Self-portrait*, 1912, by Isaac Grunewald (1899-1979). No. 1697, *Visit of an Eccentric Lady*, 1921, by Dardel. No. 1698, *Soap Bubbles*, 1927, by Nilsson. No. 1699, *The Fair*, 1915, by Grunewald.

Perf. 13 on 3 Sides
1988, Aug. 25   **Litho. & Engr.**
Size: 33x35mm (Nos. 1695, 1698)

1694	A519	2.20k shown	.75	.60
1695	A519	2.20k multi	.75	.60
1696	A519	2.20k multi	.75	.60
1697	A519	2.20k multi	.75	.60
1698	A519	2.20k multi	.75	.60
1699	A519	2.20k multi	.75	.60
a.		Bklt. pane of 6, #1694-1699	4.50	

Europa — A520

Transport and communication.

1988, Aug. 25   Engr.   Perf. 13 Vert.

1700	A520	2.20k like No. 1701	1.60	.35

Perf. 13 on 3 Sides

1701	A520	3.10k X2 high-speed train	1.00	.75
1702	A520	3.10k Steam locomotive, 1887	1.00	.75
a.		Bklt. pane, 3 each #1701-1702	4.00	
		Nos. 1700-1702 (3)	3.60	1.85

Common Swift — A521

1988, Aug. 25   Perf. 12½ Vert.

1703	A521	20k brt vio & dk vio	6.50	.60

Dan Andersson (1888-1920), Poet, and Manuscript A522

Forest and Pond, Finnmarken — A523

1988, Oct. 8   Engr.   Perf. 13 Vert.

1704	A522	2.20k vio, dk bl & dk bl grn	.70	.35
1705	A523	2.20k vio, dk bl & dk bl grn	.70	.35
a.		Pair, #1704-1705	1.40	1.25

Soccer — A524

Match scenes: No. 1706, Dribble (Torbjorn Nilsson representing local club matches). No. 1707, Heading the ball (Ralf Edstrom of the national league). No. 1708, Kick (Pia Sundhage, women's soccer).

1988, Oct. 8   Litho. & Engr.   Perf. 13

1706	A524	2.20k multi	1.25	.75
1707	A524	2.20k multi	1.25	.75
1708	A524	2.20k multi	1.25	.75
a.		Bklt. pane of 3, #1706-1708	3.75	

No. 1708a sold for 8.50k; surtax benefited stamp collecting.

Nobel Laureates in Chemistry A525

Christmas A526

Designs: No. 1709, Willard F. Libby, US, 1960, carbon-14 method of dating artifacts. No. 1710, Karl Ziegler, West Germany, and Guilio Natta, Italy, 1963, catalysts. No. 1711, Aaron Klug, South Africa, 1982, electron microscopy. No. 1712, Ilya Prigogine, Belgium, 1977, proof that molecular order can occur spontaneously out of chaos.

1988, Nov. 29   Perf. 12½ Vert.

1709	A525	3.10k multi	1.00	.80
1710	A525	3.10k multi	1.00	.80
1711	A525	3.10k multi	1.00	.80
1712	A525	3.10k multi	1.00	.80
a.		Bklt. pane, 2 each #1709-1712	8.50	
		Nos. 1709-1712 (4)	4.00	3.20

Perf. 12½x13 on 3 Sides
1988, Nov. 29

Story of Christ's birth according to Luke (2:7-20): No. 1713, Angels appear to inform shepherds of Christ's birth. No. 1714, Star of Bethlehem, angel, horse. No. 1715, Birds singing. No. 1716, Magi offering gifts. No. 1717, Holy family. No. 1718, Shepherds with palm offering.

1713	A526	2k multi	.65	.45
1714	A526	2k multi	.65	.45
1715	A526	2k multi	.65	.45
1716	A526	2k multi	.65	.45
1717	A526	2k multi	.65	.45
1718	A526	2k multi	.65	.45
a.		Bklt. pane, 2 each #1713-1718	8.00	
		Nos. 1713-1718 (6)	3.90	2.70

Nos. 1713 and 1716, 1714 and 1717, 1715 and 1718 have continuous designs.

Lighthouses A527

Designs: 1.90k, Twin masonry lighthouses, 1832, and concrete lighthouse, 1946, Nidingen, Kattegat Is. 2.70k, Soderarm, Uppland, 1839. 3.80k, Sydostbrotten, Gulf of Bothnia, 1963. 3.90k, Sandhammaren, Skane, c. 1860.

1989, Jan. 31   Engr.   Perf. 13 Vert.

1719	A527	1.90k multi	.65	.35
1720	A527	2.70k multi	.90	.45
1721	A527	3.80k multi	1.25	.70
1722	A527	3.90k multi	1.30	.85
		Nos. 1719-1722 (4)	4.10	2.35

Endangered Species — A528

1989, Jan. 31   Perf. 13 on 3 Sides

1723	A528	2.30k Gulo gulo	.75	.25
1724	A528	2.30k Strix uralensis	.75	.25
a.		Bklt. pane, 5 each #1723-1724	7.50	

Perf. 13 Horiz.

1725	A528	2.40k Dendrocopos minor	.80	.25
1726	A528	2.60k Calidris alpina schinzii	.85	.65
1727	A528	3.30k Hyla arborea	1.10	.70
1728	A528	4.60k Ficedula parva	1.50	.45
		Nos. 1723-1728 (6)	5.75	2.55

Opening of The Globe Arena, Stockholm — A529

Perf. 13 Horiz.
1989, Apr. 14   Litho. & Engr.

1729	A529	2.30k Exterior	.75	.45
1730	A529	2.30k Ice hockey	.75	.45
1731	A529	2.30k Gymnastics	.75	.45
1732	A529	2.30k Concert	.75	.45
a.		Bklt. pane of 4, #1729-1732	3.00	

Nordic Cooperation Issue — A530

Folk costumes.

Perf. 13 Horiz.
1989, Apr. 20   Litho. & Engr.

1733	A530	2.30k Woman's wool waist	.75	.30
1734	A530	3.30k Belt pouch	1.10	.70

Natl. Labor Movement, Cent. — A531

1989, May 17   Engr.   Perf. 13 Horiz.

1735	A531	2.30k dk red & blk	.75	.25

Europa 1989 — A532

Children's games: 2.30k, No. 1738, Sailing toy boats. No. 1737, Kick-sledding.

1989, May 17   Perf. 13 Vert.

1736	A532	2.30k car lake	1.25	.30

Perf. 13

1737	A532	3.30k greenish blue	1.00	.75
1738	A532	3.30k lilac	1.00	.75
a.		Bklt. pane, 3 #1737, 3 #1738	6.60	
		Nos. 1736-1738 (3)	3.25	1.80

Summer — A533

Perf. 13 on 3 Sides
1989, May 17   **Litho.**

1739	A533	2.10k Sailing	.90	.35
1740	A533	2.10k Beach ball	.90	.35
1741	A533	2.10k Cycling	.90	.35
1742	A533	2.10k Canoeing	.90	.35
1743	A533	2.10k Angling	.90	.35
1744	A533	2.10k Camping	.90	.35
1745	A533	2.10k Croquet	.90	.35
1746	A533	2.10k Badminton	.90	.35
1747	A533	2.10k Gardening	.90	.35
1748	A533	2.10k Sand sculpture	.90	.35
a.		Bklt. pane, 2 ea #1739-1748	18.00	
		Nos. 1739-1748 (10)	9.00	3.50

See note after No. 1277.

Polar Exploration A534

Swedish polar techniques used in the Arctic (Nos. 1749-1751) and Antarctic: No. 1749, Aircraft, temperature experiment. No. 1750, Settlement, Arctic pass. No. 1751, Icebreaker, experiment. No. 1752, Penguins, tall ship and longboat. No. 1753, Antarctic transports, helicopter. No. 1754, Surveying, albatross.

Perf. 13 on 3 Sides
1989, Aug. 22   Litho. & Engr.
Size: 40x43mm (Nos. 1750, 1753)

1749	A534	3.30k multi	.95	.90
1750	A534	3.30k multi	.95	.90
1751	A534	3.30k multi	.95	.90
1752	A534	3.30k multi	.95	.90
1753	A534	3.30k multi	.95	.90
1754	A534	3.30k multi	.95	.90
a.		Bklt. pane of 6, #1749-1754	5.90	

Smaland Businesses A535

Perf. 12½x12 on 3 Sides
1989, Aug. 22   **Engr.**

1755	A535	2.30k Furniture	.70	.65
1756	A535	2.30k Assembly equipment	.70	.65
1757	A535	2.30k Sewing machines	.70	.65
1758	A535	2.30k Glassware	.70	.65
1759	A535	2.30k Metal springs	.70	.65
1760	A535	2.30k Matchsticks	.70	.65
a.		Bklt. pane of 6, #1755-1760	4.25	

Eagle Owl, *Bubo bubo* A536

1989, Aug. 22   Perf. 13 Vert.

1761	A536	30k vio, blk & grn blk	9.00	.75

Conservation Type of 1983 and

Birds and Coastline, Bla Jungfrun Natl. Park — A537

Perf. 13x12½ on 3 Sides
1989, Sept. 12   **Engr.**

1762	A447	2.40k *Rhododendron lapponicum*	.75	.25
1763	A447	2.40k *Calypso bulbosa*	.75	.25
a.		Bklt. pane, 5 ea #1762-1763	7.50	

Perf. 12½ Vert.

1764	A537	4.30k dark blue, blk & brn vio	1.40	1.10
		Nos. 1762-1764 (3)	2.90	1.60

See Nos. 1776-1780.

Swedish Kennel Club, Cent. — A538

a, Large spitz. b, Fox hound. c, Small spitz.

1989, Oct. 7   Litho.   Perf. 13x12½
1765 A538   Bklt. pane of 3   3.00 3.00
a.-c.   2.40k any single   1.00 1.00
        Sold for 9.50k.

Christmas — A539

Holiday symbols: No. 1766, Top of Christmas tree, wreath. No. 1767, Candelabrum, foods. No. 1768, Star, poinsettia plant, grot pot. No. 1769, Bottom of tree, straw goat, gifts. No. 1770, Gifts, television, girl. No. 1771, Boy, grandfather, girl opening gift.

Perf. 12½x13 on 3 Sides
1989, Nov. 24   Litho.
1766 A539 2.10k multi   .65   .40
1767 A539 2.10k multi   .65   .40
1768 A539 2.10k multi   .65   .40
1769 A539 2.10k multi   .65   .40
1770 A539 2.10k multi   .65   .40
1771 A539 2.10k multi   .65   .40
 a.   Bklt. pane, 2 each #1766-1771   8.00
        Nos. 1766-1771 (6)   3.90 2.40

Nobel Laureates
in Physiology
A540

Genetics: No. 1772, Thomas Morgan (1866-1945), US, 1933, chromosomal study of fruit flies to determine laws and mechanism of heredity. No. 1773, James Watson, US, and Francis Crick with Maurice Wilkins, Great Britain, 1962, molecular structure of DNA. No. 1774, Werner Arber, Switzerland, Daniel Nathans and Hamilton Smith, US, 1978, enzymatic cutting of nucleotides to create gene hybrids. No. 1775, Barbara McClintock, botanist, US, 1983, corn color studies that led to theory of gene jumping.

Perf. 12½ Vert.
1989, Nov. 24   Litho. & Engr.
1772 A540 3.60k multi   1.10   .90
1773 A540 3.60k multi   1.10   .90
1774 A540 3.60k multi   1.10   .90
1775 A540 3.60k multi   1.10   .90
 a.   Bklt. pane, 2 each #1772-1775
        with gutter between   9.00
        Nos. 1772-1775 (4)   4.40 3.60

Natl. Parks Type of 1989

Designs: No. 1776, Campground, sailboat on lake, Angso Park. No. 1777, Hiking, Pieljekaise Park. 3.70k, Three whooper swans over wetlands, Muddus Park. 4.10k, Deer, lake, Padjelanta Park. 4.80k, Bears, forest, Sanfjallet Park.

Perf. 13 on 3 Sides
1990, Jan. 26   Engr.
1776 A537 2.50k multicolored   .80   .20
1777 A537 2.50k multicolored   .80   .20
 a.   Bklt. pane, 5 each #1776-1777   8.25
Perf. 13 Vert.
1778 A537 3.70k multicolored   1.25   .30
1779 A537 4.10k multicolored   1.40 1.10
1780 A537 4.80k multicolored   1.50 1.25
        Nos. 1776-1780 (5)   5.75 3.05

King and Queen Types of 1985-86 and

Queen   King Carl XVI
Silvia — A541   Gustaf — A542

King Carl XVI   Queen Silvia
Gustav   A544
A543

King Carl XVI
Gustaf — A545

Perf. 12½ Vert., Horiz. (A541, A542, A545)

1990-97   Engr.
1783 A436c 2.50k deep claret   .85   .20
1785 A542   2.80k dk blue   .90   .20
1786 A542   2.90k deep green   .90   .25
1789 A542   3.20k violet   .90   .20
1792 A543   3.70k dark red
                   brown   1.00   .20
1793 A543   3.85k black   1.25   .25
1796 A436d 4.60k bright org   1.50 1.00
1797 A541   5k deep rose
                   vio   1.75   .20
1797A A545   (5k) deep blue   1.50   .30
1798 A541   6k deep claret   2.00   .60
1798A A544   6k dark green   2.00   .60
1799 A541   6.50k purple   2.00   .70
1800 A544   7.50k purple   2.25 1.00
1800A A544   8k brown red   2.40 1.00
        Nos. 1783-1800A (14)   21.20 6.70

Issued: 2.50k, 4.60k, 1/26; 5k, 3/20/91; 2.80k, 11/20/91; 2.90k, #1798, 1/2/93; 3.20k, 1/17/94; 6.50k, 3/18/94; 3.70k, #1798A, 1/2/95; 3.85k, 7.50k, 1/2/96; (5k), 8k, 2/28/97.
No. 1797A is inscribed "BREV."
This is an expanding set. Numbers will change if necessary.

Viking
Heritage
A546

Designs: No. 1801, Viking head of carved bone, dragon carving found in Birka. No. 1802, Three viking longships. No. 1803, Viking town. No. 1804, Bronze statue of pagan fertility god, silver filigree cross. No. 1805, Bishop's crosier, southern Russian carved statue of a deer. No. 1806, Viking longship (stern). No. 1807, Viking longship (bow), horsemen, woman, warrior, wolf. No. 1808, Sword hilts.

Perf. 12x13 on 3 Sides
1990, Mar. 28   Litho. & Engr.
1801 A546 2.50k multicolored   .80   .65
1802 A546 2.50k multicolored   .80   .65
1803 A546 2.50k multicolored   .80   .65
1804 A546 2.50k multicolored   .80   .65
1805 A546 2.50k multicolored   .80   .65
1806 A546 2.50k multicolored   .80   .65
1807 A546 2.50k multicolored   .80   .65
1808 A546 2.50k multicolored   .80   .65
 a.   Bklt. pane of 8, #1801-1808   6.50

Nos. 1802-1803, 1806-1807 printed in a continuous design.

Swedish
Industrial Safety,
Cent. — A547

1990, Mar. 28   Engr.   Perf. 13 Horiz.
1809 A547 2.50k Lumberjack   .80   .25

Europa
1990 — A548

Post offices.

1990, Mar. 28   Perf. 13 Vert.
1810 A548 2.50k Postal Museum,
                  1720   1.10   .35
Perf. 13 on 3 Sides
1811 A548 3.80k Sollebrunn,
                  1985   1.50   .75
1812 A548 3.80k Vasteras, 1956   1.50   .75
 a.   Bklt. pane, 3 each #1811-1812   5.25
        Nos. 1810-1812 (3)   4.10 1.85

World
Equestrian
Games,
Stockholm
A549

Litho. & Engr.
1990, May 15   Perf. 12½x13
1813 A549 3.80k Endurance rid-
                  ing   1.25   .90
1814 A549 3.80k Combined train-
                  ing   1.25   .90
1815 A549 3.80k Show jumping   1.25   .90
1816 A549 3.80k Dressage   1.25   .90
1817 A549 3.80k Volting   1.25   .90
1818 A549 3.80k Four-in-hand   1.25   .90
 a.   Bklt. pane of 6, #1813-1818   7.50

Apiculture — A550

#1819, Worker bee collecting nectar. #1820, Bee, bilberry flower. #1821, Worker bee. #1822, Apiary hive. #1823, Two bees in honeycomb. #1824, Drone, 7 cells, blue green panel. #1825, Queen bee, 7 cells, yellow panel. #1826, Hive hanging from tree. #1827, Beekeeper. #1828, Honey.

1990, May 15   Litho.
1819 A550 2.30k multicolored   .95   .40
1820 A550 2.30k multicolored   .95   .40
1821 A550 2.30k multicolored   .95   .40
1822 A550 2.30k multicolored   .95   .40
1823 A550 2.30k multicolored   .95   .40
1824 A550 2.30k multicolored   .95   .40
1825 A550 2.30k multicolored   .95   .40
1826 A550 2.30k multicolored   .95   .40
1827 A550 2.30k multicolored   .95   .40
1828 A550 2.30k multicolored   .95   .40
 a.   Bklt. pane, 2 ea #1819-1828   19.00
        Nos. 1819-1828 (10)   9.50 4.00

See note after No. 1277.

Wasa Nautical
Museum — A551

Man-of-war Wasa: 2.50k, Bow. 4.60k, Stern.

1990, May 15   Engr.   Perf. 13 Vert.
1829 A551 2.50k org & blk   1.00   .30
1830 A551 4.60k dk bl & org   1.50 1.25

Dearest Brothers,
Sisters and
Friends — A552

Proud
City
A553

Allusions to poetry verses of Carl Michael Bellman (No. 1833) and Evert Taube: No. 1833, Fredmen in the gutter. No. 1834, Happy baker in San Remo. No. 1835, At sea. No. 1836, Violava.

Perf. 13 on 3 Sides
1990, Aug. 8   Litho. & Engr.
1831 A552 2.50k multicolored   .80   .65
1832 A552 2.50k multicolored   .80   .65
1833 A552 2.50k multicolored   .80   .65
1834 A552 2.50k multicolored   .80   .65
1835 A552 2.50k multicolored   .80   .65
1836 A552 2.50k multicolored   .80   .65
 a.   Bklt. pane of 6, #1831-1836   5.00

Paper
Production
A554

#1837, Paper production c. 1600. #1838, Watermark. #1839, Newspaper mastheads. #1840, Modern paper production.

1990, Aug. 8   Perf. 12½ Vert.
1837 A554 2.50k multicolored   .80   .40
1838 A554 2.50k multicolored   .80   .40
1839 A554 2.50k multicolored   .80   .40
1840 A554 2.50k multicolored   .80   .40
 a.   Bklt. pane, 2 each #1837-1840
        with gutter between   6.50
        Nos. 1837-1840 (4)   3.20 1.60

Ovedskloster Palace — A555

1990, Aug. 8   Engr.   Perf. 13 Vert.
1841 A555 40k multicolored   8.00   .50

See Nos. 1874-1877.

Photography
A556

Litho. & Engr.
1990, Oct. 6   Perf. 12½
1842 A556 2.50k Bellows camera   1.10 1.00
1843 A556 2.50k August
                  Strindberg   1.10 1.00
1844 A556 2.50k 35mm camera   1.10 1.00
 a.   Bklt. pane of 3, #1842-1844   3.30

Stamp Day. Booklet of two panes sold for 20k. Surtax benefited stamp collecting.

Clouds — A557

A558

1990, Oct. 6   Engr.   Perf. 12½ Horiz.
1845 A557 4.50k Cumulus   1.50 .45
1846 A557 4.70k Cumulonimbus   1.50 .95
1847 A557 4.90k Cirrus   1.65 .95
1848 A557 5.20k Alto cumulus   1.75 1.00
    Nos. 1845-1848 (4)   6.40 3.35

1990, Oct. 6   Perf. 12½ Vert.
1849 A558 2.50k shown   .80 .25
1850 A558 2.50k Women bathing   .80 .25
  a. Pair, #1849-1850   1.65 1.50

Moa Martinson (1890-1964), author.

Nobel Laureates in Literature — A559

Perf. 13 on 2 Sides
1990, Nov. 27   Engr.
1851 A559 3.80k Par Lagerkvist,
              1951   1.25 .90
1852 A559 3.80k Ernest Hem-
              ingway, 1954   1.25 .90
1853 A559 3.80k Albert Camus,
              1957   1.25 .90
1854 A559 3.80k Boris Paster-
              nak, 1958   1.25 .90
  a. Bklt. pane, 2 each #1851-
       1854 with gutter between   10.40
    Nos. 1851-1854 (4)   5.00 3.60

See Nos. 1914-1917.

Christmas — A560

Flowers.

Perf. 13 on 3 Sides
1990, Nov. 27   Litho.
1855 A560 2.30k Schlumbergera
              x buckleyi   .80 .35
1856 A560 2.30k Helleborus ni-
              ger   .80 .35
1857 A560 2.30k Rhododendron
              simsii   .80 .35
1858 A560 2.30k Hippeastrum x
              hortorum   .80 .35
1859 A560 2.30k Hyacinthus
              orientalis   .80 .35
1860 A560 2.30k Euphorbia
              pulcherrima   .80 .35
  a. Bklt. pane, 2 each #1855-1860   9.60
    Nos. 1855-1860 (6)   4.80 2.10

Carta Marina by
Olaus Magnus,
1572 — A561

Scandanavia by A. Bureas and J.
Blaeus, 1662 — A562

Maps: No. 1863, Celestial globe by Anders
Akerman, 1759. No. 1864, Contour map,
1938. No. 1865, Stockholm, 1989. No. 1866,
Bedrock Map, Geological Survey, 1984.

Perf. 13 on 3 Sides
1991, Jan. 30   Litho. & Engr.
1861 A561 5k multicolored   1.50 1.25
1862 A562 5k multicolored   1.50 1.25
1863 A561 5k multicolored   1.50 1.25
1864 A561 5k multicolored   1.50 1.25
1865 A562 5k multicolored   1.50 1.25
1866 A561 5k multicolored   1.50 1.25
  a. Bklt. pane of 6, #1861-1866   9.00

Fish — A563

A564

Perf. 13 on 3 Sides
1991, Jan. 30   Engr.
1867 A563 2.50k shown   .90 .25
1868 A563 2.50k Siluris glanis,
              diff.   .90 .25
  b. Bklt. pane, 5 each #1867-1868   9.00

Perf. 13 Vert.
1869 A563 5k Cobitis taenia   1.75 .20
1870 A563 5.40k Gobio gobio   1.90 1.40
1871 A563 5.50k Noemacheilus
              barbatulus   2.00 .25
1872 A563 5.60k Leucaspius de-
              lineatus   2.00 1.00
    Nos. 1867-1872 (6)   9.45 3.35

Palace Type of 1990

Designs: 10k, Stromsholm Castle. 20k,
Karlberg Castle. 25k, Drottningholm Palace.

1991-92   Engr.   Perf. 13 Vert.
1874 A555 10k blk & olive brn   2.50 .20
1876 A555 20k multicolored   5.00 .50

Size: 58x23mm
1877 A555 25k multicolored   6.00 1.50
    Nos. 1874-1877 (3)   13.50 2.20

Issued: 10k, 4/27; 25k, 3/20; 20k, 5/21/92.
This is an expanding set. Numbers will
change if necessary.

Perf. 12½x13 on 3 Sides
1991, May 15   Litho.
1883 A564 2.40k Seglora
              church   .80 .25
1884 A564 2.40k Flag above
              park   .80 .25
1885 A564 2.40k Wedding   .80 .25
1886 A564 2.40k Animals   .80 .25
  b. Bklt. pane, 5 ea #1883-1886   17.50
    Nos. 1883-1886 (4)   3.20 1.00

Skansen Park, Stockholm, 100th anniv.
See note after No. 1277. Complete booklet
of 20 stamps sold for 46k.

Kolmarden
Zoological Park,
Ostergotland
A565

Perf. 12½ Horiz.
1991, May 15   Engr.
1887 A565 2.50k Polar bears   .90 .25
1888 A565 4k Dolphin show   1.45 .65

Norden '91.

A566

Public Parks, cent.: #1890, Dancing in park.

1991, May 15   Perf. 13 Vert.
1889 A566 2.50k dark blue   .90 .30
1890 A566 2.50k dark blue   .90 .30
  a. Pair, #1889-1890   1.80 1.40

Europa — A567

Litho. & Engr.
1991, May 15   Perf. 13
1891 A567 4k Hermes space
              plane   1.10 .80
1892 A567 4k Freja satellite   1.10 .80
1893 A567 4k Tele-X satellite   1.10 .80
  a. Bklt. pane of 3, #1891-1893   4.00

Olympic
Champions
A568

Designs: No. 1894, Magda Julin, figure skating, Antwerp, 1920. No. 1895, Toini Gustaff-
son, cross country skiing, Grenoble, 1968. No.
1896, Agneta Andersson, Anna Olsson, two-
person kayak, Los Angeles, 1984. No. 1897,
Ulrika Knape, diving, Munich, 1972.

Perf. 12x13 on 3 Sides
1991, Aug. 27   Litho. & Engr.
1894 A568 2.50k multicolored   .70 .50
1895 A568 2.50k multicolored   .70 .50
1896 A568 2.50k multicolored   .70 .50
1897 A568 2.50k multicolored   .70 .50
  a. Bklt. pane, 2 each #1894-1897   5.75
    Nos. 1894-1897 (4)   2.80 2.00

See Nos. 1937-1940, 1953-1956.

Iron Mining — A569

#1898, Spetal Mine, Norberg. #1899, For-
smark Mill. #1900, Ironworks forge. #1901,
Forge welding. #1902, Dannemora Mine.
#1903, Blast furnace, Pershyttan.

Perf. 13 on 2 or 3 Sides
1991, Aug. 27   Engr.
1898 A569 2.50k multicolored   .90 .50
1899 A569 2.50k multicolored   .90 .50

Size: 31x26mm
1900 A569 2.50k multicolored   .90 .50
1901 A569 2.50k multicolored   .90 .50

Size: 31x40mm
1902 A569 2.50k multicolored   .90 .50
1903 A569 2.50k multicolored   .90 .50
  a. Bklt. pane of 6, #1898-1903   5.40

Coronation of King
Gustavus III, by
Carl Gustaf
Pilo — A570

Details from painting: No. 1904, King Gustavus III. No. 1905, Gustavus with crown held
above head. No. 1906, Chancellor Arvid Horn,
Archbishop Mattias Beronius holding crown
above Gustavus III.

1991, Oct. 5   Engr.   Perf. 13
1904 A570 10k blue   2.75 2.75
1905 A570 10k violet   2.75 2.75

Size: 76x44mm
1906 A570 10k greenish black   2.75 2.75
  a. Bklt. pane of 3, #1904-1906   8.25

Czeslaw Slania, engraver, 70th birthday.
No. 1906a sold for 35k to benefit stamp
collecting.

Rock Musicians
A571

1991, Oct. 5   Litho. & Engr.
1907 A571 2.50k Lena Philipsson   .65 .45
1908 A571 2.50k Roxette   .65 .45
1909 A571 2.50k Jerry Williams   .65 .45
  a. Bklt. pane of 3, #1907-1909   2.25

A572

A573

Christmas: No. 1910, Boy with star, girl with
snacks. No. 1911, Family dancing around
Christmas tree. No. 1912, Cat beside tree. No.
1913, Child beside bed.

Perf. 12½x13 on 3 Sides
1991, Nov. 20   Litho.
1910 A572 2.30k multicolored   .65 .35
1911 A572 2.30k multicolored   .65 .35
1912 A572 2.30k multicolored   .65 .35
1913 A572 2.30k multicolored   .65 .35
  b. Bklt. pane, 3 ea #1910-1913   8.00
    Nos. 1910-1913 (4)   2.60 1.40

Nobel Laureates Type of 1990

Nobel Peace Prize Winners: No. 1914, Jean
Henri Dunant, founder of Red Cross. No.
1915, Albert Schweitzer, physician and theologian. No. 1916, Alva Myrdal, disarmament
negotiator. No. 1917, Andrei Sakharov,
physicist.

1991, Nov. 20 Engr. Perf. 13 Horiz.
1914 A559 4k carmine   1.25 .90
1915 A559 4k dk green   1.25 .90
1916 A559 4k dk ultra   1.25 .90
1917 A559 4k dk violet   1.25 .90
  a. Bklt. pane, 2 each #1914-
       1917 with gutter between   10.00
    Nos. 1914-1917 (4)   5.00 3.60

1992, Jan. 30 Engr. Perf. 13 Horiz.
1918 A573 2.30k red, grn & blk   .65 .25

Outdoor Life Assoc., cent.

A574

Wild Animals — A575

1992-96 Engr. Perf. 13 on 3 Sides

1920	A574	2.80k Capreolus capreolus	.80	.20
1921	A574	2.80k Capreolus capreolus (with fawn)	.80	.20
b.		Bklt. pane, 5 ea #1920-1921	8.00	
1922	A574	2.90k Ursus arctos (2 cubs)	.80	.30
1923	A574	2.90k Ursus arctos (adult)	.80	.30
b.		Bklt. pane, 5 ea #1922-1923	8.00	
1924	A574	3.85k Mustela erminea	1.25	.35
1925	A574	3.85k Lutra lutra	1.25	.35
a.		Bklt. pane, 5 ea #1924-1925	12.50	
		Complete booklet, 1 #1925a	12.50	

Perf. 13 Vert.

1926	A574	1k Erinaeceus eropaeus	.30	.30
1927	A574	2.80k like #1921	.95	.20
1928	A574	2.90k like #1922	.75	.20
1929	A574	3k Mustela putorius	.78	.40
1930	A575	3.20k Castor fiber	1.00	.60
1931	A574	3.85k like #1924	1.25	.35
1932	A575	5.80k Canis lupus	1.50	.20

Perf. 13 Horiz. or Vert.

1933	A575	6k Sciurus vulgaris	2.20	.65
1934	A575	7k Alces alces	2.60	.75
1935	A574	7.70k Vulpes vulpes	2.25	.60
1936	A575	12k Lynx lynx	3.10	.85
		Nos. 1920-1936 (17)	22.38	6.80

Issued: #1920-1921, 1930, 6k, 7k, Jan. 30; #1922-1923, 1928-1929, 1932, 1936, Jan. 28, 1993; 1k, 3.20k, 3.85k, 7.70k, 1/2/96.
See Nos. 2207-2209, 2238.

Olympic Champions Type of 1991

No. 1937, Gunde Svan, cross-country skiing, Sarajevo, 1984. No. 1938, Thomas Wassberg, cross-country skiing, Lake Placid, 1980. No. 1939, Tomas Gustafson, speed skating, Sarajevo, 1984. No. 1940, Ingemar Stenmark, slalom skiing, Lake Placid, 1980.

Perf. 12x13 on 3 Sides

1992, Jan. 30   Litho. & Engr.

1937	A568	2.80k multicolored	.65	.50
1938	A568	2.80k multicolored	.65	.50
1939	A568	2.80k multicolored	.65	.50
1940	A568	2.80k multicolored	.65	.50
a.		Bklt. pane, 2 each #1937-1940	5.25	
		Nos. 1937-1940 (4)	2.60	2.00

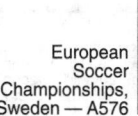

European Soccer Championships, Sweden — A576

1992, Mar. 26   Engr.   Perf. 13 Vert.

1941	A576	2.80k shown	.75	.25
1942	A576	2.80k Two players	.75	.25
a.		Pair, #1941-1942	1.50	1.00

Sweden No. 1a A577

Litho. & Engr.

1992, Mar. 26   Perf. 13

1943	A577	2.80k No. 1	1.25	1.60
1944	A577	4.50k No. 1	1.25	1.60
1945	A577	5.50k shown	1.10	.90
a.		Bklt. pane, #1943-1944, 2 #1945	5.25	
		Nos. 1943-1945 (3)	3.60	4.10

No. 1945a sold for 25k. Surtax benefited stamp collecting.

Sailing Ships — A578

1992, Mar. 26

1946	A578	4.50k Sprengtporten, 1785	1.00	.75
1947	A578	4.50k Superb, 1855	1.00	.75
1948	A578	4.50k Big T	1.00	.75
a.		Bklt. pane of 3, #1946-1948	3.00	

Europa. Discovery Race, Spain-Florida (No. 1948).

Children's Drawings A579

Perf. 13x12½ on 3 Sides

1992, May 21   Litho.

1949	A579	2.50k Rabbit	.60	.25
1950	A579	2.50k Horses	.60	.25
1951	A579	2.50k Cat	.60	.25
1952	A579	2.50k Elephant	.60	.25
a.		Bklt. pane, 5 ea #1949-1952	12.00	
		Nos. 1949-1952 (4)	2.40	1.00

See note after No. 1277.

Olympic Champions Type of 1991

Designs: No. 1953, Gunnar Larsson, swimming, 1972. No. 1954, Bernt Johansson, cycling, 1976. No. 1955, Anders Garderud, steeplechase, 1976. No. 1956, Gert Fredriksson, kayaking, 1948-1956.

Perf. 12x13 on 3 Sides

1992, May 21   Litho. & Engr.

1953	A568	5.50k multicolored	1.40	1.25
1954	A568	5.50k multicolored	1.40	1.25
1955	A568	5.50k multicolored	1.40	1.25
1956	A568	5.50k multicolored	1.40	1.25
a.		Bklt. pane, 2 each #1953-1956	11.50	
		Nos. 1953-1956 (4)	5.60	5.00

Greetings Stamps — A580

Perf. 13x12 on 3 Sides

1992, Aug. 14   Litho.

1957	A580	2.80k Hand with flower	.70	.35
1958	A580	2.80k Cheese	.70	.35
1959	A580	2.80k Baby	.70	.35
1960	A580	2.80k Hand holding pen	.70	.35
b.		Bklt. pane, 2 each #1957-1960	6.00	
		Nos. 1957-1960 (4)	2.80	1.40

88th Inter-Parliamentary Union Conference, Stockholm — A581

Swedish Patent and Registration Office, Cent. — A582

#1961, Riksdag building. #1962, First automatic lighthouse, Gustaf Dalen's sun valve.

Perf. 12½ Vert.

1992, Aug. 27   Engr.

1961	A581	2.80k violet, *tan*	.80	.25

Perf. 13 Horiz.

1962	A582	2.80k blue & black	.80	.25

Kitchen Maid, by Rembrandt A583

The Triumph of Venus, by Francois Boucher A584

Paintings: No. 1965, Portrait of a Girl, by Albrecht Durer. No. 1966, Rorstrand Vase, by Erik Wahlberg. No. 1967, Motif from the Seine/The Tree and the River Bend III, by Carl Fredrik Hill. No. 1968, Sergel in his Studio, by Carl Larsson.

Perf. 12½ on 3 Sides

1992, Aug. 27   Litho. & Engr.

1963	A583	5.50k multicolored	1.50	1.25
1964	A584	5.50k multicolored	1.50	1.25
1965	A583	5.50k multicolored	1.50	1.25
1966	A583	5.50k multicolored	1.50	1.25
1967	A584	5.50k multicolored	1.50	1.25
1968	A583	5.50k multicolored	1.50	1.25
a.		Bklt. pane of 6, #1963-1968	9.00	

National Museum of Fine Arts, 200th anniv.

Prehistoric Animals — A585

Perf. 13x12½ on 3 Sides

1992, Oct. 3   Litho. & Engr.

1969	A585	2.80k Plateosaurus	1.25	.90
1970	A585	2.80k Thoracosaurus scanicus	1.25	.90
1971	A585	2.80k Coelodonta antiquitatis	1.25	.90
1972	A585	2.80k Mammuthus primigenius	1.25	.90
a.		Bklt. pane, 2 ea #1969-1972	10.40	
		Nos. 1969-1972 (4)	5.00	3.60

No. 1972a sold for 27k to benefit stamp collecting.

1950 Automobiles A586

1992, Oct. 3   Engr.   Perf. 12½ Vert.

1973	A586	4k Saab 92	1.25	.65
1974	A586	4k Volvo P 831	1.25	.65
a.		Pair, #1973-1974	2.50	1.50

Birds of the Baltic Shores — A587

1992, Oct. 3   Litho. & Engr.   Perf. 13

1975	A587	4.50k Pandion haliaetus	1.25	.95
1976	A587	4.50k Limosa limosa	1.25	.95
1977	A587	4.50k Mergus merganser	1.25	.95
1978	A587	4.50k Tadorna tadorna	1.25	.95
a.		Bklt. pane of 4, #1975-1978	5.00	

A588   A589

A590   A591

Christmas

Icons: No. 1979, Joachim and Anna, 16th cent. No. 1980, Madonna and Child, 14th cent. No. 1981, Archangel Gabriel, 12th cent. No. 1982, St. Nicholas, 16th cent.

Perf. 12½x13 on 3 Sides

1992, Nov. 27   Litho. & Engr.

1979	A588	2.30k multicolored	.65	.30
1980	A589	2.30k multicolored	.65	.30
1981	A590	2.30k multicolored	.65	.30
1982	A591	2.30k multicolored	.65	.30
a.		Bklt. pane, 3 ea #1979-1982	8.00	
		Nos. 1979-1982 (4)	2.60	1.20

See Russia Nos. 6103-6106.

Derek Walcott, Nobel Laureate in Literature, 1992 — A592

1992, Nov. 27   Engr.   Perf. 12½ Vert.

1983	A592	5.50k Text	1.50	.85
1984	A592	5.50k Portrait	1.50	.85
a.		Pair, #1983-1984	3.25	2.25

1993 Sports Championships — A593

Perf. 12½x13 on 3 Sides

1993, Jan. 28   Litho. & Engr.

1985	A593	6k Gliding	1.75	1.25
1986	A593	6k Wrestling	1.75	1.25
1987	A593	6k Table tennis	1.75	1.25
1988	A593	6k Bowling	1.75	1.25
1989	A593	6k Team handball	1.75	1.25
1990	A593	6k Cross-country skiing	1.75	1.25
a.		Booklet pane, #1985-1990	10.50	

World Gliding Championships, Borlange (#1985). World Wrestling Championships, Stockholm (#1986). World Table Tennis Championships, Gothenburg (#1987). European Bowling Championships, Malmo (#1988). World Team Handball Championships, Gothenburg (#1989). World Cross-Country Skiing Championships, Falun (#1990).

Uppsala Convocation, 400th Anniversary
A594

Litho. & Engr.

1993, Mar. 25   **Perf. 13 Vert.**
1991 A594 2.90k Stone carving .85 .45
1992 A594 2.90k Uppsala Cathedral .85 .45
  a.   Pair, #1991-1992   1.75 1.25

A595

Tourist Attractions in Gothenburg: No. 1993, Roller coaster Liseberg Loop, Liseburg Amusement Park. No. 1994, Fountain of Poseidon, by Carl Milles.

1993, Mar. 25
1993 A595 3.50k multicolored .90 .55
1994 A595 3.50k multicolored .90 .55
  a.   Pair, #1993-1994   1.80 1.60

Fruit
A596   A596a

Perf. 12½ on 3 Sides

1993-94   **Engr.**
1995 A596 2.40k Ribes uva crispa .60 .35
1996 A596 2.40k Pyrus communis .60 .35
  b.   Bklt. pane, 5 ea #1996-1996   6.25
1997 A596 2.80k Victoria plum .70 .30
1998 A596 2.80k Opal plum .70 .30
  b.   Bklt. pane, 5 ea #1997-1998   7.00
2001 A596a 3.35k Ribes nigrum .90 .35
2002 A596a 3.35k Rubus idaeus .90 .35
  a.   Bklt. pane, 5 ea #2001-2002   9.00
    Complete booklet, #2002a   9.00

Perf. 12½ Vert.
2004 A596 2.40k Prunus avium .60 .30
2005 A596 2.80k James Grieve apple .70 .20

Perf. 12½ Horiz.
2008 A596a 3.35k Fragaria ananassa .90 .35
    Nos. 1995-2008 (9)   6.60 2.85

Issued: #1995-1996, 2004, 3/25/93; #1997-1998, 2005, 1/17/94; 3.35k, 1/2/95.
This is an expanding set. Numbers may change.

Oxe-eye Daisy — A597   Poppy — A598

Buttercup A599   Bluebell A600

Perf. 12½x13 on 3 Sides
1993, May 21   **Litho.**
2013 A597 2.60k multicolored .70 .35
2014 A598 2.60k multicolored .70 .35
2015 A599 2.60k multicolored .70 .35
2016 A600 2.60k multicolored .70 .35
  b.   Bklt. pane, 5 ea #2013-2016   14.50
    Nos. 2013-2016 (4)   2.80 1.40

See note after No. 1277.

Contemporary Art — A601

Europa: No. 2017, Oguasark, by Olle Baertling (1911-81). No. 2018, Ade-Lidic-Nander II, by Oyvind Fahlstrom (1928-76), horiz. No. 2019, The Cubist Chair, by Otto G. Carlsund (1897-1948).

Litho. & Engr.
1993, May 21   **Perf. 13**
2017 A601 5k multicolored 1.25 .90
2018 A601 5k multicolored 1.25 .90
2019 A601 5k multicolored 1.25 .90
  a.   Booklet pane of 3, #2017-2019   4.25

Butterflies — A602

1993, May 21   **Perf. 12½ Horiz.**
2020 A602 6k Papilio machaon 1.75 1.00
2021 A602 6k Nymphalis antiopa 1.75 1.00
2022 A602 6k Colias palaeno 1.75 1.00
2023 A602 6k Euphydryas maturna 1.75 1.00
  a.   Booklet pane, 2 each #2020-2023 with gutter between   14.00
    Nos. 2020-2023 (4)   7.00 4.00

A603   A604

A605   A606

Greetings

Perf. 13 on 3 Sides
1993, Aug. 6   **Litho.**
2024 A603 2.90k multicolored .90 .25
2025 A604 2.90k multicolored .90 .25
2026 A605 2.90k multicolored .90 .25
2027 A606 2.90k multicolored .90 .35
  b.   Booklet pane, 3 each #2024, 2026, 2 each #2025, 2027   9.00
    Nos. 2024-2027 (4)   3.60 1.20

Sea Birds A607

Perf. 12½ Horiz.
1993, Aug. 26   **Engr.**
2028 A607 5k Mergus serrator 1.50 .95
2029 A607 5k Melanitta fusca 1.50 .95
2030 A607 5k Aythya fuligula 1.50 .95
2031 A607 5k Somateria mollissima 1.50 .95
  a.   Booklet pane, 2 each #2028-2031 with gutter between   12.00
    Nos. 2028-2031 (4)   6.00 3.80

A608   A609

1993, Oct. 2   **Engr.**   **Perf. 13 Vert.**
2032 A608 2.90k Modern echo sounding .85 .25
2033 A608 2.90k 1643 Method .85 .25
  a.   Pair, #2032-2033   1.75 .80

Hydrographic survey.

1993, Oct. 2   **Engr.**   **Perf. 13**
2034 A609 8k King holding flag 2.25 2.00
2035 A609 10k King 2.50 2.25
2036 A609 10k Queen Silvia 2.50 2.25

Size: 75x43mm
2037 A609 12k Royal family 3.50 3.25
  a.   Booklet pane, #2034-2037   11.00
    Nos. 2034-2037 (4)   10.75 9.75

Reign of King Carl XVI Gustaf, 20th anniv.

Christmas — A610

Perf. 12½ on 3 Sides
1993, Nov. 25   **Engr.**
2038 A610 2.40k Plaited heart .65 .35
2039 A610 2.40k Straw goat .65 .35
  b.   Bklt pane, 5 ea #2038-2039   6.50

Toni Morrison, Nobel laureate in Literature, 1993 — A611

#2041, Stockholm City Hall.

1993, Nov. 25   **Engr.**   **Perf. 12½ Vert.**
2040 A611 6k red brown & brown 1.75 1.00
2041 A611 6k multicolored 1.75 1.00
  a.   Pair, #2040-2041   3.75 2.50

European Economic Assoc. Agreement A612

1994, Jan. 17   **Perf. 12½ Vert.**
2042 A612 5k Mother Svea 1.25 .50

Domestic Animals — A613

: No. 2047, North Sweden horse, vert. No. 2048, Two horses, vert. No. 2049, Red polled cattle, vert. No. 2050, Goat, vert. 3.10k, Swedish dwarf poultry. No. 2055, Gotland sheep. 6.40k, Mountain cow. 7.40k, Scanian goose. 7.50k, Yellow duck.

1994   **Engr.**   **Perf. 13 on 3 Sides**
2047 A613 3.20k multicolored .80 .25
2048 A613 3.20k multicolored .80 .25
  a.   Bklt. pane, 5 ea #2047-2048   8.00
2049 A613 3.70k multicolored 1.00 .30
2050 A613 3.70k multicolored 1.00 .30
  a.   Bklt. pane, 5 ea #2049-2050   10.00
    Complete booklet, #2050a   10.00

Perf. 13 Vert.
2054 A613 3.10k multicolored .90 .45
2055 A613 3.20k multicolored .90 .20
2059 A613 6.40k multicolored 1.60 .40
2060 A613 7.40k multicolored 2.00 .60
2060A A613 7.50k multicolored 2.00 1.00
    Nos. 2047-2060A (9)   11.00 3.75

Issued: #2047-2048, 2055, 2059, 1/17/94; #2049-2050, 3.10k, 1/2/95; 7.40k, 7.50k, 3/17/95.
This is an expanding set. Numbers may change.

Cats — A614

Litho. & Engr.
1994, Mar. 18   **Perf. 13**
2061 A614 4.50k Siamese 1.10 .90
2062 A614 4.50k Persian 1.10 .90
2063 A614 4.50k European 1.10 .90
2064 A614 4.50k Abyssinian 1.10 .90
  a.   Booklet pane of 4, #2061-2064   4.50

Roman De La Rose — A615

Swedish, French Flags A616

Swedish-French cultural relations: No. 2067, House of the Nobility, designed by Simon and Jean de la Vallee. No. 2068, Household Chores, by Hillestrom. No. 2069, Banquet for Gustavus III at the Trianon, 1784, by Lafrensen. No. 2070, Charles XIV John, by Gerard.

Litho. & Engr., Litho. (#2066)
1994, Mar. 18   **Perf. 13 on 3 Sides**
2065 A615 5k multicolored 1.25 1.25
2066 A616 5k multicolored 1.25 1.25
2067 A615 5k multicolored 1.25 1.25
2068 A616 5k multicolored 1.25 1.25
2069 A616 5k multicolored 1.25 1.25
2070 A615 5k multicolored 1.25 1.25
  a.   Booklet pane of 6, #2065-2070   7.50

See France Nos. 2410-2415.

Roses — A617   Swedish Design — A618

Perf. 12½x13 on 3 Sides
1994, May 11 — **Litho.**

2071	A617	3.20k Nyponros rosa dumalis	.85	.35
2072	A617	3.20k Rosa alba maxima	.85	.35
2073	A617	3.20k Tuscany superb	.85	.35
2074	A617	3.20k Peace	.85	.35
2075	A617	3.20k Quatre saisons	.85	.35
a.		Bklt. pane, 2 ea #2071-2075	8.50	
		Nos. 2071-2075 (5)	4.25	1.75

Perf. 12½ on 3 Sides
1994, May 11 — **Litho. & Engr.**

#2076, Vase with Irises, by Gunnar Wennerberg, 1897. #2077, Table and Chair, by Carl Malmsten; Wallpaper, by Uno Ahren, 1917. #2078, Cabinet, 1940s, and textile, 1920s, by Josef Franck. #2079, Fireworks Bowl, by Edward Hald, 1921. #2080, Silver water jug, by Wiwen Nilsson, 1941. #2081, Towel, by Astrid Sampe; Plate, by Stig Lindberg; Fork and Spoon, by Sigurd Persson, 1955.

2076	A618	6.50k multicolored	1.75	1.50
2077	A618	6.50k multicolored	1.75	1.50
2078	A618	6.50k multicolored	1.75	1.50
2079	A618	6.50k multicolored	1.75	1.50
2080	A618	6.50k multicolored	1.75	1.50
2081	A618	6.50k multicolored	1.75	1.50
a.		Bklt. pane, #2076-2081	10.50	

1994 World Cup Soccer Championships, US — A619

1994, May 11 — **Engr.** — **Perf. 12½ Vert.**

2082	A619	3.20k red & blue	1.00	.35

First Manned Moon Landing, 25th Anniv. A620

1994, May 11

2083	A620	6.50k multicolored	1.75	1.00

Greetings A621

Perf. 12½ on 3 Sides
1994, Aug. 5 — **Litho.**

2084	A621	3.20k Cat	.80	.25
2085	A621	3.20k Snail	.80	.25
2086	A621	3.20k Frog	.85	.45
2087	A621	3.20k Dog	.85	.45
a.		Booklet pane, 3 each #2084-2085, 2 each #2086-2087	8.25	
		Nos. 2084-2087 (4)	3.30	1.40

Swedish Explorers A622

Europa: No. 2088, Erland Nordenskiold (1877-1932), explored South America. No. 2089, Eric Von Rosen (1879-1948), explored Africa. No. 2090, Sten Bergman (1895-1975), explored Asia and the Pacific.

Litho. & Engr.
1994, Aug. 26 — **Perf. 12½**

2088	A622	5.50k multicolored	1.25	1.25
2089	A622	5.50k multicolored	1.25	1.25
2090	A622	5.50k multicolored	1.25	1.25
a.		Booklet pane of 3, #2088-2090	4.00	

Finland-Sweden Track and Field Meet — A623

#2091, Seppo Raty, Finland, javelin. #2092, Patrick Sjoberg, Sweden, high jump.

1994, Aug. 26 — **Perf. 12½ on 3 Sides**

2091	A623	4.50k multicolored	1.25	1.10
2092	A623	4.50k multicolored	1.25	1.10
a.		Bklt. pane, 2 ea #2091-2092	5.00	

See Finland Nos. 942-943.

Johan Helmich Roman (1694-1758), Composer A624

No. 2094, Opera House, Gothenburg.

Perf. 12½ Vert.
1994, Aug. 26 — **Engr.**

2093	A624	3.20k multicolored	.80	.25
2094	A624	3.20k multicolored	.80	.25

Yes & No Stamps — A625

1994, Oct. 1 — **Litho.** — **Perf. 12½ Vert.**

2095	A625	3.20k Ja	.85	.35
2096	A625	3.20k Nej	.85	.35

See Nos. 2107-2108.

World Wildlife Fund — A626

#2097, Sterna caspia. #2098, Haliaeetus albicilla. #2099, Dendrocopos leucotos. #2100, Anser erythropus.

Litho. & Engr.
1994, Oct. 1 — **Perf. 12½**

2097	A626	5.50k multicolored	1.50	1.25
2098	A626	5.50k multicolored	1.50	1.25
2099	A626	5.50k multicolored	1.50	1.25
2100	A626	5.50k multicolored	1.50	1.25
a.		Booklet pane of 4, #2097-2100	6.00	

Frans G. Bengtsson (1894-1954), Writer — A627

1994, Oct. 1 — **Engr.** — **Perf. 12½ Vert.**

2101	A627	6.40k multicolored	1.75	.90

Nobel Laureates in Literature A628

Christmas A629

Designs: 4.50k, Erik Axel Karlfeldt (1864-1931). 5.50k, Eyvind Johnson (1900-76). 6.50k, Harry Martinson (1904-78).

1994, Nov. 11

2102	A628	4.50k multicolored	1.25	1.00
2103	A628	5.50k multicolored	1.50	1.25
2104	A628	6.50k multicolored	1.75	1.40
		Nos. 2102-2104 (3)	4.50	3.65

Perf. 12½x13 on 3 Sides
1994, Nov. 11 — **Litho. & Engr.**

Scenes from medieval altar pieces: No. 2105, Annunciation. No. 2106, Flight to Egypt.

2105	A629	2.80k multicolored	.75	.35
2106	A629	2.80k multicolored	.75	.35
a.		Bklt. pane, 5 ea #2105-2106	7.50	

Yes & No Type of 1994
1995, Jan. 2 — **Litho.** — **Perf. 12½ Vert.**

2107	A625	3.70k Ja	1.00	.40
2108	A625	3.70k Nej	1.00	.40

Houses A630

Designs: No. 2109, Country cottage. No. 2110, Soldier's log house. No. 2111, Farmhouse courtyard. No. 2112, Timbered farmhouse. No. 2113, Manor house.

Perf. 14 Horiz.
1995, Mar. 17 — **Litho. & Engr.**

2109	A630	3.70k multicolored	1.00	.50
2110	A630	3.70k multicolored	1.00	.50
2111	A630	3.70k multicolored	1.00	.50
2112	A630	3.70k multicolored	1.00	.50
2113	A630	3.70k multicolored	1.00	.50
a.		Booklet pane of 5, #2109-2113	5.00	
		Complete booklet, #2113a	5.00	

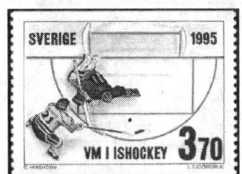

1995 Ice Hockey World Championships — A631

1995 World Track & Field Championships A632

Litho. & Engr.
1995, Mar. 17 — **Perf. 13 Vert.**

2114	A631	3.70k multicolored	1.60	.50

Perf. 13 Horiz.

2115	A632	3.70k multicolored	1.00	.50

A633

Wood Sculptures, by Bror Hjorth — A634

Europa: Nos. 2116, 2118, Walt Whitman, Christ, Socrates. Nos. 2117, 2119, Patrice Lumumba, Albert Schweitzer, children dancing.

1995, Mar. 17 — **Litho.** — **Perf. 13**

2116	A633	5k multicolored	1.25	1.00
2117	A634	5k multicolored	1.25	1.00
2118	A633	6k multicolored	1.40	1.25
2119	A634	6k multicolored	1.40	1.25
a.		Bklt. pane of 4, #2116-2119	6.25	
		Complete booklet, 2 #2119a	12.50	

Swedish Membership in European Union — A635

1995, Mar. 17 — **Perf. 13 Vert.**

2120	A635	6k multicolored	1.65	.80

Rock Speedwell A636

Cloudberry A637

Mountain Heath — A638

Alpine Arnica — A639

Perf. 13 on 3 Sides
1995, May 12 — **Litho.**

2121	A636	3.70k multicolored	1.00	.45
2122	A637	3.70k multicolored	1.10	.55
2123	A638	3.70k multicolored	1.00	.45
2124	A639	3.70k multicolored	1.10	.55
a.		Booklet pane, 3 each #2121, 2123, 2 each #2122, 2124	10.50	
		Complete booklet, #2124a	10.50	
		Nos. 2121-2124 (4)	4.20	2.00

Tourist Attractions — A640

#2125, Canal boat Wilhelm Tham on Gota Canal. #2126, Sail boat anchored on Lake Vattern.

1995, May 12 — **Engr.**

2125	A640	5k dark green	1.40	1.10
2126	A640	5k dark violet	1.40	1.10
a.		Bklt. pane, 2 ea #2125-2126	5.75	
		Complete booklet, #2126a	5.75	

Trams A641

#2127, Gothenburg, c. 1900. #2128, Norrkoping, 1905. #2129, Helsingborg, 1921. #2130, Kiruna, 1958. #2131, Stockholm, 1967.

1995, May 12 — **Perf. 13 Horiz.**

2127	A641	7.50k rose claret	2.00	1.75
2128	A641	7.50k dp brown vio	2.00	1.75
2129	A641	7.50k dk green	2.00	1.75
2130	A641	7.50k dk gray violet	2.00	1.75
2131	A641	7.50k dk violet blue	2.00	1.75
a.		Bklt. pane of 5, #2127-2131	10.00	
		Complete booklet, #2131a	10.00	

UN, 50th Anniv. A642

1995, Aug. 3 — **Engr.** — **Perf. 13 Vert.**

2132	A642	3.70k multicolored	1.00	.25

Greetings
A643

Children's drawings: No. 2133, "The Ball is Yours," by M. Angesjo. No. 2134, Happy man, by E. Sandstrom. No. 2135, Teddy Bear saying "I miss you," by L. Nordenhem. No. 2136, Mussel saying "Hello," by C. Stenbom.

1995, Aug. 3   Litho.   Perf. 13x12½

2133	A643	3.70k multicolored	1.00	.50
2134	A643	3.70k multicolored	1.00	.50
2135	A643	3.70k multicolored	1.00	.50
2136	A643	3.70k multicolored	1.00	.50
a.		Booklet pane, 3 each #2133-2134, 2 each #2135-2136	10.00	
		Complete booklet, #2136a	10.00	
		Nos. 2133-2136 (4)	4.00	2.00

1995 IAAF World Track & Field Championships, Gothenburg A644

Perf. 13 Horiz.

1995, Aug. 3   Litho. & Engr.

2137	A644	7.50k Maria Akraka	2.00	1.25

Motion Picture, Cent. A645

Scenes from films: No. 2138, Soldier Bom, 1948. No. 2139, Sir Arne's Treasure, 1919. No. 2140, Wild Strawberries, 1957. No. 2141, House of Angels, 1992. No. 2142, One Summer of Happiness, 1951. No. 2143, The Apple War, 1971.

Litho. & Engr.

1995, Oct. 7   Perf. 12½x13

Booklet Stamps

2138	A645	6k multicolored	1.75	1.25
2139	A645	6k multicolored	1.75	1.25
2140	A645	6k multicolored	1.75	1.25
2141	A645	6k multicolored	1.75	1.25
2142	A645	6k multicolored	1.75	1.25
2143	A645	6k multicolored	1.75	1.25
a.		Booklet pane, #2138-2143	10.50	
		Complete booklet, #2143a	10.50	

Fritiof Nilsson (1895-1972), Writer — A646

Litho. & Engr.

1995, Oct. 27   Perf. 13 Vert.

2144	A646	3.70k blue & claret	1.10	.40

Ancient Artifacts — A647

Designs: No. 2145, Bronze cult figures of man with beak, nude woman, Bronze Age. No. 2146, Detail of gold collar, Great Migration period. No. 2147, Bracteate pendant picturing figure on horse, Great Migration period. No. 2148, Circular bronze cult object, Bronze Age.

1995, Oct. 27   Perf. 13

2145	A647	3.70k multicolored	1.10	.55
2146	A647	3.70k multicolored	1.10	.55
2147	A647	3.70k multicolored	1.10	.55
2148	A647	3.70k multicolored	1.10	.55
a.		Booklet pane of 4, #2145-2148	4.50	
		Complete booklet, 2 #2148a	9.00	

A648   A649

Tycho Brache (1546-1601), Astronomer: 5k, Uranienborg Observatory, Ven Island. 6k, Sextant.

Litho. & Engr.

1995, Oct. 27   Perf. 13 Vert.

2149	A648	5k multicolored	1.50	.90
2150	A648	6k multicolored	1.90	1.00

See Denmark Nos. 1035-1036.

Perf. 12½x13 on 3 Sides

1995, Nov. 9   Litho.

Christmas candlesticks.

2151	A649	3.35k Santa	.95	.35
2152	A649	3.35k Apple	1.10	.50
2153	A649	3.35k Wrought iron	.95	.35
2154	A649	3.35k Red wooden	1.10	.50
a.		Booklet pane, 3 ea #2151, 2153, 2 ea #2152, 2154	10.00	
		Complete booklet, No. 2151a	10.00	
		Nos. 2151-2154 (4)	4.10	1.70

Nobel Prize Fund Established, Cent. — A650

Designs: No. 2155, Alfred Nobel, last will and testament. No. 2156, Nobel's home, 59 Avenue de Malakoff, Paris. No. 2157, Björkborn Laboratory, Karlkoga. No. 2158, Wilhelm Röntgen receiving the first physics prize, 1901.

Photo. & Engr.

1995, Nov. 9   Perf. 13 Horiz.

2155	A650	6k multicolored	1.75	1.25
2156	A650	6k multicolored	1.75	1.25
2157	A650	6k multicolored	1.75	1.25
2158	A650	6k multicolored	1.75	1.25
a.		Booklet pane, #2155-2158	7.00	
		Complete booklet, No. 2158a	7.00	

Holly — A651   Rowan Berries — A652

Rose Hips & Juniper — A653   Lingonberries & Sloe — A654

1996, Jan. 2   Litho.   Perf. 13 Horiz.

2159	A651	3.50k multicolored	1.10	.40
2160	A652	7.50k multicolored	2.25	1.10

Perf. 13 on 3 Sides

2161	A653	3.50k multicolored	1.10	.55
2162	A654	3.50k multicolored	1.10	.55
a.		Bklt. pane, 5 ea #2161-2162	11.25	
		Complete booklet, No. 2162a	11.25	
		Nos. 2159-2162 (4)	5.55	2.60

End of Railway Mail Sorting — A655

1996, Mar. 29   Engr.   Perf. 13 Vert.

2163	A655	6k multicolored	1.75	.90

King Carl XVI Gustaf, 50th Birthday — A656

King Carl XVI Gustaf: No. 2164, In forest. No. 2165, In front of portrait of King Charles XIV John. No. 2166, In carriage with King Albert of Belgium, 1994. 20kr, With family.

Litho. & Engr.

1996, Apr. 19   Perf. 13x12½

2164	A656	10k multicolored	3.00	2.50
2165	A656	10k multicolored	3.00	2.50
2166	A656	10k multicolored	3.00	2.50

Size: 80x48mm

2167	A656	20k multicolored	6.00	5.50
a.		Booklet pane, #2164-2167	15.00	

Historic Buildings — A657

Designs: No. 2168, Railway station, Halsingland. No. 2169, Motala Assembly Hall, Östergotland. No. 2170, Parish storehouse, Smaland. No. 2171, Half-timbered barn, Vasterbotten. No. 2172, Sheep shelter, Gotland. No. 2173, Old Town Hall, Lidkoping.

Perf. 13 on 2 or 3 Sides

1996, Apr. 19

2168	A657	3.85k multicolored	1.10	.40
2169	A657	3.85k multicolored	1.10	.40

Size: 28x29mm

2170	A657	3.85k multicolored	1.10	.45
2171	A657	3.85k multicolored	1.10	.45

Size: 28x38mm

2172	A657	3.85k multicolored	1.10	.45
2173	A657	3.85k multicolored	1.10	.45
a.		Booklet pane of 6, #2168-2173	6.60	

Famous Women — A658

Europa: No. 2174, Karin Kock (1891-1976), economist. No. 2175, Astrid Lindgren (b. 1907), creator of Pippi Longstocking.

Perf. 13 on 3 Sides

1996, May 3   Engr.

2174	A658	6k multicolored	1.75	1.40
2175	A658	6k multicolored	1.75	1.40
a.		Bklt. pane, 2 ea #2174-2175	6.00	
		Complete booklet, #2175a	6.00	

Summer Scenes A659

Paintings by: No. 2176, Sven X:Et Erixson (1899-1970). No. 2177, Roland Svensson (b. 1910). No. 2178, Eric Hallström (1893-1946),

No. 2179, Thage Nordholm (1927-90). No. 2180, Ragnar Sandberg (1902-72).

Perf. 13 on 2 Sides

1996, May 24   Litho.

2176	A659	3.85k multicolored	1.10	.40
2177	A659	3.85k multicolored	1.10	.40
2178	A659	3.85k multicolored	1.10	.40
2179	A659	3.85k multicolored	1.10	.40
2180	A659	3.85k multicolored	1.10	.40
a.		Bklt. pane, 2 ea #2176-2180	11.00	
		Complete booklet, #2180a	11.00	
		Nos. 2176-2180 (5)	5.50	2.00

Golf — A660

1996, Aug. 23   Engr.   Perf. 13 Horiz.

2181	A660	3.50k dark green, *buff*	1.00	.55

Greetings Stamps — A661

Designs: No. 2182, Masks of comedy, tragedy, "don't worry, be happy." No. 2183, Hearts, "Var Glad (Be happy)," vert. No. 2184, Posthorn. No. 2185, Hearts, person, "Minns du mig? (Do you remember me?)."

Perf. 13x12½ on 3 Sides

1996, Aug. 23   Litho.

2182	A661	3.85k multicolored	1.10	.40
2183	A661	3.85k multicolored	1.10	.40
2184	A661	3.85k multicolored	1.10	.55
2185	A661	3.85k multicolored	1.10	.55
a.		Booklet pane, 3 each #2182-2183, 2 each #2184-2185	11.50	
		Complete booklet, #2185a	11.50	
		Nos. 2182-2185 (4)	4.40	1.90

Mushrooms — A662

3.85k, Boletus edulis. #2187, Russula integra. #2188, Cantharellus cibarius. #2189, Craterellus cornucopioides. #2190, Coprinus comatus.

Perf. 13 Horiz.

1996, Aug. 23   Litho. & Engr.

2186	A662	3.85k multicolored	1.10	.30

Perf. 12½x13 on 3 Sides

2187	A662	5k multicolored	1.50	1.10
2188	A662	5k multicolored	1.50	1.10
2189	A662	5k multicolored	1.50	1.10
2190	A662	5k multicolored	1.50	1.10
a.		Booklet pane of 4, #2187-2190	6.00	
		Complete booklet, #2190a	6.00	
		Nos. 2186-2190 (5)	7.10	4.70

Ecopark, Stockholm A663

Designs: No. 2191, Pelousen, grassy area, Haga Park. No. 2192, Copper tents, Haga Park. No. 2193, Rosendals Palace, roe deer. No. 2194, Isbladskarret, marsh birds.

Litho. & Engr.

1996, Aug. 23   Perf. 12½Vert.

2191	A663	7.50k multicolored	2.25	1.75
2192	A663	7.50k multicolored	2.25	1.75
2193	A663	7.50k multicolored	2.25	1.75

2194	A663	7.50k multicolored	2.25	1.75
a.		Booklet pane of 4, #2191-2194	9.00	
		Complete booklet, #2194a	9.00	

Four Decades
A664

Designs: No. 2195, Errand boy, 1930's. No. 2196, Flower child, 1960's. No. 2197, Zoot-suiter, 1940's. No. 2198, Biker, 1950's.

Perf. 12½x13 on 3 Sides
1996, Oct. 5 — Litho. & Engr.

2195	A664	3.85k multicolored	1.10	.35
2196	A664	3.85k multicolored	1.10	.55
2197	A664	3.85k multicolored	1.10	.35
2198	A664	3.85k multicolored	1.10	.55
a.		Bklt. pane, 3 ea #2195, 2197, 2 ea #2196, 2198	11.50	
		Complete booklet, #2198a	11.50	
		Nos. 2195-2198 (4)	4.40	1.80

The Baroque Chair, by Endre Nemes — A665

1996, Oct. 5 — Perf. 12½ Horiz.

2199	A665	6k multicolored	1.75	1.25

See Czech Republic #2995, Slovakia #255.

Christmas
A666

Illustrations from Book of Hours (15th cent.): No. 2200, The Annunciation. No. 2201, The Birth. No. 2202, Adoration of the Magi.

Perf. 12½ Vert.
1996, Nov. 8 — Litho. & Engr.

2200	A666	3.50k multicolored	1.00	.35

Perf. 12½x13 on 3 Sides

2201	A666	3.50k multicolored	1.00	.45
2202	A666	3.50k multicolored	1.00	.45
a.		Bklt. pane, 5 ea #2201-2202	10.00	
		Complete booklet, #2202a	10.00	
		Nos. 2200-2202 (3)	3.00	1.25

Nobel Laureates in Physiology or Medicine — A667

#2203, Sune Bergström (b. 1916), medical chemist. #2204, Bengt Samuelsson (b. 1934), medical chemist. #2205, Hugo Theorell (1903-82), biochemist. #2206, Ragnar Granit (1900-91), neurophysiologist.

Perf. 13x12½ on 3 Sides
1996, Nov. 8 — Engr.

2203	A667	5k blue, grn & blk + label	1.50	1.00
2204	A667	5k grn, blue & blk+ label	1.50	1.00
2205	A667	5k blue, grn & blk+ label	1.50	1.25
2206	A667	5k green & black+ label	1.50	1.25
a.		Booklet pane, 3 each #2203-#2204, 2 each #2205-2206	15.00	
		Complete booklet, #2206a	15.00	
		Nos. 2203-2206 (4)	6.00	4.50

Wild Animal Types of 1992
1997, Jan. 2 — Engr. — Perf. 13 Vert.

2207	A574	3.20k Gulo gulo	.90	.65
2208	A574	3.50k Nyclea scandia-ca	1.00	.45

Perf. 13 Horiz.

2209	A575	7.70k Ciconia ciconia	2.25	.85
		Nos. 2207-2209 (3)	4.15	1.95

Churches — A668

Illustration reduced.

Perf. 13 Horiz.
1997, Jan. 2 — Litho. & Engr.

2210	A668	3.85k Dalby	1.10	.55
2211	A668	3.85k Vendel	1.10	.55

Size: 27x23mm
Perf. 13x12½ on 2 or 3 Sides

2212	A668	3.85k Hagby	1.10	.55
2213	A668	3.85k Overtornea	1.10	.55

Size: 27x37mm

2214	A668	3.85k Varnhem	1.10	.55
2215	A668	3.85k Ostra Amtervik	1.10	.55
a.		Booklet pane of 6, #2210-2215	7.00	
		Complete booklet, #2215a	7.00	

Kalmar Union, 600th Anniv. — A669

Design: Queen Margareta, Erik of Pomerania, coronation document. Illustration reduced.

1997, Jan. 2 — Engr. — Perf. 12½ Vert.

2216	A669	3.85k dark blue	1.10	.50

Love Stamps — A670

Perf. 13x12½ on 3 Sides
1997, Jan. 2 — Litho.

2217	A670	3.85k gray & multi	1.10	.45
2218	A670	3.85k yellow & multi	1.10	.45
a.		Bklt. pane, 5 ea #2217-2218	11.00	
		Complete booklet, #2218a	11.00	

Stamps that follow, with denominations in parenthesis, are inscribed "Brev," "Ekonomibrev," "Foreningsbrev," etc.

Wild Animals — A671

Perf. 13 on 2 Sides
1997, Feb. 28 — Engr.

2219	A671	(4.50k) Alopex lagopus	1.40	.45
2220	A671	(5k) Equus przewalskii	1.50	.35

Perf. 13 on 3 Sides

2221	A671	(5k) Panthera uni-ca, adult	1.50	.35
2222	A671	(5k) same, cubs	1.50	.35
a.		Bklt. pane, 3 ea #2221-2222	9.00	
		Complete booklet, #2222a	9.00	
		Complete booklet, 1 ea #2221-2222	3.00	
		Nos. 2219-2222 (4)	5.90	1.50

No. 2220 is 28x21mm.

Easter Stamps — A672

Perf. 13x12½ on 3 Sides
1997, Feb. 28 — Litho.

2223	A672	(5k) Rooster	1.50	.35
2224	A672	(5k) Daffodils	1.50	.35
a.		Bklt. pane, 3 ea #2223-2224	9.00	
		Complete booklet, #2224a	9.00	

Pheasants
A673

Designs: No. 2225, Phasianus colchicus. No. 2226, Chrysolophus amherstiae.

Perf. 12½ Horiz.
1997, May 9 — Litho. & Engr.

2225	A673	2k multicolored	.55	.45
2226	A673	2k multicolored	.55	.45
a.		Pair, #2225-2226	1.10	1.00

See China (PRC) Nos. 2763-2764.

Garden Flowers — A674

#2227, Iris sibirica. #2228, Lonicera periclymenum. #2229, Aquilegia vulgaris. #2230, Hemerocallis flava. #2231, Viola x wittrokiana.

1997, May 9 — Litho. — Perf. 12½x13

2227	A674	(5k) multicolored	1.25	.40
2228	A674	(5k) multicolored	1.25	.40
2229	A674	(5k) multicolored	1.25	.40
2230	A674	(5k) multicolored	1.25	.40
2231	A674	(5k) multicolored	1.25	.40
a.		Bklt. pane, 2 ea #2227-2231	13.00	
		Complete booklet, #2231a	13.00	
		Nos. 2227-2231 (5)	6.25	2.00

A675   A676

6k, Ship's figurehead, 18th cent., Naval Museum, Karlskrona. 7k, Compass rose, 18th cent. atlas. 8k, Compass rose, 1568 atlas.

Perf. 12½ Vert.
1997, May 9 — Litho. & Engr.

2232	A675	6k multicolored	1.75	.85

Litho.
Perf. 12½ Horiz.

2233	A676	7k multicolored	2.10	1.00
2234	A676	8k multicolored	2.40	1.50
		Nos. 2232-2234 (3)	6.25	3.35

18th Intl. Cartographic Conf. (#2233-2234).

Gnomes and Trolls — A677

Illustrations from "Among Trolls and Sprites:" No. 2235, Troll looking through treasure chest, gnome. No. 2236, Trolls looking at girl seated on rock. No. 2237, Troll talking with boy.

Litho. & Engr.
1997, May 9 — Perf. 12x13

2235	A677	7k multicolored	2.10	1.40
2236	A677	7k multicolored	2.10	1.40
2237	A677	7k multicolored	2.10	1.40
a.		Bklt. pane, 2 ea #2235-2237	10.00	
		Complete booklet, #2237a	10.00	
		Nos. 2235-2237 (3)	6.30	4.20

Europa.

Wild Animal Type of 1992
Perf. 12½ Horiz.
1997, Aug. 21 — Engr.

2238	A575	(3.50k) Ailurus fulgens, vert.	1.00	.65

Construction of High Coast Bridge — A678

1997, Aug. 21

2239	A678	(5k) multicolored	1.50	.50

Swedish Elk
A679

Designs: No. 2240, Elk as fantasy character. No. 2241, Bar code elk. No. 2242, Swedish elk, yellow bars. No. 2243, Forest elk, green background. No. 2244, Road sign elk, black silhouette against yellow. No. 2245, Old Norse elks, adult & calf.

1997, Aug. 21 — Litho. — Perf. 13

2240	A679	(5k) multicolored	1.50	.50
2241	A679	(5k) multicolored	1.50	.50
2242	A679	(5k) multicolored	1.50	.50
2243	A679	(5k) multicolored	1.50	.50
2244	A679	(5k) multicolored	1.50	.50
2245	A679	(5k) multicolored	1.50	.50
a.		Booklet pane, #2240-2245	9.00	
		Complete booklet, #2245a	9.00	

Perforations at each corner of Nos. 2240-2245 end in a large hole within the pane or semi-circles at the edges of the pane, giving the corners of each stamp a slightly concave appearance.

King Gustav III's Museum of Antiquities, Stockholm Palace — A680

Perf. 13x12½ on 3 Sides
1997, Aug. 21 — Engr.

2246	A680	8k Muses Gallery	2.40	1.65
2247	A680	8k Endymion	2.40	1.65
a.		Booklet pane, 2 each #2246-2247 + 4 labels	9.75	
		Complete booklet, #2247a	9.75	

Classic Cars
A681

#2248, 1958 Volvo Duett. #2249, 1955 Chevrolet Bel-Air. #2250, 1959 Porsche 356A Coupé. #2251, 1952, Citroen B11. #2252, 1963 Saab 96. #2253, 1961 E-Type Jaguar.

Perf. 12½x13 on 3 Sides

1997, Oct. 4   **Litho. & Engr.**

Booklet Stamps

2248	A681	(5k) multicolored	1.25	1.00
2249	A681	(5k) multicolored	1.25	1.00
2250	A681	(5k) multicolored	1.25	1.00
2251	A681	(5k) multicolored	1.25	1.00
2252	A681	(5k) multicolored	1.25	1.00
2253	A681	(5k) multicolored	1.25	1.00
a.		Booklet pane, #2248-2253	7.75	
		Complete booklet, #2253a	7.75	

Alfred Nobel (1833-1896), Founder of Nobel Prize — A682

Design: No. 2255, Paul Karrer (1889-1971), winner of Nobel prize for chemistry, 1937.

Perf. 12½x13 on 3 Sides

1997, Nov. 13   **Litho. & Engr.**

2254	A682	7k lt pink & black	2.00	1.25
2255	A682	7k gray & black	2.00	1.25
a.		Bklt. pane, 2 ea #2254-2255	8.00	
		Complete booklet, #2255a	8.00	

See Switzerland Nos. 1004-1005.

Christmas Gingerbread A683

Perf. 12½ Vert.

1997, Nov. 20   **Litho.**

2256	A683	(3.50k) Heart	1.00	.70

Perf. 12½ on 3 Sides

2257	A683	(3.50k) Animals	1.00	.50
2258	A683	(3.50k) People	1.00	.50
a.		Bklt. pane, 5 ea #2257-2258	10.00	
		Complete booklet, #2258a	10.00	

Christmas Angels — A684

Angels from altarpiece, Litslena Church: No. 2259, Playing horn, mandolin. No. 2260, Playing pipes, harp.

1997, Nov. 20   **Perf. 13x12½**

2259	A684	6k multicolored	1.75	1.40
2260	A684	6k multicolored	1.75	1.40
a.		Booklet pane, 5 each #2259-2260 + 10 labels	17.50	
		Complete booklet, #2260a	17.50	

Photographer Jan Lindblad (1932-87) and His Tigers — A685

Perf. 12½ Horiz.

1998, Jan. 15   **Litho. & Engr.**

2261	A685	(3.50k) shown	1.00	.75
2262	A685	(3.50k) Two tigers on rock	1.00	.75
a.		Pair, #2261-2262	2.00	2.00

New Modern Museum of Art, Stockholm A686

#2263, Fungus Sculpture, by Yves Klein. #2264, Skeppsholmen, by Göran Gidenstam. #2265, Monogram, by Robert Rauschenberg.

1998, Jan. 15   **Perf. 12½ Vert.**

2263	A686	(5k) multicolored	1.25	.50
2264	A686	(5k) multicolored	1.25	.50
2265	A686	(5k) multicolored	1.25	.50
a.		Booklet pane of 3, #2263-2265	3.75	
		Complete booklet, 2 #2265a	7.50	

Valentine's Day — A687

Perf. 13 (on 3 Sides)

1998, Jan. 15   **Litho.**

2266	A687	(5k) dp grn & org red	1.25	.50
2267	A687	(5k) dp blue & rose red	1.25	.50
a.		Bklt. pane, 3 ea #2266-2267	7.50	
		Complete booklet, #2267a	7.50	

Swedish Confederation of Trade Unions, Cent. — A688

Perf. 12½ Horiz.

1998, Mar. 19   **Engr.**

2268	A688	(5k) multicolored	1.30	.50

Public Buildings A689

#2269, Fire station, Gävle. #2270, Shoe shop, Askersund. #2271, Fish halls, Gothenburg. #2272, Rödalvarm (Red Mill) Cinema, Halmstad. #2273, Town Hotel, Eksjö.

1998, Mar. 19   **Perf. 12½ Horiz.**

2269	A689	(5k) multicolored	1.25	.50
2270	A689	(5k) multicolored	1.25	.50
2271	A689	(5k) multicolored	1.25	.50
2272	A689	(5k) multicolored	1.25	.50
2273	A689	(5k) multicolored	1.25	.50
a.		Booklet pane, #2269-2273	6.50	
		Complete booklet, #2273a	6.50	

Queen Christina, Medallion Commemorating the Peace of Westphalia, 1648 — A690

1998, Mar. 19   **Engr.**   **Perf. 12½ Vert.**

2274	A690	7k rose brn & dp grn	2.10	1.00

Handicrafts A691

Designs: (4.50k), Apron from costume, Dalecarlia. (5k), Wrought iron ornamental designs. No. 2277, Lovikka mitten. No. 2278, Boxes made from wood shavings.

1998, Mar. 19   **Perf. 13 Vert.**

2275	A691	(4.50k) multicolored	1.00	.70
2276	A691	(5k) multicolored	1.25	.40

Perf. 12½ on 3 Sides

2277	A691	8k multicolored	2.40	1.40
2278	A691	8k multicolored	2.40	1.40
a.		Bklt. pane, 2 ea #2277-2278	10.00	
		Complete booklet, #2278a + 4 labels	10.00	

Wetland Flowers
A692   A693

Perf. 13 on 3 Sides

1998, May 14   **Litho.**

2279	A692	(5k) Marsh violet	1.40	.35
2280	A693	(5k) Great willowherb	1.40	.35
a.		Bklt pane, 5 ea #2279-2280	14.00	
		Complete booklet, #2280a	14.00	

City of Stockholm — A694

Designs: Nos. 2281, 2287, Stockholm Palace. Nos. 2282, 2288, Skerry boats. No. 2283, Opera House, cent. No. 2284, Sail boats. No. 2285, Langholmen Beach, vert. No. 2286, Fireworks over City Hall, vert.
Illustration reduced.

Perf. 13 on 2 or 3 Sides

1998, May 14   **Litho. & Engr.**

2281	A694	(5k) multicolored	1.40	.50
2282	A694	(5k) multicolored	1.40	.50

Size: 27x22mm

2283	A694	(5k) multicolored	1.40	.60
2284	A694	(5k) multicolored	1.40	.60

Size: 27x36mm

2285	A694	(5k) multicolored	1.40	.60
2286	A694	(5k) multicolored	1.40	.60
a.		Booklet pane, #2281-2286	8.50	
		Complete booklet, #2286a	8.50	

Size: 58x23mm

2287	A694	7k multicolored	1.75	1.50
2288	A694	7k multicolored	1.75	1.50
a.		Bklt. pane, 2 ea #2287-2288	7.25	
		Complete booklet, #2288a	7.25	

Cruise Ship Albatros in Stockholm Harbor — A695

1998, May 14   **Perf. 13 Vert.**

Coil Stamp

2289	A695	6k multicolored	1.60	1.25

Festivals and Holidays — A696

Europa: No. 2290, Crayfish party, paper moon. No. 2291, Dancing around maypole, Midsummer in June.

Perf. 13 on 3 Sides

1998, May 14   **Litho.**

2290	A696	7k multicolored	1.75	1.50
2291	A696	7k multicolored	1.75	1.50
a.		Bklt. pane, 2 ea #2289-2290	6.50	
		Complete booklet, #2291a + 4 labels	6.50	

King Carl XVI Gustaf, 25th Anniv. of Accession to the Throne — A697

1998, May 14   **Engr.**   **Perf. 13 Vert.**

2292	A697	(5k) multicolored	1.40	.50

Vilhelm Moberg (1898-1973), Writer — A698

Litho. & Engr.

1998, Aug. 20   **Perf. 13 Vert.**

Coil Stamp

2293	A698	(5k) multicolored	1.40	.55

Pastries A699

Designs: No. 2294, Princess cake. No. 2295, Gustav Adolf pastry. No. 2296, Napoleon pastry. No. 2297, Mocha cake. No. 2298, National pastry. No. 2299, Lent bun (semla).

Perf. 13 on 3 Sides

1998, Aug. 20   **Litho.**

2294	A699	(5k) multicolored	1.40	.60
2295	A699	(5k) multicolored	1.40	.60
2296	A699	(5k) multicolored	1.40	.60
2297	A699	(5k) multicolored	1.40	.60
2298	A699	(5k) multicolored	1.40	.60
2299	A699	(5k) multicolored	1.40	.60
a.		Booklet pane, #2294-2299	8.50	
		Complete booklet, #2299a	8.50	

The Millennium — A700

Swedish developments during 1900's: No. 2300, Painting, "Flowers on the Window Sill," by Carl Larsson. No. 2301, Stockholm Stadium, poster for 1912 Olympic Games. No. 2302, Power plant, Porjus, Lapland. No. 2303, Inventions; zippers, ball bearings, vacuum cleaners, refrigerators. No. 2304, Johnson (shipping) Line. No. 2305, AB Radiotjänst, 1924. No. 2306, Jazz music, Charleston dance. No. 2307, Ellen Key, Kerstin Hesselgren, pioneers for women's rights. No. 2308, Arne Borg, swimmer, Gillis Grafström, figure skater, world champions. No. 2309, Ernst Rolf, entertainer, 1920's.

Perf. 12½ Horiz.

1998, Oct. 3   Litho. & Engr.
2300	A700 (5k) multicolored	1.40	1.00
2301	A700 (5k) multicolored	1.40	1.00
2302	A700 (5k) multicolored	1.40	1.00
2303	A700 (5k) multicolored	1.40	1.00
2304	A700 (5k) multicolored	1.40	1.00
2305	A700 (5k) multicolored	1.40	1.00
2306	A700 (5k) multicolored	1.40	1.00
2307	A700 (5k) multicolored	1.40	1.00
2308	A700 (5k) multicolored	1.40	1.00
2309	A700 (5k) multicolored	1.40	1.00
a.	Booklet pane, #2300-2309	14.00	
	Complete booklet, #2309a	14.00	

See Nos. 2327-2336, 2379-2388.

Nobel Laureates
A701

Perf. 13x12½ on 3 Sides

1998, Oct. 3   Engr.
2310	A701 6k Nadine Gordimer, 1991	1.60	1.40
2311	A701 6k Sigrid Undset, 1928	1.60	1.40
a.	Bklt. pane, 2 ea #2310-2311	6.75	
	Complete booklet, #2311a + 4 labels	6.75	

Sigismund
(1566-1632),
King of Sweden
and
Poland — A702

Perf. 12½ Horiz.

1998, Oct. 3   Litho. & Engr.
2312	A702 7k multicolored	2.00	1.25

See Poland No. 3421.

A703   A704

Perf. 12½ Horiz.

1998, Nov. 19   Litho.
2313	A703 (4k) Hyacinth	1.10	.45

Perf. 12½ on 3 Sides
2314	A703 (4k) Mistletoe	1.10	.40
2315	A703 (4k) Amaryllis	1.10	.40
a.	Bklt. pane, 5 ea #2314-2315	11.50	
	Complete booklet, #2315a	11.50	
2316	A703 6k Wreath	1.60	1.25
2317	A703 6k Azalea	1.60	1.25
a.	Bklt. pane, 5 ea #2316-2317	16.00	
	Complete booklet, #2317a	16.00	
	Nos. 2313-2317 (5)	6.50	3.75

Christmas.

1999, Jan. 14   Litho.   Perf. 13 Vert.
2318	A704 (5k) multicolored	1.40	.40

Swedish Cooperative Union, cent.

A705   A706

Swedish Coins: No. 2319, Gustav Vasa daler. No. 2320, Carl XIV John riksdaler.

Perf. 12½ Horiz.

1999, Jan. 14   Engr.   Perf. 12½ Vert.
2319	A705 (4.50k) dark green	1.25	.60
2320	A705 (5k) dark blue	1.40	.40

Perf. 12½ on 3 Sides

1999, Jan. 14   Litho.

Easter Eggs: No. 2321, Sugar egg. No. 2322, Egg filled with marzipan chicks.

Panel Color
2321	A706 (5k) green	1.40	.65
2322	A706 (5k) red	1.40	.65
a.	Bklt. pane, 3 ea #2321-2322	8.50	
	Complete booklet, #2322a	8.50	

"Little Sister
Rabbit," by Ulf
Nilsson — A707

Rabbits: No. 2323, Preparing meal over fireplace. No. 2324, Feeding Little Sister. No. 2325, Dancing to music. No. 2326, Hopping through thicket.

Perf. 12½ Vert.

1999, Jan. 14   Litho. & Engr.
2323	A707 (5k) multicolored	1.40	.50
2324	A707 (5k) multicolored	1.40	.50
2325	A707 (5k) multicolored	1.40	.50
2326	A707 (5k) multicolored	1.40	.50
a.	Booklet pane, #2323-2326	5.75	
	Complete booklet, #2326a	5.75	

The Millennium Type of 1998

Sweden in years 1939-1969: No. 2327, Scene from Bergman's film "Smiles of a Summer Night," 1955. No. 2328, Vällingby Centre. No. 2329, Silhouette of soldier, singer Ulla Bilquist. No. 2330, Cobra telephone, three-point seat belt, ASEA high voltage cables and breakers, Tetra Pak's milk carton. No. 2331, Scandinavian Airlines System formed, DC-4 over New York City, 1946. No. 2332, "Hyland's Corner," Carl-Gustaf Lindstedt, Prime Minister Tage Erlander on television. No. 2333, Protests of the 60's, Hep Stars band. No. 2334, Volvo Amazon car, family picnic. No. 2335, Ingemar Johansson, heavy-weight boxing champion, 1959, Mora-Nisse Karlsson, skiing champion, Gunder Hägg, running champion, 1941-45. No. 2336, Jazz singer Alice Babs, opera singer Jussi Björling.

Perf. 12½ Horiz.

1999, Mar. 11   Litho.
2327	A700 (5k) multicolored	1.30	1.00
2328	A700 (5k) multicolored	1.30	1.00
2329	A700 (5k) multicolored	1.30	1.00
2330	A700 (5k) multicolored	1.30	1.00
2331	A700 (5k) multicolored	1.30	1.00
2332	A700 (5k) multicolored	1.30	1.00
2333	A700 (5k) multicolored	1.30	1.00
2334	A700 (5k) multicolored	1.30	1.00
2335	A700 (5k) multicolored	1.30	1.00
2336	A700 (5k) multicolored	1.30	1.00
a.	Booklet pane, #2327-2336	13.00	
	Complete booklet, #2336a	13.00	

Construction of
the Oresund
Bridge — A708

(5k), Swan Pontoon Crane. 6k, Building bridge.

1999, Mar. 11   Perf. 12½ Vert.
2337	A708 (5k) multicolored	1.25	.40
2338	A708 6k multicolored	1.60	1.25

Swedish
Ships
A709

Perf. 12½x13 on 3 Sides

1999, Mar. 11   Litho. & Engr.
2339	A709 8k East Indiaman	2.25	1.75
2340	A709 8k Mary Anne	2.25	1.75
2341	A709 8k Beatrice	2.25	1.75
2342	A709 8k SS Austalic	2.25	1.75
a.	Booklet pane, #2339-2342	9.00	
	Complete booklet, #2342a + 4 labels	9.00	

Australia '99 World Stamp Expo.

Pyramid   Lady's
Orchid — A710   Slipper — A711

Marsh   Green-Winged
Helleborine   Ordhid
A712   A713

Perf. 12½ on 3 Sides

1999, May 20   Litho.
2343	A710 (5k) multicolored	1.25	.40
2344	A711 (5k) multicolored	1.25	.40
2345	A712 (5k) multicolored	1.25	.40
2346	A713 (5k) multicolored	1.25	.45
a.	Booklet pane, 3 each #2343, 2345, 2 each #2344, #2346	12.50	
	Complete booket, #2346a	12.50	
	Nos. 2343-2346 (4)	5.00	1.70

Council of Europe,
50th Anniv. — A714

1999, May 20   Perf. 12½ Horiz.
2347	A714 7k multicolored	1.75	1.50

Europa — A715

Perf. 12½x13 on 3 Sides

1999, May 20
2348	A715 7k Tyresta Natl. Park	1.50	1.25
2349	A715 7k Gotska Sandön Natl. Park	1.50	1.25
a.	Bklt. pane, 2 ea #2348-2349	6.25	
	Complete bklt., #2349a+4 labels	6.25	

Post Bike — A716

Racing
Bike — A717

Town
Bike — A718

Messenger
Bike — A719

Engr., Litho. (#2351)

1999, May 20   Perf. 12½ Horiz.
2350	A716 (3.50k) multicolored	.90	.65

Perf. 12½ Vert.
2351	A717 (5k) multicolored	1.25	.40
2352	A718 6k multicolored	1.50	1.25
2353	A719 8k multicolored	2.10	1.50
	Nos. 2350-2353 (4)	5.75	3.80

Signs of
the
Zodiac
A720

No. 2354: a, Aquarius. b, Pisces. c, Aries. d, Taurus. e, Gemini. f, Cancer.
No. 2355: a, Leo. b, Virgo. c, Libra. d, Scorpio. e, Sagittarius. f, Capricorn.

Litho. & Engr.

1999, Aug. 12   Perf. 13
2354	Booklet pane of 6	7.50	7.50
a.-f.	A720 (5k) any single	1.25	.65
2355	Booklet pane of 6	7.50	7.50
a.-f.	A720 (5k) any single	1.25	.65
	Complete booklet, #2354-2355	15.00	

Perforations at each corner of Nos. 2354a-2354f, 2355a-2355f end in a large hole within the pane or semi-circles at the edges of the pane, giving the corners of each stamp a slightly concave appearance.

Butterflies
A721

a, Inachis io. b, Junonia orithya wallacei. c, Hypolimnas bolina. d, Vanessa atalanta.

1999, Aug. 12   Perf. 12½x13
2356	Booklet pane of 4	6.50	6.00
a.-d.	A721 6k any single	1.60	1.40
	Complete bklt., #2356 + 4 labels	6.50	

See Singapore Nos. 903-907.

Nobel Laureates
in Peace — A722

#2357, Auguste Beernaert (1829-1912).
#2358, Henri La Fontaine (1854-1943).

Perf. 13x12½ on 3 sides

1999, Sept. 30   Litho. & Engr.
2357	A722 7k gold & blue	1.75	1.60
2358	A722 7k gold & red	1.75	1.60
a.	Bklt. pane, 2 ea #2357-2358	7.00	
	Complete booklet, #2358a + 4 labels	7.00	

See Belgium Nos. 1749-1750.

Dance Bands A723

Designs: a, Thorleifs. b, Arvingarna. c, Lotta Engbergs. d, Sten & Stanley.

Litho. & Engr.

1999, Oct. 2		Perf. 12¾	
2359	Booklet pane of 4	5.00	5.00
a.-d.	A723 (5k) any single	1.25	.65
	Complete booklet, 2 #2359	10.00	

A724

Christmas A725

Stained glass: No. 2360, Nativity, Klinte Church. No. 2361, Nativity, Hablingbro Church. No. 2362, Three kings, Hablingbro Church.
Madonna and child icons from: No. 2363, Bälinge Church. No. 2364, Skänninge Church.

Perf. 12½ Vert.

1999, Nov. 18		Litho.	
2360	A724 (4.50k) multicolored	1.10	.55

Perf. 12¾ on 3 sides

2361	A724 (4.50k) multicolored	1.10	.40
2362	A724 (4.50k) multicolored	1.10	.40
a.	Bklt. pane, 5 ea #2361-2362	11.00	
	Complete booklet, # 2362a	11.00	

Litho. & Engr.

2363	A725	6k multicolored	1.40	1.25
2364	A725	6k multicolored	1.40	1.25
a.	Booklet pane, 5 each #2363-2364 + 10 labels		14.00	
	Complete booklet, # 2364a		14.00	
	Nos. 2360-2364 (5)		6.10	3.85

Millennium — A726

Sun rays touching Heligholmen Island: No. 2365, Island rocks. No. 2366, Island map.

Perf. 12¾ Horiz.

1999, Dec. 27		Litho. & Engr.	
2365	A726 5k multicolored	1.25	1.25
2366	A726 5k multicolored	1.25	1.25
a.	Bklt. pane, 2 ea #2365-2366	5.00	
	Complete booklet, 2 #2366a	10.00	

New Year 2000 (Year of the Dragon) A727

Dragon from children's book "The Dragon with Red Eyes," by Astrid Lindgren: No. 2367, In flight (shown). No. 2368, With basket. No. 2369, In flight, diff.

Perf. 12¾ Horiz.

2000, Jan. 13		Litho.	
2367	A727 (5k) multi	1.25	.65
2368	A727 (5k) multi	1.25	.65
2369	A727 (5k) multi	1.25	.65
a.	Bklt. pane, 2 ea #2367-2369	7.50	
	Complete booklet, #2369a	7.50	

A728

A729

Love.

2000, Jan. 13   Perf. 12¾ on 3 sides

2370	A728 (5k) shown	1.25	.70
2371	A728 (5k) Heart, diff.	1.25	.70
a.	Bklt. pane, 3 ea #2370-2371	7.50	
	Complete booklet, #2371a	7.50	

2000, Jan. 13   Engr.   Perf. 12½ Vert.

Watch of King Karl XII, 1701: (4.50k), Works. (5k), Face.

2372	A729	(4.50k) blue	1.10	.40
2373	A729	(5k) brown	1.25	.65

Souvenir Sheet

Detail of "Great Deeds by Swedish Kings," by David Ehrenstrahl — A730

Litho. & Engr.

2000, Mar. 17		Perf. 12¾	
2374	A730 50k multi	11.50	11.50

Czeslaw Slania's 1000th postage stamp.

Forests — A731

Designs: (3.80k), People in forest. No. 2376, Elk in forest. No. 2377, Bird in forest. 6k, Birch forest.

Perf. 12¾ Vert.

2000, Mar. 17		Litho.	
2375	A731 (3.80k) multi	.90	.75
2376	A731 (5k) multi	1.10	.40
2377	A731 (5k) multi	1.10	.40
a.	Pair, #2376-2377	2.20	1.50
2378	A731 6k multi	1.40	1.25
	Nos. 2375-2378 (4)	4.50	2.80

Millennium Type of 1998

Sweden in the years 1970-99: No. 2379, Art in Stockholm subway stations. No. 2380, Swedish UN forces, postal clerk. No. 2381, Computer, mouse and mobile phone. No. 2382, Cullberg Ballet, Svenska Ord repertory company. No. 2383, Jönköping railway station. No. 2384, Youth with spiked hair, musical group ABBA. No. 2385, European Union flag, map of member countries. No. 2386, Scene from film, "The Apple War." No. 2387, Skiiers Pernilla Wiberg, Ingemar Stenmark, tennis player Björn Borg. No. 2388, Photo of child in womb, taken by Lennart Nilsson.

Perf. 12¾ Horiz.

2000, Mar. 17		Litho.	
2379	A700 (5k) multi	1.10	1.00
2380	A700 (5k) multi	1.10	1.00
2381	A700 (5k) multi	1.10	1.00
2382	A700 (5k) multi	1.10	1.00
2383	A700 (5k) multi	1.10	1.00
2384	A700 (5k) multi	1.10	1.00
2385	A700 (5k) multi	1.10	1.00
2386	A700 (5k) multi	1.10	1.00
2387	A700 (5k) multi	1.10	1.00
2388	A700 (5k) multi	1.10	1.00
a.	Booklet pane, #2379-2388	11.00	
	Complete booklet, #2388a	11.00	

Art by Philip von Schantz (1928-98) — A732

Designs: No. 2389, A Peck of Apples. No. 2390, A Bowl of Blueberries.

Perf. 12¾ on 3 sides

2000, May 9		Litho.	
2389	A732 (5k) multi	1.10	.50
2390	A732 (5k) multi	1.10	.50
a.	Bklt. pane, 5 ea #2389-2390	11.00	
	Complete booklet, #2390a	11.00	

A733

Oresund Bridge, Sweden-Denmark — A734

Illustration A734 reduced.

2000, May 9   Engr.   Perf. 12½ Vert.

2391	A733 (5k) blue & ultra	1.10	.40

Litho.

Perf. 12¾ Horiz.

2392	A734 6k shown	1.40	1.40
2393	A734 6k Map	1.40	1.40
a.	Booklet pane, 2 each #2392-2393, + 4 etiquettes	5.75	
	Complete booklet, #2393a	5.75	

See Denmark Nos. 1187-1188.

Europa Issue
Common Design Type

2000, May 9   Litho.   Perf. 12¾ Horiz.

2394	CD17 7k multi	1.60	1.50

2000 Summer Olympics, Sydney — A735

No. 2395: a, Hurdler Ludmila Engquist. b, Archer Magnus Petersson. c, Windsurfer Fredrik Palm. d, Beach volleyball player Lena Malm.

Perf. 12¾x12½ on 3 sides

2000, Aug. 17		Litho.	
2395	A735 Booklet pane of 4	7.25	
a.-d.	8k Any single	1.75	1.75
	Booklet, #2395 + 4 etiquettes	7.25	

Sky Conditions A736

No. 2396: a, Clouds and sun. b, Clouds and lightning. c, Clouds and rainstorm. d, Aurora borealis. e, Rainbow. f, Cumulus clouds.

2000, Aug. 17   Die Cut Perf. 9¾x10
Self-Adhesive

2396	Booklet of 6	6.75	
a.-f.	A736 (5k) Any single	1.10	.60

King Carl XVI Gustaf — A737

Design: 8k, Queen Silvia.

Perf. 12¾ Vert.

2000, Aug. 17		Engr.	
2397	A737 (5k) blue	1.10	.50
2398	A737 8k red	1.75	1.50

Nobel Laureates for Literature — A738

a, Wislawa Szymborska. b, Nelly Sachs. Illustration reduced.

Perf. 12¾x12½ on 3 sides

2000, Oct. 7		Engr.	
2399	A738 Pair	3.00	3.00
a.-b.	7k Any single	1.50	1.50
c.	Booklet pane, 2 #2399	6.00	
	Booklet #2399c + 4 etiquettes	6.00	

Toys — A739

No. 2400: a, Doll, tea set, teddy bear. b, Marbles, tin soldier, yo-yo, jump rope. c, Pine cone cow, doll, horse-drawn wagon. d, Cars and policeman. e, Model train, mechanical men. f, Lego car, robot, Furbee.

Perf. 12¾ on 3 sides

2000, Oct. 7		Litho. & Engr.	
2400	Booklet of 6	6.00	
a.-f.	A739 (5k) Any single	1.00	.70

Christmas Songs — A740

Christmas Snowflakes — A741

Designs: No. 2401, Hey, Santas.
No. 2402, vert.: a, It's Christmas Again (four children, tree). b, Three Gingerbread Men. c,

The Fox Runs Over the Ice. d, Christmas Has Come to Our House (three children, candles). No. 2403: a, White background. b, Blue background.
Illustration A741 reduced.

Perf. 12¾ Vert.

2000, Nov. 16			**Litho.**
2401	A740 (4.30k) multi	.90	.55

Perf. 12¾ on 3 sides

2402	Block of 4	3.60	2.50
a.-d.	A740 (4.30k) Any single	.90	.45
e.	Booklet pane, 3 ea #2402a, 2402c, 2 ea #2402b, 2402d	9.00	
	Booklet, #2402e	9.00	
2403	A741 Pair	2.50	2.50
a.-b.	6k Any single	1.25	1.25
c.	Booklet pane, 5 #2403 + 10 etiquettes	12.50	
	Booklet, #2403c	12.50	
	Nos. 2401-2403 (3)	7.00	5.55

Rock Carvings, Tanum World Heritage Site — A742

Swedish World Heritage Site A743

Designs: (4.50k), Rock carvings of animals and people. (5k), Rock carvings of ships.
No. 2406: a, Gammelstad Church Village. b, Karlskrona Naval Port. c, Theater, Drottningholm Palace. d, Engelsberg Ironworks.

2001, Jan. 31	**Engr.**	**Perf. 12½ Vert.**	
2404	A742 (4.50k) blue, *gray*	.95	.60
2405	A742 (5k) red, *gray*	1.10	.45
			Litho.

Perf. 12½x12¾ on 3 sides

2406	Booklet pane of 4	5.00	
a.-d.	A743 6k Any single	1.25	1.25
	Booklet, #2406 + 4 etiquettes	5.00	

New Year 2001 (Year of the Snake) — A744

No. 2407: a, Snake with tongue extended. b, Snake curled up.
Illustration reduced.

Perf. 12¾ on 3 sides

2001, Jan. 31			**Litho.**
2407	A744 Pair	2.25	1.00
a.-b.	(5k) Any single	1.10	.50
c.	Booklet pane, 3 #2407	6.75	
	Booklet, #2407c	6.75	

Dogs — A745

No. 2408: a, Golden retriever. b, German shepherd. c, Labrador retriever. d, Dachshund.

2001, Jan. 31		**Perf. 12¾ Vert.**	
2408	Booklet of 4	4.50	
a.-d.	A745 (5k) Any single	1.10	.70

Birds — A746

Designs: (3.80k), Vanellus vanellus. (5k), Pica pica. 6k, Larus argentatus. 7k, Aegithalos caudatus.

2001, Mar. 22	**Engr.**	**Perf. 12¾ Vert.**	
2409	A746 (3.80k) multi	.75	.75
2410	A746 (5k) multi	1.00	.50
2411	A746 6k multi	1.25	1.10
2412	A746 7k multi	1.40	1.40
	Nos. 2409-2412 (4)	4.40	3.75

Europa — A747

No. 2413: a, Waterways of northern Sweden. b, Large ship in Trollhätte Canal, trees. c, Waterways of southern Sweden. d, Ship "Juno" in Trollhätte Canal, duck.
Illustration reduced.

Perf. 12¾ on 3 Sides

2001, Mar. 22			**Litho.**
2413	A747 Booklet pane of 4	5.75	
a.-d.	7k Any single	1.40	1.40
	Booklet, #2413 + 4 etiquettes	5.75	

Easter A748

No. 2414: a, Orange egg. b, Purple egg. c, Chick.

2001, Mar. 22	**Die Cut Perf. 9¾x10**		
	Self-Adhesive		
2414	A748 Booklet pane of 3	3.00	
a.-c.	(5k) Any single	1.00	.65
	Booklet, 2 #2414	6.00	

Nobel Prize, Cent. A749

No. 2415: a, Alfred Nobel, Peace medal, obverse of Physics, Chemistry, Physiology or Medicine, Literature medal. b, Reverse of Physiology or Medicine medal. c, Reverse of medal for Physics or Chemistry. d, Reverse of Literature medal.

Perf. 12¾x13½ on 3 Sides

2001, Mar. 22		**Litho. & Engr.**	
2415	Vert. strip of 4	6.50	6.50
a.-d.	A749 8k Any single	1.60	1.60
e.	Booklet pane, #2415 + 4 etiquettes + 4 blank labels	6.50	
	Booklet, #2415e	6.50	

See United States No. 3504.

Ivar Lo-Johansson (1901-90), Writer — A750

No. 2416: a, Portrait. b, Lo-Johansson, truck.
Illustration reduced.

2001, May 17	**Engr.**	**Perf. 12¾ Vert.**	
2416	A750 Pair	2.00	1.90
a.-b.	(5k) Any single	1.00	.55

Peonies — A751

No. 2417: a, Fernleaf peony (two flowers, one bud). b, Chinese peony "Mons Jules Elie." c, Herbaceous peony (yellow). d, Common peony (flower and bud). e, Tree peony.

Perf. 12¾ on 3 Sides

2001, May 17			**Litho.**
2417	Horiz. strip of 5	5.00	5.00
a.-e.	A751 (5k) Any single	1.00	.40
f.	Booklet pane, 2 #2417	10.00	
	Booklet, #2417f	10.00	

Nobel Prize, Cent. — A752

Past winners: a, Doctors Without Borders. b, Red Cross.
Illustration reduced.

Perf. 12¾ Vert.

2001, Aug. 16			**Litho.**
2418	A752 Horiz. pair	3.25	3.25
a.-b.	8k Any single	1.60	1.60

Daniel Solander (1733-82), Botanist on Endeavour A753

No. 2419: a, Barringtonia calyptrata and Solander. b, Cochlospermum gillivraei and Endeavour.

Perf. 12½x12¾ on 3 Sides

2001, Aug. 16		**Litho. & Engr.**	
2419	A753 Vert. pair	3.25	3.25
a.-b.	8k Any single	1.60	1.60
c.	Booklet pane, 2 #2419	6.50	
	Booklet, #2419c + 4 etiquettes	6.50	

See Australia Nos. 1996-1997.

Fish A754

Designs: a, Perca fluviatilis. b, Abramis brama. c, Triglopsis quadricornis.

Die Cut Perf. 13½ Horiz.			
2001, Aug. 16		**Litho. & Engr.**	
	Self-Adhesive		
2420	Booklet pane of 3	3.00	
a.-c.	A754 (5k) Any single	1.00	.55
d.	Booklet, 2 #2420	6.00	

Souvenir Sheet

Aviation — A755

No. 2421: a, Lilienthal glider, 1895. b, Royal Swedish Aero Club. c, Saab J-29, 1962. d, Friedrichshafen FF49. e, Trike ultralight, 1999. f, Douglas DC-3, 1938.

Perf. 12½x12¾			
2001, Oct. 6		**Litho. & Engr.**	
2421	A755 Sheet of 6	5.75	5.25
a.-f.	5k Any single	.95	.65

Stamp Design Contest Winners — A756

No. 2422: a, Rollerblader, by Emilie Kilström, Kikebo School, Oskarshamn. b, The Letter, by Thomas Fröhling.
Illustration reduced.

Perf. 12¾ on 3 Sides

2001, Oct. 6			**Litho.**
2422	A756 Horiz. pair	1.90	.90
a.-b.	(5k) Any single	.95	.45
c.	Booklet pane, 3 #2422	5.75	
	Booklet, #2422c	5.75	

A757

Christmas — A758

Designs: No. 2423, Christmas tree.
No. 2424 — Tree ornaments (26x20mm): a, Star. b, Cracker. c, Angel. d, Heart e, Cone.
No. 2425 — Crumpled paper art by Yrjö Edelmann: a, Straw goat. b, Christmas tree.
Illustration A758 reduced.

Perf. 12¾ Vert.			
2001, Nov. 21			**Litho.**
2423	A757 (4.50k) multi	.85	.60
	Self-Adhesive		
	Die Cut Perf. 10¾x11¼		
2424	Vert. strip of 5	4.25	
a.-e.	A757 (4.50k) Any single	.85	.45
	Booklet, 2 #2424	8.50	

Water-Activated Gum
Perf. 12¾ on 3 Sides

2425	A758	Horiz. pair	2.20 2.20
a.-b.		6k Any single	1.10 1.10
c.		Booklet pane, 5 #2425 + 10 etiquettes	11.00
		Booklet, #2425c	11.00
		Nos. 2423-2425 (3)	7.30

World Ice Hockey Championships
A759

2002, Jan. 24   Litho.   Perf. 12¾ Vert.

2426	A759	(5k) multi	.95 .65

Pandion
Haliaetus
A760

2002, Jan. 24   Engr.

2427	A760	10k multi	1.90 1.10

New Year 2002 (Year of the Horse) — A761

No. 2428 — The Stones Family, by Bertil Almqvist: a, Boy and girl on horse. b, Girl on, and boy leading horse, dog running. Illustration reduced.

Perf. 12¾ on 3 Sides
2001, Jan. 24   Litho.

2428	A761	Horiz. pair	1.90 1.75
a.-b.		(5k) Any single	.95 .75
c.		Booklet pane, 5 #2428	9.50 —
		Booklet, #2428c	9.50

Love and
Miss
Terrified,
by
Joanna
Rubin
Dranger
A762

No. 2429: a, "Det tror. . ." b, "Men jag. . ." c, "Anej!!!"

Die Cut Perf. 13¾ Horiz.
2002, Jan. 24   Litho.
Self-Adhesive

2429	A762	Booklet pane of 3	2.80 —
a.-c.		(5k) Any single	.95 .75
d.		Booklet, 2 #2429	5.60

Antarctic Expedition of Otto Nordenskjöld, Cent. — A763

No. 2430: a, Scientists, ship, gull. b, Ship, penguin.

Litho. & Engr., Litho. (#2430b)
2002, Jan. 24   Perf. 12¾ Horiz.

2430	A763	Vert. pair	3.80 3.80
a.-b.		10k Any single	1.90 1.90
c.		Booklet pane, 2 #2430	7.60 —
		Booklet, #2430c + 4 etiquettes	7.60

Astrid Lindgren (1907-2002), Children's Book Writer — A764

Designs: a, Pippi Langstrump (Pippi Longstocking). b, Karlsson pa Taket. c, Bröderna Lejonhjärta, vert. d, Lindgren (24x29mm). e, Emil i Lönneberga, vert. f, Lotta pa Brakmakargatan. g, Madicken.

2002, Mar. 5   Litho.   Perf. 13x13¼

2431	A764	Booklet pane of 7	7.00 —
a.-g.		5k Any single	1.00 1.00
		Booklet, #2431	7.00

Stockholm, 750th Anniv. — A765

Painting of Stockholm, 1535: (5k), Town and Lake Mälaren. 10k, Close-up view of Cathedral and palace.

2002, Mar. 21   Engr.   Perf. 12¾ Vert.

2432	A765	(5k) shown	1.00 .50

Size: 28x28mm

2433	A765	10k claret	1.90 1.10

A766

Swedish
World
Heritage
Sites
A767

Artifacts from Birka archaeological site: (3.80k), Cross. (4.50k), Runic stone. (5k), Man's face.
No. 2437 - Scenes from Visby: a, Town and ring wall. b, Wall towers. c, Burmeister building, flowers. d, Square, walls of St. Catherine's Church.

2002, Mar. 21   Engr.   Perf. 12½ Vert.

2434	A766	(3.80k) purple	.75 .70
2435	A766	(4.50k) blue	.90 .60
2436	A766	(5k) brn & claret	1.00 .40
		Nos. 2434-2436 (3)	2.65 1.70

Litho. & Engr.
Perf. 12½x12¾ on 3 Sides

2437	A767	Booklet pane of 4	4.00 —
a.-d.		(5k) Any single	1.00 .85
		Booklet, #2437	4.00

Kristianstad Sculptures — A768

No. 2438: a, Structure by Takashi Naraha. b, Sprung From, by Pal Svensson. Illustration reduced.

Perf. 12¾ Vert.
2002, Mar. 23   Litho. & Engr.

2438	A768	Horiz. pair	3.25 3.00
a.-b.		8k Any single	1.60 1.40

Europa — A769

No. 2439: a, Charlie Rivel (1896-1983), clown. b, Clowns Without Borders (boy and clown). c, Cirkus Cirkör (performer with balloon). d, Cirkus Scott (woman on elephant). Illustration reduced.

Perf. 12¾ on 3 Sides
2002, May 2   Litho.

2439	A769	Booklet pane of 4	6.50 —
a.-d.		8k Any single	1.40 1.25
		Booklet, #2439 + 4 etiquettes	6.50

Art From
Sweden and
New
Zealand
A770

No. 2440: a, Rain Forest, glass vase blown by Ola Höglund, Sweden. b, Maori basket, by Willa Rogers, New Zealand.

Perf. 12½x12¾ on 3 Sides
2002, May 2   Litho. & Engr.

2440	A770	Vert. pair	4.00 3.00
a.-b.		10k Any single	2.00 1.25
c.		Booklet pane, 2 #2440	8.00 —
		Booklet, #2440c + 4 etiquettes	8.00

See New Zealand Nos. 1780, 1786.

A771

Summer in Bohuslän — A772

Designs: No. 2441, Waterfront building. No. 2442: a, Lighthouse and gull. b, Lighthouse and three birds. c, Bridge, sailboat, waterfront buildings. d, Boat with outboard motor.
Illustration A772 reduced.

2002, May 10   Engr.   Perf. 12¾ Vert.

2441	A771	(5k) multi	1.00 .55

Litho.
Self-Adhesive
Serpentine Die Cut 6¾

2442	A772	Block of 4	4.00
a.-d.		(5k) Any single	1.00 .70
e.		Booklet, #2442c-2442d, 2 #2442	10.00

Grönköpings Veckoblad Satirical Newspaper, Cent. — A773

No. 2443: a, Newspaper and fictitious Postmaster of Grönköping. b, Fictitious police chief and criminal.
Illustration reduced.

Perf. 12¾ Vert.
2002, Aug. 29   Litho. & Engr.

2443	A773	Pair	2.00 1.90
a.-b.		(5k) Either single	1.00 .75

Chefs
A774

No. 2444: a, Charles Emil Hagdahl (1809-97) and Cajsa Warg (1703-69). b, Marit "Hiram" Huldt, cook with cauldron and bird, flowers. c, Tore Wretman and medal. d, Leif Mannerström, fish and lobster. e, Gert Klötzke and Swedish Culinary Team. f, Christer Lingström, poultry, peas and apples.

Perf. 12½x12¾ on 3 Sides
2002, Aug. 29   Litho.

2444		Booklet pane of 6	6.00 —
a.-f.	A774	(5k) Any single	1.00 .90
		Booklet, #2444	6.00

Royal
Palaces
A775

No. 2445: a, Sweden. b, Thailand.

Perf. 12½x13 on 3 Sides

2002, Oct. 5   **Litho. & Engr.**

2445	A775	Vert. pair	2.10	1.90
a.-b.		5k Either single	1.00	.85
c.		Booklet pane, 2 #2445	4.25	
		Booklet, #2445c	4.25	

See Thailand Nos. 2040-2041.

Motorcycle Racers — A776

No. 2446: a, Hakan Carlqvist. b, Sten Lundin. c, Anders Eriksson. d, Ulf Karlsson.
No. 2447: a, Ove Fundin. b, Tony Rickardsson. c, Peter Linden. d, Varg-Olle Nygren.

2002, Oct. 5   **Litho.**   **Perf. 12¾**

2446	A776	Booklet pane of 4	5.50	—
a.-d.		5k Any single	1.40	1.40

Litho. & Engr.

2447	A776	Booklet pane of 4	5.50	—
a.-d.		5k Any single	1.40	1.40
		Booklet, #2446-2447	8.50	

Animated Film
*Karl-Bertil
Jonsson's
Christmas*
A777

Designs: No. 2448, Man with arm on Karl-Bertil's shoulder.
No. 2449: a, Karl-Bertil and mail sack of Christmas parcels. b, Karl-Bertil asleep with Robin Hood hat. c, Karl-Bertil giving parcel to poor man. d, Karl-Bertil with man, woman and child.

Perf. 12¾ Vert.

2002, Nov. 21   **Litho.**

2448	A777	(4.50k) multi	1.25	1.10

Self-Adhesive

Serpentine Die Cut 6½x6 on 3 Sides

2449		Block of 4	5.00	
a.-d.	A777	(4.50k) Any single	1.25	.85
e.		Booklet pane, 3 #2449a-2449b,		
		2 #2449c-2449d	12.50	

Churches — A778

No. 2450: a, Kiruna Church. b, Habo Church. c, Sundborn Church. d, Tensta Bell Tower.
Illustration reduced.

2002, Nov. 21   **Perf. 12¾ on 3 Sides**

2450	A778	Block of 4	8.50	—
a.-d.		8k Any single	2.10	2.00
e.		Booklet pane, 3 #2450a-		
		2450b, 2 #2450c-2450d	21.00	—
		Booklet, #2450e	21.00	

St. Bridget (1303-73) — A779

2003, Jan. 20   **Engr.**   **Perf. 12¾ Vert.**

2451	A779	(5.50k) red & brown	1.50	1.25

Swedish Sports
Federation,
Cent. — A780

No. 2452: a, Woman and child. b, Wheelchair racer. c, Snowboarder and sign language. d, Girl running.

Serpentine Die Cut 8½

2003, Jan. 20   **Litho.**

Self-Adhesive

2452		Booklet pane, 3 each		
		#2452a, 2452c, 2		
		each #2452b, 2452d	15.00	
a.-d.	A780	(5.50k) Any single	1.50	1.00

Europa — A781

Posters by: a, Anders Beckman, 1935. b, Georg Magnusson, 1930. c, Owe Gustafson, 1984. d, Carina Länk, 1993.
Illustration reduced.

Perf. 12¾x12½ on 3 Sides

2003, Jan. 20

2453	A781	Booklet pane of 4	11.00	—
a.-d.		10k Any single	2.75	2.50
		Booklet, #2453 + 4 etiquettes	11.00	

Knots — A782

Various knots.

2003, Jan. 20   **Engr.**   **Perf. 12½ Vert.**

2454	A782	(4.80k) green	1.25	1.00
2455	A782	(5k) blue	1.40	.70
2456	A782	(5.50k) red	1.50	.65
		Nos. 2454-2456 (3)	4.15	2.35

Regional
Houses — A783

Perf. 12¼ Vert. Syncopated

2003, Mar. 20   **Engr.**

2457	A783	2k Närke	.55	.55
2458	A783	4k Bohuslän	1.10	1.10
2459	A783	5k Medelpad	1.40	1.40
		Nos. 2457-2459 (3)	3.05	3.05

Nobel Prize Winners For Physiology of
Medicine From Spain — A784

No. 2460: a, Santiago Ramón y Cajal, 1906.
b, Severo Ochoa, 1959.

Perf. 12 Vert. Syncopated

2003, Mar. 20   **Litho. & Engr.**

2460	A784	Horiz. pair	5.50	5.50
a.-b.		10k Either single	2.75	2.75

See Spain No. 3204.

Flowers — A785

No. 2461: a, Hepatica nobilis. b, Primula veris. c, Tussilago farfara.

Die Cut Perf. 9¾x10

2003, Mar. 20   **Litho.**

Self-Adhesive

2461		Booklet pane of 3	4.50	
a.-c.	A785	(5.50k) Any single	1.50	1.25
		Booklet, 2 #2461	9.00	

Oland
Moorland,
UNESCO
World
Heritage
Site
A786

No. 2462: a, Windmills. b, Megaliths and windmill. c, Cow and linear village. d, Sheep and lighthouse.

Perf. 12¾ Horiz.

2003, Mar. 20   **Litho. & Engr.**

2462		Booklet pane of 4	6.00	
a.-d.	A786	(5.50k) Any single	1.50	1.25
		Booklet, #2462	6.00	

A787

Garden
Pavilions
A788

Designs: No. 2463, 1820s pavilion, by Frederik Blom.
No. 2464: a, Pavilion of Emanuel Swedenborg. b, Pavilion of Ebba Brahe. c, Västana farm pavilion, Borensberg. d, Godegard pavilion.

Perf. 12½ Vert. Syncopated

2003, May 16   **Engr.**

2463	A787	(5.50k) multi	1.50	1.40

Litho.

Self-Adhesive

Serpentine Die Cut 6½ on 3 Sides

2464		Block of 4	6.00	
a.-d.	A788	(5.50k) Any single	1.50	1.10
e.		Booklet pane, 3 #2464a-2468b,		
		2 #2464c-2464d	15.00	

Souvenir Sheet

St. Bridget (1303-73) — A789

2003, May 31   **Litho. & Engr.**   **Perf. 13**

2465	A789	40k multi	10.50	10.50

No. 2465 exists with and without numbers printed in LL and LR corners of the margin.

Royalty Type of 2000

Designs: (5.50k), King Carl XVI Gustaf. 10k, Queen Silvia.

Perf. 13 Vert. Syncopated

2003, Aug. 21   **Engr.**

2466	A737	(5.50k) red brown	1.40	.75
2467	A737	10k purple	2.50	1.50

Harvest Time — A790

No. 2468: a, Tree, radicchio, parsnip, cucumber, beet, onion. b, Pitchfork, artichoke, pear, gourd, raspberries, apple, plum, pumpkin, eggplant. c, Shovel, garlic, peas, cabbage, tomato, potato, turnip, carrots. d, Strawberries, sunflower, cherries, plums, apple, pear.

Serpentine Die Cut 6½ on 3 Sides

2003, Aug. 21   **Litho.**

Self-Adhesive

2468	A790	Block of 4	5.75	
a.-d.		(5.50k) Any single	1.40	1.25
e.		Booklet pane, 3 each		
		#2468a-2468b, 2 each		
		#2468c-2468d	14.50	

Birds — A791

No. 2469: a, Recurvirostra avosetta. b, Podiceps auritus. c, Gavia arctica. d, Podiceps cristatus.
Illustration reduced.

Perf. 12½x12¾ on 3 Sides

2003, Oct. 4   **Litho. & Engr.**
2469	A791	Booklet pane of 4	10.50	—
a.-d.		10k Any single	2.60	2.60
		Complete booklet, #2469 + 4		
		etiquettes	10.50	

See Hong Kong Nos. 1052-1055.

Building of East Indiaman
"Götheborg" — A792

No. 2470: a, Figurehead (19x23mm). b, Ship under construction (19x23mm). c, Side view of ship, horiz. (23x40mm). d, Ship at sea (39x50mm).
Illustration reduced.

2003, Oct. 4   **Perf. 12½x12¾**
2470	A792	Booklet pane of 4	13.50	
a.-b.		5.50k Either single	1.40	1.40
c.		10k multi	2.60	2.60
d.		30k multi	8.00	8.00
		Complete booklet, #2470 + label	13.50	

Christmas at Sundborn, by Carl
Larsson — A793

No. 2471: a, Martina med Frukostbrickan. b, Kerstis Slädfärd.
Illustration reduced.

Perf. 12¾ on 3 Sides

2003, Nov. 10   **Litho.**
2471	A793	Horiz. pair	4.75	4.75
a.-b.		9k Either single	2.25	2.25
c.		Booklet pane, 5 #2471 +10 etiquettes	24.00	
		Complete booklet, #2471c	24.00	

Christmas
Paintings by Carl
Larsson — A794

Designs: No. 2472, Aftonvarden.
No. 2473, vert.: a, Esbjörn pa Skidor. b, Brita med Julljus. c, Farfar och Esbjörn. d, Garden och Brygghuset.

Perf. 12¾ Vert. Syncopated

2003, Nov. 10
2472	A794	(5k) multi	1.40	1.40

Self-Adhesive

Serpentine Die Cut 6½x6 on 3 Sides

2003, Nov. 10
2473	A794	Block of 4	5.75	
a.-d.		(5k) Any single	1.40	1.40
e.		Booklet pane, #2473b, 2473d, 2 #2473	14.00	

Anna Lindh (1957-2003), Murdered
Minister of Foreign Affairs — A795

Perf. 12¾ on 3 Sides

2003, Nov. 11   **Engr.**
2474	A795	Pair	4.50	4.50
a.		(5.50k) claret	1.60	1.60
b.		10k blue	2.75	2.75

---

c.	Booklet pane, 2 each #2474a-2474b	9.00	—
	Complete booklet, #2474c	9.00	

No. 2474c sold for 35k, 4k of which went to the Anna Lindh Memorial Fund.

Woodworking
Tools — A796

Designs: (4.80k), Brace and bit. (5k), Saw. (5.50k), Plane.

Perf. 12 Vert. Syncopated

2004, Jan. 26   **Engr.**
2475	A796	(4.80k) green	1.40	1.40
2476	A796	(5k) blue	1.40	1.40
2477	A796	(5.50k) claret	1.60	1.00
		Nos. 2475-2477 (3)	4.40	3.80

Flowers
A797

No. 2478: a, Tulip. b, Lily. c, Hibiscus. d, Amaryllis. e, Calla lily.

Perf. 12¾ Horiz.

2004, Jan. 26   **Litho.**
2478		Vert. strip of 5	7.75	7.75
a.-e.	A797	(5.50k) Any single	1.50	1.50
f.		Booklet pane, 2 #2478	15.50	—
		Complete booklet, #2478f	15.50	

Europa
A798

No. 2479 - Views of Lapland: a, Mountain with purple sky. b, Tents near lake.

Perf. 12¾x13½ on 3 Sides

2004, Jan. 26
2479	A798	Pair	5.75	5.75
a.-b.		10k Either single	2.75	2.75
c.		Booklet pane, 2 #2479	11.50	—
		Complete booklet, #2479c + 4 etiquettes	11.50	

Souvenir Sheet

Norse Mythology — A799

No. 2480 - Return to Valhalla: a, Return of a warrior (denomination at LR). b, Welcoming Valkyrie (denomination at UR).

Litho. & Engr.

2004, Mar. 26   **Perf. 12¾**
2480	A799	Sheet of 2	5.25	5.25
a.-b.		10k Either single	2.60	2.60

Falun, UNESCO World Heritage
Site — A800

No. 2481: a, Excavation pit, red mine shaft entrance building. b, Yellow green and green copper weighing building, red, white and purple mining operations building. c, Gray mine entrance building. d, Miners and houses.
Illustration reduced.

Perf. 12½x12¾ on 3 Sides

2004, Mar. 26   **Litho.**
2481	A800	Block of 4	6.00	6.00
a.-d.		(5.50k) Any single	1.50	1.50
e.		Booklet pane, #2481b, 2481d, 2 each #2481a, 2481c	9.00	—
		Complete booklet, #2481e	9.00	

Swedish Soccer
Association,
Cent. — A801

No. 2482: a, Nils Liedholm. b, Hanna Ljungberg. c, Fredrik Ljungberg. d, Henrik Larsson. e, Victoria Svensson. f, Thomas Ravelli.

Serpentine Die Cut 7x6¼ on 3 Sides
2004, Mar. 26

Self-Adhesive
2482		Booklet pane of 6	9.00	
a.-f.	A801	(5.50k) Any single	1.50	1.50

Sunset Scenes — A802

No. 2483: a, Fisherman. b, Lighthouse.
Illustration reduced.

Perf. 12½ Vert. Syncopated

2004, May 13   **Engr.**
2483	A802	Horiz. pair	3.00	2.50
a.-b.		(5.50k) Either single	1.50	1.25

Stockholm
Archipelago
A803

No. 2484: a, Sailboat, red house, Gillöga. b, Rowboat, houses, Langviksskär. c, Ferry, Stora Nassa. d, Sailboat, lighthouse, Nämdöfjärden.

Serpentine Die Cut 6¾ on 3 Sides
2004, May 13   **Litho.**

Self-Adhesive
2484		Block of 4	6.00	
a.-d.	A803	(5.50k) Any single	1.50	1.50
e.		Booklet pane, 3 #2484a-2484b, 2 #2484c-2484d	15.00	

SEMI-POSTAL STAMPS

Type of 1872-91 Issues
Surcharged in Dark
Blue

Perf. 13x13½

1916, Dec. 21   **Wmk. 181**
B1	A5	5o + 5o on 2o org	5.50	7.25
B2	A5	5o + 5o on 3o yel brn	5.50	7.25
B3	A5	5o + 5o on 4o gray	5.50	7.25
B4	A5	5o + 5o on 5o grn	5.50	7.25
B5	A5	5o + 5o on 6o lilac	5.50	7.25
B6	A5	10o + 10o on 12o pale bl	5.50	7.25
B7	A5	10o + 10o on 20o red org	5.50	7.25
B8	A5	10o + 10o on 24o yel	5.50	7.25
B9	A5	10o + 10o on 30o brn	5.50	7.25
B10	A5	10o + 10o on 50o rose red	5.50	7.25
		Nos. B1-B10 (10)	55.00	72.50

The surtax on Nos. B1-B31 was for the militia. See note after No. B21.
For surcharges see Nos. B22-B31.

No. 66 Surcharged
in Dark Blue

1916, Dec. 21   **Wmk. 180**   **Perf. 13**
B11	A12	10o + 4.90k on 5k	150.00	325.00

Nos. J12-J22
Surcharged in Dark
Blue

1916, Dec. 21   **Unwmk.**   **Perf. 13**
B12	D1	5o + 5o on 1o	17.50	10.50
B13	D1	5o + 5o on 3o	5.00	5.50
B14	D1	5o + 5o on 5o	8.25	5.50
B15	D1	5o + 10o on 6o	5.00	6.00
B16	D1	5o + 15o on 12o	42.50	27.50
B17	D1	10o + 20o on 20o	15.00	21.00
B18	D1	10o + 40o on 24o	60.00	82.50
B19	D1	10o + 20o on 30o	5.50	6.00
B20	D1	10o + 40o on 50o	22.50	37.50
B21	D1	10o + 90o on 1kr	140.00	375.00
		Nos. B12-B21 (10)	321.25	577.00

The surtax on Nos. B12-B21 is indicated not in figures, but in words at bottom of surcharge: Fem, 5; Tio, 10; Femton, 15; Tjugo, 20; Fyrtio, 40; Nittio, 90.

Nos. B1-B10
Surcharged

1918, Dec. 18   **Wmk. 181**
B22	A5	7o + 3o on #B1	8.75	8.25
B23	A5	7o + 3o on #B2	2.75	1.25
B24	A5	7o + 3o on #B3	2.75	1.25
B25	A5	7o + 3o on #B4	2.75	1.25
B26	A5	7o + 3o on #B5	2.75	1.25
B27	A5	12o + 8o on #B6	2.75	1.25
B28	A5	12o + 8o on #B7	2.75	1.25
B29	A5	12o + 8o on #B8	2.75	1.25
B30	A5	12o + 8o on #B9	2.75	1.25
B31	A5	12o + 8o on #B10	2.75	1.25
		Nos. B22-B31 (10)	33.50	19.50

The 12o+8o surcharge exists on Nos. B1-B5 and the 7o+3o surcharge exists on Nos. B6-B10. Value, each $72.50.
Nos. B24, B26, B28 and B30 exist with surcharge inverted. Value unused, each $140.

SP1

King Gustaf V — SP2

Unwmk.

			Perf. 10
1928, June 16	**Engr.**		
B32	SP1	5o (+ 5o) yel grn	2.75 6.00
B33	SP1	10o (+ 5o) dk vio	2.75 6.00
B34	SP1	15o (+ 5o) car	2.75 4.50
	Complete booklet, pane of 8		
	ea. #B32, B33, B34		275.00
B35	SP1	20o (+ 5o) org	4.75 2.75
B36	SP1	25o (+ 5o) dk bl	4.75 3.25
	Nos. B32-B36 (5)		17.75 22.50
	Set, never hinged		27.50

70th birthday of King Gustaf V. The surtax was used for anti-cancer work.

Catalogue values for unused stamps in this section, from this point to the end of the section, are for Never Hinged items.

			Perf. 12½ Vertically
1948, June 16			
B37	SP2	10o + 10o green	.55 .60
B38	SP2	20o + 10o red	.80 .75
B39	SP2	30o + 10o ultra	.55 .60
	Perf. 12½ on 3 Sides		
B40	SP2	10o + 10o green	.65 .70
a.	Booklet pane of 20		9.00
B41	SP2	20o + 10o red	.80 .70
a.	Booklet pane of 20		12.00
	Nos. B37-B41 (5)		3.35 3.35

90th anniv. of the birth of King Gustaf V. The surtax provided aid for Swedish youth.

King Gustaf VI Adolf — SP3   Henri Dunant — SP4

			Perf. 12½ Horiz.
1952, Nov. 11			
B42	SP3	10o + 10o green	.35 .40
B43	SP3	25o + 10o car rose	.35 .40
B44	SP3	40o + 10o ultra	.35 .60
	Perf. 12½ on 3 Sides		
B45	SP3	10o + 10o green	.35 .40
a.	Booklet pane of 20		5.00
B46	SP3	25o + 10o car rose	.35 .40
a.	Booklet pane of 20		7.00
	Nos. B42-B46 (5)		1.75 2.20

70th birthday of King Gustaf VI Adolf. The surtax was used to promote Swedish culture.

			Perf. 12½ Horizontally
1959, May 8			
B47	SP4	30o + 10o red	.50 .65
	Perf. 12½ on 3 Sides		
B48	SP4	30o + 10o red	1.00 1.25
a.	Booklet pane of 20		18.00

Centenary of the Red Cross idea. The surtax went to the Swedish Red Cross.

King Gustav VI Adolf — SP5

			Perf. 12½ Vertically
1962, Nov. 10	**Engr.**		**Unwmk.**
	Size: 58x24mm		
B49	SP5	20o + 10o brown	.20 .20
B50	SP5	35o + 10o blue	.20 .20
	Perf. 12½ Horizontally		
B51	SP5	20o + 10o brown	.30 .30
a.	Booklet pane of 10		3.00
B52	SP5	35o + 10o blue	.30 .30
a.	Booklet pane of 10		3.00
	Nos. B49-B52 (4)		1.00 1.00

80th birthday of King Gustav VI Adolf. The surtax went to the King Gustav VI Adolf 80th anniv. Foundation for Swedish Cultural Activities.

Ship Types of Regular Issues
Imprint: "1966"

Designs (Ships): 10o, "The Lion of Smaland." 15o, "Kalmar Nyckel." 20o, Old Sailing Packet. 25o, Mail Paddle Steamship. 30o, "Kung Karl." 40o, Stern of "Amphion."

1966, Nov. 15			**Perf. 12½ on 3 Sides**
B53	A76	10o vermilion	.30 .35
B54	A50	15o vermilion	.30 .35
B55	A38	20o slate grn	.30 .35
B56	A39	25o ultra	.20 .20
B57	A76	30o vermilion	.30 .40
B58	A76	40o vermilion	.30 .40
a.	Bklt. pane. #B53-B54, B57-B58,		
	2 #B55, 4 #B56		2.75
	Nos. B53-B58 (6)		1.70 2.05

The booklet sold for 3.50k and the surtax of 1.15k went to the National Cancer Fund.

AIR POST STAMPS

Official Stamps Surcharged in Dark Blue

1920, Sept. 17		**Wmk. 181**	**Perf. 13**
C1	O3	10o on 3o brn	2.75 7.75
a.	Inverted surcharge		225.00 525.00
C2	O3	20o on 2o org	4.50 11.00
a.	Inverted surcharge		250.00 550.00
C3	O3	50o on 4o vio	20.00 25.00
a.	Inverted surcharge		225.00 550.00
	Nos. C1-C3 (3)		27.25 43.75
	Set, never hinged		55.00

		Wmk. 180	
C4	O3	20o on 2o org	2,250.
C5	O3	50o on 4o vio	160.00 350.00

Airplane over Stockholm — AP2

			Perf. 10 Vertically
1930, May 9	**Engr.**		**Unwmk.**
C6	AP2	10o deep blue	.20 .60
C7	AP2	50o dark violet	.65 1.75
	Set, never hinged		1.50

Flying Swans — AP3

1942-53			**Perf. 12½ on 3 Sides**
C8	AP3	20k brt ultra ('53)	4.50 .65
	Never hinged		6.00
a.	Bklt. pane of 20 ('53)		725.00
b.	Bklt. pane of 10 ('68)		50.00
c.	Perf. on 4 sides		65.00 12.00
	Never hinged		110.00
d.	As "c," bklt. pane of 10		1,200.

Issued: #C8c, May 4, 1942; #C8, July 7.

POSTAGE DUE STAMPS

D1

1874		**Unwmk.**	**Typo.**	**Perf. 14**
J1	D1	1o black	45.00 40.00
J2	D1	3o rose	45.00 40.00
J3	D1	5o brown	40.00 35.00
J4	D1	6o yellow	90.00 77.50
J5	D1	12o pale red	7.75 5.25
J6	D1	20o blue	62.50 40.00
J7	D1	24o violet	450.00 210.00
J8	D1	24o gray	45.00 52.50
J9	D1	30o dk grn	52.50 40.00

J10	D1	50o brown	110.00 57.50
J11	D1	1k blue & bister	225.00 72.50
	Nos. J1-J11 (11)		1,172. 670.25

1877-86			**Perf. 13**
J12	D1	1o black ('80)	2.75 4.00
J13	D1	3o rose	6.25 7.25
J14	D1	5o brown	4.50 4.50
J15	D1	6o yellow	4.50 4.50
a.	Printed on both sides		875.00
J16	D1	12o pale red ('82)	14.50 17.00
J17	D1	20o pale blue ('78)	5.25 4.50
J18	D1	24o red lilac ('86)	26.00 29.00
a.	24o violet ('84)		26.00 29.00
J19	D1	24o gray lil ('82)	125.00 140.00
J20	D1	30o yellow green	6.50 4.50
J21	D1	50o yellow breen	10.50 5.75
J22	D1	1k blue & bister	45.00 22.50
	Nos. J12-J22 (11)		250.75 243.50

Nos. J12-J17, J19-J22 exist imperf. Value, pairs, each $400.
For surcharges see Nos. B12-B21.

STAMPS FOR CITY POSTAGE

S1

		Perf. 14x13½	
1856-62		**Typo.**	**Unwmk.**
LX1	S1	(1sk or 3o) blk	950.00 450.00
LX2	S1	(3o) bis brn ('62)	600.00 475.00

From 1856 to 1858 No. LX1 was sold at 1sk, from 1858 to 1862 at 3o. The paper of the 1sk black is thin while the paper of the 3o black is medium thick.
No. LX1 was reprinted three times with perf. 14, once with perf. 13. No. LX2 was reprinted once with each perforation. Value of lowest-cost Perf. 14 reprints, $250 each. Perf. 13, $175 each.

OFFICIAL STAMPS

O1

O3

1874-77		**Unwmk.**	**Typo.**	**Perf. 14**
O1	O1	3o bister	72.50 40.00
O2	O1	4o gray ('77)	250.00 65.00
O3	O1	5o yel green	140.00 52.50
O4	O1	6o lilac	250.00 65.00
O5	O1	6o gray	525.00 175.00
O6	O1	12o blue	160.00 2.50
O7	O1	20o pale red	950.00 90.00
O8	O1	24o yellow	950.00 20.00
a.	24o orange		950.00 22.50
O9	O1	30o pale brn	425.00 35.00
O10	O1	50o rose	575.00 125.00
O11	O1	1k bl & bis	1,650. 65.00
	Nos. O1-O11 (11)		5,947. 735.00

Imperf., Pairs

O1a	O1	3o	575.
O2a	O1	4o	575.
O3a	O1	5o	900.
O4a	O1	6o	900.
O6a	O1	12o	575.
O7a	O1	20o	2,350.
O8b	O1	24o	1,800.
O9a	O1	30o	1,050.
O10a	O1	50o	1,300.
O11a	O1	1k	3,250.

1881-93			**Perf. 13**
O12	O1	2o org ('91)	1.40 2.00
O13	O1	3o bis brn	1.40 2.25
O14	O1	4o gray blk ('93)	2.50 .60
a.	4o gray ('82)		16.00 2.25
O15	O1	5o brown ('84)	5.25 .60
O16	O1	6o red lil ('82)	40.00 60.00
a.	6o lilac ('81)		45.00 65.00
O17	O1	10o car ('85)	3.00 .20
b.	10o rose		45.00 1.25
O18	O1	12o blue	57.50 21.00
O19	O1	20o ver ('82)	200.00 2.50
O20	O1	20o dk bl ('91)	5.75 .60

O21	O1	24o yellow	72.50 18.00
a.	24o orange		65.00 22.50
O22	O1	30o brown	26.00 .70
O23	O1	50o pale rose	140.00 20.00
O24	O1	50o pale gray ('93)	18.00 1.90
O25	O1	1k dk bl & yel brn	9.00 6.50
	Nos. O12-O25 (14)		582.30 136.85

Imperf., Pairs

O12a	O1	2o	250.00
O17a	O1	10o No. O17	300.00
c.	No. O17b		300.00
O20a	O1	20o	45.00
O24a	O1	50o	250.00

Surcharged in Dark Blue

1889			
O26	O1	10o on 12o blue	11.50 15.00
a.	Inverted surcharge		825.00 1,300.
b.	Perf. 14		— 2,300.
O27	O1	10o on 24o yel	15.00 20.00
a.	Inverted surcharge		1,500. 1,650.
b.	Perf. 14		2,750. 2,500.

1910-12		**Wmk. 180**	**Typo.**
O28	O3	1o black	.20 .20
O29	O3	2o orange	1.40 2.50
O30	O3	4o pale violet	2.10 3.50
O31	O3	5o green	.65 .90
O32	O3	8o claret	.65 .90
O33	O3	10o red	12.00 .70
O34	O3	15o red brown	1.10 .70
O35	O3	20o deep blue	8.25 1.10
O36	O3	25o red orange	8.25 1.60
O37	O3	30o chocolate	6.00 2.50
O38	O3	50o gray	8.25 2.75
O39	O3	1k black, yellow	7.75 7.75
O40	O3	5k claret, yellow	9.50 4.00
	Nos. O28-O40 (13)		66.10 29.10

1910-19		**Wmk. Wavy Lines (181)**	
O41	O3	1o black	3.00 3.25
O42	O3	2o orange	.20 .20
O43	O3	3o pale brown	.40 .60
O44	O3	4o pale violet	.20 .20
O45	O3	5o green	.20 .20
O46	O3	7o gray green	.45 .90
O47	O3	8o rose	20.00 27.50
O48	O3	10o red	.20 .20
O49	O3	12o rose red	.20 .20
O50	O3	15o org brown	.30 .30
O51	O3	20o deep blue	.20 .20
O52	O3	25o orange	1.00 .90
O53	O3	30o chocolate	.55 .45
O54	O3	35o dark violet	.85 .75
O55	O3	50o gray	2.50 1.90
	Nos. O41-O55 (15)		30.25 37.35

For surcharges see Nos. C1-C5.

Use of official stamps ceased on 7/1/20.

PARCEL POST STAMPS

Regular Issue of 1914 Surcharged

1917		**Wmk. 180**	**Perf. 13**
Q1	A14	1.98k on 5k claret, yel	1.40 5.25
Q2	A14	2.12k on 5k claret, yel	1.40 5.25

SWITZERLAND

'swit-sər-lənd

(Helvetia)

LOCATION — Central Europe, between France, Germany and Italy
GOVT. — Republic
AREA — 15,943 sq. mi.
POP. — 7,062,400 (1998 est.)
CAPITAL — Bern

100 Rappen or Centimes = 1 Franc

> Catalogue values for unused stamps in this country are for Never Hinged items, beginning with Scott 365 in the regular postage section, Scott B272 in the semi-postal section, Scott C46 in the airpost section, Scott CB1 in the airpost semi-postal section, and Scott 3O94, 4O40, 5O26, 7O31, 8O1, 9O1, 10O1, 11O1, 12O1 in the official sections.

Watermarks

Wmk. 182 —
Cross in Oval

Wmk. 183 —
Swiss Cross

Watermark 182 is not a true watermark, having been impressed after the paper was manufactured. There are two types:
Type 1 — width just under 9mm.
Type 2 — width just under 8½mm.

CORINPHILA
AUKTIONEN

TRADITION AND EXPERIENCE IN CLASSIC PHILATELY SINCE 1925.

We are pleased to accept suitable rarities and collections at any time for our forthcoming auctions. Confidentiality is guaranteed.

CORINPHILA AUCTIONS Ltd.

Zollikerstrasse 226
CH-8034 Zurich/Switzerland
Phone +41-1-389 91 91
Fax +41-1-389 91 95

CANTONAL ADMINISTRATION

Unused values of Nos. 1L1-3L1 are for stamps without gum.
Counterfeit and repaired copies of Nos. 1L1-3L1 abound.

Zurich

		Numerals of Value —	
		A1	A2

1843　Unwmk.　Litho.　Imperf.
Red Vertical Lines

1L1	A1	4r	black	16,500. 14,500.
1L2	A2	6r	black	5,500. 1,450.

1846　　　　Red Horizontal Lines

1L3	A1	4r	black	13,500. 18,000.
1L4	A2	6r	black	1,650. 1,350.

Five varieties of each value.
Reprints of the Zurich stamps show signs of wear and lack the red lines. Values 4r, $5,500; 6r, $1,800.

Coat of Arms — A3

1850　　Unwmk.　　Imperf.

1L5	A3	2½r	black & red	5,400. 3,600.

No. 1L5 has separation designs in the margins between stamps as shown. Values are for stamps showing part of the separation design on all four sides.

Geneva

Coat of Arms — A4

1843　Unwmk.　Litho.　Imperf.

2L1	A4	10c blk, *yel grn*	47,500. 31,500.
a.		Either half	19,000. 7,500.
b.		Stamp composed of right half at left & left half at right	65,000. 56,000.

A5　　　　　　　A6

1845-48

2L2	A5	5c blk, *yel grn*	2,500. 1,550.
2L3	A6	5c blk, *yel grn* ('46)	1,750. 1,550.
2L4	A6	5c blk, *dk grn* ('48)	3,750. 2,500.

A7　　Coat of Arms — A8

1849-50

2L5	A7	4c black & red	30,000. 18,000.
2L6	A7	5c blk & red ('50)	2,100. 1,450.

1851

2L7	A8	5c black & red	7,500. 3,500.

ENVELOPE STAMP USED AS ADHESIVE

E1

1847　　Unwmk.　　Imperf.

2LU1	E1	5c yel grn, see footnote	18,500.

Authorized for use from Feb. 19, 1847. Value is for cut-out stamp used on folded letters. Value of unused envelope (1846) or cut-out, from $400. Value of used cut-out off cover, $2,800.

Basel

Dove of Basel — A9

Typo. & Embossed

1845　　Unwmk.　　Imperf.

3L1	A9	2½r blk, crim & bl	10,500. 10,000.

Proofs are black, vermilion and green. Value, $3,600.

FEDERAL ADMINISTRATION

> Due to its tendency to damage the paper and/or the color of the stamps, the gum on Nos. 1-40 very often is removed. Unused values for Nos. 1-40 are for stamps without gum. Stamps with original gum sell for about the same prices.

A10　　　　　　　A11

1850　　Unwmk.　Litho.　Imperf.
Full Black Frame Around Cross

1	A10	2½r	black & red	2,250. 1,300.
2	A11	2½r	black & red	1,900. 1,250.

Without Frame Around Cross

3	A10	2½r	black & red	4,500. 2,100.
4	A11	2½r	blk & red	37,500. 20,000.

Forty types of each.

A12　　　　　　　A13

1850
Full Black Frame Around Cross

5	A12	5r dk bl, blk & red	4,000. 1,200.
a.		5r dk grayish bl, blk & red	4,250. 1,200.
6	A13	10r yel, blk & red	80,000.

No. 6 used, with only parts of frame around cross showing, value $175 to $900.
Beware of copies of Nos. 7-8 with faked frame added.

Without Frame Around Cross

7	A12	5r lt bl, blk & red	1,350. 400.
a.		5r dp bl, blk & red	2,750. 500.
b.		5r pur bl, blk & red	7,750. 4,500.
c.		5r grnsh bl, blk & red	1,600. 525.
8	A13	10r yel, blk & red	800. 100.
a.		10r buff, blk & red	1,200. 210.
b.		10r org yel, blk & red	1,200. 200.
c.		Half used as 5r on cover	11,250.

1851
Full Blue Frame Around Cross

9	A12	5r light blue & red	100,000

No. 9 used, with only parts of frame around cross showing, value $180 to $3,750.
Beware of copies of No. 10 with faked frame added.

Without Frame Around Cross

10	A12	5r lt blue & red	475. 110

Forty types of each.

A14　　　　　　　A15

A16

1852
Vermilion Frame Around Cross

11	A14	15r vermilion	9,000. 550
12	A15	15r vermilion	2,000. 110
13	A16	15c vermilion	10,750. 850

Ten types of each.
On October 1st, 1854, all stamps of the preceding issues were declared obsolete.

Helvetia — A17

1854　　Embossed.　　Unwmk
Thin Paper, Fine Impressions
Emerald Silk Threads

14	A17	5r orange brn	4,850. 1,350
15	A17	5r red brown	450.00 125.00
16	A17	10r blue	600.00 47.50
17	A17	15r carmine rose	750.00 125.00
a.		15r pale rose	1,000. 200.00
18	A17	40r pale yel grn	6,750. 1,000
19	A17	40r yellow grn	950. 225.00

1854-55
Emerald Silk Threads
Medium Thick Paper
Fine Impressions

20	A17	5r pale yel brn	450.00 125.00
21	A17	10r blue	1,050. 110.00
22	A17	15r rose	675.00 95.00
23	A17	20r pale orange	1,050. 140.00

1855-57
Colored ( ) Silk Threads
Medium Thick Paper
Fine to Rough Impressions

24	A17	5r yel brn (yel)	350.00 82.50
25	A17	5r dk brown (blk)	250.00 32.50
26	A17	10r mlky bl (red)	600.00 125.00
27	A17	10r blue (car)	225.00 32.50
a.		Thin paper	3,750. 375.00
28	A17	15r rose (bl)	425.00 50.00
29	A17	40r yel grn (mar)	750.00 80.00
30	A17	1fr lav (blk)	1,000. 850.00
31	A17	1fr lav (yel)	1,000. 850.00
a.		Thin paper	6,500.

1857
Thin (Emergency) Paper
Rough Impressions
Green Silk Threads

32	A17	5r pale gray brn	3,250. 950
32A	A17	10r blue	4,750. 850
33	A17	15r pale dl rose	2,500. 300
34	A17	20r pale dl org	2,500. 225

1858-62
Thick Ordinary Paper
Rough Impressions
Green Silk Threads

35	A17	2r gray	225.00 500.00
a.		One and one-half used as 3r on newspaper or wrapper	13,250
c.		Half used as 1r on cover	

36	A17	5r brown	190.00	22.50
a.		5r black brown	225.00	35.00
b.		Half used as 2r on cover		1,300.
37	A17	10r dark blue	175.00	22.50
a.		Half used as 5r on cover		7,250.
38	A17	15r dark rose	325.00	52.50
39	A17	20r dark orange	375.00	65.00
a.		Half used as 10r on cover		16,500.
40	A17	40r dk yellow grn	375.00	75.00
a.		Half used as 20r on cover		16,500.
		Nos. 35-40 (6)	1,665.	737.50

Helvetia — A18

Double embossing errors, Nos. 43c, 44a, 55b, 60a, 61a, 61b, 67b, have the design impressed twice. These do not refer to the "embossed" watermark.

Embossed

1862-64		Wmk. 182	*Perf. 11½*	
		White Wove Paper		
41	A18	2c gray	90.00	3.75
42	A18	3c black	8.00	125.00
43	A18	5c dark brown	3.00	.55
a.		5c bister brown	65.00	1.40
b.		5c gray brown	87.50	25.00
c.		Dbl. embossing, one invtd.	3,500.	375.00
d.		Double impression of lower left "5"		1,450.
44	A18	10c blue	325.00	.70
a.		Dbl. embossing, one invtd.		7,250.
45	A18	20c orange	1.90	2.75
a.		20c yellow orange	275.00	2.75
46	A18	30c vermilion	1,100.	32.50
47	A18	40c green	1,050.	52.50
48	A18	60c bronze	800.00	150.00
50	A18	1fr gold	17.50	110.00
a.		1fr yellowish bronze ('64)	1,050.	350.00

1867-78				
52	A18	2c bister brown	1.90	1.40
a.		2c red brown	625.00	250.00
53	A18	10c carmine	1.90	1.00
54	A18	15c lemon	3.25	35.00
55	A18	25c blue green	1.40	3.50
a.		25c yellow green	35.00	22.50
b.		Dbl. embossing, one invtd.		650.00
56	A18	30c ultra	425.00	8.00
a.		30c blue	1,550.	225.00
58	A18	40c gray	1.40	140.00
59	A18	50c violet	47.50	50.00
		Nos. 52-59 (7)	482.35	238.90

1881				
		Granite Paper		
60	A18	2c bister	.50	17.50
a.		Dbl. embossing, one invtd.	325.00	
61	A18	5c brown	.40	8.75
a.		Dbl. embossing, one invtd.	26.00	400.00
b.		Double embossing of lower left "5"		1,050.
62	A18	10c rose	4.50	7.75
63	A18	15c lemon	7.00	450.00
64	A18	20c orange	.50	110.00
65	A18	25c green	.40	77.50
66	A18	40c gray	.95	2,750.
67	A18	50c deep violet	9.25	400.00
b.		Dbl. embossing, one invtd.	225.00	3,250.
68	A18	1fr gold	13.00	1,200.

The granite paper contains fragments of blue and red silk threads.

Forged or backdated cancellations are found frequently on Nos. 42, 50, 54, 58 and 60-68.

All stamps of the preceding issues were declared obsolete on October 1st, 1883. Some of the remainders of Nos. 41-68 were overprinted "AUSSER KURS" (Obsolete) diagonally in black.

Numeral — A19

1882-99		Typo.	*Perf. 11½*	
		Granite Paper		
69	A19	2c bister	1.40	.70
70	A19	3c gray brown	2.25	7.75
a.		3c gray	47.50	45.00
71	A19	5c maroon	14.50	.70
a.		Tête bêche pair		
72	A19	5c deep grn ('99)	8.75	.70
73	A19	10c red	5.75	.70
a.		10c carmine	50.00	.70
b.		10c light rose	275.00	7.25
74	A19	12c ultra	7.25	.70
a.		12c chalky blue	25.00	21.00
b.		12c greenish blue	375.00	

75	A19	15c yellow	140.00	32.50
a.		15c orange	16,500.	5,000.
b.		Tête bêche pair		
76	A19	15c violet ('89)	50.00	2.50
		Nos. 69-76 (8)	229.90	46.25

Nos. 69-74, 76 are watermark type 1. Nos. 70a, 73a-73b, 75-75a are type 2.

1882				
		White Paper		
77	A19	2c bister	325.00	325.00
78	A19	5c maroon	825.00	110.00
79	A19	10c rose	2,100.	77.50
80	A19	12c chalky blue	150.00	26.00
81	A19	15c yellow	225.00	275.00

Watermark type 1.
See Nos. 113-118.

Helvetia (Large numerals) A20		Helvetia (Small numerals) A21		

1882-1904		Engr.	*Perf. 11½*	
82	A20	20c orange	150.00	6.00
83	A20	25c green	82.50	3.00
95b	A20	30c brown	—	18,500.
84	A20	40c gray	100.00	42.50
85	A21	40c gray ('04)	42.50	20.00
86	A20	50c blue	110.00	21.00
87	A20	1fr claret	210.00	6.00
88	A20	3fr yel brn ('91)	160.00	19.00

1888			*Perf. 9½*	
89	A20	20c orange	800.00	100.00
90	A20	25c yellow grn	150.00	13.00
91	A20	40c gray	800.00	650.00
92	A20	50c blue	1,000.	325.00
93	A20	1fr claret	850.00	87.50

Values for Nos. 89-93 are for well-centered stamps with slightly uneven perforations. Stamps missing perforations sell for much less.

1891-99			*Perf. 11½x11*	
82a	A20	20c orange	45.00	1.90
83a	A20	25c green	10.00	1.90
94	A20	25c blue ('99)	10.50	1.90
95	A20	30c red brn ('92)	26.00	1.90
84a	A20	40c gray	57.50	4.50
86a	A20	50c blue	42.50	10.00
96	A20	50c green ('99)	45.00	22.50
87a	A20	1fr claret	37.50	3.25
97	A20	1fr carmine	82.50	7.50
88a	A20	3fr yellow brown	150.00	25.00

1901-03			*Perf. 11½x12*	
82b	A20	20c orange	19.00	1.60
94a	A20	25c blue	9.00	1.10
95a	A20	30c red brown	35.00	1.90
84b	A20	40c gray	75.00	30.00
96a	A20	50c green	55.00	7.75
87b	A20	1fr claret	2,200.	275.00
97a	A20	1fr carmine ('03)	425.00	32.50
88b	A20	3fr yellow brown	150.00	25.00

Numerous retouches and plate flaws exist on all values of this issue.
Nos. 82-88 have wmk. type 1 and are ½mm taller (paper size) than Nos. 82b-88b, which have wmk. type 2.
See Nos. 105-112, 119-125.

UPU Allegory — A22

1900			*Perf. 11½*	
98	A22	5c gray green	32.50	1.60
99	A22	10c carmine rose	11.00	1.60
100	A22	25c blue	25.00	32.50
		Nos. 98-100 (3)	68.50	35.70

		Re-engraved		
101	A22	5c gray green	2.75	1.60
102	A22	10c carmine rose	45.00	35.00
103	A22	25c blue	775.00	11,000.

Universal Postal Union, 25th anniv.
The impression of the re-engraved stamps is much clearer, especially the horizontally lined background. The figures of value are lined instead of being solid.

Helvetia Types of 1882-1904

1905		Wmk. 183	*Perf. 11½x11*	
		White Paper		
105	A20	20c orange	2.50	2.50
106	A20	25c blue	4.50	10.00
107	A20	30c brown	3.75	2.25
108a	A21	40c gray	77.50	140.00
109	A20	50c green	25.00	6.50
110	A20	1fr carmine	72.50	3.00
111	A20	3fr yellow brn	190.00	125.00

Some clichés in the plates of the 20c, 25c, 30c, 50c and 3fr have been retouched.

1906		Re-engraved	*Perf. 11½x11*	
112	A20	25c pale blue	5.50	2.25

In the re-engraved stamp the stars are larger and the background below "FRANCO" is of horiz. or horiz. and vert. crossed lines, instead of horiz. and curved lines.

1906			*Perf. 11½*	
112a	A20	25c pale blue	77.50	7.75
108	A21	40c gray	22.50	12.50

1907			*Perf. 11½x12*	
105a	A20	20c orange	5.25	6.00
109a	A20	50c green	30.00	15.00
110a	A20	1fr carmine	87.50	11.00
111a	A20	3fr yellow brown	190.00	210.00

Numeral Type of 1882-99

1905		Typo.	*Perf. 11½*	
		Granite Paper		
113	A19	2c dull bister	4.00	2.10
114	A19	3c gray brown	5.00	57.50
115	A19	5c green	4.00	.55
116	A19	10c scarlet	4.00	.55
117	A19	12c ultra	5.00	2.75
118	A19	15c brown vio	52.50	19.00
		Nos. 113-118 (6)	74.50	82.45

Helvetia Types of 1882-1904

1907		Engr.	*Perf. 11½x12*	
		Granite Paper		
119	A20	20c orange	2.25	3.75
120	A20	25c blue	7.75	10.00
121	A20	30c red brown	6.50	17.50
122	A21	40c gray	21.00	45.00
a.		Helvetia without diadem	300.00	1,050.
123	A20	50c gray green	5.50	17.50
124	A20	1fr carmine	19.00	9.25
125a	A20	3fr yellow brown		10,500.

There are retouches and plate flaws on all values.

			Perf. 11½x11	
120a	A20	25c deep blue	10.00	6.50
121a	A20	30c red brown	140.00	325.00
122b	A21	40c gray		13,000.
124a	A20	1fr carmine		10,000.
125	A20	3fr yel brn	100.00	65.00

William Tell's Son — A23

Helvetia
A24   A25

1907-25		Typo.	*Perf. 11½*	
		Granite Paper		
126	A23	2c pale bister	.30	.55
127	A23	3c lilac brn	.25	10.00
128	A23	5c yellow grn	2.25	.50
129	A24	10c rose red	1.50	.50
130	A24	12c ocher	.30	3.50
131	A24	15c red vio	3.00	13.00
132	A25	20c red & yel ('08)	2.25	1.00
133	A25	25c dp blue ('08)	1.90	.65
a.		Tête bêche pair	17.00	55.00
134	A25	30c yel brn & pale grn ('08)	1.60	.50
135	A25	35c yel grn & yel ('08)	1.90	1.40
136	A25	40c red vio & yel ('08)	12.50	1.00
a.		Designer's name in full on the rock ('08)	6.00	82.50
137	A25	40c deep blue ('22)	1.75	.50
a.		40c light blue ('21)	5.50	1.90
138	A25	40c red vio & grn ('25)	25.00	.50
139	A25	50c dp grn & pale grn ('08)	11.00	.50
140	A25	60c brn org & buff ('18)	9.25	.65

141	A25	70c dk brn & buff ('08)	55.00	17.00
142	A25	70c vio & buff ('24)	14.50	2.25
143	A25	80c slate & buff ('15)	9.75	1.10
144	A25	1fr dp cl & pale grn ('08)	7.00	.55
145	A25	3fr bis & yel ('08)	275.00	2.10
		Nos. 126-145 (20)	436.00	57.75

No. 136 has two leaves and "CL" below sword hilt. No. 136a has three leaves and designer's full name below hilt.

For surcharges and overprints see Nos. 189, 199, O10-O13, O15, 1O6-1O8, 1O14-1O16, 2O18-2O26, 3O14-3O22.

1933				
		With Grilled Gum		
135a	A25	35c yel grn & yel ('08)	1.40	12.50
138a	A25	40c red vio & grn	32.50	1.50
139a	A25	50c dp grn & pale grn	9.00	1.50
140a	A25	60c brn org & buff	12.00	1.50
142a	A25	70c vio & buff	17.50	3.75
143a	A25	80c slate & buff	13.00	4.25
144a	A25	1fr dp cl & pale grn	6.50	
		Nos. 135a-144a (7)	104.40	31.50

"Grilled" Gum

In 1930-44 many Swiss stamps were treated with a light grilling process, applied with the gumming to counteract the tendency to curl. It resembles a faint grill of vertical and horizontal ribs covering the entire back of the stamp, and can be seen after the gum has been removed. Listings of the grilled gum varieties begin with No. 135a.

Switzerland

1843-Date. Year Units, sets, singles, specialized material. Want lists for singles, Cantonals, covers, FDC's, and specialized material.
10% Off Complete Mint NH 1958-2003 .... Only $1200.00 (Normally issued stamps , S/S)
10% Off Official Year Sets 1955-2000 .... Only $85.30

Free Price List

Complete sets, NH, Hinged and Used - Officials and B-O-Book. Also ask for our free Liechtenstein price list. *Want lists invited!*

We Buy

We buy all Switzerland including quantity material. Needed - better covers, FDC's, classical, aerophilately, rarities and all specialized material. All U.S., Europa & Worldwide stamps bought at top prices!

1-800-9-4-STAMP
(1-800-947-8267)

Henry Gitner Philatelists, Inc.

P.O. Box 3077-S
Middletown, NY 10940
Toll Free: 1-800-947-8267
Fax: 845-343-0068
E-mail: hgitner@hgitner.com
http://www.hgitner.com

Philately-The Quiet Excitement!

F/VF quality at fair
market prices.
Careful and prompt
supply subject to
your agreement.
Extensive price
list on request.

Hans P. Walser
P.O. Box 754/SC
8630 Rüti/Switzerland

WANT LIST SERVICE
SWITZERLAND
LIECHTENSTEIN
GERMANY - CEPT
AUSTRIA - FRANCE
MIXTURES

Phone 01141-55-240 44 31
Fax   01141-55-260 34 09
E-mail:walser@phila-walser-ch
www.phila-walser-ch

William Tell's
Son — A26

Bow-string in
front of stock

1909   **Perf. 11½, 12**
Granite Paper
146 A26 2c bister   .25   1.40
a.   Tête bêche pair   3.25 17.50
147 A26 3c dark violet   .25 14.00
148 A26 5c green   3.75   .20
a.   Tête bêche pair   14.00 50.00
     Nos. 146-148 (3)   4.25 15.60

See Nos. 149-163. For surcharges and
overprints see Nos. 186, 193-195, 207-208,
1O1-1O3, 1O9-1O11, 2O1-2O7, 3O1-3O5.

First Redrawing

Bow-string behind stock. Thin loop above
crossbow. Letters of "HELVETIA" without
serifs.

1910-17
Granite Paper
149 A26 2c bister ('10)   8.75   8.00
150 A26 3c dk violet ('10)   .20   .20
a.   Tête bêche pair   2.75   2.75
b.   Booklet pane of 6   12.50
151 A26 3c brown org ('17)   .20   .20
a.   Tête bêche pair   8.25 11.00
152 A26 5c green ('10)   21.00   6.50
a.   Tête bêche pair   92.50 175.00
     Nos. 149-152 (4)   30.15 14.90

Second Redrawing

Bow-string behind stock. Thick loop above
crossbow. Letters of "HELVETIA" have serifs.
7½ CENTIMES:
Type I - Top of "7" is ½mm thick. The "1" of
"½" has only traces of serifs. The two base
plates of the statue are of even thickness.
Type II - Top of "7" is 1mm thick. The "1" of
"½" has distinct serifs. The upper base plate is
thinner than the lower.

1911-30
Granite Paper
153 A26 2c bister ('11)   .20   .20
a.   Tête bêche pair   3.25   1.60
154 A26 2½c claret ('18)   .20   1.10
155 A26 2½c ol, buff ('28)   .55   2.10
156 A26 3c ultra, buff ('30)   2.75   6.00
157 A26 5c green ('11)   1.75   .20
a.   Tête bêche pair   5.50 10.00
158 A26 5c org, buff ('21)   .20   .20
a.   Bklt. pane of 6 (5 #158, 168) 14.00 47.50
159 A26 5c gray vio, buff
     ('24)   .20   .20
a.   Bklt. pane of 6 (5 #159, 168) 6.50 19.00

160 A26 5c red vio, buff ('27)   .20   .20
a.   Bklt. pane 6 (5 #160, 168) 30.00 65.00
161 A26 5c dk grn, buff ('30)   .30   .25
a.   Bklt. pane 6 (5 #161, 169) 27.50 70.00
162 A26 7½c gray (I) ('18)   1.10   .20
a.   Tête bêche pair   13.00 45.00
c.   7½c slate (II)   4.50   2.75
163 A26 7½c dp grn, buff (I)
     ('28)   .30   3.25
     Nos. 153-163 (11)   7.75 13.90

1933   **With Grilled Gum**
156a A26 3c ultra, buff   4.75 17.50
161b A26 5c dark green, buff   .55   5.00

Helvetia
A27

William Tell
A28

1909
Granite Paper
164 A27 10c carmine   .60   .40
a.   Tête bêche pair   2.25   6.00
165 A27 12c bister brn   .85   .40
166 A27 15c red violet   26.00   1.10
     Nos. 164-166 (3)   27.45   1.90
For surcharge see No. 187.

1914-30   Granite Paper   Perf. 11½
TEN CENTIMES:
Type I - Bust 16½mm high. "HELVETIA"
15½mm wide. Cross bar of "H" at middle of the
letter.
Type II - Bust 15mm high. "HELVETIA"
15mm wide. Cross bar of "H" above middle of
the letter.
167 A28 10c red, buff
     (type I)   .75   .20
a.   10c red, buff (type I)   2.50 26.00
b.   Tête bêche pair (II)   3.25   4.25
d.   Bklt. pane, #172, 167   50.00 160.00
168 A28 10c grn, buff
     (type II)   .20   .20
     ('21)
a.   Tête bêche pair   1.10   1.40
168C A28 10c bl grn, buff
     (type II)
     ('28)   .20   .20
d.   Tête bêche pair   2.50   2.50
169 A28 10c vio, buff (type
     II) ('30)   2.25   .20
a.   Tête bêche pair   9.25   1.40
170 A28 12c bis brn, buff   .20   3.25
171 A28 13c ol grn, buff
     ('15)   1.40   .50
172 A28 15c vio, buff   3.50   .20
b.   15c dk vio, buff   32.50   4.25
c.   Tête bêche pair   87.50 125.00
173 A28 15c brn red, buff
     ('28)   2.50   2.75
174 A28 20c red vio, buff
     ('21)   3.25   .20
a.   Tête bêche pair   6.50   7.50
175 A28 20c ver, buff ('24)   1.00   .50
a.   Tête bêche pair   5.75   9.25
176 A28 20c car, buff ('25)   .25   .20
a.   Tête bêche pair   2.50   .55
177 A28 25c ver, buff ('21)   2.25   1.60
178 A28 25c car, buff ('22)   1.10   .85
179 A28 25c brn, buff ('25)   3.25   1.25
180 A28 30c dp bl, buff
     ('24)   9.25   .50
     Nos. 167-180 (15)   31.35 12.60

1932-33   **With Grilled Gum**
169c A28 10c violet, buff   4.50   1.50
173a A28 15c brn red, buff ('33) 50.00 52.50
176c A28 20c carmine, buff   7.25   1.50
179a A28 25c brown, buff ('33)   125.00 35.00
180a A28 30c deep blue, buff   72.50   2.50
     Nos. 169c-180a (5)   259.25 93.00

For surcharges and overprints see Nos.
188, 196-198, 1O4-1O5, 1O12-1O13, O2O8-
2O17, 3O6-3O13.

The Mythen
A29

The
Rütli — A30

The
Jungfrau
A31

1914-30   Engr.   Granite Paper
181 A29 3fr dk green   650.00   6.50
182 A29 3fr red ('18)   87.50   1.40
183 A30 5fr dp ultra   35.00   3.00
184 A31 10fr dull violet   100.00   3.25
185 A31 10fr gray grn ('30)   225.00 37.50
     Nos. 181-185 (5)   1,097. 51.65

See No. 206. For overprints see Nos. 2O27-
2O30, 3O23-3O26.

Stamps of 1909-14 Surcharged

a   b

c

1915
186 A26(a) 1c on 2c bister   .25   1.25
187 A27(b) 13c on 12c bis brn   .25   9.25
188 A28(c) 13c on 12c brn, buff   .30   .90
     Nos. 186-188 (3)   .80 11.40

No. 141 Surcharged

189 A25 80c on 70c   25.00 17.50

Significant
of Peace
A32

"Peace"
A33

"Dawn of
Peace"
A34

Perf. 11½
1919, Aug. 1   Typo.   Unwmk.
190 A32 7½c olive drab & blk   .80   2.25
191 A33 10c red & yel   1.10   8.75
192 A34 15c violet & yel   1.90   2.75
     Nos. 190-192 (3)   3.80 13.75
Commemorating Peace after World War I.

Nos. 151, 149, 162, 171-172, 133
Surcharged in Black, Red or Dark
Blue

a

b

c

1921   **Wmk. 183**
193 A26(a) 2½c on 3c (Bl)   .20   1.10
a.   Tête bêche pair   1.10   3.25
b.   Inverted surcharge   800.00 1,550.
c.   Double surcharge   550.00 775.00
194 A26(a) 5c on 2c (R)   .20   4.50
a.   Double surcharge   450.00 450.00
195 A26(a) 5c on 7½c (R)   .20   .55
a.   Tête bêche pair   6.50 55.00
b.   Double surcharge   550.00 550.00
c.   5c on 7½c slate (II)   2,200. 4,500.
196 A28(b) 10c on 13c (R)   .20   2.25
a.   Double surcharge   550.00 550.00
197 A28(c) 20c on 15c (Bk)   .55   2.75
a.   Tête bêche pair   .55   5.50
b.   Double surcharge   875.00 875.00
198 A28(c) 20c on 15c (Bl)   2.25   5.50
b.   Double surcharge   875.00 875.00
199 A25(c) 20c on 25c dp
     bl (R)   .20   .55
a.   1.50   4.50
     Nos. 193-199 (7)   3.80 17.20

A36

1924   **Typo.   Perf. 11½**
Granite Paper, Surface Colored
200 A36 90c grn & red, grn   15.00   2.75
201 A36 1.20fr brn rose &
     red, rose   5.25   5.25
202 A36 1.50fr bl & red, bl   37.50   6.50
203 A36 2fr gray blk & red,
     gray   47.50   6.75
     Nos. 200-203 (4)   105.25 21.25
Set, never hinged   325.00

1933   **With Grilled Gum**
200a A36 90c   17.50   3.25
201a A36 1.20fr   47.50   5.50
202a A36 1.50fr   32.50   6.50
203a A36 2fr   27.50   8.25
     Nos. 200a-203a (4)   125.00 23.50
Set, never hinged   300.00

For overprints see Nos. O16-O18, 2O31-
2O34, 3O27-3O30.

Building in Bern, Location of 1st UPU Congress, 1874
A37   A38

1924, Oct. 9   Engr.   Wmk. 183
Granite Paper
204 A37 20c vermilion   .55 1.60
205 A38 30c dull blue   1.10 6.25
    Set, never hinged   3.25

50th anniv. of the UPU.

The Rütli — A39

Type of 1914 Issue
1928   Re-engraved   Perf. 11½
206 A39 5fr blue   110.00 9.75
    Never hinged   300.00
a. Imperf., pair, never hinged 10,000.

In the re-engraved stamp the picture is clearer and lighter than on No. 183. "HELVETIA" is in smaller letters. The names at foot of the stamp are "Grasset-J. Sprenger" instead of "E. GRASSET-A. BURKHARD."
For overprints see Nos. 2035, 3031.

Nos. 155 and 163 Surcharged

1930, June   Perf. 11½
207 A26 3c on 2½c ol grn, buff   .20 2.75
208 A26 5c on 7½c dp grn, buff   .20 8.00
    Set, never hinged   1.10

The Mythen
A40

1931   Engr.   Granite Paper
209 A40 3fr orange brown   65.00 5.25
    Never hinged   150.00

For overprints see Nos. 2056, 3047.

Dove on Broken Sword — A41

"Peace"
A42

1932, Feb. 2   Typo.   Perf. 11½
Granite Paper
210 A41 5c peacock blue   .20 .20
211 A41 10c orange   .20 .20
212 A41 20c cerise   .25 .20
213 A41 30c ultra   2.25 1.60
214 A41 60c olive brown   17.50 8.75

Unwmk.
Photo.
215 A42 1fr olive gray & bl   17.50 8.75
    Nos. 210-215 (6)   37.90 19.70
    Set, never hinged   95.00

Intl. Disarmament Conf., Geneva, Feb. 1932.
For overprints see #2036-2041, 3032-3037.

Louis Favre — A43   Alfred Escher — A44

Design: 30c, Emil Welti.

Wmk. 183
1932, May 31   Engr.   Perf. 11½
Granite Paper
216 A43 10c red brown   .20 .20
217 A44 20c vermilion   .25 .20
218 A44 30c deep ultra   .55 2.10
    Nos. 216-218 (3)   1.00 2.50
    Set, never hinged   3.00

Completion of the St. Gotthard tunnel, 50th anniv.
Nos. 216-218 exist imperforate.

Staubbach Falls   Mt. Pilatus
A46   A47

Chillon Castle   Rhone Glacier
A48   A49

St. Gotthard Railroad   Via Mala Gorge
A50   A51

Rhine Falls — A52

1934, July 2   Typo.   Perf. 11½
Granite Paper
219 A46 3c olive   .20 3.00
220 A47 5c emerald   .20 .20
221 A48 10c brt violet   .40 .20
222 A49 15c orange   .50 3.25
223 A50 20c red   .60 .45
224 A51 25c brown   7.75 8.25
225 A52 30c ultra   25.00 2.10
    Nos. 219-225 (7)   34.65 17.45
    Set, never hinged   100.00

Tête bêche Pairs
220a A47 5c   1.60 1.60
221a A48 10c   1.50   .85
222a A49 15c   1.75 3.00
223a A50 20c   3.50 2.25

Souvenir Sheet
1934, Sept. 29
226   Sheet of 4   500.00 550.00
    Never hinged   900.00

No. 226 was issued in connection with the Swiss National Philatelic Exhibition at Zurich, Sept. 29 to Oct. 7, 1934. It contains one each of Nos. 220-223. Size: 62x72mm.
For overprints see Nos. 2042-2046, 3048.

Staubbach Falls   Mt. Pilatus
A53   A54

Chillon Castle   Rhone Glacier
A55   A56

St. Gotthard Railroad   Via Mala Gorge
A57   A58

Rhine Falls — A59   Balsthal Pass — A60

Alpine Lake of Säntis — A61

Two types of 10c red violet:
I - Shading inside "0" of 10 has only vertical lines.
II - Shading in "0" includes two diagonal lines.

1936-42   Unwmk.   Engr.   Perf. 11½
227 A53 3c olive   .20 .20
228 A54 5c blue green   .20 .20
229 A55 10c red vio (II)   .85 .20
b.   Type I   .85 .20
230 A55 10c dk red brn ('39) .20 .20
230B A55 10c org brn ('42)   .20 .20
231 A56 15c orange   .40 1.10
232 A57 20c carmine   4.75 .20
233 A58 25c lt brown   .50 1.10
234 A59 30c ultra   .90 .20
235 A60 35c yellow grn   1.10 1.25
236 A61 40c gray   6.00 .20
    Nos. 227-236 (11)   15.30 5.05
    Set, never hinged   37.50

Two types of the 20c. See Nos. 316-321.
For overprints see Nos. O1-O4, O6-O9, O19-O19-O22, O24-O27, 2047-2055, 2068-2068A, 2070-2073, 2075-2078, 3038-3046, 3060-3060A, 3062-3065, 3067-3070, 4O1-4O4, 4O6-4O9, 4023-4024, 4027-4028, 5O1-5O2, 5O5.

Tête bêche Pairs
228a A54 5c blue green   .45 .30
229a A55 10c red violet (II) 4.50 5.50
230a A55 10c dark red brown   1.75 1.10
230d A55 10c orange brown   .50 .60
232a A57 20c carmine   25.00 35.00

1936-40   With Grilled Gum
227a A53 3c olive   .65 6.25
228d A54 5c blue green   .30 .25
229d A55 10c red violet (II) .30 .25
e.   Type I   1.00 .25
230e A55 10c dark red brn ('40) 1.90 25.00
231a A56 15c orange   .30 1.10
232c A57 20c carmine   6.75 .20
233a A58 25c light brown   1.00 5.00
234a A59 30c ultra   .95 .25
235a A60 35c yellow green   1.40 3.25
236a A61 40c gray   9.25 .50
    Nos. 227a-236a (10)   22.80 42.10
    Set, never hinged   47.50

Mobile Post Office
A62

1937, Sept. 5   Photo.
Granite Paper
237 A62 10c black & yellow   .25 .50
    Never hinged   .55

No. 237 was sold exclusively by the traveling post office. It exists on two kinds of granite paper, black and red fibers or blue and red fibers. See No. 307 for type A62 redrawn.

View of Labor Building from Lake Geneva
A63

Palace of League of Nations
A64

Main Building, Palace of League of Nations
A65

Labor Building and Albert Thomas Monument
A66

1938, May 2   Perf. 11½
Granite Paper
238 A63 20c red & buff   .20 .20
239 A64 30c blue & lt blue   .45 .20
240 A65 60c brown & buff   1.75 2.25
241 A66 1fr black & buff   7.50 17.00
    Nos. 238-241 (4)   9.90 19.65
    Set, never hinged   25.00

Opening of Assembly Hall of the Palace of the League of Nations.
For overprints see #2057-2064, 3049-3056.

Souvenir Sheet

A67

Engraved and Typographed
1938, Sept. 17   Unwmk.   Perf. 11½
Granite Paper
242 A67 Sheet of 3   37.50 32.50
     Never hinged   70.00
a.   10c on 65c gray bl & dp bl 19.00 25.00
b.   A68 20c red   1.10 2.50

Natl. Phil. Exhib. at Aarau, Sept. 17-25, and 25th anniv. of Swiss air mail. No. 242 contains 2 No. 243, but on granite paper, and a 10c on 65c similar to No. C22; no watermark.
On No. C22, wing tips touch frame lines; size is 36x21½mm; Wmk. 183. No. 242 contains a 10c on 65c similar to No. C22 but redrawn, with wing tips 1½mm from side frame lines; overall size 37x20½mm; no watermark.

Lake Lugano — A68

First Federal Pact, 1291 A69

Diet of Stans, 1481 A70

Citizens Voting A71

1938, Sept. 17 Engr. Perf. 11½

243	A68	20c red	.25	.25
a.		Tête bêche pair	.50	.85
c.		Grilled gum	.40	.40
d.		As "c," tête bêche pair	1.40	15.00

Granite Paper

244	A69	3fr brn car, *grnsh*	11.00	8.75
245	A70	5fr slate bl, *grnsh*	7.50	6.00
246	A71	10fr grn, *grnsh*	47.50	35.00
		Nos. 243-246 (4)	66.25	50.00
		Set, never hinged	190.00	

No. 243 is printed on ordinary paper. Nos. 244-246 are on granite surface-colored paper. The greenish surface coating has faded on most copies.

For type A68 in orange brown, see No. 318.

See Nos. 242b, 284-286. For overprints see Nos. O5, O23, 2O65-2O67, 2O69, 2O74, 2O88-2O90, 3O57-3O59, 3O61, 3O66, 3O80-3O82, 4O5, 4O19-4O21, O4O25, 5O3, 5O23-5O25, 7O18-7O20.

Deputation of Trades and Professions — A72

Swiss Family A73

Alpine Scenery A74

Engr., Photo. (30c)
1939, Feb. 1 Perf. 11½
Inscribed in French

247	A72	10c dl pur & red	.20	.20
248	A73	20c lake & red	.50	3.00
249	A74	30c dp blue & red	2.50	3.00

Inscribed in German

250	A72	10c dl pur & red	.20	.20
251	A73	20c lake & red	.40	.20
252	A74	30c dp blue & red	2.10	8.25

Inscribed in Italian

253	A72	10c dl pur & red	.20	.20
254	A73	20c lake & red	1.90	.20
255	A74	30c dp blue & red	2.25	9.25
		Nos. 247-255 (9)	10.25	21.70
		Set, never hinged	27.50	

National Exposition of 1939, Zurich.

Tree and Crossbow — A75

1939, May 6 Photo. Perf. 11½
Granite Paper
Inscribed in French

256	A75	5c deep green	.55	1.60
257	A75	10c gray brown	.55	1.90
258	A75	20c brt carmine	1.10	1.60
259	A75	30c violet blue	3.00	8.00

Inscribed in German

260	A75	5c deep green	.55	2.50
261	A75	10c gray brown	.55	2.50
262	A75	20c brt carmine	1.10	3.50
263	A75	30c violet blue	8.75	9.50

Inscribed in Italian

264	A75	5c deep green	.85	4.50
265	A75	10c gray brown	.55	3.50
266	A75	20c brt carmine	1.10	4.25
267	A75	30c violet blue	3.25	11.00
		Nos. 256-267 (12)	21.90	54.35
		Set, never hinged	32.50	

National Exposition of 1939.
The 5c, 10c and 20c stamps in the three languages exist se-tenant in coils.

1939 With Grilled Gum

256a	A75	5c deep green	.75	2.25
257a	A75	10c gray brown	.75	2.25
258a	A75	20c bright carmine	1.90	3.00
260a	A75	5c deep green	.75	1.60
262a	A75	20c bright carmine	1.90	1.60
264a	A75	5c deep green	1.10	3.75
265a	A75	10c gray brown	1.00	3.00
266a	A75	20c bright carmine	1.90	3.25
		Nos. 256a-266a (8)	10.05	20.70

View of Geneva A76

Perf. 11½
1939, Aug. 22 Photo. Unwmk.
Granite Paper

268	A76	20c red, car & buff	.20	.20
269	A76	30c blue, car & gray	.30	2.75
		Set, never hinged	1.40	

75th anniv. of the founding of the Intl. Red Cross Society.

"The Three Swiss" — A77

William Tell — A78

Fighting Soldier — A79

Dying Warrior — A80

Standard Bearer — A81

Ludwig Pfyffer — A82

Jürg Jenatsch — A83

Francois de Reynold — A84

Joachim Forrer — A85

1941-59 Engr. Perf. 11½
Granite Paper

270	A77	50c dp pur, *grnsh*	4.25	.20
271	A78	60c red brn, *buff*	5.50	.20
272	A79	70c rose vio, *pale lil*	2.75	1.00
273	A80	80c blk, *pale gray*	1.10	.20
a.		80c black, *pale lilac* ('58)	.80	.50
274	A81	90c dk red, *pale rose*	1.00	.20
a.		90c dark red, *buff* ('59)	1.00	1.25
275	A82	1fr dk grn, *grnsh*	1.00	.20
276	A83	1.20fr red vio, *pale gray*	1.10	.20
a.		1.20fr red vio, *pale lil* ('58)	1.90	.75
277	A84	1.50fr dk bl, *buff*	1.50	.25
278	A85	2fr *pale rose*	2.25	.20
a.		2fr maroon, *buff* ('59)	2.25	.50
		Nos. 270-278 (9)	20.45	2.65
		Set, never hinged	47.50	

For overprints see Nos. O28-O36, 2O79-2O87, 3O71-3O79, 4O10-4O18, 5O17-5O22, 6O6-6O8, 7O12-7O17.

Farmer Plowing A86

1941, Mar. 21 Photo.
Granite Paper

279	A86	10c brown & buff	.20	.50
		Never hinged	.20	

Natl. Agriculture Development Plan of 1941.

Masons, Knight and Bern Coat of Arms A87

1941, Sept. 6
Granite Paper

280	A87	10c multicolored	.20	.75
		Never hinged	.20	

750th anniversary of Bern.

"In order to Endure, Reclaim Used Materials" Inscribed in French A88

1942, Mar. 21 Unwmk. Perf. 11½

281	A88	10c shown	.35	.50
282	A88	10c German	.40	1.00
283	A88	10c Italian	6.25	4.00
		Nos. 281-283 (3)	7.00	5.50
		Set, never hinged	14.00	
		Sheet of 25	90.00	550.00

Printed in sheets of 25, containing 8 No. 281, 12 No. 282 and 5 No. 283.

Types of 1938
1955 Engr.
Cream-surfaced Granite Paper

284	A69	3fr brown car	7.00	.75
285	A70	5fr slate blue	5.00	.80
286	A71	10fr green	7.00	3.00
		Nos. 284-286 (3)	19.00	4.55

	Set, never hinged	27.50	

1942 Cream paper

284a	A69	3fr	22.50	.5(
285a	A70	5fr	10.00	.5(
286a	A71	10fr	32.50	2.0(
		Nos. 284a-286a (3)	65.00	3.0(
		Set, never hinged	160.00	

The 1955 set is on cream-surfaced granite paper with white back, and blue and red fibers. The 1942 set is on colored-through cream paper with black and red fibers.

Zurich Stamps of 1843 A91

1943, Feb. 26

287	A91	10c blk & salmon	.20	.20
		Never hinged	.20	

Centenary of postage stamps of Switzerland. See Nos. B130-B131.

Apollo Statue — A94

1944, Mar. 21 Photo.
Granite Paper

290	A94	10c org yel & gray blk	.20	1.00
291	A94	20c cer & gray blk	.30	1.00
292	A94	30c lt bl & gray blk	.60	6.00
		Nos. 290-292 (3)	1.10	8.00
		Set, never hinged	2.50	

Olympic Jubilee.

Numeral of Value — A95

Olive Branch A96

Designs: 60c, Keys of peace. 80c, Horn of plenty. 1fr, Dove of peace. 2fr, Plowing. 3fr, Field of crocus. 5fr, Clasped hands. 10fr, Aged couple.

1945, May 9 Unwmk. Perf. 12
Granite Paper

293	A95	5c gray & green	.20	.50
294	A95	10c gray & brown	.25	.25
295	A95	20c gray & car rose	.35	.25
296	A95	30c gray & ultra	.70	3.00
297	A95	40c gray & orange	2.00	10.00
298	A96	50c dark red	2.75	19.00
299	A96	60c dull gray	2.75	6.75
300	A96	80c slate green	6.25	85.00
301	A96	1fr blue	8.75	95.00
302	A96	2fr red brown	22.50	160.00

Engr.

303	A96	3fr dk sl grn, *buff*	30.00	65.00
304	A96	5fr brn lake, *buff*	100.00	325.00
305	A96	10fr rose vio, *buff*	110.00	125.00
		Nos. 293-305,B145 (14)	286.80	895.50
		Set, never hinged	525.00	

End of war in Europe.

Johann Heinrich Pestalozzi — A104

1946, Jan. 12   **Engr.**   **Perf. 11½**
306 A104 10c rose violet   .20 .20
   Never hinged   .20

200th anniversary of the birth of J. H. Pestalozzi, educational reformer.
For overprint see No. 4O22.

Mobile P.O. Type of 1937
Redrawn

1946, July 6   **Photo.**

Granite Paper
307 A62 10c black & yellow   1.10 .20
   Never hinged   3.00

The designer's and printer's names are larger on the redrawn stamp. There are many minor differences in the two designs. Sizes: 1937, 37½x21mm. 1946, 38x22½mm.

First Swiss Steam Locomotive — A105

Modern Steam Locomotive — A106

Electric Gotthard Express A107

Electric Trains Passing on Bridge A108

1947, Aug. 6   **Photo.**   **Perf. 11½**
Granite Paper
308 A105 5c dk grn, blk & yel   .20 .50
309 A106 10c dk brn, gray & blk   .20 .50
310 A107 20c dk red & red   .25 .50
311 A108 30c dk bl & bl gray   .85 1.75
   Nos. 308-311 (4)   1.50 3.25
   Set, never hinged   5.00

Centenary of the opening of the first Swiss railroad, between Zurich and Baden.

Johann Rudolf Wettstein A109

Castle at Neuchatel A110

"Helvetia" A111

Symbol of Swiss Federal State A112

1948, Feb. 27   **Granite Paper**
312 A109 5c dp grn   .20 .50
313 A110 10c gray blk   .20 .20
314 A111 20c dk red   .20 .20
315 A112 30c blk & red   .40 1.25
   Nos. 312-315 (4)   1.00 2.15
   Set, never hinged   2.00

Tercentenary of the acknowledgment of independence of the Swiss Confederation, and the centenaries of the Neuchatel Revolution and the Swiss Federal State.
See Nos. B178a and B178b for 10c and 20c denominations, type A109.

Types of 1936-42 and

Grisons National Park — A113

1948, Mar. 1   **Engr.**
316 A54   5c chocolate   .20 .20
   a.   Tête bêche pair   1.25 1.25
317 A55   10c green   .20 .20
   a.   Tête bêche pair   1.25 1.50
318 A68   20c org brn   .30 .20
   a.   Tête bêche pair   1.65 2.25
319 A113 25c carmine   1.50 1.50
320 A59   30c grnsh bl   6.25 4.00
321 A61   40c ultra   11.00 .75
   Nos. 316-321 (6)   19.45 6.85
   Set, never hinged   42.50

For overprints see Nos. 4O26, 5O4.

Figures Encircling Globe A114

Designs: 25c, Globe and inscribed ribbon. 40c, Globe and pigeons.

Perf. 11½
1949, May 16   **Photo.**   **Unwmk.**
322 A114 10c green   .20 .20
323 A114 25c dark red   .40 6.25
324 A114 40c brt blue   .50 4.00
   Nos. 322-324 (3)   1.10 10.45
   Set, never hinged   2.00

75th anniv. of the UPU.

Post Horn A115

Horse Drawn Mail Coach A116

Design: 30c, Post bus with trailer.

1949, May 16
325 A115 5c gray, yel & pink   .20 .50
326 A116 20c pur, gray & yel   .25 .30
327 A116 30c dk org brn, gray & yel   .45 6.75
   Nos. 325-327 (3)   .90 7.55
   Set, never hinged   1.50

Centenary of the establishment of the Federal Post in Switzerland.

High Tension Conductors A117

Viaducts — A118

Mountain Railway — A119

Rotary Snow Plow — A120

Reservoir, Grimsel — A121

Lake Dam — A122

Dam and Power Station — A123

Alpine Postal Road — A124

Harbor of the Rhine — A125

Suspension Railway — A126

Railway Viaduct — A127

Triangulation Point — A128

Two types of 20c:
Type I - Three lines above curved rock.
Type II - Two lines above rock.

Perf. 12x11½
1949, Aug. 1   **Engr.**   **Unwmk.**
328 A117 3c gray   1.50 4.00
329 A118 5c orange   .20 .20
   a.   Tête bêche pair   .90 .20
330 A119 10c yel grn   .20 .20
   a.   Tête bêche pair   .60 .20
331 A120 15c aqua   .20 .50
332 A121 20c brown car (II)   .30 .20
   a.   Tête bêche pair   1.75 .75
   c.   Type I   2,000. 67.50
     Type I, never hinged   3,750.
333 A122 25c red   .25 .20
334 A123 30c olive   .25 .20
335 A124 35c red brown   .45 .60
336 A125 40c deep blue   1.25 .20
337 A126 50c slate gray   1.25 .20

338 A127 60c blue green   3.75 .50
339 A128 70c purple   1.00 .30
   Nos. 328-339 (12)   10.60 7.30
   Set, never hinged   22.50

For use in vending machines, some printings of the 5c, 10c, 20c (II), 25c, 30c and 40c carry a control number on the back of every fifth stamp. The number was applied on top of the gum.
For overprints see Nos. O37-O47, 3O83-3O93, 4O29-4O39, 5O6-5O16, 6O1-6O5, 7O1-7O11.

Symbolical of the Telegraph — A129

10c, Telephone. 20c, Radio. 40c, Television.

1952, Feb. 1   **Photo.**   **Perf. 11½**
340 A129 5c org & yel   .25 .50
341 A129 10c brt grn & pink   .30 .20
342 A129 20c dp red lil & gray bl   .45 .20
343 A129 40c dp bl & lt bl   1.40 4.75
   Nos. 340-343 (4)   2.40 5.65
   Set, never hinged   5.25

"A century of telecommunications."

Zurich Airport and Tail of Plane A130

1953, Aug. 29
344 A130 40c blue, red & gray   3.25 10.50
   Never hinged   5.50

Opening of Zurich-Kloten airport.

Alpine Post Bus, Winter Background — A131

Design: 20c, Same, summer background.

1953, Oct. 8
345 A131 10c dk grn, grn & yel   .20 .20
346 A131 20c dk red, red brn & yel   .20 .20
   Set, never hinged   1.00

Sold only on Swiss alpine post buses.

Symbols of Agriculture, Forestry and Horticulture — A132

Map and Nautical Emblems A133

Alphorn Blower A135

Lausanne
Cathedral
A134

20c, Winged spoon. 40c, Football and map.

1954, Mar. 15   **Perf. 14**

347	A132	10c multicolored	.20	.25
348	A132	20c multicolored	.40	.25
349	A133	25c red, dk ol grn & gray	1.00	3.00
350	A132	40c bl, yel & brn	1.60	3.50
		Nos. 347-350 (4)	3.20	7.00
		Set, never hinged	6.00	

Nos. 347-348 were issued to publicize exhibitions at Lucerne and Bern; No. 349, fifty years of navigation on the Rhine; No. 350, the 1954 World Soccer Championships in Switzerland.

1955, Feb. 15   **Perf. 11½**

Designs: 10c, Vaud costume hat. 40c, Automobile steering wheel.

351	A134	5c multi	.20	.60
352	A134	10c grn, yel & red	.25	.50
a.		Souvenir sheet of 2	60.00	80.00
		Never hinged	90.00	
353	A134	20c red & sepia	.55	.50
354	A134	40c bl, pink & gray	1.25	2.10
		Nos. 351-354 (4)	2.25	3.70
		Set, never hinged	5.50	

No. 352a contains 10c and 20c multicolored, imperf. stamps of Cathedral type A134. Size: 104x52mm.

National Philatelic Exhibition (5c, #352a), Winegrowers' Festival (10c), Alpine Herdsman and Costume Festival (20c) and 25th Intl. Automobile Show (40c).

First Swiss
Post
Bus — A136

10c, North Gate of Simplon Tunnel and Stockalper Palace. 20c, Children crossing street and road signs. 40c, Planes and emblem of Swissair, vert.

1956, Mar. 1   **Photo.**
Granite Paper

355	A136	5c ol gray, blk & yel	.20	.50
356	A136	10c brt grn, gray & red	.25	.20
357	A136	20c multi	.45	.50
358	A136	40c blue & red	1.00	1.40
		Nos. 355-358 (4)	1.90	2.60
		Set, never hinged	4.50	

50th anniv. of the Swiss Motor Coach Service (#355); 50th anniv. of the opening of Simplon Tunnel (#356); Accident prevention (#357); 25th anniv. of the founding of Swissair (#358).

Inking Device,
Printing
Machine
A137

10c, Train on southern ramp of Gotthard Railroad. 20c, Shield of civil defense and coat of arms. 40c, Munatius Plancus and view of Basel.

Two types of 10c:
I - "Black" bottom line on train.
II - Brown bottom line.

1957, Feb. 27   **Perf. 11½**
Granite Paper

359	A137	5c multicolored	.20	.20
360	A137	10c lt bl grn, dk grn & red brn (I)	1.10	.20
a.		Type II	1.00	.50
		Never hinged	2.75	
361	A137	20c red org & gray	.25	.50
362	A137	40c multi	.75	1.25
		Nos. 359-362 (4)	2.30	2.15
		Set, never hinged	4.50	

Intl. Exhibition for Graphic Arts, Lausanne, June 1-16, 1957 (#359). 75th anniv. of St. Gotthard railroad (#360). Civil defense (#361). 2000th anniv. of Basel (#362).

Rope and
Symbol of
European
Unity — A138

1957, July 15   **Engr.**   **Perf. 11½**

363	A138	25c lt red		.50	.35
364	A138	40c blue		.80	.35
		Set, never hinged		4.50	

Issued to emphasize European unity.

Catalogue values for unused stamps in this section, from this point to the end of the section, are for Never Hinged items.

Nyon Castle
and
Corinthian
Capital
A139

Designs: 10c, Woman's head and ribbons in Swiss colors. 20c, Crossbow emblem. 40c, Salvation Army hat.

1958, Mar. 5   **Photo.**   **Unwmk.**
Granite Paper

365	A139	5c ol bis & dl pur	.20	.20
366	A139	10c grn, dk grn & red	.20	.20
367	A139	20c ver, lil & car	.50	.20
368	A139	40c multicolored	1.40	1.25
		Nos. 365-368 (4)	2.30	1.85

2000th anniv. of Nyon (#365). Saffa Exhibition, Zurich, July 17-Sept. 15 (#366). 25th anniv. of Swiss manufacturing emblem (#367). 75th anniv. of the Salvation Army in Switzerland (#368).

Symbol of
Nuclear
Fission
A140

1958, Aug. 25   **Perf. 11½**
Granite Paper

369	A140	40c blue, yel & red	.50	.50

2nd UN Atomic Conf. for peaceful uses of atomic power, Geneva, Sept. 1958.

"Transportation" — A141

Designs: 10c, Fasces and post horn. 20c, Owl, rabbit and fish. 50c, Jean Calvin, Theodore de Beze and University of Geneva.

1959, Mar. 9   **Photo.**   **Unwmk.**
Granite Paper

370	A141	5c multicolored	.20	.20
371	A141	10c emer, yel & lt gray	.30	.20
a.		Souvenir sheet of 2, imperf.	14.00	14.00
372	A141	20c multicolored	.50	.20
373	A141	50c multicolored	1.10	.75
		Nos. 370-373 (4)	2.10	1.35

Opening of the Swiss House of Transport and Communications (5c). Natl. Phil. Exhib., St. Gall, Aug. 21-30 (10c and #371a). Protection of animals (20c). 400th anniv. of the University of Geneva (50c).

No. 371a contains a 10c green, gold and light gray and a 20c deep carmine. Sold for 2fr; the money went for the St. Gall Phil. Exhib.

Chain Symbolizing
European
Unity — A142

1959, June 22   **Engr.**   **Perf. 11½**

374	A142	30c brick red	1.60	.30
375	A142	50c lt ultra	2.75	.45

Issued to emphasize European Unity.

Overprinted "REUNION DES PTT D'EUROPE 1959" in Ultramarine or Red

1959, June 22

376	A142	30c brick red	37.50	6.50
377	A142	50c lt ultra	37.50	6.50

European Conference of PTT Administrations, Montreux, June 22-July 31. Nos. 376-377 were on sale only during the conference at a special P. O. in Montreux.

"Cancer
Control"
A143

Designs: 20c, Founding charter and scepter of University of Basel. 50c, Uprooted Oak Emblem. 75c, Swissair Jet DC-8.

1960, Apr. 7   **Photo.**   **Perf. 11½**
Granite Paper

378	A143	10c brt grn & red	.55	.20
379	A143	20c car rose, gray blk & yel	.55	.20
380	A143	50c ultra & yel	.55	1.25
381	A143	75c lt bl, gray & red	3.50	4.00
		Nos. 378-381 (4)	5.15	5.65

50th anniv. of the Swiss League for Cancer Control (10c). 500th anniv. of the University of Basel (20c). World Refugee Year, July 1, 1959-June 30, 1960 (50c). Swissair's entry into the jet age (75c).

Messenger,
Fribourg
A144

Cathedral,
Lausanne
A145

Designs: 10c, Messenger, Schwyz. 15c, Messenger and pack animal. 20c, Postilion on horseback. 30c, Grossmünster (church), Zürich. 35c, 1.30fr, Woodcutters' Guildhall, Biel. 40c, Cathedral, Geneva. 50c, Spalen Gate, Basel. 60c, Clock Tower, Berne. 70c, 2.80fr, Sts. Peter and Stephen Church, Bellinzona (tower omitted on 2.80fr). 75c, Bridge and water tower, Lucerne. 80c, Cathedral, St. Gallen. 90c, Munot tower, Schaffhausen. 1fr, Townhall, Fribourg. 1.20fr, Basel gate, Solothurn. 1.50fr, Reding house, Schwyz. 1.70fr, 2fr, 2.20fr, Church, Einsiedeln.

Two types of 5c, 10c, 20c, 50c:
5 Centimes:
Type I - Four lines on pike at left of hand.
Type II - Three lines.
10 Centimes:
Type I - Dot on pike below head.
Type II - No dot.
20 Centimes:
Type I - Ten dots on horiz. harness strip.
Type II - Nine dots.
50 Centimes:
Type I - 3 shading lines at right above arch.
Type II - 2 shading lines.

1960-63   **Engr.**   **Perf. 11½**
1.30fr, 1.70fr, 2.20fr, 2.80fr on Granite Paper, Red and Blue Fibers

382	A144	5c lt ultra (I)	.20	.20
c.		Tête bêche pair	.20	.20
383	A144	10c blue grn (I)	.20	.20
c.		Tête bêche pair	.40	.20
384	A144	15c lt red brn	.20	.20
385	A144	20c rose pink (I)	.20	.20
c.		Tête bêche pair	.70	.45
386	A145	25c emerald	.25	.20
387	A145	30c vermilion	.30	.20
388	A145	35c orange red	.45	.30
389	A145	40c lilac	.45	.20
390	A145	50c lt vio bl (I)	.45	.20
c.		Tête bêche pair	2.75	2.75
391	A145	60c rose red	.50	.20
392	A145	70c orange	.60	.40
393	A145	75c lt blue	.75	.20
394	A145	80c dp claret	.75	.20
395	A145	90c olive green	.75	.20
396	A144	1fr dull orange	.95	.20
397	A144	1.20fr dull red	1.10	.30

397A	A145	1.30fr red brn, *pink* ('63)	1.40	.2
398	A144	1.50fr brt green	1.40	.3
398A	A144	1.70fr rose lil, *pink* ('63)	1.75	.2
399	A144	2fr brt blue	3.25	.5
399A	A144	2.20fr bl grn, *grn* ('63)	2.50	.5
399B	A145	2.80fr org, *buff* ('63)	3.50	.4
		Nos. 382-399B (22)	21.90	5.7

See Nos. 440-455.

1963-76
Violet Fibers, Fluorescent Paper

382d	A144	5c lt ultra (I)	.20	.2
g.		Tête bêche pair ('68)	.20	.2
383d	A144	10c bl grn (I)	.20	.2
e.		Bklt. pane of 2 + 2 labels	.65	.6
g.		Tête bêche pair ('68)	.35	.2
384a	A144	15c lt red brn	.55	.2
385d	A144	20c rose pink (I)	.30	.2
g.		Tête bêche pair ('68)	.70	.4
386a	A145	25c emerald	.35	.2
387a	A145	30c vermilion	.35	.2
c.		Tête bêche pair ('68)	1.00	.7
389a	A145	40c lilac ('67)	.55	.3
c.		Tête bêche pair ('76)	1.25	1.1
390d	A145	50c lt vio bl (I)	.65	.2
391a	A145	60c rose red ('67)	.60	.3
393a	A145	75c lt blue ('68)	1.00	.4
394a	A145	80c dp claret	1.00	.2
395a	A145	90c olive grn ('67)	1.00	.2
396a	A144	1fr dull org ('67)	1.75	.2
397b	A144	1.20fr dl red ('68)	2.75	1.7
398b	A144	1.50fr brt green ('68)	2.75	1.7
		Nos. 382d-398b (15)	14.00	6.95

Coil Stamps

1960   **White Paper**

382b	A144	5c lt ultra (II)	1.40	1.4
383b	A144	10c blue grn (II)	.85	.85
385b	A144	20c rose pink (II)	.85	.8
390b	A145	50c lt vio bl (II)	4.00	4.00
		Nos. 382b-390b (4)	7.10	7.10

The coil stamps were printed in sheets (available to collectors) and pasted into coils. Every fifth stamp has a control number on the back.

Other denominations issued in coils on white paper are: 40c, 60c, 90c, 1fr, 1.30fr, 1.70fr, 2.20fr and 2.80fr.

Denominations issued in coils on granite paper (red & blue fibers) are: 1.30fr, 1.70fr, 2.20fr and 2.80fr.

Coil Stamps

1965-68
Violet Fibers, Fluorescent Paper

382e	A144	5c lt ultra (II)	1.10	1.10
383h	A144	10c blue grn (II)	.50	.20
385e	A144	20c rose pink (II)	.50	.20
390e	A145	50c lt vio bl (II)	3.75	3.75
		Nos. 382e-390e (4)	5.85	5.30

Other denominations issued in coils on violet-fiber paper are: 40c, 60c, 90c and 1fr.

Common Design Types pictured following the introduction.

Europa Issue, 1960
Common Design Type

1960, Sept. 19   **Unwmk.**   **Perf. 11½**
Size: 33x23mm

400	CD3	30c vermilion	.50	.25
401	CD3	50c ultra	.75	.40

Wall under
Construction
and
Globe — A146

Designs: 10c, Symbolic sun (HYSPA Emblem). 20c, Ice hockey stick and puck. 50c, Wiring diagram on map of Switzerland.

1961, Feb. 20   **Photo.**   **Perf. 11½**
Granite Paper

402	A146	5c gray, brick red & grnsh bl	.35	.20
403	A146	10c aqua & yel	.35	.20
404	A146	20c multicolored	1.25	.50
405	A146	50c ultra, gray & car rose	1.10	.90
		Nos. 402-405 (4)	3.05	1.80

Development aid to new nations (5c). HYSPA 1961, Health and Sports Exhibition, Bern, May 18-July 17 (10c). Intl. Ice Hockey Championships, Lausanne and Geneva, Mar. 2-12 (20c). Fully automatic Swiss telephone service (50c).

St. Matthew and Angel — A147

Evangelists: 5fr, St. Mark and winged lion. 10fr, St. Luke and winged ox. 20fr, St. John and eagle.

Perf. 11½
1961, Sept. 18 Unwmk. Engr.
Granite Paper
406	A147	3fr rose carmine	3.25	.20
407	A147	5fr dark blue	4.75	.20
408	A147	10fr dark brown	8.25	.45
409	A147	20fr red	16.00	3.00
	Nos. 406-409 (4)		32.25	3.85

Designs are after 15th century wood carvings from St. Oswald's church, Zug.

Europa Issue, 1961
Common Design Type
1961, Sept. 18
Size: 26x21mm
| 410 | CD4 | 30c vermilion | .50 | .20 |
| 411 | CD4 | 50c blue | .75 | .35 |

Trans-Europe Express A148

10c, Rower. 20c, Jungfrau railroad station and Mönch. 50c, WHO Anti-malaria emblem.

1962, Mar. 19 Photo. Perf. 11½
412	A148	5c multicolored	.50	.20
413	A148	10c brt grn, lem & lil	.45	.20
414	A148	20c rose lil, pale bl & bis	.90	.25
415	A148	50c ultra, lt grn & rose lil	.90	.60
	Nos. 412-415 (4)		2.75	1.25

Introduction of Swiss electric TEE trains (5c). Rowing world championship, Lucerne, Sept. 6-9 (10c). 50th anniv. of the railroad station on the Jungfrau mountain (20c). WHO Anti-Malaria campaign (50c).

Europa Issue, 1962
Common Design Type
1962, Sept. 17 Unwmk. Perf. 11½
Size: 33x23mm
| 416 | CD5 | 30c orange, yel & brn | .65 | .40 |
| 417 | CD5 | 50c ultra, lt grn & brn | 1.00 | .60 |

Boy Scout — A149

Designs: 10c, Swiss Alpine Club emblem. 20c, Luegelkinn viaduct. 30c, Wheat Emblem. No. 426, 428a, Red Cross Jubilee Emblem. No. 427, Post Office Building, Paris, 1863.

1963, Mar. 21 Photo.
422	A149	5c gray, dk red & brn	.55	.20
423	A149	10c dk grn, gray & red	.40	.20
424	A149	20c dk car, brn & gray	1.10	.20
425	A149	30c yel grn, yel & org	1.60	1.60
426	A149	50c blue, sil & red	.85	.80
427	A149	50c ultra, pink, yel & gray	.90	.75
	Nos. 422-427 (6)		5.40	3.75

Souvenir Sheet
Imperf
| 428 | | Sheet of 4 | 7.00 | 5.50 |
| a. | A149 50c bl, lt bl, sil & red | | 1.75 | 1.10 |

50 years of Swiss Boy Scouts (5c). Cent. of Swiss Alpine Club (10c). 50 years Lötschberg Railroad (20c). FAO "Freedom from Hunger" campaign (30c). Red Cross Cent. (#426, 428). 1st Intl. Postal Conf., Paris 1863 (#427). No. 428 sold for 3fr.

Europa Issue, 1963
Common Design Type
1963, Sept. 16 Perf. 11½
Granite Paper
Size: 26x21mm
| 429 | CD6 | 50c ultra & ocher | .90 | .60 |

EXPO Emblem A150

50c, EXPO emblem on globe & moon ("Outlook"). 75c, EXPO emblem on globe ("Insight").

1963, Sept. 16 Unwmk. Perf. 11½
Granite Paper
430	A150	10c brt grn & dk grn	.30	.20
431	A150	20c red & maroon	.35	.20
432	A150	50c ultra & red	.45	.40
433	A150	75c purple & red	.60	.45
	Nos. 430-433 (4)		1.70	1.25

Issued to publicize the Swiss National Exhibition, Lausanne, Apr. 30-Oct. 25, 1964.

Road Tunnel Through Great St. Bernard A151

10c, Symbolic water god & waves. 20c, Soldiers of 1864 & 1964. 50c, Standards of Swiss Confederation & Geneva.

1964, Mar. 9 Photo.
Granite Paper
434	A151	5c ol, ultra & red	.20	.20
435	A151	10c Prus bl & grn	.20	.20
436	A151	20c red, ultra, blk & sal	.40	.20
437	A151	50c ultra, red, yel & blk	.95	.65
	Nos. 434-437 (4)		1.75	1.25

1st Trans-Alpine Automobile route from Switzerland to Italy (5c). "Pro Aqua" water conservation campaign (10c). Centenary of the Swiss Noncommissioned Officers' Association (20c). Sesqui. of union of Geneva with Swiss Confederation (50c).

Europa Issue, 1964
Common Design Type
1964, Sept. 14 Engr. Perf. 11½
Size: 21x26mm
Violet Fibers, Fluorescent Paper
| 438 | CD7 | 20c vermilion | .40 | .20 |
| 439 | CD7 | 50c ultra | .85 | .25 |

Type of Regular Issue, 1960-63

Designs: 5c, Lenzburg. 10c, Freuler Mansion, Näfels. 15c, St. Mauritius Church, Appenzell. 20c, Planta House, Samedan. 30c, Gabled houses, Gais. 50c, Castle and Abbey Church, Neuchâtel. 70c, Lussy House, Wolfenschiessen. 1fr, Santa Croce Church, Riva San Vitale. 1.20fr, Abbey Church, Payerne. 1.30fr, Church of St. Pierre de Clages. 1.50fr, La Porte de France, Porrentruy. 1.70fr, Frauenfeld Castle. 2fr, A Pro Castle, Seedorf. 2.20fr, Thomas Tower and Gate. Liestal. 2.50fr, St. Oswald's Church, Zug. 3.50fr, Benedictine Abbey, Engelberg.

1964-68 Engr. Perf. 11½
Violet Fibers, Fluorescent Paper
440	A144	5c car rose ('68)	.20	.20
441	A144	10c violet bl ('68)	.20	.20
b.	Tête bêche pair		.25	.20
c.	Booklet pane of 2 + 2 labels		.70	
442	A144	15c brown red ('68)	.20	.20
b.	Tête bêche pair		.35	.35
443	A144	20c blue grn ('68)	.25	.20
b.	Tête bêche pair		.50	.35
444	A144	30c vermilion ('68)	.40	.20
b.	Tête bêche pair		.90	.80
445	A144	50c ultra ('68)	.55	.20
446	A145	70c brown ('67)	.60	.20
447	A145	1fr dk green ('68)	1.00	.20
448	A145	1.20fr brown red ('68)	1.10	.20
449	A145	1.30fr violet bl ('66)	1.50	.75
450	A145	1.50fr green ('68)	1.60	.40
451	A145	1.70fr brown org ('66)	1.90	1.25
452	A145	2fr orange ('67)	2.00	.40
453	A145	2.20fr green	3.00	.80
454	A145	2.50fr Prus grn ('67)	2.25	.55
455	A145	3.50fr purple ('67)	3.25	.60
	Nos. 440-455 (16)		20.00	6.60

The 15c was issued in coils in 1972 (?) with control number on the back of every fifth stamp.

Nurse and Patient A152

Seated Helvetia, 1854 — A153

Women's Army Auxiliary A154

Intercontinental Communications Map — A155

1965, Mar. 8 Photo. Perf. 11½
Violet Fibers, Fluorescent Paper
462	A152	5c lt ultra & red	.20	.20
463	A153	10c emer, brn & blk	.20	.20
464	A154	20c red & multi	.30	.20

Granite Paper, Red and Blue Fibers
| 465 | A155 | 50c dl bl grn & mar | .70 | .50 |
| | Nos. 462-465 (4) | | 1.40 | 1.10 |

Nursing and auxiliary medical professions (5c). Natl. Postage Stamp Exhibition, NABRA, Bern, Aug. 27-Sept. 5, 1965 (10c). 20th anniv. of Women's Army Auxiliary Corps (20c). Cent. of ITU (50c).
See No. B344.

Swiss Arms, Cantonal Emblems of Valais, Neuchatel, Geneva A156

1965, June 1 Unwmk. Perf. 11½
Granite Paper, Red and Blue Fibers
| 466 | A156 | 20c multicolored | .30 | .20 |

150th anniversary of the entry of the cantons of Valais, Neuchatel and Geneva in the Swiss Confederation.

Matterhorn A157

30c, like 10c but inscribed in French "Cervin."

1965, June 1 Photo.
Granite Paper, Red and Blue Fibers
| 467 | A157 | 10c grn, slate & dk red | .20 | .20 |

Violet Fibers, Fluorescent Paper
| 468 | A157 | 30c dk red, grn & slate | .45 | .40 |

Year of the Alps; the cent. of the 1st wintertime visitors to the Alps and cent. of the 1st ascent of the Matterhorn. Nos. 467-468 on sale only at Swiss Alpine post buses.

Europa Issue, 1965
Common Design Type
1965, Sept. 14 Unwmk. Perf. 11½
Violet Fibers, Fluorescent Paper
| 469 | CD8 | 50c bl, dk bl & grn | .60 | .25 |

Figure Skating A159

1965, Sept. 14 Photo.
Violet Fibers, Fluorescent Paper
| 470 | A159 | 5c grn, dl bl & blk | .20 | .20 |

Issued to publicize the World Figure Skating Championships, Davos, Feb. 22-27, 1966.

ITU Emblem and Atom Diagram A160

Cent. of the ITU: 30c, Symbol of communications, waves.

1965, Sept. 14
Violet Fibers, Fluorescent Paper
| 471 | A160 | 10c ultra & multi | .20 | .20 |

Granite Paper, Red and Blue Fibers
| 472 | A160 | 30c org, red & gray | .35 | .35 |

Violet Fibers, Fluorescent Paper
Paper from No. 473 onward is fluorescent and has violet fibers, unless otherwise noted.

European Kingfisher A161

Mercury's Helmet and Laurel A162

Flags of 13 Member Nations and Nuclear Fission A163

1966, Feb. 21 Photo.
473	A161	10c emer & multi	.20	.20
474	A162	20c dp mag, red & brt grn	.25	.20
475	A163	50c slate blue & multi	.60	.40
	Nos. 473-475 (3)		1.05	.80

Intl. Cong. for Conservation "Pro Natura," Lucerne (10c). 50th anniv. of Swiss Trade Fair, Basel, Apr. 16-26 (20c). European Organization for Nuclear Research, CERN (50c).

Emblem of Society of Swiss Abroad — A164

1966, June 1 Photo. Perf. 11½
| 476 | A164 | 20c ultra & ver | .20 | .20 |

50th anniv. of the Society of Swiss Abroad.

Europa Issue, 1966
Common Design Type

1966, Sept. 26   **Engr.**   *Perf. 11½*
Size: 21x26mm
477 CD9 20c vermilion .25 .20
478 CD9 50c ultra .75 .35

Finsteraarhorn — A165

1966, Sept. 26   **Photo.**
479 A165 10c lt grnsh bl, dk bl & dk
red .20 .20

Automobile
Wheels and
White
Cane — A166

Flags of EFTA
Members
A167

1967, Mar. 13   **Photo.**   *Perf. 11½*
480 A166 10c bl grn, blk & yel .20 .20
481 A167 20c multicolored .20 .20

No. 480 issued to publicize the white cane
as a distinguishing mark for blind pedestrians.
No. 481 publicizes the European Free Trade
Association, EFTA. See note after Norway No.
501.

Europa Issue, 1967
Common Design Type
1967, Mar. 13
482 CD10 30c blue gray .60 .25

Cogwheel and
Swiss
Emblem
A169

Hourglass
and
Sun — A170

San
Bernardino,
from
North — A171

Railroad
Wheel
A172

1967, Sept. 18   **Photo.**   *Perf. 11½*
483 A169 10c multicolored .20 .20
484 A170 20c red, yel & blk .20 .20
485 A171 30c multicolored .35 .20
486 A172 50c multicolored .50 .35
    Nos. 483-486 (4) 1.25 .95

50th anniv. of Swiss Week (10c). 50th
anniv. of the Foundation for the Aged (20c).
Opening of the San Bernardino Road Tunnel
(30c). 75th anniv. of the Central Office for Intl.
Railroad Transportation (50c).

Mountains
and Club's
Emblem
A173

Golden Key
with CEPT
Emblem
A174

Rook and
Chessboard
A175

Aircraft Tail
and Satellites
A176

1968, Mar. 14   **Photo.**   *Perf. 11½*
487 A173 10c grn, lt ultra & red .20 .20
488 A174 20c Prus bl, yel & brn .45 .20
489 A175 30c dk ol bis & vio bl .30 .20
490 A176 50c dk blue & red .50 .35
    Nos. 487-490 (4) 1.45 .95

50th anniv. of the Swiss Women's Alpine
Club (10c). A unified Europe through postal
cooperation (20c). 18th Chess Olympics,
Lugano, Oct. 17-Nov. 6 (30c). Inauguration of
the new Geneva-Cointrin Air Terminal (50c).

Worker's
Protective
Helmet
A177

Double
Geneva and
Zurich
Stamps of
1843 — A178

Map Showing
Systematic
Planning
A179

Flag of Rhine
Navigation
Committee
A180

1968, Sept. 12   **Photo.**   *Perf. 11½*
491 A177 10c bl grn & yel .20 .20
492 A178 20c dp car, blk & yel
grn .20 .20
493 A179 30c multicolored .25 .20
494 A180 50c bl, yel & blk .55 .35
    Nos. 491-494 (4) 1.20 .95

50th anniv. of the Swiss Accident Insurance
comp., SUVA (10c). 125th anniv. of 1st Swiss
postage stamps (20c). 25th anniv. of the
Swiss Society for Territorial Planning (30c).
Cent. of the Rhine Navigation Act (50c).

Swiss Girl
Scouts'
Emblem and
Camp — A181

Pegasus
Constellation
A182

Comptoir
Suisse
Emblem and
Beaulieu
Building,
Lausanne
A183

Gymnaestrada Emblem (Man in
Circle) — A184

Swissair DC-
8 and DH-
3 — A185

1969, Feb. 12   **Photo.**   *Perf. 11½*
495 A181 10c multicolored .20 .20
496 A182 20c dark blue .25 .20
497 A183 30c red, ocher, grn &
gray .40 .20
498 A184 50c vio bl, bl, red, grn
& sil .60 .50
499 A185 2fr bl, dk bl & red 2.25 1.90
    Nos. 495-499 (5) 3.70 3.00

50th anniv. of Swiss Girl Scouts (10c).
Opening of 1st Swiss Planetarium, Lucerne,
July 1 (20c). 50th anniv. of the Comptoir
Suisse (trade fair, 30c). 5th Gymnaestrada
(gymnastic meet), Basel, July 1-5 (50c). 50th
anniv. of Swiss airmail service (2fr).

Europa Issue, 1969
Common Design Type
1969, Apr. 28
Size: 32½x23mm
500 CD12 30c brn org & multi .40 .25
501 CD12 50c chlky bl & multi .60 .35

Huldreich Zwingli
(1484-1531)
A186

Famous Swiss: 20c, Gen. Henri Guisan
(1874-1960). 30c, Francesco Borromini, architect (1599-1667). 50c, Othmar Schoeck, musician (1886-1957). 80c, Germaine de Stael,
writer (1766-1817).

1969, Sept. 18   **Engr.**   *Perf. 11½*
502 A186 10c brt purple .20 .20
503 A186 20c green .25 .20
504 A186 30c deep carmine .40 .20
505 A186 50c deep blue .90 .50
506 A186 80c red brown .95 .70
    Nos. 502-506 (5) 2.70 1.80

Kreuzberge,
Alpstein
Mountains
A187

Children
Crossing
Street — A188

Steelworker
A189

1969, Sept. 18   **Photo**
507 A187 20c blue & multi .30 .20
508 A188 30c car & multi .30 .20
509 A189 50c violet & multi .60 .30
    Nos. 507-509 (3) 1.20 .70

No. 508 publicizes the traffic safety campaign; No. 509 for 50th anniv. of the ILO.

Telex
Tape — A190

Fireman
Rescuing
Child — A191

Pro Infirmis
Emblem
A192

United
Nations
Emblem
A193

New UPU
Headquarters
A194

1970, Feb. 26   **Photo.**   *Perf. 11½*
510 A190 20c dk grn, yel & blk .25 .20
511 A191 30c dk car & multi .40 .20
512 A192 30c red & multi .40 .20
513 A193 50c dk bl, lt grnsh bl &
sil .60 .35
514 A194 80c dk pur, sep & tan 1.00 .70
    Nos. 510-514 (5) 2.65 1.65

75th anniv. of the Swiss Telegraph Agency
(20c). Cent. of the Swiss Firemen's Assoc.
(No. 511). 50th anniv. of the Pro Infirmis Foundation (No. 512). UN, 5th anniv. (50c). New
Headquarters of the UPU in Bern (80c).

Europa Issue, 1970
Common Design Type
1970, May 4   **Engr.**   *Perf. 11½*
Size: 21x26mm
515 CD13 30c vermilion .40 .20
516 CD13 50c brt blue .60 .35

Soccer
A195

Census
Form — A196

Piz Palu, Grisons A197

"Nature Conservation" A198

Numeral A199

1970, Sept. 17   Photo.   Perf. 11½

17	A195	10c green & multi	.30	.20
18	A196	20c dk grn & multi	.25	.20
19	A197	30c slate bl & multi	.40	.20
20	A198	50c dk bl & multi	.65	.55
		Nos. 517-520 (4)	1.60	1.15

75th anniv. of Swiss Soccer Association 10c). Federal Census of 1970 (20c). Swiss Alps (30c). Nature Conservation Year (50c).

Coil Stamps

1970, Sept. 17   Engr.   Perf. 11½

521	A199	10c brown lake	.20	.20
522	A199	20c olive grn	.30	.20
523	A199	50c ultra	.65	.60
		Nos. 521-523 (3)	1.15	1.00

Control number in stamp's color on back of every fifth stamp. Nos. 521-523 were regularly issued only in coils, but exist in sheets of 50.

Gymnastic Trio — A200

Rose — A201

Switzerland No. 8 — A202

Rising Spiral — A203

Intelsat 4 Satellite A204

Adaptation of 1850 Design — A205

Design: No. 525, Runners (men).

1971, Mar. 11   Photo.   Perf. 11½

524	A200	10c ol, brn & bl	.20	.20
525	A200	10c gray, brn & yel	.20	.20
a.		Pair, #524-525	.40	.30
526	A201	20c dk grn & multi	.20	.20
527	A202	30c dp car & multi	.25	.20
528	A203	50c dk bl & bis	.60	.45
529	A204	80c multicolored	.90	.90
		Nos. 524-529 (6)	2.35	2.15

Souvenir Sheet
Typo.
Imperf

530	A205	2fr blue & multi	3.00	3.00

New article on gymnastics and sports in Swiss Constitution (10c); Intl. Child Welfare Org. (20c); NABA Natl. Postage Stamp Exhibition, Basel, June 4-13 (30c, 2fr); 2nd decade of development aid (50c); Intl. Space Communications Conf., Geneva, June-July, 1971 (80c).

#525a printed checkerwise. #530 sold for 3fr.

Europa Issue, 1971
Common Design Type

1971, May 3   Engr.   Perf. 11½
Size: 26x21mm

531	CD14	30c rose car & org	.40	.20
532	CD14	50c blue & org	.60	.40

Les Diablerets, Vaud — A206

Telecommunications Symbols — A207

1971, Sept. 23   Photo.   Perf. 11½

533	A206	30c rose lil & bl gray	.35	.20
534	A207	40c ultra, yel & brt pink	.45	.45

No. 534 for the 50th anniv. of Radio-Suisse, which is also in charge of air traffic control.

Alexandre Yersin (1863-1943) Bacteriologist A208

Physicians: 20c, Auguste Forel (1848-1931), psychiatrist. 30c, Jules Gonin (1870-1935), ophthalmologist. 40c, Robert Koch (1843-1910), German bacteriologist. 80c, Frederick G. Banting (1891-1941), Canadian physiologist.

1971, Sept. 23   Engr.

535	A208	10c gray olive	.20	.20
536	A208	20c bluish green	.20	.20
537	A208	30c carmine rose	.20	.20
538	A208	40c dark blue	.60	.50
539	A208	80c brt purple	.85	.70
		Nos. 535-539 (5)	2.05	1.80

Wrench, Road Sign, Club Emblems A209

Electronic Switch Panel — A210

Boy's Head and Radio Waves A211

Symbolic Tree — A212

1972, Feb. 17   Photo.   Perf. 11½

540	A209	10c multicolored	.20	.20
541	A210	20c olive & multi	.20	.20
542	A211	30c orange & maroon	.25	.20
543	A212	40c blue, grn & pur	.50	.50
		Nos. 540-543 (4)	1.15	1.10

75th anniv. of the touring and automobile clubs of Switzerland (10c). 125th anniv. of Swiss railroads (20c). 50th anniv. of Swiss radio (30c). 50th annual congress of Swiss citizens living abroad, Bern, Aug. 25-27 (40c).

Europa Issue 1972
Common Design Type

1972, May. 2
Size: 21x26mm

544	CD15	30c multicolored	.45	.20
545	CD15	40c multicolored	.80	.35

Alberto Giacometti (1901-66), Painter and Sculptor — A213

Portraits and Signatures: 20c, Charles Ferdinand Ramuz (1878-1947), writer. 30c, Le Corbusier (Charles Edouard Jeanneret; 1887-1965) architect. 40c, Albert Einstein (1879-1955), physicist. 80c, Arthur Honegger (1892-1955), composer.

Engraved & Photogravure

1972, Sept. 21   Perf. 11½

546	A213	10c ocher & blk	.20	.20
547	A213	20c lt olive & blk	.20	.20
548	A213	30c pink & blk	.20	.20
549	A213	40c lt blue & blk	.60	.50
550	A213	80c lil rose & blk	.80	.65
		Nos. 546-550 (5)	2.00	1.75

Civil Defense Emblem A214

Spannörter, Swiss Alps — A215

Red Cross Rescue Helicopter A216

Clean Air, Fire, Earth and Water — A217

1972, Sept. 21   Photo.

551	A214	10c org, bl & yel	.20	.20
552	A215	20c bl grn & multi	.20	.20
553	A216	30c lilac, red & indigo	.25	.20
554	A217	40c lt blue & multi	.45	.35
		Nos. 551-554 (4)	1.10	.95

Earth Satellite Station, Leuk, World Map — A218

Quill Pen and Arrows in Circle — A219

INTERPOL Emblem A220

1973, Feb. 15   Photo.   Perf. 11½

555	A218	15c gray, yel & bl	.20	.20
556	A219	30c multicolored	.25	.20
557	A220	40c dp bl, lt bl & gray	.60	.30
		Nos. 555-557 (3)	1.05	.70

Opening of the satellite station at Leuk; Swiss Association of Commercial Employees, cent. (30c); International Criminal Police Organization (INTERPOL), 59th anniv.

Sottoceneri A221

Sign of Inn "Zur Sonne," Toggenburg A222

Villages: 10c, Graubunden. 15c, Central Switzerland. 25c, Jura. 30c, Simme Valley. 35c, Central Switzerland (2 buildings). 40c, Vaud. 50c, Valais. 60c, Engadine. 70c, Sopraceneri. 80c, Eastern Switzerland.
Designs: 1fr, Rose window, Lausanne Cathedral. 1.10fr, Gallus Portal, Basel Cathedral. 1.20fr, Romanesque capital (eagle), St. Jean Baptiste Church, Grandson. 1.50fr, Ceiling medallion (bird feeding nestlings), Stein am Rhein Convent. 1.70fr, Romanesque capital (St. George and dragon), St. Jean Baptiste, Grandson. 1.80fr, Gargoyle, Bern Cathedral. 2fr, Bay window, Schaffhausen. 2.50fr, Cock weather vane, St. Ursus Cathedral, Solothurn. 3fr, Font, St. Maurice Church, Saanen. 3.50fr, Astronomical clock, Bern clock tower.

1973-80   Engr.   Perf. 11½
Fluorescent, No Violet Fibers

558	A221	5c dl yel & dk bl	.20	.20
559	A221	10c rose lil & ol grn	.20	.20
560	A221	15c org & vio bl	.20	.20
561	A221	25c emer & vio bl	.25	.20
562	A221	30c brick red & dk bl	.30	.20

563	A221	35c red org & brt vio ('75)	.40	.20
564	A221	40c brt bl & blk	.45	.20
565	A221	50c ol grn & org	.60	.20
566	A221	60c yel brn & gray	.70	.20
567	A221	70c sep & dk grn	.80	.20
568	A221	80c brt grn & brick red	.80	.20

Violet Fibers, Fluorescent Paper

569	A222	1fr pur ('74)	1.10	.20
a.		Without fibers, fluorescent paper ('78)	1.10	.20
570	A222	1.10fr Prus bl ('75)	1.25	.40
571	A222	1.20fr rose red ('74)	1.40	1.00
572	A222	1.30fr ocher	2.00	.75
573	A222	1.50fr grn ('74)	1.60	.25
574	A222	1.70fr gray	2.00	.60
575	A222	1.80fr dp org	2.00	.60
576	A222	2fr ultra ('74)	2.25	.40
a.		Without fibers, fluorescent paper ('78)	2.25	.40
577	A222	2.50fr gldn brn ('75)	2.75	.40
578	A222	3fr dk car ('79)	3.00	.80
579	A222	3.50fr ol grn ('80)	3.50	1.25
		Nos. 558-579 (22)	27.75	8.85

No. 577 exists without tagging. Value, $60 unused, $30 used.

Europa Issue 1973
Common Design Type

1973, Apr. 30   Engr. and Photo.
Size: 38x28mm

580	CD16	25c brown & yel	.40	.25
581	CD16	40c ultra & yel	.70	.35

"Man and Time" — A223

Skier and Championship Emblem A224

Child — A225

1973, Aug. 30   Photo.   Perf. 11½

582	A223	15c multicolored	.20	.20
583	A224	30c pink & multi	.25	.20
584	A225	40c blue vio & blk	.45	.35
		Nos. 582-584 (3)	.90	.75

Opening of the Intl. Clock Museum, La Chaux-de-Fonds, 1974 (15c); Intl. Alpine Skiing Championships, St. Moritz, Feb. 2-10, 1974 (30c); "Terre des hommes" children's aid program (40c).

Souvenir Sheet

Medieval Postal Couriers — A226

1974, Jan. 29   Photo.   Perf. 11½

585	A226	Sheet of 4	6.00	6.00
a.		30c Basel (with staff)	1.50	1.50
b.		30c Zug (without staff)	1.50	1.50
c.		60c Uri	1.50	1.50
d.		80c Schwyz	1.50	1.50

Cent. of UPU and for INTERNABA 74 Intl. Phil. Exhib., Basel, June 7-16. No. 585 sold for 3fr.

Pine and Cabin on Globe — A227

Gymnast and Hurdlers A228

Target and Pistol — A229

1974, Jan. 29

586	A227	15c lt green & multi	.20	.20
587	A228	30c red & multi	.25	.20
588	A229	40c blue & multi	.45	.30
		Nos. 586-588 (3)	.90	.70

50th anniv. of Swiss Youth Hostels (15c); Cent. of Swiss Workers' Gymnast and Sports Association (SATUS) (30c); World Marksmanship Championships, Thun and Bern, Sept. 1974 (40c).

Old Houses, Parliament RR Station, Bern — A230

Eugéne Borel — A231

Designs: No. 590, Castle, Town Hall, Chauderon Center, Lausanne. 40c, Heinrich von Stephan. 80c, Montgomery Blair.

1974, Mar. 28   Photo.   Perf. 11½

589	A230	30c orange & multi	.30	.20
590	A230	30c scarlet & multi	.30	.20

Engr.

591	A231	30c rose & blk	.20	.20
592	A231	40c gray & blk	.30	.20
593	A231	80c lt yel grn & blk	.75	.45
		Nos. 589-593 (5)	1.85	1.25

Cent. of the UPU. Nos. 589-590 publicize the Cent. Cong., Lausanne, May 22-July 5; Nos. 591-593 honor the founders of the UPU.

"Continuity," by Max Bill — A232

Europa: 40c, "Amazon," bronze sculpture by Carl Burckhardt.

1974, Mar. 28   Photo.

594	A232	30c red & black	.40	.20
595	A232	40c ultra & sepia	.70	.35

Oath of Allegiance, by Werner Witschi — A233

Vineyard Worker, by Maurice Barraud — A241

Europa: 50c, Still Life with Guitar, by René Auberjonois.

Sports Foundation Emblem A234

Conveyor Belts, Paths of Mail Transport and Delivery A235

1974, Sept. 19   Photo.   Perf. 11½

596	A233	15c lil, ol & dk ol	.20	.20
597	A234	30c silver & multi	.30	.20
598	A235	30c plum & multi	.30	.20
		Nos. 596-598 (3)	.80	.60

Centenary of Swiss Constitution (15c); Swiss Sports Foundation (No. 597); 125th anniversary of Swiss Federal Post (No. 598).

Standard Meter, Krypton Spectrum A236

Women of Four Races A237

Red Cross Flag, Barbed Wire — A238

"Ville de Lucerne" Dirigible A239

1975, Feb. 13   Photo.   Perf. 11½

599	A236	15c grn, org & ultra	.20	.20
600	A237	30c brown & multi	.30	.20
601	A238	60c ultra, blk & red	.50	.75
602	A239	90c blue & multi	.90	.60
		Nos. 599-602 (4)	1.90	1.75

Cent. of Intl. Meter Convention, Paris, 1875 (15c); Intl. Women's Year 1975 (30c); 2nd Session of Diplomatic Conf. on Humanitarian Intl. Law, Geneva, Feb. 1975 (60c); Aviation and Space Travel exhibition in Museum of Transport and Communications, Lucerne (90c).

Mönch, by Ferdinand Hodler — A240

1975, Apr. 28   Photo.   Perf. 12x11½

603	A240	30c gray & multi	.50	.2
604	A241	50c multicolored	.90	.5
605	A241	60c bl gray & multi	1.10	.6
		Nos. 603-605 (3)	2.50	1.3

Man Pulling Wheel Chair Upstairs A242

"The Helping Hand" A243

Architectural Heritage Year Emblem A244

Beat Fischer von Reichenbach A245

1975, Sept. 11   Photo.

606	A242	15c lilac, blk & grn	.20	.20
607	A243	30c red, blk & car	.25	.20
608	A244	50c yel brn & mar	.45	.40
609	A245	60c blue & multi	.60	.55
		Nos. 606-609 (4)	1.50	1.35

Special building features for the handicapped (15c); interdenominational telephone pastoral counseling (30c); European Architectural Heritage Year 1975 (50c); Fischer Post, Bern, tercentenary (60c).

Forest A246

Fruits and Vegetables A247

Black Infant — A248

Telephones of 1876 and 1976 — A249

1976, Feb. 12   Photo.   Perf. 11½
Fluorescent, No Violet Fibers

610	A246	20c green & multi	.20	.20
611	A247	40c car & multi	.35	.20
612	A248	40c lil rose & multi	.35	.20

Engr.
Violet Fibers, Fluorescent Paper

613	A249	80c lt bl & dk bl	.75	.65
		Nos. 610-613 (4)	1.65	1.25

Centenary of Federal forest laws (20c); healthy nutrition to combat alcoholism (No. 611); fight against leprosy (No. 612); telephone centenary (80c).

Cotton and Gold Lace, St. Gall — A250

Pocket Watch, 18th Century — A251

1976, May 3   Engr.   Perf. 11½
614 A250 40c red brn & multi   .65 .25
615 A251 80c black & multi   1.40 .70

Europa. Both 40c and 80c are on fluorescent paper, the 80c having violet fibers.

Fawn, Frog and Swallow A252

"Conserve Energy" A253

St. Gotthard Mountains A254

Skater A255

1976, Sept. 16   Photo.   Perf. 11½
Fluorescent, No Violet Fibers
616 A252 20c multicolored   .20 .20
617 A253 40c multicolored   .35 .20
618 A254 40c multicolored   .40 .20
619 A255 80c multicolored   .70 .70
     Nos. 616-619 (4)   1.65 1.30

Wildlife protection (20c); energy conservation (No. 617); Pizzo Lucendro to Pizzo Rotondo, seen from Altanca (No. 618); World Men's Skating Championships, Davos, Feb. 5-6, 1977 (80c).

Oskar Bider, Bleriot Monoplane A256

Swiss Aviation Pioneers: 80c, Eduard Spelterini and balloon gondola. 100c, Armand Dufaux and Dufaux plane. 150c, Walter Mittelholzer and Dornier hydroplane.

1977, Jan. 27   Engr.   Perf. 11½
620 A256 40c multicolored   .45 .20
621 A256 80c multicolored   .95 .95
622 A256 100c multicolored   .95 .95
623 A256 150c multicolored   1.60 1.50
     Nos. 620-623 (4)   3.95 3.60

Blue Cross — A257

Festival Emblem A258

Balloons Carrying Letters A259

1977, Jan. 27   Photo.
624 A257 20c gray, bl & blk   .20 .20
625 A258 40c red, gold & brn   .40 .20
626 A259 80c lt bl & multi   .80 .80
     Nos. 624-626 (3)   1.40 1.20

Blue Cross Society (care of alcoholics and fight against alcoholism), centenary (20c); Vintage Festival, Vevey, July 30-Aug. 14 (40c); JUPHILEX 77 Youth Philatelic Exhibition, Bern, Apr. 7-11 (80c).

Fluorescent Paper
From No. 624 onward the paper lacks violet fibers but is fluorescent, unless otherwise noted.

St. Ursanne on Doubs River — A260

Europa: 80c, Sils-Baselgia on Inn River.

1977, May 2   Engr.   Perf. 11½
627 A260 40c multicolored   .65 .25
628 A260 80c multicolored   1.40 .70

Worker and Factories A261

Ionic Column and Shield A262

Swiss Cross, Arrow and Butterfly A263

1977, Aug. 25   Photo.   Perf. 11½
629 A261 20c multicolored   .20 .20
630 A262 40c multicolored   .35 .20
631 A263 80c multicolored   .85 .60
     Nos. 629-631 (3)   1.40 1.00

Federal Factories Act, centenary (20c); protection of cultural monuments (40c); Swiss hiking trails (80c).

Star Singer, Bergün — A264

Folk Customs: 10c, Horse race, Zürich. 20c, New Year's Eve costumes, Herisau. 25c, Chesslete, Solothurn. 30c, Rollelibutzen, Altstatten. 35c, Cutting off the goose, Sursee. 40c, Herald reading proclamation and men scaling wall, Geneva. 45c, Klausjagen, Kussnacht. 50c, Masked men, Laupen. 60c, Schnabelgeissen, Ottenbach. 70c, Procession (horse and masked men), Mendrisio. 80c, Griffins, Basel. 90c, Masked men, Lotschental.

1977-84   Engr.   Perf. 11½
632 A264 5c blue grn   .20 .20
  a.   Bklt. pane of 4 ('84)   .25
633 A264 10c dark red   .20 .20
  a.   Bklt. pane of 2 + 2 labels ('79)   .45
  b.   Bklt. pane of 4 ('84)   .50
634 A264 20c orange   .20 .20
  a.   Booklet pane of 4 ('79)   .25
635 A264 25c brown   .25 .20
636 A264 30c brt green   .30 .20
637 A264 35c olive   .35 .20
  a.   Bklt. pane of 4 ('84)   1.40
638 A264 40c brown lake   .40 .20
  a.   Booklet pane of 4 ('79)   1.65
  b.   Violet fibers, fluorescent paper ('78)   .35 .20
639 A264 45c gray blue   .40 .30
640 A264 50c red brown   .50 .20
  a.   Bklt. pane of 2+2 labels ('84)   1.00
  b.   Bklt. pane of 4 ('84)   2.00
641 A264 60c gray brown   .55 .45
642 A264 70c purple   .65 .25
643 A264 80c steel blue   .80 .30
644 A264 90c deep brown   .90 .35
     Nos. 632-644 (13)   5.70 3.25

Issue dates: 30c, Nov. 25, 1982; 25c, 40c, 60c, Sept. 11, 1984; others, Aug. 25, 1977.

Arms of Vaud Canton A265

Old Lucerne A266

Title Page of "Melusine" A267

Stylized Lens and Bellows A268

Steamers on Swiss Lakes — A269

1978, Mar. 9   Photo.   Perf. 11½
652 A265 20c multicolored   .20 .20
653 A266 40c multicolored   .40 .20
654 A267 70c multicolored   .65 .60
655 A268 80c multicolored   .75 .65
     Nos. 652-655 (4)   2.00 1.65

Miniature Sheet
656 A269 Sheet of 8   7.00 7.00
  a.   20c La Suisse, 1910   .30 .30
  b.   20c Il Verbano, 1826   .30 .30
  c.   40c MS Gotthard, 1970   .85 .85
  d.   40c Ville de Neuchatel, 1972   .85 .85
  e.   40c MS Romanshorn, 1958   .85 .85
  f.   40c Le Winkelried, 1871   .85 .85
  g.   70c DS Loetschberg, 1914   .90 .90
  h.   80c DS Waedenswil, 1895   1.25 1.25

LEMANEX 78 Philatelic Exhibition, Lausanne, May 26-June 4 (#652); Founding of Lucerne, 800th anniv. (#653); printing in Geneva, 500th anniv. (#654); 2nd Intl. Triennial Photography Exhibition, Fribourg, June 17-Oct. 22 (#655).
Size of No. 656: 134x129mm. Sold for 5fr.

Stockalper Palace, Brig — A270

Europa: 80c, Diet Hall, Bern.

1978, May 2   Engr.   Perf. 11½
657 A270 40c multicolored   .75 .30
658 A270 80c multicolored   1.50 .75

Machinist A271

Joseph Bovet (1879-1951), Composer — A272

#660, Chemical worker (French inscription). #661, Construction worker (Italian inscription).

1978, Sept. 14   Photo.   Perf. 11½
659 A271 40c multicolored   .40 .30
660 A271 40c multicolored   .40 .30
661 A271 40c multicolored   .40 .30
  a.   Strip of 3, #659-661   1.25 1.00

Industrial safety.

1978, Sept. 14   Engr.
Portraits: 40c, Henri Dunant (1828-1910), founder of Red Cross. 70c, Carl Gustave Jung (1875-1961), psychologist. 80c, Auguste Piccard (1884-1962), physicist and balloonist.
662 A272 20c dull green   .20 .20
663 A272 40c rose lake   .35 .20
664 A272 70c gray   .65 .60
665 A272 80c blue gray   .80 .70
     Nos. 662-665 (4)   2.00 1.70

Arms of Switzerland and Jura — A273

1978, Sept. 25   Photo.   Perf. 11½
666 A273 40c buff, red & blk   .40 .20

Admission of Jura as 23rd Canton.

Rainer Maria Rilke (1875-1926), Poet, Muzot Castle — A274

Designs: 40c, Paul Klee (1879-1940), painter and "heroic roses." 70c, Hermann Hesse (1877-1962), writer, and vines. 80c, Thomas Mann (1875-1955), writer, and Lubeck buildings.

1979, Feb. 21   Engr.   Perf. 11½
667 A274 20c gray green   .20 .20
668 A274 40c red   .35 .20
669 A274 70c brown   .65 .65
670 A274 80c gray blue   .80 .75
     Nos. 667-670 (4)   2.00 1.80

O. H. Ammann, Verrazano-Narrows Bridge, NY — A275

Target Hit with Pole and Lucerne Flag — A276

Hot Air Balloon A277

Airport, Swissair and Air France Jets — A278

1979, Feb. 21   **Photo.**

671	A275	20c multicolored	.20	.20
672	A276	40c multicolored	.35	.20
673	A277	70c multicolored	.65	.65
674	A278	80c multicolored	.80	.75
		Nos. 671-674 (4)	2.00	1.80

Othmar H. Ammann (1879-1965), engineer, bridge builder in US; 50th Federal Riflemen's Festival, Lucerne, July 7-22; World Esperanto Congress, Lucerne; new runway at Basel-Mulhouse Intl. Airport.

Letter Box, 1845, Spalentor, Basel — A279

Europa: 80c, Microwave radio relay station on Jungfraujoch.

1979, Apr. 30   **Engr.**   **Perf. 11½**

| 675 | A279 | 40c multicolored | .65 | .25 |
| 676 | A279 | 80c multicolored | 1.40 | .65 |

Helvetian Gold Quarter Stater, 2nd Century B.C. — A280

Three-stage Launcher Ariane — A283

Child and Dove — A281

Morse Key and Satellite A282

1979, Sept. 6   **Photo.**

677	A280	20c multicolored	.20	.20
678	A281	40c multicolored	.35	.20
679	A282	70c multicolored	.70	.45
680	A283	80c multicolored	.80	.70
		Nos. 677-680 (4)	2.05	1.55

Centenary of Swiss Numismatic Society; International Year of the Child; Union of Swiss Radio Amateurs, 50th anniv.; European Space Agency (ESA).

Tree in Bloom A284

Hand Carved Milk Bucket A285

Winterthur Town Hall — A286

"Pic-Pic," 1930 — A287

1980, Feb. 21   **Photo.**

681	A284	20c multicolored	.20	.20
682	A285	40c multicolored	.40	.20
683	A286	70c multicolored	.65	.55
684	A287	80c multicolored	.75	.65
		Nos. 681-684 (4)	2.00	1.60

Green '80, Swiss Horticultural & Gardening Expo., Basel, 4/12-9/9/12; Swiss Arts Crafts Centers, 50th anniv.; Soc. for Swiss Art History, cent.; 50th Intl. Automobile Show, Geneva, 3/16.

Johann Konrad Kern (1808-1888), Politician A288

Europa: 80c, Gustav Adolf Hasler (1830-1900), communications pioneer.

1980, Apr. 28   **Lith. & Engr.**
Granite Paper

| 685 | A288 | 40c multicolored | .50 | .20 |
| 686 | A288 | 80c multicolored | 1.00 | .65 |

Postal Giro System A289

Postal Bus System A290

Security Printing Plant, 50th Anniversary A291

Swiss Telephone Service Centenary A292

Swiss Meteorological Office Centenary A293

Swiss Trade Union Federation Centenary A294

Opening of St. Gotthard Tunnel for Year-round Traffic — A295

Photo., Photo. & Engr. (70c)
1980, Sept. 5   **Perf. 12**

687	A289	20c multicolored	.20	.20
688	A290	40c multicolored	.40	.20
689	A291	70c multicolored	.65	.50
690	A292	80c multicolored	.75	.55
		Nos. 687-690 (4)	2.00	1.45

1980, Sept. 5   **Photo.**

691	A293	20c multicolored	.20	.20
692	A294	40c multicolored	.40	.20
693	A295	80c multicolored	.75	.55
		Nos. 691-693 (3)	1.35	.95

Granary, Kiesen, 17th Century A296

International Year of the Disabled A297

The Parish Clerk, by Albert Anker — A298

Theodolite and Rod — A299

DC-9 (50th Anniversary of Swissair) A300

1981, Mar. 9   **Photo.**   **Perf. 11½**

694	A296	20c multicolored	.25	.20
695	A297	40c multicolored	.40	.20
696	A298	70c multicolored	.70	.50
697	A299	80c multicolored	.80	.55
698	A300	110c multicolored	1.10	.85
		Nos. 694-698 (5)	3.25	2.30

Ballenberg Open-air Museum of Rural Architecture, Furnishing and Crafts; Albert Anker (1831-1910), artist (70c); 16th Congress of the International Federation of Surveyors, Montreux, Aug. (80c).

Couple Dancing in Native Costumes — A301

1981, May 4   **Photo.**   **Perf. 11½**

| 699 | A301 | 40c shown | .45 | .25 |
| 700 | A301 | 80c Stone putting | 1.25 | .75 |

Seal of Fribourg A302

1981, Sept. 3   **Photo. & Engr.**

701	A302	40c shown	.40	.25
702	A302	40c Seal of Solothurn	.40	.25
703	A302	80c Old Town Hall, Stans	.80	.50
		Nos. 701-703 (3)	1.60	1.00

Diet of Stans, 50th anniv., and entry of Fribourg & Solothurn into the Swiss Confederation.

Voltage Regulator A303

Crossbow Quality Emblem A304

Youths A305

Flower Mosaic, St. Peter's Cathedral, Geneva A306

1981, Sept. 3   **Photo.**

704	A303	20c multi	.20	.20
705	A304	40c multi	.35	.30
706	A305	70c multi	.65	.50
707	A306	1.10fr multi	1.10	.80
		Nos. 704-707 (4)	2.30	1.80

Technorama Industrial Fair, Winterthur; Crossbow Quality Emblem, 50th anniv.; Swiss Youth Assoc., 50th anniv.; restoration of St. Peter's Cathedral.

Gotthard Railway Centenary A307

Designs: Locomotives. Nos. 708-709 setenant with label showing workers' monument.

1982, Feb. 18   **Photo.**

| 708 | A307 | 40c Steam | .45 | .20 |
| 709 | A307 | 40c Electric | .45 | .20 |

Swiss Hoteliers' Assoc. Centenary A308

Federal Gymnastic Society Sesquicentennial — A309

Intl. Gas Union, 50th Anniv. Convention, Lausanne A310

Bern Museum of Natural History Sesquicentennial — A311

Society of Chemical Industries Centenary A312

1982, Feb. 18

710	A308	20c multicolored	.20	.20
711	A309	40c multicolored	.40	.30
712	A310	70c multicolored	.70	.70
713	A311	80c multicolored	1.00	.95
714	A312	110c multicolored	1.10	1.00
		Nos. 710-714 (5)	3.40	3.15

Europa 1982 — A313

1982, May 3   Photo.   Perf. 11½

715	A313	40c Oath of Eternal Fealty	.75	.30
716	A313	80c Pact of 1291	1.50	.80

Virgo, Schwarzee above Zermatt — A314

Signs of the Zodiac and City Views.

Photogravure and Engraved

1982-86   Perf. 11½

717	A314	1fr Aquarius, Old Bern	1.10	.30
718	A314	1.10fr Pisces, Nax near Sion	1.25	.30
719	A314	1.20fr Aries, Graustock	1.40	.30
719A	A314	1.40fr Gemini, Bischofszell	1.40	1.40
720	A314	1.50fr Taurus, Basel Cathedral	1.75	.30
721	A314	1.60fr Gemini, Schonengrund	1.75	1.10
722	A314	1.70fr Cancer, Wetterhorn, Grindelwald	2.00	.30
723	A314	1.80fr Leo, Areuse Gorge, Neuchatel	2.25	1.00

724	A314	2fr Virgo, Jungfrau Monch Eiger Mts.	2.50	2.25
725	A314	2fr shown	2.25	.30
726	A314	2.50fr Libra, Fechy	2.50	.80
727	A314	3fr Scorpio, Corippo	3.25	.30
728	A314	4fr Sagittarius, Glarus	4.25	.55
728A	A314	4.50fr Capricorn, Schuls	4.50	.80
		Nos. 717-728A (14)	32.15	10.00

Issued: #717-719, 720-721, 8/23/82; #719A, 2/11/86; #722-724, 2/17/83; #725, 11/24/83; #726-727, 2/19/85; #728-728A, 2/21/84.

Zurich Tram Centenary A315

Centenary of Salvation Army in Switzerland A316

World Dressage Championship, Lausanne, Aug. 25-29 — A317

Intl. Water Supply Assoc., 14th World Congress, Zurich, Sept. 6-10 — A318

1982, Aug. 23   Photo.

729	A315	20c multicolored	.25	.20
730	A316	40c multicolored	.50	.25
731	A317	70c multicolored	.90	.50
732	A318	80c multicolored	1.00	.55
		Nos. 729-732 (4)	2.65	1.50

Fishing and Pisciculture Fed. Centenary A319

Zurich University Sesquicentennial — A320

Journalists' Fed. Centenary A321

Machine Manufacturers' Assoc. Centenary — A322

1983, Feb. 17   Photo.
Granite Paper

733	A319	20c Perch	.25	.20
734	A320	40c multicolored	.50	.30
735	A321	70c Computer print outs	.80	.50
736	A322	80c Micrometer, cycloidal computer pattern	.90	.55
		Nos. 733-736 (4)	2.45	1.55

Europa 1983 A323

Basel Seal, 1832-1848 A324

Photogravure and Engraved

1983, May 3   Perf. 11½

737	A323	40c Celestial globe, 1594	.50	.25
738	A323	80c Cog railway, 1871	1.40	.75

1983, May 26   Photo.

739	A324	40c multicolored	.45	.20

Basel Canton sesquicentennial (land division).

Octodurus Martigny Bimillenium A325

Swiss Kennel Club Centenary A326

Bicycle and Motorcycle Federation Centenary A327

World Communications Year — A328

1983, Aug. 22   Photo.

740	A325	20c multicolored	.25	.20
741	A326	40c multicolored	.40	.25
742	A327	70c multicolored	.75	.50
743	A328	80c multicolored	.85	.55
		Nos. 740-743 (4)	2.25	1.50

NABA-ZURI'84 Natl. Stamp Show, Zurich, June 22-July 1 — A329

1100th Anniv. of Saint Imier — A330

Upper City, Lausanne A331

1984, Feb. 21   Photo.

744	A329	25c multicolored	.25	.20
745	A330	50c multicolored	.55	.20
746	A331	80c multicolored	.90	.40
		Nos. 744-746 (3)	1.70	.80

Selection of Lausanne as permanent headquarters for the Intl. Olympic Committee (80c).

Europa (1959-1984) A332

1984, May 2   Photo.   Perf. 11½

747	A332	50c lilac rose	.80	.50
748	A332	80c ultra	1.25	.85

Souvenir Sheet

Panoramic View of Zurich — A333

1984, May 24

749	A333	Sheet of 4	5.25	5.25
a.-d.		50c any single	1.25	1.25

NABA-ZURI '84 Stamp Show. Sold for 3fr.

Fire Prevention A334

1984, Sept. 11   Photo.

750	A334	50c Flames, match	.55	.20

Railway Staff Association, Cent. — A335

Rheto-Roman Culture Bimillennium A336

Lake Geneva Rescue Soc., Cent. — A337

Intl. Congress on Large Dams, Lausanne A338

1985, Feb. 19   Photo.   Perf. 12x11½

751	A335	35c Conductor's hat, paraphernalia	.40	.20
752	A336	50c Engraved artifact, Chur	.55	.20
753	A337	70c Rescuing drowning victim	.75	.20

754 A338 80c Grande Dizence
               Dam, Canton
               Valais   .90   .25
        Nos. 751-754 (4)   2.60   .85

Europa
1985 — A339

Designs: 50c, Ernest Ansermet (1883-1969), composer, conductor. 80c, Frank Martin (1890-1974), composer.

1985, May 7   Photo.   Perf. 11½x12
755 A339 50c multicolored   .60   .20
756 A339 80c multicolored   1.25   .70

Swiss Master
Bakers and
Confectioners
Federation,
Bern,
Cent. — A340

Swiss Radio
Intl., 50th
Anniv.
A341

Postal, Telegraph & Telephone Intl.
Congress, Sept. 16-21, Interlaken
A342

1985, Sept. 10   Photo.   Perf. 12x11½
757 A340 50c Baker   .55   .20
758 A341 70c multi   .75   .20
759 A342 80c PTTI 75th anniv.   .90   .25
        Nos. 757-759 (3)   2.20   .65

Swiss
Worker's
Relief Org.,
50th Anniv.
A343

Battle of
Sempach,
600th Anniv.
A344

Roman Chur
Bimillennium
A345

Vindonissa
Bimillennium
A346

Zurich
Bimillennium
A347

1986, Feb. 11   Photo.   Perf. 12
772 A343 35c Knot   .40   .20
773 A344 50c Military map,
               1698   .55   .20
774 A345 80c Mercury statue   .90   .30
775 A346 90c Gallic head   1.00   .30
776 A347 1.10fr Augustus coin   1.25   .35
        Nos. 772-776 (5)   4.10 1.35

Europa 1986
A348

Mail Handling
A349

1986, Apr. 22   Photo.   Perf. 13½
777 A348 50c Woman   .65   .20
778 A348 90c Man   1.60 1.00

Photo. & Engr.
1986-89   Perf. 13½x13
779 A349 5c Franz mail van,
               1911   .20   .20
780 A349 10c Parcel sorting   .20   .20
781 A349 20c Mule post   .20   .20
782 A349 25c Letter-facing, can-
               celing   .25   .20
783 A349 30c Mail coach, 1735-
               1960   .45   .20
784 A349 35c Counter service   .35   .20
785 A349 45c Packet steamer,
               1837-40   .45   .20
786 A349 50c Postman, 1986   .65   .20
   a.   Bklt. pane of 10 ('88)   6.50
787 A349 60c Loading airmail,
               1986   .80   .25
788 A349 75c 17th Cent. courier   1.00   .40
789 A349 80c Postman, ca. 1900   1.25   .50
790 A349 90c Railroad mail car   1.00   .55
        Nos. 779-790 (12)   6.80 3.35

Issued: 5c, 10c, 25c, 35c, 80c, 90c, 9/9/86; 20c, 30c, 45c, 50c, 60c, 3/10/87; 75c, 3/7/89. For surcharge see No. B535.

Intl. Peace
Year — A351

Swiss Winter
Relief Fund,
50th Anniv.
A352

Berne
Convention for
the Protection
of Literary
and Artistic
Copyrights,
Cent. — A353

25th Intl. Red
Cross
Conference,
Geneva, Oct.
23-31
A354

1986, Sept. 9   Photo.   Perf. 12x11½
799 A351 35c multicolored   .40   .20
800 A352 50c multicolored   .55   .20
801 A353 80c multicolored   .95   .30
802 A354 90c multicolored   1.10   .35
        Nos. 799-802 (4)   3.00 1.05

Mobile P.O.,
50th Anniv.
A355

Lausanne
University,
450th Anniv.
A356

Swiss
Engineers &
Architects
Assoc.,
Sesquicent.
A357

Cointrin Airport-Geneva, Rail Link
Opening, June 1, 1987 — A358

Baden Hot
Springs,
2000th Anniv.
A359

1987, Mar. 10   Photo.
803 A355 35c multicolored   .45   .20
804 A356 50c multicolored   .60   .20
805 A357 80c multicolored   .95   .35
806 A358 90c multicolored   1.00   .40
807 A359 1.10fr multicolored   1.25   .50
        Nos. 803-807 (5)   4.25 1.65

Europa
1987 — A360

Sculpture: 50fr, Scarabaeus, 1979, by Bernard Luginbuhl. 90fr, Carnival Fountain, 1977, by Jean Tinguely, Basel Theater.

1987, May 26   Photo.   Perf. 11½
808 A360 50c multicolored   .75   .25
809 A360 90c multicolored   1.90 1.00

Swiss Master
Butchers'
Federation,
Cent. — A361

Stamp Day,
50th Anniv.
A362

Swiss Dairy
Assoc.,
Cent. — A363

1987, Sept. 4   Photo.   Perf. 12x11½
810 A361 35c multicolored   .50   .20
811 A362 50c multicolored   .70   .20
812 A363 90c Cheesemaker   1.25   .40
        Nos. 810-812 (3)   2.45   .80

Tourism Industry,
Bicent. — A364

Switzerland's four language regions: 50c Clock Tower, Zug, German. 80c, Church of San Carlo, Blenio Valley, Italian. 90c, Witches Tower, Sion Castle, French. 140c, Jorgenberg Castle ruins, Waltensburg/Vuorz, Surselva, Rhaeto-Romansh.

1987, Sept. 4   Perf. 11½
813 A364 50c multicolored   .70   .25
814 A364 80c multicolored   1.25   .40
815 A364 90c multicolored   1.40   .40
816 A364 140c multicolored   2.00   .70
   a.   Souvenir sheet of 4, #813-816   5.00
        Nos. 813-816 (4)   5.35 1.75

Swiss
Women's
Benevolent
Soc.,
Cent. — A365

Swiss
Hairdressers
Assoc.,
Cent. — A366

Battle of
Naefels, 600th
Anniv.
A367

European Campaign to Protect
Undeveloped and Developing Lands
A368

Intl. Music
Festival,
Lucerne, 50th
Anniv.
A369

1988, Mar. 8   Photo.   Perf. 12x11½
817 A365 25c multicolored   .40   .20
818 A366 35c multicolored   .50   .20
819 A367 50c Banner of St.
               Fridolin, medieval
               manuscript   .75   .25
820 A368 80c multicolored   1.25   .40
821 A369 90c Girl playing a
               shawm   1.25   .45
        Nos. 817-821 (5)   4.15 1.50

Europa
1988 — A370

1988, May 24   Photo.   Perf. 11½
822 A370 50c Arrows (transport)   .65   .25
823 A370 90c Circuitry (commu-
               nication)   1.75 1.00

Swiss Accident Prevention Office, 50th Anniv. A371.

Assoc. of Metalworkers and Watchmakers, Cent. — A372

Federal Topography Office, 150th Anniv. A373

Intl. Red Cross Museum, Geneva A374

1988, Sept. 13   Photo.   Perf. 12x11½

824	A371	35c multicolored	.45	.20
825	A372	50c multicolored	.65	.20
826	A373	80c Triangulation pyramid, theodolite, map	1.00	.35
827	A374	90c multicolored	1.25	.40
		Nos. 824-827 (4)	3.35	1.15

Metamecanique, by Jean Tinguely — A375

1988, Nov. 25   Photo.   Perf. 13x12½

828	A375	90c multicolored	1.25	.40

See France No. 2137.

Military Post, Cent. — A376

Delemont Municipal Charter, 700th Anniv. A377

Public Transport Assoc., Cent. — A378

Rhaetian Railway, Cent. — A379

Great St. Bernard Pass Bimillennium A380

25c, Army postman. 35c, Fontaine du Sauvage & the Porte au Loup, Delemont. 50c, Eye, modes of transportation. 80c, Train, viaduct. 90c, St. Bernard dog, statue of saint, hospice on summit.

1989, Mar. 2   Photo.   Perf. 12x11½

829	A376	25c multicolored	.30	.20
830	A377	35c multicolored	.45	.20
831	A378	50c multicolored	.65	.20
832	A379	80c multicolored	1.00	.35
833	A380	90c multicolored	1.25	.40
		Nos. 829-833 (5)	3.65	1.35

Europa — A381

Industry — A382

Children's games: 50c, Hopscotch. 90c, Blindman's buff.

1989, May 23   Perf. 11½

834	A381	50c multicolored	.60	.40
835	A381	90c multicolored	1.50	1.00

Engr., Litho. & Eng. (2.80, 3, 3.60, 4, 5fr)

1989-95   Perf. 13x13½

842	A382	2.75fr Bricklayer	2.75	2.00
843	A382	2.80fr Cook	3.00	1.90
843A	A382	3fr Cabinet maker	3.00	1.25
844	A382	3.60fr Pharmacist	3.75	2.50
845	A382	3.75fr Fisherman	3.75	3.00
846	A382	4fr Wine grower	4.00	1.40
847	A382	5fr Cheesemaker	5.00	1.75
848	A382	5.50fr Dressmaker	5.50	3.75
		Nos. 842-848 (8)	30.75	17.55

Issued: 2.75fr, 5.50fr, 8/29/89; 3.75fr, 3/6/90; 2.80fr, 3.60fr, 1/24/92; 5fr, 9/7/93; 4fr, 3/15/94; 3fr, 7/5/94.
This is an expanding set. Numbers will change if necessary.

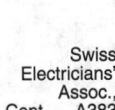

Swiss Electricians' Assoc., Cent. — A383

Swiss Travel Fund, 50th Anniv. A384

Fribourg University, Cent. — A385

Opening of the Natl. Sound-Recording Archives, 1st Anniv. — A386

Interparliamentary Union, Cent. — A387

1989, Aug. 25   Photo.   Perf. 11½

851	A383	35c multicolored	.40	.20
852	A384	50c multicolored	.60	.20
853	A385	80c "Wisdom" and "Science"	.90	.30
854	A386	90c multicolored	1.00	.35
855	A387	140c multicolored	1.60	.50
		Nos. 851-855 (5)	4.50	1.55

Union of Swiss Philatelic Societies, Cent. — A388

Urban Railway System, Zurich A389

Assistance for Mountain Communities, 50th Anniv. A390

1990 World Ice Hockey Championships — A391

1990, Mar. 6

856	A388	25c maroon type A19, 50c stamp type A20	.35	.20
857	A389	35c Locomotives	.50	.20
858	A390	50c Mountain farmer	.70	.20
859	A391	90c Athletes	1.25	.40
		Nos. 856-859 (4)	2.80	1.00

Europa 1990 — A393

Post offices.

Litho. & Engr.

1990, May 22   Perf. 13½

861	A393	50c Lucerne	.75	.25
862	A393	90c Geneva	1.90	1.00

Conrad Ferdinand Meyer (1825-1898), Writer — A394

Designs: 50c, Angelika Kaufmann (1741-1807), painter. 80c, Blaise Cendrars (1887-1961), journalist. 90c, Frank Buchser (1828-1890), artist.

1990, Sept. 5   Litho.

863	A394	35c green & blk	.45	.20
864	A394	50c blue & blk	.65	.20
865	A394	80c yellow & blk	1.00	.35
866	A394	90c vermilion & blk	1.25	.40
		Nos. 863-866 (4)	3.35	1.15

Swiss Confederation, 700th Anniv. in 1991 — A395

1990, Sept. 5   Photo.   Perf. 11½

867	A395	50c shown	.65	.20
868	A395	90c multi, diff.	1.25	.40

Natl. Census A396

1990, Nov. 20

869	A396	50c multicolored	.70	.25

Animals — A397

1990-95   Litho. & Engr.   Perf. 13

870	A397	10c Cow	.20	.20
871	A397	50c House cats	.60	.20
872	A397	70c Rabbit	.80	.40
a.		Booklet pane of 10	12.00	
		Complete booklet, #872a	12.00	
873	A397	80c Barn owls	.90	.30
874	A397	100c Horses	1.00	.25
875	A397	110c Geese	1.60	.55
876	A397	120c Dog	1.25	.40
877	A397	140c Sheep	2.25	.65
878	A397	150c Goats	1.90	.50
879	A397	160c Turkey	1.60	1.00
880	A397	170c Donkey	3.00	.75
881	A397	200c Chickens	2.75	.50
		Nos. 870-881 (12)	17.85	5.70

Issued: 50c, 3/6/90; 70c, 80c, 1/15/91; 10c, 160c, 1/24/92; 100c, 120c, 3/16/93; 150c, 200c, 7/5/94; #872a, 110c, 140c, 170c, 11/28/95.
This is an expanding set. Nos. 882-883 will be used for high values if necessary.

Swiss Confederation, 700th Anniv. — A398

Swiss Parliament, US Capitol A399

1991, Feb. 22   Photo.   Perf. 12

884	A398	50c "700 jahre"	.80	.25
885	A398	50c "700 onns"	.80	.25
886	A398	50c "700 ans"	.80	.25
887	A398	50c "700 anni"	.80	.25
a.		Block of 4, #884-887	3.25	1.00
888	A399	1.60fr multicolored	2.50	.80
		Nos. 884-888 (5)	5.70	1.80

See US No. 2532.

Bern, 800th
Anniv. — A400

1991, Feb. 22 **Perf. 11½**
889 A400 80c multicolored 1.25 .40

Europa — A401

1991, May 14 **Litho.** **Perf. 11½**
890 A401 50c Ariane payload
fairing 1.00 .25
891 A401 90c Giotto probe 1.75 1.00

Union of
Postal,
Telephone
and Telegraph
Officials,
Cent. — A402

1991, Sept. 10 **Photo.** **Perf. 11½**
892 A402 80c multicolored .95 .50

Bridges
A403

Designs: 50c, Stone bridge near
Lavertezzo. 70c, Wooden "New Bridge" near
Bremgarten. 80c, Railway bridge between
Koblenz and Felsenau. 90c, Ganter Bridge,
Simplon Pass.

1991, Sept. 10
893 A403 50c multicolored .55 .20
894 A403 70c multicolored .85 .35
895 A403 80c multicolored .85 .40
896 A403 90c multicolored 1.00 .50
Nos. 893-896 (4) 3.25 1.45

Mountain
Lakes — A404
A404a

A404b

Design: 60c, Lake de Tanay.

Litho., Litho. & Engr. (60c, #908)
1991-95 **Perf. 13½x13**
904 A404 50c blue & multi .65 .20
905 A404 60c blue & multi .85 .25
a. Booklet pane of 10 8.50
907 A404 80c red & multi, diff. 1.10 .20
908 A404a 80c multicolored 1.10 .40
909 A404b 90c multicolored 1.50 .75
a. Booklet pane of 10 15.00
Complete booklet, #909a 15.00
Nos. 904-909 (5) 5.20 1.80

Issued: 50c, #907, 12/16/91; 60c, #908,
1/19/1993; 90c, 11/28/95. This is an expanding
set. Numbers will change if necessary.
See No. 1102.

Bird Over
Rhine
River — A405

Faces of
Parents,
Child — A406

Molecular
Formula,
Structure and
Model
A407

1992, Mar. 24 **Photo.** **Perf. 11½**
911 A405 50c multicolored .65 .25
912 A406 80c multicolored 1.25 .35
913 A407 90c multicolored 1.20 .40
Nos. 911-913 (3) 3.10 1.00

Intl. Rhine Regulation, cent. (No. 911), Pro
Familia Switzerland, 50th anniv. (No. 912),
Intl. Chemical Nomenclature Conf., Geneva,
cent. (No. 913).

A408 A409

Europa: 90c, Columbus, map of voyage.

1992, Mar. 24
914 A408 50c multicolored 1.00 .25
915 A408 90c multicolored 1.75 1.00

Discovery of America, 500th anniv.

1992, May 22 **Photo.** **Perf. 12**
916 A409 90c multicolored 1.25 .40

Protect the Alps.

Comic Strips
A410

1992, May 22 **Perf. 11½**
917 A410 50c Cosey .65 .25
918 A410 80c Zep 1.10 .35
919 A410 90c Aloys 1.25 .40
Nos. 917-919 (3) 3.00 1.00

World of the
Circus
A411

50c, Clowns on trapeze. 70c, Sea lion,
clown. 80c, Clown, elephant. 90c, Lipizzaner,
harlequin.

1992, Aug. 25 **Photo.** **Perf. 12x11½**
920 A411 50c multicolored .80 .30
921 A411 70c multicolored 1.10 .40
922 A411 80c multicolored 1.25 .45
923 A411 90c multicolored 1.50 .50
Nos. 920-923 (4) 4.65 1.65

Central Office
for Intl.
Carriage by
Rail, Cent. (in
1993) — A412

1992, Nov. 24 **Photo.** **Perf. 11½**
924 A412 90c multicolored 1.25 .40

First Swiss Postage
Stamps, 150th
Anniv. — A413

Designs: 60c, Zurich Types A1, A2, Geneva
Type A1. 80c, Stylized canceled stamp. 100c,
Stylized stamps on album page.

1993, Mar. 16 **Photo.** **Perf. 11½**
925 A413 60c multicolored .80 .30
926 A413 80c multicolored 1.00 .35
927 A413 100c multicolored 1.25 .45
Nos. 925-927 (3) 3.05 1.10

Paracelsus
(1493-1541),
Physician
A414

Opening of
Olympic
Museum,
Lausanne
A415

Intl.
Metalworkers'
Federation,
Cent. — A416

1993, Mar. 16 **Photo.** **Perf. 11½**
928 A414 60c blue & sepia .80 .25
929 A415 80c multicolored 1.00 .35
930 A416 180c multicolored 2.40 .80
Nos. 928-930 (3) 4.20 1.40

Lake
Constance
Steamer
Hohentwiel
A417

1993, May 5 **Photo.** **Perf. 11½x12**
931 A417 60c multicolored .85 .30
See Austria No. 1598, Germany No. 1786.

Contemporary
Architecture
A418

Europa: 60c, Media House, Villeurbanne,
France. 80c, House, Breganzona, Switzerland.

Litho. & Engr.
1993, May 5 **Perf. 13½**
932 A418 60c multicolored .85 .40
933 A418 80c red & black 1.15 .60

Works of
Art by
Swiss
Women
A419

Designs: 60c, Work No. 095, by Emma
Kunz. 80c, Grande Cantatrice Lilas Goergens,
by Aloise Corbaz. 100c, Under the Rain
Cloud, by Meret Oppenheim. 120c, Four
Spaces in Horizontal Bands, by Sophie
Taeuber-Arp.

1993, Sept. 7 **Photo.** **Perf. 11½**
934 A419 60c multicolored .70 .30
Size: 33x33½mm
935 A419 80c multicolored .85 .40
936 A419 100c multicolored 1.10 .45
937 A419 120c multicolored 1.40 .55
Nos. 934-937 (4) 4.05 1.70

Swiss Sports
School, 50th
Anniv.
A420

Jakob
Bernoulli
(1654-1705),
Mathematician
A421

Swiss
Telecom PTT
Participation
in Unisource
A422

ICAO, 50th
Anniv.
A423

1994, Mar. 15 **Photo.** **Perf. 11½**
938 A420 60c multicolored .85 .30
939 A421 80c multicolored 1.10 .35
940 A422 100c multicolored 1.40 .45
941 A423 180c multicolored 2.50 .80
Nos. 938-941 (4) 5.85 1.90

Intl. Congress of Mathematicians, Zurich
(#939).

"Books and
the Press"
Exhibition,
Geneva
A424

1994, Mar. 15
942 A424 60c Early manuscripts .85 .30
943 A424 80c Letterpress 1.10 .35
944 A424 100c Electronic publishing 1.40 .45
Nos. 942-944 (3) 3.35 1.10

1994 World Cup Soccer
Championships, US — A425

1994, Mar. 15
945 A425 80c multicolored 1.10 .35

Research Vehicles
of August &
Jacques
Piccard — A426

Europa: 60c, Bathyscaphe Trieste. 100c,
Stratospheric balloon.

1994, May 17 Photo. Perf. 12
946 A426 60c multicolored .90 .35
947 A426 100c multicolored 1.75 .90

Georges
Simenon
(1903-89),
Writer
A427

Litho. & Engr.
1994, Oct. 15 Perf. 13
948 A427 100c multicolored 1.10 .75
See Belgium No. 1567, France No. 2443.

A428   A429

1994, Oct. 15 Photo. Perf. 11½
949 A428 60c multicolored .95 .30
Campaign to stop AIDS.

1995, Mar. 7 Photo. Perf. 11½
Endangered species.
950 A429 60c European beaver 1.00 .30
951 A429 80c Map butterfly 1.25 .40
952 A429 100c Green tree frog 1.60 .55
953 A429 120c Litte owl 1.90 .80
Nos. 950-953 (4) 5.75 2.05

Swiss Wrestling
Assoc.,
Cent. — A430

Swiss Assoc.
of Producers
& Distributors
of Electricity,
Cent. — A431

Swiss News
Agency,
Cent. — A432

UN, 50th
Anniv.
A433

1995, Mar. 7
954 A430 60c blue & black 1.00 .35
955 A431 60c multicolored 1.00 .35
956 A432 80c multicolored 1.25 .40
957 A433 180c multicolored 2.75 .90
Nos. 954-957 (4) 6.00 2.00

Peace &
Freedom
A434

Europa: 60c, Dove, faces. 100c, Zeus disguised as bull, abducting Europa, daughter of King of Phoenicia.

Litho., Engr. & Embossed
1995, May 16 Perf. 13
958 A434 60c lt blue & dk blue 1.00 .40
959 A434 100c orange & brown 1.75 .85

Switzerland-
Liechtenstein
Postal
Relationship
A435

Litho. & Engr.
1995, Sept. 5 Perf. 13½
960 A435 60c multicolored .75 .50
See Liechtenstein No. 1055.
No. 960 and Liechtenstein No. 1055 are identical. This issue was valid for postage in both countries.

Motion
Pictures,
Cent. — A436

Scenes from motion pictures: 60c, La Vocation d'Andre Carrel. 80c, Anna Goldin-The Last Witch. 150c, Pipilotti's Mistakes-Absolution.

1995, Sept. 5 Photo. Perf. 11½
961 A436 60c multicolored .75 .35
962 A436 80c multicolored .95 .65
963 A436 150c multicolored 1.75 1.25
Nos. 961-963 (3) 3.45 2.25

Telecom '95,
Geneva — A437

1995, Sept. 5
964 A437 180c multicolored 3.00 1.00

Swiss
Charities,
Solidarity
Chain, 50th
Anniv.
A438

Touring Club,
Cent. — A439

Federal Music
Festival,
Interlaken
A440

Swiss Natl.
Assoc. Pro
Filia,
Cent. — A441

Jean Piaget
(1896-1980),
Psychologist
A442

1996, Mar. 12 Photo. Perf. 11½
965 A438 70c multicolored .75 .40
966 A439 70c multicolored .75 .40
967 A440 90c multicolored .95 .55
968 A441 90c multicolored .95 .55
969 A442 180c multicolored 1.90 1.50
Nos. 965-969 (5) 5.30 3.40

Famous
Women — A443

Europa: 70c, S. Corinna Bille (1912-79), author. 110c, Iris von Roten-Meyer (1917-90), writer, painter.

Litho. & Engr.
1996, May 14 Perf. 13½
970 A443 70c multicolored .90 .40
971 A443 110c multicolored 1.60 1.00

Modern
Olympic
Games,
Cent. — A444

1996, May 14 Litho. Perf. 13½
972 A444 180c multicolored 3.00 1.00

Guinness Record
Stamp — A445

Design: Aerial view of 11,000 gymnasts arranged as No. 909, making record as world's largest living postage stamp.

1996, June 27 Litho. Perf. 13½x13
973 A445 90c multicolored 1.50 .50

Greeting
Stamps
A446

Various ornate or floral patterns.

Serpentine Die Cut 7 Vert.
1996, Sept. 10 Typo.
Self-Adhesive
Booklet Stamps
974 A446 90c yellow & black 1.00 .50
975 A446 90c blue & multi 1.00 .50
976 A446 90c red & multi 1.00 .50

977 A446 90c green & multi 1.00 .50
a. Booklet pane of 4, #974-977 4.00
Complete booklet, 2 #977a 8.00

Music Boxes
and Automata
A447

Designs: 70c, Ring with mechanical figures, musical movement, by Isaac-Daniel Piguet. 90c, Basso-piccolo mandolin cylinder music box, by Eduard Jaccard. 110c, Station automaton, by Paillard and Co. 180c, Kalliope disk music box.

1996, Sept. 10 Photo. Perf. 11½
978 A447 70c multicolored .90 .40
979 A447 90c multicolored 1.10 .50
980 A447 110c multicolored 1.40 .60
981 A447 180c multicolored 2.25 1.00
Nos. 978-981 (4) 5.65 2.50

Stamp Design
Competition
Winners — A448

Designs: 70c, Golden cow. 90c, Smiling creature. 110c, Leaves. 180c, Dove.

1996, Nov. 26 Photo. Perf. 11½
982 A448 70c blue & bister .90 .35
983 A448 90c multicolored 1.10 .50
984 A448 110c multicolored 1.40 .60
985 A448 180c multicolored 2.25 .75
Nos. 982-985 (4) 5.65 2.20

"Globi" as
Postman
A449

1997, Mar. 11 Litho. Perf. 13x13½
986 A449 70c multicolored .85 .35

Swiss
Railways,
150th Anniv.
A450

Designs: 70c, Locomotive 2000, 1990's. 90c, Red Arrow, 1930's. 140c, Pullman coach, 1920's-30's. 170c, Limmat steam locomotive, 1800's.

1997, Mar. 11 Photo. Perf. 11½
987 A450 70c multicolored .80 .30
988 A450 90c multicolored 1.00 .40
989 A450 140c multicolored 1.60 .65
990 A450 170c multicolored 2.00 .75
Nos. 987-990 (4) 5.40 2.10

Gallo-Roman
Art — A451

Archaeological finds: 70c, Venus of Octodurus. 90c, Bronze bust of Bacchus. 110c, Ceramic fragment depicting Victoria. 180c, Mosaic theatrical mask.

1997, Mar. 11
991 A451 70c multicolored .85 .30
992 A451 90c multicolored 1.00 .40
993 A451 110c multicolored 1.25 .50
994 A451 180c multicolored 2.10 .80
Nos. 991-994 (4) 5.20 2.00

Swiss Air's North Atlantic Service, 50th Anniv. — A452

1997, Mar. 11   Litho.   Perf. 13½
995 A452 180c multicolored   2.25   .80

Swiss Farmers' Union, Cent. — A453

1997, May 13   Litho.   Perf. 13½
996 A453 70c shown   .85   .35
997 A453 90c Street map   1.10   .40

Swiss Municipalities' Union, cent. (#997).

Stories and Legends — A454

Europa: Devil and Billy Goat from legend of the "Devil's Bridge."

1997, May 13   Litho. & Engr.
998 A454 90c multicolored   1.10   1.10

King of Thailand's Visit to Switzerland, Cent. — A455

King Chulalongkorn (Rama V), Pres. Adolf Deucher.

1997, Sept. 12   Litho.   Perf. 13½
999 A455 90c multicolored   1.10   .40

Energy 2000 — A456

1997, Sept. 12   Photo.   Perf. 11½
1000 A456 70c Air (clouds)   .85   .35
1001 A456 90c Fire   1.10   .40
1002 A456 110c Water   1.25   .55
1003 A456 180c Earth   2.25   .90
    Nos. 1000-1003 (4)   5.45   2.20

Paul Karrer (1889-1971), Winner of Nobel Prize for Chemistry, 1937 — A457

Design: 110c, Alfred Nobel (1833-96), founder of Nobel Prize.

Litho. & Engr.
1997, Nov. 13   Perf. 13
1004 A457 90c gray & blk   1.10   .40
1005 A457 110c lt gray brn & blk   1.25   .55

Nos. 1004-1005 each issued in sheets of 8.
See Sweden Nos. 2254-2255.

Swiss Postal Service A458

Various people from different generations, cultures. Each stamp inscribed in one of Switzerland's four national languages with message to keep in touch.

1997, Nov. 20   Litho.   Perf. 13
Color of Denomination
1006 A458 70c blue   .80   .35
1007 A458 70c yellow   .80   .35
1008 A458 70c green   .80   .35
1009 A458 70c red   .80   .35
    a.   Strip of 4, #1006-1009   3.25   1.40

Division of Swiss PTT — A459

1998, Jan. 7   Litho.   Perf. 13½
1010 A459 90c Swisscom   1.10   .40
1011 A459 90c Swiss Post   1.10   .40

Confederation, 150th Anniv. and Helvetic Republic, Bicent. — A460

Stylized design, proclamation in one of four languages, location of denomination: No. 1012, German, LL. No. 1013, Romansch, LR. No. 1014, French, UL. No. 1015, Italian, UR.

1998, Mar. 10   Photo.   Perf. 11½
1012 A460 90c multicolored   1.10   .40
1013 A460 90c multicolored   1.10   .40
1014 A460 90c multicolored   1.10   .40
1015 A460 90c multicolored   1.10   .40
    a.   Block of 4, #1012-1015   4.50   1.60

Printed in continuous design.

Swiss Old Age and Survivors' Insurance, 50th Anniv. A461

Opening of Natl. Museum, Prangins Castle A462

St. Gallen University, Cent. — A463

1998, Mar. 10
1016 A461 70c multicolored   .85   .30
1017 A462 70c multicolored   .85   .30
1018 A463 90c multicolored   1.10   .40
    Nos. 1016-1018 (3)   2.80   1.00

View of Switzerland A464

Designs: 10c, Simplon Pass. 20c, Snow-covered winter scene. 50c, Fence posts along country road. 70c, Hobbyhorses, posts. 90c, Stream, route marker. 110c, Lake, shoreline.

1998, Mar. 10   Litho.   Perf. 13x13½
1019 A464 10c multicolored   .20   .20
1020 A464 20c multicolored   .25   .20
1021 A464 50c multicolored   .55   .20
1022 A464 70c multicolored   .80   .20
1023 A464 90c multicolored   1.10   .25
1024 A464 110c multicolored   1.25   .30
    Nos. 1019-1024 (6)   4.15   1.35

See Nos. 1027-1029.

Sion, Candidate for 2006 Winter Olympic Games — A465

1998, Feb. 12   Litho.   Perf. 13½
1025 A465 90c multicolored   1.10   .40

National Day — A466

1998, May 12
1026 A466 90c multicolored   1.10   1.10

Europa.

View of Switzerland Type of 1998

140c, City of Zug. 170c, Olive grove, Castagnola. 180c, Road, mountains outside Reutigen.

1998, Sept. 8   Litho.   Perf. 13
1027 A464 140c multicolored   1.60   .40
1028 A464 170c multicolored   2.00   .45
1029 A464 180c multicolored   2.10   .50
    Nos. 1027-1029 (3)   5.70   1.35

Youth Sports — A467

Die Cut x Serpentine Die Cut
1998, Sept. 8   Photo.
Self-Adhesive
Booklet Stamps
1030 A467 70c Roller blading   .80   .30
1031 A467 70c Snow boarding   .80   .30
1032 A467 70c Mountain biking   .80   .30
1033 A467 70c Street basketball   .80   .30
1034 A467 70c Beach volleyball   .80   .30
    a.   Booklet pane, #1030-1034 + label   4.00
        Complete booklet, 2 #1034a   8.00

Universal Declaration of Human Rights, 50th Anniv. — A468

1998, Nov. 25   Litho.   Perf. 13½
1035 A468 70c multicolored   .85   .35

Christmas A469

1998, Nov. 25
1036 A469 90c multicolored   1.10   .45

Bridge 24, Slender West Lake, Yangzhou A470

Chillon Castle, Lake Geneva A470A

Photo. & Engr.
1998, Nov. 25   Perf. 13½
1037 A470 20c multicolored   .30   .20

Photo.
1038 A470A 70c multicolored   .85   .35
    a.   Sheet of 4 each, #1038-1039   4.75   1.75

Souvenir Sheet
Perf. 11½
1039 A470A 90c Castle, Bridge 24   1.10   .40

No. 1039 contains one 53x45mm stamp. See China (PRC) Nos. 2920-2921.
No. 1039 exists with China 1999 World Philatelic Exhibition emblem and a hologram in margin. These were sold for 3.50fr only canceled on cover.

Switzerland Post, 150th Anniv. A471

1999, Jan. 21   Photo.   Perf. 12
1040 A471 90c multicolored   1.10   .50

Pingu the Penguin as Postman A472

1999, Mar. 9   Litho.   Perf. 13½
1041 A472 70c Carrying package   .85   .35
1042 A472 90c In delivery cart   1.10   .45

See Nos. 1064-1065 for redrawn designs.

Comic Book, "Les Amours de Monsieur Vieux Bois," by Rodolphe Töpffer (1799-1846) A473

Vieux Bois: No. 1043, Waving out of window, lady walking away. No. 1044, Down on knees, lady. No. 1045, In air after knocking over furniture. No. 1046, Pulling lady up to lift her over wall. No. 1047, Standing with his lady to be married.

Die Cut x Serpentine Die Cut
1999, Mar. 9
Self-Adhesive
Booklet Stamps
1043 A473 90c multicolored   1.00   .45
1044 A473 90c multicolored   1.00   .45
1045 A473 90c multicolored   1.00   .45
1046 A473 90c multicolored   1.00   .45
1047 A473 90c multicolored   1.00   .45
    a.   Booklet pane, #1043-1047 + label   5.00
        Complete booklet, 2 #1047a   12.50

First Non-stop Balloon Flight Around World by Bertrand Piccard and Brian Jones — A473a

1999, Mar. 24   Litho.   Perf. 13½
1047B A473a 90c multicolored   1.25   .40

UPU, 125th Anniv. — A474

1999, May 5   Photo.   Perf. 12
1048 A474 20c shown   .25   .20
1049 A474 70c UPU emblem   .95   .35
  a. Pair, #1048-1049   1.25   .45

No. 1049 is 56x30mm. Issued in sheets of 8 stamps.

SOS Children's Village, Wabern, 50th Anniv. — A475

1999, May 5   Litho.   Perf. 13½
1050 A475 70c multicolored   .95   .35

Vintners Festival, Vevey — A476

1999, May 5
1051 A476 90c multicolored   1.25   .40
  Complete booklet, 10 #1051   12.50

Council of Europe, 50th Anniv. — A477

1999, May 5   Photo.   Perf. 11½
1052 A477 90c multicolored   1.25   .45

Swiss National Park — A478

1999, May 5   Litho.   Perf. 13½
1053 A478 90c Horns of an ibex   1.10   1.10

Europa.

Geneva Convention, 50th Anniv. — A479

1999, May 5
1054 A479 110c multicolored   1.40   .50

Field Marshal Aleksandr Suvorov's Alpine Campaign, 200th Anniv. A481

Designs: 70c, Suvorov and soldiers, monument at Schöllenen Gorge. 110c, Suvorov's vanguard by Lake Klöntal.

1999, Sept. 24   Photo.   Perf. 11¾
1056 A481 70c multicolored   .95   .30
1057 A481 110c multicolored   1.50   .50

Nos. 1056-1057 each issued in sheets of 8 stamps.
  See Russia Nos. 6534-6535.

Rights of the Child — A482

1999, Sept. 24   Litho.   Perf. 13½
1058 A482 70c multicolored   .95   .30

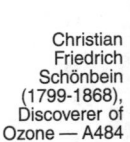

Carl Lutz (1895-1975), Diplomat, Rescuer of Jews — A483

1999, Sept. 24
1059 A483 90c multicolored   1.25   .40

Christian Friedrich Schönbein (1799-1868), Discoverer of Ozone — A484

1999, Sept. 24
1060 A484 1.10fr multicolored   1.50   .50

Midday in the Alps, by Giovanni Segantini (1858-99) A485

1999, Sept. 24
1061 A485 180c multicolored   2.40   .80

Christmas — A486

Perf. 13½x13¼
1999, Nov. 23   Litho.
1062 A486 90c multicolored   1.25   .40

Millennium A487

Perf. 11¾x11½
1999, Nov. 23   Photo.
1063 A487 90c multicolored   1.25   .40

No. 1063 was printed in sheets of 8 stamps and 8 se-tenant labels with text or blank. Swiss Post offered to print photos or artwork sent in by customers on the blank labels. Personalized sheets sold for 14fr per sheet.

Pingu The Penguin Type of 1999
Redrawn to Omit Strings on Packages
1999, Dec. 6   Litho.   Perf. 13¼x13½
1064 A472 70c Like #1041   .85   .30
1065 A472 90c Like #1042   1.10   .35

Intl. Cycling Union, Cent. — A488

2000, Mar. 7   Litho.   Perf. 13¼x13½
1066 A488 70c multicolored   .85   .30

Swiss Souvenirs — A489

Souvenirs in snow domes: 10c, Alphorn. 20c, Fondue pot. 30c, Wine pitchers. 50c, Figurine of ibex. 60c, Neuchâtel "Pendule" wall clock. 70c, St. Bernard dog.

2000, Mar. 7   Litho.   Perf. 13x13¼
1067 A489 10c multicolored   .20   .20
1068 A489 20c multicolored   .25   .20
1069 A489 30c multicolored   .35   .20
1070 A489 50c multicolored   .60   .20
1071 A489 60c multicolored   .75   .20
1072 A489 70c multicolored   .85   .30
  Nos. 1067-1072 (6)   3.00   1.35

See No. 1101.

National Council of Women, Cent. A490

2000, May 10   Litho.   Perf. 13¼
1073 A490 70c multi   .85   .30

Europa, 2000
Common Design Type
2000, May 10
1074 CD17 90c multi   1.10   .35

Embroidery — A491

Illustration reduced.

Embroidered
2000, June 21   Imperf.
Self-Adhesive
1075 A491 5fr multi   12.00   12.00
  a. Sheet of 4   175.00   175.00

A492

Designs: 120c, Payerne Church, violin. 130c, Church of St. Saphorin, waiter's tray. 180c, Vals hot springs, bather.

2000, June 21   Litho.   Perf. 13x13¼
1076 A492 120c multi   1.40   .30
1077 A492 130c multi   1.50   .30
1078 A492 180c multi   2.10   .40
  Nos. 1076-1078 (3)   5.00   1.00

See Nos. 1089-1092.

2000 Census — A493

2000, Sept. 15   Perf. 13¼x13½
1079 A493 70c multi   .80   .25

A Perfect World, by Sandra Dobler A494

My Town, by Stephanie Aerschmann A495

Stampin' the Future children's stamp design contest winners: No. 1080, Alien From Outer Space, by Yannik Kehrli. No. 1081, Looks Below the Sun, by Charlotte Bättig.

Serpentine Die Cut 5¾ Vert.
2000, June 15
Booklet Stamps
Self-Adhesive
1080 A494 70c multi   .80   .25
1081 A494 70c multi   .80   .25
1082 A494 70c shown   .80   .25
1083 A495 70c shown   .80   .25
  a. Booklet pane, #1080-1083   3.25
    Booklet, 2 #1083a   6.50

The booklet, which was sold unfolded, has rouletting between panes.

2000 Summer Olympics, Sydney A496

2000, Sept. 15   Photo.   Die Cut
Booklet Stamps
Self-Adhesive
1084 A496 90c Swimmer   1.00   .35
1085 A496 90c Cyclist   1.00   .35
1086 A496 90c Runner   1.00   .35
  a. Booklet pane, #1084-1086   3.00
    Booklet, #1086a   3.00

No. 1086a is separated from booklet cover by rouletting. The booklet was sold folded. See Nos. 1201-1202.

Stamp Day — A497

Perf. 13¼x13½

2000, Nov. 21			Litho.
1087 A497 70c multi		.80	.25

Christmas — A498

2000, Nov. 21　Photo.　Perf. 11½
Granite Paper

1088 A498 90c multi		1.00	.35

Type of 2000

Designs: 200c, Mountain, hiker. 300c, Cyclist, bridge and church, Biasca.

2000-01	Litho.	Perf. 13x13¼	
1089 A492 200c multi		2.50	.50
1090 A492 220c multi		2.50	.50
1091 A492 300c multi		3.75	.75
1092 A492 400c multi		4.50	.90

Issued: 200c, 300c, 11/21/00. 220c, 400c, 3/13/01.

Alice Rivaz (1901-98), Writer — A499

Perf. 13¼x13½

2001, Mar. 13		Litho. & Engr.
1093 A499 70c multi	.80	.25

Aero Club, Cent. A500

2001, Mar. 13	Litho.	Perf. 13¼
1094 A500 90c multi	1.00	.35

Congratulations A501

2001, Mar. 13		Perf. 13¼x13½
1095 A501 90c multi		1.00	.35

Caritas, Cent. — A502

2001, Mar. 13

1096 A502 110c multi		1.25	.40

UN High Commissioner for Refugees, 50th Anniv. — A503

2001, Mar. 13

1097 A503 130c multi		1.50	.50

Vela Museum, Ligornetto A504

2001, May 9

1098 A504 70c multi		.80	.25

Europa — A505

2001, May 9

1099 A505 90c multi		1.00	.35

Chocosuisse, Cent. — A506

2001, May 9　Photo.　Perf. 11½
Granite Paper

1100 A506 90c multi		1.00	.35

No. 1100 has a scratch-and-sniff coating with a chocolate aroma.

Swiss Souvenirs Type of 2000
Serpentine Die Cut 5¾ Horiz.

2001, May 9		Litho.
Self-Adhesive		
1101 A489 70c Like #1072	.80	.20
a. Booklet of 12	9.75	

Type of 1995
Serpentine Die Cut 5¾ Vert.

2001, May 9		Typo.
Self-Adhesive		
1102 A404b 90c multi	1.00	.20
a. Booklet of 12	12.00	

Type of 2000

Designs: 90c, Farm house, Willisau, people feeding horse. 100c, Boat on Lake Geneva, woman at water's edge. 110c, Kleine Matterhorn Glacier, skier.

2001, Sept. 20 Litho.	Perf. 13x13¼	
1103 A492 90c multi	1.10	.25
1104 A492 100c multi	1.25	.25
1105 A492 110c multi	1.40	.30
Nos. 1103-1105 (3)	3.75	.80

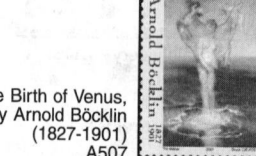

The Birth of Venus, by Arnold Böcklin (1827-1901) A507

2001, Sept. 20　　　　Perf. 13½

1106 A507 180c multi		2.25	.75

Souvenir Sheet

Flowers — A508

2001, Sept. 20		Perf. 13¼x12¾	
1107 A508	Sheet of 4	5.00	5.00
a.	70c Melastoma malabathricum	.90	.90
b.	90c Saraca cauliflora	1.10	1.10
c.	110c Leontopodium alpinum	1.40	1.40
d.	130c Gentiana clusii	1.60	1.60

See Singapore Nos. 984-988.

Illustrations from Children's Book, "The Rainbow Fish," by Marcus Pfister — A509

2001, Sept. 20 Photo.	Perf. 12¾x14	
1108 A509 70c Fish, coral	.90	.30
1109 A509 90c Fish, starfish	1.10	.35

Stamp Day Stamp Design Competition Winner — A510

Perf. 13¼x13½

2001, Nov. 20		Litho.
1110 A510 70c multi	.85	.30

Christmas — A511

2001, Nov. 20　　　　Perf. 11½
Granite Paper

1111 A511 90c multi		1.10	.35

Geneva Escalade, 400th Anniv. — A512

Perf. 13¼x13½

2002, Mar. 12		Litho.
1112 A512 70c multi	.85	.30

Federal Parliament Building, Cent. — A513

2002, Mar. 12

1113 A513 90c multi		1.10	.35

Rega Air Rescue Foundation A514

Litho. with Hologram Affixed

2002, Mar. 12		Perf. 13x13¾
1114 A514 180c multi	2.25	.75

Expo.02, Switzerland — A515

No. 1115: a, "E." b, Backwards "P." c, "0." d, "2."

2002, Mar. 12　Photo.　Perf. 14x13¼
Granite Paper

1115 A515	Block of 4	3.40	1.20
a.-d.	70c Any single	.85	.30

Swiss Railways, Cent. — A516

Designs: 70c, RABDe 500 Inter-city tilting train. 90c, Inter-city 2000 double-deck train. 120c, Seetal line railcar. 130c, Re 460 locomotive.

2002, Mar. 12	Perf. 12¾x14	
1116 A516 70c multi	.85	.30
1117 A516 90c multi	1.10	.35
1118 A516 120c multi	1.50	.50
1119 A516 130c multi	1.60	.55
Nos. 1116-1119 (4)	5.05	1.70

Souvenir Sheet

Arteplage Mobile du Jura — A517

2002, May 15	Photo.	Perf. 14
1120 A517 90c multi	1.10	.35

Expo.02, Switzerland.

Europa A518

2002, May 15 Litho.	Perf. 13¼	
1121 A518 70c Clown	.90	.30
1122 A518 90c Clown, diff.	1.10	.35

Teddy Bears, Cent. — A519

No. 1123 - Teddy bear from: a, France, 1925 (round, with tan frame, 26mm diameter). b,

Switzerland, 1950s (square with cut in corners, 25x25mm). c, Germany, 1904 (oval, 23x33mm). d, Switzerland, 2002 (rectangular, 26x23mm). e, England, c. 1920 (round, with blue and red frame, 26mm diameter).

2002, May 15   *Die Cut*
Self-Adhesive

1123	A519	Booklet pane of 5	5.50	
a.-e.		90c Any single	1.10	.35
f.		Booklet, 2 #1123	11.00	

Cessation of Production at Swiss Post Stamp Printers — A520

Litho. & Engr.
2002, Sept. 17   *Perf. 13¼*
1124 A520 70c multi   .95 .30

Ladybug — A521

Illustration reduced.

Serpentine Die Cut 12¼ Vert.
2002, Sept. 17   *Litho.*
Self-Adhesive
1125 A521 90c multi + label   1.25 .40
a.   Booklet pane of 10   12.50

Insects — A522

Minerals — A523

Designs: 10c, Anax imperator. 20c, Mesoacidalia aglaja. 50c, Rosalia alpina. 100c, Graphosoma lineatum. 200c, Quartz crystal. 500c, Titanite.

    Perf. 13¾x14¼
2002, Sept. 17   *Litho.*

1126	A522	10c multi	.20	.20
1127	A522	20c multi	.25	.20
1128	A522	50c multi	.65	.20
1129	A522	100c multi	1.40	.30

    Perf. 13¼

1130	A523	200c multi	2.75	.55
1131	A523	500c multi	6.75	1.40
		Nos. 1126-1131 (6)	12.00	2.85

Switzerland's Entry Into United Nations — A524

    Perf. 13¾x14¼
2002, Sept. 10   *Litho.*
1132 A524 90c multi   1.25 .40

Stamp Day — A525

2002, Nov. 19   *Perf. 13¾x14*
1133 A525 70c multi   .95 .30

World Alpine Skiing Championships, St. Moritz — A526

2002, Nov. 19   *Perf. 14x13¾*
1134 A526 90c multi   1.25 .40

Emblem of Switzerland Tourism — A527

Serpentine Die Cut 13¼ Vert.
2002, Nov. 19
Self-Adhesive

1135	A527	(1.30fr) blue & multi	1.75	.35
a.		Booklet pane of 6	10.50	
1136	A527	(1.80fr) red & multi	2.50	.50
a.		Booklet pane of 6	15.00	

Nos. 1135-1136 were valid only on post cards sent to European (#1135) or non-European (#1136) addresses, and could not be used in combination with other stamps. No. 1135a sold for 7.20fr, and No. 1136a for 10fr.

Christmas — A528

2002, Nov. 19   *Photo.*   *Perf. 11½*
Granite Paper
1137 A528 90c multi   1.25 .40

Swiss Natl. Association of and for the Blind, Cent. — A529

Litho. & Embossed
2003, Mar. 6   *Perf. 14¾x14½*
1138 A529 70c red & carmine   1.00 .35

100th Natl. Horse Market and Show, Saignelégier — A530

2003, Mar. 6   *Litho.*   *Perf. 13¼x13½*
1139 A530 90c multi   1.40 .45

2003 World Orienteering Championships, Rapperswil and Jona — A531

2003, Mar. 6
1140 A531 90c multi   1.40 .45

Intl. Year of Water — A532

2003, Mar. 6   *Perf. 13x13¼*
1141 A532 90c multi   1.40 .45

Medicinal Plants — A533

Designs: 70c, Hypericum perforatum. 90c, Vinca minor. 110c, Valeriana officinalis. 120c, Arnica montana. 130c, Centaurium minus. 180c, Malva sylvestris. 220c, Matricaria chamomilla.

2003, Mar. 6   *Perf. 14x13¾*

1142	A533	70c multi	1.00	.20
1143	A533	90c multi	1.40	.25
1144	A533	110c multi	1.60	.30
1145	A533	120c multi	1.75	.35
1146	A533	130c multi	1.90	.40
1147	A533	180c multi	2.60	.50
1148	A533	220c multi	3.25	.65
		Nos. 1142-1148 (7)	13.50	2.65

Europa — A534

2003, May 8   *Litho.*   *Perf. 13¼x13*
1149 A534 90c multi   1.40 .45

Comic Strip Art — A535

No. 1150 - Envelope and: a, Woman, birthday cake. b, Man, heart. c, Man, thunder cloud. d, Woman, musical note. 90c, Envelope, woman, duck.

2003, May 8   *Perf. 14¾*

1150	A535	Block of 4	4.75	1.50
a.-d.		70c Any single	1.10	.40

Souvenir Sheet
1151 A535 90c multi   1.50 .50
20th Intl. Comics Festival, Sierre.

Souvenir Sheet

Trilateral Stamp Exhibition, Ticino — A536

2003, May 8   *Perf. 14¾*

1152	A536	Sheet of 2	1.50	.50
a.		20c Eagle	.30	.20
b.		70c Gentian	1.25	.40

Switzerland's Victory in 2003 America's Cup Yacht Races — A537

2003, Mar 7   *Litho.*   *Perf. 13x13¼*
1153 A537 90c multi   1.40 .45

No. 1153 was not sent to standing order subscribers until September.

Minerals Type of 2002

Designs: 300c, Rutilated quartz. 400c, Green fluorite.

2003, Sept. 9   *Perf. 13¾x14¼*

1154	A523	300c multi	4.50	1.10
1155	A523	400c multi	5.75	1.40

Comic Strip "Diddl," by Thomas Goletz — A538

Designs: 70c, Mice reading love letters. 90c, Mouse chasing flying envelopes.

2003, Sept. 9   *Perf. 13¼x13½*

1156	A538	70c multi	1.00	.35
1157	A538	90c multi	1.40	.45

UNESCO World Heritage Sites — A539

Designs: No. 1158, Jungfrau-Aletsch-Bietschhorn. No. 1159, Three Castles, Bellinzona. No. 1160, Old City, Bern. No. 1161, Convent of St. Gall. No. 1162, Benedictine Convent of St. John, Müstair.

2003, Sept. 9   *Perf. 12¾*

1158	A539	90c multi	1.40	.45
1159	A539	90c multi	1.40	.45
1160	A539	90c multi	1.40	.45
1161	A539	90c multi	1.40	.45
1162	A539	90c multi	1.40	.45
		Nos. 1158-1162 (5)	7.00	2.25

Nos. 1158-1162 each issued in sheets of 6.

Stamp Day — A540

    Perf. 13¼x13½
2003, Nov. 19   *Litho.*
1163 A540 70c multi   1.00 .35

Four-leaf Clover — A541

Illustration reduced.

Serpentine Die Cut 12¼ Vert.
2003, Nov. 19
Self-Adhesive
1164 A541 130c multi + label   1.90 .65
a.   Booklet of 10   19.00

Christmas — A542

Ornaments: 70c, Horseman. 90c, Santa Claus.

2003, Nov. 19   Photo.   *Perf. 11½*
1165	A542	70c multi	1.00	.35
1166	A542	90c multi	1.40	.45

SEMI-POSTAL STAMPS

Nos. B1-B76, B81-B84 were sold at premiums of 2c for 3c stamps, 5c for 5c-20c stamps and 10c for 30c-40c stamps.

Helvetia and Matterhorn — SP2

Perf. 11½, 12
1913, Dec. 1   Typo.   Wmk. 183
Granite Paper
B1	SP2	5c green	2.75	8.25
		Never hinged	7.75	

Boy (Appenzell) SP3   Girl (Lucerne) SP4

1915, Dec. 1   *Perf. 11½*
B2	SP3	5c green, *buff*	3.25	8.25
a.		Tête bêche pair	82.50	875.00
l		Never hinged	160.00	
B3	SP4	10c red, *buff*	100.00	87.50
		Set, never hinged	225.00	

Girl (Fribourg) SP5   Dairy Boy (Bern) SP6

Girl (Vaud) — SP7

1916, Dec. 1
B4	SP5	3c vio, *buff*	5.00	37.50
B5	SP6	5c grn, *buff*	11.00	9.25
B6	SP7	10c brn red, *buff*	47.50	77.50
		Nos. B4-B6 (3)	63.50	124.25
		Set, never hinged	175.00	

Girl (Valais) SP8   Girl (Unterwalden) SP9

Girl (Ticino) — SP10

1917, Dec. 1
B7	SP8	3c vio, *buff*	3.25	50.00
B8	SP9	5c green, *buff*	7.75	5.50
B9	SP10	10c red, *buff*	19.00	22.50
		Nos. B7-B9 (3)	30.00	78.00
		Set, never hinged	87.50	

Uri SP11   Geneva SP12

1918, Dec. 1
Straw-Surfaced Paper
B10	SP11	10c red, org & blk	7.75	25.00
B11	SP12	15c vio, red, org & blk	9.25	11.00
		Set, never hinged	52.50	

Nidwalden SP13   Vaud SP14

Obwalden — SP15

1919, Dec. 1
Cream-Surfaced Paper
B12	SP13	7½c gray, red & blk	2.50	14.00
B13	SP14	10c lake, grn & blk	2.50	14.00
B14	SP15	15c pur, red & blk	5.00	7.25
		Nos. B12-B14 (3)	10.00	35.25
		Set, never hinged	22.50	

Schwyz SP16   Zürich SP17

Ticino — SP18

1920, Dec. 1
Cream-Surfaced Paper
B15	SP16	7½c gray & red	2.75	11.50
B16	SP17	10c red & lt bl	5.00	12.50
B17	SP18	15c violet, red & bl	2.75	6.00
		Nos. B15-B17 (3)	10.50	30.00
		Set, never hinged	25.00	

Valais SP19   Bern SP20

Switzerland — SP21

1921, Dec. 1
Cream-Surfaced Paper
B18	SP19	10c grn, red & blk	.65	3.00
B19	SP20	20c vio, red, org & blk	1.90	3.50
B20	SP21	40c blue & red	7.25	47.50
		Nos. B18-B20 (3)	9.80	54.00
		Set, never hinged	25.00	

Zug SP22   Fribourg SP23

Lucerne SP24   Switzerland SP25

1922, Dec. 1
Cream-Surfaced Paper
B21	SP22	5c org, pale bl & blk	.50	5.50
B22	SP23	10c ol grn & blk	.60	2.50
B23	SP24	20c vio, pale bl & blk	1.00	2.50
B24	SP25	40c bl & red	8.75	47.50
		Nos. B21-B24 (4)	10.85	58.00
		Set, never hinged	26.00	

Basel SP26   Glarus (St. Fridolin) SP27

Neuchâtel SP28   Switzerland SP29

1923, Dec. 1
Cream-Surfaced Paper
B25	SP26	5c org & blk	.40	3.50
B26	SP27	10c multi	.40	1.90
B27	SP28	20c multi	.45	1.90
B28	SP29	40c dk bl & red	7.75	37.50
		Nos. B25-B28 (4)	9.00	44.80
		Set, never hinged	21.00	

Appenzell SP30   Solothurn SP31

Schaffhausen SP32   Switzerland SP33

1924, Dec. 1
Cream-Surfaced Paper
B29	SP30	5c dk vio & blk	.25	1.6
B30	SP31	10c grn, red & blk	.40	1.0
B31	SP32	20c car, yel & blk	.65	1.0
B32	SP33	30c bl, red & blk	1.40	11.0
		Nos. B29-B32 (4)	2.70	14.6
		Set, never hinged	6.50	

St. Gallen (Canton) SP34   Appenzell-Ausser-Rhoden SP35

Grisons SP36   Switzerland SP37

1925, Dec. 1
Cream-Surfaced Paper
B33	SP34	5c vio, grn & blk	.25	1.1
B34	SP35	10c grn & blk	.25	.8
B35	SP36	20c multi	.25	.8
B36	SP37	30c dk bl, red & blk	1.10	8.2
		Nos. B33-B36 (4)	1.85	11.0
		Set, never hinged	4.50	

Thurgau SP38   Basel SP39

Aargau SP40   Switzerland SP41

1926, Dec. 1
Cream-Surfaced Paper
B37	SP38	5c vio, bis & grn	.25	1.4
B38	SP39	10c gray grn, red & blk	.25	1.4
B39	SP40	20c red, blk & bl	.25	1.4
B40	SP41	30c dk bl & red	1.10	12.5
		Nos. B37-B40 (4)	1.85	16.7
		Set, never hinged	4.50	

Orphan SP42   Orphan at Pestalozzi School SP43

J. H. Pestalozzi SP45   SP44

1927, Dec. 1   Typo.   Wmk. 183
Granite Paper
B41	SP42	5c red vio & yel, grysh	.20	1.60
B42	SP43	10c grn & fawn, grnsh	.20	.60

Engr.
B43	SP44	20c red	.20	.60

Unwmk.
Photo.
B44	SP45	30c gray bl & blk	1.10	6.50
		Nos. B41-B44 (4)	1.70	9.30
		Set, never hinged	3.25	

Nos. B43-B44 for the centenary of the death of Johann Heinrich Pestalozzi, the Swiss educational reformer.

Lausanne
SP46

Winterthur
SP47

St. Gallen
(City) — SP48

J. H.
Dunant
SP49

1928, Dec. 1   Typo.   Wmk. 183
Cream-Surfaced Paper.
B45	SP46	5c dk vio, red & blk	.20	1.60
B46	SP47	10c bl grn, org red & blk	.20	.90
B47	SP48	20c brn red, blk & yel	.20	.90

Unwmk.
Photo.
Thick White Paper
B48	SP49	30c dl bl & red	1.10	7.00
		Nos. B45-B48 (4)	1.70	10.40
		Set, never hinged	3.50	

No. B48 for the centenary of the birth of Jean Henri Dunant, Swiss author, philanthropist and founder of the Red Cross Society.

Lake
Lugano and
Mt.
Salvatore
SP50

Lake
Engstlen
and Mt.
Titlis
SP51

Mt.
Lyskamm
SP52

Nicholas
von der
Flüe
SP53

1929, Dec. 1   Perf. 11x11½
B49	SP50	5c dk vio & red org	.20	1.40
B50	SP51	10c ol brn & gray bl	.20	1.10
B51	SP52	20c brn garnet & bl	.25	1.10
B52	SP53	30c dk blue	1.25	12.50
		Nos. B49-B52 (4)	1.90	16.10
		Set, never hinged	4.50	

No. B52 for Nicholas von der Flüe, the Swiss patriot. By his advice the Swiss Confederation was continued and Swiss independence was saved.

Fribourg
SP54

Altdorf
SP55

Schaffhausen
SP56

Jeremias
Gotthelf
SP57

Wmk. 183
1930, Dec. 1   Typo.   Perf. 11½
Cream-Surfaced Paper
B53	SP54	5c dk bl & blk	.20	1.40
B54	SP55	10c multicolored	.20	.90
B55	SP56	20c multicolored	.30	.90

Engr.
White Paper
B56	SP57	30c slate blue	1.25	6.00
		Nos. B53-B56 (4)	1.95	9.20
		Set, never hinged	4.00	

No. B56 for Jeremias Gotthelf, pen name of Albrecht Bitzius, pastor and author.

Lakes
Silvaplana
and Sils
SP58

Wetterhorn
SP59

Lake
Geneva
SP60

Alexandre
Vinet
SP61

1931, Dec. 1   Photo.   Unwmk.
Granite Paper
B57	SP58	5c dp grn	.45	1.60
B58	SP59	10c dk vio	.40	.85
B59	SP60	20c brn red	.55	1.10

Wmk. 183
Engr.
B60	SP61	30c ultra	4.50	19.00
		Nos. B57-B60 (4)	5.90	22.55
		Set, never hinged	14.00	

No. B60 for Alexandre Rudolph Vinet, critic and theologian.

Flag Swinger
SP62

Putting the
Stone
SP63

Wrestling
SP64

Eugen Huber
SP65

1932, Dec. 1   Typo.   Unwmk.
Granite Paper
B61	SP62	5c dk grn & red	.30	1.90
B62	SP63	10c orange	.45	2.25
B63	SP64	20c scarlet	.55	1.90

Wmk. 183
Engr.
B64	SP65	30c ultra	2.25	8.75
		Nos. B61-B64 (4)	3.55	14.80
		Set, never hinged	9.50	

No. B64 for Eugen Huber, jurist and author of the Swiss Civil Law Book.

Girl of
Vaud — SP66

Girl of
Bern — SP67

Girl of Ticino
SP68

Jean Baptiste
Girard (Le Père
Grégoire)
SP69

1933, Dec. 1   Photo.   Unwmk.
Granite Paper
B65	SP66	5c grn & buff	.30	1.50
B66	SP67	10c vio & buff	.30	1.10
B67	SP68	20c red & buff	.45	2.10

Wmk. 183
Engr.
B68	SP69	30c ultra	2.50	8.50
		Nos. B65-B68 (4)	3.55	13.20
		Set, never hinged	8.25	

Girl of
Appenzell
SP70

Girl of Valais
SP71

Girl of Grisons
SP72

Albrecht von
Haller
SP73

1934, Dec. 1   Photo.   Unwmk.
B69	SP70	5c grn & buff	.30	1.60
B70	SP71	10c vio & buff	.45	1.10
B71	SP72	20c red & buff	.45	1.60

Wmk. 183
Engr.
B72	SP73	30c ultra	2.50	8.75
		Nos. B69-B72 (4)	3.70	13.05
		Set, never hinged	8.25	

Girl of Basel
SP74

Girl of Lucerne
SP75

Girl of Geneva
SP76

Stefano
Franscini
SP77

1935, Dec. 1   Photo.   Unwmk.
Granite Paper
B73	SP74	5c grn & buff	.25	1.75
B74	SP75	10c vio & buff	.45	1.10
B75	SP76	20c red & buff	.45	2.75

Wmk. 183
Engr.
B76	SP77	30c ultra	2.50	8.75
		Nos. B73-B76 (4)	3.65	14.35
		Set, never hinged	8.25	

No. B76 honors Stefano Franscini (1796-1857), political economist and educator.

Alpine
Herdsman — SP78

Perf. 11½
1936, Oct. 1   Photo.   Unwmk.
Granite Paper
B77	SP78	10c + 5c vio	.55	1.00
B78	SP78	20c + 10c dk red	.85	4.25
B79	SP78	30c + 10c ultra	3.75	20.00
		Nos. B77-B79 (3)	5.15	25.25
		Set, never hinged	11.00	

Souvenir Sheet
B80	SP78	Sheet of 3	35.00	125.00
		Never hinged	70.00	
a.		Block of 4 sheets	190.00	875.00
		Never hinged	300.00	

Swiss National Defense Fund Drive.
No. B80 contains stamps similar to Nos. B77-B79, but on grilled granite paper with blue and red fibers instead of black and red. Sold for 2fr. Size: 120x130mm.

Johann Georg
Nägeli
SP79

Girl of
Neuchâtel
SP80

Girl of Schwyz
SP81

Girl of Zurich
SP82

Wmk. 183
1936, Dec. 1   Engr.   Perf. 11½
Granite Paper
B81 SP79 5c green   .25   .70
Unwmk.
Photo.
B82 SP80 10c vio & buff   .55   .70
B83 SP81 20c red & buff   .25 1.90
B84 SP82 30c ultra & buff   3.50 30.00
  Nos. B82-B84 (3)   4.30 32.60
  Set, never hinged   11.00

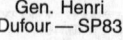

Gen. Henri
Dufour — SP83

Nicholas von
der
Flüe — SP84

Boy
SP85

Girl
SP86

Perf. 11½
1937, Dec. 1   Unwmk.   Engr.
B85 SP83 5c + 5c bl grn   .20   .55
B86 SP84 10c + 5c red vio   .20   .55
Photo.
Granite Paper
B87 SP85 20c + 5c red & silver   .30   .55
B88 SP86 30c + 10c ultra & sil   1.25 5.50
  Nos. B85-B88 (4)   1.95 7.15
  Set, never hinged   3.75

25th anniv. of the Pro Juventute (child welfare) stamps.

Souvenir Sheet
1937, Dec. 20   Imperf.
B89 Sheet of 2   6.50 57.50
  a. SP85 20c + 5c red & silver   1.60 17.00
  b. SP86 30c + 10c ultra & silver   1.60 17.00
    Never hinged   7.50

Simulated perforation in silver. Sheet sold for 1fr.

Tell
Chapel,
Lake
Lucerne
SP87

1938, June 15   Perf. 11½
Granite Paper
B90 SP87 10c + 10c brt vio & yel   .45 1.10
    Never hinged   1.10
  a. Grilled gum   22.50 77.50
    Never hinged   32.50

National Fête Day.

Salomon
Gessner
SP88

Girl of St.
Gallen
SP89

Girl of
Uri — SP90

Girl of
Aargau — SP91

1938, Dec. 1   Engr.   Perf. 11½
B91 SP88 5c + 5c dp bl grn   .20   .50
Photo.
Granite Paper
B92 SP89 10c + 5c pur & buff   .25   .55
B93 SP90 20c + 5c red & buff   .25   .55
B94 SP91 30c + 10c ultra   1.60 6.50
  Nos. B91-B94 (4)   2.30 8.10
  Set, never hinged   4.50

Castle at
Laupen
SP92

1939, June 15
B95 SP92 10c + 10c brn, gray & red   .30 1.10
    Never hinged   1.10

600th anniversary of the Battle of Laupen. The surtax was used to aid needy mothers.

Hans Herzog
SP93

Girl of Fribourg
SP94

Girl of
Nidwalden
SP95

Girl of Basel
SP96

Perf. 11½
1939, Dec. 1   Unwmk.   Engr.
B96 SP93 5c + 5c dk grn   .20   .45
Photo.
Granite Paper
B97 SP94 10c + 5c rose vio & buff   .20   .45
B98 SP95 20c + 5c org red   .30 1.40
B99 SP96 30c + 10c ultra & buff   1.60 11.50
  Nos. B96-B99 (4)   2.30 13.80
  Set, never hinged   5.00

Sempach,
1386 — SP97

Giornico,
1478 — SP98

Calven, 1499
SP99

WWI Ranger
SP100

1940, Mar. 20   Photo.
Granite Paper
B100 SP97 5c + 5c emer, blk & red   .30 1.25
B101 SP98 10c + 5c brn org, blk & car   .30   .55
B102 SP99 20c + 5c brn red, blk & car   2.25   .95
B103 SP100 30c + 10c brt bl, brn blk & red   1.60 8.25

National Fête Day. The surtax was for the National Fund and the Red Cross.

Redrawn
B104 SP99 20c + 5c brn red, blk & car   9.75 6.50
  Nos. B100-B104 (5)   14.20 17.50
  Set, never hinged   26.00

The base of statue has been heavily shaded "Calven 1499" moved nearer to bottom line of base. Top line of base removed.

Souvenir Sheet
Unwmk.
1940, July 16   Photo.   Imperf.
Granite Paper
B105 Sheet of 4   250.00 575.00
    Never hinged   425.00
  a. SP97 5c+5c yel grn, blk & red   11.00 26.00
  b. SP98 10c+5c org yel, blk & red   47.50 210.00
  c. SP99 20c+5c brn red, blk & red (redrawn)   47.50 210.00
  d. SP100 30c+10c chlky bl, blk & red   11.00 26.00

National Fete Day. Sheets measure 125x65mm and sold for 5fr.

Gottfried Keller
SP102

Girl of Thurgau
SP103

Girl of
Solothurn
SP104

Girl of Zug
SP105

1940, Dec. 1   Engr.   Perf. 11½
B106 SP102 5c + 5c dk bl grn   .20   .40
Photo.
B107 SP103 10c + 5c brn & buff   .20   .30
B108 SP104 20c + 5c org red & buff   .20   .40
B109 SP105 30c + 10c dp ultra & buff   1.40 9.50
  Nos. B106-B109 (4)   2.00 10.60
  Set, never hinged   4.00

Lake
Lucerne,
Arms of
Cantons
SP106

Tell
Chapel at
Chemin
Creux
SP107

1941, June 15
B110 SP106 10c + 10c multi   .30   .7
B111 SP107 20c + 10c org, red & lt buff   .30 1.2
  Set, never hinged   2.00

Natl. Fête Day and 650th anniv. of Swiss Independence.

Johann Lavater
SP108

Girl of
Schaffhausen
SP109

Girl of
Obwalden
SP110

Daniel Jean
Richard
SP111

1941, Dec. 1   Engr.
B112 SP108 5c + 5c dk grn   .20   .30
B113 SP111 30c + 10c dp ultra   .25   .40
Photo.
B114 SP109 10c + 5c chnt & buff   .25   .40
B115 SP110 20c + 5c ver & buff   .80 5.00
  Nos. B112-B115 (4)   1.50 6.10
  Set, never hinged   3.50

Souvenir Sheet
Imperf
B116 Sheet of 2   60.00 350.00
  a. SP109 10c +5c chnt & buff   17.00 125.00
  b. SP110 20c +5c ver & buff   17.00 125.00
    Never hinged   100.00

Issued in sheets measuring 75x70mm and sold for 2fr. The surtax was used for charity.

Ancient
Geneva
SP113

Soldiers'
Monument,
Forch
SP114

1942, June 15   Perf. 11½
B117 SP113 10c + 10c gray blk, red & yel   .25   .50
B118 SP114 20c + 10c cop red, red & buff   .25   .85
  Set, never hinged   1.25

National Fête Day, 1942. No. B117 for the 2000th anniv. of the City of Geneva.

Souvenir Sheet
Imperf
B119 Sheet of 2   50.00 225.00
  a. SP113 10c +10c gray black, red & yellow   14.00 80.00
  b. SP113 20c +10c copper red, red & buff   14.00 80.00
    Never hinged   82.50

Issued in sheets measuring 105x63mm in commemoration of National Fete and the 2000th anniv. of the City of Geneva. Sold for 2fr. The surtax was divided between the Swiss Alliance of Samaritans and the National Community Chest.

Niklaus
Riggenbach
SP116

Girl of
Appenzell
SP117

Girl of Glarus
SP118

Konrad Escher
von der Linth
SP119

1942, Dec. 1   **Engr.**   **Perf. 11½**

B120	SP116	5c + 5c deep grn	.20	.50
B121	SP119	30c + 10c royal bl	.25	.50

Photo.

B122	SP117	10c + 5c dp brn & buff	.25	.50
B123	SP118	20c + 5c org red	1.10	4.50
	Nos. B120-B123 (4)		1.80	6.00
	Set, never hinged		3.75	

Intragna
SP120

Parliament
Buildings,
Bern
SP121

1943, June 15   **Photo.**   **Perf. 11½**

B124	SP120	10c + 10c blk brn, buff & dk red	.25	.75
B125	SP121	20c + 10c cop red, buff & dk red	.30	1.50
	Set, never hinged		1.25	

National Fête Day, 1943.

Emanuel von
Fellenberg
SP122

Silver Thistle
SP123

20c+5c, Lady slipper. 30c+10c, Gentian.

1943, Dec. 1   **Engr.**

B126	SP122	5c + 5c green	.20	.50

Photo.

B127	SP123	10c + 5c sl grn & ocher	.20	.50
B128	SP123	20c + 5c copper red & yel	.25	.50
B129	SP123	30c + 10c royal bl & lt bl	1.10	8.50
	Nos. B126-B129 (4)		1.75	10.00
	Set, never hinged		3.25	

Souvenir Sheets

SP126

1943   **Engr.**   **Imperf.**

B130	SP126	Sheet of 12	37.50	60.00
a.		10c black, single stamp	1.10	3.75
		Never hinged	77.50	

Sold for 5fr. Size: 165x140mm.

SP127

Red Horizontal Lines

B131	SP127	Sheet of 2	42.50	52.50
a.		4c black & red	13.00	20.00
b.		6c black & red	13.00	20.00
		Never hinged	75.00	

Sold for 3fr. Size: 70x75mm.

Arms of Geneva — SP128

B132	SP128	Sheet of 2	40.00	40.00
a.		5c green & black	11.50	15.00
		Never hinged	65.00	

Sold for 3fr. Size: 72x72mm. Centenary of
Swiss postage stamps. The surtax aided the
Swiss Red Cross.

Heiden
SP129

St. Jacob
SP130

Mesocco
SP131

Basel
SP132

Perf. 11½

1944, June 15   **Photo.**   **Unwmk.**

B133	SP129	5c + 5c dk bl grn, red & buff	.20	2.25
B134	SP130	10c + 10c gray blk, red & buff	.20	.50
B135	SP131	20c + 10c hn, red & buff	.20	1.00
B136	SP132	30c + 10c brt ultra & red	2.10	17.50
	Nos. B133-B136 (4)		2.70	21.25
	Set, never hinged		6.00	

National Fete Day.

Numa Droz
SP133

Edelweiss
SP134

Designs: 20c+5c, Lilium martagon.
30c+10c, Aquilegia alpina.

1944, Dec. 1   **Engr.**

B137	SP133	5c + 5c green	.20	.35

Photo.

B138	SP134	10c + 5c dk sl grn, yel & gray	.25	.40
B139	SP134	20c + 5c red, yel & gray	.35	.40
B140	SP134	30c + 10c bl, gray & lt bl	1.10	8.50
	Nos. B137-B140 (4)		1.90	9.65
	Set, never hinged		4.00	

Symbol of Faith,
Hope and
Love — SP137

1945

SCHWEIZER SPENDE AN DIE KRIEGSGESCHÄDIGTEN
SPENDE DER MARKENFREUNDE

DON SUISSE POUR LES VICTIMES DE LA GUERRE
DON DES AMIS DU TIMBRE

DONO SVIZZERO PER LE VITTIME DELLA GUERRA
DONO DEGLI AMICI DEL FRANCOBOLLO

Lifeboat Making a Rescue — SP138

1945, Feb. 20   **Perf. 11½**

B141	SP137	10c + 10c multi	.30	.50
B142	SP137	20c + 60c multi	.90	5.75
	Set, never hinged		2.50	

Imperf
Souvenir Sheet

B143	SP138	3fr + 7fr bl gray	110.00	225.00
		Never hinged	200.00	

Issued in sheets measuring 70x110mm.
Surtax for the benefit of war victims.

Souvenir Sheet

Dove of Basel — SP139

1945, Apr. 14   **Typo.**

B144	SP139	Sheet of 2	70.00	95.00
a.		10c gray, maroon & black	16.00	26.00
		Never hinged	150.00	

Cent. of the Basel Cantonal Stamp. The
sheets measure 71x63mm and sold for 3fr.
The surtax was for the Pro Juventute
Foundation.

Numeral of Value
and Red
Cross — SP140

1945   **Photo.**   **Perf. 12**

B145	SP140	5c + 10c grn & red	.30	.75
		Never hinged	.65	

Weaver
SP141

Farm of
Jura
SP142

Farm of
Emmental
SP143

Frame House, Eastern
Switzerland — SP144

1945, June 15   **Engr.**   **Perf. 11½**

B146	SP141	5c + 5c bl grn & red	.35	2.00

Photo.

B147	SP142	10c + 10c brn, gray bl & red	.35	.75
B148	SP143	20c + 10c hn brn, buff & red	.55	.75
B149	SP144	30c + 10c saph & red	5.50	35.00
	Nos. B146-B149 (4)		6.75	38.50
	Set, never hinged		14.50	

The surtax was for needy mothers.

Ludwig Forrer — SP145

Susanna Orelli — SP146

Alpine Dog-Rose SP147

Crocus SP148

1945, Dec. 1   **Engr.**
B150 SP145 5c + 5c dk grn   .20   .50
B151 SP146 10c + 10c dk red brn   .20   .50

Photo.
B152 SP147 20c + 10c rose brn, rose & yel org   .30   .50
B153 SP148 30c + 10c dk bl, gray & lil   1.50   7.50
   Nos. B150-B153 (4)   2.20   9.00
   Set, never hinged   4.50

Cheese Making SP149

Farm Buildings and Vineyards SP150

House in Appenzell SP151

House in Engadine SP152

1946, June 15   **Engr.**
B154 SP149 5c + 5c bl grn & red   .35   2.00

Photo.
B155 SP150 10c + 10c brn, buff & red   .25   .75
B156 SP151 20c + 10c henna, buff & red   .35   .75
B157 SP152 30c + 10c saph & red   3.00   9.50
   Nos. B154-B157 (4)   3.95   13.00
   Set, never hinged   9.50

Rodolphe Toepffer SP153

Narcissus SP154

20c+10c, Mountain sengreen. 40c+10c, Blue thistle.

1946, Nov. 30   **Engr.**
B158 SP153 5c + 5c green   .20   .50

Photo.
B159 SP154 10c + 10c dk sl grn, gray & red org   .20   .50
B160 SP154 20c + 10c brn car, gray & yel   .20   .75
B161 SP154 30c + 10c dk bl, gray & pink   1.40   6.00
   Nos. B158-B161 (4)   2.00   7.75
   Set, never hinged   3.75

Railroad Laborers SP157

Railroad Station, Rorschach SP158

Lüen-Castiel Station — SP159

Flüelen Station SP160

Perf. 11½
1947, June 14   **Engr.**   **Unwmk.**
B162 SP157 5c + 5c dk grn & red   .25   2.10

Photo.
B163 SP158 10c + 10c gray blk, cream & red   .30   .75
B164 SP159 20c + 10c rose lil, cream & red   .30   1.00
B165 SP160 30c + 10c bl, gray & red   3.50   9.00
   Nos. B162-B165 (4)   4.35   12.85
   Set, never hinged   10.00

The surtax was for professional education of invalids and for the fight against cancer.

Jakob Burckhardt SP161

Alpine Primrose SP162

20c+10c, Red lily. 30c+10c, Cyclamen.

1947, Dec. 1   **Engr.**
B166 SP161 5c + 5c dk grn   .20   .45

Photo.
B167 SP162 10c + 10c sl blk, gray & yel   .20   .45
B168 SP162 20c + 10c red brn, gray & cop red   .20   .40
B169 SP162 30c + 10c dk bl, gray & pink   1.25   5.75
   Nos. B166-B169 (4)   1.85   7.05
   Set, never hinged   3.50

Sun and Olympic Emblem SP165

Icehockey Player SP167

10c+10c, Snowflake and Olympic Emblem. 30c+10c, Ski-runner.

1948, Jan. 15
B170 SP165 5c + 5c dk bl grn & yel   .25   1.50
B171 SP165 10c + 10c choc & bl   .30   1.00
B172 SP167 20c + 10c dp mag, gray & org yel   .40   1.50
B173 SP167 30c + 10c dk bl, bl & gray blk   1.25   5.50
   Nos. B170-B173 (4)   2.20   9.50
   Set, never hinged   5.50

Issued to publicize the 5th Olympic Winter Games, St. Moritz, Jan. 30-Feb. 8, 1948.

Frontier Guard SP169

House of Fribourg SP170

House of Valais SP171

House of Ticino SP172

1948, June 15   **Engr.**
B174 SP169 5c + 5c dk grn & red   .20   1.25

Photo.
B175 SP170 10c + 10c sl & gray   .20   .75
B176 SP171 20c + 10c brn red & pink   .20   1.00
B177 SP172 30c + 10c bl & gray   2.25   7.50
   Nos. B174-B177 (4)   2.85   10.50
   Set, never hinged   6.00

Johann R. Wettstein — SP173

1948, Aug. 21   **Perf. 11x12½**
B178 SP173   Sheet of 2   50.00   65.00
  a.   10c rose lilac   14.00   25.00
  b.   20c chalky blue   14.00   25.00
   Never hinged   77.50

Intl. Phil. Expo., Basel, Aug. 21-29, 1948. Sheet, size 110x60mm, sold for 3fr, of which the surtax was used for the exhibition and charitable purposes.

Gen. Ulrich Wille SP174

Foxglove SP175

20c+10c, Alpine rose. 40c+10c, Lily of paradise.

1948, Dec. 1   **Engr.**   **Perf. 11½**
B179 SP174 5c + 5c dk vio brn   .20   .45

Photo.
B180 SP175 10c + 10c dk grn, yel grn & yel   .25   .4
B181 SP175 20c + 10c brn, crim & buff   .30   .4
B182 SP175 40c + 10c bl, gray & org   1.25   5.5
   Nos. B180-B182 (3)   1.80   6.4
   Set, never hinged   4.50

Postman SP176

Mountain Farmhouse SP177

House of Lucerne SP178

House of Prattigau SP179

Engraved and Photogravure
1949, June 15
Shield in Carmine
B183 SP176 5c + 5c rose vio   .30   1.50

Photo.
B184 SP177 10c + 10c bl grn & car   .30   .75
B185 SP178 20c + 10c dk brn & cr   .30   .75
B186 SP179 40c + 10c bl & pale bl   2.50   10.00
   Nos. B183-B186 (4)   3.40   13.00
   Set, never hinged   7.25

The surtax was for professional education of Swiss youth.

Niklaus Wengi SP180

Anemone Sulphureous SP181

20c+10c, Alpine clematis. 40c+10c, Superb pink.

1949, Dec. 1   **Engr.**   **Perf. 11½**
B187 SP180 5c + 5c vio brn   .20   .45

Photo.
B188 SP181 10c + 10c grn, gray & yel   .20   .45
B189 SP181 20c + 10c brn, bl & yel   .25   .45
B190 SP181 40c + 10c bl, lav & yel   1.40   5.50
   Nos. B187-B190 (4)   2.05   6.85
   Set, never hinged   4.00

Adaptation of 1850 Design SP182

Putting the Stone SP183

Designs: 20c+10c, Wrestlers. 30c+10c, Runners. 40c+10c, Target shooting.

1950, June 1   **Engr. & Photo.**
Shield in Red
B191 SP182   5c + 5c black   .20   .75

Photo.
Inscribed: "I. VIII. 1950"
B192 SP183 10c + 10c green   .50   .80
B193 SP183 20c + 20c brown
    ol   .50   1.25
B194 SP183 30c + 10c rose lil   3.75   17.00
B195 SP183 40c + 10c dull bl   4.75   11.00
   Nos. B191-B195 (5)   9.70   30.80
   Set, never hinged   20.00

The surtax was for the Red Cross and the Society of Swiss History of Art.

Theophil Sprecher von Bernegg SP184

Admiral Butterfly SP185

Designs: 20c+10c, Blue Underwing Butterfly. 30c+10c, Bee. 40c+10c, Sulphur Butterfly.

1950, Dec. 1   **Engr.**
B196 SP184   5c + 5c sepia   .20   .30

Photo.
B197 SP185 10c + 10c multi   .25   .40
B198 SP185 20c + 10c multi   .30   .50
B199 SP185 30c + 10c rose lil,
    gray & dk
    brn   3.00   13.50
B200 SP185 40c + 10c bl, dk
    brn & yel   3.00   9.25
   Nos. B196-B200 (5)   6.75   23.95
   Set, never hinged   13.50

Arms of Switzerland and Zurich — SP186

Valaisan Polka SP187

20c+10c, 40c, Flag-swinging. 30c+10c, Hornussen (natl. game). 40c+10c, Blowing alphorn.

1951, June 1   **Engr.**
Shield in Red
B201 SP186   5c + 5c gray   .20   .50

Photo.
Inscribed: "1. VIII. 1951"
Shield in Red, Figure Shaded in Gray
B202 SP187 10c + 10c green   .40   .50
B203 SP187 20c + 10c ol bis   .60   .85
B204 SP187 30c + 10c red vio   4.50   11.50
B205 SP187 40c + 10c brt
    blue   4.50   13.50
   Nos. B201-B205 (5)   10.20   26.85
   Set, never hinged   20.00

The surtax was used primarily for needy mothers.

Souvenir Sheet
1951, Sept. 29   *Imperf.*
B206 SP187 40c brt bl,
    sheet   175.00   190.00
   Never hinged   275.00

No. B206 sold for 3fr, size: 74x56mm. Natl. Phil. Exhib., LUNABA, Sept. 29-Oct. 7, 1951, Lucerne. The net proceeds were used for Swiss schools abroad.

Johanna Spyri SP189   Dragonfly SP190

Butterflies: 20c+10c, Black-Veined. 30c+10c Orange-Tip. 40c+10c, Saturnia pyri.

1951, Dec. 1   **Engr.**   *Perf. 11½*
B207 SP189   5c + 5c red brn   .20   .30

Photo.
B208 SP190 10c + 10c grn &
    dk bl   .20   .30
B209 SP190 20c + 10c rose lil,
    cr & blk   .30   .50
B210 SP190 30c + 10c ol grn,
    gray & org   2.00   8.50
B211 SP190 40c + 10c bl, dk
    brn & car   2.50   8.50
   Nos. B207-B211 (5)   5.20   18.10
   Set, never hinged   10.00

Arms of Switzerland, Glarus and Zug — SP191

Doubs River — SP192

Designs: 20c+10c, Lake of St. Gotthard. 30c+10c, Moesa River. 40c+10c, Lake of Marjelen.

1952, May 31   **Engr. & Typo.**
B212 SP191   5c + 5c gray &
    red   .25   1.00

Photo.
B213 SP192 10c + 10c blue
    green   .25   .50
B214 SP192 20c + 10c brown
    car   .25   .50
B215 SP192 30c + 10c brown   2.50   6.50
B216 SP192 40c + 10c blue   3.00   8.75
   Nos. B212-B216 (5)   6.25   17.25
   Set, never hinged   12.50

The surtax was used primarily for historical research and popular culture.
See Nos. B222-B226, B233-B236, B243-B246, B253-B256.

Portrait of a Boy, by Albert Anker SP193   Ladybug SP194

20c+10c, Barred-wing butterfly. 30c+10c, Argus butterfly. 40c+10c, Silkworm moth.

    Perf. 11½
1952, Dec. 1   **Unwmk.**   **Engr.**
B217 SP193   5c + 5c brown
    car   .20   .35

Photo.
B218 SP194 10c + 10c bluish
    grn, blk &
    org red   .20   .35
B219 SP194 20c + 10c rose lil,
    cr & blk   .20   .50
B220 SP194 30c + 10c brn,
    blk & gray bl   2.00   8.25
B221 SP194 40c + 10c pale
    vio, brn &
    buff   1.90   8.75
   Nos. B217-B221 (5)   4.50   18.20
   Set, never hinged   10.00

See Nos. B227-B231, B238-B241.

Types Similar to 1952
Designs: 5c+5c, Arms of Switzerland and Bern. 10c+10c, Reuss River. 20c+10c, Sihl Lake. 30c+10c, Bisse River. 40c+10c, Lake of Geneva.

Engraved and Photogravure
1953, June 1
B222 SP191   5c + 5c gray &
    red   .20   .75

Photo.
B223 SP192 10c + 10c blue
    green   .25   .50
B224 SP192 20c + 10c brown
    car   .30   .75
B225 SP192 30c + 10c brown   2.50   7.00
B226 SP192 40c + 10c blue   2.50   6.50
   Nos. B222-B226 (5)   5.75   15.50
   Set, never hinged   12.50

The surtax was used for Swiss nationals abroad and for disabled persons.

Booklet Panes
Panes consisting of blocks, strips or pairs removed from large sheets of regular issue and fastened or enclosed within a cover or folder, often by stapling or sewing in the sheet margin, are no longer being listed. Such panes contain no straight edges and can easily be made privately.

Types Similar to 1952, Dated "1953"
5c+5c, Portrait of a girl, by Albert Anker. 10c+10c, Nun moth. 20c+10c, Camberwell beauty butterfly. 30c+10c, Purple longicorn beetle. 40c+10c, Self-portrait, Ferdinand Hodler, facing left.

1953, Dec. 1   **Engr.**   *Perf. 11½*
B227 SP193   5c + 5c rose
    brown   .20   .35

Photo.
B228 SP194 10c + 10c multi   .25   .30
B229 SP194 20c + 10c multi   .30   .50
  a.   Sheet of 24   200.00
    Never hinged   375.00
  b.   Bklt. pane, 4 #B229, 2
    #B230   32.50
B230 SP194 30c + 10c ol,
    blk & red   1.90   8.25

Engr.
B231 SP193 40c + 10c blue   2.75   7.00
   Nos. B227-B231 (5)   5.40   16.40
   Set, never hinged   12.00

No. B229a consists of 16 No. B229 and 8 No. B230, arranged to include four se-tenant pairs and four pairs which are both se-tenant and tête bêche.

Opening Bars of "Swiss Hymn" SP195   Jeremias Gotthelf SP196

Types Similar to 1952, Dated "1954"
Views: 10c+10c, Neuchatel lake. 20c+10c, Maggia river. 30c+10c, Cascade, Taubenloch gorge. 40c+10c, Sils lake.

1954, June 1   **Engr.**   *Perf. 11½*
B232 SP195   5c + 5c dk bl
    grn   .25   .75

Photo.
B233 SP192 10c + 10c blue
    grn   .25   .50
B234 SP192 20c + 10c deep
    plum   .35   .50
B235 SP192 30c + 10c dk
    brown   2.00   6.75

B236 SP192 40c + 10c dp
    blue   2.25   7.25
   Nos. B232-B236 (5)   5.10   15.75
   Set, never hinged   10.00

The surtax was used to aid vocational training and home nursing.
No. B232 commemorates the centenary of the death of Alberik Zwyssig, composer of the "Swiss Hymn."

Types Similar to 1952, Dated "1954"
Insects: 10c+10c, Garden tiger. 20c+10c, Bumble bee. 30c+10c, Ascalaphus. 40c+10c, Swallow-tail.

1954, Dec. 1   **Engr.**
B237 SP196   5c + 5c dk red
    brn   .20   .30

Photo.
B238 SP194 10c + 10c multi   .20   .30
B239 SP194 20c + 10c multi   .35   .50
B240 SP194 30c + 10c rose
    vio, brn &
    yel   2.00   6.75
B241 SP194 40c + 10c multi   2.25   7.25
   Nos. B237-B241 (5)   5.00   15.10
   Set, never hinged   11.00

Type Similar to 1952, Dated "1955," and

Federal Institute of Technology, Zurich — SP197

Views: 10c+10c, Saane river. 20c+10c, Lake of Aegeri. 30c+10c, Grappelen Lake. 40c+10c, Lake of Bienne.

1955, June 1   **Engr.**   *Perf. 11½*
B242 SP197   5c + 5c gray   .20   .75

Photo.
B243 SP192 10c + 10c dp
    green   .25   .50
B244 SP192 20c + 10c rose
    brn   .35   .50
B245 SP192 30c + 10c brown   2.00   6.00
B246 SP192 40c + 10c dp
    blue   2.25   7.50
   Nos. B242-B246 (5)   5.05   15.25
   Set, never hinged   11.50

The surtax aided mountain dwellers.
No. B242 for the centenary of the Federal Institute of Technology in Zurich.

Charles Pictet de Rochemont SP198   Peacock Butterfly SP199

Insects: 20c+10c, Great Horntail. 30c+10c, Yellow Bear moth. 40c+10c, Apollo butterfly.

1955, Dec. 1   **Engr.**   **Unwmk.**
B247 SP198   5c + 5c brn car   .20   .30

Photo.
Insects in Natural Colors
B248 SP199 10c + 10c yel grn   .20   .30
B249 SP199 20c + 10c red   .20   .50
B250 SP199 30c + 10c dk
    ocher   2.50   4.75
B251 SP199 40c + 10c ultra   2.25   5.75
   Nos. B247-B251 (5)   5.35   11.60
   Set, never hinged   11.50

Types Similar to 1952, Dated "1956", and

"Woman's Work" — SP200

Designs: 10c+10c, Rhone at St. Maurice. 20c+10c, Katzensee. 30c+10c, Rhine at Trin. 40c+10c, Lake Wallen.

1956, June 1   **Engr.**   *Perf. 11½*
B252 SP200   5c + 5c turq bl   .20   1.00

Photo.

B253	SP192	10c + 10c green	.25	.50
B254	SP192	20c + 10c brn car	.25	.75
B255	SP192	30c + 10c brown	2.00	4.75
B256	SP192	40c + 10c ultra	1.75	5.75
		Nos. B252-B256 (5)	4.45	12.75
		Set, never hinged	10.00	

The surtax was for the National Day Collection, the National Library and Academy of Arts and Letters. No. B252 was issued in honor of Swiss women.

Carlo Maderno
SP201

Burnet Moth
SP202

Insects: 20c+10c, Purple Emperor. 30c+10c, Blue ground beetle. 40c+10c, Cabbage butterfly.

1956, Dec. 1   Engr.   Perf. 11½

B257	SP201	5c + 5c brn car	.20	.30

Photo.

Granite Paper

B258	SP202	10c + 10c grn, dk grn & car rose	.20	.30
B259	SP202	20c + 10c multi	.20	.30
B260	SP202	30c + 10c yel & dp bl	1.40	4.50
B261	SP202	40c + 10c lt ultra, pale yel & sep	1.40	5.00
		Nos. B257-B261 (5)	3.40	10.40
		Set, never hinged	7.50	

Red Cross and Swiss Emblems
SP203

"Charity" — SP204

Engraved and Photogravure

1957, June 1   Unwmk.   Perf. 11½

B262	SP203	5c + 5c gray & red	.20	.55

Photo.

Granite Paper

Cross in Deep Carmine

B263	SP204	10c + 10c brt grn & gray	.20	.30
B264	SP204	20c + 10c red & bl gray	.25	.30
B265	SP204	30c + 10c brn & vio gray	1.75	4.50
B266	SP204	40c + 10c brt brl & bis	1.90	5.75
		Nos. B262-B266 (5)	4.30	11.40
		Set, never hinged	10.00	

The surtax went to the Red Cross for the needs of the sick and to combat cancer.

Leonhard Euler — SP205

Clouded Yellow — SP206

Insects: 20c+10c, Magpie moth. 30c+10c, Rose Chafer. 40c+10c, Red Underwing.

1957, Nov. 30   Engr.   Perf. 11½

B267	SP205	5c + 5c brn car	.20	.30

Photo.

Granite Paper

B268	SP206	10c + 10c multi	.20	.30
B269	SP206	20c + 10c lil rose, blk & yel	.20	.50

B270	SP206	30c + 10c rose brn, ind & brt grn	1.40	4.50
B271	SP206	40c + 10c multi	1.40	3.50
		Nos. B267-B271 (5)	3.40	9.10
		Set, never hinged	7.50	

> **Catalogue values for unused stamps in this section, from this point to the end of the section, are for Never Hinged items.**

Mother and Child — SP207

Fluorite — SP208

Designs: 20c+10c, Ammonite. 30c+10c, Garnet. 40c+10c, Rock Crystal.

Perf. 11½

1958, May 31   Unwmk.   Engr.

B272	SP207	5c + 5c brn car	.40	.40

Photo.

Granite Paper

B273	SP208	10c + 10c multi	.55	.55
B274	SP208	20c + 10c blk, red & ol bis	.75	.75
B275	SP208	30c + 10c blk, dl yel & mag	3.25	5.25
B276	SP208	40c + 10c blk, chlky bl & sl bl	3.25	5.00
		Nos. B272-B276 (5)	8.20	11.95

The surtax was for needy mothers.
See #B283-B286, B292-B295, B304-B307.

Albrecht von Haller — SP209

Pansy — SP210

Flowers: 20c+10c, China aster. 30c+10c, Morning glory. 40c+10c, Christmas rose.

1958, Dec. 1   Engr.   Perf. 11½

B277	SP209	5c + 5c brn car	.25	.30

Photo.

Granite Paper

B278	SP210	10c + 10c grn, yel & brn	.25	.30
B279	SP210	20c + 10c multi	.55	.30
B280	SP210	30c + 10c multi	2.00	3.50
B281	SP210	40c + 10c dk bl, yel & bis	2.00	3.00
		Nos. B277-B281 (5)	5.05	7.90

See Nos. B287-B291.

Mineral Type of 1958 and

Globe and Swiss Flags — SP211

Designs: 10c+10c, Agate. 20c+10c, Tourmaline. 30c+10c, Amethyst. 40c+10c, Fossil salamander (andrias).

1959, June 1   Engr.   Perf. 11½

B282	SP211	5c + 5c dl grn & red	.40	.50

Photo.

Granite Paper

B283	SP208	10c + 10c gray, yel grn & ver	.50	.50
B284	SP208	20c + 10c blk, lil rose & bl grn	.65	.50
B285	SP208	30c + 10c blk, lt brn & vio	2.25	3.00

B286	SP208	40c + 10c blk, bl & gray	2.50	3.00
		Nos. B282-B286 (5)	6.30	7.50

Types of 1958

Designs: 5c+5c, Karl Hilty. 10c+10c, Marigold. 20c+10c, Poppy. 30c+10c, Nasturtium. 50c+10c, Sweet pea.

1959, Dec. 1   Engr.   Perf. 11½

B287	SP209	5c + 5c brn car	.20	.25

Photo.

Granite Paper

B288	SP210	10c + 10c dk grn, grn & yel	.30	.25
B289	SP210	20c + 10c mag, red & grn	.50	.25
B290	SP210	30c + 10c multi	2.25	3.00
B291	SP210	50c + 10c multi	2.25	3.00
		Nos. B287-B291 (5)	5.50	6.75

Mineral Type of 1958 and

Owl, T-Square and Hammer — SP212

Designs: 5c+5c, Smoky quartz. 10c+10c, Feldspar. 20c+10c, Gryphaea, fossil. 30c+10c, Azurite.

1960, June 1   Photo.   Perf. 11½

Granite Paper

B292	SP208	5c + 5c blk, bl & ocher	.55	.75
B293	SP208	10c + 10c blk, yel grn & pink	.60	.50
B294	SP208	20c + 10c blk, lil rose & yel	.85	.50
B295	SP208	30c + 10c multi	4.00	3.75

Engr.

B296	SP212	50c + 10c bl & gold	4.75	3.50
		Nos. B292-B296 (5)	10.75	9.00

Souvenir Sheet

Imperf

Typo.

B297		Sheet of 4	40.00	20.00

#B297 contains 4 50c+10c stamps of design SP212 in gold & blue. Size: 84x75mm. Sold for 3fr.

Alexandre Calame
SP213

Dandelion
SP214

Flowers: 20c+10c, Phlox. 30c+10c, Larkspur. 50c+10c, Thorn apple.

1960, Dec. 1   Engr.   Unwmk.

B298	SP213	5c + 5c grnsh bl	.25	.20

Photo.

Granite Paper

B299	SP214	10c + 10c grn, yel & gray	.30	.20
B300	SP214	20c + 10c mag, grn & gray	.45	.20
B301	SP214	30c + 10c org brn, grn & bl	3.50	3.50
B302	SP214	50c + 10c ultra & grn	3.50	3.50
		Nos. B298-B302 (5)	8.00	7.60

See Nos. B308-B312, B329-B333, B339-B343.

Mineral Type of 1958 and

Book of History with Symbols of Time and Eternity — SP215

Designs: 10c+10c, Fluorite. 20c+10c, Petrified fish. 30c+10c, Lazulite. 50c+10c, Petrified fern.

1961, June 1   Engr.   Perf. 11½

B303	SP215	5c + 5c lt blue	.35	.5

Photo.

Granite Paper

B304	SP208	10c + 10c gray, grn & pink	.50	.3
B305	SP208	20c + 10c gray & car rose	.60	.3
B306	SP208	30c + 10c gray, org & grnsh bl	1.60	2.5
B307	SP208	50c + 10c gray, bl & bis	2.25	3.5
		Nos. B303-B307 (5)	5.30	7.2

Types of 1960

Designs: 5c+5c, Jonas Furrer. 10c+10c, Sunflower. 20c+10c, Lily of the valley. 30c+10c, Iris. 50c+10c, Silverweed.

1961, Dec. 1   Engr.   Perf. 11½

B308	SP213	5c + 5c dk blue	.20	.20

Photo.

Granite Paper

B309	SP214	10c + 10c grn, yel & org	.20	.20
B310	SP214	20c + 10c dk red, grn & gray	.30	.20
B311	SP214	30c + 10c multi	1.75	2.00
B312	SP214	50c + 10c dk bl, yel & grn	2.00	2.50
		Nos. B308-B312 (5)	4.45	5.10

Jean Jacques Rousseau
SP216

Half-Thaler, Obwalden, 1732
SP217

Coins: 20c+10c, Ducat, Schwyz, ca. 1653. 30c+10c, "Steer Head" Batzen, Uri, 1659. 50c+10c, Nidwalden Batzen.

Perf. 11½

1962, June 1   Unwmk.   Engr.

B313	SP216	5c + 5c dk blue	.20	.20

Photo.

Granite Paper

B314	SP217	10c + 10c grn & stl bl	.20	.20
B315	SP217	20c + 10c car rose & yel	.50	.50
B316	SP217	30c + 10c org & sl bl	1.25	1.65
B317	SP217	50c + 10c ultra & vio bl	1.25	1.65
		Nos. B313-B317 (5)	3.40	4.20

Apple Blossoms
SP218

Mother and Child
SP219

Designs: 10c+10c, Boy chasing duck. 30c+10c, Girl and sunflowers. 50c+10c, Forsythia. 1fr+20c, Mother and child, facing right.

1962, Dec. 1   Perf. 11½

Granite Paper

B318	SP218	5c + 5c bl gray, pink, grn & yel	.20	.20
B319	SP218	10c + 10c grn, pink & dk grn	.20	.20
B320	SP219	20c + 10c org red, brn, grn & pink	.60	.50
B321	SP218	30c + 10c org, red & yel	1.10	2.00
B322	SP218	50c + 10c dp bl, yel & brn	1.50	2.50
		Nos. B318-B322 (5)	3.60	5.40

Souvenir Sheet

Imperf

B323	SP219	1fr + 20c Sheet of 2	5.25	5.25

50th anniv. of the Pro Juventute (Youth Aid) Foundation. No. B323 sold for 3fr.

Anna Heer, M.D. — SP220

Bandage Roll — SP221

Designs: 20c+10c, Gift parcel. 30c+10c, Plasma bottles. 50c+10c, Red Cross armband.

1963, June 1   Engr.   Perf. 11½
B324 SP220   5c + 5c dk blue   .20   .20

Photo.
Granite Paper
Cross in Red

B325 SP221 10c + 10c lt & dk
                   grn & gray   .20   .20
B326 SP221 20c + 10c rose,
                   gray & blk   .50   .20
B327 SP221 30c + 10c mul-
                   ticolored   1.10 1.50
B328 SP221 50c + 10c bl, gray &
                   blk   1.25 1.50
      Nos. B324-B328 (5)   3.25 3.60

Types of 1960

Designs: 5c+5c, Portrait of a Boy by Albert Anker. 10c+10c, Daisy. 20c+10c, Geranium. 30c+10c, Cornflower. 50c+10c, Carnation.

1963, Nov. 30   Engr.   Perf. 11½
B329 SP213   5c + 5c blue   .20   .30
   a. Booklet pane of 4   3.00

Photo.
B330 SP214 10c + 10c grn,
                   gray & yel   .30 1.25
   a. Booklet pane of 4   4.00
B331 SP214 20c + 10c multi   1.40 2.50
   a. Booklet pane of 4   5.75
B332 SP214 30c + 10c multi   1.40 1.50
B333 SP214 50c + 10c ultra, lil
                   rose & grn   1.75 1.50
      Nos. B329-B333 (5)   5.05 7.05

Nos. B329-B331 were printed on two kinds of paper: I. Fluorescent, with violet fibers. II. Non-fluorescent, the 10c+10c and 20c+10c with mixed red and blue fibers. Nos. B332-B333 exist only on violet-fibered, fluorescent paper. The booklet panes Nos. B329a, B330a and B331a, exist only on non-fluorescent paper.

Johann Georg Bodmer SP222

Copper Coin, Zurich SP223

Coins: 20c+10c, Doppeldicken, Basel. 30c+10c, Silver taler, Geneva. 50c+10c, Gold half florin, Bern.

Violet Fibers, Fluorescent Paper

1964, June 1   Engr.   Perf. 11½
B334 SP222   5c + 5c blue   .20   .20

Photo.
B335 SP223 10c + 10c grn, bis &
                   blk   .20   .20
B336 SP223 20c + 10c rose car,
                   gray & blk   .30   .25
B337 SP223 30c + 10c org, gray
                   & blk   .55   .50

Granite Paper, Red and Blue Fibers
B338 SP223 50c + 10c ultra, yel
                   & brn   .80   .65
      Nos. B334-B338 (5)   2.05 1.80

Fluorescent Paper

Paper of Nos. B334-B425, B427 and B429 is fluorescent and has violet fibers.

Nos. B426, B428 and all semipostals from No. B430 onward are fluorescent but lack violet fibers, unless otherwise noted.

Types of 1960

Designs: 5c+5c, Portrait of a Girl by Albert Anker. 10c+10c, Daffodil. 20c+10c, Rose. 30c+10c, Clover. 50c+10c, Water lily.

1964, Dec. 1   Engr.   Perf. 11½
B339 SP213   5c + 5c grnsh bl   .20   .20

Photo.
B340 SP214 10c + 10c dp grn,
                   yel & org   .20   .20
B341 SP214 20c + 10c dp car,
                   rose & grn   .20   .20
B342 SP214 30c + 10c brn, lil &
                   grn   .55   .55
B343 SP214 50c + 10c multi   .75   .75
      Nos. B339-B343 (5)   1.90 1.90

Type of Regular Issue, 1965
Souvenir Sheet

10c, 20r Seated Helvetia. 20c, 40r Seated Helvetia.

1965, Mar. 8   Photo.   Imperf.
Granite Paper, Nonfluorescent
B344 A153   Sheet of 2   1.50 1.00
   a. 10c grn, pale orange & blk   .75   .50
   b. 20c dark red, yel grn & blk .75   .50

Natl. Postage Stamp Exhib., NABRA, Bern, Aug. 27-Sept. 5, 1965. Sold for 3fr, the net proceeds were used to cover expenses of the exhibition and to promote philately.

Father Theodosius Florentini SP224

The Temptation of Christ SP225

Ceiling Paintings from Church of St. Martin at Zillis, 12th century: 10c+10c, Symbol of evil (goose with fishtail). 20c+10c, Magi on horseback. 30c+10c, Fishermen on Sea of Galilee.

Perf. 11½
1965, June 1   Unwmk.   Engr.
B345 SP224   5c + 5c blue   .20   .20

Photo.
B346 SP225 10c + 10c ol grn,
                   ocher & bl   .20   .20
B347 SP225 20c + 10c dk brn,
                   red & buff   .25   .20
B348 SP225 30c + 10c dk brn,
                   sep & bl   .50   .30
B349 SP225 50c + 10c vio bl, bl
                   & brn   .60   .30
      Nos. B345-B349 (5)   1.75 1.20

See Nos. B355-B359, B365-B369.

Hedgehogs — SP226

Designs: 10c+10c, Alpine marmots. 20c+10c, Red deer. 30c+10c, European badgers. 50c+10c, Varying hares.

1965, Dec. 1   Photo.   Perf. 11½
B350 SP226   5c + 5c multi   .20   .20
B351 SP226 10c + 10c multi   .20   .20
B352 SP226 20c + 10c multi   .20   .20
B353 SP226 30c + 10c multi   .50   .20
B354 SP226 50c + 10c multi   .60   .30
      Nos. B350-B354 (5)   1.70 1.10

See Nos. B360-B364.

Types of 1965

5c+5c, Heinrich Federer (1866-1928), writer. 10c+10c, Joseph's dream. 20c+10c, Joseph on his way. 30c+10c, Virgin and Child fleeing to Egypt. 50c+10c, Angel leading the way. Nos. B356-B359 from ceiling paintings, Church of St. Martin at Zillis.

1966, June 1   Engr.   Perf. 11½
B355 SP224   5c + 5c dp blue   .20   .20

Photo.
B356 SP225 10c + 10c multi   .20   .20
B357 SP225 20c + 10c multi   .25   .24
B358 SP225 30c + 10c multi   .50   .25
B359 SP225 50c + 10c multi   .60   .35
      Nos. B355-B359 (5)   1.75 1.20

Animal Type of 1965

5c+5c, Ermine. 10c+10c, Red squirrel. 20c+10c, Red fox. 30c+10c, Hares. 50c+10c, Two chamois.

1966, Dec. 1   Photo.   Perf. 11½
Animals in Natural Colors
B360 SP226   5c + 5c grnsh bl   .20   .20
B361 SP226 10c + 10c emer   .20   .20
B362 SP226 20c + 10c ver   .20   .20
B363 SP226 30c + 10c brt lemon   .50   .20
B364 SP226 50c + 10c ultra   .60   .35
      Nos. B360-B364 (5)   1.70 1.15

Types of 1965

Designs: 5c+5c, Dr. Theodor Kocher. 10c+10c, Annunciation to the Shepherds. 20c+10c, Jesus and the Samaritan Woman at the Well. 30c+10c, Adoration of the Magi. 50c+10c St. Joseph. (Ceiling paintings, St. Martin at Zillis).

Perf. 11½
1967, June 1   Unwmk.   Engr.
B365 SP224   5c + 5c blue   .20   .20

Photo.
B366 SP225 10c + 10c multi   .20   .20
B367 SP225 20c + 10c multi   .25   .20
B368 SP225 30c + 10c multi   .50   .20
B369 SP225 50c + 10c multi   .60   .35
      Nos. B365-B369 (5)   1.75 1.15

Roe Deer — SP227

Hunter, Month of May — SP228

Designs: 20c+10c, Pine marten. 30c+10c, Alpine ibex. 50c+20c, Otter.

1967, Dec. 1   Photo.   Perf. 11½
Animals in Natural Colors
B370 SP227 10c + 10c yel grn   .20   .20
B371 SP227 20c + 10c dp car   .30   .20
B372 SP227 30c + 10c ol bis   .50   .20
B373 SP227 50c + 20c ultra   .75   .50
      Nos. B370-B373 (4)   1.75 1.15

1968, May 30   Photo.   Perf. 11½

Designs from Rose Window, Lausanne Cathedral: 20c+10c, Leo. 30c+10c, Libra. 50c+20c, Pisces.

B374 SP228 10c + 10c multi   .20   .20
B375 SP228 20c + 10c multi   .25   .20
B376 SP228 30c + 10c multi   .50   .30
B377 SP228 50c + 20c multi   .70   .70
      Nos. B374-B377 (4)   1.65 1.40

Capercaillie SP229

St. Francis SP230

Birds: 20c+10c, Bullfinch. 30c+10c, Woodchat shrike. 50c+20c, Firecrest.

1968, Nov. 28   Photo.   Perf. 11½
Birds in Natural Colors
B378 SP229 10c + 10c dull yel   .20   .20
B379 SP229 20c + 10c olive grn   .25   .20
B380 SP229 30c + 10c lilac rose   .40   .20
B381 SP229 50c + 20c dp violet   .70   .50
      Nos. B378-B381 (4)   1.55 1.10

See Nos. B386-B389.

1969, May 29   Photo.   Perf. 11½

Designs: 10c+10c, St. Francis Preaching to the Birds, Königsfelden Convent Church. 20c+10c, Israelites Drinking from Spring of Moses, Berne Cathedral. 30c+10c, St. Christopher, Laufelfinger Church (now Basel Museum). 50c+20c, Virgin and Child, Chapel at Grapplang (now National Museum).

B382 SP230 10c + 10c multi   .20   .20
B383 SP230 20c + 10c multi   .25   .20
B384 SP230 30c + 10c multi   .50   .25
B385 SP230 50c + 20c multi   .70   .45
      Nos. B382-B385 (4)   1.65 1.10

Bird Type of 1968

Birds: 10c+10c, European goldfinch. 20c+10c, Golden oriole. 30c+10c, Wall creeper. 50c+20c, Eurasian jay.

1969, Dec. 1   Photo.   Perf. 11½
Birds in Natural Colors
B386 SP229 10c + 10c gray   .20   .20
B387 SP229 20c + 10c green   .20   .20
B388 SP229 30c + 10c plum   .40   .25
B389 SP229 50c + 20c ultra   .70   .55
      Nos. B386-B389 (4)   1.50 1.20

Sailor, by Gian Casty, Gellert Schoolhouse, Basel SP231

Blue Titmice SP232

Contemporary Stained Glass Windows: 20c+10c, Abstract composition, by Celestino Piatti. 30c+10c, Bull (Assyrian god Marduk), by Hans Stocker. 50c+20c, Man and Woman, by Max Hunziker and Karl Ganz.

1970, May 29   Photo.   Perf. 11½
B390 SP231 10c + 10c multi   .20   .20
B391 SP231 20c + 10c multi   .20   .20
B392 SP231 30c + 10c multi   .50   .25
B393 SP231 50c + 20c multi   .70   .50
      Nos. B390-B393 (4)   1.60 1.15

See Nos. B398-B401.

1970, Dec. 1   Photo.   Perf. 11½

Birds: 20c+10c, Hoopoe. 30c+10c, Greater spotted woodpecker. 50c+20c, Crested grebes.

Birds in Natural Colors
B394 SP232 10c + 10c orange   .20   .20
B395 SP232 20c + 10c emerald   .25   .20
B396 SP232 30c + 10c brt rose   .50   .20
B397 SP232 50c + 20c blue   .80   .75
      Nos. B394-B397 (4)   1.75 1.35

See Nos. B402-B405.

Art Type of 1970

Contemporary Stained Glass Windows: 10c+10c, "Composition," by Jean-François Comment. 20c+10c, Cock, by Jean Prahin. 30c+10c, Fox, by Kurt Volk. 50c+20c, "Composition," by Bernard Schorderet.

1971, May 27   Photo.   Perf. 11½
B398 SP231 10c + 10c multi   .20   .20
B399 SP231 20c + 10c multi   .20   .20
B400 SP231 30c + 10c multi   .40   .25
B401 SP231 50c + 20c multi   .70   .45
      Nos. B398-B401 (4)   1.50 1.10

Bird Type of 1970

Birds: 10c+10c, European redstarts. 20c+10c, White-spotted bluethroats. 30c+10c, Peregrine falcon. 40c+20c, Mallards.

1971, Dec. 1
B402 SP232 10c + 10c multi   .20   .20
B403 SP232 20c + 10c multi   .20   .20
B404 SP232 30c + 10c multi   .50   .20
B405 SP232 40c + 20c multi   .75   .60
      Nos. B402-B405 (4)   1.65 1.20

Harpoon Heads, Late Stone Age SP233

McGredy's Sunset SP234

Archaeological Treasures: 20c+10c, Bronze hydria, Hallstadt period. 30c+10c, Gold bust of Emperor Marcus Aurelius, Roman period. 40c+20c, Horseback rider (decorative disk), early Middle Ages.

1972, June 1

B406	SP233 10c + 10c multi		.20	.20
B407	SP233 20c + 10c multi		.35	.20
B408	SP233 30c + 10c multi		.50	.20
B409	SP233 40c + 20c multi		1.25	.70
	Nos. B406-B409 (4)		2.30	1.30

1972, Dec. 1   Photo.   Perf. 11½

Famous Roses: 20c+10c, Miracle. 30c+10c, Papa Meilland. 40c+20c, Madame Dimitriu.

B410	SP234 10c + 10c multi		.25	.20
B411	SP234 20c + 10c multi		.30	.20
B412	SP234 30c + 10c multi		.50	.20
B413	SP234 40c + 20c multi		1.25	1.10
	Nos. B410-B413 (4)		2.30	1.70

Rauraric (Gallic) Jug — SP235

Chestnut — SP236

Archeologic Finds: 30c+10c, Bronze head of a Gaul. 40c+20c, Alemannic dress fasteners (fish), 6th century. 60c+20c, Gold bowl, 6th century B.C.

1973, May 29   Photo.   Perf. 11½

B414	SP235 15c + 5c multi		.20	.20
B415	SP235 15c + 10c multi		.50	.20
B416	SP235 40c + 20c multi		1.00	.60
B417	SP235 60c + 20c multi		1.25	.85
	Nos. B414-B417 (4)		2.95	1.85
	See Nos. B422-B425.			

1973, Nov. 29   Photo.   Perf. 11½

Fruits of the Forest: 30c+10c, Sweet cherries. 40c+20c, Blackberries. 60c+20c, Blueberries.

B418	SP236 15c + 5c multi		.20	.20
B419	SP236 30c + 10c multi		.20	.20
B420	SP236 40c + 20c multi		.75	.60
B421	SP236 60c + 20c multi		1.25	.70
	Nos. B418-B421 (4)		2.40	1.70

Archaeological Type of 1973

Archaeological Finds: 15c+5c, Polychrome glass bowl. 30c+10c, Bull's head. 40c+20c, Gold fibula. 60c+20c, Ceramic bird.

1974, May 30   Photo.   Perf. 11½

B422	SP235 15c + 5c multi		.20	.20
B423	SP235 30c + 10c multi		.50	.30
B424	SP235 40c + 20c multi		.90	.55
B425	SP235 60c + 20c multi		1.25	.70
	Nos. B422-B425 (4)		2.85	1.75

Laurel — SP237

Gold Fibula, 6th Century — SP238

Designs: 30c+20c, Belladonna. 50c+20c, Laburnum. 60c+25c, Mistletoe.

1974, Nov. 29   Photo.   Perf. 11½

B426	SP237 15c + 10c multi		.20	.20
B427	SP237 30c + 20c multi		.50	.30
B428	SP237 50c + 20c multi		.80	.60
B429	SP237 60c + 25c multi		1.10	.80
	Nos. B426-B429 (4)		2.60	1.80

1975, May 30   Photo.   Perf. 11½

Archaeological Treasures: 30c+20c, Bronze head of Bacchus, 2nd century. 50c+20c, Bronze daggers, 1800-1600 B.C. 60c+25c, Colored glass bottle, 1st century.

B430	SP238 15c + 10c multi		.35	.20
B431	SP238 30c + 20c multi		.60	.25
B432	SP238 50c + 20c multi		1.00	.70
B433	SP238 60c + 25c multi		1.10	.75
	Nos. B430-B433 (4)		3.05	1.90

Mail Bucket SP239

Hepatica SP240

Forest Plants: 30c+20c, Mountain ash berries. 50c+20c, Yellow nettle. 60c+25c, Sycamore maple.

1975, Nov. 27   Photo.   Perf. 11½

B434	SP239 10c + 5c multi		.20	.20
B435	SP240 15c + 10c multi		.20	.20
B436	SP240 30c + 20c multi		.50	.20
B437	SP240 50c + 20c multi		.80	.65
B438	SP240 60c + 25c multi		1.00	.75
	Nos. B434-B438 (5)		2.70	2.10
	See Nos. B443-B446.			

Castles SP241

1976, May 28   Photo.   Perf. 11½

B439	SP241 20c + 10 Kyburg		.40	.20
B440	SP241 40c + 20 Grandson		.75	.30
B441	SP241 50c + 20 Murten		.75	.30
B442	SP241 80c + 40 Bellinzona		2.25	.85
	Nos. B439-B442 (4)		4.15	1.65

See #B447-B450, B455-B458, B463-B466.

Plant Type of 1975

Medicinal Forest Plants: 20c+10c, Barberry. No. B444, Black elder. No. B445, Linden. 80+40c, Pulmonaria.

1976, Nov. 29   Photo.   Perf. 11½

B443	SP240 20c + 10c multi		.20	.20
B444	SP240 40c + 20c lil & multi		.55	.20
B445	SP240 40c + 20c terra cotta & multi		.55	.20
B446	SP240 80c + 40c multi		1.25	.80
	Nos. B443-B446 (4)		2.55	1.40

Castle Type of 1976

1977, May 26   Photo.   Perf. 11½

B447	SP241 20c + 10c Aigle		.40	.25
B448	SP241 40c + 20c Pratteln		.60	.35
B449	SP241 70c + 30c Sargans		1.25	.90
B450	SP241 80c + 40c Hallwil		1.50	1.00
	Nos. B447-B450 (4)		3.75	2.50

Wild Rose — SP242

Communal Arms — SP243

Designs: Roses.

1977, Nov. 28   Photo.   Perf. 11½

B451	SP242 20c + 10c multi		.25	.20
B452	SP242 40c + 20c multi		.60	.20
B453	SP242 70c + 30c multi		1.00	.80
B454	SP242 80c + 40c multi		1.25	1.00
	Nos. B451-B454 (4)		3.10	2.20
	See Nos. B492-B496.			

Castle Type of 1976

1978, May 26   Photo.   Perf. 11½

B455	SP241 20c + 10c Hagenwil		.30	.30
B456	SP241 40c + 20c Burgdorf		.60	.60
B457	SP241 70c + 30c Tarasp		1.25	1.25
B458	SP241 80c + 40c Chillon		1.50	1.50
	Nos. B455-B458 (4)		3.65	3.65

1978, Nov. 28   Photo.   Perf. 11½

B459	SP243 20c + 10c Aarburg		.25	.20
B460	SP243 40c + 20c Gruyeres		.60	.20
B461	SP243 70c + 30c Castasegna		1.00	1.00
B462	SP243 80c + 40c Wangen an der Aare		1.50	1.25
	Nos. B459-B462 (4)		3.35	2.70

See #B467-B470, B475-B478, B484-B487.

Castle Type of 1976

1979, May 25   Photo.   Perf. 11½

B463	SP241 20c + 10c Oron		.30	.30
B464	SP241 40c + 20c Spiez		.60	.45
B465	SP241 70c + 40c Porrentruy		1.10	1.00
B466	SP241 80c + 40c Rapperswil		1.50	1.50
	Nos. B463-B466 (4)		3.50	3.25

Arms Type of 1978

1979, Nov. 28   Photo.   Perf. 11

B467	SP243 20c + 10c Cadro		.20	.20
B468	SP243 40c + 20c Rute		.60	.25
B469	SP243 70c + 30c Schwamendingen		1.00	.85
B470	SP243 80c + 40c Perroy		1.50	1.10
	Nos. B467-B470 (4)		3.30	2.40

Masons' and Carpenters' Sign — SP244

1980, May 29   Photo.   Perf. 11½

B471	SP244 20c + 10c shown		.30	.30
B472	SP244 40c + 20c Barber		.45	.30
B473	SP244 70c + 30c Hat maker		1.00	1.00
B474	SP244 80c + 40c Baker		1.25	1.25
	Nos. B471-B474 (4)		3.00	2.85

Arms Type of 1978

1980, Nov. 26   Photo.   Perf. 11½

B475	SP243 20c + 10c Cortaillod		.20	.20
B476	SP243 40c + 20c Sierre		.55	.25
B477	SP243 70c + 30c Scuol		1.00	.90
B478	SP243 80c + 40c Wolfenschiessen		1.25	.95
	Nos. B475-B478 (4)		3.00	2.30

Icarus in Flight SP245

1981, Mar. 9   Photo.

B479	SP245 2fr + 1fr multi		3.00	3.00

Swissair, 50th Anniversary. Surtax was for Pro Aero Foundation Issued in sheet of 8.

Post Office Sign, Aarburg, 1685 — SP246

Post Office Signs (c. 1849).

1981, May 4   Photo.

B480	SP246 20c + 10c shown		.30	.30
B481	SP246 40c + 20c Fribourg		.60	.50
B482	SP246 70c + 30c Gordola		1.10	1.10
B483	SP246 80c + 40c Splugen		1.25	1.25
	Nos. B480-B483 (4)		3.25	3.15

Arms Type of 1978

1981, Nov. 26   Photo.   Perf. 11½

B484	SP243 20c + 10c Uffikon		.30	.20
B485	SP243 40c + 20c Torre		.60	.60
B486	SP243 70c + 30c Benken		1.00	.60
B487	SP243 80c + 40c Preverenges		1.10	.75
	Nos. B484-B487 (4)		3.00	1.85

Sonne Inn Sign, Willisau SP247

1982, May 27   Photo.   Perf. 11½

B488	SP247 20c + 10c shown		.30	.20
B489	SP247 40c + 20c A L'Onde, St. Saphorin		.55	.30
B490	SP247 70c + 30c Three Kings, Rheinfelden		.90	.55
B491	SP247 80c + 40c Krone, Winterthur		1.25	.70
	Nos. B488-B491 (4)		3.00	1.75
	See Nos. B497-B500.			

Rose Type of 1977

Designs: 10c+10c, Letter balance. 20c+10c, La Belle Portugaise. 40c+20c, Hugh Dickson. 70c+30c, Mermaid. 80c+40c, Madame Caroline.

1982, Nov. 25   Photo.

B492	SP242 10c + 10c multi		.25	.20
B493	SP242 20c + 10c multi		.40	.20
B494	SP242 40c + 20c multi		.70	.30
B495	SP242 70c + 30c multi		1.25	.80
B496	SP242 80c + 40c multi		1.40	1.10
	Nos. B492-B496 (5)		4.00	2.60

Inn Sign Type of 1982

1983, May 26   Photo.

B497	SP247 20c + 10c Lion Inn, Heimiswil, 1669		.40	.30
B498	SP247 40c + 20c Cross Hotel, Sachseln, 1489		.75	.50
B499	SP247 70c + 30c Tankard Inn, 1830		1.25	.80
B500	SP247 80c + 40c Au Cavalier Inn, Vaud		1.40	1.00
	Nos. B497-B500 (4)		3.80	2.60

Antique Toys — SP248

1983, Nov. 24

B501	SP248 20c + 10c Kitchen stove, 1850		.35	.20
B502	SP248 40c + 20c Rocking horse, 1826		.70	.35
B503	SP248 70c + 30c Doll, 1870		1.10	.55
B504	SP248 80c + 40c Steam locomotive, 1900		1.40	.70
	Nos. B501-B504 (4)		3.55	1.80

Ceramic Tiled Stoves — SP249

1984, May 24   Photo.   Perf. 11½

B505	SP249 35c + 15c 1566		.55	.40
B506	SP249 50c + 20c 1646		.70	.50
B507	SP249 70c + 30c 1768		1.00	.70
B508	SP249 80c + 40c 18th cent.		1.25	.90
	Nos. B505-B508 (4)		3.50	2.50

Children's Stories SP250

1984, Nov. 26   Photo.

B509	SP250 35c + 15c Heidi		.60	.40
B510	SP250 50c + 20c Pinocchio		.75	.50
B511	SP250 70c + 30c Pippi Longstocking		1.10	.70
B512	SP260 80c + 40c Max and Moritz		1.40	.90
	Nos. B509-B512 (4)		3.85	2.50

Musical
Museum
Exhibits
SP251

1985, May 28 Photo. Perf. 11½
B513 SP251 25c + 10c Music
box, 1895 .30 .20
B514 SP251 35c + 15c Rattle
box, 18th cent. .50 .20
B515 SP251 50c + 20c Em-
menthal neck-
ed zither, 1828 .70 .20
B516 SP251 70c + 30c Drum,
1571 1.00 .30
B517 SP251 80c + 40c Diatonic
accordion,
20th cent. 1.25 .35
Nos. B513-B517 (5) 3.75 1.25
Surtax for Swiss cultural programs.

Hansel and
Gretel
SP252

Fairy tales by Jakob (1785-1863) and Wilhelm (1786-1859) Grimm.

1985, Nov. 26 Photo.
B518 SP252 35c + 15c shown .55 .20
B519 SP252 50c + 20c Snow
White .80 .20
B520 SP252 80c + 40c Little Red
Riding Hood 1.25 .35
B521 SP252 90c + 40c Cinderel-
la 1.40 .40
Nos. B518-B521 (4) 4.00 1.15
Surtax for Pro Juventute Foundation and
youth welfare orgs.

Man, Vitality
and
Movement
SP253

1986, Feb. 11 Photo. Perf. 12
B522 SP253 50c + 20c multi .90 .25
Surtax for Natl. Sports Federation and cul-
tural programs.

Paintings in
Natl. Museums
SP254

Swiss art: 35c+15c, Bridge in the Sun,
1907, by Giovanni Giacometti (1868-1933).
50c+20c, The Violet Hat, 1907, by Cuno Amiet
(1868-1961). 80c+40c, After the Funeral,
1905, by Max Buri (1868-1915). 90c+40c, Still
Life, 1914, by Felix Valloton (1865-1925).

1986, Apr. 22 Photo. Perf. 11½
B523 SP254 35c + 15c multi .50 .20
B524 SP254 50c + 20c multi .70 .25
B525 SP254 80c + 40c multi 1.25 .40
B526 SP254 90c + 40c multi 1.40 .45
Nos. B523-B526 (4) 3.85 1.30
Surtax for Natl. Day Collection &monuments
preservation, social & cultural organizations.

Children's
Toys — SP255

1986, Nov. 25 Photo.
B527 SP255 35c + 15c Teddy
bear .60 .20
B528 SP255 50c + 20c Top .90 .30
B529 SP255 80c + 40c Steam-
roller 1.50 .50
B530 SP255 90c + 40c Doll 1.60 .55
Nos. B527-B530 (4) 4.60 1.55
Surtax was for youth welfare organizations
and the Pro Juventute Foundation.

Antique
Furniture
SP256

Designs: 35c+15c, Saane Valley wall cabi-
net, 1764, Vieux Pays d'Enhaut Museum,
Chateau d'Oex. 50c+20c, Raised chest, 16th
cent., Rhaetian Museum, Chur. 80c+40c,
Ticino canton cradle, 1782, Valmaggia
Museum, Cevio. 90c+40c, Appenzell region
wardrobe, 1698, St. Gallen Historical
Museum.

1987, May 26 Photo.
B531 SP256 35c + 15c multi .55 .25
B532 SP256 50c + 20c multi .80 .35
B533 SP256 80c + 40c multi 1.40 .60
B534 SP256 90c + 40c multi 1.50 .60
Nos. B531-B534 (4) 4.25 1.80
Surtax for Red Cross and patriotic funds.

**No. 786 Surcharged with Clasped
Hands and "7.9.87" in Red
Photo. & Engr.**
1987, Sept. 7 Perf. 13½x13
B535 A349 50c + 50c multi 1.25 .45
Surtaxed to benefit flood victims.

Christmas
SP257

Child
Development
SP258

1987, Nov. 24 Photo. Perf. 11½
B536 SP257 25c +10c shown .50 .20
B537 SP258 35c + 15c shown .70 .20
B538 SP258 50c + 20c Boy, build-
ing blocks .95 .30
B539 SP258 80c +40c Boy, girl
in sandbox 1.60 .55
B540 SP258 90c + 40c Father,
child 1.75 .60
Nos. B536-B540 (5) 5.50 1.85
Surtax for national youth welfare projects
and the Pro Juventute Foundation.
See Nos. B555-B558.

Junkers JU-
52, 1939, and
the
Matterhorn
SP259

1988, Mar. 8 Photo.
B541 SP259 140c +60c multi 2.50 2.50
Pro Aero Foundation, Zurich, 50th Anniv.
Issued in sheets of 8.

SP260

SP261

Minnesingers.

1988, May 24 Photo.
B542 SP260 35c +15c Count Ru-
dolf of Neu-
chatel .60 .25
B543 SP260 50c +20c Rudolf
von Rotenburg .85 .35
B544 SP260 80c +40c Master
Johannes
Hadlaub 1.50 .60
B545 SP260 90c +40c The
Hardegger 1.60 .65
Nos. B542-B545 (4) 4.55 1.85
700 Years of art and culture.

1988, Nov. 25 Perf. 11½
B546 SP261 35c +15c Reading .65 .20
B547 SP261 50c +20c Music .95 .30
B548 SP261 80c +40c Math 1.65 .55
B549 SP261 90c +40c Art 1.75 .60
Nos. B546-B549 (4) 5.00 1.65
Child development. Surtax for natl. youth
welfare projects and the Pro Juventute
Foundation.

700 Years of
Art and Culture
SP262

Illuminations in Zurich Central, Bern
Burgher and Lucerne Central libraries: No.
B550, King Friedrich II presenting Bern munic-
ipal charter, 1218, *Bendicht Tschachtlan
Chronicle*, 1470. No. B551, Capt. Adrian von
Bubenberg and troops passing through
Murten town gate, 1476, *Bern Chronicle*, by
Diebold Schilling, 1483. No. B552, Official
messenger of Schwyz before the Council of
Zurich, c. 1440, *Gerold Edlibach Chronicle*,
1485. No. B553, Schilling presenting manu-
script to the mayor and councilmen in the
council chamber, Lucerne, c. 1500, *Diebold
Schilling's Lucerne Chronicle*, 1513.

1989, May 23
B550 SP262 35c +15c multi .65 .20
B551 SP262 50c +20c multi .90 .30
B552 SP262 80c +40c multi 1.50 .50
B553 SP262 90c +40c multi 1.75 .55
Nos. B550-B553 (4) 4.80 1.55
Surtax to benefit women's and cultural
organizations.

Gymnastics
SP263

1989, Aug. 25 Photo. Perf. 11½
B554 SP263 50c +20c multi .80 .30
Surtax to benefit Swiss Natl. Sports Federa-
tion, cultural and social work.

Child Development Type of 1987
1989, Nov. 24
B555 SP258 35c +15c Community work .60 .20
B556 SP258 50c +20c Friendship .85 .25
B557 SP258 80c +40c Vocational
training 1.50 .50
B558 SP258 90c +40c Higher education and re-
search 1.60 .55
Nos. B555-B558 (4) 4.55 1.50
Surtax for natl. youth welfare projects and
the Pro Juventute Foundation.

700 Years of Art
and
Culture — SP264

Street criers: No. B559, Fly swatter and
starch-sprinkler vendor. No. B560, Clock vendor. No. B561, Knife grinder. No. B562, Pine-
wood sellers.

1990, May 22 Photo.
B559 SP264 35c +15c multi .70 .25
B560 SP264 50c +20c multi .95 .30
B561 SP264 80c +40c multi 1.60 .55
B562 SP264 90c +40c multi 1.75 .60
Nos. B559-B562 (4) 5.00 1.70

Souvenir Sheet

Natl. Philatelic Exhibition, Geneva
'90 — SP265

a, Brass badge worn by Geneva Cantonal
post drivers before 1849. b, Place du Bourg-
de-Four and entrance to Rue Etienne-Dumont.
c, Ile Rousseau and Pont des Bergues. d, No.
2L1 on cover.

1990, Sept. 5
B563 SP265 Sheet of 4 4.00 1.40
a.-d. 50c +25c any single 1.00 .35

Child
Development
SP266

1990, Nov. 20
B564 SP266 35c +15c Model
making .70 .25
B565 SP266 50c +20c Youth
groups 1.00 .30
B566 SP266 80c +40c Sports 1.70 .55
B567 SP266 90c +40c Music 1.85 .60
Nos. B564-B567 (4) 5.25 1.70

700 Years of
Art and Culture
SP267

Contemporary paintings by: 50c+20c, Wolf
Barth. 70c+30c, Helmut Federle. 80c+40c,
Matthias Bosshart. 90c+40c, Werner Otto
Leuenberger.

1991, May 14 Photo. Perf. 11½
B568 SP267 50c +20c multi 1.00 .30
B569 SP267 70c +30c multi 1.40 .45
B570 SP267 80c +40c multi 1.75 .55
B571 SP267 90c +40c multi 1.75 .60
Nos. B568-B571 (4) 5.90 1.90

Woodland
Flowers
SP268

50c+25c, Allium ursinum. 70c+30c, Geranium sylvaticum. 80c+40c, Campanula trache-
lium. 90c+40c, Hieracium murorum.

1991, Nov. 26
B572 SP268 50c +25c multi 1.00 .40
B573 SP268 70c +30c multi 1.40 .45
B574 SP268 80c +40c multi 1.60 .55
B575 SP268 90c +40c multi 1.80 .60
Nos. B572-B575 (4) 5.80 2.00
Surtax for youth and family welfare projects
and the Pro Juventute Foundation.

Swiss Folk Art — SP269

50c + 20c, Earthenware plate, Heimberg, 18th cent. 70c + 40c, Paper cutout by Johann Jakob Hauswirth (1809-1871). 80c + 40c, Cream spoon, Gruyeres. 90c + 40c, Embroidered silk carnation, Grisons.

1992, May 22   Photo.   Perf. 11½

B576	SP269	50c +20c multi	.95	.30
B577	SP269	70c +30c multi	1.25	.45
B578	SP269	80c +40c multi	1.60	.50
B579	SP269	90c +40c multi	1.75	.60
		Nos. B576-B579 (4)	5.55	1.85

Surtax for preservation of cultural heritage.

Unfinished Work, by Jean Tinguely — SP270

1992, Aug. 25   Photo.   Perf. 12

B580	SP270	50c +20c blue & black	1.10	.40

Surtax for Natl. Sports Federation and sports-related social and cultural activities.

Wood Puppet of Melchior, 18th Cent. — SP271

Trees — SP272

1992, Nov. 24   Photo.   Perf. 11½

B581	SP271	50c +25c multi	1.00	.35
B582	SP272	50c +25c Copper beech	1.00	.35
B583	SP272	70c +30c Norway maple	1.40	.50
B584	SP272	80c +40c Common oak	1.60	.55
B585	SP272	90c +40c Spruce	1.75	.60
		Nos. B581-B585 (5)	6.75	2.35

Christmas. Surtax for youth and family welfare projects and the Pro Juventute Foundation.

Swiss Folk Art — SP273

Designs: No. B586, Appenzell dairyman's earring. No. B587, Fluhli glassware. 80c + 40c, Painting of cattle drive, by Sylvestre Pidoux. 100c + 40c, Straw hat ornament.

1993, May 5   Photo.   Perf. 11½

B586	SP273	50c +30c multi	1.25	.40
B587	SP273	60c +30c multi	1.25	.40
B588	SP273	80c +40c multi	1.10	.35
B589	SP273	100c +40c multi	2.00	.70
		Nos. B586-B589 (4)	5.60	1.85

Architectural Heritage Type of 1960

Design: 80c+20c, Kapell Bridge and Water Tower, Lucerne.

1993, Sept. 7   Litho.   Perf. 13½x13

B590	A145	80c +20c orange & red	1.40	.45

Surtax for reconstruction of Kapell Bridge with any excess for preservation of architectural heritage.

SP274   SP275

Woodland plants.

1993, Nov. 23   Photo.   Perf. 11½

B591	SP274	60c +30c Christmas wreath	1.25	.40
B592	SP274	60c +30c Male fern	1.25	.40
B593	SP274	80c +40c Guelder rose	1.60	.55
B594	SP274	100c +50c Mnium punctatum	2.00	.65
		Nos. B591-B594 (4)	6.10	2.00

Christmas. Surtax for youth and family welfare projects and the Pro Juventute Foundation.

1994, May 17   Photo.   Perf. 11½

Swiss Folk Art: No. B595, Weight-driven Neuchatel clock. No. B598, Linen-embroidered pomegranate. 80c+40c, Biscuit mold for Krafli. 100c+40c, Paper bird mobile for child's cradle.

B595	SP275	60c +30c multi	1.25	.40
B596	SP275	60c +30c multi	1.25	.40
B597	SP275	80c +40c multi	1.60	.55
B598	SP275	100c +40c multi	1.90	.65
		Nos. B595-B598 (4)	6.00	2.00

Christmas SP276

Mushrooms SP277

Designs: No. B600, Wood blewit. 80c+40c, Red boletus. 100c+50c, Shaggy pholiota.

1994, Nov. 28   Litho.   Perf. 11½

B599	SP276	60c +30c multi	1.10	.45
B600	SP277	60c +30c multi	1.10	.45
B601	SP277	80c +40c multi	1.40	.60
B602	SP277	100c +50c multi	1.75	.80
		Nos. B599-B602 (4)	5.35	2.30

Surtax for youth and family welfare projects and the Pro Juventute Foundation.

Swiss Folk Art — SP278

Designs: No. B603, Wooden cream pail. No. B604, Straw hat. 80c+40c, Chest lock, c. 1580. 100c+40c, Langnau pottery sugar bowl.

1995, May 16   Photo.   Perf. 11½

B603	SP278	60c +30c multi	1.10	.50
B604	SP278	60c +30c multi	1.10	.50
B605	SP278	80c +40c multi	1.50	.70
		Complete booklet, 10 #B605	15.00	
B606	SP278	100c +40c multi	1.90	.80
		Nos. B603-B606 (4)	5.60	2.50

Surtax for Swiss Pro Patria Foundation and special cultural, social projects.

Souvenir Sheet

Basler Taube '95 Philatelic Exhibition, Basel — SP279

Designs: a, 80c+30c, like Switzerland #3L1. Engraved panorama of Basel, by Matthaus Merian, 17th cent.: b, 60c+30c, Buildings, twin church steeples. c, 100c+50c, Buildings. d, 100c+50c, Buildings, bridge.

1995, May 16   Photo.   Perf. 13x14

B607	SP279	Sheet of 4	7.00	3.00
a.		80c +30c multi	1.25	.60
b.		60c +30c black & blue	1.25	.55
c.-d.		100c +50c any single	2.50	.90

Nos. B607b-B607d are a continuous design.

Christmas SP280

Life In and Around Water — SP281

#B608, Angel from "The Annunciation," by Bartolome. #B609, River trout. 80c+40c, Grey wagtail. 100c+50c, Spotted salamander.

1995, Nov. 28   Photo.   Perf. 11½

B608	SP280	60c +30c multi	1.10	.50
		Complete booklet, 10 #B608	11.00	
B609	SP281	60c +30c multi	1.10	.50
B610	SP281	80c +40c multi	1.40	.65
B611	SP281	100c +50c multi	1.75	.80
		Nos. B608-B611 (4)	5.35	2.45

Surtax for Pro Juventute Foundation.

For Sports SP282

1996, Mar. 12   Photo.   Perf. 11½

B612	SP282	70c +30c multi	1.60	.85
		Complete booklet, 10 #B612	16.00	

SP283

Restorations, projects: No. B613, Magdalena Chapel, Wolfenschiessen. No. B614, Underground mills, Col-des-Roches. 90c+40c, Pfäfers Baroque spa complex. 110c+50c, Roman road over Great St. Bernhard.

1996, May 14   Photo.   Perf. 11½

B613	SP283	70c +35c multi	1.25	.60
B614	SP283	70c +35c multi	1.25	.60
B615	SP283	90c +40c multi	1.75	.75
		Complete booklet, 10 #B615	17.50	
B616	SP283	110c +50c multi	2.10	.90
		Nos. B613-B616 (4)	6.35	2.85

Christmas SP284

Life In and Around Water — SP285

1996, Nov. 26   Photo.   Perf. 11½

B617	SP284	70c +35c Star, constellations	1.25	.55
B618	SP285	70c +35c Grayling	1.25	.55
		Complete booklet, 10 #B618	12.50	
B619	SP285	90c +45c Crayfish	1.60	.70
B620	SP285	110c +55c Otter	1.90	.80
		Nos. B617-B620 (4)	6.00	2.60

SP286

Designs: No. B621, St. Valbert Church, Soubey. No. B622, Culture Mill, Lützelflüh. 90c+40c, Ittingen Charterhouse, Thurgau. 110c+50c, Municipal Building, Onsernone Valley.

1997, May 13   Photo.   Perf. 11½

B621	SP286	70c +35c multi	1.25	1.25
B622	SP286	70c +35c multi	1.25	1.25
B623	SP286	90c +40c multi	1.60	1.60
		Complete booklet, 10 #B623	16.00	
B624	SP286	110c +50c multi	2.00	2.00
		Nos. B621-B624 (4)	6.10	6.10

Christmas SP287

Life In and Around Water — SP288

Designs: No. B625, Mistletoe twig. No. B626, Three-spined stickleback. 90c+45c, Yellow-bellied toad. 110c+55c, Ruff.

1997, Nov. 20   Photo.   Perf. 11½

B625	SP287	70c +35c multi	1.25	1.25
B626	SP288	70c +35c multi	1.25	1.25
		Complete booklet, 10 #B626	12.50	
B627	SP288	90c +45c multi	1.60	1.60
B628	SP288	110c +55c multi	1.90	1.90
		Nos. B625-B628 (4)	6.00	6.00

Surtax for Pro Juventute Foundation.

Pro Patria Stamps, 60th Anniv. SP289

Heritage and landscapes: No. B629, St. Gall Rhine Valley. No. B630, Round Church, Saas Balen. No. B631, Natural forest preserves, Bödmeren. No. B632, St. Gotthard Refuge. 110c +50c, Blacksmiths, Corcelles.

1998, May 12		**Photo.**	**Perf. 11½**	
B629	SP289	70c + 35c multi	1.25	1.25
B630	SP289	70c + 35c multi	1.25	1.25
B631	SP289	90c + 40c multi	1.50	1.50
	Complete booklet, 10 #B631		15.00	
B632	SP289	90c + 40c multi	1.50	1.50
B633	SP289	110c + 50c multi	1.90	1.90
	Nos. B629-B633 (5)		7.40	7.40

Christmas
SP290

Life Near
Water — SP291

No. B634, Bell, holly on ribbon. No. B635, Ramshorn snail. 90c+45c, Great crested grebe. 110c+55c, Pike.

1998, Nov. 25		**Photo.**	**Perf. 11½**	
B634	SP290	70c +35c multi	1.25	1.25
B635	SP291	70c +35c multi	1.25	1.25
B636	SP291	90c +45c multi	1.60	1.60
	Complete booklet, 6 #B634, 4 #B636		16.00	
B637	SP291	110c +55c multi	1.90	1.90
	Nos. B634-B637 (4)		6.00	6.00

Pro
Patria — SP292

Heritage and landscapes: No. B638, Chestnut groves, Malcantone. No. B639, La Sarraz Castle. 90c+40c, Lake Lucerne steamship. 110c+50c, St. Paul's Chapel, Rhäzüns.

1999, May 5		**Litho.**	**Perf. 13½**	
B638	SP292	70c +35c multi	1.40	1.40
B639	SP292	70c +35c multi	1.40	1.40
B640	SP292	90c +40c multi	1.75	1.75
	Complete booklet, 10 #B640		17.50	
B641	SP292	110c +50c multi	2.10	2.10
	Nos. B638-B641 (4)		6.65	6.65

Souvenir Sheet

NABA 2000 Philatelic Exhibition, St.
Gallen — SP293

a, 70c+30c, St. Laurenzen Church spire. b, 20c+10c, Top of town house. c, 90c+30c, Oriel window.
Illustration reduced.

1999, Sept. 9		**Photo.**	**Perf. 11¾**	
		Sheet of 3		
B642	SP293	#a.-c. + label	3.50	3.50
	a.	70c+30c multicolored	1.25	1.25
	b.	20c+10c multicolored	.40	.40
	c.	90c+30c multicolored	1.60	1.60

Christmas
SP294

Nicolo the Clown
From Children's
Book by Verena
Pavoni
SP295

Designs: No. B643, Children, snowman. No. B644, Nicolo, circus tent. 90c+45c, Nicolo and his father. 110c+55c, Nicolo and donkey.

1999, Nov. 23		**Litho.**	**Perf. 13½x13¼**	
B643	SP294	70c +35c multi	1.40	1.40
B644	SP295	70c +35c multi	1.40	1.40
B645	SP295	90c +45c multi	1.75	1.75
	Complete booklet, 6 #B644, 4 #B645		16.00	
B646	SP295	110c +55c multi	2.10	2.10
	Nos. B643-B646 (4)		6.65	6.65

Surtax for Pro Juventute Foundation.

Cities With Pro
Patria
Foundation
Renovation
Projects
SP296

			Perf. 13¼x13½	
2000, May 10			**Litho. & Engr.**	
B647	SP296	70c +35c Näfles	1.25	1.25
B648	SP296	70c +35c Tengia	1.25	1.25
B649	SP296	90c +40c Brugg	1.60	1.60
B650	SP296	90c +40c Carouge	1.60	1.60
	Booklet, 10 #B650		16.00	
	Nos. B647-B650 (4)		5.70	5.70

Souvenir Sheet

NABA 2000 Philatelic Exhibition, St.
Gallen — SP297

Quadrants of stylized No. 5: a, UL. b, UR. c, LL. d, LR.
Illustration reduced.

2000, May 10		**Photo.**	**Perf. 11¾**	
B651	SP297	Sheet of 4	3.75	3.75
	a.	70c+35c multicolored	1.25	1.25
	b.-c.	20c+10c any single	.35	.35
	d.	90c+45c multicolored	1.75	1.75

Christmas
SP298

Illustrations
from Little
Albert, by Albert
Manser
SP299

Designs: No. B652, St. Nicholas and Schmutzli in sleigh. No. B653, Children at fence. No. B654, Little Albert with umbrella. No. B655, Children on sleds.

		Perf. 13¼x13½		
2000, Nov. 21			**Litho.**	
B652	SP298	70c +35c multi	1.25	1.25
B653	SP299	70c +35c multi	1.25	1.25
B654	SP299	90c +45c multi	1.50	1.50
	Booklet, 6 #B653, 4 #B654		13.50	
B655	SP299	90c +45c multi	1.50	1.50
	Nos. B652-B655 (4)		5.50	5.50

Surtax for Pro Juventute Foundation.

Landmarks
SP300

Designs: No. B656, Hauterive Abbey. No. B657, La Chaux-de-Fonds Theater. No. B658, Granary, Rorschach. No. B659, Bishop's Castle, Leuk.

2001, May 9		**Litho.**	**Perf. 13¼x13½**	
B656	SP300	70c +35c multi	1.25	1.25
B657	SP300	70c +35c multi	1.25	1.25
B658	SP300	90c +40c multi	1.50	1.50
B659	SP300	90c +40c multi	1.50	1.50
	Booklet, 10 #B659		15.00	
	Nos. B656-B659 (4)		5.50	5.50

Surtax for Pro Patria Foundation.

Pro Juventute Types of 1999

Art from children's books: No. B660, What's Santa Claus Doing?, by Karin von Oldershausen. No. B661, Leopold the Leopard, from Leopold and the Sun, by Stephan Brülhart. No. B662, Honeybear, from Leopold and the Sun. No. B663, Tom the Monkey, from Leopold and the Sun.

		Perf. 13½x13¼		
2001, Nov. 20			**Litho.**	
B660	SP294	70c +35c multi	1.25	1.25
B661	SP295	70c +35c multi	1.25	1.25
B662	SP295	90c +45c multi	1.60	1.60
	Booklet, 6 #B661, 4 #B662		14.00	
B663	SP295	90c +45c multi	1.60	1.60
	Nos. B660-B663 (4)		5.70	5.70

Surtax for Pro Juventute Foundation.

Mills — SP301

Location: No. B664, Bruzella. No. B665, Oberdorf. No. B666, Büren an der Aare. No. B667, Lussery-Villars.

2002, May 15		**Litho.**	**Perf. 13¼x13½**	
B664	SP301	70c +35c multi	1.40	1.40
B665	SP301	70c +35c multi	1.40	1.40
B666	SP301	90c +40c multi	1.60	1.60
	Booklet, 10 #B666		16.00	
B667	SP301	90c +40c multi	1.60	1.60
	Nos. B664-B667 (4)		6.00	6.00

Surtax for Pro Patria Foundation.

Roses — SP302

Designs: No. B668, Christmas rose (gold background). No. B669, Ingrid Bergman rose (white background). No. B670, Belle Vaudoise rose (orange petals). No. B671, Charmian

---

rose (pink petals). 130c+65c, Frühlingsgold rose.

		Perf. 13¾x13¼		
2002, Nov. 19			**Litho.**	
B668	SP302	70c +35c multi	1.40	1.40
B669	SP302	70c +35c multi	1.40	1.40
B670	SP302	90c +45c multi	1.90	1.90
	Booklet, 6 #B669, 4 #B670		16.00	
B671	SP302	90c +45c multi	1.90	1.90
B672	SP302	130c +65c multi	2.60	2.60
	Nos. B668-B672 (5)		9.20	9.20

Surtax for Pro Juventute Foundation. No. B668 is impregnated with a pine needle, cinnamon and clove scent, and Nos. B669-B672 with a rose scent.

Bridges
SP303

Designs: No. B673, Wynigen Bridge, Burgdorf, 1776. No. B674, Salginatobel Bridge, Schiers, 1929. No. B675, Pont St. Jean, Saint Ursanne, 15th cent. No. B676, Reuss Bridge, Rottenschwil, 1907.

2003, May 8		**Litho.**	**Perf. 13¼x13½**	
B673	SP303	70c +35c multi	1.60	1.60
B674	SP303	70c +35c multi	1.60	1.60
B675	SP303	90c +40c multi	2.00	2.00
	Booklet, 10 #B675		20.00	
B676	SP303	90c +40c multi	2.00	2.00
	Nos. B673-B676 (4)		7.20	7.20

Rights of the
Child — SP304

Children: 70c+35c, Christmas tree, toy tractor, gift. 85c+35c, Playing as storekeeper and shopper. 90c+45c, Skateboarding with dog. 100c+45c, Playing guitar and drums.

		Serpentine Die Cut 10½x11		
2003, Nov. 19			**Litho.**	
		Self-Adhesive		
B677	SP304	70c +35c multi	1.75	1.75
	a.	Block of 4 on translucent backing paper	7.00	
B678	SP304	85c +35c multi	1.90	1.90
	a.	Block of 4 on translucent backing paper	7.60	
B679	SP304	90c +45c multi	2.10	2.10
	a.	Block of 4 on translucent backing paper	8.40	
B680	SP304	100c +45c multi	2.25	2.25
	a.	Block of 4 on translucent backing paper	9.00	
	b.	Nos. B677-B680 on translucent backing paper	8.00	
	c.	Booklet, 6 each #B678, B680	22.50	
	Nos. B677-B680 (4)		8.00	8.00

Nos. B677-B680 each were printed in sheets of 20 stamps with a white paper backing.

AIR POST STAMPS

Nos. 134 and 139
Overprinted in Carmine

1919-20		**Wmk. 183**	**Perf. 11½**	
		Granite Paper		
C1	A25	30c yel brn & pale grn ('20)	110.00	*1,250.*
C2	A25	50c dp & pale grn	32.50	*110.00*
	Set, never hinged		350.00	

Counterfeits of overprint and fraudulent cancellations exist.

Airplane
AP1

Pilot at
Controls of
Airplane
AP2

Biplane
against
Sky — AP3

Allegorical
Figure of
Flight
AP4

Perf. 11½, 12 and Compound
1923-25   **Typo.**

C3	AP1 15c brn red & ap grn	2.25	8.25
C4	AP1 20c grn & lt grn ('25)	.90	6.00
C5	AP1 25c dk bl & bl	7.75	22.50
C6	AP2 35c brn & buff	11.00	42.50
C7	AP2 40c vio & gray vio	14.50	45.00
C8	AP3 45c red & ind	1.60	7.25
C9	AP3 50c blk & red	12.50	17.00

Perf. 11½

C10	AP4 65c gray bl & dp bl ('24)	3.25	16.00
C11	AP4 75c org & brn red ('24)	15.00	55.00
C12	AP4 1fr vio & dp vio ('24)	42.50	32.50
	Nos. C3-C12 (10)	111.25	252.00
	Set, never hinged	275.00	

For surcharges see Nos. C19, C22, C26.

1933-37   **With Grilled Gum**

C4a	AP1 20c grn & lt grn ('37)	.30	.40
C5a	AP1 25c dk bl & bl ('34)	5.00	50.00
C8a	AP3 45c red & indigo ('37)	2.50	52.50
C9a	AP3 50c gray grn & scar ('35)	1.10	1.60
C10a	AP4 65c gray bl & dp bl ('37)	2.75	8.50
C11a	AP4 75c org & brn red ('36)	27.50	175.00
C12a	AP4 1fr vio & deep vio	2.10	3.25
	Nos. C4a-C12a (7)	41.25	291.25
	Set, never hinged	65.00	

See Grilled Gum note after No. 145.

Allegory of
Air
Mail — AP5

Bird
Carrying
Letter
AP6

1929-30   **Granite Paper**

C13	AP5 35c red brn, bis & claret	15.00	42.50
C14	AP5 40c dl grn, yel grn & bl	57.50	82.50
C15	AP6 2fr blk brn & red brn, gray ('30)	85.00	85.00
	Nos. C13-C15 (3)	157.50	210.00
	Set, never hinged	425.00	

1933-35   **With Grilled Gum**

C13a	AP5 35c red brn, bis & cl	5.00	50.00
C14a	AP5 40c dk grn, yel grn & bl	37.50	77.50

C15a	AP6 2fr blk brn & red brn ('35)	7.25	12.00
	Nos. C13a-C15a (3)	49.75	139.50
	Set, never hinged	140.00	

Front View
of Airplane
AP7

1932, Feb. 2   **Granite Paper**

C16	AP7 15c dp grn & lt grn	.55	1.60
C17	AP7 20c dk red & buff	1.10	2.50
C18	AP7 90c dp bl & gray	7.25	30.00
	Nos. C16-C18 (3)	8.90	34.10
	Set, never hinged	22.50	

Intl. Disarmament Conf., Geneva, Feb. 1932.
For surcharges see Nos. C20, C23-C25.

Nos. C3, C10, C16-C18 Surcharged with New Values and Bars in Black or Red

1935-38

C19	AP1 10c on 15c	4.75	32.50
C20	AP1 10c on 15c	.40	.55
a.	Inverted surcharge	6,500.	12,000.
C21	AP7 10c on 20c ('36)	.45	2.25
C22	AP4 10c on 65c ('38)	.20	.40
C23	AP7 30c on 20c ('36)	3.00	14.00
C24	AP7 40c on 20c ('37)	3.75	15.00
C25	AP7 40c on 90c ('36) (R)	3.25	14.50
a.	Vermilion surcharge	92.50	800.00
	Never hinged, #C25a	150.00	
	Nos. C19-C25 (7)	15.80	79.20
	Set, never hinged	40.00	

Stamp similar to No. C22, but from souvenir
sheet, is listed as No. 242a.

Type of Air Post Stamp of 1923
Surcharged in Black

1938

«PRO AERO»
75   **75**

1938, May 22   Wmk. 183   Perf. 11½

C26	AP3 75c on 50c gray & scar	6.50	

"Pro Aero" Meeting, May 21-22.
No. C26 was not sold to the public in the
ordinary way, but affixed to air mail letters by
postal officials. It was not regularly obtainable
unused.

Jungfrau — AP8

Designs: 40c, View of Valais. 50c, Lake
Geneva. 60c, Alpstein. 70c, View of Ticino. 1fr,
Lake Lucerne. 2fr, The Engadine. 5fr,
Churfirsten.

Perf. 11½
1941, May 1   Unwmk.   Engr.
Tinted Granite Paper

C27	AP8 30c ultra	.55	.25
C28	AP8 40c gray blk	.55	.25
C29	AP8 50c slate grn	.55	.30
C30	AP8 60c chestnut	.85	.30
C31	AP8 70c plum	.90	.55
C32	AP8 1fr Prus grn	1.75	.60
C33	AP8 2fr car lake	5.75	3.50
C34	AP8 5fr deep blue	19.00	15.00
	Nos. C27-C34 (8)	29.90	20.75
	Set, never hinged	80.00	

See Nos. C43-C44.

Type of 1941
Overprinted in
Red

1941, May 12

C35	AP8 1fr blue green	5.50	19.00
	Never hinged	10.00	

Issued to commemorate special flights
between Payerne and Buochs, May 28, 1941.

Parliament
Buildings,
Bern
AP16

1943, July 13   **Photo.**

C36	AP16 1fr cop red, buff & blk	1.60	10.00
		3.75	

30th anniv. of the 1st Alpine flight, by Oscar
Bider, July 13, 1913.

DH-3
Haefeli
AP17

Fokker
AP18

Lockheed-Orion — AP19

1944, Sept. 1

C37	AP17 10c gray brn & pale grn	.20	.50
C38	AP18 20c rose car & buff	.20	.50
C39	AP19 30c ultra & pale gray	.35	1.25
	Nos. C37-C39 (3)	.75	2.25
	Set, never hinged	1.50	

25th anniv. of the 1st regular air route in
Switzerland.

Douglas
DC-3
AP20

1944, Sept. 20   **Granite Paper**

C40	AP20 1.50fr multi	5.50	17.50
	Never hinged	11.00	

25th anniv. of the Zurich-Geneva air route.

Zoegling
Training
Glider
AP21

1946, May 1   **Granite Paper**

C41	AP21 1.50fr henna brn & gray	11.50	27.50
	Never hinged	20.00	

Valid for use only on two special flights.

Douglas
DC-4
Linking
Geneva
and New
York
AP22

1947, Mar. 17   **Granite Paper**

C42	AP22 2.50fr bl gray, dk bl & red	7.00	20.00
	Never hinged	13.00	

Valid only on the Geneva-New York flight of
May 2, 1947.
Because of bad weather at NYC the flight
ended at Washington.

Types of 1941
1948, Oct. 1   **Engr.**
Tinted Granite Paper

C43	AP8 30c dk slate bl	4.50	12.50
C44	AP8 40c deep ultra	21.00	2.75
	Set, never hinged	57.50	

Glider in Symbolized Aerodynamic
Buoyancy — AP23

1949, Apr. 11   **Engr. & Typo.**

C45	AP23 1.50fr dk vio & yel	16.00	37.50
	Never hinged	30.00	

Valid only on special flights, Apr. 27-29,
1949. Proceeds were for the advancement of
national aviation.

> Catalogue values for unused
> stamps in this section, from this
> point to the end of the section, are
> for Never Hinged items.

Glider and
Jets
AP24

1963, June 1   Photo.   Perf. 11½
Granite Paper

C46	AP24 2fr multicolored	4.00	3.50

50th anniversary of the first Alpine flight by
Oscar Bider, July 13, 1913. Valid for postage
on July 13, 1963, on flights from Bern to
Locarno and Langenbruck to Bern. Proceeds
went to the Pro Aero Foundation.

AIR POST SEMI-POSTAL STAMP

> Catalogue values for unused
> stamps in this section are for
> Never Hinged items.

Boeing
747 — SPAP1

1972, Feb. 17   Photo.   Perf. 12½
Violet Fibers, Fluorescent Paper

CB1	SPAP1 2fr + 1fr dp bl, red & gray	2.50	2.25

50th anniv. of 1st Swiss Intl. flight, Zurich to
Nuremberg, and 25th anniv. of 1st Swissair
trans-Atlantic flight, Zurich to NYC. Valid on all
mail but obligatory on special flights from
Geneva to NYC in May, and from Geneva to
Nuremberg in June, 1972.
Surtax was for Pro Aero Foundation and the
training of young airmen, and for the Swiss Air
Rescue Service.

POSTAGE DUE STAMPS

D1   D2

Wmk. 182

1878-80		**Typo.**	**Perf. 11½**	
J1	D1	1c ultra	1.90	1.50
J2	D2	2c ultra	1.90	1.50
J3	D2	3c ultra	17.50	17.50
J4	D2	5c ultra	17.50	7.50
J5	D2	10c ultra	175.00	5.75
J6	D2	20c ultra	190.00	5.75
J7	D2	50c ultra	375.00	15.00
J8	D2	100c ultra	525.00	15.00
J9	D2	500c ultra	475.00	25.00
		Nos. J1-J9 (9)	1,778.	97.00

A 5c in design D1 exists.

1882-83		**Granite Paper**		
J10	D2	10c ultra	160.00	35.00
J11	D2	20c ultra	375.00	47.50
J12	D2	100c ultra	2,350.	525.00
J13	D2	100c ultra	750.00	425.00
J14	D2	500c ultra	13,750.	210.00

1883-84		**Numerals in Red**		
J15	D2	5c blue green	42.50	29.00
J16	D2	10c blue green	60.00	25.00
J17	D2	20c blue green	110.00	21.00
J18	D2	50c blue green	140.00	70.00
J19	D2	100c blue green	350.00	325.00
J20	D2	500c blue green	725.00	195.00
		Nos. J15-J20 (6)	1,427.	645.00

1884-97		**Numerals in Red**		
J21	D2	1c olive green	.60	.60
J22	D2	3c olive green	10.00	4.50
J23	D2	5c olive green	1.50	.60
a.		5c yellow green	25.00	12.00
J24	D2	10c olive green	3.50	.95
a.		10c yellow green	110.00	15.00
J25	D2	20c olive green	8.75	1.25
a.		20c yellow green	110.00	15.00
J26	D2	50c olive green	13.00	2.75
a.		50c yellow green	110.00	32.50
J27	D2	100c olive green	14.50	2.75
a.		100c yellow green	110.00	80.00
J28	D2	500c olive green	150.00	175.00
a.		500c yellow green	140.00	65.00

1908-09		**Wmk. 183**		
		Numerals in Red		
J29	D2	1c olive green	.25	1.25
J30	D2	5c olive green	.60	.90
J31	D2	10c olive green	1.50	2.50
J32	D2	20c olive green	3.00	5.50
J33	D2	50c olive green	15.00	1.10
J34	D2	100c olive green	27.50	2.25
		Nos. J29-J34 (6)	47.85	13.50

D3

1910			**Perf. 11½, 12**	
		Numerals in Red		
J35	D3	1c blue green	.20	.20
J36	D3	3c blue green	.20	.20
J37	D3	5c blue green	.20	.20
J38	D3	10c blue green	11.00	.20
J39	D3	15c blue green	.65	1.10
J40	D3	20c blue green	17.50	.20
J41	D3	25c blue green	1.25	.65
J42	D3	30c blue green	1.25	.55
J43	D3	50c blue green	1.50	1.10
		Nos. J35-J43 (9)	33.75	4.40

See Nos. S1-S12.

No. J36 Surcharged

1916				
J44	D3	5c on 3c bl grn & red	.40	.25

Nos. J35-J36, J43
Surcharged

1924				
J45	D3	10c on 1c	.25	8.25
J46	D3	10c on 3c	.25	1.50
J47	D3	20c on 50c	.95	1.50
		Nos. J45-J47 (3)	1.45	11.25

D4   D5

Wmk. 183

1924-26		**Typo.**	**Perf. 11½**	
		Granite Paper		
J48	D4	5c ol grn & red	.65	.25
J49	D4	10c ol grn & red	2.75	.20
J50	D4	15c ol grn & red ('26)	2.50	.55
J51	D4	20c ol grn & red	6.00	.20
J52	D4	25c ol grn & red	2.75	.55
J53	D4	30c ol grn & red	2.75	.85
J54	D4	40c ol grn & red ('26)	3.75	.70
J55	D4	50c ol grn & red	3.75	.70
		Nos. J48-J55 (8)	24.90	4.00

1924				
		With Grilled Gum		
J48a	D4	5c olive green & red	.65	.60
J49a	D4	10c olive green & red	2.50	1.10
J51a	D4	20c olive green & red	4.75	1.50
J52a	D4	25c olive green & red	7.25	65.00
		Nos. J48a-J52a (4)	15.15	68.20

See Grilled Gum note after No. 145.

Nos. J50, J53 and J55 Surcharged with New Value in Black

1937				
J56	D4	5c on 15c	.90	4.25
J57	D4	10c on 30c	.90	1.50
J58	D4	20c on 50c	1.50	5.00
J59	D4	40c on 50c	2.50	12.00
		Nos. J56-J59 (4)	5.80	22.75
		Set, never hinged	10.50	

1938		**Engr.**	**Unwmk.**	
J60	D5	5c scarlet	.40	.20
J61	D5	10c scarlet	.55	.20
J62	D5	15c scarlet	1.25	2.25
J63	D5	20c scarlet	.95	.20
J64	D5	25c scarlet	1.40	1.90
J65	D5	30c scarlet	1.40	1.25
J66	D5	40c scarlet	1.60	.45
J67	D5	50c scarlet	1.90	2.25
		Nos. J60-J67 (8)	9.45	8.70
		Set, never hinged	19.00	

1938				
		With Grilled Gum		
J60a	D5	5c scarlet	.65	1.60
J61a	D5	10c scarlet	.65	1.25
J62a	D5	15c scarlet	1.40	2.50
J63a	D5	20c scarlet	1.25	.55
J64a	D5	25c scarlet	1.40	9.50
J65a	D5	30c scarlet	1.40	2.25
J66a	D5	40c scarlet	2.10	2.10
J67a	D5	50c scarlet	2.50	3.50
		Nos. J60a-J67a (8)	11.35	23.25
		Set, never hinged	29.00	

See Grilled Gum note after No. 145.

OFFICIAL STAMPS

For General Use

With Perforated Cross

In 1935 the government authorized the use of regular postage issues perforated with a nine-hole cross for all government departments. Twenty-seven different stamps were so perforated. These were succeeded in 1938 by the cross overprints.

Values for canceled Official Stamps are for those canceled to order. Postally used stamps sell for considerably less. This note does not apply to Nos. 1O1-1O16, 2O27-2O30, 3O23-3O26.

Counterfeit overprints exist of most official stamps.

Official stamps without unused values were not made available to the public unused.

Regular Issues of 1908-36 Overprinted in Black

1938		**Unwmk.**	**Perf. 11½**	
O1	A53	3c olive	.20	.20
O2	A54	5c blue green	.20	.20
O3	A55	10c red violet	.95	.45
O4	A56	15c orange	.25	1.60
O5	A68	20c red	.45	.25
O6	A58	25c brown	.45	1.40
O7	A59	30c ultra	.60	1.00
O8	A60	35c yellow green	.60	1.25
O9	A61	40c gray	.60	1.00

		Wmk. 183		
		With Grilled Gum		
O10	A25	50c dp grn & pale grn	.60	1.50
O11	A25	60c brn org & buff	1.25	2.50
O12	A25	70c vio & buff	1.25	4.25
O13	A25	80c sl & buff	1.25	3.25
O14	A36	90c grn & red, grn	3.00	3.25
O15	A25	1fr dp cl & pale grn	1.50	3.25
O16	A36	1.20fr brn rose & red, rose	1.50	4.50
O17	A36	1.50fr bl & red, bl	2.50	6.00
O18	A36	2fr gray blk & red, gray	3.00	7.00
		Nos. O1-O18 (18)	20.15	42.85
		Set, never hinged	65.00	

Nos. O14, O16, O17 and O18 are on surface-colored paper.

1938		**Unwmk.**	**With Grilled Gum**	
O1a	A53	3c olive	4.50	.45
O2a	A54	5c blue green	1.25	.25
O3a	A55	10c red violet	1.50	.55
O4a	A56	15c orange	2.75	1.25
O5a	A68	20c red	1.50	.70
O6a	A58	25c brown	75.00	7.75
O7a	A59	30c ultra	2.50	1.10
O8a	A60	35c yellow green	1.90	1.90
O9a	A61	40c gray	2.50	1.00
		Nos. O1a-O9a (9)	93.40	14.95
		Set, never hinged	190.00	

See Grilled Gum note after No. 145.

Postage Stamps of 1936-42 Overprinted in Black

1942-45		**Unwmk.**	**Perf. 11½**	
O19	A53	3c olive	.30	2.10
O20	A54	5c blue green	.30	.20
O21	A55	10c dk red brn	.55	.55
O21A	A55	10c orange brn ('45)	.20	.45
O22	A56	15c orange	.60	1.90
O23	A68	20c red	.60	.45
O24	A58	25c lt brown	.60	2.25
O25	A59	30c ultra	.95	.90
O26	A60	35c yellow grn	1.25	2.75
O27	A61	40c gray	1.25	.60
O28	A77	50c dp pur, grnsh	3.75	4.25
O29	A78	60c red brn, buff	4.50	4.25
O30	A79	70c rose vio, pale lil	5.00	8.25

O31	A80	80c blk, pale gray	1.40	1.60
O32	A81	90c dk red, pale rose	1.60	2.25
O33	A82	1fr dk grn, grnsh	1.60	1.60
O34	A83	1.20fr red vio, gray	2.25	2.75
O35	A84	1.50fr dk bl, buff	2.25	3.25
O36	A85	2fr mar, pale rose	3.25	4.00
		Nos. O19-O36 (19)	32.20	44.35
		Set, never hinged	60.00	

Same Overprint on Nos. 329-339

1950		**Unwmk.**	**Perf. 12x11½**	
O37	A118	5c orange	.40	.55
O38	A119	10c yellow grn	.65	.55
O39	A120	15c aqua	5.50	15.00
O40	A121	20c brown car	2.10	.65
O41	A122	25c red	3.25	8.25
O42	A123	30c olive	2.50	3.25
O43	A124	35c red brown	3.50	11.00
O44	A125	40c deep blue	2.75	3.25
O45	A126	50c slate gray	4.50	5.75
O46	A127	60c blue green	5.50	7.75
O47	A128	70c purple	16.00	22.50
		Nos. O37-O47 (11)	46.65	78.50
		Set, never hinged	77.50	

FOR THE WAR BOARD OF TRADE

Regular Issues of 1908-18 Overprinted

1918		**Wmk. 183**	**Perf. 11½, 12**	
1O1	A26	3c brown org	110.00	225.00
1O2	A26	5c green	10.00	32.50
1O3	A26	7½c gray (I)	300.00	450.00
a.		7½c slate (II)	550.00	950.00
1O4	A28	10c red, buff	15.00	40.00
1O5	A28	15c vio, buff	12.50	45.00
1O6	A25	20c red & yel	125.00	500.00
1O7	A25	25c dp bl	125.00	500.00
1O8	A25	30c yel brn & pale grn	125.00	450.00
		Nos. 1O1-1O8 (8)	822.50	2,242.

Most unused copies of Nos. 1O1-1O8 are reprints made using the original overprint forms.
Counterfeits exist.

Overprinted

1918				
1O9	A26	3c brown orange	4.25	35.00
1O10	A26	5c green	12.00	52.50
1O11	A26	7½c gray	4.50	22.50
1O12	A28	10c red, buff	45.00	87.50
1O13	A28	15c vio, buff	87.50	
1O14	A25	20c red & yel	8.75	52.50
1O15	A25	25c dp blue	8.75	52.50
1O16	A25	30c yel brn & pale grn	14.50	87.50
		Nos. 1O9-1O16 (8)	185.25	

No. 1O13 was never placed in use.
Fraudulent cancellations are found on Nos. 1O1-1O16.

FOR THE LEAGUE OF NATIONS

Regular Issues Overprinted   SOCIÉTÉ DES NATIONS

On 1908-30 Issues

1922-31		**Wmk. 183**	**Perf. 11½, 12**	
2O1	A26	2½c ol, buff ('28)	.45	
2O2	A26	3c ultra, buff ('30)	8.25	
2O3	A26	5c orange, buff	5.50	
2O4	A26	5c gray vio, buff ('26)	2.75	
2O5	A26	5c red vio, buff ('27)	2.25	
2O6	A26	5c dk grn, buff ('31)	25.00	
2O7	A26	7½c dp grn, buff ('28)	.55	
2O8	A28	10c green, buff	.55	
2O9	A28	10c bl grn, buff ('28)	1.10	

2O10	A28	10c vio, *buff* ('31)	2.75
2O11	A28	15c brn red, *buff* ('28)	1.10
2O12	A28	20c red vio, *buff*	8.25
2O13	A28	20c car, *buff* ('26)	2.25
2O14	A28	25c ver, *buff*	8.25
2O15	A28	25c car, *buff*	1.10
2O16	A28	25c brn, *buff* ('27)	17.00
2O17	A28	30c dp bl, *buff* ('25)	8.25
2O18	A25	30c yel brn & pale grn	14.00
2O19	A25	35c yel grn & yel	10.00
2O20	A25	40c deep blue	1.40
2O21	A25	40c red vio & grn ('28)	14.00
2O22	A25	50c dp grn & pale grn	11.00
2O23	A25	60c brn org & buff	30.00 / 1.60
2O24	A25	70c vio & buff ('25)	26.00
2O25	A25	80c slate & buff	2.75
2O26	A25	1fr dp cl & pale grn	6.75
2O27	A29	3fr red	32.50
2O28	A30	5fr ultra	60.00
2O29	A31	10fr dull violet	140.00
2O30	A31	10fr gray grn ('30)	140.00
		Nos. 2O1-2O30 (30)	555.35

1930-44 — With Grilled Gum

2O2a	A26	3c ultra, *buff* ('33)	10.00
2O6a	A26	5c dk grn, *buff* ('33)	19.00
2O17a	A28	30c dp bl, *buff*	425.00
2O22a	A25	50c dp grn & pale grn ('35)	.90 / 2.25
2O23a	A25	60c brn org & buff ('44)	25.00 / 225.00
2O24a	A25	70c violet & buff ('32)	1.60 / 2.25
2O25a	A25	80c slate & buff ('42)	2.75 / 2.50
2O26a	A25	1fr dp cl & pale grn ('42)	5.25

1935-36 — With Grilled Gum

2O31	A36	90c grn & red, *grn* ('36)	5.00
2O32	A36	1.20fr brn rose & red, *rose* ('36)	2.75 / 4.50
b.		Inverted overprint	4,250.
2O33	A36	1.50fr bl & red, *bl* ('36)	2.75 / 4.50
2O34	A36	2fr gray blk & red, *gray* ('36)	2.75 / 5.25

1922-25 — Ordinary Gum

2O31a	A36	90c	14.00
2O32a	A36	1.20fr ('25)	14.00
2O33a	A36	1.50fr ('25)	13.00
2O34a	A36	2fr ('25)	12.00

1928

2O35	A39	5fr blue	87.50

On 1932 Issue — 1932

2O36	A41	5c peacock bl	19.00
2O37	A41	10c orange	1.60
2O38	A41	20c cerise	1.60
2O39	A41	30c ultra	55.00
2O40	A41	60c olive brn	15.00

Unwmk.

2O41	A42	1fr ol gray & bl	15.00
		Nos. 2O36-2O41 (6)	107.20

On 1934 Issue — 1934-35 — Wmk. 183

2O42	A46	3c olive	.25
2O43	A47	5c emerald	.65
2O44	A49	15c orange ('35)	1.50
2O45	A51	25c brown	19.00
2O46	A52	30c ultra	1.60
		Nos. 2O42-2O46 (5)	23.00

On 1936 Issue — 1937 — Unwmk.

2O47	A53	3c olive	.20 / .25
2O48	A54	5c blue green	.25 / .25
2O49	A55	10c red violet	1.10
2O50	A56	15c orange	.45 / .55
2O51	A57	20c carmine	1.90
2O52	A58	25c brown	.65 / 1.10
2O53	A59	30c ultra	.65 / 1.00
2O54	A60	35c yellow green	.65 / 1.00
2O55	A61	40c gray	.95 / 1.25
		Nos. 2O47-2O55 (9)	8.40

1937 — With Grilled Gum

2O47a	A53	3c olive	.30
2O48a	A54	5c blue green	.45
2O49a	A55	10c red violet	6.25
2O50a	A56	15c orange	.70
2O51a	A57	20c carmine	2.25
2O52a	A58	25c brown	1.40
2O53a	A59	30c ultra	1.10
2O54a	A60	35c yellow green	4.25
2O55a	A61	40c gray	4.25
		Nos. 2O47a-2O55a (9)	20.95

On 1931 Issue — 1937 — Wmk. 183

2O56	A40	3fr orange brown	190.00

On 1938 Issue — 1938 — Unwmk. — Perf. 11½ — Granite Paper

2O57	A63	20c red & buff	1.90
2O58	A64	30c blue & lt blue	3.00
2O59	A65	60c brown & buff	5.75
2O60	A66	1fr black & buff	9.25
		Nos. 2O57-2O60 (4)	19.90

Regular Issue of 1938 Overprinted in Black or Red

Granite Paper

2O61	A63	20c red & buff	2.25
2O62	A64	30c blue & lt blue	4.00
2O63	A65	60c brown & buff	7.25
2O64	A66	1fr black & buff (R)	12.50
		Nos. 2O61-2O64 (4)	26.00

Regular Issue of 1938 Overprinted in Black — 1939

2O65	A69	3fr brn car, *buff*	3.25	11.00
2O66	A70	5fr slate bl, *buff*	5.50	15.00
2O67	A71	10fr green, *buff*	11.00	32.50
		Nos. 2O65-2O67 (3)	19.75	58.50

Same Overprint in Black on Regular Issues of 1939-42 — 1942-43

2O68	A55	10c dk red brown		.85
2O68A	A55	10c orange brn ('43)	.40	.85
2O69	A68	20c red	.50	1.00
		Nos. 2O68-2O69 (3)		2.70

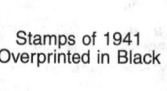

Stamps of 1936-42 Overprinted in Black — 1944

2O70	A53	3c olive	.20	.25
2O71	A54	5c blue green	.20	.25
2O72	A55	10c orange brown	.80	.40
2O73	A56	15c orange	.20	.50
2O74	A68	20c red	.40	.75
2O75	A58	25c lt brown	.40	1.00
2O76	A59	30c ultra	.50	1.00
2O77	A60	35c yellow green	.50	1.00
2O78	A61	40c gray	.55	1.25

Nos. 2O73-2O75 and 2O78 exist with grilled gum. Value each $2,000 unused, $2,250 used.

Stamps of 1941 Overprinted in Black

2O79	A77	50c dp pur, *grnsh*	1.00	1.75
2O80	A78	60c red brn, *buff*	1.25	2.50
2O81	A79	70c rose vio, *pale lil*	1.25	2.50
2O82	A80	80c blk, *pale gray*	1.10	2.00
2O83	A81	90c dk red, *pale rose*	1.10	2.00
2O84	A82	1fr dk grn, *grnsh*	1.10	2.25
2O85	A83	1.20fr red vio, *pale gray*	1.75	3.00
2O86	A84	1.50fr dk bl, *buff*	2.00	3.50
2O87	A85	2fr mar, *pale rose*	2.50	4.00

Stamps of 1942 Overprinted in Black — COURRIER DE LA SOCIÉTÉ DES NATIONS

Unwmk. — Perf. 11½

2O88	A69	3fr brn car, *cr*	4.50	9.00
2O89	A70	5fr slate bl, *cr*	7.00	12.50
2O90	A71	10fr green, *cr*	12.00	24.00
		Nos. 2O70-2O90 (21)	40.30	75.40
		Set, never hinged	65.00	

FOR THE INTERNATIONAL LABOR BUREAU

Regular Issues Overprinted — *S. d. N. Bureau international du Travail*

On 1908-30 Issues — 1923-30 — Wmk. 183 — Perf. 11½, 12

3O1	A26	2½c ol grn, *buff* ('28)		.30
3O2	A26	3c ultra, *buff* ('30)		1.10
3O3	A26	5c org, *buff*		.55
3O4	A26	5c red vio, *buff* ('28)		.20
3O5	A26	7½c dp grn, *buff* ('28)		.45
3O6	A28	10c grn, *buff*		.55
3O7	A28	10c bl grn, *buff* ('28)		1.10
3O8	A28	15c brn red, *buff* ('28)		1.10
3O9	A28	20c red vio, *buff*		17.00
3O10	A28	20c car, *buff* ('27)		5.00
3O11	A28	25c car, *buff*		1.25
3O12	A28	25c brn, *buff* ('28)		3.00
3O13	A28	30c dp bl, *buff* ('25)		2.50
3O14	A25	30c yel brn & pale grn		65.00
3O15	A25	35c yel grn & yel		11.00
3O16	A25	40c deep blue		1.25
3O17	A25	40c red vio & grn ('28)		17.00
3O18	A25	50c dp grn & pale grn		5.00
3O19	A25	'60c brn org & buff	1.60	1.90
3O20	A25	70c vio & buff ('24)		26.00
3O21	A25	80c slate & buff	14.00	2.25
3O22	A25	1fr dp cl & pale grn		2.75
3O23	A29	3fr red		25.00
3O24	A30	5fr ultra		37.50
3O25	A31	10fr dull violet		150.00
3O26	A31	10fr gray grn ('30)		150.00
		Nos. 3O1-3O26 (26)		528.75

1937-44 — With Grilled Gum

3O18a	A25	50c dp grn & pale grn ('42)	1.75	2.25
3O20a	A25	70c vio & buff	1.75	2.25
3O21a	A25	80c slate & buff ('44)	25.00	175.00
3O22a	A25	1fr dp cl & pale grn ('42)		3.25

1925-42 — With Grilled Gum

3O27	A36	90c grn & red, *grn* ('37)		9.75
a.		Ordinary gum		5.00
3O28	A36	1.20fr brn rose & red, *rose* ('42)	14.00	4.00
a.		Ordinary gum		4.50
3O29	A36	1.50fr bl & red, *bl* ('37)	2.75	3.00
a.		Ordinary gum		14.00
3O30	A36	2fr gray blk & red, *gray* ('36)	3.25	6.25
a.		Ordinary gum		32.50
		Nos. 3O27-3O30 (4)		23.00

1928

3O31	A39	5fr blue	82.50

On 1932 Issue — 1932

3O32	A41	5c peacock blue	1.10
3O33	A41	10c orange	.90
3O34	A41	20c cerise	1.25
3O35	A41	30c ultra	7.75
3O36	A41	60c olive brown	7.75

Unwmk.

3O37	A42	1fr ol gray & bl	10.00
		Nos. 3O32-3O37 (6)	28.75

On 1936 Issue — 1937

3O38	A53	3c olive	.20	.55
3O39	A54	5c blue green	.20	.55
3O40	A55	10c red violet		2.75
3O41	A56	15c orange	.45	1.10
3O42	A57	20c carmine		2.25
3O43	A58	25c brown	.60	1.40
3O44	A59	30c ultra	.60	1.10
3O45	A60	35c yellow green	.60	1.60
3O46	A61	40c gray	.95	1.90
		Nos. 3O38-3O46 (9)		13.20

1937 — With Grilled Gum

3O38a	A53	3c olive	1.10
3O39a	A54	5c blue green	1.10
3O40a	A55	10c red violet	1.60
3O41a	A56	15c orange	1.90
3O42a	A57	20c carmine	1.60
3O43a	A58	25c brown	2.25
3O44a	A59	30c ultra	2.25
3O45a	A60	35c yellow green	2.75
3O46a	A61	40c gray	2.25
		Nos. 3O38a-3O46a (9)	16.80

On 1931 Issue — 1937 — Wmk. 183

3O47	A40	3fr orange brown	175.00

On 1934 Issue

3O48	A46	3c olive	5.50

On 1938 Issue — 1938 — Unwmk. — Perf. 11½ — Granite Paper

3O49	A63	20c red & buff	1.60
3O50	A64	30c blue & lt blue	3.25
3O51	A65	60c brown & buff	6.00
3O52	A66	1fr black & buff	8.75
		Nos. 3O49-3O52 (4)	19.60

Regular Issue of 1938 Overprinted in Black or Red

3O53	A63	20c red & buff (Bk)	3.25
3O54	A64	30c bl & lt bl (Bk)	3.25
3O55	A65	60c brn & buff (Bk)	6.50
3O56	A66	1fr blk & buff (R)	7.00
		Nos. 3O53-3O56 (4)	20.00

Regular Issue of 1938 Overprinted in Black — *S. d. N. Bureau international du Travail* — 1939

3O57	A69	3fr brn car, *buff*	4.50	8.25
3O58	A70	5fr slate bl, *buff*	5.50	17.00
3O59	A71	10fr green, *buff*	10.00	30.00
		Nos. 3O57-3O59 (3)	20.00	55.25

Same Overprint in Black on Regular Issues of 1939-42 — 1942-43

3O60	A55	10c dark red brown		.80
3O60A	A55	10c orange brn ('43)	.50	.80
3O61	A68	20c red	.55	.80
		Nos. 3O60-3O61 (3)		2.40

Stamps of 1936-42 Overprinted in Black — 1944

3O62	A53	3c olive	.20	.20
3O63	A54	5c blue green	.20	.20
3O64	A55	10c orange brn	.20	.25
3O65	A56	15c orange	.50	.50
3O66	A68	20c red	.35	.60
3O67	A58	25c lt brown	.55	.70
3O68	A59	30c ultra	.50	1.10
3O69	A60	35c yellow grn	.70	1.25
3O70	A61	40c gray	.75	1.40

Stamps of 1941 Overprinted — COURRIER DU BUREAU INTERNATIONAL DU TRAVAIL

3O71	A77	50c dp pur, *grnsh*	1.50	8.00
3O72	A78	60c red brn, *buff*	1.50	8.00
3O73	A79	70c rose vio, *pale lil*	1.75	8.00
3O74	A80	80c blk, *pale gray*	.45	1.40
3O75	A81	90c dk red, *pale rose*	.45	1.40
3O76	A82	1fr dk grn, *grnsh*	.45	1.40
3O77	A83	1.20fr red vio, *pale gray*	.75	1.75
3O78	A84	1.50fr dull bl, *buff*	1.00	2.25
3O79	A85	2fr mar, *pale rose*	1.25	3.00

Stamps of 1942 Overprinted — COURRIER DU BUREAU INTERNATIONAL DU TRAVAIL

3O80	A69	3fr brown car, *cr*	3.25	6.00
3O81	A70	5fr slate blue, *cr*	5.00	10.50
3O82	A71	10fr green, *cr*	10.00	20.00
		Nos. 3O62-3O82 (21)	31.30	77.80
		Set, never hinged	60.00	

Nos. 329-339
Overprinted in Black

		1950 Unwmk.	Perf. 12x11½	
3O83	A118	5c orange	4.00	4.75
3O84	A119	10c yellow green	4.00	5.25
3O85	A120	15c aqua	5.00	7.50
3O86	A121	20c brown carmine	5.00	7.50
3O87	A122	25c red	6.00	7.75
3O88	A123	30c olive	6.00	7.75
3O89	A124	35c red brown	6.00	7.75
3O90	A125	40c deep blue	6.00	7.75
3O91	A126	50c slate gray	7.50	8.25
3O92	A127	60c blue green	9.00	12.50
3O93	A128	70c purple	10.00	17.50
		Nos. 3O83-3O93 (11)	68.50	94.25
		Set, never hinged	110.00	

Catalogue values for unused stamps in this section, from this point to the end of the section, are for Never Hinged items.

Miners — O1

Globe, Chimney and Wheel — O2

		1956-60 Unwmk. Engr.	Perf. 11½	
3O94	O1	5c dark gray	.20	.20
3O95	O1	10c green	.20	.20
3O96	O2	20c vermilion	1.25	2.25
3O97	O2	20c car rose ('60)	.20	.20
3O98	O2	30c orange ver ('60)	.25	.40
3O99	O1	40c blue	1.25	2.75
3O100	O1	50c lt ultra ('60)	.25	.50
3O101	O2	60c reddish brown	.30	.50
3O102	O2	2fr rose violet	1.10	1.50
		Nos. 3O94-3O102 (9)	5.00	8.50

Type of 1960 Overprinted: "Visite du / Pape Paul VI / Genève / 10 juin 1969"

1969, June 10
Violet Fibers, Fluorescent Paper

3O103 O2 30c orange vermilion .30 .30

Visit of Pope Paul VI to the Intl. Labor Bureau to celebrate its 50th anniv., Geneva, June 10.

ILO Headquarters, Geneva — O3

1974, May 30 Photo. Perf. 11½
Violet Fibers, Fluorescent Paper

3O104 O3 80c blue, yellow & gray .85 .80

Inauguration of the new International Labor Organization Building.

Young Man at Lathe, Cogwheels O4

Designs: 60c, Woman at drilling machine. 90c, Welder and lab assistant using protective devices and clothing. 100c, Surveyor with theodolite and topographical map. 120c, Professional education for youth.

		1975-88 Photo.	Perf. 11½	
3O105	O4	30c red brn & dk brn	.30	.30
3O106	O4	60c ultra & blk	.60	.60
3O107	O4	100c dk green & blk	1.00	1.00
3O108	O4	120c multicolored	1.25	1.25

		Perf. 12x11½		
3O109	O4	90c multicolored	1.00	1.00
		Nos. 3O105-3O109 (5)	4.15	4.15

Issued: 30c-100c, 2/13; 120c, 8/22/83; 90c, 9/13/88.

ILO, 75th Anniv. — O5

1994, May 17 Litho. Perf. 13
3O110 O5 180c multicolored 2.00 2.00

FOR THE INTERNATIONAL BUREAU OF EDUCATION

Regular Issues of 1936-42, Overprinted in Black

		1944 Unwmk.	Perf. 11½	
4O1	A53	3c olive	.40	1.00
4O2	A54	5c blue grn	.55	1.25
4O3	A55	10c orange brn	.55	1.25
4O4	A56	15c orange	.55	1.50
4O5	A68	20c red	.55	1.50
4O6	A58	25c lt brown	.65	1.75
4O7	A59	30c ultra	.85	2.25
4O8	A60	35c yellow grn	.85	2.25
4O9	A61	40c gray	1.10	2.50

Regular Issue of 1941, Overprinted in Black

4O10	A77	50c dp pur, grnsh	5.00	13.00
4O11	A78	60c red brn, buff	5.00	13.00
4O12	A79	70c rose vio, pale lil	5.00	13.00
4O13	A80	80c blk, pale gray	.60	1.50
4O14	A81	90c dk red, pale rose	.70	1.75
4O15	A82	1fr dk grn, grnsh	.85	2.25
4O16	A83	1.20fr red vio, pale gray	1.00	2.50
4O17	A84	1.50fr dk bl, buff	1.25	3.00
4O18	A85	2fr mar, pale rose	1.60	4.00

Regular Issue of 1942, Overprinted in Black

4O19	A69	3fr brn car, cr	7.00	17.00
4O20	A70	5fr slate bl, cr	10.00	25.00
4O21	A71	10fr green, cr	15.00	40.00
		Nos. 4O1-4O21 (21)	59.05	151.50
		Set, never hinged	110.00	

No. 306 Overprinted in Carmine

1946
4O22 A104 10c rose violet .20 .50
Never hinged .50

Nos. 316-321
Overprinted in Black

		1948 Unwmk.	Perf. 11½	
4O23	A54	5c chocolate	1.75	3.00
4O24	A55	10c green	1.75	3.00
4O25	A68	20c orange brn	1.75	3.00
4O26	A113	25c carmine	1.75	3.00
4O27	A59	30c grnsh blue	2.00	3.00
4O28	A61	40c ultra	2.00	3.00
		Nos. 4O23-4O28 (6)	11.00	18.00
		Set, never hinged	20.00	

Same Overprint on Nos. 329-339

1950 Perf. 12x11½
Overprint 18mm wide

4O29	A118	5c orange	.65	1.75
4O30	A119	10c yellow grn	.65	2.10
4O31	A120	15c aqua	.65	2.10
4O32	A121	20c brown car	2.00	5.75
4O33	A122	25c red	4.50	10.50
4O34	A123	30c olive	4.50	10.50
4O35	A124	35c red brn	3.50	8.75
4O36	A125	40c deep blue	3.50	8.75
4O37	A126	50c slate gray	4.00	9.75
4O38	A127	60c blue green	4.75	11.50
4O39	A128	70c purple	5.50	13.50
		Nos. 4O29-4O39 (11)	34.20	84.95
		Set, never hinged	60.00	

Catalogue values for unused stamps in this section, from this point to the end of the section, are for Never Hinged items.

Globe and Books — O1

Designs: 20c, 30c, 60c, 2fr, Pestalozzi Monument at Yverdon.

		1958-60 Engr.	Perf. 11½	
4O40	O1	5c dark gray	.20	.20
4O41	O1	10c green	.20	.20
4O42	O1	20c vermilion	2.25	2.25
4O43	O1	20c car rose ('60)	.20	.20
4O44	O1	30c org ver ('60)	.20	.35
4O45	O1	40c blue	2.75	2.75
4O46	O1	50c lt ultra ('60)	.30	.50
4O47	O1	60c reddish brn	.30	.50
4O48	O1	2fr rose violet	1.10	1.50
		Nos. 4O40-4O48 (9)	7.50	8.45

FOR THE WORLD HEALTH ORGANIZATION

No. 316-319, 321
Overprinted in Black

		1948 Unwmk.	Perf. 11½	
5O1	A54	5c chocolate	2.25	2.50
5O2	A55	10c green	2.25	3.50
5O3	A68	20c orange brn	2.25	3.50
5O4	A113	25c carmine	2.25	4.50
5O5	A61	40c ultra	2.50	5.00
		Nos. 5O1-5O5 (5)	11.50	19.00
		Set, never hinged	20.00	

Regular Issues of 1941, 1942 and 1949 Overprinted in Black

1948-50
5O6	A118	5c orange	.50	1.00
5O7	A119	10c yellow grn	.65	1.50
5O8	A120	15c aqua	.90	2.00
5O9	A121	20c brown car	2.25	6.00
5O10	A122	25c red	2.25	6.00
5O11	A123	30c olive	1.50	5.00
5O12	A124	35c red brown	2.10	7.00
5O13	A125	40c deep blue	2.10	3.50

5O14	A126	50c slate gray	2.25	6.00
5O15	A127	60c blue green	2.50	7.00
5O16	A128	70c purple	3.00	7.00
5O17	A80	80c blk, pale gray ('48)	2.00	3.75
5O18	A81	90c dk red, pale rose ('48)	4.25	8.50
5O19	A82	1fr dk grn, grnsh ('48)	2.50	4.50
5O20	A83	1.20fr red vio, pale gray	5.50	12.00
5O21	A84	1.50fr dk bl, buff	11.00	12.00
5O22	A85	2fr mar, pale rose ('48)	3.50	6.50
5O23	A69	3fr brn car, cr	22.50	37.50
5O24	A70	5fr sl bl, cr ('48)	7.50	11.50
5O25	A71	10fr grn, cr	45.00	65.00
		Nos. 5O6-5O25 (20)	123.75	213.25
		Set, never hinged	250.00	

Catalogue values for unused stamps in this section, from this point to the end of the section, are for Never Hinged items.

WHO Emblem — O2

		1957-60 Unwmk. Engr.	Perf. 11½	
5O26	O2	5c gray	.20	.20
5O27	O2	10c lt grn	.20	.20
5O28	O2	20c vermilion	2.25	2.25
5O29	O2	20c car rose ('60)	.25	.25
5O30	O2	30c org ver ('60)	.35	.35
5O31	O2	40c blue	2.75	2.75
5O32	O2	50c lt ultra ('60)	.50	.50
5O33	O2	60c red brn	.50	.50
5O34	O2	2fr rose lilac	1.50	1.50
		Nos. 5O26-5O34 (9)	8.50	8.50

No. 5O32 Overprinted:
"ERADICATION DU PALUDISME"

1962, Apr. 7
5O35 O2 50c lt ultra .75 .75

WHO drive to eradicate malaria.

World Health Organization Emblem — O3

		1975-95 Typo.	Perf. 11½	
5O36	O3	30c multi	.30	.30
5O37	O3	60c lt bl & multi	.60	.30
5O38	O3	90c lilac & multi	.90	.90
5O39	O3	100c orange & multi	1.00	1.00

		Litho. Perf. 12		
5O40	O3	140c lt grn, scar & grn	1.50	1.50

		Perf. 13½x13		
5O41	O3	180c multicolored	2.10	2.10
		Nos. 5O36-5O41 (6)	6.40	6.10

Issued: 140c, 5/27/86; 180c, 11/28/95; others, 2/13/75.

FOR THE INTERNATIONAL ORGANIZATION FOR REFUGEES

Stamps of 1941 and 1949 Overprinted in Black

		1950 Unwmk.	Perf. 12x11½, 11½	
6O1	A118	5c orange	11.00	14.00
6O2	A119	10c yellow green	11.00	14.00
6O3	A121	20c brown carmine	11.00	14.00
6O4	A122	25c red	11.00	14.00
6O5	A125	40c deep blue	11.00	14.00
6O6	A80	80c blk, pale gray	11.00	14.00
6O7	A82	1fr dk grn, grnsh	11.00	14.00

6O8 A85 2fr mar, *pale rose* 11.00 14.00
Nos. 6O1-6O8 (8) 88.00 112.00
Set, never hinged 150.00

FOR THE UNITED NATIONS EUROPEAN OFFICE

See No. 513 for postage issue commemorating the United Nations.

Stamps of 1941-49 Overprinted in Black

1950 Unwmk. Perf. 12x11½, 11½

7O1	A118	5c orange	.20	2.25
7O2	A119	10c yellow grn	.35	2.25
7O3	A120	15c aqua	.55	3.00
7O4	A121	20c brown car	.85	4.25
7O5	A122	25c red	1.10	7.50
7O6	A123	30c olive	1.40	7.50
7O7	A124	35c red brown	1.40	7.50
7O8	A125	40c deep blue	2.10	8.75
7O9	A126	50c slate gray	2.50	10.50
7O10	A127	60c blue green	2.75	12.50
7O11	A128	70c purple	3.50	12.50
7O12	A80	80c blk, *pale gray*	5.50	10.00
7O13	A81	90c dk red, *pale rose*	5.50	10.00
7O14	A82	1fr dk grn, *grnsh*	5.50	10.00
7O15	A83	1.20fr red vio, *pale gray*	6.50	13.00
7O16	A84	1.50fr dk bl, *buff*	6.50	13.00
7O17	A85	2fr mar, *pale rose*	6.50	13.00
7O18	A69	3fr brn car, *cr*	65.00	125.00
7O19	A70	5fr sl bl, *cr*	67.50	125.00
7O20	A71	10fr grn, *cr*	90.00	160.00
	Nos. 7O1-7O20 (20)		275.20	557.50
	Set, never hinged		500.00	

UN Emblem — O1

Statue from UN Building, Geneva — O2

1955-59 Engr. Perf. 11½

7O21	O1	5c dk violet brn	.20	.20
7O22	O1	10c green	.20	.20
7O23	O2	20c vermilion	2.00	4.00
7O24	O2	20c car rose ('59)	.20	.20
7O25	O2	30c org ver ('59)	.20	.30
7O26	O1	40c ultra	2.25	4.50
7O27	O1	50c ultra ('59)	.20	.40
7O28	O2	60c red brown	.25	.50
7O29	O2	2fr lilac	.80	1.60
	Nos. 7O21-7O29 (9)		6.30	11.90
	Set, never hinged		12.50	

See Nos. 7O34-7O37. For overprints see Nos. 7O31-7O32.

United Nations Emblem — O3

1955, Oct. 24 Photo.
7O30 O3 40c dark blue & bister 1.60 3.75
Never hinged 3.00

10th anniv. of the UN, Oct. 24, 1955.

Catalogue values for unused stamps in this section, from this point to the end of the section, are for Never Hinged items.

Nos. 7O24 and 7O27 Overprinted in Black or Red: "ANNEE MONDIALE DU REFUGIE 1959 1960"

1960
7O31 O2 20c carmine rose .20 .20
7O32 O1 50c ultra (R) .50 .50

World Refugee Year, 7/1/59-6/30/60.

Palace of Nations, Geneva O4

1960 Granite Paper Perf. 11½
7O33 O4 5fr blue 3.75 4.00

Types of 1955 Inscribed: "MUSEE PHILATELIQUE" (O1) or "ONU MUSEE PHILATELIQUE" (O2)

Engraved; Inscription Typographed
1962, Oct. 24 Unwmk. Perf. 11½

7O34	O1	10c green & red	.20	.20
7O35	O2	30c org ver & ultra	.30	.30
7O36	O1	50c ultra & org	.50	.50
7O37	O2	60c red brn & emer	.60	.60
	Nos. 7O34-7O37 (4)		1.60	1.60

Opening of the Philatelic Museum, UN European Office, Geneva.

O5   O6
UNCSAT Emblem

1963, Feb. 4 Engr. Perf. 11½
7O38 O5 50c ultra & car rose .50 .50
7O39 O6 2fr lilac & emer 2.00 2.00

UN Conf. on the Application of Science and Technology for the Benefit of the Less Developed Areas (UNCSAT), Geneva, Feb. 4-20.

Stamps issued, starting Oct. 4, 1969, by the UN in Swiss currency for use by UN staff members or the public are listed under "United Nations" in Vol. 1 of this catalogue and in Scott's U.S. Specialized Catalogue. These stamps are on sale in various UN post offices, but are valid only in the UN enclave in Geneva. They are not inscribed "Helvetia."

FOR THE WORLD METEOROLOGICAL ORGANIZATION

Catalogue values for unused stamps in this section are for Never Hinged items.

Sun, Cloud, Rain and Snow — O1

Design: 20c, 30c, 60c, 2fr, Direction indicator and anemometer.

1956-60 Unwmk. Engr. Perf. 11½

8O1	O1	5c dark gray	.20	.20
8O2	O1	10c green	.20	.20
8O3	O1	20c vermilion	2.25	2.25
8O4	O1	20c car rose ('60)	.25	.25
8O5	O1	30c org ver ('60)	.35	.35
8O6	O1	40c blue	2.75	2.75
8O7	O1	50c lt ultra ('60)	.50	.50
8O8	O1	60c reddish brn	.60	.60
8O9	O1	2fr rose violet	2.00	2.00
	Nos. 8O1-8O9 (9)		9.10	9.10

WMO Emblem O2

1973, Aug. 30 Engr. Perf. 11½
Violet Fibers, Fluorescent Paper

8O10	O2	30c carmine	.20	.30
8O11	O2	40c blue	.20	.30
8O12	O2	1fr ocher	1.00	1.00
	Nos. 8O10-8O12 (3)		1.40	1.60

Type O2 Inscribed: "OMI / OMM / 1873 / 1973"

1973, Aug. 30 Photo. Perf. 11½
Violet Fibers, Fluorescent Paper
8O13 O2 80c deep violet & gold .80 .80

Intl. meteorological cooperation, cent.

FOR THE INTERNATIONAL BUREAU OF THE UNIVERSAL POSTAL UNION

Catalogue values for unused stamps in this section are for Never Hinged items.

See Nos. 98-103, 204-205, 514, 589-590 for postage issues commemorating the UPU.

UPU Monument, Bern — O1

Design: 10c, 20c, 30c, 60c, Pegasus.

1957-60 Unwmk. Engr. Perf. 11½

9O1	O1	5c gray	.20	.20
9O2	O1	10c lt grn	.20	.20
9O3	O1	20c vermilion	2.25	2.25
9O4	O1	20c car rose ('60)	.20	.20
9O5	O1	30c org ver ('60)	.35	.35
9O6	O1	40c blue	2.75	2.75
9O7	O1	50c lt ultra ('60)	.50	.50
9O8	O1	60c red brn	.60	.60
9O9	O1	2fr rose lilac	2.00	2.00
	Nos. 9O1-9O9 (9)		9.05	9.05

First Class Mail — O2

Parcel Post — O3

Money Orders — O4

Technical Cooperation O5

Intl. Reply and Notication Service — O6

Express Mail Service — O7

Post NET System O8

1976-95 Photo. Perf. 11½
Fluorescent Paper

9O10	O2	40c multi	.40	.40
9O11	O3	80c multi	.80	.80
9O12	O4	90c multi	.90	.90
9O13	O5	100c multi	1.00	1.00
9O14	O6	120c multi	1.25	1.25
9O15	O7	140c multi	1.50	1.50

Perf. 13½x13

9O16	O8	180c multicolored	2.10	2.10
	Nos. 9O10-9O16 (7)		7.95	7.95

Issued: 120c, 8/22/83; 140c, 3/7/89; 180c, 11/28/95; others, 9/16/76.

UPU, 125th Anniv. O9

1999, Mar. 9 Perf. 13
9O17 O9 20c shown .30 .20
9O18 O9 70c Hand holding rainbow .85 .65

Service Quality Improvement O10

2003, Sept. 9 Litho. Perf. 13¾x14¼
9O19 O10 90c multi 1.40 .45

FOR THE INTERNATIONAL TELECOMMUNICATION UNION

Catalogue values for unused stamps in this section are for Never Hinged items.

Transmitter — O1

ITU Headquarters, Geneva — O2

Designs: 20c, 30c, 60c, 2fr, Antenna.

1958-60 Unwmk. Engr. Perf. 11½
1001	O1	5c dark gray	.20	.20
1002	O1	10c green	.20	.20
1003	O1	20c vermilion	2.25	2.25
1004	O1	20c car rose ('60)	.20	.20
1005	O1	30c org ver ('60)	.35	.35
1006	O1	40c blue	2.75	2.75
1007	O1	50c lt ultra ('60)	.50	.50
1008	O1	60c redsh brn	.60	.60
1009	O1	2fr rose vio	2.00	2.00
		Nos. 1001-1009 (9)	9.05	9.05

1973, Aug. 30 Photo. Perf. 11½
Violet Fibers, Fluorescent Paper
10010	O2	80c blue & black	.80	.80

Sound Waves, ITU Emblem O3

Airplane, Ocean Liner — O4

Radio Waves, Face on TV, Microphone O5

Photogravure and Engraved
1976, Feb. 12 Perf. 11½
Violet Fibers, Fluorescent Paper
10011	O3	40c dp org & vio bl	.40	.40
10012	O4	90c bl, vio bl & yel	.90	.90
10013	O5	1fr grn & multi	1.00	1.00
		Nos. 10011-10013 (3)	2.30	2.30

ITU activities: world telecommunications, mobile radio and mass media.

Fiber Optic Communication Links — O6

1988, Sept. 13 Litho. Perf. 12x11½
10014	O6	1.40fr multi	1.40	1.40

Radio Waves, ITU Emblem — O7

1994, May 17 Litho. Perf. 13½
10015	O7	1.80fr multicolored	2.10	2.10

Telecommunications — O8

1999, Mar. 9 Photo. Perf. 11½
10016	O8	10c Teleeducation	.20	.20
10017	O8	100c Telemedicine	1.10	1.10

Stylized Face — O9

2003, Sept. 9 Litho. Perf. 13¾x14¼
10018	O9	90c multi	1.40	.45

FOR THE WORLD INTELLECTUAL PROPERTY ORGANIZATION

Catalogue values for unused stamps in this section are for Never Hinged items.

WIPO Emblem O1

1982, May 27 Photo. Perf. 12x11½
1101	O1	40c shown	.40	.40
1102	O1	80c Headquarters, Geneva	.80	.80
1103	O1	100c Industrial symbols	1.00	1.00
1104	O1	120c Educational and artistic symbols	1.25	1.25

1985, Sept. 10 Photo. Perf. 12x11½
1105	O1	50c Mind in action	.55	.55
		Nos. 1101-1105 (5)	4.00	4.00

This is an expanding set. Numbers will change if necessary.

FOR THE INTERNATIONAL OLYMPIC COMMITTEE

Catalogue values for unused stamps in this section are for Never Hinged items.

Olympics Type of Regular Issue
Hand and plant with leaves of Olympic rings and: 20c, Orange frame. 70c, Green frame.

2000, Sept. 15 Photo. Die Cut
Booklet Stamps
Self-Adhesive
1201	A496	20c multi	.25	.25
1202	A496	70c multi	.80	.80
a.		Booklet, #1201-1202	1.10	
		Booklet, #1202a	1.10	

No. 1202a is separated from booklet cover by rouletting. The booklet was sold folded.

FRANCHISE STAMPS

These stamps were distributed to many institutions and charitable societies for franking their correspondence.

F1

Control Figures Overprinted in Black
214

Perf. 11½, 12
1911-21 Typo. Wmk. 183
Blue Granite Paper
S1	F1	2c ol grn & red	.20	.25
S2	F1	3c ol grn & red	2.50	.55
S3	F1	5c ol grn & red	1.10	.20
S4	F1	10c ol grn & red	1.40	.20
S5	F1	15c ol grn & red	21.00	4.00
S6	F1	20c ol grn & red	5.00	.60
		Nos. S1-S6 (6)	31.20	5.80

Without Control Figures
S1a	F1	2c olive green & red	.55	19.00
S2a	F1	3c olive green & red	.55	25.00
S3a	F1	5c olive green & red	4.75	32.50
S4a	F1	10c olive green & red	8.25	50.00
S5a	F1	15c olive green & red	5.25	125.00
S6a	F1	20c olive green & red	9.50	50.00
		Nos. S1a-S6a (6)	28.85	301.50

Control Figures Overprinted in Black
365

1926
S7	F1	5c ol grn & red	12.50	4.50
S8	F1	10c ol grn & red	7.75	3.25
S9	F1	20c ol grn & red	10.00	3.75
		Nos. S7-S9 (3)	30.25	11.50

Control Figures Overprinted in Black 806

1927
White Granite Paper
S10	F1	5c green & red	5.00	.40
S11	F1	10c green & red	2.50	.20
b.		Grilled gum	325.00	725.00
S12	F1	20c green & red	3.50	.30
		Nos. S10-S12 (3)	11.00	.90

Without Control Figures
S10a	F1	5c green & red	32.50	140.00
S11a	F1	10c green & red	32.50	140.00
c.		Grilled gum	150.00	650.00
S12a	F1	20c green & red	32.50	140.00

Nurse F2

Nun F3

J. H. Dunant — F4

Control Figures Overprinted in Black
1935 Perf. 11½
S13	F2	5c turq green	2.25	5.50
b.		Grilled gum	3.25	.40
S14	F3	10c lt violet	2.25	5.50
b.		Grilled gum	3.25	.20
S15	F4	20c scarlet	2.25	6.50
b.		Grilled gum	3.75	.45
		Nos. S13-S15 (3)	6.75	17.50
		Nos. S13b-S15b (3)	10.25	1.05

Without Control Figures
S13a	F2	5c turquoise green	1.40	3.75
c.		Grilled gum	15.00	1.40
S14a	F3	10c light violet	1.40	3.75
c.		Grilled gum	15.00	1.40
S15a	F4	20c scarlet	1.40	5.00
c.		Grilled gum	15.00	1.50
		Nos. S13a-S15a (3)	4.20	12.50
		Nos. S13c-S15c (3)	45.00	4.30

SYRIA

ˈsir-ē-ə

LOCATION — Asia Minor, bordering on Turkey, Iraq, Lebanon, Israel and the Mediterranean Sea
GOVT. — Republic
AREA — 71,498 sq. mi.
POP. — 14,972,000 (1997 est.)
CAPITAL — Damascus

Syria was originally part of the Turkish province of Sourya conquered by British and Arab forces in late 1918 and later partitioned. The British assumed control of the Palestine and Transjordan regions; the French were permitted to occupy the sanjaks of Lebanon, Alaouites and Alexandretta; and the remaining territory, including the vilayets of Damascus and Aleppo, was established as an independent Arab kingdom, under which the first Syrian stamps were issued.

French forces from Beirut deposed King Faisal in July 1920, and two years of military occupation followed until Syria was mandated to France in July 1922. Syrian autonomy was substituted for the mandate in 1934, but full independence was not again achieved until 1946. In 1958, Syria and Egypt merged to form the United Arab Republic. Syria left this union in 1961, adopting the name Syrian Arab Republic. UAR issues for Syria are listed following Syria's 1919-20 Issues of the Arabian Government.

10 Milliemes = 1 Piaster
40 Paras = 1 Piaster (Arabian Govt.)
100 Centimes = 1 Piaster (1920)
100 Piasters = 1 Syrian Pound

Catalogue values for unused stamps in this country are for Never Hinged items, beginning with Scott 314 in the regular postage section, Scott B13 in the semipostal section, Scott C124 in the airpost section, Scott CB5 in the airpost semipostal section, Scott J40 in the postage due section, and all of the items in the UAR sections.

Watermark

Wmk. 291 — National Emblem Multiple

Issued under French Occupation
Stamps of France, 1900-07, Surcharged

Perf. 14x13½
1919, Nov. 21 Unwmk.
1	A16	1m on 1c gray	160.00	160.00
2	A16	2m on 2c vio brn	450.00	500.00
3	A16	3m on 3c red org	200.00	200.00
4	A20	4m on 15c gray grn	32.50	32.50
5	A22	5m on 5c dp grn	17.00	17.00
6	A22	1p on 10c red	26.00	26.00
7	A22	2p on 25c blue	13.50	13.50
8	A18	5p on 40c red & pale bl	20.00	20.00
9	A18	9p on 50c bis brn & lav	45.00	45.00
10	A18	10p on 1fr cl & ol grn	72.50	72.50
		Nos. 1-10 (10)	1,036.	1,086.

The letters "T.E.O." are the initials of "Territoires Ennemis Occupés." There are two types of the numerals in the surcharges on Nos. 2, 3, 8 and 9.

Stamps of French Offices in Turkey, 1902-03, Surcharged

1919
11	A2	1m on 1c gray	.65	.65
12	A2	2m on 2c violet brn	.65	.65
13	A2	3m on 3c red orange	1.60	.65
14	A3	4m on 15c pale red	.65	.65
15	A2	5m on 5c green	.65	.65

Overprinted

16	A5	1p on 25c blue	.65	.65
17	A6	2p on 50c bis brn & lav	1.25	1.00
18	A6	4p on 1fr claret & ol grn	2.00	1.60
19	A6	8p on 2fr gray vio & yel	7.25	5.25
a.		"T.E.O." double	40.00	40.00
20	A6	20p on 5fr dk bl & buff	275.00	200.00
		Nos. 11-20 (10)	290.35	211.75

On Nos. 17-20 "T.E.O." reads vertically up.
Nos. 1-20 were issued in Beirut and mainly used in Lebanon. Nos. 16-20 were also used in Cilicia.
Inverted surcharges exist on several values of this issue.

Stamps of France, 1900-07, Surcharged

1920

21	A16	1m on 1c gray	3.25	3.25
a.		Inverted surcharge	32.50	32.50
b.		Double surcharge	19.00	
22	A16	2m on 2c vio brn	4.00	4.00
		Double surcharge	19.00	
23	A22	3m on 5c green	8.00	8.00
		Double surcharge	22.50	19.00
24	A18	20p on 5fr dk bl & buff	400.00	400.00
		Nos. 21-23 (3)	15.25	15.25

The letters "O.M.F." are the initials of "Occupation Militaire Francaise."

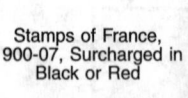

Stamps of France, 1900-07, Surcharged in Black or Red

1920

25	A16	1m on 1c gray	.65	.65
26	A16	2m on 2c violet brn	.80	.80
27	A22	3m on 5c green	1.00	1.00
28	A22	5m on 10c red	1.00	1.00
a.		Inverted surcharge		
29	A18	20p on 5fr dk bl & buff	60.00	60.00
30	A18	20p on 5fr dk bl & buff (R)	250.00	250.00
		Nos. 25-30 (6)	313.45	313.45

Stamps of France, 1900-21, Surcharged in Black or Red:

1920-22

31	A16	25c on 1c gray	.65	.65
32	A16	50c on 2c vio brn	.65	.65
33	A16	75c on 3c red org	.65	.65
34	A22	1p on 5c green (R)	.65	.65
35	A22	1p on 5c green	.30	.30
36	A22	1p on 20c red brn ('21)	.20	.20
37	A22	1.25p on 25c bl ('22)	.55	.55
38	A22	1.50p on 30c org ('22)	.55	.45
39	A22	2p on 10c red	.45	
40	A22	2p on 25c bl (R)	.45	.30
41	A18	2p on 40c red & pale bl ('21)	.65	.25
42	A20	2.50p on 50c dl bl ('22)	.75	.50
a.		Final "S" of "Piastres" omitted	8.25	8.25
43	A22	3p on 25c bl (R)	.65	.65
44	A18	3p on 60c vio & ultra ('21)	.80	.45
45	A20	5p on 15c gray grn	.65	.65
46	A18	5p on 1fr cl & ol grn ('21)	1.40	.90
47	A18	10p on 40c red & pale bl	.95	.90
48	A18	10p on 2fr org & pale bl ('21)	2.25	1.90
49	A18	25p on 50c bis brn & lav	1.40	1.40

50	A18	25p on 5fr dk bl & buff ('21)	82.50	82.50
51	A18	50p on 1fr cl & ol grn	17.50	17.50
a.		"PIASRTES"	1,200.	1,200.
52	A18	100p on 5fr dk bl & buff (R)	32.50	32.50
53	A18	100p on 5fr dk bl & buff (Bk)	225.00	225.00
a.		"PIASTRES"	1,100.	1,100.
		Nos. 31-53 (23)	372.10	369.75

In first printing, space between "Syrie" and numeral is 2mm, second printing, 1mm.
Surcharge is found inverted on Nos. 32, 35-38, 42, 44-45. Value, each $2-$3.
Surcharge is found double on Nos. 31, 37, 40, 42. Value, each $2.
For overprints see Nos. C1-C9.

Surcharged in Black or Red

1920-23

54	A16	10c on 2c violet ('23)	.40	.40
55	A22	10c on 5c org (R) ('23)	.45	.45
56	A16	25c on 1c dk gray	.30	.40
a.		50c on 1c dk gray (error)	1.40	1.40
57	A22	25c on 5c green ('21)	.45	.30
58	A22	25c on 5c orange ('22)	.55	.55
a.		"CENTIEMES" omitted	14.00	14.00
59	A22	50c on 2c vio brn	.40	.40
60	A22	50c on 10c red ('21)	.45	.45
61	A22	50c on 10c green ('22)	.60	.50
62	A16	75c on 3c red orange	.50	.45
63	A20	75c on 15c sl grn ('21)	.50	.45
		Nos. 54-63 (10)	4.60	4.20

Surcharge is found inverted on Nos. 54-55, 58-59, 62-63; double on Nos. 60, 62. Value $1.50-$2.

Preceding Issues Overprinted

1920

Black Overprint

64	A16	25c on 1c sl gray	7.75	7.75
65	A16	50c on 2c vio brn	8.75	8.75
66	A22	1p on 5c green	7.75	7.75
67	A22	2p on 25c blue	13.50	13.50
68	A20	5p on 15c gray grn	42.50	42.50
69	A18	10p on 40c red & pale bl	62.50	62.50
70	A18	25p on 50c bis brn & lav	160.00	160.00
71	A18	50p on 1fr cl & ol grn	575.00	575.00
72	A18	100p on 5fr dk bl & buff	1,650.	1,650.
		Nos. 64-72 (9)	2,527.	2,527.

Red Overprint

73	A16	25c on 1c sl gray	6.50	6.50
74	A16	50c on 2c vio brn	4.50	4.50
75	A22	1p on 5c green	5.50	6.00
76	A22	2p on 25c blue	4.50	4.50
77	A20	5p on 15c gray grn	42.50	42.50
78	A18	10p on 40c red & pale bl	62.50	62.50
79	A18	25p on 50c bis brn & lav	160.00	160.00
80	A18	50p on 1fr cl & ol grn	375.00	375.00
81	A18	100p on 5fr dk bl & buff	1,300.	1,300.
		Nos. 73-81 (9)	1,961.	1,961.

Nos. 64-81 were used only in the vilayet of Aleppo where Egyptian gold currency was still in use.

A1

Black or Red Surcharge

1921 **Perf. 11½**

82	A1	25c on ½op lt brn	.70	.50
a.		"25 Centiemes" omitted		
83	A1	50c on ⅞op grn	.70	.50
84	A1	1p on ⅜op yel	.90	.50
a.		"⅞o" for "⅞o"	8.25	8.25
85	A1	1p on 5m rose	1.00	.60
86	A1	2p on 5m rose	1.40	.60
a.		Tête bêche pair	92.50	92.50
87	A1	3p on 1p gray bl	1.40	.85
88	A1	5p on 2p bl grn	3.25	2.50
89	A1	10p on 5p vio brn	6.00	3.00
90	A1	25p on 10p gray (R)	6.50	3.75
		Nos. 82-90 (9)	21.85	12.80

Nos. 82-90 are surcharged on stamps of the Arabian Government Nos. 85, 87-93 and have the designs and sizes of those stamps.
Surcharge is found inverted on Nos. 84-88, 90; double on No. 86.

Kilis Issue

A2

Sewing Machine Perf. 9

1921 **Handstamped**
Pelure Paper

91	A2	(1p) violet	42.50 45.00

Issued at Kilis to meet a shortage of the regular issue, caused by the sudden influx of a large number of Armenian refugees from Turkey. The Kilis area was restored to Turkey in Oct. 1923.

Stamps of France, Surcharged

1921-22 **Perf. 14x13½**

92	A18	2p on 40c red & pale bl	.45	.25
93	A18	2.50p on 50c bis brn & lav ('22)	.50	.50
a.		2p on 50c bister brown & lavender (error)	37.50	30.00
94	A18	3p on 60c vio & ultra	.65	.50
95	A18	5p on 1fr cl & ol grn	4.25	4.00
96	A18	10p on 2fr org & pale bl	8.25	7.75
97	A18	25p on 5fr dk bl & buff	7.25	6.50
		Nos. 92-97 (6)	21.35	19.50

On No. 93 the surcharge reads: "2 PIASTRES 50."
Surcharge is found inverted on Nos. 92-95; double on No. 94. Value $3.
For overprints see Nos. C10-C17.

French Mandate

French Stamps of 1900-23 Surcharged

1923

104	A16	10c on 2c vio brn	.20	.20
105	A22	25c on 5c orange	.25	.25
106	A22	50c on 10c green	.25	.25
a.		25c on 10c green (error)	125.00	
107	A20	75c on 15c sl grn	.55	.55
108	A22	1p on 20c red brn	.30	.30
109	A22	1.25p on 25c blue	.85	.85
110	A22	1.50p on 30c orange	.45	.45
111	A22	1.50p on 30c red	.30	.30
112	A20	2.50p on 50c dl bl	.30	.30

On Pasteur Stamps of 1923

113	A23	50c on 10c green	.60	.60
114	A23	1.50p on 30c red	.60	.60
115	A23	2.50p on 50c blue	.60	.60

Surcharge is found inverted on #104-108, 110, 115; double on #104, 106. Value $1.50-$2.

Surcharged

116	A18	2p on 40c red & pale bl	.20	.20
a.		Inverted surcharge	14.00	
b.		Double surcharge	17.00	
c.		"Liabn"		
117	A18	3p on 60c vio & ultra	.70	.70
a.		"Liabn"		
118	A18	5p on 1fr cl & ol grn	.95	.95
a.		"Liabn"		
119	A18	10p on 2fr org & pale bl	4.75	4.75
a.		"Liabn"		
120	A18	25p on 5fr dk bl & buff	17.50	17.50
a.		Inverted surcharge		
		Nos. 104-120 (17)	29.35	29.35

Stamps of France, 1900-21, Surcharged

1924 **Perf. 14x13½**

121	A16	10c on 2c vio brn	.20	.20
a.		Double surcharge		
122	A22	25c on 5c orange	.20	.20
a.		"25" omitted	3.25	
123	A22	50c on 10c green	.30	.30
124	A20	75c on 15c sl grn	.30	.30
125	A22	1p on 20c red brn	.40	.25
a.		"1 PIASTRES"	5.00	
126	A22	1.25p on 25c blue	.65	.65
127	A22	1.50p on 30c orange	.65	.65
128	A22	1.50p on 30c red	.65	.65
129	A20	2.50p on 50c dl bl	.65	.65

Same on Pasteur Stamps of France, 1923

1924

130	A23	50c on 10c grn	.20	.20
131	A23	1.50p on 30c red	.55	.40
132	A23	2.50p on 50c blue	.20	.20
		Nos. 121-132 (12)	4.95	4.65

Olympic Games Issue
Stamps of France, 1924, Surcharged "SYRIE" and New Values

1924

133	A24	50c on 10c gray grn & yel	27.50	27.50
134	A25	1.25p on 25c rose & dk rose	27.50	27.50
135	A26	1.50p on 30c brn red & blk	27.50	27.50
136	A27	2.50p on 50c ultra & dk bl	27.50	27.50
		Nos. 133-136 (4)	110.00	110.00

See Nos. 166-169.

Stamps of France 1900-20 Surcharged

137	A18	2p on 40c red & pale bl	.25	.25
138	A18	3p on 60c vio & ultra	.45	.40
139	A18	5p on 1fr claret & ol grn	1.60	1.60
140	A18	10p on 2fr org & pale bl	1.60	1.40
141	A18	25p on 5fr dk bl & buff	3.00	3.00
		Nos. 137-141 (5)	6.90	6.60

For overprints see Nos. C18-C21.

Stamps of France 1900-21, Surcharged

or

1924-25

143	A16	10c on 2c vio brn	.20	.20
a.		Double surcharge	12.00	
b.		Inverted surcharge	14.00	
144	A22	25c on 5c orange	.20	.20
a.		Double surcharge	12.00	
145	A22	50c on 10c green	.30	.30
a.		Double surcharge	12.00	
b.		Inverted surcharge	14.00	
146	A20	75c on 15c gray grn	.30	.30
a.		Double surcharge	12.00	
b.		Inverted surcharge	14.00	
147	A22	1p on 20c red brn	.20	.20
a.		Inverted surcharge	14.00	
148	A22	1.25p on 25c blue	.30	.30
a.		Inverted surcharge	14.00	
149	A22	1.50p on 30c red	.55	.55
150	A22	1.50p on 30c orange	19.00	19.00
151	A22	2p on 35c violet ('25)	.30	.30
152	A22	2p on 40c red & pale bl	.20	.20
a.		Arabic "Piastre" in singular	1.10	1.10
153	A18	2p on 45c grn & bl ('25)	3.00	3.00
154	A18	3p on 60c vio & ultra	.65	.65
155	A20	3p on 60c lt vio ('25)	.65	.65
156	A20	4p on 85c ver	.20	.20
157	A18	5p on 1fr cl & ol grn	.65	.65
158	A18	10p on 2fr org & pale bl	1.25	1.25
159	A18	25p on 5fr dk bl & buff	1.25	1.25
		Nos. 143-159 (17)	29.20	29.20

On No. 152a, the surcharge is as illustrated. The correct fourth line ("2 Piastres" -plural), as it appears on Nos. 151, 152 and 153, has four characters, the third resembling "9."

For overprints see Nos. C22-C25.

Same Surcharge on Pasteur Stamps of France

1924-25

160	A23	50c on 10c green	.75	.75
161	A23	75c on 15c grn ('25)	.75	.75
162	A23	1.50p on 30c red	.75	.75
163	A23	2p on 45c red ('25)	.75	.75
164	A23	2.50p on 50c blue	.95	.95
165	A23	4p on 75c blue	.95	.95
		Nos. 160-165 (6)	4.90	4.90

Olympic Games Issue

Stamps of France, 1924, Surcharged "Syrie" and New Values in French and Arabic

1924

Same Colors as #133-136

166	A24	50c on 10c	19.00	22.50
167	A25	1.25p on 25c	19.00	22.50
168	A26	1.50p on 30c	19.00	22.50
169	A27	2.50p on 50c	19.00	22.50
		Nos. 166-169 (4)	76.00	90.00

Ronsard Issue

Same Surcharge on France No. 219

1925

170	A28	4p on 75c bl, bluish	.45	.45

Mosque at Hama A3

Mosque at Damascus A5

View of Merkab A4

Designs: 50c, View of Alexandretta. 75c, View of Hama. 1p, Omayyad Mosque, Damascus. 1.25p, Latakia Harbor. 1.50p, View of Damascus. 2p, View of Palmyra. 2.50p, View of Kalat Yamoun. 3p, Bridge of Daphne. 5p, View of Aleppo. 10p, View of Aleppo. 25p, Columns at Palmyra.

Perf. 12½, 13½

1925   Litho.   Unwmk.

173	A3	10c dark violet	.20	.20

Photo.

174	A4	25c olive black	.55	.55
175	A4	50c yellow green	.60	.25
176	A4	75c brown orange	.25	.20
177	A5	1p magenta	.30	.20
178	A4	1.25p deep green	1.10	1.10
179	A4	1.50p rose red	.30	.20
180	A4	2p dark brown	.85	.20
181	A4	2.50p peacock blue	.75	.50
182	A4	3p orange brn	.75	.20
183	A4	5p violet	.65	.20
184	A4	10p violet brown	1.60	.30
185	A4	25p ultra	1.90	1.25
		Nos. 173-185 (13)	9.80	5.35

For surcharges see Nos. 186-206, B1-B12, C26-C45, CB1-CB4.

Surcharged in Black or Red

1926-30

186	A4	1p on 3pi org brn ('30)	.50	.25
187	A4	2p on 1p25 dp grn (R) ('28)	.25	.25
a.		Double surcharge	8.25	8.25
188	A4	3.50p on 75c org brn	.25	.25
a.		Double surcharge	8.25	8.25
189	A4	4p on 25c ol blk	.45	.20
190	A4	4p on 25c ol blk ('27)	.45	.45
191	A4	4p on 25c ol blk (R) ('28)	.30	.20
192	A4	4.50p on 75c brn org	.40	.20
193	A4	6p on 2p50 pck bl	.25	.20
194	A4	7.50p on 2p50 pck bl	.25	.20
195	A4	7.50p on 2p50 pck bl (R) ('28)	.70	.55
a.		Double surcharge	8.25	
196	A4	12p on 1p25 dp grn	.40	.30
a.		Surcharge on face and back	42.50	42.50
197	A4	15p on 25p ultra	.55	.30
198	A4	20p on 1p25 dp grn	.60	.40
		Nos. 186-198 (13)	5.35	3.70

Size of numerals and arrangement of this surcharge varies on the different denominations.
No. 189 has slanting foot on "4."
No. 190, foot straight.

No. 173 Surcharged in Red

1928

199	A3	05c on 10c dk vio	.20	.20

Stamps of 1925 Issue Overprinted in Red or Blue

1929   Perf. 13½

200	A4	50c yellow grn (R)	1.60	1.60
201	A5	1p magenta (Bl)	1.60	1.60
202	A4	1.50p rose red (Bl)	1.60	1.60
203	A4	3p orange brn (Bl)	1.60	1.60
204	A4	5p violet (R)	1.60	1.60
205	A4	10p violet brn (Bl)	1.60	1.60
206	A4	25p ultra (R)	1.60	1.60
		Nos. 200-206 (7)	11.20	11.20

Industrial Exhibition, Damascus, Sept. 1929.

View of Hama — A6

View of Alexandretta — A9

Citadel at Aleppo A10

Great Mosque of Damascus A11

Ruins of Bosra A13

Mosque at Homs A15

View of Sednaya A16

Citadel at Aleppo A17

Ancient Bridge at Antioch A18

Mosque at Damascus A22

Designs: 20c, Great Mosque, Aleppo. 25c, Minaret, Hama. 2p, View of Antioch. 4p, Square at Damascus. 15p, Mosque at Hama. 25p, Monastery of St. Simeon the Stylite (ruins). 50p, Sun Temple (ruins), Palmyra.

Perf. 12x12½

1930-36   Litho.   Unwmk.

208	A6	10c red violet	.20	.20
209	A6	10c vio brn ('33)	.20	.20
209A	A6	10c vio brn, redrawn ('35)	.20	.20
210	A6	20c dark blue	.20	.20
211	A6	20c brn org ('33)	.20	.20
212	A6	25c gray green	.20	.20
213	A6	25c dk bl gray ('33)	.20	.20

Photo.
Perf. 13

214	A9	50c violet	.20	.20
215	A15	75c org red ('32)	.20	.20
216	A10	1p green	.20	.20
217	A10	1p bis brn ('36)	.20	.20
218	A11	1.50p bister brown	3.00	1.90
219	A11	1.50p dp grn ('33)	.25	.25
220	A9	2p dark violet	.20	.20
221	A13	3p yellow green	.60	.40
222	A10	4p yellow orange	.20	.20
223	A15	4.50p rose carmine	.60	.45
224	A16	6p grnsh black	.30	.20
225	A17	7.50p dull blue	.85	.45
226	A18	10p dark brown	.65	.20
227	A10	15p deep green	1.40	.65
228	A18	25p violet brown	1.40	.75
229	A15	50p olive brown	4.50	3.25
230	A22	100p red orange	9.25	7.50
		Nos. 208-230 (24)	25.40	18.60

On No. 209A Arabic inscriptions, upper right, are entirely redrawn with lighter lines. Hyphen added in "Helio-Vaugirard" imprint. Lines in buildings and background more distinct.

On No. 215 the letters of "VAUGIRARD" in the imprint are reversed as in a mirror.

For overprints and surcharges see Nos. 253-268, 346, M1-M2.

Autonomous Republic

Parliament Building A23

abu-al-Ala al-Maarri — A24

President Ali Bek el Abed — A25

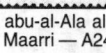

Saladin — A26

1934, Aug. 2		Engr.	Perf. 12½	
232	A23	10c olive green	.45	.45
233	A23	20c black	.45	.45
234	A23	25c red orange	.45	.45
235	A23	50c ultra	.45	.45
236	A23	75c plum	.45	.45
237	A24	1p vermilion	1.50	1.50
238	A24	1.50p green	2.50	2.50
239	A24	2p red brown	2.50	2.50
240	A24	3p Prus blue	2.50	2.50
241	A24	4p brt violet	2.50	2.50
242	A24	4.50p carmine	2.50	2.50
243	A24	5p dark blue	2.50	2.50
244	A24	6p dark brown	2.50	2.50
245	A24	7.50p dark ultra	2.50	2.50
246	A25	10p dark brown	4.00	4.00
247	A25	15p dull blue	6.00	5.25
248	A25	25p rose red	8.75	8.75
249	A26	50p dark brown	17.50	16.00
250	A26	100p lake	27.50	25.00
		Nos. 232-250 (19)	87.50	82.75

Proclamation of the Republic. See Nos. C57-C66. For surcharge see No. M3.

Stamps of 1930-36 Overprinted in Red or Black

1936, Apr. 15

253	A9	50c violet (R)	1.25	1.25
254	A10	1p bister brn (Bk)	1.25	1.25
255	A9	2p dk violet (R)	1.25	1.25
256	A13	3p yellow grn (Bk)	1.25	1.25
257	A10	4p yellow org (Bk)	1.25	1.25
258	A15	4.50p rose car (Bk)	1.25	1.25
259	A16	6p grnsh blk (R)	1.40	1.40
260	A17	7.50p dull blue (R)	1.50	1.50
261	A18	10p dk brown (Bk)	1.90	1.90
		Nos. 253-261 (9)	12.30	12.30

Industrial Exhibition, Damascus, May 1936. See Nos. C67-C71.

Stamps of 1930 Surcharged in Black

1937-38   Perf. 13½x13
262	A10	2.50p on 4p yel org ('38)	.20	.20
263	A22	10p on 100p red orange	.30	.30

Stamps of 1930-33 Surcharged in Red or Black

1938   Perf. 13½
264	A15	25c on 75c org red (Bk)	.20	.20
265	A11	50c on 1.50p dp grn (R)	.30	.20
266	A17	2p on 7.50p dl bl (R)	.30	.20
267	A17	5p on 7.50p dl bl (R)	.55	.20
268	A15	10p on 50p ol brn (Bk)	.65	.35
		Nos. 264-268 (5)	2.00	1.15

President Hashem Bek el Atassi — A27

1938-43   Photo.   Unwmk.
268A	A27	10p dp blue ('43)	.20	.20
269	A27	12.50p on 10p dp bl (R)	.30	.25
270	A27	20p dark brown	.30	.25
		Nos. 268A-270 (3)	.80	.70

The 10pi and 20pi exist imperf.

Columns at Palmyra A28

1940   Litho.   Perf. 11½
271	A28	5p pale rose	.45	.30

Exists imperf.

Museum at Damascus — A29

Hotel at Bloudan A30

Kasr-el-Heir A31

1940   Typo.   Perf. 13x14
272	A29	10c bright rose	.20	.20
273	A29	20c light blue	.20	.20
274	A29	25c fawn	.20	.20
275	A29	50c ultra	.20	.20

Engr.   Perf. 13
276	A30	1p peacock blue	.20	.20
277	A30	1.50p chocolate	.20	.20
278	A30	2.50p dark green	.20	.20
279	A31	5p violet	.20	.20
280	A31	7.50p vermilion	.30	.20
281	A31	50p sepia	.75	.70
		Nos. 272-281 (10)	2.65	2.50

For overprints see Nos. 298-299.

President Taj Eddin Hassani A32

1942, Apr. 6   Litho.   Perf. 11½
282	A32	50c sage green	2.25	1.60
283	A32	1.50p dull gray brn	2.25	1.60
284	A32	6p fawn	2.25	1.60
285	A32	15p light blue	2.25	1.60
		Nos. 282-285,C96-C97 (6)	11.80	9.20

Proclamation of independence by the Allies, Sept. 27, 1941.

President Taj Eddin Hassani — A33

President Hassani and Map of Syria — A34

1942   Photo.   Unwmk.
286	A33	6p rose lake & salmon rose	1.10	1.10
287	A33	15p dull blue & blue	1.10	1.10
		Nos. 286-287,C98 (3)	4.70	4.70

Nos. 286-287 exist imperf.

1943   Litho.
288	A34	1p light green	1.25	1.10
289	A34	4p buff	1.25	1.10
290	A34	8p pale violet	1.25	1.10
291	A34	10p salmon	1.25	1.10
292	A34	20p dull chalky blue	1.25	1.10
		Nos. 288-292,C99-C102 (9)	10.65	9.90

Proclamation of a United Syria. Exist imperf.

Stamps of 1943 Overprinted with Border in Black

1943
293	A34	1p light green	1.25	1.10
294	A34	4p buff	1.25	1.10
295	A34	8p pale violet	1.25	1.10
296	A34	10p salmon	1.25	1.10
297	A34	20p dl chalky bl	1.25	1.10
		Nos. 293-297,C103-C106 (9)	10.65	9.90

Mourning for President Hassani. Exist imperf.

Nos. 278 and 280 Overprinted in Carmine or Black

1944   Unwmk.   Perf. 13
298	A30	2.50p dk green (C)	1.60	1.60
299	A31	7.50p vermilion (Bk)	1.60	1.60
		Nos. 298-299,C114-C116 (5)	14.45	14.45

1000th anniv. of the Arab poet and philosopher, abu-al-Ala al-Maarri.

President Shukri el Kouatly — A35

1945, Mar. 15   Litho.   Perf. 11½
300	A35	4p pale lilac	.20	.20
301	A35	6p dull blue	.20	.20
302	A35	10p salmon	.20	.20
303	A35	15p dark brown	.55	.30
304	A35	20p slate green	.55	.45
305	A35	40p orange	.85	.75
		Nos. 300-305,C117-C123 (13)	9.55	5.65

Resumption of constitutional government.

A36

A37

A38

A39

Fiscal Stamps Overprinted or Surcharged in Black

1945   Typo.   Perf. 11, 11½x11
306	A36	12½p on 15p yel grn	1.10	.95
307	A37	25p buff	1.75	1.60
307A	A38	25p on 25s lt vio brn	1.25	1.10
308	A39	50p on 75p brn org	2.50	2.25
309	A39	75p brown org	3.25	3.00
310	A37	100p yellow grn	4.00	3.50
		Nos. 306-310 (6)	13.85	12.40

Type of 1945 and Nos. 308 and 310 Overprinted in Black

a   b

1945   Unwmk.   Perf. 11
311	A37(b)	50p magenta	1.25	1.25
312	A39(a)	50p on 75p brn org	1.00	.70
313	A37(b)	100p yellow green	1.50	1.25
		Nos. 311-313 (3)	3.75	3.20

Catalogue values for unused stamps in this section, from this point to the end of the section, are for Never Hinged items.

Independent Republic

A40

Fiscal Stamp Overprinted in Carmine

1946
314	A40	200p light blue	11.00	6.00

Sun and Ears of Wheat — A41

President Shukri el Kouatly — A42

1946   Litho.   Perf. 13x13½
315	A41	50c brown orange	.20	.20
316	A41	1p violet	.20	.20
317	A41	2.50p blue gray	.25	.20
318	A41	5p lt blue green	.25	.20

Photo.   Perf. 13½x13, 13x13½
319	A42	7.50p dark brown	.20	.20
320	A42	10p Prussian green	.20	.20
321	A42	12.50p deep violet	.45	.20
		Nos. 315-321 (7)	1.75	1.40

For overprints see Nos. 328-329, 335-336.

Arab Horse A44

1946-47   Litho.
325	A44	50p olive brown	1.75	.50
326	A44	100p dk blue grn ('47)	3.75	1.25
327	A44	200p rose violet ('47)	19.00	3.50
		Nos. 325-327 (3)	24.50	5.25

For overprints and surcharges see Nos. 330, 337, 356-357.

Nos. 320, 321 and 325 Overprinted in Black or Green

1946, Apr. 17
328	A42	10p Prus green	.40	.40
329	A42	12.50p deep violet	.60	.60
330	A44	50p olive brown (G)	1.50	1.50
		Nos. 328-330,C135 (4)	3.50	3.00

Evacuation of British and French troops from Syria. For surcharge see No. 347.

President Shukri el Kouatly — A45

1946   Unwmk.   Litho.   Perf. 13½x13
331	A45	15p red	.25	.20
332	A45	20p violet	.40	.20
333	A45	25p ultra	.60	.20
		Nos. 331-333 (3)	1.25	.60

No. 333 Overprinted in Magenta

1946, Aug. 28
334 A45 25p ultra   1.25 1.10
   Nos. 334,C136-C138 (4)   6.85 4.60
8th Arab Medical Cong., Aleppo, 8/28-9/4.

Nos. 328 to 330 With Additional Overprint in Black

e

f

Perf. 13½x13, 13x13½
1947, June 10
335 A42(e)   10p Prus green   .40 .20
336 A42(e)   12.50p deep violet   .60 .20
337 A44(f)   50p olive brown   1.50 .50
   Nos. 335-337,C139 (4)   3.50 1.50
Evacuation of British and French troops, 1st anniv.

Hercules and the Lion — A46

Mosaics from Omayyad Mosque, Damascus A47

1947, Nov. 15   Litho.   Perf. 11½
338 A46 12.50p slate green   .50 .40
339 A47   25p gray blue   1.00 .60
   Nos. 338-339,C140-C141 (4)   5.00 2.50
1st Arab Archaeological Cong., Damascus, Nov.
   See No. C141a.

Courtyard of Azem Palace A48

Telephone Building A49

1947, Nov. 15
340 A48 12.50p deep claret   .50 .50
341 A49   25p brt blue   1.00 .70
   Nos. 340-341,C142-C143 (4)   4.00 2.85
3rd Congress of Arab Engineers, Damascus, Nov.
   See No. C143a.

House of Parliament A50

Pres. Shukri el Kouatly — A51

1948, June 23   Unwmk.   Perf. 10½
342 A50 12.50p black & org   .35 .20
343 A51   25p deep rose   .70 .45
   Nos. 342-343,C144-C145 (4)   3.15 1.50
Reelection of Pres. Shukri el Kouatly. See No. C145a.

National Emblem — A52   Syrian Flag and Soldier — A53

1948, June 23   Litho.
344 A52 12.50p gray & choc   .40 .25
345 A53   25p multicolored   .85 .45
   Nos. 344-345,C146-C147 (4)   3.50 1.50
Inauguration of compulsory military training. See No. C147a.

Nos. 215 and 327 Surcharged with New Value and Bars in Black

1948   Perf. 13, 13x13½
346 A15 50c on 75c org red   .20 .20
347 A44 25p on 200p rose vio   2.00 .30

Col. Husni Zayim — A54   Palmyra — A56

Ain el Arous A55

1949, June 20   Litho.   Perf. 11½
348 A54 25p blue   .60 .40
Revolution of Mar. 30, 1949. See No. C153.
   A souvenir sheet comprises Nos. 348 and C153, imperf. Value $80.

1949, June 20
349 A55 12.50p violet   1.50 1.50
350 A56   25p blue   2.25 2.25
   Nos. 349-350,C154-C155 (4)   20.75 17.25
UPU, 75th anniv. See note after #C155.

Pres. Husni Zayim and Map — A57

Wmk. 291
1949, Aug. 6   Litho.   Perf. 11½
351 A57 25p blue & brown   2.00 1.25
Election of President Husni Zayim. See Nos. C156, C156a.

Tel-Chehab Waterfall — A58

Damascus Scene A59

1949
352 A58   5p gray   .20 .20
353 A58   7.50p olive gray   .20 .20
354 A59 12.50p violet brown   .40 .20
355 A59   25p blue   .80 .40
   Nos. 352-355 (4)   1.60 1.00
   See No. 376.

Nos. 327 and 326 Surcharged with New Value and Bars in Black

1950   Unwmk.   Perf. 13x13½
356 A44 2.50p on 200p rose vio   .25 .20
357 A44 10p on 100p dk bl grn   .35 .20

National Emblem — A60

Road to Damascus A61

Postal Administration Building, Damascus — A62

1950-51   Litho.   Perf. 11½
358 A60 50c orange brn   .20 .20
359 A60 2.50p pink   .20 .20
360 A61 10p purple ('51)   .25 .20
361 A61 12.50p sage grn ('51)   .45 .30
362 A62 25p blue ('51)   .90 .20
363 A62 50p black ('51)   2.75 .50
   Nos. 358-363 (6)   4.75 1.60
Nos. 358 to 363 exist imperforate.

Parliament Building, Damascus A63

1951, Apr. 14
364 A63 12.50p gray blk   .20 .20
365 A63   25p blue   .50 .35
   Nos. 364-365,C162-C163 (4)   1.60 1.35
New constitution adopted Sept. 5, 1950.
Nos. 364-365 exist imperforate.

Water Wheel, Hama A64

Palace of Justice, Damascus A65

Perf. 11½
1952, Apr. 22   Litho.   Unwmk.
366 A64 50c dark brown   .20 .20
367 A64 2.50p dark blue   .20 .20
368 A64 5p blue green   .20 .20
369 A64 10p red   .25 .20
370 A65 12.50p gray black   .55 .20
371 A65 15p lilac rose   .70 .20
372 A65 25p deep blue   1.50 .25
373 A65 100p olive brown   5.00 1.25
   Nos. 366-373 (8)   8.60 2.70
Nos. 366-373 exist imperforate.

Type of 1949 and

Crusaders' Fort — A66

Crusaders' Fort — A67

1953   Photo.
374 A67 50c rose red   .20 .20
375 A66 2.50p dark brown   .20 .20
376 A58 7.50p green   .20 .20
377 A67 12.50p deep blue   1.10 .20
   Nos. 374-377 (4)   1.70 .80

Farm Workers — A68

Family Group A69

Designs: 1pi, 5pi, Farm workers. 10pi, 12½p, Family group. 20pi, 25pi, 50pi, Factory and construction workers.

1954   Perf. 11½
378 A68 1p olive   .20 .20
379 A68 2½p brown red   .20 .20
380 A68 5p deep blue   .20 .20
381 A69 7½p brown red   .20 .20
382 A69 10p black   .25 .20
383 A69 12½p violet   .25 .20
384 A69 20p deep plum   .50 .20
385 A69 25p violet   .95 .25
386 A69 50p dark green   2.25 .60
   Nos. 378-386 (9)   5.00 2.25
For overprints see #387-388, UAR 20, 34.

Nos. 382 and 385 Overprinted in Carmine

1954, Oct. 9
387 A69 10p black .65 .35
388 A69 25p violet .70 .45
Nos. 387-388,C185-C186 (4) 3.45 2.30

Cotton Festival, Aleppo, October 1954.

Globe — A69a

Mother and Child — A70

Arab Postal Union Issue
1955 **Photo.** **Perf. 13½x13**
389 A69a 12½p green .35 .20
390 A69a 25p violet .60 .25
Nos. 389-390,C191 (3) 1.15 .65

Founding of the APU, 7/1/54. Exist imperf. For overprints see #396-399, C203, C207.

1955, May 13 **Litho.** **Perf. 11½**
391 A70 25p red .40 .25
Nos. 391,C194-C195 (3) 2.00 1.00

Mother's Day.

United Nations Emblem A71

1955 **Photo.**
392 A71 7½p crimson .35 .25
393 A71 12½p Prus green .60 .30
Nos. 392-393,C200-C201 (4) 2.45 1.20

UN, 10th anniv., Oct. 24. For overprints see Nos. 401-402.

Aqueduct at Aleppo A72

1955 **Litho.** **Unwmk.**
394 A72 7.50p lilac .20 .20
395 A72 12.50p carmine .30 .20
Nos. 394-395,C202 (3) 2.10 1.00

New aqueduct bringing water from the Euphrates to Northern Syria. Exist imperf.

Nos. 389-390 Overprinted in Ultramarine or Green

1955 **Photo.** **Perf. 13½x13**
396 A69a 12½p green .25 .20
397 A69a 25p vio (G) 1.00 .40
Nos. 396-397,C203 (3) 1.60 .80

APU Congress held at Cairo, Mar. 15.

Nos. 389-390 Overprinted in Black

مهرى زيارة جاهل الأردن
نسأه ١٩٥٦

1956
398 A69a 12½p green .35 .25
399 A69a 25p violet .60 .55
Nos. 398-399,C207 (3) 1.30 1.00

Visit of King Hussein of Jordan to Damascus, Apr. 1956.

Cotton — A73

1956 **Unwmk.** **Litho.** **Perf. 11½**
400 A73 2½p bluish green .30 .20

Issued to publicize a Cotton Festival.

Nos. 392-393 Overprinted in Black

الذكرى الحادية عشرة للأمم المتحدة
11ᵉᵐᵉ ANNIVERSAIRE de l'ONU

1956 **Photo.** **Perf. 11½**
401 A71 7½p crimson .40 .20
402 A71 12½p Prussian green .50 .35
Nos. 401-402,C221-C222 (4) 3.25 2.15

UN, 11th anniv.

People's Army A74

1957 **Litho.** **Perf. 11½**
403 A74 5p lilac rose .20 .20
404 A74 20p gray green .35 .25

Formation of the Popular Resistance Movement.
For overprints see Nos. 405-406, 413-414.

Nos. 403-404 Overprinted in Black or Red

ذكرى الجلاء عن بورسعيد ١٩٥٦/١٢/٢٢
22/12/56 EVACUATION PORT SAID

1957
405 A74 5p lilac rose .20 .20
406 A74 20p gray green (R) .35 .30

Evacuation of Port Said by British and French troops, Dec. 22, 1956.

Azem Palace, Damascus A75

1957 **Litho.** **Perf. 11½**
407 A75 12½p lilac .20 .20
408 A75 15p gray .35 .20

For overprint see UAR No. 33.

Map of Near East, Scales and Damascus Skyline — A76

Cotton, Bale and Ship — A77

1957 **Wmk. 291** **Perf. 11½**
409 A76 12½p bright green .20 .20
Nos. 409,C240-C241 (3) 1.00 .75

3rd Congress of the Union of Arab Lawyers, Damascus, Sept. 21-25.

1957
410 A77 12½p lt bl grn & blk .30 .20
Nos. 410,C242-C243 (3) 1.50 .80

Cotton Festival, Aleppo, Oct. 3-5.

Children — A78

1957, Oct. 7
411 A78 12½p olive .50 .20
Nos. 411,C244-C245 (3) 2.50 .90

Intl. Children's Day, Oct. 7.
For overprint see UAR Nos. 13A, C10-C11.

Mailing and Receiving Letter A79

1957 **Unwmk.**
412 A79 5p magenta .35 .20

Intl. Letter Writing Week, Oct. 6-12. See No. C246.

Nos. 403-404 Overprinted in Black or Red

1957 **Perf. 11½**
413 A74 5p lilac rose .20 .20
414 A74 20p gray green (R) .30 .20

Digging of fortifications along the Syrian-Israeli frontier.

Scales, Torch and Map A80

1957, Nov. 8 **Wmk. 291**
415 A80 20p olive gray .35 .20
Nos. 415,C247-C248 (3) 1.10 .75

Congress of Afro-Asian Jurists, Damascus.

Glider A81

1957, Nov. 8 **Litho.** **Perf. 11½**
416 A81 25p red brown .60 .30
417 A81 35p green .90 .40
418 A81 40p ultra 2.00 .55
Nos. 416-418 (3) 3.50 1.25

Issued to commemorate a glider festival.

Khaled ibn el Walid Mosque, Homs — A82

1957 **Unwmk.** **Perf. 12**
419 A82 2½p dull brown .20 .20

Scroll, Communications Building and Telephone — A83

1958 **Wmk. 291** **Perf. 11½**
420 A83 25p ultra .20 .20
Nos. 420,C249-C250 (3) .65 .60

Issues of 1958-61 released by the United Arab Republic are listed following the listings of Syria, Issues of the Arabian Government.

Syrian Arab Republic

Hall of Parliament, Damascus A83a

1961 **Unwmk.** **Litho.** **Perf. 12**
420A A83a 15p magenta .40 .25
420B A83a 35p olive gray .75 .25

Establishment of Syrian Arab Republic.

Water Wheel, Hama — A84

Roman Arch of Triumph, Latakia — A85

Qalb Lozah Church, Aleppo A86

7½p, 10p, Khaled ibn el Walid Mosque, Homs.

		Perf. 11½x11		
1961-62		**Unwmk.**		**Litho.**
421	A84	2½p rose red	.30	.20
422	A84	5p blue	.30	.20
423	A84	7½p blue grn ('62)	.30	.20
424	A84	10p orange ('62)	.35	.20

		Perf. 12x11½		
425	A85	12½p gray brn	.60	.20
426	A86	17½p olive gray ('62)	.50	.20
427	A85	25p dull red brown	.70	.20
428	A86	35p dull green ('62)	.65	.20
		Nos. 421-428 (8)	3.70	1.60

Types of 1961, Regular and Air Post

Designs: 2½p, 5p, 7½p, 10p, Arch, Jupiter Temple. 12½p, 15p, 17½p, 22½p, "The Beauty of Palmyra."

1962   **Perf. 11½x11**
429	A84	2½p	gray blue	.30 .20
430	A84	5p	brown orange	.30 .20
431	A84	7½p	olive bister	.30 .20
432	A84	10p	claret	.30 .20

       Perf. 12x11½
       Size: 26x38mm
433	AP68	12½p	gray olive	.35 .20
434	AP68	15p	ultra	.50 .20
435	AP68	17½p	brown	.50 .20
436	AP68	22½p	grnsh blue	.70 .20
	Nos. 429-436 (8)			3.25 1.60

Martyrs' Memorial — A87

Pres. Nazem el-Kodsi — A88

1962, June 11   **Litho.**
440	A87	12½p	tan & sepia	.30 .20
441	A87	35p	green & bl grn	.35 .20

1925 Revolution.

1962, Dec. 14   **Perf. 12x11½**
442	A88	12½p	sepia & lt bl	.30 .20

1st anniv. of the election of Pres. Nazem el-Kodsi. See No. C278.

Queen Zenobia — A89

Central Bank of Syria A90

Designs: 2½p, 5p, "The Beauty of Palmyra." 17½p, Hejaz Railway Station, Damascus. 22½p, Mouassat Hospital, Damascus. 35p, P.T.T. Jalaa Avenue Office, Damascus.

1963   **Unwmk.**   **Perf. 11½x11**
443	A89	2½p	dk bl gray	.30 .20
444	A89	5p	rose lilac	.30 .20
445	A89	7½p	dull blue	.35 .20
446	A89	10p	olive gray	.70 .20
447	A89	12½p	ultra	1.00 .20
448	A89	15p	violet brn	1.50 .20

       Perf. 11½x12
449	A90	17½p	dull violet	.60 .20
450	A90	22½p	brt violet	.30 .20
451	A90	25p	bister brown	.30 .20
452	A90	35p	bright pink	.35 .20
	Nos. 443-452 (10)			5.70 2.00

Wheat Emblem and Globe — A91

Boy Playing Ball and UN Emblem — A92

1963, Mar. 21   **Litho.**   **Perf. 12x11½**
453	A91	12½p	ultra & blk	.30 .20

FAO "Freedom from Hunger" Campaign. See No. C291 and souvenir sheet No. C291a.

Cotton Festival Type of Air Post Issue, 1962, Inscribed "1963"

1963, Sept. 26   **Perf. 12x11½**
455	AP75	17½p	multi	.30 .20
456	AP75	22½p	multi	.35 .20

The 1963 Cotton Festival, Aleppo.

1963, Oct. 24   **Perf. 12x11½**
457	A92	12½p	emer & sl grn	.30 .20
458	A92	22½p	rose red & dk grn	.30 .20

Issued for International Children's Day.

Ugharit Princess — A93

1964   **Litho.**   **Perf. 11½x11**
459	A93	2½p	gray	.30 .20
460	A93	5p	brown	.30 .20
461	A93	7½p	rose claret	.30 .20
462	A93	10p	emerald	.30 .20
463	A93	12½p	light violet	.30 .20
464	A93	17½p	ultra	.30 .20
465	A93	20p	rose carmine	.45 .20
466	A93	25p	orange	.75 .20
	Nos. 459-466 (8)			3.00 1.60

Map of North Africa and Middle East, Flag of Syria, and Crowd A94

1965, Mar. 8   **Litho.**   **Perf. 11½x12**
467	A94	12½p	multicolored	.30 .20
468	A94	17½p	multicolored	.30 .20
469	A94	20p	multicolored	.30 .20
	Nos. 467-469 (3)			.90 .60

Mar. 8 Revolution, 2nd anniv.

Weather Map and Anemometer — A95

1965, Mar. 23   **Litho.**   **Unwmk.**
470	A95	12½p	dl lilac & blk	.30 .20
471	A95	27½p	lt blue & blk	.30 .20

Fifth World Meteorological Day.

"Evacuation of Apr. 17, 1946" — A96

Peasants' Union Emblem — A97

1965, Apr. 17   **Litho.**   **Perf. 12x11½**
472	A96	12½p	bl & brt yel grn	.30 .20
473	A96	27½p	rose red & lt lil	.30 .20

19th anniv. of the evacuation of British and French troops from Syria.

1965, Aug.   **Unwmk.**   **Perf. 11½x11**
474	A97	2½p	blue green	.30 .20
475	A97	12½p	purple	.30 .20
476	A97	15p	maroon	.30 .20
	Nos. 474-476 (3)			.90 .60

Issued to publicize the Peasants' Union.

Torch, Map of Arab Countries and Farmer, Soldier, Woman, Intellectual and Worker — A98

Workers, Factory and Emblem — A99

1965, Nov. 23   **Perf. 12x11½**
477	A98	12½p	multicolored	.30 .20
478	A98	25p	multicolored	.30 .20

National Council of the Revolution, a legislative body working for a socialist and democratic society.

1966, Jan.   **Litho.**   **Perf. 11½x11**
479	A99	12½p	blue	.30 .20
480	A99	15p	carmine	.30 .20
481	A99	20p	dull violet	.30 .20
482	A99	25p	olive gray	.30 .20
	Nos. 479-482 (4)			1.20 .80

Establishment of the General Union of Trade Unions.

Roman Lamp A100

Islamic Vessel, 12th Century A101

1966   **Litho.**   **Perf. 11½x11**
483	A100	2½p	slate green	.30 .20
484	A100	5p	magenta	.30 .20
485	A101	7½p	brown	.30 .20
486	A101	10p	brt rose lilac	.30 .20
	Nos. 483-486 (4)			1.20 .80

"Evacuation of Troops" — A102

Bust of Core, Terra Cotta Vase — A103

1966, Apr. 17   **Litho.**   **Perf. 12x11½**
487	A102	12½p	multi	.30 .20
488	A102	27½p	multi	.30 .20

20th anniv. of the evacuation of British and French troops from Syria.

1967   **Perf. 11½x11**

Design: 15p, 20p, 25p, 27½p, Bronze vase in form of seated African woman.

489	A103	2½p	brt green	.30 .20
490	A103	5p	salmon pink	.30 .20
491	A103	10p	grnsh blue	.30 .20
492	A103	12½p	dull brown	.30 .20
493	A103	15p	brt pink	.30 .20
494	A103	20p	brt blue	.30 .20
495	A103	25p	green	.30 .20
496	A103	27½p	violet blue	.30 .20
	Nos. 489-496 (8)			2.40 1.60

Arab Revolution Monument, Damascus A104

1968, Mar. 8   **Litho.**   **Perf. 12x12½**
497	A104	12½p	black, yel & brn	.30 .20
498	A104	25p	blk, pink & car rose	.30 .20
499	A104	27½p	blk, lt grn & grn	.30 .20
	Nos. 497-499 (3)			.90 .60

Mar. 8 Revolution, 5th anniversary.

Map of Syria — A105

Hands Holding Wrench, Gun and Torch — A106

1968, Apr. 4   **Litho.**   **Perf. 12x12½**
500	A105	12½p	pink & multi	.30 .20
501	A105	60p	gray & multi	.40 .20

Arab Baath Socialist Party, 21st anniv.

1968, Apr. 13
502	A106	12½p	tan & multi	.30 .20
503	A106	17½p	rose & multi	.30 .20
504	A106	25p	yellow & multi	.30 .20
	Nos. 502-504 (3)			.90 .60

Issued to publicize the mobilization effort.

Rising
Sun,
Power
Lines and
Railroad
Tracks
A107

1968, Apr. 17   Litho.   Perf. 12½x12
505 A107 12½p multicolored   .30 .20
506 A107 27½p violet & multi   .30 .20

22nd anniv. of the evacuation of British and French troops from Syria.

Oil Wells and Oil Pipe Line on
Map — A108

1968, May 1
507 A108 12½p lt & dk grn & ultra   .30 .20
508 A108 17½p pink, brn & ultra   .30 .20

Syrian oil exploitation; completion of the oil pipe line to Tartus.

Map of Palestine
and
Torch — A109

Citadel of Aleppo,
Wheat and
Cogwheel
A110

1968, May   Litho.   Perf. 12x12½
509 A109 12½p ultra, blk & red   .30 .20
510 A109 25p ol bis, blk & red   .35 .20
511 A109 27½p gray, blk & red   .40 .20
     Nos. 509-511 (3)   1.05 .60

Issued for Palestine Day.

1968, July 18   Litho.   Perf. 12x12½
512 A110 12½p multi   .30 .20
513 A110 27½p multi   .30 .20

Industrial and Agricultural Fair, Aleppo.

Fair Emblem,
Globe, Grain,
Wheel and
Horse — A111

Woman Carrying
Cotton, and
Castle of
Aleppo — A112

Design: 27½p, Syrian flag, hand with torch, fair emblem, globe, grain and wheel.

Perf. 12x12½, 12½x12
1968, Aug. 25   Litho.
514 A111 12½p dp brn, blk & emer   .30 .20
515 A111 27½p multicolored   .30 .20
516 A111 60p bl gray, blk & dp
             org   .30 .20
     Nos. 514-516 (3)   .90 .60

15th Intl. Damascus Fair, Aug. 25-Sept. 20.

1968, Oct. 3   Litho.   Perf. 12½x12½
517 A112 12½p multi   .30 .20
518 A112 27½p multi   .30 .20

13th Cotton Festival, Aleppo.

Al Jahez — A113

Oil Derrick and
Pipe
Line — A114

1968, Nov. 9   Litho.   Perf. 12x12½
519 A113 12½p black & buff   .30 .20
520 A113 27½p black & gray   .60 .20

9th Science Week; Al Jahez Abu Uthman Amr ben Bahr (776-868).

1968   Perf. 12x11
521 A114   2½p grnsh bl & dk
              grn   .30 .20
522 A114   5p grn & vio bl   .30 .20
523 A114   7½p lt yel grn & bl   .30 .20
524 A114   10p brt yel & grn   .30 .20
525 A114 12½p yellow & ver   .30 .20
526 A114   15p ol bis & dk brn   .30 .20
527 A114 27½p dl org & dk red
              brn   .30 .20
     Nos. 521-527 (7)   2.10 1.40

Broken
Chains
and Sun
A115

1969, Mar. 8   Litho.   Perf. 12½x12
Sun in Yellow and Red
528 A115 12½p vio bl & blk   .30 .20
529 A115   25p gray & blk   .30 .20
530 A115 27½p dull grn & blk   .30 .20
     Nos. 528-530 (3)   .90 .60

March 8 Revolution, 6th anniversary.

"Sun of Freedom,
Young Man and
Woman" — A116

Liberation through
Knowledge and
Construction
A117

1969, Mar. 29   Perf. 12x12½
531 A116 12½p multi   .30 .20
532 A116   25p multi   .30 .20

Youth Week; 5th Youth Festival, Homs, 4/18-24.

1969, Apr. 17   Litho.   Perf. 12x12½
533 A117 12½p yellow & multi   .30 .20
534 A117 27½p gray & multi   .30 .20

23rd anniv. of the evacuation of British and French troops from Syria.

Mahatma
Gandhi — A118

Cotton — A119

1969, Oct. 7   Litho.   Perf. 12x12½
535 A118 12½p brown & dull yel   .30 .20
536 A118 27½p green & yellow   .30 .20

Mohandas K. Gandhi (1869-1948), leader in India's fight for independence.

1969, Oct. 10
537 A119 12½p multi   .30 .20
538 A119 17½p multi   .30 .20
539 A119   25p multi   .30 .20
     Nos. 537-539 (3)   .90 .60

14th Cotton Festival, Aleppo.

Map of
Arab
Countries
A120

Designs: 25p, Arab Academy. 27½p, Damascus University.

1969, Nov. 2   Litho.   Perf. 12½x12
540 A120 12½p ultra & lt grn   .30 .20
541 A120   25p dk pur & dp pink   .30 .20
542 A120 27½p dp bis & yel grn   .30 .20
     Nos. 540-542 (3)   .90 .60

10th Science Week, and 6th Arab Scientific Conf. No. 541 also for 50th anniv. of the Arab Academy and No. 542, the 50th anniv. of the Medical School of the Damascus University.

Symbols
of
Progress
A121

1970, Mar. 8   Litho.   Perf. 12½x12
543 A121 12½p brt bl, blk & bis brn .30 .20
544 A121   25p red, blk & dp bl   .30 .20
545 A121 27½p lt grn, blk & tan   .30 .20
     Nos. 543-545 (3)   .90 .60

March 8 Revolution, 7th anniversary.

Map of
Arab
League
Countries,
Flag and
Emblem
A122

1970, Mar. 22
546 A122 12½p multi   .30 .20
547 A122   25p gray & multi   .30 .20
548 A122 27½p multi   .35 .20
     Nos. 546-548 (3)   .95 .60

25th anniversary of the Arab League.

Sultan Saladin and Battle of Hattin,
1187, between Saracens and
Crusaders — A123

1970, Apr. 17   Litho.   Perf. 12½x12
549 A123 15p brn & buff   .30 .20
550 A123 35p lilac & buff   .35 .20

24th anniv. of the evacuation of British and French troops from Syria.

Development of
Agriculture and
Industry — A124

1970-71   Litho.   Perf. 11x11½
551 A124   2½p brn & red ('71)   .30 .20
552 A124   5p orange & bl   .30 .20
553 A124   7½p lil & gray ('71)   .30 .20
554 A124   10p lt & dk brn   .30 .20
555 A124 12½p blue & org ('71)   .30 .20
556 A124   15p grn & red lil   .30 .20
557 A124   20p vio & red brn   .30 .20
558 A124 22½p red brn & blk
              ('71)   .30 .20
559 A124   25p gray & vio bl
              ('71)   .30 .20
560 A124 27½p brt grn & dk brn
              ('71)   .30 .20
561 A124   35p rose red & emer
              ('71)   .35 .20
     Nos. 551-561 (11)   3.35 2.20

Young
Man and
Woman,
Map of
Arab
Countries
A125

1970, May 7   Unwmk.   Perf. 12½x12
569 A125 15p green & ocher   .30 .20
570 A125 25p brown & ocher   .30 .20

First Youth Week, Latakia, Apr. 23-29. Inscribed "Youth's First Weak" (sic.).

Refugee
Family
A126

1970, May 15
571 A126 15p multicolored   .30 .20
572 A126 25p gray & multi   .30 .20
573 A126 35p green & multi   .35 .20
     Nos. 571-573 (3)   .90 .60

Issued for Arab Refugee Week.

Cotton — A127

1970, Aug. 18   Litho.   Perf. 12½
574 A127 5p shown   .30 .20
575 A127 10p Tomatoes   .30 .20
576 A127 15p Tobacco   .30 .20
577 A127 20p Beets   .30 .20
578 A127 35p Wheat   .75 .25
 a.   Strip of 5, #574-578 2.00 2.00

Industrial and Agricultural Fair, Aleppo.

Boy Scout, Tent, Emblem and Map of Arab Countries A128

1970, Aug. 25   Perf. 12½x12
579 A128 15p gray green   .40 .20

9th Pan-Arab Boy Scout Jamboree, Damascus.

Olive Tree and Emblem A129

1970, Sept. 28   Litho.   Perf. 11½x12
580 A129 15p gray grn, yel & blk   .30 .20
581 A129 25p red brn, yel & blk   .50 .20

Issued to publicize World Olive Year.

Protection of Industry, Agriculture, Arts and Commerce — A130

1971, Mar. 8   Litho.   Perf. 12½x12
582 A130 15p olive, yel & bl   .30 .20
583 A130 22½p red brn, yel & ol   .30 .20
584 A130 27½p bl, yel & red brn   .30 .20
    Nos. 582-584 (3)   .90 .60

March 8 Revolution, 8th anniversary.

Workers Memorial, Hands with Wrench and Olive Branch A131

1971, May 1   Litho.   Perf. 12½x12
585 A131 15p brn vio, yel & bl   .30 .20
586 A131 25p dk bl, bl & yel   .30 .20

Labor Day.

Child and Traffic Lights A132

World Traffic Day: 25p, Road signs, traffic lights, children, vert.

1971, May 4   Perf. 11½x12, 12x11½
587 A132 15p black, red & bl   .30 .20
588 A132 25p gray & multi   .30 .20
589 A132 45p black, red & yel   .30 .20
    Nos. 587-589 (3)   .90 .60

Factories, Cogwheel and Cotton A133

1971, July 15   Litho.   Perf. 12½x12
590 A133 15p lt grn, bl & blk   .30 .20
591 A133 30p red & black   .30 .20

11th Industrial and Agricultural Fair, Aleppo.

Arab Postal Union Emblem — A134

Flag, Map of Syria, Egypt and Libya — A135

1971, Sep. 1   Perf. 12x12½
592 A134 15p claret & multi   .30 .20
593 A134 20p vio bl & multi   .30 .20

25th anniv. of the Conference of Sofar, Lebanon, establishing the APU.

1971, Aug. 13   Perf. 12x11½
594 A135 15p car, dl grn & blk   .30 .20

Confederation of the Arab states of Syria, Libya and Egypt.

Red Pepper and Chemical Factory (Fertilizer Industry) — A136

18th Intl. Damascus Fair: 15p, Electronics industry (TV, telephone, computer). 35p, Glass industry (old map and glass manufacture). 50p, Carpet industry (carpet and looms).

1971, Aug. 25   Perf. 12½
595 A136 5p violet & multi   .30 .20
596 A136 15p dull grn & multi   .30 .20
597 A136 35p multicolored   .30 .20
598 A136 50p yel grn & multi   .50 .20
    Nos. 595-598 (4)   1.40 .80

Pres. Hafez al Assad and Crowd — A137

UNESCO Emblem, Radar, Spacecraft, Telephone A138

1971, Nov.   Litho.   Perf. 12x12½
599 A137 15p vio bl, blk & car   .30 .20
600 A137 20p dk & lt grn, car & blk .30 .20

1st anniv. of Correctionist Movement of Nov. 16, 1970.

1971, Dec. 8
601 A138 15p vio bl & multi   .30 .20
602 A138 50p green & multi   .30 .20

25th anniv. of UNESCO.

UNICEF Emblem and Playing Children — A139

1971, Dec. 21
603 A139 15p ultra, dk bl & dp car   .30 .20
604 A139 25p grnsh bl, ocher & dk bl .30 .20

UNICEF, 25th anniv.

Conference Emblem — A140

1971, Dec.   Perf. 12½x12
605 A140 15p blk, grnsh bl & org   .30 .20

Scholars' Conference.

Book Year Emblem A141

1972, Jan. 2
606 A141 15p tan, lt bl & vio   .30 .20
607 A141 20p brn, lt grn & grn   .30 .20

International Book Year.

Wheel, "8" and Scales of Justice — A142

Baath Party Emblem — A143

1972, Mar. 8   Litho.   Perf. 12x12½
608 A142 15p blue grn & vio   .30 .20
609 A142 20p olive bis & car   .30 .20

March 8 Revolution, 9th anniversary.

1972, Mar. 7
610 A143 15p dk blue & multi   .30 .20
611 A143 20p violet & multi   .30 .20

Arab Baath Socialist Party, 25th anniv.

Eagle, Chimneys, Grain and Oil Rigs — A144

1972, Apr. 17   Perf. 12½x12
612 A144 15p gold, blk & car   .30 .20

Federation of Arab Republics, 1st anniv.

Symbolic Flower, Broken Chain — A145

Hand Holding Wrench and Spade — A146

1972, Apr. 17   Perf. 12x11½
613 A145 15p rose red & gray   .30 .20
614 A145 50p pale bl grn & gray   .30 .20

26th anniv. of the evacuation of British and French troops from Syria.

1972, May 1
615 A146 15p ol grn, bl & blk   .30 .20
616 A146 50p vio bl, brn & blk   .30 .20

Labor Day.

Environment Emblem, Crystals, Microscope A147

1972, June 5
617 A147 15p multicolored .30 .20
618 A147 50p blue & multi .35 .20

UN Conference on Human Environment, Stockholm, June 5-16.

Dove over Factory — A148

1972, July 17 Litho. Perf. 12x11½
619 A148 15p yellow & multi .30 .20
620 A148 20p yellow & multi .30 .20

Agricultural and Industrial Fair, Aleppo.

Folk Dance — A149

1972, Aug. 25 Litho. Perf. 12x12½
621 A149 15p shown .30 .20
622 A149 20p Women and tambourine player .30 .20
623 A149 50p Men and drummer .50 .20
Nos. 621-623 (3) 1.10 .60

19th International Damascus Fair.

Olympic Rings, Discus, Soccer, Swimming — A150

Warriors on Horseback, Olympic Emblems — A151

Design: 60p, Olympic rings, running, gymnastics, fencing.

1972 Litho. Perf. 12½x12
624 A150 15p ol bis, blk & vio .50 .20
625 A150 60p dull bl, blk & org .60 .20

Souvenir Sheet
Imperf
626 A151 75p lt grn, bl & blk 2.00 2.00

20th Olympic Games, Munich, Aug. 26-Sept. 11, 1972.

Emblem of Revolution and Prancing Horse A152

1973, Mar. 8 Litho. Perf. 11½x12
627 A152 15p brt grn, blk & red .30 .20
628 A152 20p dull org, blk & red .30 .20
629 A152 25p blue, blk & red .30 .20
Nos. 627-629 (3) .90 .60

March 8 Revolution, 10th anniversary.

Heart and WHO Emblem A153

1973, Mar. 21
630 A153 15p gray & multi .30 .20
631 A153 50p lt brown & multi .35 .20

WHO, 25th anniversary.

Cogwheel and Grain Emblem — A154

1973, Apr. 17 Perf. 12x12½
632 A154 15p blue & multi .30 .20
633 A154 20p multicolored .30 .20

27th anniv. of the evacuation of British and French troops from Syria.

Workers and Globe A155

1973, May 1 Perf. 11½x12
634 A155 15p rose & multi .30 .20
635 A155 50p blue & multi .35 .20

Labor Day.

UN, FAO Emblems, People and Symbols — A156

Stock — A157

1973, May 7 Perf. 12x11½
636 A156 15p lt grn & red brn .30 .20
637 A156 50p lilac & blue .35 .20

World food program, 10th anniv.

1973, May 15
638 A157 5p shown .30 .20
639 A157 10p Gardenia .30 .20
640 A157 15p Jasmine .30 .20
641 A157 20p Rose .30 .20
642 A157 25p Narcissus .30 .20
a. Strip of 5, #638-642 1.50 1.50

Intl. Flower Show, Damascus.

Children and Flame — A158

Children's Day: 3 children's heads and flame in different arrangements; 25p, 35p, 70p, vertical.

Perf. 11½x12, 12x11½
1973-74 Litho.
643 A158 2½p lt olive grn .30 .20
644 A158 5p orange .30 .20
645 A158 7½p dk brown .30 .20
646 A158 10p crimson .30 .20
647 A158 15p ultra .30 .20
648 A158 25p gray .30 .20
649 A158 35p brt blue .30 .20
650 A158 55p green .30 .20
651 A158 70p rose lilac .35 .20
Nos. 643-651 (9) 2.75 1.80

Issued: 15p, 55p, 70p, 5/73; others, 3/74.

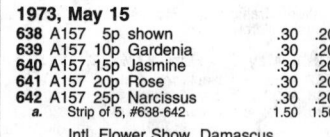

Fair Emblem A159

1973, June 17 Perf. 11½x12
652 A159 15p multicolored .30 .20

13th Agricultural and Industrial Fair, Aleppo.

Euphrates Dam and Power Plant — A160

1973, July 5 Perf. 12½x12
653 A160 15p green & multi .30 .20
654 A160 50p brown & multi .30 .20

Euphrates River diversion and dam project.

Woman from Deir Ezzor — A161

Map of Palestine, Barbed Wire, Human Rights Emblem — A162

Women's Costumes from: 10p, Hassaké. 20p, As Sahel. 25p, Zakié. 50p, Sarakeb.

1973, July 25 Litho. Perf. 12
655 A161 5p multicolored .30 .20
656 A161 10p multicolored .30 .20
657 A161 20p multicolored .30 .20
658 A161 25p multicolored .30 .20
659 A161 50p multicolored .30 .20
a. Strip of 5, #655-659 1.50 1.50

20th International Damascus Fair.

1973, Aug. 20 Perf. 12x11½
660 A162 15p lt green & multi .30 .20
661 A162 50p lt blue & multi .50 .20

25th anniversary of the Universal Declaration of Human Rights.

Citadel of Ja'abar A163

15p, Minaret of Meskeneh, vert. 25p, Statue of Psyche at Anab al Safinah, vert.

Perf. 11½x12, 12x11½
1973, Sept. 5 Litho.
662 A163 10p black, org & blue .30 .20
663 A163 15p black, org & blue .30 .20
664 A163 25p black, org & blue .30 .20
Nos. 662-664 (3) .90 .60

Salvage of monuments threatened by Euphrates Dam.

WMO Emblem A164

1973, Sept. 12 Perf. 11½x12
665 A164 70p yellow & multi .50 .20

Intl. meteorological cooperation, cent.

Maalula A165

Design: 50p, Ruins of Afamia.

1973, Oct. 22 Litho. Perf. 11½x12
666 A165 15p gray blue & blk .30 .20
667 A165 50p brown & blk .30 .20

Arab Emigrants' Congress, Buenos Aires.

Workers and Soldiers A166

1973, Nov. 16 Litho. Perf. 12½x12
668 A166 15p ultra & yellow .30 .20
669 A166 25p purple & red brn .30 .20

3rd anniv. of Correctionist Movement of Nov. 16, 1970.

Nicolaus Copernicus A167

UPU
Emblem — A169

Arms of
Syria and
Emblems
A168

Design: 25p, Abu-al-Rayhan al-Biruni.

1973, Dec. 15   Perf. 12x11½
670 A167 15p gold & black   .30 .20
671 A167 25p gold & black   .30 .20
14th Science Week.

1974, Mar. 8   Perf. 11x12
672 A168 20p gray & blue   .30 .20
673 A168 25p lt green & vio   .30 .20
11th anniversary of March 8th Revolution.

1974, Mar. 15   Perf. 12x11½, 11½x12
20p, Air mail letter and UPU emblem, horiz.
674 A169 15p gray & multi   .30 .20
675 A169 20p multicolored   .30 .20
676 A169 70p gray & multi   .50 .20
    Nos. 674-676 (3)   1.10 .60
Centenary of Universal Postal Union.

Arab
Postal
Institute
A170

1974, Apr. 10   Perf. 11½x12
677 A170 15p multicolored   .30 .20
Inauguration of the Higher Arab Postal Institute, Damascus, Apr. 10.

Sun and
Monument
A171

1974, Apr. 10
678 A171 15p emerald, blk & org   .30 .20
679 A171 20p dp org, blk & org   .30 .20
28th anniversary of the evacuation of British and French troops from Syria.

Machine Shop
Worker
A172

Abulfeda
A173

1974, May 1   Perf. 12x12½
680 A172 15p black, yel & bl   .30 .20
681 A172 50p black, buff & bl   .30 .20
Labor Day.

1974   Litho.   Perf. 11½x11
Design: 200p, al-Farabi.
682 A173 100p pale green   .50 .20
683 A173 200p lt brown   1.00 .45

Damascus Fair
Emblem — A174

Figs — A175

Design: 25p, Cog wheel and sun.

1974, July 25   Perf. 11½x11
684 A174 15p multicolored   .30 .20
685 A174 25p blue, blk & yel   .30 .20
21st International Damascus Fair.

1974, Aug. 21   Perf. 12x12½
Fruits: 15p, Grapes. 20p, Pomegranates.
25p, Cherries. 35p, Rose hips.
686 A175 5p gray & multi   .30 .20
687 A175 15p gray & multi   .30 .20
688 A175 20p gray & multi   .30 .20
689 A175 25p gray & multi   .30 .20
690 A175 35p gray & multi   .30 .20
    a.   Strip of 5, #686-690   2.50 2.50
Agricultural and Industrial Fair, Aleppo.

Burning Fuse and
Flowers — A176

Rook and
Knight — A177

20p, Bomb and star-shaped holes in target.

1974, Oct. 6   Litho.   Perf. 12x12½
691 A176 15p multicolored   .75 .20
692 A176 20p multicolored   1.00 .20
First anniv. of October Liberation War (Yom Kippur War).

1974, Nov. 23
Design: 50p, Knight and chess board.
693 A177 15p blue & black   .50 .20
694 A177 50p orange, blk & bl   .75 .35
Chess Federation, 50th anniversary.

WPY
Emblem — A178

Ishtup,
Ilum — A179

1974, Dec. 4   Litho.   Perf. 12x12½
695 A178 50p black, slate & red   .30 .20
World Population Year.

1975   Perf. 12x11½
Ancient Statuettes: 55p, Woman holding pitcher. 70p, Ur-Nina.
696 A179 20p brt green   .30 .20
697 A179 55p brown   .30 .20
698 A179 70p gray blue   .50 .20
    Nos. 696-698 (3)   1.10 .60

"A," People and
Sun — A180

Postal Savings
Bank Emblem,
Family — A181

1975, Mar. 8   Litho.   Perf. 12x11½
699 A180 15p gray & multi   .30 .20
12th anniversary, March 8th Revolution.

1975, Mar. 17
Design: 20p, Family depositing money, and stamped envelope.
700 A181 15p brt green & multi   .30 .20
701 A181 20p orange & black   .30 .20
Publicity for Savings Certificates and Postal Savings Bank.

"Sun" and
Dove — A182

1975, Apr. 17   Litho.   Perf. 12x11½
702 A182 15p bister, red & blk   .30 .20
703 A182 25p bister, grn & blk   .30 .20
29th anniversary of the evacuation of British and French troops from Syria.

"Worker and
Industry" — A183

Camomile
A184

1975, May 1   Litho.   Perf. 12x11½
704 A183 15p blue grn & blk   .30 .20
705 A183 25p brown, yel & blk   .30 .20
Labor Day.

1975, May 17
Flowers: 10p, Chincherinchi. 15p, Carnation. 20p, Poppy. 25p, Honeysuckle.
706 A184 5p ultra & multi   .30 .20
707 A184 10p lilac & multi   .30 .20
708 A184 15p blue & multi   .35 .20
709 A184 20p gray grn & multi   .40 .20
710 A184 25p vio bl & multi   .75 .25
    a.   Strip of 5, #706-710   2.10 2.10
International Flower Show, Damascus.

Kuneitra Destroyed and
Rebuilt — A185

1975, June 5   Perf. 12½
711 A185 50p black & multi   .35 .20
Re-occupation of Kuneitra by Syria.

Apples
A186

1975, July 7
712 A186 5p shown   .30 .20
713 A186 10p Quince   .30 .20
714 A186 15p Apricots   .35 .20
715 A186 20p Grapes   .40 .20
716 A186 25p Figs   .50 .20
    a.   Strip of 5, #712-716   1.90 1.90
Agricultural and Industrial Fair, Aleppo.

22nd Intl.
Damascus
Fair — A187

Farm Woman — A189

Pres. Hafez al Assad A188

1975, July 25   Litho.   Perf. 12x11½
717 A187 15p olive grn & multi   .30   .20
718 A187 35p brown & multi   .30   .20

1975, Nov. 29   Litho.   Perf. 11½x12
719 A188 15p green & multi   .30   .20
720 A188 50p blue & multi   .30   .20
5th anniv. of Correctionist Movement of Nov. 16, 1970.

1975, Nov. 29   Perf. 12x11½
IWY Emblem and: 15p, Mother. 25p, Student. 50p, Laboratory technician.
721 A189 10p buff & multi   .30   .20
722 A189 15p rose & black   .30   .20
723 A189 25p dull green & blk   .35   .20
724 A189 50p orange & blk   .50   .20
      Nos. 721-724 (4)   1.45   .80
International Women's Year.

Horse-shaped Bronze Lamp A190

Man's Head Inkstand A191

Designs: 10p, 25p, like 20p. 35p, like 30p. 50p, 60p, Nike. 75p, Hera. 100p, Imdugug-Mari (winged animal). 500p, Palmyrene coin of Vasalathus. 1000p, Abraxas coin.

1976   Perf. 11½x12, 12x11½
725 A190 10p brt bluish grn   .30   .20
726 A190 20p lilac rose   .30   .20
727 A190 25p violet blue   .30   .20
728 A191 30p brown   .30   .20
729 A191 35p olive   .30   .20
730 A191 50p brt blue   .30   .20
731 A191 60p violet   .30   .20
732 A191 75p orange   .35   .20
733 A191 100p lilac rose   .50   .20
734 A191 500p grnsh gray   2.00 1.75
735 A191 1000p dk green   4.00 2.25
      Nos. 725-735 (11)   8.95 5.80
See Nos. 798-803.

National Theater, Damascus and Pres. al Assad A192

1976, Mar. 8   Litho.   Perf. 11½x12
736 A192 25p brt grn, sil & blk   .30   .20
737 A192 35p olive, sil & blk   .30   .20
13th anniversary of March 8 Revolution.

Syria, Arabian Government #85 — A193

1976, Apr. 12   Perf. 12x12½
738 A193 25p brt green & multi   .30   .20
739 A193 35p blue & multi   .30   .20
Post's Day.

Nurse and Emblem — A194

Eagle and Stars — A195

1976, Apr. 8   Perf. 12x11½
740 A194 25p blue, blk & red   .30   .20
741 A194 100p violet, blk & red   .50   .30
Arab Red Cross and Red Crescent Societies, 8th Conference, Damascus.

1976, Apr. 17
742 A195 25p blk, red & brt grn   .30   .20
743 A195 35p blk, red & brt grn   .30   .20
30th anniversary of the evacuation of British and French troops from Syria.

Hand Holding Wrench — A196

Cotton and Factory — A197

May Day: 60p, Hand holding globe.
1976, May 1
744 A196 25p blue & black   .30   .20
745 A196 60p citron & multi   .40   .20

1976, July 1
746 A197 25p vio & multi   .30   .20
747 A197 35p bl & multi   .30   .20
Agricultural and Industrial Fair, Aleppo.

Tulips — A198

1976, July 26
748 A198 5p shown   .30   .20
749 A198 15p Yellow daisies   .30   .20
750 A198 20p Turk's-cap lilies   .30   .20
751 A198 25p Irises   .50   .20
752 A198 35p Freesia   .75   .20
a.   Strip of 5, #748-752   2.25 2.25
Intl. Flower Show, Damascus.

People, Globe and Olive Branch A199

60p, Symbolic arrow piercing darkness.
1976, Sept. 2   Perf. 11½x12
753 A199 40p yel & multi   .30   .20
754 A199 60p multi   .35   .20
5th Summit Conference of Non-aligned Countries, Colombo, Sri Lanka, Aug. 9-19.

Soccer, Pan Arab Games Emblem A200

1976, Oct. 6   Litho.   Perf. 12½
755 A200 5p shown   .30   .20
756 A200 10p Swimming   .30   .20
757 A200 25p Running   .30   .20
758 A200 35p Basketball   .30   .20
759 A200 50p Javelin   .30   .20
a.   Strip of 5, #755-759   1.50 1.50

Souvenir Sheet
Imperf
760 A200 100p Steeplechase   2.00 2.00
5th Pan Arab Sports Tournament.
Size of stamp of No. 760: 55x35mm.

"Development" A201

1976, Nov. 16   Perf. 12½x12½
761 A201 35p multi   .30   .20
Correctionist Movement pof Nov. 16, 1970.

The Fox and the Crow — A202

1976, Dec. 7   Perf. 12x12½, 12½x12
Fairy Tales: 15p, The Hare and the Tortoise, horiz. 20p, Little Red Riding Hood. 25p,

The Lamb and the Wolf, horiz. 35p, The Lamb and the Wolf.
762 A202 10p multi   .30   .20
763 A202 15p multi   .30   .20
764 A202 20p multi   .30   .20
765 A202 25p multi   .30   .20
766 A202 35p multi   .30   .20
      Nos. 762-766 (5)   1.50 1.00
Children's literature.

Syrian Airlines Boeing 747 — A203

1977, Feb.   Litho.   Perf. 12½x12
767 A203 35p multi   .30   .20
Civil Aviation Day.

Muhammad Kurd-Ali (1876-1953), Philosopher, Birth Cent. — A204

1977, Feb.   Perf. 12x12½
768 A204 25p lt grn & multi   .30   .20

Woman Holding Syrian Flag — A205

APU Emblem — A207

Warrior on Horseback — A206

1977, Mar. 8   Litho.   Perf. 12x12½
769 A205 35p multi   .30   .20
14th anniversary of March 8 Revolution.

1977, Apr. 10   Litho.   Perf. 12½
770 A206 100p multi   .30   .20
31st anniversary of the evacuation of British and French troops from Syria.

1977, Apr. 12   Litho.   Perf. 12x12½
771 A207 35p silver & multi   .30   .20
Arab Postal Union, 25th anniversary.

Tools and Factories
A208

1977, May 1   **Perf. 12½x12**
772 A208 60p multi   .35 .20
Labor Day.

ICAO Emblem, Plane and Globe
A209

1977, May 11
773 A209 100p multi   .50 .25
Intl. Civil Aviation Org., 30th anniv.

Pioneers   Citrus Fruit
A210   A211

1977, Aug. 15   **Litho.**   **Perf. 12x12½**
774 A210 35p multi   .30 .20
Al Baath Pioneer Organization.

1977, Aug. 1
775 A211 10p Lemon   .30 .20
776 A211 20p Lime   .30 .20
777 A211 25p Grapefruit   .30 .20
778 A211 35p Oranges   .30 .20
779 A211 60p Tangerines   .40 .20
    a.   Strip of 5, #775-779   1.60 1.60
Agricultural and Industrial Fair, Aleppo.

Flowers
A212

1977, Aug. 6   **Litho.**   **Perf. 12½x12**
780 A212 10p Mallow   .30 .20
781 A212 20p Coxcomb   .30 .20
782 A212 25p Morning glories   .30 .20
783 A212 35p Almond blossoms   .30 .20
784 A212 60p Lilacs   .30 .20
    a.   Strip of 5, #780-784   1.50 1.50
Intl. Flower Show, Damascus.

Coffeepot and Ornament
A213

1977, Sept. 10   **Perf. 12x12½**
785 A213 25p blk, bl & red   .30 .20
786 A213 60p blk, grn & brn   .35 .20
24th Intl. Damascus Fair.

Blind Man, Globe and Eye — A214

Globe and Measures
A215

1977, Nov. 17   **Litho.**   **Perf. 12x12½**
787 A214 55p multi   .30 .20
788 A214 70p multi   .30 .20
World Blind Week.

1977, Nov. 5
789 A215 15p grn & multi   .30 .20
World Standards Day, Oct. 14.

Microscope, Book, Harp, UNESCO Emblem — A216

1977, Nov. 5   **Perf. 12½x12**
790 A216 25p multi   .30 .20
30th anniversary of UNESCO.

Archbishop Capucci, Map of Palestine, Bars — A217

Fight Cancer Shield, Crab and Surgeon — A218

1977, Nov. 17   **Perf. 12x12½**
791 A217 60p multi   .50 .20
Palestinian Archbishop Hilarion Capucci, jailed by Israel in 1974.

1977, Nov. 17
792 A218 100p multi   .50 .20
Fight Cancer Week.

Dome of the Rock, Jerusalem — A219

1977, Dec. 6   **Perf. 12**
793 A219 5p multi   .50 .20
794 A219 10p multi   .75 .20
Palestinian fighters and their families.

Mural — A220   Pres. Hafez al Assad — A221

Designs: 10p, 15p, Murals from Dura-Europos, in National Museum, Damascus.

1978, Jan. 22   **Litho.**   **Perf. 12x11½**
795 A220 5p gray grn   .30 .20
796 A220 10p vio bl   .30 .20
797 A220 15p brown, horiz.   .30 .20
    Nos. 795-797 (3)   .90 .60

Types of 1976

Designs: 40p, Man's head inkstand. 55p, Nike. 70p, Hera. 200p, Arab-Islamic astrolabe. 300p, Palmyrene (Herod) coin.

1978   **Litho.**   **Perf. 12x11½, 11½x12**
798 A191 40p pale org   .30 .20
799 A191 55p brt rose   .30 .20
800 A191 70p vermilion   .35 .20
801 A191 80p green   .35 .20
802 A191 200p lt ultra   1.00 .30
803 A190 300p rose lil   1.50 .50
    Nos. 798-803 (6)   3.80 1.60

1978   **Perf. 12x11½**
805 A221 50p multi   .40 .20
Anniversary of "Correction Movement."

Blood Circulation, WHO Emblem — A222

Factory — A223

1978, Apr. 7   **Litho.**   **Perf. 12x11½**
806 A222 100p multi   .50 .20
World Health Day, fight against hypertension.

1978, Apr. 17
807 A223 35p multi   .30 .20
32nd anniversary of the evacuation of British and French troops from Syria.

Rosette — A224

Map of Arab Countries, Police, Flag and Eye — A225

1978, Apr. 21
808 A224 25p blk & grn   .30 .20
14th Arab Engineering Conference, Damascus, Apr. 21-26.

1978, May
809 A225 35p multi   .30 .20
6th Conf. of Arab Police Commanders.

European Goldfinch
A226

Birds: 20p, Peregrine falcon. 25p, Rock dove. 35p, Eurasian hoopoe. 60p, Old World quail.

1978   **Perf. 11½x12**
810 A226 10p multi   .40 .20
811 A226 20p multi   .40 .20
812 A226 25p multi   .40 .20
813 A226 35p multi   .50 .20
814 A226 60p multi   .60 .20
    a.   Strip of 5, #810-814   2.40 2.40

Trout
A227

Designs: Various fish.

1978, July   **Litho.**   **Perf. 11½x12**
815 A227 10p multi   .40 .20
816 A227 20p multi   .40 .20
817 A227 25p multi   .40 .20
818 A227 35p multi   .50 .20
819 A227 60p multi   .55 .25
    a.   Strip of 5, #815-819   2.25 2.25

Pres. Assad Type of Air Post, 1978
Miniature Sheet

1978, Sept.   **Litho.**   **Imperf.**
820 AP161 100p gold & multi   1.00 1.00
Reelection of President Assad. Size of stamp: 58x80mm.

Flowering Cactus
A228

Fair Emblem — A229

Designs: Flowering cacti.

1978	Litho.	Perf. 12½		
821	A228 25p multi		.50	.20
822	A228 30p multi		.50	.20
823	A228 35p multi		.50	.20
824	A228 50p multi		.50	.20
825	A228 60p multi		.50	.20
a.	Strip of 5, #821-825		2.50	2.50

International Flower Show, Damascus.

1978	Litho.	Perf. 12x12½		
826	A229 25p sil & multi		.30	.20
827	A229 35p sil & multi		.30	.20

Miniature Sheet
Imperf

828	A229 100p sil & multi	1.00	1.00

25th Intl. Damascus Fair. No. 828 shows different ornament, size of stamp: 40x46mm.

Euphrates Dam and Pres. Assad — A230

1978, Dec.	Litho.	Perf. 12½x12		
829	A230 60p multi		.50	.20

Inauguration of Euphrates Dam.

Pres. Hafez al Assad — A231

1978, Nov. 16	Litho.	Perf. 12x12½		
830	A231 60p multi		.40	.20

Nov. 16 Movement.

Racial Equality Emblem A232

1978, Mar.	Litho.	Perf. 12½		
831	A232 35p multi		.40	.20

International Year to Combat Racism.

Averroes — A233

Human Rights Flame and Globe — A234

1979, Mar.			
832	A233 100p multi	.75	.25

Averroes (1126-1198), Spanish-Arabian philosopher and physician.

1978, Dec.	Perf. 12x12½		
833	A234 60p multi	.50	.20

30th anniversary of Universal Declaration of Human Rights (in 1978).

Symbolic Design — A235

Princess, 2nd Century Shield — A236

1979, Mar.			
834	A235 100p multi	.50	.20

16th anniversary of March 8 Revolution.

1979	Litho.	Perf. 11½		
Designs: 20p, Helmet of Homs. 35p, Ishtar.				
836	A236 20p green		.30	.20
837	A236 25p rose car		.30	.20
838	A236 35p sepia		.30	.20
	Nos. 836-838 (3)		.90	.60

Molar, Emblem with Mosque — A237

Flame Emblem — A238

1979	Litho.	Perf. 12x11½		
846	A237 35p multi		.30	.20

Intl. Middle East Dental Congress.

1979			
847	A238 35p multi	.30	.20

33rd anniversary of evacuation.

Ibn Assaker, 900th Anniv. A239

1979	Perf. 11½x12		
848	A239 75p multi	.30	.20

Telephone Lineman — A240

Girl with IYC Emblem — A242

Wright Brothers' Plane A241

1979, May 1	Litho.	Perf. 12x11½		
849	A240 50p multi		.30	.20
850	A240 75p multi		.30	.20

May Day.

1979	Perf. 11½x12		
Designs: 75p, Bleriot's plane crossing English Channel. 100p, Spirit of St. Louis.			
851	A241 50p multi	.30	.20
852	A241 75p multi	.30	.20
853	A241 100p multi	.50	.20
	Nos. 851-853 (3)	1.10	.60

75th anniversary of 1st powered flight.

1979	Perf. 12x11½		
Design: 15p, Boy, globe, IYC emblem.			
854	A242 10p multi	.30	.20
855	A242 15p multi	.35	.20

International Year of the Child.

Power Plant — A243

Flags and Pavilion — A244

1979	Perf. 11x11½		
856	A243 5p blue	.30	.20
857	A243 10p lil rose	.30	.20
858	A243 15p gray grn	.30	.20
	Nos. 856-858 (3)	.90	.60

1979	Photo.	Perf. 12x11½		
Design: 75p, Lamppost and flags.				
859	A244 60p multi		.30	.20
860	A244 75p multi		.35	.20

26th International Damascus Fair.

Correction Movement, 9th Anniversary — A245

1979	Photo.	Perf. 11½x12		
861	A245 100p multi		.50	.20

Games Emblem, Running A246

1979, Nov.			
862	A246 25p shown	.30	.20
863	A246 35p Diving	.30	.20
864	A246 50p Soccer	.30	.20
	Nos. 862-864 (3)	.90	.60

8th Mediterranean Games, Split, Yugoslavia, Sept. 15-29.

Butterfly — A247

Damascus Intl. Flower Show A248

Designs: Various butterflies.

1979, Dec.	Litho.	Perf. 12x11½		
865	A247 20p multi		.50	.20
866	A247 25p multi		.50	.20
867	A247 30p multi		.50	.20
868	A247 35p multi		.50	.20
869	A247 50p multi		.50	.20
	Nos. 865-869 (5)		2.50	1.00

1980, Jan. 9	Litho.	Perf. 12½		
Design: Roses.				
870	A248 5p multi		.50	.20
871	A248 10p multi		.50	.20
872	A248 15p multi		.50	.20
873	A248 50p multi		.50	.20
874	A248 75p multi		.50	.20
875	A248 100p multi		.80	.20
	Nos. 870-875 (6)		3.30	1.20

March 8
Revolution, 17th
Anniv. — A249

Astrolabe
A250

1980, Mar. 25   Litho.   Perf. 12x11½
876 A249 40p multi   .30   .20

1980, May 2   Perf. 12½
877 A250   50p violet   .30   .20
878 A250   100p sepia   .50   .20
879 A250 1000p gray grn   4.00 1.25
     Nos. 877-879 (3)   4.80 1.65
2nd International History of Arabic Sciences
Symposium, Apr. 5.

Lit Cigarette,
Skull — A251

1980, June 25   Photo.   Perf. 12x11½
880 A251   60p Smoker   .60   .25
881 A251 100p shown   1.00   .30

World Health Day; anti-smoking campaign.

1980, June 25   Litho.
882 A252 40p multi   .30   .20
883 A252 60p multi   .35   .20

Moscow
'80
Emblem
and
Wrestling
A253

1980, July   Litho.   Perf. 11½x12
884 A253 15p shown   .30   .20
885 A253 25p Fencing   .30   .20
886 A253 35p Weight lifting   .35   .20
887 A253 50p Judo   .50   .20
888 A253 75p Boxing   1.00   .25
  a.   Strip of 5, #884-888   2.50 2.50
Souvenir Sheet
Imperf
888B A253 300p Discus, running   5.00 5.00
22nd Summer Olympic Games, Moscow,
July 19-Aug. 3.

Sinbad
the Sailor
A254

1980   Litho.   Perf. 11½x12
889 A254   15p shown   .30   .20
890 A254   25p Scheherezade
                  and Shahrayar   .30   .20
891 A254   35p Ali Baba and the
                  Forty Thieves   .35   .20
892 A254   50p Hassan the Clev-
                  er   .50   .20
893 A254 100p Aladdin's Lamp   1.00   .30
  a.   Strip of 5, #889-893   2.50 2.50
     Popular stories.

Savings Certificates — A255

1980
894 A255 25p multi   .30 .20

Hegira, 1500th Anniv. — A256

1980   Perf. 12½x12
895 A256 35p multi   .35 .20

Intl. Flower Show,
Damascus
A257

1980   Perf. 12x11½
896 A257   20p Daffodils   .50   .20
897 A257   30p Chrysanthemums   .50   .20
898 A257   40p Clematis   .55   .20
899 A257   60p Yellow roses   .60   .20
900 A257 100p Chrysanthe-
                  mums, diff.   .75   .25
  a.   Strip of 5, #896-900   3.00 3.00

May Day — A258

Children's
Day — A259

1980, May
901 A258 35p multi   .40 .20

1980
902 A259 25p multi   .40 .20

November 16th Movement, 10th
Anniv. — A260

1980   Perf. 11½x12
903 A260 100p multi   1.00 .25

Steam-powered Passenger
Wagon — A261

1980
904 A261 25p shown   .35   .20
905 A261 35p Benz, 1899   .40   .20
906 A261 40p Rolls-Royce, 1903   .60   .20
907 A261 50p Mercedes, 1906   .75   .25
908 A261 60p Austin, 1915   1.00   .30
  a.   Strip of 5, #904-908   3.25 3.25

Mother's
Day — A262

1980   Perf. 12x11½
909 A262   40p shown   .50   .20
910 A262 100p Mother and child   1.00   .20

Army Day — A264

1981, Jan. 24   Perf. 12½x12
913 A264 50p multi   .45   .20

A265

A266

1981, Mar. 8   Litho.   Perf. 12x11½
914 A265 50p multi   .35 .20
   18th anniv. of March 8th revolution.

1981, Apr. 17   Litho.   Perf. 12x11½
915 A266 50p multi   .35 .20
   35th anniversary of evacuation.

World Conference on History of Arab
and Islamic Civilization,
Damascus — A267

1981, May 30   Photo.   Perf. 12½x12
916 A267 100p multi   .60 .20

Intl. Workers'
Solidarity
Day — A268

Housing and
Population
Census — A269

1981, May 30   Litho.   Perf. 12x11½
917 A268 100p multi   .60 .20

1981, June 1
918 A269 50p multi   .35 .20

Evacuation, 34th
Anniversary
A252

27th International Damascus
Fair — A263

1981, Jan. 24   Perf. 11½x12
911 A263   50p multi   .45 .20
912 A263 100p multi   .80 .20

Umayyad
Window
A270

Abdul Malik Gold
Coin
A270a

10p, figurine. 15p, Rakkla's cavalier, Abbcid ceramic. 160p, like 5p. 500p, Umar B. Abdul Aziz gold coin.

1981   **Perf. 12x11½, 11½x12**
919 A270   5p crim rose   .20   .20
920 A270   10p brt grn   .20   .20
921 A270   15p dp rose lil   .20   .20
922 A270a 75p blue   .35   .20
923 A270 160p dk grn   .70   .35
924 A270a 500p dk brn   2.50   1.10
    Nos. 919-924 (6)   4.15   2.25

Olives
A270b

Harbor
A270c

1982   **Perf. 12x11½**
925 A270b 50p ol grn   .40   .20
926 A270b 60p bl gray   .45   .20
929 A270c 100p lilac   .55   .25
930 A270c 180p red   1.10   .55
    Nos. 925-930 (4)   2.50   1.20

Saving
Certificates
Plan — A271

Avicenna (980-
1037),
Philosopher and
Physician
A272

1981, June 22
931 A271 50p gldn brn & blk   .35   .20

1981, Aug.
932 A272 100p multi   .60   .20

Syria-P.L.O.
Solidarity, Intl.
Conference
A273

1981, June 22
933 A273 160p multi   3.50   .90

Grand Mosque, Damascus — A274

1981   **Perf. 12½**
934 A274   50p Glass lamp, 13th
                cent.   .30   .20
935 A274 180p shown   1.40   .40
936 A274 180p Hunter   1.40   .40
    Nos. 934-936 (3)   3.10   1.00

Youth
Festival
A275

1981   **Perf. 12½**
937 A275 60p multi   .40   .20

28th Intl.
Damascus
Fair — A276

Intl. Palestinian
Solidarity
Day — A277

1981   **Perf. 12x11½**
938 A276   50p Ornament   .30   .20
939 A276 160p Emblem   1.00   .45

1981
940 A277 100p multi   .75   .20

1300th
Anniv. of
Bulgaria
A278

1981   **Perf. 11½x12**
941 A278 380p multi   2.25   1.00

Intl.
Children's
Day
A279

1981
942 A279 180p multi   1.10   .45

World
Food Day,
Oct. 16
A280

1981
943 A280 180p multi   1.10   .45

9th Intl. Flower
Show, Damascus
A281

Designs: Flowers.

1981   **Perf. 12x11½**
944 A281   25p multi   .25   .20
945 A281   40p multi   .40   .25
946 A281   50p multi   .50   .30
947 A281   60p multi   .75   .35
948 A281 100p multi   1.10   .50
a.   Strip of 5, #944-948   3.00   2.00

Souvenir Sheet

Koran Competition — A282

1981   **Litho.**   **Imperf.**
949 A282 500p multi   5.00   5.00

11th Anniv. of
Correction
Movement
A283

1981, Nov.   **Perf. 12x11½**
950 A283   60p multi   .45   .30

TB
Bacillus
Centenary
A284

1982   **Litho.**   **Perf. 11½x12**
951 A284 180p multi   1.25   .65

Mothers'
Day — A285

Mar. 8th
Revolution, 19th
Anniv. — A286

1982   **Perf. 11½**
952 A285   40p green   .25   .20
953 A285   75p brown   .50   .50

1982, Mar.   **Perf. 12x11½**
954 A286   50p multi   .35   .20

Intl. Year of the
Disabled
(1981) — A287

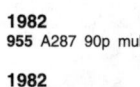
Pres. Hafez al
Assad — A288

1982   **Perf. 12x11½**
955 A287   90p multi   .75   .30

1982   **Perf. 11½**
956 A288 150p ultra   .90   .50

36th Anniv. of
Evacuation
A289

World Traffic
Day — A290

1982   **Perf. 12x11½**
957 A289   70p multi   .50   .25

1982
958 A290 180p multi   1.25   .65

Intl. Workers'
Solidarity
Day — A291

1982
959 A291 180p multi   1.25   .65

World Telecommunication Day,
May 17 — A292

1982
960 A292 180p multi 1.25 .65

Soldier Holding
Rifles — A293

1982 **Photo.** **Perf. 12x11½**
961 A293 50p multi .30 .20

Arab Postal
Union, 30th
Anniv. — A294

1982
962 A294 60p multi .45 .20

1982 World Cup — A295

Various soccer players. 300p, Ball.

1982, July **Perf. 12½**
963 A295 40p multi .25 .20
964 A295 60p multi .40 .20
965 A295 100p multi .65 .40
  Nos. 963-965 (3) 1.30 .80
  Size: 75x55mm
  Imperf
966 A295 300p multi 10.00 10.00

10th Intl. Flower
Show, Damascus
A297

1982 **Perf. 12x11½**
967 A297 50p Honeysuckle .45 .20
968 A297 60p Geraniums .60 .30

Scouting
Year
A298

1982, Nov. 4 **Perf. 11½x12**
969 A298 160p green 1.40 .75

Ladybug
A299

1982 **Perf. 12x12½**
970 Strip of 5 .75 .40
  a. A299 5p Dragonfly .20 .20
  b. A299 10p Stag Beetle .20 .20
  c. A299 20p shown .20 .20
  d. A299 40p Grasshopper .20 .20
  e. A299 50p Honeybee .30 .20

ITU Plenipotentiaries Conference,
Nairobi, Sept — A300

1982 **Perf. 11½x12**
971 A300 50p Map .30 .25
972 A300 180p Dish antenna 1.40 .75

12th
Anniv. of
Correction
Movement
A301

1982, Nov.
973 A301 50p dk bl & sil .35 .20

A302

Factory — A302a

Designs: 70p, Walled arch. 200p, Ruins.

1982-83 **Litho.** **Perf. 11½**
974 A302 30p brown .20 .20
975 A302a 50p dark green .25 .20
976 A302a 70p green .35 .20
977 A302 200p red 1.00 .55
  Nos. 974-977 (4) 1.80 1.15
Issued: 50p, 11/16/83; others, 11/4/82.

Dove and
Satellite — A303

Intl. Palestinian
Solidarity
Day — A304

1982 **Litho.** **Perf. 12x11½**
978 A303 50p multi .50 .30
  2nd UN Conference on Peaceful Uses of
  Outer Space, Vienna, Aug. 9-21.

1982
979 A304 50p multi .90 .20

20th Anniv. of March 8th
Revolution — A305

1983 **Perf. 12½x12**
980 A305 60p multi 1.00 .50

World Communications Year — A305a

1983
981 A305a 180p multi 1.25 .65

9th Anniv. of
Liberation of Al-
Kuneitra
A306

25th Anniv. of Intl.
Maritime Org.
A308

Arab Pharmacists' Day, Apr. 2 — A307

1983, June 26 **Litho.** **Perf. 11½**
982 A306 50p View 1.50 .50
983 A306 100p View, diff. 3.00 .65

1983, Apr. 2 **Perf. 11½x12**
984 A307 100p multi .75 .30

1983, June **Perf. 12x11½**
985 A308 180p multi 1.40 .75

Namibia
Day, Aug.
26
A309

1983, Aug. 26 **Perf. 11½x12**
986 A309 180p multi 1.40 .75

Eibla
Sculpture,
3rd Cent.
BC
A310

1983
987 A310 380p ol & brn 2.50 1.40

World Standards
Day — A311

11th Intl. Flower
Show, Damascus
A312

1983, Oct. 14 **Photo.** **Perf. 11½**
988 A311 50p Factory, emblem .40 .20
989 A311 100p Measuring equipment .80 .40

1983, Oct. 14 **Litho.** **Perf. 11½**
990 A312 50p multi .40 .20
991 A312 60p multi, diff. .50 .25

World Heritage
Day — A313

1983, Oct. 14 **Photo.** **Perf. 11½**
992 A313 60p dk brn .50 .25

World
Food Day
A313a

1983, Oct. 16 **Litho.** **Perf. 11½x12**
992A A313a 180p multi 1.50 .75

Waterwheels of
Hama — A314

Perf. 11x11½, 11½x11

1982-84   Litho.
993 A314 5p sepia   .20   .20
994 A314 10p violet   .20   .20
995 A314 20p red   .25   .20
997 A314 50p dk grn   .60   .30
        Nos. 993-997 (4)   1.25 .90

Issued: 50p, 11/25/82; others, 1/15/84.
On No. 997 "50" is in outlined numbers.

Statue — A316

View of Aleppo — A317

1983   Perf. 12
1003 A316 225p brown   2.00 1.00
    Intl. Symposium on History and Archaeology of Deir Ez-zor.

1983   Perf. 12x12½
1004 A317 245p multi   2.25 1.10
    Intl. Symposium on Conservation of Old City of Aleppo, Sept. 26-30.

Mar. 8th Revolution, 21st Anniv. — A318

1984, Mar. 8   Perf. 12½x12
1005 A318 60p Alassad Library   .75 .35

Massacre at Sabra and Shatilla A319

1983   Litho.   Perf. 11½x12
1006 A319 225p Victims, mother & child   2.00 .50

Mothers' Day — A320

12th Intl. Flower Show, Damascus A321

1984, Mar. 21   Perf. 12x11½
1007 A320 245p Mother & child   2.50 1.25

1984, May 25

    Various flowers.
1008 A321 245p multi   2.50 1.25
1009 A321 285p multi   2.75 1.40

1984 Summer Olympics — A322

Aleppo Agricultural & Industrial Fair — A324

9th Regional Pioneers' Festival A323

1984   Litho.   Perf. 12x11½
1010   Strip of 5   3.00 2.40
  a. A322 30p Swimming   .30 .20
  b. A322 50p Wrestling   .50 .25
  c. A322 60p Running   .60 .30
  d. A322 70p Boxing   .65 .35
  e. A322 90p Soccer   .90 .45

Souvenir Sheet
Imperf
1011 A322 200p Soccer, diff.   3.50 3.50

1984   Perf. 11½x12
1012 A323 50p Pioneers   .50 .25
1013 A323 60p Pioneers, diff.   .60 .30

1984, June 12   Litho.   Perf. 12x12½
1014 A324 150p Peppers, Aleppo Castle   1.25 .50

Supreme Council of Science, 25th Anniv. A325

1985, Feb. 23   Perf. 12½x12
1015 A325 65p multi   .40 .20

Aleppo University, 25th Anniv. A326

1985, Feb. 23
1016 A326 45p multi   .25 .20

Syrian Arab Army, 39th Anniv. A327

1985, Feb. 23
1017 A327 65p brn & gldn brn   .40 .20

Pres. Assad, Soldier Saluting, Troops A328

1984, Aug. 1   Perf. 11½x12
1018 A328 60p multi   .60 .30
    4th General Revolutionary Youth Conference.

ITU Emblem, Satellite Dish, Telephone A329

1984, Oct. 2   Perf. 12½
1019 A329 245p multi   1.75 .90
    Intl. Telecommunications Day.

APU Emblem and Administration Building, Damascus — A330

1984, Oct. 9
1020 A330 60p multi   .60 .30
    Arab Postal Union Day.

Gearwheel, Arabesque Pattern — A331

Gold Necklace — A332

1984, Oct. 27   Perf. 12x12½, 12x11½
1021 A331 45p multi   .45 .20
1022 A332 100p multi   1.00 .45
    Intl. Fair, Damascus.

Intl. Civil Aviation Org., 40th Anniv. A333

1984, Oct. 27   Perf. 11½x12
1023 A333 45p brt bl & lt bl   .25 .20
1024 A333 245p brt ultra, brt bl & lt bl   1.25 .60

14th Anniv. of 11-16-70 Movement A334

1984, Dec. 3   Perf. 12½x12
1025 A334 65p red brn, blk & org   .65 .35

Pres. Assad, Text on Scroll A335

1984, Nov. 29   Perf. 12½
1026 A335 50p grn, brn org & sep   .50 .25
    Vow of Dedication taken by Youth of the Revolution.

Agricultural Exhibition — A336

1984, June 12   Perf. 12½x12
1027 A336 65p multi   .65 .35

Al-Kuneitra Memorial, Rose — A337

1984
1028 A337 70p multi   1.25 .35

Roman Arch and Colonnades, Palmyra — A338

1984, Dec. 3
1029 A338 100p multi   1.00 .50
Intl. Tourism Day.

Woodland Conservation — A339

1984
1030 A339 45p multi   .25 .20

March 8 Revolution, 22nd Anniv. — A340

UPU Emblem, Postal Headquarters, Damascus A341

1985, Apr. 27
1031 A340 60p multi   .40 .20

1985, Apr. 27
1032 A341 285p multi   3.00 1.50
World Post Day.

APU Building, Damascus — A342

1985, Apr. 27   **Perf. 12½**
1033 A342 245p multi   2.50 1.25
Arab Parliamentary Union, 10th Anniv.

Natl. Flag, Map of Arab Countries A343

1985   **Perf. 12½x12**
1034 A343 50p multi   .50 .25
Arab League.

Re-election of President Assad A344

1985, Mar. 12   **Perf. 12½**
1035 A344 200p multi   1.25 .70
1036 A344 300p multi   2.00 1.00
1037 A344 500p multi   3.25 1.75
   a.   Souvenir sheet of 3, #1035-1037, imperf.   7.00 5.50
   Nos. 1035-1037 (3)   6.50 3.45

Arab Postal Union, 12th Congress, Damascus A345

1985, Aug. 12   **Perf. 12x12½**
1038 A345 60p multi   .60 .30

Labor Day — A346

1985, Aug. 12   **Perf. 12½**
1039 A346 60p Order of Labor   .60 .30

32nd Intl. Fair, Damascus A347

1986, Feb. 1   **Litho.**   **Perf. 12½**
1040 A347 60p multi   .50 .25

2nd Scientific Symposium — A348

1985, Nov. 16   **Perf. 12½**
1041 A348 60p Locomotives   .60 .30

UN Child Survival Campaign A349

1985, Nov. 16   **Perf. 12½x12**
1042 A349 60p Malnourished child   .50 .25

UN, 40th Anniv. — A350

1985, Nov. 16   **Perf. 12x12½**
1043 A350 245p multi   2.25 1.10

November 16th Movement, 15th Anniv. — A351

1985, Nov. 16   **Perf. 12½**
1044 A351 60p Pres. Assad, highway   .50 .25

Abdul Rahman Dakhei in Andalusia, 1200th Anniv. A352

1986, Feb. 1   **Perf. 12½x12**
1045 A352 60p beige & brn   .60 .30

Tulips — A353

World Traffic Day — A355

1986, Feb. 1   **Perf. 12½x12**
1046 A353 30p multi   .30 .20
1047 A353 60p multi, diff.   .60 .30
Intl. Flower Show, Damascus.

Dental Congress, Damascus — A354

1986, Feb. 1   **Perf. 12½**
1046 A353 30p multi   .30 .20
1047 A353 60p multi, diff.   .60 .30
Intl. Flower Show, Damascus.

1986   **Perf. 12½x12**
1048 A354 110p yel, grysh grn & bl   1.10 .55

1986   **Perf. 12x12½**
1049 A355 330p multi   3.00 1.50

Syrian Investment Certificates, 15th Anniv. — A357

Day of Internal Security Forces — A359

Liberation of Al-Kuneitra, 12th Anniv. A358

1986   **Litho.**   **Perf. 12x11½**
1055 A357 100p multi   1.00 .50

1986   **Litho.**   **Perf. 11½x12**
1056 A358 110p Government Building   .75 .40

1986   **Perf. 12x11½**
1057 A359 110p multi   .75 .40

Labor Day — A360

1986 World Cup Soccer Championships, Mexico — A361

1986, Aug. 12
1058 A360 330p multi   1.25 .60

1986, July 7
1059 A361 330p multi   3.25 1.75
1060 A361 370p multi   3.50 1.90

Booklet Stamp
Size: 105x80mm
Imperf
1061 A361 500p Hemispheres, ball   5.00 2.50
   Nos. 1059-1061 (3)   11.75 6.15

Pres. Hafez al Assad — A362

1986-90 Litho. Perf. 12x11½

1068	A362	10p rose	.20 .20
1069	A362	30p dl ultra	.20 .20
1070	A362	50p claret	.40 .20
1071	A362	100p brt lt bl	.65 .30
1072	A362	150p brn vio	1.40 .65
1073	A362	175p violet	1.60 .80
1074	A362	200p pale red brn	1.40 .65
1075	A362	300p brt rose lil	2.00 1.00
1076	A362	500p orange	3.25 1.60
1077	A362	550p pink	5.00 2.50
1078	A362	600p dull grn	5.25 2.75
1079	A362	1000p brt pink	6.50 3.25
1080	A362	2000p pale grn	13.00 6.50
		Nos. 1068-1080 (13)	40.85 20.60

Issued: 150p, 175p, 550p, 600p, 1988; 50p, 9/30/90.

Intl. Day for Solidarity with the Palestinian People — A363

Mothers' Day — A364

1986, Aug. 7 Litho.
1081 A363 110p multi 1.10 .55

1986, Aug. 7
1082 A364 100p multi 1.00 .50

March 8 Revolution, 23rd Anniv. — A365

1986, Aug. 7 Perf. 11½x12
1083 A365 110p multi 1.10 .55

Arab Post Day A366

1986, Aug. 7
1084 A366 110p multi 1.10 .55

A367

33rd Intl. Damascus Fair A368

1986, Dec. 9 Litho. Perf. 11½x12
1085 A367 110p multi .90 .45
1086 A368 330p multi 2.50 .60

14th Intl. Flower Show, Damascus — A369

Various flowers.

1986, Oct. 11 Perf. 12½
1087		Strip of 5	6.50 5.00
a.	A369	10p multi	.20 .20
b.	A369	50p multi	.50 .25
c.	A369	100p multi	1.00 .50
d.	A369	110p multi	1.10 .60
e.	A369	330p multi	3.50 1.75

Syria-Soviet Joint Space Project — A370

World Children's Day — A371

1986, Nov. 16 Litho. Perf. 12½
1088 A370 330p multi 3.50 1.75

1986 Perf. 12x12½, 12½x12
1089 A371 330p shown 1.75 .90
1090 A371 330p Youth art exhibition, horiz. 1.75 .90

World Post Day — A372

1986, Jan. 28 Perf. 12½x12
1091 A372 330p multi 1.75 .90

Intl. Tourism Day — A373

Women wearing folk costumes, landmarks.

1986
1092 A373 330p multi 1.75 .90
1093 A373 370p multi 2.00 1.00

Pres. Assad, Tishreen Palace — A374

1986, Nov. 16 Litho. Perf. 12½
1094 A374 110p multi 1.25 .60

Nov. 16 Corrective Movement.

March 8th Revolution, 24th Anniv. — A375

1987, Mar. 6
1095 A375 100p multi .60 .30

Intl. Peace Year — A376

1987, Mar. 8 Perf. 12x11½
1096 A376 370p multi 2.25 1.25

Arab Baath Socialist Party, 40th Anniv. A377

1987, Apr. 7 Litho. Perf. 12½
1097 A377 100p multi .60 .30

Arab Post Day, 35th Anniv. A378

1987, May 1 Perf. 11½x12
1098 A378 110p multi .70 .35

Evacuation, Day, 41st Anniv. — A379

1987, Apr. 17 Perf. 12½x12
1099 A379 100p multi .60 .30

Labor Day — A380

Al-Kuneitra Monument A382

Hitteen's Battle, 800th Anniv. — A381

1987, May 1 Perf. 12x11½
1100 A380 330p multi 2.00 1.00

1987, June 25 Litho. Perf. 12½
1101 A381 110p multi 1.00 .45

1987, June 25 Perf. 12x11½
1102 A382 100p multi .65 .30

Child Vaccination Campaign — A383

1987, June 25 Perf. 11½x12
1103 A383 100p multi .50 .30
1104 A383 330p multi 2.00 1.10

A384

A385

Syrian-Soviet Joint Space Flight, July 22-30 — A386

Designs: No. 1105, Launch, July 22. No. 1106, Docking at space station, July 24. No. 1107, Landing, July 30, vert. No. 1108a, Liftoff. No. 1108b, Parachute landing. No. 1108c, Docked at space station. No. 1108d, Cosmonauts.

Perf. 12½, 11½x12, 12x11½
1987 Litho.
1105	A384	330p multi	2.00 1.00
1106	A385	330p multi	2.00 1.00
1107	A385	330p multi	2.00 1.00
		Nos. 1105-1107 (3)	6.00 3.00

Souvenir Sheet
Imperf
1108		Sheet of 4	10.00 10.00
a.-d.	A386	300p, any single	2.25 2.25

6th Conference of Arab Ministers of Culture A387

1987, Apr. 21   **Litho.**   **Perf. 12½**
1109 A387 330p dull blue grn & blk   3.00 1.50

President Assad Conversing with Syrian Cosmonaut — A388

1987, Aug. 12
1110 A388 500p multi   3.50 1.75

10th Mediterranean Games, Latakia — A389

Designs: 100p, Gymnastic rings, weight lifting, vert. 330p, Phoenician sailing ship. 370p, Flags spelling "SYRIA." No. 1115a, Emblem, gymnastics. No. 1115b, Emblem, weight lifting. No. 1115c, Emblem, tennis. No. 1115d, Emblem, soccer.

Perf. 12x11½, 11½x12
1987, Sept. 10
1111 A389 100p brt rose lil & blk   .70 .35
1112 A389 110p shown   .75 .40

Size: 58x28mm
Perf. 12½
1113 A389 330p multi   2.25 1.10
1114 A389 370p multi   2.50 1.25
   Nos. 1111-1114 (4)   6.20 3.10

Souvenir Sheet
Imperf
1115   Sheet of 4   7.75 7.75
a.-d.   A389 300p any single   1.90 1.90

34th Intl. Damascus Fair — A390

Arbor Day — A392

Intl. Flower Show, Damascus A391

1987   **Perf. 12x11½**
1116 A390 330p multi   2.00 1.00

1987, Oct. 20   **Perf. 11½x12**
1117 A391 330p Poppies   1.90 1.00
1118 A391 370p Gentian   2.00 1.00

1987, Oct. 20   **Perf. 12x11½**
1119 A392 330p multi   2.00 1.00

Army Day — A393

Intl. Palestine Day — A394

1987, Oct. 20   **Litho.**   **Perf. 12x11½**
1120 A393 100p multi   .60 .30

1987, Nov. 16
1121 A394 500p multi   3.50 1.75

Corrective Movement, 17th Anniv. — A395

1987, Nov. 16   **Perf. 12½**
1122 A395 150p Assad waving to crowd   1.00 .50

World Post Day — A396

1988, Mar. 8   **Litho.**   **Perf. 12½x12**
1123 A396 500p multi   3.00 1.50

Intl. Tourism Day A397

Women wearing folk costumes and: No. 1124, Palmyra Ruins. No. 1125, Reconstructed Roman amphitheater, Busra.

1988, Feb. 25   **Litho.**   **Perf. 11½x12**
1124 A397 500p multi   3.00 1.50
1125 A397 500p multi   3.00 1.50
   See Nos. 1147-1148, 1178-1179.

Intl. Children's Day — A398

1988, Feb. 27   **Perf. 12½**
1126 A398 500p multi   3.00 1.50

March 8th Revolution, 25th Anniv. — A399

Mothers' Day — A400

1988, Mar. 15   **Litho.**   **Perf. 12x11½**
1127 A399 150p multi   1.00 .50

Size: 110x81mm
Imperf
1128 A399 500p multi, diff.   4.75 4.75

No. 1128 pictures vignette like 150p without denomination, in diff. colors, and Arab Revolt flag, text, outline map; denomination at LR in sheet.

1988, Apr. 12   **Litho.**   **Perf. 12x12½**
1129 A400 500p multi   3.00 1.50

Arab Post Day A401

1988, Apr. 17   **Perf. 12½x12**
1130 A401 150p multi   1.00 .50

1946 Evacuation A402

Labor Day — A403

1988, Apr. 17   **Perf. 12x12½**
1131 A402 150p multi   1.00 .50

1988, May 1
1132 A403 550p multi   3.00 1.50

Intl. Flower Show, Damascus A404

Arab Engineers' Union — A405

1988, May 25   **Perf. 12x11½**
1133 A404 550p Tiger Lily   3.25 1.60
1134 A404 600p Carnations   3.75 1.90

1988, May 25
1135 A405 150p multi   1.00 .50

A406

A407

1988, Aug. 28   **Litho.**   **Perf. 12x11½**
1136 A406 600p blk, grn & olive   3.50 1.75
   Intl. Children's Day.

1988, Aug. 28   **Perf. 12½**
1137 A407 550p multi   3.00 1.50
Restoration of San'a, Yemen Arab Republic.

Ebla Intl. Symposium on Archaeology of Idlib — A408

1988, Aug. 28
1138	A408	175p	Hieroglyphic tablet	1.00 .50
1139	A408	550p	Bas-relief (votive basin)	3.00 1.50
1140	A408	600p	Gold statue, 3000 B.C.	3.50 1.75
			Nos. 1138-1140 (3)	7.50 3.75

1988 Summer Olympics, Seoul A409

1988, Sept. 17   *Perf. 11½x12*
1141	A409	550p	Cycling	3.25 1.60
1142	A409	600p	Soccer	3.50 1.75

Size: 81x61mm
Imperf
1143	A409	1200p	Emblem, character trademark	12.50 12.50
			Nos. 1141-1143 (3)	19.25 15.85

35th Intl. Fair, Damascus A410

WHO, 40th Anniv. — A411

1988, Aug. 28   *Perf. 12x11½*
1144	A410	600p	multi	3.50 1.75

1988, Aug. 28   Litho.   *Perf. 12x11½*
1145	A411	600p	multi	3.25 1.60

Arab Scouting Movement, 50th Anniv. — A412

1988, Sept. 17   *Perf. 12½x12*
1146	A412	150p	multi	1.50 .75

Tourism Type of 1988

Women wearing folk costumes and: 550p, Euphrates Bridge, Deir-ez-Zor. 600p, The Tetrapylon, Latakia.

1988, Oct. 18
1147	A397	550p	multi	3.25 1.60
1148	A397	600p	multi	3.50 1.75

World Post Day — A413

Arbor Day — A414

1988, Dec. 7   Litho.   *Perf. 12x12½*
1149	A413	600p	multi	3.50 1.75

1988, Nov. 16
1150	A414	600p	multi	3.50 1.75

Shelter for the Homeless — A415

1988-89   *Perf. 12½x12*
1151	A415	150p	Arab Housing Day	.65 .35
1151A	A415	175p	Intl. Year of Shelter for the Homeless	1.25 .60
1152	A415	550p	World Housing Day	2.50 1.25
1153	A415	600p	as No. 1151A	2.75 1.50
			Nos. 1151-1153 (4)	7.15 3.70

The IYSH emblem is pictured on the 175p, 550p and 600p.
Issued: 175p, 2/6/89; others, 10/18/88.

Al-Assad University Hospital — A416

1988, Nov. 16   Litho.   *Perf. 12½*
1154	A416	150p	multi	.90 .45

Corrective Movement, 18th anniv.

World Food Day — A417

1988, Oct. 18   *Perf. 12½x12½*
1155	A417	550p	multi	2.75 1.40

Birds A418

1989, Mar. 21   Litho.   *Perf. 11½x12*
1156	A418	600p	Goldfinch	1.50 .75
1157	A418	600p	Turtledove	1.50 .75
1158	A418	600p	Bee eater	1.50 .75
			Nos. 1156-1158 (3)	4.50 2.25

Jawaharlal Nehru, 1st Prime Minister of Independent India — A419

1989, Mar. 8   *Perf. 12½*
1159	A419	550p	brn & chest	1.10 .55

Mothers' Day — A420

1989, Mar. 21
1160	A420	550p	multi	1.10 .55

Teacher's Day A421

1989, Mar. 8   Litho.   *Perf. 11½x12*
1161	A421	175p	multi	.70 .35

5th General Congress of the Union of Women A422

1989, Mar. 8   *Perf. 12½*
1162	A422	150p	multi	.30 .20

March 8th Revolution, 26th Anniv. — A423

1989, Mar. 8   *Perf. 11½x12*
1163	A423	150p	multi	.30 .20

Arab Board for Medical Specializations, 10th Anniv. — A424

1989, Feb. 6   *Perf. 12½*
1164	A424	175p	multi	.60 .30

1946 Evacuation of British and French Troops — A425

1989, Apr. 17   Litho.   *Perf. 11½x12*
1165	A425	150p	multi	.40 .20

Intl. Flower Show, Damascus A426

1989, June 3   *Perf. 12½*
1166		Strip of 5		5.00 4.00
a.	A426	150p	Snapdragon	.30 .20
b.	A426	150p	Canaria	.30 .20
c.	A426	450p	Compositae	.90 .45
d.	A426	850p	Clematis sackmani	1.75 .85
e.	A426	900p	Gesneriaceae	1.75 .90

A427

A428

1989, May 1   *Perf. 12x11½*
1167	A427	850p	blue grn & blk	1.75 .90

Labor Day.

1989, June 6   Litho.   *Perf. 12x11½*
1168	A428	175p	multi	.50 .25

13th General Congress of the Arab Teachers' Union.

Arab Post
Day — A429

Liberation of Al-
Kuneitra, 15th
Anniv. — A430

1989, June 6
169 A429 175p multi   .50 .25

1989, June 26
170 A430 450p multi   1.25 .60

17th
Congress
of the
Arab
Advocates
Union
A431

1989, June 19   **Perf. 11½x12**
171 A431 175p multi   .50 .25

World
Post Day
A432

1989, June 26
172 A432 550p multi   1.50 .75

World Telecommunications
Day — A433

1989, June 6
173 A433 550p multi   1.50 .75

Interparliamentary Union,
Cent. — A434

1989, July 12   **Perf. 12½**
174 A434 900p multi   2.50 1.25

Butterflies
A435

1989, June 6
1175 A435 550p Small white   1.50 .75
1176 A435 550p Clouded yellow   1.50 .75
1177 A435 550p Painted Lady   1.50 .75
    Nos. 1175-1177 (3)   4.50 2.25

Intl. Tourism Day Type of 1988

Women wearing folk costumes and: 550p,
Jaabar Castle, Rakka. 600p, Temple of the
Bell, Palmyra.

1989, Oct. 16   **Litho.**   **Perf. 11½x12**
1178 A397 550p multicolored   3.75 1.75
1179 A397 600p multicolored   4.00 2.00

36th Intl. Fair,
Damascus
A436

1989, Oct. 16   **Perf. 12x11½**
1180 A436 450p multicolored   3.00 1.50

Fish
A437

1989, Oct. 24   **Perf. 11½x12**
1181 A437 550p Carp   3.75 1.75
1182 A437 600p Trout   4.00 2.00

2nd Anniv. of the
Palestinian
Uprising — A438

1989, Oct. 24   **Perf. 12x11½**
1183 A438 550p Child's drawing   3.75 1.75

Corrective Movement, 19th
Anniv. — A439

1989, Nov. 16   **Litho.**   **Perf. 12½x12**
1184 A439 150p multicolored   1.00 .50

A440

A441

1990, Feb. 13   **Litho.**   **Perf. 12x11½**
1185 A440 850p multicolored   1.00 .50
    World Children's Day.

1990
1186 A441 600p multicolored   .70 .35
    March 8th Revolution, 27th anniv.

Revolutionary
Youth Union
A442

1990   **Perf. 12½**
1187 A442 150p multicolored   .20 .20

World
Food Day
A443

1990, Feb. 13   **Litho.**   **Perf. 11½x12**
1188 A443 850p multicolored   1.00 .50
    Dated 1989.

Evacuation of
British and French
Troops,
1946 — A444

1990, Apr. 17   **Perf. 12x11½**
1189 A444 175p multicolored   .20 .20

Mother's
Day — A445

1990, Apr. 17   **Perf. 12½**
1190 A445 550p multicolored   .65 .30

Labor
Day — A446

1990, May 1   **Litho.**   **Perf. 12x12½**
1191 A446 550p multicolored   .75 .35

World Cup Soccer Championships,
Italy — A447

Perf. 11½x12, 12x11½
1990, June 8   **Litho.**
1192 A447 550p shown   .40 .20
1193 A447 550p Denomination
      at right   .40 .20
1194 A447 600p Map, soccer
      ball, vert.   .45 .25
    Nos. 1192-1194 (3)   1.25 .65

Miniature Sheet
Imperf
1195 A447 1300p Stadium   3.50 1.75

Intl. Flower Show,
Damascus
A448

1990, May 27   **Perf. 12x11½**
1196 A448 600p Lily   .45 .20
1197 A448 600p Pastelkleurig   .45 .20
1198 A448 600p Marigold   .45 .20
1199 A448 600p Viburnum opu-
      lus   .45 .20
1200 A448 600p Swan river daisy   .45 .20
    Nos. 1196-1200 (5)   2.25 1.00

World Health
Day — A449

1990, May 1   **Litho.**   **Perf. 12½**
1201 A449 600p multicolored   2.50 1.25

Liberation of Al-
Kuneitra, 16th
Anniv. — A450

Intl. Literacy
Year — A451

1990, June 26   *Perf. 12x11½*
1202 A450 550p multicolored   2.50 1.25

1990, June 26
1203 A451 550p multicolored   2.25 1.10

UN Conference on Least Developed
Countries — A452

1990, July 10   *Perf. 11½x12*
1204 A452 600p multicolored   2.40 1.25

37th Damascus
Intl. Fair — A453

Arbor
Day — A455

World Meteorology Day — A454

1990, Aug. 28   *Perf. 12x11½*
1205 A453 550p multicolored   2.25 1.10

1990, Aug. 28   *Perf. 11½x12*
1206 A454 450p multicolored   1.90   .95

1990, Oct. 30   *Perf. 12x11½*
1207 A455 550p multicolored   2.25 1.10

World Food
Day — A456

1990, Oct. 30   *Perf. 12½*
1208 A456 850p multicolored   3.25 1.75

Al Maqdisi,
Cartographer
A457

1990, Nov. 6   *Perf. 12x11½*
1209 A457 550p multicolored   2.25 1.10

A458   A459

Pres.
Hafez al
Assad
A460

1990, Nov. 16   Litho.   *Perf. 11½*
1210 A458 50p claret   .20   .20
1211 A458 70p gray   .25   .20
1212 A458 100p blue   .35   .20
1213 A458 150p brown   .60   .30

Perf. 12x11½
1214 A459 175p multicolored   .70   .35
1215 A459 300p multicolored   1.25   .55
1216 A459 550p multicolored   2.25 1.10
1217 A459 600p multicolored   2.40 1.25

Perf. 11½x12
1219 A460 1000p multicolored   4.00 2.00
1220 A460 1500p multicolored   6.00 3.00
1222 A460 2000p multicolored   8.00 4.00
1224 A460 2500p multicolored   10.00 5.00
    Nos. 1210-1224 (12)   36.00 18.15

This may be an expanding set. Numbers will
change if necessary.

1992, May 19   Litho.   *Perf. 11½*
Without Date at Right
1225 A458 150p brown   .60   .30
1225A A458 300p violet   1.25   .60
1225B A458 350p gray   1.40   .70
1225C A458 400p red   1.60   .80
    Nos. 1225-1225C (4)   4.85 2.40

Souvenir Sheet

الجمهورية العربية السورية

الذكرى العشرون للحركة التصحيحية

Corrective Movement, 20th
Anniv. — A461

a, Pres. Assad with children. b, Assad
addressing crowd. c, Assad, memorial. d,
Assad, dam.

1990, Nov. 16   *Imperf.*
1227 A461 550p Sheet of 4, #a.-
              d.   9.00 9.00

UN Development Program, 40th
Anniv. — A462

1990, Dec. 11   *Perf. 11½x12*
1228 A462 550p multicolored   2.25 1.10

Arab Civil
Aviation
Day
A463

1990, Dec. 11
1229 A463 175p multicolored   1.00   .50

World Post
Day — A464

Intl. Children's
Day — A465

1990, Dec. 11   *Perf. 12x11½*
1230 A464 550p multicolored   2.25 1.10

1990, Dec. 11
1231 A465 550p multicolored   2.25 1.10

Arab-Spanish
Cultural
Symposium
A466

World AIDS
Day — A467

1990, Dec. 24
1232 A466 550p multicolored   2.25 1.10

1990, Dec. 24
1233 A467 550p multicolored   2.25 1.10

March 8th Revolution, 28th
Anniv. — A468

**1991, Mar. 8   Litho.   *Perf. 11½x1*
1234 A468 150p multicolored   .60   .3

Butterflies
A469

1991, Mar. 17   *Perf. 12*
1235 A469 550p Small tortoise-
              shell   2.25 1.1
1236 A469 550p Changeful great
              mars   2.25 1.1
1237 A469 550p Papillion
              machaon   2.25 1.1
    Nos. 1235-1237 (3)   6.75 3.3

Birds — A470

Mother's
Day — A471

1991, Mar. 17   *Perf. 12x11½*
1238 A470 600p Golden oriole   2.40 1.2
1239 A470 600p European roller   2.40 1.2
1240 A470 600p House sparrow   2.40 1.25
    Nos. 1238-1240 (3)   7.20 3.75

1991, Mar. 21
1241 A471 550p multicolored   2.25 1.1

1946 Evacuation of British and French
Troops — A472

1991, Apr. 17   *Perf. 11½x1*
1242 A472 150p multicolored   .60   .30

Labor Day
A473

1991, May 1
1243 A473 550p multicolored   2.25 1.1

Intl. Flower Show,
Damascus — A474

1991, July 8   **Perf. 12x12½**
1244 A474 550p Narcissus   2.25 1.10
1245 A474 600p Monarda
     didyma   2.40 1.25

Liberation
of
Kuneitra,
17th
Anniv.
A475

1991, July 22   **Perf. 11½x12**
1246 A475 550p multicolored   2.25 1.10

11th Mediterranean Games,
Athens — A476

1991, July 22
1247 A476   550p Running   2.25 1.10
1248 A476   550p Soccer   2.25 1.10
1249 A476   600p Equestrian   2.25 1.25

     Size: 80x64mm
         Imperf
1250 A476 1300p Dolphins play-
     ing water
     polo   5.25 5.25
   Nos. 1247-1250 (4)   12.00 8.70

38th Damascus
Intl. Fair — A477

1991, Aug. 28   **Perf. 12x12½**
1251 A477 550p multicolored   2.25 1.10

Intl.
Tourism
Day
A478

Designs: 450p, Woman at Khan Asaad
Pasha El Azem. 550p, Woman at Castle of
Arwad Island.

1991, Sept. 27   **Perf. 11½x12**
1252 A478 450p multicolored   1.90 .95
1253 A478 550p multicolored   2.25 1.10

Housing
Day — A479

Intl. Children's
Day — A480

1991, Oct. 7   **Perf. 12x11½**
1254 A479 175p multicolored   1.00 .50

1991, Oct. 16
1255 A480 600p multicolored   2.40 1.25

Physician
Abu Bakr
Al Razi
(Rhazes),
Patient
A481

1991, Nov. 2   **Litho.**   **Perf. 12½x12**
1256 A481 550p multicolored   2.25 1.10

     31st Science Week.

World
Post Day
A482

1991, Nov. 12
1257 A482 550p multicolored   2.25 1.10

World
Food Day
A483

1991, Nov. 12
1258 A483 550p multicolored   2.25 1.10

Tomb of
Unknown
Soldier,
Damascus
A484

1991, Nov. 16   **Perf. 12½**
1259 A484 600p multicolored   2.40 1.25

     Size: 65x80mm
         Imperf
1260 A484 1000p multicolored   4.00 2.00

Corrective Movement, 21st
Anniv. — A485

   Illustration reduced.

1991, Nov. 16   **Imperf.**
1261 A485 2500p multicolored   10.00 5.00

Protect the Environment — A486

1991, Nov. 20   **Perf. 12½x12**
1262 A486 175p multicolored   .70 .35

World Telecommunications
Fair — A487

1991, Nov. 20   **Perf. 12x12½**
1263 A487 600p multicolored   2.40 1.25

March 8th
Revolution,
29th Anniv.
A488

1992, Mar. 8   **Litho.**   **Perf. 12½**
1264 A488 600p multicolored   2.40 1.25

Re-election of Pres. Assad — A489

1992, Mar. 12   **Litho.**   **Imperf.**
1265 A489 5000p shown   20.00 10.00
     Size: 100x85mm
1266 A489 5000p inscription at
     right   20.00 10.00

   Nos. 1265-1266 incorporate designs of
#1036, C496 & C506.

Baath
Party,
45th
Anniv.
A490

1992, Apr. 7   **Perf. 12½x12**
1267 A490 850p multicolored   3.50 1.75

Labor
Day — A491

Mother's
Day — A492

1992, May 1   **Perf. 12x12½**
1268 A491 900p multicolored   3.50 1.75

1992, May 19
1269 A492 900p multicolored   3.50 1.75

Evacuation of British and French
Troops, 46th Anniv. — A493

1992, May 19   **Perf. 12½x12**
1270 A493 900p multicolored   3.50 1.75

Traffic Safety
Day — A494

Intl. Flower Show,
Damascus
A495

1992, May 19   **Perf. 12x12½**
1271 A494 850p multicolored   3.50 1.75

Perf. 11½x12, 12x11½
1992, July 5   **Litho.**

Designs: 300p, Linum mucronatum, horiz.
800p, Yucca filamentosa. 900p, Zinnia
elegans.
1272 A495 300p multicolored   1.25 .65
1273 A495 800p blue & multi   3.25 1.60
1274 A495 900p multicolored   3.50 1.75
    Nos. 1272-1274 (3)   8.00 4.00

1992 Summer
Olympics,
Barcelona
A496

No. 1275: a, 150p, Team handball. b, 150p,
Running. c, 450p, Swimming. d, 750p, Wrestling. 5000p, Incorporates designs of Nos.
1275a-1275d.

1992, July 25   **Litho.**   **Perf. 12x11½**
1275 A496 Strip of 4, #a.-d.   6.00 5.00
           Imperf
      Size: 80x124mm
1276 A496 5000p multicolored   20.00 10.00

Anti-Smoking
Campaign
A497

39th Intl.
Damascus
Fair — A498

1992, Aug. 28   **Perf. 12x12½**
1277 A497 750p multicolored   3.00 1.50

1992, Aug. 28
1278 A498 900p multicolored   3.50 1.75

7th Arab Games, Damascus — A499

Designs: a, 750p, Soccer. b, 850p, Pommel
horse. c, 900p, Pole vault.

1992, Sept. 4   **Perf. 12½**
1279 A499 Strip of 3, #a.-c.   10.00 5.00

World Post
Day — A500

World Children's
Day — A501

1992, Oct. 9   **Perf. 12x12½**
1280 A500 600p multicolored   2.40 1.25

1992, Nov. 7   **Perf. 12x11½**
1281 A501 850p multicolored   3.50 1.75

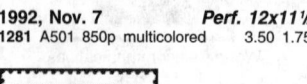

Sebtt El Mardini
(826-912)
A502

1992, Nov. 7   **Litho.**   **Perf. 12x11½**
1282 A502 850p multicolored   3.50 1.75

1992 Special
Olympics,
Madrid
A503

1992, Nov. 7   **Perf. 12½**
1283 A503 850p multicolored   3.50 1.75

Corrective Movement, 22nd
Anniv. — A504

1992, Nov. 16   **Perf. 11½x12**
1284 A504 450p multicolored   1.75 .90

Arbor
Day — A505

1992, Dec. 31   **Perf. 12x12½**
1285 A505 600p multicolored   2.40 1.25

2nd Intl. Conference of PACO — A506

Design: 1150p, Eye surrounded by scenes
of day and night, rainbow.

1993, May 12   **Litho.**   **Perf. 12**
1286 A506 1100p multicolored   1.00 .50
      Size: 35½x24mm
       Perf. 11½x12
1287 A506 1150p multicolored   1.10 .55
Syrian Ophthamological Society, 25th
anniv. (#1287).

March 8th Revolution, 30th
Anniv. — A507

1993, Mar. 8   **Litho.**   **Perf. 11½x12**
1288 A507 1100p multicolored   .80 .40

Butterflies
A508

Designs: a, 1000p, Common blue. b, 1500p,
Silver-washed fritillary. c, 2500p, Precis
orithya.

1993, Mar. 13
1289 A508 Strip of 3, #a.-c.   4.75 4.75

Mother's
Day — A509

1993, Apr. 17   **Perf. 12x11½**
1290 A509 1100p multicolored   .80 .40

Evacuation of British and French
Troops, 47th Anniv. — A510

1993, Apr. 17   **Perf. 11½x12**
1291 A510 1100p multicolored   .80 .40

A511

1993, Apr. 17   **Litho.**   **Perf. 11½x12**
1292 A511 2500p multicolored   1.75 .85

Agricultural Reform, 25th
Anniv. — A512

1993, Apr. 20   **Litho.**   **Perf. 11½x12**
1293 A512 1150p multicolored   .90 .45

A513

A514

1993, May 1   **Perf. 12x11½**
1294 A513 1100p multicolored   .80 .40
       Labor day.

1993, June 17 Litho.   Perf. 12x11½
Intl. Flower Show, Damascus: a, 1000p
Alcea setosa. b, 1100p, Primulaceae. c,
1150p, Gesneriaceae.
1295 A514 Strip of 3, #a.-c.   2.25 2.25

Tourism
A515

1993, Sept. 27   **Perf. 11½x12**
1296 A515 1000p Woman, prism
tomb   1.00 .50

World
Post Day
A516

1993, Oct. 9   **Perf. 12½x12**
1297 A516 1000p multicolored   1.00 .50

World
Child Day
A517

1993, Nov. 6   **Perf. 11½x12**
1298 A517 1150p multicolored   1.10 .55

Ibn El Bittar,
Chemist — A518

1993, Nov. 6   **Perf. 12x11½**
1299 A518 1150p multicolored   1.10 .55

Corrective Movement, 23rd
Anniv. — A519

Illustration reduced.

1993, Nov. 16   **Litho.**   **Imperf.**
1300 A519 2500p multicolored   2.50 2.50

Arabian
Horses
A520

1994, Jan.   **Litho.**   **Perf. 12½**
1301 A520 1000p shown   .60 .30
1302 A520 1000p White horse   .60 .30
1303 A520 1500p Tan horse   .90 .45
1304 A520 1500p Black horse   .90 .45
   a.   Strip of 4, #1301-1304   3.00 3.00

Arbor Day
A521

1994, Jan.   **Litho.**   **Perf. 12½x12**
1305 A521 1100p multicolored   1.75 .85

40th Intl.
Damascus
Fair
A522

1994, Jan.
1306 A522 1100p multicolored   1.75 .85

Basel Al Assad
(1962-94) — A523

1994, Mar. 1   **Perf. 12x12½**
1307 A523 2500p multicolored   4.00 2.00

March 8th Revolution, 31st
Anniv. — A524

a, Oranges. b, Mandarin oranges. c,
Lemons.

1994, Mar. 8   **Perf. 12½x12**
1308 A524 1500p Strip of 3, #a.-
   c.   7.50 7.50

Evacuation of British and French
Troops, 48th Anniv. — A525

1994, Apr. 17
1309 A525 1800p multicolored   2.75 1.40

Mother's
Day
A526

1994, May 1   **Litho.**   **Perf. 12½x12**
1310 A526 1800p multicolored   2.75 1.40

Labor Day
A527

1994, May 1
1311 A527 1700p multicolored   2.75 1.40

ILO, 75th
Anniv.
A528

1994, June 1
1312 A528 1700p multicolored   2.75 1.40

1994 World Cup Soccer
Championships, US — A529

Various soccer plays.

1994, June 17   **Perf. 12½**
1313 A529 1700p Pair, #a.-b.   5.75 2.75
   Size: 80x80mm
   Imperf
1314 A529 4000p multicolored   6.75 6.75

41st Intl. Fair,
Damascus
A530

Intl. Flower Show,
Damascus
A531

1994, Aug. 3   **Litho.**   **Perf. 12x12½**
1315 A530 1800p multicolored   1.60 .80

1994, Aug. 3   **Perf. 12x11½**
a, Daisies. b, Red flowers. c, Yellow flowers.
1316 A531 1800p Strip of 3, #a.-
   c.   4.50 4.50

Intl. Olympic Committee,
Cent. — A532

1994, Aug. 3   **Perf. 11½x12**
1317 A532 1700p multicolored   1.50 .75

Butterflies
A533

a, Apollo (shown). b, Purple emperor, value
at right. c, Birdwing, value at left.

1994, Aug. 9   **Litho.**   **Perf. 11½x12**
1318 A533 1700p Strip of 3, #a.-
   c.   8.25 8.25

4th Natl.
Census
A534

1994, Aug. 15
1319 A534 1000p multicolored   1.50 .75

Science
Week
A535

Design: £10, Al Kindi, philosopher.

1994, Nov. 5   **Perf. 12½**
1320 A535 £10 multicolored   1.50 .75

Corrective Movement, 24th
Anniv. — A536

Illustration reduced.

1994, Nov. 16   **Imperf.**
1321 A536 £25 multicolored   6.50 6.50

ICAO, 50th Anniv. — A537

1994, Dec. 7   **Litho.**   **Perf. 12½**
1322 A537 17p multicolored   1.50 .75

Martyr's Square A538

1994, Dec. 7   Litho.   *Perf. 11½x12*
1323 A538 £50 purple   7.25 3.75

Intl. Children's Day — A539

World Post Day — A540

1994, Dec. 19   *Perf. 12x11½*
1324 A539 £10 multicolored   1.50 .75

1994, Dec. 19
1325 A540 £10 multicolored   1.50 .75

Intl. Tourism Day — A541

1994, Dec. 19
1326 A541 £17 multicolored   2.50 1.25

March 8 Revolution, 32nd Anniv. — A542

1995, Mar. 8   Litho.   *Perf. 11½x12*
1327 A542 £18 multicolored   2.75 1.40

Arab League, 50th Anniv. A543

1995, Mar. 22   *Perf. 12½*
1328 A543 £17 multicolored   2.50 1.25

World Water Day — A544

1995, Apr. 9   Litho.   *Perf. 12x12½*
1329 A544 £17 multicolored   1.25 .60

Mother's Day A545

1995, Apr. 9   Litho.   *Perf. 12½x12*
1330 A545 £17 multicolored   2.00 1.00

Arbor Day — A546

1995, Apr. 9   Litho.   *Perf. 12x12½*
1331 A546 1800p multicolored   1.50 .75

A547

A548

1995, Aug. 13   Litho.   *Perf. 12x11½*
1332 A547 £18 multicolored   2.75 1.40
UN, 50th anniv.

1995, Aug. 21
1333 A548 £18 multicolored   2.75 1.40
4th World Conference on Women, Beijing.

Desert Festival, Tourism Day A549

1995, June 25   *Perf. 12½x12*
1334 A549 £18 multicolored   1.25 .65

A550

A551

1995, June 25   *Perf. 12x12½*
1335 A550 £10 Labor Day   .75 .40

1995, Apr. 30   Litho.   *Perf. 12x11½*
1336 A551 £17 multicolored   1.25 .60
Evacuation of British & French Troops, 49th anniv.

A552

A553

1995, Apr. 30   Litho.   *Perf. 12x11½*
1337 A542 £17 multicolored   1.40 .70
Intl. Year of the Family.

1995, Apr. 30   Litho.   *Perf. 12x12½*
1338 A553 £17 multicolored   2.00 1.00
Arab Apiculture Union, 1st anniv.

FAO, 50th Anniv. A554

1995, June 25   *Perf. 12½x12*
1339 A554 £15 multicolored   1.75 .85

42nd Intl. Fair, Damascus A555

1995, Aug. 28   Litho.   *Perf. 11½x12*
1340 A555 £15 multicolored   1.50 .75

Int'l Flower Show, Damascus A556

A550

1995, July 30   Litho.   *Perf. 12½*
1341 A556 £10 Astilbe   .50 .25
1342 A556 £10 Evening prim-
          rose   .50 .25
1343 A556 £10 Blue carpet   .50 .25
   a.   Strip of 3, #1341-1343   1.50 1.50

Second Congress of Arab Dentists' Assoc. — A557

1995, Sept. 16   Litho.   *Perf. 12x11½*
1344 A557 £18 multicolored   1.50 .75

Syrian Army, 50th Anniv. A558

1995, Oct. 2   Litho.   *Perf. 11½x12*
1345 A558 £18 multicolored   1.40 .70

World Post Day A559

1995, Oct. 2   Litho.   *Perf. 11½x12*
1346 A559 £15 multicolored   1.60 .85

World Children's Day — A560

1995, Oct. 2   *Perf. 12x11½*
1347 A560 £18 multicolored   2.00 1.00

Ahmed ben Maged, Cartographer, 500th Death Anniv. — A561

1995, Nov. 4   Litho.   *Perf. 11½x12*
1348 A561 £18 multicolored   2.00 1.00

Corrective Movement, 25th Anniv. A562

Design: £50, like #1349 with Nos. 1044, 720, 1227b, 903.

1995, Nov. 11   Litho.   Perf. 12½
1349 A562   £10 multicolored   1.10   .55
Imperf
Size: 100x64mm
1350 A562   £50 multicolored   5.50 2.75

Songbirds
A563

Designs: a, Group on tree branch. b, One in snow, flower. c, One on fence rail.

1995, Dec. 5   Litho.   Perf. 12½
1351 A563   £18 Strip of 3, #a.-c. 7.25 7.25

Louis
Pasteur
(1822-95)
A564

1995, Dec. 21   Perf. 12½x12
1352 A564   £18 multicolored   2.00 1.00

March 8 Revolution, 33rd
Anniv. — A565

1996, Mar. 8   Litho.   Perf. 11½x12
1353 A565   £25 Hydro-electric
plant   2.00 1.00

Evacuation Day, 50th Anniv. — A566

1996, Apr. 17   Perf. 12½
1354 A566   £10 black & multi   .85   .40
1355 A566   £25 bister & multi 2.00 1.00
Size: 57x46mm
Imperf
1356 A566   £25 bis, blk, & multi 5.25 2.75

Liberation
of
Kuneitra
A567

1996, June 26   Litho.   Perf. 11½x12
1357 A567   £10 multicolored   .60   .30

1996
Summer
Olympic
Games,
Atlanta
A568

1996, July 19   Perf. 11½x12
1358 A568   £17 Wrestling   1.10   .55
1359 A568   £17 Swimming   1.10   .55
1360 A568   £17 Running   1.10   .55
  a.   Strip of 3, #1358-1360   3.25 3.25
Size: 55x41mm
Imperf
1361 A568   £25 Soccer   1.60   .80
  Nos. 1358-1361 (4)   4.90 2.45

Intl. Flower
Show,
Damascus
A569

Cactus: No. 1362, Notocactus graessnerii.
No. 1363, Mammilaria erythosperma.

1996, July 1   Litho.   Perf. 12½
1362 A569   £18 multicolored   1.25   .65
1363 A569   £18 multicolored   1.25   .65

Ba'ath
Party,
50th
Anniv.
A570

1996, July 1   Perf. 11½x12
1364 A570   £18 multicolored   1.25   .65

Pres. Hafez al-
Assad — A571

1995   Litho.   Perf. 11½
1365 A571   100p bright blue   .20   .20
1366 A571   500p bright orange .55   .25
1367 A571   £10 bright lilac   1.10   .55
1368 A571   £17 rose lake   1.90   .95
1369 A571   £18 slate green   2.00 1.00
  Nos. 1365-1369 (5)   5.75 2.95

Issued: £10, 5/3; 100p, 500p, £17, £18,
12/31.

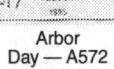

Arbor
Day — A572

Mother's
Day — A573

1996, Mar. 8   Litho.   Perf. 12¼x12½
1370 A572   £17 multicolored   .80   .40

1996, May 1   Perf. 12x11½
1370A A573 £10 multicolored   .50   .25

Labor Day — A574

1996, May 1   Perf. 12¼x12½
1371 A574   £15 multicolored   .70   .35

Radio, Cent. — A575

1996, Aug. 18   Litho.   Perf. 12½
1372 A575   £17 multicolored   1.10   .55

World AIDS
Day — A576

43rd Intl. Fair,
Damascus
A577

1996, Aug. 18   Perf. 12x11½
1373 A576   £17 multicolored   1.10   .55

1996, Aug. 28
1374 A577   £17 multicolored   1.10   .55

NICE, 5th
Anniv.
A578

1996, Sept. 5   Perf. 11½x12
1375 A578   £18 multicolored   1.10   .60

World Child
Day — A579

World Post
Day — A580

1996, Oct. 9   Perf. 12x11½
1376 A579   £10 multicolored   .65   .30

1996, Oct. 9
1377 A580   £17 multicolored   1.10   .55

UNICEF, 50th
Anniv. — A581

1996, Nov. 20
1378 A581   £17 multicolored   1.10   .55

36th Science Week — A582

Design: Musa Iben Shaker's sons.

1996, Nov. 2   Perf. 12½x12
1379 A582   £10 multicolored   .65   .35

Corrective
Movement,
26th Anniv.
A583

1996, Nov. 16   Perf. 12½
1380 A583   £10 multicolored   .65   .35
Size: 65x90mm
Imperf
1381 A583   £50 like No. 1380   3.25 1.60

Natl. Advance
Party — A584

March 8
Revolution, 34th
Anniv. — A585

1997, Mar. 7 Litho. Perf. 12x11½
1382 A584 £3 multicolored   .20 .20

1997, Mar. 8
1383 A585 £15 multicolored   1.00 .50

Arbor Day — A586

1996, Apr. 8 Litho. Perf. 12x12½
1384 A586 £10 multicolored   .75 .40

Fish — A587

1996, Apr. 8 Perf. 12½x12
1385 A587 £17 Two dorsal fins 1.00 .50
1386 A587 £17 One dorsal fin   1.00 .50
  a. Pair, #1385-1386   2.00 2.00

Mother's
Day — A588

1997, Apr. 8 Perf. 12x11½
1387 A588 £15 multicolored   1.00 .50

Baath Party
Revolution,
50th Anniv.
A589

1997, Apr. 3 Perf. 12½
1388 A589 £25 multicolored   1.60 .80
      Size: 90x65mm
      Imperf
1389 A589 £25 multicolored   1.60 .80

World Tourism
Day — A590

1997, Apr. 8 Perf. 12x11½
1390 A590 £17 multicolored   1.10 .60

Evacuation Day, 51st Anniv. — A591

1997, Apr. 17 Perf. 11½x12
1391 A591 £15 multicolored   1.00 .50

Labor
Day — A592

1997, May 1 Perf. 12x11½
1392 A592 £15 multicolored   1.00 .50

World Book
Day — A592a

1997, June 16 Litho. Perf. 12½
1392A A592a £10 multicolored   .50 .25

A592b   A593

1997, June 16 Perf. 12x11½
1392B A592b £18 multicolored   .70 .35
  No smoking day.

1997, June 21 Litho. Perf. 12x11½
No. 1393, Echino ereus. No. 1394, Iris.

1393 A593 £18 multicolored   1.10 .60
1394 A593 £18 multicolored   1.10 .60
  a. Pair, #1393-1394   2.25 2.25
  Intl. Flower Show, Damascus.
  See Nos. 1412-1413.

4th Congress of
Arab
Denistry — A594

44th Intl. Fair,
Damascus
A595

1997, Sept. 4
1395 A594 £10 multicolored   .65 .35

1997, Sept. 4
1396 A595 £17 multicolored   1.10 .55

World
Post Day
A596

1997, Sept. 27 Perf. 11½x12
1397 A596 £17 multicolored   1.10 .55

World
Children's
Day
A597

1997, Sept. 27
1398 A597 £17 multicolored   1.10 .55

Intl.
Tourism
Day
A598

1997, Sept. 27
1399 A598 £17 multicolored   1.10 .55

37th Science
Week — A599

1997, Nov. 1 Litho. Perf. 12x11½
1400 A599 £17 multicolored   1.10 .55

Corrective
Movement,
27th Anniv.
A600

1997, Nov. 16 Perf. 12½
1401 A600 £10 multicolored   .70 .35
      Size: 92x67mm
      Imperf
1402 A600 £50 like #1401   3.25 3.25

Islamic Conference, 30th
Anniv. — A601

1997, Dec. 9 Litho. Perf. 11½x12
1403 A601 £10 multicolored   .70 .35

March 8 Revolution, 35th
Anniv. — A602

1998, Mar. 8 Litho. Perf. 12½x12
1404 A602 £17 multicolored   1.10 .55

Mother's
Day
A603

1998, March 21 Perf. 11½x12
1405 A603 £10 multicolored   .70 .35

Evacuation Day,
52nd
Anniv. — A604

Labor
Day — A605

1998, Apr. 17 Litho. Perf. 12x11½
1406 A604 £10 multicolored   .70 .35

1998, May 1
1407 A605 £18 multicolored   1.10 .55

World Tourism
Day — A606

Mother Teresa
(1910-97)
A607

1998, July 22 Litho. Perf. 12x11½
1408 A606 £17 Princess of
Banias   1.10 .55

1998, July 22
1409 A607 £18 multicolored   1.10 .55

1998 World Cup
Soccer
Championships,
France — A608

1998, June 22 Perf. 12x12½
1410 A608 £10 shown   .60 .30
Size: 60x55mm
Imperf
1411 A608 £25 Soccer players,
diff.   2.25 1.10

Intl. Flower Show Type of 1997

Flowers: No. 1412, Plum-colored with yellow
centers. No. 1413, Red hibiscus.

1998, June 22 Perf. 12x11½
1412 A593 £17 multicolored   1.10 1.10
1413 A593 £17 multicolored   1.10 1.10
  a. Pair, #1412-1413   2.25 2.25

45th Intl.
Damascus
Fair
A609

1998, Sept. 26 Litho. Perf. 11½x12
1414 A609 £18 multicolored   1.10 .55

World Children's
Day — A610

1998, Sept. 26 Perf. 12x11½
1415 A610 £18 multicolored   1.10 .55

World
Post Day
A611

1998, Sept. 26 Litho. Perf. 11½x12
1416 A611 £18 multicolored   1.10 .55

Day to Stop
Smoking — A612

1998, Sept. 26 Perf. 12x11½
1417 A612 £15 multicolored   .95 .50

Arab Post Day — A613

1998, Sept. 26 Perf. 12½
1418 A613 £10 multicolored   .60 .30

Arab-Israeli October War, 25th
Anniv. — A614

Illustration reduced.

1998, Oct. 6 Imperf.
1419 A614 £25 multicolored   1.60 .80

Science
Week
A615

1998, Nov. 3 Perf. 11½x12
1420 A615 £10 multicolored   .65 .35

Camels
A616

1998, Nov. 25 Perf. 12½
1421 A616 £17 multicolored   1.10 .55

Corrective
Movement,
28th Anniv.
A617

1998, Nov. 16 Litho. Perf. 12½
1422 A617 £10 multicolored   .65 .30
Size: 99x65mm
Imperf
1423 A617 £25 multicolored   .65 .30

Jerusalem — A618

1998, Nov. 25 Perf. 12½
1424 A618 £10 multicolored   .65 .30

Re-election
of Pres.
Assad
A619

£50, Portrait with designs from Nos. 1036,
C496, C506, & portrait from No. 1265.

1999, Feb. 11 Litho. Perf. 12½
1425 A619 £10 red brn & multi .50 .25
1426 A619 £17 pale yel & multi .90 .45
1427 A619 £18 pale grn & multi .95 .45
Size: 140x110mm
Imperf
1428 A619 £50 pale grn & multi 2.50 2.50
Nos. 1425-1428 (4)   4.85 3.65

Arbor
Day — A620

1999, Apr. 29 Litho. Perf. 12½
1429 A620 £17 multicolored   1.10 .55

Evacuation Day,
53rd.
Anniv. — A621

Mother's
Day — A622

1999, Apr. 29 Perf. 12x11½
1430 A621 £18 multicolored   1.10 .55

1999, Apr. 29
1431 A622 £17 multicolored   1.10 .55

Intl. Flower Show,
Damascus
A623

Designs: a, Jasminum. b, Acanthaceae.

1999, June 20 Litho. Perf. 12x11½
1432 A623 £10 Pair, #a.-b.   .85 .45

March 8 Revolution, 36th
Anniv. — A624

1999, Mar. 8 Litho. Perf. 12¼x12½
1433 A624 £25 shown   1.50 .75
Size: 75x110mm
Imperf
1434 A624 £25 Building, monument   1.50 .75

Declaration of Human Rights, 50th
Anniv. — A625

1999, June 5 Perf. 11½x12
1435 A625 £18 multicolored   .95 .45

Labor
Day — A626

1999, June 5 Litho. Perf. 12x11½
1436 A626 £10 multicolored   .55 .30

10th
Amity
Festival
A627

1999, Aug. 1   Litho.   *Perf. 11½x12*
1437 A627 £10 multicolored   .65   .30

A628

A630

A629

1999, Oct. 12   Litho.   *Perf. 12x11½*
1438 A628 £10 multi   .65   .30
Arab Post Day.

1999, Aug. 28   *Perf. 11½x12*
1439 A629 £15 multi   .95   .45
46th Intl. Fair, Damascus.

1999, Sept. 21   *Perf. 12x11½*
1440 A630 £17 multi   1.10   .55
Arab Dentists Assoc., 7th Congress.

A631

1999, Nov. 16
1441 A631 £18 multi   1.10   .55
World Children's Day.

A632

1999, Nov. 16
1442 A632 £17 multi   1.10   .55
UPU, 125th anniv.

Corrective Movement, 29th
Anniv. — A633

#1443, Building, statue. #1444, Close-up of
statue. £25, Building statue, fountain.

1999, Nov. 16   *Perf. 12½*
1443 A633 £17 multi   1.10   .55
1444 A633 £17 multi, vert.   1.10   .55
Imperf
Size: 115x76mm
1445 A633 £25 multi   1.60 1.60
   Nos. 1443-1445 (3)   3.80 2.70

Abu Hanifah al-Deilouri,
Botanist — A634

1999, Oct. 12   *Perf. 11½x12*
1446 A634 £17 multi   1.10   .55

Christianity, 2000th Anniv. — A635

1999, Nov. 16   *Perf. 12½*
1447 A635 £17 multi   1.10   .55

March 8
Revolution,
37th Anniv.
A636

2000, Mar. 8   Litho.   *Perf. 12½*
1448 A636 £18 multi   1.10   .55

Mother's
Day — A637

2000, Mar. 21
1449 A637 £17 multi   1.00   .50

Evacuation Day, 54th Anniv. — A638

Illustration reduced.

2000, Apr. 17   *Imperf.*
1450 A638 £25 multi   1.50 1.50

Labor
Day — A639

2000, May 1   Litho.   *Perf. 12x11½*
1451 A639 £10 multi   .40   .20

Installation of
Bashar al-
Assad as
President
A640

2000, July 17   *Perf. 12¼*
1452   Strip of 4   1.90 1.90
  a. A640 £3 lt blue & multi   .20   .20
  b. A640 £10 tan & multi   .40   .20
  c. A640 £17 bl gray & multi   .65   .30
  d. A640 £18 gray & multi   .65   .35
Imperf
Size: 110x74mm
1453 A640 £50 multi   1.90 1.90

Arab Post
Day
A641

2000, Aug. 20   Litho.   *Perf. 11½x12*
1454 A641 £18 multi   1.10   .55

47th Damascus Fair — A642

2000, Aug. 20
1455 A642 £15 multi   .90   .45

2000 Summer Olympics,
Sydney — A643

No. 1456: a, £17, Weight lifting. b, £18
Women's shot put.
Illustration reduced.

2000, Oct. 1   Litho.   *Perf. 12x11½*
1456 A643 Pair, #a-b   1.40   .7?
Imperf
Size: 80x77mm
1457 A643 £25 Javelin   .95   .5?

World Tourism Day — A644

Illustration reduced.

2000, Dec. 6   Litho.   *Imperf.*
1458 A644 £50 Mosaic   3.00 3.00

World
Post Day
A645

2000, Aug. 20   *Perf. 11½x12*
1459 A645 £18 multi   1.10   .55

Nasir ad-Din
at-Tusi (1201-
74), Scientist
A646

2000, Nov. 1   Litho.   *Perf. 12½x12¼*
1460 A646 £15 multi   .60   .30
Science week.

Arbor
Day — A647

2000, May 15   *Perf. 12x11½*
1461 A647 £18 multi   .65   .35

Butterflies — A648

a, £17, Charaxes jasius. b, £18, Apaturairis.
Illustration reduced.

2000, May 15   *Perf. 12½*
1462   A648   Pair, #a-b   1.40   .70

World Children's
Day — A649

2000, Aug. 20   Litho.   *Perf. 12x11½*
1463   A649   £10 multi   .60   .30

World
Meteorological
Organization,
50th
Anniv. — A650

2000, Dec. 6
1464   A650   £10 multi   .60   .30

March 8
Revolution, 38th
Anniv. — A651

2001   Litho.   *Perf. 12x11½*
1465   A651   £25 multi   .95   .50

Mother's
Day — A652

2001
1466   A652   £10 multi   .40   .20

Evacuation Day,
55th
Anniv. — A653

2001
1467   A653   £25 multi   .95   .50

Book and
Author's
Rights — A654

2001
1468   A654   £10 multi   .40   .20

Intl. Flower Show, Damascus — A655

No. 1469: a, Weigela. b, Mertensia.
Illustration reduced.

2001
1469   A655   £10 Horiz. pair, #a-b   .75   .40

Syrian
Engineering
Syndicate,
50th Anniv.
A656

2001, Feb. 1   Litho.   *Perf. 12½*
1470   A656   £17 multi   .65   .35
       Size: 95x85mm
       Imperf
1471   A656   £25 multi   .95   .50

Martyr's Square Type of 1994
2001   *Perf. 11½x12*
1472   A538   100p brt blue grn   .20   .20
1473   A538   £10 red   .35   .20
1474   A538   £50 blue   1.90   .95
     Nos. 1472-1474 (3)   2.45   1.35

Labor Day — A657

2001   Litho.   *Perf. 12x11½*
1475   A657   £18 multi   .75   .40

48th Damascus
Fair — A658

2001   Litho.   *Perf. 12x11½*
1476   A658   £10 multi   .40   .20

Re-occupation of Kuneitra by Syria,
27th Anniv. — A659

2001   *Perf. 11½x12*
1477   A659   £17 multi   .65   .35

Anti-Smoking Campaign — A660

2001
1478   A660   £18 multi   .70   .35

UN High Commissioner for Refugees,
50th Anniv. — A661

2001
1479   A661   £17 multi   .65   .35

Tooth Cross-
section
A662

2001   *Perf. 12x11½*
1480   A662   £10 multi   .40   .20

World Children's
Day — A663

2001   *Perf. 12x11½*
1481   A663   £18 multi   .70   .35

A664

2001   *Perf. 12x11½*
1482   A664   £10 multi   .40   .20
       Size: 84x111mm
       Imperf
1483   A664   £25 multi   1.00   1.00

A665

Aga Khan Award for
Architecture — A666

2001   *Perf. 11½x12*
1484   A665   £10 multi   .40   .20
1485   A666   £17 multi   .65   .35
1486   A666   £18 multi   .70   .35
     Nos. 1484-1486 (3)   1.75   .90

Installation of Bashar al-Assad as
President, 1st Anniv. — A667

Assad and: a, £10, Silver frame. b, £17,
Gold frame.
Illustration reduced.

2001   Litho.   *Perf. 12½x12¼*
1487   A667   Horiz. pair, #a-b   1.10   .55

Arab Post
Day
A668

2001   *Perf. 11½x12*
1488   A668   £18 multi   .75   .35

World Post
Day
A669

2001
1489   A669   £10 multi   .40   .20

Arbor Day — A670

2001   *Perf. 12x11½*
1490   A670   £5 multi   .20   .20

World Tourism Day — A671

2001 **Perf. 12½**
1491 A671 £17 multi .70 .35

Palestinian Intifada — A672

2001 **Perf. 12x11½**
1492 A672 £17 multi .70 .35

Pres. Hafez al-Assad (1930-2000) — A673

2001 **Perf. 12¼x12½**
1493 A673 £25 multi 1.00 .50

Correctionist Movement, 31st Anniv. — A674

Text color: £5, Black. £15, Red.

2001 **Perf. 11½x12**
1494-1495 A674 Set of 2 .80 .40

Evacuation Day, 56th Anniv. — A675

2002, Apr. 7 Litho. Perf. 12x11½
1496 A675 £15 multi .65 .30

Labor Day — A676

2002, May 1 **Perf. 12x12½**
1497 A676 £10 multi .45 .20

Intl. Flower Show, Damascus — A677

No. 1498: a, £15, Yellow flowers. b, £17, White lilies.

2002, May 1 **Perf. 12x11½**
1498 A677 Horiz. pair, #a-b 1.40 .70

March 8 Revolution, 39th Anniv. A678

2002, Mar. 8 Litho. Perf. 11½x12
1499 A678 £15 multi .65 .30

Mother's Day — A679

2002, Mar. 21 **Perf. 12x11½**
1500 A679 £25 multi 1.10 .55

Gazelle A680

2002, Mar. 8 **Perf. 12½**
1501 A680 £15 multi .65 .30

Baath Party, 55th Anniv. A681

2002, Apr. 7 **Perf. 11½x12**
1502 A681 £15 multi .65 .30

2002 World Cup Soccer Championships, Japan and Korea — A682

No. 1503 - Various players: a, £5. b, £10. £25, Goalie making save, horiz. Illustration reduced.

2002, May 31 **Perf. 12½**
1503 A682 Horiz. pair, #a-b .65 .30
Size: 78x65mm
Imperf
1504 A682 £25 multi 1.10 .55

World Tourism Day — A683

2002, Sep. 27 **Perf. 12½**
1505 A683 £10 multi .40 .20

First Syrian Railroad, Cent. — A684

2002, Nov. 9
1506 A684 £10 multi .40 .20

Abd al-Rahman al-Kawakibi (1849-1902), Arab Nationalist — A685

2002, Aug. 13 **Perf. 12x11½**
1507 A685 £10 multi .40 .20

Intifada — A686

Designs: £10, Flag bearer, four rock throwers, tank.
£25, Flag bearer, rock thrower, tank.

2002, Sep. 28 **Perf. 12x11½**
1508 A686 £10 multi .40 .20
Size: 66x79mm
Imperf
1509 A686 £25 multi 1.10 .55

Birds A687

2002, Sep. 27 **Perf. 11½x1**
1510 Vert. strip of 4 1.40 .7(
a. A687 £3 Sand grouse .20 .2
b. A687 £5 Francolin .20 .2
c. A687 £10 Duck .40 .2
d. A687 £15 Goose .65 .3(

Arab Post Day A688

Frame color: £5, Blue. £10, Red violet.

2002, Aug. 3 **Perf. 11½x12**
1511-1512 A688 Set of 2 .65 .3(

49th Intl. Damascus Fair — A689

Emblem and: a, £5, "X's." b, £10, Squares and diamonds.

2002, Aug. 28 **Perf. 12x11½**
1513 A689 Horiz. pair, #a-b .65 .3(

World Post Day — A690

No. 1514: a, Dove, envelope, rainbow. b, Envelope, UPU emblem, horiz.

Perf. 12x11½, 11½x12 (#1514b)
2002, Oct. 9
1514 A690 £10 Horiz. pair, #a-b .80 .4(

Arbor Day — A691

2002, Dec. 26 **Perf. 12x11½**
1515 A691 £10 multi .40 .20

Intl. Children's
Day — A692

2002, Oct. 16   *Perf. 12½*
1516 A692 £10 multi   .40 .20

Corrective
Movement,
32nd
Anniv.
A693

2002, Oct. 16   *Perf. 11½x12*
1517 A693 £10 multi   .40 .20

Martyr's Square Type of 1994
2003, May 5   *Litho.*   *Perf. 11½x12*
1518 A538 300p brown   .20 .20

March 8
Revolution, 40th
Anniv. — A694

2003, Mar. 8   *Perf. 12¼x12½*
1519 A694 £15 multi   .65 .30

Teacher's
Day — A695

2003, Mar. 8   *Perf. 12x11½*
1520 A695 £17 multi   .75 .40

Mother's
Day — A696

2003, Mar. 21
1521 A696 £32 multi   1.40 .70

Evacuation Day,
57th
Anniv. — A697

2003, Apr. 17
1522 A697 £15 multi   .65 .30

Labor Day — A698

2003, May 1
1523 A698 £25 multi   1.10 .55

Intl. Flower
Show,
Damascus
A699

No. 1524: a, Damask roses and violets. b,
Anemones. c, Daisies. d, Damask roses and
gillyflowers. e, Sunflowers.

2003, June 15   *Perf. 12½x12¼*
1524   Horiz. strip of 5   2.25 1.10
a.-e. A699 £10 Any single   .45 .20

50th Intl.
Damascus
Fair — A700

Designs: £32, Flags, emblems. £50, Open
orbs, horiz.

2003   *Perf. 12x12½*
1525 A700 £32 multi   1.40 .70
     Size: 89x66mm
      Imperf
1526 A700 £50 multi   2.25 2.25

World Tourism Day — A701

2003   *Perf. 12¼x12½*
1527 A701 £32 multi   1.40 .70

Election of Pope John Paul II, 25th
Anniv. — A702

2003   *Perf. 12½x12¼*
1528 A702 £32 multi   1.40 .70

SEMI-POSTAL STAMPS

Nos. 174-185 Surcharged in Red or
Black

1926		**Unwmk.**	*Perf. 12½, 13½*		
B1	A4	25c + 25c ol blk (R)		1.50	1.40
B2	A4	50c + 25c yel grn		1.90	1.40
B3	A4	75c + 25c brown org		.90	1.40
B4	A5	1p + 50c magenta		1.40	1.40
B5	A4	1.25p + 50c dp grn (R)		1.90	1.40
B6	A4	1.50p + 50c rose red		1.25	1.40
B7	A4	2p + 75c dk brn (R)		1.90	1.40
B8	A4	2.50p + 75c pck bl (R)		1.90	1.40
B9	A4	3p + 1p org brn (R)		1.60	1.40
B10	A4	5p + 1p violet		1.60	1.40
B11	A4	10p + 2p vio brn		1.40	1.40
B12	A4	25p + 5p ultra (R)		1.90	1.40
		Nos. B1-B12 (12)		19.15	16.80
		Set, never hinged		22.50	

On No. B4 the surcharge is set in six lines to
fit the shape of the stamp.
The surcharge was a contribution to the
relief of refugees from the Djebel Druze War.
See Nos. CB1-CB4.

> **Catalogue values for unused
> stamps in this section, from this
> point to the end of the section, are
> for Never Hinged items.**

Syrian Arab Republic

Jordanian Flags
on Map of Israel,
and Arabs — SP1

1965, June 12   *Litho.*   *Perf. 12x11½*
B13 SP1 12½p + 5p multi   .20 .20
B14 SP1 25p + 5p multi   .20 .20

Issued for Palestine Week.

Father with
Children and
Red Crescent
SP2

1968, May   *Litho.*   *Perf. 12½x12*
B15 SP2 12½p + 2½p multi   .25 .25
B16 SP2 27½p + 7½p multi   .25 .25

The surtax was for refugees.

AIR POST STAMPS

a

---

b

Nos. 35, 45, 47 Handstamped Type
"a" in Violet

1920, Dec.		**Unwmk.**	*Perf. 13½*	
C1	A22	1p on 5c	125.00	35.00
C2	A20	5p on 15c	250.00	40.00
C3	A18	10p on 40c	350.00	65.00
		Nos. C1-C3 (3)	725.00	140.00

Nos. 36, 46, 48 Overprinted Type "a"
in Violet

1921, June 12				
C4	A22	1p on 20c	65.00	32.50
C5	A18	5p on 1fr	325.00	125.00
C6	A18	10p on 2fr	325.00	125.00
		Nos. C4-C6 (3)	715.00	282.50

Excellent counterfeits exist of Nos. C1-C6.

Nos. 36, 46, 48 Overprinted Type "b"

1921, Oct. 5				
C7	A22	1p on 20c	47.50	13.50
C8	A18	5p on 1fr	110.00	25.00
a.	Inverted overprint		225.00	175.00
C9	A18	10p on 2fr	150.00	37.50
a.	Double overprint		350.00	325.00
		Nos. C7-C9 (3)	307.50	76.00

Nos. 92, 94-96 Overprinted

c

1922, May 28				
C10	A18	2p on 40c	14.00	14.00
a.	Inverted overprint			
C11	A18	3p on 60c	14.00	14.00
C12	A18	5p on 1fr	14.00	14.00
C13	A18	10p on 2fr	14.00	14.00
		Nos. C10-C13 (4)	56.00	56.00

Nos. 116-119 Overprinted Type "c"

1923, Nov. 22				
C14	A18	2p on 40c	17.50	17.50
b.	Inverted surcharge			
C15	A18	3p on 60c	17.50	17.50
C16	A18	5p on 1fr	17.50	17.50
C17	A18	10p on 2fr	17.50	17.50
b.	Double overprint			
		Nos. C14-C17 (4)	70.00	70.00
		Overprinted "Liabn"		
C14a	A18	2p on 40c	300.00	300.00
C15a	A18	3p on 60c	300.00	300.00
C16a	A18	5p on 1fr	300.00	300.00
C17a	A18	10p on 2fr	300.00	300.00

Nos. 137-140 Overprinted Type "c"

1924, Jan. 13				
C18	A18	2p on 40c	1.60	1.60
a.	Double overprint			
C19	A18	3p on 60c	1.60	1.60
a.	Inverted overprint		37.50	
C20	A18	5p on 1fr	1.60	1.60
a.	Double overprint			
C21	A18	10p on 2fr	1.60	1.60
		Nos. C18-C21 (4)	6.40	6.40

Nos. 152,
154, 157-
158
Overprinted

1924, July 17				
C22	A18	2p on 40c	2.75	2.75
a.	Inverted overprint		22.50	
C23	A18	3p on 60c	2.75	2.75
a.	Inverted overprint		22.50	
b.	Double overprint		14.00	
C24	A18	5p on 1fr	2.75	2.75
C25	A18	10p on 2fr	2.75	2.75
a.	Inverted overprint		22.50	
		Nos. C22-C25 (4)	11.00	11.00

Regular
Issue of
1925
Overprinted
in Green

1925, Mar. 1

C26	A4	2p dark brown	1.10	1.10
C27	A4	3p orange brown	1.10	1.10
C28	A4	5p violet	1.10	1.10
C29	A4	10p violet brown	1.10	1.10
		Nos. C26-C29 (4)	4.40	4.40

Regular Issue of 1925 Overprinted in Red

f

1926

C30	A4	2p dark brown	1.40	1.40
a.		Inverted overprint	22.50	
C31	A4	3p orange brown	1.50	1.50
a.		Inverted overprint	22.50	
C32	A4	5p violet	1.75	1.75
a.		Inverted overprint	22.50	
b.		Double overprint	22.50	
C33	A4	10p violet brown	1.75	1.75
a.		Inverted overprint	22.50	
b.		Double overprint	22.50	
		Nos. C30-C33 (4)	6.40	6.40

Nos. C30-C33 received their first airmail use June 16, 1929, at the opening of the Beirut-Marseille line.
For surcharges see Nos. CB1-CB4.

Regular Issue of 1925 Overprinted Type "f" in Red or Black

1929

C34	A4	50c yellow green (R)	.45	.45
a.		Inverted overprint	30.00	
b.		Overprinted on face and back		
c.		Double overprint	30.00	
d.		Double overprint, one inverted	50.00	
e.		Pair, one without overprint		
C35	A5	1p magenta (Bk)	.55	.55
a.		Reversed overprint		
b.		Red overprint		
C36	A4	25p ultra (R)	2.25	2.25
a.		Inverted overprint	65.00	
b.		Pair, one without overprint		
		Nos. C34-C36 (3)	3.25	3.25

On No. C35, the overprint is vertical, with plane nose down.

No. 197 Overprinted Type "f" in Red

1929, July 9

C37	A4	15p on 25p ultra	1.25	1.25
a.		Inverted overprint		

Air Post Stamps of 1926-29 Overprinted in Various Colors

1929, Sept. 5

C38	A4	50c yellow grn (R)	1.50	1.50
C39	A5	1p magenta (Bl)	1.50	1.50
C40	A4	2p dk brown (V)	1.50	1.50
C41	A4	3p orange brn (Bl)	1.50	1.50
a.		Inverted overprint		
C42	A4	5p violet (R)	1.50	1.50
C43	A4	10p violet brn (Bl)	1.50	1.50
C44	A4	25p ultra (R)	1.50	1.50
		Nos. C38-C44 (7)	10.50	10.50

Damascus Industrial Exhibition.

AP1

Red Surcharge

1930, Jan. 30

C45	AP1	2p on 1.25p dp grn	.85	.85
a.		Inverted surcharge		
b.		Double surcharge	50.00	

Plane over Homs
AP2

Designs: 1pi, City Wall, Damascus. 2pi, Euphrates River. 3pi, Temple Ruins, Palmyra. 5pi, Deir-el-Zor. 10pi, Damascus. 15pi, Aleppo, Citadel. 25pi, Hama. 50pi, Zebdani. 100pi, Telebisse.

1931-33   Photo.   Unwmk.

C46	AP2	50c ocher	.45	.25
C47	AP2	50c black brn ('33)	.85	.85
C48	AP2	1p chestnut brown	.50	.40
C49	AP2	2p Prus blue	1.50	1.10
C50	AP2	3p blue grn	.50	.40
C51	AP2	5p red violet	.50	.40
C52	AP2	10p slate grn	.50	.40
C53	AP2	15p orange red	1.25	.85
C54	AP2	25p orange brn	1.60	1.50
C55	AP2	50p black	1.60	1.50
C56	AP2	100p magenta	1.90	1.75
		Nos. C46-C56 (11)	11.15	9.40

Nos. C46 to C56 exist imperforate. Value, $175.
For overprints see Nos. C67-C71, C110-C112, C114-C115, MC1-MC4.

Village of Bloudan
AP12

1934, Aug. 2   Engr.   Perf. 12½

C57	AP12	50c yel brown	.85	.85
C58	AP12	1p green	.85	.85
C59	AP12	2p peacock bl	.85	.85
C60	AP12	3p red	.85	.85
C61	AP12	5p plum	.85	.85
C62	AP12	10p brt violet	10.00	10.00
C63	AP12	15p orange brn	10.00	10.00
C64	AP12	25p dk ultra	12.50	12.50
C65	AP12	50p black	21.00	21.00
C66	AP12	100p red brown	47.50	47.50
		Nos. C57-C66 (10)	105.25	105.25

Proclamation of the Republic. Exist imperf.

Air Post Stamps of 1931-33 Overprinted in Red or Black

1936, Apr. 15   Perf. 13½x13, 13½

C67	AP2	50c black brown	1.90	1.90
C68	AP2	1p chnt brown (Bk)	1.90	1.90
C69	AP2	2p Prus blue	1.90	1.90
C70	AP2	3p blue green	1.90	1.90
C71	AP2	5p red violet (Bk)	1.90	1.90
		Nos. C67-C71 (5)	9.50	9.50

Industrial Exhibition, Damascus, May 1936.

Syrian Pavilion at Paris Exposition
AP13

1937, July 1   Photo.   Perf. 13½

C72	AP13	½p yellow green	.95	1.00
C73	AP13	1p green	.95	1.00
C74	AP13	2p lt brown	.95	1.00
C75	AP13	3p rose red	.95	1.00
C76	AP13	5p brown orange	.95	.95
C77	AP13	10p grnsh black	1.50	1.50
C78	AP13	15p blue	1.90	1.90
C79	AP13	25p dark violet	1.90	1.90
		Nos. C72-C79 (8)	10.05	10.25

Paris International Exposition. Exist imperf.

Ancient Citadel at Aleppo
AP14

Omayyad Mosque and Minaret of Jesus at Damascus
AP15

1937   Engr.   Perf. 13

C80	AP14	½ dark violet	.20	.20
C81	AP15	1p black	.20	.20
C82	AP14	2p deep green	.20	.20
C83	AP15	3p deep ultra	.20	.20
C84	AP14	5p rose lake	.50	.50
C85	AP15	10p red brown	.45	.45
C86	AP14	15p lake brown	1.40	1.40
C87	AP15	25p dark blue	1.75	1.75
		Nos. C80-C87 (8)	4.90	4.90

No. C80 to C87 exist imperforate.
For overprint see No. C109.

Maurice Noguès and Route of France-Syria Flight — AP16

1938, July   Photo.   Perf. 11

C88	AP16	10p dark green	1.40	1.40
a.		Souv. sheet of 4, perf. 13½	12.00	12.00
b.		Perf. 13½	2.10	2.10

10th anniversary of first Marseille-Beirut flight, by Maurice Noguès.
No. C88a exists imperf.; value $225.

Bridge at Deir-el-Zor
AP17

1940   Engr.   Perf. 13

C89	AP17	25c brown black	.20	.20
C90	AP17	50c peacock blue	.20	.20
C91	AP17	1p deep ultra	.20	.20
C92	AP17	2p dk orange brn	.20	.20
C93	AP17	5p green	.20	.20
C94	AP17	10p rose carmine	.30	.30
C95	AP17	50p dark violet	1.10	1.10
		Nos. C89-C95 (7)	2.40	2.40

Exist imperf.

President Taj Eddin Hassani
AP18

1942   Litho.   Perf. 11½

C96	AP18	10p blue gray	1.40	1.40
C97	AP18	50p gray lilac	1.40	1.40

Proclamation of Independence by the Allies, Sept. 27, 1941.

President Taj Eddin Hassani
AP19

President Hassani and Map of Syria
AP20

1942   Photo.

C98	AP19	10p sl grn & yel grn	2.50	2.50

Exists imperforate.

1943   Litho.

C99	AP20	2p dull brown	1.10	1.10
C100	AP20	10p red violet	1.10	1.10
C101	AP20	20p aqua	1.10	1.10
C102	AP20	50p rose pink	1.10	1.10
		Nos. C99-C102 (4)	4.40	4.40

Proclamation of United Syria.

Same, Overprinted with Black Border

1943, May 5

C103	AP20	2p dull brown	1.10	1.1
C104	AP20	10p red violet	1.10	1.1
C105	AP20	20p aqua	1.10	1.1
C106	AP20	50p rose pink	1.10	1.1
		Nos. C103-C106 (4)	4.40	4.4

Mourning for President Hassani. Exist imperf

President Shukri el Kouatly — AP21

1944

C107	AP21	200p sepia	4.25	4.2
C108	AP21	500p dull blue	7.25	7.2

For overprints see Nos. C113, C116.

Stamps of 1931-44 Overprinted in Black, Blue or Carmine

1944   Perf. 13, 13½, 11

C109	AP15	10p red brn (Bk)	1.25	1.2
C110	AP2	15p orange red	1.25	1.2
C111	AP2	25p org brown	1.25	1.2
C112	AP2	100p magenta	3.75	3.7
C113	AP21	200p sepia (C)	5.00	5.0
		Nos. C109-C113 (5)	12.50	12.5
		Set, never hinged	17.50	

1st congress of Arab lawyers held in Damascus, Sept. 1944.

Nos. C53-C54, C108 Overprinted in Black or Orange

1944

C114	AP2	15p orange red	1.25	1.25
C115	AP2	25p org brown	1.25	1.25
C116	AP21	500p dull blue (O)	8.75	8.75
		Nos. C114-C116 (3)	11.25	11.25
		Set, never hinged	17.50	

See note after No. 299.

President Shukri el Kouatly
AP22

1945, Mar. 15   Litho.   Perf. 11½

C117	AP22	5p pale green	.20	.20
C118	AP22	10p dull red	.20	.20
C119	AP22	15p orange	.20	.20
C120	AP22	25p lt blue	.35	.20
C121	AP22	50p lt violet	.70	.30
C122	AP22	100p deep brown	1.60	.55
C123	AP22	200p fawn	3.75	1.90
		Nos. C117-C123 (7)	7.00	3.55
		Set, never hinged	11.00	

Resumption of constitutional government.

> **Catalogue values for unused stamps in this section, from this point to the end of the section, are for Never Hinged items.**

Plane and Flock of Sheep
AP23

Kattineh
Dam
AP24

Kanawat,
Djebel
Druze
AP25

Sultan
Ibrahim
Mosque
AP26

946-47   **Perf. 13x13½**
C124	AP23	3p rose brown	.35	.20
C125	AP23	5p lt bl grn ('47)	.35	.20
C126	AP23	6p dp org ('47)	.35	.20
C127	AP24	10p sl gray ('47)	.25	.20
C128	AP24	15p scarlet ('47)	.25	.20
C129	AP24	25p blue	.30	.20
C130	AP25	50p violet	.50	.20
C131	AP25	100p blue green	1.00	.35
C132	AP25	200p brown ('47)	2.40	.75
C133	AP26	300p red brn ('47)	8.75	1.50
C134	AP26	500p ol gray ('47)	9.50	3.00
		Nos. C124-C134 (11)	24.00	7.00

For overprints and surcharges see Nos.
C135-C139, C148-C152, C157, C172.

No. C129 Overprinted in Red

946, Apr. 17
C135	AP24	25p blue	1.00	.50

Evacuation of British and French troops
from Syria.

Nos. C129-C131 Overprinted in
Magenta

946, Aug. 28
C136	AP24	25p blue	1.00	.75
C137	AP25	50p violet	1.60	1.25
C138	AP25	100p blue green	3.00	1.50
		Nos. C136-C138 (3)	5.60	3.50

See note after No. 334.

No. C135 with Additional Overprint in
Black

1947, June 10   **Perf. 13x13½**
C139	AP24	25p blue	1.00	.60

1st anniv. of the evacuation of British and
French troops from Syria.

Window at
Kasr El-
Heir El-
Gharbi
AP27

Ram-headed Sphinxes Carved in
Ivory, from King Hazael's Bed — AP28

1947, Nov. 15   **Litho.**   **Perf. 11½**
C140	AP27	12.50p dark violet	.75	.40
C141	AP28	50p brown	2.75	1.10
a.		Souv. sheet of 4, #338-339,		
		C140-C141	29.00	29.00

1st Arab Archaeological Cong., Damascus,
Nov.
No. C141a sold for 125 piasters.

Kasr El-Heir
El-Charqui
AP29

Congress
Emblem — AP30

1947, Nov. 15
C142	AP29	12.50p olive black	.75	.40
C143	AP30	50p dull violet	1.75	1.25
a.		Souv. sheet of 4, #340,		
		341, C142, C143	27.50	27.50

3rd Cong. of Arab Engineers, Damascus,
Nov.
No. C143a sold for 125 piasters.

Kouatly Types of Regular Issue

1948, June 22   **Litho.**   **Perf. 10½**
C144	A50	12.50p dp bl &		
		vio brn	.35	.20
C145	A51	50p violet brn		
		& grn	1.75	.65
a.		Souv. sheet of #342, 343,		
		C144, C145, imperf	100.00	100.00

Reelection of Pres. Shukri el Kouatly.

Military Training Types of Regular
Issue

1948, June 22
C146	A52	12.50p blue & dk		
		bl	.50	.20
C147	A53	50p green, car		
		& blk	1.75	.60
a.		Souv. sheet of 4, #344,		
		345, C146, C147, im-		
		perf.	100.00	100.00

Inauguration of compulsory military training.

Nos. C124, C126 and C132 to C134
Surcharged with New Value and Bars
in Black or Carmine

1948, Oct. 18   **Perf. 13x13½**
C148	AP23	2.50p on 3p	.20	.20
C149	AP23	2.50p on 6p	.20	.20
C150	AP25	25p on 200p (C)	.35	.20
C151	AP26	50p on 300p	1.00	.40
C152	AP26	50p on 500p	1.00	.40
		Nos. C148-C152 (5)	2.75	1.40

Husni Zayim Type of Regular Issue

1949, June 20   **Litho.**   **Perf. 11½**
C153	A54	50p brown	2.50	1.50

Revolution of March 30, 1949.

Pigeons
and Globe
AP36

Husni
Zayim and
View of
Damascus
AP37

1949, June 20   **Unwmk.**
C154	AP36	12.50p claret	4.50	4.50
C155	AP37	50p gray black	12.50	9.00

UPU, 75th anniv. A souvenir sheet of 4 contains #349, 350, C154, C155. Value $125.

Election Type of Regular Issue
Wmk. 291

1949, Aug. 6   **Litho.**   **Perf. 11½**
C156	A57	50p car rose & dk		
		grnsh bl	2.25	1.50
a.		Souv. sheet of 2, #351,		
		C156, imperf.	125.00	125.00

Election of Pres. Husni Zayim.

No. C131 Surcharged with New Value
and Bars in Black

1950   **Unwmk.**   **Perf. 13x13½**
C157	AP25	2.50p on 100p bl grn	.20	.20

Port of
Latakia
AP38

1950, Dec. 25   **Perf. 11½**
C158	AP38	2.50p dull lilac	.40	.20
C159	AP38	10p grnsh blue	.60	.20
C160	AP38	15p orange brown	1.50	.20
C161	AP38	25p bright blue	3.50	.20
		Nos. C158-C161 (4)	6.00	.80

Exist imperf. Value, $35. See No. C173. For
overprint see No. C169.

Symbolical
of
Constitution
AP39

1951, Apr. 14   **Unwmk.**
C162	AP39	12.50p crimson rose	.20	.20
C163	AP39	50p brown violet	.70	.60

New constitution adopted Sept. 5, 1950.
Exist imperf.

Ruins,
Palmyra
AP40

Citadel at
Aleppo
AP41

1952, Apr. 22   **Litho.**   **Perf. 11½**
C164	AP40	2.50p vermilion	.20	.20
C165	AP40	5p green	.20	.20
C166	AP40	15p violet	.35	.20
C167	AP41	25p deep blue	.50	.20
C168	AP41	100p lilac rose	2.75	.45
		Nos. C164-C168 (5)	4.00	1.25

Nos. C164-C168 exist imperforate.
For overprints see Nos. C170-C171, C186.

Stamps of 1946-52 Overprinted in
Black

1953, Feb. 16   **Perf. 13x13½, 11½**
C169	AP38	10p grnsh blue	1.25	.70
C170	AP40	15p violet	1.25	.70
C171	AP41	25p deep blue	2.00	1.25
C172	AP25	50p violet	5.50	1.60
		Nos. C169-C172 (4)	10.00	4.25

UN Social Welfare Seminar, Damascus,
Dec. 8-20, 1952.

Type of 1950 and

Post Office,
Aleppo
AP42

1953, Oct.   **Photo.**   **Perf. 11½**
C173	AP38	10p violet blue	.35	.20
C174	AP42	50p red brown	1.00	.25

For overprint see No. C185.

Building at Hama and
PTT Emblem — AP43

University
of Syria,
Damascus
AP44

1954
C175	AP43	5p violet	.20	.20
C176	AP43	10p brown	.20	.20
C177	AP43	15p dull green	.20	.20
C178	AP44	30p dark brown	.40	.20
C179	AP44	35p blue	.65	.20
C180	AP44	40p orange	1.10	.30
C181	AP44	50p deep plum	1.00	.40
C182	AP44	70p purple	1.75	.40
		Nos. C175-C182 (8)	5.50	2.10

For overprints see UAR Nos. C27-C28.

Monument,
Damascus
Square
AP45

Mosque and Syrian
Flag — AP46

1954, Sept. 2
C183	AP45	40p carmine rose	.60	.35
C184	AP46	50p green	.70	.40

Damascus Fair, Sept. 1954.
Nos. C183-C184 exist imperforate.

Nos. C174 and C168 Overprinted in
Blue or Black

1954, Oct. 9
C185	AP42	50p red brown (Bl)	.60	.50
C186	AP41	100p lilac rose	1.50	1.00

Cotton Festival, Aleppo, October 1954.

Virgin of
Sednaya
Concent
AP47

Omayyad
Mosque
AP48

1955, Mar. 27   **Photo.**   *Perf. 11½*
C187 AP47 25p deep purple   .35   .20
C188 AP47 75p deep blue green   1.25   .70

50th anniv. of the founding of Rotary Intl.
Exist imperforate.

1955, Mar. 26
C189 AP48 35p cerise   .50   .30
C190 AP48 65p deep green   1.00   .60

1955 Regional Cong. of Rotary Intl.,
Damascus.

Arab Postal Union Type of Regular Issue

1955, Jan. 1   *Perf. 13½x13*
C191 A69a 5p yellow brown   .20   .20

Founding of the APU, July 1, 1954.
For overprints see Nos. C203, C207.

Young
Couple and
View of
Damascus
AP49

60p, Tank and planes leading advancing
troops.

1955, Apr. 16   **Litho.**   *Perf. 11½*
C192 AP49 40p dark rose lake   .40   .30
C193 AP49 60p ultra   .60   .35

9th anniv. of the evacuation of British and
French troops from Syria.

Mother's Day Type of Regular Issue

1955, May 13   **Unwmk.**
C194 A70 35p violet   .60   .35
C195 A70 40p black   1.00   .40

Issued to publicize Mother's Day.

Emigrants
under Syrian
Flag — AP51

Mother and
Child — AP52

15p, Airplane over globe and fountain.

1955, July 26   *Perf. 11½*
C196 AP51   5p magenta   .45   .25
C197 AP51 15p light blue   .55   .30

Emigrants' Congress. Exist imperf.

1955, Oct. 3   **Photo.**
C198 AP52 25p deep blue   .50   .25
C199 AP52 50p plum   1.00   .40

International Children's Day.

Globe,
Scales and
Dove
AP53

1955, Oct. 30
C200 AP53 15p ultra   .50   .25
C201 AP53 35p brown black   1.00   .40

10th anniv. of the UN, Oct. 24, 1955.
For overprints see Nos. C221-C222.

Aqueduct Type of Regular Issue

1955, Nov. 21   **Litho.**   **Unwmk.**
C202 A72 30p dark blue   1.60   .60

No. C191
Overprinted in
Ultramarine

1955, Dec. 29   **Photo.**   *Perf. 13½x13*
C203 A69a 5p yellow brown   .35   .20

APU Congress, Cairo, Mar. 15, 1955.

Liberation
Monument — AP54

Designs: 65p, Winged figure with shield
and sword. 75p, President Shukri el Kouatly.

1956, Apr. 17   **Litho.**   *Perf. 11½*
C204 AP54 35p black brown   .50   .35
C205 AP54 65p rose red   .75   .50
C206 AP54 75p dk slate green   1.50   .70
    Nos. C204-C206 (3)   2.75   1.55

10th anniv. of the evacuation of British and
French troops from Syria.

No. C191
Overprinted in Black

1956, Apr. 11   **Photo.**   *Perf. 13½x13*
C207 A69a 5p yellow brown   .35   .20

Visit of King Hussein of Jordan to Damascus, Apr. 1956.

President
Shukri el
Kouatly
AP55

Gate of Kasr el
Heir, Palmyra
AP56

1956, July 7   **Litho.**   *Perf. 11½*
C208 AP55 100p black   1.00   .70
C209 AP55 200p violet   2.10   1.00
C210 AP55 300p dull rose   3.25   2.00
C211 AP55 500p dk bl grn   6.25   3.50
    Nos. C208-C211 (4)   12.60   7.20

Nos. CB5-CB8 Overprinted with 3
Bars Obliterating Surtax

1956
C212 SPAP1 25p gray black   .40   .20
C213 SPAP2 35p ultra   .60   .25
C214 SPAP2 40p rose lilac   1.10   .60
C215 SPAP1 70p Prus green   1.40   .90
    Nos. C212-C215 (4)   3.50   1.95

1956, Sept. 1   **Unwmk.**

Designs: 20p, Hand loom and modern mill.
30p, Ox-drawn plow and tractor. 35p, Cogwheels and galley. 50p, Textiles and vase.

C216 AP56 15p gray   .40   .35
C217 AP56 20p brt ultra   .50   .45
C218 AP56 30p blue green   .65   .60
C219 AP56 35p blue   .70   .65
C220 AP56 50p rose lilac   .85   .80
    Nos. C216-C220 (5)   3.10   2.85

3rd International Fair, Damascus.

#C200-C201 Overprinted in Red or
Green

1956, Oct. 30   **Photo.**   *Perf. 11½*
C221 AP53 15p ultra (R)   .85   .50
C222 AP53 35p brown blk (G)   1.50   1.10

United Nations, 11th anniversary.

Clay Tablet
with First
Alphabet
AP57

Helmet of Syrian
Legionary and
Ornament — AP58

50p, Lintel from Temple of the Sun, Palmyra.

1956, Oct. 8   **Typo.**
C223 AP57 20p gray   .70   .35
C224 AP58 30p magenta   .80   .45
C225 AP57 50p gray brown   1.40   .80
    Nos. C223-C225 (3)   2.90   1.60

Intl. Museum Week (UNESCO), Oct. 8-14.

Trees and
Mosque
AP59

1956, Dec. 27   **Litho.**   *Perf. 11½*
C226 AP59 10p olive bister   .30   .20
C227 AP59 40p slate green   .60   .40

Day of the Tree, Dec. 27, 1956.
See UAR #36. For overprint see UAR #49.

Mother and
Child
AP60

Sword and
Shields
AP61

Design: 60p, Mother holding infant.

1957, Mar. 21   **Unwmk**
C228 AP60 40p ultra   .50   .4
C229 AP60 60p vermilion   .85   .6

Mother's Day, 1957.

1957, Apr. 20   **Wmk. 29**

Designs: 15p, 35p, Map and "Syria" holdin
torch. 25p, Pres. Kouatly.

C230 AP61 10p redsh brn   .20   .2
C231 AP61 15p bl grn   .20   .2
C232 AP61 25p violet   .30   .2
C233 AP61 35p cerise   .40   .3
C234 AP61 40p gray   .65   .4
    Nos. C230-C234 (5)   1.75   1.3

British-French troop evacuation, 11th anniv.

Ship
Loading — AP62

Sugar
Production
AP63

30p, 40p, Harvesting grain and cotton.

1957, Sept. 1   **Unwmk.**   *Perf. 11½*
C235 AP62 25p magenta   .25   .25
C236 AP62 30p light red brown   .35   .25
C237 AP63 35p light blue   .60   .35
C238 AP62 40p blue green   .70   .40
C239 AP62 70p olive bister   .95   .50
    Nos. C235-C239 (5)   2.85   1.75

4th International Fair, Damascus.

Arab Lawyers Type of Regular Issue

1957, Sept. 21   **Litho.**   **Wmk. 291**
C240 A76   17½p red   .25   .20
C241 A76   40p black   .55   .35

Cotton Festival Type of Regular Issue

1957, Oct. 17
C242 A77   17½p org & blk   .45   .25
C243 A77   40p lt bl & blk   .75   .35

Children's Day Type of Regular Issue

1957, Oct. 3
C244 A78 17½p ultra   1.00   .35
C245 A78 20p red brn   1.00   .35

International Children's Day, Oct. 7.
For overprints see UAR Nos. C10-C11.

Family
Writing
and
Reading
Letters
AP64

1957, Oct. 18   **Litho.**   **Unwmk.**
C246 AP64 5p brt grn   .30   .20

Intl. Letter Writing Week Oct. 6-12.
For overprint see No. C26.

Afro-Asian Jurists Type of Regular Issue

1957, Nov.   **Wmk. 291**   *Perf. 11½*
C247 A80 30p lt bl grn   .30   .20
C248 A80 50p lt vio   .45   .35

Type of Regular Issue and

Radio, Telegraph and Telephone — AP65

1958, Feb. 12   **Perf. 11½**
C249 A83   10p brt grn   .20 .20
C250 AP65   15p brown   .25 .20

Syrian Arab Republic

Syrian Flag — AP67

Souvenir Sheet
1961   **Unwmk.**   **Litho.**   *Imperf.*
C253 AP67 50p multi   2.75 2.75
Establishment of Syrian Arab Republic.

"The Beauty of Palmyra" — AP68

Archway, Palmyra — AP69

Design: 200p, 300p, 500p, 1000p, Niche, King Zahir Bibar's tomb.

1961-63   **Litho.**   **Perf. 12x11½**
C255 AP68   45p citron   .40 .20
C256 AP68   50p red org   .50 .25
C257 AP69   85p sepia   1.00 .30
C258 AP69   100p lilac   1.25 .35
C259 AP69   200p slate grn ('62)   2.25 .65
C260 AP69   300p dk bl ('62)   2.75 .75
C261 AP69   500p lilac ('63)   4.00 1.50
C262 AP69   1000p dk gray ('63)   8.25 2.75
    Nos. C255-C262 (8)   20.40 6.75
    See Nos. 433-436.

Arab League Building, Cairo, and Emblem — AP70

Malaria Eradication Emblem — AP71

1962, Apr. 1   **Perf. 12x11½**
C264 AP70   17½p Prus grn & yel grn   .30 .20
C265 AP70   22½p dk & lt bl   .30 .20
C266 AP70   50p dk brn & dl org   .75 .30
    Nos. C264-C266 (3)   1.35 .70
    Arab League Week, Mar. 22-28.

1962, Apr. 7
C267 AP71   12½p ol, lt bl & pur   .40 .20
C268 AP71   50p brn, yel & grn   .75 .40
    WHO drive to eradicate malaria.

Rearing Horse — AP72

Gen. Yusef al-Azmeh AP73

1962, Apr. 17
C269 AP72   45p vio & org   .55 .20
C270 AP73   55p vio bl & lt bl   .75 .20
    Evacuation Day, 1962.

Martyrs' Square Memorial, Globe and Handshake AP74

Cotton and Cogwheel AP75

Design: 40p, 45p, Eastern Gate at Fair.

1962, Aug. 25   **Litho.**   **Perf. 12x11½**
C271 AP74   17½p rose cl & brn   .30 .20
C272 AP74   22½p ver & magenta   .30 .20
C273 AP74   40p vio brn & lt brn   .30 .20
C274 AP74   45p grnsh bl & lt grn   .50 .20
    Nos. C271-C274 (4)   1.40 .80
    9th International Damascus Fair.

1962, Sept. 20   **Perf. 12x11½**
C275 AP75   12½p multi   .35 .20
C276 AP75   50p multi   .50 .20
    Cotton Festival, Aleppo. See Nos. 455-456.

President Type of Regular Issue
1962, Dec. 14   **Unwmk.**
C278 A88   50p bl gray & tan   .75 .25
    1st anniv. of the election of Pres. Nazem el-Kodsi.

Queen Zenobia of Palmyra — AP76

Saad Allah El Jabri — AP77

1962, Dec. 28   **Perf. 12x11½**
C279 AP76   45p violet   1.00 .25
C280 AP76   50p rose red   1.00 .25
C281 AP76   85p blue green   1.00 .30
C282 AP76   100p rose claret   1.25 .55
    Nos. C279-C282 (4)   4.25 1.35

1962, Dec. 30   **Litho.**
C283 AP77   50p dull blue   .50 .20
    Saad Allah El Jabri (1894-1947), a leader in Syria's struggle for independence.

Woman from Mohardé — AP78

Eagle in Flight — AP79

Regional Costumes: 40p, Marje Sultan. 45p, Kalamoun. 55p, Jabal-Al-Arab. 60p, Afrine. 65p, Hauran.

1963   **Perf. 12**
Costumes in Original Colors
C285 AP78   40p pale lil & blk   .55 .20
C286 AP78   45p pink & blk   .60 .20
C287 AP78   50p lt grn & blk   .60 .20
C288 AP78   55p lt bl & blk   .75 .30
C289 AP78   60p tan & blk   .80 .30
C290 AP78   65p pale grn & blk   1.00 .40
    Nos. C285-C290 (6)   4.30 1.60

Hunger Type of Regular Issue

50p, Wheat emblem & bird feeding nestlings.

    Perf. 12x11½
1963, Mar. 21   **Unwmk.**
C291 A91   50p ver & blk   .45 .20
   a.   Souv. sheet of 2, #453, C291, imperf.   1.50 1.50
    FAO "Freedom from Hunger" campaign.

1963, Apr. 18   **Litho.**
C292 AP79   12½p brt grn   .30 .20
C293 AP79   50p lilac rose   .35 .20
    Revolution of Mar. 8, 1963.

Faris el Khouri — AP80

Arms and Wreath — AP81

1963, Apr. 27   **Perf. 12x11½**
C294 AP80   17½p gray   .30 .20
C295 AP81   22½p bl grn & blk   .30 .20
    Evacuation Day, 1963.

abu-al-Ala al-Maarri — AP82

Copper Pitcher, Arch and Fair — AP83

1963, Aug. 19   **Perf. 12x11½**
C296 AP82   50p violet blue   .40 .20
    abu-al-Ala al-Maarri (973-1057), poet and philosopher.

1963, Aug. 25
C297 AP83   37½p ultra, yel & brn   .45 .20
C298 AP83   50p brt bl, yel & brn   .50 .20
    10th International Damascus Fair.

Centenary Emblem — AP84

Abou Feras al Hamadani
AP85

50p, Centenary emblem and globe.

1963, Sept. 19 Litho.
C299 AP84 15p chlky bl, red & blk .40 .20
C300 AP84 50p yel grn, blk & red .50 .20
Centenary of the International Red Cross.

1963, Nov. 13 Perf. 12x11½
C301 AP85 50p yel ol & dk brn .50 .20
Abou Feras (932-968), poet.

Heads of Three Races and Flame — AP86

1964, Jan. 6 Unwmk.
C302 AP86 17½p multi .30 .20
C303 AP86 22½p grn, blk & red .30 .20
C304 AP86 50p vio, blk & red .40 .20
  a. Souv. sheet of 3 1.10 1.10
    Nos. C302-C304 (3) 1.00 .60

Universal Declaration of Human Rights, 15th anniv. #C304a contains 3 imperf. stamps similar to #C302-C304 with simulated perforations.

Flag, Torch and Map of Arab Countries AP87

1964, Mar. 8 Unwmk. Perf. 11½
C305 AP87 15p multi .30 .20
C306 AP87 17½p multi .30 .20
C307 AP87 22½p multi .30 .20
    Nos. C305-C307 (3) .90 .60
Revolution of Mar. 8, 1963, 1st anniv.

Kaaba, Mecca, and Mosque, Damascus AP88

1964, Mar. 14 Litho. Perf. 11½x12
C308 AP88 12½p bl & blk .30 .20
C309 AP88 22½p rose lil & blk .30 .20
C310 AP88 50p lt grn & blk .35 .20
    Nos. C308-C310 (3) .95 .60
First Arab Conference of Moslem Wakf Ministers, Damascus.

Young Couple and View of Damascus AP89

1964, Apr. 17 Unwmk.
C311 AP89 20p blue .30 .20
C312 AP89 25p rose car .30 .20
C313 AP89 60p emerald .35 .20
    Nos. C311-C313 (3) .95 .60
Evacuation Day, Apr. 17, 1964.

Abul Kasim (Albucasis) AP90

1964, Apr. 21 Perf. 12x11½
C314 AP90 60p brown .40 .20
4th Arab Congress of Dental and Oral Surgery, Damascus.

Mosaic, Chahba, Thalassa AP91

Perf. 11½x12
1964, June-July Litho.
C315 AP91 27½p car rose .30 .20
C316 AP91 45p gray .30 .20
C317 AP91 50p brt grn .40 .20
C318 AP91 55p slate grn .40 .20
C319 AP91 60p ultra .50 .20
    Nos. C315-C319 (5) 1.90 1.00

Hanging Lamp, Fair Emblem — AP92

Globe and Fair Emblem — AP93

1964, Aug. 28 Perf. 12x11½
C320 AP92 20p multi .30 .20
C321 AP93 25p multi .30 .20
11th International Damascus Fair.

Industrial and Agricultural Symbols — AP94

1964, Sept. 22 Litho. Unwmk.
C322 AP94 25p multi .30 .20
Same Overprinted with two Red Lines in Arabic
C323 AP94 25p multi .30 .20
Cotton Festival, Aleppo. Overprint on No. C323 translates: "Market for Industrial and Agricultural Products."

Arms of Syria and Aero Club Emblem AP95

1964, Oct. 8 Litho. Perf. 11½x12
C324 AP95 12½p emer & blk .30 .20
C325 AP95 17½p crim & blk .30 .20
C326 AP95 20p brt bl & blk .40 .20
    Nos. C324-C326 (3) 1.00 .60
10th anniversary of Syrian Aero Club.

Arab Postal Union Emblem — AP96

Grain and Hands Holding Book — AP97

1964, Nov. 12 Litho. Perf. 12x11½
C327 AP96 12½p org & blk .30 .20
C328 AP96 20p emer & blk .30 .20
C329 AP96 25p dp lil rose & blk .30 .20
    Nos. C327-C329 (3) .90 .60
10th anniv. of the permanent office of the APU.

1964, Nov. 30 Unwmk.
C330 AP97 12½p emer & blk .30 .20
C331 AP97 17½p mar & blk .30 .20
C332 AP97 20p dp bl & blk .30 .20
    Nos. C330-C332 (3) .90 .60
Burning of the library of Algiers, 6/7/62.

Tennis Player — AP98

17½p, Wrestlers and drummer. 20p, Weight lifter. 100p, Wrestlers and drummer.

1965, Feb. 7 Perf. 12x11½
C333 AP98 12½p multi .30 .20
C334 AP98 17½p multi .30 .20
C335 AP98 20p multi, horiz. .30 .20
    Nos. C333-C335 (3) .90 .60
Souvenir Sheet
C336 AP98 100p multi 1.25 1.25
18th Olympic Games, Tokyo, 10/10-25/64. #C336 contains one 45x33mm stamp.

Ramses Battling the Hittites AP99

Design: 50p, Two statues of Ramses II.

C337 AP99 22½p emer, ultra & blk .30 .20
C338 AP99 50p ultra, emer & blk .40 .20
UNESCO world campaign to save historic monuments in Nubia.

Al-Sharif Al-Radi — AP100

Dagger in Map of Palestine AP102

Hippocrates and Avicenna — AP101

1965, Apr. 3 Litho. Perf. 12x11½
C339 AP100 50p gray brn .50 .20
5th Poetry Festival held in Latakia; Al-Sharif Al-Radi (970-1015), poet.

1965, Apr. 19 Perf. 11½
C340 AP101 60p dl bl grn & blk .55 .30
"Medical Days of the Near and Middle East," a convention held at Damascus Apr. 19-25.

1965, May 15
C341 AP102 12½p multi .30 .20
C342 AP102 60p multi .35 .20
Deir Yassin massacre, Apr. 9, 1948.

ITU Emblem, Old and New Communication Equipment — AP103

Perf. 11½x12
1965, May 24 Litho. Unwmk.
C343 AP103 12½p multi .30 .20
C344 AP103 27½p multi .30 .20
C345 AP103 60p multi .50 .25
    Nos. C343-C345 (3) 1.10 .65
ITU, centenary.

Syrian Welcoming AP104

Bridge and
Gate — AP105

1965, Aug.   Unwmk.   Perf. 12x11½
C346 AP104 25p pur & multi   .30 .20
C347 AP104 100p blk & multi   .75 .25
Issued to welcome Arab immigrants.

1965, Aug. 28   Litho.
27½p, Fair emblem. 60p, Jug & ornaments.
C348 AP105 12½p blk, brt ultra &
                       brn   .30 .20
C349 AP105 27½p multi   .30 .20
C350 AP105 60p multi   .40 .20
   Nos. C348-C350 (3)   1.00 .60
12th International Damascus Fair.

Fair Emblem and
Cotton
Pickers — AP106

1965, Sept. 30   Perf. 12x11½
C351 AP106 25p olive & multi   .30 .20
10th Cotton Festival, Aleppo.

Same with Red
Overprint

1965, Sept. 30
C352 AP106 25p olive & multi   .30 .20
Industrial and Agricultural Fair, Aleppo.

View of
Damascus
and ICY
Emblem
AP107

1965, Oct. 24   Perf. 11½x12
C353 AP107 25p multi   .30 .20
International Cooperation Year.

Radio
Transmitter,
Globe, Syrian
Flag and View of
Damascus
AP108

Hand (shaped
like a dove)
Holding
Flower — AP109

1966, Feb. 16   Litho.   Perf. 12x11½
C354 AP108 25p multi   .30 .20
C355 AP108 60p multi   .35 .20
3rd Conference of Arab Information Ministers, Damascus, Feb. 14-18.

1966, Mar. 8   Perf. 12x11½, 11½x12
Design: 17½p, Stylized people, horiz.
C356 AP109 12½p multi   .30 .20
C357 AP109 17½p multi   .30 .20
C358 AP109 50p multi   .75 .25
   Nos. C356-C358 (3)   1.35 .65
March 8 Revolution, 3rd anniversary.

Statues of
Ramses II from
Abu
Simbel — AP110

1966, Mar. 15   Perf. 12x11½
C359 AP110 25p dark blue   .30 .20
C360 AP110 60p dark slate green   .40 .20
Arab "Save the Nubian Monument Week."

UN Headquarters Building and
Emblem — AP111

Design: 100p, UN Flag.

1966, Apr. 11   Litho.   Perf. 11½x12
C361 AP111 25p blk & gray   .30 .20
C362 AP111 50p blk & pale grn   .35 .20
Souvenir Sheet
Imperf
C363 AP111 100p yel, brt bl &
                         blk   1.25 1.25
20th anniv. (in 1965) of the UN. No. C363
contains one stamp 42x36mm.

Marching
Workers
AP112

1966, May 1   Litho.   Perf. 11½x12
C364 AP112 60p multi   .40 .20
Issued for May Day.

Inauguration of WHO Headquarters,
Geneva — AP113

1966, May 3
C365 AP113 60p blk, bl & yel   .40 .20

Map of Arab
Countries and
Traffic
Signals — AP114

Astarte & Tyche,
1st cent.
Basrelief,
Palmyra
AP115

1966, May 4   Perf. 12x11½
C366 AP114 25p gray & multi   .30 .20
Issued to publicize Traffic Day.

1966, July 26   Litho.   Perf. 12x11½
C367 AP115 50p pale brn   .35 .20
C368 AP115 60p slate   .50 .25

Symbolic Flag,
Wheat, Globe
and Fair Emblem
AP116

Shuttle and
Symbols of
Agriculture,
Industry and
Cotton — AP117

1966, Aug. 25   Litho.   Perf. 12x11½
C369 AP116 12½p multi   .30 .20
C370 AP116 60p multi   .35 .20
13th Intl. Damascus Fair, Aug. 25-Sept. 20.

1966, Sept. 9   Litho.   Perf. 12x11½
C371 AP117 50p sil, blk & plum   .35 .20
11th Cotton Festival, Aleppo.

Symbolic Water
Cycle — AP118

Abd-el
Kader — AP119

1966, Oct. 24   Litho.   Perf. 12x11½
C372 AP118 12½p emer, blk & org   .30 .20
C373 AP118 60p ultra, blk & org   .35 .20
Hydrological Decade (UNESCO), 1965-74.

1966, Nov. 7
C374 AP119 12½p brt grn & blk   .30 .20
C375 AP119 50p brt grn & red
                         brn   .35 .20
Transfer from Damascus to Algiers of the
ashes of Abd-el Kader (1807?-1883), Emir of
Mascara.

Clasped Hands
over Map of
South
Arabia — AP120

Pipelines and
Pigeons
AP121

1967, Feb. 8   Litho.   Perf. 12x11½
C376 AP120 20p pink & multi   .30 .20
C377 AP120 25p multi   .30 .20
3rd Congress of Solidarity with the Workers
and People of Aden, Damascus, Jan. 15-18.

1967, Mar. 8   Litho.   Perf. 12x11½
C378 AP121 17½p multi   .30 .20
C379 AP121 25p multi   .30 .20
C380 AP121 27½p multi   .30 .20
   Nos. C378-C380 (3)   .90 .60
4th anniversary of March 8 Revolution.

Soldier, Woman
and Man Holding
Flag — AP122

Workers'
Monument,
Damascus
AP123

1967, Apr. 17 Litho. Perf. 12x11½
C381 AP122 17½p green   .30 .20
C382 AP122 25p dp claret   .30 .20
C383 AP122 27½p vio blue   .30 .20
   Nos. C381-C383 (3)   .90 .60
  21st anniv. of the evacuation of British and
French troops from Syria.

1967, May 1
C384 AP123 12½p bl grn   .30 .20
C385 AP123 50p brt pink   .35 .20
   Issued for Labor Day, May 1.

Fair Emblem and
Gate, Minaret,
Omayyad
Mosque — AP124

1967, Aug. 25 Litho. Perf. 12x12½
C386 AP124 12½p multi   .30 .20
C387 AP124 60p multi   .35 .20
  14th Intl. Damascus Fair, Aug. 25-Sept. 20.

Statue of
Ur-Nina
and ITY
Emblem
AP125

1967, Sept. 2   Perf. 12½x12
C388 AP125 12½p lt bl, brt rose
    lil & blk   .30 .20
C389 AP125 25p lt bl, ver & blk   .30 .20
C390 AP125 27½p lt bl, dk bl &
    blk   .30 .20
   Nos. C388-C390 (3)   .90 .60

Souvenir Sheet
Imperf
C391 AP125 60p lt bl & vio bl   1.00 1.00
   Intl. Tourist Year.

Cotton Boll and
Cogwheel
Segment
AP126

1967, Sept. 28 Litho. Perf. 12x12½
C392 AP126 12½p ocher, brn & blk .30 .20
C393 AP126 60p ap grn, brn &
    blk   .40 .20
  12th Cotton Festival, Aleppo.

Same with Red
Overprint

1967, Sept. 28
C394 AP126 12½p multi   .30 .20
C395 AP126 60p multi   .35 .20
  Industrial and Agricultural Production Fair,
Aleppo.

Head of Young
Man, Amrith, 4th-
5th Century
B.C. — AP127

1967, Oct. 7
  100p, 500p, Bronze bust of a Princess, 2nd
cent.

C396 AP127 45p orange   .30 .20
C397 AP127 50p brt pink   .40 .20
C398 AP127 60p grnsh bl   .50 .20
C399 AP127 100p green   .60 .20
C400 AP127 500p brn red   2.25 1.50
   Nos. C396-C400 (5)   4.05 2.40

Ibn el-Naphis
AP128

1967, Dec. 28 Litho. Perf. 12x12½
C401 AP128 12½p grn & org   .30 .20
C402 AP128 27½p dk bl & lil rose   .30 .20
  700th death anniv. of Ibn el-Naphis (1210-
1288), Arab physician.

Human
Rights
Flame
and
People
AP129

  Design: 100p, Heads of various races and
Human Rights flame.

1968, Feb. 21 Litho. Perf. 12½x12
C403 AP129 12½p lt grnsh bl, bl
    & blk   .30 .20
C404 AP129 60p pink, blk & dl
    red   .40 .20

Souvenir Sheet
Imperf
C405 AP129 100p multi   1.00 1.00
  20th anniv. of the Declaration of Human
Rights; Intl. Human Rights Year.

Old Man and
Woman Reading
AP130

  Design: 17½p, 45p, Torch and book.

1968, Mar. 3   Perf. 12x12½
C406 AP130 12½p rose car, blk &
    org   .30 .20
C407 AP130 17½p multi   .30 .20
C408 AP130 25p grn, blk & org   .30 .20
C409 AP130 45p bl & multi   .30 .20
   Nos. C406-C409 (4)   1.20 .80
  Issued to publicize the literacy campaign.

Euphrates Dam Project — AP131

1968, Apr. 11 Litho. Perf. 12½x12
C410 AP131 12½p multi   .30 .20
C411 AP131 17½p multi   .30 .20
C412 AP131 25p multi   .30 .20
   Nos. C410-C412 (3)   .90 .60
  Proposed dam across Euphrates River.

WHO Emblem and Avenzoar (1091-
1162) — AP132

  WHO Emblem and: 25p, Rhazes (Razi, 850-
923). 60p, Geber (Jabir 721-776).

1968, June 10 Litho. Perf. 12½x12
C413 AP132 12½p brn, grn & sal   .30 .20
C414 AP132 25p brn, gray & sal   .30 .20
C415 AP132 60p brn, gray bl &
    sal   .40 .20
   Nos. C413-C415 (3)   1.00 .60
  WHO, 20th anniv.

Monastery
of St.
Simeon
the Stylite
AP133

  Designs: 17½p, El Tekkieh Mosque,
Damascus, vert. 22½p, Columns, Palmyra,
vert. 45p, Chapel of St. Paul, Bab Kisan. 50p,
Theater of Bosra.

Perf. 12½x12, 12x12½
1968, Oct. 10   Litho.
C416 AP133 15p pale grn &
    rose brn   .30 .20
C417 AP133 17½p redsh brn &
    dk red brn   .30 .20
C418 AP133 22½p grn gray & dk
    red brn   .30 .20
C419 AP133 45p yel & dk red
    brn   .30 .20
C420 AP133 50p lt bl & dk red
    brn   .30 .20
   Nos. C416-C420 (5)   1.50 1.00

Hammer
Throw — AP134

  Designs: 25p, Discus. 27½p, Running.
60p, Basketball. 50p, Polo, horiz.

1968, Dec. 19 Litho. Perf. 12x12½
C421 AP134 12½p brt pink, blk &
    grn   .30 .20
C422 AP134 25p red, grn & blk   .30 .20
C423 AP134 27½p blk, gray &
    grn   .30 .20
C424 AP134 60p multi   .30 .20
   Nos. C421-C424 (4)   1.20 .80

Souvenir Sheet
Imperf
C425 AP134 50p multi   1.00 1.00
  19th Olympic Games, Mexico City, Oct. 12-
27. #C425 contains one 52x80mm horiz.
stamp.

Construction of Damascus Intl.
Airport — AP135

1969, Jan. 20 Litho. Perf. 12½x1?
C426 AP135 12½p yel, brt bl &
    grn   .30 .2?
C427 AP135 17½p org, pur & lt
    grn   .30 .2?
C428 AP135 60p car, blk & yel   .40 .2?
   Nos. C426-C428 (3)   1.00 .6?

Baal
Shamin
Temple,
Palmyra
AP136

  Designs: 45p, Interior of Omayyad Mosque,
Damascus, vert. 50p, Amphitheater,
Palmyra, 60p, Khaled ibn al-Walid Mosque, Homs, ver?
100p, Ruins of St. Simeon, Djebel Samaan.

1969, Jan. 20 Photo. Perf. 12x11½
C429 AP136 25p multi   .30 .2?
C430 AP136 45p bl & multi   .30 .2?
C431 AP136 50p multi   .30 .2?
C432 AP136 60p multi   .30 .2?
C433 AP136 100p vio & multi   .60 .2?
   Nos. C429-C433 (5)   1.80 .8?

Workers,
ILO
Emblem,
Cogwheel
AP137

  Design: 60p, ILO emblem.

1969, May 1 Litho. Perf. 12½x12
C434 AP137 12½p multi   .30 .20
C435 AP137 27½p multi   .30 .20

Miniature Sheet
Imperf
C436 AP137 60p multi   .60 .60
  ILO, 50th anniv. No. C436 contains one
stamp 53½x47mm.

Ballet Dancers
AP138

  Designs: 12½p, Russian dancers. 45p,
Lebanese singer and dancers. 55p, Egyptian
dancer and musicians. 60p, Bulgarian
dancers.

1969, Aug. 25 Litho. Perf. 12½x12
C437 AP138 12½p multi   .30 .20
C438 AP138 27½p bl & multi   .30 .20
C439 AP138 45p multi   .30 .20
C440 AP138 55p multi   .30 .20
C441 AP138 60p multi   .40 .20
  a.   Strip of 5, #C437-C441   1.75 1.75
  16th Intl. Fair, Damascus, Aug. 25-Sept. 20.

Children Playing — AP139

Fortuna — AP140

1969, Oct. 6   Litho.   Perf. 12x12½
C442 AP139 12½p aqua, dk bl & emer   .30 .20
C443 AP139 25p brn red, dk bl & lt vio   .30 .20
C444 AP139 27½p ultra, dk bl & gray   .30 .20
    Nos. C442-C444 (3)   .90 .60
    Issued for Children's Day.

1969, Oct. 10
    Designs: 25p, Seated woman from Palmyra. 60p, Motherhood. All sculptures from Greco-Roman period.
C445 AP140 17½p blk, yel grn & grn   .30 .20
C446 AP140 25p dk brn, red brn & lt grn   .30 .20
C447 AP140 60p blk, lt gray & bl gray   .40 .20
    Nos. C445-C447 (3)   1.00 .60
    9th Intl. Congress for Classical Archaeology, Oct. 11-20.

Damascus Agricultural Museum — AP141

1969, Dec. 24   Litho.   Perf. 12½x12
C448 AP141 12p Cock   .30 .20
C449 AP141 17½p Cow   .30 .20
C450 AP141 20p Corn   .30 .20
C451 AP141 50p Olives   .30 .20
   a.   Strip of 4, #C448-C451 + label   1.25 1.25

Weather Satellite Tracking and UN Emblem AP142

1970, Mar. 23   Litho.   Perf. 12½x12
C452 AP142 25p blk, sl grn & yel   .30 .20
C453 AP142 60p blk, dk bl & yel   .35 .20
    10th World Meteorological Day.

Lenin (1870-1924) AP143

Workers' Syndicate Emblem AP144

1970, Apr. 15   Litho.   Perf. 12x12½
C454 AP143 15p red & dk brn   .30 .20
C455 AP143 60p red & grn   .35 .20

1970, May 1   Litho.   Perf. 12½x12
C456 AP144 15p dk brn & brt grn   .30 .20
C457 AP144 60p dk brn & org   .35 .20
    Issued for Labor Day.

Radar and Open Book AP145

1970, May 17
C458 AP145 15p brt pink & blk   .30 .20
C459 AP145 60p bl & blk   .35 .20
    International Telecommunications Day.

Opening of UPU Headquarters, Bern — AP146

1970, May 30
C460 AP146 15p multi   .30 .20
C461 AP146 60p multi   .35 .20

"Zahier Piebers and Maarouf" — AP147

    Folk Tales: 10p, Two warriors on horseback. 15p, Two warriors on white horses. 20p, Lady and warrior on horseback. 60p, Warriors, woman and lion.

1970, Aug. 12   Litho.   Perf. 12½
C462 AP147 5p lt bl & multi   .30 .20
C463 AP147 10p lt bl & multi   .30 .20
C464 AP147 15p lt bl & multi   .30 .20
C465 AP147 20p lt bl & multi   .30 .20
C466 AP147 60p lt bl & multi   .50 .20
   a.   Strip of 5, #C462-C466   1.75 1.75

Al Aqsa Mosque on Fire AP148

1970, Aug. 21   Perf. 12½x12
C467 AP148 15p multi   .30 .20
C468 AP148 60p multi   .35 .20
    1st anniv. of the burning of Al Aqsa Mosque, Jerusalem.

Wood Carving — AP149

    Handicrafts: 20p, Jewelry. 25p, Glass making. 30p, Copper engraving. 60p, Shellwork.

1970, Aug. 25   Perf. 12½
C469 AP149 15p vio & multi   .30 .20
C470 AP149 20p ol & multi   .30 .20
C471 AP149 25p multi   .30 .20
C472 AP149 30p multi   .30 .20
C473 AP149 60p multi   .50 .20
   a.   Strip of 5, #C469-C473   1.75 1.75
    17th Intl. Fair, Damascus.

Education Year Emblem AP150

1970, Nov. 2   Litho.   Perf. 12
C474 AP150 15p dl grn & dk brn   .30 .20
C475 AP150 60p vio bl & dk brn   .35 .20
    International Education Year.

UN Emblem, Symbols of Progress, Justice and Peace AP151

1970, Nov. 3
C476 AP151 15p lt ultra, red & blk   .30 .20
C477 AP151 60p bl, yel & blk   .35 .20
    United Nations, 25th anniversary.

Khaled ibn-al-Walid AP152

Woman with Garland AP153

1970-71   Perf. 12x11½, 12½x12½
C478 AP152 45p brt pink   .30 .20
C479 AP152 50p green   .35 .20
C480 AP152 60p vio brn   .50 .20
C481 AP152 100p dk bl   .60 .20
C482 AP152 200p grnsh gray ('71)   1.10 .50
C483 AP152 300p lil ('71)   1.50 .95
C484 AP152 500p gray ('71)   3.00 1.60
    Nos. C478-C484 (7)   7.35 3.85

People Dancing Around Globe AP154

1971, Apr. 17   Litho.   Perf. 12
C485 AP153 15p dl red, blk & grn   .30 .20
C486 AP153 60p grn, blk & dk red   .35 .20
    25th anniv. of the evacuation of British and French troops from Syria.

1971, Apr. 28   Litho.   Perf. 12½x12
C487 AP154 15p vio & multi   .30 .20
C488 AP154 60p grn & multi   .30 .20
    Intl. Year against Racial Discrimination.

Pres. Hafez al Assad and Council Chamber — AP155

1971, Sept. 30   Litho.   Perf. 12½x12
C489 AP155 15p grn & multi   .30 .20
C490 AP155 65p bl & multi   .60 .20
    People's Council and presidential election.

Gamal Abdel Nasser (1918-1970), President of Egypt — AP156

1971, Oct. 17   Perf. 12x12½
C491 AP156 15p lt ol grn & brn   .30 .20
C492 AP156 20p gray & brn   .30 .20

Globe and Arrows AP157

1972, May 17   Litho.   Perf. 11½
C493 AP157 15p bl, vio bl & pink   .30 .20
C494 AP157 50p org, yel & sep   .30 .20
    4th World Telecommunications Day.

Pres. Hafez al Assad — AP158

Airline Emblem, Eastern Hemisphere AP159

1972, July   Litho.   Perf. 12x11½
C495 AP158 100p dk grn   .60   .25
C496 AP158 500p dk brn   3.00 1.10

1972, Sept. 16   Litho.   Perf. 12x11½
C497 AP159 15p blk, lt bl & Prus bl   .30   .20
C498 AP159 50p blk, gray & Prus bl   .30   .20

Syrianair, Syrian airline, 25th anniversary.

Pottery — AP160

Handicraft Industries: 25p, Rugs. 30p,
Metal (weapons). 35p, Straw (baskets, mats).
100p, Wood carving.

1976, July   Litho.   Perf. 12x12½
C499 AP160 10p multi   .30   .20
C500 AP160 25p multi   .30   .20
C501 AP160 30p multi   .30   .20
C502 AP160 30p multi   .30   .20
C503 AP160 100p multi   .50   .30
  a. Strip of 5, #C499-C503   1.75 1.75

23rd Intl. Damascus Fair.

Pres. Hafez
al Assad
AP161

1978, Sept.   Litho.   Perf. 12½x12
C504 AP161 25p sil & multi   .50   .20
C505 AP161 35p grn & multi   .50   .20
C506 AP161 60p gold & multi   .50   .20
  Nos. C504-C506 (3)   1.50   .60

Reelection of Pres. Assad. See No. 820.

AIR POST SEMI-POSTAL STAMPS

Nos. C30-C33 Surcharged Like Nos.
B1-B12 in Black and Red

1926, Apr. 1   Unwmk.   Perf. 13½
CB1 A4 2p + 1p dk brown   2.25 1.75
CB2 A4 3p + 2p org brn   1.90 1.75
CB3 A4 5p + 3p violet   1.90 1.75
CB4 A4 10p + 5p vio brn   1.90 1.75
  Nos. CB1-CB4 (4)   7.95 7.00

The new value is in red and rest of the
surcharge in black on Nos. CB1-CB3. The
entire surcharge is black on No. CB4.
See note following Nos. B1-B12.

> Catalogue values for unused
> stamps in this section, from this
> point to the end of the section, are
> for Never Hinged items.

Fair Entrance
SPAP1

Industry,
Handicraft
and Farming
SPAP2

Design: 70p+10p, Fairgrounds.

1955   Perf. 11½, Imperf.
         Litho.   Unwmk.
CB5 SPAP1 25p + 5p gray black   .40   .40
CB6 SPAP2 35p + 5p ultra   .40   .40
CB7 SPAP2 40p + 10p rose lilac   .60   .60
CB8 SPAP1 70p + 10p Prus grn   1.10 1.10
  Nos. CB5-CB8 (4)   2.50 2.50

Intl. Fair, Damascus, Sept. 1955.
For overprint see Nos. C212-C215.

United
Nations
Refugee
Emblem
SPAP3

1966, Dec. 12   Litho.   Perf. 11½x12
CB9 SPAP3 12½p + 2½p ultra &   .25   .20
CB10 SPAP3 50p + 5p grn & blk   .50   .25

UN Day, 21st anniv.; Refugee Week, Oct.
24-31.

POSTAGE DUE STAMPS

Under French Occupation

Stamps of French
Offices in the Turkish
Empire, 1902-03,
Surcharged

O. M. F
Syrie
Ch. taxe
1 PIASTRE

1920   Unwmk.   Perf. 14x13½
J1 A3 1p on 10c rose red   150.00 140.00
J2 A3 2p on 20c brn vio   150.00 140.00
J3 A3 3p on 30c lil   150.00 140.00
J4 A4 4p on 40c red &
         pale bl   150.00 140.00
  Nos. J1-J4 (4)   600.00 560.00

Postage Due Stamps of
France, 1893-1920,
Surcharged in Black or
Red

O. M. F.
Syrie
2
PIASTRES

1920
J5 D2 1p on 10c brown   1.10   1.10
J6 D2 2p on 20c ol grn (R)   1.10   1.10
  a. "PIASTRE"   650.00 650.00
J7 D2 3p on 30c red   1.10   1.10
  a. "PIASTRE"
J8 D2 4p on 50c brn vio   2.75   2.75
  a. 3p in setting of 4p   400.00 400.00
  Nos. J5-J8 (4)   6.05   6.05

1921-22
J9 D2 50c on 10c brown   .45   .55
  a. "75" instead of "50"   45.00
  b. "CENTI MES" instead of "CEN-
        TIEMES"   6.00
J10 D2 1p on 20c ol grn   .45   .55
J11 D2 2p on 30c red   1.40   1.40
J12 D2 3p on 50c brn vio   1.90   1.90
J13 D2 5p on 1fr red brn,
         straw   3.50   3.50
  Nos. J9-J13 (5)   7.70   7.90

D3

D4

1921   Perf. 11½
Red Surcharge
J14 D3 50c on 1p black   2.50   2.50
J15 D3 1p on 1p black   2.50   2.50

1922
J16 D4 2p on 5m rose   4.25   4.25
  a. "AX" of "TAXE" inverted   150.00 150.00
J17 D4 3p on 1p gray bl   7.75   7.75

French Mandate

Syrie
Grand Liban
2
PIASTRES

Postage Due Stamps of
France, 1893-1920,
Surcharged

1923
J18 D2 50c on 10c brown   .95   .95
J19 D2 1p on 20c ol grn   1.25   1.25
J20 D2 2p on 30c red   1.25   1.25
J21 D2 3p on 50c vio brn   1.25   1.25
J22 D2 5p on 1fr brn brn,
         straw   2.50   2.50
  Nos. J18-J22 (5)   7.20   7.20

SYRIE
1
PIASTRE

Postage Due Stamps of
France, 1893-1920,
Surcharged

1924
J23 D2 50c on 10c brown   .45   .45
J24 D2 1p on 20c ol grn   .50   .50
J25 D2 2p on 30c red   .65   .65
J26 D2 3p on 50c vio brn   .65   .65
J27 D2 5p on 1fr red brn, straw   .75   .75
  Nos. J23-J27 (5)   3.00   3.00

Syrie
2 Piastres
سوريا
غروش ٢

Postage Due Stamps of
France, 1893-1920,
Surcharged

1924
J28 D2 50c on 10c brown   .35   .50
J29 D2 1p on 20c ol grn   .50   .55
J30 D2 2p on 30c red   .55   .70
J31 D2 3p on 50c vio brn   .70   .65
J32 D2 5p on 1fr red brn, straw 1.25   1.25
  Nos. J28-J32 (5)   3.35   3.65

Water
Wheel at
Hama
D5

Bridge at
Antioch — D6

Designs: 2p, The Tartous. 3p, View of
Banias. 5p, Chevaliers' Castle.

1925   Photo.   Perf. 13½
J33 D5 50c brown, yel   .25   .25
J34 D6 1p violet, rose   .20   .30
J35 D5 2p black, blue   .45   .55
J36 D5 3p black, red org   .75   .75
J37 D5 5p black, bl grn   .75   .75
  Nos. J33-J37 (5)   2.40   2.60

D7

Lion — D8

1931
J38 D7 8p black, gray blue   2.75   2.7
J39 D8 15p black, dull rose   4.50   4.5

> Catalogue values for unused
> stamps in this section, from this
> point to the end of the section, are
> for Never Hinged items.

Syrian Arab Republic

D9

1965   Unwmk.   Litho.   Perf. 11½x1
J40 D9 2½p violet blue   .20   .2
J41 D9   5p black brown   .20   .2
J42 D9 10p green   .20   .2
J43 D9 17½p carmine rose   .20   .2
J44 D9 25p blue   .20   .2
  Nos. J40-J44 (5)   1.00   1.0

MILITARY STAMPS

Free French Administration
Syria No. 222 Surcharged in Black

1942   Unwmk.   Perf. 13
M1 A10 50c on 4p yel org   2.75   3.00

Lebanon Nos. 155 and 142A
Surcharged in Carmine

M2 A13   1fr on 5p grnsh bl   2.75   3.00
M3 A25 2.50fr on 12½p dp ultra   2.75   3.00

Camel
Corps,
Palmyra —
M1

1942   Unwmk.   Litho.   Perf. 11½
M4 M1 1fr deep rose   .20   .20
M5 M1 1.50fr bright violet   .20   .20
M6 M1 2fr orange   .20   .20
M7 M1 2.50fr brown gray   .20   .20
M8 M1 3fr Prussian blue   .30   .30
M9 M1 4fr deep green   .55   .55
M10 M1 5fr deep claret   .55   .55
  Nos. M4-M10 (7)   2.20   2.20

Nos. M4 to M10 exist imperforate.
For surcharges see Nos. MB1-MB2, MC10.

MILITARY SEMI-POSTAL STAMPS

Free French Administration

RÉSISTANCE

Military Stamps
of 1942
Surcharged in
Black

+9F

			1943	**Unwmk.**	**Perf. 11½**
1B1	M1	1fr + 9fr deep rose		1.75	1.75
1B2	M1	5fr + 20fr deep claret		1.75	1.75

MILITARY AIR POST STAMPS

Free French Administration

Syria Nos. C55-C56 Surcharged in
Black, Carmine or Orange

			1942	**Unwmk.**	**Perf. 13**
MC1	AP2	4fr on 50p blk (C)		2.10	2.10
MC2	AP2	6.50fr on 50p blk (C)		2.10	2.10
MC3	AP2	8fr on 50p blk (O)		2.10	2.10
MC4	AP2	10fr on 100p mag		2.10	2.10
		Nos. MC1-MC4 (4)		8.40	8.40

Winged
Shields and
Cross of
Lorraine
MAP1

		1942	**Litho.**	**Perf. 11½**
MC5	MAP1	6.50fr pale pink & rose car	.45	.45
MC6	MAP1	10fr lt bl & dl vio	.45	.45

Nos. MC5 and MC6 exist imperforate.
See Nos. MC7-MC8. For surcharges see
Nos. MC9, MCB1-MCB2.

Souvenir Sheets

		1942	**Without Gum**	**Perf. 11**
MC7		Sheet of 2	9.00	9.00
a.		MAP1 6.50fr pale pink & rose carmine	2.25	2.25
b.		MAP1 10fr lt bl & dl violet	2.25	2.25
			Imperf	
MC8		Sheet of 2	9.00	9.00
a.		MAP1 6.50fr pale pink & rose carmine	2.25	2.25
b.		MAP1 10fr lt bl & dl violet	2.25	2.25

No. MC5 Surcharged in Rose Carmine
With New Value and Bars

		1942		**Perf. 11½**
MC9	MAP1	4fr on 6.50fr		.65	.55

Military Stamp of 1942 Surcharged in
Black

		1943		
MC10	M1	4fr on 3fr Prus blue	.65	.55

MILITARY AIR POST SEMI-POSTAL STAMPS

Free French Administration
Military Air Post Stamps of 1942
Surcharged in Black

		1943	**Unwmk.**	**Perf. 11½**
MCB1	MAP1	6.50fr + 48.50fr	9.50	9.50
MCB2	MAP1	10fr + 100fr	9.50	9.50

POSTAL TAX STAMPS

Revenue Stamps Overprinted in Red
or Black

R1

طابع الجيش
السوري

a

طابع
للجيش السوري

b

		1945	**Unwmk.**	**Perf. 10½x11½**
RA1	R1(a)	5p dark blue (R)	90.00	22.50

On Stamps
Overprinted

RA2	R1(a)	5p dk bl (Bk+Bk)	75.00	27.50
RA3	R1(a)	5p dk bl (Bk+R)	75.00	27.50
RA4	R1(a)	5p dk bl (R+R)	90.00	27.50
RA5	R1(b)	5p dk bl (R+R)	82.50	24.00

On Stamps Overprinted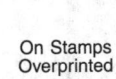

RA6	R1(a)	5p dk bl (Bk+Bk)	75.00	30.00
RA7	R1(a)	5p dk bl (Bk+R)	75.00	30.00
RA8	R1(a)	5p dk bl (R+R)	75.00	30.00
RA9	R1(b)	5p dk bl (R+R)	90.00	30.00
		Nos. RA1-RA9 (9)	727.50	249.00

The tax was for national defense.

R2

Revenue Stamp Surcharged in Black

		1945	**Unwmk.**	**Perf. 11**
RA10	R2	5p on 25c on 40c rose red	75.00	32.50

The surcharge reads "Tax (postal) for Syrian
Army."

طابع الجيش
السوري

ه ت س .

Revenue Stamp
Surcharged in
Black

		1945		
RA11	R2	5p on 25c on 40c rose red	75.00	32.50

No. RA11 Overprinted in
Black

RA12	R2	5p on 25c on 40c	67.50	

The tax on #RA11-RA12 was for the army.
This overprint exists on No. RA10.

Revenue stamps without overprints
occasionally were used as postage on
covers through at least 1948.

ISSUES OF THE ARABIAN GOVERNMENT

The following issues replaced the
British Military Occupation (E.E.F.)
stamps (Palestine Nos. 2-14) which
were used in central and eastern Syria
from Nov. 1918 until Jan. 1920.

Turkish Stamps of
1913-18
Handstamped in
Various Colors

Also Handstamp Surcharged with New
Values as:

قرش مصري
١

1 millieme   1 Egyptian
piaster

The Seal reads: "Hakuma al Arabie"
(The Arabian Government)

		1919-20	**Perf. 11½, 12, 12½, 13½**	
				Unwmk.
1	A24	1m on 2pa red lil (254)	.60	.60
2	A25	1m on 4pa dk brn (255)	.60	.60
3	A26	2m on 5pa vio brn (256)	.95	.95
4	A15	2m on 5pa on 10pa gray grn (291)	.60	.60
5	A18	2m on 5pa ocher (304)	17.50	15.00
6	A41	2m on 5pa grn (345)	225.00	160.00
7	A18	2m on 5pa ocher (378)	45.00	45.00
8	A28	4m on 10pa grn (258)	5.00	5.00
9	A28	4m on 10pa grn (271)	.60	.60
10	A22	4m on 10pa bl grn (329)	1.25	1.25
11	A41	4m on 10pa car (346)	21.00	21.00
12	A23	4m on 10pa car (415)	5.00	5.00
13	A44	4m on 10pa grn (424)	.90	.90
14	A11	4m on 10pa on 20pa vio brn (B38)	.90	.90
15	A41	4m on 10pa car (B42)	.60	.60
16	SP1	4m on 10pa red vio (B46)	.90	.90
17	SP1	4m on 10pa on 20pa car rose (B47)	.90	.90
19	A21	5pa ocher (317)		
21	A21	20pa car rose (153)	55.00	110.00
22	A29	20pa red (259)	.90	.90
23	A29	20pa red (272)	225.00	225.00
24	A17	20pa car (299)	1.75	1.75
25	A21	20pa car rose (318)	1.75	1.75
26	A22	20pa car rose (330)	9.50	9.50
27	A21	20pa car rose (342)	5.00	5.00
28	A41	20pa ultra (347)	1.60	1.60
29	A16	20pa mag (363)	7.25	7.25
30	A17	20pa car (371)	5.00	5.00
31	A18	20pa car (379)	5.00	5.00
32	A45	20pa dp rose (425)	2.50	2.50
33	A21	20pa car rose (B8)	1.50	1.50
34	A22	20pa car rose (B33)	1.75	1.75
35	A22	20pa car rose (B36)	9.75	9.75
36	A41	20pa ultra (B43)	.30	.30
37	A16	20pa mag (P140)	2.50	2.50
38	A17	20pa car (P144)	225.00	225.00
39	A30	1pi bl (260)	1.75	1.75
40	A31	1pi on 1½pi car & blk (261)	275.00	275.00
41	A30	1pi bl (273)	45.00	45.00
42	A30	1pi on 1pi bl (273)	65.00	65.00
43	A17	1pi blue (300)	3.00	3.00
44	A18	1pi blue (307)	55.00	55.00
45	A22	1pi ultra (331)	5.00	5.00
46	A21	1pi ultra (343)	9.50	9.50
47	A41	1pi vio & blk (348)	.95	.95
48	A18	1pi brt bl (389)	5.00	5.00
49	A46	1pi dl vio (426)	1.60	1.60
50	A47	1pi on 50pa ultra (428)	.60	.60
51	A21	1pi ultra (B9)	6.00	6.00
52	A22	1pi ultra (B15)	9.75	9.75
53	A18	1pi brt bl (B21)	6.00	6.00
54	A18	1pi blue (B23)	15.00	15.00
55	A22	1pi ultra (B34)	12.50	12.50
56	A41	1pi vio & blk (B44)	1.60	1.60
57	A33	2pi grn & blk (263)	45.00	40.00
58	A13	2pi brn org (289)	1.25	1.25
59	A18	2pi slate (308)	15.00	15.00
60	A18	2pi slate (314)	16.00	16.00
61	A21	2pi bl blk (320)	3.00	3.00
62	A17	2pi org (373)	3.00	3.00
63	A18	5pi brn (310)	7.25	7.25
64	A22	5pi dl vio (333)	15.00	15.00
65	A41	5pi yel brn & blk (349)	2.50	2.50
66	A41	5pi yel brn & blk (418)	2.50	2.50
67	A53	5pi on 2pa Prus bl (547)	7.75	7.75
68	A21	5pi dk vio (B10)	190.00	190.00
69	A17	5pi lil rose (B20)	32.50	32.50
70	A41	5pi yel brn & blk (B45)	3.00	3.00
72	A50	10pi dk grn (431)	65.00	65.00
73	A50	10pi dk vio (432)	60.00	60.00
74	A50	10pi dk brn (433)	375.00	
75	A18	10pi org brn (B2)	160.00	160.00
76	A37	25pi ol grn (267)	225.00	225.00
77	A40	25pi on 200pi grn & blk (287)	275.00	275.00
78	A17	25pi brn (303)	225.00	225.00
79	A51	25pi car, straw (434)	55.00	55.00
81	A52	50pi ind (438)	140.00	140.00

The variety "surcharge omitted" exists on
Nos. 1-5, 12-13, 16, 32, 49-50, 67.
A few copies of No. 377 (50pi) and No. 269
(100pi) were overprinted but not regularly
issued.

Overprinted

The Inscription reads "Hakum Soria
Arabie" (Syrian-Arabian Government)
On Stamp of 1913

83	A26	2m on 5pa vio brn (256)	3.75	3.75

On Stamp of 1916-18

84	A45	20pa dp rose (425)	.55	.55

A1

Litho.   Perf. 11½
85	A1	5m rose	.55	.55
a.		Tête bêche pair	11.00	8.25
b.		Imperf.		

Independence Issue
Arabic Overprint in Green:
"Souvenir of Syrian Independence March 8, 1920"

86	A1	5m rose	45.00	40.00
a.		Tête bêche pair		
b.		Inverted overprint	110.00	82.50

A2

Litho.
Size: 22x18mm
87	A2	¹⁄₁₀pi lt brn	.20	.20

Size: 28x22mm
88	A2	³⁄₁₀pi yel grn	.25	.20
a.		³⁄₁₀pi yellow (error)	7.00	4.50
89	A2	³⁄₁₀pi yellow	.20	.20
90	A2	1pi gray blue	.20	.20
91	A2	2pi blue grn	1.10	.50

Size: 31x25mm
92	A2	5pi vio brn	1.60	.85
93	A2	10pi gray	1.60	1.10
		Nos. 86-93 (8)	50.15	43.25

Nos. 86-93 exist imperf.
For overprint see No. J5.

PF1

PF2

Revenue Stamps Surcharged as on Postage Stamps, for Postal Use

1920		Unwmk.	Perf. 11½	
94	PF1	5m on 5pa red	.25	.25
95	PF2	1m on 5pa red	.20	.20
96	PF2	2m on 5pa red	.25	.20
97	PF2	1pi on 5pa red	.55	.45

Surcharged in Syrian Piasters

98	PF2	2pi on 5pa red	.20	.20
99	PF2	3pi on 5pa red	.20	.20
		Nos. 94-99 (6)	1.65	1.50

ISSUES OF THE ARABIAN GOVERNMENT POSTAGE DUE STAMPS

Postage Due Stamps of Turkey, 1914, Handstamped and Surcharged with New Value

1920		Unwmk.	Perf. 12	
J1	D1	2m on 5pa claret	4.50	4.50
J2	D2	20pa red	4.50	4.50
J3	D3	1pi dark blue	4.50	4.50
J4	D4	2pi slate	4.50	4.50
		Nos. J1-J4 (4)	18.00	18.00

Type of Regular Issue
Perf. 11½
Litho.
5	A2	1pi black	.85	.85

UNITED ARAB REPUBLIC

> Catalogue values for unused stamps in this section are for Never Hinged items.

See Egypt for stamps of types A1, A4, A7, A8, A14, A17, A19, A20, A24 with denomination in "M" (milliemes).

Issues for Syria

Linked Maps of Egypt and Syria — A1

Perf. 11½
1958, Feb. 1		Unwmk.	Litho.	
1	A1	12½p yellow & green	.20	.20

Establishment of UAR. See No. C1.
See also Egypt No. 436.

Freedom Monument A2

1958, May				
2	A2	5p yel & vio	.40	.20
3	A2	15p yel grn & brn red	.65	.35
		Nos. 2-3,C2-C3 (4)	3.00	1.30

British-French troop evacuation, 12th anniv.

Bronze Rattle — A3

Hand Holding Torch, Broken Chain and Flag — A4

Antique Art: 15p, Goddess. 20p, Lamgi Mari. 30p, Mithras fighting bull. 40p, Aspasia. 60p, Minerva. 75p, Flask. 100p, Enameled Vase. 150p, Mosaic from Omayyad Mosque, Damascus.

1958, Sept. 14		Litho.	Perf. 12	
4	A3	10p lt ol grn	.20	.20
5	A3	15p brown org	.20	.20
6	A3	20p rose lilac	.20	.20
7	A3	30p lt brown	.20	.20
8	A3	40p gray	.30	.20
9	A3	60p green	.50	.20
10	A3	75p blue	.80	.30

11	A3	100p brown car	1.20	.40
12	A3	150p dull purple	2.25	.60
		Nos. 4-12 (9)	5.85	2.50

Archaeological collections and museums.

1958, Oct. 14			Perf. 11½	
13	A4	12.50p car rose	.20	.20

Establishment of Republic of Iraq.
See Egypt No. 454.

Syria No. 411
Overprinted

الجمهورية العربية المتحدة
١٩٥٨/١٠/٦
RAU

1958, Oct. 6		Wmk. 291	Perf. 11½	
13A	A78	12½p olive	37.50	35.00
		Nos. 13A,C10-C11 (3)	87.50	85.00

Intl. Children's Day, 1958.

View of Damascus — A5

1958, Dec. 10			Unwmk.	
14	A5	12½p green	.20	.20

4th Near East Regional Conference, Damascus, Dec. 10-20. See No. C14.

Secondary School, Damascus — A6

1959, Feb. 26		Litho.	Perf. 12	
15	A6	12½p dull green	.20	.20

See No. 26.

Flags of UAR and Yemen A7

Perf. 13x13½
1959, Mar. 8		Photo.	Wmk. 318	
16	A7	12½p grn, red & blk	.20	.20

1st anniversary of United Arab States.
See Egypt No. 465.

Arms of UAR — A8   Mother and Children — A9

Perf. 12x11½
1959, Feb. 22		Litho.	Wmk. 291	
17	A8	12½p grn, blk & red	.20	.20

United Arab Republic, 1st anniv.
See Egypt No. 462.

1959, Mar. 21			Perf. 11½	
18	A9	15p carmine rose	.20	.20
19	A9	25p dk slate grn	.30	.25

Arab Mother's Day, Mar. 21.
For overprints see Nos. 41-42.

Syria No. 378 Surcharged "U.A.R." in Arabic and English, and New Value in Red

1959, Apr. 6		Photo.	Unwmk.	
20	A68	2½p on 1p olive	.20	.20

Type of 1959 and

A10

Boys' School, Damascus — A11

Designs: 5p, 7½p, 10p, Various arabesques. 12½p, St. Simeon's Monastery. 17½p, Hittin school. 35p, Normal School for Girls, Damascus.

1959-61		Unwmk.	Litho.	Perf. 11½	
21	A10	2½p violet		.20	.20
22	A10	5p olive bister		.20	.20
23	A10	7½p ultra		.20	.20
24	A10	10p bl grn		.20	.20
25	A11	12½p lt bl ('61)		.20	.20
26	A6	17½p brt lilac ('60)		.20	.20
27	A11	25p brt grnsh bl		.30	.20
28	A11	35p brown ('60)		.40	.20
		Nos. 21-28 (8)		1.90	1.60

Male Profile and Fair Emblem — A12

Fair Emblem and Globe — A13

1959, Aug. 30		Unwmk.	Perf. 11½	
30	A12	35p gray, grn & vio	.40	.20

Souvenir Sheet
Imperf
31	A13	30p dl yel & grn	1.50	1.50

6th International Damascus Fair.

Shield and Cogwheel — A14

Perf. 13½x13
1959, Oct. 20			Wmk. 328	
32	A14	50p sepia	.60	.35

Issued for Army Day, 1959.

See Egypt No. 491.

Syria Nos. 408 and 386 with Red Overprint Similar to

1959   Unwmk.   Litho.   Perf. 11½
33   A75 15p gray   .20 .20

Photo.
34   A69 50p dk grn   .60 .40

The overprints differ in size and lettering: No. 33 is 28x8½mm; No. 34 is 21x6mm. A period follows "R" on Nos. 33-34. The Arabic overprint means "United Arab Republic."

Cogwheel, Wheat and Cotton — A15

A. R. Kawakbi — A16

1959, Oct. 30   Litho.
35   A15 35p gray, bl & ocher   .40 .20

Industrial and Agricultural Production Fair, Aleppo. For overprint see No. 46.

Type of Syria Air Post, 1956, Inscribed "U.A.R."

1959, Dec. 31   Unwmk.   Perf. 13½
36   AP59 12½p gray ol & bister   .20 .20

Day of the Tree. For overprint see No. 49.

1960, Jan. 11   Perf. 12x11½
37   A16 15p dark green   .20 .20

Kawakbi, Arabic writer, 50th death anniv.

Arms and Flag — A17

Perf. 13½x13
1960, Feb. 22   Photo.   Wmk. 328
38   A17 12½p red & dk sl grn   .20 .20

United Arab Republic, 2nd anniversary. See Egypt No. 499.

Diesel Train and Old Town — A18

Perf. 11½x11
1960, Mar. 15   Litho.   Unwmk.
39   A18 12½p brn & brt bl   .35 .20

Construction of the Latakia-Aleppo railroad.

Arab League Center, Cairo, and Arms of UAR A19

Perf. 13x13½
1960, Mar. 22   Photo.   Wmk. 328
40   A19 12½p dl grn & blk   .20 .20

Opening of the Arab League Center and the Arab Postal Museum in Cairo. See Egypt No. 502.

Nos. 18-19 Overprinted in Black or Magenta

Wmk. 291
1960, Apr. 3   Litho.   Perf. 11½
41   A9 15p car rose   .20 .20
42   A9 25p dk slate grn (M)   .35 .20

Issued for Arab Mother's Day.

Refugees Pointing to Map of Palestine A20

Perf. 13x13½
1960, Apr. 7   Photo.   Wmk. 328
43   A20 12½p car rose   .40 .20
44   A20 50p green   .70 .30

World Refugee Year, 7/1/59-6/30/60. See Egypt Nos. 503-504.

A21

Perf. 11½
1960, May 12   Unwmk.   Litho.
45   A21 12½p vio, rose & pale grn   .20 .20

Evacuation Day, 1960.

No. 35 Overprinted in Red

1960
46   A15 35p gray, bl & ocher   .30 .20

1960 Industrial and Agricultural Production Fair, Aleppo.

Souvenir Sheet

Flags in Symbolic Design — A22

1960   Unwmk.   Imperf.
47   A22 100p gray, brn & lt bl   1.50 1.50

7th Intl. Damascus Fair.

Child — A23

1960   Litho.   Perf. 11½
48   A23 35p dk grn & fawn   .40 .20

Issued for Children's Day.

No. 36 Overprinted in Carmine

1960   Unwmk.   Perf. 11½
49   AP59 12½p gray ol & bis   .20 .20

Issued to publicize the Day of the Tree.

Coat of Arms and Victory Wreath — A24

Cogwheel, Retort and Ear of Wheat — A25

Perf. 13½x13
1961, Feb. 22   Photo.   Wmk. 328
50   A24 12½p lt vio   .20 .20

United Arab Republic, 3rd anniversary. See Egypt No. 517.

Perf. 11½
1961, June 8   Unwmk.   Litho.
51   A25 12½p multi   .20 .20

Industrial and Agricultural Fair, Aleppo.

UAR SEMI-POSTAL STAMP

Catalogue values for unused stamp in this section is for a Never Hinged item.

Postal Emblem — SP1

Perf. 13½x13
1959, Jan. 2   Photo.   Wmk. 318
B1   SP1 20p + 10p bl grn, red &   blk   .40 .40

Issued for Post Day. The surtax went to the social fund for postal employees. See Egypt No. B18 for similar stamp with denomination in "M" (milliemes).

UAR AIR POST STAMPS

Catalogue values for unused stamps in this section are for Never Hinged items.

Map Type of Regular Issue
Perf. 11½
1958, Apr. 3   Unwmk.   Litho.
C1   A1 17½p ultra & brn   .35 .20

Broken Chain, Dove and Olive Branch AP1

1958, May 17
C2   AP1 35p rose & blk   .70 .35
C3   AP1 45p bl & brn   1.25 .40

British-French troop evacuation, 12th anniv.

Scout Putting up Tent AP2

1958, Aug. 31   Perf. 12
C4   AP2 35p dk brn   1.50 1.50
C5   AP2 40p ultra   2.00 2.00

3rd Pan-Arab Boy Scout Jamboree.

View of Damascus Fair — AP3

UAR Flag and Fair Emblem AP4

Designs: 30p, Minaret, vase and emblem, vert. 45p, Mosque, chimneys and wheel, vert.

1958, Sept. 1   Litho.   Perf. 11½
C6 AP3 25p vermilion   .70   .60
C7 AP3 30p brt bl grn   1.00   .60
C8 AP3 45p violet   .80   .55
    Nos. C6-C8 (3)   2.50 1.75
Souvenir Sheet
Imperf
C9 AP4 100p brt grn, car & blk   50.00 50.00

Fifth Damascus International Fair.

Syria Nos. C244-C245
Overprinted

RAU

1958, Oct. 6   Wmk. 291   Perf. 11½
C10 A78 17½p ultra   25.00 25.00
C11 A78 20p red brn   25.00 25.00

International Children's Day.

Cotton and Cotton Material — AP5

1958, Oct. 10   Unwmk.   Perf. 12
C12 AP5 25p brn & yel   .40   .20
C13 AP5 35p brn & brick red .70   .50

Cotton Festival, Aleppo, Oct. 9-11.

Type of Regular Issue, 1958
1958, Dec. 10
C14 A5 17½p brt vio   .20   .20

Children and Glider — AP6

1958, Dec. 1   Litho.   Perf. 12
C15 AP6 7½p gray green   .50   .30
C16 AP6 12½p olive   2.00 1.25

1958 glider festival.

UN Emblem — AP7

1958, Dec. 10
C17 AP7 25p dl pur   .20   .20
C18 AP7 35p light blue   .35   .25
C19 AP7 40p brn red   .45   .30
    Nos. C17-C19 (3)   1.00   .75

10th anniv. of the signing of the Universal Declaration of Human Rights.

Globe, Radio and Telegraph — AP8

1959, Mar. 1   Perf. 12
C20 AP8 40p grn & blk   .50   .35

Arab Union of Telecommunications. See Egypt No. 464 for similar stamp with denomination in "M" (milliemes).

Same Overprinted in Red

1959, Mar. 1
C21 AP8 40p grn & blk   .40   .20

2nd Conference of the Arab Union of Telecommunications, Damascus.

Laurel and Map of Syria — AP9

Design: 35p, Torch and broken chain.

1959, Apr. 17   Perf. 12x11½
C22 AP9 15p ocher & green   .20   .20
C23 AP9 35p gray & carmine   .40   .20

British-French troop evacuation, 13th anniv.

"Emigration" — AP10

1959, Aug. 4   Unwmk.   Perf. 11½x12
C24 AP10 80p brt grn, blk & red   .70 .40

Convention of the Assoc. of Arab Emigrants in the US.

Refinery AP11

1959, Aug. 12   Litho.
C25 AP11 50p bl, blk & car   .90   .40

Opening of first oil refinery in Syria.

Syria Nos. C246 and C181-C182
Overprinted like Nos. 33-34
1959   Perf. 11½
C26 AP64 5p bright green   .20   .20
C27 AP44 50p deep plum   .40   .20
C28 AP44 70p purple   .70   .30
    Nos. C26-C28 (3)   1.30   .70

The overprints differ in size and lettering: #C26 is 25½x9½mm; #C27-C28 are 27x8mm. A period follows "R" on #C27-C28.

Cotton Boll and Thread — AP12

 ...

Boy and Building Blocks — AP13

1959, Oct. 1   Litho.   Perf. 11½
C29 AP12 45p gray blue   .40   .20
C30 AP12 50p claret   .40   .30

Cotton Festival, Aleppo. For overprints see Nos. C33-C34.

1959, Oct. 5
C31 AP13 25p dl lil, red & dk bl   .20 .20

Issued for Children's Day.

Crane and Compass AP14

1960   Unwmk.   Perf. 11½
C32 AP14 50p lt brn, crim & blk   .40 .30

7th Damascus International Fair.

Nos. C29-C30 Overprinted in Claret or Gray Blue

1960   Litho.   Perf. 11½
C33 AP12 45p gray blue (C)   .40   .20
C34 AP12 50p claret (GB)   .45   .30

1960 Cotton Festival, Aleppo.

17th Olympic Games, Rome — AP15

Globe, Laurel and "UN" — AP16

1960, Dec. 27   Unwmk.   Perf. 12
C35 AP15 15p Basketball   .20   .20
C36 AP15 20p Swimmer   .35   .20
C37 AP15 25p Fencing   .35   .20
C38 AP15 40p Horsemanship   .60   .30
    Nos. C35-C38 (4)   1.50   .90

1960, Dec. 31
C39 AP16 35p multi   .35 .2?
C40 AP16 50p bl, red & yel   .40 .2?

United Nations, 15th anniversary.

Ibrahim Hanano — AP17

Soldier with Flag — AP18

1961   Litho.   Perf. 12x11½
C41 AP17 50p buff & slate grn   .35 .2?

Hanano, leader of liberation movement.

1961, Apr. 17   Wmk. 291   Perf. 11½
C42 AP18 40p gray green   .35 .20

Issued for Evacuation Day, 1961.

Arab and Map of Palestine — AP19

Abu-Tammam AP20

1961, May 15   Perf. 12
C43 AP19 50p ultra & blk   .50 .25

Issued for Palestine Day.

1961, July 20   Unwmk.   Perf. 11½
C44 AP20 50p brown   .40 .20

Abu-Tammam (807-845?), Arabian poet.

Discus Thrower and Lyre AP21

1961, Aug. 23   Litho.   Perf. 11½
C45 AP21 15p crimson & blk   .20 .20
C46 AP21 35p bl grn & vio   .50 .20

5th University Youth Festival.

A souvenir sheet contains one each of Nos.
C45-C46 imperf.

Fair
Emblem — AP22

UAR
Pavilion — AP23

1961, Aug. 25

C47	AP22	17½p vio & grn	.20	.20
C48	AP23	50p brt lil & blk	.35	.20
a.	Black omitted			

8th International Damascus Fair.

St. Simeon's
Monastery
AP24

1961, Oct.   Litho.   Perf. 12

C49	AP24	200p violet blue	1.50	.90

No. C49 was issued by the Syrian Arab
Republic after dissolution of the UAR.

**UAR AIR POST SEMI-POSTAL
STAMP**

> **Catalogue value for the unused
> stamp in this section is for a Never
> Hinged item.**

Eye, Hand and
UN Emblem
SPAP1

Perf. 12x11½

1961, Apr. 29   Litho.   Wmk. 291

CB1	SPAP1	40p + 10p sl grn & blk	.30	.30

UN welfare program for the blind.

STOCKSHEETS

HAGNER STYLE STOCK SHEETS

Hagner-style stock pages offer convenience and flexibility.
Pages are produced on thick, archival-quality paper with
acetate pockets glued from the bottom of each pocket.
They're ideal for the topical collector who may require various page styles to store a complete collection.

- Black background makes beautiful stamp presentation.
- Pockets use pull away/snap back principle.
- Made from archival-quality heavyweight paper that
  offers unprecedented protection and clarity.
- Multi-hole punch fits most binder types.
- Available in 9 different page formats.
  8½" x 11" size accomodates every size stamp.

Sold in packages of 10.
Available with pockets on one side or both sides.
"D" in item number denotes two-sided page.

1 POCKET		**2 POCKET**		**3 POCKET**		**4 POCKET**	
242 mm		119 mm		79 mm		58 mm	
ITEM	RETAIL	ITEM	RETAIL	ITEM	RETAIL	ITEM	RETAIL
S1	$10.99	S2	$10.99	S3	$10.99	S4	$10.99
S1D	$15.99	S2D	$15.99	S3D	$15.99	S4D	$15.99

5 POCKET		**6 POCKET**		**7 POCKET**		**8 POCKET**	
45 mm		37 mm		31 mm		27 mm	
ITEM	RETAIL	ITEM	RETAIL	ITEM	RETAIL	ITEM	RETAIL
S5	$10.99	S6	$10.99	S7	$10.99	S8	$10.99
S5D	$15.99	S6D	$15.99	S7D	$15.99	S8D	$15.99

MULTI-POCKETS

36 mm
67 mm
139 mm

ITEM	RETAIL
S9	$10.99
S9D	$15.99

SCOTT.

1-800-572-6885
P.O. Box 828, Sidney OH 45365-0828
www.amosadvantage.com

AMOS
HOBBY PUBLISHING

Publishers of *Coin World, Linn's Stamp News*
and *Scott Publishing Co.*

TAHITI

tə-'hēt-ē

LOCATION — An island in the South Pacific Ocean, one of the Society group
GOVT. — A part of the French Oceania Colony
AREA — 600 sq. mi.
POP. — 19,029
CAPITAL — Papeete

The stamps of Tahiti were replaced by those of French Oceania (see French Polynesia in Vol. 2).

100 Centimes = 1 Franc

Counterfeits exist of surcharges and overprints on Nos. 1-31.

Stamps of French Colonies Surcharged in Black:

25c	**TAHITI** **25c**
a	b
TAHITI **5c**	**TAHITI** **10c**
c	d

1882		Unwmk.		Imperf.
1	A8(a)	25c on 35c dk vio, org	250.	225.
1A	A8(b)	25c on 35c dk vio, org	2,750.	4,250.
1B	A8(a)	25c on 40c ver, straw	4,600.	5,100.

Nos. 1-1B exist with surcharges inverted. Values for Nos. 1 and 1A are approximately the same as for normal copies; No. 1B with surcharge inverted is worth about half the value of a normal copy.

Surcharge exists reading either up or down on Nos. 1 and 1A, and double, one inverted on No. 1B. See *Scott Classic Specialized Catalogue of Stamps and Covers* for detailed listings of these and later Tahiti issues.

1884			Perf. 14x13½
2	A9(c)	5c on 20c red, grn	180.00 145.00
3	A9(d)	10c on 20c red, grn	210.00 200.00
			Imperf
4	A8(b)	25c on 1fr brnz grn, straw	525.00 425.00

Inverted and vertical surcharges on Nos. 2-4 are same value as normally placed surcharges.

Handstamped in Black

1893			Perf. 14x13½
5	A9	1c blk, lil bl	600.00 525.00
6	A9	2c brown, buff	2,400. 1,800.
7	A9	4c claret, lav	1,050. 800.00
8	A9	5c green, grnsh	32.50 30.00
9	A9	10c black, lav	32.50 30.00
10	A9	15c blue	32.50 30.00
11	A9	20c red, green	45.00 42.50
12	A9	25c yel, straw	6,000. 5,000.
13	A9	25c blk, rose	32.50 30.00
14	A9	35c violet, org	1,800. 1,500.
15	A9	75c carmine, rose	52.50 52.50
16	A9	1fr brnz grn, straw	52.50 52.50

Nearly all values of this set are known with overprint inverted, sloping up, sloping down and horizontal. Some occur double. Values the same as for the listed stamps.

Nos. 6, 12 and 14 are valued in the grade of Fine.

Overprinted in Black

1893

TAHITI

1893				
17	A9	1c blk, lil bl	600.00	525.00
18	A9	2c brn, buff	2,600.	2,100.
19	A9	4c claret, lav	1,300.	1,100.
20	A9	5c grn, grnsh	800.00	650.00
21	A9	10c black, lav	240.00	240.00
22	A9	15c blue	32.50	30.00
23	A9	20c red, grn	32.50	30.00
24	A9	25c yel, straw	36,000.	28,000.
25	A9	25c black, rose	32.50	30.00
26	A9	35c violet, org	1,800.	1,500.
27	A9	75c carmine, rose	32.50	30.00
b.		Double overprint	260.00	
28	A9	1fr brnz grn, straw	32.50	30.00

No. 18 is valued in the grade of Fine.

Inverted Overprint

17a	A9	1c blk, lil bl	850.	800.
18a	A9	2c brn, buff	3,000.	2,800.
19a	A9	4c claret, lav	1,450.	1,400.
20a	A9	5c grn, grnsh	1,000.	1,000.
21a	A9	10c black, lav	625.	600.
22a	A9	15c blue	150.	125.
23a	A9	20c red, grn	150.	125.
25a	A9	25c black, rose	150.	125.
26a	A9	35c violet, org	2,100.	2,000.
27a	A9	75c carmine, rose	150.	125.
28a	A9	1fr brnz grn, straw	150.	125.

Stamps of French Polynesia Surcharged in Black or Carmine:

TAHITI 10 CENTIMES	**TAHITI 10 centimes**
g	h

1903				
29	A1	(g) 10c on 15c bl (Bk)	6.50	6.50
a.		Double surcharge	40.00	40.00
b.		Inverted surcharge	40.00	40.00
30	A1	(h) 10c on 25c blk, rose (C)	6.50	6.50
a.		Double surcharge	42.50	42.50
b.		Inverted surcharge	42.50	42.50
31	A1	(h) 10c on 40c red, straw (Bk)	8.00	8.00
a.		Double surcharge	40.00	40.00
b.		Inverted surcharge	21.00	21.00
		Nos. 29-31 (3)	21.00	21.00

In the surcharges on Nos. 29-31 there are two varieties of the "1" in "10," i. e. with long and short serif.

SEMI-POSTAL STAMPS

Stamps of French Polynesia Overprinted in Red

✚ **TAHITI**

1915		Unwmk.	Perf. 14x13½
B1	A1	15c blue	190.00 190.00
a.		Inverted overprint	725.00 725.00
B2	A1	15c gray	22.50 22.50
a.		Inverted overprint	300.00 300.00

Counterfeits exist.

POSTAGE DUE STAMPS

Counterfeits exist of overprints on Nos. J1-J26.

Inverted overprints exist on most, and double overprints on many, Tahiti postage due stamps. See the *Scott Classic Specialized Catalogue of Stamps and Covers* for detailed listings.

Postage Due Stamps of French Colonies Handstamped in Black like Nos. 5-16

1893		Unwmk.	Imperf.
J1	D1	1c black	275. 275.
J2	D1	2c black	300. 300.
J3	D1	3c black	310. 310.
J4	D1	4c black	310. 310.
J5	D1	5c black	310. 310.
J6	D1	10c black	310. 310.
J7	D1	15c black	310. 310.
J8	D1	20c black	260. 260.
J9	D1	30c black	310. 310.
J10	D1	40c black	310. 310.
J11	D1	60c black	360. 360.

J12	D1	1fr brown	725. 725.
J13	D1	2fr brown	725. 725.
		Nos. J1-J13 (13)	4,815. 4,815.

Overprinted in Black like Nos. 17-28

1893				
J14	D1	1c black	1,700.	1,700.
a.		Inverted overprint	2,400.	2,400.
J15	D1	2c black	400.	400.
J16	D1	3c black	400.	400.
J17	D1	4c black	400.	400.
J18	D1	5c black	400.	400.
J19	D1	10c black	400.	400.
J20	D1	15c black	400.	400.
J21	D1	20c black	400.	400.
J22	D1	30c black	400.	400.
J23	D1	40c black	400.	400.
J24	D1	60c black	400.	400.
J25	D1	1fr brown	400.	400.
J26	D1	2fr brown	400.	400.
		Nos. J14-J26 (13)	6,500.	6,500.

Nos. J15-J20, J22-J26 exist with overprint inverted, double or both. Value, each $600.

TAJIKISTAN

tä-jik-i-'stan

(Tadzhikistan)

LOCATION — Asia, bounded by Uzbekistan, Kyrgyzstan, People's Republic of China and Afghanistan
GOVT. — Republic
AREA — 55,240 sq. mi.
POP. — 6,102,854 (1999 est.)
CAPITAL — Dushanbe

With the breakup of the Soviet Union on Dec. 26, 1991, Tajikistan became independent.

100 Kopecks = 1 Ruble
100 Tanga = 1 Ruble
100 Dinars = 1 Somoni (2000)

> Catalogue values for all unused stamps in this country are for Never Hinged items.

Gold Statue of Man on Horse — A1

1992, May 20		Litho.	Perf. 12x12½
1	A1	50k multicolored	.30 .30

For surcharge see No. 12.

Sheik Muslihiddin Mosque A2

1992, May 25		Photo.	Perf. 11½
2	A2	50k multicolored	.30 .30

Musical Instruments of Tajikistan — A3

1992, Aug. 15		**Photo. & Engr.**	Perf. 12x11½
3	A3	35k multicolored	.25 .25

For surcharges see Nos. 5-7.

Ram — A4

1992, Aug. 21		Photo.	Perf. 12x12½
4	A4	30k multicolored	.25 .25

No. 3 Surcharged in Black or Blue

		Photo. & Engr.		
1992, Nov. 12			Perf. 12x11½	
5	A3	15r on 35k	.30	.30
6	A3	15r on 35k (Bl)	1.40	1.40
7	A3	50r on 35k	.30	.30
		Nos. 5-7 (3)	2.00	2.00

Russia No. 5838 Surcharged

1992, Jan. 4		Litho.	Perf. 12x12½
8	A2765	3r on 1k	.25 .25
9	A2765	100r on 1k	1.50 1.50

No. 1 Surcharged in Black and Russia No. 5984 Surcharged in Violet Blue or Green

1992, May 7		Litho.	Perf. 12x12½
10	A2765	10r on 2k (VB)	.20 .20
11	A2765	15r on 2k (Gr)	.20 .20
12	A1	60r on 50k	1.00 1.00
		Nos. 10-12 (3)	1.40 1.40

Location and size of lettering on Nos. 10-11 varies.

No. 2 Surcharged

Methods and Perfs as Before

1992, Sept. 18			
13	A2	5r on 50k multi	.25 .25
14	A2	25r on 50k multi	.75 .75

Wild Animals A5

Designs: 3r, Ursus arctos. 10r, Cervas elaphus. 15r, Capra falconeri. 25r, Hystrix leucura. 100r, Uncia uncia.

1993, June 8   Litho.   Perf. 13½

5	A5	3r multicolored	.20	.20
6	A5	10r multicolored	.20	.20
7	A5	15r multicolored	.25	.20
8	A5	25r multicolored	.40	.25
9	A5	100r multicolored	1.60	.35
		Nos. 15-19 (5)	2.65	1.20

Fortress, 19th
Cent. — A6

1r, Statue of Rudaki, poet, vert. 5r, Mountains, river. 10r, Statue with oriental inscription, vert. 15r, Mausoleum of Aini, poet, vert. 20r, Map, flag. 35r, Post office. 50r, Aini Opera House. #29, Theater. #30, Flag, map, diff. #31, Observatory. #32, Academy.

1993-94

20	A6	1r multicolored	.20	.20
22	A6	5r multicolored	.20	.20
23	A6	10r multicolored	.20	.20
24	A6	15r multicolored	.20	.20
25	A6	20r green & multi	.20	.20
26	A6	25r multicolored	.35	.35
27	A6	35r multicolored	.20	.20
28	A6	50r multicolored	.55	.55
29	A6	100r multicolored	.50	.50
30	A6	100r blue & multi	1.00	1.00
31	A6	160r multicolored	.60	.60
32	A6	160r multicolored	.60	.60
		Nos. 20-32 (12)	4.80	4.80

Issued: 1r, 5r, 15r, 20r, 25r, 50r, No. 30, 6/8/93, others, 9/8/94.
This is an expanding set. Numbers will change if necessary.

Souvenir Sheet

1992 Summer Olympics,
Barcelona — A7

1993, June 8

33	A7	50r multicolored	5.25	5.25

For surcharge see No. 52A.

Epic Poem
"Book of
Kings", by
Ferdowsi,
1000th
Anniv.
A8

Designs: 5r, Combat with swords. 20r, Two men on horseback fighting with spears. 30r, Men in combat stopped by guide on giant bird, vert. 50r, Ferdowsi (c. 935-c. 1020), vert.

1993, June 8   Litho.   Perf. 13½

34	A8	5r multicolored	.25	.25
35	A8	20r multicolored	.75	.75
36	A8	30r multicolored	1.00	1.00
a.		Sheet, 2 each # 34-36, + 4 labels		
		Nos. 34-36 (3)	2.00	2.00

Souvenir Sheet

37	A8	50r multicolored	2.00	2.00

No. 37 contains one 30x45mm stamp.

Traditional
Art Pattern
A8a

1993, July 1   Litho.   Perf. 12x11½

37A	A8a	1.50r multicolored	.35	.35

Dated 1992.
For surcharges see Nos. 62-65.

Ali Hamadani
(1314-85), Persian
Mystic — A9

1994, Feb. 22   Litho.   Perf. 13½

38	A9	1000r multicolored	1.10	1.10
39	A9	1000r multicolored	1.10	1.10

Name in latin letters on No. 38 and in cyrillic letters on No. 39.

Natl. Arms — A10

1994, Feb. 22

40	A10	10r black brown & multi	.20	.20
41	A10	15r purple & multi	.20	.20
43	A10	35r olive & multi	.20	.20
44	A10	50r red & multi	.20	.20
46	A10	100r green & multi	.20	.20
47	A10	160r blue & multi	.20	.20

Size: 23x36mm

50	A10	500r blue & multi	.45	.45
52	A10	1000r brown & multi	.95	.95
		Nos. 40-52 (8)	2.60	2.60

This is an expanding set. Numbers will change if necessary.

No. 33 Ovptd.

1994, Apr. 13   Litho.   Perf. 13½

52A	A7	50r multicolored	4.00	4.00

Prehistoric
Animals
A11

Designs: No. 53, Diatryma. No. 54, Triceratops. No. 55, Anatosaurus. No. 56, Tyrannosaurus. No. 57, Parasaurolophus. No. 58, Incorrectly inscribed "Tyrannosaurus," with

horns, resembling an Ankalysaurus. No. 59, Spinosaurus. No. 60, Stegosaurus.

1994, Sept. 8   Litho.   Perf. 13½

53-60	A11	500r Set of 8	4.00	2.00

Issued as a sheetlet of nine, with Nos. 53-60 and one label.

No. 37A
Surcharged
in Green

1995, Mar. 10   Litho.   Perf. 12x11½

62	A8a	100r on 1.50r multi	.20	.20
63	A8a	600r on 1.50r multi	.30	.30
64	A8a	1000r on 1.50r multi	.50	.50
65	A8a	5000r on 1.50r multi	2.50	2.50
a.		Strip, #64-65, 2 ea #62-63	4.50	4.50
		Nos. 62-65 (4)	3.50	3.50

Issued in sheets of 36 stamps. Each vertical and horizontal strip has stamps in different order.
For surcharges see Nos. 111-114.

Membership Admissions — A13

Designs: No. 66, Member of UN. No. 67, Member of UPU, vert. No. 68, Member of OSCE (Organization of Security & Cooperation in Europe), vert.

1995, May 4   Litho.   Perf. 13½

66	A13	1000r multicolored	.85	.75
67	A13	1000r multicolored	.85	.75
68	A13	1000r multicolored	.85	.75
		Nos. 66-68 (3)	2.55	2.25

Lizards
A14

#69, Alsophylax loricatus. #70, Varanus griseus. #71, Phrynocephalus mystaceus. #72, Phrynocephalus helioscopus. #73, Phrynocephalus sogdianus. #74, Teratoscincus scineus.
5000r, Eumeces schneideri.

1995, May 4   Litho.   Perf. 13½

69	A14	500r multicolored	.30	.30
70	A14	500r multicolored	.30	.30
71	A14	500r multicolored	.30	.30
72	A14	500r multicolored	.30	.30
73	A14	500r multicolored	.30	.30
74	A14	500r multicolored	.30	.30
		Nos. 69-74 (6)	1.80	1.80

Souvenir Sheet

75	A14	5000r multicolored	3.00	3.00

For overprints see Nos. 77-78.

Souvenir Sheet

End of World War II, 50th
Anniv. — A15

Illustration reduced.

1995, May 8   Litho.   Perf. 13½

76	A15	5000r multicolored	2.50	2.50
a.		As #76, color diff.	2.50	2.50

On No. 76 emblem in margin is bister, black & red. No. 76a emblem is yellow, black & red with missing letter "E" from second line of text.

No. 70
Ovptd.

No. 71
Ovptd.

1995, Dec. 1   Litho.   Perf. 13½

77	A14	500r on #70	2.40	2.40
78	A14	500r on #71	2.40	2.40

Singapore '95 (#77), Beijing '95 (#78).

New Natl. Arms — A16

1995, Dec. 20

79	A16	1r olive & multi	.20	.20
80	A16	2r brown & multi	.20	.20
81	A16	5r green & multi	.20	.20
82	A16	12r red & multi	.20	.20
83	A16	40r green blue & multi	.55	.55
		Nos. 79-83 (5)	1.35	1.35

Birds
A17

Designs: No. 84, Syrrhaptes tibetana. No. 85, Perdix daurica turcomana. No. 86, Tetraogallus tibetanus. No. 87, Otis undulata macqueeni. No. 88, Larus brunnicephalus. No. 89, Anser indicus.
600r, Phasianus colchicus.

1996, Feb. 1

84	A17	200r multicolored	1.00	1.00
85	A17	200r multicolored	1.00	1.00
86	A17	200r multicolored	1.00	1.00
87	A17	200r multicolored	1.00	1.00
88	A17	200r multicolored	1.00	1.00
89	A17	200r multicolored	1.00	1.00
		Nos. 84-89 (6)	6.00	6.00

Souvenir Sheet

90	A17	600r multicolored	3.00	3.00

Two each of Nos. 84-89 were issued in sheet of 12 + label.

UN, 50th
Anniv.
A18

Designs: 100r, UN headquarters, New York. 500r, Headquarters at night.

1996

90A	A18	100r multicolored	.50	.50

Souvenir Sheet

90B	A14	500r multicolored	3.00	3.00

Issued: 100r, 4/10; 500r, 2/1.

Souvenir Sheet

Save the Aral
Sea — A19

Designs: a, Felis caracal. b, Salmo trutta aralensis. c, Hyaena hyaena. d, Pseudoscaphirhynchus kaufmanni. e, Aspiolucius esocinus.

1996, May 3   Litho.   Perf. 14
91 A19 100r Sheet of 5, #a.-e.   4.50 4.50

See Kazakhstan No. 145, Kyrgyzstan No. 107, Turkmenistan No. 52, Uzbekistan No. 113.

Octocolobus Manul — A20

Designs: Nos. 92-95, 98, Octocolobus manul (different views). No. 96, Felis chaus oxiana. No. 97, Felix lynx isabellina.

1996, June 28   Litho.   Perf. 13½
92 A20 100r brown & multi   .40 .40
93 A20 100r yellow & multi   .40 .40
94 A20 150r blue & multi   .60 .60
95 A20 150r lilac & multi   .60 .60
96 A20 200r multicolored   .80 .80
97 A20 200r multicolored   .80 .80
     Nos. 92-97 (6)   3.60 3.60

Souvenir Sheet
98 A20 500r multicolored   5.00 5.00

World Wildlife Fund (#92-95).

1996
Summer
Olympic
Games,
Atlanta
A21

1996, July 12   Litho.   Perf. 13½
99 A21 200r Judo   1.40
100 A21 200r Diving   1.40
101 A21 200r Hammer throw   1.40
102 A21 200r Soccer   1.40
103 A21 200r Pierre de Coubertin   1.40
     Nos. 99-103 (5)   7.00

Kamol Khujandi,
Poet — A22

1996, Sept. 7   Litho.   Perf. 13½
104 A22 500r Cyrillic name
       14mm long   3.25 3.25
a.   Cyrillic name 13mm long   3.25 3.25
105 A22 500r English inscriptions   3.25 3.25

Central
Asian
Postal
Union, 5th
Anniv.
A23

1996, Dec. 25   Perf. 12¾
106 A23 100r multicolored   1.75 1.75

Mountains
A24

1997, July 16   Perf. 13x12¾
107 A24 100r Communism Peak   .60 .60
108 A24 100r Peak Korzhenevskoj   .60 .60
109 A24 100r Lenin Peak   .60 .60
a.   Strip of 3, #107-109   1.80 1.80

Souvenir Sheet
110 A24 500r Mountain climber   3.00 3.00

Nos. 62-65 Surcharged

1997, Oct. 27   Litho.   Perf. 12x11½
111 A8a (A) on 100r #62   .65 .65
112 A8a (A) on 600r #63   .65 .65
113 A8a (A) on 1000r #64   .65 .65
114 A8a (A) on 5000r #65   .65 .65
a.   Strip, #113-114, 2 ea #111-112   4.00 4.00
     Nos. 111-114 (4)   2.60 2.60

A25   A27

Traditional Costumes: #115, Woman with red shawl draped over head, carrying pitcher. #116, Woman in long formal dress, cape, tiara. #117, Man wearing long striped coat. #118, Man wearing long blue coat.

1998, Feb. 20   Litho.   Perf. 12½x13
115 A25 100r multicolored   .90 .90
116 A25 100r multicolored   .90 .90
117 A25 150r multicolored   1.40 1.40
a.   Pair, #115, 117   2.30 2.30
118 A25 150r multicolored   1.40 1.40
a.   Pair, #116, 118   2.30 2.30
     Nos. 115-118 (4)   4.60 4.60

Handicrafts — A26

1998, Feb. 20   Litho.   Perf. 12¾
119 A26 30r Urn   .40 .40
119A A26 100r Cradles   1.25 1.25

Size: 64x64mm
Imperf
120 A26 300r Ceramic tile   4.00 4.00
     Nos. 119-120 (3)   5.65 5.65

1998, Apr. 3   Litho.   Perf. 12½x13
Flowers: 12r, Tulipa greigii. 30r, Crocus korolkowii. 70r, Iris darwasica. 150r, Petilium eduardii. 300r, Juno nicolai.
121 A27 12r multicolored   .20 .20
122 A27 30r multicolored   .30 .30
123 A27 70r multicolored   .65 .65

---

124 A27 150r multicolored   1.40 1.40
a.   Sheet of 4, #121-124   2.50 2.50
     Nos. 121-124 (4)   2.55 2.55

Souvenir Sheet
125 A27 300r multicolored   2.75 2.75

Stamps in No. 124a have margins continuing the background design of the sheet.

Butterflies
A28

12r, Catocala timur. 30r, Celerio chamyla apocyni. 70r, Colias sieversi. 150r, Papilio alexanor.
300r, Anthocharis tomyris.

1998, Apr. 3   Perf. 13x12½
126 A28 12r multicolored   .20 .20
127 A28 30r multicolored   .30 .30
128 A28 70r multicolored   .65 .65
129 A28 150r multicolored   1.40 1.40
a.   Sheet of 4, #126-129   2.50 2.50
     Nos. 126-129 (4)   2.55 2.55

Souvenir Sheet
130 A28 300r multicolored   2.75 2.75

Stamps of No. 129a have margins continuing the background design of the sheet.

Gems
A29

1998, Aug. 21   Litho.   Perf. 13x12¾
131 A29 1r Sapphire   .20 .20
132 A29 1r Ruby   .20 .20
133 A29 12r Lapis lazuli   .20 .20
134 A29 12r Tourmaline   .20 .20
135 A29 150r Spinel   1.40 1.40
136 A29 150r Amethyst   1.40 1.40
a.   Sheet of 6, #131-136, + 2 labels   3.75 3.75
     Nos. 131-136 (6)   3.60 3.60

Souvenir Sheet
137 A29 350r Agate   3.50 3.50

Bobojon Ghafurov,
Academician
(1908-98) — A30

1998, Aug. 21   Perf. 12¾x13
138 A30 12r blue & multi   .20 .20
139 A30 150r red & multi   1.25 1.25

Each printed in sheets of 10.

Aleksander Pushkin (1799-1837),
Russian Poet — A31

1999, June   Litho.   Perf. 13¼x13½
140 A31 100r Self-portrait drawing   .40 .40
141 A31 270r Painting by Kiprensky   1.10 1.10
a.   Pair, #140-141   1.50 1.50

"ILLEGAL" STAMPS
Tajikistan postal officials have declared as "illegal" the following items:
Sheets of nine stamps of various denominations depicting:
Elvis Presley, Barry White, Michael Douglas, Robert DeNiro, Grace Kelly, the television show "Ally McBeal," Harry Potter, Batman, Superman (two different sheets), Warner Brothers cartoon characters, U.S. Political Cartoons concerning the 2000 Presidential election, Mushrooms, Mushrooms in Art, Major League Baseball players, Sydney 2000 Olympic Games (two different sheets), Various golfers, U.S. Open Golf Championship, Golfer Eduardo Romero, Tiger Woods (two different sheets), Pope John Paul II, and Masonic emblems.
Sheet of 3 stamps of various denominations depicting Marilyn Monroe.

A32

A32a

A32b

1999, June 5   Litho.   Perf. 13½
142 A32 (40r) multi   .20 .20
143 A32a (100r) multi   .55 .55
144 A32b (270r) multi   1.40 1.40
     Nos. 142-144 (3)   2.15 2.15

Samanid
Dynasty — A33

1999, Aug.   Litho.   Perf. 12¾x13
145 A33 30r Lion figurine   .20 .20
146 A33 50r Round emblem   .35 .35
147 A33 100r Handled figurine   .70 .70
148 A33 270r Three figurines   1.90 1.90
     Nos. 145-148 (4)   3.15 3.15

Souvenir Sheet
149 A33 500r King   3.50 3.50
a.   Sheet, #149, 2 ea #145-148   10.00 10.00

Samanid Dynasty, 1100th
Anniv. — A34

Illustration reduced.
No. 150: a, 100r, King. b, 500r, Pres. Emomali Rakhmonov.

1999, Oct.   Litho.   Perf. 13½x13
150 A34 Sheet of 2, #a.-b.   4.00 4.00

Mushrooms
A35

Designs: Nos. 151, 153a, 100r, Pleurotus yngii. Nos. 152, 153b, 270r, Lepista nuda. 500r, Morchella steppicola.

1999, Nov. **Perf. 13¼x13**
151 A35 100r multi .35 .35
152 A35 270r multi 1.00 1.00
Miniature Sheet
153 A35 Sheet, 2 ea #153a-153b 2.75 2.75
Souvenir Sheet
154 A35 500r multi 1.90 1.90

Nos. 151-152 have white borders, while Nos. 153a-153b have borders which continue the sheet's central design.

Fish — A36

Designs: 40r, Ophiocephalus argus. 100r, Barbus brachycephalus. 230r, Schizopygopsis policzkai. 270r, Pseudoscaphihynchus dtschenkoi.
500r, Pseudoscaphihynchus kaufmanni.
Illustration reduced.

2000 **Litho.** **Perf. 13¼x13**
155-158 A36 Set of 4 1.75 1.75
158a Souvenir sheet, #155-158 1.75 1.75
Souvenir Sheet
159 A36 500r multi 1.40 1.40

UPU, 125th
Anniv. (in
1999) — A37

2000
160 A37 270r multi .75 .75

100 Dinars = 1 Somoni (2000)

Birds of
Prey
A38

Designs: 10d, Pandion haliaetus. 27d, Aquila chrysaetus, vert. 50d, Gyps himalayensis. 70d, Circaetus ferox, vert.
1s, Falco peregrinus, vert.

2001, Jan. 23 **Litho.** **Perf. 14**
161-164 A38 Set of 4 3.50 3.50
Souvenir Sheet
165 A38 1s multi 2.25 2.25
No. 165 contains one 42x56mm stamp. Dated 2000.

Chess — A39

Designs: 15d, Mikhail Botvinnik. 41d, Bobby Fischer.
No. 168: a, 10d, Wilhelm Steinitz. b, 25d, Chess board, five people. c, 50d, José Raul Capablanca. d, 70d, Emanuel Lasker. e, 90d, Chess board, four people. f, 1s, Alexander Alekhine.

2001, May 29 **Perf. 14¼x14**
166-167 A39 Set of 2 1.25 1.25
Souvenir Sheet
168 A39 Sheet of 6, #a-f 7.50 7.50

No. 26 Surcharged in Green, Red or
Black

a

b

c

2001, June 4 **Perf. 13½**
169 A6(a) (6d) multi (G) .25 .25
170 A6(b) (15d) multi (R) .55 .55
171 A6(c) (41d) multi (Bk) 1.50 1.50
Nos. 169-171 (3) 2.30 2.30

Souvenir Sheet

Satellite Communications — A40

2001, July 25 **Perf. 13¼x13**
172 A40 1.50s multi 2.75 2.75

Souvenir Sheets

Nurec Hydroelectric Station — A41

Pres. Emomali Rakhmonov — A42

Independence, 10th Anniv. — A43

No. 175: a, 41d, Map, flag and arms (29x29mm). b, 54d, Emblem (29x29mm). c, 95d, Ratification of constitution (49x29mm).

2001, Sept. 7 **Perf. 13¼x13¾**
173 A41 2.50s multi 1.90 1.90
Perf. 12¾x13¼
174 A42 3s multi 2.25 2.25
Perf. 14x13¾
175 A43 Sheet of 3, #a-c 1.40 1.40
Independence, 10th anniv.

___

Tajikistan postal officials have declared as "illegal" the following items:
Sheets of nine stamps of various denominations depicting Bruce Lee, Michael Jordan, Osama bin Laden, Captain America, Fantastic Four, Queen Mother's 100th Birthday, Formula 1 Racing, Motor Sports and the Netherlands Royal Wedding.
Sheets of six stamps of various denominations depicting Pope John Paul II and Motorcycle racers.
Sheet of three stamps of various denominations depicting Pope John Paul II.

___

Transportation — A44

Designs: 1s, Tu-154M Airplane.
No. 177: a, 41d, Vehicles on road. b, 90d, Locomotive.

2001, Dec. 12 Litho. Perf. 14x13¼
176 A44 1s multi .70 .70
Souvenir Sheet
177 A44 Sheet of 3, #176, 177a, 177b 1.75 1.75

Commonwealth of
Independent States,
10th Anniv. — A45

2001, Dec. 17 **Perf. 14¼x14**
178 A45 50d multi .35 .35

Souvenir Sheet

Regional Communications
Accord — A46

2001, Dec. 17
179 A46 1s multi + 2 labels .70 .70

Avesta, 2700th
Anniv. — A47

Zoroastrian: 2d, Goddess Anahita. 3d, Priest.
No. 182: a, 70d, Goddess Haoma. b, 90d, God Farroh. c, 1s, God Surush. d, 2s, Goddess Din.

2002, Jan. 1 **Litho.** **Perf. 10**
180-181 A47 Set of 2 .20 .20
Souvenir Sheet
182 A47 Sheet of 4, #a-d 3.50 3.50
No. 182 contains four 27x44mm stamps. Dated 2001.

Miniature Sheet

UN High Commissioner for Refugees,
50th Anniv. (in 2001) — A48

No. 183: a, Mothers holding children, refugees. b, Military helicopter, sun, refugees. c, Cloud, rainbow, moon, soldier, child.

2002, Jan. 1
183 A48 50d Sheet of 3, #a-c 1.10 1.10
Dated 2001.

Flora and Fauna of Central Asia — A49

No. 184: a, Bird facing right. b, Bird facing left. c, Mushrooms and snail. d, Rodent. e, Butterfly. f, Butterfly and tulip. g, Cat. h, Cat and tulip.

2002, Apr. 12 Litho. Perf. 13¾x13½
184		Miniature sheet of 8	4.75	4.75
a.	A49	6d multi	.20	.20
b.	A49	15d multi	.20	.20
c.	A49	41d multi	.30	.30
d.	A49	50d multi	.35	.35
e.	A49	95d multi	.65	.65
f.-h.	A49	1.50s any single	1.10	1.10

Worldwide Fund for Nature (WWF) — A50

Reed cats: a, 1s, Two cats. b, 1.50s, One cat walking. c, 2s, One cat resting. d, 2s, Three kittens.
Illustration reduced.

2002, Apr. 12 Perf. 14x14¼
185	A50	Block of 4, #a-d	4.75	4.75
e.		Sheet, 2 #185	9.50	9.50

Dushanbe Zoo, 40th Anniv. — A51

Designs: 2d, Pan troglodytes. 3d, Cervus nippon hortulorum. 10d, Panthera tigris altaice. 41d, Diceros bicornis michaeli. 50d, Giraffa camelopardis reticulata. 1s, Panthera leo.

2002, Aug. 29 Litho. Perf. 14¼x14
186-191	A51	Set of 6	1.40	1.40

Souvenir Sheet

Navruz — A52

No. 192: a, 1s, Wheat bundle. b, 50d, Dancers in red costumes. c, 1s, Dancer in purple costume.

2002, Aug. 29
192	A52	Sheet of 3, #a-c	1.75	1.75

A53   A54

Istravashan, 2500th Anniv.
A55   A56

2002, Sept. 6
193	A53	50d brown & multi	.35	.35
194	A54	50d green & multi	.35	.35
195	A55	50d brown & multi	.35	.35
196	A56	50d green & multi	.35	.35
		Nos. 193-196 (4)	1.40	1.40

No. 168 Overprinted "2002" on Stamps and With Text in Margin
Souvenir Sheet

Designs as before.

2002, Sept. 20 Litho. Perf. 14¼x14
197	A39	Sheet of 6, #a-f	2.40	2.40

No. 197 is overprinted in bottom sheet margin "Chess Super Championship / between teams of the World and Russia / 08-11.09.2002. Moscow" and in left sheet margin with similar text in Cyrillic characters.

Tajikistan postal officials have declared as "illegal" the following items.

Sheets of nine stamps of various denominations depicting: 20th Century Dreams (6 different sheets), Elephants and Rotary Intl. emblem, Owls, mushrooms and Rotary International emblem, Pandas, Chess, The Beatles, Locomotives, Princess Diana, the movie The Blair Witch Project, Defenders of Peace and Freedom, 2002 Brazilian World Cup Soccer Team, Harry Potter, Cartoon characters from South Park (Christmas), Warner Brothers Cartoon Characters (Christmas).

Sheets of six stamps of various denominations depicting Pokemon characters (eight sheets), Pope John Paul II, Dinosaurs.

Sheet of three stamps of various denominations depicting Elvis Presley.

Souvenir sheets of one stamp with 25.00 denomination depicting Harry Potter (2 different sheets), Penguins,

Souvenir sheet of one stamp with 20.00 denomination depicting Pope John Paul and New York fireman.

Oriental Bazaar — A58

No. 201: a, Man in donkey cart. b, Man on donkey. c, Melon vendor. d, Man cooking shashliks.

2002, Dec. 25 Litho. Perf. 14¼x14
201	A58	65d Block of 4, #a-d	1.75	1.75

Traditional Sports A59

Designs: 1d, Archery. 20d, Horse racing. 53d, Polo. 65d, Stone throwing. 1s, Buzkashi. 1.24s, Wrestling.

2002, Dec. 25 Perf. 14x14¼
202-207	A59	Set of 6	2.50	2.50

Lunar Calendar — A60

Designs: 53d, Sun and zodiac animals. 65d, Zodiac animals and ram. 1s, Ram in circle. 1.50s, Ram.

2003, Mar. 11 Perf. 14¼x14
208-210	A60	Set of 3	1.50	1.50

Souvenir Sheet
211	A60	1.50s multi + 2 labels	1.00	1.00

Monument to Ismail Somoni — A61

2003, Mar. 11 Perf. 13¼x14
212	A61	1d emerald	.20	.20
213	A61	2d red violet	.20	.20
214	A61	3d blue green	.20	.20
215	A61	4d purple	.20	.20
216	A61	12d brown	.20	.20
217	A61	20d blue	.20	.20
		Nos. 212-217 (6)	1.20	1.20

Souvenir Sheet
No. 158 Surcharged in Purple

No. 218: a, 8d on 40r, Ophiocephalus argus. b, 20d on 100r, Barbus brachycephalus. c, 53d on 230r, Schizopygopsis stoliczkai. d, 66d on 270r, Pseudoscaphihynchus fedtschenkoi.

2003, May 12 Litho. Perf. 13¼x13
218	A36	Sheet of 4, #a-d	.95	.95

2004 Summer Olympics, Athens and 2008 Summer Olympics, Beijing — A62

No. 219: a, 53d, Archery. b, 1s, Track and field. c, 1.23s, Soccer. d, 2s, Gymnastics.

2003, May 20 Perf. 14x13
219	A62	Sheet of 4, #a-d, + 2 labels	3.25	3.

Exists imperf. with additional designs margin.

Philatelic Exhibitions and Fauna — A63

No. 220: a, 8d, 16th Asian Intl. Stamp Exhibition, China. b, 20d, Panthera tigris. c, 53, Inachis io. d, 66d, Bangkok 2003 World Philatelic Exhibition. e, 1s, Rupicapra rupicapra. 1.50s, Ailuropoda melanoleuca. g, 1.50 Leontopithecus rosalia. h, 2s, Eleph. maximus.

2003, May 20
220	A63	Sheet of 8, #a-h	5.00	5.

Exists imperf.

Intl. Forum on Fresh Water — A64

Designs: No. 221, 1.50s, Peak of Moskv No. 222, 1.50s, Iskanderkul.

2003, June 7 Perf. 13
221-222	A64	Set of 2	2.00	2.

Famous Men — A65

Designs: No. 223, 1.23s, Nosir Khusr (1004-88), poet. No. 224, 1.23s, Sadridin A (1878-1954), writer.

2003, Sept. 1
223-224	A65	Set of 2	1.90	1.

Intl. Association of Academies of Science, 10th Anniv. — A66

No. 225: a, Head, satellite dish, airplane, chemicals. b, Association emblem, cosmonaut, robotic hand, computer.
Illustration reduced.

2003, Sept. 1
225 A66 1.23s Horiz. pair, #a-b 1.90 1.90

Intl. Year of Fresh Water — A67

Children's art: a, Fish above lake. b, Sun, river, tree and hills. c, River, hills and trees. d, Waterfalls.
Illustration reduced.

2003, Oct. 20   **Perf. 14x14¼**
226 A67 66d Block of 4, #a-d 1.75 1.75

Racing Airplanes — A68

No. 227: a, Aero L-29A Delfin Akrobat. b, Yak-55. c, Cessna 172. d, SIAI-Marchetti SF-260. e, Europa XS. f, MBB BO 209 Monsun. g, Mudry Cap 10. h, Soko 2.

2003, Oct. 28   **Perf. 14x13½**
227 A68 1s Sheet of 8, #a-h 5.25 5.25
Exists imperf.

Fauna of Central Asia — A69

No. 228: a, 8d, Mimas tiliae. 20d, Mustela erminea. 53d, Testudo horsfieldii. 64d, Mantis religiosa. 1.23s, Lanius collurio. 1.27s, Canis aureus. 1.76s, Capra falconeri. 2.29s, Alcedo atthis.

2003, Oct. 28
228 A69 Sheet of 8, #a-h 5.25 5.25

TANGANYIKA

ˌtan-gə-ˈnyē-kə

LOCATION — Southeastern Africa bordering on the Indian Ocean
GOVT. — Republic within British Commonwealth
AREA — 362,688 sq. mi.

POP. — 9,404,000 (est. 1961)
CAPITAL — Dar es Salaam

Before World War I, this area formed part of German East Africa. It was mandated to Britain after World War I and (in 1946) became a trust territory under the United Nations. In 1935, stamps of the mandate were replaced by those used jointly by Kenya, Uganda and Tanganyika (see Kenya, Uganda and Tanzania). On Dec. 9, 1961, Tanganyika became independent. On Dec. 9, 1962, it became a republic. April 26, 1964, it joined Zanzibar to form the United Republic of Tanganyika and Zanzibar (later renamed Tanzania). See Tanzania.

100 Cents = 1 Rupee
100 Cents = 1 Shilling (1922)
20 Shillings = 1 Pound

Catalogue values for unused stamps in this country are for Never Hinged items, beginning with Scott 45 in the regular postage section and Scott O1 in the officials section.

Stamps of Kenya, Uganda & Tanganyika Overprinted

1921   **Wmk. 4**   **Perf. 14**
1 A1 12c gray 7.50 110.00
2 A1 15c ultra 2.25 4.50
3 A1 50c dull violet & blk 10.50 97.50

Overprinted

4 A2 2r black & red, blue 37.50 140.00
5 A2 3r gray green & violet 62.50 190.00
7 A2 5r dull violet & ultra 92.50 225.00
Nos. 1-7 (6) 212.75 767.00

Overprinted in Red or Black

1922
8 A1 1c black (R) .80 19.00
9 A1 10c orange (Bk) .80 16.00

Giraffe
A3   A4

Perf. 14½x14
1922-25   **Engr.**   **Wmk. 4**
10 A3 5c dk violet & blk 2.75 .20
11 A3 5c grn & blk ('25) 2.25 1.75
12 A3 10c green & blk 2.75 .95
13 A3 10c yel & blk ('25) 4.25 1.75
14 A3 15c carmine & blk 2.25 .20
15 A3 20c orange & blk 2.00 .20
16 A3 25c black 6.25 7.50
17 A3 25c blue & blk ('25) 4.50 20.00
18 A3 30c blue & blk 5.75 5.75
19 A3 30c dull vio & blk ('25) 4.50 14.00
20 A3 40c brown & black 3.25 5.25
21 A3 50c gray black 2.25 1.75
22 A3 75c bister & black 3.75 21.00

Perf. 14
23 A4 1sh green & black 3.00 12.50
   a. Wmk. sideways 3.75 16.00
24 A4 2sh brn vio & blk 5.25 25.00
   a. Wmk. sideways 6.25 17.50
25 A4 3sh blk, wmk. sideways 15.00 32.50
26 A4 5sh red & black 15.00 85.00
   a. Wmk. sideways 29.00 97.50
27 A4 10sh dp blue & blk 57.50 110.00
   a. Wmk. sideways 110.00 225.00
28 A4 £1 orange & black 175.00 350.00
   a. Wmk. sideways 190.00 375.00
Nos. 10-28 (19) 317.25 695.30

On No. 28 the words of value are in a curve between the circle and "POSTAGE & REVENUE."

King George V
A5   A6

1927-31   **Typo.**
29 A5 5c green & black 1.75 .20
30 A5 10c yellow & black 2.25 .20
31 A5 15c red & black 1.75 .20
32 A5 20c orange & black 3.00 .20
33 A5 25c ultra & black 4.00 2.25
34 A5 30c dull violet & blk 3.25 3.00
35 A5 30c ultra & blk ('31) 27.50 .35
36 A5 40c brown & black 2.25 5.25
37 A5 50c gray & black 2.50 1.10
38 A5 75c olive grn & blk 2.25 14.00
39 A6 1sh green & black 4.50 3.25
40 A6 2sh violet brn & blk 19.00 5.25
41 A6 3sh black 19.00 55.00
43 A6 5sh scarlet & blk 19.00 19.00
43 A6 10sh ultra & black 62.50 110.00
44 A6 £1 brown org & blk 160.00 300.00
Nos. 29-44 (16) 334.50 519.25

Catalogue values for unused stamps in this section, from this point to the end of the section, are for Never Hinged items.

Independent State

Nurse and Infant — A7   Torch above Mt. Kilimanjaro — A8

5c, Teacher instructing villagers, horiz. 15c, Coffee picker. 20c, Harvesting corn. 30c, Flag, horiz. 50c, Serengeti lions. 1sh, Nurse showing infant to mother & hospital. 2sh, Dar es Salaam harbor. 5sh, Tractor & field workers. 10sh, Diamond mine & rose diamond. 1sh, 2sh, 5sh, 10sh, horiz.

Perf. 14x14½, 14½x14
1961, Dec. 9   **Photo.**   **Unwmk.**
45 A7 5c sepia & yel grn .20 .20
46 A7 10c Prussian green .20 .20
47 A7 15c sepia & blue .20 .20
   b. Blue omitted 400.00
48 A7 20c orange brown .20 .20
49 A7 30c dp green, blk & yel .20 .20
50 A7 50c sepia & yellow .20 .20
Perf. 14½
51 A8 1sh cit brn & gray bl .20 .20
52 A8 1sh30c multicolored 1.00 .20
53 A8 2sh multicolored .25 .20
54 A8 5sh Prus grn & dp org .35 .20
55 A8 10sh blk, bl & rose 8.00 2.50
   a. Rose (diamond) omitted 125.00
56 A8 20sh multicolored 2.00 4.00
Nos. 45-56 (12) 13.00 8.50

Tanganyika's independence, Dec. 9, 1961.
For overprints see Nos. O21-O28.

Pres. Julius Nyerere with Pickax — A9

Designs: 50c, Flag hoisting on Mt. Kilimanjaro. 1sh30c, Presidential emblem. 2sh50c, Independence monument, Mnazi Moja.

1962, Dec. 9   **Perf. 14½x14**
57 A9 30c bright green .20 .20
58 A9 50c multicolored .20 .20
59 A9 1sh30c multicolored .20 .20
60 A9 2sh50c dk blue, blk & red .35 .40
Nos. 57-60 (4) .95 1.00

Issued to commemorate the establishment of the Republic of Tanganyika, Dec. 9, 1962.

OFFICIAL STAMPS

Catalogue values for unused stamps in this section are for Never Hinged items.

Issued for use by the Tanganyika Government
Stamps of Kenya, Uganda & Tanganyika, 1954-59, Overprinted

Perf. 12½x13, 13x12½
1959   **Engr.**   **Wmk. 4**
O1 A18 5c choc & blk .20 .20
O2 A19 10c carmine .20 .20
O3 A20 15c lt bl & blk (on #106) .20 .20
O4 A19 20c org & blk .20 .20
   a. Double overprint 700.00
O5 A18 30c ultra & black .20 .20
O6 A19 50c dp red lilac .25 .20
O7 A19 1sh dp mag & blk .25 .25
O8 A20 1sh30c pur & red org 1.00 .75
O9 A20 2sh dp grn & gray .50 .50
O10 A20 5sh black & org 1.25 1.25
O11 A20 10sh ultra & blk 3.00 3.00
O12 A21 £1 black & ver 5.75 10.00
Nos. O1-O12 (12) 13.00 16.95

Stamps of Kenya, Uganda & Tanganyika, 1960, Overprinted

Perf. 14½x14
1960, Oct. 1   **Photo.**   **Wmk. 314**
O13 A23 5c dull blue .20 .20
O14 A23 10c lt olive green .20 .20
O15 A23 15c dull purple .20 .20
O16 A23 20c brt lilac rose .20 .20
O17 A23 30c brt vermilion .20 .20
O18 A23 50c dull violet .30 .20

Overprinted

Engr.   **Perf. 14**

O19	A24	1sh violet & lilac red	.45	.30
O20	A24	5sh rose red & lilac	6.25	1.50
		Nos. O13-O20 (8)	8.00	3.00

Nos. 45-51 and 54 Overprinted
"OFFICIAL" in Sans-serif Type of
Various Sizes

Perf. 14x14½, 14½x14

1961, Dec. 9   **Unwmk.**

O21	A7	5c sepia & yellow grn	.20	.20
O22	A7	10c Prussian green	.20	.20
O23	A7	15c sepia & blue	.20	.20
O24	A7	20c orange brown	.20	.20
O25	A7	30c dp grn blk & yel	.20	.20
O26	A7	50c sepia & yellow	.20	.20
O27	A8	1sh citron brn & gray bl	.20	.20
O28	A8	5sh Prus grn & dp org	1.00	1.00
		Nos. O21-O28 (8)	2.40	2.40

TANNU TUVA

'tä-nə 'tü-və

(Tuva People's Republic)

LOCATION — Between Siberia and northwestern Mongolia at the sources of the Yenisei, in the basin formed by the Tannu-Ola and Sayan Mountains.

GOVT. — A former republic closely identified with Soviet Russia in Asia

AREA — 64,000 sq. mi. (approx.)

POP. — 95,000 (1941 est.)

CAPITAL — Kyzyl

This region, traditionally called Uriankhai, was ruled by the Mongols until the mid-18th century, when it became part of the Chinese Empire. Russia and China struggled for control of the country 1914-21, until it became independent as the Tannu Tuva People's Republic in 1921. In 1944 it was incorporated into the U.S.S.R. as an autonomous region of the Russian Soviet Federated Socialist Republic.

Russian, later Soviet, stamps were used in Tuva prior to 1926 and after 1944.

100 Mongo=1 Tugrik

100 Kopecks = 1 Ruble

100 Kopecks = 1 Tugrik (1934)

100 Kopecks = 1 Aksha (1936)

Watermark

Wmk. 204 —
Stars and
Diamonds

Wmk. 170 — Greek Border and
Rosettes

Most used examples of Nos. 1-38, 45-52a, 54-92 and C1-C18 on the market are cancelled to order, and the used values below are for such stamps.

Tuvan stamps, except for Nos. 117-123 and most of the overprints, were

---

printed by the State Security Printers in Moscow.

Wheel of Truth — A1

1926 Litho. Wmk. 204 Perf. 13½

Size: 20x26mm

1	A1	1k red	1.25	1.00
2	A1	2k light blue	1.50	1.00
3	A1	5k orange	1.50	1.00
4	A1	8k yel green	1.75	1.00
5	A1	10k violet	2.00	1.00
6	A1	30k dark brown	1.75	1.00
7	A1	50k gray black	2.00	1.25

Size: 22½x30mm

Perf. 10½

8	A1	1r blue green	5.50	2.50
9	A1	3r red brown	8.00	4.00
10	A1	5r dark ultra	13.50	6.00
		Nos. 1-10 (10)	38.75	19.75

Nos. 1-10 have crackled white gum. Reprints can be distinguished by their smooth gum.

Nos. 1-10 in different colors are proofs.

Nos. 7-10
Surcharged in Red
or Black

1927   **Perf. 13½**

11	A1	8k on 50k	20.00	12.50

Perf. 10½

12	A1	14k on 1r	20.00	12.50
13	A1	18k on 3r (Bk)	20.00	12.50
14	A1	28k on 5r (Bk)	20.00	12.50
		Nos. 11-14 (4)	80.00	50.00

Nos. 11-14 were surcharged with a shiny ink. Reprints are overprinted with a dull ink and are often smudged.

Nos. 11-14 exist with surcharge inverted and No. 14 with surcharge double. Value $35.00 each.

Reprints exist of Nos. 1-14.

Tuvan Woman — A3

Map of
Tannu
Tuva
A8

Sheep Herding — A11

Fording a
Stream — A13

Tuvans Riding Reindeer — A16

Designs: 2k, Stag. 3k, Mountain goat. 4k, Tuvan and tent. 5k, Tuvan man. 10k, Archery competition. 14k, Camel caravan. 28k, Landscape. 50k, Weaving. 70k, Tuvan on horseback.

1927   **Typo.**   **Perf. 12½**

15	A3	1k blk, lt brn & red	1.00	.60
16	A3	2k pur, dp brn & grn	1.20	.55
17	A3	3k blk, bl grn & yel	2.00	.60
18	A3	4k vio bl & choc	.90	.60
19	A3	5k org, blk & dk bl	.90	.65

Perf. , 12½x12

20	A8	8k ol brn, pale bl & red brn	1.00	.65
21	A8	10k blk, grn & brn red	5.50	1.00
22	A8	14k vio bl & red org	10.00	3.50

Perf. 10, 10½

23	A11	18k dk bl & red brn	10.00	5.00
24	A11	28k emer & blk brn	7.25	2.75
25	A13	40k rose & bl grn	5.00	2.50
26	A13	50k blk, grn & red brn	3.50	2.00
27	A13	70k dl red & bis	7.00	4.00
28	A16	1r yel brn & vio	16.00	6.75
		Nos. 15-28 (14)	71.25	31.15

Nos. 15-28 were issued with a crackled white gum. Reprints of the 1k-5k values exist and can be distinguished by their smooth gum.

Nos. 15-28 in different colors are proofs.

Nos. 25-27, 20-22 Surcharged "Tuva",
"Posta" and New Values in Various
Colors

1932

29	A13	1k on 40k (Bk)	9.00	10.00
30	A13	2k on 50k (Br)	10.00	10.00
31	A13	3k on 70k (Bl)	10.00	10.00
a.		Inverted surcharge	300.00	
32	A8	5k on 8k (Bk)	10.00	10.00
33	A8	10k (Bk)	10.00	10.00
34	A8	15k on 14k (Bk)	15.00	15.00
		Nos. 29-34 (6)	64.00	65.00

Issued in connection with the Romanization of the alphabet.

#23-24 Surcharged in Black

No. 37

No. 38

1933   **Wmk. 204**

35	A8	10k on 8k	180.00	100.00
36	A8	15k on 14k	300.00	200.00
37	A11	35k on 18k	140.00	100.00
38	A11	35k on 28k	140.00	100.00
		Nos. 35-38 (4)	760.00	500.00

— A19

Revenue Stamps Surcharged "Posta"
and New Values

Three types: type 1, figures of value 6.7mm high; type 2, figures of value 6.7mm high, letter "p" lengthened at bottom; type 3, figures of value 5.1mm high.

1933   **Perf. 12x12½**

39	A19	15k on 6k org yel, type 1	300.00	150.00
40	A19	15k on 6k org yel, type 2	300.00	150.00
41	A19	15k on 6k org yel, type 3	500.00	300.00
42	A19	35k on 15k red brn, type 1	—	4,000.
42	A19	35k on 15k red brn, type 2	—	4,000.
44	A19	35k on 15k red brn, type 3	1,500.	800.00

Mounted
Hunter — A20

Tuvan Inside of Yurt — A21

Tuvan Milking Yak — A22

Designs: 2k, Hunter stalking game. 4k, Tractor. 10k, Camel caravan. 15k, Herdsman lassoing reindeer. 20k, Hunter shooting fox with arrow.

Two dies on 10k: Die I, Crown at center top is light and matches the shade of the sky below; Die II, Crown at center top is bold, consistent with rest of design and darker than the sky.

Printed by State Security Printers, Moscow.

Wmk. 170

1934, Apr.   **Photo.**   **Perf. 12**

45	A20	1k red orange	1.25	1.00
46	A20	2k olive green	1.25	1.00
47	A21	3k rose red	1.25	1.00
48	A21	4k slate purple	3.00	1.75
49	A22	5k ultramarine	3.00	1.75
50	A22	10k brown, die II	3.00	1.75
c.		10k brown, die I	8.00	2.00
51	A22	15k dark lilac	3.00	1.75
52	A22	20k gray black	4.00	2.75
		Nos. 45-52 (8)	19.75	12.75
		Set, never hinged	50.00	
		Set, Imperf	50.00	
		Set, imperf, never hinged	100.00	

Nos. 45-52 are inscribed "REGISTERED," but were used as regular postage stamps.

#51 Surcharged in Black
Surcharged by numbering machine in Kyzyl.

1935

53	A22	20k on 15k	175.00	325.00
a.		Inverted surcharge		400.00

Map of Tuva — A23

Rocky Outcropping — A24

Designs: 3k, 5k, 10k, Different scenes of Yenisei River. 25k, Bei-kem rapids. 50k, Mounted hunters.
Printed by State Security Printers, Moscow.

Wmk. 170

		1935, Mar.	**Photo.**	**Perf. 14**
54	A23	1k yellow orange	1.20	.90
55	A23	3k deep green	1.20	.90
56	A23	5k carmine red	1.50	1.00
57	A23	10k violet	1.60	1.00
b.		Pair, imperf between		
58	A24	15k olive green	1.75	1.25
59	A24	25k violet blue	2.00	1.25
60	A24	50k dark brown	3.00	1.50
		Nos. 54-60 (7)	12.25	7.80
		Set, never hinged	25.00	

Nos. 54-60 in different colors, perf and imperf, are proofs.

Badger
A25

Squirrel — A26

Fox — A27

Elk — A28

Yak — A29

Designs: 5k, Ermine. 25k, Otter. 50k, Lynx. 3t, Bactrian camels. 5t, Bear.
Printed by State Security Printers, Moscow.

1935, Mar.

61	A25	1k orange	1.60	1.00
62	A26	3k emerald green	1.60	1.00
a.		Imperf., pair	300.00	
63	A25	5k rose red	1.60	1.10
64	A27	10k crimson red	1.60	1.10
65	A27	25k orange red	2.50	1.20
66	A27	50k deep blue	2.50	1.20
67	A28	1t violet	2.50	1.20
a.		Pair, imperf between	—	
68	A29	2t royal blue	3.50	1.20
69	A29	3t red brown	4.00	1.35
70	A28	5t indigo	5.00	1.75
a.		Imperf., pair	300.00	
b.		Pair, imperf between	—	
		Nos. 61-70 (10)	26.40	12.10
		Set, never hinged	50.00	

Nos. 61-70 in different colors are proofs.

Tuvan Arms — A30

Wrestlers — A31

Herdsman on Bull — A32

Athletic Competitions — A33

Soldiers
A34

Designs: 2k, Pres. Ch(aumlaut char='u')rmit-Dazhy. 3k, Tuvan with Bactrian camel. 5k, Archer. 10k, 15k, Spearfishing. 12k, 20k, Bear-hunting. 30k, Camel and train. 40k, 50k, Horse race. 80k, Partisans. 3t, Partisans confiscating cattle. 5t, 1921 battle scene.
Printed by State Security Printers, Moscow.

1936, July			**Perf. 11, 14**	
71	A30	1k bronze green	1.50	.70
72	A30	2k dark brown	2.00	1.50
73	A30	3k indigo blue	2.00	.75
74a	A31	4k orange red	2.50	.75
75	A31	5k brown purple	4.00	.70
76	A31	6k myrtle green	3.75	.70
77	A31	8k plum	3.75	.70
78	A31	10k rose red	4.25	1.00
79	A31	12k black brown	5.00	1.25
80a	A31	15k bronze green	6.00	1.25
81	A31	20k deep blue	6.00	1.20
82a	A32	25k orange red	6.00	.90
83	A32	30k plum	18.00	1.25
84a	A32	35k rose red	6.00	1.25
85	A32	40k deep brown	6.00	1.50
86a	A32	50k indigo blue	6.00	1.50
87	A33	70k plum	7.25	2.00
88	A33	80k green	7.00	2.00
89	A34	1a orange red	7.00	2.00
a.		1a rose red (error)	—	—
90	A34	2a rose red	7.00	3.00
91	A33	3a indigo blue	15.00	2.00
92	A33	5a black brown	7.25	2.50
		Nos. 71-92 (22)	133.25	30.40
		Set, never hinged	260.00	

15th anniversary of independence.
Values for Nos. 71-92 are for the most common varieties. For detailed listings, see the *Scott Classic Specialized Catalogue*.
Imperfs are remainders, later sold by the Soviet Postal Museum.

Issues of 1934-36 Handstamped with Large Numerals and Old Values Obliterated with Bars or Blocks

1938, Aug.

93	A34	5k on 2a (#90a)	300.00
94	AP5	5k on 2a (#C17)	225.00
95	AP1	10k on 1t (#C8)	200.00
96	A24	20k on 50k (#60)	200.00
		On cover	—
97	AP5	30k on 2a (#C17)	200.00
98	AP5	30k on 3a (#C18)	175.00

Types of 1935-36 with Modified Designs and New Colors

1938, Dec.			**Unwmk.**
99	A25	5k deep green	100.00
100	A31	10k indigo (dates removed)	100.00
101	AP3	15k red brown ("AIR MAIL," dates removed)	100.00
102	A31	20k orange red (dates removed)	150.00
103	A33	30k maroon (dates removed)	100.00
		Nos. 99-103 (5)	550.00
		Set, never hinged	800.00

Some experts believe that these stamps were issued in March 1941.

Stamps of 1934-35 Handstamp Surcharged with New Values in Black or Violet at Kyzyl

1939

104	AP1	10k on 1t (#C8)	225.00
105	AP1	10k on 1t (#C8) (V)	225.00
106	A24	20k on 50k (#60) (V)	200.00

Old values obliterated on Nos. 104-106.

Stamps of 1934-36 Handstamp Surcharged with New Values at Kyzyl

1940, Oct.-1941

107	AP1	10k on 1t (#C8)	—	90.00
a.		Double surcharge	—	
108	A24	20k on 50k (#60)	—	100.00
109	A27	20k on 50k (#66)	—	300.00
110	A32	20k on 50k (#86a)	—	300.00
111	AP4	20k on 50k (#C14)	—	65.00
112	A33	20k on 70k (#87a)	—	
113	AP4	20k on 75k (#C15)	—	75.00
114	A33	20k on 80k (#88)	—	500.00

The old values are not obliterated on Nos. 107 or 108.

Nos. 91, 92 Handstamp Surcharged with New Values at Kyzyl

1942

115	A33	25k on 3a (#91)	1,200.	—
116	A33	25k on 5a (#92)	—	—

Government House — A35

Exhibition Hall — A36

Tuvan Woman — A37

1942	**Typo.**	**Unwmk.**	**Imperf.**	
117	A35	25k steel blue	750.00	100.00
118	A36	25k steel blue	750.00	100.00
119	A37	25k steel blue	750.00	150.00
		Nos. 117-119 (3)	2,250.	350.00

21st anniversary of independence.
Nos. 117-119 were hand-printed together in small sheetlets of five (117+119+ 118+117+119), so various se-tenant combinations are possible. Value, pane $2,000.
Two additional values, a 25k depicting a Tuvan man and a 50k depicting a soldier on a horse, were prepared, but not issued. A collective proof sheetlet of five, containing Nos. 117-119 and these two values, in the same color as the issued stamps, is also known.

Coat of Arms — A38

Government Building — A39

1943		**Perf. 11 (1 or 2 Sides)**	
		Buff Paper	
120	A38	25k slate blue	—	—
121	A38	25k black	100.00	—
122	A38	25k blue green	90.00	—
123	A39	50k blue green	90.00	—
		Nos. 120-123 (3)	280.00	
		White Paper	
120a	A38	25k slate blue	90.00	—
b.		Strip of 3, imperf between	250.00	
121a	A38	25k black	125.00	—
122a	A38	25k blue green	95.00	—
123a	A39	50k blue green	95.00	—
		With gum	175.00	
		Nos. 120a-123a (4)	405.00	

22nd anniversary of independence.
Nos. 120 and 121 were each printed in vertical strips of five, perforated 11 between stamps and imperf on outside edges, so that

these stamps may be perforated on top edge only, bottom edge only, or on both top and bottom edges. To make maximum use of limited wartime paper supplies, they were sometimes printed in strips of four. These smaller strips are rare.

Nos. 122 and 123 were printed together in blocks of four, containing a vertical pair of the 25k and a vertical pair of the 50k, perforated internally both vertically and horizontally and imperf on the outer edges. Setenant pairs, Value $225 (#122+123), $275 (#122a+123a).

Nos. 121 and 123a were issued with gum, No. 123a both with and without gum, and the balance of the set without gum.

Used examples and covers exist but are extremely rare.

AIRMAIL

Airplane and Yaks — AP1

Airplane and Capercaillie — AP2

Designs: airplane over: 5k, 15k, Camels. 25k, Argali (wild sheep). 75k, Ox and cart. 2t, Roe deer.
Printed by State Security Printers, Moscow.

Wmk. 170

1934, Apr. 4		**Photo.**		**Perf. 14**	
C1	AP1	1k orange red		1.40	1.00
C2	AP1	5k emer green		1.40	1.00
C3	AP2	10k purple brown		4.50	3.00
C4	AP2	15k rose red		2.75	1.00
C5	AP2	25k slate purple		2.75	1.00
C6	AP1	50k dp bl green		2.75	1.00
C7	AP2	75k lake		2.75	1.75
C8	AP1	1t royal blue		3.50	2.00
C9	AP2	2t ultra,			
		61x31mm		20.00	25.00
a.		54.5x29mm		40.00	
		Nos. C1-C9 (9)		41.80	36.75
		Set, never hinged		55.00	

Nos. C1-C9 imperf or perf 11½ and stamps printed in different colors are proofs.

Tuvan Leading Laden Yak — AP3

Horseman and Zeppelin
AP4

Seaplane Above Dragon — AP5

Designs: 10k, Tuvan plowing. 50k, Villagers with biplane overhead.
Printed by State Security Printers, Moscow.

1936			**Unwmk.**	
C10	AP3	5k indigo & beige	2.00	1.50
C11	AP3	10k purple & cinnamon	3.00	1.50
C12	AP3	15k black brown & pale gray	3.00	1.50
C13	AP4	25k plum & cream	5.00	2.00
c.		Horiz. pair, perf 11, imperf between	—	—
C14	AP4	50k rose red & cream	5.00	2.00
C15	AP4	75k emer grn & pale yellow	5.00	2.00
C16	AP5	1a blue green & pale bl grn	8.00	4.00
C17	AP5	2a rose red & cream	7.50	3.00
C18	AP5	3a dark brown & beige	8.00	3.00
		Nos. C10-C18 (9)	46.50	20.50
		Set, never hinged	93.00	

15th anniversary of independence.

Nos. C10-C18 exist imperf.

TANZANIA

ˌtan-zə-ˈnē-ə

(Tanganyika and Zanzibar)

LOCATION — Southeastern Africa bordering on the Indian Ocean, and a group of islands about 20 miles off the coast
GOVT. — United republic in British Commonwealth
AREA — 364,886 sq. mi.
POP. — 31,270,820 (1999 est.)
CAPITAL — Dodoma

Tanganyika joined Zanzibar on April 26, 1964, to form the United Republic of Tanganyika and Zanzibar. In October 1965 the name was changed to United Republic of Tanzania.

Zanzibar stamps include two (Nos. 331, 334) inscribed "Tanzania."

100 Cents = 1 Shilling

> **Catalogue values for all unused stamps in this country are for Never Hinged items.**

Watermark

Wmk. 387 — Squares and Rectangles

Map — A1

Design: 30c, 1sh30c, Emblem (hands holding torch and spear).

1964, July 7		**Photo.**	**Unwmk.**	
1	A1	20c blue & emerald	.20	.20
2	A1	30c brn, dk & lt bl	.20	.20
3	A1	1.30sh ultra, blk & org	.30	.30
4	A1	2.50sh ultra & purple	.60	.60
		Nos. 1-4 (4)	1.30	1.30

Union of Tanganyika and Zanzibar. Not sold in Zanzibar, nor valid there.

Flag
A2

Native
Handicraft
A3

Designs: 5c, Hale hydroelectric plant. 15c, Army squad. 20c, Road building. 40c, Giraffes. 50c, Zebras. 65c, Mt. Kilimanjaro. 1sh, Dar es Salaam harbor. 1.30sh, Zinjanthropus skull and Olduvai Gorge excavation. 2.50sh, Sailfish, dhow and map of Mafia Island. 5sh, Sisal industry. 10sh, State House, Dar es Salaam. 20sh, Tanzania coat of arms.

		Perf. 14x14½, 14½x14		
1965, Dec. 9		**Photo.**	**Unwmk.**	
		Size: 21x17½mm, 17½x21mm		
5	A2	5c orange & ultra	.20	.20
6	A2	10c ultra, grn, yel & blk	.20	.20
7	A3	15c grn, bl, brn & buff	.20	.20
8	A2	20c blue & brown	.20	.20
9	A3	30c black & red brn	.20	.20
10	A3	40c blue, yel grn & brn	.20	.20
11	A2	50c yellow grn & blue	.20	.20
12	A2	65c ultra, grn & red brn	.25	.25
		Perf. 14½		
		Size: 41½x25, 25x41½mm		
13	A2	1sh bl, grn, yel & brn	.30	.20
14	A2	1.30sh multicolored	.45	.20
15	A2	2.50sh blue & red brn	.65	.30
16	A2	5sh bl, brt grn & red brn	1.40	.45
17	A2	10sh blue & yellow	2.75	1.25
18	A3	20sh gray & multi	5.50	2.75
		Nos. 5-18 (14)	12.70	6.80

For overprints see Nos. O1-O8.

Turkeyfish — A4

Fish: 5c, Cardinalfish. 10c, Mudskipper. 15c, Toby puffer. 20c, Two sea horses. 30c, Batfish. 40c, Sweetlips. 50c, Birdfish. 65c, Butterflyfish. 70c, Grouper. 1.30sh, Surgeonfish. 1.50sh, Caesio xanthonotus. 2.50sh, Emperor snapper. 5sh, Moorish idol. 10sh, Striped triggerfish. 20sh, Squirrelfish.

1967-71		**Photo.**	**Perf. 14x14½**	
		Size: 21x17½mm		
		Fish in Natural Colors		
19	A4	5c black & citron	.20	.20
20	A4	10c brown & olive	.20	.20
21	A4	15c brown & blue	.20	.20
22	A4	20c brn & dk bl grn	.20	.20
23	A4	30c black & yel grn	.20	.20
24	A4	40c brown & emerald	.20	.20
25	A4	50c blk & dull bl grn	.20	.20
26	A4	65c blk & gray grn	.60	.60
27	A4	70c blk & olive ('69)	.50	.50
		Perf. 14½		
		Size: 41x25mm		
28	A4	1sh brown & multi	.40	.20
29	A4	1.30sh black & olive	.60	.20
30	A4	1.50sh black & ol ('69)	.70	.20
31	A4	2.50sh brn yel & grn	1.25	.20

32	A4	5sh black & bl grn	2.00	.20
33	A4	10sh brn & gray grn	4.50	.60
34	A4	20sh blk & gray olive	10.00	1.40
		Nos. 19-34 (16)	21.95	5.50

Issued: #27, 30, 9/15/69; others, 12/9/67.
Values of Nos. 28-34 are for canceled-to-order stamps with printed cancellations. Postally used copies sell for higher prices.
For overprints see Nos. O9-O16.

Papilio
Hornimani
A5

Euphaedra
Neophron
A6

Butterflies: 10c, Coiotis ione. 15c, Amauris makuyuensis. 20c, Libythea laius. 30c, Danaus chrysippus. 40c, Sallya rosa. 50c, Axiocerses styx. 60c, Eurema hecabe. 70c, Acraea insignis. 1.50sh, Precis octavia. 2.50sh, Charaxes eupale. 5sh, Charaxes pollux. 10sh, Salamis parhassus. 20sh, Papilio ophidicephalus.

1973, Dec. 3		**Photo.**	**Perf. 14½x14**	
35	A5	5c yellow grn & multi	.20	.20
36	A5	10c lt brown & multi	.20	.20
a.		Booklet pane of 4	.20	
37	A5	15c ultra & multi	.20	.20
38	A5	20c fawn & multi	.20	.20
a.		Booklet pane of 4	.20	
39	A5	30c yellow & multi	.20	.20
a.		Booklet pane of 4	.30	
40	A5	40c multicolored	.40	
a.		Booklet pane of 4	.40	
41	A5	50c citron & multi	.20	.20
a.		Booklet pane of 4	.52	
42	A5	60c multicolored	.20	.20
43	A5	70c brt green & multi	.20	.20
a.		Booklet pane of 4	.70	
		Perf. 14½		
44	A6	1sh green & multi	.30	.25
45	A6	1.50sh orange & multi	.45	.35
46	A6	2.50sh multicolored	.75	.60
47	A6	5sh multicolored	1.50	1.25
48	A6	10sh lt green & multi	3.00	2.40
49	A6	20sh blue & multi	6.00	4.75
		Nos. 35-49 (15)	13.80	11.40

For surcharges and overprints see Nos. 50-53, 135-136, O17-O26.

Nos. 42, 45-46, 49 Surcharged with New Value and 2 Bars

		Perf. 14½x14, 14½		
1975, Nov. 17			**Photo.**	
50	A5	80c on 60c multi	2.00	1.50
51	A6	2sh on 1.50sh multi	3.75	4.00
52	A6	3sh on 2.50sh multi	14.00	18.00
53	A6	40sh on 20sh multi	6.50	8.00
		Nos. 50-53 (4)	26.25	31.50

A6a

Designs: 50c, Microwave tower. 1sh, Cordless switchboard and operators, horiz. 2sh, Telephones of 1880, 1930 and 1976. 3sh, Message switching center, horiz.

1976, Apr. 15		**Litho.**	**Perf. 14½**	
54	A6a	50c blue & multi	.20	.20
55	A6a	1sh red & multi	.20	.20
56	A6a	2sh yellow & multi	.30	.25
57	A6a	3sh multicolored	.45	.35
a.		Souvenir sheet of 4	1.75	1.75
		Nos. 54-57 (4)	1.15	1.00

Telecommunications development in East Africa. No. 57a contains 4 stamps similar to Nos. 54-57 with simulated perforations.
Exist imperf. from Format International liquidation stock.

A6b

Designs: 50c, Akii Bua, Ugandan hurdler.
1sh, Filbert Bayi, Tanzanian runner. 2sh,
Steve Muchoki, Kenyan boxer. 3sh, Olympic
torch, flags of Kenya, Tanzania and Uganda.

1976, July 5		Litho.	Perf. 14½
58	A6b 50c blue & multi	.20	.20
59	A6b 1sh red & multi	.20	.20
60	A6b 2sh yellow & multi	.30	.25
61	A6b 3sh blue & multi	.40	.35
a.	Souv. sheet of 4, #58-61, perf. 13	4.50	4.50
	Nos. 58-61 (4)	1.10	1.00

21st Olympic Games, Montreal, Canada,
July 17-Aug. 1.
Exist imperf. from Format International liqui-
dation stock.

A6c

Rail Transport in East Africa: 50c, Tanzania-
Zambia Railway. 1sh, Nile Bridge, Uganda.
2sh, Nakuru Station, Kenya. 3sh, Class A
locomotive, 1896.

1976, Oct. 4		Litho.	Perf. 14½
62	A6c 50c lilac & multi	.20	.20
63	A6c 1sh emerald & multi	.30	.20
64	A6c 2sh brt rose & multi	.60	.35
65	A6c 3sh yellow & multi	.90	.60
a.	Souv. sheet of 4, #62-65, perf. 13	5.50	3.00
	Nos. 62-65 (4)	2.00	1.35

A6d

1977, Jan. 10		Litho.	Perf. 14½
66	A6d 50c Nile perch	.20	.20
67	A6d 1sh Tilapia	.35	.30
68	A6d 3sh Sailfish	1.00	.75
69	A6d 5sh Black marlin	1.75	1.50
a.	Souvenir sheet of 4, #66-69	4.25	3.25
	Nos. 66-69 (4)	3.30	2.75

A6e

50c, Masai tribesmen bleeding cow. 1sh,
Dancers from Uganda. 2sh, Makonde sculpture. 3sh, Tribesmen skinning hippopotamus.

1977, Jan. 15			Perf. 13½x14
70	A6e 50c multicolored	.20	.20
71	A6e 1sh multicolored	.25	.20
72	A6e 2sh multicolored	.45	.30
73	A6e 3sh multicolored	.75	.45
a.	Souvenir sheet of 4, #70-73	2.75	2.75
	Nos. 70-73 (4)	1.65	1.15

2nd World Black and African Festival,
Lagos, Nigeria, Jan. 15-Feb. 12.

A6f

50c, Automobile passing through village.
1sh, Winner at finish line. 2sh, Car going
through washout. 5sh, Car, elephants and Mt.
Kenya.

1977, Apr. 5		Litho.	Perf. 14
74	A6f 50c multicolored	.20	.20
75	A6f 1sh multicolored	.20	.20
76	A6f 2sh multicolored	.55	.30
77	A6f 5sh multicolored	1.40	.85
a.	Souvenir sheet of 4, #74-77	3.50	3.50
	Nos. 74-77 (4)	2.35	1.55

25th Safari rally, Apr. 7-11.

A6g

Designs: 50c, Rev. Canon Apolo Kivebulaya. 1sh, Uganda Cathedral. 2sh, Early grass-
topped Cathedral. 5sh, Early tent congregation, Kigezi.

1977, June 20		Litho.	Perf. 14
78	A6g 50c multicolored	.20	.20
79	A6g 1sh multicolored	.20	.20
80	A6g 2sh multicolored	.25	.20
81	A6g 5sh multicolored	.75	.55
a.	Souvenir sheet of 4, #78-81	3.00	3.00
	Nos. 78-81 (4)	1.40	1.15

Church of Uganda, centenary.

A6h

Endangered species: 50c, Pancake tortoise.
1sh, Nile crocodile. 2sh, Hunter's hartebeest.
3sh, Red Colobus monkey. 5sh, Dugong.

1977, Sept. 26		Litho.	Perf. 14x13½
82	A6h 50c multicolored	.40	.20
83	A6h 1sh multicolored	.45	.25
84	A6h 2sh multicolored	1.40	.45
85	A6h 3sh multicolored	2.00	.75
86	A6h 5sh multicolored	2.50	1.10
a.	Souvenir sheet of 4, #83-86	6.00	5.00
	Nos. 82-86 (5)	6.75	2.75

Prince Philip and Julius Nyerere,
1961 — A7

5sh, Queen Elizabeth II, Prince Philip,
Prime Minister Nyerere in London, 1975.
10sh, Royal crown, flags of Tanzania and
Commonwealth nations. 20sh, Coronation.

1977, Nov. 23		Litho.	Perf. 14x13½
87	A7 50c multicolored	.20	.20
88	A7 5sh multicolored	.20	.20
89	A7 10sh multicolored	.30	.30
90	A7 20sh multicolored	.55	.55
a.	Souvenir sheet of 4, #87-90	1.25	1.25
	Nos. 87-90 (4)	1.25	1.25

25th anniv. of reign of Elizabeth II.
For overprints see Nos. 99-102, 179-180.

Women Fetching Water from Stream
and Tap — A8

1sh, Flag raising. 3sh, Health care, laboratory and hospital. 5sh, Pres. Julius Nyerere.

1978, Feb. 5		Litho.	Perf. 13½x14
91	A8 50c multicolored	.20	.20
92	A8 1sh multicolored	.20	.20
93	A8 3sh multicolored	.35	.30
94	A8 5sh multicolored	.60	.50
a.	Souvenir sheet of 4, #91-94	1.25	1.25
	Nos. 91-94 (4)	1.35	1.20

First anniversary of the New Revolutionary
Party (Chama cha Mapinduzi).

A8a

50c, Soccer scene and Joe Kadenge. 1sh,
Mohammed Chuma receiving trophy, and his
portrait. 2sh, Shot on goal and Omari S.
Kidevu. 3sh, Backfield defense and Polly
Ouma.

1978, Apr. 17		Litho.	Perf. 14x13½
95	A8a 50c green & multi	.20	.20
96	A8a 1sh lt brown & multi	.20	.20
97	A8a 2sh lilac & multi	.35	.30
98	A8a 3sh dk blue & multi	.55	.40
a.	Souvenir sheet of 4, #95-98	1.75	1.75
	Nos. 95-98 (4)	1.30	1.10

World Soccer Cup Championships, Argentina '78, June 1-25.

Nos. 87-90a Overprinted in Large
Serifed Letters: "25th ANNIVERSARY /
CORONATION / 2nd JUNE 1953"

1978, June 2			
99	A7 50c multicolored	.20	.20
100	A7 5sh multicolored	.20	.20
101	A7 10sh multicolored	.30	.30
102	A7 20sh multicolored	.55	.55
a.	Souvenir sheet of 4, #99-102	1.00	1.00
	Nos. 99-102 (4)	1.25	1.25

25th anniv. of coronation of Elizabeth II.
Nos. 99-102a also exist overprinted with
smaller, sans serif letters, perf. 12. Same values or less. The perf. 12 set does not exist
without overprint.

"Do not Drink
when
Driving" — A9

Designs: 1sh, "Courtesy to the young, old
and handicapped." 3sh, "Observe highway
code." 5sh, "Do not drive faulty vehicle."

1978, July 1		Litho.	Perf. 13½x13
103	A9 50c multicolored	.20	.20
104	A9 1sh multicolored	.25	.25
105	A9 3sh multicolored	.60	.60
106	A9 5sh multicolored	2.50	2.50
a.	Souv. sheet, #103-106, perf. 14	3.00	3.00
	Nos. 103-106 (4)	3.55	3.55

Road Safety Campaign.

Lake Manyara
Hotel — A10

Designs: 1sh, Lobo Wildlife Lodge. 3sh,
Ngorongoro Crater Lodge. 5sh, Ngorongoro
Wildlife Lodge. 10sh, Mafia Island Lodge.
20sh, Mikumi Wildlife Lodge.

1978, Sept. 11		Litho.	Perf. 13½
107	A10 50c multicolored	.20	.20
108	A10 1sh multicolored	.20	.20
109	A10 3sh multicolored	.30	.30
110	A10 5sh multicolored	.55	.55
111	A10 10sh multicolored	1.10	1.10
112	A10 20sh multicolored	2.25	2.25
a.	Souvenir sheet of 6, #107-112	6.25	6.25
	Nos. 107-112 (6)	4.60	4.60

Game Lodges of Tanzania.

Chained
African — A11

1sh, Division of races (black and white
heads). 2.50sh, Racial harmony (black and
white handshake and heads). 5sh, End of sup-
pression and rise of freedom (hands breaking
loose from chains).

1978, Oct. 24		Litho.	Perf. 14½x14
113	A11 50c multicolored	.20	.20
114	A11 1sh multicolored	.20	.20
115	A11 2.50sh multicolored	.45	.45
116	A11 5sh multicolored	.90	.90
a.	Souvenir sheet of 4, #113-116	2.25	2.25
	Nos. 113-116 (4)	1.75	1.75

Anti-Apartheid Year.

Fokker Friendship at Dar Es Salaam
Airport — A12

Designs: 1sh, Single-engine Dragon, 1930,
Zanzibar. 2sh, British Airways Concorde. 5sh,
Wright Brothers' Flyer 1, 1903.

1978, Dec. 28		Litho.	Perf. 13½
117	A12 50c multicolored	.20	.20
118	A12 1sh multicolored	.30	.25
119	A12 2sh multicolored	.55	.50
120	A12 5sh multicolored	1.40	1.25
a.	Souvenir sheet of 4, #117-120	2.75	2.75
	Nos. 117-120 (4)	2.45	2.20

75th anniversary of 1st powered flight.

Emblem
A13

Design: 5sh, Headquarters buildings.

1979, Feb. 3		Litho.	Perf. 14½x14
121	A13 50c multicolored	.20	.20
122	A13 5sh multicolored	.75	.75
a.	Souvenir sheet of 2, #121-122	1.25	1.25

Tanzania Post and Telecommunications
Corporation, 1st anniversary.

Pres. Nyerere and Children — A14

Designs (UNICEF and Tanzanian IYC
Emblems and): 1sh, Kindergarten. 2sh, Vaccination of infant. 5sh, Emblems.

1979, June 25   Litho.   Perf. 14½
123 A14 50c multicolored   .20   .20
124 A14 1sh multicolored   .20   .20
125 A14 2sh multicolored   .25   .25
126 A14 5sh multicolored   .60   .60
a.   Souvenir sheet of 4, #123-126   2.25 2.25
         Nos. 123-126 (4)   1.25 1.25

International Year of the Child.

Tree Planting — A15

Forest Preservation and Expansion: 1sh, Seedling. 2sh, Rainfall. 5sh, Forest fire.

1979, Sept. 29   Litho.   Perf. 14½
127 A15 50c multicolored   .20   .20
128 A15 1sh multicolored   .25   .25
129 A15 2sh multicolored   .50   .50
130 A15 5sh multicolored   1.25 1.25
         Nos. 127-130 (4)   2.20 2.20

Mwenge Satellite Earth Station Opening A16

1979, Dec. 3   Litho.   Perf. 13½
131 A16 10c multicolored   .20   .20
132 A16 40c multicolored   .20   .20
133 A16 50c multicolored   .20   .20
134 A16 1sh multicolored   .25   .20
         Nos. 131-134 (4)   .85   .80

Nos. 36, 43 Surcharged

1979   Litho.   Perf. 14½x14
135 A5 40c (10 + 30) multi   .20   .20
136 A5 50c on 70c multi   .20   .20

Tabata Dispensary, Dar-es-Salaam, Rotary Emblem — A17

1980, Mar. 1   Litho.   Perf. 13x13½
137 A17 50c shown   .20   .20
138 A17 1sh Ngomvu water pro-
          ject   .20   .20
139 A17 5sh Flying doctor ser-
          vice   .45   .45
140 A17 20sh Torch, anniversary
          emblem   2.25 2.25
a.   Souvenir sheet of 4, #137-140   3.25 3.25
         Nos. 137-140 (4)   3.10 3.10

Rotary International, 75th anniversary.
For overprints see Nos. 149-152.

Zanzibar Nos. 49 and 309, "Stamp History" Cancel A18

Cancel and: 50c, Tanganyika #58, postal worker, vert. 10sh, Tanganyika #16, 52. 20sh, Penny Black, Rowland Hill, vert.

1980, Apr.   Perf. 14
141 A18 40c multicolored   .20   .20
142 A18 50c multicolored   .20   .20
143 A18 10sh multicolored   .70   .70
144 A18 20sh multicolored   1.40 1.40
a.   Souvenir sheet of 4, #141-144   3.00 3.00
         Nos. 141-144 (4)   2.50 2.50

Sir Rowland Hill (1795-1879), originator of penny postage; Tanzanian stamp history.

Overprinted: "LONDON 1980" / PHILATELIC EXHIBITION

1980, May 6   Litho.   Perf. 14
145 A18 40c multicolored   .20   .20
146 A18 50c multicolored   .20   .20
147 A18 10sh multicolored   .70   .70
148 A18 20sh multicolored   1.40 1.40
a.   Souvenir sheet of 4, #145-148   3.25 3.25
         Nos. 145-148 (4)   2.50 2.50

London 80 Intl. Stamp Exhib., May 6-14.

Nos. 137-140a with Additional Inscription on 1 or 2 Lines: "District 920-55th Annual / Conference, Arusha, Tanzania"

1980, June 23   Litho.   Perf. 13x13½
149 A17 50c multicolored   .20   .20
150 A17 1sh multicolored   .20   .20
151 A17 5sh multicolored   .85   .85
152 A17 20sh multicolored   3.50 3.50
a.   Souvenir sheet of 4, #149-152   5.00 5.00
         Nos. 149-152 (4)   4.75 4.75

District 920 Rotary Club, 55th Annual Conference, Arusha.

Pan African Postal Union and U.P.U. Emblems A19

1980, July 1   Perf. 13x13½
153 A19 50c purple & blk   .20   .20
154 A19 1sh ultra & blk   .20   .20
155 A19 5sh red orange & blk   .75   .75
156 A19 10sh green & blk   1.50 1.50
         Nos. 153-156 (4)   2.65 2.65

Pan African Postal Union Plenipotentiary Conference, Arusha, Jan. 8-18.

Gidamis Shahanga, Marathon — A20

Tanzanian Olympic Team: 1sh, Nzael Kyomo and sprinters. 10sh, Zakayo Malekwa and javelin. 20sh, William Lyimo and boxers.

1980, Aug. 18   Litho.   Perf. 13x13½
157 A20 50c multicolored   .20   .20
158 A20 1sh multicolored   .20   .20
159 A20 10sh multicolored   1.10 1.10
160 A20 20sh multicolored   2.25 2.25
a.   Souvenir sheet of 4, #157-160   4.00 4.00
         Nos. 157-160 (4)   3.75 3.75

22nd Summer Olympic Games, Moscow, July 19-Aug. 3.
Issued also in sheets of 20 (5 of each value).

Spring Hare — A21

1980, Oct. 1   Litho.   Perf. 14
161 A21 10c shown   .20   .20
162 A21 20c Genet   .20   .20
163 A21 40c Mongoose   .20   .20
164 A21 50c Ratel   .20   .20
165 A21 75c Rock hyrax   .20   .20
166 A21 80c Leopard   .20   .20

Perf. 14½
Size: 40x24mm
167 A21 1sh Impalas   .20   .20
168 A21 1.50sh Giraffes   .20   .20
169 A21 2sh Zebras   .20   .20
170 A21 3sh Buffalo   .25   .25
171 A21 5sh Lions   .40   .40
172 A21 10sh Rhinoceros   .80   .80
173 A21 20sh Elephants   1.60 1.60
174 A21 40sh Cheetahs   3.25 3.25
         Nos. 161-174 (14)   8.10 8.10

For overprints see Nos. O27-O36.

National Parks Emblem A22

1981, Jan. 26   Litho.   Perf. 13x13½
175 A22 50c Ngorongoro Park   .20   .20
176 A22 1sh shown   .20   .20
177 A22 5sh Friends of Ser-
          engeti   .70   .70
178 A22 20sh Friends of
          Ngorongoro   3.00 3.00
         Nos. 175-178 (4)   4.10 4.10

Ngorongoro & Serengeti Parks, 60th anniv.
For overprints see Nos. 299-302.

Nos. 89-90 Overprinted: "ROYAL WEDDING/ H.R.H. PRINCE CHARLES/ 29th JULY 1981"

1981, July 29   Litho.   Perf. 14x13½
179 A7 10sh multicolored   .35   .35
180 A7 20sh multicolored   .65   .65
a.   Souvenir sheet of 2, #179-180   5.25 5.25

Mail Runner A23

1981, Oct. 23   Litho.   Perf. 12½x12
181 A23 50c shown   .20   .20
182 A23 1sh Letter sorting   .20   .20
183 A23 5sh Post horn, carrier
          pigeon   .70   .70
184 A23 10sh Commonwealth
          members' flags   1.50 1.50
a.   Souvenir sheet of 4, #181-184   3.00 3.00
         Nos. 181-184 (4)   2.60 2.60

Commonwealth Postal Administrations Conference, Arusha, June 29-July 10.

Intl. Year of the Disabled A24

1981, Nov. 30   Litho.   Perf. 14
185 A24 50c Morris Nyunyusa,
          blind drummer   .20   .20
186 A24 1sh Sewing   .25   .25
187 A24 5sh Prostheses   1.25 1.25
188 A24 10sh Children   2.50 2.50
         Nos. 185-188 (4)   4.20 4.20

20th Anniv. of Independence — A25

1982, Jan. 13   Litho.   Perf. 13x13½
189 A25 50c Pres. Nyerere, flag   .20   .20
190 A25 1sh Zanzibar Electricity
          Plant   .20   .20
191 A25 3sh Sisal plant, weaver   .50   .50
192 A25 10sh Pupils   1.75 1.75
a.   Souvenir sheet of 4, #189-192   3.25 3.25
         Nos. 189-192 (4)   2.65 2.65

Ostrich — A26

1982, Jan. 25   Litho.   Perf. 13½
193 A26 50c shown   .20   .20
194 A26 1sh Secretary bird   .25   .25
195 A26 5sh Kori bustard   1.40 1.25
196 A26 10sh Saddle-bill stork   2.75 2.50
         Nos. 193-196 (4)   4.60 4.20

1982 World Cup A27

1982, June 2   Litho.   Perf. 14
197 A27 50c Jella Mtagwa   .20   .20
198 A27 1sh Stadium   .20   .20
199 A27 10sh Diego Armando
          Maradona   2.00 2.00
200 A27 20sh Globe   4.25 4.25
a.   Souvenir sheet of 4, #197-200   6.75 6.75
         Nos. 197-200 (4)   6.65 6.65

Jade of Seronera and her Cubs A28

Animals Appearing in Movies or TV Shows: 1sh, Wild dog and puppies, Havoc. 5sh, Fifi and sons, Gombe. 10sh, Bahati and twins Rashidi and Ramadhani, Lake Manyara.

1982, July 15   Litho.   Perf. 14
201 A28 50c multicolored   .20   .20
202 A28 1sh multicolored   .25   .25
203 A28 5sh multicolored   1.25 1.25
204 A28 10sh multicolored   2.50 2.50
a.   Souv. sheet, #201-204, perf. 14½   5.00 5.00
         Nos. 201-204 (4)   4.20 4.20

Scouting Year A29

1982, Aug. 25
205 A29 50c Brick laying   .20   .20
206 A29 1sh Camping   .20   .20
207 A29 10sh Tracing marks   1.75 1.75
208 A29 20sh Baden-Powell   3.50 3.50
a.   Souvenir sheet of 4, #205-208   5.50 5.50
         Nos. 205-208 (4)   5.65 5.65

For overprint see No. 303.

World Food Day — A30

1982, Oct. 16   Litho.   Perf. 14
209 A30 50c Plowing   .20   .20
210 A30 1sh Dairy cows   .20   .20
211 A30 5sh Corn harvest   1.00 1.00
212 A30 10sh Grain storage   2.00 2.00
a.   Souvenir sheet of 4, #209-212   3.50 3.50
         Nos. 209-212 (4)   3.40 3.40

TB Bacillus Centenary A31

1982, Dec. 5   Perf. 12½x12
213 A31 50c Child immunization   .20   .20
214 A31 1sh Koch   .20   .20
215 A31 5sh TB emblem   1.00 1.00
216 A31 10sh WHO emblem   2.00 2.00
         Nos. 213-216 (4)   3.40 3.40

A31a

1983, Mar. 14   Litho.   Perf. 14
217 A31a 50c Pres. Nyerere   .20   .20
218 A31a 1sh Running, boxing   .20   .20
219 A31a 5sh Flags   1.00 1.00
220 A31a 10sh Pres. Nyerere,
              Royal Family   2.00 2.00
  a.   Souvenir sheet of 4, #217-220 3.50 3.50
        Nos. 217-220 (4)   3.40 3.40
Commonwealth Day. For overprint see #407.

5th Anniv. of Posts and
Telecommunications Dept. — A32

1983, Feb. 3   Litho.   Perf. 12½x12
221 A32 50c Letter post   .20   .20
222 A32 1sh Training Institute   .20   .20
223 A32 5sh Satellite communi-
             cations   1.00 1.00
224 A32 10sh Emblems   2.00 2.00
  a.   Souvenir sheet of 4, #221-224 3.50 3.50
        Nos. 221-224 (4)   3.40 3.40

25th Anniv. of Economic Commission
for Africa — A33

1983, Sept. 12   Litho.   Perf. 12½x12
225 A33 50c Eastern & South-
             ern African Man-
             agement Institute,
             Arusha   .20   .20
226 A33 1sh Emblems   .25   .25
227 A33 5sh Mineral collections 1.10 1.00
228 A33 10sh Emblems, diff.   2.25 2.00
  a.   Souvenir sheet of 4, #225-228 3.75 3.25
        Nos. 225-228 (4)   3.80 3.45

World Communications Year — A34

1983, Oct. 17   Litho.   Perf. 14
229 A34 50c Rural telephone
             service   .20   .20
230 A34 1sh Emblems   .20   .20
231 A34 5sh Post Office   1.00 1.00
232 A34 10sh Microwave tower   2.00 2.00
  a.   Souvenir sheet of 4, #229-232 3.50 3.50
        Nos. 229-232 (4)   3.40 3.40

Historical
Buildings
A35

1983, Dec. 12   Litho.   Perf. 12½x12
233 A35 1sh Bagamoyo Boma   .20   .20
234 A35 1.50sh Beit-El-Ajaib   .30   .30
235 A35 5sh Anglican Church   .90   .90
236 A35 10sh State House, old
              and new   1.75 1.75
  a.   Souvenir sheet of 4, #233-236 3.50 3.50
        Nos. 233-236 (4)   3.15 3.15

20th Anniv.
of
Revolution
A36

1984, June 18   Litho.   Perf. 14
237 A36 1sh Muasisi Kwanza   .20   .20
238 A36 1.50sh Clove farming   .30   .30
239 A36 5sh Industrial devel-
             opment   1.00 1.00
240 A36 10sh Housing develop-
              ments   2.00 2.00
        Nos. 237-240 (4)   3.50 3.50

Souvenir Sheet
241 A36 15sh Map, ship   3.25 3.25

1984
Summer
Olympics
A37

1984, Aug. 6   Perf. 12½x12
242 A37 1sh Boxing   .20   .20
243 A37 1.50sh Running   .20   .20
244 A37 5sh Basketball   .75   .75
245 A37 20sh Soccer   2.25 2.25
  a.   Souvenir sheet of 4, #242-245 3.50 3.50
        Nos. 242-245 (4)   3.40 3.40
For overprints see Nos. 275-278.

Intl. Civil
Aviation
Org. 40th
Anniv.
A38

1984, Nov. 15   Litho.   Perf. 13
246 A38 1sh Icarus   .20   .20
247 A38 1.50sh Air Tanzania jets,
             traffic controller   .20   .20
248 A38 5sh Aircraft mainte-
             nance   .75   .75
249 A38 10sh ICAO emblem   1.25 1.25
  a.   Souvenir sheet of 4, #246-249 2.25 2.25
        Nos. 246-249 (4)   2.40 2.40

Traditional
Houses
A39

1984, Dec. 20   Perf. 12½x12
250 A39 1sh Sochi   .20   .20
251 A39 1.50sh Isyenga   .20   .20
252 A39 5sh Tembe   .65   .65
253 A39 10sh Banda   1.25 1.25
  a.   Souvenir sheet of 4, #250-253 2.25 2.25
        Nos. 250-253 (4)   2.30 2.30

Textile
Industry
A40

5th anniversary of the Southern Africa
Development Coordination Conference.

1985, Apr. 1   Perf. 14
254 A40 1.50sh shown   .20   .20
255 A40 4sh Mining   .45   .45
256 A40 5sh Transportation
             and communi-
             cations   .55   .55
257 A40 20sh Flags of member
             nations   2.25 2.25
  a.   Souvenir sheet of 4, #254-257 3.50 3.50
        Nos. 254-257 (4)   3.45 3.45

Rare
Species
of
Zanzibar
A41

Perf. 13½x13, 13x13½
1985, May 8   Litho.
258 A41 1sh Tortoise   .20   .20
259 A41 4sh Leopard   .50   .50
260 A41 10sh Civet cat   1.10 1.10
261 A41 17.50sh Red colobus,
              vert.   2.00 2.00
        Nos. 258-261 (4)   3.80 3.80

Souvenir Sheet
262   Sheet of 2   3.75 3.75
  a.   A41 15sh Black rhinoceros 1.50 1.50
  b.   A41 20sh Giant ground pangolin 2.25 2.25
For overprints see Nos. 408-409, 411.

Automobile Centenary — A42

Classic autos manufactured by Rolls-Royce.

1985, May 14   Perf. 14½x14
263 A42 1.50sh 1936 20/25   .20   .20
264 A42 5sh 1933 Phantom II   .20   .20
265 A42 10sh 1926 Phantom I   .25   .25
266 A42 30sh 1907 Silver
             Ghost   .75   .75
  a.   Souvenir sheet of 4, #263-266 1.25 1.25
        Nos. 263-266 (4)   1.40 1.40

Queen Mother, 85th Birthday — A43

1985, Sept. 30
267 A43 20sh Waving   .20   .20
268 A43 20sh Facing left   .20   .20
269 A43 100sh Wearing green
             hat   .40   .40
  a.   Souvenir sheet, #267, 269 .55   .55
270 A43 100sh Facing right   .40   .40
  a.   Souvenir sheet, #268, 270 .55   .55
        Nos. 267-270 (4)   1.20 1.20
For overprints see Nos. 295-298.

Tanzania Railways Locomotives — A44

1985, Oct. 7   Litho.   Perf. 14½x14
271 A44 5sh No. 3022   .20   .20
272 A44 10sh No. 3107   .20   .20
273 A44 20sh No. 6004   .30   .30
274 A44 30sh No. 3129   .50   .50
  a.   Souvenir sheet of 4, #271-274 1.40 1.40
        Nos. 271-274 (4)   1.20 1.20

Nos. 242-245 Ovptd. with Winners and
"GOLD MEDAL" in 2 or 3 Lines

1985, Oct. 22   Perf. 12½x12
275 A37 1sh Henry Tillman,
             USA   .20   .20
276 A37 1.50sh USA   .20   .20
277 A37 5sh USA   .50   .50
278 A37 20sh France   2.00 2.00
  a.   Souvenir sheet of 4, #275-278 3.00 3.00
        Nos. 275-278 (4)   2.90 2.90

Pottery
A45

1985, Nov. 4
279 A45 1.50sh Water and cook-
             ing pots   .20   .20
280 A45 2sh Frying pot and
             caldron   .20   .20
281 A45 5sh Woman selling
             pots   .50   .50
282 A45 40sh Beer pot   3.75 3.75
        Nos. 279-282 (4)   4.65 4.65

Souvenir Sheet
283 A45 30sh Water pot   3.25 3.25

Locomotives — A46

1985, Nov. 25
284 A46 1.50sh Class 64   .20   .20
285 A46 2sh Class 36   .20   .20
286 A46 5sh Shunting
             DFH1013   .55   .55
287 A46 10sh Diesel Electric
             DE1001   1.10 1.10
288 A46 30sh Zanzibar, 1906   3.25 3.25
        Nos. 284-288 (5)   5.30 5.30

Souvenir Sheet
289   Sheet of 2   4.25 4.25
  a.   A46 15sh Class 30 steam 1.75 1.75
  b.   A46 20sh Class 11 steam 2.25 2.25
For overprints see Nos. 381A-381E.

Intl. Youth
Year — A47

1986, Jan. 20   Perf. 14
290 A47 1.50sh Young Pioneers   .20   .20
291 A47 4sh Health care   .50   .50
292 A47 10sh Uhuru torch race 1.00 1.00
293 A47 20sh World map   1.75 1.75
        Nos. 290-293 (4)   3.45 3.45

Souvenir Sheet
294 A47 30sh Agriculture   3.00 3.00

Nos. 267-270 Ovptd. "CARIBBEAN/
ROYAL VISIT/ 1985" in Silver or Gold
1986, Feb. 10   Perf. 14½x14
295 A43 20sh on #267
296 A43 20sh on #268
297 A43 100sh on #269
  a.   Souvenir sheet, #295, 297
298 A43 100sh on #270
  a.   Souvenir sheet, #296, 298

See footnote following No. 303.

Nos. 175-178, 208a Ovptd.
"75th ANNIVERSARY GIRL GUIDES/
1910-1985" in Silver or Black
1986, Feb. 10   Litho.   Perf. 13x13½, 14
299 A22 50c multicolored (S)
300 A22 1sh multicolored
301 A22 5sh multicolored
302 A22 20sh multicolored

Souvenir Sheet
303   Sheet of 4
  a.   A29 50c multicolored
  b.   A29 1sh multicolored
  c.   A29 10sh multicolored
  d.   A29 20sh multicolored

The status of this set, the Caribbean Royal
Visit set and at least 12 stamps overprinted
congratulating the Duke and Duchess of York
on their marriage are in question.

Rotary Intl., World Chess
Championships — A48

1986, Mar. 17   *Perf. 14*
304 A48   20sh shown   .25   .25
305 A48 100sh Chess board   1.25   1.25
  a. Souvenir sheet of 2, #304-305   1.50   1.50

Audubon Birth Bicent. — A49

Illustrations of American bird species by
Audubon.

1986, May 22
306 A49   5sh Mallard   .20   .20
307 A49 10sh American eider   .20   .20
308 A49 20sh Scarlet ibis   .35   .35
309 A49 30sh Roseate spoonbill   .55   .55
  a. Souvenir sheet of 4, #306-309   1.50   1.50
    Nos. 306-309 (4)   1.30   1.30

Gemstones
A50

1986, May 22
310 A50 1.50sh Pearls   .30   .25
311 A50   2sh Sapphires   .35   .30
312 A50   5sh Tanzanite   .85   .75
313 A50 40sh Diamonds   6.75   6.00
    Nos. 310-313 (4)   8.25   7.30
Souvenir Sheet
314 A50 30sh Rubies   7.50   7.50

Indigenous
Flowers — A51

1986, June 2
315 A51 1.50sh Hibiscus
      calyphyllus   .20   .20
316 A51   5sh Aloe graminicola   .20   .20
317 A51 10sh Nersium olean-
      der   .20   .20
318 A51 30sh Nymphaea
      caerulea   .50   .50
  a. Souvenir Sheet of 4, #315-318 .90   .90
    Nos. 315-318 (4)   1.10   1.10

Endangered
Wildlife — A52

1986, June 30   Litho.   *Perf. 14x14½*
319 A52   5sh Oryx   .20   .20
320 A52 10sh Giraffe   .20   .20
321 A52 20sh Rhinoceros   .25   .25
322 A52 30sh Cheetah   .35   .35
  a. Miniature sheet of 4, #319-322   .80   .80
    Nos. 319-322 (4)   1.00   1.00

UN Child
Survival
Campaign
A53

1986, July 29   *Perf. 12½x12*
323 A53 1.50sh Immunization   .20   .20
324 A53   2sh Growth monitor-
      ing   .20   .20
325 A53   5sh Oral rehydration
      therapy   .20   .20
326 A53 40sh Breast feeding   1.60   1.60
    Nos. 323-326 (4)   2.20   2.20
Souvenir Sheet
327 A53 30sh Healthy child   1.25   1.25
For overprints see Nos. 406, 410, 412.

Marine
Life
A54

1986, Aug. 20
328 A54 1.50sh Butterflyfish   .50   .20
329 A54   4sh Parrotfish   1.10   .75
330 A54 10sh Sea turtle   1.75   1.75
331 A54 20sh Octopus   2.75   2.75
    Nos. 328-331 (4)   6.10   5.45
Souvenir Sheet
332 A54 30sh Coral   2.00   2.00

Queen Elizabeth II, 60th
Birthday — A55

Photographs: 5sh, Royal family, Buckingham Palace balcony. 10sh, With princes in
open carriage. 40sh, Elizabeth II. 60sh, Greeting crowd.

1987, Mar. 24   Litho.   *Perf. 14*
333 A55   5sh multicolored   .20
334 A55 10sh multicolored   .20
335 A55 40sh multicolored   .50
336 A55 60sh multicolored   .75
  a. Souvenir sheet of 4, #333-336 1.50
    Nos. 333-336 (4)   1.65

1986 World Cup Soccer
Championships, Mexico — A57

Designs: 1.50sh, Map, team captains, officials. 2sh, Foul. 10sh, Goal. 20sh, Goalie
save. 30sh, Argentine natl. team.

1986, Oct. 30   Litho.   *Perf. 14*
341 A57 1.50sh multicolored   .20   .20
342 A57   2sh multicolored   .20   .20
343 A57 10sh multicolored   .50   .50
344 A57 20sh multicolored   1.00   1.00
    Nos. 341-344 (4)   1.90   1.90
Souvenir Sheet
345 A57 30sh multicolored   1.25   1.25

Hair Styles — A58

1987, Mar. 16   *Perf. 14½*
346 A58 1.50sh Nungu Nungu   .25   .20
347 A58   2sh Upanga wa
      Jogoo   .40   .20
348 A58 10sh Morani   .75   .75
349 A58 20sh Twende Kilioni   1.25   1.75
    Nos. 346-349 (4)   2.65   2.90
Souvenir Sheet
350 A58 30sh Kusuka Nywele   2.50   2.50

Intl. Peace
Year
A59

Designs: 1.50sh, Julius K. Nyerere, Beyond
War Award winner. 2sh, Peace among
nations. 10sh, Peaceful use of outer space.
20sh, Emblem, UN building. 30sh, Emblem,
handshake.

1986, Dec. 22   Litho.   *Perf. 14½*
351 A59 1.50sh multicolored   .30   .20
352 A59   2sh multicolored   .50   .20
353 A59 10sh multicolored   1.25   1.00
354 A59 20sh multicolored   1.75   2.00
    Nos. 351-354 (4)   3.80   3.40
Souvenir Sheet
355 A59 30sh multicolored   1.75   2.00

Natl. Bank of Commerce, 20th
Anniv. — A60

1987, Feb. 6   Litho.   *Perf. 14*
356 A60 1.50sh Mobile bank   .30   .20
357 A60   2sh Headquarters   .50   .20
358 A60   5sh Pres. Mwinyi lay-
      ing foundation
      stone   .80   .75
359 A60 20sh Cotton harvest   2.00   2.25
    Nos. 356-359 (4)   3.60   3.40

New Revolutionary Party (CCM), 10th
Anniv. — A61

1987, Apr. 10   *Perf. 14½x14*
360 A61   2sh Soldiers in forma-
      tion   .20   .20
361 A61   3sh Woman picking
      coffee beans   .20   .20
362 A61 10sh Speaker at podium   .45   .45
363 A61 30sh Nyerere, Mwinyi   1.25   1.25
    Nos. 360-363 (4)   2.10   2.10

Arush Declaration, 20th anniv.

Insects
A62

1987, Apr. 22   *Perf. 12½x1*
364 A62 1.50sh Bees   .20   .20
365 A62   2sh Greater grain
      borer   .20   .4
366 A62 10sh Tse-tse fly   .40   .4
367 A62 20sh Wasp   .80   .8
    Nos. 364-367 (4)   1.60   1.6
Souvenir Sheet
368 A62 30sh Mosquito   1.25   1.2

Reptiles
A63

1987, July 2
369 A63   2sh Crocodiles   .20   .2
370 A63   3sh Black-striped grass
      snake   .20   .2
371 A63 10sh Adder   .40   .4
372 A63 20sh Green mamba   .80   .8
    Nos. 369-372 (4)   1.60   1.6
Souvenir Sheet
373 A63 30sh Tortoise   1.25   1.2

Posts and Telecommunications,
Railways Emblems — A64

1987, July 27   *Perf. 1*
374 A64   2sh shown   .20   .2
375 A64   8sh Air Tanzania, Port
      Authority   .40   .4
Souvenir Sheet
376 A64 20sh Modes of commu-
      nication and
      transportation   1.00   1.0

Traditional
Crafts
A65

1987, Dec. 15   Litho.   *Perf. 12½x1.*
377 A65   2sh Baskets   .20   .2
378 A65   3sh Gourds   .20   .2
379 A65 10sh Stools   .30   .3
380 A65 20sh Makonde carvings   .60   .6
    Nos. 377-380 (4)   1.30   1.3
Souvenir Sheet
381 A65 40sh Makonde carver at
      work   1.20   1.2

Nos. 284-288 Ovptd.

1987, Dec. 30   Litho.   *Perf. 12½x1*
381A A46 1.50sh multicolored   .20   .2
381B A46   2sh multicolored   .20   .2
381C A46   5sh multicolored   .25   .2
381D A46 10sh multicolored   .50   .5
381E A46 30sh multicolored   1.50   1.5
    Nos. 381A-381E (5)   2.65   2.6

Plateosaurus — A66

1988, Apr. 22 — Perf. 12½
382	A66	2sh shown	.20	.20
383	A66	3sh Pteranodon	.20	.20
384	A66	5sh Brontosaurus	.20	.20
385	A66	7sh Lions	.30	.30
386	A66	8sh Tiger	.30	.30
387	A66	12sh Orangutans	.35	.35
388	A66	20sh Elephants	.75	.75
389	A66	100sh Stegosaurus	1.90	1.90
		Nos. 382-389 (8)	4.20	4.20

Traditional Games A67

1988, Feb. 15 Litho. Perf. 12½x12
390	A67	2sh Mdako (marbles)	.20	.20
391	A67	3sh Mieleka (wrestling)	.20	.20
392	A67	8sh Bull fight	.20	.20
393	A67	20sh Bao (African chess)	.40	.40
		Nos. 390-393 (4)	1.00	1.00

Souvenir Sheet
394	A67	30sh Kulenga shabaha (archery)	.90	.90

Dated 1987.

Miniature Sheets

Statue of Liberty, Cent. (in 1986) — A68

No. 395: 1sh, Re-opening gala (evening), 1986. 2sh, Musicians performing. 3sh, Cheerleaders. 15sh, Statue holding tablet. 30sh, Tablet inscription. 40sh, Liberty Island. 50sh, Re-opening gala (afternoon), 1986. 60sh, Blimps over Liberty Island.

No. 396: 4sh, Statue, blimp. 5sh, Torch. 6sh, Torch and crown observatories lit at night, scaffolding. 7sh, Worker gilding torch. 8sh, Statue shrouded in scaffolding. 10sh, Two workers, torch. 12sh, Head, scaffolding. 18sh, Celebrant at re-opening (evening). 20sh, Goodyear blimp, skirt of Statue. 25sh, Boys' choir, statue. 35sh, Torch held aloft, full moon. 45sh, Worker cleaning tablet.

1988, June 15 Litho. Perf. 14
395		Sheet of 8 + label	6.00	6.00
a.	A68	1sh multicolored	.20	.20
b.	A68	2sh multicolored	.20	.20
c.	A68	3sh multicolored	.20	.20
d.	A68	15sh multicolored	.45	.45
e.	A68	30sh multicolored	1.00	1.00
f.	A68	40sh multicolored	1.25	1.25
g.	A68	50sh multicolored	1.50	1.50
h.	A68	60sh multicolored	1.75	1.75
396		Sheet of 12	6.00	6.00
a.	A68	4sh multicolored	.20	.20
b.	A68	5sh multicolored	.20	.20
c.	A68	6sh multicolored	.20	.20
d.	A68	7sh multicolored	.20	.20
e.	A68	8sh multicolored	.25	.25
f.	A68	10sh multicolored	.30	.30
g.	A68	12sh multicolored	.35	.35
h.	A68	18sh multicolored	.55	.55
i.	A68	20sh multicolored	.60	.60
j.	A68	25sh multicolored	.75	.75
k.	A68	35sh multicolored	1.00	1.00
l.	A68	45sh multicolored	1.25	1.25

No. 395 contains a center label inscribed "THE STATUE / OF LIBERTY / 100th ANNIVERSARY."

Natl. Monuments — A69

1988, June 15 Litho.
397	A69	5sh Independence Torch	.20	.20
398	A69	12sh Arusha Declaration	.20	.20

399	A69	30sh Askari	.25	.25
400	A69	60sh Independence	.50	.50
		Nos. 397-400 (4)	1.15	1.15

Souvenir Sheet
401	A69	100sh Soldier (Askari detail)	1.75	1.75

3rd Natl. Census, Aug. 28 — A70

1988, Aug. 8
402	A70	2sh shown	.20	.20
403	A70	3sh Enumeration	.20	.20
404	A70	10sh Health care	.30	.30
405	A70	20sh Population figures	.55	.55
		Nos. 402-405 (4)	1.25	1.25

Souvenir Sheet
405A	A70	40sh Segments of economy and society	.75	.75

Stamps of 1983-86 Ovptd:

A53 "125TH ANNIVERSARY / INTERNATIONAL RED CROSS / AND RED CRESCENT"
CD334 "40TH WEDDING ANNIVERSARY / H.M. QUEEN ELIZABETH II / H.R.H. THE DUKE OF EDINBURGH"
A41 "63RD ANNIVERSARY / ROTARY INTERNATIONAL / IN AFRICA"

1988, Aug. 15 Perfs. as Before
406	A53	5sh on #325	.20	.20
407	A31a	10sh on #220	.30	.30
a.		Souv. sheet of 4, #218-220, 407	.50	.50
408	A41	10sh on #260	.30	.30
409	A41	17.50sh on #261	.55	.55
410	A53	30sh on #326	1.25	1.25
		Nos. 406-410 (5)	2.60	2.60

Souvenir Sheets
411		Sheet of 2	1.00	1.00
a.	A41	15sh on #262a	.40	.40
b.	A41	20sh on #262b	.60	.60
412	A53	30sh on #327	.90	.90

1988 Olympics, Seoul and Calgary — A71

1988, Aug. 29 Perf. 14
414	A71	5sh Biathlon	.40	.40
415	A71	10sh Soccer	.20	.20
416	A71	20sh Cycling	.70	.70
417	A71	25sh Pairs figuring skating	.80	.80
418	A71	50sh Fencing	.75	.75
419	A71	50sh Downhill skiing	1.40	1.40
420	A71	70sh Volleyball	.90	.90
421	A71	75sh Bobsled	1.60	1.60
		Nos. 414-421 (8)	6.75	6.75

Souvenir Sheets
422	A71	100sh Flags, hockey sticks	2.50	2.50
423	A71	100sh Gymnastics	2.50	2.50

For overprint see No. 534A-534J.

1988 Summer Olympics, Seoul A71a

1988, Sept. 5 Litho. Perf. 12½x12
423A	A71a	2sh Javelin	.60	.60
423B	A71a	3sh Hurdles	.65	.65
423C	A71a	7sh Long distance running	1.00	1.00
423D	A71a	12sh Relay race	1.25	1.25
		Nos. 423A-423D (4)	3.50	3.50

A souvenir sheet exists.

Disney Characters, Special Occasions — A72

1988, Sept. 9 Perf. 14
424	A72	4sh Love You, Dad	.25	.25
425	A72	5sh Happy Birthday	.25	.25
426	A72	10sh Trick or Treat	.40	.40
427	A72	12sh Be Kind to Animals	.40	.40
428	A72	15sh Love	.50	.50
429	A72	20sh Let's Celebrate	.70	.70
430	A72	30sh Keep In Touch	1.50	1.50
431	A72	50sh Love You, Mom	3.00	3.00
		Nos. 424-431 (8)	7.00	7.00

Souvenir Sheet
432	A72	150sh Let's Work Together	4.00	4.00
433	A72	150sh Have a Super Sunday	4.00	4.00

Mickey Mouse, 60th anniv.

Domestic Animals A73

1988, Sept. 9
434	A73	4sh Goat, vert.	.25	.25
435	A73	5sh Rabbit	.25	.25
436	A73	8sh Cows	.35	.35
437	A73	10sh Cat	.50	.50
438	A73	12sh Horse, vert.	.65	.65
439	A73	20sh Dog, vert.	1.00	1.00
		Nos. 434-439 (6)	3.00	3.00

Souvenir Sheet
440	A73	100sh Chicken	3.00	3.00

Traditional Musical Instruments — A74

1988, Sept. 30 Litho. Perf. 14
441	A74	2sh Drums	.35	.35
442	A74	3sh Xylophones	.35	.35
443	A74	10sh Thumb pianos	.70	.70
444	A74	20sh Fiddles	1.10	1.10
		Nos. 441-444 (4)	2.50	2.50

Souvenir Sheet
445	A74	40sh Violins with calabash resonators	1.25	1.25

Dated 1987.

Butterflies A75

1988, Oct. 17 Perf. 14½
446	A75	8sh Charaxes varanes	.50	.50
447	A75	30sh Neptis melicerta	.95	.95
448	A75	40sh Mylothris chloris	1.00	1.00
449	A75	50sh Charaxes bohemani	1.25	1.25
450	A75	60sh Myrina ficedula	1.50	1.50
451	A75	75sh Papilio phorcas	2.00	2.00
452	A75	90sh Cyrestis camillus	2.40	2.40
453	A75	100sh Salamis temora	2.40	2.40
		Nos. 446-453 (8)	12.00	12.00

Souvenir Sheets
454	A75	200sh Asterope rosa	4.50	4.50
455	A75	250sh Kallima rumia	5.50	5.50

Intl. Lions Club at Dar es Salaam, 25th Anniv. A76

1988, Nov. 30 Litho. Perf. 14½
456	A76	2sh Eye operation	.20	.20
457	A76	3sh Shallow water well	.20	.20
458	A76	7sh Map, rhinoceros	.60	.60
459	A76	12sh Donating school desks	.25	.25
		Nos. 456-459 (4)	1.25	1.25

Souvenir Sheet
460	A76	40sh Emblem	1.25	1.25

Community services: Matibabu Ya Macho Eye Camp (2sh); sanitary water supply in Dar es Salaam (3sh); wildlife conservation (7sh); aid to local schools (12sh).

Intl. Red Cross and Red Crescent Organizations, 125th Annivs. — A77

Design: 2sh, Assisting the wounded and sick. 3sh, Postnatal care clinic. 7sh, Red Cross flag. 12sh, Jean-Henry Dunant, founder. 40sh, Dunant, Thomas Maunier, Louis Appia, Gustave Moynier and Gen. Guillaume Henri Dufour, members of intl. committee that sponsored the conference in 1863 where the Red Cross was founded.

1988, Dec. 30 Litho. Perf. 12½x12
461	A77	2sh multicolored	.20	.20
462	A77	3sh multicolored	.20	.20
463	A77	7sh multicolored	.25	.25
464	A77	12sh multicolored	.35	.35
		Nos. 461-464 (4)	1.00	1.00

Souvenir Sheet
465	A77	40sh multicolored	1.00	1.00

Miniature Sheet

Paradise Whydah — A78

Birds: a, Paradise whydah. b, Black-collared barbet. c, Bateleur eagle. d, Openbill storks, lilac-breasted roller. e, Scarlet-tufted malachite sunbird. f, Dark chanting goshawk. g, White-fronted bee-eater, little bee-eater, carmine bee-eater. h, Marabou stork, Narina's trocon. i, African gray parrot. j, Hoopoe. k, Yellow-collared lovebird. l, Yellow-billed hornbill. m, Hammerkop. n, Flamingos, violet-crested turaco. o, Malachite kingfisher. p, Greater flamingo. q, Yellow-billed stork. r, Shoebill stork. s, Saddle-billed stork, blacksmith plover. t, Crowned crane.

1989, Jan. 10 Perf. 14
466		Sheet of 20	14.00	14.00
a.-t.	A78	20sh any single	.70	.70

Souvenir Sheets
467	A78	350sh Helmeted guineafowl	5.00	5.00
467A	A78	350sh Ostrich	5.00	5.00

No. 466 has a continuous design.

Endangered Species
A79   A80

World Wildlife Fund: Various bushbabies, *Galago zanzibaricus*. 350sh, African palm civet.

1989, Jan. 24   *Perf. 14*
468 A79 5sh shown   .25 .25
469 A79 10sh multi, horiz.   .40 .40
470 A79 20sh multi, diff.   .60 .60
471 A79 45sh multi, diff., horiz. 1.25 1.25
        Nos. 468-471 (4)   2.50 2.50

Souvenir Sheet
472 A79 350sh multi, horiz.   5.00 5.00

1989, Jan. 24

30sh, Black cobra, umbrella acacia. 70sh, Red-tailed tropic bird, tree fern. 100sh, African tree frog, cocoa tree. 150sh, African black-necked heron, Egyptian papyrus. 350sh, Pink-backed pelicans, baobab tree.

473 A80 30sh shown   .50 .50
474 A80 70sh multicolored   2.50 2.50
475 A80 100sh multicolored   2.50 2.50
476 A80 150sh multicolored   4.50 4.50
        Nos. 473-476 (4)   10.00 10.00

Souvenir Sheet
477 A80 350sh multicolored   5.00 5.00

Steam Locomotives — A81

1989, Jan. 31
478 A81 10sh Class P36, USSR .45 .45
479 A81 25sh Class 12, Belgi-
            um   .50 .50
480 A81 60sh Class C62, Japan .75 .75
481 A81 75sh Class T1, Penn-
            sylvania R.R.   .85 .85
482 A81 80sh Class WP, India .90 .90
483 A81 90sh Class 59, East
            African Railways   1.10 1.10
484 A81 150sh People Class 4-6-
            2, China   1.60 1.60
485 A81 200sh Southern Pacific
            *Daylight Ex-
            press*, US   1.60 1.60
        Nos. 478-485 (8)   7.75 7.75

Souvenir Sheets
486 A81 350sh Stephenson's
            Planet, Britain 4.00 4.00
487 A81 350sh *Coronation Scot*,
            Britain   4.00 4.00

        Nos. 486-487 vert.

World-Class
Athletes — A82

Designs: 4sh, Juma Ikangaa, Tanzania, marathon. 8.50sh, Steffi Graf, West Germany, tennis. 12sh, Yannick Noah, France, tennis. 40sh, Pele, Brazil, soccer. 100sh, Erhard Keller, West Germany, speed skater. 125sh, Sadanoyama, Japan, Sumo wrestler. 200sh, Taino, Japan, Sumo wrestler. 250sh, I. Aoki, Japan, golfer. No. 496, Joe Louis, US, world heavyweight boxing champion, 1937-1949. No. 497, T. Nakajima, Japan, golfer.

1989, Feb. 7
488 A82 4sh multicolored   .20 .20
489 A82 8.50sh multicolored   .20 .20
490 A82 12sh multicolored   .20 .20

491 A82 40sh multicolored   .60 .60
492 A82 100sh multicolored   1.50 1.50
493 A82 125sh multicolored   1.75 1.75
494 A82 200sh multicolored   2.75 2.75
495 A82 250sh multicolored   3.50 3.50
        Nos. 488-495 (8)   10.70 10.70

Souvenir Sheets
496 A82 350sh multicolored   4.00 4.00
497 A82 350sh multicolored   4.00 4.00

History of Space Exploration and 20th Anniv. of the 1st Moon Landing — A83

1989, July 20
498 A83 20sh Luna 3   .35 .35
499 A83 30sh Rendezvous of
            Gemini 6&7   .45 .45
500 A83 40sh 1st US space
            walk   .50 .50
501 A83 60sh First man on
            Moon   .70 .70
502 A83 70sh Experiments
            on Moon   .75 .75
503 A83 100sh Apollo 15 lunar
            rover   1.00 1.00
504 A83 150sh Apollo-Soyuz   1.25 1.25
505 A83 200sh Spacelab   1.50 1.50
        Nos. 498-505 (8)   6.50 6.50

Souvenir Sheets
506 A83 250sh Futuristic
            space station   2.50 2.50
507 A83 250sh *Eagle* lunar
            module   2.50 2.50

    History of space exploration (Nos. 498-500, 503-506); others 20th anniv. of 1st Moon Landing.

St. Mary
Magdalene
in Penitence
A84

Details from paintings by Titian: 10sh, Aver-oldi Polyptych. 15sh, St. Margaret. 50sh, Venus and Adonis. 75sh, Venus and the Lutenist. 100sh, Tarquin and Lucretia. 125sh, St. Jerome. 150sh, Madonna and Child with Saints. No. 516, St. Catherine of Alexandria at Prayer. No. 517, Adoration of the Holy Trinity. No. 517A, The Supper at Emmaus.

1989, Nov. 15 Litho.   *Perf. 13½x14*
508 A84 5sh multicolored   .20 .20
509 A84 10sh multicolored   .20 .20
510 A84 15sh multicolored   .20 .20
511 A84 50sh multicolored   .45 .45
512 A84 75sh multicolored   .65 .65
513 A84 100sh multicolored .80 .80
514 A84 125sh multicolored 1.00 1.00
515 A84 150sh multicolored 1.25 1.25
        Nos. 508-515 (8)   4.75 4.75

Souvenir Sheets
516 A84 300sh multicolored 2.50 2.50
517 A84 300sh multicolored 2.50 2.50
517A A84 300sh multicolored 2.50 2.50

    500th birth anniv. of Titian.
    #517A was not available until Jan. 8, 1991.

World Cup Soccer
Championships,
Italy — A85

1989, Nov. 15   *Perf. 14*
            Uniform colors
518 A85 25sh green, red & yel .40 .40
519 A85 60sh green, yel & blue .90 .90
520 A85 75sh orange & blue   1.10 1.10
521 A85 200sh blue & white   3.00 3.00
        Nos. 518-521 (4)   5.40 5.40

Souvenir Sheets
522 A85 350sh orange & bl, diff. 4.25 4.25
523 A85 350sh grn, yel & bl, diff. 4.25 4.25

Souvenir Sheet

Union Station, Washington, DC — A86

1989, Nov. 17
524 A86 500sh multicolored   5.50 5.50

        World Stamp Expo '89.

Fish
A87

1989, Dec. 14
525 A87 9sh Tiger tilapia   .20 .20
526 A87 13sh Picasso fish   .20 .20
527 A87 20sh Powder-blue
            surgeonfish   .30 .30
528 A87 40sh Butterflyfish   .55 .55
529 A87 70sh Guenther's notho 1.00 1.00
530 A87 100sh Ansorge's
            noelebias   1.50 1.50
531 A87 150sh Lyretail panchax 2.25 2.25
532 A87 200sh Regal angelfish 3.00 3.00
        Nos. 525-532 (8)   9.00 9.00

Souvenir Sheets
533 A87 350sh Batfish   4.25 4.25
534 A87 350sh Jewel cichlid 4.25 4.25

    Nos. 533-534 each contain one 38x51mm stamp.

Nos. 414-423
Ovptd. and
Similarly

    Perfs. as Before
1989, Dec. 19   Litho.
534A A71 5sh shown   .25 .25
534B A71 10sh "Gold - USSR /
            Silver - Brazil /
            Branze - W.
            Germany"   .35 .35
534C A71 20sh "Men's Match
            Sprint / Lutz
            Hesslich,
            DDR"   1.25 1.25
534D A71 25sh "Pairs,
            Gordeeva &
            Grinkov,
            USSR"   .65 .65
534E A71 50sh "Epee, Schmitt,
            W. Germany"   1.00 1.00
534F A71 50sh "Zurbriggen,
            Switzerland"   1.00 1.00
534G A71 70sh "Men's Team,
            USA"   1.50 1.50
534H A71 75sh "Gold-USSR /
            Silver-DDR /
            Bronze-DDR"   1.25 1.25
        Nos. 534A-534H (8)   7.25 7.25

Souvenir Sheets
534I A71 100sh "Ice Hockey: /
            Gold-USSR"   5.25 5.25
534J A71 100sh "Women's
            Team, / Gold-
            USSR"   1.75 1.75

Silver and Bronze medalists overprinted on margins of souvenir sheets.

Inter-Parliamentary Union,
Cent. — A88

Designs: 9sh, Secret ballot. 13sh, Parliament, Dar Es Salaam. 40sh, Sir William Randal Cremer, Frederic Passy. 80sh, Parliament in session. 100sh, IPU emblem.

1989, Dec. 22   *Perf. 12½x12*
535 A88 9sh multicolored   .20 .20
536 A88 13sh multicolored   .20 .20
537 A88 80sh multicolored   .85 .85
538 A88 100sh lt bl, dp bl & blk 1.00 1.00
        Nos. 535-538 (4)   2.25 2.25

Souvenir Sheet
539 A88 40sh multicolored   .85 .85

Pan-African
Postal
Union, 10th
Anniv.
A89

1990, Jan. 17   *Perf. 13½*
540 A89 9sh PAPU emblem   .20 .20
541 A89 13sh Post offices box-
            es   .20 .20
542 A89 70sh Mail early, prompt
            delivery   .70 .70
543 A89 100sh Modes of mail
            delivery   1.40 1.40
        Nos. 540-543 (4)   2.50 2.50

Souvenir Sheet
544 A89 40sh Tanzania Post,
            PAPU, UPU em-
            blems   .90 .90

Extinct
Animals
A90

1990, Feb. 4   *Perf. 14*
545 A90 25sh Tecopa pupfish .40 .40
546 A90 40sh Thylacine   .60 .60
547 A90 50sh Quagga   .75 .75
548 A90 60sh Passenger pig-
            eon   .90 .90
549 A90 75sh Rodriguez sad-
            dleback tor-
            toise   1.10 1.10
550 A90 100sh Toolache walla-
            by   1.50 1.50
551 A90 150sh Texas red wolf 2.25 2.25
552 A90 200sh Utah lake scul-
            pin   3.00 3.00
        Nos. 545-552 (8)   10.50 10.50

Souvenir Sheets
553 A90 350sh Hawaiian O-O,
            vert.   4.00 4.00
554 A90 350sh South island
            whekau   4.00 4.00

Nina,
Admiral's
Flag
A91

1990, Feb. 20
555 A91 50sh shown   .75 .75
556 A91 60sh Pinta, flag   .90 .90
557 A91 75sh Santa Maria, flag 1.10 1.10

558 A91 200sh Map of Columbus' first voyage 3.00 3.00
Nos. 555-558 (4) 5.75 5.75

Souvenir Sheet

559 A91 350sh Ships, bird's head 5.25 5.25
Discovery of America, 500th anniv. (in 1992).

Modern Discoveries — A92

Designs: 9sh, Bell X-1 breaking the sound barrier. 13sh, Bathyscaph Trieste reaches the deepest ocean bottom. 150sh, Transistor and computer chips. 250sh, Discovery of DNA structure. 350sh, Voyager 2 visits Neptune.

1990, Feb. 20

560 A92 9sh multicolored .55 .55
561 A92 13sh multicolored .55 .55
562 A92 150sh multicolored 1.25 1.25
563 A92 250sh multicolored 2.10 2.10
Nos. 560-563 (4) 4.45 4.45

Souvenir Sheet

564 A92 350sh multicolored 5.25 5.25

Girl Guides, 60th Anniv. A93

1990, Feb. 22 **Perf. 12½x12**

565 A93 9sh Hiking .20 .20
566 A93 13sh Planting trees .20 .20
567 A93 50sh Teaching writing .60 .60
568 A93 100sh Teaching health
care 1.00 1.00
Nos. 565-568 (4) 2.00 2.00

Souvenir Sheet

Perf. 12x12½

569 A93 40sh Nursing school,
vert. 1.25 1.25

Disney Characters,
Automobiles — A94

1990, Mar. 20 **Perf. 14x13½**

570 A94 20sh Herbie, The
Love Bug .35 .35
571 A94 30sh The Absent-
Minded Pro-
fessor's car .40 .40
572 A94 45sh Chitty-Chitty
Bang-Bang .50 .50
573 A94 60sh Mr. Toad's wild
ride .70 .70
574 A94 75sh Scrooge's lim-
ousine .80 .80
575 A94 100sh Shaggy dog's
car 1.10 1.10
576 A94 150sh Donald Duck's
car 1.75 1.75
577 A94 200sh Firetruck in
"Dumbo" 1.90 1.90
Nos. 570-577 (8) 7.50 7.50

Souvenir Sheets

578 A94 350sh Cruella de Vil 4.00 4.00
579 A94 350sh Mickeymobile 4.00 4.00

Black Entertainers
A95

1990, Mar. 30 **Litho.** **Perf. 14**

580 A95 9sh Miriam Makeba .20 .20
581 A95 13sh Manu Dibango .20 .20
582 A95 25sh Fela .20 .20
583 A95 70sh Smokey Robinson .75 .75
584 A95 100sh Gladys Knight .90 .90
585 A95 150sh Eddie Murphy 1.75 1.75
586 A95 200sh Sammy Davis,
Jr. 2.00 2.00
587 A95 250sh Stevie Wonder 2.00 2.00
Nos. 580-587 (8) 8.00 8.00

Souvenir Sheets

Perf. 14½

588 A95 350sh Bill Cosby 2.50 2.50
589 A95 350sh Michael Jackson 2.50 2.50

Union of Tanganyika and Zanzibar,
25th Anniv. (in 1989) — A95a

Designs: 9sh, Fishing. 13sh, Grapes. 50sh, Cloves. 100sh, Presidents Nyerere and Karume exchanging Union instruments, vert. 40sh, Natl. arms, vert.

Perf. 12½x12, 12x12½

1990, Apr. 25 **Litho.**

589A A95a 9sh multicolored .20 .20
589B A95a 13sh multicolored .20 .20
589C A95a 50sh multicolored .60 .60
589D A95a 100sh multicolored 1.25 1.25
Nos. 589A-589D (4) 2.25 2.25

Souvenir Sheet

589E A95a 40sh multicolored 1.75 1.75

Southern Africa Development
Coordinating Conf. (SADCC), 10th
Anniv. — A96

1990, Aug. 8 **Perf. 13½**

590 A96 8sh Railway transport .20 .20
591 A96 11.50sh Paper industry .20 .20
592 A96 25sh Tractor production .35 .35
593 A96 100sh Flags, map 1.25 1.25
Nos. 590-593 (4) 2.00 2.00

Souvenir Sheet

Perf. 12½

594 A96 50sh Map 1.75 1.75

A97 A98

Pope John Paul II's Visit to Tanzania: 15sh, Wearing red vestments. 20sh, Wearing miter. 100sh, Papal arms. No. 599: a, Pope with arms outstretched. b, St. Joseph's Cathedral,

Dar Es Salaam. c, Christ the King Cathedral, Moshi. d, Saint Theresa's Cathedral, Tabora. e, Cathedral of the Epiphany, Bugando Mwanza. f, St. Mathias Mulumba Kalemba Cathedral, Songea.

1990, Sept. 1 **Litho.** **Perf. 14**

595 A97 10sh shown .25 .25
596 A97 15sh multicolored .35 .35
597 A97 20sh multicolored .40 .40
598 A97 100sh multicolored 1.00 1.00
Nos. 595-598 (4) 2.00 2.00

Souvenir Sheet

599 Sheet of 6 3.00 3.00
a.-f. A97 50sh any single .50 .50

1990, Sept. 28

Players from participating countries.

600 A98 10sh West Germany .50 .50
601 A98 60sh Italy .75 .75
602 A98 100sh Scotland 1.50 1.50
603 A98 300sh Yugoslavia 2.75 2.75
Nos. 600-603 (4) 5.50 5.50

Souvenir Sheets

604 A98 400sh Costa Rica 4.00 4.00
605 A98 400sh Belgium 4.00 4.00

World Cup Soccer Championships, Italy.

Birds — A99

1990-91 **Litho.** **Perf. 14**

606 A99 5sh Masked
weaver .20 .20
607 A99 9sh Emerald
cuckoo .20 .20
608 A99 13sh Little bee-
eater .35 .35
609 A99 15sh Red bishop .35 .35
610 A99 20sh Bateleur .45 .45
611 A99 25sh Scarlet-
chested
sunbird .45 .45
a. Bklt. pane, 2 ea #606-611 2.00 2.00
611B A99 30sh Pigeons .45 .45

Size: 42x28mm

612 A99 40sh Lesser fla-
mingo .45 .45
613 A99 70sh Helmeted
guineafowl .50 .50
614 A99 100sh White peli-
can .60 .60
615 A99 170sh Saddle-billed
stork .80 .80
616 A99 200sh Crowned
crane .90 .90
616A A99 300sh Pied crow 1.00 1.00
616B A99 400sh White-head-
ed vulture 1.25 1.25
617 A99 500sh Ostrich 1.25 1.25
Nos. 606-617 (15) 9.20 9.20

Souvenir Sheet

Stamp size: 42x28mm

617A Sheet of 2 2.50 2.50
b. A99 40sh Superb starling 1.00 1.00
c. A99 60sh Lilac-breasted
roller 1.50 1.50

Issued: 30sh, 300sh, 400sh, 1991; others, 10/1/90.
See Nos. 1723A, 2157-2159.

Boats
A100

1990, Oct. 10 **Litho.** **Perf. 12½x12**

618 A100 9sh Canoe .20 .20
619 A100 13sh Outrigger canoe .20 .20
620 A100 25sh Dhow .30 .30
621 A100 100sh Freighter 1.40 1.40
Nos. 618-621 (4) 2.10 2.10

Souvenir Sheet

622 A100 40sh Boat 1.50 1.50

Commonwealth Games, New
Zealand — A101

1990, Oct. 22 **Perf. 14**

623 A101 9sh Sprinting .20 .20
624 A101 13sh Netball, vert. .40 .40
625 A101 25sh Pole vault .55 .55
626 A101 100sh Long jump, vert. 1.60 1.60
Nos. 623-626 (4) 2.75 2.75

Souvenir Sheet

627 A101 40sh Boxing 1.25 1.25

Orchids — A102

1990, Nov. 12

628 A102 10sh Phalaenopsis .20 .20
629 A102 25sh Lycaste .20 .20
630 A102 30sh Vuylstekeara,
Cambria
"Plush" .25 .25
631 A102 50sh Vuylstekeara,
Monica "Burn-
ham" .40 .40
632 A102 90sh Odontocidium .70 .70
633 A102 100sh Oncidioda .85 .85
634 A102 250sh Sophrolaeliocat-
tleya 2.00 2.00
635 A102 300sh Laeliocattleya 2.40 2.40
Nos. 628-635 (8) 7.00 7.00

Souvenir Sheets

636 A102 400sh Cymbidium,
Baldoyle
"Melbury" 3.00 3.00
637 A102 400sh Cymbidium,
Tapestry "Long
Beach" 3.00 3.00

Expo '90, the Intl. Garden and Greenery Exposition, Osaka, Japan.

1990 World Cup Soccer
Championships, Italy — A102a

1990, Nov. 17 **Litho.** **Perf. 14**

637A A102a 9sh Long throw-
in .25 .25
637B A102a 13sh Penalty kick .25 .25
637C A102a 25sh Dribbling .35 .35
637D A102a 100sh Corner kick 1.40 1.40
Nos. 637A-637D (4) 2.25 2.25

Souvenir Sheet

637E A102a 50sh Trophy, map 2.00 2.00

Racing
A103

5sh, Olympic Soling Class Yacht racing. 20sh, Olympic downhill ski racing. 30sh, Tour de France bicycle race. 40sh, Le Mans 24 hour endurance auto race. 75sh, Olympic 2-man bobsled. 100sh, Belgian Grand Prix motorcycle race. 250sh, Indianapolis 500 auto race. 300sh, Power boat gold cup racing. #646, Colorado 500 enduro motorcycle race. #647, Schneider Trophy air races.

1990, Nov. 19
638	A103	5sh multicolored	.25	.25
639	A103	20sh multicolored	.50	.50
640	A103	30sh multicolored	.80	.80
641	A103	40sh multicolored	.80	.80
642	A103	75sh multicolored	.90	.90
643	A103	100sh multicolored	1.40	1.40
644	A103	250sh multicolored	1.60	1.60
645	A103	300sh multicolored	1.75	1.75
		Nos. 638-645 (8)	8.00	8.00

Souvenir Sheets
646	A103	400sh multicolored	4.25	4.25
647	A103	400sh multicolored	4.25	4.25

1992 Summer Olympics, Barcelona — A104

1990, Nov. 30
648	A104	5sh Archery	.20	.20
649	A104	10sh Women's gymnastics	.20	.20
650	A104	25sh Boxing	.20	.20
651	A104	50sh Two-man kayak race	.40	.40
652	A104	100sh Men's volleyball	.75	.75
653	A104	150sh Mens' gymnastics	1.25	1.25
654	A104	200sh 4x100 meter relay	1.60	1.60
655	A104	300sh Judo	2.40	2.40
		Nos. 648-655 (8)	7.00	7.00

Souvenir Sheets
656	A104	400sh Men's 400 meter hurdles	3.25	3.25
657	A104	400sh Men's cycling	3.25	3.25

Cog Railroads A105

Cog locomotives: 8sh, Petersberg Cog Railway, West Germany. 25sh, Engine *Waumbek* on Mt. Washington Cog Railway, US. 50sh, Doubleheaded cog engines on Dubrovnik-Sarajevo line, Yugoslavia. 100sh, Cog Railway, Budapest, Hungary 1874. 150sh, Vordenberg-Eisenerz line, Austria. 200sh, Rimutaka Incline, New Zealand, 1955. 250sh, John Stevens' cog engine, Hoboken, NJ, 1825. 300sh, Pilatusbahn Cog Railway, Switzerland, 1889. No. 666, Schneebergbahn of the OBB, Austria. No. 667, Sylvester Marsh, Mt. Washington Cog Railway, 1869.

1990, Dec. 8
658	A105	8sh multicolored	.20	.20
659	A105	25sh multicolored	.20	.20
660	A105	50sh multicolored	.40	.40
661	A105	100sh multicolored	.80	.80
662	A105	150sh multicolored	1.25	1.25
663	A105	200sh multicolored	1.60	1.60
664	A105	250sh multicolored	2.00	2.00
665	A105	300sh multicolored	2.40	2.40
		Nos. 658-665 (8)	8.85	8.85

Souvenir Sheets
666	A105	400sh multicolored	3.50	3.50
667	A105	400sh multicolored	3.50	3.50

First Postage Stamps, 150th Anniv. A106

Designs: No. 668, German Post Office at Dar Es Salaam, German East Africa No. 16. No. 669, Mailboat S.S. Reichstag, 1890, Germany No. 40 cancelled in Zanzibar. No. 670, Dhows used as mailboats, Zanzibar No. 1. No. 671, Mailplane Singapore I on Lake Victoria, 1928, Tanganyika No. 22. No. 672, Mailplane, Livingston's House, Zanzibar No. 316. No. 673, Passenger-mail train at Moshi Station, Tanganyika No. 52. No. 674, Royal mail coach, 1840. 150sh, Stephenson's *Rocket*, mail car, 1838. 200sh, Handley Page HP-42 mailplane. No. 677, Hand delivery of mail,

Thurn & Taxis No. 44 on cover. No. 678, Sir Rowland Hill.

1990, Dec. 12
668	A106	50sh multicolored	.55	.55
669	A106	50sh multicolored	.55	.55
a.		Pair, #668-669	1.10	1.10
670	A106	75sh multicolored	.75	.75
671	A106	75sh multicolored	.75	.75
a.		Pair, #670-671	1.50	1.50
672	A106	100sh multicolored	1.10	1.10
673	A106	100sh multicolored	1.10	1.10
a.		Pair, #672-673	2.25	2.25
674	A106	100sh multicolored	1.10	1.10
675	A106	150sh multicolored	1.50	1.50
676	A106	160sh multicolored	1.60	1.60
		Nos. 668-676 (9)	9.00	9.00

Souvenir Sheets
677	A106	350sh multicolored	3.25	3.25
678	A106	350sh multicolored	3.25	3.25

500th anniv. of Thurn and Taxis Post (No. 677).
For overprints see Nos. 928-934.

Intl. Literacy Year — A107

Nos. 679a-681i depict various Walt Disney characters and a letter of the alphabet.
No. 682, Mickey's train hauls Russian alphabet. No. 683, Children learning Hebrew.

1990, Dec. 27   Perf. 13½x14
Miniature Sheets
679		Sheet of 9	5.00	5.00
a.	A107	1sh "ABC"	.20	.20
b.	A107	2sh "A"	.20	.20
c.	A107	3sh "B"	.20	.20
d.	A107	15sh "C"	.20	.20
e.	A107	55sh "D"	.45	.45
f.	A107	80sh "E"	.65	.65
g.	A107	120sh "F"	.95	.95
h.	A107	145sh "G"	1.10	1.10
i.	A107	200sh "H"	1.60	1.60
680		Sheet of 9	4.75	4.75
a.	A107	10sh "I"	.20	.20
b.	A107	20sh "J"	.20	.20
c.	A107	30sh "K"	.25	.25
d.	A107	40sh "L"	.30	.30
e.	A107	50sh "M"	.40	.40
f.	A107	60sh "N"	.50	.50
g.	A107	100sh "O"	.80	.80
h.	A107	125sh "P"	1.00	1.00
i.	A107	150sh "Q"	1.25	1.25
681		Sheet of 9	5.00	5.00
a.	A107	10sh "R"	.20	.20
b.	A107	18sh "S"	.20	.20
c.	A107	25sh "T"	.20	.20
d.	A107	35sh "U"	.30	.30
e.	A107	45sh "V"	.35	.35
f.	A107	75sh "W"	.60	.60
g.	A107	90sh "X"	.70	.70
h.	A107	160sh "Y"	1.25	1.25
i.	A107	175sh "Z"	1.40	1.40

Souvenir Sheets
682	A107	600sh multicolored	4.75	4.75
683	A107	600sh multicolored	4.75	4.75

Intl. Literacy Year A108

1991, Mar. 15   Litho.   Perf. 14
684	A108	9sh Learning to read	.20	.20
685	A108	13sh Learning to write	.25	.25
686	A108	25sh Blackboard, books	.30	.30
687	A108	100sh Reading newspapers	1.75	1.75
		Nos. 684-687 (4)	2.50	2.50

Souvenir Sheet
688	A108	50sh Adult education	1.25	1.25

For surcharge see No. 1431A.

Mickey Mouse — A109

Character roles: 5sh, Western cowboy. 10sh, Boxer. 15sh, Astronaut. 20sh, Romantic lead with Minnie. 100sh, Swashbuckling hero. 200sh, Detective with Donald Duck and Pistol Pete. 350sh, King with Donald as court jester. 450sh, Sailor with Donald and Goofy. No. 697, Minnie, Mickey as archaeologists in Egypt, Donald as a mummy. No. 698, Mickey as Canadian Mountie.

1991, Feb. 11   Litho.   Perf. 14x13½
689	A109	5sh multicolored	.30	.30
690	A109	10sh multicolored	.35	.35
691	A109	15sh multicolored	.35	.35
692	A109	20sh multicolored	.35	.35
693	A109	100sh multicolored	1.40	1.40
694	A109	200sh multicolored	2.75	2.75
695	A109	350sh multicolored	3.25	3.25
696	A109	450sh multicolored	3.25	3.25
		Nos. 689-696 (8)	12.00	12.00

Souvenir Sheets
697	A109	600sh multicolored	6.00	6.00
698	A109	600sh multicolored	6.00	6.00

Craters and Caves A109a

Designs: 3sh, Ngorongoro Crater. 5sh, Kondoa Caves, prehistoric rock paintings. 9sh, Mount Kilimanjaro's inner crater. 12sh, Olduvai Gorge.
Amboni Caves: No. 698f, Open area of cave. g, People viewing cave, large stalactite. h, Woman seated beside welcome sign. i, Man climbing up to view cave.

1991, Mar. 28   Litho.   Perf. 14½
698A	A109a	3sh multicolored	.70	.70
698B	A109a	5sh multicolored	.70	.70
698C	A109a	9sh multicolored	.85	.85
698D	A109a	12sh multicolored	1.25	1.25
		Nos. 698A-698D (4)	3.50	3.50

Souvenir Sheet
698E	A109a	10sh Sheet of 4, #f.-i.	7.00	7.00

Nos. 698A-698E were not available to the philatelic community until Mar. 1994.

Miniature Sheet

Peter Paul Rubens, 350th Death Anniv. — A110

Cycle of Decius Mus: No. 699a, Proclamation of the Vision. b, Divining of the Entrails. c, Dispatch of the Lictors. d, Dedication to Death. e, Victory and Death of Decius Mus. f, Funeral Rites. No. 700, Trophy of War, vert.

1991, Apr. 10   Litho.   Perf. 14x13½
699	A110	85sh Sheet of 6, #a.-f.	7.00	7.00

Souvenir Sheet
Perf. 13½x14
700	A110	500sh multicolored	7.00	7.00

Tanzania Investment Bank, 20th Anniv. — A111

Designs: 10sh, Dairy farming. 13sh, Industrial development. 25sh, Engineering. 100sh, Tea harvesting.

1991, June 7   Perf. 14
701	A111	10sh multicolored	.20	.20
702	A111	13sh multicolored	.20	.20
703	A111	25sh multicolored	.20	.20
704	A111	100sh multicolored	1.40	1.40
a.		Souvenir sheet of 4, #701-704	2.00	2.00
		Nos. 701-704 (4)	2.00	2.00

Phila Nippon '91 A112

Japanese locomotives: 10sh, First Japanese steam. 25sh, Series 4500 steam. 35sh, C 62 steam. 50sh, Mikado steam. 75sh, Series 6250 steam. 100sh, C 11 steam. 200sh, E 10 steam. 300sh, Series 8550 steam. No. 713, EF 58 electric. No. 714, DD 51 diesel. No. 715, Series 400 electric. No. 716, EH 10 electric.

1991, Aug. 15   Litho.   Perf. 14
705	A112	10sh multicolored	.50	.50
706	A112	25sh multicolored	.75	.75
707	A112	35sh multicolored	.85	.85
708	A112	50sh multicolored	1.00	1.00
709	A112	75sh multicolored	1.25	1.25
710	A112	100sh multicolored	1.50	1.50
711	A112	200sh multicolored	1.75	1.75
712	A112	300sh multicolored	2.10	2.10
		Nos. 705-712 (8)	9.70	9.70

Souvenir Sheets
713	A112	400sh multicolored	2.25	2.25
714	A112	400sh multicolored	2.25	2.25
715	A112	400sh multicolored	2.25	2.25
716	A112	400sh multicolored	2.25	2.25

Fauna in Natl. Game Parks A113

Species and park: 10sh, Common zebra, golden-winged sunbird, Ngorongoro Crater Conservation Area. 25sh, Greater kudu, African elephant, Ruaha. 30sh, Sable antelope, red and yellow barbet, Mikumi. 50sh, Wildebeest, leopard, Serengeti. 90sh, Giraffe, white-starred bush robin, Ngurdoto Crater. 100sh, Eland, Abbot's duiker, Kilimanjaro. 250sh, Lion, impala, Lake Manyara. 300sh, Black rhinoceros, ostrich, Tarangire. No. 725, Paradise whydah, oryx, Mkomazi Game Reserve. No. 726, Blue-breasted kingfisher, defassa waterbuck, Selous Game Reserve.

1991, Aug. 22   Litho.   Perf. 14
717	A113	10sh multicolored	.20	.20
718	A113	25sh multicolored	.30	.30
719	A113	30sh multicolored	.40	.40
720	A113	50sh multicolored	.65	.65
721	A113	90sh multicolored	1.10	1.10
722	A113	100sh multicolored	1.25	1.25
723	A113	250sh multicolored	3.00	3.00
724	A113	300sh multicolored	3.75	3.75
		Nos. 717-724 (8)	10.65	10.65

Souvenir Sheets
725	A113	400sh multicolored	5.00	5.00
726	A113	400sh multicolored	5.00	5.00

Butterflies — A114

Designs: 10sh, Vine leaf vagrant. 15sh, Blue spot commodore. 35sh, Orange admiral. 75sh, Wanderer. 100sh, Jackson's leaf. 150sh, Painted empress. 200sh, Double-banded orange. 300sh, Crawshay's sapphire blue. No. 735, Noble swallowtail. No. 736, Club-tailed charaxes. No. 737, Satyr charaxes. No. 738, Green patch swallowtail.

1991, Aug. 28   Litho.   Perf. 14

727	A114	10sh multicolored	.20	.20
728	A114	15sh multicolored	.20	.20
729	A114	35sh multicolored	.45	.45
730	A114	75sh multicolored	.95	.95
731	A114	100sh multicolored	1.25	1.25
732	A114	150sh multicolored	1.90	1.90
733	A114	200sh multicolored	2.50	2.50
734	A114	300sh multicolored	3.75	3.75
		Nos. 727-734 (8)	11.20	11.20

Souvenir Sheets

735	A114	400sh multicolored	3.50	3.50
736	A114	400sh multicolored	3.50	3.50
737	A114	400sh multicolored	3.50	3.50
738	A114	400sh multicolored	3.50	3.50

While Nos. 727-736 have the same issue date as Nos. 737-738, the dollar value of Nos. 737-738 was lower when they were released.

Intelsat, 25th Anniv. A115

Designs: 10sh, Microwave link. 25sh, Earth. 100sh, Mwenge standard "B" Earth station. 500sh, Mwenge standard "A" Earth station. 50sh, World map.

1991, Sept. 5   Litho.   Perf. 14

739	A115	10sh multicolored	.20	.20
740	A115	25sh multicolored	.30	.30
741	A115	100sh multicolored	1.25	1.25
742	A115	500sh multicolored	4.75	4.75
		Nos. 739-742 (4)	6.50	6.50

Souvenir Sheet

743	A115	50sh multicolored	1.25	1.25

UN Development Program, 40th Anniv. — A116

Designs: 10sh, Irrigated rice farming. 15sh, Vocational training. 100sh, Terrace farming. 500sh, Architectural renovations, vert. 40sh, Helping people to help themselves, vert.

1991, Sept. 16   Perf. 13½

744	A116	10sh multicolored	.20	.20
745	A116	15sh multicolored	.20	.20
746	A116	100sh multicolored	1.10	1.10
747	A116	500sh multicolored	5.50	5.50
		Nos. 744-747 (4)	7.00	7.00

Souvenir Sheet
Perf. 13x12½

748	A116	40sh black & blue	1.00	1.00

All Africa Games, Cairo — A117

Telecom '91 — A118

Perf. 12x12½, 12½x12

1991, Sept. 20

749	A117	10sh Netball	.25	.25
750	A117	15sh Soccer, horiz.	.25	.25
751	A117	100sh Tennis	1.60	1.60
752	A117	200sh Running	1.90	1.90
753	A117	500sh Baseball, horiz.	4.50	4.50
		Nos. 749-753 (5)	8.50	8.50

Souvenir Sheet

754	A117	500sh Basketball	6.50	6.50

1991, Oct. 1   Perf. 13½x14, 14x13½

755	A118	10sh shown	.20	.20
756	A118	15sh Telecom '91, horiz.	.20	.20
757	A118	35sh arrows	.30	.30
758	A118	100sh like #757, horiz.	.80	.80
		Nos. 755-758 (4)	1.50	1.50

World Telecommunications Day (Nos. 757-758).

Dinosaurs A119

1991, Oct. 28   Perf. 12x12½

759	A119	10sh Stegosaurus	.20	.20
760	A119	15sh Triceratops	.20	.20
761	A119	25sh Edmontosaurus	.30	.30
762	A119	30sh Plateosaurus	.40	.40
763	A119	35sh Diplodocus	.45	.45
764	A119	100sh Iguanodon	1.25	1.25
765	A119	200sh Silviasaurus	2.50	2.50
		Nos. 759-765 (7)	5.30	5.30

Souvenir Sheet

766	A119	150sh Rhampho-rhynchus	2.25	2.25

Miniature Sheets

Animals and Fish A120

Horses: No. 767a, Shire. b, Thoroughbred. c, Kladruber. d, Appaloosa. e, Hanoverian. f, Arab. g, Breton. h, Exmoor. i, Connemara. j, Lipizzaner. k, Shetland. l, Percheron. m, Pinto. n, Orlov. o, Palomino. p, Welsh cob.
Cats: No. 768a, Japanese bobtail. b, Cornish rex. c, Malayan. d, Tonkinese. e, Abyssinian. f, Russian blue. g, Cymric. h, Somali. i, Siamese. j, Himalayan. k, Singapura. l, Manx. m, Oriental shorthair. n, Maine coon. o, Persian. p, Birman.
African elephants (all designs vert.): No. 769a, One walking left. b, Two with tusks entangled. c, One facing forward. d, One under tree. e, Adult and calf in water, zebra. f, Adult and calf walking into water. g, Two adults and calf in water. h, Adult and calf standing in water. i, One walking right. j, Two, one raising trunk in air. k, One raising trunk in air. l, One

facing forward, trunk down, zebra. m, Adult, calf at edge of water, antelope. n, Adult and calf, two more in background. o, One walking toward water. p, Adult with trunk on calf.
Aquarium fish: No. 770a, Jewel tetra. b, Five-banded barb. c, Simpson platy. d, Guppy, e, Zebra danio. f, Neon tetra. g, Siamese fighting fish. h, Tiger barb. i, Red lyretail. j, Goldfish. k, Pearl gourami. l, Angelfish. m, Clown loach. n, Red swordtail. o, Brown discus. p, Rosy barb.
Birds: No. 771a, Budgerigar. b, Rainbow bunting. c, Golden-fronted leafbird. d, Black-headed caique. e, Java sparrow. f, Diamond sparrow. g, Peach-faced lovebird. h, Golden conure. i, Military macaw. j, Celestial parrotlet. k, Sulphur-crested cockatoo. l, Spectacled Amazon parrot. m, Paradise tanager. n, Gouldian finch. o, Masked lovebird. p, Hill mynah.

1991, Oct. 28   Litho.   Perf. 14
Sheets of 16

767	A120	50sh #a.-p.	10.00	10.00
768	A120	50sh #a.-p.	9.00	9.00
769	A120	75sh #a.-p.	15.00	15.00
770	A120	75sh #a.-p.	10.00	10.00
771	A120	75sh #a.-p.	10.00	10.00
		Nos. 767-771 (5)	54.00	54.00

For overprints see Nos. 1529-1530.

Paintings by Vincent Van Gogh A121

Designs: 10sh, Peasant Woman Sewing. 15sh, Head of a Peasant Woman with Greenish Lace Cap. 35sh, Flowering Orchard. 75sh, Portrait of a Girl. 100sh, Portrait of a Woman with a Red Ribbon. 150sh, Vase with Flowers. 200sh, Houses in Antwerp. 400sh, Seated Peasant Woman with White Cap. No. 780, The Parsonage Garden at Nuenen in the Snow, horiz. No. 781, Bulb Fields, horiz.

1991, Nov. 20   Litho.   Perf. 13½x14

772	A121	10sh multicolored	.20	.20
773	A121	15sh multicolored	.20	.20
774	A121	35sh multicolored	.50	.50
775	A121	75sh multicolored	.95	.95
776	A121	100sh multicolored	1.25	1.25
777	A121	150sh multicolored	1.90	1.90
778	A121	200sh multicolored	2.50	2.50
779	A121	400sh multicolored	5.00	5.00
		Nos. 772-779 (8)	12.50	12.50

Size: 127x102mm
Imperf

780	A121	400sh multicolored	5.25	5.25
781	A121	400sh multicolored	5.25	5.25

Walt Disney Christmas Cards — A122

Design and date of card: 10sh, "Joy", 1968. 25sh, Mickey, Pluto and Goofy at fireplace, 1981. 35sh, Robin Hood and merry men celebrating, 1973. 75sh, Tree of greetings, Mickey, 1967. 100sh, Goofy, Mickey and Donald trying to catch Santa coming down chimney, 1969, vert. 150sh, Mickey on top of Christmas ornament, 1976, vert. 200sh, Clarabelle Cow with bells, 1935, vert. 300sh, Orphan mice reading book of tricks, 1935, vert. No. 790, Mickey wearing Santa hat and surrounded by Disney characters, 1968, vert. No. 791, Mickey with present for Donald, 1935, vert.

Perf. 13½x14, 14x13½
1991, Dec.   Litho.

782	A122	10sh multicolored	.20	.20
783	A122	25sh multicolored	.40	.40
784	A122	35sh multicolored	.50	.50
785	A122	75sh multicolored	1.00	1.00
786	A122	100sh multicolored	1.40	1.40
787	A122	150sh multicolored	1.75	1.75
788	A122	200sh multicolored	2.00	2.00
789	A122	300sh multicolored	2.75	2.75
		Nos. 782-789 (8)	10.00	10.00

Souvenir Sheets

790	A122	500sh multicolored	5.50	5.50
791	A122	500sh multicolored	5.50	5.50

Elephants A123

Designs: 10sh, 15sh, 25sh, 100sh, Various pictures of elephas maximus. 30sh, 35sh, 200sh, Various pictures of loxodonta africana. 400sh, Mammut mammuthus.

Perf. 12x12½, 12½x12
1991, Nov. 28   Litho.

792	A123	10sh multi, vert.	.20	.20
793	A123	15sh multi, vert.	.20	.20
794	A123	25sh multi, vert.	.30	.30
795	A123	30sh multi, vert.	.40	.40
796	A123	35sh multicolored	.45	.45
797	A123	100sh multicolored	1.25	1.25
798	A123	200sh multicolored	2.50	2.50
		Nos. 792-798 (7)	5.30	5.30

Souvenir Sheet

799	A123	400sh multicolored	4.00	4.00

Locomotives — A124

1991, Dec. 10   Perf. 12½x12, 12x12½

800	A124	10sh USSR 1930	.20	.20
801	A124	15sh Japan 1964	.20	.20
802	A124	25sh Russia 1834, vert.	.30	.30
803	A124	35sh France 1979	.45	.45
804	A124	60sh France 1972	.85	.85
805	A124	100sh United Kingdom 1972	1.25	1.25
806	A124	300sh Russia 1837, vert.	3.75	3.75
		Nos. 800-806 (7)	7.00	7.00

Souvenir Sheet

807	A124	100sh France, 1952, vert.	1.75	1.75

Miniature Sheets

Entertainers — A125

Nos. 808a-808i, 812, Various portraits of Elvis Presley.
Nos. 809a-809i, 813, Various portraits of Marilyn Monroe.
Nos. 810a-810i, 814, Various portraits of Bruce Lee.
Black entertainers: No. 811: a, Scott Joplin. b, Sammy Davis, Jr. c, Joan Armatrading. d, Louis Armstrong. e, Miriam Makeba. f, Lionel Ritchie. g, Whitney Houston, h, Bob Marley. i, Tina Turner. No. 815, Kouyate family.

1992, Feb. 15   Perf. 14
Sheets of 9

808	A125	75sh #a.-i.	8.50	8.50
809	A125	75sh #a.-i.	8.50	8.50
810	A125	75sh #a.-i.	8.50	8.50
811	A125	75sh #a.-i.	8.50	8.50
		Nos. 808-811 (4)	34.00	34.00

Souvenir Sheets

812	A125	500sh multicolored	6.25	6.25
813	A125	500sh multicolored	6.25	6.25
814	A125	500sh multicolored	6.25	6.25
815	A125	500sh multicolored	6.25	6.25
		Nos. 812-815 (4)	25.00	25.00

Nos. 812-815 each contain one 29x43mm stamp.

See #949 for #808 inscribed "15th Anniversary."

Fish of Tanzania A126

Designs: 10sh, Malacanthus latovittatus. 15sh, Lamprologus tretocephalus. 25sh, Lamprologus calvus. 35sh, Hemichromis bimaculatusl. 60sh, Aphyosemion bivittatum. No. 821, Synanceia verrucosa. 300sh, Aphyosemion ahli. No. 823, Regalecus glesne.

1992, Mar. 8   Perf. 12½x12

816	A126	10sh multicolored	.35	.35
817	A126	15sh multicolored	.45	.45
818	A126	25sh multicolored	.60	.60
819	A126	35sh multicolored	.70	.70
820	A126	60sh multicolored	.90	.90
821	A126	100sh multicolored	1.25	1.25
822	A126	300sh multicolored	3.25	3.25
		Nos. 816-822 (7)	7.50	7.50

Souvenir Sheet

823	A126	100sh multicolored	1.40	1.40

Miniature Sheet

World War II in the Pacific A127

Designs: No. 824a, British-designed radar at Pearl Harbor. b, Churchill declares war on Japan. c, Repulse destroyed. d, Prince of Wales sunk. e, Singapore falls to Japanese. f, Hermes is sunk off Ceylon. g, Airfields in Malaya attacked. h, Hong Kong falls to Japanese. i, Japanese Daihatsu landing craft. j, Japanese cruiser Haguro in Java Sea.

1992, Apr. 27   Perf. 14½x15

824	A127	75sh Sheet of 10, #a.-j.	10.00	10.00

Papal Visits — A128

Pope John Paul II's visits to: No. 825a, Dominican Republic, 1979. b, Mexico, 1979. c, Poland, 1979. d, Ireland, 1979. e, UN, New York, 1979. f, US, 1979. g, Turkey, 1979. h, Zaire, 1980. i, Congo, 1980. j, Kenya, 1980. k, Ghana, 1980. l, Upper Volta, 1980.

No. 826a, Ivory Coast, 1980. b, France, 1980. c, Brazil, 1980. d, West Germany, 1980. e, Pakistan, 1981. f, Philippines, 1981. g, Guam, 1981. h, Japan, 1981. h, Alaska, 1981. i, Nigeria, 1982. j, Benin, 1982. l. Gabon, 1982.

No. 827a, Equatorial Guinea, 1982. b, Portugal, 1982. c, Great Britain, 1982. d, Argentina, 1982. e, UN, Geneva, 1982. f, San Marino, 1982. g, Spain, 1982. h, Costa Rica, 1983. i, Panama, 1983. j, El Salvador, 1983. k, Nicaragua, 1983. l, Guatemala, 1983.

No. 828a, Honduras, 1983. b, Belize, 1983. c, Haiti, 1983. d, Poland, 1983. e, France, 1983. f, Austria, 1983. g, Alaska, 1984. h, South Korea, 1984. i, Papua New Guinea, 1984. j, Solomon Islands, 1984. k, Thailand, 1984. l, Switzerland, 1984.

No. 829a, Canada, 1984. b, Dominican Republic, 1984. c, Puerto Rico, 1984. d, Venezuela, 1985. e, Ecuador, 1985. f, Peru, 1985. g, Trinidad & Tobago, 1985. h, Netherlands, 1985. i, Luxembourg, 1985. j, Belgium, 1985. k, Togo, 1985. l, Ivory Coast, 1985.

No. 830a, Cameroun, 1985. b, Central African Republic, 1985. c, Zaire, 1985. d, Kenya,

---

1985. e, Morocco, 1985. f, Liechtenstein, 1985. g, India, 1986. h, Colombia, 1986. i, St. Lucia, 1986. j, France, 1986. k, Bangladesh, 1986. l, Singapore, 1986.

No. 831a, Fiji, 1986. b, New Zealand, 1986. c, Australia, 1986. d, Seychelles, 1986. e, Uruguay, 1987. f, Chile, 1987. g, Argentina, 1987. h, West Germany, 1987. i, Poland, 1987. j, US, 1987. k, Canada, 1987. l, Uruguay, 1988.

No. 832a, Bolivia, 1988. b, Peru, 1988. c, Paraguay, 1988. d, Austria, 1988. e, Zimbabwe, 1988. f, Botswana, 1988. g, Lesotho, 1988. h, Swaziland, 1988. i, Mozambique, 1988. j, France, 1988. k, Madagascar, 1989. l, Reunion, 1989.

No. 833a, Zambia, 1989. b, Malawi, 1989. c, Norway, 1989. d, Iceland, 1989. e, Finland, 1989. f, Denmark, 1989. g, Sweden, 1989. h, Spain, 1989. i, South Korea, 1989. j, Indonesia, 1989. k, Mauritius, 1989. l, Cape Verde, 1990.

No. 834a, Mali, 1990. b, Guinea-Bissau, 1990. c, Burkina Faso, 1990. d, Chad, 1990. e, Czechoslovakia, 1990. f, Mexico, 1990. g, Curacao, 1990. h, Malta, 1990. i, Tanzania, 1990. j, Burundi, 1990. k, Rwanda, 1990. l, Ivory Coast, 1990.

1992, Apr. 13   Perf. 14
Sheets of 12 + 4 Labels

825	A128	100sh #a.-l.	11.00	11.00
826	A128	100sh #a.-l.	11.00	11.00
827	A128	100sh #a.-l.	11.00	11.00
828	A128	100sh #a.-l.	11.00	11.00
829	A128	100sh #a.-l.	11.00	11.00
830	A128	100sh #a.-l.	11.00	11.00
831	A128	100sh #a.-l.	11.00	11.00
832	A128	100sh #a.-l.	11.00	11.00
833	A128	100sh #a.-l.	11.00	11.00
834	A128	100sh #a.-l.	11.00	11.00
		Nos. 825-834 (10)	110.00	110.00

Zanzibar Stone Town A129

Designs: No. 839a, 150sh, Old fort. b, 300sh, Maruhubi ruins.

1992, Apr. 15   Perf. 12x12½, 12½x12

835	A129	10sh Balcony	.20	.20
836	A129	20sh Bahlnara mosque	.45	.45
837	A129	30sh High Court bldg.	.60	.60
838	A129	200sh Natl. museum	3.00	3.00
		Nos. 835-838 (4)	4.25	4.25

Souvenir Sheet

839	A129	Sheet of 2, #a.-b.	4.25	4.25

Nos. 835-837 are vert.

Wolfgang Amadeus Mozart, Death Bicent. A130

Designs: 10sh, Marcella Sembrich as Zerlina in Don Giovanni. 50sh, Symphony Number 41, Jupiter. 300sh, Luciano Pavarotti as Idamente in Idomeneo. 500sn, Wolfgang Amadeus Mozart, vert.

1992, Aug. 1   Perf. 14

840	A130	10sh violet & blk	.65	.65
841	A130	50sh multicolored	1.60	1.60
842	A130	300sh violet & blk	3.75	3.75
		Nos. 840-842 (3)	6.00	6.00

Souvenir Sheet

843	A130	500sh olive brn & blk	6.25	6.25

While No. 843 has the same issue date as Nos. 840-842, the dollar value was lower when it were released.

No. 843 contains one 38x50mm stamp.

1992, Aug. 1

Designs: 10sh, Insignia, giraffe and elephant. 15sh, Scouts in canoe. 400sh, John

---

Glenn's Gemini space capsule orbiting Earth. 500sh, Boy scout, vert.

844	A130	10sh multicolored	.20	.20
845	A130	15sh multicolored	.20	.20
846	A130	400sh multicolored	5.00	5.00
		Nos. 844-846 (3)	5.40	5.40

Souvenir Sheet

847	A130	500sh multicolored	5.00	5.00

Lord Robert Baden-Powell, Founder of Boy Scouts, 50th Death Anniv. (in 1991).

While No. 847 has the same issue date as Nos. 844-846, the dollar value was lower when it were released.

No. 847 contains one 38x50mm stamp.

1992, Aug. 1

Charles de Gaulle (1890-1970): 25sh, French Resistance Monument and medal. 30sh, First Free French tank at Omaha beach, Normandy. 150sh, Concorde at de Gaulle Airport. 500sh, France #439 with Cross of Lorraine overprint and Free French stamp, vert.

848	A130	25sh multicolored	.35	.35
849	A130	30sh multicolored	.40	.40
850	A130	150sh multicolored	4.00	4.00
		Nos. 848-850 (3)	4.75	4.75

Souvenir Sheet

851	A130	500sh multicolored	6.00	6.00

While No. 851 has the same issue date as Nos. 848-850, the dollar value was lower when it was released.

No. 851 contains one 38x50mm stamp.

Common Chimpanzee A131

Various chimpanzees in natural habitat.

1992, Mar. 30

852	A131	10sh multicolored	.20	.20
853	A131	15sh multicolored	.20	.20
854	A131	35sh multicolored	.45	.45
855	A131	75sh multicolored	.95	.95
856	A131	100sh multicolored	1.25	1.25
857	A131	150sh multicolored	1.90	1.90
858	A131	200sh multicolored	2.50	2.50
859	A131	300sh multicolored	3.75	3.75
		Nos. 852-859 (8)	11.20	11.20

Souvenir Sheets

1992, Mar. 3

860	A131	400sh Swinging from tree	4.00	4.00
861	A131	400sh Eating termites	4.00	4.00

Spanish Art — A132

Drawings by Goya: 25sh, A Picador mounted on the shoulders of a Chulo, spears a Bull. 100sh, The Dream of Reason brings forth Monsters, vert. 150sh, Another Madness (of Martincho) in the Plaza de Zaragoza. 200sh, Recklessness of Martincho in the Plaza de Zaragoza.

No. 866, Seascape, by Mariana Salvador Maella.

1992   Perf. 13

862	A132	25sh blk & red brn	.30	.30
863	A132	100sh black & brn	1.10	1.10
864	A132	150sh blk & red brn	1.60	1.60
865	A132	200sh blk & red brn	1.75	1.75

Size: 120x95mm
Imperf

866	A132	400sh multicolored	2.75	2.75
		Nos. 862-866 (5)	7.50	7.50

Granada '92.

1992   Perf. 13

Drawings by Diego da Silva Velazquez: 35sh, Philip IV at Fraga. 50sh, The Head of the Stag. 75sh, The Cardinal Infante Don Fernando as a Hunter. 300sh, Pablo de Valladolid. No. 871, Two Men at Table.

867	A132	35sh multicolored	.45	.45
868	A132	50sh multicolored	.55	.55
869	A132	75sh multicolored	.85	.85
870	A132	300sh multicolored	2.40	2.40

Size: 120x95mm
Imperf

871	A132	400sh multicolored	3.25	3.25
		Nos. 867-871 (5)	7.50	7.50

Granada '92.

Chimpanzees of Gombe — A134

Designs: No. 872, Melisa and Mike. No. 873, Leakey and David Greybeard. No. 874, Fifi eating termites. No. 875 Galahad.

No. 876a, 10sh, Leakey. b, 15sh, Fifi. c, 20sh, Faben. d, 30sh, David Greybeard. e, 35sh, Mike. f, 50sh, Galahad. g, 100sh, Melisa. h, 200sh, Flo.

No. 877, Fifi, Flo, and Faben.

1992, May 29   Litho.   Perf. 14

872	A133	10sh multicolored	.40	.40
873	A133	15sh multicolored	.50	.50
874	A133	30sh multicolored	.65	.65
875	A133	35sh multicolored	.70	.70
		Nos. 872-875 (4)	2.25	2.25

Miniature Sheet

876	A134	Sheet of 8, #a.-h.	6.00	6.00

Souvenir Sheet

877	A133	100sh multicolored	2.25	2.25

Natl. Bank of Commerce, 25th Anniv. — A135

Designs: 10sh, Sorghum plants. 15sh, Samora Avenue branch, computer operator, vert. 30sh, Head office. 35sh, Bankers Training Center. 40sh, Batik tie dyeing.

1992, June 22

878	A135	10sh multicolored	.35	.35
879	A135	15sh multicolored	.40	.40
880	A135	35sh multicolored	.60	.60
881	A135	40sh multicolored	.65	.65
		Nos. 878-881 (4)	2.00	2.00

Souvenir Sheet

882	A135	30sh multicolored	1.25	1.25

A136

A137

Traditional Dress: 3sh, Gogo, central area. 5sh, Swahili, coastal area. 9sh, Hehe, southern highlands and Makonde, southern area. 12sh, Maasai, northern area. 40sh, Mwarusha.

1992, Apr. 30   Litho.   Perf. 14½
883	A136	3sh multicolored	.40	.40
884	A136	5sh multicolored	.45	.45
885	A136	9sh multicolored	.50	.50
886	A136	12sh multicolored	.65	.65
		Nos. 883-886 (4)	2.00	2.00

Souvenir Sheet

887	A136	40sh multicolored	2.25	2.25

Dated 1989.

1992, July 23   Perf. 12x12½
888	A137	40sh Basketball	.60	.60
889	A137	100sh Billiards	.90	.90
890	A137	200sh Table tennis	1.50	1.50
891	A137	400sh Darts	3.25	3.25
		Nos. 888-891 (4)	6.25	6.25

Souvenir Sheet

892	A137	500sh Weight lifting	3.50	3.50

1992 Summer Olympics, Barcelona.

Miniature Sheet

Fish
A138

#893: a, Tilapia mariae. b, Capoeta hulstaerti. c, Tropheus moorii. d, Synodontis angelicus. e, Julidochromis dickfeldi. f, Tilapia nilotica. g, Nothobranchius rachovii. h, Pseudotropheus crabro. i, Lamprologus leleupi. j, Pseudotropheus zebra. k, Julidochromis marlieri. l, Chalinochromis brichardi.
Designs: No. 894, Haplochromis "electric blue." No. 895, Lamprologus brevis. No. 896, Nothobranchius palmqvisti.

1992, Oct.   Litho.   Perf. 13½
893	A138	100sh Sheet of 12, #a.-l.	10.00	10.00

Souvenir Sheets

894	A138	500sh multicolored	3.50	3.50
895	A138	500sh multicolored	3.50	3.50
896	A138	500sh multicolored	3.50	3.50

Discovery of America, 500th Anniv.
A139

1992, Oct.   Litho.   Perf. 14
897	A139	70sh Sailing ship	.50	.50
898	A139	300sh Columbus	2.00	2.00

Souvenir Sheet

899	A139	500sh Columbus, diff.	3.50	3.50

Miniature Sheet

Flowers in Rio de Janeiro Botanical Garden — A140

Designs: No. 900a, Couroupita guianensis. b, Jacaranda acutifolia. c, Psychopsis papilio.

d, Nelumbo nucifera. e, Brownea grandiceps. f, Coffea arabica. g, Monodora myristica. h, Calaranthus rosea. i, Hibiscus schizopetalus. j, Carpobrotus edulis. k, Adenium obesum. l, Delonix regia. m, Agapanthus praecox. n, Zantedeschia aethiopica. o, Protea cynaroides. p, Cassia fistula. q, Aganisia cyanea. r, Heliconia rostrata. s, Cattelya luteola. t, Lagerstroemia speciosa.
500sh, Avenue of Royal Palms, Rio.

1992, Nov. 5   Litho.   Perf. 14½
900	A140	70sh Sheet of 20, #a.-t.	12.50	12.50

Souvenir Sheet

901	A140	500sh multicolored	3.50	3.50

Miniature Sheet

Dinosaurs
A141

Designs: a, Iguanodon. b, Saltasaurus. c, Cetiosaurus. d, Camarasaurus. e, Spinosaurus. f, Stegosaurus. g, Allosaurus. h, Ceratosaurus. i, Lesothosaurus. j, Anchisaurus. k, Ornithomimus. l, Baronyx. m, Pachycephalosaurus. n, Heterodontosaurus. o, Dryosaurus. p, Coelophysis.

1992, Nov. 5   Litho.   Perf. 14
902	A141	100sh Sheet of 16, #a.-p.	11.50	11.50

1992 Olympics, Albertville and Barcelona A142

Designs: 20sh, 4000-meter pursuit cycling, vert. 40sh, Double sculls. 50sh, Water polo. 70sh, Women's single luge. 100sh, Marathon. 150sh, Uneven parallel bars. 200sh, Ice hockey, vert, 400sh, Rings, vert.
No. 911, Tennis, vert. No. 912, Soccer, vert.

1992, Nov. 16   Litho.   Perf. 14
903	A142	20sh multicolored	.20	.20
904	A142	40sh multicolored	.30	.30
905	A142	50sh multicolored	.35	.35
906	A142	70sh multicolored	.50	.50
907	A142	100sh multicolored	.70	.70
908	A142	150sh multicolored	1.00	1.00
909	A142	200sh multicolored	1.40	1.40
910	A142	400sh multicolored	2.75	2.75
		Nos. 903-910 (8)	7.20	7.20

Souvenir Sheets

911	A142	500sh multicolored	4.50	4.50
912	A142	500sh multicolored	4.50	4.50

Mickey's Portrait Gallery A142a

Donald Duck in scenes from Disney movies: 25sh, Sea Scouts, 1939. 35sh, Fire Chief, 1940. 50sh, Truant Officer Donald, 1941. 500sh, With Daisy in Mr. Duck Steps Out, 1940.
No. 925, Daisy in Don Donald, 1937.
Disney Characters in scenes from Disney movies: No. 913, Hawaiian Holiday, 1937. No. 914, Society Dog Show, 1939. 75sh, Clock Cleaners, 1937. No. 919, Magician Mickey, 1937. No. 920, Goofy and Wilbur, 1939. 200sh, The Nifty Nineties, 1941. 300sh, Society Dog Show, 1939. 400sh, Pluto's Quin-Puplets, 1937. No. 926, Brave Little Tailor, 1938, horiz. No. 927, Forever Goofy.

1992, Nov. 30   Perf. 13½x14
913	A142a	25sh multicolored	.30	.30
914	A142a	25sh multicolored	.30	.30
915	A142a	25sh multicolored	.30	.30
916	A142a	35sh multicolored	.40	.40
917	A142a	50sh multicolored	.55	.55

918	A142a	75sh multicolored	.65	.65
919	A142a	100sh multicolored	.75	.75
920	A142a	100sh multicolored	.75	.75
921	A142a	200sh multicolored	1.25	1.25
922	A142a	300sh multicolored	1.60	1.60
923	A142a	400sh multicolored	1.75	1.75
924	A142a	500sh multicolored	1.90	1.90
		Nos. 913-924 (12)	10.50	10.50

Souvenir Sheets

925	A142a	600sh multicolored	3.00	3.00

Perf. 14x13½

926	A142a	600sh multicolored	3.00	3.00

Perf. 13½x14

927	A142a	600sh multicolored	3.00	3.00

Nos. 668-673 & 678 Ovptd. in Black or Red

1992   Litho.   Perf. 14
928	A106	50sh on #668	.35	.35
929	A106	50sh on #669	.35	.35
930	A106	75sh on #670	.55	.55
931	A106	75sh on #671	.55	.55
a.		Pair, #930-931	1.10	1.10
932	A106	100sh on #672	.75	.75
933	A106	100sh on #673	.75	.75
a.		Pair, #932-933	1.50	1.50
		Nos. 928-933 (6)	3.30	3.30

Souvenir Sheet

934	A106	350sh on #678 (R)	2.50	2.50

Overprint appears on one line in sheet margin of No. 934.

Traditional Hunting A143

Designs: 20sh, Slingshots used on birds. 40sh, Various weapons. 70sh, Bow and arrow used on gazelles. 100sh, Long knife, wooden club used on gazelles. 150sh, Spear and shield used on lion.

1992   Litho.   Perf. 13½
935	A143	20sh multicolored	.60	.60
936	A143	70sh multicolored	.75	.75
937	A143	100sh multicolored	1.25	1.25
938	A143	150sh multicolored	1.90	1.90
		Nos. 935-938 (4)	4.50	4.50

Souvenir Sheet
Perf. 12½

939	A143	40sh multicolored	2.00	2.00

Shells — A144

Designs: 10sh, Lambis truncata Humphrey. 15sh, Cypraecassis rufa. 25sh, Vexillum rugosum. 30sh, Conus litteratus. 35sh, Corculum cardissa. 50sh, Murex ramosus. 250sh, Melo melo. 300sh, Tridacha gigas.

1992, June 30   Perf. 12x12½
940	A144	10sh multicolored	.25	.25
941	A144	15sh multicolored	.30	.30
942	A144	25sh multicolored	.40	.40
943	A144	30sh multicolored	.40	.40
944	A144	35sh multicolored	.40	.40
945	A144	50sh multicolored	.60	.60
946	A144	250sh multicolored	2.40	2.40
		Nos. 940-946 (7)	4.75	4.75

Souvenir Sheet

947	A144	300sh multicolored	3.50	3.50

No. 808 Inscribed Vertically "15th Anniversary"

1992   Litho.   Perf. 14
949	A125	75sh Sheet of 9, #a.-i.	7.00	7.00

Marine Life A145

1992   Litho.   Perf. 14
950	A145	20sh Seal	.50	.50
951	A145	30sh Whale	1.25	1.25
952	A145	70sh Shark	.75	.75
953	A145	100sh Walrus	1.25	1.25
		Nos. 950-953 (4)	3.75	3.75

Souvenir Sheet

954	A145	500sh Sea turtle	4.75	4.75

A146

Anniversaries and Events — A147

Designs: 30sh, Count Ferdinand von Zeppelin. 70sh, Apollo-Soyuz. No. 957, Child being offered apple. No. 958, African elephant. No. 959, Lions Intl. emblem, man being given glasses. No. 960, Zebra. 300sh, Graf Zeppelin. No. 962, Space shuttle in Earth orbit. No. 963, Wolfgang Amadeus Mozart. No. 964, Voyager 2. No. 965, Unidentified zeppelin. No. 966, African elephant, diff. No. 967, Scene from "The Magic Flute."

1992   Litho.   Perf. 14
955	A146	30sh multicolored	.20	.20
956	A146	70sh multicolored	.50	.50
957	A146	150sh multicolored	1.00	1.00
958	A146	150sh multicolored	1.00	1.00
959	A146	200sh multicolored	1.40	1.40
960	A146	200sh multicolored	1.40	1.40
961	A146	300sh multicolored	2.00	2.00
962	A146	400sh multicolored	2.75	2.75
963	A147	400sh multicolored	2.75	2.75
		Nos. 955-963 (9)	13.00	13.00

Souvenir Sheets

964	A146	500sh multicolored	3.50	3.50
965	A146	500sh multicolored	3.50	3.50
966	A146	500sh multicolored	3.50	3.50
967	A147	800sh multicolored	5.50	5.50

Count Zeppelin, 75th death anniv. (#955, 961, 965). Intl. Space Year (#956, 962, 964). Intl. Conference on Nutrition (#957). Earth Summit, Rio de Janeiro (#958, 960, 966).Lions Intl., 75th anniv. (#959). Wolfgang Amadeus Mozart, bicent. of death (in 1991) (#963, 967).
Issued: Nos. 955-956, 961-962, 964-965, Nov.; Nos. 957-960, 966, Dec.

In 1998 Nos. 967A-967H, 978-985, 985A-985H, 985I-985P, 1128-1135, 1136-1143, 1144-1151, 1152-1159, 1160-1167, 1185-1192, 1193-1200, 1201-1208, 1209-1216, 1217-1224, 1235-1242, 1287-1294, 1295-1302, 1303-1310, 1319-1326, 1396-1403, 1422-1429, including souvenir sheets, were being sold wholesale at 42 cents per set mint, 21 cents per set used. Other sets may also be available.

Cats — A147a

1992, Dec. 3   Litho.   Perf. 12x12½

967A	A147a	20sh Abyssinian	.45	.45
967B	A147a	30sh Havana	.45	.45
967C	A147a	50sh Persian black	.55	.55
967D	A147a	70sh Persian blue	.65	.65
967E	A147a	100sh European silver tabby	.75	.75
967F	A147a	150sh Persian silver tabby	.90	.90
967G	A147a	200sh Maine	1.25	1.25
	Nos. 967A-967G (7)		5.00	5.00

Souvenir Sheet

967H	A147a	300sh European	3.00	3.00

Model Trains A148

Lionel models: 10sh, B & O Tunnel locomotive #5, 2⅞-inch gauge, 1904. 20sh, Liberty Bell #385E, standard gauge, 1930. 30sh, Armored motor car #203, standard gauge, 1917. 50sh, Open trolley #202, standard gauge, 1910-14. 70sh, Macy special #450, standrad gauge. 100sh, Milwaukee Road bipolar electric #381E, standard gauge, 1929. 200sh, New York Central "S" type, standard gauge, 1912. 300sh, 4-4-0 American #7 (thick rim), standard gauge, 1914. No. 976, Wind-up hand car with Mickey and Minnie Mouse, O-27 gauge, 1936. No. 977, Clear plastic F-3 display model, O gauge, 1947.

1992, Dec. 10   Litho.   Perf. 14

968	A148	10sh multicolored	.40	.40
969	A148	20sh multicolored	.45	.45
970	A148	30sh multicolored	.50	.50
971	A148	50sh multicolored	.75	.75
972	A148	70sh multicolored	.90	.90
973	A148	100sh multicolored	1.00	1.00
974	A148	200sh multicolored	1.40	1.40
975	A148	300sh multicolored	1.60	1.60
	Nos. 968-975 (8)		7.00	7.00

Souvenir Sheets

976	A148	500sh multicolored	3.50	3.50
977	A148	500sh multicolored	3.50	3.50

Genoa '92.

Birds — A149

Makonde Art — A149a

1992, Dec. 10   Litho.   Perf. 12x12½

978	A149	5sh Superb starling	.35	.35
979	A149	10sh Canary	.45	.45
980	A149	15sh Four-colored bush shrike	.45	.45
981	A149	25sh Grey-headed kingfisher	.50	.50
982	A149	30sh Common kingfisher	.50	.50
983	A149	35sh Yellow-billed oxpecker	.50	.50
984	A149	150sh Black throated honeyquide	1.25	1.25
	Nos. 978-984 (7)		4.00	4.00

Souvenir Sheet
Perf. 12½x12

985	A149	300sh European cuckoo, horiz.	2.50	2.50

1992, Dec. 24   Litho.   Perf. 12x12½

Various carved faces.

985A	A149a	20sh multicolored	.20	.20
985B	A149a	30sh multicolored	.20	.20
985C	A149a	50sh multicolored	.35	.35
985D	A149a	70sh multicolored	.50	.50
985E	A149a	100sh multicolored	.70	.70
985F	A149a	150sh multicolored	1.00	1.00
985G	A149a	200sh multicolored	1.40	1.40
	Nos. 985A-985G (7)		4.35	4.35

Souvenir Sheet

985H	A149a	350sh multicolored	2.50	2.50

Bicycles A149b

1992, Dec. 30   Litho.   Perf. 12½x12

985I	A149b	20sh Russia, 1813	.30	.30
985J	A149b	30sh Germany, 1840	.30	.30
985K	A149b	50sh Germany, 1818	.45	.45
985L	A149b	70sh Germany, 1850	.45	.45
985M	A149b	100sh Italy, 1988	.50	.50
985N	A149b	150sh Sweden, 1982	1.00	1.00
985O	A149b	300sh Italy, 1989	1.25	1.25
	Nos. 985I-985O (7)		4.25	4.25

Souvenir Sheet

985P	A149b	350sh Great Britain, 1887	2.50	2.50

Discovery of America, 500th Anniv. — A150

Designs: 10sh, Symbols of luck. 15sh, "Is this course right?," compass, chart. 25sh, "Earth!," first sight of land. 30sh, First meetings, horiz. 35sh, Nina, horiz. 75sh, Santa Maria, horiz. 250sh, Ship running aground, vert. 200sh, Columbus.

Perf. 12x12½, 12½x12

1992, Sept. 30   Litho.

986	A150	10sh multicolored	.20	.20
987	A150	15sh multicolored	.25	.25
988	A150	25sh multicolored	.35	.35
989	A150	30sh multicolored	.40	.40
990	A150	35sh multicolored	.45	.45
991	A150	75sh multicolored	.75	.75
992	A150	250sh multicolored	1.60	1.60
	Nos. 986-992 (7)		4.00	4.00

Souvenir Sheet

993	A150	200sh multicolored	2.50	2.50

Miniature Sheet

Louvre Museum, Bicent. A151

Paintings by Jean-Baptiste-Simeon Chardin (1699-1779): No. 994a, Young Artist. b, The Buffet. c, The Provider. d, A Mother Working. e, Grace. f, The Copper Fountain. g, House of Cards. h, Child with Teetotum. 500sh, The Ray, horiz.

1993, Mar. 8   Litho.   Perf. 12

994	A151	100sh Sheet of 8, #a.-h. + label	5.50	5.50

Souvenir Sheet
Perf. 14½

995	A151	500sh multicolored	3.50	3.50

No. 995 contains one 88x55mm stamp.

Miniature Sheet

Coronation of Queen Elizabeth II, 40th Anniv. A152

a, 100sh, Official coronation photograph. b, 150sh, Exeter salt. c, 200sh, Photograph of ceremony, 1953. d, 300sh, Queen, Prince Andrew.

500sh, Princess Elizabeth Opening the New Broadgate Coventry, by Dame Laura Knight, 1948.

1993, June 2   Litho.   Perf. 13½x14

996	A152	Sheet, 2 ea #a.-d.	7.50	7.50

Souvenir Sheet
Perf. 14

997	A152	500sh multicolored	3.25	3.25

No. 997 contains one 28x43mm stamp.

Miniature Sheet

Famous Women — A153

Designs: a, 20sh, Valentina Tereshkova. b, 40sh, Marie Curie. c, 50sh, Indira Gandhi. d, 70sh, Wilma Rudolph. e, 100sh, Margaret Mead. f, 150sh, Golda Meir. g, 200sh, Dr. Elizabeth Blackwell. h, 400sh, Margaret Thatcher. No. 999, Mother Teresa.

1993, July 15   Perf. 14

998	A153	Sheet of 8, #a.-h.	7.50	7.50

Souvenir Sheet

999	A153	500sh multicolored	3.50	3.50

Miniature Sheets

Wildlife — A154

Wildlife at watering hole: No. 1000: a, Elephant. b, Gazelles. c, Hartebeest. d, Duiker. e, Genet. f, Civet. g, Pelicans. h, Waterbuck. i, Blacksmith plovers. j, Pied kingfisher. k, Black-winged stilts. l, Bush pig.

No. 1000M: n, Brown-hooded kingfisher. o, Sable antelope (n). p, Impala (q). q, Buffalo. r, Leopard. s, Aardvark (t). t, Hippopotamus. u, Spotted hyena. v, Crowned crane (w). w, Crocodile. x, Flamingo. y, Baboon.

Wildlife on the plains: No. 1001: a, Potto. b, Flamingos. c, Grey-headed kingfisher. d, Red colobus monkey. e, Dik-dik. f, Aardwolf. g, Black-backed jackal. h, Tree pangolin. i, Serval. j, Yellow-billed hornbill. k, Pygmy mongoose. l, Bat-eared fox.

No. 1001M: n, Bushbaby. o, Egyptian vulture. p, Ostrich. q, Greater kudu. r, Diana monkey. s, Giraffe (w). t, Cheetah (s). u, Wildebeeest (t). v, Chimpanzee. w, Warthog. x, Zebra. y, Rhinoceros.

No. 1002, Lions, horiz. No. 1003, African elephants, horiz.

1993, June 30
Sheets of 12

1000	A154	100sh #a.-l.	6.00	6.00
1000M	A154	100sh #n.-y.	6.00	6.00
1001	A154	100sh #a.-l.	6.00	6.00
1001M	A154	100sh #n.-y.	6.00	6.00
	Nos. 1000-1001M (4)		24.00	24.00

Souvenir Sheets

1002	A154	500sh multi	3.00	3.00
1003	A154	500sh multi	3.00	3.00

For overprints see Nos. 1531, 1534.

Pancake Tortoise A155

1993, June 30

1004	A155	20sh On rock	.35	.35
1005	A155	30sh Drinking	.45	.45
1006	A155	50sh Crawling from under rocks	.65	.65
1007	A155	70sh Hatchling	.80	.80
	Nos. 1004-1007 (4)		2.25	2.25

World Wildlife Federation.

Mushrooms A156

Sports — A157

20sh, Macrolepiota rhacodes. 40sh, Mycena pura. 50sh, Chlorophyllum molybdites. 70sh, Agaricus campestris. 100sh, Volvariella volvacea. 150sh, Leucoagaricus naucinus. 200sh, Oudemansiella radicata. 300sh, Clitocybe nebularis. #1016, Omphalotus olearius. #1017, Lepista nuda.

1993, June 18   Litho.   Perf. 14

1008	A156	20sh multicolored	.20	.20
1009	A156	40sh multicolored	.30	.30
1010	A156	50sh multicolored	.35	.35
1011	A156	70sh multicolored	.50	.50
1012	A156	100sh multicolored	.75	.75
1013	A156	150sh multicolored	1.00	1.00
1014	A156	200sh multicolored	1.40	1.40
1015	A156	300sh multicolored	2.25	2.25
	Nos. 1008-1015 (8)		6.75	6.75

Souvenir Sheets

1016	A156	500sh multicolored	3.00	3.00
1017	A156	500sh multicolored	3.00	3.00

1992, May 28   Litho.   Perf. 12x12½

1018	A157	20sh Boxing	.20	.20
1019	A157	50sh Field hockey	.50	.50
1020	A157	70sh Horse racing	.40	.40
1021	A157	100sh Marathon	.45	.45
1022	A157	150sh Soccer	.60	.60
1023	A157	200sh Diving	.75	.75
1024	A157	400sh Basketball	1.60	1.60
	Nos. 1018-1024 (7)		4.50	4.50

Souvenir Sheet
Perf. 12½x12

1025	A157	300sh High jump, horiz.	2.00	2.00

Miniature Sheets

Animals
A158

#1026: a, Female Grant's zebra, running. b, Male Grant's zebra, standing. c, Female Grant's gazelle. d, Male Grant's gazelle. e, Thompson's gazelle. f, White-bearded gnu, calf.
#1027: a, Female cheetah, cubs. b, Young cheetah. c, Lioness carrying her cub. d, Two hunting dogs. e, Three hunting dogs. f, Hunting dogs before an attack.
No. 1028, African rhinoceros. No. 1029, African elephant.

1993, June 30   Litho.   Perf. 14
1026	A158	100sh Sheet of 6, #a.-f.	4.25	4.25
1027	A158	100sh Sheet of 6, #a.-f.	4.25	4.25

Souvenir Sheets
1028	A158	500sh multicolored	4.50	4.50
1029	A158	500sh multicolored	4.50	4.50

For overprints see Nos. 1532-1533, 1535.

A159   A160

1994 Winter Olympics, Lillehammer, Norway: 300sh, Matti Nykanen, ski jumping, 1988. 400sh, Stefan Krause, Jan Behrendt, double luge, 1992. 500sh, Downhill skiing, 1972.

1993, June 10   Litho.   Perf. 14
1030	A159	300sh multicolored	2.25	2.25
1031	A159	400sh multicolored	2.75	2.75

Souvenir Sheet
1032	A159	500sh multicolored	3.50	3.50

1993, June 10
1033	A160	100sh Telescope	.70	.70
1034	A160	300sh Radio telescope	2.25	2.25

Souvenir Sheet
1035	A160	500sh Copernicus	3.50	3.50

Copernicus, 450th anniv. of death.

Picasso (1881-1973)
A160a

Various details of painting, Guernica, 1937.

1993, June 10   Litho.   Perf. 14
1035A	A160a	30sh multi	.20	.20
1035B	A160a	200sh multi	1.40	1.40
1035C	A160a	300sh multi	2.00	2.00
		Nos. 1035A-1035C (3)	3.60	3.60

Souvenir Sheet
1035D	A160a	500sh multi	3.50	3.50

Flowers — A161   Polska '93 — A162

Designs: 20sh, Leopard orchid. 30sh, African violet. 40sh, Stapelia semota lutea. 50sh, Busy Lizzie. 60sh, Senecio petraeus. 70sh, Kalanchoe velutina. 100sh, Dwarf ginger lily. 150sh, Nymphaea colorata. 200sh, Thunbergia battiscombei. 250sh, Crossandra nilotica. 300sh, African tulip tree. 350sh, Ruttya fruticosa. No. 1048, False African violet. No. 1049, Glory lily.

1993, Nov. 8   Litho.   Perf. 13½
1036	A161	20sh multicolored	.25	.25
1037	A161	30sh multicolored	.30	.30
1038	A161	40sh multicolored	.35	.35
1039	A161	50sh multicolored	.35	.35
1040	A161	60sh multicolored	.40	.40
1041	A161	70sh multicolored	.45	.45
1042	A161	100sh multicolored	.55	.55
1043	A161	150sh multicolored	.80	.80
1044	A161	200sh multicolored	.90	.90
1045	A161	250sh multicolored	.95	.95
1046	A161	300sh multicolored	1.10	1.10
1047	A161	350sh multicolored	1.10	1.10
		Nos. 1036-1047 (12)	7.50	7.50

Souvenir Sheets
Perf. 13
1048	A161	500sh multicolored	2.50	2.50
1049	A161	500sh multicolored	2.50	2.50

1993   Litho.   Perf. 14
Paintings: 200sh, Stone Masons, by Aleksander Kobzdej, 1952. 300sh, Child Wearing Plumed Helmut, by Z. Waliszewski, 1932. 500sh, In the Marketplace, by Stanislaw Osostowicz, 1939.

1050	A162	200sh multicolored	1.40	1.40
1051	A162	300sh multicolored	2.00	2.00

Souvenir Sheet
1052	A162	500sh multicolored	3.50	3.50

Butterflies
A163

#1053: a, Gold-banded forester. b, Twin dotted border. c, Aphnaeus flavescens. d, Orange-and-lemon. e, Club-tailed charaxes. f, Broad blue-banded swallowtail. g, African map. h, Buxton's hairstreak. i, Bush charaxes. j, Lilac nymph. k, Large striped swordtail. l, Charaxes acuminatus. m, African leaf. n, African wood white. o, Trimen's false acraea. p, Red line sapphire. q, Mother-of-pearl. r, Flame-bordered charaxes. s, Large blue charaxes. t, Emperor swallowtail.
#1054: a, Angled grass yellow. b, Figtree blue. c, Iolaus ismenias. d, Green-veined charaxes. e, Commodore. f, African monarch. g, Bush scarlet. h, Eyed pansy. i, Zebra white. j, Azure hairstreak. k, Yellow pansy. l, Regal purple tip.
#1054: n, Iolaus aphnaeoides. o, Green charaxes. p, Beautiful monarch. q, Short-tailed admiral. r, Dusky dotted border. s, Charaxes anticlea. t, Blue salamis. u, Nepheronia argia. v, Acraea pseudolycia. w, Blue-banded diadem. x, Golden tip. y, Acraea bonasia.
No. 1055, Blood-red cymothoe. No. 1056, Precis octavia. No. 1056A, Noble swallowtail. No. 1056B, Violet-spotted charaxes.

1993, Nov. 8   Litho.   Perf. 13
Sheet of 20
1053	A163	100sh #a.-t.	20.00	20.00

Sheets of 12
1054	A163	100sh #a.-l.	10.00	10.00
1054M	A163	100sh #n.-y.	10.00	10.00

Souvenir Sheets
1055	A163	500sh multi	3.50	3.50
1056	A163	500sh multi	3.50	3.50
1056A	A163	500sh multi	3.50	3.50
1056B	A163	500sh multi	3.50	3.50

A164   A165

Players, country: 20sh, Gullit, Holland. 30sh, Sheedy, Ireland. 50sh, Giannini, Italy. 70sh, Cesar, Brazil. 250sh, Barnes, England. Grun, Belgium. 300sh, Chendo, Spain. 350sh, Rijkaard, Holland. 400sh, Matthaeus, Germany.
No. 1065, Berti, Italy; Caligiuri, US. No. 1066, Walker, England; Gilhaus, Holland.

1993, Dec.   Perf. 14
1057-1064	A164	Set of 8	7.00	7.00

Souvenir Sheets
1065-1066	A164	500sh each	3.50	3.50

1994 World Cup Soccer Championships, US.

1994, Feb. 10
Hummel Figurines: 20sh, Boy with accordian. 40sh, Girl with guitar, boy with banjo. 50sh, Boy with tuba. 70sh, Boy with harmonica, bird. 100sh, Bird in tree, boy seated on fence. 150sh, Boy playing horn. 200sh, Boy with horn, bird. 300sh, Girl playing banjo. 350sh, Boy with cello on back. 400sh, Girls with banjo and sheet music.
No. 1077, Four carolers. No. 1078, Two figures in tower blowing horns at angel below.

1067-1076	A165	Set of 10	7.00	7.00

Souvenir Sheets
1077-1078	A165	500sh each	3.75	3.75

Miniature Sheet

Black Athletes — A166

Designs: a, 20sh, Arthur Ashe. b, 40sh, Michael Jordan. c, 50sh, Daley Thompson. d, 70sh, Jackie Robinson. e, 100sh, Kareem Abdul-Jabbar. f, 150sh, Florence Joyner. g, 200sh, Jesse Owens. h, 400sh, Jack Johnson. 500sh, Muhammad Ali, horiz.

1993, July 15
1079	A166	Sheet of 8, #a.-h.	4.50	4.50

Souvenir Sheet
1080	A166	500sh multicolored	2.50	2.50

First US Gas Balloon Flight, Bicent.
A167

Designs: 200sh, Balloons filling with hot air. 400sh, Jean-Pierre Blanchard (1753-1809), balloon. 500sh, Hot air balloons in flight, vert.

1994, Apr. 25   Litho.   Perf. 14
1081	A167	200sh multicolored	1.40	1.40
1082	A167	400sh multicolored	2.75	2.75

Souvenir Sheet
1083	A167	500sh multicolored	3.25	3.25

Royal Air Force, 75th Anniv.
A168

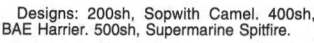

Designs: 200sh, Sopwith Camel. 400sh, BAE Harrier. 500sh, Supermarine Spitfire.

1993, Dec.
1084	A168	200sh multicolored	1.40	1.40
1085	A168	400sh multicolored	2.75	2.75

Souvenir Sheet
1086	A168	500sh multicolored	3.25	3.25

Automotive Anniversaries — A171

Designs: No. 1099, 1893 Benz, 1993 500 SEL. No. 1100, 200sh, Henry Ford, 1922 Model T. No. 1101, 400sh, Karl Benz, emblem. No. 1102, 400sh, 1893 Ford, Mustang Cobra.
No. 1103, Emblem, 1937 540 K. No. 1104, Henry Ford, first Ford factory.

1994, Apr. 25   Litho.   Perf. 14
1099-1102	A171	Set of 4	6.00	6.00

Souvenir Sheets
1103-1104	A171	500sh each	2.50	2.50

First Benz 4-wheel motor car, cent. (#1099, 1101, 1103). First Ford motor, cent. (#1100, 1102, 1104).

Miniature Sheets

Birds
A172

No. 1105: a, 20sh, African hawk eagle. b, 30sh, Shoe-bill stork. c, 50sh, Harrier eagle. d, 70sh, Casqued hornbill. e, 100sh, Crowned crane. f, 150sh, Greater flamingo.
No. 1106a, 200sh, Pelican. b, 250sh, Jacana, black crake. c, 300sh, Ostrich. d, 350sh, Helmeted guinea fowl. e, 400sh, Malachite kingfisher. f, 500sh, Saddle-billed stork.

1994, May 11
1105	A172	Sheet of 6, #a.-f.	5.00	5.00
1106	A172	Sheet of 6, #a.-f.	6.00	6.00

No. 1105 is vert.

Hong Kong '94
A173

Red-cap white pearl-scale goldfish and: No. 1107, Scarus ghobban. No. 1108, Regal angelfish.

1994, Feb. 18
1107	A173	350sh multicolored	1.50	1.50
1108	A173	350sh multicolored	1.50	1.50
a.		Pair, #1107-1108	3.00	3.00

Nos. 1107-1108 issued in sheets of 5 pairs. No. 1108a is a continuous design.
Numbers have been reserved for additional values in this set.

Mickey Mouse, 65th Anniv. — A176

Disney characters on tour: 10sh, Boarding plane. 20sh, Dancing, Tonga. 30sh, Lawn bowling, Australia. 40sh, Building igloo, Arctic region. 50sh, Royal Palace Guard, London. 60sh, Esna bazaar, Egypt. 70sh, Zsambox cowboys, Hungary, vert. 100sh, Grand Canal,

Venice, vert. 150sh, Dancing, Bali, Indonesia, vert. 200sh, Monks studying text, Bangkok, Thailand, vert. 300sh, Water skiing, Taj Mahal, India, vert. 400sh, Himalayas, Nepal.

No. 1125, Kilimanjaro Uhuru Peak, Kibo, Tanzania, vert. No. 1126, Kigoma railway station, Dar es Salaam, Tanzania, vert. No. 1127, Memorial to Dr. Livingstone, shores of Lake Tanganyika, Tanzania.

1994, Apr. 6   Perf. 14x13½, 13½x14

1113	A176	10sh multicolored	.20	.20
1114	A176	20sh multicolored	.20	.20
1115	A176	30sh multicolored	.20	.20
1116	A176	40sh multicolored	.30	.30
1117	A177	50sh multicolored	.35	.35
1118	A176	60sh multicolored	.40	.40
1119	A176	70sh multicolored	.50	.50
1120	A176	100sh multicolored	.75	.75
1121	A176	150sh multicolored	1.10	1.10
1122	A176	200sh multicolored	1.50	1.50
1123	A176	300sh multicolored	2.00	2.00
1124	A176	400sh multicolored	2.75	2.75
		Nos. 1113-1124 (12)	10.25	10.25

Souvenir Sheets

1125	A176	500sh multicolored	3.00	3.00
1126	A176	500sh multicolored	3.00	3.00
1127	A176	500sh multicolored	3.00	3.00

Reptiles A177

Designs: 20sh, Geochelone elephantopus, vert. 50sh, Iguana iguana, vert. 70sh, Varanus salvator. 100sh, Naja oxiana, vert. 150sh, Chamaeleo jacksonii. 200sh, Eunectes murinus. 250sh, Alligator mississippensis.
500sh, Vipera berus, vert.

Perf. 12x12½, 12½x12

1993, June 28   Litho.

1128-1134	A177	Set of 7	4.25	4.25

Souvenir Sheet

1135	A177	500sh multicolored	3.25	3.25

Nos. 1128-1135 were were not available until July 1994.

Sharks A178

20sh, Isurus oxyrinchus. 30sh, Etmopterus hillianus. 50sh, Galeocerdo cuvier. 70sh, Sguatina afrikana. 100sh, Pristiophorus cirratus. 150sh, Triaenodon obesus. 200sh, Sphyrna lewini.
350sh, Hexanchus grisens, vert.

1993, July 27   Perf. 12½x12

1136-1142	A178	Set of 7	3.25	3.25

Souvenir Sheet

Perf. 12x12½

1143	A178	350sh multicolored	2.00	2.00

#1136-1143 were not available until July 1994.

Dogs — A179

20sh, Gordon setter. 30sh, Zwergschnauzer. 50sh, Labrador retriever. 70sh, Wire fox terrier. 100sh, English springer spaniel. 150sh, Newfoundlander. 200sh, Moscow toy terrier.
350sh, Doberman pinscher.

1993, Sept. 27   Perf. 12x12½

1144-1150	A179	Set of 7	3.25	3.25

Souvenir Sheet

1151	A179	350sh multicolored	1.75	1.75

#1144-1151 were not available until July 1994.

Horses A180

Designs: 20sh, Norman-Arab. 40sh, Nonius. 50sh, Boulonnais. 70sh, Arab. 100sh, Anglo-Arab. 150sh, Tarpan. 200sh, Thorougbred. No. 1159, Anglo-Norman.

1993, Nov. 30   Perf. 12½x12

1152-1158	A180	Set of 7	3.50	3.50

Souvenir Sheet

Perf. 12x12½

1159	A180	400sh multicolored	2.00	2.00

#1152-1159 were not available until July 1994.

Military Aircraft A181

Designs: 20sh, ALFA jet. 30sh, Northrup F-5E. 50sh, Mirage 3NG. 70sh, MB-339C. 100sh, MIG-31. 150sh, C-101 AVIOJET. 200sh, F-16B.
500sh, EAP fighter, vert.

1994, Apr. 25 Litho. Perf. 12½x12

1160-1166	A181	Set of 7	2.75	2.75

Souvenir Sheet

Perf. 12x12½

1167	A181	500sh multicolored	1.75	1.75

A182

Customs Co-operation Council Meeting, Arusha — A183

Designs: 20sh, Trans-border trade. 50sh, Customs-international trade by ship. 100sh, Customs-air transportation. 150sh, Postal service-customs co-operation, Customs and UPU emblems.
500sh, Emblem.

1994, Aug. 23   Litho.   Perf. 13½

1168-1171	A182	Set of 4	2.25	2.25

Souvenir Sheet

Perf. 12½

1172	A183	500sh multicolored	3.00	3.00

Miniature Sheet of 8

1994 World Cup Soccer Championships, US — A184

Designs: No. 1173a, Giuseppe Signori. b, Ruud Gullit. c, Roberto Mancini. d, Marco Van Bastien. e, Dennis Bergkamp. f, Oscar Ruggeri. g, Frank Rijkaard. h, Peter Schmeichel.
1000sh, World Cup trophy.

1994, Sept. 26   Perf. 14

1173	A184	300sh #a.-h.	7.50	7.50

Souvenir Sheet

1174	A184	1000sh multicolored	4.00	4.00

1994 World Cup Soccer Championships, US — A184a

Letter in soccer ball: 40sh, B. 50sh, C. 70sh, D. 100sh, E. 170sh, A. 200sh, none. 250sh, F. 500sh, Two players and goalie.

1994, Sept. 30 Litho. Perf. 12½x12

1174A-1174G	A184a	Set of 7	5.00	5.00
	i.	Souv. sheet of 6, #1174A-1174E, 1174G + 3 labels	4.00	4.00

Souvenir Sheet

1174H	A184a	500sh multi	4.00	4.00

Miniature Sheets of 9

Dogs — A185

Designs: No. 1175a, Alsatian (German Shepherd). b, Japanese chin. c, Shetland sheepdog. d, Italian spinone. e, Great dane. f, English setter. g, Pembroke (welsh corgi). h, St. Bernard. i, Irish wolfhound.
No. 1176a, Afghan hound. b, Basenji (Congo dog). c, Siberian husky. d, Irish setter. e, Norwegian elkhound. f, Bracco Italiano (Italian hound). g, Australian cattle dog. h, German short haired pointer. i, Rhodesian ridgeback.
No. 1177a, Alaskan malamute. b, Scottish cairn terrier. c, American foxhound. d, British bulldog. e, Boston terrier. f, Borzoi (Russian wolfhound). g, Shar pei (Chinese fighting dog). h, Saluki (Persian greyhound). i, Bernese mountain dog.
No. 1178a, Doberman pinscher. b, Chihuahua. c, Bloodhound. d, Keeshond (Dutch barge dog). e, Tibetan spaniel. f, Japanese akita. g, Tervueren (Belgian shepherd dog). h, Chow chow (Chinese Spitz). i, Pharaoh hound.
#1179, like #1175e. #1180, like #1176b.

1994, Sept. 30

1175-1178	A185	120sh #a.-i, ea	3.50	3.50

Souvenir Sheets

1179-1180	A185	1000sh each	4.00	4.00

Miniature Sheets of 8

Orchids — A186

Designs: No. 1181a, Rangaeris amaniensis. b, Eulophia macowanii. c, Cyrtorchis arcuata. d, Centrostigma occultans. e, Cirrhopetalum umbellatum. f, Ansellia gigantea. g, Angraecum ramosum. h, Disa englerana.
No. 1182a, Nervilia stolziana. b, Satyrium orbiculare. c, Schzochilus sulphureus. d, Disa stolzii. e, Platycoryne mediocris. f, Satyrium breve. g, Eulophia nuttii. h, Disa ornithantha.
No. 1183, Eulophia thomsonii, horiz. No. 1184, Phaius P. tankervilliae, horiz.

1994, Oct. 7

1181-1182	A186	200sh #a.-h, each	5.00	5.00

Souvenir Sheets

1183-1184	A186	1000sh each	4.00	4.00

Natl. Parks A187

20sh, Ngorongoro Crater. 50sh, Ngurdoto Crater. 70sh, Kilimanjaro Natl. Park. 100sh, Gombe Natl. Park. 150sh, Selous Natl. Park. 200sh, Mikumi Natl. Park. 250sh, Serengeti Natl. Park.
500sh, Lake Manyara Natl. Park, vert.

1993, Oct. 29 Litho. Perf. 12

1185-1191	A187	Set of 7	2.75	2.75

Souvenir Sheet

1192	A187	500sh multicolored	2.00	2.00

Nos. 1185-1192 are dated 1993 but were not available until Oct. 1994.

Historical African Costumes A188

1994 Winter Olympics, Lillehammer A189

20sh, Berts style. 40sh, Galla style. 50sh, Guinean warrior. 70sh, Goloff style. 100sh, Peul style. 150sh, Abyssinian warrior. 200sh, Pahuin style.
350sh, Zulu style.

1993, Dec. 30

1193-1199	A188	Set of 7	2.00	2.00

Souvenir Sheet

1200	A189	350sh multicolored	1.25	1.25

Nos. 1193-1200 are dated 1993 but were not available until Oct. 1994.

1994, Feb. 12

40sh, Downhill skiing. 50sh, Ice hockey. 70sh, Speed skating. 100sh, Bobsled. 120sh, Figure skating. 170sh, Free style skiing. 250sh, Biathlon.

500sh, Slalom skiing.

1201-1207 A189 Set of 7   4.00 4.00
Souvenir Sheet
1208 A189 500sh multicolored   1.75 1.75

Sailing Ships — A190

Prehistoric Animals — A191

Designs: 40sh, Jahazi. 50sh, Caravel. 70sh, Carrack. 100sh, Galeas. 170sh, Line of battle ship. 200sh, Frigate. 250sh, Brig. No. 1210, Bark.

1994, Apr. 20
1209-1215 A190 Set of 7   2.75 2.75
Souvenir Sheet
1216 A190 500sh multicolored   1.75 1.75

1994, June 30
Designs: 40sh, Diatruma. 50sh, Tyranosaurus. 100sh, Uintaterius. 120sh, Stiracosaurus. 170sh, Diplodocus. 250sh, Archaeopteryx. 300sh, Sordes. 500sh, Dimetrodon, vert.

1217-1223 A191 Set of 7   4.25 4.25
Souvenir Sheet
1224 A191 500sh multicolored   2.00 2.00

A192

A193

Designs: 40sh, Family. 120sh, Father playing ball with children. 170sh, People at clinic, horiz. 250sh, Woman harvesting in field. 300sh, Emblem.

Perf. 12x12½, 12½x12
1994, Aug. 30   Litho.
1225-1228 A192 Set of 4   2.00 2.00
Souvenir Sheet
1229 A192 300sh multicolored   1.75 1.75
Intl. Year of the Family.

1994, Aug. 1
40sh, Pres. Salmin Amour. 70sh, Abeid Amani Karume, first president. 120sh, Processing cloves, horiz. 250sh, Zanzibar door.

500sh, Hands clasped over map.

1230-1233 A193 Set of 4   2.25 2.25
Souvenir Sheet
1234 A193 500sh multicolored   2.00 2.00
Zanzibar Revolution, 30th anniv.

Arachnids A194

Designs: 40sh, Trombidium. 50sh, Eurypelma. 100sh, Salticus. 120sh, Micrommata rosea, vert. 170sh, Araneus, vert. 250sh, Micrathena, vert. 300sh, Araneus diadematus, vert. 500sh, Hadogenes, vert.

Perf. 12½x12, 12x12½
1994, Aug. 31
1235-1241 A194 Set of 7   3.50 3.50
Souvenir Sheet
1242 A194 500sh multicolored   1.75 1.75

Miniature Sheets of 9

Butterflies & Flowers A195

#1243: a, Lunaria biennis, papilio glaucus. b, Phlox paniculata, danaus plexippus. c, Rudbeckia gloriosa, papilio troilus. d, Tithonia rotundifolia, hypolimnas antevorta. e, Osteospermum, cirrochroa imperatrix. f, Ursinia anethoides, vanessa atalanta. g, Wahlenbergia gloriosa, limenitis archippus. h, Mentzelia lindleyi, hypolimnas pandarus. i, Paeonia suffruticosa, anthocharis belia.
#1244: a, Coreopsis laneolata, limenitis sydyi. b, Lantana camara, agraulis vanillae. c, Asclepias tuberosa, danaus chrysippus. d, Verbena canadensis, eurytides marcellus. e, Lonicera japonica, artopoetes pryeri. f, Pentas bussei, heliconius charitonius. g, Echinacea purpurea, limenitis weidemeyerii. h, Myosotis alpestris, phoebis sennae. i, Aster amellus, timelaea albescens.
No. 1245, Buddleia davidii, papilio polyxenes. No. 1246, Helianthus annuus, vanessa cardui.

1994, Nov. 19   *Perf. 14*
1243-1244 A195 120sh #a.-i.,
    ea   4.50 4.50
Souvenir Sheets
1245-1246 A195 1000sh each   3.50 3.50

Miniature Sheets of 9

First Manned Moon Landing, 25th Anniv. A196

Apollo 11 mission: No. 1247: a, Map of landing site. b, Location of Sea of Tranquility shown on Moon. c, Craters. d, Launch. e, Second stage separation. f, Separation of lunar modules. g, Command module, "Columbia," landing module, "Eagle." h, "Eagle" descending. i, Inside module.
No. 1248: a, Michael Collins, Neil Armstrong, Edwin "Buzz" Aldrin. b, "Eagle" on lunar surface. c, Stepping foot on moon. d, Erecting solar wind devices. e, Gathering soil samples. f, Reflection in helmet. g, Astronaut, US flag. h, Carrying equipment. i, "Eagle" ascending from lunar surface.
No. 1249: a, "Columbia" above lunar surface, Earth on horizon. b, "Eagle" above lunar surface. c, Release of S-4B rocket. d, Heading toward Earth. e, Re-entering atmosphere. f, Splashdown. g, Pickup at sea. h, Helicopter lifting men on board. i, Astronauts in quarantine.

1994, Nov. 30
1247-1249 A196 150sh #a.-i., ea   5.50 5.50

Miniature Sheets of 16

A197

Dinosaurs — A198

#1250: a, Brontosaurus (e). b, Albertosaurus. c, Parasaurolophus. d, Pteranodon. e, Stegosaurus. f, Tyrannosaurus. g, Triceratops. h, Ornitholestes. i, Camarasaurus. j, Ankylosaurus. k, Trachodon. l, Allosaurus. m, Corythosaurus. n, Struthiomimus. o, Camptosaurus. p, Heterodontosaurus.
#1251: a, Deinonychus. b, Styracosaurus. c, Anatosaurus. d, Plateosaurus. e, Iguanodon. f, Oviraptor. g, Dimorphodon. h, Ornithomimus. i, Lambeosaurus. j, Megalosaurus. k, Cetiosaurus. l, Hypsilophodon. m, Rhamphorhynchus. n, Scelidosaurus. o, Antrodemus. p, Dimetrodon.
1000sh, Brachiosaurus, vert.

1994, Dec. 26
1250 A197 120sh #a.-p.   9.00 9.00
1251 A198 120sh #a.-p.   9.00 9.00
Souvenir Sheet
1252 A197 1000sh multicolored   4.50 4.50
No. 1250 is a continuous design.

Mickey Mouse, Safari Club — A199

Designs: No. 1253, 70sh, Donald, Mickey, lion cubs. No. 1254, 70sh, Goofy leaning on Donald. No, 1255, 100sh, Donald wearing tree disguise. No. 1256, 100sh, Donald under elephant. No. 1257, 120sh, Donald, hippopotamus. No. 1258, 120sh, Mickey writing in diary. No. 1259, 150sh, Goofy carrying gear, Donald, Mickey. No. 1260, 150sh, Mickey, elephant, Donald, Goofy in rain. No. 1261, 200sh, Donald, Goofy, Mickey reading book, lion. No. 1262, 200sh, Goofy, zebras. No. 1263, 250sh, Mickey, giraffe. No. 1264, 250sh, Donald filming picture.
No. 1265, Goofy hanging from tree, vert. No. 1266, Goofy holding camera, Donald, vert. No. 1267, Mickey holding camera, vert.

1994, Dec. 26   *Perf. 14x13½*
1253-1264 A199 Set of 12   8.50 8.50
Souvenir Sheets
Perf. 13½x14
1265-1267 A199 1000sh each   4.00 4.00

A200

Olympic Gold Medalists — A201

Designs: 350sh, Kristin Otto, Germany, 50m free-style swimming, 1988. 500sh, Carl Lewis, US, track & field, 1984, 1988. 1000sh, Oksana Baiul, Ukraine, women's figure skating, 1994.

1994, Dec. 12   Litho.   *Perf. 14*
1268 A200 350sh multicolored   1.25 1.25
1269 A200 500sh multicolored   1.75 1.75
Souvenir Sheet
1270 A201 1000sh multicolored   3.50 3.50
Intl. Olympic Committee, cent. (#1270).

D-Day, 50th Anniv. A202

350sh, Combined forces attack Atlantic wall. 600sh, Waterproofed tanks support Marines at Omaha Beach.
#1273: a, Gen. Eisenhower, US forces, Omaha Beach. b, P-51 Mustang, D-Day armada. c, US Coast Guard cutter, landing craft. d, US troops approaching Omaha Beach. e, US troops landing on Omaha Beach. f, US forces on Omaha Beach.
#1274: a, Gen. Montgomery, White Ensign flies over Normandy beach. b, British forces with Churchill Avre tank, Gold Beach. c, USS Thompson refueled en route to Omaha Beach. d, HMS Warspite fires on German positions, Sword Beach. e, Royal Marine commandoes landing, Juno Beach. f, Sherman Crab flail tank landing on Normandy beach.
#1275: a, Supermarine Spitfire over Normandy beaches. b, Bren gun carriers, Gold Beach. c, Le Regiment de la Chaudiere, Juno Beach. d, Canadian forces land on Juno Beach. e, Sherman tank on Normandy beach. f, German artillery fires on D-Day Armada.
No. 1276, US forces prepare to embark from England to Normandy beaches. No. 1277, US forces on Utah Beach. No. 1278, Beach obstacles.

1994, Dec. 12   Litho.   *Perf. 14*
1271 A202 350sh multicolored   1.25 1.25
1272 A202 600sh multicolored   2.25 2.25
Miniature Sheets of 6
1273-1275 A202 200sh #a.-f.,
    each   4.25 4.25
Souvenir Sheets
1276-1278 A202 1000sh each   3.75 3.75

Raptors A203

Designs: 40sh, Terathopius ecaudatus, vert. 50sh, Spizaetus ornatus, vert. 100sh, Pandion haliaetus, vert. 120sh, Vultur gryphus, vert. 170sh, Haliaetus vocifer. 250sh, Sarcoramphus papa, vert. 400sh, Falco peregrinus.
500sh, Pseudogyps africanus, vert.

Perf. 12x12½, 12½x12

1994, Sept. 30
1279-1285 A203   Set of 7   4.50   4.50

Souvenir Sheet
1286 A203 500sh multicolored   1.75   1.75

Endangered Species — A204

Designs: 40sh, Phascolasctos cinereus. 70sh, Ailurus fulgens. 100sh, Aguila. 120sh, Loxodonta africana. 250sh, Monachus tropicalis. 400sh, Eschrichtius gibbosus. 500sh, Cetacea.
500sh, Panthera tigris, vert.

1994, July 29   **Perf. 12½x12**
1287-1293 A204   Set of 7   4.75   4.75

Souvenir Sheet
Perf. 12x12½
1294 A204 500sh multicolored   2.00   2.00

No. 1288 shows a Giant Panda, and is incorrectly inscribed with the scientific name of the Lesser Panda.

Crabs — A205

Flowers — A206

Designs: 40sh, Astacus leptodactytus, horiz. 100sh, Eriocheir sinensis. 120sh, Caneer opillo. 170sh, Cardisoma quanhumi, horiz. 250sh, Birgus latro. 300sh, Menippe mercenaria, horiz. 400sh, Dromia vulgaris.
No. 1302, Callinectes sapidus, horiz.

Perf. 12½x12, 12x12½

1994, Nov. 30   **Litho.**
1295-1301 A205   Set of 7   4.50   4.50

Souvenir Sheet
1302 A205 500sh multicolored   1.75   1.75

1995, Oct. 31   **Perf. 12x12½**
40sh, Dicentra spectabilis. 100sh, Thunbergia alata. 120sh, Cyrtanthus minimiflorus. 170sh, Nepenthes hybrida. 250sh, Allamanda cathartica. 300sh, Encyclia pentotis. 400sh, Protea lacticolor.
500sh, Tradescantia.

1303-1309 A206   Set of 7   5.50   5.50

Souvenir Sheet
1310 A206 500sh multicolored   2.00   2.00

Dated 1994.

Woodstock Music Festival, 25th Anniv. — A207

Illustration reduced.

1995   **Litho.**   **Imperf.**
Size: 124x84mm
1311 A207 2000sh Jimi Hendrix   7.50   7.50

Souvenir Sheet
Self-Adhesive
1312 A207 2000sh Carlos
                  Santana   7.50   7.50

Size: 115x122mm
Imperf
Self-Adhesive
1313 A207 2000sh John Lee
                  Hooker   7.50   7.50

Numbers have been reserved for additional values in this set.
Issued: #1311, 2/27; #1312, 5/15; #1313, 8/22.

Space Probes & Satellites A208

Designs: 40sh, Hubble telescope. 100sh, Mariner. 120sh, Voyager 2. 170sh, Work Package 03. 250sh, Orbiting solar observatory (OSO). 300sh, Magellan. 400sh, Galileo.
500sh, FOBOS.

1994, Dec. 30 **Litho.** **Perf. 12½x12**
1319-1325 A208   Set of 7   4.50   4.50

Souvenir Sheet
1326 A208 500sh multicolored   2.00   2.00

Miniature Sheets of 9

Sierra Club, Cent. A209

No. 1327 vert: a, Black rhinoceros. b, Aye-aye. c, Aye-aye, holding claw at mouth. d, Giraffes, Masai Mara Reserve. e, Red lechwe, group. f, Red lechwe running. g, White-handed gibbon, white coat. h, White-handed gibbon, dark coat. i, White-handed gibbon, ready to climb tree.
No. 1328: a, Aye-aye. b, Black rhinoceros facing each other. c, Black rhinoceros. d, Red lechwe. e, Lions fighting, Masai Mara Reserve. f, Hyena, Masai Mara Reserve. g, Nile crocodile in water. h, Nile crocodile, mouth open. i, Nile crocodile in grass.

1995, July 6   **Litho.**   **Perf. 14**
1327-1328 A209 150sh #a.-i., ea   5.50 5.50

Fruit A210

Designs: 70sh, 500sh, Coconuts. 100sh, Pineapple. 150sh, Pawpaw. 200sh, Tomato.

1995, June 30
1329-1332 A210   Set of 4   2.00   2.00

Souvenir Sheet
1333 A210 500sh multicolored   2.00   2.00

Miniature Sheets of 9

The Beatles — A211

No. 1334: a, George Harrison. b, d, e, f, h, Various group portraits. c, Ringo Starr. g, Paul McCartney. i, John Lennon.
No. 1335a-1335i, vert: Various portraits of John Lennon.
No. 1336, John Lennon, vert. No. 1337, Paul McCartney.

1995   **Perf. 12½**
1334-1335 A211 100sh #a.-i., ea   6.25 6.25

Souvenir Sheets
1336-1337 A211 500sh each   5.25 5.25

No. 1336 contains one 51x76mm stamp. No. 1337 contains one 57x51mm stamp.

Miniature Sheets of 9

Singapore '95 — A212

Trains of the world - #1338: a, 0-6-0 Italy. b, 0-4-4-OT Mallet, Germany. c, 4-8-0 Tender Engine, Ghana. d, Mallet Tanks, Germany. e, 0-6-2T on the Zillertalbahn, Switzerland. f, Rack Lines, Austria. g, Sweden Jodemans Railway, Norway. h, 4-6-0 Portugal. i, 60CM gauge, Mine Railway, Spain.
No. 1339a, 640 Class 2-6-0s, Italy. b, Norway electric. c, Gordon Highlander 4-40s. d, High Line 9600 class 2-8-0 Japan. e, 4-6-0 Henschel, Portugal. f, Federal German State Railway 220 hydraulic. g, Caledonian 4-2-2, Scotland. h, M2 Locomotive, Denmark. i, Denver & Rio Grande, Western US.
No. 1340, Karl Golsdorf 2-6-0 tank engine, "Germany." No. 1341, High speed ET 403, Germany. No. 1342, AKO 1920, US. No. 1343 Porter 2-4-OS, Hawaii.

1995, July 5   **Litho.**   **Perf. 14**
1338-1339 A212 200sh #a.-i.,
                  ea   7.25   7.25

Souvenir Sheets
1340-1343 A212 1000sh each   4.00   4.00

A213

FAO, 50th anniv.: No. 1344a, Boy eating. b, Baby, mother eating. c, Two young people eating.
1000sh, Woman picking fruit, horiz.

1995, Aug. 14
1344 A213 250sh Strip of 3,
                  #a.-c.   4.75   4.75

Souvenir Sheet
1345 A213 1000sh multicolored   4.00   4.00

No. 1344 is a continuous design.

A214

1995, Aug. 14
Rotary, Intl., 90th Anniv.: 600sh, Paul Harris, Rotary emblem. 1000sh, Natl. flag, Rotary emblem.

1346 A214 600sh multicolored   3.25   3.25

Souvenir Sheet
1347 A214 1000sh multicolored   4.00   4.00

Queen Mother, 95th Birthday A215

No. 1348: a, Drawing. b, With Queen Elizabeth II. c, Formal portrait. d, In black outfit. 1000sh, Blue dress with pearls.

1995, Aug. 14   **Perf. 13½x14**
1348 A215   250sh Block or strip
              of 4, #a.-d.   4.75   4.75

Souvenir Sheet
1349 A215 1000sh multicolored   4.00   4.00

No. 1348 was issued in sheets of 8 stamps. Sheets of Nos. 1348-1349 exist with black borders overprinted in sheet margins and text "In Memoriam 1900-2002."

Miniature Sheets of 6 or 8

End of World War II, 50th Anniv. A216

Flags of countries shaped as "VJ:" No. 1350a: Singapore. b, Fiji. c, Malaysia. d, Marshall Islands. e, Philippines. f, Solomon Islands.
No. 1351: a, Pearl Harbor. b, North Africa. c, Battle of Atlantic. d, War in Soviet Union. e, "D" Day, June 6, 1944. f, Holocaust. g, War in Pacific. h, Hiroshima, Enola Gay, mushroom cloud.
No. 1352, Battle of Britain. No. 1353, British soldier, donkey with backpack.

1995, Aug. 14   **Litho.**   **Perf. 14**
1350 A216 250sh #a.-f. + label   6.00   6.00
1351 A216 250sh #a.-h. + label   8.00   8.00

Souvenir Sheets
1352-1353 A216 1000sh each   4.00   4.00

Miniature Sheet of 12

Reptiles A217

No. 1354: a, African rock python. b, Bell's hinged tortoise. c, Gaboon viper. d, Royal python. e, Savannah monitor. f, Nile monitor. g, Three-horned chameleon. h, Nile crocodile. i, Rough-scaled bush viper. j, Puff adder. k, Rhinocerous viper. l, Leopard tortoise.
No. 1355, Bush viper. No. 1356, Spitting cobra.

1995, Sept. 5
1354 A217 250sh #a.-l.   9.50   9.50

Souvenir Sheets
1355-1356 A217 1000sh each   4.00   4.00

UN, 50th Anniv. — A218

Various races of people, within group: No. 1357a, Woman holding baby on shoulders. b, Man holding child in arms. c, One child standing.
1000sh, UN soldier using binoculars.

1995, Aug. 14   Litho.   Perf. 14
1357 A218 250sh Strip of 3,
   #a.-c.   3.25 3.25
Souvenir Sheet
1358 A218 1000sh multicolored   4.25 4.25
   No. 1357 is a continuous design.

Miniature Sheets of 9

Summer Olympics
Gold Medal
Winners — A219

No. 1359: a, Tommie Smith, US, 1968. b, Jack Lovelock, New Zealand, 1936. c, Al Oerter, US, 1956-68. d, Daley Thompson, Great Britain, 1980. e, Greg Louganis, US, 1984-88. f, Sammy Lee, US, 1948. g, Dan Gable, US, 1972. h, Helen Meany, US, 1928. i, Sugar Ray Leonard, US, 1976.
No. 1360: a, Robert Mathias, US, 1948-52 . b, Larissa Latynina, USSR, 1956. c, Martin Sheridan, US, 1904-08. d, Vera Caslavska, Czechoslovakia, 1968. e, Edwin Moses, US, 1984. f, Jesse Owens, US, 1936. g, Mary Lou Retton, US, 1984. h, Bobby Morrow, US, 1956. i, Joan Benoit, US, 1984.
No. 1361, Florence Griffith Joyner, Jackie Joyner-Kersee, US, 1988. No. 1362, Vasily Alexeyev USSR, 1972-76.

1995, Sept. 18
1359-1360 A219 200sh #a.-i.,
   ea   7.25 7.25
Souvenir Sheets
1361-1362 A219 1000sh each   4.25 4.25

Miniature Sheets

Wild
Animals
A220

No. 1363: a, Snake, vulture. b, Vulture. c, Giraffe (d, g, h, k, l). d, African bateleur. e, Elephants (f). f, Kob, rhino (b, e, i, j, n). g, Rhinos. h, Baboon. i, Kob (m, n). j, Saddle billed stork, warthog (n). k, Cheetahs (g, j, n). l, African lion (h, k, o, p). m, Vulture. n, Dik-diks. o, Lion cubs. p, Lions (o).
No. 1364: a, Elands. b, Zebras. c, Lions. d, Baboons.
No. 1365, Rhinoceros. No. 1366, Leopard.

1995, Sept. 15
1363 A220 100sh Sheet of 16,
   #a.-p.   6.50 6.50
1364 A220 250sh Sheet of 4,
   #a.-d.   4.00 4.00
Souvenir Sheets
1365-1366 A220 1000sh each   4.25 4.25

UN, 50th
Anniv.
A221

70sh, Corn farming, vert. 100sh, Cultivating land. 150sh, Women spinning cotton in factory. 200sh, Boy drawing at desk, vert. 500sh, UN emblem, "50."

Wmk. 387
1995, Oct. 24   Litho.   Perf. 14
1367-1371 A221 Set of 4   2.00 2.00
Souvenir Sheet
1372 A221 500sh multicolored   2.00 2.00

East
African
Treaty,
2nd
Anniv.
A222

Designs: 100sh, 500sh, Heads of State. 150sh, Map, flags, vert. 180sh, Map, cotton, vert. 200sh, Fishing on Lake Victoria.

1995, Oct. 24
1373-1376 A222 Set of 4   2.50 2.50
Souvenir Sheet
1377 A222 500sh multicolored   2.00 2.00

Hoofed
Animals — A224

Cactus
Flowers — A225

Designs: 70sh, Hippopotamus amphibius, horiz. 100sh, Litocranius walleri. 150sh, Sincerus caffer, horiz. 180sh, Antilocapridae, horiz. 200sh, Alcelphus buselaphus. 260sh, Taurotragus oryx. 380sh, Strepsiceros. 500sh, Giraffa camelopardalis.

Perf. 12½x12, 12x12½
1995, May 31   Litho.
1380-1386 A224 Set of 7   5.25 5.25
Souvenir Sheet
1387 A224 500sh multicolored   2.00 2.00

1995, Aug. 31   Perf. 12x12½
Designs: 70sh, Weingartia fidaiana. 100sh, Rebutia spegazziniana. 150sh, Caralluma lugarii. 180sh, Cerochlamys pachyphylla. 200sh, Schlumbergera orssighiana. 260sh, Epiphyllum darrahii. 380sh, Ceropegia nilotica. 500sh, Neoporteria nigrihorrida.

1388-1394 A225 Set of 7   5.25 5.25
Souvenir Sheet
1395 A225 500sh multicolored   2.00 2.00

Bats
A226

70sh, Cheiromeles torquatus, vert. 100sh, Hypsignatus monstrosus, vert. 150sh, Rhinolophus ferrum-equinum, vert. 180sh, Plecotus auritus. 200sh, Syconycteris australis, vert. 260sh, Plecotus auritus, vert. 380sh, Otomops martiensseni. 500sh, Pteropus.

1995, July 31   Perf. 12x12½, 12½x12
1396-1402 A226 Set of 7   5.25 5.25
Souvenir Sheet
1403 A226 500sh multicolored   2.00 2.00

Marine
Life of
Coral
Reefs
A227

Designs: 70sh, Medusa. 100sh, Surgeonfish. 150sh, Angelfish. 180sh, Octopus. 200sh, Zebra fish. 260sh, Shark. 380sh, Ray. 500sh, Turtle.

1995, June 15   Perf. 12½x12
1404-1410 A227 Set of 7   5.25 5.25
Souvenir Sheet
1411 A227 500sh multicolored   2.00 2.00

Jerry Garcia
(d. 1995),
Musician
A228

Scenes of Grateful Dead performing on stage: #1413A, Bears. #1413B, Skeletons.

1995   Litho.   Perf. 12½
1412 A228 200sh multicolored   .80   .80
Souvenir Sheet
1413 A228 1000sh multicolored   4.00 4.00
Size: 140x92mm
Imperf
Self-Adhesive
1413A A228 2000sh multicolored 7.50 7.50
1413B A228 2000sh multicolored 7.50 7.50
   No. 1412 was issued in sheets of 9. No. 1413 contains one 51x57mm stamp.
   Issued: #1412-1413, 11/15/95; #1413A-1413B, 12/21/95.

Miniature Sheet

Rock and
Roll Stars
A229

No. 1414: a, Chuck Berry. b, Bob Dylan. c, Aretha Franklin. d, The Supremes. e, Buddy Holly. f, Bruce Springsteen. g, Elton John. h, The Rolling Stones. i, Michael Jackson.
No. 1415, The Beach Boys (Al Jardin, Mike Love, Brian Wilson, Carl Wilson, Dennis Wilson), horiz.

1995, Dec. 1   Perf. 13½x14
1414 A229 250sh Sheet of 9,
   #a.-i.   9.00 9.00
Souvenir Sheet
Perf. 14x13½
1415 A229 1000sh multicolored   4.00 4.00

Miniature Sheet

Motion
Pictures,
Cent.
A230

Bible epics: No. 1416: a, Noah's Ark, Dolores Costello. b, Ben-Hur, 1926, Ramon Novarro. c, Ben-Hur, 1926, Francis X. Bushman. d, Ben-Hur, 1959, Charlton Heston. e, Ben-Hur, 1959, Haya Harareet. f, Ben-Hur, 1959, Sam Jaffe. g, The Ten Commandments,

1923, Theodore Roberts. h, Samson and Delilah, Victor Mature. i, Samson and Delilah, Hedy Lamarr.
No. 1417, The Ten Commandments, Theodore Roberts.

1995, Dec. 1   Perf. 13½x14
1416 A230 250sh Sheet of 9,
   #a.-i.   9.00 9.00
Souvenir Sheet
1417 A230 1000sh multicolored   4.00 4.00

World Tourism Organization, 20th
Anniv. — A231

Designs: 100sh, Olduvai Gorge, "Cradle of Mankind." 300sh, First State House, Bagamoyo. 400sh, Mount Kilimanjaro. 500sh, Rhinoceroses, Ngorongoro Crater.

1995, Dec. 18   Perf. 14
1418-1420 A231 Set of 3   3.25 3.25
Souvenir Sheet
1421 A231 500sh multicolored   2.00 2.00

Predatory
Animals
A232

Designs: 70sh, Acinonyx jubatus. 100sh, Felus serval. 150sh, Huaena buana. 200sh, Otocyon megalotis. 280sh, Pantera pardus. 300sh, Pantera leo. 500sh, Alligator.

1995, Sept. 30 Litho. Perf. 12½x12
1422-1428 A232 Set of 7   5.50 5.50
Souvenir Sheet
1429 A232 500sh multicolored   2.00 2.00

Miniature Sheet

Horses — A233

Designs: a, True black Freisian. b, Appaloosa. c, Arab. d, Paint. e, Chestnut saddlebred. f, Standard thoroughbred. g, Belgian. h, Liver chestnut quarter. i, Hackney. 1000sh, Clydesdale.

1995   Perf. 14
1430 A233 250sh Sheet of 9,
   #a.-i.   9.00 9.00
Souvenir Sheet
1431 A233 1000sh multicolored   4.00 4.00

No. 685 Surcharged

70/-

X

1995?   Litho.   Perf. 14
1431A A108 70sh on 13sh #685

Miniature Sheets of 8 + Label

Paintings from the Metropolitan Museum of Art — A234

Details or entire paintings: No. 1432: a, la Orana Maria, by Gauguin. b, Young Herdsman with Cows, by Cuyp. c, Moses and the Burning Bush by, Domenichino. d, Path in the Ile Saint-Martin, Vétheuil, by Monet. e, Dances, Pink and Green, by Degas. f, Terrace at Sainte-Adresse, by Monet. g, The Rehearsal Onstage, by Degas. h, Study for "A Sunday on La Grande Jatte," by Seurat.

No. 1433: a, Madame Marsollier and Daughter, by Nattier. b, Christ and the Woman of Samaria, by Rembrandt. c, Rubens and His Wife and Son, by Rubens. d, Portrait of a Young Woman, by Vermeer. e, Portrait of a Man, by Van Dyck. f, Young Woman with a Water Jug, by Vermeer. g, Self Portrait, by Rembrandt. h, Young Man and Woman in an Inn, by Hals.

No. 1434, On the Beach at Trouville, by Boudin. No. 1435, A Dance in the Country, by G.D. Tiepolo.

1996, Mar. 7		**Perf. 13½x14**		
1432-1433	A234	200sh #a.-h.,		
		each	6.40	6.40

Souvenir Sheets
Perf. 14

1434-1435	A234	1000sh each	4.00	4.00

Nos. 1434-1435 each contain one 81x53mm stamp.

Miniature Sheet

Domestic Cats — A235

No. 1436: a, Siberian. b, Classic silver tabby Persian. c, Brown Burmese. d, Norwegian forest. e, Tabby. f, Blue & white maine coon. g, Brown California spangled cat. h, Black & white bicolor Persian. i, Shaded silver American shorthair.

Dogs: No. 1437: a, Red labrador. b, St. Bernard. c, Cocker spaniel. d, Black labrador. e, Bernese mountain dog. f, Beagle. g, Miniature pincher. h, Basset hound. i, German shepherd.

No. 1438, Silver tabby British shorthair. No. 1439, Alaskan malamute.

1996, Mar. 4		**Litho.**	**Perf. 14**	
1436	A235	250sh Sheet of 9,		
		#a.-i.	9.00	9.00
1437	A235	250sh Sheet of 9,		
		#a.-i.	9.00	9.00

Souvenir Sheets

1438	A235	1000sh multicolored	4.00	4.00
1439	A235	1000sh multicolored	4.00	4.00

Souvenir Sheets

Janis Joplin (1943-70), Rock Musician — A235a

#1439B, Joplin seated atop a psychedelically-painted Porsche, horiz. Illustration reduced.

1996, Apr. 10		**Litho.**	**Imperf.**	
Self-Adhesive				
1439A	A235a	2000sh multi	11.00	11.00
1439B	A235a	2000sh multi	11.00	11.00

Elvis Presley (1935-77) — A235b

Various photographs with EPE (Elvis Presley Enterprises) official product emblem.

1996, Mar. 13		**Litho.**	**Perf. 12½**	
1439C	A235b	200sh Sheet of 9, #d.-l.	6.00	6.00

New Year 1996 (Year of the Rat) A236

#1440: a, Arvicola oryzivora. b, Meriones hudsonicus. c, Mus missouriensis. d, Mus aureolus.
500sh, Fiber zibethicus.

1996, Apr. 12				
1440	A236	200sh Block of 4, #a.-d.	2.40	2.40

Miniature Sheet

1441	A236	200sh Sheet of 1 #1440	2.40	2.40

Souvenir Sheet

1442	A236	500sh multicolored	2.00	2.00

No. 1440 was issued in sheets of 16 stamps.

Deng Xiaoping, Chinese Communist Leader A237

Various portraits.

1996, May 6		**Litho.**	**Perf. 13**	
1443	A237	250sh Sheet of 6, #a.-f.	6.00	6.00

Souvenir Sheet

1444	A237	500sh multicolored	2.00	2.00

CHINA '96, 9th Asian Intl. Philatelic Exhibition (#1443).

Butterflies A238

Designs: 70sh, Dirphia multicolor. 100sh, Inachis io, vert. 150sh, Automerisio. 200sh, Saturnia pyri. 250sh, Arctia villica. 260sh, Arctia caja. 300sh, Celerio euforbiae, vert. 500sh, Zygaena laeta.

Perf. 12½x12, 12x12½				
1996, Jan.			**Litho.**	
1445-1451	A238	Set of 7	5.25	5.25

Souvenir Sheet

1452	A238	500sh multicolored	2.00	2.00

Frogs A239

Designs: 100sh, Bufo bufo laur. 140sh, Pyxicephalus adspersus. 180sh, Megalixalus laevis. 200sh, Xenopus laevis. 210sh, Hemisus marmoratus. 260sh, Rana beccarii. 300sh, Hyperolius cinctiventrus. 500sh, Rana goliaph.

1996, Jan. 31			**Perf. 12½x12**	
1453-1459	A239	Set of 7	5.50	5.50

Souvenir Sheet

1460	A239	500sh multicolored	2.00	2.00

Souvenir Sheet

China 1996 Intl. Philatelic Exhibition — A239a

1996, June 5		**Litho.**	**Perf. 12½**	
1460A	A239a	300sh multi	1.00	1.00

Souvenir Sheet

Shanghai Intl. Tea Culture Festival — A239b

1996		**Litho.**	**Perf. 12½**	
1460B	A239b	300sh multi	1.00	1.00

Queen Elizabeth II, 70th Birthday — A240

Designs: a, Portrait. b, As young woman in evening dress. c, Wearing tiara, jewels. 1000sh, Portrait as young woman.

1996, July 3		**Litho.**	**Perf. 13½x14**	
1461	A240	300sh Strip of 3, #a.-c.	3.50	3.50

Souvenir Sheet

1462	A240	1000sh multicolored	4.00	4.00

No. 1461 was issued in sheets of 9 stamps.

Crocodiles, Alligators — A241

Designs: 100sh, Melanosuchus niger. 150sh, Caiman latirostris. 200sh, Alligator mississpiensis. 250sh, Gavialis gangeticus. 260sh, Crocodylus niloticus. 300sh, Crocodylus cataphractus. 380sh, Crocodylus rhombifer.
500sh, Crocodile.

1996   **Perf. 12½x12**
1463-1469 A241 Set of 7   6.50 6.50
Souvenir Sheet
1470 A241 500sh multicolored   2.00 2.00

Snakes
A242

100sh, Naja pallida. 140sh, Agkistrodon contortrix. 180sh, Bungarus fasciatus. 200sh, Micrurus frontalis, vert. 260sh, Bitis gabonica, vert. 300sh, Elaphe moellendorffi, vert. 400sh, Vipera ursini, vert.
700sh, Corallus caninus, vert.

1996   **Perf. 12½x12, 12x12½**
1471-1477 A242 Set of 7   6.25 6.25
Souvenir Sheet
1478 A242 700sh multicolored   2.75 2.75

Famous People,
Events — A243

No. 1479: a, Gandhi. b, Mao Tse-tung. c, Jonas Salk. d, John F. Kennedy. e, Neil Armstrong. f, Mikhail Gorbachev. g, Nelson Mandela. h, Gen. Colin Powell.
No. 1480: a, Orville, Wilbur Wright. b, Battle of Verdun, 1916. c, Charles Lindbergh. d, Al Jolson. e, Alexander Fleming. f, Amelia Earhart. g, Franklin Roosevelt, Joseph Stalin, Winston Churchill, Yalta Conference, 1945. h, Atomic bomb blast, 1945, Enrico Fermi.
1000sh, Deng Xiaoping.

1996, July 15   **Litho.**   **Perf. 14**
Sheets of 8
1479-1480 A243 250sh #a.-h.,
    each   8.00 8.00
Souvenir Sheet
1481 A243 1000sh multicolored   4.00 4.00

A244   Birds — A245

Fruits of East Africa: 140sh, Pineapple. 180sh, Orange, lime. 200sh, Pear, apple. 300sh, Bananas.

1996, Sept. 4   **Litho.**   **Perf. 13**
1482-1485 A244 Set of 4   3.25 3.25
     Souv. sheet of 1
1485a   #1485   1.25 1.25

1996, Sept. 16   **Perf. 14**
No. 1486: a, Vidua macroura. b, Tockus erythrorynchus. c, Trachyphonus erythrocephalus. d, Bubo capensis. e, Gyps ruppellii. f, Sarkidiornis melanotus. g, Dendrocygna bicolor. h, Struthio camelus.
No. 1487: a, Gypohierax angolensis. b, Aquila chrysaetos. c, Spilornis rufipectus. d, Eutriorchis astur. e, Haliaeetus albicilla. f, Ichthyophaga ichthyaetus. g, Spilornis holospilus. h, Dryotriorchis spectabilis.
No. 1488, African paradise flycatcher. No. 1489, Haliaeetus leucocephala, horiz.

Sheets of 8
1486-1487 A245 300sh #a.-h., ea 9.50 9.50
Souvenir Sheets
1488 A245 1000sh multicolored   4.00 4.00
1489 A245 1000sh multicolored   4.00 4.00

Reef Fish
A246

100sh, Yellowtail wrasse. 150sh, Jewel grouper. 250sh, Barred thick-lipped wrasse. 500sh, Bullethead parrotfish.
No. 1494: a, Golden cardinal fish. b, Yellowhead butterfly fish. c, Common banner fish (diver). d, Zanzibar butterfly fish. e, Lemon damsel. f, Blue and gold fusilier. g, Red firegoby. h, Threadfin fairy basslet. i, Rein rock basslet.
No. 1495, African pygmy angelfish. No. 1496, Blue green chromis.

1996, Sept. 23
1490-1493 A246 Set of 4   4.00 4.00
Sheet of 9
1494 A246 200sh #a.-i.   7.25 7.25
Souvenir Sheets
1495-1496 A246 1000sh each   4.00 4.00

Ferrari
Cars
A247

Designs: a, 1964 250LM. b, 1992 456 GT. c, 1995 F50. d, 1995 F512 M "Testarossa." e, 1984 BB 512. f, 1955 410 S coupe.
1000sh, 1964 250 GTO.

1996, Sept. 27   **Litho.**   **Perf. 14**
1497 A247 250sh Sheet of 6,
    #a.-f.   6.00 6.00
Souvenir Sheet
1498 A247 1000sh multicolored   4.00 4.00
No. 1498 contains one 85x28mm stamp.

Radio, Cent.
A248

70sh, Franklin D. Roosevelt, 1st fireside chat, 1933. 100sh, Harry S. Truman announces US use of atomic bomb, 1945. 150sh, Orson Welles, "Alien Invasion" broadcast, 1938. 200sh, Fiorello La Guardia reads newspaper comics via radio.
1000sh, Robin Williams as Adrian Cronauer, "Good Morning Viet Nam."

1996, July 15   **Litho.**   **Perf. 13½x14**
1499-1502 A248 Set of 4   2.00 2.00
Souvenir Sheet
1503 A248 1000sh multicolored   4.00 4.00

Mercedes-Benz Automobiles — A249

a, 1952 300SL Coupè 1. b, 1932 680S. c, 1934 500K. d, 1934 Type 150. e, 1934 Type 150 Sport Roadster "Heck." f, 1937 W125.
1000sh, 1936 540K Roadster Class A.

1996, Sept. 27   **Perf. 14**
1504 A249 250sh Sheet of 6,
    #a.-f.   6.00 6.00
Souvenir Sheet
1505 A249 1000sh multicolored   4.00 4.00

UNICEF, 50th
Anniv. — A250

200sh, Child holding bowl. 250sh, Mother breastfeeding infant. 500sh, Tetsuko Kuroyanaga holding child.
1000sh, Girl.

1996, Oct. 4
1506-1508 A250 Set of 3   3.75 3.75
Souvenir Sheet
1509 A250 1000sh multicolored   4.00 4.00

UNESCO, 50th Anniv. — A251

200sh, Ngorongoro Conservation Area, Tanzania. 250sh, Los Katios Natl. Park, Colombia. 600sh, Kilwa Kisiwani Makutani Complex, Tanzania.
1000sh, Kilimanjaro Natl. Park, Tanzania.

1996, Oct. 4
1510-1512 A251 Set of 3   4.25 4.25
Souvenir Sheet
1513 A251 1000sh multicolored   4.00 4.00

Flowers — A252

No. 1514: a, Lily of the valley. b, Spanish iris. c, Spiderwort. d, Morning glory. e, Gazania. f, Pansy. g, Begonia. h, Madonna lily.
No. 1515: a, Snowdrop. b, Treesia. c, Cosmos. d, Daffodil. e, Blue himalayan poppy. f, Blue daisy. g, Zinnia flore-pleno. h, Oriental poppy.
No. 1516, Fuchsia. No. 1517, Hanson's lily.

1996, Oct. 25
Sheets of 8 + Label
1514-1515 A252 300sh #a.-h.,
    each   9.75 9.75
Souvenir Sheets
1516-1517 A252 1000sh each   4.00 4.00

Domestic
Cats
A253

100sh, Lilac point Siamese. 150sh, Somali. 200sh, British blue shorthair.
No. 1521: a, American shorthair silver tabby. b, Scottish fold. c, Persian blue. d, Ocicat.
1000sh, Ragdoll.

1996, Dec. 10   **Litho.**   **Perf. 14**
1518-1520 A253 Set of 3   1.75 1.75
1521 A253 300sh Sheet of 4,
    #a.-d.   3.75 3.75
Souvenir Sheet
1522 A253 1000sh multicolored   4.00 4.00

Dogs
A254

70sh, Shar-pei. 250sh, Beagle. 600sh, Keeshond.
No. 1527: a, St. Bernard. b, Shetland sheepdog. c, Samoyed. d, Australian cattle dog.
1000sh, Collie.

1996, Dec. 10   **Litho.**   **Perf. 14**
1524-1526 A254 Set of 3   3.50 3.50
1527 A254 300sh Sheet of 4,
    #a.-d.   4.75 4.75
Souvenir Sheet
1528 A254 1000sh multicolored   4.00 4.00

Nos. 767-768, 1001-1002, 1026-1028
Ovptd.

a

b

c

1996, Dec. 16
Sheets of 16, 12 & 6
1529 A120(a-b) 50sh #a.-p.
    (#767)   3.25 3.25
1530 A120(c) 50sh #a.-p.
    (#768)   3.25 3.25
1531 A154(a-b) 100sh #a.-l.
    (#1001)   4.75 4.75
1532 A158(c) 100sh #a.-l.
    (#1026)   2.40 2.40
1533 A158(c) 100sh #a.-f.
    (#1027)   2.40 2.40
Souvenir Sheets
1534 A154(c) 500sh on #1002   2.00 2.00
1535 A158(a) 500sh on #1028   2.00 2.00

Size and location of overprint varies.
Overprints types a-b appear on alternating stamps of Nos. 1529, 1531.
Nos. 1529-1533 have additional overprints in sheet margin.

Mushrooms
A255

No. 1536: a, Amanita phalloides. b, Amanita muscaria. c, Morchella vulgaris. d, Tricholoma aurantium. e, Amanita caesarea. f, Psalliota haemorrhoidaria. g, Russula virescens. h, Boletus crocipodius.
No. 1537: a, Coprinus comatus. b, Amanitopsis vaginata. c, Clitocybe geotropa. d, Cortinarius violaceus. e, Russula sardonia. f, Cortinarius collinitus. g, Boletus aereus. h, Lepiota procera.
No. 1538, Ganoderma lucidum. No. 1539, Collybia distorta.

1996, Dec. 17
Sheets of 8
1536-1537 A255 300sh #a.-h.,
                each   9.50 9.50
Souvenir Sheets
1538-1539 A255 1000sh each   4.00 4.00
Souvenir Sheet

Watercolor Painting — A256

Illustration reduced.

1996, May 6   Litho.   Perf. 13
1540 A256 500sh multicolored   2.00 2.00
China '96. No. 1540 was not available until March 1997.

Sun Yat-Sen
(1866-1925)
A257

Various portraits.

1997   Perf. 14
1541 A257 300sh Sheet of 6,
                #a.-f.   7.25 7.25
Souvenir Sheet
1542 A257 1000sh multicolored   4.00 4.00
Hong Kong '97.

Horses
A258

No. 1543: a, Blue Arabian horse. b, English thoroughbred. c, Tennessee walking horse. d, Anglo-Arab horse.
No. 1544: a, Trakehner. b, American saddlebred. c, Morgan. d, Frederiksborg. e, Mirror of #d. f, Mirror of #c. g, Mirror of #b. h, Mirror of #a.
#1545, Wielkopolski. #1546, Thiawari, vert.

1997, Mar. 20   Litho.   Perf. 14
1543 A258 250sh Strip of 4, #a.-
                d.   4.25 4.25
1544 A258 250sh Sheet of 8,
                #a.-h.   8.50 8.50
Souvenir Sheet
1545-1546 A258 1000sh each   4.25 4.25
No. 1543 was issued in sheets of 8 stamps with second strip in reverse order.

COMESA
A259

140sh, Tourism. 180sh, Fishing. 200sh, Dar es Salaam Port. 300sh, TAZARA Railway.

1997   Perf. 13
1547-1550 A259 Set of 4   3.50 3.50
Souvenir Sheet
1551 A259 500sh Cotton   2.25 2.25

UN
Volunteers,
25th Anniv.
A260

Designs: 140sh, Health of mother and child. 200sh, Food distribution. 260sh, Clean water distribution. 300sh, Public education. 500sh, Refugee camp.

1997
1552-1555 A260 Set of 4   3.75 3.75
Souvenir Sheet
1556 A260 500sh multicolored   2.25 2.25

Birds
A261

150sh, Mockingbird. 200sh, House finch. 410sh, Bridled titmouse. 500sh, Cactus wren.
No. 1561: a, Sooty tern. b, Nunbird. c, Mottled wood owl. d, Turquoise-browed mot mot. e, Emerald toucanet. f, Dusky-headed conure.
No. 1562: a, Maguari stork. b, Spoonbills. c, Flamingo. d, Hammerkop. e, Limpkin. f, Pink-backed pelican.
No. 1563, Masked booby. No. 1564, Brown pelican.

1997, May 5   Litho.   Perf. 14
1557-1560 A261 Set of 4   5.00 5.00
1561 A261 140sh Sheet of 6,
                #a.-f.   3.50 3.50
1562 A261 370sh Sheet of 6,
                #a.-f.   9.00 9.00
Souvenir Sheets
1563-1564 A261 1000sh each   4.00 4.00

Flowers
A262   A263

100sh, Plumeria rubra acutifolia. 140sh, 150sh, Liliaceae. 180sh, Alamanda. 200sh, Lilaceae, diff. 210sh, Zinnia. 260sh, Malvaviscus penduliflorus. 300sh, Carna. 380sh, Nerium oleander carneum. 400sh, Hibiscus rosa sinensis. 600sh, Cartharanthus roseus. 700sh, Bougainvillea formosa. 750sh, Acalypha.
No. 1577: a, like #1571. b, like #1569. c, like #1572. d, like #1575.

1997   Perf. 14½x15
1565 A262 100sh multi   .40 .40
1566 A262 140sh multi   .60 .60
1566A A262 150sh multi
1567 A262 180sh multi   .75 .75
1568 A262 200sh multi   .80 .80
1569 A262 210sh multi   .85 .85
1570 A262 260sh multi   1.00 1.00
1571 A262 300sh multi   1.25 1.25
1572 A262 380sh multi   1.50 1.50
1573 A262 400sh multi   1.60 1.60
1574 A262 600sh multi   2.40 2.40
1575 A262 700sh multi   2.75 2.75
1576 A262 750sh multi   3.00 3.00
  Nos. 1565-1566,1567-1576 (12) 16.90 16.90
Sheet of 4
Perf. 14½x14
1577 A263 125sh #a.-d.   2.00 2.00
Issued: #1566A, 1997; others, 5/19.
For overprint see No. O49.

Modern Olympic Games, Cent., 1996
Summer Olympic Games,
Atlanta, — A264

1996   Litho.   Perf. 11½
1578 A264 100sh Tennis   .40 .40
1579 A264 150sh Baseball   .60 .60
1580 A264 200sh Soccer   .75 .75
1581 A264 300sh Boxing   1.25 1.25
  Nos. 1578-1581 (4)   3.00 3.00

Chernobyl
Disaster,
10th Anniv.
A265

Designs: No. 1582, Chabad's Children of Chernobyl. No. 1583, UNESCO.

1997, Apr. 25   Litho.   Perf. 13½x14
1582 A265 700sh multicolored   2.75 2.75
1583 A265 700sh multicolored   2.75 2.75

Flowers
A266

No. 1583A: b, Prunus dulcis. c, Spassky Clock tower. d, Crataegus monogyna. e, Amica montana. f, Campanula patula. g, Papaver orientalis.
No. 1584: a, Malus niedzwetzkayana. b, Golden domes of the Cathedral of the Annunciation, Moscow. c, Polygonatum multiflorum. d, Leucanthemum vulgare, e, Hypencum perforatum. f, Pulsatilla vulgaris.
No. 1585, Laburnum anagyroides, St. Basil's Cathedral, vert. No. 1585A, Rosa canina, Church of Christ Resurrection, Moscow.

1997   Perf. 14x14½
1583A A266 200sh Sheet of 6,
                #b.-g.   5.00 5.00
1584 A266 300sh Sheet of 6,
                #a.-f.   7.50 7.50
Souvenir Sheets
1585-
1585A   A266 1000sh each
                                 4.25 4.25
No. 1585 contains one 30x38mm stamp.

World
AIDS Day
A267

Designs: 140sh, Condom protects against AIDS, vert. 310sh, Caution, you may contract AIDS. 370sh, Control of AIDS is our responsibility. 410sh, Care and support AIDS orphans. 500sh, like #1586.

1997   Litho.   Perf. 13
1586-1589 A267 Set of 4   5.00 5.00
Souvenir Sheet
1590 A267 500sh multicolored   2.00 2.00

Paintings by
Hiroshige
(1797-1858)
A268

No. 1591: a, Aoi Slope, Outside Toranomon Gate. b, Bikuni Bridge in Snow. c, Mount Atago, Shiba. d, Akasaka Kiribatake. f, Zojoji Pagoda & Akabane. f, Hibiya & Soto-Sakurada from Yamashita-cho.
No. 1592, Shiba Shinmei Shrine. No. 1593, Kanasugibashi Shibaura.

1997, July 21 Litho.   Perf. 13½x14
1591 A268 250sh Sheet of 6,
                #a.-f.   5.00 5.00
Souvenir Sheets
1592-1593 A268 1000sh each   3.25 3.25

Queen
Elizabeth II
and Prince
Philip, 50th
Anniv.
A269

No. 1594: a, Engagement picture of Queen. b, Royal arms. c, Queen, Prince in casual attire. d, Prince, Queen. e, Balmoral Castle. f, Prince Philip.
1500sh, Formal portrait.

1997, July 21   Litho.   Perf. 14
1594 A269 370sh Sheet of 6,
                #a.-f.   7.50 7.50
Souvenir Sheet
1595 A269 1500sh multicolored   5.00 5.00

Return of Hong Kong to
China — A270

Split design comparing modern and early photographs of: No. 1596a, Clock Tower, Tsim Sha Tsu, former terminal of Kowloon-Canton Railways. No. 1596b, Legislative Council Building, previously Supreme Court.
No. 1597: a, Signing of Sino-British Joint Declaration on Question of Hong Kong, 1984. b, Deng Xiaoping, Chinese leaders, c, C.F. Tung, first Chinese chief executive of Hong Kong, 1996.
Illustration reduced.

1997, July 21   Perf. 14½
1596 A270 1000sh Sheet of 2,
                #a.-b.   6.75 6.75
1597 A270 1000sh Sheet of 3,
                #a.-c.   10.00 10.00
No. 1597 contains 3 59x28mm stamps.

Grimm's Fairy Tales A271

Mother Goose — A272

Rumpelstiltskin: No. 1598: a, Woman at spinning wheel, Prince. b, Woman, Rumpelstiltskin at spinning wheel. c, Prince, woman playing mandolin.
#1599, Girl whistling. #1600, Rumpelstiltskin.

1997   **Perf. 13½x14**
1598 A271   400sh Sheet of 3,   #a.-c.   4.00 4.00

Souvenir Sheets
Perf. 14
1599 A272 1000sh multicolored   3.25 3.25
Perf. 13½x14
1600 A271 1500sh multicolored   5.00 5.00

1998 Winter Olympic Games, Nagano — A273

Designs: 100sh, Torvill & Dean, ice dancing. 200sh, Katarina Witt, figure skating. 500sh, First Olympic winter games, 1924, curling introduced. 600sh, Pirmin Zurbriggen, downhill skiing.
No. 1605: a, Dan Jansen, 1000m speed skating. b, Alberto Tomba, slalom & giant slalom skiing. c, Herma Plank-Szabo, figure skating. d, Donna Weinbrecht, mogul skiing.
No. 1606, Yukio Kasaya, ski jump. No. 1607, Barbara Ann Scott, figure skating.

1997, Oct. 6   **Litho.**   **Perf. 14**
1601-1604 A273   Set of 4   4.75 4.75
1605 A273 250sh Block or strip   of 4, #a.-d.   3.25 3.25

Souvenir Sheets
1606-1607 A273 1000sh each   3.25 3.25

Sinking of MV Bukoba A274

Designs: 140sh, Ship sinking. 350sh, Removing bodies. 370sh, Identification of the dead. 410sh, Mass funeral.
500sh, MV Bukoba.

1997, May 21   **Litho.**   **Perf. 14**
1608-1611 A274   Set of 4   4.25 4.25

Souvenir Sheet
Perf. 14½
1612 A274 500sh multicolored   1.75 1.75

Tourist Attractions of East Africa — A275

Designs: 140sh, Mount Kilimanjaro. 310sh, Masai. 370sh, Zanzibar old stonetown. 410sh, Buffalo, plains of Ruaha.
500sh, Mount Kilimanjaro Kibo Peak.

1997, Oct. 9   **Perf. 13½**
1613-1616 A275   Set of 4   4.25 4.25

Souvenir Sheet
1617 A275 500sh multicolored   1.75 1.75

1998 World Cup Soccer Championships, France — A276

Teams: 100sh, Italy, 1938. 150sh, Brazil, 1970. 200sh, Uruguay, 1930. 250sh, W. Germany, 1954. 500sh, Argentina, 1978. 600sh, England, 1966.
Players: No. 1624, vert: a, Muller, W. Germany. b, Kocsis, Hungary. c, Pele, Brazil. d, Schillaci, Italy. e, Fontaine, France. f, Nejedly, Czechoslovakia. g, Rahn, W. Germany. h, Lineker, England.
Stadiums: No. 1625: a, The Rose Bowl, US, 1994. b, Torino Stadium, Italy, 1934. c, Olympia Stadium, Germany, 1974. d, Azteca Satdium, Mexico, 1970, 1986. e, Wembley, England, 1966. f, Maracana, Brazil, 1950. g, Centenary Stadium, Uruguay, 1930. h, Bernabeu Stadium, Spain, 1982.
#1626, Pele, Brazil. #1627, Eusebio, Portugal.

1997, Oct. 20   **Perf. 14x13½, 13½x14**
1618-1623 A276   Set of 6   6.00 6.00
Sheets of 8 + Label
1624-1625 A276 250sh #a.-h.,   each   6.75 6.75
Souvenir Sheet
1626-1627 A276 1000sh each   4.00 4.00

Endangered Species A277

Fauna A278

Animals of Asia: No. 1628: a, Tiger. b, Japanese macaque. c, Slender loris. d, Musk deer. e, Przewalski's horse. f, Red panda.

Animals of Latin America: No. 1629: a, Night monkey. b, Woolly opossum. c, Jaguar. d, Red uakaris. e, Ringtailed coati. f, Cotton-top tamarin.
Animals of North America: No. 1630: a, Bobcat. b, Moose. c, American bison. d, Mountain goat. e, Walrus. f, Common racoon.
Animals of Africa: No. 1630G: h, Cheetah. i, Zebra. j, Gorilla. k, Brown lesser mouse lemur. l, Rhinoceros. m. Chimpanzee.
Northern wilderness: No. 1631: a, Great horned owl. b, Bald eagle. c, Coyotes. d, Grizzly bear. e, Caribou (d). f, Walrus. g, Hooded seal. h, Humpback whale (g). i, Harp seal.
African safari: No. 1632: a, Barbary macaque. b, Turaco. c, Giraffe (f). d, Mountain gorilla, African elephant (a, b, e, g, h). e, Zebra. f, Grant's gazelle. g, Monarch butterfly, meerkat. h, African lion. i, Rhinoceros (f).
#1633, Maned wolf. #1634, Giant panda. #1635, Gray wolf. #1636, African elephant, diff.

1997, Oct. 30   **Perf. 14**
Sheets of 6
1628-1630 A277   250sh #a.-f.,   each   5.25 5.25
1630G   A277   250sh #h.-m.   5.00 5.00
Sheets of 9
1631-1632 A278   250sh #a.-i.,   each   7.50 7.50
Souvenir Sheets
1633-1636 A277 1500sh each   5.25 5.25

A279

A280

Modern architecture: No. 1637: a, Sydney Opera House, Australia. b, Brasilia Cathedral, Brazil. c, Metropolitan Cathedral of Christ the King, Liverpool, England. d, Einstein Tower, Potsdam, Berlin, Germany. e, Solomon Guggenheim Museum, New York City, US. f, Palace of the Natl. Congress, Brasilia.
Ancient wonders of the world, vert.: No. 1638: a, Temple of Artemis at Ephesus. b, Great Pyramid of Cheops. c, Mausoleum at Halicarnassus. d, Statue of Zeus at Olympia. e, Hanging Gardens of Babylon. f, Colossus of Rhodes.
No. 1639, Notre Dame Du Haut Chapel, Ronchamp, France. No. 1640, Lighthouse of Alexandria.

1997, Nov. 5   **Perf. 14**
1637 A279 140sh Sheet of 6,   #a.-f.   2.75 2.75
1638 A279 370sh Sheet of 6,   #a.-f.   7.50 7.50
Souvenir Sheets
1639-1640 A279 1000sh each   3.50 3.50
Nos. 1639-1640 contain one 42x57mm or 57x42mm stamp, respectively.

1997, Nov. 28   **Wmk. 233**
Coastal Birds: 140sh, Red hornbill. 350sh, Sacred ibis, horiz. 370sh, Sea gulls, horiz. 410sh, Ring-necked dove, horiz.
500sh, Hornbill, ibis, gulls, doves, horiz.

1641-1644 A280   Set of 4   4.25 4.25
Souvenir Sheet
1645 A280 500sh multicolored   1.75 1.75

Aircraft A281

Fighter Planes: 100sh, P-51D. 200sh, Lockheed P-38J Lightning. 300sh, B-29 Superfortress. 400sh, Lockheed P-80 Shooting Star P-80 A1. 500sh, Curtiss P-36A.
Spitfires: No. 1651a, MK IX providing altitude cover for bomber formations. b, MK Vc dog fighting. c, PRMK XIX, Photographic Reconnaissance Development Unit, RAF. d, MK Vb over North Africa. e, FR XIVE firing rockets. f, MK VIII (ZPZ), Japanese bomber. g, Supermarine Seafire being catapulted from HMS Indomitable. h, MK IX during D-Day landings. i, MK XII attacking V1 Flying Bomb.

Spitfires: No. 1652: a, MK IXc, escorting crippled Lancaster Bomber. b, MK 1a dog fighting. c, PR MK XI, 14th Photo Sqdn., US 8th Air Force. d, MK Vb, North Africa. e, MK VIII with lightning bolt on nose. f, MK Vc with RAF, Yugoslav, American markings. g, Supermarine Seafire landing on British carrier. h, MK IXc D-Day. i, MK XII destroying V-1 Flying Bomb.
No. 1653: a, MKII in desert. b, Hurribomber dog fighting. c, MK 24, photo reconnaissance. d, Canadian MK 1 foreign squadron. e, Mark IXC convoy protection. f, Spitfire with clipped wings flanked by MK 22. g, Hurricanes MKII in desert. h, Hurribomber.
No. 1654, Boeing P-26. No. 1655, SR-71A. No. 1656, MK Vb. No. 1657, MK V Float plane. No. 1658, MK 1.

1997, Dec. 23   **Litho.**   **Perf. 14**
1646-1650 A281   Set of 5   5.25 5.25
Sheets of 8 or 9
1651-1652 A281 150sh #a.-i., ea   4.50 4.50
1653 A281 250sh #a.-h.   6.75 6.75
Souvenir Sheets
1654-1658 A281 1000sh each   3.50 3.50
No. 1656 contains one 85x28mm stamp. Nos. 1657-1658 each contain one 57x42mm stamp.

Jackie Chan, Movie Star A282

Various portraits.

1997, Dec. 30
1659 A282 370sh Sheet of 6,   #a.-f.   7.50 7.50

PAPU (Pan African Postal Union), 18th Anniv. A283

Designs: 150sh, Natl. flag of Tanzania, flag of PAPU. 250sh, PAPU emblem. 400sh, Delivery by EMS motorcycles. 500sh, Giraffes.

1998, Jan. 18   **Perf. 13½**
1660-1663 A283   Set of 4   4.50 4.50

A284

A285

1998   **Litho.**   **Perf. 14**
1664 A284 410sh Mt. Kilimanjaro 1.40 1.40

1998, Jan. 23
Diana, Princess of Wales (1961-97): 150sh, In red jacket. 250sh, In lilac dress.
1000sh, In teal suit with Prince Harry (in sheet margin).

1665 A285 150sh multicolored   .50 .50
1666 A285 250sh multicolored   .85 .85
Souvenir Sheet
1667 A285 1000sh multicolored   3.25 3.25
Nos. 1665-1666 were each issued in sheets of 9.

Marine Life and Sea Birds A286

No. 1668: a, Black-browed albatross. b, Unidentified bird. c, Xantusi murrelet. d, Empress angelfish. e, Bottle nosed dolphins. f, Queen angelfish. g, Red sponge. h, Unidentified red and tan fish. i, Reef shark. j, Sea star. k, Unidentified white and black fish. l, Stingray.

No. 1669: a, Black-saddled pufferfish. b, Harlequin tuskfish. c, Emperor angelfish. d, Foxface. e, Yellow tang. f, Catalina goby. g, Fifteen-spined stickleback. h, Banded pipefish. i, Weather loach.

No. 1670 vert.: a, Octopus. b, Pantherfish. c, Hawksbill turtle. d, Skate. e, Jellyfish. f, White tip shark. g, Blue starfish. h, Brain coral. i, Anemone.

No. 1671, Clown fish. No. 1672, Shark. No. 1673, Yellow seahorse, vert.

1998, Jan. 30
1668	A286	200sh Sheet of 12, #a.-l.	8.00	8.00

Sheets of 9
1669-1670	A286	250sh #a.-i., ea	7.50	7.50

Souvenir Sheets
1671-1673	A286	1000sh each	3.25	3.25

For overprints see #1697-1702, 1750-1751.

Traditional Weapons — A287

Designs: 150sh, Slingshot. 250sh, Cutlass and club. 400sh, Gun. 500sh, Bow, arrows.

1998, Mar. 16   Litho.   Perf. 14
1674-1677	A287	Set of 4	4.40	4.40

New Year 1998 (Year of the Tiger) — A288

Stylized tiger: No. 1678: a, Walking right. b, Walking left. c, Lying down. d, Seated. 1500sh, Tiger standing.

1998, Mar. 30   Litho.   Perf. 13½
1678	A288	370sh Sheet of 4, #a.-d.	5.00	5.00

Souvenir Sheet
1679	A288	1500sh multicolored	5.00	5.00

John Denver (1943-97), Rock Musician — A288a

No. 1679A: c, Wearing green sweater. d, Wearing brown sweater (shoulders in middle of stamp). e, Wearing brown sweater (shoulder near corner of stamp). f, Wearing green sweater, hand at face. 1500sh, Wearing blue shirt.

1998, Apr. 30   Litho.   Perf. 14
1679A	A288a	370sh Sheet of 4, #c-f	3.00	3.00

Souvenir Sheet
1679B	A288a	1500sh multi	3.00	3.00

Most examples of Nos. 1679A-1679B were not available in the philatelic marketplace until Dec. 2002.

Antique Automobiles — A289

No. 1680: a, 1901 Mercedes 35hp. b, 1903 Ford Model A. c, 1908 Legnano Type A. d, 1908-09 Rolls Royce 40-50hp Silver Ghost. e, 1910 Renault Petit Duc. f, 1913 Fischer Torpedo.

No. 1681: a, 1923-24 Peugeot 18cv. b, 1926 Daimler 25-85hp. c, 1932 Bugatti Type 50T. d, 1933 Pierce-Arrow V12 "Silver Arrow." e, 1934 Tatra V8. f, 1937 Grosser Mercedes Benz. #1682, 1900 Benz. #1683, 1893 Duryea.

1998, Aug. 4   Litho.   Perf. 14
Sheets of 6
1680-1681	A289	370sh #a.-f., each	7.50	7.50

Souvenir Sheets
1682-1683	A289	1000sh each	3.50	3.50

Nos. 1682-1683 each contain one 64x48mm stamp.

Flowers and Insects A290

No. 1684, vert: a, Euanthe sanderiana, teirataenia surinama. b, "Clown Mixed." c, Pansies, caterpiller of papilio polyxenes. d, "Prelude." e, Dendrobium primulinum, wasp beetle. f, Carrion beetle, clematis "Lasurstern." g, Sunflowers, "Autumn Beauty" & "Italian White," elder borer, painted daisy. h, Grape hyacinth.

No. 1685: a, Platinum sun. b, Vespid wasp, oriental poppy. c, Anemone. d, Ipomoea alba, king's bee hawkmoth. e, Aussie delight, potter wasp. f, Colorado potato beetle, Japanese iris. g, Bomarea caldasii, azure damselfly. h, Hybrid macranthe, queen bumblebee. i, Love with lace iris, click beetle.

No. 1686: a, Golden ray lily, South African longhorn beetle. b, Oncidium macianthum. c, Agelia petali, dendrobium. c, Cobaea scandens. d, Goldsmith beetle, paphiopedilum gilda. e, Iceland poppies, potter wasp. f, Pink beauty. g, Annual chrysanthemums. h, Little mal. m, femurrubrum.

No. 1687, Carolina Queen. No. 1688, Robert E. Lee daffodils. No. 1689, Orange scarlet hybrid "Tempo." No. 1690, Pansies.

1998, Aug. 18   Litho.   Perf. 14
1684	A290	250sh Sheet of 8, #a.-h.	6.75	6.75

Sheets of 9
1685-1686	A290	250sh #a.-i., ea	7.50	7.50

Souvenir Sheets
1687-1690	A290	1500sh each	5.00	5.00

A291

Endangered Species — A292

No. 1691: a, Hyacinth macaw. b, Gibbon. c, Bosman's potto. d, Scarlet crowned barbets. e, Giant anteater. f, Cacomistle. g, Tiger. h, Mara. i, Mandrill. j, Crocodile. k, Wood turtle. l, Baribusa.

No. 1692: a, Giant sable antelope. b, Cheetah. c, Giraffe. d, Black bear. e, African elephant. f, Giant panda.

No. 1693: a, Tiger. b, Bald eagle (a, c). c, Mountain gorilla. d, Sea lion. e, Green sea turtle. f, Hippopotamus.

No. 1694, Emerald tanager. No. 1695, Florida manatee. No. 1696, Orangutan.

1998, Aug. 31   Litho.   Perf. 14
1691	A291	200sh Sheet of 12, #a.-l.	8.00	8.00
1692	A292	370sh Sheet of 6, #a.-f.	7.50	7.50
1693	A292	370sh Sheet of 6, #a.-f.	7.50	7.50

Souvenir Sheets
1694	A291	1500sh multi	5.00	5.00
1695-1696	A292	1500sh each	5.00	5.00

Nos. 1692, 1695 each contain 51x38mm stamps. No. 1696 contains 43x28mm stamps.

Nos. 1668-1673 Ovptd.

1998, Sept. 2   Litho.   Perf. 14
1697	A286	200sh Sheet of 12, #a.-l.	8.00	8.00

Sheets of 9
1698-1699	A286	250sh #a.-l., each	7.50	7.50

Souvenir Sheets
1700-1702	A286	1000sh each	3.40	3.40

The stamps of Nos. 1697-1699, 1701-1702 were ovptd. with Intl. Year of the Ocean emblem and the sheet margins contain one or two emblems with words "INTERNATIONAL YEAR OF THE OCEAN." No. 1700 has overprint only on sheet margin.

Aircraft A293

No. 1703: a, Antoinette IV, 1908. b, Deperdussin Racer, 1912. c, Demoiselle, 1909. d, Bleriot XI, 1909. e, Avro FAV Roe, 1912. f, Breguet IV, 1910.

No. 1704: a, Deperdussin. b, Ultralight, 1979-86. c, Amphibian, 1929-30. d, Pitts Special, 1930. e, BAC-221, 1960. f, Avro Tutor, 1931.

No. 1705: a, KI-44 Tojo. b, Hawker Fury. c, Mustang. d, Zero. e, Travel Air Mystery Ship. f, F8F Bearcat.

No. 1706, USAAF Curtiss P-40M. No. 1707, Biplane. No. 1708, Balloon.

1998, Aug. 4   Litho.   Perf. 14
Sheets of 6
1703-1705	A293	300sh #a.-f., each	6.00	6.00

Souvenir Sheets
1706-1708	A293	1000sh each	3.50	3.50

No. 1704a incorrectly inscribed 1900.

Eagles A294

No. 1709: a, Pallas's fish. b, Bateleur. c, Martial. d, Golden. e, Wedge-tailed. f, Java hawk. 1500sh, Wedge-tailed, diff.

1998, Aug. 31
1709	A294	370sh Sheet of 6, #a.-f.	7.50	7.50

Souvenir Sheet
1710	A294	1500sh multicolored	5.00	5.00

Fauna and Flora A295

Designs: 250sh, Takahe. 410sh, Lear's macaw. 500sh, Ring-tailed lemur. 600sh, Arabian oryx.

No. 1715: a, Japanese crested ibis. b, Kuai O'o. c, Bourke's hairstreak. d, Quokka. e, Tahitian lorikeet. f, Black-faced tamarin.

No. 1716: a, Loggerhead turtle. b, Snow leopard. c, Gurney's pitta. d, Lowland gorilla. e, Echo parakeet. f, Orangutan. #1717, Giant panda. #1718, Bengal tiger.

1998, Aug. 31   Perf. 14x14½
1711-1714	A295	Set of 4	6.25	6.25

Sheets of 6
1715-1716	A295	370sh #a.-f., each	7.50	7.50

Souvenir Sheets
1717-1718	A295	1500sh each	5.00	5.00

Children's Rights A296

150sh, Equal rights for boys and girls. 250sh, #1723, Right to education. 400sh, Right not to be beaten, vert. 500sh, Right to be loved, vert.

1998   Perf. 13
1719-1722	A296	Set of 4	4.50	4.50

Souvenir Sheet
1723	A296	500sh multicolored	1.75	1.75

No. 608 Surcharged

Method and Perf. as Before
1998 (?)
1723A	A99	150sh on 13sh multi	

The editors suspect that other surcharges exist in this set and would like to examine any examples.

World Stamp Day — A297

Designs: 150sh, UPU Emblem. 250sh, Letter facing and date stamping. 400sh, Trusted messenger. 500sh, Letter posting.

No. 1728, Trusted messenger, letter posting, UPU emblem.

1998, Oct. 9   Wmk. 387   Perf. 14
1724-1727	A297	Set of 4	4.50	4.50

Souvenir Sheet
1728	A297	500sh multicolored	1.75	1.75

A298

Marine Life, Sea Birds A299

Designs: 150sh, Equal sea star. 250sh, Mountain crab. 400sh, Wolffish. 500sh, Purple sea urchin.

No. 1733: a, Barred antshrike. b, Yellow-nosed albatross, common tern. c, Common tern, killer whale. d, Crimson-rumped toucanet. e, French angelfish. f, Grey shark (e). g, Manta ray (f, h). h, Yellow-backed damselfish. i, Green parrot wrasse. j, Silver badgerfish, pyjama wrasse. k, Skate, red-knobbed starfish (h). l, Striped snapper.

No. 1734: a, Common dolphin. b, Blue marlin. c, Arctic tern. d, Blackedge moray. e, Loggerhead turtle. f, Blacktip shark. g, Two-spotted octopus. h, Manta ray. i, Sailfin tang.

No. 1735, Aequipecten opercularis. No. 1736, Chrysaora quinquecirrha. No. 1737, Skate.

1998, Oct. 12
1729-1732	A298	Set of 4	4.50	4.50
1733	A299	200sh Sheet of 12, #a.-l.	8.00	8.00
1734	A298	300sh Sheet of 9, #a.-i.	9.50	9.50

Souvenir Sheets
1735-1736	A298	1000sh each	3.25	3.25
1737	A299	1500sh multi	5.00	5.00

Intl. Year of the Ocean (1733-1737).

Mushrooms and Insects — A300

Designs: 140sh, Cardinal beetle, tricholoma batschii. 150sh, Tricholoma catigatum, painted lady. 200sh, Lyophylum decastes, speckled wood butterfly. 250sh, Tricholoma flavovfrens, speckled bush cricket. 370sh, Boletus chrysenteron, shieldbug. 410sh, Boletus zelleri, darter dragonfly. 500sh, Gyroporus castaneus, tortoise beetle. 600sh, Hissing cockroach, boletus satanas.
No. 1746: a, Hygrocybe miniata, shieldbug. b, Peacock butterfly, cystolepiata adulterina. c, Collybia dryophila, bush cricket. d, Omphalotus olearius, halloween pennant butterfly. e, Macrolepiota rhacodes, helicon butterfly. f, Macrole piota puellaris, hornet. g, Carpenter bee. h, Mycena epipteryia, South African longhorn beetle. i, Amanita muscaria, skipper butterfly.
No. 1747: vert: a, Leaf hopper cicadia, pleurotus ostreatus. b, Amanita muscaria, froghopper beetle. c, Wasp, amanita umbrinolutea. d, Butterfly, onnia tomentosa. e, Monarch butterfly, ganoderma lucidum. f, Broadbodied libellua, macrolepiota procera. g, Butterfly anthocharis, suillus granulatus. h, Egyptian grasshopper, cortinarius praestans. i, Flying bush cricket, marasmius ramealis.
No. 1748, Coprinus silvaticus, thornbug. No. 1749, Black swallowtail, chroogomphus rutilus.

1998, Nov. 27
1738-1745	A300	Set of 8	8.75	8.75

Sheets of 9
1746-1747	A300	250sh #a.-i., each	7.50	7.50

Souvenir Sheets
1748-1749	A300	1500sh each	5.00	5.00

Rudolph the Red-Nosed Reindeer A301

Characters from movie - #1752: a, Milo. b, Rudolph (face). c, Leonard. d, Stormella. e, Ridley. f. Boone.
No. 1753: a, Santa. b, Rudolph. c, Doggle. d, Edgar. e, Baby Rudolph. f, Toys.
No. 1754, Leonard, horiz. No. 1755, Rudolph. No. 1756, Baby Rudolph with ball on nose, diff. No. 1757, Santa with Rudolph.

Perf. 13½x14, 14x13½
1998, Dec. 15   Litho.
Sheets of 6
1752-1753	A301	200sh #a.-f., each	4.00	4.00

Souvenir Sheets
1754-1757	A301	1000sh each	3.50	3.50

Ferrari Automobiles — A301a

No. 1757A: c, GTO. d, F40. e, 512S. 100sh, Breadvan.
Illustration reduced.

1998, Dec. 16   Litho.   Perf. 14
1757A	A301a	500sh Sheet of 3, #c-e	4.50	4.50

Souvenir Sheet
Perf. 13¾x14¼
1757B	A301a	1000sh multi	3.00	3.00

No. 1757A contains three 39x25mm stamps.

Diana, Princess of Wales (1961-97) A302

1998, Dec. 16   Perf. 14
1758	A302	600sh multicolored	2.00	2.00

No. 1758 was issued in sheets of 6.

Picasso — A303

Paintings: #1759, 400sh, Jacquelin with Crossedhand, 1954. #1760, 400sh, Straw Hat with Blue Foilage, 1936. 500sh, Reading the Letter, 1921. 1500sh, Woman Writing, 1934.

1998, Dec. 16   Perf. 14½
1759-1761	A303	Set of 3	4.50	4.50

Souvenir Sheet
1762	A303	1500sh multicolored	5.00	5.00

Gandhi — A304

1998, Dec. 16   Perf. 14
1763	A304	370sh Portrait	1.25	1.25

Souvenir Sheet
1764	A304	1500sh Nehru speaking	5.00	5.00

No. 1763 was issued in sheets of 4.

1998 World Scout Jamboree, Chile A305

No. 1765: a, US Pres. William Howard Taft greets scouts during early years, 1908. b, Early Cub Scout pack enjoys musical camp break, 1930's. c, Dan Beard demonstrates tomahawk throw at Silver Bay, 1912.
1500sh, Ernest Thompson Seton (1860-1946), first Chief Scout.

1998, Dec. 16   Litho.   Perf. 14
1765	A305	600sh Sheet of 3, #a.-c.	6.00	6.00

Souvenir Sheet
1766	A305	1500sh multicolored	5.00	5.00

Royal Air Force, 80th Anniv. A306

#1767: a, Panavia Tornado F3. b, Sepecat Jaguar GR1A. c, Jaguar GR1A. d, Jaguar GR1A, diff.
No. 1768, Harrier, Eurofighter. No. 1769, Biplane, hawk.

1998, Dec. 16   Perf. 14
1767	A306	500sh Sheet of 4, #a.-d.	6.75	6.75

Souvenir Sheets
1768-1769	A306	1000sh each	3.50	3.50

New Year 1999 (Year of the Rabbit) A307

Color of rabbit - #1770: a, red brown. b, Spotted. c, Yellow. d, Brown.
1500sh, White.

1999, Jan. 18   Perf. 14
1770	A307	250sh Sheet of 4, #a.-d.	3.50	3.50

Souvenir Sheet
1771	A307	1500sh multicolored	5.00	5.00

Tourism in Zanzibar A308

Designs: 100sh, Dhow Harbor, vert. 150sh, Girl on giant tortoise, vert. 250sh, Children with giant tortoise. 300sh, Street in Stone Town, vert. 400sh, Old fort. 500sh, Red colobus monkeys.
600sh, Girl on tortoise, street in Stone Town.

1998, Nov. 10   Litho.   Perf. 14
1772-1777	A308	Set of 6	5.75	5.75

Souvenir Sheet
1778	A308	600sh multicolored	2.00	2.00

Tanzanian Posts Corp., 5th Anniv. A309

Designs: 150sh, Rural post office. 250sh, Overnight mail service. 350sh, Money fax service. 400sh, Post shop business.
500sh, Exterior view of high rise building, vert.

1999, Jan. 1
1779-1782	A309	Set of 4	3.75	3.75

Souvenir Sheet
1783	A309	500sh multicolored	1.60	1.60

Butterflies A310

200sh, Calycopis cecrops. 250sh, Heliconis melpomena, vert. 370sh, Citheras menander, vert. 410sh, Heliconis antiochus, vert.
No. 1788: a, Acraea cerasa. b, Acraea semivitrea. c, Euchrysops scintilla. d, Papilio phorcas. e, Euphaedra eusemoides. f, Acraea masamba. g, Phyciodes emerantia. h, Hypothiris tricolor. i, Orimba jansoni.
No. 1789: a, Papilio zagreus. b, Chlosyne narva. c, Phyciodes alsina. d, Pyronia bathseba. e, Eurema daira. f, Eurytides xanticles. g, Clossiana titania. h, Euphydryas cynthia. i, Polygonia c-album.
No. 1790, Ornithoptera priamus, vert. No. 1791, Phyciodes, vert.

1999, Feb. 18
1784-1787	A310	Set of 4	3.75	3.75

Sheets of 9
1788-1789	A310	200sh #a.-i., each	6.00	6.00

Souvenir Sheets
1790-1791	A310	1500sh each	5.00	5.00

Birds A311

No. 1792: a, Yellow billed stork. b, Black egret. c, Crowned lapwing. d, Snowy plover. e, Crowned crane. f, Saddlebilled stork.
No. 1793: a, Great blue heron. b, Chinese egret. c, Horned puffins. d, White faced ibis. e, Greater flamingo. f, Blue footed boobie.
No. 1794: a, Blacksmith plover. b, Brolga crane. c, Green-backed heron. d, Strawnecked ibis. e, Little bittern. f, Marabou stork.
No. 1795, vert: a, Sandhill crane. b, Great egret. c, Spoonbill. d, Yellow-crowned night heron. e, Glossy ibis. f, Willet.
No. 1796, Purple heron. No. 1797, Kittliz's sandplover, vert. No. 1798, Black-crowned night heron. No. 1799, Black-headed heron.

1999, Feb. 18
Sheets of 6
1792-1795	A311	370sh #a.-f., each	6.75	6.75

Souvenir sheets
1796-1799	A311	1500sh each	4.50	4.50

A312   A313

Cats A314

Nos. 1800-1803: 200sh, Bengal, horiz. 250sh, Seal lynx point birman. 370sh, Calico British shorthair, horiz. 420sh, Blue & white cornish rex.
Nos. 1804-1809: 100sh, Burmese. 140sh, Burmilla. 150sh, Turkish van. 200sh, Snowshoe. 250sh, Bombay. 370sh, Seychellois longhair.
No. 1810: a, Silver classic tabby. b, Auburn Turkish van. c, Seal bicolor ragdoll. d, European shorthair. e, Black & white British shorthair. f, Gold California spangled. g, Chocolate tipped Burmilla. h, Red classic tabby manx.
No. 1811: a, Pekeface Persian. b, American curl shorthair. c, Korat. d, Himalayan Persian. e, Exotic shorthair. f, Scottish fold.
No. 1812: a, European shorthair. b, Chartreux. c, British shorthair. d, Maine coon. e, Japanese bobtail. f, Birman.
Kittens chasing butterflies: No. 1813: a, Black & white kitten, butterfly UL. b, Black & white kitten, butterfly UR. c, Black & yellow kitten, butterfly UR. d, Yellow kitten, butterfly UL.
No. 1814, Black & white Persian, horiz. No. 1815, Cream tabby European shorthair. No.

1816, American shorthair. No. 1817, American wirehair. No. 1818, Kitten, butterfly, vert.

1999, Feb. 23

1800-1803	A312	Set of 4	4.00	4.00
1804-1809	A313	Set of 6	4.00	4.00

Sheets of 8, 6 or 4

1810	A312	250sh #a.-h.	6.25	6.25
1811-1812	A313	370sh #a.-f., ea	7.25	7.25
1813	A314	500sh #a.-d.	6.25	6.25

Souvenir Sheets

1814-1815	A312	1500sh each	5.00	5.00
1816-1817	A313	1500sh each	5.00	5.00
1818	A314	1500sh multi	5.00	5.00

19th Century Ships A315

No. 1819: a, Prince Consort (1). b, USS Kearsage (2). c, HMS Victoria (3). d, USS Brooklyn (4). e, Mount Stewart (5). f, Hougomont (6).

No. 1820: a, Charles W. Morgan (1). b, RMS Britannia (2). c, Great Britain (3). d, Flying Cloud (4). e, HMS Warrior (5). f, Lightning (6).

No. 1821, Cutty Sark. No. 1822, Great Eastern.

1999, Feb. 9   Litho.   Perf. 14

Sheets of 6

1819-1820	A315	370sh #a.-f., each	7.50	7.50

Souvenir Sheets

1821-1822	A315	1500sh each	5.00	5.00

#1821-1822 each contain one 57x43mm stamp.

Military Helicopters — A316

a, Germany DF 4. b, Germany. c, France. d, US, with rocket pods. e, US, with suspended lift sling. f, France, red on tail boom & stabilizers.

1999

1823	A316	370sh Sheet of 6, #a.-f.	7.50	7.50

Unidentified Flying Objects (UFOs) — A317

No. 1824: a, US, 1968. b, Trinidad, 1958. c, Belgium, 1990. d, Finland, 1970. e, New Zealand, 1951. f, Australia, 1954.

No. 1825: a, McMinnville, 1950. b, Albuquerque, 1963. c, Gulf Breeze, 1988. d, Madre de Dios, 1952. e, Merlin, 1964. f, Mexico City, 1991.

No. 1826, The Arnold Sighting, 1947. No. 1827, The Mantell case, 1948.

1999

Sheets of 6

1824-1825	A317	370sh #a.-f., each	7.50	7.50

Souvenir Sheets

1826-1827	A317	1500sh each	5.00	5.00

No. 1828: a, Boston terrier. b, Tyrolean hound. c, Rottweiler. d, Golden retriever. e, English bulldog. f, Spanish greyhound. g, Long-haired dachshund. h, Scottish terrier. i, Pekingese.

1500sh, English cocker spaniel.

1999

1828	A318	200sh Sheet of 9, #a.-i.	5.50	5.50

Souvenir Sheet

1829	A318	1500sh multicolored	5.00	5.00

Dinosaurs — A319

Designs: 200sh, Stegosaurus (inscribed Edmontonia). 250sh, Archaeopteryx. 370sh, Stegosaurus. 410sh, Lagosuchus.

No. 1834: a, Dromiceiomimus. b, Saurolophus. c, Camarosaurus. d, Protoceratops. e, Psittacosaurus. f, Stegoceras.

No. 1835: a, Gallimimus. b, Peteinosaurus. c, Lambeosaurus. d, Coelophysis. e, Parasaurolophus. f, Tyrannosaurus rex. #1836, Quetzalcoatlus. #1837, Rhomaleosaurus.

1999, Apr. 30   Litho.   Perf. 14

1830-1833	A319	Set of 4	4.00	4.00

Sheets of 6

1834-1835	A319	370sh #a.-f., each	7.50	7.50

Souvenir Sheets

1836-1837	A319	1500sh each	5.00	5.00

Tourism A320

Designs: a, Hoofed animals. b, Mount Kilimanjaro, crater. c, Animal life. d, Sacred ibis. e, Ngorongoro crater. f, Giraffe. g, Lions. h, Dik diks. i, Vulture. j, Lion cubs. k, Elephants. l, African lion. m, Stone Town, Zanzibar. n, National Museum. o, Carved door, Zanzibar. p, Map showing Zanzibar, Pemba, Indian Ocean. q, Herding animals. r, Fishing. s, Lion cub. t, Buildings, boats along shore. u, Masai. v, Birds wading in water. w, Buffalo stampede. x, Like #1838b, closer view.

1999   Perf. 14½x14

Booklet Stamps

1838	A320	Souvenir Booklet	11.00	
a.-x.		150sh any single	.45	.45
y.		Booklet pane, #1838a-1838f	2.75	
z.		Booklet pane, #1838g-1838l	2.75	
aa.		Bklt. pane, #1838m-1838r	2.75	
ab.		Bklt. pane, #1838s-1838x	2.75	

Space Exploration — A321

Designs: 70sh, Edward White. 100sh, Gemini 7. 150sh, Mir, Russian space station, vert. 200sh, Laika, Russian space dog. 250sh, Apollo Command & Service Modules. 370sh, Apollo Lunar Module.

1500sh, Saturn V Moon Rocket, vert.

1999   Perf. 14

1839-1844	A321	Set of 6	3.75	3.75

Souvenir Sheet

1845	A321	1500sh multicolored	5.00	5.00

Airships, Balloons — A322

No. 1846: a, Graf Zeppelin, 1935 (b). b, Knabenshue Airship, 1905. c, British R-100, 1931. d, Hindenburg, 1937 (c). e, French Balloon, 1783. f, French Balloon, 1912.

1500sh, Sport ballooning.

1999

1846	A322	370sh Sheet of 6, #a.-f.	7.00	7.00

Souvenir Sheet

1847	A322	1500sh multicolored	4.50	4.50

Marine Life A323

200sh, Powder blue surgeon. 250sh, Frilled anemone. 310sh, Red-finned batfish. 410sh, Red beard sponge.

No. 1852: a, Right whale. b, Fin whale. c, Humpback whale. d. Tucuxi. e, Gray's beaked whale. f, Sperm whale. g, Bottlenose dolphin. h, Hector's dolphin. i, Hourglass dolphin.

No. 1853: a, Horn shark. b, Nurse shark. c, Bonnethead. d, Tiger shark. e, Bull shark. f, Leopard shark. g, Blue shark. h, Zebra shark. i, Oceanic whitetip.

No. 1854, Pacific Electric ray, vert. No. 1855, Loggerhead turtle, vert.

1999, Feb. 9   Litho.   Perf. 14

1848-1851	A323	Set of 4	3.00	3.00

Sheets of 9, #a.-i.

1852-1853	A323	250sh each	7.00	7.00

Souvenir Sheets

1854-1855	A323	1500sh each	4.50	4.50

Airplanes A324

Designs: 20sh, Oiseau Bleu, 1929. 100sh, Beechcraft Model 17, 1934. No. 1858, 140sh, US Army Air Corps Beechcraft YC-43. No. 1859, 140sh, Deperdussin, 1913. 150sh, Beechcraft E17B, 1937. 200sh, Beechcraft B17L, 1936. 250sh, Beechcraft Model-G175, 1946. 370sh, Beechcraft Staggerwing Model-C17L.

No. 1864: a, Bird of Passage, Voisin Brothers, 1909. b, BS1, Geoffrey de Havilland, 1913. c, Taube-IGO Etrich, 1910. d, Curtiss Rheims Flyer, Glenn Curtiss, 1909. e, Wright Flyer III, Wright Brothers, 1905. f, Russky Vitvas, Igor Sikorsky, 1913.

No. 1865: a, Sikorsky S-38. b, EFA Eurofighter. c, F-16. d, Hawker Hurricane. e, Artiplast. f, Islander.

#1866, Piper Cherokee. #1867, MiG.

1999, Feb. 14

1856-1863	A324	Set of 8	4.25	4.25

Sheets of 6

1864	A324	370sh #a.-f.	6.75	6.75
1865	A324	370sh #a.-f.	5.50	5.50

Souvenir Sheets

1866-1867	A324	1500sh each	4.50	4.50

Nos. 1866-1867 contain one 56x42mm stamp.

Stamp inscriptions are incorrect on Nos. 1865b, 1865c, and perhaps others.

African Wildlife A325

Designs: 100sh, Black rhinoceros. 140sh, Zebra, vert. 150sh, Hippopotamus. 200sh, Nile crocodile. 250sh, African elephant, vert. 370sh, Cape buffalo.

No. 1874, Royal python. No. 1875, Giraffe.

1999, Feb. 18

1868-1873	A325	Set of 6	3.75	3.75

Souvenir Sheets

1874-1875	A325	1500sh each	4.50	4.50

Millennium — A326

Designs: 350sh, High quality health care. 400sh, Good upbringing. 700sh, An abundance of food. 750sh, Clean water for all. 1500sh, Ostrich, "Enhancement of tourism promotion," multicolored.

1999, Mar. 29

1876-1879	A326	Set of 4	6.75	6.75

Souvenir Sheet

1880	A326	1500sh multicolored	4.50	4.50

Sharks A327

Designs: 200sh, Sand tiger. 250sh, Mako. 370sh, Great white. 410sh, Bull.

No. 1885: a, Basking. b, Whale. c, Tiger. d, Thresher. e, Caribbean reef. f, Nurse. #1886, Scalloped hammerhead. #1887, Blue.

1999   Litho.   Perf. 14

1881-1884	A327	Set of 4	3.00	3.00

Sheet of 6

1885	A327	370sh Sheet of 6, #a.-f.	6.75	6.75

Souvenir Sheets

1886-1887	A327	1500sh each	4.50	4.50

Rotary Club of Dar Es Salaam, 50th Anniv. A328

150sh, Emblem. 250sh, Polio plus immunization, vert. 350sh, Paul P. Harris, founder of Rotary, Intl., vert. 400sh, Water supply. 500sh, Emblem, vert.

1999, June 30

1888-1891	A328	Set of 4	3.50	3.50

Souvenir Sheet

1892	A328	500sh multicolored	1.50	1.50

Endangered or Extinct Species — A330

No. 1898: a, Atitlan grebe. b, Cabot's tragopan. c, Spider monkey. d, Dibatag. e, Right whale. f, Imperial parrot. g, Cheetah. h, Brown-eared pheasant. i, Leatherback turtle. j, Imperial woodpecker. k, Andean condor. l, Barbary deer. m, Gray gentle lemur. n, Cuban parrot. o, Numbat. p, Short-tailed albatross. q, Green turtle. r, White rhinoceros. s, Diademed sifaka. t, Galapagos penguin.

No. 1899 - Tigers, horiz.: a, Caspian. b, Bengal. c, Javan. d, Indochinese. e, In white phase. f, Sumatran. g, Chinese. h, Bali. i, Siberian.

No. 1900, Rabbit-eared bandicoot. No. 1901, Grenada dove.

1999, Feb. 18
1898 A330	100sh Sheet of 20, #a.-t.	5.00	5.00
1899 A330	250sh Sheet of 9, #a.-i.	5.75	5.75

Souvenir Sheets
1900-1901 A330	1500sh each	3.75	3.75

Queen Mother (b. 1900) — A331

No. 1902: a, In Kenya, 1959. b, In 1980. c, With Prince Charles, 1950. d, lin 1990. 1500sh, In Kenya, 1959, diff.

1999, Aug. 4   **Litho.**   **Perf. 14**
1902 A331	600sh Sheet of 4, #a.-d. + label	6.00	6.00

Souvenir Sheet
Perf. 13¾
1903 A331	1500sh black	3.75	3.75

No. 1903 contains one 38x51mm stamp.

UPU, 125th Anniv. A332

150sh, Mail conveyance. 300sh, Letter writing competition. 350sh, UPU committee meeting. 400sh, EMS Post net track and trace. 500sh, UPU emblem.

Wmk. 387
1999, Aug. 10   **Litho.**   **Perf. 14**
1904-1907 A332	Set of 4	3.00	3.00

Souvenir Sheet
1908 A332	500sh multicolored	1.25	1.25

Souvenir Sheets

Philex France 99 — A333

Illustration reduced.
Trains: No. 1909, 4-8-2 compound express locomotive. No. 1910, TGV.

1999, Aug. 20   **Litho.**   **Perf. 13¾**
1909-1910 A333	1500sh each	3.75	3.75

Inscriptions are misspelled on Nos. 1909-1910.

Birds of Japan A334

No. 1911: a, Steller's sea eagle. b, Japanese blue flycatcher. c, Great gray shrike. d, Kingfisher. e, Hen harrier. f, Siberian meadow bunting. g, Mandarin duck. h, Red-necked grebe. i, Fairy pitta.

No. 1912: a, Black paradise flycatcher. b, Laysan albatross. c, Collared Scops owl. d, Ryukyu robin. e, Japanese green woodpecker. f, Lidth's jay. g, White-naped crane. h, Copper pheasant. i, Okinawa rail.

No. 1913, Gyrfalcon. No. 1914, Japanese yellow bunting.

1999, Aug. 20   **Sheets of 9, #a.-i.**
1911-1912 A334	250sh each	5.75	5.75

Souvenir Sheets
1913-1914 A334	1500sh each	3.75	3.75

Inscription on No. 1912b, and perhaps others, is misspelled.
APS StampShow '99 (#1911-1912).

Hokusai Paintings — A335

No. 1915: a, A Ferry Boat at Onmayagashi. b, A Drum Bridge at Kameido. c, Sea Life (fish). d, Sea Life (Octopus). e, Measuring a Pine Tree at Mishima Pass. f, Mount Fuji Seen From the Banks of Minobu River.

1500sh, Mount Fuji and Edo Castle Seen From Nihonbashi, vert.

1999, Aug. 20   **Sheet of 6**
1915 A335	400sh #a.-f.	6.00	6.00

Souvenir Sheet
1916 A335	1500sh multicolored	3.75	3.75

Masks — A336   Military Scenes — A337

Various masks: 150sh, 250sh, 300sh, 350sh.

1999, Aug. 20   **Perf. 14**
1917-1920 A336	Set of 4	2.60	2.60

Souvenir Sheet
1921 A336	1500sh multicolored	3.75	3.75

1999, Sept. 30
150sh, British defeat Spanish Armada, 1588, horiz. #1923, 250sh, Battle of Waterloo. #1924, 250sh, Rorke's Drift, 24th Regiment, South Wales Borderers. #1925, 250sh, Special Air Services, Desert Storm. #1926, 300sh, Soldier on horseback. #1927, 300sh, World War I, horiz. #1928, 300sh, Bland's Dragoons, Battle of Dettingen. #1929, 350sh, Battle of Trafalgar, horiz. #1930, 350sh, Light Brigade. #1931, 350sh, Squadron 617, the "Dam Busters." #1932, 400sh, World War I tank, horiz. #1933, 400sh, Battle of Inkerman. #1934, 400sh, Battle of Salamanca, horiz. #1935, 500sh, Gen. James Wolfe, Battle of Quebec. #1936, 500sh, Parachute Regiment, Battle of Arnhem. #1937, 500sh, Battle of the Bulge.

#1938, Battle of the Nile. #1939, Battle of Albuhera.

1922-1937 A337	Set of 16	14.00	14.00

Souvenir Sheets
1938-1939 A337	1500sh each	3.75	3.75

Ships A338

No. 1940: a, Bayan. b, Flying Cloud. c, Mayflower. d, Santa Maria. e, Morning Star. f, Ben Venue.

No. 1941: a, Georg Stag. b, E. Starr Jones. c, Indiana. d, Brazilian coasting vessel. e, Nova Queen. f, Rainbow.

No. 1942, Dutch East Indiaman. No. 1943, Junk.

1999, Sept. 30   **Sheets of 6, #a.-f.**
1940-1941 A338	400sh each	6.00	6.00

Souvenir Sheets
1942-1943 A338	1500sh each	3.75	3.75

Trains A339

No. 1944: a, Adler 2-2-2, 1835. b, Beuth 2-2-2, 1843. c, Class 500 4-6-0, 1900. d, Northumbrian 0-2-2, 1830. e, Class 4-6-2, 1901. f, Claud Hamilton class 4-4-0.

No. 1945: a, Firefly class 2-2-2, 1840. b, Single, 1854. c, 4-4-0, 1891. d, Medoc class 2-4-0, 1857. e, 4-4-0, 1893. f, Numar, 1846.

No. 1946, Planet class 2-2-0, 1830. No. 1947, Vauxhall 2-2-0, 1834. No. 1948, Class PB 4-6-0, 1906. No. 1949, 4-4-0, 1855.

1999, Sept. 30   **Sheets of 6, #a.-f.**
1944-1945 A339	400sh each	6.00	6.00

Souvenir Sheets
1946-1949 A339	1500sh each	3.75	3.75

Airplanes A340

Designs: 200sh, Amref. No. 1951, 250sh, Westwind 2. 300sh, Morning Star. 400sh, Piper Warrior III.

No. 1954: a, Glasair Super II. b, Glastar. c, Cessna 120. d, Europa XS. e, Beechcraft Bonanza. f, Comache GTO. g, Lancir IV. h, Comanche 400.

No. 1955, Glastar, diff. No. 1956, Piper Archer III.

1999, Sept. 30   **Litho.**   **Perf. 14**
1950-1953 A340	Set of 4	3.00	3.00

Sheet of 8
1954 A340	250sh #a.-h.	5.00	5.00

Souvenir Sheets
1955-1956 A340	1500sh each	3.75	3.75

Automobiles — A341

No. 1957: a, Audi TT Coupe. b, Mitsubishi SST Spyder. c, Honda Dream. d, Renault 20. e, Renault Spider. f, Hyundai Euro I.

No. 1958: a, Pininfarina Ethos. b, Jaguar XK120. c, Pininfarina Ethos II. d, Rinspeed E-GO Rocket. e, Volkswagen W12 Roadster. f, Chrysler Pronto Cruiser.

No. 1959, Ferrari Mythos. No. 1960, Hyundai Euro I, diff.

1999, Sept. 30   **Sheets of 6, #a.-f.**
1957-1958 A341	400sh each	6.00	6.00

Souvenir Sheets
1959-1960 A341	1500sh each	3.75	3.75

Flowers A342

Designs; 150sh, Lilium longiflorum. 250sh, Strelitzia reginae. 400sh, 600sh, Zantedeschia anim lily. 500sh, Iris.

1999, Oct. 6   **Litho.**   **Perf. 14**
1961-1964 A342	Set of 4	3.25	3.25

Souvenir Sheet
1965 A342	600sh multicolored	1.50	1.50

Butterflies — A343

No. 1966: a, Basilarchia archippus. b, Eueides isabella. c, Colobura dirce. d, Papilio cresphontes. e, Agrias claudia. f, Callicore maimuna.

No. 1967, Anteos clorinade, horiz. No. 1968, Tithorea harmonia, horiz.

1999, Nov. 15   **Sheet of 6**
1966 A343	1500sh #a.-f.	6.00	6.00

Souvenir Sheets
1967-1968 A343	1500sh each	3.75	3.75

Sea Birds A344

Designs: 150sh, Rockhopper penguin, vert. No. 1970, 250sh, Jackass penguin, vert. 300sh, Adelie penguin, vert. 350sh, White tern. 400sh, Great frigatebird. 500sh, Brown pelican.

No. 1975: a, Manx shearwater. b, Ring-billed gull. c, Herring gull. d, Red-tailed tropic bird. e, Laysan albatross. f, Black-headed gull. g, Blue-footed booby. h, Parakeet auklet. i, Red-legged cormorant.

No. 1976: a, Razorbill. b, Southern giant petrel. c, Atlantic puffin. d, Great cormorant. e, Northern gannet. f, Masked booby. g, Tufted puffin. h, Galapagos penguin. i, Macaroni penguin.

No. 1977, King penguin, vert. No. 1978, Emperor penguin, vert.

1999, Nov. 15
1969-1974 A344	Set of 6	5.00	5.00

Sheets of 9, #a.-i.
1975-1976 A344	250sh each	5.75	5.75

Souvenir Sheets
1977-1978 A344	1500sh each	3.75	3.75

Dogs A345

No. 1979: a, Boxer. b, Mixed breed. c, Afghan hound. d, Chihuahua. e, Basset hound. f, Cavalier King Charles.
1500sh, Cocker spaniel.

1999, Nov. 15   **Sheet of 6**
1979 A345	400sh #a.-f.	6.00	6.00

Souvenir Sheet
1980 A345	1500sh multicolored	3.75	3.75

Paintings by Xu Beihong (1895-1953) A346

No. 1981: a, Chang K'uei. b, Fisherman. c, Orchid. d, Cock and Sunflower. e, Eagle. f, Sprite of the Mountain. g, Horse. h, Geese. i, Pigeon and Bamboo. j, Cat and Bamboo.
No. 1982: a, Spring Rain of Li River, horiz. b, The Himalayas, horiz.

1999	Sheet of 10	Perf. 12½	
1981	A346	150sh #a.-j.	3.75 3.75
		Perf. 13	
1982	A346	600sh Sheet of 2, #a.-b.	3.00 3.00

China 1999 World Philatelic Exhibition.

Return of Macao to People's Republic of China — A347

Nam Van: a, In 1850s. b, In 1930s. c, At present. d, View of lakes project.

1999	Litho.	Perf. 13¾	
1983	A347	300sh Sheet of 4, #a.-d.	3.00 3.00

China 1999 World Philatelic Exhibition.

Animals of the Central American Rain Forest — A348

No. 1984: a, Red howler monkey. b, Scarlet macaw. c, Rainbow boa, tree sloth. d, Iguana. e, Fruit bat. f, Rainbow boa. g, Crocodile. h, Manatee. i, Jaguar.
1500sh, Jaguar, diff.

1999, Nov. 15	Litho.	Perf. 14	
1984	A348	350sh Sheet of 9, #a.-i.	8.00 8.00
		Souvenir Sheet	
1985	A348	1500sh multi	3.75 3.75

Dinosaurs — A349

No. 1986: a, Tyrannosaurus. b, Coelurus. c, Stegosaurus. d, Corythosaurus. e, Thadeosaurus. f, Brachiosaurus.
1500sh, Ceratosaurus.

1999, Nov. 15			
1986	A349	400sh Sheet of 6, #a.-f.	6.00 6.00
		Souvenir Sheet	
1987	A349	1500sh multi	3.75 3.75

Nos. 1986-1987 dated 1998. Inscription on No. 1986f is misspelled.

Cats A350

No. 1988: a, Si-Rex. b, Spotted Mist. c, Angora. d, Persian. e, Sphynx. f, Alaskan Snow.
1500sh, Ragdoll.

1999, Nov. 15			
1988	A350	400sh Sheet of 6, #a.-f.	6.00 6.00
		Souvenir Sheet	
1989	A350	1500sh multi	3.75 3.75

Mushrooms A351

150sh, Tricholoma portentosum. 250sh, Tricholomopsis rutilans. 300sh, Russula foetens. 350sh, Russula aeruginea. #1994, 400sh, Cortinarius varius. 500sh, Hygrocybe coccineocrenata.
No. 1996: a, Agaricus abruptibulbus. b, Anellaria semiovata. c, Cystoderma carcharias. d, Amanita rubescens. e, Amanita fulva. f, Tricholoma sulphureum.
No. 1997: a, Xerocomus rubellus. b, Geastrum rufescens. c, Lactarius salmonicolor. d, Gomphus clavatus. e, Russula rhodopoda. f, Russula paludosa.
No. 1998, Owl. No. 1999, Chipmunk and Stropharia hornemannii, horiz.

1999, Nov. 15			
1990-1995	A351	Set of 6	5.00 5.00
		Sheets of 6, #a.-f.	
1996-1997	A351	400sh each	6.00 6.00
		Souvenir Sheets	
1998-1999	A351	1500sh each	3.75 3.75

Flora & Fauna A352

Designs: No. 2000, 150sh, Lion, vert. No. 2001, 150sh, Mountain gorilla, vert. No. 2002, 250sh, Pygmy hippopotamus, vert. No. 2003, 250sh, Japanese macaque, vert. No. 2004, 300sh, Cheetah. No. 2005, 300sh, Desert hare, vert. No. 2006, 350sh, Horned puffin. No. 2007, 350sh, Salvin's Amazon parrot. No. 2008, 400sh, Blueberries. No. 2009, 400sh, Bird's foot violet. No. 2010, 500sh, Orange groundsel. No. 2011, 500sh, Iguana.
No. 2012: a, Polar bear. b, Woodland caribou. c, Snowy owl. d, Arctic fox. e, Willow ptarmigan. f, Arctic hare.
No. 2013: a, White-tailed deer. b, Monarch butterfly. c, Yellow trumpet pitcher plants. d, Great blue heron. e, Yellow mud turtle. f, American alligator.
No. 2014: a, Three-toed sloth. b, Emerald toucan. c, Praying mantis. d, Mouse opossum. e, Green palm viper. f, Phyllomedusa lemur.
No. 2015: a, Ficus stupenda. b, Slow loris. c, Sambar deer. d, Thick-billed green pigeon. e, Bush cricket. f, Monitor lizard.
No. 2016, Three-toed jacamar. No. 2017, Chuckwallas. No. 2018, Swallowtail butterfly. No. 2019, Otter, vert.

1999, Nov. 15			
2000-2011	A352	Set of 12	9.75 9.75
		Sheets of 6, #a.-f.	
2012-2015	A352	400sh each	6.00 6.00
		Souvenir Sheets	
2016-2019	A352	1500sh each	3.75 3.75

Flowers — A353

150sh, Foxglove. 250sh, Chrysanthemum. 400sh, Amaryllis. 500sh, Hidden lilies.
No. 2024, horiz.: a, Gerbara daisies. b, Begonias. c, Clematis. d, Violas. e, Southern magnolia. f, Dwarf balloon flowers. g, Camellias. h, Day lilies. i, Roses.
No. 2025, horiz.: a, Daffodils. b, Columbines. c, Nasturtiums. d, Gazanias. e, Rose. f, Crocuses. g, Trumpet vine. h, Dahlia. i, Oriental poppies.
No. 2026, Siberian iris. No. 2027, Water lily, horiz.

1999, Nov. 15	Litho.	Perf. 14	
2020-2023	A353	Set of 4	3.25 3.25
		Sheets of 9, #a.-i.	
2024-2025	A353	350sh each	8.00 8.00
		Souvenir Sheets	
2026-2027	A353	1500sh each	3.75 3.75

Military Vehicles — A354

Illustration reduced.
No. 2028: a, French Hotchkiss H35 tank. b, German Panzer IV tank. c, US M4 tank. d, German Tiger tank. e, US Half track. f, British Cromwell tank.
No. 2029: a, British MK IV tank. b, Japanese Type 95 tank. c, German Hunting Panther tank. d, French AMX30 tank. e, Israeli Merkava tank. f, US M1 tank.
No. 2030, AH-64A Apache helicopter. No. 2031, Austin armored car, vert.

1999, Sept. 30	Litho.	Perf. 14	
		Sheets of 6, #a.-f.	
2028-2029	A354	400sh each	6.00 6.00
		Souvenir Sheets	
2030-2031	A354	1500sh each	3.75 3.75

African Flowers — A355

Designs: 150sh, Canarina abyssinica. 250sh, Diaphananthe kamerunensis. 350sh, Protea barbigera. 500sh, Angraecum scottianum.
No. 2036: a, Bolusanthus speciosus. b, Cassia abbreviata. c, Erythrina lysistemon. d, Leucodendron discolor. e, Romulea fischeri. f, Lupinus princei.
No. 2037: a, Ansellia africana. b, Kigelia africana. c, Aerangis brachycarpa. d, Brachycorythis kalbreyeri. e, Begonia meyeriijohannis. f, Saintpaulia ionantha.
No. 2038, Nymphaea caerulea. No. 2039, Aloe petricola.

1999, Nov. 15			
2032-2035	A355	Set of 4	3.25 3.25
		Sheets of 6, #a.-f.	
2036-2037	A355	400sh each	6.00 6.00
		Souvenir Sheets	
2038-2039	A355	1500sh each	3.75 3.75

African Wildlife — A356

Illustration reduced.
No. 2040, horiz.: a, Mountain gorilla. b, Zebras. c, East African elephant. d, Crowned cranes. e, Cheetah. f, Tiger. g, Pygmy chimpanzee. h, Hippopotamus.
No. 2041, Giraffes. No. 2042, Rhinoceros.

1999, Nov. 15			
2040	A356	300sh Sheet of 8, #a.-h.	6.00 6.00
		Souvenir Sheets	
2041-2042	A356	1500sh each	3.75 3.75

Marine Life A357

Designs: 350sh, Beluga whale. 400sh, Ghost crab. 500sh, Emperor penguin, vert.
No. 2046: a, Herring gulls. b, Dusky dolphin. c, Sandwich tern. d, Humpback whale. e, Right whale. f, Dusky dolphin, sergeant major. g, White-tipped shark. h, Manta ray, trunkfish. i, Purple moon angel. j, Scalloped hammerhead shark. k, Manatee. l, Striped fingerfish.
No. 2047, Humpback whales. No. 2048, Tiger shark.

1999, Nov. 15			
2043-2045	A357	Set of 3	3.25 3.25
2046	A357	250sh Sheet of 12, #a.-l.	7.50 7.50
		Souvenir Sheets	
2047-2048	A357	1500sh each	3.75 3.75

Ballet A358

Designs: 300sh, Romeo and Juliet. 350sh, The Dying Swan. 400sh, Giselle, vert. 500sh, Spartacus, vert.
No. 2053, The Firebird, vert. No. 2054, Swan Lake, vert.

1999, Aug. 20	Litho.	Perf. 14	
2049-2052	A358	Set of 4	4.00 4.00
		Souvenir Sheets	
2053-2054	A358	1500sh each	3.75 3.75

17th and 18th Century Indian
Art — A359

No. 2055: a, Krishna and the Gopis (large tree). b, Krishna Painting the Feet of Radha. c, Krishna Yearning for the Moon (woman with fan). d, Games of Krishna and Radha (boat).
No. 2056: a, Balwant Singh Having His Beard Cut. b, Festival of Hou (women at right). c, Ragini Bialvali (woman with fan, woman on seat). d, Krishna Holding a Ball of Butter.
No. 2057, Portrait of Emperor Jahanoir (man with necklace), vert. No. 2058, Krishna and the Gopis, diff., vert.
Illustration reduced.

1999, Aug. 20   *Perf. 13¾*
Sheets of 4, #a-d
2055-2056 A359 500sh each   5.00 5.00
Souvenir Sheets
2057-2058 A359 1500sh each   3.75 3.75

Fashion Designers — A360

No. 2059: a, Christian Dior. b, Model wearing Dior fashions. c, Bottle of Chanel No. 5, model wearing Chanel Fashions. d, Gabrielle "Coco" Chanel. e, Gianni Versace. f, Model wearing Versace fashions. g, Model wearing Yves Saint Laurent fashions. h, Yves Saint Laurent.
1500sh, Valentino Garavani.

1999, Aug. 20   *Perf. 14*
2059 A360 300sh Sheet of 8, #a-h   6.00 6.00
Souvenir Sheet
2060 A360 1500sh multi   3.75 3.75
Nos. 2059b-2059c, 2059f-2059g are 53x39mm.

Locomotives — A361

No. 2061: a, Class EF 81 Bo-Bo, Japan. b, Class 120 Bo-Bo, West Germany. c, Shao Shan I Co-Co, China. d, TGV, France. e, F40 PH Bo-Bo, US. f, LRC Bo-Bo, Canada.
1500sh, Class 401 Intercity Express, Germany.
Illustration reduced.

1999, Sept. 30
2061 A361 400sh Sheet of 6, #a-f   6.00 6.00
Souvenir Sheet
2062 A361 1500sh multi   3.75 3.75

Marine Life A362

Designs: 150sh, Great barracuda. 250sh, Common squid. No. 2065, 300sh, Atlantic salmon. 350sh, Ocean sunfish. 400sh, Lobster. 500sh, Yellowfin tuna.
No. 2069: a, Flying fish. b, Sailfish. c, Common dolphin. d, Sperm whale. e, Spinner dolphin. f, Manta ray. g, Green turtle. h, Hammerhead shark. i, Marlin.
No. 2070: a, Walrus. b, Killer whale. c, Arctic tern. d, White shark. e, Narwhal. f, Blue whale. g, Giant clam. h, Octopus. i, Conger eel.
No. 2071, Whale shark. No. 2072, Beluga, vert.

1999, Nov. 15
2063-2068 A362 Set of 6   5.00 5.00
Sheets of 9, #a-i
2069-2070 A362 300sh each   6.75 6.75
Souvenir Sheets
2071-2072 A362 1500sh each   3.75 3.75

Pres. Julius K. Nyerere (1922-99) A363

Nyerere: 200sh, As young man and old man. 500sh, With Edward Moringe Sokonie. 600sh, The Compassionate leader, vert. 800sh, During the early days of independence, vert.
1000sh, Mausoleum.

2000, Apr. 13   *Perf. 13*
2073-2076 A363 Set of 4   5.25 5.25
Souvenir Sheet
Perf. 13x13½
2077 A363 1000sh multi   2.50 2.50
No. 2077 contains one 35x28mm stamp.

Tourism A364

400sh, Lion, Seronera Wildlife Lodge. #2079, 800sh, Hippopotami and hyenas, Selous Game Reserve. #2080, 800sh, Fish, Mafia Island. #2081, 800sh, Giraffes, Lobo Wildlife Lodge. #2082, 800sh, Rhinoceros, Ngorongoro Crater Wildlife Lodge. #2083, 800sh, Elephant, Mikumi Natl. Park. #2084, 800sh, Elephant, Lake Manyara Natl. Park. #2085, 800sh, Elephants, rhinoceros, Kibo Peak, Mt. Kilimanjaro.
1000sh, Lion, giraffes, elephant, rhinoceros, Lake Manyara Natl. Park, vert.

Perf. 13x13½, 13½x13
2000, June 10   *Litho.*
2078-2085 A364 Set of 8   15.00 15.00
Souvenir Sheet
2086 A364 1000sh multi   2.50 2.50
See Nos. 2102-2125.

Activities of World Vision A365

200sh, Children with water pots on heads. 600sh, Family preparing food. 800sh, Nurse, family. 1000sh, Education of children.

2000, July 20   *Litho.*   *Perf. 13x13¼*
2087-2090 A365 Set of 4   6.50 6.50
Souvenir Sheet
2091 A365 500sh Two children   1.25 1.25

2000 Summer Olympics, Sydney A366

Designs: 150sh, Soccer. 350sh, Basketball, vert. 400sh, Women's 1500-meter race, vert. 800sh, Boxing.
500sh, Medal ceremony, vert.

2000, Sept. 15   *Perf. 13¾*
2092-2095 A366 Set of 4   4.25 4.25
Souvenir Sheet
2096 A366 500sh multi   1.25 1.25

Universities of East Africa A367

Designs: 150sh, Medical students, Muhimbili University College of Health Sciences. 200sh, Zanzibar University. 600sh, Makerere University, Uganda, vert. 800sh, Egerton University, Kenya.
500sh, Emblem of Inter-university Council for East Africa.

2000   *Perf. 13x13¼, 13¼x13*
2097-2100 A367 Set of 4   4.50 4.50
Perf. 14½
Size: 84x83mm
2101 A367 500sh multi   1.25 1.25

Tourism Type of 2000
#2102, 400sh, #2110, 500sh, #2118, 600sh, Like No. 2079. #2103, 400sh, #2111, 500sh, #2119, 600sh, Like No. 2080. #2104, 400sh, #2112, 500sh, #2120, 600sh, Like No. 2081. #2105, 400sh, #2113, 500sh, #2121, 600sh, Like No. 2082. #2106, 400sh, #2114, 500sh, #2122, 600sh, Like No. 2083. #2107, 400sh, #2115, 500sh, #2123, 600sh, Like No. 2084. #2108, 400sh, #2116, 500sh, #2124, 600sh, Like No. 2085. #2109, 400sh, #2117, 600sh, #2125, 800sh, Like No. 2078.

2000, June 1   *Litho.*   *Perf. 13x13½*
2102-2125 A364 Set of 24   35.00 35.00

Flowers A368

150sh, Bacciflava. 250sh, Hybridus pendulus. 300sh, Rhaphiolepis umbellata. 350sh, Magnoliaeflora. 400sh, Magnolia, vert. 500sh, Margot Koster, vert.
No. 2132, 300sh: a, Viola pedata. b, Magnolia. c, Felicia amelloides. d, Lythrum. e, Hemerocallis. f, Tithonia rotundifolia. g, Lilium. h, Iris. i, Stokesia laevis.
No. 2133, 300sh, vert.: a, Prunus subhirtella. b, Sanguinaria canadensis. c, Rosa palustris. d, Gordonia lasianthius. e, Aquilegia caerulea. f, Fremontodendron. g, Hypericum calycinum. h, Anemone vitifolia. i, Clematis.
No. 2134, Iris cristata, vert. No. 2134A, Aster prikartil.

2000   *Perf. 14*
2126-2131 A368 Set of 6   5.00 5.00
Sheets of 9, #a-i
2132-2133 A368 Set of 2   13.50 13.50
Souvenir Sheet
2134- A368 Set of 2
2134A   7.50 7.50

Social Security Fund A369

Designs: 200sh, Retirement. 350sh, Employment injury. 600sh, Invalidity. 800sh, Health insurance.

2000   *Wmk. 387*   *Perf. 13¾*
2135-2138 A369 Set of 4   5.00 5.00
Souvenir Sheet
2139 A369 500sh Maternity   1.25 1.25

Environmental Care — A370

Designs: 200sh, Tree planting campaign. 400sh, Water sources protection. 600sh, Cleaning sewage. 800sh, Protecting forests.

2000   *Wmk. 387*   *Perf. 13x13¼*
2140-2143 A370 Set of 4   5.00 5.00
Souvenir Sheet
2144 A370 1000sh Mountain   2.50 2.50

Zanzibar Millennium A371

Designs: 150sh, Fishing industry. 200sh, Trade and tourism. 400sh, Child and emblem, vert. 800sh, Right to higher learning, vert. 500sh, Peace and tranquility, vert.

2000   *Wmk. 387*   *Perf. 13¾*
2145-2148 A371 Set of 4   4.00 4.00
Souvenir Sheet
2149 A371 500sh multi   1.25 1.25

Orchids A372

Designs: 200sh, Vanilla planifolia. 250sh, Pleurothallus tuerckheimii. No. 2152, 370sh, Trichopilia fragrans.
No. 2153, 370sh: a, Cyrtopodium andersonii. b, Cochleanthes discolor. c, Catasetum barbatum. d, Caularthron bicornutum. e, Broughtonia sanguinea. f, Brassavola nodosa.
No. 2154, 370sh: a, Oeceoclades maculata. b, Isochilus linearis. c, Eulophia alta. d, Ionopsis utricularioides. e, Epidendrum ciliare. f, Dimerandra emarginata.
No. 2155, 1500sh, Brassavola cucullata. No. 2156, 1500sh, Epidendrum nocturnum.

2000   *Litho.*   *Perf. 14*
2150-2152 A372 Set of 3   2.00 2.00
Sheets of 6, #a-f
2153-2154 A372 Set of 2   11.00 11.00
Souvenir Sheets
2155-2156 A372 Set of 2   7.25 7.25

Nos. 607, 612, 615 Surcharged

1999-2000?   *Litho.*   *Perf. 14*

Methods and perfs as before
2000
2157　A99　100sh on 40sh multi
2158　A99　150sh on 9sh multi
2159　A99　200sh on 170sh multi
2159A　A99　230sh on 170sh multi

An additional surcharge exists in this set. The editors would like to see any examples.

Rare Birds
A373

Designs: 150sh, Taita falcon. 300sh, Banded green. 400sh, Spotted ground thrush. 500sh, Fischer's turaco. 600sh, Blue swallow.

2000　　　Litho.　　Perf. 14
2160　A373　150sh multi
2161　A373　300sh multi
2162　A373　400sh multi
2163　A373　500sh multi
Souvenir Sheet
2164　A373　600sh multi

Architecture — A374

Designs: 150sh, Ruins of Great Mosque, Kilwa Kisiwani. 200sh, German Boma, Mikindani. 250sh, German Boma, Bagamoyo. 300sh, Butiama Museum, Mara. 350sh, Chief Government Chemist Office. 400sh, Old Post Office, Dar es Salaam. 500sh, Dr. David Livingstone Lodge, Kwihara Tabora. 600sh, Original and present State Houses, vert. 700sh, Ngoni-Nyamwezi traditional houses. 800sh, The People's Palace Beit Elajaib, Zanzibar. 900sh, Tongoni Ruins, Tanga. 1000sh, Karimjee Hall, Dar es Salaam. 1500sh, Old Boma, Mikindani.

2000 (?)　　Litho.　　Perf. 13
2165　A374　150sh multi
2166　A374　200sh multi
2166A　A374　250sh multi
2167　A374　300sh multi
2167A　A374　350sh multi
2168　A374　400sh multi
2168A　A374　500sh multi
2169　A374　600sh multi
2169A　A374　700sh multi
2170　A374　800sh multi
2170A　A374　900sh multi

2171　A374　1000sh multi
Souvenir Sheet
2172　A374　1500sh multi

Flora & Fauna — A375

Designs: 100sh, Common babbler. 140sh, Eastern blue darner. 150sh, Cavalier mushroom. 200sh, Orange-barred sulphur. 250sh, Harlequin bug. No. 2179, 370sh, Brassolae liocattleya.
No. 2180, 370sh: a, Common yellowthroat. b, Great orange tip. c, Tiger lily. d, Shaggy mane. e, Sri Lanka grasshopper. f, Woodhouse's toad.
No. 2181, 370sh: a, Golden-crowned warbler. b, Fuchsia. c, Alfalfa butterfly. d, Lycaste aquila. e, Snail. f, Ground beetle.
No. 2182, 1500sh, Rufous-collared sparrow, horiz. No. 2183, 1500sh, Monarch butterfly, horiz.

2000　　　Litho.　　Perf. 14
2174-2179　A375　Set of 6　　3.00　3.00
Sheets of 6, #a-f
2180-2181　A375　Set of 2　11.00 11.00
Souvenir Sheets
2182-2183　A375　Set of 2　　7.50　7.50

Endangered Animals
A376

Designs: 200sh, Leopard. 400sh, Rhinoceros. No. 2186, 600sh, Crocodile. 800sh, Hunting wild dogs.
No. 2188, 600sh, Cheetah.

2001, June 15　Litho.　　Perf. 13
2184-2187　A376　Set of 4　　4.50　4.50
Souvenir Sheet
2188　A376　600sh multi　　1.40　1.40

UN High Commissioner for Refugees, 50th Anniv. — A377

Designs: 200sh, Refugee child being vaccinated. 400sh, Refugees crossing Lake Tanganyika. 600sh, Refugee woman, vert. 800sh, Fleeing refugees, vert.

2001, July 31
2189-2192　A377　Set of 4　　4.50　4.50
2191a　　　Souvenir sheet of 1　1.40　1.40

Landscapes
A378

Designs: 200sh, Rufiji River, Selous Game Reserve. 400sh, Mangapwani Beach, Zanzibar. 600sh, Mountains, Mikumi Natl. Park. 800sh, Balancing Stones, Shore of Lake Victoria, Mwanza, vert.
700sh, Ruaha Natl. Park, vert.

2001, Nov. 30　Litho.　　Perf. 13
2193-2196　A378　Set of 4　　4.50　4.50
Souvenir Sheet
2197　A378　700sh multi　　1.50　1.50

Year of Dialogue Among Civilizations
A379

Designs: 200sh, Talking with children. 400sh, Formal dress. 600sh, Exchanging ideas. 800sh, Letter writing.
700sh, Communication linkages, vert.

2001, Oct. 9　　　　Litho.
2198-2201　A379　Set of 4　　4.50　4.50
Souvenir Sheet
2202　A379　700sh multi　　1.50　1.50

Conservation of Zanzibar Rare Species — A380

Designs: 250sh, Dolphins. 300sh, Coral reefs. 450sh, Coral reefs, diff. 800sh, Zanzibar red colobus, vert.
700sh, Zanzibar red colobus, diff.

2002, Aug. 30　Litho.　　Perf. 13
2203-2206　A380　Set of 4　　4.00　4.00
Souvenir Sheet
2207　A380　700sh multi　　1.60　1.60

Historic Sites of East Africa
A381

Designs: 250sh, Fort Kilwa. 300sh, Maruhubi Palace ruins, Zanzibar. 400sh, Old Provincial Office, Nairobi, 1913. 800sh, Mparu Tombs, Hoima, Uganda.
700sh, Map of East Africa, ship.

2001, Oct. 19
2208-2211　A381　Set of 4　　3.75　3.75
Souvenir Sheet
2212　A381　700sh multi　　1.50　1.50

Independence, 40th Anniv. — A382

Designs: 180sh, Tea estates. 230sh, Regional integration with Uganda and Kenya, vert. 350sh, University graduates, vert. 450sh, 1000sh, Lion, elephant, buffalo, cheetah, rhinoceros, Mt. Kilimanjaro. 650sh, Referral hospitals. 950sh, Mining industry.

2001, Dec. 30　Litho.　　Perf. 14
2213-2218　A382　Set of 6　　6.00　6.00
Souvenir Sheet
2219　A382　1000sh multi　　2.10　2.10

Ceremonial Costumes — A383

Designs: 250sh, Makonde mask dance. 350sh, Zanzibar Mwaka koga festival. 400sh, Lizombe dancer. 450sh, Zaramo bride's celebration.
500sh, Like 400sh.

Wmk. 387
2002, Mar. 30　Litho.　　Perf. 13¾
2220-2223　A383　Set of 4　　3.00　3.00
Souvenir Sheet
2224　A383　500sh multi　　1.00　1.00

Mountains
A384

Designs: 250sh, Mt. Kilimanjaro. 350sh, Usambara Mountains. 400sh, Uluguru Mountains. 450sh, Mwanihana Peak, Udzungwa Mountains.
500sh, Like 250sh.

2002, June 30　　　　Wmk. 387
2225-2228　A384　Set of 4　　3.00　3.00
Souvenir Sheet
2229　A384　500sh multi　　1.10　1.10

National Census
A385

Census emblem and: 200sh, School children, vert. 250sh, Group of people. 350sh, Family. 600sh, Boy, census figures. 800sh, Group of people, vert.

Perf. 13x13¼ Sync., 13¼x13 Sync.
2002, Aug. 13　　　　Unwmk.
2230-2233　A385　Set of 4　　3.00　3.00
Souvenir Sheet
Perf. 13x13¼
2234　A385　800sh multi　　1.60　1.60

Arts of Zanzibar
A386

Designs: 200sh, Mat making. 250sh, Handsewn hats. 350sh, Chair making. 600sh, Hina painting.
800sh, Zanzibar door.

2002, Sept. 13　Unwmk.　　Perf. 13¼
2235-2238　A386　Set of 4　　3.00　3.00
Souvenir Sheet
Perf. 13
2239　A386　800sh multi　　1.60　1.60

Souvenir Sheet

Wildlife — A387

No. 2240: a, Leopard. b, Elephant. c, Rhinoceros. d, Lion. e, Buffalo.

Perf. 13x14

002, Apr. 30 **Wmk. 387**

240 A387 250sh Sheet of 5, 2.60 2.60
#a-e

Compare No. 2240 with No. 2251.

Archaeology
A388

Designs: 250sh, Ancient city of Kisimkazi, anzibar, vert. 400sh, Ruins of Kaole town, agamoyo. 450sh, Kondoa Irangi rock paint-gs, vert. 600sh, Great Mosque, Kilwa isiwani. 1000sh, Like 450sh.

Perf. 13¼

002, Sept. 30 **Unwmk.** **Litho.**

241-2244 A388 Set of 4 3.50 3.50

Souvenir Sheet
Perf. 13

245 A388 1000sh multi 2.10 2.10

Wildlife
A389

Designs: 400sh, Rhinoceroses. 500sh, Ele-hant. 600sh, Lion. 800sh, Leopard, vert. 000sh, Buffalo.
1500sh, Rhinoceros, elephant, lion, leopard, uffalo, vert.

Perf. 13¼x12¾, 12¾x13¼

003, Apr. 22 **Litho.** **Wmk. 387**

246-2250 A389 Set of 5 6.50 6.50
Size: 85x115mm

Imperf

251 A389 1500sh multi 3.00 3.00

Compare No. 2251 with No. 2240.

Cash
Crops — A390

Designs: 250sh, Cotton. 300sh, Cashews. 00sh, Sisal. 800sh, Cloves.
1000sh, Tea, horiz.

Perf. 13x13¼ Syncopated

003, June 10 **Unwmk.**

252-2255 A390 Set of 4 3.75 3.75
Souvenir Sheet
Perf. 13¼x13 Syncopated

256 A390 1000sh multi 1.90 1.90

Activities of
World
Vision
A391

Designs: 300sh, Better nutrition with vitamin A. 600sh, Education opportunity for all chil-dren. 800sh, Clean and safe water for all, vert. 1000sh, Malaria prevention with treated mos-quito nets.
500sh, Children have a right to be heard.

2003, July 3 **Perf. 13**

257-2260 A391 Set of 4 5.25 5.25
Souvenir Sheet

261 A391 500sh multi .95 .95

Traditional
Dances
A392

Dances: 300sh, Nyamwezi. 500sh, Luo. 600sh, Pemba. 800sh, Baganda. 1000sh, Masai.

Perf. 13¼x13 Syncopated

2003, July 25

2262-2265 A392 Set of 4 4.25 4.25
Souvenir Sheet

2266 A392 1000sh multi 1.90 1.90

Nos. 612 and 1567 Surcharged

Methods and Perfs As Before

2003

2267 A99 250sh on 40sh #612 .50 .50
2268 A262 250sh on 180sh .50 .50
#1567

SEMI-POSTAL STAMPS

Natl.
Solidarity
Walk — SP1

1988, July 1 **Litho.** **Perf. 14½**

B1 SP1 2sh +1sh Flag, crowd .50 .50
B2 SP1 3sh +1sh Map, Pres. .50 .50
Mwinyi
Souvenir Sheet

B3 SP1 50sh +1sh Flag, Pres. 1.25 1.25
Mwinyi

Surtax for Chama Cha Mapinduzi party activities.

Natl.
Solidarity
Walk — SP2

1989, July 1 **Litho.** **Perf. 14½**

B4 SP2 5sh +1sh Party flag .35 .35
B5 SP2 10sh +1sh Pres. Mwinyi, .35 .35
walk
Souvenir Sheet

B6 SP2 50sh +1sh Pres. Mwinyi 1.00 1.00

Natl.
Solidarity
Walk
SP3

Designs: 4sh + 1sh, Pres. Mwinyi marching with crowd. 9sh + 1sh, Crowd around party flag. 13sh + 1sh, Pres. Mwinyi. 30sh + 1sh, Pres. Mwinyi planting tree. No. B11, Pres. Mwinyi sorting cloves. No. B12, Handshake across map, vert.

1991-92 **Litho.** **Perf. 13½**

B7 SP3 4sh +1sh multicolored .50 .50
('92)
B8 SP3 9sh +1sh multicolored .70 .70
B9 SP3 13sh +1sh multicolored .70 .70
B10 SP3 30sh +1sh multicolored 1.25 1.25
('92)
Nos. B7-B10 (4) 3.15 3.15
Souvenir Sheets
Perf. 12½

B11 SP3 50sh +1sh multicolored 2.25 2.25
B12 SP3 50sh +1sh multicolored 1.75 1.75

Issued: Nos. B8-B9, 7/6/90. Nos. B7, B10, 7/5/91.

POSTAGE DUE STAMPS

D1 D2

Perf. 14x14½

1978, July 31 **Litho.** **Unwmk.**

J1 D1 5c red .20 .20
J2 D1 10c green .20 .20
J3 D1 20c dark blue .20 .20
J4 D1 30c reddish brown .20 .20
J5 D1 40c bright rose lilac .20 .20
J6 D1 1sh orange .30 .30
Nos. J1-J6 (6) 1.30 1.30

1967, Jan. 3 **Perf. 14x13½**

J1a D1 5c red .20 .20
J2a D1 10c green .20 .20
J3a D1 20c dark blue .40 .40
J4a D1 30c reddish brown .60 .60
J5a D1 40c bright rose lilac .80 .80
J6a D1 1sh orange 2.00 2.00
Nos. J1a-J6a (6) 4.20 4.20

1969-71 **Perf. 14x15**

J1b D1 5c red .20 .20
J2b D1 10c green .20 .20
J3b D1 20c dark blue .40 .40
J4b D1 30c reddish brown .60 .60
J5b D1 40c bright rose lilac .80 .80
J6b D1 1sh orange ('71) 2.00 2.00
Nos. J1b-J6b (6) 4.20 4.20

1973, Dec. 12 **Perf. 15**

J1c D1 5c red .20 .20
J2c D1 10c green .20 .20
J3c D1 20c dark blue .30 .30
J4c D1 30c reddish brown .45 .45
J5c D1 40c bright rose lilac .60 .60
J6c D1 1sh orange 1.50 1.50
Nos. J1c-J6c (6) 3.25 3.25

1984? **Perf. 14¾x14**

J4d D1 30c reddish brown

Additional stamps of this type with this per-foration have been reported. The editors would like to examine any examples.

1990 **Litho.** **Perf. 15x14**

J7 D2 50c dark green .20 .20
J8 D2 80c bright blue .20 .20
J9 D2 1sh orange brown .20 .20
J10 D2 2sh light olive green .20 .20
J11 D2 3sh purple .20 .20
J12 D2 5sh gray .20 .20
J13 D2 10sh brown .20 .20
J14 D2 20sh bister .20 .20
Nos. J7-J14 (8) 1.60 1.60

OFFICIAL STAMPS

Nos. 5-9, 11, 13 and 16 Overprinted:
"OFFICIAL"
Perf. 14x14½, 14½x14

1965, Dec. 9 **Photo.** **Unwmk.**
Size: 21x17½mm, 17½x21mm

O1 A2 5c orange & ultra .20 .20
O2 A2 10c multicolored .20 .20
O3 A3 15c grn bl, brn & buff .20 .20
O4 A2 20c blue & brown .20 .20
O5 A3 30c black & red brn .20 .20
O6 A2 50c yellow grn & blk .20 .20

Perf. 14½
Size: 41½x25

O7 A2 1sh multicolored .30 .20
O8 A2 5sh bl, brt grn & red 1.50 1.00
brn
Nos. O1-O8 (8) 3.00 2.40

Overprint size: 17mm on 5c, 10c, 20c, 50c. 14mm on 15c, 30c. 29x3½mm on 1sh, 5sh.
The overprint was also applied in 1967 in Dar es Salaam to 50c, 1sh and 5sh. Size: 29x3mm.

Nos. 19-23, 25, 27 and 30
Overprinted: "OFFICIAL"

1967, Dec. 9 **Perf. 14x14½**
Fish in Natural Colors
Size: 21x17½mm

Overprint Litho., 17mm Wide

O9 A4 5c black & citron .20 .20
O10 A4 10c brown & olive .20 .20
O11 A4 15c brown & blue .20 .20
O12 A4 20c brown & dk blue grn .20 .20
O13 A4 30c black & yel grn .20 .20
O14 A4 50c black & dull bl grn .20 .20

Perf. 14½
Size: 41x25mm

Overprint 29mm Wide

O15 A4 1sh brown & multi .40 .20
O16 A4 5sh black & blue grn 1.75 1.25
Nos. O9-O16 (8) 3.35 2.65

1970-73
Overprint Typo., 17½mm Wide

O9a A4 5c black & citron .20 .20
O10a A4 10c brown & olive .20 .20
O12a A4 20c brn & dk bl grn .20 .20
O13a A4 30c blk & yel grn .30 .20
O13B A4 40c multicolored ('73)
Nos. O9a-O13a (4) .90 .80

The overprint was also applied in 1973 to 15c, 50c, 1sh (28mm wide), and 5sh.

Nos. 35-36, 38, 40-41, 43-47
Overprinted

a b

1973, Dec. 10 **Photo.** **Perf. 14½x14**

O17 A5(a) 5c multicolored .20 .20
O18 A5(a) 10c multicolored .20 .20
O19 A5(a) 20c multicolored .20 .20
O20 A5(a) 40c multicolored .20 .20
O21 A5(a) 50c multicolored .20 .20
O22 A5(a) 70c multicolored .20 .20

Perf. 14½

O23 A6(b) 1sh multicolored .20 .20
O24 A6(b) 1.50sh multicolored .30 .30
O25 A6(b) 2.50sh multicolored .50 .50
O26 A6(b) 5sh multicolored 1.00 1.00
Nos. O17-O26 (10) 3.20 3.20

A larger overprint (17½mm wide instead of 14½mm) was applied locally to 10c, 20c, 40c, and 50c.
Provisional use of some values for regular postage is known.

Nos. 161-171 Overprinted:
OFFICIAL

1980, Oct. 1 **Perf. 14**

O27 A21 10c multicolored .20 .20
O28 A21 20c multicolored .20 .20
O29 A21 40c multicolored .20 .20
O30 A21 50c multicolored .20 .20
O31 A21 75c multicolored .20 .20
O32 A21 80c multicolored .20 .20

Perf. 14½

O33 A21 1sh multicolored .20 .20
O33A A21 1.50sh multicolored
O34 A21 2sh multicolored .40 .40
O35 A21 3sh multicolored .60 .60
O36 A21 5sh multicolored 1.00 1.00
Nos. O27-O33,O34-O36 (10) 3.40 3.40

Overprint measures 13mm on Nos. O33-O36; reads up or down.

Nos. 606-614 Inscribed "OFFICIAL"

1990-91		Litho.	Perf. 14	
O37	A99	5sh multi	.20	.20
O38	A99	9sh multi	.20	.20
O39	A99	13sh multi	.20	.20
O40	A99	15sh multi	.20	.20
O41	A99	20sh multi	.30	.30
O42	A99	25sh multi	.35	.35
O42A	A99	30sh multi ('91)	.45	.45
O43	A99	40sh multi	.60	.60
O44	A99	70sh multi	1.00	1.00
O45	A99	100sh multi	1.50	1.50
	Nos. O37-O45 (10)		5.00	5.00

Inscription on Nos. O37-O42A is 15½mm long. Insription on Nos. O43-O45 is 19mm long.

No. 1568 Ovptd. "OFFICIAL"

1997 (?)		Litho.	Perf. 14½x15
O49	A262	200sh multi	

The editors suspect there are additional stamps in this set, and would like to examine any examples.

SCOTTMOUNTS

For stamp presentation unequaled in beauty and clarity, insist on ScottMounts. Made of 100% inert polystyrol foil, ScottMounts protect your stamps from the harmful effects of dust and moisture. Available in your choice of clear or black backs, ScottMounts are center-split across the back for easy insertion of stamps and feature crystal clear mount faces. Double layers of gum assure stay-put bonding on the album page. Discover the quality and value ScottMounts have to offer.

ScottMounts are available from your favorite stamp dealer or direct from:

Discover the quality and value ScottMounts have to offer.

For a complete list of ScottMount sizes call or write Scott Publishing Co.

SCOTT

Scott Publishing Co.
1-800-572-6885
P.O. Box 828 Sidney OH 45365-0828
www.amosadvantage.com

AMOS
HOBBY PUBLISHING

Publishers of:
Coin World, Linn's Stamp News and Scott Publishing Co.

TETE

'tāt-ə

LOCATION — In southeastern Africa between Nyasaland and Southern Rhodesia
GOVT. — A district of the Portuguese East Africa Colony
AREA — 46,600 sq. mi. (approx.)
POP. — 367,000 (approx.)
CAPITAL — Tete

This district was formerly a part of Zambezia. Stamps of Mozambique replaced those of Tete. See Mozambique.

100 Centavos = 1 Escudo

Vasco da Gama Issue of Various Portuguese Colonies Surcharged as

1913   Unwmk.   Perf. 12½, 16
On Stamps of Macao

CD20	¼c on ½a bl grn	3.00	3.00
CD21	½c on 1a red	1.75	3.00
CD22	1c on 2a red vio	1.75	3.00
CD23	2½c on 4a yel grn	1.75	3.00
CD24	5c on 8a dk blue	1.75	2.10
CD25	7½c on 12a vio brn	2.40	3.00
CD26	10c on 16a bis brn	1.75	2.10
CD27	15c on 24a bister	1.75	2.10
	Nos. 1-8 (8)	15.90	21.30

On Stamps of Portuguese Africa

CD20	¼c on 2½r bl grn	1.75	2.10
CD21	½c on 5r red	1.75	2.10
CD22	1c on 10r red vio	1.75	2.10
CD23	2½c on 25r yel grn	1.75	2.10
CD24	5c on 50r dk blue	1.75	2.10
CD25	7½c on 75r vio brn	2.40	3.00
CD26	10c on 100r bis brn	1.75	2.10
CD27	15c on 150r bister	1.75	2.10
	Nos. 9-16 (8)	14.65	17.70

On Stamps of Timor

CD20	¼c on ½a bl grn	1.75	2.10
CD21	½c on 1a red	1.75	2.10
CD22	1c on 2a red vio	1.75	2.10
a.	Inverted overprint	30.00	30.00
CD23	2½c on 4a yel grn	1.75	2.10
CD24	5c on 8a dk blue	1.75	2.10
CD25	7½c on 12a vio brn	2.40	3.00
CD26	10c on 16a bis brn	1.75	2.10
CD27	15c on 24a bister	1.75	2.10
	Nos. 17-24 (8)	14.65	17.70
	Nos. 1-24 (24)	45.20	56.70

Common Design Types pictured following the introduction.

Ceres — A1

1914   Typo.   Perf. 15x14
Name and Value in Black

25	A1	¼c olive brn	1.40	2.25
26	A1	½c black	1.40	2.25
27	A1	1c blue grn	1.40	2.25
28	A1	1½c lilac brn	1.40	2.25
29	A1	2c carmine	1.40	2.25
30	A1	2½c light vio	1.40	2.25
31	A1	5c deep blue	1.40	2.25
32	A1	7½c yel brn	2.25	3.25
33	A1	8c slate	2.25	3.25
34	A1	10c org brn	2.75	4.00
35	A1	15c plum	3.25	4.50
36	A1	20c yel green	3.25	4.50
37	A1	30c brn, *green*	3.25	4.50
38	A1	40c brn, *pink*	4.00	5.50
39	A1	50c org, *salmon*	7.00	6.00
40	A1	1e grn, *blue*	10.00	7.00
		Nos. 25-40 (16)	47.80	58.25

THAILAND

'tī-,land

(Siam)

LOCATION — Western part of the Malay peninsula in southeastern Asia
GOVT. — Republic
AREA — 198,250 sq. mi.
POP. — 60,609,046 (1999 est.)
CAPITAL — Bangkok

32 Solot = 16 Atts = 8 Sio =
4 Sik = 2 Fuang = 1 Salung
4 Salungs = 1 Tical
100 Satangs (1909) = 1 Tical
= 1 Baht (1912)

Catalogue values for unused stamps in this country are for Never Hinged items, beginning with Scott 264 in the regular postage section, Scott B34 in the semipostal section, Scott C20 in the airpost section, and Scott O1 in the official section.

Watermarks

Wmk. 176 — Chakra

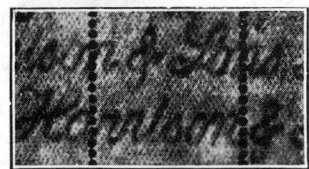

Wmk. 233 — Harrison & Sons, London in Script Letters

Wmk. 299 — Thai Characters and Wavy Lines

Wmk. 329 — Zigzag Lines

Wmk. 334 — Rectangles

Wmk. 340 — Alternating Interlaced Wavy Lines

Wmk. 356 — POSTAGE

Wmk. 368 — JEZ Multiple

Wmk. 371 — Wavy Lines

Wmk. 374 — Circles and Crosses

Wmk. 375 — Letters

Thailand We are THE LEADER in Thai philately.

Public Auctions. Mail Sales. A terrific website where our famous services are offered:
www.michaelrogersinc.com

Send only $1 for our next auction/mail sale catalog

ARE YOU SELLING? We pay FULL market value. Call us now!

Michael Rogers Inc.

660 West Fairbanks Ave. Suite 4
Winter Park FL 32789
Office/Gallery: (407) 644-2290
Toll Free: 1-800-843-3751
Fax: (407) 645-4434

ASIAN PHILATELY

E-Mail: mrogersinc@aol.com

THAILAND

BUYING
PAYING TOP DOLLAR
SHIP - WRITE - CALL - FAX
...what you have for sale with your best price or for our prompt offer.

We are also looking to buy other Asian Stamps – China (both PRC & Taiwan), Hong Kong, Indonesia, Japan, Macau, Malaysia, Philippines, Singapore, Vietnam, etc. Please contact us.

SELLING
We maintain a comprehensive stock of Thailand Stamps from 1883 to date.

The 2004 Thailand Specialized Catalogue is now available.

The price is $22.00 postpaid (domestic U.S.A.).
$25.00 overseas.

QUALITY PHILATELICS

P.O. Box 2871, Newport Beach, CA 92659
PHONE: 714-963-3257 FAX: 714-963-5121
Email:qualityphilatelics@earthlink.net

Wmk. 377 — Interlocking Circles

Wmk. 385 — CARTOR

Wmk. 387 — Squares and Rectangles

King Chulalongkorn
A1   A2

A4

Perf. 14½, 15

1883, Aug. 4		Unwmk.	Engr.	
1	A1	1sol blue	7.00	9.00
b.		Imperf., pair		4,500.
2	A1	1att carmine	8.25	7.00
3	A1	1sio vermilion	27.50	16.00
4	A2	1sik yellow	10.00	13.00
5	A4	1sa orange	40.00	40.00
a.		1sa ocher	45.00	45.00
		Nos. 1-5 (5)	92.75	85.00

There are three types of No. 1, differing mainly in the background of the small oval at the top.

A 1 fuang red, of similar design to the foregoing, was prepared but not placed in use. Value, $900.

For surcharges see Nos. 6-8, 19.

No. 1 Handstamp Surcharged in Red:

1 TICAL
a

1 Tical   **1 Tical**
b   *c*

1 Tical   **1 Tical**
d   *e*

1885, July 1

6	A1 (a)	1t on 1sol blue	400.	400.
7	A1 (b)	1t on 1sol blue	325.	325.
c.		"1" inverted	1,100.	1,100.
8	A1 (c)	1t on 1sol blue	400.	400.

Surcharges of Nos. 6-8 have been counterfeited.

Types "d" and "e" are typeset *official reprints.*

As is usual with handstamps, double impressions, etc., exist.

King
Chulalongkorn — A7

1887-91	Typo.	Wmk. 176	*Perf. 14*	
11	A7	1a green ('91)	3.00	.90
12	A7	2a green & car	4.50	.90
13	A7	3a grn & blue	11.00	3.75
14	A7	4a grn & org brn	9.00	3.00
15	A7	8a green & yel	9.00	2.40
16	A7	12a lilac & car	15.00	1.25
17	A7	24a lilac & blue	21.00	1.50
18	A7	64a lil & org brn	77.50	22.50
		Nos. 11-18 (8)	150.00	36.20

The design of No. 11 has been redrawn and differs from the illustration in many minor details.

Issue dates: #12-18, Apr. 1; #11, Feb.

For surcharges see Nos. 20-69, 109, 111, 126.

No. 3 Handstamp
Surcharged

1889, Aug.   Unwmk.   Perf. 15

19	A1	1a on 1sio	16.00	16.00

Three different handstamps were used. Doubles, etc. exist.

Nos. 12 and 13
Handstamp Surcharged

1889-90   Wmk. 176   Perf. 14

20	A7	1a on 2a	3.25	2.25
a.		"1" omitted	250.00	250.00
c.		1st Siamese character invtd.		
d.		First Siamese character omitted	300.00	300.00
21	A7	1a on 3a ('90)	8.25	8.00
a.		Inverted "1"	150.00	150.00

For surcharge see No. 29.

22	A7	1a on 2a grn & car	400.00	450.00

24	A7	1a on 2a grn & car	175.00	125.00

25	A7	1a on 2a grn & car	1,000.	1,000.

26	A7	1a on 3a grn & bl		

Some authorities consider No. 26 a forgery. Doubles, etc., exist in this issue.
Issue dates: Nov. 1889. Sept. 1890.

No. 13 Handstamp
Surcharged

1891

27	A7	2a on 3a grn & bl	55.00	50.00

28	A7	2a on 3a grn & bl	50.00	45.00
a.		Double surcharge	250.00	250.00
b.		"2" omitted	250.00	

No. 21 with Additional 2 Att Surcharge

29	A7	2a on 1a on 3a grn & bl	1,500.	1,500.

On No. 29 the 2a surcharge consists of Siamese numeral like No. 27 and English numeral like No. 28.

Most examples of No. 29 show attempts to remove the "1" of the first surcharge.

Typeset Surcharge

30	A7	2a on 3a grn & bl	40.00	32.50

There are 7 types of this surcharge in the setting.
Issued: #27-28, Jan.; #29, Feb.; #30, Mar.

No. 17 Handstamp Surcharged:

f   g

1892, Oct.

33	A7 (f)	4a on 24a lil & bl	50.00	47.50
34	A7 (g)	4a on 24a lil & bl	32.50	32.50

Surcharges exist double on Nos. 33-34 and inverted on No. 33.

Nos. 33-34 Handstamp Surcharged in English

4 atts

1892, Nov.

35	A7	4a on 24a lil & bl	8.25	6.50
c.		Inverted "s"	40.00	40.00

4 atts.

36	A7	4a on 24a lil & bl	13.00	9.00
a.		Inverted "s"	40.00	40.00

37	A7	4a on 24a lil & bl	12.00	10.00

4 atts.

38	A7	4a on 24a lil & bl	13.00	11.00

Numerous inverts., doubles, etc., exist.

Nos. 18 and 17 Typeset Surcharged in English (Shown) and Siamese

1   Atts

1894

39	A7	1a on 64a lil & org brn	3.25	3.0
a.		Inverted "s"	40.00	40.0
b.		Inverted surcharge	900.00	900.0
d.		Italic "s"	50.00	50.0
e.		Italic "1"	50.00	50.0

1 Att.

40	A7	1a on 64a lil & org brn	1.90	1.60
a.		Inverted capital "S" added to the surcharge	175.00	200.00

2 Atts.   2 Atts.
   h   *i*

2 Atts.   2 Atts.
   j   *k*

2. Atts.   2 Atts.
    l   *m*

41	A7 (h)	2a on 64a	22.50	22.50
a.		Inverted "s"	40.00	40.00
b.		Double surcharge	100.00	100.00
42	A7 (i)	2a on 64a	3,000.	3,000.
43	A7 (j)	2a on 64a	55.00	55.00
44	A7 (k)	2a on 64a	32.50	32.50
45	A7 (l)	2a on 64a	50.00	50.00
46	A7 (m)	2a on 64a	1.75	1.60
a.		"Atts."	40.00	40.00

Nos. 41-46 were in one plate of 120 subjects. The quantities were: h, 38; i, 1; j, 8; k 18; l, 11 and m, 44.

1 Att.

1894, Oct. 12

47	A7	1a on 64a	2.25	2.00
a.		Surcharged on face and back	150.00	
b.		Surcharge on back inverted	200.00	
c.		Double surcharge	400.00	
d.		Inverted surcharge	500.00	
e.		Siamese surcharge omitted	400.00	

2 Atts.

48	A7	2a on 64a	2.75	2.25
a.		"Att"	35.00	30.00
b.		Inverted surcharge	300.00	300.00
c.		Surch. on face and back	400.00	400.00
d.		Surcharge on back inverted	400.00	400.00
e.		Double surcharge	300.00	300.00
f.		Double surch., one inverted	1,100.	1,100.
g.		Inverted "s"	40.00	40.00

10 Atts.

1895, July 23

49	A7	10a on 24a lil & bl	6.75	1.75
a.		Inverted "s"	40.00	25.00
b.		Surch. on face and back	175.00	175.00
c.		Surcharge on back inverted	175.00	175.00

No. 16 Surcharged in English (Shown) and Siamese

4 Atts.

1896

50	A7	4a on 12a lil & car	10.00	5.00
a.		Inverted "s"	50.00	50.00
b.		Surch. on face and back	175.00	175.00
c.		Double surcharge on back	175.00	175.00

Two types of surcharge.

Nos. 16-18 Surcharged in English (Shown) and Siamese
Antique Surcharges:

1 Atts.   1 Att.   2 Atts.
   a   *b*   *c*

3 Atts.   4 Atts.   10 Atts.
   d   *e*   *f*

Atts.

Antique Letters

Atts.
Roman Letters

1898-99

51	A7 (a)	1a on 12a	325.00	325.00
52	A7 (b)	1a on 12a	15.00	5.00
53	A7 (c)	2a on 64a ('99)	27.50	7.50
54	A7 (d)	3a on 12a	10.00	3.00
a.		Double surcharge	350.00	350.00
55	A7 (e)	4a on 12a	10.00	3.50
a.		Double surcharge	350.00	350.00
56	A7 (e)	4a on 24a ('99)	30.00	10.00
57	A7 (f)	10a on 24a ('99)	750.00	750.00

Roman Surcharges:

2 Atts.
วากเบ ยุ

1 Atts. **1 Att.** **2 Atts.**
g   h   i

3 Atts. 4 Atts. 10 Atts.
j   k   l

58	A7 (g)	1a on 12a	400.00	400.00
59	A7 (h)	1a on 12a	40.00	10.00
60	A7 (i)	2a on 64a ('99)	35.00	9.00
61	A7 (j)	3a on 12a	85.00	17.50
62	A7 (k)	4a on 12a	40.00	12.50
a.		Double surcharge	175.00	175.00
b.		No period after "Atts."	30.00	30.00
63	A7 (k)	4a on 24a ('99)	55.00	20.00
64	A7 (l)	10a on 24a ('99)	700.00	700.00
		Nos. 58-64 (7)	1,355.	1,169.

In making the settings to surcharge Nos. 51 to 64 two fonts were mixed. Antique and Roman letters are frequently found on the same stamp.
Issued: #54-55, 61-62, Feb. 22; #51-52, 58-59, June 4; #56-57, 63-64, Oct. 3.

Nos. 16 and 18 Surcharged in English (Shown) and Siamese Surcharged:

1 Att. 1 Att.
m   n

1 Att.
o

2 Atts. 2 Atts.
p   r

1894-99

65	A7 (m)	1a on 12a	20.00	2.50
66	A7 (n)	1a on 12a	18.00	6.75
a.		Inverted "I"	150.00	150.00
b.		Inverted 1st "I"	150.00	150.00
67	A7 (o)	1a on 64a	5.00	3.75
68	A7 (p)	2a on 64a	8.50	5.00
a.		"1 Atts."	500.00	500.00
69	A7 (r)	2a on 64a	24.00	3.25
		Nos. 65-69 (5)	75.50	21.25

Issued: #67, 10/12/94; others, 2/14/99.

A13   A14

1899, Oct.   Typo.   Unwmk.

70	A13	1a dull green	125.00	70.00
71	A13	2a dl grn & rose	200.00	110.
72	A13	3a carmine & blue	300.	160.
73	A13	4a black & grn	1,850.	575.
74	A13	10a carmine & grn	2,100.	825.
		Nos. 70-74 (5)	4,575.	1,740.

The King rejected Nos. 70-74 in 1897, but some were released by mistake to three post offices in Oct. 1899. Used values are for copies canceled to order at Korat in Dec. 1899. Postally used examples sell for more.

1899-1904

75	A14	1a gray green	1.60	.70
76	A14	2a yellow green	1.60	.70
77	A14	2a scarlet & bl	3.25	.70
78	A14	3a red & blue	6.50	1.75

79	A14	3a green	19.00	10.50
80	A14	4a dark rose	3.25	1.10
81	A14	4a vio brn & rose	6.50	1.75
82	A14	6a dk rose	32.50	12.50
83	A14	8a dk grn & org	8.00	1.10
84	A14	10a ultra	8.00	2.25
85	A14	12a brn vio & rose	37.50	1.75
86	A14	14a ultra	19.00	16.00
87	A14	24a brn vio & bl	290.00	21.00
88	A14	28a vio brn & bl	22.50	22.50
89	A14	64a brn vio & org brn	65.00	8.00
		Nos. 75-89 (15)	524.20	102.30

Two types of 1a differ in size and shape of Thai "1" are in drawing of spandrel ornaments.
Issue dates: 6a, 14a, 28a, Nos. 77, 79, 81, Jan. 1, 1904; others, Sept. 1899.
For surcharges see Nos. 90-91, 112, 125, 127.

Nos. 78 and 85 With Typewritten Surcharge of 6 or 7 Siamese Characters (1 line) in Violet

1902

78a	A14	2a on 3a	4,000.	4,500.
85a	A14	10a on 12a	4,000.	4,500.

Nos. 78a and 85a were authorized provisionals, surcharged and issued by the Battambang postmaster.

Nos. 86 and 88 Surcharged in Black

1905, Feb.

90	A14	1a on 14a	10.00	7.50
a.		No period after "Att"	35.00	35.00
91	A14	2a on 28a	11.00	9.00
a.		Double surcharge	125.00	125.00

King Chulalongkorn
A15   A16

1905-08   Engr.

92	A15	1a orange & green	1.60	.50
93	A15	2a violet & slate	2.50	.90
94	A15	2a green ('08)	10.00	3.50
95	A15	3a green	3.00	1.40
96	A15	3a vio & sl ('08)	10.00	4.50
97	A15	4a gray & red	3.25	1.00
98	A15	4a car & green ('08)	5.75	1.00
99	A15	5a carmine & rose	7.50	2.50
100	A15	8a blk & ol bis	7.25	1.00
101	A15	9a blue ('08)	20.00	7.50
102	A15	12a blue	16.00	2.75
103	A15	18a red brn ('08)	50.00	13.00
104	A15	24a red brown	30.00	5.00
105	A15	1t dp bl & brn org	42.50	8.00
		Nos. 92-105 (14)	209.35	52.65

Issue dates: Dec. 1905, Apr. 1, 1908.
For surcharges and overprints see Nos. 110, 113-117, 128-138, 161-162, B15, B21.

1907, Apr. 24
Black Surcharge

106	A16	10t gray green	300.	70.
107	A16	20t gray green	3,300.	250.
108	A16	40t gray green	2,400.	400.
		Nos. 106-108 (3)	6,000.	720.00

Counterfeits of Nos. 106-108 exist. In the genuine, the surcharged figures correspond to the Siamese value inscriptions on the basic revenue stamps.

No. 17 Surcharged

1att.

1907, Dec. 16

109	A7	1a on 24a lil & bl	2.00	.80
a.		Double surcharge	400.00	

No. 99 Surcharged

1908, Sept.

110	A15	4a on 5a car & rose	11.00	3.75

The No. 110 surcharge is found in two spacings of the numerals: normally 15mm apart, and a narrow, scarcer spacing of 13 ½mm.

Nos. 17 and 84 Surcharged in Black:

2 Atts.   **9 Atts**

111	A7	2a on 24a lil & bl	2.00	.80
a.		Inverted surcharge	325.00	325.00
112	A14	9a on 10a ultra	12.00	5.00
a.		Inverted surcharge	325.00	325.00

Jubilee Issue

Nos. 92, 95, 110, 100 and 103 Overprinted in Black or Red

1908, Nov. 11

113	A15	1a	1.50	.75
a.		Siamese date "137" instead of "127"	900.00	900.00
b.		Pair, one without ovpt.		

114	A15	3a	3.00	1.75
115	A15	4a on 5a	4.50	2.50
a.		Horiz. pair, imperf. btwn.	500.00	
116	A15	8a (R)	21.00	19.00
117	A15	18a	30.00	16.00
		Nos. 113-117 (5)	60.00	40.00

40th year of the reign of King Chulalongkorn. Nos. 113 to 117 exist with a small "i" in "Jubilee."

Statue of King Chulalongkorn
A19

1908, Nov. 11   Engr.   Perf. 13½

118	A19	1t green & vio	27.50	2.75
119	A19	2t red vio & org	55.00	9.75
120	A19	3t pale ol & bl	82.50	12.50
121	A19	5t dl vio & dk grn	110.00	22.50
122	A19	10t bister & car	1,250.	82.50
123	A19	20t gray & red brn	275.00	77.50
124	A19	40t sl bl & blk brn	425.00	250.00
		Nos. 118-124 (7)	2,225.	457.50

The inscription at the foot of the stamps reads: "Coronation Commemoration-Forty-first year of the reign-1908."

The only website that gives you what you need about Thai stamps
Just click !
www.thaistamp.com

By International House of Stamps Co., Ltd.
98/2 Soi Ton Son, Langsuan Rd., Lumpinee, Pathumwan, Bangkok 10330 THAILAND
Phone + 66 (0) 2 652 2220 Fax + 66 (0) 2 652 2221
E-mail : houseofstamp@thaistamp.com

Stamps of 1887-1904
Surcharged

1909
			Perf. 14	
125	A14	6s on 6a dk rose	2.00	1.90
126	A7	14s on 12a lil & car	100.00	90.00
127	A14	14s on 14a ultra	18.00	17.50
		Nos. 125-127 (3)	120.00	109.40

Nos. 92-102
Surcharged with Bar
and

1909, Aug. 15
128	A15	2s on 1a #92	1.40	.60
129	A15	2s on 2a #93	57.50	47.50
130	A15	2s on 2a #94	1.40	.60
a.		"2" omitted	75.00	
131	A15	3s on 3a #95	2.40	.90
132	A15	3s on 3a #96	2.40	.60
133	A15	6s on 4a #97	60.00	45.00
134	A15	6s on 4a #98	3.50	.90
135	A15	6s on 5a #99	3.00	2.10
136	A15	12s on 8a #100	7.00	.90
137	A15	14s on 9a #101	10.50	1.50
138	A15	14s on 12a #102	21.00	18.00
		Nos. 128-138 (11)	170.10	118.60

King
Chulalongkorn — A20

1910
		Engr.	Perf. 14x14½	
139	A20	2s org & green	1.10	.45
140	A20	3s green	1.75	.45
141	A20	6s carmine	3.00	.45
142	A20	12s blk & ol brn	5.50	.75
143	A20	14s blue	17.50	1.25
144	A20	28s red brown	40.00	7.00
		Nos. 139-144 (6)	68.85	10.35

Issue dates: 12s, June 5. Others, May 5.
For surcharges see Nos. 163, 223-224.

A21   King
Vajiravudh — A22

Printed at the Imperial Printing Works,
Vienna

1912
			Perf. 14½	
145	A21	2s brown orange	1.25	.20
a.		Vert. pair, imperf. btwn.	500.00	500.00
b.		Horiz. pair, imperf. btwn.	500.00	500.00
146	A21	3s yellow green	1.25	.20
a.		Horiz. pair, imperf. btwn.	500.00	500.00
147	A21	6s carmine rose	2.25	.55
148	A21	12s gray blk & brn	3.25	.60
149	A21	14s ultramarine	5.25	.80
150	A21	28s chocolate	19.00	7.25
151	A22	1b blue & blk	19.00	1.40
a.		Pair, imperf. btwn.	1,250.	1,250.
152	A22	2b car rose & ol brn	22.50	2.50
153	A22	3b yel grn & bl blk	30.00	4.50
154	A22	5b vio & blk	45.00	4.50
155	A22	10b ol grn & vio brn	225.00	72.50
156	A22	20b sl bl & red brn	375.00	60.00
		Nos. 145-156 (12)	748.75	155.00

See Nos. 164-175.
For surcharges and overprints see Nos.
157-160, 176-186, 206, B1-B14, B16-B20,
B22, B31-B33.

Nos. 147-150
Surcharged in Red or
Blue

1914-15
157	A21	2s on 14s (R)		
		('15)	1.75	.35
a.		Vert. pair, imperf. btwn.	900.00	900.00
b.		Double surcharge	62.50	40.00
158	A21	5s on 6s (Bl)	3.25	.35
a.		Horiz. pair, imperf. btwn.	900.00	900.00
b.		Double surcharge	62.50	62.50
159	A21	10s on 12s (R)	4.00	.45
a.		Double surcharge	65.00	55.00
160	A21	15s on 28s (Bl)	5.00	.60
		Nos. 157-160 (4)	14.00	1.75

The several settings of the surcharges on
Nos. 157 to 160 show variations in the figures
and letters.

Nos. 92-93
Surcharged

1915, Apr. 3
161	A15	2s on 1a org & grn	4.75	2.50
a.		Pair, one without surcharge	350.00	350.00
162	A15	2s on 2a vio & slate	4.75	2.50

No. 143 Surcharged
in Red

1916, Oct.
163	A20	2s on 14s blue	2.50	1.10

Printed by Waterlow & Sons, London
Types of 1912 Re-engraved

1917, Jan. 1
			Perf. 14	
164	A21	2s orange brown	.65	.25
165	A21	3s emerald	.95	.35
166	A21	5s rose red	2.50	.25
167	A21	10s black & olive	1.60	.25
168	A21	15s blue	3.75	.50
170	A22	1b bl & gray blk	17.50	2.00
171	A22	2b car rose & brn	70.00	26.00
172	A22	3b yel grn & blk	500.00	240.00
173	A22	5b dp violet & blk	125.00	85.00
174	A22	10b ol gray & vio brn	375.00	8.50
a.		Perf. 12½	475.00	32.50
175	A22	20b sea grn & brn	475.00	47.50
a.		Perf. 12½	600.00	70.00
		Nos. 164-175 (11)	1,571.	410.60

The re-engraved design of the satang
stamps varies in numerous minute details from
the 1912 issue. Four lines of the background
appear between the vertical strokes of the "M"
of "SIAM" in the 1912 issue and only three
lines in the 1917 stamps.

The 1912 stamps with value in bahts are
37½mm high; those of 1917 are 39mm. In the
latter the king's features, especially the eyes
and mouth, are more distinct and the uniform
and decorations are more sharply defined.

The 1912 stamps have seven pearls
between the earpieces of the crown. On the
1917 stamps there are nine pearls in the same
place. Nos. 174 and 175 exist imperforate.

Nos. 164-173
Overprinted in Red

1918, Dec. 2
176	A21	2s orange brown	.55	.45
a.		Double overprint	100.00	100.00
177	A21	3s emerald	.85	.75
178	A21	5s rose red	1.40	1.25
a.		Double overprint	150.00	150.00
179	A21	10s black & olive	1.40	1.25
180	A21	15s blue	2.75	2.50
181	A22	1b bl & gray blk	21.00	15.00
182	A22	2b car rose & brn	42.50	32.50

183	A22	3b yel grn & blk	100.00	60.00
184	A22	5b dp vio & blk	350.00	250.00
		Nos. 176-184 (9)	520.45	363.70

Counterfeits of this overprint exist.

Nos. 147-148 Surcharged in Green or
Red

1919-20
185	A21	5s on 6s (G)	1.75	.30
186	A21	10s on 12s (R) ('20)	6.00	.75

Issue dates: 5s, Nov. 11. 10s, Jan. 1.

King   Throne Room
Vajiravudh   A24
A23

1920-26
		Engr.	Perf. 14-15, 12½	
187	A23	2s brn, yel ('21)	2.00	.40
188	A23	3s grn, grn ('21)	3.25	.55
189	A23	3s chocolate ('24)	3.25	.40
190	A23	5s rose, pale rose	3.75	.40
191	A23	5s green ('22)	27.50	3.25
192	A23	5s dk vio, lil ('26)	7.50	.40
193	A23	10s blk & org ('21)	5.75	.40
194	A23	15s bl, bluish ('21)	8.50	.40
195	A23	15s carmine ('22)	37.50	4.00
196	A23	25s chocolate ('21)	21.00	1.05
197	A23	25s dk blue ('22)	25.00	.75
198	A23	50s och & blk ('21)	22.50	1.10
		Nos. 187-198 (12)	167.50	13.80

For overprints see Nos. 205, B23-B30.

1926, Mar. 5
			Perf. 12½	
199	A24	1t gray vio & grn	10.50	1.60
200	A24	2t car & org red	25.00	4.75
201	A24	3t ol grn & bl	42.50	22.50
202	A24	5t dl vio & ol grn	62.50	16.00
203	A24	10t red & ol bis	275.00	19.00
204	A24	20t gray bl & brn	300.00	62.50
		Nos. 199-204 (6)	715.50	126.35

This issue was intended to commemorate
the fifteenth year of the reign of King
Vajiravudh. Because of the King's death the
stamps were issued as ordinary postage
stamps.

Nos. 195 and 150 with Surcharge
similar to 1914-15 Issue in Black or
Red

1928, Jan.
205	A23	5s on 15s car	3.75	1.75
206	A21	10s on 28s choc (R)	8.75	.60

King Prajadhipok
A25   A26

1928
		Engr.	Perf. 12½	
207	A25	2s deep red brown	.60	.20
208	A25	3s deep green	.75	.20
209	A25	3s dark violet	.60	.20
210	A25	10s deep rose	.75	.20
211	A25	15s dark blue	.90	.40
212	A25	25s black & org	3.50	.60
213	A25	50s brn org & blk	1.75	1.25
214	A25	80s blue & black	3.00	.80
215	A26	1b dk blue & blk	6.00	1.25
216	A26	2b car rose & blk brn	10.50	2.00
217	A26	3b yellow grn & blk	9.00	3.00

219	A26	5b dp vio & gray blk	18.00	4.00
220	A26	10b ol grn & red vio	35.00	8.25
221	A26	20b Prus grn & brn	75.00	14.00
222	A26	40b dk grn & ol brn	140.00	45.00
		Nos. 207-222 (15)	305.35	81.35
		Set, never hinged	400.00	

On the single colored stamps, type A25, the
lines in the background are uniform; those of
the bicolored values are shaded and do not
extend to the frame.

Issue dates: 5s, 10s, 2b-40b, Apr. 15; 2s,
3s, 15s, 25s, 50s, May 1; 1b, June 1; 80s, Nov.
15.

For overprints & surcharge see #300-301,
B34.

Nos. 142, 144
Surcharged in Red or
Blue   25 SATANG

1930
			Perf. 14	
223	A20	10s on 12s	6.00	1.00
224	A20	25s on 28s (Bl)	30.00	1.50
		Set, never hinged	37.50	

King Prajadhipok and Chao P'ya
Chakri

A27   A28

Statue of Chao P'ya
Chakri — A29

1932, Apr. 1
		Engr.	Perf. 12½	
225	A27	2s dark brown	1.00	.25
226	A27	3s deep green	2.00	.40
227	A27	5s dull violet	1.25	.25
228	A28	10s red brn & blk	2.00	.25
229	A28	15s dull blue & blk	7.75	.95
230	A28	25s violet & black	11.00	1.40
231	A28	50s claret & black	50.00	3.50
232	A29	1b blue black	75.00	11.00
		Nos. 225-232 (8)	150.00	18.00
		Set, never hinged	225.00	

150th anniv. of the Chakri dynasty, the
founding of Bangkok in 1782, and the opening
of the memorial bridge across the Chao
Phraya River.

Assembly
Hall,
Bangkok
A30

1939, June 24
		Litho.	Perf. 11, 12	
233	A30	2s dull red brown	3.25	1.00
234	A30	3s green	6.75	2.25
235	A30	3s dark violet	3.25	.20
236	A30	10s carmine	13.50	.20
237	A30	15s dark blue	32.50	1.00
		Nos. 233-237 (5)	59.25	4.65
		Set, never hinged	70.00	

7th anniv. of the Siamese Constitution.

Chakri Palace,
Bangkok — A31

1940
		Typo.	Perf. 12½	
238	A31	2s dull brown	3.25	1.00
239	A31	3s dp yellow grn	6.25	2.25
a.		Cliché of 5s in plate of 3s	900.00	725.00
240	A31	5s dark violet	4.75	.20
241	A31	10s carmine	17.50	.20
242	A31	15s dark blue	37.50	1.00
		Nos. 238-242 (5)	69.25	4.65
		Set, never hinged	90.00	

Issued: 2s, 3s, 5/13; 5s, 5/24; 15s, 5/28;
10s, 5/30.

King Ananda
Mahidol — A32

Plowing Rice
Field — A33

Royal Pavilion
at Bang-pa-in
A34

King Ananda
Mahidol
A35

1941, Apr. 17   Engr.

243	A32	2s brown	.40	.25
244	A32	3s deep green	.40	.40
245	A32	5s violet	.40	.25
246	A32	10s dark red	.40	.25
247	A33	15s dp bl & gray blk	.55	.25
248	A33	25s slate & org	.70	.40
249	A33	50s red org & gray	.80	.40
250	A34	1b brt ultra & gray	7.75	.90
251	A34	2b dk car rose & gray	14.00	2.00
252	A34	3b dp grn & gray	17.50	4.25
253	A34	5b blk & rose red	42.50	17.00
a.		Horiz. pair, imperf. btwn.		
254	A34	10b ol blk & yel	65.00	42.50
		Nos. 243-254 (12)	150.40	68.85
		Set, never hinged	225.00	

1943, May 1   Unwmk.   Perf. 11

255	A35	1b dark blue	17.50	1.60
a.		Horiz. pair, imperf. btwn.	85.00	85.00
b.		Vert. pair, imperf. btwn.	85.00	85.00

See No. 274.

Indo-China
War
Monument
A36

Bangkhaen
Monument
A37

1943   Engr.   Perf. 11, 12½

256	A36	3s dark green	17.50	17.50

Litho.
Perf. 12½x11

257	A36	3s dull green	3.00	1.00

Issue dates: #256, June 1. #257, Nov. 2.

1943, Nov. 25   Perf. 12½, 12½x11

Two types of 10s:
I - Size 19½x24mm.
II - Size 20¾x25¼mm.

258	A37	2s brown orange	2.50	1.75
259	A37	10s car rose (I)	4.00	.60
a.		Type II	8.00	5.00

10th anniv. of the quelling of a counter-revolution led by a member of the royal family on Oct. 11, 1933.

Stamps of similar design, but with values in "cents," are listed under Malaya, Occupation Stamps. See Nos. 2N1-2N6.

King Bhumibol Adulyadej
A38   A39

1947, Dec. 5   Pin-perf. 12½x11

260	A38	5s orange	1.75	1.25
261	A38	10s olive ('48)	1.75	1.25
a.		10s light brown	70.00	70.00

262	A38	20s blue	7.00	1.25
263	A38	50s blue green	14.00	2.50
		Nos. 260-263 (4)	24.50	6.25

Coming of age of King Bhumibol Adulyadej. Issued with and without gum.

> **Catalogue values for unused stamps in this section, from this point to the end of the section, are for Never Hinged items.**

1947-49   Unwmk.   Engr.   Perf. 12½
Size: 20x25mm

264	A39	5s violet	.60	.20
265	A39	10s red	1.50	.20
266	A39	20s chocolate	.90	.20
267	A39	50s olive	1.50	.20

Size: 22x27mm

268	A39	1b vio & dp bl	9.25	.30
269	A39	2b ultra & green	20.00	1.10
270	A39	3b brn red & blk	30.00	2.25
271	A39	5b bl grn & brn red	72.50	4.25
272	A39	10b dk brn & pur	260.00	1.40
273	A39	20b blk & rose brn	300.00	5.75
		Nos. 264-273 (10)	696.25	15.85

Issued: 5s, 20s, 11/15/47; 10s, 50s, 1/3/49; 1b-20b, 11/1/48.
For surcharges see Nos. 302-303.

Type of 1943
Perf. 11½, 12½x11½

1948, Jan.   Litho.

274	A35	1b chalky blue	50.00	7.50
a.		Horiz. pair, imperf. btwn.	150.00	150.00
b.		Vert. pair, imperf. btwn.	150.00	150.00

King Bhumibol Adulyadej and
Palace
A40   A41

Perf. 12½

1950, May 5   Unwmk.   Engr.

275	A40	5s red violet	.55	.20
276	A40	10s red	.55	.25
277	A40	15s purple	2.75	2.75
278	A40	20s chocolate	.90	.20
279	A40	80s green	7.25	3.50
280	A40	1b deep blue	2.25	.25
281	A40	2b orange yellow	14.50	1.10
282	A40	3b gray	72.50	9.75
		Nos. 275-282 (8)	101.25	18.00

Coronation of Bhumibol Adulyadej as Rama IX, May 5, 1950.

1951-60   Perf. 12½, 13x12½

283	A41	5s rose lilac	.30	.20
284	A41	10s deep green	.30	.20
285	A41	15s red brown	.90	.20
285A	A41	20s chocolate	.90	.20
286	A41	25s carmine	.30	.20
287	A41	50s gray olive	.90	.20
288	A41	1b deep blue	1.25	.20
289	A41	1.15b deep blue	.30	.50
290	A41	1.25b orange brn	4.50	.35
291	A41	2b dull blue grn	5.50	.35
292	A41	3b gray	9.00	.50
293	A41	5b aqua & red	37.50	.75
294	A41	10b black brn & vio	275.00	1.75
295	A41	20b gray & olive	260.00	14.00
		Nos. 283-295 (14)	596.65	19.60

Issued: 25s, 2/15; 5s, 10s, 1b, 6/4; 2b, 3b, 12/1; 15s, 2/15/52; 1.15b, 9/1/53; 1.25b, 10/1/54; 5b, 10b, 20b, 2/1/55; 50s, 10/15/56; 20s, 1960.

United Nations
Day — A42

1951, Oct. 24

296	A42	25s ultramarine	3.50	2.50

Overprinted "1952" in Carmine

1952, Oct.

297	A42	25s ultramarine	2.50	2.00

Overprinted "1953" in Carmine

1953, Oct.

298	A42	25s ultramarine	1.50	1.10

Overprinted "1954" in Carmine

1954, Oct. 24

299	A42	25s ultramarine	4.50	3.50
		Nos. 296-299 (4)	12.00	9.10

For more overprints see Nos. 315, 320.

Nos. 209 and 210
Overprinted in Black

1955, Jan. 4   Perf. 12½

300	A25	5s dark violet	8.50	7.50
301	A25	10s deep rose	8.50	7.50

No. 266 Surcharged with New Value in Black or Carmine

302	A39	5s on 20s choc	2.00	.75
303	A39	10s on 20s choc (C)	3.00	.75
		Nos. 300-303 (4)	22.00	16.50

King Naresuan
(1555-1605), on
War
Elephant — A43

Tao
Suranari — A44

Perf. 13½

1955, Feb. 15   Unwmk.   Engr.

304	A43	25s brt carmine	1.50	.20
305	A43	80s rose violet	17.50	4.75
306	A43	1.25b dark olive grn	47.50	1.60
307	A43	2b deep blue	11.00	1.25
308	A43	3b henna brown	32.50	1.10
		Nos. 304-308 (5)	110.00	8.90

1955, Apr. 15   Perf. 12x13½

309	A44	10s purple	2.10	.40
310	A44	25s emerald	1.40	.20
311	A44	1b brown	35.00	2.40
		Nos. 309-311 (3)	38.50	3.00

Lady Mo, called Tao Suranari (Brave Woman) for her role in stopping an 1826 rebellion.

King Taksin
Statue at
Thonburi
A45

Don Jedi
Monument
A46

1955, May 1   Perf. 12½x12

312	A45	5s violet blue	1.00	.30
313	A45	25s Prus green	10.00	.20
314	A45	1.25b red	29.00	2.50
		Nos. 312-314 (3)	40.00	3.00

King Somdech P'ya Chao Taksin (1734-1782).

No. 296 Overprinted "1955" in Red

1955, Oct. 24   Perf. 12½

315	A42	25s ultramarine	4.00	3.00

United Nations Day, Oct. 24, 1955.

1956, Feb. 1   Perf. 13½x13

316	A46	10s emerald	3.25	2.50
317	A46	50s reddish brown	16.00	1.00
318	A46	75s violet	5.00	.75
319	A46	1.50b brown orange	20.00	1.25
		Nos. 316-319 (4)	44.25	5.50

No. 296 Overprinted "1956" in Red Violet

1956, Oct. 24

320	A42	25s ultramarine	1.75	1.60

United Nations Day, Oct. 24, 1956.

Dharmachakra and
Deer — A47

20s, 25s, 50s, Hand of peace and Dharmachakra. 1b, 1.25b, 2b, Pagoda of Nakon Phatom.

Wmk. 329

1957, May 13   Photo.   Perf. 13½

321	A47	5s dark brown	.65	.20
322	A47	10s rose lake	.65	.20
323	A47	15s brt green	1.60	1.25
324	A47	20s orange	1.60	1.25
325	A47	25s reddish brown	.35	.20
326	A47	50s magenta	1.40	.40
327	A47	1b olive brown	2.00	.50
328	A47	1.25b slate blue	27.50	5.25
329	A47	2b deep claret	5.00	.75
		Nos. 321-329 (9)	40.75	10.00

2500th anniversary of birth of Buddha.

UN Day — A48

Thai
Archway — A49

1957, Oct. 24   Perf. 13½

330	A48	25s olive	.80	.30
331	A48	25s bright ocher ('58)	.80	.30
332	A48	25s indigo ('59)	.90	.30
		Nos. 330-332 (3)	2.50	.90

Issued: Oct. 24.

1959, Oct. 15   Photo.   Perf. 13½

Designs (inscribed "SEAP Games 1959"): 25s, Royal tiered umbrellas. 1.25b, Thai archer, ancient costume. 2b, Wat Arun pagoda and prow of royal barge.

333	A49	10s orange	.30	.20
334	A49	25s dk carmine rose	.45	.20
335	A49	1.25b bright green	3.00	1.00
336	A49	2b light blue	3.25	.60
		Nos. 333-336 (4)	7.00	2.00

Issued to publicize the South-East Asia Peninsula Games, Bangkok, Dec. 12-17.

Wat Arun, WRY
Emblem — A50

Wat Arun,
Bangkok — A51

1960, Apr. 7

337	A50	50s chocolate	.30	.20
338	A50	2b yellow green	1.50	.50

WRY, July 1, 1959-June 30, 1960.

1960, Aug.   Wmk. 329   Perf. 13½

339	A51	50s carmine rose	.40	.20
340	A51	2b ultramarine	3.50	.90

Anti-leprosy campaign.

Elephants in Teak Forest — A52

Globe and SEATO Emblem — A53

1960, Aug. 29   Photo.   Perf. 13½
341 A52 25s emerald   1.00   .20
   5th World Forestry Cong., Seattle, WA, Aug. 29-Sept. 10.

1960, Sept. 8
342 A53 50s chocolate   1.10   .20
   SEATO Day, Sept. 8.

Siamese Child — A54

Hand with Pen and Globe — A55

1960, Oct. 3   Wmk. 329
343 A54 50s magenta   .60   .20
344 A54 1b orange   5.00   .75
   Children's Day, 1960.

1960, Oct. 3
345 A55 50s carmine rose   .60   .20
346 A55 2b blue   5.00   .90
   Intl. Letter Writing Week, Oct. 3-9.

UN Emblem and Globe A56

King Bhumibol Adulyadej A57

1960, Oct. 24   Perf. 13½
347 A56 50s purple   1.00   .25
   15th anniversary of the United Nations.
   See Nos. 369, 390.

		Perf. 13½x13		
1961-68		**Engr.**	**Wmk. 334**	
348	A57	5s rose cl ('62)	.20	.20
349	A57	10s green ('62)	.20	.20
350	A57	15s red brn ('62)	.35	.20
351	A57	20s brown ('62)	.20	.20
352	A57	25s carmine ('63)	.35	.20
353	A57	50s olive ('62)	.35	.20
354	A57	80s orange ('62)	1.60	1.00
355	A57	1b vio bl & brn	1.10	.20
355A	A57	1.25b red & citron ('65)	3.25	1.25
356	A57	1.50b dk vio & yel green	1.00	.35
357	A57	2b red & violet	1.40	.20
358	A57	3b brn & bl	3.25	.35
358A	A57	4b olive bis & blk ('68)	3.25	1.40
359	A57	5b blue & green	15.00	.45
360	A57	10b red org & blk	80.00	.70
361	A57	20b emer & ultra	67.50	3.50
362	A57	25b green & blue	21.00	1.75
362A	A57	40b yellow & blk ('65)	67.50	4.50
		Nos. 348-362A (18)	267.50	16.85
   For overprint see No. 588.

Children in Garden — A58

Pen and Envelope with Map — A59

Wmk. 329
1961, Oct. 2   Photo.   Perf. 13½
363 A58 20s indigo   .60   .25
364 A58 2b purple   3.75   .70
   Issued for Children's Day.

1961, Oct. 9
1b, 2b, Pen and letters circling globe.

365 A59 25s gray green   .45   .20
366 A59 50s rose lilac   .25   .20
367 A59 1b bright rose   1.40   .40
368 A59 2b ultramarine   1.90   .45
   Nos. 365-368 (4)   4.00 1.25
   Intl. Letter Writing Week, Oct. 2-8.

UN Type of 1960
1961, Oct. 24 Wmk. 329 Perf. 13½
369 A56 50s maroon   .70   .25
   Issued for United Nations Day, Oct. 24.

Scout Emblem — A60

Scouts Saluting and Tents — A61

Design: 2b, King Vajiravudh and Scouts.

1961, Nov. 1   Photo.
370 A60 50s carmine rose   .25   .20
371 A61 1b bright green   1.25   .40
372 A61 2b bright blue   1.50   .50
   Nos. 370-372 (3)   3.00 1.10
   Thai Boy Scouts, 50th anniversary.

Malaria Eradication Emblem and Siamese Designs
A62   A63

1962, Apr. 7   Wmk. 329   Perf. 13
373 A62 5s orange brown   .30   .20
374 A62 10s sepia   .30   .20
375 A62 20s blue   .30   .20
376 A62 50s carmine rose   .30   .20
377 A63 1b green   1.10   .25
378 A63 1.50b dk car rose   2.00   .50
379 A63 2d dark blue   1.40   .35
380 A63 3b violet   4.25 2.25
   Nos. 373-380 (8)   9.95 4.15
   WHO drive to eradicate malaria.

View of Bangkok and Seattle Fair Emblem A64

1962, Apr. 21   Wmk. 329
381 A64 50s red lilac   .60   .20
382 A64 2b deep blue   6.00   .75
   "Century 21" Intl. Expo., Seattle, WA, Apr. 21-Oct. 12.

Mother and Child A65

Globe, Letters, Carrier Pigeons A66

Wmk. 329
1962, Oct. 1   Photo.   Perf. 13
383 A65 25s lt blue green   .60   .30
384 A65 50s bister brown   .65   .20
385 A65 2b bright pink   5.75   .75
   Nos. 383-385 (3)   7.00 1.25
   Issued for Children's Day.

1962, Oct. 8
Design: 1b, 2b, Quill pen and scroll.

386 A66 25s violet   .65   .30
387 A66 50s red   .35   .20
388 A66 1b lemon   3.25   .60
389 A66 2b lt bluish green 5.50   .65
   Nos. 386-389 (4)   9.75 1.75
   Intl. Letter Writing Week, Oct. 7-13.

UN Type of 1960
1962, Oct. 24   Perf. 13½
390 A56 50s carmine rose   .70   .25
   United Nations Day, Oct. 24.

Exhibition Emblem — A67

Temple Lion — A69

Woman Harvesting Rice — A68

1962, Nov. 1   Unwmk.
391 A67 50s olive bister   1.00   .20
   Students' Exhibition, Bangkok.

Wmk. 334
1963, Mar. 21   Engr.   Perf. 14
392 A68 20s green   1.25   .45
393 A68 50s ocher   1.00   .25
   FAO "Freedom from Hunger" campaign.

1963, Apr. 1   Wmk. 329   Perf. 13½
394 A69 50s green & bister 1.00   .20
   1st anniv. of the formation of the Asian-Oceanic Postal Union, AOPU.

New and Old Post and Telegraph Buildings — A70

Wmk. 334
1963, Aug. 4   Engr.   Perf. 14
395 A70 50s org, bluish blk & grn .75   .25
396 A70 3b grn, dk red & brn   6.25 1.50
   80th anniv. of the Post and Telegraph Dept.

King Bhumibol Adulyadej A71

Child with Dolls A72

		Perf. 13x13½		
1963-71		**Wmk. 329**	**Photo.**	
397	A71	5s dk car rose	.20	.20
398	A71	10s dark green	.20	.20
399	A71	15s red brown	.20	.20
400	A71	20s black brown	.20	.20
401	A71	25s carmine	.20	.20
402	A71	50s olive gray	.20	.20
402A	A71	75s brt vio ('71)	.40	.20
403	A71	80s dull orange	1.10	.45
404	A71	1b dk bl & dk brn	1.10	.20
404A	A71	1.25b org brn & ol ('65)	5.75	1.00
405	A71	1.50b vio bl & grn	1.10	.50
406	A71	2b dk red & vio	.75	.25
407	A71	3b brn & dk bl	1.90	.25
407A	A71	4b dp bis & blk ('68)	2.25	.25
408	A71	5b blue & green	13.00	.25
409	A71	10b orange & blk	22.50	.50
410	A71	20b brt grn & ind	110.00	3.75
411	A71	25b dk grn & bl	5.75	.50
411A	A71	40b yel & blk ('65)	140.00	4.50
		Nos. 397-411A (19)	306.80	13.75
   Nos. 397-403 were issued in 1963; Nos. 404, 405-407, 408-411 in 1964.
   For overprint see No. 589.

1963, Oct. 7   Litho.   Perf. 13½
412 A72 50s rose red   1.60   .25
413 A72 2b dull blue   5.25   .75
   Issued for Children's Day.

Garuda Carrying Letter — A73

Design: 2b, 3b, Thai women writing letters.

1963, Oct. 7   Wmk. 329
414 A73 50s lt blue & claret 1.00   .20
415 A73 1b lt grn & vio brn   4.75   .80
416 A73 2b yel brn & turq bl 27.50 1.00
417 A73 3b org brn & yel grn 10.00 3.00
   Nos. 414-417 (4)   43.25 5.00
   Intl. Letter Writing Week, Oct. 6-12.

UN Emblem — A74

UNICEF Emblem — A76

King Bhumibol Adulyadej — A75

1963, Oct. 24   Wmk. 329   Perf. 13½
418 A74 50s bright blue   .70   .20
   United Nations Day, Oct. 24.

1963, Dec. 5   Photo.   Perf. 13½
419 A75 1.50b blue, org & ind   4.00   .50
420 A75 5b brt lil rose, org & blk 21.00 2.50
   King Bhumibol's 36th birthday.

1964, Jan. 13   **Litho.**
421 A76 50s blue   .50 .20
422 A76 2b olive green   3.50 .45
     17th anniv. of UNICEF.

Hand (flags), Pigeon and Globe — A77

Designs: 1b, Girls and world map. 2b, Pen, pencil and unfolded world map. 3b, Globe and hand holding quill.

1964, Oct. 5   **Wmk. 329**   **Perf. 13½**
423 A77 50s lilac & lt grn   .25 .20
424 A77 1b red brown & grn   4.50 .80
425 A77 2b yellow & vio bl   11.50 1.00
426 A77 3b blue & dk brown   6.25 2.50
    Nos. 423-426 (4)   22.50 4.50
   Intl. Letter Writing Week, Oct. 5-11.

UN Emblem and Globe — A78   King and Queen — A79

1964, Oct. 24   **Photo.**   **Perf. 13½**
427 A78 50s gray   1.25 .20
    United Nations Day, Oct. 24.

1965, Apr. 28   Wmk. 329   Perf. 13½
428 A79 2b brown & multi   11.00 .40
429 A79 5b violet & multi   21.00 2.00
15th wedding anniversary of King Bhumibol Adulyadej and Queen Sirikit.

ITU Emblem, Old and New Communications Equipment — A80

1965, May 17   **Photo.**
430 A80 1b bright green   4.50 .50
     Cent. of the ITU.

World Map, Letters and Goddess — A81

2b, 3b, World map, letters and handshake.

1965, Oct. 3   Wmk. 329   Perf. 13½
431 A81 50s dp plum, gray & sal   .25 .25
432 A81 1b dk vio bl, lt vio & yel   2.75 .60
433 A81 2b dk gray, bis & dp org   11.00 .60
434 A81 3b multicolored   16.00 2.75
   Nos. 431-434 (4)   30.00 4.20
   Intl. Letter Writing Week, Oct. 3-9.

A82   A83

Gates of Royal Chapel of Emerald Buddha.

Engr. & Litho.
Perf. 13½x14
1965, Oct. 24   **Wmk. 356**
435 A82 50s slate grn, bl & ocher   1.50 .20
   International Cooperation Year, 1965.

Wmk. 329
1965, Nov. 1   **Litho.**   **Perf. 13½**
Map of Thailand and UPU monument, Bern.
436 A83 20s dk blue & lilac   .50 .20
437 A83 50s gray & blue   1.75 .20
438 A83 1b orange brn & vio bl   4.25 .35
439 A83 3b green & bister   11.50 2.25
   Nos. 436-439 (4)   18.00 3.00
80th anniv. of Thailand's admission to the UPU.

Lotus Blossom and Child — A84

Design: 1b, Boy with book walking up steps.

1966, Jan. 8   Wmk. 334   Perf. 13½
440 A84 50s henna brn & blk   .30 .20
441 A84 1b green & black   3.25 .60
   Issued for Children's Day, 1966.

Bicycling — A85

1966, Aug. 4   **Photo.**   **Wmk. 329**
442 A85 20s shown   .60 .20
443 A85 25s Tennis   .90 .30
444 A85 50s Running   .60 .20
445 A85 1b Weight lifting   2.50 .60
446 A85 1.25b Boxing   3.75 2.50
447 A85 2b Swimming   7.00 .45
448 A85 3b Netball   15.00 3.50
449 A85 5b Soccer   37.50 12.50
   Nos. 442-449 (8)   67.85 20.25
    5th Asian Games, Bangkok.

Trade Fair Emblem and Temple of Dawn — A86

1966, Sept. 1   **Litho.**   **Perf. 13½**
450 A86 50s lilac   1.10 .40
451 A86 1b brown red   2.40 .75
   1st Intl. Asian Trade Fair, Bangkok.

Letter Writer A87

Design: 50s, 1b, Letters, maps and pen.

1966, Oct. 3   **Photo.**   **Wmk. 329**
452 A87 50s scarlet   .30 .20
453 A87 1b orange brown   1.90 .60
454 A87 2b brt violet   9.50 .60
455 A87 3b brt blue grn   6.00 2.25
   Nos. 452-455 (4)   17.70 3.65
   Intl. Letter Writing Week, Oct. 6-12.

UN Emblem — A88   Pra Buddha Bata Monastery, UNESCO Emblem — A90

Rice Field A89

Wmk. 334
1966, Oct. 24   **Litho.**   **Perf. 13½**
456 A88 50s ultramarine   1.00 .20
    United Nations Day, Oct. 24.

1966, Nov. 1   **Engr.**   **Wmk. 329**
457 A89 50s dp bl & grnsh bl   1.50 .60
458 A89 3b plum & pink   13.50 4.00
   Intl. Rice Year under sponsorship of the FAO.

1966, Nov. 4   **Photo.**   **Wmk. 329**
459 A90 50s black & yel grn   .70 .20
    20th anniv. of UNESCO.

Thai Boxing A91

Designs: 1b, Takraw (three men playing ball). 2b, Kite fighting. 3b, Cudgel play.

1966, Dec. 9   Wmk. 329   Perf. 13½
460 A91 50s black, brn & red   1.25 .25
461 A91 1b black, brn & red   4.00 1.50
462 A91 2b black, brn & red   22.50 3.50
463 A91 3b black, brn & red   20.00 10.50
   Nos. 460-463 (4)   47.75 15.75
     5th Asian Games.

Snakehead — A92

Pigmy Mackerel — A93

Fish: 3b, Barb. 5b, Siamese fighting fish.

1967, Jan. 1   **Photo.**
464 A92 1b brt blue & multi   5.00 1.50
465 A93 2b multicolored   25.00 2.50
466 A93 3b yel grn & multi   12.50 7.00
467 A92 5b pale grn & multi   15.00 8.00
   Nos. 464-467 (4)   57.50 19.00

Dharmachakra, Globe and Temples — A94

Wmk. 329
1967, Jan. 15   **Litho.**   **Perf. 13½**
468 A94 2b black & yellow   4.00 .70
Establishment of the headquarters of the World Fellowship of Buddhists in Thailand.

Great Hornbill A95   Ascocentrum Curvifolium A96

Birds: 25s, Hill myna. 50s, White-rumped shama. 1b, Diard's fireback pheasant. 1.50b, Spotted dove. 2b, Sarus crane. 3b, White-breasted kingfisher. 5b, Asiatic open-bill (stork).

1967, Feb. 1   **Photo.**
469 A95 20s tan & multi   .70 .60
470 A95 25s lt gray & multi   1.00 .90
471 A95 50s yel grn & multi   1.75 .30
472 A95 1b olive & multi   4.25 1.25
473 A95 1.50b dull yel & multi   4.25 1.50
474 A95 2b pale sal & multi   22.50 1.50
475 A95 3b gray & multi   12.00 7.75
476 A95 5b multicolored   22.50 7.75
   Nos. 469-476 (8)   68.95 21.55

1967, Apr. 1   Wmk. 329   Perf. 13½
Orchids: 20s, Vandopsis parishii. 80s, Rhynchostylis retusa. 1b, Rhynchostylus gigantea. 1.50b, Dendrobium falconerii. 2b, Paphiopedilum callosum. 3b, Dendrobium formosum. 5b, Dendrobium primulinum.
477 A96 20s black & multi   .50 .45
478 A96 50s brt blue & multi   1.00 .30
479 A96 80s black & multi   1.75 1.40
480 A96 1b blue & multi   5.25 1.25
481 A96 1.50b black & multi   3.50 1.25
482 A96 2b ver & multi   19.00 1.50
483 A96 3b brown & multi   12.50 7.75
484 A96 5b multicolored   19.00 6.25
   Nos. 477-484 (8)   62.50 20.15

Thai Architecture — A97

1967, Apr. 6   **Engr.**
485 A97 50s Mansion   1.40 .40
486 A97 1.50b Pagodas   4.00 1.50
487 A97 2b Bell tower   16.00 1.50
488 A97 3b Temple   11.00 5.00
   Nos. 485-488 (4)   32.40 8.40

Grand Palace and Royal Barge on Chao Phraya River — A98

1967, Sept. 15   Wmk. 329   Perf. 13½
489 A98 2b ultra & sepia   5.25 1.00
    International Tourist Year, 1967.

Globe, Dove, People and Letters — A99

2b, 3b, Clasped hands, globe and doves.

1967, Oct. 8   **Photo.**
490	A99	50s dk blue & multi	.85	.20
491	A99	1b multicolored	2.00	.60
492	A99	2b brt yel grn & blk	5.00	.75
493	A99	3b brown & blk	8.00	3.00
		Nos. 490-493 (4)	15.85	4.55

Intl. Letter Writing Week, Oct. 6-12.

UN Emblem — A100

1967, Oct. 24   **Wmk. 329**   **Perf. 13½**
| 494 | A100 | 50s multicolored | .70 | .20 |

Issued for United Nations Day, Oct. 24.

Flag and Map of Thailand — A101

1967, Dec. 5   **Photo.**   **Perf. 13½**
| 495 | A101 | 50s greenish blue, red & vio bl | .75 | .20 |
| 496 | A101 | 2b ol gray, red & vio bl | 5.75 | 1.25 |

50th anniversary of the flag.

Elephant Carrying Teakwood — A102

1968, Mar. 1   **Engr.**   **Wmk. 329**
| 497 | A102 | 2b rose claret & gray ol | 3.75 | .75 |

See Nos. 537, 566.

Syncom Satellite over Thai Tracking Station — A103

1968, Apr. 1   **Photo.**   **Perf. 13**
| 498 | A103 | 50s multicolored | .50 | .20 |
| 499 | A103 | 3b multicolored | 3.00 | 1.25 |

Earth Goddess — A104

1968, May 1   **Wmk. 329**   **Perf. 13**
| 500 | A104 | 50s blk, gold, red & bl grn | .70 | .20 |

Hydrological Decade (UNESCO), 1965-74.

Snake-skinned Gourami — A105

Fish: 20s, Red-tailed black "shark." 25s, Tor tambroides. 50s, Pangasius sanitwongsei. 80s, Bagrid catfish. 1.25b, Vaimosa rambaiae. 1.50b, Catlocarpio siamensis. 4b, Featherback.

1968, June 1   **Photo.**   **Perf. 13**
501	A105	10s multicolored	.30	.20
502	A105	20s multicolored	.30	.20
503	A105	25s multicolored	.65	.35
504	A105	50s multicolored	.95	.20
505	A105	80s multicolored	2.50	1.50
506	A105	1.25b multicolored	4.75	3.25
507	A105	1.50b multicolored	16.00	2.75
508	A105	4b multicolored	37.50	17.00
		Nos. 501-508 (8)	62.95	25.45

Arcturus Butterfly — A106

Various butterflies.

1968, July 1   **Wmk. 329**   **Perf. 13**
509	A106	50s lt blue & multi	5.00	.30
510	A106	1b multicolored	7.75	1.25
511	A106	3b multicolored	15.00	6.25
512	A106	4b buff & multi	22.50	9.25
		Nos. 509-512 (4)	50.25	17.05

Queen Sirikit — A107

Designs: Various portraits of Queen Sirikit.

Photogravure and Engraved
Perf. 13½x14
1968, Aug. 12   **Wmk. 334**
513	A107	50s gold & multi	.55	.20
514	A107	2b gold & multi	2.10	.85
515	A107	3b gold & multi	5.50	2.50
516	A107	5b gold & multi	11.00	2.75
		Nos. 513-516 (4)	19.15	6.30

Queen Sirikit's 36th birthday, or third 12-year "cycle."

Globe, Pen and Envelope — A109

1b, 3b, Pen nib, envelope and globe.

1968, Oct. 6   **Wmk. 329**   **Perf. 13½**
518	A109	50s brown & multi	.25	.20
519	A109	1b pale brown & multi	1.25	.25
520	A109	2b multicolored	2.75	.40
521	A109	3b violet & multi	5.75	1.60
		Nos. 518-521 (4)	10.00	2.45

Intl. Letter Writing Week, Oct. 7-13.

UN Emblem and Flags — A110   King Rama II — A112

Human Rights Flame and Bas-relief — A111

1968, Oct. 24
| 522 | A110 | 50s multicolored | .70 | .20 |

Issued for United Nations Day.

1968, Dec. 10   **Photo.**   **Perf. 13½**
| 523 | A111 | 50s sl grn, red & vio | .85 | .20 |

International Human Rights Year.

1968, Dec. 30   **Engr.**   **Wmk. 329**
| 524 | A112 | 50s sepia & bister | .70 | .20 |

Rama II (1768-1824), who reigned 1809-24.

National Assembly Building — A113

Photogravure and Engraved
1969, Feb. 10   **Wmk. 329**   **Perf. 13½**
| 525 | A113 | 50s multicolored | .80 | .20 |
| 526 | A113 | 2b multicolored | 3.00 | .60 |

First constitutional election day.

ILO Emblem and Cogwheels — A114

1969, May 1   **Photo.**   **Perf. 13½**
| 527 | A114 | 50s rose vio & dk bl | .50 | .20 |

50th anniv. of the ILO.

Ramwong Dance — A115

Designs: 1b, Candle dance. 2b, Krathop Mai dance. 3b, Nohra dance.

1969, July 15   **Wmk. 329**   **Perf. 13**
528	A115	50s multicolored	.30	.20
529	A115	1b multicolored	1.10	.50
530	A115	2b multicolored	2.50	.35
531	A115	3b multicolored	4.50	1.50
		Nos. 528-531 (4)	8.40	2.55

Posting and Receiving Letters — A116

Design: 2b, 3b, Writing and posting letters.

1969, Oct. 5   **Photo.**   **Wmk. 334**
532	A116	50s multicolored	.25	.20
533	A116	1b multicolored	.80	.35
534	A116	2b multicolored	1.60	.50
535	A116	3b multicolored	2.75	1.25
		Nos. 532-535 (4)	5.40	2.30

International Letter Writing Week.

Hand Holding Globe — A117

1969, Oct. 24   **Wmk. 329**   **Perf. 13**
| 536 | A117 | 50s multicolored | .60 | .20 |

Issued for United Nations Day.

Teakwood Type of 1968
1969, Nov. 18   **Engr.**   **Perf. 13½**
| 537 | A102 | 2b Tin mine | 3.75 | .40 |

Issued to publicize tin export, and the 2nd Technical Conf. of the Intl. Tin Council, Bangkok.

Loy Krathong Festival — A118

Designs: 1b, Marriage ceremony. 2b, Khwan ceremony. 5b, Songkran festival.

1969, Nov. 23   **Photo.**   **Wmk. 329**
538	A118	50s gray & multi	.30	.20
539	A118	1b multicolored	.85	.30
540	A118	2b multicolored	1.10	.40
541	A118	5b multicolored	4.00	1.40
		Nos. 538-541 (4)	6.25	2.30

Biplane, Mailmen and Map of First Thai Airmail Flight, 1919 — A119

1969, Dec. 10   **Engr.**   **Perf. 13½**
| 542 | A119 | 1b multicolored | 1.10 | .25 |

50th anniversary of Thai airmail service.

Shadow Play — A120

Photogravure and Engraved
1969, Dec. 18   **Wmk. 329**
543	A120	50s Phra Rama	.25	.20
544	A120	2b Ramasura	3.25	.30
545	A120	3b Mekhala	2.75	1.10
546	A120	5b Ongkhot	3.75	1.40
	Nos. 543-546 (4)		10.00	3.00

Symbols of Agriculture, Industry and Shipping — A121

1970, Jan. 1   **Photo.**
547	A121	50s multicolored	.60	.20

Productivity Year 1970.

World Map, Thai Temples and Emblem — A122

1970, Jan. 31   **Litho.**
548	A122	50s brt blue & blk	.70	.20

19th triennial meeting of the Intl. Council of Women, Bangkok.

Earth Station Radar and Satellite — A123

Perf. 14½x15
1970, Apr. 1   **Litho.**   **Wmk. 356**
549	A123	50s multicolored	.55	.20

Communication by satellite.

Household and Population Statistics — A124

Perf. 13x13½
1970, Apr. 1   **Photo.**   **Wmk. 329**
550	A124	1b multicolored	.65	.20

Issued to publicize the 1970 census.

Inauguration of New UPU Headquarters, Bern — A125

Lithographed and Engraved
1970, June 15   **Wmk. 334**   **Perf. 13½**
551	A125	50s lt bl, lt grn & grn	.55	.20

Khun Ram Kamhang Teaching (Mural) — A126

1970, July 1   **Litho.**
552	A126	50s black & multi	.60	.20

Issued for International Education Year.

Swimming Stadium — A127

1.50b, Velodrome. 3b, Subhajalasaya Stadium. 5b, Kittikachorn Indoor Stadium.

Lithographed and Engraved
1970, Sept. 1   **Wmk. 329**   **Perf. 13½**
553	A127	50s yellow, red & pur	.40	.20
554	A127	1.50b ultra, grn & dk red	.90	.40
555	A127	3b gold, black & dk red	1.25	.55
556	A127	5b brt grn, ultra & dk red	2.75	.85
	Nos. 553-556 (4)		5.30	2.00

6th Asian Games, Bangkok.

Children Writing Letters — A128

Designs: 1b, Woman writing letter. 2b, Two women reading letters. 3b, Man reading letter.

1970, Oct. 4   **Photo.**   **Perf. 13½**
557	A128	50s black & multi	.35	.20
558	A128	1b black & multi	.90	.35
559	A128	2b black & multi	2.00	.35
560	A128	3b black & multi	2.75	1.10
	Nos. 557-560 (4)		6.00	2.00

Intl. Letter Writing Week, Oct. 6-12.

Royal Palace, Bangkok, and UN Emblem — A129

1970, Oct. 24   **Photo.**   **Perf. 13½**
561	A129	50s multicolored	.90	.20

25th anniversary of the United Nations.

Heroes of Bangrachan — A130

1b, Monument to Thao Thepkrasatri & Thao Srisunthorn. 2b, Queen Suriyothai riding elephant. 3b, Phraya Phichaidaphak and battle scene.

1970, Oct. 25   **Engr.**   **Perf. 13½**
562	A130	50s pink & violet	.30	.20
563	A130	1b violet & maroon	.90	.60
564	A130	2b rose & brown	3.00	.75
565	A130	3b blue & green	2.50	.90
	Nos. 562-565 (4)		6.70	2.45

Heroes from Thai history.

Teakwood Type of 1968
1970, Nov. 1   **Engr.**
566	A102	2b Rubber plantation	2.50	.30

Issued to publicize rubber export.

King Bhumibol Lighting Flame — A131

1970, Dec. 9   **Photo.**   **Wmk. 329**
567	A131	1b multicolored	1.00	.20

Opening of 6th Asian Games, Bangkok.

Woman Playing So Sam Sai — A132

Women Playing Classical Thai Musical Instruments: 2b, Khlui Phiang-O. 3b, Krachappi. 5b, Thon Rammana.

1970, Dec. 20
568	A132	50s multicolored	.40	.20
569	A132	2b multicolored	.95	.30
570	A132	3b multicolored	2.25	.65
571	A132	5b multicolored	4.25	1.10
	Nos. 568-571 (4)		7.85	2.25

Chocolate Point Siamese Cats — A133

Siamese Cats: 1b, Blue point. 2b, Seal point. 3b, Pure white cat and kittens.

Perf. 13½x14
1971, Mar. 15   **Litho.**   **Wmk. 356**
572	A133	50s multicolored	.40	.20
573	A133	1b multicolored	2.75	.50
574	A133	2b multicolored	4.50	.55
575	A133	3b multicolored	6.75	1.75
	Nos. 572-575 (4)		14.40	3.00

Muang Nakhon Temple — A134

Temples: 1b, Phanom. 3b, Pathom Chedi. 4b, Doi Suthep.

Lithographed and Engraved
1971, Mar. 30   **Wmk. 329**   **Perf. 13½**
576	A134	50s rose, black & brn	.45	.20
577	A134	1b emerald, bis & pur	.75	.30
578	A134	3b org, brn & dk brn	1.75	.40
579	A134	4b ultra, ocher & brn	3.50	2.10
	Nos. 576-579 (4)		6.45	3.00

Corn and Tractor in Field A135

1971, Apr. 20   **Engr.**   **Wmk. 329**
580	A135	2b multicolored	1.75	.30

Export promotion.

Buddha's Birthplace, Lumbini, Nepal — A136

Buddha's: 1b, Place of Enlightenment, Bihar. 2b, Place of first sermon, Benares. 3b, Place of death, Kusinara.

1971, May 9   **Engr.**   **Perf. 13½**
581	A136	50s violet blue & blk	.35	.20
582	A136	1b green & black	1.00	.30
583	A136	2b dull yellow & blk	2.40	.50
584	A136	3b red & black	2.40	1.00
	Nos. 581-584 (4)		6.15	2.00

20th anniv. of World Fellowship of Buddhists.

King Bhumibol and Subjects — A137

Floating Market — A138

Perf. 13½
1971, June 9   **Unwmk.**   **Litho.**
585	A137	50s silver & multi	1.25	.20

King Bhumibol's Silver Jubilee.

1971, June 20   **Photo.**   **Wmk. 329**
586	A138	4b gold & multi	2.00	.50

Visit Asia Year.

Boy Scouts Saluting — A139

1971, July 1   Litho.
587 A139 50s orange & multi   .95 .20
60th anniversary of Thai Boy Scouts.

Blocks of four of Nos. 354 and 403
Overprinted in Dark Blue

a

b

Perf. 13½x13
1971, Aug.   **Wmk. 334**   **Engr.**
588 A57 (a)   Block of 4   3.00 3.00
a.   80s orange, single stamp   .55 .55

Perf. 13x13½
Photo.   **Wmk. 329**
589 A71 (b)   Block of 4   3.00 3.00
a.   80s dull orange, single stamp .55 .55
THAILANDPEX '71, Philatelic Exhib., Aug.
4-8.

Woman Writing Letter — A140

Designs: 1b, Women reading mail. 2b,
Woman sitting on porch. 3b, Man handing letter to woman.

Wmk. 334
1971, Oct. 3   **Litho.**   **Perf. 13½**
590 A140 50s gray & multi   .60 .20
591 A140 1b red brown & multi   .80 .25
592 A140 2b ultra & multi   1.60 .50
593 A140 3b lt gray & multi   2.50 1.25
    Nos. 590-593 (4)   5.50 2.20

Intl. Letter Writing Week, Oct. 6-12.

Wat Benchamabopit (Marble Temple),
Bangkok — A141

Perf. 13½x14
1971, Oct. 24   **Litho.**   **Unwmk.**
594 A141 50s multicolored   .50 .20
United Nations Day, Oct. 24.

Duck Raising — A142

Rural occupations: 1b, Raising tobacco. 2b,
Fishermen. 3b, Rice winnowing.

Wmk. 329
1971, Nov. 15   **Photo.**   **Perf. 12½**
595 A142 50s lt blue & multi   .45 .20
596 A142 1b multicolored   .65 .30
597 A142 2b blue & multi   1.40 .40
598 A142 3b buff & multi   2.00 1.10
    Nos. 595-598 (4)   4.50 2.00

UNICEF Emblem, Mother and
Child — A143

1971, Dec. 11   Wmk. 334   Perf. 13½
599 A143 50s blue & multi   .50 .20
25th anniv. of UNICEF.

Thai Costumes, 17th Century — A144

Thai Costumes: 1b, 13th-14th cent. 1.50b,
14th-17th cent. 2b, 18th-19th cent.

Perf. 13½x14
1972, Jan. 12   **Litho.**   **Unwmk.**
600 A144   50s multicolored   .45 .20
601 A144   1b multicolored   .90 .25
602 A144   1.50b multicolored   1.75 .45
603 A144   2b blue & multi   2.25 .70
    Nos. 600-603 (4)   5.35 1.60

Globe
A145

Perf. 13x13½
1972, Apr. 1   Photo.   Wmk. 334
604 A145 75s violet blue   .50 .20
Asian-Oceanic Postal Union, 10th anniv.

King Bhumibol
Adulyadej — A146

Perf. 13½x13
1972-77   **Litho.**   **Wmk. 329**
Size: 21x26mm
605 A146 10s yellow green   .30 .20
606 A146 20s blue   .30 .20
607 A146 25s rose red   .30 .20
608 A146 75s lilac   .30 .20

Engr.
609 A146 1.25b yel grn &
              pink   1.25 .20
610 A146 2.75b red brn &
              blue grn   .55 .20
611 A146 3b brn & dk
              blue ('74)   2.50 .25
612 A146 4b blue & org
              red ('73)   1.25 .20
613 A146 5b dk vio & red
              brown   1.25 .35
614 A146 6b green & vio   2.50 .45
615 A146 10b ver & black   2.00 .65
616 A146 20b org & yel grn   4.00 1.10
617 A146 40b dp bis & lilac
              ('74)   32.50 3.25
618 A146 50b pur & brt grn
              ('77)   25.00 2.75
619 A146 100b dp org & dk
              bl ('77)   50.00 5.25
    Nos. 605-619 (15)   124.00 15.45
    See Nos. 835-838, 907-908.

Iko Women — A147

Hill Tribes: 2b, Musoe musician. 4b, Yao
weaver. 5b, Maeo farm woman.

Wmk. 334
1972, May 11   **Photo.**   **Perf. 13½**
620 A147 50s multicolored   .65 .20
621 A147 2b dark gray & multi   2.25 .30
622 A147 4b multicolored   5.25 3.50
623 A147 5b multicolored   6.25 1.00
    Nos. 620-623 (4)   14.40 5.00

Ruby
A148

Precious Stones: 2b, Yellow sapphire. 4b,
Zircon. 6b, Star sapphire.

1972, June 7   **Litho.**
624 A148 75s gray & multi   .70 .25
625 A148 2b multicolored   4.00 .55
626 A148 4b multicolored   8.75 4.50
627 A148 6b crimson & multi   15.00 3.50
    Nos. 624-627 (4)   28.45 8.80

Prince
Vajiralongkorn
A149

Thai Costume
A150

Perf. 13½x13
1972, July 28   Photo.   Wmk. 329
628 A149 75s tan & multi   .60 .20
20th birthday of Prince Vajiralongkorn, heir
apparent.

Perf. 14x13½
1972, Aug. 12   Litho.   Wmk. 356
Designs: Costumes of Thai women.
629 A150 75s tan & multi   .40 .20
630 A150 2b multicolored   1.60 .20
631 A150 4b yellow & multi   2.50 2.25
632 A150 5b gray & multi   4.50 1.10
a.   Souvenir sheet of 4, #629-632 32.50 8.00
    Nos. 629-632 (4)   9.00 3.75

Rambutan — A151

Fruits: 1b, Mangosteen. 3b, Durian. 5b,
Mango.

1972, Sept. 7   Wmk. 334   Perf. 13½
633 A151 75s multicolored   .80 .20
634 A151 1b multicolored   1.75 .40
635 A151 3b pink & multi   4.50 .75
636 A151 5b lt ultra & multi   7.25 2.25
    Nos. 633-636 (4)   14.30 3.60

Lod Cave, Phangnga — A152

1.25b, Kang Krachara Reservoir. 2.75b,
Erawan Waterfalls, Kanchanaburi. 3b, Nok-
Kaw Cliff, Loei.

1972, Nov. 15   **Litho.**   **Wmk. 334**
637 A152   75s multicolored   .65 .20
638 A152   1.25b multicolored   1.10 .20
639 A152   2.75b multicolored   2.75 .25
640 A152   3b multicolored   3.50 1.50
    Nos. 637-640 (4)   8.00 2.40

Intl. Letter Writing Week, Oct. 9-15.

Princess Mother Visiting Old
People — A153

1972, Oct. 21   Photo.   Wmk. 329
641 A153 75s dk green & ocher   .75 .20
Princess Mother Sisangwan, 72nd birthday.

UN Emblem and
Globe — A154

Wmk. 334

1972, Nov. 15   **Litho.**   *Perf. 14*
642 A154 75s blue & multi   .50 .20

25th anniversary of the Economic Commission for Asia and the Far East (ECAFE).

Educational Center and Book Year
Emblem — A155

1972, Dec. 8   *Perf. 13½*
643 A155 75s multicolored   .50 .20

International Book Year 1972.

Crown Prince
Vajiralongkorn
A156

1972, Dec. 28   **Photo.**   **Wmk. 329**
644 A156 2b brt blue & multi   .95 .20

Investiture of Prince Vajiralongkorn Salayacheevin as Crown Prince.

Flag, Soldiers and Civilians — A157

1973, Feb. 3   **Wmk. 334**   *Perf. 13½*
645 A157 75s multicolored   .50 .20

25th anniversary of Veterans Day.

Savings Bank,
Emblem and
Coin — A158

1973, Apr. 1   **Wmk. 329**
646 A158 75s emerald & multi   .50 .20

60th anniv. of Government Savings Bank.

WHO Emblem and Deity — A159

1973, Apr. 1   **Wmk. 329**
647 A159 75s brt green & multi   .50 .20

25th World Health Organization Day.

Water
Lily
A160

Designs: Various water lilies (Thai lotus).

Perf. 11x13
1973, May 15   **Litho.**   **Wmk. 356**
648 A160   75s violet & multi   1.00 .25
649 A160 1.50b brown & multi   2.00 .35
650 A160   2b dull grn & multi   2.75 .45
651 A160   4b black & multi   4.25 2.50
    Nos. 648-651 (4)   10.00 3.85

King Bhumibol
Adulyadej — A161

Perf. 14x13½
1973-81   **Photo.**   **Wmk. 334**
652 A161   5s purple   .50 .20
653 A161 20s blue   .55 .20
    a. Perf. 14½, wmk. 233   .55 .20
654 A161 25s rose carmine   .65 .20

        Wmk. 233   *Perf. 14½*
655 A161 25s brown red ('81)   .65 .25
656 A161 50s dk olive grn ('79)   1.25 .20
657 A161 75s violet   1.25 .20
    a. Perf. 14x13½, wmk. 334   1.25 .20

        Wmk. 334
        Engr.   *Perf. 13*
658 A161   5b violet & brown   5.50 .65
659 A161   6b green & violet   3.50 1.00
660 A161 10b red & black   11.00 1.10
661 A161 20b org & yel grn
             ('75)   100.00 4.00
    Nos. 652-661 (10)   124.85 8.00

For surcharges see Nos. 1168A, 1548.

Silversmiths — A162

1973, June 15   **Litho.**   *Perf. 13½*
662 A162   75s shown   .50 .20
663 A162 2.75b Lacquerware   2.00 .55
664 A162   4b Pottery   3.50 2.75
665 A162   5b Paper umbrel-
             las   5.00 .90
    Nos. 662-665 (4)   11.00 4.40
          Thai handicrafts.

Fresco from Temple of the Emerald
Buddha — A163

Designs: Frescoes illustrating Ramayana in Temple of the Emerald Buddha.

1973, July 17   **Photo.**   **Wmk. 329**
666 A163 25s multicolored   .20 .20
667 A163 75s multicolored   .35 .20
668 A163 1.50b multicolored   1.75 .20
669 A163 2b multicolored   2.50 .85
670 A163 2.75b multicolored   2.25 .30
671 A163 3b multicolored   7.75 1.25
672 A163 5b multicolored   11.00 2.75
673 A163 6b multicolored   4.00 1.25
    Nos. 666-673 (8)   29.80 7.00

Development of Postal
Service — A164

2b, Telecommunications development.

1973, Aug. 4   *Perf. 13½*
674 A164 75s multicolored   .55 .20
675 A164 2b multicolored   1.10 .65

90th anniv. of Post and Telegraph Dept.

No. 1 and Other Stamps — A165

Various Stamps and: 1.25b, No. 147. 1.50b, No. 209. 2b, No. 244.

1973, Aug. 4   **Photo. & Engr.**
676 A165   75s dp rose & dk bl   .90 .20
677 A165 1.25b blue & dp rose   1.25 .30
678 A165 1.50b olive & vio blk   1.50 .55
679 A165   2b orange & sl grn   2.75 1.10
    a. Souvenir sheet of 4   16.00 2.50
    Nos. 676-679 (4)   6.40 2.15

2nd Natl. Phil. Exhib., THAIPEX '73, Aug. 4-8. No. 679a contains 4 stamps with simulated perforations similar to Nos. 676-679.

INTERPOL Emblem — A166

1973, Sept. 3   **Photo.**
680 A166 75s gray & multi   .50 .20

Intl. Criminal Police Organization, 50th anniv.

"Lilid Pralaw" — A167

Designs: Scenes from Thai literature.

Perf. 11x13
1973, Oct. 7   **Litho.**   **Wmk. 368**
681 A167   75s green & multi   .65 .30
682 A167 1.50b blue & multi   1.40 .60
683 A167   2b multicolored   2.50 1.10
684 A167   5b blue & multi   5.25 2.00
    a. Souvenir sheet of 4, #681-
        684, perf. 13x14   30.00 10.00
    Nos. 681-684 (4)   9.80 4.00

Intl. Letter Writing Week, Oct. 7-13.

Wat Suan Dok,
Chiangmai; UN
Emblem — A168

1973, Oct. 24   *Perf. 13x11*
685 A168 75s blue & multi   .50 .35

United Nations Day.

Schomburgk's Deer — A169

        Wmk. 329
1973, Nov. 14   **Photo.**   *Perf. 13½*
686 A169 20s shown   .30 .20
687 A169 25s Kouprey   .40 .20
688 A169 75s Gorals   .65 .20
689 A169 1.25b Water buffalos   1.90 .20
690 A169 1.50b Javan rhinocer-
              os   3.25 .20
691 A169   2b Eld's deer   4.50 1.25
692 A169 2.75b Asiatic 2-
             horned rhi-
             noceros   8.00 .40
693 A169   4b Serows   11.00 2.25
    Nos. 686-693 (8)   30.00 4.90
          Protected animals.

Human Rights Flame — A170

        Wmk. 371
1973, Dec. 10   **Litho.**   *Perf. 12½*
694 A170 75s multicolored   .85 .20

25th anniversary of the Universal Declaration of Human Rights.

Children and
Flowers — A171

1974, Jan. 12   **Litho.**   *Perf. 13*
695 A171 75s multicolored   .70 .20

Children's Day.

Siriraj Hospital and Statue of Prince
Nakarin — A172

        Perf. 13x13½
1974, Mar. 17   **Photo.**   **Wmk. 368**
696 A172 75s multicolored   .50 .20

84th anniversary of Siriraj Hospital, oldest medical school in Thailand.

Phala Piang Lai — A173

Classical Thai Dances: 2.75b, Phra Lux Phlaeng Rit. 4b, Chin Sao Sai. 5b, Charot Phra Sumen.

Wmk. 334

1974, June 25		**Litho.**	**Perf. 14**	
697	A173	75s pink & multi	.70	.20
698	A173	2.75b gray bl & multi	1.90	.25
699	A173	4b gray & multi	3.00	2.00
700	A173	5b yellow & multi	3.50	.80
		Nos. 697-700 (4)	9.10	3.25

Large Teak Tree in Uttaradit Province — A174

1974, July 5	**Wmk. 329**	**Perf. 12½**	
701	A174 75s multicolored	.50	.20

15th Arbor Day.

People and WPY Emblem — A175

	Perf. 10½x13		
1974, Aug. 19	**Litho.**	**Wmk. 368**	
702	A175 75s multicolored	.45	.20

World Population Year, 1974.

Ban Chiang Painted Vase — A176

75s, Royal chariot. 2.75b, Avalokitesavara Bodhisattva. 3b, King Mongkut, Rama IV.

1974, Sept. 19		**Wmk. 262**	**Perf. 12½**	
703	A176	75s blue & multi	.50	.20
704	A176	2b black, brn & bis	1.25	.50
705	A176	2.75b black, brn & tan	1.50	.40
706	A176	3b black & multi	2.25	.80
		Nos. 703-706 (4)	5.50	1.90

Centenary of National Museum. Inscribed "BATH" in error.

Purging Cassia — A177

1974, Oct. 6		**Wmk. 368**	**Perf. 11x13**	
707	A177	75s shown	.45	.20
708	A177	2.75b Butea	2.00	.25
709	A177	3b Jasmine	2.25	.30

710	A177	4b Lagerstroemia	2.50	.75
a.		Souvenir sheet of 4, #707-710, perf. 13½x14	30.00	10.00
		Nos. 707-710 (4)	7.20	1.50

Intl. Letter Writing Week, Oct. 6-12.

"UPU" and UPU Emblem — A178

1974, Oct. 9	**Wmk. 371**	**Perf. 12½**	
711	A178 75s dk green & multi	.50	.20

Centenary of Universal Postal Union.

Wat Suthat Thepvararam — A179

	Wmk. 329		
1974, Oct. 24	**Photo.**	**Perf. 13**	
712	A179 75s multicolored	.50	.20

United Nations Day.

Elephant Roundup — A180

	Wmk. 371		
1974, Nov. 16	**Engr.**	**Perf. 12½**	
713	A180 4b multicolored	2.50	1.40

Tourist publicity.

Vanda Coerulea — A181

Orchids: 2.75b, Dendrobium aggregatum. 3b, Dendrobium scabrilingue. 4b, Aerides falcata.

		Perf. 11x13		
1974, Dec. 5		**Photo.**	**Wmk. 368**	
714	A181	75s red & multi	.75	.20
715	A181	2.75b multicolored	1.60	.25
716	A181	3b olive & multi	2.50	.65
717	A181	4b green & multi	3.00	1.50
a.		Souvenir sheet of 4, #714-717, perf. 13½x14	37.50	11.00
		Nos. 714-717 (4)	7.85	2.60

See Nos. 745-748.

Boy — A182

	Perf. 14x13½		
1975, Jan. 11	**Litho.**	**Wmk. 374**	
718	A182 75s vermilion & multi	.75	.20

Children's Day.

Democracy Monument — A183

Designs: 2b, Mother with children and animals, bas-relief from Democracy Monument. 2.75b, Workers, bas-relief from Democracy Monument. 5b, Top of Democracy Monument and quotation from speech of King Rama VII.

		Perf. 14x14½		
1975, Jan. 26			**Wmk. 233**	
719	A183	75s dull grn & multi	.35	.20
720	A183	2b multicolored	1.00	.20
721	A183	2.75b blue & multi	1.40	.25
722	A183	5b multicolored	2.75	1.00
		Nos. 719-722 (4)	5.50	1.65

Movement of Oct. 14, 1973, to re-establish democratic institutions.

Marbled Tiger Cat — A184

1975, Mar. 5		**Wmk. 334**	**Perf. 13½**	
723	A184	20s shown	.45	.20
724	A184	75s Gaurs	1.75	.20
725	A184	2.75b Asiatic elephant	5.00	.55
726	A184	3b Clouded leopard	6.25	1.50
		Nos. 723-726 (4)	13.45	2.45

Protected animals.

White-eyed River Martin — A185

Birds: 2b, Paradise flycatchers. 2.75b, Long-tailed broadbills. 5b, Sultan tit.

		Wmk. 371		
1975, Apr. 2		**Litho.**	**Perf. 12½**	
727	A185	75s ocher & multi	.75	.20
728	A185	2b lt blue & multi	1.90	.20
729	A185	2.75b lt violet & multi	3.00	.35
730	A185	5b rose & multi	5.75	1.25
		Nos. 727-730 (4)	11.40	2.00

King Bhumibol Adulyadej and Queen Sirikit — A186

3b, King, Queen, different background design.

		Perf. 10½x13		
1975, Apr. 28		**Photo.**	**Wmk. 368**	
731	A186	75s violet bl & multi	.25	.20
732	A186	3b multicolored	1.10	.40

25th wedding anniversary of King Bhumibol Adulyadej and Queen Sirikit.

Round-house Kick — A187

Thai Boxing: 2.75b, Reverse elbow. 3b, Flying knee. 5b, Ritual homage.

	Wmk. 371		
1975, May 20	**Litho.**	**Perf. 12½**	
733	A187	75s green & multi	.75	.20
734	A187	2.75b blue & multi	2.75	.30
735	A187	3b orange & multi	4.00	1.00
736	A187	5b orange & multi	5.75	2.00
		Nos. 733-736 (4)	13.25	3.50

Tosakanth Mask — A188

Masks: 2b, Kumbhakarn. 3b, Rama. 4b, Hanuman.

1975, June 10	**Litho.**	**Wmk. 371**	
737	A188	75s dark gray & multi	.80	.20
738	A188	2b dull vio & multi	2.25	.30
739	A188	3b purple & multi	4.25	.75
740	A188	4b multicolored	8.50	3.75
		Nos. 737-740 (4)	15.80	5.00

Thai art and literature.

THAIPEX 75 Emblem — A189

THAIPEX 75 Emblem and: 2.75b, Stamp designer. 4b, Stamp printing plant. 5b, Stamp collector.

1975, Aug. 4	**Wmk. 371**	**Perf. 12½**	
741	A189	75s yellow & multi	.35	.20
742	A189	2.75b orange & multi	1.40	.30
743	A189	4b lt blue & multi	2.00	1.00
744	A189	5b carmine & multi	2.50	.60
		Nos. 741-744 (4)	6.25	2.10

THAIPEX 75, Third National Philatelic Exhibition, Aug. 4-10.

Orchid Type of 1974

Orchids: 75s, Dendrobium cruentum. 2b, Dendrobium parishii. 2.75b, Vanda teres. 5b, Vanda denisoniana.

	Perf. 11x13		
1975, Aug. 12	**Photo.**	**Wmk. 368**	
745	A181	75s olive & multi	.75	.20
746	A181	2b multicolored	1.75	.40
747	A181	2.75b scarlet & multi	2.75	.40
748	A181	5b ultra & multi	4.25	1.25
a.		Souv. sheet, #745-748, perf 13½	35.00	9.00
		Nos. 745-748 (4)	9.50	2.25

Mytilus Smaragdinus — A190

Sea Shells: 1b, Turbo marmoratus. 2.75b, Oliva mustelina. 5b, Cypraea moneta.

Perf. 14x14½
1975, Sept. 5   Litho.   Wmk. 375
49	A190	75s yellow & multi	.85	.40
50	A190	1b ver & multi	1.40	.20
51	A190	2.75b blue & multi	4.00	.30
52	A190	5b green & multi	11.00	3.00
		Nos. 749-752 (4)	17.25	3.90

Yachting and Games Emblem — A191

Designs: 1.25b, Badminton. 1.50b, Volleyball. 2b, Target shooting.

Perf. 11x13
1975, Sept. 20   Litho.   Wmk. 368
753	A191	75s ultra & black	.30	.20
754	A191	1.25b brt rose & blk	.80	.25
755	A191	1.50b red & black	1.40	.65
756	A191	2b apple grn & blk	2.00	.60
a.		Souv. sheet, #753-756, perf 13½	26.00	8.00
		Nos. 753-756 (4)	4.50	1.70

8th SEAP Games, Bangkok, Sept. 1975.

Pataya Beach A192

Views: 2b, Samila Beach. 3b, Prachuap Bay. 5b, Laem Singha Bay.

1975, Oct. 5   Wmk. 371   Perf. 12½
757	A192	75s orange & multi	.65	.20
758	A192	2b orange & multi	1.25	.30
759	A192	3b orange & multi	1.50	.40
760	A192	5b orange & multi	4.50	1.25
		Nos. 757-760 (4)	7.90	2.15

Intl. Letter Writing Week, Oct. 6-12.

"u n," UN Emblem, Food and Education for Children — A193

1975, Oct. 24   Litho.   Wmk. 371
761	A193	75s ultra & multi	.50	.20

United Nations Day.

Morse Telegraph — A194

Design: 2.75b, Teleprinter and radar.

Perf. 14x14½
1975, Nov. 4   Litho.   Wmk. 334
762	A194	75s multicolored	.60	.20
763	A194	2.75b blue & multi	1.75	.30

Centenary of telegraph system.

Sukhrip Khrong Mueang Barge — A195

Thai ceremonial barges: 1b, Royal escort barge Anekchat Phuchong. 2b, Royal barge Anantanakarat. 2.75b, Krabi Ran Ron Rap barge. 3b, Asura Wayuphak barge. 4b, Asura paksi barge. 5b, Royal barge Sri Suphanahong. 6b, Phali Rang Thawip barge.

Wmk. 371
1975, Nov. 18   Litho.   Perf. 12½
764	A195	75s multicolored	.55	.20
765	A195	1b multicolored	.65	.30
766	A195	2b lilac & multi	2.75	.40
767	A195	2.75b multicolored	3.50	.45
768	A195	3b yellow & multi	4.25	.45
769	A195	4b multicolored	5.50	1.25
770	A195	5b gray & multi	11.00	4.00
771	A195	6b blue & multi	6.50	2.50
		Nos. 764-771 (8)	34.70	9.55

Thai Flag, Arms of Chakri Royal Family — A196

King Bhumibol Adulyadej — A197

Perf. 15x14
1975, Dec. 5   Litho.   Wmk. 375
772	A196	75s multicolored	.30	.20
773	A197	5b multicolored	1.50	.50

King Bhumibol's 48th birthday.

Shot Put and SEAP Emblem — A198

2b, Table tennis. 3b, Bicycling. 4b, Relay race.

1975, Dec. 9   Wmk. 368   Perf. 11x13
774	A198	1b orange & black	.50	.20
775	A198	2b brt green & blk	1.10	.85
776	A198	3b ocher & blk	1.75	.40
777	A198	4b violet & blk	2.00	.85
a.		Souvenir sheet of 4, #774-777, perf. 13½	27.50	8.00
		Nos. 774-777 (4)	5.35	2.30

8th SEAP Games, Bangkok, Dec. 9-20.

IWY Emblem and Globe — A199

Perf. 14x14½
1975, Dec. 20   Wmk. 375
778	A199	75s blk, org & vio bl	.50	.20

International Women's Year.

Children Writing on Slate — A200

Perf. 13x14
1976, Jan. 10   Litho.   Wmk. 368
779	A200	75s lt green & multi	.60	.20

Children's Day.

Macrobrachium Rosenbergii — A201

Designs: 2b, Penaeus merguiensis. 2.75b, Panulirus ornatus. 5b, Penaeus monodon.

1976, Feb. 18   Perf. 11x13
780	A201	75s multicolored	1.60	.20
781	A201	2b multicolored	3.25	.85
782	A201	2.75b multicolored	4.75	.20
783	A201	5b multicolored	7.25	1.75
		Nos. 780-783 (4)	16.85	3.00

Shrimp and lobster exports.

Golden-backed Three-toed Woodpecker A202

Birds: 1.50b, Greater green-billed malcoha. 3b, Pomatorhinus hypoleucos. 4b, Green magpie.

Wmk. 371
1976, Apr. 2   Litho.   Perf. 12½
784	A202	1b multicolored	.70	.20
785	A202	1.50b multicolored	1.25	.20
786	A202	3b yellow & multi	2.50	.65
787	A202	4b rose & multi	2.75	.65
		Nos. 784-787 (4)	7.20	1.70

Perf. 14½x14
1976, May 5   Litho.   Wmk. 375
Designs: Ban Chiang painted pottery, various vessels, Bronze Age.

788	A203	1b olive & multi	.90	.20
789	A203	2b dp blue & multi	2.00	.20
790	A203	3b green & multi	3.75	.35
791	A203	4b org red & multi	5.00	1.75
		Nos. 788-791 (4)	11.65	2.50

Ban Chiang Vase — A203

Mailman, 1883 — A204

Designs: 3b, Mailman, 1935. 4b, Mailman, 1950. 5b, Mailman, 1974.

Wmk. 377
1976, Aug. 4   Litho.   Perf. 12½
792	A204	1b multicolored	.55	.20
793	A204	3b multicolored	2.00	.50
794	A204	4b multicolored	3.25	.80
795	A204	5b multicolored	3.50	1.00
		Nos. 792-795 (4)	9.30	2.50

Development of mailmen's uniforms.

Kinnari — A205

Thai Mythology: 2b, Suphan-mat-cha. 4b, Garuda. 5b, Naga.

1976, Oct. 3   Wmk. 368   Perf. 11x13
796	A205	1b green & multi	.50	.20
797	A205	2b ultra & multi	1.10	.20
798	A205	4b gray & multi	3.75	.45
799	A205	5b slate & multi	4.50	.50
		Nos. 796-799 (4)	9.85	1.35

International Letter Writing Week.

UN Emblem, Drug Addicts, Alcohol, Cigarettes, Drugs — A206

Wmk. 329
1976, Oct. 24   Photo.   Perf. 13½
800	A206	1b ultra & multi	.50	.20

United Nations Day.

Old and New Telephones — A207

Perf. 14x14½
1976, Nov. 10   Litho.   Wmk. 375
801	A207	1b multicolored	.50	.20

Centenary of first telephone call by Alexander Graham Bell, Mar. 10, 1876.

Sivalaya-Mahaprasad Hall — A208

Royal Houses: 2b, Cakri-Mahaprasad. 4b, Mahisra-Prasad. 5b, Dusit-Mahaprasad.

Perf. 14x15
1976, Dec. 5 Wmk. 375 Litho.
802	A208	1b multicolored	1.00 .20
803	A208	2b multicolored	1.50 .50
804	A208	4b multicolored	5.00 .75
805	A208	5b multicolored	5.50 .80
		Nos. 802-805 (4)	13.00 2.25

Banteng — A209

Protected animals: 2b, Tapir and young. 4b, Sambar deer and fawn. 5b, Hog deer family.

Wmk. 334
1976, Dec. 26 Litho. Perf. 11
806	A209	1b multicolored	1.00 .20
807	A209	2b multicolored	1.25 .30

Wmk. 368
808	A209	4b multicolored	3.50 .60
809	A209	5b multicolored	4.25 1.00
		Nos. 806-809 (4)	10.00 2.10

Child Casting Shadow of Man — A210

Wmk. 329
1977, Jan. 8 Photo. Perf. 13½
810	A210	1b multicolored	.50 .20

National Children's Day.

Alsthom's Electric Engine — A211

Locomotives: 2b, Davenport's electric engine. 4b, Pacific's steam engine. 5b, George Egestoff's steam engine.

Perf. 11x13
1977, Mar. 26 Wmk. 368
811	A211	1b multicolored	1.90 .20
812	A211	2b multicolored	3.75 .35
813	A211	4b multicolored	8.50 2.00
814	A211	5b multicolored	11.00 .80
		Nos. 811-814 (4)	25.15 3.35

80th anniv. of State Railroad of Thailand.

Chulalongkorn University Auditorium — A212

1977, Mar. 26   Photo.
815	A212	1b multicolored	.70 .20

Chulalongkorn University, 60th anniversary.

Flags of AOPU Members — A213

Wmk. 371
1977, Apr. 1 Litho. Perf. 12½
816	A213	1b multicolored	.70 .20

Asian-Oceanic Postal Union (AOPU), 15th anniv.

Invalid in Wheelchair and Soldiers — A214

Wmk. 329
1977, Apr. 2 Photo. Perf. 13½
817	A214	5b multicolored	1.40 .45

Sai-Jai-Thai Day, to publicize Sai-Jai-Thai Foundation which helps wounded soldiers.

Phra Aphai Mani and Phisua Samut A215

Puppets: 3b, Rusi and Sutsakhon. 4b, Nang Vali and Usren. 5b, Phra Aphai Mani and Nang Laweng's portrait.

Perf. 11x13
1977, June 16 Wmk. 368
818	A215	2b multicolored	.55 .20
819	A215	3b multicolored	.75 .25
820	A215	4b multicolored	1.50 .45
821	A215	5b multicolored	2.00 .55
		Nos. 818-821 (4)	4.80 1.45

Thai plays and literature.

Drum Dance — A216

Designs: 3b, Dance of dip nets. 4b, Harvest dance. 5b, Kan dance.

1977, July 14 Photo. Perf. 13x11
822	A216	2b rose & multi	.65 .20
823	A216	3b lt green & multi	.75 .20
824	A216	4b yellow & multi	1.25 .40
825	A216	5b lt violet & multi	1.50 .40
		Nos. 822-825 (4)	4.15 1.20

Thailand No. 609, Various Stamps and Thaipex Emblem — A217

Wmk. 377
1977, Aug. 4 Litho. Perf. 12½
826	A217	75s multicolored	.70 .20

THAIPEX 77, 4th National Philatelic Exhibition, Aug. 4-12.

Scenes from Thai Literature — A218

Perf. 11x13
1977, Oct. 5 Photo. Wmk. 368
827	A218	75s multicolored	.70 .20
828	A218	2b multi, diff.	1.10 .20
829	A218	5b multi, diff.	3.00 .40
830	A218	6b multi, diff.	4.00 .65
		Nos. 827-830 (4)	8.80 1.45

Intl. Letter Writing Week, Oct. 6-12.

Old and New Buildings, UN Emblem — A219

1977, Oct. 5 Litho. Perf. 11x13
831	A219	75s multicolored	.85 .20

United Nations Day.

King Bhumibol as Scout Leader, Camp and Emblem — A220

1977, Nov. 21 Photo. Wmk. 368
832	A220	75s multicolored	1.50 .20

9th National Jamboree, Nov. 21-27.

Diseased Hand and Elbow — A221

1977, Dec. 20   Perf. 11x13
833	A221	75s multicolored	.70 .20

World Rheumatism Year.

Map of South East Asia and ASEAN Emblem — A222

Wmk. 377
1977, Dec. 1 Litho. Perf. 12½
834	A222	5b multicolored	1.75 .35

ASEAN, 10th anniv.

King Type of 1972-74 Redrawn
1976   Perf. 12½x1
Size: 21x27mm
835	A146	20s blue	2.50 .2
836	A146	75s lilac	2.50 .2

Engr.
837	A146	10b vermilion & blk	25.00 1.0
838	A146	40b bister & lilac	20.00 2.2
		Nos. 835-838 (4)	50.00 3.6

Numerals are taller and thinner and leave in background have been redrawn.

Children Carrying Flag of Thailand — A223

Wmk. 329
1978, Jan. 9 Photo. Perf. 13½
839	A223	75s multicolored	.75 .20

Children's Day.

Dendrobium Heterocarpum — A224

Orchids: 1b, Dendrobium pulchellum. 1.50b, Doritis pulcherrima. 2b, Dendrobium hercoglossum. 2.75b, Aerides odorata. 3b, Trichoglottis fasciata. 5b, Dendrobium wardianum. 6b, Dendrobium senile.

Perf. 11x14
1978, Jan. 18 Wmk. 368
840	A224	75s multicolored	.20 .20
841	A224	1b multicolored	.25 .20
842	A224	1.50b multicolored	.40 .20
843	A224	2b multicolored	.70 .60
844	A224	2.75b multicolored	2.75 .20
845	A224	3b multicolored	1.00 .30
846	A224	5b multicolored	1.50 .50
847	A224	6b multicolored	4.00 .60
		Nos. 840-847 (8)	10.80 2.80

9th World Orchid Conference.

Census Chart, Symbols of Agriculture — A225

Wmk. 377
1978, Mar. 1 Litho. Perf. 12½
848	A225	75s multicolored	.40 .20

Agricultural census, Apr. 1978.

Anabas Testudineus — A226

Fish: 2b, Datnioides microlepis. 3b, Kryptopterus apogon. 4b, Probarbus Jullieni.

Perf. 11x13
1978, Apr. 13 Photo. Wmk. 368
849	A226	1b multicolored	.30 .20
850	A226	2b multicolored	.70 .20
851	A226	3b multicolored	1.25 .35
852	A226	4b multicolored	1.75 .55
		Nos. 849-852 (4)	4.00 1.30

Birth of Prince Siddhartha — A227

Murals: 3b, Prince Siddhartha cuts his hair. 5b, Buddha descending from Tavatimsa Heaven. 6b, Buddha entering Nirvana.

1978, June 15	Photo.	Perf. 13½
853 A227 2b multicolored	1.40	.25
854 A227 3b multicolored	2.00	.50
855 A227 5b multicolored	6.00	.80
856 A227 6b multicolored	4.50	1.10
Nos. 853-856 (4)	13.90	2.65

Wmk. 329

Story of Gautama Buddha, murals in Puthi Savan Hall, National Museum, Bangkok.

Bhumibol Dam — A228

Dams and Reservoirs: 2b, Sirikit dam. 2.75b, Vajiralongkorn dam. 6b, Ubol Ratana dam.

1978, July 28	Litho.	Perf. 14x14½
		Wmk. 233
857 A228 75s multicolored	.95	.20
858 A228 2b multicolored	1.25	.20
859 A228 2.75b multicolored	1.75	.20
860 A228 6b multicolored	3.25	.90
Nos. 857-860 (4)	7.20	1.50

Idea Lynceus — A229

Butterflies: 3b, Sephisa chandra. 5b, Charaxes durnfordi. 6b, Cethosia penthesilea methypsia.

1978, Aug. 25	Litho.	Perf. 11x13
		Wmk. 368
861 A229 2b lilac, blk & red	1.60	.20
862 A229 3b multicolored	2.00	.30
863 A229 5b multicolored	3.25	.50
864 A229 6b multicolored	5.25	1.00
Nos. 861-864 (4)	12.10	2.00

Chedi Chai Mongkhon Temple — A230

Mother and Children, UN Emblem — A231

Temples: 2b, That Hariphunchai. 2.75b, Borom That Chaiya. 5b, That Choeng Chum.

1978, Oct. 8		Perf. 13x11
865 A230 75s multicolored	.90	.20
866 A230 2b multicolored	1.25	.20
867 A230 2.75b multicolored	1.75	.20
868 A230 6b multicolored	2.75	.80
Nos. 865-868 (4)	6.65	1.40

Intl. Letter Writing Week, Oct. 6-12.

Perf. 14½x14

1978, Oct. 24	Litho.	Wmk. 375
869 A231 75s multicolored	.50	.20

United Nations Day.

Boxing, Soccer, Pole Vault — A232

Designs: 2b, Javelin, weight lifting, running. 3b, Ball games and sailing. 5b, Basketball, hockey stick and boxing gloves.

	Perf. 14x14½	
1978, Oct.	Wmk. 233	Litho.
870 A232 75s multicolored	.40	.20
871 A232 2b multicolored	1.00	.20
872 A232 3b multicolored	1.40	.25
873 A232 5b multicolored	2.00	.80
Nos. 870-873 (4)	4.80	1.45

8th Asian Games, Bangkok.

Five Races and World Map A233

1978, Nov.
874 A233 75s multicolored   .45 .20

Anti-Apartheid Year.

Children Painting Thai Flag — A234

Children and Children's SOS Village, Tambol Bangpu — A235

1979, Jan. 17	Perf. 14x14½
875 A234 75s multicolored	.70 .20
876 A235 75s multicolored	.70 .20

International Year of the Child.

Matuta Lunaris — A236

Crabs: 2.75b, Matuta planipes fabricius. 3b, Portunus pelagicus. 5b, Scylla serrata.

Wmk. 377

1979, Mar. 22	Litho.	Perf. 12½
877 A236 2b multicolored	1.10	.20
878 A236 2.75b multicolored	4.25	.20
879 A236 3b multicolored	1.75	.25
880 A236 5b multicolored	5.25	.70
Nos. 877-880 (4)	12.35	1.35

A237

A238

1979, June 25

881 A237 1b Sweetsop	1.25	.20
882 A237 2b Pineapple	1.00	.20
883 A237 5b Bananas	4.00	.45
884 A237 6b Longans (litchi)	3.75	1.25
Nos. 881-884 (4)	10.00	2.10

See Nos. 1145-1148.

Perf. 13x11

1979, July 10	Litho.	Wmk. 368

Young man and woman planting tree.

885 A238 75s multicolored   .50 .20

20th Arbor Day.

Pencil, Pen, Thaipex '79 Emblem — A239

Thaipex '79 Emblem and: 2b, Envelopes. 2.75b, Stamp album. 5b, Magnifying glass and tongs.

1979, Aug. 4		Perf. 11x13
886 A239 75s multicolored	.30	.20
887 A239 2b multicolored	.80	.20
888 A239 2.75b multicolored	1.25	.20
889 A239 5b multicolored	2.00	.30
Nos. 886-889 (4)	4.35	.90

Thaipex '79, 5th National Philatelic Exhibition, Bangkok, Aug. 4-12.

Floral Arrangement A240

UN Day — A241

Designs: Decorative arrangements.

	Perf. 14½x14	
1979, Oct. 7	Litho.	Wmk. 233
890 A240 75s multicolored	.45	.20
891 A240 2b multicolored	.80	.20
892 A240 2.75b multicolored	1.25	.20
893 A240 3b multicolored	1.90	.60
Nos. 890-893 (4)	4.40	1.20

Intl. Letter Writing Week, Oct. 8-14.

1979, Oct. 24 Litho.	Perf. 14½x14
894 A241 75s multicolored	.50 .20

Frigate Makut Rajakumarn — A242

Thai Naval Ships: 3b, Frigate Tapi. 5b, Fast strike craft, Prabparapak. 6b, Patrol boat T-91.

Wmk. 329

1979, Nov. 20	Photo.	Perf. 13½
895 A242 2b multicolored	.70	.20
896 A242 3b multicolored	1.10	.25
897 A242 5b multicolored	5.25	.70
898 A242 6b multicolored	6.50	1.00
Nos. 895-898 (4)	13.55	2.15

Thai Royal Orders (Medallions and Ribbons) — A243

Designs: #900a, Rajamitrabhorn Order. #902a, House of Chakri. #904a, The nine gems. #906a, Chula Chom Klao. Pairs have continuous design.

	Perf. 13x11	
1979, Dec. 5	Litho.	Wmk. 368
899 1b multicolored	.40	.25
900 1b multicolored	.40	.25
a. A243 Pair, #899-900	.80	.50
901 2b multicolored	.85	.20
902 2b multicolored	.85	.20
a. A243 Pair, #901-902	1.75	.40
903 5b multicolored	2.00	.40
904 5b multicolored	2.00	.40
a. A243 Pair, #903-904	4.00	.80
905 6b multicolored	2.75	.60
906 6b multicolored	2.75	.60
a. A243 Pair, #905-906	5.50	1.25
Nos. 899-906 (8)	12.00	2.90

See Nos. 1278-1285.

King Type of 1972-77
Perf. 13½x13

1979, Dec. 23	Litho.	Wmk. 329
Size: 21x26mm		
907 A146 50s olive green		.50 .20
Engr.		
908 A146 2b org red & lilac		.65 .20

Rice Planting — A245

Children's Day: No. 910, Family in rice field.

Perf. 13x11

1980, Jan. 12   Litho.   Wmk. 368
909 A245 75s multicolored   .55 .20
910 A245 75s multicolored   .55 .20

Family, House, Map of Thailand — A246

Gold-fronted Leafbird — A247

Perf. 15x14

1980, Feb. 1   Litho.   Wmk. 233
911 A246 75s multicolored   .65 .30

Natl. Population & Housing Census, Apr.

Perf. 13x11

1980, Feb. 26   Wmk. 368
912 A247 75s shown   .40 .20
913 A247 2b Yellow-cheeked tit   .60 .25
914 A247 3b Chestnut-tailed si-
            va   1.40 .40
915 A247 5b Scarlet minivet   2.40 1.10
    Nos. 912-915 (4)   4.80 1.95

Intl. Commission for Bird Preservation, 9th Conf. of Asian Section, Chieng-mai, 2/26-29.

Smokers and Lungs, WHO Emblem — A248

1980, Apr. 7   Wmk. 329   Perf. 13½
916 A248 75s multicolored   .60 .25

World Health Day; fight against cigarette smoking.

Garuda and Rotary Emblem — A249

1980, May 6   Wmk. 368   Perf. 13x11
917 A249 5b multicolored   1.50 .25

Rotary International, 75th anniversary.

Sai Yok Falls, Kanchanaburi — A250

Perf. 14x15

1980, July 1   Litho.   Wmk. 233
918 A250 1b shown   .40 .20
919 A250 2b Punyaban Falls, Ra-
            nong   .60 .25
920 A250 5b Heo Suwat Falls,
            Nakhon Ratch-
            asima   2.10 .85
921 A250 6b Siriphum Falls, Chi-
            ang Mai   1.90 1.25
    Nos. 918-921 (4)   5.00 2.55

Queen Sirikit — A251

Family with Cattle, Ceres Medal (Reverse) — A252

No. 524, Ceres medal (obverse), potters.

Perf. 13½, 11x13 (5b)
Wmk. 329, 368 (5b)

1980, Aug. 12   Litho.
922 A251 75s multicolored   .40 .20
923 A252 5b multicolored   1.60 .80
924 A252 5b multicolored   1.60 .80
    Nos. 922-924 (3)   3.60 1.80

Queen Sirikit's 48th birthday.

Khao Phanomrung Temple, Buri Ram — A253

Intl. Letter Writing Week, Oct. 6-12 (Temples): 2b, Prang Ku, Chailyaphum. 2.75b, Phimai, Nakhon Ratchasima. 5b, Sikhoraphum, Surin.

Perf. 11x13
1980, Oct. 5   Litho.   Wmk. 368
925 A253 75s multicolored   .25 .20
926 A253 2b multicolored   .60 .25
927 A253 2.75b multicolored   .80 .30
928 A253 5b multicolored   1.90 1.00
    Nos. 925-928 (4)   3.55 1.75

Princess Mother — A254

Golden Mount, Bangkok — A255

Perf. 15x14
1980, Oct. 21   Litho.   Wmk. 233
929 A254 75s multicolored   1.75 .45

Princess Mother, 80th birthday.

1980, Oct. 24
930 A255 75s multicolored   .60 .25

United Nations Day.

King Bhumibol Adulyadej — A256

Perf. 11x13

1980-84(?)   Litho.   Wmk. 368
932 A256 25s salmon   2.00 .20
933 A256 50s olive green   .20 .20
   b.   Wmk. 233, perf. 14x15   5.00 .20
   c.   Wmk. 387, perf. 11x13   1.00 .20
934 A256 75s lilac   .50 .20
935 A256 1.25b yellow green   .50 .20
   a.   Wmk. 387, perf. 11x13   2.00 .20
   b.   Wmk. 233, perf. 14x15   6.00 .20

Perf. 13½x13
Engr.   Wmk. 329
936 A256 3b brown & dk bl   4.75 .20
937 A256 5b purple & brn   7.25 .30
938 A256 6b dk green & pur   9.50 .35
939 A256 8.50b grn & brn org   2.00 .50
940 A256 9.50b olive & dk grn   2.50 .55
    Nos. 932-940 (9)   29.20 2.70

Issued: 50s, 1.25b, 1981. 3b-9.50b, 1983. See Nos. 1080-1093. For surcharges see Nos. 1226-1226A.

King Rama VII Monument Inauguration A257

Perf. 15x14
1980, Dec. 10   Wmk. 233
946 A257 75s multicolored   .75 .25

Bencharongware Bowl — A258

Perf. 11x13
1980, Dec. 15   Wmk. 368
947 A258 2b shown   .80 .40
948 A258 2.75b Covered bowls   .80 .40
949 A258 3b Covered jar   1.60 .60
950 A258 5b Stem plates   1.60 1.00
    Nos. 947-950 (4)   4.80 2.40

King Vajiravudh Birth Centenary A259

1981, Jan. 1   Wmk. 233   Perf. 15x14
951 A259 75s multicolored   .85 .25

Children's Day — A260

Perf. 13x11
1981, Jan. 16   Wmk. 368
952 A260 75s multicolored   .60 .20

Hegira, 1500th Anniv. — A261

Wmk. 377
1981, Jan. 18   Litho.   Perf. 12½
953 A261 5b multicolored   2.40 .75

Dolls in Native Costumes — A262

Wmk. 368
1981, Feb. 6   Litho.   Perf. 13½
954 A262 75s Palm-leaf fish
            mobile   .45 .20
955 A262 75s Teak elephants   .45 .20
956 A262 2.75b shown   1.25 .60
957 A262 2.75b Baskets   1.25 .60
    Nos. 954-957 (4)   3.40 1.60

CONEX '81 International Crafts Exhibition.

Scout Leader and Boy on Crutches — A263

1981, Feb. 28   **Perf. 13x11**
58 A263 75s shown   .40 .20
59 A263 5b Diamond cutter in
              wheelchair   1.60 .60

International Year of the Disabled.

Dindaeng-Tarua Expressway Opening — A264

1981, Oct. 29   **Perf. 13½**
60 A264 1b Klongtoey   .25 .20
61 A264 5b Vipavadee Rangsit
              Highway   2.00 .65

Ongkhot, Khon Mask — A265

Designs: Various Khon masks.

1981, July 1   Litho.   Perf. 13x11
962 A265 75s shown   .45 .25
963 A265 2b Maiyarab   .70 .30
964 A265 3b Sukrip   1.60 .50
965 A265 5b Indrajit   1.75 1.10
        Nos. 962-965 (4)   4.50 2.15

Exhibition Emblem, No. 83 — A266

Wmk. 370
1981, Aug. 4   Litho.   Perf. 12
966 A266 75s shown   .35 .20
967 A266 75s No. 144   .35 .20
968 A266 2.75b No. 198   1.00 .60
969 A266 2.75b No. 226   1.00 .60
        Nos. 966-969 (4)   2.70 1.60

A267

A268

Perf. 15x14
1981, Aug. 26   **Wmk. 233**
970 A267 1.25b multicolored   .65 .25

Luang Praditphairo, court Musician, birth centenary. THAIPEX '81 Intl. Stamp Exhibition.

1981, Oct. 4   **Wmk. 329**

Designs: Dwarfed trees.

971 A268 75s Mai hok-hian   .40 .20
972 A268   2b Mai kam-ma-lo   .65 .40
973 A268 2.75b Mai khen   1.00 .25
974 A268   5b Mai khabuan   2.50 1.25
        Nos. 971-974 (4)   4.55 2.10

25th Intl. Letter Writing Week, Oct. 6-12.

World Food Day A269

Wmk. 370
1981, Oct. 16   Litho.   Perf. 12
975 A269 75s multicolored   .60 .25

United Nations Day — A270

1981, Oct. 24   Wmk. 368   Perf. 13½
976 A270 1.25b Samran Mukhamat
              Pavilion   .60 .25

King Cobra A271

1981, Dec. 1   Wmk. 329   Perf. 13½
977 A271 75s shown   .25 .20
978 A271   2b Banded krait   1.25 .55
979 A271 2.75b Thai cobra   1.25 .25
980 A271   5b Malayan pit viper 2.25 1.00
        Nos. 977-980 (4)   5.00 2.00

Children's Day — A272

Scouting Year — A273

1982, Jan. 9   Wmk. 370   Perf. 12
981 A272 1.25b multicolored   .75 .25

1982, Feb. 22
982 A273 1.25b multicolored   .60 .25

Bicentenary of Bangkok (Thai Capital) A274

Chakri Dynasty kings. (Rama I-Rama IX).

1982, Apr. 4   Litho.   Perf. 12
983 A274 1b Buddha Yod-
              Fa (1736-
              1809)   .45 .25
984 A274 1.25b shown   .60 .30
985 A274 2b Buddha Lert
              La Naphalai
              (1767-1824)   .90 .25
986 A274 3b Nang Klao
              (1787-1851)   1.60 .35
987 A274 4b Mongkut
              (1804-1868)   1.25 .50
988 A274 5b Chulalongkorn
              (1853-1910)   2.00 .75
989 A274 6b Vajiravudh
              (1880-1925)   2.50 .75
990 A274 7b Prachathipok
              (1893-1941)   5.25 2.50
991 A274 8b Ananda
              Mahidol
              (1925-1946)   2.75 1.50
992 A274 9b Bhumibol
              Adulyadej (b.
              1927)   2.75 1.00
  a. Souv. sheet of 10,
      205x142mm   42.50 32.50
  b. Souv. sheet of 1, 195x180mm 42.50 32.50
        Nos. 983-992 (10)   20.05 8.15

Nos. 992a-992b each contain Nos. 983-992. No. 992a sold for 60b, No. 992b for 70b. Values for #992a-992b include folder.

TB Bacillus Centenary — A275

Wmk. 368
1982, Apr. 7   Litho.   Perf. 13½
993 A275 1.25b multicolored   .60 .25

Local Flowers — A276

Perf. 14x14½
1982, June 30   **Wmk. 233**
994 A276 1.25b Quisqualis indica .35 .20
995 A276 1.50b Murraya anicu-
              lata   .55 .30
996 A276 6.50b Mesua ferrea   2.00 .80

997 A276 7b Desmos chinen-
              sis   1.60 .50
        Nos. 994-997 (4)   4.50 1.80

Buddhist Temples in Bangkok — A277

1982, Aug. 4   Wmk. 368   Perf. 13½
998 A277 1.25b shown   .40 .20
999 A277 4.25b Wat Pho   1.00 .40
1000 A277 6.50b Mahathat
              Yuwarat
              Rangsarit   1.25 .75
1001 A277 7b Phra Sri Rat-
              tana Sat-
              sadaram   2.10 .55
  a. Souv. sheet of 4, #998-
      1001, perf. 12½   70.00 55.00
        Nos. 998-1001 (4)   4.75 1.90

BANGKOK '83 Intl. Stamp Exhibition, Aug. 4-13, 1983. No. 1001a sold for 30b.
See Nos. 1025-1026.

A278

A279

1982, Aug. 9   Wmk. 370   Perf. 12
1002 A278 1.25b LANDSAT Satel-
              lite   .60 .25

2nd UN Conference on Peaceful Uses of Outer Space, Vienna, Aug. 9-21.

1982, Sept. 14   Wmk. 233   Perf. 14

Prince Purachatra of Kambaengbejra (1882-1936).

1003 A279 1.25b multicolored   .60 .25

26th Intl. Letter Writing Week, Oct. 6-12 — A280

Sangalok Pottery.

1982, Oct. 3   Wmk. 329   Perf. 13½
1004 A280 1.25b Covered glazed
              jar   .45 .25
1005 A280 3b Painted jar   1.25 .50
1006 A280 4.25b Glazed plate   .90 .65
1007 A280 7b Painted plate   1.75 1.00
        Nos. 1004-1007 (4)   4.35 2.40

UN Day — A281

1982, Oct. 24
1008 A281 1.25b Loha Prasat Tower   .60 .25

Musical Instruments — A282

1982, Nov. 30   Wmk. 370   *Perf. 12*
1009	A282	50s Chap, ching	.20	.20
1010	A282	1b Pi nai, pi nok	.60	.25
1011	A282	1.25b Klong that, taphon	.40	.20
1012	A282	1.50b Khong mong, krap	.40	.30
1013	A282	6b Khong wong yai	4.00	1.40
1014	A282	7b Khong wong lek	1.60	.50
1015	A282	8b Ranat ek	1.40	.50
1016	A282	9b Ranat thum	1.40	.50
		Nos. 1009-1016 (8)	10.00	3.85

Pileated
Gibbon — A283

ASEAN Members'
Flags — A284

1982, Dec. 26
1017	A283	1.25b shown	.60	.25
1018	A283	3b Pig-tailed macaque	2.90	.45
1019	A283	5b Slow loris	1.75	1.00
1020	A283	7b Silvered leaf monkey	2.25	1.10
		Nos. 1017-1020 (4)	7.50	2.80

1982, Dec. 26   Wmk. 233
1021 A284 6.50b multicolored   1.60 .40
    15th Anniv. of Assoc. of Southeast Asian Nations.

Children's
Day — A285

Perf. 14½x14
1983, Jan. 8   Litho.   Wmk. 233
1022 A285 1.25b multicolored   .60 .25

First
Anniv.
of
Postal
Code
A286

1983, Feb. 25   Wmk. 329   *Perf. 13½*
1023	A286	1.25b Codes	.60	.25
1024	A286	1.25b Code on envelope	.60	.25

BANGKOK '83 Type of 1982

Design: Old General Post Office.

1983, Feb. 25   Wmk. 368   Photo.
1025	A277	7b multicolored	1.60	.30
1026	A277	10b multicolored	2.40	.50
a.		Souv. sheet of 2, #1025-1026, perf. 12½	25.00	22.50

25th Anniv. of Intl. Maritime
Org. — A287

Perf. 14x14½
1983, Mar. 17   Litho.   Wmk. 233
1029 A287 1.25b Chinese junks   .60 .25

Civil Servants'
Day — A288

Prince Sithiporn
Kridakara (1883-
1971)
A289

1983, Apr. 1   Wmk. 370   *Perf. 12*
1030 A288 1.25b multicolored   .60 .25

Perf. 14½x14
1983, Apr. 11   Wmk. 233
1031 A289 1.25b multicolored   .60 .25

Domestic Satellite Communications
System Inauguration — A290

Wmk. 368
1983, Aug. 4   Litho.   *Perf. 13½*
1032 A290 2b Map, dish antenna,
      satellite   .60 .25

BANGKOK '83 Intl. Stamp Show, Aug.
4-13 — A291

1983, Aug. 4   Wmk. 370   *Perf. 12*
1033	A291	1.25b Mail collection	.25	.20
1034	A291	7.50b Posting letters	1.75	.60
1035	A291	8.50b Mail transport	1.25	.75
1036	A291	9.50b Mail delivery	1.25	.75
a.		Souv. sheet of 4, #1033-1036	32.50	29.00
		Nos. 1033-1036 (4)	4.50	2.30

    No. 1036a exist imperf, sold for 50b. Value, $140.

A292

A293

Prince Bhanurangsi memorial statue.

Perf. 15x14
1983, Aug. 4   Litho.   Wmk. 233
1037 A292 1.25b multicolored   .60 .25

Wmk. 370
1983, Sept. 27   Litho.   *Perf. 12*
1038	A293	1.25b multicolored	.25	.20
1039	A293	7b multicolored	1.50	.75

    Malaysia/ Thailand/ Singapore submarine cable inauguration.

Intl. Letter Writing Week — A294

1983, Oct. 6   Wmk. 329   *Perf. 13*
1040	A294	2b Acropora asper	.70	
1041	A294	3b Platygyra lamellina	1.60	
1042	A294	4b Fungia	.70	
1043	A294	7b Pectinia lactuca	2.00	1.1
		Nos. 1040-1043 (4)	5.00	2.3

Prince Mahidol o
Songkhla — A295

Wmk. 370
1983, Oct. 10   Litho.   *Perf. 1*
1044 A295 9.50b multicolored   1.50 .7
    Siriraj Hospital Faculty of Medicine an
Rockefeller Foundation, 60th Anniv. c
cooperation.

World Communications Year — A296

    3b, Telecommunications equipment, diff.

Perf. 14x14½
1983, Oct. 24   Litho.   Wmk. 233
1045	A296	2b multicolored	.60	.2
1046	A296	3b multicolored	.60	.2

United Nations Day — A297

1983, Oct. 24
1047 A297 1.25b multicolored   .60 .25

Thai Alphabet, 700th Anniv. — A298

    Designs: 3b, Painted pottery, Sukothai period. 7b, Thai characters, reign of King Ramkamhaeng. 8b, Buddha, Sukothai period. 9b, Mahathat Temple, Sukothai province.

1983, Nov. 17   Wmk. 370   *Perf. 12*
1048	A298	3b multicolored	1.00	.25
1049	A298	7b multicolored	1.90	.45
1050	A298	8b multi, vert.	1.00	.50
1051	A298	9b multi, vert.	1.00	.50
		Nos. 1048-1051 (4)	4.90	1.70

National Development
Program — A299

    #1052, King and Queen initiating Royal Projects. #1053, Technical aid. #1054, Terrace farming, Irrigation dam. #1055, Gathering grain. #1056, Receiving the peoples' gratitude.

1984, May 5

1052	A299	1.25b multicolored	.60	.25
1053	A299	1.25b multicolored	.60	.25
1054	A299	1.25b multicolored	.60	.25
1055	A299	1.25b multicolored	.60	.25
1056	A299	1.25b multicolored	.60	.25
a.		Strip of 5, #1052-1056	3.00	1.50

Children's Day — A300

1984, Jan. 14   Wmk. 329   Perf. 13½

1057	A300	1.25b multicolored	.60	.25

17th Natl. Games, Jan. 22-28 — A301

1984, Jan. 22

1058	A301	1.25b Running	.65	.20
1059	A301	3b Soccer	.45	.25

5th Rheumatology Congress, Jan. 22-27 — A302

Perf. 14x15

1984, Jan. 22   Wmk. 233

1060	A302	1.25b Rheumatic joints	.75	.25

Armed Forces Day — A303

50th Anniv. of Royal Institute — A304

1984, Jan. 25   Perf. 15x14

1061	A303	1.25b King Naresuan, tanks, jet, ship	.60	.25

1984, Mar. 31

1062	A304	1.25b multicolored	.60	.25

Thammasat University, 50th Anniv. — A305

1984, June 27   Perf. 14x15

1063	A305	1.25b Dome Building	.60	.25

Asia-Pacific Broadcasting Union, 20th Anniv. — A306

1984, July 1   Wmk. 387   Perf. 12

1064	A306	4b Map, emblem	1.00	.35

Seated Buddha, Chiang Saen Style — A307

Intl. Letter Writing Week — A308

Seated Buddhas in various styles.

Perf. 14½x14

1984, July 12   Wmk. 233

1065	A307	1.25b shown	.25	.20
1066	A307	7b Sukhothai	2.10	.80
1067	A307	8.50b U-Thong	1.00	1.00
1068	A307	9.50b Ayutthaya	1.00	1.00
		Nos. 1065-1068 (4)	4.35	3.00

Wmk. 385

1984, Oct. 7   Litho.   Perf. 13½

Medicinal Succulents: 1.50b, Alocasia indica. 2b, Aloe barbadensis. 4b, Gynura pseudochina DC. 10b, Rhoeo spathacea.

1069	A308	1.50b multicolored	.35	.25
1070	A308	2b multicolored	.55	.25
1071	A308	4b multicolored	.90	.45
1072	A308	10b multicolored	2.75	1.25
		Nos. 1069-1072 (4)	4.55	2.20

Princess Mother (b. 1900) — A309

UN Day — A310

Perf. 15x14

1984, Oct. 21   Wmk. 233

1073	A309	1.50b Portrait	.60	.25

1984, Oct. 24   Wmk. 233

1074	A310	1.50b Woman threshing rice	.60	.25

Local Butterflies — A311

Wmk. 329

1984, Nov. 27   Photo.   Perf. 13½

1075	A311	2b Bhutanitis lidderdalei	.65	.30
1076	A311	3b Stichophthalma louisa	.65	.30
1077	A311	5b Parthenos sylvia	1.40	.90
1078	A311	7b Stichophthalma godfreyi	2.40	.90
		Nos. 1075-1078 (4)	5.10	2.40

King Type of 1980

Perf. 13½x13, 14x15 (1.50b, 2b)
Wmk. 329, 233 (1.50b, 2b)

1984-87   Litho.

1080	A256	1b Prus blue	.25	.20
1081	A256	1.50b brt yel org ('85)	.35	.20
1082	A256	2b dk car ('85)	.45	.20
a.		Wmk. 387, perf. 11x13½ ('86?)	4.00	.50
b.		Wmk. 387, perf. 14½x14 ('87)	1.50	.30

Engr.

1083	A256	2b hn brn & gray vio	5.00	.20
1084	A256	4b turq bl & hn brn	.75	.25
1085	A256	6.50b dk yel grn & ol brn	1.00	.35
1086	A256	7b dl red brn & sep	1.25	.40
1087	A256	7.50b dk org & saph ('85)	1.25	.50
1088	A256	8b brn vio & ol grn ('85)	1.40	.50
1089	A256	9b int bl & dk ol bis ('85)	1.75	.60
1090	A256	10b hn brn & sl grn	2.00	.65
1091	A256	20b dk org & grn	7.00	1.25
1092	A256	50b dp vit & grn	8.50	3.00
1093	A256	100b dp org & dk bl	17.00	6.00
		Nos. 1080-1093 (14)	47.95	14.30

For surcharge see No. 1212.

Children's Day — A313

Children's drawings.

Wmk. 385

1985, Jan. 12   Litho.   Perf. 13½

1101	A313	1.50b Pedestrians, over-pass	.40	.20
1102	A313	1.50b Climbing over-pass, vert.	.40	.20

Bangkok Mail Center Opening — A314

1985, Feb. 25

1103	A314	1.50b multicolored	.60	.25

Phuket Province Heroes Bicent. — A315

Perf. 15x14

1985, Mar. 13   Litho.   Wmk. 233

1104	A315	2b multicolored	.35	.25

Tao-Thep-Krasattri, Tao-Sri-Sundhorn Monument.

Government Savings Bank, 72nd Anniv. — A316

1985, Apr. 1   Perf. 14x15

1105	A316	1.50b King Rama VI, headquarters	.60	.25

Intl. Telecommunications Satellite Org., 20th Anniv. — A317

1985, Apr. 6   Wmk. 387   Perf. 12

1106	A317	2b multicolored	.60	.25

Thai Airways Intl., 25th Anniv. — A318

Wmk. 385

1985, May 1   Litho.   Perf. 13

1107	A318	2b DC-6	.30	.20
1108	A318	7.50b DC-10	1.40	.65
1109	A318	8.50b Airbus A-300	1.60	.90
1110	A318	9.50b Boeing 747	1.60	1.00
		Nos. 1107-1110 (4)	4.90	2.75

Natl. Flag and UPU Emblem — A319

1985, July 1   Wmk. 387   Perf. 12
1111 A319 2b shown   .25 .20

Perf. 13½
Wmk. 385
1112 A319 10b Flag and ITU emblem   1.25 .90

Thai membership to UPU and Intl. Telecommunications Union, cent.

Natl. Communications Day, Aug. 5 — A320

1985, Aug. 4   Wmk. 329   Perf. 13½
1113 A320 2b multicolored   .60 .25

THAIPEX '85, Aug. 4-13 — A321

1985, Aug. 4   Wmk. 385
1114 A321 2b Aisvarya Pavilion, vert.   .50 .20
1115 A321 3b Varopas Piman Pavilion   .75 .25
1116 A321 7b Vehas Camrun Pavilion   1.25 .60
1117 A321 10b Vitoon Tassana Tower, vert.   1.50 .95
    a. Souv. sheet of 4, #1114-1117   57.50
    Nos. 1114-1117 (4)   4.00 2.00

No. 1117a exists imperf, sold for 40b.

Natl. Science Day, Aug. 18 — A322

1985, Aug. 18   Wmk. 387   Perf. 12
1118 A322 2b King Rama IV, solar eclipse   .60 .60

1885 Seal, Modern Map and Crest — A323

Perf. 14½x15
1985, Sept. 3   Wmk. 233
1119 A323 2b multicolored   .60 .25
Royal Thai Survey Department, Cent.

13th SEA Games, Bangkok, Dec. 8-17 — A324

Designs: a, Boxing. b, Shot put. c, Badminton. d, Javelin. e, Weight lifting.

1985, Oct. 1   Wmk. 387   Perf. 12
1120 Strip of 5   2.75 2.50
    a.-e. A324 2b, any single   .50   .20
    f. Souv. sheet of 5, #a.-e. + label 27.50 22.50

No. 1120f sold for 20b.

Climbing Plants — A325

UN Child Survival Campaign A326

1985, Oct. 6   Wmk. 385   Perf. 13½
1121 A325 2b Allemanda cathartica   .65 .25
1122 A325 3b Jasminum auriculatum   .90 .25
1123 A325 7b Passiflora laurifolia   1.40 .70
1124 A325 10b Antigonon leptopus   1.60 .80
    Nos. 1121-1124 (4)   4.55 2.00

International Letter Writing Week.

1985, Oct. 24
1125 A326 2b multicolored   .60 .25
UN Day.

Prince Kromamun Bidyalabh Bridhyakorn (1885-1974), Govt. Minister — A327

Rangsit (1885-1951), Prince of Jainad — A328

1985, Dec. 8   Wmk. 387   Perf. 12
1132 A332 1b Volleyball   .60 .30
1133 A332 2b Sepak-takraw   .60 .30
1134 A332 3b Women's gymnastics   .60 .30
1135 A332 4b Bowling   1.00 .60
    a. Souv. sheet, #1132-1135 + label 25.00 21.00
    Nos. 1132-1135 (4)   2.80 1.50

No. 1135a sold for 20b.

1985, Nov. 7
1126 A327 2b multi   5.75 1.25
1126A A327 2b multi, diff.   .75   .25
    b. Pair, #1126-1126A   35.00 29.00

No. 1126A has flower design framing portrait reversed.

Perf. 15x14½
1985, Nov. 12   Wmk. 233
1127 A328 1.50b multicolored   .60 .25

Asian-Pacific Postal Union, 5th Congress, Nov. 25-Dec. 4 — A329

1985, Nov. 25 Wmk. 385 Perf. 13½
1128 A329 2b multicolored   .20 .20
1129 A329 10b multicolored   1.00 .50

Intl. Youth Year A330

Perf. 14x15
1985, Nov. 26   Wmk. 233
1130 A330 2b multicolored   .60 .25

12th Asian-Pacific Dental Congress, Bangkok, Dec. 5-10 — A331

1985, Dec. 5
1131 A331 2b multicolored   .60 .25

13th SEA Games — A332

French Envoys — A333

1985, Dec. 12 Wmk. 385 Perf. 13
1136 A333 2b shown   .25 .2
1137 A333 8.50b Thai envoys   1.25 .7

Diplomatic relations with France, 300th anniv

Domestic Express Mail Service Inauguration — A334

1986, Jan. 1
1138 A334 2b multicolored   .60 .2
Intl. Express Mail Service, EMS, 3rd anniv.

Wildlife Conservation — A335

Marine turtles.

1986, Jan. 8   Wmk. 329
1139 A335 1.50b Chelonia mydas   .45 .25
1140 A335 3b Eretmochelys imbricata   .85 .25
1141 A335 5b Dermochelys coriacea   2.50 .45
1142 A335 10b Lepidochelys olivacea   2.10 .65
    Nos. 1139-1142 (4)   5.90 1.60

Natl. Children's Day — A336

Statue of Sunthon Phu, Poet — A337

Design: Children picking lotus, by Areeya Makarabhundhu, age 12.

1986, Jan. 11   Wmk. 385
1143 A336 2b multicolored   .60 .25

1986, June 26
1144 A337 2b multicolored   .60 .25

Fruit Type of 1979

1986, June 26   Wmk. 385
1145 A237 2b Watermelon   1.00 .25
1146 A237 2b Malay apple   1.00 .25
1147 A237 6b Pomelo   1.50 .65
1148 A237 6b Papaya   1.50 .65
    Nos. 1145-1148 (4)   5.00 1.80

Nos. 1145-1148 horiz.

Natl. Year of the Trees A338

1986, July 21
149 A338 2b multicolored   .60 .25

Communications Day — A339

1986, Aug. 4
150 A339 2b multicolored   .60 .25

Bamboo Baskets — A340

1986, Oct. 5
1151 A340 2b Chalom   .50 .20
1152 A340 2b Krabung   .50 .20
1153 A340 6b Kratib   1.00 .45
1154 A340 6b Kaleb   1.00 .45
    Nos. 1151-1154 (4)   3.00 1.30
    Intl. Letter Writing Week.

Intl. Peace Year A341

1986, Oct. 24
1155 A341 2b multicolored   .60 .25

Productivity Year — A342

1986, Oct. 24   Wmk. 329
1156 A342 2b multicolored   .60 .25

6th ASEAN Orchid Congress — A343

1986, Nov. 7   Wmk. 385
1157 A343 2b Vanda varavuth, vert.   .60 .25
1158 A343 3b Ascocenda emma, vert.   .60 .30
1159 A343 4b Dendrobium srisiam   1.10 .85

1160 A343 5b Dendrobium ekapol panda   1.10 .60
  a. Souv. sheet of 4, #1157-1160   85.00 67.50
    Nos. 1157-1160 (4)   3.40 2.00
    No. 1160a sold for 25b.

Fungi A344

Perf. 13x13½
1986, Nov. 26   Wmk. 329   Photo.
1161 A344 2b Volvariella volvacea   .55 .20
1162 A344 2b Pleurotus ostreatus   .55 .20
1163 A344 6b Auricularia polytricha   1.40 .65
1164 A344 6b Pleurotus cystidiosus   1.40 .65
    Nos. 1161-1164 (4)   3.90 1.70

Fisheries Dept., 60th Anniv. — A345

    Wmk. 385
1986, Dec. 16   Litho.   *Perf. 13½*
1165 A345 2b Morulius chrysophekadion   .60 .25
1166 A345 2b Notopterus blanci   .60 .25
1167 A345 7b Scleropages formosus   1.10 .65
1168 A345 7b Pangasianodon gigas   1.10 .65
    Nos. 1165-1168 (4)   3.40 1.80

No. 653 Surcharged in Dark Olive Green

Perf. 14x13½
1986, Dec.   Photo.   Wmk. 233
1168A A161 1b on 20s blue   .60 .25

Children's Day — A346

Child's drawing.

Perf. 14½x15
1987, Jan. 10   Litho.   Wmk. 387
1169 2b School, playground   .60 .25
1170 2b Pool   .60 .25
  a. A346 Pair, #1169-1170   1.25 1.00
    No. 1170a has continuous design.

F-16 & F-5 Fighter Planes, Pilot — A347

1987, Mar. 27   Wmk. 385   *Perf. 13½*
1171 A347 2b multicolored   .60 .25
    Royal Thai Air Force, 72nd anniv.

King Rama III (Nang Klao, 1787-1851) — A348

Perf. 15x14½
1987, Mar. 31   Wmk. 387
1172 A348 2b multicolored   .60 .25

Ministry of Communications, 75th Anniv. — A349

1987, Apr. 1
1173 A349 2b multicolored   .60 .25

Forestry Year — A350

1987, July 11   Wmk. 385   *Perf. 13½*
1174 A350 2b multicolored   .60 .25

THAIPEX '87 — A351

Gold artifacts.

1987, Aug. 4   Wmk. 385
1175 A351 2b Peacock, vert.   .40 .20
1176 A351 2b Hand mirrors, vert.   .40 .20
1177 A351 6b Water urn, finger bowls   1.10 .55
1178 A351 6b Dragon vase   1.10 .55
  a. Souv. sheet of 4, #1175-1178   57.50 47.50
    Nos. 1175-1178 (4)   3.00 1.50
    No. 1178a exists imperf.

ASEAN, 20th Anniv. — A352

1987, Aug. 20
1179 A352 2b multicolored   .30 .20
1180 A352 3b multicolored   .60 .30
1181 A352 4b multicolored   .60 .40
1182 A352 5b multicolored   .90 .45
    Nos. 1179-1182 (4)   2.40 1.35

Natl. Communications Day — A353

1987, Aug. 4
1183 A353 2b multicolored   .60 .25

Chulachamklao Royal Military Academy, Cent. — A354

Design: School crest, King Rama V, and King Rama IX conferring sword on graduating officer.

1987, Aug. 5
1184 A354 2b multicolored   1.00 .25

Intl. Literacy Day — A355

Tourism Year — A356

1987, Sept. 8
1185 A355 2b multicolored   .60 .25

1987, Sept. 18
    2b, Flower-offering ceremony, Saraburi province. 3b, Duan Sib Festival, Nakhon Si Thammarat province. 5b, Bang Fai Festival, Yasothon province. 7b, Loi Krathong Festival, Sukhothai province.
1186 A356 2b multicolored   .25 .20
1187 A356 3b multicolored   .60 .30
1188 A356 5b multicolored   .90 .40
1189 A356 7b multicolored   1.25 .60
    Nos. 1186-1189 (4)   3.00 1.50

Auditor General's Office, 72nd Anniv. — A357

1987, Sept. 18
1190 A357 2b multicolored   .60 .25

Diplomatic Relations Between
Thailand and Japan, Cent. — A358

1987, Sept. 26   **Wmk. 329**
1191 A358 2b multicolored   .60 .25

Intl. Letter Writing
Week — A359

Floral garlands.

1987, Oct. 4   **Wmk. 385**
1192	A359	2b	Floral tassel	.35 .20
1193	A359	3b	Tasselled garland	.65 .30
1194	A359	5b	Wrist garland	.75 .40
1195	A359	7b	Double-ended garland	1.25 .65

Nos. 1192-1195 (4)   3.00 1.55

Thai Pavilion — A360

1987, Oct. 9   **Wmk. 387**   **Perf. 15**
1196 A360 2b multicolored   .60 .25

Social Education and Cultural Center
inauguration.

A361

A362

King Bhumibol Adulyadej, 60th
Birthday — A363

Royal ciphers and: #1197, Adulyadej as a
child. #1198, King and Queen, wedding portrait, 1950. #1199, King taking the Oath of
Accession, 1950. #1200, King dressed as a
monk, collecting alms. #1201, Greeting 100
year-old woman. #1202, In military uniform
holding pen and with hill tribes. #1203, Royal
couple visiting wounded servicemen. #1204,
Visiting farm. #1205, Royal family. #1206,

King, Queen Sirikit. #1207, Princess Mother
Somdej Phra Sri Nakarindra Boromrajjonnani,
emblem of Medical Volunteer Assoc. #1208,
Crown Prince Maha Vajiralongkorn, crown
prince's royal standard. #1209, Princess Maha
Chakri Sirindhorn, emblem of Sai Jai Thai
Foundation. #1210, Princess Chulabhorn,
Albert Einstein gold medal awarded by
UNESCO.

         Wmk. 329
1987, Dec. 5   **Photo.**   **Perf. 13½**
1197	A361	2b	shown	.55 .25
1198	A361	2b	multicolored	.55 .25
1199	A361	2b	multicolored	.55 .25
1200	A361	2b	multicolored	.55 .25
1201	A361	2b	multicolored	.55 .25
1202	A361	2b	multicolored	.55 .25
1203	A361	2b	multicolored	.55 .25
1204	A361	2b	multicolored	.55 .25
a.			Souv. sheet, #1197-1204	35.00 30.00

       Litho.
       Wmk. 385
1205	A362	2b	multicolored	1.10 .30
1206	A362	2b	multicolored	1.10 .30
1207	A362	2b	multicolored	1.10 .30
1208	A362	2b	multicolored	1.10 .30
1209	A362	2b	multicolored	1.10 .30
1210	A362	2b	multicolored	1.10 .30

    Litho. & Embossed
1211 A363 100b vio blue &
gold   65.00 65.00
Nos. 1197-1211 (15)   76.00 68.80

Size of Nos. 1206-1210: 45x27mm. No.
1211 printed in sheets of 10. No. 1204a sold
for 40b.

No. 1081 Surcharged

1987 Litho. Wmk. 233 Perf. 14x15
1212 A256 2b on 1.50b brt yel org   .60 .25

Children's
Day — A364

Thai Agricultural
Cooperatives,
72nd
Anniv. — A365

      Perf. 14x14½
1988, Jan. 9   **Litho.**   **Wmk. 387**
1213 A364 2b multicolored   .60 .25

1988, Feb. 26   **Wmk. 387**
1214 A365 2b Prince Bridhy-
alongkorn, founder   .60 .25

Royal
Siam
Soc.,
84th
Anniv.
A366

1988, Mar. 10   **Perf. 14½x14**
1215 A366 2b multicolored   .60 .25

Cultural Heritage Preservation — A367

Ruins in Sukhothai Historic Park.

1988, Apr. 2   **Perf. 14½x14**
1216	A367	2b	Wat Phra Phai Luang	.25 .20
1217	A367	3b	Wat Traphang Thonglang	.60 .30
1218	A367	4b	Wat Maha That	.90 .60
1219	A367	6b	Thewalai Maha Kaset	1.25 .70

Nos. 1216-1219 (4)   3.00 1.80

Red
Cross
Fair
A368

1988, Apr.   **Wmk. 387**   **Perf. 14**
1220 A368 2b Prevention of rabies   .60 .25

King Rama V,
Founder — A369

Intl. Council of
Women,
Cent. — A371

Pheasants — A370

      Perf. 14x14½
1988, Apr. 26   **Wmk. 387**
1221 A369 5b multicolored   2.10 .70

Siriraj Hospital, cent.

        Wmk. 329
1988, June 15   **Photo.**   **Perf. 13½**
1222	A370	2b	Crested fireback	.30 .20
1223	A370	3b	Kalij	.60 .25
1224	A370	6b	Silver pheasant	1.25 .60
1225	A370	7b	Hume's pheasant	1.50 .75

Nos. 1222-1225 (4)   3.65 1.80

Nos. 935a, 935 Surcharged

a   b

      Perf. 11x13
1988-92   **Litho.**   **Wmk. 38?**
1226	A256(a)	1b on 1.25b		.60
1226A	A256(b)	1b on 1.25b		.75
b.		Wmk. 368		1.40 1

Issued: #1226, 1988; #1226A, Dec. 5, 1992?

1988, June 26   **Wmk. 385**   **Perf. 13**
1227 A371 2b multicolored   .60 .2

King Bhumibol Adulyadej
A372   A372a

      Perf. 13½x13
1988-95   **Litho.**   **Wmk. 387**
1228 A372 25s brown   .20 .2?

      Perf. 14x14½
1229	A372	50s olive		.20 .2
a.		Wmk. 329		.60 .2
1230	A372	1b brt blue		.20 .2
		Complete booklet, 5 #1230		1.25
a.		Photo, wmk. 233		1.00 .2?
b.		Photo., wmk. 340, perf. 13½x13¾		.20 .2?
1233	A372	2b scarlet		.75 .2?
		Complete booklet, 5 #1233		1.25
a.		Wmk. 329		.75 .2?
b.		Photo., wmk. 340, perf. 13½x13¾		.25 .2?
		Complete booklet, 5 #1233b		1.25

       Photo.
       Wmk. 233
       Perf. 14½
1236 A372 1b bright blue   .20 .2?
Nos. 1228-1236 (5)   1.55 1.0?

No. 1236 has blue background without halo
effect around head. See #1230.
Issued: 25s, 8/12/92; 1b-2b, 7/2/88; 50s,
7/28/93; #1230a, 1236, 1990; #1233a, 1992;
#1230b, 1233b, 12/5/94; #1229a, 1995.

      Perf. 13½x13
1988-90   **Engr.**   **Wmk. 329**
1241	A372a	3b brn & bluish gray	.35	.25
1242	A372a	4b brt bl & red brn	.45	.30
1243	A372a	5b violet & brn	.40	.30
1244	A372a	6b green & vio	.45	.35
1245	A372a	7b red brn & dk brn	.80	.55
1246	A372a	8b red brn & gray ol	.65	.40
1247	A372a	9b dk blue & brn	.70	.40
1248	A372a	10b henna brn & blk	1.00	.25
1249	A372a	20b brn org & sage grn	2.00	.65
1250	A372a	25b olive grn & dark blue	2.50	.90
1251	A372a	50b violet & grn	5.00	1.00
1252	A372a	100b brn org & bluish blk	10.00	2.00

Nos. 1241-1252 (12)   24.30 7.35

Issued: 3b, 10b, 50b, 100b, 12/5; 5b, 6b, 8b,
9b, 7/1/89; 4b, 7b, 20b, 12/5/89; 25b, 1/9/90.

A373

A375

King Bhumibol's Reign (since 1950) — A374

Designs: No. 1253, King Bhumibol. Regalia: No. 1254, Great Crown of Victory. No. 1255, Sword of Victory and matching scabbard. No. 1256, Scepter. No. 1257, Fan and feather fly swatter. No. 1258, Royal slippers.

Canopied thrones in the Grand Palace: No. 1259, Queen's round ottoman on 1-tier dais in front of decorative screen. No. 1260, King's throne on 1-tier dais in front of decorative screen. No. 1261, 3-Tier throne with 3 gilded trees. No. 1262, 3-Canopy throne on high gold dais. No. 1263, 3-Tier throne with 4 gilded trees, altar in background. No. 1264, 3-Canopy throne on 5-stair dais, in front of arch flanked by columns.

Wmk. 385

1988, July 2		Litho.	Perf. 13½
1253 A373	2b shown	2.00	.25

Photo.

Wmk. 329

1254 A374	2b multi, vert.	.60	.30
1255 A374	2b multicolored	.60	.30
1256 A374	2b multicolored	.60	.30
1257 A374	2b multicolored	.60	.30
1258 A374	2b multicolored	.60	.30

Litho.

Perf. 14x14½

Wmk. 387

1259 A375	2b multicolored	.60	.30
1260 A375	2b multicolored	.60	.30
1261 A375	2b multicolored	.60	.30
1262 A375	2b multicolored	.60	.30
1263 A375	2b multicolored	.60	.30
1264 A375	2b multicolored	.60	.30
a.	Souv. sheet of 6, #1259-1264	57.50	47.50
	Nos. 1253-1264 (12)	8.60	3.55

No. 1264a sold for 25b.

Arbor Year A376

Perf. 14½x14

1988, July 29		Litho.	Wmk. 387
1265 A376	2b multicolored	.60	.25

Natl. Communications Day — A377

Wmk. Alternating Interlaced Wavy Lines (340)

1988, Aug. 4			Perf. 13½
1266 A377	2b multicolored	.60	.25

Intl. Letter Writing Week — A378

Designs: Coconut leaf sculptures.

Perf. 14½x14

1988, Oct. 9			Wmk. 387
1267 A378	2b Grasshopper	.40	.20
1268 A378	2b Fish	.40	.20
1269 A378	6b Bird	1.10	.50
1270 A378	6b Takro (box)	1.10	.50
	Nos. 1267-1270 (4)	3.00	1.40

Housing Development — A379

Wmk. 233

1988, Oct. 24	Litho.		Perf. 14
1271 A379	2b multicolored	.60	.25

Traffic Safety — A380

King's Bodyguard, 120th Anniv. — A381

1988, Nov. 11	Wmk. 329		Perf. 13½
1272 A380	2b multicolored	.60	.25

1988, Nov. 11			Wmk. 385
1273 A381	2b Chulalongkorn	3.00	.40

New Year — A382

Flowers.

1988, Dec. 1			Wmk. 387
1274 A382	1b Crotalaria sessiliflora	.45	.30
1275 A382	1b Uvaria grandiflora	.45	.30
1276 A382	1b Reinwardtia trigyna	.45	.30
1277 A382	1b Impatiens griffithii	.45	.30
	Nos. 1274-1277 (4)	1.80	1.20

Thai Royal Orders Type of 1979

Floral background: Nos. 1278-1279, Knight Grand Commander, Order of Rama, 1918. Nos. 1280-1281, Knight Grand Cordon, Order of the White Elephant, 1861. Nos. 1282-1283, Knight Grand Cordon, Order of the Crown of Thailand, 1869. Nos. 1284-1285, Ratana Varabhorn Order of Merit, 1911. Pairs have continuous designs.

1988, Dec. 5			Wmk. 385
1278 A243	2b multicolored	.25	.20
1279 A244	2b multicolored	.25	.20
a.	Pair, #1278-1279	.50	.40
1280 A243	3b multicolored	.50	.25
1281 A244	3b multicolored	.50	.25
a.	Pair, #1280-1281	.50	.50
1282 A243	5b multicolored	1.00	.75
1283 A244	5b multicolored	.75	.30
a.	Pair, #1282-1283	1.50	1.10
1284 A243	7b multicolored	1.00	.40
1285 A244	7b multicolored	1.00	.40
a.	Pair, #1284-1285	2.00	1.50
	Nos. 1278-1285 (8)	5.25	2.75

A383

Buddha Monthon Celebrations, Tambol Salaya — A384

Perf. 14x15, 15x14

1988, Dec. 5			Wmk. 233
1286 A383	2b Birthplace	.35	.20
1287 A383	3b Enlightenment place	.45	.25
1288 A383	4b Location of 1st sermon	.65	.45
1289 A383	5b Place Buddha achieved nirvana	.85	.40
1290 A384	6b Statue	1.00	.50
	Nos. 1286-1290 (5)	3.30	1.80

Souvenir Sheet

Perf. 14½x14

1291 A384	6b like No. 1290	24.00	20.00

No. 1291 sold for 15b.

Children's Day — A385

"Touch" paintings by blind youth: No. 1292, *Floating Market,* by Thongbai Siyam. No. 1293, *Flying Bird,* by Kwanchai Kerd-Daeng. No. 1294, *Little Mermaid,* by Chalermpol Jiengmai. No. 1295, *Golden Fish,* by Natetip Korsantirak.

Wmk. 387

1989, Jan. 14	Litho.		Perf. 13½
1292 A385	2b multicolored	.45	.25
1293 A385	2b multicolored	.45	.25
1294 A385	2b multicolored	.45	.25
1295 A385	2b multicolored	.45	.25
	Nos. 1292-1295 (4)	1.80	1.00

Communications Authority of Thailand, 12th Anniv. — A386

1989, Feb. 25			Perf. 14½x14
1296 A386	2b multicolored	.60	.25

Chulalongkorn University, 72nd Anniv. — A387

Design: 2b, Statue of Chulalongkorn and King Vajiravudh in front of university auditorium.

1989, Mar. 26			
1297 A387	2b multicolored	.60	.25

A388

A389

1989, Mar. 31	Litho.		Wmk. 233
1298 A388	2b shown	.60	.30

Wmk. 387

Perf. 13½

1299 A388	10b Emblem	1.50	.60

Thai Red Cross Society, 96th anniv. (2b); Intl. Red Cross and Red Crescent organizations, 125th annivs. (10b).

Perf. 14x14½

1989, Apr. 2		Wmk. 387

Phra Nakhon Khiri Historical Park: 2b, Wat Phra Kaeo. 3b, Chatchawan Wiangchai Observatory. 5b, Phra That Chom Phet Stupa. 6b, Wetchayan Wichian Phrasat Throne Hall.

1300 A389	2b multicolored	.30	.20
1301 A389	3b multicolored	.90	.40
1302 A389	5b multicolored	1.25	.90
1303 A389	6b multicolored	1.25	.90
	Nos. 1300-1303 (4)	3.70	2.40

Natl. Lottery Office, 50th Anniv. — A390

1989, Apr. 5			Perf. 13½
1304 A390	2b multicolored	.50	.25

Seashells — A391

1989, June 28	Wmk. 329		Perf. 13½
1305 A391	2b Conus thailandis	.30	.20
1306 A391	3b Spondylus princeps	.60	.30
1307 A391	6b Cyprea guttata	.95	.75
1308 A391	10b Nautilus pompilius	3.00	1.50
	Nos. 1305-1308 (4)	4.85	2.75

Arts and Crafts Year A392

Wmk. 387
1989, June 28   Litho.   Perf. 13½
1309 A392 2b Ceramic figurines   .40   .20
1310 A392 2b Gold niello ginger
             jar, chicken   .40   .20
1311 A392 6b Textiles   1.10   .50
1312 A392 6b Gemstone flower
             ornament   1.10   .50
    Nos. 1309-1312 (4)   3.00 1.40

Asia-Pacific Telecommunications
Organization, 10th Anniv. — A393

APT emblem, map of submarine cable network and satellites of member nations.

1989, July 1   Wmk. 329   Perf. 13½
1313 A393 9b multicolored   1.00   .50

Phya Anuman
Rajadhon (1888-
1969),
Ethnologist
A394

1989, July 1   Wmk. 387   Perf. 13½
1314 A394 2b multicolored   .50   .20

9th Natl. Phil.
Exhib., Aug. 4-
13 — A395

1989, Aug. 4   Wmk. 233   Perf. 15x14
Various mailboxes.
1315 A395 2b multicolored   .30   .20
1316 A395 3b multi, diff.   .45   .25
1317 A395 4b multi, diff.   .60   .35
1318 A395 5b multi, diff.   .75   .40
1319 A395 6b multi, diff.   .90   .50
  a. Souv. sheet #1315-1319,
      perf 14   35.00 29.00
    Nos. 1315-1319 (5)   3.00 1.70

No. 1319a sold for 30b.

A396

A398

A397

Wmk. 387
1989, June 26   Litho.   Perf. 13½
1320 A396 2b multicolored   .50   .20

Intl. Anti-drug Day.

1989, Aug. 4   Wmk. 233   Perf. 14x15
1321 A397 2b multicolored   .50   .20

Post and Telecommunications School, cent.

1989, Aug. 4   Wmk. 387   Perf. 13½
1322 A398 2b multicolored   .50   .20

Natl. Communications Day.

Dragonflies — A399

Wmk. 329
1989, Oct. 8   Photo.   Perf. 13½
1323 A399 2b shown   .40   .20
1324 A399 5b multi, diff.   .75   .50
1325 A399 6b multi, diff.   1.25   .60
1326 A399 10b Damselfly   1.60 1.50
  a. Souv. sheet of 4, #1323-
      1326   30.00 30.00
    Nos. 1323-1326 (4)   4.00 2.80

Intl. Letter Writing Week. #1326a sold for
40b.

Transport and Communications
Decade for Asia and the
Pacific — A400

Perf. 14½x14
1989, Oct. 24   Litho.   Wmk. 387
1327 A400 2b multicolored   .50   .20

Mental Health   New Year
Care,   1990 — A402
Cent. — A401

1989, Nov. 1   Wmk. 233   Perf. 15x14
1328 A401 2b multicolored   .50   .20

Perf. 14x14½
1989, Nov. 15   Wmk. 387
Flowering plants.
1329 A402 1b Hypericum uralum   .30   .25
1330 A402 1b Uraria rufescens   .30   .25
1331 A402 1b Manglietia garrettii   .30   .25
1332 A402 1b Aeschynanthus
             macranthus   .30   .25
  a. Souv. sheet of 4, #1329-1332   6.00 6.00
    Nos. 1329-1332 (4)   1.20 1.00

No. 1332a sold for 14b.

Insects — A403

Wmk. 329
1989, Nov. 15   Photo.   Perf. 13½
1333 A403 2b Catacanthus in-
             carnatus   .40   .20
1334 A403 3b Aristobia approxi-
             mator   .60   .30
1335 A403 6b Chrysochroa
             chinensis   .90   .50
1336 A403 10b Enoplotrupes
             sharpi   1.60 1.25
    Nos. 1333-1336 (4)   3.50 2.25

Population and Housing Census of
1990 — A404

Wmk. 387
1990, Jan. 1   Litho.   Perf. 13½
1337 A404 2b multicolored   .50   .20

Children's Day   Emblems
A405   A406

Perf. 15x14
1990, Jan. 13   Wmk. 233
1338 A405 2b Jumping rope,
             horiz.   .45   .20
1339 A405 2b Sports   .45   .20

1990, Mar. 29   Wmk. 387   Perf. 13½
1340 A406 2b multicolored   .50   .20

WHO Fight AIDS Worldwide campaign and
the Natl. Red Cross Soc.

Thai Heritage Conservation
Day — A407

Prize-winning inlaid mother-of-pearl containers: No. 1341, Tiap (footed bowl with lid), vert.
No. 1342, Phan waenfa (two-tiered vessel),
vert. No. 1343, Lung (lidded bowl). No. 1344,
Chiat klom (spade-shaped lidded container
signifying noble rank).

1990, Apr. 2   Photo.   Wmk. 329
1341 A407 2b multicolored   .40   .20
1342 A407 2b multicolored   .40   .20
1343 A407 6b multicolored   1.10   .90
1344 A407 8b multicolored   1.10   .90
    Nos. 1341-1344 (4)   3.00 2.20

A408

A409

Minerals.

Perf. 14x14½
1990, June 29   Litho.   Wmk. 387
1345 A408 2b Tin   .45   .25
1346 A408 3b Zinc   .70   .40
1347 A408 5b Lead   .85   .60
1348 A408 6b Fluorite   1.00   .80
  a. Souv. sheet of 4, #1345-1348   6.25 6.25
    Nos. 1345-1348 (4)   3.00 2.05

No. 1348a sold for 30b, exists imperf.

1990, May 16
1349 A409 2b multicolored   .50   .20

Faculty of Dentistry, Chulalongkorn Univ.,
50th anniv.

Communications Day — A410

1990, Aug. 4   Perf. 14½x14
1350 A410 2b multicolored   .50   .20

Asian-Pacific Postal Training Center,
20th Anniv. — A411

1990, Sept. 10
1351 A411 2b multicolored   .35   .20
1352 A411 8b multicolored   .90   .65

Rotary Intl. in Thailand, 60th
Anniv. — A412

1990, Sept. 16   Perf. 13½
1353 A412 2b Health care   .45   .25
1354 A412 3b Immunizations   .60   .30
1355 A412 6b Literacy project   .90   .55

356 A412 8b Thai museum project | 1.50 | 1.00
Nos. 1353-1356 (4) | 3.45 | 2.10

Intl. Letter Writing Week, 1990 — A413

Illustration reduced.

1990, Oct. 7   *Perf. 14*
1357 A413 2b multicolored | .45 | .25
1358 A413 3b multi, diff. | .70 | .40
1359 A413 5b multi, diff. | .85 | .60
1360 A413 6b multi, diff. | 1.00 | .80
a.   Souv. sheet of 4, #1357-1360 | 6.25 | 6.25
Nos. 1357-1360 (4) | 3.00 | 2.05

No. 1360a sold for 30b. Exists imperf, value same as perf.

Dept. of Comptroller-General, Cent. — A414

1990, Oct. 7   *Perf. 14½x14*
1361 A414 2b multicolored | .50 | .20

A415   A416

1990, Oct. 21   *Perf. 14x14½*
1362 A415 2b multicolored | 1.75 | .25

Princess Mother, 90th birthday.

1990, Nov. 15   **Wmk. 233**   *Perf. 14½*
Flowers: No. 1363, Cyrtandromoea grandiflora. No. 1364, Rhododendron arboreum. No. 1365, Merremia vitifolia. No. 1366, Afgekia mahidolae.

1363 A416 1b multicolored | .30 | .25
1364 A416 1b multicolored | .30 | .25
1365 A416 1b multicolored | .30 | .25
1366 A416 1b multicolored | .30 | .25
a.   Sheet of 4, #1363-1366 | 3.75 | 3.75
Nos. 1363-1366 (4) | 1.20 | 1.00

New Year 1991. No. 1366a sold for 10b. Exists imperf, value same as perf.
See Nos. 1417-1420.

Wiman Mek Royal Hall — A417

Royal Throne Rooms in the Dusit Palace: 3b, Ratcharit Rungrot Royal House. 4b, Aphisek Dusit Royal Hall. 5b, Amphon Sathan Palace. 6b, Udon Phak Royal Hall. 8b, Anantasamakhom Throne Hall.

Wmk. 329
1990, Dec. 5   **Photo.**   *Perf. 13½*
1367 A417 2b multicolored | .30 | .20
1368 A417 3b multicolored | .65 | .25
1369 A417 4b multicolored | .65 | .40

1370 A417 5b multicolored | .75 | .50
1371 A417 6b multicolored | .95 | .50
1372 A417 8b multicolored | 1.10 | .75
Nos. 1367-1372 (6) | 4.40 | 2.60

Somdet Phra Maha Samanachao Kromphra Paramanuchitchinorot (1790-1853), Supreme Patriarch — A418

1990, Dec. 11   **Wmk. 387**   *Perf. 13½*
1373 A418 2b multicolored | .50 | .20

Petroleum Authority, 12th Anniv. — A419

Perf. 14½x14
1990, Dec. 29   **Litho.**   **Wmk. 387**
1374 A419 2b multicolored | .50 | .20

Locomotives — A420

Designs: 2b, No. 6, Krauss & Co., Germany, 1908. 3b, No. 32, Kyosan Kogyo, Japan, 1949. 5b, No. 715, C56, Japan, 1946. 6b, No. 953, Mikado, Japan, 1949-1951.

Perf. 14½x14
1990, Dec. 29   **Litho.**   **Wmk. 387**
1375 A420 2b multicolored | .35 | .25
1376 A420 3b multicolored | .70 | .35
1377 A420 5b multicolored | 1.00 | 1.00
1378 A420 6b multicolored | 1.40 | 1.10
a.   Souv. sheet of 4, #1375-1378 | 7.50 | 7.50
Nos. 1375-1378 (4) | 3.45 | 2.70

No. 1378a sold for 25b. Exists imperf, value same as perf.

Children's Day — A421

Children's games: 2b, Tops. 5b, Race. 6b, Blind-man's buff.

1991, Jan. 12
1379 A421 2b multicolored | .35 | .25
1380 A421 3b shown | .35 | .30
1381 A421 5b multicolored | .70 | .40
1382 A421 6b multicolored | 1.10 | .50
Nos. 1379-1382 (4) | 2.50 | 1.45

A422

A423

1991, Feb. 17   *Perf. 14x14½*
1383 A422 2b multicolored | .50 | .20

Land titling project.

Perf. 14x14½
1991, Mar. 30   **Litho.**   **Wmk. 387**
1384 A423 2b Princess Maha | 1.00 | .20
a.   Souvenir sheet of 1 | 5.00 | 5.00

Red Cross. No. 1384a sold for 8b. Exists imperf, value same as perf.

Cultural Heritage
A424

Floral decorations: 2b, Indra's heavenly abode. 3b, Celestial couch. 4b, Crystal ladder. 5b, Crocodile.

Wmk. 329
1991, Apr. 2   **Photo.**   *Perf. 13½*
1385 A424 2b multicolored | .40 | .25
1386 A424 3b multicolored | .50 | .30
1387 A424 4b multicolored | .75 | .50
1388 A424 5b multicolored | .85 | .60
a.   Souv. sheet of 4, #1385-1388 | 6.25 | 6.25
Nos. 1385-1388 (4) | 2.50 | 1.65

No. 1388a sold for 30b. Exists imperf, value same as perf.

Songkran Day — A425

Perf. 14x14½
1991, Apr. 13   **Wmk. 387**   **Litho.**
1389 A425 2b Demon on sheep | 2.50 | 1.00
a.   Souvenir sheet of 1 | 10.00 | 10.00

No. 1389a sold for 8b. Exists imperf, value same as perf.
See #1467, 1530, 1566, 1606, 1662, 1724, 1801, 1869, 1940.

Prince Narisranuvattivongs (1863-1947) — A426

1991, Apr. 28   *Perf. 14½x14*
1390 A426 2b brown & yellow | .50 | .25

Mosaics — A427

Various lotus flowers.

1991, May 28   *Perf. 13½*
1391 A427 2b multi, vert. | .30 | .20
1392 A427 3b multi, vert. | .40 | .25
1393 A427 5b multi | .65 | .45
1394 A427 6b multi | .80 | .55
Nos. 1391-1394 (4) | 2.15 | 1.45

Natl. Communications Day — A428

Wmk. 387
1991, Aug. 4   **Litho.**   *Perf. 13½*
1395 A428 2b multicolored | .60 | .25

Thaipex '91, Natl. Philatelic Exhibition A429

Various fabric designs.

1991, Aug. 4   *Perf. 14x14½*
1396 A429 2b multicolored | .45 | .25
1397 A429 4b multicolored | .70 | .35
1398 A429 6b multicolored | .85 | .50
1399 A429 8b multicolored | 1.00 | .90
a.   Souv. sheet of 4, #1396-1399 | 6.00 | 6.00
Nos. 1396-1399 (4) | 3.00 | 2.00

No. 1399a sold for 30b. Exists imperf, value $24. No. 1399a overprinted with Philanippon emblem in lower left corner of margin sold for 200b. Value, $190.

Intl. Productivity Congress — A430

Perf. 14½x14
1991, Sept. 3   **Litho.**   **Wmk. 387**
1400 A430 2b multicolored | .50 | .25

26th Intl. Council of Women Triennial — A431

Wmk. 387
1991, Sept. 23   **Litho.**   *Perf. 13½*
1401 A431 2b multicolored | .50 | .25

Bantam Chickens — A432

Wmk. 329

1991, Oct. 6	**Photo.**		**Perf. 13½**
1402 A432 2b	Black bantams	.35	.25
1403 A432 3b	Black-tailed buff		
	bantams	.65	.30
1404 A432 6b	Fancy bantams	1.00	.45
1405 A432 8b	White bantams	1.25	1.00
a.	Souv. sheet of 4, #1402-1405	7.50	7.50
	Nos. 1402-1405 (4)	3.25	2.00

No. 1405a sold for 35b. Exists imperf, value same as perf.

Intl. Letter Writing Week.

World Bank/Intl. Monetary Fund Annual Meetings — A433

Temples, meeting emblem and: 2b, Silver coin of King Rama IV. 4b, Pod Duang money. 8b, Chieng and Hoi money. 10b, Funan, Dvaravati and Srivijaya money.

Perf. 14½x14

		Litho.	**Wmk. 387**
1991, Oct. 15			
1406 A433 2b	multicolored	.20	.20
1407 A433 4b	multicolored	.45	.30
1408 A433 8b	multicolored	.90	.60
1409 A433 10b	multicolored	1.10	.75
a.	Souv. sheet of 4, #1406-1409	6.25	6.25
	Nos. 1406-1409 (4)	2.65	1.85

No. 1409a sold for 35b. Exists imperf, value same as perf.

1993 World Philatelic Exhibition, Bangkok — A434

		Perf. 14x14½
1991, Oct. 23		
1410 A434 2b	No. 118	.20	.20
1411 A434 3b	No. 119	.30	.20
1412 A434 4b	No. 120	.40	.30
1413 A434 5b	No. 121	.55	.40
1414 A434 6b	No. 122	.65	.45
1415 A434 7b	No. 123	.75	.50
1416 A434 8b	No. 124	.85	.60
a.	Souvenir sheet of 1	5.00	5.00
	Nos. 1410-1416 (7)	3.70	2.65

No. 1416a sold for 15b. Exists imperf, value same as perf.

Flower Type of 1990

		Perf. 13½
1991, Nov. 5		
1417 A416 1b	Dillenia obovata	.20	.20
1418 A416 1b	Melastoma		
	sanguineum	.20	.20
1419 A416 1b	Commelina diffusa	.20	.20
1420 A416 1b	Plumbago indica	.20	.20
a.	Souv. sheet of 4, #1417-1420	3.00	3.00
	Nos. 1417-1420 (4)	.80	.80

No. 1420a sold for 10b. Exists imperf, value same as perf.

Asian Elephants — A435

Wmk. 329

1991, Nov. 5	**Photo.**		**Perf. 13½**
1421 A435 2b	shown	.30	.20
1422 A435 4b	Pulling logs	.55	.30
1423 A435 6b	Lying down	.80	.45
1424 A435 8b	In river	1.10	.60
a.	Souvenir sheet of 1, litho.	7.50	7.50
	Nos. 1421-1424 (4)	2.75	1.55

No. 1424a sold for 22b and stamp does not have border. No. 1424a exists imperf, value same as perf.

Wild Animals — A436

Perf. 14½x14

		Wmk. 387	**Litho.**
1991, Dec. 26			
1425 A436 2b	Viverra zibetha	.25	.20
1426 A436 3b	Prionodon linsang	.40	.25
1427 A436 6b	Felis temmincki	.80	.50
1428 A436 8b	Ratufa bicolor	1.10	.65
a.	Sheet of 4, #1425-1428	6.25	6.25
	Nos. 1425-1428 (4)	2.55	1.60

No. 1428a sold for 30b. Exists imperf, value same as perf.

Prince Mahidol of Songkla (1891-1929), Medical Pioneer — A437

		Perf. 14x14½
1992, Jan. 1		
1429 A437 2b multicolored		.35	.25

Department of Mineral Resources, Cent. — A438

No. 1430, Locating fossils. No. 1431, Mining excavation. No. 1432, Drilling for natural gas and petroleum. No. 1433, Digging artesian wells.

Perf. 14½x14

		Litho.	**Wmk. 387**
1992, Jan. 1			
1430 A438 2b	multicolored	.35	.20
1431 A438 2b	multicolored	.35	.20
1432 A438 2b	multicolored	.35	.20
1433 A438 2b	multicolored	.35	.20
	Nos. 1430-1433 (4)	1.40	.80

Children's Day — A439

Children's drawings on "World Under the Sea": 2b, Divers, fish. 3b, Fish, sea grass. 5b, Mermaid.

		Perf. 13½
1992, Jan. 11	**Wmk. 329**	
1434 A439 2b	multicolored	.30	.20
1435 A439 3b	multicolored	.40	.30
1436 A439 5b	multicolored, vert.	.65	.50
	Nos. 1434-1436 (3)	1.35	1.00

Duel on Elephants, 400th Anniv. — A440

		Perf. 14½x14
1992, Jan. 18	**Litho.**	**Wmk. 387**
1437 A440 2b multicolored		.50	.20

Orchids (Paphiopedilum) — A441

1992, Jan. 20			
1438 A441 2b	Bellatulum	.25	.20
1439 A441 2b	Exul	.25	.20
1440 A441 3b	Concolor	.35	.30
1441 A441 3b	Godefroyae	.35	.30
1442 A441 6b	Niveum	.70	.55
1443 A441 6b	Villosum	.70	.55
1444 A441 10b	Parishii	1.25	.90
a.	Souv. sheet of 4, #1438, 1440, 1442, 1444	5.00	5.00
1445 A441 10b	Sukhakulii	1.25	.90
a.	Souv. sheet of 4, #1439, 1441, 1443, 1445	5.00	5.00
	Nos. 1438-1445 (8)	5.10	3.90

Fourth Asia Pacific Orchid Conference. Nos. 1444a-1445a each sold for 30b. Each exists imperf, value same as perf.

21st Intl. Society of Sugar Cane Technologists Conf. — A442

		Perf. 14x14½
1992, Mar. 5		
1446 A442 2b multicolored		.50	.25

Intl. Red Cross A443

		Perf. 14½x14
1992, Mar.	**Litho.**	**Wmk. 387**
1447 A443 2b multicolored		.50	.20

Ministry of Justice, Cent. — A444

Designs: 3b, Prince Rabi Badhanasakdi of Ratchaburi, founder of Thailand's School of Law. 5b, King Rama V, reformer of court system.

		Perf. 13½
1992, Mar. 25		
1448 A444 3b multicolored		.40	.30
1449 A444 5b multicolored		.60	.40

Ministry of Agriculture and Cooperatives, Cent. — A445

		Perf. 14½x14
1992, Apr. 1		
1450 A445 2b	gray & multi	.25	.2
1451 A445 3b	lil & multi	.40	.3
1452 A445 4b	pink & multi	.45	.3
1453 A445 5b	gray bl & multi	.60	.4
	Nos. 1450-1453 (4)	1.70	1.2

A446

A447

Ministry of Interior, Cent.: No. 1454, Prince Damrong Rajanubharb, first Minister of the Interior. No. 1455, People voting. No. 1456, Police and fire protection. No. 1457, Water and electricity provided to remote areas.

		Perf. 14x14½
1992, Apr. 1		
1454 A446 2b	multicolored	.35	.20
1455 A446 2b	multicolored	.35	.20
1456 A446 2b	multicolored	.35	.20
1457 A446 2b	multicolored	.35	.20
	Nos. 1454-1457 (4)	1.40	.80

1992, Apr. 1		
1458 A447 2b	Ships, truck	.25	.20
1459 A447 3b	Truck, bus, train	.40	.30
1460 A447 5b	Airplanes	.60	.40
1461 A447 6b	Truck, satellites	.75	.50
	Nos. 1458-1461 (4)	2.00	1.40

Ministry of Transport and Communications, 80th anniv.

Ministry of Education, Cent. — A448

		Perf. 14x14½
1992, Apr. 1	**Litho.**	**Wmk. 387**
1462 A448 2b multicolored		.30	.20

Carts A449

1992, Apr. 2   Perf. 14½x14

463	A449	2b West	.25	.20
464	A449	3b North	.35	.25
465	A449	5b Northeast	.55	.40
466	A449	10b East	1.10	.90
a.		Souv. sheet of 4, #1463-1466	4.50	
		Nos. 1463-1466 (4)	2.25	1.75

Heritage Conservation Day. No. 1466a sold or 30b and exists imperf without sheet price in margin.

Songkran Day Type of 1991

1992, Apr. 13   Perf. 14x14½

467	A425	2b Demon on mon-key, zodiac	.60	.25
a.		Souvenir sheet of 1	3.75	

No. 1467a sold for 8b and exists imperf. with sale price in different colors.

Department of Livestock Development, 50th Anniv. — A451

Perf. 14½x14

1992, May 5   Litho.   Wmk. 387

1468	A451	2b multicolored	.30	.20

Wisakhabucha Day — A452

Scenes from Buddha's life: 2b, Birth. 3b, Enlightenment. 5b, Death.

Wmk. 387

1992, May 16   Perf. 14½

1469	A452	2b multicolored	.30	.20
1470	A452	3b multicolored	.35	.25
1471	A452	5b multicolored	.60	.40
		Nos. 1469-1471 (3)	1.25	.85

Meteorological Department, 50th Anniv. — A453

1992, June 23   Perf. 14x14½

1472	A453	2b multicolored	.30	.20

1993 World Philatelic Exhibition, Bangkok — A454

Visit ASEAN Year — A455

Perf. 14x14½

1992, July 1   Litho.   Wmk. 387

1473	A454	2b No. 18	.25	.20
1474	A454	3b No. 156	.35	.25
1475	A454	5b No. 222	.55	.40
1476	A454	7b No. 255	.85	.50
1477	A454	8b No. 273	1.00	.65
a.		Souv. sheet of 5, #1473-1477 + label	6.00	6.00
		Nos. 1473-1477 (5)	3.00	2.00

No. 1477a sold for 35b. Exists imperf. with sheet price in blue, value same as #1477a.

1992, July 1

Designs: 2b, Bua Tong field, Mae Hong Son Province. 3b, Klong Larn Waterfall, Kamphaeng Phet Province. 4b, Coral, Chumphon Province. 5b, Khao Ta-Poo, Phangnga Province.

1478	A455	2b multicolored	.30	.20
1479	A455	3b multicolored	.40	.25
1480	A455	4b multicolored	.50	.35
1481	A455	5b multicolored	.60	.40
		Nos. 1478-1481 (4)	1.80	1.20

Prince Chudadhuj Dharadilok of Bejraburna (1892-1923) A456

Wmk. 368

1992, July 5   Litho.   Perf. 13½

1482	A456	2b multicolored	.30	.20

Natl. Communications Day — A457

Perf. 14½x14

1992, Aug. 4   Litho.   Wmk. 387

1483	A457	2b multicolored	.30	.20

ASEAN, 25th Anniv. — A458

Flags and: 2b, Cultures and sports. 3b, Tourist attractions. 5b, Transportation, communications. 7b, Agriculture.

1992, Aug. 8   Wmk. 368   Perf. 13½

1484	A458	2b multicolored	.25	.20
1485	A458	3b multicolored	.35	.25
1486	A458	5b multicolored	.55	.40
1487	A458	7b multicolored	.85	.55
		Nos. 1484-1487 (4)	2.00	1.40

Queen Sirikit, 60th Birthday — A459

#1488, Wedding, with King, Queen being anointed. #1489, Coronation, King and Queen on throne. #1490, Being crowned, Queen with crown, being anointed. #1491, Formal portrait, Queen seated. #1492, Visiting wounded. #1493, Visiting public.

Wmk. 329

1992, Aug. 12   Photo.   Perf. 13½

1488	A459	2b multicolored	.30	.20
1489	A459	2b multicolored	.30	.20
1490	A459	2b multicolored	.30	.20
1491	A459	2b multicolored	.30	.20
1492	A459	2b multicolored	.30	.20
1493	A459	2b multicolored	.30	.20
a.		Souv. sheet of 6, #1488-1493	3.75	
		Nos. 1488-1493 (6)	1.80	1.20

No. 1493a sold for 30b and exists imperf. with sale price in different colors.

Royal Regalia of Queen Sirikit — A460

No. 1494, Tray. No. 1495, Kettle. No. 1496, Bowl. No. 1497, Box. No. 1498, Covered dish.

1992, Aug. 12
Background Colors

1494	A460	2b dark blue	.25	.20
1495	A460	2b violet	.25	.20
1496	A460	2b yellow green	.25	.20
1497	A460	2b Prussian blue	.25	.20
1498	A460	2b dark green	.25	.20
		Nos. 1494-1498 (5)	1.25	1.00

Opening of Sirikit Medical Center — A461

Perf. 14½x14

1992, Aug. 12   Litho.   Wmk. 387

1499	A461	2b multicolored	.30	.20

Queen Sirikit, 60th Birthday — A462

Litho. & Embossed

1992, Aug. 12   Perf. 13½

1500	A462	100b blue & gold	10.00	10.00

No. 1500 printed in sheets of 10.

A463

A464

Wmk. 387

1992, Aug. 25   Litho.   Perf. 13½

1501	A463	2b multicolored	.25	.20

Prince Wan Waithayakon Krommun Naradhip Bongsprabandh (1891-1976).

1992, Sept. 15   Perf. 14x14½

1502	A464	2b multicolored	.30	.20

Professor Silpa Bhirasri, Sculptor, cent. of birth.

Coral A465

Perf. 14½x14

1992, Oct. 4   Litho.   Wmk. 387

1503	A465	2b Catalaphyllia jardinei	.25	.20
1504	A465	3b Porites lutea	.30	.25
1505	A465	6b Tubastraea coccinea	.65	.50
1506	A465	8b Favia pallida	.90	.70
a.		Souv. sheet of 4, #1503-1506	5.25	
		Nos. 1503-1506 (4)	2.10	1.65

Intl. Letter Writing Week. No. 1506a sold for for 30b.

New Year 1993 — A466

Flowers: No. 1507, Rhododendron simsii. No. 1508, Cynoglossum lanceolatum. No. 1509, Tithonia diversifolia. No. 1510, Agapetes parishii.

Perf. 14x13½

1992, Nov. 15   Wmk. 368   Litho.

1507	A466	1b multicolored	.20	.20
1508	A466	1b multicolored	.20	.20
1509	A466	1b multicolored	.20	.20
1510	A466	1b multicolored	.20	.20
a.		Souv. sheet of 4, #1507-1510	3.00	
		Nos. 1507-1510 (4)	.80	.80

Nos. 1510a sold for 10b. Exists imperf. with sheet price in green.

1st Asian
Congress of
Allergies and
Immunology
A467

1992, Nov. 22   *Perf. 13½*
1511 A467 2b black, red & yellow   .30 .20

Natl. Assembly, 60th Anniv. — A468

Wmk. 387
1992, Dec. 10   **Litho.**   *Perf. 13½*
1512 A468 2b multicolored   .30 .20

Bank of Thailand, 50th Anniv. — A469

1992, Dec. 10   *Perf. 14½x14*
1513 A469 2b multicolored   .30 .20

Children's Day — A470

Children's drawings: No. 1514, River scene.
No. 1515, Wild animals, forest. No. 1516,
Trains, planes, monorail.

1993, Jan. 9   **Wmk. 368**   *Perf. 13½*
1514 A470 2b multicolored   .25 .20
1515 A470 2b multicolored   .25 .20
1516 A470 2b multicolored   .25 .20
    Nos. 1514-1516 (3)   .75 .60

Pottery — A471

Designs: 3b, Jug with bird's neck spout, two
bottles. 6b, Pear-shaped vase, two jars. 7b,
Three bowls. 8b, Three jars.

1993, Jan. 9   **Photo.**   **Wmk. 329**
1517 A471 3b multicolored   .35 .25
1518 A471 6b multicolored   .70 .50
1519 A471 7b multicolored   .80 .55
1520 A471 8b multicolored   .95 .70
  a.   Souv. sheet of 4, #1517-1520   4.00
    Nos. 1517-1520 (4)   2.80 2.00

1993 World Philatelic Exhibition, Bangkok.
No. 1520a sold for 35b.

Thai Teachers'
Training Institute,
Cent. — A472

Perf. 13½x14
1993, Jan. 16   **Litho.**   **Wmk. 368**
1521 A472 2b multicolored   .30 .25

Kasetsart University, 50th
Anniv. — A473

1993, Feb. 2   **Wmk. 329**   *Perf. 13½*
1522 A473 2b multicolored   .30 .25

Maghapuja
Day — A474

Wmk. 387
1993, Mar. 7   **Litho.**   *Perf. 14½*
1523 A474 2b multicolored   .30 .20

Queen Sri
Bajarindra
A475

1993, Mar. 27   *Perf. 14x14½*
1524 A475 2b multicolored   .30 .20
Thai Red Cross, cent.

Office of Attorney General,
Cent. — A476

1993, Apr. 1   **Wmk. 368**   *Perf. 12½*
1525 A476 2b multicolored   .30 .20

Heritage Conservation Day — A477

Historical landmarks, Si Satchanalai Park:
3b, Wat Chedi Chet Thaeo. 4b, Wat Chang
Lom. 6b, Wat Phra Si Rattanamahathat
(Chaliang). 7b, Wat Suan Kaeo Utthayan Noi.

Wmk. 368
1993, Apr. 2   **Litho.**   *Perf. 13½*
1526 A477 3b multicolored   .30 .25
1527 A477 4b multicolored   .45 .30
1528 A477 6b multicolored   .65 .50
1529 A477 7b multicolored   .75 .55
  a.   Souv. sheet of 4, #1526-1529   4.00
    Nos. 1526-1529 (4)   2.15 1.60

   No. 1529a sold for 25b.
   See Nos. 1561-1564, 1650-1653, 1797-
1800.

Songkran Day Type of 1991

Perf. 14x14½
1993   **Litho.**   **Wmk. 387**
1530 A425 2b Demon on roost-
    er's back, zodiac   .40 .20
  a.   Souvenir sheet of 1   2.50
  b.   #1530a ovptd. in gold   7.75

No. 1530b overprinted on sheet margin in
both Thai and Chinese for Chinpex '93.
Nos. 1530a-1530b sold for 8b and exist
imperf. with sale price in different colors.
Issued: #1530, 1530a, Apr. 13.

Mushrooms — A478

Wmk. 368
1993, July 1   **Litho.**   *Perf. 13½*
1531 A478 2b Marasmius   .25 .20
1532 A478 4b Coprinus   .50 .30
1533 A478 6b Mycena   .70 .45
1534 A478 8b Cyathus   .90 .60
  a.   Souv. sheet of 4, #1531-1534   4.25
    Nos. 1531-1534 (4)   2.35 1.55

   No. 1534a sold for 30b.

Natl. Communications Day — A479

1993, Aug. 4   **Wmk. 387**   *Perf. 13½*
1535 A479 2b multicolored   .30 .20

Post and Telegraph Department, 110th
Anniv. — A480

Wmk. 387
1993, Aug. 4   **Litho.**   *Perf. 13½*
1536 A480 2b multicolored   .30 .20

Queen Suriyothai's Monument — A481

1993, Aug. 12
1537 A481 2b multicolored   .30 .25

Fruit — A482

Wmk. 368
1993, Oct. 1   **Photo.**   *Perf. 13*
1538 A482 2b Citrus reticulata   .25 .20
1539 A482 3b Musa sp.   .40 .20
1540 A482 6b Phyllanthus dis-
    tichus   .75 .45
1541 A482 8b Bouea burmanica   1.00 .60
    Nos. 1538-1541 (4)   2.40 1.50

Thai Ridgeback Dogs — A483

Various dogs.

1993, Oct. 1
1542 A483 2b multicolored   .20 .20
1543 A483 3b multicolored   .30 .20
1544 A483 5b multicolored   .50 .40
1545 A483 10b multicolored   1.00 .75
  a.   Souv. sheet of 4, #1542-1545   3.75
    Nos. 1542-1545 (4)   2.00 1.55

Intl. Letter Writing Week. No. 1545a sold for
30b.

5th Conference & Exhibition of ASEAN
Council on Petroleum
(ASCOPE) — A484

Wmk. 387
1993, Nov. 2   **Litho.**   *Perf. 13½*
1546 A484 2b multicolored   .30 .20

King Rama VII
(1893-1941)
A485

1993, Nov. 8   *Perf. 14x14½*
1547 A485 2b multicolored   .30 .20

No. 655 Surcharged

1993   **Photo.**   **Wmk. 233**   *Perf. 14½*
1548 A161 1b on 25s brown red   .50 .20

Bencharong and
Lai Nam Thong
Wares — A486

Designs: 3b, Bencharong cosmetic jar,
vinity design. 5b, Bencharong cosmetic jar,
old knob. 6b, Lai Nam Thong cosmetic jar,
oral design. 7b, Lai Nam Thong cosmetic jar,
oral design, diff.

Wmk. 368

		Photo.	**Perf. 13½**	
1549	A486	3b multicolored	.30	.20
1550	A486	5b multicolored	.55	.40
1551	A486	6b multicolored	.65	.45
1552	A486	7b multicolored	.75	.55
a.		Souv. sheet of 4, #1549-1552	4.00	
		Nos. 1549-1552 (4)	2.25	1.60

1993, Oct. 1

Bangkok '93. No. 1552a sold for 30b.

New Year
1994 — A487

Perf. 14½x14

1993, Nov. 15		**Litho.**	**Wmk. 387**	
1553	A487	1b Ipomoea cairica	.20	.20
1554	A487	1b Decaschistia parviflora	.20	.20
1555	A487	1b Hibiscus tiliaceus	.20	.20
1556	A487	1b Passiflora foetida	.20	.20
a.		Souv. sheet of 4, #1553-1556	1.25	
		Nos. 1553-1556 (4)	.80	.80

No. 1556a sold for 10b.

THAICOM, Natl.
Satellite
Project — A488

Perf. 14x14½

1993, Dec. 1				
1557	A488	2b multicolored	.30	.20

Children's Day — A489

Perf. 14½x14

1994, Jan. 8				
1558	A489	2b Play land	.25	.20

Administrative Building, Chulalongkorn
Hospital, 80th Anniv. — A490

Perf. 14½x14

1994, Mar. 30		**Litho.**	**Wmk. 387**	
1559	A490	2b multicolored	.25	.20

Thai Red Cross.

Royal Institute,
60th
Anniv. — A491

1994, Mar. 31			**Perf. 14x14½**	
1560	A491	2b multicolored	.25	.20

Heritage Conservation Day Type of
1993

Historical landmarks, Phra Nakhon Si
Ayutthaya Park: 2b, Wat Ratchaburana. 3b,
Wat Maha That. 6b, Wat Maheyong. 9b, Wat
Phra Si Samphet.

1994, Apr. 2			**Perf. 14½x14**	
1561	A477	2b multicolored	.20	.20
1562	A477	3b multicolored	.35	.25
1563	A477	6b multicolored	.65	.50
1564	A477	9b multicolored	1.25	.95
a.		Souv. sheet of 4, #1561-1564	2.50	
		Nos. 1561-1564 (4)	2.45	1.90

No. 1564a sold for 25b.

Opening of Friendship Bridge,
Thailand-Laos — A492

1994, Apr. 8				
1565	A492	9b multicolored	1.00	.75

Songkran Day Type of 1991

1994, Apr. 13		**Litho.**		
1566	A425	2b Demon on dog's back, zodiac	.25	.20
a.		Souvenir sheet of 1	1.00	
b.		As "a," inscribed in margin	.25	

No. 1566a sold for 8b and exists imperf with
frame around stamp and sale price in different
color.
Sheet margin of No. 1566b has no value
inscription and is overprinted in violet with Thai
and Chinese inscriptions for Beijing Stamp
Exhibition. Issued: May 1994. No. 1566b also
exists imperf.

Intl. Olympic Committee,
Cent. — A493

Wmk. 387

1994, June 23		**Litho.**	**Perf. 14**	
1567	A493	2b Soccer	.20	.20
1568	A493	3b Running	.30	.20
1569	A493	5b Swimming	.50	.40
1570	A493	6b Weight lifting	.60	.45
1571	A493	9b Boxing	.90	.75
		Nos. 1567-1571 (5)	2.50	2.00

Thammasat University, 60th
Anniv. — A494

Wmk. 387

1994, June 27		**Litho.**	**Perf. 14**	
1572	A494	2b multicolored	.20	.20

Asalhapuja
Day — A495

1994, July 22		**Wmk. 329**	**Perf. 13½**	
1573	A495	2b multicolored	.20	.20

Natl. Communications Day — A496

1994, Aug. 4		**Wmk. 368**		
1574	A496	2b multicolored	.20	.20

Crabs
A497

3b, Phricotelphusa limula. 5b, Thaipotamon
chulabhorn. 6b, Phricotelphusa sirindhorn.
10b, Thaiphusa sirikit.

Wmk. 340 (340)

1994, Aug. 12		**Photo.**	**Perf. 13½x13**	
1575	A497	3b multicolored	.30	.20
1576	A497	5b multicolored	.50	.40
1577	A497	6b multicolored	.60	.45
1578	A497	10b multicolored	1.00	.75
a.		Souv. sheet of 4, #1575-1578	3.00	
b.		As "a," inscribed in margin	3.00	
		Nos. 1575-1578 (4)	2.40	1.80

No. 1578b has PHILAKOREA '94 Exhibition
emblem added to sheet margin.

Intl. Letter Writing Week — A498

Winning paintings in design contest: 2b,
Gold niello bowls, octagonal footed tray. 6b,
Pumpkin shaped bowls. 8b, Silver niello betel-
nut set. 9b, Covered square bowl with gold
finial, small lotus-shaped footed tray.

Wmk. 368

1994, Oct. 9		**Photo.**	**Perf. 13½**	
1579	A498	2b multicolored	.20	.20
		Complete booklet, 5 #1579	.80	
1580	A498	6b multicolored	.50	.35
1581	A498	8b multicolored	.60	.50
1582	A498	9b multicolored	.70	.55
a.		Souv. sheet of 4, #1579-1582	2.50	
		Nos. 1579-1582 (4)	2.00	1.60

No. 1582a sold for 30b.

ILO,
75th
Anniv.
A499

		Perf. 15x14		
1994, Oct. 29		**Litho.**	**Wmk. 387**	
1583	A499	2b multicolored	.20	.20
		Complete booklet, 5 #1583	1.25	

New Year
1995 — A500

Herbs: No. 1584, Utricularia delphinioides.
No. 1585, Utricularia minutissima. No. 1586,
Eriocaulon odoratum. No. 1587, Utricularia
bifida.

1994, Nov. 15			**Perf. 14x14½**	
1584	A500	1b multicolored	.20	.20
1585	A500	1b multicolored	.20	.20
1586	A500	1b multicolored	.20	.20
1587	A500	1b multicolored	.20	.20
a.		Souv. sheet of 4, #1584-1587	1.00	
		Nos. 1584-1587 (4)	.80	.80

No. 1587a sold for 10b.

Suan Dusit Teachers College, 60th
Anniv. — A501

Perf. 14½x14

1994, Dec. 4		**Litho.**	**Wmk. 387**	
1588	A501	2b multicolored	.20	.20
		Complete booklet, 5 #1588	1.25	

Council of State, 120th Anniv. — A502

1994, Dec. 5		**Wmk. 368**	**Perf. 13½**	
1589	A502	2b multicolored	.20	.20
		Complete booklet, 5 #1589	1.25	

ICAO,
50th
Anniv.
A503

Perf. 14½x14

1994, Dec. 7			**Wmk. 387**	
1590	A503	2b multicolored	.20	.20
		Complete booklet, 5 #1590	1.25	

Pharmacy in Thailand, 80th
Anniv. — A504

Grinding stones: 2b, Dvaravati, 7th-11th
cent. 6b, Lopburi Period, 11th-13th cent. 9b,
Bangkok Period, 18th-20th cent.

1994, Dec. 13				
1591	A504	2b multicolored	.20	.20
		Complete booklet, 5 #1591	1.25	
1592	A504	6b multicolored	.45	.35
1593	A504	9b multicolored	.70	.55
		Nos. 1591-1593 (3)	1.35	1.10

Bar Assoc., 80th Anniv. — A505

Design: 2b, First Bar Assoc. headquarters, King Vajiravudh, King Bhumibol.

1995, Jan. 1   Wmk. 368   Perf. 13½
1594 A505   2b multicolored   .20   .20
    Complete booklet, 5 #1594   1.10

A506

A507

Children's drawings: No. 1595, Kites Decorate the Summer Sky. No. 1596, Trees and Streams, horiz. No. 1597, Youths and Religion, horiz.

1995, Jan. 14   Wmk. 387   Perf. 14
1595 A506   2b multicolored   .20   .20
    Complete booklet, 5 #1595   1.10
1596 A506   2b multicolored   .20   .20
    Complete booklet, 5 #1596   1.10
1597 A506   2b multicolored   .20   .20
    Complete booklet, 5 #1597   1.10
    Nos. 1595-1597 (3)   .60   .60

Children's Day.

1995, Mar. 4
1598 A507   2b multicolored   .20   .20
    Complete booklet, 5 #1598   1.10

First Thai newspaper, Bangkok Recorder, 150th anniv.

Royal Thai Air Force, 80th Anniv. A508

1995, Mar. 27   Wmk. 368   Perf. 13½
1599 A508   2b multicolored   .20   .20
    Complete booklet, 5 #1599   1.10

Red Cross Floating Clinic, Wetchapha — A509

1995, Mar. 30
1600 A509   2b multicolored   .20   .20
    Complete booklet, 5 #1600   1.10

Phimai Historical Park — A510

Paintings: 3b, Naga Bridge. 5b, Brahmin Hall. 6b, Gateway of the Inner Wall. 9b, Main Pagoda.

Perf. 14½x14
1995, Apr. 2   Wmk. 387
1601 A510   3b multicolored   .25   .20
1602 A510   5b multicolored   .40   .30
1603 A510   6b multicolored   .50   .35
1604 A510   9b multicolored   .75   .55
 a. Souv. sheet of 4, #1601-1604   2.50
    Nos. 1601-1604 (4)   1.90   1.40

Heritage Conservation Day.
No. 1604a sold for 30b.

Ministry of Defense, 108th Anniv. — A511

Design: 2b, Admin. building, King Rama V.

1995, Apr. 8   Wmk. 387   Perf. 14
1605 A511   2b multicolored   .20   .20
    Complete booklet, 5 #1605   1.10

Songkran Day Type of 1991
1995, Apr. 13   Perf. 11x13
1606 A425   2b Demon on boar's
        back, zodiac   .20   .20
 a. Souvenir sheet of 1   .60
    Complete booklet, 5 #1606   1.10

No. 1606a sold for 8b and exists imperf with sale price in different color.

Ministry of Foreign Affairs, 120th Anniv. — A512

2b, Saranrom Palace, King Rama V.

1995, Apr. 14   Perf. 14
1607 A512   2b multicolored   .20   .20
    Complete booklet, 5 #1607   1.10

Visakhapuja Day — A513

Sculptures of Buddha: 2b, Emerald Buddha, temple of Wat Phra Si Rattana Satsadaram, Bangkok. 6b, Phra Phuttha Chinnarat, Wat Phra Si Rattana Maha That, Phitsanulok Province. 8b, Phra Phuttha Sihing, Wat Phra Sing, Chiang Mai Province. 9b, Phra Sukhothai Traimit, Wat Traimit Witthayaram, Bangkok.

Wmk. 340
1995, May 13   Photo.   Perf. 13½
1608 A513   2b multicolored   .20   .20
1609 A513   6b multicolored   .45   .35
1610 A513   8b multicolored   .60   .50
1611 A513   9b multicolored   .75   .55
 a. Souv. sheet of 4, #1608-1611   2.75
    Nos. 1608-1611 (4)   2.00   1.60

No. 1611a sold for 35b.

ASEAN Environment Year — A514

1995, June 5   Litho.   Wmk. 368
1612 A514   2b multicolored   .20   .20
    Complete booklet, 5 #1612   1.10

Information Technology Year — A515

1995, June 9   Wmk. 340
1613 A515   2b multicolored   .20   .20
    Complete booklet, 5 #1613   1.10

Thailand-People's Republic of China Diplomatic Relations, 20th Anniv. — A516

#1614, Elephants walking right into water. #1615, Elephants walking left into water.

Wmk. 340
1995, July 1   Photo.   Perf. 13½
1614 A516   2b multicolored   .20   .20
1615 A516   2b multicolored   .20   .20
 a. Pair, Nos. 1614-1615   .30   .20
 b. Souv. sheet, #1614-1615   .65
 c. As "b," diff. inscriptions in
     sheet margin   18.00

No. 1615c contains Jakarta '95 exhibition emblem and does not have sheet value in margin.
#1615b sold for 8b. #1615c sold for 28b.
No. 1615b exists with serial number in sheet margin, The same number is on China (PRC) No. 2462a. These two souvenir sheets were sold as a set. Value, set $26.50.
See People's Republic of China Nos. 2579-2580.

Natl. Communications Day — A517

1995, Aug. 4   Litho.   Perf. 14½x14
1616 A517   2b multicolored   .20   .20
    Complete booklet, 5 #1616   1.10

A518

A519

Domestic cats: 3b, Khoa Manee. 6b, Korat or Si-Sawat. 7b, Seal point Siamese. 9b, Burmese.

1995, Aug. 4   Photo.   Perf. 13
1617 A518   3b multicolored   .25
1618 A518   6b multicolored   .50
1619 A518   7b multicolored   .55
1620 A518   9b multicolored   .70
 a. Souv. sheet, Nos. 1617-1620   2.00
 b. As "a," diff. inscriptions in
     margin   10.00
    Nos. 1617-1620 (4)   2.00

Thaipex '95.
No. 1620b contains Singapore '95 exhibition emblem added to sheet margin and does not have value inscription.
No. 1620a sold for 35b. No. 1620b sold for 46b.

1995, Sept. 2   Litho.   Perf. 14x14
1621 A519   2b multicolored   .20   .20
    Complete booklet, 5 #1621   1.10

Revenue Department, 80th anniv.

Natl. Auditing & Office of Auditor General, 120th Anniv. — A520

1995, Sept. 18   Perf. 14½x14
1622 A520   2b multicolored   .20   .20
    Complete booklet, 5 #1622   1.10

Intl. Letter Writing Week — A521

Wicker: No. 1623, Vase with handles, legs. No. 1624, Oval-shaped container. No. 1625, Lamp shade. No. 1626, Vase.

Wmk. 340
1995, Oct. 8   Photo.   Perf. 13
1623 A521   2b multicolored   .20   .20
    Complete booklet, 5 #1623   1.10
1624 A521   2b multicolored   .20   .20
    Complete booklet, 5 #1624   1.10
1625 A521   9b multicolored   .75   .55
1626 A521   9b multicolored   .75   .55
 a. Souv. sheet, #1623-1626   1.75
    Nos. 1623-1626 (4)   1.90   1.50

FAO, 50th Anniv. A522

1995, Oct. 16   Litho.   Perf. 14½x14
1627 A522   2b multicolored   .20   .20
    Complete booklet, 5 #1627   1.10

Total Solar Eclipse in Thailand — A523

1995, Oct. 24   *Perf. 13½*
1628   A523 2b multicolored   .20   .20
    Complete booklet, 5 #1628   1.10

UN, 50th Anniv. A524

Perf. 13½x14
1995, Oct. 24   **Wmk. 387**
1629   A524 2b multicolored   .20   .20
    Complete booklet, 5 #1629   1.10

World Agricultural and Industrial
Exhibition, Nkhon Ratchasima
Province — A525

2b, Worldtech '95 Thailand Symbol Tower, vert. 5b, Farming equipment, food products, vert. 6b, Computers, equipment. 9b, Factory, beach.

Perf. 14x14½, 14½x14
1995, Nov. 4   **Wmk. 340**
1630   A525 2b multicolored   .20   .20
    Complete booklet, 5 #1630   1.10
1631   A525 5b multicolored   .40   .30
1632   A525 6b multicolored   .50   .40
1633   A525 9b multicolored   .75   .55
    Nos. 1630-1633 (4)   1.85   1.45

New Year 1996 — A526

#1634, Adenium obesum. #1635, Bauhinia acuminata. #1636, Cananga odorata. #1637, Thumbergia erecta.

1995, Dec. 9   *Perf. 13½*
1634   A526 2b multicolored   .20   .20
1635   A526 2b multicolored   .20   .20
   a.   Souvenir sheet, #1634-1635   4.50
1636   A526 2b multicolored   .20   .20
1637   A526 2b multicolored   .20   .20
   a.   Souvenir sheet, #1634-1637   1.25
   b.   As "a," inscribed in margin   5.00
   c.   Souvenir sheet, #1636-1637   4.50
    Nos. 1634-1637 (4)   .80   .80

No. 1637a sold for 15b.
Nos. 1635a, 1637c have "CHINA '96" emblem inscribed in sheet margin and sold for 22b each. No. 1637b is inscribed in sheet margin with "Indonesia '96" emblem and has the gold 15b value removed. No. 1637b sold for 14b.
Issued: #1635a, 1637b-1637c, 5/18/96.

Veterinary Science in Thailand, 60th
Anniv. — A527

1995, Dec. 9   *Perf. 14½x14*
1638   A527 2b multicolored   .20   .20
    Complete booklet, 5 #1638   1.10

A528

A529

Perf. 14x14½
1996, Jan. 12   Litho.   **Wmk. 340**
1639   A528 2b multicolored   .20   .20
    Complete booklet, 5 #1639   1.10

Siriraj School of Nursing and Midwifery, cent.

1996, Jan. 13   **Wmk. 387**   *Perf. 13½*
Paintings of Buddha instructing people with: No. 1640, Bright light, deer. No. 1641, Children, animal, person reclined, horiz. No. 1642, Followers, large tree, river.

1640   A529 2b multicolored   .20   .20
    Complete booklet, 5 #1640   1.10
1641   A529 2b multicolored   .20   .20
    Complete booklet, 5 #1641   1.10
1642   A529 2b multicolored   .20   .20
    Complete booklet, 5 #1642   1.10
    Nos. 1640-1642 (3)   .60   .60

Natl. Children's Day.

Natl. Aviation Day — A530

Perf. 14½x14
1996, Jan. 13   **Wmk. 340**
1643   A530 2b multicolored   .20   .20
    Complete booklet, 5 #1643   1.10

Asia-Europe
Economic
Meeting — A531

Perf. 14x14½
1996, Mar. 1   Litho.   **Wmk. 340**
1644   A531 2b multicolored   .20   .20
    Complete booklet, 5 #1644   1.10

Maghapuja Day — A532

Scenes from the Ten Jataka stories: 2b, Man on knee, another holding chariot. 6b, Two people flying over sea. 8b, Archer approaching man with arrow in side. 9b, Charioteer pointing.

Wmk. 340
1996, Mar. 3   Photo.   *Perf. 13½*
1645   A532 2b multicolored   .20   .20
1646   A532 6b multicolored   .50   .35
1647   A532 8b multicolored   .60   .50
1648   A532 9b multicolored   .70   .50
   a.   Souvenir Sheet, #1645-1548   2.75
    Nos. 1645-1648 (4)   2.00   1.55

No. 1648a sold for 36b.

Cremation of Princess Mother Somdej
Phra Sri Nakharindra
Barommarajjonnani — A533

Litho. & Embossed
Perf. 14½x14
1996, Mar. 10   **Wmk. 340**
1649   A533 2b gold & multi   .20   .20
    Complete booklet, 5 #1649   1.75

Heritage Conservation Day Type of
1993

Historical landmarks, Kamphaeng Phet Park: 2b, Wat Phra Kaeo. 3b, Wat Phra Non. 6b, Wat Chang Rop. 9b, Wat Phra Si Iriyabot.

Wmk. 387
1996, Apr. 2   Litho.   *Perf. 13½*
1650   A477 2b multicolored   .20   .20
    Complete booklet, 5 No. 1650   1.10
1651   A477 3b multicolored   .25   .20
1652   A477 6b multicolored   .50   .35
1653   A477 9b multicolored   .70   .50
   a.   Souvenir sheet, #1650-1653   2.25
    Nos. 1650-1653 (4)   1.65   1.25

No. 1653a sold for 28b.

Chiang Mai, 700th Anniv. — A534

Anniv. logo of Chiang Mai and: 2b, Buddhist Pagoda of Wat Chiang Man. 6b, Sculpted angel on wall, Wat Chet Yot's Pagoda. 8b, Insignia of Wat Phan Tao's Vihara. 9b, Sattaphanta.

Wmk. 340
1996, Apr. 12   Photo.   *Perf. 13½*
1654   A534 2b multicolored   .20   .20
    Complete booklet, 5 #1654   1.10
1655   A534 6b multicolored   .50   .35
1656   A534 8b multicolored   .60   .45
1657   A534 9b multicolored   .70   .50
   a.   Souvenir sheet, #1654-1657   2.90
    Nos. 1654-1657 (4)   2.00   1.50

No. 1657a sold for 37b.

Second Intl.
Asian Hornbill
Workshop
A535

#1658, White-crowned. #1659, Rufous-necked. #1660, Plain-pouched. #1661, Rhinoceros.

1996, Apr. 12
1658   A535 3b multicolored   .25   .20
1659   A535 3b multicolored   .25   .20
1660   A535 9b multicolored   .70   .50

1661   A535 9b multicolored   .70   .50
   a.   Souvenir sheet, #1658-1661   2.75
   b.   As "a," inscribed in margin   3.75
    Nos. 1658-1661 (4)   1.90   1.40

No. 1661a sold for 35b. No. 1661b was issued 6/8/96, contains CAPEX '96 exhibition emblem in sheet margin, no value inscription, and sold for 47b.

Songkran Day Type of 1991
Perf. 13½x14
1996, Apr. 13   Litho.   **Wmk. 387**
1662   A425 2b Demon on rat's
         back, zodiac   .20   .20
    Complete booklet, 5 #1662   1.10
   a.   Souvenir sheet of 1   .65
   b.   Souv. sheet, #1389, 1467,
      1530, 1566, 1606, 1662   1.60
   c.   As "a," inscribed in margin   4.00
   d.   As "b," inscribed in margin   10.00

No. 1662c contains CHINA '96 exhibition emblem and "CHINA '96-9th Asian International Philatelic Exhibition" in Chinese and English and no value inscription in sheet margin. No. 1662d contains CHINA '96 and Hong Kong '96 exhibition emblems in margin and no value inscription.
#1662a sold for 8b. #1662b sold for 20b. #1662c, issued 5/15/96, sold for 14b. #1662d, issued 5/10/96, sold for 25b. #1662a-1662d exist imperf.

A536

King
Bhumibol
Adulyadej,
50th Anniv.
of Assession
to the
Throne
A537

Designs: No. 1663, Royal Ablutions Ceremony. No. 1664, Pouring of the Libation. No. 1665, Grand Audience. No. 1666, Royal Progress by Land. No. 1667, Audience from Balcony.

1996, June 9   Photo.   *Perf. 11½*
      Granite Paper
1663   A536 3b multicolored   .25   .20
   a.   Souvenir sheet   .65
1664   A536 3b multicolored   .25   .20
   a.   Souvenir sheet   .65
1665   A536 3b multicolored   .25   .20
   a.   Souvenir sheet   .65
1666   A536 3b multicolored   .25   .20
   a.   Souvenir sheet   .65
1667   A536 3b multicolored   .25   .20
   a.   Souvenir sheet   .65

Litho. & Typo.
Wmk. 387
Perf. 13½
1668   A537 100b gold & multi   8.00   6.00
    Nos. 1663-1668 (6)   9.25   7.00

Nos. 1663a 1664a, 1665a, 1666a, 1667a have a continuous design and each sold for 8b.

Development Programs of King
Bhumibol Adulyadej — A538

#1669, Using Vetiver grass to prevent soil erosion. #1670, Chai pattana aerator to improve water quality. #1671, Rain making project to counter droughts. #1672, Dam, natural water resource development. #1673, Reforestation.

Wmk. 340

1996, June 9	**Litho.**			**Perf. 13½**
1669	A538	3b multicolored	.25	.20
1670	A538	3b multicolored	.25	.20
1671	A538	3b multicolored	.25	.20
1672	A538	3b multicolored	.25	.20
1673	A538	3b multicolored	.25	.20
a.	Souv. sheet, #1669-1673+label		2.00	
	Nos. 1669-1673 (5)		1.25	1.00

No. 1671 has a holographic image. Soaking in water may affect the hologram. No. 1673a sold for 25b.

Royal Utensils — A539

#1674, Gold-enameled cuspidor, golden spittoon. #1675, Royal betel, areca-nut set, vert. #1676, Royal water urn, vert.

Wmk. 329

1996, June 9	**Photo.**			**Perf. 13½**
1674	A539	3b green & multi	.25	.20
1675	A539	3b blue & multi	.25	.20
1676	A539	3b purple & multi	.25	.20
a.	Souvenir sheet, #1674-1676		1.30	
	Nos. 1674-1676 (3)		.75	.60

No. 1676a sold for 17b.

Modern Olympic Games, Cent. — A540

2b, Pierre de Coubertin, grave site. 3b, 1st lighting of Olympic torch, Olympia, Greece. 5b, Olympic Stadium, Athens, Olympic flag. 9b, Discus thrower, medal from 1896 games.

Perf. 14x14½

1996, June 23	**Litho.**			**Wmk. 340**
1677	A540	2b multicolored	.20	.20
	Complete booklet, 5 #1677		1.25	
1678	A540	3b multicolored	.25	.20
1679	A540	5b multicolored	.40	.30
1680	A540	9b multicolored	.75	.55
	Nos. 1677-1680 (4)		1.60	1.25

Nat. Communications Day — A541

1996, Aug. 4				**Wmk. 340**
1681	A541	2b King using radio	.20	.20
	Complete booklet, 5 #1681		1.25	

Royal Forest Department, Cent. — A542

Perf. 14½x14

1996, Sept. 18	**Litho.**			**Wmk. 340**
Type of Forest				
1682	A542	3b Tropical rain	.25	.20
1683	A542	6b Hill evergreen	.50	.40
1684	A542	7b Swamp	.55	.30
1685	A542	9b Mangrove	.70	.55
a.	Souvenir sheet, #1682-1685		2.75	
	Nos. 1682-1685 (4)		2.00	1.45

No. 1685a sold for 35b.

Intl. Letter Writing Week — A543

Classical Thai novels, characters: No. 1686, "Ramayana," King Rama following deer. No. 1687, "Inao," Inao kidnapping Budsaba, taking her to cave. No. 1688, "Ngao Pa," Lumhap touring forest. No. 1689, "Mathanapatha," Nang Mathana being cursed.

Wmk. 340

1996, Oct. 6	**Photo.**			**Perf. 13½**
1686	A543	3b multicolored	.25	.20
1687	A543	3b multicolored	.25	.20
1688	A543	9b multicolored	.70	.55
1689	A543	9b multicolored	.70	.55
a.	Souvenir sheet, #1686-1689		3.00	
	Nos. 1686-1689 (4)		1.90	1.50

No. 1689a sold for 36b.

Rotary Intl. 1996 Asia Regional Conference A544

Perf. 14x14½

1996, Oct. 25	**Litho.**			**Wmk. 340**
1690	A544	2b multicolored	.20	.20
	Complete booklet, 5 #1609		1.10	

UNESCO, 50th Anniv. — A545

1996, Nov. 4				**Perf. 14½x14**
1691	A545	2b multicolored	.20	.20
	Complete booklet, 5 #1691		1.10	

Royal Barge — A546

Illustration reduced.

1996, Nov. 7	**Unwmk.**			**Perf. 11½**
Granite Paper				
1692	A546	9b multicolored	.70	.55
a.	Souvenir sheet of 1		1.25	.95

No. 1692a sold for 16b.

New Year 1997 — A547

Designs: No. 1693, Limnocharis flava. No. 1694, Crinum thaianum, vert. No. 1695, Monochoria hastata, vert. No. 1696, Nymphoides indicum.

Perf. 14x14½, 14½x14

1996, Nov. 15	**Litho.**			**Wmk. 387**
1693	A547	2b multicolored	.20	.20
1694	A547	2b multicolored	.20	.20
1695	A547	2b multicolored	.20	.20
1696	A547	2b multicolored	.20	.20
a.	Souvenir sheet, #1693-1696		1.20	
b.	As "a," inscribed in margin		.60	
	Nos. 1693-1696 (4)		.80	.80

No. 1696a sold for 15b. No. 1696b inscribed in sheet margin with Hong Kong '97 emblem and vertical Chinese inscription. No. 1696b issued 2/12/97.

Ducks A548

#1697, Sarkidiornis melanotos. #1698, Dendrocygna javanica, vert. #1699, Cairina scutulata, vert. #1700, Nettapus coromandelianus.

Wmk. 340

1996, Dec. 1	**Photo.**			**Perf. 13½**
1697	A548	3b multicolored	.25	.20
1698	A548	3b multicolored	.25	.20
1699	A548	7b multicolored	.55	.40
1700	A548	7b multicolored	.55	.40
a.	Souvenir sheet, #1697-1700		2.50	
	Nos. 1697-1700 (4)		1.60	1.20

No. 1700a sold for 33b.

UNICEF, 50th Anniv. — A549

1996, Dec. 11	**Litho.**			**Wmk. 340**
1701	A549	2b multicolored	.20	.20
	Complete booklet, 5 #1701		1.10	

King Bhumibol Adulyadej — A550

1996, Dec. 5	**Litho.**			**Perf. 14x14½**
1702	A550	2b carmine	.20	.20
	Complete booklet, 5 #1702		1.10	
a.	Unwmk., granite paper		.20	.20

No. 1702a issued 9/1/98. See Nos. 1725-1729, 1743-1745, 1756-1757, 1794-1795, 1819-1820, 1876-1879, 2067.

Thailand's 1st Olympic Gold Medal, 1996 — A552

Mahavajiravudh School, Songkhla, Cent. — A553

Litho. & Embossed
Perf. 14½x14

1996, Dec. 16				**Wmk. 340**
1704	A552	6b multicolored	.45	.30

Perf. 14x14½

1997, Jan. 1				**Wmk. 387**
1705	A553	2b multicolored	.20	.20
	Complete booklet, 5 #1705		1.00	

Children's Day — A554

Children' paintings: No. 1706, Children processing fish. No. 1707, Monument, children in praise.

1997, Jan. 11				**Wmk. 340**
1706	A554	2b multicolored	.20	.20
	Complete booklet, 5 #1706		1.00	
1707	A554	2b multicolored	.20	.20
	Complete booklet, 5 #1707		1.00	

Communications Authority of Thailand, 20th Anniv. — A555

Perf. 14½x14

1997, Feb. 25	**Litho.**			**Wmk. 340**
1708	A555	2b multicolored	.20	.20
	Complete booklet, 5 #1708		1.00	

Statue of Prince Bhanurangsi A556

Perf. 14½x14

1997, Feb. 25				
1709	A556	2b multicolored	.20	.20
	Complete booklet, 5 #1709		1.00	

Laksi Mail Center A557

#1710, Outside view of building. #1711, Computerized mail sorting machine.

1997, Feb. 25	**Perf. 14½x14**	
1710 A557 2b multicolored	.20	.20
1711 A557 2b multicolored	.20	.20
a. Pair, #1710-1711	.30	.25

State Railway, Cent. — A558

3b, 0-6-0 Type. 4b, Garratt. 6b, Sulzer diesel. 7b, Hitachi diesel leaving tunnel.

Wmk. 387

1997, Mar. 26 Litho.	**Perf. 13**	
1712 A558 3b multicolored	.25	.20
a. Souvenir sheet of 1	1.50	1.50
1713 A558 4b multicolored	.30	.25
1714 A558 6b multicolored	.45	.35
1715 A558 7b multicolored	.55	.40
a. Souv. sheet of 4, #1712-1715	2.25	
Nos. 1712-1715 (4)	1.55	1.20

No. 1712a sold for 20b, No. 1715a sold for 30b.

Chulalongkorn University, 80th Anniv. — A559

Designs: No. 1716, Palace of Prince Maha Vajirunhis. No. 1717, Faculty of Arts building.

Perf. 14½x14		
1997, Mar. 26	**Wmk. 340**	
1716 A559 2b yellow & multi	.20	.20
Complete booklet, 5 #1716	1.00	
1717 A559 2b rose & multi	.20	.20
Complete booklet, 5 #1717	1.00	

Thai Red Cross A560

1997, Mar. 28

1718 A560 3b Rajakarun building	.25	.20

Govt. Savings Bank, 84th Anniv. — A561

1997, Apr. 1

1719 A561 2b multicolored	.20	.20
Complete booklet, 5 #1719	1.00	

Heritage Conservation Day — A562

Phanomrung historical Park: No. 1720, Outer stairway. No. 1721, Pavilion. No. 1722, Passage, stairway to sanctuary. No. 1723, Naga balustrade, Central Gate of Eastern Gallery.

1997, Apr. 2		
1720 A562 3b multicolored	.25	.20
1721 A562 3b multicolored	.25	.20
1722 A562 7b multicolored	.55	.40
1723 A562 7b multicolored	.55	.40
a. Souvenir sheet, #1720-1723	2.25	
Nos. 1720-1723 (4)	1.60	1.20

No. 1723a sold for 30b.

Songkran Day Type of 1991

1997-2002   Wmk. 340   Perf. 14x14½

1724 A425 2b Demon on ox's back, zodiac	.20	.20
Complete booklet, 5 #1724	1.00	.75
a. Souvenir sheet of 1	.65	
b. Unwmkd., granite paper	.20	.20

Issued: Nos. 1724, 1724a, 4/13/97; No. 1724b, 4/13/02. No. 1724b issued only in No. 2017b.

No. 1724a sold for 8b and exists imperf.

King Bhumibol Adulyadej Type of 1996

Litho, Litho & Engraved (#1728-1729)

Perf. 14x14½

1997, May 5	**Wmk. 340**	
1725 A550 4b blue & red brown	.30	.25
a. Perf. 13¼, unwmkd.	.30	.25
b. Unwmkd., granite paper	.20	.20
1726 A550 5b pur & org brn	.40	.30
a. Perf. 13½, unwmk., granite paper	.25	.20
b. Unwmkd., granite paper	.20	.20
1727 A550 7b pink & green	.55	.40

Wmk. 329

Perf. 13½x13

1728 A550 10b orange & brown	.80	.60
1729 A550 20b violet & maroon	1.60	1.25
Nos. 1725-1729 (5)	3.65	2.80

Issued: No. 1726a, 12/28/98; No. 1725a, 10/8/99. 1725b, 1726b, 12/1/00.

Waterfowl — A563

Designs: No. 1730, Pheasant-tailed jacana. No. 1731, Bronze-winged jacana. No. 1732, Painted stork. No. 1733, Black-winged stilt.

Perf. 11½x12

1997, May 15   Photo.   Unwmk.

Granite Paper

1730 A563 3b multicolored	.25	.20
1731 A563 3b multicolored	.25	.20
1732 A563 7b multicolored	.55	.40
1733 A563 7b multicolored	.55	.40
a. Souvenir sheet, #1730-1733	2.25	
b. As "a", with added inscription	2.25	
Nos. 1730-1733 (4)	1.60	1.20

No. 1733a sold for 30b. No. 1733b has PACIFIC 97 emblem in sheet margin, while sales price has been removed from sheet margin. No. 1728b sold for 42b.

King Bhumibol Adulyadej, National Telecommunications — A564

2b, King using hand-held radio, "Suthee" aerial. 3b, King using hand-held radio for communication in local areas. 6b, King using computer. 9b, King, classroom using satellite information.

Perf. 14½x14

1997, June 9 Litho.	**Wmk. 340**	
1734 A564 2b multicolored	.20	.20
Complete booklet, 5 #1734	1.00	
1735 A564 3b multicolored	.25	.20
1736 A564 6b multicolored	.50	.40
1737 A564 9b multicolored	.70	.50
a. Souvenir sheet, #1734-1737	2.40	
Nos. 1734-1737 (4)	1.65	1.30

No. 1737a sold for 30b.

Motion Pictures in Thailand, Cent. — A565

Designs: No. 1738, King Rama VII filming movie, film showing King Chulalongkorn's state visit to Europe. No. 1739, Early motion picture equipment, advertisement, Prince Sanbassatra, founder of Thai motion picures. No. 1740, Poster from "Double Luck," band playing in front of movie theater. No. 1741, Open air theater, poster from "Going Astray."

1997, June 10

1738 A565 3b multicolored	.25	.20
1739 A565 3b multicolored	.25	.20
1740 A565 7b multicolored	.55	.40
1741 A565 7b multicolored	.55	.40
Nos. 1738-1741 (4)	1.60	1.20

Faculty of Medicine, Chulalongkorn University, 50th Anniv. — A566

King Rama VIII, building, operating room.

1997, June 11

1742 A566 2b multicolored	.20	.20
Complete booklet, 5 #1742	1.00	

King Bhumibol Adulyadej Type of 1996

Perf. 14x14½

1997, July 19 Litho.	**Wmk. 340**	
1743 A550 6b grn & gray vio	.40	.30
1744 A550 9b dk bl & brn org	.60	.45

Litho. & Engr. Wmk. 329 Perf. 13½x13

1745 A550 100b lem & dk bl grn	6.25	4.75
Nos. 1743-1745 (3)	7.25	5.50

Thai-Russian Diplomatic Relations, Cent. — A567

Design: Peterhof Palace, King Chulalongkorn (King Rama V).

1997, July 3 Litho.	**Perf. 14½x14**	
1746 A567 2b multicolored	.20	.20
Complete booklet, 5 #1746	.65	

Asalhapuja Day — A568

3b, Mahosathajataka (scene with man on elephant). 4b, Bhuridattajataka (scene with two men, large snake). 6b, Candakumarajataka (scene with pot of fire, three men on knees, man in sky, Buddha). 7b, Naradajataka (scene with people praising human figure with four arms hovering above roof).

Perf. 11½ Syncopated

1997, July 19   Photo.   Unwmk.

Granite Paper

1747 A568 3b multicolored	.20	.20
a. Souvenir sheet of 1	.40	
b. As "a," inscribed in margin	.20	

1748 A568 4b multicolored	.25	.20
a. Souvenir sheet of 1	.50	
b. As "a," inscribed in margin	.25	
1749 A568 6b multicolored	.40	.25
a. Souvenir sheet of 1	.65	
b. As "a," inscribed in margin	.40	
1750 A568 7b multicolored	.45	.35
a. Souvenir sheet of 1	.75	
b. Souvenir sheet, #1747-1750	1.90	
c. As "a," inscribed in margin	.45	.35
Nos. 1747-1750 (4)	1.30	1.00

#1747a sold for 6b; #1748a for 8b; #1749a for 10b; #1750a for 12b; #1750b for 30b.

Sheet margins of lack value inscriptions, but contain Shanghai '97 exhibition emblem (#1747b, 1748b), Chinese insription; Bangkok '97 exhibition emblem (#1749b, 1750c).

1997 Thailand Philatelic Exhibition — A569

Houses from: 2b, Northern region. 5b, Central region. 6b, Northeastern region. 9b, Southern region.

Wmk. 329

1997, Aug. 2 Litho.	**Perf. 13½**	
1751 A569 2b multicolored	.20	.20
Complete booklet, 5 #1751	1.00	
1752 A569 3b multicolored	.30	.25
1753 A569 6b multicolored	.40	.30
1754 A569 9b multicolored	.55	.45
a. Souvenir sheet, #1751-1754	2.00	
Nos. 1751-1754 (4)	1.45	1.20

No. 1754a sold for 32b.

Natl. Communications Day — A570

Perf. 14x14½

1997, Aug. 4	**Wmk. 340**	
1755 A570 2b multicolored	.20	.20
Complete booklet, 5 #1755	1.00	

Greeting Stamps — A570a

Lotus flowers: No. 1755A, Nymphaea capensis. No. 1755B, Nymphaea stellata.

Perf. 14x14½

1997, Aug. 4   Litho.   Wmk. 387

Booklet Stamps

1755A A570a (2b) multicolored	.30	.30
1755B A570a (2b) multicolored	.30	.30
c. Bklt. pane, 5 ea #1755A-1755B + 4 labels	3.00	
Complete bklt., #1755Bc	3.00	

Nos. 1755A-1755B were sold only at 7-11 stores, not at post offices or philatelic agencies.

King Bhumibol Adulyadej Type of 1996

Litho. & Engr.

Perf. 13½x13

1997, Aug. 8	**Wmk. 329**	
1756 A550 25b bl grn & ol blk	1.60	1.25
1757 A550 200b lil rose & vio blk	12.50	6.25

ASEAN, 30th Anniv. — A571

Designs: No. 1758, Thi Lo Su Falls, Tak. No. 1759, Luang Chiang Dao Mountain, Chiang Mai. No. 1760, Phromthep Cape, Phuket. No. 1761, Thalu Island, Chumphon.

Perf. 14½x14

				Wmk. 340	
1997, Aug. 8					
1758	A571	2b multicolored		.20	.20
		Complete booklet, 5 #1758		1.00	
1759	A571	2b multicolored		.20	.20
		Complete booklet, 5 #1759		1.00	
1760	A571	9b multicolored		.60	.45
1761	A571	9b multicolored		.60	.45
		Nos. 1758-1761 (4)		1.60	1.30

Dinosaurs — A572

Designs: 2b, Phuwiangosaurus sirindhornae. 3b, Siamotyrannus isanensis. 6b, Siamosaurus suteethorni. 9b, Psittacosaurus sattayaraki.

Perf. 13½x13 Syncopated

1997, Aug. 28		**Photo.**		**Unwmk.**	
1762	A572	2b multicolored		.20	.20
		Complete booklet, 5 #1762		1.00	
1763	A572	3b multicolored		.20	.20
1764	A572	6b multicolored		.35	.25
1765	A572	9b multicolored		.50	.35
a.		Souvenir sheet, #1762-1765		1.75	
		Nos. 1762-1765 (4)		1.25	1.00

No. 1765a sold for 30b.

King Chulalongkorn's Visit to Switzerland, Cent. — A573

Perf. 14x14½

1997, Sept. 12		**Litho.**		**Wmk. 340**	
1766	A573	2b multicolored		.20	.20
		Complete booklet, 5 #1766		.65	

Intl. Letter Writing Week — A574

Winning drawings: No. 1767, Tricycle, combining rickshaw and tricycle. No. 1768, Tricycle with side seat. No. 1769, Motor tricycle. No. 1770, Motor tricycle with light on roof.

Perf. 11½x12

1997, Oct. 5		**Photo.**		**Unwmk.**	
		Granite Paper			
1767	A574	3b multicolored		.20	.20
1768	A574	3b multicolored		.20	.20
1769	A574	9b multicolored		.40	.30
1770	A574	9b multicolored		.40	.30
a.		Souvenir sheet, #1767-1770		1.25	
		Nos. 1767-1770 (4)		1.20	1.00

No. 1770a sold for 30b.

Shells of Thailand and Singapore A575

Designs: No. 1771, Drupa morum. No. 1772, Nerita chamaelon. No. 1773, Littoraria melanostoma. No. 1774, Cryptospira elgans.

Perf. 11½

1997, Oct. 9		**Litho.**			
		Granite Paper			
1771	A575	2b multicolored		.20	.20
		Complete booklet, 5 #1771		1.00	
1772	A575	2b multicolored		.20	.20
		Complete booklet, 5 #1772		1.00	
1773	A575	9b multicolored		.40	.30
1774	A575	9b multicolored		.40	.30
a.		Souvenir sheet, #1771-7774		1.25	
		Nos. 1771-1774 (4)		1.20	1.00

No. 1774a sold for 30b. See Singapore Nos. 825-828A.

Chalerm Prakiat Energy Conserving Building — A576

Perf. 14½x14

1997, Nov. 10		**Litho.**		**Wmk. 340**	
1775	A576	2b multicolored		.20	.20
		Complete booklet, 5 #1775		1.00	

Christening of Suphannahong Royal Barge, 86th Anniv. — A577

Illustration reduced.

Perf. 11½

1997, Nov. 13		**Photo.**		**Unwmk.**	
		Granite Paper			
1776	A577	9b multicolored		.40	.30
a.		Souvenir sheet of 1		.90	
b.		As "a," ovptd. in margin		1.10	
c.		As "a," ovptd. in margin		.90	

#1776a, 1776b, 1776c sold for 20b.
The sheet margin of #1776b is ovptd in gold with Thai and Chinese inscriptions for Bangkok/China 98. Issued 10/16/98.
No. 1776c overprinted in margin with World Stamp Expo 2000 emblem in gold. Issued 7/7/00.

New Year 1998 — A578

Flowers: No. 1777, Cassia alata. No. 1778, Strophanthus caudatus. No. 1779, Clinacanthus nutans. No. 1780, Acanthus ilicifolius.

Perf. 13½x13

1997, Nov. 15		**Litho.**			
		Granite Paper			
1777	A578	2b multicolored		.20	.20
1778	A578	2b multicolored		.20	.20
1779	A578	2b multicolored		.20	.20
1780	A578	2b multicolored		.20	.20
a.		Souvenir sheet, #1777-1780		.70	
b.		As "a," with added inscription		.35	
		Nos. 1777-1780 (4)		.80	.80

No. 1780a sold for 15b. No. 1780b contains Indepex '97 exhibition emblem, but no value inscription in sheet margin.

King Bhumibol Adulyadej's 70th Birthday — A579

#1781, Playing saxophone. #1782, Painting picture. #1783, Building sailboat. #1784, Wearing gold medal, sailboats. 6b, Taking photograph. 7b, Writing book. 9b, Working at computer.

Perf. 11½

1997, Dec. 5		**Photo.**			
		Granite Paper			
1781	A579	2b multicolored		.20	.20
1782	A579	2b multicolored		.20	.20
1783	A579	2b multicolored		.20	.20
1784	A579	2b multicolored		.20	.20
1785	A579	6b multicolored		.25	.20
1786	A579	7b multicolored		.30	.25
1787	A579	9b multicolored		.40	.30
		Nos. 1781-1787 (7)		1.75	1.55

A580

A581

Winners in Yuvabadhana Foundation, "Sports Develop Mind and Body" drawing competition: No. 1788, Children in wheelchair race. No. 1789, Flying kites. No. 1790, Gymnastics. No. 1791, Windsurfing.

Perf. 14x14½

1998, Jan. 10		**Litho.**		**Wmk. 340**	
1788	A580	2b multicolored		.20	.20
		Complete booklet, 5 #1788		.45	
1789	A580	2b multicolored		.20	.20
		Complete booklet, 5 #1789		.45	
1790	A580	2b multicolored		.20	.20
		Complete booklet, 5 #1790		.45	
1791	A580	2b multicolored		.20	.20
a.		Complete booklet, 5 #1791		.45	
		Nos. 1788-1791 (4)		.80	.80

Natl. Childrens' Day.

1998, Jan. 17				**Unwmk.**	
		Granite Paper			
1792	A581	2b multicolored		.20	.20
		Complete booklet, 5 #1792		.45	

20th Asia Pacific Dental Congress.

A582

A583

1998, Feb. 3		**Litho.**		**Wmk. 340**	
1793	A582	2b multicolored		.20	.20

Veteran's Day, 50th anniv.

King Bhumibol Adulyadej Type of 1996

1998, Feb. 25		**Photo.**		**Perf. 11½x12**	
		Granite Paper			
1794	A550	50s dk ol & lt ol		.20	.20
		Litho. & Engr.			
		Wmk. 329			
		Perf. 13½x13			
1795	A550	50b dp vio & dk grn		2.50	1.90

Perf. 14x14½

1998, Mar. 27		**Litho.**		**Wmk. 340**	
1796	A583	2b Queen Sirikit		.20	.20
		Complete booklet, 5 #1796		.50	

1998 Thai Red Cross Fair.

Heritage Conservation Day Type of 1993

Paintings of Phanomrung Historical Park: 3b, Main Tower. 4b, Minor Tower. 6b, Scripture Repository. 7b, Lintel depicting Vishnu sleeping in ocean, doorway of Main Tower.

Perf. 14½x14

1998, Apr. 2		**Litho.**		**Wmk. 340**	
1797	A477	3b multicolored		.20	.20
1798	A477	4b multicolored		.20	.20
1799	A477	6b multicolored		.30	.25
1800	A477	7b multicolored		.35	.30
a.		Souvenir sheet, #1797-1800		1.40	

No. 1800a sold for 27b.

Songkran Day Type of 1991

1998-2002				**Perf. 14x14½**	
1801	A425	2b Demon on tiger's back, zodiac		.20	.20
		Complete booklet, 5 #1801		.50	
a.		Souvenir sheet of 1		.40	
b.		As "a," inscribed in margin		.40	
c.		Unwmkd., granite paper		.20	.20

Issued: Nos. 1801-1801b, 4/13/98. No. 1801c, 4/13/98. No. 1801c issued only in No. 2017b.
No. 1801a sold for 8b and exists imperf.
Sheet margin of No. 1801b contains flags of Thailand and China (PRC), Thai and Chinese inscriptions, no value inscription, and exists imperf.
No. 1801b sold for 8b and was issued 10/16/98.

Wild Cats A584

Paintings: 2b, Felis viverrina. 4b, Panthera tigris. 6b, Panthera pardus. 8b, Felis chaus.

1998, Apr. 13				**Perf. 14½x14**	
1802	A584	2b multicolored		.20	.20
		Complete booklet, 5 #1802		.50	
1803	A584	4b multicolored		.20	.20
1804	A584	6b multicolored		.30	.25
1805	A584	8b multicolored		.40	.35
a.		Souvenir sheet, #1802-1805		1.50	
		Nos. 1802-1805 (4)		1.10	1.00

No. 1805a sold for 30b.

AEROTHAI (Aeronautical Radio of Thailand, Ltd.), 50th Anniv. — A585

1998, Apr. 15
1806 A585 2b multicolored .20 .20
    Complete booklet, 5 #1806 .50

Visakhapuja Day — A586

Paintings of the "Ten Jataka Stories:" 3b, Riding horse above buildings, Vidhurajataka. 4b, In chariot, Vessantarajataka. 6b, Two figures seated before larger figure, Vessantarajataka. 7b, Figures in front of building, Vessantarajataka.

1998, May 10   *Perf. 13½*
1807 A586 3b multicolored .20 .20
1808 A586 4b multicolored .20 .20
1809 A586 6b multicolored .30 .25
1810 A586 7b multicolored .30 .25
   a.   Souvenir sheet, #1807-1810 1.00
    Nos. 1807-1810 (4) 1.00 .90

No. 1810a sold for 30b.

Adm. Abhakara Kiartiwongse (1880-1923), Father of Royal Thai Navy — A587

1998, May 19   *Perf. 14½x14*
1811 A587 2b multicolored .20 .20
    Complete booklet, 5 #1811 .50

Educational Development — A588

Perf. 14½x14
1998, June 15   **Litho.**   **Wmk. 340**
1812 A588 2b multicolored .20 .20
    Complete booklet, 5 #1812 .50

King Chulalongkorn's 1st State Visit to Europe, Cent. — A589

Illustration reduced.

Unwmk.
1998, July 1   **Litho.**   *Perf. 13*
Granite Paper
1813 A589 6b multicolored .30 .25
Litho. & Embossed
1814 A589 20b multicolored 1.00 .75

Intl. Year of the Ocean A590

2b, Orchaella brevirostris. 3b, Tursiops truncatus. 6b, Physeter catodon. 9b, Dugong dugon.

1998, July 19   **Litho.**   *Perf. 14½x14*
Granite Paper
1815 A590 2b multicolored .20 .20
    Complete booklet, 5 #1815 .50
1816 A590 3b multicolored .20 .20
1817 A590 6b multicolored .30 .30
1818 A590 9b multicolored .45 .45
   a.   Souvenir sheet, #1815-1818 1.50
    Nos. 1815-1818 (4) 1.15 1.15

No. 1818a sold for 30b.

King Bhumibol Adulyadej Type of 1996
1998 Photo. Unwmk. Perf. 11½x12
Granite Paper
1819 A550 2b carmine .20 .20
1820 A550 9b dark bl & brn org .60 .45

Irrigation Engineering in Thailand, 60th Anniv. — A591

Perf. 14½x14
1998, Aug. 1   **Litho.**   **Unwmk.**
Granite Paper
1821 A591 2b multicolored .20 .20
    Complete booklet, 5 #1821 .50

Natl. Communications Day — A592

1998, Aug. 4
Granite Paper
1822 A592 2b multicolored .20 .20
    Complete booklet, 5 #1822 .50

School of Political Science, Chulalongkorn University, 50th Anniv. — A593

1998, Aug. 19
Granite Paper
1823 A593 2b multicolored .20 .20
    Complete booklet, 5 #1823 .50

Sukhothai Thammathirat Open University, Award for Excellence — A594

1998, Sept. 5   **Litho.**   *Perf. 14½x14*
Granite Paper
1824 A594 2b multicolored .20 .20
    Complete booklet, 5 #1824 .50

Amazing Thailand, 1998-99, Thai Arts and Culture A595

1998, Sept. 15   *Perf. 13½*
Granite Paper
1825 A595 3b With bow & arrow .20 .20
1826 A595 3b Combat .20 .20
1827 A595 7b Seizing opponent .35 .25
1828 A595 7b Sky hovering .35 .25
    Nos. 1825-1828 (4) 1.10 .90

Chinese Stone Statues — A596

Warriors holding: No. 1829, Staff with loop. No. 1830, Spear with slightly curved blade. No. 1831, Mace. No. 1832, Spear with jagged blade.

1998, Sept. 15   *Perf. 14x14½*
Granite Paper
1829 A596 2b multicolored .20 .20
    Complete booklet, 5 #1829 .50
1830 A596 2b multicolored .20 .20
    Complete booklet, 5 #1830 .50
1831 A596 10b multicolored .50 .40
1832 A596 10b multicolored .50 .40
   a.   Souvenir sheet, #1829-1832, perf 13½ 1.75
   b.   As "a," with added marginal inscription 1.90
    Nos. 1829-1832 (4) 1.40 1.20

China 1999 World Philatelic Exhibition (#1832b). #1832a-1832b sold for 35b. #1832 is perf 13¼ and was issued 8/21/99.

Intl. Letter Writing Week — A597

Himavanta mythical animals created by ancient Thai artists: #1836, Kraisara Rajasiha, 3 king lions, white body, golden collars. #1837, Gajasiha, 2 tusked lions. #1838, Kesara Singha, 2 hoofed lions. #1839, Singha, 3 gray lions.

Perf. 11½
1998, Oct. 3   **Photo.**   **Unwmk.**
Granite Paper
1836 A597 2b multicolored .20 .20
    Complete booklet, 5 #1836 .55
1837 A597 2b multicolored .20 .20
    Complete booklet, 5 #1837 .55
1838 A597 12b multicolored .65 .50
1839 A597 12b multicolored .65 .50
   a.   Souvenir sheet, #1836-1839 2.25
    Nos. 1836-1839 (4) 1.70 1.40

No. 1839a sold for 40b.

Thai Presidency of the Intl. Assoc. of Lions Clubs — A598

1998, Oct. 8   **Litho.**   *Perf. 14½x14*
Granite Paper
1840 A598 2b multicolored .20 .20
    Complete booklet, 5 #1840 .55

New Year 1999 — A599

Flowers: No. 1841, Barleria lupulina. No. 1842, Gloriosa superba. No. 1843, Asclepias curassavica. No. 1844, Sesamum indicum.

Perf. 14½x14
1998, Nov. 15   **Photo.**   **Unwmk.**
Granite Paper
1841 A599 2b multicolored .20 .20
1842 A599 2b multicolored .20 .20
1843 A599 2b multicolored .20 .20
1844 A599 2b multicolored .20 .20
   a.   Souvenir sheet, #1841-1844 .85
    Nos. 1841-1844 (4) .80 .80

No. 1844a sold for 15b.

Knight Grand Cross, Most Admirable Order of the Direkgunabhorn — A600

Perf. 14x14½
1998, Dec. 5   **Litho.**   **Unwmk.**
Granite Paper
1845 15b shown .80 .60
1846 15b Decoration .80 .60
   a. A600 Pair, #1845-1846 1.60 1.40

Children's Day — A601

Paintings from competition, "Sports develop body and mind:" No. 1847, Sepak Takraw (game of kicking ball over net). No. 1848, Swimming. No. 1849, Volleyball. No. 1850, Equestrian sports.

Perf. 14½x14
1999, Jan. 9   **Litho.**   **Unwmk.**
Granite Paper
1847 A601 2b multicolored .20 .20
    Complete booklet, 5 #1847 .55
1848 A601 2b multicolored .20 .20
    Complete booklet, 5 #1848 .55
1849 A601 2b multicolored .20 .20
    Complete booklet, 5 #1849 .55
1850 A601 2b multicolored .20 .20
    Complete booklet, 5 #1850 .55
    Nos. 1847-1850 (4) .80 .80

Asian and Pacific Decade of Disabled Persons — A602

1999, Jan. 10
Granite Paper

1851	A602	2b multicolored	.20	.20
a.		Complete booklet, 5 #1851	.55	

Thai Rice Production — A603

#1852, Planting rice. #1853, Harvesting rice by hand. #1854, Harvesting rice with machinery. #1855, Rice in field, bowl of rice.

1999, Feb. 25 Litho. Perf. 14½x14
Granite Paper

1852	A603	6b multicolored	.35	.25
1853	A603	6b multicolored	.35	.25
1854	A603	12b multicolored	.65	.50
1855	A603	12b multicolored	.65	.50
a.		Souvenir sheet, #1852-1855	2.50	
		Nos. 1852-1855 (4)	2.00	1.50

No. 1855a sold for 45b.

Maghapuja Day (Buddhist Holiday) — A604

Designs: 3b, Birth of Mahajanaka. 6b, Mani Mekkhala carrying Mahajanaka to Mithila City. 9b, Two mango trees. 15b, Mahajanaka founding an educational institution.

1999, Mar. 1 Litho. Perf. 13½
Granite Paper

1856	A604	3b multicolored	.30	.25
1857	A604	6b multicolored	.35	.25
1858	A604	9b multicolored	.55	.40
1859	A604	15b multicolored	.80	.60
a.		Souvenir sheet, #1856-1859	2.40	
		Nos. 1856-1859 (4)	2.00	1.50

No. 1859a sold for 45b.

Somdetch Phra Sri Savarindira Baromma Raja Devi Phra Phan Vassa Ayika Chao, Queen Grandmother A605

Perf. 14x14½
1999, Mar. 30 Litho. Wmk. 340

1860	A605	2b multicolored	.20	.20
		Complete booklet, 5 #1860	.55	

1999 Red Cross Fair.

Bangkok 2000 World Youth Stamp Expo, 13th Asian Intl. Stamp Expo — A606

Thai children's games: No. 1861, Kite flying. No. 1862, Wheel rolling. No. 1863, Catching last one in line (children going under arms). No. 1864, Snatching baby from mother snake.

Perf. 14½x14
1999, Mar. 30 Unwmk.
Granite Paper

1861	A606	2b multicolored	.20	.20
1862	A606	2b multicolored	.20	.20
1863	A606	15b multicolored	.80	.60
1864	A606	15b multicolored	.80	.60
a.		Souvenir sheet, #1861-1864, perf. 13½	2.40	
		Nos. 1861-1864 (4)	2.00	1.60

No. 1864a sold for 45b.

Heritage Conservation Day — A607

Various Thai silk designs for "Mudmee" textiles.

1999, Apr. 2 Perf. 14x14½
Granite Paper

1865	A607	2b bl grn & multi	.20	.20
		Complete booklet, 5 #1865	.55	
1866	A607	4b red & multi	.20	.20
1867	A607	12b vermilion & multi	.65	.50
1868	A607	15b black & multi	.80	.60
a.		Souvenir sheet, #1865-1868	2.40	
		Nos. 1865-1868 (4)	1.85	1.50

No. 1868a sold for 45b.

Songkran Day Type of 1991
1999, Apr. 13
Granite Paper

1869	A425	2b Woman on rabbit's back, zodiac	.20	.20
		Complete booklet, 5 #1869	.55	
a.		Souvenir sheet of 1	.45	
b.		As "a," with added marginal inscription	.45	

China 1999 World Philatelic Exhibition (#1869b). #1869a-1869b sold for 8b and exist imperf.
Issued: #1869b, 8/21.

Consumer Protection Years, 1998-99 — A608

1999, Apr. 30 Perf. 14½x14
Granite Paper

1870	A608	2b multicolored	.20	.20
		Complete booklet, 5 #1870	.55	

King Bhumibol Adulyadej's 72nd Birthday — A609

Royal palaces: No. 1871, Chitralada Villa, Dusit Palace, Bangkok. No. 1872, Phu Phing Ratchaniwet Palace, circular drive, white fence. No. 1873, Phu Phan Ratchaniwet Palace, adjoining buildings, light posts. No. 1874, Thaksin Ratchaniwet Palace, four trees reaching to second story windows. Illustration reduced.

1999, May 5 Photo. Perf. 11½
Granite Paper

1871	A609	6b multicolored	.35	.25
1872	A609	6b multicolored	.35	.25
1873	A609	6b multicolored	.35	.25
1874	A609	6b multicolored	.35	.25
a.		Souvenir sheet, #1871-1874	2.25	
		Nos. 1871-1874 (4)	1.40	1.00

No. 1874a sold for 40b.

Political Science Dept., Thammasat University, 50th Anniv. — A610

1999, June 14 Litho. Perf. 14x14½

1875	A610	3b multicolored	.20	.20

King Bhumibol Adulyadej Type of 1996
Litho. & Engr.

			Perf. 13	
1999		**Wmk. 329**		
1876	A550	12b bl grn & bl	.60	.40
1877	A550	15b yel brn & grn	.80	.60
1878	A550	30b pink & brown	1.60	1.40

Size: 25x30mm
Perf. 12¾x13¼

1879	A550	500b org & claret	26.00	19.00
		Nos. 1876-1879 (4)	29.00	21.40

Issued: 12b, 15b, 30b, 7/1; 500b, 9/10.

UPU, 125th Anniv. A611

Designs: 2b, Floating Vessel of Light Festival. 15b, Buddhist Candle Festival, Ubon Ratchathani.

1999, July 1 Litho. Perf. 14½x14
Granite Paper

1880	A611	2b multicolored	.20	.20
		Complete booklet, 5 #1880	.55	
1881	A611	15b multicolored	.80	.60

Customs Dept., 125th Anniv. — A612

1999, July 3

1882	A612	6b multicolored	.30	.20

Natl. Communications Day — A613

1999, Aug. 4 Litho. Perf. 14½x14
Granite Paper

1883	A613	4b multicolored	.20	.20

Thaipex '99 — A614

1999, Aug. 4 Granite Paper
Color of Rabbits

1884	A614	6b black & white	.30	.20
1885	A614	6b golden brown, brown	.30	.20
1886	A614	12b white	.60	.40
1887	A614	12b gray	.60	.40
a.		Souvenir sheet, #1884-1887, perf. 13½	2.50	
		Nos. 1884-1887 (4)	1.80	1.20

No. 1887a sold for 50b and exists imperf.

Bangkok 2000 Stamp Exhibition — A615

Scenes from Thai folk tales and literature: No. 1888, Boy on dragon-like horse. No. 1889, Rishi transforming tiger cub and calf into humans. No. 1890, Boy exiting conch shell. No. 1891, Children playing with kitchenware.

1999, Aug. 4 Perf. 14½x14
Granite Paper

1888	A615	2b multicolored	.20	.20
1889	A615	2b multicolored	.20	.20
1890	A615	15b multicolored	.80	.55
1891	A615	15b multicolored	.80	.55
a.		Souvenir sheet, #1888-1891, perf. 13½	2.40	
		Nos. 1888-1891 (4)	2.00	1.50

No. 1891a sold for 45b.

King Bhumibol Adulyadej's 72nd Birthday A616

King: No. 1892, On father's knee. No. 1893, With mother, sister and brother. No. 1894, With brother, in suits. No. 1895, With brother, in military uniforms. No. 1896, With wife on wedding day. No. 1897, At coronation ceremony. No. 1898, As Buddhist monk. No. 1899, With Queen, Prince and Princesses. No. 1900, Wearing royal robe.

1999, Sept. 10 Photo. Perf. 11¾
Granite Paper

1892	A616	3b multicolored	.20	.20
1893	A616	3b multicolored	.20	.20
1894	A616	3b multicolored	.20	.20
1895	A616	6b multicolored	.30	.20
1896	A616	6b multicolored	.30	.20
1897	A616	6b multicolored	.30	.20
1898	A616	12b multicolored	.60	.40
1899	A616	12b multicolored	.60	.40
1900	A616	12b multicolored	.60	.40
a.		Souvenir sheet, #1892-1900	4.75	
		Nos. 1892-1900 (9)	3.30	2.40

No. 1900a sold for 90b.

Intl. Year of Older Persons — A617

999, Oct. 1 Litho. Perf. 14½x14
Granite Paper
901 A617 2b multi .20 .20
Complete booklet, 5 #1901 1.00

Bauhinia
Variegata — A618

Intl. Letter Writing Week: No. 1903, Bombax eiba. No. 1904, Radermachera ignea (orange owers). No. 1905, Bretschneidera sinensis ink flowers).

999, Oct. 2 Perf. 14x14½
Granite Paper
902 A618 2b shown .20 .20
Complete booklet, 5 #1902 .55
903 A618 2b multi .20 .20
Complete booklet, 5 #1903 .55
904 A618 12b multi .65 .45
905 A618 12b multi .65 .45
a. Souvenir sheet, #1902-1905, perf. 13¼ 1.90
Nos. 1902-1905 (4) 1.70 1.30
No. 1905a sold for 35b.

King Bhumibol Adulyadej's 72nd
Birthday — A619

King: #1906, And vehicle. #1907, And Buddhist monks. #1908, And Queen. #1909, And oldiers. #1910, And crowd. #1911, And disbled boy. #1912, Wearing green army uniorm. #1913, In white suit with camera. #1914, With crowd waving flags.

999, Oct. 21 Photo. Perf. 14½
Granite Paper
906 A619 3b multi .20 .20
907 A619 3b multi .20 .20
908 A619 3b multi .20 .20
909 A619 6b multi .30 .20
910 A619 6b multi .30 .20
911 A619 6b multi .30 .20
912 A619 12b multi .65 .45
913 A619 12b multi .65 .45
914 A619 12b multi .65 .45
a. Souvenir sheet, #1906-1914 4.75
Nos. 1906-1914 (9) 3.45 2.55
No. 1914a sold for 90b. Numbers have been eserved for additional stamps in this set.

Design
A39 — A620

Litho. & Embossed with Foil
Application
999, Dec. 5 Wmk. 387 Perf. 13¼
915 A620 100b blue & bronze 5.25 3.50
916 A620 100b blue & silver 5.25 3.50
917 A620 100b blue & gold 5.25 3.50
a. Souvenir sheet, #1915-1917 19.00
Nos. 1915-1917 (3) 15.75 10.50
King Bhumibol Adulyadej's 72nd birthday.
No. 1917a sold for 350b.

New Year
2000 — A621

Medicinal plants: No. 1918, Thunbergia laurifolia. No. 1919, Gmelina arborea. No. 1920, Prunus cerasoides. No. 1921, Fagraea fragrans.

Perf. 14½x14¼
1999, Nov. 15 Litho.
Granite Paper
1918 A621 2b multi .20 .20
1919 A621 2b multi .20 .20
1920 A621 2b multi .20 .20
a. Souv. sheet, 5 ea #1918-1920 + 10 labels 4.00
1921 A621 2b multi .20 .20
a. Souvenir sheet, #1918-1921 .80 .60
Nos. 1918-1921 (4) .80 .80
No. 1921a sold for 15b.
No. 1920a was issued 3/25/00 and sold for 60b. For an additional fee the blank labels could be personalized with photos taken at a booth not operated by the Thailand postal authorities at the Bangkok 2000 Stamp Exhibition.

Investiture of
Crown Prince
Vajiralongkorn,
27th
Anniv. — A622

1999, Dec. 28 Perf. 14x14½
Granite Paper
1922 A622 3b multi .20 .20

Lake of Lilies, Thale Noi — A623

Kulap Khao Flowers, Doi Chang
Dao — A624

Krachieo Flowers, Pa Hin
Ngam — A625

Bua Tong Flowers, Doi Mae
Ukor — A626

Illustrations reduced.

Perf. 14½x14¼
2000 Litho. Unwmk.
Granite Paper
1923 A623 Sheet of 12, #a-l 1.75 1.75
a.-l. 3b Any single .20 .20
1924 A624 Sheet of 12, #a-l 1.75 1.75
a.-l. 3b Any single .20 .20
1925 A625 Sheet of 12, #a-l 1.75 1.75
a.-l. 3b Any single .20 .20
1926 A625 Sheet of 12, #a-l 1.60 1.60
a.-l. 3b Any single .20 .20
Nos. 1923-1926 (4) 6.85 6.85
Issued: #1923, 1/1; #1924, 2/25; #1925, 7/16. #1926, 11/15.

Bees — A627

#1927, Apis andreniformis. #1928, Apis florea. #1929, Apis cerana. #1930, Apis dorsata.

2000, Mar. 19 Photo. Perf. 11¾
Granite Paper
1927-1930 A627 3b Set of 4 .55 .40
Souvenir Sheets of 1
1927a-1930a Set of 4 1.50
Nos. 1927a-1930a do not have white margin on stamps and sold for 8b each.

Bangkok 2000 Stamp
Exhibition — A628

Ceremonies: #1931, 2b, 1st month blessing (family & baby). #1932, 2b, Tonsure. #1933, 15b, Teacher respect (teacher, 3 children). #1934, 15b, Novice ordination.

2000, Mar. 25 Litho. Perf. 14½x14
Granite Paper
1931-1934 A628 Set of 4 1.60 1.25
1934a Souvenir sheet, #1931-1934, perf. 13 ½x14 2.10
No. 1934a sold for 45b.

Thai
Red
Cross
Fair
A629

2000, Mar. 30 Perf. 14½x14
Granite Paper
1935 A629 3b multi .20 .20

Thai Heritage Conservation — A630

Chok cloths from: 3b, Hat Seio. 6b, Mae Chaem. 8b, Ban Rai. 12b, Khu Bua.

2000, Apr. 2 Wmk. 387 Perf. 13¼
1936-1939 A630 Set of 4 1.40 1.00
1939a Souvenir sheet, #1936-1939 1.90
No. 1939a sold for 40b.

Songkran Day Type of 1991
Perf. 14x14½
2000, Apr. 13 Litho. Unwmk.
Granite Paper
1940 A425 2b Angel on serpent .20 .20
Booklet, 5 #1940 .50
a. Souvenir sheet of 1 .40
No. 1940a sold for 8b and exists imperf.

50th Wedding Anniv. of King and
Queen — A631

No. 1941 - King Bhumibol Adulyadej and Queen Sirikit: a, Sitting on grass. b, Standing. c, Sitting on thrones. d, With family. e, Standing, wearing regalia.
Illustration reduced.

2000, Apr. 28 Photo. Perf. 11¾
Granite Paper
1941 Vert. strip of 5 2.25 1.75
a.-e. A631 10b Any single .45 .35

Asalhapuja
Day — A632

2000, July 16 Litho. Perf. 14x14½
Granite Paper
1942 A632 3b multi .20 .20

Crown Prince Maha Vajiralongkorn,
48th Birthday — A633

2000, July 28 Perf. 14½x14
Granite Paper
1943 A633 2b multi .20 .20
Booklet, 5 #1943 .50
a. Souvenir sheet of 1, perf. 13¼ .40
No. 1943a sold for 8b.

Natl. Communications Day — A634

2000, Aug. 4
Granite Paper
1944 A634 3b multi .20 .20

Intl. Letter Writing Week — A636

Various tea sets.

Perf. 14½x14
2000, Oct. 7   Litho.   Unwmk.
Granite Paper
1945	A635	6b shown	.25	.20
1946	A635	6b multi, diff.	.25	.20
1947	A636	12b shown	.55	.40
1948	A636	12b multi, diff.	.55	.40
a.		Souvenir sheet, #1945-1948, perf. 13¼	2.00	
		Nos. 1945-1948 (4)	1.60	1.20

No. 1948a sold for 45b.

Princess Srinagarindra, Birth
Cent. — A637

2000, Oct. 21   Granite Paper
1949	A637	2b multi	.20	.20
		Booklet, 5 #1949	.45	
a.		Souvenir sheet of 1, perf. 13¼	.35	

No. 1949a sold for 8b.

Royal Barge Anantanakkharat — A638

Illustration reduced.

Perf. 13¼x14
2000, Nov. 15   Photo.   Wmk. 340
1950	A638	9b multi	.40	.30
a.		Souvenir sheet of 1	.65	

No. 1950a sold for 15b.

New Year
2001 — A639

Flowers: No. 1951, 2b, Clerodendrum philippinum. No. 1952, 2b, Capparis micracantha. No. 1953, 2b, Belamcanda chinensis. No. 1954, 2b, Memecylon caeruleum.

Perf. 14½x14¼
2000, Nov. 15   Litho.   Unwmk.
Granite Paper
1951-1954	A639	Set of 4	.35	.25
1954a		Souvenir sheet, #1951-1954	.65	

No. 1954a sold for 15b.

Parrots — A640

Designs: 2b, Psittacula alexandri. 5b, Psittacula eupatria. 8b, Psittinus cyanurus. 10b, Psittacula roseata.

2001, Jan. 13   Perf. 14x14½
Granite Paper
1955-1958	A640	Set of 4	1.10	.85
		Booklet, 5 #1955	.45	
a.		Souvenir sheet, #1955-1958, perf. 13¼	1.50	
b.		As "a," without price and with show emblem in margin	2.25	

No. 1955a sold for 35b. No. 1955b, Hong Kong 2001 Stamp Exhibition, sold for 50b.

King
Chulalongkorn
and Land
Deed — A641

2001, Feb. 17   Granite Paper
1959	A641	5b multi	.20	.20

Dept. of Lands, cent.

Marine Life — A642

Designs: a, Ray. b, Turtle. c, Jellyfish, fish. d, Lionfish. e, Black, yellow fish, coral. f, Eel. g, School of striped fish, angelfish, coral, vert. h, Pufferfish, blue fish, vert. i, Shark, fish.
   Stamp sizes: Nos. 1960a-1960f, 29x24mm, Nos. 1960g-1960h, 29x48mm. No. 1960i, 58x42mm.

Perf. 13¾x14¼
2001, Mar. 15   Photo.
Granite Paper
1960	A642	Sheet of 9	1.60	1.60
a.-f.		3b Any single	.20	.20
g.-i.		6b Any single	.25	.20

Gems
A643

Designs: 3b, Diamond. 4b, Green sapphire. 6b, Pearl. 12b, Blue sapphire.

2001   Litho.   Perf. 14½x14
Granite Paper
1961-1964	A643	Set of 4	1.10	.85
a.		Souvenir sheet, #1961-1964, perf. 13½x14	1.50	
b.		As "a," ovptd. in margin in gold	1.50	

Issued, Nos. 1961-1964a, 3/30; No. 1964b, 6/9.
No. 1964a sold for 35b.
No. 1964b has Belgica 2001 emblem overprint.

Red
Cross
A644

Perf. 14½x14
2001, Apr. 1   Litho.   Unwmk.
Granite Paper
1965	A644	4b multi	.20	.20

Ancient Brocades
From Nakhon Si
Thammarat
National
Museum — A645

Colors of brocade: 2b, Orange red, lilac, and gold. 3b, Green and gold. No. 1968, 10b, Orange and gold. No. 1969, 10b, Bright pink and gold.

2001, Apr. 2   Perf. 14x14½
Granite Paper
1966-1969	A645	Set of 4	1.10	.85
		Booklet, 5 #1966	.45	
a.		Souvenir sheet, #1966-1969, perf. 13¼	1.60	

Heritage Conservation Day.
No. 1969a sold for 35b.

Songkran Day Type of 1991
Perf. 13½x13¾
2001-2002   Wmk. 387
1970	A425	2b Man on snake, zodiac	.20	.20
		Booklet, 5 #1970	.45	
a.		Souvenir sheet of 1	.35	.35
b.		Unwmkd., granite paper, perf. 14x14½	.20	.20

Issued: Nos. 1970-1970a, 4/13/01. No. 1970b, 4/13/02. No. 1970b issued only in No. 2017b.
No. 1970a sold for 8b and exists imperf.

Visakhapuja
Day — A646

2001, May 7 Unwmk. Perf. 14x14½
Granite Paper
1971	A646	3b multi	.20	.20

Demon
Statues — A647

Designs: 2b, Maiyarap. 5b, Wirunchambang. 10b, Thotsakan. 12b, Sahatsadecha.

Perf. 14x14½
2001, June 13   Litho.   Unwm
Granite Paper
1972-1975	A647	Set of 4	1.40	1.
		Booklet, 5 #1972	.45	
1975a		Souvenir sheet #1972-1975, perf. 13½	1.50	

No. 1975a sold for 33b.

Prince Purachartra
Jayakara and
Rotary Intl.
Emblem — A648

2001, July 1   Granite Pape
1976	A648	3b multi	.20	.2

Rotary Intl. in Thailand, 66th anniv.

Mushrooms — A649

Designs: 2b, Schizophyllum commune. 3 Lentinus giganteus. 5b, Pleurotus cit nopileatus. 10b, Pleurotus flabellatus.

2001, July 4   Perf. 13¾x1
Granite Paper
1977-1980	A649	Set of 4	.90	.
		Booklet, 5 # 1977	.45	
1980a		Souvenir sheet, #1977-1980, perf. 13½	1.25	

No. 1980 sold for 26b.

Insect
A650

Designs: 2b, Cheirotonus parryi. 5b, Mouh tia batesi. 6b, Cladognathus giraffa. 12 Mormolyce phyllodes.

2001, July 4   Wmk. 329   Perf. 13
1981-1984	A650	Set of 4	1.10	.
		Booklet, 5 #1981	.45	
a.		Souvenir sheet, #1981-1984	1.50	
b.'		As "a," with Phila Nippon '01 emblem in margin	1.50	

No. 1984a sold for 34b.
No. 1984b sold for 34b, and was issued 8/

Natl. Communications Day — A651

Perf. 14½x14
2001, Aug. 4   Litho.   Unwmk
Granite Paper
1985	A651	4b multi	.20	.2

Thaipex '01 — A652

Various domesticated fowl: 3b, 4b, 6b, 12b.

2001, Aug. 4   Photo.   Perf. 13¼
Granite Paper
1986-1989 A652   Set of 4   1.10   .85
1989a   Souvenir sheet, #1986-
           1989   1.50   —
No. 1989 sold for 33b, also exists imperf.

Queen Suriyothai,
Heroine of
Thailand — A653

2001, Aug. 12 Litho.   Perf. 14x14¾
Granite Paper
1990 A653 3b multi   .20   .20
a.   Souvenir sheet of 1, perf. 13¼   .45   —
No. 1990a sold for 10b.

Queen Sirikit's Visit to the People's
Republic of China — A654

2001, Aug. 12   Perf. 14¾x14
Granite Paper
1991 A654 5b multi   .25   .20

Butterflies — A655

Designs: 2b, Pachliopta aristolochiae goni-
opeltis. 4b, Rhinopalpa polynice. 10b, Poritia
erycinoides. 12b, Spindasis lohita.

Perf. 13½ Syncopated
2001, Sept. 10   Photo.
1992-1995 A655 3b multi   1.25   .95
           Booklet, 5 #1992   .45
1995a   Souvenir sheet, #1992-
           1995   1.90   —
No. 1995a sold for 40b.

Intl. Letter Writing
Week — A656

Medicinal herbs: 2b, Piper nigrum. 3b, Solanum trilobatum. 5b, Boesenbergia rotunda.
10b, Ocimum tenuiflorum.

Perf. 14x14½
2001, Oct. 6   Litho.   Unwmk.
Granite Paper
1996-1999 A656 Set of 4   .90   .70
           Booklet, 5 #1996   .45
1999a   Souvenir sheet, #1996-
           1999, perf. 13½x13¼   1.10   —
No. 1999a sold for 25b.

Police Cadet Academy, Cent. — A657

2001, Oct. 13 Litho.   Perf. 14½x14
Granite Paper
2000 A657 5b multi   .25   .20

Royal Barge Anekkachat
Puchong — A658

Illustration reduced.

2001, Nov. 15 Photo.   Perf. 14¼
Granite Paper
2001 A658 9b multi   .40   .30
a.   Souvenir sheet of 1   .75   —
No. 2001a sold for 17b.

New Year
2002 — A659

Flowers: No. 2002, 2b, Pedicularis siamensis. No. 2003, 2b, Schoutenia glomerata. No.
2004, 2b, Gentiana crassa. No. 2005, 2b, Col-
quhounia coccinea.

2001, Nov. 15 Litho.   Perf. 14x14½
Granite Paper
2002-2005 A659 Set of 4   .35   .25
2005a   Souvenir sheet, #2002-
           2005   .50   —
No. 2005a sold for 11b.

Laying of Foundation Stone for
Suvarnabhumi Airport Passenger
Terminal — A660

2002, Jan. 19 Litho.   Perf. 14½x14
Granite Paper
2006 A660 3b multi   .20   .20

Rose — A661

2002, Feb. 1   Perf. 13¾
Granite Paper
2007 A661 4b multi   .20   .20

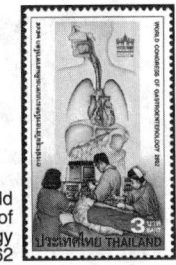

12th World
Congress of
Gastroenterology
A662

2002, Feb. 24   Perf. 14x14½
Granite Paper
2008 A662 3b multi   .20   .20

Communications Authority of Thailand,
25th Anniv. — A663

No. 2009: a, Satellite dish, CAT Telecom Co.
emblem. b, Envelope, mailbox, Thailand Post
emblem.
Illustration reduced.

2002, Feb. 25   Perf. 14½x14
Granite Paper
2009 A663 3b Horiz. pair, #a-b   .30   .20
c.   Souvenir sheet, #2009, perf.
       13¼x13½   .45   —
No. 2009c sold for 10b.

Maghapuja Day — A664

2002, Feb. 26   Perf. 14½x14
Granite Paper
2010 A664 3b multi   .20   .20

2002
Red
Cross
Fair
A665

2002, Mar. 30   Granite Paper
2011 A665 4b multi   .20   .20

Ministry of Transport and
Communications, 90th Anniv. — A666

2002, Apr. 1   Litho.   Perf. 14½x14
Granite Paper
2012 A666 3b multi   .20   .20

Heritage
Conservation
Day — A667

String puppets: No. 2013, 3b, Man. No.
2014, 3b, Woman. 4d, Demon. 15b, Monkey.

2002, Apr. 2   Perf. 14x14½
Granite Paper
2013-2016 A667 Set of 4   1.25   .90
2016a   Souvenir sheet, #2013-
           2016, perf. 13¼   1.40   —
No. 2016a sold for 30b.

Songkran Day Type of 1991
2002, Apr. 13   Perf. 14x14½
Granite Paper
2017 A425 2b Angel on horse,
           zodiac   .20   .20
a.   Souvenir sheet of 1   .35   .35
b.   Souvenir sheet, #1724b,
       1801c, 1869, 1940, 1970b,
       2017   .65   .65
c.   As "b," with Beijing 2002 em-
       blem in margin and selling
       price removed   1.40 1.40
Nos. 2017a and 2017b sold for 8b and 14b
respectively. Both exist imperf.
Issued: No. 2017c, 9/29. No. 2017c sold for
30b.

Fighting
Fish
A668

Designs: No. 2018, 3b, Betta imbellis. No.
2019, 3b, Betta splendens. 4b, Betta
splendens, diff. 15b, Betta splendens, diff.

2002, May 15 Litho.   Perf. 14½x14
Granite Paper
2018-2021 A668 Set of 4   1.25   .90
2021a   Souvenir sheet, #2018-
           2021, perf. 13½   1.40 1.40
2021b   As "a," with Amphilex 2002
           emblem and selling price
           removed   1.50 1.50
Issued: No. 2021b, 8/30. No. 2021a sold for
30b; No. 2021b sold for 31b.

Temples — A669

Designs: No. 2022, 3b, Wat Phra Si Rat-
tanasatsadaram. No. 2023, 3b, Wat Phra
Chetuphon Wimon Mangkhalaram. 4b, Wat
Arun Ratchawararam.   12b, Wat
Benchamabophit Dusit Wanaram.

2002, June 17   Perf. 14½x14
Granite Paper
2022-2025 A669 Set of 4   1.10   .85
2025a   Souvenir sheet, #2022-
           2025, perf. 13½   1.25 1.25
2025b   As "a," with Philakorea
           2002 emblem and selling
           price removed   1.25 1.25
Issued: No. 2025b, 8/2. Nos. 2025a and
2025b each sold for 27b.

Crown Prince
Maha
Vajiralongkorn,
50th
Birthday — A670

2002, July 28   Perf. 14x14½
Granite Paper
2026 A670 3b multi   .20   .20

Natl. Communications Day — A671

2002, Aug. 4   **Granite Paper**
2027 A671 4b multi   .20   .20

Thailand - Australia Diplomatic
Relations, 50th Anniv. — A672

Designs: No. 2028, 3b, Nelumbo nucifera
(pink flower). No. 2029, 3b, Nymphaea
immutabilis (purple flower).

2002, Aug. 6   **Perf. 14½x14**
Granite Paper
2028-2029 A672 Set of 2   .30   .25
2029a   Souvenir sheet, #2028-
            2029, perf. 13½   .45   .45

See Australia Nos. 2072-2073. No. 2029a
sold for 9b.

Queen Sirikit, 70th Birthday — A673

Designs: No. 2030, 3b, Queen and roses.
No. 2031, 3b, Queen Sirikit rose. 4b, Queen
Sirikit orchid. 15b, Queen Sirikit dona shrub.

2002, Aug. 12   **Perf. 14½x14**
Granite Paper
2030-2033 A673 Set of 4   1.25   .90
2033a   Souvenir sheet, #2030-
            2033, perf. 13½   1.50 1.50

No. 2033a sold for 31b.

National Archives, 50th Anniv. — A674

2002, Aug. 18   **Perf. 14½x14**
2034 A674 3b multi   .20   .20

Thai
Bank
Notes,
Cent.
A675

2002, Sept. 7   Engr.   Perf. 13½
Granite Paper
2035 A675 5b org & brown   .25   .20
  a.   Souvenir sheet of 1   .50   .50

No. 2035a sold for 11b.

Vimanmek Mansion Art
Objects — A676

Designs: No. 2036, 3b, Round, lidded betel
nut box. No. 2037, 3b, Bowl. 4b, Bowl, diff.
12b, Rectangular betel nut box.

2002, Sept. 7   Litho.   Perf. 14½x14
Granite Paper
2036-2039 A676 Set of 4   1.00   .75
2039a   Souvenir sheet, #2036-
            2039, perf. 13½   1.25 1.25

No. 2039a sold for 26b.

Royal
Palaces
A677

Designs: No. 2040, 4b, Thailand. No. 2041,
4b, Sweden.

Perf. 12½x13½ Syncopated
2002, Oct. 5   Litho. & Engr.
2040-2041 A677 Set of 2   .40   .30

See Sweden No. 2445.

Intl.
Letter
Writing
Day
A678

Designs: No. 2042, 3b, Animal-shaped
coconut grater. No. 2043, 3b, Strainer. 4b,
Coconut shell ladle. 15b, Earthenware stove
and pot.

2002, Oct. 5   Litho.   Perf. 14½x14
Granite Paper
2042-2045 A678 Set of 4   1.25   .90
2045a   Souvenir sheet, #2042-
            2045, perf. 13½   1.40 1.40

No. 2045a sold for 31b.

Bangkok 2003 World Philatelic
Exhibition — A679

Foods from: No. 2046, 3b, Central Thailand
(red tablecloth). No. 2047, 3b, Southern Thailand (brown and yellow tablecloth). 4b, Northeastern Thailand. 15b, Northern Thailand.

2002, Oct. 5   Perf. 14½x14
2046-2049 A679 Set of 4   1.25   .90
2049a   Souvenir sheet, #2046-2049,
            perf. 13½   1.40 1.40

No. 2049a sold for 30b.

New Year
2003 — A680

Flowers: No. 2050, 3b, Guaiacum officinale.
No. 2051, 3b, Nyctanthes arbor-tristis. No.
2052, 3b, Barleria cristata. No. 2053, 3b,
Thevetia peruviana.

Perf. 14½x14¼
2002, Nov. 15   Litho.
Granite Paper
2050-2053 A680 Set of 4   .55   .40
2053a   Souvenir sheet, #2050-
            2053   .75   .55

No. 2053a sold for 16b.

20th World Scout Jamboree — A681

Designs: 3b, Scouts. 12b, Jamboree site.

2002, Dec. 28   Perf. 14½x14
Granite Paper
2054-2055 A681 Set of 2   .70   .55

New Year 2003
(Year of the
Goat) — A682

2003, Jan. 1   Perf. 13
Granite Paper
2056 A682 3b multi   .20   .20

National Children's Day — A683

Pangpond and his: a, Dog, Big (blue background). b, Friend, Hanuman (orange background). c, Girlfriend, Namo (green background). d, Teacher (red background).
Illustration reduced.

2003, Jan. 11   Perf. 14½x14
Granite Paper
2057 A683 3b Block of 4, #a-d   .55   .40

Rose — A684

2003, Feb. 1   Perf. 13
Granite Paper
2058 A684 4b multi   .20   .20

No. 2058 is impregnated with rose scent.
Compare with Type A716.

Blue Green,
by Fua
Haribhitak
A685

Portrait of
Chira
Chongkon, by
Chamras
Kietkong
A686

Moonlight, by
Prasong
Padmanuja
A687

Lotus Flowers, by Thawee
Nandakwang — A688

2003, Feb. 24   Perf. 13¼
Granite Paper
2059 A685 3b multi   .20   .20
2060 A686 3b multi   .20   .20
2061 A687 3b multi   .20   .20
2062 A688 15b multi   .70   .55
      Nos. 2059-2062 (4)   1.30 1.15

Bangkok 2003 World Philatelic
Exhibition — A689

Tourist attractions: No. 2063, 3b, Doi Intha-
non Temple, Chiang Mai. No. 2064, 3b, River
Kwai Bridge, Kanchanaburi. No. 2065, 3b,
Phu Kradung (cliff), Loei. 15b, Maya Bay,
Krabi.

2003, Mar. 3   Perf. 14½x14
Granite Paper
2063-2066 A689 Set of 4   1.10   .85
2066a   Souvenir sheet, #2063-
            2066, perf. 13¼   1.40 1.10

No. 2066a sold for 29b.

**King Bhumibol Adulyadej Type of
1996**
Perf. 14x14½
2003, Mar. 14   Litho.   Unwmk.
Granite Paper
2067 A550 1b blue   .20   .20

2003 Red Cross
Fair — A690

2003, Mar. 28 — Perf. 14x14½
Granite Paper
2068 A690 3b multi .20 .20

Kick Boxing — A691

Designs: No. 2069, 3b, Boxers punching. No. 2070, 3b, Boxer in black trunks with knee raised. No. 2071, 3b, Boxer in red trunks kicking. 15b, Boxer in red trunks kicking, diff.

2003, Apr. 2 — Litho. — Perf. 13¼
Granite Paper
2069-2072	A691	Set of 4	1.10	.85
2072a		Souvenir sheet, #2069-2072	1.40	1.10
2072b		As "a," with China 2003 Philatelic Exhibition emblem in margin	1.50	1.10

No. 2072a sold for 29b.
Issued: No. 2072b, 11/20. No. 2072b sold for 29b.

Princess Maha Chakri Sirindhorn, 48th Birthday — A692

2003, Apr. 2 — Perf. 14x14½
Granite Paper
2073 A692 3b multi .20 .20

Princess Galyani Vadhana, 80th Birthday — A693

2003, May 6 — Granite Paper
2074 A693 3b multi .20 .20

Kings Chulalongkorn and Vajiravudh A694

2003, May 6 — Granite Paper
2075 A694 3b multi .20 .20
Inspector General Dept., cent.

King Prajadhipok Day — A695

2003, May 30 — Perf. 14½x14
Granite Paper
2076 A695 3b multi .20 .20

Bantam Chickens — A696

Designs: No. 2077, 3b, White ears jungle fowl. No. 2078, 3b, Sugarcane husk colored. No. 2079, 3b, Black-tailed white. 15b, Dark gray.

2003 — Litho. — Perf. 13
Granite Paper
2077-2080	A696	Set of 4	1.25	.95
2080a		Souvenir sheet, #2077-2080	1.40	1.10
2080b		As "a," with Lanka Philex 2003 emblem in margin	1.40	1.10

Issued: Nos. 2077-2080, 2080a, 6/10; No. 2080b, 7/31. Nos. 2080a and 2080b each sold for 29b.

Asalhapuja Day — A697

2003, July 13 — Perf. 14x14½
Granite Paper
2081 A697 3b multi .20 .20

National Communications Day — A698

2003, Aug. 4 — Perf. 14½x14
Granite Paper
2082 A698 3b multi .20 .20

Communications Organization Emblems — A699

No. 2083: a, Thailand Post Company Limited. b, Communications Authority of Thailand (23x27mm). c, CAT Telecom Public Company Limited.
Illustration reduced.

Perf. 14¼x14½
2003, Aug. 14 — Litho. — Wmk. 340
2083 A699 3b Horiz. strip of 3, #a-c .45 .35

King Chulalongkorn (1853-1910) A700

Litho. & Embossed
2003, Sept. 20 — Unwmk. — Perf. 13¼
2084 A700 100b gold & multi 5.25 4.00

Government Housing Bank, 50th Anniv. — A701

2003, Sept. 24 — Litho. — Perf. 14½x14
Granite Paper
2085 A701 3b multi .20 .20

Bangkok 2003 World Philatelic Exhibition — A702

Handicrafts: No. 2086, 3b, Basketry. No. 2087, 3b, Pottery. No. 2088, 3b, Leatherwork. 15b, Wood carving.

2003, Oct. 4
Granite Paper
2086-2089	A702	Set of 4	1.25	.95
2089a		Souvenir sheet, #2086-2089, perf. 13¼	1.50	1.10

A varnish with a rough surface was applied to portions of the designs. No. 2089a sold for 29b, and exists imperf.

Trees of Thailand and Canada — A703

No. 2090: a, Cassia fistula (Thailand). b, Maple leaves (Canada).

2003, Oct. 4 — Perf. 14x14½
Granite Paper
2090	A703	3b Horiz. pair, #a-b	.30	.25
c.		Souvenir sheet, #2090, perf. 13¼	.45	.35

No. 2090c sold for 9b.

Lychees — A704

Rose Apples — A705

Fruit: No. 2093, Coconuts. 15b, Jackfruit.

2003, Oct. 4
Granite Paper
2091	A704	3b shown	.20	.20
2092	A705	3b shown	.20	.20
2093	A704	3b multi	.20	.20
2094	A704	15b multi	.75	.55
a.		Souvenir sheet, #2091-2094, perf. 13¼	1.50	1.10

International Letter Writing Week. No. 2094a sold for 29b.

Oct. 14, 1973 Student Uprisings, 30th Anniv. — A706

2003, Oct. 14 — Perf. 14½x14
Granite Paper
2095 A706 3b multi .20 .20

Asia-Pacific Economic Cooperation Meeting — A707

2003, Oct. 20 — Granite Paper
2096 A707 3b multi .20 .20

New Year 2004 — A708

Flowers: No. 2097, 3b, Bougainvillea spectabilis. No. 2098, 3b, Eucrosia bicolor. No. 2099, 3b, Canna x generalis. No. 2100, 3b, Zinnia violacea.

2003, Nov. 15 — Perf. 14½x14¼
Granite Paper
2097-2100	A708	Set of 4	.60	.45
2100a		Souvenir sheet, #2097-2100	.80	.60
2100b		As "a," with 2004 Hong Kong Stamp Expo emblem in margin	.85	.60

No. 2100a sold for 16b.
Issued: No. 2100b, 1/30/04. No. 2100b sold for 16b.

Thailand Flag A709

Thai Pavilion A710

Elephants A711

Cassia Fistula A712

2003, Dec. 1 — Perf. 14¼x14½
Granite Paper
2101	A709	3b multi	.20	.20
2102	A710	3b multi	.20	.20
2103	A711	3b multi	.20	.20
2104	A712	3b multi	.20	.20
		Nos. 2101-2104 (4)	.80	.80

Elephants — A713

No. 2105: a, Asian elephant. b, African elephants.
Illustration reduced.

2003, Dec. 9   **Perf. 14½x14**
Granite Paper
2105 A713 3b Horiz. pair, #a-b   .30   .25
   c.   Souvenir sheet, #2105a, perf.
        13¼   .45   .35
   No. 2105c sold for 9b.
Thailand-South Africa diplomatic relations, 10th anniv. See South Africa No. 1330.

King Bhumibol Adulyadej Type of 1996
2003-04   Litho.   Perf. 14x14½
Granite Paper
2106 A550 50s olive brown   .20   .20
2107 A550 1b blue   .20   .20
   Issued: 50s, 12/3. 1b, 1/22/04.

Zodiac Animal Type of 2003
2004, Jan. 1   Litho.   Perf. 13
Granite Paper
2108 A682 3b Monkey   .20   .20

Children's Day — A714

2004, Jan. 10   Perf. 14½x14
Granite Paper
2109 A714 3b multi   .20   .20

Paintings of
Hem Vejakorn
A715

Designs: No. 2110, 3b, A Scene in Thai History (dancers). No. 2111, 3b, Maha Bharatayudh (charioteer). No. 2112, 3b, Khun Chang - Khun Phaen (women with horse). No. 2113, 3b, Phra Lor (woman and rooster).

2004, Jan. 17   Perf. 13¼
Granite Paper
2110-2113 A715 Set of 4   .65   .50
2113a   Souvenir sheet, #2110-
         2113   .85   .60
   No. 2113a sold for 16b.

Rose — A716

2004, Feb. 1   Perf. 13
Granite Paper
2114 A716 4b multi   .20   .20
   Compare with type A684. No. 2114 is impregnated with rose scent.

Turtles — A717

Designs: No. 2115, 3b, Cuora amboinensis. No. 2116, 3b, Platysternon megacephalum. No. 2117, 3b, Indotestudo elongata. No. 2118, 3b, Heosemys spinosa.

2004, Mar. 1   Perf. 14½x14
Granite Paper
2115-2118 A717 Set of 4   .65   .50
2118a   Souvenir sheet, #2115-
          2118, perf. 13¼   .85   .60
   No. 2118a sold for 16b.

Siam Society, Cent. — A718

2004, Mar. 10   Perf. 14½x14
2119 A718 3b multi   .20   .20

2004 Red Cross
Fair — A719

2004, Mar. 29   Perf. 14x14½
Granite Paper
2120 A719 3b multi   .20   .20

SEMI-POSTAL STAMPS

Nos. 164-175 Overprinted in Red

1918, Jan. 11   Unwmk.   Perf. 14
B1 A21 2s orange brown   2.00   .90
B2 A21 3s emerald   2.00   .90
B3 A21 5s rose red   4.50   1.75
B4 A21 10s black & olive   6.25   2.75
B5 A21 15s blue   6.25   2.75
B6 A22 1b bl & gray blk   32.50   13.00
B7 A22 2b car rose & brn   57.50   22.50
B8 A22 3b yel grn & blk   82.50   35.00
B9 A22 5b dp vio & blk   200.00   55.00
   a.   Double overprint   775.00 400.00
B10 A22 10b ol grn & vio
         brn   525.00 140.00
B11 A22 20b sea grn & brn 1,800. 500.00
   Nos. B1-B11 (11)   2,718. 774.55
Excellent counterfeit overprints are known.
These stamps were sold at an advance over face value, the excess being given to the Siamese Red Cross Society.

Stamps of 1905-19
Handstamp Overprinted

1920, Feb.
On Nos. 164, 146, 168
B12 A21 2s (+ 3s) org brn   35.00   35.00
B13 A21 3s (+ 2s) green   35.00   35.00
B14 A21 15s (+ 5s) blue   67.50   67.50
On No. 105
B15 A15 1t (+ 25s)   260.00 260.00
On Nos. 185-186
B16 A21 5s (+ 5s) on 6s   50.00   50.00
   a.   Overprint inverted
B17 A21 10s (+ 5s) on 12s   52.50   52.50
   Nos. B12-B17 (6)   500.00 500.00
   Set, never hinged   625.00
   Sold at an advance over face value, the excess being for the benefit of the Wild Tiger Corps. Counterfeits exist.

Stamps of 1905-20
Handstamp
Overprinted

On Nos. 164, 146, 168
B18 A21 2s (+ 3s) org brn   32.50   32.50
B19 A21 3s (+ 2s) green   32.50   32.50
   a.   Pair, one without ovpt.
B20 A21 15s (+ 5s) blue   47.50   47.50
On No. 105
B21 A15 1t (+ 25s)   225.00 225.00
On No. 186
B22 A21 10s on 12s (+ 5s)   47.50   47.50
On No. 190
B23 A23 5s (+ 5s)   67.50   67.50
   Nos. B18-B23 (6)   452.50 452.50
   Set, never hinged   575.00
   Sold at an advance over face value, the excess being for the benefit of the Wild Tiger Corps. Counterfeits exist.

Nos. 187-188, 190,
193-194, 196, 198
Overprinted in Blue
or Red

1920, Dec. 21
B24 A23 2s brown, yel   11.50   11.50
B25 A23 3s grn, grn (R)   11.50   11.50
B26 A23 5s rose, pale rose   11.50   11.50
B27 A23 10s blk & org (R)   11.50   11.50
B28 A23 15s bl, bluish (R)   20.00   20.00
B29 A23 25s chocolate   77.50   77.50
B30 A23 50s ocher & blk (R) 160.00 160.00
   Nos. B24-B30 (7)   303.50 303.50
   Set, never hinged   375.00
   Sold at an advance over face value, the excess being for the benefit of the Wild Tiger Corps. Counterfeits exist.

Nos. 170-172
Surcharged in Red

1939, Apr. 6   Unwmk.   Perf. 14
B31 A22 5s + 5s on 1b   18.00   18.00
B32 A22 10s + 5s on 2b   22.50   22.50
B33 A22 15s + 5s on 3b   22.50   22.50
   Nos. B31-B33 (3)   63.00   63.00
   Set, never hinged   85.00
   Founding of the Intl. Red Cross Soc., 75th anniv.
   Bottom line of overprint is different on Nos. B32-B33.

> **Catalogue values for unused stamps in this section, from this point to the end of the section, are for Never Hinged items.**

No. 214 Surcharged
in Carmine

1952   Unwmk.   Perf. 12½
B34 A25 80s + 20s blue & blk 19.00 10.00
   New constitution.

Red Cross and
Dancer — SP1

Lithographed, Cross Typographed
1953, Apr. 6   Wmk. 299   Perf. 11
Cross in Red, Dancer Dark Blue
B35 SP1 25s + 25s yellow grn 8.50   2.50
B36 SP1 50s + 50s brt rose   17.00   4.00
B37 SP1 1b + 1b lt blue   22.50   5.50
   Nos. B35-B37 (3)   48.00 12.00
   60th anniv. of the founding of the Siamese Red Cross Society.

Nos. B35-B37 Overprinted with Year
Date "24 98," in Black

1955, Apr. 3
Cross in Red, Dancer Dark Blue
B38 SP1 25s + 25s yel grn   45.00 12.00
B39 SP1 50s + 50s brt rose   95.00 22.50
B40 SP1 1b + 1b lt blue   125.00 32.50
   Nos. B38-B40 (3)   265.00 67.00
   Counterfeits exist.

Red Cross Cent. Emblem — SP2

1963   Wmk. 334   Litho.   Perf. 13½
B41 50s + 10s cross at right   .30   .20
B42 50s + 10s cross at left   .30   .20
   a.   SP2 Pair, #B41-B42   .60
   Cent. of the Intl. Red Cross.

Nos. B41-B42
Surcharged

1973, Feb. 15
B43 SP2 75s + 25s on 50s + 10s   .75   .75
B44 SP3 75s + 25s on 50s + 10s   .75   .75
   a.   Pair, #B43-B44   1.50
   Red Cross Fair, Feb. 15-19.

Nos. B41-B42
Surcharged

1974, Feb. 2
B45 SP2 75s + 25s on 50s + 10s   .40   .30
B46 SP3 75s + 25s on 50s + 10s   .40   .30
   a.   Pair, #B45-B46   .90
   Red Cross Fair, Feb. 1974. Position of surcharge reversed on No. B46.

Nos. B41-B42
Surcharged

1975, Feb 11 52
B47 SP2 75s + 25s on 50s + 10s   .50 .30
B48 SP3 75s + 25s on 50s + 10s   .50 .30
  a. Pair, #B47-B48   1.10

Red Cross Fair, Feb. 1975. Position of surcharge reversed on No. B48.

Nos. B41-B42
Surcharged

1976, Feb. 26
B49 SP2 75s + 25s on 50s + 10s   .40 .40
B50 SP3 75s + 25s on 50s + 10s   .40 .40
  a. Pair, #B49-B50   .80

Red Cross Fair, Feb. 16-Mar. 1. Position of surcharge reversed on #B50.

Nos. B41-B42
Surcharged

1977, Apr. 6   Wmk. 334   *Perf. 13½*
B51 SP2 75s + 25s on 50s + 10s   .45 .30
B52 SP3 75s + 25s on 50s + 10s   .45 .30
  a. Pair, #B51-B52   .90

Red Cross Fair 1977.

Red Cross   Eye and Blind
Blood   People
Collection   SP5
SP4

Wmk. 329
1978, Apr. 6   Photo.   *Perf. 13*
B53 SP4 2.75b + 25s multi   1.00 .25

"Give blood, save life."
For surcharge see No. B58.

Perf. 14x13½
1979, Apr. 6   Litho.   Wmk. 368
B54 SP5 75s + 25s multi   .55 .20

"Give an eye, save new life." Red Cross Fair. Surtax was for Thai Red Cross.
For surcharge see No. B59.

Extracting Snake Venom, Red
Cross — SP6

1980, Apr.   *Perf. 11x13*
B55 SP6 75s + 25s multi   .90 .90

Red Cross Fair. Surtax was for Thai Red Cross.
For surcharge see No. B60.

Nurse Helping Victim — SP7

1981, Apr. 6   Wmk. 377   *Perf. 12½*
B56 SP7 75 + 25s red & gray grn 1.25 1.25

Red Cross Fair (canceled). Surtax was for Thai Red Cross.
For surcharge see No. B65.

Red
Cross
Fair
SP8

Perf. 13x13½
1983, Apr. 6   Litho.   Wmk. 329
B57 SP8 1.25b + 25s multi   .75 .75

Surtax was for Thai Red Cross.

No. B53 Surcharged

1984, Apr.   Photo.   *Perf. 13*
B58 SP4 3.25b + 25s on 2.75b +
              25s   2.00 2.00

Red Cross Fair. Surtax was for Thai Red Cross. Overprint translates: Red Cross Donation.

No. B54
Surcharged

Wmk. 368
1985, Mar. 30   Litho.   *Perf. 13*
B59 SP5 2b + 25c on 75s + 25s 1.50 1.50

Surtax for the Thai Red Cross.

No. B55 Overprinted and Surcharged

1986, Apr. 6   Wmk. 368   *Perf. 11x13*
B60 SP6 2b + 25s on 75s + 25s 1.50 1.50

Natl. Children's Day. Surtax for Natl. Red Cross Society. Overprint translates "Red Cross Donation."

Natl. Scouting Movement, 75th Anniv.,
15th Asia-Pacific Conference,
Thailand — SP9

#B61, Scouts, saluting, community service.
#B62, Scout activities. #B63, King & queen at
ceremony. #B64, 15th Asia-Pacific conf.

1986, Nov. 7   Wmk. 385   *Perf. 13½*
B61 SP9 2b + 50s multi   .35 .35
B62 SP9 2b + 50s multi   .35 .35
B63 SP9 2b + 50s multi   .35 .35
B64 SP9 2b + 50s multi   .35 .35
  Nos. B61-B64 (4)   1.40 1.40

Surtax for the Natl. Scouting Fund.

No. B56 Surcharged
1987, Apr.   Wmk. 377   *Perf. 12½*
B65 SP7 2b + 50s on 75s + 25s   .95 .20

Sports

SP10   SP11

Designs: No. B66, Hurdles, medal winners.
No. B67, Race, nurse treating injured cyclist.
No. B68, Boxers training. No. B69, Soccer.

1989, Dec. 16   Wmk. 387   *Perf. 13½*
B66 SP10 2b +1b multi   .40 .25
B67 SP10 2b +1b multi   .40 .25
B68 SP10 2b +1b multi   .40 .25
B69 SP10 2b +1b multi   .40 .25
  Nos. B66-B69 (4)   1.60 1.00

Surtax for sports welfare organizations.

1990, Dec. 16
B70 SP11 2b +1b Judo   .40 .25
B71 SP11 2b +1b Archery   .40 .25
B72 SP11 2b +1b High jump   .40 .25
B73 SP11 2b +1b Windsurfing   .40 .25
  Nos. B70-B73 (4)   1.60 1.00

Surtax for sports welfare organization.

Sports — SP12

Wmk. 387
1991, Dec. 16   Litho.   *Perf. 13½*
B74 SP12 2b +1b Jogging   .30 .20
B75 SP12 2b +1b Cycling   .30 .20
B76 SP12 2b +1b Soccer, jump-
              ing rope   .30 .20
B77 SP12 2b +1b Swimming   .30 .20
  Nos. B74-B77 (4)   1.20 .80

Surtax for sports welfare organizations.

18th South East
Asian Games,
Chiang
Mai — SP13

No. B78: a, Water polo. b, Tennis. c, Hurdles. d, Gymnastics.
No. B79: a, Fencing. b, Pool. c, Diving. d, Pole vault.

1994, Dec. 16   Wmk. 340
B78 SP13 2b +1b Strip of 4,
              #a.-d.   1.00 .75
  e. Souvenir sheet, #B78   1.25 1.00

Wmk. 387
B79 SP13 2b +1b Strip of 4,
              #a.-d.   1.00 .75
  e. Souvenir sheet, #B79   1.25 1.25

Nos. B78e, B79e sold for 15b.
Issued: #B78, 12/16/94; #B79, 12/9/95.

SP14

13th Asian Games, Bangkok — SP15

1998, Mar. 27   *Perf. 14½x14*
B80 SP14 2b +1b Shooting   .20 .20
B81 SP14 3b +1b Rhythmic
              gymnastics   .20 .20
B82 SP14 4b +1b Swimming   .25 .20
B83 SP14 7b +1b Wind-surfing   .35 .30
  Nos. B80-B83 (4)   1.00 .90

Perf. 14½x14
1998, Dec. 6   Litho.   Unwmk.
Granite Paper
B84 SP15 2b +1b Field hockey   .20 .20
B85 SP15 3b +1b Wrestling   .20 .20
B86 SP15 4b +1b Rowing   .25 .20
B87 SP15 7b +1b Equestrian   .35 .30
  Nos. B84-B87 (4)   1.00 .90

AIR POST STAMPS

Garuda — AP1

1925   Unwmk.   Engr.   *Perf. 14, 14½*
C1 AP1 2s brown, *yel*   1.75 .25
C2 AP1 3s dark brown   2.00 .25
C3 AP1 5s green   5.50 .50
C4 AP1 10s black & org   15.00 .50
C5 AP1 15s carmine   4.25 1.00
C6 AP1 25s dark blue   4.00 1.00
C7 AP1 50s brown org & blk   32.50 7.50
C8 AP1 1b blue & brown   30.00 9.00
  Nos. C1-C8 (8)   95.00 20.00
  Set, never hinged   125.00

Issued: 2s, 50s, 4/21; others, 1/3.

Nos. C1-C8 received this overprint ("Government Museum 2468") in 1925, but were never issued. The death of King Vajiravudh caused cancellation of the fair at which this set was to have been released.

They were used during 1928 only in the interdepartmental service for accounting purposes of the money-order sections of various Bangkok post offices, and were never sold to the public. Value for canceled set, $25.

1930-37   *Perf. 12½*
C9 AP1 2s brown, *yel*   5.00 .90
C10 AP1 5s green   1.25 .20
C11 AP1 10s black & org   2.50 .20
C12 AP1 15s carmine   25.00 5.25
C13 AP1 25s dark blue ('37)   1.50 .90
  a. Vert. pair, imperf. btwn. 400.00
C14 AP1 50s brn org & blk
              ('37)   2.75 1.40
  Nos. C9-C14 (6)   38.00 8.85
  Set, never hinged   55.00

Monument of
Democracy,
Bangkok
AP2

1942-43   Engr.   Perf. 11

C15	AP2	2s dk org brn		
		('43)	1.75	.80
C16	AP2	3s dk grn ('43)	30.00	17.00
a.		Vert. pair, imperf. btwn.	100.00	100.00
C17	AP2	5s deep claret	2.00	.25
a.		Horiz. pair, imperf. btwn.	75.00	75.00
b.		Vert. pair, imperf. btwn.	75.00	75.00
C18	AP2	10s carmine ('43)	15.00	.60
a.		Vert. pair, imperf. btwn.	100.00	100.00
C19	AP2	15s dark blue	2.75	1.60
a.		Vert. pair, imperf. btwn.	100.00	100.00
		Nos. C15-C19 (5)	51.50	20.25
		Set, never hinged	70.00	

> **Catalogue values for unused stamps in this section, from this point to the end of the section, are for Never Hinged items.**

Garuda and
Bangkok
Skyline — AP3

1952-53   Perf. 13x12½

C20	AP3	1.50b red violet ('53)	4.75	.25
C21	AP3	2b dark blue	11.00	2.50
C22	AP3	3b gray ('53)	16.00	1.10
		Nos. C20-C22 (3)	31.75	3.85

Issue dates: June 15, 1952. Sept. 15, 1953.

OFFICIAL STAMPS

> **Catalogue values for unused stamps in this section are for Never Hinged items.**

O1

Perf. 10½ Rough

1963, Oct. 1   Typo.   Unwmk.
Without Gum

O1	O1	10s pink & dp car	.20	.20
O2	O1	20s brt grn & car rose	.20	.20
O3	O1	25s blue & dp car	.30	.35
O4	O1	50s deep carmine	.85	1.10
O5	O1	1b silver & car rose	1.00	1.50
O6	O1	2b bronze & car rose	1.75	1.50
		Nos. O1-O6 (6)	4.30	4.85

Issued as an official test from Oct. 1, 1963, to Jan. 31, 1964, to determine the amount of mail sent out by various government departments.

1964   Without Gum

O7	O1	20s green	.35	.30
O8	O1	25s blue	.35	.40
O9	O1	1b silver	.65	.65
O10	O1	2b bister	1.90	2.25
		Nos. O7-O10 (4)	3.25	3.60

Others values exist printed in one color.

STOCK**SHEETS**

HAGNER STYLE STOCK SHEETS

Hagner-style stock pages offer convenience and flexibility. Pages are produced on thick, archival-quality paper with acetate pockets glued from the bottom of each pocket. They're ideal for the topical collector who may require various page styles to store a complete collection.

- Black background makes beautiful stamp presentation.
- Pockets use pull away/snap back principle.
- Made from archival-quality heavyweight paper that offers unprecedented protection and clarity.
- Multi-hole punch fits most binder types.
- Available in 9 different page formats.
  8½" x 11" size accomodates every size stamp.

Sold in packages of 10.
Available with pockets on one side or both sides.
"D" in item number denotes two-sided page.

1 POCKET — 242 mm

ITEM	RETAIL
S1	$10.99
S1D	$15.99

2 POCKET — 119 mm

ITEM	RETAIL
S2	$10.99
S2D	$15.99

3 POCKET — 79 mm

ITEM	RETAIL
S3	$10.99
S3D	$15.99

4 POCKET — 58 mm

ITEM	RETAIL
S4	$10.99
S4D	$15.99

5 POCKET — 45 mm

ITEM	RETAIL
S5	$10.99
S5D	$15.99

6 POCKET — 37 mm

ITEM	RETAIL
S6	$10.99
S6D	$15.99

7 POCKET — 31 mm

ITEM	RETAIL
S7	$10.99
S7D	$15.99

8 POCKET — 27 mm

ITEM	RETAIL
S8	$10.99
S8D	$15.99

MULTI-POCKETS — 36 mm / 67 mm / 139 mm

ITEM	RETAIL
S9	$10.99
S9D	$15.99

SCOTT

1-800-572-6885
P.O. Box 828, Sidney OH 45365-0828
www.amosadvantage.com

AMOS
HOBBY PUBLISHING

Publishers of *Coin World*, *Linn's Stamp News* and *Scott Publishing Co.*

THRACE

'thrās

LOCATION — In southeastern Europe between the Black and Aegean Seas
GOVT. — Former Turkish Province
AREA — 89,361 sq. mi. (approx.)

Thrace underwent many political changes during the Balkan Wars and World War I. It was finally divided among Turkey, Greece and Bulgaria.

100 Lepta = 1 Drachma
40 Paras = 1 Piaster
100 Stotinki = 1 Leva (1919)

Giumulzina District Issue

Turkish Stamps of 1909 Surcharged in Blue or Red

1913		**Unwmk.**	**Perf. 12, 13½**	
1	A21	10 l on 20pa rose (Bl)	17.50	30.00
2	A21	25 l on 10pa bl grn	37.50	40.00
3	A21	25 l on 20pa rose (Bl)	40.00	40.00
4	A21	25 l on 1pi ultra	75.00	92.50
		Nos. 1-4 (4)	170.00	202.50

Counterfeits exist of Nos. 1-4.

Turkish Inscriptions
A1   A2

1913		**Litho.**		**Imperf.**
		Laid Paper		
		Control Mark in Rose		
		Without Gum		
5	A1	1pi blue	17.00	17.00
6	A1	2pi violet	20.00	20.00
		Wove Paper		
7	A2	10pa vermilion	35.00	32.50
8	A2	20pa blue	35.00	32.50
9	A2	1pi violet	35.00	32.50
		Nos. 5-9 (5)	142.00	134.50

Turkish Stamps of 1908-13 Surcharged in Red or Black

۱ بر عروش P.

1913			**Perf. 12**	
10	A22	1pi on 2pa ol grn (R)	9.50	9.00
10A	A22	1pi on 2pa ol grn	10.00	9.50
11	A22	1pi on 5pa ocher	16.00	14.50
11A	A22	1pi on 5pa ocher	17.50	17.00
12	A22	1pi on 20pa rose	26.00	25.00
13	A22	1pi on 5pi dk vio	47.50	47.50
13A	A21	1pi on 5pi dk vio	65.00	65.00
14	A21	1pi on 10pi dl red	90.00	90.00
15	A19	1pi on 25pi dk grn	325.00	325.00
		Nos. 10-15 (9)	606.50	602.50

On Nos. 13-15 the surcharge is vertical, reading up. No. 15 exists with double surcharge, one black, one red.
Nos. 10-15 exist with forged surcharges.

Bulgarian Stamps of 1911 Handstamp Surcharged in Red or Blue

1913				
16	A20	10pa on 1s myr grn (R)	20.00	20.00
17	A21	20pa on 2s car & blk	20.00	20.00
18	A23	1pi on 5s grn & blk (R)	20.00	20.00
19	A22	2pi on 3s lake & blk	26.00	26.00
20	A24	2½pi on 10s dp red & blk	40.00	40.00
21	A25	5pi on 15s brn bis	62.50	62.50
		Nos. 16-21 (6)	188.50	188.50

Same Surcharges on Greek Stamps
On Issue of 1911

1913		**Serrate Roulette 13½**		
22	A24	10pa on 1 l grn (R)	21.00	21.00
23	A24	10pa on 1 l grn	22.50	22.50
25	A25	10pa on 25 l ultra (R)	30.00	30.00
26	A25	20pa on 2 l car rose	20.00	20.00
27	A24	1pi on 3 l ver	20.00	20.00
28	A26	2pi on 5 l grn (R)	47.50	47.50
29	A24	2½pi on 10 l car rose	47.50	47.50
30	A25	5pi on 40 l dp bl (R)	82.50	82.50
		Nos. 22-30 (8)	291.00	291.00

On Occupation Stamps of 1912

31	O1	10pa on 1 l brn	14.00	14.00
32	O1	20pa on 1 l brn	14.00	14.00
33	O1	1pi on 1 l brn	14.00	14.00
		Nos. 31-33 (3)	42.00	42.00

These surcharges were made with handstamps, two of which were required for each surcharge. One or both parts may be found inverted, double or omitted.
Nos. 16-33 exist with forged surcharges.

OCCUPATION STAMPS

Issued under Allied Occupation

Bulgarian Stamps of 1915-19 Handstamped in Violet Blue

Perf. 11½, 11½x12, 14

1919			**Unwmk.**	
N1	A43	1s black	1.50	1.50
N2	A43	2s olive green	1.50	1.50
N3	A44	5s green	.55	.55
N4	A44	10s rose	.55	.55
N5	A44	15s violet	.70	.70
N6	A26	25s indigo & black	.70	.70
		Nos. N1-N6 (6)	5.50	5.50

The overprint on Nos. N1-N6 is frequently inverted and known in other positions.

Bulgarian Stamps of 1911-19 Overprinted in Red or Black

1919				
N7	A43	1s black (R)	.20	.20
N8	A43	2s olive green	.20	.20
N9	A44	5s green	.20	.20
N10	A44	10s rose	.20	.20
N11	A44	15s violet	.20	.20
N12	A26	25s indigo & black	.25	.25
N13	A29	1 l chocolate	3.00	3.00
N14	A37a	2 l brown orange	5.50	5.50
N15	A38	3 l claret	7.50	7.50
		Nos. N7-N15 (9)	17.25	17.25

Overprint is vertical, reading up, on Nos. N9-N13.

The following varieties are found in the setting of "INTERALLIEE": Inverted "V" for "A," second "L" inverted, "F" instead of final "E."

Bulgarian Stamps of 1919 Overprinted

1920				
N16	A44	5s green	.25	.25
N17	A44	10s rose	.25	.25
N18	A44	15s violet	.25	.25
N19	A44	50s yellow brown	.70	.70
		Nos. N16-N19 (4)	1.45	1.45

The varieties: "Irteraliiee" and final "e" inverted are found on all values.

Bulgarian Stamps of 1919 Overprinted

1920			**Perf. 12x11½**	
N20	A44	5s green	.25	.25
a.		Inverted overprint	19.00	
N21	A44	10s rose	.25	.25
a.		Inverted overprint	19.00	
N22	A44	15s violet	.25	.25
N23	A44	25s deep blue	.25	.25
N24	A44	50s ocher	.25	.25
		Imperf		
N25	A44	30s chocolate	.75	.75
		Nos. N20-N25 (6)	2.00	2.00

No. N25 is not known without overprint.

ISSUED UNDER GREEK OCCUPATION

For Use in Western Thrace

Greek Stamps of 1911-19 Overprinted

Serrate Roulette 13½

1920		**Litho.**	**Unwmk.**	
N26	A24	1 l green	.20	.35
a.		Inverted overprint	15.00	
N27	A25	2 l rose	.20	.35
N28	A24	3 l vermilion	.20	.35
N29	A26	5 l green	.20	.35
N30	A24	10 l rose	.30	.50
N31	A25	15 l dull blue	.35	.65
a.		Inverted overprint	16.00	
b.		Dbl. ovpt., one inverted	24.00	
N32	A25	25 l blue	.40	.75
N33	A26	30 l rose	29.00	50.00
N34	A25	40 l indigo	1.90	4.00
N35	A26	50 l violet brn	1.90	5.00
N36	A27	1d ultra	6.50	14.00
N37	A27	2d vermilion	17.50	32.50
		Engr.		
N38	A25	2 l car rose	.60	.60
N39	A24	3 l vermilion	.60	.60
N40	A27	1d ultra	25.00	52.50
N41	A27	2d vermilion	25.00	55.00
N42	A27	3d car rose	37.50	70.00
N43	A27	5d ultra	14.50	22.50
N44	A27	10d deep blue	14.00	20.00
		Nos. N26-N44 (19)	175.85	330.00

Nos. N42-N44 are overprinted on the reissues of Greece Nos. 210-212. See footnote below Greece No. 213. Counterfeits exist of Nos. N26-N84.

ΔΙΟΙΚΗΣΙΣ
Overprinted   ΔΥΤΙΚΗΣ
ΘΡΑΚΗΣ

N45	A28	25d deep blue	40.00	65.00

This overprint reads: "Administration Western Thrace."

With Additional Overprint

		Litho.		
N46	A24	1 l green	.55	1.10
N47	A25	2 l rose	.20	.40
a.		Inverted overprint	77.50	
N48	A24	10 l rose	.55	.65
N49	A25	20 l slate	.55	.65
N50	A26	30 l rose	.65	1.00
		Engr.		
N51	A27	2d vermilion	19.00	32.50
N52	A27	3d car rose	8.50	22.50
N53	A27	5d ultra	25.00	42.50
N54	A27	10d deep blue	19.00	32.50
a.		Double overprint	45.00	
		Nos. N46-N54 (9)	74.00	133.80

For Use in Eastern and Western Thrace

Greek Stamps of 1911-19 Overprinted

1920			**Litho.**	
N55	A24	1 l green	.20	.30
a.		Pair, one without ovpt.	22.50	
N56	A25	2 l rose	.20	.30
N57	A24	3 l vermilion	.20	.30
a.		Double overprint	11.50	
N58	A26	5 l green	.25	.45
a.		Pair, one without ovpt.	24.00	
N59	A24	10 l rose	.40	.70
a.		Double overprint	27.50	
N60	A25	20 l slate	.65	1.25
a.		Inverted overprint	15.00	
N61	A25	25 l blue	1.25	2.00
N62	A25	40 l indigo	2.40	6.50
N63	A26	50 l violet brn	3.00	8.50
N64	A27	1d vermilion	12.00	20.00
N65	A27	2d vermilion	22.50	35.00
		Engr.		
N66	A24	3 l vermilion	2.75	4.75
N67	A25	20 l gray lilac	9.50	22.50
N68	A28	25d deep blue	47.50	90.00
		Nos. N55-N68 (14)	102.80	192.55

This overprint reads "Administration Thrace."

With Additional Overprint as Nos. N46-N54

		Litho.		
N69	A25	2 l car rose	.25	.50
N70	A26	5 l green	1.50	3.00
N71	A25	20 l slate	.25	.50
N72	A26	30 l rose	.25	.50
		Engr.		
N73	A27	3d car rose	7.50	14.00
N74	A27	5d ultra	18.00	30.00
N75	A27	10d deep blue	32.50	60.00
		Nos. N69-N75 (7)	60.25	108.50

Turkish Stamps of 1916-20 Surcharged in Blue, Black or Red

1920			**Perf. 11½, 12½**	
N76	A43	1 l on 5pa org (Bl)	.40	.50
N77	A32	5 l on 3pi blue	.40	.50
N78	A30	20 l on 1pi bl grn	.50	.70
N79	A53	25 l on 5pi on 2pa Prus bl (R)	.60	.75
N80	A49	50 l on 5pi bl & blk (R)	4.25	4.50
N81	A45	1d on 20pa dp rose (Bl)	1.25	1.40
N82	A22	2d on 10pa on 2pa ol grn (R)	2.00	2.25
N83	A57	3d on 1pi dp bl (R)	9.00	9.50
N84	A38	5d on 20pa rose	8.50	9.00
		Nos. N76-N84 (9)	26.90	29.10

Nos. N77, N78 and N84 are on the 1920 issue with designs modified. Nos. N81, N82 and N83 are on stamps with the 1919 overprints.

Varieties found on some values of this issue include: inverted surcharge, double surcharge with one inverted, and surcharge on both face and back.

POSTAGE DUE STAMPS

Issued under Allied Occupation
Bulgarian Postage Due Stamps of 1919 Overprinted like Nos. N7-N15
Reading Vertically Up

1919		Unwmk.		Perf. 12x11½	
NJ1	D6	5s emerald		.30	.30
NJ2	D6	10s purple		.70	.70
NJ3	D6	50s blue		.70	.60
		Nos. NJ1-NJ3 (3)		1.70	1.60

Type of Bulgarian Postage Due Stamps of 1919-22 Overprinted

1920				Imperf.	
NJ4	D6	5s emerald		.20	.20
NJ5	D6	10s deep violet		1.40	1.40
NJ6	D6	20s salmon		.25	.25
NJ7	D6	50s blue		1.25	1.10
		Perf. 12x11½			
NJ8	D6	10s deep violet		1.00	.80
		Nos. NJ4-NJ8 (5)		4.10	3.75

TIBET

tə-'bet

LOCATION — A high tableland in Central Asia
GOVT. — A semi-independent state, nominally under control of China

TIBET NEPAL BHUTAN

PUBLIC AUCTIONS

Rare Stamps, and Postal History

Advanced materials for the specialist.

Please visit our website for our online auctions.

www.georgealevizos.com

George Alevizos

P.O. Box 1408
Topanga, CA 90290
Telephone: 310-455-2300
FAX: 310-455-2303

email:georgealevizos@msn.com

(under Communist China since 1950-51). In 1965 Tibet became a nominally autonomous region of the People's Republic of China.
AREA — 463,200 sq. mi.
POP. — 1,500,000 (approx.)
CAPITAL — Lhasa

Tibet's postage stamps were valid only within its borders.

6 ⅔ Trangka = 1 Sang

"Stamps" produced by the "Tibetan Government in Exile" have no postal value. These include four-value sets for Himalayan animals and the UPU that were put on sale in the early 1970s.

Excellent counterfeits of Nos. 1-18 exist. Numerous shades of all values.
All stamps issued without gum
Small bits of foreign matter (inclusions) are to be expected in Native Paper. These do not reduce the value of the stamp unless they have caused serious damage to the design or paper.

Lion
A1   A2

1912-50		Unwmk.	Typo.	Imperf.	
		Native Paper			
1	A1	¼t green		30.00	40.00
2	A1	⅓t blue		35.00	45.00
a.		⅓t ultramarine		40.00	55.00
3	A1	½t violet		35.00	45.00
4	A1	⅔t carmine		40.00	50.00
a.		"POTSAGE"		140.00	150.00

TIBET
STAMPS AND POSTAL HISTORY

We specialize in the Stamps and Postal History of Tibet. Maintaining one of the World's largest and most comprehensive stocks of this Mysterious Land.

SELLING?
We are always interested in Better Individual Items or Collections.

GEOFFREY FLACK
P.O. Box 16011
Lynn Valley Postal Outlet
North Vancouver, B.C.
Canada V7J-3S9
Phone (604) 986-3898
FAX: (604) 986-4777
www.tibetanpost.com
E-mail:geoffrey@tibetanpost.com

5	A1	1t vermilion		45.00	60.00
6	A1	1s sage green ('50)		90.00	100.00
		Nos. 1-6 (6)		275.00	340.00

The "POTSAGE" error is found on all shades of the ⅔t (positions 6 and 7).
Pin-perf. copies of Nos. 1 and 3 exist.
Issued in sheets of 12.
Beware of private reproductions of #1-5 that were printed in the US around 1986. Sheets of 12 bear "J. Crow Co." imprint. The set of 5 sheets was sold for $5.

Printed Using Shiny Enamel Paint

1920					
1a	A1	¼t green		50.00	30.00
2b	A1	⅓t blue		450.00	450.00
3d	A1	½t purple		90.00	100.00
4h	A1	⅔t carmine		90.00	100.00
i.		"POTSAGE"		200.00	225.00
5c	A1	1t carmine		300.00	300.00

In some 1920-30 printings, European enamel paint was used instead of ink. It has a glossy surface.

1914					
7	A2	4t milky blue		675.	725.
8	A2	8t carmine rose		160.	160.
a.		8t carmine		1,000.	1,100.

Issued in sheets of 6.

Printed Using Shiny Enamel Paint

1920					
7b	A2	4t blue		1,200.	1,250.
8b	A2	8t carmine		1,200.	1,250.

See note following No. 5c.

A3

Thin White Native Paper

1933				**Pin-perf.**	
9	A3	½t orange		82.50	95.00
10	A3	⅔t dark blue		82.50	110.00
11	A3	1t rose carmine		82.50	110.00
12	A3	2t scarlet		82.50	110.00
13	A3	4t emerald		82.50	110.00
		Nos. 9-13 (5)		412.50	535.00

Issued in sheets of 12.
Exist imperf.

Heavy Toned Native Paper

1934				**Imperf.**	
14	A3	½t yellow		13.00	16.00
15	A3	⅔t blue		10.00	11.00
16	A3	1t orange ver		8.75	10.00
a.		1t carmine		11.00	11.00
17	A3	2t red		10.00	10.00
a.		2t orange vermilion		7.75	7.75
18	A3	4t green		7.75	7.75
a.		25x25mm instead of 24x24mm		50.00	60.00
		Nos. 14-18 (5)		49.50	54.75

Nos. 14-18 are also known with a private pin-perf.
The ½t and 1t exist printed on both sides.
Issued in sheets of 12.

OFFICIAL STAMPS

O1

O2

Various Designs and Sizes Inscribed "STAMP"
Sizes: No. O1, 32½x32½mm. No. O2, 38x28½mm. No. O3, 34x33mm. No. O4, 44x44mm. No. O5, 66x66mm.

1945		Unwmk.	Typo.	Imperf.	
		Native Paper			
O1	O1	⅓t bronze green			
O2	O2	⅓t slate black			
O3	O1	⅔t reddish brown			
O4	O1	1 ⅓t olive green			
O5	O1	1s dark gray blue			

The status of Nos. O1-O5 is in question. Other values exist.

TIMOR

'tē-‚mor

LOCATION — The eastern part of Timor island, Malay archipelago
GOVT. — Portuguese Overseas Territory
AREA — 7,330 sq. mi.
POP. — 660,000 (est. 1974)
CAPITAL — Dili

The Portuguese territory of Timor was annexed by Indonesia May 3, 1976.

1000 Reis = 1 Milreis
78 Avos = 1 Rupee (1895)
100 Avos = 1 Pataca
100 Centavos = 1 Escudo (1960)

Catalogue values for unused stamps in this country are for Never Hinged items, beginning with Scott 256 in the regular postage section, Scott J31 in the postage due section, and Scott RA11 in the postal tax section.

Watermark

Wmk. 232 — Maltese Cross

Stamps of Macao Overprinted in Black or Carmine   **TIMOR**

1885		Unwmk.		Perf. 12½, 13½	
1	A1	5r black (C)		4.00	1.50
a.		Double overprint		32.50	32.50
b.		Triple overprint		100.00	
2	A1	10r green		7.00	3.00
a.		Overprint on Mozambique stamp		20.00	12.50
b.		Overprint on Portuguese India stamp		190.00	140.00
3	A1	20r rose, perf. 13½		8.00	4.00
a.		Double overprint		20.00	
b.		Perf. 12½		8.50	4.50
4	A1	25r violet		2.00	.95
a.		Perf. 13½		19.00	10.00
5	A1	40r yellow		5.00	2.75
a.		Double overprint		15.00	
b.		Inverted overprint		18.00	18.00
c.		Perf. 13½		12.50	10.00
6	A1	50r blue		4.00	1.25
a.		Perf. 13½		10.50	8.50
7	A1	80r slate		9.00	2.75
8	A1	100r lilac		5.00	1.40
a.		Double overprint		20.00	
b.		Perf. 13½		8.00	3.00
9	A1	200r org, perf. 13½		8.00	3.00
a.		Perf. 12½		10.00	3.00
10	A1	300r brown		7.00	2.75
		Nos. 1-10 (10)		59.00	23.35

The 20r brown, 25r rose and 50r green were prepared for use but not issued.
The reprints are printed on a smooth white chalky paper, ungummed, with rough perforation 13½, and on thin white paper with shiny white gum and clean-cut perforation 13½.

King Luiz — A2

King Carlos — A3

1887 Embossed   **Perf. 12½**

11	A2	5r black	1.75	1.50
12	A2	10r green	3.00	2.75
13	A2	20r bright rose	3.00	2.75
14	A2	25r violet	6.00	3.00
15	A2	40r chocolate	10.00	4.00
16	A2	50r blue	12.00	5.00
17	A2	80r gray	12.00	6.75
18	A2	100r yellow brown	17.50	8.00
19	A2	200r gray lilac	22.50	15.00
20	A2	300r orange	22.50	15.00
		Nos. 11-20 (10)	110.25	63.75

Reprints of Nos. 11, 16, 18 and 19 have clean-cut perforation 13½.
For surcharges see Nos. 34-43, 83-91.

Macao No. 44
Surcharged in Black

1892 Without Gum   **Perf. 12½, 13**

21	A7	30r on 300r orange	7.50	5.00

For surcharge see No. 44.

1894   **Typo.**   **Perf. 11½**

22	A3	5r yellow	1.00	.60
23	A3	10r red violet	1.25	.60
24	A3	15r chocolate	2.50	.85
25	A3	20r lavender	3.00	.95
26	A3	25r green	3.75	.70
27	A3	50r light blue	5.00	3.00
a.		Perf. 13½	125.00	110.00
28	A3	75r rose	6.00	2.50
29	A3	80r light green	6.50	3.75
30	A3	100r brown, *buff*	5.00	2.50
31	A3	150r car, *rose*	10.50	6.00
32	A3	200r dk bl, *lt bl*	11.00	7.25
33	A3	300r dk bl, *salmon*	14.00	9.50
		Nos. 22-33 (12)	69.50	38.20

For surcharges and overprints see Nos. 92-102, 120-122, 124-128, 131-133, 183-193, 199.

Stamps of 1887
Surcharged in Red,
Green or Black

1895 Without Gum   **Perf. 12½**

34	A2	1a on 5r black (R)	.90	.75
35	A2	2a on 10r green	1.10	.75
a.		Double surcharge	15.00	
36	A2	3a on 20r brt rose (G)	2.50	1.60
37	A2	4a on 25r violet	2.50	1.00
38	A2	6a on 40r choc	4.00	2.25
39	A2	8a on 50r blue (R)	3.50	2.00
40	A2	13a on 80r gray	12.00	8.00
41	A2	16a on 100r yellow brn	13.00	6.00
42	A2	31a on 200r gray lilac	25.00	16.00
43	A2	47a on 300r org (G)	25.00	17.50
		Nos. 34-43 (10)	89.50	55.85

5 avos

No. 21 Surcharged

1895 Without Gum   **Perf. 12½, 13**

44	A7	5a on 30r on 300r org	7.50	4.50

Common Design Types
pictured following the introduction.

Vasco da Gama Issue
Common Design Types

1898   **Engr.**   **Perf. 14 to 15**

45	CD20	½a blue green	1.50	.85
46	CD21	1a red	1.50	.85
47	CD22	2a red violet	1.50	.85
48	CD23	4a yellow green	1.50	.85
49	CD24	8a dark blue	3.00	1.25
50	CD25	12a violet brown	3.50	1.40
51	CD26	16a bister brown	4.00	1.90
52	CD27	24a bister	4.00	1.90
		Nos. 45-52 (8)	21.50	10.45

400th anniversary of Vasco da Gama's discovery of the route to India.
For overprints and surcharge see Nos. 148-155.

King Carlos

A5   A6

1898-1903   **Typo.**   **Perf. 11½**
Name & Value in Black Except #79

53	A5	½a gray	.35	.25
a.		Perf. 12½	2.50	1.75
54	A5	1a orange	.35	.30
a.		Perf. 12½	2.50	1.75
55	A5	2a light green	.35	.30
56	A5	2½a brown	1.25	1.10
57	A5	3a gray violet	1.25	1.10
58	A5	3a gray green ('03)	1.50	1.00
59	A5	4a sea green	1.60	1.00
60	A5	5a rose ('03)	1.50	1.00
61	A5	6a pale yel brn ('03)	1.50	1.00
62	A5	8a blue	2.00	1.00
63	A5	9a red brown ('03)	1.50	1.25
64	A5	10a slate blue ('00)	2.00	1.10
65	A5	10a gray brown ('03)	1.50	1.00
66	A5	12a rose	4.25	3.00
67	A5	12a dull blue ('03)	15.00	8.50
68	A5	13a violet	4.50	3.75
69	A5	13a red lilac ('03)	3.50	1.75
70	A5	15a gray lilac ('03)	5.50	3.75
71	A5	16a dark bl, *bl*	4.50	3.75
72	A5	20a brn, *yelsh* ('00)	5.25	3.75
73	A5	22a brn org, *pink* ('03)	5.25	3.50
74	A5	24a brown, *buff*	5.50	3.75
75	A5	31a red lil, *pinkish*	5.50	3.75
76	A5	31a brn, *straw* ('03)	5.75	3.50
77	A5	47a dk blue, *rose*	9.00	4.25
78	A5	47a red vio, *pink* ('03)	6.50	3.50
79	A5	78a blk & red, *bl* ('00)	11.00	6.00
80	A5	78a dl bl, *straw* ('03)	14.00	8.00
		Nos. 53-80 (28)	121.65	76.00

Most of Nos. 53-80 were issued without gum.
For surcharges & overprints see #81-82, 104-119, 129-130, 134-147, 195-196.

1899

Black Surcharge

81	A6	10a on 16a dk bl, *bl*	3.00	2.50
82	A6	20a on 31a red lil, *pnksh*	3.00	2.50

Surcharged in Black

1902

On Issue of 1887

83	A2	5a on 25r violet	2.50	1.75
84	A2	5a on 200r gray lil	4.00	2.50
85	A2	5a on 10r blue grn	75.00	40.00
86	A2	6a on 300r orange	3.75	3.50
87	A2	9a on 40r choc	4.50	3.50
88	A2	9a on 100r yel brn	4.50	3.50
89	A2	9a on 20r rose	4.50	3.50
90	A2	15a on 50r blue	75.00	40.00
91	A2	22a on 80r gray	7.50	5.00
		Nos. 83-91 (9)	181.25	103.25

Reprints of Nos. 83-88, 90-91, 104A have clean-cut perf. 13½.

On Issue of 1894

92	A3	5a on 5r yellow	1.90	1.10
a.		Inverted surcharge	40.00	30.00
93	A3	5a on 25r green	2.25	1.10
94	A3	5a on 50r lt blue	2.25	1.40
95	A3	6a on 20r lavender	2.25	1.40
96	A3	9a on 15r choc	2.25	1.40
97	A3	9a on 75r rose	2.25	1.40
98	A3	15a on 10r red vio	4.00	2.25
99	A3	15a on 100r brn, *buff*	4.00	2.25
100	A3	15a on 300r bl, *sal*	4.00	2.25
101	A3	22a on 80r lt green	6.00	4.00
102	A3	22a on 200r bl, *blue*	8.00	4.00

On Newspaper Stamp of 1893

103	N2	6a on 2½r brn	1.00	.85
a.		Inverted surcharge	27.50	27.50
		Nos. 92-103 (12)	40.15	23.40

Nos. 93-97, 99-102 issued without gum.

Stamps of 1898
Overprinted in Black

104	A5	3a gray violet	3.00	1.40
104A	A5	12a rose	6.00	3.75

Reprint noted after No. 91.

No. 67 Surcharged in
Black

1905

105	A5	10a on 12a dull blue	3.50	2.50

Stamps of 1898-1903
Overprinted in
Carmine or Green

1911

106	A5	½a gray	.30	.30
a.		Inverted overprint	11.00	11.00
107	A5	1a orange	.30	.30
a.		Perf. 12½	9.00	9.00
108	A5	2a light green	.40	.35
109	A5	3a gray green	.50	.35
110	A5	5a rose (G)	.50	.35
111	A5	6a yel brown	.50	.35
112	A5	9a red brown	.75	.45
113	A5	10a gray brown	.75	.45
114	A5	13a red lilac	.80	.50
115	A5	15a gray lilac	1.60	1.25
116	A5	22a brn org, *pink*	1.60	1.25
117	A5	31a brown, *straw*	1.60	1.25
118	A5	47a red vio, *pink*	3.00	2.50
119	A5	78a dl bl, *straw*	4.75	3.50
		Nos. 106-119 (14)	17.35	13.15

Preceding Issues
Overprinted in Red

1913

Without Gum

On Provisional Issue of 1902

120	A3	5a on 5r yellow	3.00	4.00
121	A3	5a on 25r green	3.00	4.00
122	A3	5a on 50r lt bl	5.00	7.00
123	N2	6a on 2½r brn	5.00	7.00
124	A3	6a on 20r lavender	3.00	4.00
125	A3	9a on 15r choc	3.00	4.00
126	A3	15a on 100r brn, *buff*	5.00	5.50
127	A3	22a on 80r lt grn	7.00	8.00
128	A3	22a on 200r bl, *bl*	6.00	7.50

On Issue of 1903

129	A5	3a gray green	5.00	7.50

On Issue of 1905

130	A5	10a on 12a dull bl	4.50	4.00
		Nos. 120-130 (11)	49.50	62.50

Overprinted in Green
or Red

1913

On Provisional Issue of 1902

131	A3	9a on 75r rose (G)	4.50	4.50
132	A3	15a on 10r red vio (G)	3.75	3.75
a.		Inverted overprint	27.50	27.50
133	A3	15a on 300r bl, *sal* (R)	6.50	6.50
a.		"REUBPLICA"	19.00	19.00
b.		"REPBLICAU"	19.00	19.00

On Issue of 1903

134	A5	5a rose (G)	3.00	3.00
		Nos. 131-134 (4)	17.75	17.75

Stamps of 1898-1903
Overprinted in Red

1913

135	A5	6a yellow brown	3.00	1.75
136	A5	9a red brown	3.00	1.75
137	A5	10a gray brown	3.00	1.75
138	A5	13a violet	5.00	2.50
a.		Inverted overprint	35.00	35.00
139	A5	13a red lilac	4.00	2.50
140	A5	15a gray lilac	5.00	3.25
141	A5	22a brn org, *pnksh*	6.00	3.50
142	A5	31a red lil, *pnksh*	6.00	3.50
143	A5	31a brown, *straw*	7.00	5.50
144	A5	47a blue, *pink*	8.00	5.50
145	A5	47a red vio, *pink*	10.00	8.00
146	A5	78a dl bl, *straw*	12.00	6.50

No. 79 Overprinted in
Red

147	A5	78a blk & red, *bl*	10.00	8.00
		Nos. 135-147 (13)	82.00	54.00

Vasco da Gama Issue of 1898
Overprinted or Surcharged in Black:

148	CD20	½a blue green	.65	.60
149	CD21	1a red	.65	.60
150	CD22	2a red violet	.65	.60
151	CD23	4a yellow green	.65	.60
152	CD24	8a dark blue	1.40	1.10
153	CD25	10a on 12a vio brn	2.50	2.00
154	CD26	16a bister brown	2.00	1.75
155	CD27	24a bister	2.75	2.25
		Nos. 148-155 (8)	11.25	9.50

Ceres — A7

1914-23 Typo.   **Perf. 15x14, 12x11½**
Name and Value in Black

156	A7	½a olive brown	.20	.20
157	A7	1a black	.20	.20
158	A7	1½a yel grn ('23)	.60	1.10
159	A7	2a blue green	.25	.25
160	A7	3a lilac brown	1.00	.75
161	A7	4a carmine	1.00	.75
162	A7	6a light violet	1.00	.75
163	A7	7a lt green ('23)	1.75	1.75
164	A7	7½a ultra ('23)	3.25	3.50
165	A7	9a blue ('23)	4.00	6.75
166	A7	10a deep blue	1.25	.60
167	A7	11a gray ('23)	4.00	6.75
168	A7	12a yellow brown	1.50	1.25
169	A7	15a lilac ('23)	8.00	7.25
170	A7	16a slate	2.00	3.75
171	A7	18a dp blue ('23)	10.00	6.25
172	A7	19a gray grn ('23)	10.00	6.50
173	A7	20a org brown	15.00	6.00
174	A7	36a turq blue ('23)	9.00	4.25
175	A7	40a plum	9.00	4.50
176	A7	54a choc ('23)	10.00	6.25
177	A7	58a brown, *grn*	10.00	5.00
178	A7	72a brt rose ('23)	16.00	16.00
179	A7	76a brown, *rose*	11.50	6.50
180	A7	1p org, *salmon*	20.00	11.00

181 A7　3p green, *blue*　　35.00　25.00
182 A7　5p car rose ('23)　70.00　52.50
　Nos. 156-182 (27)　255.50 184.50

For surcharges see Nos. 200-201, MR1.

Preceding Issues
Overprinted in
Carmine

1915　　　　　　　　*Perf. 11½*
On Provisional Issue of 1902
183 A3　5a on 5r yellow　1.00　.55
184 A3　5a on 25r green　1.00　.55
185 A3　5a on 50r lt blue　1.00　.55
186 A3　6a on 20r lavender　1.00　.55
187 A3　9a on 15r chocolate　1.00　.55
188 A3　9a on 75r rose　1.50　.55
189 A3　15a on 10r red vio　1.50　1.50
190 A3　15a on 100r brn, *buff*　2.00　1.50
191 A3　15a on 300r bl, *sal*　2.00　3.00
192 A3　22a on 80r lt grn　3.25　2.75
193 A3　22a on 200r bl, *bl*　5.00　5.00
On No. 103
194 N2　6a on 2½r, perf. 13½　1.00　.55
　a. Perf. 12½　　2.00　1.25
　b. Perf. 11½　　4.00　1.75
On No. 104
195 A5　3a gray violet　1.00　.60
On No. 105
196 A5　10a on 12a dull bl　1.10　.90
　Nos. 183-196 (14)　23.35　18.80

Type of 1915 with
Additional Surcharge
in Black

1915　　　　　　*Perf. 11½*
199 A3　½a on 5a on 50r lt bl　12.50　7.00
　a. Perf. 13½　　20.00　12.50

Nos. 178 and 169
Surcharged

1932　　　　　　*Perf. 12x11½*
200 A7　6a on 72a brt rose　1.50　1.25
201 A7　12a on 15a lilac　1.50　1.25

"Portugal" and Vasco
da Gama's Flagship
"San Gabriel" — A8

1935　　**Typo.**　　**Wmk. 232**
202 A8　½a bister　　.20　.20
203 A8　1a olive brown　.20　.20
204 A8　2a blue green　.20　.20
205 A8　3a red violet　.55　.30
206 A8　4a black　　.55　.55
207 A8　5a gray　　.65　.55
208 A8　6a brown　　.75　.60
209 A8　7a bright rose　.90　.90
210 A8　8a bright blue　1.00　1.00
211 A8　10a red orange　1.40　1.10
212 A8　12a dark blue　2.50　1.90
213 A8　14a olive green　3.00　1.90
214 A8　15a maroon　2.75　2.50
215 A8　20a orange　3.25　2.50
216 A8　30a apple green　3.75　2.50
217 A8　40a violet　6.75　4.00
218 A8　50a olive bister　8.00　4.00
219 A8　1p light blue　19.00　10.50
220 A8　2p brn orange　37.50　20.00
221 A8　3p emerald　47.50　30.00
222 A8　5p dark violet　75.00　40.00
　Nos. 202-222 (21)　215.40 125.40

Common Design Types
1938　**Unwmk.　Engr.**　*Perf. 13½x13*
Name and Value in Black
223 CD34　1a gray green　.20　.20
224 CD34　2a orange brown　.20　.30
225 CD34　3a dk violet brn　.20　.30
226 CD34　4a brt green　.20　.60
227 CD35　5a dk carmine　.20　1.50
228 CD35　6a slate　　.40　.20
229 CD35　8a rose violet　.60　1.00
230 CD37　10a brt red violet　.60　1.50
231 CD37　12a red　　1.00　2.25
232 CD37　15a orange　1.50　2.25
233 CD36　20a blue　　1.50　.70
234 CD36　40a gray black　3.25　1.10
235 CD36　50a brown　3.25　1.10
236 CD38　1p brown carmine　6.25　4.00
237 CD38　2p olive green　12.50　3.00
238 CD38　3p blue violet　15.00　7.00
239 CD38　5p red brown　30.00　10.00
　Nos. 223-239 (17)　76.85　37.00

For overprints see Nos. 245A-245K.

Mozambique Nos.
273, 276, 278, 280,
282 and 283
Surcharged in Black

1946　　　　　　*Perf. 13½x13*
240 CD34　1a on 15c dk vio
　　　　brn　　6.00　4.50
241 CD35　4a on 35c brt grn　6.00　4.50
242 CD35　8a on 50c brt red
　　　　vio　　6.00　4.50
243 CD36　10a on 70c brn vio　6.00　4.50
244 CD36　12a on 1e red　6.00　4.50
245 CD37　20a on 1.75e blue　6.00　4.50
　Nos. 240-245 (6)　36.00　27.00

Nos. 223-227 and 229-234
Overprinted "Libertacao"

1947
245A CD34　1a gray green　16.00　10.50
245B CD34　2a org brown　25.00　19.00
245C CD34　3a dk vio brn　10.00　6.00
245D CD34　4a brt green　10.00　8.00
245E CD35　5a dark car　4.50　2.00
245F CD35　8a rose violet　2.25　1.50
245G CD37　10a brt red vio　6.25　3.25
245H CD37　12a red　6.50　2.50
245I CD37　15a orange　5.00　2.50
245J CD36　20a blue　55.00　35.00
　m. Inverted overprint　70.00　70.00
245K CD36　40a gray black　15.00　8.25
　Nos. 245A-245K (11)　155.50　98.50

Timor　　　　　UPU
Woman — A9　Symbols — A10

Designs: 3a, Gong ringer. 4a, Girl with basket. 8a, Aleixo de Ainaro. 10a, 1p, 3p, Heads
of various chieftains. 20a, Warrior and horse.

1948　　**Litho.**　　*Perf. 14*
246 A9　1a aqua & dk brn　.50　.50
247 A9　3a gray & dk brn　1.00　.60
248 A9　4a pink & dk grn　1.00　.60
249 A9　8a red & blue blk　.50　.35
250 A9　10a blue grn & org　.75　.50
251 A9　20a ultra, aqua & bl　.70　.45
252 A9　1p org, bl & ultra　12.50　3.00
253 A9　3p vio & dk brn　9.00　5.00
　a. Sheet of 8, #246-253　55.00　55.00
　Nos. 246-253 (8)　25.95　11.00

No. 253a sold for 5p.

Lady of Fatima Issue
Common Design Type
1948, Oct.
254 CD40　8a slate gray　3.00　3.00

UPU Issue
1949　　**Unwmk.**　　*Perf. 14.*
255 A10　16a brown & buff　4.00　5.00

UPU, 75th anniversary.

Catalogue values for unused
stamps in this section, from this
point to the end of the section, are
for Never Hinged items.

Craftsman　　　Timor Woman
A11　　　　　　A12

1950　　　　　　*Perf. 14½*
256 A11　20a dull vio blue　1.10　.70
257 A12　50a dull brown　4.50　1.40

Holy Year Issue
Common Design Types
1950, May　　　　*Perf. 13x13½*
258 CD41　40a green　1.50　1.25
259 CD42　70a black brown　2.25　2.00

Blackberry
Lily — A13

Designs: Various flowers.

1950　**Unwmk.　Litho.**　*Perf. 14½*
260 A13　1a multicolored　.25　.30
261 A13　3a multicolored　.75　1.00
262 A13　10a multicolored　.75　1.00
263 A13　16a multicolored　1.50　1.25
264 A13　20a multicolored　1.00　1.00
265 A13　30a multicolored　1.10　1.10
266 A13　70a multicolored　1.50　1.25
267 A13　1p multicolored　1.50　1.50
268 A13　2p multicolored　2.00　2.00
269 A13　3p multicolored　3.00　3.00
　Nos. 260-269 (10)　13.35　13.40

Holy Year Extension Issue
Common Design Type
1951　　　　　　*Perf. 14*
270 CD43　86a bl & pale bl + la-
　　　　bel　　2.00　1.75

Stamp without label attached sells for much
less.

Medical Congress Issue
Common Design Type
Design: Weighing baby.
1952　　**Litho.**　　*Perf. 13½*
271 CD44　10a ol blk & brn　.90　.85

St. Francis Xavier Issue

Statue of St. Francis
Xavier — A14

Designs: 16a, Miraculous Arm of St. Francis. 1p, Tomb of St. Francis.

1952, Oct. 25　　　　*Perf. 14*
272 A14　1a black　　.25　.20
273 A14　16a blk brn & blk　1.00　.80
274 A14　1p dk car & gray　5.00　2.00
　Nos. 272-274 (3)　6.25　3.00

400th death anniv. of St. Francis Xavier.

Madonna and　　Stamp of Portugal
Child — A15　　and Arms of
　　　　　　　Colonies — A16

1953　　　　　　*Perf. 13x13½*
275 A15　3a dk brn & dull gray　.25　.20
276 A15　16a dk brown & cream　1.00　.60
277 A15　50a dk bl & dull gray　3.00　1.40
　Nos. 275-277 (3)　4.25　2.20

Exhibition of Sacred Missionary Art, Lisbon,
1951.

Stamp Centenary Issue
1953　　**Photo.**　　*Perf. 13*
278 A16　10a multicolored　1.10　1.00

Sao Paulo Issue
Common Design Type
1954　　**Litho.**　　*Perf. 13½*
279 CD46　16a dk brn red, bl & blk　.85　.70

Map of
Timor — A17

1956　　**Unwmk.**　　*Perf. 14x12½*
Inscription and design in brown,
red, green, ultramarine & yellow
280 A17　1a pale salmon　.20　.20
281 A17　3a pale gray blue　.25　.20
282 A17　8a buff　　.30　.20
283 A17　24a pale green　.40　.20
284 A17　32a lemon　　.50　.20
285 A17　40a pale gray　.75　.30
286 A17　1p yellow　　1.75　1.10
287 A17　3p pale blue　4.25　1.50
　Nos. 280-287 (8)　8.40　3.90

For surcharges see Nos. 291-300.

Brussels Fair Issue

Exhibition Emblems
and View — A18

1958　　　　　　*Perf. 14½*
288 A18　40a multicolored　.50　.40

Tropical Medicine Congress Issue
Common Design Type
Design: Calophyllum inophyllum.
1958　　　　　　*Perf. 13½*
289 CD47　32a multicolored　3.00　2.75

Symbolical
Globe — A19

Carved Elephant Jar — A20

1960 Unwmk. Litho. Perf. 13½
290 A19 4.50e multicolored .50 .35
500th death anniv. of Prince Henry the Navigator.

Nos. 280-287 Surcharged with New Value and Bars

1960 Unwmk. Perf. 14x12½
Inscription and design in brown, red, green, ultramarine & yellow

291 A17	5c on 1a pale salmon	.20	.20
292 A17	10c on 3a pale gray bl	.20	.20
293 A17	20c on 8a buff	.25	.20
294 A17	30c on 24a pale grn	.30	.20
295 A17	50c on 32a lemon	.40	.20
296 A17	1e on 40a pale gray	.50	.20
297 A17	2e on 40a pale gray	.60	.20
298 A17	5e on 1p yellow	.75	1.00
299 A17	10e on 3p pale blue	1.75	2.50
300 A17	15e on 3p pale blue	2.50	2.00
	Nos. 291-300 (10)	7.45	6.90

1961 Litho. Perf. 11½x12
Native Art: 10c, House on stilts. 20c, Madonna and Child. 30c, Silver rosary. 50c, Two men in boat, horiz. 1e, Silver box in shape of temple. 2.50e, Archer. 4.50e, Elephant. 5e, Man climbing tree. 10e, Woman carrying pot on head. 20e, Cockfight. 50e, House on stilts and animals.

Multicolored Designs

301 A20	5c pale violet	.20	.30
302 A20	10c pale green	.20	.30
a.	Value & legend inverted	72.50	72.50
303 A20	20c pale blue	.20	.30
304 A20	30c rose	.25	.20
305 A20	50c pale grnsh bl	.20	.20
306 A20	1e bister	.70	.20
307 A20	2.50e pale ol bis	.50	.20
308 A20	4.50e lt salmon	.50	.20
309 A20	5e lt gray	.60	.20
310 A20	10e gray	1.40	.30
311 A20	20e yellow	2.75	1.00
312 A20	50e lt bluish gray	9.25	2.50
	Nos. 301-312 (12)	16.75	5.90

Sports Issue
Common Design Type
Sports: 50c, Duck hunting. 1e, Horseback riding. 1.50e, Swimming. 2e, Gymnastics. 2.50e, Soccer. 15e, Big game hunting.

1962, Mar. 22 Unwmk. Perf. 13½
Multicolored Designs

313 CD48	50c gray & bis	.25	.20
314 CD48	1e olive bister	.60	.30
315 CD48	1.50e gray & bl grn	.70	.40
316 CD48	2e buff	.85	.35
317 CD48	2.50e gray	1.00	.50
318 CD48	15e salmon	3.00	1.90
	Nos. 313-318 (6)	6.40	3.65

Anti-Malaria Issue
Common Design Type
Design: Anopheles sundaicus.

1962 Litho. Perf. 13½
319 CD49 2.50e multicolored .75 .60

National Overseas Bank Issue
Common Design Type
Design: 2.50e, Manuel Pinheiro Chagas.

1964, May 16 Unwmk. Perf. 13½
320 CD51 2.50e grn, gray, yel, lt bl & blk .75 .60

ITU Issue
Common Design Type

1965, May 17 Litho. Perf. 14½
321 CD52 1.50e multicolored 1.50 .90

National Revolution Issue
Common Design Type
Design: 4.50e, Dr. Vieira Machado Academy and Dili Health Center.

1966, May 28 Litho. Perf. 11½
322 CD53 4.50e multicolored 1.50 .90

Navy Club Issue
Common Design Type
10c, Capt. Gago Coutinho and gunboat Patria. 4.50e, Capt. Sacadura Cabral and seaplane Lusitania.

1967, Jan. 31 Litho. Perf. 13
323 CD54 10c multicolored 2.00 1.00
324 CD54 4.50e multicolored 2.00 1.00

Sepoy Officer, 1792 — A21 | Our Lady of Fatima — A22

Designs: 1e, Officer, 1815. 1.50e, Infantry soldier, 1879. 2e, Infantry soldier, 1890. 2.50e, Infantry officer, 1903. 3e, Sapper, 1918. 4.50e, Special forces soldier, 1964. 10e, Paratrooper, 1964.

1967, Feb. 12 Photo. Perf. 13½

325 A21	35c multicolored	.25	.30
326 A21	1e multicolored	1.50	1.00
327 A21	1.50e multicolored	.60	.30
328 A21	2e multicolored	.60	.20
329 A21	2.50e multicolored	.60	.25
330 A21	3e multicolored	.75	.35
331 A21	4.50e multicolored	1.10	.45
332 A21	10e multicolored	2.25	.65
	Nos. 325-332 (8)	7.65	3.50

1967, May 13 Litho. Perf. 12½x13
333 A22 3e multicolored .60 .30
Apparition of the Virgin Mary to three shepherd children at Fatima, Portugal, 50th anniv.

Cabral Issue

Map of Brazil, by Lopo Homem-Reinéis, 1519 — A23

1968, Apr. 22 Litho. Perf. 14
334 A23 4.50e multicolored .80 .50
See note after Macao No. 416.

Admiral Coutinho Issue
Common Design Type
Design: 4.50e, Adm. Coutinho and frigate Adm. Gago Coutinho.

1969, Feb. 17 Litho. Perf. 14
335 CD55 4.50e multicolored 1.10 .85

View of Dili, 1834 — A24

1969, July 25 Litho. Perf. 14
336 A24 1e multicolored .30 .20
Bicentenary of Dili as capital of Timor.

da Gama Medal in St. Jerome's Convent — A25

Emblem of King Manuel, St. Jerome's Convent — A26

Vasco da Gama Issue
1969, Aug. 29 Litho. Perf. 14
337 A25 5e multicolored .40 .30
Vasco da Gama (1469-1524), navigator.

Administration Reform Issue
Common Design Type
1969, Sept. 25 Litho. Perf. 14
338 CD56 5e multicolored .40 .25

King Manuel I Issue
1969, Dec. 1 Litho. Perf. 14
339 A26 4e multicolored .40 .25
King Manuel I, 500th birth anniv.

Capt. Ross Smith, Arms of Great Britain, Portugal and Australia, and Map of Timor A27

1969, Dec. 9
340 A27 2e multicolored .50 .40
50th anniv. of the first England to Australia flight of Capt. Ross Smith and Lt. Keith Smith.

Marshal Carmona Issue
Common Design Type
Antonio Oscar Carmona in civilian clothes.

1970, Nov. 15 Litho. Perf. 14
341 CD57 1.50e multicolored .20 .20

Lusiads Issue

Sailing Ship and Monks Preaching to Islanders — A28

1972, May 25 Litho. Perf. 13
342 A28 1e brown & multi .20 .35
4th centenary of publication of The Lusiads by Luiz Camoens.

Olympic Games Issue
Common Design Type
Design: 4.50e, Soccer, Olympic emblem.

1972, June 20 Perf. 14x13½
343 CD59 4.50e multicolored .50 .50

Lisbon-Rio de Janeiro Flight Issue
Common Design Type
Design: 1e, Sacadura Cabral and Gago Coutinho in cockpit of "Lusitania."

1972, Sept. 20 Litho. Perf. 13½
344 CD60 1e multicolored .25 .40

WMO Centenary Issue
Common Design Type
1973, Dec. 15 Litho. Perf. 13
345 CD61 20e multicolored 1.75 2.00

United Nations Transitional Authority in East Timor
100 cents = 1 dollar (2000)

A30

2000, Apr. 29 Litho. Perf. 12x11¾
350 A30 Dom. red & multi .25 .25
351 A30 Int. blue & multi 1.25 1.25
No. 350 sold for 10c and No. 351 sold for 50c on day of issue.

Independence — A31

Designs: 25c, Crocodile. 50c, Palm fronds. $1, Coffee beans and picker. $2, Flag.

2002, May 20 Litho. Perf. 14½x14
352-355 A31 Set of 4 7.50 7.50

A32

Flag and: 10c, Pres. Xanana Gusmao. 50c, Map of country.

2002 Litho. Perf. 13x13¼
356-357 A32 Set of 2 1.25 1.25

AIR POST STAMPS

Common Design Type
1938 Unwmk. Engr. Perf. 13½x13
Name and Value in Black

C1 CD39	1a red orange	.85	.45
C2 CD39	2a purple	.90	.55
C3 CD39	3a orange	.90	.60
C4 CD39	5a ultra	1.00	.65
C5 CD39	10a lilac brown	1.60	1.10
C6 CD39	20a dark green	3.00	1.40
C7 CD39	50a red brown	6.00	4.00
C8 CD39	70a rose carmine	7.00	5.25
C9 CD39	1p magenta	13.00	6.00
	Nos. C1-C9 (9)	34.25	20.00

No. C7 exists with overprint "Exposicao Internacional de Nova York, 1939-1940" and Trylon and Perisphere. Counterfeits exist.
For overprints see Nos. C15-C23.

Mozambique Nos. C3, C4, C6, C7 and C9 Surcharged in Black

TIMOR 8 AVOS

1946 Unwmk. Perf. 13½x13

C10 CD39	8a on 50c orange	6.25	4.00
C11 CD39	12a on 1e ultra	6.25	4.00
C12 CD39	40a on 3e dk green	6.25	4.00
C13 CD39	50a on 5e red brn	6.25	4.00
C14 CD39	1p on 10e mag	6.25	4.00
	Nos. C10-C14 (5)	31.25	20.00

Nos. C1-C9 Overprinted "Libertacao"

1947

C15 CD39	1a scarlet	17.50	13.00
C16 CD39	2a purple	17.50	13.00
C17 CD39	3a orange	17.50	13.00
C18 CD39	5a ultra	17.50	13.00
C19 CD39	10a lilac brown	5.75	3.25
C20 CD39	20a dark green	5.75	3.75
C21 CD39	50a red brown	6.00	3.25
C22 CD39	70a rose carmine	24.00	8.00
C23 CD39	1p magenta	9.50	3.25
	Nos. C15-C23 (9)	121.00	73.50

POSTAGE DUE STAMPS

D1

1904　Unwmk.　Typo.　Perf. 12
Without Gum
Name and Value in Black

J1	D1	1a yellow green	.50	.50
J2	D1	2a slate	.50	.50
J3	D1	5a yellow brown	2.25	1.50
J4	D1	6a red orange	2.25	2.25
J5	D1	10a gray brown	2.50	2.00
J6	D1	15a red brown	3.75	2.75
J7	D1	24a dull blue	6.25	5.50
J8	D1	40a carmine	7.50	5.50
J9	D1	50a orange	10.50	7.50
J10	D1	1p dull violet	17.00	13.00
		Nos. J1-J10 (10)	53.00	41.00

Overprinted in
Carmine or Green

1911　　　　Without Gum

J11	D1	1a yellow green	.25	.25
J12	D1	2a slate	.30	.25
a.		Inverted overprint		
J13	D1	5a yellow brown	.60	.40
J14	D1	6a deep orange	.80	.50
J15	D1	10a gray brown	1.50	.70
J16	D1	15a brown	1.75	1.10
J17	D1	24a dull blue	2.50	2.00
J18	D1	40a carmine (G)	3.25	2.50
J19	D1	50a orange	3.75	2.50
J20	D1	1p dull violet	7.50	7.00
		Nos. J11-J20 (10)	22.20	17.20

Nos. J1-J10
Overprinted in Red
or Green

1913　　　　Without Gum

J21	D1	1a yellow green	8.00	9.00
J22	D1	2a slate	8.00	9.00
J23	D1	5a yellow brown	4.50	4.50
J24	D1	6a deep orange	4.50	4.50
a.		Inverted surcharge	30.00	
J25	D1	10a gray brown	4.50	6.00
J26	D1	15a red brown	4.50	6.00
J27	D1	24a dull blue	6.00	6.00
J28	D1	40a carmine (G)	6.00	6.00
J29	D1	50a orange	10.00	12.00
J30	D1	1p gray violet	10.00	12.00
		Nos. J21-J30 (10)	66.00	75.00

> **Catalogue values for unused stamps in this section, from this point to the end of the section, are for Never Hinged items.**

Common Design Type

1952　Photo. & Typo.　Perf. 14
Numeral in Red, Frame Multicolored

J31	CD45	1a chocolate	.40	.40
J32	CD45	3a brown	.40	.40
J33	CD45	5a dark green	.40	.40
J34	CD45	10a green	.40	.40
J35	CD45	30a purple	.65	.65
J36	CD45	1p brown carmine	1.25	1.25
		Nos. J31-J36 (6)	3.50	3.50

WAR TAX STAMP

Regular Issue of 1914
Surcharged in Red

1919　　Unwmk.　Perf. 15x14

MR1	A7	2a on ½a ol brn	17.50	15.00

See note after Macao No. MR2.

NEWSPAPER STAMPS

King Luiz — N1

Stamps of Macao Surcharged in Black

1892　　Unwmk.　Perf. 12½
Without Gum

P1	N1	2½r on 20r brt rose	2.00	.75
a.		"TIMOR" inverted		
P2	N1	2½r on 40r chocolate	2.00	.75
a.		"TIMOR" inverted		
b.		Perf. 13½	4.50	3.00
c.		As "a," perf. 13½		
P3	N1	2½r on 80r gray	2.00	.75
a.		"TIMOR" inverted	12.50	8.00
b.		Perf. 13½	6.00	2.25
		Nos. P1-P3 (3)		

N2　　　　　　N3

1893-95　Typo.　Perf. 11½, 13½

P4	N2	2½r brown	.40	.35
a.		Perf. 12½	2.00	1.50
P5	N3	½a on 2½r brn ('95)	.45	.30

For surcharges see Nos. 103, 123, 194.

POSTAL TAX STAMPS

Pombal Issue
Common Design Types

1925　　Unwmk.　Perf. 12½

RA1	CD28	2a lake & black	.30	.30
RA2	CD29	2a lake & black	.30	.30
RA3	CD30	2a lake & black	.30	.30
		Nos. RA1-RA3 (3)	.90	.90

Type of War Tax Stamp of Portuguese
India Overprinted in Red

1934-35　　　　Perf. 12

RA4	WT1	2a green & blk	6.50	8.00
RA5	WT1	5a green & blk	8.00	8.00

Surcharged in Black

RA6	WT1	7a on ½a rose & blk ('35)	9.00	7.50
		Nos. RA4-RA6 (3)	23.50	23.50

The tax was for local education.

Type of War Tax Stamp of Portuguese
India Overprinted in Black

1936　　　　Perf. 12x11½

RA7	WT1	10a rose & black	7.00	9.00

1937　　　　Perf. 11½

RA8	WT1	10a green & blk	5.50	8.25

PT1　　　　　　PT2

1948　Unwmk.　Typo.　Perf. 11½
Without Gum

RA9	PT1	10a dark blue	3.00	2.00
RA10	PT1	20a green	3.50	3.00

The 20a bears a different emblem.

> **Catalogue values for unused stamps in this section, from this point to the end of the section, are for Never Hinged items.**

1960　　Without Gum　Perf. 11½

RA11	PT2	70c dark blue	1.50	1.25
RA12	PT2	1.30e green	2.25	2.25

See Nos. RA13-RA16. For surcharges see Nos. RA20-RA25.

Type of 1960 Redrawn

1967　　Typo.　Perf. 10½
Without Gum

RA13	PT2	70c deep blue	12.00	12.00
RA14	PT2	1.30e emerald	3.00	2.50

The denominations of Nos. RA13-RA14 are 2mm high. They are 2½mm high on Nos. RA11-RA12. Other differences exist. The printed area of No. RA13 measures 18x31mm; "Republica" 16mm.

Type of 1960
Serif Type Face

1967

RA14A	PT2	70c deep blue	12.00	10.00

Type of 1960, 2nd Redrawing

1967-68　Typo.　Perf. 10½
Without Gum

RA15	PT2	70c violet blue	.60	.60
RA16	PT2	1.30e bluish grn ('68)	1.25	1.25

The printed area measures 13x30mm on Nos. RA15-RA16; "Republica" measures 10½mm.

Woman and
Star — PT3

1969-70　　Litho.　Perf. 13½

RA17	PT3	30c vio bl & lt bl ('70)	.20	.20
RA18	PT3	50c dl org & maroon	.20	.20
RA19	PT3	1e yellow & brown	.20	.20
		Nos. RA17-RA19 (3)	.60	.60

The 2.50e and 10e in design PT3 were revenue stamps.

Nos. RA15-RA16
Surcharged in Red or
Carmine

1970　　Typo.　Perf. 10½
Without Gum

RA20	PT2	30c on 70c	7.00	6.00
RA21	PT2	30c on 1.30e	6.00	6.00
RA22	PT2	50c on 70c	160.00	110.00
RA23	PT2	50c on 1.30e	6.00	6.00
RA24	PT2	1e on 70c (C)	160.00	125.00
RA25	PT2	1e on 1.30e	8.00	7.25
		Nos. RA20-RA25 (6)	347.00	260.25

POSTAL TAX DUE STAMPS

Pombal Issue
Common Design Types

1925　　Unwmk.　Perf. 12½

RAJ1	CD28	4a lake & black	.40	1.00
RAJ2	CD29	4a lake & black	.40	1.00
RAJ3	CD30	4a lake & black	.40	1.00
		Nos. RAJ1-RAJ3 (3)	1.20	3.00

TOBAGO

tə-ˈbā-ˌgō

LOCATION — An island in the West Indies lying off the Venezuelan coast north of Trinidad
GOVT. — British Colony
AREA — 116 sq. mi.
POP. — 25,358
CAPITAL — Scarborough (Port Louis)

In 1889 Tobago, then an independent colony, was united with Trinidad under the name of Colony of Trinidad and Tobago. It became a ward of that colony January 1, 1899.

12 Pence = 1 Shilling
20 Shillings = 1 Pound

Queen Victoria
A1　　　　　A2

Wmk. Crown and C C (1)
1879　　Typo.　Perf. 14

1	A1	1p rose	92.50	75.00
2	A1	3p blue	92.50	57.50
3	A1	6p orange	45.00	57.50
4	A1	1sh green	425.00	75.00
a.		Half used as 6p on cover		
5	A1	5sh slate	750.00	700.00
6	A1	£1 violet	4,500.	

Stamps of the above set with revenue cancellations sell for a small fraction of the price of postally used copies.

Stamps of Type A1, watermarked Crown and C A, are revenue stamps.

1880

Manuscript Surcharge

7	A1	1p on half of 6p org	5,250.	875.

1880

8	A2	½p brown violet	45.00	70.00
9	A2	1p red brown	110.00	62.50
a.		Half used as ½p on cover		2,250.
10	A2	4p yellow green	225.00	30.00
a.		Half used as 2p on cover		2,250.
11	A2	6p bister brown	350.00	110.00
12	A2	1sh bister	70.00	80.00
a.		Imperf.		
		Nos. 8-12 (5)	800.00	352.50

No. 11 Surcharged in Black

1883
| 13 | A2 | 2½p on 6p bister brn | 55.00 | 55.00 |
| a. | | Double surcharge | 3,250. | 1,500. |

1882-96   Wmk. Crown and C A (2)
14	A2	½p brown vio ('82)	1.10	14.00
15	A2	½p dull green ('86)	2.00	.75
16	A2	1p red brown ('82)	3.25	2.00
a.		Diagonal half used as ½p on cover		—
17	A2	1p rose ('89)	2.75	.90
18	A2	2½p ultra ('83)	5.75	.85
a.		2½p dull blue ('83)	35.00	1.60
b.		2½p bright blue	5.75	.85
19	A2	4p yel grn ('82)	210.00	100.00
20	A2	4p gray ('85)	2.75	1.50
a.		Imperf., pair	2,000.	
21	A2	6p bis brn ('84)	625.00	550.00
a.		Imperf.		
22	A2	6p brn org ('86)	2.25	5.25
23	A2	1sh olive bis ('94)	2.75	19.00
24	A2	1sh brn org ('96)	9.25	75.00

Stamps of 1882-96 Surcharged in Black:

Nos. 25-29   No. 30

1886-92
25	A2	½p on 2½p ultra	5.25	13.50
a.		Inverted surcharge	11,000.	
b.		Pair, one without surcharge	11,000.	
c.		Space between "½" and "PENNY" 3mm	22.50	57.50
d.		Double surcharge	1,900.	1,500.
26	A2	½p on 4p gray	15.00	55.00
a.		Space between "½" and "PENNY" 3mm		
b.		Double surcharge	2,250.	
27	A2	½p on 6p bis brn	3.00	22.50
a.		Inverted surcharge	1,600.	
b.		Space between "½" and "PENNY" 3mm	30.00	125.00
c.		Double surcharge	1,900.	
28	A2	½p on 6p brn org	110.00	150.00
a.		Space between "½" and "PENNY" 3mm	350.00	375.00
b.		Double surcharge		1,400.
29	A2	1p on 2½ ultra	70.00	19.00
a.		Space between "1" and "PENNY" 4mm	175.00	85.00
b.		Half used as ½p on cover		1,650.
30	A2	2½p on 4p gray	7.00	7.50
a.		Double surcharge	2,250.	2,250.
		Nos. 25-30 (6)	210.25	267.50

Revenue Stamp Type A1 Surcharged in Black

1896
| 31 | A1 | ½p on 4p lilac & rose | 62.50 | 35.00 |
| a. | | Space between "½" and "d" 1½ to 2½mm | 140.00 | 80.00 |

Tobago stamps were replaced by those of Trinidad or Trinidad and Tobago.

TOGO

'tō-ˌgō

LOCATION — Western Africa, bordering on the Gulf of Guinea
GOVT. — Republic
AREA — 20,400 sq. mi.
POP. — 4,320,000 (1997 est.)
CAPITAL — Lome

The German Protectorate of Togo was occupied by Great Britain and France in World War I, and later mandated to them. The British area became part of Ghana. The French area was

granted internal autonomy in 1956 and achieved independence in 1958.

100 Pfennig = 1 Mark
12 Pence = 1 Shilling
100 Centimes = 1 Franc

Catalogue values for unused stamps in this country are for Never Hinged items, beginning with Scott 309 in the regular postage section, Scott B11 in the semipostal section, Scott C14 in the airpost section, Scott J32 in the postage due section, and Scott O1 in the official section.

Watermark

Wmk. 125 — Lozenges

German Protectorate

AREA — 34,934 sq. mi.
POP. — 1,000,368 (1913)

Stamps of Germany Overprinted in Black

1897   Unwmk.   Perf. 13½x14½
1	A9	3pf dark brown	4.25	5.50
a.		3pf yellow brown	7.25	20.00
b.		3pf reddish brown	21.00	50.00
2	A9	5pf green	3.25	2.25
3	A10	10pf carmine	3.50	2.50
4	A10	20pf ultra	4.00	10.50
5	A10	25pf orange	26.00	45.00
6	A10	50pf red brown	26.00	45.00
		Nos. 1-6 (6)	67.00	110.75

Kaiser's Yacht, the "Hohenzollern"

A3

A4

1900   Typo.   Perf. 14
7	A3	3pf brown	.80	1.00
8	A3	5pf green	9.25	1.60
9	A3	10pf carmine	17.00	1.25
10	A3	20pf ultra	.80	1.25
11	A3	25pf org & blk, yel	.80	8.00
12	A3	30pf org & blk, sal	1.10	8.00
13	A3	40pf lake & blk	.80	8.00
14	A3	50pf pur & blk, sal	1.10	6.00
15	A3	80pf lake & blk, rose	2.00	13.00

Engr.
Perf. 14½x14
16	A4	1m carmine	2.50	42.50
17	A4	2m blue	4.25	65.00
18	A4	3m black vio	5.50	125.00
19	A4	5m slate & car	85.00	400.00
		Nos. 7-19 (13)	130.90	680.60

Counterfeit cancellations are found on Nos. 10-19 and 22.

1909-19   Wmk. 125 Typo.   Perf. 14
20	A3	3pf brown ('19)	.70	
21	A3	5pf green	1.00	1.75
22	A3	10pf carmine ('14)	1.25	85.00

Engr.
Perf. 14½x14
| 23 | A4 | 5m slate & car ('19) | 16.00 | |
| | | Nos. 20-23 (4) | 18.95 | |

Nos. 20 and 23 were never placed in use.

British Protectorate
Nos. 7, 10-19, 21-22 Overprinted or Surcharged

First (Wide) Setting
3mm between Lines
2mm between "Anglo" & "French"
Wmk. 125 (5pf, 10pf); Unwmkd.
1914, Oct. 1   Perf. 14, 14½
33	A3	½p on 3pf brown	275.00	175.00
a.		Thin "y" in "penny"	700.00	525.00
34	A3	1p on 5pf green	275.00	175.00
a.		Thin "y" in "penny"	700.00	525.00
35	A3	3pf brown	150.00	90.00
36	A3	5pf green	110.00	80.00
37	A3	10pf carmine	150.00	90.00
a.		Inverted overprint	8,500.	4,500.
b.		Unwmk.		5,500.
38	A3	20pf ultra	30.00	27.50
39	A3	25pf org & blk, yel	30.00	22.50
40	A3	30pf org & blk, sal	30.00	32.50
41	A3	40pf lake & blk	275.00	240.00
42	A3	50pf pur & blk, sal	8,750.	7,000.
43	A3	80pf lake & blk, rose	275.00	250.00
44	A4	1m carmine	5,000.	2,600.
45	A4	2m blue	7,500.	7,500.
a.		Inverted overprint		
b.		"Occupation" double		

On Nos. 33-34, the surcharge line ("Half penny" or "One penny") was printed separately and its position varies in relation to the 3-line overprint. On Nos. 46-47, the surcharge and overprint lines were printed simultaneously.

Second (Narrow) Setting
2mm between Lines
2mm between "Anglo" & "French"
1914, Oct.
46	A3	½p on 3pf brown	40.00	30.00
a.		Thin "y" in "penny"	70.00	70.00
b.		"TOG"	475.00	350.00
47	A3	1p on 5pf green	5.00	5.00
a.		Thin "y" in "penny"	15.00	17.50
b.		"TOG"	150.00	125.00
48	A3	3pf brown	5,250.	1,000.
a.		"Occupation" omitted		
49	A3	5pf green	1,400.	800.00
50	A3	10pf carmine	—	3,100.
51	A3	20pf ultra	20.00	14.00
a.		"TOG"	4,750.	4,750.
b.		Vert. pair, #51 & #38		
52	A3	25pf org & blk, yel	26.00	35.00
a.		"TOG"	13,750.	
53	A3	30pf org & blk, sal	22.50	32.50
54	A3	40pf lake & blk	5,250.	1,750.
55	A3	50pf pur & blk, sal		6,750.
56	A3	80pf lake & blk, rose	2,000.	2,000.
57	A4	1m carmine	8,500.	4,500.
58	A4	2m blue		9,750.
59	A4	3m black violet		43,500.
60	A4	5m slate & car		43,500.

Third Setting
1 ¼mm btwn. "Anglo" & "French"
2mm between Lines
"Anglo-French" 15mm Wide

1915, Jan. 7
61	A3	3pf brown	8,500.	3,250.
62	A3	5pf green	225.00	150.00
63	A3	10pf carmine	225.00	150.00
64	A3	20pf ultra	1,600.	600.
64A	A3	40pf lake & blk		8,500.
65	A3	50pf pur & blk, sal	14,000.	11,000.

Stamps of Gold Coast Overprinted Locally

1915, May   Wmk. 3   Perf. 14
66	A7	½p green	.35	1.10
a.		Double overprint	525.00	550.00
67	A8	1p scarlet	.35	.55
a.		Double ovpt.	375.00	500.00
b.		Inverted ovpt.	200.00	275.00
c.		As "b," "Togo" omitted		
68	A7	2p gray	.35	1.40
69	A7	2½p ultra	1.10	3.75

Chalky Paper
70	A7	3p violet, yel	1.00	1.60
71	A7	6p dl vio & red vio	1.00	2.00
72	A7	1sh black, grn	1.75	4.75
a.		Double overprint	1,100.	
73	A7	2sh vio & bl, bl	10.00	15.00
74	A7	2sh6p blk & red, bl	5.25	22.50
75	A7	10sh grn & red, grn	40.00	70.00
76	A7	20sh vio & blk, red	150.00	175.00

Surfaced-Colored Paper
77	A7	3p violet, yel	1.00	1.60
78	A7	5sh grn & red, yel	9.25	17.50
		Nos. 66-78 (13)	221.40	316.75

Nos. 66-78 exist with small "F" in "French" and thin "G" in "Togo." Several values are known without the hyphen between "Anglo-French" and all but No. 77 without the first "O" in "Occupation."

Stamps of Gold Coast Overprinted in London

1916, Apr.
Ordinary Paper
80	A7	½p green	.35	2.90
81	A8	1p scarlet	.35	1.00
a.		Inverted overprint		
82	A7	2p gray	.60	.70
83	A7	2½p ultra	.60	1.75

Chalky Paper
84	A7	3p violet, yel	1.75	.80
85	A7	6p dl vio & red vio	1.75	1.10
86	A7	1sh black, grn	2.25	5.25
a.		1sh black, emerald	300.00	625.00
b.		1sh black, bl grn, ol back	5.50	15.00
87	A7	2sh vio & ultra, bl	5.25	9.75
88	A7	2sh6p blk & red, bl	5.25	8.00
89	A7	5sh grn & red, yel	14.00	30.00
90	A7	10sh grn & red, bl grn, ol back	18.00	62.50
a.		10sh green & red, grn	27.50	75.00
91	A7	20sh vio & blk, red	150.00	175.00
		Nos. 80-91 (12)	200.15	298.75

The overprint on Nos. 80-91 is in heavier letters than on Nos. 66-78 and the 2nd and 3rd lines are each ½mm longer. The letter "O" on Nos. 80-91 is narrower and more oval.

Issued under French Occupation
Stamps of German Togo Surcharged:

c   d

e   f

g   h

i

Wmk. Lozenges (5pf and 10pf) (125), Unwmk. (other values)

1914			Perf. 14, 14½	
151	A3(c+d)	5c on 3pf brn	50.00	50.00
152	A3(c+e)	5c on 3pf brn	50.00	50.00
153	A3(c+f)	5c on 3pf brn	50.00	50.00
154	A3(c+g)	10c on 5pf grn	17.50	17.50
a.		Double surcharge	925.00	925.00
155	A3(c+h)	10c on 5pf grn	17.50	17.50
156	A3(c+i)	10c on 5pf grn	25.00	25.00
158	A3(c)	20pf ultra	42.50	42.50
a.		3½mm between "TOGO" and "Occupation"	650.00	600.00
159	A3(c)	25pf org & blk, yel	45.00	45.00
160	A3(c)	30pf org & blk, sal	82.50	82.50
161	A3(c)	40pf lake & blk	525.00	450.00
162	A3(c)	80pf lake & blk, rose	525.00	450.00
		Nos. 151-162 (11)	1,430.	1,280.

Surcharged or Overprinted in Sans-Serif Type:

TOGO
Occupation
franco anglaise
O5

TOGO
Occupation
franco-anglaise

1915				
164	A3	5c on 3pf brown	12,000.	3,750.
165	A3	5pf green	800.	375.
166	A3	10pf carmine	925.	375.
a.		Inverted overprint	23,000.	13,500.
167	A3	20pf ultra	1,100.	800.
168	A3	25pf org & blk, yel	12,000.	6,000.
169	A3	30pf org & blk, sal	12,000.	6,000.
170	A3	40pf lake & blk	12,000.	6,000.
171	A3	50pf pur & blk, sal	18,000.	10,000.
172	A4	1m carmine		
173	A4	2m blue		18,000.
174	A4	3m black vio		25,000.
175	A4	5m slate & car	23,000.	25,000.

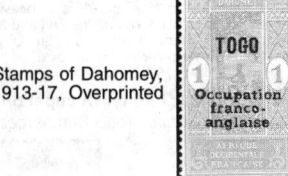

Stamps of Dahomey, 1913-17, Overprinted

1916-17		Unwmk.	Perf. 13½x14	
176	A5	1c violet & blk	.20	.20
177	A5	2c choc & rose	.20	.20
178	A5	4c black & brn	.20	.20
a.		Double overprint	350.00	350.00
179	A5	5c yel grn & bl grn	.50	.50
180	A5	10c org red & rose	.45	.45
181	A5	15c brn org & dk vio	1.10	1.10
182	A5	20c gray & choc	.50	.50
183	A5	25c ultra & dp bl	.80	.80
184	A5	30c choc & vio	.80	.80
185	A5	35c brown & blk	1.10	1.10
186	A5	40c blk & red org	1.00	1.00
187	A5	45c gray & ultra	1.10	1.10
188	A5	50c choc & brn	1.10	1.10
189	A5	75c blue & vio	4.75	4.75
190	A5	1fr bl grn & blk	6.25	6.25
191	A5	2fr buff & choc	9.25	9.25
192	A5	5fr vio & do bl	11.00	11.00
		Nos. 176-192 (17)	40.30	40.30

All values of the 1916-17 issue exist on chalky paper and all but the 15c, 25c and 35c on ordinary paper.

French Mandate

AREA - 21,893 sq. mi.
POP. - 780,497 (1938)

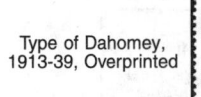

Type of Dahomey, 1913-39, Overprinted

1921				
193	A5	1c gray & yel grn	.20	.20
a.		Overprint omitted	90.00	
194	A5	2c blue & org	.20	.20
195	A5	4c ol grn & org	.20	.20
196	A5	5c dull red & blk	.20	.20
a.		Overprint omitted	300.00	
197	A5	10c bl grn & yel grn	.45	.45
198	A5	15c brown & car	.50	.50
199	A5	20c bl grn & org	.85	.85
200	A5	25c slate & org	.85	.85
201	A5	30c dp rose & ver	1.00	1.00
202	A5	35c red brn & yel grn	.85	.85
203	A5	40c bl grn & ol	1.25	1.25
204	A5	45c red brn & ol	1.00	1.00
205	A5	50c deep blue	1.00	1.00
206	A5	75c dl red & ultra	1.25	1.25
207	A5	1fr gray & ultra	1.40	1.40
208	A5	2fr ol grn & rose	4.00	4.00
209	A5	5fr orange & blk	7.25	7.25
		Nos. 193-209 (17)	22.45	22.45

Stamps and Type of 1921 Surcharged

1922-25				
210	A5	25c on 15c ol brn & rose red	.25	.25
211	A5	25c on 2fr ol grn & rose	.40	.40
212	A5	25c on 5fr org & blk	.40	.40
213	A5	60c on 75c vio, pnksh	.65	.65
a.		"60" omitted	150.00	150.00
214	A5	65c on 45c red brn & ol	1.10	1.10
a.		"TOGO" omitted	125.00	
215	A5	85c on 75c dull red & ultra	1.75	1.75
		Nos. 210-215 (6)	4.55	4.55

Issue years: #213, 1922; #211-212, 1924; others, 1925.

Coconut Grove
A6

Cacao Trees — A7

Oil Palms
A8

1924-38			Typo.	
216	A6	1c yellow & blk	.20	.20
217	A6	2c dp rose & blk	.20	.20
218	A6	4c dk blue & blk	.20	.20
219	A6	5c dp org & blk	.20	.20
220	A6	10c red vio & blk	.20	.20
221	A6	15c green & blk	.20	.20
222	A7	20c gray & blk	.20	.20
223	A7	25c grn & blk, yel	.45	.45
224	A7	30c gray grn & blk	.20	.20
225	A7	30c dl grn & lt grn ('27)	.35	.35
226	A7	35c lt brown & blk	.50	.50
227	A7	35c dp bl grn & grn ('38)	.45	.45
228	A7	40c red org & blk	.20	.20

229	A7	45c carmine & blk	.20	.20
230	A7	50c ocher & blk, bluish	.35	.35
231	A7	55c vio bl & car rose ('38)	.65	.55
232	A7	60c vio brn & blk, pnksh	.20	.20
233	A7	60c dp red ('26)	.35	.35
234	A7	65c gray lil & brn	.45	.45
235	A7	75c blue & black	.45	.45
236	A7	80c ind & dl vio ('38)	1.40	1.25
237	A7	85c brn org & brn	.85	.85
238	A7	90c brn red & cer ('27)	.65	.65
239	A8	1fr red brn & blk, bluish	.60	.60
240	A8	1fr blue ('26)	.50	.50
241	A8	1fr gray lil & grn ('28)	2.00	1.60
242	A8	1fr dk red & red org ('38)	.65	.50
243	A8	1.10fr vio & dk brn ('28)	3.00	3.00
244	A8	1.25fr mag & rose ('33)	1.10	1.10
245	A8	1.50fr bl & lt bl ('27)	.50	.50
246	A8	1.75fr bis & pink ('33)	6.50	3.75
247	A8	1.75fr vio bl & ultra ('38)	1.10	.85
248	A8	2fr bl blk & blk, bluish	.85	.85
249	A8	3fr bl grn & red org ('27)	1.10	1.10
250	A8	5fr red org & blk, bluish	1.60	1.60
251	A8	10fr bl grn & rose ('26)	1.90	1.90
252	A8	20fr brn red & blk, yel ('26)	2.00	2.00
		Nos. 216-252 (37)	32.50	28.70

For surcharges see #253, 301-302, B8-B9.

No. 240 Surcharged with New Value and Bars in Red

1926				
253	A8	1.25fr on 1fr lt bl	.45	.45

Common Design Types pictured following the introduction.

Colonial Exposition Issue
Common Design Types
Engr., "TOGO" Typo. in Black

1931, Apr. 13			Perf. 12½	
254	CD70	40c deep green	4.00	4.00
255	CD71	50c violet	4.00	4.00
256	CD72	90c red orange	4.00	4.00
257	CD73	1.50fr dull blue	4.00	4.00
		Nos. 254-257 (4)	16.00	16.00

Paris International Exposition Issue
Common Design Types

1937			Perf. 13	
258	CD74	20c deep violet	1.25	1.25
259	CD75	30c dark green	1.25	1.25
260	CD76	40c carmine rose	1.25	1.25
261	CD77	50c dark brown	1.25	1.25
262	CD78	90c red	1.25	1.25
263	CD79	1.50fr ultra	1.25	1.25
		Nos. 258-263 (6)	7.50	7.50

Colonial Arts Exhibition Issue
Souvenir Sheet
Common Design Type

1937			Imperf.	
264	CD77	3fr Prus bl & blk	5.25	6.50

Caillié Issue
Common Design Type

1939, Apr. 5			Perf. 12½x12	
265	CD81	90c org brn & org	.65	.65
266	CD81	2fr brt violet	.65	.65
267	CD81	2.25fr ultra & dk bl	.65	.65
		Nos. 265-267 (3)	1.95	1.95

New York World's Fair Issue
Common Design Type

1939, May 10				
268	CD82	1.25fr carmine lake	.75	.75
269	CD82	2.25fr ultra	.75	.75

Togolese Women
A9   A12

Mono River Bank
A10

Hunters
A11

1941		Engr.	Perf. 12½	
270	A9	2c brown vio	.20	.20
271	A9	3c yellow grn	.20	.20
272	A9	4c brown blk	.20	.20
273	A9	5c lilac rose	.20	.20
274	A9	10c light blue	.20	.20
275	A9	15c chestnut	.20	.20
276	A10	20c plum	.20	.20
277	A10	25c violet blue	.20	.20
278	A10	30c brown blk	.20	.20
279	A10	40c dk carmine	.20	.20
280	A10	45c dk green	.20	.20
281	A10	50c chestnut	.20	.20
282	A10	60c red violet	.45	.45
283	A11	70c black	.65	.65
284	A11	90c lt violet	1.00	1.00
285	A11	1fr yellow grn	.35	.35
286	A11	1.25fr cerise	.85	.85
287	A11	1.40fr orange brn	.50	.50
288	A11	1.60fr orange	.50	.50
289	A11	2fr lt ultra	.65	.65
290	A12	2.25fr ultra	1.00	1.00
291	A12	2.50fr lilac rose	.65	.65
292	A12	3fr brown vio	.65	.65
293	A12	5fr vermilion	.65	.65
294	A12	10fr rose violet	1.25	1.25
295	A12	20fr brown blk	1.90	1.90
		Nos. 270-295 (26)	13.45	13.45

For surcharges see Nos. 303-308, B7, B10.

Mono River Bank and Marshal Pétain
A12a

1941		Engr.	Perf. 12½x12	
296	A12a	1fr green		.45
297	A12a	2.50fr blue		.45

Nos. 296-297 were issued by the Vichy government in France, but were not placed on sale in Togo.
For surcharges, see Nos. B10D-B10E.

Types of 1941 Without "RF"

1942-44			Perf. 12½	
298	A9	10c blue green		.20
299	A9	15c yel brn & black		.50
300	A10	20c lilac brn & black		.65
300A	A11	1fr yellow grn		.75
300B	A11	1.50fr lilac & green		.50
300C	A12	3fr brown violet		.75
300D	A12	5fr red brown		.75
300E	A12	10fr rose violet		1.10
300F	A12	20fr black		1.25
		Nos. 298-300F (9)		6.45

Nos. 298-300F were issued by the Vichy government in France, but were not placed on sale in Togo.

Nos. 231, 238, 284 Surcharged with New Values in Various Colors

a

b

1943-44		Perf. 14x13½, 12½	Unwmk.	
301	A7(a)	1.50fr on 55c (Bk)	.65	.65
302	A7(a)	1.50fr on 90c (Bk)	.65	.65
303	A11(b)	3.50fr on 90c (Bk)	.50	.50

304	A11(b)	4fr on 90c (R)	.65	.65
305	A11(b)	5fr on 90c (Bl)	1.25	1.25
306	A11(b)	5.50fr on 90c (Br)	1.25	1.25
307	A11(b)	10fr on 90c (G)		
		('44)	1.25	1.25
308	A11(b)	20fr on 90c (R)	1.60	1.60
	Nos. 301-308 (8)		7.80	7.80

Catalogue values for unused stamps in this section, from this point to the end of the section, are for Never Hinged items.

Extracting Palm
Oil — A13

Hunter — A14

Cotton
Spinners — A15

Village of
Atakpamé
A16

Red-fronted Gazelles — A17

Houses of
the Cabrais
A18

1947, Oct. 6   Engr.   Perf. 12½

309	A13	10c dark red	.20	.20
310	A13	30c brt ultra	.20	.20
311	A13	50c bluish green	.20	.20
312	A14	60c lilac rose	.20	.20
313	A14	1fr chocolate	.35	.35
314	A14	1.20fr yellow grn	.45	.40
315	A15	1.50fr brown org	.45	.45
316	A15	2fr olive	.45	.45
317	A15	2.50fr gray blk	1.10	.90
318	A16	3fr slate	.50	.45
319	A16	3.60fr rose car	.75	.75
320	A16	4fr Prus green	.55	.35
321	A17	5fr black brn	1.25	.35
322	A17	6fr ultra	1.25	1.00
323	A17	10fr orange red	1.75	.35
324	A18	15fr dp yel grn	1.60	.50
325	A18	20fr grnsh black	1.60	.75
326	A18	25fr lilac rose	1.75	.75
	Nos. 309-326 (18)		14.60	8.60

Military Medal Issue
Common Design Type
Engr. & Typo.

1952, Dec. 1   Perf. 13

327	CD101	15fr multicolored	4.00	4.00

Gathering
Palm Nuts
A19

1954, Nov. 29   Engr.

328	A19	8fr vio & vio brn	1.00	.60
329	A19	15fr indigo & dk brn	1.25	.60

Goliath
Beetle — A20

1955, May 2

330	A20	8fr black & green	2.00	1.75

Intl. Exhibition for Wildlife Protection, Paris,
May 1955.

FIDES Issue
Common Design Type

Design: 15fr, Teacher and children planting
tree.

1956   Unwmk.   Perf. 13x12½

331	CD103	15fr dk vio brn & org brn	4.50	2.25

Republic

Woman
Holding
Flag — A21

1957, June 8   Engr.   Perf. 13

332	A21	15fr dk bl grn, sepia & red	.50	.20

Konkomba
Helmet — A22

Teak Forest
A23

Design: 4fr, 5fr, 6fr, 8fr, 10fr, Buffon's kob.

1957, Oct.   Unwmk.

333	A22	30c violet & claret	.20	.20
334	A22	50c indigo & blue	.20	.20
335	A22	1fr pur & lil rose	.20	.20
336	A22	2fr dk brn & olive	.20	.20
337	A22	3fr black & green	.20	.20
338	A22	4fr blue & gray	.40	.20
339	A22	5fr bluish gray & mag	.40	.20
340	A22	6fr crim rose & bl gray	.45	.20
341	A22	8fr bluish gray & vio	.45	.25
342	A22	10fr grn & red brn	.45	.25
343	A23	15fr multicolored	.30	.25
344	A23	20fr violet, mar & org	.35	.20
345	A23	25fr indigo & bis brn	.45	.25
346	A23	40fr dk brn, ol & dk grn	.75	.35
	Nos. 333-346 (14)		5.00	3.10

See Nos. 350-363.

Flags, Dove and UN
Emblem — A24

1958, Dec. 10   Engr.   Perf. 13

347	A24	20fr dk grn & rose red	.20	.20

Universal Declaration of Human Rights,
10th anniversary.

Flower Issue
Common Design Type

Designs: 5fr, Flower of Bombax tree
(kapok). 20fr, Tectona grandis (teakwood)
flower, horiz.

Perf. 12x12½, 12½x12

1959, Jan. 15   Photo.   Unwmk.

348	CD104	5fr dp bl, rose & grn	.20	.20
349	CD104	20fr black, yel & grn	.20	.20

Types of 1957 Inscribed: "Republique
du Togo"

1959, Jan. 15   Engr.   Perf. 13
Designs as Before

350	A22	30c ultra & gray	.20	.20
351	A22	50c org & brt grn	.20	.20
352	A22	1fr red lil & lt ol grn	.20	.20
353	A22	2fr olive & bl grn	.20	.20
354	A22	3fr vio & rose car	.20	.20
355	A22	4fr lil rose & pale pur	.20	.20
356	A22	5fr green & brown	.20	.20
357	A22	6fr ultra & gray bl	.20	.20
358	A22	8fr sl grn & bis	.20	.20
359	A22	10fr vio & lt brn	.20	.20
360	A23	15fr dk brn, bis & cl	.20	.20
361	A23	20fr blk, bl grn & brn	.20	.20
362	A23	25fr sep, red brn, ol & vio	.25	.20
363	A23	40fr dk grn, org brn & bl	.25	.20
	Nos. 350-363 (14)		2.90	2.80

"Five Continents,"
Ceiling Painting,
Palais des
Nations,
Geneva — A25

1959, Oct. 24   Engr.   Perf. 12½
Centers in Dark Ultramarine

364	A25	15fr brown	.20	.20
365	A25	20fr purple	.20	.20
366	A25	25fr dark orange	.20	.20
367	A25	40fr dark green	.30	.25
368	A25	60fr carmine rose	.35	.30
	Nos. 364-368 (5)		1.25	1.15

Issued for United Nations Day, Oct. 24.

Skier
A26

Bicyclist
A27

Sports: 50c, Ice Hockey. 1fr, Tobogganing.
15fr, Discus thrower, vert. 20fr, Boxing, vert.
25fr, Runner.

1960   Unwmk.   Perf. 13

369	A26	30c sl grn, car & bl grn	.20	.20
370	A26	50c red & black	.20	.20
371	A26	1fr red, blk & emer	.20	.20
372	A27	10fr brown, ultra & sl	.20	.20
373	A27	15fr dk red brn & grn	.20	.20

374	A27	20fr dk grn, gldn brn & brn	.25	.20
375	A27	25fr orange, mag & brn	.30	.20
	Nos. 369-375 (7)		1.55	1.40

8th Winter Olympic Games, Squaw Valley,
Calif. (Nos. 369-371); 17th Olympic Games,
Rome (Nos. 372-375).

Prime Minister
Sylvanus Olympio
and Togo
Flag — A28

1960, Apr. 27   Litho.
**Center in Green, Red, Yellow &
Brown**

376	A28	30c black & buff	.20	.20
377	A28	50c brown & buff	.20	.20
378	A28	1fr lilac & buff	.20	.20
379	A28	10fr blue & buff	.20	.20
380	A28	20fr red & buff	.20	.20
381	A28	25fr green & buff	.20	.20
	Nos. 376-381 (6)		1.20	1.20

Proclamation of Togo's full independence,
Apr. 27, 1960.
See Nos. C31-C33.

Flags of
"Big Four,"
and British
Flag — A29

1960, May 21   Perf. 14x14½

382	A29	50c shown	.20	.20
383	A29	1fr USSR	.20	.20
384	A29	20fr France	.20	.20
385	A29	25fr US	.20	.20
	Nos. 382-385 (4)		.80	.80

Summit Conference of France, Great Britain, United States and USSR, Paris, May 16.

Flag of
Togo and
UN
Emblem
A30

1961, Jan. 6   Perf. 14½x15
Flag in red, olive green & yellow

386	A30	30c red	.20	.20
387	A30	50c brown	.20	.20
388	A30	1fr ultramarine	.20	.20
389	A30	10fr maroon	.20	.20
390	A30	25fr black	.20	.20
391	A30	30fr violet	.20	.20
	Nos. 386-391 (6)		1.20	1.20

Togo's admission to United Nations.

Crowned
Cranes over
Map — A31

Augustino de
Souza — A32

1961, Apr. 1   Perf. 14½x15

392	A31	1fr multicolored	.20	.20
393	A31	10fr multicolored	.20	.20
394	A31	25fr multicolored	.25	.20
395	A31	30fr multicolored	.35	.20
	Nos. 392-395 (4)		1.00	.80

1961, Apr. 27   Litho.   Perf. 15

396	A32	50c yellow, red & blk	.20	.20
397	A32	1fr emerald, brn & blk	.20	.20
398	A32	10fr grnsh bl, vio & blk	.20	.20
399	A32	25fr salmon, grn & blk	.20	.20
400	A32	30fr rose lil, bl & blk	.20	.20
	Nos. 396-400 (5)		1.00	1.00

1st anniv. of independence; "Papa" Augustino de Souza, leader of the independence
movement.

Daniel C. Beard
A33

Designs: 1fr, Lord Baden-Powell. 10fr, Togolese Scout and emblems. 25fr, Togolese Scout and flag, vert. 30fr, Symbolic tents and fire, vert. 100fr, Three hands of different races giving Scout sign.

1961, Oct. 7   Photo.   Perf. 13
401 A33 50c brt rose & grn   .20   .20
402 A33 1fr dp violet & car   .20   .20
403 A33 10fr dk gray & brn   .20   .20
404 A33 25fr multicolored   .20   .20
405 A33 30fr grn, red & org brn   .25   .20
406 A33 100fr rose car & bl   .60   .25
     Nos. 401-406 (6)   1.65 1.25

Togolese Boy Scouts; 20th anniv. of the deaths of Daniel C. Beard and Lord Baden-Powell.

Four imperf. souvenir sheets each contain the six stamps, Nos. 401-406. Two sheets have a solid background of bright yellow, two a background of pale grayish brown. One yellow and one brown sheet have simulated perforations around the stamps. Size: 120x145mm. "REPUBLIQUE DU TOGO" is inscribed in white on bottom sheet margin. Value, each $3.

Plane, Ship and Part of Map of Africa — A34

Part of Map of Africa and: 25fr, Electric train and power mast. 30fr, Tractor and oil derricks. 85fr, Microscope and atomic symbol.

1961, Oct. 24   Litho.
Black Inscriptions; Map in Ocher
407 A34 20fr vio bl, org & yel   .20   .20
408 A34 25fr gray, org & yel   .20   .20
409 A34 30fr dk red, yel & org   .25   .20
410 A34 85fr blue, yel & org   .45   .20
     a. Souvenir sheet of 4   1.60 1.40
     Nos. 407-410 (4)   1.10   .80

UN Economic Commission for Africa. No. 410a contains one each of Nos. 407-410, imperf., printed without separating margin between the individual stamps to show a complete map of Africa.

Children Dancing around Globe — A35   Cmdr. Alan B. Shepard — A36

UNICEF Emblem, children and globe.

1961, Dec. 9   Unwmk.   Perf. 13½
Black Inscription; Multicolored Design
411 A35 1fr ultra   .20   .20
412 A35 10fr red brown   .20   .20
413 A35 20fr lilac   .20   .20
414 A35 25fr gray   .20   .20
415 A35 30fr bright blue   .25   .20
416 A35 85fr deep lilac   .45   .25
     Nos. 411-416 (6)   1.50 1.25

UNICEF, 15th anniv.
Nos. 411-416 assembled in two rows show the globe and children of various races dancing around it.

1962, Feb. 24   Perf. 15x14

Design: 1fr, 30fr, Yuri A. Gagarin.

417 A36 50c green   .20   .20
418 A36 1fr carmine rose   .20   .20
419 A36 25fr blue   .20   .20
420 A36 30fr purple   .20   .20
     Nos. 417-420 (4)   .80   .80

Astronauts of 1961.

Issued in sheets of 50 and in miniature sheets of 12 stamps plus four central labels showing photographs of Alan B. Shepard (US), Virgil I. Grissom (US), Yuri A. Gagarin (USSR), Gherman S. Titov (USSR).

No. 417 Surcharged: "100F COL. JOHN H. GLENN USA VOL ORBITAL 20 FEVRIER 1962" and Bars in Black
1962, Apr. 7
421 A36 100fr on 50c green   .75   .50
     a. Carmine surcharge   .75   .50

Orbital flight of Lt. Col. John H. Glenn, Jr., US, Feb. 20, 1962.

Independence Monument, Lomé — A37   Woman Carrying Fruit Basket — A38

1962, Apr. 27   Litho.   Perf. 13½x14
422 A37 50c multicolored   .20   .20
423 A38 1fr green & pink   .20   .20
424 A37 5fr multicolored   .20   .20
425 A38 20fr purple & yel   .20   .20
426 A37 25fr multicolored   .20   .20
427 A38 30fr red & yellow   .20   .20
     a. Souv. sheet of 3, #424-425, 427, imperf.   .35   .35
     Nos. 422-427 (6)   1.20 1.20

2nd anniversary of Togo's independence.

Malaria Eradication Emblem A39

1962, June 2   Perf. 13½x13
Multicolored Design
428 A39 10fr yellow green   .20   .20
429 A39 25fr pale lilac   .20   .20
430 A39 30fr ocher   .20   .20
431 A39 85fr light blue   .40   .20
     Nos. 428-431 (4)   1.00   .80

WHO drive to eradicate malaria.

Capitol, Pres. John F. Kennedy and Pres. Sylvanus Olympio — A40

1962, July 4   Unwmk.   Perf. 13
Inscription and Portraits in Slate Green
432 A40 50c yellow   .20   .20
433 A40 1fr blue   .20   .20
434 A40 2fr vermilion   .20   .20
435 A40 5fr lilac   .20   .20
436 A40 25fr pale violet   .45   .20
437 A40 100fr brt green   1.75   .80
     a. Souvenir sheet, imperf.   5.75 5.75
     Nos. 432-437 (6)   3.00 1.80

Visit of Pres. Sylvanus Olympio of Togo to the US, Mar. 1962.

Mail Coach and Stamps of 1897 — A41

50c, Mail ship, stamps of 1900. 1fr, Mail train, stamps of 1915. 10fr, Motorcycle truck, stamp of 1924. 25fr, Mail truck, stamp of 1941. 30fr, DC-3, stamp of 1947.

1963, Jan. 12   Photo.   Perf. 13
438 A41 30c multicolored   .20   .20
439 A41 50c multicolored   .20   .20
440 A41 1fr multicolored   .20   .20
441 A41 10fr vio, dp org & blk   .20   .20
442 A41 25fr dk red brn, blk & yel grn   .20   .20
443 A41 30fr ol brn & lil rose   .20   .20
     Nos. 438-443,C34 (7)   1.80 1.50

65th anniv. of Togolese mail service.
For souvenir sheet see No. C34a.

Hands Reaching for FAO Emblem A42

1963, Mar. 21   Perf. 14
444 A42 50c bl, org & dk brn   .20   .20
445 A42 1fr ol grn, org & dk brn   .20   .20
446 A42 25fr brn, dk brn & org   .20   .20
447 A42 30fr vio, dk brn & org   .25   .20
     Nos. 444-447 (4)   .85   .80

FAO "Freedom from Hunger" campaign.

Togolese Flag and Lomé Harbor — A43

1963, Apr. 27   Litho.   Perf. 13x12½
Flag in Red, Green and Yellow
448 A43 50c red brn & blk   .20   .20
449 A43 1fr dk car rose & blk   .20   .20
450 A43 25fr dull bl & blk   .20   .20
451 A43 30fr bister & blk   .25   .20
     Nos. 448-451 (4)   .85   .80

3rd anniversary of independence.

Centenary Emblem — A44

1963, June 1   Photo.   Perf. 14
Flag in Red, Olive Green, Yellow
452 A44 25fr blue, blk & red   .20   .20
453 A44 30fr dull grn, blk & red   .25   .20

International Red Cross centenary.

Lincoln, Broken Fetters, Maps of Africa and US. — A45

1963, Oct.   Unwmk.   Perf. 13x14
454 A45 50c multicolored   .20   .20
455 A45 1fr multicolored   .20   .20
456 A45 25fr multicolored   .20   .20
     Nos. 454-456,C35 (4)   1.25   .90

Centenary of the emancipation of the American slaves. See souvenir sheet No. C35a.
For overprints see Nos. 473-475, C41.

UN Emblem and "15" — A46   Hibiscus — A47

1963, Dec. 10   Photo.   Perf. 14x13
457 A46 50c ultra, dk bl & rose red   .20   .20
458 A46 1fr yel grn, dk bl & rose red   .20   .20
459 A46 25fr lil, dk bl & rose red   .20   .20
460 A46 85fr gold, dk bl & rose red   .65   .25
     Nos. 457-460 (4)   1.25   .85

15th anniv. of the Universal Declaration of Human Rights.

1964   Perf. 14

Designs: 50c, Orchid. 2fr, Butterfly. 5fr, Hinged tortoise. 8fr, Ball python. 10fr, Bunea alcinoe (moth). 20fr, Octopus. 25fr, John Dory (fish). 30fr, French angelfish. 40fr, Hippopotamus. 60fr, Bohor reedbuck. 85fr, Anubis baboon.

Size: 22½x31mm
461 A47 50c multicolored   .20   .20
462 A47 1fr yellow, car & grn   .20   .20
463 A47 2fr lilac, yel & blk   .20   .20
464 A47 5fr gray & multi   .20   .20
465 A47 8fr cit, red brn & blk   .20   .20
466 A47 10fr multicolored   .20   .20
467 A47 20fr dl bl, yel & brn   .20   .20
468 A47 25fr dl bl, grn & yel   .25   .20
469 A47 30fr multicolored   .25   .20
470 A47 40fr grn, red brn & blk   .30   .20
471 A47 60fr grnsh bl & red brn   .45   .20
472 A47 85fr lt grn, brn & org   .65   .25
     Nos. 461-472 (12)   3.25 2.45

See Nos. 511-515, C36-C40, J56-J63.

Nos. 454-456 Overprinted Diagonally: "En Mémoire de / JOHN F. KENNEDY / 1917-1963"
1964, Mar. 7   Perf. 13x14
473 A45 50c multicolored   .20   .20
474 A45 1fr multicolored   .20   .20
475 A45 25fr multicolored   .20   .20
     Nos. 473-475 (3)   .60   .60

Issued in memory of John F. Kennedy.
See No. C41 and note on souvenir sheets following it.

Isis of Kalabsha A48

Designs: 25fr, Head of Ramses II. 30fr, Colonnade of Birth House at Philae.

1964, Mar. 8   Litho.   Perf. 14
476 A48 20fr blk, pale grn & red   .20   .20
477 A48 25fr black & lil rose   .20   .20
478 A48 30fr black & citron   .25   .20
     a. Souvenir sheet of 3   .65   .65
     Nos. 476-478 (3)   .65   .60

UNESCO world campaign to save historic monuments in Nubia. No. 478a contains three imperf. stamps similar to Nos. 476-478 with simulated perforations.

Phosphate Mine, Kpeme A49

25fr, Phosphate plant, Kpeme. 60fr, Phosphate train. 85fr, Loading ship with phosphate.

1964, Apr. 27   Unwmk.   Perf. 14

479	A49	5fr brown & bis brn	.20 .20
480	A49	25fr dk pur & brn car	.20 .20
481	A49	60fr dk green & olive	.45 .20
482	A49	85fr vio blk & Prus bl	.65 .25
		Nos. 479-482 (4)	1.50 .85

Fourth anniversary of independence.

African Breaking Slavery Chain, and Map — A50

1964, May 25   Photo.   Perf. 14x13

483	A50	5fr dp orange & brn	.20 .20
484	A50	25fr olive grn & brn	.20 .20
485	A50	85fr rose car & brn	.50 .20
		Nos. 483-485,C42 (4)	1.55 .90

1st anniv. of the meeting of African heads of state at Addis Ababa.

Pres. Nicolas Grunitzky and Butterfly A51

1964, Aug. 18   Litho.   Perf. 14

486	A51	1fr shown	.20 .20
487	A51	5fr Dove	.20 .20
488	A51	25fr Flower	.20 .20
489	A51	45fr as 1fr	.35 .20
490	A51	85fr Flower	.65 .25
		Nos. 486-490 (5)	1.60 1.05

National Union and Reconciliation.

Soccer A52

1964, Oct.   Photo.   Perf. 14

491	A52	1fr shown	.20 .20
492	A52	5fr Runner	.20 .20
493	A52	25fr Discus	.20 .20
494	A52	45fr as 1fr	.25 .20
		Nos. 491-494,C43 (5)	1.60 1.10

18th Olympic Games, Tokyo, Oct. 10-25. For souvenir sheet see No. C43a.

Cooperation Issue
Common Design Type

1964, Nov. 7   Engr.   Perf. 13

495	CD119	25fr mag, dk brn & ol bis	.20 .20

Dirigible and Balloons — A53

25fr, 45fr, Otto Lilienthal's glider, 1894; Wright Brothers' plane, 1903; Boeing 707.

1964, Dec. 5   Photo.   Perf. 14x13

496	A53	5fr org lil & grn	.20 .20
497	A53	10fr brt grn, dl bl & dk red	.20 .20
498	A53	25fr bl, vio bl & org	.20 .20

499	A53	45fr brt pink, vio bl & grn	.25 .20
a.		Souv. sheet of 4	1.25 1.25
		Nos. 496-499,C44 (5)	1.65 1.10

Inauguration of the national airline, Air Togo. #499a contains 4 imperf. stamps similar to #497-499 and #C44 with simulated perfs.

Orbiting Geophysical Observatory and Mariner — A54

Space Satellites: 15fr, 25fr, Tiros, Telstar and Orbiting Solar Observatory. 20fr, 50fr, Nimbus, Syncom and Relay.

1964, Dec. 12   Litho.   Perf. 14

500	A54	10fr dp rose, bl & yel	.20 .20
501	A54	15fr multi	.20 .20
502	A54	20fr yel, grn & vio	.20 .20
503	A54	25fr multi	.20 .20
504	A54	45fr brt grn, dk bl & yel	.30 .20
505	A54	50fr yel, grn & org	.40 .20
a.		Souv. sheet, #502-505, imperf.	1.00 1.00
		Nos. 500-505 (6)	1.50 1.20

Intl. Quiet Sun Year.

Togo Olympic Stamps Printed in Israel — A55

Arms of Israel and Togo — A56

Pres. Nicolas Grunitzky of Togo and: 20fr, Church of the Mount of Beatitudes. 45fr, Ruins of Synagogue at Capernaum.

Perf. 13½x14½, 14x13½

1964, Dec. 26   Photo.

506	A55	5fr rose violet	.20 .20
507	A56	20fr grnsh bl, grn & dl pur	.20 .20
508	A56	25fr red & bluish grn	.20 .20
509	A56	45fr dl yel, ol & dl pur	.45 .25
510	A56	85fr mag & bluish grn	.35 .20
a.		Souv. sheet of 4, imperf.	2.50 2.50
		Nos. 506-510 (5)	1.40 1.05

Israel-Togo friendship.

Type of Regular Issue, 1964

1965, June   Unwmk.   Perf. 14

Designs: 3fr, Morpho aega butterfly. 4fr, Scorpion. 6fr, Bird-of-paradise flower. 15fr, Flap-necked chameleon. 45fr, Ring-tailed palm civet.

Size: 23x31mm

511	A47	3fr bister & multi	.20 .20
512	A47	4fr org & bluish blk	.20 .20
513	A47	6fr multi	.20 .20
514	A47	15fr brt pink, yel & brn	.20 .20
515	A47	45fr dl grn, org & brn	.30 .20
		Nos. 511-515 (5)	1.10 1.00

Syncom Satellite, Radar Station and ITU Emblem — A57

1965, June   Perf. 13x14

516	A57	10fr Prus blue	.20 .20
517	A57	20fr olive bister	.20 .20
518	A57	25fr bright blue	.20 .20
519	A57	45fr crimson	.30 .20
520	A57	50fr green	.35 .20
		Nos. 516-520 (5)	1.25 1.00

ITU, centenary.

Abraham Lincoln — A58

Discus Thrower, Flags of Togo and Congo — A59

1965, June 26   Photo.   Perf. 13x14

521	A58	1fr magenta	.20 .20
522	A58	5fr dull green	.20 .20
523	A58	20fr brown	.20 .20
524	A58	25fr slate	.20 .20
		Nos. 521-524,C45 (5)	1.70 1.10

Death cent. of Abraham Lincoln. For souvenir sheet see No. C45a.

1965, July   Unwmk.   Perf. 14x13

Flags and: 10fr, Javelin thrower. 15fr, Handball player. 25fr, Runner.

Flags in Red, Yellow and Green

525	A59	5fr deep magenta	.20 .20
526	A59	10fr dark blue	.20 .20
527	A59	15fr dark green	.20 .20
528	A59	25fr dark purple	.20 .20
		Nos. 525-528,C46 (5)	1.60 1.10

1st African Games, Brazzaville, July 18-25.

Winston Churchill and "V" — A60

Stalin, Roosevelt and Churchill at Yalta — A61

Perf. 13½x14, 14x13½

1965, Aug. 7   Photo.

529	A60	5fr dull green	.20 .20
530	A61	10fr brt vio & gray	.20 .20
531	A60	20fr brown	.20 .20
532	A61	45fr Prus bl & gray	.35 .20
		Nos. 529-532,C47 (5)	1.75 1.10

Sir Winston Spencer Churchill (1874-1965), British statesman and World War II leader.

Unisphere and New York Skyline — A62

10fr, Togolese dancers & drummer, Unisphere. 50fr, Michelangelo's Pieta & Unisphere.

1965, Aug. 28   Photo.   Perf. 14

533	A62	5fr grnsh bl & vio blk	.20 .20
534	A62	10fr yel grn & dk brn	.20 .20
535	A62	25fr brn org & dk grn	.20 .20
536	A62	50fr vio & sl grn	.30 .20
537	A62	85fr rose red & brn	.65 .30
a.		Souvenir sheet of 2	1.00 1.00
		Nos. 533-537 (5)	1.55 1.10

New York World's Fair, 1964-65. No. 537a contains two imperf. stamps similar to Nos. 536-537 with simulated perforations.

"Constructive Cooperation" and Olive Branch — A63

Designs: 25fr, 40fr, Hands of various races holding globe and olive branch. 85fr, Handclasp, olive branch and globe.

1965, Sept. 25   Unwmk.   Perf. 14

538	A63	5fr violet, lt bl & org	.20 .20
539	A63	15fr brn, org & gray	.20 .20
540	A63	25fr blue & orange	.20 .20
541	A63	40fr dp car, gray & org	.30 .20
542	A63	85fr green & org	.60 .30
		Nos. 538-542 (5)	1.50 1.10

International Cooperation Year.

Major White and Gemini 4 — A64

25fr, Lt. Col. Alexei Leonov and Voskhod 2.

1965, Nov. 25   Photo.   Perf. 13½x14

543	A64	25fr dp bl & brt car rose	.20 .20
544	A64	50fr green & brown	.35 .20

"Walks in Space" of Lt. Col. Alexei Leonov (USSR), and Major Edward H. White (US). Printed in sheets of 12 with ornamental borders.

For overprints and surcharges see Nos. 563-566.

Adlai E. Stevenson and UN Headquarters — A65

5fr, "ONU" and doves. 10fr, UN emblem and headquarters. 20fr, "ONU" and orchids.

1965, Dec. 15   Perf. 14x13½
545	A65	5fr dk brn, yel & lt bl		
546	A65	10fr org, dk bl & grn	.20	.20
547	A65	20fr dk grn, yel grn & org brn	.20	.20
548	A65	25fr brt yel, dk bl & bluish grn	.20	.20
		Nos. 545-548,C48 (5)	1.80	1.20

UN, 20th anniv.; Adlai E. Stevenson (1900-1965), US ambassador to the UN.

Pope Paul VI, Plane and UN Emblem — A66

15fr, 30fr, Pope addressing UN General Assembly & UN emblem, vert. 20fr, Pope, NYC skyline with UN Headquarters.

1966, Mar. 5   Litho.   Perf. 12
549	A66	5fr blue & multi	.20	.20
550	A66	15fr lt violet & multi	.20	.20
551	A66	20fr bister & multi	.20	.20
552	A66	30fr lt ultra & multi	.20	.20
		Nos. 549-552,C49-C50 (6)	1.80	1.20

Visit of Pope Paul VI to the UN, New York City, Oct. 4, 1965.

Surgical Operation and Togolese Flag — A67

Togolese Flag and: 10fr, 30fr, Blood transfusion. 45fr, Profiles of African man and woman.

1966, May 7   Litho.   Perf. 12
553	A67	5fr multicolored	.20	.20
554	A67	10fr multicolored	.20	.20
555	A67	15fr multicolored	.20	.20
556	A67	30fr multicolored	.20	.20
557	A67	45fr multicolored	.30	.20
		Nos. 553-557,C51 (6)	2.00	1.30

Togolese Red Cross, 7th anniversary.

Talisman Roses and WHO Headquarters, Geneva — A68

Various flowers & WHO Headquarters.

1966, May   Litho.   Perf. 12
558	A68	5fr lt yel grn & multi	.20	.20
559	A68	10fr pale pink & multi	.20	.20
560	A68	15fr dull yel & multi	.20	.20
561	A68	20fr pale gray & multi	.20	.20
562	A68	30fr tan & multi	.20	.20
		Nos. 558-562,C52-C53 (7)	2.10	1.40

Inauguration of WHO Headquarters, Geneva.

Nos. 543-544 Overprinted or Surcharged in Red

1966, July 11   Photo.   Perf. 13½x14
563	A64	50fr Envolée Surveyor 1	.30	.20
564	A64	50fr Envolée Gemini 9	.30	.20
a.		Pair, #563-564	.60	.25
565	A64	100fr on 25fr Envolée Luna 9	.75	.20
566	A64	100fr on 25fr Envolée Venus 3	.75	.20
a.		Pair, #565-566	1.50	.40
		Nos. 563-566 (4)	2.10	.80

US and USSR achievements in Space.

Wood Carver — A69

Togolese Dancer — A70

Arts and Crafts: 10fr, Basket maker. 15fr, Woman weaver. 30fr, Woman potter.

1966, Sept.   Photo.   Perf. 13x14
567	A69	5fr blue, yel & dk brn	.20	.20
568	A69	10fr emer, org & dk brn	.20	.20
569	A69	15fr ver, yel & dk brn	.20	.20
570	A69	30fr lilac, dk brn & yel	.20	.20
		Nos. 567-570,C55-C56 (6)	2.00	1.20

1966, Nov.   Photo.   Perf. 13x14

Designs: 5fr, Togolese man. 20fr, Woman dancer from North Togo holding branches. 25fr, Male dancer. 30fr, Male dancer from North Togo with horned helmet. 45fr, Drummer.

571	A70	5fr emerald & multi	.20	.20
572	A70	10fr dl yel & multi	.20	.20
573	A70	20fr lt ultra & multi	.20	.20
574	A70	25fr dp orange & multi	.20	.20
575	A70	30fr red violet & multi	.20	.20
576	A70	45fr blue & multi	.25	.20
		Nos. 571-576,C57-C58 (8)	2.15	1.60

Soccer Players and Jules Rimet Cup — A71

Various Soccer Scenes.

1966, Dec. 14   Photo.   Perf. 14x13
577	A71	5fr blue, brn & red	.20	.20
578	A71	10fr brick red & multi	.20	.20
579	A71	20fr ol, brn & dk grn	.20	.20
580	A71	25fr vio, brn & org	.20	.20
581	A71	30fr ocher & multi	.20	.20
582	A71	45fr emerald, brn & mag	.25	.20
		Nos. 577-582,C59-C60 (8)	2.15	1.60

England's victory in the World Soccer Cup Championship, Wembley, July 30. For souvenir sheet see No. C60a.

African Mouthbreeder and Sailboat — A72

Designs: 10fr, Yellow jack and trawler. 15fr, Banded distichodus and seiner. 25fr, Jewelfish and galley. 30fr, like 5fr.

1967, Jan. 14   Photo.   Perf. 14
Fish in Natural Colors
583	A72	5fr lt ultra & blk	.20	.20
584	A72	10fr brn org & brn	.20	.20
585	A72	15fr brt rose & dk bl	.20	.20
586	A72	25fr olive & blk	.20	.20
587	A72	30fr grnsh bl & blk	.25	.20
		Nos. 583-587,C61-C62 (7)	2.35	1.50

African Boy and Greyhound — A73

UNICEF Emblem and: 10fr, Boy and Irish setter. 20fr, Girl and doberman.

1967, Feb. 11   Photo.   Perf. 14x13½
588	A73	5fr orange, plum & blk	.20	.20
589	A73	10fr yel grn, red brn & dk grn	.20	.20
590	A73	15fr brt rose, brn & blk	.20	.20
591	A73	20fr bl, vio bl & blk	.20	.20
592	A73	30fr ol, sl grn & blk	.20	.20
		Nos. 588-592,C63-C64 (7)	2.05	1.45

UNICEF, 20th anniv. (in 1966).

French A-1 Satellite — A74

5fr, Diamant rocket, vert. 15fr, Fr-1 satellite, vert. 20fr, 40fr, D-1 satellite. 25fr, A-1 satellite.

Perf. 14x13½, 13½x14
1967, Mar. 18   Photo.
593	A74	5fr multi	.20	.20
594	A74	10fr multi	.20	.20
595	A74	15fr multi	.20	.20
596	A74	20fr multi	.20	.20
597	A74	25fr multi	.20	.20
598	A74	40fr multi	.25	.20
		Nos. 593-598,C65-C66 (8)	2.50	1.65

French achievements in space.

Johann Sebastian Bach and Organ — A75

UNESCO Emblem and: 10fr, Ludwig van Beethoven, violin and clarinet. 15f, Duke Ellington, saxophone, trumpet, drums. 20fr, Claude A. Debussy, piano and harp. 30fr, like 15fr.

1967, Apr. 15   Photo.   Perf. 14x13½
599	A75	5fr org & multi	.20	.20
600	A75	10fr multi	.20	.20
601	A75	15fr multi	.20	.20
602	A75	20fr lt bl & multi	.20	.20
603	A75	30fr lil & multi	.20	.20
		Nos. 599-603,C67-C68 (7)	2.10	1.40

20th anniv. (in 1966) of UNESCO.

EXPO Emblem, British Pavilion and Day Lilies — A76

10fr, French pavilion, roses. 30fr, African village, bird-of-paradise flower.

1967, May 30   Photo.   Perf. 14
604	A76	5fr brt pink & multi	.20	.20
605	A76	10fr dull org & multi	.20	.20
606	A76	30fr blue & multi	.20	.20
		Nos. 604-606,C69-C72 (7)	2.70	1.55

EXPO '67 Intl. Exhibition, Montreal, Apr. 28-Oct. 27.

For overprints see Nos. 628-630, C86-C89.

Lions Emblem — A77

20fr, 45fr, Lions emblem and flowers.

1967, July 29   Photo.   Perf. 13x14
607	A77	10fr yellow & multi	.20	.20
608	A77	20fr multicolored	.20	.20
609	A77	30fr green & multi	.25	.20
610	A77	45fr blue & multi	.35	.20
		Nos. 607-610 (4)	1.00	.80

50th anniversary of Lions International.

Montagu's Harriers — A78

5fr, Bohor reedbucks. 15fr, Zebras. 20fr, 30fr, Marsh harriers. 25fr, Leopard.

1967, Aug. 19   Photo.   Perf. 14x13½
611	A78	5fr lilac & org brn	.20	.20
612	A78	10fr dk red, yel & dl bl	.20	.20
613	A78	15fr grn, blk & lil	.20	.20
614	A78	20fr dk brn, yel & dl bl	.20	.20
615	A78	25fr brn, ol & yel	.20	.20
616	A78	30fr vio, yel & dl bl	.20	.20
		Nos. 611-616,C79-C80 (8)	2.25	1.60

Stamp Auction and Togo Nos. 16 and C42 — A79

10fr, 45fr, Exhibition, #67 (British) & 520. 15fr, 30fr, Stamp store, #230. 20fr, Stamp packet vending machine, #545.

1967, Oct. 14   Photo.   Perf. 14x13
Stamps on Stamps in Original Colors

617	A79	5fr purple	.20	.20
618	A79	10fr dk brown	.20	.20
619	A79	15fr deep blue	.20	.20
620	A79	20fr slate green	.25	.20
621	A79	30fr red brown	.35	.20
622	A79	45fr Prus blue	.50	.20
		Nos. 617-622,C82-C83 (8)	4.00	1.85

70th anniv. of the 1st Togolese stamps. For souvenir sheet see No. C82a.
See Nos. 853-855, C205.

Monetary Union Issue
Common Design Type

1967, Nov. 4   Engr.   Perf. 13

623	CD125	30fr dk bl, vio bl & brt grn	.25	.20

Broad Jump, Summer Olympics Emblem and View of Mexico City — A80

15fr, Ski jump, Winter Olympics emblem, ski lift. 30fr, Runners, Summer Olympics emblem, view of Mexico City. 45fr, Bobsledding, Winter Olympics emblem, ski lift.

1967, Dec. 2   Photo.   Perf. 13x14

624	A80	5fr orange & multi	.20	.20
625	A80	15fr multicolored	.20	.20
626	A80	30fr multicolored	.20	.20
627	A80	45fr multicolored	.25	.20
		Nos. 624-627,C84-C85 (6)	2.10	1.30

1968 Olympic Games. For souvenir sheet see No. C85a.

Nos. 604-606 Overprinted: "JOURNEE NATIONALE / DU TOGO / 29 SEPTEMBRE 1967"

1967, Dec.   Perf. 14

628	A76	5fr multicolored	.20	.20
629	A76	10fr multicolored	.20	.20
630	A76	30fr blue & multi	.25	.20
		Nos. 628-630,C86-C89 (7)	3.55	1.60

National Day, Sept. 29, 1967.

The Gleaners, by François Millet and Phosphate Works, Benin — A81

Industrialization of Togo: 20fr, 45fr, 90fr, The Weaver at the Loom, by Vincent van Gogh, and textile plant, Dadia.

1968, Jan.   Photo.   Perf. 14

631	A81	10fr olive & multi	.20	.20
632	A81	20fr multicolored	.20	.20
633	A81	30fr brown & multi	.25	.20
634	A81	45fr multicolored	.30	.20
635	A81	60fr dk blue & multi	.45	.20
636	A81	90fr multicolored	.70	.25
		Nos. 631-636 (6)	2.10	1.25

Togolese Women Brewing Beer — A82

The Beer Drinkers, by Edouard Manet — A83

Design: 45fr, Modern beer bottling plant.

1968, Mar. 26   Litho.   Perf. 14

637	A82	20fr emerald & multi	.20	.20
638	A83	30fr dk car & multi	.25	.20
639	A82	45fr orange & multi	.30	.20
		Nos. 637-639 (3)	.75	.60

Publicity for local beer industry.

Symbolic Water Cycle, Flower and Cogwheels A84

1968, Apr. 6

640	A84	30fr multicolored	.20	.20

Hydrological Decade (UNESCO), 1965-74. See No. C90.

Viking Ship and Portuguese Brigantine — A85

10fr, Fulton's steamship and modern steamship. 20fr, Harbor activities and map of Africa.

1968, Apr. 26   Photo.   Perf. 14x13½

641	A85	5fr brt green & multi	.20	.20
642	A85	10fr dp orange & multi	.20	.20
643	A85	20fr green & multi	.20	.20
644	A85	30fr yel grn & multi	.20	.20
		Nos. 641-644,C91-C92 (6)	1.90	1.20

Inauguration of Lomé Harbor.

Adenauer and 1968 Europa Emblem — A86

1968, May 25   Photo.   Perf. 14

645	A86	90fr olive grn & brn org	.60	.20

Konrad Adenauer (1876-1967), chancellor of West Germany (1949-63).

Adam and Eve Expelled from Paradise, by Michelangelo — A87

Paintings: 20fr, The Anatomy Lesson of Dr. Tulp, by Rembrandt. 30fr, The Anatomy Lesson, by Rembrandt (detail). 45fr, Jesus Healing the Sick, by Raphael.

1968, June 22   Photo.   Perf. 14

646	A87	15fr crimson & multi	.20	.20
647	A87	20fr multicolored	.20	.20
648	A87	30fr green & multi	.20	.20
649	A87	45fr multicolored	.20	.20
		Nos. 646-649,C93-C94 (6)	2.10	1.20

WHO, 20th anniv.

Olympic Monument, San Salvador Island, Bahamas — A88

1968, July 27   Perf. 14x13½

650	A88	15fr Wrestling	.20	.20
651	A88	20fr Boxing	.20	.20
652	A88	30fr Judo	.20	.20
653	A88	45fr Running	.25	.20
		Nos. 650-653,C95-C96 (6)	2.10	1.20

19th Olympic Games, Mexico City, 10/12-27.

Chick Holding Lottery Ticket — A89

Scout Before Tent — A90

45fr, Lottery ticket, horseshoe & 4-leaf clover.

1968, Oct. 5   Litho.   Perf. 14

654	A89	30fr dk green & multi	.25	.20
655	A89	45fr multicolored	.30	.20

2nd anniversary of National Lottery.

1968, Nov. 23

10fr, 45fr, Scout leader training cub scouts, horiz. 20fr, First aid practice, horiz. 30fr, Scout game.

656	A90	5fr dp org & multi	.20	.20
657	A90	10fr emerald & multi	.20	.20
658	A90	20fr multicolored	.20	.20
659	A90	30fr multicolored	.25	.20
660	A90	45fr blue & multi	.30	.20
		Nos. 656-660,C97-C98 (7)	2.65	1.60

Issued to honor the Togolese Boy Scouts.

Adoration of the Shepherds, by Giorgione — A91

Paintings: 20f, Adoration of the Magi, by Pieter Brueghel. 30fr, Adoration of the Magi, by Botticelli. 45fr, Adoration of the Magi, by Durer.

1968, Dec. 28   Litho.   Perf. 14

661	A91	15fr green & multi	.20	.20
662	A91	20fr multicolored	.20	.20
663	A91	30fr multicolored	.25	.20
664	A91	45fr multicolored	.30	.20
		Nos. 661-664,C100-C101 (6)	2.45	1.30

Christmas.

Martin Luther King, Jr. — A92

Portraits and Human Rights Flame: 20fr, Professor René Cassin (author of Declaration of Human Rights). 45fr, Pope John XXIII.

1969, Feb. 1   Photo.   Perf. 13½x14

665	A92	15fr brn org & sl grn	.20	.20
666	A92	20fr grnsh bl & vio	.20	.20
667	A92	30fr ver & slate bl	.20	.20
668	A92	45fr olive & car rose	.25	.20
		Nos. 665-668,C102-C103 (6)	1.80	1.30

International Human Rights Year.
For overprints see Nos. 683-686, C110-C111.

Omnisport Stadium and Soccer — A93

Stadium and: 15fr, Handball. 20fr, Volleyball. 30fr, Basketball. 45fr, Tennis.

1969, Apr. 26   Photo.   Perf. 14x13½

669	A93	10fr emer, dp car & dk brn	.20	.20
670	A93	15fr org, ultra & dk brn	.20	.20
671	A93	20fr yel, ol & dk brn	.20	.20
672	A93	30fr dl grn, bl & dk brn	.20	.20
673	A93	45fr org, lil & dk brn	.25	.20
		Nos. 669-673,C105-C106 (7)	2.15	1.45

Opening of Omnisport Stadium, Lomé.

Astronaut and Eagle on Moon, Earth and Stars in Sky — A94

Designs: 1f, 30fr, Lunar Module Eagle Landing on Moon. 45fr, Astronaut and Eagle on moon, earth and stars in sky.

1969, July 21   Litho.   Perf. 14

674	A94	1fr green & multi	.20	.20
675	A94	20fr brown & multi	.20	.20
676	A94	30fr scarlet & multi	.20	.20
677	A94	45fr ultra & multi	.35	.20
		Nos. 674-677,C107-C108 (6)	2.00	1.40

Man's 1st landing on the moon, 7/20/69. US astronauts Neil A. Armstrong & Col. Edwin E. Aldrin, Jr., with Lieut. Col. Michael Collins piloting Apollo 11.
For overprints see #710-712, C120-C121.

Christ at Emmaus, by Velazquez A95

Paintings: 5fr, The Last Supper, by Tintoretto. 20fr, Pentecost, by El Greco. 30fr, The Annunciation, by Botticelli. 45fr, Like 10fr.

1969, Aug. 16   Litho.   Perf. 14

678	A95	5fr red, gold & multi	.20	.20
679	A95	10fr multicolored	.20	.20
680	A95	20fr grn, gold & multi	.20	.20
681	A95	30fr multicolored	.20	.20
682	A95	45fr pur, gold & multi	.30	.20
		Nos. 678-682,C109 (6)	2.10	1.40

Nos. 665-668
Overprinted

1969, Sept. 1   Photo.   Perf. 13½x14

683	A92	15fr brn org & sl grn	.20	.20
684	A92	20fr grnsh bl & vio	.20	.20
685	A92	30fr ver & slate bl	.20	.20
686	A92	45fr olive & car rose	.25	.20
		Nos. 683-686,C110-C111 (6)	1.85	1.25

Gen. Dwight D. Eisenhower (1890-1969), 34th President of the US.

African
Development
Bank and
Emblem — A96

Designs: 45fr, Bank emblem and hand holding railroad bridge and engine.

1969, Sept. 10   Photo.   Perf. 13x14

687	A96	30fr ultra, blk gold & grn	.20	.20
688	A96	45fr grn, dk bl, gold & dk red	.30	.20

5th anniv. of the African Development Bank. See No. C112.

Louis Pasteur and Help for 1968 Flood Victims — A97

Designs: 15fr, Henri Dunant and Red Cross workers meeting Biafra refugees at airport. 30fr, Alexander Fleming and help for flood victims. 45fr, Wilhelm C. Roentgen and Red Cross workers with children in front of Headquarters.

1969, Sept. 27   Litho.   Perf. 14

689	A97	15fr red & multi	.20	.20
690	A97	20fr emerald & multi	.20	.20
691	A97	30fr purple & multi	.20	.20
692	A97	45fr brt blue & multi	.30	.20
		Nos. 689-692,C113-C114 (6)	2.00	1.40

League of Red Cross Societies, 50th anniv.

Glidji
Agricultural
Center
A98

Designs (Emblem of Young Pioneer and Agricultural Organization and): 1fr, Corn harvest. 3fr, Founding meeting of Agricultural Pioneer Youths, Mar. 7, 1967. 4fr, Class at Glidji Agricultural School. 5fr, Boys forming

human pyramid. 7fr, Farm students threshing. 8fr, Instruction in gardening. 10fr, 50fr, Cooperative village. 15fr, Gardening School. 20fr, Cattle breeding. 25fr, Chicken farm. 30fr, Independence parade. 40fr, Boys riding high wire. 45fr, Tractor and trailer. 60fr, Instruction in tractor driving.

1969-70   Litho.   Perf. 14

693	A98	1fr multi ('70)	.20	.20
694	A98	2fr multi	.20	.20
695	A98	3fr multi ('70)	.20	.20
696	A98	4fr multi ('70)	.20	.20
697	A98	5fr ultra & multi	.20	.20
698	A98	7fr multi ('70)	.20	.20
699	A98	8fr red & multi	.20	.20
700	A98	10fr bl & multi ('70)	.20	.20
701	A98	15fr red & multi ('70)	.20	.20
702	A98	20fr lilac & multi	.20	.20
703	A98	25fr multi ('70)	.20	.20
704	A98	30fr brt bl & multi	.20	.20
705	A98	40fr brt yel & multi	.25	.20
706	A98	45fr rose lil & multi	.25	.20
707	A98	50fr blue & multi	.25	.20
708	A98	60fr orange & multi	.25	.20
		Nos. 693-708,C115-C119 (21)	10.50	5.35

Books and
Map of
Africa
A99

1969, Nov. 27   Litho.   Perf. 14

709	A99	30fr lt blue & multi	.20	.20

12th anniv. of the Intl. Assoc. for the Development of Libraries in Africa.

Christmas Issue
Nos. 674-675, 677 Overprinted
"JOYEUX NOEL"

1969, Dec.   Litho.   Perf. 14

710	A94	1fr green & multi	.20	.20
711	A94	20fr brown & multi	.70	.35
712	A94	45fr ultra & multi	1.25	.65
		Nos. 710-712,C120-C121 (5)	5.30	2.20

George
Washington — A100

Portraits: 20fr, Albert Luthuli. 30fr, Mahatma Gandhi. 45fr, Simon Bolivar.

1969, Dec. 27   Photo.   Perf. 14x13½

713	A100	15fr dk brn, emer & buff	.20	.20
714	A100	20fr dk brn, org & buff	.20	.20
715	A100	30fr dk brn, grnsh bl & ocher	.20	.20
716	A100	45fr dk brn, sl grn & dl yel	.20	.20
		Nos. 713-716,C122-C123 (6)	1.80	1.30

Issued to honor leaders for world peace.
For overprint & surcharges see #764-766, C143.

Plower, by
M.K. Klodt
and ILO
Emblem
A101

Paintings and ILO Emblem: 10fr, Gardening, by Camille Pissarro. 20fr, Fruit Harvest, by Diego Rivera. 30fr, Spring Sowing, by Vincent van Gogh. 45fr, Workers, by Rivera.

1970, Jan. 24   Litho.   Perf. 12½x13

717	A101	5fr gold & multi	.20	.20
718	A101	10fr gold & multi	.20	.20
719	A101	20fr gold & multi	.20	.20

720	A101	30fr gold & multi	.25	.20
721	A101	45fr gold & multi	.35	.20
		Nos. 717-721,C124-C125 (7)	2.20	1.40

ILO, 50th anniversary.

Togolese Hair Styles — A102

Various hair styles. 20fr, 30fr, vertical.

1970, Feb. 21   Perf. 13x12½, 12½x13

722	A102	5fr multicolored	.20	.20
723	A102	10fr ver & multi	.20	.20
724	A102	20fr purple & multi	.20	.20
725	A102	30fr yellow grn & multi	.25	.20
		Nos. 722-725,C126-C127 (6)	1.60	1.30

Togo No. C127 and Independence Monument, Lomé — A103

30fr, Pres. Etienne G. Eyadéma, Presidential Palace and Independence Monument. 50fr, Map of Togo, dove and Independence Monument, vert.

Perf. 13x12½, 12½x13

1970, Apr. 27   Litho.

726	A103	20fr multicolored	.20	.20
727	A103	30fr multicolored	.20	.20
728	A103	50fr multicolored	.30	.20
		Nos. 726-728,C128 (4)	1.00	.80

10th anniv. of independence.

Inauguration of UPU Headquarters, Bern — A104

1970, May 30   Photo.   Perf. 14x13½

729	A104	30fr orange & pur	.25	.20

See No. C129.

Soccer, Jules Rimet Cup and Flags of Italy and Uruguay — A105

Designs (Various Scenes from Soccer, Rimet Cup and Flags of): 10fr, Great Britain and Brazil. 15fr, USSR and Mexico. 20fr, Germany and Morocco. 30fr, Romania and Czechoslovakia.

1970, June 27   Litho.   Perf. 13x14

730	A105	5fr olive & multi	.20	.20
731	A105	10fr pink & multi	.20	.20
732	A105	15fr yellow & multi	.20	.20
733	A105	20fr multicolored	.20	.20
734	A105	30fr emerald	.30	.20
		Nos. 730-734,C130-C132 (8)	2.35	1.70

Soccer Championships for the Jules Rimet Cup, Mexico City, May 30-June 21, 1970.

Lenin and
UNESCO
Emblem
A106

1970, July 25   Litho.   Perf. 12½

735	A106	30fr fawn & multi	.25	.20

Lenin (1870-1924), Russian communist leader. See No. C133.
For surcharge see No. C179.

EXPO '70 Emblem and View of US Pavilion — A107

Designs: 2fr, Paper carp flying over Sanyo pavilion. 30fr, Russian pavilion. 50fr, Tower of the Sun pavilion. 60fr, French and Japanese pavilions.

1970, Aug. 8   Litho.   Perf. 13

Size: 56½x35mm

736	A107	2fr gray & multi	.20	.20

Size: 50x33mm

737	A107	20fr blue & multi	.20	.20
738	A107	30fr blue & multi	.25	.20
739	A107	50fr blue & multi	.20	.20
740	A107	60fr blue & multi	.30	.20
a.		Strip of 4, #737-740	.75	.30
		Nos. 736-740 (5)	1.15	1.00

EXPO '70 Intl. Exhibition, Osaka, Japan, Mar. 15-Sept. 13. No. 740a has continuous view of EXPO. See No. C134.

Neil A.
Armstrong,
Michael
Collins and
Edwin E.
Aldrin,
Jr. — A108

Designs: 2fr, US flag, moon rocks and Apollo 11 emblem. 20fr, Astronaut checking Surveyor 3 on moon, and Apollo 12 emblem. 30fr, Charles Conrad, Jr., Richard F. Gordon, Jr., Alan L. Bean and Apollo 12 emblem. 50fr, US flag, moon rocks and Apollo 12 emblem.

1970, Sept. 26

741	A108	1fr multi	.20	.20
742	A108	2fr multi	.20	.20
743	A108	20fr multi	.20	.20
744	A108	30fr multi	.25	.20
745	A108	50fr multi	.45	.20
		Nos. 741-745,C135 (6)	2.25	1.55

Moon landings of Apollo 11 and 12.
For overprints see Nos. 746-750, C136.

Nos. 741-745 Inscribed:
"FELICITATIONS / BON RETOUR
APOLLO XIII"

1970, Sept. 26

746	A108	1fr multi	.20	.20
747	A108	2fr multi	.20	.20
748	A108	20fr multi	.20	.20
749	A108	30fr multi	.25	.20
750	A108	50fr multi	.45	.20
		Nos. 746-750,C136 (6)	2.30	1.55

Safe return of the crew of Apollo 13.

Forge of Vulcan, by Velazquez, and ILO Emblem — A109

Paintings and Emblems of UN Agencies: 15fr, Still Life, by Delacroix, and FAO emblem. 20fr, Portrait of Nicholas Kratzer, by Holbein, and UNESCO emblem. 30fr, UN Headquarters, New York, and UN emblem. 50fr, Portrait of a Little Girl, by Renoir, and UNICEF emblem.

1970, Oct. 24   Litho.   Perf. 13x12½
751 A109 1fr car, gold & dk brn   .20   .20
752 A109 15fr ultra, gold & blk   .20   .20
753 A109 20fr grnsh bl, gold &
           dk grn   .20   .20
754 A109 30fr lil & multi   .25   .20
755 A109 50fr org brn, gold & se-
           pia   .40   .20
  Nos. 751-755,C137-C138 (7)   2.15 1.50

United Nations, 25th anniversary.

Euchloron Megaera — A110

Butterflies and Moths: 2fr, Cymothoe chrysippus. 30fr, Danaus chrysippus. 50fr, Morpho.

1970, Nov. 21   Litho.   Perf. 13x14
756 A110 1fr yellow & multi   .20   .20
757 A110 2fr lt vio & multi   .20   .20
758 A110 30fr multicolored   .20   .20
759 A110 50fr orange & multi   .40   .20
  Nos. 756-759,C139-C140 (6)   2.10 1.20

For surcharge see No. 859.

Nativity, by Botticelli — A111

Paintings: 20fr, Adoration of the Shepherds, by Veronese. 30fr, Adoration of the Shepherds, by El Greco. 50fr, Adoration of the Kings, by Fra Angelico.

1970, Dec. 26   Litho.   Perf. 12½x13
760 A111 15fr gold & multi   .20   .20
761 A111 20fr gold & multi   .20   .20
762 A111 30fr gold & multi   .20   .20
763 A111 50fr gold & multi   .35   .20
  Nos. 760-763,C141-C142 (6)   2.10 1.30

Christmas.

Nos. 715, C123, 714 Surcharged and Overprinted: "EN MEMOIRE / Charles De Gaulle / 1890-1970"

1971, Jan. 9   Photo.   Perf. 14x13½
764 A100 30fr multicolored   .25   .20
765 A100 30fr on 90fr multi   .25   .20
766 A100 150fr on 20fr multi   1.10   .35
  Nos. 764-766,C143 (4)   3.10 1.35

"Aerienne" obliterated with heavy bar on No. 765.

De Gaulle and Churchill A112

De Gaulle and: 30fr, Dwight D. Eisenhower. 40fr, John F. Kennedy. 50fr, Konrad Adenauer.

1971, Feb. 20   Photo.   Perf. 13x14
767 A112 20fr blk & brt blue   .20   .20
768 A112 30fr blk & crimson   .20   .20
769 A112 40fr blk & dp green   .30   .20
770 A112 50fr blk & brown   .35   .20
  Nos. 767-770,C144-C145 (6)   2.25 1.25

Nos. 764-770 issued in memory of Charles de Gaulle (1890-1970), President of France.

Resurrection, by Raphael — A113

Easter: 30fr, Resurrection, by Master of Trebon. 40fr, like 1fr.

1971, Apr. 10   Litho.   Perf. 10½x11½
771 A113 1fr gold & multi   .20   .20
772 A113 30fr gold & multi   .20   .20
773 A113 40fr gold & multi   .20   .20
  Nos. 771-773,C146-C148 (6)   2.10 1.30

Cmdr. Alan B. Shepard, Jr. — A114

Designs: 10fr, Edgar D. Mitchell and astronaut on moon. 30fr, Stuart A. Roosa, module on moon. 40fr, Take-off from moon, and spaceship.

1971, May   Litho.   Perf. 12½
774 A114 1fr blue & multi   .20   .20
775 A114 10fr green & multi   .20   .20
776 A114 30fr dull red & multi   .20   .20
777 A114 40fr dk green & multi   .25   .20
  Nos. 774-777,C149-C151 (7)   3.25 2.00

Apollo 14 moon landing, Jan. 31-Feb. 9. For overprints see Nos. 788, C162-C164.

Cacao Tree and Pods — A115

Designs: 40fr, Sorting and separating beans and pods. 50fr, Drying cacao beans.

1971, June 6   Litho.   Perf. 14
778 A115 30fr multicolored   .30   .20
779 A115 40fr ultra & multi   .35   .20
780 A115 50fr multicolored   .35   .20
  Nos. 778-780,C152-C154 (6)   2.70 1.45

International Cacao Day, June 6.

Napoleon, Death Sesquicentennial - A115a

Die Cut Perf. 12
1971, June 11   Embossed
780A A115a 1000fr gold   12.50 12.50
  b.   Sheet of 1, imperf.   12.50 12.50

No. 780Ab contains one 48x69mm stamp.

Control Tower and Plane — A116

1971, June 26   Litho.   Perf. 14
781 A116 30fr multicolored   .25   .20

10th anniv. of the Agency for the Security of Aerial Navigation in Africa and Madagascar (ASECNA). See No. C155.

Great Market, Lomé — A117

Tourist publicity: 30fr, Bird-of-paradise flower and sculpture of a man. 40fr, Aledjo Gorge and anubius baboon.

1971, July 17
782 A117 20fr multicolored   .20   .20
783 A117 30fr multicolored   .20   .20
784 A117 40fr multicolored   .25   .20
  Nos. 782-784,C156-C158 (6)   2.05 1.35

For surcharge and overprint see Nos. 804, C172.

Great Fetish of Gbatchoume — A118

Religions of Togo: 30fr, Chief Priest in front of Atta Sakuma Temple. 40fr, Annual ceremony of the sacred stone.

1971, July 31   Litho.   Perf. 14½
785 A118 20fr multicolored   .20   .20
786 A118 30fr multicolored   .20   .20
787 A118 40fr multicolored   .25   .20
  Nos. 785-787,C159-C161 (6)   1.90 1.25

No. 777 Overprinted in Silver: "EN MEMOIRE / DOBROVOLSKY - VOLKOV - PATSAYEV / SOYUZ 11"

1971, Aug.   Perf. 12½
788 A114 40fr multicolored   .25   .20
  Nos. 788,C162-C164 (4)   2.90 1.25

Russian astronauts Lt. Col. Georgi T. Dobrovolsky, Vladislav N. Volkov and Victor I. Patsayev, who died during the Soyuz 11 space mission, June 6-30, 1971.

Sapporo '72 Emblem and Speed Skating — A119

Sapporo '72 Emblem and: 10fr, Slalom skiing. 20fr, Figure skating, pairs. 30fr, Bobsledding. 50fr, Ice hockey.

1971, Oct. 30   Perf. 14
789 A119 1fr multicolored   .20   .20
790 A119 10fr multicolored   .20   .20
791 A119 20fr multicolored   .20   .20
792 A119 30fr multicolored   .20   .20
793 A119 50fr multicolored   .35   .20
  Nos. 789-793,C165 (6)   2.55 1.50

11th Winter Olympic Games, Sapporo, Japan, Feb. 3-13, 1972.

Toy Crocodile and UNICEF Emblem — A120

Toys and UNICEF Emblem: 30fr, Fawn and butterfly. 40fr, Monkey. 50fr, Elephants.

1971, Nov. 27
794 A120 20fr multicolored   .20   .20
795 A120 30fr violet & multi   .20   .20
796 A120 40fr green & multi   .25   .20
797 A120 50fr bister & multi   .35   .20
  Nos. 794-797,C167-C168 (6)   2.00 1.25

UNICEF, 25th anniv.
For overprints see Nos. 918, C263-C264.

Virgin and Child, by Botticelli A121

Virgin and Child by: 30fr, Master of the Life of Mary. 40fr, Dürer. 50fr, Veronese.

1971, Dec. 24   Perf. 14x13
798 A121 10fr purple & multi   .20   .20
799 A121 30fr green & multi   .20   .20
800 A121 40fr brown & multi   .30   .20
801 A121 50fr dk blue & multi   .40   .20
  Nos. 798-801,C169-C170 (6)   2.20 1.45

Christmas.

St. Mark's Basilica — A122

Design: 40fr, Rialto Bridge.

1972, Feb. 26   Litho.   Perf. 14
802 A122 30fr multicolored   .20   .20
803 A122 40fr multicolored   .25   .20
    Nos. 802-803,C171 (3)   1.15   .80
    UNESCO campaign to save Venice.

No. 784 Surcharged with New Value,
Two Bars and "VISITE DU
PRESIDENT / NIXON EN CHINE /
FEVRIER 1972"

1972, Mar.   Litho.   Perf. 14
804 A117 300fr on 40fr multi   2.00 1.25

Visit of Pres. Richard M. Nixon to the People's Republic of China, Feb. 20-27.
See No. C172.

Crucifixion,
by Master
MS — A123

Easter (Paintings): 30fr, Pietà, by Botticelli.

1972, Mar. 31
805 A123 25fr gold & multi   .20   .20
806 A123 30fr gold & multi   .20   .20
807 A123 40fr gold & multi   .25   .20
    Nos. 805-807,C173-C174 (5)   1.75 1.05

Heart, Smith,
WHO Emblem
A124

Video Telephone
A125

Org. of African and Malagasy Union
Conf. - A124a

Heart, WHO Emblem and: 40fr, Typist. 60fr,
Athlete with javelin.

1972, Apr. 4
808 A124 30fr multicolored   .20   .20
809 A124 40fr multicolored   .25   .20
810 A124 60fr multicolored   .40   .20
    Nos. 808-810,C175 (4)   1.50 1.00

"Your heart is your health," World Health
Day.

Die Cut Perf. 12x12½
**1972, Apr. 24   Litho. & Embossed
Self-adhesive**
810A A124a 1000fr gold, red &
          grn

On No. 810A embossing may cut through
stamp and embossed backing paper may not
adhere well to the unused stamps.
For overprint see No. 893A.

1972, June 24   Litho.   Perf. 14
811 A125 40fr violet & multi   .25   .20

4th World Telecommunications Day. See
No. C176.
For overprints see Nos. 880, C229.

Grating Cassava
A126

Basketball
A127

25fr, Cassava collection by truck, horiz.

1972, June 30
812 A126 25fr yellow & multi   .20   .20
813 A126 40fr multicolored   .25   .20
    Nos. 812-813,C177-C178 (4)   1.45   .90
    Cassava production.
    For overprint & surcharge see #866-867.

1972, Aug. 26   Litho.   Perf. 14
814 A127 30fr shown   .20   .20
815 A127 40fr Running   .25   .20
816 A127 50fr Discus   .35   .20
    Nos. 814-816,C180-C181 (5)   2.95 1.60

20th Olympic Games, Munich, 8/26-9/11.
For overprints see Nos. C234-C235.

Pin-tailed
Whydah — A128

Paul P. Harris,
Rotary
Emblem — A129

Birds: 30fr, Broad-tailed widowbird. 40fr,
Yellow-shouldered widowbird. 60fr, Yellow-
tailed widowbird.

1972, Sept. 9
817 A128 25fr citron & multi   .20   .20
818 A128 30fr lt blue & multi   .25   .20
819 A128 40fr multicolored   .25   .20
820 A128 60fr lt green & multi   .40   .20
    Nos. 817-820,C182 (5)   1.75 1.15

1972, Oct. 7   Litho.   Perf. 14
50fr, Flags of Togo and Rotary Club.

821 A129 40fr green & multi   .20   .20
822 A129 50fr multicolored   .35   .20
  a.   Souvenir sheet of 2   .65   .65
    Nos. 821-822,C183-C185 (5)   2.00 1.35

Rotary International, Lomé. No. 822a contains 2 stamps with simulated perforations
similar to Nos. 821-822.
For overprints see Nos. 862, 898, C212-
C213, C244-C235.

Mona Lisa,
by Leonardo
da Vinci
A130

40fr, Virgin and Child, by Giovanni Bellini.

1972, Oct. 21
823 A130 25fr gold & multi   .20   .20
824 A130 40fr gold & multi   .25   .20
    Nos. 823-824,C186-C188 (5)   2.10 1.25

West African Monetary Union Issue
Common Design Type

Design: 40fr, African couple, city, village
and commemorative coin.

1972, Nov. 2   Engr.   Perf. 13
825 CD136 40fr red brn, rose red &
          gray   .25   .20

Presidents Pompidou and Eyadema,
Party Headquarters — A131

1972, Nov. 23   Litho.   Perf. 14
826 A131 40fr purple & multi   .30   .20

Visit of Pres. Georges Pompidou of France
to Togo, Nov. 1972. See No. C189.

Anunciation,
Painter
Unknown
A132

Paintings: 30fr, Nativity, Master of
Vyshchibrod.   40fr, Like 25fr.

1972, Dec. 23
827 A132 25fr gold & multi   .20   .20
828 A132 30fr gold & multi   .20   .20
829 A132 40fr gold & multi   .25   .20
    Nos. 827-829,C191-C193 (6)   2.50 1.50

Christmas.

Raoul Follereau and Lepers — A133

1973, Jan. 23   Photo.   Perf. 14x13½
830 A133 40fr violet & green   .25   .20

World Leprosy Day and 20th anniv. of the
Raoul Follereau Foundation. See No. C194.

WHO
Emblem — A134

Christ on the
Cross — A135

1973, Apr. 7   Photo.   Perf. 14x13
831 A134 30fr blue & multi   .20   .20
832 A134 40fr dp yellow & multi   .25   .20

WHO, 25th anniv.

1973, Apr. 21   Litho.   Perf. 14
833 A135 25fr shown   .20   .20
834 A135 30fr Pietá   .20   .20
835 A135 40fr Ascension   .25   .20
    Nos. 833-835,C195 (4)   1.25 1.00

Easter.

Eugene Cernan, Ronald Evans,
Harrison Schmitt, Apollo 17
Badge — A136

Design: 40fr, Lunar rover on moon.

1973, June 2   Litho.   Perf. 14
836 A136 30fr multicolored   .20   .20
837 A136 40fr multicolored   .25   .20
    Nos. 836-837,C196-C197 (4)   2.65 1.40

Apollo 17 moon mission, Dec. 7-19, 1972.

Scouts Pitching
Tent
A137

Nicolaus
Copernicus
A138

20fr, Campfire, horiz. 30fr, Rope climbing.

1973, June 30
838 A137 10fr multicolored   .20   .20
839 A137 20fr multicolored   .20   .20
840 A137 30fr violet & multi   .20   .20
841 A137 40fr ocher & multi   .25   .20
    Nos. 838-841,C198-C199 (6)   3.00 1.85

24th Boy Scout World Conference (1st in
Africa), Nairobi, Kenya, July 16-21.
For overprints see Nos. C265-C266.

1973, July 18

Designs: 10fr, Heliocentric system. 30fr,
Seated figure of Astronomy and spacecrafts
around earth and moon.   40fr, Astrolabe.

842 A138 10fr multicolored   .20   .20
843 A138 20fr multicolored   .20   .20
844 A138 30fr multicolored   .20   .20
845 A138 40fr lilac & multi   .25   .20
    Nos. 842-845,C200-C201 (6)   2.15 1.50

Red Cross
Ambulance
Crew
A139

1973, Aug. 4
846 A139 40fr multicolored   .25   .20

Togolese Red Cross. See No. C202.
For overprints see Nos. 846, C294.

Teacher and Students — A140

40fr, Hut and man reading under tree, vert.

1973, Aug. 18   Litho.   Perf. 14
847 A140 30fr multicolored   .20   .20
848 A140 40fr multicolored   .25   .20
    Nos. 847-848,C203 (3)   1.00   .75

Literacy campaign.

African Postal Union Issue
Common Design Type

1973, Sept. 12   Engr.   Perf. 14
849 CD137 100fr yel, red & claret .70   .35

INTERPOL
Emblem and
Headquarters
A141

Weather Vane
and WMO
Emblem
A142

1973, Sept. 29 Photo. *Perf. 13½x14*
850 A141 30fr yel, brn & gray grn .20 .20
851 A141 40fr yel grn, bl & mag .25 .20
50th anniv. of Intl. Criminal Police Org.

1973, Oct. 4 *Perf. 14x13*
852 A142 40fr yel, dp brn & grn .25 .20
Intl. meteorological cooperation, cent. See No. C204.

Type of 1967

Designs: 25fr, Old and new locomotives, No. 795. 30fr, Mail coach and bus, No. 613. 90fr, Mail boat and ship, Nos. C61 and 469.

1973, Oct. 20 Photo. *Perf. 14x13*
853 A79 25fr multicolored .20 .20
854 A79 30fr purple & green .25 .20
855 A79 90fr dk blue & multi .65 .30
Nos. 853-855,C205 (4) 1.90 1.00
Togolese postal service, 75th anniv.

John F.
Kennedy and
Adolf Schaerf
A143

Virgin and Child,
Italy, 15th Century
A144

Designs: 30fr, Kennedy and Harold MacMillan. 40fr, Kennedy and Konrad Adenauer.

1973, Nov. 22 Litho. *Perf. 14*
856 A143 20fr blk, gray & vio .20 .20
857 A143 30fr blk, rose & brn .20 .20
858 A143 40fr blk, lt grn & grn .25 .20
Nos. 856-858,C206-C208 (6) 3.35 2.00
John F. Kennedy (1917-1963).

No. 758 Surcharged with New Value, 2 Bars and Overprinted in Ultramarine: "SECHERESSE SOLIDARITE AFRICAINE"

1973, Dec. Photo. *Perf. 13x14*
859 A110 100fr on 30fr multi .70 .50
African solidarity in drought emergency.

1973, Dec. 22 Litho. *Perf. 14*
30fr, Adoration of the Kings, Italy, 15th cent.
860 A144 25fr gold & multi .20 .20
861 A144 30fr gold & multi .25 .20
Nos. 860-861,C210-C211 (4) 1.75 1.00
Christmas.

No. 821 Overprinted: "PREMIERE CONVENTION / 210eme DISTRICT / FEVRIER 1974 / LOME"

1974, Feb. 21 Litho. *Perf. 14*
862 A129 40fr green & multi .25 .20
Nos. 862,C212-C213 (3) 1.25 .75
First convention of Rotary Intl., District 210, Lomé, Feb. 22-24.

Soccer and
Games'
Cup
A145

Various soccer scenes and games' cup.

1974, Mar. 2 Litho. *Perf. 14*
863 A145 20fr lt blue & multi .20 .20
864 A145 30fr yellow & multi .25 .20
865 A145 40fr lilac & multi .30 .20
Nos. 863-865,C214-C216 (6) 3.90 2.10
World Soccer Championships, Munich, Germany, June 13-July 7.

Nos. 812-813 Overprinted and Surcharged: "10e ANNIVERSAIRE DU P.A.M."

1974, Mar. 25 Litho. *Perf. 14*
866 A126 40fr multicolored .35 .20
867 A126 100fr on 25fr multi .75 .50
10th anniv. of World Food Program. Overprint on No. 866 is in one line; 2 lines on No. 867 and 2 bars through old denomination.

Girl Before Mirror,
by
Picasso — A146

Mailman, UPU
Emblem — A148

Kpeme
Village and
Wharf
A147

Paintings by Picasso: 30fr, The Turkish Shawl. 40fr, Mandolin and Guitar.

1974, Apr. 6
868 A146 20fr vio blue & multi .20 .20
869 A146 30fr maroon & multi .25 .20
870 A146 40fr multicolored .30 .20
Nos. 868-870,C217-C219 (6) 3.45 1.90
Pablo Picasso (1881-1973), Spanish painter.

1974, Apr. 20
Design: 40fr, Tropicana tourist village.
871 A147 30fr multicolored .25 .20
872 A147 40fr multicolored .25 .20
Nos. 871-872,C220-C221 (4) 1.75 1.00

1974, May 10 Litho. *Perf. 14*
Design: 40fr, Mailman, different uniform.
873 A148 30fr salmon & multi .25 .20
874 A148 40fr multicolored .30 .20
Nos. 873-874,C222-C223 (4) 1.65 .95
UPU, centenary.

Map and
Flags of
Members -
A148a

1974, May 29 Litho. *Perf. 13x12½*
875 A148a 40fr blue & multi .30 .25
15th anniversary of the Council of Accord.

Fisherman
with Net
A149

40fr, Fisherman casting net from canoe.

1974, June 22 Litho. *Perf. 14*
876 A149 30fr multicolored .25 .20
877 A149 40fr multicolored .30 .20
Nos. 876-877,C224-C226 (5) 2.70 1.55
Lagoon fishing.

Pioneer Communicating with
Earth — A150

30fr, Radar station and satellite, vert.

1974, July 6 *Perf. 14*
878 A150 30fr multicolored .25 .20
879 A150 40fr multicolored .30 .20
Nos. 878-879,C227-C228 (4) 2.60 1.40
US Jupiter space probe.

No. 811 Overprinted with INTERNABA Emblem in Silver Similar to No. C229

1974, July
880 A125 40fr multicolored 1.10 .55
INTERNABA 1974 Intl. Philatelic Exhibition, Basel, June 7-16. See No. C229.

Tympanotomus
Radula — A151

Designs: Seashells.

1974, July 13 Litho. *Perf. 14*
881 A151 10fr shown .20 .20
882 A151 20fr Tonna galea .20 .20
883 A151 30fr Conus mercator .25 .20
884 A151 40fr Cardium costatum .35 .20
Nos. 881-884,C230-C231 (6) 2.00 1.40

Groom with
Horses
A152

Design: 40fr, Trotting horses.

1974, Aug. 3 Litho. *Perf. 14*
885 A152 30fr multicolored .25 .20
886 A152 40fr multicolored .30 .20
Nos. 885-886,C232-C233 (4) 1.85 1.00
Horse racing.

Leopard
A153

1974, Sept. 7 Litho. *Perf. 14*
887 A153 20fr shown .20 .20
888 A153 30fr Giraffes .20 .20
889 A153 40fr Elephants .25 .20
Nos. 887-889,C236-C237 (5) 1.80 1.25
Wild animals of West Africa.

1974, Oct. 14
890 A153 30fr Herding cattle .20 .20
891 A153 40fr Milking cow .25 .20
Nos. 890-891,C238-C239 (4) 1.50 1.00
Domestic animals.

Churchill
and Frigate
F390
A154

Design: 40fr, Churchill and fighter planes.

1974, Nov. 1 Photo. *Perf. 13x13½*
892 A154 30fr multicolored .25 .20
893 A154 40fr multicolored .30 .20
Nos. 892-893,C240-C241 (4) 2.40 1.30
Winston Churchill (1874-1965).

No. 810A Ovptd. "Inauguration de l'hotel de la Paix 9-1-75"
Litho. & Embossed
1975, Jan. 9 *Perf. 12½*
Self-adhesive
893A A124a 1000fr gold, red & grn
On No. 893A embossing may cut through stamp and embossed backing paper may not adhere well to the unused stamps.

Chlamydocarya Macrocarpa — A155

Flowers of Togo: 25fr, Strelitzia reginae, vert. 30fr, Storphanthus sarmentosus, vert. 60fr, Clerodendrum scandens.

1975, Feb. 15 Litho. *Perf. 14*
894 A155 25fr multicolored .20 .20
895 A155 30fr multicolored .20 .20
896 A155 40fr multicolored .25 .20
897 A155 60fr multicolored .35 .20
Nos. 894-897,C242-C243 (6) 2.65 1.55

No. 821 Overprinted: "70e ANNIVERSAIRE / 23 FEVRIER 1975"

1975, Feb. 23 Litho. *Perf. 14*
898 A129 40fr green & multi .30 .20
Nos. 898,C244-C245 (3) 1.35 .80
Rotary Intl., 70th anniv.

Radio
Station,
Kamina
A156

30fr, Benedictine Monastery, Zogbegan. 40fr, Causeway, Atchinedji. 60fr, Ayome Waterfalls.

1975, Mar. 1 Photo. *Perf. 13x14*
899 A156 25fr multicolored .20 .20
900 A156 30fr multicolored .20 .20
901 A156 40fr multicolored .25 .20
902 A156 60fr multicolored .35 .25
Nos. 899-902 (4) 1.00 .85

Jesus Mocked, by
El Greco — A157

Paintings: 30fr, Crucifixion, by Master Janoslet. 40fr, Descent from the Cross, by Bellini. 90fr, Pietà, painter unknown.

1975, Apr. 19   Litho.   Perf. 14
903	A157	25fr black & multi	.20	.20
904	A157	30fr black & multi	.25	.20
905	A157	40fr black & multi	.30	.20
906	A157	90fr black & multi	.60	.30
		Nos. 903-906,C246-C247 (6)	3.00	1.70

Easter.

Stilt Walking, Togolese Flag A158

Design: 30fr, Flag and dancers.

1975, Apr. 26   Litho.   Perf. 14
907	A158	25fr multicolored	.20	.20
908	A158	30fr multicolored	.20	.20
		Nos. 907-908,C248-C249 (4)	1.00	.80

15th anniv. of independence.

Rabbit Hunter with Club A159

40fr, Beaver hunter with bow and arrow.

1975, May 24   Photo.   Perf. 13x13½
909	A159	30fr multicolored	.20	.20
910	A159	40fr multicolored	.25	.20
		Nos. 909-910,C250-C251 (4)	1.50	.90

Pounding Palm Nuts A160

Design: 40fr, Man extracting palm oil, vert.

1975, June 28   Litho.   Perf. 14
911	A160	30fr multicolored	.25	.20
912	A160	40fr multicolored	.25	.20
		Nos. 911-912,C252-C253 (4)	1.50	.90

Palm oil production.

Apollo-Soyuz Link-up — A161

1975, July 15
913	A161	30fr multicolored	.20	.20
		Nos. 913,C254-C258 (6)	2.90	1.70

Apollo Soyuz space test project (Russo-American cooperation), launching July 15; link-up July 17.

Women's Heads, IWY Emblem — A162

1975, July 26   Litho.   Perf. 12½
914	A162	30fr blue & multi	.20	.20
915	A162	40fr multicolored	.25	.20

International Women's Year.

Dr. Schweitzer and Children — A163

1975, Aug. 23   Litho.   Perf. 14x13½
916	A163	40fr multicolored	.25	.20
		Nos. 916,C259-C261 (4)	1.75	1.10

Dr. Albert Schweitzer (1875-1965), medical missionary and musician.

Merchant Writing Letter, by Vittore Carpaccio A164

Virgin and Child, by Mantegna A165

1975, Oct. 9   Litho.   Perf. 14
917	A164	40fr multicolored	.25	.20

Intl. Letter Writing Week. See No. C262.

No. 797 Overprinted: "30ème Anniversaire / des Nations-Unies"

1975, Oct. 24   Litho.   Perf. 14
918	A120	50fr multi	.30	.25
		Nos. 918,C263-C264 (3)	1.10	.70

UN, 30th anniv.

1975, Dec. 20   Litho.   Perf. 14

Paintings of the Virgin and Child: 30fr, El Greco. 40fr, Barend van Orley.

919	A165	20fr red & multi	.20	.20
920	A165	30fr bl & multi	.25	.20
921	A165	40fr red & multi	.25	.20
		Nos. 919-921,C267-C269 (6)	2.90	1.60

Christmas.

Crashed Plane and Pres. Eyadema A166

1976, Jan. 24   Photo.   Perf. 13
922	A166	50fr multi	.55	.40
923	A166	60fr multi	.75	.45

Airplane crash at Sara-kawa, Jan. 24, 1974, in which Pres. Eyadema escaped injury.

1976 Summer Olympics, Montreal - A166a

Litho. & Embossed
1976, Feb. 24   Perf. 11
923A	A166a	1000fr	Diving
923B	A166a	1000fr	Track
923C	A166a	1000fr	Pole vault
923D	A166a	1000fr	Equestrian
923E	A166a	1000fr	Cycling

Exist imperf.

Frigates on the Hudson — A167

American Bicentennial: 50fr, George Washington, by Gilbert Stuart, and Bicentennial emblem, vert.

1976, Mar. 3   Litho.   Perf. 14
924	A167	35fr multicolored	.25	.20
925	A167	50fr multicolored	.35	.25
		Nos. 924-925,C270-C273 (6)	3.00	1.65

For overprints see Nos. C280-C283.

ACP and CEE Emblems A168

50fr, Map of Africa, Europe and Asia.

1976, Apr. 24   Photo.   Perf. 13x14
926	A168	10fr orange & multi	.20	.20
927	A168	50fr pink & multi	.30	.25
		Nos. 926-927,C274-C275 (4)	1.25	.85

First anniv. of signing of treaty between Togo and European Common Market, Lomé, Feb. 28, 1975.

Cable-laying Ship — A169

30fr, Telephone, tape recorder, speaker.

1976, Mar. 10   Photo.   Perf. 13x14
928	A169	25fr ultra & multi	.20	.20
929	A169	30fr pink & multi	.20	.20
		Nos. 928-929,C276-C277 (4)	1.35	1.00

Centenary of first telephone call by Alexander Graham Bell, Mar. 10, 1876.

Blind Man and Insect — A170

Marine Exhibition Hall — A171

1976, Apr. 8   Perf. 14x13
930	A170	50fr brt grn & multi	.30	.20

World Health Day: "Foresight prevents blindness." See No. C278.

Air Post Type, 1976, and Type A171

10fr, Pylon, flags of Ghana, Togo and Dahomey.

1976   Litho.   Perf. 14
931	A171	5fr multicolored	.20	.20
932	AP19	10fr multicolored	.20	.20
933	A171	50fr multicolored	.30	.25
		Nos. 931-933,C279 (4)	1.05	.85

Marine Exhibition, 10th anniv. (5fr, 50fr). Ghana-Togo-Dahomey electric power grid, 1st anniversary (10fr).
Issue dates: 50fr, May 8; 5fr, 10fr, August.

Running — A172

Montreal Olympic Emblem and: 30fr, Kayak. 50fr, High jump.

1976, June 15   Photo.   Perf. 14x13
934	A172	25fr multicolored	.20	.20
935	A172	30fr multicolored	.20	.20
936	A172	35fr multicolored	.35	.20
		Nos. 934-936,C284-C286 (6)	3.10	1.90

21st Olympic Games, Montreal, Canada, July 17-Aug. 1.
For overprints see Nos. 947, C298-C299.

Titan 3 and Viking Emblem — A173

50fr, Viking trajectory, Earth to Mars.

1976, July 15   Litho.   Perf. 14
937	A173	30fr blue & multi	.20	.20
938	A173	50fr rose & multi	.30	.20
		Nos. 937-938,C287-C290 (6)	2.90	1.70

US Viking Mars missions.

Young Routy at Celeyran, by Toulouse-Lautrec A174

Mohammed Ali Jinnah, Flags of Togo and Pakistan — A176

Adoration of the Shepherds, by Pontormo — A175

Paintings by Toulouse-Lautrec: 20fr, Model in Studio. 35fr, Louis Pascal, portrait.

1976, Aug. 7   Litho.   Perf. 14
939	A174	10fr black & multi	.20	.20
940	A174	20fr black & multi	.20	.20
941	A174	35fr black & multi	.25	.20
		Nos. 939-941,C291-C293 (6)	2.50	1.60

Henri Toulouse-Lautrec (1864-1901), French painter, 75th death anniversary.

No. 846 Overprinted: "Journée / Internationale / de l'Enfance"

1976, Nov. 27   Litho.   Perf. 14
942 A139 40fr multi   .25 .20
Intl. Children's Day. See No. C294.

1976, Dec. 18
Paintings: 30fr, Nativity, by Carlo Crivelli. 50fr, Virgin and Child, by Jacopo da Pontormo.
943 A175 25fr multi   .20 .20
944 A175 30fr multi   .20 .20
945 A175 50fr multi   .30 .20
    Nos. 943-945,C295-C297 (6)   2.70 1.70
Christmas.

1976, Dec. 24   Litho.   Perf. 13
946 A176 50fr multi   .30 .20
Jinnah (1876-1948), first Governor General of Pakistan.

No. 936 Overprinted: "CHAMPIONS OLYMPIQUES / SAUT EN HAUTEUR / POLOGNE"

1976, Dec.   Photo.   Perf. 14x13
947 A172 50fr multi   .35 .20
    Nos. 947,C298-C299 (3)   1.85 1.00
Olympic winners.

Queen Elizabeth II, Silver Jubilee
A176a

Designs: No. 947A, Portrait. No. 947B, Wearing coronation regalia.

Litho. & Embossed
1977, Jan. 10   Perf. 11
947A A176a 1000fr silver & multi
Souvenir Sheet
947B A176a 1000fr silver & multi
Exist imperf.

Kpeme Phosphate Mine, Sarakawa Crash
A177

1977, Jan. 13   Photo.   Perf. 13x14
948 A177 50fr multi   .30 .20
    Nos. 948,C300-C301 (3)   1.20 .70
Presidency of Etienne Eyadema, 10th anniv.

Musical Instruments
A178

1977, Feb. 7   Litho.   Perf. 14
949 A178   5fr Gongophone   .20 .20
950 A178 10fr Tamtam, vert.   .20 .20
951 A178 25fr Dondon   .20 .20
    Nos. 949-951,C302-C304 (6)   1.90 1.25

Victor Hugo and his Home
A179

1977, Feb. 26   Perf. 13x14
952 A179 50fr multi   .30 .20
Victor Hugo (1802-1885), French writer, 175th birth anniversary. See No. C305.

For overprints see Nos. 959, C316.

Beethoven and Birthplace, Bonn
A180

50fr, Bronze bust, 1812, & Heiligenstadt home.

1977, Mar. 7   Perf. 14
953 A180 30fr multi   .20 .20
954 A180 50fr multi   .30 .20
    Nos. 953-954,C306-C307 (4)   2.15 1.40

Benz, 1894, Germany — A181

Early Automobiles: 50fr, De Dion Bouton, 1903, France.

1977, Apr. 11   Litho.   Perf. 14
955 A181 35fr multi   .25 .20
956 A181 50fr multi   .35 .20
    Nos. 955-956,C308-C311 (6)   3.00 1.75

Lindbergh, Ground Crew and Spirit of St. Louis — A182

50fr, Lindbergh and Spirit of St. Louis.

1977, May 9
957 A182 25fr multi   .20 .20
958 A182 50fr multi   .20 .20
    Nos. 957-958,C312-C315 (6)   2.75 1.25
Charles A. Lindbergh's solo transatlantic flight from New York to Paris, 50th anniv.

No. 952 Overprinted: "10ème ANNIVERSAIRE DU / CONSEIL INTERNATIONAL / DE LA LANGUE FRANCAISE"

1977, May 17   Litho.   Perf. 14
959 A179 50fr multi   .40 .20
Intl. French Language Council, 10th anniv. See No. C316.

African Slender-snouted Crocodile — A183

Endangered wildlife: 15fr, Nile crocodile.

1977, June 13
960 A183   5fr multi   .20 .20
961 A183 15fr multi   .20 .20
    Nos. 960-961,C317-C320 (6)   3.45 1.35

Agriculture School, Tove
A184

1977, July 11   Litho.   Perf. 14
962 A184 50fr multi   .40 .20
    Nos. 962,C321-C323 (4)   2.85 1.00
Agricultural development.

Landscape with Cart, by Peter Paul Rubens (1577-1640) — A185

Rubens Painting: 35fr, Exchange of the Princesses at Hendaye, 1623.

1977, Aug. 8
963 A185 15fr multi   .20 .20
964 A185 35fr multi   .25 .20
    Nos. 963-964,C324-C325 (4)   1.50 .80

Orbiter 101 on Ground — A186

Designs: 30fr, Launching of Orbiter, vert. 50fr, Ejection of propellant tanks at take-off.

1977, Oct. 4   Litho.   Perf. 14
965 A186 20fr multi   .20 .20
966 A186 30fr multi   .25 .20
967 A186 50fr multi   .35 .20
    Nos. 965-967,C326-C328 (6)   3.30 1.35
Space shuttle trials in the US.

Lafayette Arriving in Montpelier, Vt. — A187

Design: 25fr, Lafayette, age 19, vert.

1977, Nov. 7   Perf. 14x13, 13x14
968 A187 25fr multi   .20 .20
969 A187 50fr multi   .35 .20
    Nos. 968-969,C329-C330 (4)   1.65 .80
Arrival of the Marquis de Lafayette in North America, 200th anniv.

Lenin, Cruiser Aurora, Red Flag
A188

1977, Nov. 7   Litho.   Perf. 14
970 A188 50fr multi   .35 .20
Russian October Revolution, 60th anniv.

Virgin and Child, by Lorenzo Lotto — A189

Virgin and Child by: 30fr, Carlo Bellini. 50fr, Cosimo Tura.

1977, Dec. 19   Perf. 14
971 A189 20fr multi   .20 .20
972 A189 30fr multi   .25 .20
973 A189 50fr multi   .35 .20
    Nos. 971-973,C331-C333 (6)   3.45 1.35
Christmas.

Perf. 14x13, 13x14
1978, Jan. 9   Litho.
Design: 20fr, Vaccination clinic, horiz.
974 A190   5fr multi   .20 .20
975 A190 20fr multi   .20 .20
    Nos. 974-975,C334-C335 (4)   1.15 .80
Worldwide eradication of smallpox.

Orville and Wilbur Wright — A191

Design: 50fr, Wilbur Wright flying at Kill Devil Hill, 1902.

1978, Feb. 6   Litho.   Perf. 14
976 A191 35fr multi   .25 .20
977 A191 50fr multi   .35 .20
    Nos. 976-977,C336-C339 (6)   4.85 1.75
75th anniversary of first motorized flight.

Anniversaries and Events — A192

Designs: No. 978, High jump. No. 979, Westminster Abbey. No. 980, Soccer players, World Cup. No. 981, Apollo 8. No. 982, Duke of Wellington, by Goya. No. 983, Hurdles. No. 984, Coronation coach. No. 985, Soccer players. No. 986, Apollo launch. No. 987, Dona Isabel Cobos de Porcel, by Goya.

1978, Mar. 13   Perf. 11
978 A192 1000fr gold & multi
979 A192 1000fr gold & multi
980 A192 1000fr gold & multi
981 A192 1000fr gold & multi
982 A192 1000fr gold & multi
Souvenir Sheets
983 A192 1000fr gold & multi
984 A192 1000fr gold & multi
985 A192 1000fr gold & multi
986 A192 1000fr gold & multi
987 A192 1000fr gold & multi

Nos. 978, 983, 1980 Summer Olympics, Moscow. Nos. 979, 984, Coronation of Queen Elizabeth II, 25th anniv. Nos. 980, 985, 1978 World Cup Soccer Championships, Argentina. Nos. 981, 986, 1st manned lunar orbit, 10th anniv. Nos. 982, 987, Death sesquicent. of Francisco Goya.
For overprints see Nos. 1056A-1056B, 1094A-1094B.
Exist imperf.

John, the Evangelist and Eagle — A197

Evangelists: 10fr, Luke and ox. 25fr, Mark and lion. 30fr, Matthew and angel.

1978, Mar. 20   Litho.   Perf. 13½x14
988 A197   5fr multi   .20 .20
989 A197 10fr multi   .20 .20
990 A197 25fr multi   .20 .20
991 A197 30fr multi   .25 .20
    a.   Souvenir sheet of 4   .60 .60
    Nos. 988-991 (4)   .85 .80
No. 991a contains one each of Nos. 988-991 with simulated perforations.

Anchor,
Fishing
Harbor,
Lomé
A199

1978, Apr. 26   Photo.   Perf. 13
997 A199 25fr multi   .20   .20
  Nos. 997,C340-C342 (4)   2.65 1.00

Venera I,
USSR — A200

Soccer — A201

Designs: 30fr, Pioneer, US, horiz. 50fr,
Venera, fuel base and antenna.

1978, May 8   Litho.   Perf. 14
998 A200 20fr multi   .20   .20
999 A200 30fr multi   .25   .20
1000 A200 50fr multi   .35   .20
  Nos. 998-1000,C343-C345 (6)   3.45 1.35
US Pioneer and USSR Venera space
missions.

1978, June 5   Perf. 14
50fr, Soccer players and Argentina '78
emblem.
1001 A201 30fr multi   .25   .20
1002 A201 50fr multi   .40   .20
  Nos. 1001-1002,C346-C349 (6) 5.00 1.65
11th World Cup Soccer Championship,
Argentina, June 1-25.

Celerifère,
1818
A202

History of the Bicycle: 50fr, First bicycle
sidecar, c. 1870, vert.

Perf. 13x14, 14x13
1978, July 10   Photo.
1003 A202 25fr multi   .20   .20
1004 A202 50fr multi   .35   .20
  Nos. 1003-1004,C350-C353 (6) 2.75 1.30

Thomas A.
Edison, Sound
Waves — A203

Dunant's
Birthplace,
Geneva — A204

Design: 50fr, Victor's His Master's Voice
phonograph, 1905, and dancing couple.

1978, July 8   Photo.   Perf. 14x13
1005 A203 30fr multicolored   .25   .20
1006 A203 50fr multicolored   .35   .20
  Nos. 1005-1006,C354-C357 (6) 4.80 1.65
Centenary of the phonograph, invented by
Thomas Alva Edison.

1978, Sept. 4   Photo.   Perf. 14x13
Designs: 10fr, Henri Dunant and red cross.
25fr, Help on battlefield, 1864, and red cross.
1007 A204 5fr Prus bl & red   .20   .20
1008 A204 10fr red brn & red   .20   .20
1009 A204 25fr grn & red   .20   .20
  Nos. 1007-1009,C358 (4)   1.00   .80
Dunant (1828-1910), founder of Red Cross.

Threshing, by Raoul Dufy — A205

50fr, Horsemen on Seashore, by Paul
Gauguin.

1978, Nov. 6   Litho.   Perf. 14
1010 A205 25fr multi   .20   .20
1011 A205 50fr multi   .35   .20
  Nos. 1010-1011,C359-C362 (6) 3.25 1.85

Eiffel Tower,
Paris — A206

Virgin and Child,
by Antonello da
Messina — A207

1978, Nov. 27   Photo.   Perf. 14x13
1012 A206 50fr multi   .35   .20
  Nos. 1012,C365-C367 (4)   2.85 1.40
Centenary of the Congress of Paris.

1978, Dec. 18   Litho.   Perf. 14
Paintings (Virgin and Child): 30fr, by Carlo
Crivelli. 50fr, by Francesco del Cossa.
1013 A207 20fr multi   .20   .20
1014 A207 30fr multi   .25   .20
1015 A207 50fr multi   .35   .20
  Nos. 1013-1015,C368-C370 (6) 3.30 1.90
Christmas.

Capt. Cook's Ship
off New
Zealand — A208

Entry into
Jerusalem
A209

Design: 50fr, Endeavour in drydock, N.E.
Coast of Australia, horiz.

1979, Feb. 12   Litho.   Perf. 14
1016 A208 25fr multi   .20   .20
1017 A208 50fr multi   .35   .20
  Nos. 1016-1017,C371-C374 (6) 3.40 2.40
200th death anniv. of Capt. James Cook.

1979, Apr. 9
Easter: 40fr, The Last Supper, horiz. 50fr,
Descent from the Cross, horiz.
1018 A209 30fr multi   .25   .20
1019 A209 40fr multi   .30   .20
1020 A209 50fr multi   .35   .20
  Nos. 1018-1020,C375-C377 (6) 3.35 1.80

Einstein Observatory,
Potsdam — A210

Design: 50fr, Einstein and James Ramsay
MacDonald, Berlin, 1931.

1979, July 2   Photo.   Perf. 14x13
1021 A210 35fr multi   .25   .20
1022 A210 50fr multi   .35   .20
  Nos. 1021-1022,C380-C383 (6) 3.65 1.90
Albert Einstein (1879-1955), theoretical
physicist.

Children and
Children's
Village
Emblem — A211

Man Planting
Tree — A212

IYC: 10fr, Mother and children. 15fr, Map of
Africa, Children's Village emblem, horiz. 20fr,
Woman and children walking to Children's Vil-
lage, horiz. 25fr, Children sitting under African
fan palm. 30fr, Map of Togo with location of
Children's Villages.

1979, July 30   Photo.   Perf. 14x13
1023 A211 5fr multi   .20   .20
1024 A211 10fr multi   .20   .20
1025 A211 15fr multi   .20   .20
1026 A211 20fr multi   .20   .20
1027 A211 25fr multi   .20   .20
1028 A211 30fr multi   .25   .20
  a.   Souv. sheet of 2, #1027-1028   .45
  Nos. 1023-1028 (6)   1.25 1.20

1979, Aug. 13   Perf. 14x13
1029 A212 50fr lilac & green   .35   .20
Second Arbor Day. See No. C384.

Sir Rowland Hill
(1795-1879),
Originator of
Penny
Postage — A213

Olympic Flame,
Lake Placid 80
Emblem,
Slalom — A215

Norris Locomotive, 1843 — A214

30fr, French mail-sorting office, 18th cent.,
horiz. 50fr, Mailbox, Paris, 1850.

1979, Aug. 27
1030 A213 20fr multi   .20   .20
1031 A213 30fr multi   .25   .20
1032 A213 50fr multi   .35   .20
  Nos. 1030-1032,C385-C387 (6) 3.45 1.90

1979, Oct. 1   Litho.   Perf. 14
35fr, Stephenson's "Rocket," 1829, vert.
1033 A214 35fr multi   .25   .20
1034 A214 50fr multi   .35   .20
  Nos. 1033-1034,C388-C391 (6) 3.60 1.90

1979, Oct. 18   Litho.   Perf. 13½
1980 Olympic Emblems, Olympic Flame
and: 30fr, Yachting 50fr, Discus.
1035 A215 20fr multi   .20   .20
1036 A215 30fr multi   .25   .20
1037 A215 50fr multi   .35   .20
  Nos. 1035-1037,C392-C394 (6) 3.45 1.90
13th Winter Olympic Games, Lake Placid,
NY, 2/12-24/80 (90fr); 22nd Summer Olympic
Games, Moscow, 7/19-8/3/80.

Catholic
Priests
A216

Design: 30fr, Native praying, vert.

1979, Oct. 29   Perf. 13x14
1038 A216 30fr multi   .25   .20
1039 A216 50fr multi   .35   .20
  Nos. 1038-1039,C396-C397 (4) 1.45   .85
Religions in Togo.

Astronaut Walking
on Moon — A217

Design: 50fr, Space capsule orbiting moon.

1979, Nov. 5
1040 A217 35fr multi .25 .20
1041 A217 50fr multi .35 .20
Nos. 1040-1041,C398-C401 (6) 4.85 2.50

Apollo 11 moon landing, 10th anniversary.

Telecom 79 — A218

1979, Nov. 26   Photo.   Perf. 13x14
1042 A218 50fr multi .35 .20

3rd World Telecommunications Exhibition, Geneva, Sept. 20-26. See No. C402.

Holy Family — A219

Rotary Emblem — A220

Christmas: 30fr, Virgin and Child. 50fr, Adoration of the Kings.

1979, Dec. 17   Litho.   Perf. 14
1043 A219 20fr multi .20 .20
1044 A219 30fr multi .25 .20
1045 A219 50fr multi .35 .20
Nos. 1043-1045,C403-C405 (6) 3.30 1.90

1980, Jan. 14

Rotary Emblem and: 30fr, Anniversary emblem. 40fr, Paul P. Harris, Rotary founder.

1046 A220 25fr multi .20 .20
1047 A220 30fr multi .25 .20
1048 A220 40fr multi .30 .20
Nos. 1046-1048,C406-C408 (6) 3.25 1.90

Rotary International, 75th anniversary.

Biathlon, Lake Placid '80 Emblem — A221

1980, Jan. 31   Litho.   Perf. 13½
1049 A221 50fr multi .35 .20
Nos. 1049,C409-C411 (4) 2.65 1.40

13th Winter Olympic Games, Lake Placid, NY, Feb. 12-24. See No. C412.

1980 Winter Olympics, Lake Placid — A221a

Gold medalist: No. 1049F, Hanni Wenzel, Liechtenstein, women's slalom. No. 1049G, Eric Heiden, US, men's speed skating. No. 1049H, Jouko Tormanen, Finland, 90-meter ski jumping. No. 1049I, Erich Schaerer, Josef Benz, Switzerland, 2-man bobsled. No. 1049J, US, ice hockey.

1980   Litho.   Perf. 11
Souvenir Sheets
1049F A221a 1000fr gold & multi
1049G A221a 1000fr gold & multi
1049H A221a 1000fr gold & multi
1049I A221a 1000fr gold & multi
1049J A221a 1000fr gold & multi

Exist imperf.

Swimming, Moscow '80 Emblem — A222

1980, Feb. 29   Litho.   Perf. 13½
1050 A222 20fr shown .20 .20
1051 A222 30fr Gymnastics .25 .20
1052 A222 50fr Running .45 .25
Nos. 1050-1052,C413-C415 (6) 5.90 3.15

22nd Summer Olympic Games, Moscow, July 19-Aug. 3.

Christ and the Angels, by Andrea Mantegna A223

Easter 1980 (Paintings by): 40fr, Carlo Crivelli. 50fr, Jacopo Pontormo.

1980, Mar. 31   Perf. 14
1053 A223 30fr multi .25 .20
1054 A223 40fr multi .30 .20
1055 A223 50fr multi .35 .20
Nos. 1053-1055,C416-C418 (6) 3.20 1.80

Jet over Map of Africa A224

1980, Mar. 24   Litho.   Perf. 12½
1056 A224 50fr multi .35 .20
ASECNA (Air Safety Board), 20th anniv. See No. C419.

Nos. 979, 984 Ovptd. "Londres / 1980"
Litho. & Embossed
1980, May 6   Perf. 11
1056A A192 1000fr gold & multi
Souvenir Sheet
1056B A192 1000fr gold & multi

12th World Telecommunications Day — A225

1980, May 17   Photo.   Perf. 14x13½
1057 A225 50fr multi .35 .20

See No. C420.

Red Cross over Globe Showing Lomé, Togo — A226

1980, June 16   Photo.   Perf. 14x13
1058 A226 50fr multi .35 .20

Togolese Red Cross. See No. C421.

Jules Verne (1828-1905), French Science Fiction Writer — A227

1980, July 14   Litho.   Perf. 14
1059 A227 30fr multi .25 .20
1060 A227 50fr multi .35 .20
Nos. 1059-1060,C422-C425 (6) 3.45 1.85

Baroness James de Rothschild, by Ingres — A228

50fr, Shark (20,000 Leagues Under the Sea).

1980, Aug. 29   Litho.   Perf. 14

Paintings by Jean Auguste Dominique Ingres (1780-1867): 30fr, Napoleon I on Imperial Throne. 40fr, Don Pedro of Toledo and Henri IV.

1061 A228 25fr multi .20 .20
1062 A228 30fr multi .25 .20
1063 A228 40fr multi .30 .20
Nos. 1061-1063,C426-C428 (6) 3.25 1.90

Minnie Holding Mirror for Leopard A229

Disney Characters and Animals from Fazao Reserve: 2fr, Goofy (Dingo) cleaning teeth of hippopotamus. 3fr, Donald holding snout of crocodile. 4fr, Donald dangling over cliff from horn of rhinoceros. 5fr, Goofy riding water buffalo. 10fr, Monkey taking picture of Mickey. 100fr, Mickey as doctor examining giraffe with sore throat. 200fr, Pluto in party hat. No. 1071, Elephant giving shower to Goofy. No. 1072, Lion carrying Goofy by seat of his pants. No. 1072A, Pluto.

1980, Sept. 15   Perf. 11
1064 A229 1fr multi .20 .20
1065 A229 2fr multi .20 .20
1066 A229 3fr multi .20 .20
1067 A229 4fr multi .20 .20
1068 A229 5fr multi .20 .20
1069 A229 10fr multi .20 .20
1070 A229 100fr multi .75 .35
1070A A229 200fr multi 1.50 .75
1071 A229 300fr multi 2.25 1.10
Nos. 1064-1071 (9) 5.70 3.40

Souvenir Sheets
1072 A229 300fr multi 2.25 1.10
1072A A229 300fr multi 2.25 1.10

50th anniv. of the Disney character Pluto.

Market Activities, Women Preparing Meat A230

1980-81   Perf. 14
1073 A230 1fr Grinding savo .20 .20
1074 A230 2fr shown .20 .20
1075 A230 3fr Truck going to market .20 .20
1076 A230 4fr Unloading produce .20 .20
1077 A230 5fr Sugar cane vendor .20 .20
1078 A230 6fr Barber curling child's hair, vert. .20 .20
1079 A230 7fr Vegetable vendor .20 .20
1080 A230 8fr Sampling mangos, vert. .20 .20
1081 A230 9fr Grain vendor .20 .20
1082 A230 10fr Spiced fish vendor .20 .20
1083 A230 15fr Clay pot vendor .20 .20
1084 A230 20fr Straw baskets .20 .20
1085 A230 25fr Selling lemons and onions, vert. .20 .20
1086 A230 30fr Straw baskets, diff. .25 .20
1087 A230 40fr Shore market .30 .20
1087A A230 45fr Vegatable stall .30 .20
1088 A230 50fr Women carrying produce, vert. .40 .20
1088A A230 60fr Rice wine .40 .20
Nos. 1073-1088A (18) 4.25 3.60

Issued: 45fr, 60fr, 3/8/81; others, 3/17/80. Nos. 1087A, 1088A dated 1980.
See Nos. C440-C445, J68-J71. For overprints see Nos. C486-C487.

Commemorative Wreath — A231

Famous Men of the Decade: 40fr, Mao Tsetung, vert.

1980, Feb. 11   *Perf. 14x13*
1089 A231 25fr multi   .25 .20
1090 A231 40fr emer grn & dk
    grn   .40 .20
Nos. 1089-1090,C429-C431 (5)   3.15 1.70

World Tourism Conference, Manila,
Sept. 27 — A232

1980, Sept. 15   *Litho.*   *Perf. 14*
1091 A232 50fr Hotel tourism
    emblem, vert.   .50 .25
1092 A232 150fr shown   1.50 .75

Map of
Australia
and Human
Rights
Flame
A233

1980, Oct. 13   *Photo.*   *Perf. 13x14*
1093 A233 30fr shown   .30 .20
1094 A233 50fr Europe and Asia
    map   .50 .25
Nos. 1093-1094,C432-C433 (4)   2.20 1.15

Declaration of Human Rights, 30th anniv.

#980, 985 Ovptd. in Gold & Black

**COUPE DU MONDE
DE FOOTBALL
ESPAÑA 1982**

Litho. & Embossed
1980, Nov. 24   *Perf. 11*
1094A A192 1000fr gold & multi
Souvenir Sheet
1094B A192 1000fr gold & multi

No. 1094B ovptd. with additional text and
black bars in sheet margin.

Melk
Monastery,
Austria, 18th
Century
A234

     Perf. 14½x13½
1980, Dec. 22   *Litho.*
1095 A234 20fr shown   .20 .20
1096 A234 30fr Tarragon Cathe-
    dral, Spain, 12th
    cent.   .30 .20
1097 A234 50fr St. John the Bap-
    tist, Florence,
    1964   .50 .25
Nos. 1095-1097,C435-C437 (6)   3.90 2.15

Christmas.

African Postal
Union, 5th
Anniversary
A235

1980, Dec. 24   *Photo.*   *Perf. 13½*
1098 A235 100fr multi   .75 .35

February
2nd Hotel
Opening
A236

1981, Feb. 2   *Litho.*   *Perf. 12½x13*
1099 A236 50fr multi   .50 .25

See No. C437B.

A236a

A237

1981, Dec. 21   *Litho.*   *Perf. 12½*
1100 A236a 70fr lt grn & multi   .70 .35

West African Rice Development Assoc.
See No. C461.

1981, Apr. 13   *Perf. 14½x13½*

Easter (Rembrandt Paintings): 30fr, Rembrandt's Father. 40fr, Self-portrait. 50fr, Artist's
father as an old man. 60fr, Rider on
Horseback.

1101 A237 30fr multi   .25 .20
1102 A237 40fr multi   .30 .20
1103 A237 50fr multi   .35 .20
1104 A237 60fr multi   .45 .25
Nos. 1101-1104,C438-C439 (6)   3.25 1.85

Wedding of Prince Charles and Lady
Diana Spencer — A237a

1981, July 29   *Litho.*   *Perf. 11*
1105 A237a 1000fr gold & multi
Souvenir Sheet
Litho. & Embossed
1106 A237a 1000fr Charles & Di-
    ana, diff.

No. 1105 printed with embossed se-tenant
label.
For overprints see Nos. 1143A-1143B.

Red-headed Rock Fowl — A238

1981, Aug. 10   *Perf. 13½x14½*
1107 A238 30fr shown   .20 .20
1108 A238 40fr Splendid sunbird   .25 .20
1109 A238 60fr Violet-backed
    starling   .40 .20
1110 A238 90fr Red-collared
    widowbird   .60 .30
Nos. 1107-1110,C446-C447 (6)   2.45 1.45

1982 World Soccer Championships,
Spain — A238a

Flags (Nos. 1110A-1110E) or Players (Nos.
1110F-1110J) and stadiums: Nos. 1110A,
1110F, Athletico de Madrid. Nos. 1110B,
1110G, Real Madrid C.F. Nos. 1110C, 1110H,
R.C.D. Espanol. Nos. 1110D, 1110I, Real
Zaragoza. Nos. 1110E, 1110J, Valencia.

Litho. & Embossed
1981, Aug. 17   *Perf. 11*
1110A-1110E A238a 1000fr Set of
    5
Souvenir Sheets
1110F-1110J A238a 1000fr Set of
    5

African
Postal
Union
Ministers,
6th Council
Meeting,
July 28-20
A239

1981, Aug. 31   *Litho.*   *Perf. 12½*
1111 A239 70fr Dish antenna   .50 .25
1112 A239 90fr Computer oper-
    ator, vert.   .70 .35
1113 A239 105fr Map   .80 .40
Nos. 1111-1113 (3)   2.00 1.00

Intl. Year of
the
Disabled
A240

1981, Aug. 31   *Perf. 14*
1114 A240 70fr Blind man   .70 .35
Nos. 1114,C448-C449 (3)   2.55 1.30

See No. C449A.

Woman with
Hat, by
Picasso,
1961 — A241

Picasso Birth Centenary: Sculptures.

1981, Sept. 14   *Perf. 14½x13½*
1116 A241 25fr shown   .20 .20
1117 A241 50fr She-goat   .35 .20
1118 A241 60fr Violin, 1915   .40 .20
Nos. 1116-1118,C450-C452 (6)   3.55 1.90

Aix-la-Chapelle Cathedral,
Germany — A242

World Heritage Year: 40fr, Geyser, Yellow-
stone Natl. Park. 50fr, Nahanni Natl. Park,
Canada. 60fr, Stone churches, Ethiopia.

1981, Sept. 28   *Perf. 13½x14½*
1119 A242 30fr multi   .25 .20
1120 A242 40fr multi   .30 .20
1121 A242 50fr multi   .35 .20
1122 A242 60fr multi   .45 .30
Nos. 1119-1122,C453-C454 (6)   3.60 2.00

Yuri Gagarin's Vostok I, 20th. — A243

Space Anniversaries: 50fr, 20th Anniv. of
Alan Shepard's Flight. 60fr, Lunar Orbiter I,
15th.

1981, Nov.   *Perf. 14*
1123 A243 25fr multi   .20 .20
1124 A243 50fr multi   .35 .20
1125 A243 60fr multi   .45 .25
Nos. 1123-1125,C455-C456 (5)   2.45 1.40

Christmas
A244

Rubens Paintings: 20fr, Adoration of the
Kings. 30fr, Adoration of the Shepherds. 50fr,
St. Catherine.

Perf. 14½x13½
1981, Dec. 10   Litho.
1126 A244 20fr multi .20 .20
1127 A244 30fr multi .20 .20
1128 A244 50fr multi .35 .20
   Nos. 1126-1128,C457-C459 (6)   4.80 2.60

15th Anniv. of Natl. Liberation — A245

1982, Jan. 13   Litho.   **Perf. 12½**
1129 A245 70fr Dove, flag .70 .35
1130 A245 90fr Citizens, Pres.
       Eyadema, vert. .90 .45
   Nos. 1129-1130,C462-C463 (4)   3.20 1.55

Scouting
Year
A246

1982, Feb. 25   Litho.   **Perf. 14**
1131 A246 70fr Pitching tent .45 .25
   Nos. 1131,C464-C467 (5)   3.65 1.80

Easter — A247

Designs: The Ten Commandments.

1982, Mar. 15   **Perf. 14x14½**
1132 A247 10fr multi .20 .20
1133 A247 25fr multi .20 .20
1134 A247 30fr multi .20 .20
1135 A247 45fr multi .30 .20
1136 A247 50fr multi .35 .20
1137 A247 70fr multi .45 .25
1138 A247 90fr multi .60 .30
   Nos. 1132-1138,C469-C470 (9)   3.80 2.30

Papilio
Dardanus
A248

1982, July 15   Litho.   **Perf. 14½x14**
1139 A248 15fr shown .20 .20
1140 A248 20fr Belenois calypso .20 .20
1141 A248 25fr Palla decius .20 .20
   Nos. 1139-1141,C474-C475 (5)   1.90 1.25

1982 World
Cup — A249

Designs: Various soccer players.

1982, July 26   **Perf. 14x14½**
1142 A249 25fr multi .20 .20
1143 A249 45fr multi .30 .20
   Nos. 1142-1143,C477-C479 (5)   4.50 2.40

For overprints see Nos. 1150-1155.

Nos. 1105-1106 Ovptd. "BEBE
ROYALE 21 JUIN 1982" on one or two
lines

1982, Oct. 28   Litho.   **Perf. 11**
1143A A237a 1000fr gold & multi

Souvenir Sheet
Litho. & Embossed
1143B A237a 1000fr gold & multi

Christmas
A250

Madonna of Baldacchino, by Raphael.
#1144-1148 show details; #1149 entire
painting.

1982, Dec. 24   Litho.   **Perf. 14½x14**
1144 A250 45fr multi .30 .20
1145 A250 70fr multi .45 .25
1146 A250 105fr multi .70 .35
1147 A250 130fr multi .90 .40
1148 A250 150fr multi 1.00 .50
   Nos. 1144-1148 (5)   3.35 1.70

Souvenir Sheet
Perf. 14x14½
1149 A250 500fr multi, vert. 3.50 1.60

Nos. 1142-1143, C477-C480
Overprinted: VAINQUER / COUPE DU
MONDE / FOOTBALL 82 / "ITALIE"
1983, Jan. 31   Litho.   **Perf. 14x14½**
1150 A249 25fr multi .20 .20
1151 A249 45fr multi .30 .20
1152 A249 105fr multi .70 .35
1153 A249 200fr multi 1.40 .65
1154 A249 300fr multi 2.00 1.00
   Nos. 1150-1154 (5)   4.60 2.40

Souvenir Sheet
1155 A249 500fr multi 3.50 1.60

Italy's victory in 1982 World Cup. Nos.
1152-1155 airmail.

20th Anniv. of West
African Monetary
Union
(1982) — A251

1983, May   Litho.   **Perf. 12½x12**
1156 A251 70fr Map .45 .25
1157 A251 90fr Emblem .60 .30

Visit of Pres. Mitterand of France, Jan.
13-15 — A252

1983, Jan. 13   Litho.   **Perf. 13**
1158 A252 35fr Sokode Region-
       al Hospital .25 .20
   a.   Souvenir sheet, imperf. .25 .20
1159 A252 45fr Citizens joining
       hands .30 .20
   a.   Souvenir sheet, imperf. .35 .20
1160 A252 70fr Soldiers, vert. .45 .25
   a.   Souvenir sheet, imperf. .50 .25
1161 A252 90fr Pres. Mitterand,
       vert. .60 .30
   a.   Souvenir sheet, imperf. .65 .35
1162 A252 105fr Pres. Eyadema,
       Mitterand, vert. .70 .35
   a.   Souvenir sheet, imperf. .70 .35

1163 A252 130fr Greeting crowd .90 .40
   a.   Souvenir sheet, imperf. .90 .40
   Nos. 1158-1163 (6)   3.20 1.70

Nos. 1161-1163 airmail.

Easter — A253

Paintings: 35fr, Mourners at the Death of
Christ, by Bellini. 70fr, Crucifixion, by Raphael.
90fr, Descent from the Cross, by Carracci.
500fr Christ, by Reni.

1983   Litho.   **Perf. 13½x14½**
1164 A253 35fr multi .20 .20
1165 A253 70fr multi, vert. .25 .20
1166 A253 90fr multi .30 .20
   Nos. 1164-1166 (3)   .75 .60

Souvenir Sheet
Perf. 14½x13½
1167 A253 500fr multi 1.65 .80

90fr, 500fr airmail.

Folkdances — A254

1983, Dec. 1   **Perf. 14½x14**
1168 A254 70fr Kondona .25 .20
1169 A254 90fr Kondona, diff. .30 .20
1170 A254 105fr Toubole .35 .20
1171 A254 130fr Adjogbo .40 .20
   Nos. 1168-1171 (4)   1.30 .80

90fr, 105fr, 130fr airmail.

World
Communications
Year — A255

1983, June 20   Litho.   **Perf. 14x14½**
1172 A255 70fr Drummer .25 .20
1173 A255 90fr Modern communi-
       cation .30 .20

90fr airmail.

Christmas — A256

1983, Dec.   **Perf. 13½x14½**
1174 A256 70fr Catholic
       Church, Kante .25 .20
1175 A256 90fr Altar, Dapaong
       Cathedral .30 .20
1176 A256 105fr Protestant
       Church,
       Dapaong .35 .20
   Nos. 1174-1176 (3)   .90 .60

Souvenir Sheet
1177 A256 500fr Ecumenical
       Church, Pya 1.60 .80

90fr, 105fr, 500fr airmail.

Sarakawa Presidential Assassination
Attempt, 10th Anniv. — A257

1984, Jan. 24   Litho.   **Perf. 13**
1178 A257 70fr Wrecked plane .25 .20
1179 A257 90fr Plane, diff. .30 .20
1180 A257 120fr Memorial Hall .40 .20
1181 A257 270fr Pres. Eyadema
       statue, vert. .90 .40
   Nos. 1178-1181 (4)   1.85 1.00

120fr, 270fr airmail.

20th Anniv.
of World
Food
Program
(1983)
A258

1984, May 2   Litho.   **Perf. 13**
1182 A258 35fr Orchard .20 .20
1183 A258 70fr Fruit tree .25 .20
1184 A258 90fr Rice paddy .30 .20
   Nos. 1182-1184 (3)   .75 .60

Souvenir Sheet
1185 A258 300fr Village, horiz. 1.00 .50

25th Anniv. of
Council of
Unity — A259

Easter
1984 — A260

1984, May 29   **Perf. 12**
1186 A259 70fr multi .25 .20
1187 A259 90fr multi .30 .20

1984   Litho.   **Perf. 14x14½**

Various stained-glass windows.

1188 A260 70fr multi .25 .20
1189 A260 90fr multi .30 .20
1190 A260 120fr multi .40 .20
1191 A260 270fr multi .90 .45
1192 A260 300fr multi 1.00 .50
   Nos. 1188-1192 (5)   2.85 1.55

Souvenir Sheet
1193 A260 500fr multi 1.60 .80

Nos. 1189-1193 airmail.

Centenary of German-Togolese Friendship — A261

#1194, Degbenou Catholic Mission, 1893. #1195, Kara Bridge, 1911. #1196, Treaty Site, Baguida, 1884. #1197, Degbenou Students, 1893. #1198, Sansane Administrative Post, 1908. #1199, Adjido Official School.
#1200, Sokode Cotton Market, 1910. #1201, William Fountain, Atakpame, 1906. #1202, Lome Main Street, 1895, No. 19. #1203, Police, 1905. #1204, Lome Railroad Construction. #1205, Governor's Palace, Lome, 1905. #1206, No. 9, Commerce Street, Lome.
#1207, Nos. 10, 17. #1208, Lome Wharf, 1903. #1209, G. Nachtigal. #1210, Wilhelm II. #1211, O.F. de Bismark. #1212, J. de Puttkamer. #1213, A. Koehler. #1214, W. Horn. #1215, J.G. de Zech. #1216, E. Bruckner. #1217, A.F. de Mecklenburg. #1218, H.G. de Doering. #1219, Land Development, 1908.
#1220, Postal Courier, No. 8. #1221, Treaty Signers, 1885. 150fr, German & Togolese Children, Flags. #1223, Aneho Line Locomotive, 1905. #1224, Mallet Locomotive, 1907. #1225, German Ship "Mowe," 1884. #1226, "La Sophie," 1884. 300fr, Pres. Eyadema, Helmut Kohl.

1984, July 5		Litho.	Perf. 13	
1194	A261	35fr multi	.20	.20
1195	A261	35fr multi	.20	.20
1196	A261	35fr multi, vert.	.20	.20
1197	A261	35fr multi	.20	.20
1198	A261	35fr multi	.20	.20
1199	A261	35fr multi	.20	.20
1200	A261	35fr multi	.20	.20
1201	A261	45fr multi, vert.	.20	.20
1202	A261	45fr multi	.20	.20
1203	A261	45fr multi	.20	.20
1204	A261	45fr multi	.20	.20
1205	A261	45fr multi	.20	.20
1206	A261	45fr multi	.20	.20
1207	A261	70fr multi	.25	.20
1208	A261	70fr multi	.25	.20
1209	A261	90fr multi	.30	.20
1210	A261	90fr multi, vert.	.30	.20
1211	A261	90fr multi, vert.	.30	.20
1212	A261	90fr multi, vert.	.30	.20
1213	A261	90fr multi	.30	.20
1214	A261	90fr multi	.30	.20
1215	A261	90fr multi	.30	.20
1216	A261	90fr multi	.30	.20
1217	A261	90fr multi, vert.	.30	.20
1218	A261	90fr multi, vert.	.30	.20
1219	A261	90fr multi	.30	.20
1220	A261	120fr multi, vert.	.40	.20
1221	A261	120fr multi	.40	.20
1222	A261	150fr multi, vert.	.50	.25
1223	A261	270fr multi	.90	.45
1224	A261	270fr multi	.90	.45
1225	A261	270fr multi	.90	.45
1226	A261	270fr multi	.90	.45
1227	A261	300fr multi	1.00	.50
		Nos. 1194-1227 (34)	12.30	8.15

Souvenir sheets of one exist for each design. Stamp size: 65x80mm.

Donald Duck, 50th Anniv. A262

1984, Sept. 21		Litho.	Perf. 11	
1230	A262	1fr Donald, Chip	.20	.20
1231	A262	2fr Donald, Chip and Dale	.20	.20
1232	A262	3fr Louie, Chip and Dale	.20	.20
1233	A262	5fr Donald, Chip	.20	.20
1234	A262	10fr Daisy Duck, Donald	.20	.20
1235	A262	15fr Goofy, Donald	.20	.20
1236	A262	105fr Huey, Dewey and Louie	.30	.20
1237	A262	500fr Nephews, Donald	1.40	.70

1238	A262	1000fr Nephews, Donald	3.00	1.40
		Nos. 1230-1238 (9)	5.90	3.50

Souvenir Sheets
Perf. 14

1239	A262	1000fr Surprised Donald	3.00	1.40
1240	A262	1000fr Perplexed Donald	3.00	1.40

Nos. 1236-1240 airmail.
For overprints see Nos. C551-C554.

Endangered Mammals — A263

1984, Oct. 1		Litho.	Perf. 15x14½	
1241	A263	45fr Manatee swimming	.90	.30
1242	A263	70fr Manatee eating	1.10	.30
1243	A263	90fr Manatees floating	2.25	.50
1244	A263	105fr Young manatee, mother	2.75	.50
		Nos. 1241-1244 (4)	7.00	1.60

Souvenir Sheets
Perf. 14x15, 15x14

1245	A263	1000fr Olive Colobus monkey, vert.	3.00	1.40
1246	A263	1000fr Galago (Bushbaby)	3.00	1.40

Nos. 1243-1246 airmail. See #1444-1447.

Birth Centenary of Eleanor Roosevelt A264

1984, Oct. 10		Litho.	Perf. 13½	
1247	A264	70fr shown	.20	.20
1248	A264	90fr Mrs. Roosevelt, Statue of Liberty	.25	.20

No. 1248 airmail.

Classic Automobiles — A265

1984, Nov. 15		Litho.	Perf. 15	
1249	A265	1fr 1947 Bristol	.20	.20
1250	A265	2fr 1925 Frazer Nash	.20	.20
1251	A265	3fr 1950 Healey	.20	.20
1252	A265	4fr 1925 Kissell	.20	.20
1253	A265	50fr 1927 La Salle	.20	.20
1254	A265	90fr 1921 Minerva	.25	.20
1255	A265	500fr 1950 Morgan	1.40	.70
1256	A265	1000fr 1921 Napier	3.00	1.40
		Nos. 1249-1256 (8)	5.65	3.30

Souvenir Sheets

1257	A265	1000fr 1941 Nash	3.00	1.40
1258	A265	1000fr 1903 Peugeot	3.00	1.40

Nos. 1254-1258 airmail.
For overprints see Nos. 1328-1331, C542-C544, C564-C565.

Christmas A266

Perf. 14½x13½

1984, Nov. 23		Litho.	
1259	A266	70fr Connestable Madonna	.20	.20
1260	A266	290fr Cowper Madonna	.80	.40
1261	A266	300fr Alba Madonna	.80	.45
1262	A266	500fr Madonna of the Curtain	1.40	.70
		Nos. 1259-1262 (4)	3.20	1.75

Souvenir Sheet

1263	A266	1000fr Madonna with Child	3.00	1.40

Nos. 1260-1263 airmail.

African Locomotives — A267

1984, Nov. 30		Litho.	Perf. 15	
1264	A267	1fr Decapod, Madeira	.20	.20
1265	A267	2fr 2-6-0, Egypt	.20	.20
1266	A267	3fr 4-8-2+2-8-4, Algeria	.20	.20
1267	A267	4fr Congo-Ocean diesel	.20	.20
1268	A267	50fr 0-4-0+0-4-0, Libya	.20	.20
1269	A267	90fr #49, Malawi	.25	.20
1270	A267	105fr 1907 Mallet, Togo	.30	.20
1271	A267	500fr 4-8-2, Rhodesia	1.40	.70
1272	A267	1000fr Beyer-Garratt, East Africa	2.75	1.40
		Nos. 1264-1272 (9)	5.70	3.50

Souvenir Sheets

1273	A267	1000fr 2-8-2, Ghana	2.75	1.40
1274	A267	1000fr Locomotive, Senegal	2.75	1.40

Nos. 1269-1274 airmail.
For overprints see Nos. 1343-1346, 1356-1360, C541, C566.

Economic Convention, Lome — A268

1984, Dec. 8		Litho.	Perf. 12½	
1275		100fr Map of the Americas	.30	.20
1276		130fr Map of Eurasia, Africa	.45	.20
1277		270fr Map of Asia, Australia	.75	.40
a.		A268 Strip of 3, #1275-1277	1.50	.75

Souvenir Sheet

1278	A268	500fr President Eyadema	1.40	.70

No. 1277a has continuous design.

Intl. Civil Aviation Org., 40th Anniv. A269

Map of Togo, ICAO emblem and: 70fr, Lockheed Constellation, 1944. 105fr, Boeing 707 1954. 200fr, Doubas DC-8-61, 1966. 500fr, Bac/Sud Concorde, 1966. 1000fr, Icarus, by Hans Erni.

1984, Oct. 15		Litho.	Perf. 15x1..	
1279	A269	70fr multi	.20	.2.
1280	A269	105fr multi	.25	.2.
1281	A269	200fr multi	.40	.2.
1282	A269	500fr multi	1.00	.5.
		Nos. 1279-1282 (4)	1.85	1.1.

Souvenir Sheet

1283	A269	1000fr multi	2.00	1.0.

Nos. 1280-1283 airmail.

Fresco of the 12 Apostles, Baptistry of the Aryans, Ravenna, Italy, — A270

Designs: 1fr, St. Paul. 2fr, St. Thomas. 3fr, St. Matthew. 4fr, St. James the Younger. 5fr, St. Simon. 70fr, St. Thaddeaus Judas. 90fr, St. Bartholomew. 105fr, St. Philip. 200fr, St. John. 270fr, St. James the Greater. 400fr, St. Andrew. 500fr, St. Peter. No. 1296, The Last Supper, by Andrea del Castagno, c. 1421-1457, horiz. No, 1297, Coronation of the Virgin, by Raphael, 1483-1520, horiz.

1984, Dec. 14		Litho.	Perf. 15	
1284	A270	1fr multi	.20	.20
1285	A270	2fr multi	.20	.20
1286	A270	3fr multi	.20	.20
1287	A270	4fr multi	.20	.20
1288	A270	5fr multi	.20	.20
1289	A270	70fr multi	.20	.20
1290	A270	90fr multi	.20	.20
1291	A270	105fr multi	.20	.20
1292	A270	200fr multi	.40	.20
1293	A270	270fr multi	.55	.30
1294	A270	400fr multi	.80	.40
1295	A270	500fr multi	1.00	.50
		Nos. 1284-1295 (12)	4.35	3.00

Souvenir Sheets

1296-1297	A270	1000fr each	2.00	1.00

Nos. 1290-1297 airmail.
For overprints see Nos. C545-C547.

Race Horses A271

1985, Jan. 10				
1298	A271	1fr Allez France	.20	.20
1299	A271	2fr Arkle, vert.	.20	.20
1300	A271	3fr Tingle Creek, vert.	.20	.20
1301	A271	4fr Interco	.20	.20
1302	A271	50fr Dawn Run	.20	.20
1303	A271	90fr Seattle Slew, vert.	.20	.20
1304	A271	500fr Nijinsky	1.00	.50
1305	A271	1000fr Politician	2.00	1.00
		Nos. 1298-1305 (8)	4.20	2.70

Souvenir Sheets

1306	A271	1000fr Shergar	2.00	1.00
1307	A271	1000fr Red Rum	2.00	1.00

Nos. 1303-1307 airmail.
For overprints see Nos. 1353-1355A.

Easter — A272

Paintings by Raphael (1483-1520).

Perf. 13½x14½, 14½x13½
1985, Mar. 7
1308	A272	70fr Christ and His Flock	.20	.20
1309	A272	90fr Christ and the Fishermen	.20	.20
1310	A272	135fr The Blessed Christ, vert.	.25	.20
1311	A272	150fr The Entombment, vert.	.30	.20
1312	A272	250fr The Resurrection, vert.	.50	.25
		Nos. 1308-1312 (5)	1.45	1.05

Souvenir Sheet
1313	A272	1000fr The Resurrection, diff.	2.00	1.00

Nos. 1309-1313 airmail.

Technical & Cultural Cooperation Agency, 15th Anniv. — A273

1985, Mar. 20   *Perf. 12½*
1314	A273	70fr multi	.20	.20
1315	A273	90fr multi	.20	.20

Philexafrica '85, Lome — A274

1985, May 9   *Perf. 13*
1316	A274	200fr Woman carrying fruit basket	.40	.20
1317	A274	200fr Man plowing field	.40	.20
a.		Pair, #1316-1317 + label	.80	.40

Scarification Ritual — A275

1985, May 14   *Perf. 14x15*
1318	A275	25fr Kabye (Pya)	.20	.20
1319	A275	70fr Mollah (Kotokoli)	.20	.20
1320	A275	90fr Maba (Dapaong)	.20	.20
1321	A275	105fr Kabye (Pagouda)	.25	.20
1322	A275	270fr Peda	.55	.30
		Nos. 1318-1322 (5)	1.40	1.10

Nos. 1320-1322 airmail.

Seashells A276

70fr, Clavatula muricata. 90fr, Marginella desjardini. 120fr, Clavatula nifat. 135fr, Cypraea stercoraria. 270fr, Conus genuanus. 1000fr, Dancers wearing traditional shell decorations.

1985, June 1   *Perf. 15x14*
1323	A276	70fr multi	.20	.20
1324	A276	90fr multi	.20	.20
1325	A276	120fr multi	.25	.20

1326	A276	135fr multi	.25	.20
1327	A276	270fr multi	.55	.30
		Nos. 1323-1327 (5)	1.45	1.10

Souvenir Sheet
1327A	A276	1000fr multi	2.00	1.00

Nos. 1324-1327A airmail.

Nos. 1253, 1256-1258 Overprinted "Exposition Mondiale 1985 / Tsukuba, Japon"

1985, June   *Perf. 15*
1328	A265	50fr #1253	.20	.20
1329	A265	1000fr #1256	2.00	1.00

Souvenir Sheets
1330	A265	1000fr #1257	2.00	1.00
1331	A265	1000fr #1258	2.00	1.00

EXPO '85.

Audubon Birth Bicent. — A277

Illustrations by artist-naturalist J.J. Audubon (1785-1851).

1985, Aug. 13   *Perf. 13*
1332	A277	90fr Larus bonapartii	.20	.20
1333	A277	120fr Pelecanus occidentalis	.25	.20
1334	A277	135fr Cassidix mexicanus	.25	.20
1335	A277	270fr Aquila chrysaetos	.55	.30
1336	A277	500fr Picus erythrocephalus	1.00	.50
		Nos. 1332-1336 (5)	2.25	1.40

Souvenir Sheet
1337	A277	1000fr Dendroica petechia	2.00	1.00

Nos. 1332, 1334 and 1336-1337 airmail.

Dove, UN Emblem — A278

Kara Port Construction — A279

Designs: 115fr, Hands, UN emblem. 250fr, Millet crop, Atalote Research Facility. 500fr, UN, Togo flags, statesmen.

1985, Oct. 24   Litho.   *Perf. 13*
1338	A278	90fr multi	.20	.20
1339	A278	115fr multi	.25	.20
1340	A279	150fr multi	.30	.20
1341	A279	250fr multi	.50	.25
1342	A279	500fr multi	1.00	.50
		Nos. 1338-1342 (5)	2.25	1.35

UN, 40th anniv. Nos. 1340-1342 are airmail.

Nos. 1267, 1270, 1272, 1273 Ovptd. with Rotary Emblem and "80e ANNIVERSAIRE DU / ROTARY INTERNATIONAL"

1985   Litho.   *Perf. 15*
1343	A267	4fr multi	.20	.20
1344	A267	105fr multi	.20	.20
1345	A267	1000fr multi	2.00	1.00
		Nos. 1343-1345 (3)	2.40	1.40

Souvenir Sheet
1346	A267	1000fr multi	2.00	1.00

Nos. 1344-1346 are airmail.

Christmas A280

Religious paintings and statuary: 90fr, The Garden of Roses Madonna. 115fr, Madonna and Child, Byzantine, 11th cent. 150fr, Rest During the Flight to Egypt, by Gerard David (1450-1523). 160fr, African Madonna, 16th cent. 250fr, African Madonna, c. 1900. 500fr, Mystic Madonna, by Sandro Botticelli (1444-1510).

1985, Dec. 10   *Perf. 14½x13½*   Litho.
1347	A280	90fr multi	.25	.20
1348	A280	115fr multi	.30	.20
1349	A280	150fr multi	.40	.20
1350	A280	160fr multi	.40	.20
1351	A280	250fr multi	.65	.35
		Nos. 1347-1351 (5)	2.00	1.15

Souvenir Sheet
1352	A280	500fr multi	1.40	.65

Nos. 1348-1352 air airmail. No. 1352 contains one stamp 36x51mm.

Nos. 1302, 1305-1307 Ovptd. "75e Anniversaire / du Scoutisme Feminin"

1986, Jan.   *Perf. 15*
1353	A271	50fr multi	.20	.20
1354	A271	1000fr multi	4.00	2.00

Souvenir Sheet
1355	A271	1000fr multi	4.00	2.00
1355A	A271	1000fr multi	4.00	2.00

Nos. 1354-1355A airmail.

Nos. 1268-1269, 1271, 1273-1274 Ovptd. "150e ANNIVERSAIRE / DE CHEMIN FER 'LUDWIG'"

1985, Dec. 27   Litho.   *Perf. 15*
1356	A267	50fr multi	.25	.20
1357	A267	90fr multi	.50	.25
1358	A267	500fr multi	2.75	1.40
		Nos. 1356-1358 (3)	3.50	1.85

Souvenir Sheets
1359	A267	1000fr No. 1273	5.50	2.75
1360	A267	1000fr No. 1274	5.50	2.75

Halley's Comet A281

Designs: 70fr, Suisei space probe, comets. 90fr, Vega-1 probe. 150fr, Space telescope. 200fr, Giotto probe, comet over Togo. 1000fr, Edmond Halley, Sir Isaac Newton.

1986, Mar. 27   *Perf. 13*
1361	A281	70fr multi	.40	.20
1362	A281	90fr multi	.50	.25
1363	A281	150fr multi	.80	.40
1364	A281	200fr multi	1.10	.55
		Nos. 1361-1364 (4)	2.80	1.40

Souvenir Sheet
1365	A281	1000fr multi	5.50	2.75

Nos. 1362-1365 are airmail.
For overprints see Nos. 1405-1409.

Flowering and Fruit-bearing Plants A282

1986, June   *Perf. 14*
1366	A282	70fr Anacardium occidentale	.40	.20
1367	A282	90fr Ananas comosus	.50	.25
1368	A282	120fr Persea americana	.65	.35
1369	A282	135fr Carica papaya	.75	.40
1370	A282	290fr Mangifera indica, vert.	1.60	.80
		Nos. 1366-1370 (5)	3.90	2.00

Nos. 1368-1370 airmail.

1986 World Cup Soccer Championships, Mexico — A283

Various soccer plays.

1986, May 5   Litho.   *Perf. 15x14*
1371	A283	70fr multi	.40	.20
1372	A283	90fr multi	.50	.25
1373	A283	130fr multi	.70	.35
1374	A283	300fr multi	1.60	.80
		Nos. 1371-1374 (4)	3.20	1.60

Souvenir Sheet
1375	A283	1000fr multi	5.50	2.75

Nos. 1372-1375 are airmail.
For overprints see Nos. 1394-1397.

Mushrooms — A284

1986, June 9   *Perf. 13x12½*
1376	A284	70fr Ramaria moelleriana	.40	.20
1377	A284	90fr Hygrocybe firma	.50	.25
1378	A284	150fr Kalchbrennera corallocephala	.80	.40
1379	A284	200fr Cookeina tricholoma	1.10	.55
		Nos. 1376-1379 (4)	2.80	1.40

Intl. Youth Year — A285

1986, June   *Perf. 13½x14½*
1380	A285	25fr shown	.20	.20
1381	A285	90fr Youths, doves	.50	.25

Dated 1985.

Wrestling — A286

Wedding of Prince
Andrew and Sarah
Ferguson — A287

1986, July 16   Perf. 14x15, 15x14
1382 A286 15fr Single-leg take-
　　　　down move　　　.20 .20
1383 A286 20fr Completing take-
　　　　down　　　　　　.20 .20
1384 A286 70fr Pinning combina-
　　　　tion　　　　　　　.35 .20
1385 A286 90fr Riding　　.50 .25
　　Nos. 1382-1385 (4)　1.25 .85
Nos. 1384-1385 horiz. No. 1385 is airmail.

1986, July 23   Perf. 14
1386 A287 10fr Sarah Fergu-
　　　　son　　　　　　　.20 .20
1387 A287 1000fr Prince Andrew 5.50 2.75
Souvenir Sheet
1388 A287 1000fr Couple　5.50 2.75
　　Nos. 1387-1388 are airmail.

Easter
A288

Paintings (details): 25fr, 1000fr, The Resurrection, by Andrea Mantegna (1431-1506),
vert. 70fr, The Calvary, by Paolo Veronese
(1528-1588), vert. 90fr, The Last Supper, by
Jacopo Tintoretto (1518-1594). 200fr, Christ
at the Tomb, by Alonso Berruguette (1486-
1561).

Perf. 14x15, 15x14
1986, Mar. 24　　　　Litho.
1389 A288 25fr multi　　.20 .20
1390 A288 70fr multi　　.40 .20
1391 A288 90fr multi　　.50 .25
1392 A288 200fr multi　1.10 .55
　　Nos. 1389-1392 (4)　2.20 1.20
Souvenir Sheet
1393 A288 1000fr multi　5.50 2.75
　　Nos. 1391-1393 are airmail.

Nos. 1371-1374 Ovptd. or Inscribed
"DEMI-FINALE / ARGENTINE 2 /
BELGIQUE 0,"
"DEMI-FINALE / ALLEMAGNE / DE
L'OUEST 2 / FRANCE 0,"
"3 eme et 4 eme PLACE / FRANCE 4
/ BELGIQUE 2,"
& "FINALE / ARGENTINE 3 /
ALLEMAGNE / DE L'OUEST 2"

1986, Aug. 4   Litho.   Perf. 15x14
1394 A283 70fr multi　　.40 .20
1395 A283 90fr multi　　.50 .25
1396 A283 130fr multi　.70 .35
1397 A283 300fr multi　1.60 .80
　　Nos. 1394-1397 (4)　3.20 1.60
　　Nos. 1395-1397 are airmail.

Hotels — A289

1986, Aug. 18   Perf. 12½
1398 A289 70fr Fazao　　.40 .20
1399 A289 90fr Sarakawa　.50 .25
1400 A289 120fr Le Lac　.65 .30
　　Nos. 1398-1400 (3)　1.55 .75
Nos. 1399-1400 are airmail.

Keran
Natl.
Park
A290

1986, Sept. 15   Litho.   Perf. 14½
1401 A290 70fr Wild ducks　.40 .20
1402 A290 90fr Antelope　.50 .25
1403 A290 100fr Elephant　.55 .30
1404 A290 130fr Waterbuck　.70 .35
　　Nos. 1401-1404 (4)　2.15 1.10
　　Nos. 1402-1404 are airmail.

Nos. 1361-1365 Ovptd. with Halley's
Comet Emblem in Silver

1986, Oct. 9　　　　Perf. 13
1405 A281 70fr multi　　.40 .20
1406 A281 90fr multi　　.50 .25
1407 A281 150fr multi　.80 .40
1408 A281 200fr multi　1.10 .55
　　Nos. 1405-1408 (4)　2.80 1.40
Souvenir Sheet
1409 A281 1000fr multi　5.50 2.75
　　Nos. 1406-1409 are airmail.

Frescoes from
Togoville
Church — A291

Togoville Church — A292

1986, Dec. 22   Litho.   Perf. 14½x15
1410 A291 45fr Annunciation　.25 .20
1411 A291 120fr Nativity　.65 .30
1412 A291 130fr Adoration of
　　　　the Magi　　　　.70 .35
1413 A291 200fr Flight into
　　　　Egypt　　　　　1.10 .55
　　Nos. 1410-1413 (4)　2.70 1.40
Souvenir Sheet
1414 A292 1000fr multi　5.50 2.75
Christmas. Nos. 1411-1414 are airmail.

Phosphate Mining — A293

Natl. Liberation, 20th Anniv. — A294

1987, Jan. 13   Litho.   Perf. 12½
1415 A293 35fr shown　　.25 .20
1416 A293 50fr Sugar refinery,
　　　　Anie　　　　　　.30 .20
1417 A293 70fr Nangbeto Dam　.40 .20
1418 A293 90fr Hotel, post of-
　　　　fice in Lome　　.55 .30
1419 A293 100fr Post office, Kara　.60 .30
1420 A293 120fr Peace monu-
　　　　ment　　　　　　.70 .35
1421 A293 130fr Youth vaccina-
　　　　tion campaign　.80 .45
　　Nos. 1415-1421 (7)　3.60 2.00
Souvenir Sheet
Perf. 13
1422 A294 500fr shown　3.00 1.50
　　Nos. 1419-1422 are airmail.

Easter — A295

Paintings in Nadoba Church, Keran: 90fr,
The Last Supper. 130fr, Christ on the Cross.
300fr, The Resurrection. 500fr, Evangelization
in Tamberma, fresco, horiz.

1987, Apr. 13   Litho.   Perf. 14½x15
1423 A295 90fr multi　　.55 .30
1424 A295 130fr multi　.80 .40
1425 A295 300fr multi　1.75 .90
　　Nos. 1423-1425 (3)　3.10 1.60
Souvenir Sheet
Perf. 15x14½
1426 A295 500fr multi　3.00 1.50
　　Nos. 1424-1426 are airmail.

World
Rugby Cup
A296

1987, May 11　　　　Perf. 15x14½
1427 A296 70fr Dive　　.40 .20
1428 A296 130fr Running with
　　　　the ball　　　　.85 .40
1429 A296 300fr Scrimmage　1.75 .90
　　Nos. 1427-1429 (3)　3.00 1.50
Souvenir Sheet
Perf. 14½x15
1430 A296 1000fr Stands, goal,
　　　　vert.　　　　　6.00 3.00
　　Nos. 1427-1429 are horiz. Nos. 1428-1430
are airmail.

Indigenous
Flowers
A297

1987, June 22   Litho.   Perf. 13
1431 A297 70fr Adenium
　　　　obesum　　　　.40 .20
1432 A297 90fr Amorphophallus
　　　　abyssinicus,
　　　　vert.　　　　　.50 .25
1433 A297 100fr Ipomoea
　　　　mauritana　　　.55 .30

1434 A297 120fr Salacia togoica,
　　　　vert.　　　　　.70 .35
　　Nos. 1431-1434 (4)　2.15 1.10
　　Nos. 1432-1434 are airmail.

Fish
A298

1987, Sept. 8   Litho.   Perf. 13
1435 A298 70fr Chaetodon
　　　　hoefleri　　　　.50 .25
1436 A298 90fr Tetraodon
　　　　lineatus　　　　.60 .30
1437 A298 120fr Chaetodipterus
　　　　goreensis　　　.80 .40
1438 A298 130fr Labeo parvus　.90 .45
　　Nos. 1435-1438 (4)　2.80 1.40

1988 Summer Olympics,
Seoul — A299

Buddha and athletes

1987, Sept. 14　　　　Perf. 12½
1439 A299 70fr Long jump　.50 .25
1440 A299 90fr Relay　　.60 .30
1441 A299 200fr Cycling　1.25 .70
1442 A299 250fr Javelin　1.75 .85
　　Nos. 1439-1442 (4)　4.10 2.10
Souvenir Sheet
1443 A299 1000fr Tennis　6.75 3.50
　　Nos. 1440-1443 are airmail.

World Wildlife Fund Type of 1984
1987, Dec. 15   Litho.   Perf. 14
Size: 32x24mm
1444 A263 60fr like 45fr　.65 .20
1445 A263 75fr like 70fr　.75 .25
1446 A263 80fr like 90fr　.75 .30
1447 A263 100fr like 105fr　1.00 .35
　　Nos. 1444-1447 (4)　3.15 1.10
　　No. 1447 is airmail.

Christmas
A300

Eradication of
Tuberculosis
A301

Paintings: 40fr, Springtime in Paradise,
horiz.. 45fr, Creation of Man, Sistine Chapel,
by Michelangelo, horiz.. 105fr, Presentation in
the Temple. 270fr, Original Sin. 500fr, Nativity,
horiz.

Perf. 15x14, 14x15
1987, Dec. 15　　　　Litho.
1448 A300 40fr multi　　.25 .20
1449 A300 45fr multi　　.30 .20
1450 A300 105fr multi　.75 .40
1451 A300 270fr multi　1.90 .95
　　Nos. 1448-1451 (4)　3.20 1.75
Souvenir Sheet
1452 A300 500fr multi　3.50 1.75
　　Nos. 1450-1452 are airmail.

1987, Dec. 28 *Perf. 12½x13, 13x12½*
1453 A301 80fr Inoculation, horiz. .55 .30
1454 A301 90fr Family under umbrella .65 .30
1455 A301 115fr Hospital, horiz. .80 .40
    Nos. 1453-1455 (3) 2.00 1.00

Health for all by the year 2000. Nos. 1454-1455 are airmail.

Intl. Fund for Agricultural Development (IFAD), 10th Anniv. — A302

1988, Feb. 25 **Litho.** *Perf. 13½*
1456 A302 90fr multi .65 .30

Easter 1988 — A303

Stained-glass windows: 70fr, Jesus and the Disciples at Emmaus. 90fr, Mary at the Foot of the Cross. 120fr, The Crucifixion. 200fr, St. Thomas Touching the Resurrected Christ. 500fr, The Agony of Jesus on the Mount of Olives.

1988, June 6 **Litho.** *Perf. 14x15*
1457 A303 70fr multi .40 .20
1458 A303 90fr multi .65 .30
1459 A303 120fr multi .85 .40
1460 A303 200fr multi 1.40 .70
    Nos. 1457-1460 (4) 3.30 1.60
    Souvenir Sheet
1461 A303 500fr multi 3.50 1.75

Nos. 1459-1461 are airmail.

Paintings by Picasso (1881-1973) — A304

Designs: 45fr, The Dance. 160fr, Portrait of a Young Girl. No. 1464, Gueridon. No. 1465, Mandolin and Guitar.

1988, Apr. 25 **Litho.** *Perf. 12½x13*
1462 A304 45fr multi .30 .20
1463 A304 160fr multi 1.00 .50
1464 A304 300fr multi 2.00 1.00
    Nos. 1462-1464 (3) 3.30 1.70
    Souvenir Sheet
1465 A304 300fr multi 2.00 1.00

Nos. 1464-1465 are airmail.

A305

A306

1988, Aug. 30 *Perf. 14x15*
1466 A305 70fr Basketball .45 .25
1467 A305 90fr Tennis .60 .30
1468 A305 120fr Archery .80 .40
1469 A305 200fr Discus 1.25 .65
    Nos. 1466-1469 (4) 3.10 1.60
    Souvenir Sheet
1470 A305 500fr Marathon 3.25 1.60

1988 Summer Olympics, Seoul. Nos. 1468-1470 are airmail.

1988, Oct. 28 **Litho.** *Perf. 13*
1471 A306 80fr shown .55 .30
1472 A306 125fr Emblems .85 .40

WHO, 40th anniv.

Traditional Costumes A307

1988, July 25 **Litho.** *Perf. 13½*
1473 A307 80fr Watchi chief .50 .20
1474 A307 125fr Watchi woman .80 .40
1475 A307 165fr Kotokoli 1.00 .50
1476 A307 175fr Ewe 1.10 .60
    Nos. 1473-1476 (4) 3.40 1.70
    Souvenir Sheet
1477 A307 500fr Moba 3.25 1.60

PHILTOGO 3, Aug. 11-12 — A308

Children's drawings by: 10fr, B. Gossner. 35fr, K. Ekoue-Kouvahey. 70fr, A. Abbey. 90fr, T.D. Lawson. 120fr, A. Tazzar.

1988, Dec. 3
1478 A308 10fr multi .20 .20
1479 A308 35fr multi .25 .20
1480 A308 70fr multi .45 .25
1481 A308 90fr multi .55 .30
1482 A308 120fr multi .70 .40
    Nos. 1478-1482 (5) 2.15 1.35

Christmas — A309

Paintings: 80fr, Adoration of the Magi, by Brueghel. 150fr, The Virgin, Infant Jesus, Sts. Jerome and Dominic, by Lippi. 175fr, Madonna, Infant Jesus, St. Joseph and Infant John the Baptist, by Barocci. 195fr, Virgin and Child, by Bellini. 750fr, The Holy Family and a Shepherd, by Titian.

1988, Dec. 15 *Perf. 14½x15*
1483 A309 80fr multi .50 .25
1484 A309 150fr multi .90 .45
1485 A309 175fr multi 1.10 .55
1486 A309 195fr multi 1.25 .60
    Nos. 1483-1486 (4) 3.75 1.85
    Souvenir Sheet
1487 A309 750fr multi 3.50 1.75

Nos. 1484-1487 are airmail.

Natl. Industries A310

1988, May 28 **Litho.** *Perf. 13*
1488 A310 125fr Cement factory .80 .40
1489 A310 165fr Bottling plant 1.25 .55
1490 A310 195fr Phosphate mine 1.25 .65
1491 A310 200fr Plastics factory 1.50 .70
1492 A310 300fr Manufacturing plant 2.00 1.00
    Nos. 1488-1492 (5) 6.80 3.30

John F. Kennedy A311

Designs: 125fr, Arrival in Paris, 1961. 155fr, At Hotel de Ville, vert. 165fr, With De Gaulle at Elysee Palace, vert. 180fr, Boarding Air Force One with Jackie at Orly, France. 750fr, Kennedy and De Gaulle, natl. colors, vert.

1988, July 30 **Litho.** *Perf. 14*
1493 A311 125fr multi .80 .35
1494 A311 155fr multi 1.00 .50
1495 A311 165fr multi 1.10 .55
1496 A311 180fr multi 1.25 .60
    Nos. 1493-1496 (4) 4.15 2.00
    Souvenir Sheet
    Perf. 13½x13
1497 A311 750fr multi 5.00 2.50

Hairstyles A312

1988, Nov. 20 *Perf. 13*
1498 A312 80fr shown .50 .25
1499 A312 125fr multi, diff. .80 .40
1500 A312 170fr multi, diff. 1.10 .55
1501 A312 180fr multi, diff., vert. 1.25 .60
    Nos. 1498-1501 (4) 3.65 1.80
    Souvenir Sheet
    Perf. 14
1502 A312 500fr multi, diff. 3.25 1.60

Sarakawa Plane Crash, 15th Anniv. A313

Portrait and various views of the wreckage.

1989, Jan. 24 *Perf. 13½*
1503 A313 10fr multi .20 .20
1504 A313 80fr multi, vert. .50 .25
1505 A313 125fr multi .80 .40
    Nos. 1503-1505 (3) 1.50 .85

1990 World Cup Soccer Championships, Italy — A314

ITALIA '90 emblem, flag of Togo, athletes and architecture: 80fr, Cathedral of St. Januarius, Naples. 125fr, Milan Cathedral. 165fr, Bevilacqua Palace, Verona. 175fr, Baptistery of San Giovanni, Florence. 380fr, Madama Palace, Turin. 425fr, Cathedral of San Lorenzo, Genoa. 650fr, The Colosseum, Rome.

1989, Jan. 10 **Litho.** *Perf. 13½*
1506 A314 80fr multi .50 .25
1507 A314 125fr multi .80 .40
1508 A314 165fr multi 1.00 .50
1509 A314 175fr multi 1.10 .55
1510 A314 380fr multi 2.40 1.25
1511 A314 425fr multi 2.75 1.25
    Nos. 1506-1511 (6) 8.55 4.20
    Souvenir Sheet
1512 A314 650fr multi 4.00 2.00

Nos. 1510-1512 are airmail.

A316

Prince Emanuel of Liechtenstein Foundation — A316a

1988 Summer Olympics, Seoul: Flags of Liechtenstein, Togo, athletes, Pres. Eyadema. No. 1522A, Olympic rings. No. 1522B, Tennis players Miroslav Mecir, Steffi Graf, vert.

1989, May 25 **Litho.** *Perf. 13½*
1520 A316 80fr Boxing .50 .25
1521 A316 125fr Long jump .40 .40
1522 A316 165fr Running 1.00 .50
    Nos. 1520-1522 (3) 1.90 1.15
    Litho. & Embossed
1522A A316a 1500fr gold & multi
1522B A316a 1500fr gold & multi

Nos. 1522A-1522B are airmail and exist imperf. and in souvenir sheets of 1 both perf. and imperf.

Federal Republic of Germany, 40th Anniv. A317

1989, June 1
1523 A317 90fr Palace .60 .25
1524 A317 125fr Statesmen, vert. .80 .40
1525 A317 180fr Natl. flag, crest 1.00 .50
    Nos. 1523-1525 (3) 2.40 1.15

Council for Rural Development, 30th Anniv. — A318

1989, June 19   *Perf. 15x14*
1526 A318 75fr Flags, well, trac-
             tor, field   .50   .25

See Ivory Coast No. 874.

Intl. Red
Cross,
125th
Anniv.
A319

1989, June 30   *Perf. 13½*
1527 A319 90fr shown   .60   .30
1528 A319 125fr Geneva Con-
             vention, 1864   .80   .40

French
Revolution,
Bicent.
A320

Designs: 90fr, Storming of the Bastille, vert.
125fr, Tennis Court Oath. 180fr, Abolition of
privileges. 1000fr, Declaration of Human
Rights and Citizenship, vert.

1989, July 15
1529 A320 90fr multi   .60   .30
1530 A320 125fr multi   .80   .40
1531 A320 180fr multi   1.10 .55
      Nos. 1529-1531 (3)   2.50 1.25

Souvenir Sheet
1532 A320 1000fr multi   6.25 3.10

Electric
Corp. of
Benin,
20th
Anniv.
A321

1989, July 15
1533 A321 80fr multi   .50   .25
1534 A321 125fr multi   .80   .40

A322

PHILEXFRANCE '89, French
Revolution, Bicent. — A322a

Figures and scenes from the revolution:
90fr, Jacques Necker (1732-1804), financier,
statesman, and The Three Estates. 190fr, Guy
Le Chapelier (1754-1794), politician, and abolition of feudalism (seigniorial privileges), Aug.
4, 1789. 425fr, Talleyrand-Perigord (1754-
1838), statesman, and Lafayette's Oath at the
Festival of Federation, July 14, 1790. 480fr,

Paul Barras (1755-1829), revolutionary, and
overthrowing of Robespierre during the
Revolution of 9th Thermidor, July 27, 1794.
750fr, Georges Jacques Danton (1759-1794),
revolutionary leader, and arrest of Louis XVI at
Varennes, June 21, 1791, horiz. Nos. 1537-
1539 are airmail.
   No. 1539A, Assassination of Jean-Paul
Marat (1743-93).   No. 1539B, Fabré
d'Eglantine (1750-94), making of the calendar
of the republic.

1989   **Litho.**   *Perf. 13½*
1535 A322 90fr multi   .65   .30
1536 A322 190fr multi   1.25 .65
1537 A322 425fr multi   3.00 1.50
1538 A322 480fr multi   3.50 1.75
      Nos. 1535-1538 (4)   8.40 4.20

Souvenir Sheet
1539 A322 750fr multi   5.25 2.75

Litho. & Embossed
Souvenir Sheet
1539A A322a 1500fr gold & multi

Souvenir Sheet
1539B A322a 1500fr gold & multi

#1539A-1539B are airmail and exist imperf.
   Nos. 1535-1538 exist in souvenir sheets of
1, No. 1539A in souvenir sheets of 1, perf. and
imperf.
   Issued: 90fr-750fr, 6/12; 1500fr, 7/15.

Gen.
Kpalime's
Role in Natl.
Unity and
Peace
Struggle, 20th
Anniv.
A323

1989, Aug. 21
1540 A323 90fr shown   .65   .30
1541 A323 125fr Giving speech   .90   .45

A324

A325

Butterflies.

1990, Apr. 30   Litho.   *Perf. 13½*
1542 A324 5fr Danaus
             chrysippus   .20   .20
1543 A324 10fr Morpho aega   .20   .20
1544 A324 15fr Papilio
             demodocus   .20   .20
1545 A324 90fr Papilio darda-
             nus   .70   .40
      Nos. 1542-1545 (4)   1.30 1.00

Souvenir Sheet
1545A A324 500fr Papilio zalmox-
             is   3.75 1.90

No. 1545A is airmail.

1989, Dec. 1   Litho.   *Perf. 13½*
1546 A325 40fr Apollo 11 liftoff   .30   .20
1547 A325 90fr Module transpo-
             sition   .65   .30
1548 A325 150fr Eagle   1.00 .50
1549 A325 250fr Splashdown   1.75 .90
      Nos. 1546-1549 (4)   3.70 1.90

Souvenir Sheet
1550 A325 500fr Astronaut on
             Moon   3.50 1.75

1st Moon Landing, 20th anniv.

Lome IV Conference, Dec.
1989 — A326

1989, Dec. 15   Litho.   *Perf. 13*
1551 A326 100fr "Dec. 89"   .70   .35
1552 A326 100fr "15 Dec. 89"   .70   .35

A327

Boy Scouts,
Flora and
Fauna
A327a

#1559A, *Kalchbrennera corallocephala.*
#1559B, *Spindasis mozambica.*

1990, Jan. 8   Litho.   *Perf. 13½*
1553 A327 80fr *Myrina silenus*   .60   .30
1554 A327 90fr *Phlebobus
             silvaticus*   .65   .35
1555 A327 125fr *Volvariella es-
             culenta*   .90   .45
1556 A327 165fr *Hypolicaena an-
             tifaunus*   1.10 .65
1557 A327 380fr *Termitomyces
             striatus*   2.75 1.25
1558 A327 425fr *Axiocerces
             harpax*   3.00 1.50
      Nos. 1553-1558 (6)   9.00 4.50

Souvenir Sheet
1559 A327 750fr *Cupidopsis jo-
             bates*   5.25 2.50

Litho. & Embossed
1559A A327a 1500fr gold & multi

Souvenir Sheet
1559B A327a 1500fr gold & multi

   Nos. 1557-1559B are airmail. Nos. 1559A-
1559B exist imperf. No. 1559A exists in souvenir sheet of 1 both perf. and imperf.

People's Republic of Togo, 20th
Anniv. — A328

1990, Jan. 8
1560 A328 45fr Government
             House, Kara   .35   .20
1561 A328 90fr Pres. Eyadema,
             House   .65   .30

Pan-African
Postal Union,
10th
Anniv. — A329

1990, Jan. 1   *Perf. 13½*
1562 A329 125fr bronze, blk & bl   .90   .4

US-Togo
Relations
A330

180fr, Pres. Bush, Pres. Eyadema, horiz.

1990, July 20   Litho.   *Perf. 13½*
1563 A330 125fr multicolored   .95   .50
1564 A330 180fr multicolored   1.40 .70

Size: 90 x 75mm
1565 A330 125fr multicolored   1.00 .50
1566 A330 180fr multicolored   1.40 .70
      Nos. 1563-1566 (4)   4.75 2.40

Nos. 1565-1566 printed in sheets of 1.

Reptiles
A331

1990, May 22
1567 A331 1fr Varanus niloticus   .20   .20
1568 A331 25fr Vipere bitis
             arietans   .20   .20
1569 A331 60fr Naja melaneulo-
             ca   .50   .25
1570 A331 90fr Python de sebae   .70   .35
      Nos. 1567-1570 (4)   1.60 1.00

Cowrie Shell
Ornaments
A332

1990, July, 20   Litho.   *Perf. 13½*
1571 A332 90fr shown   .70   .35
1572 A332 125fr Shell necklace   1.00 .50
1573 A332 180fr Shells on
             horned helmet   1.40 .70
      Nos. 1571-1573 (3)   3.10 1.55

Stamp
Day
A333

1990, Aug. 23
1574 A333 90fr multicolored   .70   .35

Traditional
Homes
A334

1990, Sept. 9
1575	A334	90fr shown	.70 .35
1576	A334	125fr multi, diff.	1.00 .50
1577	A334	190fr multi, diff.	1.50 .75
		Nos. 1575-1577 (3)	3.20 1.60

Charles de Gaulle (1890-1970),
Speech at Brazzaville, 1944 — A335

1990, Aug. 30   Litho.   Perf. 14
1578	A335	125fr multicolored	1.00 .50

New
Lome
Airport
A336

1990, Sept. 17   Perf. 13½
1579	A336	90fr multicolored	.70 .35

Children's
Art — A337

1990, Sept. 28   Litho.   Perf. 13½
1580	A337	90fr multicolored	.75 .35

Forest Wildlife — A342

1991, June 5   Litho.   Perf. 13½x14
1593	A342	90fr Chimpanzee	.65 .30
1594	A342	1.70fr Green parrot	1.25 .60
1595	A342	1.85fr White parrot	1.25 .65
		Nos. 1593-1595 (3)	3.15 1.55

Python
Regius
A343

Various snakes emerging from eggs.

1992, Aug. 24   Litho.   Perf. 13½
1596	A343	90fr multicolored	.70 .35
1597	A343	125fr multicolored	1.00 .50
1598	A343	190fr multicolored	1.50 .75
1599	A343	300fr multicolored	2.25 1.10
		Nos. 1596-1599 (4)	5.45 2.70
		Dated 1991.	

Voodoo
Dances
A344

Various women dancing.

1992, Aug. 24
1600	A344	90fr multicolored	.70 .35
1601	A344	125fr multicolored	1.00 .50
1602	A344	190fr multicolored	1.50 .75
		Nos. 1600-1602 (3)	3.20 1.60
		Dated 1991.	

A345

1994 World Cup Soccer
Championships, US — A346

Various soccer players in action: 5fr, 10fr,
25fr, 60fr, 90fr, 100fr, 200fr, 1000fr.
1500fr, Player in white & green uniform.
3000fr, Two players in air, horiz.

1994, Nov. 15   Litho.   Perf. 14
1603-1610	A345	Set of 8	5.75 3.00

Souvenir Sheets
1611	A346	1500fr multicolored	5.75 3.00
1612	A346	3000fr multicolored	11.50 5.75

UPU, 120th
Anniv. — A347

Stamp
Day — A348

1994, July 29   Perf. 13½
1613	A347	180fr multicolored	.70 .35
		A miniature sheet may exist.	

1994, Oct. 9
1614	A348	90fr pale bl & multi	.35 .20
1615	A348	125fr pale yel & multi	.50 .25

Intl. Olympic Committee,
Cent. — A348a

Designs: b, Pierre de Coubertin, Olympic
Hymn. c, Original members of IOC. d, Olympic
flame.
900fr, Pierre de Coubertin holding
document.

1996, Oct.   Litho.   Perf. 13½
1615A	A348a	300fr Strip of 3, #b.-d.	

Souvenir Sheet
1615E	A348a	900fr multicolored	

Nos. 1615A, 1615E exist imperf. No. 1615c
is 60x51mm. No. 1615E is airmail and contains one 36x51mm stamp.

Birds
A349

Designs: #1616, 5fr, Secretary bird, vert.
#1617, 10fr, Paradise flycather, vert. #1618,
25fr, African spoonbill. #1619, 60fr, Cordon
bleu waxbill. #1620, 90fr, Orange-breasted
sunbird, vert. #1621, 100fr, Yellow-billed hornbill, vert. #1621A, 180fr, Barn owl. #1622,
200fr, African hoopoe. #1622A, 300fr, Fire-
crowned bishop, vert. #1623, 1000fr, Red-
throated bee eater, vert.

1995   Litho.   Perf. 14
1616-1623	A349	Set of 10	7.75 3.75

Souvenir Sheet
1624	A349	1500fr Vulture	5.75 2.75

Issued: 180fr, 300fr, 8/7; others, 1/23.

A350   A351

Motion Picture, Alien: a, Alien creature. b,
Humans in combat with creature. c, Sigourney
Weaver.

1994   Litho.   Perf. 13½
1625	A350	600fr Strip of 3, #a.-c.	7.50 3.75

No. 1625b is 60x48mm. No. 1625 is a continuous design and exists in souvenir sheets of
1.

1994

No. 1626: a, Edwin "Buzz" Aldrin. b, Eagle,
olive branch, Neil Armstrong. c, Michael
Collins.
No. 1627: a, Apollo emblem, footprint. b,
Crew of Apollo 11. c, Moon rock, NASA
emblem.
1626-1627	A351	600fr Strips of 3, #a.-c., each	7.50 3.75

First manned Moon landing, 25th anniv.
Nos. 1626b, 1627b are each 60x47mm.
Nos. 1626-1627 are continuous designs and
exist in souvenir sheets of 1.

Dinosaurs — A352

125fr, Polacanthus. 180fr,
Pachycephalosaurus. 425fr, Coelophysis.
480fr, Brachiosaurus. 500fr, Dilophosaurus.
1500fr, Scutellosaurus.
No. 1634, Velociraptor, vert.

1994
1628-1633	A352	Set of 6	13.00 6.50

Souvenir Sheet
1634	A352	1500fr multicolored	6.25 3.00

No. 1634 is airmail.

Flowers — A353

Easter — A354

Designs: 15fr, Belvache de Madagascar.
90fr, Oeuillets. 125fr, Agave, horiz.

1995, May 12
1635-1637	A353	Set of 3	.90 .45

1995, May 12

Details or entire paintings: 90fr, The Resurrection, by A. Mantegna. 180fr, Calvary, by
Veronese. 190fr, The Last Supper, by Tintoretto, horiz.
1638-1640	A354	Set of 3	1.75 .90

Fish
A355

10fr, Pike. 90fr, Capitaine. 180fr, Carp.

1995, May 12
1641-1643	A355	Set of 3	1.10 .55

Miniature Sheets of 6 and 8

VJ Day,
50th Anniv.
A356

Japanese leaders: No. 1644a, Adm. Isoroko
Yamamoto. b, Gen. Hideki Tojo. c, Vice Adm.
Shigeru Fukudome. d, Adm. Shigetaro
Shimada. e, Contre-Adm. Chuichi Nagumo. f,
Gen. Shizu Ichi Tanaka.
No. 1646, Japanese signing peace
agreement.
VE Day: No. 1645a, 200fr, German fighter
planes making final attacks. b. 200fr, Allies win
Battle of the Atlantic. c, 200fr, Ludendorf
Bridge at Remagen is taken intact. d, 200fr,

Russian rockets fired at Berlin. e, 45fr, Hostilities suspended in Italy. f, 90fr, Russians capture devastated Warsaw. g, 125fr, Russian tanks enter Berlin. h, 500fr, UN flag.
No. 1647, German U-236 surrenders.

1995, July 20   **Litho.**   **Perf. 14**
1644 A356   200fr #a.-f.   4.75 2.50
1645 A356   #a.-h.   6.25 3.25

Souvenir Sheets
1646 A356   1500fr multicolored   6.00 3.00
1647 A356   1500fr multicolored   6.00 3.00

UN, 50th Anniv. — A357

No. 1648: a, 25fr, Doves, earth from space. b, 90fr, Doves, UN headquarters. c, 400fr, Doves, earth from space.
1000fr, Earth, dove.

1995, June 26
1648 A357   Strip of 3, #a.-c.   1.25 .65

Souvenir Sheet
1649 A357   1000fr multicolored   4.00 2.00

1995 Boy Scout Jamboree, Holland — A358

Designs: 90fr, Nat. flag. 190fr, Scout oath. 300fr, Lord Baden-Powell. 1500fr, Scout salute.

1995, July 20
1650-1652 A358   Set of 3   1.60 .80

Souvenir Sheet
1653 A358   1500fr multicolored   6.00 3.00

Queen Mother, 95th Birthday A359

No. 1654: a, Formal portrait. b, Cutting cake. c, As younger woman wearing jewels, waving. d, Drawing.
No. 1654E, Holding umbrella. No. 1654F, Formal portrait as young woman.
No. 1655, Royal attire, pearls.
No. 1655A, Early picture of King George VI, Queen Mother.

1995, July 20   **Perf. 13½x14**
1654 A359   250fr Strip of 4,
    #a.-d.   5.00 2.50
1654E A359   250fr multicolored   1.25 .65
1654F A359   250fr multicolored   1.25 .65
   g.   Block or strip of 4, #1654a,
     1654d, 1654E, 1654F   5.00 2.50
   Nos. 1654-1654F (3)   7.50 3.80

Souvenir Sheets
1655 A359   1000fr multicolored   4.00 2.00
1655A A359   1000fr multicolored   4.00 2.00

Nos. 1654, 1654Fg were issued in sheets of 8 stamps.
Issued: #1654, 1655, 7/20; # 1654E, 1654F, 1655A, 11/22.

FAO, 50th Anniv. — A360

No. 1656: a, 45fr, Cattle. b, 125fr, Water buffalo. c, 200fr, Boy, man with water buffaloes.
1000fr, Woman milking cow.

1995, Mar. 3   **Perf. 14**
1656 A360   Strip of 3, #a.-c.   1.50 .75

Souvenir Sheet
1657 A360   1000fr multicolored   4.25 2.00

No. 1656 is a continuous design.

A361

No. 1658: a, Elihu Root, peace, 1912. b, Alfred Fried, peace, 1911. c, Henri Moissan, chemistry, 1906. d, Charles Barkla, physics, 1917. e, Rudolf Eucken, literature, 1908. f, Carl von Ossietzky, peace, 1935. g, Sir Edward Appleton, physics. 1947. h, Camillo Golgi, physiology, 1906. i, Wilhelm Roentgen, physics, 1901.
No. 1659: a, Manfred Eigen, chemistry, 1967. b, Donald J. Cram, chemistry, 1987. c, Paul J. Flory, chemistry, 1974. d, Johann Deisenhofer, chemistry, 1988. e, P.W. Bridgman, physics, 1946. f, Otto Stern, physics, 1943. g, Arne Tiselis, chemistry, 1948. h, J. Georg Bednorz, physics, 1987. i, Albert Claude, medicine, 1974.
No. 1660, Albert Einstein, physics, 1921.
No. 1661, Woodrow Wilson, peace, 1919.

1995, Aug. 21
Miniature Sheets of 9
1658-1659 A361   200fr #a.-i., ea   7.25 3.50

Souvenir Sheets
1660-1661 A361   1500fr each   6.00 3.00
Nobel Prize winners.

1995, July 20
1662 A362   1000fr shown   4.25 2.00

Souvenir Sheet
1663 A362   1000fr Natl. flag, Rotary emblem   4.25 2.00
Rotary Intl., 90th anniv.

Miniature Sheets

Fauna A363

Primates, vert: No. 1664a, Black-faced monkey in tree. b, Brown monkey in tree. c, Black monkey. d, Baboon.
Wild animals: No. 1665a, Hyena. b, Hyrax. c, Mongoose. d, Elephant. e, Mandrill. f, Okapi. g, Hippopotamus. h, Flamingo. i, Wild boar.
1500fr, Potto.

1995, Oct. 2   **Litho.**   **Perf. 14**
1664 A363   200fr Sheet of 4,
    #a.-d.   3.25 1.60
1665 A363   200fr Sheet of 9,
    #a.-i.   7.25 3.50

Souvenir Sheet
1666 A363   1500fr multicolored   6.00 3.00

FAO, 50th Anniv. A364

1995, Mar. 3   **Litho.**   **Perf. 14**
1667 A364   125fr shown   .50 .25

Souvenir Sheet
1668 A364   300fr like No. 1667   1.25 .60

Sir Rowland Hill (1795-1879) A365

UN, 50th Anniv. — A366

1995, June 3   **Perf. 13½**
1669 A365   125fr multicolored   .50 .25

1995, June 26
1670 A366   180fr multicolored   .75 .40

Miniature Sheets of 8

Mushrooms A367

No. 1671: a, Cortinarius violaceus. b, Hygrocybe flavescens. c, Mycena haematopus. d, Coprinus micaceus. e, Helvella lacunosa. f, Flammulina velutipes. g, Aleuria aurantia. h, Geastrum triplex.
No. 1672: a, Russula laurocerasi. b, Phyllotopsis nidulans. c, Xeromphalina campanella. d, Psathyrella hydrophila. e, Entoloma murraii. f, Hygrophorus speciosus. g, Mycena leaiana. h, Cystoderma amianthinum.
No. 1673: a, Amanita muscaria. b, Amanita virosa. c, Galerina autumnalis. d, Omphalotus illudens. e, Naematoloma fasciculare. f, Paxillus involutus. g, Russula emetica. h, Scleroderma citrinum.
No. 1674: a, Armillaria ponderosa. b, Agaricus augustus. c, Gomphidius subroseus. d, Morchella esculenta. e, Stropharia rugoso. f, Boletus edulis. g, Clitocybe nuda. h, Lactarius deliciosus.
No. 1675, Trametes versicolor. No. 1676, Collybia iocephala.

1995, Nov. 1   **Perf. 14**
1671   A367   180fr #a.-h.   5.75 2.75
1672   A367   195fr #a.-h.   6.25 3.00
1673-1674 A367   200fr #a.-h.,
     each   6.50 3.25

Souvenir Sheets
1675-1676 A367   1500fr each   6.00 3.00

Miniature Sheets

History of Transportation — A368

Steam locomotives: No. 1677: a, SNC Class 231 D Le Havre-Paris Express. b, Princess Royal Class Pacific, England. c, Class 5 2-10-0, German Railroad. d, Class "15A" 4-6 4+4-6-4 Beyer-Garratt, Rhodesia. e, Japanes 2-8-0. f, Class 940, 2-8-2 engine, Italy.
Various vehicles: No. 1678: a, Semi truck. Roman chariot. c, Motorcycle. d, Hummer 4 wheel drive. e, Bicycle. f, London autobus. Lunar rover. h, 1954 Jaguar XK 140. i, Sk doo.
No. 1679, First land vehicle to break soun barrier.

1995, Dec. 1   **Litho.**   **Perf. 1**
1677 A368   200fr Sheet of 6,
    #a.-f.   4.75 2.5
1678 A368   200fr Sheet of 9,
    #a.-i.   7.25 3.5

Souvenir Sheet
1679 A368   1500fr multicolored   6.00 3.00
No. 1679 contains one 85x28mm stamp.

World Post Day A369

Designs: 220fr, Selling stamps. 315fr, Sorting stamps. 335fr, Post office workers handling large sacks of mail.

1995   **Litho.**   **Perf. 13½**
1680-1682 A369   Set of 3   4.50 2.25

Christmas A370

Paintings: 90fr, Nativity scene, vert. 325fr, Adoration of the Magi, vert. 340fr, 500fr, Adoration of the shepherds.

1995, Sept. 13   **Litho.**   **Perf. 13½**
1683-1685 A370   Set of 3   3.00 1.50

Souvenir Sheet
Perf. 12½
1686 A370   500fr multi, vert.   2.00 1.00

Sheets of 6

Wildlife of Africa A371

No. 1687: a, Gorilla. b, Uroota suraka. c, Pan troglodytes. d, Panthera pardus. e, Crocodylus niloticus. f, Leptailurus serval.
No. 1688a, Papilio tynderaeus. b, Bongo taurotragus. c, Epiphora aldiba. d, Cephalophus zebra. e, Cercopithecus cephus. f, Arctocebus calabarensis.

1996, May 10   **Litho.**   **Perf. 14**
1687 A371   150fr #a.-f., each   3.50 1.75
1688 A371   180fr #a.-f., each   4.25 2.25

China '96, 9th Asian Intl. Philatelic Exhibition.

A372

1996 Summer
Olympics,
Atlanta — A373

Designs: 50fr, Olympic Stadium, Mexico,
1968, horiz. 90fr, Yevgeny Petrov, skeet
shooter, Mexico, 1968, horiz. 220fr, Lia
Manoliu, women's discus, Mexico, 1968, horiz.
325fr, Dumb-bell lifting, discontinued sport.
Medal winners from past games: No. 1693:
a, China, Women's Volleyball, 1984. b, Wayne
Wells, wrestling, 1972. c, Bob Beamon, long
jump, 1968. d, Victor Kurentsov, weight lifting,
1968. e, Shirley Strong, 100m hurdles, 1984. f,
Nadia Comaneci, balance beam, 1976. g, Giovanni Parisi, boxing, 1988. h, Emil Zatopek,
10,000m, 1948. i, USSR, Brazil, Germany,
soccer, 1988.
1000fr, Helen Mayer, fencing, 1936.

1996, July 8	Litho.	Perf. 14
1689-1692 A372 Set of 4	2.75	1.40
1693 A372 200fr Sheet of 9, #a.-i.	7.25	3.50
Souvenir Sheet		
1694 A372 1000fr multicolored	4.00	2.00

1996, Mar. 25		Perf. 12½

100fr, Women's gymnastics. 150fr,
Women's tennis. 200fr, Javelin. 300fr, Men's
field hockey. 400fr, Weight lifting. 500fr, Men's
soccer.
1000fr, Synchronized swimming.

1695-1700 A373 Set of 6	7.50	3.75
Souvenir Sheet		
1701 A373 1000fr multicolored	5.50	2.75

Butterflies
A374

Designs: 40fr, Euphaedra eleus, vert. 90fr,
Papilio dardanus, vert. 220fr, Iolaus timon.
315fr, Charaxes cynthia.

1996, June 17	Litho.	Perf. 13
1702-1705 A374 Set of 4	2.75	1.50

Beetles — A375

Designs: 100fr, Purpuricenus kaehleri.
150fr, Carabus auronitens. 200fr, Semanotus
rassicus. 300fr, Rosalia alpina. 400fr, Mylabris
variabilis. 500fr, Odontolabis cuvera.
1000fr, Psalidognathus atys.

1996, May 5		
1706-1711 A375 Set of 6	7.75	3.75
Souvenir Sheet		
Perf. 12½		
1712 A375 1000fr multicolored	5.50	2.75
No. 1712 contains one 40x32mm stamp.

1998 World Cup
Soccer
Championships,
France — A376

French flag, various action scenes: 100fr,
150fr, 200fr, 300fr, 400fr, 500fr.

1996, Apr. 10		Perf. 12½
1713-1718 A376 Set of 6	7.75	3.75
Souvenir Sheet		
1719 A376 1000fr multicolored	5.50	2.75

World Wildlife Fund — A377

Designs: a, 325fr, Cephalophus drosalis. b,
220fr, Cephalophus maxwelli. c, 180fr,
Cephalophus rufilatus. d, 370fr, Cephalophus
syvicultor.
1500fr, Cephalophus drosalis, diff.

1996, July 30		Perf. 14
1720 A377 Block of 4, #a.-d.	4.00	2.00
Souvenir Sheet		
1721 A377 1500fr multicolored	6.25	3.00
No. 1720 was issued in sheets of 16 stamps.

Endangered Species — A378

Designs, vert: 220fr, Zebra. 315fr, Leopard.
325fr, Antelope. 335fr, Madoqua Kirki.
No. 1726: a, African elephants. b, Toucan
(c, d, e, f.) c, Mamba (f). d, Lionesses. e,
Impala. f, Nyala. g, Hippopptamus. h, Croco-
dile. i, Kingfisher.
No. 1727, Buphagus erythrorhynchus, vert.
No. 1728, Leopard, vert.

1996, July 30		
1722-1725 A378 Set of 4	6.25	3.00
1726 A378 200fr Sheet of 9, #a.-i.	7.50	3.75
Souvenir Sheets		
1727-1728 A378 1500fr each	6.25	3.00

Endangered
Species
A379

75fr, Elephant. 90fr, Crocodile. 315fr, Deer.

1996, July 30	Litho.	Perf. 13
1729-1731 A379 Set of 3	1.90	.95

Traditional
Musical
Instruments
A380

90fr, Gongs. 220fr, Cymbals (balafon).
325fr, String instrument. 500fr, Drums.

1996, July 15		
1732-1735 A380 Set of 4	4.50	2.25

Traditional
Dances
A381

Designs: 10fr, Kamou dance, Kabyes. 90fr,
Kondona dance, Kabyes. 220fr, Bassar. 315fr,
Kloto. 335fr, Voudoussin.

1996, June 30		
1736-1740 A381 Set of 5	4.00	2.00

New Year 1997
(Year of the
Ox) — A382

Paintings, by Ren Bonian (1840-95): No.
1741: a, Herdboy on Buffalo. b, Return from
the Pasture. c, Grazing by the Pond.
500fr, Reading Beside an Ox.

1997, Jan. 2	Litho.	Perf. 14
1741 A382 180fr Strip of 3, #a.-c.	2.25	2.25
d. Souvenir sheet of 3, #a-c	2.25	2.25
Souvenir Sheet		
Perf. 13½x14		
1742 A382 500fr multicolored	2.00	2.00
No. 1741 was issued in sheets of 6 stamps.
No. 1742 contains one 34x46mm stamp.

Fruits
A383

100fr, Mango. 150fr, Bananas. 200fr,
Peaches. 300fr, Papaya. 400fr, Lemon. 500fr,
Coconuts.
1000fr, Various fruits.

1996, June 2	Litho.	Perf. 12½
1743-1748 A383 Set of 6	7.25	7.25
Souvenir Sheet		
Perf. 13		
1749 A383 1000fr multicolored	5.25	5.25
No. 1749 contains one 40x32mm stamp.

Souvenir Sheet

Chinese Stone Carving — A384

Illustration reduced.

1996, May 10	Litho.	Perf. 12
1750 A384 370fr multicolored	1.50	1.50
China '96. No. 1750 was not available until
March 1997.

Jaffar Ballogou,
Boxer — A384a

1996	Litho.	Perf. 13
1750C A384a 315fr multi		
Two additional stamps were issued in this
set. The editors would like to examine them.
World Telecommunications Day.

UNESCO,
50th Anniv.
A385

World Heritage Sites: No. 1751: a, Axum
archaeological site, Ethiopia. b, Victoria Falls,
Zambia. c, Archaeological site, Zimbabwe. d,
Nature reserve, Niger. e, Arguin Natl. Park,
Mauritania. f, Goree Island, Senegal. g, Tim-
gad Ruins, Algeria. h, Ait Ben-Haddou,
Morocco.
No. 1752: a, Kyoto, Japan. b, Waterfalls,
Colombia. c, Necropolis, Egypt. d, Old Rama
Church, Finland. e, Palladian villa, Vicenza,
Italy. f, Rock paintings, China. g, Church, Ouro
Preto, Brazil. h, Rhodes, Greece.
No. 1753: a, Exterior of Cistercian Abbey,
Fontenay, France. b, Dubrovnik Village, Croa-
tia. c, Interior of Cistercian Abbey, Fontenay.
d, e, Quedlinberg, Germany. f, Ironbridge
Gorge, England. g, Grand Canyon, US. h, Vil-
lage, Ironbridge Gorge, England.
No. 1754, Kyoto, Japan, horiz. No. 1755, Mt.
Huangshan, China, horiz. No. 1756, Village,
Ironbridge, England, horiz.

1997, Mar. 24	Litho.	Perf. 14
Sheets of 8 + Label		
1751-1753 A385 235fr #a.-h., ea	7.50	7.50
Souvenir Sheet		
1754-1756 A385 1000fr each	4.00	4.00

Cats
A386

150fr, American shorthair. 200fr, Siamese,
vert. 300fr, Java. 400fr, "Ocicat," vert. 500fr,
Scottish fold. No. 1762, 1000fr, Persian, vert.
No. 1763, Colorpoint shorthair, vert.

1997	Litho.	Perf. 12½
1757-1762 A386 Set of 6	8.50	8.50
Souvenir Sheet		
1763 A386 1000fr multicolored	3.50	3.50
No. 1763 contains one 32x40mm stamp.

Military
Uniforms — A387

Designs: 150fr, Officer of cuirassiers. 200fr,
Norman regiment officer. 300fr, Volunteer bat-
talion foot soldier. 400fr, Berlin Campaign Mili-
tiaman. 500fr, Foot soldier. No. 1769, 1000fr,
Musketeer.
No. 1770, Belling Regiment Hussar.

1997
Perf. 13x12½
1764-1769 A387 Set of 6   8.50 8.50
Souvenir Sheet
1770 A387 1000fr multicolored   3.50 3.50
No. 1770 contains one 40x32mm stamp.

Return of Hong Kong to China - A388

Deng Xiaoping (1904-97) — A388a

Views of city: 220fr, Chinese flag as inscription, skyscraper. 315fr, Chinese flag as inscription, night scene. 325fr, Circular stair railing, skyscraper at night. 340fr, Chinese flag, view of city through inscription. 370fr, Deng Xiaoping (1904-97), fireworks over city. #1775A: a, shown. b, Looking left.

Illustration reduced.

1997, June 2
Perf. 14
1771-1775 A388 Set of 5   6.50 6.50
Sheet of 2
Perf. 13½
1775A A388a 500fr #a.-b.   3.75 3.75
Nos. 1771-1773 are 28x44mm and were each issued in sheets of 4. Nos. 1774-1775 were each issued in sheets of 3.

Queen Elizabeth II and Prince Philip, 50th Wedding Anniv. A389

No. 1776: a, Queen. b, Royal arms. c, Queen in yellow hat, Prince in military uniform. d, Queen in white hat, Prince. e, Windsor Castle. f, Prince.
1000fr, Portrait of Queen, Prince.

1997, June 25
1776 A389 315fr Sheet of 6, #a.-f.   6.50 6.50
Souvenir Sheet
1777 A389 1000fr multicolored   3.50 3.50

Locomotives — A390

150fr, Light locomotive, Adams Bridges. 200fr, Norris Type, England 1866. 300fr, Jones and Ports locomotive with long boiler, 1848. 400fr, Cargo and passenger locomotive, Ansaldo, 1850. 500fr, Birkenhead, Italy, 1863. #1783, 1000fr, Quarter locomotive, New York, 1890.
#1783A, Six-wheeled locomotive, Robert Stephenson, 1830, vert.

1996, Dec. 5 Litho. Perf. 12½x12
1778-1783 A390 Set of 6   8.75 8.75
Souvenir Sheet
Perf. 12½
1783A   A390 1000fr multi   3.50 3.50

Birds — A391

150fr, Poephila guttata. 200fr, Lonchura malacca. 300fr, Acanthis cannabina. 400fr, Fringilla coelebs. 500fr, Emblema guttata. #1789, 1000fr, Passerina amoena.
#1789A, Chloebia gouldiae.

1996, Nov. 27 Perf. 13
1784-1789 A391 Set of 6   8.75 8.75
Souvenir Sheet
1789A A391 1000fr multicolored   3.50 3.50
Nos. 1784-1789 are dated 1996. No. 1789A contains one 32x40mm stamp.

Turtles A392

Designs: 150fr, Asterochelys yniphora. 200fr, Staurotypus triporcatus. 300fr, Puxidea mouhoti. 400fr, Geomyda spengleri. 500fr, Cuora galbinifrons. #1795, 1000fr, Malaclemys terrapin.
#1795A, Asterochelys radiata.

1996, Nov. 30
1790-1795 A392 Set of 6   6.50 6.50
Souvenir Sheet
1795A A392 1000fr multicolored   3.50 3.50
Nos. 1790-1795 are dated 1996. No. 1795A contains one 40x32mm stamp.

Natl. Liberation, 30th Anniv. — A393

1997 Litho. Perf. 13½
1796 A393 90fr yellow & multi   .30 .30
1797 A393 220fr green & multi   .75 .75

Diana, Princess of Wales (1961-97) A394

Nos. 1798a-1798i: Various portraits of Princess Diana in designer gowns.
Views up close: No. 1799, like #1798a. No. 1800, like #1798c. No. 1801, like #1798d. No. 1802, like #1798e. No. 1803, like #1798h. No. 1804, like #1798i.

1997
1798 A394 180fr Sheet of 9, #a.-i.   7.50 7.50
Souvenir Sheets
1799-1804 A394 180fr each   5.50 5.50

Diana, Princess of Wales (1961-97) — A395

Nos. 1805-1807, Various pictures of Diana during her lifetime as Princess of Wales.
Pictures of Diana with (in margin): No. 1808, French Pres. Giscard d'Estaing. No. 1809, Mother Teresa. No. 1810, US First Lady Hillary Clinton.

1998, Jan. 2 Perf. 14
Sheets of 6
1805 A395 240fr #a.-f.   5.00 5.00
1806 A395 315fr #a.-f.   6.50 6.50
1807 A395 340fr #a.-f.   7.25 7.25
Souvenir Sheets
1808-1810 A395 1000fr each   3.50 3.50

Souvenir Sheet

Marilyn Monroe (1926-62) — A396

Illustration reduced.

1997 Litho. Perf. 13½
1811 A396 2000fr multicolored   7.25 7.25

New Year 1998 (Year of the Tiger) — A397

Various paintings of tigers, by Liu Jiyou (1918-83): No. 1812: a, 180fr. b, 200fr. No. 1813: a, 90fr. b, 100fr. c, 180fr. d, 200fr.

1998, Jan. 5 Litho. Perf. 14
1812 A397 Sheet of 2, #a.-b.   1.25 1.25
1813 A397 Sheet of 4, #a.-d.   2.00 2.00
No. 1812 contains two 26x65mm stamps.

Hiroshige (1797-1858), Painter — A398

Paintings: No. 1814: a, Sixty-Nine Stations of the Kisokaido Road: Mochizuki. b, Eight Views of Lake Biwa Evening Snow at Mt. Hira. c, Kinkizan Temple on Enoshima Island, Sagami Provence. d, Cherry Blossoms. e, Evening Snow at Asakusa. f, Myhankoshi.
No. 1815: a, Two Terrapins (Fan print). b, Swimming Carp. c, Takanawa by Moonlight. d, Night Rain at Karasaki. e, Chiryu: The Summer Horse Fair. f, Shower over the Nihonbashi.
No. 1816, vert: a, Takata Riding Grounds. b, Sugatami & Omokage Bridges & Jariba at Takata. c, Dam on the Otonashi River at Oji. d,

Basho's Hermitage and Camellia Hill. e, Fud Falls, Oji. f, Takinogawa Oji.
No. 1817, Bird in a Tree. No. 1818, Titl Page for Hiroshige's One Hundred Views o Edo, by Baisotei. No. 1819, Memorial Portra of Hiroshige, by Utagawa. No. 1820, Stree Stalls and Tradesmen in Jouricho. No. 182 Cherry Blossom, Morning Glory, Cranes an Rabbits. No. 1822, Three Wild Geese Flyin Across the Moon. No. 1823, Suwa Bluff, Nip pori. Nos. 1817-1823 are vert.

Perf. 14x13½, 13½x14
1998, Mar. 2 Litho
Sheets of 6
1814 A398 220fr #a.-f.   4.50 4.5
1815 A398 315fr #a.-f.   6.50 6.5
1816 A398 370fr #a.-f.   7.50 7.5
Souvenir Sheets
Perf. 13½x14
1817-1823 A398 1000fr each   3.50 3.50
Nos. 1817-1823 each contain one 26x72mm stamp.

Fauna, Flora, Minerals — A399

Dolphins and whales: No. 1824: a, Souffleur nesarnack. b, Lagenorhynque. c, Sotalie du cameroun. d, Petit rorqual. e, Rorqual commun. f, Faux orque.
Insects and spiders: No. 1825: a, Lasius niger. b, Sceliphron spirifex. c, Peucetia. d, Mygale. e, Theraphoside. f, Dynaste hercule.
Precious stones, minerals: No. 1826: a, Ruby. b, Diamond in kimberlite. c, Cut diamond. d, Rock salt. e, Tiger's eye. f, Uraninite.
Moths and butterflies: No. 1827: a, Pirate. b, Euchromie des liserons. c, Asterope. d, Psalis de kiriakoff. e, Sphinx de fabricius. f, Pensee bleue.
Mushrooms: No. 1828: a, Lepiote. b, Hypholome. c, Lactaire. d, Russule fetide. e, Russule doree. f, Strophaire.
No. 1829, Tricholome a odeur de savon. No. 1830, Potto.

1998(?) Litho. Perf. 13½
Sheets of 6
1824 A399 180fr #a.-f.   4.00 4.00
1825 A399 250fr #a.-f.   5.75 5.75
1826 A399 300fr #a.-f.   6.75 6.75
1827 A399 400fr #a.-f.   9.00 9.00
1828 A399 450fr #a.-f.   10.25 10.25
Souvenir Sheets
1829-1830 A399 2000fr each   7.75 7.75
Intl. Scouting, 90th Anniv. (#1825, 1827-1830). Nos. 1829-1830 each contain one 41x60mm stamp.

Jerry Garcia (1942-95) — A400

Various portraits.

1998 Litho. Perf. 13½
1831 A400 250fr Sheet of 9, #a.-i.   7.75 7.75
Souvenir Sheet
1832 A400 2000fr multicolored   7.00 7.00
No. 1832 contains one 42x51mm stamp.

Dinosaurs — A401

Various unidentified dinosaurs.

1998

1833 A401 290fr Sheet of 9,
#a.-i. 10.00 10.00

Souvenir Sheet

1834 A401 2000fr multicolored 7.50 7.50

No. 1834 contains one 42x51mm stamp.

1998 Winter Olympic Games,
Nagano — A402

No. 1835: a, Hockey. b, Speed skating. c,
Pairs figure skating. d, Luge. e, Curling. f,
Bobsledding.
No. 1836: a, Downhill skiing. b, Freestyle ski
jumping (blue skis). c, Ski jumping. d, Downhill
skiier in tuck. e, Snow boarding. f, Freestyle
skiing (red skis).

1998

Sheets of 6

1835 A402 250fr #a.-f. 5.75 5.75
1836 A402 300fr #a.-f. 6.75 6.75

Nos. 1835-1836 each have 3 labels.

1998 World Cup Soccer
Championships, France — A403

Player, country, vert: No. 1837, Kluivert,
Netherlands. No. 1838, Asprilla, Colombia.
No. 1839, Bergkamp, Netherlands. No. 1840,
Gascoigne, England. No. 1841, Ravanelli,
Italy. No. 1842, Sheringham, England.
No. 1843: a, Paul Gascoigne, England, diff.
b, Ryan Giggs, Wales. c, Roy Keane, Ireland.
d, Stuart Pearce, England. e, Tony Adams,
England. f, Teddy Sheringham, England, diff.
g, Paul Ince, England. h, Steve McManaman,
England.
No. 1844: a, Rossi, Italy. b, Lineker,
England. c, Lato, Poland. d, Futre, Poland. e,
Klinsmann, Germany. f, Hurst, England. g,
Kempes, Argentina. h, McCoist, Scotland.
World Cup Champions, year, vert.: - #1845:
a, Argentina, 1978. b, Italy, 1982. c, England,
1966. d, Uruguay, 1930. e, Germany, 1954. f,
Argentina, 1986. g, Brazil, 1994.
No. 1846: Ronaldo, Brazil, vert. No. 1847,
Gary Lineker, England, vert. No. 1848,
Shearer, England, vert.

Perf. 13½x14, 14x13½

1998, July 10 **Litho.**
1837-1842 A403 370fr Set of 6 7.50 7.50

Sheets of 8 + Label

1843 A403 220fr #a.-h. 5.00 6.00
1844 A403 315fr #a.-h. 8.50 8.50

Sheet of 7 + 2 Labels

1845 A403 325fr #a.-g. 7.75 7.75

Souvenir Sheets

1846-1848 A403 1500fr each 5.00 5.00

Bella Bellow (d.
1973), Singer -
A403a

1998 **Litho.** **Perf. 13½**
1848A A403a 5fr yel orange
1848B A403a 10fr olive green
1848C A403a 25fr emerald
1848D A403a 40fr violet
1848E A403a 50fr black
1848F A403a 75fr yel orange
1848G A403a 100fr orange
1848H A403a 125fr blue
1848I A403a 200fr brt purple
1848J A403a 240fr red violet
1848K A403a 280fr green
1848L A403a 300fr Prus blue
1848M A403a 320fr red orange
1848N A403a 340fr car lake
1848O A403a 390fr car rose

Five additional stamps were issued in this
set. The editors would like to examine them.

Star Wars Movies — A404

Return of the Jedi - #1849: a, Princess Leia.
b, Darth Vader. c, Han Solo. d, R2-D2, C-3PO.
e, Emperor Palpatine. f, Chewbacca. g, Leia
on speeder. h, Luke Skywalker. i, Storm
trooper on speeder.
Empire Strikes Back - #1850: a, Lando
Calrissian. b, Yoda. c, Chewbacca. d, C-3PO,
R2-D2. e, Luke Skywalker. f, Darth Vader. g,
Battle on snow planet. h, Leia. i, Rider on
snow planet.
2000fr, Han Solo, Luke Skywalker, Princess
Leia, R2-D2.

1997 **Litho.** **Perf. 13½**

Sheets of 9

1849 A404 190fr #a.-i. 5.75 5.75
1850 A404 350fr #a.-i. 10.50 10.50

Souvenir Sheet

1851 A404 2000fr multicolored 7.00 7.00

No. 1851 contains one 42x60mm.

Jacqueline Kennedy Onassis (1929-
94) — A405

No. 1852: Various portraits.
No. 1853: Various portraits of John F. Kennedy (1917-63).

1997

Sheets of 9

1852 A405 250fr #a.-i. 7.50 7.50
1853 A405 400fr #a.-i. 12.00 12.00

Diana, Princess of Wales (1961-
97) — A406

No. 1854: Various portraits.
2000fr, Diana in black (Mother Teresa in
sheet margin).

1997

Sheet of 8 + Label

1854 A406 500fr #a.-h. 15.00 15.00

Souvenir Sheet

1854I A406 2000fr multicolored 8.25 8.25

Marilyn Monroe (1926-62) — A407

Various portraits.

1997 **Litho.** **Perf. 13½**
1855 A407 300fr Sheet of 9, #a.-
i. 9.00 9.00

Minerals
A408

Designs: 100fr, Calcite. 150fr, Turquoise,
vert. 200fr, Pyrite, vert. 300fr, Tourmaline,
vert. 400fr, Pyrargirite, vert. 500fr, Malachite.
1000fr, Beryl, vert.

1999 **Litho.** **Perf. 12¾**
1856-1861 A408 Set of 6 5.00 5.00

Souvenir Sheet

Perf. 13

1861A A408 1000fr multicolored 3.00 3.00

No. 1861A contains one 32x40mm stamp.

Flowers — A409

Designs: No. 1862, Caralluma burchardii.
No. 1863, Dimorphotheca barberiae. No.
1864, Hoya carnosa. No. 1865, Amaryllis belladonna. No. 1866, Watsonia beatricis. No.
1867, Anthurium schezerianum. No. 1868,
Thumbergia alata. No. 1869, Arctotis brevis-
capa. No. 1870, Glauciun flavum. No. 1871,
Impatiens petersiana. No. 1872, Chrysanthemum segetum. No. 1873, Zantedeschia aethiopica, horiz.

1999 **Perf. 12¼**
1862 A409 100fr brown .30 .30
1863 A409 100fr violet .30 .30
1864 A409 100fr pale red .30 .30
1865 A409 150fr dark grn bl .45 .45
1866 A409 150fr red brown .45 .45
1867 A409 150fr violet blue .45 .45
1868 A409 200fr orange .60 .60
1869 A409 200fr bright grn bl .60 .60
1870 A409 300fr olive .90 .90
1871 A409 300fr blue .90 .90
1872 A409 500fr brown 1.50 1.50
1873 A409 1000fr bright pink 3.00 3.00
Nos. 1862-1873 (12) 9.75 9.75

1998 World Cup Soccer
Championship, France—A410

Predominant colors of player's shirts. No.
1874: a, Yellow. b, White. c, Blue. d, Red.
No. 1875: a, White. b, Blue. c, Red. d,
Green.
No. 1876: a, White, with black shorts. b,
Yellow, with blue shorts. c, Yellow, with yellow
shorts. d, White, with white shorts.
No. 1877: a, Red. b, Green. c, White. d, Red
& white striped.
No. 1878: a, Blue. b, Yellow. c, Red. d,
White.
No. 1879: a, Orange. b, White. c, Red. d,
Multicolored diamonds.
No. 1880: a, White, with black shorts. b,
White, with blue and red chest stripes. c,
White, with green trim. d, White, with red and
blue arm stripes.
No. 1881: a, Blue & white stripes. b, Red &
white checks. c, Yellow & green, d, Blue.
2000fr, Player, map of France.

1998   **Litho.**   *Perf. 13¼*
Sheets of 4

1874	A410	180fr #a.-d.	2.40	2.40
1875	A410	200fr #a.-d.	2.60	2.60
1876	A410	250fr #a.-d.	3.25	3.25
1877	A410	290fr #a.-d.	3.75	3.75
1878	A410	300fr #a.-d.	4.00	4.00
1879	A410	350fr #a.-d.	4.75	4.75
1880	A410	400fr #a.-d.	5.25	5.25
1881	A410	425fr #a.-d.	5.50	5.50
	Nos. 1874-1881 (8)		31.50	31.50

Souvenir Sheet

1882	A410	2000fr multicolored	6.50	6.50

Birds
A410a

Designs: 100fr, Luscinia svecica. 150fr, Oriolus oriolus. 200fr, Carduelis carduelis. 300fr, Parus caeruleus. 400fr, Fringilla coelebs. 500fr, Parus montanus.
1000fr, Regulus ignicapillus.

1999   **Litho.**   *Perf. 12¾*

1882A- 1882F	A410a	Set of 6	4.00	4.00

Souvenir Sheet
Perf. 13x13¼

1882G	A410a	1000fr multi	2.40	2.40

No. 1882G contains one 40x32mm stamp.

Antique Automobiles — A410b

Designs: 100fr, 1913 Peugeot Bebe. 150fr, 1950 Rolls-Royce. 200fr, 1921 Stutz Bearcat. 300fr, 1923 Ford Model T. 400fr, 1907 Packard. 500fr, 1950 Citroen II Legere sedan.
1000fr, 1929 Ford Model A Tudor sedan.

1999   **Perf. 12¾**

1882H-1882M	A410b	Set of 6	4.00	4.00

Souvenir Sheet
Perf. 13

1882N	A410b	1000fr multi	2.40	2.40

No. 1882N contains one 40x32mm stamp.

Cats — A411

No. 1883: a, 100fr, Colorpoint. b, 150fr, British shorthair.
No. 1884: a, 200fr, Ocicat. b, 300fr, Ragdoll.
No. 1885: a, 400fr, Balinese. b, 500fr, California Spangled.
1000fr, Somali.

1999   **Litho.**   *Perf. 12½*

1883	A411	Pair, #a.-b.	.75	.75
1884	A411	Pair, #a.-b.	1.50	1.50
1885	A411	Pair, #a.-b.	2.75	2.75
	Nos. 1883-1885 (3)		5.00	5.00

Souvenir Sheet

1886	A411	1000fr multicolored	3.00	3.00

Millennium
A412

No. 1886A, Invention of Paper by Chinese (with millennium emblem).
No. 1887 - Chinese Science & Technology: a, Lacquerware. b, Counting rods. c, Sericulture. d, Acupuncture. e, "Tuned chime bell." f, Piston bellows. g, Compass. h, Manufacture of steel. i. Crossbow. j, Spinning wheel. k, Water conservancy. l, Pulse taking. m, Multi-tube seed drill. n, Rotary winnowing fan. o, Like #1886A (no millennium emblem). p, Silk loom (60x40mm). q, Wheelbarrow.
No. 1888 - Highlights of the 11th Century: a, Chinese invent gunpowder. b, Islamic bronze griffin. c, Battle of Clontarf. d, William becomes Duke of Normandy. e, Norman knight. f, Spinning wheels in use in China. g, Yaroslav becomes Grand Prince of Kiev. h, Polyphonic singing introduced. i, Macbeth becomes King of Scotland. j, Edward the Confessor becomes King of England. k, Astrolabe. l, Harp introduced in Europe. m, Trier Cathedral. n, Mandingo Empire founded in Africa. o, Toltecs invade Yucatan. p, Vikings reach North Americam (60x40mm). q, Movable type used in China.
No. 1889 - Western Paintings of the 20th century by: a, Henri Matisse. b, Pablo Picasso. c, Marc Chagall. d, Wassily Kandinsky. e, Fernand Léger. f, Piet Mondrian. g, George Bellows. h, Georgia O'Keeffe. i, Salvador Dali. j, Francis Bacon. k, Edward Hopper. l, Andy Warhol. m, Helen Frankenthaler. n, Richard Anuszkiewicz. o, Audrey Flack. p, Jackson Pollack, Lee Krasner (60x40mm). q, Jean-Michel Basquiat.

1999   **Litho.**   *Perf. 13¼x13*

1886A	A412	120fr multi	.35	.35

Sheets of 17
Perf. 12½

1887	A412	120fr #a.-q. + label	6.75	6.75
1888	A412	130fr #a.-q. + label	7.00	7.00
1889	A412	140fr #a.-q. + label	7.75	7.75

Inscriptions on Nos. 1887b, 1887e, 1888i, and perhaps others, are incorrect or misspelled.
Issued: 130fr, 7/20.

US Civil War
Photographs
A413

Various Civil War photographs making up a photomosaic of Abraham Lincoln.

1999, July 20   **Litho.**   *Perf. 13½*

1890	A413	300fr Sheet of 8,		
		#a.-h.	7.50	7.50

See Nos. 1939-1940.

Free Trade
Zone, 10th
Anniv. — A414

Symbol and: 125fr, Map. 240fr, Clouds. 340fr, Wall.

1999   **Litho.**   *Perf. 12¾*

1891	A414	125fr multi	.35	.35
1892	A414	240fr multi	.65	.65
1893	A414	340fr multi	.90	.90
	Nos. 1891-1893 (3)		1.90	1.90

Rural Development Council, 40th
Anniv. - A414a

1999   **Litho.**   *Perf. 13x13¼*

1893A	A414a	240fr red & multi	
1893B	A414a	380fr vio & multi	
1893C	A414a	390fr blk & multi	

Other stamps for this subject may exist. The editors would like to examine any examples. Numbers may change.

Goldfish
A415

Various depictions of Carassius auratus auratus: 100fr, 150fr, 200fr, 300fr, 400fr, 500fr.

1999

1894-1899	A415	Set of 6	4.75	4.75

Souvenir Sheet
Perf. 13

1899A	A415	1000fr multi	3.00	3.00

No. 1899A contains one 40x31mm stamp.

SOS Children's
Villages, 50th
Anniv. — A416

1999   **Litho.**   *Perf. 13¼x13*

1900	A416	125fr multi ('01)	.35	.35
1901	A416	240fr multi		
1902	A416	340fr multi		

Additional stamps may have been issued in this set. The editors would like to examine any examples.

Sailing
Vessels -
A417

Designs: 100fr, Phoenician boat. 150fr, Roman cargo boat. 200fr, New Guinea fishing boat. 300fr, Caravel, vert. 400fr, 16th cent. English ship, vert. 500fr, 17th cent. English ship, vert.
1000fr, Steamship with sails.

1999   **Litho.**   *Perf. 12½*

1905-1910	A417	Set of 6	4.50	4.50

Souvenir Sheet
Perf. 12¼x12

1911	A417	1000fr multi	2.75	2.75

No. 1911 contains one 42x30mm stamp.

Dogs — A417a

Designs: 100fr, St. Bernard. 150fr, Teckel. 200fr, German shepherd. 300fr, Italian hound. 400fr, Yorkshire terrier. 500fr, Schnauzer.

1999   **Litho.**   *Perf. 12¾*

1911A- 1911F	A417a	Set of 6	4.00	4.00

Souvenir Sheet
Perf. 12½

1911G	A417a	1000fr Afghan hound	2.40	2.40

No. 1911G contains one 40x31mm stamp.

Trains
A417b

Designs: 100fr, Baldwin 0-4-0. 150fr, Baldwin 2-6-2. 200fr, Baldwin gasoline locomotive. 300fr, H.K. Porter 0-4-0. 400fr, H.K. Porter 2-6-2. 500fr, Vulcan 0-4-0.

1999   **Litho.**   *Perf. 12¾*

1911H-1911M	A417b	Set of 6	4.00	4.00

Souvenir Sheet

1911N	A417b	1000fr Jordanian locomotive	2.40	2.40

No. 1911N contains one 40x31mm stamp.

Orchids
A417c

Designs: 100fr, Gramangis ellisii. 150fr, Habenaria columbae. 200fr, Epidendrum atroporpureum. 300fr, Odontoglossum majale. 400fr, Oncidium splendidum. 500fr, Zygopetalum mackai.
1000fr, Paphiopedilum pairieanum.

1999, Nov. 8   **Litho.**   *Perf. 12x12¼*

1911O-1911T	A417c	Set of 6	5.25	5.25

Souvenir Sheet
Perf. 12½

1911U	A417c	1000fr multi	3.25	3.25

No. 1911U contains one 31x39mm stamp.

New Year 2000
(Year of the
Dragon) — A418

Various views of dragon: 100fr, 150fr, 200fr, 300fr, 400fr, 500fr.
1000fr, Head of dragon, horiz.

2000   *Perf. 12¾x12*
912-1917 A418 Set of 6   4.50 4.50

Souvenir Sheet
Perf. 13¼
918 A418 1000fr multi   2.75 2.75
No. 1918 contains one 40x32mm stamp.

Wild
Cats
A419

Designs: 100fr, Panthera tigris. 150fr, Acinonyx jubatus. 200fr, Felis concolor. 300fr, Panthera leo, female. 400fr, Felis pardalis. 500fr, Panthera leo, male.
1000fr, Panthera tigris, diff.

2000   *Perf. 13*
1919-1924 A419 Set of 6   4.50 4.50

Souvenir Sheet
1925 A419 1000fr multi   2.75 2.75
No. 1925 contains one 40x32mm stamp.

Flowers — A420

No. 1926, 290fr: a, Cyrtanthus contractus. b, Sandersonia aurantiaca. c, Anomateca grandiflora. d, Helichrysum ecklonis. e, Striga elegans. f, Nymphaea odorata.
No. 1927, 290fr: a, Leomotis leonii. b, Strelitzia reginae. c, Freesia refracta. d, Garzania nivea. e, Dimophoteca sinuata. f, Pelargonium domesticum.
No. 1928, 290fr: a, Gloriosa rothchiliana. b, Clematis vitalba. c, Rochea falcato. d, Plumbago capensis. e, Thunbergia alata. f, Lampranthus coccineus.
No. 1929, 1500fr, Epiphyllum hybrid. No. 1930, 1500fr, Agapanthus africanus.
Illustration reduced.

2000, July 28   Litho.   *Perf. 14*
Sheets of 6, #a-f
1926-1928 A420 Set of 3   13.50 13.50

Souvenir Sheets
1929-1930 A420 Set of 2   7.75 7.75

Wildlife
A421

Designs: 200fr, Thompson's gazelle. 300fr, Felis margarita. 400fr, Blesbok. 500fr, Kob.
No. 1935, 290fr, vert.: a, Hoopoe. b, Harpactira spider. c, Marabou. d, Bee-eater. e, Oryx. f, Okapi. g, Wart hog. h, Baboon.
No. 1936, 290fr, vert.: a, Hornbill. b, Pygmy kingfisher. c, Vulture. d, Bataleur eagle. e, Kudu. f, Hyena. g, Gorilla. h, Lizard.
No. 1937, 1500fr, Eland, vert. No. 1938, 1500fr, Mongoose, vert.

2000, July 28
1931-1934 A421 Set of 4   3.75 3.75

Sheets of 8, #a-h
1935-1936 A421 Set of 2   12.00 12.00

Souvenir Sheets
1937-1938 A421 Set of 2   7.75 7.75

Mushrooms
A421a

Designs: 100fr, Hebeloma crustuliniforme. 150fr, Polyporellus squamosus, horiz. 200fr, Morchella deliciosa. 300fr, Disciotis venosa, horiz. 400fr, Cantharellus tubiformis. 500fr, Otidea onotica, horiz.
1000fr, Ixocomus granulatus, horiz.

2000, July 30   Litho.   *Perf. 12¾*
1938A-1938F A421a Set of 6   4.75 4.75

Souvenir Sheet
Perf. 13
1938G A421a 1000fr multi   2.75 2.75
No. 1938G contains one 39x31mm stamp.

Civil War Photographs Type of 1999

No. 1939, 290fr: Various photographs with a science theme making up a photomosaic of Albert Einstein.
No. 1940, 290fr: Various photographs with an Oriental theme making up a photomosaic of Mao Zedong.

2000, Sept. 5   *Perf. 13¾*
Sheets of 8, #a-h
1939-1940 A413 Set of 2   12.00 12.00

Queen Mother, 100th Birthday — A422

No. 1941: a, With Princesses Elizabeth and Margaret, 1931. b, With daughter, 1940. c, Black and white photo. d, In 1990.
1500fr, With Princess Margaret, 1939.
Illustration reduced.

2000, Sept. 5   *Perf. 14*
1941 A422 650fr Sheet of 4, #a-d, + label   6.75 6.75

Souvenir Sheet
Perf. 13¾
1942 A422 1500fr With Princess Margaret, 1939   4.00 4.00
No. 1942 contains one 38x51mm stamp.

Popes — A423

No. 1943, 400fr: a, Anastasius I, 399-401. b, Boniface I, 418-22. c, Gaius, 283-96. d, Hilarius, 461-68. e, Hyginus, 136-40. f, Innocent I, 402-17.
No. 1944, 400fr: a, Martin I, 649-55. b, Nicholas I, 858-67. c, Paschal I, 817-24. d, Paul I, 757-67. e, Pelagius, 556-61. f, Pelagius II, 579-90.
No. 1945, 400fr: a, Sergius, 687-701. b, Sergius II, 844-47. c, Severinus, 640. d, Sisinnius, 708. e, Stephen II, 752-57. f, Stephen IV, 816-17.
No. 1946, 1500fr, Pontian, 230-35. No. 1947, 1500fr, Pelagius II, diff. No. 1948, 1500fr, Stephen V, 885-91.
Illustration reduced.

2000, Sept. 5   *Perf. 12x12¼*
Sheets of 6, #a-f
1943-1945 A423 Set of 3   19.00 19.00

Souvenir Sheets
1946-1948 A423 Set of 3   11.50 11.50

British Monarchs — A424

No. 1949, 400fr: a, Charles II, 1660-85. b, Anne, 1702-14. c, George I, 1714-27. d, George IV, 1820-30. e, James II, 1685-88. f, George II, 1727-60.
No. 1950, 400fr: a, Elizabeth II, 1952-present. b, Edward VIII, 1936. c, George VI, 1936-52. d, George V, 1910-36. e, Edward VII, 1901-10. f, William IV, 1830-37.
No. 1951, 1500fr, William III and Mary, 1689-1702. No. 1952, 1500fr, Victoria, 1837-1901.
Illustration reduced.

2000, Sept. 5
Sheets of 6, #a-f
1949-1950 A424 Set of 2   12.50 12.50

Souvenir Sheets
1951-1952 A424 Set of 2   7.75 7.75

Millennium Type of 1999

Highlights of 1950-59: a, US sends troops to defend South Korea. b, Rock and roll hits the air waves. c, Death of Eva Peron. d, Structure of DNA revealed by Watson and Crick. e, Sir Edmund Hillary and Tenzing Norgay reach peak of Mt. Everest. f, John F. Kennedy marries Jacqueline Bouvier. g, Coronation of Queen Elizabeth II. h, Millionth Volkswagen produced. i, German soccer team wins World Cup. j, Roger Bannister runs 1st 4-minute mile. k, Dr. Jonas Salk develops polio vaccine. l, 1st McDonald's franchise. m, New phone lines cross Atlantic. n, Soviet Union launches Sputnik. o, Jack Kerouac writes "On the Road." p, China begins "Great Leap Forward." q, Communist revolution in Cuba. r, Computer chip patented.

2000   *Perf. 12¾x12½*
1953 A412 200fr Sheet of 18, #a-r, + label   9.25 9.25

36th Organization of African Unity Summit. Lomé — A425

OAU emblem, map of Africa, doves and panel color of: 10fr, Bright yellow. 25fr, Green. 100fr, Dull yellow. 125fr, Blue violet. 250fr, Red violet. 375fr, Red. 400fr, Brown. 425fr, Orange.
No. 1954: a, Peace dove statue. b, Hotel du 2 Février. c, Congress building, Lomé. d, Alédjo Fault. e, Temberma hut. f, Cacao plantation.
No. 1955: a, Pres. Gnassingbé Eyadema, map of Europe and Africa, handshakes. b, Algerian Pres. Abdelazir Bouteflika, Pres. Eyadema, and map of Africa. c, Pres. Eyadema and OAU emblem. d, Map of Africa, doves, OAU emblem.
Illustration reduced.

2000   Litho.   *Perf. 14x13¾*
1953S-1953Z A425 Set of 8   5.00 5.00

Sheets of 6 and 4
1954 A425 350fr #a-f   5.50 5.50
1955 A425 550fr #a-d   6.00 6.00

Trains — A426

No. 1956, 425fr: a, Richard Trevethick's engine. b, Stephenson's Adler. c, Crampton Continent. d, Atlantic Coastlines 4--4-2. e, Great Northern Railway Ivatt Atlantic. f, Great Western Railway City of Truro 4-4-0.
No. 1957, 425fr: a, Paris-Lyon-Mediterranean Railway, compound 4-8-2. b, Canadian Pacific Railway Royal Hudson 4-6-4. c, London-Midland Railway Duchess. d, New York Central Twentieth Century Limited. e, New Zealand Government Railway J class 4-8-4. f, British Railways Evening Star 5-10-0.
No. 1958, 1800fr, Eurostar. No. 1959, 1800fr, TGV Atlantique.
Illustration reduced.

2000, Sept. 8   Litho.   *Perf. 14*
Sheets of 6, #a-f
1956-1957 A426 Set of 2   14.50 14.50

Souvenir Sheets
1958-1959 A426 Set of 2   10.50 10.50

Ships — A427

No. 1960, 425fr: a, Norse knaar. b, Hanseatic cog. c, Iberian caravel. d, Henri Grace à Dieu. e, Ark Royal. f, Dutch Hooker.
No. 1961, 425fr: a, HMS Victory. b, HMS Warrior. c, Cutty Sark. d, USS Olympia. e, Empress of Canada. f, James Clark Ross.
No. 1962, 1800fr, Discovery. No. 1963, 1800fr, Sea Cat ferry.

Illustration reduced.

2000, Sept. 8   Litho.   Perf. 14
Sheets of 6, #a-f
1960-1961 A427   Set of 2   14.50 14.50

Souvenir Sheets
1962-1963 A427   Set of 2   10.50 10.50

Dogs and
Cats — A428

Designs: 275fr, Bloodhound. 300fr, Sphinx
cat. 325fr, Basset hound. 350fr, Cocker spaniel. No. 1968, 375fr, American curl cat. 400fr,
Scottish fold cat.

No. 1970, 375fr, horiz. - Dogs: a, Bearded
collie. b, Chow chow. c, Boxer. d, Irish setter.
e, Bracco Italiano. f, Pointer.

No. 1971, 375fr, horiz. - Cats: a, Devon Rex.
b, Cornish Rex. c, Siamese. d, Balinese. e,
Birman. f, Korat.

No. 1972, 1500fr, Yorkshire terrier. No.
1973, 1500fr, Chinchilla cat.

Perf. 13½x13x13½

2001, Dec. 17   Litho.
1964-1969 A428   Set of 6   5.50 5.50

Sheets of 6, #a-f
1970-1971 A428   Set of 2   12.50 12.50

Souvenir Sheets
1972-1973 A428   Set of 2   8.25 8.25

Marine Life — A429

No. 1974, 200fr (31x31mm): a, Priacanthus
arenatus. b, Diplodus annularis. c,
Lithognathus mormgrus. d, Selene nomer. e,
Perraeus duorarum. f, Arbacia lixula. g, Ser-
ranus scriba. h, Trachurus trachurus. i, Lepas
amatifera. j, Octopus vulgaris. k, Scorpaena
scrofa. l, Dardenus arroser.

No. 1975, 250fr (31x31mm): a, Porcupine
fish. b, Blue shark. c, Sting ray. d, Physalia
physalis. e, Turtles. f, Coryphaena hippurus. g,
Carranx hippos. h, Sawfish. i, Todarupsis
eblanae. j, Pompano. k, Diplodus cervinus. l,
Barracuda.

No. 1976, 1500fr, Octopus vulgaris, diff. No.
1977, 1500fr, Blue shark, diff.

2001, Dec. 17   Perf. 12½
Sheets of 12, #a-l
1974-1975 A429   Set of 2   15.00 15.00

Souvenir Sheets
Perf. 13¼x13½
1976-1977 A429   Set of 2   8.25 8.25

African
Wildlife
A430

Designs: 150fr, Okapia johnstoni, vert.
200fr, Sagittarius serpentarius. 250fr, Lemur
catta, vert. 300fr, Gorilla gorilla. 350fr, Genetta
genetta, vert. Hippocampus. 400fr, Fennecus zerda.

No. 1984, 380fr: a, Papio hamadryas. b,
Felis serval. c, Suricata suricatta. d, Orycter-
opus afer. e, Connochataetes taurinus. f,
Tragelaphus strepsiceros.

No. 1985, 380fr: a, Panthera pardus. b, Loxodonta africana. c, Cercopithecus hamlyni. d,
Ephippiorhynchuus senegalensis. e, Hippopotamus amphibius. f, Hippotragus niger.

No. 1986, 415fr: a, Equus burchelli boehmi.
b, Ceratotherium simum. c, Achionyx jubatus.
d, Gazella dama. e, Crocuta crocuta. f, Lyacon
pictus.

No. 1987, 1500fr, Crocodylus niloticus. No.
1988, 1500fr, Panthera leo, vert. No. 1989,
1500fr, Giraffa camelopardalis.

Perf. 13½x13¼, 13¼x13½
2001, Dec. 17
1978-1983 A430   Set of 6   4.50 4.50

Sheets of 6, #a-f
1984-1986 A430   Set of 3   19.00 19.00

Souvenir Sheets
1987-1989 A430   Set of 3   12.50 12.50

United We
Stand
A431

2002, Mar. 18   Litho.   Perf. 14
1990 A431 400fr multi   1.10 1.10

SEMI-POSTAL STAMPS

Curie Issue
Common Design Type
1938   Unwmk.   Engr.   Perf. 13
B1 CD80 1.75fr + 50c brt ultra 14.50 14.50

French Revolution Issue
Common Design Type
**Photo., Name and Value Typo. in
Black**

1939
B2 CD83 45c + 25c green   6.50 6.50
B3 CD83 70c + 30c brown   6.50 6.50
B4 CD83 90c + 35c red org   6.50 6.50
B5 CD83 1.25fr + 1fr rose
                          pink   6.50 6.50
B6 CD83 2.25fr + 2fr blue   6.50 6.50
          Nos. B2-B6 (5)   32.50 32.50

French Revolution, 150th anniv. Surtax for
defense of the colonies.

Nos. 281, 236, 245,   **SECOURS**
289 Surcharged in Red   **+ 1 fr.**
or Black   **NATIONAL**

1941   Perf. 14 x 13½, 12½
B7   A10   50c + 1fr   1.25 1.25
B8   A7   80c + 2fr   4.00 4.00
B9   A8   1.50fr + 2fr   4.00 4.00
B10 A11   2fr + 3fr (R)   4.00 4.00
           Nos. B7-B10 (4)   13.25 13.25

**Catalogue values for unused
stamps in this section, from this
point to the end of the section, are
for Never Hinged items.**

Common Design Type and

Togolese
Militiaman
SP1

Military
Infirmary
SP2

1941   Photo.   Perf. 13½
B10A SP1 1fr + 1fr red   .65
B10B CD86 1.50fr + 3fr maroon .65
B10C SP2 2.50fr + 1fr blue   .65
           Nos. B10A-B10C (3) 1.95

Nos. B10A-B10C were issued by the Vichy
government in France, but were not placed on
sale in Togo.

Nos. 296-297
Surcharged in Black or Red

1944   Engr.   Perf. 12x12½
B10D 50c + 1.50fr on 2.50fr deep
              blue (R)   .45
B10E + 2.50fr on 1fr green   .45
      Colonial Development Fund.
Nos. B10D-B10E were issued by the Vichy
government in France, but were not placed on
sale in Togo.

Tropical Medicine Issue
Common Design Type
1950   Engr.   Perf. 13
B11 CD100 10fr + 2fr indigo & dk
              bl   2.75 2.75

The surtax was for charitable work.

Republic

Patient on   Uprooted Oak
Stretcher — SP3   Emblem — SP4

Designs: 30fr+5fr,   Feeding infant.
50fr+10fr, Blood transfusion.

1959   Engr.   Perf. 13
B12 SP3 20fr + 5fr multicolored .30 .25
  a. Souvenir sheet of 4   1.50 1.50
B13 SP3 30fr + 5fr bl, car & brn .30 .25
  a. Souvenir sheet of 4   1.50 1.50
14   SP3 50fr + 10fr emer, brn &
              car   .30 .30
  a. Souvenir sheet of 4   1.50 1.50
          Nos. B12-B14 (3)   .90 .80

      Issued for the Red Cross.
Nos. B12a, B13a, B14a exist imperf.; same
values.

1960   Unwmk.   Perf. 13
#B16 similar to #B15, with emblem on top.

B15 SP4 25fr + 5fr dk bl, brn & yel
              grn   .20 .20
B16 SP4 45fr + 5fr dk bl, brn & ol .35 .35
  World Refugee Year, July 1, 1959-June 30,
1960. The surtax was for aid to refugees.

AIR POST STAMPS

Common Design Type
1940   Unwmk.   Engr.   Perf. 12½x12
C1 CD85 1.90fr ultra   .30   .20
C2 CD85 2.90fr dark red   .40   .20
C3 CD85 4.50fr dk gray grn   .50   .30
C4 CD85 4.90fr yellow bister .50   .50
C5 CD85 6.90fr deep orange   .85   .85
          Nos. C1-C5 (5)   2.55 2.05

Common Design Type
Inscribed "Togo" across top
1942
C6   CD88 50c car & bl   .20
C7   CD88 1fr brn & blk   .20
C8   CD88 2fr grn & red brn   .20
C9   CD88 3fr dk bl & scar   .35
C10 CD88 5fr vio & brn red   .45

**Frame Engraved, Center
Typographed**
C11 CD89 10fr ultra, ind & org   .55
C12 CD89 20fr rose car, mag &
                gray blk   .55

C13 CD89 50fr yel grn, dl grn & lt
              vio   .90 1.6
      Nos. C6-C13 (8)   3.40

There is doubt whether Nos. C6-C12 were
officially placed in use.

**Catalogue values for unused
stamps in this section, from this
point to the end of the section, are
for Never Hinged items.**

Elephants — AP1

Plane — AP2

Plane — AP3

Post Runner and Plane — AP4

1947, Oct. 6   Engr.   Perf. 12½
C14 AP1 40fr blue   5.25 2.50
C15 AP2 50fr lt ultra, & red vio 2.50 1.10
C16 AP3 100fr emer & dk brn 4.00 1.60
C17 AP4 200fr lilac rose   6.50 2.50
          Nos. C14-C17 (4)   18.25 7.70

UPU Issue
Common Design Type
1949, July 4   Perf. 13
C18 CD99 25fr multi   5.00 5.00

Liberation Issue
Common Design Type
1954, June 6
C19 CD102 15fr indigo & pur   4.00 4.00

Freight
Highway — AP5

1954, Nov. 29
C20 AP5 500fr indigo & dk grn 32.50 30.00

Republic

Independence Allegory — AP6

Unwmk.

1957, Oct. 29		Engr.	Perf. 13	
C21	AP6	25fr bl, olive bister & ver	.40	.30

1st anniv. of Togo's autonomy.

Flag and Torch — AP7

Great White Egret — AP8

1957, Oct. 29				
C22	AP7	50fr multi	.65	.30
C23	AP7	100fr multi	1.10	.45
C24	AP7	200fr multi	2.25	.75
C25	AP8	500fr ind, lt bl & grn	7.00	3.00
		Nos. C22-C25 (4)	11.00	4.50

Types of 1957 inscribed:
"Republique du Togo" and

Flag, Plane and
Map — AP9

1959, Jan. 15		Engr.	Perf. 13	
C26	AP9	25fr ultra, emer & vio brn	.20	.20
C27	AP7	50fr dk bl, dl grn & red	.40	.20
C28	AP7	100fr multi	1.10	.40
C29	AP7	200fr dk grn, red & ultra	2.25	.85
C30	AP8	500fr blk brn, rose lil & grn	6.25	1.90
		Nos. C26-C30 (5)	10.20	3.55

Hotel Le
Benin
AP10

Eagle and Map of
Togo — AP11

Perf. 14½x15, 15x14½

1960, Apr. 27		Litho.	Unwmk.	
C31	AP10	100fr crim, emer & yel	.60	.25
C32	AP10	200fr multi	1.40	.40
C33	AP11	500fr grn & gldn brn	3.00	1.00
		Nos. C31-C33 (3)	5.00	1.65

Proclamation of Togo's full independence, Apr. 27, 1960.

Mail Service Type

100fr, Boeing 707 and stamps of 1960.

1963, Jan. 12		Photo.	Perf. 13	
C34	A41	100fr multi	.60	.30
a.	Souvenir sheet of 4		1.25	1.25

No. C34a contains 4 stamps similar to Nos. 441-443 and C34, with simulated perforations.

Emancipation Type

1963, Oct.		Unwmk.	Perf. 13x14	
C35	A45	100fr multi	.65	.30
a.	Souv. sheet of 4, #454-456, C35, imperf.		.90	.75

For overprint see No. C41.

Type of 1964 Regular Issue

50fr, Black-bellied seed-cracker. 100fr, Blue-billed mannikin. 200fr, Redheaded lovebird. 250fr, African gray parrot. 500fr, Yellow-breasted barbet.

1964-65		Photo.	Perf. 14	

Size: 22½x31mm
Birds in Natural Colors

C36	A47	50fr yel grn	.40	.25
C37	A47	100fr ocher	.80	.30
C38	A47	200fr dl bl grn	1.50	.80
C39	A47	250fr dl rose ('65)	2.00	1.00
C40	A47	500fr violet	4.00	1.50
		Nos. C36-C40 (5)	8.70	3.85

No. C35 Overprinted Diagonally: "En Mémoire de / JOHN F. KENNEDY / 1917-1963"

1964, Feb.			Perf. 13x14	
C41	A45	100fr multi	.60	.30

Issued in memory of John F. Kennedy. Same overprint was applied to stamps of No. C35a, with black border and commemorative inscription added. Two sheets exist: with and without gray silhouetted head of Kennedy covering all four stamps.

Liberation Type

1964, May 25			Perf. 14x13	
C42	A50	100fr dl bl grn & dk brn	.65	.30

Olympic Games Type

1964, Oct.		Photo.	Perf. 14	
C43	A52	100fr Tennis	.75	.30
a.	Souv. sheet of 3, #493-494, C43, imperf.		1.10	1.10

Flag of Togo and Jet — AP12

1964, Dec. 5		Unwmk.	Perf. 14x13	
C44	AP12	100fr multi	.80	.30

Inauguration of the national airline "Air Togo." For souvenir sheet see No. 499a.

Lincoln Type

1965, June		Photo.	Perf. 13½x14	
C45	A58	100fr ol gray	.90	.30
a.	Souv. sheet, #545, C45, imperf		.90	.90

Sports Type

100fr, Soccer player, flags of Togo and Congo.

1965, July		Unwmk.	Perf. 14x13	
C46	A59	100fr multi	.80	.30

Churchill Type

1965, Aug. 7		Photo.	Perf. 13½x14	
C47	A60	85fr car rose	.80	.30
a.	Souv. sheet, #532, C47, imperf		1.10	1.10

UN Type

100fr, Apple, grapes, wheat and "ONU."

1965, Dec. 15			Perf. 14x13½	
C48	A65	100fr dk bl & bis	1.00	1.00
a.	Souvenir sheet of 2		1.40	1.40

No. C48a contains two imperf. stamps similar to Nos. 548 and C48 with simulated perforations.

Pope Type

Designs: 45fr, Pope speaking at UN rostrum, world map and UN emblem. 90fr, Pope, plane and UN emblem.

1966, Mar. 5		Litho.	Perf. 12	
C49	A66	45fr emer & multi	.30	.20
C50	A66	90fr gray & multi	.70	.20
a.	Souvenir sheet of 2, #C49-C50		1.25	1.00

Red Cross Type

Jean Henri Dunant and Togolese Flag.

1966, May 7		Litho.	Perf. 12	
C51	A67	100fr multi	.90	.30

WHO Type

Flowers: 50fr, Daisies and WHO Headquarters. 90fr, Talisman roses and WHO Headquarters.

1966, May		Litho.	Perf. 12	
C52	A68	50fr lt bl & multi	.40	.20
C53	A68	90fr gray & multi	.70	.20
a.	Souvenir sheet of 2, #C52-C53		1.10	.90

Air Afrique Issue
Common Design Type

1966, Aug. 31		Photo.	Perf. 13	
C54	CD123	30fr brt grn, blk & lem	.30	.20

Arts and Crafts Type

60fr, Basket maker. 90fr, Wood carver.

1966, Sept.			Perf. 13x14	
C55	A69	60fr ultra, org & blk	.45	.20
C56	A69	90fr brt rose, yel & blk	.75	.20

Dancer Type

50fr, Woman from North Togo holding branches. 60fr, Man from North Togo with horned helmet.

1966, Nov.		Photo.	Perf. 13x14	
C57	A70	50fr multi	.40	.20
C58	A70	60fr olive & multi	.50	.20

Soccer Type

Designs: Different Soccer Scenes.

1966, Dec. 14		Photo.	Perf. 14x13	
C59	A71	50fr org, brn & pur	.40	.20
C60	A71	60fr ultra, brn & org	.50	.20
a.	Souv. sheet of 3, #582, C59-C60, imperf.		1.10	1.00

Fish Type

Designs: 45fr, Yellow jack and trawler. 90fr, Banded distichodus and seiner.

1967, Jan. 14		Photo.	Perf. 14	

Fish in Natural Colors

C61	A72	45fr org & brn	.40	.20
C62	A72	90fr emer & dk bl	.90	.30

UNICEF Type

UNICEF Emblem and: 45fr, Girl and miniature poodle. 90fr, African boy and greyhound.

1967, Feb. 11		Photo.	Perf. 14x13½	
C63	A73	45fr yel, red brn & blk	.35	.20
C64	A73	90fr ultra, dk grn & blk	.70	.25
a.	Souvenir sheet of 2		1.10	.90

No. C64a contains 2 imperf., lithographed stamps with simulated perforations similar to Nos. C63-C64.

Satellite Type

50fr, Diamant rocket. 90fr, Fr-1 satellite.

1967, Mar. 18		Photo.	Perf. 13½x14	
C65	A74	50fr multi, vert.	.45	.20
C66	A74	90fr multi, vert.	.80	.25
a.	Souvenir sheet of 2		1.25	1.00

No. C66a contains 2 imperf. stamps similar to Nos. C65-C66 with simulated perforations.

Musician Type

UNESCO Emblem and: 45fr, Johann Sebastian Bach and organ. 90fr, Ludwig van Beethoven, violin and clarinet.

1967, Apr. 15		Photo.	Perf. 14x13½	
C67	A75	45fr multi	.35	.20
C68	A75	90fr pink & multi	.75	.20
a.	Souvenir sheet of 2		1.10	.85

No. C68a contains 2 imperf. stamps similar to Nos. C67-C68 with simulated perforations.

EXPO '67 Type

EXPO '67 Emblem and: 45fr, French pavilion, roses. 60fr, British pavilion, day lilies. 90fr, African village, bird-of-paradise flower. 105fr, US pavilion, daisies.

1967, May 30		Photo.	Perf. 14	
C69	A76	45fr multi	.30	.20
C70	A76	60fr multi	.45	.20
C71	A76	90fr yel & multi	.60	.25
a.	Souv. sheet of 3, #C69-C71, imperf		1.50	1.10
C72	A76	105fr multi	.75	.30
		Nos. C69-C72 (4)	2.10	.95

For overprints see Nos. C86-C89.

Mural by José Vela Zanetti — AP13

The designs are from a mural in the lobby of the UN Conf. Building, NYC. The mural depicting mankind's struggle for a lasting peace is shown across 3 stamps twice in the set: on the 5fr, 15fr, 30fr and 45fr, 60fr, 90fr.

1967, July 15		Litho.	Perf. 14	
C73	AP13	5fr multi	.20	.20
C74	AP13	15fr org & multi	.20	.20
C75	AP13	30fr multi	.25	.20
C76	AP13	45fr multi	.40	.20
C77	AP13	60fr car & multi	.60	.20
C78	AP13	90fr ind & multi	.90	.25
a.	Souvenir sheet of 3, #C76-C78		1.90	1.50
		Nos. C73-C78 (6)	2.55	1.25

Issued to publicize general disarmament.

Animal Type

1967, Aug. 19		Photo.	Perf. 14x13½	
C79	A78	45fr Lion	.40	.20
C80	A78	60fr Elephant	.60	.20

African Postal Union Issue, 1967
Common Design Type

1967, Sept. 9		Engr.	Perf. 13	
C81	CD124	100fr bl, brt grn & ol brn	.75	.30

Stamp Anniversary Type

Designs: 90fr, Stamp auction and Togo Nos. 16 and C42. 105fr, Father and son with stamp album and No. 474.

1967, Oct. 14		Photo.	Perf. 14x13	

Stamps on Stamps in Original Colors

C82	A79	90fr olive	.90	.25
a.	Souvenir sheet of 3		2.00	1.50
C83	A79	105fr dk car rose	1.40	.40

No. C82a contains 3 imperf. stamps similar to Nos. 621-622 and C82 with simulated perforations.

Pre-Olympics Type

View of Mexico City, Summer Olympics emblem and: 60fr, Runners. 90fr, Broad jump.

1967, Dec. 2			Perf. 13x14	
C84	A80	60fr pink & multi	.50	.20
C85	A80	90fr multi	.75	.30
a.	Souv. sheet of 3, #627, C84-C85, imperf.		1.50	1.25

Nos. C69-C72 Overprinted:
"JOURNEE NATIONALE / DU TOGO / 29 SEPTEMBRE 1967"

1967, Dec.		Photo.	Perf. 14	
C86	A76	45fr multi	.40	.20
C87	A76	60fr multi	.60	.20
C88	A76	90fr yel & multi	.90	.25
C89	A76	100fr multi	1.00	.35
		Nos. C86-C89 (4)	2.90	1.00

Issued for National Day, Sept. 29, 1967.

Hydrological Decade Type

1968, Apr. 6		Litho.	Perf. 14	
C90	A84	60fr multi	.45	.20

Ship Type

Designs: 45fr, Fulton's and modern steamships. 90fr, US atomic ship Savannah and atom symbol.

1968, Apr. 26   Photo.   Perf. 14x14½
C91 A85 45fr yel & multi   .35   .20
C92 A85 90fr bl & multi   .75   .20
 a.   Souvenir sheet of 2   1.10   .90

No. C92a contains 2 imperf. stamps similar to Nos. C91-C92 with simulated perforations.

WHO Type

Paintings: 60fr, The Anatomy Lesson, by Rembrandt (detail). 90fr, Jesus Healing the Sick, by Raphael.

1968, June 22   Photo.   Perf. 14
C93 A87 60fr multi   .50   .20
C94 A87 90fr pur & multi   .75   .20
 a.   Souvenir sheet of 2   1.10   .90

No. C94a contains 2 imperf. stamps similar to Nos. C93-C94 with simulated perforations.

Olympic Games Type

1968, July 27   Perf. 14x13½
C95 A88 60fr Wrestling   .50   .20
C96 A88 90fr Running   .75   .20
 a.   Souvenir sheet of 2   1.10   .90

No. C96a contains 2 imperf. stamps similar to Nos. C95-C96 with simulated perforations.

Boy Scout Type

60fr, First aid practice, horiz. 90fr, Scout game.

1968, Nov. 23   Litho.   Perf. 14
C97 A90 60fr ol & multi   .60   .25
C98 A90 90fr org & multi   .90   .35
 a.   Souvenir sheet of 2   1.50   1.25

No. C98a contains 2 imperf. stamps with simulated perforations similar to Nos. C97-C98.

PHILEXAFRIQUE Issue

The Letter, by Jean Auguste Franquelin
AP14

1968, Nov. 9   Photo.   Perf. 12½x12
C99 AP14 100fr multi   1.00   .80

PHILEXAFRIQUE Philatelic Exhibition in Abidjan, Feb. 14-23. Printed with alternating light ultramarine label.

Christmas Type

Paintings: 60fr, Adoration of the Magi, by Pieter Brueghel. 90fr, Adoration of the Magi, by Dürer.

1968, Dec. 28   Litho.   Perf. 14
C100 A91 60fr red & multi   .60   .20
C101 A91 90fr multi   .90   .30
 a.   Souvenir sheet   1.25   1.00

No. C101a contains 2 imperf. stamps similar to Nos. C100-C101 with simulated perforations.

Human Rights Type

Human Rights Flame and: 60fr, Robert F. Kennedy. 90fr, Martin Luther King, Jr.

1969, Feb. 1   Photo.   Perf. 13½x14
C102 A92 60fr brt rose lil & vio bl   .40   .20
C103 A92 90fr emer & brn   .55   .30
 a.   Souvenir sheet   1.00   .65

No. C103a contains 2 imperf. stamps similar to Nos. C102-C103 with simulated perforations.
For overprints see Nos. C110-C111.

2nd PHILEXAFRIQUE Issue
Common Design Type

Design: 50fr, Togo #16 and Aledjo Fault.

1969, Feb. 14   Engr.   Perf. 13
C104 CD128 50fr red brn, grn & car
                           rose   .40   .40

Sports Type

Stadium and: 60fr, Boxing. 90fr, Bicycling.

1969, Apr. 26   Photo.   Perf. 14x13½
C105 A93 60fr bl, red & dk brn   .40   .20
C106 A93 90fr ultra, brt pink & dk
                           brn   .70   .25
 a.   Souvenir sheet   1.00   .80

No. C106a contains 2 imperf. stamps similar to Nos. C105-C106 with simulated perforations.

Lunar Type

Designs: 60fr, Astronaut exploring moon surface. 100fr, Astronaut gathering rocks.

1969, July 21   Litho.   Perf. 14
C107 A94 60fr dk bl & multi   .40   .20
C108 A94 100fr multi   .65   .40
 a.   Souvenir sheet of 4   4.00   3.50

No. C108a contains 4 imperf. stamps with simulated perforations similar to Nos. 676-677 and C107-C108, magenta margin. No. C108a also exists with colors of 30fr and 100fr stamps changed, and margin in orange. Value $6.
For overprints see Nos. C120-C121.

Painting Type

Painting: 90fr, Pentecost, by El Greco.

1969, Aug. 16   Litho.   Perf. 14
C109 A95 90fr multi   1.00   .40
 a.   Souvenir sheet   1.00   .75

No. C109a contains two imperf. stamps with simulated perforations similar to Nos. 682 and C109.

Nos. C102-C103 Overprinted Like
Nos. 683-686

1969, Sept. 1   Photo.   Perf. 13½x14
C110 A92 60fr brt rose lil & vio bl   .40   .20
C111 A92 90fr emer & brn   .60   .25
 a.   Souv. sheet of 2   2.50   1.90

#C111a is #C103a with Eisenhower overprint.

Bank Type

Design: 100fr, Bank emblem and hand holding cattle and farmer.

1969, Sept. 10   Photo.   Perf. 13x14
C112 A96 100fr multi   .80   .40

Red Cross Type

60fr, Wilhelm C. Roentgen & Red Cross workers with children in front of Togo Headquarters. 90fr, Henri Dunant & Red Cross workers meeting Biafra refugees at airport.

1969, Sept. 27   Litho.   Perf. 14
C113 A97 60fr brn & multi   .45   .25
C114 A97 90fr ol & multi   .65   .35
 a.   Souv. sheet of 2   1.00   .75

No. C114a contains 2 imperf. stamps with simulated perforations similar to Nos. C113-C114.

Agricultural Center Type

Emblem of Young Pioneer and Agricultural Organization and: 90fr, Manioc harvest. 100fr, Instruction in gardening. 200fr, Corn harvest. 250fr, Marching drum corps. 500fr, Parade of Young Pioneers.

1969-70   Litho.   Perf. 14
C115 A98 90fr multi   .55   .20
C116 A98 100fr org & multi   .60   .25
C117 A98 200fr multi ('70)   1.25   .35
C118 A98 250fr ol & multi   1.50   .60
C119 A98 500fr multi ('70)   3.25   .75
   Nos. C115-C119 (5)   7.15   2.15

Christmas Issue

Nos. C107-C108, C108a Overprinted:
"JOYEUX NOEL"

1969, Dec.   Litho.   Perf. 14
C120 A94 60fr multi   1.25   .40
C121 A94 100fr multi   1.90   .60
 a.   Souvenir sheet of 4   6.00   6.00

Peace Leaders Type

60fr, Friedrich Ebert. 90fr, Mahatma Gandhi.

1969, Dec. 27   Litho.   Perf. 14x13½
C122 A100 60fr dk brn, dk red &
                           yel   .40   .20
C123 A100 90fr dk brn, vio bl &
                           ocher   .60   .30

For surcharges see Nos. 765, C143.

ILO Type

Paintings and ILO Emblem: 60fr, Spring Sowing, by Vincent van Gogh. 90fr, Workers, by Diego de Rivera.

1970, Jan. 24   Litho.   Perf. 12½x13
C124 A101 60fr gold & multi   .35   .20
C125 A101 90fr gold & multi   .65   .20
 a.   Souvenir sheet of 2   1.00   .75

No. C125a contains two stamps similar to Nos. C124-C125, with simulated perforations.

Hair Styles Type

Various hair styles. 45fr, vert. 90fr, horiz.

1970, Feb. 21   Perf. 12½x13, 13x12½
C126 A102 45fr car & multi   .25   .20
C127 A102 90fr multi   .50   .30

Independence Type

Design: 60fr, Togo No. C33 and Independence Monument, Lomé.

1970, Apr. 27   Litho.   Perf. 13x12½
C128 A103 60fr yel & multi   .30   .20

UPU Type

1970, May 30   Photo.   Perf. 14x13½
C129 A104 50fr grnsh bl & dk car   .30   .20

Soccer Type

Various Scenes from Soccer, Rimet Cup and Flags of: 50fr, Sweden and Israel. 60fr, Bulgaria and Peru. 90fr, Belgium and Salvador.

1970, June 27   Litho.   Perf. 13x14
C130 A105 50fr multi   .30   .20
C131 A105 60fr lil & multi   .40   .20
C132 A105 90fr multi   .55   .30
 a.   Souvenir sheet of 4   1.50   1.50
   Nos. C130-C132 (3)   1.25   .70

No. C132a contains 4 stamps similar to Nos. 734, C130-C132, but imperf. with simulated perforations.

Lenin Type

Design: 50fr, Lenin Meeting Peasant Delegation, by V. A. Serov, and UNESCO emblem.

1970, July 25   Litho.   Perf. 12½
C133 A106 50fr multi   .35   .20

For overprint see No. C179.

EXPO '70 Type
Souvenir Sheet

150fr, Mitsubishi pavilion, EXPO '70 emblem.

1970, Aug. 8   Litho.   Perf. 13
C134 A107 150fr yel & multi   1.00   .35
 a.   Inscribed "AERINNE"

No. C134 contains one stamp 86x33mm.

Astronaut Type

Design: 200fr, James A. Lovell, Fred W. Haise, Jr. and Tom Mattingly (replaced by John L. Swigert, Jr.) and Apollo 13 emblem.

1970, Sept. 26
C135 A108 200fr multi   .95   .55
 a.   Souvenir sheet of 3   1.50   1.10

Space flight of Apollo 13. No. C135a contains 3 stamps similar to Nos. 741, 744 and C135, with simulated perforations.
For overprint see No. C136.

Nos. C135, C135a Inscribed:
"FELICITATIONS / BON RETOUR
APOLLO XIII"

1970, Sept. 26
C136 A108 200fr multi   1.00   .55
 a.   Souvenir sheet of 3   1.50   1.10

Safe return of the crew of Apollo 13.

UN Type

Paintings and Emblems of UN Agencies: 60fr, The Mailman Roulin, by van Gogh, and UPU emblem. 90fr, The Birth of the Virgin, by Vittore Carpaccio, and WHO emblem.

1970, Oct. 24   Litho.   Perf. 13x12½
C137 A109 60fr grn, gold & blk   .35   .20
C138 A109 90fr red org, gold &
                           brn   .55   .30
 a.   Souvenir sheet of 4   1.50   1.10

No. C138a contains one each of Nos. 754-755 and C137-C138 with simulated perforations.

Moth Type

Moths: 60fr, Euchloron megaera. 90fr, Pseudacraea boisduvali.

1970, Nov. 21   Photo.   Perf. 13x1
C139 A110 60fr multi   .55   .2
C140 A110 90fr multi   .55   .2

Christmas Type

Paintings: 60fr, Adoration of the Shepherd by Botticelli. 90fr, Adoration of the Kings, b Tiepolo.

1970, Dec. 26   Litho.   Perf. 12½x1
C141 A111 60fr gold & multi   .45   .3
C142 A111 90fr gold & multi   .70   .3
 a.   Souv. sheet of 2, #C141-C142 1.00   .

No. C122 Surcharged and
Overprinted: "EN MEMOIRE / Charle
De Gaulle / 1890-1970"

1971, Jan. 9   Photo.   Perf. 14x13
C143 A100 200fr on 60fr   1.50   .6

De Gaulle Type

Designs: 60fr, De Gaulle and Pope Paul V 90fr, De Gaulle and satellite.

1971, Feb. 20   Photo.   Perf. 13x1
C144 A112 60fr blk & dp vio   .50   .2
C145 A112 90fr blk & bl grn   .70   .2
 a.   Souvenir sheet of 4   1.75   1.

Nos. C143-C145 issued in memory o Charles De Gaulle (1890-1970), President o France. No. C145a contains 4 imperf. stamp similar to Nos. 769-770, C144-C145.

Easter Type

Paintings: 50fr, Resurrection, by Matthias Grunewald. 60fr, Resurrection, by Master o Trebon. 90fr, Resurrection, by El Greco.

1971, Apr. 10   Litho.   Perf. 10½x11½
C146 A113 50fr gold & multi   .35   .2
C147 A113 60fr gold & multi   .50   .2
C148 A113 90fr gold & multi   .65   .3
 a.   Souvenir sheet of 4, #773,
       C146-C148   1.60   1.
   Nos. C146-C148 (3)   1.50   .7

Apollo 14 Type

Designs: 50fr, 200f, Apollo 14 badge 100fr, Take-off from moon, and spaceship.

1971, May   Litho.   Perf. 12½
C149 A114 50fr grn & multi   .35   .2
C150 A114 100fr multi   .65   .3
C151 A114 200fr org & multi   1.40   .6
 a.   Souv. sheet of 2   3.00   2.2
   Nos. C149-C151 (3)   2.40   1.2

No. C151a contains 4 stamps similar to Nos. 777 and C149-C151 with simulated perforations.
For surcharge and overprints see Nos. C162-C164.

Cacao Type

60fr, Ministry of Agriculture. 90fr, Cacao tree and & pods. 100fr, Sorting & separating beans from pods.

1971, June 6   Litho.   Perf. 14
C152 A115 60fr multi   .40   .20
C153 A115 90fr multi   .60   .3
C154 A115 100fr multi   .70   .35
   Nos. C152-C154 (3)   1.70   .85

ASECNA Type

1971, June 26
C155 A116 100fr multi   .70   .35

Tourist Type

Designs: 50fr, Château Viale and antelope. 60fr, Lake Togo and crocodile. 100fr, Old lime furnace, Tokpli, and hippopotamus.

1971, July 17
C156 A117 50fr multi   .35   .20
C157 A117 60fr multi   .40   .20
C158 A117 100fr multi   .65   .35
   Nos. C156-C158 (3)   1.40   .75

For overprint see No. C172.

Religions Type

Designs: 50fr, Mohammedans praying in front of Lomé Mosque. 60fr, Protestant service. 90fr, Catholic bishop and priests.

1971, July 31   Litho.   Perf. 14½
C159 A118 50fr multi   .30   .20
C160 A118 60fr multi   .35   .20
C161 A118 90fr multi   .60   .30
 a.   Souvenir sheet of 4, #787,
       C159-C161   1.60   1.40
   Nos. C159-C161 (3)   1.25   .65

Nos. C149-C151 Overprinted and
Surcharged in Black or Silver: "EN
MEMOIRE / DOBROVOLSKY -
VOLKOV - PATSAYEV / SOYUZ 11"

C162	A114	90fr on 50fr multi	.60 .25
C163	A114	100fr multi (S)	.65 .30
C164	A114	200fr multi	1.40 .50
a.		Souvenir sheet of 4, #788,	
		C162-C164	2.75 2.25
		Nos. C162-C164 (3)	2.65 1.05

See note after No. 788.

Olympic Type

200fr, Sapporo '72 emblem and Ski jump.

1971, Oct. 30   Litho.   Perf. 14

C165	A119	200fr multi	1.40 .50
a.		Souvenir sheet of 4	2.00 1.90

No. C165 contains 4 stamps with simulated
perforations similar to Nos. 791-793 and C165
printed on glazed paper.

African Postal Union Issue, 1971
Common Design Type

Design: 100fr, Adjogbo dancers and
JAMPT Building, Brazzaville, Congo.

1971, Nov. 13   Photo.   Perf. 13x13½

C166	CD135	100fr bl & multi	.70 .40

Intl. Organization for the Protection of
Children (U.I.P.E.) - AP14a

Die Cut Perf. 10½

1971, Nov. 13   Embossed

C166A AP14a 1500fr gold

UNICEF Type

Toys: 60fr, Turtle. 90fr, Parrot.

1971, Nov. 27   Litho.   Perf. 14

C167	A120	60fr lt bl & multi	.40 .20
C168	A120	90fr multi	.60 .25
a.		Souvenir sheet of 4	1.90 1.90

No. C168a contains 4 stamps with simu-
lated perforations similar to Nos. 796-797 and
C167-C168.
For overprints see Nos. C263-C264.

Christmas Type

Virgin and Child by: 60fr, Giorgione. 100fr,
Raphael.

1971, Dec. 24   Perf. 14x13

C169	A121	60fr olive & multi	.40 .25
C170	A121	100fr multi	.70 .40
a.		Souvenir sheet of 4	2.00 1.60

No. C170a contains 4 stamps with simulated perforations similar to Nos. 800-801,
C169-C170.

Venice Type

Design: 100fr, Ca' d'Oro, Venice.

1972, Feb. 26   Litho.   Perf. 14

C171	A122	100fr multi	.70 .40
a.		Souvenir sheet of 3	1.50 1.50

No. C171a contains 3 stamps similar to
Nos. 802-803, C171 with simulated
perforations.

No. C156 Overprinted "VISITE DU
PRESIDENT / NIXON EN CHINE /
FEVRIER 1972"

1972, Mar.   Litho.   Perf. 14

C172	A117	50fr multi	.35 .20

Visit of Pres. Richard M. Nixon to the People's Republic of China, Feb. 20-27.

Easter Type

Paintings: 50fr, Resurrection, by Thomas
de Coloswa. 100fr, Ascension by Andrea
Mantegna.

1972, Mar. 31

C173	A123	50fr gold & multi	.45 .20
C174	A123	100fr gold & multi	.65 .25
a.		Souvenir sheet of 4	2.00 1.90

No. C174a contains 4 stamps similar to
Nos. 806-807, C173-C174 with simulated
perforations.

Heart Type

100fr, Heart, WHO emblem and smith.

1972, Apr. 4

C175	A124	100fr multi	.65 .40
a.		Souvenir sheet of 2	1.25 1.25

No. C175a contains 2 stamps similar to
Nos. 810 and C175 with simulated
perforations.

Telecommunications Type

Design: 100fr, Intelsat 4 over Africa.

1972, June 24   Perf. 14

C176	A125	100fr multi	.70 .30

For overprint see No. C229.

Cassava Type

60fr, Truck and cassava processing factory,
horiz. 80fr, Children, mother holding tapioca
cake.

1972, June 30

C177	A126	60fr multi	.45 .25
C178	A126	80fr multi	.55 .25

No. C133 Surcharged in Deep
Carmine:
"VISITE DU PRESIDENT / NIXON EN
RUSSIE / MAI 1972"

1972, July 15   Litho.   Perf. 12½

C179	A106	300fr on 50fr multi	2.50 1.40

President Nixon's visit to the USSR, May
1972. Old denomination obliterated with
6x5mm rectangle.

Olympic Type

1972, Aug. 26   Litho.   Perf. 14

C180	A127	90fr Gymnastics	.65 .35
a.		Souv. sheet of 2	1.25 1.10
C181	A127	200fr Basketball	1.50 .65

No. C180a contains 2 stamps with simu-
lated perforations similar to Nos. 816 and
C180.
For overprints see Nos. C234-C235.

Bird Type

Bird: 90fr, Rose-ringed parakeet.

1972, Sept. 9

C182	A128	90fr multi	.65 .35
a.		Souvenir sheet of 4	1.90 1.50

No. C182a contains 4 stamps similar to
Nos. 818-820, C182 with simulated
perforations.

Rotary Type

Rotary Emblem and: 60fr, Map of Togo,
olive branch. 90fr, Flags of Togo and Rotary
Club. 100fr, Paul P. Harris.

1972, Oct. 7   Litho.   Perf. 14

C183	A129	60fr brn & multi	.35 .20
C184	A129	90fr multi	.50 .35
C185	A129	100fr multi	.60 .40
		Nos. C183-C185 (3)	1.45 .95

For overprints see Nos. C212-C213, C244-
C245.

Painting Type, 1972

Designs: 60fr, Mystical Marriage of St.
Catherine, by Assistant to the P. M. Master.
80fr, Self-portrait, by Leonardo da Vinci. 100fr,
Sts. Mary and Agnes by Botticelli.

1972, Oct. 21

C186	A130	60fr gold & multi	.40 .20
C187	A130	80fr gold & multi	.45 .25
C188	A130	100fr gold & multi	.80 .40
a.		Souvenir sheet of 4	2.25 1.50
		Nos. C186-C188 (3)	1.65 .85

No. C188a contains 4 stamps with simulated perforations similar to Nos. 824, C186-
188.

Presidential Visit Type

Design: 100fr, Pres. Pompidou and Col. Etienne Eyadema, front view of party
headquarters.

1972, Nov. 23   Litho.   Perf. 14

C189	A131	100fr multi	.80 .40

Johann Wolfgang
von Goethe
(1749-1832),
German Poet and
Dramatist
AP15

1972, Dec. 2   Photo.   Perf. 13x14

C190	AP15	100fr grn & multi	.80 .40

Christmas Type

Paintings: 60fr, Nativity, by Master
Vyshchibrod. 80fr, Adoration of the Kings,
anonymous. 100fr, Flight into Egypt, by
Giotto.

1972, Dec. 23   Litho.   Perf. 14

C191	A132	60fr gold & multi	.45 .25
C192	A132	80fr gold & multi	.60 .30
C193	A132	100fr gold & multi	.80 .40
a.		Souvenir sheet of 4	2.00 2.00
		Nos. C191-C193 (3)	1.85 .90

No. C193a contains 4 stamps with simulated perforations similar to Nos. 829, C191-
C193.

Leprosy Day Type

Design: 100fr, Dr. Armauer G. Hansen,
apparatus, microscope and Petri dish.

1973, Jan. 23   Photo.   Perf. 14x13½

C194	A133	100fr rose car & bl	.70 .40

World Leprosy Day and centenary of the
discovery of the Hansen bacillus, the cause of
leprosy.

Miniature Sheets

1972 Summer Olympics,
Munich — AP15a

Medalists: #C194A, Mark Spitz, US, swimming. #C194B, L. Linsenhoff, West Germany,
equestrian. #C194C, D. Morelon, France,
cycling.

Litho. & Embossed

1973, Jan.   Perf. 13½

C194A-C194C   AP15a 1500fr multi

Exist imperf.

Miniature Sheet

Apollo 17 Moon Landing — AP15b

1973, Jan.

C194D AP15b 1500fr gold & multi

Exists imperf.

Easter Type

1973, Apr. 21   Litho.   Perf. 14

C195	A135	90fr Christ in Glory	.60 .40
a.		Souvenir sheet of 2	1.00 1.00

No. C195a contains one each of Nos. 835
and C195 with simulated perforations.

Apollo 17 Type

Designs: 100fr, Astronauts on moon and
orange rock. 200fr, Rocket lift-off at Cape
Kennedy and John F. Kennedy.

1973, June 2   Litho.   Perf. 14

C196	A136	100fr multi	.70 .40
C197	A136	200fr multi	1.50 .60
a.		Souvenir sheet of 2	2.25 2.00

No. C197a contains 2 stamps similar to
Nos. C196-C197 with simulated perforations.

Boy Scout Type

100fr, Canoeing, horiz. 200fr, Campfire,
horiz.

1973, June 30   Litho.   Perf. 14

C198	A137	100fr bl & multi	.65 .40
C199	A137	200fr bl & multi	1.50 .65
a.		Souvenir sheet of 2	2.25 2.00

No. C199a contains 2 stamps similar to
Nos. C198-C199 with simulated perforations.
For overprints see Nos. C265-C266.

Copernicus Type

Designs: 90fr, Heliocentric system. 100fr,
Nicolaus Copernicus.

1973, July 18

C200	A138	90fr multi	.60 .30
C201	A138	100fr bis & multi	.70 .40
a.		Souv. sheet of 2, #C200-C201	1.50 1.35

Red Cross Type

Design: 100fr, Dove carrying Red Cross
letter, sun, map of Togo.

1973, Aug. 4

C202	A139	100fr multi	.65 .35

For overprint see No. C294.

Literacy Type

Design: 90fr, Woman teacher in classroom.

1973, Aug. 18   Litho.   Perf. 14

C203	A140	90fr multi	.55 .35

WMO Type

1973, Oct. 4   Photo.   Perf. 14x13

C204	A142	200fr dl bl, pur & brn	1.50 .60

Type 1967

Early & contemporary planes, #758, C36.

1973, Oct. 20   Photo.   Perf. 14x13

C205	A79	100fr multi	.80 .30
a.		Souvenir sheet of 2	1.60 1.40

75th anniversary of Togolese postal service.
No. C205a contains 2 stamps similar to Nos.
855 and C205 with simulated perforations.

Kennedy Type

Designs: 90fr, Kennedy and Charles De
Gaulle. 100fr, Kennedy and Nikita Krushchev.
200fr, Kennedy and model of Apollo
spacecraft.

1973, Nov. 22   Litho.   Perf. 14

C206	A143	90fr blk & pink	.60 .35
C207	A143	100fr blk, lt bl & bl	.70 .45
C208	A143	200fr blk, buff & brn	1.40 .60
a.		Souvenir sheet of 2	2.25 2.00
		Nos. C206-C208 (3)	2.70 1.40

No. C208a contains 2 stamps similar to
Nos. C207-208 with simulated perforations.

Human Rights
Flame and
People — AP16

1973, Dec. 8　Photo.　Perf. 13x14
C209 AP16 250fr lt bl & multi　1.90　.80
25th anniversary of the Universal Declaration of Human Rights.

Christmas Type

Paintings: 90fr, Virgin and Child. 100fr, Adoration of the Kings. Both after 15th century Italian paintings.

1973, Dec. 22　Litho.　Perf. 14
C210 A144 90fr gold & multi　.60　.25
C211 A144 100fr gold & multi　.70　.35
　a.　Souvenir sheet of 2　1.60　1.50
No. C211a contains 2 stamps with simulated perforations similar to Nos. C210-C211.

Nos. C183 and C185 Overprinted: "PREMIERE CONVENTION / 210eme DISTRICT / FEVRIER 1974 / LOME"

1974, Feb. 21　Litho.　Perf. 14
C212 A129 60fr brn & multi　.40　.20
C213 A129 100fr multi　.60　.35
First convention of Rotary International, District 210, Lomé, Feb. 22-24.

Soccer Type

Various soccer scenes and games' cup.

1974, Mar. 2　Litho.　Perf. 14
C214 A145 90fr multi　.70　.35
C215 A145 100fr multi　.85　.40
C216 A145 200fr multi　1.60　.75
　a.　Souvenir sheet of 2　3.00　2.50
　　　Nos. C214-C216 (3)　3.15　1.50
No. C216a contains 2 stamps with simulated perforations similar to Nos. C215-C216.

Picasso Type

Paintings: 90fr, The Muse. 100fr, Les Demoiselles d'Avignon. 200fr, Sitting Nude.

1974, Apr. 6　Litho.　Perf. 14
C217 A146 90fr brn & multi　.60　.30
C218 A146 100fr pur & multi　.70　.35
C219 A146 200fr multi　1.40　.65
　a.　Souvenir sheet of 3　3.50　3.00
　　　Nos. C217-C219 (3)　2.70　1.30
No. C219a contains 3 stamps similar to Nos. C217-C219 with simulated perforations.

Coastal Views Type

Designs: 90fr, Fishermen on Lake Togo. 100fr, Mouth of Anecho River.

1974, Apr. 20
C220 A147 90fr multi　.60　.25
C221 A147 100fr multi　.65　.35
　a.　Souvenir sheet of 2　1.40　1.25
No. C221a contains 2 stamps similar to Nos. C220-C221 with simulated perforations.

UPU Type

Designs: Old mailmen's uniforms.

1974, May 10　Litho.　Perf. 14
C222 A148 50fr multi　.40　.20
C223 A148 100fr multi　.70　.35
　a.　Souvenir sheet of 2　10.00　8.25
No. C223a contains 2 stamps similar to Nos. C222-C223, rouletted.

Fishing Type

Designs: 90fr, Fishermen bringing in net with catch. 100fr, Fishing with rod and line. 200fr, Fishing with basket, vert.

1974, June 22　Litho.　Perf. 14
C224 A149 90fr multi　.50　.25
C225 A149 100fr multi　.55　.25
C226 A149 200fr multi　1.10　.65
　　　Nos. C224-C226 (3)　2.15　1.15
No. C226a contains 3 stamps with simulated perforations similar to Nos. C224-C226.

Jupiter Probe Type

Designs: 100fr, Rocket take-off, vert. 200fr, Satellite in space.

1974, July 6　Perf. 14
C227 A150 100fr multi　.65　.35
C228 A150 200fr multi　1.40　.65
　a.　Souvenir sheet of 2　5.00　3.75
No. C228a contains 2 stamps similar to Nos. C227-C228 with simulated perforations; imperf. or rouletted.

No. C176
Overprinted

1974, July　Perf. 14
C229 A125 100fr multi　1.60　.65
INTERNABA 1974 Intl. Philatelic Exhibition, Basel, June 7-16.

Seashell Type

1974, July 13　Litho.　Perf. 14
C230 A151 90fr Alcithoe pon-
　　　sonbyi　.45　.25
C231 A151 100fr Casmaria
　　　iredalei　.55　.35
　a.　Souvenir sheet of 2　1.25　1.10
No. C231a contains 2 stamps similar to Nos. C230-C231 with simulated perforations.

Horse Racing Type

90fr, Steeplechase. 100fr, Galloping horses.

1974, Aug. 3　Litho.　Perf. 14
C232 A152 90fr multi　.60　.25
C233 A152 100fr multi　.70　.35
　a.　Souvenir sheet of 2　1.50　1.25
No. C233a contains one each of Nos. C232-C233 with simulated perforations.

Nos. C180, C180a and C181 Overprinted: "COUPE DU MONDE / DE FOOTBALL / VAINQUEURS / REPUBLIQUE FEDERALE / d'ALLEMAGNE"

1974, Aug. 19
C234 A127 90fr multi　.60　.25
　a.　Souvenir sheet of 2　1.25　1.25
C235 A127 200fr multi　1.25　.65
World Cup Soccer Championship, Munich, 1974, victory of German Federal Republic. For description of No. C234a see note after No. C181.

Animal Type

1974, Sept. 7　Litho.　Perf. 14
C236 A153 90fr Lions　.55　.30
C237 A153 100fr Rhinoceroses　.60　.35
　a.　Souvenir sheet of 2　1.60　1.40
Wild animals of West Africa. No. C237a contains 3 stamps similar to Nos. 889, C236-C237 with simulated perforations.

1974, Oct. 14
C238 A153 90fr Herd at
　　　waterhole　.50　.25
C239 A153 100fr Village and
　　　cows　.55　.35
　a.　Souvenir sheet of 2　1.50　1.25
Domestic animals. No. C239a contains 2 stamps with simulated perforations similar to Nos. C238-C239.

Churchill Type

Designs: 100fr, Churchill and frigate. 200fr, Churchill and fighter planes.

1974, Nov. 1　Photo.　Perf. 13x13½
C240 A154 100fr multi　.60　.30
C241 A154 200fr org & multi　1.25　.60
　a.　Souvenir sheet of 2　2.25　1.90
No. C241a contains 2 stamps similar to Nos. C240-C241; perf. or imperf.

Flower Type

Flowers of Togo: 100fr, Clerodendrum thosonae. 200fr, Gloriosa superba.

Jupiter Probe Type (col 3)

1975, Feb. 15　Litho.　Perf. 14
C242 A155 100fr multi　.55　.25
C243 A155 200fr multi　1.10　.50
　a.　Souvenir sheet of 2　3.25　2.50
No. C243a contains one each of Nos. C242-C243, perf. 13x14 or imperf.

Nos. C184-C185 Overprinted: "70e ANNIVERSAIRE / 23 FÉVRIER 1975"

1975, Feb. 23　Litho.　Perf. 14
C244 A129 90fr multi　.50　.25
C245 A129 100fr multi　.55　.35
Rotary International, 70th anniversary.

Easter Type

Paintings: 100fr, Christ Rising from the Tomb, by Master MS. 200fr, Holy Trinity (detail), by Dürer.

1975, Apr. 19　Litho.　Perf. 14
C246 A157 100fr multi　.55　.25
C247 A157 200fr multi　1.10　.55
　a.　Souvenir sheet of 2　1.65　1.40
No. C247a contains 2 stamps similar to Nos. C246-C247 with simulated perforations.

Independence Type

50fr, National Day parade, flag and map of Togo. 60fr, Warriors' dance and flag of Togo.

1975, Apr. 26　Litho.　Perf. 14
C248 A158 50fr multi, vert.　.25　.20
C249 A158 60fr multi　.35　.20
　a.　Souvenir sheet of 2　.90　.50
No. C249a contains 2 stamps similar to Nos. C248-C249 with simulated perforations.

Hunt Type

Designs: 90fr, Running deer. 100fr, Wild boar hunter with shotgun.

1975, May 24　Photo.　Perf. 13x13½
C250 A159 90fr multi　.50　.25
C251 A159 100fr multi　.55　.25

Palm Oil Type

Designs: 85fr, Selling palm oil in market, vert. 100fr, Oil processing plant, Alokoegbe.

1975, June 28　Litho.　Perf. 14
C252 A160 85fr multi　.45　.25
C253 A160 100fr multi　.55　.25

Apollo-Soyuz Type and

Soyuz Spacecraft
AP17

Designs: 60fr, Donald K. Slayton, Vance D. Brand and Thomas P. Stafford. 90fr, Aleksei A. Leonov and Valery N. Kubasov. 100fr, Apollo-Soyuz link-up, American and Russian flags. 200fr, Apollo-Soyuz emblem and globe.

1975, July 15
C254 AP17 50fr yel & multi　.25　.20
C255 A161 60fr lil & multi　.35　.20
C256 A161 90fr bl & multi　.45　.25
C257 A161 100fr grn & multi　.55　.40
C258 A161 200fr yel & multi　1.10　.45
　a.　Souv. sheet of 4, #C255-C258　3.00　2.00
　　　Nos. C254-C258 (5)　2.70　1.50
See note after No. 913.

Schweitzer Type

Dr. Schweitzer: 80fr, playing organ, vert. 90fr, with pelican, vert. 100fr, and Lambarene Hospital.

1975, Aug. 23　Litho.　Perf. 14x13½
C259 A163 80fr multi　.45　.25
C260 A163 90fr multi　.50　.30
C261 A163 100fr multi　.55　.35
　　　Nos. C259-C261 (3)　1.50　.90

Letter Writing Type

80fr, Erasmus Writing Letter, by Hans Holbein.

1975, Oct. 9　Litho.　Perf. 14
C262 A164 80fr multi　.45　.25

Nos. C167-C168a Overprinted: "30ème Anniversaire / des Nations-Unies"

1975, Oct. 24　Litho.　Perf. 14
C263 A120 60fr multi　.35　.2
C264 A120 90fr multi　.45　.2
　a.　Souvenir sheet of 4　1.40　1.1
UN, 30th anniv. #C264a contains Nos. 79 (with overprint), 918, C263-C264.

Nos. C198-C199 Overprinted: "14ème JAMBOREE / MONDIAL / DES ECLAIREURS"

1975, Nov. 7
C265 A137 100fr multi　.55　.25
C266 A137 200fr multi　1.10　.50
　a.　Souvenir sheet of 2　1.60　1.50
14th World Boy Scout Jamboree, Lillehammer, Norway, July 29-Aug. 7. No. C266a contains one each of Nos. C265-C266 with simulated perforations.

Christmas Type

Paintings of the Virgin and Child: 90fr, Nativity, by Federico Barocci. 100fr, Bellini. 200fr, Correggio.

1975, Dec. 20　Litho.　Perf. 14
C267 A165 90fr bl & multi　.50　.25
C268 A165 100fr red & multi　.55　.25
C269 A165 200fr multi　1.10　.50
　a.　Souv. sheet of 2, #C268-C269　1.90　1.50
　　　Nos. C267-C269 (3)　2.15　1.00

Bicentennial Type

Paintings (and Bicentennial Emblem): 60fr, Surrender of Gen. Burgoyne, by John Trumbull. 70fr, Surrender at Trenton, by Trumbull, vert. 100fr, Signing of Declaration of Independence, by Trumbull. 200fr, Washington Crossing the Delaware, by Emanuel Leutze.

1976, Mar. 3　Litho.　Perf. 14
C270 A167 60fr multi　.35　.20
C271 A167 70fr multi　.40　.20
C272 A167 100fr multi　.55　.25
C273 A167 200fr multi　1.10　.55
　a.　Souv. sheet of 2, #C272-C273　1.60　1.60
　　　Nos. C270-C273 (4)　2.40　1.20
No. C273a also exists imperf.; same value. For overprints see Nos. C280-C283.

Common Market Type

Designs: 60fr, ACP and CEE emblems. 70fr, Map of Africa, Europe and Asia.

1976, Apr. 24　Photo.　Perf. 13x14
C274 A168 60fr lt bl & multi　.35　.20
C275 A168 70fr yel & multi　.40　.20

Telephone Type

Designs: 70fr, Thomas A. Edison, old and new communications equipment. 105fr, Alexander Graham Bell, old and new telephones.

1976, Mar. 10　Photo.　Perf. 13x14
C276 A169 70fr multi　.40　.20
C277 A169 105fr multi　.55　.40
　a.　Souv. sheet of 2, #C276-C277　1.00　.90
No. C277a exists imperf.; same value.

Eye Examination
AP18

Pylon, Flags of
Ghana, Togo,
Dahomey
AP19

1976, Apr. 8　Perf. 14x13
C278 AP18 60fr dk red & multi　.35　.20
World Health Day: "Foresight prevents blindness."

1976, May 8　Litho.　Perf. 14
C279 AP19 60fr multi　.35　.20
Ghana-Togo-Dahomey electric power grid, 1st anniv. See No. 932.

Nos. C270-C273, C273a, Overprinted: "INTERPHIL / MAI 29-JUIN 6, 1976"

1976, May 29

C280	A167	60fr multi	.35 .20
C281	A167	70fr multi	.40 .20
C282	A167	100fr multi	.55 .25
C283	A167	200fr multi	1.10 .55
a.		Souvenir sheet of 2	1.60 1.50
		Nos. C280-C283 (4)	2.40 1.20

Interphil 76 Intl. Philatelic Exhibition, Philadelphia, Pa., May 29-June 6. Overprint on No. C283 in 3 lines; overprint on No. C283a applied to each stamp.

Olympic Games Type

Montreal Olympic Emblem and: 70fr, Yachting. 105fr, Motorcycling. 200fr, Fencing.

1976, June 15   Photo.   Perf. 14x13

C284	A172	70fr multi	.45 .25
C285	A172	105fr multi	.65 .40
C286	A172	200fr multi	1.25 .65
a.		Souvenir sheet of 2, #C285-C286, perf. 14	2.50 2.25
		Nos. C284-C286 (3)	2.35 1.30

For overprints see Nos. C298-C299.

Viking Type

60fr, Viking landing on Mars. 70fr, Nodus Gordii (view on Mars). 105fr, Lander over Mare Tyrrhenum. 200fr, Landing on Mars.

1976, July 15   Litho.   Perf. 14

C287	A173	60fr bis & multi	.35 .20
C288	A173	70fr multi	.40 .20
C289	A173	105fr bl & multi	.55 .35
C290	A173	200fr multi	1.10 .55
a.		Souv. sheet of 2, #C289-C290, perf. 14x13½	1.90 1.60
		Nos. C287-C290 (4)	2.40 1.30

Toulouse-Lautrec Type, 1976

Paintings: 60fr, Carmen, portrait. 70fr, Maurice at the Somme. 200fr, "Messalina."

1976, Aug. 7   Litho.   Perf. 14

C291	A174	60fr blk & multi	.35 .20
C292	A174	70fr blk & multi	.40 .25
C293	A174	200fr blk & multi	1.10 .55
a.		Souv. sheet of 2, #C292-C293, perf. 13½x14	1.60 1.50
		Nos. C291-C293 (3)	1.85 1.00

No. C202 Overprinted: "Journeé / Internationale / de l'Enfance"

1976, Nov. 27   Litho.   Perf. 14

C294	A139	100fr multi	.55 .35

International Children's Day.

Christmas Type

Paintings: 70fr, Holy Family, by Lorenzo Lotto. 105fr, Virgin and Child with Saints, by Jacopo da Pontormo. 200fr, Virgin and Child with Saints, by Lotto.

1976, Dec. 18

C295	A175	70fr multi	.35 .20
C296	A175	105fr multi	.55 .35
C297	A175	200fr multi	1.10 .55
a.		Souv. sheet of 2, #C296-C297	1.90 1.60
		Nos. C295-C297 (3)	2.00 1.10

No. C284 Overprinted: "CHAMPIONS OLYMPIQUES / YACHTING - FLYING DUTCHMAN / REPUBLIQUE FEDERALE ALLEMAGNE"
No. C286 Overprinted: "CHAMPIONS OLYMPIQUES / ESCRIME FLEURET PAR EQUIPES / REPUBLIQUE FEDERALE ALLEMAGNE"

1976, Dec.   Photo.   Perf. 14x13

C298	A172	70fr multi	.40 .20
C299	A172	200fr multi	1.10 .60
a.		Souvenir sheet of 2	1.90 1.60

Olympic winners. No. C299a (on No. C286a) contains Nos. C285 and C299.

Eyadema Anniversary Type

60fr, National Assembly Building. 100fr, Pres. Eyadema greeting people at Aug. 30th meeting.

1977, Jan. 13   Photo.   Perf. 13x14

C300	A177	60fr multi	.35 .20
C301	A177	100fr multi	.55 .30
a.		Souv. sheet of 2, #C300-C301	.90 .85

Musical Instrument Type

Musical Instruments: 60fr, Atopani. 80fr, African violin, vert. 105fr, African flutes, vert.

1977, Feb. 7	**Litho.**	**Perf. 14**	
C302	A178	60fr multi	.35 .20
C303	A178	80fr multi	.40 .20
C304	A178	105fr multi	.55 .25
a.		Souv. sheet of 2, #C303-C304	1.25 1.00
		Nos. C302-C304 (3)	1.30 .65

Victor Hugo Type

Victor Hugo in exile on Guernsey Island.

1977, Feb. 26   Perf. 13x14

C305	A179	60fr multi	.35 .20
a.		Souvenir sheet of 2, #952, C305	.65 .60

For overprint see No. C316.

Beethoven Type

Designs: 100fr, Beethoven's piano and 1818 portrait. 200fr, Beethoven on his deathbed and Holy Trinity Church, Vienna.

1977, Mar. 7   Perf. 14

C306	A180	100fr multi	.55 .35
C307	A180	200fr multi	1.10 .65
a.		Souv. sheet of 2, #C306-C307	1.60 1.60

Automobile Type

Early Automobiles: 60fr, Cannstatt-Daimler, 1899, Germany. 70fr, Sunbeam, 1904, England. 100fr, Renault, 1908, France. 200fr, Rolls Royce, 1909, England.

1977, Apr. 11   Litho.   Perf. 14

C308	A181	60fr multi	.35 .20
C309	A181	70fr multi	.40 .20
C310	A181	100fr multi	.55 .30
C311	A181	200fr multi	1.10 .55
a.		Souv. sheet of 2, #C310-C311	1.60 1.60
		Nos. C308-C311 (4)	2.40 1.35

Lindbergh Type

Designs: 60fr, Lindbergh and son Jon, birds in flight. 85fr, Lindbergh home in Kent, England. 90fr, Spirit of St. Louis over Atlantic Ocean. 100fr, Concorde over NYC.

1977, May 9

C312	A182	60fr multi	.40 .20
C313	A182	85fr multi	.55 .20
C314	A182	90fr multi	.60 .20
C315	A182	100fr multi	.65 .25
a.		Souv. sheet of 2, #C314-C315	1.40 .85
		Nos. C312-C315 (4)	2.20 .85

No. C305 Overprinted: "10ème ANNIVERSAIRE DU / CONSEIL INTERNATIONAL / DE LA LANGUE FRANCAISE"

1977, May 17   Litho.   Perf. 14

C316	A179		.40 .20

10th anniv. of the French Language Council.

Wildlife Type

60fr, Colobus monkeys. 90fr, Chimpanzee, vert. 100fr, Leopard. 200fr, West African manatee.

1977, June 13

C317	A183	60fr multi	.40 .20
C318	A183	90fr multi	.60 .20
C319	A183	100fr multi	.65 .20
C320	A183	200fr multi	1.40 .55
a.		Souv. sheet of 2, #C319-C320	2.25 1.25
		Nos. C317-C320 (4)	3.05 .95

Agriculture Type

Designs: 60fr, Corn silo. 100fr, Hoeing and planting by hand. 200fr, Tractor on field.

1977, July 11   Litho.   Perf. 14

C321	A184	60fr multi	.40 .20
C322	A184	100fr multi	.65 .20
C323	A184	200fr multi	1.40 .40
a.		Souv. sheet of 2, #C322-C323, perf. 13x14	2.25 1.25
		Nos. C321-C323 (3)	2.45 .80

Rubens Type

Paintings: 60fr, Heads of Black Men, 1620. 100fr, Anne of Austria, 1624.

1977, Aug. 8

C324	A185	60fr multi	.40 .20
C325	A185	100fr multi	.65 .20
a.		Souv. sheet of 2, #C324-C325, perf. 14x13	1.25 .65

Orbiter Type

90fr, Retrieval of unmanned satellite in space. 100fr, Satellite's return to space after repairs. 200fr, Manned landing of Orbiter.

1977, Oct. 4   Litho.   Perf. 14

C326	A186	90fr multi, vert.	.60 .20
C327	A186	100fr multi	.65 .20
C328	A186	200fr multi	1.25 .35
a.		Souv. sheet of 2, #C327-C328	2.25 1.25
		Nos. C326-C328 (3)	2.50 .75

Lafayette Type

60fr, Lafayette landing in New York, 1824. 105fr, Lafayette and Washington at Valley Forge.

1977, Nov. 7   Perf. 13x14

C329	A187	60fr multi	.40 .20
C330	A187	105fr multi	.70 .20
a.		Souv. sheet of 2, #C329-C330	1.25 .65

Christmas Type

Virgin & Child by: 90fr, 200fr, Carlo Crivelli, diff. 100fr, Bellini.

1977, Dec. 19   Perf. 14

C331	A189	90fr multi	.60 .20
C332	A189	100fr multi	.65 .20
C333	A189	200fr multi	1.40 .35
a.		Souv. sheet of 2, #C332-C333	2.25 1.25
		Nos. C331-C333 (3)	2.65 .75

Jenner Type

Designs: 50fr, Edward Jenner. 60fr, Smallpox vaccination clinic, horiz.

1978, Jan. 9   Perf. 14x13, 13x14

C334	A190	50fr multi	.35 .20
C335	A190	60fr multi	.40 .20
a.		Souv. sheet of 2	.80 .50

No. C335a contains 2 stamps with simulated perforations similar to Nos. C334-C335.

Wright Brothers Type

Designs: 60fr, Orville Wright's 7½-minute flight. 70fr, Orville Wright injured in first aircraft accident, 1908. 200fr, Wrights' bicycle shop, Dearborn, Mich. 300fr, First flight, 1903.

1978, Feb. 6   Litho.   Perf. 14

C336	A191	60fr multi	.40 .20
C337	A191	70fr multi	.45 .20
C338	A191	200fr multi	1.40 .35
C339	A191	300fr multi	2.00 .60
a.		Souvenir sheet of 2	3.50 2.00
		Nos. C336-C339 (4)	4.25 1.35

No. C339a contains one each of Nos. C338-C339 with simulated perforations.

Port of Lomé Type, 1978

Anchor and: 60fr, Industrial harbor. 100fr, Merchant marine harbor. 200fr, Bird's-eye view of entire harbor.

1978, Apr. 26   Photo.   Perf. 13

C340	A199	60fr multi	.40 .20
C341	A199	100fr multi	.65 .20
C342	A199	200fr multi	1.40 .40
a.		Souv. sheet of 2, #C341-C342	2.25 1.25
		Nos. C340-C342 (3)	2.45 .80

Space Type

Designs: 90fr, Module camera, horiz. 100fr, Module antenna. 200fr, Pioneer, US, in orbit.

1978, May 8   Litho.   Perf. 14

C343	A200	90fr multi	.60 .20
C344	A200	100fr multi	.65 .20
C345	A200	200fr multi	1.40 .35
a.		Souv. sheet of 2, #C344-C345, perf. 13¼x14	2.25 1.25
		Nos. C343-C345 (3)	2.65 .75

Soccer Type

Various soccer scenes & Argentina '78 emblem.

1978, June 5   Perf. 14

C346	A201	60fr multi	.40 .20
C347	A201	80fr multi	.55 .20
C348	A201	200fr multi	1.40 .35
C349	A201	300fr multi	2.00 .50
a.		Souvenir sheet of 2, #C348-C349, perf. 13½x14	3.75 2.25
		Nos. C346-C349 (4)	4.35 1.25

Bicycle Type

History of Bicycle: 60fr, Bantam, 1896, vert. 85fr, Fold-up bicycle for military use, 1897. 90fr, Draisienne, 1816, vert. 100fr, Penny-farthing, 1884, vert.

Perf. 14x13, 13x14

1978, July 10   Photo.

C350	A202	60fr multi	.40 .20
C351	A202	85fr multi	.55 .20
C352	A202	90fr multi	.60 .25
C353	A202	100fr multi	.65 .25
a.		Souv. sheet of 2, #C352-C353	1.40 .85
		Nos. C350-C353 (4)	2.20 .90

Phonograph Type

60fr, Edison's original phonograph, horiz. 80fr, Emile Berliner's phonograph, 1888. 200fr, Berliner's improved phonograph, 1894, horiz. 300fr, His Master's Voice phonograph, 1900, horiz.

1978, July 8		**Photo.**	
C354	A203	60fr multi	.40 .20
C355	A203	80fr multi	.55 .20
C356	A203	200fr multi	1.25 .35
C357	A203	300fr multi	2.00 .50
a.		Souv. sheet of 2, #C356-C357	3.50 2.00
		Nos. C354-C357 (4)	4.20 1.25

Red Cross Type

Design: 60fr, Red Cross and other pavilions at Paris Exhibition, 1867.

1978, Sept. 4   Photo.   Perf. 14x13

C358	A204	60fr pur & red	.40 .20
a.		Souv. sheet, #1009, C358	.65 .40

Paintings Type

60fr, Langlois Bridge, by Vincent van Gogh. 70fr, Witches' Sabbath, by Francisco Goya. 90fr, Jesus among the Doctors, by Albrecht Dürer. 200fr, View of Arco, by Dürer.

1978, Nov. 6   Litho.   Perf. 14

C359	A205	60fr multi	.40 .20
C360	A205	70fr multi	.45 .25
C361	A205	90fr multi	.60 .35
C362	A205	200fr multi	1.25 .65
a.		Souv. sheet of 2, #C361-C362	2.00 1.25
		Nos. C359-C362 (4)	2.70 1.45

Birth and death anniversaries of famous painters.

Philexafrique II - Essen Issue
Common Design Types

#C363, Warthog and Togo No. C36. #C364, Firecrest and Thurn and Taxis No. 1.

1978, Nov. 1   Litho.   Perf. 13x12½

C363	CD138	100fr multi	.65 .35
C364	CD139	100fr multi	.65 .35
a.		Pair, #C363-C364 + label	1.30 .70

Congress of Paris Type

60fr, Mail ship "Slieve Roe" 1877, post horn. 105fr, Congress of Paris medal. 200fr, Locomotive, 1870. All horizontal.

1978, Nov. 27   Photo.   Perf. 14x13

C365	A206	60fr multi	.40 .20
C366	A206	105fr multi	.70 .35
C367	A206	200fr multi	1.40 .65
a.		Souv. sheet of 2, #C366-C367	2.25 1.25
		Nos. C365-C367 (3)	2.50 1.20

Christmas Type

Paintings (Virgin and Child): 90fr, 200fr, by Carlo Crivelli, diff. 100fr, by Cosimo Tura.

1978, Dec. 18

C368	A207	90fr multi	.60 .30
C369	A207	100fr multi	.65 .35
C370	A207	200fr multi	1.25 .65
a.		Souv. sheet of 2, #C369-C370	2.25 1.25
		Nos. C368-C370 (3)	2.50 1.30

Capt. Cook Type

Designs: 60fr, "Freelove", Whitby Harbor, horiz. 70fr, Trip to Antarctica, 1773, horiz. 90fr, Capt. Cook. 200fr, Sails of Endeavour.

1979, Feb. 12   Litho.   Perf. 14

C371	A208	60fr multi	.40 .20
C372	A208	70fr multi	.45 .25
C373	A208	90fr multi	.60 .30
C374	A208	200fr multi	1.40 1.25
a.		Souv. sheet of 2, #C373-C374	2.00 1.75
		Nos. C371-C374 (4)	2.85 2.00

Easter Type

60fr, Resurrection. 100fr, Ascension. 200fr, Jesus appearing to Mary Magdalene.

1979, Apr. 9

C375	A209	60fr multi	.40 .20
C376	A209	100fr multi	.65 .35
C377	A209	200fr multi	1.40 .65
a.		Souv. sheet of 2, #C376-C377	2.25 1.25
		Nos. C375-C377 (3)	2.45 1.20

UPU Emblem, Drummer — AP20

Design: 100fr, UPU emblem, hands passing letter, satellites.

1979, June 8   Engr.   *Perf. 13*
C378 AP20 60fr multi   .40   .20
C379 AP20 100fr multi   .65   .35

Philexafrique II, Libreville, Gabon, June 8-17.

Einstein Type

Designs: 60fr, Sights and actuality diagram. 85fr, Einstein playing violin, vert. 100fr, Atom symbol and formula of relativity, vert. 200fr, Einstein portrait, vert.

Perf. 14x13, 13x14

1979, July 2   Photo.
C380 A210 60fr multi   .40   .20
C381 A210 85fr multi   .60   .30
C382 A210 100fr multi   .65   .35
C383 A210 200fr multi   1.40   .65
  a.   Souv. sheet of 2, #C382-C383   2.25   1.25
       Nos. C380-C383 (4)   3.05   1.50

Tree Type

Design: 60fr, Man watering tree.

1979, Aug. 13   *Perf. 14x13*
C384 A212 60fr blk & brn   .40   .20

Rowland Hill Type

Designs: 90fr, Bellman, England, 1820. 100fr, "Centercycles" used for parcel delivery, 1883, horiz. 200fr, French P.O. railroad car, 1848, horiz.

1979, Aug. 27   Photo.
C385 A213 90fr multi   .60   .30
C386 A213 100fr multi   .65   .35
C387 A213 200fr multi   1.40   .65
  a.   Souv. sheet of 2, #C386-C387   2.25   2.25
       Nos. C385-C387 (3)   2.65   1.30

Train Type

Historic Locomotives: 60fr, "Le General," 1862. 85fr, Stephenson's, 1843. 100fr, "De Witt Clinton," 1831. 200fr, Joy's "Jenny Lind," 1847.

1979, Oct. 1   Litho.   *Perf. 14*
C388 A214 60fr multi   .40   .20
C389 A214 85fr multi   .55   .30
C390 A214 100fr multi   .65   .35
C391 A214 200fr multi   1.40   .65
  a.   Souv. sheet of 2, #C390-C391   2.25   2.25
       Nos. C388-C391 (4)   3.00   1.50

Olympic Type

1980 Olympic Emblems and: 90fr, Ski jump. No. C393, Doubles canoeing, Olympic flame. No. C394, Rings. No. C395a, Bobsledding, horiz. No. C395b, Gymnast, horiz.

1979, Oct. 18   Litho.   *Perf. 13½*
C392 A215 90fr multi   .60   .30
C393 A215 100fr multi   .65   .35
C394 A215 200fr multi   1.40   .65
  a.   Souvenir sheet of 2   2.25   2.25
       Nos. C392-C394 (3)   2.65   1.30

Souvenir Sheet
C395   Sheet of 2   2.25   2.25
  a.   A215 100fr multi   .65   .35
  b.   A215 200fr multi   1.40   .65

Religion Type

Designs: 60fr, Moslems praying. 70fr, Protestant ministers.

1979, Oct. 29   *Perf. 13x14*
C396 A216 60fr multi   .40   .20
C397 A216 70fr multi   .45   .24
  a.   Souv. sheet, #C396-C397   1.00   1.00

Apollo 11 Type

60fr, Astronaut leaving Apollo 11. 70fr, US flag. 200fr, Sun shield. 300fr, Lunar take-off.

1979, Nov. 5
C398 A217 60fr multi   .40   .20
C399 A217 70fr multi   .45   .25
C400 A217 200fr multi   1.40   .65
C401 A217 300fr multi   2.00   1.00
  a.   Souv. sheet of 2, #C400-C401   3.75   3.75
       Nos. C398-C401 (4)   4.25   2.10

Telecom Type

Design: 60fr, Telecom 79, dish antenna.

1979, Nov. 26   Photo.   *Perf. 14x13*
C402 A218 60fr multi   .40   .20

Miniature Sheets

President Eyadema, 10th Anniv. of the People's Republic — AP21

Illustration reduced.

Litho. & Embossed
1979, Nov. 30   *Perf. 13½*
C402A AP21 1000fr In uniform

Imperf
C402B AP21 1000fr In suit, vert.

Exist imperf.

Christmas Type

90fr, Adoration of the Kings. 100fr, Presentation of Infant Jesus. 200fr, Flight into Egypt.

1979, Dec. 17   Litho.   *Perf. 14*
C403 A219 90fr multi   .60   .30
C404 A219 100fr multi   .65   .35
C405 A219 200fr multi   1.25   .65
  a.   Souv. sheet of 2, #C404-C405   2.25   1.25
       Nos. C403-C405 (3)   2.50   1.30

Rotary Type

3-H Emblem and: 90fr, Man reaching for sun. 100fr, Fish, grain. 200fr, Family, globe.

1980, Jan. 14
C406 A220 90fr multi   .60   .30
C407 A220 100fr multi   .65   .35
C408 A220 200fr multi   1.25   .65
  a.   Souv. sheet of 2, C407-C408   2.25   1.25
       Nos. C406-C408 (3)   2.50   1.30

Rotary Intl., 75th anniv.; 3-H program (health, hunger, humanity).

Winter Olympic Type, 1980
1980, Jan. 31   Litho.   *Perf. 13½*
C409 A221 60fr Downhill skiing   .40   .20
C410 A221 100fr Speed skating   .65   .35
C411 A221 200fr Cross-country
            skiing   1.25   .65
       Nos. C409-C411 (3)   2.30   1.20

Souvenir Sheet
C412   Sheet of 2   2.00   1.00
  a.   A221 100fr Ski jump, horiz.   .65   .35
  b.   A221 200fr Hockey, horiz.   1.25   .65

Olympic Type
1980, Feb. 29   *Perf. 13½*
C413 A222 100fr Fencing   .90   .45
C414 A222 200fr Pole vault   1.60   .80
C415 A222 300fr Hurdles   2.50   1.25
  a.   Souv. sheet of 2, #C414-C415   4.75   2.50
       Nos. C413-C415 (3)   5.00   2.50

Easter Type

Easter 1980 (Paintings by): 60fr, Lorenzo Lotto. 100fr, El Greco. 200fr, Carlo Crivelli.

1980, Mar. 31   *Perf. 14*
C416 A223 60fr multi   .40   .20
C417 A223 100fr multi   .65   .35
C418 A223 200fr multi   1.25   .65
  a.   Souv. sheet of 2, #C417-C418   2.00   1.00
       Nos. C416-C418 (3)   2.30   1.20

ASECNA Type
1980, Mar. 24   Litho.   *Perf. 12½*
C419 A224 60fr multi   .40   .20

Telecommunications Type
1980, May 17   Photo.   *Perf. 13½x14*
C420 A225 60fr "17 MAI", vert.   .40   .20

Red Cross Type
1980, June 16   Photo.   *Perf. 14x13*
C421 A226 60fr Nurses, patient   .40   .20

Jules Verne Type

Designs: 60fr, Rocket (From Earth to Moon). 80fr, Around the World in 80 Days. 100fr, Rocket and moon (From Earth to Moon). 200fr, Octopus (20,000 Leagues Under the Sea).

1980, July 14   Litho.   *Perf. 14*
C422 A227 60fr multi   .40   .20
C423 A227 80fr multi   .55   .25
C424 A227 100fr multi   .65   .35

C425 A227 200fr multi   1.25   .65
  a.   Souv. sheet of 2, #C424-C425,
         perf. 13½x14   2.00   1.00
       Nos. C422-C425 (4)   2.85   1.45

Ingres Type

Ingres Paintings: 90fr, Jupiter and Thetis. 100fr, Countess d'Hassonville. 200fr, "Tu Marcellus Eris."

1980, Aug. 29   Litho.   *Perf. 14*
C426 A228 90fr multi   .60   .30
C427 A228 100fr multi   .65   .35
C428 A228 200fr multi   1.25   .65
  a.   Souv. sheet of 2, #C427-C428   2.00   1.00
       Nos. C426-C428 (3)   2.50   1.30

Famous Men Type

90fr, Salvador Allende, vert. 100fr, Pope Paul VI, vert. 200fr, Jomo Kenyatta, vert.

1980, Feb. 11   Litho.   *Perf. 14x13*
C429 A231 90fr ultra & lt bl grn   .60   .30
C430 A231 100fr pur & pink   .65   .35
C431 A231 200fr brn & yel bis   1.25   .65
  a.   Souv. sheet of 2, #C430-C431   2.00   1.00
       Nos. C429-C431 (3)   2.50   1.30

Human Rights Type
1980, Oct. 13   *Perf. 13x14*
C432 A233 60fr Map of Ameri-
            cas   .40   .20
C433 A233 150fr Map of Africa   1.00   .50
  a.   Souv. sheet of 2, #C432-C433   1.50   .65

American Order of Rosicrucians Emblem — AP22

1980, Nov. 17   Litho.   *Perf. 13*
C434 AP22 60fr multi   .40   .20

General Conclave of the American Order of Rosicrucians, meeting of French-speaking countries, Lome, Aug.

Christmas Type

Designs: 100fr, Cologne Cathedral, Germany, 13th cent. 150fr, Notre Dame, Paris, 12th cent. 200fr, Canterbury Cathedral, England, 11th cent.

1980, Dec. 22   *Perf. 14½x13½*
C435 A234 100fr multi   .65   .35
C436 A234 150fr multi   1.00   .50
C437 A234 200fr multi   1.25   .65
  a.   Souv. sheet of 2, #C436-C437   2.25   1.25
       Nos. C435-C437 (3)   2.90   1.50

Hotel Type of 1981
1981, Feb. 2   Litho.   *Perf. 12½x13*
C437B A236 60fr multi   .40   .20

Easter Type of 1981

Rembrandt Paintings: 100fr, Artist's Mother. 200fr, Man in a Ruff.

1981, Apr. 13   Litho. *Perf. 14½x13½*
C438 A237 100fr multi   .65   .35
C439 A237 200fr multi   1.25   .65
  a.   Souv. sheet of 2, #C438-C439   2.00   1.00

Market Type
1981, Mar. 8   Litho.   *Perf. 14*
C440 A230 90fr Fabric dealer   .60   .30
C441 A230 100fr Bananas   .65   .35
C442 A230 200fr Clay pottery   1.60   .80
C443 A230 250fr Setting up   1.60   .80
C444 A230 500fr Selling   3.50   1.60
C445 A230 1000fr Measuring
            grain   6.50   3.50
       Nos. C440-C445 (6)   14.25   7.20

For overprints see Nos. C486-C487.

Bird Type
Perf. 13½x14½
1981, Aug. 10   Litho.
C446 A238 50fr Violet-backed
            sunbird   .35   .20
C447 A238 100fr Red bishop   .65   .35
  a.   Souv. sheet, #C446-C447   1.00   .50

IYD Type
1981, Aug. 31   *Perf. 14*
C448 A240 90fr Carpenter   .60   .30

C449 A240 200fr Basketball
            players   1.25   .6
Souvenir Sheet
C449A A240 300fr Weaver   2.00 1.0

Picasso Type
1981, Sept. 14   *Perf. 14½x13½*
C450 A241 90fr Violin and Bot-
            tle on Table,
            1916   .60   .3
C451 A241 100fr Baboon and
            Young   .60   .3
C452 A241 200fr Mandolin and
            Clarinet, 1914   1.40   .6
  a.   Souv. sheet of 2, #C451-C452   2.00 1.0
       Nos. C450-C452 (3)   2.60 1.3

World Heritage Year Type
1981, Sept. 28   *Perf. 13½x14½*
C453 A242 100fr Cracow Muse-
            um, Poland   .75   .3
C454 A242 200fr Goree Isld., Se-
            negal   1.50   .7
  a.   Souv. sheet of 2, #C453-C454   2.25 1.1

Space Type
1981, Nov.   *Perf. 14*
C455 A243 90fr multi   .70   .35
C456 A243 100fr multi   .75   .35

Souvenir Sheet
Perf. 13x14
C456A A243 300fr multi, vert.   2.25 1.10

10th anniv. of Soyuz 10 (90fr) and Apollo 14 (100fr).

Christmas Type

Rubens Paintings: 100fr, Adoration of the Kings. 200fr, Virgin and Child. 300fr, Virgin giving Chasuble to St. Idefonso.

Perf. 14½x13½
1981, Dec. 10   Litho.
C457 A244 100fr multi   .65   .35
C458 A244 200fr multi   1.40   .65
C459 A244 300fr multi   2.00   1.00
  a.   Souv. sheet of 2, #C458-C459   3.75   1.90
       Nos. C457-C459 (3)   4.05   2.00

West African Rice Development Assoc. Type
1981, Dec. 21   Litho.   *Perf. 12½*
C461 A236a 105fr yel & multi   .70   .35

Liberation Type

Designs: 105fr, Citizens holding hands, Pres. Eyadema, vert. 130fr, Hotel.

1982, Jan. 13   Litho.   *Perf. 12½*
C462 A245 105fr multi   .70   .35
C463 A245 130fr multi   .90   .40

Scouting Year Type
1982, Feb. 25   Litho.   *Perf. 14*
C464 A246 90fr Semaphore   .60   .30
C465 A246 120fr Tower   .80   .40
C466 A246 130fr Scouts, canoe   .90   .40
C467 A246 135fr Scouts, tent   .90   .45
       Nos. C464-C467 (4)   3.20   1.55

Souvenir Sheet
Perf. 13x14
C468 A246 500fr Baden-Powell   3.50   1.60

Easter Type
1982, Apr.   *Perf. 14x14½*
C469 A247 105fr multi   .70   .35
C470 A247 120fr multi   .80   .40

Souvenir Sheet
C471 A247 500fr multi   3.50   1.60

PHILEXFRANCE '82 Intl. Stamp Exhibition, Paris, June 11-21 — AP23

1982   Litho.   *Perf. 13*
C472 AP23 90fr shown   .60   .30
C473 AP23 105fr ROMOLYMPHIL
            '82, vert.   .70   .35

Issue dates: 90fr, June 11; 105fr, May 19.

Butterfly Type

982, July 15   *Perf. 14½x14*

474	A248	90fr Euxanthe eurionome	.60	.30
475	A248	105fr Mylothris rhodope	.70	.35

Souvenir Sheet

476	A248	90fr Papilio zalmoxis	3.50	1.60

World Cup Type

982, July 26   *Perf. 14x14½*

477	A249	105fr multi	.75	.35
478	A249	200fr multi	1.25	.65
479	A249	300fr multi	2.00	1.00
		Nos. 477-479 (3)	4.00	2.00

Souvenir Sheet

480	A249	500fr multi	3.50	1.65

For overprints see Nos. 1152-1155.

Pre-Olympics, 1984 Los Angeles — AP24

1983, Oct. 3   **Photo.**   *Perf. 12½*

C481	AP24	70fr Boxing	.25	.20
C482	AP24	90fr Hurdles	.30	.20
C483	AP24	105fr Pole vault	.35	.20
C484	AP24	130fr Runner	.40	.20
		Nos. C481-C484 (4)	1.30	.80

Souvenir Sheet

C485	AP24	500fr Runner, diff.	1.60	.80

Nos. C443-C444 Overprinted: "19E CONGRES UPU HAMBOURG 1984"

1984, June 14   **Litho.**   *Perf. 14*

C486	A230	250fr multi	.80	.40
C487	A230	500fr multi	1.60	.80

1984 Summer Olympics — AP25

1984, July 27   *Perf. 13*

C488	AP25	70fr Pole vault	.25	.20
C489	AP25	90fr Bicycling	.30	.20
C490	AP25	120fr Soccer	.40	.20
C491	AP25	250fr Boxing	.80	.40
C492	AP25	400fr Running	1.25	.65
		Nos. C488-C492 (5)	3.00	1.65

Souvenir Sheet

C493	AP25	1000fr like 120fr, without flag	3.50	1.75

Nos. C488-C490, C493 vert.

Olympic Champions AP26

Peace and Human Rights — AP28

1984, Nov. 15   **Litho.**   *Perf. 15*

C494	AP26	500fr Jim Thorpe, US	1.40	.70
C495	AP26	500fr Jesse Owens, US	1.40	.70
C496	AP26	500fr Muhammad Ali, US	1.40	.70
C497	AP26	500fr Bob Beamon, US	1.40	.70
		Nos. C494-C497 (4)	5.60	2.80

Souvenir Sheets

C498	AP26	500fr Bill Steinkraus, US	1.40	.70
C499	AP26	500fr New Zealand rowing team	1.40	.70
C500	AP26	500fr Pakistani hockey team	1.40	.70
C501	AP26	500fr Yukio Endo, Japan	1.40	.70

West German Olympians

1984, Nov. 15

C502	AP26	500fr Dietmar Mogenburg	1.40	.70
C503	AP26	500fr Fredy Schmidtke	1.40	.70
C504	AP26	500fr Matthias Behr	1.40	.70
C505	AP26	500fr Sabine Everts	1.40	.70
		Nos. C502-C505 (4)	5.60	2.80

Souvenir Sheets

C506	AP26	500fr Karl-Heinz Radschinsky	1.40	.70
C507	AP26	500fr Pasquale Passarelli	1.40	.70
C508	AP26	500fr Michale Gross	1.40	.70
C509	AP26	500fr Jurgen Hingsen	1.40	.70

For overprints see Nos. C521-C536, C563.

1985, Jan. 14   **Litho.**   *Perf. 13½x14*

230fr, Map of Togo, globe, doves. 270fr, Palm tree, emblem. 500fr, Opencast mining operation. 1000fr, Human Rights Monument, UN, NYC.

C510	AP28	230fr multi	.45	.20
C511	AP28	270fr multi	.55	.30
C512	AP28	500fr multi	1.00	.50
C513	AP28	1000fr multi	2.00	1.00
		Nos. C510-C513 (4)	4.00	2.00

Tribal Dances AP29

1985, July   *Perf. 15x14*

C514	AP29	120fr Adifo, Adangbe	.25	.20
C515	AP29	135fr Fouet (whip), Kente	.25	.20
C516	AP29	290fr Idjombi, Pagouda	.60	.30
C517	AP29	500fr Moba, Dapaong	1.00	.50
		Nos. C514-C517 (4)	2.10	1.20

Visit of Pope John Paul II — AP30

90fr, The Pope outside Lome Cathedral. 130fr, Blessing crowd in St. Peter's Square. 500fr, Greeting Pres. Eyadema.

1985, Aug. 9   *Perf. 13*

C518	AP30	90fr multi	.30	.20
C519	AP30	130fr multi, vert.	.45	.25
C520	AP30	500fr multi	1.40	.50
		Nos. C518-C520 (3)	2.15	.95

Nos. C495, C497, C499, C502, C505-508 Overprinted with Winners Names, Country and Type of Olympic Medal

1985, Aug.   *Perf. 15*

C521	AP26	500fr Kirk Baptiste, US	1.00	.50
C522	AP26	500fr Carl Lewis, US	1.00	.50
C523	AP26	500fr Patrik Sjoborg, Sweden	1.00	.50
C524	AP26	500fr Glynis Nunn, Australia	1.00	.50
		Nos. C521-C524 (4)	4.00	2.00

Souvenir Sheets

C525	AP26	500fr Rowing eights, Canada	2.00	1.00
C526	AP26	500fr Rolf Milser, W. Germany	2.00	1.00
C527	AP26	500fr Takashi Irie, Japan	2.00	1.00
C528	AP26	500fr Frederic Delcourt, France	2.00	1.00

Nos. C494, C496, C503-C504, C498, C500, C501, C509 Ovptd. with Winners Names, Country and Type of Olympic Medal

1985, Sept. 19   **Litho.**   *Perf. 15*

C529	AP26	500fr Italy	1.00	.50
C530	AP26	500fr Kevin Barry	1.00	.50
C531	AP26	500fr Rolf Golz	1.00	.50
C532	AP26	500fr Philippe Boisse	1.00	.50
		Nos. C529-C532 (4)	4.00	2.00

Souvenir Sheets

C533	AP26	500fr Karen Stives	1.00	.50
C534	AP26	500fr R.F.A. (West Germany)	1.00	.50
C535	AP26	500fr Koji Gushiken	1.00	.50
C536	AP26	500fr Daley Thompson	1.00	.50

Traditional Instruments — AP31

Youth and Development — AP32

Designs: No. C537, Xylophone, Kante horn, tambour. No. C538, Bongo drums, castanets, bassar horn. No. C539, Communications. No. C540, Agriculture and industry.

1985   **Litho.**   *Perf. 13*

C537	AP31	100fr multi	.20	.20
C538	AP31	100fr multi	.20	.20
a.		Pair, #C537-C538	.40	.20
C539	AP32	200fr multi	.40	.20
C540	AP32	200fr multi	.40	.20
a.		Pair, #C539-C540	.80	.40
		Nos. C537-C540 (4)	1.20	.80

PHILEXAFRICA '85, Lome, Togo, 11/16-24. Issued: 100fr, Nov. 4; 200fr, Nov. 16.

No. 1274 Ovptd. with Organization Emblem and "80e Anniversaire du Rotary International."

1985, Nov. 15   **Litho.**   *Perf. 15*

Souvenir Sheet

C541	A267	1000fr multi	2.50	1.25

Nos. 1254-1255, 1258 Ovptd. "10e ANNIVERSAIRE DE APOLLO-SOYUZ" in 1 or 2 lines

1985, Dec. 27   **Litho.**   *Perf. 15*

C542	A265	90fr multi	.35	.20
C543	A265	500fr multi	1.90	.90

Souvenir Sheet

C544	A265	1000fr multi	3.75	1.90

Nos. 1294-1295, 1297 Ovptd. "75e ANNIVERSAIRE DE LA MORT DE HENRI DUNANT FONDATEUR DE LA CROIX ROUGE" in 2 or 4 lines

1985, Dec. 27

C545	A270	400fr multi	1.50	.70
C546	A270	500fr multi	1.90	.90

Souvenir Sheet

C547	A270	1000fr multi	3.75	1.90

Statue of Liberty, Cent. — AP33

1986, Apr. 10   *Perf. 13*

C548	AP33	70fr Eiffel Tower	.40	.20
C549	AP33	90fr Statue of Liberty	.50	.25
C550	AP33	500fr Empire State Building	2.75	1.40
		Nos. C548-C550 (3)	3.65	1.85

Nos. 1237-1240 Ovptd. with AMERIPEX '86 Emblem

1986, May 22   *Perf. 11*

C551	A262	500fr multi	2.75	1.40
C552	A262	1000fr multi	5.50	2.75

Souvenir Sheets

Perf. 14

C553	A262	1000fr No. 1239	5.50	2.75
C554	A262	1000fr No. 1240	5.50	2.75

Air Africa, 25th Anniv. AP34

1986, Dec. 29   **Litho.**   *Perf. 12½x13*

C555	AP34	90fr multi	.50	.25

Konrad Adenauer (1876-1967) West German Chancellor — AP35

1987, July 15   **Litho.**   *Perf. 12½x13*

C556	AP35	120fr At podium	.70	.35
C557	AP35	500fr With Pres. Kennedy, 1962	2.75	1.40

Souvenir Sheet

Perf. 13x12½

C558	AP35	500fr Portrait, vert.	2.75	1.40

Berlin, 750th Anniv. AP36

Designs: 90fr, Wilhelm I (1781-1864) coin, Victory statue. 150fr, Frederick III (1831-1888) coin, Brandenburg Gate. 300fr, Wilhelm II (1882-1951) coin, Reichstag building. 750fr, Otto Leopold von Bismarck (1815-1898), first chancellor of the German empire, and Charlottenburg Palace.

1987, Aug. 31   **Litho.**   *Perf. 13½*

C559	AP36	90fr multi	.60	.30
C560	AP36	150fr multi	1.00	.50
C561	AP36	300fr multi	2.00	1.00
		Nos. C559-C561 (3)	3.60	1.80

Souvenir Sheet

C562	AP36	750fr multi	5.00	2.50

Nos. C506, 1258, 1273 and 1274 Overprinted in Black for Philatelic Exhibitions

a

b

c

d

Additional overprints appear on souvenir sheets away from stamps.

1988, Apr. 25　Litho.　Perf. 15
Souvenir Sheets

C563	AP26 (a)	500fr #C506	3.25	1.60
C564	A265 (b)	1000fr #1258	7.00	3.50
C565	A265 (c)	1000fr #1273	7.00	3.50
C566	A267 (d)	1000fr #1274	6.50	3.25
	Nos. C563-C566 (4)		23.75	11.85

AIR POST SEMI-POSTAL STAMPS

Nursery — SPAP1

Perf. 13½x12½
1942, June 22　Unwmk.　Photo.

CB1	SPAP1	1.50fr + 3.50fr green	.40
CB2	SPAP1	2fr + 6fr brown	.40

Native children's welfare fund.

Nos. CB1-CB2 were issued by the Vichy government in France, but were not placed on sale in Togo.

Colonial Education Fund
Common Design Type

1942, June 22　　　　Engr.

CB3	CD86a	1.20fr + 1.80fr blue & red	.40

No. CB3 was issued by the Vichy government in France, but was not placed on sale in Togo.

POSTAGE DUE STAMPS

Postage Due Stamps of Dahomey, 1914 Overprinted

1921　　Unwmk.　Perf. 14x13½

J1	D2	5c green	.50	.50
J2	D2	10c rose	.50	.50
J3	D2	15c gray	1.10	1.10
J4	D2	20c brown	2.00	2.00
J5	D2	30c blue	2.25	2.25
J6	D2	50c black	1.75	1.75
J7	D2	60c orange	1.75	1.75
J8	D2	1fr violet	3.25	3.25
	Nos. J1-J8 (8)		13.10	13.10

Cotton Field — D3

1925　　Typo.　　Unwmk.

J9	D3	2c blue & blk	.20	.20
J10	D3	4c dl red & blk	.20	.20
J11	D3	5c ol grn & blk	.20	.20
J12	D3	10c cerise & blk	.20	.20
J13	D3	15c orange & blk	.50	.50
J14	D3	20c red vio & blk	.35	.35
J15	D3	25c gray & blk	.65	.65
J16	D3	30c ocher & blk	.35	.35
J17	D3	50c brown & blk	.75	.75
J18	D3	60c green & blk	.75	.75
J19	D3	1fr dk vio & blk	.75	.75
	Nos. J9-J19 (11)		4.90	4.90

Type of 1925 Issue Surcharged

1927

J20	D3	2fr on 1fr rose red & vio	4.25	4.25
J21	D3	3fr on 1fr org brn, blk & ultra	4.25	4.25

Mask — D4

Carved Figures — D5

1941　　Engr.　　Perf. 13

J22	D4	5c brown black	.20	.20
J23	D4	10c yellow green	.20	.20
J24	D4	15c carmine	.20	.20
J25	D4	20c ultra	.20	.20
J26	D4	30c chestnut	.45	.45
J27	D4	50c olive green	1.25	1.25
J28	D4	60c violet	.45	.45
J29	D4	1fr light blue	.75	.75
J30	D4	2fr orange vermilion	.65	.65
J31	D4	3fr rose violet	.80	.80
	Nos. J22-J31 (10)		5.15	5.15

For type D4 without "RF," see Nos. J31A-J31F.

Type of 1941 Without "RF"
1942-44

J31A	D4	5c brown black	.20
J31B	D4	10c green & violet	.20
J31C	D4	15c car rose & brn	.20
J31D	D4	30c brown & black	.40

J31E	D4	2fr brn org & brn vio	.45
J31F	D4	3fr violet & green	.45
	Nos. J31A-J31F (6)		1.90

Nos. J31A-J31F were issued by the Vichy government in France, but were not placed on sale in Togo.

Catalogue values for unused stamps in this section, from this point to the end of the section, are for Never Hinged items.

1947

J32	D5	10c brt ultra	.20	.20
J33	D5	30c red	.20	.20
J34	D5	50c dp yellow grn	.20	.20
J35	D5	1fr chocolate	.40	.40
J36	D5	2fr carmine	.40	.40
J37	D5	3fr gray blk	.40	.40
J38	D5	4fr ultra	.60	.60
J39	D5	5fr sepia	.75	.75
J40	D5	10fr dp orange	.85	.85
J41	D5	20fr dk blue vio	1.25	1.25
	Nos. J32-J41 (10)		5.25	5.25

Republic

Konkomba Helmet
D6　　　　D7

1957　　Engr.　Perf. 14x13

J42	D6	1fr brt violet	.20	.20
J43	D6	2fr brt orange	.20	.20
J44	D6	3fr dk gray	.20	.20
J45	D6	4fr brt red	.20	.20
J46	D6	5fr ultra	.20	.20
J47	D6	10fr dp green	.30	.30
J48	D6	20fr dp claret	.45	.45
	Nos. J42-J48 (7)		1.75	1.75

1959　　　　Perf. 14x13

J49	D7	1fr orange brn	.20	.20
J50	D7	2fr lt blue grn	.20	.20
J51	D7	3fr orange	.20	.20
J52	D7	4fr blue	.20	.20
J53	D7	5fr lilac rose	.20	.20
J54	D7	10fr violet blue	.30	.30
J55	D7	20fr black	.50	.50
	Nos. J49-J55 (7)		1.80	1.80

Type of Regular Issue

Shells: 1fr, Conus papilionaceus. 2fr, Marginella faba. 3fr, Cypraea stercoraria. 4fr, Strombus latus. 5fr, Costate cockle (sea shell). 10fr, Cancellaria cancellata. 15fr, Cymbium pepo. 20fr, Tympanotomus radula.

1964-65　Unwmk.　Photo.　Perf. 14
Size: 20x25 ½mm

J56	A47	1fr gray grn & red brn ('65)	.20	.20
J57	A47	2fr tan & ol grn ('65)	.20	.20
J58	A47	3fr gray, brn & yel ('65)	.20	.20
J59	A47	4fr tan & multi ('65)	.20	.20
J60	A47	5fr sep, org & grn	.30	.30
J61	A47	10fr sl bl, brn & bis	.40	.40
J62	A47	15fr grn & brn	1.00	1.00
J63	A47	20fr sl, dk brn & yel	1.25	1.25
	Nos. J56-J63 (8)		3.75	3.75

Tomatoes — D8

1969-70　　Litho.　　Perf. 14

J64	D8	5fr yellow & multi	.20	.20
J65	D8	10fr blue & multi	.20	.20
J66	D8	15fr multi ('70)	.30	.30
J67	D8	20fr multi ('70)	.40	.40
	Nos. J64-J67 (4)		1.10	1.10

Market Type

1981, Mar. 8　Litho.　Perf. 14
Size: 23x32mm, 32x23mm

J68	A230	5fr Millet, vert.	.20	.20
J69	A230	10fr Packaged goods	.20	.20
J70	A230	25fr Chickens	.20	.20
J71	A230	50fr Ivory vendor	.25	.20
	Nos. J68-J71 (4)		.85	.80

OFFICIAL STAMPS

Catalogue values for unused stamps in this section are for never hinged items.

O1

1991?　　Litho.　Perf. 13

O1	O1	15fr multicolored	—
O2	O1	100fr multicolored	—
O3	O1	125fr multicolored	—
O4	O1	500fr multicolored	—

1991?

O5	O1	10fr multicolored	—
O6	O1	90fr yellow & multi	—

1991?

O7	O1	180fr ap grn & multi

1991

O8	O1	50fr yellow & multi	.20	.20
O9	O1	300fr ap grn & multi	1.00	1.00

The editors would like information on date of issue and stamps of other denominations. The catalogue numbers will change.

TOKELAU

'tō-kə-ˌlau

(Union Islands)

LOCATION — Pacific Ocean 300 miles north of Apia, Western Samoa
GOVT. — A dependency of New Zealand
AREA — 4 sq. mi.
POP. — 1,487 (1996)

The Tokelau islands consist of three atolls: Atafu, Nukunono and Fakaofo, which span 100 miles of ocean.

12 Pence = 1 Shilling
100 Cents = 1 Dollar (1967)

Catalogue values for all unused stamps in this country are for Never Hinged items.

Map and Scene on Atafu — A1

Nukunono Dwelling and Map — A2

Fakaofo Shore Line and Map — A3

Perf. 13½x13
948, June 22   Wmk. 253   Engr.
A1 ½p red brown & rose lilac   .20   .40
A2 1p dp green & orange brn   .25   .30
A3 2p deep ultra & green   .30   .30
Nos. 1-3 (3)   .75   1.00

For surcharges see Nos. 5, 9-11.

Coronation Issue

Queen Elizabeth
II — A3a

953, May 25   Photo.   Perf. 14x14½
A3a 3p brown   3.00   2.75

No. 1 Surcharged in Black:

Perf. 13½x13
956, Mar. 27   Engr.   Wmk. 253
A1 1sh on ½p   3.00   3.00

Postal-Fiscal Type of
New Zealand, 1950,
Surcharged

Wmk. 253
1966, Nov.   Typo.   Perf. 14
6 A109 6p light blue   .75   .35
7 A109 8p light green   1.40   .75
8 A109 2sh pink   2.50   1.90
Nos. 6-8 (3)   4.65   3.00

Nos. 1-3 Surcharged with New Value
and Dots Obliterating Old
Denomination

1967, July 10   Engr.   Perf. 13½x13
9 A2 1c on 1p   .25   .25
10 A3 2c on 2p   .60   .60
11 A1 10c on ½p   2.00   2.00
Nos. 9-11 (3)   2.85   2.85

The 1c and 2c surcharges include two dots,
the 10c surcharge has only one.

Postal Fiscal Type of
New Zealand, 1950,
Surcharged

1967, July 10   Typo.   Perf. 14
12 A109 3c light lilac   .30   .30
13 A109 5c light blue   .60   .60
14 A109 7c light green   1.00   1.00
15 A109 20c pink   2.10   2.10
Nos. 12-15 (4)   4.00   4.00

1877, British
Protectorate — A4

History of Tokelau: 10c, 1916, part of Gilbert
and Ellice Islands Colony. 15c, 1925, administration transferred to New Zealand. 20c, 1948,
New Zealand Territory.

Perf. 13x12½
1969, Aug. 8   Litho.   Wmk. 253
16 A4 5c ultra, yellow & blk   1.00   .40
17 A4 10c rose red, yel & blk   1.25   .75
18 A4 15c dull grn, yel & blk   1.50   1.25
19 A4 20c brown, yel & blk   2.25   1.50
Nos. 16-19 (4)   6.00   3.90

Nativity, by   Adoration, by
Federico Fiori   Correggio
A4a   A4b

1969, Oct. 1   Photo.   Perf. 13½x14
20 A4a 2c multicolored   .40   .40
Christmas.

Perf. 12½
1970, Oct. 1   Unwmk.   Litho.
21 A4b 2c multicolored   .40   .40
Christmas.

"Dolphin,"   Fan — A6
1765, Map of
Atafu — A5

Designs: 10c, "Pandora," 1791, and map of
Nukunono. 25c, "General Jackson," 1835, and
map of Fakaofo, horiz.

1970, Dec. 9   Unwmk.   Perf. 13½
22 A5 5c yellow & multi   .75   .65
23 A5 10c multicolored   1.75   1.25
24 A5 25c pink & multi   4.25   3.50
Nos. 22-24 (3)   6.75   5.40

Discovery of Tokelau Islands.

1971, Oct. 20   Litho.   Perf. 14
Native Handicrafts: 2c, Round vessel. 3c,
Hexagonal box. 5c, Shoulder bag. 10c, Handbag. 15c, Jewelry box with beads. 20c, Outrigger canoe model. 25c, Fish hooks.

25 A6 1c olive & multi   .20   .20
26 A6 2c red & multi   .20   .20
27 A6 3c dk violet & multi   .20   .20
28 A6 5c dull blue & multi   .20   .20
29 A6 10c dp orange & multi   .45   .25
30 A6 15c emerald & multi   .70   .45
31 A6 20c multicolored   .95   .60
32 A6 25c violet blue & multi   1.10   .75
Nos. 25-32 (8)   4.00   2.85

Windmill Pump,   Horny Coral — A8
Map of
Atafu — A7

South Pacific Commission Emblem and:
10c, Community well, map of Fakaofo. 15c,
Eradication of rhinoceros beetle, map of Nukunono. 20c, members.

1972, Sept. 6   Litho.   Perf. 14x13½
33 A7 5c lt blue grn & multi   .35   .25
34 A7 10c grnsh blue & multi   .75   .45
35 A7 15c lilac & multi   1.10   .60
36 A7 20c violet bl & multi   1.50   .95
Nos. 33-36 (4)   3.70   2.25

South Pacific Commission, 25th anniversary. On 15c, "PACIFIC" reads "PACFIC."

1973, Sept. 12   Litho.   Perf. 13x13½
37 A8 3c shown   1.25   1.10
38 A8 5c Soft coral   1.25   1.25
39 A8 15c Mushroom coral   2.00   2.10
40 A8 25c Staghorn coral   2.50   2.50
Nos. 37-40 (4)   7.00   6.95

Cowrie
(Cypraea
Mauritiana)
A9

Cowrie shells: 5c, Cypraea tigris. 15c,
Cypraea talpa. 25c, Cypraea argus.

1974, Nov. 13   Litho.   Perf. 14
41 A9 3c apple grn & multi   1.25   1.10
42 A9 5c dk blue & multi   1.50   1.10
43 A9 15c blue & multi   2.00   2.25
44 A9 25c green & multi   2.25   2.50
Nos. 41-44 (4)   7.00   6.95

Moorish Idol — A10

Fish: 10c, Long-nosed butterflyfish. 15c,
Lined butterflyfish. 25c, Red firefish.

1975, Nov. 19   Litho.   Perf. 14
45 A10 5c blue & multi   .30   .20
46 A10 10c brown & multi   .70   .40
47 A10 15c lilac & multi   1.10   .70
48 A10 25c multicolored   1.90   1.25
Nos. 45-48 (4)   4.00   2.55

Canoe
Making
A11

Designs: 2c, Reef fishing. 3c, Woman preparing pandanus leaves for weaving. 5c, Communal kitchen (umu). 9c, Wood carving. 20c,
Husking coconuts. 50c, Wash day. $1, Meal
time. 9c, 20c, 50c, $1, vertical.

1976, Oct. 27   Litho.   Perf. 14
49 A11 1c pink & multi   .40   .75
50 A11 2c multicolored   .30   1.00
51 A11 3c lt blue & multi   .25   .50
52 A11 5c yellow & multi   .30   .50
53 A11 9c bister & multi   .20   .60
54 A11 20c multicolored   .20   .50
55 A11 50c tan & multi   .25   .60
56 A11 $1 multicolored   .50   1.50
Nos. 49-56 (8)   2.40   5.95

1981, July 17   Perf. 15
49a A11 1c   .90   1.40
51a A11 3c   .90   1.40
52a A11 5c   .90   1.40
53a A11 9c   1.40   1.40
54a A11 20c   1.40   1.40
55a A11 50c   1.75   1.90
56a A11 $1   2.75   2.75
Nos. 49a-56a (7)   10.00 11.65

White
Tern — A12

Birds of Tokelau: 10c, Turnstone. 15c,
White-capped noddy. 30c, Brown noddy.

1977, Nov. 16   Litho.   Perf. 14½x15
57 A12 8c multicolored   .35   .25
58 A12 10c multicolored   .45   .30
59 A12 15c multicolored   .55   .45
60 A12 30c multicolored   1.25   1.00
Nos. 57-60 (4)   2.60   2.00

Westminster
Abbey — A13

10c, King Edward's Chair. 15c, Scepter,
Crown, Orb, Bible and Staff of State. 30c, Elizabeth II.

1978, June 28   Litho.   Perf. 14
61 A13 8c multicolored   .25   .25
62 A13 10c multicolored   .35   .35
63 A13 15c multicolored   .55   .55
64 A13 30c multicolored   1.00   1.00
Nos. 61-64 (4)   2.15   2.15

25th anniv. of coronation of Elizabeth II.

Canoe
Racing
A14

Designs: Various canoe races.

1978, Nov. 8   Litho.   Perf. 13½x14
65 A14 8c multicolored   .20   .20
66 A14 12c multicolored   .25   .25
67 A14 15c multicolored   .30   .30
68 A14 20c multicolored   .50   .50
Nos. 65-68 (4)   1.25   1.25

1979, Nov. 7   Photo.   Perf. 14
69 A14 10c Rugby   .20   .20
70 A14 15c Cricket   .40   .40
71 A14 20c Rugby, diff.   .40   .40
72 A14 30c Cricket, diff.   .50   .50
Nos. 69-72 (4)   1.50   1.50

1980, Nov. 5   Litho.   Perf. 13½
73 A14 10c Surfing   .20   .20
74 A14 20c Surfing, diff.   .25   .20
75 A14 30c Swimming   .35   .30
76 A14 50c Swimming, diff.   .45   .40
Nos. 73-76 (4)   1.25   1.10

1981, Nov. 4   Photo.   Perf. 14
77 A14 10c Pole vaulting, vert.   .20   .20
78 A14 20c Volleyball, vert.   .25   .20
79 A14 30c Running, vert.   .30   .25
80 A14 50c Volleyball, vert., diff.   .35   .35
Nos. 77-80 (4)   1.10   1.00

Wood   Octopus Lure
Carving — A15   Fishing — A16

1982, May 5   Litho.   Perf. 13½x13
81 A15 10s shown   .20   .20
82 A15 22s Bow-drilling sea
shells   .20   .20
83 A15 34s Bowl finishing   .30   .30
84 A15 60s Basket weaving   .60   .60
Nos. 81-84 (4)   1.30   1.30

1982, Nov. 3   Litho.   Perf. 14
Designs: Fishing Methods.

85 A16 5s shown   .20   .20
86 A16 18s Multiple-hook   .20   .20
87 A16 23s Ruvettus   .25   .25
88 A16 34s Netting flying fish   .35   .35
89 A16 63s Noose   .60   .60
90 A16 75s Bonito   .75   .75
Nos. 85-90 (6)   2.35   2.35

Outrigger Canoe A17

1983, May 4　Litho.　Perf. 13½x14
91	A17	5s shown	.20	.20
92	A17	18s Whale boat	.20	.20
93	A17	23s Aluminium whale boat	.20	.20
94	A17	34s Alia fishing boat	.25	.25
95	A17	63s Cargo ship	.50	.50
96	A17	75s Seaplane	.65	.65
		Nos. 91-96 (6)	2.00	2.00

Traditional Games A18

1983, Nov. 2　Litho.　Perf. 14
97	A18	5s Javelin throwing	.20	.20
98	A18	18s Tifaga string game	.20	.20
99	A18	23s Fire making	.20	.20
100	A18	34s Shell throwing	.25	.25
101	A18	63s Handball	.50	.50
102	A18	75s Mass wrestling	.65	.65
		Nos. 97-102 (6)	2.00	2.00

Planting, Harvesting Copra — A19

Local Fish — A20

Copra Industry: b, Husking, splitting. c, Drying, cutting. d, Bagging, weighing. e, Shipping. Continuous design.

1984, May 2　Litho.　Perf. 13½x13
103		Strip of 5	2.40	2.40
a.-e.		A19 48s any single	.45	.45

1984, Dec. 5　Litho.　Perf. 14½x14
104	A20	1c Manini	.20	.20
105	A20	2c Hahave	.20	.20
106	A20	5c Ululo	.20	.20
107	A20	9c Ume Ihu	.20	.20
108	A20	23c Lifilafi	.25	.25
109	A20	34c Fagamea	.35	.35
110	A20	50c Kakahi	.45	.45
111	A20	75c Palu Po	.70	.70
112	A20	$1 Mokoha	.90	.90
113	A20	$2 Hakula	1.75	1.75
		Nos. 104-113 (10)	5.20	5.20

Trees, Fruits and Herbs — A21

1985, June 26　Litho.　Perf. 13½
114	A21	5c Mati	.20	.20
115	A21	18c Nonu	.20	.20
116	A21	32c Ulu	.30	.30
117	A21	48c Fala	.50	.50
118	A21	60c Kanava	.60	.60
119	A21	75c Niu	.75	.75
		Nos. 114-119 (6)	2.55	2.55

Public Buildings and Churches A22

Designs: 5c, Administration Center, Atafu. 18c, Administration Center, Nukunonu. 32c, Administration Center, Fakaofo. 48c, Congregational Church, Atafu. 60c, Catholic Church, Nukunonu. 75c, Congregational Church, Fakaofo.

1985, Dec. 4
120	A22	5c multicolored	.20	.20
121	A22	18c multicolored	.20	.20
122	A22	32c multicolored	.30	.30
123	A22	48c multicolored	.50	.50
124	A22	60c multicolored	.55	.55
125	A22	75c multicolored	.70	.70
		Nos. 120-125 (6)	2.45	2.45

Hospitals and Schools A23

Designs: 5c, Atafu Hospital. 18c, St. Joseph's Hospital, Nukunonu. 32c, Fenuafala Hospital, Fakaofo. 48c, Matauala School, Atafu. 60c, Matiti School, Nukunonu. 75c, Fenuafala School, Fakaofo.

1986, May 7　　　　Perf. 13½
126	A23	5c multicolored	.20	.20
127	A23	18c multicolored	.20	.20
128	A23	32c multicolored	.30	.30
129	A23	48c multicolored	.50	.50
130	A23	60c multicolored	.55	.55
131	A23	75c multicolored	.70	.70
		Nos. 126-131 (6)	2.45	2.45

Fauna A24

1986, Dec. 3　Litho.　Perf. 14
132	A24	5c Coconut crab	.20	.20
133	A24	18c Pigs	.20	.20
134	A24	32c Chickens	.40	.40
135	A24	48c Turtles	.60	.60
136	A24	60c Goats	.70	.70
137	A24	75c Ducks	.90	.90
		Nos. 132-137 (6)	3.00	3.00

Flora A25

1987, May 6
138	A25	5c Gahu	.50	.50
139	A25	18c Puka	.70	.70
140	A25	32c Higano	.95	.95
141	A25	48c Tialetiale	1.25	1.25
142	A25	60c Gagie	1.50	1.50
143	A25	75c Puapua	1.60	1.60
		Nos. 138-143 (6)	6.50	6.50

Olympic Sports A26

1987, Dec. 2　Litho.　Perf. 14x14½
144	A26	5c Javelin	.35	.35
145	A26	18c Shot put	.60	.60
146	A26	32c Long jump	.80	.80
147	A26	48c Hurdles	.90	.90
148	A26	60c Running	1.10	1.10
149	A26	75c Wrestling	1.50	1.50
		Nos. 144-149 (6)	5.25	5.25

Australia Bicentennial, SYDPEX '88 — A27

Re-enactment of the arrival of the First Fleet in Sydney Harbor, Jan. 26, 1988 (in a continuous design): a, Ships in harbor, building (LL). b, Ships in harbor, tall ship (LR). c, Ships in harbor, Sydney Opera House. d, Bridge. e, North Sydney.

1988, July 30　Litho.　Perf. 13½x13
150		Strip of 5	7.00	7.00
a.-e.		A27 50c any single	1.40	1.40

Political Development A28

Designs: 5c, Transfer of administration from the New Zealand Department of Maori and Island Affairs to the Ministry of Foreign Affairs, 1975. 18c, The General Fono empowered as the decision-making body of Tokelau, 1977. 32c, 1st Visit of New Zealand's prime minister, 1985. 48c, 1st Visit of UN representatives, 1976. 60c, 1st Tokelau delegation to go to the UN, 1987. 75c, 1st Tokelau appointed to the office of Official Secretary, 1987.

1988, Aug. 10　　　　Perf. 14½
151	A28	5c multicolored	.20	.20
152	A28	18c multicolored	.25	.25
153	A28	32c multicolored	.50	.50
154	A28	48c multicolored	.70	.70
155	A28	60c multicolored	.90	.90
156	A28	75c multicolored	1.10	1.10
		Nos. 151-156 (6)	3.65	3.65

Island Christmas A29

Designs: 5c, Three Wise Men (Na Makoi). 20c, Holy family (He Tala). 40c, Escape into Egypt (Fakagagalo ki Aikupito). 60c, Christmas presents (Meaalofa Kilihimahi). 70c, Christ child (Pepe ko Iesu). $1, Christmas parade (Holo Tamilo).

1988, Dec. 7　Litho.　Perf. 13½
157	A29	5c multicolored	.20	.20
158	A29	20c multicolored	.20	.20
159	A29	40c multicolored	.45	.45
160	A29	60c multicolored	.65	.65
161	A29	70c multicolored	.75	.75
162	A29	$1 multicolored	1.10	1.10
		Nos. 157-162 (6)	3.35	3.35

Food Gathering A30

Fishing and gathering coconuts. Printed setenant in continuous designs.
No. 163: a, Launching outrigger canoe. b, Outrigger canoe and sailboat starboard side. c, Outrigger canoe and sailboat stern.
No. 164: a, Outrigger and sailboat port side. b, Islander carrying baskets of coconuts. c, Gathering coconuts from palm trees.

1989, June 28　Litho.　Perf. 14x14½
163		Strip of 3	2.50	2.50
a.-c.		A30 50c any single	.85	.85
164		Strip of 3	2.50	2.50
a.-c.		A30 50c any single	.85	.85

Women's Work and Leisure — A31

1990, May 2　Litho.　Perf. 14
165	A31	5c Weavers	.50	.4
166	A31	20c Washing clothes	.85	.7
167	A31	40c Resting among palm trees	1.25	1.1
168	A31	60c Weaving mat	1.50	1.6
169	A31	80c Weaving, diff.	2.25	2.4
170	A31	$1 Basket weaver	2.40	2.5
		Nos. 165-170 (6)	8.75	8.7

Souvenir Sheet

Penny Black, 150th Anniv. — A32

1990, May 3　Litho.　Perf. 11½
171	A32	$3 multicolored	11.50	11.5

Men's Handicrafts — A33

1990, Aug. 1　Photo.　Perf. 13
172	A33	50c shown	1.00	1.0
173	A33	50c Carving pots	1.00	1.0
174	A33	50c Tying rope on pot	1.00	1.0
a.		Strip of 3, #172-174	3.00	3.0
175	A33	50c Finishing pots	1.00	1.0
176	A33	50c Shaping a canoe	1.00	1.0
177	A33	50c Three men working	1.00	1.0
a.		Strip of 3, #175-177	3.00	3.0

1992 Summer Olympics, Barcelona — A34

1992, July 8　Litho.　Perf. 13½
178	A34	40c Swimming	.55	.55
179	A34	60c Long jump	.75	.75
180	A34	$1 Volleyball	1.60	1.60
181	A34	$1.80 Running	2.10	2.10
		Nos. 178-181 (4)	5.00	5.00

Discovery of America, 500th Anniv. A35

1992, Dec. 18
182	A35	40c Santa Maria	.75	.75
183	A35	60c Columbus	1.00	1.00
184	A35	$1.20 Columbus' fleet	2.25	2.25
185	A35	$1.80 Landfall	3.00	3.00
		Nos. 182-185 (4)	7.00	7.00

Coronation
of Queen
Elizabeth II,
40th Anniv.
A36

1993, July 8   Litho.   Perf. 13½
186 A36 25c Queen, early por-
        trait   .60   .60
187 A36 40c Prince Philip   .85   .85
188 A36 $1 Queen, recent por-
        trait   1.40 1.40
189 A36 $2 Queen & Prince
        Philip   2.40 2.40
      Nos. 186-189 (4)   5.25 5.25

Birds
A37

25c, Numenius tahitiensis. 40c, Phaethon
rubricauda. $1, Egretta sacra. $2, Pluvialis
fulva.

1993-94   Litho.   Perf. 13½
190 A37 25c multicolored   .60   .60
191 A37 40c multicolored   .90   .90
192 A37 $1 multicolored   1.50 1.50
193 A37 $2 multicolored   2.00 2.00
a.   Souvenir sheet of 4, #190-193,
      perf. 14x14½   5.00 5.00
      Nos. 190-193 (4)   5.00 5.00

No. 193a contains Hong Kong '94 emblem,
inscription in Chinese and English in sheet
margin and sold for $20 HK at the show.
      Issued: #190-193, 12/15/93; #193a, 2/1/94.

PHILAKOREA '94 — A38

1994, Aug. 16   Litho.   Perf. 12
194 A38 $2 White heron   2.50 2.50
a.   Souvenir sheet of 1   2.50 2.50

No. 194a has a continuous design.

Handicrafts
A39

1995   Litho.   Perf. 13½
195 A39 5c Outrigger canoe   .20   .20
196 A39 25c Plaited fan   .30   .30
197 A39 40c Plaited baskets   .45   .45
198 A39 50c Fishing box   .60   .60
199 A39 80c Water bottle   .90   .90
200 A39 $1 Fishing hook   1.10 1.10
201 A39 $2 Coconut gourds   2.25 2.25
202 A39 $5 Shell necklace   5.75 5.75
      Nos. 195-202 (8)   11.55 11.55

Souvenir Sheet

New Year 1995 (Year of the
Boar) — A40

Illustration reduced.

1995, Feb. 3   Litho.   Perf. 14
203 A40 $5 multicolored   6.50 6.50
a.   Ovptd. in sheet margin   6.50 6.50
b.   Ovptd. in sheet margin   7.50 7.50

No. 203a ovptd. in red in sheet margin
"POST'X 95 / 3-6 February / 1995 / AUCK-
LAND" surrounded by simulated perforations.
      No. 203b ovptd. in red in sheet margin with
Singapore '95 exhibition emblem.

Pacific
Imperial
Pigeon
A41

1995, Apr. 27   Litho.   Perf. 13½
204 A41 25c shown   .60   .60
205 A41 40c Full view   .90   .90
206 A41 $1 In tree, red berries 1.50 1.50
207 A41 $2 Nesting   2.75 2.75
      Nos. 204-207 (4)   5.75 5.75

World Wildlife Fund.

Reef
Fish — A42

Designs: 25c, Long nosed butterfly fish. 40c,
Emperor angelfish. $1, Moorish idol. $2, Lined
butterfly fish.
      $3, Red fire fish.

1995, Sept. 1   Litho.   Perf. 12
208 A42 25c multicolored   .40   .40
209 A42 40c multicolored   .60   .60
210 A42 $1 multicolored   1.50 1.50
211 A42 $2 multicolored   3.00 3.00
      Nos. 208-211 (4)   5.50 5.50

Souvenir Sheet
212 A42 $3 multicolored   4.25 4.25

No. 212 contains one 40x35mm stamp and
is inscribed in sheet margin for Singapore '95.

Butterflies — A43

Designs: 25c, Danaus plexippus. 40c, Precis villida samoensis. $1, Hypolimnas bolina.
$2, Euploea lewenii.

1995, Oct. 16   Litho.   Perf. 12
213 A43 25c multicolored   .60   .60
214 A43 40c multicolored   .75   .75
215 A43 $1 multicolored   1.90 1.90
216 A43 $2 multicolored   2.75 2.75
      Nos. 213-216 (4)   6.00 6.00

Sea Turtles
A44

1995, Nov. 27   Litho.   Perf. 12
217 A44 25c Hawksbill   .60   .60
218 A44 40c Leatherback   .75   .75
219 A44 $1 Green   1.90 1.90
220 A44 $2 Loggerhead   2.75 2.75
      Nos. 217-220 (4)   6.00 6.00

Souvenir Sheet
221 A44 $3 like #220   4.75 4.75

No. 221 contains one 50x40mm stamp and
is a continuous design.

Souvenir Sheet

New Year 1996 (Year of the
Rat) — A45

Illustration reduced.

1996, Feb. 19   Litho.   Perf. 12
222 A45 $3 Pacific rat   4.00 4.00
a.   Ovptd. in sheet margin   4.00 4.00
b.   Ovptd. in sheet margin   4.00 4.00

Overprinted in sheet margin with red exhibition emblem: No. 222a, CHINA '96; No. 222b,
TAIPEI '96.

Common Design Types
pictured following the introduction.

Queen Elizabeth II, 70th Birthday
Common Design Type

Various portraits of Queen, scenes of Tokelau: 40c, Nukunonu. $1, Atafu, silhouette of
island, boat. $1.25, Atafu, building on island,
boat. $2, Atafu, huts.
      $3, Queen wearing tiara, formal dress.

1996, Apr. 22   Litho.   Perf. 13½
223 CD354 40c multicolored   .50   .50
224 CD354 $1 multicolored   1.50 1.50
225 CD354 $1.25 multicolored   1.75 1.75
226 CD354 $2 multicolored   2.50 2.50
      Nos. 223-226 (4)   6.25 6.25

Souvenir Sheet
227 CD354 $3 multicolored   4.25 4.25

Dolphins — A46

1996, July 15   Litho.   Perf. 14
228 A46 40c Fraser's   1.00 1.00
229 A46 $1 Common   2.25 2.25
230 A46 $1.25 Striped   2.25 2.25
231 A46 $2 Spotted   3.25 3.25
      Nos. 228-231 (4)   8.75 8.75

Shells
A47

Designs: 40c, Cypraea talpa. $1, Cypraea
mauritiana. $1.25, Cypraea argus. $2,
Cypraea tigris.
      $3, Cypraea mauritana, diff.

1996, Oct. 16   Litho.   Perf. 12
232 A47 40c multicolored   .60   .60
233 A47 $1 multicolored   1.40 1.40
234 A47 $1.25 multicolored   1.75 1.75
235 A47 $2 multicolored   2.75 2.75
      Nos. 232-235 (4)   6.50 6.50

Souvenir Sheet
236 A47 $3 multicolored   4.25 4.25

No. 236 contains one 50x40mm stamp with
a continuous design.

Souvenir Sheet

New Year 1997 (Year of the
Ox) — A48

Illustration reduced.

1997, Feb. 12   Litho.   Perf. 15x14
237 A48 $2 multicolored   2.75 2.75
a.   Overprinted in gold   2.75 2.75
b.   Overprinted in red   2.75 2.75

No. 237a ovptd. in sheet margin HONG
KONG '97 / STAMP EXHIBITION" in English
and Chinese.
      No. 237b overprinted in sheet margin with
Pacific 97 emblem. Issued 5/29.

Humpback
Whale
A49

Designs: 40c, With school of fish. $1, Calf,
adult, young adult. $1.25, With mouth open,
school of fish. $2, Adult, calf.
      $3, Mouth, head of whale.

1997, May 29   Litho.   Perf. 12
238 A49 40c multicolored   .60   .60
239 A49 $1 multicolored   1.40 1.40
240 A49 $1.25 multicolored   1.75 1.75
241 A49 $2 multicolored   2.75 2.75
      Nos. 238-241 (4)   6.50 6.50

Souvenir Sheet
242 A49 $3 multicolored   4.25 4.25
a.   Ovptd. in sheet margin   4.25 4.25

No. 242a ovptd. in sheet margin, "AUPEX
'97 / 13-16 NOVEMBER / NZ NATIONAL /
STAMP EXHIBITION." Issued: 11/13.

South Pacific Commission, 50th
Anniv. — A50

1997, Sept. 17   Litho.   Perf. 14
243 A50 40c Church, waterfront   .50   .50
244 A50 $1 Beach, child   1.25 1.25
245 A50 $1.25 Island   1.60 1.60
246 A50 $2 Atoll   2.50 2.50
      Nos. 243-246 (4)   5.85 5.85

Year of the
Coral
Reef — A51

Designs: No. 247, Gorgonian coral, emperor
angelfish. No. 248, Soft coral. No. 249, Mushroom coral. No. 250, Staghorn coral. No. 251,
Staghorn coral, Moorish idol.

1997, Oct. 20   Litho.   Perf. 13½
247 A51 $1 multicolored   1.25 1.25
248 A51 $1 multicolored   1.25 1.25
249 A51 $1 multicolored   1.25 1.25
250 A51 $1 multicolored   1.25 1.25
251 A51 $1 multicolored   1.25 1.25
a.   Strip of 5, #247-251   6.50 6.50

Souvenir Sheet

New Year 1998 (Year of the Tiger) — A52

Illustration reduced.

1998, Jan. 28   Litho.   Perf. 14x14½
252 A52 $2 multicolored   2.25 2.25
a.   Ovptd. in sheet margin   2.25 2.25

No. 252a overprinted in sheet margin with emblem of Singpex '98 Stamp Exhibition, Singapore.

Diana, Princess of Wales (1961-97)
Common Design Type

Designs: a, Wearing high-collared ruffled blouse. b, Wearing red beret. c, Holding yellow flowers. d, Wearing pink & yellow jacket.

1998, May 15   Litho.   Perf. 14½x14
253 CD355 $1 Sheet of 4, #a.-d.   5.00 5.00

No. 253 sold for $4 + 50c, with surtax from international sales being donated to the Princess Diana Memorial Fund and surtax from national sales being donated to designated local charity.

Souvenir Sheet

First Stamps of Tokelau, 50th Anniv. — A53

Designs: a, #3. b. #1. c, #2.

1998, June 22   Litho.   Perf. 14½
254 A53 $1 Sheet of 3, #a.-c.   3.00 3.00

Beetles A54

Designs: 40c, Oryctes rhinoceros. $1, Tribolium castaneum. $1.25, Coccinella repanda. $2, Amarygmus hyorophiloides. $3, Coccinella repanda, diff.

1998, Aug. 24   Litho.   Perf. 14
255 A54 40c multicolored   .40 .40
256 A54 $1 multicolored   1.00 1.00
257 A54 $1.25 multicolored   1.25 1.25
258 A54 $2 multicolored   1.90 1.90
   Nos. 255-258 (4)   4.55 4.55
Souvenir Sheet
259 A54 $3 multicolored   3.00 3.00

Tropical Flowers A55

40c, Ipomoea pes-caprae. $1, Ipomoea littoralis. $1.25, Scaevola taccada. $2, Thespesia populnea.

1998, Nov. 19   Litho.   Perf. 14
260 A55 40c multicolored   .40 .40
261 A55 $1 multicolored   1.00 1.00
262 A55 $1.25 multicolored   1.25 1.25
263 A55 $2 multicolored   2.00 2.00
   Nos. 260-263 (4)   4.65 4.65
Souvenir Sheet

New Year 1999 (Year of the Rabbit) — A56

Illustration reduced.

1999, Feb. 16   Litho.   Perf. 14
264 A56 $3 multicolored   3.25 3.25
a.   Ovptd. in sheet margin   3.25 3.25

No. 264a overprinted in sheet margin with emblem of IBRA '99 Intl. Stamp Exhibtion, Nuremburg. Issued: 4/27.

Souvenir Sheet

Australia '99, World Stamp Exhibition — A57

Illustration reduced.

1999, Mar. 19
265 A57 $3 HMS Pandora   3.25 3.25

First Manned Moon Landing, 30th Anniv. — A58

Designs: 25c, Lift-off. 50c, Separation of stages. 75c, Aldrin deploying instruments on moon. $1, Planting flag. $1.25, Returning to Earth. $2, Splashdown.
$3, Apollo 11, Moon, Earth.

Perf. 13½x13¼
1999, Aug. 31   Litho.
266 A58 25c multicolored   .25 .25
267 A58 50c multicolored   .50 .50
268 A58 75c multicolored   .75 .75
269 A58 $1 multicolored   1.00 1.00
270 A58 $1.25 multicolored   1.25 1.25
271 A58 $2 multicolored   2.00 2.00
   Nos. 266-271 (6)   5.75 5.75
Souvenir Sheet
272 A58 $3 multicolored   3.00 3.00

Crabs A59

1999   Litho.   Perf. 14¼x14½
273 A59 40c Coconut   .40 .40
274 A59 $1 Ghost   1.00 1.00
275 A59 $1.25 Land hermit   1.25 1.25
276 A59 $2 Purple hermit   2.00 2.00
   Nos. 273-276 (4)   4.65 4.65
Souvenir Sheet
277 A59 $3 Ghost, diff.   3.00 3.00

Black-naped Tern — A60

Designs: 40c, Chick and egg. $1, On nest. $1.25, Pair near water. $2, Pair in flight.

Perf. 13½x14
1999, Dec. 31   Litho.   Unwmk.
278-281 A60 Set of 4   4.50 4.50

Souvenir Sheet

New Year 2000 (Year of the Dragon) — A61

Illustration reduced.

2000   Litho.   Perf. 14x14¼
282 A61 $3 multi   3.00 3.00
a.   Overprinted in sheet margin   3.00 3.00

No. 282a overpritned in sheet margin with emblem "Bangkok 2000", "World Youth Stamp Exhibition" and Thai text.

Souvenir Sheet

The Stamp Show 2000, London — A62

Illustration reduced.

Unwmk.
2000, May 22   Litho.   Perf. 14
283 A62 $6 multi   5.50 5.50

Queen Mother, 100th Birthday — A63

Various photos. Denominations 40c, $1.20, $1.80, $3.

Perf. 14½x14¼
2000, Aug. 4   **Wmk. 373**
284-287 A63 Set of 4   5.25 5.25

Lizards A64

Designs: 40c, Gehyra oceanica. $1, Lepidodactylus lugubris. $1.25, Gehyra mutilata. $2, Emoia cyanura.

2001, Feb. 1   Litho.   Perf. 14
288-291 A64 Set of 4   4.00 4.00

Souvenir Sheet

New Year 2001 (Year of the Snake) — A65

2001, Feb. 1
292 A65 $3 multi   2.60 2.6
a.   With gold ovpt. in margin   2.60 2.6

Overprint in margin on No. 292a is for Hong Kong 2001 Stamp Exhibition.

Hippocampus Histrix — A66

Various views of seahorses. Denominations 40c, $1, $1.25, $2.

2001, Aug. 23   Litho.   Perf. 14
293-296 A66   Set of 4   4.00 4.00
Souvenir Sheet
297 A66 $3 multi   2.50 2.50

Island Scenery A67

Designs: 40c, Sky over Atafu. $1, Waters of Fakaofo. $2, Sunrise over Nukunonu village $2.50, Ocean, Nukunonu.

Unwmk.
2001, Dec. 17   Litho.   Perf. 14
298-301 A67   Set of 4   4.75 4.75

Reign Of Queen Elizabeth II, 50th Anniv. Issue
Common Design Type

Designs: Nos. 302, 306a, 40c, Princess Elizabeth, Prince Philip on honeymoon, 1947. Nos. 303, 306b, $1, Wearing purple hat. Nos. 304, 306c, $1.25, Holding Prince Charles, 1948. Nos. 305, 306d, $2, In 1996. No. 306e, $3, 1955 portrait by Annigoni (38x50mm).

Perf. 14¼x14½, 13¾ (#306e)
2002, Feb. 6   Litho.   Wmk. 373
With Gold Frames
302-305 CD360   Set of 4   4.00 4.00
Souvenir Sheet
Without Gold Frames
306 CD360   Sheet of 5, #a-e   6.50 6.50

Souvenir Sheet

New Year 2002 (Year of the Horse) — A68

'002, Feb. 12   Litho.   *Perf. 14*
07	A68	$4 multi	3.25 3.25
a.	As #307, with gold ovpt. in margin		3.25 3.25

No. 307a was issued 2/22 and has overprint ʳeading "STAMPEX 2002 / HONG KONG / 22-4 FEBRUARY 2002."

Worldwide Fund for Nature (WWF) — A69

Various views of Pelagic thresher shark: ₀c, $1, $2, $2.50.

'002, July 2   Litho.   *Perf. 14¼*
₀08-311	A69	Set of 4	5.75 5.75

Queen Mother Elizabeth (1900-2002)
Common Design Type

Designs: 40c, Wearing broad-brimmed hat ₍black and white photograph). $2, Wearing ₋lue hat.
No. 314: a, $2.50, Wearing hat (black and ₋hite photograph). b, $4, Wearing purple hat.

Wmk. 373
'002, Aug. 5   Litho.   *Perf. 14¼*
With Purple Frames
₋12-313	CD361	Set of 2	2.25 2.25

Souvenir Sheet
Without Purple Frames
Perf. 14¼x14¼
₋14	CD361	Sheet of 2, #a-b	6.00 6.00

New Zealand Navy Ships That Have Stopped at Tokelau — A70

Designs: 40c, HMNZS Kaniere. $1, HMNZS Endeavour. $2, HMNZS Wellington. $2.50, HMNZS Monowai.

2002, Dec. Litho. Unwmk. *Perf. 14*
₋315-318	A70	Set of 4	6.25 6.25

Souvenir Sheet

New Year 2003 (Year of the Ram) — A71

2003, Feb. 3
319	A71	$4 multi	4.50 4.50
a.	With Bangkok 2003 overprint in gold in margin		4.75 4.75

Issued: No. 319a, 10/13.

Coronation of Queen Elizabeth II, 50th Anniv.
Common Design Type

Designs: Nos. 320, 322a, $2.50, Queen with maids of honor. Nos. 321, 322b, $4, Queen with Prince Philip.

Perf. 14¼x14½
2003, June 2   Litho.   Wmk. 373
Vignettes Framed, Red Background
320-321	CD363	Set of 2	7.50 7.50

Souvenir Sheet
Vignettes Without Frame, Purple Panel
322	CD363	Sheet of 2, #a-b	7.50 7.50

Prince William, 21st Birthday
Common Design Type

No. 323: a, Color photograph at right. b, Color photograph at left.

Wmk. 373
2003, June 21   Litho.   *Perf. 14¼*
323		Horiz. pair	5.50 5.50
a.	CD364 $1.50 multi		1.75 1.75
b.	CD364 $3 multi		3.75 3.75

Souvenir Sheet

Welpex 2003 Stamp Show, Wellington, New Zealand — A72

Unwmk.
2003, Nov. 7   Litho.   *Perf. 14*
324	A72	$4 multi	5.00 5.00

Souvenir Sheet

New Year 2004 (Year of the Monkey) — A73

2004   Litho. with Foil Application
325	A73	$4 multi	5.50 5.50
a.	With 2004 Hong Kong Stamp Expo emblem in gold in margin		5.50 5.50

Issued: No. 325, 1/22; No. 325a, 1/28.

TONGA
ˈtäŋ-gə

LOCATION — A group of islands in the south Pacific Ocean, south of Samoa
GOVT. — Kingdom in British Commonwealth
AREA — 289 sq. mi.
POP. — 109,082 (1999 est.)
CAPITAL — Nuku'alofa

This group, also known as the Friendly Islands, became a British Protectorate in 1900 under the Anglo-German Agreement of 1899. On June 4, 1970, the United Kingdom ceased to have any responsibility for the external relations of Tonga.

12 Pence = 1 Shilling
20 Shillings = 1 Pound
100 Seniti = 1 Pa'anga (1967)

Catalogue values for unused stamps in this country are for **Never Hinged** items, beginning with Scott 87 in the regular postage section, Scott B1 in the semipostal section, Scott C1 in the air post section Scott CE1 in the air post special delivery section, Scott CO1 in the air post official section, and Scott O11 in the officials section.

Watermarks

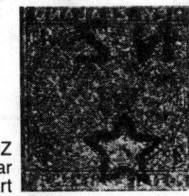

Wmk. 62 — NZ and Small Star Wide Apart

Wmk. 79 — Turtles

King George I — A1

Perf. 12x11½
1886-92   Typo.   Wmk. 62
1	A1	1p car rose ('87)	11.50	4.00
a.	Perf. 12½		450.00	7.00
b.	Perf. 12½x10			
2	A1	2p violet ('87)	32.50	3.50
a.	Perf. 12½		57.50	14.00
3	A1	6p ultra ('88)	57.50	2.75
a.	Perf. 12½		67.50	4.00
4	A1	6p org yel ('92)	18.00	30.00
5	A1	1sh blue grn ('88)	62.50	7.25
a.	Perf. 12½		110.00	4.50
b.	Half used as 6p on cover		182.00	47.50
		Nos. 1-5 (5)	182.00	47.50

For surcharges and overprints see #6-9, 24.

Nos. 1 and 2 Surcharged or Overprinted in Black:

a		b

1891, Nov. 10   *Perf. 12x11½*
6	A1(a)	4p on 1p car rose	3.50	12.50
a.	No period after "PENCE"		57.50	125.00
7	A1(a)	8p on 2p violet	40.00	100.00

1891, Nov. 23   *Perf. 12½*
Two types of overprint:
I - Solid stars, rays pointed and short.
II - Open-center stars, rays blunt and long.
8	A1(b)	1p car rose (I)	5.00	57.50
a.	Overprinted with 3 stars (I)		375.00	
b.	Overprinted with 4 stars (I)		475.00	
c.	Overprinted with 5 stars (I)		750.00	
d.	Type II		50.00	57.50
e.	Perf. 12x11½ (I or II)		350.00	
9	A1(b)	2p violet (I)	80.00	42.50
a.	Type II		80.00	42.50
b.	Perf. 12x11½ (I or II)		425.00	

Coat of Arms A4	George I A5

1892, Nov. 10   Typo.   *Perf. 12x11½*
10	A4	1p rose	14.00	19.00
a.	Diagonal half used as ½p on cover		975.00	
11	A5	2p olive gray	18.00	18.00
12	A4	4p red brown	55.00	80.00
13	A5	8p violet	62.50	200.00
14	A5	1sh brown	90.00	125.00
		Nos. 10-14 (5)	239.50	442.00

For surcharges and overprints see Nos. 15-23, 25-28, 36-37, O1-O10.

Types A4 and A5 Surcharged in Carmine or Black:

c	d

f

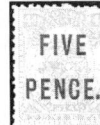

1893
15	A4	½p on 1p ultra (C)	26.00	30.00
a.	Surcharge omitted			
16	A4	½p on 1p ultra	50.00	55.00
17	A5	2½p on 2p blue grn (C)	16.00	13.50
18	A5	2½p on 2p blue grn	19.00	19.00
a.	Double surcharge		2,000.	
19	A4	5p on 4p org yel (C)	4.50	7.50
20	A5	7½p on 8p rose (C)	27.50	85.00
		Nos. 15-20 (6)	143.00	210.00

Stamps of 1886-92 Surcharged in Blue or Black:

g	h

1894
21	A4	½p on 4p red brn (Bl)	2.25	8.00
a.	"SURCHARCE"		10.00	22.50
b.	Pair, one without surcharge			
c.	"HALF PENNY" omitted			
22	A5	½p on 1sh brn (Bk)	2.75	12.50
a.	Double surcharge		310.00	
b.	"SURCHARCE"		11.50	45.00
c.	As "b," double surcharge		1,000.	
23	A5	2½p on 8p vio (Bk)	5.75	9.25
a.	No period after "SURCHARGE"		35.00	62.50
24	A1	2½p on 1sh blue grn (Bk)	62.50	27.50
a.	No period after "SURCHARGE"		200.00	
b.	Perf. 12x11½		17.50	47.50
		Nos. 21-24 (4)	73.25	57.25

Type A5 with Same Surcharges in Carmine
1895   Unwmk.
25	A5(g)	1p on 2p lt blue	50.00	25.00
26	A5(h)	1½p on 2p lt blue, perf. 12x11	55.00	32.50
a.	Perf. 12		70.00	32.50
27	A5(h)	2½p on 2p lt blue	45.00	50.00
b.	Without period		250.00	250.00
28	A5(h)	7½p on 2p lt bl, perf. 12x11	70.00	50.00
a.	Perf. 12		450.00	
		Nos. 25-28 (4)	220.00	157.50

King George II — A13

1895, Aug. 16   *Perf. 12*
29	A13	1p gray green	22.50	30.00
a.	Diagonal half used as ½p on cover		850.00	
b.	Horiz. pair, imperf. btwn.		6,900.	
30	A13	2½p dull rose	22.50	15.00
31	A13	5p brt blue, perf. 12x11	26.00	57.50
a.	Perf. 12		25.00	57.50
b.	Perf. 11		400.00	
32	A13	7½p yellow	35.00	55.00
		Nos. 29-32 (4)	106.00	157.50

Type A13 Redrawn and Surcharged "g" or "h" in Black

33	A13(g)	½p on 2½p red	35.00	37.50
a.		"SURCHARCE"	80.00	
b.		Period after "Postage"	85.00	
34	A13(g)	1p on 2½p red	70.00	45.00
a.		Period after "Postage"	125.00	
35	A13(h)	7½p on 2½p red	62.50	70.00
a.		Period after "Postage"	110.00	
	Nos. 33-35 (3)		167.50	152.50

Nos. 26 and 28 with Additional Surcharge in Violet and Black

Half Penny– *VAEUAOLENI*

1896, May   Perf. 12x11

36	A5	½p on 1½p on 2p	500.00	
a.		Tongan surch. reading up	475.00	475.00
b.		Perf. 12	475.00	475.00
c.		As "a," perf. 12	500.00	500.00
d.		"Haalf"	2,100.	
37	A5	½p on 7½p on 2p	97.50	125.00
a.		"Half penny" inverted	2,100.	
b.		"Half penny" double		
c.		Tongan surch. reading up	97.50	125.00
d.		Tongan surcharge as "c" and double		
e.		"Hafl Penny"	1,750.	1,800.
f.		"Hafl" only	3,750.	
g.		"Hwlf"		
h.		Periods instead of hyphens after words	1,000.	
j.		Perf. 12	925.00	

Coat of Arms — A17

Ovava Tree — A18

George II — A19

Prehistoric Trilithon, Tongatabu — A20

Breadfruit A21

Coral Formations A22

View of Haabai A23

Red-breasted Musk Parrot — A24

View of Vavau — A25

Two types of 2p:
I - Top of sword hilt shows above "2."
II - No hilt shows.

Wmk. 79 Sideways

1897-1934		Engr.	Perf. 14	
38	A17	½p dark blue	4.75	3.00
39	A17	½p green ('34)	1.10	1.40
40	A18	1p dp red & blk	.90	.90
41	A19	2p bis & sep (I)	18.00	6.25
a.		bister & gray, type II	35.00	3.75
42	A19	2½p lt blue & blk	7.00	1.60
a.		"½" without fraction bar	110.00	75.00
43	A20	3p ol grn & blk	4.00	9.75
44	A21	4p dull vio & grn	4.25	4.50
45	A19	5p orange & blk	35.00	16.00
46	A22	6p red	15.00	7.00
47	A19	7½p green & blk	18.00	26.00
a.		Center inverted	5,500.	
48	A19	10p carmine & blk	50.00	55.00
49	A19	1sh red brn & blk	16.00	8.50
50	A23	2sh dk ultra & blk	70.00	75.00
51	A24	2sh6p dk violet	57.50	35.00
52	A25	5sh dull red & blk	55.00	55.00
	Nos. 38-52 (15)		356.50	304.90

See Nos. 73-74, 77-78, 80-81. For surcharges see Nos. 63-69.

Stamp of 1897 Overprinted in Black

1899, June 1

53	A18	1p red & black	32.50	62.50
a.		"1889" instead of "1899"	225.00	400.00
b.		Comma omitted after June		
c.		Double overprint		

Marriage of George II to Lavinia, June 1, 1899. The letters "T L" are the initials of Taufa'ahau, the King's family name, and Lavinia.

Queen Salote — A26

Dies of 2p:
Die I - Ball of "2" smaller.
Die II - Ball of "2" larger. "U" has spur at left.

1920-35		Engr.	Wmk. 79	
54	A26	1½p gray blk ('35)	.55	3.50
55	A26	2p violet & sepia	9.75	15.00
56	A26	2p dl vio & blk (I) ('24)	9.75	2.75
a.		Die II	5.00	7.50
57	A26	2½p blue & black	5.50	45.00
58	A26	2½p ultra ('34)	2.25	1.10
59	A26	5p red org & blk	3.75	5.50
60	A26	7½p green & blk	2.00	2.00
61	A26	10p carmine & blk	2.90	5.50
62	A26	1sh red brown & blk	1.40	2.90
	Nos. 54-62 (9)		37.85	83.25

See Nos. 75-76, 79.

Stamps of 1897 Surcharged in Dark Blue or Red

1923

63	A19	2p on 5p org & blk	1.10	1.00
64	A19	2p on 7½p grn & blk	20.00	32.50
65	A19	2p on 10p car & blk	12.50	57.50
66	A19	2p on 1sh red brn & blk	55.00	25.00

67	A23	2p on 2sh ultra & blk (R)	22.50	22.50
68	A24	2p on 2sh6p dk vio (R)	35.00	7.50
69	A25	2p on 5sh dull red & blk (R)	16.00	16.00
	Nos. 63-69 (7)		162.10	162.00

Queen Salote — A27

Inscribed "1918-1938"

1938, Oct. 12			Perf. 14	
70	A27	1p carmine & blk	.50	4.00
71	A27	2p violet & blk	4.50	3.00
72	A27	2½p ultra & blk	4.50	3.75
	Nos. 70-72 (3)		9.50	10.75
	Set, never hinged		16.00	

Accession of Queen Salote Tupou, 20th anniv.
See Nos. 82-86.

Types of 1897-1920

1942		Engr.	Wmk. 4	

Die III of 2p:
Foot of "2" longer than in Die II, extending beyond curve of loop.

73	A17	½p green	.30	2.75
74	A18	1p scarlet & blk	.75	2.75
75	A26	2p dull vio & blk (II)	2.10	3.00
a.		Die III	4.25	8.25
76	A26	2½p ultra	.65	2.00
77	A20	3p green & black	.30	3.75
78	A22	6p orange red	1.40	2.25
79	A26	1sh red brown & gray blk	1.25	3.50
80	A24	2sh6p dk violet	19.00	22.50
81	A25	5sh dull red & brn blk	13.00	50.00
	Nos. 73-81 (9)		38.75	92.50
	Set, never hinged		55.00	

Type of 1938, Inscribed "1918-1943"

1944, Jan. 25				
82	A27	1p rose car & blk	.20	1.10
83	A27	2p purple & blk	.20	1.10
84	A27	3p dk yel grn & blk	.20	1.10
85	A27	6p red orange & blk	.25	2.00
86	A27	1sh dk red brn & blk	.25	2.00
	Nos. 82-86 (5)		1.10	7.30
	Set, never hinged		1.75	

25th anniv. of the accession of Queen Salote.

Catalogue values for unused stamps in this section, from this point to the end of the section, are for Never Hinged items.

UPU Issue
Common Design Types
Engr.; Name Typo. on 3p, 6p
Perf. 13½, 11x11½

1949, Oct. 10			Wmk. 4	
87	CD306	2½p ultra	.40	.90
88	CD307	3p deep olive	1.60	3.25
89	CD308	6p deep carmine	.55	.55
90	CD309	1sh red brown	.55	.55
	Nos. 87-90 (4)		3.10	5.25

Common Design Types pictured following the introduction.

A28

A29

Queen Salote — A30

1950, Nov. 1		Photo.	Perf. 12	
91	A28	1p cerise	1.00	2.
92	A29	5p green	1.00	2.
93	A30	1sh violet	1.00	3.0
	Nos. 91-93 (3)		3.00	7.7

50th anniv. of the birth of Queen Salote.

Map and Island Scene — A31

Badges and Royal Palace A32

2½p, Queen Salote & coastal scene. 3p, Queen Salote & ship "Bellona." 5p, Flag of Tonga, island view. 1sh, Arms of Tonga & Great Britain.

Perf. 13x13½ (1p), 13½x13, 12½ (3p)

1951, July 2		Engr.	Wmk. 4	
94	A31	½p deep green	.30	3.0
95	A32	1p carmine & black	.30	3.0
96	A32	2½p choc & dp grn	.60	3.0
97	A31	3p ultra & org yel	1.00	3.0
98	A32	5p dp green & car	1.25	1.10
99	A32	1sh purple & orange	2.50	1.10
	Nos. 94-99 (6)		5.95	14.20

50th anniv. of the treaty of friendship between Tonga and Great Britain.

Royal Palace, Nukualofa A33

Map of Tonga Islands — A34

Designs: 1½p, Fisherman. 2p, Canoe and schooners. 3p, Swallows' Cave, Vavau. 3½p, Map of Tongatabu. 4p, Vavau harbor. 5p, Post Office, Nukualofa. 6p, Fuaamotu airport. 8p, Wharf, Nukualofa. 2sh, Beach at Lifuka, Haapai. 5sh, Mutiny on the Bounty. 10sh, Queen Salote. £1, Arms of Tonga.

Perf. 11½x11, 11x11½

1953, July 1			Wmk. 79	
100	A33	1p chocolate & blk	.30	.20
101	A33	1½p emerald & ultra	.30	.20
102	A33	2p black & aqua	.30	.20
103	A34	3p dk grn & ultra	.30	.20
104	A33	3½p carmine & yel	.30	.20
105	A33	4p rose car & yel	.30	.20
106	A33	5p choc & ultra	.30	.20
107	A33	6p black & dp ultra	.40	.20

08	A33	8p purple & emer	.45	.25
09	A34	1sh black & ultra	.75	.40
10	A33	2sh choc & ol grn	1.60	.90
11	A33	5sh purple & yel	4.00	2.50
12	A34	10sh black & yellow	9.00	5.25
13	A34	£1 ultra, car & yel	18.00	10.50
		Nos. 100-113 (14)	36.30	21.40

For surcharges and overprints see Nos. 19-126, 158-174, 182-202, 210-215, 218-21, 237, 269-273, C34-C39, C47-C54, C87-91, CO4-CO6, CO11-CO20, CO27-CO43.

Whaling Ship and Longboat A35

1p, Stamp of 1886. 4p, Post Office, Cusoms & Treasury Building & Queen Salote. 5p, Diesel-driven ship Aoniu. 1sh, Plane over Tongatabu.

1961, Dec. 1 Photo. Perf. 14½x13½

14	A35	1p brn org & car rose	.30	.20
15	A35	2p ultra	.30	.20
16	A35	4p bright green	.30	.20
17	A35	5p purple	.50	.30
18	A35	1sh red brown	1.00	.60
		Nos. 114-118 (5)	2.40	1.50

75th anniversary of postal service.
For surcharges & overprints see Nos. 146-151, 16-221, C16-C21, C55-C57, CO1-CO3, CO9-CO10.

Stamps of 1953 and 1961 Overprinted in Red: "1862 / TAU'ATAINA / EMANCIPATION / 1962"

Perf. 11½x11, 11x11½, 14½x13

Engr.; Photo. (4p)

			Wmk. 79	
1962, Feb. 7				
19	A33	1p choc & blk	.20	.60
20	A35	4p brt green	.20	.65
21	A33	5p choc & ultra	.20	.65
22	A33	6p black & dp ultra	.20	1.00
23	A33	8p purple & emer	.40	1.50
24	A34	1sh black & ultra	.25	.75
25	A34	2sh on 3p dk grn &	.45	3.50
26	A33	5sh purple & yellow	5.50	3.50
		Nos. 119-126 (8)	7.40	12.15

Cent. of emancipation. See Nos. CO1-CO6.

Freedom from Hunger Issue
Common Design Type with Portrait of Queen Salote

Perf. 14x14½

1963, June 4		**Wmk. 79**	**Photo.**	
27	CD314	11p ultra	.70	.35

Coat of Arms, ¼ Koula Coin, Reverse A36

Designs: 2p, 9p, 2sh, Queen Salote (head), ¼-koula coin, obverse.

Litho.; Embossed on Gilt Foil

1963, July 15		**Unwmk.**	**Die Cut**	
		Diameter: 40mm		
28	A36	1p dp carmine	.20	.20
29	A36	2p violet blue	.20	.20
30	A36	6p dp green	.25	.25
31	A36	9p magenta	.30	.30
32	A36	1sh6p violet	.65	.65
33	A36	2sh emerald	.70	.70
		Nos. 128-133,C1-C6,C07 (13)	11.95	11.95

1st gold coinage of Polynesia. Backed with paper inscribed in salmon-colored alternating rows: "TONGA" and "THE FRIENDLY ISLANDS" in multiple.
For surcharges see #140-145, C11-C15, CO8.

Red Cross Centenary Issue
Common Design Type with Portrait of Queen Salote

Wmk. 79

1963, Sept. 2		**Litho.**	**Perf. 13**	
34	CD315	2p black & red	.25	.20
35	CD315	11p ultra & red	.75	1.00

Queen Salote on ¼-Koula Coin A37

Litho.; Embossed on Gilt Foil

1964, Oct. 19		**Unwmk.**	**Die Cut**	
136	A37	3p pink	.20	.20
137	A37	9p light blue	.20	.20
138	A37	2sh yellow green	.35	.35
139	A37	5sh pale lilac	.90	.90
		Nos. 136-139,C7-C10 (8)	3.85	3.85

Pan-Pacific and Southeast Asia Women's Association Conf., Nukualofa, Aug. 1964. See note on paper backing after No. 133.
For surcharges & overprints see #152-157, 263-268.

Nos. 128-133 Surcharged in Red, White or Black

1965, Mar. 18				
140	A36	1sh3p on 1sh6p (R)	.20	.20
141	A36	1sh9p on 9p (W)	.20	.20
142	A36	2sh6p on 6p (R)	.25	.25
143	A36	5sh on 1p	18.00	18.00
144	A36	5sh on 2p	3.00	3.00
145	A36	5sh on 2sh	.75	.75
		Nos. 140-145,C11-C15,CO8 (12)	65.85	65.85

Nos. 114-115 Overprinted and Surcharged in Purple or Red

Perf. 14½x13½

1966, June 18		**Photo.**	**Wmk. 79**	
146	A35	1p (P)	.20	.20
147	A35	3p on 1p (P)	.20	.20
148	A35	6p on 2p (R)	.20	.20
149	A35	1sh3p on 2p (R)	.20	.20
150	A35	2sh on 2p (R)	.35	.20
151	A35	3sh on 2p (R)	.35	.20
		Nos. 146-151,C16-C21,CO9-CO10 (14)	5.55	3.10

Centenary of Tupou College and of secondary eucation.

Nos. 136-137 Overprinted and Surcharged in Silver on Black or Ultramarine

Illustration reduced.

Litho.; Embossed on Gilt Foil

1966, Dec. 16		**Unwmk.**	**Die Cut**	
152	A37	3p pink (U)	.20	.20
153	A37	5p on 9p lt blue	.20	.20
154	A37	9p lt bl	.20	.20
155	A37	1sh7p on 3p pink (U)	.50	.50
156	A37	3sh6p on 9p lt blue	.85	.85
157	A37	6sh6p on 3p pink (U)	1.60	1.60
		Nos. 152-157,C22-C26 (11)	8.20	8.20

Nos. 100-110, 147 and 151 Surcharged in Black or Red

Perf. 11½x11, 11x11½, 14½x13½

			Wmk. 79	
1967, Mar. 25				
158	A33	1s on 1p	.20	.20
159	A33	1s on 4p	.20	.20
160	A33	3s on 5p	.20	.20
161	A33	4s on 5p	.20	.20
162	A33	5s on 3½p	.20	.20
163	A33	6s on 8p	.20	.20
164	A33	7s on 1½p	.20	.20
165	A33	8s on 6p	.20	.20
166	A34	9s on 3p	.20	.20
167	A34	10s on 1sh	.25	.25
168	A35	11s on 3p on 1p	.35	.35
169	A35	21s on 3sh on 2p	.55	.55
170	A33	23s on 1p	.60	.60
171	A33	30s on 2sh (R) (1-line surcharge	1.25	1.25
172	A33	30s on 2sh (R) (3-line surcharge	1.40	1.40
173	A33	50s on 6p (R)	1.60	1.60
174	A33	60s on 2p (R)	2.00	2.00
		Nos. 158-174 (17)	9.80	9.80

The size, typeface and arrangement of surcharge vary on the different denominations.

King Taufa'ahau IV — A38

Designs: 1s, 4s, 28s, 1pa, Coat of Arms, reverse of new palladium coins.

Litho.; Embossed on Palladium Foil

1967, July 4		**Unwmk.**	**Die Cut**	

Diameter: 1s, 44mm; 2s, 50s, 52mm; 4s, 59mm; 15s, 68mm; 28s, 40mm; 1pa, 74mm

175	A38	1s orange & brt bl	.20	.20
176	A38	2s brt bl & dp mag	.20	.20
177	A38	4s emerald & mag	.20	.20
178	A38	15s blue grn & vio	.35	.35
179	A38	28s blk & brt red lil	.60	.60
180	A38	50s red & vio bl	1.10	1.10
181	A38	1pa ultra & brt rose	2.25	2.25
		Nos. 175-181,C27-C33 (14)	12.00	12.00

Coronation of King Taufa'ahau IV, July 4, 1967. Backed with paper inscribed in yellow alternating rows: "Tonga The Friendly Islands" and "Historically The First Palladium Coinage."
For surcharges and overprints see Nos. 203-209, C40-C46, CO21-CO24,

Types of Regular Issue, 1953, Surcharged

Wmk. 79

1967, Dec. 15		**Engr.**	**Die Cut**	
182	A33	1s on 1p yellow & blk	.20	.20
183	A33	2s on 2p carmine & ultra	.20	.20
184	A34	3s on 3p brown org & yel	.20	.20
185	A33	4s on 4p purple & yel	.20	.20
186	A33	5s on 5p green & yel	.20	.20
187	A34	10s on 10p rose red & yel	.20	.20
188	A33	20s on 2sh carmine & ultra	.25	.25
189	A33	50s on 5sh sepia & yel	1.60	1.60
190	A34	1pa on 10sh orange yel	.75	.75
		Nos. 182-190,C34-C36,CO12-CO14 (15)	6.80	6.80

Arrival of US Peace Corps.

Nos. 100-111 Surcharged in Red, Black or Ultramarine

Perf. 11½x11, 11x11½

			Wmk. 79	
1968, Apr. 6		**Engr.**		
191	A33	1s on 1p (R)	.20	.20
192	A33	1s on 4p	.20	.20
193	A34	3s on 3p (U)	.20	.20
194	A33	4s on 5p (R)	.20	.20
195	A33	5s on 2p (R)	.20	.20
196	A33	6s on 6p (R)	.20	.20
197	A33	7s on 1½p (R)	.20	.20
198	A33	8s on 8p (R)	.20	.20
199	A33	9s on 3½p	.30	.30
200	A34	10s on 1sh (R)	.30	.30
201	A33	20s on 5sh (R)	1.25	1.25
202	A33	2pa on 2sh (R)	2.75	2.75
		Nos. 191-202,C37-C39,CO15-CO18 (19)	13.10	13.10

Surcharge on 3s and 10s is vertical.

Nos. 175-181 Overprinted: "H.M'S BIRTHDAY / 4 July 1968" in Gold on Red Panel on 1s, 4s, 28s and 1pa. "HIS MAJESTY'S 50th BIRTHDAY" in Silver on Blue Panel on 2s, 15s and 50s

Litho.; Embossed on Palladium Foil

1968, July 4		**Unwmk.**	**Die Cut**	
203	A38	1s orange & brt bl	.20	.20
204	A38	2s brt bl & dp mag	.20	.20
205	A38	4s emerald & mag	.20	.20
206	A38	15s blue grn & vio	.55	.55
207	A38	28s blk & brt red lil	1.10	1.10
208	A38	50s red & vio bl	1.75	1.75
209	A38	1pa ultra & brt rose	3.50	3.50
		Nos. 203-209,C40-C46,CO21-CO24 (18)	28.85	25.55

Types of 1953 Surcharged in Red, Black or Green: "Friendly Islands / Field & Track Trials / South Pacific Games / Port Moresby 1969"

Designs as before.

Wmk. 79

1968, Dec. 19		**Engr.**	**Die Cut**	
210	A33	5s on 5p green & yel (R)	.20	.20
211	A34	10s on 1sh cer & buff	.20	.20
212	A33	15s on 2sh rose car & bl	.20	.20
213	A33	25s on 2p rose car & bl	.30	.20
214	A33	50s on 1p yel & blk	.50	.30
215	A33	75s on 10sh org (G)	.85	.45
		Nos. 210-215,C47-C54,CO19-CO20 (16)	8.00	4.75

Issued to publicize the field and track trials for the third South Pacific Games, Port Moresby, 1969. The overprint is in 5 lines on the horizontal stamps, in 7 lines on vertical stamps. On the vertical stamps "Trial" is printed on the line ahead of "Field & Track." On #215 the denomination is spelled out.

Nos. 149-150 and Types of 1953 Surcharged

Perf. 14½x13½

1968		**Photo.**	**Wmk. 79**	
216	A35	1s on 1sh2p on 2p	1.00	1.00
217	A35	1s on 2sh on 2p	1.00	1.00
		Engr.		**Die Cut**
218	A33	1s on 6p yellow & blk	.40	.40
219	A33	2s on 3½p dk blue	.50	.50
220	A33	3s on 1½p lt green	.50	.50
221	A33	4s on 8p black & pale grn	.60	.60
		Nos. 216-221,C55-C57 (9)	7.00	7.00

Banana — A39

Unwmk.

1969, Apr. 21		**Typo.**	**Die Cut**	
		Self-adhesive		
222	A39	1s yellow, black & red	.75	.65
223	A39	2s yel, black & emer	.90	.80
224	A39	3s yellow, black & lil	1.00	.85

225 A39 4s yellow, black & ultra 1.10 .95
226 A39 5s yel, blk & ol grn 1.25 1.25
Nos. 222-226 (5) 5.00 4.50

Packed in boxes of 200. See Nos. 248-252, 297-301, O11-O15, design A75.

Peelable Backing Inscribed
Starting in 1969, self-adhesive stamps are attached to peelable paper backing printed with "TONGA where time begins" in multiple rows and various colors, unless otherwise stated.

Shot-putter — A40

1969, Aug. 13 Litho. Die Cut
Self-adhesive
227 A40 1s bister, red & blk .20 .20
228 A40 3s bis, red & emer .20 .20
229 A40 6s bister, red & bl .20 .20
230 A40 10s bister, red & pur .20 .20
231 A40 30s bister, red & bl .30 .30
Nos. 227-231,C58-C62,CO25-
CO26 (12) 5.50 5.50

3rd Pacific Games, Port Moresby, Papua and New Guinea, Aug. 13-23.

Oil Derrick and Map of Tonga Islands — A41

1969, Dec. 23 Litho. Die Cut
Self-adhesive
232 A41 3s brown & multi .20 .20
233 A41 7s brt blue & multi .20 .20
234 A41 20s multicolored .55 .55
235 A41 25s orange & multi .80 .80
236 A41 35s henna brn & multi 1.10 1.10

Type of Regular Issue, 1953, Surcharged in Red: "1969 / OIL / SEARCH / T$1.10" and Oil Derrick Obliterating Old Denomination
Wmk. 79 Die Cut
237 A34 1.10pa on £1 green & multi 3.50 3.50
Nos. 232-237,C63-C67,CO27 (12) 12.70 12.70

First scientific search for oil in Tonga.

British and Tongan Royal Families — A42

Litho.; Gold Embossed
1970, Mar. 7 Self-adhesive Die Cut
238 A42 3s multicolored .20 .20
239 A42 5s multicolored .20 .20
240 A42 10s multicolored .55 .40
241 A42 25s multicolored 1.25 .90
242 A42 50s multicolored 2.75 2.00
Nos. 238-242,C68-C72,CO28-
CO30 (13) 27.45 18.75

Visit of Elizabeth II, Prince Philip and Princess Anne, Mar. 1970.

Open Book, George Tupou I and II, Salote Tupou III, Taufa'ahau Tupou IV and Tonga Flag — A43

Litho.; Gold Embossed
1970, June 4 Die Cut
Self-adhesive
243 A43 3s multicolored .20 .20
244 A43 7s multicolored .25 .25
245 A43 15s multicolored .60 .60
246 A43 25s multicolored .70 .70
247 A43 50s multicolored 1.25 1.25
Nos. 243-247,C73-C77,CO31-
CO33 (13) 13.25 13.25

Tonga's independence and entry into the British Commonwealth of Nations.
For surcharges see Nos. CO49-CO51, CO71.

Banana Type of 1969 redrawn and

Coconut — A44

1970, June 9 Typo.
Self-adhesive
248 A39 1s yellow, blk & mag .35 .35
249 A39 2s yellow, blk & bl .45 .45
250 A39 3s yellow, blk & brn .45 .45
251 A39 4s yellow, blk & grn .45 .45
252 A39 5s yellow, blk & org .50 .50
Typo.; Embossed on Gilt Foil
Coconut Brown
253 A44 6s blue, grn & mag .60 .60
254 A44 7s purple & green .65 .65
255 A44 8s gold, grn & vio bl .70 .70
256 A44 9s carmine & green .80 .80
257 A44 10s gold, grn & org .80 .80
Nos. 248-257,O11-O20 (20) 14.45 14.45

Nos. 248-252 have no white shading in upper part of the banana, Nos. 222-226 have white shading. Nos. 253-256 have self-adhesive control numbers in lower left corner of paper backing. Paper backing is green on Nos. 253-257.
See Nos. 302-306, O26-O30.

Red Cross and Arms of Tonga A45

1970, Oct. 17 Die Cut
Self-adhesive
258 A45 3s red, black & grn .20 .20
259 A45 7s red, blk & vio bl .20 .20
260 A45 15s red, blk & red lil .55 .55

261 A45 25s red, black & brt grn .90 .90
262 A45 75s red, black & brn 4.50 4.50
Nos. 258-262,C78-C82,CO34-
CO36 (13) 28.25 28.25

Centenary of the British Red Cross.

Nos. 153, 152 Surcharged

Litho.; Embossed on Gilt Foil
1971, Jan. 31 Die Cut
263 A37 2s on 9p lt blue .20 .20
264 A37 3s on 9p lt blue .20 .20
265 A37 5s on 3p pink .35 .35
266 A37 15s on 9p lt blue 1.00 .60
267 A37 25s on 3p pink 1.40 .95
268 A37 50s on 3p pink 3.25 2.00
Nos. 263-268,C83-C86,CO37-
CO40 (14) 31.80 21.80

In memory of Queen Salote (1900-65). The "In Memoriam" inscription is in silver on black panel on the 2s, 3s and 15s; in silver on ultramarine panel on the 5s, 25s and 50s. The dates and denominations are all on black panels in silver and metallic red, green, bronze, magenta or gold respectively.

Type of Regular Issue, 1953, Surcharged in Red and Black

1971 Engr. Wmk. 79 Imperf
269 A33 3s on 8p black & pale grn .20 .20
270 A33 7s on 4p pur & yel .25 .20
271 A33 25s on 1p yel & blk .45 .35
272 A33 75s on 2sh car & ultra 2.75 2.0
Nos. 269-272,C87-C89,CO41-
CO43 (10) 12.25 8.75

Philatokyo 71, Philatelic Exposition, Tokyo, Apr. 19-29.

Type of Regular Issue, 1971, Surcharged

1971
273 A34 15s on 1sh car & buff .50 .50
Nos. 273,C90-C91 (3) 4.00 4.00

Centenary of Japanese postal service.

Self-adhesive & Imperf.
Starting with Nos. 274-278, all issues are self-adhesive and imperforate, unless otherwise stated.

Pole Vault — A46

Gold Medal of Merit — A47

1971, July Litho. Unwmk.
274 A46 3s green, blk & brn .20 .20
275 A46 7s red, blk & brn .20 .20
276 A46 15s green, blk & brn .30 .30

277 A46 25s rose lil, blk & brn .40 .4
278 A46 50s dk bl, blk & brn .85 .8
Nos. 274-278,C92-C96,CO44-
CO46 (13) 7.75 7.7

4th South Pacific Games, Papeete, French Polynesia, Sept. 8-19.
For surcharges see Nos. 332, C140.

1971, Oct. 30 Litho.; Embosse
24s, Silver Medal of Merit. 38s, Bronz Medal of Merit, obverse (King Taufa'ahau IV)
279 A47 3s gold & multi .20 .2
280 A47 24s silver & multi .35 .3
281 A47 38s bronze & multi .65 .6
Nos. 279-281,C99-C101,CO49-
CO51 (9) 7.75 7.7

First investiture of Tongan Medal of Merit. For surcharges see Nos. 333-336.

Juggler, UNICEF Emblem A48

1971, Dec. Litho
282 A48 2s violet & multi .20 .2
283 A48 4s multicolored .20 .2
284 A48 8s blue & multi .20 .2
285 A48 16s emerald & multi .35 .3
286 A48 30s lil rose & multi .65 .6
Nos. 282-286,C102-
C106,CO52-CO54 (13) 13.00 13.0

25th anniv. of UNICEF.

Merchant Marine Routes from Tonga and "Olovaha" — A49

1972, Apr. 14
287 A49 2s blue & multi .35 .3
288 A49 10s magenta & multi .75 .3
289 A49 17s brown & multi 1.10 .3
290 A49 21s dk green & multi 1.25 .4
291 A49 60s multicolored 5.50 3.5
Nos. 287-291,C107-
C111,CO55-CO57 (13) 35.80 26.4

Togan Merchant Marine publicity
For surcharges see Nos. C124, CO66 CO69.

King Taufa'ahau IV Coronation Coin, ¼ Hau — A50

Litho.; Embossed on Metallic Foil
1972, July 15
292 A50 5s silver & multi .20 .2
293 A50 7s silver & multi .20 .2
294 A50 10s silver & multi .20 .2

| 95 | A50 | 17s silver & multi | .40 | .40 |
| 96 | A50 | 60s silver & multi | 1.40 | 1.40 |

Nos. 292-296,C112-
C116,CO58-CO60 (13) 12.75 12.75

Coronation of King Taufa'ahau IV, 5th anniv.

Coconut Type of 1970 and

Banana
A51

Watermelon — A52

1972, Sept. 30   Typo.

297	A51	1s brt yel, red & blk	.35	.20
298	A51	2s brt yel, bl & blk	.40	.20
299	A51	3s brt yel, emer & blk	.45	.20
300	A51	4s brt yel & blk	.45	.25
301	A51	5s brt yel & brn blk	.45	.25
302	A44	6s brn, org & grn	.50	.25
303	A44	7s brn, ultra & grn	.55	.30
304	A44	8s brn, mag & grn	.55	.30
305	A44	9s brn, red & grn	.55	.30
306	A44	10s brn, bl & grn	.65	.35
307	A52	15s green, org brn & ultra	1.40	.50
308	A52	20s grn, bl & red	1.50	.70
309	A52	25s grn, red & brn	1.75	.80
310	A52	40s grn, bl & org	3.00	1.75
311	A52	50s grn, dk bl & yel	3.00	2.00

Nos. 297-311,O21-O35 (30) 27.85 16.70

Paper backing is brown on Nos. 302-311.
Nos. 302-306 have self-adhesive control number in lower left corner of paper backing.

Flag Raising, Minerva Reef — A53

1972, Dec. 9   Litho.

312	A53	5s black & multi	.20	.20
313	A53	7s green & multi	.20	.20
314	A53	10s purple & multi	.20	.20
315	A53	15s orange & multi	.30	.30
316	A53	40s ultra & multi	1.10	1.10

Nos. 312-316,C119-
C123,CO63-CO65 (13) 11.00 11.00

Tonga's proclamation of sovereignty over
the Minerva Reefs, June 1972.

Tongan Coins and Bank
Building — A54

1973, Mar. 30   Litho.

317	A54	5s silver & multi	.20	.20
318	A54	7s silver & multi	.20	.20
319	A54	10s silver & multi	.20	.20
320	A54	20s silver & multi	.45	.20
321	A54	30s silver & multi	.60	.35

Nos. 317-321,C125-
C129,CO66-CO68 (13) 15.30 14.00

Establishment of Bank of Tonga.

Handshake, Outrigger Canoe — A55

1973, June 29

322	A55	5s silver & multi	.30	.20
323	A55	7s silver & multi	.45	.20
324	A55	15s silver & multi	1.40	.55
325	A55	21s silver & multi	1.90	.70
326	A55	50s silver & multi	6.75	3.25

Nos. 322-326,C130-
C134,CO69-CO71 (13) 135.00 70.00

Tongan Boy Scout Movement, 25th anniv.

Capt. Cook's Report and Tongan
Rulers — A56

Litho.; Embossed on Gilt Foil
1973, Oct. 2

327	A56	6s multicolored	.45	.40
328	A56	8s multicolored	.45	.40
329	A56	11s multicolored	.65	.50
330	A56	35s multicolored	4.25	1.75
331	A56	40s multicolored	4.25	2.00

Nos. 327-331,C135-
C139,CO72-CO74 (13) 54.45 28.70

Bicentenary of Capt. Cook's arrival. Design
is from the manuscript in British Museum.

Nos. 278, 281, C100-C101 and 280
Surcharged and Overprinted in Silver
or Gold on Red (12s, 14s) or Black
Panels (5s, 20s, 50s): "Commonwealth
Games Christchurch 1974"

1973, Dec. 19   Litho.

| 332 | A46 | 5s on 50s (G) | .20 | .20 |

Litho.; Embossed

333	A47	12s on 38s (G)	.40	.20
334	A47	14s on 75s (G)	.40	.20
335	A47	20s on 1pa (G)	.70	.20
336	A47	50s on 24s (S)	1.50	1.25

Nos. 332-336,C140-
C144,CO75-CO77 (13) 12.75 9.75

10th British Commonwealth Games, Christchurch, N.Z., Jan. 24-Feb. 2, 1974.

Girl Guide Badges — A58

1974, Sept. 11   Litho.

342	A58	5s multicolored	.45	.30
343	A58	10s multicolored	.85	.50
344	A58	20s multicolored	1.90	1.10
345	A58	40s multicolored	3.75	2.25
346	A58	60s multicolored	5.00	3.00

Nos. 342-346,C159-
C163,CO90-CO92 (13) 45.25 26.80

Girl Guides of Tonga.
For surcharges see Nos. C189, C192.

Sailing
Ship
and
Anchors
A59

1974, Dec. 11

347	A59	5s blue & multi	.40	.35
348	A59	10s blue & multi	.85	.40
349	A59	25s blue & multi	1.90	.75
350	A59	50s blue & multi	3.75	2.50
351	A59	75s blue & multi	5.50	4.00

Nos. 347-351,C164-
C168,CO93-CO95 (13) 43.35 24.85

Establishment of Royal Marine Institute.

Dateline Hotel, Nukualofa — A60

1975, Mar. 11

352	A60	5s blue & multi	.20	.20
353	A60	10s green & multi	.20	.20
354	A60	15s scarlet & multi	.35	.35
355	A60	30s purple & multi	.75	.75
356	A60	1pa orange & multi	2.75	2.75

Nos. 352-356,C169-
C173,CO96-CO98 (13) 15.00 15.00

First meeting of South Pacific area Prime
Ministers. See note after No. 226.

Boxing and Games' Emblem — A61

1975, June 11   Litho.

357	A61	5s black & multi	.25	.25
358	A61	10s green & multi	.35	.35
359	A61	20s brown & multi	.55	.55
360	A61	25s orange & multi	.65	.65
361	A61	65s violet & multi	1.40	1.40

Nos. 357-361,C174-
C178,CO99-CO101 (13) 12.50 12.50

5th South Pacific Games, Guam, Aug. 1-10.
See note after No. 226.
For surcharges see Nos. 412, 482.

King
Taufa'ahau IV
Coin — A62

Designs (FAO Coins): 5s, Chicken. 20s, like
1pa, (small coin, 27mm). 50s, School of fish.
2pa, Animals and plants on reverse, King on
obverse (large coin, 42mm.).

1975, Sept. 3

362	A62	5s red, sil & blk	.25	.25
363	A62	20s ultra, grn, sil & blk	.55	.55
364	A62	50s blue, sil & blk	1.10	1.10
365	A62	1pa silver & black	2.25	2.25
366	A62	2pa silver & black	3.75	3.75

Nos. 362-366,C179-C183 (10) 13.00 13.00

Coinage issued for the benefit of the FAO.
Size of paper backing of 2pa: 82x50mm;
others 45x45mm. See note after No. 226.
For surcharge see Nos. 413.

Coat of Arms, 5pa Coin,
Reverse — A63

George Tupou I Coin, Reverse and
Obverse — A64

Coins: 20s, King Taufa'ahau IV. 50s, King
George Tupou II, 50pa obverse and reverse.
75s, 20pa reverse.

Litho.; Embossed on Gilt Foil
1975, Nov. 4
Pink Background

367	A63	5s black, sil & vio bl	.20	.20
368	A64	10s gold, blk & red	.35	.20
369	A63	20s black, sil & grn	.60	.35
370	A64	50s gold, blk & vio	1.25	1.25
371	A63	75s black, sil & red lil	2.25	2.25

Nos. 367-371,C184-
C188,CO102-CO104 (13) 14.90 13.25

Centenary of Constitution of Tonga. Size of
paper backing of Nos. 367 and 369:
65x60mm; of No. 371, 87x78mm. See note
after No. 226.
For surcharges see Nos. C232, C296.

Montreal Olympic Games
Emblem — A65

1976, Feb. 24				Litho.
372	A65	5s red, ultra & blk	.40	.35
373	A65	10s red, green & blk	.55	.35
374	A65	25s red, lt brown & blk	1.25	.75
375	A65	35s red, lilac & blk	1.50	1.00
376	A65	70s red, bister & blk	3.25	2.50
	Nos. 372-376,C189-C193,CO105-CO107 (13)		28.60	18.40

21st Olympic Games, Montreal, Canada, July 17-Aug. 1. See note after No. 226.
For surcharges see Nos. 414, 478.

William Hooper, William Floyd, John
Penn, Francis Lightfoot Lee — A66

Signers of Declaration of Independence, Flags of US and Tonga: 10s, Benjamin Franklin, Thomas Nelson, Jr., Benjamin Harrison, William Ellery. 15s, Oliver Wolcott, Lyman Hall, William Whipple, Carter Braxton. 25s, George Taylor, Thomas Stone, Arthur Middleton, Richard Stockton. 75s, Stephen Hopkins, Eldridge Gerry, James Wilson, Francis Hopkinson.

1976, May 26				Litho.
377	A66	9s buff & multi	.45	.20
378	A66	10s buff & multi	.45	.20
379	A66	15s buff & multi	.65	.50
380	A66	25s buff & multi	.90	.90
381	A66	75s buff & multi	5.25	4.25
	Nos. 377-381,C194-C198,CO108-CO110 (13)		28.60	19.20

American Bicentennial. Printed on peelable buff paper backing, inscribed in carmine with facsimile of Declaration of Independence.
For surcharges see #481, C233, C236-C237, C297.

Nathaniel Turner and John
Thomas — A67

1976, Aug. 25				
382	A67	5s yellow & multi	.25	.25
383	A67	10s multicolored	.40	.25
384	A67	20s multicolored	.90	.50
385	A67	25s multicolored	1.00	.55
386	A67	85s multicolored	2.75	2.75
	Nos. 382-386,C199-C203,CO111-CO113 (13)		18.75	16.65

Sesquicentennial of the arrival of Methodist missionaries and establishment of Christianity in Tonga. Printed on peelable paper backing inscribed in manuscript with segments of John Thomas's Tonga diary.

For surcharges see Nos. 415-416, 479-480.

Wilhelm I and George Tupou I — A68

1976, Nov. 1				
387	A68	9s yellow & multi	.35	.30
388	A68	15s yellow & multi	.55	.50
389	A68	22s yellow & multi	.80	.70
390	A68	50s yellow & multi	1.40	1.25
391	A68	73s yellow & multi	1.90	1.75
	Nos. 387-391,C204-C208,CO114-CO116 (13)		14.85	13.50

Tonga-Germany Friendship Treaty, centenary. Printed on peelable paper backing showing reproduction of original treaty.

Queen Salote in Coronation
Procession, 1953 — A69

1977, Feb. 7				Litho.
392	A69	11s blue & multi	.40	.40
393	A69	20s green & multi	.50	.50
394	A69	30s vio blue & multi	.30	.30
395	A69	50s lt green & multi	.45	.45
396	A69	75s violet & multi	.80	.80
	Nos. 392-396,C209-C213,CO117-CO119 (13)		20.00	15.50

25th anniv. of the reign of Elizabeth II. Printed on peelable paper backing showing replica of handwritten Proclamation of Accession.
For surcharge see No. 417.

Various Coins — A70

1977, July 4				
397	A70	10s multicolored	.20	.20
398	A70	15s multicolored	.30	.30
399	A70	25s multicolored	.40	.40
400	A70	50s multicolored	.85	.85
401	A70	75s multicolored	1.25	1.25
	Nos. 397-401,C214-C218,CO120-CO122 (13)		10.15	10.15

10th anniversary of coronation of King Taufa'ahau IV. Printed on peelable paper backing showing multicolored replicas of Tongan stamps.

Capt. Cook's Resolution — A71

1977, Sept. 27				Litho.
402	A71	10s multicolored	1.00	.75
403	A71	17s multicolored	2.25	1.25
404	A71	25s multicolored	2.50	2.50
405	A71	30s multicolored	3.00	2.50
406	A71	40s multicolored	3.00	2.50
	Nos. 402-406,C219-C223,CO123-CO125 (13)		71.45	53.90

Bicentenary of Capt. Cook's farewell voyage.

Humpback Whale — A72

1977, Dec. 16				
407	A72	15s ultra & black	4.00	.75
408	A72	22s green & black	4.25	1.25
409	A72	31s orange & black	4.75	1.75
410	A72	38s lilac & black	5.00	2.10
411	A72	64s red & black	8.50	5.25
	Nos. 407-411,C224-C228,CO126-CO128 (13)		81.00	32.50

Whale protection.

Stamps of 1975-77 Surcharged in
Black, Green, Brown or Black on Silver

1978, Feb. 17				
412	A61	15s on 20s (#359;B)	1.60	1.50
413	A62	15s on 5s (#362;B)	1.60	1.50
414	A65	15s on 10s (#373;G)	1.60	1.50
415	A67	15s on 5s (#382;Br)	1.60	1.50
416	A67	15s on 10s (#383;B)	1.60	1.50
417	A69	15s on 11s (#392;B on S)	1.60	2.50
418	OA11	15s on 38s (#CO99;B)	1.60	1.50
	Nos. 412-418,C229-C238 (17)		65.50	63.00

The surcharge on No. 413 is only the "1," and on No. 418 includes "postage."

Flags of
Canada
and
Tonga
A73

1978, May 5				Litho.
419	A73	10s red & multi	.20	.20
420	A73	15s red & multi	.35	.35
421	A73	20s red & multi	.45	.45
422	A73	25s red & multi	.60	.60
423	A73	45s red & multi	1.00	1.00
	Nos. 419-423,C239-C243,CO129-CO131 (13)		12.00	12.00

11th Commonwealth Games, Edmonton, Canada, Aug. 3-12. See note after No. 226.

King Taufa'ahau IV — A74

1978, July 4				
424	A74	2s multicolored	.20	.2
425	A74	5s multicolored	.20	.2
426	A74	10s multicolored	.25	.2
427	A74	25s multicolored	.65	.6
428	A74	75s multicolored	2.00	2.0
	Nos. 424-428,C244-C248,CO132-CO134 (13)		13.00	13.0

60th birthday of King Taufa'ahau IV. See note after No. 226.

Two Bananas
A75

Coconut — A76

Designs: 1s to 5s, Bananas. 6s to 10s Coconuts. 15s to 1pa, Pineapples.

1978, Sept. 29				Typo
429	A75	1s yellow & black	.25	.2
430	A75	2s yellow & dk blue	.25	.2
431	A75	3s multicolored	.35	.3
432	A75	4s multicolored	.35	.3
433	A75	5s multicolored	.35	.3
434	A76	6s multicolored	.50	.5
435	A76	7s multicolored	.50	.5
436	A76	8s multicolored	.50	.5
437	A76	9s multicolored	.50	.5
438	A76	10s brown & green	.50	.5
439	A76	15s green & lt brown	1.50	1.5
440	A76	20s multicolored	1.75	1.7
441	A76	30s multicolored	2.00	2.0
442	A76	50s multicolored	2.50	2.5
443	A76	1pa multicolored	3.00	3.0
	Nos. 429-443,O36-O50 (30)		28.00	28.0

Nos. 429-443 issued in coils; self-adhesive control numbers on paper backing, except on 1s and 5s. See note after No. 226.
See No. 529.

Whale — A77

1978, Dec. 15				Litho. & Typo
444	A77	15s shown	3.50	1.7
445	A77	18s Bat	3.50	1.7
446	A77	25s Turtle	3.50	1.7
447	A77	28s Parrot	5.50	2.5
448	A77	60s like 15s	9.00	6.0
	Nos. 444-448,C249-C253,CO150-CO152 (13)		73.25	40.2

Wildlife conservation. See note after No. 226.

Introduction of Metric System — A78

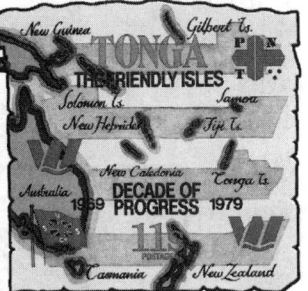

Shipping Routes, South Pacific Map — A79

Peace Corps A80

22s, New church buildings. 50s, Air routes to Auckland, Suva, Apia & Pago Pago.

		1979, Feb. 16		**Litho.**
449	A78	5s multicolored	.20	.20
450	A79	11s multicolored	.25	.20
451	A80	18s multicolored	.40	.30
452	A79	22s multicolored	.55	.40
453	A79	50s multicolored	1.25	.75
		Nos. 449-453,C254-C258,CO153-CO155 (13)	12.75	8.25

Decade of Progress. Paper backing shows map of Tonga.

Tongan First Day Covers — A81

		1979, June 1		
454	A81	5s multicolored	.20	.20
455	A81	10s multicolored	.25	.25
456	A81	25s multicolored	.60	.60
457	A81	50s multicolored	1.25	1.25
458	A81	1pa multicolored	1.75	1.75
		Nos. 454-458,C259-C263,CO156-CO158 (13)	11.55	11.55

10th anniversary of introduction of self-adhesive stamps and for Bernard Mechanick, inventor of self-adhesive, free-form stamps; death centenary of Sir Rowland Hill.
Printed on peelable paper backing showing advertisement.
For surcharges and overprints see Nos. 469-473.

Eua Island through Camera Lens — A82

		1979, Nov. 23		**Litho.**
459	A82	10s multicolored	.20	.20
460	A82	18s multicolored	.45	.45
461	A82	31s multicolored	.75	.75
462	A82	50s multicolored	1.10	1.10
463	A82	60s multicolored	1.40	1.40
		Nos. 459-463,C275-C279,CO170-CO172 (13)	11.80	11.80

Printed on peelable paper backing showing film and camera.

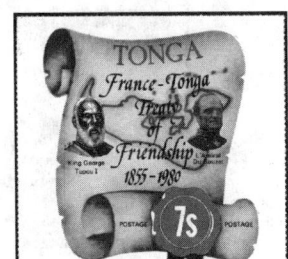

King George Tupou I, Admiral du Bouzet, Map of Tonga — A83

		1980, Jan. 9		**Litho.**
464	A83	7s multicolored	.20	.20
465	A83	10s multicolored	.25	.25
466	A83	14s multicolored	.35	.35
467	A83	50s multicolored	1.25	1.25
468	A83	75s multicolored	1.75	1.75
		Nos. 464-468,C280-C284,CO173-CO175 (13)	12.05	12.05

Tongan-French Friendship Treaty, 125th anniversary. Printed on peelable paper; multicolored backing shows map of Tonga.

Nos. 454-458 Surcharged and Overprinted in Black on Silver: "1980 OLYMPIC GAMES," Moscow '80 and Bear Emblems

		1980, Apr. 30		**Litho.**
469	A81	13s on 5s multi	.40	.40
470	A81	20s on 10s multi	.65	.50
471	A81	25s multicolored	.80	.80
472	A81	33s on 50s multi	1.00	1.00
473	A81	1pa multicolored	3.25	3.25
		Nos. 469-473,C285-C289,CO176-CO178 (13)	15.80	15.65

Boy Scout Cooking over Campfire — A84

		1980, Sept. 30		**Litho.**
474	A84	9s multicolored	.25	.25
475	A84	13s multicolored	.40	.40
476	A84	33s multicolored	.45	.45
477	A84	30s multicolored	.90	.90
		Nos. 474-477,C290-C293,CO179-CO180 (10)	14.75	14.75

Boy Scout Jamboree; Rotary Intl., 75th anniv. Peelable backing shows map of Tonga.

Nos. 361, 375, 380, 384-385 Surcharged

		1980, Dec. 3		**Litho.**
478	A65	9s on 35s multi	.20	.20
479	A67	13s on 20s multi	.30	.30
480	A67	13s on 25s multi	.30	.30
481	A66	19s on 25s multi	.45	.45
482	A61	1pa on 65s multi	2.50	2.50
		Nos. 478-482,C294-C299,CO181 (12)	13.70	13.70

Intl. Year of the Disabled — A85

		1981, Sept. 9		**Litho.**
483	A85	2pa multicolored	3.25	3.25
484	A85	3pa multicolored	5.00	5.00
		Nos. 483-484,C300-C302 (5)	10.05	10.05

Prince Charles and Lady Diana — A86

Designs: 13s, Charles, King Taufa'ahau. 47s, 1.50pa, Couple, diff.

		1981, Oct. 21		**Litho.**
485	A86	13s multicolored	.20	.20
486	A86	47s multicolored	.50	.50
487	A86	1.50pa multicolored	1.75	1.75
488	A86	3pa multicolored	3.50	3.50
		Nos. 485-488 (4)	5.95	5.95

Royal Wedding and Gt. Britain-Tonga Friendship Treaty centenary. Issued in sheets of 20 (2x10) and 5 labels in vert. center row.
For surcharge see No. B1

Bicentenary of Discovery of Vavau by Francisco Maurelle A87

18th century Spanish engravings and maps.

		1981, Nov. 25		**Litho.**
489	A87	9s multicolored	.50	.40
490	A87	13s multicolored	.80	.50
491	A87	47s multicolored	2.50	1.25
492	A87	1pa multicolored	6.25	6.25
a.		Souvenir sheet, imperf.	12.00	12.00
		Nos. 489-492 (4)	10.05	8.40

No. 492a contains one No. 492 (32x25mm).

Bible Class, 1830 Print — A88

		1981, Nov. 25		
493	A88	9s Open book	.30	.30
494	A88	13s Book, diff.	.50	.40
495	A88	32s Type	1.10	1.10
496	A88	47s shown	1.60	1.60
		Nos. 493-496 (4)	3.50	3.40

Christmas 1981 and sesquicentennial of books printed in Tonga.

175th Anniv. of Capture of The Port-au-Prince — A89

		1981, Dec. 16		**Litho.**
497	A89	29s Battle	.95	.70
498	A89	32s Battle, diff.	1.10	.80
499	A89	47s Map	1.50	1.40
500	A89	47s Sinking ship	1.50	1.40
a.		Pair, #499-500	3.25	
501	A89	1pa Ship	3.25	3.25
		Nos. 497-501 (5)	8.30	7.55

Nos. CO179-CO180 Surcharged

		1982, Jan. 4		**Litho.**
502	OA19	5pa on 25s multi	10.00	10.00
503	OA19	5pa on 2pa multi	10.00	10.00

Scouting Year — A90

		1982, Feb. 22		**Litho.**
504	A90	29s	Brownsea Isld. Camp, 1907	.85	.55
505	A90	32s	Baden-Powell, horse	.95	.60
506	A90	47s	Imperial Jamboree, 1924	1.40	.90
507	A90	1.50pa	"Scouting for Boys"	4.25	2.75
508	A90	2.50pa	Mafeking stamp	7.00	4.50
			Nos. 504-508 (5)	14.45	9.30

1982 World Cup — A91

Designs: Various soccer players, map showing match sites.

		1982, July 7		**Litho.**
509	A91	32s multicolored	.80	.55
510	A91	47s multicolored	1.10	.80
511	A91	75s multicolored	1.75	1.25
512	A91	1.50pa multicolored	3.25	2.25
		Nos. 509-512 (4)	6.90	4.85

Inter-island Transport A92

9s, 13s, Ferry Olovaha. 47s, 1pa SPIA Twin Otter (Niuatoputapu Airport opening).

		1982, Aug. 11		
513	A92	9s multicolored	.40	.20
514	A92	13s multicolored	.50	.25
515	A92	47s multicolored	1.75	.90
516	A92	1pa multicolored	3.50	2.50
		Nos. 513-516 (4)	6.15	3.85

Tin Can Mail
Centenary
A93

13s, 32s, 47s, Collecting mail. 2pa, Map.
Nos. 517-519 form continuous design.

1982, Sept. 29   **Litho.**
517 A93 13s multicolored   .20   .20
518 A93 32s multicolored   .45   .45
519 A93 47s multicolored   .75   .75
  a. Souv. sheet of 3 (13s, 32s, 47s) 1.50 1.50
520 A93 2pa multicolored   3.25   3.25
  a. Souvenir sheet of 1   3.25   3.25
       Nos. 517-520 (4)   4.65   4.65

No. 520 comes with different labels. For
surcharges see Nos. 526-528.

Tonga College Centenary — A94

1982, Oct. 25   Size: 42x30mm (5s)
521 A94 5s Students   .35   .35
522 A94 29s King George Tupou
           I   2.25   2.25
523 A94 29s Monument   2.25   2.25
  a. Pair, #522-523   5.00
       Nos. 521-523 (3)   4.85   4.85

Nos. 521-523 inscribed in English or Tongan.

12th Commonwealth Games,
Brisbane, Australia, Sept. 30-Oct.
9 — A95

1982, Oct. 25
524 A95 32s Decathlon, vert.   .75   .50
525 A95 1.50pa Opening cere-
           mony   5.50   5.50

Nos. 517-519 Overprinted in Red or
Silver in 1 or 2 Lines: "Christmas /
Greetings / 1982"

1982, Nov. 17
526 A93 13s multicolored   .30   .30
527 A93 32s multicolored   .70   .70
528 A93 47s multicolored   1.00   1.00
       Nos. 526-528 (3)   2.00   2.00

Pineapple Type of 1978 and

Fruit — A96

1982, Nov. 17
529 A76 13s multicolored   .35   .25
530 A96 2pa multicolored   5.75   4.00
531 A96 3pa multicolored   8.75   6.00
       Nos. 529-531 (3)   14.85 10.25

Capt. Cook's Resolution, 1777 and
Canberra, 1983 — A96a

32s, like 29s. 47s, 1.50pa, Montgolfier Bros.
balloon, 1783, Concorde. 2.50pa, Concorde,
Canberra. 29s se-tenant with label showing
Resolution.

1983, Feb. 22   **Litho.**
532 A96a 29s multicolored   2.25   1.50
533 A96a 32s multicolored   3.00   1.50
534 A96a 47s multicolored   4.25   2.50
535 A96a 1.50pa multicolored   11.00 11.00
       Nos. 532-535 (4)   20.50 16.50

Souvenir Sheet
536 A96a 2.50pa multicolored   5.75   5.75

Pacific Forum of Sea and Air Transport (29s,
32s, 2.50pa); manned flight bicentenary (47s,
1.50pa).
For overprints see Nos. O68-O70.

A96b

1983, Mar. 14
537 A96b 29s Map   1.40   1.40
538 A96b 32s Dancers   1.60   1.60
539 A96b 47s Fishermen   2.25   2.25
540 A96b 1.50pa King
            Taufa'ahau
            IV, flag   7.00   7.00
       Nos. 537-540 (4)   12.25 12.25

Commonwealth Day.

Niuafo'ou
Airport
Opening
A97

1983, May 11   **Litho.**
541 A97 32s De Havilland Ot-
            ter   .75   .45
542 A97 47s like 32s   1.10   .45
543 A97 1pa Boeing 707   2.00   1.25
544 A97 1.50pa like 1pa   3.50   2.00
       Nos. 541-544 (4)   7.35   4.15

World
Communications
Year — A98

1983, June 22   **Litho.**
545 A98 29s Intelsat IV   .40   .40
546 A98 32s Intelsat IV-A   .50   .50
547 A98 75s Intelsat V   1.25   1.25

Size: 45x32mm
548 A98 2pa Apollo 15 Moon
            post cover   3.25   3.25
       Nos. 545-548 (4)   5.40   5.40

10th
Anniv. of
Bank of
Tonga
A99

Various banknotes.

1983, Aug. 3   **Litho.**
549 A99 1pa multicolored   2.25   2.25
550 A99 2pa multicolored   4.25   4.25

Printing Press,
1830 — A100

1983, Sept. 22   **Litho.**
551 A100 13s shown   .25   .25
552 A100 32s Woon's arrival,
             1831   .65   .65
553 A100 1pa Print   1.60   1.60
554 A100 2pa Tonga Chronicle   3.50   3.50
       Nos. 551-554 (4)   6.00   6.00

Sesquicentennial of printing in Tonga (by
missionary William Woon).

Christmas
1983
A101

Designs: Various sailboats off Vava'u.

1983, Nov. 17   **Litho.**
555 A101 29s multicolored   .45   .35
556 A101 32s multicolored   .55   .45
557 A101 1.50pa multicolored   2.10   2.10
558 A101 2.50pa multicolored   4.00   4.00
       Nos. 555-558 (4)   7.10   6.90

Abel Tasman, Discoverer of Tonga,
and his Zeehan — A102

Navigators and Explorers of the Pacific and
their Ships.

1984, Mar. 12   **Litho.**
559 A102 32s shown   2.00   2.00
560 A102 47s Samuel Wal-
             lis, Dolphin   2.75   2.75
561 A102 90s William Bligh,
             Bounty   5.00   5.00
562 A102 1.50pa James Cook,
             Resolution   9.00   9.00
       Nos. 559-562 (4)   18.75 18.75

See Nos. 593-596.

Swainsonia
Casta — A103

Shells, fish.

1984-85   **Litho.**
563 A103 1s shown   .45   1.75
564 A103 2s Porites (coral)   1.10   1.75
565 A103 3s Holocentrus
             ruber   1.40   2.00
566 A103 5s Cypraea mappa
             viridis   .55   1.75
567 A103 6s Dardanus me-
             gistos (crab)   1.40   2.00

568 A103   9s Stegostoma fas-
              ciatum   1.40   .8
  a. Perf. 14½ ('85)   1.40   .8
569 A103 10s Conus bullatus   1.10   1.7
570 A103 13s Pterois volitans   1.75   .8
571 A103 15s Conus textile   1.10   2.0
572 A103 20s Dascyllus
              aruanus   2.60   2.6
573 A103 29s Conus aulicus   2.00   1.1
574 A103 32s Acanthurus
              leucosternon   3.50   1.1
575 A103 47s Lambis truncata   3.50   1.7

Size: 39x25mm
576 A103 1pa Millepora
              dichotama
              (coral)   11.00 11.0
577 A103 2pa Birgus latro
              (crab)   16.00 17.5
578 A103 3pa Chicoreus pal-
              ma-rosae   10.00 17.5
579 A103 5pa Thunnus alba-
              cares   12.50 20.0
       Nos. 563-579 (17)   71.35 87.2

See Nos. 682-692, 701-709, 756-759. For
surcharges and overprints see Nos. 618-625,
808-810, O52-O67, O71-O77.

Tonga
Chronicle,
20th Anniv.
A104

1984 Summer Olympics
A105

1984, June 26
580 A104 3s multicolored   .20   .20
  a. Sheet of 12   .65
581 A104 32s multicolored   .50   .50
  a. Sheet of 12   6.50

Nos. 580-581 issued in sheets of 12; sheet
backgrounds show pages of Chronicle, giving
each stamp different background.

1984, July 23
582 A105 29s Running   .40   .40
583 A105 47s Javelin   .65   .65
584 A105 1.50pa Shot put   2.00   2.00
585 A105 3pa Torch   4.25   4.25
       Nos. 582-585 (4)   7.30   7.30

Intl. Dateline Centenary — A106

1984, Aug. 20
586 A106 47s George Airy,
              Greenwich Merid-
              ian pioneer   1.50   1.00
587 A106 2pa Sandford Fleming,
              time zone pioneer   7.50   5.00

Ausipex '84 — A107

1984, Sept. 17
588 A107 32s Australia #18   1.00   .75
589 A107 1.50pa Tonga #51   5.00   3.50

Souvenir Sheet
589A Sheet of 2, #588-589   4.50   4.50

Nos. 588-589 each printed se-tenant with
label showing exhibition emblem.
No. 589A contains two imperf. stamps similar to Nos. 588-589, but with denomination
replacing logo. No. 589A without denominations was not valid for postage.

Christmas
1984 — A108

1984, Nov. 12 Litho.
Christmas Carols in local settings.
590 A108 32s Silent Night .90 .50
591 A108 47s Away in a Manger 1.40 .75
592 A108 1pa I Saw Three Ships 3.00 3.00
Nos. 590-592 (3) 5.30 4.25

Famous Mariners
Designs: 32s, Willem Schouten (c. 1580-1625), The Eendracht, 1616. 47s, Jakob Le Maire (1585-1616), The Hoorn, 1615. 90s, Lt. Fletcher Christian, The Bounty, 1789. 1.50pa, Francisco Maurelle, La Princessa, 1781.

1985, Feb. 27 Litho. *Die Cut*
593 A102 32s multicolored 2.25 1.25
a. Perf. 14 50.00
594 A102 47s multicolored 3.50 1.50
595 A102 90s multicolored 6.25 4.50
596 A102 1.50pa multicolored 11.00 7.00
Nos. 593-596 (4) 23.00 14.25

Nos. 593-596 each printed se-tenant with self-adhesive label picturing anchor.

Geological Survey of Tonga Trench for Oil — A110

Designs: 29s, Tonga Trench and islands. 32s, Marine exploration, seismic surveying. 47s, Search for oil off Tongatapu, vert. No. 600, Exploration of sea bed, vert. No. 601, Angler fish.

1985, Apr. 10
597 A110 29s multicolored 1.40 1.00
598 A110 32s multicolored 1.50 1.00
599 A110 47s multicolored 2.25 1.50
600 A110 1.50pa multicolored 7.50 7.50
Nos. 597-600 (4) 12.65 11.00

Souvenir Sheet
601 A110 1.50pa multicolored 10.00 6.00
a. Perf. 14 10.00 6.00

Nos. 597-600 printed in sheets of 40, 2 panes of 20 separated by labels inscribed "Proof 1," etc.

Adventures of Will Mariner — A111

29s, Readying Port au Prince for sail, Gravesend, 1805. 32s, Captured & set afire, 1806. 47s, Mariner taken prisoner by Chief Finow, Tonga. 1.50pa, Passage to China aboard brig Favourite. 2.50pa, Returning to England aboard East Indiaman Cuffnells, 1810.

1985, June 18 *Die Cut*
602 A111 29s multicolored .60 .50
a. Perf. 14 .60 .50
603 A111 32s multicolored .65 .55
a. Perf. 14 .65 .55
604 A111 47s multicolored 1.00 .80
a. Perf. 14 1.00 .80
605 A111 1.50pa multicolored 3.25 3.25
a. Perf. 14 3.25 3.25
606 A111 2.50pa multicolored 5.50 5.50
a. Perf. 14 5.50 5.50
Nos. 602-606 (5) 11.00 10.60
Nos. 602a-606a (5) 11.00 10.60

Mutiny on the Bounty, Film 50th Anniv. A112

Designs: a, Byron Russell (Quintal), Stanley Fields (Muspratt) and Charles Laughton (Capt. Bligh). b, Laughton, Donald Crisp (Burkitt), Eddie Quillon (Ellison) and David Thursby (Maxwell). c, Clark Gable (Fletcher Christian). d, Russell, Alec Craig (McCoy), Laughton and Fields. e, Laughton and Franchot Tone (Roger Byam).

1985, July 16 *Perf. 14*
607 Strip of 5 55.00 55.00
a.-e. A112 47s, any single 10.00 5.00

Sheets consist of four strips of 5 and a central strip of labels showing film credits.

Queen Mother, 85th Birthday A113

Designs: 32s, Age 10. 47s, At Hadfield Girl Guides rally, 1931. 1.50pa, In Guide uniform. 2.50pa, Portrait by Norman Parkinson, 1985.

1985, Aug. 20 *Imperf.*
608 A113 32s multicolored 1.00 .75
a. Perf. 14 1.50 1.25
609 A113 47s multicolored 1.60 1.25
a. Perf. 14 2.50 2.00
610 A113 1.50pa multicolored 4.75 4.75
a. Perf. 14 7.75 7.75
611 A113 2.50pa multicolored 8.00 8.00
a. Perf. 14 12.50 12.50
Nos. 608-611 (4) 15.35 14.75
Nos. 608a-611a (4) 24.25 23.50

Girl Guides movement, 75th anniv.

Christmas — A114

1985, Nov. 12
612 A114 32s No room at the inn .50 .35
613 A114 42s Shepherds follow star .65 .45
614 A114 1.50pa The three kings 2.50 2.50
615 A114 2.50pa Holy family 3.75 3.75
Nos. 612-615 (4) 7.40 7.05

Self-adhesive Discontinued
In 1986, imperforate self-adhesive stamps attached to peelable paper backing were no longer issued, unless otherwise stated.

Halley's Comet A115

Designs: Nos. 616a, 617a, Comet. Nos. 616b, 617b, Edmond Halley. Nos. 616c, 617c, Solar system. Nos. 616d, 617d, Telescope. Nos. 616e, 617e, Giotto space probe.

1986, Mar. 26 *Perf. 14*
616 Strip of 5 17.50 17.50
a.-e. A115 42s, any single 3.00 3.00
617 Strip of 5 17.50 17.50
a.-e. A115 57s, any single 3.00 3.00

Nos. 564, 570, 565, 568, 567, 572, 577 and 579 Surcharged

1986, Apr. 16 Litho. *Imperf.*
Self-adhesive
618 A103 4s on 2s, #564 1.10 2.25
619 A103 4s on 13s, #570 1.10 2.25
620 A103 42s on 3s, #565 2.90 1.75
621 A103 42s on 9s, #568 2.90 1.75
622 A103 57s on 6s, #567 3.50 2.50
623 A103 57s on 20s, #572 3.50 2.50
624 A103 2.50pa on 2pa, #577 11.00 11.00
625 A103 2.50pa on 5pa, #579 11.00 11.00
Nos. 618-625 (8) 37.00 35.00

Royal Links with the United Kingdom A116

1986, May 22 *Perf. 14*
626 A116 57s Taufa'ahau IV 1.25 1.25
627 A116 57s Elizabeth II 1.25 1.25
a. Pair, #626-627 3.00 3.00

Size: 40x40mm
628 A116 2.50pa King and queen 5.50 5.50
Nos. 626-628 (3) 8.00 8.00

Queen Elizabeth II, 60th birthday. No. 628 printed in sheets of 5 plus one label.

AMERIPEX '86, Chicago, May 22-June 1 — A117

Peace Corps activities: No. 629, Health care. No. 630, Education.

1986, May 22
629 A117 57s multicolored 1.00 1.00
630 A117 1.50pa multicolored 2.75 2.75
a. Souv. sheet, #629, 630, imperf 4.50 4.50
b. Pair, #629-630 5.50 5.50

Peace Corps in Tonga, 20th anniv.

Intl. Sporting Events — A118

Designs: 42s, 1986 Field Hockey World Cup, London. 57s, Women's basketball, 13th Commonwealth Games, Scotland. 1pa, Boxing, Commonwealth Games. 2.50pa, 1986 World Cup Soccer Championships, Mexico.

1986, July 23 Litho. *Perf. 14*
631 A118 42s multicolored 1.25 1.25
632 A118 57s multicolored 1.75 1.75
633 A118 1pa multicolored 3.00 3.00
634 A118 2.50pa multicolored 7.25 7.25
Nos. 631-634 (4) 13.25 13.25

Postage Stamp Cent. A119

Stamps on stamps: No. 635, #1. No. 636, #47a. No. 637, #91. No. 638, #628. No. 639a, #40, UL portion of #C29. No. 639b, UR portion of #C29, left side #245. No. 639c, Center of #245, Type AP10. No. 639d, Left side #245, #C148. No. 639e, LL portion of #C29, #429, #440. No. 639f, LR portion of #C29, #135. No. 639g, #507. No. 639h, #514. Nos. 639a-639h, vert.

1986, Aug. 27
635 A119 32s multicolored 2.25 1.50
636 A119 42s multicolored 2.50 1.75
637 A119 57s multicolored 3.25 1.75
638 A119 2.50pa multicolored 5.50 5.50
Nos. 635-638 (4) 13.50 10.50

Souvenir Sheet
639 Sheet of 8 14.00 14.00
a.-h. A119 50s, any single 1.50 1.50

Christmas — A120

Designs: 32s, Girls wearing shell jewelry. 42s, Boy, totem poles, vert. 57s, Folk dancers, vert. 2pa, outrigger canoe.

1986, Nov. 12 Litho. *Perf. 14*
640 A120 32s multicolored 2.25 .80
641 A120 42s multicolored 2.50 .90
642 A120 57s multicolored 2.75 1.40
643 A120 2pa multicolored 6.00 6.00
Nos. 640-643 (4) 13.50 9.10

Nos. 641-642 Ovptd. with Jamboree Emblem and "BOY SCOUT / JAMBOREE / 5th-10th DEC '86" in Silver

1986, Dec. 2 Litho. *Perf. 14*
644 A120 42s multicolored 3.50 3.50
645 A120 57s multicolored 3.75 3.75

Dumont d'Urville's Second Voyage A121

Designs: 32s, D'Urville and ship Astrolabe. 42s, Four Tongan girls, detail from D'Urville's engraving, Voyage au Pole et dans l'Oceanie. 1pa, Map of voyage. 2.50pa, Wreck of the Astrolabe.

1987, Feb. 24
646 A121 32s multicolored 4.25 2.00
647 A121 42s multicolored 4.25 2.00
648 A121 1pa multicolored 10.00 6.00
649 A121 2.50pa multicolored 16.00 16.00
Nos. 646-649 (4) 34.50 26.00

Dumont d'Urville (1790-1842), explorer and admiral.

Wildlife Conservation — A122

Fauna: a, Noah's Ark. b, Eagles. c, Giraffes, birds. d, Seagulls. e, Elephants, ostriches. f, Elephant. g, Lions, zebras, antelopes. h, Chimpanzees. i, Antelope, frogs. j, Tigers, lizard. k, Tiger, snake. l, Butterfly.

1987, May 6 *Perf. 13½*
650 Sheet of 12 52.50 52.50
a.-l. A122 42s any single 4.00 4.00

1st Inter-island
Canoe Race,
Tonga to
Samoa — A123

1987, July 1   **Perf. 14**
651 A123 32s Two paddlers   .55   .45
652 A123 42s Five paddlers   .75   .60
653 A123 57s Three paddlers   1.00   .80
654 A123 1.50pa Two, diff.   2.75 2.75
  a.   Souvenir sheet of 4, #651-654 9.50 9.50
       Nos. 651-654 (4)   5.05 4.60

Coronation of King
Taufa'ahau IV, 20th
Anniv. — A124

Booklet Stamps
1987-88   **Imperf.**
Self-Adhesive
655 A124 1s green & yel grn   .30   .75
655A A124 2s blk & pale yel
              org   3.50 3.50
656 A124 5s black & brt pink   .30   .75
  a.   Bklt. pane of 12 (6 5s plus 1
       5s, 2 10s, 3 15s with gutter
       between)   4.50
657 A124 10s black & bluish lil .40 .85
658 A124 15s brn blk & org ver .55 .85
  a.   Bklt. pane of 12 (1s, 2 2s, 3
       10s, plus 2 5s, 10s, 3 15s
       with gutter between) ('88) 12.50
659 A124 32s Prus bl & aqua   .65 .90
  a.   Bklt. pane, 4 32s, 2 15s + 4
       10s, 2 1s with gutter be-
       tween)   6.25
  b.   Bklt. pane, 6 32s + 2 2s, 4 1s
       with gutter btwn. ('88) 12.50
       Nos. 655-659 (6)   5.70 7.60

Issued: 2s, 7/4/88; others, 7/1/87.

Parliament, 125th
Anniv. — A125

1987, Sept. 2   **Litho.**   **Perf. 14½**
660 A125 32s multicolored   .50   .50
661 A125 42s multicolored   .65   .65
662 A125 75s multicolored   1.10 1.10
663 A125 2pa multicolored   2.75 2.75
       Nos. 660-663 (4)   5.00 5.00

Christmas 1987 — A126

Cartoons featuring Octopus as Santa Claus
and mouse as his helper.

1987, Nov. 18   **Litho.**   **Perf. 14**
664 A126 42s Sack of gifts   1.40   .75
665 A126 57s Delivering them
              by canoe   1.60   .90
666 A126 1pa By automobile   3.00 3.00
667 A126 3pa Sipping tropical
              drinks   7.25 7.25
       Nos. 664-667 (4)   13.25 11.90

King Taufa'ahau Tupou IV, 70th
Birthday — A127

Portrait and: 32s, M.V. *Olovaha* inter-island
ship, athlete pole vaulting and offshore oil derrick. 42s, Banknote and coins, Ha'Amonga
Trilithon and traditional craftsman. 57s, Rowing, Red Cross nurse and communications
satellite. 2.50pa, Tonga Scouts emblem, No.
506 and Friendly Islands Airways passenger
plane.

1988, July 4   **Litho.**   **Perf. 11½**
668 A127 32s multicolored   2.00   .90
669 A127 42s multicolored   1.40 1.00
670 A127 57s multicolored   1.50 1.00
671 A127 2.50pa multicolored 7.50 7.50
       Nos. 668-671 (4)   12.40 10.40

See Nos. 744-747 for stamps inscribed for
the silver jubilee.

Souvenir Sheet

Australia Bicentennial — A128

Designs: a, Cook and his journal. b, List of
stores shipped aboard the *Lady Juliana,* the
ship, Arthur Philip, 1st gov. of New South
Wales, 1788, and left half of the list of
sentences of all the prisoners tried at Glo'ster
Assizes. c, Right half of list of sentences, Australia Type A59 redrawn and aerial view of an
early settlement. d, Robert O'Hara Burke
(1820-61) and W.J. Wills (1834-61), the 1st
explorers to cross Australia from south to
north. e, Emu pictured on a Player's cigarette
card, U.R. Stuart's (gold) prospecting license
and opals. f, Australian Commonwealth Military Forces emblem, WW I recruit on cigarette
card, and war poster. g, Souv. card commemorating 1st overland mail delivery by transcontinental railway, and Australia Type A4 on
cover. h, Hand-canceled cover commemorating the 1st England-Australia transcontinental
airmail flight, Nov. 12-Dec.10, 1919, aviator
Capt. Ross Smith (1892-1922) and Great Britain #588. i, Don Bradman and Harold
Larwood, cricket champions of the 1930s, on
cigarette cards, and era newspaper frontispiece. j, Frontispiece of Hulton's natl. weekly
Picture Post Victory Special issue, and WW II
campaign medals. k, Australia #676 and a
sheep station. l, Sydney Harbor Bridge, Opera
House and theater tickets to *The Bartered
Bride.*

1988, July 11   **Litho.**   **Perf. 13½**
672 A128 Sheet of 12   37.50 37.50
  a.-l.   42s any single   3.00 3.00

1988 Summer
Olympics,
Seoul — A129

1988, Aug. 11   **Perf. 14**
673 A129 57s Running   .75   .75
674 A129 75s Yachting   1.00 1.00
675 A129 2pa Cycling   5.00 5.00

676 A129 3pa Women's ten-
              nis   6.00 6.00
       Nos. 673-676 (4)   12.75 12.75

Music of
Tonga
A130

1988, Sept. 9   **Litho.**   **Perf. 14**
677 A130 32s shown   .55   .45
678 A130 42s Choir   .75   .60
679 A130 57s Tonga Police
              Band   .95   .80
680 A130 2.50pa The Jets   4.25 4.25
       Nos. 677-680 (4)   6.50 6.10

Souvenir Sheet

681   Sheet of 2   2.25 2.25
  a.   A130 57s like 2.50pa   1.00 1.00
  b.   A130 57s Olympic eternal
       flame   1.00 1.00

SPORT AID '88.

Marine Type of 1984

Two types of background shading on No.
690:
Type I: Shading at top and sides extends to
vert. & horiz. edges of design.
Type II: Shading is oval shaped.

1988   **Litho.**   **Perf. 14½**
Size: 27x34mm
682 A103 1s like No. 563   .25   .25
683 A103 1s like No. 564   .35   .35
684 A103 5s like No. 566   .45   .45
685 A103 6s like No. 567   .90   .90
686 A103 10s like No. 569   .55   .55
687 A103 15s like No. 571   .55   .55
688 A103 20s like No. 572   .80   .80
689 A103 32s like No. 574   .90   .90
690 A103 42s Fregata ariel,
              type I   3.25   .80
  a.   Type II   30.00
691 A103 57s Sula leuco-
              gaster   4.00 1.00

Size: 41x27mm
Perf. 14
692 A103 3pa Like No. 578   2.50 7.50
       Nos. 682-692 (11)   14.50 14.05

Issued: 1s, 5s, 10s, 20s, 32s, Oct. 4; 2s, 6s,
15s, 42s, 57s, 3pa, Oct. 18.
Nos. 683-684, 686, 689 exist inscribed
"1990."
See #701-709. For surcharge see #808.

Tonga-US
Treaty,
Cent.
A131

1988, Oct. 20   **Perf. 14**
693 A131 42s *Resolution*   1.00   .75
694 A131 57s *Santa Maria*   1.40 1.00
695 A131 2pa Capt. Cook,
              Columbus   5.00 5.00
  a.   Souvenir sheet of 3, #693-
       695   6.75 6.75
       Nos. 693-695 (3)   7.40 6.75

Christmas — A132

Designs (a, Intl. Red Cross, b, Natl. Red
Cross): 15s, Girl, teddy bear. 32s, Nurse reading to child. 42s, Checking pulse. 57s, Tucking
child into bed. 1.50pa, Boy in wheelchair.

1988, Nov. 17   **Litho.**   **Perf. 14½**
696 A132 15s Pair, #a.-b.   .50   .50
697 A132 32s Pair, #a.-b.   1.00 1.00
698 A132 42s Pair, #a.-b.   1.10 1.10
699 A132 57s Pair, #a.-b.   1.90 1.90
700 A132 1.50pa Pair, #a.-b. 4.75 4.75
       Nos. 696-700 (5)   9.25 9.25

Intl. Red Cross 125th anniv. and 25th anniv.
of the natl. Red Cross.

Marine Type of 1984
1989, Mar. 2   **Lith(?)**
Size: 27x34mm
701 A103 4s like No. 570   1.60 1.6(?)
702 A103 7s Diomedea
              exulans   3.75 2.(?)
703 A103 35s Hippocampus   3.25 2.7(?)
704 A103 50s like No. 573   3.75 2.0(?)
Size: 41x27mm
Perf. 14
705 A103 1pa Chelonia
              mydas   6.00 4.5(?)
706 A103 1.50pa Megaptera
              novaean-
              gliae   12.00 7.5(?)
707 A103 2pa like No. 577   8.75 8.7(?)
709 A103 5pa like No. 579   14.00 17.(?)
       Nos. 701-709 (8)   53.10 46.6(?)

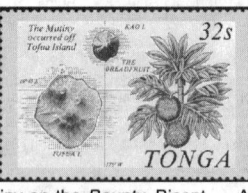

Mutiny on the *Bounty,* Bicent. — A13(?)

32s, Map of Tofua & Kao Isls., breadfru(?)
42s, *Bounty,* chronometer. 57s, William Blig(?)
& castaways in longboat. 2pa, Mutineers o(?)
the *Bounty,* vert. 3pa, Castaways.

Perf. 13½x14, 14x13½
1989, Apr. 28   **Phot(?)**
710 A133 32s multicolored   3.50 2.0(?)
711 A133 42s multicolored   5.75 2.5(?)
712 A133 57s multicolored   7.50 3.7(?)
       Nos. 710-712 (3)   16.75 8.2(?)

Souvenir Sheet
713   Sheet of 2   13.50 13.5(?)
  a.   A133 2pa multicolored   5.00 5.0(?)
  b.   A133 3pa multicolored   7.50 7.5(?)

Butterflies
A134

1989, May 15   **Litho.**   **Perf. 14**
714 A134 42s *Hypolimnas
              bolina*   1.10   .7(?)
715 A134 57s *Jamides
              bochus*   1.40 1.0(?)
716 A134 1.20pa *Melanitis le-
              da solandra*   3.25 2.5(?)
717 A134 2.50pa *Danaus plex-
              ippus*   6.25 6.2(?)
       Nos. 714-717 (4)   12.00 10.5(?)

Opening of the Natl. Sports Stadium
and the South Pacific Mini Games,
Aug. 22
A135

Rugby (No. 718): a, Rugby Public Schoo(?)
1870. b, Dave Gallaher and the Springbo(?)
vs. East Midlands, 1906. c, King George (?)
inspecting Cambridge team of 1922 an(?)
Wavell Wakefield, captain of England. d, Ern(?)
Crawford, captain of Ireland, Danie Crave(?)
demonstrating the dive pass and cigarett(?)
cards from the 1930's. e, Sioni Mafi, captain (?)
Tonga, and match scene.
Tennis (No. 719): a, Royal tennis, 1659. (?)
Walter Clopton Wingfield and game of law(?)
tennis, 1873. c, Oxford and Cambridge team(?)
of 1884. d, Bunny Ryan in 1910 and cigarett(?)
cards. e, Tennis players, 1980's.
Cricket (No. 720): a, Match in 1743 an(?)
bronze memorial to Fuller Pilch. b, W.(?)
Grace, 19th cent. c, *The Boys Own Pape(?)
1909. d, Australian team of 1909 and cigarett(?)
cards. e, The Ashes trophy and modern mat(?)
scene.

1989, Aug. 22   Litho.   Perf. 14

718		Strip of 5	6.25	6.25
a.-e.	A135	32s any single	1.00	1.00
719		Strip of 5	9.50	9.50
a.-e.	A135	42s any single	1.50	1.50
720		Strip of 5	14.50	14.50
a.-e.	A135	57s any single	2.50	2.50
	Nos. 718-720 (3)	30.25	30.25

Printed in sheets of 10 containing descriptions and emblem.

Natl. Aviation History — A136

Designs: 42s, Short S30. 57s, Vought F4U Corsair. 90s, Boeing 737. 3pa, Montgolfier brothers' hot-air balloon, the Wright Flyer, Concorde jet and space shuttle.

1989, Oct. 23   Litho.   Perf. 14½x14

721	A136	42s multicolored	3.00	1.50
722	A136	57s multicolored	3.50	1.50
723	A136	90s multicolored	6.25	5.75

Size: 97x126½mm

724	A136	3pa multicolored	14.50	14.50
	Nos. 721-724 (4)	27.25	23.50

1st Flight to Tonga, 1939 (42s); military base on the island, 1943 (57s); civil aviation, Fua'amotu Airport (90s); aviation through the ages (3pa).

Flying Home for Christmas A137

1989, Nov. 9   Perf. 14x13½

725	A137	32s Aircraft landing	1.75	.80
726	A137	42s Islanders waving, aircraft	2.00	.80
727	A137	57s Tongan in outrigger canoe, aircraft	2.25	1.00
728	A137	3pa Islanders waving, aircraft, diff.	6.50	6.50
	Nos. 725-728 (4)	12.50	9.10

World Stamp Expo '89 A138

20th UPU Congress, Washington, DC — A139

Postal history and communications (No. 730): a, Sir Rowland Hill, penny blacks on Mulready envelope. b, Clipper ship, early train. c, Pony Express advertisement, stagecoach, post rider. d, Hot-air balloon and flight cover. e, Samuel Morse, miniature, telegraph key. f, Early Royal Mail truck, mailbox. g, Biplane and early aviators. h, Zeppelin flight cover, HMS Queen Mary. i, Helicopter, truck. j, Computer

operator, facsimile machine. k, Apollo 11 mission emblem, flight cover, planetary bodies. l, American space shuttle, UPU monument.

1989, Nov. 17   Litho.   Perf. 14

729	A138	57s Pair, #730k-730 l	3.00	3.00

**Souvenir Sheet
Perf. 13½**

730	A139	Sheet of 12	35.00	35.00
a.-l.		A139 57s any single	2.50	2.50

A140   A141

1990, Feb. 14   Litho.   Perf. 14

731	A140	42s Boxing	1.25	.75
732	A140	57s Archery	2.00	1.25
733	A140	1pa Bowls	2.75	2.75
734	A140	2pa Swimming	4.50	4.50
	Nos. 731-734 (4)	10.50	9.25

1990 Commonwealth Games.

1990, Apr. 11   Litho.   Perf. 14

Protect the Environment: 32s, Wave power, ocean pollution. 57s, Wind power, acid rain. $1.20, Solar power, ozone layer. $2.50, Green earth, rain forests.

735	A141	32s multicolored	2.00	.75
736	A141	57s multicolored	3.00	1.25
737	A141	1.20pa multicolored	6.00	6.00
	Nos. 735-737 (3)	11.00	8.00

Souvenir Sheet

738	A141	2.50pa multicolored	11.00	11.00

First Postage Stamps, 150th Anniv. A142

1990   Litho.   Perf. 14

739	A142	42s G. B. #1	1.75	1.25
740	A142	42s G. B. #2	1.75	1.25
a.		Pair, #739-740	3.75	3.75
741	A142	57s Tonga #1	2.25	1.25
742	A142	1.50pa Tonga #CO180	5.00	5.00
743	A142	2.50pa Tonga #736	7.50	7.50
	Nos. 739-743 (5)	18.25	16.25

King's Birthday Type of 1988 Inscribed "Silver Jubilee of His Majesty King Taufa'ahau Tupou IV 1965-1990"

1990, July 4   Litho.   Perf. 11½

744	A127	32s like No. 668	1.50	1.00
745	A127	42s like No. 669	1.50	1.00
746	A127	57s like No. 670	2.00	1.10
747	A127	2.50pa like No. 671	7.00	7.00
	Nos. 744-747 (4)	12.00	10.10

Native Catamaran — A143

1990, June 6   Perf. 14½

748	A143	32s buff & green	1.60	.75
749	A143	42s buff & bl, diff.	1.50	.80
750	A143	1.20pa buff & brn, diff.	4.00	4.00
751	A143	3pa buff & vio, diff.	8.00	8.00
	Nos. 748-751 (4)	15.10	13.55

Banded Iguana A144

1990, Sept. 12   Litho.   Perf. 14

752	A144	32s multicolored	2.00	1.25
753	A144	42s multi, diff.	2.50	1.75
754	A144	57s multi, diff.	3.00	2.00
755	A144	1.20pa multi, diff.	7.50	4.50
	Nos. 752-755 (4)	15.00	9.50

Marine Type of 1984

**1990, July 6   Litho.   Perf. 14
Size: 20x22mm**

756	A103	2s like No. 564	1.10	.75
a.		Booklet pane of 10	11.00	11.00
757	A103	5s like No. 566	1.10	.75
a.		Booklet pane of 10	11.00	11.00
758	A103	10s like No. 569	1.10	.75
a.		Booklet pane of 10	11.00	11.00
759	A103	32s like No. 574	2.00	2.00
a.		Booklet pane of 10	20.00	20.00
	Nos. 756-759 (4)	5.30	4.25

Nos. 756-758 exist inscribed "1992."
For surcharge see No. 810.
Issue date: #756a-759a, Sept. 4.

UN Development Program, 40th Anniv. — A145

1990, Oct. 25   Litho.   Perf. 14

760	A145	57s Tourism	2.00	2.00
761	A145	57s Agriculture, fisheries	2.00	2.00
a.		Pair, #760-761	4.50	4.50
762	A145	3pa Education	10.00	10.00
763	A145	3pa Healthcare	10.00	10.00
a.		Pair, #762-763	22.50	22.50
	Nos. 760-763 (4)	24.00	24.00

Rotary Intl. — A146

Accident Prevention A147

1990, Nov. 28

764	A146	32s shown	.95	.50
765	A146	42s Two boys	1.25	.75
766	A146	2pa Three children	4.50	4.50
767	A146	3pa Two girls	6.00	6.00
	Nos. 764-767 (4)	12.70	11.75

1991, Apr. 10   Litho.   Perf. 14½

No. 768: a, d, Care at work; hard hats save lives. b, c, Keep matches and medicines out of children's reach. e, as "d," corrected inscription
No. 769: a, d, Don't drink and drive. b, c, Crash helmets save lives; mind cyclists and children.
No. 770: a, d, Listen to forecasts; learn to swim. b, c, Swim from safe beaches; beware of broken glass.
"a" and "b" have English inscriptions, denominations at top; "c" and "d" have Tongan inscriptions, denominations at bottom.

Strips of 4 + Label

768	A147	32s #a.-d.	4.50	4.50
f.		Strip of 4, #a.-c., e.		32.50
769	A147	42s #a.-d.	5.75	5.75
770	A147	57s #a.-d.	7.25	7.25
	Nos. 768-770 (3)	17.50	17.50

Center label is a progressive proof.
No. 768d was incorrectly inscribed, "Ngauo tokanga." No. 768e was issued 8/11/91 with correct inscription, "Ngaue tokanga."
For surcharge see No. 811.

A148

A149

1991, July 2   Litho.   Perf. 14½

771	A148	42s Fish	.80	.70
772	A148	57s Island, boat	.95	.85
773	A148	2pa Fruit, island	3.25	3.25
774	A148	3pa Turtle, beach	5.50	5.50
	Nos. 771-774 (4)	10.50	10.30

Heilala week.

1991, July 2

Racing yachts: a, Red spinnaker. b, Yellow spinnaker. c, Green striped spinnaker. d, Yacht at sunset. e, Yacht, moon.

Miniature Sheet of 5 + Label

775	A149	1pa #775a-775e	13.00	13.00

Around the world yacht race.

Church of Jesus Christ of Latter Day Saints in Tonga, Cent. — A150

1991, Aug. 19

776	A150	42s Tonga Temple	1.50	1.50
777	A150	57s Temple at night	2.50	2.50

Rowing Festival A151

1991, Oct. 29   Litho.   Perf. 14

778	A151	42s Women's coxed eight	1.00	1.00
779	A151	57s Men's longboat	1.50	1.50
780	A151	1pa Outrigger	2.75	2.75
781	A151	2pa Bow of large canoe	5.25	5.25
782	A151	2pa Stern of large canoe	5.25	5.25
a.		Pair, #781-782	11.00	11.00
	Nos. 778-782 (5)	15.75	15.75

For surcharges see Nos. 898-899C.

Telecommunications — A152

No. 783: a, Recording television program. b, Communications Satellite. c, Watching television program.

No. 784: a, Man on telephone, woman at computer. b, Communications satellite, diff. c, Man in city on telephone.

No. 785: a, Seaman on sinking ship broadcasting SOS. b, Man on telephone, satellite relay station. c, Rescue missions.

No. 786: a, Weather satelite. b, Men at computers. c, Television weather report, storm.

1991, Oct. 15   Litho.   Perf. 14½

783	A152	15s Strip of 3, #a.-c.	1.50	1.50
784	A152	32s Strip of 3, #a.-c.	3.00	3.00
785	A152	42s Strip of 3, #a.-c.	4.25	4.25
786	A152	57s Strip of 3, #a.-c.	6.00	6.00
		Nos. 783-786 (4)	14.75	14.75

Christmas — A153

Designs: 32s, Turtles pulling Santa's sleigh. 42s, Santa on roof. 57s, Family with presents. 3.50pa, Waving goodbye to Santa.

1991, Nov. 11

787	A153	32s multicolored	.85	.60
788	A153	42s multicolored	1.10	.80
789	A153	57s multicolored	1.60	1.60
790	A153	3.50pa multicolored	9.25	9.25
		Nos. 787-790 (4)	12.80	12.25

Armed Forces — A154

1991, Dec. 15

791		42s Royal Tonga Marine	1.00	1.00
792		42s Patrol boat Pangai	1.00	1.00
a.	A154	Pair, #791-792	2.50	2.50
793		57s Patrol boat Neiafu	1.50	1.50
794		57s Tonga Royal Guards	1.50	1.50
a.	A154	Pair, #793-794	3.50	3.50
795		2pa King Tupou IV, military parade	5.25	5.25
796		2pa Patrol boat Savea	5.25	5.25
a.	A154	Pair, #795-796	11.00	11.00
		Nos. 791-796 (6)	15.50	15.50

Miniature Sheet

Discovery of America, 500th Anniv. — A155

Designs: a, Columbus. b, Monastery of Santa Maria de la Chevas. c, Obverse and reverse of coin of Ferdinand and Isabella. d, Spain #C48. e, Compass, astrolabe. f, Santa Maria. g, Map, Columbus' signature. h, Columbus arriving in New World. i, Lucayan artifacts, parrot. j, Pineapple, artifacts. k, Columbus announcing his discovery. l, Medal of Columbus, signature.

1992, Apr. 28   Litho.   Perf. 13½

797	A155	57s Sheet of 12, #a.-l.	32.50	32.50

Marine Type of 1984 and

A155a

Perf. 13x13½, 14 (15s, 20s, 10pa)

1992-93   Litho.

798	A155a	1s Swainsonia casta	.20	.20
799	A155a	3s Holocentrus ruber	.20	.20
800	A155a	5s Cypraea mappa viridis	.20	.20
801	A155a	10s Conus bullatus	.20	.20
802	A103	15s like #567	.25	.25
803	A155a	20s Dascyllus aruanus	.30	.30
804	A155a	45s Lambis truncata	.70	.70
805	A155a	60s Conus aulicus	.90	.90
806	A155a	80s Pterois volitans	1.25	1.25

Size: 27x41mm

807	A103	10pa like #568	18.00	18.00
		Nos. 798-807 (10)	22.20	22.20

Issued: 1s, 3s, 5s, 10s, 20s, 45s, 60s, 80s, May 12, 1993. 15s, 10pa, May 5, 1992.

See Nos. 874-884. Area covered by background colors on Nos. 874, 876-879 has been reduced in size. See Nos. 920-924.

For inscribed stamps see Nos. O78-O87.

Surcharges

On #688

XX

10s

On #756 in Blue

On #759

On #769 in Red and Black

1992-93   Litho.   Perf. 14½, 14

808	A103	1s on 20s #688	.20	.20
809	A103	10s on 2s #756		
810	A103	45s on 32s #759	4.00	4.00
811	A147	60s on 42s Strip of 4, #a.-d. + label	16.00	16.00

Issued: 1s, 5/19; 45s, 60s, 8/11; 10s, 1993.

Miniature Sheet

World War II in Pacific, 50th Anniv. A156

Designs: a, Newspaper headline, Japanese attack on Pearl Harbor. b, Map of Bataan, Corregidor, and Manila, pilot's wings, airplanes. c, Newspaper headline, troops landing in Gilbert Islands, Marine Corps emblem, dogtags. d, Uniform patch, B-29 "Enola Gay," troops landing on Iwo Jima. e, Map of Battle of Midway, Admiral Nimitz. f, Southwest Pacific campaign map, Gen. MacArthur. g, Map of Saipan and Tinian, Lt. Gen. Holland Smith. h, Map outling bombing of Japan, Maj. Gen. Curtis Lemay. i, Mitsubishi A6M Zero. j, Douglas SBD Dauntless. k, Grumman F4F Wildcat. l, Supermarine Seafire.

1992, May 26   Litho.   Perf. 14

814	A156	42s Sheet of 12, #a.-l.	22.50	22.50

42

1992 Summer Olympics, Barcelona — A157

1992, June 16

815	A157	42s Boxing	1.10	.75
816	A157	57s Diving	1.60	1.00
817	A157	1.50pa Tennis	4.25	4.25
818	A157	3pa Cycling	8.75	8.75
		Nos. 815-818 (4)	15.70	14.75

King Taufa'ahau IV, 25th Anniv. of Coronation A158

Designs: 45s, 2pa, King, Queen Halaevalu. No. 820a, King, crown. b, Extract from investiture ceremony. c, King, #C33.

1992, July 4   Perf. 13½x13

819	A158	45s multicolored	1.10	.85

Size: 51x38mm

Perf. 12½x12

820	A158	80s Strip of 3, #a.- c.	6.25	6.25
821	A158	2pa multicolored	4.75	4.75
		Nos. 819-821 (3)	12.10	11.85

Sacred Bats of Kolovai — A159

Designs: No. 822a, Bats in flight. b, Close-up of flying bat. c, Flying bats, tree. d, Bats hanging in tree. e, Bat hanging from tree limb.

Origin of sacred bats: No. 823a, 45s, Kula leaving for Upolu to be tattooed as Tongan chief. b, 45s, Kula looking through path of fires. c, 2pa, Kula walking down path, Hina. d, 2pa, Hina waving, Kula leaving with pet fruit bats.

Nos. 823a-823d are horiz.

1992, Oct. 20   Litho.   Perf. 14

822	A159	60s Strip of 5, #a.-e.	13.00	13.00

Souvenir Sheet

Perf. 14½

823	A159	Sheet of 4, #a.-d.	14.00	14.00

Christmas A160

1992, Nov. 10   Perf. 14

824	A160	60s Pearls	1.50	1.10
825	A160	80s Reef fish	2.00	1.40
826	A160	2pa Pacific orchids	4.75	4.75
827	A160	3pa Eua parrots	7.25	7.25
		Nos. 824-827 (4)	15.50	14.50

For surcharges see Nos. 894-897.

Anniversaries and Events — A161

Designs: 60s, Tonga flag, Rotary emblem 80sh, John F. Kennedy, Peace Corps emblem 1.50pa, FAO, WHO emblems. 3.50pa, Globe Rotary Foundation emblem.

1992, Dec. 15   Perf. 14½

828	A161	60s multicolored	1.40	1.00
829	A161	80s multicolored	1.90	1.40
830	A161	1.50pa multicolored	3.50	3.50
831	A161	3.50pa multicolored	8.50	8.50
		Nos. 828-831 (4)	15.30	14.40

Rotary Intl. in Tonga, 25th anniv. (#828) Peace Corps in Tonga, 25th anniv. (#829). Intl Conference of FAO and WHO (#830). Rotary Foundation of Rotary Intl., 75th anniv. (#831) For overprint see No. 868.

Family Planning — A163

Outdoor silhouette scenes: No. 832, Mother, girl, butterflies. No. 833, Child on tricycle pulling kite. No. 834, Girl, kittens. No. 835, Adult, child playing chess.

1993, Jan. 26   Perf. 14x13½

832	A163	15s Pair, #a.-b.	2.10	2.10
833	A163	45s Pair, #a.-b.	3.00	3.00
834	A163	60s Pair, #a.-b.	4.25	4.25
835	A163	2pa Pair, #a.-b.	13.00	13.00
		Nos. 832-835 (4)	22.35	22.35

Nos. 832a-835a have Tongan inscriptions. Nos. 832b-835b have English inscriptions and are mirror images of Nos. 832a-835a.

Health and Fitness — A164

Designs: 60s, Fresh fruit, fish, anti-smoking and anti-drug symbols. 80s, Anti-smoking symbol, weight training. 1.50pa, Anti-drug symbol, water sports. 2.50pa, Fresh fruit, fish, cyclist, jogger. Illustration reduced.

1993, Mar. 16   Litho.   Perf. 14

836	A164	60s multicolored	1.75	1.75
837	A164	80s multicolored	2.40	2.40
838	A164	1.50pa multicolored	4.50	4.50
839	A164	2.50pa multicolored	7.25	7.25
		Nos. 836-839 (4)	15.90	15.90

Tonga Fire Service, 25th Anniv. A165

1993, May 18   Litho.   Perf. 14

840	A165	45s Fireman's badge	1.50	1.50
841	A165	45s Police van, badge	1.50	1.50
a.		Pair, #840-841	3.50	3.50
842	A165	60s Police band	2.00	2.00
843	A165	60s Putting out fire	2.00	2.00
a.		Pair, #842-843	4.50	4.50
844	A165	2pa Fire truck at station	7.00	7.00
845	A165	2pa Policeman, police dog	7.00	7.00
a.		Pair, #844-845	15.00	15.00
		Nos. 840-845 (6)	21.00	21.00

Tonga Police Training College, 25th anniv. (#841-842, 845).

For surcharges see Nos. 943-948.

A166

A167

Abel Tasman's Voyage to Eua, 350th Anniv.: 30s, Map of islands. 60s, Sailing ships, Heemskirk and Zeehaen. 80s, Sailing ships, natives in canoes. 3.50pa, Landing on Eua.

1993, June 21

846	A166	30s multicolored	.80	.50
847	A166	60s multicolored	1.75	1.10
848	A166	80s multicolored	2.25	2.25
849	A166	3.50pa multicolored	10.00	10.00
		Nos. 846-849 (4)	14.80	13.85

1993, July 1   Litho.   Perf. 13x13½

King Taufa'ahau IV, 75th Birthday: 45s, 2pa, Musical instruments.

No. 851a, Sporting events. b, Ancient landmarks. c, Royal Palace.

850	A167	45s multicolored	.65	.65

Perf. 12x12½

Size: 37x48mm

851	A167	80s Strip of 3, #a.-		
		c.	5.00	5.00
852	A167	2pa multicolored	3.00	3.00
		Nos. 850-852 (3)	8.65	8.65

A168

A168a

Children's Stamp Designs: Nos. 853a, 854a, Beach scene. Nos. 853b, 854b, "Maui—The Fisher of the Islands." Nos. 853c, 854c, Raft on ocean. Nos. 853d, 854d, Woman with hands in mixing bowl. Nos. 853e, 854e, "Maui and his Hook." Nos. 853f, 854f, "Communication in the South Pacific."

1993, Dec. 1   Litho.   Perf. 14

853	A168	10s Strip of 6, #a.-f.	2.75	2.75
854	A168	80s Strip of 6, #a.-f.	13.00	13.00

1993, Nov. 10   Litho.   Perf. 14

Christmas traditions: 60s, Festive dinner. 80s, Shooting cannon. 1.50pa, Musicians. 3pa, Going to church.

855	A168a	60s multicolored	1.40	1.10
856	A168a	80s multicolored	1.75	1.40
857	A168a	1.50pa multicolored	3.50	3.50
858	A168a	3pa multicolored	7.00	7.00
		Nos. 855-858 (4)	13.65	13.00

Miniature Sheet

Kindness to Animals — A169

Designs: a, 80s, Boy holding puppy. b, 80s, Girl holding kitten. c, 60s, Boy holding rooster (b). d, 60s, Girl with butterfly. e, 60s, Three dogs. f, 60s, Boy, puppy.

1994, Jan. 14   Perf. 14½

859	A169	Sheet of 6, #a.-f.	14.00	14.00

For overprint see No. 868.

Game Fishing — A170

1994, Feb. 28   Litho.   Perf. 12

860	A170	60s Tiger shark	1.50	1.00
861	A170	80s Dolphin fish	2.00	1.40
862	A170	1.50pa Yellow fin tuna	4.00	4.00
863	A170	2.50pa Pacific blue marlin	6.50	6.50
		Nos. 860-863 (4)	14.00	12.90

1994 World Cup Soccer Championships, US — A171

Designs: No. 864a, Player's legs. No. 864b, World Cup trophy. No. 865a, American player in red, white, & blue. No. 865b, German player in black shorts, white shirt.

1994, June 1   Perf. 14x14½

864	A171	80s Pair, #a.-b.	4.00	4.00
865	A171	2pa Pair, #a.-b.	10.00	10.00

Pan Pacific & South East Asia Women's Assoc. Conference — A172

Career women: No. 866a, Lawyer. No. 866b, Policewoman. No. 867a, Doctor. No. 867b, Nurse.

1994, Aug. 18   Litho.   Perf. 14

866	A172	45s Pair, #a.-b.	3.50	3.50
867	A172	2.50pa Pair, #a.-b.	10.50	10.50

Nos. 859a, 859c-859f Ovptd. "MERRY / CHRISTMAS"

No. 859b Ovptd. "KILISIMASI FIEFIA"

1994, Nov. 10   Litho.   Perf. 14½

868	A169	Sheet of 6, #a.-f.	8.50	8.50

No. 831 Ovptd. in Dark Blue

1994, Nov. 17   Litho.   Perf. 14½

869	A161	60s on 3.50pa multi	2.75	2.75

Types of 1969-85 and

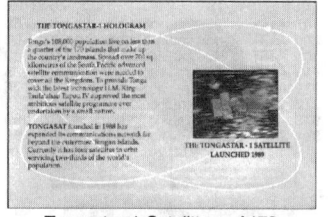

Tongastar 1 Satelitte — A173

Design: a, 10s, Type A39 banana, size 22x11mm. b, 25s, Type AP12. c, Booklet pane, 12 #870a, 3 #870b. d, 45s, like #608. e, 45s, like #609. f, 45s, like #610. g, 45s, like #611. h, Booklet pane of 3 each #870d-870e, 2 #870f, 1 #870g. i, 60s, Type A72. j, 60s, Type OA19. k, 80s, Type OA17. l, Booklet pane, #870i-870k. m, 2pa, Tongastar 1. n, Booklet pane of 1 #870m.

Unwmk.

1994, Dec. 14   Litho.   Die Cut

Self-adhesive

870	A173	Souvenir booklet	20.00

First full-scale production of self-adhesive stamps by Tonga, 25th anniv. (#870). Satellite communications network for Tongan Islands (#870m).

No. 870b is airmail. Nos. 870j-870k are air post official stamps.

No. 870m contains a holographic image. Soaking in water may affect the hologram.

Marine Type of 1992-93 Redrawn

1994-95		**Litho.**	**Perf. 14**	
874	A155a	10s like #799A	.20	.20
876	A155a	20s like #801	.30	.30
877	A155a	45s like #803	.70	.70
878	A155a	60s like #804	.95	.95
879	A155a	80s like #806	1.25	1.25

Size: 41x27mm, 41x27mm

880	A155a	1pa like #705, horiz.	1.90	1.90
881	A155a	2pa like #577, horiz.	3.75	3.75
882	A155a	3pa like #578, horiz.	5.75	5.75
883	A155a	5pa like #706	9.50	9.50
884	A155a	10pa like #568	20.00	20.00
		Nos. 874-884 (10)	44.30	44.30

Area covered by background colors on Nos. 874, 876-879 has been reduced in size.

Issued: 1pa, 2pa, 3pa, 6/21/94; 5pa, 9/21/94; 10pa, 1/18/95; 10s, 20s, 45s, 60s, 80s, 9/25/95.

This is an expanding set. Numbers may change.

FAO, 50th Anniv. A174

1995, May 16   Litho.   Perf. 14

886	A174	5pa multicolored	13.00	13.00

Tonga's Entry into British Commonwealth, 25th Anniv. — A175

Children with bicycles from parts of Commonwealth.

1995, June 6

887	A175	45s Polynesia	1.10	.90
888	A175	60s Asia	1.50	1.25
889	A175	80s Africa	1.75	1.75
890	A175	2pa India	4.50	4.50
891	A175	2.50pa Europe	6.00	6.00
		Nos. 887-891 (5)	14.85	14.40

1995 Rugby World Cup, South Africa — A176

Designs: No. 892a, Player running right with ball, two others. b, Two players. No. 893a, Three players. b, Player ready to catch ball.

1995, June 20   Perf. 14½

892	A176	80s Pair, #a.-b.	4.00	4.00
893	A176	2pa Pair, #a.-b.	9.00	9.00

Nos. 892-893 were each issued in sheets of 4 stamps.

For surcharges see Nos. 954A, 956A.

Nos. 824-827 Surcharged

i

j

1995, June 30   Litho.   Perf. 14

894		60s Pair	4.00	4.00
a.	A160(i)	on #824	1.75	1.75
b.	A160(j)	on #824	1.75	1.75
895		60s Pair	4.00	4.00
a.	A160(i)	on 80s #825	1.75	1.75
b.	A160(j)	on 80s #825	1.75	1.75
896		60s Pair	4.00	4.00
a.	A160(i)	on 2pa #826	1.75	1.75
b.	A160(j)	on 2pa #826	1.75	1.75
897		60s Pair	4.00	4.00
a.	A160(i)	on 3pa #827	1.75	1.75
b.	A160(j)	on 3pa #827	1.75	1.75
		Nos. 894-897 (4)	16.00	16.00

Nos. 779-782 Surcharged

1995, June 30   Litho.   Perf. 14

898	A151	60s on 57s #779	1.40	1.40
899	A151	80s on 2pa #781	1.75	1.75
899A	A151	80s on 2pa #782	1.75	1.75
b.		Pair, #899-899A	3.50	3.50
899C	A151	1pa on #780	2.25	2.25
		Nos. 898-899C (4)	7.15	7.15

Victory in the Pacific, 50th Anniv. — A177

Nos. 900, 901: a, Soldier climbing from rope ladder. b, Ship, soldiers. c, Ship, landing craft with troops, soldiers up close. d, Ship, landing craft with troops. e, Map.

1995, Aug. 1   Litho.   Perf. 14x14½
900 A177 60s Strip of 5, #a.-e.   8.50   8.50
901 A177 80s Strip of 5, #a.-e.   10.00 10.00

Nos. 900-901 are continuous designs and were issued together in sheet containing ten stamps.

Singapore '95 — A178

Designs: No. 902a, 45s, #887. b, 60s, #888. 2pa, Boy cycling in Singapore.

1995, Sept. 1   Litho.   Perf. 12
902 A178   Pair, #a.-b.   3.75   3.75

Souvenir Sheet
903 A178 2pa multicolored   4.75   4.75

Souvenir Sheet

Beijing Intl. Coin & Stamp Show '95 — A179

Design: 1.40pa, Mount Song, Henan Province, China. Illustration reduced.

1995, Sept. 14   Perf. 14½
904 A179 1.40pa multicolored   4.00   4.00

End of World War II, UN, 50th Anniv. — A180

No. 905a, Holocaust survivors. b, UN emblem, "50." c, Children of Holocaust survivors in celebration.
No. 906a, Mushroom cloud from atom bomb explosion. b, Like #905b. c, Space shuttle.

1995, Oct. 20   Litho.   Perf. 13
905 A180 60s Strip of 3, #a.-c.   3.75   3.75
906 A180 80s Strip of 3, #a.-c.   6.25   6.25

Nos. 905b, 906b are 23x31mm.

Christmas and New Year — A181

Orchids: 20s, Calanthe triplicata. Nos. 908, Spathoglottis plicata, inscribed "MERRY CHRISTMAS." No. 909, like #908, inscribed "A HAPPY 1996." No. 910, Dendrobium platygastrium, inscribed "MERRY CHRISTMAS". No. 911, like #910, inscribed "A HAPPY 1996." 80s, Goodyera rubunda. 2pa, Dendrobium toki. 2.50pa, Phaius tankervilliae.

1995, Nov. 15   Litho.   Perf. 14x14½
907 A181   20s multicolored   .50   .50
908 A181   45s multicolored   1.00   1.00
909 A181   45s multicolored   1.00   1.00
910 A181   60s multicolored   1.25   1.25
911 A181   60s multicolored   1.25   1.25
912 A181   80s multicolored   1.75   1.75
913 A181   2pa multicolored   4.50   4.50
914 A181 2.50pa multicolored   5.50   5.50
    Nos. 907-914 (8)   16.75 16.75

Humpback Whale — A182

1996, Jan. 7   Perf. 14
915 A182   45s In water   1.60   .50
916 A182   60s With calf   2.50   .75
917 A182 1.50pa Sounding   5.00   5.00
918 A182 2.50pa Breaching   7.50   7.50
    Nos. 915-918 (4)   16.60 13.75

World Wildlife Fund.

Miniature Sheet

New Year 1996 (Year of the Rat) — A183

Denomination: a, UR. b, UL. c, LR. d, LL.

1996, Feb. 23
919 A183   60s Sheet of 4, #a.-d.   7.50   7.50

No. 919 is a continuous design. See Nos. 930-932, 932E, 942, 986.

Marine Type of 1992-93 Redrawn
1996, May 31   Litho.   Perf. 14
Size: 40x26mm
920 A155a 1pa like #880   2.10   2.10
921 A155a 2pa like #881   4.25   4.25
922 A155a 3pa like #882   6.75   6.75
923 A155a 5pa like #883   11.00   11.00
924 A155a 10pa like #884   22.50   22.50
    Nos. 920-924 (5)   46.60 46.60

Size of "TONGA" on Nos. 920-923 is smaller than on Nos. 880-883. Name of species appears at top instead of bottom on Nos. 920-924. Background colors vary. Inscribed "1996."

1996 Summer Olympic Games, Atlanta — A184

Statues of classical Greek figures, modern athletes: 45s, Zeus, runner. 80s, The Discus Thrower. 2pa, The Javelin Thrower. 3pa, The Horseman, dressage competitor.

1996, July 2   Litho.   Perf. 14
925 A184 45s multicolored   1.25   .75
926 A184 80s multicolored   2.00   1.75
927 A184 2pa multicolored   5.25   5.25
928 A184 3pa multicolored   8.25   8.25
    Nos. 925-928 (4)   16.75 16.00

For surcharges & overprint see Nos. 949-952.

13th Congress of Intl. Union of Preshistoric and Protohistoric Sciences — A185

a, Prehistoric man using fire, knife, bow & arrow, animals. b, Ancient Egyptians, Greeks, Romans.

1996, Sept. 5   Litho.   Perf. 12
929 A185 1pa Pair, #a.-b.   5.50   5.50

No. 929 was issued in sheets of 6 stamps.

New Year 1996 (Year of the Rat) Type
Denomination: a, UR. b, UL. c, LR. d, LL.

1996, June 27   Litho.   Perf. 14
Sheets of 4
930 A183 10s #a.-d.   1.40   1.40
931 A183 20s #a.-d.   2.75   2.75
932 A183 45s #a.-d.   6.75   6.75
932E A183 60s #a.-d.   8.50   8.50

The denominations are larger on No. 932E than those on No. 919.

Christmas A186

Paintings: 20s, Virgin and Child, by Sassoferrato. 60s, Adoration of the Shepherds, by Murillo. 80s, Virgin and Child, by Delaroche. 1pa, Adoration of the Shepherds, by Champaigne.

1996, Oct. 29   Litho.   Perf. 14
933 A186 20s multicolored   .75   .50
934 A186 60s multicolored   1.75   1.25
935 A186 80s multicolored   2.25   1.75
936 A186 1pa multicolored   7.25   7.25
    Nos. 933-936 (4)   12.00 10.75

UNICEF, 50th Anniv. — A187

Children in sports activities: a, Running, playing rugby. b, Tennis. c, Cycling.

1996, Oct. 29
937 A187 80s Strip of 3, #a.-c.   7.50   7.50

No. 937 is a continuous design.

Queen Halaevalu Mata'aho, 70th Birthday — A188

Designs: 60s, Queen, natl. flag. No. 939a, Queen, coin with portrait. No. 939b, Coin with natl. arms, Queen.

1996, Nov. 27   Litho.   Perf. 12
938 A188 60s multicolored   3.00   3.00
939 A188 2pa Pair, #a.-b.   9.00   9.00

Towards the Year 2000 — A189

Year "2000" rising out of Pacific, Tonga landmarks: Nos. 940a, 941a, The Ha'amonga stone monument, globe, Kao Island. Nos. 941b, 941b, Mount Talau overlooking Port of Reguge, Royal Palance, Tongatapu, communication satellite.

1996, Dec. 9
940 A189 80s Pair, #a.-b.   4.00   4.00
941 A189 2pa Pair, #a.-b.   9.50   9.50

New Year Type of 1996 Redrawn with Ox

Denomination located: a, 60s, UR. b, 60s, UL. c, 80s, LR. d, 2pa, LL.

1997, Jan. 24   Litho.   Perf. 14
942 A183 Sheet of 4, #a.-d.   10.00 10.00

New Year 1997 (Year of the Ox).

Nos. 840-845 Surcharged

1997, Mar. 3   Litho.   Perf. 14
943 A165 10s on 45s #840   2.75   2.50
944 A165 10s on 45s #841   2.75   2.50
a.   Pair, #943-944   6.00   6.00
945 A165 10s on 60s #842   2.75   2.50
946 A165 10s on 60s #843   2.75   2.50
a.   Pair, #945-946   6.00   6.00
947 A165 20s on 2pa #844   3.25   3.00
948 A165 20s on 2pa #845   3.25   3.00
a.   Pair, #947-948   7.00   7.00
    Nos. 943-948 (6)   17.50 16.00

Nos. 925-928 Surcharged, Ovptd.

1997, Mar. 24   Litho.   Perf. 14
949 A184 10s on 45s #925   .75   .75
950 A184 10s on 80s #926   .75   .75
951 A184 10s on 2pa #927   .75   .75
952 A184 3pa #928   7.75   7.75
    Nos. 949-952 (4)   10.00 10.00

Size and location of surcharge varies.

Nos. 892-893 Surcharged

a   b

1997, Mar. 24   *Perf. 14½*
Sheets of 4
954A	A176	10s on 80s	1.50	1.50
956A	A176	1pa on 2pa	12.00	12.00

#954A contains #892b (a), #892b (a), #892b (b), #892a (b). #956A contains #893a (a), #893b ((a), #893b (b), #893a (b).

Christianity in Tonga, Birth of King George Tupou I, Bicent. — A190

#957, 961a, 962a, Arrival of missionary ship, Duff, Captain James Wilson. #958, King George Tupou I, village. #959, 961b, 962b, People in water, rowboats coming ashore from Duff. #960, 961c, 962c, Natives, missionaries, Duff.

1997, Apr. 28   *Perf. 14*
957	A190	10s multicolored	.20	.20
958	A190	10s multicolored	.20	.20
959	A190	10s multicolored	.20	.20
960	A190	10s multicolored	.20	.20
a.		Sheet of 6, #957, 959-960, 3 #958	3.75	3.75
961	A190	60s Strip of 3, #a.-c.	4.50	4.50
962	A190	80s Strip of 3, #a.-c.	6.50	6.50

Nos. 961-962 were each issued in sheets of 9 stamps.
See Nos. 972-975.

Souvenir Sheet

Pacific Swallow, Golden Gate Bridge — A191

Illustration reduced.

1997, May 30
963	A191	2pa multicolored	5.50	5.50

Pacific '97.

Tonga High School, 50th Anniv. A192

Designs: 20s, Students in uniforms outside of school. 60s, Dressed for sports. 80s, Brass band. 3.50pa, Running competition.

1997, June 4
964	A192	20s multicolored	.50	.35
965	A192	60s multicolored	1.40	1.00
966	A192	80s multicolored	1.75	1.25
967	A192	3.50pa multicolored	7.75	7.75
		Nos. 964-967 (4)	11.40	10.35

A193   A194

Nos. 968, 970: a, Queen, King with bowed heads, royal escorts. b, Coronation ceremony. c, Queen, King. 45s, 2pa, King's crown.

1997, June 30   Litho.   *Perf. 13x13½*
968	A193	10s Strip of 3, #a.-c.	1.00	1.00
969	A193	45s multicolored	1.50	1.50

Size: 34x47mm
Perf. 12
970	A193	60s Strip of 3, #a.-c.	5.75	5.75
971	A193	2pa multicolored	6.75	6.75

King Taufa'ahau IV, Queen Halaevalu Mata'aho, 50th wedding anniv., coronation, 30th anniv.

Christianity in Tonga Type of 1997

1997, Aug. 27   *Perf. 14*
Size: 27x18mm
972	A190	10s like #957	.20	.20
973	A190	10s like #958	.20	.20
974	A190	10s like #959	.20	.20
975	A190	10s like #960	.20	.20
a.		Sheet of 12, 6 #973, 2 each #972, #974-975	3.50	3.50

1997, Oct. 1   Litho.   *Perf. 14*
Mushrooms: Nos. 976a, 977a, Lenzites elegans. Nos. 976b, 977b, Marasmiellus semiustus. No. 976c, 978a, Aseroe rubra. Nos. 976d, 978b, Podoscypha involuta. Nos. 976e, 979a, Microporus xanthopus. Nos. 976f, 979b, Lentinus tuberregium.
976	A194	10s Strip of 6, #a.-f.	2.25	2.25

Size: 26x40mm
977	A194	20s Pair, #a.-b.	1.50	1.50
978	A194	60s Pair, #a.-b.	4.00	4.00
979	A194	2pa Pair, #a.-b.	13.00	13.00
c.		Sheet of 6, #977-979	20.00	20.00

No. 976 is a continuous design.

Diana, Princess of Wales (1961-97)
Common Design Type

Various portraits: a, 10s. b, 80s, c, 1pa. d, 2.50pa.

Perf. 13½x14
1998, May 29   Litho.   Unwmk.
980	CD355	Strip of 4, #a.-d.	6.75	6.75

No. 980 sold for 4.40pa + 50s with surtax from international sales going to the Princess Diana Memorial Fund and surtax from local sales going to designated local charity.

Flying Home for Christmas A195

Designs: 60s, Airplane on ground, people waving. 80s, People waving, house, plane overhead. 1.50pa, Man in outrigger canoe waving to airplane. 3.50pa, Man, woman, people in boat on lake waving, airplane overhead.

1997, Oct. 20   Litho.   *Perf. 14x13½*
981	A195	60s bister & red	.90	.90
982	A195	80s bister & red	1.20	1.20
983	A195	1.50pa bister & red	2.20	2.20
984	A195	3.50pa bister & red	5.20	5.20
		Nos. 981-984 (4)	9.50	9.50

King Taufa'ahau Tupou IV, 80th Birthday — A196

1998, July 4   Litho.   *Perf. 14*
985	A196	2.70pa multicolored	6.00	6.00
a.		Souv. sheet, #985, Niuafo'ou #207	8.50	8.50

New Year 1998 (Year of the Tiger)

Tiger: a, 55s, Leaping down. b, 80s, Lying down. c, 1pa, Leaping upward. d, 1pa, Stalking.

1998, July 23
986	A183	Sheet of 4, #a.-d.	6.00	6.00

No. 986 is a continuous design. Singpex '98.

Birds A197

5s, Fairy tern, vert. 10s, Tongan whistler, vert. 15s, Common barn owl, vert. 20s, Purple swamp hen, vert. 30s, Red-footed booby, vert. 40s, Banded rail. 50s, Swamp harrier. 55s, Blue-crowned lorikeet, vert. 60s, Great frigate bird, vert. 70s, Friendly ground dove. 80s, Red-tailed tropic bird, vert. 1pa, Red shining parrot, vert. 2pa, Pacific pigeon, vert. 3pa, Pacific golden plover. 5pa, Tongan megapode.

Perf. 14x14½, 14½x14
1998, Aug. 26   Litho.
992	A197	5s multicolored	.20	.20
993	A197	10s multicolored	.20	.20
994	A197	15s multicolored	.20	.20
995	A197	20s multicolored	.25	.25
996	A197	30s multicolored	.45	.45
997	A197	40s multicolored	.60	.60
998	A197	50s multicolored	.70	.70
999	A197	55s multicolored	.80	.80
1000	A197	60s multicolored	.85	.85
1001	A197	70s multicolored	1.00	1.00
1002	A197	80s multicolored	1.10	1.10
1003	A197	1pa multicolored	1.40	1.40
1004	A197	2pa multicolored	2.75	2.75
1005	A197	3pa multicolored	4.25	4.25
1006	A197	5pa multicolored	7.25	7.25
		Nos. 992-1006 (15)	22.00	22.00

Fish A198

Designs: a, 10s, Chaetodon pelewensis. b, 55s, Chaetodon lunula. c, 1pa, Chaetodon ephippium.

1998, Sept. 23   Litho.   *Perf. 14*
1008	A198	Strip of 3, #a.-c.	4.00	4.00

Intl. Year of the Ocean. No. 1008 was issued in sheets of 9 stamps.

Christmas A199

Designs: 10s, Angel, "Kilisimasi Fiefia." 80s, Angel, "Merry Christmas." 1pa, Children, candle, "Ta'u Fo'ou Monu'ia." 1.60pa, Children, candle, "Happy New Year."

1998, Nov. 12   Litho.   *Perf. 14x14½*
1009	A199	10s multicolored	.60	.40
1010	A199	80s multicolored	2.50	1.25
1011	A199	1pa multicolored	2.75	2.25
1012	A199	1.60pa multicolored	3.50	3.50
		Nos. 1009-1012 (4)	9.35	7.40

New Year 1999 (Year of the Rabbit) A200

a, 10s, Three rabbits. b, 55s, Rabbit eating. c, 80s, Rabbit looking upward. d, 1pa, Rabbit hopping.

1999, Feb. 16   *Perf. 14*
1013	A200	Sheet of 4, #a.-d.	3.50	3.50

Explorers — A201

Explorer, ship: 55s, Tasman, Heemskerck, 1643. 80s, La Perouse, Astrolabe, 1788. 1pa, William Bligh, Bounty, 1789. 2.50pa, James Cook, Resolution, 1777.

1999, Mar. 19   Litho.   *Perf. 14*
1014	A201	55s multicolored	1.00	.60
1015	A201	80s multicolored	1.50	1.00
1016	A201	1pa multicolored	2.00	1.75
1017	A201	2.50pa multicolored	4.75	4.75
a.		Souvenir sheet of 1	5.00	5.00
		Nos. 1014-1017 (4)	9.25	8.10

Australia '99 World Stamp Expo (#1017a).

Scenic Views, Vava'u A202

Designs: 10s, Neiafu. 55s, Boats on water, Port of Refuge. 80s, Aerial view, Port of Refuge. 1pa, Sunset, Neiafu. 2.50pa, Mounu Island.

1999, May 19   *Perf. 14½*
1018	A202	10s multicolored	.50	.40
1019	A202	55s multicolored	1.00	.60
1020	A202	80s multicolored	1.60	.80
1021	A202	1pa multicolored	1.75	1.40
1022	A202	2.50pa multicolored	3.50	3.50
		Nos. 1018-1022 (5)	8.35	6.70

Flowers
A203

Designs: 10s, Fagraea berteroana. 80s, Garcinia pseudoguttfera. 1pa, Phlaeria disperma, vert. 2.50pa, Gardenia taitensis, vert.

Perf. 13¼x13, 13x13¼

1999, Sept. 29				**Litho.**
1023	A203	10s multicolored	.25	.25
1024	A203	80s multicolored	1.25	1.25
1025	A203	1pa multicolored	1.60	1.60
1026	A203	2.50pa multicolored	4.00	4.00
		Nos. 1023-1026 (4)	7.10	7.10

Millennium — A204

Designs: a, 55s, Ha'amonga monument, people, clocks at 11:15 to 11:25. b, 80s, Monument, people, clocks at 11:30 to 11:40. c, 1pa, People, clocks at 11:45 to 11:55. d, 2.50pa, King Taufa'ahau IV, clocks at 12:00, 12:05.

1999, Dec. 1

1027	A204	Strip of 4, #a.-d.	7.00	7.00

Millennium — A205

Clock, dove and: 10s, Flowers. 1pa, Ha'amonga Monument. 2.50pa, Native boat. 2.70pa, Crown.

Litho. & Embossed

2000, Jan. 1			**Perf. and Die Cut**	
1028	A205	10s multi	.25	.25
1029	A205	1pa multi	1.50	1.50
1030	A205	2.50pa multi	3.50	3.50
1031	A205	2.70pa multi	4.00	4.00
a.		Souv. sheet #1030-1031	7.50	7.50
		Nos. 1028-1031 (4)	9.25	9.25

Values are for stamps with attached selvage.

Souvenir Sheet

New Year 2000 (Year of the Dragon) — A206

Illustration reduced.
Various dragons; a, 10s. b, 55s, c, 80s. d, 1pa.

Litho. with Foil Application

2000, Feb. 4			**Perf. 14½**	
1032	A206	Sheet of 4, #a.-d.	4.75	4.75

Souvenir Sheet

The Stamp Show 2000,
London — A207

Illustration reduced.

Litho. with Foil Application

2000, May 22			**Perf. 13x13¼**	
1033	A207	Sheet of 2	5.50	5.50
a.		1pa Queen Mother	1.50	1.50
b.		2.50pa Queen Salote Tupou III	3.50	3.50

Geostationary Orbital Slot
Program — A208

Designs: 10s, Proton RU500 lauch vehicle, vert. 1pa, LM3 launch vehicle. 2.50pa, Apstar 1. 2.70pa, Gorizont.

Litho. with Foil Application

2000, July 5		**Perf. 14½x15, 15x14½**		
1034-1037	A208	Set of 4	9.00	9.00
1037a		Souvenir sheet, #1036-1037	8.25	8.25

World Stamp Expo 2000, Anaheim.

2000 Summer
Olympics,
Sydney — A209

No. 1038: a, Runner, koalas, sailboats. b, Boxers, kangaroos, Ayers Rock. c, Torchbearers, Ayers Rock, Sydney Opera House (60x45mm). d, Discus thrower, Sydney Harbour Bridge, flower. e, Weight lifter, kookaburra, fish.

2000, Sept. 15		**Litho.**	**Perf. 14**	
1038		Horiz. strip of 5	5.50	5.50
a.-e.	A209 80s Any single		1.00	1.00

Commonwealth Membership, 30th
Anniv. — A210

Designs: 10s, Education. 55s, Arts. 80s, Health. 2.70pa, Agriculture.

2000, Oct. 25

1039-1042	A210	Set of 4	5.50	5.50

Souvenir Sheet

New Year 2001 (Year of the
Snake) — A211

No. 1043 - Various snakes: a, 10s. b, 55s, c, 80s, d, 1pa.

Litho. with Foil Application

2001, Feb. 1		**Perf. 14¼**		
1043	A211	Sheet of 4, #a-d	3.50	3.50

Hong Kong 2001 Stamp Exhibition.

Dance — A212

Designs: 10s, Ma'ulu'ulu. 55s, Me'etupaki. 80s, Tau'olunga. 2.70pa, Faha'iula.

2001, Apr. 4		**Litho.**	**Perf. 13¼**	
1044-1047	A212	Set of 4	5.50	5.50

Year of the
Mangrove
A213

Designs: 10s, Fiddler crab. 55s, Black duck, gray mullet, vert. 80s, Red mangrove, emperor fish, vert. 1pa, Reef heron, mangrove. 2.70pa, Mangrove crab.

2001, May 5		**Litho.**	**Perf. 13¾**	
1048-1052	A213	Set of 5	6.50	6.50
1052a		Souvenir sheet, #1048-1052, perf. 13½	7.00	7.00

Sport
Fishing — A214

2001, July 31		**Perf. 14¾x14**		
1053		Horiz. strip of 4 with central label	8.25	8.25
a.	A214 45s Sailfish		.50	.50
b.	A214 80s Blue marlin		1.00	1.00
c.	A214 2.40pa Wahoo		3.00	3.00
d.	A214 2.60pa Dorado		3.25	3.25

Fruit — A215

2001, Sept. 19		**Serpentine Die Cu**	
		Self-Adhesive	
1054		Horiz. strip of 5	6.00
a.	A215 10s Banana		.25	.2
b.	A215 45s Coconut		.50	.5
c.	A215 60s Pineapple		.75	.7
d.	A215 80s Watermelon		.85	.8
e.	A215 2.40pa Passion fruit		2.40	2.4

Shells
A216

Designs: 10s, Haliotis ovina. 80s, Turbo petholatus. 1pa, Trochus niloticus. 2.70pa, Turbo marmoratus.

Perf. 12¾

2001, Dec. 13		**Litho.**	**Unwmk.**	
1055-1058	A216	Set of 4	6.25	6.25

Values are for copies with surrounding selvage.

**Reign Of Queen Elizabeth II, 50th
Anniv. Issue
Common Design Type
Souvenir Sheet**

No. 1059: a, 15s, Princess Elizabeth as child. b, 90s, Wearing yellow hat. c, 1.20pa, With Princess Anne and Prince Charles. d, 1.40pa, Wearing crown. e, 2.25pa, 1955 portrait by Annigoni (38x50mm).

Perf. 14¼x14½, 13¾ (2.25pa)

2002, Feb. 6		**Litho.**	**Wmk. 373**	
1059	CD360	Sheet of 5, #a-e	8.00	8.00

Souvenir Sheet

New Year 2002 (Year of the
Horse) — A217

Various horses: a, 65s. b, 80s. c, 1pa. d, 2.50pa.

Litho. With Foil Application

2002, Feb. 12		**Unwmk.**	**Perf. 14**	
1060	A217	Sheet of 4, #a-d	6.75	6.75

Intl. Year of Ecotourism — A218

Designs: 5s, Whale, surfer. 15s, Woman, shoreline. 70s, Beach, fish. 1.40pa, Arch, man. 2.25pa, Boats, man.

2002, Apr. 9	**Litho.**	**Perf. 13¼x13¾**	
1061-1065	A218	Set of 5	6.50	6.50

Pearls
A219

Pearls and: 90s, Workers preparing oysters for pearl cultivation. 1pa, Diver checking strung oysters. 1.20pa, Woman, pearl on necklace. 2.50pa, Islands.

2002, June 12	Litho.	Perf. 13½		
1066-1069 A219	Set of 4		7.50	7.50
1069a	Souvenir sheet, #1068-1069		5.00	5.00

Values are for copies with surrounding selvage.

Participation of Tongan Team in Rugby Sevens Tournament — A220

Designs: 15s, Player leaping for ball. 30s, Players ready for scrum. 90s, Player attempting tackle. 4pa, Players on ground.

2002, July 27				
1070-1073 A220	Set of 4		7.25	7.25

Values are for copies with surrounding selvage.

Weaving — A221

Designs: 30s, Woman and young girl. 90s, Woman with work hanging on line, boy with baskets. 1.40pa, Women weaving baskets. 2.50pa, Woman weaving basket lid.

2002, Sept. 17		Perf. 12¼		
1074-1077 A221	Set of 4		7.00	7.00

'Eua National Park, 10th Anniv. — A222

Various depictions of red shining parrots 45s, 1pa, 1.50pa, 2.50pa.

2002, Nov. 27	Litho.	Perf. 12¼		
1078-1081 A222	Set of 4		7.50	7.50

New Year 2003 (Year of the Ram) — A223

No. 1082: a, 65s, One ram. 80s, Three sheep. 1pa, Three sheep, diff. 2.50pa, Two sheep.

2003, Apr. 14	Litho.	Perf. 13¼		
1082 A223	Sheet of 4, #a-d		4.75	4.75

Coronation of Queen Elizabeth II, 50th Anniv. — A224

Designs: 90s, Queen Elizabeth II in coach. 1.20pa, Queen Salote of Tonga. 1.40pa, Queen Salote in coach. 2.50pa, Queen Elizabeth II.

Litho. With Foil Application

2003, June 2				
1083-1086 A224	Set of 4		5.75	5.75

Boats of Abel Tasman — A225

Various boats: 15s, 75s, 90s, 2.50pa.

2003, Aug. 7	Litho.	Perf. 13¼		
1087-1090 A225	Set of 4		4.00	4.00
1090a	Souvenir sheet, #1087-1090		4.00	4.00

Beaches — A226

Flower and: 15s, Euakafa Beach. 90s, Pangaimotu Beach. 1.40pa, Fafa Beach. 2.25pa, Nuku Beach.

2003, Sept. 11				
1091-1094 A226	Set of 4		4.50	4.50

Churches A227

Designs: 15s, Catholic Church, Neiafu, Vava'u. 90s, Wesleyan Church, Uiha, Ha'apai. 1.40pa, Cathedral of the Immaculate Conception of Mary. 2.25pa, Free Wesleyan Church, Nuku'alofa.

2003, Nov. 10				
1095-1098 A227	Set of 4		4.75	4.75

Christmas.

SEMI-POSTAL STAMP

Catalogue values for unused stamps in this section are for Never Hinged items.

No. 488 Surcharged in Silver for Cyclone Relief

1982, Apr. 14		Litho.		
B1 A86	3pa + 50s multi		3.00	3.00

AIR POST STAMPS

Catalogue values for unused stamps in this section are for Never Hinged items.

Type of Regular Gold Coin Issue

Designs: 10p, 1sh1p, Queen Salote standing, ½-koula coin, obverse. 11p, Coat of arms, ½-koula coin, reverse. 2sh1p, 2sh9p, Queen Salote standing, 1-koula coin, obverse. 2sh4p, Coat of arms, 1-koula coin, reverse.

Litho.; Embossed on Gilt Foil

1963, July 15		Unwmk.	Die Cut	
Diameter: 54mm				
C1 A36	10p dp carmine		.35	.35
C2 A36	11p green		.50	.50
C3 A36	1sh6p violet blue		.50	.50
Diameter: 80mm				
C4 A36	2sh1p magenta		.90	.90
C5 A36	2sh4p emerald		.90	.90
C6 A36	2sh9p violet		1.25	1.25
Nos. C1-C6 (6)			4.40	4.40

See note after No. 133.

Map of Tongatabu and ¼-Koula Coin — AP1

Litho.; Embossed on Gilt Foil

1964, Oct. 19				
C7 AP1	10p deep green		.20	.20
C8 AP1	1sh2p black		.20	.20
C9 AP1	3sh6p carmine		.60	.60
C10 AP1	6sh6p purple		1.20	1.20
Nos. C7-C10 (4)			2.20	2.20

Pan-Pacific and Southeast Asia Women's Association Conf., Nukualofa, Aug. 1964. See note after No. 133.

Nos. C1-C2, C4-C6 Surcharged like Regular Issue, 1965, in Black, White or Red

1965, Mar. 18				
C11 A36	2sh3p on 10p (B)		.20	.20
C12 A36	2sh9p on 11p (W)		.25	.25
C13 A36	4sh6p on 2sh1p		14.50	14.50
C14 A36	4sh6p on 2sh4p		14.50	14.50
C15 A36	4sh6p on 2sh9p		8.50	8.50
Nos. C11-C15 (5)			37.95	37.95

Nos. 114-115, 117-118 Overprinted or Surcharged

	Perf. 14½x13½			
1966, June 18		Wmk. 79		
C16 A35	5p purple		.25	.20
C17 A35	10p on 1p brn org & car rose		.25	.20
C18 A35	1sh red brown		.30	.20
C19 A35	2sh9p on 2p ultra		.35	.20
C20 A35	3sh6p on 5p purple		.35	.20
C21 A35	4sh6p on 1sh red brn		.75	.20
Nos. C16-C21 (6)			2.25	1.20

Centenary of Tupou College and secondary education. The overprint or surcharge is spaced differently on other values.

Nos. C7-C8 Overprinted and Surcharged in Silver or Gold on Black, or in Black on Gold

Litho.; Embossed on Gilt Foil

1966, Dec. 16		Unwmk.	Die Cut	
C22 AP1	10p (S on B)		.20	.20
C23 AP1	1sh2p (B on G)		.20	.20
C24 AP1	4sh on 10p (S on B)		.90	.90
C25 AP1	5sh6p on 1sh2p (B on G)		1.25	1.25
C26 AP1	10sh6p on 1sh2p (G on B)		2.10	2.10
Nos. C22-C26 (5)			4.65	4.65

In memory of Queen Salote (1900-65).

King Taufa'ahau Type of Regular Issue, 1967

Designs: 7s, 11s, 23s, 2pa, Taufa'ahau IV, obverse of new palladium coins. 9s, 21s, 29s, Coat of Arms, reverse.

Litho.; Embossed on Palladium Foil

1967, July 4				

Diameter: 7s, 44mm; 9s, 29s, 52mm; 11s, 59mm; 21s, 68mm; 23s, 40mm; 2pa, 74mm.

C27 A38	7s red & black		.20	.20
C28 A38	9s maroon & emer		.25	.25
C29 A38	11s brt blue & org		.30	.30
C30 A38	21s black & emer		.55	.55
C31 A38	23s magenta & emer		.60	.60
C32 A38	29s vio blue & emer		.70	.70
C33 A38	2pa magenta & orange		4.50	4.50
Nos. C27-C33 (7)			7.10	7.10

See note after No. 181.

Type of Regular Issue, 1953 Surcharged in Red or Black

	Wmk. 79			
1967, Dec. 15		Engr.	Die Cut	
C34 A33	11s on 3½p ultra (R)		.20	.20
C35 A33	21s on 1½p emerald		.30	.30
C36 A33	23s on 3½p ultra (R)		.30	.30
Nos. C34-C36 (3)			.80	.80

Arrival of the United States Peace Corps.

No. 112 Surcharged in Red

1968, Apr. 6		Engr.	Perf. 11x11½	
C37 A34	11s on 10sh blk & yel		.45	.45
C38 A34	21s on 10sh blk & yel		.60	.60
C39 A34	23s on 10sh blk & yel		.60	.60
Nos. C37-C39 (3)			1.65	1.65

Nos. C27-C33 Overprinted: "HIS MAJESTY'S 50th BIRTHDAY" in Silver on Blue Panel on 7s, 11s, 23s and 2pa. "H.M.'s BIRTHDAY / 4 . JULY . 1968" in Gold on Red Panel on 9s, 21s and 29s

Litho.; Embossed on Palladium Foil

1968, July 4		Unwmk.	Die Cut	
C40 A38	7s red & black		.20	.20
C41 A38	9s maroon & emer		.20	.20
C42 A38	11s brt blue & org		.25	.25
C43 A38	21s black & emerald		.65	.30
C44 A38	23s mag & emerald		.65	.30

C45 A38 29s vio blue & emer .90 .35
C46 A38 2pa magenta & org 6.25 5.50
Nos. C40-C46 (7) 9.10 7.05

50th birthday of King Taufa'ahau IV.

Types of 1953 Surcharged: "Friendly Islands / Field & Track Trials / South Pacific Games / Port Moresby 1969 / AIRMAIL"

Designs as before.

1968, Dec. 19   Engr.   Wmk. 79
C47 A33 6s on 6p yel& blk .20 .20
C48 A33 7s on 4p purple & yel .20 .20
C49 A33 8s on 8p blk & lt grn .20 .20
C50 A33 9s on 1½p emerald .20 .20
C51 A34 11s on 3p brn org & yel .20 .20
C52 A33 21s on 3½p dk blue .30 .30
C53 A33 38s on 5sh sepia & yel 2.10 .50
C54 A34 1pa on 10sh orange yel 1.00 .60
Nos. C47-C54 (8) 4.40 2.40

Issued to publicize the field and track trials for the third South Pacific Games, Port Moresby, 1969. The overprint is in 5 lines on the horizontal stamps, in 7 lines on the vertical stamps. On the vertical stamps "Trial" is printed on the line ahead of "Field & Track." On No. C54 the denomination is spelled out.

Nos. C19-C21 Surcharged
Perf. 14½x13½
1968   Photo.   Wmk. 79
C55 A35 1s on 2sh9p on 2p ultra 1.00 1.00
C56 A35 1s on 3sh6p on 5p pur 1.00 1.00
C57 A35 1s on 4sh6p on 1sh red brown 1.00 1.00
Nos. C55-C57 (3) 3.00 3.00

Pacific Games Type of Regular Issue
Design: Boxer.

1969, Aug. 13   Litho.   Die Cut
Self-adhesive
C58 A40 9s orange, blk & pur .20 .20
C59 A40 11s orange, blk & dk bl .20 .20
C60 A40 20s org, blk & yel grn .25 .25
C61 A40 60s orange, blk & scar .75 .75
C62 A40 1pa orange, blk & grn 1.25 1.25
Nos. C58-C62 (5) 2.65 2.65

See note after No. 231.

Oil Derrick on Map of Tongatabu and King Taufa'ahau IV — AP2

Litho.; Gold Embossed
1969, Dec. 23   Self-adhesive
C63 AP2 9s multicolored .25 .25
C64 AP2 10s multicolored .25 .25
C65 AP2 24s multicolored .70 .70
C66 AP2 29s multicolored .80 .80
C67 AP2 38s multicolored 1.10 1.10
Nos. C63-C67 (5) 3.10 3.10

1st scientific search for oil in Tonga.

King Taufa'ahau IV and Queen Elizabeth II — AP3

Litho.; Gold Embossed
1970, Mar. 7   Self-adhesive
C68 AP3 7s multicolored .40 .30
C69 AP3 9s multicolored .50 .35
C70 AP3 24s multicolored 1.25 .65

C71 AP3 29s multicolored 1.50 .75
C72 AP3 38s multicolored 2.10 1.00
Nos. C68-C72 (5) 5.75 3.05

See note after No. 242.

King Taufa'ahau Tupou IV Medal — AP4

Litho.; Gold Embossed
1970, June 4   Self-adhesive
C73 AP4 9s grnsh bl, ver & gold .25 .25
C74 AP4 10s lilac, bl & gold .25 .25
C75 AP4 24s yel, grn & gold .70 .70
C76 AP4 29s ultra, org & gold .80 .80
C77 AP4 38s ocher, emer & gold 1.00 1.00
Nos. C73-C77 (5) 3.00 3.00

See note after No. 247.

Red Cross Type of Regular Issue Without Coat of Arms

1970, Oct. 17   Litho.   Die Cut
Self-adhesive
C78 A45 9s red & silver .25 .25
C79 A45 10s red & magenta .25 .25
C80 A45 18s red & brt green .75 .75
C81 A45 29s red & brt blue 2.25 2.25
C82 A45 1pa red & green 5.50 5.50
Nos. C78-C82 (5) 9.00 9.00

Centenary of the British Red Cross.

Nos. C22-C24 Surcharged

Lithographed; Embossed on Gilt Foil
1971, Jan. 31   Die Cut
C83 AP1 9s on #C22 (S on B) .65 .20
C84 AP1 24s on #C24 (G on B) 1.40 .95
C85 AP1 29s on #C23 (R on B) 2.00 1.10
C86 AP1 38s on #C23 (G on B) 3.00 1.50
Nos. C83-C86 (4) 7.05 3.75

In memory of Queen Salote (1900-1965).

Type of Regular Issue, 1953, Surcharged in Red and Black

1971   Engr.   Wmk. 79   Imperf
C87 A33 9s on 1½p green .25 .20
C88 A33 10s on 4p purple & yel .25 .20
C89 A33 38s on 1p yellow & blk 1.10 .60
Nos. C87-C89 (3) 1.60 1.00

See note after No. 272.

Types of Regular Issue Surcharged in Purple or Black: "AIRMAIL," New Denomination and "HONOURING JAPANESE POSTAL CENTENARY 1871-1971"

1971
C90 A34 18s on 1sh car & buff (P) .50 .50
C91 A33 1pa on 2sh car & ultra 3.00 3.00
Surcharge on #C90 in 6 lines, on #C91 in 4.

Self-adhesive & Imperf.
Starting with Nos. C92-C96, all airmail issues are self-adhesive and imperforate, unless otherwise stated.

High Jump — AP5

1971, July   Litho.   Unwmk.
C92 AP5 9s brown, mag & blk .20 .20
C93 AP5 10s brown, blue & blk .20 .20
C94 AP5 24s brn, dk grn & blk .40 .40
C95 AP5 29s brown, vio & blk .55 .55
C96 AP5 38s brown, red & blk .75 .75
Nos. C92-C96 (5) 2.10 2.10

4th South Pacific Games, Papeete, French Polynesia, Sept. 8-19.
For surcharges see Nos. C141-C142.

Prehistoric Trilithon, King's Watch and Portrait AP6

Litho. and Embossed
1971, July 20
C97 AP6 14s dk brown & multi .65 .65
C98 AP6 21s ocher & multi .90 .90

2nd anniversary of man's first landing on the moon and the placement of a Bulova Accutron there. See Nos. C117-118, CO47-CO48, CO61-CO62. Advertisement on peelable paper backing.

Medal Type of Regular Issue
Designs: 10s, Gold Medal of Merit, obverse (King Taufa'ahau IV). 75s, Silver Medal of Merit, obverse (King Taufa'ahau IV). 1pa, Bronze Medal of Merit, reverse.

1971, Oct. 30   Litho. & Embossed
C99 A47 10s gold & multi .20 .20
C100 A47 75s silver & multi 1.25 1.25
C101 A47 1pa bronze & multi 1.50 1.50
Nos. C99-C101 (3) 2.95 2.95

Girl with Blocks and UNICEF Emblem — AP7

1971, Dec.   Litho.
C102 AP7 10s multicolored .20 .20
C103 AP7 15s multicolored .35 .35
C104 AP7 25s multicolored .60 .60
C105 AP7 50s multicolored 1.25 1.25
C106 AP7 1pa multicolored 2.50 2.50
Nos. C102-C106 (5) 4.90 4.90

25th anniversary of UNICEF.

Ship Type of Regular Issue
Design: Map of Merchant Marine routes from Tonga and cargo ship "Niuvakai."

1972, Apr. 14
C107 A49 9s ver & multi .75 .3
C108 A49 12s multicolored .90 .3
C109 A49 14s dk purple & multi 1.10 .3
C110 A49 75s olive & multi 5.75 4.2
C111 A49 90s black & multi 6.00 5.5
Nos. C107-C111 (5) 14.50 10.8

For surcharge and overprint see No. C124.

Coin Type of Regular Issue
Design: Coins on top; panel at bottom inscribed "5th anniversary world's first palladium coinage."

Litho.; Embossed on Metallic Foil
1972, July 15
C112 A50 9s silver & multi .20 .20
C113 A50 12s silver & multi .30 .3
C114 A50 14s silver & multi .35 .35
C115 A50 21s silver & multi .50 .50
C116 A50 75s silver & multi 1.75 1.75
Nos. C112-C116 (5) 3.10 3.10

Watch Type of 1971
Litho. and Embossed
1972, July 20
C117 AP6 17s multicolored .75 .75
C118 AP6 38s multicolored 1.50 1.50

Advertisement on peelable paper backing.

Proclamation of Sovereignty — AP8

1972, Dec. 9   Litho.
C119 AP8 9s ultra & multi .20 .20
C120 AP8 12s red brown & multi .25 .25
C121 AP8 14s magenta & multi .30 .30
C122 AP8 38s brn org & multi .85 .85
C123 AP8 1pa olive & multi 2.40 2.40
Nos. C119-C123 (5) 4.00 4.00

Tonga's proclamation of sovereignty over the Minerva Reefs, June 1972.

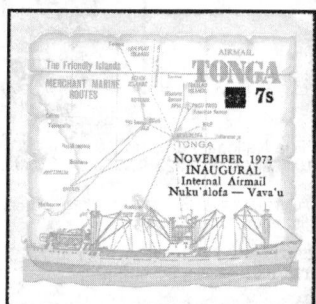

No. C107 Surcharged

1972, Nov.   Litho.
C124 A49 7s on 9s multicolored 1.50 1.50

Inauguration of internal airmail service Nukualofa-Vavau, Nov. 1972.

Tongan Bank Notes and Bank Building — AP9

1973, Mar. 30		Litho.	
C125	AP9 9s multicolored	.25	.20
C126	AP9 12s ultra & multi	.25	.20
C127	AP9 17s dp car & multi	.40	.20
C128	AP9 50s lt blue & multi	1.50	1.25
C129	AP9 90s multicolored	2.75	2.75
	Nos. C125-C129 (5)	5.15	4.60

Establishment of Bank of Tonga.

Boy Scout Emblem — AP10

1973, June 29		Litho.	
C130	AP10 9s silver & multi	.70	.35
C131	AP10 12s silver & multi	.85	.45
C132	AP10 14s silver & multi	1.25	.70
C133	AP10 17s silver & multi	1.40	.85
C134	AP10 1pa silver & multi	15.00	9.25
	Nos. C130-C134 (5)	19.20	11.60

See note after No. 326.
For surcharges see Nos. C143-C144.

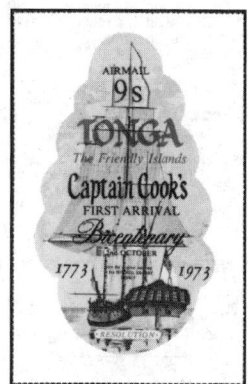

"Resolution" — AP11

1973, Oct. 2		Litho.	
C135	AP11 9s multicolored	.75	.35
C136	AP11 14s multicolored	1.40	.55
C137	AP11 29s multicolored	4.25	2.50
C138	AP11 38s multicolored	5.00	2.75
C139	AP11 75s multicolored	9.25	4.00
	Nos. C135-C139 (5)	20.65	10.15

Bicentenary of Capt. Cook's arrival.

Nos. 277, C96, C94, C130 and C132
Surcharged in Silver, Violet or Black:
"Commonwealth Games Christchurch
1974"

1973, Dec. 19			
C140	A46 7s on 25s multi (S)	.20	.20
C141	AP5 9s on 38s multi (V)	.25	.20
C142	AP5 24s multicolored (B)	.85	.35
C143	AP10 29s on 9s multi (V)	1.00	.45
C144	AP10 40s on 14s multi (B)	1.25	1.00
	Nos. C140-C144 (5)	3.55	2.20

10th British Commonwealth Games, Christchurch, New Zealand, Jan. 24-Feb. 2, 1974. No. C140 is overprinted "AIRMAIL" in black; the silver surcharge and overprint are on black panels.

Parrot of
Eua — AP12

1974, Mar. 20		Litho.	
C145	AP12 7s multicolored	.50	.25
C146	AP12 9s multicolored	.60	.30
C147	AP12 12s multicolored	.60	.30
C148	AP12 14s multicolored	.90	.45
C149	AP12 17s multicolored	1.00	.50
C150	AP12 29s multicolored	1.75	.90
C151	AP12 38s multicolored	2.50	1.25
C152	AP12 50s multicolored	3.00	1.50
C153	AP12 75s multicolored	4.50	2.25
	Nos. C145-C153 (9)	15.35	7.70

Printed in rolls of 500. Self-adhesive rose red control number in upper left corner.

Carrier Pigeon Scattering Letters over
Tonga — AP13

1974, June 20		Typo.	
C154	AP13 14s lt blue & multi	.35	.35
C155	AP13 21s lt blue & multi	.50	.50
C156	AP13 60s lt blue & multi	1.60	1.60
C157	AP13 75s lt blue & multi	1.75	1.75
C158	AP13 1pa lt blue & multi	2.25	2.25
	Nos. C154-C158 (5)	6.45	6.45

Centenary of Universal Postal Union.

Girl Guide Leaders — AP14

1974, Sept. 11		Litho.	
C159	AP14 14s blue & multi	.80	.50
C160	AP14 16s blue & multi	1.25	.75
C161	AP14 29s blue & multi	2.50	1.50
C162	AP14 31s blue & multi	3.25	1.90
C163	AP14 75s blue & multi	6.75	4.00
	Nos. C159-C163 (5)	14.55	8.65

Girl Guides of Tonga.
For surcharges and overprints see Nos. C190-C191, C193.

Freighter "James Cook" and List of
Tongan Merchantmen — AP15

1974, Dec. 11			
C164	AP15 9s blue & multi	.80	.30
C165	AP15 14s blue & multi	1.25	.50
C166	AP15 17s blue & multi	1.40	.55
C167	AP15 60s blue & multi	5.00	3.50
C168	AP15 90s blue & multi	8.00	4.50
	Nos. C164-C168 (5)	16.45	9.35

Establishment of Royal Marine Institute.

Beach
AP16

Designs: 12s, 14s, like 9s. 17s, 38s, Surf.

1975, Mar. 11		Litho.	
C169	AP16 9s gold & multi	.20	.20
C170	AP16 12s gold & multi	.25	.25
C171	AP16 14s gold & multi	.30	.30
C172	AP16 17s gold & multi	.30	.30
C173	AP16 38s gold & multi	.95	.95
	Nos. C169-C173 (5)	2.00	2.00

First meeting of South Pacific area Prime Ministers. See note after No. 226.
For surcharges see Nos. C229, C298.

Women's Discus and Games'
Emblem — AP17

1975, June 11			
C174	AP17 9s multicolored	.35	.35
C175	AP17 12s multicolored	.45	.45
C176	AP17 14s multicolored	.45	.45
C177	AP17 17s black & multi	.55	.55
C178	AP17 90s olive & multi	2.00	2.00
	Nos. C174-C178 (5)	3.80	3.80

5th South Pacific Games, Guam, Aug. 1-10. See note after No. 226.
For surcharges see Nos. C230-C231.

FAO Type of 1975

Designs (FAO Coins): 12s, Coins showing cattle, corn and pig. 14s, Cornucopias; coins showing king, family planning emblem and melons. 25s, Bananas and treasure chest. 50s, King Taufa'ahau. 1pa, Palms.

1975, Sept. 3			
C179	A62 12s multicolored	.45	.45
C180	A62 14s blue & multi	.45	.45
C181	A62 25s silver, blk & org	.70	.70
C182	A62 50s car, sil & blk	1.25	1.25
C183	A62 1pa silver & black	2.25	2.25
	Nos. C179-C183 (5)	5.10	5.10

Size of paper backing of 14s: 82x50mm; others 45x45mm. See note after No. 226.

Coin Type of 1975

Coins: 9s, King Taufa'ahau IV, obverse. 12s, Queen Salote III, 75pa reverse and obverse. 14s, 10pa reverse. 38s, King Taufa'ahau IV, 10pa reverse and observe. 1pa, Heads of four constitutional monarchs.

1975, Nov. 4			
	Light Blue Background		
C184	A63 9s black, sil & red	.35	.20
C185	A63 12s gold, blk & grn	.45	.35
C186	A63 14s black, sil & ol	.45	.35
C187	A63 38s gold, blk & org	1.00	.50
C188	A63 1pa black, sil & blue	2.60	2.60
	Nos. C184-C188 (5)	4.85	4.00

Size of paper backing of 1pa: 87x78mm, others 65x60mm. See note after No. 226.

Nos. 344-345, C160, C163
Surcharged and Overprinted in
Carmine on Silver, Green or Gold

a

b

1976, Feb. 24		Litho.	
C189	A58 (a) 12s on 20s (S)	.75	.45
C190	AP14 (b) 14s on 16s (Gr)	.75	.45
C191	AP14 (b) 16s on 9s (G)	.90	.45
C192	A58 (a) 38s on 40s (G)	2.25	.60
C193	AP14 (b) 75s (S)	4.25	2.50
	Nos. C189-193 (5)	8.90	4.45

21st Olympic Games, Montreal, Canada, July 17-Aug. 1. See note after No. 226.

Bicentennial Type of 1976

Signers of Declaration of Independence, Flags of US and Tonga: 12s, Abraham Clark, George Ross, Thomas Lynch, Jr., Charles Carroll, Roger Sherman (no flags). 14s, Robert Treat Paine, Thomas Jefferson, Thomas McKean, John Adams. 17s, Button Gwinnett, Caesar Rodney, Richard Henry Lee. 38s, John Hart, Samuel Huntington, Philip Livingstone, John Morton. 1pa, John Hancock, Joseph Hewes, Josiah Bartlett, John Witherspoon.

1976, May 26			
C194	A66 12s buff & multi	.65	.20
C195	A66 14s buff & multi	.70	.20
C196	A66 17s buff & multi	.75	.40
C197	A66 38s buff & multi	3.25	.90
C198	A66 1pa buff & multi	5.50	3.50
	Nos. C194-C198 (5)	10.85	5.20

See note after No. 381.

Missionary Ship "Triton" — AP18

1976, Aug. 25		Litho.	
C199	AP18 9s pink & multi	.35	.30
C200	AP18 12s multicolored	.55	.40
C201	AP18 14s multicolored	.60	.45
C202	AP18 17s buff & multi	.80	.55
C203	AP18 38s multicolored	1.40	.90
	Nos. C199-C203 (5)	3.70	2.60

See note after No. 386.
For surcharges see Nos. C234, C294, C299.

Treaty Signing Ceremony,
Nukualofa — AP19

1976, Nov. 1

C204	AP19	11s multicolored	.45	.40
C205	AP19	17s multicolored	.60	.55
C206	AP19	18s multicolored	.65	.60
C207	AP19	31s multicolored	1.10	1.00
C208	AP19	39s multicolored	1.40	1.25
	Nos. C204-C208 (5)		4.20	3.80

See note after No. 391.
For surcharges see Nos. C235, C295.

Elizabeth II and Taufa'ahau IV — AP20

1977, Feb. 7

C209	AP20	15s gray & multi	.20	.20
C210	AP20	17s gray & multi	.35	.35
C211	AP20	22s gray & multi	10.00	6.50
C212	AP20	31s gray & multi	.50	.50
C213	AP20	39s gray & multi	.50	.50
	Nos. C209-C213 (5)		11.55	8.05

See note after No. 396.

Coronation Coin — AP21

1977, July 4   Litho.

C214	AP21	11s multicolored	.30	.30
C215	AP21	17s multicolored	.40	.40
C216	AP21	18s multicolored	.40	.40
C217	AP21	39s multicolored	.65	.65
C218	AP21	1pa multicolored	1.75	1.75
	Nos. C214-C218 (5)		3.50	3.50

See note after No. 401.
See Nos. CO120-CO122.

Capt. Cook Medal and Journal
Quotation — AP22

1977, Sept. 27

C219	AP22	15s multicolored	.90	.75
C220	AP22	22s multicolored	1.40	1.25
C221	AP22	31s multicolored	3.00	2.50
C222	AP22	50s multicolored	9.00	4.50
C223	AP22	1pa multicolored	17.50	7.50
	Nos. C219-C223 (5)		31.80	16.50

Bicentenary of Capt. Cook's farewell voyage.
See Nos. CO123-CO125.

Sei and Fin Whales — AP23

1977, Dec. 16

C224	AP23	11s blk, vio & bl	4.00	.70
C225	AP23	17s blk, red & bl	4.50	.85
C226	AP23	18s blk, grn & bl	4.50	1.00
C227	AP23	39s blk, brn & bl	5.50	2.10
C228	AP23	50s blk, mag & bl	7.00	3.25
	Nos. C224-C228 (5)		25.50	7.90

Whale protection.
See Nos. CO126-CO128.

Stamps of 1975-77 Surcharged in
Various Colors

1978

C229	AP16	17s on 38s (#C173;Gr)	1.90	1.50
C230	AP17	17s on 9s (#C174;B)	1.90	1.50
C231	AP17	17s on 12s (#C175;Dbl)	1.90	1.50
C232	A63	17s on 38s (#C187;B)	1.90	1.50
C233	A66	17s on 12s (#C194; R on G)	1.90	1.50
C234	AP18	17s on 9s (#C199; B)	1.90	1.50
C235	AP19	17s on 18s (#C206; G on Brn)	1.90	1.50
C236	A66	1pa on 75s (#381; Gr on S)	9.25	8.00
C237	A66	1pa on 38s (#C197; Dbl on G)	9.25	8.00
C238	OA15	1pa on 1.10pa (#CO119; S on Dbl)	22.50	25.00

Edmonton Games Type of 1978

Canadian Maple leaf and Tongan coat of
arms.

1978, May 5   Litho.

C239	A73	17s red & multi	.45	.45
C240	A73	35s red & multi	.90	.90
C241	A73	38s red & multi	.95	.95
C242	A73	40s red & multi	1.00	1.00
C243	A73	65s red & multi	1.50	1.50
	Nos. C239-C243 (5)		4.80	4.80

See note after No. 423.

King Type of 1978

Design: Head of King Taufa'ahau IV within
6-pointed star.

1978, July 4

C244	A74	11s multicolored	.25	.25
C245	A74	15s multicolored	.35	.35
C246	A74	17s multicolored	.45	.45
C247	A74	39s multicolored	1.00	1.00
C248	A74	1pa multicolored	2.50	2.50
	Nos. C244-C248 (5)		4.55	4.55

See note after No. 226.

Wildlife Type of 1978

1978, Dec. 15   Litho. & Typo.

C249	A77	17s Whale	3.50	1.75
C250	A77	22s Bat	3.50	1.75
C251	A77	31s Turtle	3.50	1.75
C252	A77	39s Parrot	7.00	3.00
C253	A77	45s like 17s	7.50	3.50
	Nos. C249-C253 (5)		25.00	11.75

Wildlife conservation. See note after No. 226.

Types of 1979

Designs: 15s, like No. 453. 17s, like No.
450. 31s, Rotary emblem. 39s, Ministry and
tourism buildings, Bank of Tonga, GPO. 1pa,
Dish antenna and map of Tonga.

1979, Feb. 16   Litho.

C254	A79	15s multicolored	.30	.25
C255	A79	17s multicolored	.40	.30
C256	A78	31s vio blue & gold	.70	.40
C257	A79	39s multicolored	.95	.60
C258	A79	1pa multicolored	2.50	1.50
	Nos. C254-C258 (5)		4.85	3.05

Decade of Progress. Paper backing shows
map of Tonga.

Type of 1979

Tongan self-adhesive, free-form stamps.

1979, June 1

C259	A81	15s multicolored	.35	.35
C260	A81	17s multicolored	.45	.45
C261	A81	18s multicolored	.50	.50
C262	A81	31s multicolored	.75	.75
C263	A81	39s multicolored	.95	.95
	Nos. C259-C263 (5)		3.00	3.00

See note after No. 458.

Jet — AP24

1979, Aug. 17

C264	AP24	5s multicolored	.20	.20
C265	AP24	11s multicolored	.35	.25
C266	AP24	14s multicolored	.50	.35
C267	AP24	15s multicolored	.50	.35
C268	AP24	17s multicolored	.65	.45
C269	AP24	18s multicolored	.70	.50
C270	AP24	22s multicolored	.75	.55
C271	AP24	31s multicolored	1.10	.75
C272	AP24	39s multicolored	1.40	.95
C273	AP24	75s multicolored	2.50	1.75
C274	AP24	1pa multicolored	3.50	2.50
	Nos. C264-C274 (11)		12.15	8.60

Nos. C264-C274 issued in coils; self-adhesive control number in lower left corner of
paper backing except on 14s, 18s, 22s, 75s.
See note after No. 226.
See Nos. C303-C305.

View Type of 1979

Design: Kao Island. See note after No. 463.

1979, Nov. 23

C275	A82	5s multicolored	.20	.20
C276	A82	15s multicolored	.35	.35
C277	A82	17s multicolored	.45	.45
C278	A82	39s multicolored	.95	.95
C279	A82	75s multicolored	1.75	1.75
	Nos. C275-C279 (5)		3.70	3.70

Friendship Treaty Type of 1980

George Tupou I, Admiral du Bouzet, Adventure. See notes over #464 & after #468.

1980, Jan. 9   Litho.

C280	A83	15s multicolored	.35	.35
C281	A83	17s multicolored	.45	.45
C282	A83	22s multicolored	.50	.50
C283	A83	31s multicolored	.75	.75
C284	A83	39s multicolored	.95	.95
	Nos. C280-C284 (5)		3.00	3.00

Nos. C259-C263 Surcharged and
Overprinted in Black on Silver: "1980
OLYMPIC GAMES," Moscow '80 and
Bear Emblems

1980, Apr. 30   Litho.

C285	A81	9s on 15s multi	.25	.25
C286	A81	16s on 17s multi	.55	.55
C287	A81	29s on 18s multi	.90	.90
C288	A81	32s on 31s multi	1.00	1.00
C289	A81	47s on 39s multi	1.40	1.40
	Nos. C285-C289 (5)		4.10	4.10

22nd Summer Olympic Games, Moscow,
July 19-Aug. 3.

Scouting Activities in Rotary
Emblem — AP25

1980, Sept. 30   Litho.

C290	AP25	29s multicolored	.90	.90
C291	AP25	32s multicolored	1.00	1.00
C292	AP25	47s multicolored	1.40	1.40
C293	AP25	1pa multicolored	3.00	3.00
	Nos. C290-C293 (4)		6.30	6.30

Boy Scout Jamboree; Rotary International,
75th anniversary. Peelable backing shows
map of Tonga.

Nos. C170, C185, C195, C200-C201,
C208 Surcharged

1980, Dec. 3   Litho.

C294	AP18	29s on 14s multi	.70	.70
C295	AP19	29s on 39s multi	.70	.70
C296	A63	32s on 12s multi	.80	.80
C297	A66	32s on 14s multi	.80	.80
C298	AP16	47s on 12s multi	1.10	1.10
C299	AP18	47s on 12s multi	1.10	1.10
	Nos. C294-C299 (6)		5.20	5.20

IYD Type of 1981

1981, Sept. 9   Litho.

Size: 25x32mm

C300	A85	29s multicolored	.45	.45
C301	A85	32s multicolored	.55	.55
C302	A85	47s multicolored	.80	.80
	Nos. C300-C302 (3)		1.80	1.80

Jet Type of 1979

1982, Nov. 17   Litho.

C303	AP24	29s pink & black	1.25	.85
C304	AP24	32s pale yel & blk	1.40	1.00
C305	AP24	47s lt brown & blk	2.25	1.50
	Nos. C303-C305 (3)		4.90	3.35

AIR POST SPECIAL DELIVERY

Catalogue values for unused
stamps in this section are for
Never Hinged items.

Owl — APSD1

1990, Feb. 21	**Litho.**		**Perf. 11½**	
CE1	APSD1	10pa multi	15.00	15.00

AIR POST OFFICIAL STAMPS

Catalogue values for unused
stamps in this section are for
Never Hinged items.

Nos. 115, 117-118, 111-113
Overprinted "OFFICIAL AIR MAIL / 1862 / TAU'ATAINA / EMANCIPATION / 1962" in Red

Engr.; Photo. (A35)

1962, Feb. 7   Wmk. 79

CO1	A35	2p ultra	10.00	7.50
CO2	A35	5p purple	11.00	8.00
CO3	A35	1sh red brown	8.00	4.00
CO4	A33	5sh pur & yel	85.00	50.00
CO5	A34	10sh black & yel	40.00	20.00
CO6	A34	£1 ultra, car & yel	65.00	30.00
		Nos. CO1-CO6 (6)	219.00	119.50

Centenary of emancipation.

Type of Regular Gold Coin Issue
Design: 15sh, Queen Salote standing, 1-koula coin, obverse.

Litho.; Embossed on Gilt Foil

1963, July 15   Unwmk.   Die Cut
Diameter: 80mm

CO7	A36	15sh black	5.25	5.25

Note after No. 133 also applies to No. CO7.

No. CO7 Surcharged like Regular Issue of 1965 in Black

1965, Mar. 18

CO8	A36	30sh on 15sh black	5.50	5.50

No. 116 Surcharged in Italic Letters Similarly to Nos. C16-C21
Perf. 14½x13½

1966, June 18   Wmk. 79

CO9	A35	10sh on 4p brt green	.80	.30
CO10	A35	20sh on 4p brt green	1.00	.40

Centenary of Tupou College and secondary education.

No. 111 Surcharged in Red: "OFFICIAL / AIRMAIL / ONE PA'ANGA"

1967, Mar. 25   Engr.   Perf. 11½x11

CO11	A33	1p on 5sh pur & yel	3.00	3.00

Type of Regular Issue Surcharged

1967, Dec. 15   Wmk. 79   Die Cut

CO12	A34	30s on £1 multi	.50	.50
CO13	A34	70s on £1 multi	.70	.70
CO14	A34	1.50pa on £1 multi	1.00	1.00
		Nos. CO12-CO14 (3)	2.20	2.20

Arrival of US Peace Corps.

No. 113 Surcharged with New Value and "OFFICIAL/AIRMAIL"

1968, Apr. 6   Engr.   Perf. 11x11½

CO15	A34	40s on £1 multi	.75	.75
CO16	A34	60s on £1 multi	1.00	1.00
CO17	A34	1pa on £1 multi	1.25	1.25
CO18	A34	2pa on £1 multi	2.25	2.25
		Nos. CO15-CO18 (4)	5.25	5.25

Type of 1953 Surcharged: "Friendly Islands / Trials / Field & Track / South Pacific / Games / Port Moresby / 1969 / OFFICIAL AIRMAIL"
Wmk. 79

1968, Dec. 19   Engr.   Die Cut

CO19	A34	20s on £1 grn & multi	.35	.20
CO20	A34	1pa on £1 grn & multi	1.00	.60

No. 176 Overprinted and Surcharged in Gold on Colored Panels (Green, Emerald, Violet or Lilac) like Nos. 203-209.

Litho.; Embossed on Palladium Foil

1968   Unwmk.

CO21	A38	40s on 2s (G)	1.50	.75
CO22	A38	60s on 2s (E)	2.00	1.50
CO23	A38	1pa on 2s (V)	3.25	3.25
CO24	A38	2pa on 2s (L)	5.50	5.50
		Nos. CO21-CO24 (4)	12.25	11.00

50th birthday of King Taufa'ahau IV.

Pacific Games Type of Regular Issue
Design: Boxer.

1969, Aug. 13   Litho.   Die Cut
Self-adhesive

CO25	A40	70s gray, red & grn	.80	.80
CO26	A40	80s gray, red & org	.95	.95

See note after No. 231.

Type of Regular Issue, 1953, Surcharged: "OFFICIAL AIRMAIL / 1969 OIL / SEARCH / 90s" and Oil Derrick Obliterating Old Denomination

1969, Dec. 23   Die Cut Wmk. 79

CO27	A34	90s on £1 grn & multi	3.25	3.25

First scientific search for oil in Tonga.

Type of Regular Issue, 1953, Surcharged: "Royal Visit / MARCH / 1970 / OFFICIAL / AIRMAIL" in Black, Violet Blue or Emerald

1970, Mar. 7   Engr.   Wmk. 79

CO28	A34	75s on 1sh	4.25	3.00
CO29	A34	1pa on 1sh (VBl)	5.50	4.00
CO30	A34	1.25pa on 1sh (E)	7.00	5.00
		Nos. CO28-CO30 (3)	16.75	12.00

See note after No. 242.

Type of Regular Issue Surcharged in Black, Red or Emerald

1970, June 4   Wmk. 79   Die Cut

CO31	A33	50s on 5sh (B)	1.50	1.50
CO32	A33	90s on 5sh (R)	2.25	2.25
CO33	A33	1.50pa on 5sh (E)	3.50	3.50
		Nos. CO31-CO33 (3)	7.25	7.25

See note after No. 247.

Type of Regular Issue, 1953, Surcharged in Red and Purple or Black:

1970, Oct. 17   Engr.   Die Cut

CO34	A33	30s on 1½p (B & R)	1.90	1.90
CO35	A33	80s on 5sh (P & R)	5.00	5.00
CO36	A33	90s on 5sh (P & R)	6.00	6.00
		Nos. CO34-CO36 (3)	12.90	12.90

Centenary of the British Red Cross.

Type of Regular Issue, 1953, Surcharged in Black, Purple, Blue or Green

1971, Jan. 31   Engr.   Die Cut

CO37	A34	20s on 10sh (Bk)	1.10	.80
CO38	A34	30s on 10sh (P)	2.00	1.10
CO39	A34	50s on 10sh (Bl)	3.25	2.00
CO40	A34	2pa on 10sh (G)	12.00	10.00
		Nos. CO37-CO40 (4)	18.35	13.90

In memory of Queen Salote (1900-1965).

Type of Regular Issue, 1953, Surcharged in Red and Blue, Black or Purple

1971   Engr.   Wmk. 79   Imperf
Colors: Green & Yellow

CO41	A33	30s on 5p (R & Bl)	1.25	.75
CO42	A33	80s on 5p (R & Bk)	2.75	2.00
CO43	A33	90s on 5p (R & P)	3.00	2.25
		Nos. CO41-CO43 (3)	7.00	5.00

See note after No. 272.

Self-adhesive & Imperf.
Starting with Nos. CO44-CO46, all airmail official issues are self-adhesive and imperforate, unless otherwise stated.

Soccer Ball — OA1

1971, July   Litho.   Unwmk.

CO44	OA1	50s multi	.85	.85
CO45	OA1	90s multi	1.10	1.10
CO46	OA1	1.50pa multi	1.75	1.75
		Nos. CO44-CO46 (3)	3.70	3.70

4th South Pacific Games, Papeete, French Polynesia, Sept. 8-19.
For overprints see Nos. CO75-CO77.

Watch Type of Air Post Issues
Litho. and Embossed

1971, July 20

CO47	AP6	14s brown & multi	.65	.65
CO48	AP6	21s brn red & multi	.90	.90

Advertisement on peelable paper backing.

Nos. 243-244, 246 Surcharged

Reduced illustration.

Litho.; Gold Embossed

1971, Oct. 30

CO49	A43	60s on 3s multi	.95	.95
CO50	A43	80s on 25s multi	1.25	1.25
CO51	A43	1.10pa on 7s multi	1.40	1.40
		Nos. CO49-CO51 (3)	3.60	3.60

First investiture of Tongan Medal of Honor.

"UNICEF" — OA2

1971, Dec.   Litho.

CO52	OA2	70s black & multi	2.00	2.00
CO53	OA2	80s multicolored	2.25	2.25
CO54	OA2	90s multicolored	2.25	2.25
		Nos. CO52-CO54 (3)	6.50	6.50

25th anniversary of UNICEF.
For overprint see No. CO70.

Ship Type of Regular Issue
Design: Map of Merchant Marine routes from Tonga and tanker "Aoniu."

1972, Apr. 14

CO55	A49	20s multicolored	1.60	.90
CO56	A49	50s multicolored	3.50	2.75
CO57	A49	1.20pa multicolored	7.25	7.00
		Nos. CO55-CO57 (3)	12.35	10.65

Coin Type of Regular Issue
Design: Coins in center, inscription panel above, date below coins.

Litho.; Embossed on Metallic Foil

1972, July 15

CO58	A50	50s silver & multi	1.50	1.50
CO59	A50	70s silver & multi	2.00	2.00
CO60	A50	1.50pa silver & multi	3.75	3.75
		Nos. CO58-CO60 (3)	7.25	7.25

Watch Type of Air Post Issue

1972, July 20   Litho.; Embossed

CO61	AP6	17s multicolored	.60	.60
CO62	AP6	38s ocher & multi	1.25	1.25

Advertisement on peelable paper backing.

Flags and Map of Tonga Islands — OA3

1972, Dec. 9   Litho.

CO63	OA3	25s black & multi	.50	.50
CO64	OA3	75s multicolored	1.50	1.50
CO65	OA3	1.50pa multicolored	3.00	3.00
		Nos. CO63-CO65 (3)	5.00	5.00

Tonga's proclamation of sovereignty over the Minerva Reefs, June 1972.

No. 290 Surcharged in Black, Ultramarine or Green

1973

ESTABLISHMENT BANK OF TONGA
40s
OFFICIAL AIRMAIL

1973, Mar. 30   Litho.

CO66	A49	40s on 21s (B)	1.50	1.25
CO67	A49	85s on 21s (U)	3.25	3.25
CO68	A49	1.25pa on 21s (G)	3.75	3.75
		Nos. CO66-CO68 (3)	8.50	8.25

Establishment of Bank of Tonga.

Nos. CO55, CO53 and 247 Overprinted or Surcharged in Silver:
No. CO69: New value, 4 wavy lines, fleur-de-lis and "SILVER JUBILEE/ TONGAN SCOUTING / 1948-1973"
No. CO70: "SILVER / JUBILEE" (vertically), fleur-de-lis and "1948 1973"
No. CO71: Silver surcharge and overprint on dark blue panels "OFFICIAL AIRMAIL / T$1.40," "1948-1973" "SILVER / JUBILEE/ TONGAN / SCOUTING," "1948-1973" in dark blue

1973, June 29

CO69	A49	30s on 20s	15.00	4.00
CO70	OA2	80s multi	37.50	14.50
CO71	A43	1.40pa on 50s	52.50	35.00
		Nos. CO69-CO71 (3)	105.00	53.50

25th anniv. of Tongan Boy Scout movement.

Tanker James Cook and Cook
Medal — OA4

1973, Oct. 2 **Litho.**
CO72 OA4 25s multi 3.50 1.50
CO73 OA4 80s multi 9.25 4.50
CO74 OA4 1.30pa multi 11.00 7.50
Nos. CO72-CO74 (3) 23.75 13.50
Bicentenary of Capt. Cook's arrival.

Nos. CO44-CO46 Overprinted in Dark
Blue, Black or Green with Games'
Emblems and: "1974 / Commonwealth
/ Games / Christchurch"

1973, Dec. 19
CO75 OA1 50s multi (DBl) 1.10 1.10
CO76 OA1 90s multi (B) 2.00 1.75
CO77 OA1 1.50pa multi (G) 2.90 2.50
Nos. CO75-CO77 (3) 6.00 5.35

10th British Commonwealth Games, Christchurch, N.Z., Jan. 24-Feb. 2, 1974.

Peace
Dove
OA5

1974, Mar. 20 **Litho.**
CO78 OA5 7s multicolored .40 .25
CO79 OA5 9s multicolored .50 .30
CO80 OA5 12s multicolored .50 .30
CO81 OA5 14s multicolored .75 .45
CO82 OA5 17s multicolored .80 .50
CO83 OA5 29s multicolored 1.50 .90
CO84 OA5 38s multicolored 2.00 1.25
CO85 OA5 50s multicolored 2.50 1.50
CO86 OA5 75s multicolored 3.75 2.25
Nos. CO78-CO86 (9) 12.70 7.70

Printed in rolls of 500. Self-adhesive lilac
control number in upper left corner.

"UPU Centenary" — OA6

1974, June 20 **Typo.**
CO87 OA6 25s red, green & blk .75 .75
CO88 OA6 35s yel, red lil & blk .85 .85
CO89 OA6 70s dp org, bl & blk 1.75 1.75
Nos. CO87-CO89 (3) 3.35 3.35
Centenary of Universal Postal Union.

Lady Baden-Powell — OA7

1974, Sept. 11 **Litho.**
CO90 OA7 45s emer & multi 4.25 2.50
CO91 OA7 55s emer & multi 6.00 3.50
CO92 OA7 1pa emer & multi 8.50 5.00
Nos. CO90-CO92 (3) 18.75 11.00
Girl Guides of Tonga.
For overprints see Nos. CO105-CO107.

Handshake and Institute's
Emblem — OA8

Institute's Emblem and
Banknotes — OA9

1974, Dec. 11
CO93 OA8 30s multicolored 3.00 1.50
CO94 OA8 35s multicolored 3.50 2.00
CO95 OA9 80s red & multi 8.00 4.00
Nos. CO93-CO95 (3) 14.50 7.50
Establishment of Royal Marine Institute.

Arch and Palms — OA10

Designs: 75s, 1.25pa, Dawn over lagoon.

1975, Mar. 11 **Litho.**
CO96 OA10 50s multi 1.75 1.75
CO97 OA10 75s multi 3.00 3.00
CO98 OA10 1.25pa multi 4.00 4.00
Nos. CO96-CO98 (3) 8.75 8.75
First meeting of South Pacific area Prime
Ministers. See note after No. 226.

Track and Games' Emblem — OA11

1975, June 11
CO99 OA11 38s multi 1.00 1.00
CO100 OA11 75s multi 1.75 1.75
CO101 OA11 1.20pa multi 2.75 2.75
Nos. CO99-CO101 (3) 5.50 5.50
5th South Pacific Games, Guam, Aug. 1-10.
See note after No. 226.
For surcharge see No. 418.

Four Constitutional Monarchs — OA12

Litho.; Embossed on Gilt Foil
1975, Nov. 4
CO102 OA12 17s multicolored .80 .65
CO103 OA12 60s multicolored 2.00 1.75
CO104 OA12 90s multicolored 2.60 2.60
Nos. CO102-CO104 (3) 5.40 5.00

No. CO90-CO92 Overprinted in
Carmine on Blue, Silver or Gold

1976, Feb. 24 **Litho.**
CO105 OA7 45s multicolored
(B) 3.25 1.25
CO106 OA7 55s multicolored
(S) 3.25 1.50
CO107 OA7 1pa multicolored
(G) 6.25 6.25
Nos. CO105-CO107 (3) 12.75 9.00
21st Olympic Games, Montreal, Canada,
July 17-Aug. 1. See note after No. 226.

Bicentennial Type of 1976

Signers of Declaration of Independence:
20s, William Paca, Francis Lewis, George
Read, Edward Rutledge, Thomas Heyward,
Jr. 50s, George Walton, Matthew Thornton,
Robert Morris, William Williams, James
Smith. 1.15pa, Benjamin Rush, Samuel
Adams, Samuel Chase, George Wythe,
George Clymer.

1976, May 26
CO108 A66 20s buff & multi .90 .70
CO109 A66 50s buff & multi 2.90 2.25
CO110 A66 1.15pa buff & multi 6.25 5.00
Nos. CO108-CO110 (3) 10.05 7.95
See note after No. 381.

Inside View of Lifuka Chapel — OA13

1976, Aug. 25 **Litho.**
CO111 OA13 65s multi-
colored 2.75 2.75
CO112 OA13 85s multi-
colored 3.00 3.00
CO113 OA13 1.15pa mul-
ticolored 4.00 4.00
Nos. CO111-CO113 (3) 9.75 9.75
See note after No. 386.
For surcharge see No. CO181.

OA14

1976, Nov. 1
CO114 OA14 30s silver &
multi .80 .70
CO115 OA14 60s silver &
multi 1.60 1.50
CO116 OA14 1.25pa silver &
multi 3.25 3.00
Nos. CO114-CO116 (3) 5.65 5.20
See note after No. 391.

Flags and Arms of Great Britain and
Tonga — OA15

1977, Feb. 7 **Litho.**
CO117 OA15 35s multi 4.00 3.25
CO118 OA15 45s multi .50 .50
CO119 OA15 1.10pa multi 1.50 1.25
Nos. CO117-CO119 (3) 6.00 5.00
See note after No. 396.
For surcharge see No. C238.

Coin Type of Air Post Stamps 1977

Design: Coronation coin, inscriptions in
round upper panel.

1977, July 4
CO120 AP21 20s multicolored .55 .55
CO121 AP21 40s multicolored 1.00 1.00
CO122 AP21 80s multicolored 2.10 2.10
Nos. CO120-CO122 (3) 3.65 3.65
See note after No. 401.

**Capt. Cook Type of Air Post Stamps
1977**

Design: Inscription and flying dove.

1977, Sept. 27

CO123	AP22	20s gold & multi	1.40	1.40
CO124	AP22	55s on 20s multi	8.50	8.50
CO125	AP22	85s on 20s multi	18.00	18.00
	Nos. CO123-CO125 (3)		27.90	27.90

Printed on peelable paper backing showing dark brown replica of entry in Capt. Cook's diary.

Whale Type of Air Post Stamps 1977

Design: Blue whale.

1977, Dec. 16

CO126	AP23	45s multicolored	7.00	3.00
CO127	AP23	65s multicolored	10.00	4.75
CO128	AP23	85s multicolored	12.00	5.75
	Nos. CO126-CO128 (3)		29.00	13.50

Whale protection.

Games' Emblem and Athletes OA16

1978, May 5   **Litho.**

CO129	OA16	30s red & multi	.70	.70
CO130	OA16	60s red & multi	1.40	1.40
CO131	OA16	1pa red & multi	2.50	2.50
	Nos. CO129-CO131 (3)		4.60	4.60

See note after No. 423.

King Type of 1978

Head of King Taufa'ahau IV on medal.

1978, July 4

CO132	A74	26s multicolored	.65	.65
CO133	A74	85s multicolored	2.00	2.00
CO134	A74	90s multicolored	2.50	2.50
	Nos. CO132-CO134 (3)		5.15	5.15

See note after No. 226.

Wildlife Type of 1978

1978, Dec. 15   **Litho. & Typo.**

CO150	A77	40s Whale	7.00	3.50
CO151	A77	50s Bat	7.00	3.50
CO152	A77	1.10pa Turtle	9.25	7.75
	Nos. CO150-CO152 (3)		23.25	14.75

Wildlife conservation. See note after No. 226.

Types of 1979

Designs: 38s, Red Cross and star. 74s, like No. 451. 80s, like No. 450.

1979, Feb. 16   **Litho.**

CO153	A78	38s multicolored	1.00	.60
CO154	A80	74s multicolored	2.00	1.25
CO155	A79	80s multicolored	2.25	1.50
	Nos. CO153-CO155 (3)		5.25	3.35

Decade of Progress. Paper backing shows map of Tonga.

Hands Peeling off No. CO118 — OA17

1979, June 1

CO156	OA17	45s multicolored	1.10	1.10
CO157	OA17	65s multicolored	1.50	1.50
CO158	OA17	80s multicolored	1.90	1.90
	Nos. CO156-CO158 (3)		4.50	4.50

See note after No. 458.
For surcharges see Nos. CO176-CO178.

Parrot — OA18

1979, Aug. 1

CO159	OA18	5s multicolored	.20	.20
CO160	OA18	11s multicolored	.25	.25
CO161	OA18	14s multicolored	.35	.35
CO162	OA18	15s multicolored	.35	.35
CO163	OA18	17s multicolored	.45	.45
CO164	OA18	18s multicolored	.50	.50
CO165	OA18	22s multicolored	.55	.55
CO166	OA18	31s multicolored	.75	.75
CO167	OA18	39s multicolored	.95	.95
CO168	OA18	75s multicolored	1.75	1.75
CO169	OA18	1pa multicolored	2.25	2.25
	Nos. CO159-CO169 (11)		8.35	8.35

Nos. CO159-CO169 issued in coils. See note after No. 226.
The 5s exists with denomination in magenta and the leaves behind the bird missing. This seems to be a special printing that was not available for postal purposes.

View Type of 1979

Design: Niuatoputapu and Tafahi Islands. See note after No. 463.

1979, Nov. 23   **Litho.**

CO170	A82	35s multicolored	.85	.85
CO171	A82	45s multicolored	1.10	1.10
CO172	A82	1pa multicolored	2.25	2.25
	Nos. CO170-CO172 (3)		4.20	4.20

Friendship Treaty Type of 1980

Design: Church. See note after No. 468.

1980, Jan. 9   **Litho.**

CO173	A83	40s multicolored	1.00	1.00
CO174	A83	55s multicolored	1.25	1.25
CO175	A83	1.25pa multicolored	3.00	3.00
	Nos. CO173-CO175 (3)		5.25	5.25

Nos. CO156-CO158 Surcharged and Overprinted in Black on Silver: "1980 OLYMPIC GAMES," Moscow '80 and Bear Emblems

1980, Apr. 30   **Litho.**

CO176	OA17	26s on 45s	.85	.85
CO177	OA17	40s on 65s	1.25	1.25
CO178	OA17	1.10pa on 80s	3.50	3.50
	Nos. CO176-CO178 (3)		5.60	5.60

22nd Summer Olympic Games, Moscow, July 19-Aug. 3.

Tents and Rotary Emblem — OA19

1980, Sept. 30   **Litho.**

CO179	OA19	25s multicolored	.70	.70
CO180	OA19	2pa multicolored	5.75	5.75

Boy Scout Jamboree; Rotary Intl., 75th anniv. Peelable backing shows map of Tonga. For surcharges see Nos. 502-503.

No. CO111 Surcharged

1980, Dec. 3   **Litho.**

CO181	OA13	2pa on 65s multi	4.75	4.75

OFFICIAL STAMPS

Types of Postage Issue of 1892 Overprinted in Carmine

Perf. 12x11½

1893, Feb. 13   **Wmk. 62**

O1	A4	1p ultra	11.50	55.00
a.	*Half used as ½p on cover*			
O2	A5	2p ultra	30.00	62.50
O3	A4	4p ultra	55.00	110.00
O4	A5	8p ultra	100.00	200.00
O5	A5	1sh ultra	110.00	210.00
	Nos. O1-O5 (5)		306.50	637.50

Values are for copies of good color. Faded and discolored copies sell for much less.
The overprinted initials stand for "Gaue Faka Buleaga" (On Government Service).

Nos. O1-O5 with Additional Surcharge Handstamped in Black

1893

O6	A4	½p on 1p ultra	20.00	57.50
O7	A5	2½p on 2p ultra	27.50	50.00
O8	A4	5p on 4p ultra	27.50	50.00
O9	A5	7½p on 8p ultra	27.50	92.50
O10	A5	10p on 1sh ultra	32.50	95.00
	Nos. O6-O10 (5)		135.00	345.00

> Catalogue values for unused stamps in this section, from this point to the end of the section, are for Never Hinged items.

Redrawn Banana and Coconut Types of Regular Issue, 1970, Inscribed "Official Post"

1970, June 9   **Typo.**   *Die Cut*
Self-adhesive

O11	A39	1s yel, blk & dp car	.50	.50
O12	A39	2s yel, blk & blue	.65	.65
O13	A39	3s yel, blk & brn	.65	.65
O14	A39	4s yel, blk & emer	.65	.65
O15	A39	5s yel, blk & org	.75	.75

Litho.; Embossed on Gilt Foil

O16	A44	6s brown & multi	.90	.90
O17	A44	7s brown & multi	.95	.95
O18	A44	8s brown & multi	1.00	1.00
O19	A44	9s brown & multi	1.25	1.25
O20	A44	10s brown & multi	1.40	1.40
	Nos. O11-O20 (10)		8.70	8.70

Nos. O13, O17-O18 and O20 have self-adhesive control numbers in lower left corner of paper backing.

Types of Regular Issue 1970-72

1972, Sept. 30   **Typo.**
Self-adhesive

O21	A51	1s yel, red & brn	.20	.20
O22	A51	2s yel, grn & brn	.25	.25
O23	A51	3s yel, emer & brn	.35	.20
O24	A51	4s yel, blk & brn	.35	.25
O25	A51	5s yellow & brn	.35	.25
O26	A44	6s brown & green	.40	.25
O27	A44	7s brown & green	.45	.30
O28	A44	8s brown & green	.45	.30
O29	A44	9s brown & green	.45	.30
O30	A44	10s brown & green	.55	.35
O31	A52	15s green & ultra	.90	.50
O32	A52	20s green & ver	1.10	.70
O33	A52	25s green & dk brn	1.25	.80
O34	A52	40s green & org	2.50	1.75
O35	A52	50s green & vio bl	2.75	2.00
	Nos. O21-O35 (15)		12.30	8.35

Paper backing is brown on Nos. O26-O35. Nos. O30-O35 have self-adhesive control number in lower left corner, Nos. O21-O29 lower right corner.

Types of Regular Issue 1978

Designs: 1s-5s, Bananas (similar to type A75). 6s-10s, Coconuts. 15s-1pa, Pineapples.

1978, Sept. 29   **Typo.**

O36	A75	1s yellow & lilac	.25	.25
O37	A75	2s yellow & brown	.25	.25
O38	A75	3s multicolored	.35	.35
O39	A75	4s multicolored	.35	.35
O40	A75	5s multicolored	.35	.35
O41	A76	6s multicolored	.50	.50
O42	A76	7s multicolored	.50	.50
O43	A76	8s multicolored	.50	.50
O44	A76	9s multicolored	.50	.50
O45	A76	10s multicolored	.50	.50
O46	A76	15s multicolored	1.25	1.25
O47	A76	20s multicolored	1.40	1.40
O48	A76	30s multicolored	1.50	1.50
O49	A76	50s multicolored	2.00	2.00
O50	A76	1pa multicolored	3.00	3.00
	Nos. O36-O50 (15)		13.20	13.20

Nos. O36-O50 issued in coils; self-adhesive control numbers on paper backing except on 1s. See note after No. 226.

Type of 1984 Overprinted "OFFICIAL"

1984-85   **Litho.**   *Die Cut*

O52	A103	1s multicolored	.50	.50
O53	A103	2s multicolored	.50	.50
O54	A103	3s multicolored	.50	.50
O55	A103	5s multicolored	.50	.50
O56	A103	6s multicolored	.50	.50
O57	A103	9s multicolored	.75	.75
a.	*Perf. 14½ ('85)*		.75	.75
O58	A103	10s multicolored	.75	.75
O59	A103	13s multicolored	1.25	1.25
O60	A103	15s multicolored	1.25	1.25
O61	A103	20s multicolored	1.50	1.50
O62	A103	29s multicolored	1.75	1.75
O63	A103	32s multicolored	1.75	1.75
O64	A103	47s multicolored	2.00	2.00
O65	A103	1pa multicolored	4.00	4.00
O66	A103	2pa multicolored	7.00	7.00
O67	A103	5pa multicolored ('85)	12.00	12.00
	Nos. O52-O67 (16)		36.50	36.50

Nos. 532-534 Ovptd. "OFFICIAL"

1983, Feb. 22   **Litho.**   *Die Cut*

O68	A96a	29s multicolored	4.75	4.75
O69	A96a	32s multicolored	4.75	4.75
O70	A96a	47s multicolored	10.00	10.00
	Nos. O68-O70 (3)		19.50	19.50

O68-O70 handstamped.

Nos. 564-565, 567-568, 570, 572 and 577 Surcharged "OFFICIAL"

1986, Apr. 16   *Die Cut*
Self-adhesive

O71	A103	4s on 2s, #564	1.00	1.00
O72	A103	4s on 13s, #570	1.00	1.00
O73	A103	42s on 3s, #565	3.25	3.25
O74	A103	42s on 9s, #568	3.25	3.25
O75	A103	57s on 6s, #567	3.50	3.50
O76	A103	57s on 20s, #572	3.50	3.50
O77	A103	2.50pa on 2pa, #577	12.00	12.00
	Nos. O71-O77 (7)		27.50	27.50

Marine Type Inscribed "POSTAGE & REVENUE" and "OFFICIAL"

1995-96   **Litho.**   *Perf. 14*

O78	A155a	10s multicolored	.60	.60
O79	A155a	20s multicolored	.90	.40
O80	A155a	45s multicolored	1.10	.70
O81	A155a	60s multicolored	1.40	.95
O82	A155a	80s multicolored	1.75	1.25
O83	A155a	1pa multicolored	2.25	1.75
O84	A155a	2pa multicolored	4.00	4.00
O85	A155a	3pa multicolored	5.00	5.00
O86	A155a	5pa multicolored	9.75	9.75
O87	A155a	10pa multicolored	14.00	14.00
	Nos. O78-O87 (10)		40.75	38.40

Issued: 10s-80s, 9/25/95; 1pa-10pa, 5/31/96.

NIUAFO'OU

Tin Can Island

> Catalogue values for all unused stamps in this country are for Never Hinged items.

Nos. 1-63 are self-adhesive stamps on peelable inscribed backing paper and imperforate.

Niuafo'ou Airport Type of Tonga

1983, May 11   **Litho.**   *Die Cut*

1	A97	29s multicolored	1.75	1.75
2	A97	1pa multicolored	4.50	4.50

Map of
Niuafo'ou — A1

1983, May 11
3	A1	1s buff, blk & red	.35	.35
4	A1	2s buff, blk & brt green	.35	.35
5	A1	3s buff, blk & brt blue	.35	.35
6	A1	3s buff, blk & brn org	.35	.35
7	A1	5s buff, blk & deep rose lil	.35	.35
8	A1	6s buff, blk & grnsh blue	.35	.35
9	A1	9s buff, blk & lt ol grn	.35	.35
10	A1	10s buff, blk & brt bl	.35	.35
11	A1	13s buff, blk & brt grn	.40	.40
12	A1	15s buff, blk & brn org	.50	.50
13	A1	20s buff, blk & grnsh blue	.65	.65
14	A1	29s buff, blk & deep rose lil	1.00	1.00
15	A1	32s buff, blk & lt ol grn	1.10	1.10
16	A1	47s buff, blk & red	1.60	1.60
		Nos. 3-16 (14)	8.05	8.05

See Nos. 19-22.

Tonga No. 520 Surcharged or
Ovptd. in Purple or Gold
"NIUAFO'OU / Kingdom of Tonga"

1983, May 11
17	A93	1pa on 2pa multi (P)	3.25	3.25
18	A93	2pa multicolored (G)	6.75	6.75

Nos. 17-18 each exist se-tenant with label.

Map Type of 1983
Value Typo. in Violet Blue

1983, May 30
19	A1	3s buff & black	.30	.30
20	A1	5s buff & black	.30	.30
21	A1	32s buff & black	1.50	1.50
22	A1	2pa buff & black	8.00	8.00
		Nos. 19-22 (4)	10.10	10.10

The denomination on Nos. 19-22 added like
a surcharge and is larger than on Nos. 5-7, 15,
covering part of the design.
Nos. 19-22 each exist se-tenant with label.

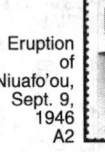

Eruption
of
Niuafo'ou,
Sept. 9,
1946
A2

1983, Sept. 29
23	A2	5s shown	.50	.35
24	A2	29s Lava flow	1.75	1.25
25	A2	32s Moving to high ground	1.90	1.25
26	A2	1.50pa Evacuation to Eua	6.00	6.00
		Nos. 23-26 (4)	10.15	8.85

Birds — A3

1983, Nov. 15
27	A3	1s Purple swamphen	1.00	1.00
28	A3	2s White-collared kingfisher	1.00	1.00
29	A3	3s Red-headed parrotfinch	1.00	1.00
30	A3	5s Banded rail	1.25	1.25
31	A3	6s Niuafo'ou megapode	1.60	1.60
32	A3	9s Giant forest honeyeater	2.25	2.25
33	A3	10s Purple swamphen, drinking	2.25	2.25
34	A3	13s Banded rail, diff.	2.50	2.50
35	A3	15s Niuafo'ou megapode, diff.	2.50	2.50

Size: 25x39mm
36	A3	20s like #34	3.00	3.00
37	A3	29s Red-headed parrotfinch, diff.	3.25	3.25
38	A3	32s White-collared kingfisher, diff.	3.25	3.25
39	A3	47s like #35	4.00	4.00

Size: 32x42mm
40	A3	1pa like #33	7.75	9.00
41	A3	2pa like #35	10.00	13.00
		Nos. 27-41 (15)	46.60	50.85

Nos. 34-36, 39 and 41 horiz.
For surcharges see Nos. 66-73.

Wildlife
A4

1984, Mar. 7
42	A4	29s Green turtle	.85	.85
43	A4	32s Flying fox, vert.	.85	.85
44	A4	47s Humpback whale	3.00	2.00
45	A4	1.50pa Niuafo'ou megapode, vert.	5.50	7.50
		Nos. 42-45 (4)	10.20	11.20

Map
A5

1984, Aug. 20
46	A5	47s Intl. Date Line, Cent.	.70	.70
47	A5	2pa shown	3.00	3.00

AUSIPEX
'84 — A6   A7

1984, Sept. 17
48	A6	32s Australia No. 15	.90	.90
49	A6	1.50pa No. 10	4.50	4.50

Souvenir Sheet
50	Sheet of 2	4.50	4.50

No. 50 contains two imperf. stamps similar
to Nos. 48-49, but with denomination replacing
logo. No. 50 without denominations was not
valid for postage.

1985, Feb. 20

Jacob Le Maire, 400th Birth Anniv.: 13s,
Dutch band entertaining natives. 32s, Natives
preparing kava. 47s, Native outrigger canoes.
1.50pa, Le Maire's ship at anchor.
51	A7	13s multicolored	.50	.50
52	A7	32s multicolored	1.10	1.10
53	A7	47s multicolored	1.50	1.50
54	A7	1.50pa multicolor	4.50	5.50
		Nos. 51-54 (4)	7.60	8.60

Souvenir Sheet
55	A7	1.50pa multicolored	4.00	4.00

Mail
Ships
A8

1985, May 22   *Die Cut*
56	A8	9s Ysabel, 1902	.60	.60
a.		Perf. 14		.90

57	A8	13s Tofua I, 1908	1.25	1.25
a.		Perf. 14	1.90	1.90
58	A8	47s Mariposa, 1934	1.90	1.90
a.		Perf. 14	2.75	2.75
59	A8	1.50pa Matua, 1936	4.25	6.00
a.		Perf. 14	6.50	9.00
		Nos. 56-59 (4)	8.00	9.75
		Nos. 56a-59a (4)	12.05	14.55

Rocket
Mail — A9

Designs: 32s, Preparing to fire rocket. 42s,
Rocket airborne. 57s, Captain watching
rocket's progress. 1.50pa, Islanders reading
mail.

1985, Nov. 5
60	A9	32s multicolored	1.50	.90
61	A9	42s multicolored	1.90	1.10
62	A9	57s multicolored	2.50	1.50
63	A9	1.50pa multicolored	5.25	6.00
		Nos. 60-63 (4)	11.15	9.50

Self-adhesive stamps discontinued.

Halley's
Comet — A10

Nos. 64, 65: a, Drawing of Comet in 684. b,
Comet shown in Bayeux Tapestry, 1066. c,
Edmond Halley. d, Comet, 1910. e, Infrared
photography, 1986.

1986, Mar. 26   *Perf. 14*
64	A10	42s Strip of #a.-e.	36.00	32.50
65	A10	57s Strip of #a.-e.	36.00	32.50

Nos. 32-39
Surcharged
in Blue

1986, Apr. 16   *Die Cut*
Self-Adhesive
66	A3	4s on 9s #32	1.00	2.25
67	A3	4s on 10s #33	1.00	2.25
68	A3	42s on 13s #34	3.00	2.25
69	A3	42s on 15s #35	3.00	2.25
70	A3	57s on 29s #37	3.75	2.50
71	A3	57s on 32s #38	3.75	2.50
72	A3	2.50pa on 20s #36	10.00	11.00
73	A3	2.50pa on 47s #39	10.00	11.00
		Nos. 66-73 (8)	35.50	36.00

Placement of surcharge varies.

AMERIPEX '86 Type of Tonga

1986, May 22   *Perf. 14*
74	A117	57s Surveying	3.00	3.00
75	A117	1.50pa Agriculture	5.50	5.50
a.		Souv. sheet of 2, #74-75, imperf.	9.25	9.25

Peace Corps in Tonga, 25th anniv.

First
Tongan
Postage
Stamps,
Cent.
A11

1986, Aug. 27
76	A11	42s Swimmers with mail	1.50	1.50
77	A11	57s Loading tin can mail into canoe	1.90	1.90
78	A11	1pa Rocket mail	3.50	3.50

79	A11	2.50pa Outrigger canoe	6.00	6.00
		Nos. 76-79 (4)	12.90	12.90

Souvenir Sheet
80	A11	2.50pa Outrigger canoe, diff.	13.00	13.00

Red
Cross — A12

1987, Mar. 11   *Perf. 14x14½*
81	A12	15s Balanced diet	1.00	1.00
82	A12	42s Post-natal care	2.75	2.75
83	A12	1pa Insects spread disease	4.25	4.25
84	A12	2.50pa Fight against drugs, alcohol, smoking	6.75	6.75
		Nos. 81-84 (4)	14.75	14.75

Sharks
A13

1987, Apr. 29   *Perf. 14*
85	A13	29s Hammerhead	2.75	2.50
86	A13	32s Tiger	2.75	2.50
87	A13	47s Gray nurse	3.50	3.00
88	A13	1pa Great white	5.50	7.50
		Nos. 85-88 (4)	14.50	15.50

Souvenir Sheet
89	A13	2pa Shark attack	16.00	16.00

Aviators
and
Aircraft
A14

Designs: 42s, Capt. E. C. Musick and Sikorsky S-42. 57s, Capt. J.W. Burgess and Shorts
S-30. 1.50pa, Sir Charles Kingsford Smith and
Fokker F.VIIb-3m. 2pa, Amelia Earhart and
Lockheed Electra 10A.

1987, Sept. 2
90	A14	42s multicolored	2.50	1.75
91	A14	57s multicolored	3.00	2.00
92	A14	1.50pa multicolored	4.50	4.50
93	A14	2pa multicolored	5.25	5.25
		Nos. 90-93 (4)	15.25	13.50

First
Niuafo'ou
Postage
Stamps,
5th
Anniv.
A15

Designs: 42s, 57s, Niuafo'ou megapode,
No. 15. 1pa, 2pa, Concorde, No. 1.

1988, May 18
94	A15	42s multicolored	1.25	.90
95	A15	57s multicolored	1.25	1.00
96	A15	1pa multicolored	4.75	3.50
97	A15	2pa multicolored	5.50	4.50
		Nos. 94-97 (4)	12.75	9.90

#96-97, Niuafo'ou Airport Inauguration, 5th
anniv.

Settlement of Australia, Bicent.
Type of Tonga
Miniature Sheet

Designs: a, Arrival of First Fleet, Sydney
Cove, Jan. 1788. b, Aborigines. c, Early settlement. d, Soldier on guard. e, Herd of sheep. f,
Horseman. g, Locomotive, kangaroos. h,
Train, kangaroos. i, Flying doctor service. j,
Cricket players. k, Stadium, batsman guarding
wicket. l, Sydney Harbor Bridge, Opera
House.

1988, July 11 — Perf. 13½

98	A128	42s Sheet of 12, #98a-98 I	42.50	42.50

Polynesian Islands — A16

Birds and landmarks: 42s, Audubon's shearwater, blowholes at Houma, Tonga. 57s, Kiwi, Akaroa Harbor, New Zealand. 90s, Red-tailed tropicbird, Rainmaker Mountain, Samoa. 2.50pa, Laysan albatross, Kapoho Volcano, Hawaii.

1988, Aug. 18 — Perf. 14

99	A16	42s multicolored	1.50	1.00
100	A16	57s multicolored	2.25	1.50
101	A16	90s multicolored	2.50	2.50
102	A16	2.50pa multicolored	5.00	5.00
		Nos. 99-102 (4)	11.25	10.00

Miniature Sheet

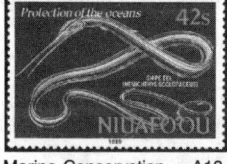

Mutiny on the Bounty, Bicent. — A17

Designs: a, Sextant. b, William Bligh. c, Royal Navy lieutenant. d, Midshipman. e, Contemporary newspaper, Tahitian girl. f, Breadfruit. g, *Mutiny on the Bounty* excerpt, pistol grip. h, Pistol barrel, illustration of Bounty castaways. i, Tahitian girl, newsprint. j, Bligh's and Fletcher Christian's signatures. k, Christian, Pitcairn Island. l, Tombstone of John Adams.

1989, Apr. 28 — Perf. 13½

103	A17	42s Sheet of 12, #a.-l.	25.00	25.00

Marine Conservation — A18

1989, June 2 — Perf. 14

104	A18	32s Hatchet fish	1.25	1.25
105	A18	42s Snipe eel	1.50	1.50
106	A18	57s Viper fish	1.90	1.90
107	A18	1.50pa Angler fish	4.50	4.50
		Nos. 104-107 (4)	9.15	9.15

Evolution of the Earth — A19

Designs: 1s, Formation of the crust. 2s, Cross-section of crust. 5s, Volcanism. 10s, Surface cools. 13s, Gem stones. 15s, Oceans form. 20s, Mountains develop. 32s, River valley. 42s, Silurian Era plant life. 45s, Early marine life. 50s, Trilobites, Cambrian Era marine life. 57s, Carboniferous Era forest, coal

seams. 60s, Dinosaurs feeding. 80s, Dinosaurs fighting. 1pa, Carboniferous Era insect, amphibians. 1.50pa, Stegosaurus, Jurassic Era. 2pa, Birds and mammals, Jurassic Era. 5pa, Hominid family, Pleistocene Era. 10pa, Mammoth, saber tooth tiger.

1989-93 — Perf. 14½

108	A19	1s multicolored	.60	.60
109	A19	2s multicolored	.60	.60
110	A19	5s multicolored	.80	.80
111	A19	10s multicolored	.80	.80
111A	A19	13s multicolored	1.00	1.00
112	A19	15s multicolored	.80	.80
113	A19	20s multicolored	.80	.80
114	A19	32s multicolored	1.00	1.00
115	A19	42s multicolored	1.40	1.40
115A	A19	45s multicolored	1.40	1.40
116	A19	50s multicolored	1.50	1.50
117	A19	57s multicolored	1.50	1.50
117A	A19	60s multicolored	1.60	1.60
117B	A19	80s multicolored	2.00	2.00

Size: 26x40mm
Perf. 14

118	A19	1pa multicolored	2.75	2.75
119	A19	1.50pa multicolored	4.25	4.25
120	A19	2pa multicolored	4.25	4.25
121	A19	5pa multicolored	8.50	8.50

Perf. 14

121A	A19	10pa multicolored	14.50	14.50
		Nos. 108-121A (19)	50.05	50.05

Issued: 1s-10s, 15s-42s, 50s-57s, 6/6/89; 13s, 45s, 60s, 80s, 5/3/93; 10pa, 9/14/93; others, 8/1/89.

1989, Nov. 17 — Perf. 14

122	A20	57s multicolored	1.90	1.90

Miniature Sheet

Nos. 108-121 with UPU emblem: Nos. 123a-123e, #108-112, Nos. 123f-123j, #113-117, Nos. 123k-123n, #118-121.

123		Sheet of 15, #a.-n., 122	25.00	25.00
a.-e.	A19 42s any single, perf. 14½		1.00	1.00
f.-j.	A19 42s any single, perf. 14½		1.50	1.50
k.-n.	A19 57s any single, perf. 14		2.00	2.00

Miniature Sheet

Lake Vai Lahi, Niuafo'ou A21

a, d, Left part of lake. b, e, Small islands in center of lake. c, f, Small islet in right side of lake.

1990, Apr. 4 — Perf. 14

124		Sheet of 6	10.00	10.00
a.-c.	A21 42s any single		1.00	1.00
d.-f.	A21 1pa any single		2.25	2.25

Nos. 124a-124c and 124d-124f printed in continuous designs.

Penny Black, 150th Anniv. A22

Tin Can Mail and: 42s, Penny Black. 57s, US #2. 75s, Western Australia #1. 2.50pa, Cape of Good Hope #178.

1990, May 1

125	A22	42s multicolored	1.60	1.25
126	A22	57s multicolored	1.75	1.50
127	A22	75s multicolored	2.00	2.00
128	A22	2.50pa multicolored	6.50	6.50
		Nos. 125-128 (4)	11.85	11.25

Polynesian Whaling — A23

Designs: 15s, Whale surfacing. 42s, Whale diving beneath outrigger canoe. 57s, Tail flukes. 1pa, 2pa, Old man, two whales.

1990 — Perf. 11½

129	A23	15s multicolored	2.50	2.50
130	A23	42s multicolored	3.50	3.50
131	A23	57s multicolored	3.75	3.75
132	A23	2pa multicolored	9.75	9.75
		Nos. 129-132 (4)	19.50	19.50

Souvenir Sheet
Perf. 14x14½

133	A23	1pa multicolored	17.00	17.00

Issue dates: #133, Sept. 4, others, June 6.
The entire souvenir sheet, No. 133, shows a modified No. 132. The 37½x30½mm stamp shows the two whales.
For surcharges see Nos. 139, 174-178.

UN Development Program, 40th Anniv. — A24

Designs: No. 134a, Agriculture and fisheries. No. 134b, Education. No. 135a, Health care. No. 135b, Communications.

1990, Oct. 25 — Perf. 14

134	A24	Pair, #a.-b.	2.50	2.50
135	A24	2.50pa Pair, #a.-b.	11.50	11.50

Charting of Niuafo'ou, Bicent. — A24a

Designs: No. 136a, 32s, The Bounty. b, 42s, Chart showing location of Niuafo'ou and Tonga. c, 57s, The Pandora.
No. 137a, 2pa, Capt. Edwards of the Pandora. b, 3pa, Capt. Bligh of the Bounty.

1991, July 25 — Litho. — Perf. 14½

136	A24a	Strip of 3, #a.-c.	5.50	5.50

Souvenir Sheet

137	A24a	Sheet of 2, #a.-b.	17.00	17.00

No. 133 Surcharged in Dark Blue Violet

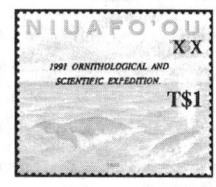

1991, July 31 — Litho. — Perf. 14x14½

139	A23	1pa on 1pa #133	10.00	10.00

"1991 Ornithological and Scientic Expedition" overprint appears on souvenir sheet at top center.

Ceresium Unicolor — A25

1991, Sept. 11 — Perf. 14½x14

140	A25	42s Larva stage	1.00	1.00
141	A25	57s Mature beetle	1.40	1.40
142	A25	1.50pa Larva stage, diff.	3.50	3.50
143	A25	2.50pa Mature beetle on tree limb	6.00	6.00
		Nos. 140-143 (4)	11.90	11.90

Christmas A26

Legend of the origin of the coconut tree: 15s, No. 146a, Heina bathing in lake being watched by eel. 42s, No. 146b, Heina weeping over plant growing from eel's grave. No. 146c, 1.50pa, Heina's boy climbing coconut tree. No. 146d, 3pa, "Eel's face" on coconut.

1991, Nov. 12 — Litho. — Perf. 14½

144	A26	15s multicolored	.75	.75
145	A26	42s multicolored	2.00	2.00
146	A26	Sheet of 4, #a.-d.	16.00	16.00
		Nos. 144-146 (3)	18.75	18.75

Nos. 144-145 inscribed "Christmas Greetings 1991." No. 146 contains Nos. 144-145, 146a-146d inscribed "A Love Story."

Miniature Sheet

Discovery of America, 500th Anniv. — A27

Designs: a, Columbus. b, Queen Isabella, King Ferdinand. c, Columbus being blessed by Abbot of Palos. d, Men in boat, 15th century compass. e, Wooden traverse, wind rose, Nina. f, Bow of Santa Maria. g, Stern of Santa Maria. h, Pinta. i, Two men raising cross. j, Explorers, natives. k, Columbus kneeling before King and Queen. l, Columbus' second coat of arms.

1992, Apr. 28 — Litho. — Perf. 13½

147	A27	57s Sheet of 12, #a.-l.	27.50	27.50

Miniature Sheet

World War II in Pacific, 50th Anniv. A28

Newspaper headline and: a, Battleship ablaze at Pearl Harbor. b, Destroyed aircraft. c, Japanese A6M Zero fighter. d, Declaration of war, Pres. Franklin D. Roosevelt. e, Japanese T95 tank, Gen. MacArthur, Japanese naval ensign. f, Douglas SBD Dauntless dive bomber, Admiral Nimitz. g, Bren gun, Gen. Sir Thomas Blamey. h, Australian mortar crew, Kokoda Trail. i, US battleship, Maj. Gen. Julian C. Smith. j, Aircraft carrier USS Enterprise. k, American soldier, flag, Maj. Gen. Curtis Lemay. l, B-29 bomber, surrender ceremony on USS Missouri in Tokyo bay.

1992, May 12 — Litho. — Perf. 14

148	A28	42s Sheet of 12, #a.-l.	22.50	22.50

King Taufa'ahau IV, 25th Anniv. of Coronation A29

45s, 2pa, King, Queen Halaevalu during coronation. No. 150a, King, Tongan national anthem. b, Extract from investiture ceremony. c, Tongan national anthem, singers.

1992, July 4 — Perf. 13½x13

149	A29	45s multicolored	1.00	1.00

Size: 51x38mm
Perf. 12½x12

150	A29	80s Strip of 3, #a.-c.	5.50	5.50
151	A29	2pa multicolored	4.50	4.50
		Nos. 149-151 (3)	11.00	11.00

Megapodius Pritchardii — A30

1992, Sept. 15　Litho.　Perf. 14
152	A30	45s Female & male	1.75	1.75
153	A30	60s Female with egg	2.00	2.00
154	A30	80s Chick	2.75	2.75
155	A30	1.50pa Head of male	5.00	5.00
		Nos. 152-155 (4)	11.50	11.50

World Wildlife Fund.

First Niuafo'ou Postage Stamps, 10th Anniv. A31

1993, May 3　Litho.　Perf. 14x14½
156	A31	60s Nos. 4, 117A	1.75	1.75
157	A31	80s Nos. 7, 117B	2.25	2.25

Aviation in Niuafo'ou, 10th Anniv. — A32

Airplanes of: 1pa, South Pacific Island Airways. 2.50pa, Friendly Islands Airways.

1993, May 3
158	A32	1pa multicolored	1.75	1.75
159	A32	2.50pa multicolored	4.25	4.25

King's 75th Birthday Type of Tonga

King and: 45s, 2pa, Patrol boat Pangai. No. 161a, Sporting events. b, Aircraft and communications. c, Musical instruments.

1993, July 1　Perf. 13x13½
160	A167	45s multicolored	1.00	1.00

Perf. 12x12½
Size: 37x48mm
161	A167	80s Strip of 3, #a.-c.	5.50	5.50
162	A167	2pa multicolored	4.25	4.25
		Nos. 160-162 (3)	10.75	10.75

Wildlife — A33

Designs: a, Two parrots. b, Bird with fish. c, Butterfly, beetle. d, Birds, dragonfly, butterfly. e, Bird in flight, two on ground.

1993, Aug. 10　Litho.　Perf. 14
163	A33	60s Strip of 5, #a.-e.	7.50	7.50

No. 163 is a continuous design.

Winners of Children's Painting Competition — A34

Designs: Nos. 164a, 165a, Ofato Beetle Grubs of Niuafo'ou, by Peni Finau. Nos. 164b, 165b, Crater Lake Megapode, Volcano, by Paea Puletau.

1993, Dec. 1　Litho.　Perf. 14
164	A34	10s Pair, #a.-b.	.75	.75
165	A34	1pa Pair, #a.-b.	7.25	7.25

Beetles A35

1994, Mar. 15　Litho.　Perf. 14
168	A35	60s Scarabaeidea	1.50	1.50
169	A35	80s Coccinellidea	1.90	1.90
170	A35	1.50pa Cerambycidea	3.50	3.50
171	A35	2.50pa Pentatomidae	6.25	6.25
		Nos. 168-171 (4)	13.15	13.15

A36　　　　　　A37

Sailing Ships: a, Stern of HMS Bounty. b, Bow of HMS Bounty. c, HMS Pandora. d, Whaling ship. e, Trading schooner.

1994, June 21　Litho.　Perf. 14
172	A36	80s Strip of 5, #a.-e.	15.00	15.00

No. 172 is a continuous design.

1994, Sept. 21　Litho.　Perf. 14½

1946 Volcanic Eruption: a, Blue-crowned lorikeet, lava flow. b, Black Pacific ducks, lava flow. c, Megapodes, palm trees (b). d, White-tailed tropic birds, people evacuating island (c). e, People wading out to sailboats, Pacific reef heron.
173	A37	80s Strip of 5, #a.-e.	9.50	9.50

No. 173 is a continuous design.

Nos. 129-133 Surcharged in Blue

1995, June 30　Litho.　Perf. 11½
174	A23	60s on 42s #130	1.90	1.90
175	A23	80s on 15s #129	2.50	2.50
176	A23	80s on 57s #131	2.75	2.75
177	A23	2pa on #132	6.75	6.75
		Nos. 174-177 (4)	13.90	13.90

Souvenir Sheet
178	A23	1.50pa on 1pa #133	6.75	6.75

Size and location of surcharge varies. Surcharge on No. 178 includes "COME

WHALE WATCHING / IN THE SOUTH PACIFIC."

Victory in the Pacific Type of Tonga

Nos. 179, 180: a, Soldier holding rifle. b, Soldier aiming rifle, tank. c, Front of tank. d, Troops coming off boat, firing weapons. e, Troops on beach.

1995, Aug. 1　Litho.　Perf. 14x14½
179	A177	60s Strip of 5, #a.-e.	8.50	8.50
180	A177	80s Strip of 5, #a.-e.	10.50	10.50

Nos. 179-180 are continuous designs and were issued together in sheets containing 10 stamps.

Singapore '95 Type of Tonga

Designs, vert: No. 181a, 45s, like #117A. b, 60s, like #117B.
2pa, Plesiosaurus.

1995, Sept. 1　Litho.　Perf. 12
181	A178	Pair, #a.-b.	4.00	4.00

Souvenir Sheet
182	A178	2pa multicolored	5.50	5.50

Beijing Intl. Coin & Stamp Show '95 Type of Tonga
Souvenir Sheet

Design: 1.40pa, The Great Wall of China.

1995, Sept. 14　Perf. 14½
183	A179	1.40pa multicolored	4.25	4.25

End of World War II, UN, 50th Anniv. Type of Tonga

No. 184: a, London blitz. b, UN emblem, "50." c, Concorde.
No. 185: a, Building of Siam-Burma Railway by Allied prisoners of war. b, Like #184b. c, Japanese bullet train.

1995, Oct. 20　Litho.　Perf. 14
184	A180	60s Strip of 3, #a.-c.	4.25	4.25
185	A180	80s Strip of 3, #a.-c.	5.75	5.75

Nos. 184b, 185b are 23x31mm.

Mailmen of Niuafo'ou A38

Portrait, illustration of postal history: 45s, Charles Stuart Ramsey, companions, floating with poles. 60s, Ramsey with can of mail encountering shark. 1pa, Walter George Quensell, mail being lowered from ship to canoes. 3pa, Quensell, original "tin can" mail cancels.

1996, Aug. 21　Litho.　Perf. 14
186	A38	45s multicolored	1.25	1.25
187	A38	60s multicolored	1.60	1.60
188	A38	1pa multicolored	2.75	2.75
189	A38	3pa multicolored	8.50	8.50
		Nos. 186-189 (4)	14.10	14.10

Congress of Preshistoric and Protohistoric Sciences Type of Tonga

a, Prehistoric man making drawings, fire, living in huts, animals. b, Ancient Egyptians, Romans.

1996, Sept. 5　Perf. 12
190	A185	1pa Pair, #a.-b.	5.50	5.50

Evacuation of Niuafo'ou, 50th Anniv. — A39

a, Island, two canoes. b, Volcano, four canoes. c, Edge of island, canoe. d, Canoe. e, People boarding MV Matua.

1996, Dec. 2　Perf. 14
191	A39	45s Strip of 5, #a.-e.	5.50	5.50
192	A39	60s Strip of 5, #a.-e.	7.50	7.50

Nos. 191-192 are continuous designs and were issued together in sheet containing 10 stamps.

UNICEF, 50th Anniv. Type of Tonga

Children's toys on checkerboard: a, Dolls, truck, balls on pegs. b, Tricycle, car, balls on pegs, teddy bear, train. c, Car, helicopter, ice skates, books, blocks.

1996, Oct. 29　Litho.　Perf. 14
193	A187	80s Strip of 3, #a.-c.	6.00	6.00

No. 193 is a continuous design.

Ocean Environment — A40

Various zooplankton and phytoplankton.

1997, May 19　Litho.　Perf. 14
194	A40	60s red & multi	1.40	1.40
195	A40	80s brown & multi	1.75	1.75
196	A40	1.50pa blue & multi	3.50	3.50
197	A40	2.50pa green & multi	5.75	5.75
		Nos. 194-197 (4)	12.40	12.40

Pacific '97 Type of Tonga
Souvenir Sheet

Design: Oakland Bay Bridge, back-naped tern.

1997, May 30
198	A191	2pa multicolored	5.00	5.00

1997 Wedding Anniv., Coronation Anniv. Type of Tonga

No. 199: a, King Taufa'ahau, Queen Halaevalu Mata'aho on wedding day. b, King in coronation regalia.
5pa, King in coronation procession, horiz.

1997, June 30　Litho.　Perf. 12
Size: 34x47mm
199	A193	80s vert. pair, #a.-b.	3.75	3.75

Souvenir Sheet
200	A193	5pa multicolored	11.00	11.00

No. 199 was issued in sheets of 6 stamps.

Diana, Princess of Wales (1961-97)
Common Design Type

Various portraits: a, 10s. b, 80s, c, 1pa. d, 2.50pa.

Perf. 13½x14
1998, May 29　Litho.　Unwmk.
201	CD355	Sheet of 4, #a.-d.	7.75	7.75

No. 201 sold for 4.40pa + 50s with surtax from international sales going to the Princess Diana Memorial Fund and surtax from local sales going to designated local charity.

Blue Crowned Lorikeet — A41

World Wildlife Fund: 10s, Young birds in nest. 55s, Adult on branch of flower. 80s, Adult on branch of bush. 3pa, Two adults on tree branch.

1998, May 15　Litho.　Perf. 14½x15
202	A41	10s multicolored	.85	.85
203	A41	55s multicolored	1.75	1.75
204	A41	80s multicolored	2.10	2.10
205	A41	3pa multicolored	7.25	7.25
a.		Sheet, 2 each #202-205	24.00	24.00
		Nos. 202-205 (4)	11.95	11.95

King Taufa'ahau Tupou IV Type of Tonga

1998, July 4   **Litho.**   *Perf. 14*
207 A196   2.70pa multicolored   3.75   3.75

See Tonga #985a for souvenir sheet containing one #207.

Fish A43

a, 10s, Amphipiron melanopus. b, 55s, Amphipiron perideraion. c, 80s, Amphipiron chrysopterus.

1998, Sept. 23   **Litho.**   *Perf. 14*
208 A43   Strip of 3, #a.-c.   2.00   2.00

Intl. Year of the Ocean. No. 208 was issued in sheets of 9 stamps.

Year of the Tiger Type of Tonga

Designs: a, 55s, Head of tiger with mouth open. b, 80s, Two tigers standing. c, 1pa, Two tigers lying down. 1pa, Head of tiger.

1998, July 23   **Litho.**   *Perf. 14*
209 A183   Sheet of 4, #a.-d.   5.00   5.00

No. 209 is a continuous design. Singpex '98.

Christmas A44

Designs: 20s, Angel playing mandolin. 55s, Angel playing violin. 1pa, Children singing, bells. 1.60pa, Children singing, candles.

1998, Nov. 12   *Perf. 14x14½*
210 A44   20s multicolored   .35   .35
211 A44   55s multicolored   .95   .95
212 A44   1pa multicolored   1.75   1.75
213 A44   1.60pa multicolored   2.90   2.90
    Nos. 210-213 (4)   5.95   5.95

New Year 1999 (Year of the Rabbit) A45

Stylized rabbits: a, 10s. b, 55s. c, 80s. d, 1pa.

1999, Feb. 16   *Perf. 14*
214 A45   Sheet of 4, #a.-d.   3.75   3.75

Jakob le Maire (1585-1616), Explorer — A46

1999, Mar. 19   **Litho.**   *Perf. 14*
215 A46   80s shown   1.10   1.10
216 A46   2.70pa Tongiaki canoe   3.75   3.75
    a.   Souvenir sheet, #215-216   5.00   5.00

Australia '99 World Stamp Expo (#216a).

Flowers A47

55s, Cananga odorata. 80s, Gardenia tannaensis, vert. 1pa, Coleus amboinicus, vert. 2.50pa, Hernandia moerenhoutiana.

1999, Sept. 29   *Perf. 13x13¼, 13¼x13*   **Litho.**
217 A47   55s multicolored   .75   .75
218 A47   80s multicolored   1.10   1.10
219 A47   1pa multicolored   1.40   1.40
220 A47   2.50pa multicolored   3.50   3.50
    Nos. 217-220 (4)   6.75   6.75

Souvenir Sheet

Millennium — A48

a, 1pa, Dove. b, 2.50pa, Native boat.

2000, Jan. 1   **Litho.**   *Perf. 14½x15*
221 A48   Sheet of 2, #a.-b.   5.00   5.00

Souvenir Sheet

New Year 2000 (Year of the Dragon) — A49

Illustration reduced.
Various dragons; a, 10s. b, 55s, c, 80s. d, 1pa.

Litho. with Foil Application

2000, Feb. 4   *Perf. 14½*
222 A49   Sheet of 4, #a.-d.   3.50   3.50

Souvenir Sheet

The Stamp Show 2000, London — A50

Illustration reduced.

Litho. with Foil Application

2000, May 22   *Perf. 13x13¼*
223 A50   Sheet of 2   5.75   5.75
    a. $1.50 Queen Mother   2.00   2.00
    b. $2.50 Queen Salote Tupou III   3.25   3.25

Souvenir Sheet

World Stamp Expo 2001, Anaheim — A51

No. 224: a, 10s, Man and woman. b, 2.50pa, Satellite dish. c, 2.70pa, Intelsat.

2000, July 7   **Litho.**   *Perf. 13x13¼*
224 A51   Sheet of 3, #a-c   7.50   7.50

Butterflies — A52

Designs: 55s, Jamides bochus. 80s, Blue moon. 1pa, Eurema hecabe aprica. 2.70pa, Monarch.

2000, Oct. 25   *Perf. 14*
225-228 A52   Set of 4   6.75   6.75

Souvenir Sheet

New Year 2001 (Year of the Snake) — A53

No. 229 - Various snakes: a, 10s. b, 55s, c, 80s, d, 1pa.

Litho. with Foil Application

2001, Feb. 1   *Perf. 14¼*
229 A53   Sheet of 4, #a-d   3.25   3.25

Hong Kong 2001 Stamp Exhibition.

Fish — A54

Designs: 80s, Prognichthys sealei. 1pa, Xiphias gladius. 2.50pa, Katsuwonus pelamis.

2001, June 5   **Litho.**   *Perf. 13¾*
230-232 A54   Set of 3   6.00   6.00
   232a   Souvenir sheet, #230-232   6.00   6.00

Souvenir Sheet

Fruit — A55

No. 233: a, 55s, Papaya. b, 80s, Limes. c, 1pa, Mangos. d, 2.50pa, Bananas.

2001, Sept. 19   *Perf. 14¼x14*   Unwmk.
233 A55   Sheet of 4, #a-d   6.75   6.75

Barn Owl A56

Designs: Nos. 234, 238a, 10s, Owl in flight. Nos. 235, 238b, 55s, Adult feeding young. Nos. 236, 238c, 2.50pa, Four owls. Nos. 237, 238d, 2.70pa, Owl's head.

2001, Nov. 21   *Perf. 12¾x13¼*
Without Vertical Bister Line Separating Panels
234-237 A56   Set of 4   8.50   8.50

Souvenir Sheet
With Vertical Bister Line Separating Panels
238 A56   Sheet of 4, #a-d   8.50   8.50

Reign Of Queen Elizabeth II, 50th Anniv. Issue
Common Design Type
Souvenir Sheet

No. 239: a, 15s, Princess Elizabeth with Queen Mother. b, 90s, Wearing purple hat. c, 1.20pa, As young woman. d, 1.40pa, Wearing red hat. e, 2.25pa, 1955 portrait by Annigoni (38x50mm).

2002, Feb. 6   *Perf. 14¼x14½, 13¾ (2.25pa)*   **Litho.**   **Wmk. 373**
239 CD360   Sheet of 5, #a-e   6.25   6.25

Souvenir Sheet

New Year 2002 (Year of the Horse) — A517

Various horses: a, 65s. b, 80s. c, 1pa. d, 2.50pa.

Litho. With Foil Application

2002, Feb. 12   Unwmk.   *Perf. 14*
240 A57   Sheet of 4, #a-d   6.75   6.75

Megapodius Pritchardii A58

Designs: 15s, Bird, eggs. 70s, Two birds. 90s, Bird, vert. 2.50pa, Two birds, vert.

2002, Apr. 9   *Perf. 14x13½, 13½x14*   **Litho.**
241-244 A58   Set of 4   6.00   6.00
   244a   Souvenir sheet, #243-244   5.00   5.00

Nos. 243-244 lack white frame around stamp.

Cephalopods A59

Designs: 80s, Octopus vulgaris. 1pa, Sepioteuthis lessoniana. 2.50pa, Nautilus belauensis.

2002, July 25   **Litho.**   *Perf. 13¾*
245-247 A59   Set of 3   4.00   4.00
   247a   Souvenir sheet, #245-247   4.00   4.00

Souvenir Sheet

Mail Planes — A60

No. 248: a, 80c, Casa C-212 Aviocar. b, 1.40pa, Britten-Norman Islander. c, 2.50pa, DHC 6-300 Twin Otter.

2002, Nov. 27   **Litho.**   *Perf. 12¾*
248   A60   Sheet of 3, #a-c   4.25   4.25

**New Year 2003 (Year of the Ram)
Type of Tonga**

No. 249: a, 65s, One ram. 80s, Three sheep. 1pa, Three sheep, diff. 2.50pa, Two sheep.

2003, Apr. 14   **Litho.**   *Perf. 13¼*
249   A223   Sheet of 4, #a-d   4.75   4.75

**Coronation of Queen Elizabeth II,
50th Anniv. Type of Tonga**

Designs: 90s, Queen Elizabeth II. 1.20pa, Queen Elizabeth II seated. 1.40pa, Queen Salote of Tonga in coach. 2.50pa, Queen Salote.

2003, June 2   **Litho.**
250-253   A224   Set of 4   5.75   5.75

SCOTTMOUNTS

For stamp presentation unequaled in beauty and clarity, insist on ScottMounts. Made of 100% inert polystyrol foil, ScottMounts protect your stamps from the harmful effects of dust and moisture. Available in your choice of clear or black backs, ScottMounts are center-split across the back for easy insertion of stamps and feature crystal clear mount faces. Double layers of gum assure stay-put bonding on the album page. Discover the quality and value ScottMounts have to offer.

ScottMounts are available from your favorite stamp dealer or direct from:

Discover the quality and value ScottMounts have to offer.

For a complete list of ScottMount sizes call or write Scott Publishing Co.

Scott Publishing Co.
1-800-572-6885
P.O. Box 828 Sidney OH 45365-0828
www.amosadvantage.com

AMOS
HOBBY PUBLISHING

Publishers of:
Coin World, Linn's Stamp News and Scott Publishing Co.

TRANSCAUCASIAN FEDERATED REPUBLICS

ˌtranˌt͜s-ko-ˈkā-zhən ˈfe-də-rāted ri-ˈpə-bliks

LOCATION — In southeastern Europe, south of the Caucasus Mountains between the Black and Caspian Seas
GOVT. — Former republic
AREA — 71,255 sq. mi.
POP. — 5,851,000 (approx.)
CAPITAL — Tiflis

The Transcaucasian Federation was made up of the former autonomies of Armenia, Georgia and Azerbaijan. Its stamps were replaced by those of Russia.

100 Kopecks = 1 Ruble

Russian Stamps of 1909-17 Overprinted in Black or Red

1923		**Unwmk.**	**Perf. 14½x15**	
1	A15	10k dark blue	3.00	5.00
2	A14	10k on 7k lt bl	3.00	5.00
3	A11	25k grn & gray vio	3.00	5.00
4	A11	35k red brn & grn (R)	3.00	5.00
a.		Double overprint	40.00	40.00
5	A8	50k brn red & grn	3.00	5.00
6	A9	1r pale brn, brn & org		7.50 10.00
7	A12	3½r mar & lt grn	25.00	
		Imperf		
8	A9	1r pale brn, brn & red org	3.00	6.00
		Nos. 1-8 (8)	50.50	
		Nos. 1-6,8 (7)		41.00

No. 7 was prepared but not issued.

Overprinted on Stamps of Armenia Previously Handstamped:

 a   c

		Perf. 14½x15		
9	A11(c)	25k grn & gray vio	200.00	225.00
10	A8(c)	50k vio & grn	100.00	150.00
		Perf. 13½		
11	A9(a)	1r pale brn, brn & org	50.00	40.00
12	A9(c)	1r pale, brn, brn & org	50.00	40.00
		Imperf		
13	A9(c)	1r pale brn, brn & red org	32.50	32.50
		Nos. 9-13 (5)	432.50	487.50

Counterfeit overprints exist.

Oil Fields — A1

Soviet Symbols — A2

1923			**Perf. 11½**	
14	A1	40,000r red violet	1.50	3.00
15	A1	75,000r dark grn	1.50	3.00
16	A1	100,000r blk vio	1.50	3.00
17	A1	150,000r red	1.50	3.00
18	A2	200,000r dull grn	1.50	3.00
19	A2	300,000r blue	1.50	3.00
20	A2	350,000r dark brn	1.50	3.00
21	A2	500,000r rose	1.50	3.00
		Nos. 14-21 (8)	12.00	24.00

Nos. 14-15 Surcharged in Brown

1923				
22	A1	700,000r on 40,000r	3.00	5.00
a.		Imperf., pair	13.00	
23	A1	700,000r on 75,000r	3.00	5.00
a.		Imperf., pair	13.00	

Types of Preceding Issue with Values in Gold Kopecks

1923, Oct. 24				
25	A2	1k orange	1.75	3.00
26	A2	2k blue green	1.75	3.00
27	A2	3k rose	2.50	3.00
28	A2	4k gray brown	1.50	3.00
29	A1	5k dark violet	1.50	3.00
30	A1	9k deep blue	1.50	3.00
31	A1	18k slate	1.50	3.00
		Nos. 25-31 (7)	12.00	21.00

Nos. 14-21, 25-31 exist imperf. but are not known to have been issued in that condition. Value, $12 each.

TRANSVAAL

tranˌt͜s-ˈväl

(South African Republic)

LOCATION — Southern Africa
GOVT. — A former British Colony
AREA — 110,450 sq. mi.
POP. — 1,261,736 (1904)
CAPITAL — Pretoria

Transvaal was known as the South African Republic until 1877 when it was occupied by the British. The republic was restored in 1884 and continued until 1900 when it was annexed to Great Britain and named "The Transvaal."

12 Pence = 1 Shilling
20 Shillings = 1 Pound

Most unused stamps between Nos. 1-96, 119-122 and 136-137 were issued with gum, but do not expect gum on scarcer stamps as few examples retain their original gum. In many cases removal of the remaining gum may enhance the preservation of the stamps. Otherwise, values for unused stamps are for examples with original gum as defined in the catalogue introduction.

Very fine imperforate stamps will have adequate to large margins. However, rouletted stamps are valued as partly rouletted, with straight edges, and rouletted just into the design, as the rouletting methods were quite inaccurate.

First Republic

Coat of Arms
A1   A2
Mecklenburg Printings
By Adolph Otto, Gustrow
Fine Impressions
Thin Paper

A1 has spread wings on eagle.

1869		**Unwmk.**	**Imperf.**	
1	A1	1p brown lake	350.00	
a.		1p red	350.00	350.00

2	A1	6p ultra	125.00	125.00
3	A1	1sh dark green	550.00	550.00
a.		Tete beche pair		
		Rouletted 15½, 16		
4	A1	1p red		70.00
		1p brown lake	87.50	
5	A1	6p ultra	65.00	65.00
6	A1	1sh blue green	85.00	110.00
a.		1sh yellow green	100.00	100.00
b.		1sh deep green	140.00	140.00

Nos. 1-6 were printed from 2 sets of plates, differing in the spacing between the stamps. The only known example of No. 3a is in a museum.
See Nos. 9-24, 26-33, 35-36, 38-39, 41-42, 43-49, 119, 122. For overprints see Nos. 53-61, 63-66, 68-72, 75-78, 81-83, 86-87, 90-91, 94.

1871-74				
7	A2	3p lilac	82.50	90.00
a.		3p violet	87.50	90.00
8	A2	6p brt ultra ('74)	60.00	27.50
a.		Half used as 3p on cover		1,400.

Many forgeries exist in colors duller or lighter than the genuine stamps.

In forgeries of type A1, all values, the "D" of "EENDRAGT" is not noticeably larger than the other letters and does not touch the top of the ribbon. In type A1 genuine stamps, the "D" is large and touches the ribbon top. The eagle's eye is a dot and its face white on the genuine stamps; the eye is a loop or blob attached to the beak, and the beak is strongly hooked, on the forgeries. Many forgeries of the 1sh have the top line of the ribbon broken above "EENDRAGT."

Forgeries of type A2 usually can be detected only by color.

A sharply struck cancellation of a numeral in three rings is found on many of these forgeries. The similar genuine cancellation is always roughly or heavily struck.

See Nos. 25, 34, 437, 40, 42B, 120-121. For overprints see Nos. 50-52, 62, 67, 73-74, 79-80, 84-85, 88-89, 92-93, 95-96.

Local Printings
(A) By M. J. Viljoen, Pretoria
Poor Impressions,
Overinked and Spotted
Thin Soft Paper

1870			**Imperf.**	
9	A1	1p pink	65.00	
a.		1p rose red	72.50	
b.		1p carmine	80.00	65.00
10	A1	6p dull ultra	250.00	75.00
a.		Tete beche pair		

The only known examples of No. 10a are in museums.

		Rouletted 15½, 16		
11	A1	1p carmine	700.00	250.00
a.		Rouletted 6½		850.00
12	A1	6p dull ultra	200.00	125.00

Hard Paper, Thick to Medium
Imperf

13	A1	1p carmine	62.50	60.00
14	A1	6p ultra		
15	A1	1sh gray green	80.00	75.00
a.		1sh dark green	650.00	300.00
b.		Tete beche pair	10,000.	
c.		Half used as 6p on cover		1,350.

The existence of No. 14 is questionable.

		Rouletted 15½, 16		
16	A1	1p light carmine	80.00	40.00
a.		1p carmine	60.00	70.00
17	A1	6p ultra	100.00	95.00
a.		Tete beche pair	20,000.	15,000.
18	A1	1sh dark green	80.00	60.00
a.		1sh gray green	300.00	165.00

Copies of Nos. 16 to 18 are sometimes so heavily inked as to be little more than blots of color.

(B) By J. P. Borrius, Potchefstroom
Clearer Impressions Though Often
Overinked
Thick Porous Paper

1870			**Imperf.**	
19	A1	1p black	110.00	95.00
20	A1	6p indigo	250.00	
		Rouletted 15½, 16		
21	A1	1p black	18.00	25.00
22	A1	6p gray blue	125.00	70.00
a.		6p indigo	100.00	60.00
b.		6p bright ultra		

Thin Transparent Paper

23	A1	1p black	200.00	550.00
24	A1	1p brt carmine	175.00	50.00
a.		1p deep carmine	55.00	45.00
25	A2	3p gray lilac	100.00	50.00
26	A1	6p ultra	60.00	30.00
27	A1	1sh yellow green	70.00	40.00
a.		1sh deep green	70.00	40.00

b.		Half used as 6p on cover		—
		Thick Soft Paper		
28	A1	1p dull rose	450.00	75.00
a.		1p brown rose	450.00	100.00
b.		Printed on both sides		
29	A1	6p dull blue	90.00	45.00
a.		6p bright blue	190.00	70.00
b.		6p ultramarine	175.00	75.00
c.		Rouletted 6½		
30	A1	1sh yellow green	800.00	600.00

The paper of Nos. 28 to 30 varies considerably in thickness.

(C) By P. Davis & Son, Natal
Thin to Medium Paper

1874			**Perf. 12½**	
31	A1	1p red	90.00	40.00
a.		1p brownish red	90.00	40.00
32	A1	6p deep blue	125.00	60.00
a.		6p blue	110.00	55.00
b.		Horiz. pair, imperf. between		

(D) By the Stamp Commission,
Pretoria
Pelure Paper

1875-76			**Imperf.**	
33	A1	1p pale red	50.00	50.00
a.		1p orange red	45.00	22.50
b.		1p brown red	50.00	30.00
c.		Pin perf.	425.00	225.00
34	A2	3p gray lilac	50.00	40.00
a.		3p dull violet	60.00	45.00
b.		Pin perf.	400.00	225.00
35	A1	6p blue	50.00	45.00
a.		6p pale blue	50.00	50.00
b.		6p dark blue	60.00	47.50
c.		Tete beche pair		
d.		Pin perf.		200.00

The only known examples of No. 35c are in museums.

		Rouletted 15½, 16		
36	A1	1p orange red	400.00	150.00
a.		Rouletted 6½	750.00	175.00
37	A2	3p dull violet	500.00	175.00
a.		Rouletted 6½	650.00	250.00
38	A1	6p blue	165.00	95.00
a.		Rouletted 6½	750.00	125.00

The paper of this group varies slightly in thickness and is sometimes divided into pelure and semipelure. We believe there was only one lot of the paper and that the separation is not warranted.

Thick Hard Paper
Imperf

39	A1	1p orange red ('76)	22.50	17.50
40	A2	3p lilac	350.00	110.00
41	A1	6p deep blue	60.00	20.00
a.		6p blue	100.00	22.50
b.		Tete beche pair		5,500.

		Rouletted 15½, 16		
42	A1	1p orange red ('76)	425.00	150.00
a.		Rouletted 6½ ('75)	525.00	175.00
42B	A2	3p lilac	300.00	
43	A1	6p deep blue	600.00	85.00
a.		6p blue	600.00	125.00
b.		Rouletted 6½ ('75)	500.00	250.00

Soft Porous Paper
Imperf

44	A1	1p orange red	125.00	62.50
45	A1	6p deep blue	175.00	60.00
a.		6p dull blue	300.00	100.00
46	A1	1sh yellow green	325.00	125.00

		Rouletted 15½, 16		
47	A1	1p orange red		275.00
a.		Rouletted 6½		375.00
48	A1	6p deep blue		150.00
a.		Rouletted 6½		850.00
49	A1	1sh yellow grn	700.00	350.00
a.		Rouletted 6½		900.00
b.		Rouletted 15½-16x16½	500.00	325.00

First British Occupation

Stamps and Types of
1875 Overprinted

Red Overprint
Pelure Paper

1877		**Unwmk.**	**Imperf.**	
50	A2	3p lilac	1,150.	250.00
a.		Overprinted on back	3,500.	3,500.
b.		Double ovpt., red and black	6,500.	

		Rouletted 15½, 16		
51	A2	3p lilac		1,700.
a.		Rouletted 6½		1,400.

Thin Hard Paper
Imperf

52	A2	3p lilac	1,400.	300.00

Soft Porous Paper

53	A1	6p blue	1,500. 200.00
a.		6p deep blue	275.00
b.		Inverted overprint	5,750.
c.		Double overprint	4,900.
54	A1	1sh yellow grn	425.00 225.00
a.		Inverted overprint	3,750.
b.		Half used as 6p on cover	1,900.

Rouletted 15½, 16

55	A1	6p blue	. 1,700.
a.		Rouletted 6½	1,400.
56	A1	1sh yellow grn	1,500. 600.00
a.		Rouletted 6½	3,500. 1,200.

Black Overprint
Pelure Paper
Imperf

57	A1	1p red	200.00 110.00

Rouletted 15½, 16

58	A1	1p red	. 1,200.

Thick Hard Paper
Imperf

59	A1	1p red	22.50 22.50
a.		Inverted overprint	450.00 375.00

Rouletted 15½, 16

60	A1	1p red	160.00 55.00
a.		Rouletted 6½	550.00 160.00
b.		Rouletted 6½	
c.		Double overprint	

Soft Porous Paper
Imperf

61	A1	1p red	22.50 22.50
a.		Double overprint	1,100.
62	A2	3p lilac	80.00 40.00
a.		3p deep lilac	160.00 90.00
b.		Inverted overprint	3,500.
63	A1	6p dull blue	100.00 35.00
a.		6p bright blue	175.00 27.50
b.		6p dark blue	175.00 27.50
d.		Inverted overprint	1,500. 250.00
e.		Double overprint	4,000.
64	A1	6p blue, rose	85.00 55.00
a.		Tete beche pair	
b.		Inverted overprint	100.00 55.00
c.		Overprint omitted	3,250. 2,500.
d.		Half used as 3p on cover	
65	A1	1sh yellow grn	100.00 50.00
a.		Tete beche pair	10,000. 10,000.
b.		Inverted overprint	1,100. 225.00
c.		Half used as 6p on cover	1,250.

The only known examples of No. 64a are in museums.

Rouletted 15½, 16

66	A1	1p red	75.00 75.00
a.		Rouletted 6½	650.00 160.00
67	A2	3p lilac	160.00 65.00
a.		Rouletted 6½	700.00
68	A1	6p dull blue	175.00 55.00
a.		Inverted overprint	5,000. 700.00
b.		Rouletted 6½	5,000. 1,250.
c.		As "a," rouletted 6½	4,000.
69	A1	6p blue, rose	175.00 70.00
a.		Inverted overprint	525.00 75.00
b.		Rouletted 6½	
c.		Tete beche pair	
d.		Overprint omitted	
e.		As "d," rouletted 6½	
f.		As "d," rouletted 6½	
70	A1	1sh yellow grn	200.00 100.00
a.		Inverted overprint	1,000. 575.00
b.		Rouletted 6½	400.00 140.00
c.		As "a," rouletted 6½	1,500. 550.00

In this issue the space between "V. R." and "TRANSVAAL" is normally 8½mm but in position 11 it is 12mm. In this and the following issues there are numerous minor varieties of the overprint, missing periods, etc.
The only known examples of No. 69c are in museums.

Types A1 and A2 Overprinted

V. R. Transvaal

1877-79 Imperf.

71	A1	1p red, blue	50.00 25.00
a.		"Transvral"	5,000. 2,500.
b.		Inverted overprint	700.00 375.00
c.		Double overprint	3,500.
d.		Overprint omitted	
72	A1	1p red, org ('78)	18.00 17.00
a.		Printed on both sides	
b.		Pin perf.	
73	A2	3p lilac, buff	40.00 25.00
a.		Inverted overprint	625.00
b.		Pin perf.	575.00 575.00
74	A2	3p lilac, grn ('79)	150.00 50.00
a.		Inverted overprint	1,600.
b.		Double overprint	
c.		Pin perf.	
75	A1	6p blue, grn	80.00 40.00
a.		Tete beche pair	12,500.
b.		Inverted overprint	750.00
c.		Half used as 3p on cover	
d.		Pin perf.	
76	A1	6p blue, bl ('78)	50.00 24.00
a.		Tete beche pair	
b.		Overprint omitted	1,700.
c.		Inverted overprint	800.00
d.		Half used as 3p on cover	800.00

e.		Double overprint	2,750.
f.		Pin perf.	
		Nos. 71-76 (6)	388.00 181.00

The only known examples of No. 76a are in museums.

Rouletted 15½, 16

77	A1	1p red, blue	75.00 35.00
a.		"Transvral"	2,250.
b.		Inverted overprint	
c.		Double overprint	
78	A1	1p red, org ('78)	29.00 25.00
a.		Horiz. pair, imperf. vert.	525.00
b.		Rouletted 6½	275.00 125.00
79	A2	3p lilac, buff	90.00 25.00
a.		Inverted overprint	2,700.
b.		Vert. pair, imperf. horiz.	
c.		Rouletted 6½	125.00
80	A2	3p lilac, grn ('79)	525.00 125.00
a.		Inverted overprint	
b.		Rouletted 6½	400.00 300.00
81	A1	6p blue, green	75.00 32.50
a.		Inverted overprint	525.00
b.		Overprint omitted	3,250.
c.		Tete beche pair	
d.		Half used at 3p on cover	700.00
e.		Rouletted 6½	900.00
82	A1	6p blue, bl ('78)	190.00 55.00
a.		Inverted overprint	— 1,000.
b.		Overprint omitted	2,700.
c.		Tete beche pair	
d.		Horiz. pair, imperf. vert.	
e.		Half used as 3p on cover	700.00
f.		Double overprint	
g.		Rouletted 6½	300.00
h.		As "a," rouletted 6½	
		Nos. 77-82 (6)	984.00 297.50

The only known examples of No. 81c are in museums. The existence of No. 82c is questioned.

Types A1 and A2 Overprinted

Imperf

83	A1	1p red, org ('78)	50.00 40.00
84	A2	3p lilac, buff ('78)	60.00 35.00
a.		Pin perf.	800.00 750.00
85	A2	3p lilac, grn ('79)	100.00 40.00
a.		Inverted overprint	1,600.
b.		Overprint omitted	2,750.
c.		Printed on both sides	
86	A1	6p blue, bl ('78)	90.00 27.50
a.		Tete beche pair	10,000.
b.		Inverted overprint	550.00
		Nos. 83-86 (4)	300.00 142.50

Rouletted 15½, 16

87	A1	1p red, org ('78)	140.00 125.00
a.		Rouletted 6½	275.00
88	A2	3p lilac, buff ('78)	150.00 110.00
a.		Vert. pair, imperf. horiz.	
b.		Rouletted 6½	325.00
89	A2	3p lilac, grn ('79)	550.00 150.00
a.		Inverted overprint	
b.		Overprint omitted	
c.		Rouletted 6½ ('97)	325.00
90	A1	6p blue, bl ('78)	375.00 110.00
a.		Tete beche pair	
b.		Inverted overprint	— 800.00
d.		Rouletted 6½	325.00
e.		As "b," rouletted 6½	

Types A1 and A2 Overprinted

1879 Imperf.

91	A1	1p red, orange	35.00 25.00
a.		1p red, yellow	37.50 32.50
b.		Small capital "T"	200.00 165.00
92	A2	3p lilac, green	75.00 20.00
a.		Small capital "T"	225.00 165.00
93	A2	3p lilac, blue	40.00 20.00
a.		Small capital "T"	165.00 75.00
		Nos. 91-93 (3)	150.00 65.00

Rouletted 15½, 16

94	A1	1p red, yellow	200.00
a.		1p red, orange	325.00
b.		Small capital "T"	775.00 265.00
c.		Rouletted 6½	650.00
d.		Pin perf.	500.00
95	A2	3p lilac, green	825.00 200.00
a.		Small capital "T"	
b.		Rouletted 6½	
96	A2	3p lilac, blue	115.00
a.		Small capital "T"	800.00
b.		Rouletted 6½	
c.		Pin perf.	

Queen Victoria — A3

1878-80 Engr. Perf. 14, 14½

97	A3	½p vermilion ('80)	19.00 70.00
98	A3	1p red brown	8.75 3.50
99	A3	3p claret	10.00 4.25
100	A3	4p olive green	14.50 5.25
101	A3	6p slate	6.75 3.50
a.		Half used as 3p on cover	
102	A3	1sh green	110.00 35.00
103	A3	2sh blue	150.00 77.50
		Nos. 97-103 (7)	319.00 199.00

For surcharges see Nos. 104-118, 138-139.

No. 101 Surcharged in Red or Black:

(a) Surcharged **1 PENNY**

1879

104	A3	1p on 6p slate (R)	82.50 65.00
105	A3	1p on 6p slate (Bk)	35.00 24.00

(b) Surcharged **1 Penny**

106	A3	1p on 6p slate (R)	350.00 275.00
107	A3	1p on 6p slate (Bk)	160.00 85.00

(c) Surcharged **1 Penny**

108	A3	1p on 6p slate (R)	200.00 115.00
109	A3	1p on 6p slate (Bk)	65.00 32.50

(d) Surcharged   **1 Penny**

110	A3	1p on 6p slate (R)	210.00 125.00
111	A3	1p on 6p slate (Bk)	55.00 50.00
a.		Pair, one without surcharge	

(e) Surcharged **1 Penny**

112	A3	1p on 6p slate (R)	350.00 225.00
113	A3	1p on 6p slate (Bk)	150.00 75.00

(f) Surcharged **1 Penny**

114	A3	1p on 6p slate (R)	325.00 150.00
115	A3	1p on 6p slate (Bk)	90.00 55.00

(g) Surcharged **1 Penny**

116	A3	1p on 6p slate (R)	1,500.
117	A3	1p on 6p slate (Bk)	500.00 150.00

Surcharge distinctions: a, "PENNY" in gothic capitals. b, "1" has heavy serif at base; "P," thin serif at base. c, No serif at base of "1." d, Heavy serifs at base of "1" and "p." e, Italics. f, "1" has long, sloping serif at top, thin serif at base. g, Tail of "y" missing.

Second Republic

No. 100 Surcharged

Een Penny

1882 Unwmk. Perf. 14, 14½

118	A3	1p on 4p olive grn	7.00 4.25
a.		Inverted surcharge	250.00 250.00

1883 Perf. 12

119	A1	1p black	3.00 1.10
a.		Imperf.	
b.		Vert. pair, imperf. horiz.	
c.		Horiz. pair, imperf. vert.	
120	A2	3p red	6.00 2.00
a.		Horiz. pair, imperf. vert.	
b.		Half used as 1p on cover	
121	A2	3p black, rose	15.00 2.50
a.		Half used as 6p on cover	750.00
122	A1	1sh green	25.00 3.00
a.		Tete beche pair	450.00 100.00
b.		Half used as 6p on cover	400.00
		Nos. 119-122 (4)	49.00 10.60

The so-called reprints of this issue are forgeries. They were made from the counterfeit plates described in the note following No. 8, plus a new false plate for the 3p. The false 3p plate has many small flaws and defects.

Forgeries of No. 120 are in dull orange red, clearly printed on whitish paper, and those of No. 121 in brownish or grayish black on bright rose. Genuine copies of No. 120 lack the orange tint and the paper is yellowish; genuine copies of No. 121 are in black without gray or brown shade, on dull lilac rose paper.

A 6p in slate on white, apparently of this issue, is a late print from the counterfeit plate.

 A4

Perf. 13½, 11½x12, 12½, 12½x12
1885-93 Typo.

123	A4	½p gray	.20 .20
124	A4	1p rose	.20 .20
125	A4	2p brown	1.00 .75
126	A4	2p olive bis ('87)	.40 .20
127	A4	2½p purple ('93)	1.10 .40
128	A4	3p violet	1.10 .50
129	A4	4p bronze green	2.00 .40
130	A4	6p blue	2.75 1.75
a.		Imperf.	
131	A4	1sh green	2.25 .25
132	A4	2sh6p yellow	3.00 1.25
133	A4	5sh steel blue	4.25 2.00
134	A4	10sh pale brown	22.50 4.50
135	A4	£5 dark green ('92)	
		Nos. 123-134 (12)	40.75 12.40

Reprints of Nos. 123-137, 140-163, 166-174 closely resemble the originals. Paper is whiter; perf. 12½, large holes.
Excellent counterfeits of No. 135 exist.
For overprint and surcharges see Nos. 140-147, 163, 213.

Nos. 120, 122 Surcharged

1885 Perf. 12

136	A2	½p on 3p red	3.50 5.00
a.		Surcharge reading down	3.50 5.00
137	A1	½p on 1sh green	9.50 15.00
a.		Surcharge reading down	9.50 15.00
b.		Tete beche pair	450.00 250.00

Almost all copies of No. 137b have telegraph cancellations. Postally used examples are rare.

Nos. 101, 128 Surcharged in Red or Black

Perf. 14

138	A3	½p on 6p slate	15.00 27.50
139	A3	2p on 6p slate	2.25 2.50
a.		Horiz. pair, imperf. vert.	

Perf. 11½x12, 12½x12

140	A4	½p on 3p vio (Bk)	1.75 1.75
a.		"PRNNY"	125.00
b.		2nd "N" of "PENNY" invtd.	125.00

No. 128 Surcharged

No. 141   No. 142

1887

141	A4	2p on 3p violet	.50 .90
a.		Double surcharge	150.00
142	A4	2p on 3p violet	4.00 4.00
a.		Double surcharge	225.00

Nos. 126, 130, 131 Surcharged

Nos. 143-144   Nos. 145-146

No. 147

Red Surcharge

1893

143	A4	½p on 2p olive bis	.65	.50
a.		Inverted surcharge	2.25	2.25
b.		Bars 14mm apart	1.50	1.50
c.		As "b," inverted	6.50	6.50

Black Surcharge

144	A4	½p on 2p olive bis	.70	.50
a.		Inverted surcharge	4.25	4.25
b.		Bars 14mm apart	1.25	1.25
c.		As "b," inverted	13.00	11.00
145	A4	1p on 6p blue	.40	.30
a.		Inverted surcharge	1.25	1.25
b.		Double surcharge	50.00	50.00
c.		Pair, one without surcharge	175.00	
d.		Bars 14mm apart	.55	.55
e.		As "d," inverted	5.50	5.50
f.		As "d," double		90.00
146	A4	2½p on 1sh green	.75	.90
a.		Inverted surcharge	5.00	6.00
b.		Fraction line misplaced "²⁵⁄₁₂"	27.50	27.50
c.		As "b," inverted	325.00	275.00
d.		Bars 14mm apart	1.50	1.50
e.		As "d," inverted	7.25	10.00
147	A4	2½p on 1sh green	2.50	2.00
a.		Inverted surcharge	6.50	6.50
b.		Bars 14mm apart	5.00	5.00
c.		As "b," inverted	32.50	20.00
d.		Double surcharge	60.00	75.00
		Nos. 143-147 (5)	5.00	4.20

A13

Wagon with Two Shafts

		1894	**Typo.**	**Perf. 12½**
148	A13	½p gray	.20	.20
149	A13	1p rose	.20	.20
150	A13	2p olive bister	.20	.20
151	A13	6p blue	.85	.40
152	A13	1sh yellow grn	4.75	5.00
		Nos. 148-152 (5)	6.20	6.00

Counterfeits of #148-152 are plentiful.
See note following No. 135 for reprints.

		1895-96	**Wagon with Pole**	
153	A13	½p gray	.20	.20
154	A13	1p rose	.20	.20
155	A13	2p olive bister	.20	.20
156	A13	3p violet	.40	.20
157	A13	4p slate	.95	.45
158	A13	6p blue	.95	.30
159	A13	1sh green	1.40	.60
160	A13	5sh slate blue ('96)	7.75	13.50
161	A13	10sh red brown ('96)	7.75	2.75
		Nos. 153-161 (9)	19.80	18.40

Most of the unused specimens of Nos. 153-161 now on the market are reprints.
See Nos. 166-174. For surcharge and overprints see Nos. 162, 214-220, 232-235.
See note following No. 135 for reprints.

Nos. 159, 127 Surcharged in Red or Green

1895

162	A13	½p on 1sh green (R)	.20	.20
a.		Inverted surcharge	5.25	5.25
b.		"Pennij" instead of "Penny"	60.00	60.00
c.		Double surcharge	60.00	60.00
163	A4	1p on 2½p pur (G)	.20	.20
a.		Inverted surcharge	20.00	20.00
b.		Surcharge sideways		
c.		Surcharge on back		
d.		Space between "1" and "d"	1.25	1.25

A16

1895   **Perf. 11½**

164	A16	6p rose (G)	.65	.65
a.		Vertical pair, imperf. between		

Counterfeits of No. 164 are on the 6p dark red revenue stamp of 1898, and have a shiny green ink for the overprint. The false overprint is also found on other revenue denominations, though only the 6p rose was converted to postal use.

Coat of Arms, Wheat Field and Railroad Train — A17

1895, Sept. 6   **Litho.**

165	A17	1p red	.20	.20
a.		Imperf.		
b.		Vertical pair, imperf. between	25.00	25.00

Penny Postage in Transvaal. Horiz. pair, imperf. between also exists.
For overprint see No. 245.

With Pole

		1896	**Typo.**	**Perf. 12½**
166	A13	½p green	.20	.20
167	A13	1p rose & grn	.20	.20
168	A13	2p brown & grn	.20	.20
169	A13	2½p ultra & grn	.20	.20
170	A13	3p red vio & grn	.50	.50
171	A13	4p olive & grn	.50	.50
172	A13	6p violet & grn	.25	.20
173	A13	1sh bister & grn	.30	.20
174	A13	2sh6p lilac & grn	1.00	1.00
		Nos. 166-174 (9)	3.35	3.20

See note following No. 135 for reprints.
For overprints and surcharges see Nos. 202-212, 214-235, 237-244, 246-251, Cape of Good Hope Nos. N5-N8.

Pietersburg Issue

Date large; "P" in Postzegel large — A18   Date small; "P" in Postzegel large — A19

Date small; "P" in Postzegel small — A20

1901   **Typeset**   **Imperf.**

Initials in Red

175	A18	½p black, *green*	37.50
a.		Initials omitted	125.00
b.		Initials in black	45.00
176	A19	½p black, *green*	50.00
a.		Initials omitted	125.00
b.		Initials in black	45.00
177	A20	½p black, *green*	50.00
a.		Initials omitted	125.00
b.		Initials in black	45.00

Initials in Black

178	A18	1p black, *rose*	10.00
179	A19	1p black, *rose*	13.00
180	A20	1p black, *rose*	16.00
181	A18	2p black, *orange*	15.00
182	A19	2p black, *orange*	20.00
183	A20	2p black, *orange*	22.50
184	A18	4p black, *dull blue*	25.00
185	A19	4p black, *dull blue*	30.00

186	A20	4p black, *dull blue*	40.00	
187	A18	6p black, *green*	32.50	
188	A19	6p black, *green*	47.50	
189	A20	6p black, *green*	65.00	
190	A18	1sh black, *yellow*	75.00	
191	A19	1sh black, *yellow*	55.00	
192	A20	1sh black, *yellow*	140.00	

Perf. 11½

Initials in Red

193	A18	½p black, *green*	13.00	
194	A19	½p black, *green*	15.00	
195	A20	½p black, *green*	20.00	

Initials in Black

196	A18	1p black, *rose*	10.00	
a.		Horiz. pair, imperf. vert.	125.00	
197	A19	1p black, *rose*	13.00	
a.		Horiz. pair, imperf. vert.	150.00	
198	A20	1p black, *rose*	13.00	
a.		Horiz. pair, imperf. vert.	150.00	
199	A18	2p black, *orange*	15.00	
200	A19	2p black, *orange*	17.00	
201	A20	2p black, *orange*	17.00	

Nos. 193 to 201 inclusive are always imperforate on one side.
The setting consisted of 12 stamps of type A18, 6 of type A19, and 6 of type A20. Numerous type-setting varieties exist. The perforated stamps are from the first printing and were put into use first. Used copies are not valued as all seen show evidence of having been canceled to order.

Second British Occupation
Issued under Military Authority

Nos. 166-174, 160-161, 135 Overprinted

		1900	**Unwmk.**	**Perf. 12½**
202	A13	½p green	.20	.20
a.		"V.I.R."	650.00	
203	A13	1p rose & grn	.20	.20
204	A13	2p brown & grn	1.40	.40
a.		"V.I.R."	650.00	
205	A13	2½p ultra & grn	.50	.40
206	A13	3p red vio & grn	.50	.20
207	A13	4p olive & grn	1.10	.20
a.		"V.I.R."	650.00	
208	A13	6p violet & grn	1.10	.40
209	A13	1sh bister & grn	1.10	.80
210	A13	2sh6p hel & grn	1.75	2.25
211	A13	5sh slate blue	3.50	4.00
212	A13	10sh red brown	5.25	4.50
213	A4	£5 dark green		
		Nos. 202-212 (11)	16.60	13.55

Nos. 202 to 213 have been extensively counterfeited. The overprint on the forgeries is clear and clean, with small periods and letters showing completely. In the genuine, letters are worn and lack many or all serifs; the periods are large and oval.
The genuine overprint exists inverted; double; with period missing after "V," after "R," after "I," etc.

Issued in Lydenburg

Overprinted in Black

1900

214	A13	½p green	110.00	110.00
215	A13	1p rose & grn	100.00	80.00
216	A13	2p brown & grn	800.00	700.00
217	A13	2½p ultra & grn		800.00
218	A13	4p olive & grn	2,250.	650.00
219	A13	6p violet & grn	2,250.	575.00
220	A13	1sh bister & grn	2,500.	

Beware of counterfeits.

No. 167 Surcharged

221	A13	3p on 1p rose & green	80.00	70.00

Issued in Rustenburg

Nos. 166-170, 172-174 Handstamped in Violet

1900   **Perf. 12½**

223	A13	½p green	100.00	100.00
224	A13	1p rose & grn	95.00	60.00
225	A13	2p brown & grn	200.00	190.00
226	A13	2½p ultra & grn	120.00	80.00
227	A13	3p red vio & grn	190.00	110.00
229	A13	6p violet & grn	650.00	500.00
230	A13	1sh bister & grn	1,300.	650.00
231	A13	2sh6p hel & grn		4,250.

Issued in Schweizer Reneke

Nos. 166-168 and 172 Handstamped "BESIEGED" in Black

1900   **Typo.**   **Perf. 12½**

232	A13	½p green	250.00
233	A13	1p rose & green	275.00
234	A13	2p brown & green	450.00
235	A13	6p violet & green	900.00
		Nos. 232-235 (4)	1,875.

Same Overprint on Cape of Good Hope No. 59 and Type of 1893

Perf. 14

236	A15	½p green	650.00
236A	A15	1p carmine	650.00

In 1902 five revenue stamps overprinted "V.R.I." are said to have been used postally in Volksrust. There seems to be some doubt that this issue was properly authorized for postal use.

Issued in Wolmaransstad

Nos. 166-173 Handstamped in Blue or Red

1900

237	A13	½p green	175.00	
238	A13	1p rose & grn	160.00	175.00
239	A13	2p brown & grn	1,400.	1,400.
240	A13	2½p ultra & grn (R)	2,000.	2,000.
241	A13	3p red vio & grn	2,500.	
242	A13	4p olive & grn	3,000.	3,750.
243	A13	6p violet & grn	2,750.	4,250.
244	A13	1sh bister & grn		

No. 165 Overprinted in Blue

245	A17	1p red	160.00	150.00

Regular Issues

Nos. 166-168, 170-171, 174 Surcharged or Overprinted

1901-02

246	A13	½p on 2p brn & grn	.35	.20
247	A13	½p green	.20	.20
248	A13	1p rose & grn	.20	.20
a.		Overprint "E" omitted	65.00	
249	A13	3p red vio & grn	1.40	.40
250	A13	4p olive & grn	1.40	.50
251	A13	2sh6p hel & grn	4.50	5.00
		Nos. 246-251 (6)	8.05	7.00

Excellent counterfeits of Nos. 246 to 251 are plentiful. See note after No. 213 for the recognition marks of the counterfeits.

Edward VII — A27

Nos. 260, 262 to 267 and 275 to 280 have "POSTAGE" at each side; the other stamps of type A27 have "REVENUE" at the right.

Wmk. Crown and C A (2)

1902-03		Typo.	Perf. 14	
252	A27	½p gray grn & blk	1.10	.20
253	A27	1p rose & blk	1.10	.20
254	A27	2p violet & blk	1.75	.20
255	A27	2½p ultra & blk	2.75	.80
256	A27	3p ol grn & blk	3.50	.30
257	A27	4p choc & blk	3.50	.35
258	A27	6p brn org & blk	1.75	.50
259	A27	1sh ol grn & blk	8.00	3.25
260	A27	1sh red brn & blk	6.25	1.00
261	A27	2sh brown & blk	21.00	18.00
262	A27	2sh yel & blk	10.00	7.00
263	A27	2sh6p black & vio	10.50	6.50
264	A27	5sh vio & blk, yel	16.00	13.00
265	A27	10sh vio & blk, red	35.00	17.00
266	A27	£1 violet & grn	125.00	75.00
267	A27	£5 violet & org	900.00	525.00
		Nos. 252-266 (15)	247.20	143.30

Issue dates: 3p, 4p, Nos. 260, 262, £1, £5, 1903. Others, Apr. 1, 1902.

1904-09			Wmk. 3	
268	A27	½p gray grn & blk	2.25	1.00
269	A27	1p rose & blk	2.25	.20
270	A27	2p violet & blk	3.00	.30
271	A27	2½p ultra & blk	4.00	2.25
272	A27	3p ol grn & blk	2.25	.20
273	A27	4p choc & blk	2.25	.20
274	A27	6p brn org & blk	2.25	.20
275	A27	1sh red brn & blk	2.25	.20
276	A27	2sh yellow & blk	11.00	3.00
277	A27	2sh6p blk & red vio	20.00	1.50
278	A27	5sh vio & blk, yel	10.00	1.25
279	A27	10sh vio & blk, red	24.00	2.00
280	A27	£1 violet & grn	125.00	14.00
		Nos. 268-280 (13)	210.50	26.30

The 2p and 3p are on chalky paper, the 2½p, 4p, 6p and £1 on both chalky and ordinary, and the other values on ordinary paper only.

Issue years: ½p, 1p, 5sh, 1904. 2½p, 6p, 1sh, 1905. 2p, 3p, 4p, 2sh, 1906. 10sh, 1907. £1, 1908. 2sh6p, 1909.

1905-10				
281	A27	½p green	1.25	.20
a.		Booklet pane of 6		
282	A27	1p carmine	.85	.20
a.		Wmk. 16 (anchor) ('07)	275.00	
b.		Booklet pane of 6		
283	A27	2p dull vio ('10)	2.75	.20
284	A27	2½p ultra ('10)	7.50	2.00
		Nos. 281-284 (4)	12.35	2.60

Wmk. 16 is illustrated in the Cape of Good Hope.

Some of the above stamps are found with the overprint "C. S. A. R." for use by the Central South African Railway, the control mark being applied after the stamps had left the post office.

POSTAGE DUE STAMPS

D1

Wmk. Multiple Crown and C A (3)

1907		Typo.	Perf. 14	
J1	D1	½p green & blk	2.25	1.10
J2	D1	1p carmine & blk	3.00	.65
J3	D1	2p brown & org	3.00	1.00
J4	D1	3p blue & blk	5.25	2.75
J5	D1	5p violet & blk	1.60	10.00
J6	D1	6p red brown & blk	3.50	11.00
J7	D1	1sh black & car	6.50	4.50
		Nos. J1-J7 (7)	25.10	31.00

Most canceled copies of #J1-J7 were used outside the Transvaal under the Union of South Africa administration in 1910-16.

The stamps of Transvaal were replaced by those of South Africa.

TRINIDAD

ˈtri-nə-ˌdad

LOCATION — West Indies, off the Venezuelan coast
GOVT. — British Colony which became part of the Colony of Trinidad and Tobago in 1889
AREA — 1,864 sq. mi.
POP. — 387,000
CAPITAL — Port of Spain

12 Pence = 1 Shilling
20 Shillings = 1 Pound

In 1847 David Bryce, owner of the "Lady McLeod," issued a blue, lithographed, imperf. stamp to prepay his 5-cent rate for carrying letters on his sail-equipped steamer between Port of Spain and San Fernando, another Trinidad port. The stamp pictures the "Lady McLeod" above the monogram "LMcL," expressing no denomination. Value, unused, $50,000, used (pen canceled), $12,500. Used stamps canceled by having a corner skinned off are worth less.

Values for unused stamps are for examples with original gum as defined in the catalogue introduction. However, Nos. 9-12 are seldom found with gum, and these are valued without gum.

Values for Nos. 18-26 are for stamps with pin perforations on two or three sides. Stamps with pin perforations on all four sides are not often seen and command large premiums.

Very fine examples of Nos. 27-47 will have perforations touching the design on one or more sides due to the narrow spacing of the stamps on the plates and imperfect perforating methods. These stamps with perfs clear of the design on all four sides are scarce and command substantially higher prices.

"Britannia"

A1   A2

1851-53		Unwmk. Engr.	Imperf.	
		Blued Paper		
1	A1	(1p) brick red ('56)	175.00	75.00
a.		(1p) brown red ('53)	350.00	70.00
2	A1	(1p) purple brown	12.50	80.00
3	A1	(1p) blue	12.50	32.50
a.		(1p) deep blue, deeply blued paper	175.00	92.50
4	A1	(1p) gray brn ('53)	45.00	80.00
a.		(1p) gray ('52)	75.00	70.00
		Nos. 1-4 (4)	245.00	267.50

1854-57				
		White Paper		
6	A1	(1p) brown red ('57)	1,950.	70.00
7	A1	(1p) gray	40.00	85.00
8	A1	(1p) black violet	26.00	92.50

See Nos. 14, 18, 22, 27, 33, 39, 43, 45, 48, 58. For surcharges see Nos. 62-64.

1852			Litho.	
		Fine Impressions		
		Yellowish Paper		
9	A2	(1p) blue	10,000.	1,850.
a.		(1p) deep blue	11,500.	1,750.
b.		White paper		1,675.

1853				
		Bluish Paper		
10	A2	(1p) blue	9,000.	2,400.

Same, Lines of Background More or Less Worn

1855-60				
		Thin Paper		
11	A2	(1p) slate blue	4,500.	750.00
12	A2	(1p) blue	5,000.	1,150.
a.		(1p) greenish blue		1,050.
13	A2	(1p) rose	15.00	700.00
a.		(1p) dull red	15.00	700.00

A3

1859		Engr.	Imperf.	
		White Paper		
14	A1	(1p) dull rose	750.00	300.00
15	A3	4p gray lilac	92.50	375.00
		4p dull lilac		400.00
16	A3	6p green	25,000.	500.00
17	A3	1sh slate blue	92.50	375.00
		Pin-perf. 12½		
18	A1	(1p) dull rose red	1,750.	65.00
a.		(1p) lake	2,100.	57.50
19	A3	4p brown lilac	10,000.	1,050.
a.		4p dull purple	7,000.	1,050.
20	A3	6p deep green	3,150.	225.00
a.		6p yellow green	3,150.	225.00
21	A3	1sh black violet	7,500.	1,500.
		Pin-perf. 14		
22	A1	(1p) rose red	150.00	26.00
a.		(1p) carmine	325.00	25.00
23	A3	4p brown lilac	125.00	125.00
a.		4p violet	1,400.	92.50
b.		4p dull violet	425.00	125.00
24	A3	6p deep green	575.00	80.00
25	A3	6p yellow green	575.00	85.00
a.		Vert. pair, imperf. between	5,250.	
26	A3	1sh black violet	7,500.	925.00

1860		Clean-cut Perf. 14 to 15½		
27	A1	(1p) dull rose	125.00	62.50
a.		(1p) lake	140.00	60.00
b.		Horiz. pair, imperf. vert.	1,250.	
29	A3	4p violet brown	140.00	92.50
a.		4p dull violet		350.00
30	A3	6p deep green	275.00	160.00
31	A3	6p yellow green	475.00	100.00
32	A3	1sh black violet		

1861		Rough Perf. 14 to 16½		
33	A1	(1p) dull rose	125.00	30.00
34	A3	4p gray lilac	375.00	60.00
35	A3	4p brown lilac	275.00	92.50
a.		4p dull violet	700.00	92.50
36	A3	6p green	275.00	92.50
a.		6p blue green	450.00	80.00
37	A3	1sh indigo	925.00	325.00
a.		1sh purplish blue	1,350.	450.00

1863		Perf. 11½ to 12		
		Thick Paper		
39	A1	(1p) carmine	110.00	20.00
a.		Perf. 11½-12x11	1,900.	550.00
40	A3	4p dull violet	175.00	70.00
41	A3	6p dp blue green	1,150.	97.50
a.		Perf. 11½-12x11		7,500.
42	A3	1sh indigo	2,300.	100.00
		Perf. 12½		
43	A1	(1p) lake	45.00	19.00
		Perf. 13		
45	A1	(1p) lake	40.00	20.00
46	A3	6p emerald	525.00	62.50
47	A3	1sh brt violet	4,500.	325.00

1864-72		Wmk. 1	Perf. 12½	
48	A1	(1p) red	52.50	2.00
a.		(1p) lake	52.50	5.50
b.		(1p) rose	52.50	2.00
c.		(1p) carmine	42.50	2.25
d.		Imperf., pair	800.00	800.00
49	A3	4p brt violet	110.00	10.50
a.		4p pale violet	210.00	15.00
b.		Imperf.	600.00	
50	A3	4p lilac	160.00	15.00
a.		4p gray lilac		
51	A3	4p gray ('72)	125.00	5.25
52	A3	6p blue green	140.00	7.50
a.		6p emerald	77.50	11.00
53	A3	6p yellow grn	80.00	4.25
a.		6p dp grn	425.00	8.50
b.		Imperf., pair	800.00	
54	A3	1sh purple	100.00	5.00
a.		1sh lilac	110.00	7.50
b.		1sh violet	110.00	7.50
c.		1sh red lilac	150.00	7.50
d.		Imperf.	750.00	
55	A3	1sh orange yel ('72)	150.00	1.50
		Nos. 48-55 (8)	917.50	51.00

See Nos. 59-61A, 65. For surcharge see No. 67.

Queen Victoria — A4

1869-94		Typo.	Perf. 12½	
56	A4	5sh dull lake	190.00	85.00
a.		Imperf., pair	1,250.	
		Perf. 14		
57	A4	5sh claret ('94)	57.50	92.50

For overprint see No. O7.

1876		Engr.	Perf. 14	
58	A1	(1p) carmine	25.00	1.10
a.		(1p) red	45.00	.85
b.		(1p) lake	25.00	1.10
c.		Half used as ½p on cover		625.00
59	A3	4p gray	110.00	.80
60	A3	6p yellow green	97.50	1.50
a.		6p deep green	125.00	1.50
61	A3	1sh orange yellow	110.00	3.00
		Nos. 58-61 (4)	342.50	6.40
		Perf. 14x12½		
61A	A3	6p yellow green		5,750.

Value for No. 61A is for stamp with perfs barely touching the design.

Type A1 Surcharged in Black

1879		Wmk. 1	Perf. 14	
62	A1	½p lilac	11.50	8.00

Same Surcharge

1882		Wmk. Crown and C A (2)		
63	A1	½p lilac	210.00	75.00
64	A1	1p carmine	32.50	.90
a.		Half used as ½p on cover		625.00

Type of 1859

1882			Wmk. 2	
65	A3	4p gray	200.00	7.50

No. 60 Surcharged by pen and ink in Black or Red

1882			Wmk. 1	
67	A3	1p on 6p green (R)	8.00	5.25
a.		Half used as ½p on cover		350.00
b.		Black surcharge		2,000.

Counterfeits of No. 67b are plentiful. Various handwriting exists on both 60 and 60a.

A7   A8

A9

1883-84		Typo.	Wmk. 2	
68	A7	½p green	4.50	1.50
69	A7	1p rose	11.50	.55
a.		Half used as ½p on cover		800.00
70	A7	2½p ultra	12.50	.70
a.		2½p blue	12.50	.70

71	A7	4p slate	3.00	.70
72	A7	6p olive brn ('84)	3.75	5.00
73	A7	1sh orange brn ('84)	4.25	2.75
		Nos. 68-73 (6)	39.50	11.20

For overprints see Nos. O1-O6.

1896-1904 — Perf. 14

ONE PENNY:
Type I - Round "O" in "ONE."
Type II - Oval "O" in "ONE."

74	A8	½p lilac & green	3.75	.35
75	A8	½p gray grn ('02)	.75	2.25
76	A8	1p lil & car, type I	4.00	.20
77	A8	1p lil & car, type II ('00)	375.00	4.50
78	A8	1p blk, red, type II ('01)	1.50	.20
a.		Value omitted	32,500.	
79	A8	2½p lilac & ultra	5.50	.20
80	A8	2½p vio & bl, bl ('02)	17.50	.30
81	A8	4p lilac & orange	7.50	20.00
82	A8	4p grn & ultra, buff ('02)	1.75	10.00
83	A8	5p lilac & violet	7.50	16.00
84	A8	6p lilac & black	8.50	6.25
85	A8	1sh grn & org brn	8.00	7.50
86	A8	1sh blk & bl, yel ('04)	21.00	6.25

Wmk. C A over Crown (46)

87	A9	5sh green & org	50.00	85.00
88	A9	5sh lil & red vio ('02)	50.00	75.00
89	A9	10sh grn & ultra	175.00	325.00
		Revenue cancel		25.00
90	A9	£1 grn & car	150.00	225.00
		Nos. 74-90 (17)	887.25	784.00

No. 82 also exists on chalky paper. Nos. 88 and 90 exist on both ordinary and chalky paper.
Circular "Registrar General" cancels are revenue usage and of minimal value.
See Nos. 92-104.

Landing of Columbus — A10

1898 — Engr. Wmk. 1

| 91 | A10 | 2p gray vio & yel brn | 3.00 | 1.50 |

400th anniv. of the discovery of the island of Trinidad by Columbus, July 31, 1498.

1904-09 — Wmk. 3
Chalky Paper

92	A8	½p gray green	4.50	2.75
93	A8	1p blk, red, type II	6.25	.20
94	A8	2½p vio & bl, bl	25.00	1.00
95	A8	4p blk & car, yel ('06)	1.75	9.25
96	A8	6p lilac & blk ('05)	17.50	17.50
97	A8	6p vio & dp vio ('06)	8.00	10.50
98	A8	1sh blk & bl, yel	22.50	9.25
99	A8	1sh vio & bl, yel	11.50	15.00
100	A8	1sh blk, grn ('06)	2.00	1.50
101	A9	5sh lil & red vio ('07)	50.00	92.50
102	A9	£1 grn & car ('07)	150.00	275.00
		Nos. 92-102 (11)	299.00	434.45

The ½p and 1p also exist on ordinary paper.
For overprints see Nos. O8-O9.

1906-07

| 103 | A8 | 1p carmine ('07) | 1.50 | .20 |
| 104 | A8 | 2½p ultramarine | 3.00 | .20 |

 A11   A12

1909
Ordinary Paper

105	A11	½p gray green	3.75	1.10
106	A12	1p carmine	3.50	.20
107	A11	2½p ultramarine	11.50	3.75
		Nos. 105-107 (3)	18.75	5.05

For overprint see No. O10.

POSTAGE DUE STAMPS

 D1

Wmk. Crown and C A (2)
1885, Jan. 1   Typo.   Perf. 14

J1	D1	½p black	15.00	45.00
J2	D1	1p black	4.25	.20
J3	D1	2p black	22.50	.20
J4	D1	3p black	47.50	.40
J5	D1	4p black	27.50	3.25
J6	D1	5p black	22.50	.65
J7	D1	6p black	37.50	4.00
J8	D1	8p black	60.00	3.00
J9	D1	1sh black	60.00	5.00
		Nos. J1-J9 (9)	296.75	61.70

1906-07 — Wmk. 3

J10	D1	1p black	3.25	.20
J11	D1	2p black	19.00	.20
J12	D1	3p black	9.00	2.75
J13	D1	4p black	11.00	10.00
J14	D1	5p black	11.00	10.00
J15	D1	6p black	6.00	9.50
J16	D1	8p black	12.00	14.00
J17	D1	1sh black	12.00	32.50
		Nos. J10-J17 (8)	83.25	79.15

See Trinidad and Tobago Nos. J1-J16.

OFFICIAL STAMPS

Postage Stamps of 1869-84 Overprinted in Black

1893-94 — Wmk. 2   Perf. 14

O1	A7	½p green	32.50	55.00
O2	A7	1p rose	35.00	60.00
O3	A7	2½p ultra	45.00	92.50
O4	A7	4p slate	45.00	100.00
O5	A7	6p olive brown	45.00	100.00
O6	A7	1sh orange brown	65.00	140.00

Wmk. Crown and C C (1)
Perf. 12½

| O7 | A4 | 5sh dull lake | 175.00 | 525.00 |
| | | Nos. O1-O7 (7) | 442.50 | 1,072. |

Nos. 92 and 103 Overprinted

1909-10 — Wmk. 3   Perf. 14

O8	A8	½p gray green	1.00	5.50
O9	A8	1p carmine	1.00	5.50
a.		Double overprint		300.00
b.		Inverted overprint	850.00	225.00
c.		Vertical overprint	100.00	125.00

Same Overprint on No. 105

1910

| O10 | A11 | ½p gray green | 4.00 | 5.50 |

Stamps of Trinidad have been superseded by those inscribed "Trinidad and Tobago."

TRINIDAD AND TOBAGO

ˈtri-nə-ˌdad and tə-ˈbā-ˌgō

LOCATION — West Indies off the coast of Venezuela
GOVT. — Republic
AREA — 1,980 sq. mi.
POP. — 1,102,096 (1999 est.)
CAPITAL — Port-of-Spain

The two British colonies of Trinidad and Tobago were united from 1889 until 1899, when Tobago became a ward of the united colony. From 1899 until 1913 postage stamps of Trinidad were used. The two islands became a state in

August 1962, and the independent Republic of Trinidad and Tobago on August 1, 1976.

12 Pence = 1 Shilling
20 Shillings = 1 Pound
100 Cents = 1 Dollar (1935)

> Catalogue values for unused stamps in this country are for Never Hinged items, beginning with Scott 62 in the regular postage section and Scott J9 in the postage due section.

 A1

 "Britannia" — A2

1913 — Typo.   Wmk. 3   Perf. 14
Ordinary Paper

1	A1	½p green	1.60	.20
2	A1	1p scarlet	.80	.20
a.		1p carmine	2.00	.20
4	A1	2½p ultra	5.50	.50

Chalky Paper

5	A1	4p scar & blk, yel	.70	6.00
6	A1	6p red vio & dull vio	8.50	3.75
7	A1	1sh black, emerald	1.50	3.00
a.		1sh black, green	1.75	4.50
b.		1sh black, bl grn, ol back	7.50	9.00
		Nos. 1-2,4-7 (6)	18.60	13.65

1914
Surface-colored Paper

| 8 | A1 | 4p scar & blk, yel | 1.75 | 10.00 |
| 9 | A1 | 1sh black, green | 1.00 | 3.25 |

Chalky Paper

10	A2	5sh dull vio & red vio	55.00	100.00
11	A2	£1 green & car	125.00	175.00
		Nos. 8-11 (4)	182.75	288.25

1921-22 — Wmk. 4
Ordinary Paper

12	A1	½p green	.45	1.40
13	A1	1p scarlet	.25	.20
14	A1	1p brown ('22)	.25	.90
15	A1	2p gray ('22)	1.90	.90
16	A1	2½p ultra	.75	8.00
17	A1	3p ultra ('22)	1.50	2.00

Chalky Paper

18	A1	6p red vio & dull vio	1.40	11.00
19	A2	5sh dull vio & red vio	32.50	87.50
20	A2	£1 green & car	80.00	140.00
		Nos. 12-20 (9)	119.00	251.90

For overprints see #B2-B3, MR1-MR13, O1-O5.

"Britannia" and King George V — A3

1922-28
Ordinary Paper

21	A3	½p green	.20	.20
22	A3	1p brown	.20	.20
23	A3	1½p rose red	.40	.20
24	A3	2p gray	.40	.95
25	A3	3p ultra	.75	.95

Chalky Paper

26	A3	4p red & blk, yel ('28)	2.50	2.40
27	A3	6p red vio & dl vio	5.00	18.00
28	A3	6p red & grn, emer ('24)	1.25	.35
29	A3	1sh blk, emer ('25)	1.25	1.25
30	A3	5sh vio & dull vio	20.00	26.00

| 31 | A3 | £1 rose & green | 90.00 | 150.00 |

Wmk. Multiple Crown and C A (3)
Chalky Paper

32	A3	4p red & blk, yel	.60	4.00
33	A3	1sh blk, emerald	3.00	6.75
		Nos. 21-33 (13)	125.55	211.25

 First Boca — A4

Designs: 2c, Agricultural College. 3c, Mt. Irvine Bay, Tobago. 6c, Discovery of Lake Asphalt. 8c, Queen's Park, Savannah. 12c, Town Hall, San Fernando. 48c, Memorial Park. 72c, Blue Basin.

1935-37 — Engr.   Wmk. 4   Perf. 12

34	A4	1c emer & bl, perf. 12½ ('36)	.30	.50
a.		Perf. 12	.25	.25
35	A4	2c lt brn & ultra, perf. 12	.40	.50
a.		Perf. 12½ ('36)	.50	.20
36	A4	3c red & black, perf. 12½ ('36)	.60	.20
a.		Perf. 12	1.50	.20
37	A4	6c bl & brn, perf. 12	3.25	1.60
a.		Perf. 12½ ('37)	4.00	2.25
38	A4	8c red org & yel grn	2.75	2.75
39	A4	12c dk violet & blk	2.75	1.25
a.		Perf. 12½ ('37)	3.00	3.50
40	A4	24c ol grn & blk	2.00	1.25
a.		Perf. 12½ ('37)	7.50	5.00
41	A4	48c slate green	6.00	11.00
42	A4	72c mag & sl grn	22.50	24.00
		Nos. 34-42 (9)	40.55	43.05

Common Design Types pictured following the introduction.

Silver Jubilee Issue
Common Design Type
1935, May 6   Perf. 11x12

43	CD301	2c black & ultra	.25	.45
44	CD301	3c car & blue	.25	.80
45	CD301	6c ultra & brn	1.25	1.75
46	CD301	24c brn vio & ind	4.25	12.00
		Nos. 43-46 (4)	6.00	15.00
		Set, never hinged		9.50

Coronation Issue
Common Design Type
1937, May 12   Perf. 13½x14

47	CD302	1c deep green	.20	.20
48	CD302	2c yellow brown	.20	.20
49	CD302	8c deep orange	.50	.50
		Nos. 47-49 (3)	.90	.90
		Set, never hinged	1.25	

 First Boca — A13

 George VI — A14

Various Frames and: 2c, Agricultural College. 3c, Mt. Irvine Bay, Tobago. 4c, Memorial Park. 5c, General Post Office and Treasury. 6c, Discovery of Lake Asphalt. 8c, Queen's Park, Savannah. 12c, Town Hall, San Fernando. 24c, Government House. 60c, Blue Basin.

Perf. 11½x11
1938-41   Wmk. 4   Engr.

50	A13	1c emer & blue	.25	.20
51	A13	2c lt brn & ultra	.25	.20
52	A13	3c dk car & blk	6.75	.65
52A	A13	3c vio brn & bl grn ('41)	.20	.20
53	A13	4c brown	18.00	.70
53A	A13	4c red ('41)	.25	.25
54	A13	5c mag ('41)	.20	.20
55	A13	6c brt bl & sep	.90	.40
56	A13	8c red org & yel grn	.85	.50
57	A13	12c dk vio & blk	1.50	.20
58	A13	24c dk ol grn & blk	.45	.20
59	A13	60c mag & sl grn	5.25	.90

Perf. 12

60	A14	$1.20 dk grn ('40)	6.25	.60
61	A14	$4.80 rose pink ('40)	12.50	15.00
	Nos. 50-61 (14)		53.60	20.20
	Set, never hinged			85.00

Watermark sideways on Nos. 50-59.

> **Catalogue values for unused stamps in this section, from this point to the end of the section, are for Never Hinged items.**

Peace Issue
Common Design Type
Perf. 13½x14

1946, Oct. 1   Engr.   Wmk. 4

62	CD303	3c brown	.20	.20
63	CD303	6c deep blue	.25	.25

Silver Wedding Issue
Common Design Types

1948, Nov. 22   Photo.   Perf. 14x14½

64	CD304	3c red brown	.20	.20

Engr.   Perf. 11½x11

65	CD305	$4.80 rose car	17.00	22.50

UPU Issue
Common Design Types
Engr.; Name Typo. on 6c, 12c
Perf. 13½, 11x11½

1949, Oct. 10   Wmk. 4

66	CD306	5c red violet	.20	.20
67	CD307	6c indigo	.20	.20
68	CD308	12c rose violet	.50	.45
69	CD309	24c olive	.85	.80
	Nos. 66-69 (4)		1.75	1.65

University Issue
Common Design Types
Inscribed: "Trinidad"

1951, Feb. 16   Engr.   Perf. 14x14½

70	CD310	3c chocolate & grn	.25	.20
71	CD311	12c purple & blk	.60	.50

Types of 1938 with Portrait of Queen Elizabeth II

1953, Apr. 20   Perf. 11½x11

72	A13	1c yel grn & dp blue	.20	.20
73	A13	2c org brn & sl blue	.20	.20
74	A13	3c vio brn & blue grn	.20	.20
75	A13	4c red	.20	.20
76	A13	5c magenta	.20	.20
77	A13	6c blue & brown	.30	.20
78	A13	8c red org & dp grn	1.00	.20
79	A13	12c dk violet & blk	.20	.20
80	A13	24c dk ol grn & blk	.85	.20
81	A13	60c rose car & grnsh blk	13.50	.50

Perf. 11½

82	A14	$1.20 dark green	.65	.50
a.		Perf. 12	2.25	1.50
83	A14	$4.80 rose pink	5.00	10.00
a.		Perf. 12	9.25	11.00
	Nos. 72-83 (12)		22.50	12.80

For surcharge see No. 85.

Coronation Issue
Common Design Type

1953, June 3   Perf. 13½x13

84	CD312	3c dark green & blk	.20	.20

No. 73 Surcharged "ONE CENT"
Perf. 11½x11

1956, Dec. 20   Wmk. 4

85	A13	1c on 2c org brn & sl blue	.65	.75

West Indies Federation
Common Design Type
Perf. 11½x11

1958, Apr. 22   Engr.   Wmk. 314

86	CD313	5c green	.20	.20
87	CD313	6c blue	.20	.40
88	CD313	12c carmine rose	.30	.25
	Nos. 86-88 (3)		.70	.85

Cipriani Memorial, Port-of-Spain
A27

Queen's Hall, Port-of-Spain
A28

Designs: 5c, Whitehall. 6c, Treasury Building. 8c, Governor General's House. 10c, General Hospital, San Fernando. 12c, Oil refinery. 15c, Crest of colony. 25c, Scarlet ibis. 35c, Lake Asphalt (Pitch). 50c, Jinnah Memorial Mosque. 60c, Anthurium lilies. $1.20, Copper-rumped hummingbird and hibiscus. $4.80, Map.

Perf. 13½x14, 14x13½

1960, Sept. 24   Photo.   Wmk. 314
Size: 22½x25mm, 25x22½mm

89	A27	1c dark gray & buff	.20	.20
a.		Wmkd. sideways ('66)	.50	.50
90	A28	2c ultra	.20	.20
91	A28	5c dark blue	.20	.20
92	A28	6c lt red brown	.20	.20
93	A28	8c yellow green	.20	.35
94	A28	10c light purple	.20	.20
95	A28	12c bright red	.20	.20
96	A28	15c orange	.60	.30
97	A28	25c dk blue & crim	.55	.20
98	A28	35c green & black	1.75	.20
99	A28	50c blue, yel & olive	.30	.35
100	A27	60c multicolored	.45	.20
a.		Perf. 14 ('65)	160.00	24.00

Size: 48x25mm

101	A28	$1.20 multicolored	10.00	1.75
102	A28	$4.80 lt bl & lt yel grn	5.75	6.25
	Nos. 89-102 (14)		20.80	10.80

See #116. For overprints see #123-124, 126.

Scouts and Map of Trinidad and Tobago — A29

1961, Apr. 4   Perf. 13½x14

103	A29	8c multicolored	.20	.20
104	A29	25c multicolored	.35	.35

2nd Caribbean Scout Jamboree, Valsayn Park, Trinidad, Apr. 4-14.

Independent State

Underwater Scene from Painting by Carlisle Chang — A30

Designs: 8c, Elizabeth II and new Terminal Building, Piarco Airport. 25c, Elizabeth II and Hilton Hotel. 35c, Map and greater bird of paradise. 60c, Map and scarlet ibis.

1962, Aug. 31   Photo.   Perf. 14½

105	A30	5c blue green	.20	.20
106	A30	8c slate	.20	.20
107	A30	25c purple	.20	.20
108	A30	35c emer, yel, brn & blk	1.40	.20
109	A30	60c ultra, black & ver	1.60	1.75
	Nos. 105-109 (5)		3.60	2.55

Issued to mark Trinidad and Tobago's independence, Aug. 31, 1962.

Freedom from Hunger Issue

Protein Food — A31

1963, June 1   Perf. 14x13½

110	A31	5c henna brown	.20	.20
111	A31	8c citron	.20	.20
112	A31	25c violet blue	.30	.30
	Nos. 110-112 (3)		.70	.70

See note in Common Design section.

Girl Guide Emblem
A32

Perf. 14½x14

1964, Sept. 15   Wmk. 314

113	A32	6c red, dk blue & yel	.20	.20
114	A32	25c brt blue, dk bl & yel	.20	.20
115	A32	35c lt green, dk bl & yel	.30	.30
	Nos. 113-115 (3)		.70	.70

50th anniv. of the Trinidad and Tobago Girl Guide Association.

Arms of Independent State — A33

1964, Sept. 15   Perf. 14x13½

116	A33	15c orange	.40	.40

For overprint see No. 125.

ICY Emblem
A34

Unwmk.

1965, Nov. 15   Litho.   Perf. 12
Granite Paper

117	A34	35c dull yel, red brn & grn	.35	.35

International Cooperation Year, 1965.

Eleanor Roosevelt — A35

Perf. 13½x14

1965, Dec. 10   Wmk. 314

118	A35	25c vio blue, red & blk	.25	.25

Issued to honor Eleanor Roosevelt and to publicize the Eleanor Roosevelt Memorial Foundation.

"Redhouse," Parliament Building — A36

8c, Map of Trinidad & Tobago, royal yacht "Britannia," arms of State. 25c, Flag, map. 35c, Flag, Trinity Hills, General Post Office, sugar cane, coconut palms, derricks.

1966, Feb. 8   Photo.   Wmk. 314

119	A36	5c ultra, red, blk & grn	.25	.20
120	A36	8c ultra, sil, blk & yel brn	1.25	.25
121	A36	25c red, blk & emerald	.75	.20
122	A36	35c ultra, red, blk & grn	1.25	1.00
	Nos. 119-122 (4)		4.00	2.15

Visit of Elizabeth II and Prince Philip.

Nos. 93, 94, 116 and 100 Overprinted: "FIFTH YEAR OF / INDEPENDENCE / 31st AUGUST 1967"
Perf. 14x13½, 13½x14

1967, Aug. 31   Photo.   Wmk. 314

123	A28	8c yellow green	.20	.20
124	A28	10c lt purple	.20	.20
125	A33	15c orange	.20	.20
126	A27	60c multicolored	.30	.30
	Nos. 123-126 (4)		.90	.90

On 60c, the overprint is arranged in 5 lines.

Carnival Symbols
A37

Designs: 10c, Calypso King, vert. 15c, Steel band. 25c, Chinese masks. 35c, Carnival King, vert. 60c, Carnival Queen, vert.

Unwmk.

1968, Feb. 16   Litho.   Perf. 12

127	A37	5c pink & multi	.20	.20
128	A37	10c vio blue & multi	.20	.20
129	A37	15c multicolored	.20	.20
130	A37	25c multicolored	.20	.20
131	A37	35c dk purple & multi	.20	.20
132	A37	60c brown ol & multi	.35	.35
	Nos. 127-132 (6)		1.35	1.35

Issued to publicize the Trinidad Carnival.

WHO Emblem and Eye Examination
A38

Dancing Children and Human Rights Flame
A39

Wmk. 314

1968, May 7   Photo.   Perf. 14

133	A38	5c rose red, gold & blk	.20	.20
134	A38	25c orange, gold & blk	.30	.30
135	A38	35c brt blue, gold & blk	.40	.40
	Nos. 133-135 (3)		.90	.90

1968, Aug. 5   Perf. 14

136	A39	5c carmine, yel & blk	.20	.20
137	A39	10c org, yel & blk	.20	.20
138	A39	25c yel grn, yel & blk	.25	.25
	Nos. 136-138 (3)		.65	.65

International Human Rights Year.

Bicycling and Map
A40

Designs (Olympic Rings, Map of Trinidad and Tobago and): 15c, Weight lifting. 25c, Relay race. 35c, Running. $1.20, Map of Mexico and flags of Mexico and Trinidad and Tobago.

Photo.; Gold Impressed (except $1.20)

1968, Oct. 12   Perf. 14

139	A40	5c vio, gold & multi	.20	.20
140	A40	15c red, gold & multi	.20	.20
141	A40	25c org, gold & multi	.20	.20
142	A40	35c brt grn, gold & multi	.25	.20
143	A40	$1.20 blue, gold & multi	1.00	.20
	Nos. 139-143 (5)		1.85	1.50

19th Olympic Games, Mexico City, 10/12-27.

Cacao
A41

Designs: 3c, Sugar refinery. 5c, Redtailed chachalaca. 6c, Oil refinery. 8c, Fertilizer plant. 10c, Green hermit (hummingbird) vert. 12c, Citrus fruit, vert. 15c, Coat of arms, vert. 20c, 25c, Flag and map of islands, vert. 30c, Wild poinsettia, vert. 40c, Scarlet ibis. 50c, Maracas Bay. $1, Blooming tabebuia (tree) vert. $2.50, Fishermen hauling in net. $5, Red House, Port-of-Spain.

Photo.; Silver or Gold Impressed

			1969, Apr. 1	**Wmk. 314**	**Perf. 14**
144	A41	1c silver & multi		.20	.20
145	A41	3c gold & multi		.20	.20
a.		Wmk. upright ('74)		.50	.50
146	A41	5c gold & multi		.20	.20
a.		Wmk. upright ('73)		7.50	4.00
147	A41	6c gold & multi		.30	.25
a.		Wmk. upright ('74)			
148	A41	8c gold & multi		.20	.20
149	A41	10c gold & multi		.20	.20
b.		Wmk. 373 ('76)		.30	.25
150	A41	12c silver & multi		.20	.20
151	A41	15c silver & multi		.20	.20
152	A41	20c gold & multi		.20	.20
153	A41	25c gold & multi		.25	.20
154	A41	30c gold & multi		.30	.20
155	A41	40c gold & multi		.40	.25
156	A41	50c silver & multi		.50	.30
157	A41	$1 gold & multi		1.00	.75
158	A41	$2.50 gold & multi		3.00	3.00
159	A41	$5 gold & multi		6.00	5.50
		Nos. 144-159 (16)		13.25	12.00

For overprint see No. 187.

Capt. A. A. Cipriani, ILO Emblem and Gate
A42

ILO, 50th Anniv.: 15c, Industrial Court's & ILO emblems, & Woodford Square gate.

Unwmk.

			1969, May 1	**Photo.**	**Perf. 12**
160	A42	6c dp car, gold & blk		.20	.20
161	A42	15c brt blue, gold & blk		.20	.20

Union Jack and Flags of CARIFTA Members
A43

Designs: 6c, Cornucopia, vert. 30c, Map of Caribbean, vert. 40c, Jet plane and "Strength through Unity" emblem.

			1969, Aug. 1	**Perf. 14x13½, 13½x14**
162	A43	6c lilac, gold & multi	.20	.20
163	A43	10c multicolored	.20	.20
164	A43	30c red, emer, blk &	.25	.25
165	A43	40c blue, blk, grn & gold	.35	.35
		Nos. 162-165 (4)	1.00	1.00

Caribbean Free Trade Area (CARIFTA).

Moon Landing and Earth — A44

40c, Lunar landing module & astronauts on moon. $1, Astronauts Aldrin at control panel, Armstrong collecting rocks.

			1969, Sept. 1	**Litho.**	**Perf. 14**
166	A44	6c multi		.20	.20
167	A44	40c multi, vert.		.30	.30
168	A44	$1 multi		.75	.75
		Nos. 166-168 (3)		1.25	1.25

See note after US No. C76.

Maces of Senate and House of Representatives — A45

10c, Chamber of Parliament. 15c, View of Kennedy Complex, University of the West Indies at St. Augustine. 40c, Cannon & view of Scarborough from Fort King George.

Perf. 14x13½

			1969, Oct. 23	**Photo.**	**Wmk. 314**
169	A45	10c multicolored		.20	.20
170	A45	15c multicolored		.20	.20
171	A45	30c lt blue & multi		.25	.25
172	A45	40c multicolored		.25	.25
		Nos. 169-172 (4)		.90	.90

15th Conf. of the Commonwealth Parliamentary Assoc., Port-of-Spain, Oct. 4-19.

Congress Emblem and Landscape
A46

Carnival King as "Man in the Moon"
A47

6c, Congress emblem (steel drum and bird). 30c, Palms, landscape and emblem, horiz.

Perf. 14x13½, 13½x14

			1969, Nov. 2	**Litho.**	**Unwmk.**
173	A46	6c red, black & gold		.20	.20
174	A46	30c lt blue, plum & gold		.25	.25
175	A46	40c ultra, black & gold		.25	.25
		Nos. 173-175 (3)		.70	.70

24th Cong. of the Intl. Junior Chamber of Commerce.

			1970, Feb. 2	**Wmk. 314**	**Perf. 14**

Designs: 6c, Carnival Queen as "City Beneath the Sea." 15c, Bambara god (antelope) from the Band of the Year. 30c, Pheasant Queen (Chanticleer) of Malaya. 40c, Steel Band of the Year with 1969 Calypso and Road March Kings, horiz.

176	A47	5c dk brown & multi		.20	.20
177	A47	6c dk blue & multi		.20	.20
178	A47	15c violet bl & multi		.20	.20
179	A47	30c dk green & multi		.25	.25
180	A47	40c green & multi		.25	.25
		Nos. 176-180 (5)		1.10	1.10

Issued to publicize the Trinidad Carnival.

Mahatma Gandhi and Indian Flag — A48

Design: 10c, Gandhi monument, vert.

Unwmk.

			1970, Mar. 2	**Photo.**	**Perf. 12**
181	A48	10c ultra & multi		.35	.25
182	A48	30c crimson & multi		.90	.70

Mohandas K. Gandhi (1869-1948), leader in India's fight for independence.

"Culture, Science, Arts and Technology"
A49

UN, 25th Anniv.: 10c, Children of various races, map of Trinidad and Tobago and

"UNICEF." 20c, Noah's ark, rainbow, dove and UN emblem.

			1970, June 26	**Photo.**	**Perf. 13½**
183	A49	5c multicolored		.20	.20
184	A49	10c multicolored		.25	.25
185	A49	20c multicolored		.30	.30
		Nos. 183-185 (3)		.75	.75

UPU Headquarters, Bern — A50

			1970, June 26	**Unwmk.**	**Perf. 12**
186	A50	30c ultra & multi		.50	.50

Opening of new UPU Headquarters in Bern.

No. 146 Overprinted:
"NATIONAL / COMMERCIAL / BANK / ESTABLISHED / 1.7.70"

Photo.; Gold Embossed

			1970, July 1	**Wmk. 314**	**Perf. 14**
187	A41	5c gold & multi		.30	.20

San Fernando Town Hall — A51

Designs: 3c, East Indian Immigrants, 1820, after painting by Cazabon, vert. 40c, Ships in San Fernando Harbor, 1860, after painting by Michel J. Cazabon.

Perf. 14x13½, 13½x14

			1970, Nov.	**Litho.**	**Wmk. 314**
188	A51	3c bister & multi		.20	.20
189	A51	5c lemon & multi		.20	.20
190	A51	40c lemon & multi		.50	.50
		Nos. 188-190 (3)		.90	.90

Municipality of San Fernando, 125th anniv.

Madonna and Child, by Titian — A52

Paintings: 3c, Adoration of the Shepherds, School of Saville. 30c, Adoration of the Shepherds, by Louis Le Nain. 40c, Virgin and Child with St. John and Angel, by Morando. $1, Adoration of the Magi, by Paolo Veronese.

Perf. 13½

			1970, Dec. 8	**Unwmk.**	**Litho.**
191	A52	3c dull org & multi		.20	.20
a.		Booklet pane of 2		.20	
192	A52	5c brt pink & multi		.20	.20
a.		Booklet pane of 2		.25	
193	A52	30c lt utra & multi		.25	.25
a.		Booklet pane of 2		.60	
194	A52	40c yellow grn & multi		.25	.25
a.		Booklet pane of 2		.75	
b.		Souvenir sheet of 4, #191-194		2.00	2.00
195	A52	$1 pale lilac & multi		.60	.60
		Nos. 191-195 (5)		1.50	1.50

Brocket Deer — A53

Perf. 14x13½

			1971, Aug. 9	**Litho.**	**Wmk. 314**
196	A53	3c shown		.40	.25
197	A53	5c Collared peccary		.50	.20
198	A53	6c Paca		.60	.40
199	A53	30c Agouti		1.75	3.25
200	A53	40c Ocelot		1.75	2.40
		Nos. 196-200 (5)		5.00	6.50

Capt. A. A. Cipriani
A54

Virgin and Child with St. John, by Bartolommeo
A55

Design: 30c, Chaconia medal (for distinction in social field).

			1971, Aug. 31		**Perf. 14**
201	A54	5c multicolored		.20	.20
202	A54	30c multicolored		.30	.30

9th anniversary of independence. Capt. Arthur Andrew Cipriani (died 1945) was mayor of Port of Spain and member of First Executive Council.

			1971, Oct. 25	**Litho.**	**Perf. 14x14½**

Christmas: 5c, Local creche. 10c, Virgin and Child with Sts. Jerome and Dominic, by Filipino Lippi. 15c, Virgin and Child with St. Anne, by Gerolamo dai Libri.

203	A55	3c yellow & multi		.20	.20
204	A55	5c dull blue & multi		.20	.20
205	A55	10c red & multi		.25	.25
206	A55	15c orange & multi		.35	.35
		Nos. 203-206 (4)		1.00	1.00

Satellite Earth Station, Matura
A56

Dish Antenna
A57

Design: 40c, Satellite over earth (Africa).

			1971, Nov. 18		**Perf. 14**
207	A56	10c ultra & multi		.20	.20
208	A57	30c green & multi		.25	.25
209	A57	40c black & multi		.35	.35
a.		Souvenir sheet of 3		1.40	1.40
		Nos. 207-209 (3)		.80	.80

Opening of Satellite Earth Station at Matura. No. 209a contains 3 imperf. stamps with simulated perforations similar to Nos. 207-209.

Morpho
Hybrid
A58

Butterflies: 5c, Purple mort bleu. 6c, Jaune
d'abricot. 10c, Purple king shoemaker. 20c,
Southern white pape. 30c, Little jaune.

1972, Feb. 18   Photo.   Wmk. 314
210 A58   3c olive & multi   .25   .25
211 A58   5c ocher & multi   .40   .20
212 A58   6c yellow & multi   .50   .50
213 A58 10c yel grn & multi   1.10   .25
214 A58 20c lilac & multi   2.25 1.90
215 A58 30c dull grn & multi   3.50 2.40
    Nos. 210-215 (6)   8.00 5.50

S.S.
Lady
McLeod
and
Stamp
A59

10c, Map of Trinidad and Tobago. 30c, Commemorative inscription.

1972, Apr. 12   Litho.   Perf. 14½x14
216 A59   5c blue & multi   .20   .20
217 A59 10c blue & multi   .25   .25
218 A59 30c blue & multi   .65   .65
    a. Souvenir sheet of 3, #216-218 1.25 1.25
        Nos. 216-218 (3)   1.10 1.10

125th anniv. of the Lady McLeod stamp.

Trinity
Cross — A60

Medals: 10c, Chaconia medal. 20c, Hummingbird medal. 30c, Medal of Merit.

1972, Aug. 28   Photo.   Perf. 13½x13
219 A60   5c blue & multi   .20   .20
220 A60 10c multicolored   .20   .20
221 A60 20c yellow grn & multi   .25   .30
222 A60 30c brt rose & multi   .25   .40
    a. Souvenir sheet of 4, #219-222 1.00 1.00
        Nos. 219-222 (4)   .90 1.10

10th anniversary of independence.
See Nos. 235-238.

Olympic
Rings,
Relay
Race
Medal,
1964
A61

Olympic Rings and: 20c, Bronze medal,
200-meters, 1964. 30c, Bronze medals,
weight lifting, 1952. 40c, Silver medal, 400-
meters, 1964. 50c, Silver medal, weight lifting,
1948.

1972, Sept. 7   Litho.   Perf. 14
223 A61 10c yellow & multi   .20   .20
224 A61 20c multicolored   .30   .30
225 A61 30c lilac & multi   .40   .40
226 A61 40c lt blue & multi   .50   .50
227 A61 50c orange & multi   .60   .60
    a. Souv. sheet, #223-227 + label 2.00 2.00
        Nos. 223-227 (5)   2.00 2.00

20th Olympic Games, Munich, 8/26-9/11.

Holy
Family, by
Titian
A62

Christmas: 3c, Adoration of the Kings, by
Dosso Dossi. 30c, Like 5c.

1972, Nov. 9   Photo.   Wmk. 314
228 A62   3c blue & multi   .20   .20
229 A62   5c rose lilac & multi   .20   .20
230 A62 30c lt green & multi   .50   .50
    a. Souvenir sheet of 3, #228-230 1.50 1.50
        Nos. 228-230 (3)   .90   .90

ECLA Headquarters, Santiago,
Chile — A63

Designs: 20c, INTERPOL emblem. 30c,
WHO emblem. 40c, University of West Indies
Administration Building.

1973, Aug. 15   Litho.   Wmk. 314
231 A63 10c orange & multi   .20   .20
232 A63 20c multicolored   .25   .25
233 A63 30c ultra & multi   .35   .35
234 A63 40c lilac & multi   .45   .45
    a. Souvenir sheet of 4, #231-234 1.25 1.25
        Nos. 231-234 (4)   1.25 1.25

Economic Commission for Latin America,
25th anniv. (10c); Intl. Criminal Police Organization, 50th anniv. (20c); Intl. Meteorological
cooperation, cent. (30c); Admission of 1st students to the University of West Indies, 25th
anniv. (40c).

Medal Type of 1972 Redrawn

Medals: 10c, Trinity Cross. 20c, Medal of
Merit. 30c, Chaconia medal. 40c, Hummingbird medal.

1973, Aug. 30   Photo.   Perf. 14½x14
235 A60 10c dark green & multi   .20   .20
236 A60 20c dark brown & multi   .20   .20
237 A60 30c dark blue & multi   .20   .20
238 A60 40c deep violet & multi   .40   .40
    a. Souv. sheet, #235-238, perf. 14 1.25 1.25
        Nos. 235-238 (4)   1.00 1.00

11th anniv. of independence. "Trinidad and
Tobago" in one line on #235-238.

General
Post
Office,
Port of
Spain
A64

40c, Conference Hall & flags, Chagaramas.

1973, Oct. 8   Photo.   Perf. 14
239 A64 30c multicolored   .25   .25
240 A64 40c multicolored   .40   .40
    a. Souvenir sheet of 2, #239-240 1.00 1.00

2nd Commonwealth Conf. of Postal Administrations, Trinidad, Oct. 8-20. On #240a the
perforations extend through margin and divide
map.

Virgin and Child,
by Murillo — A65

1973, Oct. 22   Perf. 14½x14
241 A65   5c pink & multi   .20   .20
242 A65 $1 lt blue & multi   .80   .80
    a. Souv. sheet, #241-242, perf. 14 1.10 1.10

Christmas 1973.

Post Office and UPU Emblem — A66

UPU, Cent.: 50c, Map of Islands, UPU
emblem, means of transportation.

1974, Nov. 18   Photo.   Perf. 13½x14
243 A66 40c brt purple & multi   .40   .40
244 A66 50c blue gray & multi   .60   .60
    a. Souvenir sheet of 2, #243-244 20.00 22.50

Humming Bird I, Transatlantic
Crossing, 1960 — A67

Design: 50c, Globe, Humming Bird II, Harold and Kwailan La Borde.

1974, Dec. 2   Perf. 14½
245 A67 40c multicolored   .50   .50
246 A67 50c multicolored   .70   .70
    a. Souvenir sheet of 2, #245-246 2.50 2.50

First anniversary of the voyage around the
world by Harold and Kwailan La Borde aboard
Humming Bird II, 1969-1973.

"Equality"
and IWY
Emblem
A68

1975, June 23   Litho.   Wmk. 314
247 A68 15c multicolored   .20   .20
248 A68 30c multicolored   .40   .40

International Women's Year 1975.

Dr. Pawan and Laboratory
Equipment — A69

25c, Vampire bat, microscope, syringe, bat's
head.

**   Perf. 14x14½**
1975, Sept. 23   Photo.   Wmk. 373
249 A69 25c yellow & multi   .45   .45
250 A69 30c lt blue & multi   .55   .55

Isolation of rabies virus by Dr. Joseph Len-
nox Pawan (1887-1957).

Boeing
707,
BWIA
Emblem,
Air
Routes
A70

Designs: 30c, Boeing 707 on ground. 40c,
Boeing 707 in the air.

**   Wmk. 373**
1975, Nov. 27   Litho.   Perf. 14½
251 A70 20c dark blue & multi   .40   .40
252 A70 30c deep ultra & multi   .60   .60
253 A70 40c dull green & multi   .75   .75
    a. Souvenir sheet of 3, #251-253 1.75 1.75
        Nos. 251-253 (3)   1.75 1.75

British West Indian Airways, 35th anniv.

Land of the Hummingbird
Costume — A71

Carnival 1976: $1, Carib Prince riding pink
ibis. Designs show prize-winning costumes
from 1974 carnival.

1976, Jan. 12   Photo.   Perf. 14½
254 A71 30c multicolored   .20   .20
255 A71 $1 multicolored   .70   .70
    a. Souvenir sheet of 2, #254-255 1.10 1.10

Angostura
Building,
Port of
Spain
A72

Designs (Exposition Medals, obverse and
reverse): 35c, New Orleans, 1885-86. 45c,
Sydney, 1879. 50c, Brussels, 1897.

1976, July 14   Litho.   Perf. 13
256 A72   5c bister & multi   .20   .20
257 A72 35c yellow grn & multi   .20   .20
258 A72 45c blue & multi   .30   .30
259 A72 50c violet & multi   .30   .30
    a. Souv. sheet #256-259, perf. 14 1.10 1.10
        Nos. 256-259 (4)   1.00 1.00

Sesquicentennial of the manufacture of
Angostura Bitters.

Map of
West
Indies,
Bats,
Wicket
and Ball
A72a

Prudential
Cup — A72b

1976, Oct. 4   Unwmk.   Perf. 14
260 A72a 35c lt blue & multi   .55   .55
261 A72b 45c lilac rose & blk   .75   .75
    a. Souvenir sheet of 2, #260-261 2.00 2.00

World Cricket Cup, won by West Indies
Team, 1975.

Columbus Sailing through the Bocas,
by A. Camps-Campins — A73

Paintings: 10c, View, by Jean Michael
Cazabon. 20c, Landscape, by Cazabon. 35c,
Los Gallos Point, by Cazabon. 45c, Corbeaux
Town, by Cazabon.

1976, Nov. 1   Litho.   Wmk. 373
262 A73   5c ocher & multi   .20   .20
263 A73 10c lilac & multi   .20   .20
264 A73 20c green & multi   .20   .20
265 A73 35c red orange & multi   .20   .20
266 A73 45c blue & multi   .25   .25
    a. Souvenir sheet of 5, #262-266 .80   .80
        Nos. 262-266 (5)   1.05 1.05

For overprints see Nos. 325, 327.

Hasely Crawford and Gold Medal A74

1977, Jan. 4   Litho.   Perf. 12½
267	A74	25c multicolored	.50 .45
a.		Souvenir sheet of 1	.60 .50

Hasely Crawford, winner of 100-meter dash at Montreal Olympic Games.

Sikorsky S-38 (Lindbergh's Plane) — A75

Designs: 35c, Charles Lindbergh delivering first airmail to Port of Spain, 1927. 45c, Boeing 707, British West Indies Airways. 50c, Boeing 747, British Airways.

1977, Apr.   Wmk. 373   Perf. 13
268	A75	20c lt blue & multi	.30 .30
269	A75	35c lt blue & multi	.50 .50
270	A75	45c lt blue & multi	.60 .60
271	A75	50c lt blue & multi	1.10 .75
a.		Souv. sheet, #268-271, perf. 14	2.50 2.15
		Nos. 268-271 (4)	2.50 2.15

Airmail to Trinidad & Tobago, 50th anniv.

Trinidad and Tobago Flag — A76

White Poinsettia — A77

35c, Coat of arms. 45c, Government House.

1977, July 26   Litho.   Perf. 13½x13
272	A76	20c yellow & multi	.20 .20
273	A76	35c red & multi	.35 .35
274	A76	45c lt blue & multi	.45 .45
a.		Souv. sheet #272-274, perf. 14	1.25 1.25
		Nos. 272-274 (3)	1.00 1.00

Inauguration of the Republic, Aug. 1, 1976.

1977, Oct. 11   Litho.   Perf. 14½

Christmas: 45c, 50c, Red poinsettia.
275	A77	10c multicolored	.20 .20
276	A77	35c multicolored	.30 .30
277	A77	45c multicolored	.40 .40
278	A77	50c multicolored	.45 .45
a.		Souvenir sheet of 4, #275-278	1.40 1.40
		Nos. 275-278 (4)	1.35 1.35

Robinson Crusoe Hotel, Tobago A78

15c, Turtle Beach Hotel, Tobago. 25c, Mount Irvine Hotel, Tobago. 70c, Mount Irvine beach, Tobago. $5, Holiday Inn, Trinidad.

Wmk. 373
1978, Jan. 17   Litho.   Perf. 14
279	A78	6c multicolored	.20 .20
280	A78	15c multicolored	.20 .20
281	A78	25c multicolored	.20 .20
282	A78	70c multicolored	.45 .45
283	A78	$5 multicolored	3.25 3.25
a.		Souvenir sheet of 5, #279-283	4.50 4.50
		Nos. 279-283 (5)	4.30 4.30

For overprint see No. 326.

Paphinia Cristata A79

Orchids: 30c, Caularthron bicornutum. 40c, Miltassia. 50c, Oncidium ampiliatum. $2.50, Oncidium papilio.

1978, June 7   Wmk. 373   Perf. 14
284	A79	12c multicolored	.20 .20
285	A79	30c multicolored	.25 .25
286	A79	40c multicolored	.30 .30
287	A79	50c multicolored	.40 .40
288	A79	$2.50 multicolored	2.00 2.00
a.		Souvenir sheet of 5, #284-288	3.50 3.50
		Nos. 284-288 (5)	3.15 3.15

Miss Universe and Trophy — A80

Designs: 35c, Portrait with crown. 45c, Miss Universe in evening dress.

1978, Aug. 2   Litho.   Perf. 14½
289	A80	10c multicolored	.20 .20
290	A80	35c multicolored	.30 .30
291	A80	45c multicolored	.35 .35
a.		Souvenir sheet of 3, #289-291	1.00 1.00
		Nos. 289-291 (3)	.85 .85

Janelle (Penny) Commissiong, Miss Universe, 1977.

Tayra A81

1978, Nov. 7   Perf. 13½x14
292	A81	15c shown	.20 .20
293	A81	25c Ocelot	.30 .25
294	A81	40c Porcupine	.45 .40
295	A81	70c Yellow anteater	.95 .65
a.		Souvenir sheet of 4, #292-295	2.00 2.00
		Nos. 292-295 (4)	1.90 1.50

"Burst of Beauty" — A82

Day Care Center — A83

Costumes: 10c, Rain worshipper. 35c, Zodiac. 45c, Praying mantis. 50c, Eye of the hurricane. $1, Steel orchestra.

1979, Feb. 1   Litho.   Perf. 13½
296	A82	5c multicolored	.20 .20
297	A82	10c multicolored	.20 .20
298	A82	35c multicolored	.25 .25
299	A82	45c multicolored	.30 .30

300	A82	50c multicolored	.35 .35
301	A82	$1 multicolored	.70 .70
		Nos. 296-301 (6)	2.00 2.00

Unwmk.
1979, June 5   Litho.   Perf. 13

IYC Emblem and: 10c, School lunch program. 35c, Dental care. 45c, Nursery school. 50c, Free school bus. $1, Medical care.
302	A83	5c multicolored	.20 .20
303	A83	10c multicolored	.20 .20
304	A83	35c multicolored	.25 .25
305	A83	45c multicolored	.30 .30
306	A83	50c multicolored	.30 .30
307	A83	$1 multicolored	.65 .65
a.		Souvenir sheet of 6, #302-307	1.90 1.90
		Nos. 302-307 (6)	1.90 1.90

International Year of the Child.

Geothermal Exploration A84

Designs: 35c, Hydrogeology. 45c, Petroleum exploration. 70c, Preservation of the environment.

1979, July 3   Wmk. 373
308	A84	10c multicolored	.20 .20
309	A84	35c multicolored	.30 .30
310	A84	45c multicolored	.35 .35
311	A84	70c multicolored	.55 .55
a.		Souvenir sheet of 4, #308-311	1.50 1.50
		Nos. 308-311 (4)	1.40 1.40

4th Latin American Geological Cong., July 7-15.

Map of Tobago and Tobago No. 1 — A85

15c, Tobago #2, 7. 35c, Tobago #28, 11. 45c, Tobago #25, 4. 70c, Great Britain #28 used in Scarborough and Tobago #5. $1, General Post Office, Scarborough and Tobago #6.

Perf. 13½x14
1979, Aug. 1   Litho.   Wmk. 373
312	A85	10c multicolored	.20 .20
313	A85	15c multicolored	.20 .20
314	A85	35c multicolored	.25 .25
315	A85	45c multicolored	.30 .30
316	A85	70c multicolored	.45 .45
317	A85	$1 multicolored	.65 .65
a.		Souvenir sheet of 6, #312-317	1.90 1.90
		Nos. 312-317 (6)	2.05 2.05

Centenary of Tobago's postage stamps.

Rowland Hill, Trinidad and Tobago No. 109 — A86

Hill and: 45c, Trinidad and Tobago #273. $1, Trinidad #62, Tobago #10.

1979, Oct. 4   Perf. 13
318	A86	25c multicolored	.20 .20
319	A86	45c multicolored	.30 .30
320	A86	$1 multicolored	.60 .60
a.		Souvenir sheet of 3, #318-320	1.25 1.25
		Nos. 318-320 (3)	1.10 1.10

Sir Rowland Hill (1795-1879), originator of penny postage.

Poui Tree A87

Designs: 10c, Court House. 50c, Royal Train locomotive. $1.50, Bacchante freighter.

Wmk. 373
1980, Jan. 21   Litho.   Perf. 14½
321	A87	5c multicolored	.20 .20
322	A87	10c multicolored	.20 .20
323	A87	50c multicolored	.45 .45
324	A87	$1.50 multicolored	1.40 1.40
a.		Souvenir sheet of 4, #321-324	2.00 2.00
		Nos. 321-324 (4)	2.25 2.25

Princes Town centenary.

Nos. 262, 279, 263 Overprinted in 3 or 5 Lines:
"1844-1980 POPULATION CENSUS 12th MAY 1980"

1980, Apr. 8   Litho.   Perf. 14
325	A73	5c multicolored	.20 .20
326	A78	6c multicolored	.20 .20
327	A73	10c multicolored	.20 .20
		Nos. 325-327 (3)	.60 .60

Scarlet Ibis Hen and Nest — A88

Scarlet Ibis: b, Nest and eggs. c, Chick in nest. d, Male. e, Male and female.

Wmk. 373
1980, May 6   Litho.   Perf. 14½
328		Strip of 5, multi	4.50 4.50
a.-e.		A88 single stamp	.90 .90

Bronze and Silver Medals, 1948, 1952 A89

Wmk. 373
1980, July 22   Litho.   Perf. 14
329	A89	10c shown	.20 .20
330	A89	15c Hasely Crawford, 1976 gold medal	.20 .20
331	A89	70c 1964 silver, bronze medals	.65 .65
		Nos. 329-331 (3)	1.05 1.05

Souvenir Sheet
332	A89	$2.50 Moscow '80 emblem, vert.	1.60 1.60

22nd Summer Olympic Games, Moscow, July 19-Aug. 3.

Charcoal Production — A90

Wmk. 373
1980, Sept. 8   Litho.   Perf. 14
333	A90	10c shown	.20 .20
334	A90	55c Logging	.30 .30
335	A90	70c Teak plantation	.40 .40
336	A90	$2.50 Watershed management	1.50 1.50
a.		Souvenir sheet of 4, #333-336	3.00 3.00
		Nos. 333-336 (4)	2.40 2.40

11th Commonwealth Forestry Conference.

Elizabeth Bourne, Judiciary and
Isabella Tesbier, Government — A91

Decade for Women: No. 338, Beryl
McBurnie, dance and culture; Audrey Jeffers,
social work. No. 339, Dr. Stella Abidh, public
health; Louise Horne, nutrition.

1980, Sept. 29
337	A91	$1 multicolored	.70	.70
338	A91	$1 multicolored	.70	.70
339	A91	$1 multicolored	.70	.70
		Nos. 337-339 (3)	2.10	2.10

Stadium and Netball League
Emblem — A92

1980, Oct. 21
340	A92	70c multicolored	.55	.55

1979 World Netball Tournament, Port-of-
Spain.

Athlete, Man in Wheelchair, IYD
Emblem — A93

Wmk. 373
1981, Apr. 6   Litho.   Perf. 14½
341	A93	10c shown	.20	.20
342	A93	70c Amputee with crutch	.35	.35
343	A93	$1.50 Blind people	.85	.85
344	A93	$2 IYD emblem	1.10	1.10
		Nos. 341-344 (4)	2.50	2.50

International Year of the Disabled.

Marine Preservation — A94

1981, July 7   Litho.   Perf. 13x13½
345	A94	10c Land	.20	.20
346	A94	55c shown	.40	.40
347	A94	$3 Sky	2.50	2.50
a.		Souvenir sheet of 3, #345-347	3.00	3.00
		Nos. 345-347 (3)	3.10	3.10

World
Food
Day — A95

1981, Oct. 16   Litho.   Perf. 14½x14
348	A95	10c Produce	.20	.20
349	A95	15c Rice threshing, mill	.20	.20
350	A95	45c Bigeye	.30	.30
351	A95	55c Cow, pig, goats	.40	.40
352	A95	$1.50 Poultry	1.00	1.00
353	A95	$2 Smallmouth grunt	1.40	1.40
a.		Souvenir sheet of 6, #348-353	3.50	3.50
		Nos. 348-353 (6)	3.50	3.50

President
Awards — A96

1981, Nov. 30   Perf. 14
354	A96	10c First aid	.20	.20
355	A96	70c Motor mechanics	.50	.50
356	A96	$1 Hiking	.70	.70
357	A96	$2 President giving award	1.40	1.40
		Nos. 354-357 (4)	2.80	2.80

Commonwealth
Pharmaceutical
Conference
— A97

1982, Feb. 12   Litho.   Perf. 14½x14
358	A97	10c Pharmacist	.20	.20
359	A97	$1 Pluchea symphitfolia	.85	.85
360	A97	$2 Nopalea cochenilifera	1.60	1.60
		Nos. 358-360 (3)	2.65	2.65

Scouting
Year — A98

1982, June 28   Litho.   Perf. 14
361	A98	15c Production	.20	.20
362	A98	55c Tolerance	.45	.45
363	A98	$5 Discipline	4.00	4.00
		Nos. 361-363 (3)	4.65	4.65

25th Anniv. of
Tourist
Board — A99

Perf. 13½x14
1982, Oct. 18   Litho.   Wmk. 373
364	A99	55c Charlotteville	.45	.45
365	A99	$1 Boating	.85	.85
366	A99	$3 Fort George	2.50	2.50
		Nos. 364-366 (3)	3.80	3.80

Pa Pa
Bois — A100

Designs: Various folklore characters.

1982, Nov. 8
367	A100	10c multicolored	.20	.20
368	A100	15c multicolored	.20	.20
369	A100	65c multicolored	.55	.55
370	A100	$5 multicolored	4.25	4.25
a.		Souvenir sheet of 4, #367-370	5.50	5.50
		Nos. 367-370 (4)	5.20	5.20

Canefarmers' Centenary — A101

1982, Dec. 13   Litho.   Perf. 14
371	A101	30c Harvest	.40	.40
372	A101	70c Loading bullock cart	.95	.95
373	A101	$1.50 Field	2.00	2.00
a.		Souvenir sheet of 3, #371-373, perf. 14½	5.50	5.50
		Nos. 371-373 (3)	3.35	3.35

20th Anniv. of Independence — A102

1982, Dec. 28   Perf. 13½x14
374	A102	10c Natl. Stadium	.20	.20
375	A102	35c Caroni Arena Water Treatment Plant	.25	.25
376	A102	50c Mount Hope Maternity Hospital	.40	.40
377	A102	$2 Natl. Insurance Board Mall, Tobago	1.50	1.50
		Nos. 374-377 (4)	2.35	2.35

Commonwealth Day — A103

1983, Mar. 14   Perf. 14
378	A103	10c Flags	.20	.20
379	A103	55c Satellite view	.40	.40
380	A103	$1 Oil industry, vert.	.75	.75
381	A103	$2 Maps, vert.	1.50	1.50
		Nos. 378-381 (4)	2.85	2.85

10th Anniv. of CARICOM — A104

1983, July 11   Litho.   Perf. 14
382	A104	35c Jet, map	.65	.65

World Communications Year — A105

1983, Aug. 5   Perf. 14½
383	A105	15c Operator	.20	.20
384	A105	55c Scarborough PO, Tobago	.45	.45
385	A105	$1 Textel Building	.85	.85
386	A105	$3 Morne Bleu Receiving Station	2.50	2.50
		Nos. 383-386 (4)	4.00	4.00

Commonwealth Finance Ministers
Conference — A106

Wmk. 373
1983, Sept. 19   Litho.   Perf. 14
387	A106	$2 multicolored	1.50	1.50

World Food
Day — A107

1983, Oct. 17   Perf. 14x13½
388	A107	10c Kingfish	.20	.20
389	A107	55c Flying fish	.40	.40
390	A107	70c Queen conch	.50	.50
391	A107	$4 Red shrimp	3.00	3.00
		Nos. 388-391 (4)	4.10	4.10

Flowers — A108

1983, Dec. 14   Wmk. 373   Perf. 14
392	A108	5c Bois pois	.20	.20
393	A108	10c Maraval Lily	.20	.20
394	A108	15c Star grass	.20	.20
395	A108	20c Bois caco	.20	.20
396	A108	25c Strangling fig	.20	.20
397	A108	30c Cassia moschata	.20	.20
398	A108	50c Chalice flower	.35	.35
399	A108	65c Black stick	.45	.45
400	A108	80c Columnea scandens	.55	.55
401	A108	95c Cats Claws	.65	.65
402	A108	$1 Bois l'agli	.70	.70
403	A108	$1.50 Eustoma exeltatum	1.00	1.00

Size: 38½x26mm
404	A108	$2 Chaconia, horiz.	1.40	1.40
405	A108	$2.50 Chysothemis pulchella, horiz.	1.75	1.75
406	A108	$5 Centratherum punctatum, horiz.	3.50	3.50
407	A108	$10 Savanna flower, horiz.	6.75	6.75
		Nos. 392-407 (16)	18.30	18.30

"1984" imprint: #392, 393, 394, 396.
"1986:" #393.
"1989:" #392.

1985-89   Wmk. 384
392a	A108	5c	.20	.20
393a	A108	10c	.20	.20
395a	A108	20c ('89)	.20	.20
396a	A108	25c ('89)	.20	.20
397a	A108	30c ('87)	.20	.20
399a	A108	65c ('87)	.35	.35
400a	A108	80c ('87)	.45	.45
401a	A108	95c	.65	.65
402a	A108	$1	.70	.70
403a	A108	$1.50 ('87)	.80	.80
404a	A108	$2 ('87)	1.10	1.10
405a	A108	$2.50 ('89)	1.40	1.40
406a	A108	$5	3.25	3.25
407a	A108	$10	6.75	6.75
		Nos. 392a-407a (14)	16.45	16.45

"1985" imprint: #392, 393a, 401a, 402a, 406a, 407a.
"1987:" #393a, 397a, 399a, 400a-404a, 406a-407a.
"1988:" #393a, 395a-397a, 399a-402a, 406a-407a.
"1989:" #393a, 395a-397a, 399a, 402a-407a.

Castles on Chess
Board
A109

1984 Summer
Olympics
A110

World Chess Federationn, 60th Anniv.: Various chess pieces.

Wmk. 373

1984, Sept. 12		**Litho.**	**Perf. 14**	
408	A109	50c multicolored	.35	.35
409	A109	70c multicolored	.50	.50
410	A109	$1.50 multicolored	1.00	1.00
411	A109	$2 multicolored	1.40	1.40
		Nos. 408-411 (4)	3.25	3.25

1984, Sept. 21			**Perf. 14x14½**	
412	A110	15c Swimming	.20	.20
413	A110	55c Running	.45	.45
414	A110	$1.50 Yachting	1.10	1.10
415	A110	$4 Bicycling	3.00	3.00
a.		Souvenir sheet of 4, #412-415	5.00	5.00
		Nos. 412-415 (4)	4.75	4.75

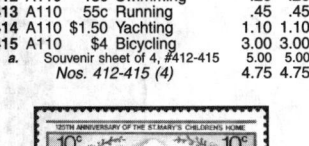

St. Mary's Children's Home, 125th
Anniv. — A111

1984, Nov. 13		**Litho.**	**Perf. 13½**	
416	A111	10c Children's band	.20	.20
417	A111	70c St. Mary's Home	.65	.65
418	A111	$3 Group scene	3.00	3.00
		Nos. 416-418 (3)	3.85	3.85

Christmas
1984
A112

1984, Nov.		**Litho.**	**Perf. 14**	
419	A112	10c Parang Band	.20	.20
420	A112	30c Musical notes, Poinsettia	.25	.25
421	A112	$1 Bandola, Cuatro, Bandolin	.85	.85
422	A112	$3 Fiddle, Guitar, Double Bass	2.50	2.50
		Nos. 419-422 (4)	3.80	3.80

Emancipation, 150th
Anniv. — A113

1984, Oct. 22		**Litho.**	**Perf. 13½x13**	
423	A113	35c Slave ship	.50	.50
424	A113	55c Map, Slave Triangle	.80	.80
425	A113	$1 Book by Eric Williams	1.50	1.50
426	A113	$2 Toussaint L'Ouverture	3.00	3.00
a.		Souvenir sheet of 4, #423-426	5.00	5.00
		Nos. 423-426 (4)	5.80	5.80

Labor
Day — A114

Labor leaders: No. 427, A.A. Cipriani and T.U.B. Butler. No. 428, A. Cola Rienzi and C.T.W.E. Worrell. No. 429, C.P. Alexander and Q. O'Connor.

Wmk. 373

1985, June 17		**Litho.**	**Perf. 14**	
427	A114	55c dull rose & blk	.65	.65
428	A114	55c brt green & blk	.65	.65
429	A114	55c lt orange & blk	.65	.65
		Nos. 427-429 (3)	1.95	1.95

Ships
A115

Wmk. 373

1985, Aug 20		**Litho.**	**Perf. 14½**	
430	A115	30c Lady Nelson	.25	.25
431	A115	95c Lady Drake	.75	.75
432	A115	$1.50 Federal Palm	1.10	1.10
433	A115	$2 Federal Maple	1.50	1.50
		Nos. 430-433 (4)	3.60	3.60

UN
Decade
for
Women
A116

Women in the arts, public service and education: No. 434, Sybill Atteck, Marjorie Padmore. No. 435, May Cherrie, Evelyn Tracey. No. 436, Jessica Smith-Phillips, Irene Omilta McShine.

1985, Oct. 30		**Wmk. 384**	**Perf. 14**	
434	A116	$1.50 multicolored	1.10	1.10
435	A116	$1.50 multicolored	1.10	1.10
436	A116	$1.50 multicolored	1.10	1.10
		Nos. 434-436 (3)	3.30	3.30

Intl. Youth
Year — A117

Anniversaries and events: 10c, Natl. Cadet Force, 75th anniv. 65c, Girl Guides, 75th anniv.

1985, Nov. 27			**Perf. 14x14½**	
437	A117	10c Cadet emblem	.20	.20
438	A117	65c Badges, anniv. emblem	.50	.50
439	A117	95c shown	.70	.70
		Nos. 437-439 (3)	1.40	1.40

A118   A119

Sisters of St. Joseph de Cluny in Trinidad, 150th Anniv.: 10c, Sister Anne-Marie Javouhey, founder. 65c, St. Joseph's Convent, Port-of-Spain. 95c, Statue of Sr. Anne-Marie.

Perf. 14x14½

1986, Mar. 19		**Litho.**	**Wmk. 384**	
440	A118	10c multicolored	.20	.20
441	A118	65c multicolored	.45	.45
442	A118	95c multicolored	.70	.70
		Nos. 440-442 (3)	1.35	1.35

Wmk. 384

1986, Apr. 21		**Litho.**	**Perf. 14½**	
443	A119	10c At the Cenotaph	.20	.20
444	A119	15c Aboard HMY Britannia	.20	.20
445	A119	30c With Pres. Clarke	.20	.20
446	A119	$5 Receiving bouquet	2.50	2.50
		Nos. 443-446 (4)	3.10	3.10

Queen Elizabeth II, 60th birthday.

Locomotives, AMERIPEX '86 — A120

Perf. 14½x14

1986, May 26			**Wmk. 373**	
447	A120	65c Arma tank locomotive	.30	.30
448	A120	95c Canadian-built No. 22	.55	.55
449	A120	$1.10 Tender engine	.60	.60
450	A120	$1.50 Saddle tank	.85	.85
a.		Souvenir sheet of 4, #447-450	2.50	2.50
		Nos. 447-450 (4)	2.30	2.30

Boy Scouts,
75th Anniv.
A121

1986, July 21		**Wmk. 384**	**Perf. 14**	
451	A121	$1.70 Campsite	1.00	1.00
452	A121	$2 Uniforms, 1911, 1986	1.25	1.25

Dr. Eric Williams (1911-1981), First
Prime Minister — A122

Wmk. 373

1986, Sept. 25		**Litho.**	**Perf. 14**	
453	A122	10c Graduating college, 1935	.20	.20
454	A122	30c Wearing red tie	.20	.20
a.		Black tie		.20
455	A122	95c Pro-Chancellor of UWI	.60	.60
456	A122	$5 Williams, prime minister's residence	3.00	3.00
a.		Souvenir sheet of 4, #453-456	4.00	4.00
		Nos. 453-456 (4)	4.00	4.00

Nos. 453-454 vert.

Intl. Peace
Year
A123

1986, Oct. 30			**Wmk. 384**	
457	A123	95c shown	.60	.60
458	A123	$3 Dove	2.40	2.40

Giselle LaRonde,
Miss World
1986 — A124

Wmk. 384

1987, July 27		**Litho.**	**Perf. 14**	
459	A124	10c Wearing folk costume	.40	.20
460	A124	30c Bathing suit	.85	.25
461	A124	95c Crown	1.90	1.50
462	A124	$1.65 Crown and sash	3.00	3.00
		Nos. 459-462 (4)	6.15	4.95

Republic
Bank,
150th
Anniv.
A125

Designs: 10c, Colonial Bank, Port of Spain. 65c, Cocoa plantation. 95c, Oil fields. $1.10, Tramcar, Belmont Tramway Co.

Wmk. 373

1987, Dec. 21		**Litho.**	**Perf. 14**	
463	A125	10c buff, red brn & blk	.20	.20
464	A125	65c buff, red brn & blk	.30	.30
465	A125	95c buff, red brn & blk	.50	.50
466	A125	$1.10 buff, red brn & blk	.60	.60
		Nos. 463-466 (4)	1.60	1.60

Defense Force,
25th
Anniv. — A126

Various army, coast guard and navy uniforms.

Wmk. 384

1988, Feb. 29		**Litho.**	**Perf. 14**	
467	A126	10c Army	.40	.20
468	A126	30c Army (women)	1.10	.25
469	A126	$1.10 Navy, army, coast guard	2.00	1.75
470	A126	$1.50 Navy	2.50	2.50
		Nos. 467-470 (4)	6.00	4.70

Cricket
A127

Bat, wicket posts, ball, 18th cent. belt buckle and batters: 30c, George John. 65c, Learie Constantine. 95c, Sonny Ramadhin. $1.50, Gerry Gomez. $2.50, Jeffrey Stollmeyer.

Wmk. 373

1988, June 6		**Litho.**	**Perf. 14**	
471	A127	30c multicolored	.70	.25
472	A127	65c multicolored	1.25	.60
473	A127	95c multicolored	1.40	1.00
474	A127	$1.50 multicolored	1.75	1.75
475	A127	$2.50 multicolored	2.25	2.50
		Nos. 471-475 (5)	7.35	6.10

Oilfield Workers'
Trade Union, 50th
Anniv. — A128

50, Star, oil well and: 10c, Uriah Buzz Butler, labor leader. 30c, Adrian C. Rienzi, pres. from 1937-42. 65c, John Rojas, pres. from 1943-62. $5, George Weekes, pres. from 1962-87.

Wmk. 384

1988, July 11		**Litho.**	**Perf. 14½**	
476	A128	10c multicolored	.20	.20
477	A128	30c multicolored	.20	.20
478	A128	65c multicolored	.40	.40
479	A128	$5 multicolored	2.00	2.00
		Nos. 476-479 (4)	2.80	2.80

Borough of
Arima, Cent.
A129

20c, Mary Werges, Santa Rosa Church.
30c, Gov. W. Robinson, royal charter. $1.10,
Mayor C.P. Lopez greeting Gov. Robinson at
train station. $1.50, Mayor J.F. Wallen, centen-
nial emblem.

Wmk. 384

1988, Aug. 22	**Litho.**	**Perf. 14½**	
480	A129	20c multicolored	.20 .20
481	A129	30c multicolored	.20 .20
482	A129	$1.10 multicolored	.60 .60
483	A129	$.85 multicolored	.85 .85
		Nos. 480-483 (4)	1.85 1.85

Lloyds of London, 300th Anniv.
Common Design Type

Designs: 30c, Queen Mother at the "Topping
Out" ceremony of new Lloyds's building, 1984.
$1.10, BWIA Tristar 500, horiz. $1.55, ISCOTT
iron and steel mill, horiz. $2, *Atlantic Empress*
on fire off Tobago.

1988, Nov. 21	**Litho.**	**Perf. 14**	
484	CD341	30c multicolored	.50 .20
485	CD341	$1.10 multicolored	1.75 1.00
486	CD341	$1.55 multicolored	1.60 1.40
487	CD341	$2 multicolored	3.00 2.00
		Nos. 484-487 (4)	6.85 4.60

Unification of the Islands,
Cent. — A130

Torch and: 40c, Natl. arms, 1889, and 1p
Type A1. $1, Badge from Tobago flag and
Tobago No. 31. $1.50, Badge from Trinidad
flag and Trinidad No. 71. $2.25, Natl. arms,
1889, and No. 274.

Wmk. 384

1989, Mar. 20	**Litho.**	**Perf. 14½**	
488	A130	40c multicolored	.40 .20
489	A130	$1 multicolored	1.10 .60
490	A130	$1.50 multicolored	1.50 1.50
491	A130	$2.25 multicolored	1.90 2.00
		Nos. 488-491 (4)	4.90 4.30

Rare
Species
A131

Designs: a, *Pipile pipile*. b, *Phyllodytes
auratus*. c, *Cebus albifrons trinitatis*. d, *Tamandua tetradactyla*. e, *Lutra longicaudis*. Printed
in a continuous design.

Perf. 14x14½

1989, July 31		**Wmk. 373**	
492		Strip of 5	10.00 10.00
a.-e.	A131	$1 any single	2.00 2.00

A132

A133

1989, Oct. 2		**Perf. 14½**	
493	A132	10c Men using walking sticks	.35 .20
494	A132	40c City Hall	.30 .20
495	A132	$1 Guides and leader	1.00 .50
496	A132	$2.25 Volunteers, anniv. emblem	1.50 1.50
		Nos. 493-496 (4)	3.15 2.40

Blind Welfare, 75th anniv. (10c), Port-of-
Spain City Hall, 75th anniv. (40c), Girl Guides,
75th anniv. ($1), and Red Cross, 50th anniv.
($2.25).

Perf. 14½x14

1989, Nov. 30		**Wmk. 384**	

Drum instruments played in a steel band.

497	A133	10c Tenor	.20 .20
498	A133	40c Guitar	.20 .20
499	A133	$1 Cello	.40 .45
500	A133	$2.25 Bass	1.00 1.10
		Nos. 497-500 (4)	1.80 1.95

Mushrooms
A134

1990, May 3		**Perf. 14x13½**	
501	A134	10c *Xeromphalina tenuipes*	.20 .20
502	A134	40c *Dictyophora indusiata*	.30 .30
503	A134	$1 *Leucocoprinus birnbaumii*	.75 .75
504	A134	$2.25 *Crinipellis perniciosa*	1.60 1.60
		Nos. 501-504 (4)	2.85 2.85

Stamp World London '90.

Scarlet
Ibis
A135

1990, Sept. 7		**Perf. 14**	
505	A135	40c Immature bird	1.25 .25
506	A135	80c Mating display	1.50 1.00
507	A135	$1 Adult male	1.75 1.00
508	A135	$2.25 Adult, egg & young	2.75 2.50
		Nos. 505-508 (4)	7.25 4.75

World Wildlife Fund.

Yellow
Oriole — A136

1990, Dec. 17	**Litho.**	**Wmk. 384**	
509	A136	20c shown	.20 .20
510	A136	25c Green rumped parrotlet	.35 .25
511	A136	40c Fork-tailed flycatcher	.20 .20
512	A136	50c Copper rumped hummingbird	.40 .30
513	A136	$1 Bananaquit	.45 .30
514	A136	$2 Semp	.75 .65
515	A136	$2.25 Channel-billed toucan	.35 .35

516	A136	$2.50 Bay headed tanager	.40 .40
517	A136	$5 Green honeycreeper	2.50 2.50
a.		Souvenir sheet of 1, wmk. 373	1.60 1.60
518	A136	$10 Cattle egret	1.75 1.75
519	A136	$20 Golden olive woodpecker	5.00 5.00
520	A136	$50 Peregrine falcon	12.50 12.50
		Nos. 509-520 (12)	24.85 24.40

No. 517a issued 2/3/97 for Hong Kong '97.
For overprints & surcharge see #565-568,
597A.

1994-98		**Wmk. 373**	
510a	A136	25c	.30 .30
512a	A136	50c	.20 .20
513a	A136	$1	.30 .30
514a	A136	$2	.65 .65
516a	A136	$2.50	.80 .80
517b	A136	$5	1.60 1.60
518a	A136	$10	3.25 3.25
519a	A136	$20	6.50 6.50
		Nos. 510a-519a (8)	13.60 13.60

Issued: #510a, 8/94; #512a, 4/95; #510a,
8/94; #513a, 3/3/97; #516a, 518a, 519a,
10/14/98; #517b, 6/1996.
#510a, 513a, 514a, 517b dated 1990;
#517a dated 1997.

University of
the West
Indies
A137

Chancellors and Campus Buildings: 40c,
HRH Princess Alice, Administration Building.
80c, Sir Hugh Wooding, Main Library. $1, Sir
Allen Lewis, Faculty of Engineering. $2.25, Sir
Shridath Ramphal, Faculty of Medical Studies.

Perf. 13½x14

1990, Oct. 15	**Litho.**	**Wmk. 373**	
521	A137	40c multicolored	.20 .20
522	A137	80c multicolored	.40 .40
523	A137	$1 multicolored	.50 .50
524	A137	$2.25 multicolored	1.10 1.10
		Nos. 521-524 (4)	2.20 2.20

British
West
Indies
Airways,
50th
Anniv.
A138

Airplanes: 40c, Lockheed Lodestar. 80c,
Vickers Viking 1A. $1, Vickers Viscount 702.
$2.25, Boeing 707. $5, Lockheed TriStar 500.

1990, Nov. 27		**Perf. 14**	
525	A138	40c multicolored	.75 .25
526	A138	80c multicolored	1.00 .75
527	A138	$1 multicolored	1.10 .75
528	A138	$2.25 multicolored	2.00 2.50
		Nos. 525-528 (4)	4.85 4.25

Souvenir Sheet

529	A138	$5 multicolored	3.25 3.25

Ferns
A139

1991, July 1		**Perf. 13½**	
530	A139	40c *Lygodium volubile*	.20 .20
531	A139	80c *Blechnum occidentale*	.40 .40
532	A139	$1 *Gleichenia bifida*	.50 .50
533	A139	$2.25 *Polypodium lycopodioides*	1.10 1.10
		Nos. 530-533 (4)	2.20 2.20

Trinidad & Tobago in World War
II — A140

Designs: 40c, Firing practice by Trinidad &
Tobago regiment. 80c, Fairey Barracuda sur-
prises U-boat. $1, Avro Lancaster returns from
bombing raid. $2.25, River class frigate on
convoy duty. No. 538a, Supermarine Spitfire.
b, Vickers Wellington.

Perf. 13½x14

1991, Dec. 7	**Litho.**	**Wmk. 384**	
534	A140	40c multicolored	.20 .20
535	A140	80c multicolored	.40 .40
536	A140	$1 multicolored	.50 .50
537	A140	$2.25 multicolored	1.10 1.10
		Nos. 534-537 (4)	2.20 2.20

Souvenir Sheet of 2

538	A140	$2.50 #a.-b.	2.50 2.50

H. E.
Rapsey — A141

Inca Clathrata
Quesneli — A142

Holy Name
Convent — A143

Religions of
Trinidad and
Tobago — A145

1992, Mar. 30	**Wmk. 373**	**Perf. 14**	
539	A141	40c multicolored	.20 .20
540	A142	80c multicolored	.40 .40
541	A143	$1 multicolored	.50 .50
		Nos. 539-541 (3)	1.10 1.10

#539, Building and Loan Assoc., cent. #540,
Trinidad & Tobago Field Naturalists' Club.
#541, Holy Name Convent, cent.

1992, Apr. 21	**Litho.**	**Perf. 14**	

#544, Baptist, baptism by immersion. #545,
Muslim, minaret. #546, Hindu, Brahman..the
source of all. #547, Christianity, cross. #548,
Baha'i, slogan.

544	A145	40c multicolored	.20 .20
545	A145	40c multicolored	.20 .20
546	A145	40c multicolored	.20 .20

547 A145 40c multicolored .20 .20
548 A145 40c multicolored .20 .20
  Nos. 544-548 (5) 1.00 1.00

BWIA Aircraft A146

Wmk. 373
1992, Aug. 6 **Litho.** *Perf. 14*
549 A146 $2.25 MD83 1.10 1.10
550 A146 $2.25 L1011 1.10 1.10

Natl. Museum and Art Gallery, Cent. A147

Wmk. 384
1992, Dec. 7 **Litho.** *Perf. 14½*
551 A147 $1 multicolored .50 .50

Christmas — A148

1992, Dec. 21
552 A148 40c multicolored .20 .20

Trinidad Guardian, 75th Anniv. — A149

1992, Dec. 23
553 A149 40c multicolored .20 .20

Philatelic Society of Trinidad & Tobago, 50th Anniv. A150

1992, Dec. 30
554 A150 $2.25 multicolored 1.10 1.10

CARICOM (Caribbean Economic Community), 20th Anniv. — A151

Map of CARICOM nations, portraits of West Indian men: 50c, $1.50, $2.75, $3, Derek Walcott, Sir Shridath Ramphal, William Demas.
$6, Order of the Caribbean Community. Illustration reduced.

Perf. 13x13½
1994, Jan. 31 **Litho.** **Wmk. 373**
555 A151 50c pink & multi .20 .20
556 A151 $1.50 green & multi .50 .50
557 A151 $2.75 gray & multi .95 .95
558 A151 $3 violet & multi 1.00 1.00
  Nos. 555-558 (4) 2.65 2.65

Souvenir Sheet
Perf. 13½x13
559 A151 $6 multicolored 2.00 2.00
No. 559 contains one 34x56mm stamp.

Drum Instruments Played in a Steel Band — A152

1994, Feb. 11 *Perf. 14x15*
560 A152 50c Quadrophonic pan .20 .20
561 A152 $1 Tenor base pan .35 .35
562 A152 $2.25 Six pan .80 .80
563 A152 $2.50 Rocket pan .90 .90
  Nos. 560-563 (4) 2.25 2.25

Alwyn Roberts Kitchener, Calypso Singer — A153

1994, Feb. 11 *Perf. 14*
564 A153 50c multicolored .20 .20

Nos. 510-511, 514, 518 Ovptd. with Hong Kong '94 Exhibition Emblem
Wmk. 384
1994, Feb. 18 **Litho.** *Perf. 14*
565 A136 25c multicolored .20 .20
566 A136 40c multicolored .20 .20
567 A136 $2 multicolored .70 .70
568 A136 $10 multicolored 3.50 3.50
  Nos. 565-568 (4) 4.60 4.60

Hotels & Lodges A154

#569, Trinidad Hilton. #570, Sandy Point Village, Tobago. #571, Asa Wright Nature Center and Lodge. #572, ML's Bed and Breakfast.

Wmk. 373
1994, Aug. 10 **Litho.** *Perf. 14*
569 A154 $3 multicolored 1.10 1.10
570 A154 $3 multicolored 1.10 1.10
571 A154 $3 multicolored 1.10 1.10
572 A154 $3 multicolored 1.10 1.10
  Nos. 569-572 (4) 4.40 4.40

Snakes A155

50c, Boa constrictor. $1.25, Horse whip or vine snake. $2.50, Bushmaster. $3, Large coral snake.

Wmk. 373
1994, Sept. 19 **Litho.** *Perf. 14*
573 A155 50c multicolored .20 .20
574 A155 $1.25 multicolored .45 .45
575 A155 $2.50 multicolored .90 .90
576 A155 $3 multicolored 1.10 1.10
  Nos. 573-576 (4) 2.65 2.65

Trinidad Art Society, 50th Anniv. — A156

Artworks: No. 577, Copper sculpture, by Ken Morris. No. 578, Fisherman, by Sybil Atteck. No. 579, Snowballman, by Mahmoud P. Alladin.

1995, Mar. 6 **Wmk. 384**
577 A156 50c multicolored .20 .20
578 A156 50c multicolored .20 .20
579 A156 50c multicolored .20 .20
  Nos. 577-579 (3) .60 .60

Conservation — A157

Designs: $1.25, Leatherback turtle. $2.50, POS Lighthouse, vert. $3, "Knowsley" Ministry of Foreign Affairs.

1995, Aug. 7
580 A157 $1.25 multicolored .45 .45
581 A157 $2.50 multicolored .90 .90
582 A157 $3 multicolored 1.10 1.10
  Nos. 580-582 (3) 2.45 2.45

Brian Lara, Cricket Hero — A158

Designs: $1.25, Batting. $2.50, In batting stance. $3, Batting, diff.
No. 587: a, $3.75, With arms raised at crowd. b, $5.01, Down on one knee with bat.

Perf. 13x13½
1996, May 15 **Litho.** **Wmk. 373**
583 A158 50c multicolored .20 .20
584 A158 $1.25 multicolored .45 .45
585 A158 $2.50 multicolored .90 .90
586 A158 $3 multicolored 1.00 1.00
  Nos. 583-586 (4) 2.55 2.55
Souvenir Sheet
587 A158 Sheet of 2, #a.-b. 3.00 3.00

Trinidad & Tobago Remembers World War II — A159

50c, Red Cross Economy Label. $1.25, Battleship USS Missouri. $2.50, US servicemen playing baseball, Queen's Park, Savannah, 1942. $3, Fulmar 1, Royal Naval Air Station.
No. 592: a, Grumman Goose seaplane. b, US Navy Airship.

Wmk. 373
1996, June 7 **Litho.** *Perf. 14*
588 A159 50c multicolored .20 .20
589 A159 $1.25 multicolored .45 .45
590 A159 $2.50 multicolored .90 .90
591 A159 $3 multicolored 1.00 1.00
  Nos. 588-591 (4) 2.55 2.55
Souvenir Sheet of 2
592 A159 $3 #a.-b. 2.00 2.00

A160   A161

Wendy Fitzwilliam, 1998 Miss Universe: $1.25, Lying on beach. $2.50, In traditional costume. $3, Wearing evening gown. $5, After coronation.

1999, May 3 **Litho.** *Perf. 14*
593 A160 50c multicolored .20 .20
594 A160 $1.25 multicolored .40 .40
595 A160 $2.50 multicolored .80 .80
596 A160 $3 multicolored .95 .95
  Nos. 593-596 (4) 2.35 2.35
Souvenir Sheet
597 A160 $5 multicolored 1.60 1.60

No. 511 Surcharged **75c**

1999 **Method and Perf. as Before**
597A A136 75c on 40c multi

Serpentine Die Cut
2000, Jan. 27 **Litho.**

Angostura Bitters, 175th Anniv.: 75c, Angostura Bitters bottle. $3, Distillery. $4.50, Bitters bottle, cocktails.

Self-Adhesive
598 A161 75c multi .25 .25
599 A161 $3 multi .90 .90
600 A161 $4.50 multi 1.25 1.25
  a. Souvenir sheet, #598-600 2.40 2.40

Tourism A162

Shoreline scenes: 75c, Maracas Bay. $1, Pirates Bay. $3.75, Pigeon Point. $5, Toco, North Coast.

2000, July 25 Litho. *Perf. 14¼x14½*
601 A162 75c multi — —
602 A162 $1 multi — —
603 A162 $3.75 multi — —
604 A162 $5 multi — —

An additional stamp was issued in this set. The editors would like to examine it.

Christmas A163

Design: 75c, Caroni landscape. $3.75, Pastelles, sorrel and ginger beer. $4.50, Musicians under palm trees. $5.25, Angels with steel drums.

Perf. 14¼x14½
2000, Nov. 14 **Litho.**
605 A163 75c multi — —
606 A163 $3.75 multi — —
607 A163 $4.50 multi — —
608 A163 $5.25 multi — —

No. 515
Surcharged

Method and Perf. as Before
2001?
609 A136 75c on $2.25 multi

Endangered
Fauna
A165

Designs: 25c, Pacca, 50c, Prehensile-tailed porcupine. 75c, Iguana. $1, Leatherback turtle. $2, Golden tegu. $2, Red howler monkey. $4, Weeping capuchin monkey, vert. $5, River otter. $10, Ocelot. $20, Trinidad piping guan, vert.

Perf. 14¼x14½, 14½x14¼				
2001, Feb. 6			**Litho.**	
612	A165	25c multi	.20	.20
613	A165	50c multi	.20	.20
614	A165	75c multi	.25	.25
615	A165	$1 multi	.30	.30
616	A165	$2 multi	.65	.65
617	A165	$3 multi	.95	.95
618	A165	$4 multi	1.25	1.25
619	A165	$5 multi	1.60	1.60
620	A165	$10 multi	3.25	3.25
621	A165	$20 multi	6.50	6.50
	Nos. 612-621 (10)		15.15	15.15

Salvation Army in
Trinidad & Tobago,
Cent. — A166

Designs: 75c, Emblem. $2, William Booth Memorial Hall.

2001, Aug. 9		**Perf. 14½x14¼**		
622-623	A166	Set of 2	.90	.90
623a		Souvenir sheet, #622-623, perf. 13¾x14¼	.90	.90

Natl. Library,
150th Anniv.
A167

Designs: 75c, Port of Spain Public Library, Carnegie Free Library. $3.25, New National Library building.

2001, Aug. 9		**Perf. 14¼x14½**		
624-625	A167	Set of 2	1.40	1.40
625a		Souvenir sheet, #624-625	1.40	1.40

Under 17 World Soccer
Championships — A168

Designs: $2, Emblem of Soca Warriors. $3.25, National flag. $4.50, Lion holding flag. $5.25, Stadiums.

2001, Sept. 6		**Perf. 14½x14**		
626-629	A168	Set of 4	5.00	5.00
629a		Souvenir sheet, #626-629	5.00	5.00

Flowers — A169

Designs: $1, Pachystachys coccinea. $2.50, Heliconia psittacorum. $3.25, Brownea latifolia, horiz. $3.75, Oncidium papilio.

2001		**Perf. 14½x14¼, 14¼x14½**		
630-633	A169	Set of 4	3.50	3.50

Christmas — A170

Designs: People and: $1, Boats, church. $3.75, Flowers. $4.50, House, flowers. $5.25, Church, post office.

2001		**Perf. 14½x14¼**		
634-637	A170	Set of 4	4.75	4.75
637a		Souvenir sheet, #634-637	4.75	4.75

Butterflies
A171

Designs: $1, Cracker. $3.75, Tiger . $4.50, Four continent. $5.25, "89."

2002, June 19	**Litho.**	**Perf. 13¼x13**		
638-641	A171	Set of 4	4.75	4.75

Hummingbirds
A172

Designs: $1, Rufous-breasted hermit. $2.50, Black-throated mango. $3.25, Tufted coquette. $3.75, White-chested emerald.

2002 ?		**Perf. 13x13¼**		
642-645	A172	Set of 4	3.50	3.50

Historic
Forts — A173

Designs: $1, Fort Picton. $3.75, Fort George. $4.50, Fort King George. $5.25, Fort James.

2002 ?		**Perf. 13¼x13**		
646-649	A173	Set of 4	4.75	4.75
649a		Souvenir sheet, #646-649	4.75	4.75

Reign of
Queen
Elizabeth II,
50th Anniv.
A174

Queen: $3.75, At Governor General's House. $4.50, With Mayor E. Taylor of Port of Spain. $5.25, At Red House, addressing Parliament, #119, and former personal flag of the Queen.
$10, In limousine, waving to crowd.

2002	**Litho.**	**Perf. 13¾**		
650-652	A174	Set of 3	4.50	4.50
	Souvenir Sheet			
653	A174	$10 multi	3.25	3.25

Independence, 40th Anniv. — A175

2002				
654	A175	$1 multi	.35	.35

Christmas
A176

Designs: $1, Child opening gift of steel drum, vert. $2.50, People, musicians, house. $3.75, Houses. $5.25, Santa Claus on horse-drawn cart, vert.

Perf. 14½x14¼, 14¼x14½				
2002, Nov. 20			**Litho.**	
655-658	A176	Set of 4	4.25	4.25

Pan-American
Health
Organization,
Cent. — A177

Designs: $1, Emblem. $2.50, National headquarters, Port of Spain. $3.25, Steel drum with symbols. $4.50, Joseph L. Pawan (1887-1957), discoverer of vampire bat rabies.

2002, Dec. 2		**Perf. 14½x14¼**		
659-662	A177	Set of 4	3.75	3.75

Cricket
Players — A178

Designs: $1, Ian Raphael Bishop. $2.50, Deryck Lance Murray. $4.50, Augustine Lawrence Logie. $5.25, Ann Browne John.

2003, Feb. 7		**Perf. 13**		
663-666	A178	Set of 4	4.50	4.50

Carnival
A179

Various costumed participants: $1, $2.50, $3.75, vert., $4.50, vert., $5.25, vert.

Perf. 14¼x14½, 14½x14¼				
2003, Feb. 25			**Litho.**	
667-671	A179	Set of 5	5.75	5.75
671a		Souvenir sheet of 1	1.75	1.75

Inauguration of Intl. Criminal
Court — A180

Designs: $1, Trinidad & Tobago Pres. Arthur N. R. Robinson and UN Secretary General Kofi Annan. $2.50, Robinson, Prof. Benjamin Ferencz, Prof. Cherif Bassiouni, Philippe Kirsch, UN Undersecretary for Legal Affairs Hans Corell. $3.75, Robinson and Corell. $4.50, Robinson, Emma Bonino, and Italian Pres. Carlo Ciampi.
$6, Robinson, vert.

Perf. 14¾x14½, 14½x14¾				
2003, Feb. 25				
672-675	A180	Set of 4	4.00	4.00
	Souvenir Sheet			
676	A180	$6 multi	2.00	2.00

Rainforest Flora &
Fauna — A181

No. 677: a, Mountain immortelle. b, Blue-crowned motmot. c, Red howler monkey. d, Butterfly orchid. e, Channel-billed toucan. f, Ocelot. g, Bromeliads. h, Lineated woodpecker. i, Tamandua. j, Emperor butterfly.

Serpentine Die Cut 12½				
2003, Feb. 24			**Litho.**	
	Self-Adhesive			
677		Booklet pane of 10	3.25	
a.-j.	A181	$1 any single	.30	.30

Lighthouses
A182

Designs: $1, Port-of-Spain. $3.75, Chacachacare. $4.50, Port-of-Spain, diff. $5.25, Chacachacare, diff.

2003, May 26		**Perf. 14½x14¼**		
678-681	A182	Set of 4	4.75	4.75
681a		Souvenir sheet, #678-681	4.75	4.75

Scenes of Village
Life — A183

Designs: $1, Dancing the cocoa. $2.50, Dirt oven. $3.75, River washing. $4.50, Box cart racing. $5.25, Pitching marbles.

2003, Oct. 28
682-686 A183 Set of 5   5.50 5.50

Marine Life — A184

Designs: $1, Boulder brain coral. $2.50, Hawksbill turtle. $3.75, Green moray eel. $4.50, Creole wrasse. $5.25, Black-spotted sea goddess.
$10, Queen angelfish.

2003, Oct. 28   *Perf. 14¼x14½*
687-691 A184 Set of 5   5.50 5.50
Souvenir Sheet
692 A184 $10 multi   3.25 3.25

Christmas — A185

Paintings by Jean Michel Cazabon (1813-88): $1, View of Port-of-Spain from Laventille Hill. $2.50, View of Diego Martin from Fort George. $3.75, Corbeaux Town, Trinidad. $4.50, Rain Clouds over Cedros. $5.25, Los Galos, Icacos Bay.
No. 698: a, $5, River at St. Ann's. b, $6.50, House in Trinidad.

2003, Nov. 17   *Perf. 13¾*
693-697 A185 Set of 5   5.50 5.50
Souvenir Sheet
698 A185 Sheet of 2, #a-b   3.75 3.75

World
AIDS
Day
A186

Designs: $1, Unite against AIDS. $2.50, Stigma isolates. $3.75, Care stops AIDS, vert. $4.50, Family protects, vert.
$10, People and AIDS ribbon.

2003, Nov. 21
699-702 A186 Set of 4   4.00 4.00
Souvenir Sheet
703 A186 $10 multi   3.25 3.25

2004
Carnival — A187

Calypso musicians: $1, Aldric Farrel, "The Lord Pretender." $2.50, Roy Lewis, "The Mystic Prowler." $3.75, Lord Kitchener, The Mighty Sparrow and The Roaring Lion. $4.50, McArthur Linda Sandy-Rose, "Calypso Rose." $5.25, Nap Hepburne, Lord Brynner and The Mighty Sparrow.
$10, McArthur Linda Sandy-Rose, diff.

2004, Feb. 18
704-708 A187 Set of 5   5.50 5.50
Souvenir Sheet
709 A187 $10 multi   3.25 3.25

SEMI-POSTAL STAMPS

Emblem of
Red Cross
SP1

Perf. 11, 12
1914, Sept. 18   **Typo.**   **Unwmk.**
B1 SP1 (½p) red (on cover)   210.00

This stamp was allowed to pay ½p postage on one day, Sept. 18, 1914, on circulars distributed by the Red Cross. Value on cover is for proper Red Cross usage. Value unused, $12.50.

No. 2 Overprinted in Red (Cross) and Black (Date):

a   b

1915, Oct. 21   **Wmk. 3**   **Perf. 14**
B2 A1 (a) 1p scarlet   1.50 1.50

1916, Oct. 19
B3 A1 (b) 1p scarlet   .50 *2.00*
  a. Date omitted

POSTAGE DUE STAMPS

D1   D2

1923-45   **Typo.**   **Wmk. 4**   **Perf. 14**
J1	D1	1p black	.75	*1.50*
J2	D1	2p black	1.50	1.50
J3	D1	3p black ('25)	1.50	*2.25*
J4	D1	4p black ('29)	2.75	20.00
J5	D1	5p black ('45)	35.00	92.50
J6	D1	6p black ('45)	55.00	35.00
J7	D1	8p black ('45)	42.50	160.00
J8	D1	1sh black ('45)	72.50	110.00
		Nos. J1-J8 (8)	211.50	422.75

Catalogue values for unused stamps in this section, from this point to the end of the section, are for Never Hinged items.

Denominations in Cents
1947, Sept. 1
J9	D1	2c black	1.40	.75
J10	D1	4c black	.80	1.00
J11	D1	6c black	1.00	2.00
J12	D1	8c black	1.00	6.00
J13	D1	10c black	1.00	.90
J14	D1	12c black	1.00	5.00
J15	D1	16c black	1.90	11.50
J16	D1	24c black	6.75	2.50
		Nos. J9-J16 (8)	14.85	29.65

Nos. J9-J16 also exist on chalky paper.

Wmk. 4a (error)
J9a	D1	2c	50.00
J11a	D1	6c	100.00
J14a	D1	12c	125.00

1970   **Unwmk. Litho.**   *Perf. 14x13½*
Size: 18x23mm
J17	D2	2c green	.20	.55
J18	D2	4c carmine rose	.20	.85
J19	D2	6c brown	.40	1.10
J20	D2	8c lt violet	.50	1.25
J21	D2	10c brick red	.50	1.25
J22	D2	12c dull orange	.65	1.25
J23	D2	16c brt yellow grn	.65	.85
J24	D2	24c gray	.65	.90
J25	D2	50c blue	.65	1.00
J26	D2	60c olive green	.65	1.00
		Nos. J17-J26 (10)	5.05	10.00

Perf. 13½x14
1976-77   **Litho.**   **Unwmk.**
Size: 17x21mm
J27	D2	2c green	.20	.45
J28	D2	4c carmine rose	.25	.45
J29	D2	6c brown	.25	.60
J30	D2	8c lt violet	.30	.60
J31	D2	10c brick red	.30	.60
J32	D2	12c dull orange	.45	.80
		Nos. J27-J32 (6)	1.75	3.50

Issued: 4c, 12c, 4/1/76; 2c, 6c, 8c, 10, 1977.
The letters in the top label on Nos. J27-J32 are larger with D's and O's more squarish than the oval letters on Nos. J17-J26. "Postage Due" is 13mm long and is composed of finer letters than on Nos. J17-J26, which have a 14mm inscription.

WAR TAX STAMPS

Nos. 1-2 Overprinted

1917   **Wmk. 3**   **Perf. 14**
MR1 A1 1p scarlet   2.00 *2.75*
  a. Invtd. overprint   175.00 225.00

Overprinted

MR2 A1 ½p green   .20 .20
  a. Overprinted on face and back   400.00
  b. Pair, one without overprint   250.00
MR3 A1 1p scarlet   .60 *1.75*
  a. Pair, one without overprint   400.00 750.00
  b. Double overprint   110.00

Overprinted

MR4 A1 ½p green   .20 *5.00*
MR5 A1 1p scarlet   .20 .75

Overprinted

MR6 A1 ½p green   .20 *2.50*
MR7 A1 1p scarlet   2.75 1.00

Overprinted

MR8 A1 ½p green   .20 *2.50*
MR9 A1 1p scarlet   27.50 22.50

Overprinted

MR10 A1 1p scarlet   .60 *1.00*
  a. Inverted overprint   92.50 92.50

Overprinted

MR11 A1 1p scarlet   1.25 .20
  a. Double overprint   175.00 175.00
  b. Inverted overprint   100.00 100.00

Overprinted

1918
MR12 A1 ½p green   .20 1.60
MR13 A1 1p scarlet   .75 1.25
  a. Double overprint   110.00

The War Tax Stamps show considerable variations in the colors, thickness of the paper, distinctness of the watermark, and the gum. Counterfeits exist of the errors of Nos. MR1-MR13.

OFFICIAL STAMPS

Regular Issue of 1913
Overprinted

1913   **Wmk. 3**   *Perf. 14*
O1 A1 ½p green   .80 5.50

Same Overprinted

1914
O2 A1 ½p green   1.50 10.00

Same Overprinted

1916
O3 A1 ½p green   1.00 2.50
  a. Double overprint   22.50

Same Overprint without Period
1917
O4 A1 ½p green   .50 5.50

Same Overprinted

1917, Aug. 22
O5 A1 ½p green   1.00 14.00

The official stamps are found in several shades of green and on paper of varying thickness.

TRIPOLITANIA

tri-pä-lə-'tā-nyə

LOCATION — In northern Africa, bordering on Mediterranean Sea
GOVT. — A former Italian Colony
AREA — 350,000 sq. mi. (approx.)
POP. — 570,716 (1921)
CAPITAL — Tripoli

Formerly a Turkish province, Tripolitania became part of Italian Libya. See Libya.

100 Centesimi = 1 Lira

Used values in italics are for postaly used stamps. CTO's or stamps with fake cancels sell for about the same as unused, hinged stamps.

Watermark

Wmk. 140 — Crowns

Propaganda of the Faith Issue

Italian Stamps Overprinted

1923, Oct. 24   Wmk. 140   Perf. 14

1	A68	20c ol grn & brn org	5.50	24.00
2	A68	30c claret & brn org	5.50	24.00
3	A68	50c vio & brn org	3.75	24.00
4	A68	1 l blue & brn org	3.75	32.50
		Nos. 1-4 (4)	18.50	104.50
		Set, never hinged	36.00	

Fascisti Issue

Italian Stamps Overprinted in Red or Black

1923, Oct. 29   Unwmk.

5	A69	10c dk green (R)	5.50	9.50
6	A69	30c dk violet (R)	5.50	9.50
7	A69	50c brown car	5.50	10.50

Wmk. 140

8	A70	1 l blue	5.50	25.00
9	A70	2 l brown	5.50	27.50
10	A71	5 l blk & bl (R)	5.50	40.00
		Nos. 5-10 (6)	33.00	122.00
		Set, never hinged	62.50	

Manzoni Issue

Stamps of Italy, 1923, Overprinted in Red

1924, Apr. 1   Wmk. 140   Perf. 14

11	A72	10c brown red & blk	6.25	29.00
12	A72	15c blue grn & blk	6.25	29.00
13	A72	30c black & slate	6.25	29.00

14	A72	50c org brn & blk	6.25	29.00
15	A72	1 l blue & blk	60.00	190.00
16	A72	5 l violet & blk	600.00	1,400.
		Nos. 11-16 (6)	685.00	1,706.
		Set, never hinged		1,700.

On Nos. 15 and 16 the overprint is placed vertically at the left side.

Victor Emmanuel Issue

Italy Nos. 175-177 Overprinted

1925-26   Unwmk.   Perf. 11

17	A78	60c brown car	.80	5.25
18	A78	1 l dark blue	1.25	5.25
a.		Perf. 13½	4.00	19.00

Perf. 13½

19	A78	1.25 l dk blue ('26)	2.10	17.50
a.		Perf. 11	750.00	850.00
		Nos. 17-19 (3)	4.15	28.00
		Set, #17-19, 18a, 19a, never hinged	1,150.	

Saint Francis of Assisi Issue

Italy Nos. 178-180 Overprinted

1926, Apr. 12   Wmk. 140   Perf. 14

20	A79	20c gray green	1.90	8.50
21	A80	40c dark violet	1.90	8.50
22	A81	60c red brown	1.90	14.50

Italy No. 182 and Type of A83 Overprinted in Red

Unwmk.

23	A82	1.25 l dark blue	1.90	20.00
24	A83	5 l + 2.50 l ol grn	4.00	40.00
a.		Double overprint		
		Nos. 20-24 (5)	11.60	91.50
		Set, never hinged	25.00	

Volta Issue

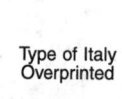

Type of Italy Overprinted

1927, Oct. 10   Wmk. 140   Perf. 14

25	A84	20c purple	5.25	22.50
26	A84	50c deep orange	8.50	15.00
a.		Double overprint	165.00	
27	A84	1.25 l brt blue	11.50	30.00
		Nos. 25-27 (3)	25.25	67.50
		Set, never hinged	52.50	

Monte Cassino Issue

Types of Italy Overprinted in Red or Blue

1929, Oct. 14

28	A96	20c dk green (R)	5.25	10.50
29	A96	25c red org (Bl)	5.25	10.50
30	A98	50c + 10c crim (Bl)	5.25	12.50
31	A98	75c + 15c ol brn (R)	5.25	12.50

| 32 | A96 | 1.25 l + 25c dk vio (R) | 10.00 | 21.00 |
| 33 | A98 | 5 l + 1 l saph (R) | 10.00 | 25.00 |

Victor Emmanuel Issue

Overprinted in Red

Unwmk.

34	A100	10 l + 2 l gray brn	10.00	32.50
		Nos. 28-34 (7)	51.00	124.50
		Set, never hinged	100.00	

Royal Wedding Issue

Type of Italy Overprinted

1930, Mar. 17   Wmk. 140

35	A101	20c yellow green	1.25	3.75
36	A101	50c + 10c dp org	.85	5.25
37	A101	1.25 l + 25c rose red	.85	12.00
		Nos. 35-37 (3)	2.95	21.00
		Set, never hinged	6.00	

Ferrucci Issue

Types of Italy Overprinted in Red or Blue

1930, July 26

38	A102	20c violet (R)	1.60	2.10
39	A103	25c dk green (R)	1.60	2.10
40	A103	50c black (R)	1.60	4.00
41	A103	1.25 l deep blue (R)	1.60	7.00
42	A104	5 l + 2 l dp car (Bl)	4.00	16.00
		Nos. 38-42,C1-C3 (8)	23.70	63.95
		Set, never hinged	45.00	

Virgil Issue

Types of Italy Overprinted in Red or Blue

1930, Dec. 4   Photo.

43	A106	15c violet black	.85	4.50
44	A106	20c orange brown	.85	2.40
45	A106	25c dark green	.85	1.90
46	A106	30c lt brown	.85	2.40
47	A106	50c dull violet	.85	1.90
48	A106	75c rose red	.85	3.25
49	A106	1.25 l gray blue	.85	4.50

Unwmk.   Engr.

50	A106	5 l + 1.50 l dk vio	3.50	25.00
51	A106	10 l + 2.50 l ol brn	3.50	40.00
		Nos. 43-51,C4-C7 (13)	25.15	156.35
		Set, never hinged	52.50	

Saint Anthony of Padua Issue

Types of Italy Overprinted in Blue or Red

1931, May 7   Photo.   Wmk. 140

52	A116	20c brown (Bl)	1.40	8.50
53	A116	25c green (R)	1.40	4.00
54	A118	30c gray brn (Bl)	1.40	4.00
55	A118	50c dull vio (Bl)	1.40	4.00
56	A120	1.25 l slate bl (R)	1.40	19.00

Overprinted in Red or Black

Unwmk.   Engr.

57	A121	75c black (R)	1.40	8.50
58	A122	5 l + 2.50 l dk brn (Bk)	4.00	45.00
		Nos. 52-58 (7)	12.40	93.00
		Set, never hinged	25.00	

Native Village Scene A14

1934, Oct. 16   Wmk. 140

73	A14	5c ol grn & brn	3.50	10.00
74	A14	10c brown & black	3.50	10.00
75	A14	20c scar & indigo	3.50	8.25
76	A14	50c purple & brown	3.50	8.25
77	A14	60c org brn & ind	3.50	11.00
78	A14	1.25 l dk bl & grn	3.50	19.00
		Nos. 73-78,C43-C48 (12)	40.50	133.00
		Set, never hinged	75.00	

2nd Colonial Arts Exhibition, Naples.

SEMI-POSTAL STAMPS

Many issues of Italy and Italian Colonies include one or more semipostal denominations. To avoid splitting sets, these issues are generally listed as regular postage, airmail, etc., unless all values carry a surtax.

Holy Year Issue

Italian Stamps of 1924 Overprinted in Black or Red

1925   Wmk. 140   Perf. 12

B1	SP4	20c + 10c dk grn & brn	3.00	12.50
B2	SP4	30c + 15c dk brn & brn	3.00	16.00
B3	SP4	50c + 25c vio & brn	3.00	12.50
B4	SP4	60c + 30c dp rose & brn	3.00	18.00
B5	SP8	1 l + 50c dp bl & vio (R)	3.00	22.50
B6	SP8	5 l + 2.50 l org brn & vio (R)	3.00	32.50
		Nos. B1-B6 (6)	18.00	114.00
		Set, never hinged	35.00	

Colonial Institute Issue

Peace Substituting Spade for Sword — SP1

1926, June 1   Typo.   Perf. 14

B7	SP1	5c + 5c brown	.60	4.50
B8	SP1	10c + 5c brown	.60	4.50
B9	SP1	20c + 5c bl grn	.60	4.50
B10	SP1	40c + 5c brn red	.60	4.50

B11	SP1	60c + 5c orange	.60	4.50
B12	SP1	1 l + 5c blue	.60	7.00
		Nos. B7-B12 (6)	3.60	29.50
		Set, never hinged	7.50	

The surtax was for the Italian Colonial Institute.

Fiera Campionaria Tripoli

See Libya for stamps with this inscription.

Types of Italian Semi-Postal Stamps of 1926 Overprinted like Nos. 17-19

1927, Apr. 21   Unwmk.   *Perf. 11*

B19	SP10	40c + 20c dk brn & blk	2.10	16.00
B20	SP10	60c + 30c brn red & ol brn	2.10	16.00
B21	SP10	1.25 l + 60c dp bl & blk	2.10	32.50
B22	SP10	5 l + 2.50 l dk grn & blk	3.25	45.00
		Nos. B19-B22 (4)	9.55	109.50
		Set, never hinged	19.00	

The surtax was for the charitable work of the Voluntary Militia for Italian National Defense.

Allegory of Fascism and Victory — SP2

1928, Oct. 15   Wmk. 140

B29	SP2	20c + 5c bl grn	1.90	6.50
B30	SP2	30c + 5c red	1.90	6.50
B31	SP2	50c + 10c pur	1.90	9.50
B32	SP2	1.25 l + 20c dk bl	1.90	11.50
		Nos. B29-B32 (4)	7.60	34.00
		Set, never hinged	15.00	

46th anniv. of the Società Africana d'Italia. The surtax aided that society.

Types of Italian Semi-Postal Stamps of 1928 Overprinted

1929, Mar. 4   Unwmk.   *Perf. 11*

B33	SP10	30c + 10c red & blk	3.50	14.00
B34	SP10	50c + 20c vio & blk	3.50	16.00
B35	SP10	1.25 l + 50c brn & blk	3.50	22.50
B36	SP10	5 l + 2 l ol grn & blk	3.50	42.50
		Nos. B33-B36 (4)	14.00	95.00
		Set, never hinged	30.00	

The surtax on these stamps was for the charitable work of the Voluntary Militia for Italian National Defense.

Types of Italian Semi-Postal Stamps of 1926, Overprinted in Black or Red Like Nos. B33-B36

1930, Oct. 20

B50	SP10	30c + 10c dp grn & bl (Bk)	15.00	21.00
B51	SP10	50c + 10c dk grn & vio (R)	15.00	25.00
B52	SP10	1.25 l + 30c blk brn & red (R)	15.00	40.00
B53	SP10	5 l + 1.50 l ind & grn (R)	52.50	85.00
		Nos. B50-B53 (4)	97.50	171.00
		Set, never hinged	190.00	

Ancient Arch — SP3

1930, Nov. 27   Photo.   Wmk. 140

B54	SP3	50c + 20c ol brn	2.50	11.50
B55	SP3	1.25 l + 20c dp bl	2.50	11.50
B56	SP3	1.75 l + 20c green	2.50	14.50
B57	SP3	2.55 l + 50c purple	3.75	22.50
B58	SP3	5 l + 1 l deep car	3.75	32.50
		Nos. B54-B58 (5)	15.00	92.50
		Set, never hinged	30.00	

25th anniv. of the Italian Colonial Agricultural Institute. The surtax was for the benefit of that institution.

AIR POST STAMPS

Ferrucci Issue
Type of Italian Air Post Stamps Overprinted in Blue or Red like #38-42

1930, July 26   Wmk. 140   *Perf. 14*

C1	AP7	50c brown vio (Bl)	2.40	3.50
C2	AP7	1 l dk blue (R)	2.40	6.75
C3	AP7	5 l + 2 l dp car (Bl)	8.50	22.50
		Nos. C1-C3 (3)	13.30	32.75
		Set, never hinged	27.50	

Virgil Issue
Types of Italian Air Post Stamps Overprinted in Red or Blue like #43-51

1930, Dec. 4   Photo.

C4	AP8	50c deep green	2.10	5.25
C5	AP8	1 l rose red	2.10	5.25

Unwmk.   Engr.

C6	AP8	7.70 l + 1.30 l dk brn	4.00	30.00
C7	AP8	9 l + 2 l gray	4.00	30.00
		Nos. C4-C7 (4)	12.20	70.50
		Set, never hinged	25.00	

Airplane over Columns of the Basilica, Leptis — AP1

Arab Horseman Pointing at Airplane AP2

1931-32   Photo.   Wmk. 140

C8	AP1	50c rose car	.60	.20
C9	AP1	60c red org	2.40	7.00
C10	AP1	75c dp bl ('32)	2.40	6.00
C11	AP1	80c dull violet	6.50	11.50
C12	AP2	1 l deep blue	1.00	.20
C13	AP2	1.20 l dk brown	19.00	12.50
C14	AP2	1.50 l org red	6.50	12.50
C15	AP2	5 l green	21.00	19.00
		Nos. C8-C15 (8)	59.40	68.90
		Set, never hinged	125.00	

For surcharges and overprint see Nos. C29-C32.

Airplane over Ruins AP3

1931, Dec. 7

C16	AP3	50c dp blue	3.00	11.50
C17	AP3	80c violet	3.00	11.50
C18	AP3	1 l gray black	3.00	17.50

C19	AP3	2 l deep green	4.50	22.50
C20	AP3	5 l + 2 l rose red	5.50	42.50
		Nos. C16-C20 (5)	19.00	105.50
		Set, never hinged	40.00	

Graf Zeppelin Issue

Mercury, by Giovanni da Bologna, and Zeppelin AP4

Designs: 3 l, 12 l, Mercury. 10 l, 20 l, Guido Reni's "Aurora." 5 l, 15 l, Arch of Marcus Aurelius.

1933, May 5

C21	AP4	3 l dark brown	7.00	70.00
C22	AP4	5 l purple	7.00	70.00
C23	AP4	10 l deep green	7.00	125.00
C24	AP4	12 l deep blue	7.00	150.00
C25	AP4	15 l carmine	7.00	150.00
C26	AP4	20 l gray black	7.00	160.00
		Nos. C21-C26 (6)	42.00	725.00
		Set, never hinged	85.00	

For overprints and surcharges see Nos. C38-C42.

North Atlantic Flight Issue

Airplane, Lion of St. Mark AP7

1933, June 1

C27	AP7	19.75 l blk & ol brn	15.00	350.00
C28	AP7	44.75 l dk bl & lt grn	15.00	350.00
		Set, never hinged	60.00	

Type of 1931 Overprinted or Surcharged

1934, Jan. 20

C29	AP2	2 l on 5 l org brn	2.50	32.50
C30	AP2	3 l on 5 l grn	2.250	32.50
C31	AP2	5 l ocher	2.50	35.00
C32	AP2	10 l on 5 l rose	3.00	35.00
		Nos. C29-C32 (4)	12.50	135.00
		Set, never hinged	21.00	

For use on mail to be carried on a special flight from Rome to Buenos Aires.

Types of Libya Airmail Issue Overprinted in Black or Red

CIRCUITO DELLE OASI
TRIPOLI
MAGGIO 1934-XII

1934, May 1   Wmk. 140

C38	AP4	50c rose red	10.50	62.50
C39	AP4	75c lemon	10.50	62.50
C40	AP4	5 l + 1 l brn	10.50	62.50
C41	AP4	10 l + 2 l dk bl	210.00	350.00
C42	AP5	25 l + 3 l pur	210.00	350.00
		Nos. C38-C42,CE1-CE2 (7)	472.50	1,012.
		Set, never hinged	925.00	

"Circuit of the Oases."

Plane Shadow on Desert AP11

Designs: 25c, 50c, 75c, Plane shadow on desert. 80c, 1 l, 2 l, Camel corps.

1934, Oct. 16   Photo.

C43	AP11	25c sl bl & org red	3.25	10.00
C44	AP11	50c dk grn & ind	3.25	8.25
C45	AP11	75c dk brn & org red	3.25	8.25
C46	AP11	80c org brn & ol grn	3.25	10.00
C47	AP11	1 l scar & ol grn	3.25	11.00
C48	AP11	2 l dk bl & brn	3.25	19.00
		Nos. C43-C48 (6)	19.50	66.50
		Set, never hinged	37.50	

Second Colonial Arts Exhibition, Naples.

AIR POST SEMI-POSTAL STAMPS

King Victor Emmanuel III SPAP1

1934, Nov. 5   Wmk. 140   *Perf. 14*

CB1	SPAP1	25c + 10c gray grn	3.75	5.50
CB2	SPAP1	50c + 10c brn	3.75	5.50
CB3	SPAP1	75c + 15c rose red	3.75	5.50
CB4	SPAP1	80c + 15c blk brn	3.75	5.50
CB5	SPAP1	1 l + 20c red brn	3.75	5.50
CB6	SPAP1	2 l + 20c brt bl	3.75	5.50
CB7	SPAP1	3 l + 25c pur	17.50	45.00
CB8	SPAP1	5 l + 25c org	17.50	45.00
CB9	SPAP1	10 l + 30c rose vio	17.50	45.00
CB10	SPAP1	25 l + 2 l grn	17.50	45.00
		Nos. CB1-CB10 (10)	92.50	213.00
		Set, never hinged	190.00	

65th birthday of King Victor Emmanuel III; non-stop flight from Rome to Mogadiscio. For overprint see No. CBO1.

AIR POST SEMI-POSTAL OFFICIAL STAMP

Type of Air Post Semi-Postal Stamps Overprinted Crown and "SERVIZIO DI STATO" in Black

1934   Wmk. 140   *Perf. 14*

CBO1	SPAP1	25 l + 2 l cop red	2,100.	2,500.
		Never hinged	2,500.	

AIR POST SPECIAL DELIVERY STAMPS

Type of Libya Overprinted in Black Like Nos. C38-c42

1934, May 1   Wmk. 140   *Perf. 14*

CE1	APSD1	2.25 l red orange	10.50	62.50
CE2	APSD1	4.50 l + 1 l dp rose	10.50	62.50
		Set, never hinged	45.00	

AUTHORIZED DELIVERY STAMP

Authorized Delivery Stamp of Italy 1930, Overprinted like Nos. 38-42

1931, Mar.   Wmk. 140   *Perf. 14*

EY1	AD2	10c dark brown	12.00	12.00
		Never hinged	24.00	

TRISTAN DA CUNHA

ˌtris-tən-də-'kü-nə

LOCATION — Group of islands in the south Atlantic Ocean midway between the Cape of Good Hope and South America
GOVT. — A dependency of St. Helena
AREA — 40 sq. mi.
POP. — 313 (1988)

12 Pence = 1 Shilling
100 Cents = 1 Rand (1961)
12 Pence = 1 Shilling (1963)
20 Shillings = 1 Pound
100 Pence = 1 Pound (1971)

> Catalogue values for all unused stamps in this country are for Never Hinged items.

Stamps of St. Helena, 1938-49, Overprinted in Black

1952, Jan. 1   Wmk. 4   Perf. 12½
1	A24	½p purple	.20	2.00
2	A24	1p blue grn & blk	.80	1.75
3	A24	1½p car rose & blk	.80	1.75
4	A24	2p carmine & blk	.80	1.75
5	A24	3p gray	1.10	1.75
6	A24	4p ultra	4.25	2.75
7	A24	6p gray blue	5.00	2.75
8	A24	8p olive	4.50	6.25
9	A24	1sh sepia	5.00	2.25
10	A24	2sh6p deep claret	22.50	15.00
11	A24	5sh brown	24.00	22.50
12	A24	10sh violet	45.00	35.00
		Nos. 1-12 (12)	113.95	95.50
		Set, hinged	65.00	

Common Design Types pictured following the introduction.

Coronation Issue
Common Design Type
1953, June 2   Engr.   Perf. 13½x13
13	CD312	3p dk green & black	.75	1.25

Tristan Crayfish — A1

Carting Flax — A2

Designs: 1½p, Rockhopper penguin. 2p, Factory. 2½p, Mollymauk. 3p, Island boat. 4p, View of Tristan. 5p, Potato patches. 6p, Inaccessible Island. 9p, Nightingale Island. 1sh, St. Mary's Church. 2sh 6p, Elephant seal. 5sh, Flightless rail. 10sh, Island spinning wheel.

1954-58   Perf. 12½
14	A1	½p choc & red	.20	.20
a.	Bklt. pane of 4 ('58)		2.50	
15	A2	1p green & choc	.20	.55
a.	Bklt. pane of 4 ('58)		4.00	
16	A1	1½p dp plum & blk	1.75	1.25
a.	Bklt. pane of 4 ('58)		6.00	
17	A2	2p org & vio blue	.30	.20
18	A2	2½p carmine & blk	1.50	.65
19	A1	3p ol grn & ultra	.70	1.25
a.	Bklt. pane of 4 ('58)		9.00	
20	A2	4p dp bl & aqua	.70	.70
a.	Bklt. pane of 4 ('58)		11.00	
21	A2	5p gray & bl grn	.70	.70
22	A2	6p vio & dk ol grn	.70	.70
23	A2	9p henna brn & rose lil	.70	.50
24	A2	1sh choc & ol grn	.70	.50
25	A2	2sh6p blue & choc	21.00	10.50

26	A2	5sh red org & blk	47.50	14.00
27	A2	10sh red vio & org	22.50	16.00
		Nos. 14-27 (14)	99.15	47.70
		Set, hinged	60.00	

Starfish — A3

Fish: 1p, Concha. 1½p, Klipfish. 2p, Heron fish (saury). 2½p, Snipefish ("swordfish"). 3d, Tristan crawfish. 4p, Soldier fish. 5p, Five finger fish. 6p, Mackeral scad. 9p, Stumpnose. 1sh, Bluefish. 2sh6p, Snoek (snake mackerel). 5sh, Shark. 10sh, Atlantic right whale.

Perf. 12½x13
1960, Feb. 1   Engr.   Wmk. 314
28	A3	½p orange & black	.20	.20
a.	Booklet pane of 4		1.50	
29	A3	1p rose lilac & blk	.25	.20
a.	Booklet pane of 4		2.50	
30	A3	1½p grnsh bl & blk	.35	.25
a.	Booklet pane of 4		2.75	
31	A3	2p green & black	.45	.30
32	A3	2½p brown & black	.50	.30
33	A3	3p rose red & blk	.55	.35
a.	Booklet pane of 4		3.75	
34	A3	4p gray ol & blk	.65	.45
a.	Booklet pane of 4		4.00	
35	A3	5p org yel & blk	.80	.55
36	A3	6p blue & black	.90	.65
37	A3	9p rose car & blk	1.60	.90
38	A3	1sh brn org & blk	2.00	1.10
39	A3	2sh6p vio blue & blk	9.00	10.00
40	A3	5sh emerald & blk	15.00	12.50
41	A3	10sh violet & blk	37.50	30.00
		Nos. 28-41 (14)	69.75	57.75

1961, Apr. 15   Perf. 12½x13
42	A3	½c like No. 28	.20	.20
43	A3	1c like No. 29	.20	.20
44	A3	1½c like No. 30	.20	.20
45	A3	2c like No. 32	.25	.20
46	A3	2½c like No. 33	.30	.20
47	A3	3c like No. 34	.40	.30
48	A3	4c like No. 35	.50	.35
49	A3	5c like No. 36	.70	.50
50	A3	7½c like No. 37	1.00	.80
51	A3	10c like No. 38	1.60	1.25
52	A3	25c like No. 39	7.00	7.50
53	A3	50c like No. 40	16.00	17.50
54	A3	1r like No. 41	42.50	30.00
		Nos. 42-54 (13)	70.85	59.20

Nos. 46, 49-51 surcharged for "Tristan Relief" are listed as St. Helena Nos. B1-B4.

Types of St. Helena, 1961 Overprinted

Perf. 11½x12, 12x11½
1963, Apr. 12   Photo.   Wmk. 4
55	A29	1p rose, ultra, yel & grn	.20	.85
56	A29	1½p bis, sep, yel & grn	.20	.40
57	A29	2p gray & red	.20	.85
58	A30	3p dk bl, rose & grnsh bl	.25	.70
a.	Double overprint			
59	A29	4½p slate, brn & grn	.45	.70
60	A29	6p cit, brn & dp car	.75	.40
61	A29	7p vio, blk & red brn	.45	.40
62	A29	10p bl & dp claret	.45	.40
63	A29	1sh red brn, grn & yel	.45	.40
64	A29	1sh6p gray bl & blk	3.00	.85
65	A29	2sh6p grnsh bl, yel & red	.85	.75
66	A29	5sh grn, brn & yel	5.25	1.75
67	A29	10sh gray bl, blk & sal	5.75	1.75
		Nos. 42-67 (13)	18.25	10.20

Freedom from Hunger Issue
Common Design Type
Perf. 14x14½
1963, Oct. 2   Photo.   Wmk. 314
68	CD314	1sh6p rose carmine	1.00	.40

Red Cross Centenary Issue
Common Design Type
1964, Jan. 2   Litho.   Perf. 13
69	CD315	3p black & red	.75	.40
70	CD315	1sh6p ultra & red	1.25	.60

Flagship of Tristão da Cunha, 1506 — A4

Queen Elizabeth II — A5

½p, Map of South Atlantic Ocean. 1½p, Dutch ship Heemstede, first landing, 1643. 2p, New England whaler. 3p, Confederate ship Shenandoah. 4½p, H.M.S. Galatea, 1867. 6p, H.M.S. Cilicia, 1942. 7p, H.M. Royal Yacht Britannia, 1957. 10p, H.M.S. Leopard, Evacuation, 1961. 1sh, Dutch ship Tjisadane, 1961. 1sh6p, M.V. Tristania. 2sh6p, M.V. Boissevain, returning islanders, 1963. 5sh, M.S. Bornholm, returning islanders, 1963.

Perf. 11x11½
1965, Feb. 17   Engr.   Wmk. 314
71	A4	½p black & dk blue	.20	.20
a.	Booklet pane of 4		.25	
72	A4	1p black & emerald	.20	.20
a.	Booklet pane of 4		.40	
73	A4	1½p black & ultra	.20	.20
a.	Booklet pane of 4		.60	
74	A4	2p black & lilac	.20	.20
75	A4	3p blk & grnsh bl	.25	.20
a.	Booklet pane of 4		1.00	
76	A4	4½p black & brown	.50	.35
77	A4	6p black & green	.40	.30
a.	Booklet pane of 4		1.60	
78	A4	7p black & ver	.55	.40
79	A4	10p black & dk brn	.70	.40
80	A4	1sh black & lil rose	.75	.50
81	A4	1sh6p black & olive	1.50	1.00
82	A4	2sh6p black & brn org	2.75	1.50
83	A4	5sh black & violet	5.25	3.50

Perf. 11½x11
84	A5	10sh lil rose & dk bl	6.75	4.50
		Nos. 71-84 (14)	20.20	13.45

See Nos. 113-115. For surcharges see Nos. 108, 141-152. For overprints see No. 132.

ITU Issue
Common Design Type
1965, May 11   Litho.   Perf. 11x11½
85	CD317	3p vermilion & gray	.55	.25
86	CD317	6p purple & orange	.85	.40

Intl. Cooperation Year Issue
Common Design Type
1965, Oct. 25   Wmk. 314   Perf. 14½
87	CD318	1p blue grn & claret	.20	.30
88	CD318	6p lt violet & green	1.25	.45

Churchill Memorial Issue
Common Design Type
Wmk. 314
1966, Jan. 24   Photo.   Perf. 14
Design in Black, Gold and Carmine Rose
89	CD319	1p bright blue	.20	.20
90	CD319	3p green	.30	.20
91	CD319	6p brown	1.40	.70
92	CD319	1sh6p violet	4.25	1.50
		Nos. 89-92 (4)	6.15	2.60

World Cup Soccer Issue
Common Design Type
1966   Litho.   Perf. 14
93	CD320	3p multicolored	.25	.20
94	CD321	2sh6p multicolored	1.25	.55

Nos. 93-94 were issued Oct. 1 in Tristan da Cunha, but on July 1 in St. Helena.

Light Dragoon of 19th Century and Sailing Ship — A6

Wmk. 314
1966, Aug. 15   Litho.   Perf. 14½
95	A6	3p pale green & multi	.20	.2_
96	A6	6p tan & multi	.20	.2_
97	A6	1sh6p gray & multi	.50	.3_
98	A6	2sh6p multicolored	.85	.4
		Nos. 95-98 (4)	1.75	1.1_

150th anniv. of the establishment of a garrison on Tristan da Cunha.

WHO Headquarters Issue
Common Design Type
1966, Oct. 1   Litho.   Perf. 1_
99	CD322	6p multicolored	.35	.2_
100	CD322	5sh multicolored	1.90	1.0_

UNESCO Anniversary Issue
Common Design Type
1966, Dec. 1   Litho.   Perf. 1_
101	CD323	10p "Education"	.35	.2_
102	CD323	1sh6p "Science"	.75	.4
103	CD323	2sh6p "Culture"	1.40	.7_
		Nos. 101-103 (3)	2.50	1.3_

Calshot Harbor A7

Perf. 14x14½
1967, Jan. 2   Litho.   Unwmk.
104	A7	6p dull green & multi	.20	.2_
105	A7	10p brown & multi	.20	.2_
106	A7	1sh6p dull blue & multi	.20	.2_
107	A7	2sh6p orange brn & multi	.25	.3_
		Nos. 104-107 (4)	.85	.9_

Opening of the artificial Calshot Harbor.

No. 76 Surcharged with New Value and Three Bars
Perf. 11x11½
1967, May 10   Engr.   Wmk. 314
108	A4	4p on 4½p blk & brn	.25	.2_

Tristan da Cunha, Prince Alfred, Queen Elizabeth II and Prince Philip — A8

1967, July 10   Litho.   Perf. 14x14½
109	A8	3p blue grn, dk grn & blk	.20	.20
110	A8	6p dk carmine & blk	.20	.20
111	A8	1sh6p brt grn, gray grn & blk	.20	.20
112	A8	2sh6p dull ultra, sep & blk	.25	.30
		Nos. 109-112 (4)	.85	.90

Cent. of the visit of Prince Alfred, First Duke of Edinburgh, to Tristan da Cunha.

Types of 1965
Designs: 4p, H.M.S. Challenger, 1870. 10sh, South African research vessel, R.S.A. £1, Queen Elizabeth II.

Perf. 11x11½
1967, Sept. 1   Engr.   Wmk. 314
113	A4	4p black & orange	5.25	3.75
114	A4	10sh black & dull grn	16.00	14.00

Perf. 11½x11
115	A5	£1 brn org & dk grn	16.00	17.50
		Nos. 113-115 (3)	37.25	35.25

Wandering Albatross Nest — A9

Birds: 1sh, Big-billed buntings. 1sh6p, Tristan thrushes. 2sh6p, Great shearwaters.

Perf. 14x14½

1968, May 15		**Photo.**	**Wmk. 314**	
116	A9	4p multicolored	.20	.20
117	A9	1sh multicolored	.50	.30
118	A9	1sh6p multicolored	.85	.50
119	A9	2sh6p multicolored	1.25	.85
		Nos. 116-119 (4)	2.80	1.85

Union Jack and St. Helena Flag — A10

Design: 9p, 2sh6p, Map showing locations of St. Helena and Tristan da Cunha.

1968, Nov. 1		**Litho.**	**Wmk. 314**	
120	A10	6p violet & multi	.20	.20
121	A10	9p brn, bl grn & vio bl	.20	.20
122	A10	1sh6p green & multi	.25	.25
123	A10	2sh6p dp car, bl grn & vio bl	.35	.35
		Nos. 120-123 (4)	1.00	1.00

30th anniv. of Tristan da Cunha as a Dependency of St. Helena.

Frigate A11

Designs: 1sh, Cape Horner. 1sh6p, Barque. 2sh6p, Tea Clipper.

Perf. 11x11½

1969, June 1		**Engr.**	**Wmk. 314**	
124	A11	4p brt blue	.20	.20
125	A11	1sh rose carmine	.45	.40
126	A11	1sh6p green	.65	.50
127	A11	2sh6p sepia	1.10	.90
		Nos. 124-127 (4)	2.40	2.00

Islanders Going to First Religious Service, 1851 — A12

Designs: 4p, Tristan da Cunha, birds and ship. 1sh6p, Landing at the beach. 2sh6p, St. Mary's Church, 1969, and procession.

Perf. 14½x14

1969, Nov. 1		**Litho.**	**Wmk. 314**	
128	A12	4p multicolored	.20	.40
129	A12	9p multicolored	.20	.40
130	A12	1sh6p multicolored	.35	.55
131	A12	2sh6p multicolored	.50	.55
		Nos. 128-131 (4)	1.25	1.90

Issued to honor the work of the United Society for the Propagation of the Faith.

No. 77 Overprinted in Deep Orange: "NATIONAL / SAVINGS"

Perf. 11x11½

1970, May 15		**Engr.**	**Wmk. 314**	
132	A4	6p black & green	.30	.25

Issued to promote national savings. No. 132 also used as savings stamp.

In 1971, No. 132 was locally surcharged "2½p" and 3 short bars by means of a rubber handstamp.

Globe and Red Cross A13

1sh9p, 2sh6p, British & Red Cross flags, vert.

Perf. 13½x13, 13x13½

1970, June 1		**Litho.**		
133	A13	4p emer, red & grnsh bl	.30	.20
134	A13	9p bister, red & grnsh bl	.45	.20
135	A13	1sh9p gray, vio bl & red	.75	.35
136	A13	2sh6p rose cl, vio bl & red	1.00	.60
		Nos. 133-136 (4)	2.50	1.35

Centenary of the British Red Cross Society.

Rock Lobster and Lobster Men Placing Trap — A14

10p, 2sh6p, Workers in processing plant and side view of rock lobster (jasus tristani).

Perf. 12½x13

1970, Nov. 1		**Litho.**	**Wmk. 314**	
137	A14	4p lilac rose & multi	.20	.30
138	A14	10p dull yel & multi	.25	.35
139	A14	1sh6p brown org & multi	.75	.60
140	A14	2sh6p olive & multi	1.10	.75
		Nos. 137-140 (4)	2.30	2.00

Tristan da Cunha rock lobster (crawfish) industry.

Nos. 72-74, 77-83, 113-114 Surcharged with New Value and Three Bars

Perf. 11x11½

1971, Feb. 15		**Engr.**	**Wmk. 314**	
141	A4	½p on 1p	.20	.20
142	A4	1p on 2p	.20	.20
143	A4	1½p on 4p	.35	.20
144	A4	2½p on 6p	.35	.20
145	A4	3p on 7p	.35	.20
146	A4	4p on 10p	.35	.20
147	A4	5p on 1sh	.35	.20
148	A4	7½p on 1sh6p	2.10	1.50
149	A4	12½p on 2sh6p	3.00	2.10
150	A4	15p on 1½p	3.00	2.50
151	A4	25p on 5sh	3.00	4.50
152	A4	50p on 10sh	4.25	9.00
		Nos. 141-152 (12)	17.50	21.00

"Quest" — A15

4p, Presentation of Scout Troop flag in front of Tristan school. 7½p, Great Britain #167a with Tristan da Cunha cancellation. 12½p, Sir Ernest Henry Shackleton, boat & expedition cancellations.

Perf. 13½x14

1971, June 1		**Litho.**	**Wmk. 314**	
153	A15	1½p lt blue & multi	1.00	.20
154	A15	4p buff, yel grn & blk	1.00	.40
155	A15	7½p pale grn, rose lil & blk	1.00	.90
156	A15	12½p buff & multi	1.25	1.50
		Nos. 153-156 (4)	4.25	3.00

50th anniversary of the Shackleton-Rowett South Atlantic expedition.

"Victory" at Trafalgar and Thomas Swain Catching Nelson — A16

Ships and Island Families: 2½p, "Emily of Stonington" and inscribed P. W. Green, 1836. 4p, "Italia" and inscribed Gaetano Lavarello, 1892, and Andrea Repetto. 7½p, "Falmouth" and Corp. William Glass, 1816. 12½p, American Whaler and inscribed 1836 Joshua Rogers, 1849, Capt. Andrew Hangan.

1971, Nov. 1				
157	A16	1½p bister & multi	.20	.20
158	A16	2½p multicolored	.25	.25
159	A16	4p gray & multi	.50	.55
160	A16	7½p multicolored	.80	.85
161	A16	12½p blue & multi	1.25	1.40
		Nos. 157-161 (5)	3.00	3.25

Cow Pudding — A17

Coxswain — A18

Native Flora: 1p, Peak berry and crater lake. 1½p, Sand flower, horiz. 2½p, New Zealand flax, horiz. 3p, Island tree. 4p, Bog fern and snow-capped mountain. 5p, Dog catcher and albatrosses. 7½p, Celery and terns. 12½p, Pepper tree and waterfall. 25p, Foul berry, horiz. 50p, Tussock and penguins. £1, Tussac and islands, horiz.

Perf. 13½x13, 13x13½

1972, Feb. 26			**Wmk. 314**	
162	A17	½p gray & multi	.20	.20
163	A17	1p salmon & multi	.20	.20
164	A17	1½p green & multi	.25	.25
165	A17	2½p multicolored	.25	.25
166	A17	3p multicolored	.25	.25
167	A17	4p lemon & multi	.30	.30
168	A17	5p yel grn & multi	.40	.30
169	A17	7½p dull yel & multi	1.25	1.25
170	A17	12½p multicolored	.85	.75
171	A17	25p gray & multi	1.75	1.75

Litho. and Engr.

172	A17	50p multicolored	4.25	3.25
173	A17	£1 lt blue & multi	7.50	3.25
		Nos. 162-173 (12)	17.45	12.00

1972, June 1		**Litho.**	**Perf. 14**	

2½p, Launching longboat. 4p, Men rowing longboat. 12½p, Longboat under sail.

174	A18	2½p multi, horiz.	.20	.20
175	A18	4p multi, horiz.	.20	.20
176	A18	7½p multi	.45	.30
177	A18	12½p multi	.75	.40
		Nos. 174-177 (4)	1.60	1.10

Silver Wedding Issue, 1972
Common Design Type

Design: Queen Elizabeth II, Prince Philip, thrush and wandering albatrosses.

Perf. 14x14½

1972, Nov. 20		**Photo.**	**Wmk. 314**	
178	CD324	2½p multicolored	.20	.20
179	CD324	7½p ultra & multi	.50	.45

Altar, St. Mary's Church — A19

1973, July 8		**Litho.**	**Perf. 13½**	
180	A19	25p dk blue & multi	1.40	1.40

St. Mary's Church, Tristan da Cunha, 50th anniv.

"Challenger" off Tristan, Steil's Sounding Instrument — A20

Designs: 4p, Challenger's laboratory. 7½p, Challenger off Nightingale Island. 12½p, Map of Challenger's voyage. Each stamp shows an instrument for deep sea soundings.

Perf. 13½x14

1973, Oct. 15			**Wmk. 314**	
181	A20	4p multicolored	.20	.20
182	A20	5p multicolored	.30	.30
183	A20	7½p multicolored	.50	.50
184	A20	12½p multicolored	1.00	1.00
a.		Souv. sheet, #181-184, perf. 13½	2.25	2.25
		Nos. 181-184 (4)	2.00	2.00

Centenary of "Challenger's" visit to Tristan da Cunha during oceanographic exploration world trip, 1872-76.

View of English Port from Shipboard — A21

5p, Inspectors at volcano rim. 7½p, Islanders disembarking from "Bornholm." 12½p, Islanders on board ship approaching Tristan da Cunha.

1973, Nov. 10			**Perf. 14½**	
185	A21	4p yellow, blk & gold	.20	.20
186	A21	5p multicolored	.25	.20
187	A21	7½p multicolored	.40	.30
188	A21	12½p multicolored	.55	.40
		Nos. 185-188 (4)	1.40	1.10

10th anniversary of return of islanders to Tristan da Cunha.

Princess Anne's Wedding Issue
Common Design Type

1973, Nov. 14		**Wmk. 314**	**Perf. 14**	
189	CD325	7½p multicolored	.20	.20
190	CD325	12½p bl grn & multi	.25	.20

Rockhopper Penguin — A22

Designs: Rockhopper penguins.

1974, May 1			**Litho.**	
191	A22	2½p shown	2.50	1.25
192	A22	5p Colony	2.75	1.65
193	A22	7½p Penguins fishing	3.25	2.00
194	A22	25p Penguin and fledgling	7.50	5.00
		Nos. 191-194 (4)	16.00	9.90

Souvenir Sheet

Map of Tristan da Cunha, Penguin and
Sea Gull — A23

1974, Oct. 1   **Wmk. 314**   *Perf. 13½*
195   A23   35p multicolored   3.75   3.25

Blenheim
Palace
A24

25p, Churchill and Queen Elizabeth II.

Wmk. 373
1974, Nov. 30   **Litho.**   *Perf. 14*
196   A24   7½p black & yellow   .20   .20
197   A24   25p black & brown   .50   .40
   a.   Souvenir sheet of 2, #196-197   1.10   1.10

Sir Winston Churchill (1874-1965).

Plocamium Fuscorubrum — A25

Aquatic Plants: 5p, Ulva lactuca. 10p,
Epymenia flabellata. 20p, Macrocystis pyrifera.

    Perf. 13x14
1975, Apr. 16   **Wmk. 314**
198   A25   4p lilac & multi   .20   .20
199   A25   5p ultra & multi   .20   .20
200   A25   10p yellow & multi   .40   .30
201   A25   20p lt green & multi   .75   .65
    Nos. 198-201 (4)   1.55   1.35

Killer Whales — A26

Wmk. 314
1975, Nov. 1   **Litho.**   *Perf. 13½*
202   A26   2p shown   .30   .20
203   A26   3p Rough-toothed dol-
          phins   .45   .20
204   A26   5p Atlantic right whale   1.25   .60
205   A26   20p Finback whales   3.00   1.40
    Nos. 202-205 (4)   5.00   2.40

Tristan
da
Cunha
No. 1
A27

Designs: 9p, Tristan da Cunha #13, vert.
25p, Freighter Tristania II.

    Perf. 13½x14, 14x13½
1976, May 6   **Wmk. 373**
206   A27   5p lilac, vio & blk   .20   .20
207   A27   9p bluish gray, grn &
          blk   .25   .25

---

208   A27   25p multicolored   .85   .85
   a.   Souvenir sheet of 3   2.75   2.75
    Nos. 206-208 (3)   1.30   1.30

Festival of Stamps 1976. #208a contains
one each of Ascension #214, St. Helena #297
and Tristan da Cunha #208.

The
Patches
A28

Views, by Roland Svensson: 3p, Tristan
house, vert. 10p, Tristan Settlement and Cliffs.
20p, Huts at Nightingale, vert.

1976, Oct. 4   **Litho.**   *Perf. 14*
209   A28   3p multicolored   .20   .20
210   A28   5p multicolored   .20   .20
211   A28   10p multicolored   .25   .25
212   A28   20p multicolored   .45   .45
   a.   Souvenir sheet of 4, #209-211   1.25   1.10
    Nos. 209-212 (4)   1.10   1.10

An artist's view of Tristan da Cunha.
See Nos. 234-237, 268-271.

Royal Yacht Britannia — A29

15p, Royal standard. 25p, Royal family.

1977, Feb. 7   **Wmk. 373**   *Perf. 13*
213   A29   10p multicolored   .20   .20
214   A29   15p multicolored   .20   .20
215   A29   25p multicolored   .25   .25
    Nos. 213-215 (3)   .65   .65

25th anniv. of the reign of Elizabeth II.
For surcharges see Nos. 220-221.

H.M.S.
Eskimo,
Sept.
1970
A30

Royal Naval Ships and Arms: 10p, Naiad,
Nov. 1968. 15p, Jaguar, Mar. 1964. 20p,
London, Dec. 1964. Dates of visits to island.

1977, Oct. 1   **Litho.**   *Perf. 14½*
216   A30   5p multicolored   .20   .20
217   A30   10p multicolored   .20   .20
218   A30   15p multicolored   .25   .25
219   A30   20p multicolored   .35   .35
   a.   Souvenir sheet of 4, #216-219   1.25   1.25
    Nos. 216-219 (4)   1.00   1.00

Nos. 214-215 Surcharged with New
Value and Bar

1977, Oct. 13   **Wmk. 373**   *Perf. 13*
220   A29   4p on 15p multi   1.75   4.25
221   A29   7½p on 25p multi   1.75   4.25

Giant Fulmars — A31

    Perf. 13½x14, 14x13½
1977, Dec. 1   **Litho.**
222   A31   1p Pterodroma
          macroptera,
          horiz.   .20   .40
223   A31   2p Fregetta marina,
          horiz.   .20   .65
224   A31   3p Macronectes gi-
          ganteus   .20   .65
225   A31   4p Pterodroma mol-
          lis   .20   .75
226   A31   5p Diomedea exu-
          lans   .20   .75

---

227   A31   10p Pterodroma
          brevirostris   .30   .75
228   A31   15p Sterna vittata   .50   .95
229   A31   20p Puffinus gravis   .65   .95
230   A31   20p Pachyptila vittata   .80   .95
231   A31   50p Catharacta skua   1.75   .95
232   A31   £1 Pelecanoides
          urinatrix   2.50   1.75
233   A31   £2 Diomedea
          chlororynchos   5.50   2.50
    Nos. 222-233 (12)   13.00   12.00

Nos. 224-233 are vertical. For overprints
see Nos. 318-319.

Painting Type of 1976

Views by Roland Svensson: 5p, St. Mary's
Church. 10p, Longboats. 15p, A Tristan home.
20p, Harbor, 1970.

Wmk. 373
1978, Mar. 1   **Litho.**   *Perf. 14½*
234   A28   5p multicolored   .20   .20
235   A28   10p multicolored   .20   .20
236   A28   15p multicolored   .25   .25
237   A28   20p multicolored   .35   .35
   a.   Souvenir sheet of 4, #234-237   1.25   1.25
    Nos. 234-237 (4)   1.00   1.00

An artist's view of Tristan da Cunha.

Elizabeth II Coronation Anniversary
Common Design Types
Souvenir Sheet

1978, Apr. 21   **Unwmk.**   *Perf. 15*
238   Sheet of 6   1.40   1.40
   a.   CD326 25p King's Bull   .25   .25
   b.   CD327 25p Elizabeth II   .25   .25
   c.   CD328 25p Tristan crawfish   .25   .25

No. 238 contains 2 se-tenant strips of Nos.
238a-238c, separated by horizontal gutter with
commemorative and descriptive inscriptions
and showing central part of coronation procession with coach.

Sodalite — A32

Local Minerals: 5p, Aragonite. 10p, Sulphur.
20p, Lava containing pyroxene crystal.

    Perf. 13½x14
1978, June 9   **Litho.**   **Wmk. 373**
239   A32   3p multicolored   .30   .30
240   A32   5p multicolored   .35   .35
241   A32   10p multicolored   .55   .55
242   A32   20p multicolored   .80   .80
    Nos. 239-242 (4)   2.00   2.00

Fish
A33

1978, Sept. 29   **Litho.**   *Perf. 14*
243   A33   5p Klipfish   .20   .20
244   A33   10p Fivefinger   .20   .20
245   A33   15p Concha   .30   .30
246   A33   20p Soldier   .40   .40
    Nos. 243-246 (4)   1.10   1.10

Orangeleaf
and Navy
Flag — A34

Royal Fleet Auxiliary Vessels: 10p, Tarbat-
ness. 20p, Tidereach. 25p, Reliant.

1978, Nov. 24   **Litho.**   *Perf. 12½*
247   A34   5p multicolored   .25   .25
248   A34   10p multicolored   .25   .25
249   A34   20p multicolored   .35   .35
250   A34   25p multicolored   .40   .40
   a.   Souvenir sheet of 4, #247-250   1.50   2.75
    Nos. 247-250 (4)   1.25   1.25

Fur Seals — A35

Wildlife conservation: 5p, Elephant seal.
15p, Tristan thrush. 20p, Tristan buntings.

Wmk. 373
1979, Jan. 3   **Litho.**   *Perf. 14*
251   A35   5p multicolored   .20   .20
252   A35   10p multicolored   .20   .20
253   A35   15p multicolored   .25   .25
254   A35   20p multicolored   .35   .35
    Nos. 251-254 (4)   1.00   1.00

Tristan Longboat — A36

Ships: 10p, Queen Mary. 15p, Queen Elizabeth. 20p, QE II. 25p, QE II, longboat, view of
Tristan.

1979, Feb. 8   *Perf. 14½*
255   A36   5p multicolored   .20   .20
256   A36   10p multicolored   .20   .20
257   A36   15p multicolored   .25   .25
258   A36   20p multicolored   .35   .35
    Nos. 255-258 (4)   1.00   1.00

Souvenir Sheet
259   A36   25p multicolored   1.00   1.50

Visit of cruise ship QE II, Feb. 8.

Tristan
da
Cunha
No. 12
A37

Tristan da Cunha Stamps: 10p, No. 26. 25p,
No. 58, vert. 50p, 1p-local "potatoe" stamp.

    Perf. 14½x14, 14x14½
1979, Aug. 27   **Litho.**   **Wmk. 373**
260   A37   5p multicolored   .20   .20
261   A37   10p multicolored   .20   .20
262   A37   25p multicolored   .35   .35
    Nos. 260-262 (3)   .75   .75

Souvenir Sheet
263   A37   50p multicolored   .75   .75

Sir Rowland Hill (1795-1879), originator of
penny postage.

The
Padre's
House,
IYC
Emblem
A38

IYC Emblem, Children's Drawings: 10p,
"Houses in the Village." 15p, "St. Mary's
Church." 20p, "Rockhopper Penguins."

1979, Nov. 26   **Litho.**   *Perf. 14*
264   A38   5p multicolored   .20   .20
265   A38   10p multicolored   .20   .20
266   A38   15p multicolored   .20   .20
267   A38   20p multicolored   .25   .25
    Nos. 264-267 (4)   .85   .85

International Year of the Child.

Painting Type of 1976

Views (Sketches by Roland Svensson): 10p,
Nightingale from the East. 15p, The Administrator's abode, vert. 20p, "Ridge where the
goat jumped off," vert.

1980, Feb. Litho. Perf. 14
268	A28	5p multicolored	.20	.20
269	A28	10p multicolored	.20	.20
270	A28	15p multicolored	.20	.20
271	A28	20p multicolored	.25	.25
a.		Souvenir sheet of 4, #268-271	.90	.90
		Nos. 268-271 (4)	.85	.85

Mail Pickup Boat — A40

Golden Hinde — A41

1980, May 6 Litho. Perf. 14
272	A40	5p shown	.20	.20
273	A40	10p Unloading mail	.20	.20
274	A40	15p Truck transport	.20	.20
275	A40	20p Delivery bell	.20	.20
276	A40	25p Distribution	.30	.30
		Nos. 272-276 (5)	1.10	1.10

London 80 Intl. Stamp Exhib., May 6-14.

Queen Mother Elizabeth Birthday
Common Design Type
1980, Aug. 11 Litho. Perf. 14
277	CD330	14p multicolored	.30	.30

1980, Sept. 6 Perf. 14½
278	A41	5p shown	.20	.20
279	A41	10p Drake's route	.20	.20
280	A41	20p Sir Francis Drake	.25	.25
281	A41	25p Queen Elizabeth I	.35	.35
		Nos. 278-281 (4)	1.00	1.00

Sir Francis Drake's circumnavigation, 400th anniversary.

Humpty Dumpty A42

Wmk. 373
1980, Oct. 31 Litho. Perf. 13½
282		Sheet of 9	1.75	1.75
a.	A42	15p shown	.20	.20
b.	A42	15p Mary had a Little Lamb	.20	.20
c.	A42	15p Little Jack Horner	.20	.20
d.	A42	15p Hey Diddle Diddle	.20	.20
e.	A42	15p London Bridge	.20	.20
f.	A42	15p Old King Cole	.20	.20
g.	A42	15p Sing a Song of Sixpence	.20	.20
h.	A42	15p Tom Tom the Piper's Son	.20	.20
i.	A42	25p Owl and the Pussy Cat	.20	.20

Christmas 1980.

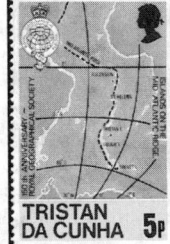

Islands on Mid-Atlantic Ridge, Society Emblem — A43

Royal Geographical Soc., 150th Anniv. (Maps and Expeditions): 10p, Tristan da Cunha, Francis Beaufort, 1806. 15p, Tristan Island, Norwegian expedition, 1937-1938. 20p, Gough Island, scientific survey, 1955-1956.

1980, Dec. 15
283	A43	5p multicolored	.20	.20
284	A43	10p multicolored	.20	.20
285	A43	15p multicolored	.25	.25
286	A43	20p multicolored	.35	.35
		Nos. 283-286 (4)	1.00	1.00

Rev. Edwin Dodgson A44

Wmk. 373
1981, Mar. 23 Litho. Perf. 14
287	A44	10p portrait, vert.	.20	.20
288	A44	20p shown	.35	.35
289	A44	30p Dodgson preaching, vert.	.45	.45
a.		Souvenir sheet of 3, #287-289	1.00	1.00
		Nos. 287-289 (3)	1.00	1.00

Centenary of arrival of Rev. Edwin H. Dodgson, who saved population from starvation.

Map of Tristan da Cunha showing L'heure du Berger Route, 1767 (Dalrymple's Map, 1781) — A45

Early Maps and Charts By: 5p, 21p, Capt. Denham, 1853 (diff.). 35p, Ivan Keulen, 1700.

1981, May 22
290	A45	5p multicolored	.20	.20
291	A45	14p multicolored	.40	.30
292	A45	21p multicolored	.50	.50
		Nos. 290-292 (3)	1.10	1.00

Souvenir Sheet
293	A45	35p multicolored	.60	.75

Royal Wedding Issue
Common Design Type
Wmk. 373
1981, July 22 Litho. Perf. 14
294	CD331	5p Bouquet	.20	.20
295	CD331	20p Charles	.20	.20
296	CD331	50p Couple	.35	.35
		Nos. 294-296 (3)	.75	.75

Hiking — A46

1981, Sept. 14
297	A46	5p shown	.20	.20
298	A46	10p Camping	.20	.20
299	A46	20p Map reading	.25	.25
300	A46	25p Prince Philip	.35	.25
		Nos. 297-300 (4)	1.00	.90

Duke of Edinburgh's Awards, 25th anniv.

Inaccessible Island Rail — A47

1981, Nov. 1 Litho. Perf. 13½x14
301		Strip of 4	1.40	1.40
a.	A47	10p Nest	.30	.30
b.	A47	10p Eggs	.30	.30
c.	A47	10p Chicks	.30	.30
d.	A47	10p Adult rail	.30	.30

Six-gilled Shark A48

1982, Feb. 8 Litho. Perf. 13½x14
302	A48	5p shown	.20	.20
303	A48	14p Porbeagle shark	.40	.25
304	A48	21p Blue shark	.60	.45
305	A48	35p Hammerhead shark	.90	.70
		Nos. 302-305 (4)	2.10	1.60

Marcella — A49

1982, Apr. 5 Litho. Perf. 14
306	A49	5p shown	.35	.35
307	A49	15p Eliza Adams	.35	.50
308	A49	30p Corinthian	.45	.70
309	A49	50p Samuel & Thomas	.75	.95
		Nos. 306-309 (4)	1.90	2.50

See Nos. 324-327.

Princess Diana Issue
Common Design Type
Perf. 14½x14
1982, July 1 Litho. Wmk. 373
310	CD333	5p Arms	.25	.20
311	CD333	15p Diana	.75	.20
312	CD333	30p Wedding	1.50	.35
313	CD333	50p Portrait	2.25	.60
		Nos. 310-313 (4)	4.75	1.35

Scouting Year — A50

Perf. 13½x13, 13x13½
1982, Aug. 23 Litho.
314	A50	5p Baden-Powell, vert.	.20	.20
315	A50	20p Brownsea Isld. camp, 1907, vert.	.35	.35
316	A50	50p Saluting	.95	.95
		Nos. 314-316 (3)	1.50	1.50

Souvenir Sheet
Perf. 14
317	A50	50p Tree illustration, vert.	1.25	1.10

Nos. 226, 230 Overprinted: "1st PARTICIPATION / COMMONWEALTH / GAMES 1982"

Perf. 13½x14
1982, Sept. 28 Litho. Wmk. 373
318	A31	5p multicolored	.20	.20
319	A31	25p multicolored	.40	.40

12th Commonwealth Games, Brisbane, Australia, Sept. 30-Oct. 9.

Formation of Volcanic Island A51

1982, Nov. 1 Perf. 14x14½
320	A51	5p shown	.25	.25
321	A51	15p Surface cinder cones	.40	.40
322	A51	25p Eruption	.50	.50
323	A51	35p 1961 eruption	.60	.60
		Nos. 320-323 (4)	1.75	1.75

Ship Type of 1982
1983, Feb. 1 Litho. Perf. 14
324	A49	5p Islander, vert.	.20	.20
325	A49	20p Roscoe	.50	.50
326	A49	35p Columbia	.90	.75
327	A49	50p Emeline, vert.	1.25	1.10
		Nos. 324-327 (4)	2.85	2.55

Tractor Pulling Trailer A52

1983, May 2 Litho. Perf. 14
328	A52	5p shown	.20	.20
329	A52	15p Pack mules	.25	.20
330	A52	30p Oxen pulling cart	.50	.40
331	A52	50p Jeep	.80	.60
		Nos. 328-331 (4)	1.75	1.40

Map of South Atlantic A53

Island History.

Wmk. 373
1983, Aug. 1 Litho. Perf. 14
332	A53	1p shown	.20	.20
333	A53	3p Tristao d'Acunha's flag-ship	.20	.20
334	A53	4p Landing, 1643	.20	.20
335	A53	5p 17th cent. views	.20	.20
336	A53	10p Landing party, 1815	.25	.20
337	A53	15p Settlement	.35	.30
338	A53	18p Governor Glass's house	.45	.35
339	A53	20p Rev. W.F. Taylor, Peter Green	.50	.40
340	A53	25p Three-master John and Eliza-beth	.60	.50
341	A53	50p Dependency dec-laration of St. Helena, 1938	1.25	1.00
342	A53	£1 Commissioning ceremony	2.50	2.00
343	A53	£2 Evacuation, 1961	5.00	4.00
		Nos. 332-343 (12)	11.70	9.55

Raphael, 500th Birth Anniv. — A54

1983, Oct. 27 Litho. Perf. 14½
344	A54	10p multicolored	.25	.20
345	A54	25p multicolored	.65	.50
346	A54	40p multicolored	1.10	.90
		Nos. 344-346 (3)	2.00	1.60

Souvenir Sheet
347	A54	50p multi, horiz.	1.50	1.25

Details from Christ's Charge to St. Peter.

St. Helena Colony Sesquicentenary — A55

1984, Jan. 3 Litho. Perf. 14
348	A55	10p No. 7	.20	.20
349	A55	15p No. 9	.30	.25
350	A55	25p No. 10	.50	.40
351	A55	60p No. 12	1.25	1.00
		Nos. 348-351 (4)	2.25	1.85

Local Fungi A56

1984, Mar. 26
352	A56	10p Agrocybe praecox, vert.	.35	.25
353	A56	20p Laccaria tetraspora, vert.	.65	.50
354	A56	30p Agrocybe cylindracea	1.00	.75
355	A56	50p Sarcoscypha coccinea	1.60	1.25
		Nos. 352-355 (4)	3.60	2.75

Constellations A57

Sheep Shearing — A58

1984, July 30 Perf. 14½
356	A57	10p Orion	.25	.20
357	A57	20p Scorpius	.55	.45
358	A57	25p Canis Major	.65	.55
359	A57	50p Crux	1.25	1.10
		Nos. 356-359 (4)	2.70	2.30

1984, Oct. 1
360	A58	9p shown	.25	.20
361	A58	17p Carding wool	.40	.35
362	A58	29p Spinning	.70	.60
363	A58	45p Knitting	1.10	1.00
a.		Souvenir sheet of 4, #360-363	2.60	2.25
		Nos. 360-363 (4)	2.45	2.15

Stamps from No. 363a do not have white border around the design.

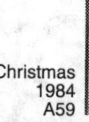

Christmas 1984 A59

1984, Dec. 3 Perf. 14
364	A59	10p Three angels, Christmas dinner	.25	.20
365	A59	20p Two angels, cart	.50	.45
366	A59	30p Candles, sailboat	.80	.70
367	A59	50p Trees, Nativity	1.25	1.10
		Nos. 364-367 (4)	2.80	2.45

Shipwrecks — A60

1985, Feb. 4 Perf. 14x13½, 13½x14
368	A60	10p HMS Julia, 1817, vert.	.35	.25
369	A60	25p Bell from Mabel Clark, 1878, vert.	.80	.65
370	A60	35p Barque Glenhuntley, 1898	1.10	.85
		Nos. 368-370 (3)	2.25	1.75

Souvenir Sheet
371	A60	60p Map of shipwreck sites	2.00	1.60

No. 371 contains one 48x32mm stamp.
See Nos. 393-396, 412-415.

Queen Mother 85th Birthday
Common Design Type
Perf. 14½x14

1985, June 7 Litho. Wmk. 384
372	CD336	10p With Prince Charles, 1954	.30	.30
373	CD336	20p With Margaret at Ascot	.55	.55
374	CD336	30p Queen Mother	.80	.80
375	CD336	50p Holding Prince Henry	1.00	1.00
		Nos. 372-375 (4)	2.65	2.65

Souvenir Sheet
376	CD336	80p With Anne	2.50	2.50

Flags A61

10p, Jonathan Lambert & flag of 1811, Isles of Refreshment. 15p, Cannon & flag of 21st Light Dragoons, 1816-17, Fort Malcolm. 25p, HMS Falmouth, 1816, & flag of HMS Atlantic Isle, HMS JOB 9, 1942-46. 60p, View of Tristan & Union Jack, 1816 to date.

1985, Sept. 30 Wmk. 373 Perf. 14
377	A61	10p multicolored	.35	.30
378	A61	15p multicolored	.45	.40
379	A61	25p multicolored	.80	.70
380	A61	60p multicolored	2.10	1.60
		Nos. 377-380 (4)	3.70	3.00

Nos. 378-380 vert.

Loss of The Lifeboat, Cent. — A62

1985, Nov. 28
381	A62	10p Lifeboat, barque West Riding	.30	.30
382	A62	30p Map	.90	.90
383	A62	50p Death toll	1.50	1.50
		Nos. 381-383 (3)	2.70	2.70

Halley's Comet A63

1986, Mar. 3 Wmk. 384
384	A63	10p Bayeux Tapestry, c. 1092	.30	.30
385	A63	20p Trajectory around Earth	.55	.55
386	A63	30p Comet over Inaccessible Is.	.80	.80
387	A63	50p Ship Paramour	1.25	1.25
		Nos. 384-387 (4)	2.90	2.90

Queen Elizabeth II 60th Birthday
Common Design Type

Designs: 10p, With Prince Charles, 1950. 15p, Birthday Parade, wearing uniform of Scots Guards, 1976. 25p, At Westminster Abbey, London, 1972, wearing mantle and robes of the Most Noble Order of Bath. 45p, Silver Jubilee Tour, Canada, 1977. 65p, Visiting Crown Agents' offices, 1983.

1986, Apr. 21 Perf. 14½
388	CD337	10p scarlet, blk & sil	.25	.25
389	CD337	15p ultra & multi	.35	.35
390	CD337	25p green & multi	.60	.60
391	CD337	45p violet & multi	1.00	1.00
392	CD337	65p rose vio & multi	1.40	1.40
		Nos. 388-392 (5)	3.60	3.60

For overprints see Nos. 429-433.

Shipwrecks Type of 1985

1986, June 2 Perf. 13½
393	A60	9p SV Allanshaw, 1893	.30	.30
394	A60	20p Church font from Edward Vittery, 1881	.70	.65
395	A60	40p Figurehead, 1940	1.50	1.40
		Nos. 393-395 (3)	2.50	2.35

Souvenir Sheet
Perf. 13½x13
396	A60	65p Barque Italia, 1892	2.75	2.50

Nos. 394-395 vert.

Royal Wedding Issue, 1986
Common Design Type

Designs: 10p, Informal portrait. 40p, Andrew operating helicopter.

1986, July 23 Perf. 14
397	CD338	10p multicolored	.25	.25
398	CD338	40p multicolored	1.25	1.25

A64　　A65

1986, Sept. 30
399	A64	5p Wandering albatross	.20	.20
400	A64	10p Daisy	.40	.35
401	A64	20p Vanessa butterfly	.75	.70
402	A64	25p Wilkins's bunting	.95	.85
403	A64	50p Ring-eye	1.90	1.75
		Nos. 399-403 (5)	4.20	3.85

Flora & fauna of Inaccessible Island.

1987, Jan. 23 Perf. 14½

Indigenous Flightless Species and Habitats: 10p, Flightless moth, Edinburgh Settlement. 25p, Strap-winged fly, Crater Lake. 35p, Flightless rail, Inaccessible Island. 50p, Gough Island moorhen, Gough Island.
404	A65	10p multicolored	.30	.30
405	A65	25p multicolored	.80	.80
406	A65	35p multicolored	1.10	1.10
407	A65	50p multicolored	1.60	1.60
		Nos. 404-407 (4)	3.80	3.80

Rockhopper Penguins A66

1987, June 22
408	A66	10p Swimming	.35	.35
409	A66	20p Nesting	.75	.75
410	A66	30p Adult and young	1.10	1.10
411	A66	50p Adult's head	2.00	2.00
		Nos. 408-411 (4)	4.20	4.20

Shipwrecks Type of 1985

Designs: 11p, Castaways attacking sea elephant, vert. 17p, Henry A. Paull, 1879, Sandy Point. 45p, Gustav Stoltenhoff, Stoltenhoff Is., vert. 70p, Map of wrecks off Inaccessible Is.

1987, Apr. 2 Perf. 14
412	A60	11p olive gray & blk	.30	.30
413	A60	17p dark violet & blk	.50	.50
414	A60	45p myrtle green & blk	1.50	1.50
		Nos. 412-414 (3)	2.30	2.30

Souvenir Sheet
415	A60	70p light blue, royal blue & apple grn	2.10	2.10

Norwegian Scientific Expedition, 50th Anniv. — A67

10p, Microscope and textbooks symbolic of expedition results. 20p, Scientists tagging a mollymawk. 30p, Expedition headquarters on the island. 50p, S.S. Thorshammer.

Wmk. 384
1987, Dec. 7 Litho. Perf. 14
416	A67	10p multicolored	.50	.40
417	A67	20p multicolored	1.00	.75

Wmk. 373
418	A67	30p multicolored	1.60	1.60
419	A67	50p multicolored	2.50	1.90
		Nos. 416-419 (4)	5.60	4.15

Fauna of Nightingale Island — A68

1988, Mar. 21 Wmk. 384 Perf. 14
420	A68	5p Tristan bunting	.20	.20
421	A68	10p Tristan thrush	.40	.40
422	A68	20p Yellow-nosed albatross	.75	.75
423	A68	25p Great shearwater	.90	.90
424	A68	50p Elephant seal	2.00	2.00
		Nos. 420-424 (5)	4.25	4.25

Handicrafts A69

1988, May 30 Perf. 14½
425	A69	10p Painted penguin eggs	.25	.25
426	A69	15p Moccasins	.35	.35
427	A69	35p Woolen clothing	.90	.90
428	A69	50p Model canvas boats	1.25	1.25
		Nos. 425-428 (4)	2.75	2.75

Nos. 388-392 Ovptd. "40TH WEDDING ANNIVERSARY" in Silver

1988, Mar. 9
429	CD337	10p scar, blk & sil	.25	.25
430	CD337	15p ultra & multi	.40	.40
431	CD337	25p green & multi	.65	.65
432	CD337	45p violet & multi	1.10	1.10
433	CD337	65p rose vio & multi	1.60	1.60
		Nos. 429-433 (5)	4.00	4.00

19th Cent. Whaling A70

1988, Oct. 6 Perf. 14x14½
434	A70	10p "Trying out" blubber	.40	.40
435	A70	20p Harpoon guns	.75	.75
436	A70	30p Scrimshaw	1.10	1.10
437	A70	50p Ships	1.90	1.90
		Nos. 434-437 (4)	4.15	4.15

Souvenir Sheet
438	A70	£1 Right whale	3.50	3.50

Lloyds of London, 300th Anniv.
Common Design Type

10p, Lloyds's new building, 1988. 25p, Cargo ship *Tristania II*, horiz. 35p, Supply ship *St. Helena*, horiz. 50p, Square-rigger *Kobenhavn*, lost at sea.

1988, Nov. 7 — Perf. 14

439	CD341	10p multicolored	.30	.30
440	CD341	25p multicolored	.85	.85
441	CD341	35p multicolored	1.25	1.25
442	CD341	50p multicolored	1.60	1.60
		Nos. 439-442 (4)	4.00	4.00

Paintings of the Island, 1824, by Augustus Earle (1793-1838) — A71

Designs: 1p, Government House. 3p, Squall off Tristan. 4p, Rafting Blubber. 5p, Tristan. 10p, Man Killing an Albatross. 15p, View on the Summit. 20p, Nightingale Island. 25p, Tristan, diff. 35p, "Solitude," Watching the Horizon. 50p, North Eastern. £1, Tristan, diff. £2, Governor Glass and His Companions.

1988, Dec. 10

443	A71	1p multicolored	.20	.20
444	A71	3p multicolored	.20	.20
445	A71	4p multicolored	.20	.20
446	A71	5p multicolored	.20	.20
447	A71	10p multicolored	.30	.30
448	A71	15p multicolored	.40	.40
449	A71	20p multicolored	.55	.55
450	A71	25p multicolored	.70	.70
451	A71	35p multicolored	1.00	1.00
452	A71	50p multicolored	1.40	1.40
453	A71	£1 multicolored	2.75	2.75
454	A71	£2 multicolored	5.50	5.50
		Nos. 443-454 (12)	13.40	13.40

Gough Is. Fauna — A72

Ferns — A73

1989, Feb. 6 — Litho. — Wmk. 384

455	A72	5p Giant petrel	.25	.25
456	A72	10p Gough moorhen	.50	.50
457	A72	20p Gough bunting	.90	.90
458	A72	25p Sooty albatross	1.10	1.10
459	A72	50p Amsterdam fur seal	2.25	2.25
		Nos. 455-459 (5)	5.00	5.00

1989, May 22 — Wmk. 373 — Perf. 14

460	A73	10p Eriosorus cheilanthoides	.35	.35
461	A73	25p Asplenium alvarezense	.90	.90
462	A73	35p Elaphoglossum hybridum	1.25	1.25
463	A73	50p Ophioglossum opacum	1.75	1.75
		Nos. 460-463 (4)	4.25	4.25

A74

1989, Nov. 20 — Wmk. 384

464	A74	10p Cattle egret	.65	.50
465	A74	25p Spotted sandpiper	1.40	1.10
466	A74	35p Purple gallinule	2.10	1.60
467	A74	50p Barn swallow	2.75	2.25
		Nos. 464-467 (4)	6.90	5.45

Artifacts on Exhibit in the Nautical Museum A75

1989, Sept. 25

468	A75	10p Surgeon's mortar	.35	.35
469	A75	20p Parts of a harpoon	.65	.65
470	A75	30p Compass with binnacle hood	1.00	1.00
471	A75	60p Rope-twisting device	1.90	1.90
		Nos. 468-471 (4)	3.90	3.90

Moths A76

1990, Feb. 1 — Perf. 14

472	A76	10p Peridroma saucia	.35	.35
473	A76	15p Ascalapha odorata	.55	.55
474	A76	35p Agrius cingulata	1.25	1.25
475	A76	60p Eumorpha labruscae	2.25	2.25
		Nos. 472-475 (4)	4.40	4.40

Starfish (Echinoderms) A77

1990, June 12 — Perf. 14x13½

476	A77	10p shown	.35	.35
477	A77	20p multi, diff.	.70	.65
478	A77	30p multi, diff.	1.10	.95
479	A77	60p multi, diff.	2.00	1.90
		Nos. 476-479 (4)	4.15	3.85

Queen Mother, 90th Birthday
Common Design Types

1990, Aug. 4 — Wmk. 384 — Perf. 14x15

480	CD343	25p Queen Mother at the Coliseum	.95	.85

Perf. 14½

481	CD344	£1 Broadcasting to women of the empire, 1939	3.75	3.50

Dunnottar Castle, 1942 — A78

Designs: 15p, RMS St. Helena, 1977-1990. 35p, Launching new RMS St. Helena, 1989. 60p, Duke of York launching new RMS St. Helena. £1, New RMS St. Helena.

1990, Sept. 13 — Wmk. 373 — Perf. 14½

482	A78	10p multicolored	.35	.35
483	A78	15p multicolored	.55	.55
484	A78	35p multicolored	1.40	1.25
485	A78	60p multicolored	2.25	2.00
		Nos. 482-485 (4)	4.55	4.15

Souvenir Sheet

486	A78	£1 multicolored	3.75	3.50

See Ascension Nos. 493-497, St. Helena Nos. 535-539.

Royal Navy Warships A79

Perf. 14½x14

1990, Nov. 30 — Litho. — Wmk. 373

487	A79	10p Pyramus, 1829	.45	.40
488	A79	25p Penguin, 1815	1.10	1.00
489	A79	35p Thalia, 1886	1.50	1.40
490	A79	50p Sidon, 1858	2.25	2.00
		Nos. 487-490 (4)	5.30	4.80

See Nos. 547-550.

1991, Feb. 4

491	A79	10p Milford, 1938	.45	.40
492	A79	25p Dublin, 1923	1.10	1.00
493	A79	35p Yarmouth, 1919	1.50	1.40
494	A79	50p Carlisle, 1938	2.25	2.00
		Nos. 491-494 (4)	5.30	4.80

Souvenir Sheet

Royal Viking Sun — A80

Wmk. 384

1991, Apr. 1 — Litho. — Perf. 14

495	A80	£1 multicolored	4.00	3.75

Prince Philip, 70th Birthday A81

Designs: 10p, HMS Galatea, Prince Alfred. 25p, Royal Visit, 1957. 30p, HMY Britannia, Prince Philip. 50p, Settlement of Edinburgh, Prince Philip.

1991, June 10 — Wmk. 373

496	A81	10p multicolored	.45	.40
497	A81	25p multicolored	1.10	1.00
498	A81	30p multicolored	1.40	1.25
499	A81	50p multicolored	2.25	2.00
		Nos. 496-499 (4)	5.20	4.65

Birds A82

1991, Oct. 1

500	A82	8p Gough moorhens	1.50	1.00
501	A82	10p Gough bunting	1.60	1.10
502	A82	12p Gough moorhen in nest	1.75	1.10
503	A82	15p Gough bunting with chicks	1.90	1.25
		Nos. 500-503 (4)	6.75	4.45

World Wildlife Fund.

Discovery of America, 500th Anniv. — A83

Royal Navy Warships A79

1992, Jan. 23

504	A83	10p STV Eye of the Wind	.50	.40
505	A83	15p STV Soren Larsen	.70	.60
506	A83	35p STV Pinta, Nina, Santa Maria	1.60	1.40
507	A83	60p Columbus, Santa Maria	3.00	2.50
		Nos. 504-507 (4)	5.80	4.90

World Columbian Stamp Expo '92, Chicago and Genoa '92 Intl. Philatelic Exhibitions.

Queen Elizabeth II's Accession to the Throne, 40th Anniv.
Common Design Type

1992, Feb. 6

508	CD349	6p multicolored	.40	.35
509	CD349	20p multicolored	.75	.70
510	CD349	25p multicolored	.95	.85
511	CD349	35p multicolored	1.40	1.25
512	CD349	65p multicolored	2.50	2.25
		Nos. 508-512 (5)	6.00	5.40

Fish — A84

Designs: 10p, Caesioperca coatsii. 15p, Mendosoma lineatum. 35p, Physiculus karrerae. 60p, Decapterus longimanus.

1992, June 1

513	A84	10p multicolored	.50	.35
514	A84	15p multicolored	.80	.55
515	A84	35p multicolored	1.60	1.25
516	A84	60p multicolored	3.00	2.25
		Nos. 513-516 (4)	5.90	4.40

Wreck of the Italia, Cent. — A85

Designs: 10p, Italia leaving Greenock. 45p, In mid-Atlantic. 65p, Driving ashore on Stony Beach. £1, Italia in peaceful waters.

1992, Sept. 18 — Perf. 13½x14

517	A85	10p multicolored	.40	.35
518	A85	45p multicolored	1.75	1.60
519	A85	65p multicolored	2.50	2.25
		Nos. 517-519 (3)	4.65	4.20

Souvenir Sheet

520	A85	£1 multicolored	4.00	3.50

Genoa '92 Intl. Philatelic Exhibition (#520).

Insects — A86

15p, Stenoscelis hylastoides. 45p, Trogloscaptomyza brevilamellata. 60p, Senilites tristanicola.

Perf. 14x13½

1993, Feb. 2 — Litho. — Wmk. 384

521	A86	15p multicolored	.55	.55
522	A86	45p multicolored	1.75	1.75
523	A86	60p multicolored	2.25	2.00
		Nos. 521-523 (3)	4.55	4.30

Coronation of Queen Elizabeth II, 40th Anniv. — A87

Designs: 10p, Ampulla, spoon. 15p, Orb. 35p, Imperial State Crown. 60p, St. Edward's Crown.

1993, June 14			**Perf. 14½**	
524	A87	10p green & black	.35	.30
525	A87	15p red vio & black	.50	.45
526	A87	35p purple & black	1.10	1.00
527	A87	60p blue & black	1.90	1.75
		Nos. 524-527 (4)	3.85	3.50

Resettlement to Tristan, 30th Anniv. — A88

Ships: No. 528, Tristania, Frances Repetto. No. 529, Boissevain. 50p, Bornholm.

1993, Nov. 10			**Perf. 13½x14**	
528	A88	35p multicolored	1.10	1.00
529	A88	35p multicolored	1.10	1.00
a.		Pair, #528-529	2.25	2.00
530	A88	50p multicolored	1.50	1.40
		Nos. 528-530 (3)	3.70	3.40

Christmas — A89

Entire paintings or details: 5p, Madonna with Child, School of Botticelli. 15p, The Holy Family, by Daniel Gran. 35p, The Holy Virgin and Child, by Rubens. 65p, The Mystical Marriage of St. Catherine with the Holy Child, by Jan Van Balen.

1993, Nov. 30	**Wmk. 373**		**Perf. 13**	
531	A89	5p multicolored	.20	.20
532	A89	15p multicolored	.55	.45
533	A89	35p multicolored	1.25	1.00
534	A89	65p multicolored	2.10	1.75
		Nos. 531-534 (4)	4.10	3.40

Ships A90

Designs: 1p, Duchess of Atholl, 1929. 3p, Empress of Australia, 1935. 5p, Anatolia, 1937. 8p, Viceroy of India, 1939. 10p, Rangitata, 1943. 15p, Caronia, 1950. 20p, Rotterdam, 1960. 25p, Leonardo da Vinci, 1972. 35p, Vistafjord, 1974. £1, World Discoverer, 1984. £2, Astor, 1984. £5, RMS St. Helena, 1992.

1994, Feb. 3	**Wmk. 384**		**Perf. 14**	
535	A90	1p multicolored	.20	.20
536	A90	3p multicolored	.20	.20
537	A90	5p multicolored	.20	.20
538	A90	8p multicolored	.20	.20
539	A90	10p multicolored	.30	.30
540	A90	15p multicolored	.40	.40
541	A90	20p multicolored	.55	.55
542	A90	25p multicolored	.70	.70
543	A90	35p multicolored	1.00	1.00
544	A90	£1 multicolored	2.75	2.75
545	A90	£2 multicolored	5.50	5.50
546	A90	£5 multicolored	14.00	14.00
		Nos. 535-546 (12)	26.00	26.00

Royal Navy Warships Type of 1990

1994, May 2			**Wmk. 373**	
547	A79	10p HMS Nigeria, 1948	.30	.30
548	A79	25p HMS Phoebe, 1949	.75	.75
549	A79	35p HMS Liverpool, 1949	1.00	1.00
550	A79	50p HMS Magpie, 1955	1.50	1.50
		Nos. 547-550 (4)	3.55	3.55

Sharks A91

1994, Aug.			**Wmk. 384**	
551	A91	10p Blue shark	.35	.35
552	A91	45p Seven-gill shark	1.50	1.50
553	A91	65p Mako shark	2.00	2.00
		Nos. 551-553 (3)	3.85	3.85

Farm Animals — A92

1994, Nov.			**Wmk. 373**	
554	A92	10p Donkeys	.30	.30
555	A92	20p Cattle	.60	.60
556	A92	35p Ducks, geese	1.10	1.10
557	A92	60p Girl feeding lamb	1.90	1.90
		Nos. 554-557 (4)	3.90	3.90

Local Transport A93

Designs: 15p, Pick-up truck. 20p, Leyland Daf Sherpa van. 45p, Yamaha motorcycle, scooter. 60p, Administrator's Landrover.

	Wmk. 384			
1995, Feb. 27	**Litho.**		**Perf. 14**	
558	A93	15p multicolored	.50	.50
559	A93	20p multicolored	.65	.65
560	A93	45p multicolored	1.40	1.40
561	A93	60p multicolored	1.90	1.90
		Nos. 558-561 (4)	4.45	4.45

End of World War II, 50th Anniv.
Common Design Types

Designs: 15p, Lewis gun instruction, 1943. 20p, Tristan defense volunteers, 1943-46. 45p, Radio, weather stations. 60p, HNS Birmingham, 1942.
£1, Reverse of War Medal, 1939-45.

	Perf. 13x13½			
1995, June 19	**Litho.**		**Wmk. 373**	
562	CD351	15p multicolored	.50	.50
563	CD351	20p multicolored	.65	.65
564	CD351	45p multicolored	1.40	1.40
565	CD351	60p multicolored	1.90	1.90
		Nos. 562-565 (4)	4.45	4.45
Souvenir Sheet				
	Perf. 14			
566	CD352	£1 multicolored	3.25	3.25

Souvenir Sheet

Queen Mother, 95th Birthday — A94

1995, Aug. 4	**Litho.**		**Perf. 14½x14**	
567	A94	£1.50 multicolored	4.75	4.75

UN, 50th Anniv.
Common Design Type

20p, Bedford 4-ton truck. 30p, Saxon armored personnel carrier. 45p, Mi26 heavy lift helicopter. 50p, RFA Sir Tristram transporting UN vehicles.

1995, Oct. 24			**Perf. 13½x13**	
568	CD353	20p multicolored	.65	.65
569	CD353	30p multicolored	1.00	1.00
570	CD353	45p multicolored	1.40	1.40
571	CD353	50p multicolored	1.60	1.60
		Nos. 568-571 (4)	4.65	4.65

Seals A95

Sub Antarctic fur seal: 10p, On rock. 35p, Coming out of water with young. Southern elephant seal: 45p, On beach with young. 50p, In water.

1995, Nov. 3			**Perf. 13½**	
572	A95	10p multicolored	.30	.30
573	A95	35p multicolored	1.10	1.10
574	A95	45p multicolored	1.50	1.50
575	A95	50p multicolored	1.60	1.60
		Nos. 572-575 (4)	4.50	4.50

Queen Elizabeth II, 70th Birthday
Common Design Type

Various portraits of Queen, island scenes: 15p, Queen from sea. 20p, Traditional cottage. 45p, The Residency. 60p, With Prince Philip.

1996, Apr. 22	**Litho.**		**Perf. 13½**	
576	CD354	15p multicolored	.45	.45
577	CD354	20p multicolored	.60	.60
578	CD354	45p multicolored	1.40	1.40
579	CD354	60p multicolored	1.75	1.75
		Nos. 576-579 (4)	4.20	4.20

New Harbor — A96

15p, View of Old Harbor. 20p, Earthmoving, New Harbor construction. 45p, Crane, new construction. 60p, View of New Harbor. Nos. 581-582 are 45x28mm.

1996, July 5	**Wmk. 373**		**Perf. 13**	
580	A96	15p multicolored	.45	.45
581	A96	20p multicolored	.60	.60
582	A96	45p multicolored	1.40	1.40
583	A96	60p multicolored	1.75	1.75
		Nos. 580-583 (4)	4.20	4.20

Nos. 581-582 are 45x28mm.

A97

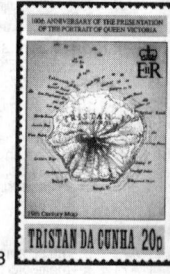

A98

Gough Island Birds: 15p, Gough moorhen. 20p, Wandering albatross. 45p, Sooty albatross. 60p, Gough bunting.

1996, Oct. 1			**Perf. 14**	
584	A97	15p multicolored	.50	.50
585	A97	20p multicolored	.65	.65
586	A97	45p multicolored	1.50	1.50
587	A97	60p multicolored	2.00	2.00
a.		Souvenir sheet of 1	2.00	2.00
		Nos. 584-587 (4)	4.65	4.65

No. 587a for return of Hong Kong to China, July 1, 1997. Issued 6/20/97.

1996, Dec. 18			**Perf. 13½**	

Presentation of Portrait of Queen Victoria, Cent.: 20p, 19th cent. map of Trista da Cunha. 30p, HMS Magpie. 45p, Peter Green, former governor. 50p, Detail of portrait of Queen Victoria, by Heinrich Von Angell.

588	A98	20p multicolored	.65	.65
589	A98	30p multicolored	1.00	1.00
590	A98	45p multicolored	1.50	1.50
591	A98	50p multicolored	1.60	1.60
		Nos. 588-591 (4)	4.75	4.75

Atlantic Marine Fauna of the Cretaceous — A99

Designs: a, Archelon. b, Trinacromerum. c, Platecarpus. d, Clidastes.

1997, Feb. 10	**Wmk. 384**		**Perf. 14**	
592	A99	35p Sheet of 4, #a.-d.	4.50	4.50

See No. 619.

Visual Communications — A100

Designs: No. 593, Smoke signals. No. 594, HMS Eurydice. No. 595, HMS Challenger. No. 596, Flag hoists. No. 597, Semaphore. No. 598, HMS Carlisle. No. 599, Light signals. No. 600, HMS Cilicia.

1997	**Litho.**	**Wmk. 384**	**Perf. 14½**	
593		10p multicolored	.35	.35
594		10p multicolored	.35	.35
a.		A100 Pair, #593-594	.70	.70

95	15p multicolored	.50	.50
96	15p multicolored	.50	.50
a.	A100 Pair, #595-596	1.00	1.00
97	20p multicolored	.60	.60
98	20p multicolored	.60	.60
a.	A100 Pair, #597-598	1.25	1.25
99	35p multicolored	1.10	1.10
00	35p multicolored	1.10	1.10
a.	Pair, #599-600	2.25	2.25
	Nos. 593-600 (8)	5.10	5.10

Farm Animals Type of 1994

1997, Aug. 26   **Litho.**   **Perf. 14**

01	A92	20p Chickens	.65	.65
02	A92	30p Cattle	1.00	1.00
03	A92	45p Sheep	1.50	1.50
04	A92	50p Dogs	1.60	1.60
		Nos. 601-604 (4)	4.75	4.75

Queen Elizabeth II and Prince Philip, 50th Wedding Anniv. — A101

Designs: No. 605, Queen up close. No. 606, Prince riding polo pony. No. 607, Queen with horse. No. 608, Prince up close. No. 609, Prince in military attire, Queen in green coat. No. 610, Princess Anne riding horse.
£1.50, Queen, Prince riding in open carriage, horiz.

1997, Nov. 20   **Wmk. 373**   **Perf. 14**

605		15p multicolored	.50	.50
606		15p multicolored	.50	.50
a.	A101	Pair, #605-606	1.00	1.00
607		20p multicolored	.70	.70
608		20p multicolored	.70	.70
a.	A101	Pair, #607-608	1.40	1.40
609		45p multicolored	1.50	1.50
610		45p multicolored	1.50	1.50
a.	A101	Pair, #609-610	3.00	3.00
		Nos. 605-610 (6)	5.40	5.40

Souvenir Sheet

611	A101	£1.50 multicolored	5.00	5.00

First Lobster Survey, 50th Anniv. — A102

Ships: 15p, Hilary, Melodie. 20p, Tristania II, Hekla. 30p, Pequena, Frances Repetto. 45p, Tristania, Gillian Gaggins. 50p, MFV. Kelso, MV. Edinburgh.
£1.20, Fr. C.P. Lawrence, lobster.

1998, Feb. 6   **Perf. 14½**

612	A102	15p multicolored	.50	.50
613	A102	20p multicolored	.65	.65
614	A102	30p multicolored	1.00	1.00
615	A102	45p multicolored	1.50	1.50
616	A102	50p multicolored	1.60	1.60
		Nos. 612-616 (5)	5.25	5.25

Souvenir Sheet

617	A102	£1.20 multicolored	4.00	4.00

Diana, Princess of Wales (1961-97)
Common Design Type

a, In beige dress. b, In white top with black collar. c, In striped top. d, In lilac & white print dress.

1998, May 15   **Perf. 14½x14**

618	CD355	35p Strip of 4, #a.-d.	4.75	4.75

No. 618 sold for £1.40 + 20p with surtax from international sales going to the Princess Diana Memorial Fund and surtax from local sales going to a designated local charity.

Atlantic Marine Fauna Type of 1997

Fauna of the Miocene Epoch: a, Carcharodon. b, Orycterocetus. c, Eurhinodelphis. d, Hexanchus (six gilled shark), myliobatis.

1998, July 8   **Perf. 14**

619	A99	45p Sheet of 4, #a.-d.	5.75	5.75

Visiting Cruise Ships A103

1998, Sept. 15   **Perf. 14**

620	A103	15p Livonia	.50	.50
621	A103	20p Professor Molchanov	.65	.65
622	A103	45p Explorer	1.50	1.50
623	A103	60p Hanseatic	2.00	2.00
		Nos. 620-623 (4)	4.65	4.65

Sailing Ships A104

1998, Nov. 23   **Wmk. 373**   **Perf. 14½**

624	A104	15p H.G. Johnson, 1892	.50	.50
625	A104	35p Theodore, 1893	1.10	1.10
626	A104	45p Hesperides, 1893	1.50	1.50
627	A104	50p Bessfield, 1894	1.60	1.60
		Nos. 624-627 (4)	4.70	4.70

1999, Mar. 19

628	A104	20p Derwent, 1895	.65	.65
629	A104	30p Strathgryffe, 1898	.95	.95
630	A104	50p Celestial Empire, 1898	1.60	1.60
631	A104	60p Lamorna, 1902	1.90	1.90
		Nos. 628-631 (4)	5.10	5.10
		Nos. 624-631 (8)	9.80	9.80

Wandering Albatross — A105

World Wildlife Fund: 5p, Two adults. 8p, Adult, juvenile in nest. 12p, Adult spreading wings. 15p, Two in flight.

1999, Apr. 27   **Wmk. 373**   **Perf. 14**

632	A105	5p multicolored	.20	.20
633	A105	8p multicolored	.25	.25
634	A105	12p multicolored	.40	.40
635	A105	15p multicolored	.50	.50
a.		Strip of 4, #632-635	1.25	1.25
		Nos. 632-635 (4)	1.35	1.35

Issued in sheets of 16.

Wedding of Prince Edward and Sophie Rhys-Jones
Common Design Type
Perf. 13¾x14

1999, June 18   **Litho.**   **Wmk. 384**

636	CD356	45c Separate portraits	1.40	1.40
637	CD356	£1.20 Couple	3.75	3.75

Queen Mother's Century
Common Design Type

Queen Mother: 20p, With Princess Elizabeth on her 18th birthday. 30p, With King George VI at Balmoral. 50p, With Royal Family, 94th birthday. 60p, As colonel-in-chief of Black Watch.
£1.50, Age 5 photo, airplanes from Battle of Britain, 1940.

1999, Aug. 18   **Wmk. 384**   **Perf. 13½**

638	CD358	20p multicolored	.65	.65
639	CD358	30p multicolored	1.00	1.00
640	CD358	50p multicolored	1.60	1.60
641	CD358	60p multicolored	2.00	2.00
		Nos. 638-641 (4)	5.25	5.25

Souvenir Sheet

642	CD358	£1.50 black	5.00	5.00

Millennium — A106

Various birds.

2000, Jan. 1   **Wmk. 373**   **Perf. 14**
Color of Queen's Head

643	A106	20p bister	.60	.60
644	A106	30p green	.90	.90
645	A106	50p blue	1.50	1.50
646	A106	60p brown	1.90	1.90
		Nos. 643-646 (4)	4.90	4.90

Royalty — A107

British monarchs on 8p-£5: 1p, King Manuel I of Portugal. 3p, Frederick Henry, Prince of Orange. 5p, Empress Maria Theresa of Austria. 8p, King George III. 10p, King George IV. 15p, King Willian IV. 20p, Queen Victoria. 25p, Edward VII. 35p, George V. £1, Edward VIII. £2, George VI. £5, Elizabeth II.

2000, Feb. 1   **Wmk. 384**   **Perf. 14**

647	A107	1p multi	.20	.20
648	A107	3p multi	.20	.20
649	A107	5p multi	.20	.20
650	A107	8p multi	.25	.25
651	A107	10p multi	.30	.30
652	A107	15p multi	.45	.45
653	A107	20p multi	.60	.60
654	A107	25p multi	.75	.75
655	A107	35p multi	1.10	1.10
656	A107	£1 multi	3.00	3.00
657	A107	£2 multi	6.25	6.25
658	A107	£5 multi	15.00	15.00
		Nos. 647-658 (12)	28.30	28.30

The Stamp Show 2000, London A108

Designs: 15p, Longboat under oars. 45p, Longboat under sail. 50p, Cutty Sark, 1876. 60p, Cutty Sark, 2000.
£1.50, Cutty Sark visiting Tristan da Cunha, 1876.

2000, May 22   **Litho.**   **Perf. 14**

659	A108	15p multi	.45	.45
660	A108	45p multi	1.40	1.40
661	A108	50p multi	1.50	1.50
662	A108	60p multi	1.75	1.75
		Nos. 659-662 (4)	5.10	5.10

Souvenir Sheet

663	A108	£1.50 multi	4.50	4.50

Prince William, 18th Birthday
Common Design Type

William: Nos. 664, 668a, As toddler, with Princes Charles and Harry, vert. Nos. 665, 668b, Holding paper, vert. Nos. 666, 668c, Wearing scarf. Nos. 667, 668d, Wearing suit and wearing sweater. Nos. 668e, As child, with Shetland pony.

Perf. 13¾x14¼, 14¼x13¾

2000, June 21   **Litho.**   **Wmk. 373**
Stamps With White Border

664	CD359	45p multi	1.40	1.40
665	CD359	45p multi	1.40	1.40
666	CD359	45p multi	1.40	1.40
667	CD359	45p multi	1.40	1.40
		Nos. 664-667 (4)	5.60	5.60

Souvenir Sheet
Stamps Without White Border
Perf. 14¼

668	CD359	45p Sheet of 5, #a-e	7.00	7.00

Ships and Helicopters — A109

No. 669, 10p: a, SA Agulhas. b, SA 330J Puma, 1999.
No. 670, 15p: a, HMS London. b, Westland Wessex HAS 1, 1964.
No. 671, 20p: a, HMS Endurance. b, Westland Lynx HAS 3, 1996.
No. 672, 50p: a, USS Spiegel Grove. b, Sikorsky UH-19F, 1963.
Illustration reduced.

Wmk. 373

2000, Sept. 4   **Litho.**   **Perf. 14**
Pairs, #a-b

669-672	A109	Set of 4	5.50	5.50

First Election of Winston Churchill to Parliament, Cent. — A110

Designs: 20p, During siege of Sidney Street, 1911. 30p, With Franklin D. Roosevelt, 1941. 50p, VE Day broadcast, 1945. 60p, Greeting Queen Elizabeth, 1955.

Perf. 13¾x14

2000, Oct. 2   **Wmk. 373**

673-676	A110	Set of 4	4.75	4.75

Souvenir Sheet

New Year 2001 (Year of the Snake) — A111

No. 677: a, 30p, Inaccessible Island rail. b, 45p, Black-faced spoonbill.
Illustration reduced.

Wmk. 373

2001, Feb. 1   **Litho.**   **Perf. 14½**

677	A111	Sheet of 2, #a-b	2.25	2.25

Hong Kong 2001 Stamp Exhibition.

Age of Victoria A112

Designs: 15p, Letter, 1846. 20p, Prince Alfred, Duke of Edinburgh, vert. 30p, HMS Galatea. 35p, Queen Victoria, vert. 50p, Charles Dickens, vert. 60p, Resupplying ships.
£1.50, Jubilee celebrations.

Wmk. 373

2001, May 24   **Litho.**   **Perf. 14**

678-683	A112	Set of 6	6.00	6.00

Souvenir Sheet

684	A112	£1.50 multi	4.25	4.25

Longboats — A113

No. 685: a, Boat with dark and light blue striped sails, island in distance. b, Boat with red and blue striped and white sails, boat with blue, red and yellow striped and blue and white striped sails. c, Prow and sail of boat, two boats in distance. d, Boat with blue red and yellow striped and blue and white striped sails. e, Boat with dark and light blue sails near shore. f, Boat with red and blue striped and white sails. g, Boat with gray, red and white sails. h, Boat with sails down.

2001, July 12
685　A113　30p Sheet of 8, #a-h　　6.75 6.75

Nos. 669-672 Overprinted in Blue Violet

Illustration reduced.

Wmk. 373
2001, Sept. 17　Litho.　Perf. 14
686　A109　10p Pair, #a-b　.60　.60
687　A109　15p Pair, #a-b　.85　.85
688　A109　20p Pair, #a-b　1.10 1.10
689　A109　50p Pair, #a-b　3.00 3.00
　　Nos. 686-689 (4)　　5.55 5.55

Souvenir Sheet

Birdlife International World Bird Festival — A114

Spectacled petrel: a, Head. b, Diving (island in background). c, In flight with legs extended. d, Diving (sea in background). e, Chick.

Wmk. 373
2001, Oct. 1　Litho.　Perf. 14½
690　A114　35p Sheet of 5, #a-e　5.25 5.25

Royal Navy Ships A115

Designs: No. 691, 20p, HMS Penguin, 1815. No. 692, 20p, HMS Julia, 1817. No. 693, 35p, HMS Beagle, 1901. No. 694, 35p, HMS Puma, 1962. No. 695, 60p, HMS Monmouth, 1997. No. 696, 60p, HMS Somerset, 1999.

Wmk. 373
2001, Oct. 31　Litho.　Perf. 14
691-696 A115　Set of 6　　6.75 6.75

Churches A116

Designs: No. 697, 35p, Exterior, St. Joseph's Catholic Church. No. 698, 35p, Exterior, St. Mary's Anglican Church. No. 699, 60p, Stained glass window, St. Joseph's. No. 700, 60p, Altar, St. Mary's.

Perf. 13¼x13½, 13½x13¼
2001, Nov. 27
697-700 A116　Set of 4　　5.50 5.50

Christmas, Arrival of first USPG missionary, 150th anniv.

Tristan da Cunha Postage Stamps, 50th Anniv. A117

Designs: Nos. 701, 45p, 705a, 45p, #5, 6, 9, 10 canceled. Nos. 702, 20p, 705, 45p, #7, 8, 11, 12 canceled. Nos. 703, 50p, 705c, 45p, #1-4 canceled. Nos. 704, 60p, 705d, 45p, Men at post office, 1952.

2002, Jan. 1　　　　Perf. 13½
Without "Tristan da Cunha" in Script
701-704 A117　Set of 4　　4.25 4.25

Souvenir Sheet
With "Tristan da Cunha" in Script at Top or Bottom of Stamps
705　A117　45p Sheet of 4, #a-d　5.25 5.25

Reign Of Queen Elizabeth II, 50th Anniv. Issue
Common Design Type

Designs: Nos. 706, 710a, 15p, Princess Elizabeth, 1947. Nos. 707, 710b, 30p, Wearing tiara, 1991. Nos. 708, 710c, 45p, Wearing red coat. Nos. 709, 710d, 50p, Wearing purple hat, 1997. No. 710e, 60p, 1955 portrait by Annigoni (38x50mm).

Perf. 14¼x14½, 13¾ (#710e)
2002, Feb. 6　　Wmk. 373
With Gold Frames
706-709 CD360　Set of 4　　4.00 4.00

Souvenir Sheet
Without Gold Frames
710　CD360　Sheet of 5, #a-e　5.75 5.75

Fishing Industry A118

Designs: 20p, Pelagic armorhead. 35p, Yellowtail. 50p, Splendid alfonsino. 60p, Ship San Liberatore.

Wmk. 373
2002, May　Litho.　Perf. 14
711-713 A118　Set of 3　　3.25 3.25
714　　Souvenir sheet, #711-713, 714a　　5.00 5.00
　a.　A118 60p multi　　1.75 1.75

Queen Mother Elizabeth (1900-2002)
Common Design Type

Designs: 20p, Wearing hat (black and white photograph). £1.50, Wearing blue green hat. No. 717: a, 75p, Holding baby (black and white photograph). b, 75p, Wearing dark blue hat.

Wmk. 373
2002, Aug. 5　Litho.　Perf. 14¼
With Purple Frames
715-716 CD361　Set of 2　　5.25 5.25

Souvenir Sheet
Without Purple Frames
Perf. 14½x14¼
717　CD361　Sheet of 2, #a-b　4.75 4.75

Marine Mammals — A119

No. 718: a, Gray's beaked whale. b, Dusky dolphin. c, False killer whale. d, Long-finned pilot whale. e, Sperm whale. f, Shepherd's beaked whale. £2, Humpback whale.

Wmk. 373
2002, Sept. 24　Litho.　Perf. 13¼
718　A119　30p Sheet of 6, #a-f　5.75 5.75

Souvenir Sheet
719　A119　£2 multi　　6.25 6.25

HMS Herald Survey, 150th Anniv. — A120

Designs: 20p, Captain Denham and officers. 35p, HMS Herald in Bay of Biscay. 50p, Surveying, Oct. 30, 1852. 60p, HMS Herald and Torch at sunset, 1852.

2002, Nov. 11　　　Perf. 14x14¾
720-723 A120　Set of 4　　5.25 5.25

Guinness Book of World Records — A121

No. 724: a, Great Barrier Reef (longest reef). b, Greenland (biggest island). c, Sahara Desert (biggest desert). d, Amazon and Nile Rivers (longest rivers). e, Mt. Everest (biggest mountain). f, Tristan da Cunha (most remote inhabited island). £2, Like No. 724f.

Wmk. 373
2003, Jan. 10　　　Perf. 13¾
724　A121　30p Sheet of 6, #a-f　5.75 5.75

Souvenir Sheet
725　A121　£2 multi　　6.50 6.50

Atlantic Yellow-nosed Albatross A122

Designs: Nos. 726, 730a, 15p, Heads of two birds. Nos. 727, 730b, 30p, Bird on nest, vert. Nos. 728, 730c, 45p, Bird in flight, vert. Nos. 729, 730d, Two birds in flight. No. 730e, £1, Two birds in flight, diff.

Perf. 14¼x13¾, 13¾x14¼
2003, May 7　　　　Litho.
Stamps With White Frames
726-729 A122　Set of 4　　4.50 4.5(

Souvenir Sheet
Stamps Without Frames
Perf. 14¼x14½
730　A122　Sheet of 5, #a-e　7.75 7.7
　Birdlife International.

Head of Queen Elizabeth II
Common Design Type
Wmk. 373
2003, June 2　Litho.　Perf. 13¾
731　CD362　£2.80 multi　　9.25 9.2

Coronation of Queen Elizabeth II, 50th Anniv.
Common Design Type

Designs: Nos. 732, 20p, 734a, Queen an(extended family. Nos. 733, £1.50, 734b, Bishops paying homage to Queen at coronation.

Perf. 14¼x14½
2003, June 2　　　Wmk. 373
Vignettes Framed, Red Background
732-733 CD363　Set of 2　　5.50 5.5(

Souvenir Sheet
Vignettes Without Frame, Purple Panel
734　CD363　75p Sheet of 2, #a-b　5.00 5.0(

Prince William, 21st Birthday
Common Design Type

No. 735: a, William in polo uniform at right. b, In sweater at left.

Wmk. 373
2003, June 21　Litho.　Perf. 14¼
735　　Horiz. pair　　3.25 3.25
　a.-b.　CD364 50p Either single　1.60 1.60

William Glass (1787-1853), Governor — A123

No. 736: a, Arrival of Glass on HMS Falmouth, 1816. b, As corporal, stationed on Tristan da Cunha. c, Glass and family onshore, 1817. d, Glass family with dog. e, Gov. Glass conducting daughter's marriage ceremony, 1833. f, Glass as old man.

Perf. 14¼x14½
2003, Nov. 24　Litho.　Wmk. 373
736　A123　30p Sheet of 6, #a-f, + 6 labels　　6.00 6.00

Royal Navy Ships — A124

No. 737, 20p: a, RFA Tideflow. b, RFA Tidespring.
No. 738, 35p: a, RFA Gold Rover. b, RFA Diligence.
No. 739, 60p: a, RFA Wave Chief. b, HMY Britannia.
Illustration reduced.

Wmk. 373
2003, Dec. 8　Litho.　Perf. 14
Horiz. pairs, #a-b
737-739 A124　Set of 3　　8.00 8.00

History of Writing Implements — A125

Designs: 15p, Cave paintings and pigment
blocks. 20p, Clay tablet. 35p, Egyptian writing
palette. 45p, Goose quill pen. 50p, Fountain
pen. 60p, Ballpoint pen.
£1.50, Word processing.

2004, Jan. 8			*Perf. 13¾*	
740-745	A125	Set of 6	8.50	8.50

Souvenir Sheet

Litho. with Margin Embossed

746	A125	£1.50 multi	5.75	5.75

POSTAGE DUE STAMPS

Type of Barbados 1934-47

Perf. 14

1957, Feb. 1		**Wmk. 4**		**Typo.**

Chalky Paper

J1	D1	1p rose red	2.75	4.75
J2	D1	2p orange yellow	3.50	6.25
J3	D1	3p green	3.75	7.75
J4	D1	4p ultramarine	4.50	9.00
J5	D1	5p deep claret	5.75	11.00
		Nos. J1-J5 (5)	20.25	38.75

Numeral — D2

Perf. 13½x14

1976, Sept. 3		**Litho.**	**Wmk. 373**	
J6	D2	1p lilac rose	.20	.20
J7	D2	2p grayish green	.20	.20
J8	D2	4p violet	.20	.20
J9	D2	5p light blue	.25	.40
J10	D2	10p brown	.65	.85
		Nos. J6-J10 (5)	1.50	1.85

1976, May 31			**Wmk. 314**	
J6a	D2	1p lilac rose	.20	.20
J7a	D2	2p grayish green	.20	.20
J8a	D2	4p violet	.20	.20
J9a	D2	5p light blue	.30	.30
J10a	D2	10p brown	.70	.70
		Nos. J6a-J10a (5)	1.60	1.60

Outline Map of Tristan
da Cunha — D3

Perf. 15x14

1986, Nov. 20		**Litho.**	**Wmk. 384**	
J11	D3	1p pale yel brn & brn	.20	.20
J12	D3	2p orange & brown	.20	.20
J13	D3	5p crimson rose & brn	.20	.20
J14	D3	7p lt lilac & black	.20	.20
J15	D3	10p pale ultra & blk	.25	.25
J16	D3	25p lt green & blk	.70	.70
		Nos. J11-J16 (6)	1.75	1.75

TRUCIAL STATES

'trü-shəl 'stāts

LOCATION — Qatar Peninsula, Persian
  Gulf
GOVT. — Sheikdoms under British
  Protection
AREA — 32,300 sq. mi.
POP. — 86,000
CAPITAL — Dubai

  The Trucial States are: Abu Dhabi,
Ajman, Dubai, Fujeira, Ras al Khaima,
Sharjah and Kalba, and Umm al
Qiwain.
  Stamps inscribed "Trucial States"
were issued and used only in Dubai.

Beginning Aug. 1972 all Trucial States
used the stamps of United Arab
Emirates.

  100 Naye Paise = 1 Rupee

> **Catalogue values for all unused
> stamps in this country are for
> Never Hinged items.**

7 Palm
Trees — A1

Dhow — A2

Perf. 14½x14

1961, Jan. 7		**Photo.**	**Unwmk.**	
1	A1	5np emerald	.90	.20
2	A1	15np red brown	.45	.20
3	A1	20np ultra	.90	.20
4	A1	30np orange	.45	.20
5	A1	40np purple	.45	.20
6	A1	50np brown olive	.45	.20
7	A1	75np gray	.60	.20

		Engr.	*Perf. 13x12½*	
8	A2	1r emerald	4.50	2.00
9	A2	2r black	3.50	11.50
10	A2	5r rose red	6.00	17.50
11	A2	10r violet blue	12.00	20.00
		Nos. 1-11 (11)	30.20	52.40

  Stamps inscribed "Trucial States" were withdrawn in June, 1963, when the individual
states began issuing their own stamps.

LOOKING UP LISTINGS IN THE CATALOGUE HAS NEVER BEEN EASIER WITH

Scott Catalogue Tabs

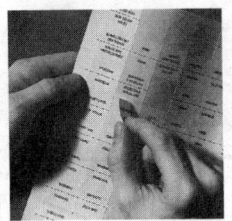

1. Select the country name or
specialty area from the sheet.

2. Affix a portion of the tab to the
appropriate page. Fold tab in half
at dotted line.

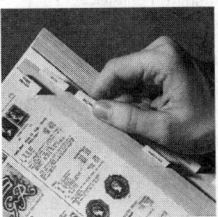

3. Use the tabs to reference catalogue
listings. Blank tabs also included.

Tabs available for each Volume of the Scott Catalogue

ITEM	DESCRIPTION	RETAIL
CT1	Tabs Volume 1 *U.S. & Countries A - B*	$2.95
CT2	Tabs Volume 2 *Countries C - F*	$2.95
CT3	Tabs Volume 3 *Countries G - I*	$2.95
CT4	Tabs Volume 4 *Countries J - O*	$2.95
CT5	Tabs Volume 5 *Countries P - Slovenia*	$2.95
CT6	Tabs Volume 6 *Countries Solomon Islands - Z*	$2.95
CLGT6	Tabs *U.S. Specialized*	$2.95
CLGTC	Tabs Classic Specialized	$2.95

Catalogue Tabs are available from your favorite stamp dealer
or direct from

1-800-572-6885
P.O. Box 828, Sidney OH 45365
www.amosadvantage.com

AMOS
HOBBY PUBLISHING

TUNISIA

tü-'nē-zhē̦ə

LOCATION — Northern Africa, bordering on the Mediterranean Sea
GOVT. — Republic
AREA — 63,362 sq. mi.
POP. — 9,513,603 (1999 est.)
CAPITAL — Tunis

The former French protectorate became a sovereign state in 1956 and a republic in 1957.

100 Centimes = 1 Franc
1000 Millimes = 1 Dinar (1959)

Catalogue values for unused stamps in this country are for Never Hinged items, beginning with Scott 163 in the regular postage section, Scott B78 in the semi-postal section, Scott C13 in the airpost section, Scott CB1 in the airpost semi-postal section, and Scott J33 in the postage due section.

Coat of Arms — A1

Perf. 14x13½

		1888, July 1	Typo.	Unwmk.
1	A1	1c black, *blue*	1.75	1.10
2	A1	2c pur brn, *buff*	1.75	1.25
3	A1	5c green, *grnsh*	13.50	7.50
4	A1	15c blue, *grysh*	32.50	12.00
5	A1	25c black, *rose*	62.50	35.00
6	A1	40c red, *straw*	60.00	32.50
7	A1	75c car, *rose*	62.50	35.00
8	A1	5fr gray vio, *grysh*	325.00	200.00
		Nos. 1-8 (8)	559.50	324.35

All values exist imperforate.

Reprints were made in 1893 and some values have been reprinted twice since then. The shades usually differ from those of the originals and some reprints have white gum instead of grayish. All values except the 15c and 40c have been reprinted from retouched designs, having a background of horizontal ruled lines.

A2   A3

1888-1902

9	A2	1c blk, *lil bl*	.80	.25
10	A2	2c pur brn, *buff*	.85	.25
11	A2	5c grn, *grnsh*	5.00	.45
12	A2	5c yellow grn ('99)	5.00	.40
13	A2	10c blk, *lav* ('93)	5.00	.25
14	A2	10c red ('01)	4.25	.35
15	A2	15c blue, *grysh*	35.00	.40
16	A2	15c gray ('01)	5.50	.75
17	A2	20c red, *grn* ('99)	12.00	1.10
18	A2	25c blk, *rose*	13.00	.80
19	A2	25c blue ('01)	8.50	1.00
20	A2	35c brown ('02)	30.00	1.60
21	A2	40c red, *straw*	10.50	.75
22	A2	75c car, *rose*	100.00	60.00
23	A2	75c dp vio, *org* ('93)	17.50	4.00
24	A3	1fr olive, *olive*	22.50	5.00
25	A3	2fr dull violet ('02)	125.00	90.00
26	A3	5fr red lil, *lav*	125.00	75.00
		Bar cancellation		.50

Quadrille Paper

27	A2	15c bl, *grysh* ('93)	30.00	.30
		Nos. 9-27 (19)	555.40	242.65

For surcharges see Nos. 28, 58-61.

No. 27 Surcharged in Red

1902

28	A2	25c on 15c blue	1.75	1.60

Mosque at Kairouan A4

Plowing A5

Ruins of Hadrian's Aqueduct A6

Carthaginian Galley — A7

		1906-26		Typo.
29	A4	1c blk, *yel*	.20	.20
30	A4	2c red brn, *straw*	.20	.20
31	A4	3c lt red ('19)	.20	.20
32	A4	5c grn, *grnsh*	.20	.20
33	A4	5c orange ('21)	.20	.20
34	A5	10c red	.20	.20
35	A5	10c green ('21)	.25	.20
36	A5	15c vio, *pnksh*	.40	.20
a.		Imperf., pair		
37	A5	15c brn, *org* ('23)	.20	.20
38	A5	20c brn, *pnksh*	.20	.20
39	A5	25c deep blue	.75	.20
a.		Imperf., pair		
40	A5	25c violet ('21)	.25	.20
41	A6	30c red brn & vio ('19)	.50	.35
42	A5	30c pale red ('21)	.70	.50
43	A5	35c ol grn & brn	8.00	.55
44	A6	40c blk brn & red brn	4.00	.25
45	A5	40c blk, *pnksh* ('23)	.80	.50
46	A5	40c gray grn ('26)	.20	.20
47	A5	50c blue ('21)	.50	.40
48	A6	60c ol grn & vio ('21)	.50	.25
49	A6	60c ver & rose ('25)	.25	.25
50	A6	75c red brn & red	.35	.25
51	A6	75c ver & dl red ('26)	.25	.25
52	A7	1fr brn & dk brn	.70	.25
53	A7	1fr ind & ultra ('25)	.30	.25
54	A7	2fr brn & ol grn	4.00	.90
55	A7	2fr grn & red, *pink* ('25)	.40	.25
56	A7	5fr violet & blue	9.50	3.75
57	A7	5fr gray vio & grn ('25)	.75	.25
		Nos. 29-57 (29)	34.95	11.90

For surcharges and overprints see Nos. 62-64, 70-73115-116, B1-B23, B25-B27, B29-B30, B32-B36, C1-C6.

Stamps and Type of 1888-1902 Surcharged

1908, Sept.

58	A2	10c on 15c gray, *lt gray* (R)	1.00	.90
59	A3	35c on 1fr ol, *ol* (R)	1.75	1.60
60	A3	40c on 2fr dl vio (Bl)	4.50	4.00
61	A3	75c on 5fr red lil, *lav* (Bl)	3.75	3.50
		Nos. 58-61 (4)	11.00	10.00

No. 36 Surcharged

1911

62	A5	10c on 15c vio, *pinkish*	1.25	.40

No. 34 Surcharged

1917, Mar. 16

63	A5	15c on 10c red	.50	.20
a.		"15c" omitted	13.00	
b.		Double surcharge	40.00	

No. 36 Surcharged

1921

64	A5	20c on 15c vio, *pinkish*	.60	.20

Arab and Ruins of Dougga — A9

		1922-26	Typo.	**Perf. 13½x14**
65	A9	10c green	.20	.20
66	A9	10c rose ('26)	.20	.20
67	A9	30c rose	1.00	.40
68	A9	30c lilac ('26)	.35	.20
69	A9	50c blue	.60	.25
		Nos. 65-69 (5)	2.35	1.25

For surcharges see #117, B24, B28, B31.

Stamps and Type of 1906 Surcharged in Red or Black

    a   b

1923-25

70	A4(a)	10c on 5c grn, *grnsh* (R)	.30	.30
a.		Double surcharge	40.00	
71	A5(b)	20c on 15c vio (Bk)	.70	.25
72	A5(b)	30c on 20c yel brn (Bk) ('25)	.20	.20
73	A5(b)	50c on 25c blue (R)	.75	.25
		Nos. 70-73 (4)	1.95	1.00

Arab Woman Carrying Water — A10

Grand Mosque at Tunis — A11

Mosque, Tunis — A12

Roman Amphitheater, El Djem (Thysdrus) — A13

		1926-46	Typo.	**Perf. 14x13½**
74	A10	1c lt red	.20	.20
75	A10	2c olive grn	.20	.20
76	A10	3c slate blue	.20	.20
77	A10	5c yellow grn	.20	.20
78	A10	10c rose	.20	.20
78A	A12	10c brown ('46)	.20	.20
79	A11	15c gray lilac	.20	.20
80	A11	20c deep red	.20	.20
81	A11	25c gray green	.30	.20
82	A11	25c lt violet ('28)	.20	.20
83	A11	30c lt violet	.20	.20
84	A11	30c blue grn ('28)	.20	.20
84A	A12	30c dk ol grn ('46)	.20	.20

85	A11	40c deep brown	.20	.20
85A	A12	40c lil rose ('46)	.20	.20
86	A11	45c emerald ('40)	.45	.20
87	A12	50c black	.20	.20
88	A12	50c ultra ('34)	.25	.20
88B	A12	50c emerald ('40)	.20	.20
88C	A12	50c lt blue ('46)	.20	.20
89	A12	60c red org ('44)	.20	.20
89A	A12	60c ultra ('45)	.20	.20
90	A12	65c ultra ('38)	.55	.20
91	A12	70c dark red ('40)	.20	.20
92	A12	75c vermilion	.25	.25
93	A12	75c lil rose ('28)	1.00	.20
94	A12	80c blue green	1.40	.25
94A	A12	80c blk brn ('40)	.20	.20
94B	A12	80c emerald ('45)	.20	.20
95	A12	90c org red ('28)	.20	.20
96	A12	90c ultra ('39)	12.50	10.00
97	A12	1fr brown violet	.40	.20
97A	A12	1fr rose ('40)	.20	.20
98	A13	1.05fr dl bl & mag	.40	.20
98A	A12	1.20fr blk brn ('45)	.20	.20
99	A13	1.25fr gray bl & dk bl	.35	.20
100	A13	1.25fr car rose ('40)	1.00	.65
100A	A13	1.30fr bl & vio bl ('42)	.20	.20
101	A13	1.40fr brt red vio ('40)	.40	.40
102	A13	1.50fr bl & dp bl ('28)	.75	.20
102A	A13	1.50fr rose red & red org ('42)	.25	.20
102B	A12	1.50fr rose lil ('46)	.20	.20
103	A13	2fr rose & ol brn	1.10	.20
104	A13	2fr red org ('39)	1.00	.20
104A	A12	2fr Prus grn ('45)	.20	.20
105	A13	2.25fr ultra ('39)	.55	.55
105A	A13	2.40fr red ('46)	.30	.30
106	A13	2.50fr green ('40)	.55	.55
107	A13	3fr dl bl & org	1.10	.40
108	A13	3fr violet ('39)	.20	.20
108A	A13	3fr blk brn ('46)	.20	.20
108B	A13	4fr ultra ('45)	.40	.40
109	A13	5fr red & grn, *grnsh*	2.75	.20
110	A13	5fr dp red brn ('40)	.55	.55
110A	A13	5fr dk green ('46)	.25	.25
110B	A13	6fr dp ultra ('45)	.30	.30
111	A13	10fr brn red & blk, *bluish*	8.50	1.40
112	A13	10fr rose pink ('40)	.45	.30
112A	A13	10fr ver ('46)	.30	.30
112B	A13	10fr ultra ('46)	.25	.25
112C	A13	10fr rose lil ('45)	.25	.25
113	A13	20fr lil & red, *pnksh* ('28)	1.50	.50
113A	A13	20fr dk green ('45)	.30	.30
113B	A13	25fr violet ('45)	.40	.20
113C	A13	50fr carmine ('45)	.80	.30
113D	A13	100fr car rose ('45)	1.10	.20
		Nos. 74-113D (66)	49.05	28.45

See Nos. 152A-162, 185-189, 199-206. For surcharges and overprints see Nos. 114, 118-121, 143-152, B74-B77, B87-B88, B91-B95, B98, C7-C12.

No. 99 Surcharged with New Value and Bars in Red

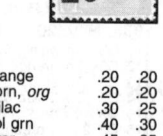

1927, Mar. 24

114	A13	1.50fr on 1.25fr	.30	.20

Stamps of 1921-26 Surcharged

≡3c

1928, May 1

115	A4	3c on 5c orange	.20	.20
116	A5	10c on 15c brn, *org*	.20	.20
117	A9	25c on 30c lilac	.30	.25
118	A12	40c on 80c bl grn	.40	.30
119	A12	50c on 75c ver	.45	.45
		Nos. 115-119 (5)	1.55	1.30

No. 83 Surcharged

≡ 10

1929

120	A11	10c on 30c lt violet	3.50	2.00

No. 120 exists precanceled only. The value in first column is for a stamp which has not been through the post and has original gum. The value in the second column is for a postally used, gumless stamp. See No. 199a.

No. 85 Surcharged with New Value and Bars

1930

121	A11	50c on 40c dp brn	3.00	.85

A14   A15

A16

A17

Perf. 11, 12½, 12½x13

1931-34   **Engr.**

122	A14	1c deep blue	.20	.20
123	A14	2c yellow brn	.20	.20
124	A14	3c black	.25	.25
125	A14	5c yellow grn	.20	.20
126	A14	10c red	.20	.20
127	A15	15c dull violet	.30	.25
128	A15	20c dull brown	.20	.20
129	A15	25c rose red	.20	.20
130	A15	30c deep green	.20	.20
131	A15	40c red orange	.20	.20
132	A16	50c ultra	.20	.20
133	A16	75c yellow	1.40	1.40
134	A16	90c red	.40	.25
135	A16	1fr olive black	.20	.20
136	A16	1fr dk brown ('34)	.20	.20
137	A17	1.50fr brt ultra	.35	.25
138	A17	2fr deep brown	.35	.25
139	A17	3fr blue green	6.25	6.00
140	A17	5fr car rose	15.00	13.00
a.		Perf. 12½	22.50	20.00
141	A17	10fr black	26.00	21.00
142	A17	20fr dark brown	37.50	30.00
		Nos. 122-142 (21)	90.00	75.00

For surcharges see Nos. B54-B73.

Nos. 88, 102 Surcharged in Red or Black:

1937   **Perf. 14x13½**

143	A12	65c on 50c (R)	.35	.20
b.		Double surcharge	55.00	50.00
144	A13	1.75fr on 1.50fr (R)	3.50	.85
a.		Double surcharge	50.00	50.00

1938

145	A12	65c on 50c (Bk)	.55	.20
146	A13	1.75fr on 1.50fr (R)	6.00	4.50

Stamps of 1938-39 Surcharged in Red or Carmine:

1940

147	A12	25c on 65c ultra (C)	.20	.20
148	A12	1fr on 90c ultra (R)	.30	.20

Stamps of 1938-40 Surcharged in Red or Black:

1941

149	A12	25c on 65c ultra (R)	.20	.20
150	A13	1fr on 1.25fr car rose	.30	.30
151	A13	1fr on 1.40fr brt red vio	.30	.30
152	A13	1fr on 2.25fr ultra (R)	.30	.30
		Nos. 149-152 (4)	1.10	1.10

Types of 1926 Without RF

1941-45   **Typo.**   **Perf. 14x13½**

152A	A11	30c carmine ('45)	.20	.20
152B	A12	1.20fr int blue ('45)	.20	.20
153	A12	1.50fr brn red ('42)	.50	.25
154	A13	2.40fr car & brt pink ('42)	.25	.25
155	A13	2.50fr dk bl & lt bl	.25	.25
156	A13	3fr lt violet ('42)	.25	.25
157	A13	4fr blk & bl vio ('42)	.30	.30
158	A13	4.50fr ol grn & brn ('42)	.25	.25
159	A13	5fr brown blk ('42)	.25	.25
160	A13	10fr lil & dull vio	.30	.30
161	A13	15fr henna brn ('42)	2.75	2.25
162	A13	20fr lt vio & car	1.25	.55
		Nos. 152A-162 (12)	6.70	5.25

> Catalogue values for unused stamps in this section, from this point to the end of the section, are for Never Hinged items.

One Aim Alone - Victory   Mosque and Olive Tree
A18   A19

1943   **Litho.**   **Perf. 12**

163	A18	1.50fr rose	.20	.20

1944-45   **Unwmk.**   **Perf. 11½**

Size: 15½x19mm

165	A19	30c yellow ('45)	.20	.20
166	A19	40c org brn ('45)	.20	.20
168	A19	60c red org ('45)	.35	.35
169	A19	70c rose pink ('45)	.20	.20
170	A19	80c Prus grn ('45)	.20	.20
171	A19	90c violet ('45)	.20	.20
172	A19	1fr red ('45)	.20	.20
173	A19	1.50fr dp bl ('45)	.20	.20

Size: 21¼x26½mm

175	A19	2.40fr red	.35	.35
176	A19	2.50fr red brn	.35	.35
177	A19	3fr lt vio	.50	.50
178	A19	4fr brt bl vio	.35	.35
179	A19	4.50fr apple grn	.35	.35
180	A19	5fr gray	.50	.50
181	A19	6fr choc ('45)	.35	.35

182	A19	10fr brn lake ('45)	.50	.50
183	A19	15fr copper brn	.50	.50
184	A19	20fr lilac	.75	.75
		Nos. 165-184 (18)	6.25	6.25

For surcharge see No. B79.

Types of 1926

1946-47   **Typo.**   **Perf. 14x13½**

185	A12	2fr emerald ('47)	.40	.40
186	A12	3fr rose pink	.20	.20
187	A12	4fr violet ('47)	.40	.40
188	A13	4fr violet ('47)	.40	.40
189	A12	6fr carmine ('47)	.20	.20
		Nos. 185-189 (5)	1.60	1.60

Neptune, Bardo Museum A20

1947-49   **Engr.**   **Perf. 13**

190	A20	5fr dk grn & bluish blk	.60	.60
191	A20	10fr blk brn & bluish blk	.25	.25
192	A20	18fr dk bl gray & Prus bl ('48)	.75	.60
193	A20	25fr dk bl & bl grn ('49)	1.00	.75
		Nos. 190-193 (4)	2.60	2.20

For surcharge see No. B108.

Detail from Great Mosque at Kairouan A21

1948-49

194	A21	3fr dk bl grn & bl grn	.60	.45
195	A21	4fr dk red vio & red vio	.40	.25
196	A21	6fr red brn & red	.20	.20
197	A21	10fr purple ('49)	.25	.20
198	A21	12fr henna brn	.60	.45
198A	A21	12fr dk brn & org brn ('49)	.40	.30
198B	A21	15fr dk red ('49)	.40	.30
		Nos. 194-198B (7)	2.85	2.15

See No. 225. For surcharge see No. B103.

Types of 1926

1947-49   **Typo.**   **Perf. 14x13½**

199	A12	2.50fr brown orange	.20	.20
a.		2.50fr brown	.85	.35
200	A12	4fr brown org ('49)	.30	.20
201	A12	4.50fr lt ultra	.20	.20
202	A12	5fr blue ('48)	.40	.25
203	A12	5fr lt bl grn ('49)	.40	.40
204	A13	6fr rose red	.20	.20
205	A12	15fr rose red	.40	.40
206	A13	25fr red orange	.75	.55
		Nos. 199-206 (8)	2.85	2.40

No. 199a is known only precanceled. See note after No. 120.

Dam on the Oued Mellegue A22

1949, Sept. 1   **Engr.**   **Perf. 13**

207	A22	15fr grnsh black	2.50	1.50

UPU Symbols and Tunisian Post Rider — A23   Berber Hermes at Carthage — A24

1949, Oct. 28

Bluish Paper

208	A23	5fr dark green	1.00	1.00
209	A23	15fr red brown	1.00	1.00
		Nos. 208-209,C13 (3)	3.25	3.25

UPU, 75th anniversary.
Nos. 208-209 exist imperf.

1950-51

210	A24	15fr red brown	.45	.35
211	A24	25fr indigo ('51)	.45	.40
212	A24	50fr dark green ('51)	1.25	.40
		Nos. 210-212 (3)	2.15	1.15

Horse, Carthage Museum — A25

1950, Dec. 26   **Typo.**   **Perf. 13½x14**

Size: 21½x17½mm

213	A25	10c aquamarine	.20	.25
214	A25	50c brown	.20	.80
215	A25	1fr rose lilac	.20	.20
216	A25	2fr gray	.20	.20
217	A25	4fr vermilion	.25	.20
218	A25	5fr blue green	.25	.20
219	A25	8fr deep blue	.25	.25
220	A25	12fr red	.60	.25
221	A25	15fr carmine rose ('50)	.25	.25
		Nos. 213-221 (9)	2.35	2.55

See Nos. 222-224, 226-228.

1951-53   **Engr.**   **Perf. 13x14**

Size: 22x18mm

222	A25	15fr carmine rose	.50	.20
223	A25	15fr ultra ('53)	.75	.30
224	A25	30fr deep ultra	1.50	.30
		Nos. 222-224 (3)	2.75	.80

Type of 1948-49

1951, Aug. 1   **Perf. 13**

225	A21	30fr dark blue	.55	.30

Horse Type of 1950

1952   **Typo.**   **Perf. 13½x14**

226	A25	3fr brown orange	.25	.20
227	A25	12fr carmine rose	.75	.20
228	A25	15fr ultra	.25	.20
		Nos. 226-228 (3)	1.25	.60

Charles Nicolle — A26   Flags, Pennants and Minaret — A27

1952, Aug. 4   **Engr.**   **Perf. 13**

229	A26	15fr black brown	1.00	.60
230	A26	30fr deep blue	1.00	.60

Founding of the Society of Medical Sciences of Tunisia, 50th anniv.

1953, Oct. 18

231	A27	8fr black brn & choc	.60	.60
232	A27	12fr dk green & emer	.60	.60
233	A27	15fr indigo & ultra	.60	.60
234	A27	18fr dk pur & pur	.60	.60
235	A27	30fr dk car & car	.60	.60
		Nos. 231-235 (5)	3.00	3.00

First International Fair of Tunis.

Courtyard at Sousse — A28

Sidi Bou
Maklouf
Mosque
A29

Designs: 1fr, Courtyard at Sousse. 2fr, 4fr, Citadel, Takrouna. 5fr, 8fr, View of Tatahouine. 10fr, 12fr, Ruins at Matmata. 15fr, Street Corner, Sidi Bou Said. 20fr, 25fr, Genoese fort, Tabarka. 30fr, 40fr, Bab-El-Khadra gate. 50fr, 75fr, Four-story building, Medenine.

Perf. 13½x13 (A28), 13

1954, May 29
236	A28	50c emerald	.20	.20
237	A28	1fr carmine rose	.20	.20
238	A28	2fr violet brown	.20	.20
239	A28	4fr turq blue	.20	.20
240	A28	5fr violet	.20	.20
241	A28	8fr black brown	.20	.20
242	A28	10fr dk blue grn	.20	.20
243	A28	12fr rose brown	.20	.20
244	A28	15fr dp ultra	1.60	.20
245	A28	18fr chocolate	.90	.40
246	A29	20fr dp ultra	.65	.20
247	A29	25fr indigo	.50	.20
248	A29	30fr dp claret	.40	.20
249	A29	40fr dk Prus grn	.50	.20
250	A29	50fr dk violet	1.60	.20
251	A29	75fr carmine rose	1.60	1.10

Typo.
Perf. 14x13½
252	A28	15fr ultra	.50	.20
		Nos. 236-252 (17)	9.85	4.50

Imperforates exist. See Nos. 271-287. For surcharge see No. B125.

Mohammed al-
Amin, Bey of
Tunis — A30

1954, Oct.   *Perf. 13*
253	A30	8fr bl & dk bl	.50	.50
254	A30	12fr lil gray & indigo	.50	.50
255	A30	15fr dp car & brn lake	.50	.50
256	A30	18fr red brn & blk brn	.50	.50
257	A30	30fr bl grn & dk bl grn	1.00	1.00
		Nos. 253-257 (5)	3.00	3.00

Theater
Drapes,
Dove and
Sun — A31

1955
258	A31	15fr dk red brn, bl & org	.50	.40

Essor, Tunisian amateur theatrical society.

Rotary Emblem, Map and Symbols of
Punic, Roman, Arab and French
Civilizations
A32

1955, May 14   **Unwmk.**
259	A32	12fr vio brn & blk brn	.50	.50
260	A32	15fr vio gray & dk brn	.50	.50
261	A32	18fr rose vio & dk pur	.50	.50
262	A32	25fr blue & dp ultra	.50	.50
263	A32	30fr dk Prus grn & ind	.75	.75
		Nos. 259-263 (5)	2.75	2.75

Rotary International, 50th anniv.

Bey of Tunis
A33

Embroiderers
A34

1955   **Engr.**   *Perf. 13½x13*
264	A33	15fr dark blue	.40	.20

1955, July 25   *Perf. 13*

15fr, 18fr, Potters. 20fr, 30fr, Florists.
265	A34	5fr rose brown	.55	.55
266	A34	15fr ultra	.55	.55
267	A34	15fr Prussian green	.55	.55
268	A34	18fr red	.55	.55
269	A34	20fr dark violet	.75	.75
270	A34	30fr violet brown	.75	.75
		Nos. 265-270 (6)	3.70	3.70

For surcharge see No. B126.

Independent Kingdom
Types of 1954 Redrawn with "RF" Omitted

1956, Mar. 1   *Perf. 13½x13, 13 (A29)*
271	A28	50c emerald	.20	.20
272	A28	1fr carmine rose	.20	.20
273	A28	2fr violet brown	.20	.20
274	A28	4fr turquoise blue	.20	.20
275	A28	5fr violet	.20	.20
276	A28	8fr black brown	.20	.20
277	A28	10fr dk blue grn	.20	.20
278	A28	12fr rose brown	.20	.20
279	A28	15fr deep ultra	.75	.20
280	A29	18fr chocolate	.30	.20
281	A29	20fr deep ultra	.20	.20
282	A29	25fr indigo	.20	.20
283	A29	30fr deep claret	.70	.20
284	A29	40fr dk Prus grn	.70	.20
285	A29	50fr dark violet	.50	.20
286	A29	75fr carmine rose	.85	.55

Perf. 14x13
Typo.
287	A28	15fr ultra	.20	.20
		Nos. 271-287 (17)	6.00	3.75

Mohammed al-
Amin Bey of
Tunis — A35

Farhat
Hached — A36

Designs: 12fr, 18fr, 30fr, Woman and Dove. 5fr, 20fr, Bey of Tunis.

1956   **Unwmk.**   **Engr.**   *Perf. 13*
288	A35	5fr deep blue	.20	.20
289	A35	12fr brown violet	.20	.20
290	A35	15fr red	.25	.20
291	A35	18fr dk blue gray	.35	.20
292	A35	20fr dark green	.35	.30
293	A35	30fr copper brown	.65	.30
		Nos. 288-293 (6)	2.00	1.40

Issued to commemorate Tunisian autonomy.

1956, May 1
294	A36	15fr rose brown	.25	.20
295	A36	30fr indigo	.25	.25

Farhat Hached (1914-1952), nationalist leader.

Grapes — A37

Fruit
Market
A38

Designs: 15fr, Hand holding olive branch. 18fr, Wheat harvest. 20fr, Man carrying food basket ("Gifts for the wedding").

1956-57   **Unwmk.**   **Engr.**   *Perf. 13*
296	A37	12fr lil, vio & vio brn	.40	.20
297	A37	15fr ind, dk ol grn & red brn	.60	.20
298	A37	18fr brt violet blue	.70	.20
299	A37	20fr brown orange	.70	.20
300	A38	25fr chocolate	1.00	.40
301	A38	30fr deep ultra	1.10	.40
		Nos. 296-301 (6)	4.50	1.60

Habib
Bourguiba — A39

Farmers and
Workers
A40

Perf. 14 (A39), 11½x11 (A40)
1957, Mar. 20
302	A39	5fr dark blue	.20	.20
303	A40	12fr magenta	.20	.20
304	A39	20fr ultra	.20	.20
305	A40	25fr green	.30	.20
306	A39	30fr chocolate	.35	.20
307	A40	50fr crimson rose	.75	.25
		Nos. 302-307 (6)	2.00	1.25

First anniversary of independence.

Dove and
Handclasp
A41

Labor Bourse,
Tunis — A42

1957, July 5   **Engr.**   *Perf. 13*
308	A41	18fr dk red violet	.20	.20
309	A42	20fr crimson	.30	.30
310	A41	25fr green	.30	.30
311	A42	30fr dark blue	.30	.30
		Nos. 308-311 (4)	1.10	1.10

5th World Congress of the Intl. Federation of Trade Unions, Tunis, July 5-13.

Republic

Officer and
Soldier — A43

1957, Aug. 8   **Typo.**   *Perf. 11*
312	A43	20fr rose pink	10.00	10.00
313	A43	25fr light violet	10.00	10.00
314	A43	30fr brown orange	10.00	10.00
		Nos. 312-314 (3)	30.00	30.00

Proclamation of the Republic.

Bourguiba
in Exile, Ile
de la Galité
A44

1958, Jan. 18   **Engr.**   *Perf. 13*
315	A44	20fr blue & dk brn	.35	.25
316	A44	25fr lt blue & vio	.35	.25

6th anniv. of Bourguiba's deportation.

Map of
Tunisia — A45

25fr, Woman & child. 30fr, Hand holding flag.

1958, Mar. 20   *Perf. 13*
317	A45	20fr dk brown & emer	.20	.20
318	A45	25fr blue & sepia	.20	.20
319	A45	30fr red brown & red	.25	.20
		Nos. 317-319 (3)	.65	.60

2nd anniv. of independence. See No. 321.

Andreas Vesalius and Abderrahman
ibn Khaldoun — A46

1958, Apr. 17   **Unwmk.**
320	A46	30fr bister & slate grn	.30	.20

World's Fair, Brussels, Apr. 17-Oct. 19.

Redrawn Type of 1958
1958, June 1   **Engr.**   *Perf. 13*
321	A45	20fr brt bl & ocher	.30	.20

Date has been changed to "1 Juin 1955-1958."

3rd anniv. of the return of Pres. Habib Bourguiba.

Gardener — A47

A48

1958, May 1
322	A47	20fr multicolored	.30	.30

Labor Day, May 1.

1958, July 25   **Unwmk.**   *Perf. 13*
Blue Paper
323	A48	5fr dk vio brn & ol	.40	.20
324	A48	10fr dk grn & yel grn	.40	.20
325	A48	15fr org red & brn lake	.40	.20
326	A48	20fr vio, ol grn & yel	.40	.20
327	A48	25fr red lilac	.40	.20
		Nos. 323-327 (5)	2.00	1.00

First anniversary of the Republic.

Pres. Habib
Bourguiba — A49

Fishermen
Casting
Net — A50

1958, Aug. 3   Unwmk.   Perf. 13
328 A49 20fr vio & brn lake   .25 .25
Pres. Bourguiba's 55th birthday.

1958, Oct. 18   Engr.   Perf. 13
329 A50 25fr dk brn, grn & red   .40 .20
6th International Fair, Tunis.

UNESCO
Building,
Paris
A51

1958, Nov. 3
330 A51 25fr grnsh black   .40 .20
Opening of UNESCO Headquarters, Nov. 3.

Woman
Opening
Veil — A52

Hand Planting
Symbolic
Tree — A53

Habib
Bourguiba
at Borj le
Boeuf
A54

1959, Jan. 1   Engr.   Perf. 13
331 A52 20m greenish blue   .30 .20
Emancipation of Tunisian women.

1959, Mar. 2   Unwmk.   Perf. 13
10m, Shield with flag and people holding
torch. 20m, Habib Bourguiba at Borj le Boeuf,
Sahara.

332 A53 5m vio brn, car & sal   .20 .20
333 A53 10m multicolored   .20 .20
334 A53 20m blue   .20 .20
335 A54 30m grnsh bl, ind & org
         brn   .40 .40
    Nos. 332-335 (4)   1.00 1.00
25th anniv. of the founding of the Neo-
Destour Party at Kasr Helal, Mar. 2, 1934.

"Independence" — A55

1959, Mar. 20
336 A55 50m olive, blk & red   .40 .25
3rd anniversary of independence.

Map of Africa and
Drawings — A56

1959, Apr. 15   Litho.   Perf. 13
337 A56 40m lt bl & red brn   .40 .30
Africa Freedom Day, Apr. 15.

Camel
Camp and
Mosque,
Kairouan
A57

Horseback
Rider — A58

Olive
Picker — A59

Open
Window
A58a

Designs: ½m, Woodcock in Ain-Draham forest. 2m, Camel rider. 3m, Saddler's shop. 4m,
Old houses of Medenine, gazelle and youth.
6m, Weavers. 8m, Woman of Gafsa. 10m,
Unveiled woman holding fruit. 12m, Ivory
craftsman. 15m, Skanes Beach, Monastir, and
mermaid. 16m, Minaret of Ez-Zitouna University, Tunis. 20m, Oasis of Gabès. 25m, Oil,
flowers and fish of Sfax. 30m, Modern and
Roman aqueducts. 40m, Festival at Kairouan
(drummer and camel). 45m, Octagonal minaret, Bizerte (boatman). 50m, Three women of
Djerba island. 60m, Date palms, Djerid. 70m,
Tapestry weaver. 75m, Pottery of Nabeul.
90m, Le Kef (man on horse). 100m, Road to
Sidi-bou-Said. 200m, Old port of Sfax. ½d,
Roman temple, Sbeitla. 1d, Farmer plowing
with oxen, Beja.

1959-61   Unwmk.   Engr.   Perf. 13
338 A58   ½m emer, brn &
           bl grn ('60)   .20 .20
339 A57   1m lt bl & ocher   .20 .20
340 A57   2m multicolored   .20 .20
341 A58   3m slate green   .20 .20
342 A57   4m red brn ('60)   .20 .20
343 A58   5m gray green   .20 .20
344 A58   6m rose violet   .20 .20
345 A58   8m vio brn ('60)   .45 .20
346 A58 10m ol, dk grn &
           car   .20 .20
347 A58 12m vio bl & ol
           bis ('61)   .50 .20
348 A57 15m brt blue ('60)   .35 .20
349 A57 16m grnsh blk
           ('60)   .25 .20
350 A58a 20m grnsh blue   .65 .20
351 A58 20m grnsh blk, ol
           & mar ('60)   1.25 .20
352 A57 25m multi ('60)   .20 .20
353 A58a 30m brn, grnsh bl
           & ol   .30 .20
354 A59 40m dp grn ('60)   1.00 .20
355 A58a 45m grn & blk ('60)   .45 .20
356 A58 50m Prus grn, dk
           bl & rose
           ('60)   .60 .20
357 A58a 60m grn & red
           brn ('60)   .75 .20
358 A59 70m multi ('60)   .90 .25
359 A58 75m ol gray ('60)   .90 .30
360 A58a 90m brt grn, ultra
           & choc ('60)   1.00 .30
361 A59 95m multicolored   1.10 .50
362 A58a 100m dk bl, ol &
           brn   1.25 .50
363 A58a 200m brt bl, bis &
           car   3.00 1.25
363A A59 ½d lt brn ('60)   11.00 3.50

363B A58a 1d sl grn & bis
            ('60)   17.50 7.00
     Nos. 338-363B (28)   45.00 17.60

UN Emblem and
Clasped
Hands — A60

Dancer and
Coin — A61

1959, Oct. 24
364 A60 80m org brn, brn & ultra   .60 .40
UN Day, Oct. 24.

1959, Nov. 4
365 A61 50m grnsh bl & blk   .40 .40
Central Bank of Tunisia, first anniversary.

Uprooted Oak
Emblem — A62

Doves and
WRY
Emblem
A63

1960, Apr. 7   Engr.   Perf. 13
366 A62 20m blue black   .35 .20
367 A63 40m red lil & dk grn   .40 .30
World Refugee Year, 7/1/59-6/30/60.

Girl, Boy and
Scout
Badge — A64

Cyclist — A65

Designs: 25m, Hand giving Scout sign.
30m, Bugler and tent. 40m, Peacock and
Scout emblem. 60m, Scout and campfire.

1960, Aug. 9
368 A64 10m lt blue green   .20 .20
369 A64 25m green, red & brn   .20 .20
370 A64 30m vio bl, grn & mar   .25 .20
371 A64 40m black, car & bl   .30 .20
372 A64 60m dk brn, vio blk &
         lake   .65 .35
    Nos. 368-372 (5)   1.60 1.15
4th Arab Boy Scout Jamboree, Tunis, Aug.

1960, Aug. 25
Designs: 10m, Olympic rings forming flower.
15m, Girl tennis player and minaret. 25m,
Runner and minaret. 50m, Handball player
and minaret.

373 A65 5m dk brown & olive   .20 .20
374 A65 10m sl, red vio & emer   .20 .20
375 A65 15m rose red & rose car   .20 .20
376 A65 25m grnsh bl & gray bl   .35 .35
377 A65 50m brt green & ultra   .65 .60
    Nos. 373-377 (5)   1.60 1.55
17th Olympic Games, Rome, 8/25-9/11.

Symbolic Forest
Design — A66

National Fair
Emblems — A67

Designs: 15m, Man working in forest. 25m,
Tree superimposed on leaf. 50m, Symbolic
tree and bird.

1960, Aug. 29
378 A66 8m multicolored   .20 .20
379 A66 15m dark green   .20 .20
380 A66 25m dk pur, crim & brt
         grn   .30 .20
381 A66 50m Prus grn, yel grn &
         rose lake   .40 .30
    Nos. 378-381 (4)   1.10 .90
5th World Forestry Congress, Seattle,
Wash., Aug. 29-Sept. 10.

1960, June 1
382 A67 100m black & green   .55 .35
5th Natl. Fair, Sousse, May 27-June 12.

Pres. Bourguiba
Signing
Constitution
A68

Pres. Bourguiba
A69

1960, June 1
383 A68 20m choc, red & emer   .20 .20
384 A69 20m grayish blk   .20 .20
385 A69 30m blue, dl red & blk   .20 .20
386 A69 75m grn, dl red & blk   .25 .20
    Nos. 383-386 (4)   .85 .80
Promulgation of the Constitution (No. 383).

UN Emblem and
Arms — A70

Dove and
"Liberated
Tunisia" — A71

1960, Oct. 24   Engr.   Perf. 13
387 A70 40m mag, ultra & gray grn   .45 .35
15th anniversary of the United Nations.

1961, Mar. 20   Perf. 13
Design: 75m, Globe and arms.

388 A71 20m maroon, bis & bl   .20 .20
389 A71 30m blue, vio & brn   .20 .20
390 A71 40m yel grn & ultra   .40 .30
391 A71 75m bis, red lil & Prus
         bl   .50 .40
    Nos. 388-391 (4)   1.30 1.10
5th anniversary of independence.

Map of Africa, Woman and Animals — A72

Mother and Child with Flags — A73

Map of Africa: 60m, Negro woman and Arab. 100m, Arabic inscription and Guinea masque. 200m, Hands of Negro and Arab.

1961, Apr. 15   Engr.   Unwmk.
392 A72 40m bis brn, red brn & dk grn .... .20 .20
393 A72 60m sl grn, blk & org brn .... .20 .20
394 A72 100m sl grn, emer & vio .... .35 .20
395 A72 200m dk brn & org brn .... .75 .65
    Nos. 392-395 (4) 1.50 1.25

Africa Freedom Day, Apr. 15.

1961, June 1   Unwmk.   Perf. 13
Designs: 50m, Tunisians. 95m, Girl with wings and half-moon.

396 A73 25m pale vio, red & brn .... .20 .20
397 A73 50m bl grn, sep & brn ...... .35 .20
398 A73 95m pale vio, rose lil & ocher .... .45 .30
    Nos. 396-398 (3) .... 1.00 .70

National Feast Day, June 1.

Dag Hammarskjold A74

Arms of Tunisia A75

1961, Oct. 24   Photo.   Perf. 14
399 A74 40m ultramarine .... .30 .20

UN Day; Dag Hammarskjold (1905-1961), Secretary General of the UN, 1953-61.

1962, Jan. 18   Perf. 11½
Arms in Original Colors
400 A75 1m black & yellow .... .20 .20
401 A75 2m black & pink .... .20 .20
402 A75 3m black & lt blue .... .20 .20
403 A75 6m black & gray .... .20 .20
    Nos. 400-403 (4) .... .80 .80

Tunisia's campaign for independence, 10th anniv.

Mosquito in Spider Web and WHO Emblem — A76

Designs: 30m, Symbolic horseback rider spearing mosquito. 40m, Hands crushing mosquito, horiz.

1962, Apr. 7   Engr.   Perf. 13
404 A76 20m chocolate .... .40 .20
405 A76 30m red brn & slate grn .... .35 .20
406 A76 40m dk brn, mar & grn .... .50 .25
    Nos. 404-406 (3) .... 1.25 .65

WHO drive to eradicate malaria.

Boy and Map of Africa — A77

African Holding "Africa" — A78

1962, Apr. 15   Photo.   Perf. 14
407 A77 50m brown & orange ...... .35 .20
408 A78 100m blue, blk & org ...... .50 .25

Africa Freedom Day, Apr. 15.

Farm Worker — A79

Industrial Worker — A80

1962, May 1   Unwmk.
409 A79 40m multicolored .... .30 .20
410 A80 60m dark red brown .... .40 .25

Labor Day.

"Liberated Tunisia" — A81

Woman of Gabès — A82

1962, June 1   Typo.   Perf. 13½x14
411 A81 20m salmon & blk .... .20 .20

National Feast Day, June 1.

1962-63   Photo.   Perf. 11½
Women in costume of various localities: 10m, 30m, Mahdia. 15m, Kairouan. 20m, 40m, Hammamet. 25m, Djerba. 55m, Ksar Hellal. 60m, Tunis.

412 A82 5m multi .... .25 .20
413 A82 10m multi .... .30 .20
414 A82 15m multi ('63) .... .40 .25
415 A82 20m multi ('63) .... .50 .30
416 A82 25m multi ('63) .... .50 .30
417 A82 30m multi .... .65 .35
418 A82 40m multi .... .70 .40
419 A82 50m multi .... .70 .45
420 A82 55m multi ('63) .... .85 .55
421 A82 60m multi ('63) .... 1.25 .85
    Nos. 412-421 (10) 6.10 3.85

6 stamps issued July 25, 1962 (July 25) for the 6th anniv. of Tunisia's independence. 4 issued June 1, 1963 for Natl. Feast Day. See Nos. 470-471.

UN Emblem, Flag and Dove — A83

Aboul-Qasim Chabbi — A84

30m, Leaves, globe, horiz. 40m, Dove, globe.

1962, Oct. 24   Unwmk.
422 A83 20m gray, blk & scar ...... .25 .20
423 A83 30m multicolored .... .30 .20
424 A83 40m claret brn, blk & bl .... .55 .30
    Nos. 422-424 (3) .... 1.10 .70

Issued for United Nations Day, Oct. 24.

1962, Nov. 20   Engr.   Perf. 13
425 A84 15m purple .... .20 .20

Aboul-Qasim Chabbi (1904-34), Arab poet.

Pres. Habib Bourguiba A85

Hached Telephone Exchange A86

1962, Dec. 7   Photo.   Perf. 12½x13½
426 A85 20m bright blue .... .20 .20
427 A85 30m rose claret .... .20 .20
428 A85 40m green .... .20 .20
    Nos. 426-428 (3) .... .60 .60

1962, Dec. 7   Litho.
Designs: 10m, Carthage Exchange. 15m, Sfax telecommunications center. 50m, Telephone operators. 100m, Symbol of automatization. 200m, Belvedere Central Exchange.

429 A86 5m multicolored .... .20 .20
430 A86 10m multicolored .... .20 .20
431 A86 15m multicolored .... .30 .20
432 A86 50m multicolored .... .50 .25
433 A86 100m multicolored .... 1.40 .55
434 A86 200m multicolored .... 1.90 .90
    Nos. 429-434 (6) 4.50 2.30

1st Afro-Asian Philatelic Exhibition; automation of the telephone system.

Dove over Globe — A87

"Hunger" — A88

1963, Mar. 21   Engr.   Perf. 13
435 A87 20m brt bl & brn .... .20 .20
436 A88 40m bis brn & dk brn ...... .30 .20

FAO "Freedom from Hunger" campaign.

Runner and Walker — A89

Centenary Emblem — A90

1963, Feb. 17   Litho.   Perf. 13
437 A89 30m brn, blk & grn .... .30 .20

Army Sports Day; 13th C.I.S.M. cross country championships.

1963, May 8   Engr.   Perf. 13
438 A90 20m brn, gray & red ...... .20 .20

Centenary of International Red Cross.

"Human Rights" — A91

Hand Raising Gateway of Great Temple Philae — A92

1963, Dec. 10   Unwmk.   Perf.
439 A91 30m grn & dk brn .... .20

15th anniv. of the Universal Declaration Human Rights.

1964, Mar. 8   Eng
440 A92 50m red brn, bis & bluish blk .... .35

UNESCO world campaign to save histo monuments in Nubia.

Sunshine, Rain and Barometer — A93

Mohammed Ali — A94

1964, Mar. 8   Unwmk.   Perf.
441 A93 40m brn, red lil & slate .... .30

4th World Meteorological Day, Mar. 23.

1964, May 15   Eng
442 A94 50m sepia .... .25

Mohammed Ali (1894-1928), labor leader.

Map of Africa and Symbolic Flower — A95

Pres. Habib Bourguiba — A96

1964, May 25   Photo.   Perf. 13x1
443 A95 60m multicolored .... .35

Addis Ababa charter on African Unity, 1s anniv.

1964, June 1   Engr.   Perf. 12½x13
444 A96 20m vio bl .... .20
445 A96 30m black .... .20

"Ship and Torch" — A97

1964, Oct. 19 Photo. Perf. 11½x11
446 A97 50m blk & grn .20 .20

Neo-Destour Congress, Bizerte. "Bizerte" in Arabic forms the ship and "Neo-Destour Congress 1964" the torch of the design.

Communication Equipment and ITU Emblem — A98

1965, May 17 Engr. Perf. 13
447 A98 55m gray & blue .35 .20
ITU, centenary.

Carthaginian Coin — A99   Girl with Book — A100

Perf. 12½x14

1965, July 9 Photo. Unwmk.
448 A99 5m grn & blk brn .20 .20
449 A99 10m bis & blk brn .20 .20
450 A99 75m bl & blk brn .50 .20
Nos. 448-450 (3) .90 .60
Festival of Popular Arts, Carthage.

1965, Oct. 1 Engr. Perf. 13
451 A100 25m brt bl, blk & red .20 .20
452 A100 40m blk, bl & red .25 .20
453 A100 50m red, bl & blk .30 .20
a. Souvenir sheet of 3, #451-453 3.00 3.00
Nos. 451-453 (3) .75 .60

Girl Students' Center; education for women.
No. 453a sold for 200m. Issued perf. and imperf.; same value.

Links and ICY Emblem — A101   Man Pouring Water — A102

1965, Oct. 24
454 A101 40m blk, brt bl & rose lil .30 .20
International Cooperation Year.

1966, Jan. 18 Photo. Perf. 13x14
Symbolic Designs: 10m, Woman and pool. 30m, Woman pouring water. 100m, Mountain and branches.

Inscribed "Eaux Minerales"
455 A102 10m gray, ocher & dk red .20 .20
456 A102 20m multicolored .20 .20
457 A102 30m yel, bl & red .25 .20
458 A102 100m ol, bl & yel .65 .40
Nos. 455-458 (4) 1.30 1.00
Mineral waters of Tunisia.

President Bourguiba and Hands A103

"Promotion of Culture" — A104

25m, "Independence" (arms raised), flag and doves. 40m, "Development."

1966, June 1 Engr. Perf. 13
459 A103 5m dl pur & vio .20 .20
460 A103 10m gray grn & sl grn .20 .20

Perf. 11½
Photo.
461 A104 25m multi .20 .20
462 A104 40m multi, horiz. .35 .20
463 A104 60m multi .50 .20
Nos. 459-463 (5) 1.45 1.00
10th anniversary of independence.

Map of Africa through View Finder, Plane and UN Emblem — A105

1966, Sept. 12 Engr. Perf. 13
464 A105 15m lilac & multicolored .20 .20
465 A105 35m blue & multi .20 .20
466 A105 40m multicolored .25 .20
a. Souvenir sheet, #464-466 7.50 7.50
Nos. 464-466 (3) .65 .60

2nd UN Regional Cartographic Conference for Africa, held in Tunisia, Sept. 12-24.
No. 466a sold for 150m. Issued perf. and imperf.; same value.

UNESCO Emblem and Nine Muses A106

1966, Oct. 24 Perf. 13
467 A106 100m blk & brn .60 .25
UNESCO, 20th anniv.

Runners and Mediterranean Map — A107

1967, Mar. 20 Engr. Perf. 13
468 A107 20m dk red, brn ol & bl .20 .20
469 A107 30m brt bl & blk .20 .20
Mediterranean Games, Sept. 8-17.

Types of 1962-63 and 1965-66 with EXPO '67 Emblem and Inscription and

Symbols of Various Activities — A108

Designs: 50m, Woman of Djerba. 75m, Woman of Gabes. 155m, Pink flamingoes.

Photo.; Engr. (A108)
1967, Apr. 28 Perf. 11½, 13 (A108)
470 A82 50m multicolored .25 .20
471 A82 75m multicolored .35 .25
472 A108 100m dk grn, sl bl & blk .45 .45
473 A108 110m dk brn, ultra & red .55 .30
474 AP6 155m multicolored .90 .30
Nos. 470-474 (5) 2.50 1.50

EXPO '67, Intl. Exhibition, Montreal, Apr. 28-Oct. 27.

Tunisian Pavilion, Pres. Bourguiba and Map of Tunisia — A109

Designs: 105m, 200m, Tunisian Pavilion and bust of Pres. Bourguiba.

1967, June 13 Engr. Perf. 13
475 A109 65m red lil & dp org .20 .20
476 A109 105m multicolored .30 .20
477 A109 120m brt bl .40 .25
478 A109 200m red, lil & blk .65 .35
Nos. 475-478 (4) 1.55 1.00
Tunisia Day at EXPO '67.

"Tunisia" Holding 4-leaf Clovers A110

Woman Freeing Doves — A111

1967, July 25 Litho. Perf. 13½
479 A110 25m multicolored .20 .20
480 A111 40m multicolored .20 .20
10th anniversary of the Republic.

Tennis Courts, Players and Games' Emblem — A112

10m, Games' emblem & sports emblems, vert. 15m, Swimming pool & swimmers. 35m, Sports Palace & athletes. 75m, Stadium & athletes.

1967, Sept. 8 Engr. Perf. 13
481 A112 5m sl grn & hn brn .20 .20
482 A112 10m brn red & multi .20 .20
483 A112 15m black .20 .20
484 A112 35m dk brn & Prus bl .30 .20
485 A112 75m dk car rose, vio & bl grn .55 .35
Nos. 481-485 (5) 1.45 1.15
Mediterranean Games, Tunis, Sept. 8-17.

Bird, Punic Period — A113

"Mankind" and Human Rights Flame — A114

History of Tunisia: 20m, Sea horse, medallion from Kerkouane. 25m, Hannibal, bronze bust, Volubilis. 30m, Stele, Carthage. 40m, Hamilcar, coin. 60m, Mask, funereal pendant.

1967, Dec. 1 Litho. Perf. 13½
486 A113 15m gray grn, pink & blk .20 .20
487 A113 20m dp bl, red & blk .20 .20
488 A113 25m dk grn & org brn .20 .20
489 A113 30m grnsh gray, pink & blk .25 .20
490 A113 40m red brn, yel & blk .30 .20
491 A113 60m multicolored .35 .20
Nos. 486-491 (6) 1.50 1.20

1968, Jan. 18 Engr. Perf. 13
492 A114 25m brick red .20 .20
493 A114 60m deep blue .25 .20
International Human Rights Year.

Computer Fantasy A115

1968, Mar. 20 Engr. Perf. 13
494 A115 25m mag, bl vio & ol .20 .20
495 A115 40m ol grn, red brn & brn .25 .20
496 A115 60m ultra, slate & brn .30 .20
Nos. 494-496 (3) .75 .60
Introduction of electronic equipment for postal service.

Physician and Patient — A116   Arabian Jasmine — A117

1968, Apr. 7 Engr. Perf. 13
497 A116 25m dp grn & brt grn .20 .20
498 A116 60m magenta & carmine .30 .20
WHO, 20th anniversary.

1968-69 Photo. Perf. 11½
Flowers: 5m, Flax. 6m, Canna indica. 10m, Pomegranate. 15m, Rhaponticum acaule. 20m, Geranium. 25m, Madonna lily. 40m, Peach blossoms. 50m, Caper. 60m, Ariana rose. 100m, Jasmine.

Granite Paper

499 A117	5m multicolored	.20	.20
500 A117	6m multicolored	.20	.20
501 A117	10m multicolored	.20	.20
502 A117	12m multicolored	.20	.20
503 A117	15m multicolored	.20	.20
504 A117	20m multicolored	.20	.20
505 A117	25m multicolored	.20	.20
506 A117	40m multicolored	.30	.20
507 A117	50m multicolored	.30	.20
508 A117	60m multicolored	.55	.30
509 A117	100m multicolored	.85	.45
	Nos. 499-509 (11)	3.40	2.55

Issued: 12, 50, 60, 100m, 4/9/68; others, 3/20/69.

Flower with Red Crescent and Globe — A118

Flutist — A119

25m, Dove with Red Crescent and globe.

1968, May 8   **Engr.**   *Perf. 13*
510 A118	15m Prus bl, grn & red	.20	.20
511 A118	25m brt rose lil & red	.25	.20

Red Crescent Society.

1968, June 1   **Litho.**   *Perf. 13*
512 A119	20m vio & multi	.20	.20
513 A119	50m multicolored	.25	.20

Stamp Day.

Jackal A120

Animals: 8m, Porcupine. 10m, Dromedary. 15m, Dorcas gazelle. 20m, Desert fox (fennec). 25m, Desert hedgehog. 40m, Arabian horse. 60m, Boar.

1968-69   **Photo.**   *Perf. 11½*
514 A120	5m dk brn, lt bl & bis	.20	.20
515 A120	8m dk vio brn & yel grn	.20	.20
516 A120	10m dk brn, lt bl & ocher	.25	.20
517 A120	15m dk brn, ocher & yel grn	.25	.20
518 A120	20m dl yel & dk brn	.35	.30
519 A120	25m blk, tan & brt grn	.55	.30
520 A120	40m blk, lil & pale grn	.70	.55
521 A120	60m dk brn, buff & yel grn	1.00	.80
	Nos. 514-521 (8)	3.50	2.75

Issued: 5, 8, 20, 60m, 9/15/68; others, 1/18/69.

Worker and ILO Emblem — A121

60m, Young man & woman holding banner.

1969, May 1   **Engr.**   *Perf. 13*
522 A121	25m Prus bl, blk & bis	.20	.20
523 A121	60m rose car, bl & yel	.30	.20

ILO, 50th anniversary.

Veiled Women and Musicians with Flute and Drum A122

1969, June 20   **Litho.**   *Perf. 14x13½*
524 A122	100m dp yel grn & multi	.50	.30

Stamp Day.

Tunisian Coat of Arms — A123

Symbols of Industry — A124

1969, July 25   **Photo.**   *Perf. 11½*
525 A123	15m yel & multi	.20	.20
526 A123	25m pink & multi	.20	.20
527 A123	40m gray & multi	.20	.20
528 A123	60m lt bl & multi	.25	.20
	Nos. 525-528 (4)	.85	.80

1969, Sept. 10   *Perf. 13x12*
529 A124	60m blk, red & yel	.25	.20

African Development Bank, 5th anniv.

Lute — A125

Nurse and Maghrib Flags — A126

Musical Instruments: 50m, Zither, horiz. 70m, Rebab (2-strings). 90m, Drums and flute, horiz.

1970, Mar. 20   **Photo.**   *Perf. 11½*
Granite Paper
530 A125	25m multicolored	.25	.20
531 A125	50m multicolored	.35	.20
532 A125	70m multicolored	.55	.25
533 A125	90m multicolored	.60	.35
	Nos. 530-533 (4)	1.75	1.00

1970, May 4   **Photo.**   *Perf. 11½*
534 A126	25m lilac & multi	.20	.20

6th Medical Seminar of Maghrib Countries (Morocco, Algeria, Tunisia and Libya), Tunis, May 4-10.

Common Design Types pictured following the introduction.

UPU Headquarters Issue
Common Design Type

1970, May 20   **Engr.**   *Perf. 13*
535 CD133	25m dl red & dk ol bis	.25	.20

Mail Service Symbol A127

35m, Mailmen of yesterday and today, vert.

1970, Oct. 15   **Litho.**   *Perf. 12½x13*
Size: 37x31½mm
536 A127	25m pink & multi	.30	.20

Size: 22x37½mm
Perf. 13x12½
537 A127	35m blk & multi	.40	.20

United Nations, 25th anniversary.

Dove, Laurel and UN Emblem A128

1970, Oct. 24   **Photo.**   *Perf. 13x12½*
538 A128	40m multicolored	.25	.20

United Nations, 25th anniversary.

Jasmine Vendor and Veiled Woman — A129

Lenin, after N.N. Joukov — A130

Scenes from Tunisian Life: 25m, "The 3rd Day of the Wedding." 35m, Perfume vendor. 40m, Fish vendor. 85m, Waiter in coffeehouse.

1970, Nov. 9   **Photo.**   *Perf. 14*
539 A129	20m dk grn & multi	.20	.20
540 A129	25m multicolored	.20	.20
541 A129	35m multicolored	.20	.20
542 A129	40m dp car & multi	.25	.20
543 A129	85m brt bl & multi	.40	.20
a.	Souvenir sheet of 5, #539-543	3.50	3.50
	Nos. 539-543 (5)	1.25	1.00

No. 543a sold for 500m. Issued perf. and imperf.; same value.

1970, Dec. 28   **Engr.**   *Perf. 13*
544 A130	60m dk car rose	.25	.20

Lenin (1870-1924), Russian communist leader.

Radar, Flags and Carrier Pigeon — A131

1971, May 17   **Litho.**   *Perf. 13x12½*
545 A131	25m lt bl & multi	.22	.20

Coordinating Committee for Post and Telecommunications Administrations of Maghrib Countries.

UN Headquarters, Symbolic Flower — A132

1971, May 10   **Photo.**   *Perf. 12½x13*
546 A132	80m brt rose lil, blk & yel	.30	.20

Intl. year against racial discrimination.

"Telecommunications" — A133

1971, May 17   *Perf. 13x12*
547 A133	70m sil, blk & lt grn		.35

3rd World Telecommunications Day.

Earth, Moon, Satellites A134

Design: 90m, Abstract composition.

1971, June 21   **Photo.**   *Perf. 13x12*
548 A134	15m brt bl & blk	.20	
549 A134	90m scar & blk	.40	

Conquest of space.

"Pottery Merchant" A135

Life in Tunisia (stylized drawings): 30m, Esparto weaver selling hats and mats. 40m, Poultry man. 50m, Dyer.

1971, July 24   **Photo.**   *Perf. 14x13*
550 A135	25m gold & multi	.20	.2
551 A135	30m gold & multi	.20	.2
552 A135	40m gold & multi	.20	.2
553 A135	50m gold & multi	.25	.2
a.	Sheet of 4, #550-553, perf. 13½	2.50	2.5
	Nos. 550-553 (4)	.85	.8

No. 553a sold for 500m. Issued perf. and imperf.; same value.

Pres. Bourguiba Sick in 1938 A136

Designs: 25m, Bourguiba and "8," vert. 50m, Bourguiba carried in triumph, vert. 80m, Bourguiba and irrigation dam.

1971, Oct. 11   *Perf. 13½x13, 13x13½*
554 A136	25m multicolored	.20	.20
555 A136	30m multicolored	.20	.20
556 A136	50m multicolored	.20	.20
557 A136	80m blk, ultra & grn	.25	.20
	Nos. 554-557 (4)	.85	.80

8th Congress of the Neo-Destour Party.

Shah Mohammed Riza Pahlavi and Stone Head 6th Century B.C. — A137

50m, King Bahram-Gur hunting, 4th cent. 100m, Coronation, from Persian miniature, 1614.

1971, Oct. 17   **Perf. 11½**

Granite Paper

8	A137	25m multicolored	.20 .20
9	A137	50m multicolored	.20 .20
0	A137	100m multicolored	.40 .20
a.		Souvenir sheet of 3, #558-560	2.25 2.25
		Nos. 558-560 (3)	.80 .60

2500th anniv. of the founding of the Persian mpire by Cyrus the Great. No. 560a sold for 00m. Issued perf. and imperf.; same value.

Pimento and Warrior A138

2m, Mint & farmer. 5m, Pear & 2 men under ear tree. 25m, Oleander & girl. 60m, Pear & heep. 100m, Grapefruit & fruit vendor.

1971, Nov. 15   **Perf. 13**

61	A138	1m lt bl & multi	.20 .20
62	A138	2m gray & multi	.20 .20
63	A138	5m citron & multi	.20 .20
64	A138	25m lilac & multi	.20 .20
65	A138	60m multicolored	.40 .20
66	A138	100m buff & multi	.80 .25
a.		Souvenir sheet of 6, #561-566	2.50 2.50
		Nos. 561-566 (6)	2.00 1.25

Fruit, flowers and folklore. No. 566a sold for 00m. Exists imperf.; same value.

Dancer and Musician — A139

1971, Nov. 22   **Photo.**   **Perf. 11½**

67 A139 50m blue & multi   .25 .20

Stamp Day.

Map of Africa, Communica-tion Symbols A139a

UNICEF Emblem, Mother and Child A140

Perf. 13½x12½

1971, Nov. 30   **Litho.**

68 A139a 95m multicolored   .35 .20

Pan-African telecommunications system.

1971, Dec. 6   **Photo.**   **Perf. 11½**

69 A140 110m multicolored   .35 .20

UNICEF, 25th anniv.

Symbolic Olive Tree and Oil Vat — A141

Gondolier in Flood Waters — A142

1972, Jan. 9   **Litho.**   **Perf. 13½**

570 A141 60m multicolored   .20 .20

International Olive Year.

1972, Feb. 7   **Photo.**   **Perf. 11½**

Designs: 30m, Young man and Doge's Palace. 50m, Gondola's prow and flood. 80m, Rialto Bridge and hand holding gondolier's hat, horiz.

571	A142	25m lt bl & multi	.20 .20
572	A142	30m blk & multi	.20 .20
573	A142	50m yel grn, gray & blk	.25 .20
574	A142	80m bl & multi	.35 .20
		Nos. 571-574 (4)	1.00 .80

UNESCO campaign to save Venice.

Man Reading and Book Year Emblem — A143

"Your Heart is Your Health" — A144

1972, Mar. 27   **Photo.**   **Perf. 11½**
Granite Paper

575 A143 90m brn & multi   .35 .20

International Book Year.

1972, Apr. 7   **Perf. 13x13½**

World Health Day: 60m, Smiling man pointing to heart.

576	A144	25m grn & multi	.20 .20
577	A144	60m red & multi	.25 .20

"Only one Earth" Environment Emblem — A145

1972, June 5   **Engr.**   **Perf. 13**

578 A145 60m lemon & slate green   .30 .20

UN Conference on Human Environment, Stockholm, June 5-16.

Hurdler, Olympic Emblems A146

1972, Aug. 26   **Photo.**   **Perf. 11½**

579	A146	5m Volleyball	.20 .20
580	A146	15m shown	.20 .20
581	A146	20m Athletes	.20 .20
582	A146	25m Soccer	.20 .20
583	A146	60m Swimming, women's	.20 .20

584	A146	80m Running	.35 .20
a.		Souv. sheet of 6	2.25 2.25
		Nos. 579-584 (6)	1.35 1.20

20th Olympic Games, Munich, Aug. 26-Sept. 11. No. 584a contains 6 imperf. stamps similar to Nos. 579-584. Sold for 500m.

Chessboard and Pieces — A147

Fisherman A148

1972, Sept. 25   **Photo.**   **Perf. 11½**

585 A147 60m grn & multi   1.00 .50

20th Men's Chess Olympiad, Skopje, Yugoslavia, Sept.-Oct.

1972, Oct. 23   **Litho.**   **Perf. 13½**

586	A148	5m shown	.20 .20
587	A148	10m Basket maker	.20 .20
588	A148	25m Musician	.20 .20
589	A148	50m Married Berber woman	.30 .20
590	A148	60m Flower merchant	.30 .20
591	A148	80m Festival	.40 .20
a.		Souvenir sheet of 6, #586-591	2.25 2.25
		Nos. 586-591 (6)	1.60 1.20

Life in Tunisia. No. 591a sold for 500m; exists imperf.

Post Office, Tunis A149

Litho. & Engr.

1972, Dec. 8   **Perf. 13**

592 A149 25m ver, org & blk   .20 .20

Stamp Day.

Dome of the Rock, Jerusalem A150

1973, Jan. 22   **Photo.**   **Perf. 13½**

593 A150 25m multicolored   .65 .35

Globe, Pen and Quill — A151

Family — A152

Design: 60m, Lyre and minaret.

1973, Mar. 19   **Photo.**   **Perf. 14x13½**

594	A151	25m gold, brt mag & brn	.20 .20
595	A151	60m bl & multi	.20 .20

9th Congress of Arab Writers.

1973, Apr. 2   **Perf. 11½**

Family Planning: 25m, profiles and dove.

596	A152	20m grn & multi	.20 .20
597	A152	25m lil & multi	.20 .20

"10" and Bird Feeding Young A153

Design: 60m, "10" made of grain and bread, and hand holding spoon.

1973, Apr. 26   **Photo.**   **Perf. 11½**

598	A153	25m multicolored	.20 .20
599	A153	60m multicolored	.20 .20

World Food Program, 10th anniversary.

Roman Head and Ship A154

Drawings of Tools and: 25m, Mosaic with ostriches and camel. 30m, Mosaic with 4 heads and 4 emblems. 40m, Punic stele to the sun, vert. 60m, Outstretched hand & arm of Christian preacher; symbols of 4 Evangelists. 75m, 17th cent. potsherd with Arabic inscription, vert.

1973, May 6

600	A154	5m multicolored	.20 .20
601	A154	25m multicolored	.20 .20
602	A154	30m multicolored	.20 .20
603	A154	40m multicolored	.25 .20
604	A154	60m multicolored	.30 .20
605	A154	75m multicolored	.35 .20
a.		Souvenir sheet of 6	2.75 2.75
		Nos. 600-605 (6)	1.50 1.20

UNESCO campaign to save Carthage. No. 605a contains 6 imperf. stamps similar to Nos. 600-605. Sold for 500m.

Overlapping Circles — A155

Map of Africa as Festival Emblem — A156

Design: 75m, Printed circuit board.

1973, May 17   **Photo.**   **Perf. 14x13½**

606	A155	60m yel & multi	.20 .20
607	A155	75m vio & multi	.25 .20

5th Intl. Telecommunications Day.

1973, July 15   **Photo.**   **Perf. 13½x13**

40m, African heads, festival emblem in eye.

608	A156	25m multicolored	.20 .20
609	A156	40m multicolored	.25 .20

Pan-African Youth Festival, Tunis.

Scout Emblem and Pennants — A157

1973, July 23   **Litho.**   **Perf. 13½x13**

610 A157 25m multicolored   .20 .20

International Boy Scout Organization.

Crescent-shaped Racing Cars — A158

1973, July 30   **Perf. 13x13½**
611 A158 60m multicolored   .25 .20
    2nd Pan-Arab auto race.

Highway
Cloverleaf
A159

Traffic Lights and   Stylized
Signs — A160   Camel — A161

Perf. 12½x13, 13x12½
1973, Sept. 28   **Litho.**
612 A159 25m lt bl & multi   .20 .20
613 A160 30m multicolored   .25 .20
    Highway safety campaign.

1973, Oct. 8   **Photo.**   **Perf. 13½**
    Stamp Day: 10m, Stylized bird and phila-
telic symbols, horiz.
614 A161 10m multicolored   .20 .20
615 A161 65m multicolored   .25 .20

Copernicus   African Unity
A162   A163

Lithographed and Engraved
1973, Oct. 16   **Perf. 13x12½**
616 A162 60m blk & multi   .25 .20

1973, Nov. 4   **Photo.**   **Perf. 14x13½**
617 A163 25m blk & multi   .25 .20
    10th anniv. of the OAU.

Handshake and   Globe, Hand
Emblems   Holding
A164   Carnation
             A165

1973, Nov. 15   **Litho.**   **Perf. 14½x14**
618 A164 65m yel & multi   .30 .20
    25th anniv. of Intl. Criminal Police Org.

1973, Dec. 10   **Photo.**   **Perf. 11½**
619 A165 60m blk & multi   .30 .20
    25th anniv. of Universal Declaration of
Human Rights.

WMO Headquarters and
Emblem — A166

    Design: 60m, Globe and emblem.

1973, Dec. 24   **Litho.**   **Perf. 14x14½**
620 A166 25m multicolored   .20 .20
621 A166 60m multicolored   .25 .20
    Intl. meteorological cooperation, cent.

Bourguiba in the
Desert,
1945 — A167

Scientist with
Microscope
A168

    Portraits of Pres. Habib Bourguiba: 25m,
Exile transfer from Galite Island to Ile de la
Groix, France, 1954. 60m, Addressing crowd,
1974. 75m, In Victory Parade, 1955. 100m, In
1934.

1974, Mar. 2   **Photo.**   **Perf. 11½**
622 A167 15m plum & multi   .20 .20
623 A167 25m multicolored   .20 .20
624 A167 60m multicolored   .20 .20
625 A167 75m multicolored   .30 .20
626 A167 100m multicolored   .35 .25
    a.   Souvenir sheet of 5, #622-626   1.50 1.50
          Nos. 622-626 (5)   1.25 1.05

    40th anniv. of the Neo-Destour Party. No.
626a sold for 500m. Issued perf. and imperf.;
same value.

1974, Mar. 21   **Perf. 14**
627 A168 60m multicolored   .40 .20
    6th African Congress of Micropaleontology,
Mar. 21-Apr. 3.

Woman with   Pres. Bourguiba
Telephones and   and Sun Flower
Globe — A169   Emblem — A171

WPY
Emblem
and
Symbolic
Design
A170

    60m, Telephone dial, telephones, wires.

1974, July 1   **Photo.**   **Perf. 11½**
628 A169 15m multicolored   .20 .20
629 A169 60m multicolored   .35 .20
    Introduction of international automatic tele-
phone dialing system.

1974, Aug. 19   **Photo.**   **Perf. 11½**
630 A170 110m multicolored   .40 .20
    World Population Year.

1974, Sept. 12   **Photo.**   **Perf. 11½**
    60m, Bourguiba and cactus flower, horiz.
200m, Bourguiba and verbena, horiz.
631 A171 25m blk, ultra & grnsh
              bl   .20 .20
632 A171 60m red, car & yel   .20 .20
633 A171 200m blk, brt lil & grn   .60 .40
    a.   Souv. sheet, #631-633, imperf.   1.50 1.50
          Nos. 631-633 (3)   1.00 .80
    Congress of the Socialist Destour Party.

Jets
Flying
over
Old
World
Map
A172

1974, Sept. 23   **Litho.**   **Perf. 12½**
634 A172 60m brn & multi   .35 .20
    25th anniversary of Tunisian aviation.

Symbolic Carrier
Pigeons — A173

Handshake,
Letter, UPU
Emblem — A174

1974, Oct. 9   **Photo.**   **Perf. 13**
635 A173 25m multicolored   .20 .20
636 A174 60m multicolored   .30 .20
    Centenary of Universal Postal Union.

Le Bardo, National
Assembly — A175

Pres. Bourguiba
Ballot — A176

1974, Nov. 3   **Photo.**   **Perf. 11**
637 A175 25m grn, bl & blk   .20 .
638 A176 100m org & blk   .35 .
    Legislative (25m) and presidential electio
(100m), Nov. 1974.

Mailman with   Water
Letters and   Carrier — A17
Bird — A177

1974, Dec. 5   **Litho.**   **Perf. 14½x**
639 A177 75m lt vio & multi   .30 .
    Stamp Day.

1975, Feb. 17   **Photo.**   **Perf. 13**
640 A178 5m shown   .20 .
641 A178 15m Perfume vendor   .20 .
642 A178 25m Laundresses   .20 .
643 A178 60m Potter   .30 .
644 A178 110m Fruit vendor   .50 .
    a.   Souvenir sheet of 5, #640-644   3.00 3.
          Nos. 640-644 (5)   1.40 1.
    Life in Tunisia. No. 644a sold for 500
Issued perf. and imperf.; same value.

Steel Tower,
Skyscraper — A179

Geometri
Designs
and Arrow
A180

Perf. 14x13½, 13½x14
1975, Mar. 17   **Phot**
645 A179 25m yel, org & blk   .20 .
646 A180 65m ultra & multi   .20 .
    Union of Arab Engineers, 13th Conferenc
Tunis, Mar. 17-21.

Brass Coffeepot and Plate — A181

15m, Horse and rider. 25m, Still life. 30m, Bird cage. 40m, Woman with earrings. 60m, Design patterns.

1975, Apr. 14   Perf. 13x14, 14x13
647 A181 10m blk & multi   .20   .20
648 A181 15m blk & multi   .20   .20
649 A181 25m blk & multi   .20   .20
650 A181 30m blk & multi, vert.   .20   .20
651 A181 40m blk & multi, vert.   .20   .20
652 A181 60m blk & multi   .20   .20
        Nos. 647-652 (6)   1.20   1.20

Artisans and their works.

Communications and Weather
Symbols — A182

1975, May 17   Photo.   Perf. 11½
653 A182 50m lt bl & multi   .20   .20

World Telecommunications Day (communications serving meteorology).

Youth and   Tunisian Woman,
Hope — A183   IWY
                   Emblem — A184

65m, Bourguiba arriving at La Goulette, Tunis.

1975, June 1   Photo.   Perf. 11½
654 A183 25m multi   .20   .20
655 A183 65m multi, horiz.   .20   .20

Victory (independence), 20th anniversary.

1975, June 19   Litho.   Perf. 14x13½
656 A184 110m multicolored   .40   .25

International Women's Year.

Children
Crossing
Street
A185

1975, July 5   Photo.   Perf. 13½x14
657 A185 25m multicolored   .20   .20

Highway safety campaign, July 1-Sept. 30.

Djerbian
Minaret,
Hotel
and
Marina,
Jerba
A186

Old & new Tunisia: 15m, 17th cent. minaret & modern hotel, Tunis. 20m, Fortress, earring & hotel, Monastir. 65m, View of Sousse, hotel & pendant. 500m, Town wall, mosque &

---

palms, Tozeur. 1d, Mosques & Arab ornaments, Kairouan.

1975, July 12   Litho.   Perf. 14x14½
658 A186 10m multicolored   .20   .20
659 A186 15m multicolored   .20   .20
660 A186 20m multicolored   .20   .20
661 A186 65m multicolored   .25   .25
662 A186 500m multicolored   2.40   .80
663 A186 1d multicolored   3.75   2.00
        Nos. 658-663 (6)   7.00   3.65

Victors — A187

Symbolic
Ship
A188

1975, Aug. 23   Photo.   Perf. 13½
664 A187 25m olive & multi   .20   .20
665 A188 50m blue & multi   .20   .20

7th Mediterranean Games, Algiers, 8/23-9/6.

Flowers in Vase,
Birds Holding
Letters — A189

1975, Sept. 29   Litho.   Perf. 13½x13
666 A189 100m blue & multi   .30   .20

Stamp Day.

Sadiki College, Young
Bourguiba — A190

Engr. & Litho.
1975, Nov. 17   Perf. 13
667 A190 25m sepia, orange & olive   .20   .20

Sadiki College, centenary.

Duck — A191

Vergil — A192

Mosaics: 10m, Fish. 25m, Lioness, horiz. 60m, Head of Medusa, horiz. 75m, Circus spectators.

1976, Feb. 16   Photo.   Perf. 13
668 A191 5m multicolored   .20   .20
669 A191 10m multicolored   .20   .20
670 A192 25m multicolored   .40   .30
671 A192 60m multicolored   .40   .30
672 A192 75m multicolored   .50   .30
673 A192 100m multicolored   .70   .30
  a. Souvenir sheet of 6, #668-673   4.00   4.00
        Nos. 668-673 (6)   2.40   1.60

Tunisian mosaics, 2nd-5th centuries. No. 673a sold for 500m. Issued perf. and imperf.; same value.

Telephone
A193

1976, Mar. 10   Litho.   Perf. 14x13½
674 A193 150m blue & multi   .40   .25

Centenary of first telephone call by Alexander Graham Bell, Mar. 10, 1876.

Pres.
Bourguiba
and
"20" — A194

Pres. Bourguiba and: 100m, "20" and symbolic Tunisian flag. 150m, "Tunisia" rising from darkness, and 20 flowers.

1976, Mar. 20   Photo.   Perf. 11½
675 A194 40m multicolored   .20   .20
676 A194 100m multicolored   .20   .20
677 A194 150m multicolored   .30   .20
        Nos. 675-677 (3)   .70   .60
Souvenir Sheets
Perf. 11½, Imperf.
678   Sheet of 3   1.50   1.50
  a.   A194 50m like 40m   .20   .20
  b.   A194 200m like 100m   .35   .20
  c.   A194 250m like 150m   .45   .25

20th anniversary of independence.

Blind Man with   Procession and
Cane   Buildings
A195   A196

1976, Apr. 7   Engr.   Perf. 13
679 A195 100m black & red   .40   .20

World Health Day: "Foresight prevents blindness."

1976, May 31   Photo.   Perf. 12x11½
680 A196 40m multicolored   .20   .20

Habitat, UN Conf. on Human Settlements, Vancouver, Canada, May 31-June 11.

Face and Hands
Decorated with
Henna — A197

Old and new Tunisia: 50m, Sponge fishing at Jerba. 65m, Textile industry. 110m, Pottery of Guellala.

1976, June 15   Photo.   Perf. 13x13½
681 A197 40m multicolored   .20   .20
682 A197 50m multicolored   .20   .20
683 A197 65m multicolored   .20   .20
684 A197 110m multicolored   .40   .20
        Nos. 681-684 (4)   1.00   .80

The
Spirit of
'76, by
Archibald
M.
Willard
A198

1976, July 4   Perf. 13x14
685 A198 200m multicolored   .80   .50
Souvenir Sheets
Perf.   13x14, Imperf.
686 A198 500m multicolored   2.00   2.00

American Bicentennial.

Running
A199

Montreal Olympic Games Emblem and: 75m, Bicycling. 120m, Peace dove.

1976, July 17   Photo.   Perf. 11½
687 A199 50m gray, red & blk   .20   .20
688 A199 75m red, yel & blk   .20   .20
689 A199 120m orange & multi   .35   .20
        Nos. 687-689 (3)   .75   .60

21st Olympic Games, Montreal, Canada, July 17-Aug. 1.

Child   Heads and
Reading — A200   Bird — A201

1976, Aug. 23   Litho.   Perf. 13
690 A200 100m brown & multi   .35   .20

Books for children.

1976, Sept. 30   Litho.   Perf. 13
691 A201 150m orange & multi   .40   .20

Non-aligned Countries, 15th anniv. of 1st Conference.

Mouradite
Mausoleum, 17th
Century — A202

Electronic Tree and ITU Emblem — A204

Globe and Emblem A203

Cultural Heritage: 100m, Minaret, Kairawan Great Mosque and psalmodist. 150m, Monastir Ribat monastery and Alboracq (sphinx). 200m, Barber's Mosque, Kairawan andman's bust.

1976, Oct. 25   Photo.   Perf. 14
692	A202	85m multicolored	.25 .20
693	A202	100m multicolored	.25 .20
694	A202	150m multicolored	.40 .20
695	A202	200m multicolored	.60 .30
	Nos. 692-695 (4)		1.50 .90

1976, Dec. 24   Photo.   Perf. 13x14
696	A203	150m multicolored	.50 .25

25th anniv. of UN Postal Administration.

1977, May 17   Photo.   Perf. 14x13½
697	A204	150m multicolored	.50 .30

9th World Telecommunications Day.

"Communication," Sassenage Castle, Grenoble — A205

1977, May 19   Litho.   Perf. 13½x13
698	A205	100m multicolored	.50 .30

10th anniv. of Intl. French Language Council.

Soccer A206

1977, June 27   Photo.   Perf. 13½
699	A206	150m multicolored	.50 .30

Junior World Soccer Tournament, Tunisia, June 27-July 10.

Gold Coin, 10th Century — A207

Cultural Heritage: 15m, Stele, Gorjani Cemetery, Tunis, 13th century. 20m, Floral design, 17th century illumination. 30m, Bird and flowers, glass painting, 1922. 40m, Antelope, from 11th century clay pot. 50m, Gate, Sidi Bou Said, 20th century.

1977, July 9   Photo.   Perf. 13
700	A207	10m multicolored	.20 .20
701	A207	15m multicolored	.20 .20
702	A207	20m multicolored	.20 .20
703	A207	30m multicolored	.20 .20
704	A207	40m multicolored	.20 .20
705	A207	50m multicolored	.20 .20
a.	Miniature sheet of 6, #700-705		1.00 1.00
	Nos. 700-705 (6)		1.20 1.20

"The Young Republic" and Bourguiba — A208

Diseased Knee, Gears and Globe — A210

Symbolic Cancellation, APU Emblem — A209

Habib Bourguiba and: 100m, "The Confident Republic" and 20 doves. 150m, "The Determined Republic" and 20 roses.

1977, July 25   Photo.   Perf. 13x13½
706	A208	40m multicolored	.20 .20
707	A208	100m multicolored	.40 .20
708	A208	150m multicolored	.65 .20
a.	Souvenir sheet of 3, #706-708		2.00 2.00
	Nos. 706-708 (3)		1.25 .60

20th anniv. of the Republic. No. 708a sold for 500m. Exists imperf., same value.

1977, Aug. 16   Litho.   Perf. 13x12½
709	A209	40m multicolored	.20 .20

Arab Postal Union, 25th anniversary.

1977, Sept. 26   Photo.   Perf. 14x13½
710	A210	120m multicolored	.40 .20

World Rheumatism Year.

Farmer, Road, Water and Electricity — A211

1977, Dec. 15   Photo.   Perf. 13½
711	A211	40m multicolored	.20 .20

Rural development.

Factory Workers — A212

Pres. Bourguiba, Torch and "9" — A213

Designs: 20m, Bus driver and trains, horiz. 40m, Farmer driving tractor, horiz.

1978, Mar. 6   Perf. 13x14, 14x13
712	A212	20m rose red & multi	.20 .20
713	A212	40m black & green	.20 .20
714	A212	100m multicolored	.30 .20
	Nos. 712-714 (3)		.70 .60

5th development plan, creation of new jobs.

1978, Apr. 9   Engr.   Perf. 13
715	A213	40m shown	.20 .20
716	A213	60m Bourguiba and "9"	.20 .20

40th anniv. of 1st fight for independence, 4/9/38.

A214

1978, May 2   Photo.   Perf. 13x13½
717	A214	150m Policeman	.50 .20

6th Regional African Interpol Conference, Tunis, May 2-5.

A215

1978, June 1   Photo.   Perf. 13x14

Designs: 40m, Tunisian Goalkeeper. 150m., Soccer player, maps of South America and Africa, flags.
718	A215	40m multicolored	.20 .20
719	A215	150m multicolored	.50 .30

11th World Cup Soccer Championship, Argentina, June 1-25.

Destruction of Apartheid, Map of South Africa — A216

Fight Against Apartheid: 100m, White and black doves flying in unison.

1978, Aug. 30   Litho.   Perf. 13½x14
720	A216	50m multicolored	.20 .20
721	A216	100m multicolored	.30 .20

"Pollution is a Plague" A217

"Eradication of Smallpox" A218

Designs: 50m, "The Sea, mankind's patrimony." 120m, "Greening of the desert."

1978, Sept. 11   Photo.   Perf. 14x13
722	A217	10m multicolored	.20 .20
723	A217	50m multicolored	.20 .20
724	A217	120m multicolored	.50 .20
	Nos. 722-724 (3)		.90 .60

Protection of the environment.

1978, Oct. 16   Litho.   Perf. 12½
725	A218	150m multicolored	.40 .25

Global eradication of smallpox.

Jerba Weddin A219

5m, Horseman from Zlass. 75m, Wom potters from the Mogods. 100m, Dove o Marabout Sidi Mahrez cupolas, Tunis. 500 Plowing in Jenduba. 1d, Spring Festival Tozeur (man on swing).

1978, Nov. 1   Photo.   Perf.
726	A219	5m multi, vert.	.20
727	A219	60m multi	.20
728	A219	75m multi	.25
729	A219	100m multi	.35
730	A219	500m multi	2.25
731	A219	1d multi	3.50 1.
	Nos. 726-731 (6)		6.75 3.

Traditional Arab calligraphy.

Lenin and Red Banner over Kremlin — A220

Farhat Hached, Union Emblem — A221

1978, Nov. 7   Perf. 13
732	A220	150m multicolored	.40 .2

Russian October Revolution, 60th anniv.

1978, Dec. 5   Photo.   Perf. 1
733	A221	50m multicolored	.20 .2

Farhat Hached (1914-1952), founder o General Union of Tunisian Workers.

Family — A222

Sun with Man's Face — A223

1978, Dec. 15   Photo.   Perf. 13½
734	A222	50m multicolored	.20 .2

Tunisian Family Planning Assoc., 10th anniv.

1978, Dec. 25   Perf. 1
735	A223	100m multicolored	.40 .2

Sun as a source of light and energy.

Plane, Weather Map and Instruments — A224

1978, Dec. 29

736 A224 50m multicolored .20 .20
Tunisian civil aviation and meteorology, 20th anniv.

Habib Bourguiba and Constitution — A225

1979, May 31 Photo. Perf. 14x13½

737 A225 50m multicolored .20 .20
20th anniversary of Constitution.

El Kantaoui Port A226

1979, June 3 Perf. 13½x14

738 A226 150m multicolored .40 .20
Development of El Kantaoui as a resort area.

Landscapes — A227

1979, July 14 Perf. 12½x13½

739 A227 50m Korbous .20 .20
740 A227 100m Mides .20 .20

Bow Net Weaving — A228   Pres. Bourguiba, "10" and Hands — A229

1979, Aug. 15 Photo. Perf. 11½

741 A228 10m shown .20 .20
742 A228 50m Beekeeping .20 .20

1979, Sept. 5

743 A229 50m multicolored .20 .20
Socialist Destour Party, 10th Congress.

Modes of Communication, ITU Emblem — A230

1979, Sept. 20 Litho. Perf. 11½

744 A230 150m multicolored .50 .30
3rd World Telecommunications Exhibition, Geneva, Sept. 20-26.

Arab Achievements — A231

1979, Oct. 1 Perf. 14½

745 A231 50m multicolored .20 .20

Children Crossing Street, IYC Emblem — A232

1979, Oct. 16 Perf. 14x13½

746 A232 50m shown .20 .20
747 A232 100m Child and birds .35 .20
International Year of the Child.

Dove, Olive Tree, Map of Tunisia — A233   Woman Wearing Crown — A234

1979, Nov. 1 Litho. Perf. 12

748 A233 150m multicolored .50 .30
2nd International Olive Oil Year.

1979, Nov. 3 Perf. 14½

749 A234 50m multicolored .20 .20
Central Bank of Tunisia, 20th anniversary.

Children and Jujube Tree — A235

1979, Dec. 25 Litho. Perf. 15x14½

750 A235 20m shown .20 .20
751 A235 30m Peacocks .20 .20
752 A235 70m Goats .25 .20
753 A235 85m Girl, date palm .30 .20
Nos. 750-753 (4) .95 .80

Postal Code Introduction — A236

1980, Mar. 20 Photo. Perf. 14

754 A236 50m multicolored .20 .20

Fight Against Cigarette Smoking A237

1980, Apr. 7

755 A237 150m multicolored .40 .20

Pres. Bourguiba in Flower, Open Book — A238

1980, June 1 Photo. Perf. 11½

756 A238 50m shown .20 .20
757 A238 100m Dove, Bourguiba, mosque .45 .20
Victory (independence), 25th anniversary.

Butterfly and Gymnast A239

1980, June 3 Photo. Perf. 12x11½
Granite Paper

758 A239 100m multicolored .45 .20
Turin Gymnastic Games, June 1-7.

Artisans
A240   A241

1980, July 21 Photo. Perf. 13½

759 A240 30m multicolored .20 .20
760 A241 75m multicolored .30 .20

ibn-Khaldun (1332-1406), Historian — A242

Avicenna (Arab Physician), Birth Millenium — A243

1980, July 28 Perf. 14

761 A242 50m multicolored .20 .20

1980, Aug. 18 Engr. Perf. 12½x13

762 A243 100m redsh brn & sepia .40 .20

Arab Achievements — A244

1980, Aug. 25 Photo. Perf. 13½x14

763 A244 50m multicolored .20 .20

Port Sidi bou Said A245

1980, Sept. 4 Perf. 14

764 A245 100m multicolored .50 .20

World Tourism Conference, Manila, Sept. 27 — A246

1980, Sept. 27 Photo. Perf. 14

765 A246 150m multicolored .55 .20

Wedding in Jerba, by Yahia (1903-1969) — A247

1980, Oct. 1 Perf. 12

766 A247 50m multicolored .30 .20

Tozeur-Nefta International Airport Opening — A248

1980, Oct. 13 Photo. Perf. 13x13½

767 A248 85m multicolored .35 .20

Eye and Text
A249

1980, Oct. 26　Litho.　Perf. 13½x14
768 A249 100m multicolored　.45 .20
7th Afro-Asian Ophthalmologic Congress.

Hegira, 1500th Anniv.
A250

1980, Nov. 9
769 A250 50m Spiderweb　.20 .20
770 A250 80m City skyline　.35 .20

Film Strip and Woman's Head — A251

1980, Nov. 15　Photo.　Perf. 14x13½
771 A251 100m multicolored　.45 .20
Carthage Film Festival.

Orchid
A252

1980, Nov. 17　Perf. 13½x14
772 A252 20m shown　.20 .20
773 A252 25m Wild cyclamen　.20 .20
Size: 39x27mm
Perf. 14
774 A252 50m Mouflon　.20 .20
775 A252 100m Golden eagle　.25 .20
　Nos. 772-775 (4)　.85 .80

Campaign to Save Kairouan Mosque
A253

1980, Dec. 29　Photo.　Perf. 12
Granite Paper
776 A253 85m multicolored　.30 .20

Heinrich von Stephan (1831-1897), Founder of UPU — A254

Blood Donors' Assoc., 20th Anniv. — A255

1981, Jan. 7
777 A254 150m multicolored　.55 .30

1981, Mar. 5　Litho.　Perf. 14x13½
778 A255 75m multicolored　.25 .20

Pres. Bourguiba and Flag — A256

1981, Mar. 20　Photo.　Perf. 12x11½
Granite Paper
779 A256 50m shown　.20 .20
780 A256 60m Dove, "25"　.20 .20
781 A256 85m Doves　.30 .20
782 A256 120m Victory on winged horse　.40 .20
a.　Souvenir sheet of 4, #779-782　1.25 1.25
　Nos. 779-782 (4)　1.10 .80

25th anniversary of independence. No. 782 sold for 500m. Exists imperf., same value.

Pres. Bourguiba and Flower
A257

1981, Apr. 10　Photo.　Perf. 12x11½
783 A257 50m shown　.20 .20
784 A257 75m Bourguiba, flower, diff.　.20 .20
Destourien Socialist Party Congress.

Mosque Entrance, Mahdia
A258

1981, Apr. 20　Perf. 13½
785 A258 50m shown　.20 .20
786 A258 85m Tozeur Great Mosque, vert.　.50 .20
787 A258 100m Needle Rocks, Tabarka　.55 .20
　Nos. 785-787 (3)　1.25 .60

A259

Youth Festival — A260

1981, May 17　Litho.　Perf. 14x15
788 A259 150m multicolored　.40 .25
13th World Telecommunications Day.

1981, June 2　Photo.　Perf. 11½
Granite Paper
789 A260 100m multicolored　.40 .20

A261　　A262

1981, June 15　Photo.　Perf. 14
790 A261 150m multicolored　.85 .25
Kemal Ataturk (1881-1938), 1st president of Turkey.

1981, July 15　Photo.　Perf. 11½x12
791 A262 150m Skifa, Mahdia　.55 .30

Mohammed Tahar Ben Achour (1879-1973), Scholar — A263

1981, Aug. 6　Perf. 13
792 A263 200m multicolored　1.10 .35

25th Anniv. of Personal Status Code (Women's Liberation) — A264

1981, Aug. 13
793 A264 50m Woman　.20 .20
794 A264 100m shown　.30 .20

Intl. Year of the Disabled — A265

1981, Sept. 21　Photo.　Perf. 13½
795 A265 250m multicolored　.85 .50

Pilgrimage to Mecca — A266

World Food Day — A267

1981, Oct. 7　Photo.　Perf. 13
796 A266 50m multicolored　.20

1981, Oct. 16　Litho.　Perf.
Granite Paper
797 A267 200m multicolored　.65

Traditional Jewelry
A268

150m, Mneguech silver earrings. 180 Mahfdha (silver medallion worn by marrie women). 200m, Essalta gold headdress.

1981, Dec. 7　Photo.　Perf.
798 A268 150m multi, vert.　.60
799 A268 180m multi　.80
800 A268 200m multi, vert.　1.00
　Nos. 798-800 (3)　2.40

Bizerta Bridge
A269

1981, Dec. 14　Litho.　Perf. 12x11
Granite Paper
801 A269 230m multicolored　.90

A270

A271

Chemist compounding honey mixture, ma uscript miniature, 1224.

1982, Apr. 3　Photo.　Perf. 1
802 A270 80m multicolored　.40
Arab Chemists' Union, 16th anniv.

1982, May 12　Photo.　Perf. 13
803 A271 150m multicolored　.75 .3
Oceanic Enterprise Symposium, Tunis 5/12-14.

A272

A273

982, June 26   *Perf. 12½*
Granite Paper
04 A272 80m multicolored   .30 .20
The Productive Family Employment
ampaign.

982, July 25   Litho.   *Perf. 14x13½*
25th Anniv. of Republic: Pres. Bourguiba
nd Various Women.

05 A273 80m multicolored   .30 .20
06 A273 100m multicolored   .45 .20
07 A273 200m multicolored   .75 .30
    Nos. 805-807 (3)   1.50 .70

Scouting
Year — A274

Tunisian
Fossils — A274a

Perf. 14½x14, 14x14½
1982, Aug. 23
808 A274 80m multicolored   .30 .20
809 A274 200m multicolored   .60 .20
75th anniv. of scouting and 50th anniv. of
scouting in Tunisia (80m, horiz.).

1982, Sept. 20   Photo.   *Perf. 11½x12*
Designs: 80m, Pseudophillipsia azzouzi,
vert. 200m, Mediterraneotrigonia cherahilen-
sis, vert. 280m, Numidiopleura enigmatica.
300m, Micreschara tunisiensis, vert. 500m,
Mantelliceras pervinquieri, vert. 1000m,
Elephas africanavus.

809A A274a 80m multi   .20 .20
809B A274a 200m multi   .20 .20
809C A274a 280m multi   .90 .45
809D A274a 300m multi   1.00 .50
809E A274a 500m multi   1.60 .80
809F A274a 1000m multi   3.50 1.60
    Nos. 809A-809F (6)   7.40 3.75

A275   A276

1982, Sept. 29   *Perf. 14x13½*
810 A275 80m shown   .20 .20
    Size: 23x40mm
811 A275 200m Woman, buildings   .50 .20
    30th Anniv. of Arab Postal Union.

1982, Oct. 1   Photo.   *Perf. 12*
Granite Paper
812 A276 200m multicolored   .50 .35
    ITU Plenipotentiaries Conf., Nairobi

World Food Day
A277

Tahar Haddad
(1899-1935),
Social Reformer
A278

1982, Oct. 16   Litho.   *Perf. 13*
813 A277 200m multicolored   .50 .20

1982, Oct. 25   Engr.
814 A278 200m dark brown   .50 .20

TB Bacillus
Centenary
A279

Folk Songs and
Stories — A280

1982, Nov. 16   Litho.   *Perf. 13½*
815 A279 100m multicolored   .25 .20

1982, Nov. 22   Photo.   *Perf. 14*
816 A280 20m Dancing in the
          Rain   .20 .20
817 A280 30m Woman Sweep-
          ing   .20 .20
818 A280 70m Fisherman and
          the Child   .20 .20
819 A280 80m Rooster and the
          Oranges, horiz.   .20 .20
820 A280 100m Woman and the
          Mirror, horiz.   .35 .20
821 A280 120m The Two Girls,
          horiz.   .45 .20
    Nos. 816-821 (6)   1.60 1.20

Intl. Palestinian Solidarity Day — A281

1982, Nov. 30   Litho.   *Perf. 13x12*
822 A281 80m multicolored   .20 .20

Farhat Hached
(1914-1952)
A282

Bourguiba Dam
Opening
A283

1982, Dec. 6   Engr.   *Perf. 13*
823 A282 80m brown red   .20 .20

1982, Dec. 20   Litho.   *Perf. 13½*
824 A283 80m multicolored   .20 .20

Environmental Training
College
Opening — A284

1982, Dec. 29   Photo.   *Perf. 11½*
Granite Paper
825 A284 80m multicolored   .20 .20

World Communications Year — A285

1983, May 17   Litho.   *Perf. 13½x14*
826 A285 200m multicolored   .40 .20

20th Anniv. of Org.
of African
Unity — A286

Aly Ben Ayed
(1930-1972),
Actor — A288

30th Anniv. of Customs Cooperation
Council — A287

1983, May 25   Photo.   *Perf. 12*
Granite Paper
827 A286 230m ultra & grnsh bl   .55 .35

1983, May 30   Litho.   *Perf. 13½*
828 A287 100m multicolored   .25 .20

1983, Aug. 15   Engr.   *Perf. 13*
829 A288 80m dk car, dl red & gray   .20 .20

Stone-carved
Face, El-
Mekta — A289

Pre-historic artifacts: 20m, Neolithic neck-
lace, Kel el-Agab. 30m, Mill and grindstone,
Redeyef. 40m, Orynx head rock carving,
Gafsa. 80m, Dolmen Mactar. 100m, Acheulian
Bi-face flint, El-Mekta.

1983, Aug. 20   Photo.   *Perf. 11½x12*
830 A289 15m multicolored   .20 .20
831 A289 20m multicolored   .20 .20
832 A289 30m multicolored   .20 .20
833 A289 40m multicolored   .20 .20
834 A289 80m multicolored   .20 .20
835 A289 100m multicolored   .20 .20
    Nos. 830-835 (6)   1.20 1.20

Sports
for All
A290

1983, Sept. 27   Litho.   *Perf. 12½*
836 A290 40m multicolored   .20 .20

World
Fishing
Day
A291

1983, Oct. 17   *Perf. 14½*
837 A291 200m multicolored   .40 .20

Evacuation of
French Troops,
20th
Anniv. — A292

1983, Oct. 17   Litho.   *Perf. 14x13½*
838 A292 80m multicolored   .20 .20

Tapestry Weaver, by Hedi Khayachi
(1882-1948) — A293

1983, Nov. 22   Photo.   *Perf. 11½*
Granite Paper
839 A293 80m multicolored   .20 .20

Natl. Allegiance
A294

Jet, Woman's
Head, Emblem
A295

1983, Nov. 30   Litho.   *Perf. 14½*
840 A294 100m Children, flag   .25 .20

1983, Dec. 21   *Perf. 13½*
841 A295 150m multicolored   .35 .20

Pres.
Bourguiba
A296

4th Molecular
Biology
Symposium
A297

Destourien Socialist Party, 50th Anniv.: Portraits of Bourguiba. 200m, 230m horiz.

Perf. 12½x12, 12x12½
1984, Mar. 2   Photo.
Granite Paper
842 A296 40m multicolored   .20 .20
843 A296 70m multicolored   .20 .20
844 A296 80m multicolored   .20 .20
a.   Pair, #843-844   .35 .30
845 A296 150m multicolored   .35 .20
a.   Pair, #842, 845   .50 .30
846 A296 200m multicolored   .40 .20
847 A296 230m multicolored   .55 .35
a.   Pair, #846-847   1.00 .60
    Nos. 842-847 (6)   1.90 1.35

Nos. 844a, 845a and 847a were printed checkerwise in sheets of ten.

1984, Apr. 3   *Perf. 13½x13*
848 A297 100m Map, diagram   .25 .20

Ibn El Jazzar,
Physician — A298

Economic
Development
Program, 20th
Anniv. — A299

1984, May 15   Photo.   *Perf. 14x13*
849 A298 80m multicolored   .20 .20

1984, June 15   *Perf. 11½*
Granite Paper
850 A299 230m Merchant, worker   .50 .20

Coquette,
The
Sorceress
and the
Fairy
Carabosse
A300

Perf. 13½x14, 14x13½
1984, Aug. 27   Photo.
851 A300 20m shown   .20 .20
852 A300 80m Counting with fingers   .20 .20
853 A300 100m Boy riding horse, vert.   .25 .20
    Nos. 851-853 (3)   .65 .60
    Legends and folk tales.

Family and Education Org., 20th
Anniv. — A301

1984, Sept. 4   *Perf. 13x14*
854 A301 80m Family looking into future   .20 .20

Natl. Heritage
Protection
A302

Aboul-Qasim
Chabbi, Poet
(1909-1934)
A303

1984, Sept. 13   *Perf. 14*
855 A302 100m Medina Mosque Minaret, hand   .25 .20

1984, Oct. 9   Engr.   *Perf. 12½x13*
856 A303 100m multicolored   .25 .20

40th
Anniv.,
ICAO
A304

1984, Oct. 25   Photo.   *Perf. 13*
857 A304 200m Aircraft tail, bird   .50 .25

Sahara
Festival
A305

1984, Dec. 3   Litho.   *Perf. 14½*
858 A305 20m Musicians   .20 .20

20th
Anniv.,
Intelsat
A306

Perf. 13½x14½
1984, Dec. 25   Photo.
859 A306 100m Tunisian Earth Station   .25 .20

Mediterranean Landscape, by Jilani
Abdelwaheb (Abdul) — A307

1984, Dec. 31   Photo.   *Perf. 14½*
860 A307 100m multicolored   .25 .20

EXPO '85,
Tsukuba,
Japan
A308

1985, Mar. 20   Photo.   *Perf. 12*
861 A308 200m multicolored   .35 .20

Civil Protection
Week — A309

1985, May 13   Litho.   *Perf. 14*
862 A309 100m Hands, water and fire   .20 .20

Pres. Habib Bourguiba, Crowded
Pier — A310

Pres. Bourguiba: 75m, On horseback, vert. 200m, Wearing hat, vert. 230m, Waving to crowd.

1985, June 1   *Perf. 12½*
863 A310 75m multicolored   .20 .20
864 A310 100m multicolored   .20 .20
865 A310 200m multicolored   .30 .20
866 A310 230m multicolored   .40 .20
    Nos. 863-866 (4)   1.10 .80
    Natl. independence, 30th anniv.

Head of a
Statue,
Carthage
and Pres.
Bourguiba
A311

1985, June 4   *Perf. 14*
867 A311 250m multicolored   .40 .20
    EXPO '85.

Intl. Amateur Film
Festival,
Kelibia — A312

Natl. Folk
Tales — A313

1985, July 20   *Perf. 14½x1*
868 A312 250m multicolored   .40 .

1985, July 29   *Perf.*
869 A313 25m Sun, Sun Shine Again, horiz.   .20 .
870 A313 50m I Met a Man With Seven Wives   .20 .
871 A313 100m Uncle Shisbene   .20 .
    Nos. 869-871 (3)   .60 .

Intl. Youth
Year — A314

1985, Sept. 30   *Perf. 14½x13*
872 A314 250m multicolored   .40 .

The Perfumers' Courtyard, 1912, by
Hedi Larnaout — A315

1985, Oct. 4   *Perf.*
873 A315 100m multicolored   .20 .

Regional Bridal
Costumes
A316

UN, 40th Anniv
A317

1985, Oct. 22   *Perf.*
874 A316 20m Matmata   .20 .
875 A316 50m Moknine   .20 .
876 A316 100m Tunis   .25 .
    Nos. 874-876 (3)   .65 .

1985, Oct. 24   *Perf. 14x13*
877 A317 250m multicolored   .50 .

Self-Sufficiency in Food
Production — A318

Perf. 13½x14½

1985, Nov. 26   **Photo.**
878 A318 100m Makhtar stele of
             feast   .20 .20

League of
Arab
States,
40th Anniv.
A319

1985, Nov. 29   Litho.   Perf. 13½x14
879 A319 100m multicolored   .20 .20

Aziza Othmana   Land Law,
(d.   Cent. — A321
1669) — A320

1985, Dec. 16   Engr.   Perf. 12½x13
880 A320 100m dk grn, hn brn &
             brn   .20 .20

1985, Dec. 25   Litho.   Perf. 13½
881 A321 100m multicolored   .20 .20

Natl. Independence, 30th
Anniv. — A322

Perf. 13x13½, 13½x13
1986, Mar. 20   **Photo.**
882 A322 100m Dove, vert.   .30 .20
883 A322 120m Rocket   .35 .20
884 A322 280m Horse and rider   .75 .35
885 A322 300m Balloons, vert.   .85 .40
  a.   Souvenir sheet of 4, #882-885 2.25 1.10
       Nos. 882-885 (4)   2.25 1.15
    No. 885a exists imperf.

A323   A324

1986, Apr. 30   Litho.   Perf. 14x13½
886 A323 300m multicolored   .85 .40
887 A324 380m multicolored   1.00 .50
   Prof. Hulusi Behcet (1889-1948), discovered virus causing Behcet's Disease affecting
eyes and joints. 3rd Mediterranean Rheumatology Day (#886). Intl. Geographical
Ophtalmological Soc. Cong. (#887).

12th
Destourian
Socialist Party
Congress
A325

1986, June 19   Photo.   Perf. 12
888 A325 120m shown   .35 .20
889 A325 300m Torchbearer   .85 .40

A326

A327

Regional bridal costumes.

1986, Aug. 25   Litho.   Perf. 14
890 A326 40m Homi-Souk   .20 .20
891 A326 280m Mahdia   .80 .40
892 A326 300m Nabeul   .80 .40
       Nos. 890-892 (3)   1.80 1.00

1986, Sept. 20   Engr.   Perf. 13
893 A327 160m dark red   .45 .20
   Hassen Husni Abdul-Wahab (1883-1968),
historian, archaeologist

Founding of Carthage, 2800th
Anniv. — A328

1986, Oct. 18   Engr.   Perf. 13
894 A328 2d dark violet   8.00 4.00

Protohistoric
Artifacts — A329

Bedouins, by
Ammar
Farhat — A330

   Design: 10m, Flint arrowhead, El Borma, c.
3000 B.C. 20m, Rock cut-out dwelling,
Sejnane, c. 1000 B.C. 50m, Lintel bas-relief
from a cult site in Tunis, c. 1000 B.C., horiz.
120m, Base of a Neolithic vase, Kesra. 160m,
Phoenician trireme, petroglyph, c. 800 B.C.,
horiz. 250m, Ceramic pot, c. 700 B.C., found
at Sejnane, vert.

1986, Oct. 30   Litho.   Perf. 13½
895 A329 10m multicolored   .20 .20
896 A329 20m multicolored   .20 .20
897 A329 50m multicolored   .20 .20
898 A329 120m multicolored   .50 .25

---

899 A329 160m multicolored   .70 .35
900 A329 250m multicolored   1.00 .50
       Nos. 895-900 (6)   2.80 1.70

1986, Nov. 20   Photo.   Perf. 13½
901 A330 250m multicolored   .70 .35

Intl.
Peace
Year
A331

1986, Nov. 24   Perf. 13½x13
902 A331 300m multicolored   .85 .40

FAO, 40th
Anniv. — A332

Computer
Education
Inauguration
A333

1986, Nov. 27   Perf. 13x13½
903 A332 280m multicolored   .80 .40

1986, Dec. 8   Perf. 13½
904 A333 2d multicolored   5.50 2.75

Breast-feeding for   Wildlife, Natl.
     Child   Parks — A335
Survival — A334

1986, Dec. 22   Photo.   Perf. 14
905 A334 120m multicolored   .50 .25

1986, Dec. 29   Perf. 12
   Designs: 60m, Mountain gazelle, Chambi
Natl. Park. 120m, Addax, Bou. Hedma.
350m, Seal, Zembretta. 380m, Greylag
goose, Ichkeul.

Granite Paper
906 A335 60m multicolored   .20 .20
907 A335 120m multicolored   .45 .25
908 A335 350m multicolored   1.40 .70
909 A335 380m multicolored   1.50 .75
       Nos. 906-909 (4)   3.55 1.90

City of
Monastir,
Cent. — A336

1987, Jan. 24   Litho.   Perf. 12x11½
Granite Paper
910 A336 120m Pres. Bourguiba,
             city arms   .40 .25

Invention of the Telegraph by Samuel
F.B. Morse, 150th Anniv.
A337

1987, June 15   Litho.   Perf. 13½x14
911 A337 500m multicolored   1.75 1.00

30th
Anniv. of
the
Republic
A338

   Pres. Bourguiba and women of various
sects.

1987, July 25   Photo.   Perf. 13½
912 A338 150m multi   .60 .30
913 A338 250m multi   1.00 .50
914 A338 350m multi, diff.   1.40 .70
915 A338 500m multi, diff.   2.00 1.00
  a.   Souvenir sheet of 4, #912-915 6.00 3.00
       Nos. 912-915 (4)   5.00 2.50
   No. 915a sold for 1.50d. Exists imperf.

UN Universal
Vaccination by 1990
Campaign — A339

1987, Sept. 14   Perf. 12
Granite Paper
916 A339 250m multicolored   1.00 .50

The Street,
by Azouz
ben Raiz
(1902-1962)
A340

1987, Sept. 22   Granite Paper
917 A340 250m multicolored   1.00 .50

Arab Day
for Shelter
of the
Homeless
A341

1987, Oct. 5   Photo.   Perf. 12x11½
Granite Paper
918 A341 150m multicolored   .50 .25

Advisory
Council
for Postal
Research,
30th
Anniv.
A342

1987, Oct. 9   Perf. 14
919 A342 150m Express mail   .50 .25
920 A342 350m Use postal code   1.10 .60

The Arabs, by Ibn-Mandhour (1233-1312), Lexicographer
A343

1987, Oct. 26   Engr.   Perf. 13
921 A343 250m plum   1.00 .50

Pasteur Institute, Tunis
A344

1987, Nov. 21   Perf. 13x12½
922 A344 250m blk, grn & rose lake   1.00 .50

Pasteur Institute, Paris, cent.

Intl. Year of the Vine (Wine) — A345

1987, Nov. 27   Photo.   Perf. 14
923 A345 250m multicolored   1.00 .50

6th Volleyball Championships of African Nations — A346

1987, Dec. 2   Litho.   Perf. 14x13½
924 A346 350m multicolored   1.40 .70

African Basketball Championships A347   Folk Costumes A348

1987, Dec. 15
925 A347 350m multicolored   1.40 .70

1987, Dec. 25   Photo.
926 A348 20m Midoun   .20 .20
927 A348 30m Tozeur   .20 .20
928 A348 150m Sfax   .85 .40
Nos. 926-928 (3)   1.25 .80

Flowering Plants — A349

1987, Dec. 29   Perf. 14½
929 A349 30m Narcissus tazetta   .20 .20
930 A349 150m Gladiolus communis   .60 .30
931 A349 400m Iris xiphium   1.60 .80
932 A349 500m Tulipa sylvestris   2.10 1.00
Nos. 929-932 (4)   4.50 2.30

Declaration of Nov. 7, 1987
A350

Cameo portrait of Pres. Zine el Abidine Ben Ali and: 150m, Scales of Justice. 200m, Girl with flowers (party badges) in her hair, vert. 350m, Mermaid, doves, natl. coat of arms. 370m, "CMA," emblem of the Maghreb states (Tunisia, Mauritania, Morocco, Algeria and Libya), vert.

1988, Mar. 21   Photo.   Perf. 12
Granite Paper
933 A350 150m multicolored   .50 .25
934 A350 200m multicolored   .60 .30
935 A350 350m multicolored   1.10 .55
936 A350 370m multicolored   1.10 .60
Nos. 933-936 (4)   3.30 1.70

Youth and Change A351

1988, Mar. 22   Litho.   Perf. 14x14½
937 A351 75m shown   .25 .20
938 A351 150m Happy family   .50 .25

Martyr's Day, 50th Anniv. A352

Perf. 13x13½, 13½x13
1988, Apr. 9   Photo.
939 A352 150m shown   .45 .25
940 A352 500m Monument, vert.   1.50 .75

Opening Conference of the Constitutional Democratic Assembly — A353

1988, July 30   Perf. 12x11½
Granite Paper
941 A353 150m Flag, Pres. Ben Ali   .50 .25

1988 Summer Olympics, Seoul A354

1988, Sept. 20   Photo.   Perf. 13½
942 A354 150m shown   .30 .20
943 A354 430m Running, boxing, weight lifting, wrestling   .95 .45

A355

1988, Sept. 21
944 A355 200m multicolored   .40 .20

Restoration of the City of San'a, Yemen.

A356

1988, Nov. 7   Photo.   Perf. 14
945 A356 150m multicolored   .70 .35

Appointment of Pres. Zine El Abidine Ben Ali, 1st anniv.

Amilcar Beach, 1942, by A. Debbeche — A357

1988, Nov. 21   Photo.   Perf. 13½x13
946 A357 100m multicolored   .20 .20

Tunis Air, 40th Anniv. A358

1988, Nov. 28   Photo.   Perf. 12x11½
Granite Paper
947 A358 500m multicolored   1.60 .80

UN Declaration of Human Rights, 40th Anniv. — A359

1988, Dec. 10   Perf. 12
Granite Paper
948 A359 370m black   1.25 .65

Tunisian Postage Stamp Cent. — A360

1988, Dec. 16   Perf. 12½
Granite Paper
949 A360 150m multicolored   .50 .25

A361   A362

Decorative doorways.

1988, Dec. 26   Perf. 14x13½
950 A361 50m multi   .20 .20
951 A361 70m multi, diff.   .20 .20
952 A361 100m multi, diff.   .20 .20
953 A361 370m multi, diff.   .35 .20
954 A361 370m multi, diff.   .80 .40
955 A361 400m multi, diff.   .85 .40
Nos. 950-955 (6)   2.60 1.60

1989, Mar. 7   Engr.   Perf. 13½x13
956 A362 1000m dark blue   2.25 1.10

Ali Douagi (1909-49).

Natl. Day for the Handicapped A363

1989, May 30   Photo.   Perf. 13½
957 A363 150m multicolored   .35 .20

Education A364

1989, July 10   Perf. 14
958 A364 180m multicolored   .40 .20

Family Planning Assoc., 20th Anniv. — A365

1989, Aug. 14   Litho.   Perf. 14
959 A365 150m multicolored   .35 .20

Family Care A366

1989, Aug. 14   Litho.   Perf. 14
960 A366 150m multicolored   .35 .20

Fauna A367

989, Aug. 28 Photo. Perf. 13½x14
61 A367 250m Tortoise .55 .30
62 A367 350m Oryx .80 .40

Intl. Fair, Tunis
A368

Mohamed
Beyram V (1840-1889)
A369

989, Oct. 16 Photo. Perf. 14
63 A368 150m shown .35 .20
64 A368 370m Pavilion, horiz. .85 .40

989, Oct. 28 Engr. Perf. 13
65 A369 150m blk & dp rose lil .35 .20

Theater, Carthage
A370

Monument
A371

989, Nov. 3 Photo. Perf. 14
66 A370 300m multicolored .70 .35

989, Nov. 7 Perf. 11½x12
Granite Paper
67 A371 150m multicolored .35 .20

Appointment of Pres. Zine El Abidine Ben
li, 2nd Anniv.

Nehru — A372

Flags — A373

989, Nov. 29 Engr. Perf. 13
68 A372 300m dark brown .70 .35

Jawaharlal Nehru, 1st prime minister of
dependent India.

990, Jan. 15 Photo. Perf. 12x11½
Granite Paper
69 A373 200m multicolored .50 .25

Maghreb Union summit, Tunis.

Museum
of Bardo,
Cent.
A374

990, Feb. 20 Litho. Perf. 13½
70 A374 300m multicolored .65 .30

Pottery
A375

1990, Mar. 22 Perf. 14
971 A375 75m multicolored .20 .20
972 A375 100m multi, diff. .20 .20

Sheep Museum — A376

1990, Apr. 13 Litho. Perf. 13½
973 A376 400m Sheep 1.00 .50
974 A376 450m Ram's head 1.10 .55
a. Souvenir sheet of 2, #973-974 2.50 1.25

No. 974a sold for 1000m, exists imperf. Nos.
973-974 inscribed 1989.

Tunisian Olympic Movement — A377

1990, May 27
975 A377 150m multicolored .40 .20

Child's
Drawing
A378

1990, June 5 Perf. 14
976 A378 150m multicolored .40 .20

A379

1990, July 13 Photo. Perf. 14x14½
977 A379 150m Sbiba .40 .20
978 A379 500m Bou Omrane 1.25 .65

1990, Aug. 1 Litho. Perf. 14
Relic from Punic city of Dougga.
979 A380 300m multicolored .80 .40

A380

Traditional costumes.

Intl.
Literacy
Year
A381

1990, Sept. 8 Photo. Perf. 12x11½
Granite Paper
980 A381 120m multicolored .30 .20

A382

A383

1990, Oct. 15 Perf. 11½x12
Granite Paper
981 A382 150m multicolored .40 .20
Importance of water.

1990, Nov. 7
Granite Paper
982 A383 150m shown .40 .20
983 A383 150m Clock tower .40 .20

Appointment of Pres. Zine El Abidine Ben
Ali, 3rd anniv.

A384

A385

1990, Nov. 16 Engr. Perf. 13½x13
984 A384 150m green .40 .20
Kheireddine Et-Tounsi (1822-1889), politician.

1990, Dec. 17 Photo. Perf. 13½
Fauna and flora.
985 A385 150m Cervus elaphus
barbarus .40 .20
986 A385 200m Cynara
cardenculus .50 .25
987 A385 300m Bubalus bubalis .80 .40
988 A385 600m Ophris lutea 1.50 .80
Nos. 985-988 (4) 3.20 1.65

Maghreb Arab
Union, 2nd
Anniv. — A386

Harbor of
Tabarka — A387

1991, Jan. 21 Photo. Perf. 13½
989 A386 180m multicolored .45 .20

1991, Mar. 17
990 A387 450m multicolored 1.00 .50

Fish — A388

1991, Sept. 10 Photo. Perf. 14x13
991 A388 180m Pagre .45 .20
992 A388 350m Rouget de roche .85 .40
993 A388 450m Maquereau 1.10 .55
994 A388 550m Pageot commun 1.40 .65
Nos. 991-994 (4) 3.80 1.80

Child
Welfare — A389

1991, Sept. 29 Perf. 14
995 A389 450m multicolored 1.10 .55

A390

1991, Oct. 9 Perf. 13½x14
996 A390 400m multicolored 1.00 .50

A391

A392

Jewelry.

Perf. 14x13, 13x14
1991, Oct. 22 Litho.
997 A391 120m Ring, bracelets,
horiz. .30 .20
998 A391 180m Necklace .40 .20
999 A391 220m Earrings .55 .25
1000 A391 730m shown 1.75 .90
Nos. 997-1000 (4) 3.00 1.55

1991, Nov. 7 Perf. 11½
1001 A392 180m multicolored
Appointment of Pres. Zine El Abidine Ben
Ali, 4th anniv.

Tunis-Carthage Center — A393

1991, Nov. 22   Engr.   Perf. 13
1002 A393 80m red, blue & green

A394

A395

1991, Dec. 12   Photo.   Perf. 14
1003 A394 450m bright blue   1.10 .55

World Day of the Rights of Man.

1991, Dec. 26   Engr.   Perf. 12½x13
1004 A395 200m blue   .50 .25

Mahmoud Bayram Et Tounsi (1893-1960), poet.

Expo '92, Seville — A396

General Post Office, Tunis, Cent. — A397

1992, Apr. 20   Photo.   Perf. 13½
1005 A396 180m multicolored   .35 .20

Perf. 13x12½, 12½x13
1992, June 15   Engr.
1006 A397 180m red brn, horiz.   .35 .20
1007 A397 450m dark brown   .90 .45

"When the Subconscious Awakes," by Moncef ben Amor — A398

1992, July 21   Litho.   Perf. 13½
1008 A398 500m multicolored   1.00 .50

1992 Summer Olympics, Barcelona A399

1992, Aug. 4
1009 A399 180m Running   .35 .20
1010 A399 450m Judo, vert.   .90 .45

Birds — A400   A401

1992, Sept. 22   Photo.   Perf. 11½
Granite Paper
1011 A400 100m Merops apiaster   .20 .20
1012 A400 180m Carduelis carduelis   .35 .20
1013 A400 200m Serinus serinus   .45 .20
1014 A400 500m Carduelis chloris   1.00 .50
Nos. 1011-1014 (4)   2.00

1992, Oct. 21   Perf. 11½x12
Granite Paper
1015 A401 180m multicolored   .35 .20

UN Conference on Rights of the Child.

African Human Rights Conference, Tunis — A402

1992, Nov. 2   Photo.   Perf. 11½
Granite Paper
1016 A402 480m multicolored   .95 .50

A403   A404

1992, Nov. 7
Granite Paper
1017 A403 180m multicolored   .35 .20
1018 A404 730m multicolored   1.50 .75

Appointment of Pres. Zine El Abidine Ben Ali, 5th anniv.

Arbor Day A405

1992, Nov. 8   Perf. 11½x12
Granite Paper
1019 A405 180m Acacia tortilis   .35 .20

Intl. Conference on Nutrition, Rome — A406

1992, Dec. 15   Litho.   Perf. 13½
1020 A406 450m multicolored   .90 .45

Traditional Costumes — A407

1992, Dec. 23
1021 A407 100m Chemesse   .20 .20
1022 A407 350m Hanifites   .70 .35

Mosaics A408

1992, Dec. 29
1023 A408 100m Goat   .20 .20
1024 A408 180m Duck   .35 .20
1025 A408 350m Horse   .70 .35
1026 A408 450m Gazelle   .90 .45
Nos. 1023-1026 (4)   2.15 1.20

Arab-African Fair of Tunisia — A410

1993, July 10   Litho.   Perf. 13½x14
1028 A410 450m multicolored   .90 .45

Relaxation in the Patio, by Ali Guermassi A411

Reassembly of the Democratic Congress A412

1993, July 20   Litho.   Perf. 13
1029 A411 450m multicolored   .90

1993, July 29   Perf. 13
1030 A412 180m multicolored   .35

A413

A414

1993   Perf.
1031 A413 20m Wolf   .20
1032 A414 60m Hoya carnosa   .20

Appointment of Pres. Zine El Abidine, 6th Anniv.
A414A   A415

1993, Nov. 7   Perf. 13
1033 A414A 180m multicolored   .35
1034 A415 450m multicolored   .90

Kairouan Tapestries — A416

Designs: Various ornate patterns.

1993, Dec. 13   Perf. 13
1035 A416 100m multicolored   .20
1036 A416 120m multicolored   .25
1037 A416 180m multicolored   .35
1038 A416 350m multicolored   .70
Nos. 1035-1038 (4)   1.50 1.

Pasteur Institute of Tunis, Cent. A417

Design: 450m, Charles Nicolle (1866-1936), bacteriologist, 1928 Nobel medal.

1993, Oct. 12   Litho.   Perf. 13½
1039 A417 450m multicolored   .90 .45

A418

ILO, 75th Anniv. — A423

1994, May 12   Perf. 13½x14
1048 A423 350m multicolored   .70 .35

School Activities A419

1993, Dec. 30   Litho.   Perf. 13½
1040 A418 180m Music   .35 .20
1041 A419 180m Art, reading   .35 .20

Intl. Year of the Family — A424   Plants — A425

1994, May 15   Litho.   Perf. 14x13½
1049 A424 180m multicolored   .50 .25

1994, June 2
1050 A425 50m Prunus spinosa   .20 .20
1051 A425 100m Xeranthemum inapertum   .25 .20
1052 A425 200m Orchis simia   .55 .30
1053 A425 1d Scilla peruviana   3.00 1.50
    Nos. 1050-1053 (4)   4.00 2.20

19th African Cup of Nations Soccer Tournament — A420

1994, Mar. 26
1042 A420 180m shown   .35 .20
1043 A420 350m Two players, diff.   .75 .35
1044 A420 450m Map, player   .90 .45
    Nos. 1042-1044 (3)   2.00 1.00

Organization of African Unity Summit Meeting, Tunis — A426

1994, June 3   Perf. 13½
1054 A426 480m multicolored   1.50 .75

Presidential and Legislative Elections — A421

1994, Mar. 20
1045 A421 180m multicolored   .35 .20

Intl. Olympic Committee, Cent. A427

1994, July 7   Litho.   Perf. 13½
1055 A427 450m multicolored

Election of Pres. Zine El Abidine ben Ali — A422

1994, May 15   Photo.   Perf. 11½
Granite Paper
1046 A422 180m multicolored   .35 .20
1047 A422 350m multicolored   .70 .35
    a.   Souvenir sheet, #1046-1047   1.10 .55
    No. 1047a exists imperf.

A429   A430

Butterflies: 100m, Colias croceus, horiz. 180m, Vanessa atalanta, horiz. 300m, Papilio podalirius. 350m, Danaus chrysippus, horiz. 450m, Vanessa cardui. 500m, Papilio machaon.

Perf. 13½x14, 14x13½
1994, Oct. 13   Litho.
1057 A429 100m multicolored   .30 .20
1058 A429 180m multicolored   .55 .25
1059 A429 300m multicolored   .90 .45
1060 A429 350m multicolored   1.00 .50
1061 A429 1.25m multicolored   1.25 .65
1062 A429 500m multicolored   1.50 .75
    Nos. 1057-1062 (6)   5.50 2.80

1994, Nov. 16   Perf. 13½
1063 A430 350m Pres. Ali, "7," horiz.   1.00 .50
1064 A430 730m "7," Emblem   2.00 1.00
    Pres. Zine El Abdine, 7th anniv. of taking office.

41st Military Boxing World Championships A431

1994, Nov. 18   Litho.   Perf. 13½x14
1065 A431 450m multicolored   1.40 .70

500

Wildlife — A433

1994, Dec. 27   Litho.   Perf. 13½
1067 A433 180m Anser anser
1068 A433 350m Aythya ferina, Aythya fuligula
1069 A433 500m Bubalus bubalis
1070 A433 1d Lutra lutra, horiz.

"Composition," by Ridha Bettaieb — A434

1994, Dec. 29   Litho.   Perf. 13
1071 A434 500m multicolored

Arab League, 50th Anniv. — A435   Art of Glass Blowing — A436

1995, May 29   Litho.   Perf. 13½
1072 A435 180m multicolored   .55 .30

1995, June 29
1073 A436 450m Water bottle   1.40 .70
1074 A436 730m Incense burner   2.25 1.10

Aboulkacem Chebbi (1909-34), Poet — A437

1995, Aug. 12   Litho.   Perf. 13½
1075 A437 180m multicolored   .55 .30

4th World Conference on Women, Beijing A438

1995, Sept. 6   Litho.   Perf. 13½
1076 A438 180m multicolored   .55 .25

FAO, 50th Anniv. A439

1995, Oct. 2   Litho.   Perf. 13½x13
1077 A439 350m multicolored   .90 .45

Hannibal (247-183BC), Carthaginian General — A440

1995, Nov. 14   Engr.   Perf. 14x13½
1078 A440 180m maroon   .50 .25
    a.   Souvenir sheet of 1   2.50 1.25
    No. 1078a sold for 1d and exists imperf.

United Nations, 50th Anniv. A441

1995, Oct. 24   Litho.   Perf. 14x13½
1079 A441 350m multicolored   .90 .45

A442   A443

1995, Nov. 7   Litho.   Perf. 13x13½
1080 A442 180m multicolored   .50 .25
1081 A443 350m multicolored   .95 .45

    Appointment of Pres. Zine El Abidine ben Ali, 8th anniv.

Human Rights
Day — A445

1995, Dec. 10 Litho. *Perf. 13x13½*
1083 A445 350m multicolored .95 .45

Pedestrian
Security
A446

1995, Dec. 19 *Perf. 13½x13*
1084 A446 350m multicolored .95 .45

Flora and Fauna
A447

Traditional
Costumes
A448

Designs: 50m, Ophrys lapethica. 180m, Gazella dorcas. 300m, Scupellaria cypria. 350m, Chlamydotis undulata.

1995, Dec. 28 *Perf. 13½*
1085 A447 50m multicolored .20 .20
1086 A447 180m multicolored .50 .25
1087 A447 300m multicolored .80 .40
1088 A447 350m multicolored .95 .45
Nos. 1085-1088 (4) 2.45 1.30

1996, Mar.16 *Perf. 14x13½*
1089 A448 170m Jebra, Khamri .45 .20
1090 A448 200m Kaftan brode, Hammamet .55 .30

A449 A450

Independence, 40th Anniv.: 390m, Dove, rainbow, "20, 40."

1996, Mar. 20 *Perf. 13x13½*
1091 A449 200m multicolored .55 .30
1092 A449 390m multicolored 1.00 .50

1996, Jan. 20 Litho. *Perf. 13x13½*
1093 A450 440m multicolored 1.50 .75
Natl. Trade Union, 50th anniv.

Painting, "Hannana," by Noureddine
Khayachi (1917-87) — A451

1996, Apr. 25 Litho. *Perf. 13½*
1094 A451 810m multicolored 1.60 .80

A451a A452

1996, June 5 Litho. *Perf. 13x13½*
1094A A451a 390m multicolored
Environment Day.

1996, June 8 Litho. *Perf. 13x13½*
1095 A452 200m multicolored .65 .35
CAPEX '96.

Insects
A453

1996, May 23 Litho. *Perf. 14x13½*
1096 A453 200m Coccinella septempunctata .50 .25
1097 A453 810m Apis mellifica 1.90 .95

1996
Summer
Olympic
Games,
Atlanta
A455

Olympic emblem, and: 20m, Flags, Olympic rings, athletic field. 200m, Torch bearer, fireworks, "100," globe, vert. 390m, Early Olympic wrestlers.

1996, July 19 Litho. *Perf. 13*
1099 A455 20m multicolored .20 .20
1100 A455 200m multicolored .50 .25
1101 A455 390m multicolored .95 .50
Nos. 1099-1101 (3) 1.65 .95

Code of Personal
Status (Women's
Liberation), 40th
Anniv. — A456

1996, Aug. 13 *Perf. 14*
1102 A456 200m multicolored .50 .25

Landmarks
A457

Intl. Year to Fight
Poverty
A458

Designs: 20m, Ramparts of Sousse, horiz. 200m, Numidian Mausoleum, Dougga. 390m, Arch of Trajan, Makthar, horiz.

1996, Sept. 16 Photo. *Perf. 11½*
Granite Paper

1103 A457 20m multicolored .20 .20
1104 A457 200m multicolored .45 .20
1105 A457 390m multicolored .85 .45
Nos. 1103-1105 (3) 1.50 .85

1996, Oct. 17 Litho. *Perf. 13x13½*
1106 A458 390m multicolored .85 .40

Appointment of Pres. Zine El Abidine, 9th Anniv.
A459 A460

1996, Nov. 7
1107 A459 200m multicolored .45 .20
1108 A460 390m multicolored .65 .30

Ezzitouna Mosque, 1300th
Anniv. — A462

1996, Nov. 25 Litho. *Perf. 14x13½*
1111 A462 250m multicolored .55 .30

Natl. Solidarity Day
A463 A464

1996, Dec. 8 *Perf. 13x13½*
1112 A463 500m multicolored 1.10 .55
1113 A464 500m multicolored 1.10 .55

World Human
Rights
Day — A465

UNICEF, 50th
Anniv. — A466

1996, Dec. 10
1114 A465 500m multicolored 1.10 .5

1996, Dec. 11
1115 A466 810m multicolored 1.75 .9

Musical Instruments — A467

1996, Dec. 26 Litho. *Perf. 13¹*
1116 A467 250m Mezoued .60 .3
1117 A467 300m Gombri .75 .4
1118 A467 360m Tabla .85 .4
1119 A467 500m Tar Tounsi (Riq) 1.25 .6
Nos. 1116-1119 (4) 3.45 1.7

World
Book and
Copyright
Day
A468

1997, Apr. 23 Litho. *Perf. 13¹*
1120 A468 1d multicolored 2.40 1.25

Marine
Life
A469

Designs: 50m, Mytilus galloprovincialis. 70m, Tapes decussatus. 350m, Octopus vulgaris. 500m, Sepia officinalis.

1997, May 13
1121 A469 50m multicolored .20 .20
1122 A469 70m multicolored .20 .20
1123 A469 350m multicolored .85 .45
1124 A469 500m multicolored 1.25 .60
Nos. 1121-1124 (4) 2.50 1.45

PACIFIC 97, Intl.
Stamp Exhibition,
San
Francisco — A470

1997, May 29 Photo. *Perf. 11½x12*
Granite Paper
1125 A470 250m multicolored .70 .35

A471 A472

1997, June 16   Litho.   Perf. 13½
1126 A471 350m multicolored   1.10 .55
Mediterranean Games, Bari.

1997, July 15
1127 A472 250m multicolored   .70 .35
Tunis, 1997 Cultural Capital.

A473

Republic, 40th Anniv. A474

1997, July 25
1128 A473 130m multicolored   .35 .20
1129 A474 500m multicolored   1.25 .65

Reptiles A475

100m, Uromastix acanthinurus. 350m, Chamaeleo chamaeleon, vert. 500m, Varanus griseus.

1997, Sept. 9   Litho.   Perf. 13½
1130 A475 100m multicolored   .25 .20
1131 A475 350m multicolored   1.00 .50
1132 A475 500m multicolored   1.25 .65
    Nos. 1130-1132 (3)   2.50 1.35

Rosa Gallica Flore Pleno — A476

1997, Sept. 23   Litho.   Perf. 13½
1134 A476 350m multicolored   .80 .40

Intl. Day for Protection of the Elderly A477

1997, Oct. 1   Litho.   Perf. 13½
1135 A477 250m multicolored   .60 .30

Tunisian Works of Art — A478

#1136, "L'Automne," by Ammar Farhat. #1137, Sculpture, "Pecheur D'Hommes," by Hedi Selmi. #1138, "Au Cafe-Maure," by Farhat. #1139, "Le Viellard au Kanoun," by Farhat. #1140, "Cafe Des Nattes-Sidi Bou Said," by Hedi Khayachi. #1141, "Le Kouttab," by Yahia Turki. 1000d, "La Fileuse," by Farhat.

1997, Nov. 5
1136 A478 250m multi, vert.   .55 .30
1137 A478 250m multi, vert.   .55 .30
1138 A478 250m multi, vert.   .55 .30
1139 A478 250m multi, vert.   .55 .30
1140 A478 500m multi   1.10 .55
1141 A478 500m multi   1.10 .55
1142 A478 1000m multi, vert.   2.25 1.10
  a. Sheet of 7, #1136-1142, + 3 labels   7.25 7.25
    Nos. 1136-1142 (7)   6.65 3.40
    No. 1142a issued 11/7.

A479

A480

1997, Nov. 7
1143 A479 250m multicolored   .60 .30
1144 A480 500m multicolored   1.10 .55
Pres. Zine El Abdine, 10th anniv. of taking office.

Desert Rose — A481

1997, Nov. 29
1145 A481 250m multicolored   .60 .30

Intl. Human Rights Day — A482

1997, Dec. 10   Litho.   Perf. 13½
1146 A482 500m multicolored   1.25 .60

Horses A483

Designs: 50m, Arabian. 70m, Barb. 250m, Arabian barb, vert. 500m, Arabian, vert.

1997, Dec. 18   Perf. 12½x13
1147 A483 50m multicolored   .20 .20
1148 A483 70m multicolored   .20 .20
1149 A483 250m multicolored   .75 .40
1150 A483 500m multicolored   1.50 .75
    Nos. 1147-1150 (4)   2.65 1.55

Bombing of Sakiet Sidi Yoncef, 40th Anniv. A484

1998, Feb. 8
1151 A484 250m multicolored   .60 .30

School Health Week A485

1998, Feb. 16   Litho.   Perf. 12½x13
1152 A485 250m multicolored   .60 .30

Bar Assoc. of Tunisia, Cent. — A486

1998, Mar. 27   Perf. 13x12½
1153 A486 250m multicolored   .60 .30

Martyr's Day, 60th Anniv.
A487   A488

1998, Apr. 9
1154 A487 250m multicolored   .60 .30
1155 A488 520m multicolored   1.25 .60

Okba Ibn Nafaa Mosque, Kairouan — A489

1998, May 28   Litho.   Perf. 13
1156 A489 500m multicolored   1.40 .70

1998 World Cup Soccer Championships, France — A490

250m, Tunisian team. 500m Player, trophy.

1998, June 10   Litho.   Perf. 13
1157 A490 250m multi   .60 .30
1158 A490 500m multi, vert.   1.25 .60

Crustaceans — A491

1998, July 8   Perf. 12½x13
1159 A491 110m Crab   .25 .20
1160 A491 250m Shrimp   .60 .30
1161 A491 1000m Lobster   2.25 1.10
    Nos. 1159-1161 (3)   3.10 1.60

21st Reassembly of the Democratic Congress (RCD) — A492

#1162, Pres. Zine El Abidine ben Ali, flag, emblems. #1163, People holding torches, flag, dove.

1998, July 30   Perf. 13
1162 A492 250m multi   .60 .30
1163 A492 250m multi, vert.   .60 .30

36th Intl. Congress on the History of Medicine — A493

1998, Sept. 6   Litho.   Perf. 13
1164 A493 500m multicolored   1.25 .60

Paintings — A494

#1165, "The Weaver," by Ali Guermassi (1923-92). #1166, "Woman Musician," by Noureddine Khayachi (1917-87). 500m, Still life by Ali Khouja (1947-91).

1998, Oct. 8
1165 A494 250m multi   .60 .30
1166 A494 250m multi, vert.   .60 .30
1167 A494 500m multi, vert.   1.25 .60
    Nos. 1165-1167 (3)   2.45 1.20

Central Bank of Tunisia, 40th Anniv. A495

1998, Nov. 10   Litho.   Perf. 13
1168 A495 250m multicolored   .60 .30

A496

1998, Nov. 7
1169 A496 250m multicolored   .60 .30
Appointment of Pres. Zine El Abidine ben Ali, 11th anniv.

Universal Declaration of Human Rights, 50th Anniv. A497

1998, Dec. 10   Litho.   Perf. 12½x13
1170 A497 250m multicolored   .65 .35

Averroes (Ibn Rushd) (1126-1198), Philosopher — A498

1998, Dec. 12
1171 A498 500m multicolored   1.25 .60

Musicians A499

1998, Dec. 21   Perf. 12½x13, 13x12½
1172 A499 250m Kaddour Srarfi   .60 .30
1173 A499 250m Saliha, vert.   .60 .30
1174 A499 500m Ali Riahi, vert.   1.25 .60
    Nos. 1172-1174 (3)   2.45 1.20

Boukornine Natl. Park — A500

1998, Dec. 29   Litho.   Perf. 13
1175 A500 70m Gazelles   .20 .20
1176 A500 110m Rabbit   .25 .20
1177 A500 250m Eagles   .60 .30
1178 A500 500m Cyclamens   1.25 .60
    Nos. 1175-1178 (4)   2.30 1.30

Fruit Trees A501

1999, Feb. 27   Litho.   Perf. 13
1179 A501 250m Orange   .65 .30
1180 A501 250m Date, vert.   .65 .30
1181 A501 500m Olive   1.25 .60
    Nos. 1179-1181 (3)   2.55 1.20

Archaeological Sites — A502

50m, Gate, Thuburbo Majus. 250m, Thermal baths, Bulla Regia. 500m, Zaghouan Aqueduct.

1999, Mar. 31   Litho.   Perf. 13
1182 A502 50m multi, vert.   .20 .20
1183 A502 250m multi   .55 .30
1184 A502 500m multi   1.25 .60
    Nos. 1182-1184 (3)   2.00 1.10

Paintings by Tunisian Artists A503

Designs: No. 1185, "L'Intemporel," by Moncef Ben Amor. No. 1186, "Fiancailles," by Ali Guermassi. No. 1187, "La Poterie," by Ammar Farhat. No. 1188, "Vendeur d'ombrelles et d'eventails," by Yahia Turki.

1999, May 6   Litho.   Perf. 13
1185 A503 250m multicolored   .55 .30
1186 A503 250m multicolored   .55 .30
1187 A503 500m multicolored   1.10 .55
1188 A503 500m multicolored   1.10 .55
    Nos. 1185-1188 (4)   3.30 1.70

Constitution, 40th Anniv. — A504

1999, June 1   Litho.   Perf. 13
1189 A504 250m multicolored   .85 .40

Flowers — A505

70m, Acacia cyanophilla. #1191, Bouganvillea spectabilis. #1192, Papaver rhoeas. 500m, Dianthus caryophylius.

1999, June 25   Litho.   Perf. 12¾
1190 A505 70m multicolored   .20 .20
1191 A505 250m multicolored   .55 .25
1192 A505 250m multicolored   .55 .25
1193 A505 500m multicolored   1.10 .55
  a. Souvenir sheet, #1190-1193, imperf.   4.00 4.00
    Nos. 1190-1193 (4)   2.40 1.25

No. 1193a sold for 1.50d.

Philex France 99 — A506

1999, July 2   Perf. 13x12¾
1194 A506 500m multicolored   1.10 .55

Tahar Haddad (b. 1899), Women's Rights Advocate — A507

1999, Aug. 13   Litho.
1195 A507 500m multicolored   1.10 .50

Marine Life A508

1999, Sept. 22   Perf. 12¾
1196 A508 250m Caretta caretta   .55 .25
1197 A508 500m Epinephelus marginatus   1.10 .55

National Organ Donation Day — A509

1999, Oct. 2   Perf. 13x12¾
1198 A509 250m multicolored   .55 .25

UPU, 125th Anniv. — A510   Elections — A511

1999, Oct. 9   Perf. 12¾
1199 A510 500m multicolored   1.10 .55

1999, Oct. 10   Litho.
1200 A511 500m multicolored   1.10 .55

Tamarisk A512

1999, Oct. 28   Litho.   Perf. 12¾x13
1201 A512 250m shown   .55 .25
1202 A512 500m Dromedary   1.10 .55

Appointment of Pres. Zine El Abidine Ben Ali, 12th Anniv. — A513

1999, Nov. 7   Perf. 13x12¾
1203 A513 250m multi   .60 .30

Human Rights Day — A514   Famous Tunisians — A515

1999, Dec. 10   Litho.   Perf. 13x12¾
1204 A514 250m multi   .60 .30

1999, Dec. 28   Perf. 13x12¾, 12¾x13
#1205, Ahmed Ibn Abi Dhiaf (1802-74), historian. #1206, Abdelaziz Thaalbi (1876-1944), anti-colonial leader. 500m, Khemaies Tarnane (1894-1964), musician.
1205 A515 250m multi   .60 .30
1206 A515 250m multi   .60 .30
1207 A515 500m multi, horiz.   1.25 .60
    Nos. 1205-1207 (3)   2.45 1.20

Millennium — A516

1999, Dec. 31   Perf. 13
1208 A516 250m multi   .60 .30

A517

A518

Archaeology A519

Design: 100m, Methred cup. 110m, Aghlabide plate. 250m, Zaghouan water temple. 500m, Ulysses and the Sirens mosaic. Illustration A517 reduced.

000, Apr. 22   Litho.   Perf. 13x13¼
209 A517 100m multi   .20 .20
210 A517 110m multi   .20 .20
            Perf. 13¼
211 A518 250m multi   .45 .25
212 A519 500m multi   .90 .45
        Nos. 1209-1212 (4)   1.75 1.10

Ferry Carthage — A520

000, Apr. 29   Perf. 13¼x13
213 A520 500m multi   .90 .45
   a.   Souvenir sheet, imperf.   3.75 1.90
        No. 1213a sold for 2d.

Expo 2000, Hanover — A521

000, June 1   Perf. 13¼x13
214 A521 1d multi   2.10 1.10

Trees
A522

Designs: 50m, Carob. 100m, Apricot. 250m,
Avocado, vert. 400m, Apple.

000, July 5   Litho.   Perf. 12¾
215-1218 A522   Set of 4   1.60 .80

2001 Mediterranean Games,
Tunis — A523

000, Sept. 2   Litho.   Perf. 13
219 A523 500m multi   .90 .45
   a.   Souvenir sheet of 1, imperf. 2.60 1.40
        No. 1219a sold for 1500m.

2000 Summer
Olympics,
Sydney — A524

000, Sept. 22   Perf. 12¾
1220 A524 500m multi   .90 .45

Souvenir Sheet
Imperf
1221 A524 1500m multi   2.60 1.40

Flowers — A525

Designs: 110m, Freesias. 200m, Chrysanthemums. No. 1224, 250m, "Golden Times"
roses. No. 1225, 250m, Vase with flowers
(33x49mm). 500m, "Calibra" roses.

2000, Oct. 21   Perf. 12¾, 13 (#1225)
1222-1226 A525   Set of 5   2.25 1.10

Appointment
of Pres. Zine
El Abidine
Ben Ali, 13th
Anniv.
A526

2000, Nov. 7   Perf. 13
1227 A526 250m multi   .60 .30

Art — A527

Designs: 100m, Still Life, by Hédi Khayachi.
No. 1229, 250m, Landscape, by Abdelaziz
Berraies. No. 1230, 250m, The Knife Sharp-
ener, by Ali Guermassi. 400m, Date and Milk
Seller, by Yahia Turki, vert.

2000, Nov. 18
1228-1231 A527   Set of 4   2.00 1.00

Intl. Human
Rights
Day — A528

2000, Dec. 10
1232 A528 500m multi   .90 .45

Shells — A529

Designs: 50m, Neverita josephinia. No.
1234, 250m, Phyllonotus trunculus. No. 1235,
250m, Columbella rustica. 1d, Arca noe.

Illustration reduced.

2000, Dec. 29   Perf. 13x13¼
1233-1236 A529   Set of 4   3.00 1.50

A530

Famous
Tunisians
A531

Designs: No. 1237, 250m, Imam Sahnoun.
No. 1238, 250m, Imam Ibn Arafa. No. 1239,
250m, Ali Belhaouane (1909-58), vert. 1d,
Mohamed Jamoussi (1910-82), musician.

2000, Dec. 30   Perf. 12¾
1237 A530 250m shown   .45 .25
1238 A530 250m multi   .45 .25
1239 A531 250m multi   .45 .25
1240 A531   1d shown   1.90 .95
        Nos. 1237-1240 (4)   3.25 1.70

Tunisian Presidency of UN Security
Council — A532

2001, Feb. 19   Litho.   Perf. 13
1241 A532 250m multi   .45 .25

World Fund of
Solidarity
A533

2001, Mar. 29
1242 A533 500m multi   .90 .45

Year of Digital
Culture — A534

2001, May 17   Perf. 12¾
1243 A534 250m multi   .45 .25

Mohamed Dorra, Child Killed in Israeli-
Palestinian Violence — A535

2001, May 30
1244 A535 600m multi   1.10 .55

A536   A537

Designs: No. 1245, 19th cent. ceramic tile,
Qallaline. No. 1246, Gigthis, horiz. No. 1247,
Tunis City Hall, horiz. 500m, Needles of
Tabarka.

2001, Aug. 24
1245 A536 250m multi   .45 .25
1246 A537 250m multi   .45 .25
1247 A537 250m multi   .45 .25
1248 A537 500m multi   .90 .45
        Nos. 1245-1248 (4)   2.25 1.20

2001
Mediterranean
Games,
Tunis — A538

Designs: No. 1249, 250m, No. 1251b, Track,
stadium. No. 1250, 500m, No. 1251a, Runners, medal.

2001, Sept. 2   Perf. 12¾
1249-1250 A538   Set of 2   1.40 .70
Souvenir Sheet
Imperf
1251 A538 750m Sheet of 2,
              #a-b   2.75 1.40

Paintings — A539

Designs: No. 1252, 250m, Sidi Bou Said, by
Pierre Boucherle. No. 1253, 250m, Still Life,
by Boucherle. No. 1254, 250m, Dream in
Traditional Space, by Aly Ben Salem, vert.
500m, Traditional Open-air Marriage, by Ben
Salem.

2001, Sept. 29   Litho.   Perf. 13
1252-1255 A539   Set of 4   2.25 1.20

Year of
Dialogue
Among
Civilizations
A540

2001, Oct. 9   Perf. 12¾x13
1256 A540 500m multi   .90 .45

National Employment Fund — A541

2001, Oct. 10
1257 A541 250m multi   .45   .25

Appointment of
Pres. Zine El
Abidine Ben Ali,
14th Anniv. — A542

2001, Nov. 7   *Perf. 13x12¾*
1258 A542 250m multi   .45   .25

Butterflies — A543

Designs: Nos. 1259, 1263a, 250m, Ariane.
No. 1260, 250m, No. 1263c, 500m, Pacha à
deux queues. Nos. 1261, 1263b, 250m, Demi-
deuil. Nos. 1262, 1263d, 500m, Grand paon
de nuit.
Illustration reduced.

2001, Nov. 15   *Perf. 13x13¼*
1259-1262 A543   Set of 4   2.25 1.10
Souvenir Sheet
Imperf
1263 A543   Sheet of 4, #a-d   2.75 1.40

Birds — A544

Designs: No. 1264, 250m, No. 1268a,
300m, Bec-croise des sapins. 500m, Mesange
charbonnière. No. 1266, 600m, Cigogne
blanche. No. 1267, 600m, Geai des chenes.

2001, Nov. 22   *Perf. 13*
1264-1267 A544   Set of 4   3.25 1.75
Souvenir Sheet
1268 A544   Sheet, #1265-1267,
             1268a   3.50 1.75

Intl. Human Rights
Day — A545

2001, Dec. 10   *Perf. 13x12¾*
1269 A545 250m multi   .45   .25

Famous
Men
A546

Designs: No. 1270, 250m, Ibrahim ibn al-
Aghlab (757-812), founder of Aghlabid
dynasty. No. 1271, 250m, Ibn Rachiq al
Kairaouani (1000-71). 350m, Abdelaziz Laroui

(1898-1971). 650m, Assad ibn al-Fourat (759-
828).

2001, Dec. 29   *Perf. 12¾x13*
1270-1273 A546   Set of 4   2.75 1.40

Arabic
Calligraphy
A547

Designs: No. 1274, 350m, Shown. No.
1275, 350m, Calligraphy, vert.

2001, Dec. 31 *Perf. 12¾x13, 13x12¾*
1274-1275 A547   Set of 2   1.25   .65

Archaeology
A548   A549

Designs: 250m, Kef casbah. 390m, Amphitheater, Oudhna, horiz. No. 1278, Baron of
Erlanger Palace. No. 1279, Mosaic of Virgil.

Perf. 13x12¾, 12¾x13
2002, Mar. 26   Litho.
1276 A548 250m multi   .35   .20
1277 A548 390m multi   .55   .25
1278 A549 600m multi   .80   .40
1279 A549 600m multi   .80   .40
          Nos. 1276-1279 (4)   2.50 1.25

Animals of Zembra
and Zembretta Natl.
Park — A550

Designs: No. 1280, 250m, No. 1284a,
400m, Ovis musimon. No. 1281, 250m, No.
1284b, Oryctolagus cuniculus. No. 1282,
600m, Falco peregrinus brookei. No. 1283,
600m, Larus audouinii.

2002, Apr. 10   *Perf. 13*
1280-1283 A550   Set of 4   2.25 1.10
Souvenir Sheet
1284 A550   Sheet, #1282-1283,
             1284a-1284b   2.75 1.40

Sahara Desert
Tourism
A551

Designs: No. 1285, 250m, No. 1289a,
400m, Gazella leptoceros. No. 1286, 390m,
No. 1289b, 400m, Sahara village. No. 1287,
600m, Horseman. No. 1288, 600m,
Tamaghza.

2002, May 22   *Perf. 13¼*
1285-1288 A551   Set of 4   2.60 1.25
Souvenir Sheet
1289 A551   Sheet, #1287-1288,
             1289a-1289b, im-
             perf.   2.75 1.40

2002 World Cup Soccer
Championships, Japan and
Korea — A552

World Cup, Emblem of Tunisia and World
Cup tournament and: No. 1290, 390m, No.
1292a, 500m, Player, map of Japan and
Korea. No. 1291, 600m, 1292b, 1000m, Ball in
goal net.

2002, May 29   *Perf. 13*
1290-1291 A552   Set of 2   1.40   .70
Souvenir Sheet
1292 A552   Sheet of 2, #a-b   2.10 1.10

Famous
Men — A553

Designs: 100m, Sheikh Mohamed Senoussi
(1851-1900). No. 1294, 250m, Mosbah Jarbou
(1914-58). No. 1295, 250m, Mohamed
Daghbaji (1885-1924). 1.10d, Abou al-Hassen
al-Housri (1029-95).

2002, July 18   *Perf. 12¾*
1293-1296 A553   Set of 4   2.50 1.25

World Handicapped Games — A554

Tunisian flag and: 100m, Wheelchair racer.
700m, Discus thrower, vert.

2002, July 20
1297-1298 A554   Set of 2   1.25   .60

27th World
Veterinary
Congress,
Tunis
A555

2002, Sept. 25 Litho.   *Perf. 12¾*
1299 A555 600m multi   .90   .45

Travel International Club, 20th
Anniv. — A556

2002, Oct. 25 Litho.   *Perf. 13x13¼*
1300 A556 600m multi   .90   .45

Appointment of
Pres. Zine El
Abidine Ben Ali,
15th Anniv. — A557

2002, Nov. 7   *Perf. 13x12¾*
1301 A557 390m multi   .60   .30

Assassination of
Farhat Hached
(1914-52) — A558

2002, Dec. 3 Litho.   *Perf. 13x12¾*
1302 A558 390m multi   .60   .30

Intl. Human Rights
Day — A559

2002, Dec. 10
1303 A559 700m multi   1.00   .50

Art Type of 2001

Designs: No. 1304, 250m, Space for Gaze-
les, by Aly Ben Salem. No. 1305, 250m, Popular Arts, by Ammar Farhat, vert. No. 1306,
250m, Marriage, by Habib Bouabana, vert.
900m, Still Life, by Pierre Boucherle, vert.

2002, Dec. 28   *Perf. 13*
1304-1307 A539   Set of 4   2.50 1.25

Mosaics
A560

Designs: 390m, Spinner. 600m, Africa.

2003, Feb. 28
1308-1309 A560   Set of 2   1.50   .75

Scouting in Tunisia, 70th
Anniv. — A561

"70" and scouts: 250m, Reading map, at
computer, planting tree. 600m, Saluting flag
at computer, vert.

2003, Mar. 29 Litho.   *Perf. 13*
1310-1311 A561   Set of 2   1.25   .60

National Book
Year — A562

2003, Apr. 23
312 A562 390m multi   .65 .30

The Washerwoman, by Yahia
Turki — A563

2003, June 13
313 A563 1d multi   1.60 .80

National
Tourism
Day — A564

2003, June 28   Perf. 13¼
314 A564 600m multi   .95 .45

Parks — A565

Designs: 200m, Farhat Hached Park, ades. 250m, Friguia Animal Park. 390m, La arsa Park. 1d, Ennahli Park.

2003, June 28   Perf. 13
15-1318 A565 Set of 4   3.00 1.50

A566   A567

2003, July 28 Litho. Perf. 13x12¾
19 A566 250m multi   .45 .25
Congress of Ambition.

2003, Aug. 3
20 A567 390m multi   .65 .30
Pres. Habib Bourguiba (1903-2000).

A568

Flora and Fauna — A569

Designs: Nos. 1321a, 50m, 1326, 600m, Oryx dammah. Nos. 1321b, 50m, 1324, 250m, Nyctanthes sambac. Nos. 1321c, 100m, 1323, 250m, Aries. Nos. 1321d, 100m, 1327, 1d, Myrtus communis. Nos. 1321e, 200m, 1325, 390m, Struthio camelus. Nos. 1321f, 200m, 1322, 100m, Rosa canina.

2003, Sept. 25   Perf. 12¾
1321   Strip of 6   1.25 .65
 a.-b. A568 50m Either single   .20 .20
 c.-d. A568 100m Either single   .20 .20
 e.-f. A568 200m Either single   .35 .20
1322-1327 A569 Set of 6   4.50 2.25
No. 1321 was issued in a sheet of 6 strips that sold for 4500m.

Appointment of
Pres. Zine El
Abidine Ben Ali,
16th Anniv. — A570

2003, Nov. 7 Litho. Perf. 13x12¾
1328 A570 250m multi   .40 .20

First 5+5
Dialogue
Summit,
Tunis — A571

2003, Dec. 5   Perf. 13¼
1329 A571 600m multi   1.00 .50

Universal
Declaration of
Human
Rights — A572

2003, Dec. 10   Perf. 13x12¾
1330 A572 350m multi   .60 .30

Silver Items
A573

Designs: No. 1331, 600m, Machmoum. No. 1332, 600m, Jewelry.

2003, Dec. 18   Perf. 12¾x13
1331-1332 A573 Set of 2   2.00 1.00
1332a   Souvenir sheet, #1331-1332   2.50 2.50
No. 1332a sold for 1.50d.

African Soccer
Championships — A574

Designs: 250m, Stylized soccer players, African cup, map. 600m, Map of Africa as soccer player.

2004, Jan. 24   Perf. 13
1333-1334 A574 Set of 2   1.40 .70
Values are for stamps with surrounding selvage.

SEMI-POSTAL STAMPS

No. 36 Overprinted in Red

1915, Feb. Unwmk. Perf. 14x13½
B1 A5 15c vio, pnksh   .75 .60

No. 32 Overprinted in Red

1916, Feb. 15
B2 A4 5c grn, grnsh   .75 .60

Types of Regular
Issue of 1906 in New
Colors and
Surcharged

1916, Aug.
B3 A5 10c on 15c brn vio, bl   .60 .60
B4 A5 10c on 20c brn, org   .65 .65
B5 A5 10c on 25c bl, grn   2.25 2.25
B6 A6 10c on 35c ol grn & vio   4.00 4.00
B7 A6 10c on 40c bis & blk   2.25 2.25
B8 A6 10c on 75c vio brn & grn   5.50 5.50
B9 A7 10c on 1fr red & grn   2.25 2.25
B10 A7 10c on 2fr bis & bl   57.50 57.50
B11 A7 10c on 5fr vio & red   75.00 75.00
Nos. B3-B11 (9)   150.00 150.00
Nos. B3 to B11 were sold at their face value but had a postal value of 10c only. The excess was applied to the relief of prisoners of war in Germany.

Types of Regular
Issue of 1906 in New
Colors and
Surcharged in
Carmine

1918
B12 A5 15c on 20c blk, grn   1.00 1.00
B13 A5 15c on 25c dk bl, buff   1.00 1.00
B14 A6 15c on 35c gray grn & red   1.25 1.25
B15 A6 15c on 40c brn & lt bl   2.75 2.75
B16 A6 15c on 75c red brn & blk   4.50 4.50
B17 A7 15c on 1fr red & vio   12.50 12.50
B18 A7 15c on 2fr bis brn & red   47.50 47.50
B19 A7 15c on 5fr vio & blk   95.00 95.00
Nos. B12-B19 (8)   165.50 165.50
The different parts of the surcharge are more widely spaced on the stamps of types A6 and A7. These stamps were sold at their face

value but had a postal value of 15c only. The excess was intended for the relief of prisoners of war in Germany.

Types of 1906-22
Surcharged

1923
B20 A4 0c on 1c blue   .35 .35
B21 A4 0c on 2c ol brn   .35 .35
B22 A4 1c on 3c green   .35 .35
B23 A4 2c on 5c red vio   .35 .35
B24 A9 3c on 10c vio, bluish   .35 .35
B25 A5 5c on 15c ol grn   .35 .35
B26 A5 5c on 20c bl, pink   1.00 1.00
B27 A5 5c on 25c vio, bluish   1.00 1.00
B28 A9 5c on 30c orange   1.00 1.00
B29 A6 5c on 35c bl & vio   1.10 1.10
B30 A6 5c on 40c bl & brn   1.10 1.10
B31 A9 10c on 50c blk, bluish   1.50 1.50
B32 A6 10c on 60c ol brn & bl   1.50 1.50
B33 A6 10c on 75c vio & lt grn   2.75 2.75
B34 A7 25c on 1fr mar & vio   2.75 2.75
B35 A7 25c on 2fr bl & rose   10.00 10.00
B36 A7 25c on 5fr grn & ol brn   45.00 45.00
Nos. B20-B36 (17)   70.80 70.80
These stamps were sold at their original values but had postal franking values only to the amounts surcharged on them. The difference was intended to be used for the benefit of wounded soldiers.
This issue was entirely speculative. Before the announced date of sale most of the stamps were taken by postal employees and practically none of them were offered to the public.

Mail Delivery — SP1

Type of Parcel Post Stamps, 1906,
with Surcharge in Black
1925, June 7   Perf. 13½x14
B37 SP1 1c on 5c brn & red, pink   .40 .40
 a. Surcharge omitted   85.00 85.00
B38 SP1 2c on 10c brn & bl, yel   .40 .40
B39 SP1 3c on 20c red vio & rose, lav   .50 .50
B40 SP1 5c on 25c sl grn & rose, bluish   .60 .60
B41 SP1 5c on 40c rose & grn, yel   .60 .60
B42 SP1 10c on 50c vio & bl, lav   1.50 1.50
B43 SP1 10c on 75c grn & ol, grnsh   1.00 1.00
B44 SP1 25c on 1fr bl & grn, bluish   1.00 1.00
B45 SP1 25c on 2fr rose & vio, pnksh   5.50 5.50
B46 SP1 25c on 5fr red & brn, lem   27.50 27.50
Nos. B37-B46 (10)   39.00 39.00
These stamps were sold at their original values but paid postage only to the amount of the surcharged values. The difference was given to Child Welfare societies.

Tunis-Chad
Motor
Caravan
SP2

1928, Feb. Engr. Perf. 13½
B47 SP2 40c + 40c org brn   .65 .65
B48 SP2 50c + 50c dp vio   .65 .65
B49 SP2 75c + 75c dk bl   .75 .75
B50 SP2 1fr + 1fr carmine   .75 .75
B51 SP2 1.50fr + 1.50fr brt bl   .75 .75

B52	SP2	2fr + 2fr dk grn	.95	.95
B53	SP2	5fr + 5fr red brn	1.00	1.00
		Nos. B47-B53 (7)	5.50	5.50

The surtax on these stamps was for the benefit of Child Welfare societies.

Nos. 122-135, 137-142 Surcharged in Black

a

b

1938   **Perf. 11, 12½, 12½x13**

B54	A14(a)	1c + 1c	1.10	1.10
B55	A14(a)	2c + 2c	1.10	1.10
B56	A14(a)	3c + 3c	1.10	1.10
B57	A14(a)	5c + 5c	1.10	1.10
B58	A14(a)	10c + 10c	1.10	1.10
B59	A15(a)	15c + 15c	1.10	1.10
B60	A15(a)	20c + 20c	1.10	1.10
B61	A15(a)	25c + 25c	1.10	1.10
B62	A15(a)	30c + 30c	1.10	1.10
B63	A15(a)	40c + 40c	1.10	1.10
B64	A16(a)	50c + 50c	1.10	1.10
B65	A16(a)	75c + 75c	1.10	1.10
B66	A16(a)	90c + 90c	1.10	1.10
B67	A16(a)	1fr + 1fr	1.10	1.10
B68	A17(b)	1.50fr + 1fr	1.10	1.10
B69	A17(b)	2fr + 1.50fr	2.00	2.00
B70	A17(b)	3fr + 2fr	2.00	2.00
B71	A17(b)	5fr + 3fr	11.00	11.00
a.		Perf. 12½	60.00	60.00
B72	A17(b)	10fr + 5fr	26.00	26.00
B73	A17(b)	20fr + 10fr	42.50	42.50
		Nos. B54-B73 (20)	100.00	100.00

50th anniversary of the post office.

Nos. 86, 100-101, 105 Surcharged in Black, Blue or Red

1941   **Perf. 14x13½**

B74	A11	1fr on 45c (Bk)	.35	.35
B75	A13	1.30fr on 1.25fr (Bl)	.35	.35
B76	A13	1.50fr on 1.40fr (Bk)	.35	.35
B77	A13	2fr on 2.25fr (R)	.35	.35
		Nos. B74-B77 (4)	1.40	1.40

The surcharge measures 11x14mm on #B74.

> **Catalogue values for unused stamps in this section, from this point to the end of the section, are for Never Hinged items.**

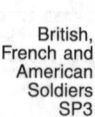

British, French and American Soldiers SP3

1943   **Litho.**   **Perf. 12**

B78 SP3 1.50fr + 8.50fr crimson   .20 .20

Liberation of Tunisia.

Children — SP3a

1944   **Engr.**   **Perf. 13½**

B78A	SP3a	1.20fr + 1.30fr brown	.30	
B78B	SP3a	1.50fr + 2fr black brown	.30	

B78C	SP3a	2fr + 3fr dark green	.30	
B78D	SP3a	3fr + 4fr red orange	.30	
		Nos. B78A-B78D (4)	1.20	

National welfare fund.

Nos. B78A-B78D were issued by the Vichy government in France, but were not issued in Tunisia.

Native Scene — SP4

Surcharged in Black: "+ 48frcs / pour nos / Combattants"

1944   **Perf. 11½**

B79 SP4 2fr + 48fr red   .35 .35

The surtax was for soldiers.

Sidi Mahrez Mosque — SP5

Ramparts of Sfax — SP6

Fort Saint — SP7

Sidi-bou-Said — SP8

1945 **Unwmk.** **Litho.** **Perf. 11½**

B80	SP5	1.50fr + 8.50fr choc & red	.40	.40
B81	SP6	3fr + 12fr dk bl grn & red	.40	.40
B82	SP7	4fr + 21fr brn org & red	.50	.50
B83	SP8	10fr + 40fr red & blk	.50	.50
		Nos. B80-B83 (4)	1.80	1.80

The surtax was for soldiers.

France No. B193 Overprinted in Black

c   **TUNISIE**

1945   **Perf. 14x13½**

B84 SP147 2fr + 1fr red org   .25 .25

The surtax was for the aid of tuberculosis victims.

Same Overprint on Type of France, 1945

1945   **Engr.**   **Perf. 13**

B85 SP150 2fr + 3fr dk grn   .30 .30

Stamp Day.

Same Overprint on France No. B192

1945

B86 SP146 4fr + 6fr dk vio brn   .30 .25

The surtax was for war victims of the P.T.T.

Types of 1926 Surcharged in Carmine

1945   **Typo.**   **Perf. 14x13½**

B87	A10	4fr + 6fr on 10c ultra	.35	.25
B88	A12	10fr + 30fr on 80c dk grn	.35	.25

The design of type A12 is redrawn, omitting "RF." The surtax was for war veterans.

Tunisian Soldier — SP9

1946 **Unwmk.** **Engr.** **Perf. 13**

B89 SP9 20fr + 30fr grn, red & blk .80 .80

The surtax aided Tunisian soldiers in Indo-China.

Type of France Overprinted Type "c" in Carmine

1946

B90 SP160 3fr + 2fr dk bl   .55 .55

Stamp Day.

Stamps and Types of 1926-46 Surcharged in Carmine and Black

1946   **Perf. 14x13½**

B91	A12	80c + 50c emerald	.50	.50
B92	A12	1.50fr + 1.50fr rose lil	.50	.50
B93	A12	2fr + 2fr Prus grn	.50	.50
B94	A12	2.40fr + 2fr sal pink	.50	.50
B95	A13	4fr + 4fr ultra	.50	.50
		Nos. B91-B95 (5)	2.50	2.50

The two parts of the surcharge are more widely spaced on stamps of type A13.

Type of France Overprinted Type "c" in Carmine

1947   **Perf. 13**

B96 SP172 4.50fr + 5.50fr sepia   .50 .50

On Type of France Surcharged in Carmine with New Value and Bars

B97 SP158 10fr + 15fr on 2fr + 3fr brt ultra   .50 .50

Type of 1926 Surcharged in Carmine

1947   **Typo.**   **Perf. 14x13½**

B98 A13 10fr + 40fr black   .55 .50

Feeding Young Bird — SP10

1947   **Engr.**   **Perf. 1**

B99	SP10	4.50fr + 5.50fr dk bl grn	.60	.6
B100	SP10	6fr + 9fr brt ultra	.60	.6
B101	SP10	8fr + 17fr dp car	.60	.6
B102	SP10	10fr + 40fr dk pur	.60	.6
		Nos. B99-B102 (4)	2.40	2.4

The surtax was for child welfare.

Type of Regular Issue of 1948 Surcharged in Blue

1948

B103 A21 4fr + 10fr ol grn & org   .40 .4

The surtax was for anti-tuberculosis work.

Arch of Triumph, Sbeitla SP11

1948

B104	SP11	10fr + 40fr ol grn & olive	.60	.6
B105	SP11	18fr + 42fr dk bl & indigo	.60	.60

Surtax for charitable works of the army.

Arago Type of France Overprinted in Carmine

1948

B106 SP176 6fr + 4fr brt car   .60 .60

Stamp Day, Mar. 6-7.

Sleeping Child SP12

1949, June 1

B107 SP12 25fr + 50fr dk grn   1.10 1.10

The surtax was for child welfare.

Neptune Type of 1947 Surcharged in Black with Lorraine Cross and "FFL+15F"

1949, Dec. 8

B108 A20 10fr + 15fr dp ultra & car   .40 .40

The surtax was for the Tunisian section of the Association of Free French.

Type of France Overprinted in Carmine

e

1949, Mar. 26
B109 SP180 15fr + 5fr indigo .60 .60
Stamp Days, Mar. 26-27.

Type of France, 1950, Ovptd. Like No. B106 in Ultramarine

1950, Mar. 11 Unwmk. Perf. 13
B110 SP183 12fr + 3fr dk grn .60 .60
Stamp Days, Mar. 11-12.

Tunisian and French Woman Shaking Hands SP13

1950, June 5
B111 SP13 15fr + 35fr red .60 .60
B112 SP13 25fr + 45fr dp ultra .60 .60
The surtax was for Franco-Tunisian Mutual Assistance.

Arab Soldier — SP14

1950, Aug. 21 Engr.
B113 SP14 25fr + 25fr dp bl .80 .80
The surtax was for old soldiers.

Type of France Overprinted Type "c" in Black

1951, Mar. 10
B114 SP186 12fr + 3fr brnsh gray .50 .40
Stamp Days, Mar. 10-11.

Mother Carrying Child SP15

1951, June 19 Engr. Perf. 13
B115 SP15 30fr + 15fr dp ultra 1.25 1.25
The surtax was for child welfare.

National Cemetery of Gammarth SP16

1952, June 15
B116 SP16 30fr + 10fr blue 1.10 1.10
Surtax aided orphans of the military services.

Type of France Overprinted Type "e" in Lilac

1952, Mar. 8 Unwmk.
B117 SP190 12fr + 3fr purple .70 .70
Stamp Day, Mar. 8.

Stucco Work, Bardo SP17

Boy Campers SP18

1952, May 5 Engr. Perf. 13
B118 SP17 15fr + 1fr ultra & indigo .50 .50
Surtax for charitable works of the army.

1952, June 15
B119 SP18 30fr + 10fr dk grn .80 .80
The surtax was for the Educational League vacation camps.

Type of France Surcharged Type "c" and Surtax

1952, Oct. 15
B120 A226 15fr + 5fr bl grn .90 .90
Creation of the French Military Medal, cent.

Type of France Overprinted Type "c"

1953, Mar. 14
B121 SP193 12fr + 3fr vermilion .40 .40
"Day of the Stamp."

Type of France Overprinted Type "c"

1954, Mar. 20
B122 SP196 12fr + 3fr indigo .40 .40
Stamp Day.

Balloon Post, 1870 SP19

1955, Mar. 19
B123 SP19 12fr + 3fr red brown .50 .50
Stamp Days, Mar. 19-20.

Independent Kingdom

Franz von Taxis SP20

1956, Mar. 17
B124 SP20 12fr + 3fr dark green .40 .40
Stamp Days, Mar. 17-18

Republic

No. 246 Surcharged in Red

1957, Aug. 8 Engr.
B125 A29 20fr + 10fr dp ultra .40 .40
15th anniversary of the army.

Florist Type of 1955 with Added Inscriptions, Surcharged in Red

1957, Oct. 19 Perf. 13
B126 A34 20fr + 10fr dk vio .35 .35
No. B126 is inscribed "5e. Foire Internationale" at bottom and lines of Arabic at either side.

Mailman Delivering Mail — SP21

Ornamental Cock — SP22

1959, May 1 Engr. Perf. 13
B127 SP21 20fr + 5fr dk brn & org brn .35 .35
Day of the Stamp. The surtax was for the Post Office Mutual Fund.

1959, Oct. 24 Litho. Perf. 13
B128 SP22 10m + 5m yel, lt bl & red .25 .25
Surtax for the Red Crescent Society.

Mailman on Camel Phoning — SP23

Dancer of Kerkennah Holding Stamp — SP24

1960, Apr. 16 Engr. Perf. 13
B129 SP23 60m + 5m ol, org & ultra .50 .50
Day of the Stamp.

1961, May 6 Unwmk. Perf. 13
Stamp Day: 15m+5m, Mail truck, horiz. 20m+6m, Hand holding magnifying glass and stamps. 50m+5m, Running boy, symbols of mail.
B130 SP24 12m + 4m multi .30 .30
B131 SP24 15m + 5m multi .40 .40
B132 SP24 20m + 6m multi .40 .40
B133 SP24 50m + 5m multi .50 .50
Nos. B130-B133 (4) 1.60 1.60

Nos. B130-B133 Overprinted

1963, Oct. 24
B134 SP24 12m + 4m cl, vio & ol .20 .20
B135 SP24 15m + 5m ol, cl & vio bl .30 .30
B136 SP24 20m + 6m multi .40 .40
B137 SP24 50m + 5m multi .60 .60
Nos. B134-B137 (4) 1.50 1.50
United Nations Day.

Old Man, Red Crescent SP25

Nurse Holding Bottle of Blood SP26

Tunisian Red Crescent: 75m+10m, Mother, child and Red Crescent.

1972, May 8 Engr. Perf. 13
B138 SP25 10m + 10m pur & dk red .25 .20
B139 SP25 75m + 10m bis brn & dl red .35 .25

1973, May 10 Engr. Perf. 13
Design: 60m+10m, Red Crescent and blood donors' arms, horiz.
B140 SP26 25m + 10m multi .25 .20
B141 SP26 60m + 10m gray & car .35 .20
Red Crescent appeal for blood donors.

Blood Donors — SP27

Man Holding Scales with Balanced Diet — SP28

Red Crescent Society: 75m+10m, Blood transfusion, symbolic design.

1974, May 8 Photo. Perf. 14x13
B142 SP27 25m + 10m multi .35 .20
B143 SP27 75m + 10m multi .50 .30

1975, May 8 Photo. Perf. 11½
B144 SP28 50m + 10m multi .25 .25
Tunisian Red Crescent fighting malnutrition.

Blood Donation, Woman and Man — SP29

1976, May 8 Photo. Perf. 11½
B145 SP29 40m + 10m multi .25 .20
Tunisian Red Crescent Society.

Litter Bearers and Red Crescent SP30

1977, May 8 Photo. Perf. 13½x14
B146 SP30 50m + 10m multi .25 .20
Tunisian Red Crescent Society.

Blood Donors
SP31

Hand and Red
Crescent
SP32

1978, May 8   Photo.   Perf. 13x14
B147 SP31 50m + 10m multi   .25 .20
Blood drive of Tunisian Red Crescent
Society.

1979, May 8   Photo.   Perf. 13½
B148 SP32 50m + 10m multi   .40 .25
Tunisian Red Crescent Society.

Red Crescent Society
SP33   SP34

1980, May 8   Photo.   Perf. 13½
B149 SP33 50m + 10m multi   .25 .20

1981, May 8   Perf. 14½x13½
B150 SP34 50m + 10m multi   .35 .20

Dome of
the Rock,
Jerusalem
SP35

1981, Nov. 29   Photo.   Perf. 13½
B151 SP35 50m + 5m multi   .35 .20
B152 SP35 150m + 5m multi   .65 .30
B153 SP35 200m + 5m multi   1.00 .50
     Nos. B151-B153 (3)   2.00 1.00
Intl. Palestinian Solidarity Day.

Red
Crescent
Society
SP36

1982, May 8   Photo.   Perf. 13½
B154 SP36 80m + 10m multi   .25 .20

Red Crescent
Society — SP37

1983, May 8   Litho.   Perf. 14x13½
B155 SP37 80m + 10m multi   .25 .20

Sabra and Chatilla Massacre — SP38

1983, Sept. 20   Photo.   Perf. 13
B156 SP38 80m + 5m multi   .20 .20

Red Crescent Society — SP39

1984, May 8   Litho.   Perf. 12½
B157 SP39 80m + 10m First aid   .25 .20

Red Crescent Society
SP40   SP41

1985, May 8   Litho.   Perf. 14
B158 SP40 100m + 10m multi   .25 .20

1986, May 9   Litho.   Perf. 14½x13½
B159 SP41 120m + 10m Map of
         Tunisia   .50 .25

Red
Crescent
Society
SP42

1987, May 8   Litho.   Perf. 13x13½
B160 SP42 150m + 10m multi   .65 .30

Intl. Red Cross and Red Crescent
Organizations, 125th Annivs. — SP43

1988, May 9   Photo.   Perf. 14
B161 SP43 150m + 10m multi   .50 .25

Red Crescent
Society
SP44

1989, May 8   Photo.   Perf. 11½
Granite Paper
B162 SP44 150m +10m multi   .40 .20

Red Crescent Society
SP45   SP46

1990, May 8   Litho.   Perf. 14x13½
B163 SP45 150m +10m multi   .35 .20

1991, May 8   Litho.   Perf. 13½
B164 SP46 180m +10m multi   .45 .20

Red Crescent
Society — SP47

1993, Aug. 17   Litho.   Perf. 14x13½
B165 SP47 120m +30m multi   .30 .20

AIR POST STAMPS

No. 43 Surcharged in Red

1919, Apr.   Unwmk.   Perf. 14x13½
C1 A6 30c on 35c ol grn &
       brn   .90 .90
a. Inverted surcharge   100.00 100.00
b. Double surcharge   100.00 100.00
c. Double inverted surcharge   110.00 110.00
d. Double surcharge, one in-
     verted   100.00 100.00

Type A6, Overprinted in Rose

1920, Apr.
C2 A6 30c ol grn, bl & rose   .40 .40

Nos. 53 and 55 Overprinted in Red

1927, Mar. 24
C3 A7 1fr indigo & ultra   .75 .65
C4 A7 2fr grn & red, pink   2.25 1.60

Nos. 51 and 57 Surcharged in Black
or Red

C5 A6 1.75fr on 75c (Bk)   .75 .50
C6 A7 1.75fr on 5fr (R)   2.25 1.50

Type A13 Ovptd. like #C3-C4 in Blue

1928, Feb.
C7 A13 1.30fr org & lt vio   2.75 1.10
C8 A13 1.80fr gray grn & red   3.50 .60
C9 A13 2.55fr lil & ol brn   1.50 .60
     Nos. C7-C9 (3)   7.75 2.30

Type A13 Surcharged like #C5-C6 in
Blue

1930, Aug.
C10 A13 1.50fr on 1.30fr org &
       lt vio   1.25 .50
C11 A13 1.50fr on 1.80fr gray
       grn & red   2.25 .50
C12 A13 1.50fr on 2.55fr lil & ol
       brn   4.25 1.00
     Nos. C10-C12 (3)   7.75 2.00

Catalogue values for unused
stamps in this section, from this
point to the end of the section, are
for Never Hinged items.

UPU Type of Regular Issue
1949, Oct. 28   Engr.   Perf. 1
C13 A23 25fr dk bl, bluish   1.25 1.2
UPU, 75th anniv. Exists imperf.; value $35.

Bird from
Antique
Mosaic,
Museum of
Sousse
AP2

(Arabic on
one
line) — AP3

1949   Unwmk
C14 AP2 200fr dk bl & indigo   3.00 .7

1950-51
C15 AP3 100fr bl grn & brn   1.25 .4
C16 AP3 200fr dk bl & ind ('51)   2.75 1.4

Monastir
AP4

Coast at
Korbous
AP5

Design: 1000fr, Air view of Tozeur mosque

1953-54
C17 AP4 100fr dk bl, ind & dk
       grn ('54)   2.25 .5
C18 AP4 200fr cl, blk brn &
       red brn ('54)   3.00 .9
C19 AP5 500fr dk brn & ultra   15.00 7.5
C20 AP5 1000fr dk green   27.50 15.0
     Nos. C17-C20 (4)   47.75 23.9
     Imperforates exist.

Independent Kingdom
Types of 1953-54 Redrawn with "RF"
Omitted
1956, Mar. 1
C21 AP4 100fr slate bl, indigo
       & dk grn   1.00 .2
C22 AP4 200fr multi   1.75 .5
C23 AP5 500fr dk brn & ultra   5.50 2.0
C24 AP5 1000fr dk green   10.00 3.7
     Nos. C21-C24 (4)   18.25 6.5

Republic

Desert
Swallows — AP6

Birds: #C26, Butcherbird. #C27, Cream-
colored courser. 100m, European chaffinch.
150m, Pink flamingoes. 200m, Barbary par-
tridges. 300m, European roller. 500m,
Bustard.

1965-66		**Photo.**	**Perf. 12½**	
		Size: 23x31mm		
C25	AP6	25m multi	.80	.30
C26	AP6	55m blk & lt bl	1.00	.40
C27	AP6	55m multi ('66)	1.25	.65
		Size: 22½x33mm		
		Perf. 11½		
C28	AP6	100m multi	1.50	.65
C29	AP6	150m multi ('66)	5.75	2.00
C30	AP6	200m multi ('66)	6.00	2.25
C31	AP6	300m multi ('66)	9.00	4.25
C32	AP6	500m multi ('66)	10.00	5.50
		Nos. C25-C32 (8)	35.30	16.00
		See No. 474.		

AIR POST SEMI-POSTAL STAMP

> Catalogue value for the unused
> stamp in this section is for a Never
> Hinged item.

Window, Great
Mosque of
Kairouan — SPAP1

		Unwmk.		
1952, May 5		**Engr.**	**Perf. 13**	
CB1	SPAP1	50fr + 10fr blk & gray grn	1.00	1.00

Surtax for charitable works of the army..

POSTAGE DUE STAMPS

Regular postage stamps perforated
with holes in the form of a "T," the holes
varying in size and number, were used
as postage due stamps from 1888 to
1901.

D1   D2

		Perf. 14x13½		
1901-03		**Unwmk.**		**Typo.**
J1	D1	1c black	.20	.20
J2	D1	2c orange	.25	.20
J3	D1	5c blue	.30	.20
J4	D1	10c brown	.25	.20
J5	D1	20c blue green	1.90	.40
J6	D1	30c carmine	1.00	.45
J7	D1	50c brown violet	.85	.45
J8	D1	1fr olive green	.65	.45
J9	D1	2fr carmine, *grn*	2.00	.80
J10	D1	5fr blk, *yellow*	35.00	25.00
		Nos. J1-J10 (10)	42.40	28.35

No. J10 Surcharged in
Blue

1914, Nov.
J11 D1 2fr on 5fr blk, *yellow*   .75   .60

In Jan. 1917 regular 5c postage stamps
were overprinted "T" in an inverted triangle
and used as postage due stamps.

1922-49

J12	D2	1c black	.25	.25
J13	D2	2c black, *yellow*	.25	.25
J14	D2	5c violet brown	.35	.25
J15	D2	10c blue	.25	.25
J16	D2	10c yel green ('45)	.20	.20
J17	D2	20c orange, *yel*	.25	.25
J18	D2	30c brown ('23)	.20	.20
J19	D2	50c rose red	.40	.25
J20	D2	50c blue vio ('45)	.20	.20
J21	D2	60c violet ('28)	.40	.20
J22	D2	80c bister ('28)	.25	.20
J23	D2	90c orange red ('28)	.60	.40
J24	D2	1fr green	.30	.20
J25	D2	2fr olive grn, *straw*	.60	.20
J26	D2	2fr car rose ('45)	.20	.20
J27	D2	3fr vio, *pink* ('29)	.20	.20
J28	D2	4fr grnsh bl ('45)	.25	.25
J29	D2	5fr violet	.45	.30
J30	D2	10fr cerise ('49)	.25	.25
J31	D2	20fr olive gray ('49)	.60	.35
		Nos. J12-J31 (20)	6.45	5.00

Inscribed: "Timbre Taxe"

1950		**Unwmk.**	**Perf. 14x13½**	
J32	D2	30fr blue	.75	.50

> Catalogue values for unused
> stamps in this section, from this
> point to the end of the section, are
> for Never Hinged items.

Independent Kingdom

Grain and Fruit — D3

1957, Apr. 1		**Engr.**	**Perf. 14x13**	
J33	D3	1fr bright green	.20	.20
J34	D3	2fr orange brown	.20	.20
J35	D3	3fr bluish green	.25	.25
J36	D3	4fr indigo	.30	.30
J37	D3	5fr lilac	.25	.25
J38	D3	10fr carmine	.25	.25
J39	D3	20fr chocolate	.80	.80
J40	D3	30fr blue	1.00	1.00
		Nos. J33-J40 (8)	3.25	3.25

Republic

Inscribed "Republique Tunisienne"

1960-77				
J41	D3	1m emerald	.20	.20
J42	D3	2m red brown	.20	.20
J43	D3	3m bluish green	.20	.20
J44	D3	4m indigo	.20	.20
J45	D3	5m lilac	.20	.20
J46	D3	10m carmine rose	.25	.25
J47	D3	20m violet brown	.40	.40
J48	D3	30m blue	.50	.50
J49	D3	40m lake ('77)	.20	.20
J50	D3	100m blue green ('77)	.25	.20
		Nos. J41-J50 (10)	2.60	2.55

PARCEL POST STAMPS

Mail
Delivery — PP1

Gathering
Dates — PP2

1906		**Unwmk. Typo.**	**Perf. 13½x14**	
Q1	PP1	5c grn & vio brn	.30	.25
Q2	PP1	10c org & red	.60	.30
Q3	PP1	20c dk brn & org	.85	.25
Q4	PP1	25c blue & brn	1.25	.25
Q5	PP1	40c gray & rose	1.75	.30
Q6	PP1	50c vio brn & vio	1.25	.20
Q7	PP1	75c bis brn & bl	2.50	.25
Q8	PP1	1fr red brn & red	1.50	.20
Q9	PP1	2fr carmine & bl	4.50	.30
Q10	PP1	5fr vio & vio brn	12.50	.60
		Nos. Q1-Q10 (10)	27.00	2.90
1926				
Q11	PP2	5c pale brn & dk bl	.20	.20
Q12	PP2	10c rose & vio	.25	.20
Q13	PP2	20c yel grn & blk	.25	.20
Q14	PP2	25c org brn & blk	.30	.20
Q15	PP2	40c dp rose & dp grn	1.25	.35
Q16	PP2	50c lt vio & blk	1.25	.55
Q17	PP2	60c ol & brn red	1.25	.25
Q18	PP2	75c gray vio & bl grn	1.25	.25
Q19	PP2	80c ver & ol brn	1.25	.25
Q20	PP2	1fr Prus bl & dp rose	1.25	.25
Q21	PP2	2fr vio & mag	2.25	.35
Q22	PP2	4fr red & blk	2.75	.25
Q23	PP2	5fr red brn & dp vio	4.00	.25
Q24	PP2	10fr dl red & grn, *grnsh*	7.50	.50
Q25	PP2	20fr yel grn & dp vio, *lav*	15.00	.90
		Nos. Q11-Q25 (15)	40.00	5.00

Parcel post stamps were discontinued July
1, 1940.

ADVANTAGE STOCKSHEETS

Designed with the collector in mind, Advantage
stock sheets fit directly in your 2-post or 3-ring
National or Specialty album. For unprecedented
durability and flexibility choose Advantage
Stocksheets. Choose from 1 to 8 pockets.
Sheets are sold in packages of 10.

- Stock sheets match album pages in every
  respect, including border, size, and color.

- Punched and drilled to fit perfectly in binder.

- Available with 1 to 8 pockets.
  Ideal for storing minor varieties and
  collateral material. A great place to keep
  new issues until the next supplement is
  available.

- Provide the protection and durability of
  crystal clear acetate pockets on
  heavyweight pages.

NATIONAL BORDER

ITEM			RETAIL
AD11	1 Pocket	242mm	$15.99
AD12	2 Pockets	119mm	$15.99
AD13	3 Pockets	79mm	$15.99
AD14	4 Pockets	58mm	$15.99
AD15	5 Pockets	45mm	$15.99
AD16	6 Pockets	37mm	$15.99
AD17	7 Pockets	31mm	$15.99
AD18	8 Pockets	31mm	$15.99

SPECIALTY BORDER

AD21	1 Pocket	242mm	$15.99
AD22	2 Pockets	119mm	$15.99
AD23	3 Pockets	79mm	$15.99
AD24	4 Pockets	58mm	$15.99
AD25	5 Pockets	45mm	$15.99
AD26	6 Pockets	37mm	$15.99
AD27	7 Pockets	31mm	$15.99
AD28	8 Pockets	31mm S	$15.99

Available from your favorite stamp
dealer or direct from:

1-800-572-6885
P.O. Box 828,
Sidney OH 45365
www.amosadvantage.com

AMOS
HOBBY PUBLISHING

TURKEY

'tər-kē

LOCATION — Southeastern Europe and Asia Minor, between the Mediterranean and Black Seas
GOVT. — Republic
AREA — 300,947 sq. mi.
POP. — 65,599,206 (1999 est.)
CAPITAL — Ankara

The Ottoman Empire ceased to exist in 1922, and the Republic of Turkey was inaugurated in 1923.

40 Paras = 1 Piaster
40 Paras = 1 Ghurush (1926)
40 Paras = 1 Kurush (1926)
100 Kurush = 1 Lira

> **Catalogue values for unused stamps in this country are for Never Hinged items, beginning with Scott 817 in the regular postage section, Scott B69 in the semipostal section, Scott C1 in the airpost section, Scott J97 in the postage due section, Scott O1 in the official section, Scott P175 in the newspaper section, and Scott RA139 in the postal tax section.**

Watermark

Wmk. 394 — "PTT," Crescent and Star

Turkish (Arabic) Numerals

"Tughra," Monogram of Sultan Abdul-Aziz
A1   A2

A3   A4

1863   Unwmk.   Litho.   Imperf.
Red Band: 20pa, 1pi, 2pi
Blue Band: 5pi
Thin Paper

1	A1	20pa blk, *yellow*		57.50	17.50
a.		Tête bêche pair		200.00	200.00
b.		Without band		80.00	
c.		Green band			
2	A2	1pi blk, *dl vio*		77.50	24.00
a.		1pi black, *gray*		77.50	24.00
b.		Tête bêche pair		300.00	300.00
c.		Without band		90.00	
d.		Design reversed			175.00
e.		1pi blk, *yel (error)*		200.00	150.00
4	A3	2pi blk, *grnsh bl*		77.50	24.00
a.		2pi black, *ind*		77.50	24.00
b.		Tête bêche pair		300.00	300.00
c.		Without band		85.00	

5	A4	5pi blk, *rose*		150.00	50.00
a.		Tête bêche pair		400.00	400.00
b.		Without band		175.00	
c.		Green band		200.00	
d.		Red band		200.00	

Thick, Surface Colored Paper

6	A1	20pa blk, *yellow*		175.00	57.50
a.		Tête bêche pair		400.00	400.00
b.		Design reversed		275.00	275.00
c.		Without band		175.00	175.00
d.		Paper colored through		175.00	175.00
7	A2	1pi blk, *gray*		200.00	57.50
a.		Tête bêche pair		750.00	750.00
b.		Design reversed			
c.		Without band			
d.		Paper colored through		225.00	190.00
		Nos. 1-7 (6)		737.50	230.50

The 2pi and 5pi had two printings. In the common printing, the stamps are more widely spaced and alternate horizontal rows of 12 are inverted. In the first and rare printing, the stamps are more closely spaced and no rows are tête bêche.
See Nos. J1-J4.

Crescent and Star, Symbols of Turkish Caliphate — A5

Surcharged

The bottom characters of this and the following surcharges denote the denomination. The characters at top and sides translate, "Ottoman Empire Posts."

1865   Typo.   Perf. 12½

8	A5	10pa deep green		8.50	35.00
c.		"1" instead of "10" in each corner		300.00	300.00
9	A5	20pa yellow		3.00	3.00
a.		Star without rays		4.25	7.75
10	A5	1pi lilac		7.50	5.00
a.		Star without rays		8.50	7.00
11	A5	2pi blue		5.50	5.00
12	A5	5pi carmine		4.50	5.00
d.		Inverted surcharge			

Imperf., Pairs

8b	A5	10pa		125.00	125.00
9b	A5	20pa		125.00	125.00
10b	A5	1pi		90.00	90.00
11a	A5	2pi		90.00	90.00
12b	A5	5pi		110.00	110.00
13a	A5	25pi		700.00	700.00
13	A5	25pi red orange		300.00	300.00

See Nos. J6-J35. For overprints and surcharges see Nos. 14-52, 64-65, 446-461, 467-468, J71-J77, Eastern Rumelia 1.

Surcharged

1867

14	A5	10pa gray green		4.25	
a.		Imperf., pair		50.00	
15	A5	20pa yellow		9.25	
a.		Imperf., pair		70.00	
16	A5	1pi lilac		9.25	
a.		Imperf., pair		95.00	
b.		Imperf., with surcharge of 5pi		15.00	
17	A5	2pi blue		3.50	10.00
a.		Imperf.			
18	A5	5pi rose		3.50	10.00
a.		Imperf.			
19	A5	25pi orange		2,400.	
		Nos. 14-18 (5)		29.75	

Nos. 14, 15, 16 and 19 were never placed in use.

Surcharged

1869   Perf. 13½

20	A5	10pa dull violet		80.00	7.00
a.		Printed on both sides			
b.		Imperf., pair		80.00	80.00
c.		Inverted surcharge			90.00
d.		Double surcharge			
e.		10pa yellow (error)			300.00

21	A5	20pa pale green		275.00	140.00
a.		Printed on both sides		350.00	275.00
22	A5	1pi yellow		3.50	2.75
c.		Inverted surcharge		80.00	
d.		Double surcharge			
e.		Surcharged on both sides			
f.		Printed on both sides			
23	A5	2pi orange red		57.50	6.75
b.		Imperf., pair		125.00	125.00
c.		Printed on both sides			125.00
d.		Inverted surcharge		70.00	70.00
e.		Surcharged on both sides			140.00
24	A5	5pi blue		2.75	7.00
25	A5	5pi gray		27.50	19.00
26	A5	25pi dull rose		30.00	70.00
		Nos. 20-26 (7)		476.25	252.50

Pin-perf., Perf. 5 to 11 and Compound

1870-71

27	A5	10pa lilac		350.00	25.00
28	A5	10pa brown		350.00	10.00
29	A5	20pa gray green		30.00	5.50
a.		Printed on both sides			
30	A5	1pi yellow		350.00	5.50
a.		Inverted surcharge		100.00	80.00
b.		Without surcharge			
31	A5	2pi red		3.50	3.50
a.		Imperf.		20.00	20.00
b.		Printed on both sides			40.00
c.		Surcharged on both sides			
32	A5	5pi blue		2.75	7.00
a.		5pi greenish blue		2.75	8.00
33	A5	5pi slate		27.50	27.50
a.		Printed on both sides			
b.		Surcharged on both sides			40.00
34	A5	25pi dull rose		30.00	40.00
		Nos. 27-34 (8)		1,143.	124.00

1873   Perf. 12, 12½

35	A5	10pa dark lilac		80.00	20.00
a.		Inverted surcharge			90.00
36	A5	10pa olive brown		100.00	15.00
a.		10pa bister		110.00	11.00
37	A5	2pi vermilion		2.50	3.00
a.		Surcharged on both sides		22.50	22.50
		Nos. 35-37 (3)		182.50	38.00

Surcharged

1874-75   Perf. 13½

38	A5	10pa red violet		20.00	5.00
a.		Imperf., pair		70.00	50.00
39	A5	20pa yellow green		15.00	4.00
b.		Inverted surcharge		30.00	13.00
c.		Double surcharge			
40	A5	1pi yellow		30.00	12.00
a.		Imperf., pair		100.00	80.00

Perf. 12, 12½

41	A5	10pa red violet		21.00	7.50
a.		Inverted surcharge		45.00	60.00
		Nos. 38-41 (4)		86.00	28.50

Surcharged

1876, Apr.   Perf. 13½

42	A5	10pa red lilac		.50	.30
a.		Inverted surcharge		70.00	
b.		Imperf., pair		15.00	15.00
43	A5	20pa pale green		.50	.50
b.		Inverted surcharge		70.00	
c.		Imperf., pair		15.00	15.00
44	A5	1pi yellow		.50	.60
a.		Imperf., pair		27.50	27.50
46	A5	5pi gray blue		250.00	
47	A5	25pi dull rose		250.00	
		Nos. 42-44 (3)		1.50	

Nos. 46 and 47 were never placed in use.

Surcharged

1876, Jan.

48	A5	¼pi on 10pa violet		1.00	1.25
49	A5	½pi on 20pa yel grn		2.00	1.50
50	A5	1¼pi on 50pa rose		.75	1.00
a.		Imperf., pair			
51	A5	2pi on 2pi redsh brn		20.00	6.00
52	A5	5pi on 5pi gray blue		10.00	10.00
		Nos. 48-52 (5)		33.75	19.75

The surcharge on Nos. 48-52 restates in French the value originally expressed in Turkish characters.

A7

1876, Sept.   Typo.   Perf. 13½

53	A7	10pa black & rose lil		.35	.40
54	A7	20pa red vio & grn		30.00	3.50
55	A7	50pa blue & yellow		.35	2.00
56	A7	2pi black & redsh brn		.35	1.10
57	A7	5pi red & blue		1.75	3.00
b.		Cliché of 25pi in plate of 5pi		400.00	375.00
58	A7	25pi claret & rose		12.00	12.50
a.		Imperf.		160.00	
		Nos. 53-58 (6)		44.80	22.50

Nos. 56-58 exist perf. 11½, but were not regularly issued.

See Nos. 59-63, 66-91, J36-J38. For overprints see Nos. 462-466, 469-476, J78-J79, P10-P14, Eastern Rumelia 2-40.

1880-84   Perf. 13½

59	A7	5pa black & ol ('81)		.30	.20
a.		Imperf.		30.00	
60	A7	10pa black & grn ('84)		.40	.65
61	A7	20pa black & rose		3.00	.35
62	A7	1pi blk & bl (*piastres*)		7.00	7.00
a.		1pi black & gray blue		7.00	
b.		Imperf.		40.00	
63	A7	1pi blk & bl (*piastre*) ('81)		26.00	3.00
		Nos. 59-63 (5)		36.70	6.20

A cliché of No. 63 was inserted in a plate of the Eastern Rumelia 1pi (No. 13). This was found in the remainder stock.

Nos. 60-61 and 63 exist perf. 11½, but were not regularly issued.

1881-82
Surcharged like Apr., 1876 Issue

64	A5	20pa gray		.30	.25
a.		Inverted surcharge		13.50	
b.		Imperf., pair		25.00	
65	A5	2pi pale salmon		.20	.30
a.		Inverted surcharge		22.50	

1884-86   Perf. 11½, 13½

66	A7	5pa lil & pale lil ('86)		30.00	35.00
67	A7	10pa grn & pale grn		.40	.20
68	A7	20pa rose & pale rose		.20	.20
69	A7	1pi blue & lt blue		.20	.20

Perf. 11½

70	A7	2pi och & pale och		.20	.20
71	A7	5pi red brn & pale brn		10.00	4.50
c.		5pi och & pale och (error)		12.00	12.00

Perf. 11½, 13½

73	A7	25pi blk & pale gray ('86)		110.00	125.00
		Nos. 66-73 (7)		151.00	165.30

Imperf

66a	A7	5pa		60.00	
67a	A7	10pa		20.00	
68b	A7	20pa		20.00	
69b	A7	1pi		20.00	
73a	A7	25pi		150.00	

1886   Perf. 13½

74	A7	5pa black & pale gray		.30	.20
75	A7	2pi orange & lt bl		.30	.20
76	A7	5pi grn & pale grn		.40	.30
77	A7	25pi bis & pale bis		20.00	42.50
		Nos. 74-77 (4)		21.00	43.20

Imperf

74a	A7	5pa		20.00	
75b	A7	2pi		20.00	
76b	A7	5pi		20.00	
77a	A7	25pi		35.00	

Stamps of 1884-86, bisected and surcharged as above, 10pa, 20pa, 1pi and 2pi or surcharged "2" in red are stated to have been made privately and without authority. With the aid of employees of the post office, copies were passed through the mails.

1888 — Perf. 13½

83	A7	5pa green & yellow	.35	.20
84	A7	2pi red lilac & bl	.40	.25
85	A7	5pi dk brown & gray	4.00	6.00
86	A7	25pi red & yellow	30.00	40.00
		Nos. 83-86 (4)	34.75	46.45

Imperf

83a	A7	5pa	20.00	
84a	A7	2pi	20.00	
85a	A7	5pi	20.00	
86a	A7	25pi	25.00	

Nos. 74-86 exist perf. 11½, but were not regularly issued.

1890 — Perf. 11½, 13½

87	A7	10pa green & gray	.75	.50
88	A7	20pa rose & gray	.60	.50
89	A7	1pi blue & gray	9.00	1.00
90	A7	2pi yellow & gray	1.00	1.25
91	A7	5pi buff & gray	1.75	5.00
		Nos. 87-91 (5)	13.10	8.25

Imperf

87a	A7	10pa	20.00	
88a	A7	20pa	20.00	
89a	A7	1pi	20.00	
90b	A7	2pi	25.00	
91a	A7	5pi	25.00	

Arms and Tughra of "El Gazi" (The Conqueror) Sultan Abdul Hamid

A10   A11

A12   A13

A14   No. 100

1892-98 — Typo. — Perf. 13½

95	A10	10pa gray green	1.00	.20
96	A11	20pa violet brn ('98)	.20	.20
a.		20pa dark pink	7.50	.30
		20pa pink	10.00	.30
97	A12	1pi pale blue	15.00	1.00
98	A13	2pi brown org	2.00	.50
a.		Tête bêche pair	5.00	5.00
99	A14	5pi dull violet	7.00	10.00
a.		Turkish numeral in upper right corner reads "50" instead of "5"	12.50	12.50
		Nos. 95-99 (5)	25.20	11.90

See Nos. J39-J42. For surcharges and overprints see Nos. 100, 288-291, 350, 355-359, 477-478, B38, B41, J80-J82, P25-P34, P36, P121-P122, P134-P137, P153-P154.

Red Surcharge

1897

100	A10	5pa on 10pa gray grn	1.25	.25
a.		"Cinq" instead of "Cinq"	10.00	10.00

Turkish stamps of types A11, A17-18, A21-A24, A26, A28-A39, A41 with or without Turkish overprints and English surcharges with "Baghdad" or "Iraq" are listed under Mesopotamia in Vol. 4.
Turkish stamps of types A19 and A21 with "Double-headed Eagle and Shqipenia" handstamp are listed under Albania in Vol. 1.

A16   A17

1901 — Typo. — Perf. 13½
For Foreign Postage

102	A16	5pa bister	1.00	.60
103	A16	10pa yellow green	1.00	.60
104	A16	20pa magenta	1.00	.40
a.		Perf. 12	1.25	.40
105	A16	1pi violet blue	1.50	1.00
106	A16	2pi gray blue	2.00	.80
107	A16	5pi ocher	3.50	1.25
108	A16	25pi dark green	35.00	20.00
109	A16	50pi yellow	80.00	35.00
		Nos. 102-109 (8)	125.00	59.65

For Domestic Postage
Perf. 12, 13½

110	A17	5pa purple	1.00	.30
111	A17	10pa green	1.00	.30
112	A17	20pa carmine	1.00	.30
113	A17	1pi blue	1.25	.25
a.		Imperf.	20.00	
114	A17	2pi orange	1.50	.50
115	A17	5pi lilac rose	3.50	.75

Perf. 13½

116	A17	25pi brown	4.00	1.50
a.		Perf. 12	20.00	1.50
117	A17	50pi yellow brown	7.50	3.00
a.		Perf. 12	20.00	3.00
		Nos. 110-117 (8)	20.75	6.90

Nos. 110-113 exist perf. 12x13½.
For overprints and surcharges see Nos. 165-180, 292-303, 340-341, 361-377, 479-493, B19-B20, B37, J43-J46, P37-P48, P69-P80, P123-P126, P138-P146, P155-P164.

A18   A19

1905 — Perf. 12, 13½ and Compound

118	A18	5pa ocher	.25	.20
119	A18	10pa dull green	.25	.20
a.		Imperf.	4.00	3.50
120	A18	20pa carmine	.20	.20
a.		Imperf.	4.00	3.50
121	A18	1pi blue	.30	.20
122	A18	2pi slate	1.00	.25
123	A18	2½pi red violet	1.50	.40
a.		Imperf.	11.00	9.00
124	A18	5pi brown	1.50	.40
125	A18	10pi orange brn	1.50	.40
126	A18	25pi olive green	6.25	5.00
127	A18	50pi deep violet	12.00	8.50

See Nos. J47-J48. For overprints and surcharges see Nos. 128-131, 181-182, 304-314, 351-354, 378-389, 494-508, B1-B3, B21-B23, B39-B40, P49-P54, P127-P129, P147-P150, P165-P171.

Overprinted in Carmine or Blue

1906

128	A18	10pa dull green (C)	.65	.50
129	A18	20pa carmine (Bl)	.65	.50
130	A18	1pi blue (C)	1.10	.60
131	A18	2pi slate (C)	4.00	3.00
		Nos. 118-131 (14)	31.15	20.35

Stamps bearing this overprint were sold to merchants at a discount from face value to encourage the use of Turkish stamps on foreign correspondence, instead of those of the various European powers which maintained post offices in Turkey. The overprint is the Arab "B," for "Béhié," meaning "discount."

1908

132	A19	5pa ocher	.35	.20
133	A19	10pa blue green	.90	.30
134	A19	20pa carmine	3.25	.50
135	A19	1pi bright blue	8.00	.90
a.		1pi ultramarine	15.00	2.25
136	A19	2pi blue black	8.00	.90
137	A19	2½pi violet brown	6.00	.90
138	A19	5pi dark violet	6.50	.90

139	A19	10pi red	8.00	.90
140	A19	25pi dark green	7.00	2.50
141	A19	50pi red brown	12.50	3.75

See Nos. J49-J50. For overprints and surcharges see Nos. 142-145, 314B-316B, 390-396, 509-516A, B4-B6, B17, B24-B27, P55-P60, P130-P131, P151, P172, Thrace 15.

Overprinted in Carmine or Blue

142	A19	10pa blue green	2.00	1.60
143	A19	20pa carmine (Bl)	2.00	1.75
144	A19	1pi brt blue (C)	3.25	2.00
145	A19	2pi blue black (C)	7.50	4.50
		Nos. 132-145 (14)	75.25	21.60

A20

Perf. 12, 13½ & Compound
1908, Dec. 17

146	A20	5pa ocher	.30	.20
147	A20	10pa blue green	.35	.20
148	A20	20pa carmine	.50	.30
149	A20	1pi ultra	1.00	.35
150	A20	2pi gray black	6.50	2.50
		Nos. 146-150 (5)	8.65	3.55

Imperf

146a	A20	5pa	1.75	1.75
147a	A20	10pa	2.00	2.00
148a	A20	20pa	2.75	2.75
149a	A20	1pi	1.75	1.75

Granting of a Constitution, the date of which is inscribed on the banderol: "324 Temuz 10" (July 24, 1908).
For overprints see Nos. 397, 517.

Tughra and "Reshad" of Sultan Mohammed V — A21

1909, Dec.

151	A21	5pa ocher	.20	.20
152	A21	10pa blue green	.30	.20
a.		Imperf.	1.75	1.75
153	A21	20pa carmine rose	.20	.20
154	A21	1pi ultra	.30	.20
a.		1pi bright blue	5.00	.40
155	A21	2pi blue black	.40	.20
156	A21	2½pi dark brown	17.00	12.00
157	A21	5pi dark violet	9.00	.50
158	A21	10pi dull red	13.00	3.00
159	A21	25pi dark green	100.00	65.00
160	A21	50pi red brown	40.00	17.00

The 2pa olive green, type A21, is a newspaper stamp, No. P68.
Two types exist for the 10pa, 20pa and 1pi. In the second type, the damaged crescent is restored.
See Nos. J51-J52. For overprints and surcharges see Nos. 161-164, 317-327, 342-343, 398-406, 518-528, 567, B7-B14, B18, B28-B32, P61-P68, P81, P132-P133, P152, P173, Turkey in Asia 67, 72, Thrace 1-4, 13, 13A, 14.

Overprinted in Carmine or Blue

161	A21	10pa blue grn (C)	.75	.20
a.		Imperf.		
162	A21	20pa car rose (Bl)	.75	.20
a.		Imperf.		
163	A21	1pi ultra (C)	2.00	.35
a.		Imperf.	4.00	
b.		1pi bright blue	2.00	.30
164	A21	2pi blue black (C)	15.00	6.00
a.		Imperf.		
		Nos. 151-164 (14)	198.90	105.25

Stamps of 1901-05 Overprinted in Carmine or Blue

The overprint was applied to 18 denominations in four settings with change of city name, producing individual sets for each city: "MONASTIR," "PRISTINA," "SALONIKA" and "USKUB."

1911, June 26 — Perf. 12, 13½

165	A16	5pa bister	1.50	
166	A16	10pa yellow green	1.50	
167	A16	20pa magenta	5.00	
168	A16	1pi violet blue	5.00	
169	A16	2pi gray blue	5.00	
170	A16	5pi ocher	30.00	
171	A16	25pi dark green	35.00	
172	A16	50pi yellow	40.00	
173	A17	5pa purple	1.50	
174	A17	10pa green	1.50	
175	A17	20pa carmine	5.00	
176	A17	1pi blue	5.00	
177	A17	2pi orange	5.00	
178	A17	5pi lilac rose	30.00	
179	A17	5pi chocolate	40.00	
180	A17	50pi yellow brown	50.00	
181	A18	2½pi red violet	35.00	
182	A18	10pi orange brown	35.00	
		Nos. 165-182 (18)	331.00	

Sultan's visit to Macedonia. The Arabic overprint reads: "Souvenir of the Sultan's Journey, 1329." Value for Salonika and Uskub sets, each $350. See Nos. P69-P81.

General Post Office, Constantinople
A22

1913, Mar. 14 — Perf. 12

237	A22	2pa olive green	.20	.20
238	A22	5pa ocher	.20	.20
239	A22	10pa blue green	.20	.20

SULTAN STAMP CENTER

Specializing in Turkey, Turkey in Asia & Turkish Cyprus

Old Collections Wanted!

WANT LISTS WELCOME!

P.O. Box 30846
Charlotte, NC 28230
Tel/Fax 704-643-2041
e-mail:SultanStamps@aol.com

240 A22 20pa carmine rose .20 .20
241 A22 1pi ultra .20 .20
242 A22 2pi indigo .35 .20
243 A22 5pi dull violet 1.00 .60
244 A22 10pi dull red 4.00 .80
245 A22 25pi gray green 12.00 6.50
246 A22 50pi orange brown 25.00 15.00

See Nos. J53-J58. For overprints and surcharges see Nos. 247-250, 328-339, 344, 407-414, 529-538, 568, B15-B16, B33-B36, Turkey in Asia 68, Thrace 10, 10A, 11, 11A, 12, N82.

Overprinted in Carmine or Blue

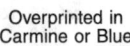

247 A22 10pa blue green (C) .20 .20
248 A22 20pa car rose (Bl) .20 .20
249 A22 1pi ultra (C) .20 .20
250 A22 2pi indigo (C) 5.50 3.00
Nos. 237-250 (14) 49.55 27.70

Mosque of Selim, Adrianople — A23

1913, Oct. 23   Engr.
251 A23 10pa green .30 .20
252 A23 20pa red 1.10 .55
253 A23 40pa blue 2.25 1.10
Nos. 251-253 (3) 3.65 1.85

Recapture of Adrianople (Edirne) by the Turks.
See Nos. 592, J59-J62. For overprints and surcharge see Nos. 415-417, 539-540, J59-J62, J67-J70, J83-J86, Thrace N84.

Obelisk of Theodosius in the Hippodrome A24

Column of Constantine A25

Leander's Tower — A26

One of the Seven Towers — A27

Fener Bahçe (Garden Lighthouse) A28

The Castle of Europe on the Bosporus A29

Mosque of Sultan Ahmed — A30

Monument to the Martyrs of Liberty A31

Fountains of Suleiman A32

Cruiser "Hamidie" A33

View of Kandili on the Bosporus A34

War Ministry (Later Istanbul University) A35

Sweet Waters of Europe Park — A36

Mosque of Suleiman A37

The Bosporus A38

Sultan Ahmed's Fountain A39

Sultan Mohammed V — A40

Designs A24-A39: Views of Constantinople.

1914, Jan. 14   Litho.
254 A24 2pa red lilac .30 .20
255 A25 4pa dark brown .30 .20
256 A26 5pa violet brown .30 .20
257 A27 6pa dark blue .30 .20

Engr.
258 A28 10pa green .30 .20
259 A29 20pa red .25 .20
260 A30 1pi blue .30 .20
  b. Booklet pane of 2+2 labels
261 A31 1½pi car & blk .40 .20
262 A32 1¾pi sl & red brn .25 .20
263 A33 2pi green & blk 1.25 .25
264 A34 2½pi org & ol grn .75 .30
265 A35 5pi dull violet 1.50 .40
266 A36 10pi red brown 7.00 .75
267 A37 25pi olive green 80.00 8.00
268 A38 50pi carmine 6.00 2.00
269 A39 100pi deep blue 55.00 27.50
  Cut cancellation 12.00
270 A40 200pi green & blk 550.00 400.00
  Cut cancellation 25.00
Nos. 254-270 (17) 704.20 441.00

See Nos. 590-591, 593-598.
For overprints and surcharges see Nos. 271-287, 419, 541, 552-553, 574A, 601, 603-604, P174, Turkey in Asia 1-3, 5-9, 73-74, Thrace N77, N78.

Stamps of Preceding Issue Overprinted in Red or Blue

271 A28 10pa green (R) .25 .20
272 A29 20pa red (Bl) 3.50 .50
273 A30 1pi blue (R) .75 .30
275 A32 1¾pi sl & red brn (Bl) .90 .80
276 A33 2pi green & blk (R) 15.00 2.25
Nos. 271-276 (5) 20.40 4.05

No. 261 Surcharged

1914, July 23
277 A31 1pi on 1½pi car & blk .35 .20
  a. "1330" omitted 2.50 1.50
  b. Double surcharge
  c. Triple surcharge 5.00 5.00

7th anniv. of the Constitution. The surcharge reads "10 July, 1330, National fête" and has also the numeral "1" at each side, over the original value of the stamp.

Stamps of 1914 Overprinted in Black or Red

278 A26 5pa violet brn (Bk) .40 .20
279 A28 10pa green (R) 1.25 .20
280 A29 20pa red (Bk) 3.00 .35
281 A30 1pi blue (R) 4.50 1.00
282 A33 2pi grn & blk (R) 4.50 1.25
283 A35 5pi dull violet (R) 22.50 3.50
284 A36 10pi red brown (R) 82.50 25.00
Nos. 278-284 (7) 118.65 31.50

This overprint reads "Abolition of the Capitulations, 1330".

No. 269 Surcharged

1915
286 A39 10pi on 100pi 40.00 27.50
  a. Inverted surcharge —

No. 270 Surcharged

287 A40 25pi on 200pi 22.50 8.00

Preceding Issues Overprinted in Carmine or Black

1915
On Stamps of 1892
288 A10 10pa gray green .25 .2
  a. Inverted overprint 7.50 7.5
289 A13 2pi brown orange .25 .2
  a. Inverted overprint 7.50 7.5
290 A14 5pi dull violet 2.50 .2
  a. On No. 99a 17.00 17.0

On Stamp of 1897
291 A15 5pa on 10pa gray grn .25 .2
  a. Inverted overprint 5.00 5.0
  b. On No. 100a 10.00 10.0

On Stamps of 1901
292 A16 5pa bister .20 .2
293 A16 1pi violet blue 3.00 1.0
294 A16 2pi gray blue 2.50 .2
295 A16 5pi ocher 10.00 .2
296 A16 25pi dark green 15.00 12.0
297 A16 5pa purple .20 .2
298 A17 10pa green 1.00 .2
299 A17 20pa carmine 1.00 .2
  a. Inverted overprint 7.50 7.5
300 A17 1pi blue 1.00 .2
  a. Inverted overprint 5.00 5.0
301 A17 2pi orange 1.90 .2
  a. Inverted overprint 7.50 7.5
  b. Double ovpt. (R and Bk) 5.00 5.0
302 A17 5pi lilac rose 2.50 .4
303 A17 25pi brown 3.50 1.1

On Stamps of 1905
304 A18 5pa ocher .20 .2
305 A18 10pa dull green .20 .2
  a. Inverted overprint 5.00 5.0
306 A18 20pa carmine .20 .2
  a. Inverted overprint 5.00 5.0
307 A18 1pi brt blue .80 .2
  a. Inverted overprint 5.00 5.0
308 A18 2pi slate 2.50 .2
  a. Inverted overprint 10.00 10.0
309 A18 2½pi red violet 1.50 .2
310 A18 5pi brown 2.00 .2
  a. Inverted overprint 10.00 10.0
311 A18 10pi orange brown 8.00 .5
312 A18 25pi olive green 12.50 3.5

On Stamps of 1906
313 A18 10pa dull green 1.00 .2
314 A18 2pi slate 3.00 .2
  a. Inverted overprint 5.00 5.0

On Stamps of 1908
314B A19 2pi blue black 75.00 25.0
315 A19 2½pi violet brown 3.00 .3
315A A19 5pi dark violet 75.00 10.0
315B A19 10pi red 15.00 7.5
316 A19 25pi dark green 30.00 5.0
  a. Inverted overprint 17.00 17.0

With Additional Overprint

316B A19 2pi blue black 10.00 5.0

On Stamps of 1909
317 A21 5pa ocher .30 .2
  a. Inverted overprint 10.00 10.
  b. Double overprint 10.00 5.
318 A21 20pa car rose .30 .2
  a. Inverted overprint 5.00 .3
319 A21 1pi ultra 1.00 .3
  a. Inverted overprint 5.00 .3
320 A21 2pi blue black 1.00 .2
  a. Inverted overprint 5.00 .5
321 A21 2½pi dark brown 27.50 15.0
322 A21 5pi dark violet .30 .5
  a. Inverted overprint 6.50 6.
323 A21 10pi dull red 6.00 .5
324 A21 25pi dark green 400.00 250.0

With Additional
Overprint

25	A21	20pa carmine rose	1.00	.30
26	A21	1pi ultra	1.00	.30
27	A21	2pi blue black	1.00	.30

On Stamps of 1913

28	A22	5pa ocher	.20	.20
a.		Inverted overprint	7.50	7.50
29	A22	10pa blue green	.20	.20
a.		Inverted overprint	10.00	10.00
30	A22	20pa carmine rose	.20	.20
a.		Inverted overprint	7.50	7.50
31	A22	1pi ultra	.25	.20
a.		Inverted overprint	5.00	5.00
32	A22	2pi indigo	1.50	.20
a.		Inverted overprint	5.00	5.00
33	A22	5pi dull violet	1.50	.20
34	A22	10pi dull red	3.00	.50
a.		Inverted overprint	10.00	10.00
35	A22	25pi gray green	10.00	10.00

With Additional
Overprint

36	A22	10pa blue green	.25	.20
37	A22	20pa carmine rose	.45	.30
38	A22	1pi ultra	.60	.30
39	A22	2pi indigo	3.50	1.00
a.		Inverted overprint	10.00	10.00

See Nos. P121-P133.

Stamps of 1901-13
Overprinted

1916

40	A17	5pa purple	.50	.25
a.		5pa purple, #P43	80.00	80.00
41	A17	10pa green	.50	.25
a.		Double overprint	6.50	6.50
b.		10pa yellow green, #103	80.00	80.00
42	A21	20pa car rose, #153	.75	.25
a.		20pa carmine rose, #162	110.00	110.00
43	A21	1pi ultra	2.50	.60
44	A22	5pi dull violet	4.25	3.50
		Nos. 340-344 (5)	8.50	4.85

Occupation of the Sinai Peninsula.

Old General Post
Office of
Constantinople
A41

1916, May 29 Litho. Perf. 12½, 13½

45	A41	5pa green	.30	.20
46	A41	10pa carmine	.45	.20
47	A41	20pa ultra	.60	.20
48	A41	1pi violet & blk	1.25	.90
49	A41	5pi yel brn & blk	14.00	2.50
		Nos. 345-349 (5)	16.60	4.00

Introduction of postage in Turkey, 50th anniv.
For overprints see Nos. 418, B42-B45.

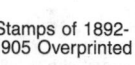

Stamps of 1892-
1905 Overprinted

1916

50	A10	10pa gray grn (R)	1.00	.55
51	A18	20pa carmine (Bl)	3.00	.50
52	A18	1pi blue (R)	6.00	.90

353	A18	2pi slate (Bk)	6.00	.90
354	A18	2½pi red violet (Bk)	6.00	.90
		Nos. 350-354 (5)	22.00	3.75

National Fête Day. Overprint reads "10
Temuz 1332" (July 23, 1916).

**Preceding Issues Overprinted or
Surcharged in Red or Black:**

a   b

1916

On Stamps of 1892-98

355	A10(a)	10pa gray green	.50	.20
355A	A11(a)	20pa violet brown	.55	.30
b.		Inverted overprint	10.00	10.00
356	A12(a)	1pi gray blue	25.00	15.00
357	A13(a)	2pi brown org	3.00	1.50
358	A14(a)	5pi dull violet	9.00	7.50

On Stamp of 1897

359	A15(b)	5pa on 10pa gray grn	.75	.30

On Stamps of 1901

361	A16(a)	5pa bister	.50	.30
a.		Double overprint	7.50	7.50
362	A16(a)	10pa yel grn	1.00	.30
363	A16(a)	20pa magenta	.50	.30
364	A16(a)	1pi violet blue	.50	.30
a.		Inverted overprint	7.50	7.50
365	A16(a)	2pi gray blue	1.00	.35
366	A16(b)	5pi on 25pi dk grn	20.00	20.00
367	A16(b)	10pi on 25pi dk grn	20.00	20.00
368	A16(a)	25pi dark green	20.00	20.00
369	A17(a)	5pa purple	20.00	15.00
370	A17(a)	10pa green	1.00	1.00
371	A17(a)	20pa carmine	.35	.20
a.		Inverted overprint	7.50	7.50
372	A17(a)	1pi blue	.50	.20
a.		Inverted overprint	7.50	7.50
373	A17(a)	2pi orange	.50	.40
374	A17(b)	10pi on 25pi brown	3.00	1.00
375	A17(b)	10pi on 50pi yel brn	5.00	.90
376	A17(a)	25pi brown	5.00	.90
377	A17(a)	50pi yel brn	5.00	1.50

On Stamps of 1905

378	A18(a)	5pa ocher	.30	.20
379	A18(a)	20pa carmine	.40	.20
a.		Inverted overprint	10.00	5.00
380	A18(a)	1pi brt blue	2.00	.50
a.		Inverted overprint	10.00	5.00
381	A18(a)	2pi slate	1.00	.50
382	A18(a)	2½pi red violet	2.00	1.00
383	A18(a)	10pi on 25pi ol grn	3.00	1.00
384	A18(b)	10pi on 50pi dp vio	3.00	1.00
385	A18(a)	25pi olive green	5.00	3.00
386	A18(a)	50pi deep violet	6.00	3.00

On Stamps of 1906

387	A18(a)	10pa dull green	1.00	.60
388	A18(a)	20pa carmine	1.00	.60
389	A18(a)	1pi brt blue	1.00	.60

On Stamps of 1908

390	A19(a)	2½pi violet brown	10.00	15.00
391	A19(b)	10pi on 25pi dk grn	4.00	2.50
392	A19(b)	10pi on 50pi red brn	15.00	15.00
393	A19(b)	25pi on 50pi red brn	15.00	15.00
394	A19(a)	25pi dark green	15.00	15.00
395	A19(a)	50pi red brown	12.50	12.50

With Additional
Overprint

396	A19(a)	2pi blue black	12.50	12.50

On Stamps of 1908-09

397	A20(a)	5pa ocher	12.50	12.50
398	A21(a)	5pa ocher	.60	.40
399	A21(a)	10pa blue green	15.00	12.50
400	A21(a)	20pa carmine rose	15.00	15.00
401	A21(a)	1pi ultra	1.00	.50
402	A21(a)	2pi blue black	1.00	1.00
403	A21(a)	2½pi dark brown	20.00	17.50
404	A21(a)	5pi dark violet	20.00	17.50

With Additional
Overprint

405	A21(a)	1pi ultra	15.00	12.50
406	A21(a)	2pi blue black	15.00	12.50

On Stamps of 1913

407	A22(a)	5pa ocher	.50	.20
408	A22(a)	20pa carmine rose	.90	1.00
409	A22(a)	1pi ultra	1.00	.35
410	A22(a)	2pi indigo	.50	.45
411	A22(b)	10pi on 50pi org brn	5.00	2.50
412	A22(a)	25pi gray green	5.00	2.50
413	A22(a)	50pi orange brown	5.00	2.50

With Additional Overprint

414	A22(a)	1pi ultra	.50	.50

On Commemorative Stamps of 1913

415	A23(a)	10pa green	.40	.25
416	A23(a)	20pa red	1.75	.90
417	A23(a)	40pi blue	4.25	1.50

On Commemorative Stamp of 1916

418	A41(a)	5pi yel brn & blk	1.00	.50

No. 277 Surcharged in Blue

419	A31	60pa on 1pi on 1½pi	1.75	1.00
a.		"1330" omitted	10.00	10.00

See Nos. P134-P152, J67-J70.

Turkish
Artillery
A42

Mosque at Orta Köy,
Constantinople — A43

Lighthouse on   Monument to
Bosporus — A44   Martyrs of
                     Liberty — A45

Map of the
Dardanelles;
Sultan
Mohammed
V — A46

Map of the
Dardanelles
A47

Istanbul
Across the
Golden
Horn
A48

Pyramids
of Egypt
A49

Dolma
Bahçe
Palace and
Mohammed
V — A50

Sentry and   Sultan
Shell — A51   Mohammed
                  V — A52

1916-18 Typo. Perf. 11½, 12½

420	A42	2pa violet	.20	.20
421	A43	5pa orange	.20	.20
424	A44	10pa green	.20	.20

Engr.

425	A45	20pa deep rose	.25	.20
426	A46	1pi dull violet	.30	.20

Typo.

428	A47	50pa ultra	.90	.30
429	A48	2pi org brn & ind	.30	.20
430	A49	5pi pale blue & blk	12.00	2.25

Engr.

431	A50	10pi dark green	6.00	.75
432	A50	10pi dark violet	20.00	.90
433	A50	10pi dark brown	10.00	1.25
434	A51	25pi carmine, straw	1.00	.50
437	A52	50pi carmine	3.50	1.40
438	A52	50pi indigo	2.50	1.25
439	A52	50pi green, straw	3.50	3.50
		Nos. 420-439 (15)	60.85	13.30

For overprints and surcharges see Nos.
541B-541E, 554-560, 565-566, 569-574, 575,
577-578, 579A-580, Turkey in Asia 4, 10, 64-
66, Thrace N76, N80, N81. Compare designs
A42-A43 with A53-A54.

Forgeries of Nos. 446-545 abound.

Preceding Issues Overprinted or
Surcharged in Red, Black or Blue:

d   e

f   g

1917

On Stamps of 1865

446	A5(d)	20pa yellow (R)	45.00	45.00
a.		Star without rays (R)	50.00	35.00

447 A5(d) 1pi pearl gray (R) 45.00 45.00
a. Star without rays (R) 50.00 35.00
448 A5(d) 2pi blue (R) 35.00 35.00
449 A5(d) 5pi carmine (Bk) 45.00 45.00

On Stamp of 1867

450 A5(d) 5pi rose (Bk) 45.00 45.00

On Stamps of 1870-71

451 A5(d) 2pi red (Bl) 45.00 45.00
452 A5(d) 5pi blue (Bk) 45.00 45.00
453 A5(d) 25pi dull rose (Bl) 45.00 45.00

On Stamp of 1874-75

454 A5(d) 10pa red violet (Bl) 45.00 45.00

On Stamps of April, 1876

455 A5(d) 10pa red lilac (Bl) 45.00 45.00
a. 10pa red violet (Bl) 50.00 50.00
457 A5(d) 20pa pale green (R) 45.00 45.00
458 A5(d) 1pi yellow (Bl) 45.00 45.00

On Stamps of January, 1876

459 A5(d) ¼pi on 10pa rose lil (R) 45.00 45.00
460 A5(d) ½pi on 20pa yel grn (R) 45.00 45.00
461 A5(d) 1¼pi on 50pa rose (Bl) 45.00 45.00

On Stamps of September, 1876

462 A7(d) 50pa blue & yel (R) 45.00 45.00
463 A7(d) 2pi blk & redsh brn (R) 45.00 45.00
464 A7(d) 25pi claret & rose (Bk) 45.00 45.00

On Stamps of 1880-84

465 A7(d) 5pa black & ol (R) 45.00 45.00
466 A7(d) 10pa black & grn (R) 45.00 45.00

On Stamps of 1881-82

467 A5(d) 20pa gray (Bl) 45.00 45.00
468 A5(d) 2pi pale sal (Bl) 45.00 45.00

On Stamps of 1884-86

469 A7(d) 10pa grn & pale grn (Bk) 45.00 45.00
470 A7(d) 2pi ocher & pale ocher (Bk) 45.00 45.00
471 A7(d) 5pi red brn & pale brn (Bk) 45.00 45.00

On Stamps of 1886

472 A7(d) 5pa blk & pale gray (R) 2.00 1.75
a. Inverted overprint 30.00 30.00
473 A7(d) 2pi org & bl (Bk) 3.00 2.50
a. Inverted overprint 35.00 35.00
474 A7(d) 5pi grn & pale grn (R) 45.00 45.00
475 A7(d) 25pi bis & pale bis (Bk) 45.00 45.00

On Stamp of 1888

476 A7(d) 5pi dk brn & gray (Bk) 45.00 45.00

On Stamps of 1892-98

477 A11(d) 20pa vio brn (R) 4.00 3.00
478 A13(d) 2pi brn org (R) 4.00 3.50
a. Tête bêche pair 13.50 13.50

On Stamps of 1901

479 A16(d) 5pa bister (R) 3.00 3.00
a. Inverted overprint 20.00 20.00
480 A16(d) 20pa mag (Bk) 2.00 1.50
a. Inverted overprint 25.00 25.00
481 A16(d) 1pi vio bl (R) 3.00 3.00
a. Inverted overprint 20.00 20.00
482 A16(d) 2pi gray bl (R) 3.00 2.50
483 A16(d) 5pi ocher (R) 45.00 45.00
484 A16(e) 10pi on 50pi yel (R) 45.00 45.00
485 A16(d) 25pi dk grn (R) 35.00 35.00
486 A17(d) 5pa purple (Bk) 45.00 45.00
487 A17(d) 10pa green (R) 5.00 5.00
488 A17(d) 20pa car (Bk) 2.00 1.50
a. Inverted overprint 20.00 20.00
489 A17(d) 1pi blue (R) 1.00 .90
490 A17(d) 2pi org (Bk) 3.00 3.00
a. Inverted overprint 20.00 20.00
491 A17(d) 5pi lil rose (R) 45.00 45.00
492 A17(e) 10pi on 50pi yel brn (R) 50.00 50.00
493 A17(d) 25pi brown (R) 3.00 3.00

On Stamps of 1905

494 A18(d) 5pa ocher (R) 2.00 1.00
a. Inverted overprint 20.00 20.00
495 A18(d) 10pa dl grn (R) 45.00 45.00
496 A18(d) 20pa car (Bk) 1.00 1.00
a. Double ovpt., one invtd. 35.00 35.00
b. Inverted overprint 35.00 35.00
497 A18(d) 1pi blue (R) 1.50 1.00
a. Inverted overprint 35.00 35.00
498 A18(d) 2pi slate (Bk) 5.00 5.00
499 A18(d) 2½pi red vio (Bk) 5.00 5.00
a. Inverted overprint 20.00 20.00
500 A18(d) 5pi brown (R) 35.00 35.00
501 A18(d) 10pi orange brn (R) 35.00 35.00

---

502 A18(e) 10pi on 50pi dp vio (R) 35.00 35.00
503 A18(d) 25pi ol grn (R) 35.00 35.00

On Nos. 128-131

504 A18(d) 10pa dl grn (R) 1.50 1.00
a. Inverted overprint 20.00 20.00
505 A18(d) 20pa car (Bk) 1.00 .75
a. Double ovpt., one invtd. 20.00 20.00
b. Inverted overprint 20.00 20.00
506 A18(d) 1pi brt bl (Bk) 1.00 .75
a. Inverted overprint 20.00 20.00
507 A18(d) 1pi brt bl (R) 1.50 1.25
a. Inverted overprint 20.00 20.00
508 A18(d) 2pi slate (Bk) 35.00 35.00
Nos. 494-508 (15) 239.50 236.75

On Stamps of 1908

509 A19(d) 5pa ocher (R) 1.50 1.25
510 A19(d) 10pa bl grn (R) 20.00 20.00
510A A19(d) 1pi brt blue (R) 250.00 250.00
511 A19(d) 2pi bl blk (R) 35.00 35.00
512 A19(d) 2½pi violet brn (Bk) 35.00 35.00
512A A19(d) 10pi red (R) 250.00 250.00
513 A19(e) 10pi on 50pi red brn (R) 35.00 35.00
514 A19(d) 25pi dark green (R) 35.00 35.00

With Additional Overprint

514A A19(d) 10pa bl grn (Bk) 75.00 75.00
515 A19(d) 1pi brt bl (Bk) 45.00 45.00
516 A19(d) 2pi bl blk (R) 8.00 8.00
516A A19(d) 2pi bl blk (Bk) 45.00 45.00

On Stamps of 1908-09

517 A20(d) 5pa ocher (R) 3.00 3.00
518 A21(d) 5pa ocher (R) 2.00 1.50
a. Double overprint 20.00 20.00
b. Dbl. ovpt., one inverted 20.00 20.00
519 A21(d) 10pa brn (R) 2.00 1.50
520 A21(d) 20pa carmine rose (Bk) 2.00 1.50
a. Double overprint 35.00 35.00
521 A21(d) 1pi ultra (R) 1.00 .75
a. 1p bright blue (R) 30.00 30.00
522 A21(d) 2pi bl blk (Bk) 5.00 5.00
523 A21(d) 2½pi dk brn (Bk) 45.00 45.00
524 A21(d) 5pi dk vio (R) 45.00 45.00
525 A21(d) 10pi dull red (R) 45.00 45.00

With Additional Overprint

525A A21(d) 10pa bl grn (Bk) 175.00 175.00
526 A21(d) 1pi ultra (Bk) 35.00 35.00
527 A21(d) 1pi ultra (R) 5.00 5.00
a. 1pi bright blue (R) 45.00 30.00
528 A21(d) 2pi bl blk (Bk) 35.00 35.00

On Stamps of 1913

529 A22(d) 5pa ocher (R) 2.50 2.50
530 A22(d) 10pa bl grn (R) 35.00 35.00
531 A22(d) 20pa car rose (Bk) 2.50 2.50
532 A22(d) 1pi ultra (R) 5.00 3.50
533 A22(d) 2pi indigo (R) 5.00 3.50
534 A22(d) 5pi dl vio (R) 35.00 35.00
535 A22(d) 10pi dl red (Bk) 45.00 45.00

With Additional Overprint

536 A22(d) 10pa bl grn (Bk) 2.50 2.00
a. Inverted overprint 20.00 20.00
537 A22(d) 1pi ultra (Bk) 5.00 5.00
a. Inverted overprint 20.00 20.00
538 A22(d) 2pi indigo (Bk) 35.00 35.00

On Commemorative Stamps of 1913

539 A23(d) 10pa green (R) 5.00 5.00
a. Inverted overprint 20.00 20.00
540 A23(d) 40pa blue (R) 5.00 5.00
a. Inverted overprint 20.00 20.00

On No. 277, with Addition of New Value

541 A31 60pa on 1pi on 1½pi (Bk) 5.00 4.00
a. "1330" omitted 45.00 45.00

On Stamps of 1916-18

541B A51(f) 25pi car, straw 15.00 10.00
541C A52(g) 50pi carmine 35.00 25.00
541D A52(g) 50pi indigo 35.00 25.00
541E A52(g) 50pi green, straw 35.00 30.00

Ovptd. on Eastern Rumelia No. 12

542 A4(d) 20pa blk & rose (Bl) 35.00 35.00

Ovptd. in Black on Eastern Rumelia #15-17

543 A4(d) 5pa lilac & pale lilac 45.00 45.00
544 A4(d) 10pa green & pale green 45.00 45.00
545 A4(d) 20pa carmine & pale rose 45.00 45.00

Some experts question the status of Nos. 510A, 512A and 525A.
See Nos. J71-J86, P153-P172.

Soldiers in Trench — A52a

Surcharged ❂ ٥. باد.ه ❂ ٥

1917
545A A52a 5pa on 1pi red .30 .20

It is stated that No. 545A was never issued without surcharge.
See Nos. 548f, 545A, 602.

Turkish Artillery A53

1917 Typo. Perf. 11½, 12½
546 A53 2pa Prussian blue 65.00

In type A42 the Turkish inscription at the top is in one group, in type A53 it is in two groups. It is stated that No. 546 was never placed in use. Copies were distributed through the Universal Postal Union at Bern.
For surcharges see Nos. 547-548, Turkey in Asia 69-70.

Surcharged

547 A53 5pi on 2pa Prus bl 5.00 .90
a. Inverted surcharge 9.00 9.00
b. Turkish "5" omitted at lower left

Surcharged

1918
548 A53 5pi on 2pa Prus blue 5.00 .90
g. Inverted surcharge 10.00 10.00

Top line of surcharge on Nos. 547-548 reads "Ottoman Posts."
For surcharge see Thrace No. N79.

No. 545A Surcharged

1918
548A A52a 2pa on 5pa on 1pi red .30 .2
b. Double surcharge 10.00 10.0
c. Inverted surcharge 10.00 10.0
d. Double surcharge inverted 10.00 10.0
e. Dbl. surch., one inverted 10.00 10.0
f. In pair with No. 545A 17.50 17.5

Enver Pasha and Kaiser Wilhelm II on Battlefield A54

St. Sophia and Obelisk o the Hippodrome A55

1918 Typo. Perf. 12, 12
549 A54 5pa brown red 75.00
550 A55 10pa gray green 75.00

The stamps, of which very few saw post use, were converted into paper money b pasting on thick yellow paper ar reperforating.
Values are for copies with original gun Copies removed from the yellow paper a worth $8 each.

Armistice Issue

Overprinted in Black or Red

1919, Nov. 30
On Stamps of 1913
552 A34 2½pi org & ol grn 50.00 50.0
553 A38 50pi carmine 50.00 50.0

On Stamps of 1916-18
554 A46 1pi dull violet (R) .60 .6
555 A47 50pa ultra (R) .55 .
556 A48 2pi org brn & ind .55 .
557 A49 5pi pale bl & blk (R) .25 .
558 A50 10pi dark green (R) 2.25 1.4
559 A51 25pi carmine, straw 2.25 1.4
560 A52 50pi grn, straw (R) 2.25 1.4

Fountain in Desert near Sinai — A56

Sentry at Beersheba — A57

Turkish Troops at Sinai A58

Typo.

562	A56	20pa claret	.40	.20
563	A57	1pi blue (R)	50.00	50.00
564	A58	25pi slate blue (R)	50.00	50.00
		Nos. 552-564 (12)	209.10	205.85

The overprint reads: "Souvenir of the Armistice, 30th October 1334." Nos. 562 to 564 are not known to have been regularly issued without overprint.

See No. J87. For overprints and surcharges see Nos. 576, 579, 582, 583-584, 586, Turkey in Asia 71, Thrace N83.

Stamps of 1911-19 Overprinted in Turkish
"Accession to the Throne of His Majesty, 3rd July 1334-1918," the Tughra of Sultan Mohammed VI and sometimes Ornaments and New Values

Dome of the Rock, Jerusalem — A59

1919

565	A42	2pa violet	.30	.25
566	A43	5pa orange	.20	.20
567	A21	5pa on 2pa ol grn	.20	.20
a.		Inverted surcharge	10.00	10.00
568	A22	10pa on 2pa ol grn	.25	.20
569	A44	10pa green	.60	.50
a.		Inverted overprint	25.00	25.00
570	A45	20pa deep rose	.25	.20
a.		Inverted overprint	12.00	12.00
571	A46	1pi dull violet	.30	.20
572	A47	60pa on 50pa ultra	1.40	.75
573	A48	60pa on 2pi org brn & ind	.25	.20
574	A48	2pi orange brn & ind	.20	.25
574A	A34	2½pi orange & ol grn	15.00	12.50
575	A49	5pi pale blue & blk	.40	.30
576	A56	10pi on 20pa cl	.40	.30
577	A50	10pi dark brown	.80	.80
578	A51	25pi carmine, straw	1.25	1.25
579	A57	35pi on 1pi blue	1.10	.45
579A	A52	50pi carmine	20.00	20.00
580	A52	50pi green, straw	6.00	3.50
581	A59	100pi on 10pa green	6.00	3.25
582	A58	250pi on 25pi sl bl	6.00	3.25
		Nos. 565-582 (20)	60.90	48.55

See note after #586. See #J88-J91. For overprint and surcharge see Nos. 585, Thrace N82.

Surcharged with Ornaments, New Values and

Perf. 11½, 12½

583	A56	20pa claret	1.00	.25
584	A57	1pi deep blue	1.25	.50
585	A59	60pa on 10pa green	1.50	2.00
586	A58	25pi slate blue	7.00	2.50
a.		Inverted overprint		100.00
		Nos. 583-586 (4)	10.75	5.25

#576, 579, 581, 582, 583-586 were prepared in anticipation of the invasion and conquest of Egypt by the Turks. They were not issued at that time but subsequently received various overprints in commemoration of Sultan Mehmet Sadi's accession to the throne (#565-582) and of the 1st anniv. of this event (#583-586).

For surcharge see Thrace No. N83.

Designs of 1913 Modified

1920		**Litho.**	**Perf. 11, 12**	
590	A26	5pa brown orange	.20	.20
		Engr.		
591	A28	10pa green	.20	.25
592	A23	20pa rose	.20	.20
593	A30	1pi blue green	1.50	.30
594	A32	3pi blue	.20	.20
595	A34	5pi gray	9.00	1.25
596	A36	10pi gray violet	6.50	.80
597	A37	25pi dull violet	1.50	.65
598	A38	50pi brown	2.00	2.75
		Nos. 590-598 (9)	21.30	6.60

On most stamps of this issue the designs have been modified by removing the small

Turkish word at right of the tughra of the Sultan. In the 3pi and 5pi the values have been altered, while for the 25pi the color has been changed.

For surcharges see Thrace Nos. N77, N78, N84.

Black Surcharge

1921-22

600	SP1	30pa on 10pa red vio	.40	.30
a.		Double surcharge	37.50	37.50
b.		Imperf.		
601	A28	60pa on 10pa green	.25	.20
a.		Double surcharge	22.50	22.50
602	A52a	4½pi on 1pi red	.40	.25
a.		Inverted surcharge	20.00	20.00
603	A32	7½pi on 3pi blue	4.25	.90
604	A32	7½pi on 3pi bl (R) ('22)	4.25	1.25
a.		Double surcharge	30.00	30.00
		Nos. 600-604 (5)	9.55	2.90

ΕΛΛΗΝΙΚΗ ΚΑΤΟΧΗ ΛΕΠΤΑ·50

Turkish Stamps of 1916-21 with Greek surcharge as above in blue or black are of private origin.

Issues of the Republic

Crescent and Star — A64

TWO PIASTERS:
Type I — "2" measures 3¼x1¾mm
Type II — "2" measures 2¾x1½mm

FIVE PIASTERS:
Type I — "5" measures 3½x2¼mm
Type II — "5" measures 3x1¾mm

Perf. 11, 12, 13½, 13½x12

1923-25				**Litho.**
605	A64	10pa gray black	.20	.20
606	A64	20pa citron	.20	.20
607	A64	1pi deep violet	.25	.20
a.		Slanting numeral in lower left corner	.50	.25
608	A64	1½pi emerald	.25	.20
609	A64	2pi bluish grn (I)	1.25	.25
a.		2pi deep green (II)	4.00	.20

610	A64	3pi yel brn	1.00	.20
611	A64	3¾pi lilac brown	1.25	.20
612	A64	4½pi carmine	1.25	.20
613	A64	5pi purple (I)	2.25	.25
a.		5pi violet (II)	7.50	.25
614	A64	7½pi blue	1.00	.20
615	A64	10pi slate	6.00	1.00
a.		10pi blue	7.50	.30
616	A64	11¼pi dull rose	1.50	.30
617	A64	15pi brown	6.00	.50
618	A64	18¾pi myrtle green	4.50	.50
619	A64	22½pi orange	3.00	.50
620	A64	25pi black brown	10.00	.60
621	A64	50pi gray	30.00	1.75
622	A64	100pi dark violet	52.50	1.90
623	A64	500pi deep green	225.00	125.00
		Cut cancellation		1.60
		Nos. 605-624 (19)	347.40	134.15

#605-610, 612-617 exist imperf. & part perf.

Bridge of Sakarya and Mustafa Kemal — A65

1924, Jan. 1   **Perf. 12**

625	A65	1½pi emerald	.30	.20
626	A65	3pi purple	.40	.30
627	A65	4½pi pale rose	1.00	.80
628	A65	5pi yellow brown	1.00	.80
629	A65	7½pi deep blue	1.00	.80
630	A65	50pi orange	12.00	6.50
631	A65	100pi brown violet	42.50	16.00
632	A65	200pi olive brown	62.50	30.00
		Nos. 625-632 (8)	120.70	55.40

Signing of Treaty of Peace at Lausanne.

The Legendary Blacksmith and his Gray Wolf — A66   Sakarya Gorge — A67

Fortress of Ankara — A68   Mustafa Kemal Pasha — A69

1926				**Engr.**
634	A66	10pa slate	.20	.20
635	A66	20pa orange	.20	.20
636	A66	1g brt rose	.20	.20
637	A67	2g green	.20	.20
638	A67	2½g gray black	.20	.20
639	A67	3g copper red	.30	.20
640	A68	5g lilac gray	.40	.20
641	A68	6g red	.50	.20
642	A68	10g deep blue	2.25	.25
643	A68	15g deep orange	4.50	.25
644	A69	25g dk green & blk	7.75	.35
645	A69	50g carmine & blk	11.00	.55
646	A69	100g olive grn & blk	22.50	2.00
647	A69	200g brown & blk	42.50	3.50
		Nos. 634-647 (14)	92.70	8.50

Stamps of 1926 Overprinted in Black, Silver or Gold

1927, Sept. 9

648	A66	1g brt rose	.20	.20
649	A67	2g green	.20	.20
650	A67	2½g gray black	.20	.20
651	A67	3g copper red	.30	.20
652	A68	5g lilac gray	.50	.20

653	A68	6g red	.45	.40
654	A68	10g deep blue	2.75	1.10
655	A68	15g deep orange	3.25	1.50
656	A69	25g dk green & blk (S)	11.00	7.00
657	A69	50g car & blk (S)	22.50	22.50
658	A69	100g ol grn & blk (G)	30.00	27.50
		Nos. 648-658 (11)	71.35	61.00

Agricultural and industrial exhibition at Izmir, Sept. 9-20, 1927.

The overprint reads: "1927" and the initials of "Izmir Dokuz Eylul Sergisi" (Izmir Exhibition, September 9).

Second Izmir Exhibition Issue
Nos. 634-647 Overprinted in Red or Black

On A66-A68   On A69

1928, Sept. 9

659	A66	10pa slate (R)	.20	.20
660	A66	20pa orange	.20	.20
661	A66	1g brt rose	.20	.20
662	A67	2g green (R)	.20	.20
663	A67	2½g gray blk (R)	.50	.20
664	A67	3g copper red	.90	.20
665	A68	5g lilac gray (R)	.90	.40
666	A68	6g red	.60	.20
667	A68	10g deep blue	1.25	.25
668	A68	15g deep orange	2.50	.75
669	A69	25g dk grn & blk (R)	7.50	3.00
670	A69	50g car & blk	16.00	7.50
671	A69	100g ol grn & blk (R)	27.50	19.00
672	A69	200g brn & blk (R)	40.00	20.00
		Nos. 659-672 (14)	98.45	52.30

The overprint reads "Izmir, September 9, 1928."

Nos. 636, 652, 654 Surcharged in Black (#673) or Red (#674-675)

2½ kuruslur

1929

673	A66	20pa on 1g brt rose	.25	.20
a.		Inverted surcharge	3.50	3.50
674	A68	2½k on 5g lilac gray	.40	.25
a.		Inverted surcharge	7.50	7.50
675	A68	6k on 10g deep blue	5.50	.40
		Nos. 673-675 (3)	6.15	.85

Railroad Bridge over Kizil Irmak — A70   A71

A72   A73

Latin Inscriptions
Without umlaut over first "U" of "CUMHURIYETI"

1929				**Engr.**
676	A70	2k gray black	1.75	.20
677	A70	2½k green	.80	.20
678	A70	3k violet brown	1.25	.20
679	A71	6k dark violet	12.50	.25
680	A72	12½k deep blue	19.00	.55
681	A73	50k carmine & blk	35.00	.90
		Nos. 676-681 (6)	70.30	2.30

See Nos. 682-691, 694-695, 697, 699. For surcharges & overprints see #705-714, 716-717, 719, 721, 727, 765-766, 770-771, 777, C2, C7.

Sakarya
Gorge — A74

Mustafa
Kemal
Pasha — A75

With umlaut over first "U" of "CUMHURIYETI"

1930

682	A71	10pa green	.20	.20
683	A70	20pa gray violet	.20	.20
684	A70	1k olive green	.25	.20
685	A71	1½k olive black	.20	.20
686	A70	2k dull violet	2.00	.20
687	A70	2½k deep green	1.00	.20
688	A70	3k brown orange	12.50	.50
689	A71	4k deep rose	6.75	.50
690	A72	5k rose lake	8.00	.50
691	A71	6k indigo	8.00	.50
692	A74	7½k red brown	.20	.20
694	A72	12½k deep ultra	.55	.20
695	A72	15k deep orange	.55	.20
696	A74	17½k dark gray	.60	.20
697	A72	20k black brown	4.00	.45
698	A74	25k olive brown	1.25	.20
699	A72	30k yellow brown	1.75	.20
700	A74	40k red violet	1.75	.20
701	A75	50k red & black	3.50	.30
702	A75	100k olive grn & blk	20.00	.20
703	A75	200k dk green & blk	3.75	.60
704	A75	500k chocolate & blk	20.00	3.25
		Nos. 682-704 (22)	80.50	9.50

For surcharges and overprints see Nos. 715, 718, 720, 722-726, 767-769, 772-773, 775-776, 778-780, 823-828, 848-850, C1, C3-C6, C8-C11.

Nos. 682-704 Surcharged in Red or Black:

Sivas
D. Y.
30 ag. 930
1 K.
a

D. Y. Sivas
30 ag. 930
10 P.
b

Sivas
c

D.   Y.
30 ag. 930
40 K.

1930, Aug. 30

705	A71(a)	10pa on 10pa (R)	.20	.20
706	A70(b)	10pa on 20pa	.20	.20
707	A70(b)	20pa on 1ku	.20	.20
708	A71(a)	1k on 1½k (R)	.20	.20
709	A70(b)	1½k on 2k	.30	.20
710	A70(b)	2k on 2½k (R)	.55	.20
711	A70(b)	2½k on 3k	.50	.20
712	A71(a)	3k on 4k	.60	.20
713	A72(a)	4k on 5k	1.25	.25
714	A71(a)	5k on 6k (R)	.60	.30
715	A74(a)	6k on 7½k	.70	.20
716	A72(a)	7½k on 12½k (R)	.80	.20
717	A72(a)	12½k on 15k	2.25	.30
718	A74(b)	15k on 17½k (R)	2.00	.60
719	A72(b)	17½k on 20k (R)	2.75	.60
720	A74(b)	20k on 25k (R)	2.75	.60
721	A72(b)	25k on 30k	3.00	.65
722	A74(b)	30k on 40k	4.25	.80
723	A75(c)	40k on 50k	4.25	.70
724	A75(c)	50k on 100k (R)	32.50	9.00
725	A75(c)	100k on 200k (R)	35.00	14.00
726	A75(c)	250k on 500k (R)	37.50	12.00
		Nos. 705-726 (22)	132.35	41.80

Inauguration of the railroad between Ankara and Sivas.

There are numerous varieties in these settings as: "309," "390," "930" inverted, no period after "D," no period after "Y" and raised period before "Y."

No. 685 Surcharged in Red

1931, Apr. 1

727	A71	1k on 1½k olive blk	.60	.20

Olive Tree with Roots Extending to All Balkan Capitals — A76

1931, Oct. 20   Engr.   Perf. 12

728	A76	2½k dark green	.20	.20
729	A76	4k carmine	.20	.20
730	A76	6k steel blue	.20	.20
731	A76	7½k dull red	.20	.20
732	A76	12k deep orange	.25	.20
733	A76	12½k dark blue	.40	.20
734	A76	30k dark violet	.90	.30
735	A76	50k dark brown	1.90	.35
736	A76	100k brown violet	5.00	2.00
		Nos. 728-736 (9)	9.25	3.85

Second Balkan Conference.

A77   A78

Mustafa Kemal Pasha
(Kemal Atatürk) — A79

1931-42   Typo.   Perf. 11½, 12

737	A77	10pa blue green	.20	.20
738	A77	20pa deep orange	.20	.20
739	A77	30pa brt violet ('38)	.20	.20
740	A78	1k dk slate green	.20	.20
740A	A77	1½k magenta ('42)	.55	.20
741	A78	2k dark violet	.20	.20
741A	A78	2k yel grn ('40)	.25	.20
742	A77	2½k green	.20	.20
743	A78	3k brn org ('38)	.20	.20
744	A78	4k slate	.20	.20
745	A78	5k rose red	.20	.20
745A	A78	5k brown blk ('40)	1.25	.30
746	A78	6k deep blue	.25	.20
746A	A78	6k rose ('40)	.80	.30
747	A77	7½k deep rose ('38)	.20	.20
747A	A78	8k brt blue ('38)	.20	.20
	b.	8k dark blue ('36)	.20	.20
748	A77	10k black brn ('32)	3.00	.20
748A	A77	10k deep blue ('40)	4.00	.40
749	A77	12k bister ('32)	.40	.20
750	A79	12½k indigo ('32)	.25	.20
751	A77	15k org yel ('32)	.40	.20
752	A77	20k olive grn ('32)	.40	.20
753	A77	25k Prus blue ('32)	.40	.20
754	A77	30k magenta ('32)	7.50	.20
755	A79	100k maroon ('32)	10.00	.20
756	A79	200k purple ('32)	12.50	.20
757	A79	250k chocolate ('32)	35.00	.40
		Nos. 737-757 (27)	79.15	6.00

See Nos. 1015-1033, 1117B-1126. For overprints see Nos. 811-816.

Symbolizing 10th Anniversary of Republic — A80

President Atatürk — A81

1933, Oct. 29   Perf. 10

758	A80	1½k blue green	.50	.20
759	A80	2k olive brown	.50	.20
760	A81	3k red brown	.50	.20
761	A81	6k deep blue	.50	.25
762	A80	12½k dark blue	1.50	1.40
763	A80	25k dark brown	3.00	2.50
764	A81	50k orange brown	6.50	6.00
		Nos. 758-764 (7)	13.00	10.75

10th year of the Turkish Republic. The stamps were in use for three days only.

Nos. 682, 685, 692, 694, 696-698, 702 Overprinted or Surcharged in Red:

Izmir
9 Eylül 934
Sergisi

Izmir
9 Eylül 934
2 Kuruş

1934, Aug. 26   Perf. 12

765	A71	10pa green	.20	.20
766	A71	1k on 1½k	.25	.20
767	A74	2k on 25k	.45	.20
768	A74	5k on 7½k	1.25	.30
769	A74	6k on 17½k	1.25	.35
770	A72	12½k deep ultra	3.50	.75
771	A72	15k on 20k	32.50	14.00
772	A74	20k on 25k	27.50	13.00
773	A75	50k on 100k	27.50	13.00
		Nos. 765-773 (9)	94.40	42.00

Izmir Fair, 1934.

Nos. 696, 698, 701-704 Surcharged in Black

1936, Oct. 26

775	A74	4k on 17½k	.80	.40
776	A74	5k on 25k	.80	.40
777	A73	6k on 50k	.80	.40
778	A75	10k on 100k	1.25	.50
779	A75	20k on 200k	4.50	1.40
780	A75	50k on 500k	8.00	2.25
		Nos. 775-780 (6)	16.15	5.35

"1926" in Overprint

775a	A74	4k on 17½k	6.50	3.75
776a	A74	5k on 25k	7.00	3.75
777a	A73	6k on 50k	7.00	3.75
778a	A75	10k on 100k	9.00	4.50
779a	A75	20k on 200k	20.00	10.00
780a	A75	50k on 500k	55.00	27.50
		Nos. 775a-780a (6)	104.50	53.25

Re-militarization of the Dardanelles.

Hittite Bronze
Stag — A82

Thorak's Bust
of Kemal
Atatürk — A83

1937, Sept. 20   Litho.   Perf. 12

781	A82	3k light violet	.65	.50
782	A83	6k blue	.85	.50
783	A82	7½k bright pink	1.60	1.00
784	A83	12½k indigo	3.75	3.50
		Nos. 781-784 (4)	6.85	5.50

2nd Turkish Historical Congress, Istanbul, Sept. 20-30.

Arms of Turkey, Greece, Romania and Yugoslavia — A84

1937, Oct. 29   Perf. 11½

785	A84	8k carmine	6.75	3.50
786	A84	12½k dark blue	15.00	4.75

The Balkan Entente.

Street in
Izmir
A85

Fig Tree — A87

30pa, View of Fair Buildings. 3k, Tower, Government Square. 5k, Olive branch. 6k, Woman with grapes. 7½k, Woman picking grapes. 8k, Izmir Harbor through arch. 12k, Statue of Pres. Atatürk. 12½k, Pres. Atatürk.

1938, Aug. 20   Photo.   Perf. 11½

Inscribed: "Izmir Enternasyonal Fuari 1938"

789	A85	10pa dark brown	.30	.20
790	A85	30pa purple	.30	.20
791	A87	2½k brt green	.60	.20
792	A87	3k brown orange	.50	.25
793	A85	5k olive green	.60	.30
794	A85	6k brown	1.75	.40
795	A87	7½k scarlet	1.75	.60
796	A87	8k brown lake	1.75	.80
797	A87	12k rose violet	1.75	.80
798	A87	12½k deep blue	2.75	1.40
		Nos. 789-798 (10)	12.05	5.15

Izmir International Fair.

President Atatürk Teaching Reformed Turkish Alphabet A95

1938, Nov. 2

799	A95	2½k brt green	.20	.35
800	A95	3k orange	.20	.35
801	A95	6k rose violet	.40	.45
802	A95	7½k deep rose	.40	.80
803	A95	8k red brown	.80	.95
804	A95	12½k brt ultra	1.40	1.10
		Nos. 799-804 (6)	3.40	4.00

Reform of the Turkish alphabet, 10th anniv.

Army and
Air Force
A96

Atatürk Driving
Tractor — A98

3k, View of Kayseri. 7½k, Railway bridge. 8k, Scout buglers. 12½k, President Atatürk.

1938, Oct. 29
Inscribed: "·Cumhuriyetin 15 inc yil donumu hatirasi"

605	A96	2½k dark green	.20	.25
606	A96	3k red brown	.25	.25
607	A98	6k bister	.30	.30
608	A96	7½k red	.70	.70
609	A96	8k rose violet	2.50	2.00
610	A98	12½k deep blue	1.75	1.50
		Nos. 805-810 (6)	5.70	5.00

15th anniversary of the Republic.

Stamps of 1931-38 Overprinted in Black

1938, Nov. 21 Perf. 11½x12

811	A78	3k brown orange	.25	.20
812	A78	5k rose red	.25	.20
813	A78	6k deep blue	.25	.20
814	A77	7½k deep rose	.50	.25
815	A78	8k dark blue	.75	.40
a.		8k bright blue	40.00	60.00
816	A79	12½k indigo	1.00	.65
		Nos. 811-816 (6)	3.00	1.90

President Kemal Atatürk (1881-1938). The date is that of his funeral.

> **Catalogue values for unused stamps in this section, from this point to the end of the section, are for Never Hinged items.**

Turkish and American Flags — A102

Presidents Inönü and F. D. Roosevelt and Map of North America A103

Designs: 3k, 8k, Inonu and Roosevelt. 7½k, 12½k, Kemal Ataturk and Washington.

1939, July 15 Photo. Perf. 14

817	A102	2½k ol grn, red & bl	.25	.20
818	A103	3k dk brn & bl grn	.25	.20
819	A102	6k purple, red & bl	.45	.20
820	A103	7½k org ver & bl grn	.45	.40
821	A103	8k dp cl & bl grn	.60	.40
822	A103	12½k brt bl & bl grn	1.50	.85
		Nos. 817-822 (6)	3.50	2.25

US constitution, 150th anniversary.

Nos. 698, 702-704 Surcharged in Black

1939, July 23 Unwmk. Perf. 13

823	A74	3k on 25k	.35	.20
824	A75	6k on 200k	.35	.20
825	A74	7½k on 25k	.65	.20
826	A75	12k on 100k	.65	.20
827	A75	12½k on 200k	1.00	.30
828	A75	17½k on 500k	2.25	.60
		Nos. 823-828 (6)	5.25	1.70

Annexation of Hatay.

Railroad Bridge A105

Locomotive A106

Track Through Mountain Pass A107

Design: 12½k, Railroad tunnel, Atma Pass.

1939, Oct. 20 Typo. Perf. 11½

829	A105	3k lt orange red	2.50	1.00
830	A106	6k chestnut	5.25	2.00
831	A107	7½k rose pink	5.50	2.25
832	A107	12½k dark blue	8.25	3.75
		Nos. 829-832 (4)	21.50	9.00

Completion of the Sivas to Erzerum link of the Ankara-Erzerum Railroad.

Atatürk Residence in Ankara — A109

Kemal Atatürk — A110

TÜRKİYE POSTALARI

KEMAL ATATÜRK
1880-1938

A111

Designs: 5k, 6k, 7½k, 8k, 12½k, 17½k, Various portraits of Ataturk, "1880-1938."

1939-40 Photo.

833	A109	2½k brt green	.60	.25
834	A110	3k dk blue gray	.60	.30
835	A110	5k chocolate	.65	.30
836	A110	6k chestnut	1.25	.25
837	A110	7½k rose red	1.90	.70
838	A110	8k gray green	1.25	.55
839	A110	12½k brt blue	1.50	.25
840	A110	17½k brt rose	2.50	.90
		Nos. 833-840 (8)	10.25	3.50

Souvenir Sheet

841	A111	100k blue black	50.00	25.00

Death of Kemal Ataturk, first anniversary. Size of No. 841: 90x120mm.
Issued: 2½k, 6k, 12½k, 11/11/39; others, 1/3/40.

Namik Kemal A118

Arms of Turkey, Greece, Romania and Yugoslavia A119

1940, Jan. 3

842	A118	6k chestnut	.60	.20
843	A118	8k dk olive grn	.75	.40
844	A118	12k brt rose red	1.75	.40
845	A118	12½k brt blue	2.50	1.10
		Nos. 842-845 (4)	5.60	2.10

Birth cent. of Namik Kemal, poet and patriot.

Perf. 11½
1940, Jan. 1 Typo. Unwmk.

846	A119	8k light blue	3.00	.75
847	A119	10k deep blue	4.50	.75

The Balkan Entente.

Nos. 703-704 Surcharged in Red or Black

1940, Aug. 20 Perf. 12

848	A75	6k on 200k dk grn & blk (R)	.40	.20
849	A75	10k on 200k dk grn & blk	.55	.30
850	A75	12k on 500k choc & blk	.65	.30
		Nos. 848-850 (3)	1.60	.80

13th International Izmir Fair.

Map of Turkey and Census Figures A120

1940, Oct. 1 Typo. Perf. 11½

851	A120	10pa dark blue green	.20	.20
852	A120	3k orange	.25	.20
853	A120	6k carmine rose	.55	.25
854	A120	10k dark blue	2.00	.50
		Nos. 851-854 (4)	3.00	1.15

Census of Oct. 20, 1940.

Runner — A121

Pole Vaulter — A122

Hurdler A123

Discus Thrower — A124

1940, Oct. 5

855	A121	3k olive green	2.25	.75
856	A122	6k rose	4.50	1.60
857	A123	8k chestnut brown	3.00	1.00
858	A124	10k dark blue	4.50	2.00
		Nos. 855-858 (4)	14.25	5.35

11th Balkan Olympics.

Mail Carriers on Horseback A125

Postman of 1840 and 1940 — A126

Old Sailing Vessel and Modern Mailboat — A127

Design: 12k, Post Office, Istanbul.

1940, Dec. 31 Typo. Perf. 10

859	A125	3k gray green	.25	.20
860	A126	6k rose	.30	.20
861	A127	10k dark blue	1.00	.60
862	A127	12k olive brown	1.00	.50
		Nos. 859-862 (4)	2.55	1.50

Centenary of the Turkish post.

Harbor Scene A129

Statue of Atatürk — A132

Designs: 3k, 6k, 17½k, Various Izmir Fair buildings. 12k, Girl picking grapes.

1941, Aug. 20 Litho. Perf. 11½
Inscribed: "Izmir Enternasyonal Fuari 1941"

863	A129	30pa dull green	.20	.20
864	A129	3k olive gray	.20	.20
865	A129	6k salmon rose	.45	.20
866	A129	10k blue	.20	.20
867	A129	12k dull brown vio	.45	.20
868	A129	17½k dull brown	.85	.40
		Nos. 863-868 (6)	2.35	1.40

Izmir International Fair, 1941.

Tomb of Barbarossa II — A135

Barbarossa II (Khair ed-Din) — A137

Barbarossa's Fleet in Battle — A136

1941
869	A135	20pa dark violet	.20	.20
870	A136	3k light blue	.20	.20
871	A136	6k rose red	.30	.20
872	A136	10k deep ultra	.50	.20
873	A136	12k dull brn & bis	1.50	.40
874	A137	17½k multicolored	2.50	1.50
	Nos. 869-874 (6)		5.20	2.70

400th death anniv. of Barbarossa II.

President Inönü
A138   A138a

1942-45   **Perf. 11½x11, 11**
875	A138	0.25k yellow bis	.20	.20
876	A138	0.50k lt yellow grn	.20	.20
877	A138	1k gray green	.20	.20
877A	A138	1½k brt vio ('45)	.20	.20
878	A138	2k bluish green	.20	.20
879	A138	4k fawn	.20	.20
880	A138	4½k slate	.20	.20
881	A138	5k light blue	.35	.20
882	A138	6k salmon rose	.20	.20
883	A138	6¾k ultra	.20	.20
884	A138	9k blue violet	1.10	.20
885	A138	10k dark blue	.20	.20
886	A138	13½k brt pink	.20	.20
887	A138	16k Prus green	.20	.20
888	A138	17½k rose lake	.30	.20
889	A138	20k brown violet	.80	.20
890	A138	27½k orange	.60	.20
891	A138	37k buff	.75	.20
892	A138	50k purple	1.60	.20
893	A138	100k olive bister	4.50	.50
894	A138a	200k brown	11.00	.70
	Nos. 875-894 (21)		23.40	5.00

Ankara — A139   Antioch — A141

0.50k, Mohair goats. 1½k, Ankara Dam. 2k, Oranges. 4k, Merino sheep. 4½k, Train. 5k, Tile decorating. 6k, Atatürk statue, Ankara. 6¾k, 10k, Pres. Ismet Inonu. 13½k, Grand National Assembly. 16k, Arnavutkoy, Istanbul. 17½k, Republic monument, Istanbul. 20k, Safety monument, Ankara. 27½k, Post Office,

Istanbul. 37k, Monument at Afyon. 50k, "People's House," Ankara. 100k, Atatürk & Inonu. 200k, Pres. Inonu.

1943, Apr. 1   **Perf. 11**
896	A139	0.25k citron	.20	.20
897	A139	0.50k brt green	.25	.20
898	A141	1k yellow olive	.20	.20
899	A141	1½k deep violet	.20	.20
900	A139	2k brt blue green	.40	.20
901	A139	4k copper red	.70	.20
902	A139	4½k black	.60	.20
903	A141	5k sapphire	.45	.20
904	A139	6k carmine rose	.20	.20
905	A139	6¾k brt ultra	.20	.20
906	A139	10k dark blue	.20	.20
907	A141	13½k brt red violet	.20	.20
908	A141	16k myrtle green	1.10	.20
909	A139	17½k brown orange	.60	.20
910	A139	20k sepia	.75	.20
911	A139	27½k dk orange	1.50	.40
912	A139	37k lt yellow brn	1.25	.40
913	A141	50k purple	3.00	.20
914	A139	100k dk olive grn	5.25	.20
915	A139	200k dark brown	6.75	.30
a.	Souvenir sheet		32.50	17.50
	Nos. 896-915 (20)		24.00	4.50

No. 915a contains one stamp similar to No. 915, perf. 13½ and printed in sepia. Issued Apr. 20.

For surcharge see No. 928.

Girl with Grapes — A158

Entrance to Izmir Fair A159

Fair Building A160

1943, Aug. 20   Litho.   Perf. 11½
916	A158	4½k dull olive	.25	.20
917	A159	6k carmine rose	.20	.20
918	A160	6¾k blue	.25	.20
919	A159	10k dark blue	.30	.20
920	A158	13½k sepia	.90	.20
921	A160	27½k dull gray	.90	.30
	Nos. 916-921 (6)		2.80	1.30

Izmir International Fair.

Soccer Team on Parade A161

Turkish Flag and Soldier — A162

Designs: 6¾k, Bridge. 10k, Hospital. 13½k, View of Ankara. 27½k, President Inonu.

1943, Oct. 29   Perf. 11x11½, 11½x11
Inscribed: "Cumhuriyetin 20 nci Yildonomu Hatirasi"
922	A161	4½k lt olive grn	.80	.30
923	A162	6k rose red	.25	.20
924	A161	6¾k ultra	.25	.20
925	A161	10k violet blue	.25	.20

926	A161	13½k olive	.50	.20
927	A162	27½k lt brown	.80	.40
	Nos. 922-927 (6)		2.85	1.50

Republic, 20th anniv. Nos. 922-927 exist imperf.

No. 905 Surcharged with New Value in Red

1945   **Perf. 11**
928	A139	4½k on 6¾k brt ultra	.25	.20

Recording Census Data — A167   President Ismet Inönü — A169

1945, Oct. 21   Litho.   Perf. 11½
929	A167	4½k olive black	.55	.20
930	A167	9k violet	.60	.20
931	A167	10k violet blue	.60	.20
932	A167	18k dark red	1.25	.50
	Nos. 929-932 (4)		3.00	1.10

Souvenir Sheet
Imperf
933	A167	1 l chocolate	35.00	6.50

Census of 1945.

Perf. 11½ to 12½
1946, Apr. 1   **Unwmk.**
934	A169	0.25k brown red	.20	.20
935	A169	1k dk slate grn	.20	.20
936	A169	1½k plum	.20	.20
937	A169	9k purple	.35	.20
938	A169	10k deep blue	1.10	.20
939	A169	50k chocolate	3.25	.20
	Nos. 934-939 (6)		5.30	1.20

U.S.S. Missouri A170

1946, Apr. 5   Perf. 11½
940	A170	9k dark purple	.25	.20
941	A170	10k dk chalky blue	.25	.20
942	A170	27½k olive green	.90	.30
a.	Imperf., pair		25.00	
	Nos. 940-942 (3)		1.40	.70

Visit of the USS Missouri to Istanbul, 4/5.

Sower A171   Dove and Flag-Decorated Banderol A172

1946, June 16   Perf. 11½ to 12½
943	A171	9k violet	.20	.20
944	A171	10k dark blue	.20	.20
945	A171	18k olive green	.30	.20
946	A171	27½k red orange	.75	.20
	Nos. 943-946 (4)		1.45	.80

Passing of legislation to distribute state lands to poor farmers.

1947, Aug. 20   Photo.   Perf. 12
947	A172	15k violet & dk bl	.20	.20
948	A172	20k blue & dk blue	.20	.20
949	A172	30k brown & gray blk	.20	.20
950	A172	1 l grn & dk green	.80	.40
	Nos. 947-950 (4)		1.40	1.00

Izmir International Fair.

Victory Monument, Afyon Karahisar A173   Ismet Inönü as General A174

Kemal Atatürk as General — A175

1947, Aug. 30
951	A173	10k dk brn & pale brn	.20	.20
952	A174	15k brt violet & gray	.20	.20
953	A175	20k dp blue & gray	.20	.20
954	A173	30k grnsh blk & gray	.20	.20
955	A174	60k ol gray & pale brn	.50	.30
956	A175	1 l dk green & gray	1.50	.50
	Nos. 951-956 (6)		2.80	1.60

25th anniv. of the Battle of Dumlupinar, Aug. 30, 1922.

Grapes and Istanbul Skyline A176

1947, Sept. 22
957	A176	15k rose violet	.20	.20
958	A176	20k deep blue	.20	.20
959	A176	60k dark brown	.60	.40
	Nos. 957-959 (3)		1.00	.80

International Vintners' Congress, Istanbul.

Approaching Train, Istanbul Skyline and Sirkeci Terminus — A177

1947, Oct. 9
960	A177	15k rose violet	.40	.20
961	A177	20k brt blue	.60	.20
962	A177	60k olive green	1.00	.60
	Nos. 960-962 (3)		2.00	1.00

International Railroad Congress, Istanbul.

President Ismet Inönü
A178   A179

1948   Unwmk.   Engr.   Perf. 12, 14
963	A178	0.25k dark red	.20	.20
964	A178	1k olive black	.20	.20
965	A178	2k brt rose lilac	.20	.20
966	A178	3k red orange	.20	.20
967	A178	4k dark green	.20	.20
968	A178	5k blue	.20	.20
969	A178	10k chocolate	.20	.20
970	A178	12k deep red	.20	.20
971	A178	15k violet	.20	.20
972	A178	20k deep blue	.30	.20
973	A178	30k brown	.60	.20
974	A178	60k black	.90	.20
975	A179	1 l olive green	1.90	.25
976	A179	2 l dark brown	18.00	1.75
977	A179	5 l deep plum	14.00	10.50
	Nos. 963-977 (15)		37.50	14.90

For overprints see Nos. O13-O42.

President Ismet Inönü and Lausanne Conference — A180

Conference Building A180a

1948, July 23   Photo.   Perf. 11½
978 A180 15k rose lilac   .20 .20
979 A180 20k blue   .20 .20
980 A180a 40k gray green   .30 .20
981 A180 1 l brown   1.10 .40
    Nos. 978-981 (4)   1.80 1.00

25th anniversary of Lausanne Treaty.

Statue of Kemal Atatürk, Ankara — A181

1948, Oct. 29
982 A181 15k violet   .20 .20
983 A181 20k blue   .20 .20
984 A181 40k gray green   .25 .20
985 A181 1 l brown   1.50 .65
    Nos. 982-985 (4)   2.15 1.25

25th anniv. of the proclamation of the republic.

A182   A183

A184

Wrestlers A185

1949, June 3
986 A182 15k rose lilac   2.00 1.00
987 A183 20k blue   2.50 1.40
988 A184 30k brown   2.50 1.60
989 A185 60k green   3.50 2.75
    Nos. 986-989 (4)   10.50 6.75

5th European Wrestling Championships, Istanbul, June 3-5, 1949.

Ancient Galley A186

Galleon Mahmudiye A187

Monument to Khizr Barbarossa A188

Designs: 15k, Cruiser Hamidiye. 20k, Submarine Sakarya. 30k, Cruiser Yavuz.

1949, July 1
990 A186   5k violet   .20 .20
991 A187 10k brown   .25 .20
992 A186 15k lilac rose   .30 .20
993 A186 20k gray blue   .40 .20
994 A186 30k gray   .85 .30
995 A188 40k olive gray   1.00 .55
    Nos. 990-995 (6)   3.00 1.65

Fleet Day, July 1, 1949.

A189

UPU Monument, Bern A190

Perf. 11½
1949, Oct. 9   Unwmk.   Photo.
996 A189 15k violet   .20 .20
997 A189 20k blue   .20 .20
998 A190 30k dull rose   .30 .30
999 A190 40k green   .65 .65
    Nos. 996-999 (4)   1.35 1.35

UPU, 75th anniversary.

Istanbul Fair Building A191

1949, Oct. 1   Litho.   Perf. 10
1000 A191 15k brown   .20 .20
1001 A191 20k blue   .20 .20
1002 A191 30k olive   .60 .25
    Nos. 1000-1002 (3)   1.00 .65

Istanbul Fair, Oct. 1-31.

Boy and Girl and Globe — A192

Aged Woman Casting Ballot — A193

Kemal Atatürk and Map A194

1950, Aug. 13   Perf. 11½
1003 A192 15k purple   .20 .20
1004 A192 20k deep blue   .20 .20

2nd World Youth Council Meeting, 1950. No. 1004 exists imperf. Value $3.

1950, Aug. 30
1005 A193 15k dark brown   .20 .20
1006 A193 20k dark blue   .20 .20
1007 A194 30k dk blue & gray   .30 .20
    Nos. 1005-1007 (3)   .70 .60

Election of May 14, 1950.

Hazel Nuts — A195   Symbolical of 1950 Census — A196

Designs: 12k, Acorns. 15k, Cotton. 20k, Symbolical of the fair. 30k, Tobacco.

1950, Sept. 9
1008 A195   8k gray grn & buff   .20 .20
1009 A195 12k magenta   .30 .20
1010 A195 15k brn blk & lt brn .50 .20
1011 A195 20k dk blue & aqua   .90 .40
1012 A195 30k brn blk & dull org 1.40 .65
    Nos. 1008-1012 (5)   3.30 1.65

Izmir International Fair, Aug. 20-Sept. 20.

1950, Oct. 9   Litho.   Perf. 11½
1013 A196 15k dark brown   .20 .20
1014 A196 20k violet blue   .30 .20

General census of 1950.

Atatürk Types of 1931-42
Perf. 10x11½, 11½x12

1950-51			Typo.	
1015	A77	10p dull red brn	.20	.20
1016	A77	10p vermilion ('51)	.35	.20
1017	A77	20p blue green	.20	.20
1018	A78	1k olive green	.20	.20
1019	A78	2k plum	.25	.20
1020	A78	2k dp yellow ('51)	.75	.30
1021	A78	3k yellow orange	.55	.20
1022	A78	3k gray ('51)	.75	.20
1023	A78	4k green ('51)	.75	.20
1024	A78	5k blue	.25	.20
1025	A78	5k plum ('51)	3.50	.30
1026	A77	10k brown orange	1.10	.20
1027	A77	15k purple	1.25	.20
1028	A77	15k brown carmine	12.00	.20
1029	A77	20k dark blue	7.00	.20
1030	A77	30k pink ('51)	15.00	.50
1031	A79	100k red brown ('51)	1.90	.30
1032	A79	200k dark brown	8.00	1.00
1033	A79	200k rose violet ('51)	8.50	1.50
		Nos. 1015-1033 (19)	62.50	6.50

16th Century Flight of Hezarfen Ahmet Celebi — A197

Plane over Istanbul A198

40k, Biplane over Taurus Mountains.

1950, Oct. 17   Litho.   Perf. 11
1034 A197 20k dk green & blue   .35 .20
1035 A197 40k dk brown & blue   .55 .35
1036 A198 60k purple & blue   .90 .60
    Nos. 1034-1036 (3)   1.80 1.15

Regional meeting of the ICAO, Istanbul, Oct. 17.

Farabi A199

1950, Dec. 1   Unwmk.   Perf. 11½
Multicolored Center
1037 A199 15k blue   .75 .20
1038 A199 20k blue violet   1.00 .30
1039 A199 60k red brown   2.50 1.00
1040 A199   1 l gold & bl vio   2.25 2.50
    Nos. 1037-1040 (4)   6.50 4.00

Death millenary of Farabi, Arab philosopher.

Mithat Pasha and Security Bank Building — A200

Design: 20k, Agricultural Bank.

1950, Dec. 21   Photo.
1041 A200 15k rose violet   .35 .20
1042 A200 20k blue   .45 .30

3rd Congress of Turkish Cooperatives, Istanbul, Dec. 25, 1950.

Floating a Ship A201

Lighthouse — A202

1951, July 1
1043 A201 15k shown   .35 .20
1044 A201 20k Steamship   .35 .20
1045 A201 30k Diver rising   .75 .40
1046 A202   1 l shown   1.75 .80
    Nos. 1043-1046 (4)   3.20 1.60

25th anniv. of the recognition of coastal rights in Turkish waters to ships under the Turkish flag.

Mosque of
Sultan
Ahmed
A203

Henry Carton de
Wiart — A204

Designs: 20k, Dolma Bahce Palace. 60k,
Rumeli Hisari Fortress.

1951, Aug. 31   Photo.   Perf. 13½
1047 A203 15k dark green   .25   .20
1048 A203 20k deep ultra   .30   .20
1049 A204 30k brown   .35   .30
1050 A203 60k purple brown   1.10   .70
     Nos. 1047-1050 (4)   2.00 1.40

40th Interparliamentary Conf., Istanbul.

Allegory of
Food and
Agriculture
A205

Designs: 20k, Dam. 30k, United Nations
Building. 60k, University, Ankara.

1952, Jan. 3   Unwmk.   Perf. 14
Inscribed: "Akdeniz Yetistirme
Merkezi. Ankara 1951."
1051 A205 15k green   .50   .20
1052 A205 20k blue violet   .60   .20
1053 A205 30k blue   .90   .35
1054 A205 60k red   2.25 1.40
   a. Souvenir sheet of 4   45.00 35.00
     Nos. 1051-1054 (4)   4.25 2.15

UN Mediterranean Economic Instruction
Center.
No. 1054a contains one each of Nos. 1051-
1054, imperf., with inscriptions in dark blue
gray.

Abdulhak Hamid
Tarhan, Poet,
Birth
Cent. — A206

1952, Feb. 5   Photo.   Perf. 13½
1055 A206 15k dark purple   .20   .20
1056 A206 20k dark blue   .20   .20
1057 A206 30k brown   .30   .20
1058 A206 60k dark olive grn   .70   .40
     Nos. 1055-1058 (4)   1.40 1.00

Ruins, Bergama   Tarsus Cataract
A207   A208

Designs: 2k, Ruins, Milas. 3k, Karatay Gate,
Konya. 4k, Kozak plateau. 5k, Urgup. 10k,
12k, 15k, 20k, Kemal Ataturk. 30k, Mosque,
Bursa. 40k, Mosque, Istanbul. 75k, Rocks,
Urgup. 1 l, Palace, Istanbul. 2 l, Pavilion, Istan-
bul. 5 l, Museum interior, Istanbul.

1952, Mar. 15   Perf. 13½
1059 A207 1k brown orange   .20   .20
1060 A207 2k olive green   .20   .20
1061 A207 3k rose brown   .20   .20
1062 A207 4k blue green   .20   .20

1063 A207 5k brown   .20   .20
1064 A207 10k dark brown   .20   .20
1065 A207 12k brt rose car   .20   .20
1066 A207 15k purple   .20   .20
1067 A207 20k chalky blue   .65   .20
1068 A207 30k grnsh gray   .40   .20
1069 A207 40k slate blue   .90   .20
1070 A208 50k olive   1.00   .20
1071 A208 75k slate   .95   .25
1072 A208 1 l deep purple   .95   .20
1073 A208 2 l brt ultra   2.00   .30
1074 A208 5 l sepia   15.00 3.00
     Nos. 1059-1074 (16)   23.45 6.15

Imperfs, value, set $75.
For surcharge & overprint see #1075, 1255.

No. 1059 Surcharged with New Value
in Black

1952, June 1
1075 A207 0.50k on 1k brn org   .25   .20

Technical
Faculty
Building
A209

1952, Aug. 20   Perf. 12x12½
1076 A209 15k violet   .25   .20
1077 A209 20k blue   .35   .20
1078 A209 60k brown   1.00   .75
     Nos. 1076-1078 (3)   1.60 1.15

8th Intl. Congress of Theoretic and Applied
Mechanics.

Turkish   Pigeons
Soldier — A210   Bandaging
                     Wounded
                     Hand — A212

20k, Soldier with Turkish flag. 30k, Soldier &
child with comic book. 60k, Raising Turkish
flag.

1952, Sept. 25   Perf. 14
1079 A210 15k Prus blue   .30   .20
1080 A210 20k deep blue   .30   .20
1081 A210 30k brown   .50   .35
1082 A210 60k olive blk & car   .90   .75
     Nos. 1079-1082 (4)   2.00 1.50

Turkey's participation in the Korean war.

1952, Oct. 29   Perf. 12½x12

20k, Flag, rainbow and ruined homes.

Dated "1877-1952"
1085 A212 15k dk green & red   .55   .25
1086 A212 20k blue & red   1.25   .45

Turkish Red Crescent Society, 75th anniv.

Relief From Panel
of Aziziye
Monument — A213

Aziziye
Monument
A214

Design: 40k, View of Erzerum.

1952, Nov. 9   Perf. 11
1087 A213 15k purple   .30   .20
1088 A214 20k blue   .35   .25
1089 A214 40k olive gray   .60   .55
     Nos. 1087-1089 (3)   1.25 1.00

75th anniv. of the Battle of Aziziye at
Erzerum.

Rumeli
Hisari
Fortress
A215

Troops Entering   Sultan Mohammed
Constan-   II — A217
tinople — A216

Designs: 8k, Soldiers moving cannon. 10k,
Mohammed II riding into sea, and Turkish
armada. 12k, Landing of Turkish army. 15k,
Ancient wall, Constantinople. 30k, Mosque of
Faith. 40k, Presenting mace to Patriarch
Yenadios. 60k, Map of Constantinople, c.
1574. 1 l, Tomb of Mohammed II. 2.50 l, Por-
trait of Mohammed II.

1953, May 29   Photo.   Perf. 11½
Inscribed: "Istanbulun Fethi 1453-
1953"
1090 A215   5k brt blue   .25   .20
1091 A215   8k gray   .40   .20
1092 A215 10k blue   .50   .20
1093 A215 12k rose lilac   .60   .20
1094 A215 15k brown   .75   .20
1095 A216 20k vermilion   1.00   .20
1096 A216 30k dull green   1.25   .20
1097 A215 40k violet blue   1.50   .25
1098 A215 60k chocolate   1.50   .35
1099 A215   1 l blue green   2.75   .60
              Perf. 12
1100 A217   2 l multi   6.25 2.50
1101 A217 2.50 l multi   9.50 4.00
   a. Souvenir sheet   95.00 65.00
     Nos. 1090-1101 (12)   26.25 9.10

Conquest of Constantinople by Sultan
Mohammed II, 500th anniv.

Ruins of
the
Odeon,
Ephesus
A218

15k, Church of St. John the Apostle. 20k,
Shrine of Virgin Mary, Panaya Kapulu. 40k,
Ruins of the Double Church. 60k, Shrine of
the Seven Sleepers. 1 l, Restored house of the
Virgin Mary.

1953, Aug. 16   Litho.   Perf. 13½
Multicolored Center
1102 A218 12k sage green   .20   .20
1103 A218 15k lilac   .20   .20
1104 A218 20k dk slate blue   .20   .20
1105 A218 40k light green   .35   .20
1106 A218 60k violet blue   .55   .35
1107 A218 1 l brown red   1.50 1.40
     Nos. 1102-1107 (6)   3.00 2.55

Pres. Celal Bayar, Mithat Pasha.
Herman Schulze-Delitzsch and
People's Bank — A219

Design: 20k, Pres. Bayar, Mithat Pasha and
University of Ankara.

1953, Sept. 2   Photo.   Perf. 10½
1108 A219 15k orange brown   .25   .20
1109 A219 20k Prus green   .50   .40

5th Intl. People's Circuit Congress, Istanbul
Sept.

Combined
Harvester
A220

Kemal
Atatürk — A221

Designs: 15k, Berdan dam. 20k, Military
parade. 30k, Diesel train. 35k, Yesilkoy airport.

1953, Oct. 29   Perf. 14
1110 A220 10k olive bister   .20   .20
1111 A220 15k dark gray   .20   .20
1112 A220 20k rose red   .20   .20
1113 A220 30k olive green   .40   .20
1114 A220 35k dull blue   .30   .20
1115 A221 55k dull purple   .90   .60
     Nos. 1110-1115 (6)   2.20 1.60

Turkish Republic, 30th anniv.

Kemal Atatürk and Mausoleum at
Ankara — A222

1953, Nov. 10
1116 A222 15k gray black   .30   .25
1117 A222 20k violet brown   .60   .40

15th death anniv. of Kemal Ataturk.

Type of 1931-42
Without umlaut over first "U" of
"CUMHURIYETI"
Perf. 11½x12, 10x11½

1953-56	Typo.		Unwmk.	
1117B	A77	20p yellow	.30	.20
1118	A78	1k brown orange	.30	.20
1119	A78	2k rose pink ('53)	.25	.20
1120	A78	3k yellow brn ('53)	.25	.20
1120A	A78	4k slate ('56)	1.50	.40
1121	A78	5k blue	2.00	.20
1121A	A78	8k violet ('56)	.25	.20
1122	A77	10k dark olive ('53)	.25	.20
1123	A77	12k brt car rose ('53)	.25	.20
1124	A77	15k fawn	.60	.20
1125	A77	20k rose lilac	3.50	.40
1126	A77	30k lt blue grn ('54)	1.25	.20
		Nos. 1117B-1126 (12)	10.70	2.80

Compass
and Map
A223

Designs: 20k, Globe, crescent and stars.
40k, Tree symbolical of 14 NATO members.

1954, Apr. 4   Photo.   Perf. 14
1127 A223 15k brown   1.50 1.10
1128 A223 20k violet blue   2.00 1.50
1129 A223 40k dark green   14.00 12.00
     Nos. 1127-1129 (3)   17.50 14.60

NATO, 5th anniv.

Industry, Engineering and Agriculture — A224

Justice and Council of Europe Flag — A225

1954, Aug. 8   Litho.   Perf. 10½
1130 A224 10k brown   3.75 2.50
1131 A225 15k dark green   3.50 2.50
1132 A225 20k blue   3.75 2.50
1133 A224 30k brt violet   19.00 15.00
    Nos. 1130-1133 (4)   30.00 22.50
Council of Europe, 5th anniv.

Flag Signals to Plane — A226

Amaury de La Grange and Plane A227

Design: 45k, Kemal Ataturk and air fleet.

1954, Sept. 20   Perf. 12½
1134 A226 20k black brown   .20 .20
1135 A227 35k dull violet   .25 .20
1136 A227 45k deep blue   .45 .30
    Nos. 1134-1136 (3)   .90 .70
47th Congress of the Intl. Aeronautical Federation, Istanbul, 1954.

Souvenir Sheet

A228

1954, Oct. 18   Imperf.
1137 A228 Sheet of 3   12.50 5.50
a.   20k aquamarine   .65 .65
b.   30k violet blue   .65 .65
c.   1 l red violet   1.40 1.40
First anniv. of Law of Oct. 17, 1953, reorganizing the Department of Post, Telephone and Telegraph.

Ziya Gokalp A229

Kemal Ataturk A230

1954, Oct. 25   Perf. 11
1138 A229 15k rose lilac   .25 .20
1139 A229 20k dark green   .35 .20
1140 A229 30k crimson   .60 .35
    Nos. 1138-1140 (3)   1.20 .75
30th death anniv. of Ziya Gokalp, author and historian.

1955, Mar. 1   Perf. 12½
1141 A230 15k carmine rose   .20 .20
1142 A230 20k blue   .20 .20
1143 A230 40k dark gray   .30 .20
1144 A230 50k blue green   .55 .20
1145 A230 75k orange brown   .65 .20
    Nos. 1141-1145 (5)   1.90 1.00

Relief Map of Dardanelles — A231

Artillery Loaders — A232

30k, Minelayer Nusrat. 60k, Col. Kemal Ataturk.

1955, Mar. 18   Perf. 10½
1146 A231 15k green   .20 .20
1147 A232 20k orange brown   .20 .20
1148 A231 30k ultra   .25 .20
1149 A232 60k olive gray   .80 .40
    Nos. 1146-1149 (4)   1.45 1.00
Battle of Gallipoli, 40th anniversary.

Aerial Map A233

1955, Apr. 14   Perf. 11
1150 A233 15k gray   .20 .20
1151 A233 20k aquamarine   .20 .20
1152 A233 50k brown   .35 .20
1153 A233 1 l purple   .80 .30
    Nos. 1150-1153 (4)   1.55 .90
City Planning Congress, Ankara, 1955.

Carnation — A234

1955, May 19   Litho.   Perf. 10
1154 A234 10k shown   .25 .20
1155 A234 15k Tulip   .20 .20
1156 A234 20k Rose   .25 .20
1157 A234 50k Lily   1.60 1.00
    Nos. 1154-1157 (4)   2.30 1.60
National Flower Show, Istanbul, May 20-Aug. 20.

Battle First Aid Station A235

30k, Gulhane Military Hospital, Ankara.

1955, Aug. 28   Unwmk.   Perf. 12
1158 A235 20k red, lake & gray   .25 .20
1159 A235 30k dp grn & yel grn   .50 .20
XVIII Intl. Congress of Military Medicine, Aug. 8-Sept. 1, Istanbul.

Soccer Game A236

Emblem and Soccer Ball — A237

1 l, Emblem with oak & olive branches.

1955, Aug. 30   Perf. 10
1160 A236 15k light ultra   .50 .20
1161 A237 20k crimson rose   .60 .20
1162 A236 1 l light green   1.25 .75
    Nos. 1160-1162 (3)   2.35 1.15
Intl. Military Soccer Championship games, Istanbul, Aug. 30.

Sureté Monument, Ankara A238

20k, Dolma Bahce Palace. 30k, Police College, Ankara. 45k, Police Martyrs' Monument, Istanbul.

1955, Sept. 5   Perf. 10
Inscribed: "Enterpol Istanbul 1955"
1163 A238 15k blue green   .20 .20
1164 A238 20k brt violet   .20 .20
1165 A238 30k gray black   .30 .20
1166 A238 45k lt brown   .70 .40
    Nos. 1163-1166 (4)   1.40 1.00
24th general assembly of the Intl. Criminal Police, Istanbul, Sept. 5-9.

Early Telegraph Transmitter A239

Modern Transmitter A240

Perf. 13½x14, 14x13½
1955, Sept. 10   Photo.
1167 A239 15k olive   .20 .20
1168 A240 20k crimson rose   .20 .20
1169 A239 45k fawn   .40 .20
1170 A240 60k ultra   .40 .40
    Nos. 1167-1170 (4)   1.20 1.00
Centenary of telecommunication.

Academy of Science, Istanbul A241

Designs: 20k, University. 60k, Hilton Hotel. 1 l, Kiz Kulesi (Leander's Tower).

1955, Sept. 12   Perf. 13½x14
1171 A241 15k yellow orange   .20 .20
1172 A241 20k crimson rose   .20 .20
1173 A241 60k purple   .30 .20
1174 A241 1 l deep green   .55 .40
    Nos. 1171-1174 (4)   1.25 1.00
10th meeting of the governors of the Intl. Bank of Reconstruction and Development and the Intl. Monetary Fund, Istanbul, Sept. 12-16.

Surlari, Istanbul A242

Mosque of Sultan Ahmed — A243

Congress Emblem — A244

Designs: 30k, Haghia Sophia. 75k, Map of Constantinople, by Christoforo Buondelmonti, 1422.

1955, Sept. 15   Litho.   Perf. 11½
1175 A242 15k grnsh blk & Prus grn   .35 .20
1176 A243 20k vermilion & org   .25 .20
1177 A242 30k sepia & vio brn   .25 .20
1178 A243 75k ultramarine   .70 .50
    Nos. 1175-1178 (4)   1.55 1.10
10th Intl. Congress of Byzantine Research, Istanbul, Sept. 15-21, 1955.

1955, Sept. 26   Perf. 10½x11
30k, Chalet in Istanbul. 55k, Bridges.

Inscribed: "Beynelmiel X. Vol Kongresi Istanbul 1955"
1179 A244 20k red violet   .20 .20
1180 A244 30k dk grn & yel grn   .20 .20
1181 A244 55k dp bl & brt bl   .75 .40
    Nos. 1179-1181 (3)   1.15 .80
10th International Transportation Congress.

Map of Turkey, Showing Population Increase A245

1955, Oct. 22 Unwmk. Perf. 10
Map in Rose
1182 A245 15k lt & dk gray & red .30 .20
1183 A245 20k lt & dk vio & red .20 .20
1184 A245 30k lt & dk ultra & red .25 .20
1185 A245 60k lt & dk bl grn & red .60 .25
Nos. 1182-1185 (4) 1.35 .85
Census of 1955.

Waterfall, Antalya — A246

Alanya and Seljukide Dockyards A247

Designs: 30k, Theater at Aspendos. 45k, Ruins at Side. 50k, View of Antalya. 65k, St. Nicholas Church at Myra (Demre) and St. Nicholas.

Perf. 14x13½, 13½x14
1955, Dec. 10 Photo. Unwmk.
1186 A246 18k bl, ol grn & ultra .20 .20
1187 A247 20k blue, ultra & brn .20 .20
1188 A247 30k dl grn, ol bis & grn .20 .20
1189 A246 45k yel grn & brn 1.00 .45
1190 A246 50k Prus grn & ol bis .25 .20
1191 A247 65k orange ver & blk .40 .30
Nos. 1186-1191 (6) 2.25 1.55

Kemal Atatürk — A248

1955-56 Litho. Perf. 12½
1192 A248 0.50k carmine .20 .20
1193 A248 1k yellow orange .20 .20
1194 A248 2k brt blue .20 .20
1195 A248 3k scarlet .20 .20
1196 A248 5k lt brown .20 .20
1197 A248 6k lt blue grn .20 .20
1198 A248 10k blue green .20 .20
1199 A248 18k rose violet .20 .20
1200 A248 20k lt violet bl .25 .20
1201 A248 25k olive green .30 .20
1202 A248 30k violet .35 .20
1203 A248 40k fawn .45 .20
1204 A248 75k slate blue 1.25 .20
Nos. 1192-1204 (13) 4.20 2.60
Issue dates: 3k, 1955. Others, 1956.

Tomb at Nigde — A249

Zubeyde Hanum — A250

1956, Apr. 12 Perf. 10½
1205 A249 40k violet bl & bl .20 .20
25th anniv. of the Turkish History Society. The tomb of Hüdavent Hatun, a sultan's daughter, exemplifies Seljukian architecture of the 14th century.

1956, May 13 Perf. 11
1206 A250 20k pale brn & dk brn .20 .20
Imperf
1207 A250 20k lt grn & dk grn .45 .25
Mother's Day; Zubeyde Hanum, mother of Kemal Ataturk.

Shah and Queen of Iran A251

1956, May 15 Unwmk. Perf. 11
1208 A251 100k grn & pale grn 1.50 1.00
Imperf
1209 A251 100k red & pale grn 10.00 5.00
Visit of the Shah and Queen of Iran to Turkey, May 15.

Erenkoy Sanitarium A252

1956, July 31 Perf. 11
1210 A252 50k dk bl grn & pink .40 .20
Anti-Tuberculosis work among PTT employees.

Symbol of Izmir Fair — A253

A254

1956, Aug. 20 Perf. 11
1211 A253 45k brt green .20 .20
Souvenir Sheet
Imperf
1212 A254 Sheet of 2 1.40 .80
a. 50k rose red .25 .20
b. 50k bright ultramarine .25 .20
25th Intl. Fair, Izmir, 8/20-9/20. See #C28.

Hands Holding Bottled Serpent — A255

1956, Sept. 10 Litho. Perf. 10½
1213 A255 25k multicolored .20 .20
a. Tete beche pair 1.25
25th Intl. Anti-Alcoholism Congress, Istanbul Sept. 10-15.
Printed both in regular sheets and in sheets with alternate vertical rows inverted.

Medical Center at Kayseri — A256

Sariyar Dam — A257

1956, Nov. 1 Perf. 12½x12
1214 A256 60k violet & yel .20 .20
750th anniv. of the first medical school and clinic in Anatolia.

1956, Dec. 2 Litho. Perf. 10½
1215 A257 20k vermilion .20 .20
1216 A257 20k bright blue .20 .20
Inauguration of Sariyar Dam.

Freestyle Wrestling A258

Mehmet Akif Ersoy — A259

Design: 65k, Greco-Roman wrestling.

1956, Dec. 8 Unwmk. Perf. 10½
1217 A258 40k brt yel grn & brn .35 .20
1218 A258 65k lt bluish gray & dp car .45 .25
16th Olympic Games, Melbourne, Nov. 22-Dec. 8, 1956.

1956, Dec. 26
1219 A259 20k brn & brt yel grn .25 .20
1220 A259 20k rose car & lt gray .25 .20
1221 A259 20k vio bl & brt pink .25 .20
Nos. 1219-1221 (3) .75 .60
20th death anniv. of Mehmet Akif Ersoy, author of the Turkish National Anthem.
Each value bears a different verse of the anthem.

Theater in Troy — A260

Trojan Vase — A261

Design: 30k, Trojan Horse.

Perf. 13½x14, 14x13½
1956, Dec. 31 Photo. Unwmk.
1222 A260 15k green 1.00 .60
1223 A261 20k red violet 1.00 .60
1224 A260 30k chestnut 1.50 .60
Nos. 1222-1224 (3) 3.50 1.80
Excavations at Troy.

Mobile Chest X-Ray Unit A262

Kemal Atatürk — A263

1957, Jan. 1 Litho. Perf. 12
1225 A262 25k ol brn & red .20 .20
Fight against tuberculsois.

1956-57 Perf. 12½
1226 A263 ½k blue green .20 .20
1227 A263 1k yellow orange .20 .20
1228 A263 3k gray olive .20 .20
1229 A263 5k violet .20 .20
1230 A263 6k rose car ('57) .35 .20
1231 A263 10k rose violet .20 .20
1232 A263 12k fawn ('57) .30 .20
1233 A263 15k lt violet bl .20 .20
1234 A263 18k carmine ('57) .30 .20
1235 A263 20k lt brown .20 .20
1236 A263 25k lt blue green .20 .20
1237 A263 30k slate blue .20 .20
1238 A263 40k olive ('57) .40 .20
1239 A263 50k orange .35 .20
1240 A263 60k brt blue ('57) .50 .20
1241 A263 70k Prus green ('57) 1.75 .25
1242 A263 75k brown 1.00 .25
Nos. 1226-1242 (17) 6.75 3.50

Pres. Heuss of Germany — A264

1957, May 5 Unwmk. Perf. 10½
1243 A264 40k yellow & brown .20 .20
Visit of Pres. Theodor Heuss of Germany to Turkey, May 5. See No. C29.

View of Bergama and Ruin A265

40k, Dancers in kermis at Bergama.

1957, May 24
1244 A265 30k brown .20 .20
1245 A265 40k green .25 .20
20th anniv. of the kermis at Bergama (Pergamus).

Symbols of Industry and Flags A266

1957, July 1 Photo. Perf. 13½x14
1246 A266 25k violet .20 .20
1247 A266 40k gray blue .20 .20
Turkish-American collaboration, 10th anniv.

Osman Hamdi Bey A267

Hittite Sun Course from Alaça Höyük — A268

1957, July 6   *Perf. 10½*
1248 A267 20k beige, pale brn & blk   .30 .20
1249 A268 30k Prussian green   .35 .20

75th anniv. of the Academy of Art. The 20k exists with "cancellation" omitted.

King of Afghanistan — A269

1957, Sept. 1   Litho.   *Perf. 10½*
1250 A269 45k car lake & pink   .20 .20

Visit of Mohammed Zahir Shah, King of Afghanistan, to Turkey. See No. C30.

Medical Center, Amasya A270

Design: 65k, Suleiman Medical Center.

1957, Sept. 29   Unwmk.   *Perf. 10½*
1251 A270 25k vermilion & yellow   .20 .20
1252 A270 65k brt grnsh bl & citron .30 .20

11th general meeting of the World Medical Assoc.

Mosque of Suleiman A271

Architect Mimar Koca Sinan (1489-1587) A272

1957, Oct. 18   *Perf. 11*
1253 A271 20k gray green   .20 .20
1254 A272 100k brown   .30 .25

400th anniv. of the opening of the Mosque of Suleiman, Istanbul.

No. 1073 Surcharged with New Value and "ISTANBUL Filatelik n. Sergisi 1957"

1957, Nov. 11   Photo.   *Perf. 13½*
1255 A208 50k on 2 l brt ultra   .25 .20

1957 Istanbul Philatelic Exhibition.

Forestation Map of Turkey — A273

25k, Forest & hand planting tree, vert.

1957, Nov. 18   Litho.   *Perf. 10½*
1256 A273 20k green & brown   .20 .20
1257 A273 25k emerald & bl grn   .20 .20

Centenary of forestry in Turkey. Nos. 1256-1257 each come with two different tabs attached (four tabs in all) bearing various quotations.

A274

A275

1957, Nov. 23
1258 A274 50k pink, vio, red & yel   .30 .20

400th death anniv. of Fuzuli (Mehmet Suleiman Ogioui), poet.

1957, Nov. 28   Photo.   *Perf. 14x13½*
1259 A275 65k dk Prus blue   .20 .20
1260 A275 65k rose violet   .20 .20

Benjamin Franklin (1707-1790).

Green Dome, Tomb of Mevlana, at Konya — A276   Mevlana — A278

Konya Museum A277

Perf. 11x10½, 10½x11
1957, Dec. 17   Litho.   Unwmk.
1261 A276 50k green, bl & vio   .20 .20
1262 A277 100k dark blue   .30 .20

Miniature Sheet
Imperf
1263 A278 100k multicolored   1.25 1.00

Jalal-udin Mevlana (1207-1273), Persian poet and founder of the Mevlevie dervish order. No. 1263 contains one stamp 32x42mm.

Kemal Atatürk (Double Frame; Serifs) — A279

1957   Unwmk.   *Perf. 11½*
    Size: 18x22mm
1264 A279 ½k lt brown   .20 .20
1265 A279 1k lt violet bl   .20 .20
1266 A279 2k black violet   .20 .20
1267 A279 3k orange   .20 .20
1268 A279 5k blue green   .20 .20
1269 A279 6k dk slate grn   .20 .20
1270 A279 10k violet   .20 .20
1271 A279 12k brt green   .20 .20
1272 A279 15k dk blue grn   .20 .20
1273 A279 18k rose carmine   .20 .20
1274 A279 20k brown   .20 .20
1275 A279 25k brown red   .20 .20
1276 A279 30k brt blue   .20 .20
1277 A279 40k slate blue   .20 .20
1278 A279 50k yellow orange   .20 .20
1279 A279 60k black   .25 .20
1280 A279 70k rose violet   .25 .20
1281 A279 75k gray olive   .30 .20
    Size: 21x29mm
1282 A279 100k carmine   .65 .20
1283 A279 250k olive   2.00 .20
    Nos. 1264-1283 (20)   6.45 4.00

College Emblem — A280   View of Adana — A281

1958, Jan. 16   Litho.   *Perf. 10½x11*
1288 A280 20k bister, ind & org   .20 .20
1289 A280 25k dk blue, bis & org   .20 .20

"Turkiye" on top of 25k. 75th anniv. of the College of Economics and Commerce, Istanbul.

1958   Photo.   *Perf. 11½*
    Size: 26x20½mm
1290 A281 5k Adana   .20 .20
1291 A281 5k Adapazari   .20 .20
1292 A281 5k Adiyaman   .20 .20
1293 A281 5k Afyon   .20 .20
1294 A281 5k Amasya   .20 .20
1295 A281 5k Ankara   .20 .20
1296 A281 5k Antakya   .20 .20
1297 A281 5k Antalya   .20 .20
1298 A281 5k Artvin   .20 .20
1299 A281 5k Aydin   .20 .20
1300 A281 5k Balikesir   .20 .20
1301 A281 5k Bilecik   .20 .20
1302 A281 5k Bingol   .20 .20
1303 A281 5k Bitlis   .20 .20
1304 A281 5k Bolu   .20 .20
1305 A281 5k Burdur   .20 .20
1306 A281 5k Bursa   .20 .20
1307 A281 5k Canakkale   .20 .20
1308 A281 5k Cankiri   .20 .20
1309 A281 5k Corum   .20 .20
1310 A281 5k Denizli   .20 .20
1311 A281 5k Diyarbakir   .20 .20
    Size: 32½x22mm
1312 A281 20k Adana   .30 .20
1313 A281 20k Adapazari   .30 .20
1314 A281 20k Adiyaman   .30 .20
1315 A281 20k Afyon   .30 .20
1316 A281 20k Amasya   .30 .20
1317 A281 20k Ankara   .30 .20
1318 A281 20k Antakya   .30 .20
1319 A281 20k Antalya   .30 .20
1320 A281 20k Artvin   .30 .20
1321 A281 20k Aydin   .30 .20
1322 A281 20k Balikesir   .30 .20
1323 A281 20k Bilecik   .30 .20
1324 A281 20k Bingol   .30 .20
1325 A281 20k Bitlis   .30 .20
1326 A281 20k Bolu   .30 .20
1327 A281 20k Burdur   .30 .20
1328 A281 20k Bursa   .30 .20
1329 A281 20k Canakkale   .30 .20

1330 A281 20k Cankiri   .30 .20
1331 A281 20k Corum   .30 .20
1332 A281 20k Denizli   .30 .20
1333 A281 20k Diyarbakir   .30 .20
    Nos. 1290-1333 (44)   11.00 8.80

1959
    Size: 26x20½mm
1334 A281 5k Edirne   .20 .20
1335 A281 5k Elazig   .20 .20
1336 A281 5k Erzincan   .20 .20
1337 A281 5k Erzurum   .20 .20
1338 A281 5k Eskisehir   .20 .20
1339 A281 5k Gaziantep   .20 .20
1340 A281 5k Giresun   .20 .20
1341 A281 5k Gumusane   .20 .20
1342 A281 5k Hakkari   .20 .20
1343 A281 5k Isparta   .20 .20
1344 A281 5k Istanbul   .20 .20
1345 A281 5k Izmir   .20 .20
1346 A281 5k Izmit   .20 .20
1347 A281 5k Karakose   .20 .20
1348 A281 5k Kars   .20 .20
1349 A281 5k Kastamonu   .20 .20
1350 A281 5k Kayseri   .20 .20
1351 A281 5k Kirklareli   .20 .20
1352 A281 5k Kirsehir   .20 .20
1353 A281 5k Konya   .20 .20
1354 A281 5k Kutahya   .20 .20
1355 A281 5k Malatya   .20 .20
    Size: 32½x22mm
1356 A281 20k Edirne   .30 .20
1357 A281 20k Elazig   .30 .20
1358 A281 20k Erzincan   .30 .20
1359 A281 20k Erzurum   .30 .20
1360 A281 20k Eskisehir   .30 .20
1361 A281 20k Gaziantep   .30 .20
1362 A281 20k Giresun   .30 .20
1363 A281 20k Gumusane   .30 .20
1364 A281 20k Hakkari   .30 .20
1365 A281 20k Isparta   .30 .20
1366 A281 20k Istanbul   .30 .20
1367 A281 20k Izmir   .30 .20
1368 A281 20k Izmit   .30 .20
1369 A281 20k Karakose   .30 .20
1370 A281 20k Kars   .30 .20
1371 A281 20k Kastamonu   .30 .20
1372 A281 20k Kayseri   .30 .20
1373 A281 20k Kirklareli   .30 .20
1374 A281 20k Kirsehir   .30 .20
1375 A281 20k Konya   .30 .20
1376 A281 20k Kutahya   .30 .20
1377 A281 20k Malatya   .30 .20
    Nos. 1334-1377 (44)   11.00 8.80

1960
    Size: 26x20½mm
1378 A281 5k Manisa   .20 .20
1379 A281 5k Maras   .20 .20
1380 A281 5k Mardin   .20 .20
1381 A281 5k Mersin   .20 .20
1382 A281 5k Mugla   .20 .20
1383 A281 5k Mus   .20 .20
1384 A281 5k Nevsehir   .20 .20
1385 A281 5k Nigde   .20 .20
1386 A281 5k Ordu   .20 .20
1387 A281 5k Rize   .20 .20
1388 A281 5k Samsun   .20 .20
1389 A281 5k Siirt   .20 .20
1390 A281 5k Sinop   .20 .20
1391 A281 5k Sivas   .20 .20
1392 A281 5k Tekirdag   .20 .20
1393 A281 5k Tokat   .20 .20
1394 A281 5k Trabzon   .20 .20
1395 A281 5k Tunceli   .20 .20
1396 A281 5k Urfa   .20 .20
1397 A281 5k Usak   .20 .20
1398 A281 5k Van   .20 .20
1399 A281 5k Yozgat   .20 .20
1400 A281 5k Zonguldak   .20 .20
    Size: 32½x22mm
1401 A281 20k Manisa   .30 .20
1402 A281 20k Maras   .30 .20
1403 A281 20k Mardin   .30 .20
1404 A281 20k Mersin   .30 .20
1405 A281 20k Mugla   .30 .20
1406 A281 20k Mus   .30 .20
1407 A281 20k Nevsehir   .30 .20
1408 A281 20k Nigde   .30 .20
1409 A281 20k Ordu   .30 .20
1410 A281 20k Rize   .30 .20
1411 A281 20k Samsun   .30 .20
1412 A281 20k Siirt   .30 .20
1413 A281 20k Sinop   .30 .20
1414 A281 20k Sivas   .30 .20
1415 A281 20k Tekirdag   .30 .20
1416 A281 20k Tokat   .30 .20
1417 A281 20k Trabzon   .30 .20
1418 A281 20k Tunceli   .30 .20
1419 A281 20k Urfa   .30 .20
1420 A281 20k Usak   .30 .20
1421 A281 20k Van   .30 .20
1422 A281 20k Yozgat   .30 .20
1423 A281 20k Zonguldak   .30 .20
    Nos. 1378-1423 (46)   11.50 9.20
    Nos. 1290-1423 (134)   33.50 26.80

Ruins at Pamukkale
A282

Designs: 25k, Travertines at Pamukkale.

1958, May 18   Litho.   Perf. 12
1424 A282 20k brown   .20 .20
1425 A282 25k blue   .20 .20

"Industry"
A283

Symbolizing New
Europe
A284

1958, Oct. 10   Unwmk.   Perf. 10½
1426 A283 40k slate blue   .20 .20

National Industry Exhibition.

Europa Issue
1958, Oct. 10
1427 A284 25k vio & dull pink   .50 .25
1428 A284 40k brt ultra   .50 .25

Letters
A285

1958, Oct. 5
1429 A285 20k orange & blk   .20 .20

Intl. Letter Writing Week, Oct. 5-11.

Atatürk 20th Anniv. Death — A286

1958, Nov. 10   Perf. 12
1430   25k Flame and mausoleum   .20 .20
1431   75k Atatürk   .25 .20
a. A286 Pair, #1430-1431   .45 .25

20th death anniv. of Kemal Ataturk.

Emblem — A288

1959, Jan. 10   Litho.   Perf. 10
1432 A288 25k dk violet & yel   .20 .20

25th anniv. of the Agricultural Faculty of Ankara University.

Blackboard and School
Emblem — A289

1959, Jan. 15   Perf. 10½
1433 A289 75k black & yellow   .20 .20

75th anniv. of the establishment of a secondary boys' school in Istanbul.

State
Theater,
Ankara
A290

Design: 25k, Portrait of Sinasi.

1959, Mar. 30   Unwmk.   Perf. 10½
1434 A290 20k red brn & emer   .20 .20
1435 A290 25k Prus grn & org   .20 .20

Centenary of the Turkish theater; Sinasi, writer of the first Turkish play in 1859.

Globe and
Stars
A291

1959, Apr. 4   Perf. 10
1436 A291 105k red   .20 .20
1437 A291 195k green   .40 .25

10th anniversary of NATO.

Aspendos
Theater
A292

1959, May 1   Litho.   Perf. 10½
1438 A292 20k bis brn & vio   .20 .20
1439 A292 20k grn & ol bis   .20 .20

Aspendos (Belkins) Festival.

No. B70 Surcharged in Ultramarine

1959, May 5
1440 SP25 105k on 15k + 5k org   .35 .20

Council of Europe, 10th anniversary.

Basketball — A293

1959, May 21   Perf. 10
1441 A293 25k red org & dk bl   .20 .20

11th European and Mediterranean Basketball Championship.

"Karadeniz"
A294

Telegraph
Mast — A295

Kemal
Atatürk — A296

Designs: 1k, Turkish Airlines' SES plane. 10k, Grain elevator, Ankara. 15k, Iron and Steel Works, Karabück. 20k, Euphrates Bridge, Birecik. 25k, Zonguldak Harbor. 30k, Gasoline refinery, Batman. 40k, Rumeli Hisari Fortress. 45k, Sugar factory, Konya. 55k, Coal mine, Zonguldak. 75k, Railway. 90k, Crane loading ships. 100k, Cement factory, Ankara. 120k, Highway. 150k, Harvester. 200k, Electric transformer.

Perf. 10½, 11, 11½, 12½, 13½
1959-60   Litho.   Unwmk.
1442 A294   1k indigo   .20 .20
1443 A294   5k brt blue ('59)   .20 .20
1444 A294   10k blue   .20 .20
1445 A294   15k brown   .20 .20
1446 A294   20k slate green   .20 .20
1447 A294   25k violet   .20 .20
1448 A294   30k lilac   .25 .20
1449 A294   40k blue   .20 .20
1450 A294   45k dull violet   .20 .20
1451 A294   55k olive brown   .25 .20
1452 A295   60k green   .65 .20
1453 A295   75k gray olive   2.25 .20
1454 A294   90k dark blue   3.25 .20
1455 A295 100k gray   2.25 .20
1456 A294 120k magenta   1.90 .20
1457 A294 150k orange   3.25 .30
1458 A294 200k yellow green   3.25 .30
1459 A296 250k black brown   3.25 .40
1460 A296 500k dark blue   6.75 .60
  Nos. 1442-1460 (19)   28.90 4.60

Postage Due Stamps of 1936 Surcharged

1959, June 1   Perf. 11½
1461 D6 20k on 20pa brown   .20 .20
1462 D6 20k on 2k lt blue   .20 .20
1463 D6 20k on 3k lt blue   .20 .20
1464 D6 20k on 5k Prus bl   .20 .20
1465 D6 20k on 12k brt rose   .20 .20
  Nos. 1461-1465 (5)   1.00 1.00

Anchor
Emblem — A297

Design: 40k, Sea Horse emblem.

1959, July 4   Perf. 11
1466 A297 30k multicolored   .20 .20
1467 A297 40k multicolored   .20 .20

50th anniv. of the Merchant Marine College.

11th
Century
Warrior
A298

1959, Aug. 26   Litho.   Perf. 11
1468 A298 2½ l rose lil & lt bl   .70 .50

Battle of Malazkirt, 888th anniversary.

A299

Ornament — A300

Design: 40k, Mosque.

1959, Oct. 19   Unwmk.   Perf. 12½
1469 A299 30k black & red   .20 .20
1470 A299 40k lt blue, blk & ocher .20 .20
1471 A300 75k dp blue, yel & red   .30 .20
  Nos. 1469-1471 (3)   .70 .60

Turkish Artists Congress, Ankara.

Kemal
Atatürk — A301

Litho.; Center Embossed
1959, Nov. 10   Perf. 14
1472 A301 500k dark blue   1.75 .90
a. Min. sheet of 1, red, imperf.   2.75 2.00

School
of
Political
Science,
Ankara
A302

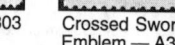

Emblem — A303

Crossed Swords
Emblem — A304

1959, Dec. 4   Photo.   Perf. 13½
1473 A302 40k green & brown   .20 .20
1474 A302 40k red brown & bl   .20 .20
1475 A303 1 l lt & dk vio & buff   .30 .20
  Nos. 1473-1475 (3)   .70 .60

Political Science School, Ankara, cent.

Inscribed: "Kara Harbokulunum 125 Yili"

Design: 40k, Bayonet and flame.

1960, Feb. 28   Litho.   Perf. 10½
1476 A304 30k vermilion & org   .20 .20
1477 A304 40k brown, car & yel   .20 .20

125th anniv. of the Territorial War College.

Window on
World and
WRY Emblem
A305

Spring Flower Festival — A306

150k, Symbolic shanties & uprooted oak emblem.

1960, Apr. 7

1478	A305	90k brt grnsh bl & blk	.20	.20
1479	A305	105k yellow & blk	.30	.20

World Refugee Year, 7/1/59-6/30/60.

1960, June 4   Photo.   Perf. 11½
Granite Paper

1480	A306	30k Carnations	.20	.20
1481	A306	40k Jasmine	.25	.20
1482	A306	75k Rose	.45	.20
1483	A306	105k Tulip	.65	.30
	Nos. 1480-1483 (4)		1.55	.90

Atatürk Square, Nicosia A307

Design: 105k, Map of Cyprus.

1960, Aug. 16   Litho.   Perf. 10½

1484	A307	40k blue & pink	.20	.20
1485	A307	105k blue & yellow	.25	.20

Independence of the Republic of Cyprus.

Women and Nest A308

Design: 30k, Globe and emblem.

1960, Aug. 22   Photo.   Perf. 11½

1486	A308	30k lt vio & yel	.20	.20
1487	A308	75k grnsh bl & gray	.25	.20

16th meeting of the Women's Intl. Council.

Soccer A309

#1489, Basketball. #1490, Wrestling. #1491, Hurdling. #1492, Steeplechase.

1960, Aug. 25

1488	A309	30k yellow green	.20	.20
1489	A309	30k black	.20	.20
1490	A309	30k slate blue	.20	.20
1491	A309	30k purple	.20	.20
1492	A309	30k brown	.20	.20
a.	Sheet of 25, #1488-1492		12.00	7.00
	Nos. 1488-1492 (5)		1.00	1.00

17th Olympic Games, Rome, 8/25-9/11. Printed in sheets of 25 (5x5) with every horizontal and every vertical row containing one of each design. Also printed in normal sheets of 100.

Common Design Types
pictured following the introduction.

Europa Issue, 1960
Common Design Type
1960, Sept. 19
Size: 33x22mm

1493	CD3	75k green & bl grn	.85	.50
1494	CD3	105k dp bl & lt bl	1.25	.85

Agah Efendi and Front Page of Turcamani Ahval — A310

UN Emblem and Torch — A311

1960, Oct. 21   Photo.   Perf. 11½

1495	A310	40k brown blk & sl	.20	.20
1496	A310	60k brn blk & bis brn	.20	.20

Centenary of Turkish journalism.

1960, Oct. 24   Unwmk.

Design: 105k, UN headquarters building and UN emblem forming "15," horiz.

1497	A311	90k brt bl & dk bl	.20	.20
1498	A311	105k lt bl grn & brn	.25	.20

15th anniversary of the United Nations.

Army Emblem A312

Tribunal A313

Design: 195k, "Justice," vert.

1960, Oct. 14   Litho.   Perf. 13

1499	A312	40k violet & bister	.20	.20
1500	A313	105k red, gray & brn	.25	.20
1501	A313	195k grn, rose red & brn	.45	.20
	Nos. 1499-1501 (3)		.90	.60

Trial of ex-President Celal Bayar and ex-Premier Adnan Menderes.

Revolutionaries and Statue — A314

Prancing Horse, Broken Chain — A315

Designs: 30k, Ataturk and hand holding torch. 105k, Youth, soldier and broken chain.

1960, Dec. 1   Photo.   Perf. 14½

1502	A314	10k gray & blk	.20	.20
1503	A314	30k purple	.20	.20
1504	A315	40k brt red & blk	.20	.20
1505	A314	105k blue blk & red	.40	.20
	Nos. 1502-1505 (4)		1.00	.80

Revolution of May 27, 1960.

Faculty Building A316

Sculptured Head of Atatürk — A317

Designs: 40k, Map of Turkey and sun disk.

1961, Jan. 9   Litho.   Perf. 13

1506	A316	30k slate grn & gray	.20	.20
1507	A316	40k brn blk & bis brn	.20	.20
1508	A317	60k dk green & buff	.25	.20
	Nos. 1506-1508 (3)		.65	.60

25th anniv. of the Faculty of Languages, History and Geography, University of Ankara.

Communication and Transportation — A318

40k, Highway construction, telephone & telegraph. 75k, New parliament building, Ankara.

1961, Apr. 27   Unwmk.   Perf. 13

1509	A318	30k dull vio & blk	.20	.20
1510	A318	40k green & black	.35	.20
1511	A318	75k dull blue & blk	.45	.20
	Nos. 1509-1511 (3)		1.00	.60

9th conference of ministers of the Central Treaty Org. (CENTO), Ankara.

Flag and People — A319

Legendary Wolf and Osman Warriors A320

Design: 60k, "Progress" (Atatürk showing youth the way).

1961, May 27   Litho.

1512	A319	30k multicolored	.20	.20
1513	A320	40k sl grn & yel	.20	.20
1514	A319	60k grn, pink & dk red	.25	.20
	Nos. 1512-1514 (3)		.65	.60

First anniversary of May 27 revolution.

Rockets A321

Designs: 40k, Crescent and star emblem, "50" and Jet. 75k, Atatürk, eagle and jets, vert.

1961, June 1

1515	A321	30k brn, org yel & blk	.20	.20
1516	A321	40k violet & red	.25	.20
1517	A321	75k slate blk & bis	.55	.25
	Nos. 1515-1517 (3)		1.00	.65

50th anniversary of Turkey's air force.

Europa Issue, 1961
Common Design Type
1961, Sept. 18   Perf. 13
Size: 32x22mm

1518	CD4	30k dk violet bl	.55	.35
1519	CD4	40k gray	.65	.35
1520	CD4	75k vermilion	1.25	.60
	Nos. 1518-1520 (3)		2.45	1.30

Tulip and Cogwheel A322

Open Book and Olive Branch A324

Torch, Hand and Cogwheel A323

1961, Oct. 21   Unwmk.   Litho.

1521	A322	30k slate, pink & sil	.20	.20
1522	A323	75k ultra, org & blk	.35	.20

Technical and professional schools, cent.

1961, Oct. 29

1523	A324	30k red, blk & olive	.20	.20
1524	A324	75k brt blue, blk & grn	.30	.20

Inauguration of the new Parliament.

Kemal Atatürk

A325	A326

1961-62   Litho.   Perf. 10x10½
Size: 20x25mm

1525	A325	1k brown org ('62)	.25	.20
1526	A325	5k blue	.25	.20
1527	A325	10k sepia	.40	.20
1528	A326	10k car rose	.40	.20
1529	A325	30k dull grn ('62)	2.25	.25
	Size: 21½x31mm			
1530	A325	10 l violet ('62)	7.00	1.00
	Nos. 1525-1530 (6)		10.55	2.05

NATO Emblem and Dove — A327

Scouts at Campfire A328

Design: 105k, NATO emblem, horiz.

1962, Feb. 18   Unwmk.   Perf. 13

1545	A327	75k dl bl, blk & sil	.20	.20
1546	A327	105k crimson, blk & sil	.30	.20

10th anniv. of Turkey's admission to NATO.

1962, July 22   **Litho.**

60k, Scouts with flag. 105k, Scouts saluting.

1547	A328	30k lt grn, blk & red	.20	.20
1548	A328	60k gray, blk & red	.25	.20
1549	A328	105k tan, blk & red	.35	.20
		Nos. 1547-1549 (3)	.80	.60

Turkish Boy Scouts, 50th anniversary.

Soldier Statue — A329

Oxcart from Victory Monument, Ankara A330

Design: 75k, Atatürk.

1962, Aug. 30   **Unwmk.**   **Perf. 13**

1550	A329	30k slate green	.20	.20
1551	A330	40k gray & sepia	.20	.20
1552	A329	75k gray blk & lt gray	.30	.20
		Nos. 1550-1552 (3)	.70	.60

40th anniv. of Battle of Dumlupinar.

Europa Issue, 1962
Common Design Type

1962, Sept. 17

Size: 37x23mm

1553	CD5	75k emerald & blk	.65	.40
1554	CD5	105k red & blk	.85	.50
1555	CD5	195k blue & blk	1.50	.65
		Nos. 1553-1555 (3)	3.00	1.55

Brown imprint.

Virgin Mary's House, Ephesus A331

20pa Stamp of 1863 A332

40k, Inside view after restoration, horiz. 75k, Outside view, horiz. 105k, Statue of Virgin Mary.

1962, Dec. 8   **Photo.**   **Perf. 13½**

1556	A331	30k multicolored	.20	.20
1557	A331	40k multicolored	.20	.20
1558	A331	75k multicolored	.25	.20
1559	A331	105k multicolored	.35	.20
		Nos. 1556-1559 (4)	1.00	.80

1963, Jan. 13   **Perf. 13x13½**

Issue of 1863: 30k, 1pi. 40k, 2pi. 75k, 5pi.

1560	A332	10k yellow, brn & blk	.20	.20
1561	A332	30k rose, lil & blk	.20	.20
1562	A332	40k lt bl, bluish grn & blk	.25	.20
1563	A332	75k red brn, rose & blk	.45	.20
		Nos. 1560-1563 (4)	1.10	.80

Centenary of Turkish postage stamps. See No. 1601, souvenir sheet.

Starving People A333

Designs: 40k, Sowers. 75k, Hands protecting Wheat Emblem, and globe.

1963, Mar. 21   **Unwmk.**   **Perf. 13**

1564	A333	30k dp bl & dk bl	.20	.20
1565	A333	40k brn org & brn	.20	.20
1566	A333	75k grn & dk grn	.25	.20
		Nos. 1564-1566 (3)	.65	.60

FAO "Freedom from Hunger" campaign.

Julian's Column, Ankara — A334

Ethnographic Museum A335

10k, Ankara Citadel. 30k, Gazi Institute of Education. 50k, Atatürk's mausoleum. 60k, President's residence. 100k, Ataturk's home, Cankaya. 150k, Parliament building.

1963   **Litho.**   **Perf. 13**

1568	A334	1k sl grn & yel grn	.20	.20
1569	A334	1k purple	.20	.20
1570	A335	5k sepia & buff	.20	.20
1571	A335	10k lil rose & pale bl	.40	.20
1573	A335	30k black & violet	.90	.20
1574	A335	50k blue & yellow	1.90	.20
1575	A335	60k dk blue gray	1.50	.40
1576	A335	100k olive brown	1.75	.40
1577	A335	150k dull green	6.50	.40
		Nos. 1568-1577 (9)	13.55	2.40

Map of Turkey and Atom Symbol A336

Designs: 60k, Symbols of medicine, agriculture, industry and atom. 100k, Emblem of Turkish Atomic Energy Commission.

1963, May 27   **Unwmk.**   **Perf. 13**

1584	A336	50k red brn & blk	.20	.20
1585	A336	60k grn, dk grn, yel & red	.25	.20
1586	A336	100k violet bl & bl	.55	.30
		Nos. 1584-1586 (3)	1.00	.70

Turkish nuclear research center, 1st anniv.

Meric Bridge A337

Sultan Murad I — A338

Designs: 10k, Üçserefeli Mosque. 60k, Summerhouse, Edirne Palace.

1963, June 17

1587	A338	10k dp bl & yel grn	.20	.20
1588	A337	30k red org & ultra	.20	.20
1589	A337	60k dk bl, red & brn	.20	.20
1590	A338	100k multicolored	.65	.25
		Nos. 1587-1590 (4)	1.25	.85

600th anniv. of the conquest of Edirne (Adrianople).

Soldier and Rising Sun A339

1963, June 28

1591	A339	50k red, blk & gray	.20	.20
1592	A339	100k red, blk & ol	.30	.20

600th anniversary of the Turkish army.

Plowing A340

Mithat Pasha — A341

Design: 50k, Agriculture Bank, Ankara.

Perf. 13x13½, 13½x13

1963, Aug. 27   **Photo.**   **Unwmk.**

1593	A340	30k brt yel grn, red brn & grn	.20	.20
1594	A340	50k pale vio & Prus bl	.20	.20
1595	A341	60k gray & green	.30	.20
		Nos. 1593-1595 (3)	.70	.60

Centenary of Agriculture Bank, Ankara.

Sports and Exhibition Palace, Istanbul and #5 — A342

Designs: 50k, Sultan Ahmed Mosque & Turkey in Asia #22. 60k, View of Istanbul & Turkey in Asia #87. 100k, Rumeli Hisari Fortress & #679. 130k, Ankara Fortress & #C2.

1963, Sept. 7   **Litho.**   **Perf. 13**

1596	A342	10k blk, yel & rose	.20	.20
a.		Rose omitted		
1597	A342	50k blk, grn & rose lil	.30	.20
1598	A342	60k dk brn, dk bl & blk	.50	.20
1599	A342	100k dk vio & lil rose	.75	.20
1600	A342	130k brn, tan & dp org	1.00	.20
		Nos. 1596-1600 (5)	2.75	1.00

"Istanbul 63" Intl. Stamp Exhibition.

Type of 1963 Inscribed: "F.I.P. GÜNÜ" Souvenir Sheet

Issues of 1963: 10k, 20pa. 50k, 1pi. 60k, 2pi. 130k, 5pi.

Unwmk.

1963, Sept. 13   **Litho.**   **Imperf.**

1601	Sheet of 4	1.75	1.50
a.	A332 10k yel, brown & blk	.20	.20
b.	A332 50k lilac, blk & blk	.20	.20
c.	A332 60k bluish grn, lt bl & blk	.30	.20
d.	A332 130k red brn, pink & blk	.35	.20

Intl. Philatelic Federation.

Europa Issue, 1963
Common Design Type

1963, Sept. 16

Size: 32x24mm

1602	CD6	50k red & black	.60	.25
1603	CD6	130k bl grn, blk & bl	.80	.35

Atatürk and First Parliament Building A343

Atatürk and: 50k, Turkish flag. 60k, New Parliament building.

1963, Oct. 29   **Photo.**   **Perf. 13½**

1604	A343	30k blk, gold, yel & mar	.20	.20
1605	A343	50k dk grn, gold, yel & red	.30	.20
1606	A343	60k dk brn, gold & yel	.40	.20
		Nos. 1604-1606 (3)	.90	.60

40th anniversary of Turkish Republic.

Atatürk, 25th Death Anniv. — A344

1963, Nov. 10

1607	A344	50k red, gold, grn & brn	.25	.20
1608	A344	60k red, gold, bl & brn	.35	.20

NATO, 15th Anniv. A346

130k, NATO emblem and olive branch.

1964, Apr. 4   **Litho.**   **Perf. 13**

1610	A346	50k grnsh bl, vio bl & red	.25	.20
1611	A346	130k red & black	.45	.40

12 Stars and Europa with Torch A347

Design: 130k, Torch and stars.

1964, May 5   **Litho.**   **Perf. 12**

1612	A347	50k red brn, yel & vio bl	.35	.20
1613	A347	130k vio bl, lt bl & org	.60	.40

15th anniversary of Council of Europe.

Recaizade Mahmut Ekrem, Writer — A348

Portraits: 1k, Hüseyin Rahmi Gürpinar, novelist. 5k, Ismail Hakki Izmirli, scientist. 10k, Sevket Dag, painter. 60k, Gazi Ahmet Muhtar Pasha, commander. 100k, Ahmet Rasim, writer. 130k, Salih Zeki, mathematician.

1964   **Litho.**   **Perf. 13½x13**

1614	A348	1k red & blk	.20	.20
1615	A348	5k dull grn & blk	.20	.20
1616	A348	10k tan & blk	.20	.20
1617	A348	50k ultra & dk bl	.70	.20
1618	A348	60k gray & blk	.80	.20
1619	A348	100k grnsh bl & dk bl	.90	.20
1620	A348	130k brt grn & dk grn	4.00	.40
		Nos. 1614-1620 (7)	7.00	1.60

Mosque of Sultan Ahmed A349

Kiz Kulesi, Mersin — A350

Designs: No. 1622, Zeus Temple, Silifke. No. 1623, View of Amasra. No. 1625, Augustus' Gate and minaret, Ankara.

1964, June 11   Unwmk.   Perf. 13
1621	A349	50k gray ol & yel grn	.25	.20
1622	A349	50k claret & car	.25	.20
1623	A349	50k dk bl & vio bl	.25	.20
1624	A350	60k sl grn & dk gray	.35	.20
1625	A350	60k dk brn & org brn	.35	.20
		Nos. 1621-1625 (5)	1.45	1.00

Kars Castle — A351   Alp Arslan, Conqueror of Kars, 1064 — A352

1964, Aug. 16   Unwmk.   Perf. 13
1626	A351	50k blk & pale vio	.20	.20
1627	A352	130k blk, gold, sal & pale vio	.35	.20

900th anniversary of conquest of Kars.

Europa Issue, 1964
Common Design Type
1964, Sept. 14   Litho.   Perf. 13
Size: 22x33mm
1628	CD7	50k org, ind & sil	.90	.50
1629	CD7	130k lt bl, mag & cit	1.75	.85

Fuat, Resit and Ali Pashas — A353

Design: 60k, Mustafa Resit Pasha, vert.

1964, Nov. 3   Perf. 13
Sizes: 48x33mm (50k, 100k); 22x33mm (60k)
1630	A353	50k multicolored	.20	.20
1631	A353	60k multicolored	.30	.20
1632	A353	100k multicolored	.50	.30
		Nos. 1630-1632 (3)	1.00	.70

125th anniversary of reform decrees.

Parachutist — A354

Designs: 90k, Glider, horiz. 130k, Ataturk watching squadron in flight.

1965, Feb. 16   Litho.   Perf. 13
1633	A354	60k lt bl, blk, red & yel	.20	.20
1634	A354	90k bister & multi	.30	.20
1635	A354	130k lt blue & multi	.50	.20
		Nos. 1633-1635 (3)	1.00	.60

Turkish Aviation League, 40th anniv.

Emblem A355

Designs: 50k, Radio mast and waves, vert. 75k, Hand pressing button.

1965, Feb. 24   Unwmk.   Perf. 13
1636	A355	30k multicolored	.20	.20
1637	A355	50k multicolored	.20	.20
1638	A355	75k multicolored	.35	.20
		Nos. 1636-1638 (3)	.75	.60

Telecommunications meeting of the Central Treaty Org., CENTO.

Coast of Ordu — A356

50k, Manavgat Waterfall, Antalya. 60k, Sultan Ahmed Mosque, Istanbul. 100k, Hali Rahman Mosque, Urfa. 130k, Red Tower, Alanya.

1965, Apr. 5   Litho.
1639	A356	30k multicolored	.20	.20
1640	A356	50k multicolored	.25	.20
1641	A356	60k multicolored	.25	.20
1642	A356	100k multicolored	.45	.20
1643	A356	130k multicolored	.65	.20
		Nos. 1639-1643 (5)	1.80	1.00

ITU Emblem, Old and New Communication Equipment — A357

1965, May 17   Perf. 13
1644	A357	50k multicolored	.20	.20
1645	A357	130k multicolored	.55	.25

ITU, centenary.

ICY Emblem A358

1965, June 26   Litho.   Unwmk.
1646	A358	100k red org, red brn & brt grn	.30	.20
1647	A358	130k gray, lil & ol grn	.45	.25

International Cooperation Year.

Hands Holding Book A358a

Map and Flags of Turkey, Iran and Pakistan A358b

1965, July 21   Unwmk.   Perf. 13
1648	A358a	50k org brn, yel & dk brn	.30	.20
1649	A358b	75k dl bl, red, grn blk & org	.45	.20

1st anniv. of the signing of the Regional Cooperation Development Pact by Turkey, Iran and Pakistan.

Kemal Ataturk — A359

1965   Litho.   Perf. 12½
1650	A359	1k brt green	.20	.20
1651	A359	5k violet blue	.20	.20
1652	A359	10k blue	.45	.20
1653	A359	25k gray	1.25	.20
1654	A359	30k magenta	1.50	.20
1655	A359	50k brown	2.50	.25
1656	A359	150k orange	3.00	.50
		Nos. 1650-1656 (7)	9.10	1.75

Europa Issue, 1965
Common Design Type
1965, Sept. 27   Perf. 13
Size: 32x23mm
1665	CD8	50k gray, ultra & grn	1.25	.70
1666	CD8	130k tan, blk & grn	2.25	1.40

Map of Turkey and People A360

Designs: 50k, "1965." 100k, "1965," symbolic eye and man, vert.

Unwmk.
1965, Oct. 24   Litho.   Perf. 13
1667	A360	10k multicolored	.20	.20
1668	A360	50k grn, blk & lt yel grn	.20	.20
1669	A360	100k orange, sl & blk	.40	.20
		Nos. 1667-1669 (3)	.80	.60

Issued to publicize the 1965 census.

Plane over Ankara Castle A361

Designs: 30k, Archer and Ankara castle. 50k, Horsemen with spears (ancient game). 100k, Three stamps and medal. 150k, Hands holding book, vert.

1965, Oct. 25
1670	A361	10k brt vio, yel & red	.20	.20
1671	A361	30k multicolored	.20	.20
1672	A361	50k lt gray ol, ind & red	.20	.20
1673	A361	100k gray & multi	.40	.25
		Nos. 1670-1673 (4)	1.00	.85

Souvenir Sheet
Imperf
1674	A361	150k multicolored	1.10	1.00

1st Natl. Postage Stamp Exhibition "Ankara 65."

Resat Nuri Guntekin, Novelist — A362

Portraits: 5k, Besim Omer Akalin, M.D. 10k, Tevfik Fikret, poet. 25k, Tanburi Cemil, composer. 30k, Ahmet Vifik Pasha, playwright. 50k, Omer Seyfettin, novelist. 60k, Kemalettin Mimaroglu, architect. 150k, Halit Ziya Usakligil, novelist. 220k, Yahya Kemal Beyatli, poet.

1965   Litho.   Perf. 13½x13
Black Portrait and Inscriptions
1675	A362	1k rose	.20	.20
1676	A362	5k blue	.30	.20
1677	A362	10k buff	.30	.20
1678	A362	25k dull red brn	.50	.20
1679	A362	30k gray	.60	.20
1680	A362	50k orange	1.25	.20
1681	A362	60k red lilac	1.25	.20
1682	A362	150k lt green	1.50	.20
1683	A362	220k tan	2.50	.30
		Nos. 1675-1683 (9)	8.40	1.90

Training Ship Savarona A363

Designs: 60k, Submarine "Piri Reis." 100k, Cruiser "Alpaslan." 130k, Destroyer "Gelibolu." 220k, Destroyer "Gemlik."

1965, Dec. 6   Photo.   Perf. 11½
1684	A363	50k blue & brown	.35	.20
1685	A363	60k blue & black	.50	.20
1686	A363	100k blue & black	.80	.25
1687	A363	130k blue & vio blk	1.25	.40
1688	A363	220k blue & indigo	1.75	.65
		Nos. 1684-1688 (5)	4.65	1.70

First Congress of Turkish Naval Society.

Kemal Ataturk — A364   Halide Edip Adivar, Writer — A365

1965   Litho.   Perf. 13½
Imprint: "Apa Ofset Basimevi"
Black Portrait and Inscriptions
1689	A364	1k rose lilac	.20	.20
1690	A364	5k lt green	.20	.20
1691	A364	10k blue gray	.30	.20
1692	A364	50k olive bister	.50	.20
1693	A364	150k silver	1.50	.20
		Nos. 1689-1693 (5)	2.70	1.00

See Nos. 1724-1728.

1966   Litho.   Perf. 13½

Portraits: 25k, Huseyin Sadettin Arel, writer and composer. 30k, Kamil Akdik, graphic artist. 60k, Abdurrahman Seref, historian. 130k, Naima, historian.

1694	A365	25k gray & brn blk	.50	.20
1695	A365	30k rose vio & blk brn	.50	.20
1696	A365	50k blue & black	.55	.20
1697	A365	60k lt grn & blk brn	.55	.20
1698	A365	130k lt vio bl & blk	1.00	.20
		Nos. 1694-1698 (5)	3.10	1.00

Tiles, Green Mausoleum, Bursa — A366

Tiles: 60k, Spring flowers, Hurrem Sultan Mausoleum, Istanbul. 130k, Stylized flowers, 16th century.

1966, May 15   Litho.   Perf. 13½x13
1699	A366	50k multicolored	.50	.20
1700	A366	60k multicolored	.80	.30
1701	A366	130k multicolored	1.25	.35
		Nos. 1699-1701 (3)	2.55	.85

On No. 1700 the black ink was applied by a thermographic process and varnished, producing a shiny, raised effect to imitate the embossed tiles of the design source.

Volleyball
A367

View of Bodrum
A368

1966, May 20   *Perf. 13x13½*
1702 A367 50k tan & multi   .35 .20
    4th Intl. Military Volleyball Championship.

1966, May 25   *Perf. 13x13½, 13½x13*
Views: 30k, Kusadasi. 50k, Anadolu Hisari, Istanbul. 90k, Marmaris. 100k, Izmir.
1703 A368 10k multi   .20 .20
1704 A368 30k multi   .60 .20
1705 A368 50k multi, horiz.   .30 .20
1706 A368 90k multi   .30 .20
1707 A368 100k multi, horiz.   .40 .20
    Nos. 1703-1707 (5)   1.80 1.00

Inauguration of Keban Dam — A369

Design: 60k, View of Keban Dam area.

1966, June 10   *Perf. 13½*
1708 A369 50k multicolored   .20 .20
1709 A369 60k multicolored   .40 .20

Visit of King Faisal of Saudi Arabia
A370

1966, Aug. 29   *Litho.*   *Perf. 13½x13*
1710 A370 100k car rose & dk car   .55 .20

Symbolic Postmark and Stamp
A371

Designs: 60k, Flower made of stamps. 75k, Stamps forming display frames. 100k, Map of Balkan states, magnifying glass and stamp.

1966, Sept. 3   *Perf. 13½x13*
1711 A371 50k multicolored   .20 .20
1712 A371 60k multicolored   .20 .20
1713 A371 75k multicolored   .40 .20
    Nos. 1711-1713 (3)   .80 .60

Souvenir Sheet
Imperf
1714 A371 100k multicolored   1.50 1.25
    2nd "Balkanfila" stamp exhibition, Istanbul.

Sultan Suleiman on Horseback
A372

90k, Mausoleum, Istanbul. 130k, Suleiman.

1966, Sept. 6   *Perf. 13½x13*
1715 A372 60k multicolored   .40 .20
1716 A372 90k multicolored   .70 .25
1717 A372 130k multicolored   1.40 .40
    Nos. 1715-1717 (3)   2.50 .85

Sultan Suleiman the Magnificent (1496?-1566). On No. 1717 a gold frame was applied by raised thermographic process.

Europa Issue, 1966
Common Design Type
1966, Sept. 26   *Litho.*   *Perf. 13x13½*
Size: 22x33mm
1718 CD9 50k lt bl, vio bl & blk   1.10 .65
  a.   Black (inscriptions & imprint) omitted   65.00
1719 CD9 130k lil, dk red lil & blk   2.25 1.10

Symbols of Education, Science and Culture
A373

1966, Nov. 4   *Litho.*   *Perf. 13*
1720 A373 130k brn, bis brn & yel   .45 .20
    UNESCO, 20th anniversary.

University of Technology
A374

Designs: 100k, Atom symbol. 130k, design symbolizing sciences.

1966, Nov. 15
1721 A374 50k multicolored   .20 .20
1722 A374 100k multicolored   .30 .20
1723 A374 130k multicolored   .50 .30
    Nos. 1721-1723 (3)   1.00 .70

10th anniv. of the Middle East University of Technology.

Ataturk Type of 1965
Imprint: "Kiral Matbaasi - Ist"
1966   *Litho.*   *Perf. 12½*
Black Portrait and Inscriptions
1724 A364 25k yellow   .25 .20
1725 A364 30k pink   .30 .20
1726 A364 50k rose lilac   1.25 .20
1727 A364 90k pale brown   .70 .20
1728 A364 100k gray   1.00 .20
    Nos. 1724-1728 (5)   3.50 1.00

Statue of Ataturk, Ankara — A375

Equestrian Statues of Ataturk: No. 1729A, Statue in Izmir. No. 1729B, Statue in Samsun.

Without Imprint
1967   *Litho.*   *Perf. 13x12½*
Size: 23x16mm
1729 A375 10k black & yellow   .30 .20

Inscribed "1967"
Imprint: Kiral Matbaasi
Size: 22x15mm
1729A A375 10k black & salmon   .30 .20
1729B A375 10k black & lt grn   .30 .20
    Nos. 1729-1729B (3)   .90 .60

Issued for use on greeting cards. See Nos. 1790-1791A, 1911.

Puppets Karagöz and Hacivat — A376

Intl. Tourist Year Emblem and: 60k, Sword and shield game. 90k, Traditional military band. 100k, raised effect.

Perf. 13x13½, 13½x13
1967, Mar. 30   *Litho.*
1730 A376 50k multicolored   .30 .20
1731 A376 60k multicolored   .45 .20
1732 A376 90k multicolored   .55 .25
1733 A376 100k multicolored   .70 .35
    Nos. 1730-1733 (4)   2.00 1.00

Intl. Tourist Year. On No. 1733 the black ink was applied by a thermographic process and varnished, producing a shiny, raised effect.

Woman Vaccinating Child, Knife and Lancet — A377

Fallow Deer — A378

1967, Apr. 1   *Perf. 13x13½*
1734 A377 100k multicolored   .60 .25

250th anniv. of smallpox vaccination (variolation) in Turkey. The gold was applied by a thermographic process and varnished, producing a shiny, raised effect.

1967, Apr. 23   *Litho.*   *Perf. 13x13½*
1735 A378 50k shown   .20 .20
1736 A378 60k Wild goat   .30 .20
1737 A378 100k Brown bear   .45 .20
1738 A378 130k Wild boar   .70 .25
    Nos. 1735-1738 (4)   1.65 .85

Soccer Players and Emblem with Map of Europe
A379

130k, Players at left, smaller emblem.

1967, May 1   *Perf. 13*
1739 A379 50k multicolored   .20 .20
1740 A379 130k yellow & multi   .50 .30
    20th Intl. Youth Soccer Championships.

Sivas Hospital
A380

1967, July 1   *Litho.*   *Perf. 13*
1741 A380 50k multicolored   .40 .20
    750th anniversary of Sivas Hospital.

Selim Sirri Tarcan
A381

60k, Olympic Rings, Baron Pierre de Coubertin.

1967, July 20
1742 A381 50k lt blue & multi   .25 .2
1743 A381 60k lilac & multi   .25 .2
  a.   Pair, #1742-1743   .50 .4
    1st Turkish Olympic competitions.

Ahmed Mithat, Writer — A382

Portraits: 5k, Admiral Turgut Reis. 50k, Sokullu Mehmet, statesman. 100k, Nedim, poet. 150k, Osman Hamdi, painter.

1967   *Litho.*   *Perf. 12½*
1744 A382 1k green & blk   .40 .20
1745 A382 5k dp bister & blk   .40 .20
1746 A382 50k brt violet & blk   .80 .20
1747 A382 100k citron & blk   1.50 .20
1748 A382 150k yellow & blk   2.50 .20
    Nos. 1744-1748 (5)   5.60 1.00

Ruins of St. John's Church, Ephesus
A383

Design: 130k, Inside view of Virgin Mary's House, Ephesus.

1967, July 26   *Perf. 13*
1749 A383 130k multicolored   .25 .20
1750 A383 220k multicolored   .55 .30
    Visit of Pope Paul VI to the House of the Virgin Mary in Ephesus, July 26.

Plate on Firing Grid and Ornaments
A384

1967, Sept. 1
1751 A384 50k pale lil, blk, ind & bl   .30 .20
    5th International Ceramics Exhibition.

View of Istanbul and Emblem
A385

1967, Sept. 4   *Litho.*   *Perf. 13*
1752 A385 130k dk blue & gray   .30 .20
    9th Congress of the Intl. Commission of Large Dams.

Stamps, Ornament and Map of Turkey
A386

Kemal Ataturk
A387

Design: 60k, Grapes and stamps.

1967
1753 A386 50k multicolored .20 .20
1754 A386 60k multicolored .25 .20
a. Souvenir sheet, #1753-1754 1.00 1.00

Intl. Trade Fair, Izmir.

1967 **Litho.** **Perf. 11½x12**
Booklet Stamps
1755 A387 10k black & lt ol grn .30 .30
a. Booklet pane of 10 6.00
b. Booklet pane of 25 12.00
1756 A387 50k black & pale rose .90 .30
a. Booklet pane of 2 2.50
b. Bklt. pane, 5 #1755, 4 #1756 + label 15.00

Symbolic Water Cycle — A388

Human Rights Flame — A390

Child and Angora Cat, Man with Microscope — A389

1967, Dec. 1 **Litho.** **Perf. 13**
1757 A388 90k lt grn, blk & org .25 .20
1758 A388 130k lilac, blk & org .30 .25

Hydrological Decade (UNESCO), 1965-74.

1967, Dec. 23 **Perf. 13**
60k, Horse and man with microscope.
1759 A389 50k multicolored .35 .20
1760 A389 60k multicolored .45 .25

125th anniv. of Turkish veterinary medicine.

1968, Jan. 1 **Perf. 13x13½**
1761 A390 50k rose lil, dk bl & org .20 .20
1762 A390 130k lt bl, dk bl & red org .35 .20

International Human Rights Year.

Archer on Horseback — A391

Miniatures, 16th Century: 50k, Investiture. 60k, Sultan Suleiman the Magnificent receiving an ambassador, vert. 100k, Musicians.

Perf. 13x13½, 13½x13
1968, Mar. 1 **Litho.**
1763 A391 50k multicolored .20 .20
1764 A391 60k multicolored .25 .20
1765 A391 90k multicolored .50 .20
1766 A391 100k multicolored .75 .30
Nos. 1763-1766 (4) 1.70 .90

Kemal Ataturk — A392

1968 **Litho.** **Perf. 12½**
1767 A392 1k dk & lt blue .20 .20
1768 A392 5k dk & lt green .20 .20
1769 A392 50k org brn & yel 1.10 .20
1770 A392 200k dk brown & pink 3.00 .25
Nos. 1767-1770 (4) 4.50 .85

Law Book and Oak Branch A393

Mithat Pasha and Scroll A394

1968, Apr. 1 **Perf. 13**
1771 A393 50k multicolored .30 .20
1772 A394 60k multicolored .35 .20

Centenary of the Court of Appeal.

1968, Apr. 1
Designs: 50k, Scales of Justice. 60k, Ahmet Cevdet Pasha and scroll.
1773 A393 50k multicolored .25 .20
1774 A394 60k multicolored .35 .20

Centenary of the Supreme Court.

Europa Issue, 1968
Common Design Type
1968, May 6 **Litho.** **Perf. 13**
Size: 31½x23mm
1775 CD11 100k pck bl, yel & red 1.75 .75
1776 CD11 130k green, yel & red 3.25 1.25

Yacht Kismet — A395

"Fight Usury" A396

1968, June 15 **Litho.** **Perf. 13**
1777 A395 50k lt ultra & multi .35 .20
Round-the-world trip of the yacht Kismet, Aug. 22, 1965-June 14, 1968.

1968, June 19
1778 A396 50k multicolored .25 .20
Centenary of the Pawn Office, Istanbul.

Sakarya Battle and Independence Medal — A397

130k, Natl. anthem & reverse of medal.

1968, Aug. 30 **Perf. 13x13½**
1779 A397 50k gold & multi .25 .20
1780 A397 130k gold & multi .45 .20

Turkish Independence medal. The gold on Nos. 1779-1780 was applied by a thermographic process and varnished, producing a shiny, raised effect.

Ataturk and Galatasaray High School — A398

50k, "100" and old and new school emblems. 60k, Portraits of Beyazit II and Gulbaba.

1968, Sept. 1 **Litho.**
1781 A398 50k gray & multi .20 .20
1782 A398 60k tan & multi .30 .20
1783 A398 100k lt blue & multi .50 .25
Nos. 1781-1783 (3) 1.00 .65

Centenary of Galatasaray High School.

Charles de Gaulle — A399

1968, Oct. 25 **Litho.** **Perf. 13**
1784 A399 130k multicolored .90 .50

Visit of President Charles de Gaulle of France to Turkey.

Kemal Ataturk — A400

Ataturk and his Speech to Youth — A401

50k, Ataturk's tomb and Citadel of Ankara. 60k, Ataturk looking out a train window. 250k, Framed portrait of Ataturk in military uniform.

1968, Nov. 10
1785 A400 30k orange & blk .30 .20
1786 A400 50k brt grn & sl grn .30 .20
1787 A400 60k bl grn & blk .35 .20
1788 A401 100k blk, gray & brt grn .70 .20
1789 A401 250k multicolored 1.25 .40
Nos. 1785-1789 (5) 2.90 1.20

30th death anniv. of Kemal Ataturk.

Ataturk Statue Type of 1967
Equestrian Statues of Ataturk: No. 1790, Statue in Zonguldak. No. 1791, Statue in Antakya. No. 1791A, Statue in Bursa.

Imprint: Kiral Matbaasi 1968
1968-69 **Litho.** **Perf. 13x12½**
Size: 22x15mm
1790 A375 10k black & lt blue .25 .20
1791 A375 10k blk & brt rose lil .25 .20

Perf. 13½
Imprint: Tifdruk Matbaacilik Sanayii A. S. 1969
Size: 21x16½mm
1791A A375 10k dk grn & tan ('69) .30 .20
Nos. 1790-1791A (3) .80 .60

Ince Minare Mosque, Konya — A402

ILO Emblem A403

Historic Buildings: 10k, Doner Kumbet (tomb), Kayseri. 50k, Karatay Medresse (University Gate), Konya. 100k, Ortakoy Mosque, Istanbul. 200k, Ulu Mosque, Divriki.

1968-69 **Photo.** **Perf. 13x13½**
1792 A402 1k dk brn & buff ('69) .20 .20
1793 A402 10k plum & dl rose ('69) .30 .20
1794 A402 50k dk ol grn & gray .40 .20
1795 A402 100k dk & lt grn ('69) 1.10 .25
1796 A402 200k dp bl & lt bl ('69) 1.75 .35
Nos. 1792-1796 (5) 3.75 1.20

1969, Apr. 15 **Litho.** **Perf. 13**
1797 A403 130k dk red & black .30 .20

ILO, 50th anniv.

Sultana Hafsa, Medical Pioneer A404

1969, Apr. 26 **Litho.** **Perf. 13½x13**
1798 A404 60k multicolored .35 .20

Europa Issue, 1969
Common Design Type
1969, Apr. 28 **Perf. 13**
Size: 32x23mm
1799 CD12 100k dull vio & multi 1.60 .65
1800 CD12 130k gray grn & multi 2.25 1.60

Kemal Ataturk — A405

Map of Istanbul — A407

Ataturk and S.S. Bandirma A406

1969, May 19 **Litho.** **Perf. 13**
1801 A405 50k multicolored .20 .20
1802 A406 60k multicolored .25 .20

50th anniv. of the landing of Kemal Ataturk at Samsun.

1969, May 31
1803 A407 130k vio bl, lt bl, gold & red .35 .20

22nd Congress of the Intl. Chamber of Commerce, Istanbul.

Educational
Progress
A408

Agricultural
Progress
A409

Designs: 90k, Pouring ladle and industrial symbols. 100k, Road sign (highway construction). 180k, Oil industry chart and symbols.

1969   **Litho.**   **Perf. 13½x13**
1804	A408	1k black & gray	.20	.20
1805	A408	1k black & bis brn	.20	.20
1806	A408	1k black & lt grn	.20	.20
1807	A408	1k black & lt vio	.20	.20
1808	A408	1k black & org red	.20	.20
1809	A409	50k brown & ocher	.40	.20
1810	A409	90k blk & grnsh gray	.65	.20
1811	A408	100k black & org red	.90	.20
1812	A408	180k violet & orange	1.60	.20
		Nos. 1804-1812 (9)	4.55	1.80

Issued: 1, 100k, 4/8; 50k, 6/11; 90, 180k, 8/15.

Sultan
Suleiman
Receiving
Sheik Abdul
Latif — A410

Kemal
Ataturk — A411

Designs: 80k, Lady Serving Wine, Safavi miniature, Iran. 130k, Lady on Balcony, Mogul miniature, Pakistan.

1969, July 21   **Litho.**   **Perf. 13**
1813	A410	50k yellow & multi	.30	.20
1814	A410	80k yellow & multi	.50	.20
1815	A410	130k yellow & multi	.85	.35
		Nos. 1813-1815 (3)	1.65	.75

5th anniv. of the signing of the Regional Cooperation for Development Pact by Turkey, Iran and Pakistan.

1969, July 23

Design: 60k, Ataturk monument and bas-relief showing congress.

1816	A411	50k black & gray	.20	.20
1817	A411	60k black & grnsh gray	.30	.20

50th anniversary, Congress of Erzerum.

Sivas
Congress
Delegates
A412

Design: 50k, Congress Hall.

1969, Sept. 4   **Litho.**   **Perf. 13**
1818	A412	50k dk brn & dp rose	.20	.20
1819	A412	60k olive blk & yel	.20	.20

50th anniv. of the Congress of Sivas (preparation for the Turkish war of independence).

Bar Dance — A413

Folk Dances: 50k, Candle dance (çaydaçira). 60k, Scarf dance (halay). 100k, Sword dance (kiliç-kalkan). 130k, Two male dancers (zeybek), vert.

1969, Sept. 9
1820	A413	30k brown & multi	.20	.20
1821	A413	50k multicolored	.35	.20
1822	A413	60k multicolored	.45	.20
1823	A413	100k yellow & multi	.60	.20
1824	A413	130k multicolored	1.00	.40
		Nos. 1820-1824 (5)	2.60	1.20

1914
Airplane
"Prince
Celaleddin"
A414

75k, First Turkish letter carried by air.

1969, Oct. 18   **Litho.**   **Perf. 13**
1825	A414	60k dk blue & blue	.25	.20
1826	A414	75k black & bister	.35	.20

55th anniv. of the first Turkish mail transported by air.

"Kutadgu
Bilig"
A415

1969, Nov. 20   **Litho.**   **Perf. 13**
1827	A415	130k ol bis, brn & gold	.35	.20

900th anniv. of "Kutadgu Bilig," a book about the function of the state, compiled by Jusuf of Balasagun in Tashkent, 1069.

Ataturk's Arrival in Ankara, after a
Painting — A416

Design: 60k, Ataturk and his coworkers in automobiles arriving in Ankara, after a photograph.

1969, Dec. 27   **Litho.**   **Perf. 13**
1828	A416	50k multicolored	.30	.20
1829	A416	60k multicolored	.50	.30

50th anniv. of Kemal Ataturk's arrival in Ankara, Dec. 27, 1919.

Bosporus Bridge, Map of Europe and
Asia — A417

Design: 60k, View of proposed Bosporus Bridge and shore lines.

1970, Feb. 20   **Litho.**   **Perf. 13**
1830	A417	60k gold & multi	1.25	.30
1831	A417	130k gold & multi	2.50	.65

Foundation ceremonies for the bridge across the Bosporus linking Europe and Asia.

Kemal Ataturk
and Signature
A418

Kemal Ataturk
A419

1970   **Litho.**   **Perf. 13**
1832	A418	1k dp orange & brn	.20	.20
1833	A419	5k silver & blk	.20	.20
1834	A419	30k citron & blk	.20	.20
1835	A418	50k lt olive & blk	.45	.20
1836	A419	50k pink & blk	.35	.20
1837	A419	75k lilac & blk	.65	.20
1838	A419	100k blue & blk	.85	.20
		Nos. 1832-1838 (7)	2.90	1.40

Education Year
Emblem — A420

Turkish EXPO
'70
Emblem — A421

1970, Mar. 16
1839	A420	130k ultra, pink & rose lil	.45	.20

International Education Year.

1970, Mar. 27

100k, EXPO '70 emblem & Turkish pavilion.

1840	A421	50k gold & multi	.20	.20
1841	A421	100k gold & multi	.30	.20

EXPO '70 International Exhibition, Osaka, Japan, Mar. 15-Sept. 13.

Opening of
Grand
National
Assembly
A422

Design: 60k, Session of First Grand National Assembly, 1920.

1970, Apr. 23
1842	A422	50k multicolored	.20	.20
1843	A422	60k multicolored	.30	.20

Turkish Grand National Assembly, 50th anniv.

Emblem of
Cartographic
Service
A423

Map of Turkey and Gen. Mehmet
Sevki Pasha — A424

Designs: 60k, Plane and aerial mapping survey diagram. 100k, Triangulation point in mountainous landscape.

Perf. 13½x13 (A423), 13x13½ (A424)
1970, May 2   **Litho.**
1844	A423	50k blue & multi	.20	.20
1845	A424	60k blk, gray grn & brick red	.20	.20
1846	A423	100k multicolored	.30	.20
1847	A424	130k multicolored	.50	.35
		Nos. 1844-1847 (4)	1.20	.90

Turkish Cartographic Service, 75th anniv.

Europa Issue, 1970
Common Design Type

1970, May 4   **Perf. 13**
Size: 37x23mm
1848	CD13	100k ver, blk & org	1.50	.65
1849	CD13	130k dk bl grn, blk & org	3.50	1.10

Inauguration of UPU Headquarters,
Bern — A425

1970, May 20
1850	A425	60k blk & dull blue	.25	.20
1851	A425	130k blk & dl ol grn	.45	.20

Lady with
Mimosa, by
Osman Hamdi
(1842-1910)
A426

Paintings: No. 1853, Deer, by Seker Ahmet (1841-1907). No. 1854, Portrait of Fevzi Cakmak, by Avni Lifij (d. 1927). No. 1855, Sailboats, by Nazmi Ziya (1881-1937); horiz.

1970   **Litho.**   **Perf. 13**
Size: 29x49mm
1852	A426	250k multicolored	1.10	.35
1853	A426	250k multicolored	1.10	.35

Size: 32x49mm
1854	A426	250k multicolored	1.10	.35

Size: 73½x33mm
1855	A426	250k multicolored	1.10	.35
		Nos. 1852-1855 (4)	4.40	1.40

Issued: #1852-1853, 6/15; #1854-1855, 12/15.

Turkish Folk
Art — A427

1970, June 15
1856	A427	50k multicolored	.40	.20

3rd National Stamp Exhibition, ANKARA 70, Oct. 28-Nov. 4. Pane of 50, each stamp setenant with label. This 50k, in pane of 50 without labels, was re-issued Oct. 28 with Nos. 1867-1869.

View of
Fethiye
A428

80k, Seeyo-Se-Pol Bridge, Esfahan, Iran. 130k, Saiful Malook Lake, Pakistan.

1970, July 21   Litho.   *Perf. 13*
1857	A428	60k multicolored	.25	.20
1858	A428	80k multicolored	.30	.20
1859	A428	130k multicolored	.45	.25
		Nos. 1857-1859 (3)	1.00	.65

6th anniv. of the signing of the Regional Cooperation for Development Pact by Turkey, Iran and Pakistan.

Sultan Balim's Tomb — A429

Haci Bektas Veli — A430

30k, Tomb of Haci Bektas Veli, horiz.

1970, Aug. 16   Litho.   *Perf. 13*
1860	A429	30k multicolored	.20	.20
1861	A429	100k multicolored	.40	.20
1862	A430	180k multicolored	.80	.20
		Nos. 1860-1862 (3)	1.40	.60

700th death anniv. of Haci Bektas Veli, mystic.

Hittite Sun Disk and "ISO" A431

1970, Sept. 15
| 1863 | A431 | 110k car rose, gold & blk | .20 | .20 |
| 1864 | A431 | 150k ultra, gold & blk | .30 | .20 |

8th General Council Meeting of the Intl. Standardization Org., Ankara.

UN Emblem, People and Globe — A432

Stamp "Flower" and Book — A433

100k, UN emblem and propeller, horiz.

1970, Oct. 24   Litho.   *Perf. 13*
| 1865 | A432 | 100k gray & multi | .30 | .20 |
| 1866 | A432 | 220k multicolored | .55 | .25 |

25th anniversary of the United Nations.

1970, Oct. 28
Designs: 60k, Ataturk monument and stamps, horiz. 130k, Abstract flower.

| 1867 | A433 | 10k multicolored | .20 | .20 |
| 1868 | A433 | 60k blue & multi | .20 | .20 |

Souvenir Sheet
| 1869 | A433 | 130k dk green & org | 2.00 | 1.50 |

3rd National Stamp Exhibition, ANKARA 70, Oct. 28-Nov. 4. See note below No. 1856.

InönüBattle Scene — A434

Design: No. 1871, Second Battle of Inönü.

1971   Litho.   *Perf. 13*
| 1870 | A434 | 100k multicolored | .50 | .20 |
| 1871 | A434 | 100k multicolored | .50 | .20 |

1st and 2nd Battles of Inönü, 50th anniv. Issue dates: #1870, Jan. 10; #1871, Apr. 1.

Village on River Bank, by Ahmet Sekür — A435

Painting: No. 1872, Landscape, Yildiz Palace Garden, by Ahmet Ragip Bicakcilar.

1971, Mar. 15   Litho.   *Perf. 13*
| 1872 | A435 | 250k multicolored | 1.25 | .40 |
| 1873 | A435 | 250k multicolored | 1.25 | .40 |

See #1901-1902, 1909-1910, 1937-1938.

Campaign Against Discrimination A436

1971, Mar. 21   Litho.   *Perf. 13*
| 1874 | A436 | 100k multicolored | .20 | .20 |
| 1875 | A436 | 250k gray & multi | .45 | .25 |

Intl. Year against Racial Discrimination.

Europa Issue, 1971
Common Design Type
1971, May 3   Litho.   *Perf. 13*
Size: 31½x22½mm
| 1876 | CD14 | 100k lt bl, cl & mag | 2.10 | .70 |
| 1877 | CD14 | 150k dp org, grn & red | 3.50 | 1.00 |

Kemal Ataturk
| A437 | A438 |

1971
1878	A437	5k gray & ultra	.20	.20
1879	A437	25k gray & dk red	.20	.20
1880	A438	25k brown & pink	.20	.20
1881	A437	100k gray & violet	.40	.20
1882	A438	100k green & salmon	.40	.20
1883	A438	250k blue & gray	1.00	.20
1884	A437	400k tan & olive grn	1.10	.20
		Nos. 1878-1884 (7)	3.50	1.40

Pres. Kemal Gürsel — A439

Mosque of Selim, Edirne — A440

1971, May 27   Litho.   *Perf. 13*
| 1885 | A439 | 100k multicolored | .35 | .20 |

Revolution of May 27, 1960; Kemal Gürsel (1895-1966), president.

1971, July 21   Litho.   *Perf. 13*
150k, Religious School, Chaharbagh, Iran. 200k, Badshahi Mosque, Pakistan.

1886	A440	100k multi	.25	.20
1887	A440	150k multi	.35	.20
1888	A440	200k multi, horiz.	.50	.20
		Nos. 1886-1888 (3)	1.10	.60

Regional Cooperation by Turkey, Iran and Pakistan, 7th anniversary.

Alp Arslan and Battle of Malazkirt — A441

Design: 250k, Archers on horseback.

1971, Aug. 26   Litho.   *Perf. 13x13½*
| 1889 | A441 | 100k multicolored | 1.00 | .20 |
| 1890 | A441 | 250k red, org & blk | 1.50 | .40 |

900th anniversary of the Battle of Malazkirt, which established the Seljuk Dynasty in Asia Minor.

Battle of Sakarya — A442

1971, Sept. 13
| 1891 | A442 | 100k violet & multi | .80 | .45 |

50th anniversary of the victory of Sakarya.

Turkey-Bulgaria Railroad — A443

Designs: 110k, Ferry and map of Lake Van. 250k, Turkey-Iran railroad.

1971
1892	A443	100k multicolored	.85	.20
1893	A443	110k multicolored	.85	.20
1894	A443	250k yellow & multi	1.90	.60
		Nos. 1892-1894 (3)	3.60	1.00

Turkish railroad connections with Bulgaria &Iran. Issued: 110, 250k, 9/27; 100k, 10/4.

Netball and Map of Mediterranean A444

200k, Runner and stadium, vert. 250k, Shot put and map of Mediterranean, vert.

1971, Oct. 6
| 1895 | A444 | 100k dull vio & blk | .35 | .20 |
| 1896 | A444 | 200k brn, blk & emer | .55 | .25 |

Souvenir Sheet
Imperf
| 1897 | A444 | 250k ol bis & slate grn | .95 | .85 |

Mediterranean Games, Izmir.

Tomb of Cyrus the Great — A445

Designs: 100k, Harpist, Persian mosaic, vert. 150k, Ataturk and Riza Shah Pahlavi.

1971, Oct. 13
1898	A445	25k lt blue & multi	.25	.20
1899	A445	100k multicolored	.65	.20
1900	A445	150k dk brown & buff	1.10	.25
		Nos. 1898-1900 (3)	2.00	.65

2500th anniversary of the founding of the Persian empire by Cyrus the Great.

Painting Type of 1971
No. 1901, Sultan Mohammed I and his Staff. No. 1902, Palace with tiled walls.

1971, Nov. 15   Litho.   *Perf. 13*
| 1901 | A435 | 250k multicolored | 1.25 | .40 |
| 1902 | A435 | 250k multicolored | 1.25 | .40 |

Yunus Emre — A446

1971, Dec. 27   Litho.   *Perf. 13*
| 1903 | A446 | 100k brown & multi | .65 | .20 |

650th death anniv. of Yunus Emre, Turkish folk poet.

First Turkish World Map and Book Year Emblem — A447

1972, Jan. 3   *Perf. 13*
| 1904 | A447 | 100k buff & multi | .50 | .20 |

International Book Year.

Doves and NATO
Emblem — A448

Fisherman, by
Cevat
Dereli — A449

1972, Feb. 18   Litho.   Perf. 13
1905 A448 100k dull grn, blk &
           gray   .80 .25
1906 A448 250k dull bl, blk & gray 1.00 .60
Turkey's membership in NATO, 20th anniv.

Europa Issue 1972
Common Design Type
1972, May 2   Litho.   Perf. 13
Size: 22x33mm
1907 CD15 110k blue & multi   3.00 1.00
1908 CD15 250k brown & multi   4.50 1.50

Painting Type of 1971
No. 1909, Forest, Seker Ahmet. No. 1910,
View of Gebze, Anatolia, by Osman Hamdi.

1972, May 15   Litho.
1909 A435 250k multicolored   1.25 .35
1910 A435 250k multicolored   1.25 .35

Ataturk Statue Type of 1967
Design: 25k, Ataturk Statue in front of Ethnographic Museum, Ankara.

Imprint: Ajans - Turk/Ankara 1972
Perf. 12½x11½
1972, June 12   Litho.
Size: 22x15½mm
1911 A375 25k black & buff   .20 .20

1972, July 21   Litho.   Perf. 13
Paintings: 125k, Young Man, by Abdur
Rehman Chughtai (Pakistan). 150k, Persian
Woman, by Behzad.

1912 A449 100k gold & multi   .60 .20
1913 A449 125k gold & multi   .90 .25
1914 A449 150k gold & multi   1.00 .35
      Nos. 1912-1914 (3)   2.50 .80

Regional Cooperation for Development Pact
among Turkey, Iran and Pakistan, 8th anniv.

Ataturk and Commanders at Mt.
Koca — A450

Designs: No. 1916, Battle of the Com-
mander-in-chief. No. 1917, Turkish army
entering Izmir. 110k, Artillery and cavalry.

1972   Perf. 13x13½
1915 A450 100k lt ultra & blk   .35 .20
1916 A450 100k pink & multi   .50 .20
1917 A450 100k yellow & multi   .50 .20
1918 A450 110k orange & multi   .75 .25
      Nos. 1915-1918 (4)   2.10 .85

50th anniv. of fight for establishment of independent Turkish republic. Issued: #1915,
1918, 8/26; #1916, 8/30; #1917, 9/9.

"Cancer is
Curable"
A451

International
Railroad Union
Emblem — A452

1972, Oct. 10   Litho.   Perf. 12½x13
1919 A451 100k blk, brt bl & red   .35 .20
Fight against cancer.

1972, Dec. 31   Litho.   Perf. 13
1920 A452 100k sl grn, ocher & red .30 .20
Intl. Railroad Union, 50th anniv.

Kemal
Ataturk — A453

1972-76   Litho.   Perf. 13½x13
Size: 21x26mm
1921 A453   5k gray & blue   .20 .20
1922 A453 25k orange ('75)   .25 .20
1923 A453 100k buff & red brn
              ('73)   .55 .20
1924 A453 100k lt gray & gray
              ('75)   .50 .25
1925 A453 110k lt bl & vio bl   .60 .20
1926 A453 125k dull grn ('73)   .80 .20
1927 A453 150k tan & brown   .75 .20
1928 A453 150k lt grn & grn
              ('75)   .75 .30
1929 A453 175k yel & lil ('73)   1.00 .20
1930 A453 200k buff & red   .80 .20
1931 A453 250k pink & pur
                                    1.40 .20
1931A A453 400k gray & Prus
              bl ('76)   1.25 .20
1932 A453 500k pink & violet   2.00 .20
1933 A453 500k gray & ultra
              ('75)   1.50 .40
Size: 22x33mm
Perf. 13
1934 A453 10 l pink & car
              rose ('75)   2.00 .30
      Nos. 1921-1934 (15)   14.35 3.45
      See Nos. 2060-2061.

Europa Issue 1973
Common Design Type
1973, Apr. 4   Litho.   Perf. 13
Size: 32x23mm
1935 CD16 110k gray & multi   3.25 1.50
1936 CD16 250k multicolored   6.75 2.25

Painting Type of 1971
Paintings: No. 1937, Beyazit Almshouse,
Istanbul, by Ahmet Ziya Akbulut. No. 1938,
Flowers, by Suleyman Seyyit, vert.

1973, June 15   Litho.   Perf. 13
1937 A435 250k multicolored   .85 .35
1938 A435 250k multicolored   .85 .35

Helmet, Sword
and Oak
Leaves — A454

Mausoleum of
Antiochus
I — A455

Design: 100k, Helmet, sword and laurel.

1973, June 28   Perf. 13x12½
1939 A454 90k brown, gray & grn   .25 .20
1940 A454 100k brown, lem & grn   .25 .20
Army Day.

1973, July 21   Litho.   Perf. 13
Designs: 100k, Colossal heads, mausoleum
of Antiochus I (69-34 B.C.), Commagene, Turkey. 150k, Statue, Shahdad Kerman, Persia,
3000 B.C. 200k, Street, Mohenjo-daro,
Pakistan.

1941 A455 100k lt blue & multi   .25 .20
1942 A455 150k olive & multi   .30 .20
1943 A455 200k brown & multi   .45 .60
      Nos. 1941-1943 (3)   1.00 1.00

Regional Cooperation for Development Pact
among Turkey, Iran and Pakistan, 9th anniv.

Minelayer
Nusret
A456

Designs: 25k, Destroyer Istanbul. 100k,
Speedboat Simsek and Naval College. 250k,
Two-masted training ship Nuvid-i Futuh.

1973, Aug. 1
Size: 31½x22mm
1944 A456   5k Prus bl & multi   .20 .20
1945 A456 25k Prus bl & multi   .20 .20
1946 A456 100k Prus bl & multi   .60 .20
Size: 48x32mm
1947 A456 250k blue & multi   1.50 .25
      Nos. 1944-1947 (4)   2.50 .85

abu-al-Rayhan
al-Biruni
A457

Emblem of
Darussafaka
Foundation
A458

1973, Sept. 4   Litho.   Perf. 13x12½
1948 A457 250k multicolored   .70 .70
abu-al-Rayhan al-Biruni (973-1048), philosopher and mathematician.

1973, Sept. 15   Perf. 13
1949 A458 100k silver & multi   .30 .20
Centenary of the educational and philanthropic Darussafaka Foundation.

BALKANFILA IV
Emblem — A459

Designs: 110k, Symbolic view and stamps.
250k, "Balkanfila 4."

1973   Litho.   Perf. 13
1950 A459 100k gray & multi   .35 .20
1951 A459 110k multicolored   .20 .20
1952 A459 250k multicolored   .45 .20
      Nos. 1950-1952 (3)   1.00 .60

BALKANFILA IV, Philatelic Exhibition of Balkan Countries, Izmir, Oct. 26-Nov. 5.
Issued: 100k, Sept. 26; 110k, 250k, Oct. 26.

Sivas
Shepherd
A460

Kemal
Ataturk — A461

1973, Oct. 4
1953 A460 25k shown   .20 .20
1954 A460 100k Angora cat   .60 .20

1973, Oct. 10   Litho.   Perf. 13
1955 A461 100k gold & blk brn   .40 .20
35th death anniv. of Kemal Ataturk.

Flower and
"50" — A462

Ataturk — A463

250k, Torch & "50." 475k, Grain & cogwheel.

1973, Oct. 29
1956 A462 100k purple, red & bl   .20 .20
1957 A462 250k multicolored   .45 .20
1958 A462 475k brt blue & org   .70 .35
      Nos. 1956-1958 (3)   1.35 .75

Souvenir Sheet
Imperf
1959 A463 500k multicolored   1.25 .90

50th anniv. of the Turkish Republic. #1959
contains one stamp with simulated
perforations.

Bosporus
Bridge
A464

150k, Istanbul & Bosporus Bridge. 200k,
Bosporus Bridge, children & UNICEF emblem,
vert.

1973, Oct. 30   Perf. 13
1960 A464 100k multicolored   .30 .20
1961 A464 150k multicolored   .50 .30
1962 A464 200k multicolored   .55 .30
      Nos. 1960-1962 (3)   1.35 .80

Inauguration of the Bosporus Bridge from
Istanbul to Uskudar, Oct. 30, 1973; UNICEF;
children from East and West brought closer
through Bosporus Bridge (No. 1962).

Mevlana's Tomb and Dancers — A465

Jalal-udin Mevlana — A466

1973, Dec. 1   *Perf. 13x12½*
963 A465 100k blk, lt ultra & grn   .30   .20
964 A466 250k blue & multi   .55   .25

Jalal-udin Mevlana (1207-1273), poet and founder of the Mevlevie dervish order.

Cotton and Ship — A467

Export Products: 90k, Grapes. 100k, Figs. 250k, Citrus fruits. 325k, Tobacco. 475k, Hazelnuts.

1973, Dec. 10   Litho.   *Perf. 13*
1965 A467   75k black, gray & bl   .20   .20
1966 A467   90k black, olive & bl   .30   .20
1967 A467 100k black, emer & bl   .40   .20
1968 A467 250k blk, brt yel & bl   1.10   .25
1969 A467 325k blk, yel & bl   1.10   .25
1970 A467 475k blk, org brn & bl   1.60   .40
     Nos. 1965-1970 (6)   4.70   1.50

Pres. Inönü — A468

Hittite King, 8th Century B.C. — A469

1973, Dec. 25   Litho.   *Perf. 13*
1971 A468 100k sepia & buff   .30   .20

Ismet Inönü, (1884-1973), first Prime Minister and second President of Turkey.

1974, Apr. 29   Litho.   *Perf. 13*
Europa: 250k, Statuette of a Boy, (2nd millenium B.C.).
1972 A469 110k multicolored   5.50   1.25
1973 A469 250k lt blue & multi   9.50   1.75

Silver and Gold Figure, 3000 B.C. — A470

Child Care — A471

Archaeological Finds: 175k, Painted jar, 5000 B.C., horiz. 200k, Vessels in bull form, 1700-1600 B.C., horiz. 250k, Pitcher, 700 B.C.

1974, May 24   Litho.   *Perf. 13*
1974 A470 125k multicolored   .45   .20
1975 A470 175k multicolored   .70   .20
1976 A470 200k multicolored   .85   .20
1977 A470 250k multicolored   1.25   .40
     Nos. 1974-1977 (4)   3.25   1.00

1974, May 24
1978 A471 110k gray blue & blk   .30   .20
Sisli Children's Hospital, Istanbul, 75th anniv.

Anatolian Rug, 15th Century A472

Designs: 150k, Persian rug, late 16th century. 200k, Kashan rug, Lahore.

1974, July 21   Litho.   *Perf. 12½x13*
1979 A472 100k blue & multi   .65   .20
1980 A472 150k brown & multi   1.00   .20
1981 A472 200k red & multi   2.00   .25
     Nos. 1979-1981 (3)   3.65   .65

10th anniversary of the Regional Cooperation for Development Pact among Turkey, Iran and Pakistan.

Dove with Turkish Flag over Cyprus A473

1974, Aug. 26   Litho.   *Perf. 13*
1982 A473 250k multicolored   .80   .40
Cyprus Peace Operation.

Wrestling A474

Arrows Circling Globe A475

90k, 250k, various wrestling holds, horiz.

1974, Aug. 29
1983 A474   90k multicolored   .25   .20
1984 A474 100k multicolored   .40   .20
1985 A474 250k multicolored   .70   .25
     Nos. 1983-1985 (3)   1.35   .65

World Freestyle Wrestling Championships.

1974, Oct. 9   Litho.   *Perf. 13*
UPU Emblem and: 110k, "UPU" in form of dove. 200k, Dove.
1986 A475 110k bl, gold & dk bl   .25   .20
1987 A475 200k green & brown   .30   .20
1988 A475 250k multicolored   .55   .30
     Nos. 1986-1988 (3)   1.10   .70

Centenary of Universal Postal Union.

"Law Reforms" A476

"National Economy" A477

"Education" A478

1974, Oct. 29
1989 A476   50k blue & black   .20   .20
1990 A477 150k red & multi   .25   .20
1991 A478 400k multicolored   .65   .30
     Nos. 1989-1991 (3)   1.10   .70

Works and reforms of Kemal Ataturk.

Arrows Pointing Up — A479

Cogwheel and Map of Turkey A480

1974, Nov. 29   Litho.   *Perf. 13*
1992 A479   25k brown & black   .20   .20
1993 A480 100k brown & gray   .35   .20
3rd 5-year Development Program (#1992), and industrialization progress (#1993).

Volleyball — A481

1974, Dec. 30
1994 A481 125k shown   .35   .20
1995 A481 175k Basketball   .55   .20
1996 A481 250k Soccer   .90   .20
     Nos. 1994-1996 (3)   1.80   .60

Automatic Telex Network A482

Postal Check A483

Radio Transmitter and Waves A484

1975, Feb. 5   Litho.   *Perf. 13*
1997 A482   5k black & yellow   .20   .20
1998 A483   50k ol grn & org   .20   .20
1999 A484 100k blue & black   .30   .20
     Nos. 1997-1999 (3)   .70   .60

Post and telecommunications.

Child Entering Classroom A485

Children's paintings: 50k, View of village. 100k, Dancing children.

Karacaoglan Monument in Mut, by Huseyin Gezer — A486

1975, Apr. 23   Litho.   *Perf. 13*
2000 A485   25k multicolored   .20   .20
2001 A485   50k multicolored   .20   .20
2002 A485 100k multicolored   .30   .20
     Nos. 2000-2002 (3)   .70   .60

1975, Apr. 25
2003 A486 110k dk grn, bis & red   .30   .25
Karacaoglan (1606-1697), musician.

Orange Harvest in Hatay, by Cemal Tollu — A487

Europa: 250k, Yoruk Family on Plateau, by Turgut Zaim.

1975, Apr. 28
2004 A487 110k bister & multi   2.75   .95
2005 A487 250k bister & multi   4.25   1.25

Porcelain Vase, Turkey A488

Designs: 200k, Ceramic plate, Iran, horiz. 250k, Camel leather vase, Pakistan.

       Perf. 13½x13, 13x13½
1975, July 21   Litho.
2006 A488 110k multicolored   .35   .20
2007 A488 200k multicolored   .65   .25
2008 A488 250k ultra & multi   1.00   .40
     Nos. 2006-2008 (3)   2.00   .85

Regional Cooperation for Development Pact among Turkey, Iran and Pakistan.

Horon Folk Dance — A489

Regional Folk Dances: 125k, Kasik. 175k, Bengi. 250k, Kasap. 325k, Kafkas, vert.

1975, Aug. 30   Litho.   *Perf. 13*
2009 A489 100k blue & multi   .35   .20
2010 A489 125k green & multi   .55   .20
2011 A489 175k rose & multi   .65   .20
2012 A489 250k multicolored   .95   .25
2013 A489 325k orange & multi   1.50   .40
     Nos. 2009-2013 (5)   4.00   1.25

Knight Slaying Dragon — A490

The Plunder of Salur Kazan's House — A491

Design: 175k, Two Wanderers, horiz.

1975, Oct. 15   Litho.   Perf. 13
2014 A490 90k multicolored .25 .20
2015 A490 175k multicolored .40 .30
2016 A491 200k multicolored .60 .40
    Nos. 2014-2016 (3) 1.25 .90

Illustrations for tales by Dede Korkut.

Common Carp A492

1975, Nov. 27   Litho.   Perf. 12½x13
2017 A492 75k Turbot .40 .20
2018 A492 90k shown .40 .20
2019 A492 175k Trout .90 .20
2020 A492 250k Red mullet 1.10 .30
2021 A492 475k Red bream 2.50 .45
    Nos. 2017-2021 (5) 5.30 1.35

Women's Participation A493

Insurance Nationaliza-tion — A494

Fine Arts — A495

1975, Dec. 5   Perf. 12½x13, 13x12½
2022 A493 100k bis, blk & red .20 .20
2023 A494 110k violet & multi .30 .20
2024 A495 250k multicolored .40 .20
    Nos. 2022-2024 (3) .90 .60

Works and reforms of Ataturk.

Ceramic Plate — A496

Europa: 400k, Decorated pitcher.

1976, May 3   Litho.   Perf. 13
2025 A496 200k purple & multi 3.75 1.10
2026 A496 400k multicolored 8.00 2.00

Sultan Ahmed Mosque A497

1976, May 10
2027 A497 500k gray & multi .80 .40

7th Islamic Conference, Istanbul.

Lunch in the Field A498

Children's Drawings: 200k, Boats on the Bosporus, vert. 400k, Winter landscape.

1976, May 19   Litho.   Perf. 13
2028 A498 50k multicolored .20 .20
2029 A498 200k multicolored .25 .20
2030 A498 400k multicolored .45 .20
    Nos. 2028-2030 (3) .90 .60

Samsun 76, First National Junior Philatelic Exhibition, Samsun.

Storks, Sultan Marsh A499

Conservation Emblem and: 200k, Horses, Manyas Lake. 250k, Borabay Lake. 400k, Manavgat Waterfall.

1976, June 5
2031 A499 150k multicolored 2.50 .60
2032 A499 200k multicolored .65 .20
2033 A499 250k multicolored 1.10 .20
2034 A499 400k multicolored 1.50 .25
    Nos. 2031-2034 (4) 5.75 1.25

European Wetland Conservation Year.

Nasreddin Hodja Carrying Liver — A500

Montreal Olympic Emblem and Flame — A501

Turkish Folklore: 250k, Friend giving recipe for cooking liver. 600k, Hawk carrying off liver and Hodja telling hawk he cannot enjoy liver without recipe.

1976, July 5   Litho.   Perf. 13
2035 A500 150k multicolored .25 .20
2036 A500 250k multicolored .40 .20
2037 A500 600k multicolored .95 .35
    Nos. 2035-2037 (3) 1.60 .75

1976, July 17
Designs: 400k, "76", Montreal Olympic emblem, horiz. 600k, Montreal Olympic emblem and ribbons.

2038 A501 100k red & multi .20 .20
2039 A501 400k red & multi .50 .25
2040 A501 600k red & multi .90 .40
    Nos. 2038-2040 (3) 1.60 .85

21st Olympic Games, Montreal, Canada, 7/17-8/1.

Kemal Ataturk A502

Designs: 200k, Riza Shah Pahlavi. 250k, Mohammed Ali Jinnah.

1976, July 21   Litho.   Perf. 13½
2041 A502 100k multicolored .25 .20
2042 A502 200k multicolored .35 .20
2043 A502 250k multicolored .50 .25
    Nos. 2041-2043 (3) 1.10 .65

Regional Cooperation for Development Pact among Turkey, Pakistan and Iran, 12th anniversary.

"Ataturk's Army" A503

Ataturk's Speeches A504

"Peace at Home and in the World" A505

1976, Oct. 29   Litho.   Perf. 13
2044 A503 100k black & red .20 .20
2045 A504 200k gray grn & multi .25 .20
2046 A505 400k blue & multi .55 .25
    Nos. 2044-2046 (3) 1.00 .65

Works and reforms of Ataturk.

Hora A506

1977, Jan. 19   Litho.   Perf. 13
2047 A506 400k multicolored .70 .25

MTA Sismik 1 "Hora" geophysical explora-tion ship.

Keyboard and Violin Sound Hole — A507

1977, Feb. 24   Litho.   Perf. 13x13½
2048 A507 200k multicolored .40 .20

Turkish State Symphony Orchestra, sesquicentennial.

Ataturk and "100" — A508

Design: 400k, Hand holding ballot.

1977, Mar. 21   Litho.   Perf. 13
2049 A508 200k black & red .25 .20
2050 A508 400k black & brown .50 .25

Centenary of Turkish Parliament.

Hierapolis (Pamukkale) A509

Europa: 400k, Zelve (mountains and poppies).

1977, May 2   Litho.   Perf. 13½x1..
2051 A509 200k multicolored 4.75 2.0.
2052 A509 400k multicolored 8.75 2.7.

Terra Cotta Pot, Turkey A510

Designs: 225k, Terra cotta jug, Iran. 675k, Terra cotta bullock cart, Pakistan.

1977, July 21   Litho.   Perf. 1..
2053 A510 100k multicolored .25 .2.
2054 A510 225k multicolored .75 .2.
2055 A510 675k multicolored 1.50 .5.
    a.   Souv. sheet, #2053-2055 11.00 11.0.
    Nos. 2053-2055 (3) 2.50 1.0.

Regional Cooperation for Development Pact among Turkey, Iran and Pakistan, 13th anniv...

Finn-class Yacht A511

Kemal Ataturk A512

200k, Three yachts. 250k, Symbolic yacht.

1977, July 28
2056 A511 150k lt bl, bl & blk .25 .20
2057 A511 200k ultra & blue .40 .20
2058 A511 250k ultra & black .55 .20
    Nos. 2056-2058 (3) 1.20 .60

European Finn Class Sailing Champion-ships, Istanbul, July 28.

Ataturk Type of 1972

1977, June 13   Litho.   Perf. 13½x13..
2060 A453 100k olive .50 .20
2061 A453 200k brown .75 .25

Imprint: "GUZEL SANATLAR MATBAASI A.S. 1977"

1977, Sept. 23   Litho.   Perf. 13.
    Size: 20½x22mm
2062 A512 200k blue .30 .20
2063 A512 250k Prussian blue .35 .20

Imprint: "TIFDRUK-ISTANBUL 1978"

1978, June 28   Photo.   Perf. 13.
    Size: 20x25mm
2065 A512 10k brown .20 .20
2066 A512 50k grnsh gray .20 .20
2067 A512 1 l fawn .20 .20
2068 A512 2½ l purple .30 .20
2069 A512 5 l blue .55 .20
2072 A512 25 l dl grn & lt bl 2.25 .30
2073 A512 50 l dp org & tan 3.50 1.40
    Nos. 2065-2073 (7) 7.20 2.70

No. 1832 Surcharged with New Value and Wavy Lines

1977, Aug. 17
2078 A418 10k on 1k dp org & brn .30 .20

"Rationalism" A513

"National Sovereignty" A514

"Liberation of Nations" — A515

1977, Oct. 29   Litho.   Perf. 13
2079	A513	100k multicolored	.20	.20
2080	A514	200k multicolored	.20	.20
2081	A515	400k multicolored	.40	.20
		Nos. 2079-2081 (3)	.80	.60

Works and reforms of Ataturk.

Mohammad Allama Iqbal — A516

Trees and Burning Match — A517

1977, Nov. 9   Perf. 13x12½
2082	A516	400k multicolored	.45	.20

Mohammad Allama Iqbal (1877-1938), Pakistani poet and philosopher.

1977, Dec. 15   Litho.   Perf. 13

Design: 250k, Sign showing growing tree.
2083	A517	50k green, blk & red	.20	.20
2084	A517	250k gray, grn & blk	.25	.20

Forest conservation. See type A542.

Wrecked Car — A518

Passing on Wrong Side — A519   Traffic Sign, "Slow!" — A520

Two types of 50k:
I - Number on license plate.
II - No number on plate.

Traffic Safety: 250k, Tractor drawing overloaded farm cart. 800k, Accident caused by incorrect passing. 10 l, "Use striped crossings."

1977-78   Perf. 13½x13, 13x13½
2085	A518	50k ultra, blk & red,		
		II	1.10	.55
a.		Type I	1.40	.55
2086	A519	150k red, gray & blk	.25	.20
2087	A518	250k ocher, blk & red	.50	.20
2088	A520	500k gray, red & blk	.50	.20

2089	A520	800k multicolored	1.10	.25
2090	A520	10 l dl grn, blk & brn	1.75	.35
		Nos. 2085-2090 (6)	5.20	1.75

Issued: 500k, 1977; others, 1978.

Ishak Palace, Dogubeyazit — A521

Europa: 5 l, Anamur Castle.

1978, May 2   Litho.   Perf. 13
2091	A521	2½ l multicolored	5.00	2.50
2092	A521	5 l multicolored	10.00	3.50

Riza Shah Pahlavi — A522

1978, June 16   Litho.   Perf. 13x13½
2093	A522	5 l multicolored	.70	.70

Riza Shah Pahlavi (1877-1944) of Iran, birth centenary.

Yellow Rose, Turkey A523

3½ l, Pink roses, Iran. 8 l, Red roses, Pakistan.

1978, July 21   Litho.   Perf. 13
2094	A523	2½ l multi	.20	.20
2095	A523	3½ l multi	.30	.20
2096	A523	8 l multi	.70	.25
		Nos. 2094-2096 (3)	1.20	.65

Regional Cooperation for Development Pact among Turkey, Iran and Pakistan.

Anti-Apartheid Emblem — A524

1978, Aug. 14   Litho.   Perf. 13½x13
2097	A524	10 l multicolored	.85	.25

Anti-Apartheid Year.

View of Ankara — A525

Design: 5 l, View of Tripoli, horiz.

Perf. 13x12½, 12½x13
1978, Aug. 17
2098	A525	2½ l multi	.30	.20
2099	A525	5 l multi	.75	.20

Turkish-Libyan friendship.

Souvenir Sheet

Bridge and Mosque — A526

1978, Oct. 25   Imperf.
2100	A526	15 l multicolored	1.25	.80

Edirne '78, 2nd Natl. Phil. Youth Exhib.

Independence Medal A527

Latin Alphabet A529

Speech Reform A528

1978, Oct. 29   Perf. 13x13½, 13½x13
2101	A527	2½ l multi	.20	.20
2102	A528	3½ l multi	.25	.20
2103	A529	5 l multi	.35	.20
		Nos. 2101-2103 (3)	.80	.60

Ataturk's works and reforms.

House on Bosporus, 1699 — A530

Turkish Houses: 2½ l, Izmit, 1774, vert. 3½ l, Kula, 17th cent., vert. 5 l, Milas, 18th-19th cent., vert. 8 l, Safranbolu, 18th-19th cent.

Perf. 13x12½, 12½x13
1978, Nov. 22
2104	A530	1 l multi	.20	.20
2105	A530	2½ l multi	.30	.20
2106	A530	3½ l multi	.40	.20
2107	A530	5 l multi	.60	.20
2108	A530	8 l multi	.95	.25
		Nos. 2104-2108 (5)	2.45	1.05

Carrier Pigeon, Plane, Horseback Rider, Train A531

Europa: 5 l, Morse key, telegraph and Telex machine. 7½ l, Telephone dial and satellite.

1979, Apr. 30   Litho.   Perf. 13
2109	A531	2½ l multicolored	2.00	.35
2110	A531	5 l org brn & blk	3.00	.65
2111	A531	7½ l brt blue & blk	5.00	1.00
		Nos. 2109-2111 (3)	10.00	2.00

Plowing, by Namik Ismail A532

Paintings: 7½ l, Potters, by Kamalel Molk, Iran. 10 l, At the Well, by Allah Baksh, Pakistan.

1979, Sept. 5   Litho.   Perf. 13½x13
2112	A532	5 l multi	.20	.20
2113	A532	7½ l multi	.35	.20
2114	A532	10 l multi	.55	.25
		Nos. 2112-2114 (3)	1.10	.65

Regional Cooperation for Development Pact among Turkey, Pakistan and Iran, 15th anniversary.

A533

A534

1979, Sept. 17   Perf. 13
2115	A533	5 l Colemanite	.35	.20
2116	A533	7½ l Chromite	.60	.20
2117	A533	10 l Antimonite	1.00	.20
2118	A533	15 l Sulphur	1.25	.30
		Nos. 2115-2118 (4)	3.20	.90

10th World Mining Congress.

1979, Sept. 24

8-shaped road, train tunnel, plane and emblem.
2119	A534	5 l multicolored	.30	.20

European Ministers of Communications, 8th Symposium.

Youth — A535

Secularization A536

Design: 5 l, National oath.

1979, Oct. 29   Perf. 13x12½, 12½x13
2120	A535	2½ l multi	.20	.20
2121	A536	3½ l multi	.20	.20
2122	A535	5 l black & orange	.30	.20
		Nos. 2120-2122 (3)	.70	.60

Ataturk's works and reforms.

Poppies — A537

1979, Nov. 26   Litho.   Perf. 13x13½
2123	A537	5 l	shown	.25	.20
2124	A537	7½ l	Oleander	.45	.20
2125	A537	10 l	Late spider orchid	.80	.20
2126	A537	15 l	Mandrake	1.25	.25
		Nos. 2123-2126 (4)		2.75	.85

See Nos. 2154-2157.

Kemal Ataturk
A538   A538a
Perf. 12½x11½, 13x12½(No. 2131)

1979-81   Litho.
2127	A538	50k	olive ('80)	.20	.20
2128	A538	1 l	grn & lt grn	.20	.20
2129	A538	2½ l	purple	.25	.20
2130	A538	2½ l	bl grn & lt bl ('80)	.20	.20
2131	A538	2½ l	orange ('81)	.20	.20
2132	A538	5 l	ultra & gray	.50	.20
a.		Sheet of 8		3.00	3.00
2133	A538	7½ l	brown	.60	.20
2134	A538	7½ l	red ('80)	.80	.20
2135	A538	10 l	rose carmine	.90	.20
2136	A538	20 l	gray ('80)	1.50	.30
		Nos. 2127-2136 (10)		5.35	2.10

No. 2132a for Ankara '79 Philatelic Exhibition, Oct. 14-20.
For surcharge see No. 2261.

1980-82   Photo.   Perf. 13½
2137	A538a	7½ l	red brown	.20	.20
c.		Sheet of 4		.70	.30
2137A	A538a	10 l	brown	.75	.20
2138	A538a	20 l	lilac	.75	.20
2138A	A538a	30 l	gray	.90	.30
2139	A538a	50 l	orange red	1.60	.30
2140	A538a	75 l	brt green	2.40	.60
2141	A538a	100 l	blue	3.50	.75
		Nos. 2137-2141 (7)		10.10	2.55

No. 2137c for ANTALYA '82 4th Natl. Junior Stamp Show.
Issued: #2137, 7/15/81; #2137c, 10/3/82; 30 l, 9/23/81; others, 12/10/80.
See Nos. 2164-2169.

Turkish Printing, 250th
Anniversary — A539

1979, Nov. 30   Litho.   Perf. 13
2142	A539	10 l	multicolored	.60	.45

2nd
International
Olive Oil
Year — A540

Perf. 12½x13, 13x12½
1979, Dec. 20   Litho.
2143	A540	5 l	shown	.20	.20
2144	A540	10 l	Globe, oil drop, vert.	.45	.20

Uskudarli Hoca Ali Riza Bey (1857-
1930), Painter — A541

Europa: 15 l, Ali Sami Boyar (1880-1967),
painter. 20 l, Dr. Hulusi Behcet (1889-1948),
physician, discovered Behcet skin disease.

1980, Apr. 28   Perf. 13
2145	A541	7½ l	multi	1.25	.40
2146	A541	15 l	multi	2.10	.60
2147	A541	20 l	multi	2.75	.80
		Nos. 2145-2147 (3)		6.10	1.80

Forest   Earthquake
Conservation   Destruction
A542   A543

1980, July 3   Perf. 13½x13
2148	A542	50k	ol grn & red org	.45	.20

See type A517. For surcharge see No. 2262.

1980, Sept. 8   Perf. 13
2149	A543	7½ l	shown	.50	.25
2150	A543	20 l	Seismograph	1.00	.50

7th World Conference on Earthquake Engineering, Istanbul.

Games' Emblem,   Hegira — A545
Sports — A544

1980, Sept. 26   Perf. 13x13½
2151	A544	7½ l	shown	.45	.20
2152	A544	20 l	Emblem, sports, diff.	1.00	.20

First Islamic Games, Izmir.

1980, Nov. 9
2153	A545	20 l	multicolored	1.10	.70

Plant Type of 1979
1980, Nov. 26   Perf. 13
2154	A537	2½ l	Manisa tulip	.20	.20
2155	A537	7½ l	Ephesian bellflower	.50	.20
2156	A537	15 l	Angora crocus	.95	.20
2157	A537	20 l	Anatolian orchid	1.50	.20
		Nos. 2154-2157 (4)		3.15	.80

Avicenna
Treating
Patient
A546

Avicenna (Arab Physician), Birth Millenium:
20 l, Portrait, vert.

1980, Dec. 15
2158	A546	7½ l	multi	.40	.20
2159	A546	20 l	multi	.70	.30

Balkanfila
VIII Stamp
Exhibition,
Ankara
A547

1981, Jan. 1   Litho.   Perf. 13
2160	A547	10 l	red & black	.60	.20

Kemal
Ataturk — A548

1981, Feb. 4   Perf. 13
2163	A548	10 l	lilac rose	.60	.20

Ataturk Type of 1980
1983-84   Perf. 13x13½
2164	A538a	15 l	grnsh blue	.25	.20
2165	A538a	20 l	orange ('84)	.30	.20
2167	A538a	65 l	bluish grn	.95	.20
2169	A538a	90 l	lilac rose	1.25	.20
		Nos. 2164-2169 (4)		2.75	.80

Issued: #2164, 2167, 2169, 11/30; #2165, 7/25.

Sultan Mehmet the
Conqueror (1432-
1481) — A549

1981, May 3   Litho.   Perf. 13x12½
2173	A549	10 l	multicolored	.30	.25
2174	A549	20 l	multicolored	.65	.50

Gaziantep
(Folk
Dance)
A550

Antalya
A551

1981, May 4   Litho.   Perf. 13
2175	A550	7½ l	shown	.25	.20
2176	A550	10 l	Balikesir	.35	.20
2177	A550	15 l	Kahramanmaras	.55	.25
2178	A550	35 l	shown	3.00	.65
2179	A551	70 l	Burdur	4.50	1.00
		Nos. 2175-2179 (5)		8.65	2.30

Nos. 2178-2179 show CEPT (Europa)
emblem.

Nos. C40, 1925, 1931A, 2089
Surcharged in Black with New Value
and Wavy Lines
1981, June 3   Perf. 13½x13
2179A	AP7	10 l	on 60k	.40	.20
2180	A453	10 l	on 10k	.40	.20
2181	A453	10 l	on 400k	.40	.20
2182	A520	10 l	on 800k	.40	.20
		Nos. 2179A-2182 (4)		1.60	.80

A552

Kemal Ataturk
A553

1981, June 22   Perf. 13x12
2183	A552	7½ l	Rug, Bilecik	.20	.20
2184	A552	10 l	Embroidery	.25	.20
2185	A552	15 l	Drum, zurna players	.40	.20
2186	A552	20 l	Embroidered napkin	.40	.20
2187	A552	30 l	Rug, diff.	.75	.20
		Nos. 2183-2187 (5)		2.00	1.00

22nd Intl. Turkish Folklore Congress.

1981, May 19   Litho.   Perf. 14x1...
2188	A553	2½ l	No. 1801	.20	.20
2189	A553	7½ l	No. 1816	.20	.20
2190	A553	10 l	No. 1604	.20	.20
2191	A553	20 l	No. 804	.95	.20
2192	A553	25 l	No. 777	1.25	.20
2193	A553	35 l	No. 1959	1.60	.20
		Nos. 2188-2193 (6)		4.40	1.20

Souvenir Sheet
2194		Sheet of 6		11.00	5.50
a.	A553	2½ l	like 2½ l	.20	.20
b.	A553	37½ l	like 7½ l	.40	.20
c.	A553	50 l	like 10 l	.60	.20
d.	A553	100 l	like 20 l	1.25	.40
e.	A553	125 l	like 25 l	1.50	.50
f.	A553	175 l	like 35 l	2.25	.65

Souvenir Sheet

Balkanfila VIII Stamp Exhibition,
Ankara — A554

1981, Aug. 8   Litho.   Perf. 13
2195	A554	Sheet of 2		6.50	6.50
a.		50 l	No. B68	2.50	2.50
b.		50 l	No. 733	2.50	2.50

5th General Congress of European
Physics Society
A555

1981, Sept. 7   Perf. 12½x13
2196	A555	10 l	red & multi	.25	.20
2197	A555	30 l	blue & multi	.60	.20

World
Food Day
A556

1981, Oct. 16
2198	A556	10 l	multicolored	.25	.20
2199	A556	30 l	multicolored	.60	.20

Constituent Assembly
Inauguration — A557

1981, Oct. 23   Perf. 13
2200	A557	10 l	multicolored	.25	.20
2201	A557	30 l	multicolored	.60	.20

Ataturk — A558

Portraits of Ataturk.

1981-82 *Perf. 11½x12½, 13 (#2204)*
2202	A558	1 l	green	.20 .20
2203	A558	2½ l	purple	.20 .20
2204	A558	2½ l	gray & org	.50 .20
2205	A558	5 l	blue	.20 .20
2206	A558	10 l	orange	.20 .20
2207	A558	35 l	brown	.70 .20
		Nos. 2202-2207 (6)		2.00 1.20

Issued: #2204, 12/10/81; others, 1/27/82.

Literacy
Campaign
A559

Energy
Conservation
A560

1981, Dec. 24 *Perf. 13½*
2217 A559 2½ l Procession .35 .20

1982, Jan. 11 *Perf. 13*
2218 A560 10 l multicolored .45 .20

Magnolias, by
Ibrahim Calli
(b. 1882)
A561

Sultanhan
Caravanserai
A562

1982, Mar. 17 *Perf. 13x13½, 13½x13*
2219	A561	10 l	shown	.25 .20
2220	A561	20 l	Fishermen, horiz.	.50 .20
2221	A561	30 l	Sewing Woman	.65 .20
		Nos. 2219-2221 (3)		1.40 .60

Europa Issue

1982, Apr. 26 *Perf. 13x12½*
2222	A562	30 l	shown	.60 .25
2223	A562	70 l	Silk Route	1.40 .60
a.		Min. sheet, 2 each #2222-2223		5.00 5.00
b.		Pair, #2222-2223		1.10 .50

1250th Anniv. of
Kul-Tigin
Monument, Kosu
Saydam,
Mongolia — A563

1982, June 9 *Perf. 13*
2224 A563 10 l Monument .20 .20
2225 A563 30 l Kul-Tigin (685-732),
Gok-Turkish com-
mander .40 .20

Pendik
Shipyard
Opening
A564

1982, July 1 *Perf. 12½x13*
2226 A564 30 l Ship, emblem .40 .20

Mountains
of Anatolia
A565

1982, July 17 *Perf. 13*
2227	A565	7½ l	Agri Dagi, vert.	.20 .20
2228	A565	10 l	Buzul Dagi	.30 .20
2229	A565	15 l	Demirkazik, vert.	.60 .20
2230	A565	20 l	Erciyes	.70 .20
2231	A565	30 l	Kackar Dagi,	
				.90 .20
2232	A565	35 l	Uludag	1.25 .20
		Nos. 2227-2232 (6)		3.85 1.20

Beyazit
State
Library
Centenary
A566

1982, Sept. 27
2233 A566 30 l multicolored .50 .25

Musical Instruments of
Anatolia — A567

1982, Oct. 13
2234	A567	7½ l	Davul	.30 .20
2235	A567	10 l	Baglama	.40 .20
2236	A567	15 l	shown	.60 .20
2237	A567	20 l	Kemence	.90 .20
2238	A567	30 l	Mey	1.10 .20
		Nos. 2234-2238 (5)		3.30 1.00

Roman
Temple
Columns,
Sart
A568

1982, Nov. 3
2239 A568 30 l multi 1.00 .60

Family
Planning and
Mother-Child
Health
A569

1983, Jan. 12 *Litho.* *Perf. 13*
2240 A569 10 l Family on map .25 .20
2241 A569 35 l Mother and child .75 .20

30th Anniv. of Customs Cooperation
Council — A570

1983, Jan. 26
2242 A570 45 l multi .75 .20

1982 Constitution — A571

1983, Jan. 27
2243 A571 10 l Ballot box .20 .20
2244 A571 30 l Open book, scale .35 .20

Manastirli
Bey
A572

1983, Mar. 16 *Litho.*
2245 A572 35 l multi .45 .20

Manastirli Hamdi Bey (1890-1945), telegrapher of news of Istanbul's occupation to Ataturk, 1920.

Europa Issue

Piri Reis,
Geographer
A573

1983, May 5 *Litho.* *Perf. 12½x13*
2246 A573 50 l shown 12.50 8.50
2247 A573 100 l Ulug Bey
(1394-1449),
astronomer 32.50 15.00

Youth
Week
A574

1983, May 16
2248 A574 15 l multi .25 .20

World Communications Year — A575

1983, May 16 *Perf. 13*
2249	A575	15 l	Carrier pigeon, vert.	.30 .20
2250	A575	50 l	Phone lines	.60 .20
2251	A575	70 l	Emblem, vert.	1.10 .20
		Nos. 2249-2251 (3)		2.00 .60

50th
Anniv. of
State Civil
Aviation
A576

1983, May 20 *Litho.* *Perf. 13*
2252 A576 50 l Plane, jet .50 .20
2253 A576 70 l Airport .70 .20

18th
Council of
Europe Art
Exhibition
A577

15 l, Eros, 2nd cent. BC, vert. 35 l, Two-
headed duck, Hittite, 14th cent BC. 50 l, Zinc
jugs, plate, 16th cent., vert. 70 l, Marcus Aurelius and his wife Faustina the Young, 2nd cent.

1983, May 22 *Perf. 13*
2254	A577	15 l	multi	.40 .20
2255	A577	35 l	multi	.90 .20
2256	A577	50 l	multi	1.00 .20
2257	A577	70 l	multi	1.10 .20
		Nos. 2254-2257 (4)		3.40 .80

Council of Europe's
"The Water's Edge"
Campaign — A578

Coastal Views.

1983, June 1 *Litho.* *Perf. 13x12½*
2258	A578	10 l	Oldeniz	.20 .20
2259	A578	25 l	Olympus	.50 .20
2260	A578	35 l	Kekova	.70 .20
		Nos. 2258-2260 (3)		1.40 .60

Nos. 2127, 2148 Surcharged
Perf. 12½x11½, 13½x13

1983, June 8
2261 A538 5 l on 50k olive .20 .20
2262 A542 5 l on 50k ol grn & red org .20 .20

Kemal
Ataturk
A579

Aga Khan
Architecture Award
A580

1983, June 22 *Perf. 13*
2263	A579	15 l	bl grn & bl	.25 .20
a.		Sheet of 5 + label		1.75 1.25
2264	A579	50 l	green & blue	.80 .20
2265	A579	100 l	orange & blue	1.75 .30
		Nos. 2263-2265 (3)		2.80 .70

For surcharge see No. 2432.

1983, Sept. 4 *Photo.* *Perf. 11½*
2266 A580 50 l View of Istanbul .75 .20

60th Anniv. of
the Republic
A582

1983, Oct. 29 *Perf. 13½x13*
2268 A582 15 l multi .25 .20
2269 A582 50 l multi .75 .20

Columns, Aphrodisias — A583

1983, Nov. 2 *Perf. 13*
2270 A583 50 l multi 1.00 .75

UNESCO Campaign
for Istanbul and
Goreme — A584

1984, Feb. 15 *Litho.* *Perf. 13*
2271	A584	25 l	St. Sophia Basili-ca	.30 .20
2272	A584	35 l	Goreme	.45 .20
2273	A584	50 l	Istanbul	.60 .20
		Nos. 2271-2273 (3)		1.35 .60

Natl. Police
Org. Emblem
A585

1984, Apr. 10   Litho.   Perf. 13
2274 A585 15 l multi   .30 .25

Europa (1959-
84)
A586

1984, Apr. 30   Perf. 13½x13
2275 A586 50 l blue & multi   9.00 1.25
2276 A586 100 l gray & multi 26.00 5.00

Mete
Khan, Hun
Ruler, 204
BC, Flag
A587

Sixteen States (Hun Rulers and Flags): 20 l,
Panu, Western Hun empire (48-216). 50 l,
Attila, 375-454. 70 l, Aksunvar, Ak Hun
empire, 420-562.

1984, June 20   Litho.   Perf. 13
2277 A587 10 l multi   .30 .20
2278 A587 20 l multi   .60 .20
2279 A587 50 l multi   1.25 .20
2280 A587 70 l multi   2.50 .20
    Nos. 2277-2280 (4)   4.65 .80

See Nos. 2315-2318, 2349-2352, 2382-2385.

Occupation of
Cyprus, 10th
Anniv.
A588

1984, July 20   Litho.   Perf. 13
2281 A588 70 l Dove, olive
               branch   1.10 .50

Wild Flowers   Armed Forces Day
A589   A590

1984, Aug. 1   Perf. 11½x12½
2282 A589 10 l Marshmallow
               flower   .20 .20
2283 A589 20 l Red poppy   .25 .20
2284 A589 70 l Sowbread   .85 .20
2285 A589 200 l Snowdrop   2.50 .30
2286 A589 300 l Tulip   4.00 .40
    Nos. 2282-2286 (5)   7.80 1.30

See Nos. 2301-2308. For surcharges see
Nos. 2465, 2467, 2479-2480.

1984, Aug. 26   Perf. 13½x13
2287 A590 20 l Soldier, dove,
               flag   .20 .20
2288 A590 50 l Sword   .40 .20
2289 A590 70 l Arms, soldier,
               flag   .55 .20
2290 A590 90 l Map, soldier   .65 .20
    Nos. 2287-2290 (4)   1.80 .80

Trees and Wood   Pres. Ismet
Products   Inonu (1884-
A591   1973),
                     A592

Seed, Tree and Product: 10 l, Liquidambar,
liquidambar grease. 20 l, Oriental spruce,
stringed instrument. 70 l, Oriental beech,
chair. 90 l, Cedar of Lebanon, ship.

1984, Sept. 19   Litho.   Perf. 13x12½
2291 A591 10 l multi   .25 .20
2292 A591 20 l multi   .30 .20
2293 A591 70 l multi   1.00 .20
2294 A591 90 l multi   1.25 .20
    Nos. 2291-2294 (4)   2.80 .80

1984, Sept. 24   Perf. 13
2295 A592 20 l Portrait   .30 .20

First Intl. Turkish
Carpet
Congress — A593

1984, Oct. 7   Perf. 13x13½
2296 A593 70 l Seljukian carpet,
               13th cent.   .60 .30

Ruins of
Ancient
City of
Harran
A594

1984, Nov. 7   Perf. 13½x13
2297 A594 70 l Columns, arch   1.00 .60

Turkish
Women's
Suffrage, 50th
Anniv.
A595

1984, Dec. 5   Litho.   Perf. 13
2298 A595 20 l Women voting   .25 .20

40th Anniv.,
ICAO — A596

1984, Dec. 7   Litho.   Perf. 13
2299 A596 100 l Icarus, ICAO
               emblem   1.10 .60

Souvenir Sheet

No. 1047 — A597

1985, Jan. 13   Litho.   Imperf.
2300 A597 Sheet of 4, 2 each
           #a.-b.   4.00 3.00
    a.-b. 70 l, any single   .35 .20

Istanbul '87. No. 2300b has denomination in
lower right.

Flower Type of 1984

1985   Perf. 11½x12½
2301 A589 5 l Narcissus   .20 .20
           Perf. 12½x13
2308 A589 100 l Daisy   .60 .20

Issue dates: #2301, Feb. 6; #2308, July 31.

Turkish
Aviation
League,
60th Anniv.
A598

1985, Feb. 16   Perf. 13
2310 A598 10 l Parachutist, glider .25 .20
2311 A598 20 l Hot air balloon,
               vert.   .55 .20

INTELSAT, 20th
Anniv. — A599

1985, Apr. 3
2312 A599 100 l multi   .60 .20

Europa Issue

Ulvi Cemal Erkin (1906-1972) and
Kosekce — A600

Composers and music: 200 l, Mithat
Fenmen (1916-1982) and Concertina.

1985, Apr. 29   Perf. 13½x13
2313 A600 100 l multi   25.00 3.50
2314 A600 200 l multi   35.00 5.00

Turkish States Type of 1984

Sixteen States (Kagan rulers and flags): 10
l, Bilge, Gokturk Empire (552-743) and Orhon-
Turkish alphabet. 20 l, Bayan, Avar Empire
(565-803). 70 l, Hazar, Hazar Empire (651-
983). 100 l, Kutlug Kul Bilge, Uygur State
(774-1335).

1985, June 20
2315 A587 10 l multi   .30 .20
2316 A587 20 l multi   .60 .20
2317 A587 70 l multi   1.25 .20
2318 A587 100 l multi   2.50 .20
    Nos. 2315-2318 (4)   4.65 .80

Intl. Youth
Year
A601

1985, Aug. 8
2319 A601 100 l multi   .80 .20
2320 A601 120 l multi   1.50 1.00

Postal Code
Inauguration
A602

1985, Sept. 4   Perf. 1.
Background Color
2321 A602 10 l pale yel brn   .20 .2(
2322 A602 20 l fawn   .30 .2(
2323 A602 20 l gray green   .30 .2(
2324 A602 20 l brt blue   .30 .2(
2325 A602 70 l rose lilac   .65 .2(
2326 A602 100 l gray   .90 .3(
    Nos. 2321-2326 (6)   2.65 1.3(

Symposium of Natl. Palaces — A603

1985, Sept. 25   Perf. 13½x13
2327 A603 20 l Aynalikavak, c.
               1703   .20 .20
2328 A603 100 l Beylerbeyi, 1865 .55 .20

UN, 40th
Anniv.
A604

1985, Oct. 24
2329 A604 100 l multi   .90 .20

Alanya
Fortress
and City
A605

1985, Nov. 7
2330 A605 100 l multi   1.25 .20

A606   A607

1985, Nov. 12   Perf. 13x13½
2331 A606 100 l multi   1.00 .20

Turkish Meteorological Service, 60th anniv.

1985, Dec. 14
2332 A607 20 l multi   .30 .20

Isik Lyceum, Istanbul, cent.

Ataturk — A608

Perf. 11½x12½

1985, Dec. 18   Litho.

334	A608	10 l pale bl & ultra	.20 .20
336	A608	20 l beige & brn	.25 .20
340	A608	100 l lt pink & claret	1.25 .20
		Nos. 2334-2340 (3)	1.70 .60

This is an expanding set. Numbers will change if necessary.

7th Intl. Children's Festival, Ankara A609

Various children's drawings.

1986, Apr. 23   Litho.   **Perf. 12½x13**

2342	A609	20 l multi	.20 .20
2343	A609	100 l multi	.60 .20
2344	A609	120 l multi	.75 .20
		Nos. 2342-2344 (3)	1.55 .60

Europa Issue

Pollution A610

1986, Apr. 28   **Perf. 13**

2345	A610	100 l shown	8.50 1.50
2346	A610	200 l Bandaged leaf	13.00 2.50

1st Ataturk Intl. Peace Prize — A611

Kirkpinar Wrestling Matches, Edirne — A613

1st Turkish Submarine, Cent. — A612

1986, May 19   Litho.   **Perf. 13**

2347	A611	20 l gold & multi	.35 .20
2348	A611	100 l silver & multi	.75 .20

States Type of 1984

Sixteen States (Devleti rulers and flags): 10 l, Bilge Kul Kadir Khan, Kara Khanids State (840-1212). 20 l, Alp-Tekin, Ghaznavids State (963-1183). 100 l, Seldjuk Bey, Seldjuks State (1040-1157). 120 l, Muhammed Harezmsah, Khwarizm-Shahs State (1157-1231).

1986, June 20

2349	A587	10 l multi	.30 .20
2350	A587	20 l multi	.60 .20
2351	A587	100 l multi	1.25 .20
2352	A587	120 l multi	2.50 .20
		Nos. 2349-2352 (4)	4.65 .80

1986, June 16   Litho.   **Perf. 13**

2353	A612	20 l Torpedo sub Abdulhamid	.45 .20

1986, June 30

2354	A613	10 l Oiling bodies	.20 .20
2355	A613	20 l Five wrestlers	.20 .20
2356	A613	100 l Two wrestlers	.60 .20
		Nos. 2354-2356 (3)	1.00 .60

Organization for Economic Cooperation and Development, 25th Anniv. — A614

1986, Sept. 30   Litho.   **Perf. 13½x13**

2357	A614	100 l multi	.60 .25

Automobile, Cent. — A615

1986, Oct. 15

2358	A615	10 l Benz Veloci-pede, 1886	.30 .20
2359	A615	20 l Rolls-Royce Sil-ver Ghost, 1906	.50 .20
2360	A615	100 l Mercedes Tour-ing Car, 1928	1.10 .35
2361	A615	200 l Abstract speed-ing car	2.25 .60
		Nos. 2358-2361 (4)	4.15 1.35

Paintings A616

Celal Bayar (1883-1986), 3rd President — A617

Designs: 100 l, Bouquet with Tulip, by Feyhaman Duran (1886-1970). 120 l, Landscape with Fountain, by H. Avni Lifij (1886-1927), horiz.

1986, Oct. 22   **Perf. 13½x13, 13x13½**

2362	A616	100 l multi	.35 .20
2363	A616	120 l multi	1.00 .20

1986, Oct. 27   **Perf. 13**

2364	A617	20 l shown	.50 .20
2365	A617	100 l Profile	.75 .20

Kubad-Abad Ruins, Beysehir Lake — A618

1986, Nov. 7   **Perf. 13½x13**

2366	A618	100 l multi	.50 .20

Mehmet Akif Ersoy (1873-1936), Composer of the Turkish National Anthem — A619

1986, Dec. 27   Litho.   **Perf. 13½x13**

2367	A619	20 l multi	.35 .20

Road Safety A620

Intl. Year of Shelter for the Homeless A622

Butterflies A621

1987, Feb. 4   Litho.   **Perf. 13x13½**

2368	A620	10 l Use seatbelts	.20 .20
2369	A620	20 l Don't drink alcohol and drive	.20 .20
2370	A620	150 l Observe speed limit	.75 .20
		Nos. 2368-2370 (3)	1.15 .60

For surcharges see Nos. 2466, 2477-2478.

1987, Feb. 25   **Perf. 13½x13**

2371	A621	10 l Celerio euphorbiae	.30 .20
2372	A621	20 l Vanessa atalanta	.30 .20
2373	A621	100 l Euplagia quadripunctaria	.90 .20
2374	A621	120 l Colias crocea	1.50 .20
		Nos. 2371-2374 (4)	3.00 .80

1987, Mar. 18   Litho.   **Perf. 13x13½**

2375	A622	200 l multi	.70 .20

Karabuk Iron and Steel Works, 50th Anniv. A623

1987, Apr. 3   Litho.   **Perf. 13½x13**

2376	A623	50 l Interior	.30 .20
2377	A623	200 l Exterior	.80 .20

Natl. Sovereignty — A624

1987, Apr. 23   **Perf. 13½x13**

2378	A624	50 l multi	.35 .20

Founding of the Turkish state, 67th anniv.

Architecture — A625

Europa: 50 l, Turkish History Institute, 1951-67, designed by Turgut Cansever with Ertur Yener. 200 l, Social Insurance Institute, 1963, designed by Sedad Hakki Eldem.

1987, Apr. 28   **Perf. 13**

2379	A625	50 l multi	7.00 2.00
2380	A625	200 l multi	19.00 4.00

92nd Session, Intl. Olympic Committee, Istanbul, May 9-12 — A626

1987, May 9   Litho.   **Perf. 13x13½**

2381	A626	200 l multi	1.00 .20

Turkish States Type of 1984

Sixteen states (Devleti and Imparatorlugu rulers and flags): 10 l, Batu Khan, Golden Horde State (1227-1502). 20 l, Kutlug Timur Khan, Great Timur Empire (1368-1507). 50 l, Babur Shah, Babur Empire (1526-1858). 200 l, Osman Bey Gasi, Ottoman Empire (1299-1923).

1987, June 20   **Perf. 12½x13**

2382	A587	10 l multi	.30 .20
2383	A587	20 l multi	.60 .20
2384	A587	50 l multi	1.25 .20
2385	A587	200 l multi	2.50 .20
		Nos. 2382-2385 (4)	4.65 .80

Album of the Conqueror, Mehmet II, 15th Cent., Topkapi Palace Museum — A627

Untitled paintings by Mehmet Siyah Kalem: 10 l, Two warriors, vert. 20 l, Three men, donkey. 50 l, Blackamoor whipping horse. 200 l, Demon, vert.

Perf. 13½x13, 13x13½

1987, July 1   Litho.

2386	A627	10 l multi	.20 .20
2387	A627	20 l multi	.20 .20
2388	A627	50 l multi	.35 .20
2389	A627	200 l multi	1.50 .20
		Nos. 2386-2389 (4)	2.25 .80

Natl. Palaces A628

1987, Sept. 25   **Perf. 13½x13**

2390	A628	50 l Ihlamur, c. 1850	.20 .20
2391	A628	200 l Kucuksu Pavilion, 1857	.65 .20

See Nos. 2425-2426.

"Tughra," Suleiman's Calligraphic Signature — A629

Designs: 30 l, Portrait, vert. 200 l, Suleiman Receiving a Foreign Minister, contemporary miniature, vert. 270 l, Bust, detail of bas-relief, The Twenty-Three Law-Givers, entrance to the gallery of the US House of Representatives.

Litho., Litho. & Engr. (270 l)
1987, Oct. 1   Perf. 13½x13, 13x13½

2392	A629	30 l	multi	.30	.20
2393	A629	50 l	shown	.60	.20
2394	A629	200 l	multi	1.25	.20
2395	A629	270 l	multi	2.50	.20
	Nos. 2392-2395 (4)			4.65	.80

Suleiman the Magnificent (1494-1566), sultan of the Turkish Empire (1520-1566). On No. 2395, the gold ink was applied by a thermographic process producing a shiny, raised effect.

A630

Presidents: a, Cemal Gursel (1961-1966). b, Cevdet Sunay (1966-1973). c, Fahri S. Koruturk (1973-1980). d, Kenan Evren (1982-). e, Ismet Inonu (1938-1950). f, Celal Bayar (1950-1960). g, Mustafa Kemal Ataturk (1923-1938).

1987, Oct. 29   Litho.   Imperf.
Souvenir Sheet

2396	A630	Sheet of 7	2.25	1.50
a.-f.		50 l any single	.20	.20
g.		100 l multi, 26x37mm	.25	.20

A631

1988, Apr. 9   Litho.   Perf. 13

2397	A631	50 l	shown	.75	.50
2398	A631	200 l	Mosque, architectural elements	2.25	1.00

Joseph (Mimar) Sinan (1489-1588), architect.

Health — A632

1988, May 4

2399	A632	50 l	Immunization, horiz.	.20	.20
2400	A632	200 l	Fight drug abuse	.35	.20
2401	A632	300 l	Safe work conditions, horiz.	.45	.20
2402	A632	600 l	Organ donation	1.10	.30
	Nos. 2399-2402 (4)			2.15	.90

Europa Issue

Telecommunications — A633

Transport and communication: 200 l, Modes of transportation, vert.

1988, May 2   Litho.   Perf. 13, 12½

2403	A633	200 l	multi	3.75	1.50
2404	A633	600 l	multi	11.00	2.50

Steam, Electric and Diesel Locomotives A634

50 l, American Standard steam engine, c. 1850. 100 l, Steam engine produced in Esslingen for Turkish railways, 1913. 200 l, Henschel Krupp steam engine, 1926. 300 l, E 43001 Toshiba electric engine produced in Japan, 1987. 600 l, MTE-Tulomsas #24361 diesel-electric high-speed engine, 1984.

1988, May 24   Perf. 13

2405	A634	50 l	buff, brn & blk	.30	.20
2406	A634	100 l	buff, brn & blk	.50	.20
2407	A634	200 l	buff, brn & blk	.80	.20
2408	A634	300 l	buff, brn & blk	1.25	.20
2409	A634	600 l	buff, brn & blk	2.00	.30
	Nos. 2405-2409 (5)			4.85	1.10

Court of Cassation (Supreme Court), 120th Anniv. A635

1988, July 1   Litho.   Perf. 13½x13

2410	A635	50 l	multi	.25	.20

Bridge Openings — A636

Designs: 200 l, Fatih Sultan Mehmet Bridge, Kavacik-Hisarustu. 300 l, Seto Ohashi (Friendship) Bridges, the Minami and Kita.

1988, July 3   Litho.   Perf. 13x13½

2411	A636	200 l	multi	.75	.20
2412	A636	300 l	multi	1.25	.20

Telephone System A637

1988, Aug. 24   Litho.   Perf. 13½x13

2413	A637	100 l	multi	.30	.20

1988 Summer Olympics, Seoul A638

Perf. 12½x13, 13x12½
1988, Sept. 17   Litho.

2414	A638	100 l	Running	.50	.20
2415	A638	200 l	Archery	1.50	.20
2416	A638	400 l	Weight lifting	2.00	.25
2417	A638	600 l	Gymnastics, vert.	3.00	.35
	Nos. 2414-2417 (4)			7.00	1.00

Naim Suleymanoglu, 1988 Olympic Gold Medalist, Weight Lifting — A639

1988, Oct. 5   Litho.   Perf. 13x12½

2418	A639	1000 l	multi	2.75	2.00

Aerospace Industries A640

1988, Oct. 28   Perf. 13½x13, 13x13½

2419	A640	50 l	Gear, aircraft, vert.	.20	.20
2420	A640	200 l	shown	.60	.20

Butterflies A641

1988, Oct. 28   Perf. 13½x13

2421	A641	100 l	Gonepteryx rhamni	.30	.20
2422	A641	200 l	Chazara briseis	.50	.20
2423	A641	400 l	Allancastria cerisyi godart	1.00	.20
2424	A641	600 l	Nymphalis antiopa	1.50	.40
a.		Souvenir sheet of 4, #2421-2424	3.50	3.00
	Nos. 2421-2424 (4)			3.30	1.00

ANTALYA '88.

Natl. Palaces Type of 1987
1988, Nov. 3   Litho.   Perf. 13

2425	A628	100 l	Maslak Royal Lodge, c. 1890	.20	.20
2426	A628	400 l	Yildiz Sale Pavilion, 1889	.70	.20

Souvenir Sheet

Kemal Ataturk — A642

1988, Nov. 10   Perf. 13x13½

2427	A642	400 l	multi	1.50	.40

Medicinal Plants of Anatolia A643

1988, Dec. 14   Litho.   Perf. 13

2428	A643	150 l	Tilia rubra	.45	.20
2429	A643	300 l	Malva silvestris	.65	.20
2430	A643	600 l	Hyoscyamus niger	1.25	.20
2431	A643	900 l	Atropa belladonna	2.50	.30
	Nos. 2428-2431 (4)			4.85	.90

Stamps of 1983-85 Surcharged

Perf. 13, 11½x12½
1989, Feb. 8   Litho.

2432	A579	50 l	on 15 l	No. 2263	.20	.20
2433	A608	75 l	on 10 l	No. 2334	.20	.20
2434	A608	150 l	on 20 l	No. 2336	.30	.20
	Nos. 2432-2434 (3)				.70	.60

Surcharge on No. 2432 is slightly different.

Artifacts in the Museum of Anatolian Civilizations, Ankara — A644

Designs: 150 l, Seated Goddess with Child, neolithic bisque figurine, Hacilar, 6th millennium B.C. 300 l, Lead figurine, Alisar Huyuk, Assyrian Trading Colonies Era, c. 19th cent. B.C. 600 l, Human-shaped vase, Kultepe, Assyrian Trading Colonies Era, 18th cent. B.C. 1000 l, Ivory mountain god, Bogazkoy, Hittite Empire, 14th cent. B.C.

1989, Feb. 8   Litho.   Perf. 13½x13

2435	A644	150 l	multi	.40	.20
2436	A644	300 l	multi	.60	.20
2437	A644	600 l	multi	1.00	.20
2438	A644	1000 l	multi	2.50	.30
	Nos. 2435-2438 (4)			4.50	.90

See Nos. 2458-2461, 2495-2498, 2520-2523, 2617-2620.

NATO, 40th Anniv. A645

Wmk. 394
1989, Apr. 4   Litho.   Perf. 13½

2439	A645	600 l	multi	.90	.20

Europa Issue

Children's Games — A646

Perf. 13x12½
1989, Apr. 23   Wmk. 394

2440	A646	600 l	Leapfrog	13.50	2.00
2441	A646	1000 l	Open the door, Headbezirgan	21.00	3.50

Steamships — A647

Perf. 13½x13
1989, July 1   Litho.   Wmk. 394

2442	A647	150 l	Sahilbent	.40	.20
2443	A647	300 l	Ragbet	.60	.20
2444	A647	600 l	Tari	1.00	.20
2445	A647	1000 l	Guzelhisar	2.00	.30
	Nos. 2442-2445 (4)			4.00	.90

French Revolution, Bicent. — A648

Kemal Ataturk — A649

Wmk. 394

1989, July 14   **Litho.**   *Perf. 14*
2446	A648	600 l multi	1.25	.20

1989, Aug. 16   *Perf. 13x13½*
2447	A649	2000 l gray & bluish gray	2.00	.50
2448	A649	5000 l gray & deep red brn	5.00	1.25

See Nos. 2485-2486, 2538-2541. For surcharges see Nos. 2655-2656.

No. 2336 Surcharged in Bright Blue
Perf. 11½x12½

1989, Aug. 31   **Litho.**   **Unwmk.**
2449	A608	500 l on 20 l	.70	.20

Photography, 150th Anniv. — A650

1989, Oct. 17   *Perf. 13½x13*
2450	A650	175 l Camera	.25	.20
2451	A650	700 l Shutter	.85	.20

State Exhibition of Paintings and Sculpture A651

Designs: 200 l, *Manzara*, by Hikmet Onat. 700 l, *Sari Saz*, by Bedri Rahmi Eyuboglu. 1000 l, *Kadin*, by Zuhtu Muridoglu.

Perf. 13½x13

1989, Oct. 30   **Litho.**   **Wmk. 394**
2452	A651	200 l multicolored	.25	.20
2453	A651	700 l multicolored	.80	.20
2454	A651	1000 l multicolored	1.10	.30
		Nos. 2452-2454 (3)	2.15	.70

Jawaharlal Nehru, 1st Prime Minister of Independent India — A652

1989, Nov. 14   *Perf. 13½x12½*
2455	A652	700 l multicolored	.80	.20

Sea Turtles A653

1989, Nov. 16   *Perf. 13½x13*
2456	A653	700 l Caretta caretta	1.50	.20
2457	A653	1000 l Chelonia mydas	1.75	.30
a.		Souv. sheet of 2, #2456-2457	4.50	1.25

Artifacts Type of 1989
Perf. 13x12½, 12½x13

1990, Feb. 8   **Litho.**   **Wmk. 394**
2458	A644	100 l Ivory female deity	.20	.20
2459	A644	200 l Ceremonial vessel	.25	.20
2460	A644	500 l Seated goddess pendant	.65	.20
2461	A644	700 l Carved lion	.90	.20
		Nos. 2458-2461 (4)	2.00	.80

Nos. 2458 and 2460 vert.

Wars of Dardanelles, 1915 — A654

1990, Mar. 18   *Perf. 13*
2462	A654	1000 l multicolored	.85	.20

EXPO '90 Intl. Garden and Greenery Exposition, Osaka — A655

Illustration reduced.

Perf. 12½x13

1990, Apr. 1   **Litho.**   **Wmk. 394**
2463		1000 l Bridge at left	1.00	.25
2464		1000 l Pavilion at left	1.00	.25
a.		A655 Pair, #2463-2464	2.00	.75

Nos. 2301, 2368 and 2284 Surcharged
Perfs. as Before

1990, Apr. 4   **Litho.**
2465	A589	50 l on 5 l #2301	.20	.20
2466	A620	100 l on 10 l #2368	.20	.20
2467	A589	200 l on 70 l #2284	.20	.20
		Nos. 2465-2467 (3)	.60	.60

Grand Natl. Assembly, 70th Anniv. — A657

Europa 1990 — A658

1990, Apr. 23   *Perf. 13*
2468	A657	300 l multicolored	.30	.20

1990, May 2
Post offices.
2469	A658	700 l Ulus, Ankara	3.75	1.00
2470	A658	1000 l Sirkeci, Istanbul, horiz.	6.25	1.50

8th European Supreme Courts Conf. A659

1990, May 7   **Litho.**   *Perf. 12½x13*
2471	A659	1000 l multicolored	1.00	.25

Salamandra Salamandra — A660

World Environment Day: No. 2473, Trituris vittatus. No. 2474, Bombina bombina. No. 2475, Hyla arborea, vert.

1990, June 5   *Perf. 13½x13*
2472	A660	300 l multicolored	.25	.20
2473	A660	500 l multicolored	.40	.20
2474	A660	1000 l multicolored	.85	.40
2475	A660	1500 l multicolored	1.25	.60
		Nos. 2472-2475 (4)	2.75	1.40

Turkey-Japan Relations, Cent. — A661

1990, June 13   *Perf. 12½x13*
2476	A661	1000 l multicolored	1.00	.50

Traffic Types of 1987 and Nos. 2283-2284 Surcharged

1990, June 20   *Perf. 14*
2477	A620	150 l on 10 l	.50	.20
2478	A620	300 l on 20 l	.80	.20

Perf. 11½x12½
2479	A589	300 l on 70 l #2284	.80	.20
2480	A589	1500 l on 20 l #2283	3.00	.60
		Nos. 2477-2480 (4)	5.10	1.20

Boats in Saintes Marines — A662

Paintings by Vincent Van Gogh (1853-1890): 300 l, Self-portrait, vert. 1000 l, Vase with Sunflowers, vert. 1500 l, Road of Cypress and Stars.

Wmk. 394

1990, July 29   **Litho.**   *Perf. 13*
2481	A662	300 l multicolored	.50	.20
2482	A662	700 l multicolored	.85	.30
2483	A662	1000 l multicolored	1.60	.40
2484	A662	1500 l multicolored	2.25	.65
		Nos. 2481-2484 (4)	5.20	1.55

Ataturk Type of 1989

1990, Aug. 1   **Unwmk.**   *Perf. 14*
2485	A649	500 l gray & olive grn	.40	.20
2486	A649	1000 l gray & rose vio	.85	.40

A664   A665

Perf. 13x13½

1990, Aug. 22   **Wmk. 394**
2487	A664	300 l multicolored	.35	.20

Intl. Literacy Year.

1990, Oct. 17   **Litho.**   *Perf. 13x13½*

State exhibition of paintings and sculpture by: 300 l, Nurullah Berk. 700 l, Cevat Dereli. 1000 l, Nijad Sirel.
2488	A665	300 l multicolored	.30	.20
2489	A665	700 l multicolored	.60	.25
2490	A665	1000 l multicolored	.90	.35
		Nos. 2488-2490 (3)	1.80	.80

PTT, 150th Anniv. A666

Past and present communication methods: 200 l, Post rider, truck, train, airplane, ship. 250 l, Telegraph key, computer terminal. 400 l, Telephone switchboard, computerized telephone exchange. 1500 l, Power lines, satellite.

1990, Oct. 23   *Perf. 14*
2491	A666	200 l multicolored	.20	.20
2492	A666	250 l multicolored	.20	.20
2493	A666	400 l multicolored	.30	.20
2494	A666	1500 l multicolored	1.10	2.25
a.		Souv. sheet of 4, #2491-2494	3.00	2.25
		Nos. 2491-2494 (4)	1.80	2.85

For surcharges see Nos. 2657-2659.

Artifacts Type of 1989

300 l, Figurine of a woman, c. 5000-4500 BC. 500 l, Sistrum, c. 2100-2000 BC. 1000 l, Spouted vessel with 3-footed pedestal, c. 2000-1750 BC. 1500 l, Ceremonial vessel, 1900-1700 BC.

1991, Feb. 8   **Litho.**   *Perf. 13x12½*
2495	A644	300 l multi	.20	.20
2496	A644	500 l multi	.40	.20
2497	A644	1000 l multi	.70	.35
2498	A644	1500 l multi	1.10	.55
		Nos. 2495-2498 (4)	2.40	1.30

Nos. 2495-2498 are vert.

Lakes of Turkey A667

Wmk. 394

1991, Apr. 24   **Litho.**   *Perf. 13*
2499	A667	250 l Abant	.20	.20
2500	A667	500 l Egridir	.40	.20
2501	A667	1500 l Van	1.10	.60
		Nos. 2499-2501 (3)	1.70	1.00

Europa — A668

Unwmk.

1991, May 6   **Litho.**   *Perf. 13*
2502	A668	1000 l multicolored	9.00	2.00
2503	A668	1500 l multi, diff.	13.50	3.00

Natl. Statistics Day — A669

1991, May 9   *Perf. 13½x13*
2504	A669	500 l multicolored	.40	.20

Eastern Mediterranean Fiber Optic
Cable System — A670

1991, May 13
2505 A670 500 l multicolored   .40   .20

European Conf. of
Transportation
Ministers — A671

1991, May 22   *Perf. 13*
2506 A671 500 l multicolored   .40   .20

Caricature
Art
A672

500 l, "Amcabey" by Cemal Nadir Guler.
1000 l, "Abdulcanbaz" by Turhan Selcuk, vert.

                          Wmk. 394
1991, Sept. 11   Litho.   *Perf. 13*
2507 A672 500 l multicolored   .40   .20
2508 A672 1000 l multicolored   .80   .40

Ceramics
A673

Wall facings: 500 l, 13th cent. Seljuk bird.
1500 l, 16th cent. Ottoman floral pattern.

1991, Sept. 23   *Perf. 13½x13*
2509 A673 500 l multicolored   .40   .20
2510 A673 1500 l multicolored   1.25   .60

Symposium on Intl.
Protection of Human
Rights,
Antalya — A674

1991, Oct. 4   *Perf. 13x12½*
2511 A674 500 l multicolored   .40   .20

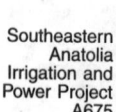

Southeastern
Anatolia
Irrigation and
Power Project
A675

1991, Oct. 6   Unwmk. *Perf. 13½x13*
2512 A675 500 l multicolored   .40   .20

Turkish Fairy
Tales — A676

Baldboy: 500 l, With genie. 1000 l, At party.
1500 l, Plowing field.

1991, Oct. 9   *Perf. 13x13½*
2513 A676 500 l multicolored   .40   .20
2514 A676 1000 l multicolored   .80   .40
2515 A676 1500 l multicolored   1.25   .60
      Nos. 2513-2515 (3)   2.45 1.20

Snakes
A677

               Perf. 12½x13
1991, Oct. 23   **Wmk. 394**
2516 A677 250 l Eryx jaculus   .20   .20
2517 A677 500 l Elaphe
                 quatuorlineata   .40   .20
2518 A677 1000 l Vipera
                 xanthina   .80   .40
2519 A677 1500 l Vipera
                 kaznakovi   1.25   .60
      Nos. 2516-2519 (4)   2.65 1.40
      World Environment Day.

Antiquities Type of 1989

300 l, Statuette of Mother Goddess, Neolithic, 6000 B.C., vert. 500 l, Hasanoglan statuette, Early Bronze Age, 3000 B.C., vert.
1000 l, Inandik vase, Old Hittite, 18th cent.
B.C., vert. 1500 l, Lion statuette, Urartian, 8th
cent. B.C., vert.

                          Wmk. 394
1992, Feb. 12   Litho.   *Perf. 13*
2520 A644 300 l multicolored   .25   .20
2521 A644 500 l multicolored   .40   .20
2522 A644 1000 l multicolored   .80   .40
2523 A644 1500 l multicolored   1.25   .60
      Nos. 2520-2523 (4)   2.70 1.40

Discovery
of
America,
500th
Anniv.
A678

                          Wmk. 394
1992, May 4   Litho.   *Perf. 13*
2524 A678 1500 l shown   5.00 1.00
2525 A678 2000 l Balloons, vert.   7.50 1.50
      Europa.

Settlement
of Jews in
Turkey,
500th
Anniv.
A679

1992, May 15   *Perf. 12½x13*
2526 A679 1500 l multicolored   .55   .30

A681

A682

                          Wmk. 394
1992, June 1   Litho.   *Perf. 13*
2529 A681 500 l multicolored   .25   .20
      Turkish Court of Accounts, 130th anniv.

1992, June 4
2530 A682 1500 l multicolored   .60   .30
      Economics Congress, Izmir.

World Environment Day — A683

1992, June 5   Litho.   *Perf. 13*
2531 A683 500 l Vanellus vanel-
                 lus   .20   .20
2532 A683 1000 l Oriolus oriolus   .35   .20
2533 A683 1500 l Tadorna
                 tadorna   .55   .30
2534 A683 2000 l Halcyon
                 smyrnensis,
                 vert.   .70   .40
      Nos. 2531-2534 (4)   1.80 1.10

Ataturk Type of 1989 and:

Kemal
Ataturk — A683a

A683b

10,000 l, Full face. 100,000 l, Facing left.

**Perf. 13, 14 (#2539, 2541, 2543-
2544A)**

1992-96		Litho.		Unwmk.	
2538	A649	250 l	gold, brn & org	.20	.20
2539	A649	5000 l	gold & vio	.80	.40
2540	A649	10,000 l	gold & blue	3.75	1.90
2541	A649	20,000 l	gold & lil rose	3.25	1.60
2542	A683a	50,000 l	multi	3.50	1.75
2543	A683b	50,000 l	lake & pink	1.75	.90
2544	A683a	100,000 l	grn bl & yel org	3.50	1.75
	Nos. 2538-2544 (7)			16.75	8.50

Issued: 250 l, 10,000 l, 5/28/92; 5000 l,
20,000 l, 9/29/93; #2542, 11/10/94; #2543,
100,000 l, 6/1/96.
For surcharges see Nos. 2655, 2732.

Black Sea
Economic
Cooperation
Summit — A684

                          Wmk. 394
1992, June 25   Litho.   *Perf. 13*
2545 A684 1500 l multicolored   .60   .30

1992
Summer
Olympics,
Barcelona
A685

Wmk. 394
1992, July 25   **Wmk. 39**
2546 A685 500 l Doves   .20
2547 A685 1000 l Boxing   .45
2548 A685 1500 l Weight lifting   .60
2549 A685 2000 l Wrestling   .90
      Nos. 2546-2549 (4)   2.15 1.2

Anatolian
Folktales — A686

Scenes: 500 l, Woman carrying milk to
soldiers. 1000 l, Pouring milk into trough.
1500 l, Soldiers dipping into trough.

                          Perf. 13x12½
1992, Sept. 23   Litho.   Wmk. 394
2550 A686 500 l multicolored   .20   .20
2551 A686 1000 l multicolored   .30   .20
2552 A686 1500 l multicolored   .50   .25
      Nos. 2550-2552 (3)   1.00   .65

Turkish Handicrafts — A687

500 l, Embroidered flowers. 1000 l, Dolls in
traditional costumes, vert. 3000 l, Saddlebags.

1992, Oct. 21   *Perf. 13½x13, 13x13½*
2553 A687 500 l multicolored   .20   .20
2554 A687 1000 l multicolored   .35   .20
2555 A687 3000 l multicolored   .95   .50
      Nos. 2553-2555 (3)   1.50   .90
      See Nos. 2585-2588, 2611-2612.

Fruits — A688

                          Wmk. 394
1992, Nov. 25   Litho.   *Perf. 13*
2556 A688 500 l Cherries   .20   .20
2557 A688 1000 l Peaches   .30   .20
2558 A688 3000 l Grapes   .90   .45
2559 A688 5000 l Apples   1.50   .75
      Nos. 2556-2559 (4)   2.90 1.60
      See Nos. 2565-2568.

Famous
Men — A689

Designs: No. 2560, Sait Faik Abasiyanik
(1906-54), writer. No. 2561, Fikret Mualla
Saygi (1904-67), artist. No. 2562, Cevat Sakir
Kabaagacli (1886-1973), author. No. 2563,
Muhsin Ertugrul (1892-1979), actor and pro-
ducer. No. 2564, Asik Veysel Satiroglu (1894-
1973), composer.

Perf. 14, 13½x13 (#2561, 2564)
1992, Dec. 30   **Litho.**
2560 A689 T multicolored   .20   .20
2561 A689 T multicolored   .20   .20
2562 A689 M multicolored   .30   .20
2563 A689 M multicolored   .30   .20
2564 A689 M multicolored   .30   .20
      Nos. 2560-2564 (5)   1.30 1.00

Value on day of issue: Nos. 2560-2561,
500 l. Nos. 2562-2564, 1000 l.
See Nos. 2577-2581.

Fruit Type of 1992
Wmk. 394
993, Apr. 28   **Litho.**   **Perf. 13**

565	A688	500 l	Bananas	.20	.20
566	A688	1000 l	Oranges	.25	.20
567	A688	3000 l	Pears	.75	.35
568	A688	5000 l	Pomegranates	1.25	.65
		Nos. 2565-2568 (4)		2.45	1.40

Europa — A690

Sculptures by: 1000 l, Hadi Bara. 3000 l, Zuhtu Muridoglu.

1993, May 3

2569	A690	1000 l	multicolored	.70	.30
2570	A690	3000 l	multicolored	2.00	.60

A691

Wmk. 394
1993, July 6   **Litho.**   **Perf. 13**

2571	A691	2500 l	lt bl, dk bl & gold	.50	.25

Economic Cooperation Organization Meeting, Istanbul.

Houses — A692

1993, July 7

Various houses from Black Sea region.

2572	A692	1000 l	multicolored	.25	.20
2573	A692	2500 l	multi, horiz.	.50	.25
2574	A692	3000 l	multicolored	.65	.30
2575	A692	5000 l	multi, horiz.	1.00	.50
		Nos. 2572-2575 (4)		2.40	1.25

See Nos. 2604-2607, 2631-2634, 2647-2650, 2676-2679.

Hodja Ahmet Yesevi (1093-1166), Poet — A693

1993, July 28

2576	A693	3000 l	lt bl, dk bl & gold	.65	.30

Famous Men Type of 1992

Designs: No. 2577, Haci Arif Bey (1831-84), composer. No. 2578, Neyzen Tevfik Kolayli (1878-1953), poet. No. 2579, Munir Nurettin Selcuk (1900-81), composer, musician. No. 2580, Cahit Sitki Taranci (1910-56), poet. No. 2581, Orhan Veli Kanik (1914-50), writer.

Perf. 14, 13½x13 (2578-2580)
1993, Aug. 4   **Litho.**   **Unwmk.**

2577	A689	T	brown & red brown	.20	.20
2578	A689	T	brown & red brown	.20	.20
2579	A689	M	brown & red brown	.25	.20
2580	A689	M	brown & red brown	.25	.20
2581	A689	M	brown & red brown	.25	.20
		Nos. 2577-2581 (5)		1.15	1.00

Value on day of issue: Nos. 2577-2578, 500 l. Nos. 2579-2581, 1000 l.

Istanbul, Proposed Site for 2000 Olympics A694

1993, Aug. 11   **Perf. 12½x13**

2582	A694	2500 l	multicolored	.50	.25

Protection of Mediterranean Sea Against Pollution — A695

Unwmk.
1993, Oct. 12   **Litho.**   **Perf. 13**

2583	A695	1000 l	Amphora on sea floor	.20	.20
2584	A695	3000 l	Dolphin jumping	.50	.25

Handicrafts Type of 1992
Perf. 12½x13, 13x12½
1993, Oct. 21   **Wmk. 394**

2585	A687	1000 l	Painted rug	.20	.20
2586	A687	2500 l	Earrings	.40	.20
2587	A687	5000 l	Money purse, vert.	.80	.40
		Nos. 2585-2587 (3)		1.40	.80

Republic, 70th Anniv. — A696

1993, Oct. 29   **Wmk. 394**   **Perf. 13**

2588	A696	1000 l	multicolored	.20	.20

Civil Defence Organization — A697

Perf. 12½x13
1993, Nov. 25   **Unwmk.**

2589	A697	1000 l	multicolored	.20	.20

Turksat Satellite — A698   **Natl. Water Project — A699**

Designs: 1500 l, Satellite, globe, map of Turkey. 5000 l, Satellite transmissions to areas in Europe and Asia.

Perf. 13x13½
1994, Jan. 21   **Litho.**   **Wmk. 394**

2590	A698	1500 l	multicolored	.20	.20
2591	A698	5000 l	multicolored	.40	.20

1994, Feb. 28   **Perf. 13x12½**

2592	A699	1500 l	multicolored	.20	.20

Native Cuisine A700

Perf. 12½x13
1994, Mar. 23   **Litho.**   **Wmk. 394**

2593	A700	1000 l	Ezogel in corbasi	.20	.20
2594	A700	1500 l	Mixed dolma	.20	.20
2595	A700	3500 l	Shish kebabs	.30	.20
2596	A700	5000 l	Baklava	.40	.20
		Nos. 2593-2596 (4)		1.10	.80

Europa A701

1500 l, Marie Curie (1867-1934), chemist, vert. 5000 l, Albert Einstein (1879-1955), physicist.

Unwmk.
1994, May 2   **Litho.**   **Perf. 13**

2597	A701	1500 l	multicolored	.75	.40
2598	A701	5000 l	multicolored	1.50	.70

World Environment Day — A703

Views of: 6000 l, Antalya. 8500 l, Mugla, vert.

Wmk. 394
1994, June 5   **Litho.**   **Perf. 13**

2602	A703	6000 l	multicolored	.40	.20
2603	A703	8500 l	multicolored	.60	.30

Houses Type of 1993

2500 l, 2-story housing complex. 3500 l, 3-story home with balconies. 6000 l, Tri-level country home. 8500 l, 2-story home.

1994, July 7

2604	A692	2500 l	multi, horiz.	.20	.20
2605	A692	3500 l	multi, horiz.	.25	.20
2606	A692	6000 l	multi, horiz.	.45	.20
2607	A692	8500 l	multi, horiz.	.60	.30
		Nos. 2604-2607 (4)		1.50	.90

Tourism A704

1994, Aug. 3

2608	A704	5000 l	Hiking	.35	.20
2609	A704	10,000 l	Rafting	.70	.35

Project of the Year 2001 A705

1994, Aug. 27

2610	A705	2500 l	multicolored	.20	.20

Handicrafts Type of 1992

Designs: 7500 l, Kusak pattern used on 18th cent. clothing, vert. 12,000 l, Pacalik pattern used on 19th cent. clothing.

1994, Oct. 21

2611	A687	7500 l	multicolored	.40	.20
2612	A687	12,500 l	multicolored	.70	.35

Mushrooms — A706

1994, Nov. 16

2613	A706	2500 l	Morchella conica	.20	.20
2614	A706	5000 l	Agaricus bernardii	.35	.20
2615	A706	7500 l	Lactarius deliciosus	.50	.20
2616	A706	12,500 l	Macrolepiota procera	.85	.45
		Nos. 2613-2616 (4)		1.90	1.10

See Nos. 2637-2640.

Antiquities Type of 1989

Lydian Treasures, 6th cent. B.C.: 2500 l, Silver pitcher, vert. 5000 l, Silver incense burner, vert. 7500 l, Gold, glass necklace. 12,500 l, Gold brooch.

1994, Dec. 7

2617	A644	2500 l	multicolored	.20	.20
2618	A644	5000 l	multicolored	.35	.20
2619	A644	7500 l	multicolored	.50	.25
2620	A644	12,500 l	multicolored	.85	.45
		Nos. 2617-2620 (4)		1.90	1.10

Nevruz, New Day A707

1995, Mar. 21

2621	A707	3500 l	multicolored	.20	.20

Europa — A708

1995, May 5

2622	A708	3500 l	Flowers	.60	.30
2623	A708	15,000 l	Olive branch	1.50	.50

Istanbul '96 World Stamp Exhibition — A709

a, 7000 l, Buildings. b, 25,000 l, Tower, buildings. c, 7000 l, Mosque, city along harbor. c, 25,000 l, Residential area, mosque, harbor.

1995, May 24

2624	A709	Block of 4, #a.-d.		3.25	1.50

Nos. 2624a-2624b and 2624c-2624d are each continuous designs.

European Nature Conservation Year — A710

1995, June 5
2625	A710	5000 l	Field of poppies	.30 .20
2626	A710	15,000 l	Trees	.85 .40
2627	A710	25,000 l	Mountain valley	1.40 .70
			Nos. 2625-2627 (3)	2.55 1.30

A711   A712

1995, Feb. 1
2628	A711	15,000 l	red & blue	.80 .40

Motion Pictures, cent.

1995, Apr. 23
2629	A712	5000 l	multicolored	.25 .20

1sh Conference of the Moslem Women Parliamentaries, Pakistan.

Houses Type of 1993

5000 l, 2-story block house. 10,000 l, Tower of part-stone house. 15,000 l, Interior view of 2-story house, horiz. 20,000 l, Three unit-connecting apartment, horiz.

1995, July 7
2631	A692	5000 l	multicolored	.25 .20
2632	A692	10,000 l	multicolored	.50 .25
2633	A692	15,000 l	multicolored	.80 .40
2634	A692	20,000 l	multicolored	1.00 .50
			Nos. 2631-2634 (4)	2.55 1.35

UN, 50th Anniv. — A713

1995, Oct. 24
2635	A713	15,000 l	shown	.80 .40
2636	A713	30,000 l	UN emblem, "50"	1.60 .80

Mushroom Type of 1994

Designs: 5000 l, Amanita phalloides. 10,000 l, Lepiota helveola. 20,000 l, Gyromitra esculenta. 30,000 l, Amanita gemmata.

1995, Nov. 16
2637	A706	5000 l	multicolored	.20 .20
2638	A706	10,000 l	multicolored	.40 .20
2639	A706	20,000 l	multicolored	.80 .40
2640	A706	30,000 l	multicolored	1.25 .60
			Nos. 2637-2640 (4)	2.65 1.40

Children's Rights A714

6,000 l, Rainbow, hearts, flower, sun in sky. 10,000 l, Child's hand drawing letter "A."

1996, Mar. 13
2641	A714	6,000 l	multicolored	.20 .20
2642	A714	10,000 l	multicolored	.40 .20

Fauna — A715

Designs: a, 5,000 l, Bee. b, 10,000 l, Dog. c, 15,000 l, Rooster. d, 30,000 l, Fish.

1996, Apr. 10   **Unwmk.**
2643	A715	Sheet of 4, #a.-d.		2.25 1.10

Instanbul '96.

Famous Women A716

Perf. 12½x13
1996, May 5   **Litho.**   **Unwmk.**
2644	A716	10,000 l	Nene Hatun	.60 .30
2645	A716	40,000 l	Halide Edip Adivar	2.40 .50

Europa.

World Environment Day — A717

Unwmk.
1996, June 3   **Litho.**   **Perf. 13**
2646	A717	50,000 l	multicolored	1.75 .90

Houses Type of 1993

Designs: 10,000 l, Tri-level block house, horiz. 15,000 l, Two story with bay window, gate at entrance to side courtyard, horiz. 25,000 l, Two story townhouse, double wooden doors at bottom. 50,000 l, Flat-roofed, two-story townhouse.

1996, July 7   **Perf. 13**
2647	A692	10,000 l	multicolored	.35 .20
2648	A692	15,000 l	multicolored	.60 .30
2649	A692	25,000 l	multicolored	.90 .45
2650	A692	50,000 l	multicolored	1.75 .90
			Nos. 2647-2650 (4)	3.60 1.85

1996 Summer Olympic Games, Atlanta — A718

a, 10,000 l, Archery. b, 15,000 l, Wrestling. c, 25,000 l, Weight lifting. d, 50,000 l, Hurdles.

1996, July 19
2651	A718	Sheet of 4, #a.-d.		2.75 1.75

ISTANBUL '96.

Turkish Press, 50th Anniv. A719

1996, July 24   **Perf. 12½x13**
2652	A719	15,000 l	multicolored	.60 .30

Euro '96, European Soccer Championships, Great Britain — A720

1996, June 8   **Perf. 13**
2653	A720	15,000 l	Player, vert.	.60 .30
2654	A720	50,000 l	Soccer ball, flags	1.75 .90

Nos. 2447, 2491, 2493-2494, 2538 Surcharged in Orange or Deep Violet Blue

or

Perfs., Printing Methods as Before
1996, July 22
2655	A649	T on 250 l #2537 (O)		.25 .20
2656	A649	T on 2000 l #2447		.25 .20
2657	A666	M on 200 l #2491		.40 .20
2658	A666	M on 400 l #2493		.40 .20
2659	A666	M on 1500 l #2494		.40 .20
		Nos. 2655-2659 (5)		1.70 1.00

Nos. 2655-2656 and 2657-2659 had face values of 10,000 l and 15,000 l on day of issue.
See No. 2732.

Methods of Transportation — A721

a, 25,000 l, Airplane (b). b, 50,000 l, Helicopter, ship (d). c, 75,000 l, Train. d, 100,000 l, Bus (c).

Unwmk.
1996, Sept. 27   **Litho.**   **Perf. 13**
2660	A721	Sheet of 4, #a.-d.		7.00 3.50

Istanbul '96.

New Year A722

Unwmk.
1996, Oct. 23   **Litho.**   **Perf. 13**
2661	A722	15,000 l	multicolored	.55 .30

Social and Cultural Heritage A723

10,000 l, Public Library, Bayezit, Amasy
15,000 l, Mosque and hospital, Divrigi.

1996, Dec. 17   **Litho.**   **Perf.**
2662	A723	10,000 l	multicolored	.20 .2
2663	A723	15,000 l	multicolored	.30 .2

Stories and Legends — A724

Europa: 25,000 l, Little children dressed in flowers and leaves riding a giant peacock 70,000 l, Genie, man being riding a giant bird

1997, May 5   **Litho.**   **Perf. 13**
2664	A724	25,000 l	multicolored	.65 .30
2665	A724	70,000 l	multicolored	1.90 .55

White Cat — A725

Designs: a, 25,000 l, Tail, hindquarters. b, 50,000 l, Back legs. c, 75,000 l, Front legs. d, 150,000 l, Face.

1997, Apr. 23
2666	A725	Sheet of 4, #a.-d.		5.00 3.50

Language Day — A726

1997, May 13   **Litho.**   **Perf. 13**
2667	A726	25,000 l	multicolored	.30 .20

World Environment Day — A727

1997, June 5
2668	A727	35,000 l	multicolored	.45 .20

Orchids — A728

Designs: 25,000 l, Ophrys tenthredinifera. 70,000 l, Ophrys apifera.

1997, May 28
2669	A728	25,000 l	multicolored	.30 .20
2670	A728	70,000 l	multicolored	.90 .45

25th Intl.
Istanbul
Festival
A729

1997, June 13 — Perf. 13½
Background Color

2671	A729	15,000 l	blue	.20	.20
2672	A729	25,000 l	pink	.40	.20
2673	A729	70,000 l	blue green	1.00	.50
2674	A729	75,000 l	purple	1.40	.70
2675	A729	100,000 l	green blue	1.40	.70
		Nos. 2671-2675 (5)		4.00	2.10

House Type of 1993

Inscribed: 25,000 l, Bir Urfa Evi, vert. 40,000 l, Bir Mardin Evi. 80,000 l, Bir Diyarbakir Evi. 100,000 l, Kemaliye'de Bir Ev, vert.

1997, July 7 — Litho. — Perf. 13

2676	A692	25,000 l	multicolored	.35	.20
2677	A692	40,000 l	multicolored	.55	.30
2678	A692	80,000 l	multicolored	1.10	.55
2679	A692	100,000 l	multicolored	1.40	.70
		Nos. 2676-2679 (4)		3.40	1.75

A730

A731

Flowers: 40,000 l, Lilium candidum. 100,000 l, Euphorbia pulcherima.

1997, Sept. 8 — Litho. — Perf. 13

2680	A730	40,000 l	multicolored	.40	.20
2681	A730	100,000 l	multicolored	1.00	.50

1997, Sept. 13

World Air Games: No. 2682, Hang gliding. No. 2683, Sailplane. No. 2684, Man pointing up at biplanes. No. 2685, Hot air balloon.

2682	A731	40,000 l	multicolored	.40	.20
2683	A731	40,000 l	multicolored	.40	.20
2684	A731	100,000 l	multicolored	1.00	.60
2685	A731	100,000 l	multicolored	1.00	.60
		Nos. 2682-2685 (4)		2.80	1.60

Forestry
Congress
A732

1997, Oct. 13 — Litho. — Perf. 13

2686	A732	50,000 l	multicolored	.50	.25

15th European
Gymnastics
Congress — A733

1997, Oct. 13

2687	A733	100,000 l	multicolored	1.00	.50

Traditional
Women's
Headcovers
A734

1997, Nov. 19 — Litho. — Perf. 13

2688	A734	50,000 l	Gaziantep	.60	.30
2689	A734	50,000 l	Canakkale	.60	.30
2690	A734	100,000 l	Isparta	1.25	.60
2691	A734	100,000 l	Bursa	1.25	.60
		Nos. 2688-2691 (4)		3.70	1.80

See Nos. 2711-2714, 2748-2751, 2765-2768.

1998 Winter Olympic Games,
Nagano — A735

Slalom skiers: No. 2692, #1 on bib. No. 2693, #119 on bib.

1998, Feb. 7 — Litho. — Perf. 13

2692		125,000 l	multicolored	1.00	.50
2693		125,000 l	multicolored	1.00	.50
a.		A735 Pair, #2692-2693		2.25	1.00

Intl. Year of the Ocean — A736

Designs: a, 50,000 l, Turtle, jellyfish. b, 75,000 l, Fish, octopus. c, 125,000 l, Coral, crab. d, 125,000 l, Fish, coral, starfish.

1998, Apr. 18 — Litho. — Perf. 13

2694	A736	Sheet of 4, #a.-d.	3.25	2.25

Dardenelles
Campaign — A737

Memorial Statues: #2695, "Mother with Children," Natl. War Memorial, Wellington. #2696, "With Great Respect to the Mehmetcik, Gallipoli" (Turkish soldier carrying wounded ANZAC).

1998, Mar. 18 — Litho. — Perf. 13

2695	A737	125,000 l	multicolored	1.00	.50
2696	A737	125,000 l	multicolored	1.00	.50

See New Zealand Nos. 1490-1491.

A739

Europa (National Festivals and Holidays): 100,000 l, Kemal Ataturk, natl. flag, people celebrating. 150,000 l, Ataturk, natl. flag, children of different races celebrating together.

1998, May 5

2697	A738	100,000 l	multicolored	*1.25*	*.35*
2698	A738	150,000 l	multicolored	*1.75*	*.50*

1998, May 1 — Litho. — Perf. 13

Tulips: 50,000 l, Sylvestris. 75,000 l, Armena (pink). 100,000 l, Armena (violet). 125,000 l, Saxatilis.

2699	A739	50,000 l	multicolored	.50	.25
2700	A739	75,000 l	multicolored	.75	.40
2701	A739	100,000 l	multicolored	1.00	.60
2702	A739	125,000 l	multicolored	1.25	.60
		Nos. 2699-2702 (4)		3.50	1.75

Souvenir Sheet

World Environment Day — A740

Owls: a, Two on branches. b, One flying, one standing.

1998, June 5 — Litho. — Perf. 13½

2703	A740	150,000 l	Sheet of 2, #a.-b.	3.00	1.50

Contemporary Arts — A741

75,000 l, Couple dancing. 100,000 l, Man playing cello. 150,000 l, Ballerina.

1998, Aug. 14 — Litho. — Perf. 13

2704	A741	75,000 l	multi	.70	.35
2705	A741	100,000 l	multi, vert.	.90	.45
2706	A741	150,000 l	multi, vert.	1.40	.70
		Nos. 2704-2706 (3)		3.00	1.50

Kemal
Ataturk — A742

1998, Aug. 20 — Litho. — Perf. 13

2707	A742	150,000 l	cl & brn	1.10	.50
2708	A742	175,000 l	bl & rose brn	1.25	.65
2709	A742	250,000 l	brn & cl	1.90	.95
2710	A742	500,000 l	brn & dk bl	3.75	1.90
		Nos. 2707-2710 (4)		8.00	4.00

Traditional Headcovers Type of 1997

1998, Nov. 24 — Litho. — Perf. 13

2711	A734	75,000 l	Afyon	.70	.35
2712	A734	75,000 l	Ankara	.70	.35
2713	A734	175,000 l	Mus	1.60	.80
2714	A734	175,000 l	Mugla	1.60	.80
		Nos. 2711-2714 (4)		4.60	2.30

Turkish Republic, 75th Anniv. — A743

275,000 l, Flag, silhouette of Ataturk.

1998, Oct. 29 — Litho. — Perf. 13

2715	A743	175,000 l	shown	1.75	.90
a.		Souvenir sheet of 1, imperf.		1.75	1.25
2716	A743	275,000 l	red & blk	2.75	1.40
a.		Souvenir sheet of 1, imperf.		2.75	2.00

Nos. 2715a, 2716a have simulated perforations.

Famous
People
A744

#2717, Ihap Hulusi Görey (1898-1986). #2718, Bedia Muvahht (1897-1993). No. 2719, Feza Gürsey (1921-92). #2720, Haldun Taner (1915-86). #2721, Vasfi Riza Zobu (1902-92).

1998, Dec. 31 — Photo. — Perf. 13

2717	A744	M	gray bl, bl & plum	.25	.20
2718	A744	M	lil, dp lil & plum	.25	.20
2719	A744	T	org, brn & plum	.50	.25
2720	A744	T	gray vio, vio & plum	.50	.25
2721	A744	T	grn, blk & plum	.50	.25
		Nos. 2717-2721 (5)		2.00	1.15

On day of issue, Nos. 2717-2718 were valued at each, and Nos. 2719-2721 were valued at each.

NATO,
50th Anniv.
A745

1999, Apr. 4 — Litho. — Perf. 13

2722	A745	200,000 l	multicolored	1.00	.50

Ottoman
Empire, 700th
Anniv.
A746

Designs: No. 2723, Man on horse surrounded by people in buildings. No. 2724, Man on horse, three men in foreground. No. 2725, Men seated.
No. 2726, Man on white horse, castle. No. 2727, Group of women, horiz.

1999, Apr. 12

2723	A746	175,000 l	multicolored	.85	.45
2724	A746	175,000 l	multicolored	.85	.45
2725	A746	175,000 l	multicolored	.85	.45
		Nos. 2723-2725 (3)		2.55	1.35

Size: 79x119mm, 119x79mm
Imperf

2726	A746	200,000 l	multicolored	.95	.50
2727	A746	200,000 l	multicolored	.95	.50

Europa
A747

Natl. Parks: 175,000 l, Köprülü Canyon, vert. 200,000 l, Kackarlar.

A738

Perf. 13¼x13, 13x13¼
1999, May 5   **Litho.**
2728	A747	175,000 l multicolored	1.00	.40
2729	A747	200,000 l multicolored	1.25	.50

World Environment Day — A748

No. 2730: a, 100,000 l, Tetrax tetrax. 200,000 l, Hoplopterus spinosus.
No. 2731: a, 100,000 l, Marbled duck. b, 200,000 l, Sitta kruperi.

1999, June 3   Litho.   Perf. 13¼
2730	A748	Sheet of 2, #a.-b.	1.40	.70
2731	A748	Sheet of 2, #a.-b.	1.40	.70

See Nos. 2763-2764.

No. 2538 Surcharged in Violet Blue

1999   Litho.   Perf. 13
2732	A649	T on 250 l #2537	.35	.20

No. 2732 sold for 50,000 l on day of issue.

Souvenir Sheet

National Congress During the War for Independence — A749

Designs: a, 100,000 l, Ataturk, two other men, building. b, 100,000 l, Ataturk, two other men seated. c, 200,000 l, Two men standing in front of building. d, 200,000 l, Ataturk standing in front of building.

Perf. 13¼x13
1999, June 22   Litho.   Unwmk.
2733	A749	Sheet of 4, #a.-d.	2.50	1.25

Art — A750

1999, July 8   Litho.   Perf. 13x13¼
2734	A750	250,000 l shown	1.00	.50
2735	A750	250,000 l multi, diff.	1.00	.50

Tourism — A751

Perf. 13x13¼, 13¼x13
1999, Sept. 19   **Litho.**

No. 2736, Temple to Zeus. No. 2737, Antakya Archaelogical Museum, horiz. No. 2738, Golf course, Antalya. No. 2739, Sailboat off Bodrum.

2736	A751	125,000 l multi	1.00	.50
2737	A751	125,000 l multi	1.00	.50
2738	A751	225,000 l multi	1.00	.50
2739	A751	225,000 l multi	1.00	.50
		Nos. 2736-2739 (4)	4.00	2.00

Dams A752

225,000 l, Cubuk 1. 250,000 l, Atatürk.

1999, Sept. 19   Litho.   Perf. 13¼x13
2740	A752	225,000 l multi	1.10	.55
2741	A752	250,000 l multi	1.40	.65

Kemal Atatürk — A753

1999, Sept. 27   Litho.   Perf. 13¾
2742	A753	225,000 l grn & brn	1.10	.55
2743	A753	250,000 l brn & lil	1.40	.65
2744	A753	500,000 l pink & grn	2.75	1.40
2745	A753	1,000,000 l bl & red	5.25	2.75
		Nos. 2742-2745 (4)	10.50	5.35

Thanks for Earthquake Rescue Efforts — A754

Designs: 225,000 l, Hands holding wreckage, flowers, vert. 250,000 l, Rescuers, handclasp.

Perf. 13¼x13, 13x13¼
1999, Oct. 15   **Litho.**
2746	A754	225,000 l multi	1.10	.55
2747	A754	250,000 l multi	1.40	.65

Women's Headcovers Type of 1997
1999, Nov. 24   Litho.   Perf. 13¼
2748	A734	150,000 l Manisa	.80	.40
2749	A734	150,000 l Nigde	.80	.40
2750	A734	250,000 l Antalya	1.40	.65
2751	A734	250,000 l Amasya	1.40	.65
		Nos. 2748-2751 (4)	4.40	2.10

Caravansaries — A755

1999, Dec. 24   Litho.   Perf. 13¼x13
2752	A755	150,000 l Sarapsa	.50	.25
2753	A755	250,000 l Obruk	.85	.45

Millennium A756

Designs: 275,000 l, Earth, brain, satellite. 300,000 l, Monachus monachus.

2000, Feb. 1   Litho.   Perf. 13¼
2754	A756	275,000 l multi	1.00	.50
2755	A756	300,000 l multi	1.10	.55

Merchant Ships A757

125,000 l, Bug. 150,000 l, Gülcemal. 275,000 l, Nusret. 300,000 l, Bandirma.

2000, Mar. 16
2756	A757	125,000 l multi	.40	.20
2757	A757	150,000 l multi	.50	.25
2758	A757	275,000 l multi	.90	.45
2759	A757	300,000 l multi	1.00	.50
		Nos. 2756-2759 (4)	2.80	1.40

Grand National Assembly, 80th Anniv. — A758

Perf. 13x13¼, 13¼x13
2000, Apr. 23   **Litho.**
2760	A758	275,000 l shown	.90	.45
2761	A758	300,000 l Sprouts, horiz.	1.00	.50

Europa, 2000
Common Design Type
2000, May 9   Perf. 13x13¼
2762	CD17	300,000 l multi	1.00	.50

World Environment Day Type of 1999
Souvenir Sheets

No. 2763, 275,000 l: a, Aquila heliaca. b, Picus viridis.
No. 2764, 275,000 l: a, Oxyura leucocephala. b, Recurvirostra avosetta.

2000, June 5   Litho.   Perf. 13¼
Sheets of 2, #a-b
2763-2764	A748	Set of 2	3.75	1.90

Women's Headcover Type of 1997
Designs: No. 2765, 275,000 l, Trabzon. No. 2766, 275,000 l, Tunceli. No. 2767, 275,000 l, Corum. No. 2768, 275,000 l, Izmir.

2000, July 15
2765-2768	A734	Set of 4	3.25	1.60

Souvenir Sheet

Nomadic Life A759

a, Woman at loom, woman seated. b, Women & containers. c, Women, 2 goats, carpet on tent rope. d, Woman, children, 6 goats, carpet on rope.

2000
2769		Sheet of 4	3.50	1.7
a.-d.	A759	300,000 l Any single	.85	.4

Military Leaders — A760

Designs: 100,000 l, Gen. Yakup Sevki Subasi. 200,000 l, Lt. Gen. Musa Kazim Karabekir (c. 1882-1948). 275,000 l, Marshal Mustafa Fevzi Cakmak (1876-1950). 300,000 l, Gen. Cevat Cobanli (1871-1938).

2000
2770-2773	A760	Set of 4	2.50	1.25

2000 Summer Olympics, Sydney A761

Designs: 125,000 l, Rhythmic gymnastics. 150,000 l, Swimming. 275,000 l, High jump. 300,000 l, Archery.

2000
2774-2777	A761	Set of 4	2.50	1.25

Crocuses — A762

Designs: 250,000 l, Crocus chrysanthus. 275,000 l, Crocus olivieri. 300,000 l, Crocus biflorus. 1,250,000 l, Crocus sativus.

2000, Oct. 9   Litho.   Perf. 13¾x14
2778-2781	A762	Set of 4	5.75	3.00

Architecture — A763

Designs: 200,000 l, Arslan Baba. 275,000 l, Karasaç Ana. 300,000 l, Hoca Ahmet Yesevi.

2000, Oct. 19   Litho.   Perf. 13¼x13
2782-2784	A763	Set of 3	2.25	1.10

Turksat 2A — A764

Women's Clothing — A765

2001, Jan. 25   Litho.   Perf. 13x13¾
2785	A764	200,000 l multi	.35	.20

2001, Mar. 19

Designs: No. 2786, 200,000 l, Afyon. No. 2787, 200,000 l, Balikesir. No. 2788, 325,000 l, Kars. No. 2789, 325,000 l, Tokat.

2786-2789	A765	Set of 4	1.90	.95

Women's Headcovers Type of 1997

Designs: 200,000 l, Mersin-Silifke. 50,000 l, Sivas. 425,000 l, Aydin. 450,000 l, akkari.

2001, Apr. 16	Litho.	Perf. 13¼	
790-2793 A734	Set of 4	1.90	.90

Europa — A766

Waterfalls: 450,000 l, Düdenbasi. 500,000 l, erköprü.

2001, May 5		Perf. 13	
794-2795 A766	Set of 2	1.40	.70

Aviators A767

Designs: 250,000 l, Capt. Ismail Hakki Bey. 300,000 l, Lieut. Nuri Bey. 450,000 l, Lieut. Sadik Bey. 500,000 l, Capt. Fethi Bey.

2001, May 15			
2796-2799 A767	Set of 4	2.10	1.00

World Environment Day Type of 1999

No. 2800, 300,000 l: a, Turdus pilaris. b, Carduelis carduelis.
No. 2801, 450,000 l: a, Merops apiaster. b, Upupa epops.

2001, June 5		Perf. 13¼	
	Sheets of 2, #a-b		
2800-2801 A748	Set of 2	2.10	1.00

Kemal Ataturk — A768

Medicinal Plants — A769

Ataturk (1881-1938) and: 300,000 l, Turkish flag. 450,000 l, Birthplace

2001, May 19	Litho.	Perf. 13	
2802-2803 A768	Set of 2	1.25	.60

2001, June 27		Perf. 13¾	

Designs: 250,000 l, Myrtus communis. 300,000 l, Achillea millefolium. 450,000 l, Hypericum perforatum. 500,000 l, Rosa moyesii. 1,750,000 l, Crataegus oxyacantha.

2804-2808 A769	Set of 5	4.50	2.25

Horses A770

Designs: 300,000 l, Horse and foal. No. 2810, 450,000 l, Three horses. No. 2811, 450,000 l, Two horses galloping. 500,000 l, Horse, vert.

2001, July 16		Perf. 13	
2809-2812 A770	Set of 4	2.40	1.25

Merchant Ships Type of 2000

Designs: 250,000 l, Resitpasa. No. 2814, 300,000 l, Mithatpasa. No. 2815, 300,000 l, Gülnihal, 500,000 l, Aydin.

2001, Sept. 3		Perf. 13¼	
2813-2816 A757	Set of 4	1.60	.80

Architecture A771

Designs: No. 2817, 300,000 l, Sirvansahlar Palace, Baku, Azerbaijan. No. 2818, 300,000 l, Sultan Tekes Mausoleum, Urgench, Uzbekistan. 450,000 l, Timur Mausoleum, Samarkand, Uzbekistan. 500,000 l, While Tlightning Mausoleum, Bursa.

2001, Oct. 15			
2817-2820 A771	Set of 4	1.90	.95

Sultan Nevruz A772

2002, Mar. 21	Litho.	Perf. 13¼	
2821 A772	400,000 l multi	.55	.30

Women's Clothing Type of 2001

Designs: 350,000 l, Kastamonu. 400,000 l, Canakkale. 500,000 l, Amasya-Ilisu. 600,000 l, Elazig.

2002, Apr. 16		Perf. 13x13¼	
2822-2825 A765	Set of 4	2.25	1.10

Europa — A773

2002, May 5	Litho.	Perf. 13x13¼	
2826 A773	500,000 l multi	.70	.35

2002 World Cup Soccer Championships, Japan and Korea — A774

Designs: 400,000 l, Players, referee. 600,000 l, Crowd, player making scissors kick.

2002, May 31	Litho.	Perf. 13¼x13	
2827-2828 A774	Set of 2	1.25	.60

Famous Men — A775

Designs: 100,000 l, Muzaffer Sarisözen (1898-1963), musician. 400,000 l, Arif Nihat Asya (1904-75), writer. 500,000 l, Vedat Tek (1873-1942), architect. 600,000 l, Hilmi Ziya Ulken (1901-74), philosopher. 2,500,000 l, Ibrahim Calli (1882-1960), painter.

2002, June 3		Perf. 13¾x14	
2829-2833 A775	Set of 5	5.00	2.50

Souvenir Sheet

Wild Cats — A776

No. 2834: a, Panthera pardus tulliana. b, Lynx lynx. c, Panthera tigris. d, Caracal caracal.

2002, June 20		Perf. 13¼x13	
2834 A776	400,000 l Sheet of 4,		
	#a-d	1.90	.95

Souvenir Sheet

Shells — A777

Various shells: a, 400,000 l. b, 500,000 l. c, 600,000 l. d, 750,000 l.

2002, June 25			
2835 A777	Sheet of 4, #a-d	2.75	1.40

Third Place Finish of Turkish Team in World Cup Soccer Championships — A778

Designs: 400,000 l, Players in action. 700,000 l, Team photo.

2002, July 29		Perf. 13x13¼	
2836-2837 A778	Set of 2	1.40	.70

String Instruments A779

Designs: 450,000 l, Violin. 700,000 l, Bass.

2002, Oct. 10		Perf. 13¼x13	
2838-2839 A779	Set of 2	1.25	.60

Merchant Ships Type of 2000

Designs: 450,000 l, Ege. 500,000 l, Ayvalik. No. 2842, 700,000 l, Karadeniz. No. 2843, 700,000 l, Marakaz.

2002, Nov. 4	Litho.	Perf. 13	
2840-2843 A757	Set of 4	3.00	1.50

Souvenir Sheet

Turkish and Hungarian Buildings — A780

No. 2844: a, 450,000 l, Gazi Kassim Pasha Mosque, Pécs, Hungary. b, 700,000 l, Rakoczi House, Tekirdag, Turkey.

2002, Dec. 2	Litho.	Perf. 13¼	
2844 A780	Sheet of 2, #a-b	1.40	1.40

See Hungary Nos. 3819-3820.

BJK Soccer Team, Cent. — A781

Team emblem and: 500,000 l, Eagle, Turkish and team flags. 700,000 l, Eagle, stadium. 750,000 l, Soccer players. 1,000,000 l, Eagle's head.

2003, Mar. 3		Perf. 13x13¼	
2845-2848 A781	Set of 4	3.50	3.50

A782   A783

Europa: 500,000 l, Travel poster. 700,000 l, Ankara State Theater poster.

2003, May 9	Litho.	Perf. 13	
2849-2850 A782	Set of 2	1.50	.75

2003, May 29			

Conquest of Constantinople, 550th Anniv.: No. 2851, 500,000 l, Leaders at table. No. 2852, 500,000 l, Sultan Mehmet II seated. 700,000 l, Robe. 1,500,000 l, Sultan Mehmet II and cartouche.

2851-2854 A783	Set of 4	4.50	2.25

Souvenir Sheet

World Environment Day — A784

No. 2855: a, Gazella subgutturosa. b, Cervus elaphus. c, Capreolus capreolus. d, Cervus dama.

2003, June 5			
2855 A784	500,000 l Sheet of 4,		
	#a-d	3.00	1.50

Zodiac
A785

2003, June 19   *Perf. 13¼*
2856 A785 500,000 l multi   .70   .35

Women's Clothing Type of 2001

Designs: No. 2857, 500,000 l, Sivas. No. 2858, 500,000 l, Gaziantep. No. 2859, 700,000 l, Erzincan. No. 2860, 700,000 l, Ankara-Beypazari.

2003, July 8   *Perf. 13*
2857-2860 A765 Set of 4   3.50 1.75

Fruit
Blossoms — A786

Blossoms: 500,000 l, Ayva cicegi (quince). 700,000 l, Erik cicegi (plum). 750,000 l, Kiraz cicegi (cherry) . 1,000,000 l, Nar cicegi (pomegranate). 3,000,000 l, Portakal cicegi (orange).

2003, July 25   *Perf. 13¾x14*
2861-2865 A786 Set of 5   8.50 4.25

Brass
Instruments
A787

Designs: 600,000 l, French horn. 800,000 l, Trumpet.

2003, Sept. 23 Litho. Perf. 13¼x13
2866-2867 A787 Set of 2   2.00 1.00

SEMI-POSTAL STAMPS

Regular Issues
Overprinted in
Carmine or Black

Overprint reads: "For War Orphans"
Perf. 12, 13½ and Compound
1915   Unwmk.
On Stamps of 1905
B1 A18 10pa dull grn (#119)   .75   .35
B2 A18 10pi orange brown   9.00   .80
On Stamp of 1906
B3 A18 10pa dull grn (#128)   40.00 8.50
On Stamps of 1908
B4 A19 10pa blue green   1.50   .75
B5 A19 5pi dark violet   40.00 8.50
      Nos. B1-B5 (5)   91.25 18.90

With Additional
Overprint

B6 A19 10pa blue green   125.00 85.00
On Stamps of 1909
B7   A21 10pa blue green   1.00   .75
  a.   Inverted overprint   22.50 22.50
  b.   Double overprint, one invtd. 30.00 30.00
B8   A21 20pa carmine rose   1.00   .75
  a.   Inverted overprint   27.50 27.50
B9   A21 1pi ultra   1.00   .75
B10 A21 5pi dark violet   4.00 1.50
      Nos. B7-B10 (4)   7.00 3.75

With Additional
Overprint

B11 A21 10pa blue green   1.00   .75
  b.   Double overprint, one inverted 5.00 5.00
B12 A21 20pa carmine rose   1.50   .75
B13 A21 1pi ultra   2.00   .75
On Stamps of 1913
B14 A22 10pa blue green   1.00   .75
  a.   Inverted overprint   22.50 22.50
B15 A22 1pi ultra   1.00   .75
  a.   Double overprint   5.00 5.00
      Nos. B11-B15 (5)   6.50 3.75

With Additional
Overprint

B16 A22 10pa blue green   1.25   .75
  a.   Inverted overprint   27.50 27.50
On Newspaper Stamp of 1908
B17 A19 10pa blue green   175.00 65.00
On Newspaper Stamp of 1909
B18 A21 10pa blue green   1.25 1.00

Regular Issues
Overprinted in
Carmine or Black

1916
On Stamps of 1901
B19 A17 1pi blue   1.00   .50
B20 A17 5pi lilac rose   5.50 1.50
On Stamps of 1905
B21 A18 1pi brt blue   7.00 2.00
B22 A18 5pi brown   7.50 4.50
On Stamp of 1906
B23 A18 1pi brt blue   1.00   .75
On Stamps of 1908
B24 A19 20pa carmine (Bk)   300.00
B25 A19 10pi red   400.00 150.00

With Additional
Overprint

B26 A19 20pa carmine   1.00   .75
B27 A19 1pi brt blue (C)   20.00 5.00
On Stamps of 1909
B28 A21 20pa carmine rose   1.00   .75
B29 A21 1pi ultra   .50   .75
B30 A21 10pi dull red   150.00 90.00

With Additional
Overprint

B31 A21 20pa carmine rose   .75   .50
B32 A21 1pi ultra   1.00   .75
On Stamps of 1913
B33 A22 20pa carmine rose   1.00   .75
B34 A22 1pi ultra   1.00   .35
  a.   Inverted overprint   5.00 5.00
B35 A22 10pi dull red   18.00 14.00

With Additional
Overprint

B36 A22 20pa carmine rose   1.00   .75
On Newspaper Stamps of 1901
B37 A16 5pi ocher   9.00 6.00
  a.   5pa bister, No. P37   150.00 150.00

Regular Issues
Surcharged in Black

On Stamp of 1899
B38 A11 10pa on 20pa vio brn   1.00   .75
On Stamp of 1905
B39 A18 10pa on 20pa carmine   1.00   .75
On Stamp of 1906
B40 A18 10pa on 20pa carmine   .90   .75
On Newspaper Stamp of 1893-99
B41 A11 10pa on 20pa violet brn 2.00 1.50
      Nos. B38-B41 (4)   4.90 3.75

Nos. 346-349
Overprinted

B42 A41 10pa carmine   1.00   .75
  a.   Inverted overprint   6.75 6.75
B43 A41 20pa ultra   1.00   .75
  a.   Inverted overprint   6.75 6.75
B44 A41 1pi violet & blk   1.00   .90
  a.   Inverted overprint   6.75 6.75
B45 A41 5pi yel brn & blk   1.00   .75
  a.   Inverted overprint   11.00 11.00
      Nos. B42-B45 (4)   4.00 3.15

Nos. B42-B45 formed part of the Postage Commemoration issue of 1916.

A Soldier's
Farewell — SP1

1917, Feb. 20 Engr. Perf. 12½
B46 SP1 10pa red violet   .70   .20

For surcharges see Nos. 600, B47.

Stamp of Same
Design Surcharged

B47 SP1 10pa on 20pa car rose   1.10   .20

Badge of the
Society — SP9

School
Teacher — SP1

Carrie
Chapman Catt
SP16

Kemal Atatür
SP23

Designs: 2k+2k, Woman farmer. 2½k+2½ Typist. 4k+4k, Aviatrix and policewoma 5k+5k, Women voters. 7½k+7½k, Yildiz Pa ace, Istanbul. 12½k+12½k, Jane Addam 15k+15k, Grazia Deledda. 20k+20k, Selm Lagerlof. 25k+25k, Bertha von Suttne 30k+30k, Sigrid Undset. 50k+50k, Mar Sklodowska Curie.

1935, Apr. 17   Photo.   Perf. 11
Inscribed: "XII Congres Suffragiste International"

B54	SP9	20pa + 20pa brn	.50	.2
B55	SP10	1k + 1k rose car	.75	.2
B56	SP10	2k + 2k sl bl	.75	.2
B57	SP10	2½k + 2½k yel grn	.75	.2
B58	SP10	4k + 4k blue	.75	.3
B59	SP10	5k + 5k dl vio	1.00	.4
B60	SP10	7½k + 7½k org red	2.00	.7
B61	SP16	10k + 10k org	2.50	.8
B62	SP16	12½k + 12½k dk bl	6.50	2.2
B63	SP16	15k + 15k violet	6.50	2.2
B64	SP16	20k + 20k red org	12.00	3.7
B65	SP16	25k + 25k grn	21.00	7.2
B66	SP16	30k + 30k ultra	47.50	35.0
B67	SP16	50k + 50k dk sl grn	82.50	60.0
B68	SP23	100k + 100k brn car	77.50	57.5
		Nos. B54-B68 (15)	262.50	171.0

12th Congress of the Women's Intl. Alliance.

Catalogue values for unused stamps in this section, from this point to the end of the section, are for Never Hinged items.

Katip
Chelebi — SP24

Perf. 10½
1958, Sept. 24 Litho. Unwmk
B69 SP24 50k + 10k gray   .25 .2

Mustafa ibn 'Abdallah Katip Chelebi Haj Khalifa (1608-1657), Turkish author.

Road
Building
Machine
SP25

Kemal
Atatürk — SP26

Ruins,
Göreme
SP27

Design: 25k+5k, Tanks and planes.

1958, Oct. 29
B70 SP25 15k + 5k orange .20 .20
B71 SP26 20k + 5k lt red brn .20 .20
B72 SP25 25k + 5k brt grn .20 .20
Nos. B70-B72 (3) .60 .60

The surtax went to the Red Crescent Society and to the Society for the Protection of Children.
For surcharge see No. 1440.

1959, July 8   Litho.   Perf. 10
B73 SP27 105k + 10k pur & buff .30 .20

Issued for tourist publicity.

Istanbul
SP28

1959, Sept. 11
B74 SP28 105k + 10k lt bl & red .25 .20

15th International Tuberculosis Congress.

Manisa
Asylum
SP29

Merkez
Muslihiddin
SP30

Kermis at Manisa: 90k+5k, Sultan Camil Mosque, Manisa, vert.

1960, Apr. 17   Unwmk.   Perf. 13
B75 SP29 40k + 5k grn & lt bl .25 .20
B76 SP29 40k + 5k vio & rose lil .25 .20
B77 SP29 90k + 5k dp cl & car rose .60 .20
B78 SP30 105k + 10k multi .80 .20
Nos. B75-B78 (4) 1.90 .80

Census Chart
SP31

Census
Symbol — SP32

1960, Sept. 23   Photo.   Perf. 11½
Granite Paper
B79 SP31 30k + 5k bl & rose pink .20 .20
B80 SP32 50k + 5k grn, dk bl & ultra .25 .20

Issued for the 1960 Census.

Old
Observatory
SP33

Fatin
Gökmen — SP34

Designs: 30k+5k, Observatory emblem. 75k+5k, Building housing telescope.

1961, July 1   Litho.   Perf. 13
B81 SP33 10k + 5k grnsh bl & grn .20 .20
B82 SP33 30k + 5k vio & blk .30 .20
B83 SP34 40k + 5k brown .30 .20
B84 SP33 75k + 5k olive grn .50 .20
Nos. B81-B84 (4) 1.30 .80

Kandill Observatory, 50th anniversary.

Anti-Malaria
Work — SP35

UNICEF, 10th anniv.: 30k+5k, Mother and infant, horiz. 75k+5k, Woman distributing pasteurized milk.

1961, Dec. 11   Unwmk.   Perf. 13
B85 SP35 10k + 5k Prus green .20 .20
B86 SP35 30k + 5k dull violet .30 .20
B87 SP35 75k + 5k dk violet bis .60 .20
Nos. B85-B87 (3) 1.10 .60

Malaria
Eradication
Emblem,
Map and
Mosquito
SP36

1962, Apr. 7   Litho.
B88 SP36 30k + 5k dk & lt brn .20 .20
B89 SP36 75k + 5k blk & lil .20 .20

WHO drive to eradicate malaria.

Poinsettia
SP37

Wheat and
Census Chart
SP38

Flowers: 40k+10k, Bird of paradise flower. 75k+10k, Water lily.

1962, May 19   Perf. 12½x13½
Flowers in Natural Colors
B90 SP37 30k + 10k lt bl & blk .20 .20
B91 SP37 40k + 10k lt bl & blk .30 .20
B92 SP37 75k + 10k lt bl & blk .80 .30
Nos. B90-B92 (3) 1.30 .70

Inscribed: "Umumi Ziraat Sayimi"
1963, Apr. 14   Photo.   Perf. 11½
Design: 60k+5k, Wheat and chart, horiz.
B93 SP38 40k + 5k gray grn & yel .20 .20
B94 SP38 60k + 5k org yel & blk .20 .20

1961 agricultural census. Two black bars obliterate "Kasim 1960" inscription.

Red Lion and
Sun, Red
Crescent, Red
Cross and
Globe
SP39

Designs: 60k+10k, Emblems in flowers, vert. 100k+10k, Emblems on flags.

1963, Aug. 1   Perf. 13
B95 SP39 50k + 10k multi .20 .20
B96 SP39 60k + 10k multi .25 .20
B97 SP39 100k + 10k multi .40 .30
Nos. B95-B97 (3) .85 .70

Centenary of International Red Cross.

Angora
Goat — SP40

Olympic Torch
Bearer — SP41

Animals: 10k+5k, Steppe cattle, horiz. 50k+5k, Arabian horses, horiz. 60k+5k, Three Angora goats. 100k+5k, Montofon cattle, horiz.

1964, Oct. 4   Litho.   Perf. 13
B98 SP40 10k + 5k multi .30 .20
B99 SP40 30k + 5k multi .30 .20
B100 SP40 50k + 5k multi .50 .20
B101 SP40 60k + 5k multi .70 .20
B102 SP40 100k + 5k multi .90 .20
Nos. B98-B102 (5) 2.70 1.00

Issued for Animal Protection Day.

1964, Oct. 10   Unwmk.
Designs: 10k+5k, Running, horiz. 60k+5k, Wrestling. 100k+5k, Discus.
B103 SP41 10k + 5k org brn, blk & red .30 .20
B104 SP41 50k + 5k ol, blk & red .30 .20
B105 SP41 60k + 5k bl, blk & red .70 .20
B106 SP41 100k + 5k vio, blk, red & sil 1.00 .30
Nos. B103-B106 (4) 2.30 .90

18th Olympic Games, Tokyo, Oct. 10-25.

Map of
Dardanelles
and Laurel
SP42

Designs: 90k+10k, Soldiers and war memorial, Canakkale. 130k+10k, Turkish flag and arch, vert.

1965, Mar. 18   Litho.   Perf. 13
B107 SP42 50k + 10k vio, yel & gold .20 .20
B108 SP42 90k + 10k vio bl, bl, yel & grn .25 .20
B109 SP42 130k + 10k dk brn, red & yel .45 .40
Nos. B107-B109 (3) .90 .80

50th anniversary of Battle of Gallipoli.

Tobacco
Plant — SP43

Goddess, Basalt
Carving — SP44

50k+5k, Tobacco leaves and Leander's tower, horiz. 100k+5k, Tobacco leaf.

1965, Sept. 16   Unwmk.   Perf. 13
B110 SP43 30k + 5k brn, lt brn & grn .20 .20
B111 SP43 50k + 5k vio bl, ocher & pur .30 .20
B112 SP43 100k + 5k blk, ol grn & ocher .50 .25
Nos. B110-B112 (3) 1.00 .65

Second International Tobacco Congress.

Perf. 13½x13, 13x13½
1966, June 6   Litho.
Archaeological Museum, Ankara: 30k+5k, Eagle and rabbit, ivory carving, horiz. 60k+5k, Bronze bull. 90k+5k, Gold pitcher.
B113 SP44 30k + 5k multi .20 .20
B114 SP44 50k + 5k multi .30 .20
B115 SP44 60k + 5k multi .45 .25
B116 SP44 90k + 5k multi .60 .35
Nos. B113-B116 (4) 1.55 1.00

Grand
Hotel
Ephesus
SP45

Designs: 60k+5k, Konak Square, Izmir, vert. 130k+5k, Izmir Fair Grounds.

1966, Oct. 18   Litho.   Perf. 12
B117 SP45 50k + 5k multi .20 .20
B118 SP45 60k + 5k multi .25 .20
B119 SP45 130k + 5k multi .55 .35
Nos. B117-B119 (3) 1.00 .75

33rd Congress of the Intl. Fair Assoc.

Europa Issue, 1967
Common Design Type
1967, May 2   Litho.   Perf. 13x13½
Size: 22x33mm
B120 CD10 100k + 10k multi 1.00 .50
a. Dark blue ("Europa") omitted
B121 CD10 130k + 10k multi 1.50 1.00

Cloverleaf
Crossing,
Map of
Turkey
SP46

130k+5k, Highway E5 & map of Turkey.

1967, June 30   Litho.   Perf. 13
B122 SP46 60k + 5k multi .30 .20
B123 SP46 130k + 5k multi, vert. .60 .30

Inter-European Express Highway, E5.

WHO
Emblem
SP47

1968, Apr. 7   Litho.   Perf. 13
B124 SP47 130k + 10k lt ultra, blk & yel .35 .20

WHO, 20th anniversary.

Efem Pasha, Dr. Marko Pasha and View of Istanbul — SP48

60k+10k, Omer Pasha, Dr. Abdullah Bey & wounded soldiers. 100k+10k, Ataturk & Dr. Refik Say in front of Red Crescent headquarters, vert.

1968, June 11   Litho.   Perf. 13
B125 SP48 50k + 10k multi   .40   .20
B126 SP48 60k + 10k multi   .50   .25
B127 SP48 100k + 10k multi   .80   .40
      Nos. B125-B127 (3)   1.70   .85

Centenary of Turkish Red Crescent Society.

NATO Emblem and Dove SP49

NATO, 20th anniv.: 130k+10k, NATO emblem and globe surrounded by 15 stars, symbols of the 15 NATO members.

1969, Apr. 4   Litho.   Perf. 13
B128 SP49 50k + 10k brt grn, blk & lt bl   .25 .20
B129 SP49 130k + 10k bluish blk, bl & gold .45 .30

Red Cross, Crescent, Lion and Sun Emblems SP50

Design: 130k+10k, Conference emblem and Istanbul skyline.

1969, Aug. 29   Litho.   Perf. 13
B130 SP50 100k + 10k dk & lt bl & red   .30 .20
B131 SP50 130k + 10k red, lt bl & blk   .45 .25

21st Intl. Red Cross Conf., Istanbul.

Erosion Control SP51

60k+10k, Protection of flora (dead tree). 130k+10k, Protection of wildlife (bird of prey).

1970, Feb. 9   Litho.   Perf. 13
B132 SP51 50k + 10k multi   .25   .25
B133 SP51 60k + 10k multi   .40   .40
B134 SP51 130k + 10k multi   .95   .95
      Nos. B132-B134 (3)   1.60 1.60

1970 European Nature Conservation Year.

Globe and Fencer SP52

Design: 130k+10k, Globe, fencer and folk dancer with sword and shield.

1970, Sept. 13   Litho.   Perf. 13
B135 SP52 90k + 10k bl & blk   .30   .20
B136 SP52 130k + 10k ultra, lt bl, blk & org   .40   .20

International Fencing Championships.

"Children's Protection" SP53

Designs: 100k+15k, Hand supporting child, vert. 110k+15k, Mother and child.

1971, June 30   Litho.   Perf. 13
Star and Crescent Emblem in Red
B137 SP53 50k + 10k lil rose & blk   .20 .20
B138 SP53 100k + 15k brn, rose & blk .25 .20
B139 SP53 110k + 15k org brn, bis & blk .30 .20
      Nos. B137-B139 (3)   .75 .60

50th anniv. of the Child Protection Assoc.

UNICEF, 25th Anniv. — SP54   "Your Heart is your Health" — SP55

1971, Dec. 11
B140 SP54 100k + 10k multi   .25   .20
B141 SP54 250k + 15k multi   .60   .40

1972, Apr. 7   Litho.   Perf. 13
B142 SP55 250k + 25k gray, blk & red   .55 .40

World Health Day.

Olympic Emblems, Runners SP56

100k+15k, Olympic rings & motion emblem. 250k+25k, Olympic rings & symbolic track ('72).

1972, Aug. 26
B143 SP56 100k + 15k multi   .25   .20
B144 SP56 110k + 25k multi   .35   .20
B145 SP56 250k + 25k multi   .50   .30
      Nos. B143-B145 (3)   1.10   .70

20th Olympic Games, Munich, 8/26-9/11.

Emblem of Istanbul Technical University SP57

1973, Apr. 21   Litho.   Perf. 13
B146 SP57 100k + 25k multi   .35   .20

Istanbul Technical University, 200th anniv.

Dove and "50" SP58

1973, July 24   Litho.   Perf. 12½x13
B147 SP58 100k + 25k multi   .35   .20

Peace Treaty of Lausanne, 50th anniversary.

World Population Year — SP59

1974, June 15   Litho.   Perf. 13
B148 SP59 250k + 25k multi   .75   .35

Guglielmo Marconi (1874-1937), Italian Electrical Engineer and Inventor SP60

1974, Nov. 15   Litho.   Perf. 13½
B149 SP60 250k + 25k multi   .75   .35

Dr. Albert Schweitzer SP61   Africa with South-West Africa SP62

1975, Jan 14   Litho.   Perf. 13
B150 SP61 250k + 50k multi   .90   .45

Dr. Albert Schweitzer (1875-1965), medical missionary and music scholar.

1975, Aug. 26   Litho.   Perf. 13x12½
B151 SP62 250k + 50k multi   .70   .35

Namibia Day (independence for South-West Africa).

Ziya Gökalp SP63   Spoonbill SP64

1976, Mar. 23   Litho.   Perf. 13
B152 SP63 200k + 25k multi   .35   .20

Ziya Gökalp (1876-1924), philosopher.

1976, Nov. 19   Litho.   Perf. 13
Birds: 150k+25k, European roller. 200k+25k, Flamingo. 400k+25k, Hermit ibis, horiz.
B153 SP64 100k + 25k multi   .40   .20
B154 SP64 150k + 25k multi   .45   .20
B155 SP64 200k + 25k multi   .85   .25
B156 SP64 400k + 25k multi   1.50   .35
      Nos. B153-B156 (4)   3.20 1.00

Decree by Mehmet Bey, and Ongun Holy Bird — SP65

1977, May 13   Litho.   Perf. 13
B157 SP65 200k + 25k grn & blk   .40   .20

700th anniv. of Turkish as official language.

10th World Energy Conference SP66

Design: 600k+50k, Conference emblem and globe with circles.

1977, Sept. 19   Litho.   Perf. 12
B158 SP66 100k + 25k multi   .40
B159 SP66 600k + 50k multi   1.25

Running SP67

Designs: 2½ l+50k, Gymnastics. 5 l + 50, Table tennis. 8 l+50k, Swimming.

1978, July 18   Litho.   Perf. 1
B160 SP67 1 l + 50k multi   .20
B161 SP67 2½ l + 50k multi   .20
B162 SP67 5 l + 50k multi   .60
B163 SP67 8 l + 50k multi   1.00
      Nos. B160-B163 (4)   2.00

GYMNASIADE '78, World School Game Izmir.

Ribbon and Chain SP68

Design: 5 l+50k, Ribbon and flower, vert.

Perf. 12½x13, 13x12½
1978, Sept. 3   Litho
B164 SP68 2½ l + 50k multi   .75
B165 SP68 5 l + 50k multi   1.00

European Declaration of Human Rights 25th anniversary.

Children, Head of Ataturk SP69   Black Francolin SP70

IYC Emblem and: 5 l+50k, Children with globe as balloon. 8 l+50k, Kneeling person and child, globe.

1979, Apr. 23   Litho.   Perf. 13x13½
B166 SP69 2½ l + 50k multi   .25   .20
B167 SP69 5 l + 50k multi   .40   .20
B168 SP69 8 l + 50k multi   .60   .25
      Nos. B166-B168 (3)   1.25   .65

International Year of the Child.

1979, Dec. 3   Litho.   Perf. 13x13½
#B170, Great bustard. #B171, Crane. #B172, Gazelle. #B173, Mouflon muffelwild.
B169 SP70 5 l + 1 l multi   1.00   .20
B170 SP70 5 l + 1 l multi   1.00   .20
B171 SP70 5 l + 1 l multi   1.00   .20
B172 SP70 5 l + 1 l multi   1.00   .20
B173 SP70 5 l + 1 l multi   1.00   .20
  a. Strip of 5, #B169-B173   6.00 2.00

European Wildlife Conservation Year. No. B173a has continuous design.

Flowers, Trees and Sun
SP71

Rodolia Cardinalis
SP72

Environment Protection: 7½ l+ 1 l, Sun, water. 15 l+1 l, Industrial pollution, globe. l+1 l, Flower in oil puddle.

1980, June 4   Litho.   Perf. 13
174	SP71	2½ l + 1 l multi	.20 .20
175	SP71	7½ l + 1 l multi	.25 .20
176	SP71	15 l + 1 l multi	.45 .25
177	SP71	20 l + 1 l multi	.50 .35
	Nos. B174-B177 (4)		1.40 1.00

1980, Dec. 3   Litho.   Perf. 13

Useful Insects: 7½ l+1 l, Bracon hebetor; 15 1 l, Calosoma sycophanta; 20 l+1 l, Deraeocoris rutilus.

178	SP72	2½ l + 1 l multi	.25 .20
179	SP72	7½ l + 1 l multi	.45 .20
180	SP72	15 l + 1 l multi	.80 .20
181	SP72	20 l + 1 l multi	1.00 .20
	Nos. B178-B181 (4)		2.50 .80

Intl. Year of the Disabled
SP73

TB Bacillus Centenary
SP75

Insects
SP74

1981, Mar. 25   Litho.   Perf. 13
182	SP73	10 l + 2½ l multi	.30 .20
183	SP73	20 l + 2½ l multi	.45 .20

1981, Dec. 16   Litho.   Perf. 13

Useful Insects: No. B184, Cicindela ampestris. No. B185, Syrphus vitripennis. o. B186, Ascalaphus macaronius. No. B187, mpusa fasciata.

184	SP74	10 l + 2½ l multi	.30 .20
185	SP74	20 l + 2½ l multi	.50 .20
186	SP74	30 l + 2½ l multi	.75 .25
187	SP74	40 l + 2½ l multi	1.00 .35
	Nos. B184-B187 (4)		2.55 1.00

See Nos. B190-B194, B196-B200.

1982, Mar. 24   Perf. 13x12½

Portraits: #B188, Dr. Tevfik Saglam (1882-963). #B189, Robert Koch.

188	SP75	10 l + 2½ l multi	.30 .20
189	SP75	30 l + 2½ l multi	.70 .20

Insect Type of 1981

Useful Insects: 10 l+2½ l, Eurydema pectabile. 15 l+2½ l, Dacus oleae. 20 l+2½ l, lapperichicen viridissima. 30 l+2½ l, Leptinotarsa decemlineata. 35 l+2½ l, Rhynchites uratus.

1982, Aug. 18   Litho.   Perf. 13
190	SP74	10 l + 2½ l multi	.25 .20
191	SP74	15 l + 2½ l multi	.45 .20
192	SP74	20 l + 2½ l multi	.45 .20
193	SP74	30 l + 2½ l multi	.65 .20
194	SP74	35 l + 2½ l multi	.70 .20
	Nos. B190-B194 (5)		2.50 1.00

Richard Wagner (1813-1883), Composer — SP76

1983, Feb. 13
B195	SP76	30 l + 5 l multi	1.10 1.00

Insect Type of 1981

Harmful Insects: 15 l+5 l, Eurygaster Intergriceps Put. 25 l+5 l, Phyllobius nigrofasciatus Pes. 35 l+5 l, Cercopis intermedia Kbm. 50 l+10 l, Graphosoma lineatum (L). 75 l+10 l, Capnodis miliaris (King).

1983, Sept. 14   Litho.   Perf. 13
B196	SP74	15 l + 5 l multi	.50 .20
B197	SP74	25 l + 5 l multi	.65 .20
B198	SP74	35 l + 5 l multi	.85 .20
B199	SP74	50 l + 10 l multi	1.25 .25
B200	SP74	75 l + 10 l multi	1.75 .40
	Nos. B196-B200 (5)		5.00 1.25

Topkapi Museum Artifacts
SP77

1984 Summer Olympics
SP78

1984, May 30   Litho.   Perf. 13
B201	SP77	20 l + 5 l Kaftan, 16th cent.	.30 .20
B202	SP77	70 l + 15 l Ewer	.95 .40
B203	SP77	90 l + 20 l Swords	1.60 .45
B204	SP77	100 l + 25 l Lock, key	1.90 .55
	Nos. B201-B204 (4)		4.75 1.60

Surtax was for museum. See Nos. B208-B211, B213-B216, B218-B221.

1984, July 28

Designs: 20 l+5 l, Banners, horiz. 70 l+15 l, Medalist Oyunlan. 100 l+20 l, Running, horiz.

B205	SP78	20 l + 5 l multi	.30 .20
B206	SP78	70 l + 15 l multi	.90 .40
B207	SP78	100 l + 20 l multi	1.40 .55
	Nos. B205-B207 (3)		2.60 1.15

Artifacts Type of 1984

Ceramicware: 10 l+5 l, Iznik plate. 20 l+10 l, Iznik boza pitcher and mug, 16th cent. 100 l+15 l, Du Paquier ewer and basin, 1730. 120 l+20 l, Ching dynasty plate, 1522-1566.

1985, May 30   Litho.   Perf. 13
B208	SP77	10 l + 5 l multi	.20 .20
B209	SP77	20 l + 10 l multi	.50 .25
B210	SP77	100 l + 15 l multi	1.50 .75
B211	SP77	120 l + 20 l multi	2.50 1.10
	Nos. B208-B211 (4)		4.70 2.30

Rabies Vaccine, Cent. — SP79

1985, July 16   Perf. 13x13½
B212	SP79	100 l + 15 l Pasteur	1.10 .60

Artifacts Type of 1984

20 l+5 l, Metal and ceramic incense burner, c. 17th cent. 100 l+10 l, Jade lidded mug decorated with precious gems, 16th cent. 120 l+15 l, Dagger designed by Mahmut I, 1714. 200 l+30 l, Willow buckler, defensive shield, undated.

1986, May 30   Litho.   Perf. 13x12½
B213	SP77	20 l + 5 l multi	.50 .25
B214	SP77	100 l + 10 l multi	1.00 .40
B215	SP77	120 l + 15 l multi	1.10 .50
B216	SP77	200 l + 30 l multi	2.25 .75
	Nos. B213-B216 (4)		4.85 1.90

General Assembly of NATO
SP80

1986, Nov. 13   Litho.   Perf. 13½x13
B217	SP80	100 l + 20 l multi	1.25 .40

Artifacts Type of 1984

Designs: 20 l+5 l, Crystal and gold ewer, 16th cent., vert. 50 l+10 l, Emerald and gold pendant, 17th cent. 200 l+15 l, Sherbet jug, 19th cent., vert. 250 l+30 l, Crystal and gold pen box, 16th cent.

1987, May 30   Litho.   Perf. 13
B218	SP77	20 l + 5 l multi	.30 .20
B219	SP77	50 l + 10 l multi	.45 .20
B220	SP77	200 l + 15 l multi	1.10 .50
B221	SP77	250 l + 30 l multi	1.50 .65
	Nos. B218-B221 (4)		3.35 1.55

15th Intl. Chemotherapy Congress, Istanbul — SP81

1987, July 19   Litho.   Perf. 13
B222	SP81	200 l + 25 l multi	.85 .20

Intl. Road Transport Union (IRU) 21st World Congress
SP82

1988, June 13   Litho.   Perf. 12½x13
B223	SP82	200 l + 25 l multi	.55 .20

European Environmental Campaign Balancing Nature and Development — SP83

Designs: 100 l+25 l, Hands, desert reclamation. 400 l+50 l, Eye, road, planted field.

1988, Oct. 19   Litho.   Perf. 12½x13
B224	SP83	100 l + 25 l multi	.35 .20
B225	SP83	400 l + 50 l multi	1.25 .30

Silkworm Industry
SP84

Perf. 13½x13
1989, Apr. 15   Litho.   Wmk. 394
B226	SP84	150 l + 50 l Silkworm	.30 .20
B227	SP84	600 l + 100 l Cocoon, strands	1.10 .25

Council of Europe, 40th Anniv.
SP85

1989, May 5   Litho.   Perf. 13
B228	SP85	600 l + 100 l multi	.90 .25

European Tourism Year
SP86

1990, Apr. 26   Wmk. 394
B229	SP86	300 l + 50 l Antalya	.35 .20
B230	SP86	1000 l + 100 l Istanbul	1.10 .30

Fight Against Addictions — SP87

Fight Against: No. B231, Smoking. No. B232, Drugs, horiz.

1990, June 26   Litho.   Perf. 13
B231	SP87	300 l + 50 l multi	.30 .20
B232	SP87	1000 l + 100 l multi	.90 .45

Yunus Emre (died c.1321), Poet
SP88   SP89

1991, June 26   Litho.   Perf. 13
B233	SP88	500 l + 100 l multi	.50 .25
B234	SP89	1500 l + 100 l multi	1.25 .65

Wolfgang Amadeus Mozart (1756-1791), Composer — SP90

1991, July 24
B235	SP90	1500 l + 100 l multi	1.25 .65

Turkish Supreme Court, 30th Anniv.
SP91

1992, Apr. 25
B236	SP91	500 l + 100 l multi	.50 .25

Scouts Planting Tree
SP92

#B238 Mountain climber on rope, vert.

1992, Dec. 18
B237 SP92 1000 l +200 l multi .30 .20
B238 SP92 3000 l +200 l multi .80 .40

Travertine, Pamukkale — SP93

Different views of rock formations.

1993, June 6
B239 SP93 1000 l +200 l multi .30 .20
B240 SP93 3000 l +500 l multi .80 .40

Intl. Day for Natural Disaster Reduction SP94

1993, Oct. 13 *Perf. 12½x13*
B241 SP94 3000 l + 500 l multi .60 .30

Intl. Olympic Committee, Cent. — SP95

1994, Aug. 17 *Perf. 13*
B242 SP95 12,500 l +500 l multi .90 .45

Trees SP96

Designs: No. B243, Platanus orientalis. No. B244, Cupressus sempervirens, vert.

1994, Nov. 30
B243 SP96 7500 l +500 l multi .50 .25
B244 SP96 12,500 l +500 l multi .85 .40

TBMM (Great Natl. Assembly), 75th Anniv. SP97

1995, Apr. 23
B245 SP97 3500 l +500 l multi .25 .20

The Epic of Manas SP98

Designs: No. B246, Lancers charging. No. B247, Abay Kunanbay (1845-1904), poet, vert.

1995, June 28
B246 SP98 3500 l +500 l multi .25 .20
B247 SP98 3500 l +500 l multi .25 .20

For the People of Bosnia-Herzegovina — SP99

1996, Feb. 28
B248 10,000 l +2500 l multi .45 .20

Ankara University, 50th Anniv. SP100

Unwmk.
1996, Nov. 20 *Litho.* *Perf. 13*
B249 15,000 l +2500 l multi .65 .30

Fight Against Cancer, 50th Anniv. SP101

1997, Feb. 18 *Litho.* *Perf. 12½x13*
B250 25,000 l +5000 l multi .65 .30

Pakistan Independence, 50th Anniv. — SP102

Mohammed Ali Jinnah (1876-1948).

1997, Mar. 23 *Litho.* *Perf. 13*
B251 25,000 l +5000 l multi .60 .30

Universal Declaration of Human Rights SP103

Stylized designs: 75,000 l, Puzzle piece with outlines of people's faces. 175,000 l, Heart-shaped kite with people as tail.

1998, Dec. 10 *Litho.* *Perf. 13½*
B252 SP103 75,000 l +25,000 l 1.00 .50
B253 SP103 175,000 l +25,000 l 2.00 1.00

GATA 100, Yilinda SP104

1998, Dec. 30 *Litho.* *Perf. 13*
B254 75,000 l +10,000 l multi .60 .30

Kemal Ataturk's Entry Into War College, Cent. — SP105

1999, Mar. 13 *Litho.* *Perf. 13*
B255 75,000 l +5,000 l multi .40 .20

Council of Europe, 50th Anniv. SP106

1999, Apr. 30 *Litho.* *Perf. 13¼*
B256 SP106 175,000 l +10,000 l .85 .45

Church, Mosque and Synagogue — SP107

Dancers SP108

2000, May 25 *Litho.* *Perf. 13¼*
B257 SP107 275,000 l +10,000 l .95 .45
B258 SP108 300,000 l +10,000 l 1.00 .50

Tombs and Mausoleums — SP109

150,000 l+25,000 l, Usta Sagirt Kumbeti Ahlat, vert. 200,000 l+25,000 l, Kocbasli Mezar Tasi Tunceli. 275,000 l+25,000 l, Isabey Turbesi, Uskup, vert. 300,000 l+25,000 l, Yusuf bin Kuseyr Turbesi, Nahcivan, vert.

2000
B259- SP109 Set of 4
B262 3.00 1.50

Coins SP110

Various coins with background colors of: No. B263, 300,000 l + 25,000 l, Red. No. B264, 300,000 l + 25,000 l, Blue green. 450,000 l + 25,000 l, Dark carmine. 500,000 l + 25,000 l, Blue violet.

2001, Oct. 1 *Litho.* *Perf. 13*
B263- SP110 Set of 4
B266 2.00 1.00

Caravansaries — SP111

Designs: 300,000 l + 25,000 l, Ashab i Ke Han, Afsin. 500,000 l + 25,000 l, Horozlu Ha Konya.

2001, Nov. 19 *Litho.* *Perf. 1*
B267- SP111 Set of 2
B268 1.00 .5

Turkey's Admission to NATO, 50th Anniv. SP112

2002, Feb. 18
B269 SP112 400,000 l + 25,000 l .60 .3

Trains SP113

Designs: 500,000 l + 25,000 l, Steam loco motive. 700,000 l + 25,000 l, Electri locomotive.

2002, Sept. 16 *Litho.* *Perf. 13¼x1*
B270- SP113 Set of 2
B271 1.50 .7

Trains SP114

Designs: 600,000 l+50,000 l, Trolley 800,000 l+50,000 l, Subway.

2003, Sept. 9 *Litho.* *Perf. 13¼x1*
B272-B273 SP114 Set of 2 2.10 1.1

AIR POST STAMPS

Catalogue values for unused stamps in this section are for Never Hinged items.

Nos. 692, 695, 698, 700 Overprinted or Surcharged in Brown or Blue

1934, July 15 Unwmk. *Perf. 12*
C1 A74 7½k (Br) .20 .20
C2 A72 12½k on 15k (Br) .30 .20
C3 A74 20k on 25k (Br) .30 .20
C4 A74 25k (Bl) .50 .25
C5 A74 40k (Br) .95 .60
Nos. C1-C5 (5) 2.25 1.45

Regular Stamps of 1930 Surcharged in Brown

37
A74	4½k on 7½k red brn		1.25	.75
A72	9k on 15k dp org		27.50	20.00
A74	35k on 40k red vio		6.00	4.25
	Nos. C6-C8 (3)		34.75	25.00

Nos. 698, 703-704
Surcharged in Black

41, Dec. 18
A74	4½k on 25k		2.00	1.50
A75	9k on 200k		9.75	8.25
A75	35k on 500k		6.25	5.25
	Nos. C9-C11 (3)		18.00	15.00

Plane over
Izmir
AP1

Planes over: 5k, 40k, Izmir. 20k, 50k, Ankara. 30k, 1 l, Istanbul.

949, Jan. 1   Photo.   Perf. 11½
12	AP1	5k gray & vio	.20	.20
13	AP1	20k bl gray & brn	.30	.20
14	AP1	30k bl gray & ol brn	.45	.20
15	AP1	40k bl & dp ultra	.60	.20
16	AP1	50k gray vio & red brn	.65	.25
17	AP1	1 l gray bl & dk grn	1.10	.65
	Nos. C12-C17 (6)		3.30	1.70

For overprints see Nos. C19-C21.

Plane Over
Rumeli
Hisari
Fortress
AP2

950, May 19   Unwmk.
18	AP2	2½ l gray bl & dk grn	22.50	10.00

Nos. C12, C14 and C16 Overprinted
in Red

951, Apr. 9   Perf. 11½
C19	AP1	5k gray & vio	1.75	.50
C20	AP1	30k bl gray & ol brn	2.25	.60
C21	AP1	50k gray vio & red brn	2.75	.70
	Nos. C19-C21 (3)		6.75	1.80

Industrial Congress, Ankara, Apr. 9.

Yesilkoy
Airport and
Plane
AP3

Designs: 20k, 45k, Yesilkoy Airport and plane in flight. 35k, 55k, Ankara Airport and plane. 40k, as No. C22.

1954, Nov. 1   Perf. 14
C22	AP3	5k red brn & bl	.25	.20
C23	AP3	20k brn org & bl	.20	.20
C24	AP3	35k dk grn & bl	.20	.20
C25	AP3	40k dp car & bl	.20	.20
C26	AP3	45k violet & bl	.25	.20
C27	AP3	55k black & bl	.55	.45
	Nos. C22-C27 (6)		1.65	1.45

Symbol of Izmir
Fair — AP4

1956, Aug. 20   Litho.   Perf. 10½
C28	AP4	25k reddish brown	.20	.20

25th Intl. Fair at Izmir, Aug. 20-Sept. 20.

Heuss Type of Regular Issue, 1957

1957, May 5
C29	A264	40k sal pink & magenta	.20	.20

Zahir Shah Type of Regular Issue,
1957

1957, Sept. 1
C30	A269	25k grn & lt grn	.20	.20

Hawk — AP5

Crane — AP6

Birds: 40k, 125k, Swallows. 65k, Cranes. 85k, 195k, Gulls. 245k, Hawk.

1959, Aug. 13   Litho.   Perf. 10½
C31	AP5	40k bright lilac	.20	.20
C32	AP5	65k blue green	.25	.20
C33	AP5	85k bright blue	.30	.20
C34	AP5	105k yel & sepia	.30	.20
C35	AP6	125k brt violet	.50	.20
C36	AP6	155k yel green	.70	.20
C37	AP6	195k violet blue	.70	.25
C38	AP6	245k brn & brn org	1.50	.45
	Nos. C31-C38 (8)		4.45	1.90

De Havilland
Rapide
Biplane
AP7

Kestrel — AP8

Designs: 60k, Fokker Friendship transport plane. 130k, DC9-30. 220k, DC-3. 270k, Viscount 794.

1967, July 13   Litho.   Perf. 13½x13
C39	AP7	10k pink & blk	.25	.20
C40	AP7	60k lt grn, red & blk	.30	.20
C41	AP7	130k bl, blk & red	.65	.20
C42	AP7	220k lt brn, blk & red	.95	.30
C43	AP7	270k org, blk & red	1.40	.35
	Nos. C39-C43 (5)		3.55	1.25

For surcharge see No. 2179A.

1967, Oct. 10   Litho.   Perf. 13
Birds: 60k, Golden eagle. 130k, Falcon. 220k, Sparrow hawk. 270k, Buzzard.
C44	AP8	10k brown & salmon	.60	.20
C45	AP8	60k brown & yellow	.45	.20
C46	AP8	130k brown & lt bl	1.10	.20
C47	AP8	220k brown & lt grn	1.75	.25
C48	AP8	270k org brn & gray	2.50	.35
	Nos. C44-C48 (5)		6.40	1.20

F-104 Jet
Plane — AP9

Turkish Air
Force
Emblem
and Jets
AP10

Designs: 200k, Victory monument, Afyon, and Jets. 325k, F-104 jets and pilot. 400k, Bleriot XI plane with Turkish flag. 475k, Flight of Hezarfen Ahmet Celebi from Galata Tower to Uskudar.

1971, June 1   Litho.   Perf. 13
C49	AP9	110k multi	.50	.20
C50	AP9	200k multi	1.10	.20
C51	AP10	250k multi	1.10	.25
C52	AP9	325k multi	1.75	.25
C53	AP10	400k multi	1.90	.30
C54	AP10	475k multi	2.50	.35
	Nos. C49-C54 (6)		8.85	1.55

The gold ink on No. C51 is applied by a thermographic process which gives a raised and shiny effect.

F-28
Plane — AP11

1973, Dec. 11   Litho.   Perf. 13
C55	AP11	110k shown	.45	.25
C56	AP11	250k DC-10	.90	.30

POSTAGE DUE STAMPS

Same Types as Regular Issues of
Corresponding Dates

1863   Unwmk.   Imperf.
Blue Band
J1	A1	20pa blk, *red brn*	65.00	30.00
a.	Tête bêche pair		225.00	225.00
b.	Without band		50.00	
c.	Red band		90.00	45.00
J2	A2	1pi blk, *red brn*	125.00	45.00
a.	Tête bêche pair		225.00	225.00
b.	Without band		50.00	
J3	A3	2pi blk, *red brn*	200.00	125.00
a.	Tête bêche pair		650.00	450.00
J4	A4	5pi blk, *red brn*	150.00	140.00
a.	Tête bêche pair		425.00	425.00
b.	Without band		100.00	
c.	Red band		150.00	
	Nos. J1-J4 (4)		540.00	340.00

1865   Perf. 12½
J6	A5	20pa brown	2.50	4.00
J7	A5	1pi brown	2.50	4.00
b.	Half used as 20pa on cover			
c.	Printed on both sides		25.00	
J8	A5	2pi brown	6.00	6.00
a.	Half used as 1pi on cover			
J9	A5	5pi brown	4.25	5.00
a.	Half used as 2½pi on cover			
J10	A5	25pi brown	37.50	50.00
	Nos. J6-J10 (5)		52.75	69.00

Exist imperf. Values, $60 to $100 each.
The 10pa brown is an essay. Value about
$700.

1867
J11	A5	20pa bister brn	9.50	40.00
J12	A5	1pi bister brn	5.00	
a.	With surcharge of 5pi		13.50	
b.	Imperf., pair		65.00	
J13	A5	2pi fawn	40.00	
J14	A5	3pi fawn	35.00	
J15	A5	25pi bister brn	3,000.	
	Nos. J11-J14 (4)		89.50	

Nos. J12-J15 were not placed in use.

1869   Perf. 13½
With Red Brown Border
J16	A5	20pa bister brn	5.50	4.00
a.	Without surcharge			

J17	A5	1pi bister brn	82.50	20.00
a.	Without surcharge			
J18	A5	1pi bister brn	125.00	15.00
J19	A5	5pi bister brn	1.25	1.50
b.	Without border			
c.	Printed on both sides		14.00	
J20	A5	25pi bister brn	27.50	50.00
	Nos. J16-J20 (5)		241.75	90.50

With Black Brown Border
J21	A5	20pa bister brn	22.50	12.00
a.	Inverted surcharge			
b.	Without surcharge			
J22	A5	1pi bister brn	125.00	25.00
a.	Without surcharge			
J23	A5	2pi bister brn	190.00	22.50
b.	Inverted surcharge			
J24	A5	5pi bister brn	3.50	6.00
b.	Without surcharge			
J25	A5	25pi bister brn	35.00	40.00
	Nos. J21-J25 (5)		376.00	105.50

Pin-perf., Perf. 5 to 11 and
Compound
1871
With Red Brown Border
J26	A5	20pa bister brn	60.00	15.00
J27	A5	1pi bister brn		400.00
J28	A5	2pi bister brn	10.00	6.25
J29	A5	5pi bister brn	3.75	4.00

With Black Brown Border
J31	A5	20pa bister brn	20.00	3.50
b.	Half used as 10pa on cover			
c.	Imperf., pair			16.50
c.	Printed on both sides		40.00	
J32	A5	1pi bister brn	20.00	2.00
a.	Half used as 20pa on cover			
c.	Inverted surcharge		50.00	35.00
d.	Printed on both sides			
J33	A5	2pi bister brn	2.50	8.00
a.	Half used as 1pi on cover			
c.	Imperf., pair			16.50
J34	A5	5pi bister brn	1.50	15.00
a.	Half used as 2½pi on cover			
c.	Printed on both sides			
J35	A5	25pi bister brn	35.00	45.00
a.	Inverted surcharge			
	Nos. J31-J35 (5)		79.00	73.50

1888   Perf. 11½ and 13½
J36	A7	20pa black	5.00	10.00
J37	A7	1pi black	5.00	10.00
J38	A7	2pi black	5.00	10.00
b.	Diagonal half used as 1pi			
	Nos. J36-J38 (3)		15.00	30.00

Imperf
J36a	A7	20pa		11.00
J37a	A7	1pi		11.00
J38a	A7	2pi		11.00

1892   Perf. 13½
J39	A11	20pa black	3.00	3.00
J40	A12	1pi black	9.00	3.75
a.	Printed on both sides			
J41	A13	2pi black	2.50	3.00
	Nos. J39-J41 (3)		14.50	9.75

1901
J42	A11	20pa black, *deep rose*	2.25	3.00

1901
J43	A17	10pa blk, *deep rose*	2.25	3.00
J44	A17	20pa blk, *deep rose*	2.25	3.00
J45	A17	1pi blk, *deep rose*	3.00	3.50
J46	A17	2pi blk, *deep rose*	4.50	5.50
	Nos. J43-J46 (4)		12.00	15.00

1905   Perf. 12
J47	A18	1pi black, *deep rose*	3.00	5.00
J48	A18	2pi black, *deep rose*	6.25	10.00

1908,   Perf. 12, 13½ and Compound
J49	A19	1pi black, *deep rose*	4.00	2.00
J50	A19	2pi black, *deep rose*	5.00	2.00

1909
J51	A21	1pi black, *deep rose*	1.00	1.00
J52	A21	2pi black, *deep rose*	20.00	20.00
a.	Imperf.		65.00	

1913   Perf. 12
J53	A22	2pa blk, *deep rose*	1.00	.50
J54	A22	5pa blk, *deep rose*	1.00	.50
J55	A22	10pa blk, *deep rose*	1.00	.50
J56	A22	20pa blk, *deep rose*	1.00	.50
J57	A22	1pi blk, *deep rose*	2.50	2.25
J58	A22	2pi blk, *deep rose*	5.25	6.00
	Nos. J53-J58 (6)		11.75	10.25

Adrianople Issue

Nos. 251-253
Surcharged in
Black, Blue or
Red

تاقسیه بولی

۲ بار، ۲

1913
J59	A23	2pa on 10pa green (Bk)	1.50	.35
J60	A23	5pa on 20pa red (Bl)	1.50	.35

J61 A23 10pa on 40pa bl (R)   3.00   .80
J62 A23 20pa on 40pa bl (Bk) 16.00 11.00
   Nos. J59-J62 (4)   22.00 12.50

For surcharges see Nos. J67-J70, J83-J86.

D1

D2

D3

D4

1914   **Engr.**
J63 D1 5pa claret   1.00 10.00
J64 D2 20pa red   1.00 10.00
J65 D3 1pi dark blue   1.00 10.00
J66 D4 2pi slate   1.25 10.00
   Nos. J63-J66 (4)   4.25 40.00

For surcharges and overprints see Nos. J87-J91.

Nos. J59 to J62 Surcharged in Red or Black

1916
J67 A23 10pa on 2pa on
        10pa (R)   30.00 30.00
J68 A23 20pa on 5pa on
        20pa   30.00 30.00
J69 A23 40pa on 10pa on
        40pa   30.00 30.00
J70 A23 40pa on 20pa on
        40pa (R)   40.00 35.00
   Nos. J67-J70 (4)   130.00 125.00

Preceding Issues Overprinted in Red, Black or Blue

1917
On Stamps of 1865
J71 A5 20pa red brn (Bl)   45.00 45.00
J72 A5 1pi red brn (Bl)   45.00 45.00
J73 A5 2pi bis brn (Bl)   45.00 45.00
J74 A5 5pi bis brn (Bl)   45.00 45.00
J75 A5 25pi dk brn (Bl)   75.00 75.00
   Nos. J71-J75 (5)   255.00 255.00
On Stamp of 1869
Red Brown Border
J76 A5 5pi bis brn (R)   45.00 35.00
On Stamp of 1871
Black Brown Border
J77 A5 5pi bis brn   75.00 50.00
On Stamps of 1888
J78 A7 1pi black (R)   45.00 45.00
J79 A7 2pi black (R)   45.00 45.00
On Stamps of 1892
J80 A11 20pa black (R)   2.50   2.50
J81 A12 1pi black (R)   2.50   2.50
J82 A13 2pi black (R)   2.50   2.50
   Nos. J80-J82 (3)   7.50   7.50

Adrianople Issue
On Nos. J59 to J62 with Addition of New Value
J83 A23 10pa on 2pa on 10pa
        (R)   1.00   .60
J84 A23 20pa on 5pa on 20pa
        (Bk)   .75   .50
J85 A23 40pa on 10pa on 40pa
        (Bk)   2.00   2.00
   a. "40pa" double

J86 A23 40pa on 20pa on 40pa
        (R)   5.00   3.00
   Nos. J83-J86 (4)   8.75   6.10

Nos. J71-J86 were used as regular postage stamps.

Armistice Issue

No. J65 Overprinted

1919, Nov. 30
J87 D3 1pi dark blue   70.00 65.00

Accession to the Throne Issue
Postage Due Stamps of 1914 Overprinted in Turkish "Accession to the Throne of His Majesty. 3rd July, 1334-1918"

1919
J88 D1 10pa on 5pa claret   18.00 18.00
J89 D2 20pa red   18.00 18.00
J90 D3 1pi dark blue   18.00 18.00
J91 D4 2pi slate   18.00 18.00
   Nos. J88-J91 (4)   72.00 72.00

Railroad Bridge over Kizil Irmak — D5

Kemal Atatürk — D6

1926   **Engr.**
J92 D5 20pa ocher   .60   .35
J93 D5 1g red   .70   .45
J94 D5 2g blue green   1.00   .80
J95 D5 3g lilac brown   1.25   .90
J96 D5 5g lilac   2.25   2.00
   Nos. J92-J96 (5)   5.80   4.50

Catalogue values for unused stamps in this section, from this point to the end of the section, are for Never Hinged items.

1936   **Litho.**   **Perf. 11½**
J97 D6 20pa brown   .20   .20
J98 D6 2k light blue   .20   .20
J99 D6 3k bright violet   .20   .20
J100 D6 5k Prussian blue   .20   .20
J101 D6 12k bright rose   .35   .20
   Nos. J97-J101 (5)   1.15   1.00

For surcharges see Nos. 1461-1465.

Local Issues

Type I

Type II

Type III   Type IV

Type V

Type VI

During 1873//1882 Turkish stamps with the above overprints were used for local postage in Constantinople (types 1-5) and Mount Athos (type 6).

MILITARY STAMPS
For the Army in Thessaly

Tughra and Bridge at Larissa — M1

1898, Apr. 21   Unwmk.   Perf. 13
M1 M1 10pa yellow green   2.25   1.10
M2 M1 20pa rose   2.25   1.10
M3 M1 1pi dark blue   2.25   1.10
M4 M1 2pi orange   2.25   1.10
M5 M1 5pi violet   2.25   1.10
   Nos. M1-M5 (5)   11.25   5.50

Issued for Turkish occupation forces to use in Thessaly during the Greco-Turkish War of 1897-98.

Forgeries of Nos. M1-M5 are perf. 11½.

OFFICIAL STAMPS

Catalogue values for unused stamps in this section are for Never Hinged items.

O1

Perf. 10 to 12 and Compound
1948   Typo.   Unwmk.
O1 O1 10pa rose brown   .30   .20
O2 O1 1k gray green   .30   .20
O3 O1 2k rose violet   .30   .20
O4 O1 3k orange   .30   .20
O5 O1 5k blue   15.00   .90
O6 O1 10k brown org   5.00   .20
O7 O1 15k violet   1.75   .20
O8 O1 20k dk blue   1.75   .20
O9 O1 30k olive bister   3.00   .80
O10 O1 50k black   3.00   .80
O11 O1 1 l bluish grn   3.00   .80
O12 O1 2 l lilac rose   4.00   1.00
   Nos. O1-O12 (12)   37.70   5.70

Regular Issue of 1948 Overprinted Type "a" in Black

1951
O13 A178 5k blue   .20   .20
O14 A178 10k chocolate   .30   .20
O15 A178 20k deep blue   .60   .20
O16 A178 30k brown   .90   .20
   Nos. O13-O16 (4)   2.00   .80

Overprint "a" is 15½mm wide. Points of crescent do not touch star. The 0.25k (No. 963) exists with overprint "a" but its status is questionable.

b

c

Overprinted Type "b" in Dark Brown
1953
O17 A178 0.25k dk red   .20   .20
O18 A178 5k blue   .30   .20
O19 A178 10k chocolate   .40   .20
O20 A178 15k violet   1.00   .20
O21 A178 20k deep blue   2.75   1.00

O22 A178 30k brown   .90
O23 A178 60k black   1.40
   Nos. O17-O23 (7)   6.95 2.

Overprint "b" is 14mm wide. Lettering t[?] with sharp, clean corners.

Overprinted Type "c" in Black or Gree[?] Black

1953-54
O23A A178 0.25k dk red (G Bk) .20
        ('53)
   f. Black overprint   4.00 4
   g. Violet overprint ('53) 4.00 4
O23B A178 10k chocolate   5.00
O23C A178 15k violet   7.00 1.
O23D A178 30k brown   3.00
O23E A178 60k black   4.00 1.
   Nos. O23A-O23E (5)   19.20 3.[?]

Lettering of type "c" heavy with rounde[?] corners.

Small Star — d

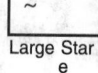
Large Star – e

Overprinted or Surcharged Type "d" i[?] Black

1955
O24 A178 0.25k dark red   .20   .2
O25 A178 1k olive black   .20   .2
O26 A178 2k brt rose lil   .20   .2
O27 A178 3k red orange   .30   .2
O28 A178 4k dk green   .30   .2
O29 A178 5k on 15k vio   .30   .2
O31 A178 10k on 15k vio   .30   .2
O32 A178 15k violet   .40   .2
O33 A178 20k deep blue   .40   .2
O35 A179 40k on 1 l ol grn   .60   .2
O36 A179 75k on 2 l dk brn   1.00   .6
O37 A179 75k on 5 l dp
        plum   8.00   8.0
   Nos. O24-O37 (12)   12.10 10.6

Type "d" is 15x16mm wide. Overprint o[?] Nos. O35-O37 measures 19x22mm. Nos[?] O29, O31, O35-O37 have two bars and new value added.

Overprinted or Surcharged Type "e" i[?] Black

1955
O25a A178 1k olive black   .20   .2
O29a A178 5k on 15k violet   .20   .2
O30 A178 5k blue   .55   .2
O31a A178 10k on 15k violet 2.75   2.0
   c. "10" without serif   .20   .2
O33a A178 20k deep blue   .45   .2
O34 A178 30k brown   .80   .2

Heavy crescent — f

Thin crescent — g

Overprinted or Surcharged Type "f" in Black

1957
O24b A178 0.25k dark red   .30   .20
O38b A178 ½k on 1k ol blk   .20   .20
O25b A178 1k olive black   .20   .20
O31b A178 10k on 15k violet   .70   .35
O35b A179 75k on 1 l olive grn 8.00 2.0
   Nos. O24b-O35b (5)   9.40 2.35

Type "f" crescent is larger and does no[?] touch wavy line. The surcharged "10" on No[?] O31b exists only without serifs. The overprin[?] on O35b measures 17x22½mm.

Overprinted or Surcharged Type "g" in Black

1957
O38 A178 ½k on 1k ol blk   .20   .20
O39 A178 1k ol blk   .20   .20
O40 A179 2k on 4k dk grn   .20   .20
O41 A178 3k on 4k dk grn   .20   .20
O42 A178 10k on 12k dp red   1.00   1.00
   Nos. O38-O42 (5)   1.00 1.00

The shape of crescent and star on type "g[?] varies on each value. Overprint measures[?] 14x18mm. The surcharged stamps have two bars and new value added.

O2

O3

O4

1957 | **Litho.** | **Perf. 10½**
O43 O2 5k blue .25 .20
O44 O2 10k orange brn .25 .20
O45 O2 15k lt violet .25 .20
O46 O2 20k red .25 .20
O47 O2 30k gray olive .25 .20
O48 O2 40k brown vio .25 .20
O49 O2 50k grnsh blk .25 .20
O50 O2 60k lt yel grn .30 .25
O51 O2 75k yellow org .50 .25
O52 O2 100k green .75 .25
O53 O2 200k deep rose 1.25 .50
Nos. O43-O53 (11) 4.55 2.60

1959 | **Unwmk.** | **Perf. 10**
O54 O2 5k rose .20 .20
O55 O2 10k ol grn .20 .20
O56 O2 15k car rose .20 .20
O57 O2 20k lilac .20 .20
O58 O2 40k blue .20 .20
O59 O2 60k orange .25 .20
O60 O2 75k gray .50 .20
O61 O2 100k violet .65 .20
O62 O2 200k red brn 1.10 .65
Nos. O54-O62 (9) 3.50 2.25

1960 | **Litho.** | **Perf. 10½**
O63 O3 1k orange .20 .20
O64 O3 5k vermilion .20 .20
O65 O3 10k gray grn .35 .20
O67 O3 30k red brn .25 .20
O69 O3 60k green .30 .20
O71 O3 1 l rose lilac .95 .20
O72 O3 1½ l brt ultra 1.50 .35
O74 O3 2½ l violet 3.50 .85
O75 O3 5 l blue 7.45 2.60
Nos. O63-O75 (9)

For surcharge see No. O83.

1962 | **Typo.** | **Perf. 13**
O76 O4 1k olive bister .20 .20
O77 O4 5k brt green .20 .20
O78 O4 10k red brown .20 .20
O79 O4 15k dk blue .20 .20
O80 O4 25k carmine .30 .20
O81 O4 30k ultra .20 .20
Nos. O76-O81 (6) 1.30 1.20

For surcharge see No. O82.

Nos. O81 and O70 Surcharged

1963
O82 O4 50k on 30k ultra .35 .20

Perf. 10½
Litho.
O83 O3 100k on 60k green .50 .20

O5

O6

O7

1963 | **Litho.** | **Perf. 12½**
O84 O5 1k gray .20 .20
O85 O5 5k salmon .20 .20
O86 O5 10k green .20 .20
O87 O5 50k car rose .20 .20
O88 O5 100k ultra .55 .20
Nos. O84-O88 (5) 1.35 1.00

For surcharge see No. O139.

1964 | **Unwmk.** | **Perf. 12½**
O89 O6 1k gray .20 .20
O90 O6 5k blue .20 .20
O91 O6 10k yellow .20 .20
O92 O6 30k red .20 .20
O93 O6 50k lt green .25 .20
O94 O6 60k brown .60 .20
O95 O6 80k pale grnsh bl 1.10 .40
O96 O6 130k indigo 2.00 .60
O97 O6 200k lilac 5.00 .80
Nos. O89-O97 (9) 9.75 3.00

For surcharge see No. O140.

1965 | **Litho.** | **Perf. 13**
O98 O7 1k emerald .20 .20
O99 O7 10k ultra .25 .20
O100 O7 50k orange .35 .20
Nos. O98-O100 (3) .80 .60

For surcharge see No. O141.

Carpet
Designs
O8

Seljuk Tile,
13th Century
O9

1k, Usak. 50k, Bergama. 100k, Ladik.
150k, Seljuk. 200k, Nomad. 500k, Anatolia.

1966 | **Litho.** | **Perf. 13**
O101 O8 1k orange .20 .20
O102 O8 50k green .20 .20
O103 O8 100k brt pink .20 .20
O104 O8 150k violet blue .35 .20
O105 O8 200k olive bister .60 .20
O106 O8 500k lilac 1.90 .40
Nos. O101-O106 (6) 3.45 1.40

For surcharge see No. O142.

1967 | **Litho.** | **Perf. 11½x12**
O107 O9 1k dk bl & lt bl .20 .20
O108 O9 50k org & dk bl .30 .20
O109 O9 100k lil & dk bl .40 .20
Nos. O107-O109 (3) .90 .60

For surcharge see No. O143.

Leaf Design — O10

1968 | **Litho.** | **Perf. 13**
O110 O10 50k brn & lt grn .20 .20
O111 O10 150k blk & dl yel .50 .20
O112 O10 500k red brn & lt bl 1.60 .20
Nos. O110-O112 (3) 2.30 .60

O11

O12

O13

1969, Aug. 25 | **Litho.** | **Perf. 13**
O113 O11 1k lt grn & red .20 .20
O114 O11 10k lt grn & bl .20 .20
O115 O11 50k lt grn & brn .20 .20
O116 O11 100k lt grn & red vio .40 .20
Nos. O113-O116 (4) 1.00 .80

1971, Mar. 1 | **Litho.** | **Perf. 11½x12**
O117 O12 5k brown & blue .20 .20
O118 O12 10k vio bl & ver .20 .20
O119 O12 30k org & vio bl .20 .20
O120 O12 50k Prus bl & sepia .35 .20
O121 O12 75k yellow & green .60 .20
Nos. O117-O121 (5) 1.55 1.00

1971, Nov. 15 | **Litho.** | **Perf. 11½x12**
O122 O13 5k lt bl & gray .20 .20
O123 O13 25k cit & lt brn .20 .20
O124 O13 100k org & olive .20 .20
O125 O13 200k dk brn & bis .40 .20
O126 O13 250k rose lil & vio .60 .20
O127 O13 500k dk bl & brt bl .95 .45
Nos. O122-O127 (6) 2.55 1.45

O14

O15

O16

1972, Apr. 7 | **Litho.** | **Perf. 13**
O128 O14 5k buff & blue .20 .20
O129 O14 100k buff & olive .25 .20
O130 O14 200k buff & carmine .55 .20
Nos. O128-O130 (3) 1.00 .60

1973, Sept 20 | **Litho.** | **Perf. 13**
O131 O15 100k violet & buff .65 .20

1974, June 17 | **Litho.** | **Perf. 13½x13**
O132 O16 10k sal pink & brn .20 .20
O133 O16 25k blue & dk brn .20 .20
O134 O16 50k brt pink & brn .40 .20
O135 O16 150k lt grn & brn .40 .20
O136 O16 250k rose & brn .65 .20
O137 O16 500k yellow & brn 1.25 .25
Nos. O132-O137 (6) 2.90 1.25

O17

O18

O19

1975, Nov. 5 | **Litho.** | **Perf. 12½x13**
O138 O17 100k lt blue & maroon .20 .20

Nos. O84, O89, O98, O101, O107
Surcharged in Red or Black

Perf. 12½, 13, 11½x12
1977, Aug. 17 | | **Litho.**
O139 O5 5k on 1k gray .20 .20
O140 O6 5k on 1k gray .20 .20
O141 O7 5k on 1k emer .20 .20
O142 O8 5k on 1k org (B) .20 .20
O143 O9 5k on 1k dk & lt bl .20 .20
Nos. O139-O143 (5) 1.00 1.00

1977, Dec. 29 | **Litho.** | **Perf. 13½x13**
O144 O18 250k lt bl & grn .35 .20

1978 | **Photo.** | **Perf. 13½**
O145 O19 50k pink & rose .20 .20
O146 O19 2½ l buff & grnsh blk .25 .20
O147 O19 4½ l lil rose & sl grn .40 .20
O148 O19 5 l lt blue & pur .40 .20
O149 O19 10 l lt grn & grn .85 .20
O150 O19 25 l yellow & red 2.25 .20
Nos. O145-O150 (6) 4.35 1.20

O20

O21

O22

1979 | **Litho.** | **Perf. 13½**
O151 O20 50k dp org & brn .20 .20
O152 O20 2½ l bl & dk bl .25 .20

1979, Dec. 20 | **Litho.** | **Perf. 13½**
O153 O21 50k sal & dk bl .20 .20
O154 O21 1 l lt grn & red .20 .20
O155 O21 2½ l lil rose & red .30 .20
O156 O21 5 l lt bl & mag .65 .20
O157 O21 7½ l lt lil & dk bl .90 .20
O158 O21 10 l yel & dk bl 1.10 .20
O159 O21 35 l gray & rose ('81) 1.00 .20
O160 O21 50 l pnksh & dk bl ('81) 1.50 .20
Nos. O153-O160 (8) 5.85 1.60

1981, Oct. 23 | **Litho.** | **Perf. 13½**
O161 O22 5 l yel & red .30 .20
O162 O22 10 l salmon & red .50 .20
O163 O22 35 l gray & rose .80 .20
O164 O22 50 l pink & dk bl 1.00 .20
O165 O22 75 l pale grn & grn 2.00 .20
O166 O22 100 l lt bl & dk bl 2.50 .20
Nos. O161-O166 (6) 7.10 1.20

O23

O24

1983-84 | **Litho.** | **Perf. 12½x13**
| | **Background Color** | |
O167 O23 5 l yellow .20 .20
O168 O23 15 l yellow bister .20 .20
O169 O23 20 l gray ('84) .20 .20
O170 O23 50 l sky blue .60 .20
O171 O23 65 l pink .75 .20
O172 O23 70 l pale rose ('84) .55 .20
O173 O23 90 l bister brn 1.10 .20
O174 O23 90 l bl gray ('84) .65 .20
O175 O23 100 l lt green ('84) .75 .20
O176 O23 125 l lt green 1.60 .20
O177 O23 230 l pale salmon ('84) 1.90 .35
Nos. O167-O177 (11) 8.50 2.35

For surcharges see Nos. O184, O186-O190.

1986-87
O178 O24 5 l yel & vio .20 .20
O179 O24 10 l org & vio .20 .20
O180 O24 20 l gray & vio .20 .20
O180A O24 50 l pale blue & dp ultra ('87) .30 .20
O181 O24 100 l lt yel grn & vio 1.00 .20
O182 O24 300 l pale vio & dk blue ('87) 1.50 .20
Nos. O178-O182 (6) 3.40 1.20

For surcharges see Nos. O183, O185.

Nos. O179, O168, O180, O172, O173,
O177 Surcharged in Dark Orange

1989
O183 O24 500 l on 10 l .50 .20
O184 O23 500 l on 15 l .50 .20
O185 O24 500 l on 20 l .50 .20
O186 O23 1000 l on 70 l 1.00 .25
O187 O23 1000 l on 90 l 1.10 .25
O188 O23 1250 l on 230 l 1.25 .30
Nos. O183-O188 (6) 4.85 1.40

Issued: #O183, O185-O188, 8/9; #O184, 6/7.

Nos. O171 & O174
Surcharged in Black

1991, Mar. 27
O189 O23 100 l on 65 l .20 .20
O190 O23 250 l on 90 l .20 .20

O25

O26

O27

Perf. 11½x12½

1992, Mar. 24   **Litho.**
O191 O25 3000 l lt brn & dk brn   1.00   .50
O192 O25 5000 l lt grn & dk grn   1.75   .90

1992, Dec. 2 Litho. Perf. 12½x13
O193 O26 1000 l bl grn & vio
                              bl   .30   .20
O194 O26 10,000 l vio bl & bl
                              grn   3.00 1.50

1993, Sept. 27 Litho. Perf. 12½x13
O195 O27 1000 l brown & green .20   .20
O196 O27 1500 l brown & green .25   .20
O197 O27 1000 l green & claret .80   .40
        Nos. O195-O197 (3)   1.25   .80

O28

O29

O30

1994, May 9 Litho. Perf. 11½x12
O198 O28 2500 l pink & violet .20   .20
O199 O28 25,000 l yel & brn   2.00 1.00

1995, Jan. 25
O200 O29 3500 l violet & lt vio .20   .20
O201 O29 17,500 l bl grn & lt grn .90   .45

1995, May 17
O202 O30 50,000 l ol & apple
                              grn   3.25 1.60

O31

1995, Nov. 8 Litho. Perf. 12½x13
O203 O31 5000 l salmon & org   .20   .20

O32   O32a

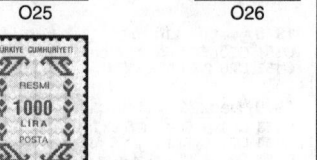

O32b   O32c

1996, July 10 Litho. Perf. 11½x12¼
O204 O32   15,000 l bl & red   .35   .20
O205 O32a   20,000 l grn & pur   .50   .25
O206 O32b   50,000 l pur & grn 1.25   .60
O207 O32c 100,000 l red & bl   2.50 1.25
        Nos. O204-O207 (4)   4.60 2.30

O33

O34

O35

1997, Feb. 5 Litho. Perf. 12½x13
O208 O33 25,000 l red & blue   .55   .30

1997, Aug. 4 Litho. Perf. 12½x13
O209 O34 40,000 l multicolored .55   .30
O210 O35 250,000 l multicolored 3.50 1.75

O36   O37

O38   O39

1998, June 10 Litho. Perf. 12½x13
O211 O36 40,000 l dk bl & lt bl .40   .20
O212 O37 100,000 l purple   1.00   .50
O213 O38 200,000 l brn & pale
                              bl grn 2.00 1.00
O214 O39 500,000 l brn & pale
                              bl grn 5.00 2.50
        Nos. O211-O214 (4)   8.40 4.20

O40

O41

1998, July 29 Litho. Perf. 12½x13
O215 O40 75,000 l multicolored .60   .30

1999 Litho. Perf. 11½x12¼
O216 O41 (R) vio & blue grn   .90   .45
O217 O42 (RT) black & pink   .90   .45

O43   O44

O45   O46

2000, Apr. 3 Litho. Perf. 11½x12¼
O218 O43   50,000 l blue &
                              pink   .20   .20
O219 O44   75,000 l brn & gray .20   .20
O220 O45   500,000 l red brn &
                              lt bl   1.60   .80
O221 O46 1,250,000 l dk bl &
                              buff   4.00 2.00
        Nos. O218-O221 (4)   6.00 3.20

O47

Perf. 11½x12¼
2001, Dec. 13   **Litho.**
O222 O47 R blue & yel org   .35   .20
        Sold for 300,000 l on day of issue.

O48   O49

O50   O51

O52

Perf. 11½x12¼
2002, Dec. 10   **Litho.**
O223 O48   50,000 l multi   .20   .20
O224 O49   100,000 l multi   .20   .20
O225 O50   250,000 l multi   .30   .30
O226 O51   500,000 l multi   .60   .60
O227 O52 1,500,000 l multi   1.75 1.75
        Nos. O223-O227 (5)   3.05 3.05

O53   O54

O55   O56

Perf. 11½x12¼
2003, Aug. 18   Lith...
O228 O53   500,000 l bl & red   .70   ...
O229 O54   750,000 l bl & yel   1.10 1....
O230 O55 1,000,000 l bl & grn   1.40 1....
O231 O56 3,000,000 l bl & yel   4.25 4.2...
        Nos. O228-O231 (4)   7.45 7....

NEWSPAPER STAMPS

N1

Black Overprint
1879 Unwmk. Perf. 11½ and 13
P1 N1 10pa blk & rose lilac   55.00 40.0...

Other stamps found with this "IMPRIMES...
overprint were prepared on private order ar...
have no official status as newspaper stamps...
Counterfeits exist of No. P1.

The 10pa surcharge, on half of 20p...
rose and pale rose was made privatel...
See note after No. 77.

Regular Issue of 1890
Handstamped in Black

There are two types of this handstamp...
varying slightly in size.

1891   **Perf. 13½, 11**
P10 A7 10pa grn & gray   10.00   3.5...
  a.   Imperf.   22.50 12.5...
P11 A7 20pa rose & gray 12.00   4.0...
P12 A7 1pi blue & gray 25.00 14.0...
P13 A7 2pi yel & gray 100.00 40.0...
P14 A7 5pi buff & gray 225.00 110.0...
        Nos. P10-P14 (5) 372.00 171.5...

Blue Handstamp
P10b A7 10pa green & gray 25.00 10.0...
P11a A7 20pa rose & gray   25.00 10....
P12a A7 1pi blue & gray 110.00 30.0...
        Nos. P10b-P12a (3) 160.00 50.0...

This overprint in red and on 2pi and 5pi i...
blue is considered bogus.

Same Handstamp on Regular Issue o...
1892

1892   **Perf. 13...**
P25 A10 10pa gray green   25.00 20.0...
P26 A11 20pa rose   42.50 35.0...
P27 A12 1pi pale blue   12.50 10.0...
P28 A13 2pi brown org   14.00 10.0...
P29 A14 5pi pale violet 150.00 125.0...
  a.   On No. 99a   500.00
        Nos. P25-P29 (5) 244.00 200.0...

The handstamps on Nos. P10-P29 ar...
found double, inverted and sideways. Counter...
feit overprints comprise most of the copie...
offered for sale in the marketplace.

Regular Issues of
1892-98 Overprinted
in Black

1893-98
P30 A10 10pa gray grn   1.00   .3...
P31 A11 20pa vio brn ('98) .80   .5...
  a.   20pa dark pink   .60   .6...
  b.   20pa pink   15.00   8.0...
P32 A12 1pi pale blue   2.00   .5...
P33 A13 2pi brown org   12.50 5.0...
  a.   Tete beche pair   22.5...

34	A14	5pi pale violet	40.00	20.00
a.		On No. 99a	140.00	65.00
		Nos. P30-P34 (5)	56.30	26.35

For surcharge and overprints see Nos. B41, 134-P136, P153-P154.

No. 95 Surcharged

36	A10	5pa on 10pa gray grn	1.50	.20
a.		"Cinq" instead of "Cinq"	7.50	7.50

For overprint see No. P137.

Nos. 102-107
Overprinted in Black

901 *Perf. 12, 13½ and Compound*

37	A16	5pa bister	.20	.25
a.		Inverted overprint		
38	A16	10pa yellow grn	1.60	1.25
39	A16	20pa magenta	6.00	4.00
40	A16	1pi violet blue	15.00	9.00
41	A16	5pa gray blue	40.00	20.00
42	A16	5pi ocher	65.00	22.50
		Nos. P37-P42 (6)	127.80	57.00

For overprints see Nos. B37, P69-P74, 123, P138-P141, P155-P158.

Same Overprint on Nos. 110-115

901

43	A17	5pa purple	2.00	.60
44	A17	10pa green	15.00	.60
45	A17	20pa carmine	1.25	.35
a.		Overprinted on back		
46	A17	1pi blue	7.00	.70
47	A17	2pi orange	30.00	1.75
a.		Inverted overprint		
48	A17	5pi lilac rose	35.00	18.00
		Nos. P43-P48 (6)	90.25	22.00

For overprints see Nos. P75-P80, P124-126, P142-P146, P159-P164.

Same Overprint on Regular Issue of 1905

905

49	A18	5pa ocher	1.00	.50
50	A18	10pa dull green	10.00	1.00
51	A18	20pa carmine	1.25	.50
52	A18	1pi pale blue	1.00	.50
53	A18	2pi slate	25.00	3.75
54	A18	5pi brown	35.00	9.00
		Nos. P49-P54 (6)	73.25	15.25

For overprints see Nos. P127-P129, P147-150, P165-P171.

Regular Issue of 1908
Overprinted in Carmine
or Blue

908

55	A19	5pa ocher (Bl)	8.00	.50
56	A19	10pa blue grn (C)	6.00	.50
57	A19	20pa carmine (Bl)	7.00	1.00
58	A19	1pi brt blue (C)	11.00	2.00
59	A19	2pi blue blk (C)	22.50	5.00
60	A19	5pi dk violet (C)	25.00	12.00
		Nos. P55-P60 (6)	79.50	21.00

For overprints see Nos. B17, P130-P131, P151, P172.

Same Overprint on Regular Issue of 1909

909

61	A21	5pa ocher (Bl)	2.00	1.00
a.		Imperf.		
62	A21	10pa blue grn (C)	2.00	1.25
63	A21	20pa car rose (Bl)	15.00	1.75
a.		Imperf.		

P64	A21	1pi brt blue (C)	25.00	7.50
P65	A21	2pi blue blk (C)	40.00	21.00
P66	A21	5pi dk violet (C)	45.00	32.50
		Nos. P61-P66 (6)	129.00	65.00

For surcharge and overprints see Nos. B18, P67-P68, P81, P132-P133, P152.

No. 151 Surcharged in
Blue

1910 *Perf. 12, 13½ and Compound*

P67	A21	2pa on 5pa ocher	.25	.20

1911 *Perf. 12*

P68	A21	2pa olive green	.25	.20

Newspaper Stamps of
1901-11 Overprinted in
Carmine or Blue

The overprint was applied to 13 denominations in four settings with change of city name, producing individual sets for each city: "MONASTIR," "PRISTINA," "SALONIKA" and "USKUB."

1911 *Perf. 12, 13½*

P69	A16	5pa bister	1.75
P70	A16	10pa yellow grn	1.75
P71	A16	20pa magenta	1.75
P72	A16	1pi violet blue	1.75
P73	A16	2pi gray blue	2.75
P74	A16	5pi ocher	4.25
P75	A17	5pa purple	1.75
P76	A17	10pa green	1.75
P77	A17	20pa carmine	1.75
P78	A17	1pi blue	3.00
P79	A17	2pi orange	2.75
P80	A17	5pi lilac rose	4.75
P81	A21	2pa olive green	1.00
		Nos. P69-P81 (13)	30.75

Values for each of the 4 city sets of 13 are as printed.
The note after No. 182 will also apply to Nos. P69-P81.

Preceding Newspaper
Issues with additional
Overprint in Carmine
or Black

1915

On Stamps of 1893-98

P121	A10	10pa gray green	3.00	.20
a.		Inverted overprint	10.00	10.00
P122	A13	2pi yellow brn	1.50	1.00
a.		Inverted overprint	10.00	10.00

On Stamps of 1901

P123	A16	10pa yellow grn	.50	.20
P124	A17	5pa purple	.50	.30
P125	A17	20pa carmine	2.00	.50
P126	A17	5pi lilac rose	12.00	2.00

On Stamps of 1905

P127	A18	5pa ocher	.50	.30
a.		Inverted overprint	7.50	7.50
P128	A18	2pi slate	3.00	2.25
P129	A18	5pi brown	2.50	.60

On Stamps of 1908

P130	A19	2pi blue blk	250.00	75.00
P131	A19	5pi dk violet	7.50	1.25

On Stamps of 1909

P132	A21	5pa ocher	.30	.20
P133	A21	5pi dk violet	35.00	20.00
		Nos. P121-P129, P131-P133 (12)	68.30	28.80

Preceding
Newspaper Issues
with additional
Overprint in Red or
Black

1916

On Stamps of 1893-98

P134	A10	10pa gray green	.50	.30
P135	A11	20pa violet brn	.50	.30
P136	A14	5pi dull violet	11.00	11.00

On Stamp of 1897

P137	A10	5pa on 10pa gray grn	.50	.30

On Stamps of 1901

P138	A16	5pa bister	.50	.30
P139	A16	10pa yellow grn	.90	.90
P140	A16	20pa magenta	1.00	.90
a.		Inverted overprint	10.00	10.00
P141	A16	1pi violet blue	1.00	1.00
P142	A17	5pa purple	20.00	15.00
P143	A17	10pa green	20.00	15.00
P144	A17	20pa carmine	1.50	.90
P145	A17	1pi blue	1.50	.90
P146	A17	2pi orange	1.50	.90

On Stamps of 1905

P147	A18	5pa ocher	1.00	.75
P148	A18	10pa dull green	12.50	12.50
P149	A18	20pa carmine	12.50	12.50
P150	A18	1pi pale blue	1.75	1.00

On Stamp of 1908

P151	A19	5pa ocher	8.00	6.50

On Stamp of 1909

P152	A21	5pa ocher	15.00	12.00
		Nos. P134-P152 (19)	111.15	92.95

Preceding
Newspaper Issues
with additional
Overprint in Red or
Black

1917

On Stamps of 1893-98

P153	A12	1pi gray (R)	2.50	2.00
P154	A11	20pa vio brn (R)	2.75	2.00

On Stamps of 1901

P155	A16	5pa bister (Bk)	1.50	1.25
a.		Inverted overprint	20.00	20.00
P156	A16	10pa yel grn (R)	1.50	1.25
P157	A16	20pa mag (Bk)	1.50	1.25
P158	A16	2pi gray bl (R)	40.00	30.00
P159	A17	5pa purple (Bk)	1.50	1.25
a.		Inverted overprint	20.00	20.00
b.		Double overprint	20.00	20.00
c.		Double ovpt., one inverted	25.00	25.00
P160	A17	10pa green (R)	15.00	15.00
P161	A17	20pa car (Bk)	1.50	1.25
P162	A17	1pi blue (R)	2.50	2.50
P163	A17	2pi orange (Bk)	1.50	1.25
P164	A17	5pi lil rose (R)	20.00	20.00

On Stamps of 1905

P165	A18	5pa ocher (R)	2.50	2.00
a.		Inverted overprint	10.00	10.00
P166	A18	5pa ocher (Bk)	3.00	2.50
a.		Inverted overprint	10.00	10.00
P167	A18	10pa dull grn (R)	2.50	2.00
P168	A18	20pa car (Bk)	2.50	2.00
a.		Double overprint	15.00	15.00
P169	A18	1pi blue (R)	2.50	2.00
a.		Inverted overprint	25.00	25.00
P170	A18	2pi slate (R)	45.00	45.00
P171	A18	5pi brown (R)	45.00	45.00

On Stamp of 1908

P172	A19	5pa ocher (R)	20.00	20.00
		Nos. P153-P172 (20)	214.75	199.50

Nos. P153-P172 were used as regular postage stamps.

#P173

#P174

1919
Blue Surcharge and Red Overprint

P173	A21	5pa on 2pa ol grn	.30	.20
a.		Red overprint double	12.50	5.00
b.		Blue surcharge double	12.50	5.00

1920 **Red Surcharge**

P174	A25	5pa on 4pa brn	.20	.20

Catalogue values for unused
stamps in this section, from this
point to the end of the section, are
for Never Hinged items.

Dove and Citadel of
Ankara — N6

1952-55		Litho.	*Perf. 12½*	
P175	N6	0.50k grnsh gray	.20	.20
P176	N6	0.50k violet ('53)	.20	.20
		Perf. 10½, 10		
P177	N6	0.50k red org ('54)	.20	.20
P178	N6	0.50k brown ('55)	.20	.20
		Nos. P175-P178 (4)	.80	.80

POSTAL TAX STAMPS

Map of Turkey
and Red
Crescent
PT1

1928	Unwmk.	Typo.	*Perf. 14*	
		Crescent in Red		
RA1	PT1	½pi lt brown	.30	.20
RA2	PT1	1pi red violet	.30	.20
RA3	PT1	2½pi orange	.30	.20
		Engr.		
		Various Frames		
RA4	PT1	5pi dk brown	.60	.45
RA5	PT1	10pi yellow green	.75	.55
RA6	PT1	20pi slate	1.25	.60
RA7	PT1	50pi dark violet	3.75	1.40
		Nos. RA1-RA7 (7)	7.25	3.60

The use of these stamps on letters, parcels, etc. in addition to the regular postage, was obligatory on certain days in each year.
For surcharges see Nos. RA16, RA21-RA22.

Cherubs Upholding
Star — PT2

1932				
RA8	PT2	1k ol bis & red	.50	.20
RA9	PT2	2½k dk brn & red	.65	.20
RA10	PT2	5k green & red	.85	.20
RA11	PT2	25k black & red	2.75	.90
		Nos. RA8-RA11 (4)	4.75	1.50

For surcharges and overprints see Nos. RA12-RA15, RA28-RA29, RA36-RA38.

No. RA8 Surcharged

RA12	PT2	20pa on 1k	.25	.20
RA13	PT2	3k on 1k	1.00	.40
a.		3 "kruus"	2.50	2.50

By a law of Parliament the use of these stamps on letters and telegraph forms, in addition to the regular fees, was obligatory from

Apr. 20-30 of each year. The inscription in the tablet at the bottom of the design states that the money derived from the sale of the stamps is devoted to child welfare work.

No. RA8 Surcharged

1933
RA14 PT2 20pa on 1k ol bis & red .25 .20
RA15 PT2 3k on 1k ol bis & red 1.00 .60

No. RA5 Surcharged

RA16 PT1 5k on 10pi yel grn & red .95 .45
Nos. RA14-RA16 (3) 2.20 1.25

PT3   PT4

1933   **Perf. 11, 11½**
RA17 PT3 20pa gray vio & red .65 .20
RA18 PT4 1k violet & red .80 .20
RA19 PT4 5k dk brown & red 2.50 .50
RA20 PT3 15k green & red 3.50 .50
Nos. RA17-RA20 (4) 7.45 1.40

Nos. RA17 and RA20 were issued in Ankara; Nos. RA18 and RA19 in Izmir. For overprint see No. RA27.

Nos. RA3, RA1 Surcharged in Black

1933-34
RA21 PT1 1k on 2½pi orange .25 .20
RA22 PT1 5k on ½pi lt brown .70 .25

Map of Turkey PT5

1934-35   **Crescent in Red**   **Perf. 12**
RA23 PT5 ½k blue ('35) .20 .20
RA24 PT5 1k red brown .20 .20
RA25 PT5 2½k brown ('35) .50 .20
RA26 PT5 5k blue green ('35) 1.25 .20
Nos. RA23-RA26 (4) 2.15 .80

Frame differs on No. RA26.
See Nos. RA30-RA35B. For surcharge see No. RA63.

Nos. RA17, RA8-RA9 Overprinted "P.Y.S." in Roman Capitals

1936   **Perf. 11, 14**
RA27 PT3 20pa gray vio & red .40 .20
RA28 PT2 1k ol bis & red .40 .20
RA29 PT2 3k on 2½k dk brn & red .75 .30
Nos. RA27-RA29 (3) 1.55

Type of 1934-35, Inscribed "Türkiye Kizilay Cemiyeti"
1938-46   **Perf. 8½-11½**

Type I - Imprint, "Devlet Basimevi". Crescent red.
Type II - Imprint, "Alaeddin Kiral Basimevi". Crescent carmine.
Type III - Imprint, "Damga Matbaasi". Crescent red.

Crescent in Red or Carmine
RA30 PT5 ½k blue (I) .20 .20
   a.   Type II 3.50 1.00
   b.   Type III .30
RA31 PT5 1k red vio (I) .20 .20
   a.   Type II 6.50 2.00
   b.   Type III .30
RA32 PT5 2½k orange (I) .20 .20
   a.   Type III 1.25 .25
RA33 PT5 5k blue grn (I) .35 .20
RA33A PT5 5k choc (III) ('42) 1.00 .20
RA34 PT5 10k pale grn (I) .95 .30
   a.   Type III 1.25 .30
RA35 PT5 20k black (I) 1.40 .45
RA35A PT5 50k pur (III) ('46) 5.00 .55
RA35B PT5 1 l blue (III) ('44) 22.50 2.50
Nos. RA30-RA35B (9) 31.80 4.80

No. RA9 Surcharged in Black

1938   **Perf. 14**
RA36 PT2 20pa on 2½k .40 .20
RA37 PT2 1k on 2½k .60 .20

No. RA9 Surcharged in Black

1938   **Unwmk.**   **Perf. 14**
RA37A PT2 20pa on 2½k .90 .50
RA37B PT2 1k on 2½k 1.10 .65

No. RA9 Surcharged "1 Kurus" in Black
1939   **Perf. 14**
RA38 PT2 1k on 2½k dk brn & red .50 .50

Child — PT6   Nurse with Child — PT7

1940   **Typo.**   **Perf. 12**
Star in Carmine
RA39 PT6 20pa bluish grn .30 .20
RA40 PT6 1k violet .30 .20
RA41 PT7 1k lt blue .30 .20
RA42 PT7 2½k pale red lil .30 .20
RA43 PT6 3k black .35 .20
RA44 PT7 5k pale violet .30 .20
RA45 PT7 10k blue green 1.00 .40
RA46 PT6 15k dark blue .75 .30
RA47 PT7 25k olive bister 2.50 1.25
RA48 PT7 50k olive gray 6.00 2.50
Nos. RA39-RA48 (10) 12.10 5.65

Soldier and Map of Turkey — PT8

1941-44   **Perf. 11½**
RA49 PT8 1k purple .40 .20
RA50 PT8 2k light blue 2.50 .20
RA51 PT8 3k chestnut 2.75 .50
RA51A PT8 4k mag ('44) 9.50 .35
RA52 PT8 5k brt rose 7.75 2.50
RA53 PT8 10k dk blue 11.00 4.00
Nos. RA49-RA53 (6) 33.90 7.75

The tax was used for national defense.

Baby — PT9   Nurse and Baby — PT13

Nurse and Children PT10

Nurse Feeding Child PT11

Nurse and Child PT12   President Inonu Holding Child — PT15

Nurse and Child — PT14   Children PT16

1942   **Unwmk.**   **Typo.**   **Perf. 11½**
Star in Red
RA54 PT9 20pa brt violet .40 .20
RA55 PT9 20pa chocolate .40 .20
RA56 PT10 1k dk slate grn .40 .20
RA57 PT11 2½k yellow grn .40 .20
RA58 PT12 3k dark blue .40 .30
RA59 PT13 5k brt pink .40 .30
RA60 PT14 10k lt blue .70 .40
RA61 PT15 15k dk red brn 1.10 .70
RA62 PT16 25k brown 1.75 1.00
Nos. RA54-RA62 (9) 5.95 3.60

See Nos. RA175, RA179-RA180.

No. RA32 Surcharged with New Value in Brown
1942   **Perf. 10**
RA63 PT5 1k on 2½k org & red (I) .20 .20

Child Eating — PT17

Nurse and Child — PT18

Nurse and Child PT19

Child and Red Star — PT20   President Inönü and Child — PT21

Inscribed: "Sefcat Pullari 23 Nisan 1943 Cocuk Esirgeme Kurumu."

1943   **Star in Red**   **Perf. 11**
RA64 PT17 50pa lilac .20 .20
RA65 PT17 50pa gray green .25 .20
RA66 PT18 1k lt ultra .25 .20
RA67 PT19 3k dark red .30 .20
RA68 PT20 15k cream & blk 1.50 .40
RA69 PT21 100k brt violet blue 2.50 1.60
   a.   Souvenir sheet, #RA64-RA69, imperf. 5.50 5.50
Nos. RA64-RA69 (6) 5.00 2.80

Star and Crescent PT23   Hospital PT24

Nurse and Children PT25   Baby PT26

Nurse Bathing
Baby — PT27

Nurse Feeding
Child — PT28

Baby with
Bottle — PT29

Child — PT30

Hospital — PT31

Perf. 10 to 12 and Compound
1943-44

Star in Red

RA71	PT23	20pa deep blue	.40	.30
RA72	PT24	1k gray green	.40	.20
RA73	PT25	3k pale gray brn	.40	.20
RA74	PT26	5k yellow orange	.70	.30
RA75	PT26	5k violet brn	.30	.20
RA76	PT27	10k red	.40	.30
RA77	PT28	15k red violet	.60	.40
RA78	PT29	25k pale violet	.90	.50
RA79	PT30	50k lt blue	2.00	1.00
RA80	PT31	100k lt green	5.00	4.00
		Nos. RA71-RA80 (10)	11.10	7.40

For surcharge see No. RA156.

Nurse Holding
Baby — PT32

Nurse Feeding
Child — PT33

Child — PT34

Star and
Crescent
PT35

1945-47 Unwmk. Litho. Perf. 11½

Star in Red

RA81	PT32	1k lilac brn	.40	.20
a.		1k rose violet	.50	.20
RA82	PT33	5k yellow grn	.70	.20
a.		5k green	.70	.20
RA83	PT34	10k red brown	.50	.20
RA84	PT35	250k gray black	9.50	3.50
RA84A	PT35	500k dull vio ('47)	37.50	12.50
		Nos. RA81-RA84A (5)	48.60	16.60

Imprint on No. RA82: "Kagit ve Basim isleri A.S. ist." On No. RA82a: "Guzel Sanatlar Matbaasi - Ankara."

Nurse and
Wounded Soldier
PT36

President Inönü
and Victim of
Earthquake
PT37

Removing
Wounded from
Hospital
Ship — PT38

Nurse and
Soldier — PT39

Feeding the
Poor — PT40

Wounded
Soldiers on
Landing
Raft — PT41

Symbolical of
Red Crescent
Relief — PT42

1945   Perf. 12x10, 10x12

Crescent in Red

RA85	PT36	20pa dp bl & brn org	.30	.20
RA86	PT37	1k ol grn & ol bis	.30	.20
RA87	PT38	2½k dp bl & red	.50	.20
RA88	PT39	5k dp bl & red	1.25	.30
RA89	PT40	10k dp bl & lt grn	1.25	.40
RA90	PT41	50k blk & gray grn	3.00	1.00
RA91	PT42	1 l black & yel	12.00	4.00
		Nos. RA85-RA91 (7)	18.60	6.30

See Nos. RA181-RA182.

Ankara
Sanatorium
PT43

1946   Perf. 12

RA92	PT43	20k red & lt bl	.65	.30

See No. RA210. For surcharge see No. RA186.

Covering Sleeping
Child — PT44

Designs: 1k, Mother and child. 2½k, Nurse at playground. 5k, Doctor examining infant. 15k, Feeding child. 25k, Bathing child. 50k, Weighing baby. 150k, Feeding baby.

1946 Litho. Perf. 12½
Inscribed: "25ci Yil Hatirasi 1946"
Star in Carmine

RA93	PT44	20pa brown	.35	.20
RA94	PT44	1k blue	.35	.20
RA95	PT44	2½k carmine	.35	.20
RA96	PT44	5k vio brn	.60	.20
RA97	PT44	15k violet	.90	.50
RA98	PT44	25k gray grn	1.25	.60
RA99	PT44	50k bl grn	1.75	1.50
RA100	PT44	150k gray brn	3.25	1.75
		Nos. RA93-RA100 (8)	8.80	5.15

For surcharge see No. RA155.

Hospital
Ship — PT52

Ambulance
Plane — PT53

Hospital
Train — PT54

Ambulance
PT55

Boy Scout and Red
Crescent
Flag — PT56

Stretcher
Bearers and
Wounded
Soldier
PT57

Nurse and
Hospital — PT58

Sanatorium
PT59

1946   Perf. 11½

RA101	PT52	1k multi	1.25	1.25
RA102	PT53	4k multi	1.25	1.25
RA103	PT54	10k multi	3.50	3.50
RA104	PT55	25k multi	4.50	4.50
RA105	PT56	40k multi	8.50	8.50
RA106	PT57	70k multi	6.00	6.00
RA107	PT58	1 l multi	5.50	5.50
RA108	PT59	2½ l multi	12.50	12.50
		Nos. RA101-RA108 (8)	43.00	43.00

For overprints see Nos. RA139-RA146.

Souvenir Sheet

Pres. Inönü and Child — PT60

1946 Unwmk. Typo. Imperf.
Without Gum

RA109	PT60	250k slate blk, pink & red	20.00 17.50

Turkish Society for the Prevention of Cruelty to Children, 25th anniv.

Nurse and
Wounded Soldier
PT61

Pres. Inönü and
Victim of
Earthquake
PT62

Nurse and
Soldier — PT64

Symbolical of
Red Crescent
Relief — PT67

1946-47 Litho. Perf. 11½
Crescent in Red

RA113	PT61	20pa dk bl vio & ol ('47)	.20	.20
RA114	PT62	1k dk brn & yel	.45	.20
RA115	PT64	5k dp bl & red	.45	.25
RA116	PT67	1 l brn blk & yel	1.90	1.25
		Nos. RA113-RA116 (4)	3.00	1.90

PT68

Nurse and
Wounded
Soldier — PT69

Victory and
Soldier — PT70

1947
Crescent in Red

RA117	PT68	250k brn blk & grn	5.25	2.00
RA118	PT69	5 l sl gray & org	8.75	3.50

Booklet Pane of One
Perf. 11½ (top) x Imperf.

RA119	PT70	10 l deep blue	22.50	—

Black numerals above No. RA119 indicate position in booklet.

President Inönü and Victim of Earthquake
PT71

Nurse and Child
PT72

1947
Perf. 11½

RA120	PT71	1k dk brn, pale bl & red	.20	.20
RA121	PT72	2½k bl vio & car	.20	.20

See Nos. RA221-RA223. For surcharge see No. RA154.

Nurse Offering Encouragement
PT73

Plant with Broken Stem
PT74

Perf. 8½, 11½x10, 11x10½

1948-49   Typo.   Unwmk.
Crescent in Red

RA122	PT73	½k ultra ('49)	.55	.20
RA123	PT73	1k indigo	.20	.20
RA124	PT73	2k lilac rose	.20	.20
RA125	PT73	2½k org ('49)	.20	.20
RA126	PT73	3k bl grn	.20	.20
RA127	PT73	4k gray ('49)	.35	.20
RA128	PT73	5k blue	.70	.20
RA129	PT73	10k pink	1.25	.20
RA130	PT73	25k chocolate	1.60	.25

Perf. 10

RA130A	PT74	50k ultra & bl gray ('49)	2.25	.75
RA130B	PT74	100k grn & pale grn ('49)	5.25	1.00
		Nos. RA122-RA130B (11)	12.75	3.60

For surcharges see Nos. RA151-RA153, RA187.

Nurse and Children — PT75

Various Scenes with Children.

Inscribed: "1948 Cocuk Yili Hatirasi"

1948   Litho.   Perf. 11
Star in Red

RA131	PT75	20pa dp ultra	.20	.20
RA132	PT75	20pa rose lilac	.20	.20
RA133	PT75	1k dp Prus bl	.30	.20
RA134	PT75	3k dk brn vio	.40	.25
RA135	PT75	15k slate black	1.25	1.00
RA136	PT75	30k orange	2.75	2.50

RA137	PT75	150k yellow grn	3.75	3.50
RA138	PT75	300k brown red	5.75	5.50
		Nos. RA131-RA138 (8)	14.60	13.35

No. RA136 is arranged horizontally. For overprints and surcharges see Nos. RA199-RA206.

> **Catalogue values for unused stamps in this section, from this point to the end of the section, are for Never Hinged items.**

Nos. RA101 to RA108 Overprinted in Carmine

1949   Perf. 11½

RA139	PT52	1k multi	.35	.35
RA140	PT53	4k multi	.60	.60
RA141	PT54	10k multi	3.50	3.50
RA142	PT55	25k multi	1.75	1.75
RA143	PT56	40k multi	2.75	2.75
RA144	PT57	70k multi	4.50	4.50
RA145	PT58	1 l multi	6.25	6.25
RA146	PT59	2½ l multi	27.50	27.50
		Nos. RA139-RA146 (8)	47.20	47.20

Ruins and Tent
PT76

"Protection"
PT77

Booklet Panes of One

1949   Perf. 10 (top) x Imperf.

RA149	PT76	5k gray, vio gray & red	.50	.20
RA150	PT76	10k red vio, sal & red	.60	.25

Black numerals above each stamp indicate its position in the booklet.

No. RA124 Surcharged in Black

1950   Unwmk.   Perf. 8½

RA151	PT73	20pa on 2k	.20	.20

Postal Tax Stamps of 1944-48 Surcharged with New Value in Black or Carmine

Perf. 8½ to 12½ and Compound

1952

RA152	PT73	20pa on 3k bl grn	.20	.20
RA153	PT73	20pa on 4k gray	.20	.20
RA154	PT72	1k on 2½k bl vio & car (C)	.20	.20
RA155	PT44	1k on 2½k car	.20	.20
RA156	PT25	1k on 3k pale gray brn	.40	.20
		Nos. RA152-RA156 (5)	1.20	1.00

Various Symbolical Designs Inscribed "75 iNCi" etc.

1952   Typo.   Perf. 10
Crescent in Carmine

RA157	PT77	5k bl grn & bl	.60	.50
RA158	PT77	15k yel grn, bl & cr	.60	.50
RA159	PT77	30k bl, grn & brn	.60	.50
RA160	PT77	1 l blk, bl & cr	.90	.80
a.		Souvenir sheet, #RA157-RA160, imperf.	15.00	15.00
		Nos. RA157-RA160 (4)	2.70	2.30

Printed in sheets of 20 containing one horizontal row of each value.

Nurse and Children
PT78

Design: 1k, Nurse and baby.

1954   Litho.   Perf. 10½
Star in Red

RA161	PT78	20pa aqua	.20	.20
RA162	PT78	20pa yellow	.20	.20
RA163	PT78	1k deep blue	.25	.20
		Nos. RA161-RA163 (3)	.65	.60

Globe and Flag — PT79

Designs: 5k, Winged nurse in clouds. 10k, Protecting arm of Red Crescent.

1954

RA164	PT79	1k multi	.20	.20
RA165	PT79	5k multi	.50	.20
RA166	PT79	10k car, grn & gray	1.00	.20
		Nos. RA164-RA166 (3)	1.70	.60

See Nos. RA208, RA211-RA213. For surcharges see Nos. RA187A-RA187B.

Florence Nightingale — PT80

Selimiye Barracks
PT81

30k, Florence Nightingale, full-face.

1954, Nov. 4
Crescent in Carmine

RA167	PT80	20k gray grn & dk brn	.40	.40
RA168	PT80	30k dl brn & blk	.40	.40
RA169	PT81	50k buff & blk	.80	.80
		Nos. RA167-RA169 (3)	1.60	1.60

Arrival of Florence Nightingale at Scutari, cent.

Type of 1942 and

Children Kissing — PT82

Nurse Holding Baby — PT83

1955, Apr. 23
Star in Red

RA170	PT82	20pa chalky bl	.20	.20
RA171	PT82	20pa org brn	.20	.20
RA172	PT82	1k lilac	.20	.20
RA173	PT82	3k gray bis	.20	.20
RA174	PT82	5k orange	.20	.20
RA175	PT12	10k green	.50	.50
RA176	PT83	15k dk blue	.25	.20
RA177	PT83	25k brn car	.70	.20
RA178	PT83	50k dk gray grn	1.75	.80
RA179	PT12	2½ l dull brn	42.50	40.00
RA180	PT12	10 l rose lil	100.00	90.00
		Nos. RA170-RA180 (11)	146.70	132.70

Types of 1945
Inscribed: "Turkiye Kizilay Dernegi"

1955   Litho.   Perf. 10½x11½, 10½
Crescent in Red

RA181	PT36	20pa vio brn & lem	.20	.20
RA182	PT41	1k blk & gray grn	.20	.20

Nurse — PT85

Nurses on Parade
PT86

Design: 100k, Two nurses under Red Cross and Red Crescent flags and UN emblem.

Perf. 10½

1955, Sept. 5   Unwmk.   Litho
Crescent and Cross in Red

RA183	PT85	10k blk & pale brn	.75	.4
RA184	PT86	15k dk grn & pale yel grn	.75	.4
RA185	PT85	100k lt ultra	1.90	.6
		Nos. RA183-RA185 (3)	3.40	1.4

Meeting of the board of directors of the Int Council of Nurses, Istanbul, Aug. 29-Sept. 5 1955.

Nos. RA92 and RA130B Surcharged "20 Para"

1955

RA186	PT43	20p on 20k		.40	.20

Typo.

RA187	PT74	20p on 100k (surch. 11½x2mm)	.60	.20
c.		Surcharge 13½x2½mm	.60	.20

No. RA164 Surcharged with New Value and Two Bars

1956   Litho.   Perf. 10½

RA187A	PT79	20p on 1k multi	.20	.20
RA187B	PT79	2.50k on 1k multi	.20	.20

Woman and Children — PT87

Designs: 10k, 25k, 50k, Flag and building. 250k, 5 l, 10 l, Mother nursing baby.

1956   Litho.   Perf. 10½
Star in Red

RA188	PT87	20pa red org	.20	.20
RA189	PT87	20pa gray grn	.20	.20
RA190	PT87	1k purple	.20	.20
RA191	PT87	1k grnsh bl	.20	.20
RA192	PT87	3k lt red brn	.25	.20
RA193	PT87	10k rose car	.40	.20
RA194	PT87	25k brt grn	1.00	.50
RA195	PT87	50k brt ultra	1.60	.90
RA196	PT87	250k red lilac	8.50	5.00
RA197	PT87	5 l sepia	20.00	5.00
RA198	PT87	10 l dk sl grn	40.00	7.50
		Nos. RA188-RA198 (11)	72.55	20.10

Nos. RA131-RA138 Overprinted and Surcharged in Black or Red: "IV. DUNYA Cocuk Gunu 1 Ekim 1956"

1956, Oct. 1   Unwmk.   Perf. 11

RA199	PT75	20pa (R)	10.00	10.00
RA200	PT75	20pa	10.00	10.00
RA201	PT75	1k (R)	10.00	10.00
RA202	PT75	3k (R)	10.00	10.00
RA203	PT75	15k (R)	10.00	10.00
RA204	PT75	25k on 30k	10.00	10.00
RA205	PT75	100k on 150k (R)	12.00	12.00
RA206	PT75	250k on 300k	14.00	14.00
		Nos. RA199-RA206 (8)	86.00	86.00

The tax was for child welfare.

Type of 1954, Redrawn Type of 1946, and

Flower
PT88

Children
PT89

1957   **Unwmk.**   **Perf. 10½**
Crescent in Red

A207	PT88	½k lt ol gray & brn	.20	.20
A208	PT79	1k ol bis, blk & grn	.20	.20
A209	PT88	2½k yel grn & bl grn	.20	.20
A210	PT43	20k red & lt bl	.20	.20
A211	PT79	25k lt gray, blk & grn	.60	.30
A212	PT79	50k bl, dk grn & grn	.95	.30
A213	PT79	100k vio, blk & grn	1.40	.60
			3.75	2.00

No. RA210 inscribed "Türkiye Kizilay emiyeti." No. RA92 inscribed ". . . . Dernegi."

1957   **Unwmk.**   **Perf. 10½**

A214	PT89	20pa car & red	.20	.20
A215	PT89	20pa grn & red	.20	.20
A216	PT89	1k ultra & car	.20	.20
A217	PT89	3k red org & car	.50	.20
	Nos. RA214-RA217 (4)		1.10	.80

Blood Donor and
Recipient"
PT90

Child and
Butterfly
PT91

Designs: 75k, Figure showing blood circulation. 150k, Blood transfusion symbolism.

1957, May 22
Size: 24x40mm

A218	PT90	25k gray, blk & red	.25	.20

Size: 22½x37½mm

A219	PT90	75k grn, blk & red	.40	.30
A220	PT90	150k yel grn & red	.65	.50
	Nos. RA218-RA220 (3)		1.30	1.00

Redrawn Type of 1947
Inscribed: "V Dunya Cocuk Gunu"

1957   **Star in Red**   **Perf. 10½**

A221	PT72	100k blk & bis brn	.65	.60
A222	PT72	150k blk & yel grn	.65	.60
A223	PT72	250k blk & vio	.70	.65
	Nos. RA221-RA223 (3)		2.00	1.85

The tax was for child welfare.

1958   **Litho.**   **Unwmk.**

Various Butterflies. 50k, 75k horiz.

A224	PT91	20k gray & red	.30	.25
A225	PT91	25k multi	.30	.25
A226	PT91	50k multi	.40	.30
A227	PT91	75k grn, yel & blk	.50	.40
A228	PT91	150k multi	.80	.65
	Nos. RA224-RA228 (5)		2.30	1.85

Florence
Nightingale — PT92

1958
Crescent in Red

RA229	PT92	1 l bluish green	.40	.25
RA230	PT92	1½ l gray	.60	.50
RA231	PT92	2½ l blue	.80	.60
	Nos. RA229-RA231 (3)		1.80	1.35

Turkey stopped issuing postal tax stamps in June, 1958. Similar stamps of later date are private charity stamps issued by the Red Crescent Society and the Society for the Protection of Children.

POSTAL TAX AIR POST STAMPS

Air Fund Issues

These stamps were obligatory on all air mail for 21 days a year. Tax for the Turkish Aviation Society: 20pa for a postcard, 1k for a regular letter, 2 1/2k for a registered letter, 3k for a telegram, 5k-50k for a package, higher values for air freight. Postal tax air post stamps were withdrawn Aug. 21, 1934 and remainders destroyed later that year.

Biplane
PTAP1

Perf. 11, Pin Perf.
1926   **Unwmk.**   **Litho.**
Type PTAP1
Size: 35x25mm

RAC1	20pa brn & pale grn		2.25	.30
RAC2	1g blue grn & buff		1.25	.30

Size: 40x29mm

RAC3	5g vio & pale grn		5.00	1.00
RAC4	5g car lake & pale grn		25.00	15.00
	Nos. RAC1-RAC4 (4)		33.50	16.60

PTAP2

PTAP3

1927-29
Type PTAP2

RAC5	20pa dl red & pale grn		.50	.20
RAC6	1k green & yel		.45	.20

Type PTAP3
Perf. 11½

RAC7	2k dp cl & yel grn		.60	.35
RAC8	2½k red & yel grn		4.50	1.60
RAC9	5k dk bl gray & org		.45	.45
RAC10	10k dk grn & rose		3.75	1.60
RAC11	15k green & yel		3.75	2.00
RAC12	20k ol brn & yel		3.75	1.50
RAC13	50k dk bl & cob bl		6.00	3.25
RAC14	100k car & lt bl		60.00	35.00
	Nos. RAC5-RAC14 (10)		83.75	46.15

#RAC1, RAC5, RAC7 and RAC11
Surcharged in Black (RAC15-RAC16,
RAC18-RAC19) or Red (Others)

1930-31

RAC15	1k ("Bir kurus") on RAC1		80.00	70.00
RAC16	1k ("Bir Kurus") on RAC5		.75	.50
RAC17	100pa ("Yuz Para") on RAC7		1.00	.75
RAC18	5k ("Bes Kurus") on RAC5		1.00	.75

RAC19	5k ("5 Kurus") on RAC5		1.00	.75
RAC20	10k ("On kurus") on RAC7		1.50	1.25
RAC21	50k ("Elli kurus") on RAC7		8.00	7.00
RAC22	1 l ("Bir lira") on RAC7		12.00	25.00
RAC23	5 l ("Bes lira") on RAC11		500.00	400.00
	Nos. RAC15-RAC23 (9)		605.25	506.00

PTAP4

PTAP5

1931-32   **Litho.**   **Perf. 11½**

RAC24	PTAP4	20pa black	.50	.30

Typo.

RAC25	PTAP5	1k brown car ('32)	.60	.20
RAC26	PTAP5	5k red ('32)	.60	.25
RAC27	PTAP5	10k green ('32)	1.50	.50
	Nos. RAC24-RAC27 (4)		3.20	1.25

PTAP6

1933
Type PTAP6

RAC28	10pa ("On Para") grn		.60	.20
RAC29	1k ("Bir Kurus") red		.75	.20
RAC30	5k ("Bes Kurus") lil		1.50	1.00
	Nos. RAC28-RAC30 (3)		2.85	1.40

TURKEY IN ASIA

'tər-kē in 'ā-zhə

(Anatolia)

40 Paras = 1 Piaster

This designation, which includes all of Turkey in Asia Minor, came into existence during the uprising of 1919, led by Mustafa Kemal Pasha. Actually there was no separation of territory, the Sultan's sovereignty being almost immediately reduced to a small area surrounding Constantinople. The formation of the Turkish Republic and the expulsion of the Sultan followed in 1923. Subsequent issues of postage stamps are listed under Turkey (Republic).

Issues of the Nationalist Government

Turkish Stamps of
1913-18 Surcharged
in Black or Red

(The Surcharge reads "Angora 3
Piastres")

1920   **Unwmk.**   **Perf. 12**
On Stamps of 1913

1	A24	3pi on 2pa red lilac	2.50	2.00
2	A25	3pi on 4pa dk brn	10.00	7.50
3	A27	3pi on 6pa dk bl	25.00	22.50

On Stamp of 1916-18

4	A42	3pi on 2pa vio (Bk)	15.00	12.50
	Nos. 1-4 (4)		52.50	44.50

Turkish Stamps of 1913-18
Handstamped in Black or Red

(The Surch. reads "Post, Piastre 3")
1921   **Perf. 12**
On Stamps of 1913

5	A24	3pi on 2pa red lilac	8.00	5.50
a.	On No. 1		20.00	20.00
6	A25	3pi on 4pa dk brown	22.50	7.00
a.	On No. 2		20.00	20.00
7	A25	3pi on 4pa dk brn (R)	30.00	27.50
a.	On No. 2		12.00	12.00
8	A27	3pi on 6pa dk blue	35.00	35.00
a.	On No. 3		32.50	32.50
9	A27	3pi on 6pa dk bl (R)	70.00	55.00
a.	On No. 3		40.00	40.00

On Stamps of 1916-18

10	A42	3pi on 2pa vio (R)	30.00	30.00
a.	On No. 4		40.00	40.00
	Nos. 5-10 (6)		195.50	160.00

Turkish Revenue Stamps
Handstamped in Turkish "Osmanli
Postalari, 1336" (Ottoman Post,
1920).

عثمانلى پوسترلرى

١٣٣٦

Dash at upper left is set high. Bottom (date) line is 8½mm long.

عثمانلى پوستەرلرى

١٣٣٦

Dash at upper left is set lower. Bottom (date) line is 10mm long.

عثمانلى پوسترلرى

١٣٣٦

Dash at upper left is set lower. Bottom (date) line is 9mm long.

Religious
Tribunals
Revenue — R1

12	R1	1pi green (a, b, c)	275.00	195.00
13	R1	5pi ultra (a, b)	16,000.	15,500.
14	R1	50pi gray grn (a, b, c)	12.00	12.00
	Cut cancellation			1.50
15	R1	100pi buff (a)	55.00	55.00
a.	100pi yellow (a)		70.00	35.00
	Cut cancellation			6.00
16	R1	500pi orange (a)	110.00	70.00
	Cut cancellation			15.00
17	R1	1000pi brown (a)	2,000.	1,175.
	Cut cancellation			100.00

See Nos. 29-32.

Court Costs
Revenue — R2

Black Overprint

18	R2	10pa green		
		(b, c)	90.00	85.00
19	R2	1pi ultra (a,		
		c)	—	14,000.
20	R2	5pi rose (c)	*14,000.*	—
21	R2	50pi ocher		
		(a, b,		
		c)	6.75	5.75
a.	50pi yellow (a, b, c)		12.00	8.00
	Cut cancellation, #21,			
	21a			1.50
22	R2	100pi brown		
		(a)	95.00	55.00
	Cut cancellation			15.00
23	R2	500pi slate (a)	200.00	200.00
	Cut cancellation			10.00

See Nos. 24, 33-39.

Notary Public
Revenue — R3

Design R2 Overprinted "Katibi Adliye
Masus dur" in Red

24	R3	50pi ocher (a)	550.00	55.00
	Cut cancellation			15.00

Laborer's   **Notary Public**
Passport Tax   **Revenue — R5**
Stamp — R4

Black Overprint

25	R4	2pi emerald (a, c)		20,000.
26	R5	100pi yellow brn (a)	700.00	70.00
	Cut cancellation			15.00

See Nos. 46-48.

Theater Tax
Stamp — R6

Land Registry
Revenue — R7

27	R6	20pa black	3,500.	3,500.
28	R7	2pi blue black	6,250.	6,250.

See Nos. 40, 45.

Hejaz Railway Tax
Stamp — R8

Perf. 11½

28A	R8	2pi dk red & bl		
		(b)	1,200.	1,200.

Turkish Revenue Stamps
Overprinted in Turkish "Osmanli
Postalari, 1337" (Ottoman Post,
1921)

عثمانلی پوسته لری

۱۳۳۷   On #29-63

Perf. 12

29	R1	10pa slate	12.00	9.50
a.	Handstamped overprint		15.00	27.50
b.	Double overprint			
30	R1	1pi green	12.00	9.50
a.	Inverted overprint		16.00	13.00
b.	Handstamped overprint		2,000.	2,000.
31	R1	5pi ultra	12.00	5.50
a.	"1337" inverted		90.00	82.50
b.	Half used as 2½pi on cover			
c.	Handstamped overprint		550.00	550.00
	Nos. 29-31 (3)		36.00	24.50

Handstamped Overprint

32	R1	50pi green	3,500.	3,500.

Design R2 Overprinted

33	R2	10pa green	20.00	8.00
a.	Handstamped overprint		2,000.	2,000.
34	R2	1pi ultra	42.50	20.00
a.	Handstamped overprint		550.00	350.00
35	R2	5pi red	20.00	20.00
a.	Inverted overprint			
b.	"1337" inverted		50.00	50.00
c.	Half used as 2½pi on cover		3,500.	3,500.
d.	Handstamped overprint			
36	R2	50pi ocher	55.00	52.50
a.	Handstamped overprint		95.00	60.00
	As "a," cut cancellation			10.00
	Nos. 33-36 (4)		137.50	100.50

Design R3 Overprinted
Additional Turkish Overprint in Red or
Black

37	R3	10pa green (R)	55.00	50.00
38	R3	1pi ultra (R)	50.00	50.00
39	R3	5pi rose (Bk)	60.00	60.00
a.	"1337" inverted		150.00	150.00
b.	Handstamped overprint		4,250.	4,250.
	Nos. 37-39 (3)		165.00	160.00

Design R7 Overprinted

40	R7	2pi blue black	95.00	95.00
a.	Handstamped overprint		3,500.	3,500.

R12

1921   *Perf. 12*
Overprinted in Black

41	R12	5pi green	140.00	140.00
	Cut cancellation			10.00
a.	Handstamped overprint			

Museum Tax
Stamp — R13

Overprinted in Black

42	R13	1pi ultra	325.00	325.00
a.	Handstamped overprint		3,500.	3,500.
43	R13	5pi deep green	400.00	400.00
a.	Handstamped overprint		3,500.	3,500.

Handstamped Overprint

44	R13	5pi dark vio	5,500.	5,500.

The overprint variety "337" for "1337" exists on Nos. 42-43.

Design R6 Overprinted
Perf. 12, 12½

45	R6	20pa black	12.50	4.25
a.	Date 4½mm high		15.00	
b.	"337" for "1337"		25.00	

Design R5 Overprinted

46	R5	10pa green	14.00	5.50
a.	Overprint 21mm long			
b.	"131" for "1337"			
47	R5	1pi ultra	24.00	12.00
a.	"13" for "1337"		50.00	50.00
b.	"131" for "1337"		50.00	50.00
c.	Inverted overprint		75.00	75.00
d.	Handstamped overprint		2,800.	2,800.
48	R5	5pi red	42.50	20.00
a.	"13" for "1337"		85.00	85.00
b.	"131" for "1337"		85.00	85.00
c.	Handstamped overprint		2,400.	2,400.
	Nos. 46-48 (3)		80.50	37.50

R16

Perf. 11½, 11½x11
Overprinted in Black

49	R16	10pa pink	1.50	1.00
a.	Imperf.			
b.	Date "1237"		2.00	2.00
d.	Inverted overprint			
e.	Handstamped overprint		1,550.	1,550.
50	R16	1pi yellow	4.00	2.25
a.	Overprint 18mm long		5.00	2.00
b.	Date "1332"		6.00	
c.	Date "1317"			
d.	Inverted overprint			
e.	Handstamped overprint		1,550.	1,550.
51	R16	2pi yellow grn	7.75	2.50
a.	Date "1237"		8.00	
b.	Date "1317"			
c.	Imperf.			
d.	Inverted overprint		25.00	5.00
e.	Handstamped overprint		1,600.	1,600.
52	R16	5pi red	8.00	2.25
a.	Horiz. pair, imperf. vert.			
b.	Inverted overprint		12.50	7.50
c.	Double overprint		15.00	12.50
d.	Date "1332"		22.50	
e.	Half used as 2½pi on cover			
f.	Overprint 18mm long		10.00	7.50
g.	Handstamped overprint		1,600.	1,600.
	Nos. 49-52 (4)		21.25	8.00

Design R8 Overprinted
TURKISH INSCRIPTIONS:

20 Paras   1 Piaster

2 Piasters   5 Piasters

1921   *Perf. 11½*
Dark Red & Blue

53	R8	20pa on 1pi	60.00	24.00
54	R8	1pi on 1pi	3.25	3.25
55	R8	2pi on 1pi	3.25	3.25
a.	Inverted surcharge			
56	R8	5pi on 1pi	5.00	3.25
	Nos. 53-56 (4)		71.50	33.75

See No. 57.

No. 54 Overprinted

57	R8	1pi on 1pi dk red & bl	40.00	24.0

Hejaz Railway Tax
Stamp — R19

Overprinted in Black

58	R19	1pi grn & brn red	2.50	1.?
a.	Double overprint			
b.	Handstamped overprint			

The errors "1307," "1331" and "2337" occu[r] once in each sheet of Nos. 53-58.

Naval League
Labels — R20

1921   *Perf. 12x11*
Overprinted in Black

59	R20	1pa orange	2.75	2.7
a.	Date "1327"		3.50	3.5
60	R20	2pa indigo	2.75	2.7
61	R20	5pa green	2.75	2.7
62	R20	10pa brown	25.00	25.0
63	R20	40pa red brown	75.00	75.0
	Nos. 59-63 (5)		108.25	108.2

The error "2337" occurs on all values of th[is] issue.

The Naval League stamps have pictures [of] three Turkish warships. They were sold for th[e] benefit of sailors of the fleet but did not pa[y] postage until they were overprinted in 1921.

Turkish Stamps of 1915-20
Overprinted

a   b

The overprints on Nos. 64-77 read "Adan[a,] December 1st, 1921." This issue commemo[-] rated the withdrawal of the French from Cilicia[.] On No. 71 the lines of the overprint are fu[r-] ther apart than on Nos. 68-70 and 73-74.

1921   *Perf. 1[2]*

64	A44 (a)	10pa grn (424)	6.00	6.0
65	A45 (a)	20pa deep rose		
		(425)	6.00	6.0
a.	Inverted overprint		17.00	
66	A51 (a)	25pi car, *straw*		
		(434)	21.00	20.0
a.	Double overprint			
b.	Inverted overprint		37.50	37.5
	Nos. 64-66 (3)		33.00	32.0

On Newspaper Stamp of 1915

67	A21 (a)	5pa och (P132)	150.00	120.0

On Stamp of 1915

68	A22 (b)	5pa och (328)	425.00	425.0

On Stamps of 1917-18

69	A53 (b)	5pi on 2pa		
		(547)	12.00	12.0
70	A53 (b)	5pi on 2pa		
		(548)	12.00	12.0

On Stamp of 1919
71 A57 (b) 35pi on 1pi bl
(Bk; 579) 42.50 42.50
a. Inverted surcharge

On Newspaper Stamp of 1915
72 A21 (b) 5pa och (P132) 200.00 200.00
On No. 72 the overprint is vertical, half reading up and half reading down.

On Stamps of 1920
73 A32 (b) 3pi blue (594) 8.00 8.00
74 A36 (b) 10pi gray vio
(596) 12.00 12.00

On Postage Due Stamps of 1914
75 D1 (a) 5pa claret (J63) 425.00 425.00
76 D2 (a) 20pa red (J64) 425.00 425.00
a. Inverted overprint
77 D3 (b) 1pi dk bl (J65) 425.00 425.00
a. Inverted overprint 750.00 750.00
Nos. 75-77 (3) 1,275. 1,275.
Withdrawal of the French from Cilicia.
Forged overprints exist.

Pact of Revenge, Burning Village at Top — A21

Izmir Harbor — A22

Mosque of Selim, Adrianople A23

Mosque of Selim, Konya — A24

Soldier — A25

Legendary Gray Wolf — A26

Snake Castle and Seyhan River, Adana — A27

Parliament Building at Sivas — A28

A29

Mosque at Urfa — A30

Map of Anatolia — A31

Declaration of Faith from the Koran — A32

1922		Litho.		Perf. 11½
78	A21	10pa violet brn	.20	.20
79	A22	20pa blue grn	.30	.20
80	A23	1pi dp blue	.60	.20
81	A24	2pi red brown	1.50	.20
82	A25	5pi dk blue	1.50	.20
83	A26	10pi dk brown	4.00	.20
84	A27	25pi rose	12.00	.20
85	A28	50pi indigo	.55	.40
86	A29	50pi dk gray	.60	.30
87	A30	100pi violet	72.50	2.75
		Cut cancellation		1.00
88	A31	200pi slate	195.00	32.50
		Cut cancellation		1.25
89	A32	500pi green	110.00	16.00
		Cut cancellation		2.50
		Nos. 78-89 (12)	398.75	53.35
		Set, never hinged	1,950.	

Imperf

79a	A22	20pa	25.00	30.00
80a	A23	1pi	15.00	20.00
82a	A25	5pi	15.00	20.00
84a	A27	25pi	25.00	30.00
85a	A28	50pi	27.50	30.00

Stamps of Type A23 Overprinted

1922				
90	A23	1pi deep blue	8.00	—
91	A23	5pi deep blue	8.00	—
92	A23	10pi brown	8.00	—
93	A23	25pi rose	9.50	—
94	A23	50pi slate	11.00	—
95	A23	100pi violet	17.00	—
96	A23	200pi black vio	17.00	—
97	A23	500pi blue green	24.00	—
		Nos. 90-97 (8)	102.50	.00
		Set, never hinged	200.00	

Withdrawal of the French from Cilicia and the return of the Kemalist Natl. army. The overprint reads: "Adana, Jan. 5, 1922."
No. 90-97 without overprint were presented to some high government officials.

First Parliament House, Ankara — A33

1922				Litho.
98	A33	5pa violet	.40	.40
99	A33	10pa green	.75	.40
100	A33	20pa pale red	1.00	.75
101	A33	1pi brown org	4.75	1.10
102	A33	2pi red brown	11.50	3.25
103	A33	3pi rose	2.25	.40
a.		Arabic "13" in right corner	6.50	3.50
b.		Thin grayish paper	40.00	4.00
		Nos. 98-103 (6)	20.65	6.30
		Set, never hinged	60.00	

Nos. 98-103, 103b exist imperf. In 1923 several stamps of Turkey and Turkey in Asia were overprinted in Turkish for advertising purposes. The overprint reads: "Izmir Economic Congress, 17 Feb., 1339."

POSTAGE DUE STAMPS

D1

1922		Litho.		Perf. 11½
J1	D1	20pa dull green	.50	—
a.		Imperf.		
J2	D1	1pi gray green	.75	—
J3	D1	2pi red brown	1.25	—
J4	D1	3pi rose	2.25	—
J5	D1	5pi dark blue	2.75	—
		Nos. J1-J5 (5)	7.50	.00
		Set, never hinged	42.50	

ADVANTAGE STOCKSHEETS

Designed with the collector in mind, Advantage stock sheets fit directly in your 2-post or 3-ring National or Specialty album. For unprecedented durability and flexibility choose Advantage Stocksheets. Choose from 1 to 8 pockets.
Sheets are sold in packages of 10.

- Stock sheets match album pages in every respect, including border, size, and color.

- Punched and drilled to fit perfectly in binder.

- Available with 1 to 8 pockets.
  Ideal for storing minor varieties and collateral material. A great place to keep new issues until the next supplement is available.

- Provide the protection and durability of crystal clear acetate pockets on heavyweight pages.

NATIONAL BORDER

ITEM			RETAIL
AD11	1 Pocket	242mm	$15.99
AD12	2 Pockets	119mm	$15.99
AD13	3 Pockets	79mm	$15.99
AD14	4 Pockets	58mm	$15.99
AD15	5 Pockets	45mm	$15.99
AD16	6 Pockets	37mm	$15.99
AD17	7 Pockets	31mm	$15.99
AD18	8 Pockets	31mm	$15.99

SPECIALTY BORDER

AD21	1 Pocket	242mm	$15.99
AD22	2 Pockets	119mm	$15.99
AD23	3 Pockets	79mm	$15.99
AD24	4 Pockets	58mm	$15.99
AD25	5 Pockets	45mm	$15.99
AD26	6 Pockets	37mm	$15.99
AD27	7 Pockets	31mm	$15.99
AD28	8 Pockets	31mm S	$15.99

Available from your favorite stamp dealer or direct from:

1-800-572-6885
P.O. Box 828,
Sidney OH 45365
www.amosadvantage.com

AMOS
HOBBY PUBLISHING

TURKISH REPUBLIC OF NORTHERN CYPRUS

'tər-kish ri-'pə-blik of 'nor-tḥəɾn 'sī-prəs

LOCATION — Northern 40% of the Island of Cyprus in the Mediterranean Sea off the coast of Turkey.

Established following Turkish invasion of Cyprus in 1974. On Nov. 15, 1983 Turkey declared the Turkish Republic of Northern Cyprus to be independent. No other country has recognized this country.

1000 Milliemes = 1 Pound

100 Kurus = 1 Turkish Lira (1978)

Catalogue values for all unused stamps in this country are for Never Hinged items.

Letters bearing these stamps enter international mail via the Turkish Post Office.

Watermark

Wmk. 390

Republic of Turkey, 50th Anniv.
A1   A2

Designs: 3m, Woman sentry. 5m, Military parade. 10m, Flag bearers. 15m, Anniversary emblem. 20m, Ataturk statue. 50m, Painting, "The Fallen." 70m, Turkish flag, map of Cyprus.

1974, July 27   Litho.   Unwmk.
Perf. 12x11½, 11½x12

1	A1	3m multicolored	37.50	37.50
2	A2	5m multicolored	.35	.20
3	A1	10m multicolored	.50	.50
4	A2	15m multicolored	.60	.50
5	A1	20m multicolored	.70	.70
6	A1	50m multicolored	3.00	2.75
7	A2	70m multicolored	27.50	15.00
		Nos. 1-7 (7)	70.15	56.85

First day covers are dated 1/29/73.

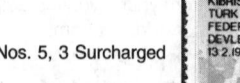

Nos. 5, 3 Surcharged

1975, Mar. 3   Perf. 12x11½
8	A1	30m on 20m, #5	1.25	1.00
9	A1	100m on 10m, #3	3.00	2.25

Surcharge appears in different positions.

Historical Sites and Landmarks A3

Designs: 3m, Namik Kemal's bust, Famagusta. 5m, 30m, Kyrenia Harbor. 10m, Ataturk Statue, Nicosia. 15m, St. Hilarion Castle. 20m, Ataturk Square, Nicosia. 25m, Coastline, Famagusta. 50m, Lala Mustafa Pasha Mosque, Famagusta vert. 100m, Kyrenia Castle. 250m, Kyrenia Castle, exterior walls. 500m, Othello Tower, Famagusta vert.

1975-76   Perf. 13
10	A3	3m pink & multi	.25	.25
11	A3	5m bl & multi	.20	.20
12	A3	10m pink & multi	.25	.25
13	A3	15m pink & multi	.30	.30
14	A3	15m bl & multi	.20	.20
15	A3	20m pink & multi	2.25	.40
16	A3	20m bl & multi	.20	.20
17	A3	25m pink & multi	.50	.50
18	A3	30m pink & multi	1.25	.75
19	A3	50m pink & multi	1.40	.75
20	A3	100m pink & multi	1.60	1.10
21	A3	250m pink & multi	1.75	1.75
22	A3	500m pink & multi	2.40	2.40
		Nos. 10-22 (13)	12.55	9.05

Issued: #10, 12-13, 15, 17-22, 4/21; #11, 14, 16, 8/2/76. #1, 14, 16 have different inscriptions and "1976."
For surcharges see Nos. 28-29.

Peace in Cyprus — A4

Designs: 50m, Map, olive branch, severed chain. 150m, Map, globe, olive branch, vert.

1975, July 20   Perf. 13½x13, 13x13½
23	A4	30m multicolored	.40	.25
24	A4	50m multicolored	.50	.35
25	A4	150m multicolored	1.10	1.00
		Nos. 23-25 (3)	2.00	1.60

Europa — A5

Paintings: 90m, Pomegranates by I.V. Guney. 100m, Harvest Time by F. Direkoglu.

1975, Dec. 29   Perf. 13
26	A5	90m multicolored	2.25	1.25
27	A5	100m multicolored	3.75	2.25

Nos. 19, 20 Surcharged

1976, Apr. 28   Perf. 13
28	A3	10m on 50m, #19	.30	.30
29	A3	30m on 100m, #20	1.00	1.00

Europa — A6   Olympic Games, Montreal — A8

Fruits — A7

1976, May 3
30	A6	60m Expectation	1.00	.35
31	A6	120m Man in Meditation	2.00	.75

1976, June 28
32	A7	10m Ceratonia siliqua	.20	.20
33	A7	25m Citrus nobilis	.30	.20
34	A7	40m Fragaria vesca	.40	.20
35	A7	60m Citrus sinensis	.50	.30
36	A7	80m Citrus limon	.75	.45
		Nos. 32-36 (5)	2.15	1.35

For surcharges see Nos. 66-69.

1976, July 17
Design: 100m, Olympic rings, doves, horiz.
37	A8	60m multicolored	.25	.20
38	A8	100m multicolored	.40	.35

Liberation Monument — A9

1976, Nov. 1   Perf. 13x13½
39	A9	30m multi	.20	.20
40	A9	150m multi, diff.	.45	.45

Europa — A10

1977, May 2   Perf. 13
41	A10	80m Salamis Bay	3.00	1.00
42	A10	100m Kyrenia Port	4.50	1.50

Handicrafts A11

1977, June 27
43	A11	15m Pottery	.20	.20
44	A11	30m Gourds, vert.	.20	.20
45	A11	125m Baskets	.30	.30
		Nos. 43-45 (3)	.70	.70

Landmarks A12

Designs: 20m, Arap Ahmet Pasha Mosque, Nicosia, vert. 40m, Paphos Castle. 70m, Bekir Pasha aqueduct, Larnaca. 80m, Sultan Mahmut library, Nicosia.

1977, Dec. 2   Perf. 13x13½, 13½x13
46	A12	20m multicolored	.20	.20
47	A12	40m multicolored	.20	.20
48	A12	70m multicolored	.20	.20
49	A12	80m multicolored	.25	.25
		Nos. 46-49 (4)	.85	.85

Namik Kemal (1840-1888), Writer — A13

1977, Dec. 21   Perf. 13
50	A13	30m Bust, home	.20	.20
51	A13	140m Portrait, vert.	.50	.50

Social Security — A14   Europa — A15

Designs: 275k, Man with sling, crutch. 375k, Woman with children.

1978, Apr. 17   Perf. 13x13½
52	A14	150k blk, bl & yel	.20	.20
53	A14	275k blk, grn & red org	.20	.20
54	A14	375k blk, red org & bl	.25	.25
		Nos. 52-54 (3)	.65	.65

1978, May 2   Perf. 13x13½, 13½x13
225k, Oratory in Buyuk Han, Nicosia. 450k, Reservoir, Selimiye Mosque, Nicosia.
55	A15	225k multi	4.25	1.25
56	A15	450k multi, horiz.	8.50	2.25

Transportation A16

1978, July 10   Perf. 13½x13
57	A16	75k Roadway	.20	.20
58	A16	100k Hydrofoil	.20	.20
59	A16	650k Airplane	.50	.50
		Nos. 57-59 (3)	.90	.90

National Oath — A17

Kemal Ataturk — A18

1978, Sept. 13
60	A17	150k Dove, olive branch	.20	.20
61	A17	225k Stylized pen, vert.	.20	.20
62	A17	725k Stylized dove	.25	.25
		Nos. 60-62 (3)	.65	.65

1978, Nov. 10
63	A18	75k bl grn & lt grn	.20	.20
64	A18	450k brn & buff	.20	.20
65	A18	650k Prus bl & lt bl	.30	.30
		Nos. 63-65 (3)	.70	.70

Nos. 33-36 Surcharged

1979, June 4
66	A7	50k on 25m	.20	.20
67	A7	1 l on 40m	.20	.20
68	A7	3 l on 60m	.20	.20
69	A7	5 l on 80m	.25	.20
		Nos. 66-69 (4)	.85	.80

Souvenir Sheet

5th ANNIVERSARY OF THE TURKISH PEACE OPERATION IN CYPRUS

Turkish Invasion of Cyprus, 5th Anniv. — A19

Illustration reduced.

1979, July 2   *Imperf.*
70   A19   15 l multicolored   2.75   2.75

Europa
A20

Communications: 3 l, Stamps, building, map. 8 l, Early and modern telephones, globe, satellite.

1979, Aug. 20   *Litho.*   *Perf. 13*
71   A20   2 l multicolored   1.75   .50
72   A20   3 l multicolored   2.50   .75
73   A20   8 l multicolored   5.75   1.50
    Nos. 71-73 (3)   10.00   2.75

Intl. Consultative
Radio Committee,
50th Anniv. — A21

1979, Sept. 24
74   A21   2 l blue & multi   .20   .20
75   A21   5 l gray & multi   .25   .20
76   A21   6 l green & multi   .35   .30
    Nos. 74-76 (3)   .80   .70

Intl. Year
of the
Child
A22

Childrens' drawings of children.

1979, Oct. 29
77   A22   1½ l multi, vert.   .20   .20
78   A22   4½ l multicolored   .35   .30
79   A22   6 l multi, vert.   .45   .40
    Nos. 77-79 (3)   1.00   .90

Press reports in Jan. 1980 state that the 1979 UPU Congress declared Turkish Cyprus stamps invalid for international mail.

A23   Europa — A24

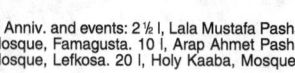

Anniv. and events: 2½ l, Lala Mustafa Pasha Mosque, Famagusta. 10 l, Arap Ahmet Pasha Mosque, Lefkosa. 20 l, Holy Kaaba, Mosque.

1980, Mar. 23
80   A23   2½ l multicolored   .20   .20
81   A23   10 l multicolored   .30   .25
82   A23   20 l multicolored   .50   .45
    Nos. 80-82 (3)   1.00   .90

1st Islamic Conference in Turkish Cyprus (2½ l). General Assembly of World Islam Congress (10 l). Moslem year 1400 AH (20 l).

1980, May 23
83   A24   5 l Ebu-Suud Efendi   1.00   .50
84   A24   30 l Sultan Selim II   3.50   1.00

Historic
Landmarks
A25

Designs: 2½ l, Omer's Shrine, Kyrenia. 3½ l, Entrance gate, Famagusta. 5 l, Funerary monuments, Famagusta. 10 l, Bella Paise Abbey, Kyrenia. 20 l, Selimiye Mosque, Nicosia.

1980, June 25
Blue Paper
85   A25   2½ l buff & Prus bl   .20   .20
86   A25   3½ l pale pink & dk grn   .20   .20
87   A25   5 l pale bl grn & dk car   .20   .20
88   A25   10 l lt grn & red lil   .25   .20
89   A25   20 l buff & dk bl   .40   .35
    Nos. 85-89 (5)   1.25   1.15

For overprints and surcharges see Nos. 198-200.

Cyprus
Postage
Stamps,
Cent.
A26

1980, Aug. 16
90   A26   7½ l No. 5, vert.   .20   .20
91   A26   15 l No. 199   .20   .20
92   A26   50 l Social welfare, vert.   .80   .75
    Nos. 90-92 (3)   1.20   1.15

Palestinian
Solidarity
A27

15 l, Dome of the Rock, entrance, vert.

1980, Mar. 24
93   A27   15 l multicolored   .30   .25
94   A27   35 l multicolored   .75   .60

World Muslim
Congress
Statement — A28

1981, Mar. 24
95   A28   1 l In Turkish   .20   .20
96   A28   35 l In English   .75   .65

Ataturk by Feyhamam Duran — A29

1981, May 19
97   A29   20 l multicolored   .65   .65
Printed with se-tenant label promoting Ataturk Stamp Exhibition.

Europa
A30

Folk dances.

1981, June 29
98   A30   10 l multicolored   .95   .45
99   A30   30 l multi, diff.   2.75   1.10

Souvenir Sheet

Ataturk, Birth Cent. — A31

Illustration reduced.

1981, July 23   *Imperf.*
100   A31   150 l multicolored   2.00   1.40
No. 100 has simulated perfs.

Flowers
A32

Designs: 1 l, Convolvulus althaeoides, vert. 5 l, Cyclamen persicum. 10 l, Mandragara officinarum. 25 l, Papaver rhoeas, vert. 30 l, Arum dioscoridis, vert. 50 l, Chrysanthemum segetum. 100 l, Cistus salviaefolius, vert. 150 l, Ferula communis.

1981-82   *Perf. 13*
101   A32   1 l multicolored   .20   .20
102   A32   5 l multicolored   .20   .20
103   A32   10 l multicolored   .25   .25
104   A32   25 l multicolored   .40   .40
105   A32   30 l multicolored   .45   .45
106   A32   50 l multicolored   .75   .75
107   A32   100 l multicolored   1.50   1.50
108   A32   150 l multicolored   2.25   2.25
    Nos. 101-108 (8)   6.00   6.00

Issue dates: 1 l, 10 l, 25 l, 150 l, Sept. 28; 5 l, 30 l, 50 l, 100 l, Jan. 22, 1982.
For surcharge & overprints see #138-141, 201.

Intl. Year
for
Disabled
Persons
A33

Fight Against   World Food
Apartheid — A34   Day — A35

1981, Oct. 16
109   A33   7½ l multicolored   .20   .20
110   A34   10 l multicolored   .35   .30
111   A35   20 l multicolored   .65   .50
    Nos. 109-111 (3)   1.20   1.00

Palestinian
Solidarity
A36

1981, Nov. 29
112   A36   10 l multicolored   .25   .25

Royal Wedding of
Prince Charles and
Lady Diana
Spencer — A37

1981, Nov. 30
113   A37   50 l multicolored   1.00   .70

Souvenir Sheet

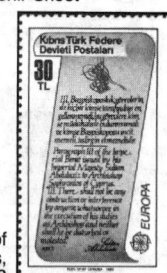

Charter of
Cyprus,
1865 — A38

Turkish Forces
Landing in
Tuzla — A39

1982, July 30
114   Sheet of 4   7.00   7.00
   a.   A38   30 l multicolored   1.00   1.00
   b.   A39   70 l multicolored   1.00   1.00

Europa. #114 contains 2 each #114a, 114b.

Buffavento
Castle — A40

Windsurfing — A41

Kantara
Castle
A42

Tourism: 30 l, Shipwreck museum.

Perf. 12½x12, 12x12½

1982, Aug. 20
116	A40	5 l multicolored	.20	.20
117	A41	10 l multicolored	.20	.20
118	A42	15 l multicolored	.25	.20
119	A42	30 l multicolored	.50	.40
		Nos. 116-119 (4)	1.15	1.00

Art Treasures — A43

Designs: 30 l, The Wedding by Aylin Orek. 50 l, Carob Pickers by Ozden Nazim, vert.

1982, Dec. 3   Perf. 13x13½, 13½x13
120	A43	30 l multicolored	.30	.30
121	A43	50 l multicolored	.50	.50

Robert
Koch, TB
Bacillus
A44

World Cup Soccer Championships,
Spain — A45

Scouting, 75th
Anniv. — A46

1982, Dec. 15   Perf. 12½
122	A44	10 l multicolored	.25	.20
123	A45	30 l multicolored	.75	.60
124	A46	70 l multicolored	2.00	1.50
		Nos. 122-124 (3)	3.00	2.30

Paintings
A47

30 l, Calloused Hands by Salih Oral. 35 l,
Malya-Limassol Bus by Emin Cizenel.

1983, May 16   Perf. 13½x13
125	A47	30 l multicolored	.90	.75
126	A47	35 l multicolored	1.25	1.00

Miniature Sheet

Europa — A48

a, Map by Piri Reis. b, Cyprus seen from
Skylab.

1983, June 30   Perf. 13
127	A48	Sheet of 2	100.00	100.00
a.-b.		100 l any single	20.00	20.00

25th Anniv.
of Turkish
Resistance
A49

Designs: 15 l, No. 3. 20 l, Exploitation, Sup-
pression & Resurrection by Aziz Hasan. 25 l,
Resistance by Guner Pir.

1983, Aug. 1   Perf. 13
129	A49	15 l multi, vert.	.30	.30
130	A49	20 l multi	.45	.45
131	A49	25 l multi, vert.	.50	.50
		Nos. 129-131 (3)	1.25	1.25

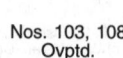

World Communications Year — A50

1983, Aug. 1
132	A50	30 l shown	.60	.60
133	A50	50 l Letters	1.00	1.00

Birds
A51

1983, Oct. 10
134	A51	10 l Merops apiaster	.20	.20
135	A51	15 l Carduelis cardue-lis	.25	.20
136	A51	50 l Erithacus rubecu-la	.90	.65
137	A51	65 l Oriolus oriolus	1.25	.85
a.		Block of 4, #134-137	3.25	2.50
		Nos. 134-137 (4)	2.60	1.90

Nos. 103, 108
Ovptd.

Nos. 101, 104 Ovptd. or Surcharged

1983, Dec. 7
138	A32	10 l multicolored	.20	.20
139	A32	15 l on 1 l multi	.20	.20
140	A32	25 l multicolored	.35	.35
141	A32	150 l multicolored	2.00	2.00
		Nos. 138-141 (4)	2.75	2.75

Europa,
25th Anniv.
A52

1984, May 30   Perf. 12x12½
142	A52	50 l blk, yel & brn	1.25	.65
143	A52	100 l blk, bl & ultra	2.75	1.75
a.		Pair, #142-143	4.00	4.00

Olympics,
Los
Angeles
A53

Perf. 12½x12, 12x12½
1984, June 19
144	A53	10 l Olympic flame, vert.	.20	.20
145	A53	20 l Olympic rings	.20	.20
146	A53	70 l Judo	.60	.60
		Nos. 144-146 (3)	1.00	1.00

Ataturk
Cultural
Center
A54

Perf. 12x12½
1984, July 20   Wmk. 390
147	A54	120 l blk, yel & brn	.90	.90

Turkish
Invasion of
Cyprus,
10th
Anniv.
A55

1984, July 20
148	A55	20 l shown	.20	.20
149	A55	70 l Map, flag, olive branch	.55	.55

Forest Conservation — A56

1984, Aug. 20
150	A56	90 l multicolored	.80	.75

Paintings — A57

20 l, Old Turkish Houses in Nicosia by
Cevdet Cagdas. 70 l, Scenery by Olga Rauf.

1984, Sept. 21   Perf. 13
151	A57	20 l multicolored	.30	.30
152	A57	70 l multicolored	.85	.85

Proclamation of
Turkish Republic of
Northern
Cyprus — A58

Unanimous Vote by Legislative
Assembly — A59

Perf. 12½x12, 12x12½
1984, Nov. 15
153	A58	20 l multicolored	.20	.20
154	A59	70 l multicolored	.55	.55

Independence, 1st Anniv.

European Taekwondo Championship,
Kyrenia — A60

1984, Dec. 10
155	A60	10 l Competitors	.20	.20
156	A60	70 l Flags	.55	.55

Balance of the Spirit — A61

Paintings by Saulo Mercader: 20 l, The
Look, vert.

1984, Dec. 10   Perf. 12½x13, 13x12½
157	A61	20 l multicolored	.20	.20
158	A61	70 l multicolored	.50	.50

 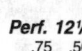

Visit by
Nuremburg
Chamber
Orchestra
A62

1984, Dec. 10   Perf. 12½
159	A62	70 l multicolored	.75	.50

Dr. Fazil Kucuk (1906-1984), Politician — A63

70 l, Kucuk reading newspaper, c. 1970.

1985, Jan.

160	A63	20 l multicolored	.20	.20
161	A63	70 l multicolored	.50	.50

Domestic Animals A64

1985, May 29   *Perf. 12x12½*

162	A64	100 l Capra	.55	.55
163	A64	200 l Bos taurus	1.10	1.10
164	A64	300 l Ovis aries	1.60	1.60
165	A64	500 l Equus asinus	2.75	2.75
		Nos. 162-165 (4)	6.00	6.00

Europa — A65   Paintings — A66

Composers: No. 166, George Frideric Handel (1685-1759). No. 167, Domenico Scarlatti (1685-1757). No. 168, Johann Sebastian Bach (1685-1750). No. 169, Buhurizade Mustafa Itri (1640-1712).

1985, June 26   *Perf. 12½x12*

166	A65	20 l grn & multi	.40	.30
167	A65	20 l brn lake & multi	.40	.30
168	A65	100 l bl & multi	1.60	1.00
169	A65	100 l brn & multi	1.60	1.00
a.		Block of 4, #166-169	4.00	4.00

Printed in sheets of 16, containing 4 No. 69a.

1985, Aug.   *Perf. 12½x13*

Paintings: 20 l, Pastoral Life by Ali Atakan. 50 l, Woman Carrying Water by Ismet V. Guney.

70	A66	20 l multicolored	.20	.20
71	A66	50 l multicolored	.30	.30

Intl. Youth Year A67

1985, Oct. 29   **Wmk. 390**   *Litho.*   *Perf. 12½*

72	A67	20 l shown	.20	.20
73	A67	100 l Globe, dove	.60	.60

Northern Cyprus Air League — A68

Development of Rabies Vaccine, Cent. — A69

Ismet Inonu (1884-1973), Turkish Pres. — A70

UN, 40th Anniv. A71

Blood Donor Services A72

1985, Nov. 29

174	A68	20 l multicolored	.20	.20
175	A69	50 l Pasteur	.30	.30
176	A70	100 l brown	.60	.60
177	A71	100 l multicolored	.60	.60
178	A72	100 l multicolored	.60	.60
		Nos. 174-178 (5)	2.30	2.30

Paintings — A73

20 l, House with Arches by Gonen Atakol. 100 l, Ataturk Square by Yalkin Muhtaroglu.

1986, June 20   *Perf. 13*

179	A73	20 l multicolored	.20	.20
180	A73	100 l multicolored	.40	.40

Miniature Sheet

Europa — A74

1986, June 20   *Perf. 12x12½*

181	A74	Sheet of 2	17.50	17.50
a.		100 l Gyps fulvus	4.75	3.00
b.		200 l Roadside litter	9.50	5.00

Karagoz Puppets — A75

1986, July 25   *Perf. 12½x13*

182	A75	100 l multicolored	.40	.40

Anatolian Artifacts A76

Designs: 10 l, Ring-shaped composite pottery, Kernos, Old Bronze Age (2300-1050 B.C.). 20 l, Bird-shaped lidded pot, Skuru Hill tomb, Morphou, late Bronze Age (1600-1500 B.C.), vert. 50 l, Earthenware jug, Vryse, Kyrenia, Neolithic Age (4000 B.C.). 100 l, Terra sigillata statue of Artemis, Sea of Salamis, Roman Period (200 B.C.), vert.

1986, Sept. 15   *Perf. 12½*

183	A76	10 l multicolored	.20	.20
184	A76	20 l multicolored	.20	.20
185	A76	50 l multicolored	.25	.25
186	A76	100 l multicolored	.50	.50
		Nos. 183-186 (4)	1.15	1.15

For surcharge see No. 295A.

Defense Forces, 10th Anniv. — A77

World Food Day — A78

World Cup Soccer Championships, Mexico — A79

Halley's Comet A80

1986, Oct. 13

187	A77	20 l multicolored	.20	.20
188	A78	50 l multicolored	.30	.30
189	A79	100 l multicolored	.35	.35
190	A80	100 l multicolored	.40	.40
		Nos. 187-190 (4)	1.25	1.25

Development Projects — A81

1986, Nov. 17

191	A81	20 l Water resources	.20	.20
192	A81	50 l Housing	.20	.20
193	A81	100 l Airport	.45	.45
		Nos. 191-193 (3)	.85	.85

Royal Wedding of Prince Andrew and Sarah Ferguson — A82

Anniv. and events: No. 195, Queen Elizabeth II, 60th birthday.

     Perf. 12½x13

1986, Nov. 20   **Wmk. 390**

194	A82	100 l multicolored	.35	.35
195	A82	100 l multicolored	.35	.35
a.		Pair, #194-195	.70	.70

Trakhoni Station, 1904 A83

1986, Dec. 31

196	A83	100 l shown	.20	.20
197	A83	100 l Locomotive #1, 1904	.50	.30

Rail transport, 1904-1951.

Nos. 86, 88-89, 105 Overprinted or Surcharged

a

b

1987, May 18   **Unwmk.**   *Perf. 13*

198	A25(a)	10 l on #89	.40	.20
199	A25(a)	15 l on 3 ½ l, #86	.40	.20
200	A25(a)	20 l on #88	.50	.25
201	A32(b)	30 l on #105	.80	.35
		Nos. 198-201 (4)	2.10	1.00

Paintings — A84

Folk Dancers — A86

Europa A85

Designs: 50 l, Shepherd by Feridun Isiman. 125 l, Pear Woman by Mehmet Uluhan.

Perf. 12½x13

1987, May 27   **Wmk. 390**
202 A84 50 l multicolored   .25   .20
203 A84 125 l multicolored   .65   .40

1987, June 30   **Perf. 12½**
Modern architecture: 50 l, Bauhaus-style house, designed by A. Vural Behaeddin, 1973. 200 l, House, designed by Necdet Turgay, 1979.

204 A85 50 l multicolored   2.00   .50
205 A85 200 l multicolored   6.00 2.50
a.   Bklt. pane, 2 each #204-205   15.00

No. 205a contains two copies each of Nos. 204-205, printed alternately, with unprinted selvage at each end of the pane, perf between stamps and selvage and imperf on outside edges. Thus, singles from the pane gauge 12½ by imperf.

1987, Aug. 20
206 A86 20 l multicolored   .20   .20
207 A86 50 l multi, diff.   .20   .20
208 A86 200 l multi, diff.   .50   .50
209 A86 1000 l multi, diff.   2.50 2.50
     Nos. 206-209 (4)   3.40 3.40

For surcharge see No. 295B.

Infantry Regiment, 1st Anniv. — A87   5th Islamic Summit Conf., Kuwait — A88

Pharmaceutical Federation — A89

1987, Sept. 30
210 A87 50 l multicolored   .20   .20
211 A88 200 l multicolored   .50   .50
212 A89 200 l multicolored   .50   .50
     Nos. 210-212 (3)   1.20 1.20

Ahmet Belig Pasha (1851-1924), Egyptian Judge — A90   Mehmet Emin Pasha (1813-1871), Turkish Grand Vizier — A91

Famous men: 125 l, Mehmet Kamil Pasha (1832-1913), grand vizier.

1987, Oct. 22
213 A90 50 l brn & yel   .20   .20
214 A91 50 l multicolored   .20   .20
215 A91 125 l multicolored   .35   .30
     Nos. 213-215 (3)   .75   .70

Pres. Rauf Denktash, Turkish Prime Minister Turgut Ozal A92

1987, Nov. 2
216 A92 50 l multi   .20   .20

New Kyrenia Harbor A93

Wmk. 390
1987, Nov. 20   Litho.   Perf. 12½
217 A93 150 l shown   .40   .40
218 A93 200 l Eastern Mediterranean University   .55   .55

Chair Weaver, by Osman Guvenir — A94

Paintings: 20 l, Woman Making Pastry, by Ayhan Mentes, vert. 150 l, Woman Weaving a Rug, by Zekai Yesiladali, vert.

Wmk. 390
1988, May 2   Litho.   Perf. 13
219 A94 20 l multi   .20   .20
220 A94 50 l multi   .20   .20
221 A94 150 l multi   .45   .35
     Nos. 219-221 (3)   .85   .75

Europa A95

1988, May 31   Perf. 12½
222 A95 200 l Tugboat *Piyale Pasha*   3.50 1.25
223 A95 500 l Satellite dish, broadcast tower, vert.   5.50 1.75

Bayrak Radio and Television Corporation, 25th anniv. (500 l).

Tourism A96

Photographs: 150 l, Nicosia, by Aysel Erduran. 200 l, Famagusta, by Sonia Halliday and Laura Lushington. 300 l, Kyrenia, by Halliday and Lushington.

1988, June 17
224 A96 150 l multi   .25   .25
225 A96 200 l multi   .35   .35
226 A96 300 l multi   .50   .50
     Nos. 224-226 (3)   1.10 1.10

Turkish Prime Ministers — A97

No. 227, Bulent Ecevit, 1970's. No. 228, Bulent Ulusu, Sept. 21, 1980-Dec. 13, 1983. No. 229, Turgut Ozal, from Dec. 13, 1983.

1988, July 20
227 A97 50 l shown   .20   .20
228 A97 50 l multi   .20   .20
229 A97 50 l multi   .20   .20
     Nos. 227-229 (3)   .60   .60

Civil Defense A98

1988, Aug. 8   Perf. 12x12½
230 A98 150 l multicolored   .35   .35

Summer Olympics, Seoul A99

1988, Sept. 17   Perf. 12½
231 A99 200 l shown   .30   .30
232 A99 250 l Women's running   .40   .40
233 A99 400 l Seoul   .65   .65
     Nos. 231-233 (3)   1.35 1.35

Sedat Simavi (1896-1953), Turkish Journalist — A100

Intl. Conferences, Kyrenia — A101

North Cyprus Intl. Industrial Fair — A102   Intl. Red. Cross and Red Crescent Organizations, 125th Anniv. — A103

US-USSR Summit Meeting on Nuclear Arms Reduction A104

WHO, 40th Anniv. — A105

1988, Oct. 17   Perf. 12½x12, 12x12½
234 A100 50 l olive grn   .20   .20
235 A101 100 l multi   .25   .25
236 A102 300 l multi   .55   .55
237 A103 400 l multi   .85   .85
238 A104 400 l Gorbachev and Reagan   .85   .85
239 A105 600 l multi   1.10 1.10
     Nos. 234-239 (6)   3.80 3.80

Miniature Sheet

Atatürk'ün Ölümünün 50.Yılı

10 Kasım, 1938-1988

Portraits and Photographs of Kemal Ataturk — A106

b, Holding canteen. c, In uniform. d, Facing left.

1988, Nov. 10   Perf. 12½
240 A106 Sheet of 4   1.75 1.75
a.-d.   250 l any single   .30   .30

Souvenir Sheet

Turkish Republic of Northern Cyprus, 5th Anniv. — A107

1988, Nov. 15   Imperf.
241 A107 500 l multicolored   1.25 1.00

Dervis Pasha Mansion, 19th Cent., Nicosia — A108

Designs: 400 l, Gamblers' Inn, 17th cent., Asmaalti Meydani. 600 l, Camii Cedit Mosque, 1902, Paphos, vert.

1989, Apr. 28   Perf. 13
242 A108 150 l shown   .30   .30
243 A108 400 l multi   .80   .80
244 A108 600 l multi   1.25 1.25
     Nos. 242-244 (3)   2.35 2.35

Europa — A109

1989, May 31   Perf. 12½x12
245 A109 600 l Girl, doll   2.25 1.25
246 A109 1000 l Flying kite   3.25 1.25
a.   Bklt. pane, 2 each #245-246, perf. 12½   10.50

Geneva
Peace
Summit,
Aug. 24,
1988
A110

1989, June 30   **Perf. 12½**
47 A110 500 l blk & dark red   1.00 1.00

Wildlife
A111

1989, July 31
48 A111 100 l Alectoris chukar   .20   .20
49 A111 200 l Lepus cyprius   .40   .40
50 A111 700 l Francolinus
           francolinus   1.40 1.40
51 A111 2000 l Vulpes vulpes   4.00 4.00
     Nos. 248-251 (4)   6.00 6.00

Natl. Development Projects — A112

Perf. 12½x12, 12x12½
1989, Sept. 29
52 A112 100 l Road construc-
           tion   .20   .20
53 A112 150 l Sanitary water
           supply   .30   .30
54 A112 200 l Afforestation   .40   .40
55 A112 450 l Telecommunica-
           tions   .90   .90
56 A112 650 l Power station   1.25 1.25
57 A112 700 l Irrigation ponds   1.40 1.40
     Nos. 252-257 (6)   4.45 4.45

Nos. 253-256 vert.

Free Port, Famagusta, 15th
Anniv. — A113

Turkish Cypriot
Post, 25th
Anniv. — A114

Saded Newspaper, Cent. — A115

Intl. Marine Organization, 30th
Anniv. — A116

Erenkoy
Uprising,
25th
Anniv.
A117

Perf. 12x12½, 12½x13 (450 l)
1989, Nov. 17
258 A113 100 l multicolored   .20   .20
259 A114 450 l multicolored   .90   .90
260 A115 500 l multicolored   1.00 1.00
261 A116 600 l multicolored   1.25 1.25
262 A117 1000 l multicolored   2.00 2.00
     Nos. 258-262 (5)   5.35 5.35

Erdal Inonu   Agriculture
A118   A119

1989, Dec. 15   **Perf. 12½x12**
263 A118 700 l multicolored   1.40 1.40

Visit of Inonu, Turkish politician, to northern
Cyprus.

1989, Dec. 25   **Perf. 12x12½, 12½x12**
264 A119 150 l Mule drawn   .30   .30
265 A119 450 l Ox drawn   .90   .90
266 A119 550 l Millstone, olive
           press   1.10 1.10
     Nos. 264-266 (3)   2.30 2.30

Nos. 264-265 horiz.

World
Health
Day
A120

Perf. 12x12½
1990, Apr. 19   **Litho.**   **Wmk. 390**
267 A120 200 l shown   .40   .20
268 A120 700 l Cigarette, heart   1.50   .40

Europa
A121

Post offices.

Perf. 12x12½
1990, May 31   **Litho.**   **Wmk. 390**
269 A121 1000 l Yenierenkoy   4.00   1.75
270 A121 1500 l Ataturk
            Meydani   6.00   2.25
   a.   Souv. sheet, 2 #269, 2 #270   21.00 21.00

World Cup Soccer Championships,
Italy — A122

1990, June 8
271 A122 300 l Turkish Cypriot
            team   .65   .65
272 A122 1000 l Ball, emblem,
            globe   2.00 2.00

A123   A126

A125

World Environment Day: Birds.

1990, June 5   **Perf. 12**
273 A123 150 l Turdus
           philomelos   3.00   .60
274 A123 300 l Sylvia atri-
           capilla   4.50 1.00
275 A123 900 l Phoenicurus
           ochruros   10.00 2.25
276 A123 1000 l Phyllosopus
           collybita   12.00 4.50
     Nos. 273-276 (4)   29.50 8.35

For surcharge see No. 386.

1990, July 31   **Perf. 13x12½, 12½x13**
Designs: 300 l, Painting by Filiz Ankac. 1000
l, Sculpture by Sinasi Tekman, vert.
279 A125 300 l multicolored   .65   .65
280 A125 1000 l multicolored   2.00 2.00

Wmk. 390
1990, Aug. 24   **Litho.**   **Perf. 12½**
281 A126 150 l Amphitheater,
           Soli   .35   .35
282 A126 1000 l Mosaic, Soli   2.00 2.00

European Tourism Year.

Visit by
Turkish
President
Kenan
Evren
A127

1990, Sept. 19
283 A127 500 l multicolored   1.00 1.00

Traffic
Safety
A128

1990, Sept. 21
284 A128 150 l Wear seat belts   .35   .35
285 A128 300 l Obey the speed
           limit   .65   .65
286 A128 1000 l Obey traffic sig-
           nals   2.00 2.00
     Nos. 284-286 (3)   3.00 3.00

A129   Flowers — A130

1990, Oct. 1
287 A129 1000 l multicolored   2.00 2.00

Visit by Turkish Prime Minister Yildirim
Akbulut.

Perf. 12½x12
1990, Oct. 31   **Litho.**   **Wmk. 390**
288 A130 150 l Rosularia cypria   .35   .20
289 A130 200 l Silene fraudra-
           trix   .40   .20
290 A130 300 l Scutellaria
           sibthorpii   .65   .20
291 A130 600 l Sedum
           lampusae   1.25   .30
292 A130 1000 l Onosma caes-
           pitosum   2.00   .50
293 A130 1500 l Arabis cypria   3.25   .80
     Nos. 288-293 (6)   7.90 2.20

For surcharges see Nos. 295C, 387.

Intl.
Literacy
Year
A131

1990, Nov. 24   **Perf. 12x12½**
294 A131 300 l Ataturk as teach-
           er   .65   .20
295 A131 750 l A, b, c, books,
           map   1.60   .40

Nos. 183, 206, 288 Surcharged

1991, June 3
Perfs. & Printing Methods as Before
295A A76 250 l on 10 l #183   .20   .20
295B A86 250 l on 20 l #206   .20   .20
295C A130 500 l on 150 l #288   .35   .25
     Nos. 295A-295C (3)   .75   .65

Shape of obliterator varies.

Orchids — A132

Wmk. 390
1991, July 8   **Litho.**   **Perf. 14**
296 A132 250 l Ophrys lapethica   .55   .55
297 A132 500 l Ophrys kotschyi   1.60 1.60

See Nos. 303-306.

A133

Perf. 12½x12
1991, July 29   **Litho.**   **Wmk. 390**
Europa: a, Hermes space shuttle. b,
Ulysses probe.

Miniature Sheet
298 A133 2000 l Sheet of 2, #a.-
            b.   8.00 8.00

Public Fountains A134

Wmk. 390

1991, Sept. 9		Litho.	*Perf. 12*	
299	A134	250 l Kuchuk Medrese	.20	.20
300	A134	500 l Djafer Pasha	.35	.35
301	A134	1500 l Sarayonu Square	1.10	1.10
302	A134	5000 l Arabahmet Mosque	3.50	3.50
		Nos. 299-302 (4)	5.15	5.15

Orchid Type of 1991

1991, Oct. 10			*Perf. 14*	
303	A132	100 l Serapias levantina	.20	.20
304	A132	500 l Dactylorhiza romana	.40	.40
305	A132	2000 l Orchis simia	1.40	1.40
306	A132	3000 l Orchis sancta	2.00	2.00
		Nos. 303-306 (4)	4.00	4.00

Hindiler by Salih M. Cizel — A135

Painting: 500 l, Dusme by Asik Mene.

Wmk. 390

1991, Nov. 5		Litho.	*Perf. 13*	
307	A135	250 l multicolored	.20	.20
308	A135	500 l multicolored	.25	.25

See type A143. For surcharge see No. 381.

World Food Day A136

Basbakan Mustafa Cagatay (1937-1989) A137

Eastern Mediterranean University — A138

Wolfgang Amadeus Mozart, Death Bicent. A139

1991, Nov. 20			*Perf. 12*	
309	A136	250 l multicolored	.20	.20
310	A137	500 l multicolored	.30	.30
311	A138	500 l multicolored	.30	.30
312	A139	1500 l multicolored	.85	.85
		Nos. 309-312 (4)	1.65	1.65

For surcharge see No. 380.

World AIDS Day A140

1991, Dec. 13			*Perf. 12*	
313	A140	1000 l multicolored	.55	.55

Lighthouses — A141

1991, Dec. 16			*Perf. 12x12½*	
314	A141	250 l Canbulat Burcu, Famagusta	.20	.20
315	A141	500 l Yat Limani, Kyrenia	.30	.30
316	A141	1500 l Turizm Limani, Kyrenia	.85	.85
		Nos. 314-316 (3)	1.35	1.35

Tourism A142

Designs: 250 l, Elephant and hippopotamus fossils, Kyrenia. 500 l, Roman fish ponds, Lambusa (58 BC-398 AD). 1500 l, Roman tomb and church, Lambusa (58 BC-1192 AD).

1991, Dec. 27				
317	A142	250 l multicolored	.20	.20
318	A142	500 l multicolored	.30	.30
319	A142	1500 l multicolored	.85	.85
		Nos. 317-319 (3)	1.35	1.35

Paintings A143

Designs: 500 l, Ebru, by Arife Kandulu. 3500 l, Nicosia, by Ismet Tartar.

Wmk. 390

1992, Mar. 31		Litho.	*Perf. 14*	
320	A143	500 l multicolored	.25	.25
321	A143	3500 l multicolored	1.75	1.75

See type A135.

Tourism A144

No. 322, Ancient building, Famagusta. No. 323, Trap shooting range, Nicosia. 1000 l, Salamis Bay resort, Famagusta. 1500 l, Casino, Kyrenia.

1992, Apr. 21		*Perf. 13½x14, 14x13½*		
322	A144	500 l multi	.25	.25
323	A144	500 l multi	.25	.25
324	A144	1000 l multi	.50	.50
325	A144	1500 l multi, vert.	.75	.75
		Nos. 322-325 (4)	1.75	1.75

Souvenir Sheet

Discovery of America, 500th Anniv. — A145

Europa: a, 1500 l, Santa Maria, Nina and Pinta. b, 3500 l, Columbus.

1992, May 29		*Perf. 13½x14*		
326	A145	Sheet of 2, #a.-b.	10.00	10.00

Sea Turtles A146

1992, June 30		Litho.	**Wmk. 390**	
327	A146	1000 l Green turtle	.75	.50
328	A146	1500 l Loggerhead turtle	1.00	.75
a.		Souv. sheet, 2 ea #327-328	3.75	3.75

World Wildlife Fund.

1992 Summer Olympics, Barcelona A147

#329: a, Women's gymnastics, vert. b, Tennis, vert. 1000 l, High jump. 1500 l, Cycling.

1992, July 25		*Perf. 14x13½*		
329	A147	500 l Pair, #a-b.	.75	.75

		Perf. 13½x14		
330	A147	1000 l multicolored	.50	.50
331	A147	1500 l multicolored	.75	.75
		Nos. 329-331 (3)	2.00	2.00

Electric Power Plant, Kyrenia A148

Social Insurance, 15th Anniv. A149

Intl. Federation of Women Artists A150

Veterinary Services A151

Souvenir Sheet

1992, Sept. 30		Litho.	**Wmk. 390**	
332	A148	500 l multicolored	.25	.2
333	A149	500 l multicolored	.25	.2
334	A150	1500 l multicolored	.75	.7
335	A151	1500 l multicolored	.75	.7
		Nos. 332-335 (4)	2.00	2.0

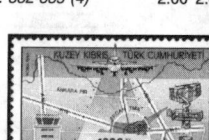

Civil Aviation Office, 17th Anniv. A152

Meteorology Office, 18th Anniv. — A153

Mapping, 14th Anniv. A154

1992, Nov. 20		Litho.	**Wmk. 390**	
336	A152	1000 l multicolored	.50	.50
337	A153	1000 l multicolored	.50	.50
338	A154	1200 l multicolored	.60	.60
		Nos. 336-338 (3)	1.60	1.60

Native Cuisine A155

Food: 2000 l, Zulbiye (pastry). 2500 l, Cicek Dolmasi (stuffed squash flowers). 3000 l, Tatar Boregi (flaky pastry dish). 4000 l, Seftali kebab (meat dish).

1992, Dec. 14				
339	A155	2000 l multicolored	1.00	1.00
340	A155	2500 l multicolored	1.25	1.25
341	A155	3000 l multicolored	1.50	1.50
342	A155	4000 l multicolored	2.00	2.00
		Nos. 339-342 (4)	5.75	5.75

Intl. Conference on Nutrition, Rome. See Nos. 388-390.

Tourism A156

Designs: 500 l, Church and Monastery of St. Barnabas. 10,000 l, Bowl.

1993, Apr. 1		Litho.	**Wmk. 390**	
343	A156	500 l multi	.25	.25
344	A156	10,000 l multi	5.00	5.00

Souvenir Sheet

Europa — A157

Contemporary paintings by: a, 2000 l, Turksal Ince. b, 3000 l, Ilkay Onsoy.

Perf. 14x13½
1993, May 5   Litho.   Wmk. 390
345 A157 Sheet of 2, #a.-b.   2.00 2.00

Trees — A158

1993, June 11   Perf. 14x13½
346 A158 500 l Olea europea   .25 .20
347 A158 1000 l Eucalyptus camaldulensis   .50 .50
348 A158 3000 l Platanus orientalis   1.50 1.50
349 A158 4000 l Pinus brutia tenore   2.00 2.00
Nos. 346-349 (4)   4.25 4.20

Arabahmet Rehabilitation Project — A159

Perf. 13½x14
1993, Sept. 20   Litho.   Wmk. 390
350 A159 1000 l shown   .20 .20
351 A159 3000 l Homes, diff.   .50 .50

Creation of Turkish Republic of Northern Cyprus, 10th Anniv. A160

Designs: No. 353, Flags changing to dove, vert. 1000 l, Dove flying from flag. 5000 l, Flowers forming "10," map.

Perf. 13½x14, 14x13½
1993, Nov. 15   Litho.   Wmk. 390
352 A160 500 l multicolored   .20 .20
353 A160 500 l multicolored   .20 .20
354 A160 1000 l multicolored   .20 .20
355 A160 5000 l multicolored   .80 .80
Nos. 352-355 (4)   1.40 1.40

Ataturk, 55th Death Anniv. — A161

State Theaters, 30th Anniv. A162

Turkish Resistance Organization, 35th Anniv. — A163

Turkish News Agency, 20th Anniv. A164

Tchaikovsky, Death Cent. — A165

Perf. 14x13½, 13½x14
1993, Dec. 27   Litho.   Wmk. 390
356 A161 500 l multicolored   .20 .20
357 A162 500 l multicolored   .20 .20
358 A163 1500 l multicolored   .30 .30
359 A164 2000 l multicolored   .40 .40
360 A165 5000 l multicolored   1.10 1.10
Nos. 356-360 (5)   2.20 2.20

Soyle Falci, by Goral Ozkan A166

Design: 6500 l, Sculpture, IV Hareket, by Senol Özdevrim.

1994, Mar. 31   Perf. 14
361 A166 1000 l multicolored   .20 .20
362 A166 6500 l multicolored   1.40 1.40

Fazil Kucuk (1906-84), Physician and Political Leader — A167

1994, Apr. 1
363 A167 1500 l multicolored   .30 .30

Souvenir Sheet

Archaeological Discoveries — A168

Europa: a, Neolithic village, Ayios Epectitos Vrysi. b, Neolithic man, early tools found in excavation.

1994, May 16   Perf. 13½
364 A168 8500 l Sheet of 2, #a.-b.   3.25 3.25

1994 World Cup Soccer Championships, US — A169

1994, June 30
365 A169 2500 l Trophy, vert.   .20 .20
366 A169 10,000 l US map   .80 .80

Turkish Postal Service in Northern Cyprus, 30th Anniv. A170

1994, June 30
367 A170 50,000 l multicolored   4.00 4.00

A171

A172

Turkish Peace Operation, 20th Anniv. A173

1994, July 20   Perf. 14
368 A171 2500 l shown   .20 .20
369 A172 5000 l Monument   .40 .40
370 A172 7000 l Monument, diff.   .50 .50
371 A173 8500 l shown   .65 .65
Nos. 368-371 (4)   1.75 1.75

First Rural Postal Cancellations, Cent. — A174

Postmarks, stamps: 1500 l, Karpas, Cyprus #131. 2500 l, Gazi Magusa (Famagusta), #71. 5000 l, Bey Keuy, Cyprus #150. 7000 l, Aloa, Cyprus, #179. 8500 l, Pyla, Cyprus #152.

1994, Aug. 15   Perf. 13½
372 A174 1500 l multicolored   .20 .20
373 A174 2500 l multicolored   .20 .20
374 A174 5000 l multicolored   .35 .35
375 A174 7000 l multicolored   .55 .55
376 A174 8500 l multicolored   .70 .70
Nos. 372-376 (5)   2.00 2.00

Sea Shells — A175

1994, Nov. 15   Perf. 14
377 A175 2500 l Charonia tritonis   .20 .20
378 A175 12,500 l Tonna galea   .70 .35
379 A175 12,500 l Cypraea talpa   .70 .35
Nos. 377-379 (3)   1.60 .90

Nos. 307, 309 Surcharged

1994, Dec. 12   Perfs., etc. as Before
380 A136 1500 l on 250 l multi   .20 .20
381 A135 2500 l on 250 l multi   .20 .20

Size and location of surcharge varies.

European Nature Conservation Year — A176

Designs: 2000 l, Donkeys on mountain top. 3500 l, Shoreline. 15,000 l, Donkeys in field.

1995, Feb. 10   Wmk. 390   Perf. 14
382 A176 2000 l multicolored   .20 .20
383 A176 3500 l multicolored   .20 .20
384 A176 15,000 l multicolored   1.00 1.00
Nos. 382-384 (3)   1.40 1.40

Souvenir Sheet

Peace and Freedom — A177

Europa: a, Globe, dove. b, Doves over Europe.
Illustration reduced.

1995, Apr. 20   Perf. 13½x14
385 A177 15,000 l Sheet of 2, #a.-b.   2.75 2.75

Nos. 275 & 290 Surcharged

1995, Apr. 21   Perfs., etc. as Before
386 A174 2000 l on 900 l #275   .20 .20
387 A130 3500 l on 300 l #290   .20 .20

Size and location of surcharge varies.

Native Cusine Type of 1992

Food: 3500 l, Sini katmeri. 10,000 l, Kolokas musakka, Bullez kizartma. 14,000 l, Enginar dolmasi.

1995, May 29 **Litho.** **Wmk. 390**
Perf. 13½x14

388	A155	3500 l	multicolored	.20 .20
389	A155	10,000 l	multicolored	.55 .55
390	A155	14,000 l	multicolored	.80 .80
	Nos. 388-390 (3)			1.55 1.55

Butterflies
A178

1995, June 30

391	A178	3500 l	Papilio machaon	.20 .20
392	A178	4500 l	Charaxes jasius	.20 .20
393	A178	15,000 l	Cynthia cardui	.65 .65
394	A178	30,000 l	Vanessa atalanta	1.25 1.25
	Nos. 391-394 (4)			2.30 2.30

Visit by Turkish Pres. Suleyman Demirel
A179

1995, Aug. 21 *Perf. 13½*

395	A179	5000 l	multicolored	.25 .25

Tourism
A180

Designs: 3500 l, Beach scene, Kyrenia. 7500 l, Sailboats. 15,000 l, Ruins, Famagusta, vert. 20,000 l, St. George Cathedral, Famagusta, vert.

1995, Aug. 21

396	A180	3500 l	multicolored	.20 .20
397	A180	7500 l	multicolored	.40 .40
398	A180	15,000 l	multicolored	.80 .80
399	A180	20,000 l	multicolored	1.00 1.00
	Nos. 396-399 (4)			2.40 2.40

State Printing Office, 20th Anniv.
A181

Turkish Natl. Assembly, 75th Anniv.
A182

Louis Pasteur (1822-95)
A183

UN, 50th Anniv.
A184

G. Marconi (1874-1937), Radio, Cent. — A185

Motion Pictures, Cent. — A186

Perf. 13½x14, 14x13½

1995, Nov. 7 **Litho.** **Wmk. 390**

400	A181	3000 l	multicolored	.20 .20
401	A182	3000 l	multicolored	.20 .20
402	A183	5000 l	multicolored	.25 .25
403	A184	22,000 l	multicolored	1.25 1.25
404	A185	30,000 l	multicolored	1.60 1.60
405	A186	30,000 l	multicolored	1.60 1.60
	Nos. 400-405 (6)			5.10 5.10

A187 A188

Tombstone inscriptions, Orhon and Yenisey river region: 5000 l, Kültigin Heykelinin Basi. 10,000 l, Kültigin Yaziti.

1995, Dec. 28 *Perf. 14x13½*

406	A187	5000 l	multicolored	.25 .25
407	A187	10,000 l	multicolored	.55 .55

Reading of Orhon Epitaphs, cent.

1996, Jan. 31

408	A188	10,000 l	multicolored	.55 .55

Bosnia-Herzegovina.

Fish
A189

Designs: 60,000 l, Mullus surmuletus. 10,000 l, Thalassoma pavo. 28,000 l, Diplodus vulgaris. 40,000 l, Epinephelus guaza.

1996, Mar. 29 *Perf. 14*

409	A189	6,000 l	multicolored	.20 .20
410	A189	10,000 l	multicolored	.30 .30
411	A189	28,000 l	multicolored	.80 .80
412	A189	40,000 l	multicolored	1.10 1.10
	Nos. 409-412 (4)			2.40 2.40

Tourism
A190

Designs: 100,000 l, Pomegranate tree, vert. 150,000 l, Pomegranate fruit, vert. 250,000 l, Bellapais Monastery. 500,000 l, Folk dancing.

Perf. 14x13½, 13½x14

1996, Apr. 26 **Litho.** **Wmk. 390**

413	A190	100,000 l	multi	2.50 2.50
414	A190	150,000 l	multi	3.75 3.75
415	A190	250,000 l	multi	6.25 6.25
416	A190	500,000 l	multi	12.50 12.50
	Nos. 413-416 (4)			25.00 25.00

Famous Women
A191

Europa: 15,000 l, Beria Remzi Ozoran. 50,000 l, Kadriye Hulusi Hacibulgur.

1996, May 31 *Perf. 13½x14*

417	A191	15,000 l	multicolored	.50 .50
418	A191	50,000 l	multicolored	2.00 2.00

World Environment Day — A192

Designs: a, Older, dying trees in mountainous area. b, Newly-planted trees.

1996, June 28 *Perf. 13½*

419	A192	50,000 l	Sheet of 2, #a.-b.	1.10 1.10

1996 Summer Olympic Games, Atlanta — A193

a, 15,000 l, Basketball. b, 50,000 l, Javelin. c, 15,000 l, Discus. d, 50,000 l, Volleyball.

1996, July 31

420	A193	Sheet of 4, #a.-d.		3.00 3.00

Euro '96, European Soccer Championship, Great Britain — A194

1996, Oct. 31 *Perf. 13½x14*

421	A194	15,000 l	shown	.40 .40
422	A194	35,000 l	Flags, soccer ball	1.40 1.40
a.			Pair, #421-422	2.00 2.00

Civil Defense
A195

Security Forces — A196

Nasreddin Hodja
A197

Children's Rights
A198

Perf. 13½x14, 14x13½

1996, Dec. 23 **Litho.** **Wmk. 390**

423	A195	10,000 l	multicolored	.25 .25
424	A196	20,000 l	multicolored	.50 .50
425	A197	50,000 l	multicolored	1.25 1.25
426	A198	75,000 l	multicolored	1.90 1.90
	Nos. 423-426 (4)			3.90 3.90

Paintings — A199

Designs: 25,000 l, Buildings, people, by Lebibe Sonuc. 70,000 l, Woman seated beside plant, by Ruzen Atakan.

1997, Jan. 31 *Perf. 14*

427	A199	25,000 l	multicolored	.65 .65
428	A199	70,000 l	multicolored	1.75 1.75

Mushrooms
A200

Natl. Flag on Mountainside
A201

Designs: 15,000 l, Amanita phallioides. No. 430, Morchella esculenta. No. 431, Pleurotus eryngii. 70,0000 l, Amanita muscaria.

1997, Mar. 31

429	A200	15,000 l	multicolored	.45 .45
430	A200	25,000 l	multicolored	.65 .65
431	A200	25,000 l	multicolored	.65 .65
432	A200	70,000 l	multicolored	1.75 1.75
	Nos. 429-432 (4)			3.50 3.50

1997, Apr. 23

433	A201	60,000 l	multicolored	1.50 1.50

Stories and Legends
A202

Europa: 25,000 l, Woman with broom, children playing, man with donkey. 70,000 l, Well, apple tree, man behind bushes.

1997, May 30   *Perf. 13½x14*
434 A202 25,000 l multicolored   .75 .75
435 A202 70,000 l multicolored   1.75 1.75

Visit by Turkish Leaders
A203

Designs: 15,000 l, Prime Minister Necmeddin Erbakan, vert. 80,000 l, Pres. Süleyman Demirel.

Perf. 14x13½, 13½x14
1997, June 20
436 A203 15,000 l multicolored   .30 .30
437 A203 80,000 l multicolored   1.50 1.50

A204   A205

Raptors: No. 438, Aquila chrysaetos. No. 439, Falco eleanorae. 75,000 l, Falco tinnunculus. 100,000 l, Pernis apivorus.

1997, July 31   *Perf. 14x13½*
438 A204 40,000 l multicolored   .55 .55
439 A204 40,000 l multicolored   .55 .55
440 A204 75,000 l multicolored   1.00 1.00
441 A204 100,000 l multicolored   1.40 1.40
     Nos. 438-441 (4)   3.50 3.50

1997, Oct. 28

Old Coins Used in Cyprus: 25,000 l, 1861 Abdül Aziz gold lira. 40,000 l, 1808 Mahmud II gold rumi. 75,000 l, 1566 Selim II gold lira. 100,000 l, 1909 Mehmed V gold besibirlik.

442 A205 25,000 l multicolored   .35 .35
443 A205 40,000 l multicolored   .55 .55
444 A205 75,000 l multicolored   1.00 1.00
445 A205 100,000 l multicolored   1.40 1.40
     Nos. 442-445 (4)   3.30 3.30

Turk Lisesi, Cent.
A206

Scouting, 90th Anniv.
A207

Fight Against AIDS — A208

Diesel Engine, Cent.
A209

Perf. 13½x14, 14x13½
1997, Dec. 22   Litho.   Wmk. 390
446 A206 25,000 l multicolored   .30 .30
447 A207 40,000 l multicolored   .50 .50
448 A208 100,000 l multicolored   1.25 1.25
449 A209 150,000 l multicolored   1.75 1.75
     Nos. 446-449 (4)   3.80 3.80

Ismet Sevki (1884-1957) and Ahmet Sevki (1874-1959), Photographers — A210

1998, Jan. 28   *Perf. 13½x14*
450 A210 40,000 l shown   .50 .50
451 A210 105,000 l Ahmet Sevki, vert.   1.25 1.25

Insects
A211

Designs: 40,000 l, Agrion splendens. 65,000 l, Ascalaphus macaronius. 125,000 l, Podalonia hirsuta. 150,000 l, Rhyssa persuasoria.

1998, Mar. 30
452 A211 40,000 l multicolored   .40 .40
453 A211 65,000 l multicolored   .65 .65
454 A211 125,000 l multicolored   1.25 1.25
455 A211 150,000 l multicolored   1.50 1.50
     Nos. 452-455 (4)   3.80 3.80

Doors — A212

1998, Apr. 30   *Perf. 14x13½*
456 A212 115,000 l shown   1.10 1.10
457 A212 140,000 l Door, steps   1.40 1.40

Natl. Festival
A213

Europa: 150,000 l, Globe, map of Cyprus, flags, vert.

1998, May 30   *Perf. 13½x14, 14x13½*
458 A213 40,000 l multicolored   .65 .65
459 A213 150,000 l multicolored   2.10 2.10

Intl. Year of the Ocean
A214

Various marine life.

1998, June 30   *Perf. 13½x14*
460 A214 40,000 l multicolored   .30 .30
461 A214 90,000 l multicolored   .65 .65

Visit by Turkish Prime Minister Mesut Yilmaz
A215

1998, July 20
462 A215 75,000 l multicolored   .55 .55

Turkish Pres. Süleyman Demirel — A216

1998 World Cup Soccer Championships, France — A217

Design: 175,000 l, Pres. Demirel, Pres. Rauf R. Denktash, view of ocean, horiz.

1998, July 25   *Perf. 13½x14, 14x13½*
463 A216 75,000 l multicolored   .55 .55
464 A216 175,000 l multicolored   1.25 1.25

Establishment of Yaylacik water program.

1998, July 31   *Perf. 13½x14, 13x13½*

75,000 l, Team coming across field, fans in stadium. 175,000 l, Holding up World Cup trophy.

465 A217 75,000 l multi, horiz.   .55 .55
466 A217 175,000 l multi   1.25 1.25

Visit of Turkish Deputy Prime Minister Bülent Ecevit — A218

Traditional Crafts — A219

1998, Sept. 5   *Perf. 14*
467 A218 200,000 l multicolored   1.50 1.50

1998, Oct. 26   *Perf. 13½x14, 14x13½*
468 A219 50,000 l Kalayci, horiz.   .40 .40
469 A219 75,000 l Sepetci   .60 .60
470 A219 130,000 l Bileyici   1.00 1.00
471 A219 400,000 l Oymaci, horiz.   3.00 3.00
     Nos. 468-471 (4)   5.00 5.00

Bayrak Radio & Television, 35th Anniv.
A220

Turkish Cyprus, 15th Anniv.
A221

Turkish Republic, 75th Anniv.
A222

Universal Declaration of Human Rights, 50th Anniv. — A223

No. 476a, 75,000 l, Natl. flag, map of Turkish Cyprus.

1998, Nov. 15
472 A220 50,000 l multicolored   .40 .40
473 A221 75,000 l multicolored   .55 .55
474 A222 75,000 l multicolored   .55 .55
475 A223 175,000 l multicolored   1.25 .65
     Nos. 472-475 (4)   2.75 2.15
         Souvenir Sheet
476   Sheet of 2, #473, #476a   1.10 1.10

A224

1999, Jan. 15   *Perf. 14*
477 A224 75,000 l multicolored   .55 .55

Dr. Fazil Kücük (1906-84), politician.

A225

1999, Jan. 30

Scene from "Othello," by Verdi: a, Singers standing. b, Singer on floor.

478 A225 200,000 l Sheet of 2, #a.-b.   1.60 1.60

Snakes
A226

Designs: 50,000 l, Malpolon monspessulanus insignitus. 75,000 l, Hierophis jugularis. 195,000 l, Vipera lebetina. 220,000 l, Natrix natrix.

1999, Mar. 26   *Perf. 13½x14*
479 A226 50,000 l multicolored   .40 .40
480 A226 75,000 l multicolored   .60 .60
481 A226 195,000 l multicolored   1.60 1.60
482 A226 220,000 l multicolored   1.75 1.75
     Nos. 479-482 (4)   4.35 4.35

Europa
A227

1999, May 17   *Perf. 14*
483 A227 75,000 l | Sütunlu Cave   .75   .75
484 A227 200,000 l | Incirli Cave,
        vert.   1.75 1.75

Turkish
Peace
Operation,
25th
Anniv.
A228

Wmk. 390
1999, July 20   **Litho.**   *Perf. 13¾*
485 A228 150,000 l | shown   1.25 1.25
486 A228 250,000 l | Dove, map,
          sun   2.00 2.00

Turkish Postal Administration in
Cyprus, 35th Anniv. — A229

1999, Nov. 12   **Litho.**   *Perf. 13¾*
487 A229 75,000 l | multicolored   .25   .25

UPU,
125th
Anniv.
A230

1999, Nov. 12
488 A230 225,000 l | multicolored   .80   .80

Total Solar
Eclipse,
Aug.
11 — A231

1999, Nov. 12
489 A231 250,000 l | multicolored   .90   .90

Destruction of Turkish Heritage in
Southern Cyprus — A232

Photos of: 75,000 l, Building, Limassol. 150,000 l, Mosque, Evdim. 210,000 l, Bayraktar Mosque, Nicosia (Lefkosa). 1,000,000 l, Cami-i Kebir Mosque, Paphos (Baf), vert.

1999, Dec. 3
490 A232   75,000 l | multi   .20   .20
491 A232   150,000 l | multi   .55   .55
492 A232   210,000 l | multi   .75   .75
493 A232 1,000,000 l | multi   3.75 3.75
     Nos. 490-493 (4)   5.25 5.25

Millennium
A233

Designs: 75,000 l, Cellular phone. 150,000 l, "Welcome 2000." 275,000 l, Computer. 300,000 l, Satellite.

2000, Mar. 3   **Litho.**   *Perf. 13¾*
494 A233   75,000 l | multi   .25   .25
495 A233 150,000 l | multi   .50   .50
496 A233 275,000 l | multi   .95   .95
497 A233 300,000 l | multi   1.00 1.00
     Nos. 494-497 (4)   2.70 2.70

Beach
Scenes
A234

Designs: 300,000 l, Umbrella, pail, shovel, beach ball, sailboats. 340,000 l, Beach chair.

2000, Apr. 29   **Litho.**   *Perf. 13¾*
498 A234 300,000 l | multi   1.00 1.00
499 A234 340,000 l | multi   1.10 1.10

Europa, 2000
Souvenir Sheet
Common Design Type and

A235

2000, May 31   **Wmk. 390**   *Perf. 14*
500   Sheet of 2   1.90 1.90
  a.   CD17 300,000 l | multi   .95   .95
  b.   A235 300,000 l | multi   .95   .95

4th Intl.
Music
Festival,
Bellapais
Abbey
A236

Designs: 150,000 l, Bellapais Abbey. 350,000 l, Blended colors, vert.

2000, June 21   *Perf. 13¾*
501 A236 150,000 l | multi   .45   .45
502 A236 350,000 l | multi   1.10 1.10

Visit of Turkish
Pres. Ahmet N.
Sezer — A237

2000, June 22
503 A237 150,000 l | multi   .45   .45

2000
Summer
Olympics,
Sydney
A238

125,000 l, Torch and Olympic rings, vert. 200,000 l, Runner.

2000, July 25
504-505 A238 Set of 2   .90   .90

No. 409 Surcharged

Method & Perf. as Before
2000, Sept. 28   **Wmk. 390**
506 A189 50,000 l | on 6000 l   .20   .20

Flora and
Fauna — A239

Designs: 125,000 l, Praying mantis on flower. 200,000 l, Butterfly on flower. 275,000 l, Bee on flower. 600,000 l, Snail on flower stem.

Wmk. 390
2000, Oct. 16   **Litho.**   *Perf. 13¾*
507-510 A239 Set of 4   3.75 3.75

Kerchief
Borders
A240

Background colors: 125,000 l, Yellow. 200,000 l, Lilac. 265,000 l, Green. 350,000 l, Brown.

2000, Nov. 28
511-514 A240 Set of 4   3.00 3.00

Restored
Buildings,
Lefkosa
A241

Designs: 125,000 l, Lusignan House. 200,000 l, Eaved House.

Wmk. 390
2001, Mar. 28   **Litho.**   *Perf. 13¾*
515-516 A241 Set of 2   .75   .75

Art — A242

Works by: 125,000 l, Inci Kansu. 200,000 l, Emel Samioglu. 350,000 l, Ozden Selenge, vert. 400,000 l, Ayhatun Atesin.

2001, Mar. 30
517-520 A242 Set of 4   2.50 2.50

Europa — A243   World
                     Environment
                     Day — A244

Designs: 200,000 l, Degirmenlik Reservoir. 500,000 l, Waterfall, Sinar.

2001, May 31
521-522 A243 Set of 2   1.60 1.60

2001, June 22
Designs: 125,000 l, Atomic model, x-ray images. 450,000 l, X-ray images, radiation symbol.
523-524 A244 Set of 2   1.10 1.10

Police
Uniforms — A245

Uniforms from: 125,000 l, 1885. 200,000 l, 1933. 500,000 l, 1934. 750,000 l, 1983.

2001, Aug. 24
525-528 A245 Set of 4   2.75 2.75

Automobiles — A246

Designs: 175,000 l, 1954 MG TF. 300,000 l, 1948 Vauxhall 14. 475,000 l, 1922 Bentley. 600,000 l, 1955 Jaguar XK 120.

Wmk. 390
2001, Nov. 2   **Litho.**   *Perf. 13¾*
529-532 A246 Set of 4   1.90 1.90

Publication of The
Genocide Files, by
Harry Scott
Gibbons — A247

2001, Dec. 24
533 A247 200,000 l | multi   .30   .30

July 20th
Technical
School,
Cent.
A248

2001, Dec. 24
534 A248 200,000 l | multi   .30   .30

Cartoon
Art — A249

Designs: 250,000 l, Chef with grinder and book, by Utku Karsu, vert. 300,000 l, People singing "We Are the World," malnourished Africans, by Musa Kayra. 475,000 l, Can of diet cola airdropped for a malnourished African, by Serhan Gazi, vert. 850,000 l, Child viewing city and painting a country scene, by Mustafa Tozaki, vert.

Wmk. 390
2002, Feb. 28   **Litho.**   *Perf. 13¾*
535-538 A249 Set of 4   2.60 2.60

Tourism
A250

Underwater photographs: 250,000 l, Turtle swimming. 300,000 l, Starfish on coral. 500,000 l, Fish. 750,000 l, Shipwreck.

2002, Mar. 27
539-542 A250 Set of 4   2.50 2.50

Souvenir Sheet

Europa — A251

No. 543: a, Man on stilts. b, Tightrope walker.

Wmk. 390
2002, May 27   Litho.   Perf. 13¾
543 A251 600,000 l   Sheet of 2,
#a-b   1.50 1.50

2002 World Cup Soccer Championships, Japan and Korea — A252

Designs: 300,000 l, Soccer team. 1,000,000 l, "Lift Embargo on Sports."

2002, June 24
544-545 A252   Set of 2   1.60 1.60

Native Costumes — A253

Designs: 250,000 l, Woman. 300,000 l, Man. 425,000 l, Man, diff. 700,000 l, Woman, diff.

2002, Aug. 8
546-549 A253   Set of 4   2.00 2.00

Children's Art — A254

Art by: 300,000 l, M. A. Alpdogan. 600,000 l, S. Avci, vert.

Wmk. 390
2002, Sept. 30   Litho.   Perf. 13¾
550-551 A254   Set of 2   .90   .90

Sports Personalities A255

Famous Men A256

Designs: 300,000 l, Sureyya Ayhan, winner of women's 1500m race at 2002 European Track and Field Championships. 1,000,000 l,

---

Park Jung-tae (1944-2002), father of modern taekwondo.

2002, Oct. 28
552-553 A255   Set of 2   1.60 1.60

2002, Dec. 3
Designs: 100,000 l, Oguz Karayel (1933-96), soccer player. 175,000 l, Mete Adanir (1961-89), soccer player. 300,000 l, M. Necati Ozkan (1899-1970). 575,000 l, Osman Turkay (1927-2001), poet, horiz.

554-557 A256   Set of 4   1.40 1.40

Art — A257

Paintings by: 250,000 l, S. Bayraktar. 1,000,000 l, F. Sükan.

Wmk. 390
2003, Feb. 21   Litho.   Perf. 13¾
558-559 A257   Set of 2   1.50 1.50

Souvenir Sheet

Europa — A258

Poster art: a, Tree. b, Question mark.

2003, May 8
560 A258 600,000 l   Sheet of 2,
#a-b   1.60 1.60

Birds A259

Designs: 100,000 l, Oenanthe cypriaca. 300,000 l, Sylvia melanothorax. 500,000 l, Phalacrocorax pygmeus, vert. 600,000 l, Phoenicopterus ruber, vert.

2003, June 3
561-564 A259   Set of 4   2.10 2.10

Chests A260

Chest from: 250,000 l, Seher. 300,000 l, Lapta. 525,000 l, Baf. 1,000,000 l, Karpaz ve Akatu.

Perf. 13¾x14
2003, July 25   Litho.   Wmk. 390
565-568 A260   Set of 4   3.00 3.00

Flowers — A261

Designs: 150,000 l, Gladiolus triphyllus. 175,000 l, Tulipa cypria. 500,000 l, Ranunculus asiaticus. 525,000 l, Narcissus tazetta.

2003, Oct. 21   Perf. 14x13¾
569-572 A261   Set of 4   1.75 1.75

National Anniversaries — A262

No. 573 - Kemal Ataturk and flag of: a, Turkey. b, Turkish Republic of Northern Cyprus.

2003, Nov. 14   Perf. 13¾x14
573 A262 3,000,000 l   Horiz. pair,
#a-b   8.50 8.50

Republic of Turkey, 80th anniv. (#573a), Turkish Republic of Northern Cyprus, 20th anniv. (#573b).

Federation of Agricultural Producers, 60th Anniv. A263

2003, Dec. 12
574 A263 300,000 l multi   .45   .45

Lions International in Turkish Republic of Northern Cyprus, 40th Anniv. — A264

2003, Dec. 12
575 A264 500,000 l multi   .70   .70

POSTAL TAX STAMP

Trees — PT1

1995, July 24   Litho.   Perf. 14
RA1 PT1 1000 l black & green   1.00 1.00

TURKMENISTAN

tərk-ˌme-nə-'stan

LOCATION — Southern Asia, bounded by Kazakhstan, Uzbekistan, Iran and Afghanistan
GOVT. — Independent republic, member of the Commonwealth of Independent States
AREA — 188,417 sq. mi.
POP. — 4,366,383 (1999 est.)
CAPITAL — Ashgabat

With the breakup of the Soviet Union on Dec. 26, 1991, Turkmenistan and ten former Soviet republics established

---

the Commonwealth of Independent States.

100 Kopecks = 1 Ruble
Manat (1994)

Catalogue values for all unused stamps in this country are for Never Hinged items.

Dagdan Necklace, 19th Century — A1

Designs: No. 3, Girl in traditional costume, horiz. No. 4, Akhaltekin horse and rider in native riding dress. No. 5, Mollanepes Theater, horiz. 15r, National arms. No. 7, Pres. Saparmurad Niyazov at left, national flag, horiz. No. 8, Niyazov at right, flag, horiz. No. 9, Map of Turkmenistan.

1992		**Litho.**	**Perf. 12x12½**	
1	A1	50k multicolored	.20	.20
		Perf. 12½		
2	A1	10r multicolored	.25	.25
3	A1	10r multicolored	.30	.30
4	A1	10r multicolored	.30	.30
5	A1	10r multicolored	.30	.30
6	A1	15r multicolored	.40	.40
7	A1	25r multicolored	.75	.75
8	A1	25r multicolored	1.50	1.50
		Nos. 1-8 (8)	4.00	4.00
		Size: 112x79mm		
		Imperf		
9	A1	10r multicolored	3.50	3.50

Issued: 50k, 1992; #8, 12/8; others, 8/27. Nos. 2-8 exist imperf.

Nos. 4, 6 Ovptd. with Horse's Head
1992, Dec. 12
Color of Overprint

10	A1	10r black	2.00	2.00
11	A1	10r brown	2.00	2.00
12	A1	10r red	2.00	2.00
13	A1	10r vermilion	2.00	2.00
14	A1	10r carmine	2.00	2.00
15	A1	10r green	2.00	2.00
16	A1	15r black	2.00	2.00
17	A1	15r brown	2.00	2.00
18	A1	15r red	2.00	2.00
19	A1	15r pink	2.00	2.00
20	A1	15r blue	2.00	2.00
21	A1	15r yellow	2.00	2.00
		Nos. 10-21 (12)	24.00	24.00

1992 Summer Olympics, Barcelona A2

Designs: a, 1r, Weight lifting. b, 3r, Equestrian. c, 5r, Wrestling. d, 10r, Rowing. e, 15r, Emblem of Turkmenistan Olympic Committee. No. 23, Flags, symbols for modern pentathalon, weight lifting, rowing, gymnastics.

1992, Dec. 15   Photo.   Perf. 10½x10
22 A2   Strip of 5, #a.-e.   3.00 3.00
Imperf
Size: 108x82mm
23 A2 15r multicolored   3.50 3.50
For surcharge see No. 33.

Musical Instruments — A3

Photo. & Engr.

1992, Sept. 13   **Perf. 12x11½**
28   A3   35k buff, red brn, gold &
         black   .20   .20

Horse
A4

1992, Aug. 9   **Photo.**   **Perf. 12**
29   A4   20k shown   .20   .20
30   A4   40k Snake, vert.   .25   .25

A5

1992, Nov. 29   **Litho.**   **Perf. 12x11½**
31   A5   1r multicolored   .25   .25

US Pres. Bill Clinton, Pres.
Saparmurad Niyazov — A6

Designs dated: a. 21.30.93. b. 22.03.93. c,
23.03.93. d, 24.03.93. e, 25.03.93.

1993, Mar. 21   **Litho.**   **Perf. 10½**
32   A6   100r Strip of 5, #a.-e.   4.00   4.00
Pres. Niyazov's visit to New York City &
Washington DC.
   Exists imperf.

No. 22 Surcharged

1993, Apr. 1   **Photo.**   **Perf. 10½x10**
33   A2   Strip of 5   4.25   4.25
  a.   25r on 1r   .80   .80
  b.   10r on 3r   .30   .30
  c.   15r on 5r   .45   .45
  d.   15r on 10r   .45   .45
  e.   50r on 15r   1.60   1.60
     Size of surcharge varies.

Phoca Caspica — A7

World
Wildlife
Fund
A8

Phoca caspica: #34a, 25r, Facing right.
#34b, 500r, Facing left. 15r, Lying in snow.
50r, On rocks. 100r, Mother and young. 150r,
Swimming.

1993, Oct. 11   **Litho.**   **Perf. 13½**
34   A7   Pair #a.-b.   3.25   3.25
35   A8   15r multicolored   .20   .20
36   A8   50r multicolored   .45   .45
37   A8   100r multicolored   1.00   1.00
38   A8   150r multicolored   1.40   1.40
  a.   Bklt. pane, 2 ea #34-38   12.00   12.00
     Booklet, #38a   12.00
     Nos. 34-38 (5)   6.30   6.30

Formation of Tovarishch Society for
Exploitation of Turkmen Oil Fields,
115th Anniv. — A9

Designs: 1m, Two men viewing oil field.
1.5m, Early tanker Turkmen. 2m, Oil well. 3m,
Alfred Nobel, Ludwig Nobel, Robert Nobel,
Petr Bilderling, vert. 5m, Early oil field.

1994, June 26   **Litho.**   **Perf. 13**
39   A9   1m multicolored   .35   .35
40   A9   1.5m multicolored   .50   .50
41   A9   2m multicolored   .75   .75
42   A9   3m multicolored   1.00   1.00
  a.   Miniature sheet of 8 + label   9.00   9.00
     Nos. 39-42 (4)   2.60   2.60

Souvenir Sheet

43   A9   5m multicolored   1.00   1.00
    See Azerbaijan Nos. 416-419.

Repetek
Natl. Park
A10

Designs: 3m, Repetek Institute. No. 45,
Desert, camels. No. 46, Echus carinatus. No.
47, Varanus griseus. 20m, Testudo horsfieldi.
No. 49, Haloxylon ammodendron.

1994, Dec. 11   **Litho.**   **Perf. 13**
44   A10   3m multicolored   .50   .50
45   A10   5m multicolored   .55   .55
46   A10   5m multicolored   .55   .55
  a.   Miniature sheet of 8 + label   5.00   5.00
47   A10   10m multicolored   1.10   1.10
48   A10   20m multicolored   2.00   2.00
     Nos. 44-48 (5)   4.70   4.70

Souvenir Sheet

49   A10   10m multicolored   1.10   1.10

Intl. Olympic Committee, Cent. — A11

1994, Dec. 30   **Litho.**   **Perf. 14**
50   A11   11.25m multicolored   1.50   1.50

Souvenir Sheet

51   A11   20m multicolored   3.00   3.00

Miniature Sheet

Save the Aral Sea — A12

Designs: a, Feis caracal. b, Salmo trutta
aralensis. c, Hyaena hyaena. d, Pseudoscaphirhynchus kaufmanni. e, Aspiolucius
esocinus.

1996, Apr. 29   **Litho.**   **Perf. 14**
52   A12   100m Sheet of 5, #a.-e.   3.75   3.75

Independence, 5th Anniv. — A13

#53, Map of Turkmenistan on globe, vert.
#54, Train pulling into station. #55, Natl. Air-
port, vert. #56, Iranian Pres. Rafsanjani, Turkmenistan Pres. Saparmurad Niyazov, Turkish
Pres. Demirel. 500m, UN Secretary-General
Boutros Boutros-Gali, Pres. Niyazov, vert.
1000m, Natl. flag, arms.

1996, Oct. 27   **Litho.**   **Perf. 14**
53   A13   100m multicolored   .20   .20
54   A13   100m multicolored   .20   .20
55   A13   300m multicolored   .45   .45
56   A13   300m multicolored   .45   .45
57   A13   500m multicolored   .65   .65
58   A13   1000m multicolored   1.40   1.40
     Nos. 53-58 (6)   3.35   3.35

1996
Summer
Olympic
Games,
Atlanta
A14

1997, May 5   **Litho.**   **Perf. 14x14½**
59   A14   100m Judo   .40   .40
60   A14   300m Boxing   1.10   1.10
61   A14   300m Track & field   1.10   1.10
62   A14   300m Wrestling   1.10   1.10
63   A14   500m Shooting   2.00   2.00
     Nos. 59-63 (5)   5.70   5.70

Souvenir Sheet

64   A14   1000m Olympic torch   3.75   3.75

Items inscribed "Turkmenistan" that
were not authorized but which have
appeared on the market in recent
months include:
   Single stamps of 100m depicting
Princess Diana (3 different stamps),
Mother Teresa, Pope John Paul II and
Mother Teresa, 50th Anniv. of India, and
50th Anniv. of Pakistan.
   Sheets of 4 stamps with denomina-
tions of 100m depicting JAPEX 98 /
Cats.
   Sheets of 9 stamps with denomina-
tions of 100m depicting the Titanic,
Trains, Golfers, Japanese Armor, Japa-
nese Paper Dolls, and Japanese Art.
   Sheets of 6 stamps with denomina-
tions of 120m depicting Millennium (8
different sheets).
   Sheets of 6 stamps with denomina-
tions of 120m depicting Pokémon, and
Brad Pitt.
   Sheets of 4 stamps with denominations of 195m depicting Greenpeace,
Elvis Presley, Birds, Orchids, and Japanese Fashion.
   Sheets of 6 stamps with denomina-
tions of 195m depicting Marilyn
Monroe.
   Sheets of 9 stamps with denominations of 195m depicting Cacti, and Minerals.
   Sheets of 4 stamps with denominations of 250m depicting Akira
Kurosawa.
   Sheets of 2 stamps with denomina-
tions of 390m depicting Brazilian soccer
players from 1998 World Cup.
   Sheets of 9 stamps with denomina-
tions of 1000m depicting IBRA / Mush-
rooms (2 different sheets).
   Souvenir sheets of 1 stamp with vari-
ous denominations depicting Hokusai
Artwork (2 different sheets), Pope John
Paul II (2 different sheets), the Titanic (2
different sheets), 1998 Winter Olympics
(2 sheets), Year of the Tiger (2 sheets),
50th Anniv. of Israel, Princess Diana,
Queen Mother, Che Guevara, Frank
Sinatra, Marilyn Monroe, Elvis Presley,
International Year of Older Persons /
Bob Hope, 1998 World Cup Soccer
Championships, Severiano Ballasteros,
Jacques Villeneuve, Leaders of the
World / Automobiles, and Maria de
Medici / Millennium.

Women's
Traditional
Clothing — A15

Various costumes.

1999, July 5   **Litho.**   **Perf. 14**
65   A15   500m multi   .30   .30
66   A15   1000m multi   .55   .55
67   A15   1200m multi   .70   .70
68   A15   2500m multi   1.40   1.40
69   A15   3000m multi   1.75   1.75
     Nos. 65-69 (5)   4.70   4.70

Falcons — A16

a, 1000m, Falco tinnunculus. b, 1000m, Falco peregrinus, looking left. c, 1000m, Falco peregrinus, looking right. d, 2500m, Falco tinnunculus, diff. e, 3000m, Falco peregrinus, diff.

2000, Mar. 30   Litho.   Perf. 14
70 A16   Sheet of 5, #a-e   4.75 4.75

Horn — A17

2000, Oct.   Litho.   Imperf.
Self-Adhesive
71 A17 A multi   .50   .50
Sold for 5000m on day of issue.

UN Resolution on the Permanent Neutrality of Turkmenistan, 5th Anniv. — A18

UN emblem, "5," and flags of Turkmenistan and resolution co-sponsors: a, Afghanistan. b, Armenia. c, Azerbaijan. d, Bangladesh. e, Belarus. f, Colombia. g, Czech Republic. h, Egypt. i, France. j, Georgia. k, India. l, Indonesia. m, Iran. n, Kenya. o, Kyrgyzstan. p, Malaysia. q, Mauritius. r, Pakistan. s, Moldova. t, Russia. u, Senegal. v, Tajikistan. w, Turkey. x, Ukraine.

2000, Dec.   Litho.   Perf. 14
72   Sheet of 24 + label   27.50 27.50
a.-x. A18 3000m Any single   1.10 1.10

Trade Center Building
A19

Flag and Arms
A20

2001, Apr. 24   Litho.   Imperf.
Self-Adhesive
73 A19 B multi   .45   .45
74 A20 U multi   1.00 1.00

Horses — A21

No. 75, horiz.: a, Perenli. b, Garader. c, Pyyada. d, Tyllanur. e, Arkadas. f, Yanardag.
No. 76, 5000m, Yanardag, diff., horiz. (denomination at LR). No. 77, 5000m, Yanardag, diff., horiz. (denomination at UR).
No. 78: a, Bitarap. b, Yanardag, diff.

2001, Aug. 20   Litho.   Perf. 14½x14
75 A21 3000m Sheet of 6, #a-f   7.00 7.00
Size: 116x90mm
Imperf
76-77 A21   Set of 2   4.00 4.00
Souvenir Sheet
Perf. 14x14½
78 A21 5000m Sheet of 2, #a-b   4.00 4.00

Items inscribed "Turkmenistan" that were not authorized by Turkmenistan postal officials but have appeared on the market in recent months include:
Sheets of 9 stamps with denominations of 50m depicting Kim Basinger, Matt Damon, and Pope John Paul II.
Sheets of 9 stamps with denominations of 100m depicting Leading Personalities of the 20th Century.
Sheets of 6 stamps with denominations of 120m depicting Leonardo DiCaprio, and Princess Diana.
Sheets of 8 stamps and one label depicting scenes and people from the 20th Century (3 different sheets).
Sheets of 9 stamps with denominations of 120m depicting Princess Diana, Musical group V.I.P., Television show "Xena, Warrior Princess," Elizabeth Taylor, Bruce Lee, Jackie Chan, Tiger Woods, Muhammad Ali, Monaco Grand Prix race cars, Auto racer David Coulthard, Soccer player David Beckham, Euro 2000 European Football Championships, Rugby players, Tennis Stars of the Millennium, Sportsmen of the Millennium, Elephants, Cats, Butterflies, and Pokémon.
Sheets of 2 stamps with denominations of 390m depicting Soccer players from the 1998 World Cup (2 different sheets depicting French and Japanese players).
Souvenir sheets of 1 with denominations of 975m depicting the Mona Lisa, Marilyn Monroe, and Lucille Ball.

A22

Independence, 10th Anniv. — A23

No. 79 - 500m coins with reverses showing: a, Building with domed roof, coin denomination at right. b, Building with domed roof and tower, coin denomination at left. c, Building with pointed, conical roof. d, Building with archway. e, Building with domed roof on cubic base. f, Statue.
No. 80 - Archaeological sites: a, Soltan Sanjar. b, Nusay. c, Gyz Gala. d, Urgenç. e, Anew. f, Köne Urgenç.
No. 81 - Items in National museum: a, Horn. b, 19th cent. carpet. c, Musical instrument. d, Statue of nude woman. e, Vase. f, 20th cent. decoration.
No. 82, horiz. - Hotels: a, Ahal. b, Gara Altyn. c, Demiryolçy. d, Altyn Suw. e, Köpetdag. f, Aziya.
No. 83 - Buildings: a, Altyn Asyryn Yasayys Jaylary. b, Bitaraplyk Binasy (Arch of Neutrality). c, Türkmendöwletätiyaçlandyrys. d, Random Tower. e, Türkmenbasy Bank. f, Altyn Asyr Söwda Merkezi (Trade Center Building).
No. 84 - Monuments to: a, Oguz Han. b, Seljuk Bay. c, Bayram Han. d, Soltan Sanjar. e, Gorkut Ata. f, Görogly Beg.
No. 85 - Monuments to: a, Sahyrlary Bayram Han. b, Sahyrlary Kemine. c, Sahyrlary Zelili. d, Sahyrlary Seydi. e, Sahyrlary Mollanepes. f, Sahyrlary Mätäji.

2001   Litho.   Imperf.
79 A22 500m Sheet of 6, #a-f   1.90 1.90
80 A23 1000m Sheet of 6, #a-f   3.75 3.75
81 A23 1200m Sheet of 6, #a-f   4.50 4.50
82 A23 1250m Sheet of 6, #a-f   4.75 4.75
83 A23 1250m Sheet of 6, #a-f   4.75 4.75
84 A23 3000m Sheet of 6, #a-f   11.00 11.00
85 A23 3000m Sheet of 6, #a-f   11.00 11.00
       Nos. 79-85 (7)   41.65 41.65
Issued: Nos. 79-80, 10/17; No. 81, 10/19; Nos. 82-83, 10/23; Nos. 84-85, 10/21.

Mohammed Ali Jinnah (1876-1948), First Governor General of Pakistan — A24

2001, Dec. 25   Litho.   Perf. 13
86 A24 500m multi   .40   .40

Birds — A25

No. 87, 3000m: a, Motacilla flava. b, Lanius isabellinus. c, Oenanthe oenanthe. d, Corvus monedula. e, Corvus cornix. f, Upupa pyrrhocorax.
No. 88, 3000m: a, Sylvia communis. b, Cuculus canorus. c, Sylvia curruca. d, Corvus pica. e, Corvus frugilegus. f, Corvus corax.
No. 89, 5000m, Anas crecca. No. 90, 5000m, Riparia riparia.

2002, Dec. 1   Litho.   Perf. 14
Sheets of 6, #a-f
87-88 A25   Set of 2   14.00 14.00
Souvenir Sheets
89-90 A25   Set of 2   3.75 3.75

Butterflies — A26

No. 91, 3000m, vert.: a, Vanessa indica. b, Cynthia cardui. c, Pararge aegeria. d, Pieris rapae. e, Lysandra bellargus. f, Anthocharis cardamines.
No. 92, 3000m, vert.: a, Pandoriana pandora. b, Chazara briseis. c, Aphantopus hyperantus. d, Iolana iolas. e, Pararge schakra. f, Maniola jurtina.
No. 93, 5000m, Hamearis lucina. No. 94, 5000m, Quercusia quercus.

2002, Dec. 1
Sheets of 6, #a-f
91-92 A26   Set of 2   14.00 14.00
Souvenir Sheets
93-94 A26   Set of 2   3.75 3.75

TURKS AND CAICOS ISLANDS

'tərks ənd͵ ' kā-kəs 'i-lənds

LOCATION — A group of islands in the West Indies, at the southern extremity of the Bahamas
GOVT. — British colony; a dependency of Jamaica until 1959
AREA — 192 sq. mi.
POP. — 16,863 (1999 est.)
CAPITAL — Grand Turk

12 Pence = 1 Shilling
20 Shillings = 1 Pound
100 Cents = 1 US Dollar (1969)

Catalogue values for unused stamps in this country are for Never Hinged items, beginning with Scott 90.

Dependency's Badge
A6   A7

				Perf. 14
1900-04	A6		**Wmk. 2**	
1	A6	½p green	1.90	2.25
2	A6	1p rose	1.70	1.90
3	A6	2p black brown	.50	.65
4	A6	2½p gray blue ('04)	.75	.75
a.		2½p blue ('00)	7.25	14.00
5	A6	4p orange	.95	1.65
6	A6	6p violet	1.60	3.25
7	A6	1sh purple brn	1.60	3.25
		Wmk. 1		
8	A7	2sh violet	45.00	67.50
9	A7	3sh brown lake	50.00	72.50
		Nos. 1-9 (9)	104.00	153.70

1905-08				**Wmk. 3**
10	A6	½p green	3.75	.20
11	A6	1p carmine	11.50	.55
12	A6	3p violet, yel ('08)	1.75	5.50
		Nos. 10-12 (3)	17.00	6.25

King Edward VII — A8

1909, Sept. 2				**Perf. 14**
13	A8	½p yellow green	.65	.25
14	A8	1p carmine	1.10	.25
15	A8	2p gray	2.00	1.25
16	A8	2½p ultra	2.00	3.50
17	A8	3p violet, yel	2.00	1.75
18	A8	4p red, yel	2.75	6.50
19	A8	6p violet	6.00	6.50
20	A8	1sh black, blue	6.00	7.50
21	A8	2sh red, grn	24.00	42.50
22	A8	3sh black, red	24.00	30.00
		Nos. 13-22 (10)	70.50	100.00

Turk's-Head Cactus   George V
A9   A10

1910-11				**Wmk. 3**
23	A9	¼p claret	1.25	1.00
24	A9	¼p red ('11)	.50	.50
		See Nos. 36, 44.		

1913-16				
25	A10	½p yellow green	.35	1.25
26	A10	1p carmine	.80	1.75
27	A10	2p gray	1.25	2.75
28	A10	2½p ultra	1.75	2.00
29	A10	3p violet, yel	1.50	7.50

30	A10	4p scarlet, yel	.85	7.25
31	A10	5p olive grn ('16)	5.25	16.00
32	A10	6p dull violet	2.00	2.75
33	A10	1sh orange	1.25	3.75
34	A10	2sh red, bl grn	6.50	20.00
a.		2sh red, grnsh white ('19)	22.50	60.00
b.		2sh red, emerald ('21)	45.00	60.00
35	A10	3sh black, red	13.00	20.00
		Nos. 25-35 (11)	34.50	85.00

Issued: 5p, 5/18/16; others, 4/1/13.
For overprints see Nos. MR1-MR13.

1921, Apr. 23				**Wmk. 4**
36	A9	¼p red	.40	7.25
37	A10	½p green	.55	3.25
38	A10	1p scarlet	.55	3.25
39	A10	2p gray	.75	9.75
40	A10	2½p ultra	2.00	4.50
41	A10	5p olive green	3.50	24.00
42	A10	6p dull violet	5.25	24.00
43	A10	6p brown orange	11.00	14.00
		Nos. 36-43 (8)	24.00	90.00

A11   A12

Inscribed "Postage"

1922-26				
44	A9	¼p gray black ('26)	.35	.60
45	A11	½p green	.35	1.75
46	A11	1p brown	.35	1.90
47	A11	1½p rose red ('25)	4.00	8.25
48	A11	2p gray	.35	3.00
49	A11	2½p violet, yel	.35	1.00
50	A11	3p ultra	.35	3.00
51	A11	4p red, yel	.75	8.00
52	A11	5p yellow grn	.65	13.00
53	A11	6p dull violet	.55	2.50
54	A11	1sh orange	.60	9.25
55	A11	2sh red, green	1.75	5.25
		Wmk. 3		
56	A11	2sh red, green ('25)	22.50	37.50
57	A11	3sh black, red ('25)	4.50	15.00
		Nos. 44-57 (14)	37.40	110.00

Issued: #47, 56-57, 11/24; #44, 10/11; others, 11/20.

Inscribed "Postage and Revenue"

1928, Mar. 1				**Wmk. 4**
60	A12	½p green	.20	.20
61	A12	1p brown	.20	.20
62	A12	1½p red	.35	.25
63	A12	2p dk gray	.95	.25
64	A12	2½p vio, yel	.40	.70
65	A12	3p ultra	.45	1.00
66	A12	6p brown vio	1.25	2.50
67	A12	1sh brown org	1.60	3.75
68	A12	2sh red, grn	5.25	14.00
69	A12	5sh green, yel	15.00	50.00
70	A12	10sh violet, bl	40.00	80.00
		Nos. 60-70 (11)	65.65	152.85

Common Design Types pictured following the introduction.

Silver Jubilee Issue
Common Design Type

1935, May 6				**Perf. 11x12**
71	CD301	½p green & blk	.35	.50
72	CD301	3p ultra & brn	.75	3.25
73	CD301	6p ol grn & lt bl	1.40	3.75
74	CD301	1sh brn vio & ind	3.50	2.50
		Nos. 71-74 (4)	6.00	10.00

Coronation Issue
Common Design Type

1937, May 12				**Perf. 13½x14**
75	CD302	½p deep green	.20	.20
76	CD302	2p gray	.30	.25
77	CD302	3p brt ultra	.40	.25
		Nos. 75-77 (3)	.90	.70
		Set, never hinged	1.25	

Raking Salt — A13

Salt Industry — A14

1938-45			**Wmk. 4**	**Perf. 12½**
78	A13	¼p black	.20	.20
79	A13	½p green	1.50	.20
80	A13	1p brown	.30	.20
81	A13	1½p carmine	.30	.20
82	A13	2p gray	.45	.25
83	A13	2½p orange	1.60	.70
84	A13	3p ultra	.25	.25
85	A13	6p rose violet	3.75	1.10
85A	A13	6p blk brn ('45)	.20	.20
86	A13	1sh bister	1.50	6.25
86A	A13	1sh dk ol grn ('45)	.20	.20
87	A14	2sh rose car	16.00	10.50
88	A14	5sh green	19.00	12.00
89	A14	10sh dp violet	4.75	5.25
		Nos. 78-89 (14)	50.00	37.50
		Set, never hinged	80.00	

Catalogue values for unused stamps in this section, from this point to the end of the section, are for Never Hinged items.

Peace Issue
Common Design Type

1946, Nov. 4		**Engr.**	**Perf. 13½x14**
90	CD303	2p gray black	.20	.20
91	CD303	3p deep blue	.25	.20

Silver Wedding Issue
Common Design Types

1948, Sept. 13		**Photo.**	**Perf. 14x14½**
92	CD304	1p red brown	.20	.20
		Perf. 11½x11		
		Engr.; Name Typo.		
93	CD305	10sh purple	7.50	10.00

Dependency's Badge — A17

Flag and Merchant Ship — A18

Map of the Islands A19

Victoria and George VI A20

1948, Dec. 14		**Engr.**	**Perf. 12½**
94	A17	½p green	.20	.20
95	A17	2p carmine	.25	.20
96	A18	3p deep blue	.40	.40
97	A19	6p violet	.50	.45
98	A20	2sh ultra & blk	.75	.75
99	A20	5sh blue grn & blk	2.25	2.00
100	A20	10sh chocolate & blk	3.50	5.00
		Nos. 94-100 (7)	7.85	9.00

Cent. of political separation from the Bahamas.

UPU Issue
Common Design Types
Engr.; Name Typo. on 3p, 6p
Perf. 13½, 11x11½

1949, Oct. 10				**Wmk. 4**
101	CD306	2½p red orange	.20	.20
102	CD307	3p indigo	1.00	1.00
103	CD308	6p chocolate	.40	.40
104	CD309	1sh olive	.40	.40
		Nos. 101-104 (4)	2.00	2.00

Loading Bulk Salt — A21

Dependency's Badge — A22

Designs: 1p, Salt Cay. 1½p, Caicos mail 2p, Grand Turk. 2½p, Sponge diving. 3p, South Creek. 4p, Map. 6p, Grand Turk Light 1sh, Government House. 1sh6p, Cockburn Harbor. 2sh, Government offices. 5sh, Salt Loading.

1950, Aug. 2		**Engr.**	**Perf. 12½**
105	A21	½p deep green	.55	.40
106	A21	1p chocolate	.45	.80
107	A21	1½p carmine	.80	.60
108	A21	2p red orange	.25	.40
109	A21	2½p olive green	.70	.50
110	A21	3p ultra	.25	.40
111	A21	4p rose car & blk	2.25	.75
112	A21	6p ultra & blk	1.75	.50
113	A21	1sh bl gray & blk	.75	.40
114	A21	1sh6p red & blk	5.75	3.50
115	A21	2sh ultra & emer	2.50	3.75
116	A21	5sh black & ultra	14.50	7.50
117	A22	10sh purple & blk	14.50	18.00
		Nos. 105-117 (13)	45.00	37.50

Coronation Issue
Common Design Type

1953, June 2				**Perf. 13½x14**
118	CD312	2p red orange & blk	.30	.75

M. S. Kirksons A23

Design: 8p, Flamingos in flight.

1955, Feb. 1		**Wmk. 4**	**Perf. 12½**
119	A23	5p emerald & blk	.50	.50
120	A23	8p yellow brn & blk	2.00	.50

Queen Elizabeth II — A24

Bonefish A25

Pelican and Salinas A26

Designs: 2p, Red grouper. 2½p, Spiny lobster. 3p, Albacore. 4p, Muttonfish snapper. 5p,

Permit. 6p, Conch. 8p, Flamingos. 1sh, Spanish mackerel. 1sh6p, Salt Cay. 2sh, Caicos
sloop. 5sh, Cable office. 10sh, Dependency's
badge.

Perf. 13½x14 (1p), 13½x13
1957-60   Engr.   Wmk. 314

121	A24	1p lil rose & dk bl	.20	.20
122	A25	1½p orange & slate	.20	.20
123	A25	2p ol & brn red	.20	.20
124	A25	2½p brt grn & car	.20	.20
125	A25	3p purple & blue	.20	.20
126	A25	4p blk & dp rose	.60	.20
127	A25	5p brown & grn	.80	.40
128	A25	6p ultra & car	1.60	.45
129	A25	8p black & ver	2.75	.20
130	A25	1sh blk & dk blue	.65	.20
131	A25	1sh6p vio bl & dk brn	7.75	1.10
132	A25	2sh lt brn & vio bl	7.75	2.10
133	A25	5sh brt car & blk	1.60	1.60

Perf. 14
| 134 | A26 | 10sh purple & blk | 10.50 | 6.75 |

Perf. 14x14½   Photo.
| 135 | A26 | £1 dk red & brn | 32.50 | 13.50 |
| | | Nos. 121-135 (15) | 67.50 | 27.50 |

Issued: £1, 11/1/60; others, 11/25/57.

Map of
Islands
A27

Perf. 13½x14
1959, July 4   Wmk. 4   Photo.
| 136 | A27 | 6p ol grn & salmon | .25 | .25 |
| 137 | A27 | 8p violet & salmon | .30 | .30 |

Granting of a new constitution.

Freedom from Hunger Issue
Common Design Type
Perf. 14x14½
1963, June 4   Wmk. 314
| 138 | CD314 | 8p carmine rose | .50 | .50 |

Red Cross Centenary Issue
Common Design Type
1963, Sept. 2   Litho.   Perf. 13
| 139 | CD315 | 2p black & red | .20 | .20 |
| 140 | CD315 | 8p ultra & red | .70 | .70 |

Shakespeare Issue
Common Design Type
1964, Apr. 23 Photo. Perf. 14x14½
| 141 | CD316 | 8p green | .30 | .30 |

ITU Issue
Common Design Type
Perf. 11x11½
1965, May 17   Litho.   Wmk. 314
| 142 | CD317 | 1p ver & brown | .20 | .20 |
| 143 | CD317 | 2sh emer & lt blue | .80 | .80 |

Intl. Cooperation Year Issue
Common Design Type
1965, Oct. 25 Wmk. 314 Perf. 14½
| 144 | CD318 | 1p blue grn & claret | .20 | .20 |
| 145 | CD318 | 8p lt violet & green | .60 | .60 |

Churchill Memorial Issue
Common Design Type
1966, Jan. 24   Photo.   Perf. 14
Design in Black, Gold and Carmine
Rose
146	CD319	1p bright blue	.20	.20
147	CD319	2p green	.20	.20
148	CD319	8p brown	.40	.40
a.		Gold impression double	200.00	
149	CD319	1sh6p violet	.90	.90
		Nos. 146-149 (4)	1.70	1.70

Royal Visit Issue
Common Design Type
1966, Feb. 4   Litho.   Perf. 11x12
Portraits in Black
| 150 | CD320 | 8p violet blue | .30 | .30 |
| 151 | CD320 | 1sh6p dk car rose | .55 | .55 |

Andrew Symmers Landing with Union
Jack — A28

Designs: 8p, Andrew Symmers, his signa-
ture, Royal Warrant and Union Jack. 1sh6p,
New coat of arms, Royal Cypher and St.
Edward's crown.

Perf. 13½
1966, Oct. 1   Unwmk.   Photo.
152	A28	1p dk blue & dp org	.20	.20
153	A28	8p dk blue, dl yel & car	.20	.20
154	A28	1sh6p multicolored	.35	.35
		Nos. 152-154 (3)	.75	.75

200th anniv. of the landing of Andrew Symmers, British agent, establishing the ties with
Great Britain.

UNESCO Anniversary Issue
Common Design Type
Wmk. 314
1966, Dec. 1   Litho.   Perf. 14
155	CD323	1p "Education"	.20	.20
156	CD323	8p "Science"	.30	.30
157	CD323	1sh6p "Culture"	.50	.50
		Nos. 155-157 (3)	1.00	1.00

Turk's-head
Cactus — A29

Boat
Building
A30

Designs: 2p, Donkey cart. 3p, Sisal industry.
4p, Conch industry. 6p, Salt industry. 8p, Skin
diving. 1sh, Fishing. 1sh6p, Water skiing. 2sh,
Crawfish industry. 3sh, Map of Islands. 5sh,
Fishing industry. 10sh, Coat of arms. £1,
Queen Elizabeth II.

Perf. 14½x14, 14x14½
1967, Feb. 1   Photo.   Wmk. 314
158	A29	1p vio, red & yel	.20	.20
159	A30	1½p choc & org yel	.20	.20
160	A29	2p gray, yel & sl	.20	.20
161	A29	3p green & dk brn	.20	.20
162	A30	4p grnsh bl, blk & pink	.20	.20
163	A29	6p blue & dk brn	.20	.20
164	A29	8p aqua, dk bl & yel	.20	.20
165	A30	1sh grnsh bl & red brn	.20	.20
166	A29	1sh6p brt grnsh bl, yel & brn	.30	.30
167	A30	2sh multicolored	.40	.40
168	A30	3sh grnsh bl & mar	.55	.55
169	A30	5sh sky bl, dk bl & yel	.95	.95
170	A30	10sh multicolored	1.90	1.90
171	A29	£1 dk car rose, sil & dk bl	4.00	4.00
		Nos. 158-171 (14)	9.70	9.70

See #181, 217-230. For surcharges see
#182-195.

Turks
Islands
No. 1
A31

Designs: 6p, Turks Islands No. 2 and portrait of Queen Elizabeth on simulated stamp.
1sh, Turks Islands No. 3 (like 1p).

1967, May 1   Photo.   Perf. 14½
172	A31	1p lilac rose & blk	.20	.20
173	A31	6p gray & black	.20	.20
174	A31	1sh Prus blue & blk	.45	.45
		Nos. 172-174 (3)	.85	.85

Centenary of Turks Islands stamps.

Human
Rights
Flame
A32

1968, Apr. 1   Perf. 14x14½
175	A32	1p lt green & multi	.20	.20
176	A32	8p lt blue & multi	.20	.20
177	A32	1sh6p multicolored	.45	.45
		Nos. 175-177 (3)	.85	.85

International Human Rights Year.

Martin
Luther
King, Jr.
and
Protest
March of
1968
A33

1968, Oct. 1   Photo.   Wmk. 314
178	A33	2p dk blue, dk & lt brn	.20	.20
179	A33	8p dk car rose, dk & lt brn	.20	.20
180	A33	1sh6p dp vio, dk & lt brn	.70	.70
		Nos. 178-180 (3)	.70	.70

Martin Luther King, Jr. (1929-68), American
civil rights leader.

Nos. 158-171 **4c**
Surcharged

Designs as before and: ¼c, Coat of arms
like 10sh.

Perf. 14x14½, 14½x14
1969, Sept. 8   Photo.   Wmk. 314
181	A30	¼c lt gray & multi	.20	.20
182	A29	1c on 1p multi	.20	.20
183	A29	2c on 2p multi	.20	.20
184	A29	3c on 3p multi	.20	.20
185	A30	4c on 4p multi	.20	.20
186	A29	5c on 6p multi	.20	.20
187	A29	7c on 8p multi	.20	.20
188	A30	8c on 1½p multi	.20	.20
189	A30	10c on 1sh multi	.20	.20
190	A30	15c on 1sh6p multi	.20	.20
191	A30	20c on 2sh multi	.30	.30
192	A30	30c on 3sh multi	.40	.40
193	A30	50c on 5sh multi	.60	.60
194	A30	$1 on 10sh multi	1.40	1.40
195	A29	$2 on £1 multi	6.00	6.00
		Nos. 181-195 (15)	10.70	10.70

The surcharge is differently arranged on
each denomination to fit the design; the old
denomination is obliterated with a rectangle on
the 8c and 15c.
See Nos. 217-230.

1969   Wmk. 314 Sideways
182a	A29	1c on 1p	.20	.20
183a	A29	2c on 2p	.20	.20
184a	A29	3c on 3p	.20	.20
186a	A29	5c on 6p	.20	.20
187a	A29	7c on 8p	.20	.20
190a	A29	15c on 1sh6p	.30	.30
195a	A29	$2 on £1	3.00	3.00
		Nos. 182a-195a (7)	4.30	4.30

Nativity with
John the
Baptist — A34

Designs from the Book of Hours of Elea-
nora, Duchess of Tuscany: 3c, 30c, Flight into
Egypt.

Coat of
Arms — A35

Perf. 13x12½
1969, Oct. 20   Litho.   Wmk. 314
196	A34	1c plum & multi	.20	.20
197	A34	3c dk blue & multi	.20	.20
198	A34	15c olive & multi	.20	.20
199	A34	30c yellow brn & multi	.30	.30
		Nos. 196-199 (4)	.90	.90

Christmas.

1970, Feb. 2   Litho.   Perf. 13x12½
| 200 | A35 | 7c brown & multi | .20 | .20 |
| 201 | A35 | 35c violet blue & multi | .75 | .75 |

New Constitution, inaugurated 6/16/69.
See No. 769.

Christ Bearing
the Cross, by
Dürer — A36

Albrecht Dürer Engravings: 7c, Christ on the
Cross. 50c, The Lamentation for Christ.

Perf. 13½x14
1970, Mar. 17   Engr.   Wmk. 314
202	A36	5c dp blue & blk	.20	.20
203	A36	7c vermilion & blk	.20	.20
204	A36	50c dk brown & multi	.75	.75
		Nos. 202-204 (3)	1.15	1.15

Easter.

Dickens
and
"Oliver
Twist"
Scene
A37

Charles Dickens and Scene from: 3c, "A
Christmas Carol." 15c, "Pickwick Papers." 30c,
"The Old Curiosity Shop."

Litho. & Engr.
1970, June 17   Perf. 13½x13
205	A37	1c yel, red brn & blk	.20	.20
206	A37	3c sal pink, sl & blk	.20	.20
207	A37	15c salmon, bl & blk	.25	.25
208	A37	30c lt blue, ol & blk	.55	.55
		Nos. 205-208 (4)	1.20	1.20

Charles Dickens (1812-70), English novelist.

Red Cross Ambulance, 1870 — A38

5c, 30c, Red Cross ambulance, 1970.

1970, Aug. 4   Litho.   Perf. 13½x14
209	A38	1c orange & multi	.20	.20
210	A38	5c ocher & multi	.20	.20
211	A38	15c brt pink & multi	.30	.30
212	A38	30c multicolored	.55	.55
		Nos. 209-212 (4)	1.25	1.25

Centenary of British Red Cross Society.

Gen. George Monck, Duke of Albemarle, and his Coat of Arms — A39

Designs: 8c, 35c, Coats of arms of Charles II and Queen Elizabeth II.

1970, Dec. 1   Litho.   Perf. 12½x13½
213	A39	1c multicolored	.20	.20
214	A39	8c multicolored	.20	.20
215	A39	10c multicolored	.30	.30
216	A39	35c multicolored	1.00	.95
		Nos. 213-216 (4)	1.70	1.65

Tercentenary of the issue of Letters Patent to the Six Lords Proprietors.

Types of 1967
Values in Cents and Dollars

Designs: 1c, Turk's-head cactus. 2c, Donkey cart. 3c, Sisal industry. 4c, Conch industry. 5c, Salt industry. 7c, Skin diving. 8c, Boat building. 10c, Fishing. 15c, Water skiing. 20c, Crawfish industry. 30c, Map of Islands. 50c, Fishing industry. $1, Arms of Colony. $2, Queen Elizabeth II.

Perf. 14x14½, 14½x14

1971, Feb. 2   Photo.   Wmk. 314
217	A29	1c violet, red & yel	.20	.20
218	A29	2c gray, yel & slate	.20	.20
219	A29	3c green & dk brn	.20	.20
220	A30	4c grnsh bl, blk & pink	.20	.20
221	A29	5c blue & dk brown	.20	.20
222	A29	7c aqua, dk bl & yel	.20	.20
223	A30	8c choc & org yel	.20	.20
224	A30	10c grnsh bl & red brn	.25	.25
225	A29	15c brt grnsh bl, yel & brn	.45	.45
226	A30	20c multicolored	.65	.65
227	A30	30c grnsh bl & mar	1.00	1.00
228	A30	50c sky bl, dk bl & yel	1.50	1.50
229	A30	$1 blue & multi	3.00	3.00
230	A29	$2 dk car rose, sil & dk blue	5.75	5.75
		Nos. 217-230 (14)	14.00	14.00

The ¼c, released with this set is a shade of No. 181, the background being a greenish, slightly darker gray.

Queen Conch and Emblem A40

Tourist publicity (Sun, Sea and Sand Emblem and): 1c, Seahorse, vert. 15c, American oyster catcher. 30c, Blue Marlin.

Perf. 14½x14, 14x14½

1971, May 2   Litho.   Wmk. 314
232	A40	1c multicolored	.20	.20
233	A40	3c multicolored	.20	.20
234	A40	15c multicolored	.40	.40
235	A40	30c multicolored	.75	.75
		Nos. 232-235 (4)	1.55	1.55

Pirate Sloop A41

Designs: 3c, Pirates burying treasure. 15c, Marooned pirate. 30c, Buccaneers.

1971, July 17   Perf. 14½x14
236	A41	2c multicolored	.20	.20
237	A41	3c multicolored	.20	.20
238	A41	15c multicolored	.60	.60
239	A41	30c multicolored	1.10	1.10
		Nos. 236-239 (4)	2.10	2.10

A42

Adoration of the Virgin and Child, from Wilton Diptych, French School, c. 1395 — A43

1971, Oct. 12   Litho.   Perf. 14x13½
240	A42	2c dull brn & multi	.20	.20
241	A43	2c dull brn & multi	.20	.20
242	A42	8c green & multi	.20	.20
243	A43	8c green & multi	.20	.20
244	A42	15c dk blue gray & multi	.30	.30
245	A43	15c dk blue gray & multi	.30	.30
		Nos. 240-245 (6)	1.40	1.40

Christmas.

Rocket Launch, Cape Canaveral — A44

10c, Space capsule in orbit around earth. 15c, Map of Turks and Caicos Islands & splashdown. 20c, Distinguished Service Medal, vert.

1972, Feb. 21   Perf. 13½
246	A44	5c lt blue & blk	.20	.20
247	A44	10c multicolored	.20	.20
248	A44	15c lt green & multi	.30	.30
249	A44	20c blue & multi	.40	.40
		Nos. 246-249 (4)	1.10	1.10

First orbital flight by US astronaut Lt. Col. John H. Glenn, Jr., and splashdown off Turks and Caicos Islands, 10th anniversary.

The Three Crosses, by Rembrandt — A45

Details from Etchings by Rembrandt: 2c, Christ Before Pilate, vert. 30c, Descent from the Cross, vert.

1972, Mar. 17   Perf. 14x13½, 13½x14
250	A45	2c lilac & black	.20	.20
251	A45	15c pink & black	.30	.30
252	A45	30c yellow & black	.60	.60
		Nos. 250-252 (3)	1.10	1.10

Easter.

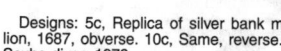

Richard Grenville and "Revenge" — A46

Discoverers and explorers of the Americas: ¼c, Christopher Columbus, Niña, Pinta and Santa Maria, vert. 10c, Capt. John Smith and three-master, vert. 30c, Juan Ponce de León and three-master.

1972, July 4
253	A46	¼c multicolored	.20	.20
254	A46	8c multicolored	.60	.20
255	A46	10c multicolored	.75	.25
256	A46	30c multicolored	2.00	.75
		Nos. 253-256 (4)	3.55	1.40

Silver Wedding Issue, 1972
Common Design Type

Design: Queen Elizabeth II, Prince Philip, turk's-head cactus and spiny lobster.

Perf. 14x14½

1972, Nov. 20   Photo.   Wmk. 314
257	CD324	10c ultra & multi	.20	.20
258	CD324	20c multicolored	.40	.40

Treasure Hunting, c. 1700 — A47

Designs: 5c, Replica of silver bank medallion, 1687, obverse. 10c, Same, reverse. 30c, Scuba diver, 1973.

Perf. 14x14½

1973, Jan. 18   Litho.   Wmk. 314
259	A47	3c Prus blue & multi	.20	.20
260	A47	5c plum & multi	.20	.20
261	A47	10c brt rose, silver & blk	.20	.20
262	A47	30c violet blue & multi	.65	.65
a.		Souvenir sheet of 4, #259-262	2.25	2.25
		Nos. 259-262 (4)	1.25	1.25

Treasure hunting.

Arms of Jamaica, Turks and Caicos Islands — A48

1973, Apr. 16   Litho.   Perf. 13½x14
263	A48	15c buff & multi	.35	.35
264	A48	35c lt green & multi	.75	.75

Centenary of annexation to Jamaica.

Sooty Tern — A49

Birds: 1c, Magnificent frigate bird. 2c, Noddy tern. 3c, Blue gray gnatcatcher. 4c, Little blue heron. 5c, Catbird. 7c, Black-whiskered vireo. 8c, Osprey. 10c, Flamingo. 15c, Brown pelican. 20c, Parula warbler. 30c, Northern mockingbird. 50c, Ruby-throated hummingbird. $1, Bahama bananaquit. $2, Cedar waxwing. $5, Painted bunting.

Wmk. 314 Sideways

1973, Aug. 1   Litho.   Perf. 14
265	A49	¼c yellow & multi	.20	.20
266	A49	1c pink & multi	.20	.20
267	A49	2c orange & multi	.20	.20
268	A49	3c lilac rose & multi	.40	.30
269	A49	4c lt blue & multi	.20	.20
270	A49	5c lt green & multi	.30	.20
271	A49	7c salmon & multi	.35	.25
272	A49	8c blue & multi	.40	.30
273	A49	10c brt blue & multi	.50	.40
274	A49	15c tan & multi	.75	.55
275	A49	20c brt yel & multi	2.00	1.50

276	A49	30c yellow & multi	1.75	1.25
277	A49	50c yellow & multi	2.75	2.00
278	A49	$1 blue & multi	5.25	4.25
279	A49	$2 gray & multi	11.50	8.50
		Nos. 265-279 (15)	26.75	20.30

1974-75   Wmk. 314 Upright
266a	A49	1c pink & multi ('75)	.45	.25
267a	A49	2c orange & multi	.95	.50
268a	A49	3c lil rose & multi ('75)	1.50	.75
275a	A49	20c brt yel & multi ('75)	4.75	2.50
		Nos. 266a-275a (4)	7.65	4.00

1976-77   Wmk. 373
265a	A49	¼c yellow & multi ('77)	.20	.20
266b	A49	1c pink & multi ('77)	.20	.20
267b	A49	2c orange & multi ('77)	.20	.20
268b	A49	3c lilac rose & multi	.20	.20
269a	A49	4c lt bl & multi ('77)	.20	.20
270a	A49	5c lt grn & multi ('77)	.20	.20
273a	A49	10c brt bl & multi ('77)	.25	.25
274a	A49	15c tan & multi ('77)	.35	.35
275b	A49	20c brt yel & multi	.45	.45
276a	A49	30c yel & multi ('77)	.65	.65
277a	A49	50c yel & multi ('77)	1.10	1.10
278a	A49	$1 blue & multi ('77)	2.25	2.25
279b	A49	$2 gray & multi ('77)	4.50	4.50
279A	A49	$5 yel grn & multi ('77)	11.50	11.50
		Nos. 265a-279A (14)	22.25	22.25

Bermuda Sloop — A50

Old Sailing Ships: 5c, HMS Blanche. 8c, US privateer Grand Turk and packet Hinchinbrooke. 10c, HMS Endymion. 15c, RMS Medina. 20c, HMS Daring.

1973, July 19   Litho.   Perf. 13½
280	A50	2c multicolored	.20	.20
281	A50	5c multicolored	.20	.20
282	A50	8c multicolored	.35	.35
283	A50	10c multicolored	.45	.45
284	A50	15c multicolored	.70	.70
285	A50	20c multicolored	.95	.95
a.		Souvenir sheet of 6, #280-285	3.00	3.00
		Nos. 280-285 (6)	2.85	2.85

Princess Anne's Wedding Issue
Common Design Type

1973, Nov. 14   Wmk. 314   Perf. 14
286	CD325	12c blue grn & multi	.20	.20
287	CD325	18c slate & multi	.25	.25

Lucayan Stool A51

Designs: Lucayan artifacts.

1974, July 17   Litho.   Perf. 14½
288	A51	6c shown	.20	.20
289	A51	10c Broken wood bowl	.20	.20
290	A51	12c Greenstone axe	.20	.20
291	A51	18c Wood bowl	.20	.20
292	A51	35c Animal head, fragment of stool	.30	.30
a.		Souvenir sheet of 5, #288-292	1.40	1.40
		Nos. 288-292 (5)	1.10	1.10

Carvings made by Lucayan Indians, first inhabitants of the islands.

Grand Turk G.P.O. A52

UPU Emblem and: 12c, Map of Turks and Caicos Islands and local mail sloop. 18c, "United Service" (globe and "UPU"). 55c, Design symbolic of the Islands joining the UPU in 1881.

1974, Oct. 9   Wmk. 314   Perf. 14

293	A52	4c yellow & multi	.20 .20
294	A52	12c blue & multi	.20 .20
295	A52	18c violet & multi	.20 .20
296	A52	55c lt blue & multi	.50 .50
		Nos. 293-296 (4)	1.10 1.10

Centenary of Universal Postal Union.

"His Finest Hour" A53

12c, Churchill and Franklin D. Roosevelt.

1974, Nov. 30   Wmk. 373

297	A53	12c multicolored	.20 .20
298	A53	18c multicolored	.35 .35
a.		Souvenir sheet of 2, #297-298	.70 .70

Sir Winston Churchill (1874-1965).

Spanish Captain, c. 1492 — A54

Old Windmill, Salt Cay — A55

Uniforms: 20c, Officer, Royal Artillery, 1783. 25c, Officer, 67th Foot, 1798. 35c, Private, First West India Regiment, 1833.

1975, Mar. 26   Wmk. 314   Perf. 14½

299	A54	5c blue & multi	.20 .20
300	A54	20c blue & multi	.30 .30
301	A54	25c blue & multi	.40 .40
302	A54	35c blue & multi	.55 .55
a.		Souvenir sheet of 4, #299-302	1.75 1.75
		Nos. 299-302 (4)	1.45 1.45

1975, Oct. 16   Litho.   Wmk. 373

Salt industry: 10c, Pink salt pans, horiz. 20c, Salt raking at Salt Cay, horiz. 25c, Unprocessed salt ready for shipment.

303	A55	6c violet & multi	.20 .20
304	A55	10c lt brown & multi	.20 .20
305	A55	20c red & multi	.25 .25
306	A55	25c magenta & multi	.35 .35
		Nos. 303-306 (4)	1.00 1.00

Star Coral A56

1975, Dec. 4   Litho.   Wmk. 373

307	A56	6c shown	.20 .20
308	A56	10c Elkhorn coral	.30 .25
309	A56	20c Brain coral	.60 .50
310	A56	25c Staghorn coral	.75 .60
		Nos. 307-310 (4)	1.85 1.55

Schooner A57

American Bicentennial: 20c, Ship of the line. 25c, Frigate Grand Turk. 55c, Ketch.

1976, May 28   Perf. 14x13½

311	A57	6c orange & multi	.20 .20
312	A57	20c violet blue & multi	.40 .30
313	A57	25c brown & multi	.50 .35

314	A57	55c multicolored	.90 .80
a.		Souvenir sheet of 4, #311-314	2.75 2.75
		Nos. 311-314 (4)	2.00 1.65

Turks and Caicos Islands No. 151 A58

25c, Turks and Caicos Islands No. 150.

1976, July 14   Wmk. 373   Perf. 14½

315	A58	20c carmine & multi	.50 .45
316	A58	25c violet blue & multi	.60 .55

Visit of Queen Elizabeth II and Prince Philip to the Caribbean, 10th anniversary.

Virgin and Child, by Carlo Dolci — A59

Christmas: 10c, Virgin and Child with St. John, by Botticelli. 20c, Adoration of the Kings, from Retable by the Master of Paradise. 25c, Adoration of the Kings, illuminated page, French, 15th century.

1976, Nov. 10   Litho.   Perf. 14x13½

317	A59	6c multicolored	.20 .20
318	A59	10c orange & multi	.20 .20
319	A59	20c red lilac & multi	.25 .25
320	A59	25c multicolored	.35 .35
		Nos. 317-320 (4)	1.00 1.00

Queen with Regalia — A60

Designs: 6c, Queen presenting Order of British Empire to E. T. Wood, Grand Turk, 1966. 55c, Royal family on balcony of Buckingham Palace. $5, Portrait of Queen from photograph taken during her 1966 visit to Grand Turk.

1977   Litho.   Perf. 14x13½

321	A60	6c multicolored	.20 .20
322	A60	25c multicolored	.20 .20
323	A60	55c multicolored	.50 .50
		Nos. 321-323 (3)	.90 .90

Souvenir Sheet
Perf. 14

324	A60	$5 multicolored	1.40 1.40

25th anniv. of the reign of Elizabeth II. Nos. 322 and 323 were also issued in booklet panes of 2.
Issued: #321-323, Feb. 7; #324, Dec. 6.

Friendship 7 Capsule — A61

Designs: 3c, Lunar rover, vert. 6c, Tracking Station on Grand Turk. 20c, Moon landing craft, vert. 25c, Col. Glenn's rocket leaving launching pad, vert. 50c, Telstar 1 satellite.

Wmk. 373
1977, June 20   Litho.   Perf. 13½

325	A61	1c multicolored	.20 .20
326	A61	3c multicolored	.20 .20
327	A61	6c multicolored	.20 .20
328	A61	20c multicolored	.20 .20
329	A61	25c multicolored	.25 .25
330	A61	50c multicolored	.55 .55
		Nos. 325-330 (6)	1.60 1.60

US Tracking Station on Grand Turk, 25th anniversary.

Adoration of the Kings, 1634 by Rubens — A63

Rubens Paintings: ¼c, Flight into Egypt. 1c, Adoration of the Kings, 1624. 6c, Madonna with Garland. 20c, $1, Virgin and Child Adored by Angels. $2, Adoration of the Kings, 1618.

1977, Dec. 23

331	A63	¼c multicolored	.20 .20
332	A63	½c multicolored	.20 .20
333	A63	1c multicolored	.20 .20
334	A63	6c multicolored	.20 .20
335	A63	20c multicolored	.20 .20
336	A63	$2 multicolored	1.60 1.60
		Nos. 331-336 (6)	2.60 2.60

Souvenir Sheet

337	A63	$1 multicolored	1.90 1.90

Christmas and 400th birth anniversary of Peter Paul Rubens (1577-1640).

Map of Turks Island Passage A64

Designs: 20c, Grand Turk lighthouse and sailboat (LUG cargo vessel). 25c, Deepsea fishing yacht. 55c, S.S. Jamaica Planter.

Wmk. 373, Unwmkd.
1978, Feb. 2   Litho.   Perf. 13½

338	A64	6c multicolored	.20 .20
339	A64	20c multicolored	.40 .35
340	A64	25c multicolored	.50 .45
341	A64	55c multicolored	1.10 1.10
a.		Souv. sheet of 4, #338-341, unwmkd.	2.50 2.50
		Nos. 338-341 (4)	2.20 2.10

Turks Island Passage, a major Caribbean shipping route.
No. 341a exists watermarked.

Queen Victoria in Coronation Regalia — A65

British Monarchs in Coronation Regalia: 10c, Edward VII. 25c, George V. $2, George VI. $2.50, Elizabeth II.

1978, June 2   Litho.   Perf. 14

342	A65	6c multicolored	.20 .20
343	A65	10c multicolored	.20 .20
344	A65	25c multicolored	.20 .20
345	A65	$2 multicolored	.75 .75
		Nos. 342-345 (4)	1.35 1.35

Souvenir Sheet

346	A65	$2.50 multicolored	1.10 1.10

25th anniversary of coronation of Queen Elizabeth II. Nos. 342-345 also issued in sheets of 3 plus label, perf. 12.

Wilbur Wright and Flyer 3 A66

Aviation Progress: 6c, Cessna 337 and Wright brothers. 10c, Southeast Airlines' Electra and Orville Wright. 15c, C47 cargo plane on South Caicos runway. 35c, Norman-Britten Islander at Grand Turk airport. $1, Orville Wright and Flyer, 1902. $2, Wilbur Wright and Flyer.

1978, June 29   Litho.   Perf. 14½

347	A66	1c multicolored	.20 .20
348	A66	6c multicolored	.20 .20
349	A66	10c multicolored	.20 .20
350	A66	15c multicolored	.20 .20
351	A66	35c multicolored	.45 .45
352	A66	$2 multicolored	2.10 1.75
		Nos. 347-352 (6)	3.35 3.00

Souvenir Sheet

353	A66	$1 multicolored	.85 .85

Queen Elizabeth II — A67

Designs: 15c, Ampulla and anointing spoon. 25c, St. Edward's crown.

Imperf. x Roulette 5
1978, July 24   Litho.

Self-adhesive

354		Souvenir booklet	2.75
a.		A67 Bklt. pane of 3, 15c, 25c, $2	1.60
b.		A67 Bklt. pane, 3 each, 15c, 25c	1.00

25th anniv. of coronation of Queen Elizabeth II. #354 contains #354a-354b printed on peelable paper backing with music and text of hymns.

11th Commonwealth Games, Edmonton, Canada, Aug. 3-12 — A68

1978, Aug. 3   Litho.   Perf. 15

355	A68	6c shown	.20 .20
356	A68	20c Weight lifting	.20 .20
357	A68	55c Boxing	.35 .35
358	A68	$2 Bicycling	1.25 1.25
		Nos. 355-358 (4)	2.00 2.00

Souvenir Sheet

359	A68	$1 Sprinting	1.40 1.40

Fish A69

1978-79   Litho.   Perf. 14

360	A69	1c Indigo hamlet	.20 .20
361	A69	2c Tobacco fish	.20 .20
362	A69	3c Passing Jack	.20 .20
363	A69	4c Porkfish	.20 .20
364	A69	5c Spanish grunt	.20 .20
365	A69	7c Yellowtail snapper	.20 .20
366	A69	8c Foureye butterflyfish	.20 .20
367	A69	10c Yellow fin grouper	.20 .20
368	A69	15c Beau Gregory	.25 .25
369	A69	20c Queen angelfish	.35 .35
370	A69	30c Hogfish	.50 .50
371	A69	50c Fairy Basslet	.85 .85
372	A69	$1 Clown wrasse	1.60 1.60

373 A69 $2 Stoplight par-
          rotfish   3.50   3.50
374 A69 $5 Queen triggerfish   8.50   8.50
          Nos. 360-374 (15)   17.15 17.15
     Issue dates: 1c, 3c, 5c, 10c, 15c, 20c, Nov.
17, 1978; others Feb. 6, 1979.
     Nos. 368-369, 372-374 exist dated 1983.

1981, Dec. 15   **Perf. 12½x12**
360a A69   1c   .20   .20
364a A69   5c   .20   .20
367a A69 10c   .20   .20
369a A69 20c   .45   .35
371a A69 50c   1.10   .85
372a A69 $1   2.10   1.60
373a A69 $2   4.50   3.50
374a A69 $5   11.00   8.50
          Nos. 360a-374a (8)   19.75 15.40

Virgin with the
Goldfinch, by
Dürer — A70

     Dürer Paintings: 20c, Virgin and Child with
St. Anne. 35c, Nativity, horiz. $1, Adoration of
the Kings, horiz. $2, Praying Hands.

1978, Dec. 11   **Litho.**   **Perf. 14**
375 A70   6c multicolored   .20   .20
376 A70 20c multicolored   .20   .20
377 A70 35c multicolored   .30   .30
378 A70 $2 multicolored   1.75   1.75
          Nos. 375-378 (4)   2.45   2.45

          Souvenir Sheet
379 A70 $1 multicolored   2.40   2.40
     Christmas and 450th death anniversary of
Albrecht Dürer (1471-1528), German painter.

Ospreys
A71

     Endangered Species: 20c, Green turtle.
25c, Queen conch. 55c, Rough-toothed
dolphin. $1, Humpback whale. $2, Iguana.

1979, May 17   **Litho.**   **Perf. 14**
380 A71   6c multicolored   .25   .20
381 A71 20c multicolored   .60   .30
382 A71 25c multicolored   .75   .35
383 A71 55c multicolored   1.60   .75
384 A71 $1 multicolored   3.00   1.40
          Nos. 380-384 (5)   6.20   3.00

          Souvenir Sheet
385 A71 $2 multicolored   3.00   2.50

The
Beloved,
by Dante
Gabriel
Rossetti
A72

     Paintings and IYC Emblem: 25c, Tahitian
Girl, by Paul Gauguin. 55c, Calmady Children,
by Sir Thomas Lawrence. $1, Mother and
Daughter (detail), by Gauguin. $2, Marchesa
Elena Grimaldi, by Van Dyck.

1979, July 2   **Litho.**   **Perf. 14**
386 A72   6c multicolored   .20   .20
387 A72 25c multicolored   .20   .20
388 A72 55c multicolored   .40   .40
389 A72 $1 multicolored   .70   .70
          Nos. 386-389 (4)   1.50   1.50

          Souvenir Sheet
390 A72 $2 multicolored   .85   .85
     International Year of the Child.

Stampless Cover and "Medina" — A73

     Designs: 20c, Map of Islands and Rowland
Hill. 45c, Stamped envelope and "Orinoco."
75c, Paddlewheeler "Shannon" and letter. $1,
Royal Packet "Trent," map of Islands. $2, New
and old seals.

1979, Sep. 10   **Litho.**   **Perf. 14**
391 A73   6c multicolored   .20   .20
392 A73 20c multicolored   .20   .20
393 A73 45c multicolored   .35   .35
394 A73 75c multicolored   .55   .55
395 A73 $1 multicolored   .75   .75
          Perf. 12
396 A73 $2 multicolored ('80)   3.25   3.25
  a.   Souv. sheet of 1, perf. 14 ('79) 1.75 1.75
          Nos. 391-396 (6)   5.30   5.30
     Nos. 391-395 were issued in sheets of 40,
and in sheets of 5 stamps plus label, in
changed colors, perf. 12.
     No. 396 issued May 6, 1980 in sheet of 5
plus label picturing signal flags and map.

No. 396a overprinted: "BRASILIANA
79"
          Souvenir Sheet
1979, Sept. 10   **Litho.**   **Perf. 14**
397 A73 $2 multicolored   1.00   1.00
     Brasiliana 79 Intl. Philatelic Exhibition, Rio
de Janeiro, Sept. 15-23.

Cuneiform Script — A74

     Designs: 5c, Egyptian papyrus; Chinese
writing. 15c, Greek runner; Roman post horse;
Roman ship. 25c, Pigeon post; railway post;
steamship postal packet. 40c, Balloon post;
first airmail plane; supersonic airmail jet. $1,
Original stamp press (3 designs each of 5c,
15c, 25c, 40).

Imperf. x Roulette 5, Imperf. ($1)
1979, Sept. 27   **Litho.**
          Self-adhesive
398   Souvenir booklet   6.00
  a.   A74 Bklt. pane of 1 ($1)
  b.   A74 Bklt. pane, 3 each 5c, 15c
  c.   A74 Bklt. pane, 3 each 25c, 40c
     Sir Rowland Hill (1795-1879), originator of
penny postage. No. 398 contains 3 booklet
panes on peelable paper backing with descriptions of stamp designs.

International
Year of the
Child
A74a

     Designs: Aquatic scenes.

1979, Nov. 2   **Litho.**   **Perf. 11**
399 A74a ¼c Pluto and starfish   .20   .20
400 A74a ½c Minnie Mouse   .20   .20
401 A74a   1c Mickey Mouse
              skin-diving   .20   .20
402 A74a   2c Goofy riding turtle   .20   .20
403 A74a   3c Donald and
              dolphin   .20   .20
404 A74a   4c Mickey Mouse
              and fish   .20   .20
405 A74a   5c Goofy surfing   .20   .20
406 A74a 25c Pluto and lobster   .60   .25

407 A74a $1 Daisy Duck water-
               skiing   2.50   1.00
          Nos. 399-407 (9)   4.50   2.65
          Souvenir Sheet
          Perf. 13½x14
408 A74a $1.50 Goofy   1.90   1.50

St. Nicholas, Icon,
17th
Century — A75

     Icons or Illuminations: 3c, Emperor Otto II,
10th century. 6c, St. John, Book of Lindis-
farne. 15c, Christ and angels. 20c, Christ
attended by angels, Book of Kells, 9th century.
25c, St. John the Evangelist. 65c, Christ
enthroned, 17th century. $1, St. John, 8th cen-
tury. $2, St. Matthew, Book of Lindisfarne.

1979, Nov. 26
409 A75   1c multicolored   .20   .20
410 A75   3c multicolored   .20   .20
411 A75   6c multicolored   .20   .20
412 A75 15c multicolored   .20   .20
413 A75 20c multicolored   .20   .20
414 A75 25c multicolored   .20   .20
415 A75 65c multicolored   .50   .50
416 A75 $1 multicolored   .75   .75
          Nos. 409-416 (8)   2.45   2.45

          Souvenir Sheet
417 A75 $2 multicolored   1.10   1.10

Christina's World, by Andrew
Wyeth — A76

     Art Treasures: 10c, Ivory leopards, Benin,
19th century. 20c, The Kiss, by Gustav Klimt,
vert. 25c, Portrait of a Lady, by Rogier van der
Weyden, vert. 80c, Sumerian bull's head harp,
2600 B.C., vert. $1, The Wave, by Hokusai.
$2, Holy Family, by Rembrandt, vert.

1979, Dec. 19   **Litho.**   **Perf. 13½**
418 A76   6c multicolored   .20   .20
419 A76 10c multicolored   .20   .20
420 A76 20c multicolored   .20   .20
421 A76 25c multicolored   .20   .20
422 A76 80c multicolored   .65   .65
423 A76 $1 multicolored   .80   .80
          Nos. 418-423 (6)   2.25   2.25

          Souvenir Sheet
424 A76 $2 multicolored   1.90   1.90

Pied-billed Grebe — A77

1980, Feb. 20   **Litho.**   **Perf. 14**
425 A77 20c shown   .60   .30
426 A77 25c Ovenbirds   .70   .35
427 A77 35c Marsh hawks   1.00   .50
428 A77 55c Yellow-bellied sap-
              sucker   1.60   .70
429 A77 $1 Blue-winged teals   2.75   1.40
          Nos. 425-429 (5)   6.65   3.25

          Souvenir Sheet
430 A77 $2 Glossy ibis   3.75   3.75

Stamp
Under
Magnifier,
Perforation
Gauge,
London 1980
Emblem
A78

1980, May 6   **Litho.**   **Perf. 14x14½**
431 A78 25c shown   .20   .20
432 A78 40c Stamp in tongs,
              gauge   .35   .35
          Souvenir Sheet
433 A78 $2 Exhibition Hall   1.00   1.00
     London 1980 International Stamp Exhibi-
tion, May 6-14.

Trumpet
Triton
A79

1980, June 26   **Litho.**   **Perf. 14**
434 A79 15c shown   .25   .25
435 A79 20c Measled cowry   .35   .35
436 A79 30c True tulip   .50   .50
437 A79 45c Lion's paw   .75   .75
438 A79 55c Sunrise tellin   .90   .90
439 A79 70c Grown cone   1.25   1.25
          Nos. 434-439 (6)   4.00   4.00

Queen Mother
Elizabeth, 80th
Birthday — A80

1980, Aug. 4   **Litho.**   **Perf. 14**
440 A80 80c multicolored   .80   .80
          Souvenir Sheet
          Perf. 12
441 A80 $1.50 multicolored   1.40   1.40

Pinocchio — A81

     Christmas: Scenes from Walt Disney's
Pinocchio.

1980, Sept. 25   **Perf. 11**
442 A81   ¼c multicolored   .20   .20
443 A81   ½c multicolored   .20   .20
444 A81   1c multicolored   .20   .20
445 A81   2c multicolored   .20   .20
446 A81   3c multicolored   .20   .20
447 A81   4c multicolored   .20   .20
448 A81   5c multicolored   .20   .20
449 A81   75c multicolored   1.10   1.10
450 A81 $1 multicolored   1.50   1.50
          Nos. 442-450 (9)   4.00   4.00

          Souvenir Sheet
451 A81 $2 multi, vert.   4.00   4.00

Medical Examination, Lions — A82

1980, Oct. 8   Litho.   Perf. 14
452	A82	10c shown	.20 .20
453	A82	15c Scholarships, Kiwanis	.20 .20
454	A82	45c Education, Soroptimists	.50 .50
455	A82	$1 Lobster boat, Rotary	1.10 1.10
		Nos. 452-455 (4)	2.00 2.00

Souvenir Sheet
456	A82	$2 Funds for schools, Rotary	2.25 2.25

Lions, Rotary, Kiwanis and Soroptimists service organizations; 75th anniv. of Rotary Intl.

Martin Luther King, Jr. (1929-68) — A83

Human Rights Leaders: 30c, John F. Kennedy. 45c, Roberto Clemente (1934-72), baseball player. 70c, Frank Worrel (1927-67), cricket player. $1, Harriet Tubman (1823-1913), born slave, helped others escape to freedom. $2, Marcus Garvey (1887-1940), Jamaican black nationalist leader.

1980, Dec. 22   Litho.   Perf. 14
457	A83	20c multicolored	.25 .25
458	A83	30c multicolored	.35 .35
459	A83	45c multicolored	.55 .55
460	A83	70c multicolored	.90 .90
461	A83	$1 multicolored	1.25 1.25
		Nos. 457-461 (5)	3.30 3.30

Souvenir Sheet
462	A83	$2 multicolored	1.75 1.75

Racing Yachts A84

Designs: Racing yachts.

1981, Jan. 29   Litho.   Perf. 14
463	A84	6c multicolored	.20 .20
464	A84	15c multicolored	.20 .20
465	A84	35c multicolored	.40 .40
466	A84	$1 multicolored	1.10 1.10
		Nos. 463-466 (4)	1.90 1.90

Souvenir Sheet
467	A84	$2 multicolored	1.75 1.75

South Caicos Regatta. No. 467 contains one 28x42mm stamp.

Pluto Listening to Sea Shell — A85

1981, Feb. 16   Perf. 13½x14
468	A85	10c shown	.20 .20
469	A85	75c Pluto on raft, dolphin	1.00 1.00

Souvenir Sheet
470	A85	$1.50 Pluto	2.75 2.75

50th anniversary of Walt Disney's Pluto.

Night Queen Cactus — A86

1981, Feb. 10   Perf. 14
471	A86	25c shown	.30 .30
472	A86	35c Ripsaw cactus	.40 .40
473	A86	55c Royal strawberry cactus	.65 .65
474	A86	80c Caicos cactus	.95 .95
		Nos. 471-474 (4)	2.30 2.30

Souvenir Sheet
475	A86	$2 Turks head cactus	1.90 1.90

Donald Duck and Louie with Easter Egg — A87

Easter: Various Disney characters with Easter eggs.

1981, Mar. 20   Litho.   Perf. 11
476	A87	10c multicolored	.20 .20
477	A87	25c multicolored	.45 .45
478	A87	60c multicolored	1.25 1.25
479	A87	80c multicolored	1.50 1.50
		Nos. 476-479 (4)	3.40 3.40

Souvenir Sheet
480	A87	$4 multicolored	6.25 6.25

Woman with Fan, 1909 — A88

1981, May 28   Litho.   Perf. 14
481	A88	20c multicolored	.20 .20
482	A88	45c Woman with Pears, 1909	.50 .50
483	A88	80c The Accordionist, 1911	.95 .95
484	A88	$1 The Aficionado, 1912	.95 .95
		Nos. 481-484 (4)	2.60 2.60

Souvenir Sheet
485	A88	$2 Girl with a Mandolin, 1910	2.75 2.75

Pablo Picasso (1881-1973).

Royal Wedding Issue
Common Design Type and

A88a

1981, June 23   Litho.   Perf. 14
486	CD331	35c Couple	.20 .20
487	CD331	65c Kensington Palace	.30 .30
488	CD331	90c Charles	.40 .40
		Nos. 486-488 (3)	.90 .90

Souvenir Sheet
489	CD331	$2 Glass coach	1.00 1.00

Self-adhesive
Imperf. x Roulette 5 (20c, $1),
Imperf. ($2)

1981, July 7
490		Booklet	3.00
a.		A88a Pane of 6 (3x20c, Lady Diana, 3x$1, Charles)	1.90
b.		A88a Pane of 1, $2, Couple	1.10

Nos. 486-488 also printed in sheets of 5 plus label, perf. 12, in changed colors.

Underwater Marine Biology Observation — A89

1981, Aug. 21   Litho.   Perf. 14
491	A89	15c shown	.20 .20
492	A89	40c Underwater photography	.55 .55
493	A89	75c Diving for wreckage	1.00 1.00
494	A89	$1 Diver, dolphins	1.25 1.25
		Nos. 491-494 (4)	3.00 3.00

Souvenir Sheet
495	A89	$2 Diving flag	2.50 2.50

Br'er Rabbit Barricading his Door — A90

Christmas: Scenes from Walt Disney's Uncle Remus.

1981, Nov. 2   Litho.   Perf. 14x13½
496	A90	¼c multicolored	.20 .20
497	A90	½c multicolored	.20 .20
498	A90	1c multicolored	.20 .20
499	A90	2c multicolored	.20 .20
500	A90	3c multicolored	.20 .20
501	A90	4c multicolored	.20 .20
502	A90	5c multicolored	.20 .20
503	A90	75c multicolored	1.25 1.25
504	A90	$1 multicolored	1.75 1.75
		Nos. 496-504 (9)	4.40 4.40

Souvenir Sheet
505	A90	$2 multicolored	3.00 3.00

Flags of Turks and Caicos Islands A91

Maps of Various Islands: a, Grand Turk. b, Salt Cay. c, South Caicos. d, East Caicos. e, Middle Caicos. f, North Caicos. g, Caicos Cays. h, Providenciales. i, West Caicos.

1981, Dec. 1   Perf. 14
506		Strip of 10	4.00 4.00
a.-j.		A91 20c any single	.40 .40

Caribbean Buckeyes — A92

Scouting Year — A93

1982, Jan. 21   Litho.   Perf. 14
507	A92	20c shown	.35 .35
508	A92	35c Clench's hairstreaks	.65 .65
509	A92	65c Gulf fritillarys	1.10 1.10
510	A92	$1 Bush sulphurs	1.90 1.90
		Nos. 507-510 (4)	4.00 4.00

Souvenir Sheet
511	A92	$2 Turk Isld. leaf butterfly	4.00 4.00

1982, Feb. 17   Litho.   Perf. 14
512	A93	40c Flag ceremony	.65 .65
513	A93	50c Building raft	.85 .85
514	A93	75c Cricket match	1.10 1.10
515	A93	$1 Nature study	1.40 1.40
		Nos. 512-515 (4)	4.00 4.00

Souvenir Sheet
516	A93	$2 Baden-Powell, salute	3.50 3.50

1982 World Cup Soccer — A94

Designs: Various soccer players.

1982, Apr. 30   Litho.   Perf. 14
517	A94	10c multicolored	.20 .20
518	A94	25c multicolored	.30 .30
519	A94	45c multicolored	.55 .55
520	A94	$1 multicolored	1.25 1.25
		Nos. 517-520 (4)	2.30 2.30

Souvenir Sheet
521	A94	$2 multi, horiz.	1.90 1.90

#517-520 issued in sheets of 5 + label.

Phillis Wheatley (1753-1784), Poet, and Washington Crossing Delaware — A95

Washington's 250th Birth Anniv. and F.D. Roosevelt's Birth Centenary: 35c, Washington, Benjamin Banneker (1731-1806), astronomer and mathematician, map. 65c, FDR, George Washington Carver (1864-1943). 80c, FDR with stamp collection. $2, FDR examining Washington stamp.

1982, May 3   Litho.   Perf. 14
522	A95	20c multicolored	.25 .25
523	A95	35c multicolored	.50 .50
524	A95	65c multicolored	1.00 1.00
525	A95	80c multicolored	1.25 1.25
		Nos. 522-525 (4)	3.00 3.00

Souvenir Sheet
526	A95	$2 multicolored	3.00 3.00

Second Thoughts, by Norman Rockwell — A96

1982, June 23   Litho.   Perf. 14x13½
527	A96	8c shown	.20	.20
528	A96	15c The Proper Gratuity	.25	.25
529	A96	20c Before the Shot	.30	.30
530	A96	25c The Three Umpires	.40	.40
		Nos. 527-530 (4)	1.15	1.15

Princess Diana Issue
Common Design Type

1982   Litho.   Perf. 14½x14
530A	CD332	8c Sandringham	.30	.20
530B	CD332	35c Wedding	1.40	.55
530C	CD332	$1.10 Diana	4.50	1.75
		Nos. 530A-530C (3)	6.20	2.50

1982, July 1   Perf. 14½x14
531	CD332	55c Sandringham	1.60	1.00
532	CD332	70c Wedding	1.60	1.00
533	CD332	$1 Diana	3.00	1.75
		Nos. 531-533 (3)	6.20	3.75

Also issued in sheetlets of 5 + label.

Souvenir Sheet
534	CD332	$2 Diana, diff.	6.00	4.00

Skymaster over Caicos Cays — A97

1982, Aug. 26   Litho.   Perf. 14
535	A97	8c shown	.20	.20
536	A97	15c Jetstar, Grand Turk	.30	.30
537	A97	65c Helicopter, South Caicos	.90	.90
538	A97	$1.10 Seaplane, Providenciales	1.60	1.60
		Nos. 535-538 (4)	3.00	3.00

Souvenir Sheet
539	A97	$2 Boeing 727	3.00	3.00

Christmas — A98

Christmas: Scenes from Walt Disney's Mickey's Christmas Carol.

1982, Dec. 1   Litho.   Perf. 13½
540	A98	1c multicolored	.20	.20
541	A98	1c multicolored	.20	.20
542	A98	2c multicolored	.20	.20
543	A98	2c multicolored	.20	.20
544	A98	3c multicolored	.20	.20
545	A98	3c multicolored	.20	.20
546	A98	4c multicolored	.20	.20
547	A98	65c multicolored	1.10	1.10
548	A98	$1.10 multicolored	2.50	1.50
		Nos. 540-548 (9)	5.00	4.00

Souvenir Sheet
549	A98	$2 multicolored	4.00	4.00

Trams and Locomotives — A99

1983, Jan. 18   Litho.   Perf. 14
550	A99	15c West Caicos trolley tram	.25	.25
551	A99	55c West Caicos steam locomotive	.90	.90
552	A99	90c Mule-drawn tram, East Caicos	1.40	1.40
553	A99	$1.60 Sisal locomotive, East Caicos	2.60	2.60
		Nos. 550-553 (4)	5.15	5.15

Souvenir Sheet
554	A99	$2.50 Steam engine	4.50	4.50

A99a

1983, Mar. 14
555	A99a	1c Woman crossing guard	.20	.20
556	A99a	8c Wind and solar energy sources	.20	.20
557	A99a	65c Sailing	1.10	1.10
558	A99a	$1 Cricket game	1.75	1.75
a.		Block or strip of 4, #555-558	3.25	3.25

Commonwealth Day.

Easter — A100

Crucifixion, by Raphael. $2.50 shows entire painting.

1983, Apr. 7   Litho.   Perf. 14
559	A100	35c Mary Magdalene, St. John	.30	.30
560	A100	50c Mary	.45	.45
561	A100	95c Angel looking to heaven	.85	.85
562	A100	$1.10 Angel looking to earth	1.00	1.00
		Nos. 559-562 (4)	2.60	2.60

Souvenir Sheet
563	A100	$2.50 multicolored	5.00	5.00

Piked Whale A101

1983   Litho.   Perf. 14
564	A101	50c shown	1.10	1.10
565	A101	65c Right whale	1.50	1.50
566	A101	70c Killer whale	1.60	1.60
567	A101	95c Sperm whale	2.25	2.25
568	A101	$1.10 Gooseback whale	2.50	2.50
569	A101	$2 Blue whale	4.50	4.50
570	A101	$2.20 Humpback whale	5.00	5.00
571	A101	$3 Longfin pilot whale	6.75	6.75
		Nos. 564-571 (8)	25.20	25.20

Souvenir Sheet
572	A101	$3 Fin whale	6.75	6.75

Issued: 50c, $2.20, #571, 5/16; 70c, 95c, $2, 6/13; others 7/11. Issued in sheets of 4.
For overprints see Nos. 637-639.

Christmas A104

Designs: Scenes from Walt Disney's Oh Christmas Tree.

1983, Nov.   Perf. 11
593	A104	1c Fifer Pig	.20	.20
594	A104	1c Fiddler Pig	.20	.20
595	A104	2c Practical Pig	.20	.20
596	A104	2c Pluto	.20	.20
597	A104	3c Goofy	.20	.20

Manned Flight Bicentenary A102

1983, Aug. 30   Litho.   Perf. 14
573	A102	25c 1st hydrogen balloon, 1783	.30	.30
574	A102	35c Friendship 7, 1962	.45	.45
575	A102	70c Montgolfiere, 1783	.90	.90
576	A102	95c Columbia space shuttle	1.25	1.25
		Nos. 573-576 (4)	2.90	2.90

Souvenir Sheet
577	A102	$2 Montgolfiere, Columbia	3.00	3.00

Ships A103

1985   Litho.   Perf. 12½x12
578	A103	4c Dug-out canoe	.20	.20
579	A103	5c Santa Maria	.20	.20
580	A103	8c Spanish treasure galleons	.20	.20
581	A103	10c Bermuda sloop	.25	.20
582	A103	20c Privateer Grand Turk	.55	.30
583	A103	25c Nelson's Frigate Boreas	.65	.35
584	A103	30c Warship Endymion	.90	.50
585	A103	35c Bark Caesar	1.10	.60
586	A103	50c Schooner Grapeshot	1.40	.75
587	A103	65c Invincible	2.00	1.10
588	A103	95c Magicienne	2.75	1.50
589	A103	$1.10 Durban	3.25	1.75
590	A103	$2 Sentinel	5.50	3.00
591	A103	$3 Minerva	8.75	4.75
592	A103	$5 Caicos sloop	13.00	7.00
		Nos. 578-592 (15)	40.70	22.40

Issued: 4c, 8c, 10c, 30c, 65c, $1.10, $5, Mar.; 5c, 20c, 25c, 35c, 50c, 95c, $2, Aug. 12; $3, Dec.

1983-84   Perf. 14
578a	A103	4c	.20	.20
579a	A103	5c	.20	.20
580a	A103	8c	.20	.20
581a	A103	10c	.25	.20
582a	A103	20c	.55	.40
583a	A103	25c	.65	.50
584a	A103	30c	.90	.55
585a	A103	35c	1.10	.65
586a	A103	50c	1.40	.95
587a	A103	65c	2.00	1.25
588a	A103	95c	2.75	1.75
589a	A103	$1.10	3.25	2.00
590a	A103	$2	5.50	3.75
591a	A103	$3	8.75	5.75
592a	A103	$5	13.00	9.50
		Nos. 578a-592a (15)	40.70	27.85

Issued: 10c, 30c, 65c, $1.10-$3, 10/5/83; 8c, 25c, 50c, 95c, 12/16/83; 4c, 5c, 20c, 35c, $5, 1/9/84.
For overprints see Nos. 744-746.

John F. Kennedy (1917-1963), 20th Death Anniv. — A105

1983, Aug. 30   Litho.   Perf. 14
598	A104	3c Mickey Mouse	.20	.20
599	A104	35c Gyro Gearloose	.50	.50
600	A104	50c Ludwig Von Drake	.70	.70
601	A104	$1.10 Huey, Dewey and Louie	1.50	1.50
		Nos. 593-601 (9)	3.90	3.90

Souvenir Sheet
Perf. 13½
602	A104	$2.50 Around the tree	4.75	4.75

1983, Dec. 22   Litho.   Perf. 14
603	A105	20c multicolored	.30	.30
604	A105	$1 multicolored	1.60	1.60

Classic Cars A106

1984, Mar. 15   Litho.   Perf. 14
605	A106	4c Cadillac V-16, 1933 + label	.20	.20
606	A106	8c Rolls Royce Phantom III, 1937 + label	.20	.20
607	A106	10c Saab 99, 1969 + label	.20	.20
608	A106	25c Maserati Bora, 1973 + label	.45	.45
609	A106	40c Datsun 260Z, 1970 + label	.70	.70
610	A106	55c Porsche 917, 1971 + label	1.00	1.00
611	A106	80c Lincoln Continental, 1939 + label	1.50	1.50
612	A106	$1 Triumph TR3A, 1957 + label	1.75	1.75
		Nos. 605-612 (8)	6.00	6.00

Souvenir Sheet
613	A106	$2 Daimler, 1886	2.75	2.75

125th anniv. of first commercially productive oil well, Drake's Rig, Titusville, Pa. Nos. 605-612 se-tenant with labels showing flags and auto museum names. No. 613 for 150th birth anniv. of Gotlieb Daimler, inventor of high speed internal combustion engine.

Easter — A107

450th death anniv. of Antonio Allegri Correggio (Various cameo portraits of Correggio, paintings): 15c, Rest on the Flight to Egypt with St. Francis. 40c, St. Luke and St. Ambrose. 60c, Diana and her Chariot. 95c, Deposition of Christ. $2, Nativity with St. Elizabeth and the Infant St. John.

1984, Apr. 9
614	A107	15c multicolored	.20	.20
615	A107	40c multicolored	.45	.45
616	A107	60c multicolored	.70	.70
617	A107	95c multicolored	1.10	1.10
		Nos. 614-617 (4)	2.45	2.45

Souvenir Sheet
618	A107	$2 multi, horiz.	3.00	3.00

1984 Los Angeles Olympics — A108

Various Disney characters participating in Olympic sports.

1984, Feb. 21   Litho.   Perf. 14
619	A108	1c 500-meter	.20	.20
620	A108	1c Diving	.20	.20
621	A108	2c Single kayak	.20	.20
622	A108	2c 1000-meter kayak	.20	.20
623	A108	3c Highboard diving	.20	.20
624	A108	3c Kayak slalom	.20	.20
625	A108	25c Freestyle swimming	.50	.50
626	A108	75c Water polo	1.50	1.50
627	A108	$1 Yachting	2.00	2.00
		Nos. 619-627 (9)	5.20	5.20

Souvenir Sheet
| 628 | A108 | $2 Platform diving | 4.75 | 4.75 |

1984, Apr.   Perf. 12½x12
Same Designs
619a	A108	1c	.20	.20
620a	A108	1c	.20	.20
621a	A108	2c	.20	.20
622a	A108	2c	.20	.20
623a	A108	3c	.20	.20
624a	A108	3c	.20	.20
625a	A108	25c	.50	.50
626a	A108	75c	1.50	1.50
627a	A108	$1	2.00	2.00
		Nos. 619a-627a (9)	5.20	5.20

Souvenir Sheet
| 628a | A108 | $2 | 4.75 | 4.75 |

Nos. 619a-628a inscribed with Olympic rings emblem. Printed in sheets of 5.

Sir Arthur Conan Doyle (1859-1930) — A109

Scenes from the Adventures of Sherlock Holmes.

1984, July 16   Litho.   Perf. 14
629	A109	25c Second Stain	1.25	.75
630	A109	45c Final Problem	1.75	1.25
631	A109	70c Empty House	2.50	2.00
632	A109	85c Greek Interpreter	3.00	2.50
		Nos. 629-632 (4)	8.50	6.50

Souvenir Sheet
| 633 | A109 | $2 Doyle, vert. | 6.25 | 7.50 |

Nos. 567-568, 572 Overprinted with UPU Emblem and: "19TH UPU CONGRESS / HAMBURG, WEST GERMANY./ 1874-1984"

1984   Litho.   Perf. 14
| 637 | A101 | 95c multicolored | 2.50 | 1.90 |
| 638 | A101 | $1.10 multicolored | 2.50 | 2.25 |

Souvenir Sheet
| 639 | A101 | $3 multicolored | 5.50 | 5.50 |

AUSIPEX '84
A110

Darwin, Ship, Map of Australia, Fauna.

1984, Aug. 22   Perf. 14x13½
640	A110	5c Clown fish	.40	.30
641	A110	35c Monitor lizard	1.40	1.25
642	A110	50c Rainbow lorikeets	1.90	1.50
643	A110	$1.10 Koalas	2.40	2.00
		Nos. 640-643 (4)	6.10	5.05

Souvenir Sheet
| 644 | A110 | $2 Grey kangaroo | 4.00 | 4.00 |

Christmas — A111

Scenes from Walt Disney's The Toy Tinkers.

1984   Litho.   Perf. 14
645	A111	20c multicolored	.75	.35
646	A111	35c multicolored	1.00	.50
647	A111	50c multicolored	1.40	.75
648	A111	75c multicolored	2.00	1.25
649	A111	$1.10 multicolored	2.25	1.75
		Nos. 645-649 (5)	7.40	4.60

Souvenir Sheet
| 650 | A111 | $2 multicolored | 4.00 | 4.00 |

No. 648 issued in sheets of 8. Issue dates: 75c, Nov. 26, others, Oct. 8.

Audubon Birth Bicentenary A112

Cameo portrait of Audubon, signature and illustrations from Birds of North America.

1985, Jan. 28   Litho.   Perf. 14
651	A112	25c Dendroica magnoliae	1.00	.50
652	A112	45c Asio flammeus	1.60	1.00
653	A112	70c Zenaida macroura	1.75	1.75
654	A112	85c Progne subis	1.75	2.00
		Nos. 651-654 (4)	6.10	5.25

Souvenir Sheet
| 655 | A112 | $2 Haematopus ostralegus | 4.50 | 4.00 |

Intl. Civil Aviation Org., 40th Anniv. A113

Pioneers & inventions: 8c, Leonardo da Vinci, 15th century glider wing. 25c, Sir Alliott Verdon Roe, 1949 C. 102 Jet. 65c, Robert H. Goddard, first liquid fuel rocket launch, 1926. $1, Igor Sikorsky, 1939 Sikorsky VS300. $2, Aviator Amelia Earhart, 1937 Lockheed 10E Electra.

1985, Feb. 21
656	A113	8c multicolored	.35	.20
657	A113	25c multicolored	1.10	.25
658	A113	65c multicolored	1.75	1.00
659	A113	$1 multicolored	2.75	2.25
		Nos. 656-659 (4)	5.95	3.70

Souvenir Sheet
| 660 | A113 | $2 multicolored | 3.50 | 3.50 |

Arrival of the Statue of Liberty in New York, Cent. A114

Designs: 20c, Flags of US, France, Franklin, Lafayette. 30c, Designer Frederic A. Bartholdi, engineer Gustave Eiffel, Statue, Eiffel Tower. 65c, Isere, arriving in New York with Statue, 1885. $1.10, Fund raisers Louis Agassiz, H. W. Longfellow, Charles Sumner, Joseph Pulitzer. $2, Dedication day, Oct. 28, 1886.

1985, Mar. 28
661	A114	20c multicolored	.70	.50
662	A114	30c multicolored	.95	.60
663	A114	65c multicolored	2.10	1.25
664	A114	$1.10 multicolored	2.25	1.50
		Nos. 661-664 (4)	6.00	3.85

Souvenir Sheet
| 665 | A114 | $2 multicolored | 4.25 | 4.25 |

Royal Navy A115

Designs: 20c, Sir Edward Hawke, Royal George. 30c, Lord Nelson, H.M.S. Victory. 65c, Adm. Sir George Cockburn, H.M.S. Albion. 95c, Adm. Sir David Beatty, H.M.S. Indefatigable. $2, 18th century naval gunner, cannons.

1985, Apr. 17
666	A115	20c multicolored	1.40	1.00
667	A115	30c multicolored	1.60	1.40
668	A115	65c multicolored	2.25	2.00
669	A115	95c multicolored	2.75	3.00
		Nos. 666-669 (4)	8.00	7.40

Souvenir Sheet
| 670 | A115 | $2 multicolored | 5.00 | 5.00 |

Intl. Youth Year A116

Anniversaries: 25c, Return of Halley's Comet, 1986. 35c, Mark Twain (1835-1910), Mississippi river boat. 50c, Jakob Grimm (1785-1863), Hansel & Gretel, vert. 95c, Grimm, Rumpelstiltskin, vert. $2, Twain, Grimm, portraits.

1985, May 17
671	A116	25c multicolored	1.00	.30
672	A116	35c multicolored	1.60	.40
673	A116	50c multicolored	1.75	.60
674	A116	95c multicolored	2.60	1.25
		Nos. 671-674 (4)	6.95	2.55

Souvenir Sheet
| 675 | A116 | $2 multicolored | 4.25 | 4.25 |

Queen Mother, 85th Birthday — A117

Designs: 30c, Queen Mother outside Clarence House, vert. 50c, Visiting Biggin Hill Airfield by helicopter. $1.10, 80th birthday portrait, vert. $2, With Prince Charles at the 1968 Garter Ceremony, Windsor Castle, vert.

1985, July 15
676	A117	30c multicolored	.65	.65
677	A117	50c multicolored	1.00	1.00
678	A117	$1.10 multicolored	2.25	2.25
		Nos. 676-678 (3)	3.90	3.90

Souvenir Sheet
| 679 | A117 | $2 multicolored | 4.00 | 4.00 |

George Frideric Handel — A118   Johann Sebastian Bach — A119

Handel or Bach and: 4c, King George II, Zadok the Priest music, 1727. 10c, Queen Caroline, Funeral Anthem, 1737. 15c, Bassoon, Invention No. 3 in D Major. 40c, Natural horn, Invention No. 3 in D Major. 50c, King George I, Water Music, 1714. 60c, Viola d'amore, Invention No. 3 . . . 95c, Clavichord, Invention No. 3 . . . $1.10, Queen Anne, Or la Tromba from Rinaldo. No. 688, Handel, portrait. No. 689, Bach, portrait.

1985, July 17   Perf. 15
680	A118	4c multicolored	.45	.35
681	A118	10c multicolored	.70	.35
682	A119	15c multicolored	.70	.30
683	A119	40c multicolored	1.40	.60
684	A119	50c multicolored	1.90	1.50
685	A119	60c multicolored	1.75	.75
686	A119	95c multicolored	2.00	1.50
687	A118	$1.10 multicolored	3.25	3.00
		Nos. 680-687 (8)	12.15	8.35

Souvenir Sheets
| 688 | A118 | $2 multicolored | 5.00 | 5.00 |
| 689 | A119 | $2 multicolored | 4.25 | 4.00 |

Motorcycle Centenary — A120

Flag of US, UK, Fed. Rep. of Germany or Japan and: 8c, 1915 dual cylinder Harley-Davidson. 25c, 1950 Thunderbird Triumph. 55c, 1985 BMW K100RS. $1.20, 1985 Honda 1100 Shadow. $2, 1885 Daimler Single Track, vert.

1985, Sept. 4   Perf. 14
690	A120	8c multicolored	.55	.20
691	A120	25c multicolored	1.10	.55
692	A120	55c multicolored	1.75	1.25
693	A120	$1.20 multicolored	2.50	4.00
		Nos. 690-693 (4)	5.90	6.00

Souvenir Sheet
| 694 | A120 | $2 multicolored | 4.25 | 4.25 |

Pirates of the Caribbean — A121

Disneyland, 30th Anniv.: No. 695, Fate of Capt. Kidd. No. 696, Pirates imprisoned. No. 697, Bartholomew Roberts, church-going pirate. No. 698, Buccaneers in battle. No. 699, Bride auction. No. 700, Plunder. No. 701, Singing pirates. No. 702, Blackbeard. No. 703, Henry Morgan. No. 704, Mary Read, Anne Bonney.

1985, Oct. 4   Litho.   Perf. 14
695	A121	1c multicolored	.20	.20
696	A121	1c multicolored	.20	.20
697	A121	2c multicolored	.20	.20
698	A121	2c multicolored	.20	.20
699	A121	3c multicolored	.20	.20
700	A121	3c multicolored	.20	.20
701	A121	35c multicolored	1.25	.50
702	A121	75c multicolored	2.25	2.50
703	A121	$1.10 multicolored	2.50	3.00
		Nos. 695-703 (9)	7.20	7.20

Souvenir Sheet
| 704 | A121 | $2.50 multicolored | 6.00 | 6.00 |

Girl Guides, 75th Anniv. A122

Uniforms of Turks and Caicos and: 10c, Papua New Guinea and China brownies. 40c, Surinam and Korea brownies. 70c, Australia and Canada girl guides. 80c, West Germany and Israel girl guides.

1985, Nov. 4

705	A122	10c multicolored	.50	.35
706	A122	40c multicolored	1.25	.90
707	A122	70c multicolored	1.75	2.00
708	A122	80c multicolored	2.00	2.25
		Nos. 705-708 (4)	5.50	5.50

Souvenir Sheet

709	A122	$2 Anniv. emblem	4.00	4.00

Grand Turk Chapter, 35th anniv.

World Wildlife Fund A123

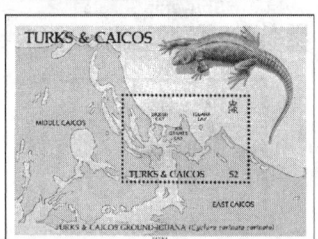

Map of the Islands — A124

Turks & Caicos ground iguanas.

1986, Nov. 20   *Perf. 14*

710	A123	8c multicolored	1.00	.75
711	A123	10c multicolored	1.00	.75
712	A123	20c multicolored	1.75	1.50
713	A123	35c multicolored	7.50	6.50
		Nos. 710-713 (4)	11.25	9.50

Souvenir Sheet

714	A124	$2 multicolored	8.50	9.00

A125

Christmas — A126

Wedding pictures.

1986, Dec. 19   **Litho.**   *Perf. 14*

715	A125	35c Couple	.70	.70
716	A125	65c Sarah in coach	1.25	1.25
717	A125	$1.10 Couple, close-up	2.25	2.25
		Nos. 715-717 (3)	4.20	4.20

Souvenir Sheet

718	A125	$2 In Westminster Abbey	4.00	4.00

Wedding of Prince Andrew and Sarah Ferguson.

1987, Dec. 9   **Litho.**   *Perf. 14*

Illuminations by miniaturist Giorgio Giulio Clovio (1498-1578) from the Farnese Book of Hours: 35c, Prophecy of the Birth of Christ to King Achaz. 50c, The Annunciation. 65c, The Circumcision. 95c, Adoration of the Kings. $2, The Nativity, from the Townley Lectionary.

719	A126	35c multicolored	1.00	.60
720	A126	50c multicolored	1.50	1.40
721	A126	65c multicolored	1.75	1.75
722	A126	95c multicolored	2.50	3.00
		Nos. 719-722 (4)	6.75	6.75

Souvenir Sheet

723	A126	$2 multicolored	4.00	4.75

Accession of Queen Victoria to the Throne of England, 150th Anniv. A127

Ships and memorials: 8c, HMS Victoria, Victoria Cross. 35c, SS Victoria, coin. 55c, Victoria & Albert I, Great Britain No. 1. 95c, Victoria & Albert II, Victoria Public Library, Turks & Caicos. $2, Bark Victoria.

1987, Dec. 24

724	A127	8c multicolored	1.75	.75
725	A127	35c multicolored	1.75	1.50
726	A127	55c multicolored	2.00	2.00
727	A127	95c multicolored	2.50	3.25
		Nos. 724-727 (4)	8.00	7.50

Souvenir Sheet

728	A127	$2 multicolored	5.25	5.75

US Constitution Bicentennial — A128

Designs: 10c, NJ state flag. 35c, Freedom of Worship, vert. 65c, US Supreme Court, vert. 80c, John Adams, vert. $2, George Mason, vert.

1987, Dec. 31

729	A128	10c multicolored	.20	.20
730	A128	35c multicolored	.50	.50
731	A128	65c multicolored	1.40	1.40
732	A128	80c multicolored	2.00	2.00
		Nos. 729-732 (4)	4.10	4.10

Souvenir Sheet

733	A128	$2 multicolored	3.00	3.50

Discovery of America, 500th Anniv. (in 1992) A129

4c, Caravel, first sighting of land, Oct. 12, 1492. 25c, Columbus meets with Indians, Oct. 14. 70c, Fleet anchored in harbor, Oct. 15. $1, Landing, Oct. 16. $2, Nina, Pinta and Santa Maria.

1988, Jan. 20

734	A129	4c multicolored	.40	.25
735	A129	25c multicolored	.80	.50
736	A129	70c multicolored	2.40	2.75
737	A129	$1 multicolored	2.40	2.75
		Nos. 734-737 (4)	6.00	6.25

Souvenir Sheet

738	A129	$2 multicolored	4.75	4.75

Sea Scouts Salute Jamboree and Australia A130

Australia Bicent.: 8c, Arawak artifact, scouts exploring cave on Middle Caicos, vert. 35c,

Santa Maria, scouts rowing to Hawks Nest. 65c, Scouts diving to explore a sunken Spanish galleon, vert. 95c, Plantation worker cutting sisal, scouts exploring plantation ruins. $2, Splashdown of Friendship 7, piloted by John Glenn, Feb. 20, 1962, vert.

1988, Feb. 12   **Litho.**   *Perf. 14*

739	A130	8c multicolored	.20	.20
740	A130	35c shown	.70	.70
741	A130	65c multicolored	1.25	1.25
742	A130	95c multicolored	1.90	1.90
		Nos. 739-742 (4)	4.05	4.05

Souvenir Sheet

743	A130	$2 multicolored	4.00	4.50

Nos. 581, 583 and 590 Ovptd. "40th WEDDING ANNIVERSARY / H.M. QUEEN ELIZABETH II / H.R.H. THE DUKE OF EDINBURGH"

1988, Mar. 14   **Litho.**   *Perf. 14*

744	A103	10c multicolored	.20	.20
745	A103	25c multicolored	.50	.50
746	A103	$2 multicolored	4.00	4.00
		Nos. 744-746 (3)	4.70	4.70

A131

A132

1988, Aug. 29   **Litho.**

747	A131	8c Soccer	.35	.20
748	A131	30c Yachting	.55	.55
749	A131	70c Cycling	2.25	2.00
750	A131	$1 Running	1.75	2.25
		Nos. 747-750 (4)	4.90	5.00

Souvenir Sheet

751	A131	$2 Swimming	4.00	4.00

1988 Summer Olympics, Seoul.

1988, Sept. 5   **Litho.**

Billfish Tournament: 8c, Passenger jet, fishing boat and fisherman reeling-in giant swordfish. 10c, Photographing prize catch. 70c, Fishing boat, lighthouse. $1, Blue marlin. $2, Sailfish.

752	A132	8c multicolored	.85	.20
753	A132	10c multicolored	.45	.20
754	A132	70c multicolored	1.90	2.10
755	A132	$1 multicolored	2.25	2.50
		Nos. 752-755 (4)	5.45	5.00

Souvenir Sheet

756	A132	$2 multicolored	4.75	4.75

Christmas A133

Paintings by Titian: 15c, Madonna and Child with St. Catherine and the Infant John the Baptist, c. 1530. 25c, Madonna with a Rabbit, c. 1526. 35c, Virgin and Child with Sts. Stephen, Jerome and Mauritius, c. 1520. 40c, The Gypsy Madonna, c. 1510. 50c, The Holy Family and a Shepherd, c. 1510. 65c, Madonna and Child, c. 1510. $3, Madonna and Child with St. John the Baptist and St. Catherine, c.

1530. No. 764, Adoration of the Magi, c. 1560. No. 765, The Annunciation, c. 1560.

1988, Oct. 24   **Litho.**

757	A133	15c multicolored	.30	.30
758	A133	25c multicolored	.50	.50
759	A133	35c multicolored	.70	.70
760	A133	40c multicolored	.80	.80
761	A133	50c multicolored	1.00	1.00
762	A133	65c multicolored	1.25	1.25
763	A133	$3 multicolored	6.00	6.00
		Nos. 757-763 (7)	10.55	10.55

Souvenir Sheets

764	A133	$2 multicolored	4.00	4.00
765	A133	$2 multicolored	4.00	4.00

Visit of Princess Alexandra, 1st Cousin of Queen Elizabeth II — A134

Various portraits and: 70c, Government House. $1.40, Map. $2, Flora, vert.

1988, Nov. 14   **Litho.**   *Perf. 14*

766	A134	70c multicolored	1.75	1.50
767	A134	$1.40 multicolored	3.75	4.00

Souvenir Sheet

768	A134	$2 multicolored	6.00	6.00

Arms Type of 1970 Without Inscription
Perf. 14½x15

1988, Dec. 15   **Litho.**   **Unwmk.**

769	A35	$10 multicolored	17.50	17.50

Pre-Columbian Societies and Their Customs — A135

UPAE and discovery of America anniv. emblems and: 10c, Hollowing-out tree to make a canoe, vert. 50c, Body painting and statue. 65c, Three islanders with body paint. $1, Canoeing, vert. $2, Petroglyph.

1989, May 15   **Litho.**   *Perf. 14*

770	A135	10c multicolored	.20	.20
771	A135	50c multicolored	1.00	1.00
772	A135	65c multicolored	1.25	1.25
773	A135	$1 multicolored	2.00	2.00
		Nos. 770-773 (4)	4.45	4.45

Souvenir Sheet

774	A135	$2 multicolored	4.25	4.50

Discovery of America 500th anniv. (in 1992).

Souvenir Sheet

Lincoln Memorial, Washington, D.C. — A136

1989, Nov. 17   **Litho.**   *Perf. 14*

775	A136	$1.50 multicolored	3.50	3.50

World Stamp Expo '89.

Miniature Sheets

American Presidential Office, 200th Anniv. — A137

US presidents, historic events and monuments.

No. 776: a, Jackson, early train. b, Van Buren, origins of baseball and Moses Fleetwood Walker, 1st black to play professional baseball. c, Harrison, Harrison's "Keep the Ball Rollin'" slogan and parade. d, Tyler, annexation of Texas, 1845. e, Polk, 1st US postage stamps (#2), 1847, and discovery of gold in California, 1849. f, Taylor, Mexican-American War, 1847.

No. 777: a, Hayes, end of Civil War reconstruction. b, Garfield, Garfield leading Union soldiers in the Battle of Shiloh. c, Arthur, opening of the Brooklyn Bridge, 1883. d, Cleveland, Columbian Exposition, 1893 (US #245). e, Benjamin Harrison, Pan-American Union building, map. f, McKinley, Spanish-American War (Rough Riders Monument, by Solon Borglum).

No. 778: a, Hoover, 1933 Olympic Games, Los Angeles and Lake Placid (American sprinter Ralph Metcalf and Norwegian figure skater Sonja Henie). b, Franklin Delano Roosevelt, Roosevelt's support of the March of Dimes (dime, 1946). c, 150th anniv. of inauguration of Washington, New York World's Fair, 1939. d, Truman, founding of the U.N., 1945. e, Eisenhower, invasion of Normandy, 1944. f, Kennedy, Apollo 11 mission, 1969.

1989, Nov. 19		Perf. 14	
776	Sheet of 6	6.00	6.00
a.-f.	A137 50c any single	1.00	1.00
777	Sheet of 6	6.00	6.00
a.-f.	A137 50c any single	1.00	1.00
778	Sheet of 6	6.00	6.00
a.-f.	A137 50c any single	1.00	1.00

Fraser is incorrectly spelled "Frazer" on No. 778c.

Christmas — A138

Religious paintings by Giovanni Bellini: 15c, Madonna and Child. 25c, The Madonna of the Shrubs. 35c, The Virgin and Child. 40c, The Virgin and Child with a Greek Inscription. 50c, The Madonna of the Meadow. 70c, The Madonna of the Pear. 70c, The Virgin and Child, diff. $1, Madonna and Child, diff. No. 787, The Madonna with John the Baptist and Another Saint. No. 788, The Virgin and Child Enthroned.

1989, Dec. 18				
779	A138	15c multicolored	.30	.30
780	A138	25c multicolored	.50	.50
781	A138	35c multicolored	.70	.70
782	A138	40c multicolored	.85	.85
783	A138	50c multicolored	1.00	1.00
784	A138	65c multicolored	1.25	1.25
785	A138	70c multicolored	1.40	1.40
786	A138	$1 multicolored	4.00	4.00
	Nos. 779-786 (8)		10.00	10.00

Souvenir Sheets

787	A138	$2 multicolored	5.00	5.00
788	A138	$2 multicolored	5.00	5.00

Souvenir Sheet

1st Moon Landing, 20th Anniv. — A139   Flowers — A140

Designs: a, Liftoff. b, Eagle lunar module on Moon's surface. c, Aldrin obtaining soil samples. d, Neil Armstrong walking on Moon. e, Columbia and Eagle in space.

1990, Jan. 8			
789	Sheet of 5	5.00	5.00
a.-e.	A139 50c any single	1.00	1.00

1990, Jan. 11			Litho.	Perf. 14
790	A140	8c Zephyranthes rosea	.20	.20
791	A140	10c Sophora tomentosa	.20	.20
792	A140	15c Coccoloba uvifera	.30	.30
793	A140	20c Encyclia gracilis	.40	.40
794	A140	25c Tillandsia streptophylla	.50	.50
795	A140	30c Maurandella antirrhiniflora	.60	.60
796	A140	35c Tillandsia balbisiana	.70	.70
797	A140	50c Encyclia rufa	1.00	1.00
798	A140	65c Aechmea lingulata	1.25	1.25
799	A140	80c Asclepias curassavica	1.60	1.60
800	A140	$1 Caesalpinia bahamensis	2.00	2.00
801	A140	$1.10 Capparis cynophallophora	2.25	2.25
802	A140	$1.25 Stachytarpheta jamaicensis	2.50	2.50
803	A140	$2 Cassia biflora	4.00	4.00
804	A140	$5 Clusia rosea	10.00	10.00
805	A140	$10 Opuntia bahamana	20.00	20.00
	Nos. 790-805 (16)		47.50	47.50

1994				Perf. 12
790a	A140	8c	.20	.20
791a	A140	10c	.20	.20
792a	A140	15c	.30	.30
793a	A140	20c	.40	.40
794a	A140	25c	.50	.50
795a	A140	30c	.60	.60
796a	A140	35c	.70	.70
797a	A140	50c	1.00	1.00
798a	A140	65c	1.25	1.25
799a	A140	80c	1.60	1.60
800a	A140	$1	2.00	2.00
801a	A140	$1.10	2.25	2.25
802a	A140	$1.25	2.50	2.50
803a	A140	$2	4.00	4.00
804a	A140	$5	10.00	10.00
805a	A140	$10 ('95)	20.00	20.00
	Nos. 790a-805a (16)		47.50	47.50

Birds A141

1990, Feb. 19				
806	A141	10c Yellow-billed cuckoo	.70	.45
807	A141	15c White-tailed tropic bird	.80	.45
808	A141	20c Kirtland's warbler	1.00	.60
809	A141	30c Yellow-crowned night heron	1.25	.60
810	A141	50c West Indian tree duck	1.75	.90
811	A141	80c Yellow-bellied sapsucker	2.25	2.00
812	A141	$1 American kestrel	3.00	3.50
813	A141	$1.40 Mockingbird	2.75	2.50
	Nos. 806-813 (8)		13.50	11.00

Souvenir Sheets

814	A141	$2 Osprey	6.00	6.00
815	A141	$2 Yellow warbler	6.00	6.00

Fish A142

1990, Feb. 12			Litho.	Perf. 14
816	A142	8c Queen parrotfish	.20	.20
817	A142	10c Queen triggerfish	.20	.20
818	A142	25c Sergeant major	.50	.50
819	A142	40c Spotted goatfish	.80	.80
820	A142	50c Neon goby	1.00	1.00
821	A142	75c Nassau grouper	1.50	1.50
822	A142	80c Jawfish	1.60	1.60
823	A142	$1 Blue tang	2.00	2.00
	Nos. 816-823 (8)		7.80	7.80

Souvenir Sheets

824	A142	$2 Butter hamlet	5.50	5.50
825	A142	$2 Queen angelfish	5.50	5.50

Butterflies A143

1990, Mar. 19				
826	A143	15c White peacock	.60	.45
827	A143	25c Cloudless sulphur	.75	.55
828	A143	35c Mexican fritillary	1.00	.65
829	A143	40c Fiery skipper	1.10	.75
830	A143	50c Chamberlain's sulphur	1.10	.85
831	A143	60c Pygmy blue	1.25	1.25
832	A143	90c Dusky swallowtail	2.10	2.50
833	A143	$1 Antillean dagger wing	2.10	2.50
	Nos. 826-833 (8)		10.00	9.50

Souvenir Sheets

834	A143	$2 Thomas's blue	4.75	4.75
835	A143	$2 9 Queen species	4.75	4.75

Nos. 826, 831 and 833 vert.

America Issue A144

Fish, UPAE and discovery of America 500th anniv. emblems.

1990, Apr. 2				
836	A144	10c Rock beauty	.45	.30
837	A144	15c Coney	.55	.40
838	A144	25c Red hind	.75	.50
839	A144	50c Banded butterflyfish	1.10	1.10
840	A144	60c French angelfish	1.40	1.25
841	A144	75c Blackbar soldierfish	1.50	1.60
842	A144	90c Stoplight parrotfish	1.60	2.00
843	A144	$1 French grunt	1.90	2.10
	Nos. 836-843 (8)		9.25	9.25

Souvenir Sheets

844	A144	$2 Gray angelfish	4.00	4.00
845	A144	$2 Blue chromis	4.00	4.00

Penny Black, 150th Anniv. — A145

British Pillar Boxes — A146

25c, 1p essay in blue, without letters. 35c, Letter Box #1, 1855. 50c, Penfold Box, 1866. 75c, Great Britain #3, essay. $1, 2p blue essay. $1.25, Air mail box, 1935. #852, Great Britain #1. #853, K type box, 1979.

1990, May 3				Perf. 14
846	A145	25c bluish blk	1.00	.65
847	A146	35c gray & pale brn	.75	.75
848	A145	50c gray & dk blue	1.00	1.00
849	A145	75c red brown	2.25	1.60
850	A145	$1 dk blue	2.75	2.75
851	A146	$1.25 gray & blue	2.25	3.25
	Nos. 846-851 (6)		10.00	10.00

Souvenir Sheets

852	A145	$2 black	4.75	4.75
853	A146	$2 blk & red brn	4.75	4.75

Stamp World London '90.

Queen Mother, 90th Birthday — A147

1990, Aug. 20			Litho.	Perf. 14
854	A147	10c multicolored	.30	.25
855	A147	25c multi, diff.	.60	.40
856	A147	75c multi, diff.	1.10	1.10
857	A147	$1.25 multi, diff.	1.75	2.00
	Nos. 854-857 (4)		3.75	3.75

Souvenir Sheet

858	A147	$2 multi, diff.	4.00	4.00

Birds A148

1990, Sept. 24			Litho.	Perf. 14
859	A148	8c Stripe-headed tanager, vert.	.55	.40
860	A148	10c Black-whiskered vireo	.55	.40
861	A148	25c Blue-grey gnatcatcher	.75	.40
862	A148	40c Lesser scaup	1.40	.80
863	A148	50c White-cheeked pintail	1.40	.85
864	A148	75c Common stilt	1.75	1.75
865	A148	80c Common oystercatcher, vert.	1.75	2.00
866	A148	$1 Tricolored heron	2.10	2.40
	Nos. 859-866 (8)		10.25	9.00

Souvenir Sheets

867	A148	$2 Bahama woodstar	4.50	4.50
868	A148	$2 American coot	4.50	4.50

Christmas A149

Different details from paintings by Rubens: 10c, 50c, 75c, No. 876, Triumph of Christ over Sin and Death. 35c, 45c, 65c, $1.25, No. 877,

St. Theresa Praying for the Souls in Purgatory.
Nos. 876-877 show entire painting.

1990, Dec. 17 Litho. Perf. 14

869	A149	10c multicolored	.30	.20
870	A149	35c multicolored	.85	.70
871	A149	45c multicolored	1.00	.90
872	A149	50c multicolored	1.10	.95
873	A149	65c multicolored	1.50	1.25
874	A149	75c multicolored	1.75	1.50
875	A149	$1.25 multicolored	2.50	2.50
		Nos. 869-875 (7)	9.00	8.00

Souvenir Sheets

876	A149	$2 multicolored	4.50	4.50
877	A149	$2 multicolored	4.50	4.50

1992 Summer
Olympics,
Barcelona — A150

1991, Jan. 17

878	A150	10c Kayaking	.20	.20
879	A150	25c Track	.50	.50
880	A150	75c Pole vault	1.50	1.50
881	A150	$1.25 Javelin	2.50	2.50
		Nos. 878-881 (4)	4.70	4.70

Souvenir Sheet

882	A150	$2 Baseball	4.00	4.50

No. 878 inscribed Canoeing.

Voyages
of
Discovery
A151

Designs: 5c, Henry Hudson, 1611. 10c,
Roald Amundsen (airship), 1926. 15c, Amundsen (ship), 1906. 50c, USS Nautilus, 1958.
75c, Robert Scott, 1911. $1, Richard Byrd,
Floyd Bennett, 1926. $1.25, Lincoln Ellsworth,
1935. $1.50, Cook, 1772-75. No. 891, The
Nina. No. 892, The search for land.

1991, Apr. 15 Litho. Perf. 14

883	A151	5c multicolored	.35	.25
884	A151	10c multicolored	.35	.25
885	A151	15c multicolored	.55	.35
886	A151	50c multicolored	.75	.55
887	A151	75c multicolored	1.25	.95
888	A151	$1 multicolored	1.50	1.25
889	A151	$1.25 multicolored	1.90	2.40
890	A151	$1.50 multicolored	2.10	2.75
		Nos. 883-890 (8)	8.75	8.75

Souvenir Sheets

891	A151	$2 multicolored	4.50	4.50
892	A151	$2 multicolored	4.50	4.50

Discovery of America, 500th anniv. (in 1992).

Butterflies
A152

1991, May 13 Litho. Perf. 14

893	A152	5c White peacock	.20	.20
894	A152	25c Orion	.50	.50
895	A152	35c Gulf fritillary	.70	.70
896	A152	45c Caribbean buckeye	.90	.90
897	A152	55c Flambeau	1.10	1.10
898	A152	65c Malachite	1.25	1.25
899	A152	70c Florida white	1.40	1.40
900	A152	$1 Great southern white	2.00	2.00
		Nos. 893-900 (8)	8.05	8.05

Souvenir Sheets

901	A152	$2 Giant hairstreak	5.00	5.00
902	A152	$2 Orange-barred sulphur	5.00	5.00

Extinct
Animals
A153

1991, June 3

903	A153	5c Protohy-drochoerus	.20	.20
904	A153	10c Phororhacos	.20	.20
905	A153	15c Prothylacynus	.30	.30
906	A153	50c Borhyaena	1.00	1.00
907	A153	75c Smilodon	1.50	1.50
908	A153	$1 Thoatherium	2.00	2.00
909	A153	$1.25 Cuvieronius	2.50	2.50
910	A153	$1.50 Toxodon	3.00	3.00
		Nos. 903-910 (8)	10.70	10.70

Souvenir Sheets

911	A153	$2 Mesosaurus	4.50	4.50
912	A153	$2 Astrapotheri-um	4.50	4.50

Royal Family Birthday, Anniversary
Common Design Type

1991 Litho. Perf. 14

913	CD347	10c multicolored	.40	.40
914	CD347	25c multicolored	.55	.45
915	CD347	35c multicolored	.65	.55
916	CD347	45c multicolored	1.50	.80
917	CD347	50c multicolored	1.75	1.10
918	CD347	65c multicolored	1.25	1.25
919	CD347	80c multicolored	1.50	1.75
920	CD347	$1 multicolored	2.10	2.40
		Nos. 913-920 (8)	9.70	8.50

Souvenir Sheets

921	CD347	$2 Elizabeth, Philip	4.00	4.50
922	CD347	$2 Diana, sons, Charles	4.50	5.00

10c, 45c, 50c, $1, No. 922, Charles and
Diana, 10th wedding anniv., issued: July 29.
Others, Queen Elizabeth II, 65th birthday,
issued: June 8.
For overprints see Nos. 1020-1022.

Mushrooms — A154

10c, Pluteus chrysophlebius. 15c,
Leucopaxillus gracillimus. 20c, Marasmius
haematocephalus. 35c, Collybia subpruinosa.
50c, Marasmius atrorubens, vert. 65c,
Leucocoprinus birnbaumii, vert. $1.10, Trogia
cantharelloides, vert. $1.25, Boletellus cuben-
sis, vert. No. 931, Gerronema citrinum. No.
932, Pyrrhoglossum pyrrhum, vert.

1991, June 24 Litho. Perf. 14

923	A154	10c multicolored	.20	.20
924	A154	15c multicolored	.30	.30
925	A154	20c multicolored	.40	.40
926	A154	35c multicolored	.70	.70
927	A154	50c multicolored	1.00	1.00
928	A154	65c multicolored	1.25	1.25
929	A154	$1.10 multicolored	2.25	2.25
930	A154	$1.25 multicolored	2.50	2.50
		Nos. 923-930 (8)	8.60	8.60

Miniature Sheets

931	A154	$2 multicolored	4.50	4.75
932	A154	$2 multicolored	4.50	4.75

Paintings by Vincent Van
Gogh — A155

Paintings: 15c, Weaver Facing Left, with
Spinning Wheel. 25c, Head of a Young Peasant with Pipe, vert. 35c, The Old Cemetery
Tower at Nuenen, vert. 45c, Cottage at Night-
fall. 50c, Still Life with Open Bible. 65c, Lane
at the Jardin du Luxembourg. 80c, The Pont
du Carrousel and the Louvre. $1, Vase with
Poppies, Cornflowers, Peonies and Chrysanthemums, vert. No. 941, Entrance to the Public Park. No. 942, Plowed Field.

1991, Aug. 26 Perf. 13

933	A155	15c multicolored	.30	.30
934	A155	25c multicolored	.50	.50
935	A155	35c multicolored	.70	.70
936	A155	45c multicolored	.90	.90
937	A155	50c multicolored	1.00	1.00
938	A155	65c multicolored	1.25	1.25
939	A155	80c multicolored	1.60	1.60
940	A155	$1 multicolored	2.00	2.00
		Nos. 933-940 (8)	8.25	8.25

Size: 107x80mm
Imperf

941	A155	$2 multicolored	4.00	4.00
942	A155	$2 multicolored	4.00	4.00

Phila
Nippon
'91
A156

Japanese steam locomotives.

1991, Nov. 4 Litho. Perf. 14

943	A156	8c Series 8550	.30	.30
944	A156	10c C 57	.30	.30
945	A156	45c Series 4110	.90	.65
946	A156	50c C 55	.95	.65
947	A156	65c Series 6250	1.25	1.25
948	A156	80c E 10	1.50	1.50
949	A156	$1 Series 4500	1.60	1.75
950	A156	$1.25 C 11	2.00	2.10
		Nos. 943-950 (8)	8.80	8.50

Souvenir Sheets

951	A156	$2 C 62	4.00	4.00
952	A156	$2 C 58	4.00	4.00

Christmas
A157

Details or entire paintings by Gerard David:
8c, Adoration of the Shepherds. 15c, Virgin
and Child Enthroned with Two Angels. 35c,
The Annunciation (outside wings). 45c, The
Rest on the Flight into Egypt. 50c, The Rest on
the Flight into Egypt, diff. 65c, Virgin and Child
with Angels. 80c, The Adoration of the Shepherds, diff. $1.25, The Perussis Altarpiece.
No. 961, The Adoration of the Kings. No. 962,
The Nativity.

1991, Dec. 23 Perf. 12

953	A157	8c multicolored	.20	.20
954	A157	15c multicolored	.30	.30
955	A157	35c multicolored	.70	.70
956	A157	45c multicolored	.90	.90
957	A157	50c multicolored	1.00	1.00
958	A157	65c multicolored	1.25	1.25
959	A157	80c multicolored	1.60	1.60
960	A157	$1.25 multicolored	2.50	2.50
		Nos. 953-960 (8)	8.45	8.45

Souvenir Sheets
Perf. 14½

961	A157	$2 multicolored	4.00	4.00
962	A157	$2 multicolored	4.00	4.00

Boy
Scouts
A160

No. 968, Member of Boy Scout Service
Corps at New York World's Fair, 1964-65. No.
969, Lord Robert Baden-Powell, vert. $2, Sil-
ver Buffalo Award.

1992, July 6 Litho. Perf. 14

968	A160	$1 multicolored	2.75	2.75
969	A160	$1 multicolored	2.75	2.75

Souvenir Sheet

970	A160	$2 multicolored	5.50	5.50

17th World Scout Jamboree, Korea.

Anniversaries and Events — A161

Designs: 25c, Astronaut releasing communications satellite. 50c, Tree with dead side,
healthy side. 65c, Emblems, globe, food products. 80c, Fish in polluted, clean water. $1,
Runners, Lions Intl. emblem. $1.25, Orbiting
quarantine facility modules. No. 977, Planned
orbital transfer vehicle for Mars. No. 977A,
Industrial pollution, clean beach.

1992-93 Litho. Perf. 14

971	A161	25c multicolored	.50	.50
972	A161	50c multicolored	1.00	1.00
973	A161	65c multicolored	1.25	1.25
974	A161	80c multicolored	1.60	1.60
975	A161	$1 multicolored	2.00	2.00
976	A161	$1.25 multicolored	2.50	2.50
		Nos. 971-976 (6)	8.85	8.85

Souvenir Sheets

977	A161	$2 multicolored	5.00	5.00
977A	A161	$2 multicolored	5.00	5.00

Intl. Space Year (#971, 976-977). Earth
Summit, Rio de Janeiro (#972, 974, 977A).
Intl. Conf. on Nutrition, Rome (#973). Lions
Intl., 75th anniv. (#975).
Issued: #972, 974, 977A, 1/93; others,
12/92.

**Queen Elizabeth II's Accession to
the Throne, 40th Anniv.**
Common Design Type

1992, Feb. 6 Litho. Perf. 14

978	CD348	10c multicolored	.40	.40
979	CD348	20c multicolored	.75	.75
980	CD348	25c multicolored	.85	.85
981	CD348	35c multicolored	.90	.90
982	CD348	50c multicolored	1.25	1.25
983	CD348	65c multicolored	1.50	1.50
984	CD348	80c multicolored	1.60	1.60
985	CD348	$1.10 multicolored	1.75	1.75
		Nos. 978-985 (8)	9.00	9.00

Souvenir Sheets

986	CD348	$2 Queen at left, boat dock	4.25	4.25
987	CD348	$2 Queen at right, shoreline	4.25	4.25

Spanish
Art — A162

Paintings: 8c, St. Monica, by Luis Tristan.
20c, 45c, The Vision of Ezekiel: The Resurrection of the Flesh (different details) by Francisco
Collantes. 50c, The Martyrdom of St. Philip, by
Jose de Ribera. 65c, St. John the Evangelist,
by Juan Ribalta. 80c, Archimedes by Jose de
Ribera. $1, St. John the Baptist in the Desert
by de Ribera. $1.25, The Martyrdom of St.
Philip (detail), by de Ribera. No. 992, The Baptism of Christ by Juan Fernandez Navarrete.
No. 997, Battle between Christians and Moors
at El Sotillo, by Francisco de Zurbaran.

1992, May 26 Litho. Perf. 13

988	A162	8c multicolored	.20	.20
989	A162	20c multicolored	.40	.40
990	A162	45c multicolored	.95	.90
991	A162	50c multicolored	1.00	1.00
992	A162	65c multicolored	1.25	1.25
993	A162	80c multicolored	1.60	1.60
994	A162	$1 multicolored	2.00	2.00
995	A162	$1.25 multicolored	2.50	2.50
		Nos. 988-995 (8)	9.90	9.85

Size: 95x120mm
Imperf

996	A162	$2 multicolored	4.00	4.00
997	A162	$2 multicolored	4.00	4.00

Granada '92.

Discovery of America, 500th Anniv. A163

Commemorative coins, scenes of first voyage: 10c, Nina, ship. 15c, Pinta, ship. 20c, Santa Maria, Columbus' second coat of arms. 25c, Fleet at sea, ships. 30c, Landfall, sailing ship. 35c, Setting sail, Columbus departing. 50c, Columbus sighting New World, Columbus. 65c, Columbus exploring Caribbean, ship. 80c, Claiming land for Spain, Columbus, priest and cross. $1.10, Columbus exchanging gifts with native, Columbus, native.
No. 1008, Coins like #998-1000. No. 1009, Coins like #1004, 1006-1007.

1992, Oct.		Litho.	Perf. 14	
998	A163	10c multicolored	.30	.30
999	A164	15c multicolored	.45	.45
1000	A164	20c multicolored	.45	.45
1001	A164	25c multicolored	.65	.65
1002	A164	30c multicolored	.65	.65
1003	A164	35c multicolored	.75	.75
1004	A164	50c multicolored	.85	.85
1005	A164	65c multicolored	1.25	1.25
1006	A164	80c multicolored	1.25	1.25
1007	A164	$1.10 multicolored	1.40	1.40
	Nos. 998-1007 (10)		8.00	8.00

Souvenir Sheets

1008	A164	$2 multicolored	4.00	4.00
1009	A164	$2 multicolored	4.00	4.00

Christmas A164

Details or entire paintings by Simon Bening: 8c, Nativity. 15c, Circumcision. 35c, Flight to Egypt. 50c, Massacre of the Innocents.
By Dirk Bouts: 65c, The Annunciation. 80c, The Visitation. $1.10, The Adoration of the Angels. $1.25, The Adoration of the Wise Men. No. 1018, The Virgin and Child. No. 1019, The Virgin Seated with the Child.

1992, Nov.		Litho.	Perf. 13½x14	
1010	A164	8c multicolored	.25	.25
1011	A164	15c multicolored	.50	.50
1012	A164	35c multicolored	.75	.75
1013	A164	50c multicolored	.90	.90
1014	A164	65c multicolored	1.25	1.25
1015	A164	80c multicolored	1.60	1.60
1016	A164	$1.10 multicolored	1.75	1.75
1017	A164	$1.25 multicolored	1.75	1.75
	Nos. 1010-1017 (8)		8.75	8.75

Souvenir Sheets

1018	A164	$2 multicolored	4.50	4.50
1019	A164	$2 multicolored	4.50	4.50

Nos. 915, 918 & 921 Ovptd. in Red or Black

1993, Mar. 20		Litho.	Perf. 14	
1020	CD347	35c on #915	.70	.70
1021	CD347	65c on #918	1.25	1.25

Souvenir Sheet

1022	CD347	$2 on #921 (Bk)	4.00	4.00

Miniature Sheet

Coronation of Queen Elizabeth II, 40th Anniv. — A165

Designs: a, 15c, Chalice and paten from royal collection. b, 50c, Official coronation photograph. c, $1, Coronation ceremony. d, $1.25, Queen, Prince Philip.
$2, New Portrait.

1993, June 2		Litho.	Perf. 13½x14	
1023	A165	Sheet, 2 ea #a.-d.	10.00	10.00

Souvenir Sheet
Perf. 14

1024	A165	$2 multicolored	4.00	4.00

No. 1024 contains one 28x42mm stamp.

Christmas A166

Details or entire woodcut, Mary, Queen of the Angels, by Durer: 8c, 20c, 35c, $1.25.
Details or entire paintings by Raphael: 50c, $1, Virgin and Child with St. John the Baptist. 65c, The Canagiani Holy Family. 80c, The Holy Family with the Lamb.
No. 1033, Mary, Queen of the Angels, by Durer. No. 1034, The Canagiani Holy Family, diff., by Raphael.

Perf. 13½x14, 14x13½

1993, Dec.			Litho.	
1025-1032	A166	Set of 8	9.50	9.50

Souvenir Sheets

1033-1034	A166	$2 each	4.00	4.00

Dinosaurs A167

8c, Omphalosaurus. 15c, Coelophysis. 20c, #1043, Triceratops. 35c, #1044, Dilophosaurus. 50c, Pterodactylus. 65c, Elasmosaurus. 80c, Stegosaurus. $1.25, Euoplocephalus.

1993, Nov. 15		Litho.	Perf. 14	
1035-1042	A167	Set of 8	8.00	8.00

Souvenir Sheets

1043-1044	A167	$2 each	4.00	4.00

Birds A168

Designs: 10c, Killdeer. 15c, Yellow-crowned night heron, vert. 35c, Northern mockingbird. 50c, Eastern kingbird, vert. 65c, Magnolia warbler. 80c, Cedar waxwing, vert. $1.10, Ruby-throated hummingbird. $1.25, Painted bunting, vert. No. 1053, American kestrel. No. 1054, Ruddy duck.

1993, Dec.				
1045	A168	10c multicolored	.20	.20
1046	A168	15c multicolored	.30	.30
1047	A168	35c multicolored	.75	.75
1048	A168	50c multicolored	1.00	1.00
1049	A168	65c multicolored	1.40	1.40
1050	A168	80c multicolored	1.60	1.60
1051	A168	$1.10 multicolored	2.25	2.25
1052	A168	$1.25 multicolored	2.50	2.50
	Nos. 1045-1052 (8)		10.00	10.00

Souvenir Sheets

1053	A168	$2 multicolored	4.00	4.00
1054	A168	$2 multicolored	4.00	4.00

Fish A169

Designs: 10c, Bluehead wrasse. 20c, Honeycomb cowfish. 25c, Glasseye snapper. 35c, Spotted drum. 50c, Jolthead porgy. 65, Smallmouth grunt. 80c, Peppermint bass. $1.10, Indigo hamlet.
No. 1063, Bonnethead shark. No. 1064, Sharpnose shark.

1993, Dec. 15				
1055-1062	A169	Set of 8	8.00	8.00

Souvenir Sheets

1063-1064	A169	$2 each	4.00	4.00

1994 World Cup Soccer Championships, US — A170

Designs: 8c, Sergio Goycoechea, Argentina. 10c, Bado Illgner, Germany. 15c, Nico Claesen, Belgium. 65c, West German team. 80c, Cameroun team. $1, Santin, Francescoli, Uruguay; Cuciuffo, Argentina. $1.10, Sanchez, Mexico.
No. 1072, Imre Garaba, Hungary, vert. No. 1073, Pontiac Silverdome.

1994, Sept. 26		Litho.	Perf. 14	
1065-1071	A170	Set of 7	8.50	8.50

Souvenir Sheets

1072-1073	A170	$2 each	4.00	4.00

Mushrooms — A171

Designs: 5c, Xerocomus guadelupae, vert. 10c, Volvariella volvacea, vert. 35c, Hygrocybe atrosquamosa. 50c, Pleurotus ostreatus. 65c, Marasmius pallescens. 80c, Coprinus plicatilis, vert. $1.10, Bolbitius vitellinus. $1.50, Pyroglossum lilaceipes, vert.
No. 1082, Lentinus edodes. No. 1083, Russula cremeolilacina, vert.

1994, Oct. 10				
1074-1081	A171	Set of 8	8.25	8.25

Souvenir Sheets

1082-1083	A171	$2 each	4.00	4.00

Christmas A172

Illustrations from French Book of Hours: 25c, The Annunciation. 50c, The Visitation. 65c, Annunciation to the Shepherds. 80c, The Nativity. $1, Flight into Egypt. $2, The Adoration of the Magi.

1994, Dec. 5		Litho.	Perf. 14	
1084-1088	A172	Set of 5	6.50	6.50

Souvenir Sheet

1089	A172	$2 multicolored	4.00	4.00

Butterflies A173

Designs: 15c, Dryas julia. 20c, Urbanus proteus. 25c, Colobura dirce. 50c, Papilio homerus. 65c, Chiodes catillus. 80c, Eurytides zonaria. $1, Hypolymnas misippus. $1.25, Phoebis avellaneda.
No. 1098, Eurema adamsi. No. 1099, Morpho peleides.

1994, Dec. 12				
1090-1097	A173	Set of 8	9.50	9.50

Souvenir Sheets

1098-1099	A173	$2 each	4.00	4.00

D-Day, 50th Anniv. A174

Designs: 10c, Gen. Montgomery, British landing on Juno Beach. 15c, Adm. Sir Bertram Ramsay, British commandos at Sword Beach. 35c, Gun crew aboard HMS Belfast. 50c, Montgomery, Eisenhower, Tedder review battle scene. 65c, Gen. Eisenhower, 101st Airborne Div. paratroopers. 80c, Gen. Omar Bradley, US landings on Omaha Beach. $1.10, Second wave of US troops on D-Day. $1.25, Supreme Commander Eisenhower presents Operation Overlord.
No. 1108, Eisenhower, Montgomery seated at table. No. 1109, Beachhead secured.

1994, Dec. 19				
1100-1107	A174	Set of 8	10.00	10.00

Souvenir Sheets

1108-1109	A174	$2 each	4.00	4.00

Orchids A175

Designs: 8c, Cattleya deckeri. 20c, Epidendrum carpophorum. 25c, Epidendrum ciliare. 50c, Encyclia phoenicea. 65c, Bletia patula. 80c, Brassia caudata. $1, Brassavola nodosa. $1.25, Bletia purpurea.
No. 1118, Ionopsis utricularioides. No. 1119, Vanilla planifolia.

1995, Jan. 5				
1110-1117	A175	Set of 8	9.50	9.50

Souvenir Sheets

1118-1119	A175	$2 each	4.00	4.00

Miniature Sheet of 12

PHILAKOREA '94 — A176

Jurassic marine reptiles: a, Elasmosaurus. b, Plesiosaurus. c, Ichthyosaurus. d, Arcfielon. e, Askeptosaurus. f, Macroplata. g, Ceresiosaurus. h, Lipoleurodon. i, Henodus. j, Muraenosaurus. k, Placodus. l, Kronosaurus.

1995, Jan. 23
1120 A176 35c #1120a-1120 l   8.50 8.50

First Manned Moon Landing, 25th Anniv. A177

Designs: 10c, Apollo XI in flight. 20c, Simulated moon landing. 25c, Painting, Astronauts on the Moon, by Kovales. 35c, First foot, footprint on moon. 50c, Aldrin, solar wind experiment. 65c, Armstrong, Aldrin setting up flag on moon. 80c, Command module Columbia in Lunar orbit. $1.10, Recovery of Apollo XI in Pacific.
No. 1129, Lift-off at Cape Canaveral, vert. No. 1130, Moon rock on display in Houston.

1995, Jan. 9   Litho.   Perf. 14
1121-1128 A177 Set of 8   8.00 8.00
Souvenir Sheets
1129-1130 A177 $2 each   4.00 4.00

Intl. Olympic Committee, Cent. — A178

Summer, Winter Olympic events: 8c, Fencing. 10c, Speed skating. 15c, Diving. 20c, Cycling. 25c, Ice hockey. 35c, Figure skating. 50c, Soccer. 65c, Bobsled. 80c, Super giant slalom. $1.25, Equestrian.
#1141, Gymnastics. #1142, Downhill skiing.

1995, Feb. 6
1131-1140 A178 Set of 10   8.75 8.75
Souvenir Sheets
1141-1142 A178 $2 each   4.00 4.00

Domestic Cats A179

Various cats, kittens: 15c, 20c, 35c, 50c, 65c, 80c, $1, $1.25.
No. 1151, Two sleeping. No. 1152, Kitten, ladybugs in flowers.

1995, July 3   Litho.   Perf. 14
1143-1150 A179 Set of 8   10.00 10.00
Souvenir Sheets
1151-1152 A179 $2 each   4.00 4.00

Birds — A180

A180a

10c, Belted kingfisher. 15c, Clapper rail. 20c, American redstart. 25c, Roseate tern.

35c, Purple gallinule. 45c, Ruddy turnstone. 50c, Barn owl. 60c, Brown booby. 80c, Great blue heron. $1, Antillean nighthawk. $1.25, Thick-billed vireo. $1.40, American flamingo. $2, Wilson's plover. $5, Blue-winged teal. $10, Reddish egret.

1995, Aug. 2   Litho.   Perf. 13
1153 A180 10c multi   .20   .20
1154 A180 15c multi   .30   .30
1155 A180 20c multi   .40   .40
1156 A180 25c multi   .50   .50
1157 A180 35c multi   .70   .70
1158 A180 45c multi   .90   .90
1159 A180 50c multi   1.00 1.00
1160 A180 60c multi   1.25 1.25
1161 A180 80c multi   1.60 1.60
1162 A180 $1 multi   2.00 2.00
1163 A180 $1.25 multi   2.50 2.50
1164 A180 $1.40 multi   2.75 2.75
1165 A180 $2 multi   4.00 4.00
1166 A180 $5 multi   10.00 10.00
1166A A180a $10 multi   20.00 20.00
Nos. 1153-1166A (15)   48.10 48.10

Queen Mother, 95th Birthday A181

No. 1167: a, Drawing. b, Wearing crown jewels. c, Formal portrait. d, Blue dress with pearls.
$2, Green blue outfit.

1995, Aug. 4   Perf. 13½x14
1167 A181 50c Block or strip of
            4, #a.-d.   4.00 4.00
Souvenir Sheet
1168 A181 $2 multicolored   4.00 4.00
No. 1167 was issued in sheets of 8 stamps.

VE Day, 50th Anniv. A182

Designs: 10c, "Big Three" meet at Yalta. 15c, Allied war prisoners released. 20c, American, Soviets meet at Elbe River. 25c, Death of Franklin D. Roosevelt. 60c, US 9th Army confirms cease fire. 80c, New York City celebrates VE Day. $1, Nuremberg War Crimes trials begin.
$2, Big Ben, US Capitol, St. Basil's Cathedral.

1995, Aug. 14   Litho.   Perf. 14
1169-1175 A182 Set of 7   3.25 3.25
Souvenir Sheet
1176 A182 $2 multicolored   4.00 4.00

Miniature Sheet of 9

Singapore '95 — A183

Diving equipment: No. 1177a, Wm. James, scuba, 1825. b, Rouquayrol apparatus, 1864. c, Fluess oxygen rebreathing apparatus, 1878. d, Armored diving suit, 1900. e, Jim Janett explores sunken Lusitania in Peress armored diving suit, 1935. f, Cousteau-Gagnan aqualung, 1943. g, Underwater camera, 1955. h, Sylvia Earle dives to 1,520 ft. in Jim suit, 1979. i, Spider propeller-driven rigid suit, 1984.
No. 1178, Helmet diver, 1935. No. 1179, Jacques-Yves Cousteau.

1995, Sept. 1   Perf. 14½
1177 A183 60c #a.-i.   11.00 11.00
Souvenir Sheets
1178-1179 A183 $2 each   4.00 4.00

Christmas A184

Details or entire paintings, by Piero di Cosimo (1462-1521): 20c, Madonna and Child with Young St. John. 25c, Adoration of the Child. 60c, Madonna and Child with Young St. John, St. Margaret, and An Angel. $1, Madonna and Child with An Angel.
$2, Madonna and Child with Angels and Saints.

1995, Dec. 29   Litho.   Perf. 14
1180-1183 A184 Set of 4   4.00 4.00
Souvenir Sheet
1184 A184 $2 multicolored   4.00 4.00

UN, 50th Anniv. — A185

Designs: 15c, Rights of women and children. 60c, Peace. 80c, Human rights. $1, Education.
No. 1189, Flags of nations forming "50." No. 1190, Tractor, portions of UN, FAO emblems.

1996, Feb. 26   Litho.   Perf. 14
1185-1188 A185 Set of 4   5.25 5.25
Souvenir Sheets
1189-1190 A185 $2 each   4.00 4.00

Queen Elizabeth II, 70th Birthday A186

No. 1191: a, Portrait. b, Wearing blue hat. c, In uniform, on horseback.
$2, As younger woman wearing white and yellow hat.

1996, Apr. 21   Litho.   Perf. 13½x14
1191 A186 80c Strip of 3, #a.-c.   4.75 4.75
Souvenir Sheet
1192 A186 $2 multicolored   4.00 4.00
No. 1191 was issued in sheets of 9 stamps.

History of Underwater Exploration A187

No. 1193: a, Glaucus, God of Divers, 2500BC. b, Alexander the Great decends to ocean bottom, 332BC. c, Salvage diver, 1430. d, Borelli's rebreathing device, 1680. e, Edmond Halley's diving bell, 1690. f, John Lethbridge's diving machine, 1715. g, Klingert's diving apparatus, 1789. h, Drieberg's triton, 1808. i, Seibe's diving helmet, 1819.
No. 1194: a, Jim Jarrat in "Iron Man" armored diving suit explores Lusitania, 1935.

b, Cousteau, team excavate first shipwreck using scuba gear, 1952. c, Oldest shipwreck ever found, coast of Turkey, 1959. d, Swedish warship Vasa raised, 1961. e, Mel Fisher discovers Spanish galleon Atocha, 1971. f, Whydah, first pirate ship found, is discovered by Barry Clifford, 1984. g, Dr. Robert Ballard, using robot sub Argo finds battleship Bismarck, 1989. h, Radeau "Land Tortoise" scuttled in 1758 during French and Indian War found in Lake George, NY, 1991. i, Deep-diving nuclear submarine recovers ancient Roman shipwreck cargo, 1994.
No. 1195, Arab diver Issa, 12th cent. No. 1196, Pearl diver in Caribbean, 1498. No. 1197, Diver in Newtsuit investigates Edmund Fitzgerald. No. 1198, Submarine Alvin explores Titanic, 1985.

1996, May 13   Litho.   Perf. 14
1193 A187 55c Sheet of 9,
            #a.-i.   10.00 10.00
1194 A187 60c Sheet of 9,
            #a.-i.   11.00 11.00
Souvenir Sheets
1195-1198 A187 $2 each   4.00 4.00
CHINA '96 (Nos. 1193, 1195-1196). CAPEX '96 (Nos. 1194, 1197-1198).

1996 Summer Olympics, Atlanta A188

Olympic gold medals for: No. 1199, Equestrian. No. 1200, Cycling. No. 1201, Fencing. No. 1202, Gymnastics. No. 1203, Hurdles. No. 1204, Pole vault. No. 1205, Sprints. No. 1206, Swimming. No. 1207, Diving. No. 1208, Running.

1996, May 27   Perf. 13½
1199-1208 A188 55c Set of 10   11.00 11.00
1208a   Sheet of 10, #1199-1208 11.00
Nos. 1199-1208 issued in sheets as well as in No. 1208a.

A189   A190

James A.G.S. McCartney (1945-80), 1st Chief Minister of Turks & Caicos Islands,

1996, July 8   Litho.   Perf. 14
1209 A189 60c multicolored   1.25 1.25
Ministerial Government, 20th anniv.
No. 1209 was issued in sheets of 9.

1996, Sept. 8   Litho.   Perf. 14
Working Dogs: No. 1210: a, Space research. b, Racing. c, Rescue. d, Military. e, Sporting. f, Companion. g, Hearing ear. h, Sled. i, Police. j, Guarding. k, Watch. l, Security.
No. 1211, Guide. No. 1212, Sheep dog.
1210 A190 25c Sheet of 12, #a.-l. 6.00 6.00
Souvenir Sheets
1211-1212 A190 $2 each   4.00 4.00

Winnie the Pooh, Christmas A191

Designs: 15c, Pooh trying to stay awake. 20c, Piglet, star. 35c, Ribbons and bows. 50c, Jingle bells. 60c, "Pooh loves Christmas." 80c, "Big hearts come in bouncy packages." $1, Santa Pooh. $1.25, "My most favorite."
No. 1221, Piglet, cookie. No. 1222, Piglet placing star atop tree.

1996, Nov. 25   Litho.   Perf. 13½x14
1213-1220 A191 Set of 8   9.75 9.75
Souvenir Sheets
1221 A191 $2 multicolored   4.00 4.00
1222 A191 $2.60 multicolored   5.20 5.20

Flowers — A192

A193

No. 1223: a, Giant milkweed. b, Geiger tree. c, Passion flower. d, Hibiscus.
No. 1224: a, Yellow elder. b, Prickly poppy. c, Frangipani. d, Seaside mahoe.
No. 1225, Chain of love. No. 1226, Firecracker.

1997, Feb. 10   Litho.   Perf. 14
1223 A192 20c Strip or block of
            4, #a.-d.   3.25 3.25
1224 A192 60c Strip or block of
            4, #a.-d.   4.75 4.75
Souvenir Sheets
1225-1226 A192 $2 each   4.00 4.00
Nos. 1223-1224 were each issued in sheets of 8 stamps.

1997, Mar. 24   Litho.   Perf. 14
UNICEF, 50th Anniv.: a, Dove flying right. b, Three children. c, Dove flying left. d, Boy with dog, girl holding cat.
1227 A193 60c Sheet of 4, #a.-d. 3.00 3.00
Souvenir Sheets

UNESCO, 50th Anniv. — A194

Canterbury Cathedral: No. 1228, View from rear. No. 1229, Interior view. Illustration reduced.

1997, Mar. 24   Litho.   Perf. 14
1228 A194 $2 multicolored   4.00 4.00
1229 A194 $2 multicolored   4.00 4.00

Queen Elizabeth II, Prince Philip, 50th Wedding Anniv. A195

Designs: a, Queen waving. b, Royal arms. c, Queen, Prince riding in car. d, Prince, Queen seated. e, Windsor Castle. f, Prince Philip.
$2, Wedding portrait.

1997, Apr. 21   Litho.   Perf. 14
1230 A195 60c Sheet of 6, #a.-f. 7.25 7.25
Souvenir Sheet
1231 A195 $2 multicolored   4.00 4.00

Heinrich von Stephan (1831-97), Founder of UPU A196

Portrait of Von Stephan and: No. 1232: a, British mail coach, 1700's. b, UPU emblem. c, Space shuttle, future transport.
$2, Von Stephan, Hemerodrome, messenger of ancient Greece.

1997, July 1   Litho.   Perf. 14
1232 A196 50c Sheet of 3, #a.-c. 3.00 3.00
Souvenir Sheet
1233 A196 $2 multicolored   4.00 4.00
PACIFIC 97.

Underwater Exploration A197

No. 1234: a, Edgerton camera taking photos at 6,000 ft., 1954. b, Conshelf Habitat, 1963. c, Sealab II, 1965. d, Research Habitat, Tektite, 1970. e, Discovery of Galapagos Volcanic Rift, 1974. f, Epaulard, robot survey craft, 1979. g, Sea life discovered thriving in undersea oil field, 1995. h, Deep flight, 1996. i, one-man research vessel. i, Sea ice is studied from above, under sea, Okhotsk Tower, off Japan, 1996.
No. 1235, Coelacanth. No. 1236, John Williamson makes first underwater movies, 1914.

1997, Aug. 21   Litho.   Perf. 14
1234 A197 20c Sheet of 9, #a.-i. 3.50 3.50
Souvenir Sheet
1235-1236 A197 $2 each   4.00 4.00
Stampshow 97.

Christmas A198

Entire paintings or details: 15c, Adoration of an Angel, by Studio of Fra Angelico. 20c, Scenes from the Life of St. John the Baptist, by Master of Saint Severin. 35c, Archangel Gabriel, by Masolino de Panicale. 50c, 60c, Jeremiah with Two Angels, by Gherardo Starnina (diff. angels). 80c, The Annunciation, by Giovanni di Palo di Grazia. $1, The Annunciation, by Carlo di Bracceso. $1.25, The Nativity, by Benvenuto di Giovanni Guasta.
No. 1245, The Wilton Diptych (right panel), by unknown English or French artist, c. 1395. No. 1246, Adoring Angels, from The Journey of the Magi, by Benozzo Gozzoli.

1997, Dec. 8   Litho.   Perf. 14
1237-1244 A198 Set of 8   9.75 9.75
Souvenir Sheets
1245-1246 A198 $2 each   4.00 4.00

World Wildlife Fund — A199

Snapper: a, Blackfin. b, Dog. c, Cubera. d, Mahogany.

1998, Feb. 24   Litho.   Perf. 14
1247 A199 25c Block of 4, #a.-d. 1.75 1.75
No. 1247 was issued in sheets of 16 stamps. Intl. Year of the Reef.

Marine Life — A200

Underwater photographs: 20c, Spotted flamingo tongue. 50c, Feather duster. 60c, Squirrel fish. 80c, Queen angelfish. $1, Barracuda. $1.25, Fairy basslet.
No. 1254, Rough file clam. No. 1255, Spotted cleaning shrimp.

1998, May 1   Litho.   Perf. 14
1248-1253 A200 Set of 6   8.75 8.75
Souvenir Sheets
1254-1255 A200 $2 each   4.00 4.00

A201   A202

Stylized designs showing symbol for earth, water, and - #1256: a, Dove. b, Crab. c, Fish. d, Clover leaf.
$2, Symbol for earth and water.

1998, July 30   Litho.   Perf. 14
1256 A201 50c Sheet of 4, #a.-d. 4.00 4.00
Souvenir Sheet
1257 A201 $2 multicolored   4.00 4.00
Intl. Year of the Ocean.

Royal Air Force, 80th Anniv.
Common Design Type Re-Inscribed

Designs: 20c, SE 5A. 50c, Sopwith Camel. 60c, Supermarine Spitfire. 80c, Avro Lancaster. $1, Panavia Tornado. $1.25, Hawker Hurricane.
No. 1264, Hawker Siddeley Harrier. No. 1265, Avro Vulcan.

1998, Aug. 18   Litho.   Perf. 14
1258-1263 CD350 Set of 6   8.75 8.75
Souvenir Sheets
1264-1265 CD350 $2 each   4.00 4.00

1998, July 30   Litho.   Perf. 14
Anniversaries and Events: 20c, University of the West Indies, 50th anniv. 60c, UNESCO, World Summit Program. 80c, Universal Declaration of Human Rights. $1, John Glenn's return to space.

$2, NASA Space Shuttle leaving launching pad.

1266-1269 A202 Set of 4   5.25 5.25
Souvenir Sheet
1270 A202 $2 multicolored   4.00 4.00

A203

A204

1998, Aug. 31
1271 A203 60c multicolored   1.25 1.25
Diana, Princess of Wales (1961-97). No. 1271 was issued in sheets of 6.

1998, Nov. 30   Litho.   Perf. 14
Paintings by Sister Thomasita Fessler - #1272: a, Magi's Visit. b, Flight Into Egypt. c, Wedding Feast. d, Maria. e, Annunciation & Visitation. f, Nativity. $2, Queen of Mothers.

1272 A204 50c Sheet of 6, #a.-f. 6.00 6.00
Souvenir Sheet
1273 A204 $2 multicolored   4.00 4.00
Christmas. Nos. 1272e-1272f are each 58x48mm.

Coral Gardens A205

No. 1274: a, Flamingos in flight. b, Sailboats. c, Seagulls, lighthouse. d, House along shore, seagulls. e, Pillar coral, yellowtail snapper (f). f, Eliptical star coral. g, Porkfish. h, Spotted eagle ray. i, Large ivory coral. j, Mustard hill coral, shy hamlet. k, Blue crust coral. l, Fused staghorn coral. m, Queen angelfish, massive starlet coral. n, Pinnate spiny sea fan. o, Knobby star coral, squirrelfish. p, Lowridge cactus coral, juvenile porkfish. q, Orange telesto coral. r, Spanish hogfish (q), Knobby ten-ray star coral. s, Boulder brain coral, clown wrasse. t, Rainbow parrotfish, regal sea fan. u, Great star coral, bluestriped grunt. v, Stinging coral, blue tang. w, Lavender thin finger coral. x, Juvenile french grunt (w), brilliant sea fingers.
No. 1275, Sea fan. No. 1276, Elkhorn coral.

1999, June 7   Litho.   Perf. 14¼x14½
1274 A205 20c Sheet of 24, #a.-
            x.   9.50 9.50
Souvenir Sheets
1275-1276 A205 $2 each   4.00 4.00

Wedding of Prince Edward and Sophie Rhys-Jones — A206

Portraits - #1277: a, Couple facing forward. b, Edward. c, Sophie. d, Couple walking arm in arm.
No. 1278, Couple facing forward. No. 1279, Couple facing each other.

1999, June 19   Litho.   Perf. 14
1277 A206 60c Sheet of 4, #a.-d.   4.75 4.75
Souvenir Sheets
1278-1279 A206 $2 each   4.00 4.00

Queen Mother (b. 1900) A207

Designs: a, At age 7. b, At age 19. c, At wedding. d, With daughters. e, With King George VI during World War II. f, In 1958. g, At age 60. h, In 1970. i, With Princes Charles and William, 1983. j, Current photograph.

1999, Aug. 4   Litho.   Perf. 13½x13¾
1280 A207 50c Sheet of 10,
    #a.-j.   10.00 10.00

Stamp inscription on No. 1280f is incorrect.
No. 1280 was reissued in 2002 with added inscription in margin, "Good Health and Happiness to her Majesty The Queen Mother on her 101st Birthday."

2nd World Underwater Photography Competition Winners A208

No. 1281: a, 10c, Painted tunicates (8th place). b, 20c, Peacock flounder (7th). c, 50c, Squirt anemone shrimps (6th). d, 60c, Juvenile drum (5th). e, 80c, Batwing coral crab (4th). f, $1, Moon jellyfish (3rd).
No. 1282, Christmas tree worms (2nd). No. 1283, Longhorn nudibranch (1st).

1999, Oct. 11   Litho.   Perf. 14¼x13¾
1281 A208   Sheet of 6, #a.-f.   6.50 6.50
Souvenir Sheets
    Perf. 13¾
1282-1283 A208 $2 each   4.00 4.00
Nos. 1282-1283 each contain one 50x38mm stamp.

Christmas A209

Paintings by Anthony Van Dyck: 20c, The Mystic Marriage of Saint Catherine. 50c, Rest on the Flight into Egypt. No. 1286, $2, Holy Family with Saints John and Elizabeth.
No. 1287, The Madonna of the Rosary.

1999, Dec. 7   Perf. 13¾
1284-1286 A209 Set of 3   5.50 5.50
Souvenir Sheet
1287 A209 $2 multicolored   4.00 4.00

Millennium A210

Perf. 14½x14¼
1999, Nov. 15   Litho.
1288 A210 20c silver & multi   .40 .40
1289 A210 $1 gold & multi   2.00 2.00

Millennium A211

Globe, clock and: No. 1290: a, London. b, Turks & Caicos Islands. c, New York. d, Rome. e, Jerusalem. f, Paris.
No. 1291, Flag of Islands. No. 1292, Arms of Islands.

2000, Jan. 18   Litho.   Perf. 14x13¾
1290 A211 50c Sheet of 6, #a.-f.   6.00 6.00
Souvenir Sheets
1291-1292 A211 $2 each   4.00 4.00

Mushrooms — A212

No. 1293, vert.: a, Pholiota squarroides. b, Psilocybe squamosa. c, Spathularia velutipes. d, Russula. e, Clitocybe clavipes. f, Boletus frostii.
No. 1294, Strobilurus conigenoides. No. 1295, Stereum ostrea.
Illustration reduced.

2000, July 6   Litho.   Perf. 14
1293 A212 50c Sheet of 6, #a-f   6.00 6.00
Souvenir Sheets
1294-1295 A212 $2 Set of 2   8.00 8.00

Souvenir Sheet

2000 Summer Olympics, Sydney — A213

No. 1296: a, Johan Gabriel Oxenstierna. b, Javelin. c, Aztec Stadium, Mexico City and Mexican flag. d, Ancient Greek runners.

2000, Sept. 25
1296 A213 50c Sheet of 4, #a-d   4.00 4.00

Birds A214

Designs: No. 1297, Chickadee. No. 1298, Scrub turkey. No. 1299, Sickle-bill gull.
No. 1300: a, Egret. b, Tern. c, Osprey. d, Great blue heron. e, Pelican. f, Bahama pintail.
No. 1301, Flamingo, vert. No. 1302, Macaw, vert.

2000, Oct. 2
1297-1299 A214 50c Set of 3   3.00 3.00
1300 A214 60c Sheet of 6, #a-f   7.25 7.25
Souvenir Sheets
1301-1302 A214 $2 Set of 2   8.00 8.00

Dogs and Cats — A215

No. 1303, 60c: a, Airedale terrier. b, Beagle. c, Dalmatian. d, Chow chow. e, Chihuahua. f, Pug.
No. 1304, 80c: a, Egyptian mau. b, Manx. c, Burmese. d, Korat. e, Maine coon cat. f, American shorthair.
No. 1305, $2, Collie. No. 1306, $2, Devon rex.

2000, Nov. 13   Litho.   Perf. 14
    Sheets of 6, #a-f
1303-1304 A215   Set of 2   17.00 17.00
Souvenir Sheets
1305-1306 A215   Set of 2   8.00 8.00

Battle of Britain, 60th Anniv. A216

Designs: No. 1307, 50c, Douglas Robert Stewart Bader. No. 1308, 50c, Alan Christopher "Al" Deere. No. 1309, 50c, James Edgar "Johnny" Johnson. No. 1310, 50c, Edgar James "Cobber" Kain. No. 1311, 50c, James Harry "Ginger" Lacey. No. 1312, 50c, Air Vicemarshal Trafford Leigh. No. 1313, 50c, Adolph Gysbert "Sailor" Malan. No. 1314, Air Vicemarshal Keith Park.
No. 1315: a, Winston Churchill. b, Barrage balloon. c, Heinkel He-111 Casa 2 111E. d, Soldier's farewell kiss to son. e, Hawker Hurricane. f, Dr. Jocelyn Henry Temple Peakins, clergyman in Home Guard. g, RAF fighter pilots scramble after an alert. h, Civilian volunteers scan the skies.
No. 1316, $2, Churchill, British flag. No. 1317, $2, London children.

2000, Dec. 4   Perf. 14
    Stamps + labels
1307-1314 A216   Set of 8   8.00 8.00
1315 A216 50c Sheet of 8, #a-h   8.00 8.00
Souvenir Sheets
1316-1317 A216   Set of 2   8.00 8.00

Butterflies — A217

No. 1318, 50c: a, Clorinde. b, Blue night. c, Small lace-wing. d, Mosaic. e, Monarch. f, Grecian shoemaker.
No. 1319, 50c: a, Giant swallowtail. b, Common morpho. c, Tiger pierid. d, Banded king shoemaker. e, Figure-of-eight. f, Polydamas swallowtail.
No. 1320, $2, Orange-barred sulphur. No. 1321, $2, White peacock.

2000, Dec. 11   Litho.
    Sheets of 6, #a-f
1318-1319 A217   Set of 2   12.00 12.00
Souvenir Sheets
1320-1321 A217   Set of 2   8.00 8.00

Ships A218

Designs: No. 1322, 60c, Neptune. No. 1323, 60c, Eagle. No. 1324, 60c, Gloria. No. 1325, 60c, Clipper ship, vert.
No. 1326, 60c: a, Viking long ship. b, Henri Grace à Dieu. c, Golden Hind. d, Endeavor. e, Anglo-Norman. f, Libertad.
No. 1327, 60c: a, Northern European cog. b, Carrack. c, Mayflower. d, Queen Anne's Revenge. e, Holkar. f, Amerigo Vespucci.
No. 1328, $2, USS Constitution, vert. No. 1329, $2, Denmark, vert.

2001, May 15   Litho.   Perf. 14
1322-1325 A218   Set of 4   4.75 4.75
    Sheets of 6, #a-f
1326-1327 A218   Set of 2   14.50 14.50
Souvenir Sheets
1328-1329 A218   Set of 2   8.00 8.00

Whales A219

Designs: No. 1330, 50c, Beluga. No. 1331, 50c, Killer. No. 1332, 50c, Dwarf sperm. No. 1333, 50c, Shortfin pilot.
No. 1334, 50c: a, Bowhead. b, Two killer. c, Pygmy sperm. d, Right. e, Sperm. f, California gray.
No. 1335, 50c: a, Narwhal. b, One killer (in air). c, Bryde's. d, Belugas. e, Sperm (and starfish). f, Pilot.
No. 1336, $2, Cuvier's beaked. No. 1337, $2, Humpback (with calf).

2001, May 15
1330-1333 A219   Set of 4   4.00 4.00
    Sheets of 6, #a-f
1334-1335 A219   Set of 2   12.00 12.00
Souvenir Sheets
1336-1337 A219   Set of 2   8.00 8.00

UN Women's
Human Rights
Campaign — A220

Designs: 60c, Woman. 80c, Woman, bird, torch.

2001, June 18   Litho.   Perf. 14
1338-1339 A220   Set of 2   3.00 3.00

Phila Nippon
'01 — A221

Designs: No. 1340, 60c, Autumn Moon in Mirror, by Suzuki Harunobu. No. 1341, 60c, Rikaku II as a Fisherman, by Hirosada. No. 1342, 60c, Musical Party, by Hishikawa Moronobu. No. 1343, 60c, Kannon and Four Farmers, by H. Gatto. No. 1344, 60c, Rain in Fifth Month, by Kunisada I. No. 1345, 60c, The Lives of Women, by Kuniyoshi Utagawa.

2001, July 30   Perf. 12x12¼
1340-1345 A221   Set of 6   7.25 7.25

Queen Victoria (1819-1901) — A222

No. 1346, 60c, oval frames: a, Wearing white headcovering. b, Wearing crown as young woman. c, Wearing black hat. d, Wearing crown as old woman.
No. 1347, 60c, rectangular frames: a, Wearing white headcovering. b, Holding flowers. c, Wearing white dress. d, Wearing crown, white dress with blue sash.
No. 1348, $2, Brown orange background. No. 1349, $2, Holding umbrella.

2001, July 2   Perf. 14
Sheets of 4, #a-d
1346-1347 A222   Set of 2   9.75 9.75
Souvenir Sheets
1348-1349 A222   Set of 2   8.00 8.00

Queen Elizabeth II, 75th
Birthday — A223

No. 1350: a, In pink hat. b, With crown looking left. c, In green hat. d, With crown looking forward. e, In red orange hat. f, With crown and veil.
$2, Wearing robe.

2001, July 2
1350 A223 60c Sheet of 6, #a-f   7.25 7.25
Souvenir Sheet
1351 A223 $2 multi   4.00 4.00

Butterflies — A224

Designs: 10c, Cuban mimic. 15c, Gundlach's swallowtail, vert. 20c, Graphium androcles. 25c, Eastern black swallowtail. 35c, Papilio velvois, vert. 45c, Schaus swallowtail, vert. 50c, Pipevine swallowtail, vert. 60c, Euploea mniszecki, vert. 80c, Poey's black swallowtail, vert. $1, Graphium encelades, vert. $1.25, Jamaican ringlet. $1.40, Eastern tiger swallowtail. $2, Graphium milon, vert. $5, Palamedes swallowtail. $10, Zebra swallowtail.

Perf. 14x14¾, 14¾x14
2001, Sept. 27
1352 A224 10c multi   .20 .20
1353 A224 15c multi   .30 .30
1354 A224 20c multi   .40 .40
1355 A224 25c multi   .50 .50
1356 A224 35c multi   .70 .70
1357 A224 45c multi   .90 .90
1358 A224 50c multi   1.00 1.00
1359 A224 60c multi   1.25 1.25
1360 A224 80c multi   1.60 1.60
1361 A224 $1 multi   2.00 2.00
1362 A224 $1.25 multi   2.50 2.50
1363 A224 $1.40 multi   2.75 2.75
1364 A224 $2 multi   4.00 4.00
1365 A224 $5 multi   10.00 10.00
1366 A224 $10 multi   20.00 20.00
Nos. 1352-1366 (15)   48.10 48.10
25c, 35c, $5, $10 exist dated "2003."

Reign of Queen
Elizabeth II, 50th
Anniv. — A225

No. 1367: a, Crossing Place Trail, Middle Caicos. b, Wades Green Plantation, North Caicos. c, Underwater scenery, Grand Turk. d, St. Thomas Anglican Church, Grand Turk. e, Ripsaw band, Grand Turk. f, Basketweaving.
No. 1368: a, Visit of Princess Royal, 1960. b, Visit of Queen Elizabeth II, 1966. c, Visit of Princess Alexandra, 1988. d, Visit of Duke of Edinburgh, 1993. e, Visit of Prince Andrew, 2000.

No. 1369: a, Salt Industry, 1952-62. b, Space splashdown, 1962-72. c, Ministerial government system, 1972-82. d, Quincentennial of Columbus' landfall, 1982-92. e, National Museum, 1992-2002.

2002, June 1   Litho.   Perf. 14¼
1367   Sheet of 6   3.00 3.00
a.-f.   A225 25c Any single   .50 .50
Perf. 13¾
1368   Sheet of 5   6.25 6.25
a.-e.   A225 60c Any single   1.25 1.25
Perf. 13¾x14¼
1369   Sheet of 5   8.00 8.00
a.-e   A225 80c Any single   1.60 1.60
No. 1368 contains five 31x31mm stamps; No. 1369 contains five 30x34mm stamps.

20th World Scout Jamboree,
Thailand — A226

No. 1370: a, Scout with mallet and chisel. b, Scout with rifle. c, Scout hanging on rope above water. d, Scouts and lantern.
$2, Handicapped Scouts.

2002, July 15   Perf. 14
1370 A226 80c Sheet of 4, #a-d   6.50 6.50
Souvenir Sheet
1371 A226 $2 multi   4.00 4.00

Intl. Year of Ecotourism — A227

No. 1372, vert.: a, Humpback whale. b, Water sports. c, Regattas. d, Queen angelfish. e, Manta ray. f, Turtle.
$2, Jojo dolphin.

2002, July 15
1372 A227 60c Sheet of 6, #a-f   7.25 7.25
Souvenir Sheet
1373 A227 $2 multi   4.00 4.00
No. 1372 contains six 28x42mm stamps.

Intl. Year of Mountains — A228

No. 1374: a, Devil's Peak, South Africa. b, Mt. Drakensburg, South Africa. c, Mt. Blanc, France. d, Roan Mountain, US. e, Mt. Sefton, New Zealand. f, Mt. Cook, New Zealand.
$2, Northwest Highlands, Scotland.

2002, July 22
1374 A228 80c Sheet of 6, #a-f   9.75 9.75
Souvenir Sheet
1375 A228 $2 multi   4.00 4.00

United We
Stand — A229

2002, Aug. 5
1376 A229 50c multi   1.00 1.00
Printed in sheets of 4.

Insects and Birds — A230

No. 1377, 60c: a, Hawk moth. b, Burnet moth. c, Mammoth wasp. d, Branch-boring beetle. e, Flower mantid, Pseudocrebotra species. f, Flower mantid, Creobroter species.
No. 1378, 60c: a, Sooty tern. b, Magnificent frigatebird. c, American white pelican. d, Northern shoveler. e, Baltimore oriole. f, Roseate spoonbill.
No. 1379, $2, Tiphiid wasp. No. 1380, $2, Greater flamingo, vert.

2002, Aug. 12   Perf. 14
Sheets of 6, #a-f
1377-1378 A230   Set of 2   14.50 14.50
Souvenir Sheets
1379-1380 A230   Set of 2   8.00 8.00

Queen Mother Elizabeth (1900-
2002) — A231

No. 1381: a, Without hat. b, With hat.

2002, Oct. 21
1381 A231 80c Sheet, 2 each #a-
    b   6.50 6.50

First Nonstop Solo Transatlantic Flight, 75th Anniv. — A232

No. 1382: a, Charles Lindbergh's early exploits as a barnstormer. b, Lindbergh standing in front of Spirit of St. Louis. c, Spirit of St. Louis. d, Take-off from Roosevelt Field. e, Crossing the Atlantic. f, Arrival and welcome in Paris.

2002, Nov. 18   Litho.   Perf. 14
1382 A232 60c Sheet of 6, #a-f   7.25 7.25

Pres. John F. Kennedy (1917-63) — A233

No. 1383 - Portrait color: a, Orange brown. b, Red violet. c, Greenish gray. d, Blue violet. e, Purple. f, Dull brown.

2002, Nov. 18
1383 A233 60c multi   7.25 7.25

Christmas A234

Designs: 20c, Madonna and Child, by Giovanni Bellini, vert. 25c, Adoration of the Magi, by Correggio. 60c, Transfiguration of Christ, by Bellini, vert. 80c, Polyptych of St. Vincent Ferrer, by Bellini, vert. $1, Miraculous Mass, by Simone Martini, vert.
$2, Christ in Heaven with Four Saints, by Domenico Ghirlandaio.

2002, Nov. 25
1384-1388 A234   Set of 5   5.75 5.75
Souvenir Sheet
1389 A234 $2 multi   4.00 4.00

Japanese Art — A235

Designs: 25c, Nagata no Taro Nagamune, by Kuniyoshi Utagawa. 35c, Danjuro Ichikawa VII, by Kunisada Utagawa. 60c, Nagata no Taro Nagamune, by Kuniyoshi Utagawa, diff. $1, Nagata no Taro Nagamune, by Kuniyoshi Utagawa, diff.

No. 1394 - Scroll of Actors, by Chikanobu Toyohara and others: a, Smiling man holding fan. b, Man holding sword at mouth. c, Man holding sword vertically. d, Man with tree branch above head.
$2, Two Women by a River, by Chikanobu Hashimoto.

2003, June 17   Litho.   Perf. 14¼
1390-1393 A235   Set of 4   4.50 4.50
1394 A235 80c Sheet of 4, #a-d   6.50 6.50
Souvenir Sheet
1395 A235 $2 multi   4.00 4.00

Rembrandt Paintings A236

Designs: 25c, Portrait of a Young Man Resting His Chin on His Hand. 50c, A Woman at an Open Door. No. 1398, $1, The Return of the Prodigal Son. No. 1399, $1, Portrait of an Elderly Man.
No. 1400: a, Nicolaas van Bambeeck. b, Agatha Bas, Wife of Nicolaas van Bambeeck. c, Portrait of a Man Holding His Hat. d, Saskia in a Red Hat.
$2, Christ Driving the Money Changers from the Temple.

Perf. 14¼, 13¼ (#1400)
2003, June 17
1396-1399 A236   Set of 4   5.50 5.50
1400 A236 60c Sheet of 4, #a-d   5.00 5.00
Souvenir Sheet
1401 A236 $2 multi   4.00 4.00

Paintings by Joan Miró — A237

Designs: 25c, Portrait of a Young Girl. 50c, Table with Glove. 60c, Self-portrait, 1917. $1, The Farmer's Wife.
No. 1406: a, Portrait of Ramon Sunyer. b, Self-portrait, 1919. c, Portrait of a Spanish Dancer. d, Portrait of Joana Obrador.
No. 1407, Flowers and Butterfly. No. 1408, Still Life of the Coffee Grinder, horiz.

2003, June 17   Perf. 14¼
1402-1405 A237   Set of 4   4.75 4.75
1406 A237 80c Sheet of 4, #a-d   6.50 6.50
Imperf
Size: 104x83mm
1407 A237 $2 multi   4.00 4.00
Size: 83x104mm
1408 A237 $2 multi   4.00 4.00

Caribbean Community, 30th Anniv. — A238

2003, July 4   Perf. 14
1409 A238 60c multi   1.25 1.25

Tanya Streeter, World Champion Freediver — A239

No. 1410: a, Wearing wetsuit in water. b, Diving underwater, portrait. c, Wearing bathing suit at shore. d, Standing in front of map. e, Holding on to diving apparatus.

2003, July 15
1410 A239 20c Sheet of 5, #a-e   2.00 2.00

Coronation of Queen Elizabeth II, 50th Anniv. — A240

No. 1411: a, Wearing crown and white robe. b, Wearing lilac dress. c, Wearing tiara and red dress.
$2, Wearing hat and blue cape. $5, Profile portrait.

2003, Aug. 25
1411 A240 80c Sheet of 3, #a-c   5.00 5.00
Souvenir Sheets
1412-1413 A240   Set of 2   14.00 14.00

Prince William, 21st Birthday — A241

No. 1414: a, Portrait in blue. b, Pink background. c, Purple background.
$2, Dark blue background.

2003, Aug. 25
1414 A241 $1 Sheet of 3, #a-c   6.00 6.00
Souvenir Sheet
1415 A241 $2 multi   4.00 4.00

Tour de France Bicycle Race, Cent. — A242

No. 1416: a, Eddy Merckx, 1974. b, Bernard Thévenet, 1975. c, Lucien Van Impe, 1976. d, Thévenet, 1977.
$2, Bernard Hinault, 1979.

2003, Aug. 25   Perf. 13¾x14¼
1416 A242 $1 Sheet of 4, #a-d   8.00 8.00
Souvenir Sheet
1417 A242 $2 multi   4.00 4.00

Powered Flight, Cent. — A243

No. 1418: a, Vought F4U Corsair. b, Messerschmidt Me 262. c, A6M. d, Hawker Hurricane.
$2, Supermarine Spitfire Mk IX.

2003, Aug. 25   Perf. 14
1418 A243 60c Sheet of 4, #a-d   5.00 5.00
Souvenir Sheet
1419 A243 $2 multi   4.00 4.00

German Teddy Bears — A244

No. 1420, vert.: a, Bear with red and yellow uniform. b, Bear with dress. c, Bear with violin case. d, Bear with sword.
$2, Bear on beer mug.

2003, Aug. 25   **Perf. 12x12¼**
1420 A244 50c Sheet of 4, #a-d   4.00 4.00

Souvenir Sheet
Perf. 12¼x12
1421 A244 $2 multi   4.00 4.00

Butterflies
A245

Designs: 50c, Papilio thersites. 60c, Papilio andraemon. 80c, Papilio pelaus. $1, Consul hippona.
$2, Papilio pelaus, diff.

2003, Nov. 17   **Perf. 14**
1422-1425 A245   Set of 4   6.00 6.00

Souvenir Sheet
1426 A245 $2 multi   4.00 4.00

Orchids
A246

Designs: 50c, Laelia anceps. 60c, Laelia briegeri. 80c, Laelia fidelensis. $1, Laelia cinnabarina.
$2, Laelia rubescens.

2003, Nov. 17
1427-1430 A246   Set of 4   6.00 6.00

Souvenir Sheet
1431 A246 $2 multi   4.00 4.00

Dogs
A247

Designs: 50c, Beagle. 60c, Sabueso Espanol, vert. 80c, Basset hound, vert. $1, Jack Russell terrier, vert.
$2, Dachshund.

2003, Nov. 17
1432-1435 A247   Set of 4   6.00 6.00

Souvenir Sheet
1436 A247 $2 multi   4.00 4.00

Cats
A248

Designs: 50c, Persian. 60c, Cymric. 80c, Main Coon, vert. $1, Tiffany.
$2, Kurile Island bobtail.

2003, Nov. 17
1437-1440 A248   Set of 4   6.00 6.00

Souvenir Sheet
1441 A248 $2 multi   4.00 4.00

Christmas
A249

Paintings: 25c, Madonna of the Harpies, by Andrea del Sarto. 60c, Madonna and Child with St. John, by del Sarto. 80c, Madonna and Child with St. Joseph and St. Peter Martyr, by del Sarto. $1, Madonna and Child with the Angels, by del Sarto.
$2, Montefeltro Altarpiece, by Piero della Francesca.

2003, Nov. 24   **Perf. 14¼**
1442-1445 A249   Set of 4   5.50 5.50

Souvenir Sheet
1446 A249 $2 multi   4.00 4.00

WAR TAX STAMPS

Regular Issue of 1913-16 Overprinted

1917   **Wmk. 3**   **Perf. 14**
Black Overprint at Bottom of Stamp
MR1 A10 1p carmine   .20 .30
   a. Double overprint   150.00
   b. "TAX" omitted
   c. Pair, one without ovpt.
MR2 A10 3p violet, yel   .70 .70
   a. Double overprint   90.00

Black Overprint at Top or Middle of Stamp
1917
MR3 A10 1p carmine   .20 .20
   a. Inverted overprint   25.00
   b. Double overprint   37.50 16.00
   c. Pair, one without overprint   200.00
MR4 A10 3p violet, yel   .50 .85
   a. Double overprint   17.50
   b. Dbl. ovpt., one inverted   37.50

Same Overprint in Violet or Red
1918-19
MR5 A10 1p car (V) ('19)   .20 .25
   a. Double overprint   14.00
   b. "WAR" omitted   100.00
MR6 A10 3p violet, yel (R)   6.75 6.75
   a. Double overprint   75.00

Regular Issue of 1913-16 Overprinted in Black

1918
MR7 A10 1p carmine   .20 .20
MR8 A10 3p violet, yel   .25 .50

Same Overprint in Red
1919
MR9 A10 3p violet, yel   .20 .25

Regular Issue of 1913-16 Overprinted in Black

MR10 A10 1p carmine   .20 .20
   a. Double overprint   100.00 100.00
MR11 A10 3p violet, yel   .25 .35

W·A·R

TAX

Regular Issue of 1913-16 Overprinted

MR12 A10 1p carmine   .20 .20
   a. Double overprint   100.00
MR13 A10 3p violet, yel   .20 .40

CAICOS

Catalogue values for all unused stamps in this country are for Never Hinged items.

Turks & Caicos Nos. 360, 364, 366, 369, 371-373 Ovptd. with Black Bar and "CAICOS ISLANDS"

Unwmk.
1981, July 24   **Litho.**   **Perf. 14**
1 A69 1c Indigo hamlet   .20 .20
2 A69 5c Spanish grunt   .20 .20
3 A69 8c Foureye butterfly-
     lyfish   .20 .20
4 A69 20c Queen angelfish   .40 .40
5 A69 50c Fairy basslet   .95 .95
6 A69 $1 Clown wrasse   1.90 1.90
7 A69 $2 Stoplight parrotfish   3.75 3.75
   Nos. 1-7 (7)   7.60 7.60

Common Design Types pictured following the introduction.

Royal Wedding Issue
Common Design Type
Turks & Caicos Nos. 486-489 Ovptd. with Black Bar and "Caicos Islands"
1981, July 24
8 CD331 35c Charles & Di-
     ana   .85 .85
9 CD331 65c Kensington Pal-
     ace   1.60 1.60
10 CD331 90c Prince Charles   2.25 2.25
   Nos. 8-10 (3)   4.70 4.70

Souvenir Sheet
11 CD331 $2 Glass coach   17.50 17.50

Roulette x Imperf. (#12a), Imperf. (#12b)
1981, Oct. 29
Self-Adhesive
12   Souvenir booklet   27.50
   a. A88a Pane, 3 each 20c, Diana, $1, Charles)   15.00
   b. A88a Pane of 1 $2, Couple   10.00

Nos. 8-11 exist with overprint in all capital letters, value about five times above. Nos. 8-10, in both overprint types, also exist in sheets of 5 plus label in changed colors, perf. 12.

Hawksbill turtle
C1

1983-84   **Perf. 14**
13 C1 8c Diver with lobster and conch shell   .20 .20
14 C1 10c shown   .20 .20
15 C1 20c Stone idol, Ara-
     wak Indians   .40 .40
16 C1 35c Sloop construc-
     tion   .70 .70
17 C1 50c Marine biology   1.00 1.00
18 C1 95c 707 Jetliner   1.90 1.90
19 C1 $1.10 15th cent. Span-
     ish ship   2.25 2.25
20 C1 $2 British soldier, Fort St. George   4.00 4.00

---

21 C1 $3 Pirates Anne Bon-
     ny, Calico Jack   6.00 6.00
   Nos. 13-21 (9)   16.65 16.65
Issued: #13-19, 6/6/83; #20-21, 5/18/84.
For overprints see Nos. 47-49.

Christmas Type of Turks and Caicos
Walt Disney characters in Santa Claus is Coming to Town.

1983, Nov. 7   **Perf. 11**
22 A104 1c Chip 'n Dale   .20 .20
23 A104 1c Goofy & Patch   .20 .20
24 A104 2c Morty, Ferdie & Pluto   .20 .20
25 A104 2c Morty   .20 .20
26 A104 3c Donald, Huey, Dewey & Louie   .20 .20
27 A104 3c Goofy & Louie   .20 .20
28 A104 50c Uncle Scrooge   1.25 1.25
29 A104 70c Mickey Mouse & Ferdie   1.75 1.75
30 A104 $1.10 Pinocchio, Jiminy Cricket and Figaro   2.50 2.50
   Nos. 22-30 (9)   6.70 6.70

Souvenir Sheet
Perf. 13½x14
31 A104 $2 Morty & Ferdie, fire-
     place   6.00 6.00

Drawings by Raphael — C2   1984 Summer Olympics, Los Angeles — C3

Designs: 35c, Leda and the Swan. 50c, Study of Apollo for Parnassus. 95c, Study of two figures for The Battle of Ostia. $1.10, Study for the Madonna of the Goldfinch. $2.50, The Garvagh Madonna.

1983, Dec. 15   **Perf. 14**
32 C2 35c multicolored   .70 .70
33 C2 50c multicolored   1.00 1.00
34 C2 95c multicolored   1.90 1.90
35 C2 $1.10 multicolored   2.25 2.25
   Nos. 32-35 (4)   5.85 5.85

Souvenir Sheet
36 C2 $2.50 multicolored   5.00 5.00

500th birth anniv. of Raphael.

1984, Mar. 1
37 C3 4c High jump   .20 .20
38 C3 25c Archery   .50 .50
39 C3 65c Cycling   1.25 1.25
40 C3 $1.10 Soccer   2.25 2.25
   Nos. 37-40 (4)   4.20 4.20

Souvenir Sheet
41 C3 $2 Show jumping, horiz.   4.00 4.00

Easter — C4

Walt Disney characters: 35c, Horace Horsecollar, Clarabelle Cow. 45c, Mickey, Minnie & Chip. 75c, Gyro Gearloose, Chip 'n Dale. 85c, Mickey, Chip 'n Dale. $2.20, Donald sailing with nephews.

1984, Apr. 15   **Perf. 14x13½**
42 C4 35c multicolored   .70 .70
43 C4 45c multicolored   .90 .90
44 C4 75c multicolored   1.50 1.50
45 C4 85c multicolored   1.75 1.75
   Nos. 42-45 (4)   4.85 4.85

Souvenir Sheet
46 C4 $2.20 mulitcolored   4.75 4.75

Nos. 18-19 Ovptd. with emblem and "Universal Postal Union 1874-1984"

1984, June 19   *Perf. 14*
47	C1	95c multicolored	1.90	1.90
48	C1	$1.10 multicolored	2.25	2.25

No. 20 Ovptd. "AUSIPEX 1984"

1984, Aug. 22
49	C1	$2 multicolored	4.00	4.00

Columbus' First Landfall — C5

1984, Sept. 21
50	C5	10c Sighting manatees	.20	.20
51	C5	70c Fleet	1.40	1.40
52	C5	$1 West Indies landing	2.00	2.00
		Nos. 50-52 (3)	3.60	3.60

Souvenir Sheet
53	C5	$2 Fleet, map	4.00	4.00

Columbus' first landing, 492nd anniv.

Christmas
C6

Walt Disney characters: 20c, Santa Claus, Donald and Mickey. 35c, Donald at refrigerator. 50c, Donald, Micky riding toy train. 75c, Donald carrying presents. $1.10, Huey, Louie, Dewey and Donald singing carols. $2, Donald as Christmas tree.

Perf. 13½x14, 12x12½ (75c)

1984, Nov. 26
54	C6	20c multicolored	.50	.50
55	C6	35c multicolored	.85	.85
56	C6	50c multicolored	1.25	1.25
57	C6	75c multicolored	1.75	1.75
58	C6	$1.10 multicolored	2.75	2.75
		Nos. 54-58 (5)	7.10	7.10

Souvenir Sheet

Perf. 13½x14
59	C6	$2 multicolored	4.50	4.50

No. 57 printed in sheets of 8.

Audubon Birth Bicentenary — C7

1985, Feb. 12   *Perf. 14*
60	C7	20c Thick-billed vireo	.40	.40
61	C7	35c Black-faced grassquit	.70	.70
62	C7	50c Pearly-eyed thrasher	1.00	1.00
63	C7	$1 Greater Antillean bullfinch	2.00	2.00
		Nos. 60-63 (4)	4.10	4.10

Souvenir Sheet
64	C7	$2 Stripe-headed tanagers	4.00	4.00

No. 64 exists imperf.

Intl. Youth Year — C8

1985, May 8
65	C8	16c Education	.30	.30
66	C8	35c Health	.70	.70
67	C8	70c Love	1.40	1.40
68	C8	90c Peace	1.75	1.75
		Nos. 65-68 (4)	4.15	4.15

Souvenir Sheet
69	C8	$2 Peace dove, child	4.00	4.00

UN 40th anniv.

Intl. Civil Aviation Org., 40th Anniv.
C9

1985, May 26
70	C9	35c DC-3	.70	.70
71	C9	75c Convair 440	1.50	1.50
72	C9	90c TCNA Islander	1.75	1.75
		Nos. 70-72 (3)	3.95	3.95

Souvenir Sheet
73	C9	$2.20 Hang glider	4.50	4.50

Queen Mother, 85th Birthday Type of Turks & Caicos

1985, July 7
74	A117	35c Wearing green hat	.70	.70
75	A117	65c With Princess Anne, horiz.	1.25	1.25
76	A117	95c Wearing white hat	1.90	1.90
		Nos. 74-76 (3)	3.85	3.85

Souvenir Sheet
77	A117	$2 Inspecting guardsmen	4.00	4.00

Mark Twain, 150th Birth Anniv. — C10

Walt Disney characters in Tom Sawyer, Detective (Intl. Youth Year): 8c, Mickey and Goofy as Tom and Huck reading reward poster. 35c, Meeting Jake Dunlap. 95c, Spying on Jubiter Dunlap. $1.10, With Pluto finding body. No. 86, Unmasking Jubiter Dunlap.

Walt Disney characters portraying Six Soldiers of Fortune (The Brothers Grimm, Bicent.): 16c, Donald receiving his meager pay. 25c, Donald meets Horace Horsecollar as strong man. 65c, Donald meets Mickey the marksman. $1.35, Goofy wins footrace against Princess Daisy. No. 87, Soldiers with sack of gold.

1985, Dec. 5   *Perf. 14x13½*
78	C10	8c multicolored	.20	.20
79	C10	16c multicolored	.30	.30
80	C10	25c multicolored	.50	.50
81	C10	35c multicolored	.70	.70
82	C10	65c multicolored	1.25	1.25
83	C10	95c multicolored	1.90	1.90
84	C10	$1.10 multicolored	2.25	2.25
85	C10	$1.35 multicolored	2.75	2.75
		Nos. 78-85 (8)	9.85	9.85

Souvenir Sheet
86	C10	$2 multicolored	4.50	4.50
87	C10	$2 multicolored	4.50	4.50

Stamps are no longer being produced for Caicos.

TURKS ISLANDS

'tərks 'i-lənds

LOCATION — West Indies, at the southern extremity of the Bahamas
GOVT. — Former dependency of Jamaica
POP. — 2,000 (approx.)
CAPITAL — Grand Turk

In 1848 the Turks Islands together with the Caicos group, lying to the northwest, were made a British colony. In 1873 the Colony became a dependency under the government of Jamaica although separate stamp issues were continued. Postage stamps inscribed Turks and Caicos Islands have been used since 1900.

12 Pence = 1 Shilling

Values for unused stamps are for examples with original gum as defined in the catalogue introduction. Very fine examples of Nos. 1-42 will have generally rough perforations that cut into the design on one or more sides due to the narrow spacing of the stamps on the plates and imperfect perforating methods. Stamps with perfs clear of the design on all four sides are extremely scarce and will command substantially higher prices.

Because of the printing and imperfect perforating methods, stamps are often found scissor separated. Prices will not be adversely affected on those stamps where the scissor cut does not remove the perforations.

Watermark

Wmk. 5 — Small Star

Queen Victoria — A1

Perf. 11½ to 13

1867   Unwmk.   Engr.
1	A1	1p rose	45.00	45.00
2	A1	6p gray black	80.00	90.00
3	A1	1sh slate blue	80.00	60.00
		Nos. 1-3 (3)	205.00	195.00

Perf. 11 to 13x14 to 15

1873-79   Wmk. 5
4	A1	1p lake	45.00	40.00
5	A1	1p dull red ('79)	50.00	60.00
a.		Horiz. pair, imperf. btwn.	12,500.	
b.		Perf. 11-12	1,000.	
6	A1	1sh violet	4,500.	2,000.

Stamps offered as No. 6 are often copies from which the surcharge has been removed.

Stamps of 1867-79 Surcharged in Black:

a   b

c

---

d   e

12 settings of the ½p, 9 of 2½p, and 6 of 4p

1881   Unwmk.   *Perf. 11 to 1*
7	(a)	½p on 6p gray blk	70.00	110.0
7A	(b)	½p on 6p gray blk	60.00	90.0
8	(b)	½p on 1sh slate bl	80.00	140.0
a.		Double surcharge	4,500.	
8B	(c)	½p on 1sh slate bl	11,000.	
c.		Without fraction bar		

Perf. 11 to 13x14 to 15
Wmk. 5
9	(a)	½p on 1p dull red	150.00	200.0
a.		Double surcharge		
10	(b)	½p on 1p dull red	55.00	90.0
11	(c)	½p on 1p dull red	50.00	90.0
a.		Double surcharge	3,000.	
12	(d)	½p on 1p dull red	200.00	
a.		Without fraction bar	1,000.	
b.		Double surcharge		
13	(e)	½p on 1p dull red	500.00	
14	(a)	½p on 1sh violet	140.00	200.0
a.		Double surcharge	4,000.	
15	(b)	½p on 1sh violet	125.00	175.0
a.		Without fraction bar	550.00	
16	(c)	½p on 1sh violet	80.00	140.0

(2½ figures) f g h

Perf. 11 to 13
Unwmk.
17	(f)	2½p on 6p gray blk	7,500.
18	(g)	2½p on 6p gray blk	325.00	350.0
a.		Horiz. pair, imperf. between	9,500.	
b.		Double surcharge	4,500.	
19	(h)	2½p on 6p gray blk	150.00	200.0

(2½ figures) i j

Perf. 11 to 13x14 to 15
Wmk. 5
20	(i)	2½p on 1sh violet	1,750.
21	(h)	2½p on 1sh violet	575.00	750.0
22	(j)	2½p on 1sh violet	6,500.

(2½ figures) k l

(2½ figures) m n

Perf. 11 to 13
Unwmk.
24	(k)	2½p on 6p gray blk	8,250.
25	(k)	2½p on 1sh slate bl	10,000.
26	(l)	2½p on 1sh slate bl	650.00
27	(m)	2½p on 1sh slate bl	1,750.
a.		Without fraction bar	4,500.	
28	(n)	2½p on 1sh slate bl	6,500.

(2½ figure) o

Perf. 11 to 13x14 to 15
Wmk. 5
29	(l)	2½p on 1p dull red	550.00
30	(o)	2½p on 1p dull red	1,000.
31	(l)	2½p on 1sh violet	500.00
a.		Double surcharge of "½"	4,000.	
32	(o)	2½p on 1sh violet	1,250.
b.		Double surcharge of "½"	5,750.	

1 d.
2

No. 50 Surcharged
in Black

p   q

r

Perf. 11 to 13
Unwmk.

33	(p) 4p on 6p gray black	65.	75.
34	(q) 4p on 6p gray black	350.00	375.00
35	(r) 4p on 6p gray black	275.00	325.00

Copies of No. 33 with top of "4" painted in
are sometimes offered as No. 35.

Perf. 11 to 13x14 to 15
Wmk. 5

36	(r) 4p on 1p dull red	750.00	450.00
a.	Inverted surcharge	3,000.	
37	(r) 4p on 1p dull red	575.00	450.00
a.	Inverted surcharge		
38	(p) 4p on 1sh violet	425.00	425.00
39	(q) 4p on 1sh violet	2,750.	

Wmk. Crown and C C (1)
		Engr.	**Perf. 14**
40	A1	1p brown red	55.00 65.00
a.	Diagonal half used as ½p on cover		
41	A1	6p olive brown	80.00 100.00
42	A1	1sh slate green	110.00 100.00
		Nos. 40-42 (3)	245.00 265.00

A2

A3

1881   Typo.
43	A2	4p ultramarine	90.00 60.00

1882-95   Engr.   Wmk. 2
44	A1	1p orange brn ('83)	55.00 30.00
a.	Half used as ½p on cover		3,750.
45	A1	1p car lake ('89)	1.75 2.25
46	A1	6p yellow brn ('89)	2.25 3.00
47	A1	1sh black brn ('87)	3.50 3.00
a.	1sh deep brown		3.50 3.00

Typo.
Die A
48	A2	½p gray green ('85)	2.00 3.50
a.	½p blue green ('82)		7.50 12.00
49	A2	2½p red brown ('82)	13.00 12.00
50	A2	4p gray ('84)	9.00 2.25
a.	Half used as 2p on cover		1,500.

Die B
51	A2	½p green ('94)	1.50 1.25
52	A2	2½p ultra ('93)	1.25 .90
53	A2	4p dk vio & bl ('95)	7.00 10.00

For explanation of dies A and B see back of
this volume.

1887   Engr.   Perf. 12
54	A1	1p carmine lake	9.00 3.00

No. 49 Surcharged in
Black

1889
55	A2	1p on 2½p red brown	6.00 7.50
a.	Double surcharge		
b.	Double surcharge, one inverted		
c.	"One" omitted		1,600.
d.	Half used as ½p on cover		5,000.

No. 55c caused by the misplacement of the
surcharge. Stamps also exist from the same
sheet reading "Penny One."

No. 50 Surcharged
in Black

Two types of surcharge:
Type I - Upper bar continuous across sheet.
Type II - Upper bar breaks between stamps.

1893
56	A2	½p on 4p gray (I)	140.00 125.00
a.	Type II		2,000. 850.00

This surcharge exists in five settings.

1894   Typo.
57	A3	5p olive grn & carmine	3.00 10.00
a.	Diag. half used as 2½p on cover		3,000.

TUVALU

tü-Vä-͵ü

LOCATION — A group of islands in the
Pacific Ocean northeast of Australia.
GOVT. — Independent state in the
British Commonwealth
AREA — 9½ sq. mi.
POP. — 10,588 (1999 est.)
CAPITAL — Funafuti

Tuvalu, formerly Ellice Islands, consists of nine islands.

Australian dollar

> **Catalogue values for all unused
> stamps in this country are for
> Never Hinged items.**

Watermark

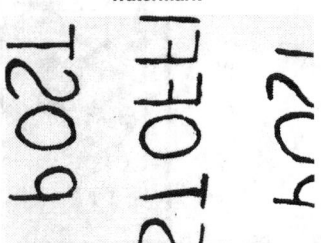

Wmk. 380 — "POST OFFICE"

Gilbert and Ellice Islands Types of
1971
Overprinted "TUVALU" and Bar
in Violet Blue or Silver (35c)
Wmk. 373

1976, Jan. 1		Litho.	Perf. 14
1	A18	1c	.85 .60
2	A19	2c	1.10 .85
a.	Wmk. 314 sideways		160.00 25.00
b.	Wmk. 314 upright		1,000. 140.00
3	A19	3c Wmk. 314	1.75 1.25
a.	Wmk. 373		.55 .55
4	A19	4c	1.10 .90
5	A19	5c Wmk. 314	1.10 1.25
6	A18	6c	1.10 .85
7	A18	8c Wmk. 314	1.10 1.25
8	A18	10c Wmk. 314	1.10 1.60
9	A18	15c	1.75 1.00
10	A19	20c	1.10 1.25
11	A19	25c Wmk. 314	7.25 3.50
a.	Wmk. 373		.60 .75
12	A19	35c	1.75 1.40
13	A18	50c	1.10 1.25
a.	Wmk. 314		32.50 22.50
14	A18	$1	1.10 1.60
a.	Wmk. 314		77.50 70.00
15	A18	$2	1.40 1.60
		Nos. 1-15 (15)	24.65 20.15

Men from Gilbert and Ellice — A1

Designs: 10c, Map of Gilbert and Ellice
Islands, vert. 35c, Gilbert and Ellice canoes.

1976, Jan. 1			Wmk. 373
16	A1	4c multicolored	.40 .50
17	A1	10c multicolored	.55 .60
18	A1	35c multicolored	.80 .90
		Nos. 16-18 (3)	1.75 2.00

Separation of the Gilbert and Ellice Islands.

50c Coin and
Octopus — A2

New coinage: 10c, 10c-coin and red-dyed
crab. 15c, 20c-coin and flyingfish. 35c, $1-coin
and green turtle.

		Wmk. 373	
1976, Apr. 21		Litho.	Perf. 14
19	A2	5c bister & multi	.20 .20
20	A2	10c ultra & multi	.55 .40
21	A2	15c blue & multi	.85 .50
22	A2	35c lt green & multi	1.40 .90
		Nos. 19-22 (4)	3.00 2.00

Map of Niulakita,
Leathery
Turtle — A3

Te
Ano
Game
A4

2c, Map of Nukulaelae and sleeping mat.
4c, Map of Nui and talo vegetable. 5c, Map of
Nanumanga and grass dancing skirt. 6c, Map
of Nukufetau and coconut crab. 8c, Map of
Funafuti and banana tree. 10c, Map of Tuvalu
Islands. 15c, Map of Niutao and flyingfish. 20c,
Map of Vaitupu and maneapa (house). 25c,
Map of Nanumea and palu fish hook. 50c,
Canoe pole fishing. $1, Reef fishing by flare.
$2, House. $5, Colony Ship M.V. Nivanga.

1976		Wmk. 373 Litho.	Perf. 13½
23-37	A3	Set of 15	27.50 18.00

Issue dates: $5, Sept. 1; others July 1.
See #58-70. For overprints see #85-91.

New
Testament
A5

Designs: 20c, Lotolelei Church, Nanumea.
25c, Kelupi Church, Nui. 30c, Mataloa o
Tuvalu Church, Vaitupu. 35c, Palataiso o
Keliso Church, Nanumanga.

Perf. 14x14½
1976, Oct. 6		Litho.	Wmk. 373
38-42	A5	Set of 5	2.50 2.00

Christmas 1976. Printed in sheets of 10
stamps and 2 labels.

Prince Philip Carried Ashore at
Vaitupu — A6

Designs: 15c, Queen and Prince Philip on
Buckingham Palace balcony. 50c, Queen
Leaving Buckingham Palace for coronation.

1977, Feb. 9		Litho.	Perf. 13½x14
43	A6	15c multicolored	.70 .60
44	A6	35c multicolored	.90 1.00
45	A6	50c multicolored	1.40 1.40
a.	Souv. sheet, #43-45, perf. 15		2.00 2.50
		Nos. 43-45 (3)	3.00 3.00

25th anniv. of the reign of Elizabeth II.

Health (Microscope) — A7

20c, Education (blackboard). 30c, Fruit
growing (palm). 35c, Map of South Pacific
Territory.

1977, May 4		Litho.	Perf. 13½x14
46	A7	5c lilac & multi	.45 .35
47	A7	20c orange & multi	.45 .35
48	A7	30c yellow grn & multi	.45 .35
49	A7	35c lt blue & multi	.65 .45
		Nos. 46-49 (4)	2.00 1.50

South Pacific Commission, 30th anniv.

Swearing-in Ceremony and Scout
Emblem — A8

Designs (Scout Emblem and): 20c, Scouts
in outrigger canoe. 30c, Scouts under sun
shelter. 35c, Lord Baden-Powell.

Perf. 13½x14
1977, Aug. 10		Litho.	Wmk. 373
50	A8	5c multicolored	.20 .20
51	A8	20c multicolored	.20 .20
52	A8	30c multicolored	.30 .30
53	A8	35c multicolored	.30 .30
		Nos. 50-53 (4)	1.00 1.00

Scouting in Tuvalu (Ellice Islands), 50th
anniv.

Hurricane Beach and Coral — A9

Designs: 20c, Boring apparatus on "Porpoise," vert. 30c, Map of islands showing line
of dredgings to prove Darwin's theory, vert.
35c, Charles Darwin and "Beagle."

Perf. 13½
1977, Nov. 2		Unwmk.	Litho.
54	A9	5c multicolored	.35 .35
55	A9	20c multicolored	.35 .35
56	A9	30c multicolored	.50 .40
57	A9	35c multicolored	.50 .40
		Nos. 54-57 (4)	1.70 1.50

1896-97 Royal Soc. of London Expeditions
to explore coral reefs by dredging and boring.

Types of 1976

Designs: 30c, Fatele, local dance. 40c, Screw pine. Others as before.

1977-78 Unwmk. Perf. 13½
58	A3	1c multicolored	.20	.20
59	A3	2c multicolored	.20	.20
60	A3	4c multicolored	.20	.20
61	A3	5c multicolored	.20	.20
62	A3	6c multicolored	.20	.20
63	A3	8c multicolored	.20	.20
64	A3	10c multicolored	.20	.20
66	A3	20c multicolored	1.50	1.00
67	A3	25c multicolored	1.00	.35
68	A4	30c multicolored	.40	.40
69	A4	40c multicolored	.55	.55
70	A4	$5 multicolored	4.00	4.00
		Nos. 58-70 (12)	8.85	7.70

Issued: #58, 61, 63-64, 67, 1977; others, 1978.

Pacific Pigeon — A10

Wild Birds of Tuvalu: 20c, Reef heron. 30c, Fairy tern. 40c, Lesser frigate bird.

Perf. 14x13½
1978, Jan. 25 Litho. Unwmk.
73	A10	8c lilac & multi	.45	.25
74	A10	20c ocher & multi	.60	.40
75	A10	30c dull green & multi	.70	.50
76	A10	40c brt green & multi	.75	.60
		Nos. 73-76 (4)	2.50	1.75

Lawedua — A11

Ships: 20c, Tug Wallacia. 30c, Freighter Cenpac Rounder. 40c, Pacific Explorer.

1978, Apr. 5 Unwmk. Perf. 13½x14
77	A11	8c multicolored	.20	.20
78	A11	20c multicolored	.30	.30
79	A11	30c multicolored	.50	.40
80	A11	40c multicolored	.60	.55
		Nos. 77-80 (4)	1.60	1.45

Canterbury Cathedral — A12

Designs: 30c, Salisbury Cathedral. 40c, Wells Cathedral. $1, Hereford Cathedral.

1978, June 2 Litho. Perf. 13½x14
81	A12	8c multicolored	.25	.25
82	A12	30c multicolored	.25	.25
83	A12	40c multicolored	.25	.25
84	A12	$1 multicolored	.65	.65
a.		Souv. sheet, #81-84, perf. 15	1.25	1.25
		Nos. 81-84 (4)	1.40	1.40

25th anniv. of coronation of Elizabeth II. #81-84 were also issued in bklt. panes of 2.

Types of 1976 Overprinted:
"INDEPENDENCE 1ST OCTOBER 1978"

1978, Oct. 1 Litho. Perf. 13½
85	A3	8c multicolored	.20	.20
86	A3	10c multicolored	.20	.20
87	A3	15c multicolored	.20	.20
88	A3	20c multicolored	.20	.20
89	A4	30c multicolored	.20	.20

90	A4	35c multicolored	.20	.20
91	A4	40c multicolored	.25	.25
		Nos. 85-91 (7)	1.45	1.45

Independence, Oct. 1, 1978. Overprint in 3 lines on vert. stamps, 1 line on horiz.

White Frangipani — A13

Wild Flowers: 20c, Zephyrantes rosea. 30c, Gardenia taitensis. 40c, Clerodendron inerme.

1978, Oct. 4 Unwmk. Perf. 14
92	A13	8c multicolored	.20	.20
93	A13	20c multicolored	.20	.25
94	A13	30c multicolored	.25	.30
95	A13	40c multicolored	.35	.50
		Nos. 92-95 (4)	1.00	1.25

Squirrelfish — A14

Fish: 2c, Yellow-banded goatfish. 4c, Imperial angelfish. 5c, Rainbow butterfly. 6c, Blue angelfish. 8c, Blue striped snapper. 10c, Orange clownfish. 15c, Chevroned coralfish. 20c, Fairy cod. 25c, Clown triggerfish. 30c, Long-nosed butterfly. 35c, Yellowfin tuna. 40c, Spotted eagle ray. 45c, Black-tipped rock cod. 50c, Hammerhead shark. 70c, Lionfish, vert. $1, White-barred triggerfish, vert. $2, Beaked coralfish, vert. $5, Tiger shark, vert.

1979, Jan. 24 Litho. Perf. 14
96	A14	1c multicolored	.20	.20
97	A14	2c multicolored	.20	.20
98	A14	4c multicolored	.20	.20
99	A14	5c multicolored	.20	.20
100	A14	6c multicolored	.20	.20
101	A14	8c multicolored	.20	.20
102	A14	10c multicolored	.20	.20
103	A14	15c multicolored	.20	.20
104	A14	20c multicolored	.20	.20
105	A14	25c multicolored	.20	.20
106	A14	30c multicolored	.25	.25
107	A14	35c multicolored	.30	.30
108	A14	40c multicolored	.35	.35
108A	A14	45c multicolored	.75	.55
109	A14	45c multicolored	.55	.55
110	A14	50c multicolored	.55	.55
111	A14	70c multicolored	.60	.60
112	A14	$1 multicolored	.80	.80
113	A14	$2 multicolored	1.90	1.90
	A14	$5 multicolored	4.50	4.50
		Nos. 96-113 (19)	12.00	11.80

No. 108A issued June 16, 1981. #101, 104, 106, 108 and #102, 105, 107, 108A were also issued in booklet panes of 4. For surcharge & overprints see #150, O1-O19.

Capt. Cook — A15

Designs: 30c, Flag raising on new island. 40c, Observation of transit of Venus. $1, Death of Capt. Cook.

1979, Feb. 14 Perf. 14x14½
114	A15	8c multicolored	.20	.20
115	A15	30c multicolored	.20	.20
116	A15	40c multicolored	.20	.20
117	A15	$1 multicolored	.40	.40
a.		Strip of 4, #114-117	1.00	1.00

Bicentenary of death of Capt. James Cook (1728-1779). Nos. 114-117 printed se-tenant horizontally in sheets of 12 (4x3) with gutters between horizontal rows.

Grumman Goose over Nukulaelae — A16

Grumman Goose over: 20c, Vaitupu. 30c, Nui. 40c, Funafuti.

1979, May 16 Litho. Perf. 14x13½
118	A16	8c multicolored	.20	.20
119	A16	20c multicolored	.20	.20
120	A16	30c multicolored	.25	.30
121	A16	40c multicolored	.35	.35
		Nos. 118-121 (4)	1.00	1.05

Inauguration of internal air service.

Hill, Tuvalu No. 16, Letterbox, London, 1855 — A17

Hill, Stamps of Tuvalu and: 40c, No. 17, Penny Black. $1, No. 18, mail coach.

1979, Aug. 20 Litho. Perf. 13½x14
122	A17	30c multicolored	.20	.20
123	A17	40c multicolored	.20	.20
124	A17	$1 multicolored	.50	.50
a.		Souvenir sheet of 3, #122-124	1.00	1.00
		Nos. 122-124 (3)	.90	.90

Sir Rowland Hill (1795-1879), originator of penny postage.

Boy — A18

Designs: Children of Tuvalu.

1979, Oct. 20 Litho. Perf. 14
125	A18	8c multicolored	.20	.20
126	A18	20c multicolored	.20	.20
127	A18	30c multicolored	.25	.25
128	A18	40c multicolored	.30	.30
		Nos. 125-128 (4)	.95	.95

International Year of the Child.

Cowry Shells — A19

1980, Feb. Litho. Perf. 14
129	A19	8c Cypraea Argus	.20	.20
130	A19	20c Cypraea scurra	.20	.20
131	A19	30c Cypraea carneola	.25	.25
132	A19	40c Cypraea aurantium	.35	.35
		Nos. 129-132 (4)	1.00	1.00

Philatelic Bureau, Funafuti, Tuvalu No 28, Arms, London 1980 Emblem — A20

Coat of Arms, London 1980 Emblem and 20c, Gilbert and Ellice #41, Nukulaelae cancel, Tuvalu #24. 30c, US airmail cover. $1, Map of Tuvalu.

1980, Apr. 30 Litho. Perf. 13½x1
133	A20	10c multicolored	.20	.2
134	A20	20c multicolored	.20	.2
135	A20	30c multicolored	.25	.2
136	A20	$1 multicolored	.60	.6
a.		Souvenir sheet of 4, #133-136	1.25	1.2
		Nos. 133-136 (4)	1.25	1.2

London 80 Intl. Stamp Exhib., May 6-14.

Queen Mother Elizabeth, 80th Birthday — A21

1980, Aug. 14 Litho. Perf. 14
137	A21	50c multicolored	.50	.50

Issued in sheets of 10 plus 2 labels.

Aethaloessa Calidalis — A22

1980, Aug. 20 Litho. Perf. 14
138	A22	8c shown	.20	.20
139	A22	20c Parotis suralis	.20	.20
140	A22	30c Dudua aprobola	.30	.30
141	A22	40c Decadarchis simulans	.40	.40
		Nos. 138-141 (4)	1.10	1.10

Air Pacific Heron (First Regular Air Service to Tuvalu, 1964) — A23

Aviation Anniversaries: 20c, Hawker Siddeley 748 (air service to Tuvalu). 30c, Sunderland Flying Boat (War time service to Funafuti, 1945. 40c, Orville Wright and Flyer (Wright brothers' first flight, 1903).

1980, Nov. 5 Litho. Perf. 14
142	A23	8c multicolored	.20	.20
143	A23	20c multicolored	.20	.20
144	A23	30c multicolored	.25	.20
145	A23	40c multicolored	.35	.30
		Nos. 142-145 (4)	1.00	.90

Hypolimnas Bolina Elliciana — A24

1981, Feb. 3   Litho.   Perf. 14½
146 A24 8c shown .20 .20
147 A24 20c Hypolimnas, diff. .25 .25
148 A24 30c Hypolimnas, diff. .30 .30
149 A24 40c Junonia vallida .50 .50
Nos. 146-149 (4) 1.25 1.25

No. 109 Surcharged
1981, Feb. 24   Litho.   Perf. 14
150 A14 45c on 50c multicolored .60 .60

Elizabeth, 1809
A25

Wmk. 373
1981, May 13   Litho.   Perf. 14
151 A25 10c shown .20 .20
152 A25 25c Rebecca, 1819 .20 .20
153 A25 35c Independence II, 1821 .25 .25
154 A25 40c Basilisk, 1872 .30 .30
155 A25 45c Royalist, 1890 .35 .35
156 A25 50c Olivebank, 1920 .45 .45
Nos. 151-156 (6) 1.75 1.75

See Nos. 216-221, 353-356, 410-413.

Prince Charles, Lady Diana, Royal Yacht Charlotte A25a

Prince Charles and Lady Diana — A25b

Illustration A25b is reduced.

Wmk. 380
1981, July 10   Litho.   Perf. 14
157 A25a 10c Couple, Carolina .20 .20
a. Blkt. pane of 4, perf. 12, unwmkd. .30
158 A25b 10c Couple .20 .20
159 A25a 45c Victoria and Albert III .25 .25
160 A25b 45c like #158 .25 .25
a. Blkt. pane of 2, perf. 12, unwmkd. .50
161 A25a $2 Britannia 1.00 1.00
162 A25b $2 like #158 1.00 1.00
Nos. 157-162 (6) 2.90 2.90

Royal wedding. Issued in sheets of 7 (6 design A25a; 1 design A25b).
For surcharges see Nos. B1-B2.

Souvenir Sheet
1981, Dec.   Litho.   Perf. 12
163 A25b $1.50 Couple .85 .85

Admission to UPU — A26

Wmk. Harrison's, London
1981, Nov. 19   Engr.   Perf. 14½x14
164 A26 70c dark blue .50 .50
165 A26 $1 dark red brown .75 .75
a. Souv. sheet of 2, #164-165, unwmkd. 1.50 1.50

Amatuku Maritime School — A27

1982, Feb. 17   Litho.   Perf. 13½x14
166 A27 10c Map .20 .20
167 A27 25c Motorboat .20 .20
168 A27 35c School, dock .25 .25
169 A27 45c Flag, ship .35 .35
Nos. 166-169 (4) 1.00 1.00

A27a

Wmk. 380
1982, May 19   Litho.   Perf. 14
170 A27a 10c Caroline of Brandenburg-Ansbach, 1714 .20 .20
171 A27a 45c Brandenburg-Ansbach arms .25 .25
172 A27a $1.50 Diana 1.00 1.00
Nos. 170-172 (3) 1.45 1.45

21st birthday of Princess Diana, July 1.

#170-172 Overprinted: "ROYAL BABY"
1982, July 14   Litho.   Perf. 14
173 A27a 10c multicolored .30 .30
174 A27a 45c multicolored .30 .30
175 A27a $1.50 multicolored .90 .90
Nos. 173-175 (3) 1.50 1.50

Birth of Prince William of Wales, June 21.

Scouting Year — A28

1982, Aug. 18
176 A28 10c Emblems .20 .20
177 A28 25c Campfire .35 .30
178 A28 35c Parade .45 .35
179 A28 45c Scout .60 .40
Nos. 176-179 (4) 1.60 1.25

Visit of Queen Elizabeth II and Prince Philip — A29

1982, Oct. 26   Litho.   Perf. 14
180 A29 25c Arms, Duke of Edinburgh's Personal Standard .20 .20
181 A29 45c Flags .35 .35
182 A29 50c Queen Elizabeth II, maps .40 .40
a. Souvenir sheet of 3, #180-182 1.00 1.00
Nos. 180-182 (3) .95 .95

Handicrafts — A30

1c, Fisherman's hat, lures, hooks. 2c, Cowrie shell handbags. 5c, Wedding & baby food baskets. 10c, Canoe model. 15c, Women's sun hats. 20c, Climbing rope. 25c, Pandanus baskets. 30c, Tray, coconut stands. 35c, Pandanus pillows, shell necklaces. 40c, Round baskets, fans. 45c, Reef sandals, fish trap. 50c, Rat trap, vert.. 60c, Waterproof boxes. $1, Pump drill, adze, vert. $2, Fisherman's hat, canoe bailers, vert. $5, Fishing rod, lures, scoop nets, vert.

1983-84   Litho.   Perf. 14
183 A30 1c multicolored .25 .20
184 A30 2c multicolored .25 .20
185 A30 5c multicolored .25 .20
186 A30 10c multicolored .25 .20
186A A30 15c multicolored 1.75 2.00
187 A30 20c multicolored .25 .20
188 A30 25c multicolored .25 .20
188A A30 30c multicolored 1.60 1.60
189 A30 35c multicolored .35 .30
190 A30 40c multicolored .25 .40
191 A30 45c multicolored .30 .45
192 A30 50c multicolored .35 .50
192A A30 60c multicolored 2.25 1.60
193 A30 $1 multicolored .35 .50
194 A30 $2 multicolored .50 .60
195 A30 $5 multicolored .80 .85
Nos. 183-195 (16) 10.00 10.00

Issued: 15c, 1984; others, 3/14/83.
For surcharges & overprints see #207, 230, O20-O32.

Commonwealth Day — A31

Wmk. 373
1983, Mar. 14   Litho.   Perf. 14
196 A31 20c Fishing industry .35 .20
197 A31 35c Traditional dancing .35 .30
198 A31 45c Satellite view .45 .40
199 A31 50c First container ship .60 .50
Nos. 196-199 (4) 1.75 1.40

Dragonflies — A32

1983, May 25   Wmk. 380
200 A32 10c Pantala flavescens .20 .20
201 A32 35c Anax guttatus .50 .50
202 A32 40c Tholymis tillarga .55 .55
203 A32 50c Diplacodes bipunctata .65 .65
Nos. 200-203 (4) 1.90 1.90

Boys Brigade Centenary — A33

1983, Aug. 10   Wmk. 373
204 A33 10c Running, emblem .20 .20
205 A33 35c Canoeing .45 .30
206 A33 $1 Officer, boys 1.10 1.25
Nos. 204-206 (3) 1.75 1.75

No. 193 Surcharged in Black
1983, Aug. 26   Wmk. 380
207 A30 60c on $1 multi .65 .40

First Manned Flight Bicentenary — A34

1983, Sept. 21   Wmk. 373
208 A34 25c Montgolfier balloon, vert. .20 .20
209 A34 35c McKinnon Turbo Goose .25 .25
210 A34 45c Beechcraft Super King Air 200 .30 .30
211 A34 50c Double Eagle II Balloon, vert. .35 .35
a. Souvenir sheet of 4, #208-211 1.25 1.25
Nos. 208-211 (4) 1.10 1.10

World Communications Year — A35

1983, Nov. 18   Wmk. 380
212 A35 25c Conch Shell Trumpet, vert. .20 .20
213 A35 35c Radio Operator, vert. .30 .30
214 A35 45c Teleprinter .40 .40
215 A35 50c Transmitting station .45 .45
Nos. 212-215 (4) 1.35 1.35

Ship Type of 1981
1984, Feb. 16   Wmk. 380
216 A25 10c Titus, 1897 .20 .20
217 A25 20c Malaita, 1905 .20 .20
218 A25 25c Aymeric, 1906 .25 .25
219 A25 35c Anshun, 1965 .35 .35
220 A25 45c Beaverbank, 1970 .45 .45
221 A25 50c Benjamin Bowring, 1981 .55 .55
Nos. 216-221 (6) 2.00 2.00

Leaders of the World
Large quantities of some Leaders of the World issues were sold at a fraction of face value when the printer was liquidated.

Historic Locomotives — A36

Perf. 12½x13
1984, Feb. 29   Unwmk.
Se-tenant Pairs, #a.-b.
a. — Side and front views.
b. — Action scene.
222 A36 1c Class GS-4, US, 1941 .20 .20
223 A36 15c AD-60, Australia, 1952 .25 .25
224 A36 40c C38, Australia, 1943 .65 .65
225 A36 60c Achilles England, 1892 1.00 1.00
Nos. 222-225 (4) 2.10 2.10

See Nos. 235-246, 291-294, 320-323.

No. 191 Surcharged
Wmk. 380
1984, Feb. 1   Litho.   Perf. 14
230 A30 30c on 45c multi .45 .45

For overprint see No. O25.

Beach Flowers A38

1984, May 30
231 A38 25c Ipomoea pes-caprae .30 .30
232 A38 45c Ipomoea macrantha .45 .45
233 A38 50c Triumfetta procumbens .55 .55
234 A38 60c Portulaca quadrifida .70 .70
Nos. 231-234 (4) 2.00 2.00

Train Type of 1984
1984 Litho. Perf. 12½x13
Se-tenant Pairs, #a.-b.
a.-Side and front views.
b.-Action scene.
235 A36 1c Class 9700, Japan, 1897 .20 .20
236 A36 10c Casey Jones, US, 1896 .20 .20
237 A36 15c Class 2310K, France, 1909 .20 .20
238 A36 15c Triplex, US, 1914 .20 .20
239 A36 20c Class 370, Gt. Britain, 1981 .20 .20
240 A36 25c Class 4F, Gt. Britain, 1924 .25 .25
241 A36 30c Glass 640, Italy, 1907 .30 .30
242 A36 40c Tornado, Gt. Britain, 1888 .40 .40
243 A36 50c Broadlands, Gt. Britain, 1967 .55 .55
244 A36 60c Locomotion, Gt. Britain, 1825 .70 .70
245 A36 $1 C57, Japan, 1937 1.00 1.00
246 A36 $1 Class 4500, France, 1906 1.00 1.00
Nos. 235-246 (12) 5.20 5.20

Issued: #235, 237, 241, 245, 10/4; others, 6/27.

15th South Pacific Forum A38a

1984, Aug. 21 Litho. Perf. 14
255 A38a 60c National flag .30 .30
256 A38a 60c Tuvalu crest .30 .30

Ausipex '84 A38b

1984, Aug. 21 Perf. 14
257 A38b 60c Exhib. emblem .50 .50
258 A38b 60c Royal Exhibi. Building .50 .50

A. Shrewsbury Playing Cricket — A39

Cricket players in action or portrait.

1984, Nov. 5 Litho. Perf. 12½
Se-tenant Pairs #a.-b.
259 A39 5c shown .20 .20
260 A39 30c H. Verity .55 .55
261 A39 50c E.H. Hendren .55 .50
262 A39 60c J. Briggs .70 .55
Nos. 259-262 (4) 2.00 1.75

Drawings, Christmas 1984 — A40

1984, Nov. 14 Litho. Perf. 14½x14
267 A40 15c By Eli Faalata .20 .20
268 A40 40c By Toakai Niutao .25 .25
269 A40 50c By Falesa Teuila .30 .30
270 A40 60c By Piuani Talie .40 .40
Nos. 267-270 (4) 1.15 1.15

Classic Automobiles — A41

Sketch listed first followed by angled view.

1984, Dec. 7 Litho. Perf. 12½x13
Se-tenant Pairs, #a.-b.
a. — Side and front views.
b. — Action scene.
271 A41 1c Morris Minor, 1949 .20 .20
272 A41 15c Studebaker Avanti, 1963 .20 .20
273 A41 50c Chevrolet International Six, 1929 .50 .50
274 A41 $1 Allard J2, 1950 .95 .95
Nos. 271-274 (4) 1.85 1.85

See Nos. 299-302, 332-339, 396-396E, 414-425.

John J. Audubon — A42

#279a, Common flicker. #279b, Say's phoebe. #280a, Townsend's warbler. #280b, Bohemian waxwing. #281a, Prothonotary warbler. #281b, Worm-eating warbler. #282a, Broad-winged hawk. #282b, Northern harrier.

1985, Feb. 12 Litho. Perf. 12½
279 A42 1c Pair, #a.-b. .20 .20
280 A42 25c Pair, #a.-b. .40 .40
281 A42 50c Pair, #a.-b. .80 .80
282 A42 70c Pair, #a.-b. 1.00 1.00
Nos. 279-282 (4) 2.40 2.40

Birds and Eggs A43

1985, Feb. 27 Perf. 14
287 A43 15c Black-naped tern .40 .30
288 A43 40c Black noddy 1.00 .75
289 A43 50c White-tailed tropicbird 1.10 .85
290 A43 60c Sooty tern 1.50 1.10
Nos. 287-290 (4) 4.00 3.00

Train Type of 1984
1985, Mar. 19 Perf. 12½
Se-tenant Pairs, #a.-b.
a. — Side and front views.
b. — Action scene.
291 A36 5c Churchward, U.K. .20 .20
292 A36 10c Class K.F., China .20 .20
293 A36 30c Class 99.77, East Germany .50 .50
294 A36 $1 Pearson, U.K. 1.60 1.60
Nos. 291-294 (4) 2.50 2.50

Automobile Type of 1984
1985, Apr. 3
Se-tenant Pairs, #a.-b.
a. — Side and front views.
b. — Action scene.
299 A41 1c Rickenbacker, 1923 .20 .20
300 A41 20c Detroit-Electric, 1914 .20 .20
301 A41 50c Packard Clipper, 1941 .55 .55
302 A41 70c Audi Quattro, 1982 .75 .75
Nos. 299-302 (4) 1.70 1.70

World War II Aircraft A44

1985, May 29 Litho. Perf. 14
307 A44 15c Curtiss P-40N 1.10 .20
308 A44 40c Consolidated B-24D Liberator 1.50 .55
309 A44 50c Lockheed PV-1 Ventura 1.50 .70
310 A44 60c Douglas C-54 Skymaster 1.50 .80
a. Souvenir sheet of 4, #307-310 5.50 3.00
Nos. 307-310 (4) 5.60 2.25

Queen Mother, 85th Birthday — A45

#310a, Facing right. #310b, Facing left. #311a, Facing right. #311b, 317b, Facing front. #312a, 316a, Waving to crowd. #312b, 316b, Facing front. #313a, Facing front. #313b, Facing left. #314a, As a young woman. #314b, as Queen Consort.

1985-86 Litho. Perf. 12½
311 A45 5c Pair, #a.-b. .20 .20
312 A45 30c Pair, #a.-b. .30 .30
313 A45 60c Pair, #a.-b. .60 .60
314 A45 $1 Pair, #a.-b. .90 .90
Nos. 311-314 (4) 2.00 2.00
Souvenir Sheets
315 A45 $1.20 #a.-b. 1.25 1.25
316 A45 $2 #a.-b. 3.00 3.00
317 A45 $3 #a.-b. 4.25 4.25
Issued: #316-317, 6/10/86; others, 7/4/85.

Train Type of 1984
1985, Sept. 18
Se-tenant Pairs, #a.-b.
a. — Side and front views.
b. — Action scene.
320 A36 10c 1936 Green Arrow, U.K. .20 .20
321 A36 40c 1982 G.M. (EMD) SD-50, US .55 .55
322 A36 65c 1932 DRG Flying Hamburger, Germany .70 .70
323 A36 $1 1908 JNR Class 1070, Japan .80 .80
Nos. 320-323 (4) 2.25 2.25

Girl Guides, 75th Anniv. — A46

1985, Aug. 28 Litho. Perf. 14
328 A46 15c Playing guitar .25 .25
329 A46 40c Camping .50 .50
330 A46 50c Flag bearer .60 .60
331 A46 60c Guides' salute .75 .75
a. Souvenir sheet of 4, #328-331 2.25 2.25
Nos. 328-331 (4) 2.10 2.05

Car Type of 1984
5c, 1929 Cord L-29, US. 10c, 1932 Horch 670 V-12, Germany. 15c, 1901 Lanchester, UK. 35c, 1950 Citroen 2 CV, France. 40c, 1957 MGA, UK. 55c, 1962 Ferrari 250-GTO, Italy. $1, 1932 Ford V-8, US. $1.50, 1977 Aston Martin-Lagonda, UK.

1985, Oct. 8 Perf. 12½
a. — Side and front views.
b. — Action scene.
332-339 A41 Set of 8 pairs 3.25 3.25

Crabs A47

1986, Jan. 7 Perf. 15
348 A47 15c Stalk-eyed ghost .35 .35
349 A47 40c Red and white painted .90 .90
350 A47 50c Red-spotted 1.10 1.10
351 A47 60c Red hermit 1.40 1.40
Nos. 348-351 (4) 3.75 3.75

Souvenir Sheet of 2

Events — A48

#352a, American and Soviet flags, chess board & knight. #352b, Rotary Intl. emblem.

1986, Mar. 19 Litho. Perf. 13x12½
352 A48 $3 #a.-b. 6.50 6.50

Fischer and Karpov, world chess champions; Rotary Intl., 80th anniv.
No. 352 exists with plain or decorated border.

Ship Type of 1981
1986, Apr. 14 Perf. 15
353 A25 15c Messenger of Peace .25 .25
354 A25 40c John Wesley .75 .75
355 A25 50c Duff .90 .90
356 A25 60c Triton 1.00 1.00
Nos. 353-356 (4) 2.90 2.90

Queen Elizabeth II, 60th Birthday — A49

Various portraits.

1986, Apr. 21   **Perf. 12½**
357 A49 10c multicolored   .20   .20
358 A49 90c multicolored   .30   .30
359 A49 $1.50 multicolored   .50   .50
360 A49 $3 multi, vert.   1.00 1.00
         Nos. 357-360 (4)   2.00 2.00

Souvenir Sheet
361 A49 $4 multicolored   4.00 4.00

Peace Corps, 25th Anniv. A50

1986, May 22   **Perf. 14**
362 A50 50c multicolored   .85   .85
         For overprint see No. 374.

A51

1986, May 22   **Perf. 14x13½**
363 A51 60c multicolored   .90   .90
                     AMERIPEX '86.

1986, June 30   **Litho.**   **Perf. 15**
  Players and teams.
364 A52 1c So. Korea   .20   .20
365 A52 5c France   .20   .20
366 A52 10c W. Germany,
             1974   .20   .20
367 A52 40c Italy   .40   .40

Size: 60x40mm
Perf. 13x12½
368 A52 60c W. Germany vs.
             Holland, 1974   .50   .50
369 A52 $1 Canada   .85   .85
370 A52 $2 No. Ireland   1.90 1.90
371 A52 $3 England   2.50 2.50
         Nos. 364-371 (8)   6.75 6.75

Souvenir Sheets
372 A52 $1.50 like #369   1.75 1.75
373 A52 $2.50 like #370   3.00 3.00

  1986 World Cup Soccer Championships.
Nos. 366 and 368 picture emblem; others picture character trademark.

No. 362 Ovptd. with STAMPEX '86 Emblem

1986, Aug. 4   **Litho.**   **Perf. 14**
374 A50 50c multicolored   .70   .70

A53

Wedding of Prince Andrew and Sarah Ferguson — A54

#381a, Andrew, vert. #381b, Couple, vert. #382a, Andrew. #382b, Princess Diana, Sarah.

Perf. 12½
1986, July 18   **Litho.**   **Unwmk.**
381 A53 60c Pair, #a.-b.   .50   .50
382 A53 $1 Pair, #a.-b.   .90   .90

Souvenir Sheet
Perf. 13x12½
383 A54 $6 Newlyweds   3.75 3.75

No. 382a pictures Westminster Abbey in LR. For overprints see Nos. 389-390.

Geckos A55

1986, July 30   **Litho.**   **Perf. 14**
384 A55 15c Mourning gecko   .40   .30
385 A55 40c Oceanic stump-toed   1.00 .80
386 A55 50c Azure-tailed skink   1.25 1.00
387 A55 60c Moth skink   1.75 1.40
         Nos. 384-387 (4)   4.40 3.50

Souvenir Sheet

South Pacific Forum, 15th Anniv. A56

Flags and maps: a, Australia. b, Cook Islands. c, Micronesia. d, Fiji. e, Kiribati. f, Nauru. g, New Zealand. h, Niue. i, Papua New Guinea. j, Solomon Islands. k, Tonga. l, Tuvalu. m, Vanuatu. n, Western Samoa.

Wmk. 380
1986, Aug. 4   **Litho.**   **Perf. 15**
388   Sheet of 14 + label   7.00 7.00
  a.-n.   A56 40c any single   .50   .50

  No. 388 has center label picturing Executive Committee headquarters, Suva, Fiji.

Nos. 381-382 Ovptd. "Congratulations to T.R.H. The Duke & Duchess of York" in Silver

1986   **Unwmk.**   **Perf. 12½**
389 A53 60c Pair, #a.-b.   1.75 1.75
390 A53 $1 Pair, #a.-b.   2.75 2.75

         Exist tete-beche.

Car Type of 1984
  15c, 1953 Cooper, UK. 40c, 1964 Rover 2000, UK. 50c, 1930 Ruxton, US. 60c, 1950 Jowett Jupiter, UK. 90c, 1964 Cobra Daytona Coupe, US. $1.50, 1903 Packard Model F "Old Pacific," US.

1986, Oct.   **Litho.**   **Perf. 12½**
  Se-tenant Pairs, #a.-b.
   a. — Side and front views.
     b. — Action scene.
391-396 A41 Set of 6 pairs   3.75 3.75

Marine Life A57

1986, Nov. 5   **Unwmk.**   **Perf. 14**
397 A57 15c Sea star   .75   .75
398 A57 40c Pencil urchin   1.25 1.25
399 A57 50c Fragile coral   1.40 1.40
400 A57 60c Pink coral   1.60 1.60
         Nos. 397-400 (4)   5.00 5.00
         See Nos. 465-468, 524-527.

Souvenir Sheets

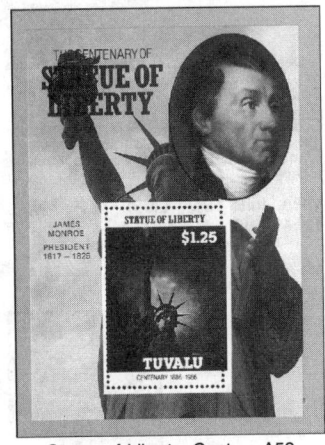

Statue of Liberty, Cent. — A58

Various views of the statue.

1986, Nov. 24
401 A58 $1.25 multicolored   .45   .45
402 A58 $1.50 multicolored   .60   .60
403 A58 $1.80 multicolored   .75   .75
404 A58 $2 multicolored   .85   .85
405 A58 $2.25 multicolored   .95   .95
406 A58 $2.50 multicolored   1.00 1.00
407 A58 $3 multicolored   1.25 1.25
408 A58 $3.25 multicolored   1.40 1.40
409 A58 $3.50 multicolored   1.50 1.50
         Nos. 401-409 (9)   8.75 8.75

Ships Type of 1981
1987, Feb. 4   **Unwmk.**   **Perf. 14**
410 A25 15c Southern Cross IV   .75   .75
411 A25 40c John Williams VI   1.60 1.60
412 A25 50c John Williams IV   1.75 1.75
413 A25 60c M.S. Southern
             Cross   1.75 1.75
         Nos. 410-413 (4)   5.85 5.85

Car Type of 1984
  1c, 1938 Talbot-Lago, France. 2c, 1930 Dupont Model G, US. 5c, 1950 Riley RM, U.K. 10c, 1915 Chevrolet Baby Grand, US. 20c, 1968 Shelby Mustang GT 500 KR, US. 30c, 1952 Ferrari 212 Export Barchetta, Italy. 40c, 1912 Peerless Model 48-Six, US. 50c, 1954 Sunbeam Alpine, U.K. 60c, 1969 Matra-Ford MS80, France. 70c, 1934 Squire 1-Litre, U.K. 75c, 1931 Talbot 105, U.K. $1, 1928 Plymouth Model Q, US.

Perf. 12½
1987, May 7   **Litho.**   **Unwmk.**
  Se-tenant Pairs, #a.-b.
   a. — Side and front views.
     b. — Action scene.
414-425 A41 Set of 12 pairs   6.25 6.25
425a   Souv. sheet of 2   3.00 3.00

Ferns — A59

1987, July 7   **Wmk. 380**   **Perf. 14**
438 A59 15c Nephrolepis
             saligna   .20   .20
439 A59 40c Asplenium nidus   .60   .45
440 A59 50c Microsorum
             scolopendria   .75   .55
441 A59 60c Pteris tripartita   .95   .70
         Nos. 438-441 (4)   2.50 1.90

Souvenir Sheet
442 A59 $1.50 Psilotum nudum   2.50 2.50

A60

#443a, 444b, 445a, 456b, Flowers, all diff. #443b, 444a, 445b, 456a, Woman wearing fou, all diff.

1987, Aug. 12   **Wmk. 380**
443 A60 15c Pair, #a.-b.   .40   .40
444 A60 40c Pair, #a.-b.   1.10 1.10
445 A60 50c Pair, #a.-b.   1.25 1.25
446 A60 60c Pair, #a.-b.   1.60 1.60
         Nos. 443-446 (4)   4.35 4.35

Crayfish and Coconut Crabs A61

1987, Nov. 11   **Litho.** **Wmk. 380** **Perf. 14**
451 A61 40c Coconut crabs   .80   .60
452 A61 50c Painted crayfish   1.00 .75
453 A61 60c Ocean crayfish   1.10 .90
         Nos. 451-453 (3)   2.90 2.25

Photograph of Queen Victoria, 1897, by Downey — A62

  60c, Elizabeth and Philip on their wedding day, 1947. 80c, Elizabeth, Charles, Philip, c. 1950. $1, Elizabeth, Anne, 1950. $2, Elizabeth, 1970. $3, Elizabeth, children, 1950.

1987, Nov. 20   **Unwmk.**   **Perf. 15**
454-458 A62 Set of 5   5.00 5.00

Souvenir Sheet
459   A62 $3 red org & blk   3.00 3.00

  Accession of Queen Victoria to the throne of England, sesquicentennial; wedding of Queen Elizabeth II and Prince Philip, 40th anniv.

16th World Scout Jamboree, Australia, 1987-88 — A63

Jamboree and Australia bicentennial emblems plus: 40c, Aborigine, Ayer's Rock. 60c, Capt. Cook, by Dance, and HMS Endeavor. $1, Scout and Scout Park Arch. $1.50, Koala and kangaroo. $2.50, Lord and Lady Baden-Powell.

Perf. 13x12½
1987, Dec. 2   Litho.   Unwmk.

460	A63	40c multicolored	.35	.35
461	A63	60c multicolored	.50	.50
462	A63	$1 multicolored	.90	.90
463	A63	$1.50 multicolored	1.25	1.25
		Nos. 460-463 (4)	3.00	3.00

Souvenir Sheet

464	A63	$2.50 multicolored	2.75	2.75

Marine Life Type of 1986
Unwmk.
1988, Feb. 29   Litho.   Perf. 15

465	A57	15c Spanish dancer	.50	.25
466	A57	40c Hard corals	1.25	.60
467	A57	50c Feather stars	1.50	.75
468	A57	60c Staghorn corals	1.75	.90
		Nos. 465-468 (4)	5.00	2.50

Birds A64

1988, Mar. 2   Perf. 15

469	A64	5c Jungle fowl	.20	.20
470	A64	10c White tern	.20	.20
471	A64	15c Brown noddy	.20	.20
472	A64	20c Phoenix petrel	.20	.20
473	A64	25c Pacific golden plover	.25	.25
474	A64	30c Crested tern	.30	.30
475	A64	35c Sooty tern	.35	.35
476	A64	40c Bristle-thighed curlew	.40	.40
477	A64	45c Eastern bar-tailed godwit	.45	.45
478	A64	50c Reef heron	.50	.50
479	A64	55c Greater frigatebird	.55	.55
480	A64	60c Red-footed booby	.60	.60
481	A64	70c Red-necked stint	.70	.70
482	A64	$1 New Zealand long-tailed cuckoo	1.10	1.10
483	A64	$2 Red-tailed tropicbird	2.00	2.00
484	A64	$5 Banded rail	5.00	5.00
		Nos. 469-484 (16)	13.00	13.00

For overprints see Nos. 676-679, 796-799, O33-O48.

Intl. Red Cross and Red Crescent Organizations, 125th Annivs. — A65

Perf. 12½
1988, May 9   Litho.   Unwmk.

485	A65	15c Jean-Henri Dunant	.20	.20
486	A65	40c Junior Red Cross	.25	.25
487	A65	50c Care for the handicapped	.35	.35
488	A65	60c First aid training	.40	.40
		Nos. 485-488 (4)	1.20	1.20

Souvenir Sheet

489	A65	$1.50 Lecture	1.90	1.90

A66

Voyages of Capt. Cook — A67

Designs: 20c, HMS *Endeavour* (starboard side). 40c, *Endeavour* (stern). 50c, Landing, Tahiti, 1769, vert. 60c, Maori chief, vert. 80c, *Resolution* and native Hawaiian sail ship. $1, Cook, by Sir Nathaniel Dance-Holland (1735-1811), vert. $2.50, Antarctic icebergs surrounding the *Resolution*. Illustration A67 reduced.

1988, June 15   Litho.   Perf. 12½

490-495	A66	Set of 6	5.75	5.75

Souvenir Sheet

496	A67	$2.50 shown	4.25	4.25

Fungi — A68

1988, July 25   Litho.   Perf. 15

497	A68	40c Ganoderma applanatum	.65	.65
498	A68	50c Pseudoepicoccum cocos	.85	.85
499	A68	60c Rigidoporus zonalis	1.00	1.00
500	A68	90c Rigidoporus microporus	1.50	1.50
		Nos. 497-500 (4)	4.00	4.00

See Nos. 520-523.

1988 Summer Olympics, Seoul — A69

Perf. 12½
1988, Aug. 19   Litho.   Unwmk.

501	A69	10c Rifles, target	.20	.20
502	A69	20c Judo	.30	.30
503	A69	40c One-man kayak	.65	.65
504	A69	60c Swimming	1.00	1.00
505	A69	80c Yachting	1.25	1.25
506	A69	$1 Balance beam	1.75	1.75
		Nos. 501-506 (6)	5.15	5.15

Natl. Independence, 10th Anniv. — A70

Wmk. 380
1988, Sept. 28   Litho.   Perf. 14

507	A70	60c Queen Elizabeth in boat	1.00	1.00
a.		Souvenir sheet of 1	1.00	1.00
508	A70	90c In sedan chair	1.40	1.40
a.		Souvenir sheet of 1	1.40	1.40
509	A70	$1 shown	1.60	1.60
a.		Souvenir sheet of 1	1.60	1.60
510	A70	$1.20 Seated at dais	2.00	2.00
a.		Souvenir sheet of 1	2.00	2.00
		Nos. 507-510 (4)	6.00	6.00

Nos. 507-508 and 510 vert.

Christmas — A71

Unwmk.
1988, Dec. 5   Litho.   Perf. 14

511	A71	15c Mary	.30	.30
512	A71	40c Christ child	.70	.70
513	A71	60c Joseph	1.10	1.10
		Nos. 511-513 (3)	2.10	2.10

Souvenir Sheet

514	A71	$1.50 Heraldic angel	2.75	2.75

Palm-frond or Pandanus-leaf Skirts — A72

1989, Mar. 31   Litho.   Perf. 14

515	A72	40c multi	.70	.70
516	A72	50c multi, diff.	.80	.80
517	A72	60c multi, diff.	1.00	1.00
518	A72	90c multi, diff.	1.50	1.50
		Nos. 515-518 (4)	4.00	4.00

Souvenir Sheet

519	A72	$1.50 multi, vert.	2.50	2.50

Fungi Type of 1988
1989, May 24   Litho.   Perf. 14

520	A68	40c Trametes muelleri	.60	.60
521	A68	50c Pestalotiopsis palmarum	.75	.75
522	A68	60c Trametes cingulata	.90	.90
523	A68	90c Schizophyllum commune	1.40	1.40
		Nos. 520-523 (4)	3.65	3.65

Marine Life Type of 1986
1989, July 31   Litho.   Perf. 14

524	A57	40c Pennant coralfish	.60	.60
525	A57	50c Anemone fish	.80	.80
526	A57	60c Batfish	.90	.90
527	A57	90c Threadfin coralfish	1.40	1.40
a.		Miniature sheet of 4, #524-527	3.75	3.75
		Nos. 524-527 (4)	3.70	3.70

Souvenir Sheet

Maiden Voyage of M.V. *Nivaga II*, 1988 — A73

1989, Oct. 9   Litho.   Perf. 14

528	A73	$1.50 multicolored	2.25	2.25

Christmas — A74

Tropical Trees — A75

Unwmk.
1989, Nov. 29   Litho.   Perf. 14

529	A74	40c Conch shell	.60	.60
530	A74	50c Flower bouquet	.80	.80
531	A74	60c Germinated coconut	.95	.95
532	A74	90c Shell jewelry	1.40	1.40
		Nos. 529-532 (4)	3.75	3.75

1990, Feb. 28   Litho.   Perf. 14½

533	A75	15c Cocus nucifera	.25	.25
534	A75	30c Rhizophora samoensis	.45	.45
535	A75	40c Messerschmidia argentea	.60	.60
536	A75	50c Pandanus tectorius	.75	.75
537	A75	60c Hernandia nymphaeifolia	.90	.90
538	A75	90c Pisonia grandis	1.40	1.40
		Nos. 533-538 (6)	4.35	4.35

Penny Black, 150th Anniv. A76

1990, May 3   Litho.   Perf. 14

539	A76	15c multicolored	.25	.25
540	A76	40c multicolored	.65	.65
541	A76	90c multicolored	1.50	1.50
		Nos. 539-541 (3)	2.40	2.40

Souvenir Sheet

542	A76	$2 multicolored	3.25	3.25

Stamp World London '90.

World War II Ships A77

Designs: 15c, Japanese merchant conversion, 1940. 30c, USS Unimak, seaplane tender, 1944. 40c, Amagari, Japanese Hubuki class, 1942. 50c, AO-24 USS Platte, Nov. 1, 1943. 60c, Japanese Shumushu Class (Type A) escort. 90c, CV-22 USS Independence.

1990

543-548	A77	Set of 6	5.90	5.90

Flowers — A78

990, Sept. 21   Litho.   Perf. 14½
9	A78	15c Erythrina fusca	.25	.25
0	A78	30c Capparis cordifolia	.50	.50
1	A78	40c Portulaca pilosa	.65	.65
2	A78	50c Cordia subcordata	.80	.80
3	A78	60c Scaevola taccada	1.00	1.00
4	A78	90c Suriana maritima	1.50	1.50
		Nos. 549-554 (6)	4.70	4.70

UN Development Program, 40th
Anniv. — A79

990, Nov. 20   Litho.   Perf. 14
55	A79	40c Surveyor	.65	.65
56	A79	60c Communications station	1.00	1.00
57	A79	$1.20 Fishing boat Te Tautai	1.90	1.90
		Nos. 555-557 (3)	3.55	3.55

Christmas
A80

Seashells — A81

1990, Nov. 20
558	A80	15c Mary and Joseph	.25	.25
559	A80	40c Nativity	.65	.65
560	A80	60c Shepherds	1.00	1.00
561	A80	90c Three Kings	1.50	1.50
		Nos. 558-561 (4)	3.40	3.40

1991, Jan. 18   Litho.   Perf. 14
562	A81	40c Murex ramosus	.65	.65
563	A81	50c Conus marmoreus	.85	.85
564	A81	60c Trochus niloticus	1.00	1.00
565	A81	$1.50 Cypraea mappa	2.25	2.25
		Nos. 562-565 (4)	4.75	4.75

Insects
A82

1991, Mar. 22   Litho.   Perf. 14
566	A82	40c Cylas formicarius	.65	.65
567	A82	50c Heliothis armiger	.80	.80
568	A82	60c Spodoptera litura	1.00	1.00
569	A82	$1.50 Agrius convolvuli	2.25	2.25
		Nos. 566-569 (4)	4.70	4.70

A84

Endangered marine life.

1991, May 31   Litho.   Perf. 14
570	A83	40c Green turtle	.65	.65
571	A83	50c Humpback whale	.80	.80
572	A83	60c Hawksbill turtle	1.00	1.00
573	A83	$1.50 Sperm whale	2.25	2.25
		Nos. 570-573 (4)	4.70	4.70

1991, July 31   Litho.   Perf. 14
574	A84	40c Soccer	.65	.65
575	A84	50c Volleyball	.80	.80
576	A84	60c Lawn tennis	1.00	1.00
577	A84	$1.50 Cricket	2.25	2.25
		Nos. 574-577 (4)	4.70	4.70

9th South Pacific Games.

World War II Ships A85

1991, Oct. 15   Litho.   Perf. 14
578	A85	40c USS Tennessee	.65	.65
579	A85	50c IJN Haguro	.85	.85
580	A85	60c HMS Achilles	1.00	1.00
581	A85	$1.50 USS North Carolina	2.50	2.50
		Nos. 578-581 (4)	5.00	5.00

A86

A87

Christmas: various traditional dance costumes.

1991, Dec. 13
582	A86	40c multicolored	.65	.65
583	A86	50c multicolored	.85	.85
584	A86	60c multicolored	1.00	1.00
585	A86	$1.50 multicolored	2.50	2.50
		Nos. 582-585 (4)	5.00	5.00

1992, Jan. 29   Litho.   Perf. 14

Constellations.
586	A87	40c Southern Fish	.65	.65
587	A87	50c Scorpio	.80	.80
588	A87	60c Sagittarius	.95	.95
589	A87	$1.50 Southern Cross	2.25	2.25
		Nos. 586-589 (4)	4.65	4.65

British Annexation of the Gilbert &
Ellice Islands, Cent. — A88

1992, Mar. 23   Litho.   Perf. 14
590	A88	40c King George VI	.60	.60
591	A88	50c King George V	.75	.75
592	A88	60c King Edward VII	.90	.90
593	A88	$1.50 Queen Victoria	2.25	2.25
		Nos. 590-593 (4)	4.50	4.50

Discovery of America, 500th Anniv. A89

Columbus and: 40c, Queen Isabella & King Ferdinand of Spain. 50c, Polynesians. 60c, South American Indians. $1.50, North American Indians.

1992, May 22   Litho.   Perf. 14
594	A89	40c black & dk blue	.60	.60
595	A89	50c black & dk plum	.75	.75
596	A89	60c black & dk green	.90	.90
597	A89	$1.50 black & dk purple	2.25	2.25
		Nos. 594-597 (4)	4.50	4.50

World Columbian Stamp Expo '92, Chicago.

Fish A90

Designs: 15c, Bluespot butterflyfish. 20c, Pink parrotfish. 25c, Stripe surgeonfish. 30c, Moon wrasse, 35c, Harlequin filefish. 40c, Bird wrasse. 45c, Black-finned pigfish. 50c, Blue-green chromis. 60c, Hump-headed Maori wrasse. 70c, Ornate coralfish, vert. 90c, Saddled butterflyfish, vert. $1, Vagabond butterflyfish, vert. $2, Longfin bannerfish, vert. $3, Moorish idol, vert.

1992, July 15
598-611	A90	Set of 14	17.00	17.00

For overprints & surcharge see #629-632, 716.

1992 Summer Olympics, Barcelona — A91

1992, July 27   Litho.   Perf. 14
612	A91	40c Discus	.60	.60
613	A91	50c Javelin	.75	.75
614	A91	60c Shotput	.90	.90
615	A91	$1.50 Track & field	2.25	2.25
		Nos. 612-615 (4)	4.50	4.50

Souvenir Sheet
616	A91	$2 Olympic stadium	3.00	3.00

Blue Coral A92

Various views of blue coral.

1992, Sept. 1
617	A92	10c multicolored	.75	.60
618	A92	25c multicolored	1.75	1.25
619	A92	30c multicolored	1.90	1.50
620	A92	35c multicolored	2.00	1.75
		Nos. 617-620 (4)	6.40	5.10

World Wildlife Fund.

Christmas — A93   Wild Flowers — A94

Designs: 40c, Fishermen seeing angel. 50c, Fishermen sailing canoes toward island. 60c, Adoration of the fishermen. $1.50, Flowers, shell necklaces.

1992, Dec. 25   Litho.   Perf. 14
621	A93	40c multicolored	.55	.55
622	A93	50c multicolored	.70	.70
623	A93	60c multicolored	.80	.80
624	A93	$1.50 multicolored	2.00	2.00
		Nos. 621-624 (4)	4.05	4.05

1993, Feb. 2   Litho.   Perf. 14
625	A94	40c Calophyllum inophyllum	.60	.60
626	A94	50c Hibiscus tiliaceus	.70	.70
627	A94	60c Lantana camara	.85	.85
628	A94	$1.50 Plumeria rubra	2.00	2.00
		Nos. 625-628 (4)	4.15	4.15

Nos. 601, 603, & 605-606 Ovptd.

1992, Sept. 1   Litho.   Perf. 14
629	A90	30c on #601	.50	.50
630	A90	40c on #603	.65	.65
631	A90	50c on #605	.85	.85
632	A90	60c on #606	1.00	1.00
		Nos. 629-632 (4)	3.00	3.00

World War II in the Pacific, 50th Anniv. A95

1993, Apr. 23   Litho.   Perf. 14
633	A95	40c Japanese bombers	.60	.60
634	A95	50c Anti-aircraft gun, vert.	.70	.70
635	A95	60c Using flame thrower	.85	.85
636	A95	$1.50 Map of Funafuti Atoll, vert.	2.25	2.25
		Nos. 633-636 (4)	4.40	4.40

Souvenir Sheet

6th ASIAN INTERNATIONAL PHILATELIC EXHIBITION
MAY 29 — JUNE 4 1993   SURABAYA INDONESIA

$1.50   TUVALU

PAMERAN INTERNASIONAL KE VI
KOLEKSI PERANGKO ASIA   MEI 29 — JUNI 4
                          SURABAYA INDONESIA

Indopex '93 — A96

1993, May 29   **Perf. 14x14½**
637 A96 $1.50 Cepora perimale   2.25 2.25

Marine
Life
A97

1993, June 29   Litho.   Perf. 14
638 A97   40c Giant clam   .55 .55
639 A97   50c Anemone crab   .70 .70
640 A97   60c Octopus   .85 .85
641 A97 $1.50 Green turtle   2.00 2.00
        Nos. 638-641 (4)   4.10 4.10

Coronation of Queen Elizabeth II, 40th
Anniv. — A98

Queen: 40c, Riding in parade with Prince
Phillip. 50c, Drinking coconut milk. 60c, Holding umbrella. $1.50, With natives. $2, Coronation ceremony.

1993, July 5
642 A98   40c multicolored   .55 .55
643 A98   50c multicolored   .70 .70
644 A98   60c multicolored   .85 .85
645 A98 $1.50 multicolored   2.00 2.00
        Nos. 642-645 (4)   4.10 4.10
        Souvenir Sheet
646 A98 $2 multicolored   2.75 2.75

Souvenir Sheet

ASIAN INTERNATIONAL INVITATION STAMP EXHIBITION
14-19 AUGUST 93
TAIPEI

TUVALU $1.50

Taipei '93 — A99

Illustration reduced.

Litho. & Typo.
1993, Aug. 14   **Perf. 14½x14**
647 A99 $1.50 Geoffroyi godart 2.00 2.00

Souvenir Sheet

BANGKOK WORLD PHILATELIC EXHIBITION
1ST OCTOBER — 10TH OCTOBER 93
1993
TUVALU $1.50

Bangkok '93 — A100

Illustration reduced.

1993, Oct. 1   Litho.   Perf. 14x14½
648 A100 $1.50 Paradisea staud-
               inger   2.00 2.00

Greenhouse   Christmas — A102
Effect — A101

Beach scene with: 40c, Sun at UR. 50c, Sun
at UL. 60c, Crab on beach. $1.50, Sea gull in
flight.

1993, Nov. 2   Litho.   Perf. 13½
649 A101 40c multicolored   .50 .50
650 A101 50c multicolored   .65 .65
651 A101 60c multicolored   .85 .85
652 A101 $1.50 multicolored   2.00 2.00
 a.   Souvenir sheet of 4, #649-652,
      perf. 14½x14   4.00 4.00
        Nos. 649-652 (4)   4.00 4.00

1993, Dec. 6   Litho.   Perf. 13½
653 A102 40c shown   .55 .55
654 A102 50c Candle, flowers .70 .70
655 A102 60c Angel, flowers .85 .85
656 A102 $1.50 Palm tree, can-
               dles   2.00 2.00
        Nos. 653-656 (4)   4.10 4.10

Souvenir Sheet

HONG KONG '94 STAMP EXHIBITION

Tuvalu $2.00

18-21 February 1994

Hong Kong '94 — A103

Illustration reduced.

1994, Feb. 18   **Perf. 14½x14**
657 A103 $2 Monarch   2.75 2.75

Scenic
Views
A104

1994, Feb. 18   Litho.   Perf. 14
658 A104 40c shown   .60 .60
659 A104 50c Beach, trees,
               diff.   .70 .70

660 A104 60c Boats, ocean   .85 .85
661 A104 $1.50 Boats, beach   2.25 2.25
        Nos. 658-661 (4)   4.40 4.40

New Year 1994
(Year of
the Dog) — A105

1994, Apr. 23   Litho.   Perf. 14
662 A105 40c Irish setter   .60 .60
663 A105 50c Golden retriever .70 .70
664 A105 60c West Highland
               terrier   .85 .85
665 A105 $1.50 German shep-
               herd   2.25 2.25
        Nos. 662-665 (4)   4.40 4.40

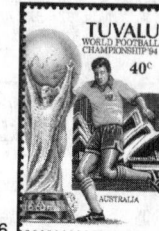

TUVALU WORLD FOOTBALL CHAMPIONSHIP '94 40c

AUSTRALIA

A106

1994, June 7
666 A106 40c Australia   .60 .60
667 A106 50c England   .75 .75
668 A106 60c Argentina   .90 .90
669 A106 $1.50 Germany   2.25 2.25
        Nos. 666-669 (4)   4.50 4.50
        Souvenir Sheet
670 A106 $2 US   3.00 3.00
1994 World Cup Soccer Championships, US.

Umbonium
giganteum   40c

TUVALU   A107

1994, Aug. 16   Litho.   Perf. 14
Seashells.

671 A107 40c Umbonium gi-
               ganteum   .60 .60
672 A107 50c Turbo petholatus .75 .75
673 A107 60c Planaxis savignyi .90 .90
674 A107 $1.50 Hydatina physis 2.25 2.25
        Nos. 671-674 (4)   4.50 4.50

Souvenir Sheet

KOEX
Korea
Exhibition
Centre
PHILAKOREA
1994
WORLD
STAMP
EXHIBITION
SEOUL
12-21
AUGUST
1994

$1.50
TUVALU

PHILAKOREA '94 — A108

Illustration reduced.

1994, Aug. 16
675 A108 $1.50 Pekinese dog   2.25 2.25

TUVALU
SINGPEX
Jungle Fowl
Gallus gallus

Nos. 469-
470, 476-
477
Ovptd.

1994, Aug. 31   Litho.   Perf. 14
676 A64   5c multicolored   .20 .20
677 A64 10c multicolored   .20 .20
678 A64 40c multicolored   .60 .60
679 A64 45c multicolored   .65 .65
        Nos. 676-679 (4)   1.65 1.65

First Manned Moon Landing, 25th
Anniv. — A109

a, 40c, Saturn V. b, 50c, Apollo 11. c, 60c,
Neil Armstrong. d, $1.50, Splash-down.

1994, Oct. 31   **Perf. 14**
680 A109 Strip of 4, #a.-d. 4.50 4.50

TUVALU
40c

Christmas — A110

40c, Boys playing in water. 50c, Islanders
fish being gathered. 60c, People seated under
canopy, food. $1.50, Traditional dancers.

1994, Dec. 15   Litho.   Perf. 14
681 A110 40c multicolored   .60 .60
682 A110 50c multicolored   .75 .75
683 A110 60c multicolored   .90 .90
684 A110 $1.50 multicolored   2.25 2.25
        Nos. 681-684 (4)   4.50 4.50

New Year
1995
(Year of
the Boar)
A111

CHINESE LUNAR YEAR OF THE PIG
TUVALU 40c

40c, One pig. 50c, Pig, piglet. 60c, Three
pigs. $1.50, Sow nursing litter.

1995, Jan. 30   Litho.   Perf. 14
685-688 A111 Set of 4   4.50 4.50

TUVALU
40c

FAO,
50th
Anniv.
A112

40c, Men with vegetables in wheelbarrow.
50c, Man with sack of vegetables. 60c, Girl
cleaning vegetables. $1.50, Girl mixing food.

1995, Mar. 31   Litho.   Perf. 14
689-692 A112 Set of 4   4.00 4.00

40c
Tuvalu

VISIT
SOUTH
PACIFIC
YEAR 95

Visit
South
Pacific
Year
A113

1995, May 26   Litho.   Perf. 14
693 A113 40c shown   .60 .60
694 A113 50c Sailboat   .75 .75
695 A113 60c Hut   .90 .90
696 A113 $1.50 Home, beach   2.25 2.25
        Nos. 693-696 (4)   4.50 4.50

Pacific Coastal Orchids A114

40c, Dendrobium comptonii. 50c, Dendrobium aff. involutum. 60c, Dendrobium rum. $1.50, Grammatophyllum scriptum.

1995, July 28   Litho.   Perf. 14
697-700 A114 Set of 4   4.50 4.50

Souvenir Sheet

Jakarta '95, Asian World Stamp Exhibition — A116

Illustration reduced.

1995, Aug. 19   Litho.   Perf. 12
702 A116 $1 Traditional dancer   1.50 1.50

For overprint see No. 702.

Souvenir Sheet

Singapore '95 World Stamp Exhibition — A117

Illustration reduced.

1995, Sept. 1
703 A117 $1 Phalaenopsis
amabillis   1.50 1.50

End of World War II, 50th Anniv. A118

40c, Soldier with sub-machine gun, map of Japan, Tuvalu. 50c, Soldier holding rifle, landing exercise on beach. 60c, US Marine, offshore air and sea battle. $1.50, Soldier firing rifle, atomic mushroom cloud.

1995, Aug. 19   Perf. 14
704-707 A118 Set of 4   4.50 4.50

Souvenir Sheet

UN, 50th Anniv. — A119

a, Rowing in outrigger canoes. b, UN New York headquarters. Illustration reduced.

1995, Oct. 24   Perf. 14½
708 A119 $1 Sheet of 2, #a.-b.   3.00 3.00

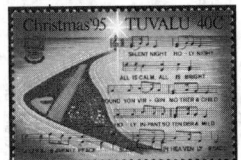

Christmas — A120

Scores and verses to Christmas carols and: 40c, Map of island, "Silent Night." 50c, Boy carolers, "O Come All Ye Faithful." 60c, Girl carolers, "The First Noel." $1.50, Angel, "Hark the Herald Angels Sing."

1995, Dec. 15   Litho.   Perf. 14
709-712 A120 Set of 4   4.50 4.50

Miniature Sheet

Independence, First Tuvalu Postage Stamps, 20th Anniv. — A121

a, 40c, #16. b, 60c, #17. c, $1, #18.

1996, Jan. 1   Litho.   Perf. 14
713 A121 Sheet of 3, #a.-c.   3.00 3.00

Miniature Sheet

New Year 1996 (Year of the Rat) — A122

Stylized rats: a, Looking right. b, Facing left, drinking from container.

1996, Feb. 23 Litho.   Perf. 14x14½
714 A122 50c Sheet of 2, #a.-b. 1.60 1.60
c.   Ovptd. in sheet margin   1.60 1.60
d.   With added inscription in sheet
      margin   1.60 1.60

No. 714c is overprinted in sheet margin with exhibition emblem of Hongpex '96.
No. 714d is inscribed in sheet margin with two exhibition emblems of China '96. Issued: 5/18.

No. 702
Ovptd. in Gold

1996, Mar. 21   Litho.   Perf. 12
715 A116 $1 multicolored   1.60 1.60

No. 715 also contains same overprint in sheet margin.

No. 604 Surcharged in Black, Red & Blue

1996, Oct. 21   Litho.   Perf. 14
716 A90 $1 on 45c multi   1.60 1.60

1996 Summer Olympic Games, Atlanta A123

1996, Sept. 11   Litho.   Perf. 14
717 A123 40c Beach volleyball   .60 .60
718 A123 50c Swimming   .75 .75
719 A123 60c Weight lifting   .90 .90
720 A123 $1.50 David Tua, boxer 2.25 2.25
      Nos. 717-720 (4)   4.50 4.50

UNICEF, 50th Anniv. A124

1996, Oct. 28
721 A124 40c Immunization   .60 .60
722 A124 50c Education for life .75 .75
723 A124 60c Water tank pro-
          ject   .90 .90
724 A124 $1.50 Hydroponic farm 2.25 2.25
      Nos. 721-724 (4)   4.50 4.50

Christmas A125

Designs: 40c, Magi following star. 50c, Shepherds seeing star. 60c, Adoration of the Magi. $1.50, Nativity scene.

1996, Nov. 25   Perf. 14½
725 A125 40c multicolored   .60 .60
726 A125 50c multicolored   .75 .75
727 A125 60c multicolored   .90 .90
728 A125 $1.50 multicolored   2.25 2.25
      Nos. 725-728 (4)   4.50 4.50

Fish A126

1997, Mar. 15   Perf. 14
729 A126 25c Bluetail mullet   .40 .40
730 A126 30c Queen fish
         leatherskin   .45 .45
731 A126 40c Paddletail   .60 .60
732 A126 45c Long-nose em-
         peror   .70 .70
   Complete bklt., 4 ea #729-
         732   8.75
733 A126 50c Long-snouted
         unicornfish   .75 .75
734 A126 55c Brigham's snap-
         per   .80 .80
735 A126 60c Red bass   .90 .90
736 A126 70c Red jobfish   1.00 1.00
737 A126 90c Leopard floun-
         der   1.40 1.40
738 A126 $1 Red snapper   1.50 1.50
739 A126 $2 Longtail snapper   3.00 3.00
   a.   Souv. sheet of 1, wmk. 373 3.00 3.00
740 A126 $3 Black trevally   4.50 4.50
      Nos. 729-740 (12)   16.00 16.00

No. 739a for return of Hong Kong to China, July 1, 1997.

Souvenir Sheet

New Year 1997 (Year of the Ox) — A127

1997, June 20   Litho.   Perf. 14
741 A127 $2 multicolored   5.25 5.25

Hong Kong '97.

Ducks and Drakes A128

1997, May 29   Litho.   Perf. 14
742 A128 40c White pekin   .60 .60
743 A128 50c Muscovy   .75 .75
744 A128 60c Pacific black   .90 .90
745 A128 $1.50 Mandarin   2.25 2.25
      Nos. 742-745 (4)   4.50 4.50

PACIFIC 97.

Domestic Cats — A129

40c, Korat king. 50c, Long-haired ginger kitten. 60c, Shaded cameo. $1.50, American Maine coon.

1997, June 20
746 A129 40c multicolored   .60 .60
747 A129 50c multicolored   .75 .75
748 A129 60c multicolored   .90 .90
749 A129 $1.50 multicolored   2.25 2.25
      Nos. 746-749 (4)   4.50 4.50

Queen Elizabeth II and Prince Philip, 50th Wedding Anniv. — A130

Designs: No. 750, Queen, Prince standing in open vehicle. No. 751, Queen in yellow hat. No. 752, Queen holding umbrella. No. 753, Queen reading, Prince up close. No. 754, Three pictures of Queen. No. 755, Prince in top hat, Queen.
$2, Queen, Prince riding in open carriage, horiz.

Wmk. 373

		1997, Oct. 1	**Litho.**	**Perf. 14½**
750		40c multicolored	.60	.60
751		40c multicolored	.60	.60
a.		A130 Pair, #750-751	1.25	1.25
752		50c multicolored	.75	.75
753		50c multicolored	.75	.75
a.		A130 Pair, #752-753	1.50	1.50
754		60c multicolored	.85	.85
755		60c multicolored	.85	.85
a.		A130 Pair, #754-755	1.75	1.75
		Nos. 750-755 (6)	4.40	4.40

Souvenir Sheet

756	A130	$2 multicolored	3.00	3.00

No. 756 contains one 38x32mm stamp.

Traditional Activities — A131

Christmas: 40c, Turtle hunting. 50c, Pole fishing. 60c, Canoe racing. $1.50, Traditional dance.

Perf. 13½x13

		1997, Nov. 25	**Litho.**	**Wmk. 373**
757	A131	40c multicolored	.55	.55
758	A131	50c multicolored	.65	.65
759	A131	60c multicolored	.80	.80
760	A131	$1.50 multicolored	2.00	2.00
		Nos. 757-760 (4)	4.00	4.00

Souvenir Sheet

New Year 1998 (Year of the Tiger) — A132

Illustration reduced.

		1998, Feb. 2	**Litho.**	**Perf. 13**
761	A132	$1.40 multicolored	1.90	1.90

Diana, Princess of Wales (1961-97)
Common Design Type

Designs: a, Wearing red evening dress. b, Wearing black evening dress. c, Wearing tiara. d, With collar up on coat.

Perf. 14½x14

		1998, Mar. 31	**Litho.**	**Wmk. 373**
762	CD355	80c Sheet of 4, #a.-d.	4.50	4.50

No. 762 sold for $3.20 + 20c, with surtax from international sales being donated to the Princess Diana Memorial Fund and surtax from national sales being donated to designated local charity.

Royal Air Force, 80th Anniv.
Common Design Type of 1993 Reinscribed

Designs: 40c, Hawker Woodcock. 50c, Vickers Victoria. 60c, Bristol Brigand $1.50, De Haviland DHC 1 Chipmunk.

No. 766: a, Sopwith Pup. b, Armstrong Whitworth FK8. c, North American Harvard. d, Vultee Vengeance.

Wmk. 384

		1998, Apr. 1	**Litho.**	**Perf. 13½**
763	CD350	40c multicolored	.55	.55
764	CD350	50c multicolored	.65	.65
765	CD350	60c multicolored	.80	.80
766	CD350	$1.50 multicolored	2.00	2.00
		Nos. 763-766 (4)	4.00	4.00

Souvenir Sheet

767	CD350	$1 Sheet of 4, #a.-d.	5.25	5.25

Ships A133

Designs: 40c, "Los Reyes," "Santiago," 1567. 50c, "Morning Star," missionary topsail schooner, 1867. 60c, "The Light," brigantine of Church of the Resurrection, 1870. $1.50, New Zealand missionary schooner, 1900.

Wmk. 373

		1998, May 19	**Litho.**	**Perf. 14**
768	A133	40c multicolored	.50	.50
769	A133	50c multicolored	.60	.60
770	A133	60c multicolored	.75	.75
771	A133	$1.50 multicolored	1.75	1.75
		Nos. 768-771 (4)	3.60	3.60

Dolphins and Porpoises — A134

40c, Bottlenose dolphin. 50c, Dall's porpoise. 60c, Harbor porpoise. $1.50, Common dolphin.

Perf. 13½x13

		1998, Aug. 21	**Litho.**	**Wmk. 384**
772	A134	40c multicolored	.45	.45
773	A134	50c multicolored	.60	.60
774	A134	60c multicolored	.70	.70
775	A134	$1.50 multicolored	1.75	1.75
		Nos. 772-775 (4)	3.50	3.50

Greenpeace, Save Our Seas A135

Marine life: 20c, Bleached platygyra daedalea, psammocora digitata. 30c, Bleached acropora robusta. 50c, Bleached acropora hyacinthus. $1, Bleached acropora danai, montastrea curta.
$1.50, Bleached seriatopora, bleached stylophora.

Wmk. 373

		1998, Nov. 6	**Litho.**	**Perf. 14½**
776	A135	20c multicolored	.25	.25
777	A135	30c multicolored	.40	.40
778	A135	50c multicolored	.65	.65
779	A135	$1 multicolored	1.25	1.25
		Nos. 776-779 (4)	2.55	2.55

Souvenir Sheet

780	A135	$1.50 multicolored	1.90	1.90

Intl. Year of the Ocean (#780).

Christmas — A136

40c, Flight into Egypt. 50c, Angel speaking to shepherds. 60c, Nativity. $1.50, Adoration of the Magi.

		1998, Nov. 20	**Perf. 14½x14**
781	A136	40c multicolored	.50 .50
782	A136	50c multicolored	.65 .65
783	A136	60c multicolored	.75 .75
784	A136	$1.50 multicolored	1.90 1.90
		Nos. 781-784 (4)	3.80 3.80

Independence, 20th Anniv. — A137

Stamps on stamps, Prime Ministers: 40c, #722, Bikenibeu Paeniu. 60c, Kamuta Latasi. 90c, Tomasi Puapua. $1.50, Design like #166, Toaripi Lauti.

Wmk. 384

		1998, Oct. 1	**Litho.**	**Perf. 14**
785	A137	40c multicolored	.50	.50
786	A137	60c multicolored	.75	.75
787	A137	90c multicolored	1.10	1.10
788	A137	$1.50 multicolored	1.75	1.75
a.		Souvenir sheet, #785-788	4.25	4.25
		Nos. 785-788 (4)	4.10	4.10

Souvenir Sheet

New Year 1999 (Year of the Rabbit) — A138

Illustration reduced.

		1999, Feb. 16	**Perf. 14½x14**	
			Litho.	**Wmk. 373**
789	A138	$2 multicolored	2.50	2.50

Australia '99, World Stamp Expo A139

Maritime history: 40c, Heemskerck, 1642. 50c, HMS Endeavour, 1769. 90c, PS Sophie Jane, 1831. $1.50, P&O SS Chusan, 1852. $2, HM Brig "Supply."

		1999, Mar. 19	**Perf. 14**
790	A139	40c multicolored	.55 .55
791	A139	50c multicolored	.65 .65
792	A139	90c multicolored	1.25 1.25
793	A139	$1.50 multicolored	2.00 2.00
		Nos. 790-793 (4)	4.45 4.45

Souvenir Sheet

794	A139	$2 multicolored	2.50	2.50

Nos. 472, 475, 479, 482 Ovptd.

		1999, June 11	**Litho.**	**Perf. 15**
796	A64	20c on #472	.25	.25
797	A64	35c on #475	.45	.45
798	A64	55c on #479	.70	.70
799	A64	$1 on #482	1.25	1.25
		Nos. 796-799 (4)	2.65	2.65

50% of the sales of Nos. 796-799 will be donated to the Kosovo Relief Fund.

1st Manned Moon Landing, 30th Anniv.
Common Design Type

40c, Lift-off. 60c, Lunar module prepares touchdown. 90c, Ascent stage approaches Command module. $1.50, Recovery.
$2, Looking at earth from moon.

Perf. 14x13¾

		1999, July 20	**Litho.**	**Wmk. 384**
800	CD357	40c multicolored	.55	.55
801	CD357	60c multicolored	.75	.75
802	CD357	90c multicolored	1.25	1.25
803	CD357	$1.50 multicolored	2.00	2.00
		Nos. 800-803 (4)	4.55	4.55

Souvenir Sheet
Perf. 14

804	CD357	$2 multicolored	2.50	2.50

No. 804 contains one circular stamp 40mm in diameter.

Queen Mother's Century
Common Design Type

Queen Mother: 40c, With King George VI inspecting bomb damage. 60c, With daughters at Balmoral. 90c, With Princes Harry and William, 95th birthday. $1.50, As colonel-in-chief of Queen's Dragoon Guards.
$2, Age 6 photo, photo of Yuri Gagarin.

Wmk. 384

		1999, Aug. 16	**Litho.**	**Perf. 13½**
805	CD358	40c multicolored	.55	.55
806	CD358	60c multicolored	.80	.80
807	CD358	90c multicolored	1.25	1.25
808	CD358	$1.50 multicolored	2.00	2.00
		Nos. 805-808 (4)	4.60	4.60

Souvenir Sheet

809	CD358	$2 multicolored	2.60	2.60

Flowers — A141

No. 810: a, Fetai. b, Ateate. c, Portulacacae lueta. d, Tamoloc. e, Beach pea. f, Pomegranate (red letters).
No. 811: a, Cup of gold. b, Rock rose. c, Bower plant. d, Lavender star. e, Hybrid mandevilla. f, Pomegranate (white letters).
No. 812, Scrambled eggs, vert.

Perf. 13¾

		1999, Nov. 22	**Litho.**	**Unwmk.**
810	A141	90c Sheet of 6, #a.-f.	6.75	6.75
811	A141	90c Sheet of 6, #a.-f.	6.75	6.75

Souvenir Sheet

812	A141	$3 multi	3.75	3.75

A142

Millennium — A143

No. 813, Lady of peace with frame.
No. 814: a, Like No. 813, no frame. b, Olive branch. c, Dove. d, Lion. e, Lamb. f, War crowning peace.

No. 815: Sun on horizon, clock, computer keyboard.

Perf. 14½x14¼

1999, Dec. 31		Litho.		
813	A142	90c multi	1.10	1.10
814	A142	90c Sheet of 6, #a.-f.	6.75	6.75

Souvenir Sheet
Perf. 14

| 815 | A143 | $2 multi | 2.50 | 2.50 |

No. 813 printed in sheets of 6.

Worldwide Fund for Nature — A144

Sand tiger shark: a, 10c, Close-up of head. b, 30c, Facing left. c, 50c, Swimming above seaweed. d, 60c, Three sharks.

Perf. 13¼x13½

2000, Feb. 7		Litho.		Unwmk.	
816	A144	Strip of 4, #a.-d.		1.75	1.75
e.		Souvenir sheet, 2 #816		4.00	4.00

Souvenir Sheet
Stamps Without WWF Emblem

| 817 | A144 | Sheet of 4, #a.-d | 1.75 | 1.75 |

Marine Life and Birds — A145

Illustration reduced.
No. 818: a, Common tern. b, White-tailed tropicbird. c, Red emperor snapper. d, Clown triggerfish. e, Longfin bannerfish. f, Harlequin tuskfish.
No. 819: a, Wilson's storm petrel. b, Common dolphin. c, Spotted seahorse. d, Three-band demoiselle. e, Coral hind. f, Palette surgeonfish.
No. 820: a, Great frigatebird. b, Brown booby. c, Dugong. d, Red knot. e, Common starfish. f, Hawksbill turtle.
No. 821: a, Manta ray. b, White shark. c, Hammerhead shark. d, Tiger shark. e, Great barracuda. f, Leatherback turtle.
No. 822: a, Whale shark. b, Sixspot grouper. c, Bluestreak cleaner wrasse. d, Lemon shark. e, Spotted trunkfish. f, Long-nosed butterflyfish.
No. 823: a, Chevroned butterflyfish. b, Mandarinfish. c, Bicolor angelfish. d, Copper-banded butterflyfish. e, Clown anemonefish. f, Lemonpeel angelfish.
No. 824, Picassofish. No. 825, Pygmy parrotfish. No. 826, Sailfish.

2000, Mar. 8			Perf. 14	
Sheets of 6, #a.-f.				
818-823	A145	90c each	6.25	6.25
Souvenir Sheets				
824-826	A145	$3 each	3.50	3.50

Butterflies — A146

Illustration reduced.
No. 827: a, Birdwing. b, Tailed emperor. c, Orchid swallowtail. d, Union Jack. e, Long-tailed blue. f, Common Jezabel.
No. 828: a, Caper white. b, Common Indian crow. c, Eastern flat. d, Cairns birdwing. e, Monarch. f, Meadow argus.
No. 829, horiz.: a, Glasswing. b, Leftwing. c, Moth butterfly. d, Blue triangle. e, Beak. f, Plane.
No. 830, Great egg-fly. No. 831, Palmfly, horiz.

2000, May 1		Sheets of 6, #a.-f.		
827-829	A146	90c each	6.25	6.25
Souvenir Sheets				
830-831	A146	$3 each	3.50	3.50

Birds — A147

#832: a, Red-billed leiothrix. b, Gray shrike-thrush. c, Great frigatebird. d, Common kingfisher. e, Chestnut-breasted finch. f, White tern.
#833: a, White-collared kingfisher. b, Scaled petrel. c, Superb blue wren. d, Osprey. e, Great cormorant. f, Peregrine falcon.
#834: a, Rainbow lorikeet. b, White-throated tree creeper. c, White-tailed kingfisher. d, Golden whistler. e, Black-bellied plover. f, Beach thick-knee.
#835, Morepork. #836, Broad-billed prion, horiz.
Illustration reduced.

2000, June 1		Litho.		Perf. 14
Sheets of 6, #a-f				
832-834	A147	90c each	6.25	6.25
Souvenir Sheets				
835-836	A147	$3 each	3.50	3.50

Dogs and Cats — A148

No. 837: a, Fox terrier. b, Collie. c, Boston terrier. d, Pembroke Welsh corgi. e, Pointer. f, Dalmatian.
No. 838, vert.: a, Dalmatian. b, Boston terrier. c, Fox terrier. d, Pointer. e, Pembroke Welsh corgi. f, Collie.
No. 839, vert. (denominations in orange): a, Ticked taboy oriental shorthair. b, Balinese. c, Somali. d, Chinchilla Persian. e, Tonkinese. f, Japanese bobtail.
No. 840, vert. (denominations in green): a, Lilac oriental shorthair. b, Balinese. c, Somali. d, Chinchilla Persian. e, Tonkinese. f, Japanese bobtail.
No. 841, Scottish terrier. No. 842, Oriental shorthair, vert.
Illustration reduced.

2000, July 3		Litho.		Perf. 14	
Sheets of 6, #a-f					
837-840	A148	90c Set of 4		22.50	22.50
Souvenir Sheets					
841-842	A148	$3 Set of 2		6.50	6.50

Birds and Animals — A149

No. 843, horiz.: a, Brown noddy. b, Great frigatebird. c, Emperor angelfish. d, Common dolphin. e, Hermit crab. f, Threadfin butterflyfish.
No. 844, horiz.: a, Red-footed booby. b, Red-tailed tropicbird. c, Black-bellied plover. d, Common tern. e, Ruddy turnstone. f, Sanderling.
$3, Great frigatebird.
Illustration reduced.

2000, Aug. 3				
Sheets of 6, #a-f				
843-844	A149	90c Set of 2	11.50	11.50
Souvenir Sheet				
845	A149	$3 Great frigatebird	3.25	3.25

New Year 2000 and 2001 (Years of the Dragon and Snake) A150

Designs: 40c, Dragon. 60c, Snake. 90c, Snake, diff. $1.50, Dragon, diff.

2001, Jan. 15		Litho.	Perf. 13½x13¼
846-849	A150	Set of 4	3.75 3.75

Motofoua Secondary School Fire, 1st Anniv. A151

Fire trucks: 60c, Anglo specialist rescue uUnit. 90c, Anglo 4800 water/foam tender. $1.50, Bronto 33-2T1 combined telescopic ladder/hydralulic platform. $2, Anglo 450 LRX water tender. $3, Wormold "Arrestor" ARFFV.

2001, Mar. 9		Litho.	Perf. 13¼	
850-853	A151	Set of 4	5.25	5.25
Souvenir Sheet				
854	A151	$3 multi	3.25	3.25

.tv Corporation A152

Palm fronds, satellite dish and: 40c, Woman. 60c, Dancers. 90c, Man. $1.50, Child. $2, Map.

2001, May 30		Litho.	Perf. 14¼x14½	
855-858	A152	Set of 4	3.75	3.75
Souvenir Sheet				
859	A152	$2 multi	2.10	2.10

Souvenir Sheet

Phila Nippon '01 — A153

2001, Aug. 1			Perf. 13	
860	A153	$3 multi	3.25	3.25

No. 805 Surcharged in Gold like No. 861 and Nos. 806-808 Overprinted in Gold

Wmk. 384

2001, Aug. 4		Litho.	Perf. 13½	
860A	CD358	60c multi	.65	.65
860B	CD358	90c multi	.95	.95
860C	CD358	$1.50 multi	1.60	1.60
860D	CD358	$2 on 40c multi	2.25	2.25
		Nos. 860A-860D (4)	5.45	5.45

No. 809 Surcharged in Gold

2001, Aug. 4	Wmk. 384	Perf. 13½
Souvenir Sheet		
861	CD358 $5 on $2 multi	5.50 5.50

Fauna
A154

Designs: 25c, Mosquito. 30c, Giant African snail. 40c, Cockroach. 45c, Stick insect. 50c, Green stink bug. 55c, Dragonfly. 60c, Monarch caterpillar. 70c, Coconut beetle. 90c, Honeybee. $1, Monarch butterfly. 42, Common eggfly butterfly. $3, Painted lady butterfly.

Unwmk.

2001, Oct. 31   Litho.   *Perf. 13*
862	A154	25c multi	.25	.25
863	A154	30c multi	.30	.30
864	A154	40c multi	.40	.40
865	A154	45c multi	.45	.45
866	A154	50c multi	.50	.50
867	A154	55c multi	.55	.55
868	A154	60c multi	.60	.60
869	A154	70c multi	.70	.70
870	A154	90c multi	.90	.90
871	A154	$1 multi	1.00	1.00
872	A154	$2 multi	2.00	2.00
873	A154	$3 multi	3.00	3.00
	Nos. 862-873 (12)		10.65	10.65

United We
Stand — A155

Statue of Liberty and Tuvalu flag: No. 874, $2, Blue background. No. 875, $2, Yellow background.

2002, Jan. 10   *Perf. 14*
874-875	A155	Set of 2	4.25 4.25

Paintings Depicting Chapter Scenes
From "The Tale of Genji" — A156

No. 876, 40c — Chapter: a, 1. b, 2. c, 3. d, 4. e, 5. f, 6.
No. 877, 60c — Chapter: a, 8, b, 9. c, 10. d, 11. e, 12. f, 13.
No. 878, 90c — Chapter: a, 15. b, 16, c, 17. d, 18. e, 19, f, 20.
No. 879, $4, Chapter 7. No. 880, $4, Chapter 14. No. 881, $4, Chapter 21.

2002, Apr. 24   Litho.   *Perf. 14¼*
Sheets of 6, #a-f
876-878	A156	Set of 3	12.50 12.50

Imperf
879-881	A156	Set of 3	13.00 13.00

Nos. 876-878 each contain six 37x50mm stamps.

UN Special Session on Children and
Convention on Rights of the Child
A157

Designs: 40c, Boy in wheelchair. 60c, Boy and girl sitting near fence. 90c, Nauti Primary School, Funafuti. $4, Mother and child.
No. 886: a, Taulosa Karl. b, Simalua Jacinta Enele.

2002, May 8   Litho.   *Perf. 13¼x13½*
882-885	A157	Set of 4	6.50 6.50

Souvenir Sheet
886	A157	$1 Sheet of 2, #a-b	2.25 2.25

Reign of Queen Elizabeth II, 50th
Anniv. — A158

No. 887: a, Princes William and Harry. b, Queen in blue green suit. c, Queen and Prince Philip. d, Queen wearing red hat.
$4, Queen on horseback.

2002, June 17   *Perf. 14¼*
887	A158	$1.50 Sheet of 4, #a-d	6.75 6.75

Souvenir Sheet
888	A158	$4 multi	4.50 4.50

2002 World Cup Soccer
Championships, Japan and
Korea — A159

No. 889: a, Tom Finney. b, Poster from 1974 World Cup. c, Portuguese player and flag. d, Uruguayan player and flag. e, Suwon World Cup Stadium, Seoul (56x42mm).
$4, Johann Cruyff.

2002, July 15   *Perf. 14*
889	A159	90c Sheet of 5, #a-e	5.00 5.00

Souvenir Sheet
890	A159	$4 multi	4.25 4.25

Queen Mother Elizabeth (1900-
2002) — A160

No. 891: a, 60c, Wearing tiara (lilac shading at UL) (26x29mm). b, 60c, Wearing tiara (lilac shading at UR) (26x29mm). c, 90c, In crowd, holding bouquet of flowers (lilac shading at UL) (28x23mm). d, 90c, Receiving flowers from children (lilac shading at UR) (28x23mm). e, 90c, With teddy bear (lilac shading at UL) (28x23mm). f, With man, woman and children (lilac shading at UR) (28x23mm). g, Color photograph (40x29mm).
No. 892, $2, lilac shading at UL: a, As child, with another young girl. b, As older woman.
No. 893, $2, lilac shading at UR: a, Smelling flower. b, Wearing brooch.

Perf. Compound x14¼ (60c),
13¼x10¾ (90c), 13¼x14¼ ($1.50)
2002, Aug. 12
891	A160	Sheet of 7, #a-g	6.75 6.75

Souvenir Sheets
Perf. 14¾
892-893	A160	Set of 2	8.50 8.50

20th World Scout Jamboree,
Thailand — A161

No. 894 — Merit badges: a, Citizenship in the World. b, First Aid. c, Personal Fitness. d, Environmental Science.
$5, Lord Robert Baden-Powell.

2002, Oct. 2   *Perf. 14¼*
894	A161	$1.50 Sheet of 4, #a-d	6.50 6.50

Souvenir Sheet
895	A161	$5 multi	5.50 5.50

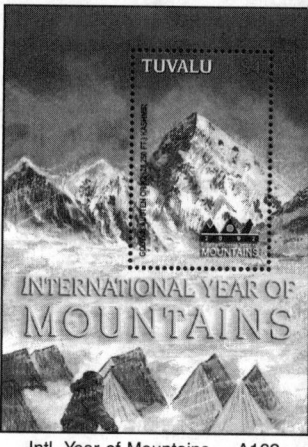

Intl. Year of Mountains — A162

No. 896, horiz.: a, Mt. Fitzroy, Chile. b, Mt Foraker, US. c, Mt. Fuji, Japan. d, Mt. Malaku Nepal and China.
$4, Mt. Godwin Austen, Kashmir.

2002, Oct. 2
896	A162	$1.50 Sheet of 4, #a-d	6.50 6.50

Souvenir Sheet
897	A162	$4 multi	4.50 4.50

Elvis Presley
(1935-77)
A163

2002, Dec. 27   Litho.   *Perf. 14¼*
898	A163	$1 multi	1.10 1.10

No. 898 was printed in sheets of 6.

Princess Diana (1961-97) — A164

No. 899 — Diana wearing: a, Black dress, no necklace. b, Black dress, choker necklace. c, Blue dress. d, Blue green scarf. e, Pink blouse, hand at chin. f, Pink dress.
$4, Black dress, hand on chin.

2002, Dec. 27   *Perf. 14*
899	A164	$1 Sheet of 6, #a-f	7.00 7.00

Souvenir Sheet
900	A164	$4 multi	4.50 4.50

Year of the Horse (in 2002) — A165

Various horses: 40c, 60c, 90c, $2.
No. 905: a, Head of horse, seahorse. b, Heads of horse, three seahorses.

2003, Jan. 23   **Perf. 13¼**
901-904 A165   Set of 4   4.75 4.75
Souvenir Sheet
905 A165 $1.50 Sheet of 2, #a-b   3.50 3.50

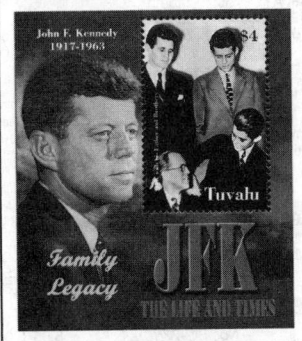

New Year 2003
(Year of the
Ram) — A166

No. 906: a, Green and black background. b, White background. c, Blue background.

2003, Feb. 1   **Perf. 14x13¾**
906 A166 75c Vert. strip of 3,
    #a-c   2.75 2.75
No. 906 printed in sheets containing two strips.

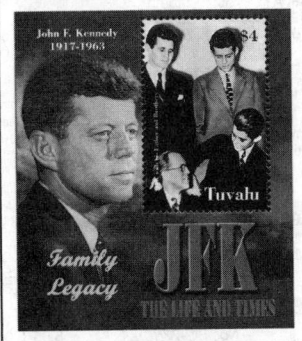

Pres. John F. Kennedy (1917-63) — A167

No. 907: a, In Solomon Islands, 1943. b, On PT 109, 1942. c, Receiving medal for gallantry, 1944. d, Campaigning for Senate, 1952.
$4, With father and brothers.

2003, Mar. 24   **Perf. 14**
907 A167 $1.75 Sheet of 4, #a-d   8.50 8.50
Souvenir Sheet
908 A167 $4 multi   5.00 5.00

Powered Flight, Cent. — A168

No. 909, $1.75: a, Orville Wright in early plane, 1903. b, Wilbur Wright and King Alfonso XIII of Spain, 1909. c, Wilbur Wright's plane, 1908. d, Gabriel Voisin's plane piloted by Léon Delagrange, 1907.
No. 910, $1.75: a, Voisin's motor boat powered glider, 1905. b, Trajan Vuia's single winged plane, 1906. c, Santos-Dumont's biplane, 1906. d, Orville Wright circles parade ground, 1908.
No. 911, $4, Wright Brothers biplane in flight, 1908. No. 912, $4, Glenn Curtiss pilots June Bug, 1908.

2003, May 19   **Litho.**   **Perf. 14**
Sheets of 4, #a-d
909-910 A168   Set of 2   19.00 19.00
Souvenir Sheets
911-912 A168   Set of 2   10.50 10.50

Coronation of Queen Elizabeth II, 50th Anniv. — A169

No. 913: a, Wearing gray dress. b, Wearing tiara. c, Wearing yellow hat.
$4, Wearing hat and pearl necklace.

2003, Aug. 11
913 A169 $2 Sheet of 3, #a-c   8.00 8.00
Souvenir Sheet
914 A169 $4 multi   5.25 5.25

Prince William, 21st Birthday — A170

No. 915: a, Wearing school cap. b, Wearing blue shirt. c, Wearing polo helmet.
$4, Wearing suit and tie.

2003, Aug. 11
915 A170 $1.50 Sheet of 3, #a-c   6.00 6.00
Souvenir Sheet
916 A170 $4 multi   5.25 5.25

General Motors Automobiles — A171

No. 917, $1 — Corvettes: a, Yellow 1979. b, Red 1979. c, Silver 1979. d, 1980.
No. 918, $1.50 — Cadillacs: a, 1931 V-16 Sport Phaeton. b, 1959 Eldorado convertible. c, 1979 Seville Elegante. d, 1983 Seville Elegante.
No. 919, $4, 1990 Corvette. No. 920, $4, 1954 Cadillac Coupe de Ville.

2003, Sept. 8   **Perf. 13¾**
Sheets of 4, #a-d
917-918 A171   Set of 2   13.50 13.50
Souvenir Sheets
919-920 A171   Set of 2   10.50 10.50
Corvettes, 50th anniv.; Cadillacs, 100th anniv.

Tour de France Bicycle Race, Cent. — A172

No. 921: a, Gastone Nencini, 1960. b, Jacques Anquetil, 1961. c, Anquetil, 1962. d, Anquetil, 1963.
$4, Jan Janssen, 1968.

2003, Oct. 6   **Perf. 13¾x13¼**
921 A172 $1 Sheet of 4, #a-d   5.50 5.50
Souvenir Sheet
922 A172 $4 multi   5.50 5.50

Butterflies — A173

No. 923, horiz.: a, Malachite. b, White M hairstreak. c, Giant swallowtail. d, Bahamian swallowtail.
$3, Polydamas swallowtail.

2003, Dec. 16   **Perf. 14**
923 A173 $1.25 Sheet of 4, #a-d   7.75 7.75
Imperf
924 A173 $3 multi   4.50 4.50
No. 923 contains four 42x28mm stamps.

Flowers — A174

No. 925: a, Rhododendron. b, Golden Artist tulip. c, Golden Splendor lily. d, Flamingo flower.
$3, Candy Bianca rose.

2003, Dec. 16   **Perf. 14**
925 A174 $1.25 Sheet of 4, #a-d   7.75 7.75
Imperf
926 A174 $3 multi   4.50 4.50
No. 925 contains four 28x42mm stamps.

Orchids — A175

No. 927, vert.: a, Dimerandra emarginata. b, Oncidium lanceanum. c, Isochilus linearis. d, Oeceoclades maculata.
$3, Oncidium ampliatum.

2003, Dec. 16   **Perf. 14**
927 A175 $1.25 Sheet of 4, #a-d   7.75 7.75
Souvenir Sheet
928 A175 $3 multi   4.50 4.50

Orchids — A176

No. 929: a, Blue-gray gnatcatcher. b, White-eyed vireo. c, Clapper rail. d, Sandhill crane.
$3, Grasshopper sparrow.

2003, Dec. 16
929 A176 $1.25 Sheet of 4, #a-d   7.75 7.75
Souvenir Sheet
930 A176 $3 multi   4.50 4.50

New Year 2004 (Year of the Monkey) A177

Paintings by Chang Dai-chen: 75c, Monkey and Old Tree. $1.50, Two Monkeys.

2004, Jan. 4   **Perf. 13½**

931	A177	75c multi	1.25	1.25

Souvenir Sheet

932	A177	$1.50 multi	2.40	2.40

No. 931 printed in sheets of 4.

Paintings by Norman Rockwell — A178

No. 933, vert.: a, 100th Year of Baseball. b, The Locker Room (The Rookie). c, The Dugout. d, Game Called Because of Rain. $3, New Kids in the Neighborhood.

2004, Jan. 30   **Perf. 14¼**

933	A178	$1.25 Sheet of 4, #a-d	7.75	7.75

Souvenir Sheet

934	A178	$3 multi	4.75	4.75

2004 AmeriStamp Expo, Norfolk, Va. (#933).

SEMI-POSTAL STAMPS

Nos. 159-160 Surcharged and Overprinted: "TONGA CYCLONE / RELIEF / 1982" in 1 or 3 Lines

Wmk. 380

1982, May 20   **Litho.**   **Perf. 14**

B1	A25a	45c + 20c multi	.45	.45
B2	A25b	45c + 20c multi	.45	.45

POSTAGE DUE STAMPS

Arms of Tuvalu — D1

1981, May 13   **Litho.**   **Perf. 14**

J1	D1	1c brt rose lil & blk	.20	.20
J2	D1	2c grnsh bl & blk	.20	.20
J3	D1	5c yellow brn & blk	.20	.20
J4	D1	10c blue grn & blk	.20	.20
J5	D1	20c chocolate & blk	.20	.20
J6	D1	30c orange & blk	.20	.20
J7	D1	40c ultra & blk	.20	.20
J8	D1	50c yellow grn & blk	.25	.25
J9	D1	$1 brt lilac & blk	.40	.45
		Nos. J1-J9 (9)	2.05	2.10

1982-83   **Perf. 14x15**

J1a	D1	1c bright rose lilac & black	.20	.20
J2a	D1	2c greenish blue & black	.20	.20
J3a	D1	5c yellow brown & black	.20	.20
J4a	D1	10c blue green & black	.20	.20
J5a	D1	20c chocolate & black	.25	.25
J6a	D1	30c orange & black	.40	.35
J7a	D1	40c ultra & black	.50	.35
J8a	D1	50c yellow green & black	.60	.45
J9a	D1	$1 bright lilac & black	.95	.65
		Nos. J1a-J9a (9)	3.50	2.80

Issued: 1c-20c, 11/25/82 (inscribed "1982"); 30c-$1, 5/25/83 (inscribed "1983").

OFFICIAL STAMPS

Nos. 96-113 Overprinted: "OFFICIAL"

1981   **Litho.**   **Unwmk.**   **Perf. 14**

O1	A14	1c multicolored	.20	.20
O2	A14	2c multicolored	.20	.20
O3	A14	4c multicolored	.20	.20
O4	A14	5c multicolored	.20	.20
O5	A14	6c multicolored	.20	.20
O6	A14	8c multicolored	.20	.20
O7	A14	10c multicolored	.20	.20
O8	A14	15c multicolored	.20	.20
O9	A14	20c multicolored	.20	.20
O10	A14	25c multicolored	.25	.25
O11	A14	30c multicolored	.30	.30
O12	A14	35c multicolored	.35	.35
O13	A14	40c multicolored	.40	.40
O14	A14	45c multicolored	.45	.45
O15	A14	50c multicolored	.50	.50
O16	A14	70c multicolored	.65	.65
O17	A14	$1 multicolored	.90	.90
O18	A14	$2 multicolored	1.90	1.90
O19	A14	$5 multicolored	4.50	4.50
		Nos. O1-O19 (19)	12.00	12.00

No. 193 Surcharged and Overprinted "OFFICIAL"

Wmk. 380

1983, Aug.   **Litho.**   **Perf. 14**

O20	A30	60c on $1 multi	.75	.75

Nos. 185-186A, 188, 230, 188A-195 Overprinted: "OFFICIAL"

1984   **Litho.**   **Wmk. 380**   **Perf. 14**

O21	A30	5c multicolored	.20	.35
O22	A30	10c multicolored	.20	.35
O23	A30	15c multicolored	.20	.65
O24	A30	25c multicolored	.30	.55
O25	A30	30c on 45c multi	.65	.65
O25A	A30	30c multicolored	.40	.65
O26	A30	35c multicolored	.50	.70
O27	A30	40c multicolored	.55	.70
O28	A30	45c multicolored	.65	.70
O29	A30	50c multicolored	.65	.65
O29A	A30	60c multicolored	.75	.90
O30	A30	$1 multicolored	.95	.90
O31	A30	$2 multicolored	1.50	1.00
O32	A30	$5 multicolored	3.50	2.25
		Nos. O21-O32 (14)	11.00	11.00

Issued: #O23, O29A, Apr. 30; others Feb. 1.

Nos. 469-484 Overprinted "OFFICIAL"

1989, Feb. 22   **Litho.**   **Perf. 15**

O33	A64	5c multicolored	.20	.20
O34	A64	10c multicolored	.20	.20
O35	A64	15c multicolored	.20	.20
O36	A64	20c multicolored	.25	.25
O37	A64	25c multicolored	.30	.30
O38	A64	30c multicolored	.40	.40
O39	A64	35c multicolored	.45	.45
O40	A64	40c multicolored	.50	.50
O41	A64	50c multicolored	.60	.60
O42	A64	55c multicolored	.65	.65
O43	A64	55c multicolored	.70	.70
O44	A64	60c multicolored	.75	.75
O45	A64	70c multicolored	.90	.90
O46	A64	$1 multicolored	1.25	1.25
O47	A64	$2 multicolored	2.50	2.50
O48	A64	$5 multicolored	6.50	6.50
		Nos. O33-O48 (16)	16.35	16.35

For the following islands all are types of Tuvalu unless otherwise specified.
See note following Tuvalu No. 221.

Leaders of the World

Large quantities of some Leaders of the World sets, including unissued stamps, were sold at a fraction of face value when the printer was liquidated.

FUNAFUTI

Catalogue values for all unused stamps in this country are for Never Hinged items.

Locomotive Type of 1984
Perf. 12½x13

1984-86   **Litho.**   **Unwmk.**

Se-tenant Pairs, #a.-b.
a. — Side and front views.
b. — Action scene.

1		5c 1919 Class C51, Japan	.20	.20
2		5c 1935 F.C.C. Andes Class, Peru	.20	.20
3		15c 1934 Kolhapur Class, UK	.20	.20
4		15c 1941 V.R. Class H, Australia	.20	.20
5		15c 1885 S.A.R. Class Y, Australia	.20	.20
6		20c 1951 Class 4, UK	.20	.20
7		20c 1928 Class U, UK	.20	.20
8		25c 1923 Eryri Cog, UK	.25	.25
9		30c 1927 Royal Scot Class, UK	.30	.30
10		35c 1828 Lancashire Witch, UK	.35	.35
11		35c 1906 NY, NH & H RR Class EP-1, US	.35	.35
12		40c 1942 Springbok Class B1, UK	.40	.40
13		40c 1827 Royal George, UK	.40	.40
14		40c 1926 Northern Pacific Class A5, US	.40	.40
15		40c 1900 Aberdare Class 2600, UK	.40	.40
16		50c 1829 Sans Pareil, UK	.55	.55
17		50c 1924 EST Class 241A, France	.55	.55
18		55c 1911 Class 8K, UK	.60	.60
19		60c 1913 Sir Gilbert Claughton, UK	.70	.70
20		60c 1920 Sherlock Holmes, UK	.70	.70
21		60c 1949 Class K1, UK	.70	.70
22		$1 1925 Class P1, UK	1.10	1.10
23		$1 1940 SNCF Class 232R, France	1.10	1.10
24		$1.50 1904 B&O Class DD-1	1.60	1.60
		Nos. 1-24 (24)	11.85	11.85

Issued: #3, 6, 9, 12, 16, 19, 4/16/84; 1, 4, 8, 10, 13, 18, 20, 22, 12/24/84; 2, 5, 11, 14, 17, 23, 4/29/85; 7, 15, 21, 24, 12/30/86. 1986 stamps not inscribed "Leaders of the World."

Automobile Type of 1984

1984-87

Se-tenant Pairs, #a.-b.
a. — Side and front views.
b. — Action scene.
Design A41

25		1c 1957 Triumph TR3A, UK	.20	.20
26		1c 1932 Nash Special 8 Convertible, US	.20	.20
27		10c 1937 Cord 812 Supercharged, US	.20	.20
28		10c 1925 AC Six, UK	.20	.20
29		20c 1924 Alfa Romeo P2, Italy	.40	.40
30		30c 1935 Aston Martin Ulster, UK	.60	.60
31		40c 1948 Morgan 4+4, UK	.85	.85
32		40c 1906 Renault GP, France	.85	.85
33		55c 1903 Cadillac Model A	1.10	1.10
34		60c 1971 Porsche 917K, Germany	1.25	1.25
35		60c 1913 Simplex 75HP, US	1.25	1.25
36		75c 1939 Delahaye Type 165, France	1.50	1.50
37		80c 1938 Opel Admiral, Germany	1.60	1.60
38		$1 1936 Jaguar SS 100, UK	2.00	2.00
39		$1 1965 Aston Martin DB5, UK	2.00	2.00
40		$1.50 1977 Porsche 935	3.25	3.25
		Nos. 25-40 (16)	17.45	17.45

Issued: #25, 27, 31, 38, 9/13/84; 26, 30, 33, 34, 2/8/85; 28-29, 32, 35-37, 39-40, 8/27/87. 1987 stamps not inscribed "Leaders of the World."

Queen Mother Type of 1985

Hats: #45a, Blue feathered. #45b, White. #46a, 50a, Pink. #46b, 50b, Tiara. #47a, 51a, Blue. #47b, 51b, Blue with veil covering face.

#48a, Blue. #48b, Tiara. #49a, Headband. #49b, Hat.

1985-86   **Perf. 13x12**

45	A45	5c Pair, #a.-b.	.20	.20
46	A45	25c Pair, #a.-b.	.30	.3
47	A45	80c Pair, #a.-b.	.90	.9
48	A45	$1.05 Pair, #a.-b.	1.10	1.1

Souvenir Sheets of 2

49	A45	$1.05 #a.-b.	2.25	2.2
50	A45	$2 #a.-b.	2.50	2.5
51	A45	$3 #a.-b.	3.75	3.7

Issued: #45-49, 8/26; #50-51, 1/3/86.

Elizabeth II 60th Birthday Type

1986, Apr. 21   **Perf. 13x12½, 12½x1.**

52	A49	10c Trooping the colors	.20	.2
53	A49	50c Tiara	.55	.5
54	A49	$1.50 As young woman, 1952	1.75	1.7
55	A49	$3.50 Tiara, diff., vert.	3.75	3.7
		Nos. 52-55 (4)	6.25	6.2

Souvenir Sheet

56	A49	$5 Scarf	6.25	6.25

Royal Wedding Type of 1986

#59a, Andrew holding rifle, vert. #59b, Sarah Ferguson, vert. #60a, Couple. #60b, Prince Philip and Andrew.

1986, July 23

59	A53	60c Pair, #a.-b.	1.25	1.25
60	A53	$1 Pair, #a.-b.	2.00	2.00

Souvenir Sheet

61	A56	$4 Newlyweds	4.00	4.00

Nos. 59-60 Ovptd. in Silver "Congratulations to T.R.H. The Duke & Duchess of York"

1986, July 23

62	A53	60c Pair, #a.-b.	1.40	1.40
63	A53	$1 Pair, #a.-b.	2.25	2.25

Royal Anniversaries — A1

1987   **Perf. 15**

66	A1	20c Queen Victoria	.20	.20
67	A1	50c George VI, Family	.55	.55
68	A1	75c Elizabeth	.85	.85
69	A1	$1.20 Elizabeth, Philip	1.40	1.40
70	A1	$1.75 Elizabeth, diff.	2.00	2.00
		Nos. 66-70 (5)	5.00	5.00

Souvenir Sheet

71	A1	$3 Elizabeth, Family	3.25	3.25

Elizabeth's 40th wedding anniv., Queen Victoria's accession to the throne, sesquicentennial.

Summer Olympics Type of 1988

1988, Aug. 19   **Perf. 13x12½**

72	A69	10c Hurdles	.20	.20
73	A69	20c High jump	.25	.25
74	A69	40c Running	.50	.50
75	A69	50c Discus	.60	.60
76	A69	80c Pole vault	1.00	1.00
77	A69	90c Javelin	1.10	1.10
		Nos. 72-77 (6)	3.65	3.65

NANUMAGA

Automobile Type of 1984
Perf. 12½x13

1984-87   **Litho.**   **Unwmk.**

Se-tenant Pairs, #a.-b.
a. — Side and front views.
b. — Action scene.
Design A41

1		5c 1903 De Dion-Bouton Single Cylinder	.20	.20
2		5c 1955 Ford Thunderbird	.20	.20
3		5c 1966 Lotus Elan, UK	.20	.20
4		10c 1915 Stutz Bearcat	.20	.20
5		10c 1915 Dodge 4-Cylinder Touring Car	.20	.20
6		10c 1976 Jaguar XJ-S, UK	.20	.20

	10c	1928 Morgan Super Sports, UK	.20	.20
	15c	1906 Spyker, Holland	.30	.30
	20c	1957 Dual-Ghia, US	.40	.40
	25c	1966 Lamborghini P400 Miura Coupe, Italy	.50	.50
1	25c	1947 Kaiser Traveler, US	.50	.50
2	25c	1951 Lancia Aurelia, Italy	.50	.50
3	30c	1963 Chevrolet Corvette Coupe	.60	.60
4	40c	1949 Jaguar XK 120, UK	.85	.85
5	40c	1930 Renault Reinastella, France	.85	.85
6	50c	1938 Alvis Speed 25, US	1.00	1.00
7	60c	1956 Studebaker Golden Hawk	1.25	1.25
8	75c	1909 Alco, US	1.50	1.50
9	$1	1966 Shelby GT-350 Coupe, US	2.00	2.00
0	$1	1968 Mercedes 300 SEL, Germany	2.00	2.00
1	$1	1953 BRM V-16, UK	2.00	2.00
2	$1	1910 Lozier Briarcliff, US	2.00	2.00
		Nos. 1-22 (22)	17.65	17.65

Issued: #1, 4, 10, 14, 19, 6/11/84; #2, 5, 16, 0, 12/24/84; #6, 11, 18, 21, 7/23/85; #3, 7-9, 2, 15, 17, 22, 8/6/87.
1987 stamps not inscribed "Leaders of the World."

British Monarchs — A2

1984, Nov. 27   *Perf. 13x12½*
Se-tenant Pairs, #a.-b.
a. — Left stamp.
b. — Right stamp.

3	A2	10c	Richard I	.20	.20
4	A2	20c	Richard I, diff.	.30	.30
5	A2	30c	Third Crusade	.50	.50
6	A2	40c	Alfred the Great	.65	.65
7	A2	50c	Alfred, diff.	.80	.80
8	A2	$1	Battle of Edington	1.60	1.60
			Nos. 23-28 (6)	4.05	4.05

Locomotive Type of 1984
1985, Apr. 3   *Perf. 12½x13*
Se-tenant Pairs, #a.-b.
a. — Side and front views.
b. — Action scene.
Design A36

9	A36	10c	1906 NYC & HR Class S	.20	.20
0	A36	25c	1884 T.R. Class B, Australia	.55	.55
1	A36	50c	1902 Decapod, UK	1.00	1.00
2	A36	60c	1846 Coppernob, UK	1.25	1.25
			Nos. 29-32 (4)	3.00	3.00

Flowers — A3

#33a, Tecophilaea cyanocrocus. #33b, ilium pardalinum. #34a, Canarina abyssinica. '34b, Vanda coerulea. #35a, Lathyrus marimus. #35b, Narcissus tazetta. #36a, Bauera essiflora. #36b, Thelymitra venosa.

985, May 3   *Perf. 13x12½*

3	A3	25c	Pair, #a.-b.	.60	.60
4	A3	30c	Pair, #a.-b.	.70	.70
5	A3	40c	Pair, #a.-b.	1.00	1.00
6	A3	50c	Pair, #a.-b.	1.25	1.25
			Nos. 33-36 (4)	3.55	3.55

Queen Mother Type of 1985
Hats: #45a, White. #45b, Blue feathered. *46a, 50a, Violet blue wide-brimmed. #46b, 0b, Blue green wide-brimmed. #47a, 51a,

---

Tiara. #47b, 51b, Light blue. #48a, Dark blue. #48b, Black.
#49a, As young girl. #49b, As young woman.

1985-86

45	A45	15c	Pair, #a.-b.	.25	.25
46	A45	55c	Pair, #a.-b.	1.00	1.00
47	A45	65c	Pair, #a.-b.	1.10	1.10
48	A45	90c	Pair, #a.-b.	1.50	1.50
				3.85	3.85

Souvenir Sheets of 2

49	A45	$1.15	#a.-b.	2.75	2.75
50	A45	$2.10	#a.-b.	3.25	3.25
51	A45	$2.50	#a.-b.	3.75	3.75

Issued: #41-49, 9/5; 50-51, 1/3/86.

Elizabeth II 60th Birthday Type
1986, Apr. 21   *Perf. 13x12½, 12½x13*

52	A49	5c	White hat	.20	.20
53	A49	$1	As young woman	.60	.60
54	A49	$1.75	Tam	1.10	1.10
55	A49	$2.50	Tiara, vert.	1.50	1.50
			Nos. 52-55 (4)	3.40	3.40

Souvenir Sheet

56		$4	Portrait	4.25	4.25

World Cup Soccer Championships, Mexico — A4

Players and teams from participating countries.

Perf. 12½x13, 13x12½
1986, June 30

57	A4	1c	Uruguay, vert.	.20	.20
58	A4	5c	Morocco, vert.	.20	.20
59	A4	5c	Hungary, vert.	.20	.20
60	A4	10c	Poland, vert.	.20	.20
61	A4	20c	Argentina, vert.	.20	.20
62	A4	35c	Bulgaria	.20	.20
63	A4	55c	Portugal, vert.	.25	.25
64	A4	60c	Belgium	.30	.30
65	A4	75c	France	.40	.40
66	A4	$1	Canada, vert.	.55	.55
67	A4	$2	Spain	1.10	1.10
68	A4	$4	Scotland, vert.	2.10	2.10
			Nos. 57-68 (12)	5.90	5.90

Royal Wedding Type of 1986
#71a, Prince Andrew, vert. #71b, Sarah Ferguson, vert. #72a, Prince Philip, Andrew. #72b, Prince Andrew.

1986, July 23

71	A53	60c	Pair, #a.-b.	1.25	1.25
72	A53	$1	Pair, #a.-b.	2.00	2.00

Souvenir Sheet

73	A56	$4	Couple	4.00	4.00

Nos. 71-72 Ovptd. in Silver "Congratulations to T.R.H. The Duke & Duchess of York"

1986, Oct. 26

74	A53	60c	Pair, #a.-b.	1.40	1.40
75	A53	$1	Pair, #a.-b.	2.25	2.25

Royal Anniversaries — A5

1987, Oct. 15   *Perf. 15*

78	A5	15c	Queen Victoria	.20	.20
79	A5	35c	Princesses Margaret and Elizabeth	.40	.40
80	A5	60c	Elizabeth holding Princess Anne	.65	.65
81	A62	$1.50	Elizabeth, Philip	1.75	1.75

82	A62	$1.75	Elizabeth wearing tiara	2.00	2.00
			Nos. 78-82 (5)	5.00	5.00

Souvenir Sheet

83	A5	$3	Elizabeth	3.25	3.25

Elizabeth's 40th wedding anniv.; Victoria's accession to the throne, sesquicentennial.

NANUMEA

Locomotive Type of 1984
Perf. 12½x13
1984-85   Litho.   Unwmk.
Se-tenant Pairs, #a.-b.
a. — Side and front views.
b. — Action scene.
Tuvalu Design A36

1	1c	1940 Class E94, Germany	.20	.20
2	15c	1946 Class 2251, UK	.25	.25
3	20c	1941 Bantam Cock Class V4, UK	.35	.35
4	30c	1902 Class C1, UK	.55	.55
5	35c	1902 S.N.C.F. CC 7121, France	.65	.65
6	40c	1903 La France Frenchmen Class, UK	.75	.75
7	50c	1929 5700 Class, UK	.95	.95
8	50c	1954 S.N.C.F. Class BB 1200, France	.95	.95
9	60c	1881 Fairlight Class G, UK	1.10	1.10
10	60c	1928 V.R. Class S, Australia	1.10	1.10
		Nos. 1-10 (10)	6.85	6.85

Issued: #2-4, 6-7, 9, 4/30; others, 2/8/85.

Cricket Players Type of 1984
1984, Oct. 9   *Perf. 13x12½*
Se-tenant Pairs, #a.-b.
Tuvalu Design A39

11	1c	J.A. Snow	.20	.20
12	10c	C.J. Tavare	.20	.20
13	40c	G.B. Stevenson	.55	.55
14	$1	P. Carrick	1.25	1.25
		Nos. 11-14 (4)	2.20	2.20

Automobile Type of 1984
1985-86   *Perf. 12½x13*
Se-tenant Pairs, #a.-b.
a. — Side and front views.
b. — Action scene.
Tuvalu Design A41

15	5c	1965 Humber Super-snipe, UK	.20	.20
16	10c	1934 Singer 9, UK	.20	.20
17	15c	1948 Holden FX 2.1 Liter Sedan, Australia	.30	.30
18	20c	1953 Buick Skylark	.40	.40
19	20c	1951 Simca Aronde, France	.40	.40
20	35c	1967 Toyota 2000 GT, Japan	.75	.75
21	40c	1960 Elva Courier, UK	.85	.85
22	50c	1952 Bentley Continental, UK	1.10	1.10
23	50c	1938 Hispano-Suiza V12 Saoutchik Cabriolet, Spain/France	1.10	1.10
24	50c	1913 Peugeot Bebe, France	1.10	1.10
25	60c	1935 Bluebird V (LSR), UK	1.25	1.25
26	60c	1978 Mazda RX7, Japan	1.25	1.25
27	75c	1970 Lola T70, UK	1.50	1.50
28	$2	1908 Locomobile, US	4.25	4.25
		Nos. 15-28 (14)	14.65	14.65

Issued: #15, 21-22, 25, 1/14; #17-18, 23, 26, 2/22; #16, 19-20, 24, 27-28, 12/30/86.

Cats — A6

#29a, American short-hair. #29b, Turkish Angora. #30a, Korat. #30b, American Maine Coon. #31a, Himalayan. #31b, Shaded Cameo. #32a, Long-haired ginger. #32b, Siamese Seal Point.

1985, May 28				*Perf. 13x12½*
29	A6	5c	Pair, #a.-b.	.20	.20
30	A6	30c	Pair, #a.-b.	.50	.50
31	A6	50c	Pair, #a.-b.	.80	.80
32	A6	$1	Pair, #a.-b.	1.50	1.50
			Nos. 29-32 (4)	3.00	3.00

Queen Mother Type of 1985
Hats: #41a, 47a, Light gray. #41b, 47b, Light blue. #42a, Lavender. #42b, Blue. #43a, Purple. #43b, Pink. #44a, 46a, Blue. #44b, 46b, Blue flowered. #45a, Feathered. #45b, Veiled.

1985-86

41	A45	5c	Pair, #a.-b.	.20	.20
42	A45	30c	Pair, #a.-b.	.60	.60
43	A45	75c	Pair, #a.-b.	1.60	1.60
44	A45	$1.05	Pair, #a.-b.	2.00	2.00
			Nos. 41-44 (4)	4.40	4.40

Souvenir Sheets of 2

45	A45	$1.20	#a.-b.	2.75	2.75
46	A45	$1	#a.-b.	1.40	1.40
47	A45	$4	#a.-b.	5.50	5.50

Issued: #41-45, 9/5; 46-47, 1/10/86.

Elizabeth II 60th Birthday Type
1986, Apr. 21   *Perf. 13x12½, 12½x13*

48	A49	10c	As teenager	.20	.20
49	A49	80c	As young woman	.50	.50
50	A49	$1.75	Red hat	1.10	1.10
51	A49	$3	Tiara, vert.	1.90	1.90
			Nos. 48-51 (4)	3.70	3.70

Souvenir Sheet

52	A49	$4	Green print hat	4.75	4.75

1986 World Cup Soccer Championships, Mexico — A7

1986, June 10   *Perf. 13x12½*

53	A7	1c	Italy, 1934	.20	.20
54	A7	2c	Italy, 1938	.20	.20
55	A7	5c	Uruguay, 1950	.20	.20
56	A7	10c	Brazil, 1958	.20	.20
57	A7	25c	Argentina vs. Holland, 1978	.20	.20
58	A7	40c	Brazil vs. Czechoslovakia, 1962	.25	.25
59	A7	50c	Uruguay vs. Argentina, 1930	.35	.35
60	A7	75c	West Germany vs. Hungary, 1954	.50	.50
61	A7	90c	Brazil, 1970	.55	.55
62	A7	$1	West Germany, 1974	.65	.65
63	A7	$2.50	Italy vs. West Germany, 1982	1.60	1.60
64	A7	$4	England, 1966	2.60	2.60
			Nos. 53-64 (12)	7.50	7.50

Royal Wedding Type of 1986
1986, July 23   *Perf. 13x12½, 12½x13*

65	A53	60c	Prince Andrew in jeep, vert.	.50	.50
66	A53	60c	Sarah Ferguson, vert.	.50	.50
67	A53	$1	Couple	.80	.80
68	A53	$1	Prince Andrew, Princess Anne and parents	.80	.80
			Nos. 65-68 (4)	2.60	2.60

Souvenir Sheet

69	A56	$4	Newlyweds	4.00	4.00

Nos. 65-68 Ovptd. in Silver "Congratulations to T.R.H. The Duke & Duchess of York"

#70a, Prince Andrew in jeep. #70b, Sarah Ferguson. #71a, Couple. #71b, Prince Andrew, Princess Anne and parents.

1986, Oct. 28

70	A53	60c	Pair, #a.-b.	1.40	1.40
71	A53	$1	Pair, #a.-b.	2.25	2.25

Elizabeth 40th Wedding Anniv. Type
1987, Oct. 15   *Perf. 15*

74	A62	40c	Victoria	.45	.45
75	A62	60c	Elizabeth & Philip, wedding portrait	.70	.70
76	A62	80c	Elizabeth, Philip & Prince Charles	.90	.90

77	A62	$1 Elizabeth, Princess Anne	1.10	1.10
78	A62	$2 Elizabeth	2.25	2.25
		Nos. 74-78 (5)	5.40	5.40

Souvenir Sheet

79	A62	$3 Royal family, diff.	3.25	3.25

Queen Victoria's accession to the throne, 150th anniv.

NIUTAO

Automobile Type of 1984
Perf. 12½x13

1984-85		Litho.		Unwmk.

Se-tenant Pairs, #a.-b.
a. — Side and front views.
b. — Action scene.

Tuvalu Design A41

1		15c 1930 Bentley 4½ Liter Supercharged, UK	.30	.30
2		20c 1935 Wolseley Hornet Special, UK	.40	.40
3		25c 1920 Crossley 25/30HP, UK	.50	.50
4		30c 1976 Cadillac Eldorado 7-Liter V-8	.60	.60
5		40c 1968 Austin Mini Cooper, UK	.85	.85
6		40c 1958 BMW 507 Cabriolet, W. Germany	.85	.85
7		50c 1963 Porsche 365C Cabriolet, W. Germany	1.10	1.10
8		60c 1971 Tyrrell Ford 001, UK	1.25	1.25
		Nos. 1-8 (8)	5.85	5.85

Issued: #1, 4-5, 7, 4/16; #2-3, 6, 8, 5/2/85.

Locomotive Type of 1984
1984-85

Se-tenant Pairs, #a.-b.
a. — Side and front views.
b. — Action scene.

Tuvalu Design A36

9		5c 1830 Planet, UK	.20	.20
10		10c 1863 Prince, UK	.20	.20
11		10c 1943 Gordon Austerity Class, UK	.20	.20
12		20c 1830 Northumbrian, UK	.35	.35
13		30c 1879 Merddin Emrys, UK	.55	.55
14		40c 1829 Agenoria, UK	.75	.75
15		45c 1909 Atchison, Topeka & Santa Fe, 1301	.85	.85
16		50c 1897 Class 6200, Japan	.95	.95
17		60c 1938 F.M.S.R. Class O, Malaya	1.10	1.10
18		75c 1880 1F, UK	1.40	1.40
19		$1 1908 Class E550, Italy	2.00	2.00
20		$1.20 1914 J.N.R. Class 6760, Japan	2.25	2.25
		Nos. 9-20 (12)	10.80	10.80

Issue dates: Nos. 9-10, 12, 14, 16, 19, Sept. 17; Nos. 11, 13, 15, 18, 20, Aug. 21, 1985.

Cricket Players Type of 1984
1985, Jan. 7　　Perf. 13x12½

Se-tenant Pairs, #a.-b.
a. — Head.
b. — Action scene.

Tuvalu Design A39

21		1c S.G. Hinks	.20	.20
22		15c C. Penn	.35	.35
23		50c T.M. Alderman	1.25	1.25
24		$1 K.B.S. Jarvis	2.50	2.50
		Nos. 21-24 (4)	4.30	4.30

Audubon Bicentennial Type

#25a, Purple finch. #25b, White-throated sparrow. #26a, Anna's hummingbird. #26b, Smith's longspur. #27a, White-tailed kite. #27b, Harris' hawk. #28a, Northern oriole. #28b, Great crested flycatcher.

1985, Apr. 4

25	A42	5c Pair, #a.-b.	.20	.20
26	A42	15c Pair, #a.-b.	.35	.35
27	A42	25c Pair, #a.-b.	.60	.60
28	A42	$1 Pair, #a.-b.	2.50	2.50
		Nos. 25-28 (4)	3.65	3.65

Queen Mother Type of 1985

Hat: #37a, Light blue. #37b, Yellow. #38a, 43a, Black. #38b, 43b, Blue. #39a, Tiara. #39b, Pink. #40a, 42a, White. #40b, 42b, Blue. #41a, As young woman. #41b, Feathered.

1985-86

37	A45	15c Pair, #a.-b.	.35	.35
38	A45	35c Pair, #a.-b.	.80	.80
39	A45	70c Pair, #a.-b.	1.60	1.60
40	A45	95c Pair, #a.-b.	2.25	2.25
		Nos. 37-40 (4)	5.00	5.00

Souvenir Sheets

41	A45	$1.05 #a.-b.	2.50	2.50
42	A45	$1.50 #a.-b.	3.50	3.50
43	A45	$4 #a.-b.	8.75	8.75

Issued: #37-41, 9/4; #42-43, 1/10/86.

Elizabeth II 60th Birthday Type
1986, Apr. 21　Perf. 13x12½, 12½x13

44	A49	5c White & gray hat	.20	.20
45	A49	60c Infant	.40	.40
46	A49	$1.50 Flowered white hat	1.00	1.00
47	A49	$3.50 Tiara, vert.	2.40	2.40
		Nos. 44-47 (4)	4.00	4.00

Souvenir Sheet

48	A49	$5 With tiara, diff.	6.25	6.25

For overprints see Nos. 58-62.

Royal Wedding Type

#51a, Couple, vert. #51b, Sarah Ferguson, vert. #52a, Prince Andrew. #52b, Sarah in evening gown.

1986, July 23　Perf. 12½x13, 13x12½

51	A53	60c Pair, #a.-b.	1.00	1.00
52	A53	$1 Pair, #a.-b.	2.00	2.00

Souvenir Sheet

53	A56	$4 Newlyweds	4.00	4.00

Nos. 51-52 Ovptd. in Silver "Congratulations to T.R.H. The Duke & Duchess of York"

1986, Oct. 28

54	A53	60c Pair, #a.-b.	1.40	1.40
55	A53	$1 Pair, #a.-b.	2.25	1.10

Nos. 44-48 Ovptd. in Gold "40th WEDDING ANNIVERSARY OF H.M. QUEEN ELIZABETH II"

1987, Mar.　Perf. 13x12½, 12½x13

58	A49	5c multicolored	.20	.20
59	A49	60c multicolored	.75	.75
60	A49	$1.50 multicolored	1.90	1.90
61	A49	$3.50 multicolored	4.50	4.50
		Nos. 58-61 (4)	7.35	7.35

Souvenir Sheet

62	A49	$5 multicolored	6.25	6.25

NUI

Locomotives Type of 1984
1984-88　Litho.　Perf. 12½x13

Se-tenant Pairs, #a.-b.
a. — Side and front views.
b. — Action scene.

Tuvalu Design A36

1		5c 1911 Class 8800, Japan	.20	.20
2		5c 1932 Soviet Union Railways Class SU	.20	.20
3		10c 1847 Jenny Lind Type, UK	.20	.20
4		10c 1907 Victorian Government Railways Class A2, Australia	.20	.20
5		15c same, 1950 Class R	.30	.30
6		15c 1913 Class 9600, Japan	.30	.30
7		20c 1934 LMS Stanier Tilbury Class 4P, UK	.40	.40
8		25c 1924 Jinty Class 3, UK	.55	.55
9		25c 1928 Boston & Albany Class D12	.55	.55
10		25c 1847 Iron Duke Class, UK	.55	.55
11		25c 1917 Wabash Railroad Class L	.55	.55
12		30c 1943 South Australian Government Railways 520 Class	.65	.65
13		35c 1885 Tennant Class 1463, UK	.75	.75
14		40c 1947 No. 10000, UK	.85	.85
15		40c 1848 Padarn Railway Fire Queen, UK	.85	.85
16		50c 1935 Princess Margaret Rose Class 8P, UK	1.10	1.10
17		50c 1932 Soviet Union Railways Class IS	1.10	1.10
18		60c 1973 D.B. Class ET403, W. Germany	1.25	1.25
19		60c 1916 E. Tenn. & W. N. Carolina R.R. No. 10	1.25	1.25
20		75c 1973 D.B. Class 151, W. Germany	1.60	1.60
21		75c 1909 Tasmanian Goverment Railways Class K Garratt	1.60	1.60
22		$1 1927 B&O President Class	2.25	2.25
23		$1 1832 Mohawk & Hudson Railroad Experiment	2.25	2.25
24		$1.25 1934 Union Pacific Railroad, M-10000 Streamliner	2.75	2.75
		Nos. 1-24 (24)	22.25	22.25

Issued: #5, 8, 12, 16, 3/19; #1, 6, 9, 22, 2/22/85; #3, 10, 14, 18, 20, 24, 8/7/87; #2, 4, 7, 11, 15, 17, 19, 21, 1/29/88.
1987 and 1988 stamps not inscribed "Leaders of the World."

British Monarchs Type of Nanumaga
1984, July 18　Perf. 13x12½

Se-tenant Pairs, #a.-b.

25	A2	1c Queen Anne	.20	.20
26	A2	5c Henry V	.20	.20
27	A2	15c Henry V, diff.	.20	.20
28	A2	40c Queen Anne, diff.	.50	.50
29	A2	50c Queen Anne, diff.	.70	.70
30	A2	$1 Henry V, diff.	1.25	1.25
		Nos. 25-30 (6)	3.05	3.05

Automobile Type of 1984
1985　　　　　Perf. 12½x13

Se-tenant Pairs, #a.-b.
a. — Side and front views.
b. — Action scene.

Tuvalu Design A41

31		5c 1909 Buick	.20	.20
32		15c 1966 Oldsmobile Toronado	.30	.30
33		25c 1947 Railton Mobil Special, UK	.55	.55
34		30c 1924 Opel Laubfrosch, Germany	.60	.60
35		40c 1966 Jensen FF, UK	.85	.85
36		40c 1963 Lotus-Climax GP MK 25, UK	.85	.85
37		50c 1910 Delaunay Belleville, France	1.10	1.10
38		60c 1956 Jensen 541, UK	1.25	1.25
39		90c 1924 Hispano-Suiza H6 Boulogne, France	1.75	1.75
40		$1.10 1972 Citroen-Maserati S.M. Coupe, France	2.25	2.25
		Nos. 31-40 (10)	9.70	9.70

Issued: #33-35, 37, 4/2; #31-32, 36, 38-40, 10/9.

Cricket Players Type of 1984
1985, May 27　　Perf. 13x12½

Se-tenant Pairs, #a.-b.

Tuvalu Design A39

41		1c S.C. Goldsmith	.20	.20
42		40c S.N.V. Waterton	.85	.85
43		60c A. Sidebottom	1.25	1.25
44		70c A.A. Metcalfe	1.60	1.60
		Nos. 41-44 (4)	3.90	3.90

Queen Mother Type of 1985

#49a, 54a, Purple. #49b, 54b, Tiara. #50a, Light blue. #50b, Lavender. #51a, Violet. #51b, White. #52a, 55a, Light blue. #52b, Tiara. #53a, White. #53b, Black.

1985-86

49	A45	5c Pair, #a.-b.	.20	.20
50	A45	50c Pair, #a.-b.	1.10	1.10
51	A45	75c Pair, #a.-b.	1.75	1.75
52	A45	85c Pair, #a.-b.	2.00	2.00
		Nos. 49-52 (4)	5.05	5.05

Souvenir Sheets of 2

53	A45	$1.15 #a.-b.	2.75	2.75
54	A45	$1.50 #a.-b.	2.50	2.50
55	A45	$3.50 #a.-b.	6.00	6.00

Issued: #49-53, 9/4; 54-55, 1/8/86.

Elizabeth II 60th Birthday Type
1986, Apr. 21　Perf. 13x12½, 12½x13

56	A49	10c Feathered hat	.20	.20
57	A49	80c As young woman	.65	.65
58	A49	$1.75 Tiara	1.40	1.40
59	A49	$3 Tiara, diff., vert.	2.40	2.40
		Nos. 56-59 (4)	4.65	4.65

Souvenir Sheet

60	A49	$4 Portrait	5.00	5.00

Royal Wedding Type of 1986

#63a, Couple, vert. #63b, Prince Andrew, vert. #64a, Couple, Queen Elizabeth II. #64b, Andrew as young boy.

1986, July 23　Perf. 12½x13, 13x12½

63	A53	60c Pair, #a.-b.	1.10	1.10
64	A53	$1 Pair, #a.-b.	1.75	1.75

Souvenir Sheet

65	A56	$4 Sarah in wedding dress	4.00	4.00

Nos. 63-64 Ovptd. in Silver "Congratulations to T.R.H. The Duke Duchess of York"

1986, Oct. 28

66	A53	60c Pair, #a.-b.	1.40	1.40
67	A53	$1 Pair, #a.-b.	2.25	2.25

Elizabeth 40th Wedding Anniv. Type of Funafuti

1987, Oct. 15　　　　Perf.

70	A1	20c Queen Victoria	.20	.20
71	A1	50c George VI, Family	.60	.60
72	A1	75c Elizabeth	.85	.85
73	A1	$1.20 Elizabeth, Philip	1.40	1.40
74	A1	$1.75 Elizabeth, diff.	2.00	2.00
		Nos. 70-74 (5)	5.05	5.00

Souvenir Sheet

75	A1	$3 Elizabeth, Family	3.50	3.50

Queen Victoria's accession to the throne, sesquicentennial.

NUKUFETAU

Automobile Type of 1984
Perf. 12½x13

1984-85		Litho.		Unwmk.

Se-tenant Pairs, #a.-b.
a. — Side and front views.
b. — Action scene.

Tuvalu Design A41

1		5c 1904 Mercedes 28 PS, Germany	.20	.20
2		10c 1966 Ford GT40 Mark II	.20	.20
3		10c 1911 Vauxhall Prince Henry, UK	.20	.20
4		15c 1956 Lincoln Continental Mark II	.30	.30
5		20c 1950 Bristol 400, UK	.40	.40
6		25c 1913 Morris Oxford "Bullnose," UK	.55	.55
7		30c 1923 Austin Seven Tourer	.60	.60
8		50c 1921 Bugatti Type 13 "Brescia," France	1.10	1.10
9		50c 1967 Monteverdi, Switzerland	1.10	1.10
10		60c 1925 Lancia Lambda, Italy	1.25	1.25
11		60c 1938 Panhard Dynamic, France	1.25	1.25
12		75c 1960 A.C. Ace, UK	1.50	1.50
13		$1.50 1950 Land Rover Model 80, UK	3.25	3.25
		Nos. 1-13 (13)	11.90	11.90

Issued: #2, 6-8, 10, 5/23; others, 6/26/85.

British Monarchs Type of Nanumaga
1984, Nov. 27　Perf. 13x12½

Se-tenant Pairs, #a.-b.

14	A2	1c Mary II	.20	.20
15	A2	10c Mary II, diff.	.20	.20
16	A2	30c Mary II, diff.	.35	.35
17	A2	50c Henry IV	.65	.65
18	A2	60c Henry IV, diff.	.75	.75
19	A2	$1 Henry IV, diff.	1.25	1.25
		Nos. 14-19 (6)	3.40	3.40

Cricket Players Type of 1984
1985, Jan. 7

Se-tenant Pairs, #a.-b.

20	A39	1c D.G. Aslett	.20	.20
21	A39	10c N.R. Taylor	.20	.20
22	A39	55c S. Oldham	1.10	1.10
23	A39	$1 C.W.J. Athey	2.10	2.10
		Nos. 20-23 (4)	3.60	3.60

Locomotive Type of 1984
1985-88
Se-tenant Pairs, #a.-b.
a. — Side and front views.
b. — Action scene.
Tuvalu Design A36

4	1c	1900 Class XV, Germany	.20	.20
5	5c	1859 ECR Class Y, UK	.20	.20
6	10c	1923 Nord Super Pacific, France	.20	.20
7	10c	1905 LNWR Experimental Class, UK	.20	.20
8	15c	1941 SR Merchant Navy Class, UK	.30	.30
9	20c	1830 S. Carolina Railroad Best Friend of Charleston	.40	.40
10	25c	1941 SR No. 1, UK	.55	.55
11	30c	1987 Class 89, UK	.65	.65
12	40c	1923 Southern Pacific Railroad Class 4300, US	.85	.85
13	50c	1956 New South Wales Government Railways Class 46	1.10	1.10
14	60c	1953 D.B. Class V200, Germany	1.25	1.25
15	60c	1936 Union Railroad Class S-7, US	1.25	1.25
16	60c	1877 Phildelphia & Reading Railroad Camelback	1.25	1.25
17	70c	1968 J.N.R. Class 381, Japan	1.50	1.50
18	$1	1933 Rio Grande Southern Railroad Galloping Goose Railcar, US	2.25	2.25
a.	Souvenir sheet of 2		2.50	2.50
19	$1.50	1935 Chicago, Milwaukee, St. Paul & Pacific Class A	3.25	3.25
		Nos. 24-39 (16)	15.40	15.40

Issued: #24, 26, 34, 37, 4/2/85; #29, 32, 35, 39, 3/20/86; #25, 27-28, 30-31, 33, 36, 38, 38a, 9/10/87.
1986 and 1987 stamps not inscribed "Leaders of the World."

Queen Mother Type of 1985

Hat: #44a, Wide-brimmed blue. #44b, Tiara. #45a, Tiara. #45b, Lavender. #46a, Blue. #46b, White stole. #47a, 50a, White. #47b, 50b, Blue. #48a, 49a, White. #48b, 49b, Wide-rimmed.

1985, Sept. 5   Perf. 13x12½

44	A45	10c Pair, #a.-b.	.20	.20
45	A45	40c Pair, #a.-b.	.90	.90
46	A45	65c Pair, #a.-b.	1.40	1.40
47	A45	$1 Pair, #a.-b.	2.25	2.25
		Nos. 44-47 (4)	4.75	4.75

Souvenir Sheets of 2

48	A45	$1.10 #a.-b.	2.50	2.50
49	A45	$1.75 #a.-b.	2.60	2.60
50	A45	$3 #a.-b.	4.25	4.25

Elizabeth II 60th Birthday Type

1986, Apr. 21   Perf. 13x12½, 12½x13

51	A49	5c Scarf	.20	.20
52	A49	40c Tiara	.25	.25
53	A49	$2 Bareheaded	1.10	1.10
54	A49	$4 Tiara, vert.	2.40	2.40
		Nos. 51-54 (4)	3.95	3.95

Souvenir Sheet

55	A49	$5 Blue hat	6.25	6.25

For overprints see Nos. 65-69.

Royal Wedding Type of 1986

#58a, Couple, vert. #58b, Andrew, vert. #59a, Andrew, parents. #59b, Andrew.

1986, July 22

58	A53	60c Pair, #a.-b.	1.25	1.25
59	A53	$1 Pair, #a.-b.	2.00	2.00

Souvenir Sheet

60	A56	$4 Wedding ceremony	4.00	4.00

Nos. 58-59 Ovptd. in Silver
"Congratulations to T.R.H. The Duke & Duchess of York"

1986, Oct. 28

61	A53	60c Pair, #a.-b.	1.40	1.40
62	A53	$1 Pair, #a.-b.	2.25	2.25

Nos. 51-55 Ovptd. in Gold
"40th WEDDING ANNIVERSARY OF H.M. QUEEN ELIZABETH II"

1987, Oct. 15

65	A49	5c multicolored	.20	.20
66	A49	40c multicolored	.50	.50
67	A49	$2 multicolored	2.50	2.50
68	A49	$4 multicolored	5.00	5.00
		Nos. 65-68 (4)	8.20	8.20

Souvenir Sheet

69	A49	$5 multicolored	6.25	6.25

NUKULAELAE

Locomotive Type of 1984
Perf. 12½x13
1984-86   Litho.   Unwmk.
Se-tenant Pairs, #a.-b.
a. — Side and front views.
b. — Action scene.
Tuvalu Design A36

1	5c	1891 Calbourne Class 02, UK	.20	.20
2	5c	1912 K.P.E.V. Class T18, Germany	.20	.20
3	10c	1942 SNCF Class 141P, France	.20	.20
4	10c	1962 Class 47, UK	.20	.20
5	15c	1941 Union Pacific Big Boy, US	.20	.20
6	15c	1955 DRB 83-10, Germany	.20	.20
7	20c	1940 S.N.C.F. 160-A-1, France	.30	.30
8	25c	1901 Class AEG High Speed Railcar, Germany	.35	.35
9	25c	1839 Albion Railroad Samson, Canada	.35	.35
10	40c	1907 Saint Class, UK	.60	.60
11	40c	1900 Nord De Glehn Atlantic, France	.60	.60
12	40c	1851 Folkstone Class, UK	.60	.60
13	50c	1914 J.N.R. Class 8620, Japan	.75	.75
14	50c	1936 Class 8F, UK	.75	.75
15	80c	1857 Shannon, UK	1.25	1.25
16	$1	1948 Class A1, UK	1.60	1.60
17	$1	1955 E.A.R. Class 59, Kenya	1.60	1.60
18	$1	1897 V.R. Class Na, Australia	1.60	1.60
19	$1	1859 Undine Class, UK	1.60	1.60
20	$1.50	1935 Turbomotive, UK	2.25	2.25
		Nos. 1-20 (20)	15.40	15.40

Issued: #1, 5, 10, 16, 5/23; #2, 7, 11, 17, 12/12; #3, 8, 13, 18, 3/24/85; #4, 6, 9, 14, 19-20, 7/11/86.
1986 stamps not inscribed "Leaders of the World."

Cricket Players Type of 1984

1984, Aug. 8   Perf. 13x12½
Se-tenant Pairs, #a.-b.

21	A39	5c D.B. Close	.20	.20
22	A39	15c G. Boycott	.35	.35
23	A39	30c D.L. Bairstow	.75	.75
24	A39	$1 T.G. Evans	2.50	2.50
		Nos. 21-24 (4)	3.80	3.80

Automobile Type of 1984

1985   Perf. 12½x13
Se-tenant Pairs, #a.-b.
a. — Side and front views.
b. — Action scene.
Tuvalu Design A41

25	5c	1924 Bugatti Type 35, France	.20	.20
26	10c	1908 Sizaire-Naudin, France	.20	.20
27	25c	1965 Sunbeam Tiger, UK	.40	.40
28	35c	1907 Napier 60HP Touring Car, UK	.55	.55
29	35c	1975 BMW 2002 TII, Germany	.55	.55
30	50c	1910 Austro-Daimler Prince Henry, Austria	.85	.85
31	50c	1927 La Salle, US	.85	.85
32	70c	1901 Oldsmobile Curved Dash Buckboard	1.10	1.10
33	75c	1955 Rover 90, UK	1.25	1.25
34	$1	1948 Chrysler Town & Country	1.50	1.50
		Nos. 25-34 (10)	7.45	7.45

Issue dates: #25, 28, 30, 32, Feb. 8; #26-27, 29, 31, 33-34, July 23.

Dogs — A8

#35a, Hungarian vizsla. #35b, Bearded collie. #36a, Bernese mountain dog. #36b, Boxer. #37a, Labrador retriever. #37b, Shetland sheepdog. #38a, Welsh springer spaniel. #38b, Scottish terrier.

1985, Apr. 30

35	A8	5c Pair, #a.-b.	.20	.20
36	A8	20c Pair, #a.-b.	.35	.35
37	A8	50c Pair, #a.-b.	.90	.90
38	A8	70c Pair, #a.-b.	1.25	1.25
		Nos. 35-38 (4)	2.70	2.70

Queen Mother Type of 1985

Hat: #47a, Purple. #47b, Blue. #48a, 52a, Tiara. #48b, 52b, Lavender. #49a, 53a, Pink. #49b, 53b, Dark blue. #50a, Light purple. #50b, Light blue. #51a, As young girl. #51b, Lace.

1985-86

47	A45	5c Pair, #a.-b.	.20	.20
48	A45	25c Pair, #a.-b.	.50	.50
49	A45	85c Pair, #a.-b.	1.75	1.75
50	A45	$1 Pair, #a.-b.	2.25	2.25
		Nos. 47-50 (4)	4.70	4.70

Souvenir Sheets of 2

51	A45	$1.20 #a.-b.	2.75	2.75
52	A45	$1.20 #a.-b.	2.10	2.10
53	A45	$3.50 #a.-b.	6.25	6.25

Issued: #46-51, 9/4; #52-53, 1/8/86.

Elizabeth II 60th Birthday Type

1986, Apr. 21   Perf. 13x12½, 12½x13

54	A49	10c White hat	.20	.20
55	A49	$1 As young woman	.70	.70
56	A49	$1.50 In orange dress	1.00	1.00
57	A49	$3 Tiara, vert.	2.00	2.00
		Nos. 54-57 (4)	3.90	3.90

Souvenir Sheet

58	A49	$4 In brown dress	4.50	4.50

Royal Wedding Type of 1986

#61a, Andrew, vert. #61b, Couple, vert. #62a, Sarah Ferguson and Princess Diana. #62b, Andrew.

1986, July 23   Perf. 12½x13, 13x12½

61	A53	60c Pair, #a.-b.	1.25	1.25
62	A53	$1 Pair, #a.-b.	2.00	2.00

Souvenir Sheet

63	A56	$4 Sarah in wedding dress	4.00	4.00

Nos. 61-62 Ovptd. in Silver
"Congratulations to T.R.H. The Duke & Duchess of York"

1986, Oct. 28

64	A53	60c Pair, #a.-b.	1.40	1.40
65	A53	$1 Pair, #a.-b.	2.25	2.25

Queen Elizabeth II 40th Wedding Anniv. Type of Nanumaga

1987, Oct. 15   Perf. 15

68	A5	15c Queen Victoria	.20	.20
69	A5	35c Princesses Margaret and Elizabeth	.40	.40
70	A5	60c Elizabeth holding Princess Anne	.65	.65
71	A5	$1.50 Elizabeth, Philip	1.75	1.75
72	A5	$1.75 Elizabeth wearing tiara	2.00	2.00
		Nos. 68-72 (5)	5.00	5.00

Souvenir Sheet

73	A5	$3 Elizabeth	3.50	3.50

Queen Victoria's accession to the throne, sesquicentennial.

VAITUPU

Automobile Type of 1984
Perf. 12½x13
1984-85   Litho.   Unwmk.
Se-tenant Pairs, #a.-b.
a. — Side and front views.
b. — Action scene.
Tuvalu Design A41

1	5c	1961 Lotus Elite, UK	.20	.20
2	15c	1950 MG TD Midget, UK	.20	.20
3	15c	1932 Hillman Minx, UK	.20	.20
4	15c	1905 White Model E Steam Car, US	.20	.20
5	25c	1935 Auburn Supercharged 851, US	.40	.40
6	25c	1981 Renault RE20, France	.40	.40
7	30c	1928 Lea-Francis Hyper	.45	.45
8	30c	1940 Packard Darrin	.45	.45
9	30c	1938 Graham, US	.45	.45
10	40c	1968 Chevrolet Camaro	.65	.65
11	40c	1957 Renault Dauphine-Gordini, France	.65	.65
12	50c	1930 Packard Eight	.85	.85
13	50c	1926 Miller Special, US	.85	.85
14	60c	1950 Healey Silverstone, UK	1.00	1.00
15	60c	1970 De Tomaso Pantera, Italy	1.00	1.00
16	$1	1927 Bentley 3-Liter, UK	1.60	1.60
		Nos. 1-16 (16)	9.55	9.55

Issued: #2, 5, 7, 12, Mar. 19; #1, 3, 6, 8, 10, 13-14, 16, Dec. 12; #4, 9, 11, 15, Apr. 4, 1985.

British Monarchs Type of Nanumaga

1984, July 18   Perf. 13x12½
Se-tenant Pairs, #a.-b.

17	A2	1c Richard III	.20	.20
18	A2	5c Charles I	.20	.20
19	A2	15c Charles I, diff.	.20	.20
20	A2	40c Richard III, diff.	.55	.55
21	A2	50c Richard III, diff.	.70	.70
22	A2	$1 Charles I, diff.	1.40	1.40
		Nos. 17-22 (6)	3.25	3.25

Locomotive Type of 1984
1985-87   Perf. 12½x13
Se-tenant Pairs, #a.-b.
a. — Side and front views.
b. — Action scene.
Tuvalu Design A36

23	5c	1929 D.R.G. V3201, Germany	.20	.20
24	10c	1841 G.W.R. Leo Class, UK	.20	.20
25	10c	1937 New York Central Railroad Class J3a	.20	.20
26	15c	1949 Richmond, Fredericksburg & Potomac Railroad Class E8	.30	.30
27	25c	1845 Columbine, UK	.55	.55
28	25c	1954 BR Class 2MT, UK	.55	.55
29	25c	1980 Amtrak Class AEM-7	.55	.55
30	35c	1981 Via Rail LRC Class MPA-27a, Canada	.75	.75
31	45c	1983 British Columbia Railway Class GF6C	.95	.95
32	50c	1888 D&H Class B, India	1.10	1.10
33	60c	1936 D.R. Class 45, Germany	1.25	1.25
34	65c	1904 Northern Pacific Railway Class W, US	1.40	1.40
35	80c	1855 W. & A. R.R. General, US	1.75	1.75
36	85c	1938 Chicago & North Western Railway Class E-4	1.90	1.90
37	$1	1911 J.N.R. Class 9020 Mallet, Japan	2.25	2.25
38	$1	1977 Chicago Regional Transportation Authority Class F40	2.25	2.25
		Nos. 23-38 (16)	16.15	16.15

Issued: #24, 27, 32-33, 3/7/85; #23, 28, 35, 37, 1/16/86; #25-26, 29-31, 34, 36, 38, 9/10/87.
1986 and 1987 stamps not inscribed "Leaders of the World."

A9

Butterfly illustrations by Roger V. Vigurs:
#39a, Marpesia petreus. #39b, Pseudoly-
caena marsyas. #40a, Charaxes jasius. #40b,
Junonia coenia. #41a, Palaeochrysophanus
hippothoe. #41b, Sticopthalma camadeva.
#42a, Phoebis avellaneda. #42b, Apatura iris.

1985, Mar. 12   **Perf. 13x12½**
39	A9	5c Pair, #a.-b.	.20	.20
40	A9	15c Pair, #a.-b.	.40	.40
41	A9	50c Pair, #a.-b.	1.25	1.25
42	A9	90c Pair, #a.-b.	1.90	1.90
		Nos. 39-42 (4)	3.75	3.75

Queen Mother Type of 1985

Hat: #51a, 57a, Light blue. #51b, 57b,
White. #52a, Tiara. #52b, Lavender. #53a,
56a, Violet. #53b, 56b, Green. #54a, Blue.
#54b, Pink. #55a, Looking up. #55b, Looking
forward.

1985-86
51	A45	15c Pair, #a.-b.	.30	.30
52	A45	40c Pair, #a.-b.	.90	.90
53	A45	65c Pair, #a.-b.	1.40	1.40
54	A45	95c Pair, #a.-b.	2.25	2.25
		Nos. 51-54 (4)	4.85	4.85

Souvenir Sheets of 2
55	A45	$1.10 #a.-b.	2.75	2.75
56	A45	$2 #a.-b.	3.00	3.00
57	A45	$2.50 #a.-b.	4.00	4.00

Issued: #51-55, 8/28; 56-57, 1/8/86.

Elizabeth II 60th Birthday Type

1986, Apr. 21   **Perf. 13x12½, 12½x13**
58	A49	5c Green hat	.20	.20
59	A49	60c As young woman	.30	.30
60	A49	$2 Flowered hat	1.00	1.00
61	A49	$3.50 Tiara, vert.	1.75	1.75
		Nos. 58-61 (4)	3.25	3.25

Souvenir Sheet
62	A49	$5 Straw hat	6.25	6.25

For overprints see Nos. 72-76.

Royal Wedding Type of 1986

#65a, Andrew, vert. #65b, Sarah Ferguson,
vert. #66a, Charles, Andrew. #66b, Couple.

1986, July 18   **Perf. 12½x13, 13x12½**
65	A53	60c Pair, #a.-b.	1.25	1.25
66	A53	$1 Pair, #a.-b.	2.00	2.00

Souvenir Sheet
67	A56	$4 Newlyweds	4.00	4.00

Nos. 65-66 Ovptd. in Silver
"Congratulations to T.R.H. The Duke &
Duchess of York"

1986, Oct. 28
68	A53	60c Pair, #a.-b.	1.40	1.40
69	A53	$1 Pair, #a.-b.	2.25	2.25

Nos. 58-62 Ovptd. in Gold
"40th WEDDING ANNIVERSARY OF
H.M. QUEEN ELIZABETH II"

1987, Oct. 15   **Perf. 13x12½, 12½x13**
72	A49	5c multicolored	.20	.20
73	A49	60c multicolored	.75	.75
74	A49	$2 multicolored	2.50	2.50
75	A49	$3 multicolored	3.75	3.75
		Nos. 72-75 (4)	7.20	7.20

Souvenir Sheet
76	A49	$5 multicolored	6.25	6.25

UBANGI-SHARI

ü-'baŋ-gē 'shär-ē

(Ubangi-Shari-Chad)

LOCATION — In Western Africa, north
   of the equator
GOVT. — French Colony
AREA — 238,767 sq. mi.
POP. — 833,916
CAPITAL — Bangui

In 1910 French Congo was divided
into the three colonies of Gabon, Middle
Congo and Ubangi-Shari and officially
named "French Equatorial Africa."
Under that name in 1934 the group,
with the territory of Chad included,
became a single administrative unit.
See Gabon.

100 Centimes = 1 Franc

Stamps of Middle Congo Overprinted
in Black

1915-22   **Unwmk.**   **Perf. 14x13½**
           Chalky Paper
1	A1	1c ol gray & brn	.20	.20
a.		Double overprint	140.00	
b.		Imperf.	42.50	
2	A1	2c violet & brn	.20	.20
3	A1	4c blue & brn	.30	.30
4	A1	5c dk grn & bl	.30	.30
5	A1	5c yel & bl ('22)	.55	.55
6	A1	10c carmine & bl	.75	.75
7	A1	10c dp grn & bl grn		
		('22)	.60	.60
8	A1	15c brn vio & rose	1.00	1.00
9	A1	20c brown & blue	2.40	2.40

No. 8 is on ordinary paper.

Overprinted

1922
10	A2	25c blue & grn	1.10	1.10
11	A2	25c bl grn & gray ('22)	.80	.80
12	A2	30c scarlet & grn	.85	.85
13	A2	30c dp rose & rose		
		('22)	.75	.75
14	A2	35c vio brn & bl	3.25	3.25
15	A2	40c dl grn & brn	4.25	4.25
16	A2	45c vio & red	4.25	4.25
17	A2	50c bl grn & red	4.00	4.00
18	A2	50c blue & grn ('22)	.65	.65
19	A2	75c brown & bl	9.25	9.25
20	A3	1fr dp grn & vio	9.25	9.25
21	A3	2fr vio & gray grn	10.00	10.00
22	A3	5fr blue & rose	27.50	27.50
		Nos. 1-22 (22)	82.20	82.20

For surcharges see Nos. B1-B2.

Types of Middle Congo, 1907-22,
Overprinted in Black or Red

1922
23	A1	1c violet & grn	.30	.30
a.		Overprint omitted	125.00	
b.		Imperf.	25.00	
24	A1	2c grn & salmon	.45	.45
25	A1	4c ol brn & brn	.65	.65
a.		Overprint omitted	150.00	
26	A1	5c indigo & rose	.65	.65
27	A1	10c dp grn & gray grn	1.00	1.00
28	A1	15c lt red & dl bl	1.10	1.10
29	A1	20c choc & salmon	3.50	3.50

Overprinted

30	A2	25c vio & salmon	5.25	5.25
31	A2	30c rose & pale rose	2.00	2.00
32	A2	35c vio & grn	3.25	3.25
33	A2	40c ind & vio (R)	3.25	3.25
34	A2	45c choc & vio	3.25	3.25
35	A2	50c dk bl & pale bl	2.00	2.00
36	A2	60c on 75c vio, pnksh	2.50	2.50
37	A2	75c choc & sal	4.00	4.00
38	A3	1fr grn & dl bl (R)	6.00	6.00
a.		Overprint omitted		
39	A3	2fr grn & salmon	8.00	8.00
40	A3	5fr grn & ol brn	13.00	13.00
		Nos. 23-40 (18)	60.15	60.15

Stamps of 1922 Issue with Additional
Overprint in Black, Blue or Red

1924-33
41	A1	1c vio & grn (Bl)	.20	.20
a.		"OUBANGUI CHARI" omitted	92.50	
42	A1	2c grn & sal (Bl)	.20	.20
a.		"OUBANGUI CHARI" omitted	92.50	
b.		Double overprint	100.00	
43	A1	4c ol brn & brn (Bl)	.20	.20
a.		Double overprint (Bl + Bk)	125.00	
b.		"OUBANGUI CHARI" omitted	125.00	
44	A1	5c ind & rose	.20	.20
a.		"OUBANGUI CHARI" omitted	92.50	
45	A1	10c dp grn & gray grn	.20	.20
46	A1	10c red org & bl ('25)	.55	.55
47	A1	15c sal & dl bl	.55	.55
48	A1	15c sal & dl bl (Bl)		
		('26)	.55	.55
49	A1	20c choc & salmon (Bl)	.60	.60

On Nos. 41-49 the color in ( ) refers to the
overprint "Afrique Equatoriale Francaise."

50	A2	25c vio & salmon (Bl)	.45	.45
a.		Imperf.		
51	A2	30c rose & pale rose		
		(Bl)	.25	.25
52	A2	30c choc & red ('25)	.45	.45
a.		"OUBANGUI CHARI" omitted	100.00	
53	A2	30c dk grn & grn ('27)	.85	.85
54	A2	35c vio & grn (Bl)	.45	.45
a.		"OUBANGUI CHARI" omitted		
55	A2	40c ind & vio (Bl)	.45	.45
56	A2	45c choc & vio (Bl)	.55	.55
57	A2	50c dk bl & pale bl (R)	.30	.30
58	A2	50c gray & bl vio ('25)		
		(R)	.90	.90
59	A2	60c on 75c dk vio,		
		pnksh (R)	.30	.30
60	A2	65c org brn & bl ('28)	1.00	1.00
61	A2	75c choc & sal (Bl)	1.10	1.10
62	A2	75c dp bl & lt bl ('25)		
		(R)	.75	.75
a.		"OUBANGUI CHARI" omitted	100.00	
63	A2	75c rose & dk brn ('28)	1.60	1.60
64	A2	90c brn red & pink ('30)	3.50	3.50
65	A3	1fr & ind (Bk + Bl)	.55	.55
66	A3	1fr grn & ind (R + Bl)	.85	.85
67	A3	1.10fr bister & bl ('28)	1.75	1.75
68	A3	1.25fr mag & lt grn		
		('33)	6.00	6.00
69	A3	1.50fr ultra & bl ('30)	4.50	4.50
70	A3	1.75fr dk brn & dp		
		buff ('33)	7.50	7.50
71	A3	2fr grn & red	.85	.85
a.		"OUBANGUI CHARI" omitted	850.00	650.00

72	A3	3fr red vio ('30)	4.00	4.⬤
73	A3	5fr grn & ol brn		
		(Bl)	3.00	3.⬤
		Nos. 41-73 (33)	45.15	45.⬤

On Nos. 65, 66 the first overprint color refe⬤
to OUBANGUI CHARI.
For surcharges see Nos. 74-81.

Types of 1924 Issue Surcharged with
New Values in Black or Red

1925-26
74	A3	65c on 1fr vio & ol	1.25	1.⬤
a.		"65" omitted	92.50	
75	A3	85c on 1fr vio & ol	1.25	1.⬤
a.		"AFRIQUE EQUATORIALE		
		FRANCAISE" omitted	92.50	
b.		Double surcharge	100.00	
76	A3	1.25fr on 1fr dk bl &		
		ultra (R) ('26)	.80	
a.		"1f25" omitted	110.00	110.⬤

Bars cover old denomination on No. 76.

Types of 1924 Issue Surcharged with
New Values and Bars

1927
77	A2	90c on 75c brn red &		
		rose red	1.25	1.⬤
78	A3	1.50fr on 1fr ultra & bl	1.25	1.⬤
79	A3	3fr on 5fr org brn &		
		dl red	2.10	2.⬤
80	A3	10fr on 5fr ver & vio	12.00	11.⬤
81	A3	20fr on 5fr vio & gray	18.00	17.⬤
		Nos. 77-81 (5)	34.60	33.⬤

Common Design Types
pictured following the introduction.

Colonial Exposition Issue
Common Design Types

1931   **Engr.**   **Perf. 12**
Name of Country Typo. in Black
82	CD70	40c deep green	3.50	3.⬤
83	CD71	50c violet	3.50	3.⬤
84	CD72	90c red orange	3.50	3.⬤
a.		Imperf.	72.50	
85	CD73l	1.50fr dull blue	3.50	3.⬤
		Nos. 82-85 (4)	14.00	14.⬤

SEMI-POSTAL STAMPS

Regular
Issue of
1915
Surcharged

1916   **Unwmk.**   **Perf. 14x13⬤**
         Chalky Paper
B1	A1	10c + 5c car & blue	2.00	2.⬤
a.		Inverted surch.	90.00	90.⬤
b.		Double surcharge	90.00	90.⬤
c.		Double surch., one invtd.	125.00	125.⬤
d.		Vertical surcharge	90.00	90.⬤
e.		No period under "C"	10.50	10.⬤

Regular
Issue of
1915
Surcharged
in Carmine

B2	A1	10c + 5c car & blue	1.10	1.⬤

POSTAGE DUE STAMPS

Postage Due Stamps of
France Overprinted

1928   **Unwmk.**   **Perf. 14x13⬤**
J1	D2	5c light blue	1.00	1.⬤
J2	D2	10c gray brown	1.10	1.⬤
J3	D2	20c olive green	1.25	1.⬤
J4	D2	25c bright rose	1.25	1.⬤
J5	D2	30c light red	1.25	1.⬤
J6	D2	45c blue green	1.25	1.⬤
J7	D2	50c brown violet	1.60	1.⬤
J8	D2	60c yellow brown	2.00	2.⬤
J9	D2	1fr red brown	2.50	2.⬤

10	D2	2fr orange red	3.50	4.00
11	D2	3fr bright violet	3.50	4.00
		Nos. J1-J11 (11)	20.20	21.85

Landscape D3

Emile Gentil — D4

930 Typo.

12	D3	5c dp bl & olive	.50	.50
13	D3	10c dk red & brn	.70	.70
14	D3	20c green & brn	.85	.85
15	D3	25c lt bl & brn	.90	.90
16	D3	30c bis brn & Prus bl	1.75	1.75
17	D3	45c Prus bl & ol	2.10	2.10
18	D3	50c red vio & brn	3.75	3.75
19	D3	60c gray lil & bl blk	4.00	4.00
20	D4	1fr bis brn & bl blk	3.75	3.75
21	D4	2fr violet & brown	4.25	4.25
22	D4	3fr dp red & brn	5.00	5.00
		Nos. J12-J22 (11)	27.55	27.55

Stamps of Ubangi-Shari were replaced in 1936 by those of French Equatorial Africa.

STOCKSHEETS

HAGNER STYLE STOCK SHEETS

Hagner-style stock pages offer convenience and flexibility. Pages are produced on thick, archival-quality paper with acetate pockets glued from the bottom of each pocket. They're ideal for the topical collector who may require various page styles to store a complete collection.

- Black background makes beautiful stamp presentation.
- Pockets use pull away/snap back principle.
- Made from archival-quality heavyweight paper that offers unprecedented protection and clarity.
- Multi-hole punch fits most binder types.
- Available in 9 different page formats.
  8½" x 11" size accomodates every size stamp.

Sold in packages of 10.
Available with pockets on one side or both sides.
"D" in item number denotes two-sided page.

1 POCKET — 242 mm

Item	Retail
S1	$10.99
S1D	$15.99

2 POCKET — 119 mm

Item	Retail
S2	$10.99
S2D	$15.99

3 POCKET — 79 mm

Item	Retail
S3	$10.99
S3D	$15.99

4 POCKET — 58 mm

Item	Retail
S4	$10.99
S4D	$15.99

5 POCKET — 45 mm

Item	Retail
S5	$10.99
S5D	$15.99

6 POCKET — 37 mm

Item	Retail
S6	$10.99
S6D	$15.99

7 POCKET — 31 mm

Item	Retail
S7	$10.99
S7D	$15.99

8 POCKET — 27 mm

Item	Retail
S8	$10.99
S8D	$15.99

MULTI-POCKETS — 36 mm, 67 mm, 139 mm

Item	Retail
S9	$10.99
S9D	$15.99

SCOTT
1-800-572-6885
P.O. Box 828, Sidney OH 45365-0828
www.amosadvantage.com

AMOS
HOBBY PUBLISHING

Publishers of *Coin World, Linn's Stamp News* and *Scott Publishing Co.*

UGANDA

ü-'gan-də

LOCATION — East Africa, at the Equator and separated from the Indian Ocean by Kenya and Tanzania
GOVT. — Independent state
AREA — 91,343 sq. mi.
POP. — 21,619,700 (1999 est.)
CAPITAL — Kampala

Stamps of 1898-1902 were replaced by those issued for Kenya, Tanganyika and Uganda. Uganda became independent October 9, 1962.

Cowries (50 = 4 Pence)
16 Annas = 1 Rupee (1896)
100 Cents = 1 Shilling (1962)

Catalogue values for unused stamps in this country are for Never Hinged items, beginning with Scott 79 in the regular postage section and Scott J1 in the postage due section.

Unused values for Nos. 1-68 are for copies without gum. Very fine examples will be evenly cut and will show at least two full typewritten framelines.

A1

A2

Nos. 1-53 were produced with a typewriter by Rev. Ernest Millar of the Church Missionary Society. They were 20-26mm wide, with nine stamps in a horizontal row. Later two more were added to each row, and the stamps became narrower, 16-18mm.
Rev. Millar got a new typewriter in 1895, and the stamps he typed on it have a different appearance. A violet ribbon in the machine, inserted late in 1895, resulted in Nos. 35-53.
Nos. 1-53 are on thin, tough, white paper, laid horizontally with traces of a few vertical lines.
Forgeries of Nos. 1-53 are known.

Without Gum
Wide Letters
Typewritten on Thin Laid Paper
Stamps 20 to 26mm wide

1895			Unwmk.	Imperf.
1	A1	10(c) black	5,750.	3,750.
2	A1	20(c) black	5,250.	1,600.
3	A1	30(c) black	1,800.	1,800.
4	A1	40(c) black	3,250.	1,550.
5	A1	50(c) black	1,550.	1,300.
6	A1	60(c) black	2,100.	2,100.

Surcharged with New Value in Black, Pen-written

10	A1	10 on 50(c) black	—
11	A1	15 on 50(c) black	—
12	A1	15 on 20(c) black	—
13	A1	15 on 40(c) black	—
14	A1	15 on 50(c) black	—
15	A1	15 on 60(c) black	—
16	A1	50 on 60(c) black	—

Stamps 16 to 18mm wide

17	A1	5(c) black	1,750.	1,100.
18	A1	10(c) black	1,750.	1,500.
19	A1	15(c) black	1,150.	1,500.
20	A1	20(c) black	1,500.	750.
21	A1	25(c) black	1,100.	1,100.
22	A1	30(c) black	8,750.	8,750.
23	A1	40(c) black	8,000.	8,000.
24	A1	50(c) black	3,750.	5,750.
25	A1	60(c) black	6,250.	

Narrow Letters
Stamps 16 to 18mm wide

26	A2	5(c) black	875.
27	A2	10(c) black	875.
28	A2	15(c) black	875.
29	A2	20(c) black	625.
30	A2	25(c) black	875.
31	A2	30(c) black	875.
32	A2	40(c) black	925.
33	A2	50(c) black	750.
34	A2	60(c) black	1,600.
35	A2	5(c) violet	575.	575.

36	A2	10(c) violet	550.	550.
37	A2	15(c) violet	700.	500.
38	A2	20(c) violet	425.	325.
39	A2	25(c) violet	800.	800.
40	A2	30(c) violet	1,100.	800.
41	A2	40(c) violet	925.	925.
42	A2	50(c) violet	1,000.	1,150.
43	A2	100(c) violet	3,250.	3,750.

As a favor to a philatelist, 35c and 45c denominations were made in black and violet. They were not intended for postal use and no rate called for those denominations.

A3

A4

1896

44	A3	5(c) violet	550.	950.
45	A3	10(c) violet	500.	575.
46	A3	15(c) violet	550.	950.
47	A3	20(c) violet	325.	275.
48	A3	25(c) violet	325.	
49	A3	30(c) violet	575.	1,150.
50	A3	40(c) violet	625.	1,150.
51	A3	50(c) violet	700.	900.
52	A3	60(c) violet	1,600.	
53	A3	100(c) violet	1,400.	2,250.

Overprinted "L" in Black

1896	Typeset		White Paper
54	A4	1a black (thin "1")	200.00	175.00
a.		Small "O" in "POSTAGE"	1,050.	925.00
55	A4	2a black	92.50	110.00
a.		Small "O" in "POSTAGE"	350.00	425.00
56	A4	3a black	225.00	250.00
a.		Small "O" in "POSTAGE"	1,100.	1,250.
57	A4	4a black	100.00	160.00
a.		Small "O" in "POSTAGE"	500.00	

Yellowish Paper

58	A4	8a black	190.00	225.00
a.		Small "O" in "POSTAGE"	975.00	1,150.
59	A4	1r black	375.00	425.00
a.		Small "O" in "POSTAGE"	1,400.	
60	A4	5r black	37,500.	37,500.

Without Overprint
White Paper

61	A4	1a black (thin "1")	110.00	97.50
a.		Small "O" in "POSTAGE"	575.00	550.00
62	A4	1a black (thick "1")	18.00	24.00
a.		Small "O" in "POSTAGE"	75.00	92.50
63	A4	2a black	25.00	30.00
a.		Small "O" in "POSTAGE"	97.50	110.00
64	A4	3a black	27.50	32.50
a.		Small "O" in "POSTAGE"	100.00	125.00
65	A4	4a black	26.00	30.00
a.		Small "O" in "POSTAGE"	97.50	110.00

Yellowish Paper

66	A4	8a black	30.00	32.50
a.		Small "O" in "POSTAGE"	110.00	140.00
67	A4	1r black	87.50	110.00
a.		Small "O" in "POSTAGE"	350.00	450.00
68	A4	5r black	210.00	350.00
a.		Small "O" in "POSTAGE"	750.00	975.00

Queen Victoria
A5   A6

1898-1902	Engr.	Wmk. 2	Perf. 14
69	A5	1a red	2.00	2.25
70	A5	1a car rose ('02)	2.25	1.10
71	A5	2a brown	2.25	8.00
72	A5	3a gray	9.25	27.50
73	A5	4a dark green	4.00	7.50
74	A5	8a olive gray	7.50	27.50

Wmk. 1

75	A6	1r ultra	37.50	47.50
76	A6	5r brown	80.00	110.00
		Nos. 69-76 (8)	144.75	231.35

A7

1902	Wmk. 2	Black Overprint
77	A7	½a yellow green	2.25	1.60
a.		Inverted overprint	1,750.	
b.		Double overprint	1,850.	
c.		Pair, one without overprint	4,250.	

Red Overprint

78	A7	2½a dark blue	3.25	3.50
a.		Double overprint	750.00	

Catalogue values for unused stamps in this section, from this point to the end of the section, are for Never Hinged items.

Ripon Falls and Speke Monument
A8

Wmk. 314

1962, July 28	Engr.	Perf. 14
79	A8	30c vermilion & blk	.20	.20
80	A8	50c violet & blk	.20	.20
81	A8	1.30sh green & blk	.35	.35
82	A8	2.50sh ultra & blk	1.25	1.25
		Nos. 79-82 (4)	2.00	2.00

Cent. of the discovery of the source of the Nile by John Hanning Speke.

Independent State

Murchison Falls — A9

Mulago Hospital, X-Ray Service
A10

Designs: 10c, Tobacco growing. 15c, Coffee growing. 20c, Ankole cattle. 30c, Cotton growing. 50c, Mountains of the Moon. 1.30sh, Rubaga and Namirembe Cathedrals and Kibuli Mosque. 2sh, Makerere College and students. 5sh, Copper mining. 10sh, Cement factory. 20sh, Parliament.

Perf. 14½x14, 14x14½			
1962, Oct. 9	Photo.	Unwmk.	
83	A9	5c Prus green	.20	.20
84	A9	10c red brown	.20	.20
85	A9	15c grn, blk & car	.20	.20
86	A9	20c bister & pur	.20	.20
87	A9	30c brt blue	.20	.20
88	A9	50c bluish grn & blk	.20	.20
89	A10	1sh bl grn, sep & red	.20	.20
90	A10	1.30sh pur & ocher	.35	.20
91	A10	2sh grnsh bl, blk & dk car	.45	.25
92	A10	5sh dk green & red	1.10	.55
93	A10	10sh red brn & slate	2.25	1.10
94	A10	20sh blue & pale brn	6.25	3.00
		Nos. 83-94 (12)	11.80	6.50

Uganda's independence, Oct. 9, 1962.

Crowned Crane — A11

1965, Feb. 20	Photo.	Perf. 14½
95	A11	30c bl grn, blk, yel & red	.25	.20
96	A11	1sh30c ultra, blk, yel & red	.75	.50

Intl. Trade Fair at Lugogo Stadium, Kampala, Feb. 20-28.

Black Bee-eater
A12

African Jacana
A13

Arms of Uganda and Birds: 15c, Orange weaver. 20c, Narina trogon. 30c, Sacred ibis. 40c, Blue-breasted kingfisher. 50c, Whale-headed stork. 65c, Black-winged red bishop. 1sh, Ruwenzori turaco. 1.30sh, African fish eagle. 2.50sh, Great blue turaco. 5sh, Lilac-breasted roller. 10sh, Black-collared lovebird. 20sh, Crowned crane.

Perf. 14½x14, 14x14½

1965, Oct. 9	Photo.	Unwmk.
Birds in Natural Colors		
Size: 17x21mm, 21x17mm		
97	A12	5c lt vio bl & blk	.20	.2
98	A13	10c dull blue & red	.20	.2
99	A12	15c dk brown & org	.20	.2
100	A12	20c bister & brt grn	.20	.2
101	A13	30c hn brn & blk	1.40	.2
102	A12	40c lt yel grn & red	.80	.3
103	A12	50c dp pur & gray	.25	.2
104	A13	65c gray & brick red	2.00	1.1

Perf. 14½
Size: 41x25mm, 25x41mm

105	A13	1sh lt blue & blk	.50	.2
106	A12	1.30sh yel & red brn	5.00	.2
107	A13	2.50sh brt yel grn & blk	4.00	.3
108	A12	5sh lil gray & vio bl	6.25	2.1
109	A13	10sh lt brown & blk	10.00	5.5
110	A13	20sh olive grn & blk	19.00	19.0
		Nos. 97-110 (14)	50.00	30.0

Parliament Building — A14

13th Commonwealth Parliamentary Assoc. Conf.: 30c, Animal carvings from entrance hall of Uganda Parliament. 50c, Arms of Uganda. 2.50sh, Parliament Chamber.

1967, Oct. 26	Photo.	Perf. 14
111	A14	30c multicolored	.20	.2
112	A14	50c multicolored	.20	.2
113	A14	1.30sh multicolored	.35	.3
114	A14	2.50sh multicolored	.70	.6
		Nos. 111-114 (4)	1.45	1.3

Cordia Abyssinica
A15

Black-galled Acacia
A16

Flowers: 10c, Grewia similis. 15c, Cassia didymobotrya. 20c, Coleus barbatus. 30c, Ochna ovata. 40c, Ipomoea spathulata (morning glory). 50c, Spathodea nilotica (flame tree). 60c, Oncoba spinosa. 70c, Carissa edulis. 1.50sh, Clerodendrum myricoides (blue butterfly bush). 2.50sh, Acanthus arboreus. 5sh, Kigelia aethiopium (sausage tree). 10sh, Erythrina abyssinica (Uganda coral). 20sh, Monodora myristica.

Perf. 14½x14

1969, Oct. 9	Photo.	Unwmk.
115	A15	5c multicolored	.20	.2
116	A15	10c multicolored	.20	.2
117	A15	15c multicolored	.20	.2
118	A15	20c multicolored	.20	.2
119	A15	30c multicolored	.20	.2
120	A15	40c gray & multi	.20	.2
121	A15	50c tan & multi	.20	.2
122	A15	60c multicolored	.20	.2
123	A15	70c multicolored	.20	.2

Perf. 14

24	A16	1sh multicolored	.35	.20
25	A16	1.50sh multicolored	.55	.20
26	A16	2.50sh multicolored	.70	.20
27	A16	5sh multicolored	1.25	.20
28	A16	10sh multicolored	3.00	.55
29	A16	20sh tan & multi	7.75	1.25
		Nos. 115-129 (15)	15.40	4.40

Values of Nos. 124-129 are for canceled-to-order stamps. Cancellations were printed on Nos. 128-129. Postally used copies sell for higher prices.

Nos. 125-126, 129 Surcharged

		1975, Sept. 29	Photo.	Perf. 14	
30	A16	2sh on 1.50sh multi		.95	.95
31	A16	3sh on 2.50sh multi		19.00	19.00
32	A16	40sh on 20sh multi		7.75	7.75
		Nos. 130-132 (3)		27.70	27.70

Millet — A17

Ugandan Crops: 20c, Sugar cane. 30c, Tobacco. 40c, Onions. 50c, Tomatoes. 70c, Tea. 80c, Bananas. 1sh, Corn. 2sh, Pineapple. 3sh, Coffee. 5sh, Oranges. 10sh, Peanuts. 20sh, Cotton. 40sh, Beans.

1975, Oct. 9   Photo.   Perf. 14x14½
Size: 21x17mm
Multicolored, Name Panel as follows

133	A17	10c lt brown	.20	.20
134	A17	20c blue	.20	.20
135	A17	30c vermilion	.20	.20
136	A17	40c lilac	.20	.20
137	A17	50c olive	.20	.20
138	A17	70c brt green	.20	.20
139	A17	80c purple	.20	.20

Perf. 14½
Size: 41x25mm

140	A17	1sh ocher	.20	.20
141	A17	2sh slate	.35	.25
142	A17	3sh blue	.55	.40
143	A17	5sh yellow green	.70	.55
144	A17	10sh brown red	1.40	1.10
145	A17	20sh rose lilac	2.75	2.25
146	A17	40sh orange	5.75	4.25
		Nos. 133-146 (14)	13.10	10.40

See #195-198. For surcharge & overprints see #175, 203-206, 227-244, 253-257.

Communications Type of Tanzania 1976

Designs: 50c, Microwave tower. 1sh, Cordless switchboard and operators, horiz. 2sh, Telephones of 1880, 1930 and 1976. 3sh, Message switching center, horiz.

1976, Apr. 15   Litho.   Perf. 14½

147	A6a	50c blue & multi	.20	.20
148	A6a	1sh red & multi	.20	.20
149	A6a	2sh yellow & multi	.35	.25
150	A6a	3sh multicolored	.50	.40
a.		Souvenir sheet of 4	1.75	1.75
		Nos. 147-150 (4)	1.25	1.05

Telecommunications development in East Africa. No. 150a contains 4 stamps similar to Nos. 147-150 with simulated perforations.

Olympics Type of Tanzania 1976

Designs: 50c, Akii Bua, Ugandan hurdler. 1sh, Filbert Bayi, Tanzanian runner. 2sh, Steve Muchoki, Kenyan boxer. 3sh, Olympic torch, flags of Kenya, Tanzania and Uganda.

1976, July 5   Litho.   Perf. 14½

151	A6b	50c blue & multi	.20	.20
152	A6b	1sh red & multi	.25	.20
153	A6b	2sh yellow & multi	.45	.40
154	A6b	3sh blue & multi	.70	.60
a.		Souv. sheet of 4, #151-154, perf. 13	7.50	5.25
		Nos. 151-154 (4)	1.60	1.40

21st Olympic Games, Montreal, Canada, July 17-Aug. 1.

Railway Type of Tanzania 1976

Designs: 50c, Tanzania-Zambia Railway. 1sh, Nile Bridge, Uganda. 2sh, Nakuru Station, Kenya. 3sh, Class A locomotive, 1896.

1976, Oct. 4   Litho.   Perf. 14

155	A6c	50c lilac & multi	.20	.20
156	A6c	1sh emerald & multi	.40	.20
157	A6c	2sh brt rose & multi	.80	.45
158	A6c	3sh yellow & multi	1.25	.65
a.		Souv. sheet #155-158, perf 13	3.50	3.50
		Nos. 155-158 (4)	2.65	1.50

Rail transport in East Africa.

Fish Type of Tanzania 1977
1977, Jan. 10   Litho.   Perf. 14½

159	A6d	50c Nile perch	.20	.20
160	A6d	1sh Tilapia	.30	.20
161	A6d	3sh Sailfish	.85	.60
162	A6d	5sh Black marlin	1.25	1.00
a.		Souvenir sheet of 4, #159-162	3.25	2.75
		Nos. 159-162 (4)	2.60	2.00

Festival Type of Tanzania 1977

Festival Emblem and: 50c, Masai tribesmen bleeding cow. 1sh, Dancers from Uganda. 2sh, Makonde sculpture, Tanzania. 3sh, Tribesmen skinning hippopotamus.

1977, Jan. 15   Perf. 13½x14

163	A6e	50c multicolored	.20	.20
164	A6e	1sh multicolored	.25	.20
165	A6e	2sh multicolored	.45	.40
166	A6e	3sh multicolored	.70	.60
a.		Souvenir sheet of 4, #163-166	2.60	2.25
		Nos. 163-166 (4)	1.60	1.40

2nd World Black and African Festival, Lagos, Nigeria, Jan. 15-Feb. 12.

Rally Type of Tanzania 1977

Safari Rally Emblem and: 50c, Automobile passing through village. 1sh, Winner at finish line. 2sh, Car passing through washout. 5sh, Car, elephants and Mt. Kenya.

1977, Apr. 5   Litho.   Perf. 14

167	A6f	50c multicolored	.20	.20
168	A6f	1sh multicolored	.20	.20
169	A6f	2sh multicolored	.45	.30
170	A6f	5sh multicolored	1.10	.85
a.		Souvenir sheet of 4, #167-170	2.00	2.00
		Nos. 167-170 (4)	1.95	1.55

25th Safari Rally, Apr. 7-11.

Church Type of Tanzania 1977

Designs: 50c, Rev. Canon Apolo Kivebulaya. 1sh, Uganda Cathedral. 2sh, Early grass-topped Cathedral. 5sh, Early tent congregation, Kigezi.

1977, June 30   Litho.   Perf. 14

171	A6g	50c multicolored	.20	.20
172	A6g	1sh multicolored	.20	.20
173	A6g	2sh multicolored	.40	.20
174	A6g	5sh multicolored	1.00	.75
a.		Souvenir sheet of 4, #171-174	2.00	2.00
		Nos. 171-174 (4)	1.80	1.45

Church of Uganda, centenary.

Type of 1975 Surcharged with New Value and 2 Bars

1977, Aug. 22   Photo.   Perf. 14x14½

175	A17	80c on 60c bananas	.30	.20

No. 175 was not issued without surcharge.

Wildlife Type of Tanzania 1977

Wildlife Fund Emblem and: 50c, Pancake tortoise. 1sh, Nile crocodile. 2sh, Hunter's hartebeest. 3sh, Red colobus monkey. 5sh, Dugong.

1977, Sept. 26   Litho.   Perf. 14x13½

176	A6h	50c multicolored	.25	.20
177	A6h	1sh multicolored	.40	.30
178	A6h	2sh multicolored	1.75	.75
179	A6h	3sh multicolored	2.50	1.00
180	A6h	5sh multicolored	2.50	2.00
a.		Souvenir sheet of 4, #177-180	7.00	4.00
		Nos. 176-180 (5)	7.40	4.25

Endangered species.

Soccer Type of Tanzania

Soccer Cup and: 50c, Soccer scene and Joe Kadenge. 1sh, Mohammed Chuma receiving trophy, and his portrait. 2sh, Shot on goal and Omari S. Kidevu. 5sh, Backfield defense and Polly Ouma.

1978, May 3   Litho.   Perf. 14x13½

181	A8a	50c green & multi	.20	.20
182	A8a	1sh lt brown & multi	.20	.20
183	A8a	2sh lilac & multi	.40	.30
184	A8a	5sh dk blue & multi	1.10	.90
a.		Souvenir sheet of 4, #181-184	2.25	2.25
		Nos. 181-184 (4)	1.90	1.45

World Soccer Cup Championships, Argentina, June 1-25.
See Nos. 203-206.

Crop Type of 1975

Designs as before.

1978, June   Litho.   Perf. 14½
Size: 41x25mm
Multicolored, Name Panel as follows

195	A17	5sh blue	.50	.25
196	A17	10sh rose lilac	.95	.50
197	A17	20sh brown	1.90	1.00
198	A17	40sh deep orange	3.75	2.10
		Nos. 195-198 (4)	7.10	3.85

Shot Put
A18

1978, July 10   Litho.   Perf. 14

199	A18	50c shown	.20	.20
200	A18	1sh Broad jump	.20	.20
201	A18	2sh Running	.40	.40
202	A18	5sh Boxing	1.00	1.00
a.		Souv. sheet, #199-202, perf 12	2.75	2.75
		Nos. 199-202 (4)	1.80	1.80

Commonwealth Games, Edmonton, Canada, Aug. 3-12.
For overprints see Nos. 249-252.

Soccer Type of 1978 Inscribed: "WORLD CUP 1978"

Designs: 50c, Backfield defense and Polly Ouma. 2sh, Shot on goal and Omari S. Kidevu. 5sh, Soccer scene and Joe Kadenge. 10sh, Mohammed Chuma receiving trophy, and his portrait.

1978, Sept. 11   Perf. 14x13½

203	A8a	50c dk blue & multi	.20	.20
204	A8a	2sh lilac & multi	.45	.35
205	A8a	5sh green & multi	1.00	.90
206	A8a	10sh lt brown & multi	2.00	1.75
a.		Souv. sheet of 4, #203-206, perf. 12	4.00	4.00
		Nos. 203-206 (4)	3.65	3.20

World Cup Soccer Championship winners.

Blood Pressure Gauge and
Chart — A19

1978, Sept. 25   Litho.   Perf. 14

207	A19	50c shown	.20	.20
208	A19	1sh Heart	.20	.20
209	A19	2sh Retina	.40	.35
210	A19	5sh Kidneys	1.00	.95
a.		Souvenir sheet of 4, #207-210	2.00	2.00
		Nos. 207-210 (4)	1.80	1.70

World Health Day and Hypertension Month.

Cattle Unloaded from Plane A20

Flyer 1 and: 1.50sh, "Islander" on runway, Kampala. 2.70sh, Coffee loaded on transport jet. 10sh, Concorde.

1978, Dec. 16

211	A20	1sh multicolored	.20	.20
212	A20	1.50sh multicolored	.25	.20
213	A20	2.70sh multicolored	.45	.40
214	A20	10sh multicolored	1.90	1.40
a.		Souvenir sheet of 4, #211-214	3.00	3.00
		Nos. 211-214 (4)	2.80	2.20

75th anniversary of 1st powered flight.
For overprints see Nos. 258-261.

Elizabeth II Leaving Owen Falls
Dam — A21

Designs: 1.50sh, Coronation regalia. 2.70sh, Coronation ceremony. 10sh, Royal family on balcony of Buckingham Palace.

1979, Mar. 1   Litho.   Perf. 12½x12

215	A21	1sh multicolored	.20	.20
216	A21	1.50sh multicolored	.20	.20
217	A21	2.70sh multicolored	.35	.30
218	A21	10sh multicolored	1.40	1.10
a.		Souvenir sheet of 4, #215-218	2.40	2.40
		Nos. 215-218 (4)	2.15	1.80

25th anniv. of coronation of Elizabeth II.
For overprints see Nos. 245-248.

Bishop
Joseph
Kiwanuka
A22

Designs: 1.50sh, Lubaga Cathedral. 2.70sh, Ugandan pilgrims and St. Peter's, Rome. 10sh, Friar Lourdel-Mapeera, missionary.

1979, Feb. 15   Perf. 14

219	A22	1sh multicolored	.20	.20
220	A22	1.50sh multicolored	.20	.20
221	A22	2.70sh multicolored	.35	.30
222	A22	10sh multicolored	1.40	1.10
a.		Souvenir sheet of 4, #219-222	2.40	2.40
		Nos. 219-222 (4)	2.15	1.80

Ugandan Catholic Church, centenary.
See No. 274. For overprints see Nos. 262-265.

Child Receiving Vaccination — A23

IYC Emblem and: 1.50sh, Handicapped children playing. 2.70sh, Ugandan IYC emblem. 10sh, Teacher and pupils.

1979, July 16   Litho.   Perf. 14

223	A23	1sh multicolored	.20	.20
224	A23	1.50sh multicolored	.20	.20
225	A23	2.70sh multicolored	.25	.25
226	A23	10sh multicolored	1.10	.90
a.		Souvenir sheet of 4, #223-226	2.00	2.00
		Nos. 223-226 (4)	1.75	1.55

International Year of the Child.
For overprints see Nos. 266-269.

Nos. 133-146, 195-198, 215-218 Overprinted: "UGANDA / LIBERATED / 1979"

1979, July 12   Photo.   Perf. 14x14½
Size: 21x17mm

227	A17	10c multicolored	.20	.20
228	A17	20c multicolored	.20	.20
229	A17	30c multicolored	.20	.20
230	A17	40c multicolored	.20	.20
231	A17	50c multicolored	.20	.20
232	A17	70c multicolored	.20	.20
233	A17	80c multicolored	.20	.20

Perf. 14½
Size: 41x25mm

234	A17	1sh multicolored	.20	.20
235	A17	2sh multicolored	.25	.20
236	A17	3sh multicolored	.40	.30
237	A17	5sh multicolored	.55	.45
238	A17	10sh multicolored	1.10	.90
239	A17	20sh multicolored	2.25	2.00
240	A17	40sh multicolored	4.50	3.75
		Nos. 227-240 (14)	10.65	9.20

1979 Litho. Perf. 14½
Multicolored, name panel as follows
241	A17	5sh blue	.75	.55
242	A17	10sh rose lilac	1.40	1.10
243	A17	20sh brown	2.60	2.25
244	A17	40sh deep orange	5.25	4.50
		Nos. 241-244 (4)	10.00	8.40

1979, July 12 Litho. Perf. 12½x12
245	A21	1sh multicolored	.20	.20
246	A21	1.50sh multicolored	.20	.20
247	A21	2.70sh multicolored	.25	.25
248	A21	15sh on 10sh multi	1.60	1.10
a.		Souvenir sheet of 4	3.00	
		Nos. 245-248 (4)	2.25	1.75

No. 248a contains Nos. 245-247 and a 15sh in design of No. 218. Issued Aug. 1.

Nos. 199-202; 203, 204-206; 211-214;
219-222, 223-226 Overprinted:
"UGANDA LIBERATED 1979"

1979, Aug. 1 Litho. Perf. 14
249	A18	50c multicolored	.20	.20
250	A18	1sh multicolored	.20	.20
251	A18	2sh multicolored	.35	.25
252	A18	5sh multicolored	.85	.75

Type A17 of Kenya
1979, Aug. 1 Perf. 14x13½
253	A17	50c multi	.20	.20
255	A17	2sh multi (#204)	.30	.25
256	A17	5sh multi	.85	.70
257	A17	10sh multi	1.75	1.40

Overprint exists on No. 183.

1979, Aug. 1 Perf. 14
258	A20	1sh multicolored	.20	.20
259	A20	1.50sh multicolored	.30	.25
260	A20	2.70sh multicolored	.60	.50
261	A20	10sh multicolored	2.10	1.75

1979, Aug. 1
262	A22	1sh multicolored	.20	.20
263	A22	1.50sh multicolored	.25	.20
264	A22	2.70sh multicolored	.45	.40
265	A22	10sh multicolored	1.60	1.40

1979, Aug. 16
266	A23	1sh multicolored	.20	.20
267	A23	1.50sh multicolored	.25	.20
268	A23	2.70sh multicolored	.50	.45
269	A23	10sh multicolored	1.75	1.60
a.		Souvenir sheet of 4, #266-269	2.75	2.75
		Nos. 249-269 (20)	13.10	11.30

ITU Emblem, Radio Waves A24

1979, Sept. 11
270	A24	1sh lt gray & multi	.20	.20
271	A24	1.50sh orange & multi	.20	.20
272	A24	2.70sh yellow & multi	.20	.20
273	A24	10sh blue & multi	.90	.75
		Nos. 270-273 (4)	1.50	1.35

50th anniv. of Intl. Radio Consultative Committee (CCIR) of the ITU.

No. 222a Redrawn and Inscribed:
FREEDOM OF WORSHIP
DECLARED
Souvenir Sheet
1979, Sept. Perf. 12
274		Sheet of 4	2.25	2.25
a.		A22 1sh No. 219	.20	.20
b.		A22 1.50sh No. 220	.20	.20
c.		A22 2.70sh No. 221	.35	.35
d.		A22 10sh No. 222	1.40	1.40

In top panel of margin scrolls and coat of arms have been replaced by inscription.

A25

1979, Nov. 12 Litho. Perf. 14
275	A25	1sh #110	.20	.20
276	A25	1.50sh #112	.20	.20
277	A25	2.70sh #94	.40	.35

278	A25	10sh #69	1.50	1.25
a.		Souvenir sheet of 4, #275-278	2.25	2.25
		Nos. 275-278 (4)	2.30	2.00

Sir Rowland Hill (1795-1879), originator of penny postage.
For overprints see Nos. 293-296.

Thomson's Gazelle — A26

Designs: 10c, Impalas. 20c, Large-spotted genet. 50c, Bush babies. 80c, Wild hunting dogs. 1sh, Lions. 1.50sh, Mountain gorillas. 2sh, Zebras. 2.70sh, Leopards. 3.50sh, Black rhinoceroses. 5sh, Defassa waterbucks. 10sh, African black buffaloes. 20sh, Hippopotami. 40sh, African elephants.

1979, Dec. 3 Litho. Perf. 14
Size: 21x17mm
279	A26	10c multicolored	.20	.20
280	A26	20c multicolored	.20	.20
281	A26	30c multicolored	.20	.20
282	A26	50c multicolored	.20	.20
283	A26	80c multicolored	.20	.20

Size: 39x25mm
284	A26	1sh multicolored	.20	.20
285	A26	1.50sh multicolored	.20	.20
286	A26	2sh multicolored	.25	.20
287	A26	2.70sh multicolored	.30	.30
288	A26	3.50sh multicolored	.40	.35
289	A26	5sh multicolored	.60	.55
290	A26	10sh multicolored	1.10	1.00
291	A26	20sh multicolored	2.50	2.10
292	A26	40sh multicolored	5.25	4.25
		Nos. 279-292 (14)	11.80	10.15

Nos. 284, 286, 289 reissued inscribed 1982.
See Nos. 400-406. For surcharges see Nos. 386-392.

Nos. 275-278a Overprinted: "LONDON 1980"

1980, May 6 Litho. Perf. 14
293	A25	1sh multicolored	.20	.20
294	A25	1.50sh multicolored	.20	.20
295	A25	2.70sh multicolored	.40	.35
296	A25	10sh multicolored	1.40	1.40
a.		Souvenir sheet of 4, #293-296	2.25	2.25
		Nos. 293-296 (4)	2.20	2.15

London 80 Intl. Stamp Exhib., May 6-14.

Paul Harris Wheeling Rotary Cart A27

1980, Aug. Litho. Perf. 14
297	A27	1sh Rotary emblem, vert.	.20	.20
298	A27	20sh shown	2.10	1.60
a.		Souvenir sheet of 2, #297-298	3.00	

Rotary International, 75th anniversary.

Soccer, Flags of Olympic Participants, Flame — A28

1980, Dec. 29 Litho. Perf. 14
299	A28	1sh shown	.20	.20
300	A28	2sh Relay race	.20	.20
301	A28	10sh Hurdles	.80	.80
302	A28	20sh Boxing	1.60	1.60
		Nos. 299-302 (4)	2.80	2.80

Souvenir Sheet
303		Sheet of 4	3.00	3.00
a.		A28 2.70sh like #299	.20	.20
b.		A28 3sh like #300	.25	.20
c.		A28 5sh like #301	.40	.35
d.		A28 25sh like 302	2.10	1.75

22nd Summer Olympic Games, Moscow, July 19-Aug. 3.

Nos. 299-303 Overprinted with Sport,
Winner and Country

1980, Dec. 29
304	A28	1sh multicolored	.20	.20
305	A28	2sh multicolored	.20	.20
306	A28	10sh multicolored	.80	.80
307	A28	20sh multicolored	1.60	1.60
		Nos. 304-307 (4)	2.80	2.80

Souvenir Sheet
308		Sheet of 4	3.00	3.00
a.		A28 2.70sh like #304	.20	.20
b.		A28 3sh like #305	.25	.20
c.		A28 5sh like #306	.40	.35
d.		A28 25sh like #307	2.10	1.75

Souvenir Sheet

Christ in the Storm on the Sea of Galilee, by Rembrandt — A29

1980, Dec. 31 Imperf.
309	A29	25sh multicolored	5.25	4.50

Christmas 1980.

Heinrich von Stephan and UPU Emblem A30

1981, June 2 Litho. Perf. 14
310	A30	1sh shown	.20	.20
311	A30	2sh UPU headquarters	.30	.25
312	A30	2.70sh Mail plane, 1935	.40	.35
313	A30	10sh Mail train, 1927	1.40	1.25
a.		Souvenir sheet of 4, #310-313	3.50	3.50
		Nos. 310-313 (4)	2.30	2.05

Von Stephan (1831-97), UPU founder.

Common Design Types pictured following the introduction.

Royal Wedding Issue
Common Design Type
1981 Litho. Perf. 14
314	CD331	10sh Couple	.20	.20
a.		10sh on 1sh	.20	.20
315	CD331	50sh Tower of London	.30	.25
a.		50sh on 5sh	.30	.25
316	CD331	200sh Prince Charles	1.50	1.25
a.		200sh on 20sh	1.50	1.25
		Nos. 314-316 (3)	2.00	1.70
		Nos. 314a-316a (3)	2.00	1.70

Souvenir Sheet
317	CD331	250sh Royal mews	1.50	1.50
a.		250sh on 25sh, light orange	1.50	1.50

Royal wedding. Issue dates: surcharges, July 13; others, July 29. Nos. 314-316 also issued in sheets of 5 plus label, perf. 12, in changed colors.
For overprints see Nos. 342-345.

Sleeping Woman Before Green Shutters, by Picasso — A31

Picasso Birth Centenary: 20sh, Bullfight. 30sh, Nude Asleep on a Landscape. 200sh, Interior with a Girl Drawing. 250sh, Minotaur.

1981, Sept. 21 Litho. Perf. 1
318	A31	10sh multicolored	.20	.2
319	A31	20sh multicolored	.35	.3
320	A31	30sh multicolored	.50	.4
321	A31	200sh multicolored	3.50	2.7

Size: 120x146mm
Imperf
322	A31	250sh multicolored	5.00	4.0
		Nos. 318-322 (5)	9.55	7.6

Intl. Year of the Disabled A32

1981, Dec. Perf. 1
323	A32	1sh Sign language	.20	.2
324	A32	10sh Teacher in wheelchair	.80	.6
325	A32	50sh Retarded children	.80	.6
326	A32	200sh Blind man	3.25	2.6
a.		Souvenir sheet of 4, #323-326	5.25	4.5
		Nos. 323-326 (4)	4.45	3.6

1982 World Cup Soccer A33

Designs: Various soccer players.

1982, Jan. 11 Litho. Perf. 1
327	A33	1sh multicolored	.20	.2
328	A33	10sh multicolored	.20	.2
329	A33	50sh multicolored	.85	.7
330	A33	200sh multicolored	3.50	3.0
		Nos. 327-330 (4)	4.75	4.1

Souvenir Sheet
331	A33	250sh World Cup	4.50	4.5

TB Bacillus Centenary — A34

1982, June 14 Litho.
332	A34	1sh Koch	.20	.2
333	A34	10sh Microscope	.35	.2
334	A34	50sh Inoculation	1.75	.95
335	A34	100sh Virus under microscope	3.50	1.90
		Nos. 332-335 (4)	5.80	3.25

Souvenir Sheet
336	A34	150sh Medical School	5.00	3.00

Peaceful Uses of Outer Space A35

1982, May 17 Litho. Perf. 1
337	A35	5sh Mpoma Satellite Earth Station	.20	.2
338	A35	10sh Pioneer II	.20	.2
339	A35	50sh Columbia space shuttle	1.00	.85
340	A35	100sh Voyager II, Saturn	2.00	1.65
		Nos. 337-340 (4)	3.40	2.9

Souvenir Sheet
341	A35	150sh Columbia shuttle	3.50	3.00

Nos. 314-317 Overprinted: "21st
BIRTHDAY / HRH Princess of Wales /
JULY 1 1982"

1982, July 7   **Perf. 14**
342 CD331 10sh multicolored .20 .20
343 CD331 50sh multicolored .55 .45
344 CD331 200sh multicolored 2.25 1.75
     Nos. 342-344 (3) 3.00 2.40

Souvenir Sheet
345 CD331 250sh multicolored 3.50 3.00

Also issued in sheets of 5 + label in
changed colors, perf. 12x12½.

20th Anniversary of Independence
A 150sh souvenir sheet showing the
Coat of Arms was not issued.

Hornbill — A36

1982, July 12
346 A36 1sh shown .20 .20
347 A36 20sh Superb starling .55 .45
348 A36 50sh Bateleur eagle 1.25 1.10
349 A36 100sh Saddle-bill stork 2.75 2.25
     Nos. 346-349 (4) 4.75 4.00

Souvenir Sheet
350 A36 200sh Laughing dove 6.00 4.00

Scouting
Year
A37

1982, Aug. 23
351 A37 5sh Scouts .20 .20
352 A37 20sh Trophy presenta-
       tion .45 .35
353 A37 50sh Helping disabled 1.10 .95
354 A37 100sh First aid instruc-
       tion 2.25 1.90
     Nos. 351-354 (4) 4.00 3.40

Souvenir Sheet
355 A37 150sh Baden-Powell 3.50 3.00

For overprints see Nos. 376-380.

Franklin D. Roosevelt (1882-
1945) — A38

Roosevelt and Washington: 50sh, 200sh,
inaugurations. No. 358, Mount Vernon. No.
359, Hyde Park.

1982, Sept.   **Litho.**
356 A38 50sh multicolored .70 .60
357 A38 200sh multicolored 2.75 2.40

Souvenir Sheets
358 A38 150sh multicolored 2.00 1.90
359 A38 150sh multicolored 2.00 1.90

Italy's
Victory
in 1982
World
Cup
A39

1982, Oct.   **Litho.**   **Perf. 14½**
359A A39 10sh Players .20 .20
359B A39 200sh Team 3.00 3.00
Souvenir Sheet
359C A39 250sh Globe 3.00 3.00

A39a

1983, Mar. 14   **Litho.**   **Perf. 14**
360 A39a 5sh Dancers .20 .20
361 A39a 20sh Traditional cur-
       rency .30 .30
362 A39a 50sh Village .70 .70
363 A39a 100sh Drums 1.40 1.40
     Nos. 360-363 (4) 2.60 2.60

Commonwealth Day.

St. George
and the
Dragon, by
Raphael
A40

1983, Apr.
364 A40 5sh shown .20 .20
365 A40 20sh St. George and
       the Dragon,
       1505 .35 .35
366 A40 50sh Moses Parts
       the Red Sea .90 .90
367 A40 200sh Expulsion of
       Heliodorus 3.25 3.25
     Nos. 364-367 (4) 4.70 4.70

Souvenir Sheet
368 A40 250sh Leo the Great
       and Attila,
       1513 3.25 3.25

A41

7th Non-aligned Summit
Conference — A42

1983, Aug. 15   **Litho.**   **Perf. 14½**
369 A41 5sh multicolored .20 .20
370 A42 200sh multicolored 2.00 2.00

African
Elephants
and World
Wildlife
Emblem
A43

5sh, Three adults with elephant bones.
10sh, Three adults walking. 30sh, Elephants
standing in water hole. 70sh, Adults with calf.

1983, Aug. 22   **Perf. 15**
371 A43 5sh multicolored .75 .75
372 A43 10sh multicolored 1.25 1.25
373 A43 30sh multicolored 3.00 3.00
374 A43 70sh multicolored 7.50 7.50
     Nos. 371-374 (4) 12.50 12.50

Souvenir Sheet
375 A43 300sh Zebras, vert. 5.50 4.50

No. 375 does not have the WWF emblem.
See Nos. 948-953.

Nos. 351-355 Overprinted or
Surcharged: "BOYS BRIGADE
CENTENARY 1883-1983"

1983, Sept. 19   **Litho.**   **Perf. 14**
376 A37 5sh multicolored .20 .20
377 A37 20sh multicolored .20 .20
378 A37 50sh multicolored .55 .55
379 A37 400sh on 100sh multi 4.50 4.50
     Nos. 376-379 (4) 5.45 5.45

Souvenir Sheet
380 A37 150sh multicolored 1.75 1.75

World Communications Year — A44

Designs: 20sh, Mpoma Satellite Earth Station. 50sh, Railroad, Computer Operator.
70sh, Filming Lions. 100sh, Pilots, Radio
Communications. 300sh, Communications
Satellite.

1983, Oct. 3   **Litho.**   **Perf. 15**
381 A44 20sh multicolored .20 .20
382 A44 50sh multicolored .60 .60
383 A44 70sh multicolored .85 .85
384 A44 100sh multicolored 1.25 1.25
     Nos. 381-384 (4) 2.90 2.90

Souvenir Sheet
385 A44 300sh multicolored 3.50 3.50

Nos. 279, 281-285, 289 Surcharged

1983, Nov. 7   **Litho.**   **Perf. 14**
386 A26 100sh on 10c multi
387 A26 135sh on 1sh multi
388 A26 175sh on 30c multi
389 A26 200sh on 50c multi
390 A26 400sh on 80c multi
391 A26 700sh on 5sh multi
392 A26 1000sh on 1.50sh
     Nos. 386-392 (7) 15.00 15.00

World
Food Day
A45

1984, Jan. 12   **Litho.**   **Perf. 14**
393 A45 10sh Plowing .20 .20
394 A45 200sh Banana crop 2.75 2.75

Christmas — A46

1983, Dec. 12   **Litho.**   **Perf. 14**
395 A46 10sh Navitity .20 .20
396 A46 50sh Sheperds and
       Angel .40 .40
397 A46 175sh Flight into Egypt 1.25 1.25
398 A46 400sh Angels Blowing
       Trumpets 3.00 3.00
     Nos. 395-398 (4) 4.85 4.85

Souvenir Sheet
399 A46 300sh Three Kings 2.25 2.25

Animal Type of 1979

1983, Dec. 19
400 A26 100sh like No. 284 .60 .60
401 A26 135sh like No. 285 .75 .75
402 A26 175sh like No. 286 .90 .90
403 A26 200sh like No. 287 1.25 1.25
404 A26 400sh like No. 288 2.60 2.60

405 A26 700sh like No. 292 4.25 4.25
406 A26 1000sh like No. 291 6.00 6.00
     Nos. 400-406 (7) 16.35 16.35

1984
Summer
Olympics
A48

1983   **Perf. 14½**
417 A48 5sh Ruth Kyalisiima .20 .20
418 A48 115sh Javelin .50 .50
419 A48 155sh Wrestling .65 .65
420 A48 175sh Rowing .85 .85
     Nos. 417-420 (4) 2.20 2.20

Souvenir Sheet
421 A48 500sh Akii-Bua 2.40 2.40

For overprints see Nos. 458-462.

Intl. Civil
Aviation
Org., 40th
Anniv.
A49

1984, Sept.
422 A49 5sh Passenger ser-
       vice .20 .20
423 A49 115sh Cargo service .65 .65
424 A49 155sh Police airwing .90 .90
425 A49 175sh Soroti Flying
       School plane 1.25 1.25
     Nos. 422-425 (4) 3.00 3.00

Souvenir Sheet
426 A49 250sh Hot air balloon 1.75 1.75

Butterflies
A50

1984, Oct.   **Litho.**   **Perf. 14½**
427 A50 5sh Silver-barred
       Charaxes .20 .20
428 A50 115sh Western Emperor
       Swallowtail .70 .70
429 A50 155sh African Giant
       Swallowtail .95 .95
430 A50 175sh Blue Salamis 1.25 1.25
     Nos. 427-430 (4) 3.10 3.10

Souvenir Sheet
431 A50 250sh Veinted Yellow 1.75 1.75

Freshwater Fish — A51

1985   **Litho.**   **Perf. 15**
432 A51 5sh Nothobranchi-
       us taeni-
       opygus .35 .35
433 A51 10sh Bagrus
       dogmac .50 .35
434 A51 50sh Polypterus
       senegalus .90 .25
435 A51 100sh Clarias 1.00 .25
436 A51 135sh Mormyrus
       kannume 1.50 .85
437 A51 175sh Synodontis
       victoriae 1.50 1.40
438 A51 205sh Haplochromis
       brownae 1.50 1.75
439 A51 400sh Lates niloticus 1.50 1.90
440 A51 700sh Protopterus
       aethiopicus 1.50 2.25
441 A51 1000sh Barbus rad-
       cliffii 1.50 2.50
442 A51 2500sh Malapterus
       electricus 1.75 3.25
     Nos. 432-442 (11) 13.50 15.10

Issued: #432-435, 437-441, 4/1; #436, 442,
6/10.
For overprints see Nos. 490-494.

Easter
A52

1985, May 13   Litho.   Perf. 14
443 A52   5sh The Last Supper   .20   .20
444 A52 115sh Jesus confronts
                    doubting
                    Thomas   1.10 1.10
445 A52 155sh Crucifixion   1.25 1.75
446 A52 175sh Pentecost   1.60 2.10
      Nos. 443-446 (4)   4.15 5.15

Souvenir Sheet
447 A52 250sh Last prayer in
                    garden   1.00 1.25

UN Child
Survival
Campaign
A53

1985, July 1
448 A53   5sh Mother
                    breastfeeding   .20   .20
449 A53 115sh Growth
                    monitorization   1.10 1.10
450 A53 155sh Immunization   1.40 1.40
451 A53 175sh Oral rehydration
                    therapy   1.50 1.50
      Nos. 448-451 (4)   4.20 4.20

Souvenir Sheet
452 A53 500sh Expectant Moth-
                    er, food   3.50 3.50

Audubon Birth   UN Decade for
Bicent. — A54   Women — A56

1985, July
453 A54 115sh Acrocephalus
                    schoenobaenus 1.25 1.00
454 A54 155sh Ardeola ibis   1.50 1.10
455 A54 175sh Galerida gristata   1.25 1.50
456 A54 500sh Aythya fuligula   2.00 2.90
      Nos. 453-456 (4)   6.00 6.50

Souvenir Sheet
457 A54 1000sh Strix aluco   7.00 7.00

      See Nos. 469-473.

Nos. 417-421 Ovptd. or Surcharged
with Winners Names, Medals and
Countries in Gold

Gold medalists: 5sh, Benita Brown-Fitzger-
ald, US, 100-meter hurdles. 115sh, Arto
Haerkoenen, Finland, javelin. 155sh, Atsuji
Miyahara, Japan, 115-pound Greco-Roman
wrestling. 100sh, West Germany, quadruple
sculls. 1200sh, Edwin Moses, US, 400-meter
hurdles.

1985, July   Perf. 15
458 A48   5sh multicolored   .20   .20
459 A48 115sh multicolored   .30   .30
460 A48 155sh multicolored   .40   .40
461 A48 1000sh on 175sh multi   2.40 2.40
      Nos. 458-461 (4)   3.30 3.30

Souvenir Sheet
462 A48 1200sh on 500sh multi   3.00 3.00

1985   Litho.   Perf. 14

5sh, Natl. Women's Day, Mar. 8. 115sh, Girl
Guides 75th anniv., horiz. 155sh, Mother Theresa, 1979 Nobel Peace Prize laureate.
1000sh, Queen Mother. #467, Queen Mother
inspecting troops. #468, like 115sh, horiz.

463 A56   5sh multicolored   .20   .20
464 A56 115sh multicolored   1.75 1.60
465 A56 155sh multicolored   2.90 2.50
466 A56 1000sh multicolored   1.40 1.75
      Nos. 463-466 (4)   6.25 6.05

Souvenir Sheets
467 A56 1500sh multicolored   3.50 3.50
468 A56 1500sh multicolored   5.00 5.00
Issued: #466-467, Aug. 21; others, Nov. 1.

Audubon Type of 1985

1985, Dec. 23   Perf. 12½x12
469 A54   5sh Rock ptarmigan   .35   .20
470 A54 155sh Sage grouse   1.25 1.10
471 A54 175sh Lesser yellow-
                    legs   1.25 1.50
472 A54 500sh Brown-headed
                    cowbird   2.10 2.75
      Nos. 469-472 (4)   4.95 5.55

Souvenir Sheet
Perf. 14
473 A54 1000sh Whooping crane   6.50 6.50

UN, 40th
Anniv.
A57

Designs: 10sh, Forest resources, vert.
180sh, UN Peace-keeping Force. 200sh,
Emblem, UN Development Project. 250sh,
Intl. Peace Year. 2000sh, Natl., UN flags, vert.
2500sh, Flags, UN Building, New York, vert.

1986, Feb.   Perf. 15
474 A57   10sh multicolored   .20   .20
475 A57 180sh multicolored   .25   .25
476 A57 200sh multicolored   .35   .35
477 A57 250sh multicolored   .40   .40
478 A57 2000sh multicolored   3.25 3.25
      Nos. 474-478 (5)   4.45 4.45

Souvenir Sheet
479 A57 2500sh multicolored   3.00 3.25

1986 World Cup Soccer
Championships, Mexico — A58

Various soccer plays.

1986, Mar.   Perf. 14
480 A58   10sh multicolored   .20   .20
481 A58 180sh multicolored   .70   .45
482 A58 250sh multicolored   .80   .55
483 A58 2500sh multicolored   4.50 5.00
      Nos. 480-483 (4)   6.20 6.20

Souvenir Sheet
484 A58 3000sh multicolored   4.50 4.50
No. 484 contains vert. stamp.
For overprints see Nos. 514-518.

A59

Halley's Comet — A60

Designs: 50sh, Arecibo radio telescope,
Puerto Rico, and Tycho Brahe (1546-1601),
Danish astronomer. 100sh, Recovery of
Astronaut John Glenn, US space capsule,
Caribbean, 1962. 140sh, Adoration of the
Magi, 1301, by Giotto (1276-1337). 2500sh,
Sighting, 1835, Davy Crockett at The Alamo.

1986, Mar.   Litho.   Perf. 14
485 A59   50sh multicolored   .25   .20
486 A59 100sh multicolored   .40   .20
487 A59 140sh multicolored   .60   .35
488 A59 2500sh multicolored   4.50 5.75
      Nos. 485-488 (4)   5.75 6.50

Souvenir Sheet
489 A60 3000sh multicolored   6.00 6.00

For overprints see Nos. 519-523.

Nos. 437, 440-442 and 468 Ovptd.
"NRA LIBERATION / 1986" in Silver or
Black

1986, Apr.   Perf. 15
490 A51 175sh multi   .75   .60
491 A51 700sh multi   2.10 2.00
492 A51 1000sh multi (Bk)   2.40 2.40
493 A51 2500sh multi (Bk)   3.75 5.00
      Nos. 490-493 (4)   9.00 10.00

Souvenir Sheet
Perf. 14
494 A56 1500sh multi (Bk)   5.00 4.00
No. 494 ovptd. in one line in margin. A
400sh also exists with silver overprint. All
stamps exist with overprint colors transposed.

Queen Elizabeth II, 60th Birthday
Common Design Type

1986, Apr. 21   Perf. 14
495 CD339 100sh At London
                    Zoo, c. 1938   .20   .20
496 CD339 140sh At the races,
                    1970   .20   .20
497 CD339 2500sh San-
                    dringham,
                    1982   3.75 3.75
      Nos. 495-497 (3)   4.15 4.15

Souvenir Sheet
498 CD339 3000sh Engagement,
                    1947   4.50 4.50

AMERIPEX '86 — A61

1986, May 22   Perf. 15
499 A61   50sh Niagara Falls   .20   .20
500 A61 100sh Jefferson Memo-
                    rial   .20   .20
501 A61 250sh Liberty Bell   .35   .35
502 A61 1000sh The Alamo   1.40 1.40
503 A61 2500sh George Wash-
                    ington Bridge   3.50 3.50
      Nos. 499-503 (5)   5.65 5.65

Souvenir Sheet
504 A61 3000sh Grand Canyon   3.00 3.00

Statue of Liberty, cent.

A62

Statue of Liberty, Cent. — A63

Tall ships, Operation Sail: 50sh, Gloria,
Colombia, vert. 100sh, Mircea, Romania, vert.
140sh, Sagres II, Portugal. 2500sh, Gazela
Primero, US.

1986, July   Perf. 1
505 A62   50sh multicolored   .40   .2
506 A62 100sh multicolored   .60   .2
507 A62 140sh multicolored   1.00   .6
508 A62 2500sh multicolored   4.50 6.0
      Nos. 505-508 (4)   6.50 7.0

Souvenir Sheet
509 A63 3000sh multicolored   4.25 4.2

Royal Wedding Issue, 1986
Common Design Type

Designs: 50sh, Prince Andrew and Sara
Ferguson. 140sh, Andrew and Princess Anne
2500sh, At formal affair. 3000sh, Couple dif
Nos. 510-512 horiz.

1986, July 23
510 CD340   50sh multicolored   .20   .2
511 CD340 140sh multicolored   .20   .2
512 CD340 2500sh multicolored   2.75 3.5
      Nos. 510-512 (3)   3.15 3.9

Souvenir Sheet
513 CD340 3000sh multicolored   3.50 3.5

Nos. 480-484 Ovptd. or Surcharged
"WINNERS Argentina 3 W. Germany
2" in Gold in 2 or 3 Lines

1986, Sept. 15   Litho.   Perf. 1
514 A58   50sh on 10sh multi   .20   .2
515 A58 180sh multicolored   .25   .2
516 A58 250sh multicolored   .30   .3
517 A58 2500sh multicolored   3.75 3.2
      Nos. 514-517 (4)   4.50 3.9

Souvenir Sheet
518 A58 3000sh multicolored   4.75 4.2

Nos. 485-489 Ovptd. with Halley's
Comet Emblem

1986, Oct. 15   Litho.   Perf. 1
519 A59   50sh multicolored   .20   .2
520 A59 100sh multicolored   .35   .2
521 A59 140sh multicolored   .45   .3
522 A59 2500sh multicolored   4.50 5.5
      Nos. 519-522 (4)   5.50 6.2

Souvenir Sheet
523 A60 3000sh multicolored   5.00 5.0

Christian
Martyrs
A64

Designs: 50sh, St. Kizito. 150sh, St. Kizit
educating Ganda converts. 200sh, Executio
of Bishop James Hannington. 1000sh
Mwanga's execution of converts, cent
1500sh, King Mwanga sentencing Christian
to death.

1986, Oct. 15
524 A64   50sh multicolored   .20   .2
525 A64 150sh multicolored   .20   .2
526 A64 200sh multicolored   .35   .3
527 A64 1000sh multicolored   1.50 1.5
      Nos. 524-527 (4)   2.25 2.2

Souvenir Sheet
528 A64 1500sh multicolored   2.25 2.2

A65

Christmas — A66

Paintings by Albrecht Durer and Titian:
[10]sh, Madonna of the Cherries. 150sh,
[M]adonna and Child, vert. 200sh, Assumption
[o]f the Virgin, vert. 2500sh, Praying Hands,
[v]ert. No. 533, Adoration of the Magi. No. 534,
[P]resentation of the Virgin in the Temple.

[1]986, Nov. 26		**Litho.**	**Perf. 14**	
[5]29	A65	50sh multicolored	.20	.20
[5]30	A65	150sh multicolored	.45	.25
[5]31	A65	200sh multicolored	.60	.25
[5]32	A65	2500sh multicolored	4.25	5.50
		Nos. 529-532 (4)	5.50	6.15

Souvenir Sheets

[5]33	A66	3000sh multicolored	3.25	3.25
[5]34	A66	3000sh multicolored	3.25	3.25

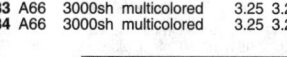

Birds and
Animals
A67

[1]987			**Perf. 15**	
[5]35	A67	2sh Red-billed firefinch	.35	.30
[5]36	A67	5sh African pygmy kingfisher	.45	.30
[5]37	A67	10sh Scarlet-chested sunbird	.55	.30
[5]38	A67	25sh White rhinoceros	1.00	.70
[5]39	A67	35sh Lion	1.00	1.00
[5]40	A67	45sh Cheetahs	1.25	1.40
[5]41	A67	50sh Cordon bleu	1.40	1.75
[5]42	A67	100sh Giant eland	2.25	3.00
		Nos. 535-542 (8)	8.25	8.75

Souvenir Sheets

[5]43	A67	150sh Carmine bee-eaters	3.75	3.75
[5]44	A67	150sh Cattle egret, zebra	3.75	3.75

Issue dates: Nos. 535-537, 541, 543, Nov.
; Nos. 538-540, 542-544, July 22.

Transportation Innovations — A68

[1]987, Aug. 14				
[5]45	A68	2sh Eagle, 1987	.20	.20
[5]46	A68	3sh Bremen, 1928	.20	.20
[5]47	A68	5sh Winnie Mae, 1933	.25	.25
[5]48	A68	10sh Voyager, 1986	.35	.35
[5]49	A68	15sh Chanute biplane glider, 1896	.55	.55
[5]50	A68	25sh Norge, 1926	.80	.80
[5]51	A68	35sh Curtis biplane, USS Pennsylvania, 1911	1.25	1.25
[5]52	A68	45sh Freedom 7, 1961	1.40	1.40
[5]53	A68	100sh Concorde, 1976	4.00	5.00
		Nos. 545-553 (9)	9.00	10.00

1988
Summer
Olympics,
Seoul
A69

Flags and athletes.

1987, Oct. 5			**Perf. 14½x14**	
554	A69	5sh Torch bearer	.20	.20
555	A69	10sh Swimming	.25	.25
556	A69	50sh Cycling	1.25	1.25
557	A69	100sh Gymnastic rings	2.50	2.50
		Nos. 554-557 (4)	4.20	4.20

Souvenir Sheet

558	A69	150sh Boxing	3.50	3.75

A70

Natl. Independence, 25th
Anniv. — A71

1987, Oct. 8				
559	A70	5sh shown	.20	.20
560	A70	10sh Mulago Hospital	.35	.35
561	A70	25sh Independence Monument	.85	.85
562	A70	50sh High Court	1.60	1.60
		Nos. 559-562 (4)	3.00	3.00

Souvenir Sheet

563	A71	100sh shown	2.75	2.75

A72

Science and Space — A73

Birds — A74

Designs: 5sh, Hippocrates, father of modern
medicine, caduceus and surgeons. 25sh,
Albert Einstein and Theory of Relativity equation. 35sh, Sir Isaac Newton and Optics Theory. 45sh, Karl Benz (1844-1929), German
engineer, automobile pioneer, and the Velocipede, Mercedes-Benz sports coupe and manufacturers' emblems.

1987, Nov. 2			**Perf. 14½x14**	
564	A72	5sh multicolored	.40	.40
565	A72	25sh multicolored	1.60	1.60
566	A72	35sh multicolored	1.75	1.75
567	A72	45sh multicolored	2.25	2.25
		Nos. 564-567 (4)	6.00	6.00

Souvenir Sheet

Perf. 14x14½

568	A73	150sh shown	3.75	3.75

1987, Nov. 2		**Litho.**	**Perf. 14**	
569	A74	5sh Golden-backed weaver	.50	.55
570	A74	10sh Hoopoe	1.10	.75
571	A74	15sh Red-throated bee-eater	1.25	.75
572	A74	25sh Lilac-breasted roller	1.50	1.25
573	A74	35sh Pygmy goose	1.60	1.40
574	A74	45sh Scarlet-chested sunbird	1.90	1.90
575	A74	50sh Crowned crane	1.90	1.90
576	A74	100sh Long-tailed fiscal shrike	3.25	3.50
		Nos. 569-576 (8)	13.00	12.00

Souvenir Sheets

577	A74	150sh African barn owl, horiz.	5.00	5.00
578	A74	150sh African fish-eagle, horiz.	5.00	5.00

14th World Boy Scout Jamboree,
Australia, 1987-88 — A75

Activities: 5sh, Stamp collecting, Uganda
Nos. 84 and 116. 25sh, Planting trees, Natl.
flag. 35sh, Canoeing on Lake Victoria. 45sh,
Hiking and camping. 150sh, Logo of 1987 jamboree and natl. Boy Scout organization
emblem.

1987, Nov. 20				
579	A75	5sh multicolored	.20	.20
580	A75	25sh multicolored	.85	.85
581	A75	35sh multicolored	1.25	1.25
582	A75	45sh multicolored	1.50	1.50
		Nos. 579-582 (4)	3.80	3.80

Souvenir Sheet

583	A75	150sh multicolored	4.50	4.50

Christmas
A76

The life of Christ and the Virgin pictured on
bas-reliefs, c. 1250, and a tapestry from
France: 5sh, The Annunciation. 10sh, The
Nativity. 50sh, Flight into Egypt. 100sh, The
Adoration of the Magi. 150sh, The Mystic
Wine Tapestry.

1987, Dec. 18				
584	A76	5sh multicolored	.20	.20
585	A76	10sh multicolored	.20	.25
586	A76	50sh multicolored	1.25	1.40
587	A76	100sh multicolored	2.25	2.75
		Nos. 584-587 (4)	3.90	4.60

Souvenir Sheet

588	A76	150sh multicolored	5.00	5.00

Locomotives — A77

Designs: 5sh, Class 12 2-6-2T light shunter.
10sh, Class 92 1Co-Co1 diesel electric. 15sh,
Class 2-8-2. 25sh, Class 2-6-2T light shunter.
35sh, Class 4-8-0. 45sh, Class 4-8-2. 50sh,
Class 4-8-4+4-8-4 Garratt. 100sh, Class 87
1Co-Co1 diesel electric. No. 597, Class 59 4-8-2+2-8-4 Garratt. No. 598, Class 31 2-8-4.

1988, Jan. 18				
589	A77	5sh multicolored	.20	.20
590	A77	10sh multicolored	.35	.35
591	A77	15sh multicolored	.55	.50
592	A77	25sh multicolored	.80	.75
593	A77	35sh multicolored	1.25	1.00
594	A77	45sh multicolored	1.50	1.25
595	A77	50sh multicolored	1.60	1.50
596	A77	100sh multicolored	3.50	2.25
		Nos. 589-596 (8)	9.75	7.80

Souvenir Sheets

597	A77	150sh multicolored	3.25	3.25
598	A77	150sh multicolored	3.25	3.25

Minerals — A78

1988, Jan. 18				
599	A78	1sh Columbite-tantalite	.20	.20
600	A78	2sh Galena	.20	.20
601	A78	5sh Malachite	.20	.20
602	A78	10sh Cassiterite	.35	.35
603	A78	35sh Ferberite	1.25	1.25
604	A78	50sh Emerald	1.75	1.75
605	A78	100sh Monazite	3.25	3.25
606	A78	150sh Microcline	5.00	5.00
		Nos. 599-606 (8)	12.20	12.20

1988
Summer
Olympics,
Seoul
A79

1988, May 16		**Litho.**	**Perf. 14**	
607	A79	5sh Hurdles	.20	.20
608	A79	25sh High jump	.35	.50
609	A79	35sh Javelin	.40	.55
610	A79	45sh Long jump	.55	.75
		Nos. 607-610 (4)	1.50	2.00

Souvenir Sheet

611	A79	150sh Medals, five-ring emblem	1.50	1.50

For overprints see Nos. 651-655.

Flowers
A80

1988, July 28		**Litho.**	**Perf. 15**	
612	A80	5sh Spathodea campanulata	.25	.20
613	A80	10sh Gloriosa simplex	.25	.20
614	A80	20sh Thevetica peruviana, vert.	.35	.25
615	A80	25sh Hibiscus schizopetalus	.35	.35
616	A80	35sh Aframomum sceptrum	.35	.40
617	A80	45sh Adenium obesum	.35	.50
618	A80	50sh Kigelia africana, vert.	.45	.60
619	A80	100sh Clappertonia ficifolia	.65	1.00
		Nos. 612-619 (8)	3.00	3.50

Souvenir Sheets

620	A80	150sh Costus spectabilis	1.50	1.50
621	A80	150sh Canarina abyssinica, vert.	1.50	1.50

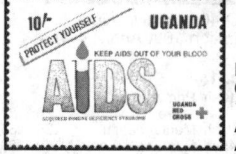

Intl. Red
Cross,
125th
Anniv.
A81

1988, Oct. 28		**Litho.**	**Perf. 14**	
622	A81	10sh "AIDS"	.20	.20
623	A81	40sh Immunize children	.65	.65
624	A81	70sh Relief distribution	1.40	1.40
625	A81	90sh First aid	1.75	1.75
		Nos. 622-625 (4)	4.00	4.00

Souvenir Sheet

626	A81	150sh Jean-Henri Dunant, vert.	1.40	1.40

Paintings by
Titian — A82

Designs: 10sh, Portrait of a Lady, c. 1508.
20sh, Portrait of a Man, 1507. 40sh, Portrait of
Isabella d'Este, c. 1534. 50sh, Portrait of Vin-
cenzo Mosti, 1520. 70sh, Pope Paul III
Farnese, c. 1545. 90sh, Violante, 1515.
100sh, Lavinia, Titian's Daughter, c. 1565.
250sh, Portrait of Dr. Parma, c. 1515. No. 635,
The Speech of Alfonso D'Avalos, c. 1540. No.
636, Cain and Abel.

1988, Oct. 31   **Perf. 14**
627 A82 10sh multicolored   .25   .25
628 A82 20sh multicolored   .40   .40
629 A82 40sh multicolored   .60   .60
630 A82 50sh multicolored   .75   .75
631 A82 70sh multicolored   .85   .85
632 A82 90sh multicolored   1.00 1.00
633 A82 100sh multicolored   1.25 1.25
634 A82 250sh multicolored   2.40 2.40
     Nos. 627-634 (8)   7.50 7.50

Souvenir Sheets
635 A82 350sh multicolored   4.75 4.75
636 A82 350sh multicolored   4.75 4.75

Game
Preserves — A83

Designs: 10sh, Giraffes, Kidepo Valley Natl.
Park. 25sh, Zebras, Lake Mburo Natl. Park.
100sh, African buffalo, Murchison Falls Natl.
Park. 250sh, Pelicans, Queen Elizabeth Natl.
Park. 350sh, Roan antelopes, Lake Mburo
Natl. Park.

1988, Nov. 18   Litho.   Perf. 14
637 A83 10sh multicolored   .35   .20
638 A83 25sh multicolored   .80   .30
639 A83 100sh multicolored   1.60 1.75
640 A83 250sh multicolored   4.25 5.25
     Nos. 637-640 (4)   7.00 7.50

Souvenir Sheet
641 A83 350sh multicolored   4.25 4.25

WHO 40th Anniv., Alma Ata
Declaration 10th Anniv. — A84

1988, Dec. 1
642 A84 10sh Primary health
                 care   .20   .20
643 A84 25sh Mental health   .35   .35
644 A84 45sh Rural health care   .60   .60
645 A84 100sh Dental care   1.40 1.40
646 A84 200sh Postnatal care   2.75 2.75
     Nos. 642-646 (5)   5.30 5.30

Souvenir Sheet
647 A84 350sh Conference Hall,
                 Alma-Ata, USSR 4.00 4.00

Miniature Sheet

Christmas, Mickey Mouse 60th
Birthday — A85

Walt Disney characters: No. 648a, Santa
Claus. b, Goofy. c, Mickey Mouse. d, Huey at
conveyor belt. e, Dewey packing building
blocks. f, Donald Duck. g, Chip-n-Dale. h,
Louie at conveyor belt controls. No. 649, Preparing reindeer for Christmas eve flight. No.
650, Mickey loading sleigh with toys, horiz.

1988, Dec. 2   Perf. 13½x14, 14x13½
648   A85 50sh any single   6.50 6.50
a.-h.   A85 50sh any single   .80   .80
         Sheet of 8
Souvenir Sheets
649 A85 350sh multicolored   4.75 4.75
650 A85 350sh multicolored   4.75 4.75

Nos. 607-611 Ovptd. or Surcharged to
Honor Olympic Winners
   5sh: "110 M HURDLES / R. KING-
DOM / USA"
   25sh: "HIGH JUMP / G. AVDEENKO /
USSR"
   35sh: "JAVELIN / T. KORJUS /
FINLAND"
   300sh: "LONG JUMP / C. LEWIS /
USA"

1989, Jan. 30   Litho.   Perf. 14
651 A79 5sh multicolored   .20   .20
652 A79 25sh multicolored   .25   .25
653 A79 35sh multicolored   .30   .30
654 A79 300sh on 45sh multi   2.60 2.60
     Nos. 651-654 (4)   3.35 3.35

Souvenir Sheet
655 A79 350sh on 150sh multi   4.50 4.50

1990 World Cup Soccer
Championships, Italy — A86

Various action scenes.

1989, Apr. 24   Litho.   Perf. 14
656 A86 10sh multi, vert.   .20   .20
657 A86 25sh multicolored   .35   .35
658 A86 75sh multicolored   1.00 1.00
659 A86 200sh multi, vert.   2.60 2.60
     Nos. 656-659 (4)   4.15 4.15

Souvenir Sheet
660 A86 300sh multicolored   3.25 3.25

Mushrooms — A87

1989, Aug. 14   Litho.   Perf. 14
661 A87 10sh Suillus granu-
                 latus   .40   .40
662 A87 15sh Omphalotus
                 olearius   .50   .50
663 A87 45sh Oudemansiella
                 radicata   1.00 1.00
664 A87 50sh Clitocybe nebu-
                 laris   1.00 1.00
665 A87 60sh Macrolepiota
                 rhacodes   1.10 1.10
666 A87 75sh Lepista nuda   1.25 1.25
667 A87 150sh Suillus luteus   2.25 2.25
668 A87 200sh Agaricus
                 campestris   2.50 2.50
     Nos. 661-668 (8)   10.00 10.00

Souvenir Sheets
669 A87 350sh Schizophyllum
                 commune   5.50 5.50
670 A87 350sh Bolbitius vitel-
                 linus   5.50 5.50

"The Thirty-six Views of Mt.
Fuji" — A88

Prints by Hokusai (1760-1849): 10sh, Fuji
and the Great Wave off Kanagawa. 15sh, Fuji
from Lake Suwa. 20sh, Fuji from Kajikazawa.
60sh, Fuji from Shichirigahama. 90sh, Fuji
from Ejiri in Sunshu. 120sh, Fuji Above Lightning. 200sh, Fuji from Lower Meguro in Edo.
250sh, Fuji from Edo. No. 679, The Red Fuji
from the Foot. No. 680, Fuji from Umezawa.

1989, May 15   Litho.   Perf. 14x13½
671 A88 10sh multicolored   .20   .20
672 A88 15sh multicolored   .20   .20
673 A88 20sh multicolored   .20   .20
674 A88 60sh multicolored   .60   .60
675 A88 90sh multicolored   .90   .90
676 A88 120sh multicolored   1.25 1.25
677 A88 200sh multicolored   2.00 2.00
678 A88 250sh multicolored   2.50 2.50
     Nos. 671-678 (8)   7.85 7.85

Souvenir Sheets
679 A88 500sh multicolored   5.00 5.00
680 A88 500sh multicolored   5.00 5.00

Hirohito (1901-1989), Showa emperor, and
Akihito, Heisei emperor of Japan.

PHILEXFRANCE
'89 — A89

1989, July 7   Litho.   Perf. 14
681 A89 20sh No. 1   .50   .50
682 A89 70sh No. 10   1.25 1.25
683 A89 100sh No. 48   1.50 1.50
684 A89 250sh No. 67   2.75 2.75
a.   Souvenir sheet of 4, #681-684 7.00 7.00
     Nos. 681-684 (4)   6.00 6.00

No. 684a sold for 500sh.

2nd All African Scout Jamboree, Aug.
3-15 — A90

1989, Aug. 3   Litho.   Perf. 14
685 A90 10sh Fatal child ail-
                 ments   .30   .30
686 A90 70sh Raising poultry   1.40 1.40
687 A90 90sh Immunization   1.90 1.90
688 A90 100sh Brick-making   1.90 1.90
     Nos. 685-688 (4)   5.50 5.50

Souvenir Sheet
689 A90 500sh Natl. emblem,
                 vert.   5.00 5.00

Scouting, 75th anniv.
For surcharges see Nos. 1301-1304.

Miniature Sheet

Wildlife at
Waterhole — A91

Designs: a, Saddle-billed stork. b, Whit
pelican. c, Marabou stork. d, Egyptian vulture
giraffes. e, Bateleur eagle, antelope. f, Africa
elephant. g, Giraffe. h, Goliath heron. i, Blac
rhinoceros, zebras. j, Zebras, oribi. k, Africa
fish eagle. l, Hippopotamus. m, Black-backe
jackal, white pelican. n, Cape buffalo. o, Oliv
baboon. p, Bohor reedbuck. q, Lesser fla
mingo, serval. r, Shoebill stork. s, Crowne
crane. t, Impala. No. 691, Lion. No. 692, Long
crested eagle.

1989, Sept. 12   Perf. 14½x1
690   Sheet of 20   12.00 12.0
a.-t.   A91 30sh any single   .60   .6
Souvenir Sheets
691 A91 500sh multicolored   5.00 5.0
692 A91 500sh multicolored   5.00 5.0

1st Moon Landing,   Butterflies — A93
20th Anniv. — A92

Quotations and scenes from the Apollo 11
mission.

1989, Oct. 20   Litho.   Perf. 14
693 A92 10sh Launch vehicle,
                 Moon   .20   .20
694 A92 20sh Eagle lower
                 stage on
                 Moon   .20   .20
695 A92 30sh Columbia   .35   .35
696 A92 50sh Eagle landing   .50   .50
697 A92 75sh Aldrin on Moon   .75   .75
698 A92 250sh Armstrong on
                 ladder   2.50 2.50
699 A92 300sh Eagle ascend-
                 ing   3.00 3.00
700 A92 350sh Aldrin, diff.   3.50 3.50
     Nos. 693-700 (8)   11.00 11.00

Souvenir Sheets
701 A92 500sh Liftoff   4.50 4.50
702 A92 500sh Parachute
                 landing   4.50 4.50

Nos. 693-697 and 699 horiz.

1989, Nov. 13
"UGANDA" in Black
703 A93 5sh Ioalus pallene   .35   .35
704 A93 10sh Hewitsonia
                 boisduvali   .40   .40
705 A93 20sh Euxanthe
                 wakefeildi   .60   .60
706 A93 30sh Papilio echer-
                 ioides   .70   .70
707 A93 40sh Acraea
                 semivitrea   .75   .75
708 A93 50sh Colotis
                 antevippe   .75   .75
709 A93 70sh Acraea peren-
                 na   .90   .90
710 A93 90sh Charaxes
                 cynthia   .90   .90
711 A93 100sh Euphaedra
                 neophroa   .90   .90
712 A93 150sh Cymothoe
                 beckeri   1.25 1.25
713 A93 200sh Vanessula
                 milca   1.25 1.25
714 A93 400sh Mimacraea
                 marshalli   1.75 1.75
715 A93 500sh Axiocerses
                 amanga   2.00 2.00
716 A93 1000sh Precis hierta   2.50 2.50
     Nos. 703-716 (14)   15.00 15.00

See Nos. 826-839 for "UGANDA" in blue.

UGANDA

Explorers of Africa
A94

Designs: 10sh, John Speke (1827-64), satellite view of Lake Victoria. 25sh, Sir Richard Burton (1821-90), satellite view of Lake Tanyika. 40sh, Richard Lander (1804-34), bronze ritual figure of the Bakota tribe. 90sh, Rene Caillie (1799-1838), mosque. 125sh, Dorcas gazelle and Sir Samuel Baker (1821-93), discoverer of Lake Albert. 150sh, Phoenician galley and Necho II (d. 595 B.C.), king of Egypt credited by Herodotus with sending an expedition to circumnavigate Africa. 250sh, Vasco da Gama (c. 1460-1524), 1st European to sail around the Cape of Good Hope, and caravel. 300sh, Sir Henry Stanley (1841-1904), discoverer of Lake Edward, and Lady Alice . No. 725, Dr. David Livingstone (1813-73), discoverer of Victoria Falls, and steam launch Ma-Robert. No. 726, Mary Kingsley (1862-1900), ethnologist, and tail-spot climbing perch.

1989, Nov. 15   Litho.   Perf. 14

717	A94	10sh multicolored	.20	.20
718	A94	25sh multicolored	.25	.25
719	A94	40sh multicolored	.40	.40
720	A94	90sh multicolored	.90	.90
721	A94	125sh multicolored	1.25	1.25
722	A94	150sh multicolored	1.50	1.50
723	A94	250sh multicolored	2.50	2.50
724	A94	300sh multicolored	3.00	3.00
		Nos. 717-724 (8)	10.00	10.00

Souvenir Sheets

725	A94	500sh multicolored	5.00	5.00
726	A94	500sh multicolored	5.00	5.00

Anniversaries and Events — A95

1989, Dec. 12

727	A95	10sh Bank emblem	.20	.20
728	A95	20sh Satellite dishes, arrows	.20	.20
729	A95	75sh Nehru	1.60	1.60
730	A95	90sh Pan-American Dixie Clipper	1.60	1.60
731	A95	100sh Locomotion, Stephenson	1.60	1.60
732	A95	150sh Concorde cockpit	2.75	2.75
733	A95	250sh Wapen von Hamburg, Leopoldus Primus	2.75	2.75
734	A95	300sh Concorde cockpit, crew	3.25	3.25
		Nos. 727-734 (8)	13.95	13.95

Souvenir Sheets

735	A95	500sh Storming of the Bastille	4.50	4.50
736	A95	500sh Emperor Frederick I Barbarossa, charter	4.50	4.50

African Development Bank 25th anniv. (10sh); World Telecommunications Day, May 17 (20sh); Birth cent. of Jawaharlal Nehru, 1st prime minister of independent India (75sh); 1st scheduled transatlantic airmail flight, 50th anniv. (90sh); 175th anniv. of the invention of the 1st steam locomotive by George Stephenson and opening of the Stockton & Darlington Railway in 1825 (100sh); 1st test flight of the Concorde, 20th anniv. (150sh, 300sh); Port of Hamburg, 800th anniv. (250sh, No. 736); and French revolution bicent. (No. 735).

Christmas — A96

Orchids — A97

Religious paintings by Fra Angelico: 10sh, Madonna and Child. 20sh, Adoration of the Magi. 40sh, Virgin and Child Enthroned with Saints. 75sh, The Annunciation. 100sh, St. Peter Martyr triptych center panel. 150sh, Virgin and Child Enthroned with Saints, diff. 250sh, Virgin and Child Enthroned. 350sh, Annalena Altarpiece. No. 745, Bosco ai Frati Altarpiece. No. 746, Madonna and Child with Twelve Angels.

1989, Dec. 18

737	A96	10sh multicolored	.20	.20
738	A96	20sh multicolored	.20	.20
739	A96	40sh multicolored	.45	.45
740	A96	75sh multicolored	.75	.75
741	A96	100sh multicolored	.90	.90
742	A96	150sh multicolored	1.25	1.25
743	A96	250sh multicolored	1.75	1.75
744	A96	350sh multicolored	2.00	2.00
		Nos. 737-744 (8)	7.50	7.50

Souvenir Sheets

745	A96	500sh multicolored	3.00	3.00
746	A96	500sh multicolored	3.00	3.00

1989, Dec. 18

747	A97	10sh Aerangis kotschyana	.20	.20
748	A97	15sh Angraecum infundibulare	.20	.20
749	A97	45sh Cyrtorchis chailluana	.45	.45
750	A97	50sh Aerangis rhodosticta	.50	.50
751	A97	100sh Eulophia speciosa	1.00	1.00
752	A97	200sh Calanthe sylvatica	2.00	2.00
753	A97	250sh Vanilla imperialis	2.50	2.50
754	A97	350sh Polystachya vulcanica	3.50	3.50
		Nos. 747-754 (8)	10.35	10.35

Souvenir Sheets

755	A97	500sh Ansellia africana	4.00	4.00
756	A97	500sh Ancistrochilus rothschildianus	4.00	4.00

For overprints see Nos. 782-786A.

EXPO '90, Osaka — A98

Flowering trees.

1990, Apr. 17   Litho.   Perf. 14

757	A98	10sh *Thevetia peruviana*	.20	.20
758	A98	20sh *Acanthus eminens*	.20	.20
759	A98	90sh *Gnidia glauca*	.60	.60
760	A98	150sh *Oncoba spinosa*	.85	.85
761	A98	175sh *Hibiscus rosa-sinensis*	.90	.90
762	A98	400sh *Jacaranda mimosifolia*	1.50	1.50
763	A98	500sh *Erythrina abyssinica*	1.75	1.75
764	A98	700sh *Bauhinia purpurea*	2.00	2.00
		Nos. 757-764 (8)	8.00	8.00

Souvenir Sheets

765	A98	1000sh *Delonix regia*	4.25	4.25
766	A98	1000sh *Cassia didymobatrya*	4.25	4.25

World War II Milestones — A99

Designs: 5sh, Allies penetrate west wall, Dec. 3, 1944. 10sh, VE Day, May 8, 1945. 20sh, US forces capture Okinawa, June 22, 1945. 75sh, DeGaulle named commander of all Free French forces, Apr. 4, 1944. 100sh, US troops invade Saipan, June 15, 1944. 150sh, Allied troops launch Operation Market Garden, Sept. 17, 1944. 200sh, Gen. MacArthur returns to Philippines, Oct. 20, 1944. 300sh, US victory at Coral Sea, May 8, 1942. 350sh, First battle of El Alamein, July 1, 1942. 500sh, Naval battle at Guadalcanal, Nov. 12, 1942. 1000sh, Battle of Britain.

1990, June 8   Litho.   Perf. 14

767	A99	5sh multicolored	.20	.20
768	A99	10sh multicolored	.20	.20
769	A99	20sh multicolored	.20	.20
770	A99	75sh multicolored	.40	.40
771	A99	100sh multicolored	.55	.55
772	A99	150sh multicolored	.85	.85
773	A99	200sh multicolored	1.10	1.10
774	A99	300sh multicolored	1.75	1.75
775	A99	350sh multicolored	2.00	2.00
776	A99	500sh multicolored	2.75	2.75
		Nos. 767-776 (10)	10.00	10.00

Souvenir Sheet

777	A99	1000sh multicolored	5.00	5.00

Queen Mother, 90th Birthday — A100

1990, July 5

778	250sh Hands clasped	1.00	1.00
779	250sh Facing left	1.00	1.00
780	250sh Holding dog	1.00	1.00
a.	A100 Strip of 3, #778-780	3.00	3.00
	Nos. 778-780 (3)	3.00	3.00

Souvenir Sheet

781	A100	1000sh like No. 778	3.50	3.50

Nos. 747-754
Ovptd. in Silver

Nos. 755-756 Ovptd. in Silver in Sheet Margin

1990   Litho.   Perf. 14

782	A97	10sh on No. 747	.50	.50
782A	A97	15sh on No. 748	.50	.50
782B	A97	45sh on No. 749	.75	.75
783	A97	50sh on No. 750	.75	.75
783A	A97	100sh on No. 751	1.10	1.10
784	A97	200sh on No. 752	1.40	1.40
785	A97	250sh on No. 753	1.40	1.40
785A	A97	350sh on No. 754	1.60	1.60
		Nos. 782-785A (8)	8.00	8.00

Souvenir Sheet

786	A97	500sh on No. 755	4.00	4.00
786A	A97	500sh on No. 756	4.00	4.00

Issue dates: 15sh, 45sh, 100sh, 350sh, No. 786A, Nov.; others, July 30.

Pan African Postal Union, 10th Anniv. A101

Designs: 750sh, UN Conference on the least developed countries, Paris, Sept. 3-14.

1990, Aug. 3   Litho.   Perf. 14

787	A101	80sh multicolored	.70	.70

Souvenir Sheet

788	A101	750sh multicolored	3.00	3.00

Great Britain
No. O1 — A102

Designs: 50sh, Canada #12. 100sh, Baden #4b. 150sh, Switzerland #3L1. 200sh, US #C3a. 300sh, Western Australia #1. 500sh, Uganda #29. 600sh, Great Britain #2. No. 797, Uganda #29. No. 798, Sir Rowland Hill.

1990, Aug. 6   Litho.   Perf. 14

789	A102	25sh multicolored	.20	.20
790	A102	50sh multicolored	.35	.35
791	A102	100sh multicolored	.65	.65
792	A102	150sh multicolored	.80	.80
793	A102	200sh multicolored	.90	.90
794	A102	300sh gray & black	1.25	1.25
795	A102	500sh multicolored	1.40	1.40
796	A102	600sh multicolored	1.40	1.40
		Nos. 789-796 (8)	6.95	6.95

Souvenir Sheets
Size: 108x77mm

797	A102	1000sh multicolored	3.50	3.50

Size: 119x85mm

798	A102	1000sh scarlet & blk	3.50	3.50

Penny Black, 150th anniversary. Nos. 797-798, Stamp World London '90.

Birds
A103

1990, Sept. 3   Litho.   Perf. 14

799	A103	10sh African jacana	.55	.55
800	A103	15sh Ground hornbill	.60	.60
801	A103	45sh Kori bustard, vert.	.75	.75
802	A103	50sh Secretary bird	.75	.75
803	A103	100sh Egyptian geese	1.10	1.10
804	A103	300sh Goliath heron, vert.	2.00	2.00
805	A103	500sh Ostrich, vert.	2.50	2.50
806	A103	650sh Saddlebill stork, vert.	2.75	2.75
		Nos. 799-806 (8)	11.00	11.00

Souvenir Sheets

807	A103	1000sh Volturine guinea fowl, vert.	4.50	4.50
808	A103	1000sh Lesser flamingo, vert.	4.50	4.50

World Cup Soccer Championships, Italy — A104

Players from various national teams.

1990, Sept. 24

809	A104	50sh Cameroun	.25	.25
810	A104	100sh Egypt	.50	.50
811	A104	250sh Ireland	1.25	1.25
812	A104	600sh West Germany	3.00	3.00
		Nos. 809-812 (4)	5.00	5.00

Souvenir Sheets

813	A104	1000sh Sweden	4.00	4.00
814	A104	1000sh Scotland	4.00	4.00

WHO, Promote Better Health — A105

Walt Disney characters in scenes promoting improved health: 10sh, Mickey, Minnie Mouse having a good breakfast. 20sh, Huey, Dewey and Louie looking before crossing street. 50sh, Mickey, Donald Duck against smoking. 90sh, Mickey saving Donald from choking. 100sh, Mickey, Goofy using seat belts. 250sh, Mickey, Minnie avoiding drugs. 500sh, Donald, Daisy exercising. 600sh, Mickey showing bicycle safety. No. 823, Mickey, friends at doctor's office. No. 824, Mickey, friends walking.

1990, Oct. 19		**Litho.**	**Perf. 13½x13**	
815	A105	10sh multicolored	.20	.20
816	A105	20sh multicolored	.20	.20
817	A105	50sh multicolored	.30	.30
818	A105	90sh multicolored	.50	.50
819	A105	100sh multicolored	.55	.55
820	A105	250sh multicolored	1.25	1.25
821	A105	500sh multicolored	2.75	2.75
822	A105	600sh multicolored	3.25	3.25
		Nos. 815-822 (8)	9.00	9.00

Souvenir Sheets

823	A105	1000sh multicolored	4.00	4.00
824	A105	1000sh multicolored	4.00	4.00

**Butterfly Type of 1989
"Uganda" in Blue**

1990-92		**Litho.**	**Perf. 14**	
826	A93	10sh like #704	.30	.30
827	A93	20sh like #705	.40	.40
828	A93	30sh like #706	.40	.40
829	A93	40sh like #707	.40	.40
830	A93	50sh like #708	.50	.50
831	A93	70sh like #709	.50	.50
832	A93	90sh like #710	.60	.60
833	A93	100sh like #711	.60	.60
834	A93	150sh like #712	.80	.80
835	A93	200sh like #713	1.00	1.00
836	A93	400sh like #714	1.25	1.25
837	A93	500sh like #715	1.25	1.25
838	A93	1000sh like #716	2.50	2.50
839	A93	2000sh like #716	6.00	6.00
839A	A93	3000sh Euphaedra eusemoides	7.50	7.50
839B	A93	4000sh Acraea natalica	8.00	8.00
839C	A93	5000sh Euphaedra themis	8.00	8.00
		Nos. 826-839C (17)	40.00	40.00

Issue dates: 50sh, 400sh, 500sh, 1000sh, 1991. 3000sh, 4000sh, Jan. 2, 1992. Nos. 827, 833, 835 and 839 exist dated 1991.
This is an expanding set, numbers may change.

Christmas
A106

Details from paintings by Rubens: 10sh, 500sh, The Baptism of Christ. 20sh, 150sh, 400sh, 600sh, St. Gregory the Great and Other Saints. 100sh, Saints Nereus, Domitilla and Achilleus. 300sh, Saint Augustine. No. 853, Victory of Eucharistic Truth Over Heresy, horiz. No. 854, Triumph of Faith, horiz.

1990, Dec. 17		**Litho.**	**Perf. 14**	
845	A106	10sh multicolored	.20	.20
846	A106	20sh multicolored	.20	.20
847	A106	100sh multicolored	.65	.65
848	A106	150sh multicolored	.90	.90
849	A106	300sh multicolored	1.50	1.50
850	A106	400sh multicolored	1.60	1.60
851	A106	500sh multicolored	1.75	1.75
852	A106	600sh multicolored	1.90	1.90
		Nos. 845-852 (8)	8.70	8.70

Souvenir Sheets

853	A106	1000sh multicolored	4.50	4.50
854	A106	1000sh multicolored	4.50	4.50

Natl. Census
A107

1000sh, Counting on fingers, houses, people.

1990, Dec. 28		**Litho.**	**Perf. 14**	
855	A107	20sh multicolored	.30	.30

Souvenir Sheet

856	A107	1000sh multicolored	4.50	4.50

Wetlands Fauna — A108

Designs: No. 857a, Damselfly. b, Purple gallinule. c, Sitatunga. d, Purple heron. e, Bushpig. f, Vervet monkey. g, Long reed frog. h, Malachite kingfisher. i, Marsh mongoose. j, Painted reed frog. k, Jacana. l, Charaxes butterfly. m, Nile crocodile. n, Herald snake. o, Dragonfly. p, Lungfish.
No. 858, Nile monitor, horiz.

1991, Jan. 1		**Litho.**	**Perf. 14**	
857	A108	70sh Min. sheet, #a-p.	9.00	9.00
858	A108	1000sh Souv. sheet of 1	6.50	6.50

Fish A109

Designs: 10sh, Haplochromis limax. 20sh, Notobranchius palmqvisti. 40sh, Distichodus affinis. 90sh, Haplochromis sauvagei. 100sh, Aphyosemion calliurum. 350sh, Haplochromis johnstoni. 600sh, Haplochromis dichrourus. 800sh, Hemichromis bimaculatus. No. 867, Haplochromis sp. No. 868, Aphyosemion striatum.

1991, Jan. 18		**Litho.**	**Perf. 14**	
859	A109	10sh multicolored	.20	.20
860	A109	20sh multicolored	.20	.20
861	A109	40sh multicolored	.20	.20
862	A109	90sh multicolored	.40	.40
863	A109	100sh multicolored	.50	.50
864	A109	350sh multicolored	1.25	1.25
865	A109	600sh multicolored	2.50	2.50
866	A109	800sh multicolored	2.75	2.75
		Nos. 859-866 (8)	8.00	8.00

Souvenir Sheets

867	A109	10sh multicolored	5.00	5.00
868	A109	1000sh multicolored	5.00	5.00

1992 Summer Olympics, Barcelona — A110

1991, Feb. 25		**Litho.**	**Perf. 14**	
869	A110	20sh Women's hurdles	.20	.20
870	A110	40sh Long jump	.20	.20
871	A110	125sh Table tennis	.60	.60
872	A110	250sh Soccer	1.25	1.25
873	A110	500sh 800-meter race	2.50	2.50
		Nos. 869-873 (5)	4.75	4.75

Souvenir Sheets

874	A110	1200sh Women's 4x100-meter relay, horiz.	4.50	4.50
875	A110	1200sh Opening ceremony, horiz.	4.50	4.50

Trains A111

Designs: 10sh, 10th Class, Zimbabwe. 20sh, 12th Class, Zimbabwe. 80sh, Tribal class, Tanzania and Zambia. 200sh, 4-6-0 Type, Egypt. 300sh, Mikado, Sudan. 400sh, Mountain class Garrat, Uganda. 500sh, Mallet Type, Uganda. 1000sh, 5 F 1 Electric locomotive, South Africa. No. 884, 4-8-2 Type, Zimbabwe. No. 885, Atlantic type, Egypt. No. 886, 4-8-2 Type, Angola. No. 887, Mallet Compound Type, Natal.

1991, Apr. 2		**Litho.**	**Perf. 14**	
876	A111	10sh multicolored	.20	.20
877	A111	20sh multicolored	.20	.20
878	A111	80sh multicolored	.35	.35
879	A111	200sh multicolored	1.00	1.00
880	A111	300sh multicolored	1.50	1.50
881	A111	400sh multicolored	2.00	2.00
882	A111	500sh multicolored	2.25	2.25
883	A111	1000sh multicolored	4.50	4.50
		Nos. 876-883 (8)	12.00	12.00

Souvenir Sheets

884	A111	1200sh multicolored	4.00	4.00
885	A111	1200sh multicolored	4.00	4.00
886	A111	1200sh multicolored	4.00	4.00
887	A111	1200sh multicolored	4.00	4.00

Even though Nos. 886-887 have the same issue date as Nos. 876-885, their dollar value was lower when they were released.

Phila Nippon '91 — A112

Walt Disney characters in Japan: 10sh, Scrooge McDuck celebrating Ga-No-Iwai. 20sh, Mickey removes shoes before entering Minnie's home. 70sh, Cartman Goofy leading horse. 80sh, Daisy, Minnie exchange gifts. 300sh, Minnie kneels at entrance to home. 400sh, Mickey, Donald in volcanic sand bath. 500sh, Clarabelle Cow enjoys incense burning. 1000sh, Mickey, Minnie writing New Year cards. No. 896, Mickey, Donald and Goofy in public bath. No. 897, Mickey and friends playing Japanese music.

1991, May 29		**Litho.**	**Perf. 14x13½**	
888	A112	10sh multicolored	.20	.20
889	A112	20sh multicolored	.20	.20
890	A112	70sh multicolored	.40	.40
891	A112	80sh multicolored	.45	.45
892	A112	300sh multicolored	1.50	1.50
893	A112	400sh multicolored	2.00	2.00
894	A112	500sh multicolored	2.50	2.50
895	A112	1000sh multicolored	4.50	4.50
		Nos. 888-895 (8)	11.75	11.75

Souvenir Sheets

896	A112	1200sh multicolored	6.00	6.00
897	A112	1200sh multicolored	6.00	6.00

17th World Scout Jamboree, Korea — A113

20sh, Lord Baden-Powell. 80sh, Scouts collecting stamps. 100sh, Scout encampment, NY World's Fair, 1939. 150sh, Cover of 1st Scout Handbook. 300sh, Cooking over campfire. 400sh, Neil Armstrong, Edwin Aldrin, 1st scouts on moon. 500sh, Hands raised for Scout Pledge. 1000sh, Statue to Unknown Scout, Gilwell Park, England. No. 906, William

D. Boyce, Lord Baden-Powell, Rev. L. Hadley No. 907, 17th Jamboree Emblem.

1991, May 27			**Perf. 14**	
898	A113	20sh multicolored	.25	.25
899	A113	80sh multicolored	.40	.40
900	A113	100sh multicolored	.50	.50
901	A113	150sh grn & blk	.75	.75
902	A113	300sh multicolored	1.50	1.50
903	A113	400sh multicolored	2.10	2.10
904	A113	500sh multicolored	2.50	2.50
905	A113	1000sh multicolored	5.00	5.00
		Nos. 898-905 (8)	13.00	13.00

Souvenir Sheets

906	A113	1200sh multicolored	6.00	6.00
907	A113	1200sh cream & blk	6.00	6.00

For surcharge see No. 1305.

Paintings by Vincent Van Gogh — A114

Paintings: 10sh, Snowy Landscape with Arles in the Background. 20sh, Peasant Woman Binding Sheaves, vert. 60sh, The Drinkers. 80sh, View of Auvers. 200sh, Mourning Man, vert. 400sh, Still Life: Vase with Roses. 800sh, The Raising of Lazarus. 1000sh, The Good Samaritan, vert. No. 916, First Steps. No. 917, Village Street and Steps in Auvers with Figures.

1991, June 26		**Litho.**	**Perf. 13½**	
908	A114	10sh multicolored	.20	.20
909	A114	20sh multicolored	.20	.20
910	A114	60sh multicolored	.30	.30
911	A114	80sh multicolored	.40	.40
912	A114	200sh multicolored	1.00	1.00
913	A114	400sh multicolored	2.00	2.00
914	A114	800sh multicolored	4.00	4.00
915	A114	1000sh multicolored	5.00	5.00
		Nos. 908-915 (8)	13.10	13.10

Size: 102x76mm

Imperf

916	A114	1200sh multicolored	6.00	6.00
917	A114	1200sh multicolored	6.00	6.00

**Royal Family Birthday, Anniversary
Common Design Type**

1991, July 5		**Litho.**	**Perf. 14**	
918	CD347	20sh multi	.20	.20
919	CD347	70sh multi	.35	.35
920	CD347	90sh multi	.45	.45
921	CD347	100sh multi	.50	.50
922	CD347	200sh multi	1.00	1.00
923	CD347	500sh multi	2.50	2.50
924	CD347	600sh multi	3.00	3.00
925	CD347	1000sh multi	5.00	5.00
		Nos. 918-925 (8)	13.00	13.00

Souvenir Sheets

926	CD347	1200sh Elizabeth, Philip	6.00	6.00
927	CD347	1200sh Sons, Diana, Charles	6.00	6.00

20sh, 100sh, 200sh, 1000sh, No. 927, Charles and Diana, 10th wedding anniversary. Others, Queen Elizabeth II, 65th birthday.

Charles de Gaulle, Birth Cent.
A115

Designs: 20sh, Portrait, vert. 70sh, Liberation of Paris, 1944, vert. 90sh, With King George VI, 1940, vert. 100sh, Reviewing Free French forces, 1940. 200sh, Making his appeal on BBC, 1940. 500sh, In Normandy, 1944. 600sh, At Albert Hall, 1940. 1000sh, Becoming President of France, 1959, vert. No. 936, Entering Paris, 1944, vert. No. 937, With Eisenhower, 1942.

1991, July 15			**Perf. 14**	
928	A115	20sh multicolored	.20	.20
929	A115	70sh multicolored	.35	.35
930	A115	90sh multicolored	.45	.45
931	A115	100sh multicolored	.50	.50
932	A115	200sh multicolored	1.00	1.00

33	A115	500sh multicolored	2.50	2.50
34	A115	600sh multicolored	3.00	3.00
35	A115	1000sh multicolored	5.00	5.00
		Nos. 928-935 (8)	13.00	13.00

Souvenir Sheets

36	A115	1200sh multicolored	6.00	6.00
37	A115	1200sh multicolored	6.00	6.00

Mushrooms
A116

Designs: 20sh, Volvariella bingensis. 70sh, Agrocybe broadwayi. 90sh, Camarophyllus lilidus. 140sh, Marasmius arborescens. 80sh, Marasmiellus subcinereus. 200sh, Agaricus campestris. 500sh, Chlorophyllum molybdites. 1000sh, Agaricus bingensis. No. 46, Leucocoprinus cepaestipes, horiz. No. 47, Laccaria lateritia, horiz.

1991, July 19   Litho.   Perf. 14

38	A116	20sh multicolored	.20	.20
39	A116	70sh multicolored	.35	.35
40	A116	90sh multicolored	.45	.45
41	A116	140sh multicolored	.70	.70
42	A116	180sh multicolored	.90	.90
43	A116	200sh multicolored	1.00	1.00
44	A116	500sh multicolored	2.50	2.50
45	A116	1000sh multicolored	5.00	5.00
		Nos. 938-945 (8)	11.10	11.10

Souvenir Sheets

46	A116	1200sh multicolored	6.00	6.00
47	A116	1200sh multicolored	6.00	6.00

World Wildlife Type of 1983

1991, Aug. 1

48	A43	100sh as No. 371	.60	.60
49	A43	140sh as No. 372	.80	.80
50	A43	200sh as No. 373	1.10	1.10
51	A43	600sh as No. 374	3.25	3.25
		Nos. 948-951 (4)	5.75	5.75

Souvenir Sheets
Perf. 13x12½

52	A43	1200sh Giraffe	6.00	6.00
53	A43	1200sh Rhinoceros	6.00	6.00

World Wildlife Fund. Nos. 952-953 do not have the WWF emblem.

Miniature Sheet

Flowers in Royal Botanical Gardens, Kew — A118

#954: a, Cypripedium calceolus. b, Rhododendron thomsonii. c, Ginkgo biloba. d, Magnolia campbellii. e, Wisteria sinensis. f, Clerodendrum ugandense. g, Eulophia horsfallii. h, Aerangis rhodosticta. i, Abelmoschus moschatus. j, Gloriosa superba. k, Carissa edulis. l, Ochna kirkii. m, Canarina abyssinica. n, Nymphaea caerulea. o, Ceropegia succulenta. p, Strelitzia reginae. q, Strongylodon macrobotrys. r, Victoria amazonica. s, Orchis militaris. Sophora microphylla. #956, The Pagoda, Kew.

Royal Botanic Gardens, Melbourne, Australia: #955: a, Anigozanthos manglesii. b, Banksia grandis. c, Clianthus formosus. d, Gossypium sturtianum. e, Callistemon lanceolatus. f, Saintpaulia ionantha. g, Halodendrum capense. h, Aloe ferox. i, Eucalanthus speciousus. j, Lithops schwantesii k, Protea repens. l, Plumbago capensis. m, Clerodendrum thomsoniae. n, Thunbergia alata. o, Schotia latifolia. p, Ipacris impressa. q, Acacia pycnantha. r, Telopea speciosissima. s, Wahlenbergia gloriosa. t, Eucalyptus globulus. #957, Temple of the Winds, Melbourne.

1991, Nov. 25   Litho.   Perf. 14½

54	A118	100sh Sheet of 20,		
		#a.-t.	8.00	8.00
55	A118	90sh Sheet of 20,		
		#a.-t.	5.25	5.25

Souvenir Sheets

956	A118	1400sh multicolored	5.50	5.50
957	A118	1400sh multicolored	4.00	4.00

No. 956 contains one 30x38mm stamp.
While Nos. 955 and 957 have the same issue date as Nos. 954 and 956, their dollar value was lower when released. Numbers have been reserved for additional values in this set.

Christmas
A120

Paintings by Piero Della Francesca: 20sh, Madonna with Child and Angels. 50sh, The Baptism of Christ. 80sh, Polyptych of Mercy. 100sh, The Madonna of Mercy. 200sh, The Legend of the True Cross: The Annunciation. 500sh, Pregnant Madonna. 1000sh, Polyptych of St. Anthony: The Annunciation. 1500sh, The Nativity. No. 968, The Brera Altarpiece. No. 969, Polyptych of St. Anthony.

1991, Dec. 18   Litho.   Perf. 12

960	A120	20sh multicolored	.20	.20
961	A120	50sh multicolored	.25	.25
962	A120	80sh multicolored	.40	.40
963	A120	100sh multicolored	.50	.50
964	A120	200sh multicolored	1.00	1.00
965	A120	500sh multicolored	2.50	2.50
966	A120	1000sh multicolored	5.00	5.00
967	A120	1500sh multicolored	7.50	7.50
		Nos. 960-967 (8)	17.35	17.35

Souvenir Sheets
Perf. 14½

968	A120	1800sh multicolored	9.00	9.00
969	A120	1800sh multicolored	9.00	9.00

Boy Scouts
A121

Designs: 20sh, Boy Scout Monument, Silver Bay, NY and Ernest Thompson Seton, first chief scout. 50sh, Tree house and Daniel Beard, Boy Scout pioneer, vert. 1500sh, Boy Scout emblem.

1992, Jan. 6   Litho.   Perf. 14

970	A121	20sh multicolored	.20	.20
971	A121	50sh multicolored	.25	.25

Souvenir Sheet

972	A121	1500sh multicolored	7.50	7.50

YMCA-Boy Scouts partnership, Lord Robert Baden-Powell, 50th death anniv. in 1991 (#970) and 17th World Scout Jamboree, Korea (#971-972).
A number has been reserved for an additional value in this set.

Miniature Sheet

Balloons
A122

Balloons: a, Modern Hot Air. b, Sport. c, Pro Juventute. d, Blanchard's. e, Nadar's Le Geant. f, First trans-Pacific balloon crossing. g, Montgolfier's. h, Paris, Double Eagle II, used in first trans-Atlantic balloon crossing. i, Tethered.

1992, Jan. 6   Litho.   Perf. 14

974	A122	200sh Sheet of 9, #a.-i.	5.25	5.25

Miniature Sheet

Japanese Attack on Pearl Harbor, 50th Anniv. (in 1991) A123

Designs: a, Japanese bombers attack USS Vestal. b, Japanese Zero fighter. c, Zeros over burning USS Arizona. d, Battleship Row, USS Nevada under way. e, Japanese Val dive bomber. f, US Dauntless dive bomber attacking Hiryu. g, Japanese planes over Midway Island. h, US Buffalo fighter plane. i, US Wildcat fighters over carrier. j, USS Yorktown and Hammann torpedoed by Japanese submarine.

1992, Jan. 6   Perf. 14½x15

975	A123	200sh Sheet of 10, #a.-j.	5.75	5.75

Battle of Midway, 50th anniv. (#975f-975j). Inscription for No. 975i incorrectly describes fighters as Hellcats.

Anniversaries and Events — A124

Designs: 400sh, Glider No. 8. 500sh, Man breaking pieces from Berlin Wall. 700sh, Portrait of Mozart and scene from "The Magic Flute." 1200sh, Electric locomotive.

1992, Jan. 6   Litho.   Perf. 14

976	A124	400sh multicolored	2.00	2.00
977	A124	500sh multicolored	2.50	2.50
978	A124	700sh multicolored	3.50	3.50
		Nos. 976-978 (3)	8.00	8.00

Souvenir Sheet

979	A124	1200sh multicolored	6.00	6.00

Otto Lillienthal, hang glider, cent. (in 1991) (#976). Brandenburg Gate, Bicent. (#977). Wolfgang Amadeus Mozart, death bicent. (#978), Trans-Siberian Railway, cent. (#979).

Walt Disney Characters on World Tour — A125

20sh, Safari surprise in Africa. 50sh, Pluto's tail of India. 80sh, Donald's calypso beat in Caribbean. 200sh, Goofy pulling rickshaw in China. 500sh, Minnie, Mickey on camel in Egypt. 800sh, Wrestling, Japanese style. 1000sh, Goofy bullfighting in Spain. 1500sh, Mickey scoring in soccer game. #988, Daisy singing opera in Germany. #989, Mickey and Pluto as Cossack dancers in Moscow.

1992, Feb.   Perf. 13

980	A125	20sh multi	.20	.20
981	A125	50sh multi	.20	.20
982	A125	80sh multi	.20	.20
983	A125	200sh multi	.50	.50
984	A125	500sh multi	1.25	1.25
985	A125	800sh multi	2.00	2.00
986	A125	1000sh multi	2.50	2.50
987	A125	1500sh multi	3.75	3.75
		Nos. 980-987 (8)	10.60	10.60

Souvenir Sheets

988	A125	2000sh multi, vert.	5.00	5.00
989	A125	2000sh multi, vert.	5.75	5.75

Queen Elizabeth II's Accession to the Throne, 40th Anniv.
Common Design Type

1992, Feb. 6   Litho.   Perf. 14

990	CD348	100sh multi	.50	.50
991	CD348	200sh multi	1.00	1.00
992	CD348	500sh multi	2.50	2.50
993	CD348	1000sh multi	5.00	5.00
		Nos. 990-993 (4)	9.00	9.00

Souvenir Sheets

994	CD348	1800sh Queen, waterfalls	9.00	9.00
995	CD348	1800sh Queen, dam	9.00	9.00

Dinosaurs
A126

1992, Apr. 8   Litho.   Perf. 14

996	A126	50sh Kentrosaurus	.20	.20
997	A126	200sh Iguanodon	.40	.40
998	A126	250sh Hypsilophodon	.70	.70
999	A126	300sh Brachiosaurus	.60	.60
1000	A126	400sh Peloneustes	1.10	1.10
1001	A126	500sh Pteranodon	1.00	1.00
1002	A126	800sh Tetralophodon	1.60	1.60
1003	A126	1000sh Megalosaurus	2.75	2.75
		Nos. 996-1003 (8)	8.35	8.35

Souvenir Sheets

1004	A126	2000sh like #1003	5.75	5.75
1005	A126	2000sh like #998	4.00	4.00

Nos. 1004-1005 printed in continuous design.
While Nos. 997, 999, 1001-1002, 1005 have the same release date as Nos. 996, 998, 1000, 1003-1004, their value in relation to the dollar was lower when they were released.

Easter
A127

Paintings: 50sh, The Entry into Jerusalem (detail), by Giotto. 100sh, Pilate and the Watch from psalter of Robert de Lisle. 200sh, The Kiss of Judas (detail), by Giotto. 250sh, Christ Washing the Feet of the Disciples, illumination from Life of Christ. 300sh, Christ Seized in the Garden from Melissande Psalter. 500sh, Doubting Thomas, illumination from Life of Christ. 1000sh, The Marys at the Tomb (detail), artist unknown. 2000sh, The Ascension, from 14th century Florentine illuminated manuscript.
Limoge enamels: No. 1014, Agony at Gethsemane. No. 1015, The Piercing of Christ's Side.

1992   Litho.   Perf. 13½x14

1006	A127	50sh multi	.20	.20
1007	A127	100sh multi	.30	.30
1008	A127	200sh multi	.60	.60
1009	A127	250sh multi	.70	.70
1010	A127	300sh multi	.85	.85
1011	A127	500sh multi	1.40	1.40
1012	A127	1000sh multi	2.75	2.75
1013	A127	2000sh multi	5.75	5.75
		Nos. 1006-1013 (8)	12.55	12.55

Souvenir Sheets

1014	A127	2500sh multi	7.00	7.00
1015	A127	2500sh multi	7.00	7.00

Musical Instruments
A128

1992, July 20   Litho.   Perf. 14

1016	A128	50sh Adungu	.20	.20
1017	A128	100sh Endingidi	.30	.30
1018	A128	200sh Akogo	.60	.60
1019	A128	250sh Nanga	.70	.70
1020	A128	300sh Engoma	.85	.85
1021	A128	400sh Amakondere	1.10	1.10
1022	A128	500sh Akakyenkye	1.40	1.40
1023	A128	1000sh Ennanga	2.75	2.75
		Nos. 1016-1023 (8)	7.90	7.90

Discovery of America, 500th Anniv. A129

50sh, World map, 1486. 100sh, Map of Africa, 1508. 150sh, New World, 1500. 200sh, Nina, astrolabe. 600sh, Quadrant, Pinta. 800sh, Hour glass. 900sh, 15th century compass. 2000sh, World map, 1492. #1032, 1490 Map by Henricus Martellus, 1490. #1033, Sections of 1492 globe.

1992, July 24   Litho.   Perf. 14

1024	A129	50sh multicolored	.20	.20
1025	A129	100sh multicolored	.20	.20
1026	A129	150sh multicolored	.20	.20
1027	A129	200sh multicolored	.60	.60
1028	A129	600sh multicolored	1.75	1.75
1029	A129	800sh multicolored	2.25	2.25
1030	A129	900sh multicolored	2.60	2.60
1031	A129	2000sh multicolored	2.00	2.00
		Nos. 1024-1031 (8)	9.80	9.80

Souvenir Sheets

1032	A129	2500sh multi, vert.	7.25	7.25
1033	A129	2500sh multi	5.00	5.00

World Columbian Stamp Expo '92, Chicago.
While Nos. 1024-1026, 1031 and 1033 have the same issue date as Nos. 1027-1030 and 1032, their value in relation to the dollar was lower when they were released.

Hummel Figurines — A130   1992 Summer Olympics, Barcelona — A131

#1042: a, like #1034. b, like #1035. c, like #1036. d, like #1037.
#1043: a, like #1039. b, like #1038. c, like #1040. d, like #1041.

1992, Aug. 28   Litho.   Perf. 14

1034	A130	50sh Little Laundry Girl	.20	.20
1035	A130	200sh Scrub Girl	.60	.60
1036	A130	250sh Sweeper Girl	.70	.70
1037	A130	300sh Little Mother	.85	.85
1038	A130	600sh Little Mountaineer	1.25	1.25
1039	A130	900sh Little Knitter	1.75	1.75
1040	A130	1000sh Little Cowboy	2.00	2.00
1041	A130	1500sh Little Astronomer	4.25	4.25
		Nos. 1034-1041 (8)	11.60	11.60

Souvenir Sheets of 4

1042	A130	500sh #a.-d.	5.75	5.75
1043	A130	500sh #a.-d.	4.00	4.00

While Nos. 1034, 1038-1040, 1043 have the same release date as Nos. 1035-1037, 1041-1042, their value in relation to the dollar was lower when they were released.

1992   Litho.   Perf. 14

1044	A131	50sh Javelin	.20	.20
1045	A131	100sh High jump, horiz.	.20	.20
1046	A131	200sh Pentathlon (Fencing)	.40	.40
1047	A131	250sh Volleyball	.50	.50
1048	A131	300sh Women's platform diving	.60	.60
1049	A131	500sh Team cycling	1.00	1.00
1050	A131	1000sh Tennis	2.00	2.00
1051	A131	2000sh Boxing, horiz.	4.00	4.00
		Nos. 1044-1051 (8)	8.90	8.90

Souvenir Sheets

1052	A131	2500sh Baseball	5.00	5.00
1053	A131	2500sh Basketball	5.00	5.00

Wild Animals A132

1992, Sept. 25   Litho.   Perf. 14

1054	A132	50sh Spotted hyena	.20	.20
1055	A132	100sh Impala	.20	.20
1056	A132	200sh Giant forest hog	.40	.40
1057	A132	250sh Pangolin	.50	.50
1058	A132	300sh Golden monkey	.60	.60
1059	A132	800sh Serval	1.60	1.60
1060	A132	1000sh Bush genet	2.00	2.00
1061	A132	3000sh Defassa waterbuck	6.00	6.00
		Nos. 1054-1061 (8)	11.50	11.50

Souvenir Sheets

1062	A132	2500sh Mountain gorilla	5.00	5.00
1063	A132	2500sh Hippopotamus	5.00	5.00

Birds — A133

Designs: 20sh, Red necked falcon. 30sh, Yellow-billed hornbill. 50sh, Purple heron. 100sh, Regal sunbird. 150sh, White-brown robin chat. 200sh, Shining-blue kingfisher. 250sh, Great blue turaco. 300sh, Emerald cuckoo. 500sh, Abyssinian roller. 800sh, Crowned crane. 1000sh, Doherty's bush shrike. 2000sh, Splendid glossy starling. 3000sh, Little bee eater. 4000sh, Red-headed lovebird.

1992, Aug.   Litho.   Perf. 15x14

1064	A133	20sh multi	.20	.20
1065	A133	30sh multi	.20	.20
1066	A133	50sh multi	.20	.20
1067	A133	100sh multi	.20	.20
1068	A133	150sh multi	.30	.30
1069	A133	200sh multi	.40	.40
1070	A133	250sh multi	.50	.50
1071	A133	300sh multi	.55	.55
1072	A133	500sh multi	1.00	1.00
1073	A133	800sh multi	1.60	1.60
1074	A133	1000sh multi	2.00	2.00
1075	A133	2000sh multi	4.00	4.00
1076	A133	3000sh multi	6.00	6.00
1076A	A133	4000sh multi	8.00	8.00
		Nos. 1064-1076A (14)	25.15	25.15

Issued: 3000sh, Oct.; others, Aug.?

Walt Disney's Goofy, 60th Anniv. — A134

Scenes from Disney animated films: 50sh, Hawaiian Holiday, 1937, vert. 100sh, The Nifty Nineties, 1941, vert. 200sh, Mickey's Fire Brigade, 1935, vert. 250sh, The Art of Skiing, 1941. 300sh, Mickey's Amateurs, 1937. 1000sh, Boat Builders, 1938. 1500sh, The Olympic Champ, 1942, vert. 2000sh, The Olympic Champ, 1942, vert. No. 1085, Goofy and Wilbur, 1939. No. 1086, Goofy's family tree, vert.

Perf. 13½x14, 14x13½

1992, Nov. 2   Litho.

1077	A134	50sh multi	.20	.20
1078	A134	100sh multi	.20	.20
1079	A134	200sh multi	.40	.40
1080	A134	250sh multi	.50	.50
1081	A134	300sh multi	.60	.60
1082	A134	1000sh multi	2.00	2.00
1083	A134	1500sh multi	3.00	3.00
1084	A134	2000sh multi	4.00	4.00
		Nos. 1077-1084 (8)	10.90	10.90

Souvenir Sheets

1085	A134	3000sh multi	6.00	6.00
1086	A134	3000sh multi	6.00	6.00

Souvenir Sheet

UN Headquarters, New York City — A135

1992, Oct. 28   Litho.   Perf. 14

1087	A135	2500sh multi	5.00	5.00

Postage Stamp Mega Event '92, NYC.

Christmas A136

Details or entire paintings by Zurbaran: 50sh, The Annunciation (angel at left). 200sh, The Annunciation (angel at right). 250sh, The Virgin of the Immaculate Conception. 300sh, The Virgin of the Immaculate Conception (detail). 800sh, 900sh, The Holy Family with Saints Anne, Joachim and John the Baptist (800sh, entire; 900sh, detail). 1000sh, Adoration of the Magi (entire). 2000sh, Adoration of the Magi. No. 1096, The Virgin of the Immaculate Conception (Virgin with arms outstretched). No. 1097, The Virgin of the Immaculate Conception (Virgin with arms folded).

1992, Nov. 16   Litho.   Perf. 13½x14

1088	A136	50sh multi	.20	.20
1089	A136	200sh multi	.35	.35
1090	A136	250sh multi	.50	.50
1091	A136	300sh multi	.60	.60
1092	A136	800sh multi	1.60	1.60
1093	A136	900sh multi	1.75	1.75
1094	A136	1000sh multi	2.00	2.00
1095	A136	2000sh multi	4.00	4.00
		Nos. 1088-1095 (8)	11.00	11.00

Souvenir Sheets

1096	A136	2500sh multi	5.00	5.00
1097	A136	2500sh multi	5.00	5.00

World Health Organization — A137

Anniversaries and Events — A138

Designs: 50sh, Improving household food security. 200sh, Continue to breastfeed. 250sh, At four months old, give breast milk and soft food. No. 1101, Drink water from a safe and protected source. No. 1102, Jupiter, Voyager 2. No. 1103, Mother holding baby. No. 1104, Impala. No. 1105, Zebra. No. 1106, Count Ferdinand von Zeppelin, zeppelin. 2000sh, Neptune, Voyager 2. 3000sh, Count Zeppelin, zeppelin, diff. No. 1109, Voyager 2, Jupiter, diff. No. 1110, Wart hog. No. 1111, Doctor examining child, Lions Intl. emblem. No. 1112, Count Zeppelin, balloon.

1992   Litho.   Perf. 14

1098	A137	50sh multi	.20	.20
1099	A137	200sh multi	.40	.40
1100	A137	250sh multi	.50	.50
1101	A137	300sh multi	.60	.60
1102	A138	300sh multi	.60	.60
1103	A137	800sh multi	1.60	1.60
1104	A138	800sh multi	1.60	1.60
1105	A138	1000sh multi	2.00	2.00
1106	A138	1000sh multi	2.00	2.00
1107	A138	2000sh multi	4.00	4.00
1108	A138	3000sh multi	6.00	6.00
		Nos. 1098-1108 (11)	19.50	19.50

Souvenir Sheets

1109	A138	2500sh multi	5.00	5.00
1110	A138	2500sh multi	5.00	5.00
1111	A138	2500sh multi	5.00	5.00
1112	A138	2500sh multi	5.00	5.00

WHO (#1098-1101, 1103). Intl. Space Year (#1102, 1107, 1109). Earth Summit, Rio de Janeiro (#1104-1105, 1110). Count Zeppelin, 75th anniv. of death (#1106, 1108, 1112). Lions Intl., 75th anniv. (#1111).
Issue dates: Nos. 1098-1103, 1106, 1109, 1112, Nov.; others, Dec.

1993 Visit of Pope John Paul II to Uganda A139

A139a

Designs: 50sh, Cathedral in Kampala, site of Papal Mass, Kampala, hands releasing doves. 200sh, Site of Papal Mass, Pope. 250sh, Ugandan man, Pope. 300sh, Three Ugandan Catholic leaders, Pope. 800sh, Pope waving, Ugandan map and flag. 900sh, Ugandan woman, Pope wearing mitre. 1000sh, Pope, Ugandan flag, site of Papal Mass. 2000sh, Ugandan flag, Pope waving.
No. 1121, Pope at door of airplane, vert. No. 1122, Pope delivering message at podium, vert.
No. 1123, Pope John Paul II. No. 1124, Pope with hands raised.

1993, Feb. 1   Litho.   Perf. 14

1113	A139	50sh multi	.20	.20
1114	A139	200sh multi	.40	.40
1115	A139	250sh multi	.50	.50
1116	A139	300sh multi	.60	.60
1117	A139	800sh multi	1.60	1.60
1118	A139	900sh multi	1.75	1.75
1119	A139	1000sh multi	2.00	2.00
1120	A139	2000sh multi	4.00	4.00
		Nos. 1113-1120 (8)	11.05	11.05

Souvenir Sheets

1121	A139	3000sh multi	6.00	6.00
1122	A139	3000sh multi	6.00	6.00

Embossed

Embossed Perf. 12

1123	A139a	5000sh gold		

Souvenir Sheet

Imperf

1124	A139a	5000sh gold		

Miniature Sheet

Louvre Museum, Bicent. A140

Details or entire paintings by Rembrandt: No. 1125a, Self-Portrait with an Easel. b, Birds of Paradise. c, The Beef Carcass. d, The Supper at Emmaus. e, Hendrickje Stoffels. f, Titus, Son of the Artist. g, The Holy Family (left). h, The Holy Family (right).

2500sh, Philosopher in Meditation, horiz.

1993, Apr. 5   Litho.   Perf. 12

1125	A140	500sh Sheet of 8, #a.-h. + label	8.00	8.00

Souvenir Sheet
Perf. 14½

1126	A140	2500sh multicolored	4.25	4.25

Dogs A141

1993, May 28   Litho.   Perf. 14

1127	A141	50sh Afghan hound	.20	.20
1128	A141	100sh Newfoundland	.20	.20
1129	A141	200sh Siberian huskies	.35	.35
1130	A141	250sh Briard	.45	.45
1131	A141	300sh Saluki	.60	.60
1132	A141	800sh Labrador retriever, vert.	1.50	1.50
1133	A141	1000sh Greyhound	1.75	1.75
1134	A141	1500sh Pointer	2.75	2.75
		Nos. 1127-1134 (8)	7.80	7.80

Souvenir Sheets

1135	A141	2500sh Cape hunting dog	4.25	4.25
1136	A141	2500sh Norwegian elkhound	4.25	4.25

Miniature Sheet

Coronation of Queen Elizabeth II, 40th Anniv. A142

#1137: a, 50sh, Official coronation photograph. b, 200sh, Orb, Rod of Equity & Mercy. c, 500sh, Queen during coronation ceremony. d, 1500sh, Queen Elizabeth II, Princess Margaret.

2500sh, The Crown, by Grace Wheatley, 1959.

1993, June 2   Litho.   Perf. 13½x14

1137	A142	Sheet, 2 each #a.-d.	7.50 7.50

Souvenir Sheet
Perf. 14

1138	A142	2500sh multicolored	4.25 4.25

No. 1138 contains one 28x42mm stamp.

Miniature Sheet

Taipei '93 — A143

Funerary objects: No. 1139a, Tomb guardian god. b, Civil official. c, Tomb guardian god, diff. d, Civil official, diff. e, Chimera. f, Civil official, diff.

2500sh, Statue of Sacred Mother, Ceremonial Hall, Taiyuan, Shanxi.

1993, Sept. 22   Litho.   Perf. 14x13½

1139	A143	600sh Sheet of 6, #a.-f.	6.00 6.00

Souvenir Sheet

1140	A143	2500sh multicolored	4.25 4.25

With Bangkok '93 Emblem

Thai sculpture: No. 1141a, Standing Buddha, 13th-15th cent. b, Crowned Buddha, 13th cent. c, Thepanom, 15th cent. d, Crowned Buddha, 12th cent. e, Four-armed Avalokitesvara, 9th cent. f, Lop Buri standing Buddha, 13th cent.

2500sh, Buddha, interior of Wat Mahathat.

1993, Sept. 22

1141	A143	600sh Sheet of 6, #a.-f.	6.00 6.00

Souvenir Sheet

1142	A143	2500sh multicolored	4.25 4.25

With Indopex '93 Emblem
Miniature Sheet

Japanese Wayang Puppets, Indonesia: No. 1143a, Bupati karma, Prince of Wangga. b, Rahwana. c, Sondjeng Sandjata. d, Raden Damar Wulan. e, Klitik figure. f, Hanaman. 2500sh, Candi Mendut in Kedu Plain, Java, Indonesia.

1993, Sept. 22   Litho.   Perf. 13½x14

1143	A143	600sh Sheet of 6, #a.-f.	6.00 6.00

Souvenir Sheet

1144	A143	2500sh multicolored	4.25 4.25

A144   A145

1993, Oct. 1   Litho.   Perf. 14

1145	A144	50sh Gutierrez, Voeller	.20	.20
1146	A144	200sh Tomas Brolin	.35	.35
1147	A144	250sh Gary Lineker	.45	.45
1148	A144	300sh Munoz, Butragueno	.50	.50
1149	A144	800sh Carlos Valderrama	1.40	1.40
1150	A144	900sh Diego Maradona	1.50	1.50
1151	A144	1000sh Pedro Troglio	1.75	1.75
1152	A144	2000sh Enzo Scifo	3.50	3.50
		Nos. 1145-1152 (8)	9.65	9.65

Souvenir Sheets

1153	A144	2500sh Brazil coaches	4.25	4.25
1154	A144	2500sh De Napoli, Skuhravy, horiz.	4.25	4.25

1994 World Cup Soccer Championships, US.

1993, Nov. 3   Perf. 14

Cathedrals of the World: 50sh, York Minster, England. 100sh, Notre Dame, Paris. 200sh, Little Metropolis, Athens. 250sh, St. Patrick's, New York. 300sh, Ulm, Germany. 800sh, St. Basil's, Moscow. 1000sh, Roskilde, Denmark. 2000sh, Seville, Spain. No. 1163, Namirembe, Uganda. No. 1163A, St. Peter's, Vatican City.

1155	A145	50sh multi	.20	.20
1156	A145	100sh multi	.20	.20
1157	A145	200sh multi	.35	.35
1158	A145	250sh multi	.40	.40
1159	A145	300sh multi	.50	.50
1160	A145	800sh multi	1.40	1.40
1161	A145	1000sh multi	1.75	1.75
1162	A145	2000sh multi	3.50	3.50
		Nos. 1155-1162 (8)	8.30	8.30

Souvenir Sheets

1163	A145	2500sh multi	4.25	4.25
1163A	A145	2500sh multi	4.25	4.25

Christmas A146

Details or entire woodcut, The Virgin with Carthusian Monks, by Durer: 50sh, 200sh, 300sh, 2000sh.

Details or entire paintings by Raphael: 100sh, 800sh, Sacred Family. 250sh, The Virgin of the Rose. 1000sh, Holy Family (Virgin with Beardless Joseph).

No. 1172, The Virgin with Carthusian Monks, by Durer. No. 1173, Sacred Family, by Raphael.

1993, Nov. 19   Litho.   Perf. 13½x14

1164-1171	A146	Set of 8	8.50	8.50

Souvenir Sheets

1172-1173	A146	2500sh Set of 2	8.50	8.50

Mickey Mouse, Friends with Dinosaurs — A147

Disney characters depicted with: 50sh, Stegosaurus. 100sh, Pterandom. 200sh, Mamenchisaurus. 250sh, Rock painting. 300sh, Dino "sails." 500sh, Diplodocus. 800sh, Mamenchisaurus, diff. 1000sh, Triceratops.

No. 1182, Tyrannosaurus rex, Mickey. No. 1183, Minnie, Mickey, mamenchisaurus, diff.

1993, Dec. 22   Litho.   Perf. 14x13½

1174-1181	A147	Set of 8	5.00	5.00

Souvenir Sheets

1182-1183	A147	2500sh Set of 2	8.00	8.00

Rinderpest Campaign A148

Picasso (1881-1973) A149

1993, Dec. 29   Perf. 14

1184	A148	200sh multicolored	.35	.35

1993, Dec. 29

Paintings: 100sh, Woman in Yellow, 1907. 250sh, Gertrude Stein, 1906. 2500sh, Woman by a Window, 1956.

1185-1186	A149	Set of 2	.50	.50

Souvenir Sheet

1187	A149	2500sh multicolored	4.25	4.25

Copernicus (1473-1543) — A150

Polska '93 — A151

Telescopes: 500sh, Early. 1000sh, Modern. 2500sh, Copernicus.

1993, Dec. 29

1188-1189	A150	Set of 2	2.50	2.50

Souvenir Sheet

1190	A150	2500sh multicolored	4.25	4.25

1993, Dec. 29

Paintings: 800sh, Creation of the World, by S. I. Witkiewicz par J. Gloqowski, 1921. 1000sh, For the Right to Work, by Andrezej Strumillo, 1952. 2500sh, Temptation of St. Anthony I, by S. I. Witkiewicz (1908-21), horiz.

1191-1192	A151	Set of 2	3.00	3.00

Souvenir Sheet

1193	A151	2500sh multicolored	4.25	4.25

World Meteorological Day — A152

Fruits and Crops — A153

Designs: 50sh, Weather station, horiz. 200sh, Observatory at Meteorological Training School, Entebbe. 250sh, Satellite receiver at National Meteorological Center, horiz. 300sh, Reading temperatures, National Center, Entebbe, horiz. 400sh, Automatic weather station. 800sh, Destruction by hail storm, horiz. 2500sh, Barograph, horiz.

1993, Dec. 29

1194-1199	A152	Set of 6	3.75	3.75

Souvenir Sheet

1200	A152	2500sh multicolored	4.25	4.25

1993, Dec. 29

Designs: 50sh, Passiflora edulis. 100sh, Helianthus annus. 150sh, Musa sapientum. 200sh, Vanilla fragrans. 250sh, Ananas comosus. 300sh, Artocarpus heterophyllus. 500sh, Sorghum bo\icolor. 800sh, Zea mays. No. 1209, Sesamum indicum. No. 1210, Coffea canephora.

1201-1208	A153	Set of 8	4.50	4.50

Souvenir Sheets

1209-1210	A153	2000sh Set of 2	8.50	8.50

Automotive Anniversaries — A154

No. 1211: a, 1903 Model A Ford, Henry Ford. b, Model T Snowmobile at 1932 Winter Olympics, Jack Shea. c, Lee Iacocca, Ford Mustang at New York World's Fair. d, Jim Clark, Lotus-Ford winning 1965 Indianapolis 500 race.

No. 1212: a, 1994 Mercedes Benz S600 Coupe. b, 1955 Mercedes Benz W196 Grand Prix Champion car, Juan Manuel Fangio. c, 1938 Mercedes Benz W125 road speed record holder, Rudolph Caracciola. d, Carl Benz, 1893 Benz Viktoria.

No. 1213, Carl Benz, vert. No. 1214, Henry Ford, vert.

1994, Jan. 18   Litho.   Perf. 14

1211	A154	700sh Strip of 4, #a.-d.	6.25	6.25
1212	A154	800sh Strip of 4, #a.-d.	7.25	7.25

Souvenir Sheets

1213	A154	2500sh multicolored	4.50	4.50
1214	A154	2500sh multicolored	4.50	4.50

First Ford motor, cent. (#1211, #1214). First Benz four-wheel car, cent. (#1212, #1213).

A155

Hong Kong
'94 — A156

Stamps, religious shrines, Repulse Bay: No. 1215, Hong Kong #531. No. 1216, #1163.

Snuff boxes, Qing Dynasty: No. 1217a, Glass painted enamel with pavilion. b, Porcelain with floral design. c, Porcelain with quail design. d, Porcelain with openwork design. e, Agate with pair of dogs. f, Agate with man on donkey.

1994, Feb. 18   Litho.   Perf. 14
1215 A155 500sh multicolored   .90 .90
1216 A155 500sh multicolored   .90 .90
   a.   Pair, #1215-1216   1.75 1.75

Miniature Sheet
1217 A156 200sh Sheet of 6, #a.-f.   2.25 2.25

Nos. 1215-1216 issued in sheets of 5 pairs. No. 1216a is continuous design.
New Year 1994 (Year of the Dog) (#1217e).

Miniature Sheet

1994 World Cup Soccer Championships, US — A157

Designs: No. 1218a, Georges Grun, Belgium. b, Oscar Ruggeri, Argentina. c, Frank Rijkaard, Holland. d, Magid "Tyson" Musisi, Uganda. e, Donald Keeman, Holland. f, Igor Shallmov, Russia.
No. 1219, RFK Stadium, Washington DC. No. 1220, Ruud Gullit, Holland.

1994, June 27   Litho.   Perf. 14
1218 A157 500sh Sheet of 6, #a.-f.   5.50 5.50

Souvenir Sheets
1219-1220 A157 2500sh each   4.50 4.50

Heifer Project Intl., 50th Anniv. A158

1994, June 29   Litho.   Perf. 14
1221 A158 100sh multicolored   .20 .20

Moths — A159   Native Crafts — A160

100sh, Lobobunaea goodii. 200sh, Bunaeopsis hersilia. 300sh, Rufoglanis rosea. 350sh, Acherontia atropos. 400sh, Rohaniella pygmaea. 450sh, Euchloron megaera. 500sh,

---

Epiphora rectifascia. 1000sh, Polyphychus coryndoni.
Lobobunaea goodii: No. 1230, Wings down. No. 1231, Wings extended.

1994, July 13
1222-1229 A159 Set of 8   6.75 6.75

Souvenir Sheets
1230-1231 A159 2500sh each   5.00 5.00

1994, July 18
100sh, Wood stool. 200sh, Wood & banana fiber chair. 250sh, Raffia & palm leaves basket. 300sh, Wool tapestry showing tree planting. 450sh, Wool tapestry showing hair grooming. 500sh, Wood sculpture, drummer. 800sh, Decorated gourds. 1000sh, Lady's bag made from bark cloth.
No. 1240, Raffia baskets. No. 1241, Papyrus hats.

1232-1239 A160 Set of 8   7.00 7.00

Souvenir Sheets
1240-1241 A160 2500sh each   5.00 5.00

Cats — A161   ILO, 75th Anniv. — A162

Cat, historic landmark: 50sh, Turkish angora, Blue Mosque, Turkey, horiz. 100sh, Japanese bobtail, Mt. Fuji, Japan, horiz. 200sh, Norwegian forest cat, windmill, Holland, horiz. 300sh, Egyptian mau, pyramids, Egypt. 450sh, Rex, Stonehenge, England. 500sh, Chartreux, Eiffel Tower, France, horiz. 1000sh, Burmese, Shwe Dagon Pagoda, Burma. 1500sh, Maine coon, Pemaquid Point Lighthouse, Maine.
#1250, Russian blue, horiz. #1251, Manx, horiz.

1994, July 22
1242-1249 A161 Set of 8   8.25 8.25

Souvenir Sheets
1250-1251 A161 2500sh each   5.00 5.00

1994, July 29
1252 A162 350sh multicolored   .70 .70

PHILAKOREA '94 — A163

Designs: 100sh, Eight story Sari pagoda, Paekyangsa. 350sh, Ch'omsongdae (Natl. treasure). 1000sh, Pulguksa Temple exterior. 2500sh, Bronze mural, Pagoda Park, Seoul.

1994, Aug. 8
1253-1255 A163 Set of 3   3.00 3.00

Souvenir Sheet
1256 A163 2500sh multicolored   5.00 5.00

Intl. Year of the Family A164

1994, Aug. 11
1257 A164 100sh multicolored   .20 .20

D-Day, 50th Anniv. A165

Designs: 300sh, Mulberry Harbor pierhead moves into position. 1000sh, Mulberry Harbor floating bridge lands armor.
2500sh, Ships, Mulberry Harbor.

1994, Aug. 11
1258 A165 300sh multicolored   .60 .60
1259 A165 1000sh multicolored   2.00 2.00

Souvenir Sheet
1260 A165 2500sh multicolored   5.00 5.00

A166

Intl. Olympic Committee, Cent. — A167

Designs: 350sh, John Akii-bua, Uganda, 100-meter hurdles, 1972. 900sh, Heike Herkel, Germany, high jump, 1992.
2500sh, Aleksei Urmanov, Russia, figure skating, 1994.

1994, Aug. 11
1261 A166 350sh multicolored   .70 .70
1262 A167 900sh multicolored   1.75 1.75

Souvenir Sheet
1263 A166 2500sh multicolored   5.00 5.00

Miniature Sheet of 7

First Manned Moon Landing, 25th Anniv. A168

Project Mercury astronauts: No. 1264a, 50sh, Alan B. Shepard, Jr., Freedom 7. b, 100sh, M. Scott Carpenter, Aurora 7. c, 200sh, Virgil I. Grissom, Liberty Bell 7. d, 300sh, L. Gordon Cooper, Jr., Faith 7. e, 400sh, Walter M. Schirra, Jr., Sigma 7. f, 500sh, Donald K. Slayton, Apollo-Soyuz, 1975. g, John H. Glenn, Jr., Friendship 7.
3000sh, Apollo 11 anniv. emblem.

1994, Aug. 11
1264 A168 #a.-g, + 2 labels   4.25 4.25

Souvenir Sheet
1265 A168 3000sh multicolored   6.00 6.00

Miniature Sheets of 9

A169

Disney's The Lion King — A169a

Designs: No. 1266a, Baby Simba. b, Mufasa, Simba, Sarabi. c, Young Simba, Nala. d, Timon. e, Rafiki. f, Pumbaa. g, Hyenas. h, Scar. i, Zazu.
No. 1267a, Rafiki, Mufasa. b, Rafiki, Mufasa, Sarabi. c, Rafiki, Simba. d, Scar, Zazu. e, Rafiki seeing vision. f, Simba, Scar. g, Simba, Nala. h, Simba trying on mane. i, Simba, Nala, Zazu.
No. 1268a, Scar plots evil plan. b, Mufasa rescues Simba. c, Destroying Mufasa. d, Simba escaping hyenas. e, Timon, Pumbaa, Simba. f, Simba, Timon, Pumbaa sing Hakuna Matata. g, Rafiki. h, Simba, Nala. i, Simba seeing reflection.
No. 1269, Simba, Timon. No. 1270, Characters of the Lion King, vert. No. 1271, Simba's colorful animal kingdon.
No. 1271A, Mufasa, Simba. No. 1271B, Mufasa, Simba on back, standing on rock.
Illustration A169a reduced.

Perf. 14x13½, 13½x14
1994, Sept. 30
1266 A169 100sh #a.-i.   1.75 1.75
1267 A169 200sh #a.-i.   3.75 3.75
1268 A169 250sh #a.-i.   4.50 4.50
   Nos. 1266-1268 (3)   10.00 10.00

Souvenir Sheets
1269-1271 A169 2500sh each   5.00 5.00

Litho. & Embossed
Perf. 11½
1271A A169a 5000sh gold
1271B A169a 5000sh gold

Miniature Sheets of 7 or 8

Sierra Club, Cent. — A170

Various animals: No. 1272, horiz. a, 200sh, Cheetahs. b, 250sh, Cheetah kittens. c-d, 300sh, 500sh, African wild dog. e, 600sh, Grevy's zebra. f, 800sh, Chimpanzee. g, 1000sh, Grevy's zebra.
No. 1273a-1273b, 100sh, 200sh, Chimpanzee. c, 250sh, African wild dog. d, 300sh, Cheetah. e-f, 500sh, 600sh, Gelada baboon. g, 800sh, Grevy's zebra. h, 1000sh, Gelada baboon.

1994, Nov. 9
1272 A170 #a.-g. + label   8.00 8.00
1273 A170 #a.-h.   8.25 8.25

ICAO, 50th Anniv. A171

Designs: 100sh, Entebbe Intl. Airport terminal building. 250sh, Entebbe control tower.

1994, Nov. 14   Litho.   Perf. 14
1274 A171 100sh multicolored   .20 .20
1275 A171 250sh multicolored   .55 .55

Environmental Protection — A172

Designs: 100sh, Stop poaching. 250sh, Waste disposals. 350sh, Overfishing is a threat. 500sh, Deforestation.

1994, Nov. 15
1276-1279 A172 Set of 4   2.50 2.50

Christmas
A173

Paintings: 100sh, Adoration of the Christ Child, by Fillipino Lippi. 200sh, The Holy Family Rests on the Flight into Egypt, by Annibale Carracci. 300sh, Madonna with Christ Child ant St. John, by Piero di Cosimo. 350sh, The Conestabile Madonna, by Raphael. 450sh, Madonna and Child with Angels, after Antonio Rossellino. 500sh, Madonna and Child with St. John, by Raphael. 900sh, Madonna and Child, by Luca Signorelli. 1000sh, Madonna with the Child Jesus, St. John and an Angel, in style of Pier Francesco Fiorentino.

No. 1288, The Madonna of the Magnificat, by Sandro Botticelli. No. 1289, Adoration of the Magi, by Fra Angelico & Filippo Lippi.

1994, Dec. 5   Litho.   Perf. 13½x14
1280-1287 A173 Set of 8   8.50 8.50
Souvenir Sheets
1288-1289 A173 2500sh each   5.50 5.50

Tintoretto (1518-94)
A174

Details or entire paintings: 100sh, Self-portrait. 300sh, A Philosopher. 400sh, The Creation of the Animals, horiz. 450sh, The Feast of Belshazzar, horiz. 500sh, The Raising of the Brazen Serpent. 1000sh, Elijah Fed by the Angel.

No. 1296, Finding of Moses. No. 1297, Moses Striking Water from a Rock.

1995, Feb. 7   Litho.   Perf. 13½
1290-1295 A174 Set of 6   5.75 5.75
Souvenir Sheets
1296-1297 A174 2000sh each   4.25 4.25

Miniature Sheet of 16

Birds
A175

Designs: a, White-faced tree duck. b, European shoveler. c, Hartlaub's duck. d, Milky eagle-owl. e, Avocet. f, African fish eagle. g, Spectacled weaver. h, Black-headed gonolek. i, Great crested grebe. j, Red-knobbed coot. k, Woodland kingfisher. l, Pintail. m, Squacco heron. n, Purple gallinule. o, African darter. p, African jacana.

No. 1299, Fulvous tree duck. No. 1300, Pygmy goose.

1995, Apr. 24   Litho.   Perf. 14
1298 A175 200sh #a.-p.   7.00 7.00
Souvenir Sheets
1299-1300 A175 2500sh each   5.50 5.50

Nos. 685-688, 906 Surcharged

1995, June 1   Litho.   Perf. 14
1301 A90 100sh on #688 multi   .20 .20
1302 A90 450sh on 70sh #686   1.00 1.00
1303 A90 800sh on 90sh #687   1.75 1.75
1304 A90 1500sh on 10sh #685   3.25 3.25
   Nos. 1301-1304 (4)   6.20 6.20
Souvenir Sheet
1305 A113 2500sh on 1200sh multi   5.50 5.50

UN, 50th Anniv. — A176

Designs: 1000sh, Hands releasing butterflies, dragonfly, dove.
No. 1308, Infant's hand holding adult's finger.

1995, July 6   Litho.   Perf. 14
1306 A176 450sh shown   1.25 1.25
1307 A176 1000sh multicolored   2.75 2.75
Souvenir Sheet
1308 A176 2000sh multicolored   4.50 4.50

FAO, 50th Anniv. — A177

Husking corn: No. 1309a, 350sh, Young woman. b, 500sh, Old woman, girl. c, 1000sh, Woman with baby on back.
2000sh, Boy beside bore well for livestock, irrigation.

1995, July 6
1309 A177 Strip of 3, #a.-c.   4.00 4.00
Souvenir Sheet
1310 A177 2000sh multicolored   4.50 4.50

Miniature Sheets of 6 or 8

A178

End of World War II, 50th Anniv.
A179

No. 1311: a, Russian 152mm gun fires into center of Berlin. b, Soviets capture Moltke Bridge. c, Emperor William Memorial Church, now war memorial. d, Brandenburg Gate falls to Russian tanks. e, US B-17's continue to devastate industrial Germany. f, Soviet tanks enter Berlin. g, Hitler's chancellery lies in ruins. h, Reichstag burns.

Flags of countries each forming "VJ:" No. 1312a, Australia. b, Great Britain. c, New Zealand. d, US. e, China. f, Canada.
No. 1313, Waving Soviet flag from atop building in Berlin. No. 1314, US flag, combat soldier.

1995, July 6
1311 A178 500sh #a.-h. + label   9.00 9.00
1312 A179 600sh #a.-f. + label   8.00 8.00
Souvenir Sheets
1313 A178 2500sh multicolored   5.50 5.50
1314 A179 2500sh multicolored   5.50 5.50

No. 1313 contains one 56x42mm stamp.

Rotary Intl., 90th Anniv. — A180

Rotary emblem and: No. 1315, Paul Harris. No. 1316, Natl. flag.

1995, July 6   Litho.   Perf. 14
1315 A180 2000sh multicolored   4.50 4.50
Souvenir Sheet
1316 A180 2000sh multicolored   4.50 4.50

Queen Mother, 95th Anniv.
A181

No. 1317: a, Drawing. b, Waving. c, Formal portrait. d, Green blue outfit.
2500sh, Pale blue outfit.

1995, July 6   Perf. 13½x14
1317 A181 500sh Block or strip of 4, #a.-d.   4.50 4.50
Souvenir Sheet
1318 A181 2500sh multicolored   5.50 5.50

No. 1317 was issued in sheets of 8 stamps.
Sheets of Nos. 1317-1318 exist with black border and text "In Memoriam/1900-2002" in sheet margins.

...

Dinosaurs
A182

Designs: 150sh, Velociraptor. 200sh, Psittacosaurus. 350sh, Dilophosaurus. 400sh, Kentrosaurus. 500sh, Stegosaurus. 1500sh, Pterodaustro.

No. 1325, vert: a, Archaeopteryx. b, Quetzalcoatlus. c, Pteranodon (b, d). d, Brachiosa (g, h). e, Tsintaosaur. f, Allosaur (g-h). g, Tyranosaur (f, i-k). h, Apatosaur (l). i, Giant dragonfly. j, Dimorphodon. k, Triceratops (l). l, Compsognathus.
No. 1326, Parasaurolophus. No. 1327, Shunosaurus.

1995, July 15   Perf. 14
1319-1324 A182 Set of 6   6.75 6.75
Miniature Sheet of 12
1325 A182 300sh #a.-l.   8.00 8.00
Souvenir Sheets
1326-1327 A182 2000sh each   4.50 4.50

Reptiles — A183

1995   Litho.   Perf. 14x15
1328 50sh Rough scaled bush viper   .20 .20
1329 100sh Pygmy python   .20 .20
1330 150sh Three horned chameleon   .30 .30
1331 200sh African rock python   .40 .40
1332 350sh Nile monitor   .70 .70
1333 400sh Savannah monitor   .85 .85
1334 450sh Bush viper   .95 .95
1335 500sh Nile crocodile   1.00 1.00
Size: 38x24mm
Perf. 14
1336 700sh Bell's hinged tortoise   1.40 1.40
1337 900sh Rhinoceros viper   1.90 1.90
1338 1000sh Gaboon viper   2.00 2.00
1339 2000sh Spitting cobra   4.00 4.00
1340 3000sh Leopard tortoise   6.25 6.25
1341 4000sh Puff adder   8.25 8.25
1341A 5000sh Common house gecko   10.00 10.00
1341B 6000sh Dwarf chameleon   12.00 12.00
1341C 10,000sh Boomslang   20.00 20.00
   Nos. 1328-1341C (17)   70.40 70.40

Issued: 5000sh, 6000sh, 10,000sh, 11/20; others, 8/21.
Compare with Nos. 1550-1552.

Nsambya Church
A184

Designs: 450sh, Namilyango College. 500sh, Intl. Cooperative Alliance, cent. 1000sh, UN Volunteers, 25th anniv.

1995, Sept. 7   Litho.   Perf. 14
1342-1345 A184 Set of 4   4.50 4.50
Mill Hill Missionaries in Uganda, cent. (#1342-1343).

Scenic Landscapes & Waterfalls of Uganda — A185

Designs: No. 1346, 50sh, Bwindi Forest. No. 1347, 50sh, Sipi Falls, vert. No. 1348, 100sh, Karamoja. No. 1349, 100sh, Murchison Falls. No. 1350, 450sh, Sunset, Lake Mburo Natl. Park. No. 1351, 450sh, Bujagali Falls. No. 1352, 500sh, Sunset, Gulu District. No. 1353, 500sh, Two Falls, Murchison. No. 1354, 900sh, Kabale District. No. 1355, 900sh, Falls, Rwenzoris, vert. No. 1356, 1000sh, Rwenzori Mountains. No. 1357, 1000sh, Falls, Rwenzoris, diff., vert.

1995, Sept. 14
1346-1357 A185 Set of 12   12.50 12.50

1996 Summer Olympics, Atlanta
A186

Athletes: 50sh, Peter Rono, runner. 350sh, Reiner Klimke, dressage. 450sh, German cycling team. 500sh, Grace Birungi, runner. 900sh, Francis Ogola, track. 1000sh, Nyakana Godfrey, welter-weight boxer.

No. 1364, Rolf Dannenberg, discus, vert.
No. 1365, Sebastian Coe, runner.

1995, Sept. 21

1358-1363	A186	Set of 6	7.25	7.25

Souvenir Sheets

1364-1365	A186	2500sh each	5.50	5.50

Miniature Sheet of 16

Domestic Animals A187

No. 1366: a, Peafowl (e). b, Pouter pigeon. c, Rock dove. d, Rouen duck. e, Guinea fowl. f, Donkey. g, Shetland pony. h, Palomino. i, Pigs. j, Border collie. k, Merino sheep. l. Milch goat. m, Black dutch rabbit. n, Lop rabbit. o, Somali cat (p). p, Asian cat.
No. 1367, Saddle bred horses. No. 1368, Oxen.

1995, Oct. 2

1366	A187	200sh #a.-p.	7.00	7.00

Souvenir Sheets

1367-1368	A187	2500sh each	5.50	5.50

Boy Scouts at Immunization Centers — A188

Designs: 150sh, Dressing children for weighing, vert. 350sh, Helping mothers carry children, vert. 450sh, Checking health cards. 800sh, Assisting in immunization. 1000sh, Weighing children, vert.

1995, Oct. 18   Litho.   Perf. 14

1369-1373	A188	Set of 5	6.00	6.00

Miniature Sheets of 12

Nobel Prize Fund Established, Cent. — A189

Recipients: No. 1374: a, Hideki Yukawa, physics, 1949. b, F.W. DeKlerk, peace, 1993. c, Nelson Mandela, peace, 1993. d, Odysseus Elytis, literature, 1979. e, Ferdinand Buisson, peace, 1927. f, Lev Landau, physics, 1962. g, Halldor Laxness, literature, 1955. h, Wole Soyinka, literature, 1986. i, Desmond Tutu, peace, 1984. j, Susumu Tonegawa, physiology or medicine, 1987. k, Louis de Broglie, physics, 1929. l, George Seferis, literature, 1963.
No. 1375: a, Hermann Staudinger, chemistry, 1953. b, Fritz Haber, chemistry, 1918. c, Bert Sakmann, physiology or medicine, 1991. d, Adolf O.R. Windaus, chemistry, 1928. e, Wilhelm Wien, physics, 1911. f, Ernest Hemingway, literature, 1954. g, Richard M. Willstätter, chemistry, 1915. h, Stanley Cohen, physiology or medicine, 1986. i, J. Hans D. Jensen, physics, 1963. j, Otto H. Warburg, physiology or medicine, 1931. k, Heinrich O. Wieland, chemistry, 1927. l, Albrecht Kossel, physiology or medicine, 1910.
No. 1376, Werner Forssmann, physiology or medicine, 1956. No. 1377, Nelly Sachs, literature, 1966.

1995, Oct. 31

1374-1375	A189	300sh #a.-l., each	8.00	8.00

Souvenir Sheets

1376-1377	A189	2000sh each	4.50	4.50

Christmas A190

Details or entire paintings of the Madonna and Child, by: 150sh, Hans Holbein the Younger. 350sh, Procaccini. 500sh, Pisanello. 1000sh, Crivelli. 1500sh, Le Nain.
No. 1383, The Holy Family, by Andrea Del Sarto. No. 1384, Madonna and Child, by Bellini.

1995, Nov. 30   Litho.   Perf. 13½x14

1378-1382	A190	Set of 5	7.75	7.75

Souvenir Sheets

1383-1384	A190	2500sh each	5.00	5.00

Orchids — A191

Designs: 150sh, Ansellia africana. 450sh, Satyricum crassicaule. 500sh, Polystachya cultriformis. 800sh, Disa erubescens.
No. 1389: a, Aerangis luteoalba. b, Satyrium sacculatum. c, Bolusiella maudiae. d, Habenaria attenuata. e, Cyrtorchis arcuata. f, Eulophia angolensis. g, Tridactyle bicaudata. h, Eulophia horsfallii. i, Diaphananthe fragrantissima.
No. 1390, Diaphananthe pulchella. No. 1391, Rangaeris amaniensis.

1995, Dec. 8   Perf. 14

1385-1388	A191	Set of 4	3.75	3.75

Miniature Sheet

1389	A191	350sh Sheet of 9, #a.-i.	6.25	6.25

Souvenir Sheets

1390-1391	A191	2500sh each	5.00	5.00

New Year 1996 (Year of the Rat) A192

Rat eating: a, Purple grapes. b, Radishes. c, Corn. d, Squash.
2000sh, Green grapes.

1996, Jan. 29   Litho.   Perf. 14

1392	A192	350sh Block of 4, #a.-d.	2.75	2.75
	e.	Miniature sheet, No. 1392	2.75	2.75

Souvenir Sheet

1393	A192	2000sh multicolored	4.00	4.00

No. 1392 issued in sheets of 16 stamps.

Miniature Sheet

Wildlife A193

No. 1394: a, 150sh, Wild dogs. b, 200sh, Fish eagle. c, 250sh, Hippopotamus. d, 350sh, Leopard. e, 400sh, Lion. f, 450sh, Lioness. g, 500sh, Meerkat. h, 550sh, Black rhinoceros. No. 1395: a, 150sh, Gorilla. b, 200sh, Cheetah. c, 250sh, Elephant. d, 350sh, Thomson's gazelle. e, 400sh, Crowned crane. f, 450sh, Sattlebill. g, 500sh, Vulture. h, 550sh, Zebra.
No. 1396, Giraffe, vert. No. 1397, Gray heron.

1996, Mar. 27   Litho.   Perf. 14

1394	A193	Sheet of 8, #a.-h.	5.75	5.75
1395	A193	Sheet of 8, #a.-h.	6.00	6.00

Souvenir Sheets

1396-1397	A193	2000sh each	4.00	4.00

Disney Characters on the Orient Express — A194

50sh, From London to Constantinople via Calais. 100sh, From Paris to Athens. 150sh, Ticket for the Pullman. 200sh, Pullman Corridor. 250sh, Dining car. 300sh, Staff beyond reproach. 600sh, Fun in the Pullman. 700sh, 1901 Unstoppable train enters the buffet in Frankfurt station. 800sh, 1929 passage detained five days by snowstorm. 900sh, Filming "Murder on the Orient Express."
No. 1408, Donald Duck in engine. No. 1409, Mickey, Goofy, Minnie waving from back of train.

1996, Apr. 15   Perf. 14x13½

1398-1407	A194	Set of 10	8.25	8.25

Souvenir Sheets

1408-1409	A194	2500sh each	5.00	5.00

Paintings by Qi Baishi (1864-1957) A195

No. 1410: a, 50sh, Autumn Pond. b, 100sh, Partridge and Smartweed. c, 150sh, Begonias and Mynah. d, 200sh, Chrysanthemums, Cocks and Hens. e, 250sh, Crabs. f, 300sh, Wisterias and Bee. g, 350sh, Smartweed and Ink-drawn Butterflies. h, 400sh, Lotus and Mandarin Ducks. i, 450sh, Lichees and Locust. j, 500sh, Millet and Preying Mantis.
No. 1411: a, Locust, flowers. b, Crustaceans.

1996, May 8   Litho.   Perf. 15x14

1410	A195	Sheet of 10, #a.-j.	6.00	6.00

Souvenir Sheet

Perf. 14

1411	A195	800sh Sheet of 2, #a.-b.	3.50	3.50

No. 1411 contains two 48x34mm stamps. The captions on Nos. 1410c and 1410d are transposed.
CHINA '96, 9th Asian Intl. Philatelic Exhibition.
See Nos. 1475-1476.

Queen Elizabeth II, 70th Birthday — A196

a, Portrait. b, As young woman, wearing crown jewels. c, Wearing red hat, coat. 2000sh, Portrait, diff.

1996, July 10   Perf. 13½x14

1412	A196	500sh Strip of 3, #a.-c.	3.00	3.00

Souvenir Sheet

1413	A196	2000sh multicolored	4.00	4.00

No. 1412 was issued in sheets of 9 stamps.

Jerusalem, 3000th Anniv. — A197

Designs: a, 300sh, Knesset Menorah. b, 500sh, Jerusalem Theater. c, 1000sh, Israel Museum.
2000sh, Grotto of the Nativity.

1996, July 10   Perf. 14

1414	A197	Sheet of 3, #a.-c.	3.50	3.50

Souvenir Sheet

1415	A197	2000sh multicolored	4.00	4.00

For overprint see Nos. 1556-1557.

Radio, Cent. A198

Entertainers: 200sh, Ella Fitzgerald. 300sh, Bob Hope. 500sh, Nat "King" Cole. 800sh, Burns & Allen.
2000sh, Jimmy Durante.

1996, July 10   Perf. 13½x14

1416-1419	A198	Set of 4	3.50	3.50

Souvenir Sheet

1420	A198	2000sh multicolored	4.00	4.00

Mushrooms A199

No. 1421: a, 150sh, Coprinus disseminatus. b, 300sh, Caprinus radians. c, 350sh, Hygrophorus coccineus. d, 400sh, Marasmius siccus. e, 450sh, Cortinarius collinitus. f, 500sh, Cortinarius cinnabarinus. g, 550sh, Coltricia cinnamomea. h, 1000sh, Mutinus elegans.
No. 1422, Inocybe soroia. No. 1423, Flammulina velutipes.

1996, June 24   Perf. 14

1421	A199	Sheet of 8, #a.-h.	7.50	7.50

Souvenir Sheets

1422-1423	A199	2500sh each	5.00	5.00

Butterflies A200

No. 1424: a, 50sh, Catopsilia philea. b, 100sh, Dione vanillae. c, 150sh, Metemorpha Hido. d, 200sh, Papilio sesotris. e, 250sh, Papilio neophilus. f, 300sh, Papilio thoas. g, 350sh, Diorina periander. h, 400sh, Morpho cipris. i, 450sh, Catonephele numilia. j, 500sh, Heliconius doris. k, 550sh, Prepona antimache. l, 600sh, Eunica alcmena.

No. 1425, Caligo martia. No. 1426, Heliconius doris.

1996, June 26
1424 A200 Sheet of 12, #a.-l.   7.75 7.75
Souvenir Sheets
1425-1426 A200 2500sh each   5.00 5.00

UNICEF, 50th Anniv. A201

450sh, Two children. 500sh, Two children wearing hats. 550sh, Boy in classroom. 2000sh, Mother and child, vert.

1996, July 10   Litho.   Perf. 14
1427-1429 A201 Set of 3   3.00 3.00
Souvenir Sheet
1430 A201 2000sh multicolored   4.00 4.00

UNESCO, 50th Anniv. — A202

Natl. Parks: 450sh, Darien, Panama. 500sh, Los Glaciares, Argentina. 550sh, Tubbataha Reef Marine Park, Philippines. 2500sh, Rwenzori Mountains, Uganda.

1996, July 10
1431-1433 A202 Set of 3   3.00 3.00
Souvenir Sheet
1434 A202 2500sh multicolored   5.00 5.00

Trains — A203

Designs: No. 1435: a, Loco Type B.B.B., Japan, 1968. b, Stephenson's "Rocket," 1829. c, "Austria," 1843. d, 19th cent. type. e, Loco Anglo-Indian, India, 1947. f, Type CoCo DB, Germany.

No. 1436: a, "Lady of Lynn," Great Western, England. b, Chinese type, 1930. c, Meyer-Ritson, Chile. d, Union Pacific "Centennial," US. e, "581" Japanese Natl. Railway, Japan, 1968. f, Co.Co. Series "120" DB, Germany.

No. 1437, Mallard, Great Britain. No. 1438, "99" Type 1-5-0, Germany.

1996, July 25
1435 A203 450sh Sheet of 6,
   #a.-f.   5.50 5.50
1436 A203 550sh Sheet of 6,
   #a.-f.   6.50 6.50
Souvenir Sheets
1437-1438 A203 2500sh each   5.00 5.00

Uganda Post Office, Cent. A204

Designs: 150sh, Emblem. 450sh, Post bus service. 500sh, Modern mail transportation means. 550sh, "100," #48, #59.

1996, Aug. 30   Litho.   Perf. 14
1439-1442 A204 Set of 4   3.25 3.25

Fruits A205

Designs: 150sh, Mango, vert. 350sh, Orange, vert. 450sh, Paw paw, vert. 500sh, Avocado, vert. 550sh, Watermelon.

1996, Oct. 8   Litho.   Perf. 14
1443-1447 A205 Set of 5   4.00 4.00

Christmas A206

Details or entire paintings: 150sh, Annunciation, by Lorenzo Di Credi. 350sh, Madonna of the Loggia (detail), by Botticelli. 400sh, Virgin in Glory with Child and Angels, by Lorenzetti P. 450sh, Adoration of the Child, by Filippino Lippi. 500sh, Madonna of the Loggia, by Botticelli. 550sh, The Strength, by Botticelli.

No. 1454, Holy Allegory, by Giovanni Bellini, horiz. No. 1455, The Virgin on the Throne with Child and Saints, by Ghirlandaio, horiz.

1996, Nov. 18   Perf. 13½x14
1448-1453 A206 Set of 6   4.75 4.75
Souvenir Sheets
Perf. 14x13½
1454-1455 A206 2500sh each   5.00 5.00

Sylvester Stallone in Movie, "Rocky III" — A207

1996, Nov. 21   Litho.   Perf. 14
1456 A207 800sh Sheet of 3   4.75 4.75

1996 Summer Olympic Games, Atlanta A208

Scenes from first Olympic Games in US, St. Louis, 1904: 350sh, Steamboat race, stadium. 450sh, Boxer George Finnegan. 500sh, Quadriga race (ancient games). 800sh, John Flanagan, hammer throw, vert.

1996, Dec. 8
1457-1460 A208 Set of 4   4.25 4.25

Traditional Attire — A209

150sh, Western region, vert. 350sh, Karimo Jong women, vert. 450sh, Ganda. 500sh, Acholi.

Headdresses, vert: No. 1465: a, Acholi. b, Alur. c, Bwola dance. d, Madi. e, Karimojong. f, Karimojong with feathers.

1997, Jan. 2
1461-1464 A209 Set of 4   3.00 3.00
1465 A209 300sh Sheet of 6,
   #a.-f.   3.50 3.50

New Year 1997 (Year of the Ox) A210

Paintings of oxen: #1466a, 1467b, Walking left. #1466b, 1467b, Calf nursing. #1466c, 1467d, Calf lying down, adult. #1466d, 1467c, Adult lying down.
1500sh, Calf, vert.

1997, Jan. 24   Litho.   Perf. 14
1466 A210 350sh Strip of 4,
   #a.-d.   2.75 2.75
1467 A210 350sh Sheet of 4,
   #a.-d.   2.75 2.75
Souvenir Sheet
1468 A210 1500sh multicolored   3.00 3.00

No. 1466 was issued in sheets of 4 vert. strips.

World Wildlife Fund — A211

Rothschild's giraffe: No. 1469: a, Running. b, One bending neck across another's back. c, Head up close. d, Young giraffe, adult facing opposite directions.
2500sh, like #1469d, horiz.

1997, Feb. 12
1469 A211 300sh Strip of 4,
   #a.-d.   2.25 2.25
Souvenir Sheet
1470 A211 2500sh multicolored   5.00 5.00

No. 1469 was issued in sheets of 4 strips with each strip in a different order.
No. 1470 does not have the WWF emblem.

Souvenir Sheet

Mural from Tomb in Xian — A212

Illustration reduced.

1996, May 8   Litho.   Perf. 14
1471 A212 500sh multicolored   1.00 1.00

China '96. No. 1471 was not available until March 1997.

Promulgation of the Constitution, Oct. 8, 1995 — A213

Designs: 150sh, shown. 350sh, Scroll. 550sh, Closed book, vert.

1997, Feb. 25   Perf. 14x13½
1472-1474 A213 Set of 3   2.10 2.10

Paintings Type of 1996

Paintings by Wu Changshuo (1844-1927): a, 50sh, Red Plum Blossom and Daffodil. b, 100sh, Peony. c, 150sh, Rosaceae. d, 200sh, Pomegranate. e, 250sh, Peach, Peony, and Plum Blossom. f, 300sh, Calyx canthus. g, 350sh, Chrysanthemum. h, 400sh, Calabash. i, 450sh, Chrysanthemum, diff. j, 500sh, Cypress tree.

No. 1476: a, 550sh, Litchi. b, 1000sh, Water lily.

1997, Mar. 5   Perf. 14x15
1475 A195 Sheet of 10, #a.-j.   5.50 5.50
Souvenir Sheet
Perf. 14
1476 A195 Sheet of 2, #a.-b.   3.00 3.00

Hong Kong '97. No. 1476 contains two 51x38mm stamps.

Summer Olympic Winners — A214

No.1477: a, 150sh, Sohn Kee-chung, marathon, 1936. b, 200sh, Walter Davis, high jump, 1952. c, 250sh, Roland Matthes, swimming, 1968. d, 300sh, Akii Bua, 400m hurdles, 1972. e, 350sh, Wolfgang Nordwig, pole vault, 1972. f, 400sh, Wilma Rudolph, 4x100m relay, 1960. g, 450sh, Abebe Bikila, marathon, 1964. h, 500sh, Edwin Moses, 400m hurdles, 1984. i, 550sh, Randy Williams, long jump, 1972.

No. 1478: a, 150sh, Bob Hayes, 100m, 1964. b, 200sh, Rod Milburn, 110m hurdles, 1972. c, 250sh, Filbert Bayi, running, 1976. d, 300sh, H. Kipchoge Keino, steeple chase, 1972. e, 350sh, Ron Ray, running, 1976. f, 400sh, Joe Frazier, boxing, 1976. g, 450sh, Carl Lewis, 100m race, 1984. h, 500sh, Gisela Mauermayer, discus, 1936. i, 550sh, Dietmar Mogenburg, high jump, 1984.

1997, Mar. 3   Litho.   Perf. 14
Sheets of 9
1477-1478 A214 #a.-i., each   6.25 6.25

No. 1478h is inscribed shot put in error.

Disney's "Toy Story" — A215

Designs, vert: No. 1479: a, Woody. b, Buzz Lightyear. c, Bo Peep. d, Hamm. e, Slinky. f, Rex.

No. 1480: a, Woody on Andy's bed. b, "Get this wagon train a-movin." c, Bo Peep, blocks. d, Buzz Lightyear. e, Slinky, Rex. f, Woody hides. g, Buzz, Woody. h, Rex, Slinky, Buzz. i, Buzz, Woody on bed.

No. 1481: a, Woody telling Buzz he's sheriff. b, Green Army on alert. c, Woody, Buzz compete. d, Woody sights alien. e, Buzz ponders fate. f, "The Cla-a-a-a-a-w." g, Intergalactic

emergency. h, Buzz, Woody argue at gas station. i, Buzz, Woody give chase.
No. 1482, Woody spots an intruder, vert. No. 1483, Andy's toys, vert. No. 1484, Buzz Lightyear in space, vert.

1997, Apr. 2　　Perf. 14x13½, 13½x14
1479　A215　100sh Sheet of 6,　　　　1.25　1.25
　　　　　　　#a.-f.
1480　A215　150sh Sheet of 9,　　　　2.75　2.75
　　　　　　　#a.-i.
1481　A215　200sh Sheet of 9,　　　　3.50　3.50
　　　　　　　#a.-i.

Souvenir Sheets
1482-1484　A215　2000sh each　　4.00　4.00

Man in Space
A216

#1484A: b, Pioneer 10. c, Voyager 1. d, Viking Orbiter. e, Pioneer, Venus 1. f, Mariner 9. g, Galileo Entry Probe. h, Mariner 10. i, Voyager 2.
#1485: a, Sputnik 1. b, Apollo. c, Soyuz. d, Intelsat 1. e, Manned maneuvering unit. f, Skylab. g, Telstar 1. h, Hubble telescope.
No. 1486, Space shuttle Challenger. No. 1486A, Mars Viking Lander Robot.

1997, Apr. 16　　Litho.　　Perf. 14
Sheets of 8
1484A　A216　250sh #b.-i.　　4.25　4.25
1485　A216　300sh #a.-h.　　4.75　4.75

Souvenir Sheet
1486　A216　2000sh multicolored　4.00　4.00
1486A　A216　2000sh multicolored　4.25　4.25

No. 1486 contains one 34x61mm stamp, No. 1486A one 61x35mm stamp.

Deng Xiaoping (1904-97), Chinese Leader — A217

Designs: a, 500sh. b, 550sh. c, 1000sh. 2000sh, Portrait, diff.

1997, May 9
1487　A217　Sheet of 3, #a.-c.　4.00　4.00
Souvenir Sheet
1488　A217　2000sh multicolored　4.00　4.00

Environmental Protection — A218

#1489a-1489d: Various water hyacinths.
No. 1490: a, Buffalo. b, Uganda kob. c, Guinea fowl. d, Malibu stork.
2500sh, Gorilla.

1997, May 14
1489　A218　500sh Sheet of 4,　　4.00　4.00
　　　　　　　#a.-d.
1490　A218　550sh Sheet of 4,　　4.50　4.50
　　　　　　　#a.-d.

Souvenir Sheet
1491　A218　2500sh multicolored　5.00　5.00

Queen Elizabeth II, Prince Philip, 50th Wedding Anniv. A219

No. 1492: a, Queen. b, Royal arms. c, Queen in purple outfit, Prince. d, Prince, Queen in white hat. e, Buckingham Palace. f, Prince Philip.
2000sh, Queen in wedding dress.

1997, June 2　　Litho.　　Perf. 14
1492　A219　200sh Sheet of 6,　　2.50　2.50
　　　　　　　#a.-f.

Souvenir Sheet
1493　A219　2000sh multicolored　4.00　4.00

Paul E. Harris (1868-1947), Founder of Rotary, Intl. — A220

1000sh, Combating hunger, Harris. 2500sh, First Rotarians, Gustavus H. Loehr, Sylvester Schiele, Hiram E. Shorey, Paul E. Harris.

1997, June 2
1494　A220　1000sh multicolored　2.00　2.00
Souvenir Sheet
1495　A220　2500sh multicolored　5.00　5.00

Heinrich von Stephan (1831-97) A221

Portrait of Von Stephan and: a, Chinese post boat. b, UPU emblem. c, Russian special post.
2500sh, Von Stephan, French postman on stilts.

1997, June 2
1496　A221　800sh Sheet of 3,　　4.75　4.75
　　　　　　　#a.-c.
Souvenir Sheet
1497　A221　2500sh multicolored　5.00　5.00
　　　　PACIFIC 97.

Chernobyl Disaster, 10th Anniv. A222

Designs: 500sh, UNESCO. 700sh, Chabad's Children of Chernobyl.

1997, May 21　　Litho.　　Perf. 14x13½
1498　A222　500sh multicolored　1.00　1.00
1499　A222　700sh multicolored　1.50　1.50

1998 Winter Olympic Games, Nagano A223

Designs: 350sh, Men's slalom, vert. 450sh, Two-man bobsled, vert. 800sh, Women's slalom. 2000sh, Men's speed skating.
No. 1504: a, Ski jumping. b, Giant slalom. c, Cross-country skiing. d, Ice hockey. e, Man, pairs figure skating. f, Woman, pairs figure skating.
No. 1505, Downhill skiing. No. 1506, Women's figure skating.

1997, June 23　　Litho.　　Perf. 14
1500-1503　A223　Set of 4　　7.25　7.25

1504　A223　500sh Sheet of 6,　　6.25　6.25
　　　　　　　#a.-f.
Souvenir Sheets
1505-1506　A223　2500sh each　　5.00　5.00

Makerere University, 75th Anniv. — A224

Designs: 150sh, Main building, administration block. 450sh, East African School of Librarianship, vert. 500sh, Buyana stock farm. 550sh, Ceramic dish, School of Architectural and Fine Arts.

1997, July 31　　Perf. 14x13½, 13½x14
1507-1510　A224　Set of 4　　4.00　4.00

Mahatma Gandhi (1869-1948) A225

Various portraits.

1997, Oct. 5　　Litho.　　Perf. 14
1511　A225　600sh multicolored　1.25　1.25
1512　A225　700sh multicolored　1.40　1.40

Souvenir Sheet
1513　A225　1000sh multicolored　2.00　2.00

1998 World Cup Soccer Championships, France — A226

No. 1514, vert: a, 200sh, Fritz Walter, Germany. b, 300sh, Daniel Passarella, Argentina. c, 450sh, Dino Zoff, Italy. d, 500sh, Bobby Moore, England. e, 600sh, Diego Maradona, Argentina. f, 550sh, Franz Beckenbauer, West Germany.
Argentina vs. West Germany, Mexico City, 1986: Nos. 1515a, d, e, f, h, Action scenes. b, Azteca Stadium. c, Argentine player holding World Cup. g, Argentina team picture.
Top tournament scorers: No. 1516: a, Paulo Rossi. b, Mario Kempes. c, Gerd Muller. d, Grzegorz Lato. e, Ademir. f, Eusebio Ferreica da Silva. g, Salvatore (Toto) Schillaci. h, Leonidas da Silva. i, Gary Lineker.
No. 1517, England, 1966. No. 1518, W. Germany, 1990.

1997, Oct. 3　　Litho.　　Perf. 14
1514　A226　Sheet of 6, #a.-f.　10.50　10.50
Sheet of 8 + Label or 9
1515　A226　250sh #a.-h.　　8.00　8.00
1516　A226　250sh #a.-i.　　9.00　9.00
Souvenir Sheets
1517-1518　A226　2000sh multi　4.25　4.25

Diana, Princess of Wales (1961-97) A227

1997, Dec. 1
1519　A227　60sh multicolored　1.25　1.25
No. 1519 was issued in sheets of 6.

Christmas A228

Sculpture, entire paintings or details: 200sh, Putto and Dolphin, by Andrea del Verrocchio. 300sh, The Fall of the Rebel Angels, by Pieter Bruegel the Elder. 400sh, The Immaculate Conception, by Murillo. 500sh, Music-making Angel, by Rosso Fiorentino. 600sh, Cupid and Psyche, by Adolphe-William Bouguereau. 700sh, Cupid and Psyche, by Antonio Canova.
No. 1526, Virgin, Angels from The Assumption of the Virgin, by El Greco. No. 1527, Angel from The Assumption of the Virgin, by El Greco.

1997, Dec. 1
1520-1525　A228　Set of 6　　5.50　5.50
Souvenir Sheets
1526-1527　A228　2500sh each　5.00　5.00

New Year 1998 (Year of the Tiger) A229

Various paintings of tigers: No. 1528: a, Looking backward. b, Jumping. c, Lying, looking forward. d, Lying, mouth open.
1500sh, On cliff.

1998, Jan. 16　　Litho.　　Perf. 13½
1528　A229　350sh Sheet of 4,　2.75　2.75
　　　　　　　#a.-d.
Souvenir Sheet
1529　A229　1500sh multicolored　3.00　3.00

Tourist Attractions — A230

300sh, Namugongo Martyrs Shrine, vert. 400sh, Kasubi Tombs. 500sh, Tourist boat, Kazinga Channel. 600sh, Elephant. 700sh, Bujagali Falls, Jinja.

1998, Feb. 6　　Litho.　　Perf. 14
1530-1534　A230　Set of 5　　5.00　5.00

Mother Teresa (1910-97) — A231

#1535a-1535h, Various portraits. #1536, With Diana, Princess of Wales (1961-97).

1998, Feb. 9   Litho.   Perf. 14
1535 A231 300sh Sheet of 8,
#a.-h.   4.75 4.75
Souvenir Sheet
1536 A231 2000sh multicolored   4.00 4.00
Nos. 1535a, 1535d-1535e, 1535h are each 22x36mm.

UNICEF in
Uganda,
30th Anniv.
A232

Designs: 300sh, "Support for children with disabilities." 400sh, "Safeguard children against polio." 600sh, "Sanitation... responsibility for all." 700sh, "Children's right to basic education."

1998, Mar. 6   Perf. 13½x14
1537-1540 A232 Set of 4   4.50 4.50

A233

A234

Dinosaurs, horiz: 300sh, Pteranodon. 400sh, Diplodocus. 500sh, Lambeosaurus. 600sh, Centrosaurus. 700sh, Parasaurolophus.
No. 1546: a, Cetiosaurus. b, Brontosaurus. c, Brachiosaurus. d, Deinonychus. e, Dimetrodon. f, Megalosaurus.
No. 1547, Tyrannosaurus. No. 1548, Iguanodon.

1998, Mar. 24   Litho.   Perf. 14
1541-1545 A233 Set of 5   5.00 5.00
1546 A233 600sh Sheet of 6,
#a.-f.   7.25 7.25
Souvenir Sheets
1547-1548 A233 2500sh each   5.00 5.00
Nos. 1547-1548 each contain one 43x57mm stamp.

1998, Apr. 6
20th century writers: a, Rita Dove. b, Mari Evans. c, Sterling A. Brown. d, June Jordan. e, Stephen Henderson. f, Zora Neale Hurston.
1549 A234 300sh Sheet of 6,
#a.-f.   3.75 3.75

Reptiles — A235

300sh, Armadillo girdled lizard. 600sh, Spotted sandveld lizard. 700sh, Bell's ringed tortoise.

1998, Apr. 21   Perf. 13½
1550 A235 300sh multicolored   .60 .60
1551 A235 600sh multicolored   1.25 1.25
1552 A235 700sh multicolored   1.40 1.40
Nos. 1550-1552 (3)   3.25 3.25
Compare with Nos. 1328-1335.

Mickey Mouse, 70th Birthday — A236

Scenes from cartoon, "Runaway Brain:" No. 1553: a, Mickey afraid of shadow. b, Mickey petting Pluto, newspaper. c, Mickey playing computer game, Pluto. d, Mickey, Minnie running. e, Mickey as target of experiment. f, Minnie being held captive by Pete on top of skyscraper. g, Mickey throwing lasso. h, Mickey surrounding Pete with rope. i, Mickey, Minnie holding onto rope above skyscrapers.
No. 1554, Mickey, Minnie embracing on top of skyscraper. No. 1555, Micky, Minnie kissing on raft, vert.

1998, May 4   Litho.   Perf. 14x13½
1553 A236 400sh Sheet of 9,
#a.-i.   7.25 7.25
Souvenir Sheets
1554-1555 A236 3000sh each   6.00 6.00

Nos. 1414-1415
Ovptd.

1998, May 13   Litho.   Perf. 14
1556 A197 Sheet of 3, #a.-c.   3.50 3.50
Souvenir Sheet
1557 A197 2000sh multicolored   4.00 4.00
Sheet margins of Nos. 1556-1557 each contain additional overprint, "ISRAEL 98 — WORLD STAMP EXHIBITION/TEL-AVIV 13-21 MAY 1998."

Sailing
Ships
A237

No. 1558: a, Fishing schooner. b, Chesapeake oyster boat. c, Java Sea schooner.
No. 1559: a, Santa Maria, 15th cent. galleon. b, Mayflower, 15th cent. galleon. c, Bark.
No. 1560, Boat with lateen sails. No. 1561, Thames River barge, vert.

1998, June 2   Litho.   Perf. 13x13½
Sheets of 3 + Label
1558-1559 A237 1000sh #a.-c.,
each   6.00 6.00
Souvenir Sheets
1560-1561 A237 3000sh each   6.00 6.00
Nos. 1560-1561 are continuous designs.

Aircraft
A238

No. 1562: a, US F4F Wildcat. b, Japanese Zero. c, British Spitfire. d, British Harrier. e, S3A Viking. f, US Corsair.
No. 1563: a, Dornier Do-X transatlantic flyer, 1929. b, German Zucker mail rocket, 1930. c, X-15 Rocket Plane, 1955. d, Goddard's Rocket, 1930's. e, Wright brothers' flight, 1903. f, 160R Sikorsky helicopter, 1939.
#1564, P40 Tomahawk. #1565, SH346 Seabat.

1998, July 24   Litho.   Perf. 14
1562 A238 500sh Sheet of 6,
#a.-f.   6.00 6.00
1563 A238 600sh Sheet of 6,
#a.-f.   7.25 7.25
Souvenir Sheets
1564-1565 A238 2500sh each   5.00 5.00

Flowers of the Mediterranean — A239

No. 1566, vert: a, Onosma. b, Rhododendron luteum. c, Paeonia mascula. d, Geranium macorrhizum. e, Cyclamen graecum. f, Lilium rhodopaedum. g, Narcissus pseudonarcissus. h, Paeonia rhodia. i, Aquilegia amaliae.
No. 1567: a, Paeonia peregrina. b, Muscari comutatum. c, Sternbergia. d, Dianthus. e, Verbascum. f, Aubrieta gracilis. g, Galanthus nivalis. h, Campanula incurva. i, Crocus sieberi.
No. 1568, Paeonia parnassica, vert. No. 1569, Pancratium maritimum, vert.

1998, Sept. 23   Litho.   Perf. 14
Sheets of 9
1566 A239 300sh #a.-i.   5.50 5.50
1567 A239 600sh #a.-i.   11.00 11.00
Souvenir Sheets
1568-1569 A239 2000sh each   4.00 4.00

Christmas
A240

Birds: 300sh, Bohemian waxwing. 400sh, House sparrow. 500sh, Black-capped chickadee. 600sh, Eurasian bullfinch. 700sh, Painted bunting. 1000sh, Northern cardinal.
No. 1576, Winter wren, vert. No. 1577, Redwinged blackbird, vert.

1998, Dec. 3   Litho.   Perf. 14
1570-1575 A240 Set of 6   7.00 7.00
Souvenir Sheets
1576-1577 A240 2500sh each   5.00 5.00

Diana, Princess
of Wales (1961-
97)
A241

1998, Dec. 28   Litho.   Perf. 14½
1578 A241 700sh multicolored   2.00 2.00

Picasso
A242

Paintings: 500sh, Woman Reading, 1935, vert. 600sh, Portrait of Dora Maar, 1937, vert. 700sh, Des Moiselles D'Avignon, 1907.
2500sh, Night Fishing at Antibes, 1939, vert.

1998, Dec. 28   Perf. 14½x13, 13x14½
1579-1581 A242 Set of 3   3.75 3.75
Souvenir Sheet
1582 A242 2500sh multicolored   5.25 5.25

Gandhi — A243

1998, Dec. 28   Perf. 14
1583 A243 600sh Portrait   1.25 1.25
Souvenir Sheet
1584 A243 2500sh Family portrait, horiz.   5.25 5.25
No. 1583 was issued in sheets of 4.

1998 World Scouting Jamboree,
Chile — A244

No. 1585: a, Cub Scouts greet Pres. Eisenhower, Georgia, 1956. b, Uncle Dan Beard at 90th birthday party, 1990. c, Future Vice President Hubert Humphrey leads South Dakota troop, 1934.
2000sh, Young scout, tamed beaver, vert.

1998, Dec. 28
1585 A244 700sh Sheet of 3,
#a.-c.   6.00 6.00
Souvenir Sheet
1586 A244 2000sh multicolored   4.00 4.00

New Year
1999
(Year of
the
Rabbit)
A245

Rabbits - #2587: a, White. b, With carrot. c, Brown & white. e, Black & white.

1999, Jan. 4
1587 A245 350sh Sheet of 4,
#a.-d.   2.50 2.50
Souvenir Sheet
1588 A245 1500sh Rabbit, diff.   2.50 2.50

Uganda
Post
Office
A246

1999, Jan. 18
1589 A246 300sh multicolored   1.75 1.75

Traditional
Hairstyles — A247

Hairstyle, region: 300sh, Iru, Bairu. 500sh, Enshunju, Bahima. 550sh, Elemungole, Karamojong. 600sh, Longo, Langi. 700sh, Ekikuura, Bahima.

1999, Feb. 1
1590-1594 A247 Set of 5   5.25 5.25

Marine
Life
A248

No. 1595: a, Wolfish. b, Equal sea star. c, Purple sea urchin. d, Mountain crab.
No. 1596: a, Blue marlin. b, Arctic tern. c, Common dolphin. d, Blacktip shark. e, Manta ray. f, Blackedge moray. g, Loggerhead turtle. h, Sailfin tang. i, Two-spotted octopus.
No. 1597, Sea nettle jellyfish. No. 1598, Decatopecten striatus.

1999, Mar. 15   **Litho.**   **Perf. 14**
1595 A248 500sh Sheet of 4,
   #a.-d.   3.25 3.25
1596 A248 500sh Sheet of 9,
   #a.-i.   9.00 9.00
Souvenir Sheets
1597-1598 A248 2500sh each   4.25 4.25
Intl. Year of the Ocean.

Intl. Year of
the Elderly
A249

Designs: 300sh, Income generating activity. 500sh, Learning from each other. 600sh, Leisure time for the aged. 700sh, Distributing food to the aged.

1999, July 19   **Litho.**   **Perf. 13x13½**
1599-1602 A249 Set of 4   3.00 3.00

First Manned
Moon Landing,
30th
Anniv. — A250

No. 1603: a, Apollo 11 launch. b, Apollo 11 command and service modules. c, Edwin E. Aldrin, Jr. on lunar module ladder. d, Saturn V ready to launch. e, Lunar module descending. f, Aldrin on moon.
No. 1604: a, Freedom 7. b, Gemini 4. c, Apollo 11 command and service modules, diff.

d, Vostok 1. e, Saturn V. f, Lunar module on moon.
No. 1605, Aldrin with scientific experiment. No. 1606, Command module re-entry.

1999, Nov. 24   **Litho.**   **Perf. 13¾**
Sheets of 6
1603 A250 600sh #a.-f.   4.75 4.75
1604 A250 700sh #a.-f.   5.50 5.50
Souvenir Sheets
1605-1606 A250 3000sh each   4.00 4.00

Queen Mother (b.
1900) — A251

No. 1607: a, With stole. b, At wedding. c, With tiara (black and white photo). d, With tiara (color photo).
3000sh, Visiting Cambridge, 1961.

1999, Nov. 24   **Perf. 14**
1607 A251 1200sh Sheet of 4,
   #a.-d.   6.50 6.50
Souvenir Sheet
Perf. 13¾
1608 A251 3000sh multicolored   4.00 4.00
No. 1608 contains one 38x51mm stamp.

Hokusai
Paintings
A252

No. 1609: a, Dragon Flying Over Mount Fuji (dragon). b, Famous Poses From the Kabuki Theater (one figure). c, Kitsune No Yomeiri. d, Dragon Flying Over Mount Fuji (Mount Fuji). e, Famous Poses From the Kabuki Theater (two figures). f, Girl Holding Cloth.
3000sh, Japanese Spaniel.

1999, Nov. 24   **Litho.**   **Perf. 13¾**
1609 A252 700sh Sheet of 6,
   #a.-f.   5.50 5.50
Souvenir Sheet
1610 A252 3000sh multicolored   4.00 4.00

A253

A254

Birds: 300sh, African penduline tit. 1000sh, Yellow-fronted tinkerbird. 1200sh, Zebra waxbill. 1800sh, Sooty anteater chat.
No. 1615: a, Gray-headed kingfisher. b, Green-headed sunbird. c, Speckled pigeon. d, Gray parrot. e, Barn owl. f, Gray crowned crane. g, Shoebill. h, Black heron.

No. 1616: a, Scarlet-chested sunbird. b, Lesser honeyguide. c, African palm swift. d, Swamp flycatcher. e, Lizard buzzard. f, Osprey. g, Cardinal woodpecker. h, Pearl-spotted owlet.
No. 1617: a, Fox's weaver. b, Chin-spot flycatcher. c, Blue swallow. d, Purple-breasted sunbird. e, Knob-billed duck. f, Red-collared widowbird. g, Ruwenzori turaco. h, African cuckoo hawk.
No. 1618, Four-banded sandgrouse. No. 1619, Paradise whydah.

1999, Dec. 6   **Perf. 14**
1611-1614 A253   Set of 4   5.75 5.75
Sheets of 8
1615 A253 500sh #a.-h.   5.25 5.25
1616 A253 600sh #a.-h.   6.50 6.50
1617 A253 700sh #a.-h.   7.50 7.50
Souvenir Sheets
1618-1619 A253 3000sh each   4.00 4.00

1999, Nov. 19   **Litho.**   **Perf. 13½x14**
Primates: 300sh, L'hoesti monkey. 400sh, Blue monkey. 500sh, Patas monkey. 600sh, Red-tailed monkey. 700sh, Black and white colobus. 1000sh, Mountain gorilla.
2500sh, Olive baboon.

1620-1625 A254   Set of 6   4.75 4.75
Souvenir Sheet
1626 A254 2500sh multicolored   3.50 3.50

Butterflies
A255

Designs: 300sh, Epiphora bauhiniae, vert. 400sh, Phylloxiphia formosa. 500sh, Bunaea alcinoe, vert. 600sh, Euchloron megaera. 700sh, Argema mimosae, vert. 1800sh, Denephila nerii.
3000sh, Lobobunaea angasana.

Perf. 13½x13¼, 13¼x13½
2000, Jan. 19   **Litho.**
1627-1632 A255   Set of 6   5.75 5.75
Souvenir Sheet
1633 A255 3000sh multi   4.00 4.00

A256   A257

UPU, 125th Anniv. (in 1999): 600sh, Postman, two women, girl. 700sh, Woman, girl, mail box. 1200sh, Postman in horse-drawn wagon.

2000, Jan. 28   **Litho.**   **Perf. 14**
1634-1636 A256   Set of 3   3.50 3.50

2000, Feb. 18
Orchids - No. 1637: a, Angraecum eichcerianum. b, Angraecum leonis. c, Arpophyllum giganteum. d, Bulbophyllum barbigerum. e, Angraecum ciryamae. f, Aerangis ellisii. g, Disa umiflora. h, Eulophia alta. i, Ancistrochilius stylosa.
No. 1638: a, Eulophia paivenna. b, Ansellia gigantea. c, Anglaecopsis gracillima. d, Bonatea steudneri. e, Bulbophyllum falcatum. f, Aerangis citrata. g, Eulophiella elisabethae. h, Aerangis rhodosticta. i, Angraecum scottianum.
No. 1639: a, Grammangis ellisii. b, Eulophia stenophylia. c, Oeoniella polystachys. d, Cymbidiella humblotti. e, Polystachya bella. f, Vanilla polycepis. g, Eulophileea roemplerana. h, Habenaria englerana. i, Ansellia frallana.
No. 1640: a, Eulophia orthoplectra. b, Cirrhopetalum umbellatum. c, Eulophiella rolfei. d, Eulophia porphyroglossa. e, Eulopia petersii. f, Cyrtorchis arcuata. g, Eurychone rothschildiana. h, Eulophia quartiniana. i, Eulophia stenophylia (one flower).
No. 1641: Polystachya tayloriana, horiz. No. 1642, Ancistrochilus rothschildianus, horiz. No. 1643, Calanthe corymbosa, horiz. No. 1644, Cymbidiella rhodochila, horiz.

Butterflies — A258

Sheets of 9, #a.-i.
1637-1638 A257 600sh each   7.25 7.2_
1639-1640 A257 700sh each   8.50 8.5_
Souvenir Sheets
1641-1644 A257 3000sh each   4.00 4.0_

Designs: 300sh, Short-tailed admiral. 400sh, Guineafowl. 1200sh, Club-taile_ charaxes. 1800sh, Cymothoe egesta.
No. 1649: a, Charaxes anrticlea. b, Epitol_ posthumus. c, Beautiful monarch. d, Blue-banded nymph. e, Euxanthe crossleyi. f, Afri_ can map. g, Western blue charaxes. h, Noble _
No. 1650: a, Green-veined charaxes. b_ Ansorge's leaf butterfly. c, Crawshay's sap_ phire blue. d, Palla ussheri. e, Friar. f, Blood_ red cymothoe. g, Mocker. h, Charaxes eupale_
No. 1651: a, Aeraea pseudolycia. b, Veine_ yellow. c, Buxton's hairstreak. d, Iolau_ isomenias. e, Veined swallowtail. f, Figtre_ blue. g, Scarlet tip. h, Precis octavia.
No. 1652, African monarch. No. 1653_ Kigezi swordtail.

2000, May 24   **Litho.**   **Perf. 1_**
1645-1648 A258   Set of 4   4.50 4.5_
Sheets of 8, #a-h
1649 A258 500sh multi   4.75 4.7_
1650 A258 600sh multi   5.75 5.7_
1651 A258 700sh multi   6.75 6.7_
Souvenir Sheets
1652-1653 A258 3000sh each   3.50 3.5_
The Stamp Show 2000, London (Nos. 1649_ 1653).

Popes — A259

No. 1654: a, Agapetus II (946-55). b, Alex_ ander II (1061-73). c, Anastasius IV (1153-54_ d, Benedict VIII (1012-24). e, Benedict V_ (974-83). f, Calixtus II (1119-24).
No. 1655, Celestine III (1191-98).
Illustration reduced.

2000, June 28   **Perf. 13_**
1654 A259 900sh Sheet of 6,
   #a-f   6.50 6.5_
Souvenir Sheet
1655 A259 3000sh multi   3.50 3.5_

Monarchs Type of 2000
No. 1655A: b, Philip II of France (1180_ 1223). c, Richard I of England (1189-99). c_ William I of England (1066-87).
No. 1657A, Cwa II Kabaleega.

2000, June 28   **Litho.**   **Perf. 13_**
1655A A260 900sh Sheet of 3,
   #b-d   3.25 3.2_
Souvenir Sheet
1657A A260 3000sh multi   3.50 3.5_

Monarchs — A260

No. 1656: a, Boris III of Bulgaria (1918-43). b, Holy Roman Emperor Charles V (1519-58). c, Pedro II of Brazil (1831-89). d, Empress Elizabeth of Austria (1854-98). e, Francis Joseph of Austria (1848-1916). f, Frederick I of Bohemia (1619-20).
No. 1657, Mutesa I of Buganda (1191-98). Illustration reduced.

2000, June 28   **Perf. 13¾**
1656 A260 900sh Sheet of 6,
          #a-f   6.50 6.50
Souvenir Sheet
1657 A260 3000sh multi   3.50 3.50

Millennium — A261

No. 1658 — Highlights of 1850-1900: a, Opening of Japan. b, First safe elevator. c, Bessemer process of steel production. d, Florence Nightingale establishes nursing as a profession. e, Louis Pasteur proposes germ theory of disease. f, First oil well drilled. g, Charles Darwin publishes The Origin of Species. h, Gregor Mendel discovers laws of heredity. i, Alfred Nobel invents dynamite. j, Suez Canal opens. k, Invention of the telephone. l, Invention of the electric light. m, World's time zones established. n, Invention of the electric motor. o, Motion pictures appear. p, US Civil War (57x37mm). q, Restoration of the Olympic Games.
Illustration reduced.

2000, June 28   **Perf. 12¾x12½**
1658 A261 300sh Sheet of 17,
          #a-q + label   6.00 6.00

Millennium — A262

Designs: 300sh, Education for all. 600sh, Nile River. 700sh, Non-traditional exports. 1800sh, Tourism.

2000, July 24   **Perf. 14½**
1659-1662 A262 Set of 4   4.00 4.00

Common Market for Eastern and Southern Africa A263

Designs: 500sh, Border checkpoint before and after COMESA treaty. 1400sh, Open border checkpoint.

2000, July 24
1663-1664 A263 Set of 2   2.25 2.25

Modern British Commonwealth, 50th Anniv. — A264

Designs: 600sh, Flags. 1200sh, Map.

2000, July 24
1665-1666 A264 Set of 2   2.10 2.10

Trains A265

Designs: 300sh, Kenya Railways A 60 Class 4-8-2+2-8-4. 400sh, Mozambique Railways Baldwin 2-8-0. 600sh, Uganda Railways 73 Class German locomotive. 700sh, South Africa Railways Baby Garratt. 1200sh, Uganda Railways 82 Class French locomotive. 1400sh, East Africa Railway Beyer Garratt 4-8-2+2-8-4. 1800sh, Rhodesian Railways 2-8-2+2-8-2 Beyer Garratt. 2000sh, East African Railways Garratt.
No. 1675: a, Uganda Railways 36 Class German locomotive. b, South African Railways Class 19D 4-8-2. c, Algeria Railways Garratt 4-8-2+2-8-4. d, Cameroon Railways French locomotive. e, South Africa railways electric freight locomotive. f, Rhodesia Railways 14A Class 2-8-2. g, British-built Egyptian railways locomotive. h, Uganda Railways 73 Class German locomotive, diff.
No. 1676: a, 36 Class German locomotive (no country specified). b, Rhodesian Railways 12th Class locomotive. c, Rhodesian Railways Garratt. d, 62 Class German locomotive. e, South Africa Railways Beyer Garratt. f, Sudan Railways locomotive. g, Nigerian Railways locomotive. h, 4-8-0 South Africa Railways.
No. 1677, East African Railways locomotive. No. 1678, Rhodesian Railways Alco 2-8-0. No. 1679, Egyptian State Railways 4-8-2.

2000, Aug. 14   **Perf. 14**
1667-1674 A265 Set of 8   10.00 10.00
Sheets of 8, #a-h
1675-1676 A265 700sh each   6.75 6.75
Souvenir Sheets
1677-1679 A265 3500sh each   4.25 4.25
Nos. 1677-1679 each contain one 56x42mm stamp.

Christmas — A266

Artwork by: 300sh, Drateru Fortunate Oliver, vert. 400sh, Brenda Tumwebaze. 500sh, Joseph Mukiibi, vert. 600sh, Paul Serunjogi. 700sh, Edward Maswere. 1200sh, Ndeba Harriet. 1800sh, Jude Kasagga, vert.
No. 1687, 3000sh, Nicole Kwiringira, vert. No. 1688, 3000sh, Michael Tinkamanyire, vert.

2000, Dec. 14   **Litho.**   **Perf. 14**
1680-1686 A266 Set of 7   6.50 6.50
Souvenir Sheets
1687-1688 A266 Set of 2   7.00 7.00

New Year 2001 (Year of the Snake) — A267

No. 1689: a, Snake with tongue out. b, Snake wrapped around person. c, Snake with open mouth. d, Snake hanging from branch.

2001, Jan. 5
1689 A267 600sh Sheet of 4,
          #a-d   2.75 2.75
Souvenir Sheet
1690 A267 2500sh shown   2.75 2.75

Holy Year 2000 — A269

Designs: 300sh, Holy Family. 700sh, Madonna and Child. 1200sh, Nativity, horiz.

2001, Apr. 4   **Litho.**   **Perf. 13¼**
1694-1696 A269 Set of 3   2.50 2.50

East African School of Library and Information Science, Makerere University, Kampala — A270

(Wildlife — A268)

No. 1691: a, Bongo, horiz. b, Black rhinoceros, horiz. c, Leopard.
No. 1692, 3000sh, Parrot. No. 1693, 3000sh, Mountain gorillas, horiz.

Perf. 13¼x13¾, 13¾x13¼
2001, Feb. 5
1691 A268 600sh Strip of 3, #a-c 2.00 2.00
Souvenir Sheets
1692-1693 A268 Set of 2   6.75 6.75

Nairobi University, Kenya — A271

Universities and Flags on Map — A272

Design: 1200sh, Nkrumah Hall, University of Dar es Salaam, Tanzania.

2001, Apr. 23
1697 A270 300sh multi   .35 .35
1698 A271 400sh multi   .45 .45
1699 A270 1200sh multi   1.40 1.40
1700 A272 1800sh multi   2.10 2.10
     Nos. 1697-1700 (4)   4.30 4.30

World Meteorological Organization, 50th Anniv. (in 2000) — A273

Designs: 300sh, Anemometer, vert. 2000sh, Tropical sun recorder.

2001, May 28
1701-1702 A273 Set of 2   2.60 2.60

UN High Commissioner for Refugees — A274

Designs: 300sh, Ensure crop production. 600sh, Ensure community participation. 700sh, Ensure improved skills. 1800sh, Ensure improved health and water services.

2001, June 15
1703-1706 A274 Set of 4   4.00 4.00

Phila Nippon '01, Japan — A275

Designs: 600sh, Kikunojo Segawa I and Danjuro Ichikawa as Samurai, by Kiyonobu II. 700sh, Kamezo Tchimura as a Warrior, by Kiyohiro. 1000sh, Danjuro Ichikawa as Shirobei, by Kiyomitsu. 1200sh, Actor Sangoro Arashi, by Shunsho. 1400sh, Koshiro Matsumoto IV as Sukenari Juro, by Kiyonaga. 2000sh, Pheasant on Pine Branch, by Kiyomasu II.
3500sh, Tale of Ise, by Eishi.

2001, Aug. 1   **Litho.**   **Perf. 14**
1707-1712 A275 Set of 6   7.75 7.75
Souvenir Sheet
1713 A275 3500sh multi   4.00 4.00

Cats and Dogs — A276

Designs: 400sh, Tabby British shorthair. 900sh, Turkish cat.

No. 1716, 600sh, horiz.: a, Blue and cream shorthair. b, Manx. c, Angora. d, Red and white British shorthair. e, Turkish cat, diff. f, Egyptian mau.

No. 1717, 1400sh, horiz.: a, Red tabby shorthair. b, Japanese bobtail. c, Siamese. d, Tabby Persian. e, Black and white Persian. f, Blue Russian.

No. 1718, 3500sh, Blue-eyed British shorthair. No. 1719, 3500sh, Calico American shorthair.

2001, Aug. 23
1714-1715	A276	Set of 2	1.50	1.50

Sheets of 6, #a-f
1716-1717	A276	Set of 2	13.50	13.50

Souvenir Sheets
1718-1719	A276	Set of 2	8.00	8.00

2001, Aug. 23

Designs: 1100sh, German shepherd. 1200sh, Irish setter.

No. 1722, 700sh, horiz.: a, Rottweiler. b, Flat-coated retriever. c, Samoyed. d, Poodle. e, Maltese. f, Irish terrier.

No. 1723, 1300sh, horiz: a, English sheep-dog. b, German shepherd, diff. c, Great Dane. d, Boston terrier. e, Bull terrier. f, Australian terrier.

No. 1724, 3500sh, Bloodhound. No. 1725, 3500sh, Pointer, horiz.

1720-1721	A276	Set of 2	2.60	2.60

Sheets of 6, #a-f
1722-1723	A276	Set of 2	13.50	13.50

Souvenir Sheets
1724-1725	A276	Set of 2	8.00	8.00

APS Stampshow, Chicago (#1723).

Royal Navy Submarines, Cent. — A277

No. 1726, vert.: a, HMS Tribune. b, HMS Royal Oak. c, HMS Invincible. d, HMS Dread-nought. e, HMS Ark Royal. f, HMS Cardiff.

2001, Aug. 27
1726	A277	1000sh Sheet of 6, #a-f	6.75	6.75

Souvenir Sheet
1727	A277	3500sh HMS Triad	4.00	4.00

Queen Victoria (1819-1901) — A278

No. 1728: a, Wearing tiara. b, Wearing white head covering, looking right. c, Wearing black hat. d, Wearing red dress with blue sash. e, Wearing white head covering, looking left. f, With hand on chin.

3500sh, Wearing black, hat, diff.

2001, Aug. 27
1728	A278	1000sh Sheet of 6, #a-f	6.75	6.75

Souvenir Sheet
1729	A278	3500sh multi	4.00	4.00

Queen Elizabeth II, 75th Birthday — A279

No. 1730: a, In 1926. b, In 1931. c, In 1939. d, In 1955. e, In 1963. f, In 1999. 3500sh, Wearing cap.

2001, Aug. 27
1730	A279	1000sh Sheet of 6, #a-f	6.75	6.75

Souvenir Sheet
1731	A279	3500sh multi	4.00	4.00

Toulouse-Lautrec Paintings — A280

No. 1732: a, Woman Combing Her Hair. b, The Toilette. c, The English Girl at the Star in Le Havre. 3500sh, Ambassadeurs: Aristide Bruant.

2001, Aug. 27 Litho. Perf. 13¾
1732	A280	1500sh Sheet of 3, #a-c	5.25	5.25

Souvenir Sheet
1733	A280	3500sh multi	4.00	4.00

Monet Paintings — A281

No. 1734, horiz.: a, Storm, Belle-Ile Coast. b, The Manneporte, Etretat. c, The Rocks at Pourville, Low Tide. d, The Wild Sea.

3500sh, Sunflowers.

2001, Aug. 27
1734	A281	1200sh Sheet of 4, #a-d	5.50	5.50

Souvenir Sheet
1735	A281	3500sh multi	4.00	4.00

Year of Dialogue Among Civilizations A282

Perf. 13¾x13¼
2001, Nov. 16 Litho.
1736	A282	3000sh multi	3.50	3.50

Intl. Volunteers Year A283

Designs: 300sh, Ebola outbreak. 700sh, Save life, donate blood. 2000sh, Collective effort for clean water.

2001, Nov. 16 Perf. 13¼x13¾
1737-1739	A283	Set of 3	3.50	3.50

Mushrooms — A284

Designs: 300sh, Amanita excelsa. 500sh, Coprinus cinereus. 600sh, Scleroderma aurantium. 700sh, Armillaria mellea. 1200sh, Leopiota procera. 2000sh, Flammulina velutipes.

3000sh, Amanita phalloides.

2001, Nov. 26 Perf. 14½
1740-1745	A284	Set of 6	6.25	6.25

Souvenir Sheets
1746	A284	3000sh multi	3.50	3.50
1746A	A284	3000sh multi	3.50	3.50

Christmas — A285

Musical instruments: 400sh, Single skin long drum. 800sh, Animal horn trumpet, horiz. 1000sh, Bugisu clay drum. 1200sh, Musical bow. 1400sh, Pan pipes. 2000sh, Log xylophones, horiz.

No. 1753, 3500sh, Eight-stringed giant bow harp. No. 1754, Nativity scene, horiz.

2001 Perf. 13¾x13¼, 13¼x13¾
1747-1752	A285	Set of 6	8.00	8.00

Souvenir Sheets
1753-1754	A285	Set of 2	8.25	8.25

New Year 2002 (Year of the Horse) — A286

No. 1755: a, White horse facing left. b, Dark brown and gray brown horse facing right with all feet on ground. c, Tan and brown horse facing right, with two feet raised. 3000r, Rearing horse.

2002, May 8 Litho. Perf. 14x14¼
1755	A286	1200sh Sheet of 3, #a-c	4.00	4.00

Souvenir Sheet
1756	A286	3000sh multi	3.25	3.25

Historic Sites of East Africa A287

Designs: 400sh, Namugongo Shrine Church, Uganda. 800sh, Maruhubi Palace Ruins, Zanzibar, Tanzania. 1200sh, Kings' Burial Grounds, Mparo, Uganda. 1400sh, Old Law Courts, Mombasa, Kenya, vert.

2002, May 8 Perf. 14½
1757-1760	A287	Set of 4	4.25	4.25

Reign of Queen Elizabeth II, 50th Anniv. — A288

No. 1761: a, Wearing blue dress. b, Wearing blue and red hat. c, Without hat. d, Wearing blue hat. 3500sh, Wearing brown hat.

2002, June 17 Perf. 14¼
1761	A288	1500sh Sheet of 4, #a-d	6.75	6.75

Souvenir Sheet
1762	A288	3500sh multi	4.00	4.00

8th Intl. Interdisciplinary Congress on Women, Kampala — A289

Designs: 400sh, Women, building. 1200sh, Makerere University arms, vert.

Perf. 13¼x13¾, 13¾x13¼
2002, July 8
1763-1764 A289   Set of 2   1.75 1.75

United We Stand — A290

2002, July 15   **Perf. 13¾x13¼**
1765 A290 1500sh multi   1.75 1.75
    Printed in sheets of 4.

Intl. Year of Mountains — A291

No. 1766: a, Tateyama, Japan. b, Mt. Nikko, Japan. c, Mt. Hodaka, Japan. 3500sh, Mt. Fuji, Japan.

2002, July 15   **Perf. 13¼x13¾**
1766 A291 2000sh Sheet of 3,
              #a-c   6.75 6.75
        Souvenir Sheet
1767 A291 3500sh multi   4.00 4.00

2002 Winter Olympics, Salt Lake City — A292

Designs: No. 1768, 1200sh, Cross-country skiing. No. 1769, 1200sh, Ski jumping.

2002, July 15   **Perf. 13¾x13¼**
1768-1769 A292   Set of 2   2.75 2.75
1769a   Souvenir sheet, #1768-
              1769   2.75 2.75

20th World Scout Jamboree, Thailand — A293

No. 1770: a, Scout in forest, 1930s. b, Scout saluting. c, Scouts hiking. d, Scout badge. 3500sh, Lord Robert Baden-Powell.

2002   **Perf. 13¼x13¾**
1770 A293 1400sh Sheet of 4,
              #a-d   6.25 6.25
        Souvenir Sheet
        Perf. 13¾x13¼
1771 A293 3500sh multi   4.00 4.00

Mammals, Insects, Flowers and Mushrooms — A294

Designs: 400sh, Ceratotherium simum. 800sh, Macrotermes subhyalinus. No. 1774, 1200sh, Gloriosa superba. 1400sh, Cyptotrama asprata.

No. 1776, 1000sh, horiz. — Insects: a, Nudaurelia cytherea. b, Locusta migratoria. c, Anacridium aegyptium. d, Sternotomis bohemanni. e, Papilio dardanus. f, Mantis polyspilota.

No. 1777, 1000sh, horiz. — Mushrooms: a, Termitomyces microcarpus. b, Agaricus trisulphuratus. c, Macrolepiota zeyheri. d, Lentinus stupeus. e, Lentinus sajor-caju. f, Lentinus velutinus.

No. 1778, 1200sh, horiz. — Flowers: a, Canarina eminii. b, Vigna unguiculata. c, Gardenia ternifolia. d, Canavalia rosea. e, Hibiscus calyphyllus. f, Nymphaea lotus.

No. 1779, 1200sh, horiz. — Mammals: a, Kobus kob. b, Alcelaphus buselaphus. c, Damalliscus lunatus. d, Papio anubis. e, Panthera leo. f, Phacochoerus africanus.

No. 1780, 4000sh, Glossina austeni, horiz. No. 1781, 4000sh, Podoscypha parvula, horiz. No. 1782, 4000sh, Abutilon grandiflorum, horiz. No. 1783, 4000sh, Kobus ellipsiprymnus.

2002, Nov. 6   **Litho.**   **Perf. 14**
1772-1775 A294   Set of 4   4.25 4.25
        Sheets of 6, #a-f
1776-1779 A294   Set of 4   30.00 30.00
        Souvenir Sheets
1780-1781 A294   Set of 4   17.50 17.50

A295

Pres. John F. Kennedy (1917-63) — A296

Various photos.

2002, Dec. 30
1784 A295 1200sh Sheet of 4,
              #a-d   5.25 5.25
1785 A296 1400sh Sheet of 4,
              #a-d   6.00 6.00

A297

Pres. Ronald Reagan — A298

Various photos.

2002, Dec. 30
1786 A297 1200sh Sheet of 4,
              #a-d   5.25 5.25
1787 A298 1400sh Sheet of 4,
              #a-d   6.00 6.00

A299

Princess Diana (1961-97) — A300

2002, Dec. 30
1788 A299 1200sh Sheet of 4,
              #a-d   5.25 5.25
1789 A300 2000sh Sheet of 4,
              #a-d   8.75 8.75

New Year 2003 (Year of the Ram) — A301

No. 1790: a, Ram on stage. b, Ram on hill. c, Ram on hill, six ram's heads. d, Six rams. e, Ram in field. f, Ram on mountainside.

2003, Feb. 1   **Perf. 14¼x14**
1790 A301 1000sh Sheet of 6,
              #a-f   6.50 6.50

Japanese Art — A302

Designs: 400sh, Beauty Arranging Her Hair, by Eisen Keisai. 1000sh, Geishas, by Tsukimaro Kitagawa. 1200sh, True Beauties, by Chikanobu Toyohara. 1400sh, Geishas, by Kitagawa, diff.

No. 1795: a, Scene in a Villa (basin in foreground), by Kinichika Toyohara. b, Scene in a Villa (screen at left), by Kinichika Toyohara. c, Visiting a Flower Garden (two people), by Kunisada Utagawa. d, Visiting a Flower Garden (one person), by Utagawa. 5000sh, Woman and Children, by Chikakazu.

2003, May 26   **Litho.**   **Perf. 14¼**
1791-1794 A302   Set of 4   4.00 4.00
1795 A302 1200sh Sheet of 4,
              #a-d   4.75 4.75
        Souvenir Sheet
1796 A302 5000sh multi   5.00 5.00

Rembrandt
Paintings
A303

Designs: 400sh, Jacob Blessing the Sons of Joseph. 1000sh, A Young Woman in Profile With Fan. 1200sh, The Apostle Peter Kneeling. 1400sh, The Painter Hendrick Martensz Sorgh.

No. 1801: a, Portrait of Margaretha de Geer. b, Portrait of a White Haired Man. c, Portrait of Nicolaes Ruts. d, Portrait of Catrina Hooghsaet.

5000sh, Joseph Accused by Potiphar's Wife.

2003, May 26
1797-1800 A303   Set of 4   4.00 4.00
1801 A303 1400sh Sheet of 4,
     #a-d   5.75 5.75
Souvenir Sheet
1802 A303 5000sh multi   5.00 5.00

Paintings of Joan Miró — A304

Designs: 400sh, Group of Personages in the Forest. 800sh, Nocturne. 1200sh, The Smile of a Tear. 1400sh, Personage Before the Sun.

No. 1807, vert: a, Man's Head III. b, Catalan Peasant by Moonlight. c, Woman in the Night. d, Seated Woman.

No. 1808, 3500sh, Self-portrait II. No. 1809, 3500sh, Woman with Three Hairs, Birds and Constellations.

2003, May 26   **Perf. 14¼**
1803-1806 A304   Set of 4   3.75 3.75
1807 A304 1400sh Sheet of 4,
     #a-d   5.75 5.75
Imperf
Size: 103x82mm
1808-1809 A304   Set of 2   7.00 7.00

Buganda Princess Katrina-Sarah
Ssangalyambogo, 2nd
Birthday — A305

Princess and: 400sh, Bulange (government office building). 1200sh, Twekobe (palace), vert. 1400sh, Drummer, vert.

Perf. 13x13¼, 13¼x13
2003, June 16
1810-1812 A305   Set of 3   3.00 3.00

Coronation of Queen Elizabeth II, 50th
Anniv. — A306

No. 1813: a, As toddler. b, As young woman, wearing flowered hat. c, Wearing robe and feathered hat.
3500sh, Wearing crown.

2003, July 15   **Perf. 14**
1813 A306 2000sh Sheet of 3,
     #a-c   6.00 6.00
Souvenir Sheet
1814 A306 3500sh multi   3.50 3.50

Prince William, 21st Birthday — A307

No. 1815: a, Wearing cap. b, Wearing blue striped shirt. c, Wearing white shirt.
5000sh, With hand on chin.

2003, July 15   **Perf. 14**
1815 A307 2000sh Sheet of 3,
     #a-c   6.00 6.00
Souvenir Sheet
1816 A307 5000sh multi   5.00 5.00

General Motors Automobiles — A308

No. 1817, 1200sh — Cadillacs: a, 1979 Seville Elegante. b, 1998 Eldorado Touring Coupe. c, 2002 Escalade. d, 1983 Seville Elegante.

No. 1818, 1400sh — Corvettes: a, 1970. b, 1972. c, 1982 Collector Edition. d, 1977.

No. 1819, 3500sh, Cadillac Eldorado convertible, 1950s. No. 1820, 3500sh, 1982 Collector Edition Corvette, diff.

2003, July 15   **Perf. 14¼**
Sheets of 4, #a-d
1817-1818 A308   Set of 2   10.50 10.50
Souvenir Sheets
1819-1820 A308   Set of 2   7.00 7.00

Millennium Development
Goals — A309

Designs: No. 1821, 400sh, Promote gender equity and empower women. No. 1822, 400sh, Improve maternal health. 600sh, Ensure environmental sustainability. 1000sh, Reduce child mortality. No. 1825, 1200sh, Eradicate extreme poverty and hunger. No. 1826, 1200sh, Combat HIV, AIDS, malaria and other diseases. 1400sh, Achieve universal primary education. 2000sh, Develop a global partnership for development.

2003, Oct. 24   **Perf. 14½**
1821-1828 A309   Set of 8   8.25 8.25

Dances and
Costumes — A310

Dances: 400sh, Entogoro. 800sh, Karimojong. 1400sh, Teso.
No. 1832 — Costumes: a, Kiga. b, Acholi. c, Karimojong. d, Ganda.

2003, Nov. 10   **Perf. 14**
1829-1831 A310   Set of 3   2.75 2.75
1832 A310 1200sh Sheet of 4,
     #a-d   5.00 5.00

Christmas — A311

Dances: 300sh, Journey to Bethlehem. 400sh, Shepherds and angels. 1200sh, Nativity. 1400sh, Adoration of the Magi.
3000sh, Holy Family.

2003, Nov. 10
1833-1836 A311   Set of 4   3.50 3.50
1837 A311 3000sh multi   3.25 3.25

SEMI-POSTAL STAMPS

Catalogue values for all unused stamps in this section are for never Hinged items.

PAPU (Pan African Postal Union), 18th Anniv. — SP1

1998, Jan. 18   Litho.   **Perf. 14**
B1 SP1 300sh +150sh Mountain gorilla   .90 .90

POSTAGE DUE STAMPS

Catalogue values for unused stamps in this section are for Never Hinged items.

Type of Kenya, 1967
Perf. 14x13½
1967, Jan. 3   Litho.   Unwmk.
J1 D1 5c red   .20 .20
J2 D1 10c green   .20 .20
J3 D1 20c dark blue   .25 .25
J4 D1 30c reddish brown   .35 .35
J5 D1 40c red lilac   .60 .60
J6 D1 1sh orange   1.50 1.50
   Nos. J1-J6 (6)   3.10 3.10

1970, Mar. 31   **Perf. 14x15**
J1a D1 5c red   .20 .20
J2a D1 10c green   .20 .20
J3a D1 20c dark blue   .25 .25
J4a D1 30c reddish brown   .30 .30
J5a D1 40c red lilac   .50 .50
   Nos. J1a-J5a (5)   1.45 1.45

1973   **Perf. 15**
J1b D1 5c red   .20 .20
J2b D1 10c green   .20 .20
J3b D1 20c dark blue   .45 .25
J4b D1 30c reddish brown   .60 .30
J5b D1 40c red lilac   1.00 .50
J6b D1 1sh orange   2.50 1.25
   Nos. J1b-J6b (6)   4.95 2.70

Nos. J1-J6 Overprinted in Black:
"LIBERATED / 1979"
1979, Dec.   Litho.   **Perf. 14**
J7 D1 5c red   .20 .20
J8 D1 10c green   .20 .20
J9 D1 20c violet blue   .20 .20
J10 D1 30c reddish brown   .20 .20
J11 D1 40c red lilac   .25 .20
J12 D1 1sh orange   .70 .50
   Nos. J7-J12 (6)   1.75 1.50

Wildlife — D2

1985, Mar. 11   Litho.   **Perf. 15x14**
J13 D2 5sh Lion   .20 .20
J14 D2 10sh African buffalo   .20 .20
J15 D2 20sh Kob antelope   .20 .20
J16 D2 40sh Elephant   .20 .20
J17 D2 50sh Zebra   .20 .20
J18 D2 100sh Rhinoceros   .40 .40
   Nos. J13-J18 (6)   1.40 1.40

UKRAINE
yü-'krān

LOCATION — In southeastern Europe, bordering on the Black Sea
GOVT. — Republic
AREA — 231,900 sq. mi.
POP. — 48,760,474 (2001)
CAPITAL — Kiev

Following the collapse of the Russian Empire, a national assembly met at Kiev and declared the Ukrainian National Republic on Jan. 22, 1918. During three years of civil war, the Ukrainian army, as well as Bolshevik, White Russian, Allied and Polish armies, fought back and forth across the country. By November, 1920, Ukraine was finally occupied by Soviet forces, and Soviet stamps were used from that time, until the recreation of the independent Ukraine on Dec. 26, 1991.

200 Shahiv = 100 Kopiyok (Kopecks)
= 1 Karbovanets (Ruble)

100 Shahiv = 1 Hryvnia

100 Kopecks = 1 Ruble (1992)

100 Kopiyok = 1 Karbovanets (1992)

100 Kopiyok = 1 Hryvnia (1996)

Catalogue values for unused stamps in this country are for Never Hinged items, beginning with Scott 100 in the regular postage section, Scott B9 in the semipostal section, and Scott F1 in the registration section.

Watermarks

Wmk. 116 — Crosses and Circles

Wmk. 399

Republic's Trident Emblem — A1

Ukrainian Peasant — A2

Allegorical Ukraine — A3

Trident — A4

Inscription of Value — A5

1918, July   Typo.   Imperf.
Thin Paper

1	A1	10sh buff	.20	.25
2	A2	20sh brown	.20	.25
3	A3	30sh ultra	.20	.25
a.		30sh blue	.65	1.25
4	A4	40sh green	.20	.25
5	A5	50sh red	.20	.25
		Nos. 1-5 (5)	1.00	1.25

The stamps of this issue exist perforated or pin-perforated unofficially.

Forgeries of this set exist on a very thin, glossy paper.

These designs were earlier (April, 1918) utilized for money tokens, printed on thin cardboard, perforated 11½, and bearing an inscription on the reverse "Circulates on par with coins" in Ukrainian. These tokens exist favor canceled but were not postage stamps. Value uncanceled, $6 each.

Stamps of Russia Overprinted in Violet, Black, Blue, Red, Brown or Green

This trident-shaped emblem was taken from the arms of the Grand Prince Volodymyr and adopted as the device of the Ukrainian Republic.

In the early months of independence, Russian stamps were commonly used, but the influx of large quantities of stamps from Russia made it necessary to take measures to protect postal revenue. In August, 1918, local post offices were ordered to send their existing stocks of Russian stamps to regional centers, where they were overprinted with the trident arms. Unoverprinted Russian stamps were declared invalid after October 1, although they were often accepted for use.

This overprint was handstamped, typographed or lithographed. It was applied in various cities in the Ukraine and there are numerous types.

Nos. 6-47 represent the basic Russian stamps that received these overprints. Values are for the most common overprint variety.

For a more detailed listing of these overprints, see the Scott Classic Specialized Catalogue.

The basic Russian stamps to which Trident overprints were applied:

A8

A9

A13

A14

A15

On Stamps of 1902-03

1918		**Wmk. 168**	**Perf. 13½**	
6	A12	3½r black & gray	25.00	30.00
7	A12	7r black & yellow	20.00	25.00

On Stamps of 1909-18
Lozenges of Varnish on Face
Perf. 14, 14½x15
Unwmk.

8	A14	1k orange	.20	.25
9	A14	2k green	.20	.25
10	A14	3k red	.20	.25
11	A15	4k carmine	.20	.25
12	A14	5k claret	.20	.25
13	A15	7k light blue	.20	.25
14	A15	10k dark blue	.20	.25
15	A11	14k blue & rose	.20	.40
16	A11	15k red brn & bl	.20	.25
17	A8	20k blue & car	.20	.25
18	A11	25k grn & gray vio	.20	.25
19	A11	35k red brn & grn	.20	8.00
20	A8	50k violet & grn	.20	.25
21	A11	70k brown & org	.20	.25

Perf. 13½

22	A9	1r lt brn, brn & org	.35	.60
23	A12	3½r mar & lt grn	.75	1.75
24	A13	5r dk bl, grn & pale bl	5.00	7.00
25	A12	7r dk grn & pink	6.00	8.00
26	A13	10r scar, yel & gray	7.00	10.00
		Nos. 6-26 (21)	66.90	86.00

On Stamps of 1917
Perf. 14, 14½x15

27	A14	10k on 7k light blue	.25	.30
28	A11	20k on 14k bl & rose	.20	.25

On Stamps of 1917-18
Imperf

29	A14	1k orange	.20	.25
30	A14	2k gray green	.20	.25
31	A14	3k red	.20	.25
32	A14	4k carmine	.20	.25
33	A14	5k claret	.75	1.00
34	A11	15k red brn & bl	.20	.25
35	A8	20k bl & car	.50	1.50
36	A11	25k grn & gray vio	50.00	—
37	A11	35k red brn & grn	.20	.25
38	A8	50k violet & grn	.25	.75
39	A11	70k brown & org	.20	.25
40	A9	1r pale brn, brn & red org	.30	.35
41	A12	3½r mar & lt grn	.45	1.00
42	A13	5r dk bl, grn & pale bl	.50	1.25
43	A12	7r dk grn & pink	1.50	1.75
44	A13	10r scar, yel & gray	40.00	50.00
		Nos. 29-44 (16)	95.65	59.35

On Postal Savings Bank Stamps

		Wmk. 171	**Litho.**	
		Perf. 14, 14½x14¾		
45		1k red, buff	.75	15.00
46		5k green, buff	7.00	70.00
47		10k brown, buff	1.75	200.00
		Nos. 45-47 (3)	9.50	285.00

Nos. 45-47 were used and accepted as postage stamps during stamp shortages.

The trident overprint was applied by favor to Russia Nos. 88-104, 110-111, the Romanov issue.

For surcharges see Russian Offices in the Turkish Empire Nos. 320-339.

A6

1919, Jan.   Litho.
48	A6	20hr red & green	3.00	15.00

Because of its high face value, No. 48 was used primarily on money transfer forms or parcel receipts.

Nos. 1 and 5 Surcharged   35 K.

1919   Unwmk.   Imperf.
49	A1	35k on 10sh buff	7.50	10.00
50	A5	70k on 50sh red	20.00	30.00
a.		Surcharge inverted		45.00

Some authorities state that Nos. 49-50 were issued by the Soviets in the Ukraine in April 1919.

Excellent forged surcharges exist.

Directorate® Publishing House **"Marka Ukrainy"**

Issues: Postage stamps, stamped and pre-stamped covers and cards, philatelic and souvenir production.

You can order and buy them at the addreses:
Directorate "Publishing House" "Marka Ukrainy" USEP "Ukrposhta", Khreschatyk st. 22, Kyiv-1, Ukraine, 01001,
Tel./Fax: 38 (044) 229-21-82.
Tel: 38 (044) 228-26-68.

**http://www.stamp.kiev.ua,
stamp@stamp.kiev.ua**

Nos. 1-5 surcharged in grivni (hryven) with the Polish eagle were sold as Polish occupation issues. They are of private origin.

Nos. 1-3 and 5 overprinted diagonally as above ("South Russia") are believed to be of private origin.

A lithographed set of 14 stamps (1hr-200hr) of these types, perf. 11½, was prepared in 1920, but never placed in use. Value, set $3.

All values exist imperf., some with inverted centers. Trial printings exist on various papers, including inverted, multiple, omitted and misaligned center vignettes. These are from the printer's waste.

This set handstamped "VILNA UKRAINA / 1921" and 6 values additionally overprinted "DOPLATA" are of private origin.

In 1923 the Ukrainian government-in-exile in Warsaw prepared an 11-value set, consisting of the 10h, 20h and 40h denominations surcharged and overprinted with the Cyrillic "UPP," supposedly intended as a Field Post issue for a planned invasion of the Ukraine. The invasion never occurred, and the stamps were never issued.

For German stamps overprinted "Ukraine" see Russia Nos. N29-N48.

Catalogue values for unused stamps in this section, from this point to the end of the section, are for Never Hinged items.

Cossacks in Ukraine, 500th Anniv. — A20

Design: No. 101, Ukrainian emigrants to Canada.

1992, Mar. 1   Litho.   Perf. 12
100 A20 15k multicolored   .50   .50
101 A20 15k multicolored   .50   .50

Ukrainian emigration to Canada, centennial (No. 101). Dated 1991.

Mykola V. Lysenko (1842-1912), Composer — A21

1992, Mar. 22   Perf. 13
102 A21 1r multicolored   .50   .50

Numerous trident overprints on Soviet stamps exist. Many of them are legitimate local issues and were in official use. Locally produced stamps also exist.

Ukrainian Girl — A22

1992   Litho.   Perf. 12x12½
118 A22 50k bright blue   .20   .20
119 A22 70k bister   .20   .20
121 A22 1kb yellow green   .20   .20
122 A22 2kb purple   .20   .20
124 A22 5kb blue   .20   .20
126 A22 10kb red   .25   .25
128 A22 20kb green   .85   .85
130 A22 50kb brown   1.50   1.50
    Nos. 118-130 (8)   3.60   3.60

Issued: Nos. 124, 126, 128, 130, 5/16; 118-119, 121-122, 6/17.

Mykola I. Kostomarov (1817-1885), Writer — A23

1992, May 16   Photo.   Perf. 12x11½
133 A23 20k olive green   .50   .50

1992 Summer Olympics, Barcelona

    A24   A25

1992, July 25   Litho.   Perf. 13
134 A24 3kb yel green & multi   .30   .30
135 A25 4kb multicolored   .40   .40
136 A24 5kb buff & multi   .55   .55
    Nos. 134-136 (3)   1.25   1.25

World Forum of Ukrainians, Kiev — A26

1992, Aug. 19   Litho.   Perf. 13
137 A26 2kb multicolored   .45   .45

Declaration of Independence from the Soviet Union — A27

1992, Aug. 19   Perf. 13½x13
138 A27 2kb multicolored   .45   .45

Souvenir Sheet

Union of Ukrainian Philatelists, 25th Anniv. — A28

1992, Aug. 21   Perf. 12
139 A28 2kb multicolored   .50   .50

Intl. Letter Writing Week A29

1992, Oct. 4   Perf. 13x13½
140 A29 5kb multicolored   .50   .50

World Congress of Ukrainian Lawyers, Kiev — A30

1992, Oct. 18   Litho.   Perf. 13
141 A30 15kb multicolored   .50   .50

Ukrainian Diaspora in Austria A31

     Perf. 13½x14½
1992, Nov. 27   Litho.
142 A31 5kb multicolored   .50   .50

Embroidery A32

1992, Nov. 16   Litho.   Perf. 11½x12
143 A32 50k black & orange   .45   .45

Mohyla Academy, Kiev, 360th Anniv. A33

1992, Nov. 27   Litho.   Perf. 12x12½
144 A33 1.50kb multicolored   .50   .50

Souvenir Sheet

Ukrainian Medal Winners, 1992 Summer Olympics, Barcelona — A34

1992, Dec. 14   Litho.   Perf. 1
145 A34 10kb multicolored   1.75   1.7

Coats of Arms — A35

1993, Feb. 15   Litho.   Perf. 14x13
148 A35 3kb Lviv   .50
150 A35 5kb Kiev   .90

See No. 292.

Cardinal Joseph Slipyj (1892-1984) A36

1993, Feb. 17   Litho.   Perf. 14x13
166 A36 15kb multicolored   .80

1st Vienna-Cracow-Lviv-Kiev Air Mail Flight, 75th Anniv. — A37

1993, Mar. 31   Perf. 13½x1
167 A37 35kb Biplane   .65
168 A37 50kb Jet   1.00

Easter
A39

1993, Apr. 8   Litho.   Perf. 13½
169 A39 15kb multicolored   1.00

UN Declaration of
Human Rights,
45th
Anniv. — A40

Design: 5kb, Country Wedding in Lower
Austria, by Ferdinand Georg Waldmuller.

Perf. 14½x13½
1993, June 11   Litho.
170 A40 5kb multicolored   .85

A41   A41a

A41b   A41c

A41d   A41e

A41f   A41g

A41h

Villagers at Work: 50kb, #177, Reaper with
scythe. 100kb, #185, Ox carts. #173A, 200kb,
500kb, Reaper with sickle. #173B, Farmer with
oxen. 150kb, 300kb, #184, Shepherd. #183,
Bee keeper. #184A, Fisherman. #186, Potter.
(Illustrations A41a-A41h help identify the Cyrillic characters, not the designs.)

Perf. 12x12½, 14 (#173B, 183, 184A, 186)

1993-98   Litho.
171	A41	50kb green	.20
173	A41	100kb blue	.20
173A	A41c	(100kb) brown	.20
173B	A41e	(100kb) magenta	.35
174	A41	150kb red	.20
176	A41	200kb orange	.25
177	A41d	(250kb) green	.40
179	A41	300kb violet	.25
182	A41	500kb brown	.30
183	A41f	(1800kb) org brn	.45
184	A41a	(5000kb) red	2.00
184A	A41g	(5300kb) blue	.95

185 A41b (10,000kb) blue   .20   .20
  a.   Perf. 14   1.60
186 A41h (17,000kb) red brn   2.00
     Nos. 171-186 (14)   8.00

Nos. 173B, 184 issued for domestic letter
rate; Nos. 177, 183 for letters within the Commonwealth of Independent States; Nos. 185-
186 for mail abroad, surface and airmail.
Actual amounts sold for varied with inflation.
No. 185a sold for 30k on date of issue and
was used for the domestic rate..
    Issued: 50, 100, 150, 200, 300, 500kb,
12/18/93; #184, 185a, 5/28/94; #173A, 177,
7/2/94; #173B, 184A, 10/15/94; #183, 186,
11/12/94; #185, 12/30/98.

Famine Deaths,
60th Anniv. — A42

1993, Sept. 12   Litho.   Perf. 12
188 A42 75kb brown   .25

First
Ukrainian
Postage
Stamp,
75th Anniv.
A43

1993, Oct. 9
189 A43 100kb blue & brown   .25

Stamp Day.

Liberation
of Kiev,
50th Anniv.
A44

1993, Nov. 6   Litho.   Perf. 12
190 A44 75kb multicolored   .25

A45

A46

1994, Jan. 15   Litho.   Perf. 12
191 A45 200kb black & red   .40

Ahapit, Kievan Rus physician, Middle Ages.

1994, Feb. 19   Perf. 12x12½
Endangered species: No. 192, Erythronium
dens, canis. No. 193, Cypripedium calceolus.
192 A46 200kb multicolored   .20
193 A46 200kb multicolored   .20

Independence Day — A47

Illustration reduced.

1994, Sept. 3   Litho.   Imperf.
194 A47 5000kb multicolored   1.50

No. 194 has simulated perforations.

Kiev
University
A47a

Litho. & Engr.
1994, Sept. 24   Perf. 13x13½
194A   A47a 10,000kb mul-
             ticolored   1.00

Souvenir Sheet
Perf. 12½x13
194B   A47a 25,000kb mul-
             ticolored   2.50

No. 194B contains one 40x27mm stamp.

Liberation
of Soviet
Areas,
50th
Anniv.
A48

Battle maps and: a, Katyusha rockets, liber-
ation of Russia. b, Fighter planes, liberation of
Ukraine. c, Combined offensive, liberation of
Belarus.

1994, Oct. 8   Litho.   Perf. 12½x12
195 A48 500kb Block of 3 + label   .45

See Russia No. 6213, Belarus No. 78.

Excavation of
Trypillia culture,
Cent. — A49

1st Books Printed
in Ukrainian, 500th
Anniv. — A50

1994, Dec. 17   Litho.   Perf. 12x12½
196 A49 4000kb multicolored   .25

1994, Dec. 17   Perf. 13½
197 A50 4000kb multicolored   .30

Sofiyivka
Natural
Park,
Bicent.
A51

1994, Dec. 17   Perf. 12½x12
198 A51 5000kb multicolored   .30

Ilya Y. Repin
(1844-1930),
Painter — A52

1994, Dec. 17   Perf. 12x12½
199 A52 4000kb multicolored   .30

City of Uzhhorod, 1100th
Anniv. — A53

1995, Jan. 28   Litho.   Perf. 12
200 A53 5000kb multicolored   .25

Ivan Franko (1856-1916),
Writer — A54

Ivan Puliuj (1845-
1918),
Physicist — A55

No. 203, Lesia Ukrainka (1871-1913), poet.

1995, Feb. 2   Perf. 13½
201 A54 3000kb multicolored   .35
202 A55 3000kb multicolored   .40
203 A54 3000kb multicolored   .35
     Nos. 201-203 (3)   1.10

Falco Peregrinus — A56

1995, Apr. 15   Litho.   Perf. 12
204 A56 5000kb shown   .20
205 A56 10,000kb Grus grus   .25

Maksym T. Rylskyi (1895-1964), Writer — A57

1995, Apr. 15   Perf. 13½x14
206 A57 50,000kb multicolored   .95

End of World War II, 50th Anniv. — A58

1995, May 9   Litho.   Perf. 13½
207 A58 100,000kb multicolored   1.75

Artek, Intl. Children's Camp A59

1995, June 16   Litho.   Perf. 13½
208 A59 5000kb multicolored   .20

Famous Writers A60

Design: 1000kb, Ivan Kotliarevskyi (1769-1838), depiction of his poem, "Eneida." 3000kb, Taras Shevchenko (1814-61), his book, "Kobzar."

1995, July 8
209 A60 1000kb multicolored   .20
210 A60 3000kb multicolored   .20

Hetman Petro Konashevych-Sahaidachny — A61

1995, July 22   Litho.   Perf. 13½
211 A61 30,000kb multicolored   .60

Arms of Luhansk — A62

1995   Litho.   Perf. 13½
212 A62 10,000kb shown   .35
213 A62 10,000kb Chernihiv   .25
Issued: No. 212, 9/15; No. 213, 10/22.

Hetman Bohdan Khmelnytsky (Khmelnytskyi; 1593?-1657) — A63

1995, Sept. 23   Litho.   Perf. 12½x12
214 A63 40,000kb multi   .70

Hetman Ivan Mazepa (1640?-1709) — A64

1995, Oct. 14   Perf. 13½
215 A64 30,000kb multi   .50

A65   A66

1995, Oct. 14
216 A65 50,000kb multi   .90
European Nature Protection Year.

1995, Oct. 22
217 A66 50,000kb multi   .90
Intl. Children's Day.

UN, 50th Anniv. A67

1995, Oct. 24   Perf. 12x12½
218 A67 50,000kb multi   .90

A68   A69

1995, Dec. 9   Perf. 13½
219 A68 50,000kb multi   .90
Ivan Karpenko-Karyi, playwright, actor.

1995, Dec. 23
220 A69 50,000kb multi   .90
Mikhailo Hrushevskyi, 1st Ukrainian president.

P. Safarik (1795-1861), Writer — A70

1995, Dec. 27
221 A70 30,000kb green   .60

Trolleybus A71   Streetcar A72

City Bus — A73

1995, Dec. 27   Litho.   Perf. 14
222 A71 (1000kb) blue violet   .20
223 A72 (2000kb) green   2.00
224 A73 (3000kb) red   .20
   Nos. 222-224 (3)   2.40
The postal rate that No. 223 paid was sharply increased greatly affecting the cost of the stamp at the post offices.

Taras Shevchenko University Astronomical Observatory, Kiev, 150th Anniv. — A74

a, 20,000 l, Early astronomical instruments. b, 30,000 l, Telescope. c, 50,000 l, Observatory, sun.

1996, Jan. 13   Perf. 12
225 A74 Strip of 3, #a.-c.   1.90

Souvenir Sheet

1994 Winter Olympics, Lillehammer — A75

Medalists: a, 40,000kb, Valentina Tserbe, bronze, biathlon. b, 50,000kb, Oksana Baiul, gold, figure skating.

1996, Jan. 13
226 A75 Sheet of 2, #a.-b.   2.25

Ahatanhel Krymskyi (1871-1942), Writer — A76   Kharkiv Zoo, Cent. — A77

1996, Jan. 15   Perf. 13½
227 A76 20,000kb bister & brown .70

1996, Mar. 23   Perf. 12½x12
228 A77 20,000kb multicolored   .55

Ivan S. Kozlovskyi (1900-93), Opera Singer — A78

1996, Mar. 23   Perf. 13½
229 A78 20,000kb multicolored   .45

Motion Pictures, Cent. A79

Oleksandr Dovzhenko, film maker, house.

1996, Mar. 23   Perf. 12½x12
230 A79 4000kb multicolored   .35
No. 230 was issued se-tenant with two labels showing scenes from films.

Chernobyl Nuclear Disaster, 10th Anniv. — A80

1996, Apr. 26   Litho.   Perf. 13½
231 A80 20,000kb multicolored   .40

Symyrenky Family
A81

Vasyl Fedorovych (1835-1915), Volodymyr
Levkovych (1891-1938), Levko Platonovych
1855-1920).

1996, May 25
232 A81 20,000kb multicolored .40

Vasil Stefanyk (1871-1936),
Writer — A82

1996, June 29
233 A82 20,000kb multicolored .35

Mykola M. Myklukho-Maklai (1846-88),
Explorer, Philologist — A83

Litho. & Engr.
1996, July 17 **Perf. 13½**
234 A83 40,000kb multicolored .65

1996 Summer
Olympic Games,
Atlanta — A84

Modern
Olympic
Games,
Cent.
A85

1996, July 19 **Litho.** **Perf. 13½**
235 A84 20,000kb Wrestling .45
236 A84 40,000kb Handball .90
237 A85 40,000kb Greek athletes .90
Nos. 235-237 (3) 2.25
Souvenir Sheet
Perf. 12
238 A84 100,000kb Gymnast 1.75

Independence,
5th Anniv. — A86

First Ukrainian
Satellite, "Sich-
1" — A87

1996, Aug. 24 **Perf. 13½**
239 A86 20,000kb multicolored .40

1996, Aug. 31
240 A87 20,000kb multicolored .40

Locomotives — A88

Designs: 20,000kb, Steam, class OD.
40,000kb, Diesel class 2 TE-116.

1996, Aug. 31
241 A88 20,000kb multicolored .40
242 A88 40,000kb multicolored .85
a. Pair, #241-242 1.25

Airplanes
Designed
by O.K.
Antonov
(1906-84)
A89

No. 243, Glider A-15, portrait of Antonov.
No. 244, AN-2. No. 245, AN-124. No. 246, AN-
225.

1996, Sept. 14
243 A89 20,000kb multicolored .35
244 A89 20,000kb multicolored .35
245 A89 40,000kb multicolored .65
246 A89 40,000kb multicolored .65
a. Block of 4, #243-246 2.00

Ivan Piddubnyi
(1871-1949),
Wrestler — A90

1996, Nov. 16
247 A90 40k multicolored .70

First
Ukrainian
Antarctic
Expedition
A91

1996, Nov. 23
248 A91 20k multicolored 1.50 1.50

A92 A93

Flowers: 20k, Leontopodium alpinum. 40k,
Narcissus anqustifolius.

1996, Nov. 23
249 A92 20k multicolored .40
250 A92 40k multicolored .70
a. Pair, #249-250 + label 1.10

1996, Dec. 7 **Litho.** **Perf. 13½**
251 A93 20k multicolored .45
UNESCO, 50th anniv.

Viktor S.
Kosenko,
Composer,
Birth Cent.
A94

1996, Dec. 21 **Litho.** **Perf. 13½**
252 A94 20k multicolored .40

St.
Sophia's
Cathedral,
Kiev — A95

Illinska (St.
Elijah)
Church,
Subotiv
A96

St. George
Church,
Drohobych
A97

#256, Troitska Cathedral, Novomoskovsk.

1996, Dec. 25
253 A95 20k multicolored .35
254 A96 20k multicolored .35
255 A97 20k multicolored .35
256 A97 20k multicolored .35
a. Block of 4, #253-256 1.40

UNICEF,
50th Anniv.
A98

1996, Dec. 31
257 A98 20k multicolored .40

Petro Mohyla (1596-1647),
Metropolitan of Kiev — A99

1996, Dec. 31
258 A99 20k multicolored .40

Wild
Animals — A100

1997, Mar. 22 **Litho.** **Perf. 13½**
259 A100 20k Lynx lynx .35
260 A100 20k Ursos arctos .35
a. Pair, #259-260 + label .70

Cathedral
of the
Exaltation
of the Holy
Cross,
Poltava,
17th Cent.
A101

Designs: No. 262, St. George's Cathedral,
Lviv, 18th cent. No. 263, Protection Fortified
Church, Sutkivtsi, 14-15th cent.

1997, Apr. 19 **Litho.** **Perf. 13½**
261 A101 20k multicolored .40 .40
262 A101 20k multicolored .40 .40
263 A101 20k multicolored .40 .40
Nos. 261-263 (3) 1.20

Legendary Founders of Kiev — A101a

Europa: a, Kyi (holding staff and shield) and
Shchek (holding sword). b, Khoriv (holding
sword, leaning on shield) and sister, Lybid.

1997, May 6 **Litho. & Engr.** **Perf. 13**
264 A101a 40k Sheet of 2, #a.-b. 2.00 2.00

4th Natl.
Philatelic
Exhibition,
Cherkassy
A102

Design: Statue of Taras Shevchenko,
stamps, exhibition hall.

1997, May 17 **Litho.** **Perf. 13½**
265 A102 10k multicolored .20

Yurii V. Kondratiuk (1897-1942), Space
Pioneer — A103

1997, June 21 **Perf. 12½x12**
266 A103 20k multicolored .35

Constitution, 1st Anniv. — A104

1997, June 28 **Perf. 13½**
267 A104 20k multicolored .35

Midsummer Festival of Ivan
Kupalo — A104a

1997, July 5 **Litho.** **Perf. 13½**
268 A104a 20k multicolored .50

Princess Olha
A105

Sultana
Roksoliana
A106

1997, July 12   Litho.   Perf. 13½
269 A105 40k multicolored   .65
270 A106 40k multicolored   .65

First
Ukrainian
Emigration
to
Argentina,
Cent.
A107

Design: Monument to poet Taras
Shevchenko, Buenos Aires.

1997, Aug. 16   Litho.   Perf. 13½
271 A107 20k multicolored   .30

For Exceptional
Service — A108

Order of Yaroslav the Wise — A109

Medals for: No. 273, Military Service. 30k,
Bravery. 40k, Order of Bohdan Khmelnytsky.
No. 276, Honored Service.
No. 277: a, Medal hanging from chain. b, 8-
point star.
Illustration A109 reduced.

Litho. & Engr.
1997, Aug. 20   Perf. 13½
272 A108 20k multicolored   .35
273 A108 20k multicolored   .35
274 A108 30k multicolored   .50
275 A108 40k multicolored   .70
276 A108 60k multicolored   1.00
  a.   Strip of 5, #272-276   3.00

Souvenir Sheet
Perf. 13
277 A109 60k Sheet of 2, #a.-b.   2.50
   Nos. 277a-277b are each 35x50mm.

Hetman — A110

No. 278, Dmytro "Baida" Vyshnevetskyj (?-
1563), boats, archers. No. 279, Pylyp Orlyk
(1672-1742), Stockholm harbor, crowd in
Thessaloniki street.

1997, Sept. 13   Litho.   Perf. 12½x12
278 A110 20k multicolored   .30
279 A110 20k multicolored   .30
   See Nos. 357-358, 376-377.

Solomiia
Krushelnytska
(Salomea
Krusceniski, 1872-
1952), Actress,
Singer — A111

1997, Sept. 23   Litho.   Perf. 13½
280 A111 20k multicolored   .30

Airplanes
A112

Designs: 20k, Antonov An-74 TK-200. 40k,
Antonov An-38-100.

1997, Oct. 30
281 A112 20k multicolored   .30
282 A112 40k multicolored   .65

Ships
A113

1997, Dec. 6   Litho.   Perf. 13½
283 A113 20k Zavyietnyj, 1903   .30
284 A113 40k Serhii Korolev,
              1970, Academi-
              cian   .65

A114

1997, Dec. 6   Litho.   Perf. 12x12½
285 A114 40k multi + label   1.40 1.40
Participation of Ukrainian astronaut in US
space shuttle mission.

A115

1997, Dec. 20   Perf. 13½
Vasyl Krychevskyi (1872-1952), painter,
architect.
286 A115 10k multicolored   .20

Christmas — A116

1997, Dec. 20
287 A116 20k multicolored   .30

Traditional
Handicrafts
A117

Region: #288, Rooster, Dnipropetrovsk.
#289, Vest, Chernivtsi. #290, Ram, Poltava.
#291, Molded design, Ivano-Frankivsk.

1997, Dec. 20
288 A117 20k multicolored   .30   .30
289 A117 20k multicolored   .30   .30
290 A117 40k multicolored   .65   .65
291 A117 40k multicolored   .65   .65
      Nos. 288-291 (4)   1.90

Perf. 11½
288a   20k   .30   .30
289a   20k   .30   .30
290a   40k   .65   .65
291a   40k   .65   .65
      b. Sheet, 2 each #288a-291a   3.80
Nos. 288-291 have colored border. Nos.
288a-291a do not.

Arms Type of 1993
Arms of Transcarpathia (Zakarpattya).

1997, Dec. 30   Litho.   Perf. 13½
292 A35 20k multicolored   .35

A118   A119

Wildlife: a, 20k, Skylark. b, 40k, White-tailed
eagle. c, 20k, Black stork. d, 40k, Long-eared
hedgehog. e, 20k, Garden dormouse. f, 40k,
Wild boar.

1997, Dec. 30   Litho.   Perf. 11½
293 A118 Sheet of 6, #a.-f.   3.00

Litho. & Engr.
1997, Dec. 20   Perf. 13½
294 A119 60k multicolored   1.00
Hryhorii Skovoroda (1722-94), philosopher.

A120   A121

1998, Jan. 6   Litho.   Perf. 13½
295 A120 20k multicolored   .30
Volodymyr Sosiura (1898-1965), poet.

1998, Feb. 14   Litho.   Perf. 13½
296 A121 20k Figure skating   .30
297 A121 20k Biathlon   .30
   1998 Winter Olympic Games, Nagano.

Bilhorod Dnistrovskyi Fortress, 2500th
Anniv. — A122

1998, Apr. 21   Litho.   Perf. 13½
298 A122 20k multicolored   .30   .30

UKRFILEKS 98 Natl. Philatelic
Exhibition, Sevastopol — A123

Design: Frigate, "Hetman Sahaidachnyi."

1998, Apr. 28   Litho.   Perf. 13½
299 A123 30k multi + label   .45

European Bank of Reconstruction and
Development — A124

Obverse, reverse of Ukrainian coins: a, 1k,
Gold, 11th cent. b, 1k, Silver, 11th cent. c, 60k,
500h St. Sophia Cathedral gold coin. d, 60k,
200h Taras Shevchenko gold coin. e, 30k,
1,000,000k Bohdan Khmelnytsky silver coin. f,
30k, 10h Petro Mohyla silver coin.

Litho. & Engr.
1998, May 8   Perf. 13½
300 A124 Sheet of 6, #a.-f.   5.00 5.00

Ivan Kupalo Natl.
Festival — A125

1998, May 16   Litho.   Perf. 13½
301 A125 40k multicolored   .60
              Europa.

Souvenir Sheet

Askania Nova Nature Preserve,
Cent. — A126

a, 40k, Deer. b, 60k, Przewalski horses.
Illustration reduced.

1998, May 16   Litho.   Perf. 11½
302 A126 Sheet of 2, #a.-b.   1.50 1.50

Paintings from Lviv Picture Gallery — A127

Designs: No. 303, Portrait of Maria Theresa, by J.E. Liotard. No. 304, Man with a Cello, by Gerard von Honthorst. 40k, Madonna and Child, 17th cent. Lviv School. 1.20h, Madonna and Child and Two Saints, by 16th cent. Italian school.

1998, June 20		Perf. 13½	
303	A127 20k multicolored	.30	.30
304	A127 20k multicolored	.30	.30
305	A127 40k multicolored	.60	.60
a.	Strip of 3, #303-305	1.25	1.25

Souvenir Sheet

306	A127 1.20h multicolored	1.60	1.60

Souvenir Sheet

Polytechnic Institute, Kiev, Cent. — A128

Illustration reduced.

1998, June 27	Litho.	Perf. 11½	
307	A128 1h multicolored	.90	.90

Askold & Dyr A129

Litho. & Engr.

1998, July 4		Perf. 13½	
308	A129 3h multi + label	4.00	4.00

Hetman Bohdan Khmelnytsky A130

Designs: a, 30k, Battle scene, denomination LR. b, 2k, Portrait of Khmelnytsky. c, 30k, Battle scene, denomination LL. d, 40k, denomination LR. e, 60k, Battle scene. f, 40k, Battle scene, denomination LL.

1998, July 25		Litho. & Engr.	
309	A130 Sheet of 6, #a.-f.	5.25	5.25

Ukrainian uprising, 350th anniv.

Town of Halych, 1100th Anniv. A131

1998, Aug. 8		Litho.	
310	A131 20k multicolored	.30	.30

Queen Anna Yaroslavna (1024?-75) A132

1998, Aug. 8			
311	A132 40k multicolored	.55	.55

Yurii Lysianskyi (1773-1837), Explorer — A133

1998, Aug. 13			
312	A133 40k multicolored		.50

Natalia Uzhvii (1898-1986), Stage Actress — A134

1998, Sept. 8	Litho.	Perf. 13½	
313	A134 40k multicolored	.35	.35

Polytechnical Institute, Kiev, Cent. — A135

Designs: 10k, W.L. Kirpichov, first president. No. 315, E.O. Paton, bridge. No. 316, S.P. Timoschenko, mathematical formula. 30k, Igor I. Sikorsky, biplane. 40k, Sergei P. Korolev, rocket, satellite.

1998, Sept. 10		Perf. 12½x12	
314	A135 10k multicolored	.20	.20
315	A135 20k multicolored	.20	.20
316	A135 20k multicolored	.20	.20
317	A135 30k multicolored	.30	.30
318	A135 40k multicolored	.35	.35
a.	Strip of 5, #314-318	1.10	1.10

A136   A137

1998, Sept. 19	Litho.	Perf. 13½	
319	A136 10k multicolored	.20	.20

World Post Day.

1998, Sept.19			
320	A137 20k multicolored	.20	.20

Ukrainian book, 1000th anniv.

Church Architecture A138

Designs: No. 321, Church of the Transfiguration, Chernihiv, 11th cent. No. 322, Church of the Holy Protection, Kharkiv, 17th cent.

1998, Sept. 21			
321	A138 20k multicolored	.20	.20
322	A138 20k multicolored	.20	.20

World Wildlife Fund A139

Branta ruficollis: a, f, 20k, Adults. b, g, 30k, Female on nest. c, h, 40k, Female with goslings. d, i, 60k, Adults, goslings.

1998, Oct. 10	Litho.	Perf. 13½	
323	A139 Block of 4, #a.-d.	2.50	2.50
e.	Block of 4, perf. 11½, #f.-i.	2.50	2.50
j.	Sheet of 2, #323e	5.00	

Antonov Airplanes A140

1998, Nov. 28	Litho.	Perf. 13½	
324	A140 20k Antonov 140	.20	.20
325	A140 40k Antonov 70	.35	.35

Hetman Type of 1997

Design: Petro Doroshenko (1627-98).

1998, Nov. 28	Litho.	Perf. 12½x12	
326	A141 20k multicolored	.20	.20

Borys D. Hrinchenko (1863-1910), Writer — A142

1998, Dec. 4	Litho.	Perf. 13½	
327	A142 20k multicolored	.20	.20

Christmas — A143

1998, Dec. 11			
328	A143 30k multicolored	.25	.25

Ukrainians in Australia, 50th Anniv. A144

1998, Dec. 20			
329	A144 40k multicolored	.35	.35

Illintsi Meteor Impact Area A145

1998, Dec. 25			
330	A145 40k multicolored	.35	.35

Universal Declaration of Human Rights, 50th Anniv. — A146

Paintings of various flowers by Kateryna Bilokur (1900-61): 30k, 1940. 50k, 1959.

1998, Dec. 25			
331	A146 30k multicolored	.25	.25
332	A146 50k multicolored	.45	.45
a.	Pair, #331-332 +label	.70	.70

Serhii Paradzhanov (1924-90), Film Director — A147

1999, Feb. 27	Litho.	Perf. 13½	
333	A147 40k multi + label	.35	.35

Volodymyr Ivasiuk (1949-79), Composer A148

1999, Mar. 4			
334	A148 30k multicolored	.25	.25

Scythian
Gold
A149

1999, Mar. 20
335   A149   20k Clasp   .20   .20
336   A149   40k Boar   .35   .35
337   A149   50k Young elk   .40   .40
338   A149   1h Necklace   .80   .80
   a.   Block of 4, #335-338   1.75   1.75

Spring Easter
Dance — A150

1999, Apr. 7
339   A150   30k multicolored   .25   .25

A151

Synevyr Natl. Park: a, 50k, Wooden monuments on bank of Tereblyia River. b, 1h, Thymallus thymallus, river scene.

1999, Apr. 24
340   A151   Pair, #a.-b.   1.25   1.25
   Europa.

A152

1999, May 13
341   A152   40k multicolored   .35   .35
   Panas Myrnyi (1849-1920), writer.

Honoré de Balzac (1799-1850),
Writer — A153

1999, May 20
342   A153   40k multicolored   .35   .35

Council of
Europe,
50th Anniv.
A154

1999, May 22
343   A154   40k multicolored   .35   .35

Aleksandr Pushkin
(1799-1837),
Poet — A155

1999, June 6
344   A155   40k + label   .35   .35

Sailboats — A156

No. 345: a, Bark (Baidak), double sails, one man at tiller. b, Cossack (Chaika), single sail, rowers.

1999, June 26
345   A156   30k Pair, #a.-b.   .50   .50

Souvenir Sheet

Yaroslav the Wise — A157

1999, July 2   Litho.   Perf. 11½
346   A157   1.20h multicolored   1.50   1.50

Principality of Halytsko-Volynskyi,
800th Anniv. — A158

1999, July 27   Perf. 13½
347   A158   50k multicolored   .60   .60

A159   A160

Designs: a, 30k, Icon of St. George. b, 60, Girl in a Red Hat, by O.O. Murashko.

1999, July 27
348   A159   Pair, #a.-b. + label   1.10   1.10
   Natl. Museum of Art, Cent.

1999, Aug. 7
349   A160   30k Bee on flower   .35   .35
   Bee keeping in Ukraine.

A161   A162

1999, Aug. 14   Litho.   Perf. 13½
350   A161   30k multicolored   .35   .35
   UPU, 125th anniv.

1999, Aug. 14
351   A162   30k multicolored   .35   .35
   Poltava, 1100th anniv.

Presidential
Medals — A163

Designs: 30k, Order of Princess Olga. No. 353: a, Medal with trident. b, Medal with star.

1999, Aug. 17   Litho. & Engr.
352   A163   30k multicolored   .35   .35
   Souvenir Sheet of 2
353   A163   2.50h #a.-b.   5.75   5.75
   No. 353 contains two 35x50mm stamps.

Polish-Ukrainian Cooperation in Nature
Conservation — A164

a, Cervus elaphus. b, Felis silvestris.

1999, Sept. 22   Litho.   Perf. 13½
354   A164   1.40h Pair, #a.-b.   2.00   2.00
   See Poland Nos. 3477-3478.

National
Bank — A165

1999, Sept. 28   Litho. & Engr.
355   A165   3h multicolored   2.10   2.10
   Souvenir Sheet
356   A165   5h multicolored   3.50   3.50

Hetman Type of 1997

Designs: No. 357, Ivan Vyhovskyi (d. 1664), cavalry in water. No. 358, Pavlo Polubotok (1660-1724), ships in water.

1999   Litho.   Perf. 12¼x12
357   A110   30k multi   .20   .20
358   A110   30k multi   .20   .20

   Issued: No. 357, 11/20; No. 358, 12/22.

A166

Christmas
A167

1999, Nov. 26   Wmk. 399   Perf. 13½
359   A166   30k multi   .20   .20
   Unwmk.
360   A167   60k multi   .45   .45

Children's Art — A168

a, Spacecraft, alien creatures. b, Elephant in space. c, Rocket and space car on planet.

1999, Nov. 30   Unwmk.   Perf. 11½
361   A168   10k Strip of 3, #a.-c.   .25   .25

Fauna
A169

Designs: a, 40k, Desmana moschata. b, 60k, Gyps fulvus. c, 40k, Lucanus cervus.

1999, Dec. 9   Perf. 13½
362   A169   Strip of 3, #a.-c.   1.00   1.00

Church of St. Andrew, Kiev — A170

1999, Dec. 12
363   A170   60k multi + label   .35   .35

Mushrooms
A171

Designs: a, 30k, Armillariella mellea. b, 30k, Paxillus atrotomentosus. c, 30k, Pleurotus ostratus. d, 40k, Cantharellus cibarius. e, 60k, Agaricus campester.

1999, Dec. 15   Perf. 11½
364   A171   Sheet of 5, #a.-e., + label   1.25   1.25

New Year 2000 — A172

1999, Dec. 18   **Perf. 13½**
365 A172 50k multi + label   .45 .45

Motor Vehicles — A173

a, Kraz-65032 truck. b, Tavriia Nova car.

1999, Dec. 18   **Litho.**
366 A173 30k Pair, #a.-b.   .45 .45

Works of Maria Prymachenko — A174

Denomination colors: a, Green. b, Violet.

1999, Dec. 22
367 A174 30k Pair, #a.-b., + central label   .45 .45

Halshka
Hulevychivna,
Philanthropist
A175

1999, Dec. 25   **Perf. 13½**
368 A175 30k multi   .20 .20

Zoogeographic Endowment
Fund — A176

Animals from: a, 10k, Carpathian Reserve.
b, 30k, Polissia Reserve. c, 40k, Kaniv
Reserve. d, 60k, Trakhtemyriv Reserve. e, 1h,
Askaniia-Nova Reserve (ram, birds). f, 1h,
Kara-Dag Reserve (birds).

1999, Dec. 28   **Perf. 11½**
369 A176 Sheet of 6, #a.-f.   2.40 2.40

Christianity, 2000th Anniv. — A177

Designs: a, Mother of God mosaic, St. Sofia
Cathedral, Kiev, 11th cent. b, Christ
Pantocrator fresco, Church of the Savior's
Transfiguration, Polotsk, Belarus, 12th cent. c,
Volodymyr Madonna, Tretiakov Gallery, Moscow, 12th cent.

2000, Jan. 5   **Litho.**   **Perf. 11½**
370 A177 80k Sheet of 3, #a.-c. 1.60 1.60

Souvenir Sheet

Opera and Ballet Theaters — A178

No. 371: a, National Academic, Kiev. b,
Odessa State, Odessa. c, Kharkov State Academic, Kharkov. d, Ivan Franko State Academic, Lviv.
Illustration reduced.

2000, Jan. 29   **Litho.**   **Perf. 11½**
371 A178 40k Sheet of 4, #a.-d.   .95 .95

Kiev Bridges — A179

No. 372: a, 10k, Moscow Bridge. b, 30k, Y.
O. Paton Bridge. c, 40k, Pedestrian park
bridge. d, 60k, Subway bridge.
Illustration reduced.

2000, Jan. 29   **Perf. 12¼x12**
372 A179 Block of 4, #a.-d.   .80 .80

Souvenir Sheet

Peresopnytsia Gospel — A180

Illustration reduced.

2000, Feb. 8   **Perf. 11½**
373 A180 1.50h multi   .85 .85

A181   A182

2000, Feb. 11   **Perf. 13½**
374 A181 30k multi   .20 .20
  Oksana Petrusenko (1900-40), opera singer

2000, Feb. 18
375 A182 40k multi   .25 .25
  Marusia Churai, 17th cent. singer

Hetman Type of 1997

Designs: No. 376, Danylo Apostol (1654-
1734), church, burning castle. No. 377, Ivan
Samoylovych (d. 1690), tent, winter scene.

2000   **Perf. 12¼x12**
376 A110 30k multi   .20 .20
377 A110 30k multi   .20 .20
  Issued: No. 376, 2/22; No. 377, 3/3.

World
Meteorological
Organization, 50th
Anniv. — A183

2000, Mar. 10   **Litho.**   **Perf. 13½**
378 A183 30k multi   .20 .20

Europa, 2000
Common Design Type

2000, Mar. 29   **Litho.**   **Perf. 13½**
379 CD17 3h multi   1.75 1.75

Souvenir Sheets

Easter Eggs — A184

No. 380: a, 30k, Egg with black and red star
design, Podillia region. b, 30k, Flower egg,
Chernihiv region. c, 30k, Egg with leaf design,
Kiev region. d, 30k, Egg with green, white and
yellow geometric design, Odessa region. e,
70k, Egg with reindeer design, Hutsulschyna
region. f, 70k, Egg with cross design, Volyn
region.

2000, Apr. 28   **Perf. 11½**
380 A184 Sheet of 6, #a-f   1.50 1.50

Stamp Exhibitions — A185

No. 381: a, Woman in native costume, Austria #2. b, Man in native costume, Great Britain
#1.
  Illustration reduced.

2000, May 20
381 A185 80k Sheet of 2, #a-b   .90 .90
  WIPA 2000 Stamp Exhibition, Vienna; The
Stamp Show 2000, London.

Donetsk Oblast — A186

City of Kiev — A187

2000   **Perf. 12¼x12**
382 A186 30k multi   .20 .20
383 A187 30k multi   .20 .20
  Regional and administrative areas.
  Issued: No. 382, 5/26; No. 383, 5/28.

6th Natl. Philatelic Exhibition,
Donetsk — A188

2000, May 28   **Litho.**   **Perf. 12¼x12**
384 A188 30k multi   .20 .20

City of Ostroh,
900th
Anniv. — A189

2000, June 16   **Litho.**   **Perf. 13½**
385 A189 30k multi   .20 .20

2000 Summer
Olympics,
Sydney — A190

2000, June 26
386 A190 30k High jump   .20 .20
387 A190 30k Boxing   .20 .20
388 A190 70k Yachting   .40 .40
389 A190 1h Rhythmic gymnastics   .55 .55
  Nos. 386-389 (4)   1.35 1.35

Petro Prokopovych (1775-1850),
Apiarist — A191

2000, July 12   **Litho.**   **Perf. 13½**
390 A191 30k multi   .20 .20

Shipbuilding — A192

Illustration reduced.

2000, July 14
391	A192	Pair	.80	.80
a.		40k Ship St. Paul	.30	.30
b.		70k Ship St. Nicholas	.50	.50

Tetiana Pata (1884-1976),
Artist — A193

No. 392: a, Leafy Plants with Flowers, 1950s. b, Viburnum Berries and Bird, 1957. Illustration reduced.

2000, July 21
392	A193	Horiz. pair, #a-b + central label	.60	.60
a.-b.		40k Any single	.30	.30

Dubno, 900th
Anniv. — A194

2000, July 26
393	A194	30k multi	.20	.20

Harvest
Festival — A195

2000, Aug. 4
394	A195	30k multi	.20	.20

Souvenir Sheet

Presidential Symbols — A196

Designs: a, Flag. b, Mace. c, Seal. d, Badge.

2000, Aug. 18   Litho.   Perf. 11½
395	A196	60k Sheet of 4, #a-d	1.10	1.10

Regional and Administrative Areas

Volynska Oblast — A197

Autonomous Republic of
Crimea — A198

2000   Perf. 12¼x12
396	A197	30k multi	.20	.20
397	A198	30k multi	.20	.20

Issued: No. 396, 8/23; No. 397, 10/20.

Kiev Post Office, 225th Anniv. — A199

Illustration reduced.

2000, Sept. 3   Perf. 11½
398	A199	30k multi	.20	.20

Endangered Amphibians — A200

No. 399: a, 30k, Triturus vulgaris. b, 70k, Salamandra salamandra. Illustration reduced.

2000, Sept. 8   Perf. 13½
399	A200	Pair, #a-b	.45	.45

Yurij
Drohobych
(1450-94),
Writer
A201

2000, Sept. 12
400	A201	30k multi	.20	.20

Souvenir Sheet

Carpathian National Park — A202

No. 401: a, Mt. Breskul, 1911 meters. b, Mt. Hoberla, 2061 meters.

2000, Sept. 15   Perf. 11½
401	A202	80k Sheet of 2, #a-b	.80	.80

Flowers — A203

Designs: a, Marigolds. b, Chamomiles. c, Hollyhocks. d, Poppies. e, Periwinkles. f, Cornflowers. g, Morning glories. h, Martagon lilies. i, Peonies. j, Bluebells.

2000, Oct. 6
402	A203	30k Sheet of 10, #a-j	1.50	1.50

Children's Folk Tales — A204

Designs: a, "Ivasyk and Telesyk," (boy in boat, witch). b, "The Crooked Duck," (couple with duck). c, "The Cat and the Rooster."

2000, Nov. 3
403		30k Horiz. strip of 3	.45	.45
a.-c.		A204 Any single	.20	.20

New
Year
2001
A205

2000, Nov. 24
404	A205	30k multi	.20	.20

St. Onufius'	Church of Christ's
Church,	Birth,
Lviv — A206	Velyke — A207

Design: 70k, Church of the Resurrection, Sumy.

2000, Dec. 8   Perf. 13½
405	A206	30k multi	.20	.20
406	A207	30k multi	.20	.20
407	A207	70k multi	.35	.35
		Nos. 405-407 (3)	.75	.75

Souvenir Sheet

St. Vladimir (c. 956-1015), Kievan
Prince — A208

2000, Dec. 15   Perf. 11½
408	A208	2h multi	.95	.95

Dmytro Rostovskyi (1651-1709),
Religious Leader — A209

2001, Jan. 16   Litho.   Perf. 13½
409	A209	75k multi	.50	.50

Love — A210

2001, Jan. 26
410	A210	30k multi	.20	.20

Souvenir Sheet

Prince Danylo Romanovych (1201-64) — A211

2001, Feb. 1   Perf. 11½
411	A211	3h multi	2.00	2.00

Hetman Type of 1997

Designs: 30k, Yuryi Khmelnytski (1641-85), as monk in Turkish prison, Kamianets-Podilskyi fortifications. 50k, Mykhailo Khanenko (1620-80), leading troops, relinquishing power.

2001, Feb. 20   Perf. 12¼x12
412-413	A110	Set of 2	.55	.55

Invention of the Telephone, 125th Anniv. A212

2001, Mar. 6   *Perf. 13½*
414 A212 70k multi   .50   .50

Children's Art — A213

Art by: 10k, Alyna Nochvaj. 30k, Olyia Pynych. 40k, Dasha Chemberzhi.

2001, Mar. 7   *Perf. 11½*
415-417 A213   Set of 3   .55   .55

Hollyhocks A214

Marigolds A215

Sunflower A216

Viburnum Opulus Berries A217

Wheat — A218

**2001, Apr. 4   Litho.   *Perf. 13¾*
418 A214   (10k) multi   .20   .20
419 A215   (30k) multi   .20   .20
420 A216   (71k) multi   .50   .50
421 A217   (2.66h) multi   1.75 1.75
422 A218   (3.65h) multi   2.50 2.50
      Nos. 418-422 (5)   5.15 5.15
      See Nos. 453-454.

Folktales — A219

No. 423: a, The Fox and Wolf (fox on sleigh, fish). b, The Mitten (bear, fox, wolf, rabbit mouse, frog). c, Sirko the Dog (wolf with bottle, dog).
Illustration reduced.

2001, Apr. 14   *Perf. 13½*
423 A219 30k Horiz. strip of 3,
         #a-c   .60   .60

Ships — A220

No. 424: a, 20k, Twelve Apostles. b, 30k, Three Priests.

Illustration reduced.
2001, Apr. 20
424 A220   Horiz. pair, #a-b   .35   .35

Europa — A221

Fish, jellyfish, seaweed: a, 28x40mm. b, 56x40mm.
Illustration reduced.

2001, Apr. 27
425 A221 1h Horiz. pair, #a-b   1.40 1.40

Holy Trinity A222

2001, May 15
426 A222 30k multi   .25   .25

Souvenir Sheet

Apiculture — A223

No. 427: a, Bee on flower. b, Plant cutting, jar of honey, bowl of pollen, jars. c, Worker on honeycomb. d, Queen. e, Hive. f, Drone.

2001, May 22   *Perf. 11½*
427 A223 50k Sheet of 6, #a-f   2.10 2.10

Souvenir Sheet

Kyievo-Pecherska Monastery, 950th Anniv. — A224

2001, May 25
428 A224 1.50h multi   1.00 1.00

Visit of Pope John Paul II, June 23-27 A225

2001, June 15   *Perf. 13½*
429 A225 3h multi   2.10 2.10

Regional and Administrative Areas

Zakarpatska Oblast — A226

Kharkivska Oblast — A227

2001   *Perf. 12¼x12*
430 A226 30k multi   .25   .25
431 A226 30k multi   .25   .25
      Issued: No. 430, 6/29; No. 431, 8/18.

Regional and Administrative Areas

Chernihivska Oblast — A228

Kirovohradska Oblast — A229

**2001   Litho.   *Perf. 12¼x12*
432 A228 30k multi   .25   .25
433 A229 30k multi   .25   .25
      Issued: No. 432, 9/21; No. 433, 9/22.

Souvenir Sheet

Icons From Khanenko Art Museum — A230

No. 434: a, 20k, Virgin and Child, 28x40mm. b, 30k, St. John the Baptist, 28x40mm. c, Saints Serhyi and Bacchus, 56x40mm.

**2001, July 12   Litho.   *Perf. 11½*
434 A230   Sheet of 3, #a-c   .75   .75

Endangered Species A231

No. 435: a, Milvus milvus. b, Scirtopoda telum.

2001, July 24   *Perf. 13*
435 A231 1h Vert. pair, #a-b   1.50 1.50

Dmytro Bortnianskyi (1751-1825), Composer — A232

2001, July 26
436 A232 20k multi   .20   .20

Soccer — A233

2001, Aug. 10
437 A233 50k multi   .35   .35

Souvenir Sheet

Independence, 10th Anniv. — A234

2001, Aug. 15   *Perf. 11½*
438 A234 3h multi   2.25 2.25

7th Natl. Philatelic Exhibition, Dnipropetrovsk — A235

**2001, Oct. 7   Litho.   *Perf. 12¼x12*
439 A235 30k multi   .25   .25

Year of Dialogue Among Civilizations A236

2001, Oct. 9   *Perf. 13*
440 A236 70k multi   .50   .50

Souvenir Sheet

Black Sea Marine Life — A237

No. 441: a, 30k, Seahorses. b, 70k, Dolphins, birds.

2001, Oct. 19   *Perf. 11½*
441 A237   Sheet of 2, #a-b   .75   .75

Christmas — A238

2001, Nov. 9   *Perf. 12¼x12*
442 A238 30k multi   .25   .25

St. Nicholas
A239

2001, Nov. 16   *Perf. 13*
443 A239 30k multi   .25   .25

Happy New
Year — A240

2001, Nov. 23
444 A240 30k multi   .25   .25

Poets — A241

No. 445: a, Taras Shevchenko (1814-61), Ukrainian poet. b, Akakii Tsereteli (1840-1915), Georgian poet.

2001, Dec. 19
445 A241 40k Horiz. pair, #a-b   .60   .60
    See Georgia No. 276.

Regional Costumes

Kyivshchyna Region — A242

Chernihivshchyna Region — A243

Poltavshchyna Region — A244

No. 446: a, 20k, Two women. b, 50k, Man and woman.
No. 447: a, 20k, Musicians and girl. b, 50k, Bride and groom, boy.
No. 448: a, 20k, Priest and family. b, 50k, Two women.

2001, Dec. 20   *Perf. 13¼*
446 A242   Horiz. pair, #a-b   .50   .50
447 A243   Horiz. pair, #a-b   .50   .50
448 A244   Horiz. pair, #a-b   .50   .50
  c.   Souvenir sheet, #446-448, perf.
     11½   1.50   1.50
    Nos. 446-448 (3)   1.50   1.50

Hetman Type of 1997

Designs: No. 449, 40k, Pavlo Teteryia (d. 1670) holding scepter, people in town, horsemen and carriage heading for town. No. 450, 40k, Demyian Mnohohrishnyi, receiving scepter, boats in river. No. 451, 40k, Ivan Briukhovetskyi (d. 1668), battle scenes.

2002, Jan. 17   *Perf. 12¼x12*
449-451 A110   Set of 3   .85   .85

Scythian Military History — A245

No. 452: a, Archer on horseback. b, Swordsman in battle. c, Commander on horseback, warrior. d, Female warrior.
Illustration reduced.

2002, Jan. 29   *Perf. 13*
452 A245 40k Block of 4, #a-d   1.10   1.10

Flower Type of 2001 and

Periwinkle — A246

2002   **Litho.**   *Perf. 13¾*
453 A246 5k multi   .20   .20
454 A214 10k multi   .20   .20
    Issued: 5k, 2/1; 10k, 2/26.

Sporting Achievements — A247

Designs: No. 455, 40k, Zhanna Pintusevich-Block winning 100-meter dash at 2001 World Track and Field Championships. No. 456, 40k, Swimmer at 2000 Summer Olympics.

2002, Feb. 15   *Perf. 13*
455-456 A247   Set of 2   .50   .50

Regional and Administrative Areas

Kyivska Oblast — A248

2002, Feb. 18   *Perf. 12¼x12*
457 A248 40k multi   .25   .25

Shipbuilding — A249

No. 458: a, Frigate Sizopol and coast. b, Brigantine Perseus.
Illustration reduced.

2002, Feb. 22   *Perf. 13½*
458 A249 40k Horiz. pair, #a-b   .55   .55

Issuance of First Stamp After
Independence, 10th Anniv. — A250

2002, Mar. 1
459 A250 40k No. 100   .25   .25

Leonid Hlibov
(1827-93),
Writer — A251

2002, Mar. 4   **Litho.**   *Perf. 13¼*
460 A251 40k multi   .25   .25

Ruslan Ponomariov, Winner of 16th
World Chess Championships — A252

2002, Mar. 29   *Perf. 13½*
461 A252 3.50h multi   1.75   1.75

Souvenir Sheet

Europa — A253

No. 462: a, Lion. b, Tiger, horiz.

2002, Apr. 4   *Perf. 11½*
462 A253 1.75h Sheet of 2, #a-b   1.75   1.75

Palm
Sunday — A254

2002, Apr. 19   *Perf. 13½*
463 A254 40k multi   .25   .25

Worldwide Fund for Nature
(WWF) — A255

Various views of Elaphe situla: a, 40k. b, 70k. c, 80k. d, 2.50h.
Illustration reduced.

2002, May 25   *Perf. 13½*
464 A255   Block of 4, #a-d   2.25   2.25

Souvenir Sheet

Opera and Ballet Theaters — A256

No. 465: a, Donetsk (tree at center). b, Dnipropetrovsk (trees at side).

2002, May 31   *Perf. 11½*
465 A256 1.25h Sheet of 2, #a-b   1.25   1.25

Flower Type of 2001 and

Blue
Cornflower
A257

Lilac
A258

2002   **Litho.**   *Perf. 13¾*
466 A215 30k multi   .20   .20
467 A257 45k multi   .30   .30
468 A258 (80k) multi   .55   .55
    Issued: 30k, 6/1; 45k, 9/18; (80k), 7/5.

Regional and Administrative Areas

Luhanska Oblast — A259

Chernivetska Oblast — A260

Odeska Oblast — A261

Cherkaska Oblast — A262

Sumska Oblast — A263

2002		Perf. 12¼x12	
69	A259 40k multi	.25	.25
70	A260 40k multi	.25	.25
71	A261 45k multi	.30	.30
72	A262 45k multi	.30	.30
73	A263 45k multi	.30	.30
	Nos. 469-473 (5)	1.40	1.40

Issued: No. 469, 6/2; No. 470, 6/27; No.
71, 9/20. No. 472, 10/9; No. 473, 10/21.

Endangered
Species
A264

No. 474: a, Phalacrocorax aristotelis. b,
Phocoena phocoena.

2002, June 14   Litho.   Perf. 13
74 A264 70k Pair, #a-b   .90   .90

Mykola Leontovich
(1877-1921),
Composer — A265

2002, June 21   Perf. 13½
75 A265 40k multi   .25   .25

Souvenir Sheet

Black Sea Nature Reserve — A266

No. 476: a, Haematopus ostralegus
40x28mm). b, Larus genei (40x28mm). c, Iris
umila (22x26mm). d, Numenius arquata

(26x22mm). e, Charadrius alexandrinus
(26x22mm).

2002, July 13   Perf. 11½
476 A266 50k Sheet of 5, #a-e   1.50 1.50

Folk Tales — A267

No. 477: a, Fox and Pancake. b, Mr. Cat. c,
Speckled Chicken.
Illustration reduced.

2002, July 19   Perf. 14¼x14
477 A267 40k Horiz. strip of 3,
             #a-c   .80   .80

Art of Hanna Sobachko-
Shostak — A268

No. 478: a, Cage for Starlings, 1963 (peach
background). b, Vase with Flowers, 1964 (red
background). c, Chamomile Flowers, 1964
(yellow background).

2002, Aug. 9   Perf. 14x14¼
478   Horiz. strip of 3   .90   .90
a.-c. A268 45k Any single   .30   .30

Space Pioneers — A269

Designs: 40k, Yurii V. Kondratiuk (1897-
1942). 45k, Mykhailo Yianhel (1911-71). 50k,
Mykola Kybalchych (1853-81). 70k, Serhii
Korolov (1907-66).

2002, Aug. 23   Perf. 12¼x12
479-482 A269   Set of 4   1.25   1.25

Marine Life — A270

No. 483: a, Phoca caspica. b, Huso huso
ponticus.
Illustration reduced.

2002, Sept. 6   Perf. 14x14¼
483 A270 75k Horiz. pair, #a-b   1.00 1.00
          See Kazakhstan No. 386.

Khotyn, 1000th Anniv. — A271

2002, Sept. 21   Perf. 12¼x12
484 A271 40k multi   .25   .25

Odessaphil 2002
Stamp Exhibition,
Odessa — A272

2002, Oct. 5   Litho.   Perf. 14¼x14
485 A272 45k multi   .30   .30

Paintings of Kiev by Taras Shevchenko
(1814-61) — A273

Designs: 45k, Askold's Tomb. 75k, Dnieper
River Shoreline. 80k, St. Alexander's Church.

Perf. 13¾x14½
2002, Nov. 15   Litho.
486-488 A273   Set of 3   1.25   1.25

Happy New
Year — A274

2002, Nov. 22   Perf. 14x14¼
489 A274 45k multi   .30   .30

Regional Costumes

Vinychyna Region — A275

Cherkashchyna Region — A276

Ternopilska Region — A277

No. 490: a, Family, rainbow. b, Family, fruit
tree.
No. 491: a, Four girls holding hands. b,
Couple gathering crops.
No. 492: a, Priest blessing family. b, People
with Easter baskets.

2002, Dec. 6   Perf. 13¼
490 A275 45k Horiz. pair, #a-b   .55   .55
491 A276 45k Horiz. pair, #a-b   .55   .55
492 A277 45k Horiz. pair, #a-b   .55   .55
c.   Souvenir sheet, #490-492, perf.
      11½   1.75   1.75
      Nos. 490-492 (3)   1.65   1.65

Folk Tales — A278

No. 493: a, Koza-Dezera (cow on bridge). b,
The Straw Bull. c, The Fox and Crane.
Illustration reduced.

2003, Jan. 17   Litho.   Perf. 14¼x14
493 A278 45k Horiz. strip of 3,
             #a-c   .75   .75

Speed
Skating
A279

2003, Jan. 24   Perf. 14x14¼
494 A279 65k multi   .35   .35

Military History — A280

No. 495: a, War with Goths, 4th cent. (soldier with spear and shield) b, Battles with
Huns, 5th cent. (archer). c, Balkan campaigns,
6th cent. (soldier with hatchet). d, Battles with
the Avars, 6th cent. (soldier with spears).
Illustration reduced.

2003, Feb. 7
495 A280 45k Block of 4, #a-d   1.00   1.00

Shipbuilding — A281

No. 496: a, Steamship Grozny (denomination at left. b, Steamship Odessa (denomination at right).
Illustration reduced.

2003, Feb. 14
496 A281 1h Horiz. pair, #a-b   1.10   1.10

Mikola Arkas (1853-1909),
Composer — A282

2003, Feb. 21
497 A282 45k multi   .25   .25

Souvenir Sheet

Javorivsky National Nature
Park — A283

No. 498: a, 1h, Alcede atthis (32x44mm). b, 1h, Cypripedium calceolus (36x41mm). c, 1.50h, Eudia pavonia, horiz. (44x32mm)

2003, Mar. 3   *Perf. 11½*
498 A283   Sheet of 3, #a-c   1.90 1.90

Europa — A284

Poster by Oleksiy Shtanko: a, Virgin Mary with dove. b, Guardian angel. Illustration reduced.

2003, Mar. 21   *Perf. 11½*
499 A284   1.75h Horiz. pair, #a-b   2.25 2.25
c.   Booklet pane, 2 #499 + central label   4.50 —
    Complete booklet, #499c   4.50

Space Pioneers Type of 2002

Designs: 45k, Olkeksandr Zasiadko (1779-1837). 65k, Kostyantin Konstantinov (1817-71). 70k, Valyntyn Hlushko (1908-89). 80k, Volodymyr Chelomei (1914-84).

2003, Apr. 11 Litho.   *Perf. 13¾x14½*
500-503 A269   Set of 4   1.40 1.40

Ukrainian Red Cross Society, 85th Anniv. — A285

2003, Apr. 18
504 A285 45k multi   .25 .25

Regional and Administrative Areas

Dnipropetrovska Oblast — A286

Lvivska Oblast — A287

Khmelnytska Oblast — A288

Mykolayivska Oblast — A289

Zaporizhiya Oblast — A290

2003
505 A286 45k multi   .25 .25
506 A287 45k multi   .25 .25
507 A288 45k multi   .25 .25
508 A289 45k multi   .25 .25
509 A290 45k multi   .25 .25
    Nos. 505-509 (5)   1.25 1.25

   Issued: No. 505, 4/21; No. 506, 5/8; No. 507, 9/8; No. 508, 10/4; No. 509, 10/11.

Hetman Type of 1997

Designs: No. 510, 45k, Ivan Skoropadskiy (1646-1722) wearing robe, serfs in field, subjects bowing. No. 511, 45k, Kyrylo Rozumovskiy (1728-1803) holding scepter, attack of palace, palace ruins.

2003, May 22
510-511 A110   Set of 2   .50 .50

Souvenir Sheet

Volodymyr Monomakh (1053-1125), Grand Prince of Kiev — A291

2003, May 28   *Perf. 11½*
512 A291   3.50h multi   1.90 1.90

Owls — A292

No. 513: a, Bubo bubo. b, Strix uralensis. c, Strix aluco. d, Strix nebulosa. e, Glaucidium passerinum. f, Aegolius funereus. g, Otus scops. h, Athene noctua. i, Tyto alba. j, Asio otus. k, Asio flammeus. l, Surnia ulula. Size of # 513e-513h: 25x27mm; others: 25x36mm.

2003, June 14
513 A292   45k Sheet of 12, #a-l   2.75 2.75

Oleksandr Myshuha (1853-1922), Opera Singer — A293

2003, June 20   *Perf. 13¼*
514 A293 45k multi   .25 .25

Sweet Pea — A294

2003, July 4   *Perf. 13¾*
515 A294 65k multi   .35 .35

Paintings Type of 2002

Paintings of Kiev: No. 516, 45k, Podil, by Mykhailo Sazhyn, 1840. No. 517, 45k, Kiev-Pecherska Monastery, by Vasyl Timm, 1857. No. 518, 45k, Ruins of St. Irene Monastery, by

---

Sazhyn, 1846. No. 519, 45k, View of Old City from Yaroslav Embankment, by Timm, 1854.

2003, July 18   *Perf. 13¾x14½*
516-519 A273   Set of 4   1.00 1.00

Customs and Traditions — A295

No. 520: a, Celebration of the Harvest (Church, flowers and insects). b, Ascension (Church, fruit).

2003, July 25   *Perf. 14¼x14*
520 A295   45k Horiz. pair, #a-b   .50 .50

Borys Hmyryia (1903-69), Composer A296

2003, Aug. 5   *Perf. 14x14¼*
521 A296 45k multi   .25 .25

Souvenir Sheet

Manyiavskyi Monastery — A297

No. 522: a, Denomination at LL. b, Denomination at LR.

2003, Aug. 15   *Perf. 11x11½*
522 A297   1.25h Sheet of 2, #a-b   1.40 1.40

Yevpatoriya, 2500th Anniv. — A298

2003, Aug. 29   *Perf. 13¾x14½*
523 A298 45k multi   .25 .25

Ancient Trade Routes — A299

No. 524: a, Arrival of Scandinavian seamen in rowboat, coin of Danish King Svend Estridsen. b, Silver coin of Prince Volodymyr Sviatoslavovych, Slavic warship with sail.

2003, Sept. 17   *Perf. 11½*
524 A299   80k Vert. pair, #a-b, + central label   .90 .90
c.   Booklet pane, #524   2.40
d.   Booklet pane, #524a   1.25
e.   Booklet pane, #524b   1.25
    Complete booklet, #524c, 524d, 524e   5.00

Hryhoryi Kvitka-Osnovyianenko (1778-1843), Writer — A300

2003, Nov. 14 Litho.   *Perf. 14¼x14*
525 A300 45k multi   .25 .25

Famine of 1932-33 — A301

2003, Nov. 21   *Perf. 13¾x14½*
526 A301 45k multi   .25 .25

Christmas A302

Litho. with Foil Application
2003, Nov. 25   *Perf. 13¼x13½*
527 A302 45k multi   .25 .25

New Year's Greetings A303

2003, Nov. 25 Litho.   *Perf. 13½*
528 A303 45k multi   .25 .25

Regional Costumes

Kharkiv Region — A304

Sumy Region — A305

Donetsk Region — A306

No. 529: a, Women, religious icons. b, Fam-
ly, lute.
No. 530: a, Woman, men. b, Group of
women.
No. 531: a, Family, sled. b, Workers in field.

2003, Dec. 19			**Perf. 13¼**	
529	A304	45k Horiz. pair, #a-b	.50	.50
530	A305	45k Horiz. pair, #a-b	.50	.50
531	A306	45k Horiz. pair, #a-b	.50	.50
c.		Souvenir sheet, #529-531, perf. 11½	1.50	1.50

SEMI-POSTAL STAMPS

Ukrainian Soviet Socialist Republic

"Famine" — SP1

Taras H.
Shevchenko
SP2

"Death" Stalking
Peasant — SP3

"Ukraine"
Distributing
Food — SP4

Perf. 14½x13½, 13½x14½				
1923, June		**Litho.**	**Unwmk.**	
B1	SP1	10k + 10k gray bl & blk	.30	2.00
B2	SP2	20k + 20k vio brn & org brn	.30	2.00
B3	SP3	90k + 30k db & blk, *straw*	.30	2.00
B4	SP4	150k + 50k red brn & blk	.30	2.00
		Nos. B1-B4 (4)	1.20	8.00
		Imperf., Pairs		
B1a	SP1	10k + 10k	60.00	80.00
B2a	SP2	20k + 20k	60.00	80.00
B3a	SP3	90k + 30k	60.00	80.00
B4a	SP4	150k + 50k	60.00	80.00

The values of these stamps are in
karbovanets, which by 1923 converted to
rubles at 100 to 1.

Wmk. 116				
Same Colors				
B5	SP1	10k + 10k	30.00	45.00
B6	SP2	20k + 20k	30.00	45.00
a.		Imperf., pair	2,000.	

B7	SP3	90k + 30k	30.00	45.00
B8	SP4	150k + 50k	30.00	45.00
		Nos. B5-B8 (4)	120.00	180.00

> **Catalogue values for unused
> stamps in this section, from this
> point to the end of the section, are
> for Never Hinged items.**

Mercy and Health
Fund — SP5

1994, Jan. 15		**Litho.**	**Perf. 12**	
B9	SP5	150kb +20kb multi		.35

Third Natl.
Philatelic
Exhibition,
Lviv — SP6

1995, Sept. 23		**Litho.**	**Perf. 13½**	
B10	SP6	50,000kb +5000kb multi	1.00	

Souvenir Sheet

Zymnenska Icon of Madonna and
Child — SP7

Illustration reduced.

1999, Sept. 4		**Litho.**	**Perf. 11½**	
B11	SP7	1.20h +10k multicolored	.90	.90

Intl. Year of the Elderly.

REGISTRATION STAMP

> **Catalogue values for unused
> stamps in this section are for
> Never Hinged items.**

Trident — R1

2001, Apr. 1		**Litho.**	**Perf. 13¾**	
F1	R1	(10.84h) multi	7.25	7.25

MILITARY STAMPS

COURIER FIELD POST ISSUE

Nos. 1-5, 48
Surcharged

1920, Aug. 26

M1	A1	10hr on 10sh buff	15.00	—
a.		Inverted surcharge	60.00	
M2	A2	10hr on 20sh brown	30.00	—
M3	A3	10hr on 30sh ul- tramarine	35.00	—
M4	A4	10hr on 40sh green	40.00	—
a.		Inverted surcharge	160.00	
M5	A5	10hr on 50sh red	35.00	—
M6	A1	20hr on 10sh buff	40.00	—
M7	A2	20hr on 20sh brown	10.00	—
a.		Inverted surcharge	40.00	
M8	A3	20hr on 30sh ul- tramarine	30.00	—
a.		Inverted surcharge	120.00	
M9	A4	20hr on 40sh green	30.00	—
M10	A5	20hr on 50sh red	30.00	—
a.		Inverted surcharge	120.00	
M11	A1	40hr on 10sh buff	150.00	—
M12	A2	40hr on 20sh brown	75.00	—
M13	A3	40hr on 30sh ul- tramarine	300.00	—
M14	A4	40hr on 40sh green	150.00	—
M15	A5	40hr on 50sh red	300.00	—
M16	A6	40hr on 20hr red & green	—	—

Nos. M1-M16 were prepared to facilitate
communications between the Ukrainian government-in-exile at Tarnow, Poland, and its
military units in the field.
Only two copies of No. M16 are known, one
unused and one used on cover.
Forged surcharges and cancellations exist.

UMM AL QIWAIN

'um-al-kī-'wīn

LOCATION — Oman Peninsula, Arabia,
on Arabian Gulf
GOVT. — Sheikdom under British
protection
AREA — 300 sq. mi.
POP. — 5,700

Umm al Qiwain is one of six Persian
Gulf sheikdoms to join the United Arab
Emirates which proclaimed indepen-
dence Dec. 2, 1971. See United Arab
Emirates.

100 Naye Paise = 1 Rupee
100 Dirham = 1 Riyal (1967)

> **Catalogue values for all unused
> stamps in this country are for
> Never Hinged items.**

Sheik
Ahmed bin
Rashid al
Mulla and
Gazelles
A1

Photogravure and Lithographed

1964, June 29		**Unwmk.**	**Perf. 14**	
Size: 35x22mm				
1	A1	1np shown	.20	.20
2	A1	2np Snake	.20	.20
3	A1	3np Hyena	.20	.20
4	A1	4np Conspicuous trig- gerfish	.20	.20
5	A1	5np Fish	.20	.20
6	A1	10np Silver angelfish	.20	.20
7	A1	15np Palace	.20	.20
8	A1	20np Umm al Qiwain	.20	.20
9	A1	30np Tower	.20	.20
Size: 42x26mm				
10	A1	40np as 1np	.20	.20
11	A1	50np as 2np	.20	.20
12	A1	70np as 3np	.25	.20
13	A1	1r as 4np	.55	.25
14	A1	1.50r as 4np	.65	.30
15	A1	2r as 10np	.90	.50
Size: 52x33mm				
16	A1	3r as 15np	1.25	.80
17	A1	5r as 20np	2.10	1.10
18	A1	10r as 30np	3.50	2.25
		Nos. 1-18 (18)	11.40	7.60

National Stadium, Tokyo, and
Discobolus — A2

Designs: 1r, 2r, National Stadium,
Tokyo. 1.50r, Indoor swimming arena. 3r,
Komazawa Gymnasium. 4r, Stadium
entrance.

1964, Nov. 25		**Photo.**		
19	A2	50np multi	.20	.20
20	A2	1r multi	.30	.20
21	A2	1.50r multi	.45	.20
22	A2	2r multi	.60	.20
23	A2	3r multi	.85	.35
24	A2	4r multi	1.60	.50
25	A2	5r multi	2.00	.65
		Nos. 19-25 (7)	6.00	2.30

18th Olympic Games, Tokyo, Oct. 10-25,
1964. Perf. and imperf. souvenir sheets contain 4 stamps similar to #22-25 in changed
colors. Size: 145x115mm.

A3

A4

Designs: 10np, Pres. Kennedy's funeral cor-
tege leaving White House. 15np, Mrs. Kennedy with children, and Robert Kennedy following coffin. 50np, Horse-drawn caisson. 1r,
Presidents Truman and Eisenhower, and Margaret Truman Daniels. 2r, Pres. Charles de
Gaulle, Emperor Haile Selassie, Chancellor
Ludwig Erhart, Sir Alec Douglas-Home and
King Frederick IX. 3r, Kennedy family on steps
of St. Matthew's Cathedral. 5r, Honor guard at
tomb. 7.50r, Portrait of Pres. John F.
Kennedy.

			Perf. 14½	
1965, Jan. 20		**Unwmk.**	**Photo.**	
Black Design with Gold Inscriptions				
Size: 29x44mm				
26	A3	10np pale blue	.20	.20
27	A3	15np pale yellow	.20	.20
28	A3	50np pale green	.20	.20
29	A3	1r pale pink	.30	.20
30	A3	2r pale green	.60	.20
Size: 33x51mm				
31	A3	3r pale gray	1.00	.20
32	A3	5r pale blue	1.75	.30
33	A3	7.50r pale yellow	2.50	.50
		Nos. 26-33 (8)	6.75	2.00

Pres. John F. Kennedy. A souvenir sheet
contains 2 stamps similar to Nos. 32-33 with
pale green (5r) and pale salmon (7.50r) backgrounds, size: 29x44mm. Size of sheet:
114x70mm.

1969, Nov. 19		**Litho.**	**Perf. 14½**	

Designs: 10d, Astronaut on Moon. 20d,
Landing module approaching moon. 30d,
Apollo XII on launching pad. 50d, Com-
manders Charles Conrad, Jr., Alan L. Bean,
Richard F. Gordon, Jr., earth and moon, horiz.
75d, Earth and Apollo XII, horiz. 1r, Sheik
Ahmed, rocket and lunar landing module,
horiz.

34	A4	10d multi		.20
35	A4	20d multi		.20
36	A4	30d multi		.20

37	A4	50d emerald & multi	.25
38	A4	75d purple & multi	.40
39	A4	1r dk bl & multi	.60
		Nos. 34-39 (6)	1.85

US Apollo XII moon landing mission, 11/14-24/69.

Two imperf. souvenir sheets of 3 exist, containing stamps similar to Nos. 34-36 and Nos. 37-39.

A5   A7

A6

1970, May 29   Litho.   Perf. 14

40	A5	10d James A. Lovell	.20
41	A5	30d Fred W. Haise, Jr.	.20
42	A5	50d John L. Swigert, Jr.	.20
a.		Souv. sheet of 3, #40-42	.40
		Nos. 40-42 (3)	.60

Safe return of the crew of Apollo 13.

1970, Aug. 14   Litho.   Perf. 13½x14

Designs: 5d, 1.25r, EXPO '70 Emblem. 10d, 20d, Japanese Pavilion.

43	A6	5d yellow & multi	.20
44	A6	10d blue & multi	.20
45	A6	20d red & multi	.20
48	A6	1.25r red & multi	.25
		Nos. 43-48 (4)	.85

EXPO '70 Intl. Exhib., Osaka, Japan, Mar. 15-Sept. 13, 1970.

A 40d and 1r, showing the Emperor and Empress of Japan, and a souvenir sheet containing these and Nos. 43-45, 48 were prepared, but not issued.

1970, Oct. 12   Litho.   Perf. 14½x14

Uniforms: 10d, Private, North Lancashire Regiment. 20d, Royal Navy seaman. 30d, Officer, North Lancashire (Loyal) Regiment. 50d, Private, York and Lancaster Regiment. 75d, Royal Navy officer. 1r, Officer, York and Lancaster Regiment.

49	A7	10d multi	.20
50	A7	20d multi	.25
51	A7	30d multi	.35
a.		Souv. sheet of 3, #49-51	1.50
52	A7	50d buff & multi	.70
53	A7	75d multi	1.00
54	A7	1r buff & multi	1.50
a.		Souv. sheet of 3, #52-54	3.50
		Nos. 49-54 (6)	4.00

British landings on the Trucial Coast, 150th anniv.

Stamps of Umm al Qiwain were replaced in 1972 by those of United Arab Emirates.

AIR POST STAMPS

Type of Regular Issue, 1964
Photogravure and Lithographed

1965		Unwmk.		Perf. 14

Size: 42x26mm

C1	A1	15np as #1	.20	.20
C2	A1	25np as #2	.20	.20
C3	A1	35np as #3	.20	.20
C4	A1	50np as #4	.20	.20
C5	A1	75np as #5	.40	.20
C6	A1	1r as #6	.40	.20

Size: 52x33mm

C7	A1	2r as #7	.85	.20
C8	A1	3r as #8	1.10	.20
C9	A1	5r as #9	1.60	.30
		Nos. C1-C9 (9)	5.15	1.90

Issued: #C7-C9, Nov. 6; others, Oct. 18.

AIR POST OFFICIAL STAMPS

Type of Regular Issue, 1964
Photogravure and Lithographed

1965, Dec. 22		Unwmk.		Perf. 14

Size: 42x26mm

CO1	A1	75np as #6	.20	.20

Size: 52x33mm

CO2	A1	2r as #7	.40	.20
CO3	A1	3r as #8	.60	.20
CO4	A1	5r as #9	1.00	.30
		Nos. CO1-CO4 (4)	2.20	.90

OFFICIAL STAMPS

Type of Regular Issue, 1964
Photogravure and Lithographed

1965, Dec. 22		Unwmk.		Perf. 14

Size: 42x26mm

O1	A1	25np as #1	.20	.20
O2	A1	40np as #2	.20	.20
O3	A1	50np as #3	.20	.20
O4	A1	75np as #4	.40	.20
O5	A1	1r as #5	.80	.20
		Nos. O1-O5 (5)	1.80	1.00

UNITED ARAB EMIRATES

yu-ˌnī-təd ˈar-əb i-ˈmiˌəˌr-əts

(Trucial States)

LOCATION — Arabia, on Arabian Gulf
GOVT. — Federation of sheikdoms
AREA — 32,300 sq. mi.
POP. — 2,377,453 (1995)
CAPITAL — Abu Dhabi

The UAE was formed Dec. 2, 1971, by the union of Abu Dhabi, Ajman, Dubai, Fujeira, Sharjah and Umm al Qiwain. Ras al Khaima joined in Feb. 1972.

1,000 Fils = 1 Dinar
100 Fils = 1 Dirham (1973)

> **Catalogue values for all unused stamps in this country are for Never Hinged items.**

Abu Dhabi Nos. 56-67 Overprinted

دولة الامارات العربية المتحدة

UAE

1972, Aug.   Litho. Unwmk.   Perf. 14

1	A10	5f multicolored	
2	A10	10f multicolored	
3	A10	25f multicolored	
4	A10	35f multicolored	
5	A10	50f multicolored	
6	A10	60f multicolored	
7	A10	70f multicolored	
8	A10	90f multicolored	
9	A11	125f multicolored	
10	A11	150f multicolored	
11	A11	500f multicolored	
12	A11	1d multicolored	
		Nos. 1-12 (12)	275.00

The overprint differs.
#1-12 were used in Abu Dhabi. #2-3 were placed on sale later in Dubai & Sharjah.

Map and Flag of UAE
A1

Almagta Bridge, Abu Dhabi — A2

Designs: 10f, Like 5f. 15f, 35f, Coat of arms of UAE (eagle). 75f, Khor Fakkan, Sharjah. 1d, Steel Clock Tower, Dubai. 1.25d, Buthnah Fort, Fujeira. 2d, Alfalaj Fort, Umm al Qiwain. 3d, Khor Khwair, Ras al Khaima. 5d, Palace of Sheik Rashid bin Humaid al Nuaimi, Ajman. 10d, Sheik Zaid bin Sultan al Nahayan, Abu Dhabi.

1973, Jan. 1   Unwmk.   Perf. 14½

Size: 41x25mm

13	A1	5f multicolored	.20	.20
14	A1	10f multicolored	.20	.20
15	A1	15f blue & multi	.25	.20
16	A1	35f olive & multi	.40	.30

Perf. 14x15
Size: 45x29½mm

17	A2	65f multicolored	.85	.75
18	A2	75f multicolored	1.00	.75
19	A2	1d multicolored	1.40	1.00
20	A2	1.25d multicolored	2.50	2.00
21	A2	2d multicolored	30.00	7.00
22	A2	3d multicolored	4.75	4.75
23	A2	5d multicolored	7.50	5.00
24	A2	10d multicolored	15.00	10.00
		Nos. 13-24 (12)	64.05	32.15

For surcharge see No. 68.

Festival Emblem
A3

1973, Mar. 27   Litho.   Perf. 13½x14

25	A3	10f shown	3.50	.20
26	A3	1.25d Trophy	9.00	6.50

National Youth Festival, Mar. 27.

Pedestrian Crossing in Dubai — A4

35f, Traffic light school crossing sign, vert. 1.25d, Traffic policemen with car & radio, vert.

1973, Apr. 1   Perf. 13½x14, 14x13½

27	A4	35f green & multi	2.00	1.10
28	A4	75f blue & multi	4.00	2.00
29	A4	1.25d violet & multi	6.75	3.00
		Nos. 27-29 (3)	12.75	6.10

Traffic Week, Apr. 1-7.

Human Rights Flame and People — A5

1973, Dec. 10   Litho.   Perf. 14½x1

30	A5	35f blue, blk & org	1.25	.5
31	A5	65f red, blk & org	3.00	1.0
32	A5	1.25d olive, blk & org	4.75	1.9
		Nos. 30-32 (3)	9.00	3.4

25th anniversary of the Universal Declaration of Human Rights.

UPU and Arab Postal Union Emblems — A6

1974, Aug. 5   Litho.   Perf. 14x14½

33	A6	25f multicolored	.95	.4
34	A6	60f emerald & multi	1.90	.7
35	A6	1.25d lt brown & multi	3.75	1.7
		Nos. 33-35 (3)	6.60	2.9

Centenary of Universal Postal Union.

Health Care — A7

Education — A8

Designs: 65f, Construction. 1.25d, UAE flag, UN and Arab League emblems.

1974, Dec. 2   Litho.   Perf. 13½

36	A7	10f multicolored	.75	.2
37	A8	35f multicolored	1.50	.6
38	A8	65f blue & brown	2.10	1.0
39	A8	1.25d multicolored	4.50	2.5
		Nos. 36-39 (4)	8.85	4.3

Third National Day.

Arab Man and Woman Holding Candle over Book — A9

Man and Woman Reading Book — A10

1974, Dec. 27   Perf. 14x14½, 14½x1

40	A9	35f deep ultra & multi	1.75	.4
41	A10	65f orange brn & multi	2.00	.7
42	A10	1.25d gray & multi	4.00	1.5
		Nos. 40-42 (3)	7.75	2.6

World Literacy Day.

Oil De-gassing Station — A11

50f, Off-shore drilling platform. 100f, Underwater storage tank. 125f, Oil production platform.

1975, Mar. 10   Litho.   Perf. 13x13½

43	A11	25f multicolored	1.00	.30
44	A11	50f multicolored	1.40	.60
45	A11	100f multicolored	2.75	1.40
46	A11	125f multicolored	3.75	1.50
a.		Souvenir sheet of 4, #43-46	9.00	5.25
		Nos. 43-46 (4)	8.90	3.80

9th Arab Petroleum Conference.

Three stamps to commemorate the 2nd Gulf Long Distance Swimming Championship were prepared in June, 1975, but not issued. Value $200.

Jabal Ali Earth Station — A12

Jabal Ali Earth Station: 35f, 65f, Communications satellite over globe.

1975, Nov. 8   Litho.   Perf. 13

47	A12	15f multicolored	.50	.20
48	A12	35f multicolored	1.75	.50
49	A12	65f multicolored	2.75	.80
50	A12	2d multicolored	5.50	2.50
		Nos. 47-50 (4)	10.50	4.00

Various Scenes — A13

Sheik Hamad, Fujeira Ruler — A14

Supreme Council Members (Sheikdom rulers): 60f, Sheik Rashid bin Humaid al Naimi, Ajman. 80f, Sheik Ahmed bin Rashid al Mulla, Umm al Qiwain. 90f, Sheik Sultan bin Mohammed al Qasimi, Sharjah. 1d, Sheik Saqr bin Mohammed al Qasimi, Ras al Khaima. 140f, Sheik Rashid bin Said al Maktum, Dubai. 5d, Sheik Zaid bin Sultan al Nahayan, Abu Dhabi.

1975, Dec. 2   Litho.   Perf. 14

51	A13	10f multicolored	.50	.20
52	A14	35f multicolored	1.50	.45
53	A14	60f multicolored	2.00	.60
54	A14	80f multicolored	3.00	1.00
55	A14	90f multicolored	3.25	1.50
56	A14	1d multicolored	3.25	1.50
57	A14	140f multicolored	5.00	2.75
58	A14	5d multicolored	19.00	10.00
		Nos. 51-58 (8)	37.50	18.00

Fourth National Day.

Students and Lamp of Learning — A15

Arab Literacy Day: 15f, Lamp of learning.

1976, Feb. 8   Litho.   Perf. 14

59	A15	15f orange & multi	.60	.20
60	A15	50f ultra & multi	1.00	.60
61	A15	3d multicolored	5.75	3.25
		Nos. 59-61 (3)	7.35	4.05

Children Crossing Street

A16

Traffic Week: 15f, Traffic lights and signals, vert. 80f, Road and traffic lights.

Perf. 14½x14, 14x14½

1976, Apr. 1   Litho.

62	A16	15f brt blue & multi	.60	.60
63	A16	80f blue & multi	2.75	2.75
64	A16	140f ocher & multi	5.00	5.00
		Nos. 62-64 (3)	8.35	8.35

Waves and Ear Phones, ITU Emblem, Coat of Arms — A17

1976, May 17   Litho.   Perf. 14

65	A17	50f gray grn & multi	.85	.45
66	A17	80f pink & multi	1.65	.65
67	A17	2d tan & multi	3.50	1.65
		Nos. 65-67 (3)	6.00	2.75

International Telecommunications Day.

No. 18 Surcharged

━━   ━━

50   **o·**

1976   Litho.   Perf. 14x15

68	A2	50f on 75f multi	22.50 7.50

Coat of Arms — A18

1976, Aug. 15   Litho.   Perf. 11½

69	A18	5f dull rose	.20	.25
70	A18	10f golden brown	.20	.20
71	A18	15f orange	.35	.25
72	A18	35f dull red brn	.60	.20
73	A18	50f bright lilac	.75	.20
74	A18	60f bister	.85	.20
75	A18	80f yellow green	1.10	.30
76	A18	90f ultra	1.25	.50
77	A18	1d blue	1.75	.50
78	A18	140f olive green	2.25	1.10
79	A18	150f rose violet	2.25	1.25
80	A18	2d slate	3.00	1.75
81	A18	5d blue green	7.75	4.25
82	A18	10d lilac rose	15.00	8.75
		Nos. 69-82 (14)	37.30	19.70

See Nos. 91-104.

Sheik Zaid — A19

1976, Dec. 12   Litho.   Perf. 13

83	A19	15f rose & multi	1.50	.25
84	A19	140f blue & multi	3.75	2.50

5th National Day.

Symbolic Falcon and Globe — A20

1976, Dec. 15   Perf. 14x13½

85	A20	80f yellow & multi	1.90	.80
86	A20	2d red & multi	4.00	2.25

International Falconry Congress, Abu Dhabi, Dec. 1976.

A21

1976, Dec. 30   Litho.   Perf. 13

87	A21	50f multicolored	2.75	1.00
88	A21	80f multicolored	3.00	1.60

Mohammed Ali Jinnah (1876-1948), 1st Governor General of Pakistan.

A22

1977, Apr. 12   Litho.   Perf. 13½x14

APU emblem, members' flags.

89	A22	50f multicolored	2.00	1.10
90	A22	80f multicolored	3.00	1.50

Arab Postal Union, 25th anniversary.

Arms Type of 1976

1977, July 25   Litho.   Perf. 11½

91	A18	5f dull rose & blk	.20	.20
92	A18	10f gldn brn & blk	.20	.20
93	A18	15f dull org & blk	.25	.25
94	A18	35f lt brown & blk	.45	.20
95	A18	50f brt lilac & blk	.65	.25
96	A18	60f bister & blk	1.00	.50
97	A18	80f yel grn & blk	1.00	.30
98	A18	90f ultra & blk	1.25	.20
99	A18	1d blue & blk	1.75	.40
100	A18	140f ol grn & blk	2.25	1.00
101	A18	150f rose vio & blk	2.75	1.10
102	A18	2d slate & blk	3.25	1.50
103	A18	5d bl grn & blk	7.50	3.75
104	A18	10d lil rose & bl	14.00	7.25
		Nos. 91-104 (14)	36.50	17.10

Man Reading Book, UAE Arms, UN Emblem A23

1977, Sept. 8   Litho.   Perf. 14x13½

105	A23	50f green, brn & gold	2.00	.50
106	A23	3d blue & multi	8.00	3.50

International Literacy Day.

A set of three stamps for the 6th Natl. Day was withdrawn from sale on the day of issue, Dec. 2, 1977.

Post Horn and Sails — A24

1979, Apr. 14   Photo.   Perf. 12x11½

107	A24	50f multicolored	.50	.30
108	A24	5d multicolored	4.75	3.00

Gulf Postal Organization, 2nd Conf., Dubai.

Arab Achievements — A25

1980, Mar. 22   Litho.   Perf. 14x14½

109	A25	50f multicolored	.50	.35
110	A25	140f multicolored	1.25	1.00
111	A25	3d multicolored	2.75	2.25
		Nos. 109-111 (3)	4.50	3.60

9th National Day — A26

1980, Dec. 2   Litho.   Perf. 13½

112	A26	15f multicolored	.55	.20
113	A26	50f multicolored	1.40	.55
114	A26	80f multicolored	1.90	.90
115	A26	150f multicolored	2.75	1.75
		Nos. 112-115 (4)	6.60	3.40

Souvenir Sheet

Perf. 13½x14

116	A26	3d multicolored	7.50	5.00

Family on Graph — A27

Hegira
(Pilgrimage
Year) — A28

1980, Dec. 15
117	A27	15f shown	.50	.25
118	A27	80f Symbols	1.75	1.00
119	A27	90f like #118	2.25	1.25
120	A27	2d like #117	4.50	2.50
		Nos. 117-120 (4)	9.00	5.00

1980 population census.

1980, Dec. 18   Perf. 14x13½
121	A28	15f multicolored	.25	.20
122	A28	80f multicolored	1.00	.50
123	A28	90f multicolored	1.25	.75
124	A28	140f multicolored	2.00	1.10
		Nos. 121-124 (4)	4.50	2.55

Souvenir Sheet
125	A28	2d multicolored	6.50	3.50

No. 125 contains one 36x57mm stamp.

OPEC Emblem — A29

1980, Dec. 21   Perf. 14
126	A29	50f Men holding OPEC emblem, vert.	.65	.50
127	A29	80f like #126	1.00	.85
128	A29	90f shown	1.10	.90
129	A29	140f like #128	1.75	1.40
		Nos. 126-129 (4)	4.50	3.65

Souvenir Sheet
130	A29	3d like #128	9.00	4.50

Traffic Week — A30

15f, 80f, Crossing guard, students, traffic light. 50f, 5d, Crossing guard, traffic light and signs.

1981, Mar. 26   Litho.   Perf. 14½
131	A30	15f multicolored	.35	.25
132	A30	50f multicolored	.65	.50
133	A30	80f multicolored	1.25	.75
134	A30	5d multicolored	5.25	4.50
		Nos. 131-134 (4)	7.50	6.00

Size of Nos. 131 and 133: 25½x35mm.

10th Natl.
Day — A31

1981, Dec. 2   Litho.   Perf. 15x14
135	A31	25f Cogwheel	.35	.20
136	A31	150f Soldiers	2.50	1.10
137	A31	2d UN emblem	3.00	1.50
		Nos. 135-137 (3)	5.85	2.80

Intl. Year of the
Disabled — A32

Perf. 14½x14, 14x14½

1981, Dec. 26   Litho.
138	A32	25f Couple	.45	.30
139	A32	45f Man in wheelchair, vert.	.80	.55
140	A32	150f like #139	2.75	2.00
141	A32	2d like #138	4.00	3.00
		Nos. 138-141 (4)	8.00	5.85

Natl. Arms — A33

1982-86
142	A33	5f multicolored	.20	.20
143	A33	10f multicolored	.20	.20
144	A33	15f multicolored	.20	.20
145	A33	25f multicolored	.20	.20
145A	A33	35f multicolored	.20	.20
146	A33	50f multicolored	.35	.35
147	A33	75f multicolored	.55	.55
148	A33	100f multicolored	.75	.75
149	A33	110f multicolored	.85	.85
150	A33	125f multicolored	.95	.95
151	A33	150f multicolored	1.10	1.00
151A	A33	175f multicolored	1.25	.75

Size: 23x27mm
Perf. 13
152	A33	2d multicolored	1.25	1.00
152A	A33	250f multicolored	1.40	.75
153	A33	3d multicolored	2.00	1.50
154	A33	5d multicolored	3.25	2.25
155	A33	10d multicolored	6.75	4.00
156	A33	20d multicolored	13.50	10.00
157	A33	50d multicolored	27.00	15.00
		Nos. 142-157 (19)	61.95	40.70

Issued: 35f, 175f, 250f, 12/15/84; 50d, 2/6/86; others, 3/7/82.

6th Arab Gulf Soccer
Championships — A34

1982, Apr. 4   Litho.   Perf. 14
167	A34	25f Emblem, flags	.50	.30
168	A34	75f Eagle, soccer ball, stadium, vert.	1.50	.95
169	A34	125f Players, vert.	2.00	1.60
170	A34	3d like 75f, vert.	4.50	3.75
		Nos. 167-170 (4)	8.50	6.60

2nd
Disarmament
Meeting
A35

1982, Oct. 24   Litho.   Perf. 13x13½
171	A35	25f multicolored	.35	.25
172	A35	75f multicolored	1.00	.80
173	A35	125f multicolored	1.75	1.40
174	A35	150f multicolored	1.90	1.65
		Nos. 171-174 (4)	5.00	4.10

11th Natl.
Day — A36

Designs: 25f, 150f, Skyscraper, communications tower, natl. crest, castle turret, open book, flag. 75f, 125f, Sun, bird, vert.

1982, Dec. 2   Litho.   Perf. 14½
175	A36	25f multicolored	.40	.25
176	A36	75f multicolored	1.25	.75
177	A36	125f multicolored	2.00	1.25
178	A36	150f multicolored	2.25	1.75
		Nos. 175-178 (4)	5.90	4.00

A37

1983, Dec. 20   Litho.   Perf. 14x14½
179	A37	25f multicolored	.25	.20
180	A37	150f multicolored	1.75	1.40
181	A37	2d multicolored	2.25	1.75
182	A37	3d multicolored	3.25	2.75
		Nos. 179-182 (4)	7.50	6.10

World Communications Year.

A38

1983, Jan. 8   Litho.   Perf. 14½

Arab Literacy Day: 25f, 75f, Oil lamp, open Koran. 35f, 3d, Scribe.
183	A38	25f multicolored	13.00	25.00
184	A38	35f multicolored	.30	.30
185	A38	75f multicolored	14.00	25.00
186	A38	3d multicolored	2.25	2.25

Nos. 183 and 185 withdrawn from sale on day of issue because of an error in Koranic inscription.

INTELSAT, 20th Anniv. — A39

1984, Nov. 24   Litho.   Perf. 14½
187	A39	2d multicolored	3.00	2.50
188	A39	2.50d multicolored	4.00	3.50

13th Natl.
Day
A40

Flag, portrait of an Emir and building or view from each capital.

1984, Dec. 2   Perf. 14½x13½
189	A40	1d Building, pavilion	1.25	1.00
190	A40	1d Fortress, cannon	1.25	1.00
191	A40	1d Port, boats	1.25	1.00
192	A40	1d Fortress	1.25	1.00
193	A40	1d Oil refinery	1.25	1.00
194	A40	1d Building, garden	1.25	1.00
195	A40	1d Oil well, palace	1.25	1.00
		Nos. 189-195 (7)	8.75	7.00

Tidy Week — A41

A42

1985, Mar. 15   Perf. 12½
196	A41	5d multicolored	6.00	4.50

1985, Sept. 10   Perf. 13½x14½
197	A42	2d multicolored	2.50	1.75
198	A42	250f multicolored	3.50	2.00

World Junior Chess Championships Sharjah, Sept. 10-27.

14th Natl.
Day — A43

1985, Dec. 2   Perf. 14x13½
199	A43	50f multicolored	.65	.30
200	A43	3d multicolored	4.00	1.75

Population
Census — A44

1985, Dec. 16
201	A44	50f multicolored	.50	.30
202	A44	1d multicolored	1.25	.60
203	A44	3d multicolored	3.25	1.75
		Nos. 201-203 (3)	5.00	2.65

Intl.
Youth
Year
A45

1985, Dec. 23   Perf. 14½
204	A45	50f Silhouettes, sapling, vert.	.65	.35
205	A45	175f Globe, open book	1.90	1.10
206	A45	2d Youth carrying world, vert.	2.25	1.50
		Nos. 204-206 (3)	4.80	2.95

Women and
Family
Day — A46

1986, Mar. 21   *Perf. 13½*
207 A46 1d multicolored   1.00   .75
208 A46 3d multicolored   3.00 2.25

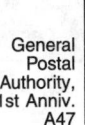

General
Postal
Authority,
1st Anniv.
A47

Designs: 50f, 250f, Posthorn, map, natl.
flag, globe. 1d, 2d, Emblem, globe, vert.

1986, Apr. 1
209 A47 50f multicolored   .40   .35
210 A47 1d multicolored   .90   .75
211 A47 2d multicolored   1.75 1.50
212 A47 250f multicolored   2.00 1.75
       Nos. 209-212 (4)   5.05 4.35

United
Arab
Shipping
Co., 10th
Anniv.
A48

1986, Aug. 20   *Perf. 13x13½*
213 A48 2d shown   2.50 1.50
214 A48 3d Ship's bow, vert.   3.00 2.25

A49

A51

Hawk — A50

1986, Sept. 1   *Perf. 13½x13*
215 A49 250f multicolored   2.50 1.65
216 A49 3d multicolored   3.00 1.90

Emirates Telecommunications Corp., Ltd.,
10th anniv.

1986, Sept. 9   Photo.   *Perf. 15x14*
Booklet Stamps
Background Color
217 A50 50f pale green   .60   .60
218 A50 75f pink   .90   .90
219 A50 125f gray   1.50 1.50
  a.   Bklt. pane, 75f, 125f, 2 50f   4.50
       Nos. 217-219 (3)   3.00 3.00

1986, Oct. 25   *Perf. 13½*
220 A51 50f Jet, camel   .75   .50
221 A51 175f Jet   2.50 2.25

Emirates Airlines, 1st anniv.

State
Crests,
GCC
Emblem
A52

1986, Nov. 2   *Perf. 13*
222 A52 50f shown   .55   .40
222A A52 175f like no. 223   1.90 1.60
223 A52   3d Tree, emblem   3.25 3.00
        Nos. 222-223 (3)   5.70 5.00

Gulf Cooperation Council supreme council
7th session, Abu Dhabi, Nov. 1986. No. 222A
incorrectly inscribed "1.75f."

15th Natl.
Day — A53

1986, Dec. 2   Litho.   *Perf. 13½*
224 A53 50f shown   .50   .20
225 A53   1d like 50f   1.00   .50
226 A53 175f Flag, emblem   1.75 1.40
227 A53   2d like 175f   2.00 1.90
       Nos. 224-227 (4)   5.25 4.00

27th Chess Olympiad, Dubai — A54

1986, Nov. 14   *Perf. 12½*
228 A54 50f Skyscraper, vert.   .65   .65
229 A54   2d shown   2.50 2.50
230 A54 250f Tapestry, diff.   3.25 3.25
  a.   Souv. sheet, #228-230, perf 13 8.50 8.50
       Nos. 228-230 (3)   6.40 6.40

No. 230a exists imperf. Value, $10.

Arab Police
Day — A55

1986, Dec. 18   *Perf. 13½*
231 A55 50f multicolored   .70   .50
232 A55   1d multicolored   1.25 1.00

A56

A57

1987, Mar. 15
233 A56 50f multicolored   .70   .50
234 A56   1d multicolored   1.25 1.10

Municipalities and Environment Week.

1987, Apr. 10
235 A57 200f multicolored   2.50 2.50
236 A57 250f multicolored   3.00 3.00

UAE Flight Information Region, 1st anniv.

A58

A59

1987, May 25
237 A58 50f Water   .50   .50
238 A58   2d Solar energy, oil
            well   5.00 5.00
        Conservation.

1987, June 23
239 A59 1d multicolored   1.00 1.00
240 A59 3d multicolored   2.50 2.50

United Arab Emirates University, 10th anniv.

1st Shipment of Crude Oil from Abu
Dhabi, 25th Anniv. — A60

1987, July 4   *Perf. 13*
241 A60 50f Oil rig   .65   .65
242 A60   1d Drilling well, vert.   1.10 1.10
243 A60 175f Crew, drill   2.00 2.00
244 A60   2d Oil tanker   2.25 2.25
        Nos. 241-244 (4)   6.00 6.00

Arab Palm Tree
and Date
Day — A61

1987, Sept. 15   Litho.   *Perf. 14x15*
245 A61 50f shown   .65   .65
246 A61   1d Tree, fruit, diff.   1.25 1.25

A62

A63

1987, Nov. 21   Litho.   *Perf. 13x13½*
247 A62 2d multicolored   1.75 1.75
248 A62 250f multicolored   2.25 2.25

Intl. Year of Shelter for the Homeless.

1987, Dec. 15   *Perf. 13½*
249 A63 1d multicolored   1.10 1.10
250 A63 2d multicolored   2.40 2.40

Salim Bin Ali Al-Owais (b. 1887), poet.

UN Child
Survival
Campaign
A64

Abu Dhabi Intl.
Airport, 6th Anniv.
A65

1987, Oct. 25   Litho.   *Perf. 13*
251 A64 50f Growth monitoring   .40   .40
252 A64   1d Immunization   .85   .85
253 A64 175f Oral rehydration
            therapy   1.60 1.60
254 A64   2d Breast feeding,
            horiz.   1.75 1.75
        Nos. 251-254 (4)   4.60 4.60

1988, Jan. 2
255 A65 50f Control tower   .50   .50
256 A65 50f Terminal interior   .50   .50
257 A65 100f Aircraft over airport 1.00 1.00
258 A65 100f Aircraft at gates   1.00 1.00
        Nos. 255-258 (4)   3.00 3.00

Natl. Arts
Festival
A66

1988, Mar. 21   Litho.   *Perf. 13½*
259 A66 50f multicolored   .60   .60
260 A66 250f multicolored   2.40 2.40

Youth
Cultural
Festival
A67

Winning children's drawings of a design
contest sponsored by the Ministry of Education and the Sharjah Cultural and Information
Department.

Perf. 13x13½, 13½x13
1988, May 25   **Litho.**

261	A67	50f Net fisherman	.55	.40
262	A67	1d Woman	.90	.70
263	A67	1.75d Youth as flower	1.60	1.25
264	A67	2d Recreation	1.75	1.40
		Nos. 261-264 (4)	4.80	3.75

Palestinian
Uprising — A68

1988, June 28   **Litho.**   **Perf. 13½**

265	A68	2d multicolored	2.25	2.25
266	A68	250f multicolored	2.75	2.75

A69

Banks — A70

1988, July 16   **Litho.**   **Perf. 13½**

267	A69	50f multicolored	.90	.90
268	A70	50f multicolored	.90	.90

Abu Dhabi Natl. Bank, Ltd., 20th anniv. (No. 267); Natl. Bank of Dubai, Ltd., 25th anniv. (No. 268).

Port Rashid,
Dubai, 16th
Anniv. — A71

1988, Aug. 31   **Litho.**   **Perf. 13½**

269	A71	50f Ground transportation	.40	.40
270	A71	1d Piers	.75	.75
271	A71	175f Ship at dock	1.40	1.40
272	A71	2d Ship, unloading cranes	1.75	1.75
		Nos. 269-272 (4)	4.30	4.30

1988 Summer Olympics, Seoul — A72

1988, Sept. 17   **Perf. 15x14½**

273		2d Swimming	1.60	1.60
274		250f Cycling	2.00	2.00
	a.	A72 Pair, #273-274	3.60	3.60

Ras Al Khaima Natl. Museum, 1st
Anniv. — A74

1988, Nov. 19   **Litho.**   **Perf. 14**

275	A74	50f Vase, vert.	.35	.35
276	A74	3d Gold crown	2.10	2.10

18th Arab Scout Conference, Nov. 29-
Dec. 3, Abu Dhabi — A75

1988, Nov. 29   **Perf. 12½**

277	A75	1d multicolored	.80	.80

10th Arbor
Day — A76

Perf. 13½x13, 13x13½
1989, Mar. 6   **Litho.**

278	A76	50f Ghaf, vert.	.40	.40
279	A76	100f Palm	.70	.70
280	A76	250f Dahlia blossom	1.90	1.90
		Nos. 278-280 (3)	3.00	3.00

Sharjah
Intl. Airport,
10th Anniv.
A77

1989, Apr. 21   **Litho.**   **Perf. 13½**

281	A77	50f multicolored	.40	.40
282	A77	100f multicolored	.80	.80

Postal
Service,
80th Anniv.
A78

1989, Aug. 19   **Litho.**   **Perf. 13x13½**

283	A78	50f Seaplane	.40	.40
284	A78	3d Ship	2.75	2.75

Al-Ittihad
Newspaper, 20th
Anniv. — A79

1989, Oct. 20   **Litho.**   **Perf. 13½**

285	A79	50f shown	.40	.40
286	A79	1d Al Ittihad Press	.80	.80

Gulf Investment Corporation, 5th
Anniv. — A80

1989, Nov. 25

287	A80	50f multicolored	.35	.35
288	A80	2d multicolored	1.40	1.40

Child on
Crutches,
Hands — A81

Bank
Building — A82

Designs: 2d, Crouched youth, cracked earth, bread in hand, horiz.

1989, Dec. 5   **Perf. 15x14, 14x15**

289	A81	2d multicolored	1.40	1.40
290	A81	250f shown	1.60	1.60

Intl. Volunteer's Day, Red Crescent Soc.

1989, Dec. 20   **Perf. 13½**

291	A82	50f Emblem, architecture	.60	.60
292	A82	1d shown	1.10	1.10

Commercial Bank of Dubai, Ltd., 20th Anniv.

Astrolabe,
Manuscript
Page and
Ship of Bin
Majid, 15th
Cent.
Navigator
and Writer
A83

1989, Dec. 25   **Perf. 13x13½, 13½x13**

293	A83	1d shown	.75	.75
294	A83	3d Ship, page, vert.	2.25	2.25

Heritage revival.

A84

Falcon — A85

1990, Jan. 17   **Perf. 13½**

295	A84	50f multicolored	.60	.60
296	A84	1d multicolored	1.10	1.10

3rd Al Ain festival.

1990, Feb. 17   **Litho.**   **Perf. 11½**
Granite Paper

297	A85	5f multicolored	.20	.20
298	A85	20f multicolored	.20	.20
299	A85	25f multicolored	.20	.20
301	A85	50f multicolored	.30	.25
302	A85	100f multicolored	.60	.40
303	A85	150f multicolored	1.00	.60
304	A85	175f multicolored	1.10	.75

Size: 21x26mm
Perf. 11½x12

306	A85	2d multicolored	1.25	1.00
307	A85	250f multicolored	1.50	1.10
309	A85	3d multicolored	1.75	1.00
310	A85	5d multicolored	2.50	2.00
311	A85	10d multicolored	5.50	4.00
312	A85	20d multicolored	10.00	7.50
313	A85	50d multicolored	25.00	16.00
		Nos. 297-313 (14)	51.10	35.60

A86

A87

1990, Mar. 10   **Litho.**   **Perf. 13½**

316	A86	50f multicolored	.45	.45
317	A86	250f multicolored	2.00	2.00

Children's cultural festival.

1990, Aug. 5   **Litho.**   **Perf. 14x15**

318	A87	175f shown	1.40	1.40
319	A87	2d Starving child	1.60	1.60

Red Crescent Society.

Dubai
Chamber
of
Commerce
and
Industry,
25th Anniv.
A88

1990, July 1   **Perf. 13½**

320	A88	50f multicolored	.40	.40
321	A88	1d multicolored	1.00	1.00

World Cup Soccer Championships,
Italy — A89

UAE emblem, character trademark and: 1d, Leaning Tower of Pisa, desert, vert. 2d, Soccer ball, vert. 250f, Circle of flags. 3d, Map, vert.

1990, June 8   **Perf. 13½**

322	A89	50f multicolored	.40	.40
323	A89	1d multicolored	.80	.80
324	A89	2d multicolored	1.50	1.50
325	A89	250f multicolored	1.90	1.90
		Nos. 322-325 (4)	4.60	4.60

Souvenir Sheet
Perf. 12½

326	A89	3d multicolored	3.00	3.00

A90

A91

Grand
Mosque, Abu
Dhaki — A95

2d, Al Jumeirah Mosque, Dubai, vert.

Perf. 13½x13, 13x13½

1990, Nov. 26
344 A95 1d multicolored .80 .80
345 A95 2d multicolored 1.60 1.60

A96

A98

A101

A103

20th Natl. Day — A107

#374, Emir at left, fortress, cannon. #377,
Fortress on rocky outcropping. #378, Emir at
right, fortress, cannon. 3d, Sheikh Said bin
Sultan al Nahayan, Defense Forces.

1991, Dec. 2   Litho.   Perf. 13
372 A104 75f multicolored .60 .60
373 A105 75f multicolored .60 .60
374 A105 75f multicolored .60 .60
375 A106 75f multicolored .60 .60
376 A107 75f multicolored .60 .60
377 A107 75f multicolored .60 .60
378 A107 75f multicolored .60 .60

Imperf
Size: 70x90mm
378A A107 3d multicolored 4.00 4.00
Nos. 372-378A (8) 8.20 8.20

On Nos. 372-378 portions of the design
were applied by a thermographic process producing a shiny, raised effect.

A108

A109

360 A100 1d Three banded
grunt .75 .75
361 A100 1d Rabbit fish .75 .75
362 A100 1d Black bream .75 .75
363 A100 1d Greasy grouper .75 .75
a.   Min. sheet of 8, #356-363 4.75 4.75
Nos. 356-363 (8) 4.40 4.40

1990, Sept. 22   Litho.   Perf. 13½
327 A90 50f shown .35 .35
328 A90 1d Emblem, 30 years .75 .75
329 A90 175f Emblem, drop of oil 1.25 1.25
Nos. 327-329 (3) 2.35 2.35

Organization of Petroleum Exporting Coun-
ries (OPEC), 30th anniv.

1990, Aug. 25   Perf. 14x14½

Flowers.
330 A91 50f Argyrolobeum rose-
um .40 .40
331 A91 50f Lamranthus roseus .40 .40
332 A91 50f Centavrea pseudo
sinaica .40 .40
333 A91 50f Calotropis procera .40 .40
a.   Souvenir sheet of 4, #330-333 1.60 1.60
334 A91 50f Nerium oleander .40 .40
335 A91 50f Catharanthus roseus .40 .40
336 A91 50f Hibiscus rosa sinensis .40 .40
337 A91 50f Bougainvillea glabra .40 .40
a.   Souvenir sheet of 4, #334-337 1.60 1.60
Nos. 330-337 (8) 3.20 3.20

A92

A93

1990, Oct. 8   Litho.   Perf. 13
338 A92 50f Water pollution .40 .40
339 A92 3d Air pollution 2.25 2.25
Environmental pollution.

1990, Dec. 2   Perf. 13½
340 A93 50f shown .35 .35
341 A93 175f Bank building,
horiz. 1.40 1.40
Central Bank, 10th anniv.

Intl. Conference
on High Salinity
Tolerant
Plants — A94

1990, Dec. 8   Perf. 13x13½
342 A94 50f Tree .40 .40
43 A94 250f Water, trees 2.00 2.00

Children's
Paintings
A99

Designs: 50f, Celebration. 1d, Women waving flags. 175f, Women playing blind-man's
buff. 250f, Women dancing for men.

1991, July 15   Litho.   Perf. 14x13½
352 A99 50f multicolored .35 .35
353 A99 1d multicolored .75 .75
354 A99 175f multicolored 1.40 1.40
355 A99 250f multicolored 1.90 1.90
Nos. 352-355 (4) 4.40 4.40

Fish
A100

1991, Aug. 5   Litho.   Perf. 13½x14
356 A100 50f Yellow marked butterflyfish .35 .35
357 A100 50f Golden trevally .35 .35
358 A100 50f Two banded porgy .35 .35
359 A100 50f Red snapper .35 .35

Perf. 13½x13, 13x13½

1991, Jan. 16   Litho.   Perf. 13x13½
346 A96 50f multicolored .40 .40
347 A96 2d multicolored 1.75 1.75
Abu Dhabi Intl. Fair.

1991, May 17   Litho.   Perf. 14x13½
348 A97 2d multicolored 1.50 1.50
349 A97 3d multicolored 2.25 2.25
World Telecommunications Day.

A97

1991, June 18   Perf. 13½
350 A98 1d Sheikh Saqr Mosque .80 .80
351 A98 2d King Faisal Mosque 1.60 1.60

A104

A105

A106

Al-Jahli
Castle Al-
Ain
A110

1992, Apr. 20   Litho.   Perf. 13½
383 A110 2d multicolored 1.25 1.25
384 A110 250f multicolored
Expo '92, Seville.
No. 384 was withdrawn because of poor
rendition of Arabic word for "postage."

A111

A102

Intl. Aerospace Exhibition, Dubai: 175f, Jet
fighter over Dubai Intl. Airport. 2d, Fighter silhouette over airport.

1991, Nov. 3   Litho.   Perf. 13½
364 A101 175f multicolored 1.25 1.25
365 A101 2d multicolored 1.50 1.50

1991, Oct. 7   Perf. 13
Sheikh Rashid Bin Said Al Maktum (1912-
90), Ruler of Dubai and: 50f, Airport, vert.
175f, City skyline, vert. 2d, Waterfront, satellite
dish.
366 A102 50f multicolored .35 .35
367 A102 1d multicolored .75 .75
368 A102 175f multicolored 1.25 1.25
369 A102 2d multicolored 1.50 1.50
Nos. 366-369 (4) 3.85 3.85

1991, Oct. 8   Litho.   Perf. 13½
370 A103 50f multicolored .45 .45
371 A103 1d multicolored .90 .90
Civil Defense Day.

1991, Nov. 16   Perf. 13½
379 A108 50f lt green & multi .35 .35
380 A108 3d orange & multi 2.25 2.25
Gulf Cooperaton Council, 10th anniv.

1992, Jan. 15   Litho.   Perf. 13½
381 A109 175f pink & multi 1.10 1.10
382 A109 250f lt blue & multi 1.60 1.60
Abu Dhabi National Oil Co., 20th anniv.

A112

Mosques: 50f, Sheikh Rashid bin Humaid al Nuaimi, Ajman. 1d, Sheikh Ahmed Bin Rashid Al Mualla, Umm Al Quwain.

1992, Mar. 26   **Perf. 14x13½**
385 A111   50f multicolored   .35   .35
386 A111   1d multicolored   .65   .65

See Nos. 417-418.

1992, Apr. 20   **Perf. 13½x13**
387 A112   1d shown
388 A112   3d Ear with hearing aid   1.90   1.90

Week of the deaf child.

Zayed Seaport, 20th Anniv. — A113

1992, June 28   **Litho.**   **Perf. 13½**
389 A113   50f Aerial view   .35   .35
390 A113   1d Cargo transport   .65   .65
391 A113 175f Ship docked   1.10   1.10
392 A113   2d Map   1.25   1.25
      Nos. 389-392 (4)   3.35   3.35

1992 Summer
Olympics,
Barcelona
A114

1992, July 25   **Litho.**   **Perf. 14x13½**
393 A114   50f Yachting   .35   .35
394 A114   1d Running   .65   .65
395 A114 175f Swimming   1.10   1.10
396 A114 250f Cycling   1.60   1.60
      Nos. 393-396 (4)   3.70   3.70

Souvenir Sheet
396A A114   3d Equestrian   2.00   2.00

Children's
Paintings
A115

1992, Aug. 15   **Perf. 13½x14**
397 A115   50f Playing soccer   .35   .35
398 A115   1d Playing in field   .65   .65
399 A115   2d Playground   1.25   1.25
400 A115 250f Children among
           trees   1.60   1.60
      Nos. 397-400 (4)   3.85   3.85

Intl. Bank of
United Arab
Emirates, 15th
Anniv. — A116

Design: 175f, Bank emblem.

Litho. & Embossed
1992, Sept. 9   **Perf. 11**
401 A116   50f gold & multi   .30   .30

Size: 35x41mm
Perf. 11½
402 A116 175f lake, gold & vio   1.10   1.10

Traditional Musical
Instruments — A116a

1992, Oct. 17   **Litho.**   **Perf. 13½**
402A A116a 50f Tambourah,
            vert.   .35   .35
402B A116a 50f Oud, vert.   .35   .35
402C A116a 50f Rababah, vert.   .35   .35
402D A116a   1d Mizmar, shindo   .65   .65
402E A116a   1d Tabel, hibban   .65   .65
402F A116a   1d Marwas, duff   .65   .65
      Nos. 402A-402F (6)   3.00   3.00

Camels
A117

Designs: 50f, Race. 1d, Used for transportation, vert. 175f, Harnessed for obtaining water from well. 2d, Roaming free, vert.

1992, Dec. 23   **Litho.**   **Perf. 13½**
403 A117   50f multicolored   .30   .30
404 A117   1d multicolored   .65   .65
405 A117 175f multicolored   1.10   1.10
406 A117   2d multicolored   1.25   1.25
      Nos. 403-406 (4)   3.30   3.30

A118

A119

1992, Dec. 21
407 A118   50f multicolored   .30   .30
408 A118   2d yellow & multi   1.25   1.25

Gulf Cooperation Council, 13th session.

1993, Jan. 28   **Litho.**   **Perf. 13½**
409 A119   2d shown   1.25   1.25
410 A119 250f Building, fishing
            boat   1.60   1.60

Dubai Creek Golf and Yacht Club.

A120

A121

1993, Jan. 16
411 A120   50f Golf, horiz.   .30   .30
412 A120   1d Fishing   .65   .65
413 A120   2d Boating, horiz.   1.25   1.25
414 A120 250f Motor vehicle
            touring, horiz.   1.60   1.60
      Nos. 411-414 (4)   3.80   3.80

Tourism.

1993, Mar. 27   **Litho.**   **Perf. 14x13½**
415 A121   50f violet & multi   .30   .30
416 A121   3d red brown & multi   1.90   1.90

Natl. Youth Festival.

Mosque Type of 1992
1993, Feb. 16   **Perf. 13½**
50f, Thabit bin Khalid Mosque, Fujeira. 1d, Sharq al Morabbah Mosque, Al Ain.

417 A111   50f multicolored   .35   .35
418 A111   1d multicolored   .65   .65

Shells
A122

1993, Apr. 3   **Litho.**   **Perf. 13**
419 A122   25f Conus textile   .20   .20
420 A122   50f Pinctada radiata   .35   .35
421 A122 100f Murex scolopax   .65   .65
422 A122 150f Natica pulicaris   .95   .95
423 A122 175f Lambis truncata
            sebae   1.40   1.40
424 A122 200f Cardita bicolor   1.60   1.60
425 A122 250f Cypraea grayana   1.90   1.90
426 A122 300f Cymatium
            trilineatum   2.50   2.50
      Nos. 419-426 (8)   9.55   9.55

Campaign
Against
Drugs
A123

Design: 1d, Skull, drugs, vert.

1993, Aug. 21   **Litho.**   **Perf. 13½**
427 A123   50f multicolored   .35   .35
428 A123   1d multicolored   .65   .65

A124

A125

Natl. Bank of Abu Dhabi, 25th Anniv.: 50f, Abu Dhabi skyline, bank emblem. 1d, Bar emblem. 175f, Bank building, emblem. 2d, Skyline, emblem, diff.

Litho. & Typo.
1993, Sept. 15   **Perf. 11**
429 A124   50f silver & multi   .30   .3
430 A124   1d silver & multi   .65   .6
431 A124 175f silver & multi   1.10   1.1
432 A124   2d silver & multi   1.25   1.2
      Nos. 429-432 (4)   3.30   3.3

1993, Nov. 10   **Litho.**   **Perf. 13**
Dubai Ports Authority: 50f, Aerial view of port. 1d, Loading cargo. 2d, Aerial view, diff. 250f, Globe.

433 A125   50f purple & multi   .30   .3
434 A125   1d green & multi   .65   .6
435 A125   2d orange & multi   1.25   1.2
436 A125 250f pink & multi   1.50   1.5
      Nos. 433-436 (4)   3.70   3.7

Natl. Day
A126

Children's paintings: 50f, Soldiers saluting flag. 1d, Two women sitting, one standing, flag, vert. 175f, Flag, boat. 2d, Flags atop castle tower.

1993, Dec. 2   **Litho.**   **Perf. 13**
437 A126   50f multicolored   .45   .4
438 A126   1d multicolored   .85   .8
439 A126 175f multicolored   1.50   1.5
440 A126   2d multicolored   1.60   1.6
      Nos. 437-440 (4)   4.40   4.4

Archaeological Discoveries — A127

Designs: 50f, Tomb. 1d, Rectangular artifact. 175f, Animal-shaped artifact. 250f, Bowl.

1993, Dec. 15   **Perf. 14x13**
441 A127   50f multicolored   .50   .5
442 A127   1d multicolored   .95   .9
443 A127 175f multicolored   1.60   1.6
444 A127 250f multicolored   2.25   2.2
      Nos. 441-444 (4)   5.30   5.3

10th
Childrens'
Festival,
Sharjah
A128

Children's paintings: 50f, Children with balloons, flags. 1d, Children playing, three trees. 175f, Child with picture, girls with balloons. 2d, House, children playing outdoors.

1994, Mar. 19   **Litho.**   **Perf. 13x13**
445 A128   50f green & multi   .40   .4
446 A128   1d blue & multi   .85   .8
447 A128 175f red violet & multi   1.40   1.4
448 A128   2d carmine & multi   1.60   1.6
      Nos. 445-448 (4)   4.25   4.2

Arabian Horses A129

50f, Brown horse on hind feet, vert. 1d, White horse. 175f, Head of brown horse, vert. 50f, Head of white and brown horse.

1994, Jan. 25   Perf. 13x13½, 13½x13
449 A129 50f multicolored   .40   .40
450 A129 1d multicolored   .75   .75
451 A129 175f multicolored   1.25 1.25
452 A129 250f multicolored   1.75 1.75
     Nos. 449-452 (4)   4.15 4.15

10th Conference of Arab Towns, Dubai A130

Perf. 13x13½, 13½x13
1994, May 15   Litho.
453 A130 50f Map, city, vert.   .45   .45
454 A130 1d shown   .85   .85

Pilgrimage to Mecca — A131

1994, Apr. 29   Litho.   Perf. 13x13½
455 A131 50f shown   .45   .45
456 A131 2d Holy Ka'aba   1.75 1.75

Intl. Year of the Family A132

Intl. Olympic Committee, Cent. A133

Arab Housing Day — A134

Writers Assoc., 10th Anniv. — A135

1994, June 15   Perf. 13x13½
457 A132 1d multicolored   .85   .85
458 A133 1d multicolored   .85   .85

Perf. 13½x13
459 A134 1d multicolored   .85   .85
460 A135 1d multicolored   .85   .85
     Nos. 457-460 (4)   3.40 3.40

Archaeological Finds, Al Qusais, Dubai — A136

Designs: 50f, Lidded pitcher, vert. 1d, Pointed-handle pitcher. 175f, Pitcher, arm-shaped handle. 250f, Short round vase.

1994, Aug. 16   Litho.   Perf. 13½
461 A136 50f multicolored   .40   .40
462 A136 1d multicolored   .75   .75
463 A136 175f multicolored   1.25 1.25
464 A136 250f multicolored   1.75 1.75
     Nos. 461-464 (4)   4.15 4.15

Environmental Protection — A137

Designs: 50f, Arabian leopard. 1d, Gordon's wildcat. 2d, Caracal. 250f, Sand cat.

1994, Oct. 10   Litho.   Perf. 13½
465 A137 50f multicolored   .40   .40
466 A137 1d multicolored   .80   .80
467 A137 2d multicolored   1.50 1.50
468 A137 250f multicolored   1.90 1.90
     Nos. 465-468 (4)   4.60 4.60

12th Arab Gulf Soccer Championships, Abu Dhabi — A138

1994, Nov. 3   Litho.   Perf. 13½
469 A138 50f Ball, emblem, vert.   .45   .45
470 A138 3d Soccer players   2.50 2.50

Birds A139

50f, Merops orientalis. 175f, Halcyon chloris. 2d, Dromas ardeola. 250f, Coracias benghalensis. 3d, Phoenicopterus ruber.

1994, Dec. 12
471 A139 50f multicolored   .40   .40
472 A139 175f multicolored   1.50 1.50
473 A139 2d multicolored   1.60 1.60
474 A139 250f multicolored   2.00 2.00
     Nos. 471-474 (4)   5.50 5.50

Souvenir Sheet
475 A139 3d multi, vert.   2.75 2.75

Archaeological Finds, Mulaiha, Sharjah — A140

Designs: 50f, Front of carved horse, vert. 175f, Ancient coin, vert. 2d, Inscription on metal, vert. 250f, Inscription on stone.

1995, Jan. 25   Litho.   Perf. 13½
476 A140 50f multicolored   .35   .35
477 A140 175f multicolored   1.25 1.25
478 A140 2d multicolored   1.40 1.40
479 A140 250f multicolored   1.60 1.60
     Nos. 476-479 (4)   4.60 4.60

Natl. Dances A141

1995, Feb. 14
480 A141 50f Al-Naashat   .35   .35
481 A141 175f Al-Ayaalah   1.10 1.10
482 A141 2d Al-Shahhoh   1.25 1.25
     Nos. 480-482 (3)   2.70 2.70

A142

A143

1995, Mar. 19   Litho.   Perf. 13½
483 A142 50f Helicopters   .35   .35
484 A142 1d Emblem   .70   .70
485 A142 175f Warships, horiz.   1.25 1.25
486 A142 2d Artillery, horiz.   1.40 1.40
     Nos. 483-486 (4)   3.70 3.70

Intl. Defense Exhibition & Conf., Abu Dhabi.

1995, Mar. 22
487 A143 1d Arab League emblem   .70   .70
488 A143 2d FAO emblem   1.40 1.40
489 A143 250f UN emblem   1.75 1.75
     Nos. 487-489 (3)   3.85 3.85

50th Anniv. of Arab League, FAO & UN.

General Post Office Authority, 10th Anniv. — A144

1995, Apr. 1
490 A144 50f multicolored   .25   .25

First Gulf Cooperation Council Philatelic Exhibition, Abu Dhabi — A145

1995, Apr. 11   Litho.   Perf. 13½
491 A145 50f multicolored   .30   .30

Traditional Games, Ajman Museum — A146

50f, Boy with hoop, stick. 175f, Girl on swing. 2d, Boy, girl playing stick game within marked boundary. 250f, Two girls playing game with stones.

1995, Aug. 28   Litho.   Perf. 13½x13
492 A146 50f multicolored   .30   .30
493 A146 175f multicolored   1.10 1.10
494 A146 2d multicolored   1.25 1.25
495 A146 250f multicolored   1.50 1.50
     Nos. 492-495 (4)   4.15 4.15

A147

A148

Birds: 50f, Falco naumanni. 175f, Phalacrocorax nigrogularis. 2d, Cursorius cursor. 250f, Upupa epops.

1995, Sept. 25
496 A147 50f multicolored   .30   .30
497 A147 175f multicolored   1.10 1.10
498 A147 2d multicolored   1.25 1.25
499 A147 250f multicolored   1.50 1.50
     Nos. 496-499 (4)   4.15 4.15

See Nos. 528-532.

1995, Nov. 20

Natl. Census: 50f, Stylized family, building. 250f, Mosque, skyscrapers, stylized family.

500 A148 50f multicolored   .30   .30
501 A148 250f multicolored   1.50 1.50

National Day A149

Children's paintings: 50f, People wearing feathered headdresses, palm trees, building. 175f, Girls with flags, balloons, flowers. 2d, Trees, family in front of house holding balloons, flags. 250f, Groups of children along street watching parade of cars.

1995, Dec. 2   Perf. 13x13½
502 A149 50f multicolored   .30   .30
503 A149 175f multicolored   1.10 1.10
504 A149 2d multicolored   1.25 1.25
505 A149 250f multicolored   1.50 1.50
     Nos. 502-505 (4)   4.15 4.15

Environmental Protection — A150

1996, Jan. 25   **Litho.**   *Perf. 13x13½*
506 A150 50f Dugong dugon .30 .30
507 A150 2d Delphinus delphis 1.30 1.30
508 A150 3d Megaptera novae-
           angliae 2.00 2.00
   a.   Souvenir sheet, #506-508 3.75 3.75
      Nos. 506-508 (3) 3.60 3.60

A151

A152

1996, Feb. 27   *Perf. 13½*
509 A151 50f shown .30 .30
510 A151 3d Building, beach 2.00 2.00

Hobie Cat 16 World Sailing Championships.

1996, Apr. 15
   Archaeological Finds, Fujeira Museum: 50f,
Two-handled pitcher. 175f, Kettle. 250f, Brace-
let. 3d, Metal ornament, horiz.

511 A152 50f multicolored .30 .30
512 A152 175f multicolored 1.10 1.10
513 A152 250f multicolored 1.75 1.75
514 A152 3d multicolored 2.00 2.00
      Nos. 511-514 (4) 5.15 5.15

1996
Summer
Olympic
Games,
Atlanta
A153

Perf. 13½x14, 14x 13½
1996, July 19   **Litho.**
515 A153 50f Shooting .35 .35
516 A153 1d Cycling, vert. .65 .65
517 A153 250f Running, vert. 1.75 1.75
518 A153 350f Swimming 2.25 2.25
      Nos. 515-518 (4) 5.00 5.00

Women's
Union, 21st
Anniv.
A154

Perf. 14x13½, 13½x14
1996, Aug. 15
519 A154 50f Emblem, vert. .30 .30
520 A154 3d shown 2.00 2.00

A155

A156

1996, Sept. 15   *Perf. 14x13½*
521 A155 1d shown .65 .65
522 A155 250f Soccer player 1.75 1.75

   11th Asian Soccer Cup Championship.

1996, Oct. 15   *Perf. 13½*
   UN Campaign Against Illegal Use of Drugs:
50f, World with snake around it. 3d, Half of
man's face, half of skull, hypodermic needle,
pills.

523 A156 50f multicolored .30 .30
524 A156 3d multicolored 2.00 2.00

Sheikh Saeed Al-Maktoum House,
Cent. — A157

   Designs: 250f Sheikh Saeed, close-up view
of house. 350f, Overall view of house.

1996, Nov. 12   **Litho.**   *Perf. 13x13½*
525 A157 50f multicolored
526 A157 250f multicolored
527 A157 350f multicolored

Bird Type of 1995

   Designs: 50f, Pterocles exustus. 150f, Otus
brucei. 250f, Hypocolus ampelinus. 3d, Irania
gutturalis. 350f, Falco concolor.

1996, Nov. 18   *Perf. 14x13½*
528 A147 50f multicolored
529 A147 150f multicolored
530 A147 250f multicolored
531 A147 3d multicolored
532 A147 350f multicolored

Children's
Paintings
A158

   50f, Face. 1d, Boats. 250f, Flowers. 350f,
Woman in long dress, palm tree, tent.

Perf. 14x13½, 13½x14
1996, Nov. 19
533 A158 50f multi, vert.
534 A158 1d multi
535 A158 250f multi, vert.
536 A158 350f multi, vert.

Sheik Zaid
bin Sultan
al
Nahayan,
Accession
to the
Throne of
Abu
Dhabi,
30th
Anniv.
A158a

A159

   Sheik and: 50f, 250f, Flowers. 1d, 350f,
Date palm.

1996, Dec. 2   **Photo.**   *Perf. 12*
537 A158a 50f red & multi .30 .30
538 A158a 1d olive & multi .60 .60
539 A158a 250f purple & multi 1.50 1.50
540 A158a 350f gray & multi 2.00 2.00
      Nos. 537-540 (4) 4.40 4.40

Photo. & Embossed
Imperf
Size: 90x70mm
541 A159 5d On horseback,
           gazelles 1.60 1.60

Anniversaries   Natl. Day, 25th
A160   Anniv.
                 A161

Photo. & Embossed
1996, Dec. 2   *Perf. 12*
542 A160 50f red violet & multi .30 .30
543 A160 1d silver & multi

   Sheik Zaid bin Sultan al Nahayan's accession to the throne of Abu Dhabi, 30th anniv.,
Creation of United Arab Emirates, 25th anniv.

1996, Dec. 2
   50f, 150f, Seven rulers of United Arab Emirates. 1d, 3d, Heraldic eagle, national flag. 5d,
Score of Natl. Anthem.

Granite Paper
544 A161 50f green & multi
545 A161 150f tan & multi
546 A161 1d multicolored
547 A161 3d multicolored

Photo. & Embossed
Imperf
Size: 70x90mm
547A A161 5d multicolored 1.60 1.60

Butterflies
A162

1997, Jan. 28   **Litho.**   *Perf. 14x13½*
548 A162 50f Agrodiaetus
            loewii .30 .30
549 A162 1d Papilio machaon
550 A162 150f Orithya .80 .80
551 A162 250f Chrysippus 1.40 1.40

Dubai
Shopping
Festival
A163

Perf. 13¼x13¾, 13¾x13¼
1997, Feb. 22   **Litho**
552 A163 50f shown
553 A163 250f Shopping bag,
            vert.

Intl. Defense
Exhibition &
Conference
A164

   50f, Helicopter airlifting jeep. 1d, Emblem.
250f, Artillery, emblem. 350f, Ships, emblem.

1997, Mar. 16   **Litho.**   *Perf. 13*
554 A164 50f multicolored .30 .3
555 A164 1d multicolored
556 A164 250f multicolored
557 A164 350f multicolored

Emirates Bank
Group, 20th
Anniv. — A165

Perf. 13¾x13¼
1997, Mar. 23   **Litho**
568 A165 50f multi
569 A165 1d buff & multi
   a.   Souv. sheet, #568-569, imperf.

   No. 569a sold for 5d.

Technical
Education and
National
Development
Conference
A166

1997, Apr. 6   *Perf. 13¾x13*
570 A166 50f shown
571 A166 250f Emblem

Sharjah
Heritage
A167

   Designs: 50f, Coins. 3d, Museum.

1997, June 17   **Litho.**   *Perf. 13*
572 A167 50f multicolored .30 .3
573 A167 3d multicolored 1.75 1.7

Emirates Philatelic
Association
A168

Perf. 13¾x13¼, 13¼x13¾
1997, June 24   **Litho**
574 A168 50f shown
575 A168 250f Stamps, horiz.

Children's
Paintings
A169

50f, Cats. 1d, Children playing. 250f, Children, moon, vert. 3d, Abstract.

1997, Sept. 15   Litho.   Perf. 13½
576 A169 50f multicolored
577 A169 1d multicolored
578 A169 150f multicolored
579 A169 3d multicolored

Reunion, by
Sheikha Hassan
Maktoum al
Maktoum — A170

Mindscape, by Sarah Majid al
Futtaim — A170a

Blue Musings, by Maha Abdulla Al
Mazroui — A170b

The
Pause,
by
Khulood
Mattar
Rashid
A170c

The Seas I, by
Sheikha Sawsan
Abdulaziz Al
Qasimi — A170d

Still Life, by
Sheikha Bodour
Sultan Al
Qasimi — A170e

The Opening, by Tina Ahmed and
Others — A170f

Illustration A170f reduced.

1997, Oct. 25   Litho.   Perf. 13¾
580 A170   50f multi
581 A170a 50f multi
582 A170b 50f multi

583 A170c 50f multi
584 A170d 50f multi
585 A170e 50f multi

Imperf
586 A170f 5d multi

Intl.
Aerospace
Exhibition,
Dubai
A171

Perf. 13½x13¾
1997, Nov. 16   Litho.
587 A171 250f Jet fighter
588 A171   3d VTOL airplane

26th
National
Day
A172

Sheikh Zaid bin Sultan al Nahayan and: 50f, Gardens. 1d, Trees and mountains. 150f, Water, trees and mountains. 250f, Roadway.

1997, Dec. 2   Litho.   Perf. 13½x13¾
589 A172   50f multi
590 A172   1d multi
591 A172 150f multi
592 A172 250f multi

3rd Afro-
Arab Trade
Fair — A173

Perf. 13x13¼, 13¼x13
1997, Dec. 6   Litho.
593 A173 150f Emblem, vert.
594 A173 350f Handshake

Arthropods
A174

50f, Blepharopsis mendica. 150f, Galeodes sp. 250f, Crocothemis arythraea. 350f, Xylocopa aestuans.

1998, Feb. 25   Litho.   Perf. 13¼
595 A174   50f multicolored
596 A174 150f multicolored
597 A174 250f multicolored
598 A174 350f multicolored
              Nos. 595-598 (4)   4.50

ISAF World Sailing
Championship — A175

Various sailboats.

Perf. 13¼x13, 13x13¼
1998, Mar. 2   Litho.
599 A175   50f multi, vert.   .30   .30
600 A175   1d multi   .55   .55
601 A175 250f multi   1.40 1.40
602 A175   3d multi, vert. 1.75 1.75
              Nos. 599-602 (4)   4.00 4.00

A176

A177

Triple Intl. Defense Exhibition & Conf., Abu Dhabi: 50f, Combat soldiers in protective gear, horiz. 1d, Emblem over world map, skyline of Abu Dhabi. 150f, Electronic gear. 350f, Missile battery, electronic warfare components.

1998, Mar. 15   Litho.   Perf. 13½
603 A176   50f multicolored   .30   .30
604 A176   1d multicolored   .55   .55
605 A176 150f multicolored   .80   .80
606 A176 350f multicolored   2.00 2.00
              Nos. 603-606 (4)   3.65 3.65

1998, Apr. 20   Litho.   Perf. 13½
607 A177   50f shown   .30   .30
608 A177   3d Emblem, monu-
                 ment   1.75 1.75

Sharjah, 1998 Arab cultural capital.

World
Environment
Day — A178

1998, May 17   Litho.   Perf. 13½
609 A178   1d Landscape, oryx 1.40 1.40
610 A178 350f multicolored   1.90 1.90

Henna
A179

Various designs painted on hands.

1998, Sept. 9   Litho.   Perf. 13½
611 A179   50f multicolored   .70   .70
612 A179   1d multicolored   1.40 1.40
613 A179 150f multicolored   2.10 2.10
614 A179   2d multicolored   2.75 2.75
615 A179 250f multicolored   3.50 3.50
616 A179   3d multicolored   4.25 4.25
              Nos. 611-616 (6) 14.70 14.70

Art — A180

1998, Oct. 20   Litho.   Perf. 13½
617 A180   50f Fish
618 A180   1d shown
619 A180 250f Mosque, palm
                 trees, vert.
620 A180 350f Door, jar
              Nos. 617-620 (4)   4.20

27th
National
Day
A181

1998, Dec. 2   Litho.   Perf. 13x13¼
621 A181   50f Mountain road
622 A181 350f Boat, city skyline
              Nos. 621-622 (2)   2.25

Flowers — A182

Designs: 25f, Indigofera arabica. 50f, Centaureum pulchellum. 75f, Lavandula citriodora. 1d, Taverniera glabra. 150f, Convolvulus deserti. 2d, Capparis spinosa. 250f, Rumex vesicrius. 3d, Anagallis arvensis. 350f, Tribulus arabicus. 5d, Reichardia tinitana.

1998, Dec. 8   Litho.   Perf. 13¼x13¾
623 A182   25f multicolored   .20   .20
624 A182   50f multicolored   .30   .30
625 A182   75f multicolored   .40   .40
626 A182   1d multicolored   .55   .55
627 A182 150f multicolored   .85   .85
628 A182   2d multicolored   1.10 1.10
629 A182 250f multicolored   1.40 1.40
630 A182   3d multicolored   1.75 1.75
631 A182 350f multicolored   1.90 1.90
632 A182   5d multicolored   2.75 2.75
              Nos. 623-632 (10) 11.20 11.20

Arthropods
A183

50f, Anthia duodecimguttata. 150f, Daphnis nerii. 250f, Acorypha glaucopsis. 350f, Androctonus crassicauda.

1999, Mar. 15   Litho.   Perf. 13½x14
633 A183   50f multicolored
634 A183 150f multicolored
635 A183 250f multicolored
636 A183 350f multicolored

Intl. Day for
Monuments
and Sites
A184

1999, Apr. 18   Litho.   Perf. 13x13½
637 A184 150f shown   .85   .85
638 A184 250f Fort   1.40 1.40

UPU, 125th
Anniv. — A185

1999   Litho.   Perf. 13½x13
639 A185   50f shown   .30   .30
640 A185 350f Emblem, "125" 2.00 2.00

Imperf
Size: 90x70mm
641 A185   5d Hemispheres   2.75 2.75

Environmental Protection — A186

Marine life: 50f, Lamprometra klunzingeri. 150f, Pelagia noctiluca. 250f, Hexabranchus sanguineus. 3d, Siphonochalina siphonella.

1999, Nov. 3   Litho.   Perf. 13½x14
642 A186 50f multi   .30   .30
643 A186 150f multi   .85   .85
644 A186 250f multi   1.40   1.40
645 A186 3d multi   1.60   1.60
          Nos. 642-645 (4)   4.15   4.15

Handicrafts A187

Designs: 50f, Lacemaking. 1d, Embroidery. 250f, Woman with wickerwork. 350f, Finished wickerwork.

1999, Nov. 8   Perf. 14x13½
646 A187 50f multi   .30   .30
647 A187 1d multi   .55   .55
648 A187 250f multi   1.40   1.40
649 A187 350f multi   1.90   1.90
          Nos. 646-649 (4)   4.15   4.15

14th Pro World Ten-pin Bowling Championships A188

Designs: 50f, Emblem. 250f, Bowler, pins, Abu Dhabi skyline.

1999, Nov. 16   Litho.   Perf. 14x13½
650-651 A188 Set of 2   1.60   1.60

Children's Art — A189

Art by: 50f, Nooran Khaleefa. 1d, Khawla Al Hawal. 150f, Khawla Salem. 250f, Fatimah Ibrahim.

1999, Dec. 15   Perf. 13x13½
652-655 A189 Set of 4   3.00   3.00

Millennium A190

Falcon and "2000" in: 50f, Gray and silver. 250f, Blue and gold.

1999, Dec. 22   Perf. 13½x13
656-657 A190 Set of 2   1.60   1.60

Dubai Ports and Customs, Cent. A191

50f, Old building. 3d, Modern building.

2000, Jan. 26   Perf. 13x13½
658-659 A191 Set of 2   1.90   1.90

Intl. Desertification Conference, Dubai — A192

2000, Feb. 12   Perf. 13½x13
660 A192 250f multi   1.40   1.40

Environmental Protection — A193

Designs: 50f, Palm trees, Al Gheel. 250f, Aggah Beach.

2000, Feb. 29   Litho.   Perf. 13x13½
661 A193 50f multi   .20   .20
662 A193 250f multi   .70   .70

2000 Summer Olympics, Sydney A194

Emblem and: 50f, Swimmer. 2d, Runner. 350f, Shooter.

2000, Sept. 16   Litho.   Perf. 13x13½
663-665 A194 Set of 3   3.25   3.25

Dubai Intl. Holy Koran Award — A195

50f, Medal on ribbon of flags. 250f, Sheikh Zaid bin Sultan al Nahayan and UAE flag.

2000, Sept. 23   Perf. 13½x13
666-667 A195 Set of 2   1.60   1.60

World Meteorological Organization, 50th Anniv. — A196

Designs: 50f, Barometer and modern map. 250f, Gauge's pointer and old map .

2000
668-669 A196 Set of 2   1.60   1.60

Expansion of Dubai Intl. Airport A197

2000, Nov. 4   Litho.   Perf. 13x13½
670-671 A197 Set of 2   2.25   2.25

Development and Environment A198

Designs: 50f, Smile. 250f, Flower. 3d, Heart as leaf. 350f, Heart as globe.

2001, Mar. 20   Litho.   Perf. 13¼x13
672-675 A198 Set of 4   5.25   5.25

Dubai Millennium, Winner of 2000 Dubai World Cup A199

Designs: 3d, Horse's head. 350f, Horse at track.

2001, Mar. 24   Perf. 13x13¼
676-677 A199 Set of 2   3.50   3.50

Sultan Bin Ali Al Owais (1925-2000), Poet — A200

Designs: 50f, Calligraphy. 1d, Portrait.

2001, Apr. 30   Perf. 13¼x13
678-679 A200 Set of 2   .80   .80

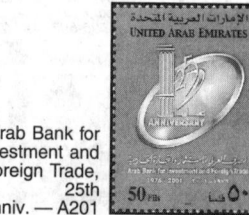

Arab Bank for Investment and Foreign Trade, 25th Anniv. — A201

Designs: 50f, Emblem. 1d, Emblem, diff.

2001, July 7   Litho.   Perf. 13¼x13
680-681 A201 Set of 2   .85   .85

7th GCC Postage Stamp Exhibition, Dubai — A202

2001, July 10
682 A202 50f multi   .30   .3

Traditional Boats A203

Designs: 50f, Shahoof. 250f, Bagarah. 3d Sam'aa. 350f, Jalboot.

2001, Aug. 25   Perf. 14x13½
683-686 A203 Set of 4   5.25   5.2

Year of Dialogue Among Civilizations A204

Designs: 50f, Emblem. 250f, Branch with multicolored leaves.

2001, Oct. 9   Perf. 13¼x13
687-688 A204 Set of 2   1.60   1.60

Emirates Post A205

Falcons and inscription: 50f, Changing. 250f, Growing. 3d, Achieving.

2001, Sept. 15   Perf. 13x13¼
689-691 A205 Set of 3   3.25   3.25

Children's Art — A206

Designs: 1d, Mosque. 250f, Boatbuilding. 3d, Man pouring coffee, vert. 350f, Falconry.

Perf. 14x13¼, 13¼x14
2001, Nov. 12   Litho.
692-695 A206 Set of 4   5.50   5.50

Unification of Armed Forces, 25th Anniv. — A207

2001, Dec. 30   Perf. 13¼x13
696 A207 1d multi   .55   .55

Intl. Water Resources and Management Conference, Dubai — A208

2002, Feb. 2
697 A208 50f multi   .30   .30

UAE University, 25th Anniv. — A209

Background colors: 50f, Blue. 1d, Red.

2002, Mar. 25   Perf. 13¼x14
698-699 A209   Set of 2   .80   .80

Arabian Saluki A210

Various salukis: 50f, 150f, 250f, 3d.

2002, Apr. 29 Litho.   Perf. 13½x13¼
700-703 A210   Set of 4   4.25   4.25

Emirates Post, 1st Anniv. — A211

"1" and: 50f, Ring of text. 3d, Emblem.

2002, May 29   Perf. 13¼x13
704 A211 50f blue   .30   .30

Souvenir Sheet
Perf. 14¼
705 A211 3d multi   1.60   1.60
No. 705 contains one 45x35mm stamp.

Rashid Bin Salim Al-Suwaidi Al-Khadhar (1905-80), Poet A212

Designs: 50f, Text. 250f, Portrait.

2002, July 17 Litho. Perf. 13½x13¼
706-707 A212   Set of 2   1.60   1.60

Children's Creativity A213

Designs: 50f, Antelope and boat, by Amna al-Bloushi. 1d, Children, by Fahd al-Habsi. 2d, Earth holding flower, by Hana Mohammed.

250f, Fish, by Hatem al-Dhaheri. 3d, Child holding Earth, by Abdulla Ridha. 350f, Stick figures, by Yousef al-Sind. 5d, Emblem of Latifa Bint Mohammed Award for Childhood Creativity (29x39mm).

Perf. 13x13¼, 13¼x13 (5d)
2002, Oct. 9
708-714 A213   Set of 7   9.50   9.50

Sheikh Hamdan Bin Rashid Al-Maktoum Award for Medical Sciences A214

Designs: 50f, Award, emblem, sand dunes. 250f, Caduceus, map.

2002, Oct. 21   Perf. 13x13¼
715-716 A214   Set of 2   1.60   1.60

31st National Day — A215

Landmarks in the Emirates: Nos. 717, 724a, 50f, Ajman. Nos. 718, 724b, 50f, Sharjah. Nos. 719, 724c, 50f, Dubai. Nos. 720, 724d, 50f, Abu Dhabi. Nos. 721, 724e, 50f, Ras al Khaima. Nos. 722, 724f, Fujeira. Nos. 723, 724g, Umm al Qiwain.

2002, Dec. 2 Litho.   Perf. 13¼x14
717-723 A215   Set of 7   1.90   1.90
Souvenir Sheet
Litho. & Embossed
Imperf
724   Sheet of 7   2.75   2.75
a.-g. A215 50f Any single   .35   .35
No. 724 sold for 5d.

Thuraya Satellite Communications A216

Denominations: 25f, 250f.

2002   Litho.   Perf. 14
725-726 A216   Set of 2   1.50   1.50
Issued: 25f, 1/27; 250f, 1/6.

Items in Al Ain National Museum A217

Designs: 50f, Jar from Hili tombs. 275f, Pottery from Umm an-Nar tombs. 4d, Bronze axe. 6d, Soapstone vessel.

2003, Feb. 25   Perf. 14x13½
727-730 A217   Set of 4   7.25   7.25

National Bank of Dubai, 40th Anniv. A218

Panel color: 50f, Blue. 4d, Orange. 6d, Red.

2003, Apr. 15 Litho.   Perf. 14x13¼
731-733 A218   Set of 3   5.75   5.75

Coins A219

Designs: 50f, Dirham of Caliph Al Walid bin Abdul Malik. 125f, Arab Sasanian Dirham of Caliph Abdul Malik Bin Marwan. 275f, Dinar of Al Mustansir Billah Al Fatimi. 375f, Dinar of Caliph Abdul Malik bin Marwan.
5d, Dirham of Caliph Muhammed Al Ameen to mark election of Mousa Al Natiq Bilhaq.

2003, July 20 Litho. Perf. 13¼x13¾
734-737 A219   Set of 4   4.50   4.50
Size: 106x73mm
Imperf
738 A219 5d multi   2.75   2.75

Sheikh Zaid bin Sultan al Nahayan, 37th Anniv. of Accession as Ruler of Abu Dhabi A220

Sheikh Zaid and: 50f, Camel and sand dune. 175f, Modern buildings.

2003, Aug. 6   Litho.   Perf. 13
739-740 A220   Set of 2   1.25   1.25

World Youth Soccer Championships, United Arab Emirates — A221

2003, Sept. 7   Perf. 13x13¼
741 A221 375f multi   2.10   2.10

World Bank Boards of Governors Annual Meetings, Dubai — A222

Emblem and: 50f, Emirates Tower. 175f, Falcon. 275f, Mosque domes, horiz. 375f, Dhow. 5d, English and Arabic text.

Perf. 13¼x13, 13x13¼
2003, Sept. 23   Litho.
742-745 A222   Set of 4   4.75   4.75
Imperf
Size: 118x74mm
746 A222 5d multi   2.75   2.75

Peace A223

Dove and: 50f, Zakharafs. 225f, Door and wind tower. 275f, Columns. 325f, Water taxi.

2003, Oct. 1   Perf. 13x13¼
747-750 A223   Set of 4   4.75   4.75

Traditional Housing A224

Designs: 50f, Palm frond house. 175f, Mud house. 275f, Stone house. 325f, Tent.

2003, Oct. 20   Perf. 13½x14
751-754 A224   Set of 4   4.50   4.50

Falcons — A225

Designs: 50f, Peregrine falcon. 125f, Hybrid gyr-peregrine falcon. 275f, Gyrfalcon. 375f, Saker falcon.

2003, Nov. 17   Perf. 13¼x14
755-758 A225   Set of 4   4.50   4.50

Poetry of Saeed Bin Ateej Al Hamli (1875-1919) A226

Poetry: 125f, Four short lines. 175f, Four long lines.

2003, Dec. 29   Perf. 13x13¼
759-760 A226   Set of 2   1.75   1.75

Mohammed Bin Saeed Bin Ghubash (1899-1969), Religious Scholar — A227

Designs: 50f, Portrait. 175f, Books.

2004, Apr. 5   Litho.   Perf. 13¼x14
761-762 A227   Set of 2   1.25   1.25

Fourth Family Meeting — A228

Color of hands: 375f, Orange. 4d, Purple.

2004, Apr. 19
763-764 A228   Set of 2   4.25   4.25

UPPER SENEGAL AND NIGER

'ə-pər ˌse-nə-gäl and 'nī-jər

LOCATION — In Northwest Africa, north of French Guinea and Ivory Coast
GOVT. — A former French Colony
AREA — 617,600 sq. mi.
POP. — 2,474,142
CAPITAL — Bamako

In 1921 the name of this colony was changed to French Sudan and postage stamps so inscribed were placed in use.

100 Centimes = 1 Franc

Gen. Louis Faidherbe — A1

Oil Palms — A2

Dr. N. Eugène Ballay — A3

1906-07   Unwmk.   Typo.
Perf. 14x13½
Name of Colony in Red or Blue

1	A1	1c slate	1.10	1.10
2	A1	2c brown	1.25	1.10
3	A1	4c brn, gray bl	1.50	1.00
4	A1	5c green	4.25	2.00
5	A1	10c car (B)	4.25	2.00
6	A1	15c vio ('07)	3.25	3.25
7	A2	20c bluish gray	4.00	3.25
8	A2	25c bl, pnksh	12.50	3.25
9	A2	30c vio brn, pnksh	5.25	3.50
10	A2	35c blk, yellow	4.00	3.25
11	A2	40c car, az (B)	7.00	5.00
12	A2	45c brn, grnsh	8.25	6.50
13	A2	50c dp vio	8.00	6.50
14	A2	75c bl, org	8.00	8.00
15	A3	1fr blk, azure	20.00	16.00
16	A3	2fr bl, pink	35.00	35.00
17	A3	5fr car, straw (B)	77.50	77.50
		Nos. 1-17 (17)	205.10	178.20

Camel with Rider — A4

1914-17
Perf. 13½x14

18	A4	1c brn vio & vio	.20	.20
19	A4	2c gray & brn vio	.20	.20
20	A4	4c black & blue	.20	.20
21	A4	5c yel grn & bl grn	.60	.25
22	A4	10c red org & rose	1.60	1.25
23	A4	15c choc & org ('17)	1.40	.55
24	A4	20c brn vio & blk	1.40	.90
25	A4	25c ultra & bl	1.10	.90
26	A4	30c ol brn & brn	1.40	.90
27	A4	35c car rose & vio	2.00	1.25
28	A4	40c gray & car rose	1.60	.75
29	A4	45c bl & ol brn	1.40	1.25
30	A4	50c black & green	1.60	1.25
31	A4	75c org & ol brn	1.60	1.25
32	A4	1fr brown & brn vio	1.60	1.25

33	A4	2fr green & blue	2.00	1.90
34	A4	5fr violet & black	8.50	8.00
		Nos. 18-34 (17)	28.40	22.25

See Burkina Faso for types of this issue that escaped overprinting.
For surcharge see No. B1.

SEMI-POSTAL STAMP

Regular Issue of 1914 Surcharged in Red

1915   Unwmk.   Perf. 13½x14

B1	A4	10c + 5c red orange & rose	1.10	1.10

POSTAGE DUE STAMPS

Natives — D1   D2

1906   Unwmk.   Typo.   Perf. 14x13½

J1	D1	5c green, greenish	2.50	2.00
J2	D1	10c red brown	6.00	5.00
J3	D1	15c dark blue	8.00	7.00
J4	D1	20c black, yellow	10.00	4.00
J5	D1	50c violet	18.00	16.00
J6	D1	60c black, buff	13.00	13.00
J7	D1	1fr black, pinkish	25.00	22.50
		Nos. J1-J7 (7)	82.50	69.50

1914

J8	D2	5c green	.80	.80
J9	D2	10c rose	.80	.80
J10	D2	15c gray	.80	.80
J11	D2	20c brown	1.00	1.00
J12	D2	30c blue	1.40	1.40
J13	D2	50c black	1.10	1.10
J14	D2	60c orange	4.50	4.50
J15	D2	1fr violet	4.50	4.50
		Nos. J8-J15 (8)	14.90	14.90

Stamps of Upper Senegal and Niger were superceded in 1921 by those of French Sudan.

UPPER SILESIA

'ə-pər sĭ'lē-zh̄ē-ˌə

LOCATION — Formerly in eastern Germany and prior to World War I a part of Germany.

A plebiscite held under the terms of the Treaty of Versailles failed to determine the status of the country, the voting resulting about equally in favor of Germany and Poland. Accordingly, the League of Nations divided the territory between Germany and Poland.

100 Pfennig = 1 Mark
100 Fennigi = 1 Marka

Plebiscite Issues

A1

Perf. 14x13½
1920, Feb. 20   Typo.   Unwmk.

1	A1	2½pf slate	.35	.55
2	A1	3pf brown	.35	.85
3	A1	5pf green	.20	.35
4	A1	10pf dull red	.35	.90
5	A1	15pf violet	.20	.40
6	A1	20pf blue	.20	.40
a.		Imperf., pair	275.00	—
b.		Half used as 10pf on cover		85.00
7	A1	50pf violet brn	3.25	6.50
8	A1	1m claret	4.00	9.25
9	A1	5m orange	3.25	9.25
		Nos. 1-9 (9)	12.15	28.45
		Set, never hinged	35.00	—

Black Surcharge

5	5	5	5
Pf.	Pf.	Pf.	Pf.
I	II	III	IV

10	A1	5pf on 15pf vio (I)	13.00	42.50
		Never hinged	35.00	
a.		Type II	13.00	42.50
b.		Type III	13.00	42.50
c.		Type IV	13.00	42.50
11	A1	5pf on 20pf blue (I)	.65	2.00
		Never hinged	1.60	
a.		Type II	.80	2.25
b.		Type III	1.00	2.50
c.		Type IV	1.25	3.25

Red Surcharge

10	10	10	10
Pf.	Pf.	Pf.	Pf.
I	II	III	IV

12	A1	10pf on 20pf bl (I)	.65	1.60
		Never hinged	1.25	
a.		Type II	.65	1.60
b.		Type III	.65	1.60
c.		Type IV	.65	1.60
d.		Imperf.	50.00	

Black Surcharge

50	50	50	50	50
Pf.	Pf.	Pf.	Pf.	Pf.
I	II	III	IV	V

13	A1	50pf on 5m org (I)	12.50	42.50
		Never hinged	65.00	
a.		Type II	13.00	45.00
b.		Type III	14.50	80.00
c.		Type IV	14.50	80.00
d.		Type V	24.00	100.00

Nos. 10-13 are found with many varieties including surcharges inverted, double and double inverted.

Dove with Olive Branch Flying over Silesian Terrain — A2

A3

1920, Mar. 26   Typo.   Perf. 13½x1[...]

15	A2	2½pf gray	.25	.[...]
16	A2	3pf red brown	.25	.[...]
17	A2	5pf green	.25	.[...]
18	A2	10pf dull red	.25	.[...]
19	A2	15pf violet	.65	1.2[...]
20	A2	20pf blue	.25	.[...]
21	A2	25pf dark brown	.25	.[...]
22	A2	30pf orange	.25	.[...]
23	A2	40pf olive green	.25	.9[...]

Perf. 14x13½

24	A3	50pf gray	.25	.4[...]
25	A3	60pf blue	.25	1.2[...]
26	A3	75pf deep green	.85	1.6[...]
27	A3	80pf red brown	.65	.8[...]
28	A3	1m claret	.50	.4[...]
29	A3	2m dark brown	.50	.4[...]
30	A3	3m violet	.70	.4[...]
31	A3	5m orange	2.25	3.2[...]
		Nos. 15-31 (17)	8.60	13.5[...]
		Set, never hinged 26.00		

Nos. 18-28 Overprinted in Black or Red

Plébiscite 20 mars 1921.

1921, Mar. 20

32	A2	10pf dull red	3.25	8.0[...]
33	A2	15pf violet	3.25	8.0[...]
34	A2	20pf blue	4.50	11.0[...]
35	A2	25pf dk brn (R)	10.00	25.0[...]
36	A2	30pf orange	8.50	16.0[...]
37	A2	40pf olive grn (R)	8.50	16.0[...]

Overprinted

Plébiscite 20 mars 1921.

38	A3	50pf gray (R)	8.50	22.5[...]
39	A3	60pf blue	10.00	20.0[...]
40	A3	75pf deep green	10.00	22.5[...]
41	A3	80pf red brown	16.00	30.0[...]
42	A3	1m claret	20.00	52.5[...]
		Nos. 32-42 (11)	102.50	231.5[...]
		Set, never hinged	450.00	

Inverted or double overprints exist on Nos[...] 32-33, 35-40. Counterfeit overprints exist.

Type of 1920 and Surcharged

10 M

1922, Mar.

45	A3	4m on 60pf ol grn	.70	1.6[...]
46	A3	10m on 75pf red	.70	2.5[...]
47	A3	20m on 80pf orange	5.25	13.0[...]
		Nos. 45-47 (3)	6.65	17.1[...]
		Set, never hinged 18.00		

Stamps of the above design were [...] private issue not recognized by the [...] Inter-Allied Commission of Govern[...]ment. Value, set of 7, $27.50 unused [...] $52.50 never hinged, $125 used.

OFFICIAL STAMPS

German Stamps of 1905-20 Handstamped in Blue

1920, Feb. Wmk. 125 Perf. 14, 14½
On Stamps of 1906-19

1	A22	2pf gray	1.10	1.25
3	A22	2½pf gray	.55	.65
4	A16	3pf brown	.55	.65
5	A16	5pf green	.55	.65
6	A22	7½pf orange	.55	.65
7	A16	10pf car rose	.55	.65
8	A22	15pf dk violet	.55	.65
9	A16	20pf blue violet	.55	.65
10	A16	25pf org & blk, yel	5.25	6.50
11	A16	30pf org & blk, buff	.55	.65
12	A22	35pf red brown	.55	.65
13	A16	40pf lake & blk	.55	.65
14	A16	50pf vio & blk, buff	.55	.65
15	A16	60pf magenta	.55	.65
16	A16	75pf green & blk	.55	.65
17	A16	80pf lake & blk, rose	6.50	8.00
18	A17	1m car rose	1.10	1.25
19	A21	2m gray blue	5.25	6.50

On National Assembly Stamps of 1919-20

25	A23	10pf car rose	.90	1.10
26	A24	15pf choc & bl	1.60	2.00
27	A25	25pf green & red	3.25	4.00
28	A25	30pf red vio & red	2.50	3.00

On Semi-Postal Stamps of 1919

30	A16	10pf + 5pf carmine	6.50	8.00
31	A22	15pf + 5pf dk vio	6.50	8.00
	Nos. O1-O31 (24)		47.60	58.05

Red Handstamp

5a	A16	5pf	10.00	14.00
8a	A22	15pf	6.50	10.00
9a	A16	20pf	6.50	10.00
13a	A16	40pf	20.00	30.00
16a	A16	75pf	20.00	30.00
26a	A24	15pf	1.10	1.25
	Nos. O5a-O26a (6)		64.10	95.25

Values of Nos. O1-O31 are for reprints made with a second type of handstamp differing in minor details from the original (example: period after "S" is round instead of the earlier triangular form). Originals are scarce. Counterfeits exist.

Germany No. 65C with this handstamp is considered bogus by experts.

Local Official Stamps of Germany, 1920, Overprinted

1920, Apr.   Perf. 14

O32	LO2	5pf green	.25	.45
O33	LO3	10pf carmine	.25	.45
O34	LO4	15pf violet brn	.25	.45
O35	LO5	20pf deep ultra	.25	.45
O36	LO6	30pf orange, buff	.25	.45
O37	LO7	50pf violet, buff	.50	1.40
O38	LO8	1m red, buff	6.00	10.00
	Nos. O32-O38 (7)		7.75	13.65

Same Overprint on Official Stamps of Germany, 1920-21

1920-21

O39	O1	5pf green	1.00	2.00
O40	O2	10pf carmine	.20	.20
O41	O3	15pf violet brn	.20	.20
O42	O4	20pf deep ultra	.20	.20
O43	O5	30pf orange, buff	.20	.20
O44	O6	40pf carmine rose	.20	.20
O45	O7	50pf violet, buff	.20	.20
O46	O8	60pf red brown	.20	.20
O47	O9	1m red, buff	.20	.20
O48	O10	1.25m dk blue, yel	.20	.20
O49	O11	2m dark blue	4.75	7.25
O50	O12	5m brown, yel	.20	.20

1922, Feb.   Wmk. 126

O51	O11 2m dark blue		.20	.20
	Nos. O39-O51 (13)		7.95	11.45

This overprint is found both horizontal and vertical, reading up or down. It also exists on most values inverted, double and double, one inverted.

SCOTTMOUNTS

For stamp presentation unequaled in beauty and clarity, insist on ScottMounts. Made of 100% inert polystyrol foil, ScottMounts protect your stamps from the harmful effects of dust and moisture. Available in your choice of clear or black backs, ScottMounts are center-split across the back for easy insertion of stamps and feature crystal clear mount faces. Double layers of gum assure stay-put bonding on the album page. Discover the quality and value ScottMounts have to offer.

ScottMounts are available from your favorite stamp dealer or direct from:

Discover the quality and value ScottMounts have to offer.

For a complete list of ScottMount sizes call or write Scott Publishing Co.

SCOTT

Scott Publishing Co.
1-800-572-6885
P.O. Box 828 Sidney OH 45365-0828
www.amosadvantage.com

AMOS
HOBBY PUBLISHING

Publishers of:
Coin World, Linn's Stamp News and Scott Publishing Co.

URUGUAY

ˈyu̇r-ə-ˌgwä

LOCATION — South America, between Brazil and Argentina and bordering on the Atlantic Ocean
GOVT. — Republic
AREA — 68,037 sq. mi.
POP. — 3,137,668 (1996)
CAPITAL — Montevideo

120 Centavos = 1 Real
8 Reales = 1 Peso
100 Centesimos = 1 Peso (1859)
1000 Milesimos = 1 Peso (1898)

Watermarks

Wmk. 187 — R O in Diamond

Wmk. 188 — REPUBLICA O. DEL URUGUAY

Wmk. 189 — Caduceus

Wmk. 227 — Greek Border and REPUBLICA O. DEL URUGUAY in Alternate Curved Lines

Wmk. 327 — Coat of Arms

Wmk. 332 — Large Sun and R O U

Catalogue values for unused stamps in this country are for Never Hinged items, beginning with Scott 534 in the regular postage section, Scott B5 in the semipostal section, Scott C113 in the airpost section, Scott CB1 in the airpost semi-postal section, Scott E9 in the special delivery section, and Scott Q64 in the parcel post section.

Carrier Issues
Issued by Atanasio Lapido, Administrator-General of Posts

"El Sol de Mayo"
A1   A1a

1856, Oct. 1   Litho.   Imperf.
1	A1	60c blue	350.	
2	A1	80c green	325.	
3	A1	1r vermilion	300.	

1857, Oct. 1
3B	A1a	60c blue	2,500.	

Nos. 1-3d were spaced very closely on the stone. Very fine examples will have clear margins on three sides and touching or slightly cut into the frames on the fourth (consult the grading illustrations in the catalogue introduction). All genuinely used examples are pen canceled. Certification by a recognized authority is recommended.

Stamps with tiny faults, such as small thin spots, sell for about 75% of the values of sound copies.

See Nos. 410-413, 771A.

A2

1858, Mar.
4	A2	120c blue	250.	—
a.		Tête bêche pair		7,500.
5	A2	180c green	100.00	200.00
c.		Thick paper	450.00	
d.		Tête bêche pair		—
6	A2	240c dull ver	150.00	1,500.
c.		180c in stone of 240c		—
d.		Thick paper (dull ver)		—
e.		240c setenant with a vacant place	5,000.	
		Nos. 4-6 (3)	500.00	1,700.

Government Issues

A3

A4

1859, June 26
Thin Numerals
7	A3	60c lilac	25.00	20.00
a.		60c gray lilac	25.00	20.00
8	A3	80c yellow	190.00	35.00
a.		80c orange	275.00	50.00
9	A3	100c brown lake	55.00	45.00
a.		100c brown rose	55.00	45.00
10	A3	120c blue	35.00	15.00
a.		120c slate blue	50.00	17.50
11	A3	180c green	15.00	17.50
12	A3	240c vermilion	50.00	50.00
		Nos. 7-12 (6)	370.00	182.50

1860
Thick Numerals
13	A4	60c dull lilac	15.00	8.00
a.		60c gray lilac	17.50	10.00
b.		60c brown lilac	17.50	12.00
c.		60c red lilac	17.50	12.00
d.		As "a," fine impression (1st printing)	70.00	40.00
14	A4	80c yellow	20.00	16.00
a.		80c orange	45.00	18.00
15	A4	100c rose	45.00	35.00
a.		100c carmine	45.00	35.00
16	A4	120c blue	21.00	16.00
17	A4	180c yellow grn	175.00	225.00
a.		180c deep green	225.00	250.00
		Nos. 13-17 (5)	276.00	300.00

No. 13 was first printed (1860) in sheets of 192 (16x12) containing 24 types. The impressions are very clear; paper is whitish and of better quality than that of the later printings. In the 1861-62 printings, the layout contains 12 types and the subjects are spaced farther apart.

Coat of Arms — A5

1864, Apr. 13
18	A5	6c rose	12.00	7.00
a.		6c carmine	20.00	12.00
b.		6c red	30.00	20.00
c.		6c brick red	30.00	20.00
20	A5	6c salmon	300.00	
21	A5	8c green	15.00	15.00
a.		Tête bêche pair	500.00	
22	A5	10c yellow	20.00	16.00
a.		10c ocher	20.00	20.00
23	A5	12c blue	15.00	15.00
a.		12c dark blue	25.00	15.00
b.		12c slate blue	30.00	50.00

No. 20, which is on thicker paper, was never placed in use.

Stamps of 1864 Surcharged in Black

1866, Jan. 1
24	A5	5c on 12c blue	16.00	35.00
a.		5c on 12c slate blue	25.00	45.00
b.		Inverted surcharge	150.00	
c.		Double surcharge	150.00	
d.		Pair, one without surcharge	150.00	
e.		Triple surcharge	55.00	
25	A5	10c on 8c brt grn	16.00	35.00
a.		10c on 8c dl grn	16.00	35.00
b.		Tête bêche pair	300.00	
c.		Double surcharge	150.00	
26	A5	15c on 10c ocher	17.00	50.00
a.		15c on 10c yellow	17.00	50.00
b.		Inverted surcharge	150.00	
c.		Double surcharge	150.00	
27	A5	20c on 6c rose	22.50	50.00
a.		20c on 6c rose red	30.00	50.00
b.		Inverted surcharge	150.00	
c.		Double surcharge	150.00	
d.		Pair, one without surcharge	150.00	
28	A5	20c on 6c brick red	350.00	
a.		Double surcharge	400.00	
		Nos. 24-27 (4)	71.50	170.00

Many counterfeits exist.
No. 28 was not issued.

Coat of Arms and Numeral of Value — A7

A8

A8b

A8a

A8c

ONE CENTESIMO:
Type I — The wavy lines behind "CENTESIMO" are clear and distinct. Stamps 4mm apart.
Type II — The wavy lines are rough and blurred. Stamps 3mm apart.

1866, Jan. 10   Imperf.
29	A7	1c black (type II)	2.50	15.00
a.		1c black (type I)	2.50	15.00
30	A8	5c blue	2.50	1.50
a.		5c dull blue	2.50	1.50
b.		5c ultramarine	25.00	10.00
c.		Numeral with white flag	20.00	9.00
d.		"ENTECIMOS"	20.00	9.00
e.		"CENTECIMO"	20.00	9.00
f.		"CENTECIMOS" with small "S"	20.00	9.00
g.		Pelure paper	100.00	100.00
h.		Thick paper		
31	A8a	10c yellow green	15.00	5.00
a.		10c blue green	17.00	6.00
b.		"I" of "CENTECIMOS" omitted	27.50	14.00
c.		"CENIECIMOS"	27.50	14.00
d.		"CENTRCIMOS"	27.50	14.00
32	A8b	15c orange yel	25.00	8.00
a.		15c yellow	25.00	8.00
33	A8c	20c rose	30.00	10.00
a.		20c lilac rose	30.00	10.00
b.		Thick paper	35.00	15.00
		Nos. 29-33 (5)	75.00	39.50

See Nos. 34-38. For overprint see No. O11.
Engraved plates were prepared for Nos. 36 to 33 but were not put in use. The stamps were printed from lithographic transfers from the plate. In 1915 a few reprints of the 15c were made from the engraved plate by a California philatelic society, each sheet being numbered and signed by officers of the society; then the plate was defaced.

1866-67   Perf. 8½ to 13½
34	A7	1c black	4.00	20.00
35	A8	5c blue	5.00	1.00
a.		5c dark blue	5.00	1.00
b.		Numeral with white flag	15.00	8.00
c.		"ENTECIMOS"	15.00	8.00
d.		"CENTECIMO"	15.00	8.00
e.		"CENTECIMOS" with small "S"	15.00	8.00
f.		Pelure paper	90.00	20.00
36	A8a	10c green	12.00	4.00
a.		10c yellow green	14.00	4.00
b.		"CENIECIMOS"	20.00	10.00
c.		"I" of "CENTECIMOS" omitted	20.00	10.00
d.		"CENTRCIMOS"	20.00	10.00
e.		Pelure paper	90.00	10.00
37	A8b	15c orange yel	21.00	6.00
a.		15c yellow	21.00	6.00
b.		Thin paper	25.00	10.00
38	A8c	20c rose	25.00	10.00
a.		20c brown rose	25.00	10.00
b.		Thin paper	30.00	15.00
c.		Thick paper	30.00	15.00
		Nos. 34-38 (5)	67.00	41.00

A9

A10

A11   A12

1877-79   Engr.   Rouletted 8
39	A9	1c red brown	.40	.30
40	A10	5c green	.50	.30
a.		Thick paper	3.00	1.10
41	A11	10c vermilion	.75	.40
42	A11	20c bister	.85	.40
43	A11	50c black	6.00	3.00
43A	A12	1p blue ('79)	30.00	13.50
		Nos. 39-43A (6)	38.50	17.90

The first printing of the 1p had the coat of arms smaller with quarterings reversed. These "error" stamps were not issued, and all were ordered burned. A copy is known to have been in a celebrated Uruguayan collection and a few others exist.

See No. 44. For overprints and surcharges see Nos. 52-53, O1-O8, O10, O19.

1880, Nov. 10   Litho.   Rouletted 6
44	A9	1c brown	.20	.20
a.		Imperf., pair	10.00	
b.		Rouletted 12½	2.50	

Joaquin Suárez — A13

1881, Aug. 25 — **Perf. 12½**
45	A13	7c blue	1.50	1.10
a.		Imperf., pair	9.00	9.00

For overprint see No. O9.

Devices from Coat of Arms
A14   A14a

1882, May 15
46	A14	1c green	1.00	1.00
a.		1c yellow green	3.25	1.75
b.		Imperf., pair	13.00	
47	A14a	2c rose	.80	.70
a.		Imperf., pair	15.00	

These stamps bear numbers from 1 to 100 according to their position on the sheet. Counterfeits of Nos. 46 and 47 are plentiful. See Nos. 1132-1133. For overprints see Nos. 54, O12-O13, O20.

Coat of Arms
A15   A16

Gen. Máximo   General José
Santos — A17   Artigas — A18

Perf. 12, 12x12½, 12x13, 13x12

1883, Mar. 1
48	A15	1c green	1.00	.75
49	A16	2c red	1.25	1.00
50	A17	5c blue	2.00	1.00
51	A18	10c brown	2.50	1.60
		Nos. 48-51 (4)	6.75	4.60

Imperf., Pairs
48a	A15	1c	7.00
49a	A16	2c	7.00
50a	A17	5c	6.50
51a	A18	10c	11.00

For overprints see Nos. O14-O18.

1883

No. 40 Overprinted in Black

Provisorio

1883, Sept. 24 — **Rouletted 8**
52	A10	5c green	.80	.60
a.		Double overprint	15.00	15.00
b.		Overprint reading down	4.50	4.50
c.		"Provisorio" omitted	7.00	7.00
d.		"1883" omitted	4.50	4.50

No. 52 with overprint in red is a color essay.

No. 41 Surcharged in Black

1884, Jan. 15
53	A11	1c on 10c ver	.40	.40
a.		Small figure "1"	3.50	3.50
b.		Inverted surcharge	3.50	3.50
c.		Double surcharge	8.00	5.00

No. 47 Overprinted in Black

Perf. 12½
54	A14a	2c rose	.60	.60
a.		Double overprint	14.00	
b.		Imperf., pair	35.00	

A22   A23

Thick Paper

1884, Jan. 25 — **Litho.** — **Unwmk.**
55	A22	5c ultra	1.50	.75
a.		Imperf., pair	7.50	4.00

Thin Paper
Perf. 12½, 13 and Compound
56	A23	5c blue	1.00	.50
a.		Imperf., pair	14.00	

For overprints see Nos. O21-O22.

A24   A24a

A24b   Artigas — A25

Santos — A26   A27

A28

1884-88 — **Engr.** — **Rouletted 8**
57	A24	1c gray	.70	.30
58	A24	1c olive	.50	.25
59	A24	1c green	.40	.20
60	A24a	2c vermilion	.40	.20
60A	A24a	2c rose ('88)	.40	.20
61	A24b	5c deep blue	.70	.25
61A	A24b	5c blue, *blue*	1.25	.60
62	A24b	5c violet ('86)	.30	.20
63	A24b	5c lt bl ('88)	.40	.20
64	A25	7c dk brown	1.25	.60
65	A25	7c org ('88)	.80	.35
66	A26	10c olive brn	.80	.35
67	A27	20c red violet	2.00	1.00
68	A27	20c bis brn ('88)	2.00	1.00
69	A28	25c gray violet	4.00	1.50
70	A28	25c ver ('88)	3.00	1.00
		Nos. 57-70 (16)	18.90	8.20

Water dissolves the blue in the paper of No. 61A.

For overprints see Nos. 73, 98-99, O23-O34, O36-O39, O61.

A29   A30

1887, Oct. 17 — **Litho.** — **Rouletted 9**
71	A29	10c lilac	2.00	1.00
a.		10c gray lilac	3.00	1.25

For overprint see No. O40.

1888, Jan. 1 — **Engr.** — **Rouletted 8**
72	A30	10c violet	.50	.25

For overprint see No. O35.

No. 62 Overprinted in Black

1889, Oct. 14
73	A24b	5c violet	.20	.20
a.		Inverted overprint	5.00	3.00
b.		Inverted "A" for "V" in "Provisorio"	3.00	

No. 73 with overprint in red is a color essay.

Coat of   Numeral of
Arms — A32   Value — A33

A34   A35

A36   A37

Justice   Mercury
A38   A39

A40

Perf. 12½ to 15½ and Compound
1889-1901 — **Engr.**
74	A32	1c green	.40	.20
a.		Imperf., pair	13.00	
75	A33	1c dull bl ('94)	.40	.20
76	A33	2c rose	.40	.20
77	A33	2c red brn ('94)	.45	.25
78	A33	2c org ('99)	.45	.20
79	A34	5c dp blue	.40	.20
80	A34	5c rose ('94)	.45	.20
81	A35	7c bister brn	.75	.30
82	A35	7c green ('94)	4.00	2.25
83	A35	7c car ('00)	3.00	1.25
84	A36	10c blue grn	3.00	.75
a.		Printed on both sides	20.00	
85	A36	10c org ('94)	3.00	.45
86	A37	20c orange	2.00	.45
87	A37	20c brown ('94)	4.00	1.50

88	A37	20c lt blue ('00)	2.25	.35
a.		20c greenish blue	2.50	.35
89	A38	25c red brown	2.75	.75
90	A38	25c ver ('94)	5.50	3.00
91	A38	25c bis brn ('01)	3.00	.40
92	A39	50c lt blue	7.50	5.00
93	A39	50c lilac ('94)	10.00	5.00
94	A39	50c car ('01)	6.00	1.00
95	A40	1p lilac	18.00	5.00
96	A40	1p lt blue ('94)	20.00	6.00
97	A40	1p dp grn ('01)	18.00	2.25
a.		Imperf., pair	30.00	
		Nos. 74-97 (24)	115.70	37.20

For surcharges and overprints see Nos. 100-101, 142, 180, 185, C1-C3, O41-O60, O89-O91, O108-O109.

Nos. 59 and 62 Overprinted in Red

a   b

1891-92 — **Rouletted 8**
98	A24 (a)	1c green ('92)	.25	.25
a.		Inverted overprint	4.25	3.75
b.		Double overprint	5.50	5.00
c.		Double ovpt., one invtd.	3.00	2.50
d.		"PREVISORIO"	2.75	2.50
99	A24b (b)	5c violet	.20	.20
a.		"1391"	2.50	1.75
b.		Double overprint	2.50	1.75
c.		Inverted overprint	2.50	1.75
d.		Double ovpt., one invtd.	5.00	3.00

Nos. 86 and 81 Surcharged in Black or Red

c   d

Perf. 12½ to 15½ and Compound
1892
100	A37 (c)	1c on 20c org (Bk)	.20	.20
a.		Inverted surcharge	3.00	3.00
101	A35 (d)	5c on 7c bis brn (R)	.20	.20
a.		Inverted surcharge	1.00	1.00
b.		Double surcharge, one invtd.	3.00	3.00
c.		Double surcharge	3.00	3.00
d.		Vertical surcharge	10.00	
e.		"PREVISORIO"	2.00	2.00
f.		"Cinco" omitted	4.50	

No. 101 with surcharge in green is a color essay.

Several surcharge errors of date and misspelling of "Centésimos" exist. Value $12.50.

A45   A46

Arms   Peace
A47   A48

1892 — **Engr.**
102	A45	1c green	.40	.20
103	A46	2c rose	.40	.20
104	A47	5c blue	.45	.20
105	A48	10c orange	1.75	.75
		Nos. 102-105 (4)	3.00	1.35

Issued: 1c, 2c, 3/9; 5c, 4/19; 10c, 12/15.

Liberty
A49

Arms
A50

1894, June 2
106 A49 2p carmine   24.00 14.00
107 A50 3p dull violet   24.00 14.00

Gaucho
A51

Solis Theater
A52

Locomotive
A53

Bull's Head
A54

Ceres — A55

Sailing
Ship — A56

Liberty
A57

Mercury
A58

Coat of
Arms — A59

Montevideo
Fortress — A60

Cathedral in
Montevideo
A61

Perf. 12 to 15½ and Compound
1895-99
108 A51 1c bister   .40 .20
109 A51 1c slate bl ('97)   .40 .20
  a.   Printed on both sides   14.00
110 A52 2c blue   .40 .20
111 A52 2c claret ('97)   .40 .20
112 A53 5c red   .40 .20
113 A53 5c green ('97)   .55 .20
  a.   Imperf., pair   3.50
114 A53 5c grnsh bl ('99)   .45 .20
115 A54 7c deep green   7.00 2.00
116 A54 7c orange ('97)   3.00 1.00
117 A55 10c brown   1.75 .40
118 A56 20c green & blk   6.00 .75
119 A56 20c cl & blk ('97)   4.00 .50
120 A57 25c red brn & blk   4.50 1.10
  a.   Center inverted   2,000.
121 A57 25c pink & bl ('97)   3.00 .50
122 A58 50c blue & blk   6.00 3.00
123 A58 50c grn & brn ('97)   4.00 1.00

124 A59 1p org brn & blk   12.00 5.00
125 A59 1p yel brn & bl ('97)   8.00 2.50
126 A60 2p violet & grn   27.50 16.00
127 A60 2p bis & car ('97)   8.00 1.50
128 A61 3p carmine & blue   27.50 16.00
129 A61 3p lil & car ('97)   10.00 2.00
      Nos. 108-129 (22)   135.25 54.65

All values of this issue exist imperforate but
they were not issued in that form.
  For overprints and surcharges see Nos.
138-140, 143, 145, 147, O62-O78.

President Joaquin Suárez
A62   A63

Statue of President
Suárez — A64

Perf. 12½ to 15 and Compound
1896, July 18
130 A62 1c brown vio & blk   .20 .20
131 A63 5c pale bl & blk   .20 .20
132 A64 10c lake & blk   .60 .30
      Nos. 130-132 (3)   1.00 .70

Dedication of Pres. Suárez statue.
  For overprints and surcharge see Nos. 133-
135, 144, 146, 152, O79-O81.

Same Overprinted in Red:

e   f

1897, Mar. 1
133 A62 (e) 1c brn vio & blk   .30 .20
  a.   Inverted overprint   3.50 3.00
134 A63 (e) 5c pale blue & blk   .30 .20
  a.   Inverted overprint   6.00 4.50
135 A64 (f) 10c lake & blk   .65 .45
  a.   Inverted overprint   8.50 7.50
  b.   Double overprint   7.50
      Nos. 133-135 (3)   1.25 .85

"Electricity" — A68

1897-99   **Engr.**
136 A68 10c red   1.10 .30
137 A68 10c red lilac ('99)   .40 .25

For overprints see Nos. 141, O82-O83.

Regular Issues
Overprinted in Red or
Blue

1897, Sept. 26
138 A51 1c slate bl (R)   .50 .40
  a.   Inverted overprint   4.00 4.00
139 A52 2c claret (Bl)   .75 .75
  a.   Inverted overprint   3.00 3.00
140 A53 5c green (Bl)   1.10 1.00
  a.   Inverted overprint   6.00 6.00
  b.   Double overprint
141 A68 10c red (Bl)   1.75 1.75
  a.   Inverted overprint   12.00 12.00
      Nos. 138-141 (4)   4.10 3.90

Commemorating the Restoration of Peace
at the end of the Civil War.
  Issue for use only on the days of the
National Fête, Sept. 26-28, 1897.

Regular Issues
Surcharged in Black,
Blue or Red

1898, July 25
142 A32 ½c on 1c bl (Bk)   .20 .20
  a.   Inverted surcharge   3.00 3.00
143 A51 ½c on 1c bis (Bl)   .20 .20
  a.   Inverted surcharge   3.00
  b.   Double surcharge   2.50
144 A62 ½c on 1c brn vio & blk   .20 .20
         (R)
145 A52 ½c on 2c blue (Bk)   .20 .20
146 A63 ½c on 5c pale bl & blk   .20 .20
         (R)
  a.   Double surcharge   6.25
147 A54 ½c on 7c dp grn (R)   .20 .20
      Nos. 142-147 (6)   1.20 1.20

The 2c red brown of 1894 (#77) was also
surcharged like #142-147 but was not issued.

Liberty — A69

Statue of
Artigas — A70

1898-99   **Litho.**   **Perf. 11, 11½**
148 A69 5m rose   .20 .20
149 A69 5m purple ('99)   .20 .20

1899-1900 Engr. Perf. 12½, 14, 15
150 A70 5m lt blue   .20 .20
151 A70 5m orange ('00)   .20 .20

No. 135 With
Additional Surcharge
in Black

1900, Dec. 1
152 A64 5c on 10c lake & blk   .30 .20
  a.   Black bar covering "1897" omitted 15.00

Cattle — A72

Girl's
Head — A73

Shepherdess — A74

Perf. 13½ to 16 and Compound
1900-10   **Engr.**
153 A72 1c yellow green   .25 .20
154 A73 5c dull blue   .50 .20
155 A73 5c slate grn ('10)   .50 .20
156 A74 10c gray violet   .60 .20
      Nos. 153-156 (4)   1.85 .80

For surcharges and overprints see Nos.
179, 184, O84, O86, O88, O106-O107.

Eros and
Cornucopia
A75

Basket of Fruit
A76

1901, Feb. 11
157 A75 2c vermilion   .35 .2
158 A76 7c brown orange   1.10 .2

For surcharges and overprints see No
197-198, O85, O87, O105.

General
Artigas — A78

Cattle — A79

Eros — A80

Cow — A81

Shepherdess
A82

Numeral
A83

Justice — A84

1904-05   Litho.   Perf. 11½
160 A78 5m orange   .25 .20
  a.   5m yellow   .20 .20
161 A79 1c green   .40 .20
  a.   Imperf., pair   3.50
162 A80 2c dp orange   .20 .20
  a.   2c orange red   .20 .20
  b.   Imperf., pair   3.00
163 A81 5c blue   .50 .20
  a.   Imperf., pair   3.50
164 A82 10c dk violet ('05)   .30 .20
165 A83 20c gray grn ('05)   1.75 .30
166 A84 25c olive bis ('05)   2.00 .50
      Nos. 160-166 (7)   5.40 1.80

For overprints see Nos. 167-169, O92-O98,
O101-O103.

Overprinted Diagonally
in Carmine or Black

1904, Oct. 15
167 A79 1c green (C)   .40 .20
168 A80 2c deep orange (Bk)   .40 .25
169 A81 5c dark blue (C)   .75 .40
      Nos. 167-169 (3)   1.55 .85

End of the Civil War of 1904. In the first
overprinting, "Paz 1904" appears at a 50-
degree angle; in the second, at a 63-degree
angle.

A85

A86

1906, Feb. 23   Litho.   Unwmk.
170 A85 5c dark blue   .80 .20
  a.   Imperf., pair   6.00

1906-07
171 A86 5c deep blue   .30 .30
172 A86 7c orange brn ('07)   .70 .50
173 A86 50c rose   5.00 1.25
      Nos. 171-173 (3)   6.00 2.05

Cruiser "Montevideo" — A87

908, Aug. 23   Typo.   Rouletted 13

74	A87	1c car & dk grn	2.00	1.50
75	A87	2c green & dk grn	2.00	1.50
76	A87	5c org & dk grn	2.00	1.50
		Nos. 174-176 (3)	6.00	4.50

Center Inverted

74a	A87	1c	300.00	300.00
75a	A87	2c	300.00	300.00
76a	A87	5c	300.00	300.00
		Nos. 174a-176a (3)	900.00	900.00

Imperf., Pairs

74b	A87	1c	30.00
75b	A87	2c	30.00
76b	A87	5c	30.00

Independence of Uruguay, declared Aug. 25, 1825. Counterfeits exist.
For surcharges and overprints see Nos. 86, O99-O100, O104, O110.

View of the Port of Montevideo — A88

Wmk. 187

909, Aug. 24   Engr.   Perf. 11½

177	A88	2c lt brown & blk	1.25	1.00
178	A88	5c rose red & blk	1.25	1.00

Issued to commemorate the opening of the Port of Montevideo, Aug. 25, 1909.

Nos. 156, 91
Surcharged

Perf. 14 to 16

1909, Sept. 13   Unwmk.

179	A74	8c on 10c dull vio	.50	.20
a.		"Contesimos"	2.00	1.10
180	A38	23c on 25c bis brn	1.00	.40

Centaur — A89

Wmk. 187

1910, May 22   Engr.   Perf. 11½

182	A89	2c carmine red	.60	.30
183	A89	5c deep blue	.60	.30

Cent. of Liberation Day, Aug. 25, 1810.
The 2c in deep blue and 5c in carmine red were prepared for collectors.

Stamps of 1900-06 Surcharged

g   h

i

Perf. 14 to 16, 11½

1910, Oct. 6   Unwmk.

Black Surcharge

184	A72	(a) 5m on 1c yel grn	.20	.20
a.		Inverted surcharge	4.50	3.75

Dark Blue Surcharge

185	A39	(b) 5c on 50c dull red	.20	.20
a.		Inverted surcharge	4.50	4.50

Blue Surcharge

186	A86	(c) 5c on 50c rose	.50	.45
a.		Double surcharge	20.00	
b.		Inverted surcharge	10.00	8.75
		Nos. 184-186 (3)	.90	.85

Artigas
A90

"Commercial
Progress"
A91

1910, Nov. 21   Engr.   Perf. 14, 15

187	A90	5m dk violet	.20	.20
188	A90	1c dp green	.20	.20
189	A90	2c orange red	.20	.20
190	A90	5c dk blue	.30	.20
191	A90	8c gray blk	.30	.20
192	A90	20c brown	.50	.20
193	A91	23c dp ultra	1.50	.30
194	A91	50c orange	3.00	1.00
195	A91	1p scarlet	7.50	1.00
		Nos. 187-195 (9)	13.60	3.50

See Nos. 199-210. For overprints see Nos. 211-213, O118-O124.

Symbolical of the
Posts — A92

1911, Jan. 6   Wmk. 187   Perf. 11½

196	A92	5c rose car & blk	.45	.35

1st South American Postal Cong., at Montevideo, Jan. 1911.

No. 158 Surcharged
in Red or Dark Blue

Perf. 14 to 16

1911, May 17   Unwmk.

197	A76	2c on 7c brn org (R)	.25	.20
198	A76	5c on 7c brn org (Bl)	.25	.20
a.		Inverted surcharge	8.00	6.00

Centenary of the battle of Las Piedras, won by the forces under Gen. Jose Gervasio Artigas, May 8, 1811.

Types of 1910

FOUR AND FIVE CENTESIMOS:
Type I - Large numerals about 3mm high.
Type II - Small numerals about 2¼mm high.

1912-15   Typo.   Perf. 11½

199	A90	5m violet	.20	.20
a.		5m purple	.20	.20
200	A90	5m magenta	.20	.20
a.		5m dull rose	.20	.20
201	A90	1c green ('13)	.20	.20
202	A90	2c brown org	.20	.20
203	A90	2c rose red ('13)	.20	.20
a.		2c deep red ('14)	.20	.20
204	A90	4c org (I) ('14)	.20	.20
a.		4c orange (II) ('15)	.20	.20
b.		4c yellow (II) ('13)	.20	.20
205	A90	5c dull bl (I)	.20	.20
a.		5c blue (II)	.20	.20
206	A90	8c ultra ('13)	.30	.20
207	A90	20c brown ('13)	.90	.20
a.		20c chocolate	.90	
208	A91	23c dk blue ('15)	2.50	.50
209	A91	50c orange ('14)	3.50	1.50
210	A91	1p vermilion ('15)	8.00	1.00
		Nos. 199-210 (12)	16.60	4.80

Stamps of 1912-15
Overprinted

1913, Apr. 4

211	A90	2c brown orange	.40	.30
a.		Inverted overprint	5.00	4.50
212	A90	4c yellow	.40	.30
213	A90	5c blue	.40	.30
		Nos. 211-213 (3)	1.20	.90

Cent. of the Buenos Aires Cong. of 1813.

Liberty
Extending
Peace to the
Country — A93

1918, Jan. 3   Litho.

214	A93	2c green & red	.45	.30
215	A93	5c buff & blue	.45	.30

Promulgation of the Constitution.

Statue of
Liberty, New
York Harbor
A94

Harbor of
Montevideo
A95

Perf. 14, 15, 13½

1919, July 15   Engr.

217	A94	2c carmine & brn	.25	.20
218	A94	4c orange & brn	.40	.20
219	A94	5c blue & brn	.45	.20
220	A94	8c org brn & ind	.65	.25
221	A94	20c ol bis & blk	1.75	.50
222	A94	23c green & blk	2.50	.90
		Nos. 217-222 (6)	6.00	2.25

Peace at end of World War I.
Perf 13½ used only on 2c, 20c, 23c.

1919-20   Litho.   Perf. 11½

225	A95	5m violet & blk	.20	.20
226	A95	1c green & blk	.20	.20
227	A95	2c red & blk	.20	.20
228	A95	4c orange & blk	.20	.20
229	A95	5c ultra & slate	.25	.20
230	A95	8c gray bl & lt brn	.35	.20
231	A95	20c brown & blk	1.25	.20
232	A95	23c green & brn	1.75	.45
233	A95	50c brown & blue	3.50	1.25
234	A95	1p dull red & bl	6.50	3.00
		Nos. 225-234 (10)	14.40	6.10

For overprints see Nos. O125-O131.

José Enrique
Rodó — A96

Mercury — A97

1920, Feb. 28   Engr.   Perf. 14, 15

235	A96	2c car & blk	.45	.35
236	A96	4c org & bl	.50	.40
237	A96	5c bl & brn	.65	.45
		Nos. 235-237 (3)	1.60	1.20

Issued to honor José Enrique Rodó, author.
For surcharges see Nos. P2-P4.

1921-22   Litho.   Perf. 11½

238	A97	5m lilac	.20	.20
239	A97	5m gray blk ('22)	.20	.20
240	A97	1c lt grn	.20	.20
241	A97	1c vio ('22)	.20	.20
242	A97	2c fawn	.35	.20
243	A97	2c red ('22)	.35	.20
244	A97	3c bl grn ('22)	.50	.20
245	A97	4c orange	.35	.20
246	A97	5c ultra	.35	.20
247	A97	5c choc ('22)	.50	.20
248	A97	12c ultra ('22)	1.50	.35
249	A97	36c ol grn ('22)	6.00	2.00
		Nos. 238-249 (12)	10.70	4.35

See Nos. 254-260. For overprint and surcharge see Nos. E1, P1.

Dámaso A.
Larrañaga (1771-
1848), Bishop,
Writer, Scientist and
Physician — A98

1921, Dec. 10   Unwmk.

250	A98	5c slate	1.00	.75

Mercury Type of 1921-22

1922-23   Wmk. 188

254	A97	5m gray blk	.20	.20
255	A97	1c violet ('23)	.20	.20
a.		1c red violet	.20	.20
256	A97	2c pale red	.25	.20
257	A97	2c deep rose ('23)	.30	.20
259	A97	5c yel brn ('23)	.50	.20
260	A97	8c salmon pink ('23)	.75	.65
		Nos. 254-260 (6)	2.20	1.65

Equestrian
Statue of
Artigas — A99

Unwmk.

1923, Feb. 26   Engr.   Perf. 14

264	A99	2c car & sepia	.20	.20
265	A99	5c vio & sepia	.20	.20
266	A99	12c blue & sepia	.30	.20
		Nos. 264-266 (3)	.70	.60

Southern
Lapwing
A100

Battle Monument
A101

Perf. 12½, 11½x12½

1923, June 25   Litho.   Wmk. 189
Size: 18x22½mm

267	A100	5m gray	.20	.20
268	A100	1c org yel	.20	.20
269	A100	2c lt vio	.20	.20
270	A100	3c gray grn	.25	.20
271	A100	5c lt bl	.25	.20
272	A100	8c rose red	.40	.20
273	A100	12c dp bl	.55	.20
274	A100	20c brn org	.90	.20
275	A100	36c emerald	3.00	1.00
276	A100	50c orange	4.50	2.00
277	A100	1p brt rose	18.00	11.00
278	A100	2p lt grn	18.00	11.00
		Nos. 267-278 (12)	46.45	26.60

See #285-298, 309-314, 317-323, 334-339.
For surcharges and overprints see Nos. 345-348, O132-O148, P5-P7.

1923, Oct. 12   Wmk. 188   Perf. 11½

279	A101	2c dp grn	.45	.35
280	A101	5c scarlet	.45	.35
281	A101	12c dk bl	.45	.35
		Nos. 279-281 (3)	1.35	1.05

Unveiling of the Sarandi Battle Monument by José Luis Zorrilla, Oct. 12, 1923.

"Victory of Samothrace" — A102

Unwmk.

1924, July 29   Typo.   Perf. 11

282	A102	2c rose	13.50	10.00
283	A102	5c mauve	13.50	10.00
284	A102	12c brt bl	13.50	10.00
		Nos. 282-284 (3)	40.50	30.00

Olympic Games. Sheets of 20 (5x4). Five hundred sets of these stamps were printed on yellow paper for presentation purposes. They were not on sale at post offices. Value for set, $550.

Lapwing Type of 1923
First Redrawing
Imprint: "A. BARREIRO Y RAMOS"

1924, July 26   Litho.   Perf. 12½, 11½
Size: 17¼x21½mm

285	A100	5m gray blk	.20	.20
286	A100	1c fawn	.20	.20
287	A100	2c rose lil	.30	.20
288	A100	3c gray grn	.20	.20
289	A100	5c chalky blue	.20	.20
290	A100	8c pink	.35	.20
291	A100	10c turq blue	.30	.20
292	A100	12c slate blue	.40	.25
293	A100	15c lt vio	.40	.20
294	A100	20c brown	.75	.30
295	A100	36c salmon	3.00	.70
296	A100	50c greenish gray	5.00	2.00
297	A100	1p buff	8.00	4.00
298	A100	2p dl vio	14.00	8.00
		Nos. 285-298 (14)	33.30	16.85

Landing of the 33 "Immortals" Led by Juan Antonio Lavalleja — A103

Perf. 11, 11½

1925, Apr. 19   Wmk. 188

300	A103	2c salmon pink & blk	1.00	.80
301	A103	5c lilac & blk	1.00	.80
302	A103	12c blue & blk	1.00	.80
		Nos. 300-302 (3)	3.00	2.40

Cent. of the landing of the 33 Founders of the Uruguayan Republic.

Legislative Palace — A104

Perf. 11½

1925, Aug. 24   Unwmk.   Engr.

303	A104	5c vio & blk	1.00	.80
304	A104	12c bl & blk	1.00	.80

Dedication of the Legislative Palace.

General Fructuoso Rivera — A105

Wmk. 188
1925, Sept. 24   Litho.   Perf. 11

305	A105	5c light red	.30	.30

Centenary of Battle of Rincón. See No. C9.

Battle of Sarandí A106

1925, Oct. 12   Perf. 11½

306	A106	2c bl grn	.75	.70
307	A106	5c dl vio	.75	.70
308	A106	12c dp bl	1.00	.80
		Nos. 306-308 (3)	2.50	2.20

Centenary of the Battle of Sarandí.

Lapwing Type of 1923
Second Redrawing
Imprint: "Imprenta Nacional"

1925-26   Perf. 11, 11½, 10½
Size: 17½x21¾mm

309	A100	5m gray blk	.50	.20
310	A100	1c dl vio	.65	.20
311	A100	2c brt rose	.65	.20
312	A100	3c gray grn	.65	.25
313	A100	5c dl bl ('26)	.75	.20
314	A100	12c slate blue	3.00	.25
		Nos. 309-314 (6)	6.20	1.30

The design differs in many small details from that of the 1923-24 issues. These stamps may be readily identified by the imprint and perforation.

Lapwing Type of 1923
Third Redrawing
Imprint: "Imp. Nacional" at center

1926-27   Perf. 11, 11½, 10½
Size: 17½x21¾mm

317	A100	5m gray	.20	.20
318	A100	1c lt vio	1.00	.20
319	A100	2c red	.75	.20
320	A100	3c gray grn	1.00	.30
321	A100	5c lt bl	.75	.20
322	A100	8c pink ('27)	1.50	.40
323	A100	36c rose buff	8.00	3.00
		Nos. 317-323 (7)	13.20	4.50

These stamps may be distinguished from preceding stamps of the same design by the imprint.

Philatelic Exhibition Issue

Post Office at Montevideo A107

Unwmk.
1927, May 25   Engr.   Imperf.

330	A107	2c green	2.00	2.00
a.		Sheet of 4	10.00	10.00
331	A107	5c dull red	2.00	2.00
a.		Sheet of 4	10.00	10.00
332	A107	8c dark blue	2.00	2.00
a.		Sheet of 4	10.00	10.00
		Nos. 330-332 (3)	6.00	6.00

Printed in sheets of 4 and sold at the Montevideo Exhibition. Lithographed counterfeits exist.

Lapwing Type of 1923
Fourth Redrawing
Imprint: "Imp. Nacional" at right
Perf. 11, 11½

1927, May 6   Litho.   Wmk. 188
Size: 17¾x21¾mm

334	A100	1c gray vio	.20	.20
335	A100	2c vermilion	.20	.20
336	A100	3c gray grn	.40	.20
337	A100	5c blue	.25	.20
338	A100	8c rose	2.00	.30
339	A100	20c gray brn	2.50	.80
		Nos. 334-339 (6)	5.55	1.90

The design has been slightly retouched in various places. The imprint is in italic capitals and is placed below the right numeral of value.

Inauguración
Ferrocarril
SAN CARLOS
a ROCHA
14/1/928
5 cts. 5

No. 292 Surcharged in Red

1928, Jan. 13   Unwmk.   Perf. 11½

345	A100	2c on 12c slate blue	1.10	1.10
346	A100	5c on 12c slate blue	1.10	1.10
347	A100	10c on 12c slate blue	1.10	1.10
348	A100	15c on 12c slate blue	1.10	1.10
		Nos. 345-348 (4)	4.40	4.40

Issued to celebrate the inauguration of the railroad between San Carlos and Rocha.

General Rivera — A108

1928, Apr. 19   Engr.   Perf. 12

349	A108	5c car rose	.25	.20

Centenary of the Battle of Las Misiones.

Artigas (7 dots in panels below portrait.) — A109

Imprint: "Waterlow & Sons. Ltd., Londres"
Perf. 11, 12½, 13x13½, 12½x13, 13x12½

1928-43
Size: 16x19½mm

350	A109	5m black	.20	.20
350A	A109	5m org ('43)	.20	.20
351	A109	1c dk vio	.20	.20
352	A109	1c brn vio ('34)	.20	.20
352A	A109	1c vio bl ('43)	.20	.20
353	A109	2c dp grn	.20	.20
353A	A109	2c brn red ('43)	.20	.20
354	A109	3c bister	.20	.20
355	A109	3c dp grn ('32)	.20	.20
355A	A109	3c brt grn ('43)	.20	.20
356	A109	5c red	.20	.20
357	A109	5c ol grn ('33)	.20	.20
357A	A109	5c dl pur ('43)	.20	.20
358	A109	7c car ('32)	.20	.20
359	A109	8c dk bl	.20	.20
360	A109	8c brn ('33)	.20	.20
361	A109	10c orange	.20	.20
362	A109	10c red org ('32)	.40	.25
363	A109	12c dp bl ('32)	.20	.20
364	A109	15c dl bl	.40	.20
365	A109	17c dk vio ('32)	.50	.20
366	A109	20c ol brn	.40	.20
367	A109	20c red brn ('33)	.65	.35
368	A109	24c car rose	.90	.35
369	A109	24c yel ('33)	.50	.30
370	A109	36c ol grn ('33)	.90	.30
371	A109	50c gray	2.25	1.25
372	A109	50c blk ('33)	3.00	1.10
373	A109	50c blk brn ('33)	2.25	.90
374	A109	1p yel brn	7.00	4.00
		Nos. 350-374 (30)	22.75	13.00

1929-33   Perf. 12½
Size: 22 to 22½x28½ to 29½mm

375	A109	1p ol brn ('33)	3.75	2.00
376	A109	2p dk grn	10.00	5.00
377	A109	2p dl red ('32)	14.00	10.00
378	A109	3p dk bl	13.00	7.00
379	A109	3p blk ('32)	12.50	8.00
380	A109	4p violet	15.00	11.00
381	A109	4p dk ol grn ('32)	15.00	10.00
382	A109	5p car brn	20.00	14.00
383	A109	5p red org ('32)	17.50	10.00
384	A109	10p lake ('33)	55.00	35.00
385	A109	10p dp ultra ('33)	55.00	35.00
		Nos. 375-385 (11)	230.75	147.00

See Nos. 420-423, 462. See type A135.

Equestrian Statue of Artigas — A110

1928, May 1

386	A110	2p Prus bl & choc	12.50	6.█
387	A110	3p dp rose & blk	17.50	10.0█

Symbolical of Soccer Victory — A111

Gen. Eugenio Garzón — A11█

1928, July 29

388	A111	2c brn vio	8.25	6.7█
389	A111	5c dp red	8.25	6.7█
390	A111	8c ultra	8.25	6.7█
		Nos. 388-390 (3)	24.75	20.2█

Uruguayan soccer victories in the Olymp█ Games of 1924 and 1928. Printed in sheets █ 20, in panes of 10 (5x2).

1928, Aug. 25   Imper█

391	A112	2c red	1.00	1.0█
a.		Sheet of 4	5.00	5.█
392	A112	5c yel grn	1.00	1.0█
a.		Sheet of 4	5.00	5.█
393	A112	8c dp bl	1.00	1.0█
a.		Sheet of 4	5.00	5.█
		Nos. 391-393 (3)	3.00	3.0█

Dedication of monument to Garzon. Issue█ in sheets of 4. Lithographed counterfeits exis█

Black River Bridge A113

Gauchos Breaking a Horse — A114█

Peace A115

Montevideo A116

Liberty and Flag of Uruguay A117

Liberty with Torch and Caduceus A118

Statue of Artigas A124

Artigas Dictating Instructions fo█ 1813 Congress A119

Seascape
A120

Montevideo
Harbor,
1830 — A121

Liberty and
Coat of
Arms
A122

Montevideo
Harbor,
1930 — A123

1930, June 16   Perf. 12½, 12

394	A113	5m gray blk	.20	.20
395	A114	1c dk brn	.20	.20
396	A115	2c brn rose	.20	.20
397	A116	3c yel grn	.20	.20
398	A117	5c dk bl	.20	.20
399	A118	8c dl red	.25	.20
400	A119	10c dk vio	.35	.20
401	A120	15c bl grn	.40	.35
402	A121	20c indigo	.55	.40
403	A122	24c red brn	.75	.40
404	A123	50c org red	2.00	1.25
405	A124	1p black	3.75	2.00
406	A124	2p bl vio	9.00	5.75
407	A124	3p dk red	13.00	9.00
408	A124	4p red org	15.00	11.00
409	A124	5p lilac	22.50	13.00
		Nos. 394-409 (16)	68.55	44.55

Cent. of natl. independence and the promulgation of the constitution.

Type of 1856 Issue
Values in Centesimos
Wmk. 227

1931, Apr. 11   Litho.   Imperf.

410	A1	2c gray blue	3.00	2.00
a.		Sheet of 4	15.00	15.00
411	A1	8c dull red	3.00	2.00
a.		Sheet of 4	15.00	15.00
412	A1	15c blue black	3.00	2.00
a.		Sheet of 4	15.00	15.00

Wmk. 188

413	A1	5c light green	3.00	2.00
a.		Sheet of 4	15.00	15.00
		Nos. 410-413 (4)	12.00	8.00

Sold only at the Philatelic Exhibition, Montevideo, Apr. 11-15, 1931. Issued in sheets of 4.

Juan Zorrilla de San
Martin, Uruguayan
Poet — A125

1932, June 6   Unwmk.   Perf. 12½

414	A125	1½c brown violet	.20	.20
415	A125	3c green	.20	.20
416	A125	7c dk blue	.25	.20
417	A125	12c lt blue	.35	.25
418	A125	1p deep brown	15.00	10.00
		Nos. 414-418 (5)	16.00	10.85

Semi-Postal Stamp
No. B2 Surcharged

1932, Nov. 1   Perf. 12
419   SP1   1½c on 2c + 2c dp grn   .20 .20

Artigas Type of 1928
Imprint: "Imprenta Nacional" at center

1932-35   Litho.   Perf. 11, 12½
Size: 15¾x19¼mm

420	A109	5m lt brown ('35)	.20	.20
421	A109	1c pale violet ('35)	.20	.20
422	A109	15m black	.20	.20
423	A109	5c bluish grn ('35)	.30	.20
		Nos. 420-423 (4)	.90	.80

Gen. J. A.
Lavalleja
A126

Flag of the
Race and Globe
A127

1933, July 12   Engr.   Perf. 12½
429   A126   15m brown lake   .20 .20

Perf. 11, 11½, 11x11½
1933, Aug. 3   Litho.

430	A127	3c blue green	.20	.20
431	A127	5c rose	.25	.20
432	A127	7c lt blue	.25	.20
433	A127	8c dull red	.75	.45
434	A127	12c deep blue	.30	.20
435	A127	17c violet	1.00	.50
436	A127	20c red brown	2.00	1.25
437	A127	24c yellow	2.50	1.25
438	A127	36c orange	3.00	1.50
439	A127	50c olive gray	4.25	2.50
440	A127	1p bister	12.00	5.50
		Nos. 430-440 (11)	26.50	13.75

Raising of the "Flag of the Race" and of the 441st anniv. of the sailing of Columbus from Palos, Spain, on his first voyage to America.

Sower
A128

Juan Zorrilla
de San
Martin
A129

1933, Aug. 28   Unwmk.   Perf. 11½

441	A128	3c blue green	.20	.20
442	A128	5c dull violet	.25	.20
443	A128	7c lt blue	.20	.20
444	A128	8c deep red	.50	.30
445	A128	12c ultra	2.00	1.00
		Nos. 441-445 (5)	3.15	1.90

3rd Constituent National Assembly.

1933, Nov. 9   Engr.   Perf. 12½
446   A129   7c slate   .20 .20

Albatross Flying over Map of the
Americas — A130

1933, Dec. 3   Typo.   Perf. 11½

447	A130	3c green, blk & brn	1.40	1.40
448	A130	7c turq bl, brn & blk	.80	.60
449	A130	12c dk bl, gray & ver	2.00	1.50
450	A130	17c ver, gray & vio	4.00	4.00
451	A130	20c yellow, bl & grn	5.00	5.00
452	A130	36c red, blk & yel	6.00	6.00
		Nos. 447-452 (6)	19.20	18.50

7th Pan-American Conf., Montevideo. Issued in sheets of 6. For overprints see Nos. C61-C62.

General Rivera — A131

1934, Feb.   Engr.   Perf. 12½
453   A131   3c green   .20 .20

Stars Representing the Three
Constitutions — A132

1934, Mar. 23   Typo.

454	A132	3c yellow grn & grn	.30	.20
455	A132	7c org red & red	.30	.20
456	A132	12c ultra & blue	.80	.40

Perf. 11½

457	A132	17c brown & rose	1.00	.90
458	A132	20c yellow & gray	1.25	1.00
459	A132	36c dk vio & bl grn	1.25	1.25
460	A132	50c black & blue	4.00	3.00
461	A132	1p dk car & vio	10.00	6.00
		Nos. 454-461 (8)	18.90	12.95

First Year of Third Republic.

Artigas Type of 1928
Imprint: "Barreiro & Ramos S. A."

1934, Nov. 28   Litho.
462   A109   50c brown black   2.50 1.00

"Uruguay" and
"Brazil" Holding
Scales of Justice
A133

Florencio
Sánchez
A134

1935, May 30   Unwmk.   Perf. 11

463	A133	5m brown	.40	.20
464	A133	15m black	.20	.20
465	A133	3c green	.20	.20
466	A133	7c orange	.25	.20
467	A133	12c ultra	.65	.40
468	A133	50c yellow green	2.50	2.00
		Nos. 463-468 (6)	4.20	3.20

Visit of President Vargas of Brazil.

1935, Nov. 7

469	A134	3c green	.20	.20
470	A134	7c brown	.20	.20
471	A134	12c blue	.40	.25
		Nos. 469-471 (3)	.80	.65

Florencio Sanchez (1875-1910), author.

Artigas (6 dots in panels
below portrait) — A135

Imprint: "Imprenta Nacional" at center

1936-44   Perf. 11, 12½

474	A135	5m org brn ('37)	.20	.20
475	A135	5m lt brown ('39)	.20	.20
476	A135	1c lt violet ('37)	.20	.20
477	A135	2c dk brown ('37)	.20	.20
478	A135	2c green ('39)	.20	.20
479	A135	5c brt blue ('37)	.20	.20
480	A135	5c bluish grn ('39)	.20	.20
481	A135	12c dull blue ('38)	.20	.20
482	A135	20c fawn	.75	.25
482A	A135	20c rose ('44)	.50	.20
483	A135	50c brown black	2.00	.50

Size: 21½x28½mm

483A	A135	1p brown	6.00	2.00
483B	A135	2p blue	10.00	9.00
483C	A135	3p gray black	15.00	12.00
		Nos. 474-483C (14)	35.85	25.55

See Nos. 488, 576. See type A109.

Power Dam on
Black
River — A136

1937-38

484	A136	1c dull violet	.20	.20
485	A136	10c blue	.25	.20
486	A136	15c rose	1.00	.40
487	A136	1p choc ('38)	4.00	1.50
		Nos. 484-487 (4)	5.45	2.30

Imprint: "Imprenta Nacional" at right

1938
488   A135   1c bright violet   .20 .20

International Law Congress,
1889 — A137

1939, July 16   Litho.   Perf. 12½

489	A137	1c brown orange	.20	.20
490	A137	2c dull green	.20	.20
491	A137	5c rose ver	.20	.20
492	A137	12c dull blue	.40	.25
493	A137	50c lt violet	1.50	1.00
		Nos. 489-493 (5)	2.50	1.85

50th anniversary of the Montevideo Congress of International Law.

Artigas
A138   A138a

1939-43   Litho.   Unwmk.
Size: 15¾x19mm

494	A138	5m dl brn org ('40)	.20	.20
495	A138	1c lt blue	.20	.20
496	A138	2c lt violet	.20	.20
497	A138	5c violet brn	.20	.20
498	A138	8c rose red	.20	.20
499	A138	10c green	.20	.20
500	A138	15c dull blue	.45	.20

Size: 24x29½mm

501	A138	1p dull brn ('41)	1.60	.40
502	A138	2p dl rose vio ('40)	6.00	2.00
503	A138	4p orange ('43)	7.00	3.00
504	A138	5p ver ('41)	12.00	5.00
		Nos. 494-504 (11)	28.25	11.80

See No. 578.

Redrawn: Horizontal lines in portrait
background

1940-44
Size: 17x21mm

505	A138a	5m brn org ('41)	.20	.20
506	A138a	1c lt blue	.20	.20
507	A138a	2c lt violet ('41)	.20	.20
508	A138a	5c violet brn	.20	.20
509	A138a	8c sal pink ('44)	.20	.20
510	A138a	10c green ('41)	.20	.20
511	A138a	50c olive bis ('42)	3.75	.80
511A	A138a	50c yel grn ('44)	2.75	1.00
		Nos. 505-511A (8)	7.70	3.00

See Nos. 568-575, 577, 601, 632, 660-661. For surcharges see Nos. 523, 726.

Juan Manuel
Blanes, Artist
A139

Francisco
Acuna de
Figueroa
A140

1941, Aug. 11   Engr.   Perf. 12½
512 A139 5m ocher   .20   .20
513 A139 1c henna brown   .20   .20
514 A139 2c green   .20   .20
515 A139 5c rose carmine   .40   .20
516 A139 12c deep blue   .75   .35
517 A139 50c dark violet   3.50   2.75
    Nos. 512-517 (6)   5.25   3.90

1942, Mar. 18   Unwmk.
518 A140 1c henna brown   .20   .20
519 A140 2c deep green   .20   .20
520 A140 5c rose carmine   .20   .20
521 A140 12c deep blue   .75   .40
522 A140 50c dark violet   2.25   2.00
    Nos. 518-522 (5)   3.60   3.00

Issued in honor of Francisco Acuna de
Figueroa, author of the National anthem.

No. 506 Surcharged in
Red

1943, Jan. 27
523 A138a 5m on 1c lt bl   .20   .20

Coat of
Arms — A141

Clio — A142

1943, Mar. 12   Litho.
524 A141 1c on 2c dl vio brn
         (R)   .20   .20
525 A141 2c on 2c dl vio brn
         (V)   .20   .20
 a.   Inverted surcharge   12.50 12.50

Nos. 524-525 are unissued stamps
surcharged. See Nos. 546-555, Q67, Q69,
Q74-Q76.

1943, Aug. 24
526 A142 5m lt violet   .20   .20
527 A142 1c lt ultra   .20   .20
528 A142 2c brt rose   .25   .20
529 A142 5c buff   .25   .20
    Nos. 526-529 (4)   .90   .80

100th anniversary of the Historic and Geo-
graphic Institute of Uruguay.

Swiss Colony
Monument
A143

YMCA Seal
A144

Overprinted "1944" and Surcharged in
Various Colors

1944, May 18
530 A143 1c on 3c dull grn (R)   .20   .20
531 A143 5c on 7c brn red (B)   .20   .20
532 A143 10c on 12c dk bl (Br)   .30   .20
    Nos. 530-532 (3)   .70   .60

Founding of the Swiss Colony, 50th anniv.

1944, Sept. 8
533 A144 5c blue   .20   .20

100th anniv. of the YMCA.

Catalogue values for unused
stamps in this section, from this
point to the end of the section, are
for Never Hinged items.

"La Educación
del Pueblo"
A145

José Pedro
Varela
A146

A147

Monument
A148

Perf. 11½
1945, June 13   Litho.   Unwmk.
534 A145 5m brt green   .20   .20
535 A146 1c dp brown   .20   .20

Perf. 12½
536 A147 2c rose red   .20   .20
537 A148 5c blue   .20   .20
 a.   Perf. 11½   .20   .20
    Nos. 534-537 (4)   .80   .80

José Pedro Varela, author, birth cent.

Santiago
Vazquez
A149

Silvestre
Blanco
A150

Eduardo
Acevedo
A151

Bruno
Mauricio de
Zabala
A152

José Pedro
Varela — A153

José
Ellauri — A154

Gen. Luis de
Larrobla — A155

**Engraved (5m, 5c, 10c);
Lithographed**
1945-47   Perf. 10½, 11, 11½, 12½
538 A149 5m purple ('46)   .20   .20
539 A150 1c yel brn ('46)   .20   .20
540 A151 2c brown vio   .20   .20
541 A152 3c grn & dp grn ('47)   .20   .20
542 A153 5c brt carmine   .20   .20
543 A154 10c ultra   .30   .20
544 A155 20c dp grn & choc
         ('47)   .85   .35
    Nos. 538-544 (7)   2.15   1.55

No. C86A Surcharged in Blue

1946, Jan. 9   Perf. 12½
545 AP7 20c on 68c pale vio brn   .85   .45

Inauguration of the Black River Power Dam.
See No. C120.

Type A141 Overprinted

1946-51   Unwmk.   Litho.   Perf. 12½
546 A141 5m orange ('49)   .20   .20
 a.   Inverted overprint
547 A141 2c dl vio brn ('47)   .20   .20
548 A141 3c green   .20   .20
549 A141 5c ultra ('51)   .20   .20
550 A141 10c orange brn   .20   .20
551 A141 20c dk green   .45   .20
552 A141 50c brown   1.40   .50
553 A141 3p lilac rose   5.50   3.00
    Nos. 546-553 (8)   8.35   4.70

Type A141 Surcharged

1947-48
554 A141 2c on 5c ultra ('48)   .20   .20
555 A141 3c on 5c ultra   .20   .20

Statue of
Ariel — A158

Bas-relief
A160

Bust of José Enrique
Rodó — A159

Bas-relief
A161

Perf. 12½
1948, Jan. 30   Unwmk.   Eng
Center in Orange Brown
556 A158 1c grnsh gray   .20   .2
557 A159 2c purple   .20   .2
558 A160 3c green   .20   .2
559 A161 5c red violet   .20   .2
560 A160 10c dp orange   .20   .2
561 A161 12c ultra   .25   .2
562 A158 20c rose violet   .55   .2
563 A159 50c dp carmine   2.00   .9
    Nos. 556-563 (8)   3.80   2.3

Dedication of the Rodó monument.

View of the Port,
Paysandú — A162

Arms of
Paysandú
A163

1948, Oct. 9   Litho
564 A162 3c blue green   .20   .2
565 A163 7c ultra   .30   .2

Exposition of Industry and Agriculture
Paysandú, October-November 1948.

Santa Lucia
River
Highway
Bridge
A164

1948, Dec. 10
566 A164 10c dark blue   .40   .20
567 A164 50c green   1.60   .65

Redrawn Artigas Types of 1940, 1936,
1939

1948-51   Litho.   Perf. 12½
568 A138a 5m gray ('49)   .20   .20
569 A138a 1c rose vio ('50)   .20   .20
570 A138a 2c orange   .20   .20
571 A138a 2c choc ('50)   .20   .20
572 A138a 3c blue green   .20   .20
572A A138a 7c violet blue   .20   .20
573 A138a 8c rose car ('49)   .20   .20
574 A138a 10c orange brn ('51)   .20   .20
575 A138a 12c blue ('51)   .20   .20
576 A135 20c violet   .30   .20
577 A138a 20c rose pink ('51)   .55   .20

Size: 18x21¾mm
578 A138 1p lilac rose ('51)   1.10   .25
    Nos. 568-578 (12)   3.75   2.45

Nos. 571-572A also exist perf. 11.

Plowing
A165

Mounted
Cattle
Herder
A166

949, Apr. 29   Unwmk.   Perf. 12½
9 A165 3c green   .20 .20
0 A166 7c blue   .30 .20
n Regional American Conf. of Labor, 1949.

Cannon, Rural and Urban Views — A167

Symbolical of Soccer Matches — A168

950, Oct. 11   Litho.
81 A167 1c lilac rose   .20 .20
82 A167 3c green   .20 .20
83 A167 7c deep blue   .20 .20
    Nos. 581-583 (3)   .60 .60

200th anniv. of the founding of Cordón, a strict of Montevideo.

951, Mar. 20   Perf. 12½, 11
84 A168 3c green   .50 .20
85 A168 7c violet blue   1.00 .25

4th World Soccer Championship, Rio de aneiro.

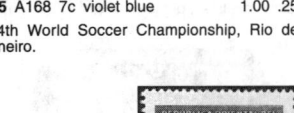

Gen. José Artigas — A169

Flight of the People A170

1c, 2c, 5c, Various equestrian portraits of rtigas. 7c, Dictating instructions. 8c, In congress. 10c, Artigas' flag. 14c, At the citadel. 0c, Arms of Artigas. In Paraguay. 1p, ust.

Engraved and Photogravure

952, Jan. 7   Unwmk.   Perf. 13½
86 A169 5m slate   .20 .20
87 A169 1c bl & blk   .20 .20
88 A169 2c pur & red brn   .20 .20
89 A170 3c aqua & dk brn   .20 .20
90 A169 5c red org & blk   .20 .20
91 A170 7c ol & blk   .20 .20
92 A170 8c car & blk   .25 .20
93 A170 10c choc, brt ultra & crim   .30 .20
94 A169 14c dp bl   .30 .20
95 A169 20c org yel, dp ultra & car   .40 .20
96 A169 50c org brn & blk   .85 .30
97 A169 1p bl gray & cit   2.75 1.25
    Nos. 586-597 (12)   6.05 3.55

Centenary (in 1950) of the death of Gen. osé Artigas.

Plane and Stagecoach A171

1952, Oct. 9   Photo.   Perf. 13½x13
598 A171 3c bl grn   .20 .20
599 A171 7c blk brn   .20 .20
600 A171 12c ultra   .30 .20
    Nos. 598-600 (3)   .70 .60

75th anniv. (in 1949) of the UPU.

Redrawn Artigas Type of 1940-44

1953, Feb. 23   Litho.   Perf. 11
Size: 24x29½mm
601 A138a 2p fawn   11.00 8.50

Franklin D. Roosevelt — A172

1953, Apr. 9   Engr.   Perf. 13½
602 A172 3c green   .20 .20
603 A172 7c ultra   .20 .20
604 A172 12c blk brn   .25 .20
    Nos. 602-604 (3)   .65 .60

5th Postal Cong. of the Americas & Spain.

Ceibo, Natl. Flower — A173   Horse Breaking — A174

Legislature Building A175

"Island of Seals" (Southern Sea Lions) — A176

Fair Entrance — A177

Designs: 2c, 10c, 5p, Ombu tree. 3c, 50c, Passion Flower. 7c, 3p, Montevideo fortress. 12c, 2p, Outer gate, Montevideo.

Perf. 13x13½, 13½x13, 12½x13, 13x12½
Photo. (5m, 3c, 20c, 50c); Engr.
1954, Jan. 14   Unwmk.
605 A173 5m multi   .20 .20
606 A174 1c car & blk   .20 .20
607 A174 2c brn & grn   .20 .20
608 A173 3c multi   .20 .20
609 A175 5c pur & red brn   .20 .20
610 A173 7c brn & grn   .20 .20
611 A176 8c car & ultra   .25 .20
612 A174 10c org & grn   .20 .20
613 A175 12c dp ultra & dk brn   .20 .20
614 A174 14c rose lil & blk   .20 .20
615 A173 20c grn, brn, gray & car   .35 .20
616 A173 50c car & multi   .75 .20
617 A175 1p car & red brn   1.25 .35
618 A175 2p car & blk brn   2.50 .75
619 A173 3p lil & blk   3.50 1.25
620 A176 4p dp brn & dp ultra   9.00 4.50
621 A174 5p vio bl & grn   8.50 4.00
    Nos. 605-621 (17)   27.90 13.25

For surcharges see Nos. 637-639, 750, C299.

1956, Jan. 19   Litho.   Perf. 11
622 A177 3c pale olive green   .20 .20
623 A177 7c blue   .25 .20
    Nos. 622-623,C166-C168 (5)   1.95 1.30

First Exposition of National Products.

José Batlle y Ordonez, Birth Centenary A178

Design: 7c, Full length portrait.

Perf. 13½
1956, Dec. 15   Wmk. 90   Photo.
624 A178 3c rose red   .20 .20
625 A178 7c sepia   .25 .20
    Nos. 624-625,C169-C172 (6)   1.95 1.50

Same Surcharged with New Values

1957-58
626 A178 5c on 3c ('58)   .20 .20
627 A178 10c on 7c   .25 .20
    a.   Surcharge inverted   17.00 17.00

Diver — A179   Eduardo Acevedo — A180

Design: 10c, Swimmer at start, horiz.

Perf. 10½, 11½
1958, Feb. 15   Litho.   Unwmk.
628 A179 5c brt bl grn   .20 .20
629 A179 10c brt bl   .35 .20

14th South American swimming meet, Montevideo.

1958, Mar. 19   Perf. 11½, 10½
630 A180 5c lt ol grn & blk   .20 .20
631 A180 10c ultra & blk   .25 .20

Eduardo Acevedo (1856-1948), lawyer, legislator, minister of foreign affairs, birth cent.

Artigas Type of 1940-44

1958, Sept. 25   Litho.   Perf. 11
632 A138a 5m blue   .25 .20

Baygorria Hydroelectric Works — A181

1958, Oct. 30   Unwmk.   Perf. 11
633 A181 5c yel grn & blk   .20 .20
634 A181 10c brn org & blk   .20 .20
635 A181 1p bl gray & blk   .50 .25
636 A181 2p rose & blk   .90 .45
    Nos. 633-636 (4)   1.80 1.10

Nos. 608, 610 and 605 Surcharged Similarly to

Photogravure and Engraved
1958-59   Perf. 13x13½
637 A173 5c on 3c multi ('59)   .30 .20
638 A173 10c on 7c brn & grn   .30 .20
639 A173 20c on 5m multi   .30 .20
    Nos. 637-639 (3)   .90 .60

Gabriela Mistral — A182   Carlos Vaz Ferreira — A183

Wmk. 327
1959, July 6   Litho.   Perf. 11½
640 A182 5c green   .20 .20
641 A182 10c dark blue   .20 .20
642 A182 20c red   .20 .20
    Nos. 640-642 (3)   .60 .60

Gabriela Mistral, Chilean poet and educator.

1959, Sept. 3   Perf. 11
643 A183 5c blk & lt bl   .20 .20
644 A183 10c blk & ocher   .20 .20
645 A183 20c blk & ver   .20 .20
646 A183 50c blk & vio   .25 .25
647 A183 1p blk & grn   .40 .25
    Nos. 643-647 (5)   1.25 1.10

Ferreira (1872-1958), educator and author.

A184   A185

Wmk. 332
1960, May 16   Litho.   Perf. 12
648 A184 3c red lil & blk   .20 .20
649 A184 5c dp vio & blk   .20 .20
650 A184 10c brt bl & blk   .20 .20
651 A184 20c chocolate & blk   .20 .20
652 A184 1p gray & blk   .25 .20
653 A184 2p org & blk   .50 .20
654 A184 3p olive grn & blk   .85 .35
655 A184 4p yel brn & blk   2.00 .75
656 A184 5p brt red & blk   2.50 .75
    Nos. 648-656 (9)   6.90 3.05

Dr. Martin C. Martinez (1859-1940), statesman.

1960, June 6   Wmk. 332   Perf. 12
657 A185 10c Uprooted oak emblem   .25 .20

Issued to publicize World Refugee Year, July 1, 1959-June 30, 1960. See No. C207.

Revolutionists and Cabildo, Buenos Aires — A186

1960, Nov. 4   Litho.   Perf. 12
658 A186 5c bl & blk   .20 .20
659 A186 10c bl & ocher   .20 .20
    Nos. 658-659,C208-C210 (5)   1.10 1.00

150th anniv. of the May Revolution of 1810.

Artigas Type of 1940-44

1960-61   Wmk. 332   Perf. 11
660 A138a 2c gray   .20 .20
661 A138a 50c brn ('61)   .20 .20

Gen. Manuel Oribe
(1796?-1857),
Revolutionary
Leader, Pres. of
Uruguay (1835-
38) — A187

1961, Mar. 4   Litho.   Perf. 12
671 A187 10c brt bl & blk   .25 .20
672 A187 20c bis & blk   .25 .20
673 A187 40c grn & blk   .25 .20
        Nos. 671-673 (3)   .75 .60

Cavalry
Charge
A188

1961, June 12   Wmk. 332   Perf. 12
674 A188 20c bl & blk   .20 .20
675 A188 40c emer & blk   .30 .20

150th anniversary of the revolution.

Welfare, Justice   Gen. José
and   Fructuoso
Education — A189   Rivera — A190

1961, Aug. 14   Wmk. 322   Perf. 12
676 A189 2c bister & lilac   .25 .20
677 A189 5c bister & orange   .25 .20
678 A189 10c bister & scarlet   .25 .20
679 A189 20c bister & yel grn   .25 .20
680 A189 50c bister & light vio .25 .20
681 A189 1p bister & blue   .35 .20
682 A189 2p bister & citron   .80 .20
683 A189 3p bister & gray   1.10 .45
684 A189 4p bister & light bl   1.75 .75
685 A189 5p bister & chocolate 1.90 1.00
        Nos. 676-685 (10)   7.15 3.60

Inter-American Economic and Social Con-
ference of the Organization of American
States, Punta del Este, August, 1961. See
Nos. C233-C244.

**   Wmk. 332**
1962, May 29   Litho.   Perf. 12
686 A190 10c brt red & blk   .20 .20
687 A190 20c bis & blk   .20 .20
688 A190 40c grn & blk   .20 .20
        Nos. 686-688 (3)   .60 .60

Issued to honor Gen. José Fructuoso Rivera
(1790-1854), first President of Uruguay.

Spade, Grain,
Swiss "Scarf" and
Hat — A191

Bernardo
Prudencio
Berro — A192

1962, Aug. 1   Wmk. 332   Perf. 12
689 A191 10c bl, blk & car   .20 .20
690 A191 20c lt grn, blk & car   .25 .20
        Nos. 689-690,C245-C246 (4) 1.05 .90

Swiss Settlement in Uruguay, cent.

1962, Oct. 22   Litho.   Perf. 12
691 A192 10c grnsh bl & blk   .20 .20
692 A192 20c yel brn & blk   .20 .20

Pres. Bernardo P. Berro (1803-1868).

Damaso
Larrañaga
A193

1963, Jan. 24   Wmk. 332   Perf. 12
693 A193 20c lt bl grn & dk brn .20 .20
694 A193 40c tan & dk brn   .20 .20

Damaso Antonio Larranaga (1771-1848),
teacher, writer and founder of National Library.

Rufous-bellied Thrush — A194

Birds: 50c, Rufous ovenbird. 1p, Chalk-
browed mockingbird. 2p, Rufous-collared
sparrow.

1963, Apr. 1   Wmk. 332   Perf. 12
695 A194 2c rose, brn & blk   .20 .20
696 A194 50c lt brn & blk   .45 .20
697 A194 1p tan, brn & blk   1.10 .20
698 A194 2p lt brn, blk & gray 2.25 .60
        Nos. 695-698 (4)   4.00 1.20

Thin frame on No. 696, no frame on No.
698.

UPAE
Emblem
A195

1963, May 31   Litho.
699 A195 20c ultra & blk   .25 .20
        Nos. 699,C252-C253 (3)   .70 .60

50th anniv. of the founding of the Postal
Union of the Americas and Spain, UPAE. For
surcharge see No. C321.

Wheat
Emblem — A196

Anchors — A197

1963, July 8   Wmk. 332   Perf. 12
700 A196 10c grn & yel   .20 .20
701 A196 20c brn & yel   .25 .20
        Nos. 700-701,C254-C255 (4) 1.05 1.00

FAO "Freedom from Hunger" campaign.

1963, Aug. 16
702 A197 10c org & vio   .20 .20
703 A197 20c dk red & gray   .25 .20
        Nos. 702-703,C256-C257 (4) 1.25 1.00

Voyage around the world by the Uruguayan
sailing vessel "Alferez Campora," 1960-63.

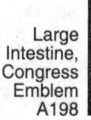

Large
Intestine,
Congress
Emblem
A198

1963, Dec. 9   Litho.
704 A198 10c lt grn, blk & dk car .20 .20
705 A198 20c org, yel, blk & dk car .25 .20

1st Uruguayan Proctology Cong., Montevideo, Dec. 9-15.

Red Cross
Centenary
Emblem
A199

Imprint: "Imp. Nacional"

1964, June 5   Wmk. 332   Perf. 12
706 A199 20c blue & red   .20 .20
707 A199 40c gray & red   .25 .20

Centenary of International Red Cross.
No. 706 exists with imprint missing. Value
$4.

Luis
Alberto de
Herrera
A200

1964, July 22   Litho.   Unwmk.
708 A200 20c dl grn, bl & blk   .20 .20
709 A200 40c lt bl, bl & blk   .20 .20
710 A200 80c yel org, bl & blk   .20 .20
711 A200 1p lt vio, bl & blk   .30 .25
712 A200 2p gray, bl & blk   .40 .35
        Nos. 708-712 (5)   1.30 1.20

Herrera (1873-1959), leader of Herrerista
party and member of National Government
Council.

Nile Gods
Uniting
Upper and
Lower
Egypt
(Abu
Simbel)
A201

1964, Oct. 30   Wmk. 332   Perf. 12
713 A201 20c multi   .25 .20
        Nos. 713,C266-C267 (3)   1.15 .90

UNESCO world campaign to save historic
monuments in Nubia. See No. C267a.

Pres. John
F. Kennedy
A202

1965, Mar. 5   Wmk. 327   Perf. 11½
714 A202 20c gold, emer & blk   .20 .20
  a. Gold omitted

1965
715 A202 40c gold, redsh brn &
            blk   .25 .2■
  a. Gold omitted
        Nos. 714-715,C269-C270 (4)   1.05 1.■

Tete
Beche
Pair of
1864, No.
21a
A203

1965, Mar. 19   Wmk. 332   Perf. 1■
716 A203 40c black & green   .25 .2■

1st Rio de la Plata Stamp Show, sponsore■
jointly by the Argentine and Uruguayan phi■
telic associations, Montevideo, Mar. 19-2■
See No. C271.

Benito
Nardone
A204

40c, Benito Nardone before microphone.

1965, Mar. 25   Lith■
717 A204 20c blk & emer   .20 .2■
718 A204 40c blk & emer, vert. .25 .2■

1st anniversary of the death of Benito Na■
done, president of the Council of Governmen■

Artigas Quotation — A205

40c, Artigas bust, quotation. 80c, José
Artigas.

**   Perf. 12x11½**
1965, May 17   Litho.   Wmk. 32■
719 A205 20c bl, yel & red   .20 .2■
720 A205 40c vio bl, cit & blk .20 .2■
721 A205 80c brn, yel, red & bl .30 .2■
        Nos. 719-721,C273-C275 (6) 1.65 1.4■

José Artigas (1764-1850), leader of the
independence revolt against Spain.

Soccer
A206

Designs: 40c, Basketball. 80c, Bicycling. 1p,
Woman swimmer.

1965, Aug. 3   Litho.   Wmk. 327
722 A206 20c grn, org & blk   .25 .2■
723 A206 40c hn brn, cit & blk .25 .2■
724 A206 80c gray, red & blk   .25 .2■
725 A206 1p bl, yel grn & blk   .25 .2■
        Nos. 722-725,C276-C281 (10) 3.70 2.8■

18th Olympic Games, Tokyo, 10/10-25/64.

No. 572A Surcharged
in Red

1965   Unwmk.   Perf. 12½
726 A138a 10c on 7c vio bl   .25 .2■

No. B5 Surcharged:

966, Jan. 25 Wmk. 327 *Perf. 11½*
27 SP2 4c on 5c + 10c grn & org .25 .20
Association of Uruguayan Architects, 50th
anniv.

Winston
Churchill
A207

Wmk. 332
966, Apr. 29 Litho. *Perf. 12*
28 A207 40c car, dp ultra & brn .25 .20
Sir Winston Spencer Churchill, statesman
and World War II leader. See No. C284.

Arms of Rio
de Janeiro
and Sugar
Loaf
Mountain
A208

966, June 9 Litho. **Wmk. 332**
29 A208 40c emer & brn .25 .20
400th anniversary of the founding of Rio de
Janeiro. See No. C285.

Army
Engineer — A209

Daniel Fernandez
Crespo — A210

966, June 17 Litho.
30 A209 20c blk, red, vio bl & yel .25 .20
50th anniversary of the Army Engineers
Corps.

966, Sept. 16 Wmk. 332 *Perf. 12*
Portraits: No. 732, Washington Beltran. No.
733, Luis Batlle Berres.
731 A210 20c lt bl & blk .25 .20
732 A210 20c lt bl & dk brn .25 .20
733 A210 20c brick red & blk .25 .20
  Nos. 731-733 (3) .75 .60
Issued to honor political leaders.

Old Printing
Press — A211

966, Oct. 14 Photo. *Perf. 12*
734 A211 20c tan, grnsh gray & dk
  brn .25 .20
50th anniversary of State Printing Office.

Fireman
A212

1966 Litho.
735 A212 20c red & blk .40 .25
Issued to publicize fire prevention. Printed
with alternating red and black labels inscribed:
"Prevengase del fuego! Del pueblo y para el
pueblo."

No. 716 Overprinted in Red: "Segunda
Muestra y / Jornadas Rioplatenses /
de Filatelia / Abril 1966 / Centenario
del Sello / Escudito Resellado"
1966, Nov. 4
736 A203 40c blk & grn .25 .20
2nd Rio de la Plata Stamp Show, Buenos
Aires, Apr. 1966, and cent. of Uruguay's 1st
surcharged issue. See No. C298.

General Leandro
Gomez — A213

#738, Gen. Juan Antonio Lavalleja. #739,
Aparicio Saravia, revolutionary, on horseback.

Wmk. 332
1966, Nov. 24 Litho. *Perf. 12*
737 A213 20c slate, blk & dp bl .20 .20
738 A213 20c red, blk & bl .20 .20
739 A213 20c blue & blk, horiz. .20 .20
  Nos. 737-739 (3) .60 .60

Montevideo
Planetarium
A214

1967, Jan. 13 Wmk. 332 *Perf. 12*
740 A214 40c pink & blk .30 .20
10th anniv. of the Montevideo Municipal
Planetarium. See No. C301.

Sunflower, Cow
and
Emblem — A215

Church of San
Carlos — A216

1967, Jan. 13 Litho.
741 A215 40c dk brn & yel .30 .20
Young Farmers' Movement, 20th anniv.

1967, Apr. 17 Wmk. 332 *Perf. 12*
742 A216 40c lt bl, blk & dk red .25 .20
Bicentenary of San Carlos.

Eduardo
Acevedo
A217

1967, Apr. 17
743 A217 20c grn & brn .20 .20
744 A217 40c org & grn .25 .20
Issued to honor Eduardo Acevedo, lawyer,
legislator and Minister of Foreign Affairs.

Arms of
Carmelo
A218

José Enrique Rodó
A219

1967, Aug. 11 Litho. *Perf. 12*
745 A218 40c lt & dk bl & ocher .25 .20
Founding of Carmelo, 150th anniv.

1967, Oct. 6 Wmk. 332 *Perf. 12*
2p, Portrait of Rodó and sculpture, horiz.
746 A219 1p gray, brn & blk .20 .20
747 A219 2p rose claret, blk & tan .20 .20
50th anniversary of the death of José
Enrique Rodó, author.

Senen M.
Rodriguez
and
Locomotive
A220

1967, Oct. 26 Litho. *Perf. 12*
748 A220 2p ocher & dk brn .35 .20
Centenary of the founding of the first
national railroad company.

Child and Map
of Americas
A221

Cocoi Heron
A222

1967, Nov. 10 Wmk. 332 *Perf. 12*
749 A221 1p vio & red .20 .20
Inter-American Children's Institute, 40th
anniv.

No. 610 Surcharged
in Red

Perf. 13x13½
1967, Nov. 10 Engr. Unwmk.
750 A173 1p on 7c brn & grn .25 .20

1968-70 Wmk. 332 Litho. *Perf. 12*
Birds: 1p, Great horned owl. 3p, Brown-
headed gull, horiz. No. 754, White-faced tree
duck, horiz. No. 754A, Black-tailed stilts. 5p,
Wattled jacanas, horiz. 10p, Snowy egret,
horiz.
751 A222 1p dl yel & brn 1.75 .30
752 A222 2p bl grn & blk 1.50 .30
753 A222 3p org, gray & blk
  ('69) 1.00 .25
754 A222 4p brn, tan & blk 2.40 .45
754A A222 4p ver & blk ('70) 1.00 .25

755 A222 5p lt red brn, blk
  & yel 3.00 .45
756 A222 10p lil & blk 5.25 .60
  Nos. 751-756 (7) 15.90 2.60

Concord
Bridge,
Presidents
of
Uruguay,
Brazil
A223

1968, Apr. 3
757 A223 6p brown .20 .20
Opening of Concord Bridge across the Uru-
guay River by Presidents Jorge Pacheco
Areco of Uruguay and Arthur Costa e Silva of
Brazil.

Soccer Player and
Trophy — A224

1968, May 29 Litho.
758 A224 1p blk & yel .25 .20
Victory of the Penarol Athletic Club in the
Intercontinental Soccer Championships of
1966.

St. John
Bosco,
Symbols of
Education
and Industry
A225

1968, July 31 Wmk. 332 *Perf. 12*
759 A225 2p brn & blk .25 .20
75th anniv. of the Don Bosco Workshops of
the Salesian Brothers.

Sailors'
Monument,
Montevideo
A226

Designs: 6p, Lighthouse and buoy, vert.
12p, Gunboat "Suarez" (1860).
1968, Nov. 12 Litho. *Perf. 12*
760 A226 2p gray ol & blk .20 .20
761 A226 6p grn & blk .20 .20
762 A226 12p brt bl & blk .20 .20
  Nos. 760-762,C340-C343 (7) 1.50 1.40
Sesquicentennial of National Navy.
For surcharge see No. Q101.

Oscar D.
Gestido
A227

1968, Dec. 6 Wmk. 332 *Perf. 12*
763 A227 6p brn, dp car & bl .25 .20
First anniversary of the death of President
Oscar D. Gestido.

Gearwheel, Grain and Two Heads A228

1969, Mar. 17　Litho.　Perf. 12
764　A228　2p blk & ver　.25 .20

25th anniversary of Labor University.

Bicyclists A229

1969, Mar. 21　Wmk. 332
765　A229　6p dk bl, org & emer　.30 .20

1968 World Bicycle Championships. See No. C347.

Gymnasts and Club Emblem A230

1969, May 8　Wmk. 332　Perf. 12
766　A230　6p blk & ver　.30 .20

75th anniversary of L'Avenir Athletic Club.

Baltasar Brum (1883-1933) A231

Former presidents: No. 768, Tomas Berreta (1875-1947).

1969　　Litho.　Perf. 12
767　A231　6p rose red & blk　.20 .20
768　A231　6p car rose & blk　.20 .20

Fair Emblem — A232

1969, Aug. 15　Wmk. 332　Perf. 12
769　A232　2p multi　.25 .20

Issued to publicize the 2nd Industrial World's Fair, Montevideo, 1970.

Diesel Locomotive A233

Design: No. 771, Old steam locomotive and modern railroad cars.

1969, Sept. 19　Litho.　Wmk. 332
770　A233　6p car, blk & ultra　.30 .25
771　A233　6p car, blk & ultra　.30 .25
　e.　Pair, #770-771　.60 .60

Centenary of Uruguayan railroads. No. 771e has continuous design and label between pairs.

For surcharges see Nos. Q102-Q103.

Souvenir Sheet

Diligencia Issue, 1856 — A233a

1969, Oct. 1　　Imperf.
771A　A233a　Sheet of 3　4.50 4.50
　b.　60p blue　1.40 1.40
　c.　80p green　1.75 1.75
　d.　100p red　2.00 2.00

Stamp Day 1969. No. 771A contains stamps similar to No. 1-3, with denominations in pesos.

No. 771A was re-issued Apr. 15, 1972, with black overprint for 15th anniv. of 1st Lufthansa flight from Uruguay to Germany and the Munich Olympic Games. Value $27.50.

"Combat" and Sculptor Belloni — A234

1969, Oct. 22　Wmk. 332　Perf. 12
772　A234　6p olive, slate grn & blk　.25 .20

José L. Belloni (1882-), sculptor.

Reserve Officers' Training Center Emblem A235

Design: 2p, Training Center emblem, and officer in uniform and as civilian.

1969, Nov. 5　　Litho.
773　A235　1p yel & dk bl　.20 .20
774　A235　2p dk brn & lt bl　.25 .20

Reserve Officers' Training Center, 25th anniv.

Map of Americas and Sun — A236　　Stylized Pine — A237

1970, Apr. 20　Wmk. 332　Perf. 12
775　A236　10p dp bl & gold　.25 .20

11th meeting of the governors of the Inter-American Development Bank, Punta del Este.

1970, May 14
776　A237　2p red, blk & brt grn　.25 .20

2nd National Forestry and Wood Exhibition.

Artigas' Ancestral Home in Sauce A238

1970, June 18　Wmk. 332　Perf. 12
777　A238　15p ver, ultra & blk　.30 .25

Map of Uruguay, Sun and Sea A239

1970, July 8　　Litho.
778　A239　5p greenish blue　.25 .20

Issued for tourist publicity.

EXPO '70 Emblem, Mt. Fuji and Uruguay Coat of Arms A240

EXPO '70 Intl. Exhibition, Osaka, Japan, 3/15-9/13: No. 780, Geisha. No. 781, Sun Tower. No. 782, Youth pole.

1970, Aug. 5　Wmk. 332　Perf. 12
779　A240　25p grn, slate bl & yel　.30 .30
780　A240　25p org, slate bl & grn　.30 .30
781　A240　25p yel, slate bl & pur　.30 .30
782　A240　25p pur, slate bl & org　.30 .30
　a.　Block of 4, #779-782　1.25 1.25

Cobbled Street in Colonia del Sacramento A241

Mother and Son by Edmundo Prati in Salto — A242

1970, Oct. 21　Litho.　Perf. 12
783　A241　5p blk & multi　.25 .20

290th anniv. of the founding of Colonia del Sacramento, the 1st European settlement in Uruguay.

1970, Nov. 4　　Litho.
784　A242　10p grn & blk　.35 .30

Issued to honor mothers.

URUEXPO Emblem A243

1970, Dec. 9　Wmk. 332　Perf. 12
785　A243　15p bl, brn org & vio　.30 .30

URUEXPO '70, National Philatelic Exposition, Montevideo, Sept. 26-Oct. 4.

Children Holding Hands, and UNESCO Emblem — A244

Children's Drawings: No. 786, Two girls holding hands, vert. No. 788, Boy sitting school desk, vert. No. 789, Astronaut and monster.

1970, Dec. 29　Litho.　Perf. 12
786　A244　10p multi　.20 .20
787　A244　10p multi　.20 .20
788　A244　10p dp car & multi　.20 .20
789　A244　10p bl & multi　.20 .20
　a.　Block of 4, #786-789 + 2 labels　.80 .80

International Education Year.

Alfonso Espinola (1845-1905), Physician, Professor and Philanthropist A245

1971, Jan. 13　Wmk. 332　Perf. 12
790　A245　5p dp org & blk　.25 .20

Exposition Poster — A246

1971　　Litho.　Perf. 12
791　A246　15p multi　.25 .20

Uruguay Philatelic Exposition, 1971, Montevideo, March 26-Apr. 19.

5c Coin of 1840, Obverse A247

Design: #793, 1st coin of Uruguay, reverse.

1971, Apr. 16　Wmk. 332　Perf. 12
792　A247　25p bl, brn & blk　.45 .45
793　A247　25p bl, brn & blk　.45 .45
　a.　Pair, #792-793　1.00 1.00

Numismatists' Day.

Domingo Arena, Lawyer and Journalist — A248

1971, May 3　Wmk. 332　Perf. 12
794　A248　5p dk car　.25 .20

National
Anthem
A249

1971, May 19   Litho.
5 A249 15p bl, blk & yel   .30 .30

José F. Arias,
Physician — A250

1971, May 25   Wmk. 332   Perf. 12
6 A250 5p sepia   .25 .20

Eduardo
Fabini,
Bar from
"Campo"
A251

1971, June 2   Litho.
7 A251 5p dk car rose & blk   .30 .30
Eduardo Fabini (1882-1950), composer,
nd 40th anniversary of first radio concert.

José E.
Rodó,
UPAE
Emblem
A252

1971, July 15   Wmk. 332   Perf. 12
8 A252 15p ultra & blk   .25 .20
José Enrique Rodó (1871-1917), writer, first
ruguayan delegate to Congress of the Postal
nion of the Americas and Spain.

Water
Cart and
Faucet
A253

1971, July 17
9 A253 5p ultra & multi   .25 .20
Centenary of Montevideo's drinking water
stem.

Sheep
and Cloth
A254

Design: 15p, Sheep, cloth and bale of wool.

1971, Aug. 7
00 A254 5p grn & gray   .20 .20
01 A254 15p dk bl, grnsh bl & gray .25 .20
Wool Promotion.

José
Maria
Elorza
and
Merilin
Sheep
A255

1971, Aug. 10
802 A255 5p lt bl, grn & blk   .20 .20
José Maria Elorza, developer of the Merilin
sheep.

Criollo
Horse
A256

1971, Aug. 11
803 A256 5p blk, gray bl & org   .25 .20

Bull and
Ram
A257

1971, Aug. 13
804 A257 20p red, grn, blk & gold   .30 .30
Centenary of Rural Association of Uruguay;
19th International Cattle Breeding Exposition,
and 66th National Cattle Championships at
Prado, Aug. 1971.

Symbol of
Liberty
and Order
A258

20p, Policemen, flag of Uruguay and
emblem.

1971
805 A258 10p gray, blk & bl   .20 .20
806 A258 20p dk bl, blk, lt bl & gold .25 .25
To honor policemen killed on duty. Issue
dates: 10p, Sept. 9; 20p, Nov. 4.

10p Banknote of 1896 — A259

Design: No. 808, Reverse of 10p note.

1971, Sept. 23
807 A259 25p dl grn, gold & blk   .30 .30
808 A259 25p dl grn, gold & blk   .30 .30
   a.   Pair, #807-808 + label   .80 .80
75th anniversary of Bank of the Republic.

Farmer
and Arms
of
Durazno
A260

1971, Oct. 11
809 A260 20p gold, bl & blk   .25 .20
Sesquicentennial of the founding of Durazno.

Emblem and Laurel — A261

1971, Oct. 20
810 A261 10p vio bl, gold & red   .25 .20
Winners of Liberator's Cup, American Soccer Champions, 1971.
For surcharge see No. 825.

Voter Casting
Ballot — A262

Design: 20p, Citizens voting, horiz.

1971, Nov. 22   Wmk. 332   Perf. 12
811 A262 10p bl & blk   .20 .20
812 A262 20p bl & blk   .20 .20
Universal, secret and obligatory franchise.

Map of
Uruguay on
Globe
A263

1971, Dec. 23
813 A263 20p lt bl & vio brn   .25 .20
7th Littoral Expo., Paysandu, 3/26-4/11.

Juan Lindolfo
Cuestas — A264

1971, Dec. 27
814 A264 10p shown   .20   .20
815 A264 10p Julio Herrera y
          Obes   .20   .20
816 A264 10p Claudio Williman   .20   .20
817 A264 10p José Serrato   .20   .20
818 A264 10p Andres Martinez
          Truebá   .20   .20
   a.   Horiz. strip of 5, #814-818   1.25 1.25
Presidents of Uruguay.

Souvenir Sheet

Uruguay No. 4, Cathedral of
Montevideo and Plaza de la
Constitucion — A265

1972, Jan. 17   Imperf.
819 A265 120p brn, bl & dp rose   .65   .65
Stamp Day 1971 (release date delayed).
See Nos. 834-835, 863.

Bartolomé
Hidalgo — A266

Missa Solemnis, by
Beethoven — A267

1972, Feb. 28   Perf. 12
820 A266 5p lt brn, blk & red   .20 .20
Bartolomé Hidalgo (1788-1822), Uru-
guayan-Argentine poet.

1972, Apr. 20   Litho.   Wmk. 332
822 A267 20p lil, emer & blk   .20 .20
12th Choir Festival of Eastern Uruguay.

Dove and
Wounded
Bird — A268

Columbus Arch,
Colon — A269

1972, May 9
823 A268 10p ver & multi   .20 .20
To honor Dionision Disz (age 9), who died
saving his sister.

1972, June 21
824 A269 20p red, bl & blk   .25 .20
Centenary of Colon, now suburb of
Montevideo.

No. 810 Surcharged in Silver

(Surcharge 69mm wide)

1972, June 30
825 A261 50p on 10p multi   .25 .25
Winners of the 1971 Intl. Soccer Cup.

Tree Planting — A270

"Collective Housing" — A271

1972, Aug. 5   Wmk. 332   Perf. 12
826 A270 20p grn & blk   .25 .20
Afforestation program.

1972, Sept. 30   Litho.
827 A271 10p dp bl & multi   .25 .20
Publicity for collective housing plan.

Amethyst A272

Uruguayan Gem Stones: 9p, Agate. 15p, Chalcedony.

1972, Oct. 7
828 A272 5p gray & multi   .20 .20
829 A272 9p gray bl & multi   .20 .20
830 A272 15p gray grn & multi   .25 .25
     Nos. 828-830 (3)   .65 .65

Uniform of 1830 — A273

Design: 20p, Lancer.

1972, Nov. 21   Litho.
831 A273 10p multi   .20 .20
832 A273 20p rose red & multi   .25 .25

Red Cross and Map of Uruguay A274

1972, Dec. 11   Wmk. 332   Perf. 12
833 A274 30p multi   .25 .25
75th anniv. of the Uruguayan Red Cross.

Stamp Day Type of 1972
Souvenir Sheets

Designs: 200p, Coat of arms type of 1864 similar to Nos. 18, 20-21, but 60p and 80p. 220p, Similar to Nos. 22-23, but 100p and 120p.

1972, Dec. 20   Imperf.
834 A265 200p multi   .60 .60
835 A265 220p multi   .75 .75
Stamp Day 1972. 1st printed cancellations, 200th anniv,. #834; Decree establishing regular postal service, cent., #835.

Scales of Justice, Olive Branch A275

1972, Dec. 27   Wmk. 332   Perf. 12
836 A275 10p gold, dk & lt bl   .25 .20
Civil Rights Law for Women, 25th anniv.

Gen. José Artigas A276

Hand Holding Cup; Grain, Map of Americas A277

1972-74   Wmk. 332   Litho.   Perf. 12
837 A276 5p yel ('74)   .20 .20
838 A276 10p dk bis ('74)   .20 .20
839 A276 15p emer ('74)   .20 .20
840 A276 20p lilac ('73)   .20 .20
841 A276 30p lt bl ('73)   .20 .20
842 A276 40p dp org ('73)   .20 .20
843 A276 50p ver ('73)   .20 .20
844 A276 75p ap grn ('73)   .20 .20
845 A276 100p emerald   .20 .20
846 A276 150p choc ('73)   .20 .20
847 A276 200p dk bl ('73)   .35 .30
848 A276 250p pur ('73)   .40 .35
849 A276 500p gray ('73)   1.00 .60
849A A276 1000p blue ('73)   2.00 1.25
     Nos. 837-849A (14)   5.75 4.50
For surcharges see Nos. 929-932.

1973, Jan. 9
850 A277 30p rose red, yel & blk   .25 .20
Intl. Institute for Agricultural Research, 39th anniv.

Elbio Fernandez and José P. Varela — A278

1973, Jan. 16
851 A278 10p dl grn, gold & blk   .25 .20
Society of Friends of Public Education, cent.

Map of Americas, "1972" and Columbus A279

1973, Jan. 30
852 A279 50p purple   .20 .20
Tourist Year of the Americas 1972.

Carlos Maria Ramirez, Scales and Books A280

1973, Feb. 15
853 A280 10p shown   .20 .20
854 A280 10p Justino Jimenez
           de Arechaga   .20 .20
855 A280 10p Juan Andres Ra-
           mirez   .20 .20
856 A280 10p Justino E. Jimenez
           de Arechaga   .20 .20
  a.   Horiz. strip, #853-856 + label 1.00 1.00
Professorship of Constitutional Rights, cent.

Provincial Map of Uruguay A281

1973, Feb. 27   Litho.   Perf. 12½x12
857 A281 20p bl & multi   .25 .20
See No. 1167.

Francisco de los Santos A282

1973, May 16   Wmk. 332   Perf. 12
858 A282 20p grn & blk   .20 .20
Soldiers' Day and Battle of Piedras. Santos was a courier who went through enemy lines.

No. C319 Surcharged with New Value and: "HOMENAJE AL 4 CENTENARIO DE CORDOBA . ARGENTINA . 1973"

1973, May 9   Litho.   Imperf.
Souvenir Sheet
859 AP57 100p on 5p multi   .75 .75
Founding of Cordoba in Argentina, 400th anniv.

Friar, Indians, Church — A283

1973, July 25   Perf. 12
860 A283 20p lt ultra, pur & blk   .25 .20
Villa Santo Domingo Soriano, first Spanish settlement in Uruguay.

Symbolic Fish A284

1973, Aug. 15
861 A284 100p bl & multi   .30 .25
First station of Oceanographic and Fishery Service, Montevideo.

A285

Sun over flower in Italian colors.

1973, Sept.
862 A285 100p multi   .20 .2
Italian Chamber of Commerce of Uruguay.

Stamp Day Type of 1972
Souvenir Sheet

Design: 240p, Thin numeral sun type 1859 and street scene.

Wmk. 332
1973, Oct. 1   Litho.   Imper
863 A265 240p grn, org & blk   .90 .9
Stamp Day 1973.

Herrera — A286

1973, Nov. 12   Perf. 1
866 A286 50p gray, brn & dk brn   .20 .2
Centenary of the birth of Luis Alberto d Herrera.

Emblem of Social Coordination Volunteers A287

Wmk. 352
1973, Nov. 19   Litho.   Perf. 1
867 A287 50p bl & multi   .25 .2
Festival of Nations, Montevideo.

Arm with Arteries and Heart A288

1973, Nov. 22
868 A288 50p blk, red & pink   .20 .2
3rd Cong. of the Pan-American Federatio of Blood Donors, Montevideo, Nov. 23-25.

Madonna, by Rafael Perez Barradas — A289

1973, Dec. 10   Litho.   Wmk. 33
869 A289 50p grn, gray & yel grn   .30 .2
Christmas 1973.

Nicolaus Copernicus — A290

1973, Dec. 26 **Litho.**
870 A290 50p grn & multi .25 .20

500th anniversary of the birth of Nicolaus Copernicus (1473-1543), Polish astronomer.

Praying Hands and Andes — A291

75p, Statue of Christ on mountain, and tower.

1973, Dec. 26 **Litho.**
871 A291 50p blk, lt grn & ultra .20 .20
872 A291 75p bl, blk & org .25 .20

Survival and rescue of victims of airplane crash.

OAS Emblem and Map of Americas A292

1974, Jan. 14 **Wmk. 332** **Perf. 12**
873 A292 250p gray & multi .60 .40

25th anniversary of the Organization of American States (OAS).

Scout Emblems and Flame A293

1974, Jan. 21
874 A293 250p multi .60 .40

1st Intl. Boy Scout Games, Montevideo, 1974.

Hector Suppici Sedes and Car — A294

1974, Jan. 28 **Perf. 12**
875 A294 50p sep, grn & blk .25 .20

70th anniversary of the birth of Hector Suppici Sedes (1903-1948), automobile racer.

Three Gauchos — A295

1974, Mar. 20 **Litho.** **Wmk. 332**
876 A295 50p multi .25 .20

Centenary of the publication of "Los Tres Gauchos Orientales" by Antonio D. Lussich.

Rifle, Target and Swiss Flag A296

1974, Apr. 2
877 A296 100p multi .25 .20

Centenary of the Swiss Rifle Association.

Map of Uruguay and Compass Rose A297

1974, Apr. 23 **Litho.**
878 A297 50p multi .25 .20

Military Geographical Service.

Montevideo Stadium Tower — A298

Design: 75p, Soccer player, Games' emblem, horiz. 1000p, similar to 75p.

1974, May 7 **Wmk. 332** **Perf. 12**
879 A298 50p multi .20 .20
880 A298 75p multi .20 .20
881 A298 1000p multicolored 16.00 6.25

World Cup Soccer Championship, Munich, June 13-July 7.
No. 881 had limited distribution. A souvenir sheet of one No. 881 was not valid for postage.

Tourism — A299

Wmk. 332
1974, June 6 **Litho.** **Perf. 12**
882 A299 1000p multicolored 35.00 35.00

No. 882 had limited distribution.

Old and New School and Founders A300

1974, May 21
883 A300 75p black & bister .25 .20

Centenary of the Osimani-Llerena Technical School at Salto, founded by Gervasio Osimani and Miguel Llerena.

Gardel and Score — A301

Volleyball and Net — A302

Wmk. 332
1974, June 24 **Litho.** **Perf. 12**
884 A301 100p multi .30 .25

Carlos Gardel (1887-1935), singer and motion picture actor. See No. 1173.

1974, July 11 **Wmk. 332** **Perf. 12**
885 A302 200p lil, yel & blk .30 .25

First anniversary of Women's Volleyball championships, Montevideo, 1973.

"Protect your Heart" — A303

Portrait and Statue — A304

1974, July 24 **Litho.**
886 A303 75p ol grn, yel & red .20 .20

Heart Foundation publicity.

1974, Aug. 5
887 A304 75p dk & lt bl .25 .20

Centenary (in 1973) of the founding of San José de Mayo by Eusebio Vidal.

A305 A306

Artigas statue, Buenos Aires, flags of Uruguay and Argentina.

1974, Aug. 13 **Perf. 12½**
888 A305 75p multi .30 .20

Unveiling of Artigas monument, Buenos Aires.

1974, Sept. 24 **Wmk. 332** **Perf. 12**
889 A306 100p Radio tower and waves .20 .20

50th anniv. of Broadcasting in Uruguay.

URUEXPO 74 Emblem — A307

URUEXPO Emblem and Old Map of Montevideo Bay — A308

1974
890 A307 100p blk, dk bl & red .20 .20
891 A308 300p sepia, red & grn .50 .50

URUEXPO 74 Philatelic Exhibition, 10th anniversary of Philatelic Circle of Uruguay (100p) and 250th anniversary of fortification of Montevideo.
Issue dates: 100p, Oct. 1; 300p, Oct. 19.

Letters and UPU Emblem
A309

UPU Cent.: 200p, UPU emblem, letter, and globe.

1974, Oct. 9
892 A309 100p lt bl & multi   .20 .20
893 A309 200p lil, blk & gold   .30 .20
  Nos. 892-893,C395-C396 (4)   1.80 1.70

A 1000p souvenir sheet was not valid for postage. Value $45.

Artigas Statue and Map of Lavalleja
A310

1974, Oct. 17   *Perf. 12*
894 A310 100p ultra & multi   .30 .20

Unveiling of Artigas statue in Minas, Lavalleja.

Ship in Dry Dock, Arsenal's Emblem
A312

1974, Nov. 15   Litho.   Wmk. 332
896 A312 200p multi   .30 .30

Centenary of Naval Arsenal, Montevideo.

Globe Hydrogen Balloon — A313

1974, Nov. 20
897 A313 100p shown   .25 .20
898 A313 100p Farman biplane   .25 .20
899 A313 100p Castaibert mono-
            plane   .25 .20
900 A313 100p Bleriot mono-
            plane   .25 .20
  a.   Strip of 4, #897-900   1.50 1.50
901 A313 150p Military and civil-
            ian pilots' em-
            blems   .25 .20
902 A313 150p Nieuport biplane .25 .20
903 A313 150p Breguet-Bidon
            fighter   .25 .20
904 A313 150p Caproni bomber   .25 .20
  a.   Strip of 4, #901-904   1.50 1.50
      Nos. 897-904 (8)   2.00 1.60

Aviation pioneers.

Sugar Loaf Mountain and Summit Cross — A314

1974, Nov. 30
905 A314 150p multi   .25 .20

Cent. of the founding of Sugar Loaf City.

Adoration of the Kings — A315

1974   *Perf. 12*
906 A315 100p shown   .20 .20
907 A315 150p Three Kings   .20 .20
  Nos. 906-907,C400 (3)   .70 .60

Christmas 1974. See No. C401. Issue dates: 100p, Dec. 17; 150p, Dec. 19.

Nike, Fireworks, Rowers and Club Emblem — A316

1975, Jan. 27   Litho.   Wmk. 332
908 A316 150p gray & multi   .20 .20

Centenary of Montevideo Rowing Club.

Treaty Signing, by José Zorilla de San Martin — A317

1975, Feb. 12   *Perf. 12*
909 A317 100p multi   .30 .20

Commercial Treaty between Great Britain and Uruguay, 1817.

Rose — A318

1975, Mar. 18   Litho.   Wmk. 332
910 A318 150p multi   .45 .30

Bicentenary of city of Rosario.

"The Oath of the 33," by Juan M. Blanes — A319

1975, Apr. 16   *Perf. 12*
911 A319 150p gold & multi   .35 .20

Sesquicentennial of liberation movement.

Ship, Columbus and Ancient Map — A320

1975, Oct. 9   Litho.   Wmk. 332
912 A320 1p gray & multi   .95 .60

Hispanic Stamp Day.

Leonardo Olivera and Santa Teresa Fort — A321

Artigas as Young and Old Man A322

1975   Litho.   Wmk. 332   *Perf. 12*
913 A321 10c org & multi   .20 .20
914 A322 50c vio bl & multi   .50 .40

Sesquicentennial of the capture of Fort Santa Teresa (10c) and of Uruguay's declaration of independence (50c).
  Issue dates: 10c, Oct. 20; 50c, Oct. 17.

Battle of Rincon, by Diogenes Hequet — A323

#916, Artigas' Home, Ibiray, Paraguay. 25c, Battle of Sarandi, by J. Manuel Blanes.

1975   **Lith**
915 A323 15c ol & blk   .20
916 A323 15c ol & multi   .20
917 A323 25c ol & multi   .30
  Nos. 915-917 (3)   .70

Uruguayan independence. Nos. 915 an 917, 150th anniversary of Battles of Rinco and Sarandi. No. 916, 50th anniversary school at Artigas mansion.
  Issued: #915, 10/23; #916, 11/18; #91 11/28.

"En Familia," by Sanchez A324

Florencio Sanchez A325

Plays by Sanchez: #919, Barranca Abajo #920, M'Hijo el Doctor. #921, Canillita.

1975, Oct. 31   Wmk. 332   *Perf. 1*
918 A324 20c gray, red & blk   .20 .2
919 A324 20c bl, grn & blk   .20 .2
920 A324 20c red, bl & blk   .20 .2
921 A324 20c grn, gray & blk   .20 .2
922 A325 20c multi   .20 .2
  a.   Block of 5 stamps + 4 labels 1.50

Florencio Sanchez (1875-1910), dramatist birth centenary. Nos. 918-922 printed se-ten-ant in sheets of 30 stamps and 20 labels.

Maria Eugenia Vaz Ferreira A326

Design: No. 924, Julio Herrera y Reissig.

1975
923 A326 15c yel, blk & brn   .20 .2
924 A326 15c org, blk & maroon .20 .2

Maria Eugenia Vaz Ferreira (1875-1924), poetess, and Julio Herrera y Reissig (1875-1910), poet, birth anniversaries.
  Issue dates: #923, Dec. 9; #924, Dec. 29.

A327

Virgin and Child — A328

Fireworks — A329

1975
925 A327 20c bl & multi .30 .30
926 A328 30c blk & multi .45 .45
927 A329 60c multi .60 .60
Nos. 925-927 (3) 1.35 1.35
Christmas 1975.
Issued: 20c, 12/16; 30c, 12/15; 60c, 12/11.

Col. Lorenzo Latorre (1840-1916), Pres. of Uruguay (1876-80) A330

1975, Dec. 30 **Perf. 12**
928 A330 15c multi .30 .20

Nos. 840, 842-843, 849A Surcharged

1975
929 A276 10c on 20p lilac .25 .25
930 A276 15c on 40p orange .25 .25
931 A276 50c on 50p ver .45 .45
932 A276 1p on 1000p blue .95 .95
Nos. 929-932 (4) 1.90 1.90
There are two surcharge types for Nos. 929 and 930. Values are the same.

Ariel, Stars, Book and Youths A331

1976, Jan. 12 **Litho.** **Wmk. 332**
933 A331 15c grn & multi .20 .20
75th anniversary of publication of "Ariel," by Jose Enrique Rodo (1872-1917), writer.

Water Sports — A332

Telephone A333

1976, Mar. 12 **Litho.** **Wmk. 332**
934 A332 30c multi .25 .20
23rd South American Swimming, Diving and Water Polo Championships.

1976, Apr. 9 **Perf. 12**
935 A333 83c multi .45 .30
Centenary of first telephone call by Alexander Graham Bell, Mar. 10, 1876.

"Plus Ultra" and Columbus' Ships — A334

Wmk. 332
1976, May 10 **Litho.** **Perf. 12**
936 A334 63c gray & multi .50 .30
Flight of Dornier "Plus Ultra" from Spain to South America, 50th anniversary.

A335 A336

Dornier "Wal" and Boeing 727, hourglass.

1976, May 24
937 A335 83c gray & multi .75 .30
Lufthansa German Airline, 50th anniv.

1976, June 3 **Perf. 11½**
Designs: 10c, Olympics. 15c, Telephone, cent. 25c, UPU, cent., UN #2. 50c, World Cup Soccer Championships, Argentina, 1978.
938 A336 10c shown 1.40 .50
939 A336 15c multicolored 1.40 .50
940 A336 25c multicolored 1.40 .50
941 A336 50c multicolored 1.40 .50
Nos. 938-941 (4) 5.60 2.00
Nos. 938-941 had limited distribution.
A souvenir sheet containing one each, Nos. 938-941, was not valid for postage. Value $25.

Louis Braille A340

1976, June 7
942 A340 60c blk & brn .75 .30
Sesquicentennial of the invention of the Braille system of writing for the blind by Louis Braille (1809-1852).

Signing of US Declaration of Independence A341

1976, June 21
943 A341 1.50p multi 1.75 1.40
American Bicentennial.

The Candombe, by P. Figari — A342

Wmk. 332
1976, July 29 **Litho.** **Perf. 12**
944 A342 30c ultra & multi .25 .20
Abolition of slavery, sesquicentennial.

Gen. Fructuoso Rivera Statue A343

1976, Aug. 2
945 A343 5p on 10p multi 3.50 1.75
No. 945 was not issued without surcharge.

General Accounting Office — A344

Wmk. 332
1976, Aug. 24 **Litho.** **Perf. 12**
946 A344 30c bl, blk & brn .30 .20
National General Accounting Office, sesquicentennial.

Old Pump, Emblem and Flame — A345

1976, Sept. 6
947 A345 20c red & blk .20 .20
First official fire fighting service, centenary.

Southern Lapwing A346

Mburucuya Flower A347

Spearhead A348

Figurine A349

La Yerra, by J. M. Blanes A350

The Gaucho, by Blanes A351

Artigas — A352

Designs: 15c, Ceibo flower.

1976-79 **Litho.** **Wmk. 332** **Perf. 12**
948 A346 1c violet .20 .20
949 A347 5c lt grn .20 .20
950 A347 15c car rose .20 .20
951 A348 20c gray .20 .20
952 A349 30c gray blue .20 .20
953 A352 45c brt bl ('79) .20 .20
954 A350 50c grnsh bl ('77) .20 .20
955 A351 1p dk brn ('77) .40 .20
956 A352 1p brt yel ('79) .20 .20
957 A352 1.75p bl grn ('79) .30 .30
958 A352 1.95p gray ('79) .30 .30
959 A352 2p dl grn ('77) .85 .40
960 A352 2p lil rose ('79) .40 .35
961 A352 2.65p vio ('79) .40 .40
962 A352 5p dk bl 2.50 1.75
963 A352 10p brn ('77) 4.50 1.75
Nos. 948-963 (16) 11.25 7.05

"Diligencia" Uruguay No. 1 — A353

Wmk. 332
1976, Sept. 26 **Litho.** **Perf. 12**
964 A353 30c bister, red & blue .30 .20
Philatelic Club of Uruguay, 50th anniv.

Games' Emblem — A354

1976, Oct. 26 **Litho.** **Perf. 12**
965 A354 83c gray & multi .75 .40
5th World University Soccer Championships.

World Cup Soccer Championships, Argentina — A355

Anniversaries and Events: 30c, 1976 Summer Olympics, Montreal. 50c, Viking spacecraft. 80c, Nobel prizes, 75th anniv.

1976, Nov. 12   *Perf. 12*
966 A355   10c multicolored   1.25   .65
967 A355   30c multicolored   1.25   .65
968 A355   50c multicolored   1.25   .65
969 A355   80c multicolored   1.25   .65
       Nos. 966-969 (4)   5.00 2.60

Nos. 966-969 had limited distribution.
See Nos. C424-C425.

Eye and
Spectrum
A356

1976, Nov. 24
970 A356   20c blk & multi   .30   .20
       Foresight prevents blindness.

Map of Montevideo, 1748 — A357

45c, Montevideo Harbor, 1842. 70c, First
settlers, 1726. 80c, Coin with Montevideo
arms, vert. 1.15p, Montevideo's first coat of
arms, vert.

                           Wmk. 332
1976, Dec. 30   *Litho.*   *Perf. 12*
971 A357 30c multi   .30   .20
972 A357 45c multi   .45   .20
973 A357 70c multi   .60   .35
974 A357 80c multi   .85   .35
975 A357 1.15p multi   1.40   .45
       Nos. 971-975 (5)   3.60 1.55

Founding of Montevideo, 250th anniversary.

Symbolic
of Flight
A358

1977, May 7   *Litho.*   *Perf. 12*
976 A358   80c multi   .75   .50
       50th anniversary of Varig airlines.

Artigas Mausoleum — A359

1977, June 17   *Litho.*   *Perf. 12*
977 A359   45c multi   .45   .30

A360

A361

1977, July 5   **Wmk. 332**
978 A360 45c Map of Uruguay,
              arch   .45   .30
Centenary of Salesian Brothers' educational
system in Uruguay.

1977, July 21
Anniversaries and events: 20c, Werner
Heisenberg, Nobel Prize for Physics. 30c,
World Cup Soccer Championships, Uruguay
Nos. 282, 390. 50c, Lindbergh's trans-Atlantic
flight, 50th anniv. 1p, Rubens 400th birth
anniv.

979 A361 20c shown   1.00   .60
980 A361 30c multicolored   1.00   .60
981 A361 50c multicolored   1.00   .60
982 A361 1p multicolored   1.00   .60
  a.   Strip, 2 ea #979-982 + 2 labels —   —
       Nos. 979-982 (4)   4.00 2.40

Nos. 979-982 had limited distribution.
A souvenir sheet containing Nos. 979-982,
imperf., was not valid for postage. It sold for
8p. See Nos. C426-C427.

Children — A362

Windmills — A364

"El Sol de
Mayo"
A363

1977, Aug. 10   *Litho.*   *Perf. 12*
983 A362   45c multi   .45   .30
Interamerican Children's Inst., 50th anniv.

1977, Oct. 1   *Litho.*   *Perf. 12*
984 A363   45c multi   .35   .35
       Stamp Day 1977.

1977, Sept. 29   **Wmk. 332**
985 A364 70c yel, car & blk   .55   .35
       Spanish Heritage Day.

Souvenir Sheet

View of Sans (Barcelona), by
Barradas — A365

1977, Oct. 7   *Litho.*   *Perf. 12*
986   A365   Sheet of 2   4.00 4.00
  a.-b.   5p, single stamp   1.75 1.75
ESPAMER '77 Philatelic Exhibition, Barcelona, Oct. 7-13.

Planes,
UN
Emblem,
Globe
A366

1977, Oct. 17
987 A366 45c multi   .25   .20
       30th anniv. of Civil Aviation Organization.

Holy
Family — A367

Santa Claus — A368

1977, Dec. 1   **Wmk. 332**
988 A367 45c multi   .20   .20
989 A368 70c blk, yel & red   .20   .20
       Christmas 1977.

Map of
Rio Negro
Province
A369

1977, Dec. 16
990 A369 45c multi   .20   .20
Rio Negro Dam; development of argiculture,
livestock and beekeeping. See Nos. 1021-
1033.

Mail Collection
A370

1977, Dec. 21
991   A370 50c shown   .20   .2
992   A370 50c Mail truck   .20   .2
993   A370 50c Post office
               counter   .20   .2
994   A370 50c Postal boxes   .20   .2
995   A370 50c Mail sorting   .20   .2
996   A370 50c Pigeonhole sort-
               ing   .20   .2
997   A370 50c Route sorting
               (seated carriers)   .20   .2
998   A370 50c Home delivery   .20   .2
999   A370 50c Special delivery
               (motorcyclists)   .20   .2
1000 A370 50c Airport counter   .20   .2
  a.   Strip of 10, #991-1000   2.40 2.4
       Uruguayan postal service, 150th anniv.

Edison's Phonograph, 1877 — A371

1977, Dec. 30
1001 A371 50c vio brn & yel   .20   .20
Centenary of invention of the phonograph.

"R",
Rainbow
and
Emblem
A372

1977, Dec. 30   **Wmk. 332**
1002 A372 50c multi   .20   .20
       World Rheumatism Year.

Emblem
and
Diploma
A373

1978, Mar. 27   *Litho.*   *Perf. 12*
1003 A373 50c multi   .25   .20
       50th anniversary of Military College.

Erhard Schon by Albrecht Durer
(1471-1528) — A374

Painting: 50c, Self-Portrait by Peter Paul
Rubens (1577-1640).

1978, June 13   *Perf. 12½*
1004 A374 25c blk & brn   .80   .75
1005 A374 50c brn & blk   1.40 1.10

Nos. 1004-1005 had limited distribution.
See Nos. C430-C432.

Map and Arms of Artigas Department — A375

Wmk. 332

1978, June 16   Litho.   Perf. 12
1006 A375 45c multi   .30 .20

Souvenir Sheet

Anniversaries — A376

Designs: 2p, Papilio thoas. No. 1007b, "100." No. 1007c, Argentina '78 emblem and globes. 5p, Model T Ford.

Wmk. 332

1978, Aug. 24   Litho.   Perf. 12
1007 A376 Sheet of 4   15.00 15.00
  a.   2p multi   1.75   1.75
  b.   4p multi   3.50   3.50
  c.   4p multi   3.50   3.50
  d.   5p multi   4.25   4.25

75th anniv. of 1st powered flight; URUEXPO '78 Phil. Exhib.; Parva Domus social club, cent.; 11th World Cup Soccer Championship, Argentina, June 1-25; Ford motor cars, 75th anniv.

Visiting Angels, by Solari — A377

Designs (Details from No. 1008b): No. 1008a, Second angel. No. 1008c, Third angel.

1978, Sept. 13   Unwmk.
1008 Strip of 3   1.60 1.60
  a.   A377 1.50p, 19x30mm   .30   .30
  b.   A377 1.50p, 38x30mm   .30   .30
  c.   A377 1.50p, 19x30mm   .30   .30

Solari, Uruguayan painter.

Bernardo O'Higgins A378

#1010, José de San Martin and monument.

1978   Wmk. 332
1009 A378 1p multi   .25 .20
1010 A378 1p multi   .25 .20

Benardo O'Higgins (1778-1842) and José de San Martin (1778-1850), South American liberators.
Issued: #1009, Sept. 13; #1010, Oct. 10.

Telephone Dials A379

1978, Sept. 25
1011 A379 50c multi   .30 .20

Automation of telephone service.

Symbolic Stamps A380

Iberian Tile Pattern — A381

1978, Oct. 31
1012 A380 50c multi   .20 .20
1013 A381 1p multi   .25 .20

Stamp Day (50c) and Spanish heritage (1p).

Boeing 727 A382

1978, Nov. 27
1014 A382 50c multi   .50 .20

Inauguration of Boeing 727 flights by PLUNA Uruguayan airlines, Nov. 1978.

Angel Blowing Horn — A383

1978, Dec. 7
1015 A383 50c multi   .20 .20
1016 A383 1p multi   .30 .20

Christmas 1978.

A384

A385

1978, Dec. 15   Perf. 12½
1017 A384 1p Flag flying on Plaza
            of the Nation   .25 .20

Wmk. 332

1978, Dec. 27   Litho.   Perf. 12
1018 A385 1p blk, red & yel   .25 .20

Horacio Quiroga (1868-1928), short story writer.

Arch, Olympic Rings, Lake Placid and Moscow Emblems A386

7p, Olympic Rings, Lake Placid '80 emblem.

1979, Apr. 28   Litho.   Perf. 12
1019 A386 5p multi   1.40 1.40
1020 A386 7p multi   1.75 1.00

81st Session of Olympic Organizing Committee, Apr. 3-8 (5p), and 13th Winter Olympic Games, Lake Placid, NY, Feb. 12-24.

Souvenir Sheets
1021   Sheet of 4   15.00 15.00
  a. A386 3p similar to #1019
  b. A386 5p Olympic rings
  c. A386 7p Rider looking back
  d. A386 10p Rider facing forward
1022   Sheet of 4   15.00 15.00
  a. A386 3p similar to #1020
  b. A386 5p Uruguay '79
  c. A386 7p World Chess Olym-
            pics '78
  d. A386 10p Sir Rowland Hill,
            Great Britain stamp

No. 1022d shows Great Britain No. 836, but with 11p denomination. No. 1021c-1021d have continuous design.
Nos. 1021-1022 had limited distribution. Except for No. 1022d, singles were sold for postal use in 1980. Nos. 1021-1022 exist imperf.

Map and Arms of Paysandu A387

Map and Arms of Maldonado A388

1979-81
1023 A387 45c shown   .20 .20
1024 A387 45c Salto   .20 .20
1025 A388 45c shown   .20 .20
1026 A387 45c Cerro Largo   .20 .20
1027 A387 50c Treinta y Tres   .20 .20
1028 A387 50c Durazno ('80)   .20 .20
1029 A388 2p Rocha ('81)   .35 .35
1030 A388 2p Flores   .35 .35
      Nos. 1023-1030 (8)   1.90 1.90

See No. 990.

Sapper with Pickax, 1837 — A389

Army Day: No. 1039, Artillery man with cannon, 1830.

1979, May 18   Litho.   Perf. 12
1038 A389 5p multi   1.90 1.00
1039 A389 5p multi   1.90 1.00

Madonna and Child by Durer A390

Anniversaries and events: 80c, World Cup Soccer Championships, Spain. 1.30p, Sir Rowland Hill, Greece No. 117.

1979, June 18   Perf. 12
1040 A390 70c brn & gray   5.25 2.75
1041 A390 80c multicolored   4.00 2.10
1042 A390 1.30p multicolored   4.00 2.10
      Nos. 1040-1042 (3)   13.25 6.95

Nos. 1040-1042 had limited distribution. Issued in sheets of 24 containing 6 blocks of 4 with margin around. See #C437-C438.

Salto Dam A391

1979, June 19
1043 A391 2p multi   .45 .30

Crandon Institute Emblem, Grain A392

1979, July 19
1044 A392 1p vio bl & bl   .30 .20

Crandon Institute (private Methodist school), centenary.

IYC Emblem, Smiling Kites — A393

Cinderella A394

1979
1045 A393 2p multi   .35 .25
1046 A394 2p multi   .35 .25

International Year of the Child. Issue dates: No. 1045, July 23; No. 1046, Aug. 29.

Uruguay Coat of Arms 150th Anniversary — A395

1979, Sept. 6
1047 A395 8p multi   2.25 1.40

Virgin and Child — A396

Symbols, by Torres-Garcia A397

    Wmk. 332
1979, Nov. 19   Litho.   Perf. 12
1048 A396 10p multi   2.75 1.60
Christmas 1979; Intl. Year of the Child.

1979, Nov. 12
1049 A397 10p yel & blk   2.75 1.60
J. Torres-Garcia (1874-1948), painter.

UPU and Brazilian Postal Emblems — A398

1979, Oct. 11
1050 A398 5p multi   1.25 .80
18th UPU Congress, Rio, Sept.-Oct.

Dish Antenna and Sun — A400

    Perf. 12x11½
1979, Nov. 26   Litho.   Wmk. 332
1052 A400 10p multi   2.75 1.25
Telecom '79, 3rd World Telecommunications Exhibition, Geneva, Sept. 20-26.

Spanish Heritage Day — A401

1979, Dec. 3   Perf. 12
1053 A401 10p multi   1.25 1.60

Silver Coin Centenary A402

Designs: Obverse and reverse of coins in denominations matching stamps.

1979, Dec. 26
1054 A402 10c multi   .20 .20
1055 A402 20c multi   .20 .20
1056 A402 50c multi   .20 .20
1057 A402   1p multi   .30 .20
    Nos. 1054-1057 (4)   .90 .80

    Souvenir Sheet

Security Agent — A403

1980, Jan. 10
1058   Sheet of 4   3.00 3.00
  a. A403 1p Police emblem   .30 .30
  b. A403 2p shown   .50 .50
  c. A403 3p Policeman, 1843   .75 .75
  d. A403 4p Cadet, 1979   1.00 1.00
   Police force sesquicentennial.

Light Bulb, Thomas Edison — A404

1980, Jan. 18
1059 A404 2p multi   .40 .30
   Centenary of electric light (1979).

Bass and Singer — A405

1980, Jan. 30
1060   Sheet of 4   3.00 3.00
  a. A405 2p Radio waves   .65 .65
  b. A405 2p shown   .65 .65
  c. A405 2p Ballerina   .65 .65
  d. A405 2p Television waves   .65 .65
Performing Arts Society, 50th anniversary.

Stamp Day — A406

La Leyenda Patria — A407

1980, Feb.
1061 A406 1p multi   .30 .20

1980, Feb. 26
1062 A407 1p multi   .30 .20

Printers' Association, 50th Anniversary A408

1980, Feb.
1063 A408 1p multi   .30 .20

Lufthansa Cargo Container Service Inauguration — A409

1980, Apr. 12   Unwmk.   Perf. 12½
1064 A409 2p multi   .45 .25

Conf. Emblem, Banners — A410

1980, Apr. 28   Wmk. 332   Perf. 12
1065 A410 2p multi   .60 .35
8th World Hereford Conf., Punta del Este and Livestock Exhib., Prado/Montivideo.

1980   Litho.   Perf. 12
1066 A411 1p multi   .30 .20
  International Year of the Child (1979).

Man, Woman and Birds — A411

Latin-American Lions, 9th Forum — A412

1980, May 6   Wmk. 332   Perf. 1
1067 A412 1p multi   .30 .2[0]

    Souvenir Sheet

Rifleman, 1814 — A413

1980, May 16
1068   Sheet of 4   3.50 3.50
  a. A413 2p shown   .80 .80
  b. A413 2p Cavalry officer, 1830   .80 .80
  c. A413 2p Private Liberty Dragoons, 1826   .80 .80
  d. A413 2p, Artigas Militia officer, 1815   .80 .80
   Army Day, May 18.

Arms of Colonia — A414

Colonia, 1680 A415

1980, June 17   Litho.   Perf. 12
1069 A414 50c multi   1.25 .20
    Souvenir Sheet
1070   Sheet of 4   1.10 1.10
  a. A415 1p shown   .25 .25
  b. A415 1p 1680, diff.   .25 .25
  c. A415 1p 1980   .25 .25
  d. A415 1p 1980, diff.   .25 .25
   Colonia, 300th anniversary.

Rotary Emblem on Globe — A416

Hand Putting Out Cigarette — A417

980, July 8
071 A416 5p multi 1.50 .90
Rotary International, 75th anniversary.

980, Sept. 8 **Photo.**
072 A417 1p multi .25 .20
World Health Day and anti-smoking campaign.

Artigas — A418

Christmas 1980 A419

Wmk. 332
980-85 **Litho.** **Perf. 12½**
073 A418 10c blue ('81) .20 .20
074 A418 20c orange .20 .20
075 A418 50c red .20 .20
076 A418 60c yellow .20 .20
077 A418 1p gray .45 .25
078 A418 2p brown .85 .30
079 A418 3p brt grn 1.50 .35
080 A418 4p brt bl ('82) 1.75 .45
081 A418 5p green ('82) .95 .25
082 A418 6p brt org ('85) .35 .20
083 A418 7p lil rose ('82) 4.50 .75
084 A418 10p blue ('82) 1.75 .35
085 A418 12p blk ('85) .95 .25
086 A418 15.50p emer ('85) 1.25 .30
087 A418 20p dk vio ('82) 3.75 .75
088 A418 30p lt brn ('82) 5.50 .75
089 A418 50p gray bl ('82) 9.00 1.90
Nos. 1073-1089 (17) 33.35 7.65

980, Dec. 15 **Litho.** **Perf. 12**
090 A419 2p multi .50 .25

Constitution Title Page — A420

980, Dec. 23 **Perf. 12½**
091 A420 4p brt bl & gold 1.25 .65
Sesquicentennial of Constitution.

A421

A422

1980, Dec. 30 **Perf. 12**
1092 A421 5p Montevideo Stadium 1.50 .90
1093 A421 5p Soccer gold cup 1.50 .90
Size: 25x79mm
1094 A421 10p Flags 1.50 .90
a. Souv. sheet of 3, #1092-1094 7.75 7.75
Nos. 1092-1094 (3) 4.50 2.70
Soccer Gold Cup Championship, Montevideo.

1981, Jan. 27
1095 A422 2p multi .60 .20
Spanish Heritage Day.

UPU Membership Centenary — A423

1981, Feb. 6
1096 A423 2p multi .60 .20

Alexander von Humboldt (1769-1859), German Explorer and Scientist — A424

1981, Feb. 19
1097 A424 2p multi .60 .25

Intl. Education Congress and Fair, Montevideo (1980) — A425

1981, Mar. 31
1098 A425 2p multi .60 .20

Hand Holding Gold Cup — A426

Eighth Notes on Map of Americas — A427

1981, Apr. 8
1099 A426 2p multi .60 .25
1100 A426 5p multi 1.40 .50
1980 victory in Gold Cup Soccer Championship.

1981, Apr. 28
1101 A427 2p multi .60 .20
Inter-American Institute of Musicology, 40th anniv.

World Tourism Conference, Manila, Sept. 27, 1980 — A428

Wmk. 332
1981, June 1 **Litho.** **Perf. 12**
1102 A428 2p multi .60 .25

Inauguration of PLUNA Flights to Madrid — A429

1981, May 12
1103 A429 2p multi .40 .25
1104 A429 5p multi .95 .45
1105 A429 10p multi 1.90 .95
Nos. 1103-1105 (3) 3.25 1.65

Army Day — A430

Natl. Atomic Energy Commission, 25th Anniv. — A431

Wmk. 332
1981, May 18 **Litho.** **Perf. 12**
1106 A430 2p Cavalry soldier, 1843 .60 .25
1107 A430 2p Infantryman, 1843 .60 .25

1981, July 20
1108 A431 2p multi .60 .25

Europe-South American Soccer Cup — A432

1981, Aug. 4
1109 A432 2p multi .75 .25

Stone Tablets, Salto Grande Excavation — A433

1981, Sept. 10
1110 A433 2p multi .60 .25

10th Lavalleja Week — A434

1981, Oct. 3
1111 A434 4p multi 1.40 .45

Intl. Year of the Disabled A435

Wmk. 332
1981, Oct. 26 **Litho.** **Perf. 12**
1112 A435 2p multi .60 .25

UN Environmental Law Meeting Montevideo, Oct. 28-Nov. 6 — A436

1981, Oct. 28
1113 A436 5p multi 1.40 .45

A437

A439

1981, Oct. 13
1114 A437 2p multi .60 .25

50th anniv. of ANCAP (Natl. Administration of Combustible Fuels, Alcohol and Cement).

1981, Dec. 5 *Perf. 12*
1116 A439 2p multi .60 .25

Topographical Society sesqu. See No. 1407.

Bank of Uruguay, 85th Anniv. — A440

1981, Dec. 17 *Perf. 12½*
1117 A440 2p multi .60 .25

Palmar Dam — A441

1981, Dec. 22 *Perf. 12*
1118 A441 2p multi .60 .25

Christmas
1981
A442

1981, Dec. 23
1119 A442 2p multi .60 .25

Pres. Joaquin
Suarez
Bicentenary
A443

1982, Mar. 15
1120 A443 5p multi .95 .45

Artillery Captain,
1872, Army
Day — A444

Cent. (1981) of
Pinocchio, by
Carlo
Collodi — A445

Wmk. 332
1982, May 18 **Litho.** *Perf. 12*
1121 A444 3p shown .90 .25
1122 A444 3p Florida Battalion, 1865 .90 .25

See Nos. 1136-1137.

1982, June 17
1123 A445 2p multi .60 .25

2nd UN
Conference on
Peaceful Uses
of Outer
Space,
Vienna, Aug.
9-21 — A446

1982, June 3
1124 A446 3p multi .90 .60

World
Food Day
A447

1982
1125 A447 2p multi .60 .20

25th Anniv. of Lufthansa's Uruguay-
Germany Flight — A448

1982, Apr. 14 **Unwmk.** *Perf. 12½*
1126 A448 3p Lockheed L-1049-
G Super Constel-
lation .80 .35
1127 A448 7p Boeing 747 1.90 .65

American Air
Forces
Cooperation
System — A449

1982, Apr. 14 **Wmk. 332** *Perf. 12*
1128 A449 10p Emblem 2.65 .80

Juan Zorilla de San Martin (1855-
1931), Painter — A450

1982, Aug. 18 *Perf. 12½*
1129 A450 3p Self-portrait .65 .35

165th Anniv. of Natl. Navy — A451

1982, Nov. 15 *Perf. 12*
1130 A451 3p Navy vessel Capitan
Miranda .75 .30

Natl. Literacy
Campaign — A452   Stamp
Day — A453

1982, Nov. 30
1131 A452 3p multi .60 .25

1982, Dec. 23 *Perf. 12½*
1132 A453 3p like #46 .30 .20
1133 A453 3p like #47 .30 .20
a. Pair, #1132-1133 1.10 1.10

These stamps bear numbers from 1 to 100 according to their position on the sheet.

Christmas 1982 — A454

1983, Jan. 4 *Perf. 12*
1134 A454 3p multi .50 .25

Eduardo Fabini (1882-1950),
Composer — A455

1983, May 10
1135 A455 3p gold & brn .50 .2●

Army Day Type of 1982
1983, May 18
1136 A444 3p Military College cadet, 1885 .45 .2●
1137 A444 3p 2nd Cavalry Regiment officer, 1885 .45 .2●

Visit of King Juan Carlos and Queen
Sofia of Spain, May — A456

1983, May 20 **Unwmk**
1138 A456 3p Santa Maria, globe .65 .3●
1139 A456 7p Profiles, flags 1.40 .6●

Size of No. 1138: 29x39mm.

Brasiliana '83
Emblem — A457

80th Anniv. of
First Automobile
in
Uruguay — A458

Opening of UPAE
Building,
Montevideo
A459

Jose Cuneo
(1887-1977),
Painter — A460

1982 World Cup A461

Graf Zeppelin Flight Over Montevideo, 50th Anniv. (1984) — A462

J.W. Goethe (1749-1832), 150th Death Anniv. — A463

First Space Shuttle Flight A464

1983	Litho.	Wmk. 332	Perf. 12	
140	A457	3p multi	1.00	1.00
141	A458	3p multi	1.00	1.00
142	A459	3p multi	1.00	1.00
143	A460	3p multi	1.00	1.00
a.		Souvenir sheet of 4	6.00	6.00
144	A461	7p multi	1.50	1.50
145	A462	7p multi	1.50	1.50
146	A463	7p multi	1.50	1.50
147	A464	7p multi	1.50	1.50
a.		Souvenir sheet of 4	7.50	7.50
		Nos. 1140-1147 (8)	10.00	10.00

No. 1143a contains stamps similar to Nos. 140-1143. No. 1147a stamps similar to Nos. 144-1147. Nos. 1143a and 1147a for URUEXPO '83 and World Communications Year.

Issued: #1142, 6/8; #1143, 1146, 9/29; #1143a, 1147a, 6/9; #1140, 7/22; #1144, 2/13; #1146, 9/20; #1145, 12/8.

Bicentenary of City of Minas — A465

Wmk. 332
1983, Oct. 17	Litho.	Perf. 12	
148	A465	3p Founder	.65	.20

World Communications Year — A466

1983, Nov. 30
| 149 | A466 | 3p multi | .25 | .20 |

Garibaldi Death Centenary A467

1983, Dec. 5
| 1150 | A467 | 7p multi | .75 | .30 |

Christmas 1983 A468

Lithographed and Embossed (Braille)
1983, Dec. 21   Perf. 12½
| 1151 | A468 | 4.50p multi | .55 | .25 |

50th Anniv. of Automatic Telephones — A469

1983, Dec. 27   Perf. 12
| 1152 | A469 | 4.50p multi | .50 | .20 |

Simon Bolivar, Battle Scene A470

Wmk. 332
1984, Mar. 28   Litho.   Perf. 12
| 1153 | A470 | 4.50p brn & gldn brn | .95 | .30 |

Gen. Leandro Gomez — A471

1984, Jan. 2
| 1154 | A471 | 4.50p multi | .40 | .25 |

American Women's Day — A472

Reunion Emblem A473

1984, Feb. 18
| 1155 | A472 | 4.50p Flags, emblem | .40 | .25 |

1984, Mar. 23
| 1156 | A473 | 10p multi | .95 | .45 |

Intl. Development Bank Governors, 25th annual reunion, Punta del Este.

50th Anniv. of Radio Club of Uruguay (1983) A474

1984, Apr. 11
| 1157 | A474 | 7p multi | .60 | .30 |

A475

A476

1984, Feb. 7   Litho.   Perf. 12
| 1158 | A475 | 4.50p multi | .40 | .25 |

Intl. Maritime Org., 25th anniv.

1984, May 2   Litho.   Perf. 12
| 1159 | A476 | 4.50p multi | .40 | .25 |

1930 World Soccer Championships, Montevideo.

Department of San José de Mayo, 200th Anniv. — A477

1984, May 9   Litho.   Perf. 12
| 1160 | A477 | 4.50p multi | .40 | .25 |

50 años de Turismo 1933-1983

Tourism, 50th Anniv. A478

1984, May 15   Litho.   Perf. 12
| 1161 | A478 | 4.50p multi | .40 | .25 |

Military Uniforms — A479

Artigas on the Plains — A480

1984, June 19   Litho.   Perf. 12
| 1162 | A479 | 4.50p Artillery Regiment, 1895 | .45 | .20 |
| 1163 | A479 | 4.50p Cazadores, 2nd battalion | .45 | .20 |

1984, July 2   Litho.   Perf. 12
| 1164 | A480 | 4.50p bl & blk | .40 | .25 |
| 1165 | A480 | 8.50p bl & redsh brn | .75 | .40 |

A. Penarol Soccer Club A481

1984, Aug. 21   Litho.   Perf. 12
| 1166 | A481 | 4.50p Championship trophy | .45 | .25 |

Provincial Map Type of 1973
1984, Sept. 21   Litho.   Perf. 12
| 1167 | A281 | 4.50p multi | .40 | .25 |

Childrens Council, 50th Anniv. A482

1984, Oct. 11   Litho.   Perf. 12
| 1168 | A482 | 4.50p multi | .40 | .25 |

Christmas A483

A484

1984 Litho. *Perf. 12*
1169 A483 6p multi .50 .30

1985, Feb. 13 Litho. *Perf. 12*
1170 A484 4.50p multi .40 .25

1st Jr. World Basketball Championships.

Don Bruno Mauricio de Zabala, 300th Birth Anniv. — A485

1985, Apr. 16 Litho. *Perf. 12*
1171 A485 4.50p multi .30 .20

Intl. Olympic Committee, 90th Anniv. — A486

Design: Olympic rings, Los Angeles and Sarajevo 1984 Games emblems.

1985, May 22 *Perf. 12½*
1172 A486 12p multi .70 .40

Carlos Gardel, (1890-1935), Entertainer A487

Catholic Circle of Workers, Cent. — A488

1985, June 21 *Perf. 12*
1173 A487 6p lt gray, red brn & bl .35 .20

Wmk. 332
1985, June 21 Litho. *Perf. 12*
1174 A488 6p Cross, clasped hands .20 .20

Icarus, by Hans Erni — A489

1985, July Photo. Wmk. 332
1175 A489 4.50p multi .25 .20

Intl. Civil Aviation Org., 40th anniv.

American Air Forces Cooperation System, 25th Anniv. — A490

1985, July
1176 A490 12p Emblem, flags .30 .20

FUNSA, Natl. Investment Funds Corp., 50th Anniv. — A491

1985, July 31 Litho. Wmk. 332
1177 A491 6p multi .25 .20

Intl. Youth Year A492

1985, Aug. 28
1178 A492 12p mar & blk .30 .20

Installation of Democratic Government — A493

1985, Aug. 30
1179 A493 20p brt pur, yel ocher & dk grnsh bl .75 .30

Intl. Book Fair — A494

1985
1180 A494 20p multi .75 .30

Military School, Cent. A495

1985, Nov. 29 Litho. *Perf. 12*
1181 A495 10p multi .40 .20

Department of Flores, Cent. — A496

Day of Hispanic Solidarity — A498

Christmas 1985 A497

1985, Dec. 9
1182 A496 6p Map, arms .20 .20

1985, Dec. 23
1183 A497 10p multi .30 .20
1184 A497 22p multi .55 .30

1985, Dec. 27
1185 A498 12p Isabel Monument .30 .20

3rd Inter-American Agricultural Congress — A499

Wmk. 332
1986, Jan. 7 Photo. *Perf. 12*
1186 A499 12p blk, dl yel & red .30 .20

UPU Day A500

1986, Jan. 14 Litho. *Perf. 12*
1187 A500 15.50p multi .45 .25

1985 Census A501

1986, Jan. 21
1188 A501 10p multi .25 .2

Conaprole, 50th Anniv. — A502

1986, Jan. 25
1189 A502 10p gold, brt ultra & bl .30 .2

UN, 40th Anniv. A503

Wmk. 332
1986, Feb. 26 Litho. *Perf. 12*
1190 A503 20p multi .45 .25

Brokers and Auctioneers Assoc., 50th Anniv. — A504

1986, Mar. 19
1191 A504 10p multi .20 .20

Gen. Manuel Ceferino Oribe (1792-1857), President — A505

Portraits: Nos. 1196, 1200, 2p, 7p, 15p, 20p, Oribe. Nos. 1195, 1209, 1211, 3p, Lavalleja. Nos. 1199, 1208, 1210, 30p, 100p, 200p, Artigas. No. 1198, 17p, 22p, 26p, 45p, 75p, Rivera.

1986-89				**Perf. 12½**
1192	A505	1p dl grn	.20	.20
1193	A505	2p scarlet	.20	.20
1194	A505	3p ultra	.20	.20
1195	A505	5p dark blue	.20	.20
1196	A505	5p violet blue	.20	.20
1197	A505	7p tan	.20	.20
1198	A505	10p lilac rose	.25	.20
1199	A505	10p brt green	.20	.20
1200	A505	10p bluish grn	.20	.20
1201	A505	15p dull blue	.20	.20
1202	A505	17p deep blue	.25	.20
1203	A505	20p light brown	.20	.20
1204	A505	22p violet	.20	.20
1205	A505	26p olive blk	.30	.20
1206	A505	30p pale org	.30	.25
1207	A505	45p dark red	.30	.20
1208	A505	50p dp bis	.55	.45
1209	A505	50p bright pink	.20	.20
1210	A505	60p dark gray	.75	.45
1211	A505	60p orange	.20	.20
1211A	A505	75p red orange	.30	.25
1211B	A505	100p dl red brn	1.10	.60
1211C	A505	200p brt yel grn	1.50	.75
Nos. 1192-1211C (23)			8.20	6.15

The 22p is airmail.
Issued: 1p, 7p, 4/18; #1195, 30p, 6/16; #1198, 22p, 9/24; #1208, 8/5; 100p, 7/2; 2p, 6/16/87; 3p, #1210, 8/14/87; #1199, 17p, 8/4/87; 26p, 9/2/87; 15p, 9/9/88; 45p, 12/20/88; 200p, 10/19/88; #1211A, 5/19/89;

#1211, 7/27/89; #1196, 1203, 8/15/89; #1209, 12/12/89; #1200, 1989.
See Nos. 1321-1329.

Italian Chamber of Commerce in Uruguay — A506

1986, May 5   *Perf. 12*
1212 A506 20p multi   .60 .20

A507

A508

1986, May 28   **Photo.**   *Perf. 12*
1213 A507 20p multi   .45 .25
1986 World Cup Soccer Championships, Mexico.

      Wmk. 332
1986, May 19   **Litho.**   *Perf. 12*
1214 A508 10p multi   .20 .20
Genocide of the Armenian people, 71st anniv.

A509

A510

1986, June 16
1215 A509 10p multi   .20 .20
El Dia Newspaper, cent.

1986, July 14
1216 A510 20p Garcia, Peruvian flag   .40 .20
State visit of Pres. Alan Garcia of Peru.

Simon Bolivar, Gen. Sucre, Map A511

1986, July 24
1217 A511 20p multi   .45 .25
State visit of Pres. Jaime Lusinchi of Venezuela.

State Visit of Pres. Jose Sarney of Brazil — A512

Zelmar Michelini, Assassinated Liberal Senator — A513

1986, July 31
1218 A512 20p multi   .30 .20

1986, Aug. 21
1219 A513 10p vio bl & rose lake   .20 .20

B'nai B'rith of Uruguay, 50th Anniv. A514

1986, Sept. 10
1220 A514 10p red, gold & red brn   .25 .20

General Agreement on Tariffs & Trade (GATT) Committee Meeting, Punta del Este — A515

1986, Sept. 15
1221 A515 10p multi   .20 .20

Scheduled Flights between Uruguay and Spain, 40th Anniv. — A516

1986, Sept. 22
1222 A516 20p multi   .30 .20

Fish Exports A517

1986, Oct. 1
1223 A517 20p multi   .30 .20

Wool Exports A518

1986, Oct. 15
1224 A518 20p multi   .30 .20

Pres. Blanco, Natl. and Dominican Flags A519

1986, Oct. 29
1225 A519 20p multi   .25 .20
State visit of Pres. Salvador Jorge Blanco of the Dominican Republic.

State Visit of Pres. Sandro Pertini of Italy — A520

State Visit of Pres. Raul Alfonsin of Argentina A521

1986, Oct. 31
1226 A520 20p grn & buff   .25 .25

1986, Nov. 10
1227 A521 20p multi   .30 .20

Hispanic Solidarity Day A522

Design: Felipe and Santiago, the patron saints of Montevideo, and cathedral.

      Wmk. 332
1987, Jan. 12   **Litho.**   *Perf. 12*
1228 A522 10p rose lake & blk   .20 .20

JUVENTUS, 50th Anniv. (in 1986) — A523

1987, Jan. 28
1229 A523 10p brt yel, blk & ultra   .20 .20
Juventus, a Catholic sports, culture and leisure organization.

Hector Gutierrez Ruiz (1934-1976), Politician — A524

Intl. Symposium on Science and Technology A525

1987, Feb. 23
1230 A524 10p brn & deep mag   .20 .20
1231 A525 20p multi   .25 .25
Ruiz represented Uruguay at an earlier science and technology symposium.

Visit of Pope John Paul II to La Plata Region — A526

Dr. Jose F. Arias (1885-1985), Founder of the University of Crafts — A527

1987, Mar. 31
1232 A526 50p blk & deep org   .60 .30

1987, Apr. 28
1233 A527 10p multi   .20 .20

Jewish Community in Uruguay, 70th Anniv. — A528

1987, July 8
1234 A528 10p blk, org & brt bl   .25 .20

Pluna Airlines, 50th Anniv. (in 1986) A529

1987, Sept. 16
1235	A529	10p Dragon Fly	.20	.20
1236	A529	20p Douglas DC-3	.25	.20
1237	A529	25p Vickers Viscount	.30	.20
1238	A529	30p Boeing 707	.40	.25
		Nos. 1235-1238 (4)	1.15	.85

Artigas Antarctic Station A530

1987, Sept. 28
1239	A530	20p multi	.25	.20

Uruguay Mortgage Bank, 75th Anniv. A531

1987, Oct. 14
1240	A531	26p multi	.30	.25

Exports — A532

1987, Oct. 28
1241	A532	51p Beef	.50	.30
1242	A532	51p Milk products	.50	.30

Christmas 1987 — A533

1987, Dec. 21
1243	A533	17p Nativity, vert.	.30	.20
1244	A533	66p shown	.65	.40

State Visit of Jose Napoleon Duarte, President of El Salvador — A534

VARIG Airlines, 60th Anniv. (in 1987) — A535

1988, Jan. 12
1245	A534	20p brt olive grn & Prus blue	.25	.20

1988, Feb. 9
1246	A535	66p blk, blue & brt yel	.75	.75

Post Office Stamp Foundation A536

Wmk. 332
1988, Feb. 9   Litho.   *Perf. 12*
1247	A536	30p on 10+5p brt blue, blk & yel	.25	.20

No. 1247 not issued without surcharge.

Intl. Peace Year A537

1988, Feb. 11
1248	A537	10p multi	.20	.20

Euskal Erria, 75th Anniv. (in 1987) — A538

1988, Mar. 9
1249	A538	66p multi	.55	.30

Basque-Uruguayan diplomatic relations.

Air Force, 75th Anniv. A539

1988, Mar. 11
1250	A539	17p multi	.25	.20

Interamerican Children's Institute, 60th Anniv. — A540

Wmk. 332
1988, Mar. 28   Litho.   *Perf. 12*
1251	A540	30p apple grn, blk & grn	.30	.20

State Hydroelectric Works (UTE), 75th Anniv. — A541

1988, Apr. 20
1252	A541	17p shown	.20	.20
1253	A541	17p Baygorria Dam	.20	.20
1254	A541	51p Gabriel Terra Dam	.45	.25
1255	A541	51p Constitucion Dam	.45	.25
1256	A541	66p Dams on map	.60	.30
		Nos. 1252-1256 (5)	1.90	1.20

Dated 1987.

Postal Union of America and Spain (UPAE), 75th Anniv. (in 1987) A542

1988, May 10
1257	A542	66p multi	.55	.45

Israel, 40th Anniv. A543

1988, May 17
1258	A543	66p lt ultra & blk	.55	.35

Postal Messenger of Peace — A544

1988, May 24
1259	A544	66p multi	.55	.35

Portrait, *La Cumparsita* Tango — A545

Firemen, Cent. — A546

1988, June 7
1260	A545	17p Parade, horiz.	.35	.20
1261	A545	51p Score	.95	.45

Gerardo H. Matos Rodrigues, composer.

1988, June 21
1262	A546	17p Pablo Banales, founder	.25	.20
1263	A546	26p Fireman, 1900	.30	.25
1264	A546	34p Emblem, horiz.	.35	.25
1265	A546	51p Merry Weather fire engine, 1907, horiz.	.50	.30
1266	A546	66p Fire pump, 1888, horiz.	.70	.50

Size: 44x24½mm
1267	A546	100p Ladder truck, 1921	1.10	.85
		Nos. 1262-1267 (6)	3.20	2.40

Capitan Miranda Trans-world Voyage, Cent. — A547

1988, July 28
1268	A547	30p multi	.30	.20

Exports A548

1988
1269	A548	30p Citrus fruit	.25	.20
1270	A548	45p Rice	.40	.25
1271	A548	55p Footwear	.45	.25
1272	A548	55p Leather and furs	.45	.30
		Nos. 1269-1272 (4)	1.55	1.00

Issued: 30p, #1272, 9/14; 45p, #1271, 8/23.

Natl. Museum of Natural History, 150th Anniv. — A549

30p, *Usnea densirostra* fossil. 90p, *Toxodon platensis* bone, Quaternary period.

1988, Sept. 20
1273	A549	30p blk, yel & red brn	.30	.20
1274	A549	90p blk, ultra & beige	.80	.50
a.		Pair, #1273-1274	1.10	1.10

Battle of Carpinteria, 150th Anniv. (in 1986) — A550

1988, Nov. 23
1275	A550	30p multi	.25	.20

Horiz. row contains two stamps, label, then two more stamps.

A551

A552

1988, Dec. 21
1276 A551 115p multi   .70   .70

Christmas.

1988, Dec. 27

Paintings: a, *Manolita Pina, 1920,* by J. Torres Garcia. b, *78 Squares and Rectangles,* by J.P. Costigliolo. c, Print publicizing an exhibition of works by Pedrero Figari, 1945. d, *Self-portrait, 1947,* by J. Torres Garcia.

1277   Block or strip of 4 + label   3.25   3.25
    a.-d. A552 115p any single   .75   .50

No. 1277 can be collected as a vert. or horiz. strip of 4, or block of 4, with label.

Spanish Heritage Day A553

1989, Jan. 9
1278 A553 90p multi   .55   .30
1279 A553 115p multi   .70   .40

Armenian Organization Hnchakian, Cent. — A554

Wmk. 332
1989, June 7   Litho.   Perf. 12
1280 A554 210p red, yel & blue   1.25   .50

French Revolution, Bicentennial — A555

1989, July 3
1281 A555 50p Plumb line, frame   .25   .20
1282 A555 50p Liberty tree   .25   .20
1283 A555 210p Eye in sunburst   1.10   .45
1284 A555 210p Liberty   1.10   .45
    Nos. 1281-1284 (4)   2.70   1.30

Use Postal Codes — A556

1989, July 25
1285 A556 50p Montevideo Dept. map   .25   .20
1286 A556 210p National map, vert.   .95   .30

3rd Pan American Milk Congress A557

1989, Aug. 24
1287 A557 170p sky blue & ultra   .85   .30

A558

A559

Wmk. 332
1989, Aug. 29   Photo.   Perf. 12
1288 A558 170p multicolored   .85   .30

Joaquin Jose da Silva Xavier.

1989, Aug. 31
1289 A559 210p blk, red & bl   1.00   .35

Inter-Parliamentary Union Conf., London.

FAO Emblem, Map, Citrus Slice — A560

1989, Sept. 11
1290 A560 180p multicolored   .70   .30

8th Conf., Intergovernmental Group on Citrus Fruits.

UN Decade for the Disabled — A561

1989, Oct. 4
1291 A561 50p shown   .30   .20
1292 A561 210p Disabled people   .85   .35

America Issue — A562

Nacurutu artifact and UPAE emblem.

1989, Oct. 11   Perf. 12½
1293 A562 60p multicolored   .45   .20
1294 A562 180p multicolored   1.10   .45

City of Pando, Bicentennial — A563

1989, Dec. 27   Litho.   Perf. 12
1295 A563 60p multicolored   .25   .20

Christmas A564

1989, Dec. 19
1296 A564 70p Virgin of Trienta y Tres   .35   .20
1297 A564 210p Barradas, horiz.   .95   .45

Charity Hospital, Bicent. (in 1988) — A565

1990, Jan. 23   Wmk. 332
1298 A565 60p multicolored   .60   .60

Provincial Arms and Maps A566

1990
1299 A566 70p Soriano   .30   .30
1300 A566 70p Florida, vert.   .35   .35
1301 A566 90p Canelones   .40   .40
1302 A566 90p Lavalleja, vert.   .40   .40
1303 A566 90p San Jose, vert.   .40   .40
1304 A566 90p Rivera   .40   .40
    Nos. 1299-1304 (6)   2.25   2.25

Dated 1989.

Writers — A567

Designs: a, Luisa Luisi (1883-1940). b, Javier de Viana (1872-1926). c, Delmira Agustini (1886-1914). d, J. Zorrilla de San Martin (1855-1931). e, Alfonsina Storni (1892-1938). f, Julio Casal (1889-1954). g, Juana de Ibarbourou (1895-1979). h, Carlos Roxlo (1861-1926).

1990, Mar. 20
1320   Block of 8 + 2 labels   3.50   3.50
    a.-b. A567 60p any single   .20   .20
    c.-d. A567 75p any single   .25   .25
    e.-f. A567 170p any single   .55   .55
    g.-h. A567 210p any single   .70   .70

Printed in sheets of 4 blocks of 4 separated by vert. and horiz. rows of 5 labels. Position of denomination varies to form border around each block.
Dated 1989.

Portraits Type of 1986

25p, 30p, Lavalleja. 60p, 90p, Rivera. 100p, 150p, 300p, 500p, 1000p, Artigas.

1990   Litho.   Wmk. 332   Perf. 12½
1321 A505 25p orange   .20   .20
1322 A505 30p ultra   .20   .20
1323 A505 60p purple   .20   .20
1324 A505 90p org red   .45   .30
1325 A505 100p brown   .35   .35
1326 A505 150p dk blue green   .60   .40
1327 A505 300p blue   1.00   .65
1328 A505 500p orange red   1.75   .75
1329 A505 1000p red   3.50   2.25
    Nos. 1321-1329 (9)   8.25   5.30

Issued: 30p, 60p, 7/17; 90p, 3/24; 150p, 6/22; 300p, 7/5; 500p, 3/22; 1000p, 7/24.

A568

A569

1990, Apr. 3   Perf. 12
1346 A568 70p multicolored   .35   .35

City of Mercedes, bicent. Dated 1989.

1990, Apr. 24
1347 A569 210p multicolored   .95   .95

Intl. Agricultural Development Fund, 10th anniv. Dated 1989.

Traffic Safety — A570

Designs: a, Bus, car. b, Don't drink and drive. c, Cross on the green light. d, Obey traffic signs.

1990, May 28
1348 A570 70p Block of 4, #a.-d. .95 .95

General Artigas A571

1990, June 18
1349 A571 60p red & blue .35 .35

A572

A573

1990, June 26
1350 A572 70p multicolored .30 .30
Intl. Mothers' Day. Dated 1989.

1990, July 10
Treaty of Montevideo, 1889: a, Gonzalo Ramirez. b, Ildefonso Garcia. c, Flags at left. d, Flags at right.
1351 A573 60p Block of 4, #a.-d. .95 .95
Nos. 1351c-1351d printed in continuous design. Dated 1989.

Microphone, Tower — A574

b, Newspaper boy. c, Television camera. d, Books.

1990, Sept. 26
1352 A574 70p Block of 4, #a.-d. 1.25 1.25

Carlos Federico Saez (1878-1901) — A575

Portraits: b, Pedro Blanes Viale (1879-1926). c, Edmundo Prati (1889-1970). d, Jose L. Zorrilla de San Martin (1891-1975).

1990, Dec. 26
1353 Block of 4 2.75 2.75
a.-b. A575 90p any single .40 .40
c.-d. A575 210p any single .90 .90

Prevent Forest Fires — A576

Wmk. 332
1990, Oct. 26 Litho. Perf. 12
1354 A576 70np multicolored 1.25 1.25

America Issue — A577

1990, Nov. 6
1355 A577 120p Odocoileus bezoarticus .55 .55
1356 A577 360p Peltophorum dubium, vert. 1.40 1.40

Army Corps of Engineers, 75th Anniv. — A578

1991, Jan. 21
1357 A578 170p multicolored .70 .70

The Nativity by Brother Juan B. Maino — A579

1990, Dec. 24
1358 A579 170p bister & multi .70 .70
1359 A579 830p silver & multi 3.25 3.25

Organization of American States, Cent. (in 1989) A580

Wmk. 332
1991, Mar. 21 Litho. Perf. 12
1360 A580 830p bl, blk & yel 3.50 3.50

Prevention of AIDS — A581

1991, Mar. 8
1361 A581 170p bl & multi .70 .70
1362 A581 830p grn & multi 3.25 3.25

Carnival — A582

1991, Feb. 19
1363 A582 170p multicolored .70 .70

Education — A583

Expanding youth's horizons: a, Stone ax, megalithic monument. b, Wheel, pyramids. c, Printing press, solar system. d, Satellite, diagram.

Wmk. 332
1991, Apr. 23 Litho. Perf. 12
1364 Block of 4 2.00 2.00
a.-b. A583 120p any single .25 .25
c.-d. A583 330p any single .75 .75

Natl. Cancer Day — A584

1991, June 17
1365 A584 360p red & black .75 .75

A585

Exports of Uruguay — A586

Perf. 12½x13, 13x12½
1991 Litho. Wmk. 332
1366 A585 120p Textiles .25 .25
1367 A586 120p Clothing .30 .20
1368 A585 400p Semiprecious stones, granite .95 .95
Nos. 1366-1368 (3) 1.50 1.40
Issued: #1366, 400p, 4/23; #1367, 6/26.

7th Pan American Maccabiah Games — A587

1991, July 4 Perf. 12½x13
1369 A587 1490p multicolored 3.00 3.00

Dornier Wal, Route Map — A588

1991, July 5 Perf. 12
1370 A588 1510p multicolored 3.50 3.50
Espamer '91.

Entrance to Sacramento Colony A589

Railroads and Trains: 540p, 825p, First locomotive, 1869. 600p, like 360p. 800p, Entrance to Sacramento Colony. 1510p, 2500p, Horse-drawn streetcar.

1991-93 Litho. Wmk. 332 Perf. 12
1378 A589 360p ol bis & yel .75 .50
1378A A589 540p dk bl & gray 1.00 .75
1379 A589 600p brn, yel & blk .75 .70
1379A A589 800p grn & yel grn .75 .75
1379B A589 825p bl, gray & blk 1.10 .90
1380 A589 1510p ol bis & emer 3.50 2.25
1382 A589 2500p ol bis, emer & blk 3.00 2.50
Nos. 1378-1382 (7) 10.85 8.35
Issued: 360p, 540p, 1510p, July 19; 825p, Feb. 11, 1992; 2500p, May 29, 1002; 600p, June 18, 1992; 800p, Feb. 9, 1993.

Sagrada Family College, Cent. — A590

College of the Immaculate Heart of Mary, Cent. — A591

Wmk. 332

1991, June 26		**Litho.**	**Perf. 12**	
1383	A590	360p multicolored	.75	.75
1384	A591	1370p multicolored	3.00	3.00

Constitutional Oath — A592

1991, July 17				
1385	A592	360p multicolored	.80	.80

Swiss Confederation, 700th Anniv. — A593

1991, Aug. 1		**Perf. 13x12½**		
1386	A593	1510p multicolored	4.25	4.25
Souvenir Sheet				
Perf. 12				
1387	A593	3000p multicolored	8.50	8.50

Photography, 150th Anniv. — A594

Perf. 12½x13				
1991, Sept. 12	**Litho.**	**Wmk. 332**		
1388	A594	1370p multi	2.50	2.50

Actors Society of Uruguay, 50th Anniv. — A595

1991, Aug. 24		**Perf. 12**		
1389	A595	450p blk & red	.85	.85

CREA (Agriculture Association), 25th Anniv. — A596

1991, Sept. 14		**Perf. 12½x13**		
1390	A596	450p multicolored	.85	.85

Whitbread Around the World Race — A597

1991, Aug. 20		**Perf. 13x12½**		
1391	A597	1510p multicolored	3.00	3.00

Amerigo Vespucci (1454-1512) — A598

America Issue: 450p, First landing at River Plate, 1602, vert.

1991, Oct. 11		**Perf. 12**		
1392	A598	450p yel & brn	.85	.85
1393	A598	1740p ol & brn	3.00	3.00

Automobiles — A599

Designs: 350p, Gladiator, 1902. 1370p, E.M.F., 1909. 1490p, Renault, 1912. 1510p, Clement-Bayard, 1903, vert.

1991, Oct. 18		**Perf. 12½x13, 13x12½**		
1394	A599	360p multicolored	.65	.65
1395	A599	1370p multicolored	2.50	2.50
1396	A599	1490p multicolored	2.50	2.50
1397	A599	1510p multicolored	3.00	3.00
		Nos. 1394-1397 (4)	8.65	8.65

Team Nacional Montevideo, Winners of Toyota and Europe-South America Soccer Cups — A600

		Wmk. 332		
1991, Nov. 8		**Litho.**	**Perf. 12**	
1398	A600	450p shown	.85	.85
1399	A600	450p Emblem, trophy, vert.	.85	.85

Margarita Xirgu (1888-1969), Actress — A601

1991, Oct. 4				
1400	A601	360p yel & brn	.65	.65

INTERPOL, 60th Congress A602

1991, Oct. 30				
1401	A602	1740p multicolored	3.00	3.00

Maria Auxiliadora Institute, Cent. — A603

1991, Nov. 11				
1402	A603	450p multicolored	.85	.85

Technological Laboratory, 25th Anniv. — A604

1991, Nov. 11				
1403	A604	1570p dk bl & lt bl	2.75	2.75

The Table by Zoma Baitler — A605

1991, Oct. 18				
1404	A605	360p multicolored	.65	.65

World Food Day A606

1991, Oct. 16		**Perf. 12½x13**		
1405	A606	1740p multicolored	3.00	3.00

Ships A607

Designs: a, Steam yacht, Gen. Rivera. b, Coast Guard cutter, Salto. c, Cruiser, Uruguay. d, Tanker, Pte. Oribe.

		Wmk. 332		
1991, Oct. 4		**Litho.**	**Perf. 12**	
1406		Block of 4	7.25	7.25
a.-b.	A607	450p any single	.85	.85
c.-d.	A607	1570p any single	2.50	2.50

Topographical Society Type of 1981

1991, Dec. 3		**Perf. 12½**		
1407	A439	550p multi	.75	.75

Topographical Society, 160th anniv.

World AIDS Day — A608

1991, Dec. 1				
1408	A608	550p bl, blk & brt yel	.75	.75
1409	A608	2040p lt grn, blk & lil	2.75	2.75

Export Industies A609

		Wmk. 332		
1991, Mar. 20		**Litho.**	**Perf. 12½**	
1410	A609	120p multicolored	.20	.20

Christmas A610

1991, Dec. 24		**Perf. 12**		
1411	A610	550p Angel	.75	.75
1412	A610	2040p Adoration of the Angels	2.75	2.75

Muscians — A611

Designs: No. 1413a, Francisco Canaro. No. 1413b, Anibal Troilo. No. 1414a, Juan de Dios Filiberto. No. 1414b, Pintin Castellanos.

		Wmk. 332		
1992, Jan. 20		**Photo.**	**Perf. 12**	
1413	A611	450p Pair, #a.-b.	1.25	1.25
1414	A611	450p Pair, #a.-b.	1.25	1.25

Patricio Aylwin, Pres. of Chile — A612

Perf. 11½x12
1992, Mar. 23 **Litho.** **Unwmk.**
1415 A612 550p multicolored .65 .65

Penarol, Winners of Liberator's Cup in Club Soccer — A612a

La Paz City, 120th Anniv. — A612b

Perf. 13x12½
1992, May 29 **Litho.** **Wmk. 332**
1415A A612a 600p yel & blk .70 .70
Souvenir Sheet
Perf. 12
1415B A612a 3000p yel & blk 3.75 3.75

1992, May 25 **Perf. 13x12½**
1415C A612b 550p multicolored .65 .65

World No-Smoking Day — A613

Wmk. 332
1992, May 31 **Litho.** **Perf. 12**
1416 A613 2500p multicolored 3.00 3.00

United Nations World Health Day A614

Wmk. 332
1992, July 28 **Litho.** **Perf. 13**
1417 A614 2500p bl, lt bl & red 3.00 3.00

Mercosur A615

1992, Aug. 5 **Photo.** **Perf. 12**
1418 A615 2500p multicolored 2.75 2.75

Olymphilex '92, Barcelona — A616

Wmk. 332
1992, Aug. 8 **Photo.** **Perf. 12**
1419 A616 2900p multicolored 3.50 3.50

Discovery of America, 500th Anniv. — A617

Perf. 11½x12, 12x11½
1992, Oct. 10 **Litho.** **Unwmk.**
1420 A617 700p Ship, masts, vert. .75 .75
1421 A617 2900p Globe, ship 3.00 3.00

Jose Pedro Varela Natl. Teachers College, 50th Anniv. A618

1992, Oct. 22 **Perf. 12x11½**
1422 A618 700p multicolored .75 .75

22nd Regional FAO Conference — A619

Designs: 2500p, Emblems. 2900p, Emblems, children with food basket.

1992, Sept. 28
1423 A619 2500p multicolored 2.50 2.50
1424 A619 2900p multicolored 3.00 3.00
Intl. Conf. on Nutrition, Rome, Italy (#1424).

Cesar Vallejo (1892-1938), Poet — A620

1992, Sept. 30
1425 A620 2500p brn & dk brn 2.50 2.50

A621

A622

1992, Oct. 26 **Perf. 11½x12**
1426 A621 700p gray, red & blk .75 .75
Assoc. of Wholesalers and Retailers, cent.

Perf. 11½x12
1992, Oct. 10 **Litho.** **Unwmk.**
1427 A622 700p black, blue & grn 1.00 1.00
Monument to Columbus, cent.

A623

A624

Ruins and lighthouse, Colonia del Sacramento.

1992, Oct. 10
1428 A623 700p multicolored .70 .70
Discovery of America, 500th anniv.

1992, Oct. 19
1429 A624 700p red lil, rose lil & blk .70 .70
Columbus Philanthropic Society, cent.

A625

A626

1992, Oct. 19
1430 A625 2900p multicolored 3.00 3.00
Judaism in the Americas, 500th anniv.

1992, Oct. 30
1431 A626 2900p multicolored 3.00 3.00
Lebanon Society of Uruguay, 50th anniv.

Pan American Health Organization, 90th Anniv. — A627

Perf. 12x11½
1992, Dec. 15 **Litho.** **Unwmk.**
1432 A627 3200p blk, bl & yel 3.00 3.00

22nd Lions Club Forum for Latin America and the Caribbean — A628

1992, Dec. 2
1433 A628 2700p multicolored 2.50 2.50

Christmas A629

1992, Dec. 1 **Perf. 11½x12**
1434 A629 800p Nativity scene .75 .75
1435 A629 3200p Star in sky 3.00 3.00

General Manuel Oribe, Birth Bicent. A630

Designs: No. 1436, Oribe, Oriental College. No. 1437, Oribe in military dress uniform, vert.

Perf. 12x11½, 11½x12

1992, Dec. 8   Litho.   Unwmk.
1436 A630 800p multicolored .75 .75
1437 A630 800p multicolored .75 .75

Logosofia, 60th Anniv. — A631

1992, Dec. 29   Perf. 12x11½
1438 A631 800p blue & yellow .75 .75

Immigrants' Day — A632

1992, Dec. 4   Perf. 11½x12
1439 A632 800p black & green .75 .75

ANDEBU, 70th Anniv. — A633

Caritas of Uruguay, 30th Anniv. A634

1992, Dec. 22   Photo.   Perf. 12x11½
1440 A633 2700p Satellite 2.50 2.50
1441 A634 3200p Map, huts by water 3.00 3.00

A635

A636

1992, Dec. 18   Perf. 11½x12
1442 A635 800p brown & yellow .75 .75
Jose H. Molaguero S. A., 50th anniv.

Perf. 11½x12

1993, Mar. 1   Litho.   Unwmk.
1443 A636 80c multicolored .65 .65
Wilson Ferreira Aldunate.

Economic Science and Accountancy College, Cent. — A637

Perf. 12x11½

1993, Apr. 15   Photo.   Unwmk.
1444 A637 1p multicolored .80 .80

Souvenir Sheet

Polska '93, Intl. Philatelic Exhibition — A638

a, Lech Walesa. b, Pope John Paul II.

1993, May 3   Perf. 11½x12
1445 A638 2p Sheet of 2, #a.-b. 3.75 3.75

A639   A639a

A639b

MENSAJERIAS ... A639c   A639d

MENSAJERIAS ... A639e   EL CORREO ... A639f

A639g   A639h

Design A639g shows the Postal Administration Tower.

ONE PESO (Letter Box — A639):
Type I — "Bugon vecinal 1879" 21½mm, letter box 23½mm high.
Type II — "Bugon vecinal 1879" 22mm, letter box 22½mm high.
Type III — "Bugon vecinal 1879" 19½mm, letter box 21mm high.
There are other differences among the three types.

Wmk. 332

1993-99   Litho.   Perf. 12½
1446 A639 50c gray ol & yel .20 .20
1447 A639 1p lt brn & yel (I) .40 .40
    a.   Type II .50 .50
    b.   Type III, unwatermarked .25 .25
    c.   Type III, photo., unwmkd. .25 .25
1448 A639a 1p org yel & bl .80 .80

Perf. 12

1449 A639b 1p org & bl .55 .55
1450 A639c (1.20p) blue .60 .60
1451 A639c (1.40p) green .65 .65
1452 A639d 1.40p yel & bl .65 .65
1453 A639c (1.60p) red 1.00 1.00
1454 A639 1.80p bl & yel 1.10 1.10
1455 A639c (1.80p) brown 1.00 1.00
1456 A639c (2p) gray 1.00 1.00
1457 A639c (2.30p) lilac 1.25 1.25
1458 A639 2.60p bl, yel & grn 1.25 1.25
1459 A639e (2.60p) grn & yel 1.25 1.25
1460 A639e (2.90p) bl & yel 1.25 1.25
1460A A639e (3p) gray & brt yel grn .85 .85
    b.   Unwmk. .85 .85
1461 A639e (3.10p) red & pink .90 .90
1462 A639e (3.20p) rose brn & lt brn 2.75 2.75
1462B A639e (3.80p) brt blue
1463 A639e (4p) bis & yel, litho. .95 .95
1464 A639f 5p bl & yel, perf. 12½ 2.00 2.00
1465 A639g 6p blue & blk 1.40 1.40
1465A A639f 7p blue & yel 2.70 2.70
1465B A639 7.50p vio & yel 3.00 3.00
1465C A639h 8p bl & yel 3.00 3.00
    Nos. 1446-1465C (24) 30.5030.50

The design of Nos. 1460A, 1462-1463 does not include "PORTE MINIMO." There are minor design differences between #1464 and 1465A.

Issued: #1448, 4/15/93; #1450, 8/2/93; #1451, 12/1/93; #1452, 1/4/94; #1453, 4/4/94; #1455, 8/1/94; #1454 8/9/94; #1449, 10/3/94; 1456, 12/1/94. #1457, 4/1/95; #1458, (2.60p), 8/10/95; 50c, #1447, 8/27/96; #1460, (3.10p), (3.50p), 4/1/96; 7.50p, 5/21/96; 5p, 1997; #1463, 8/1/97; 6p, 8/13/97; (3p), 2/1/99. #1460Ab, 1999. (3.80p), 5/9/97

Interior Fire Service, 50th Anniv. — A640

15th Congress of UPAEP — A641

Perf. 11½x12

1993, May 28   Litho.   Unwmk.
1466 A640 1p multicolored .75 .75

1993, June 21
1467 A641 3.50p multicolored 2.50 2.50

Uruguayan Navy, 175th Anniv. — A642

Sailing ship, Pedro Campbell, first admiral.

Perf. 12x11½

1993, June 28   Litho.   Wmk. 332
1468 A642 1p multicolored .75 .75

Intl. University Society, 25th Anniv. — A643

1993, July 2
1469 A643 1p multicolored .75 .75

Automobile Club of Uruguay, 75th Anniv. — A644

1993, July 19   Photo.   Unwmk.
1470 A644 3.50p 1910 Hupmobile 2.50 2.50

Uruguay Battalion in UN Peacekeeping Force, Cambodia — A645

Perf. 12x11½

1993, Aug. 6   Litho.   Unwmk.
1471 A645 1p multicolored .75 .75

Souvenir Sheet

Brasiliana '93 — A646

World Cup Soccer Champions: a, Uruguay, 1930, 1950. b, Brazil, 1958, 1962, 1970.

1993, July 28   Perf. 11½x12
1472 A646 2.50p Sheet of 2, #a.-b. 3.75 3.75

State Television Channel 5, 30th Anniv. — A647

1993, Aug. 19   Perf. 12x11½
1473 A647 1.20p multicolored .90 .90

ANDA, 60th Anniv. A648

Perf. 12½

1993, Sept. 24   Litho.   Unwmk.
1474 A648 1.20p multicolored .85 .85

Natl. Police Academy, 50th Anniv. A649

1993, Sept. 24
1475 A649 1.20p multicolored .90 .90

Newspaper Diario El Pais, 75th Anniv. — A650

1993, Sept. 30 Litho. Unwmk.
Perf. 12½
1476 A650 1.20p multicolored .85 .85

Latin American Conference on Rural Electrification — A651

1993, Oct. 11
1477 A651 3.50p multicolored 2.50 2.50

B'nai B'rith, 150th Anniv. A652

1993, Oct. 13
1478 A652 3.70p multicolored 2.75 2.75

A653

Fauna — A654

1993 Photo. Wmk. 332 Perf. 12½
1482 A653 20c Seriema bird .20 .20
1484 A653 30c Dragon bird .20 .20
1486 A653 50c Anteaters, horiz. .35 .35
1492 A654 1.20p Giant armadillo .90 .90
  Nos. 1482-1492 (4) 1.65 1.65

Issued: 1.20p, 8/3/93; 20c, 30c, 50c, 10/22/93.
This is an expanding set. Numbers may change.

America Issue A655

Perf. 12½
1993, Oct. 6 Litho. Unwmk.
1504 A655 1.20p Caiman latirostris .85 .85
1505 A655 3.50p Athene cunicularia, vert. 2.50 2.50

Souvenir Sheet

Whitbread Trans-Global Yacht Race — A656

1993, Oct. 22 Perf. 11½x12
1506 A656 5p multicolored 3.50 3.50

Beatification of Mother Francisca Rubatto — A657

Intl. Year of Indigenous People — A658

1993, Oct. 29 Wmk. 332 Perf. 12
1507 A657 1.20p multicolored .85 .85

Perf. 13x12½
1993, Oct. 29 Unwmk.
1508 A658 3.50p multicolored 2.50 2.50

Rotary Club of Montevideo, 75th Anniv. — A658a

Perf. 12½
1993, Nov. 10 Litho. Unwmk.
1508A A658a 3.50p dk bl & bis 2.50 2.50

Rhea Americana A659

1993, Dec. 20 Litho. Perf. 12
1509 A659 20c shown .40 .20
1510 A659 20c With chicks .45 .20
1511 A659 50c Head .70 .35
1512 A659 50c Two walking .70 .35
  Nos. 1509-1512 (4) 2.25 1.10
World Wildlife Fund.

Children's Rights Day A660

1994, Jan. 4 Perf. 12½
1513 A660 1.40p multicolored .95 .95

Independence of Lebanon, 50th Anniv. — A661

1993, Nov. 22
1514 A661 3.70p multicolored 2.50 2.50

Eduardo Victor Haedo — A662

1993, Nov. 24
1515 A662 1.20p multicolored .85 .85

Christmas A663

Intl. AIDS Day — A664

1993, Dec. 7
1516 A663 1.40p shown .90 .90
1517 A663 4p Nativity, diff. 2.75 2.75

1993, Dec. 1
1518 A664 1.40p multicolored 1.90 1.90

Souvenir Sheets of 4 & 2

Anniversaries & Events — A665

Designs: No. 1519a, Switzerland #3L1, 1913 Swiss private air mail stamp. b, Germany #C40, Uruguay #C426c. c, Uruguay #C372, US #C76. d, Uruguay #C282a, US #C104.
No. 1520a, Switzerland Types A1, A2. b, Switzerland #B541.

1993, Nov. 18
1519 A665 1p #a.-d. 7.50 7.50
1520 A665 2.50p #a.-b. 7.50 7.50
Swiss postage stamps, 150th anniv. (#1519a, 1520). Dr. Hugo Eckener, 125th anniv. of birth (#1519b). First man on moon, 25th anniv. (#1519c). 1994 World Cup Soccer Championships, US (#1519d).
Nos. 1519-1520 exist imperf.

17th Inter-American Naval Conference — A666

1994, Mar. 21 Litho. Perf. 12½
1521 A666 3.70p multicolored 2.50 2.50

A667

1994, Mar. 11 Perf. 12½
1522 A667 4p multicolored 2.75 2.75
5th World Sports Congress, Punta del Este.

A668

Unwmk.
1994, Apr. 4 Litho. Perf. 12
1523 A668 3.90p multicolored 2.50 2.50
Latin America Youth Organization, 7th conference.

A669

1994, Apr. 18
1524 A669 4.30p multicolored 2.75 2.75
4th World Congress on Merino Wool.

A670

1994, Apr. 28 Perf. 12½
1525 A670 4.30p multicolored 2.75 2.75
ILO, 75th anniv.

Miniature Sheet

1994 Winter Olympic Medal Winners A671

Designs: a, Katja Seizinger. b, Markus Wasmeier. c, Vreni Schneider. d, Gustav Weder.

1994, May 6   **Perf. 12**
1526 A671 1.25p Sheet of 4, #a.-
        d.   6.25 6.25

No. 1526 exists demonitized and imperf on paper with watermark 322. This item was sold with No. 1526 and has a matching serial number.

Miniature Sheet

1994 World Cup Soccer Championships, US — A672

a, Soccer ball, flags of Uruguay, Brazil. b, Ball, flags of Italy, Argentina. c, Ball, flags of Germany, Great Britain. d, Olympic Rings.

1994, May 16
1527 A672 1.25p Sheet of 4, #a.-
        d.   6.25 6.25

Uruguay, Olympic soccer gold medalists, 1924-1928 (#1527d).
See note after No. 1526.

Clemente Estable (1894-1976), Biologist — A673

1994, May 23   Litho.   Perf. 12½
1528 A673 1.60p olive & black   1.00 1.00

Electoral Court, 70th Anniv. — A674

1994, June 7
1529 A674 1.60p multicolored   1.00 1.00

Natl. Commission to Prevent Tapeworms — A675

**   Perf. 12½**
1994, June 17   Litho.   Unwmk.
1530 A675 1.60p multicolored   .95 .95

Souvenir Sheet

Cesareo L. Berisso, First Aviator to Land at Natl. Airport, Carrasco — A676

1994, June 21   **Perf. 12**
1531 A676 5p multicolored   3.00 3.00

Intl. Cooperatives, 150th Anniv. — A677

1994, July 1   **Perf. 12½**
1532 A677 4.30p multicolored   2.50 2.50

Commission on Integration of Regional Electricity, 30th Anniv. — A678

1994, July 8
1533 A678 1.60p multicolored   .95 .95

Abate Pierre A679

**   Perf. 12½**
1994, Aug. 5   Litho.   Unwmk.
1534 A679 4.80p multicolored   2.75 2.75

Intl. Year of the Family A680

1994, July 28
1535 A680 4.80p multicolored   2.75 2.75

The Man of Lugano, by Goffredo Sommavilla (1850-1944) — A681

**   Perf. 12½**
1994, Aug. 15   Litho.   Unwmk.
1536 A681 4.80p multicolored   2.75 2.75

First Manned Moon Landing, 25th Annvi. A682

1994, July 20
1537 A682 3p multicolored   1.75 1.75

Intl. Olympic Committee, Cent. — A683

1994, Aug. 23
1538 A683 4.80p multicolored   2.75 2.75

Elbio Fernandez School, 125th Anniv. A684

**   Perf. 12½**
1994, Aug. 29   Litho.   Unwmk.
1539 A684 1.80p multicolored   1.00 1.00

A685

1994, Sept. 10   **Perf. 12**
1540 A685 1.80p black & blue   1.00 1.00
Gral. Aparicio Saravia, 90th Death Anniv.

A686

1994, Sept. 30   **Perf. 12½**
1541 A686 4.80p multicolored   2.50 2.50
6th Latin American Urban Congress.

General Assoc. of Uruguayan Authors, 65th Anniv. — A687

**   Perf. 12½**
1994, Sept. 26   Litho.   Unwmk.
1542 A687 1.80p multicolored   .95 .95

America Issue A688

1994, Oct. 10
1543 A688 1.80p Stagecoach   .95 .95
1544 A688 4.80p Paddle steamer   2.75 2.75

A689

A690

**   Perf. 12½**
1994, Oct. 28   Litho.   Unwmk.
1545 A689 2p multicolored   1.10 1.10
Assoc. of Directors of Marketing, 50th anniv.

1994, Nov. 25
1546 A690 2p multicolored   1.10 1.10
YMCA in Uruguay, 85th anniv.

Lottery, 55th Anniv. A691

1994, Nov. 21
1547 A691 2p multicolored   1.10 1.10

First Intl. Seminar to Promote Roads in Uruguay, Punta del Este A692

1994, Oct. 14
1548 A692 2p multicolored   1.10 1.10

Uruguayan Press Assoc., 50th Anniv. — A693

1994, Oct. 24
1549 A693 2p multicolored   1.10 1.10

Miniature Sheet

Natl. Mint, 150th Anniv. A694

Portions of old coin press and: a, Mint building. b, 1844 Copper coin. c, 1844 Silver coin. d, Montevideo silver peso.

1994, Oct. 17 *Perf. 12*
1550 A694 1.50p Sheet of 4, #a.-
        d.   3.25 3.25

No. 1550 exists demonitized and imperf. on paper with watermark 332. This item was sold with No. 1550 and has matching serial numbers.

Miniature Sheet

Natl. Navy A695

Ships: a, ROU Uruguay, ROU Artigas. b, ROU Fortuna. c, ROU Uruguay. d, ROU Cte. Pedro Campbell.

1994, Nov. 15
1551 A695 1.50p Sheet of 4, #a.-
        d.   3.25 3.25

Latin American Peace Movement, 25th Anniv. — A696

1994, Nov. 15 *Perf. 12½*
1552 A696 4.30p multicolored   2.25 2.25

4th Conference of the Latin American and Caribbean Organization of High Fiscal Entities, Montevideo — A697

1994, Dec. 5
1553 A697 5.50p multicolored   3.00 3.00

Christmas A698

1994, Dec. 2
1554 A698   2p shown   1.10 1.10
1555 A698   5.50p Star, tree,
               house   3.00 3.00

Uruguayan Red Cross & Red Crescent Societies, 75th Anniv. — A699

1994, Dec. 20 *Litho.* *Unwmk.*
1556 A699 5p multicolored   2.50 2.50

City Post Office — A700

1995-97 Litho. *Wmk. 332* *Perf. 12*
1557 A700 20c yellow green   .25 .25
1565 A700 10p brown   3.75 3.75
1566 A700 10p dark brown   2.25 2.25
        Unwmk.
1566A A700 10p claret & black   2.25 2.25
    Nos. 1557-1566A (4)   8.50 8.50

Issued: 20c, 1/11/95; 10p, 5/21/96; #1566, 1566A, 1997.
Denomination has no decimal places on Nos. 1566-1566A.
This is an expanding set. Number may change.

Naval Aviation, 70th Anniv. A704

1995, Feb. 7 *Litho.* *Unwmk.*
1567 A704 2p multicolored   1.10 1.10

World Tourism Organization — A705

Designs: No. 1568, Ranch house, sheep herders. No. 1569, Water recreation park. No. 1570, Native wildlife. No. 1571, Beach resort.

1995, Feb. 13
1568 A705 5p multicolored   2.50 2.50
1569 A705 5p multicolored   2.50 2.50
1570 A705 5p multicolored   2.50 2.50
1571 A705 5p multicolored   2.50 2.50
    Nos. 1568-1571 (4)   10.00 10.00

Rotary Intl., 90th Anniv. A707

1995, Feb. 22
1573 A707 5p multicolored   2.50 2.50

ICAO, 50th Anniv. A708

1995, Mar. 14
1574 A708 5p multicolored   2.50 2.50

Pietro Mascagni (1863-1945), Composer — A709

Perf. 12½
1995, Mar. 30 *Litho.* *Unwmk.*
1575 A709 5p multicolored   2.50 2.50

Miniature Sheet

Butterflies A710

Designs: a, Phoebis neocypris. b, Diogas erippus. c, Euryades duponcheli. d, Automeris coresus.

1995, June 15 *Litho.* *Perf. 12½*
1576 A710 5p Sheet of 4, #a.-
        d.   10.00 10.00

Wild Dog A711

1995, May 17 *Litho.* *Perf. 12½*
1577 A711 2.30p multicolored   1.25 1.25

America Cup Soccer Championships A712

Game scenes, flags of participating countries, match sites: a, Paysandu. b, Rivera. c, Ball (no site). d, Montevideo. e, Maldonado.

1995, July 4
1578 A712 2.30p Strip of 5, #a.-
        e.   5.25 5.25

No. 1578 is a continuous design.

FAO, 50th Anniv. — A713

1995, July 7
1579 A713 5.50p multicolored   2.50 2.50

UN Peace-Keeping Missions — A714

1995, July 14 *Litho.* *Perf. 12½*
1580 A714 2.30p multicolored   1.25 1.25

Visit of Italy's Pres. Oscar Luigi Scalfaro A715

1995, July 21
1581 A715 5.50p multicolored   2.50 2.50

A716

A717

1995, July 24
1582 A716 5p multicolored   2.25 2.25
    Rotary Intl., 90th anniv.

1995, Sept. 22
1583 A717 2.60p multicolored   1.25 1.25
    Jose Pedro Varela, 150th birth anniv.

Miniature Sheet

Shells A718

a, Zidona dufresnei. b, Boccinanops duartei. c, Dorsanum moniliferum. d, Olivancillaria uretai.

1995, Aug. 4
1584 A718 5p Sheet of 4, #a.-
        d.   10.00 10.00

America Issue A719

Designs: 3p, Dicksonia sellowiana, vert. 6p, Chrysocyon brachyurus.

Unwmk.
1995, Oct. 10   Litho.   Perf. 12
1585 A719 3p multicolored   1.40 1.40
1586 A719 6p multicolored   2.75 2.75

Carlos Gardel, Musician A720

1995, Sept. 4   Perf. 12½
1587 A720 5.50p blue & black   2.50 2.50

Flowers — A721

Designs: a, Notocactus roseinflorus. b, Verbena chamaedryfolia. c, Bauhinia candicans. d, Tillandsia aeranthos. e, Eichhornia crassipes.

1995, Sept. 12
1588 A721 3p Strip of 5, #a.-e.   6.75 6.75

Miniature Sheet

Uruguay's Artigas Antarctic Scientific Research Base, 10th Anniv. A722

Designs: a, 2.50p, Albatross. b, 4p, Fairchild FAU572. c, 4p, ROU Vanguard. d, 2.50p, PTS/M Amphibian transporter.

1995, Oct. 13
1589 A722 Sheet of 4, #a.-d.   6.00 6.00

Uruguayan Antarctic Institute, 20th anniv.
No. 1589 exists demonitized and imperf. on paper with watermark 332. This item was sold with No. 1589 and has matching serial numbers.

Holocaust Memorial — A723

1995, Sept. 27   Litho.   Perf. 13x12½
1590 A723 6p multicolored   2.75 2.75

UN, 50th Anniv. — A724

1995, Oct. 24   Litho.   Perf. 12
1591 A724 6p multicolored   2.75 2.75

Early Locomotives — A725

No. 1592, Beyer & Peacock, 1876. No. 1593, Criollo, 1895. No. 1594, Beyer & Peacock, 1910.

1995, Nov. 7
1592 A725 3p multicolored   1.40 1.40
1593 A725 3p multicolored   1.40 1.40
1594 A725 3p multicolored   1.40 1.40
    Nos. 1592-1594 (3)   4.20 4.20

Uruguayan Navy, 178th Anniv. — A726

No. 1595, Sailing ship, Artiguista. No. 1596, ROU Pte. Rivera. No. 1597, ROU Montevideo.

1995, Nov. 15   Perf. 12½
1595 A726 3p multicolored   1.40 1.40
1596 A726 3p multicolored   1.40 1.40
1597 A726 3p multicolored   1.40 1.40
    Nos. 1595-1597 (3)   4.20 4.20

Motion Pictures, Cent. A727

1995, Dec. 13
1598 A727 6p Lumiere Brothers   2.75 2.75

A728

Christmas A729

1995, Dec. 15
1599 A728 2.90p multicolored   1.25 1.25
1600 A729 6.50p multicolored   3.00 3.00

Modern Olympic Games, Cent. A730

Designs: a, Equestrian event, Atlanta 1996. b, Ski jumper, Nagano 1988. c, Torch bearer, Sydney 2000. d, Skier, Salt Lake City 2002.

1996, Jan. 30   Litho.   Perf. 12½
1601 A730 2.50p Sheet of 4, #a.-
    d.   6.50 6.50

Latin America Philatelic Exposition.
No. 1601 exists demonitized and imperf. on paper with watermark 332. This item was sold with No. 1601 and has matching serial numbers.

Carnival Personalities A732

1996, Feb. 16   Litho.   Perf. 12½
1603 A732 2.90p Rosa Luna   1.25 1.25
1604 A732 2.90p Pepino   1.25 1.25
1605 A732 2.90p Santiago Luz   1.25 1.25
    Nos. 1603-1605 (3)   3.75 3.75

Golf in Uruguay A733

Designs: a, Cantegril Country Club. b, Cerro Golf Club. c, Fay Crocker. d, Lago Golf Club. e, Golf Club of Uruguay.

1996, Feb. 27
1606 A733 2.90p Strip of 5, #a.-
    e.   6.00 6.00

No. 1606 was issued in sheets of 25 stamps.

Famous People, Events A734

Designs: a, Statue, Cardinal Barbieri (1892-1979). b, Yitzhak Rabin (1922-95), Nobel Peace Prize. c, Soccer players, First World Cup Soccer Championship, Grand Park Central, July 13, 1930. d, Robert Stolz (1880-1975), composer.

1996, Mar. 8
1607 A734 2.50p Sheet of 4, #a.-
    d.   5.75 5.75

Philatelic Academy of Uruguay. The Stamp of Today, SODRE TV Chanel 5, 10th anniv.

Montevideo, Capital of Latin American Culture — A735

1996, Mar. 5
1608 A735 2.90p Solis Theater,
    1837   1.25 1.25
  a.   Booklet pane of 3   4.25
        Complete booklet, #1608a 4.25

General Census A736

1996, Apr. 29
1609 A736 3.20p multicolored   1.25 1.25

1998 World Cup Soccer Championships, France — A737

a, Player in early uniform, Olympic champions, 1924-28, world cup champions, 1930-50, older trophy. b, Trophy, player. d, Two children playing, UNICEF emblem, soccer emblems. e, Olympic rings, two players, eliminations for Atlanta '96.

1996, Apr. 10
1610 A737 2.50p Sheet of 4, #a.-
    d.   6.50 6.50

Latin America Philatelic Exposition.
No. 1610 exists demonitized and imperf. on paper with watermark 332. This item was sold with No. 1610 and has matching serial numbers.

Bones from Indian Burial Grounds — A738

1996, Apr. 18
1611 A738 3.20p multicolored   1.25 1.25

Alfredo Zitarrosa (1936-89), Guitarist A739

1996, Mar. 15   Perf. 12
1612 A739 3p multicolored   1.25 1.25

Prehistoric Animals — A740

Designs: a, Glyptodon claripes. b, Macrauchenia patachonica. c, Toxodon platensis. d, Glossotherium robustum. e, Titanosaurus.

1996, Apr. 18   Perf. 12½
1613 A740 3.20p Strip of 5, #a.-
    e.   6.50 6.50

No. 1613 was issued in sheets of 25 stamps.

Taking Care of Planet Earth, Everyone's Responsibility, by Soraya Campanella — A741

Unwmk.
1996, June 5   Litho.   Perf. 12
1614 A741 3.20p multicolored   1.25 1.25

Souvenir Sheet

Calidris Canutus — A742

1996, May 28   Perf. 12½
1615 A742 12p multicolored   9.00 9.00
CAPEX '96.

Early Methods of Transportation — A743

Designs: a, 1912 Dion-Buton omnibus. b, 1928 Ford Model A. c, 1940 Raleigh bicycle. d, 1926 Magirus firetruck. e, 1917 Hotchkiss ambulance.

1996, May 21
1616 A743 3.20p Strip of 5, #a.-
    e.   6.25 6.25
No. 1616 was issued in sheets of 25 stamps.

Sailing Ships A744

Designs: a, Our Lady of Encina, 1726. b, San Francisco. c, Ships of E. Moreau. d, Bold Lady. e, Our Lady of the Light.

1996, June 17   Perf. 12½
1617 A744 3.20p Strip of 5, #a.-
    e.   6.25 6.25
No. 1617 was issued in sheets of 25 stamps.

Landscape in Las Flores, by Carmelo de Arzadun — A745

1996, July 15   Litho.   Perf. 12½
1618 A745 3.50p multicolored   1.40 1.40

Jewish Community in Uruguay, 80th Anniv. — A746

1996, July 29
1619 A746 7.50p multicolored   3.00 3.00

A747

Scientists from Uruguay A748

No. 1620, Enrique Legrand (1861-1939). No. 1621, Victor Bertullo (1919-79). No. 1622, Tomas Beno Hirschfeld (1939-86). No. 1623, Miguel C. Rubino (1886-1945).

1996, July 30
1620 A747 3.50p multicolored   1.40 1.40
1621 A747 3.50p multicolored   1.40 1.40
1622 A748 3.50p multicolored   1.40 1.40
1623 A748 3.50p multicolored   1.40 1.40
    Nos. 1620-1623 (4)   5.60 5.60

Bank of Uruguay, Cent. — A749

1996, Sept. 9   Perf. 12
1624 A749 3.50p 10p note   1.40 1.40
  a.   Booklet pane, #1624   2.00
1625 A749 3.50p 500p note   1.40 1.40
  a.   Booklet pane, #1625   2.00
       Complete bkl., #1624a, 1625a 4.00

Souvenir Sheet

Otto Lilienthal (1848-1896) — A750

Illustration reduced.

1996, Aug. 30
1626 A750 12p multicolored   4.75 4.75
AEROFILA '96.

Scientists A751

No. 1627, Albert Einstein. No. 1628, Aristotle. No. 1629, Isaac Newton.

1996, Sept. 3   Perf. 12½
1627 A751 7.50p multicolored   3.00 3.00
1628 A751 7.50p multicolored   3.00 3.00
1629 A751 7.50p multicolored   3.00 3.00
    Nos. 1627-1629 (3)   9.00 9.00

National Heritage — A752

Designs: No. 1630, Map of Gorriti Island showing locations of Spanish forts, 18th cent. No. 1631, Narbona Church, 18th cent.

                        Perf. 13x12½
1996, Sept. 12   Litho.   Unwmk.
1630 A752 3.50p multicolored   1.40 1.40
1631 A752 3.50p multicolored   1.40 1.40

Rural Assoc., 125th Anniv. A753

1996, Sept. 20   Perf. 12½x13
1632 A753 3.50p multicolored   1.40 1.40

Marine Life A754

a, Carchardon carcharias. b, Alopias vulpinus. c, Notorynchus cepedianus. d, Squatina dumerili.

1996, Sept. 23
1633 A754 3.50p Sheet of 4, #a.-
                    d.   5.50 5.50
Istanbul '96.

Sports Champions from Uruguay — A755

Designs: a, Angel Rodriguez, boxing, 1917. b, Leandro Noli, cycling, 1939. c, Eduardo G. Risso, rowing, 1948. d, Estrella Puente, javelin, 1949. e, Oscar Moglia, basketball, 1956.

1996, Oct. 1
1634 A755 3.50p Strip of 5, #a.-
    e.   7.00 7.00

Traditional Costumes A756

America issue: 3.50p, Gaucho. 7.50p, Woman of the campana.

1996, Oct. 11   Perf. 13x12½
1635 A756 3.50p multicolored   1.40 1.40
1636 A756 7.50p multicolored   3.00 3.00

3rd Space Conference of the Americas — A757

1996, Nov. 4   Wmk. 332   Perf. 12
1637 A757 3.50p multicolored   1.40 1.40

Comic Strips, Cent. A758

"Peloduro," by Julio E. Suarez.

1996, Nov. 7
1638 A758 4p multicolored   1.60 1.60

Health Institute, Cent. A759

1996, Nov. 20
1639 A759 4p multicolored   1.60 1.60

Church of the 7th Day Adventists in Uruguay, Cent. — A760

Wmk. 332
1996, Nov. 26   Litho.   Perf. 12½
1640 A760 3.50p multicolored   1.40 1.40

Felix de Azara (1746-1811), Naturalist — A761

1996, Nov. 20   Perf. 12
1641 A761 4p multicolored   1.60 1.60

Fish A762

Designs: No. 1642, Cynolebia nigripinnis. No. 1643, Cynolebia viarius.

Unwmk.
1997, Feb. 24   Litho.   Die Cut
Self-Adhesive
1642 A762 4p multicolored   1.60 1.60
1643 A762 4p multicolored   1.60 1.60

Popular Festivals
A763

#1644, Natl. Folklore Festival, Durazno. #1645, Traditional Gaucho Festival, Tacuarembo.

1997	Wmk. 332	Perf. 12½
1644 A763 4p multi		1.60 1.60
1645 A763 4p multi, vert.		1.60 1.60

Issued: #1644, 1/30; #1645, 3/10.
See Nos. 1653-1656.

Mushrooms — A764

Designs: a, Tricholoma nudum. b, Agaricus xanthodermus. c, Russula sardonia. d, Microsporum canis. e, Polyporus versicolor.

1997, Feb. 7
1646 A764 4p Strip of 5, #a.-e.   8.00 8.00
No. 1646 was issued in sheets of 25 stamps.

Ports
A765

No. 1647, Colonia. No. 1648, Punta del Este. No. 1649, Santiago Vázquez. No. 1650, Buceo.

1997, Feb. 28	Litho.	Die Cut
Self-Adhesive		
1647 A765 4p multicolored		1.60 1.60
1648 A765 4p multicolored		1.60 1.60
1649 A765 4p multicolored		1.60 1.60
1650 A765 4p multicolored		1.60 1.60
Nos. 1647-1650 (4)		6.40 6.40

Artigas' Lancers, Bicent.
A766

1997, Mar. 10   Wmk. 332   Perf. 12½
1651 A766 4p multicolored   1.60 1.60

Military Academy, 50th Anniv. — A767

1997, Mar. 13
1652 A767 4p multicolored   1.60 1.60

Popular Festivals Type of 1997

Coat of arms and: No. 1653, Performers under outdoor pavilion, Beer Week. No. 1654, Ruben Lena, bridge, river, Olimar River Festival, vert. No. 1655, Guitar, man on horse, Festival de Minas Y Abril. No. 1656, Family around person on horseback, Roosevelt Park.

1997	Litho.
1653 A763 5p multicolored	2.00 2.00
1654 A763 5p multicolored	2.00 2.00

1655 A763 5p multicolored	2.00 2.00
Die Cut	
Unwmk.	
Self-Adhesive	
1656 A763 5p multicolored	2.00 2.00
Nos. 1653-1656 (4)	8.00 8.00

Lions Intl. (#1656). Issued: #1653, 3/23; #1654, 3/24; #1655, 4/26; #1656, 3/21.

United Mobile Coronary Unit (UCM), 20th Anniv.
A768

1997, Apr. 4   Unwmk.   Die Cut
Self-Adhesive
1657 A768 5p multicolored   2.00 2.00

UNICEF, 50th Anniv. — A769

1997, Apr. 8   Die Cut
Self-Adhesive
1658 A769 5p multicolored   2.00 2.00

Lighthouses
A770

Various birds and: a, Anchorena Tower, 1920. b, Farallón Lighthouse, 1870. c, José Ignacio Lighthouse, 1877. d, Santa Maria Lighthouse, 1874. e, Vigía Tower, 18th cent.

1997, Apr. 22   Die Cut
Self-Adhesive
1659 A770 5p Strip of 5, #a.-e.   10.00 10.00

Prehistoric Animals
A771

Designs: a, Devincenzia gallinali. b, Smilodon populator. c, Mesosaurus tenuidens. d, Doedicurus clavicaudatus. e, Artigasia magna.

1997, May 5   Die Cut
Self-Adhesive
1660 A771 5p Strip of 5, #a.-e.   10.00 10.00

A772

Ecclesiastical Provinces — A772a

#1661, Church, diocese of Salto. #1662, Church, diocese of Melo. #1663, Bishop Jacinto Vera, 1st bishop of Montevideo. #1664, Msgr. Mariano Soler, 1st archbishop of Montevideo.

	Wmk. 332	
1997, May 9	Litho.	Perf. 12½
1661 A772 5p multicolored		2.00 2.00
1662 A772 5p multicolored		2.00 2.00
1663 A772a 2p multicolored		2.00 2.00
1664 A772a 5p multicolored		2.00 2.00
Nos. 1661-1664 (4)		8.00 8.00

Youth Stamp Collecting
A773

Designs: a, 2p, Boy, "Philately?" b, 2p, Boy thinking of stamps. c, 2p, Girl with soccer ball, boy. d, 1p, Boy looking at stamps in album. e, 1p, Boy with tongs and magnifying glass.

1997, May 25   Unwmk.
1665 A773 Strip of 5, #a.-e.   3.25 3.25

PACIFIC 97 — A774

1997, May 29   Perf. 12
1666 A774 10p Rynchops niger   4.00 4.00

Maccio Theater of San Jose, 85th Anniv.
A775

1997, June 5   Wmk. 332   Perf. 12½
1667 A775 5p multicolored   2.00 2.00

Inter-American Institute of Children, 70th Anniv. — A776

1997, June 9   Unwmk.
1668 A776 5p multicolored   2.00 2.00

Colony of Sacramento — A777

1997, July 4
1669 A777 5p multicolored   2.00 2.00

Punta del Este, 90th Anniv.
A778

1997, July 1
1670 A778 5p multicolored   2.00 2.00

Uruguayan Comics — A779

Scenes from comics by: No. 1671, Julio E. Suarez (Peloduro). No. 1672, Geoffrey Foladori.

	Perf. 12½	
1997, June 30	Litho.	Unwmk.
1671 A779 5p multicolored		1.50 1.50
1672 A779 5p multicolored		1.50 1.50

Zionism, Cent.
A780

Design: Theodor Herzl (1860-1904), founder of Zionist movement.

1997, July 17
1673 A780 5p multicolored   1.50 1.50

Children's Painting
A781

Geranoaetus Melanoleucus
A782

1997, July 21	Litho.	Die Cut
Self-Adhesive		
1674 A781 15p multicolored		4.50 4.50
1675 A782 25p multicolored		7.75 7.75

Nos. 1674, 1675 exist dated 1999.
See No. 1850.

Isolation of Acetylsalicylic Acid from Willow Trees, Cent. — A783

1997, Aug. 12	Litho.	Perf. 12½
1676 A783 6p multicolored		1.40 1.40
a.	Booklet pane of 2	4.50
	Complete booklet, #1676a	4.50

Department of Salto — A784

1997, Aug. 26
1677 A784 6p multicolored   1.75 1.75

Felix Mendelssohn (1809-47) — A785

No. 1679, Johannes Brahms (1833-97).

1997, Sept. 1
1678　A785　6p multicolored　　　　1.60　1.60
1679　A785　6p multicolored　　　　1.60　1.60
　a.　　Pair, #1678-1679　　　　　　3.50　3.50

Natural History Museum of
Montevideo, 160th Anniv. — A786

Designs: a, Lucas Kraguevich, paleontologist. b, Jose Arechavaleta, botantist. c, Garibaldi J. Devincenzi, zoologist. d, Antonio Taddei, archaelogist.

1997, Sept. 3
1680　A786　6p Strip of 4, #a.-d.　5.75　5.75

Mercosur
(Common
Market of
Latin America)
A787

1997, Sept. 26　　　　　　**Perf. 12**
1681　A787　11p multicolored　　　3.00　3.00
　See Argentina, No. 1975; Brazil, No. 2646; Paraguay, No. 2564.

Souvenir Sheet

Passiflora Coerulea — A788

Illustration reduced.

1997, Sept. 26　　　　　　**Perf. 12½**
1682　A788　15p multicolored　　　4.00　4.00
　1st Philatelic Exhibition of Mercosur countries.

Heinrich von
Stephan (1831-
97)
A789

1997, Oct. 9
1683　A789　11p multicolored　　　3.00　3.00

Souvenir Sheet

Spanish-Uruguayan
Monument — A790

Illustration reduced.

1997, Oct. 9
1684　A790　15p Monument　　　　4.00　4.00
　Philatelic Exhibition, Spain 1997.

America
Issue — A791

Designs: 6p, Woman carrying mail. 11p, Man delivering letters.

1997, Oct. 10
1685　A791　6p multicolored　　　　1.60　1.60
1686　A791　11p multicolored　　　3.00　3.00

Artigas Scientific Base,
Antarctica — A792

1997, Oct. 15　　　　　　**Perf. 12**
1687　A792　6p Pygoscelis papua　1.60　1.60

Painting, by Domingo Laporte (1855-
1928) — A793

1997, Oct. 21　　　　　　**Perf. 12½**
1688　A793　6p multicolored　　　　1.75　1.75

Galicia
House,
80th
Anniv.
A794

1997, Oct. 24
1689　A794　6p multicolored　　　　1.75　1.75

3rd Intl. Congress of Aeronautical and
Space History, Montevideo — A795

1997, Oct. 27　**Litho.**　**Unwmk.**
1690　A795　6p Arme 2 Biplane　1.75　1.75

1st Biennial Interparliamentary
Exhibition of MERCOSUR Paintings,
Montevideo — A796

1997, Oct. 28
1691　A796　11p multicolored　　　3.00　3.00

Souvenir Sheet

Pope John Paul II, Holy Year
2000 — A797

Illustration reduced.

1997, Nov. 7
1692　A797　10p multicolored　　　4.50　4.50
　Third Intl. Assembly Punta del Este, and of arrival of first Polish colonists at River Plate, cent.

Uruguayan Navy, 180th Anniv. — A798

1997, Nov. 14
1693　A798　6p multicolored　　　　1.75　1.75

Shanghai
'97 Intl.
Stamp
and Coin
Exhibition
A799

No. 1694: a, 3.50p, Front and back of 1 peso coin. b, 3.50p, Chinese flag, Hong Kong harbor, flower, junk. c, 4p, Michael Schumacher, Formula 1 driving champion, Ferrari. d, 4p, Sojourner on Mars, Pathfinder Mission.
　No. 1695: a, 3.50p, Martina Hingis, 1997 Wimbledon Ladies' champion. b, 3.50p, Jan Ullrich, 1997 Tour de France winner. c, 4p, Soccer players, 1998 World Cup Soccer Championship, France. d, 4p, Ski jumper, 1998 Winter Olympic Games, Nagano.

1997, Nov. 19
1694　A799　Sheet of 4, #a.-d.　4.25　4.25
1695　A799　Sheet of 4, #a.-d.　4.25　4.25

Christmas
A800

1997, Nov. 20
1696　A800　6p Magi　　　　　　1.75　1.75
1697　A800　11p Madonna & Child　3.00　3.00

Uruguayan Sportsmen — A801

Designs: a, Adesio Lombardo, Olympic bronze medalist, basketball, Helsinki, 1952. b, Guillermo Douglas, Olympic bronze medalist, single sculls, Rome, 1932. c, Obdulio Varela, soccer player on 1950 World Cup championship team. d, Atilio Francois, silver medalist, 1947 World Cycling Championships, Paris. e, Juan López Testa, South American 100 meters champion, 1947.

1997, Nov. 26
1698　A801　6p Strip of 5, #a.-e.　8.50　8.50

Mevifil '97, 1st Intl. Exhibition of
Philatelic Audio-Visual and Computer
Systems — A802

1997, Dec. 1　　　　　　**Perf. 12**
1699　A802　11p multicolored　　　3.00　3.00

INDEPEX
'97
A803

Early vehicles, inventors: a, 1st Land Rover, 1947. b, Henry Ford (1863-1947), Model A. c, Robert Bosch (1861-1942), inventor of automotive components. d, Rudolf Diesel (1858-1913), patented first diesel engine, 1897.

1997, Dec. 8　　　　　　**Perf. 12½**
1700　A803　6p Strip of 4, #a.-d.　6.50　6.50

Naval
Academy
of
Uruguay,
90th
Anniv.
A804

1997, Dec. 12
1701　A804　6p multicolored　　　　1.60　1.60

Supreme Court of Uruguay, 90th Anniv. A805

1997, Dec. 12
1702 A805 6p multicolored   1.60 1.60

Uruguayan Post Office, 170th Anniv. — A806

1997, Dec. 19
1703 A806 6p multicolored   1.60 1.60

MEVIR (Movement for Eradication of Unsanitary Rural Housing), 90th Anniv. — A807

Design: Homes, Dr. A. Gallinal, logo.

1997, Dec. 26
1704 A807 6p multicolored   1.60 1.60

Construction Projects — A808

a, Preparation. b, Planning. c, Execution.

1997, Dec. 29   **Perf. 12**
1705 A808 6p Strip of 3, #a.-c.   5.00 5.00
   d.   Booklet pane, #1705   6.00
       Complete booklet, #1705d   6.00

Souvenir Sheet

1897 Revolution, Cent. — A809

Design: Gen. Antonio "Chiquito" Saravia and Col. Diego Lamas. Illustration reduced.

1997, Dec. 30   **Perf. 12½**
1706 A809 15p multicolored   4.00 4.00

Painting by Héctor Ragni (b. 1898) — A810

1998, Feb. 6
1707 A810 6p multicolored   1.60 1.60

Naval Station, Montevideo — A811

1998, Feb. 13
1708 A811 6p multicolored   1.60 1.60

Native Trees — A812

a, Butia capitata. b, Grove of butia capitata. c, Grove of phytolacca dioica. d, Phytolacca dioica.

1998, Mar. 20   **Perf. 12**
1709 A812 6p Block of 4, #a.-d.   6.25 6.25

Museum of Humor — A813

Cartoons: No. 1710, by Oscar Abín. No. 1711, by Emilio Cortinas.

1998, Mar. 13   **Perf. 12½**
1710 A813 6p multicolored   1.60 1.60
1711 A813 6p multicolored   1.60 1.60
   a.   Pair, #1710-1711   3.25 3.25

Wilson Ferreira Aldunate (1919-88) A814

1998, Mar. 17   **Perf. 12**
1712 A814 6p multicolored   1.60 1.60

Fossilized Animals — A815

Designs: a, Testudinites sellowi. b, Proborhyaena gigantea. c, Propachyrucos schiaffinos. d, Stegomastodon platensis.

1998, Mar. 26
1713 A815 6p Block of 4, #a.-d.   6.25 6.25

Israel '98, State of Israel, 50th Anniv. — A816

1998, Mar. 31   **Perf. 12**
1714 A816 12p multicolored   3.25 3.25

Birds — A820

a, Plyborus plancus. b, Cygnus melancoryphus. c, Platalea ajaja. d, Theristicus caudatus.

1998, Apr. 30
1718 A820 6p Block of 4, #a.-d.   6.25 6.25

Organization of American States, 50th Anniv. — A821

1998, Apr. 14 Litho.   Perf. 12¾x12½
1719 A821 12p multi   3.00 3.00

61st World Congress of Sports Journalism A822

1998, Apr. 21   **Litho.**   **Perf. 12**
1720 A822 6p multicolored   1.60 1.60

Land Settlement Institute, 50th Anniv. — A823

1998, Apr. 22 Litho.   Perf. 12¾x12½
1721 A823 6p multi   1.50 1.50

Souvenir Sheet

Intl. Topical Philatelic Exhibition, Nueva Helvecia A824

Cross and: a, 3.50p, Switzerland #5, Uruguay #1. b, 3.50p, Obverse and reverse of Euro coin. c, 4p, Olympic rings and mountain. d, 4p, Space station.

1998, May 12   **Perf. 12½x12¾**
1722 A824 Sheet of 4, #a.-d.   3.75 3.75
       Swiss Republic, bicent.

Souvenir Sheet

Whales A825

a, 3.50p, Balaenoptera physalus (b). b, 3.50p, Balaenoptera acutorostrata. c, 4p, Megaptera novaeangliae (d). d, 4p, Eubalaena australis (c).

1998, May 15   **Litho.**   **Perf. 12½**
1723 A825 Sheet of 4, #a.-d.   3.75 3.75
    Ambiente '98, Maia, Portugal; Intl. Year of the Ocean; Expo '98, Lisbon.

1983 Labor Day Democracy Demonstrations — A826

Perf. 12¼x12¾
1998, May 27   **Litho.**   **Wmk. 332**
1724 A826 6p brn & blk   1.50 1.50
      See Nos. 1740, 1775.

Street Cars — A827

Historic Montevideo trams: a, English "La Comercial," 1906. b, German Transatlantica Co., 1907. c, Transatlantica, 1908. d, Transatlantica double decker, 1916.

1998, May 29 Litho. Perf. 12
1725 A827 6p Block of 4, #a.-d. 6.25 6.25

Juvalux '98 — A828

Wildcats: a, Felis colocola. b, Felis pardalis. c, Felis wiedil. d, Panthera onca.

Unwmk.
1998, June 18 Litho. Perf. 12
1726 A828 6p Block of 4, #a.-d. 6.00 6.00

Ships A829

a, "Sirius." b, Gunboat "18 de Julio." c, Transport, "Maldonado." d, "Instituto de Pesca No. 1."

1998, June 25 Litho. Perf. 12
1727 A829 6p Block of 4, #a.-d. 6.00 6.00

Jesuit Mission Church, Calera de las Huérfanas A830

Perf. 12½x12¾
1998, July 24 Litho. Unwmk.
1728 A830 12p multi 3.00 3.00

Monument to the Peace of 1872, San José de Mayo, 125th Anniv. — A831

1998, July 31 Perf. 12¾x12½
1729 A831 6p multi 1.50 1.50

155mm Artillery Unit No. 5, Cent. A832

1998, Aug. 7 Perf. 12½x12¾
1730 A832 6p multi 1.50 1.50

Butterflies — A833

1998, Aug. 14 Litho. Perf. 12
1731 A833 6p Eacles imperialis 1.50 1.50
1732 A833 6p Protoparce luceti-
us 1.50 1.50
a. Pair, #1731-1732 3.00 3.00

First Monument to José Artigas, San José de Mayo, Cent. — A834

Perf. 12¾x12½
1998, Aug. 24 Litho.
1733 A834 6p multi 1.50 1.50

A835

1998, Aug. 28
1734 A835 6p multi 1.50 1.50
Dr. Mauricio López Lombo (1918-93), zoo founder.

A836

1998, Aug. 31
1735 A836 6p multi 1.50 1.50
Falleri-Balzo Music Conservatory, Montevideo, cent.

José Fernández Vergara (1810-1906), Founder of Pueblo Vergara — A837

1998, Sept. 8
1736 A837 6p multi 1.50 1.50

Souvenir Sheet

El Pais Newspaper, 80th Anniv. — A838

Illustration reduced.

1998, Sept. 14 Perf. 12½x12¾
1737 A838 12p multi 3.00 3.00

Collective Medical Assistance Institute, 145th Anniv. — A839

1998, Sept. 24 Perf. 12¾x12½
1738 A839 6p multi 1.50 1.50

Postal Link Between Montevideo and Corunna, Spain, 230th Anniv. — A840

1998, Sept. 24
1739 A840 12p multi 3.00 3.00
Espamer '98, Buenos Aires.

Democracy Demonstration Type

6p, March of the Social and Cultural Assoc. of Public School Students, 9/25/83.

Perf. 12½x12¾
1998, Sept. 25 Wmk. 332
1740 A826 6p brn & blk 1.50 1.50

Iberoamericana '98 Philatelic Exhibition, Maia, Portugal — A841

Airplanes: a, Junkers J52. b, Spad VII. c, Ansaldo SVA-10. d, Neybar.

Unwmk.
1998, Oct. 2 Litho. Perf. 12
1741 A841 6p Block of 4, #a.-d. 6.00 6.00

Death of Chilean Pres. Salvador Allende, 25th Anniv. A842

Perf. 12¼x12¾
1998, Oct. 2 Litho. Unwmk.
1742 A842 12p multi 3.00 3.00

50th Anniv. of Enrique Rodríguez Fabregat (1885-1976) as UN Commissioner for Palestine — A843

1998, Oct. 5 Perf. 12¾x12½
1743 A843 6p multi 1.50 1.50

Radio Carve, 70th Anniv. A844

1998, Oct. 7 Litho. Perf. 12½x12¾
1744 A844 6p multi 1.50 1.50

World Post Day A845

1998, Oct. 9 Litho. Perf. 12½x12¾
1745 A845 12p multi 3.00 3.00
Ilsapex '98, Johannesburg.

America Issue — A846

Famous women: 6p, Julia Guarino (1897-1985), first woman architect in South America. 12p, Dr. Paulina Luisi (1875-1950).

1998, Oct. 9 Litho. Perf. 12
1746 A846 6p multi 1.50 1.50
1747 A846 12p multi 3.00 3.00

Assoc. of Inland Pharmacies, 50th Anniv. — A847

1998, Oct. 10 Perf. 12½x12¾
1748 A847 6p multi 1.50 1.50

Postal Services A847a

Serpentine Die Cut 11¼
1998, Oct. 15 Litho. Unwmk.
Self-Adhesive
1748A A847a 25p multi 6.00 6.00
Exists dated 1999.

Classic Vehicles — A848

Designs: a, 1950 Lancia fire engine. b, 1946 Maserati San Remo. c, 1954 Alfa Romeo trolley bus. d, 1936 Fiat Topolino.

1998, Oct. 23   Litho.   Perf. 12
1749 A848 6p Block of 4, #a.-d.   5.50 5.50

Italia'98.

Artists
A849

Designs: No. 1750, Sculpture, "Motherhood," and self-portrait of Nerses Ounanian (1920-57). No. 1751, Illustrations from book "Piquín y Chispita," by Serafín J. García (1905-85), vert. No. 1752, Musical score by Héctor M. Artola (1903-82), vert.

Perf. 12½x12¾, 12¾x12½
1998, Oct. 27   Litho.
1750 A849 6p multi   1.50 1.50
1751 A849 6p multi   1.50 1.50
1752 A849 6p multi   1.50 1.50
   Nos. 1750-1752 (3)   4.50 4.50

Juvenalia
'98 — A850

1998, Oct. 30 Litho.   Perf. 12¾x12½
1753 A850 6p multi   1.50 1.50

Souvenir Sheet

Uruguay-Germany Philatelic Exhibition, Montevideo — A851

Designs: a, 3.50p, Zeppelin cover, Zeppelin NT. b, 3.50p, Germany #1592, Germany Berlin #9N584, German Democratic Republic #2791, mail box. c, 4p, Brandenburg Gate, Volkswagen Beetle, Konrad Adenauer. d, 4p, Airplane, German mark note and coin.

1998, Nov. 6 Litho.   Perf. 12½x12¾
1754 A851 Sheet of 4, #a.-d.   3.75 3.75

IBRA '99, 150th anniv. of German stamps (#1754a, 1754b), 50th anniv. of Federal Republic of Germany (#1754c), 50th anniv. of German mark (#1754d).

16th Congress of Expenditure Control Boards — A852

1998, Nov. 9
1755 A852 12p blue & silver   3.00 3.00

Uruguayan Chamber of Industries, Cent. — A853

1998, Nov. 9
1756 A853 6p multi   1.50 1.50

Flowers — A854

Serpentine Die Cut 11¼
1998-99   Litho.
Self-Adhesive
1757 A854 1p Oxalis pudica   .25   .25
1760 A854 4p Oxalis pudica
              (white)   .90   .90
1761 A854 5p Oxalis pudica
              (purple)   .70   .70
1762 A854 6p Eugenia
              uniflora   1.50 1.50
1763 A854 7p Eugenia
              uniflora   1.60 1.60
1765 A854 9p Eugenia
              uniflora   —   —
1766 A854 10p Aechmea
              recurvata   2.50 2.50
1770 A854 14p Acca sellowi-
              ana   3.25 3.25
1771 A854 50p Acca sellowi-
              ana   8.75 8.75
   Nos. 1757-1770 (7)   10.70 10.70

Issued: 7p, 2/4/99; 4p, 12/23/99; 14p, 8/6/99; 1p, 6p, 10p, 50p, 1998. 9p, 1999. 5p, 2/19/02.
No. 1757 exists dated 1999, 2000, 2001, 2002. No. 1766 exists dated 1999. No. 1766 exists dated 2003.

Christmas — A855

Designs: 6p, The Virgin's Descent to Reward St. Ildefons' Writings (detail), by El Greco. 12p, St. Peter's Tears (detail), by Bartolomé Esteban Murillo.

1998, Nov. 23   Litho.   Perf. 12
1772 A855 6p multi   1.50 1.50
1773 A855 12p multi   3.00 3.00

Paso Del Molina Neighborhood of Montevideo, 250th Anniv. — A856

1998, Nov. 26   Perf. 12½x12¾
1774 A856 6p multi   1.50 1.50

Labor Day Type
6p, Proclamation at the Obelisk, 11/27/83.

Perf. 12¼x12¾
1998, Nov. 27   Litho.   Wmk. 332
1775 A826 6p brn & blk   1.50 1.50

Morosoli Cultural Awards — A857

Perf. 12¾x12½
1998, Nov. 27   Litho.   Unwmk.
1776 A857 6p multi   1.50 1.50

Universal Declaration of Human Rights, 50th Anniv. — A858

1998, Dec. 10   Perf. 12½x12¾
1777 A858 6p multi   1.50 1.50

Uruguayan Olympic Committee, 75th Anniv. — A859

1998, Dec. 15   Perf. 12
1778 A859 6p multi   1.50 1.50

Uruguayan Sportsmen
A860

Designs: a, Juan Lopez (1907-83), soccer coach. b, Hector Scarone (1899-1967), soccer player. c, Leandro Gomez Harley (1902-79), basketball player, hurdler. d, Liberto Corney (1905-55), boxer.

1998, Dec. 15   Perf. 12¾x12½
1779 A860 6p Block of 4, #a.-d. 6.00 6.00

Famous Uruguayans — A861

Designs: No. 1780: Dr. Roberto Caldeyro Barcia (1921-96), physiologist. No. 1781, Dr. José Verocay (1876-1923), pathologist. No. 1782, Dr. José L. Duomarco (1905-85), medical researcher.

Perf. 12¼x12¾
1998, Dec. 18   Litho.   Unwmk.
1780 A861 6p multi   1.50 1.50
1781 A861 6p multi   1.50 1.50
1782 A861 6p multi   1.50 1.50
   Nos. 1780-1782 (3)   4.50 4.50

Emile Zola's "J'accuse" Letter, Cent. (in 1998) A862

1999, Jan. 4   Litho.   Perf. 12½x12¾
1783 A862 14p multicolored   3.50 3.50

Las Cañas Resort, Fray Bentos A863

1999, Feb. 26
1784 A863 7p multicolored   1.60 1.60

Rio de la Plata Boundary Treaty, 25th Anniv. A864

1999, Mar. 15
1785 A864 7p multicolored   1.60 1.60

Famous Uruguayans — A865

Designs: No. 1786, Joaquin Torres Garcia (1874-1949), painter. No. 1787, Luis Ernesto Aroztegui (1930-94), textile artist. No. 1788, Juan José Morosoli (1899-1957), writer.

1999, Mar. 26
1786 A865 7p multicolored   2.50 2.50
1787 A865 7p multicolored   2.50 2.50
1788 A865 7p multicolored   2.50 2.50
   Nos. 1786-1788 (3)   7.50 7.50

Birds and Flowering Trees A866

a, Psidium cattleianum, Pipraeidea melanonota. b, Tabebuia ipe, Chlorostilbon aureoventris. c, Duranta repens, Tangara preciosa. d,

Citharexylum montevidense, Tachuris rubigastra.

1999, Apr. 14 Litho. Perf. 12¼x12¾
1789 A866 7p Block of 4, #a.-d. 6.00 6.00

Carriages A867

Designs: a, Break de chasse. b, Mylord. c, Coupé trois quarts. d, Break de champ.

1999, Apr. 29 Litho. Perf. 12½x12¾
1790 A867 7p Block of 4, #a.-d. 6.50 6.50

National Soccer Team, Cent. — A868

Designs: a, B. Céspedes, M. Nebel, C. Céspedes, team's first field. b, H. Castro, P. Cea, A. Ciocca, team flag. c, R. Porta, A García, S. Gambetta, team headquarters.

1999, May 5 Litho. Perf. 12
1791 A868 7p Strip of 3, #a.-c. 5.75 5.75
Complete booklet, #1791 6.75

Children's Millennium Stamp Design Contest Winners A869

Designs: a, By Stefani Andrea Furtado. b, By Pilar Trujillo. c, By Lucia Lavie. d, By Cecilia Chopitea.

1999, May 6 Litho. Perf. 12½x12¾
1792 A869 7p Block of 4, #a.-d. 6.50 6.50

Jorge Chebataroff (1909-84), Geographer, Botanist — A870

1999, May 14
1793 A870 7p multicolored 1.60 1.60

Formation of Infantry Brigade No. 1, 60th Anniv. A871

Paintings: No. 1794, Infantry Battalion No. 2 at Battle of Montecaseros, 1852. No. 1795, Infantry Brigade No. 1 at Battle of Estero Bellaco, 1866. No. 1796, Infantry Battalion No. 1 at Battle of Boquerón, 1866.

1999, May 18
1794 A871 7p multicolored 1.75 1.75
1795 A871 7p multicolored 1.75 1.75
1796 A871 7p multicolored 1.75 1.75
Nos. 1794-1796 (3) 5.25 5.25

Villa de la Restauracion, 150th Anniv. — A872

1999, May 24 Perf. 12¾x12½
1797 A872 7p multicolored 1.60 1.60

Souvenir Sheet

Barcelona, Spain Soccer Team, Cent. — A873

Illustration reduced.

1999, May 28 Litho. Perf. 12½x12¾
1798 A873 15p multi 3.25 3.25

1st Festival of Film Critics, Montevideo A874

1999, June 2 Perf. 12¾x12¼
Booklet Stamp
1799 A874 7p multi 1.60 1.60
a. Booklet pane, 2 #1799 3.25
Complete booklet, #1799a 3.25

Philex France 99 A875

Horses: a, Arabian. b, Quarter horse. c, Thoroughbred. d, Shetland pony.

Perf. 12½x12¾
1999, June 10 Litho.
1800 A875 7p Block of 4, #a.-d. 6.25 6.25

Publication "Marcha," 60th Anniv. — A876

Perf. 12¼x12¾
1999, June 23 Litho.
1801 A876 7p multi 1.60 1.60

Permanent Home for "Espacio Ciencia" Science Exhibits — A877

1999, July 2 Perf. 12¾x12¼
1802 A877 7p multi 1.60 1.60

Artigas Antarctic Scientific Base, 25th Anniv. A878

1999, July 12 Perf. 12¼x12¾
1803 A878 7p multi 1.60 1.60

Republic of Uruguay University, 150th Anniv. A879

1999, July 19
1804 A879 7p yel & blk 1.60 1.60

UNESCO Regional Office, 50th Anniv. — A880

1999, July 20 Perf. 12¾x12¼
1805 A880 7p multi 1.60 1.60

The Last Charruas — A881

a, One seated, one standing. b, Two seated.

1999, July 22 Litho. Perf. 12¾x12½
1806 A881 7p Pair, #a.-b. 3.25 3.25

Souvenir Sheet

Millennium A882

a, 3.50p, Apollo space program. b, 3.50p, Soccer players, 2000 Olympic Games, Sydney. c, 4p, Centenary of Zeppelins. d, 4p, #C60.

1999, July 30 Litho. Perf. 12½x12¾
1807 A882 Sheet of 4, #a.-d. 3.25 3.25
UPU, 125th anniv., Bangkok 2000, Espana 2000, WIPA 2000, Hanover World's Fair.

El Galpón Theater, Montevideo, 50th Anniv. — A883

1999, Aug. 3 Perf. 12¾x12¼
1808 A883 7p multi 1.60 1.60

China 1999 World Philatelic Exhibition — A884

Sea planes: a, Piper J-3. b, Short Sunderland.

1999, Aug. 18 Perf. 12¼x12¾
1809 A884 7p Pair, #a.-b. 3.25 3.25

Dogs — A885

Designs: a, Cocker spaniel. b, German shepherd. c, Dalmatian. d, Basset hound.

Perf. 12¾x12½
1999, Aug. 24 Litho.
1810 A885 7p Block of 4, #a.-d. 6.00 6.00

Insects & Flowers A886

a, Halictidae, Oxalis sp. b, Apanteles sp., Epidendrum paniculosum. c, Metabolosia univita, Baccharis trimera. d, Compositae, Cantarido.

Perf. 12½x12¾
1999, Sept. 10 Litho.
1811 A886 7p Block of 4, #a.-d. 6.00 6.00

A887

A888

Uruguayan Artists: No. 1812, Orlando Aldama (1904-87), writer. No. 1813, Julio Martínez Oyanguren (1901-73), guitarist.

Perf. 12¾x12½

1999, Sept. 13   **Litho.**
1812 A887 7p multi   1.60 1.60
1813 A887 7p multi   1.60 1.60

Perf. 12¾x12¼

1999, Sept. 18   **Litho.**
1814 A888 7p multi   1.60 1.60

Cultural heritage of Mercosur countries.

First Uruguayan Participation in
Olympics, Paris, 1924 — A889

Designs: a, Poster, medal. b, Medal, medal-
winning soccer team.

1999, Sept. 30   **Perf. 12¼x12¾**
1815 A889 7p Pair, #a.-b.   3.25 3.25

Intl. Year
of Older
Persons
A890

1999, Oct. 1 Litho. Perf. 12¼x12¾
1816 A890 7p multi   1.60 1.60

Aquellare Filatélico, by Mariano
Barbasán — A891

1999, Oct. 1   **Perf. 12**
1817 A891 7p multi   1.60 1.60

Stamp Day.

America Issue, A
New Millennium
Without
Arms — A892

7p, Arms in trash can. 14p, Earth, satellites.

1999, Oct. 6   **Perf. 13¾x12¼**
1818 A892 7p multi   1.60 1.60
1819 A892 14p multi   3.25 3.25

Inter-American Development Bank,
40th Anniv. — A893

1999, Oct. 6   **Perf. 12¼x12¾**
1820 A893 7p multi   1.60 1.60

Winner of
Older
Person's
Stamp
Design
Contest
A894

1999, Oct. 8
1821 A894 7p multi   1.60 1.60

El Ceibo
Society,
50th
Anniv.
A895

1999, Oct. 8
1822 A895 7p multi   1.60 1.60

Third Intl.
Conference of
Ministers for
Sports, Punta
del
Este — A896

1999, Oct. 13   **Perf. 12**
1823 A896 7p multi   1.60 1.60

Souvenir Sheets

Official Service of Broadcasting,
Television and Entertainment — A897

Illustration reduced.
No. 1824: a, 4p, Television cameraman. b,
4p, Building. c, 3p, Radio studio. d, 3p, Film
cameraman.
No. 1825: a, 4p, Symphony orchestra. b, 4p,
Chamber music group. c, 3p, Chorus. d, 3p,
Ballet dancers.

1999, Oct. 22   **Perf. 12¼x12¾**
1824 A897 Sheet of 4, #a.-d.   3.25 3.25
1825 A897 Sheet of 4, #a.-d.   3.25 3.25

Uruguayan Standards Institute, 60th
Anniv. — A898

1999, Nov. 3
1826 A898 7p multi   1.60 1.60

A899

1999, Nov. 3   **Perf. 12¾x12¼**
1827 A899 7p multi   1.60 1.60

Vice-President Hugo Batalla (1926-98).

A900

1999, Nov.12

Cover of 4/29/29 Mundo Uruguayo
magazine.

1828 A900 7p multi   1.60 1.60

Exhibition of art and design from the 1920s,
Blanes Museum, Montevideo.

Millennium — A901

Illustration reduced.
No. 1829 — Various buildings and: a,
"1999." b, "2000."

1999, Nov. 23   **Litho.**   **Perf. 12**
1829 A901 3.50p Pair, #a.-b.   1.60 1.60

Celmar Poumé
(1924-83),
Cartoonist
A902

1999, Nov. 26   **Perf. 12¾x12¼**
1830 A902 7p multi   1.60 1.60

Christmas
A903

9p, Tree with ornaments. 18p, Carolers.

Perf. 12¼x12¾, 12¾x12¼
1999, Dec. 3
1831 A903 9p multi   2.00 2.00
1832 A903 18p multi, vert.   4.00 4.00

Tannat Wines,
20th
Anniv. — A904

1999, Dec. 9   **Perf. 12**
1833 A904 9p shown   2.00 2.00
1834 A904 9p Wine drinker   2.00 2.00

New Maldonado Department
Governmental Building — A905

1999, Dec. 11   **Perf. 12¼x12¾**
1835 A905 9p multi   2.00 2.00

Types of 1997 and

Crow's
Gorge
Nature
Reserve
A907

Design: 2p, Penitente Waterfall, vert. No.
1841, Gruta del Palacio, vert. 100p, Sierra de
los Caracoles.

*Serpentine Die Cut 11¼, Die Cut
(#1840, 1850, 1853)*

2000-01   **Litho.**

Self-Adhesive
1836 A907 2p multi   .30 .30
1838 A907 11p multi   2.00 2.00
1840 A781 20p multi   4.50 4.50
1841 A907 20p multi   — —
1850 A782 32p multi   7.25 7.25
1853 A782 80p multi   18.00 18.00
1854 A907 100pmulti   14.00 14.00

Issued: 32p, 1/20. No. 1840, 80p, 12/12.
11p, 3/16/01. No. 1841, 4/26/01. 2p, 8/1/01.
100p, 2/13/02. This is an expanding set. Numbers may change.
No. 1836 exists dated "2002."

50th Anniv of Artistic Career of Carlos
Páez Vilaró — A916

2000, Jan. 15   **Litho.**   **Perf. 12**
1856 A916 9p multi   2.00 2.00

Orchids — A917

No. 1857: a, 5p, Laelia purpurata. b, 4p, Cattleya corcovado. c, 4p, Cattleya sp. "hybrid." d, 5p, Laelia tenebrosa.

2000, Mar. 3
1857 A917 Block of 4, #a.-d.   4.00 4.00

Lighthouses — A918

No. 1858: a, 5p, Isla de Flores, 1828. b, 4p, Punta del Este, 1860. c, 4p, Cabo Polonio, 1881. d, 5p, Punta Brava, 1876.

2000, Mar. 14
1858 A918   Block of 4, #a.-d.   4.00 4.00

Carlos Quijano (1900-84), Economics Journalist — A919

2000, Mar. 30   *Perf. 12¼x12¾*
1859 A919 9p multi   2.00 2.00

The Gold Rush, Starring Charlie Chaplin, 75th Anniv. A920

2000, Apr. 7   Litho.   *Perf. 12¼x12¾*
1860 A920 18p multi   4.00 4.00
Lubrapex 2000 Stamp Show, Brazil.

El Cordón Neighborhood of Montevideo, 250th Anniv. — A921

2000, Apr. 10   Litho.   *Perf. 12¼x12¾*
1861 A921 9p multi   2.00 2.00

Mural "Espina de la Cruz," by Children of Mercedes — A922

a, 5p, Branches. b, 4p, Two red flowers.

2000, Apr. 26   *Perf. 12¼x12*
1862 A922 Pair, #a-b   2.00 2.00

Francisco García y Santos (1856-1921), Government Official — A923

2000, May 2   *Perf. 12¾x12¼*
1863 A923 9p multi   2.00 2.00

Uruguayan Notaries Assoc., 125th Anniv. — A924

2000, May 9   Litho.   *Perf. 12¾x12¼*
1864 A924 9p multi   2.00 2.00

Intl. Museum Day — A925

2000, May 18   Litho.   *Perf. 12¾x12¼*
1865 A925 9p multi   2.00 2.00

Stampin' the Future Children's Stamp Design Contest Winners — A926

Artwork by: a, 5p, Helena Perez. b, 4p, Maria Pia Pereyra. c, 4p, Virginia Regueiro. d, 5p, Blanca E. Lima.
Illustration reduced.

2000, June 2   Litho.   *Perf. 12*
1866 A926 Block of 4, #a-d   4.00 4.00

Club Soriano, 90th Anniv. A927

2000, June 9   Litho.   *Perf. 12¼x12¾*
1867 A927 9p multi   2.00 2.00

Antonio Rupenian, Founder of Radio Armenia — A928

2000, June 16   *Perf. 12¾x12¼*
1868 A928 18p multi   4.00 4.00

"1900 Generation" Writers, Cent. — A929

Perf. 12¾x12¼
2000, June 22   Litho.
1869 A929 9p multi   2.00 2.00

Cacti — A930

No. 1870: a, 5p, Notocactus ottonis. b, 4p, Echinopsis multiplex.

2000, July 4   *Perf. 12¼*
1870 A930   Horiz. pair, #a-b   2.00 2.00

Uruguayan Soccer Association, Cent. — A931

No. 1871: a, 5p, Players marching. b, 4p, Team photo. c, 4p, Stadium, World Cup. d, 5p, Players in action, World Cup.
Illustration reduced.

2000, July 14   Litho.   *Perf. 12¼x12*
1871 A931   Block of 4, #a-d   8.75 8.75

Opera Anniversaries — A932

No. 1872: a, 9p, Scene from Carmen, composer Georges Bizet. b, 9p, Scene from Tosca, composer Giacomo Puccini.
Illustration reduced.

2000, July 20
1872 A932   Pair, #a-b   4.00 4.00
Carmen, 125th anniv.; Tosca, cent.

Latin American Integration Association, 20th Anniv. — A933

2000, Aug. 11   *Perf. 12¾x12¼*
1873 A933 18p multi   4.00 4.00

Naval Aviation, 75th Anniv. A934

2000, Aug. 18   *Perf. 12¼x12¾*
1874 A934 9p multi   2.00 2.00

ORT, 120th Anniv. A935

2000, Aug. 28
1875 A935 9p multi   2.00 2.00

Luis de la Robla (1780-1844), First Postmaster General — A936

2000, Aug. 28   *Perf. 12¾x12¼*
1876 A936 9p multi   2.00 2.00

Gonzalo Rodriguez (1971-99), Race Car Driver — A937

a, 9p, Rodriguez, dark blue car. b, 9p, Rodriguez holding trophy, light blue car.
Illustration reduced.

2000, Sept. 11   *Perf. 12x12¼*
1877 A937   Pair, #a-b   4.00 4.00

Gen. José Artigas (1764-1850) A938

2000, Sept. 22   **Litho.**   **Perf. 12¼**
1878 A938 9p multi + label   1.60 1.60

España 2000 Intl. Philatelic Exhibition — A939

Birds: a, 5p, Donacospiza albifrons. b, 4p, Geositta cunicularia. c, 4p, Phacellodomus striaticollis. d, 5p, Cacicus chrysopterus. Illustration reduced.

2000, Sept. 27   **Perf. 12**
1879 A939   Block of 4, #a-d   3.25 3.25

Soka Gakkai International, 25th Anniv. — A940

2000, Oct. 2   **Perf. 12¼x12¾**
1880 A940 18p multi   3.25 3.25

America Issue, Fight Against AIDS — A941

No. 1881: a, 9p, Tic-tac-toe game with condoms and crosses. b, 18p, Syringe and red ribbon.

2000, Oct. 10   **Perf. 12¼**
1881 A941   Horiz. pair, #a-b   4.75 4.75

Mercosur Cultural Heritage Day — A942

2000, Oct. 14   **Perf. 12¾x12¼**
1882 A942 18p multi   3.25 3.25

Dragon, by Luis Mazzey (1895-1983) — A943

2000, Oct. 19   **Perf. 12¼x12¾**
1883 A943 9p multi   1.60 1.60

Fire Fighters A944

Designs: No. 1884, 9p, At car crash. No. 1885, 9p, Searching for victims, vert.

Perf. 12¼x12¾, 12¾x12¼
2000, Oct. 26
1884-1885 A944   Set of 2   3.25 3.25

Prof. Julio Ricaldoni (1906-93), Structural Engineer A945

2000, Nov. 13   **Perf. 12¼x12¾**
1886 A945 9p multi   1.60 1.60

29th Conference on Structural Engineering, Punta del Este.

Training Ship "Capitan Miranda," 70th Anniv. A946

2000, Nov. 15
1887 A946 9p multi   1.60 1.60

Holy Roman Emperor Charles V (1500-58) A947

2000, Nov. 22   **Litho.**
1888 A947 22p multi   4.00 4.00

Christmas A948

Designs: 11p, Fireworks. 22p, Holy Family.

2000, Dec. 1
1889-1890 A948   Set of 2   5.75 5.75

Sarandi del Yi, 125th Anniv. — A949

2000, Dec. 14   **Perf. 12¾x12¼**
1891 A949 11p multi   2.00 2.00

Forest Fire Prevention Service A950

2001, Feb. 9   **Litho.**   **Perf. 12½x12¾**
1892 A950 11p multi   2.00 2.00

Amphibians and Reptiles — A951

No. 1893: a, Phyllomedusa iheringii. b, Acanthochelys spixii. c, Phrynops hilarii. d, Scinax sqalirostris.

2001, Feb. 15   **Perf. 12**
1893 A951 11p Block of 4, #a-d   8.00 8.00

Paysandú Rowing Club, Cent. A952

2001, Feb. 28   **Perf. 12½x12¾**
1894 A952 11p multi   2.00 2.00

17th Congress of Latin American Confederation of Congress Organizers A953

2001, Mar. 2   **Perf. 12¾x12½**
1895 A953 11p multi   2.00 2.00

City of Belén, Bicent. — A954

2001, Mar. 14
1896 A954 11p multi   2.00 2.00

David, by Michelangelo, 500th Anniv. — A955

2001, Mar. 22
1897 A955 22p multi   4.00 4.00

Uruguayan Society of Performers, 50th Anniv. — A956

2001, Mar. 26   **Perf. 12½x12¾**
1898 A956 11p multi   2.00 2.00

Casal Catalá, 75th Anniv. — A957

2001, Apr. 20   **Perf. 12¾x12½**
1899 A957 11p multi   2.00 2.00

Universidad Mayor de la República Engineering Faculty, 85th Anniv. — A958

2001, Apr. 30
1900 A958 11p blue   2.00 2.00

Rodolfo V. Tálice (1899-1999), Biologist — A959

2001, May 2   **Perf. 12½x12¾**
1901 A959 11p multi   2.00 2.00

Montevideo Lions Club, 50th Anniv. — A960

2001, May 14   *Perf. 12¾x12½*
1902 A960 11p multi   2.00 2.00

Invention of the Telephone, 125th Anniv. A961

2001, May 22   *Perf. 12½x12¾*
1903 A961 22p multi   4.00 4.00

Snakes — A962

No. 1904: a, Philodryas olfersii. b, Bothrops alternatus.
Illustration reduced.

2001, May 28   *Perf. 12*
1904 A962 11p Horiz. pair, #a-b   4.00 4.00

Juan Manuel Blanes (1830-1901), Painter — A963

2001, June 8   Litho.   *Perf. 12½x12¾*
1905 A963 11p multi   1.75 1.75

Start of Pediatrics Teaching by Dr. Luis Morquio, Cent. — A964

2001, June 15   *Perf. 12¾x12½*
1906 A964 11p multi   1.75 1.75

The Ring of the Nibelung, by Richard Wagner — A965

No. 1907: a, The Rhinegold (El Oro del Rin). b, The Valkyrie (La Walquiria). c, Siegfried (Sigfrido). d, The Twilight of the Gods (El Ocaso de los Dioses).

2001, June 29   *Perf. 12*
1907 A965 11p Block of 4, #a-d   6.50 6.50

Intl. Organization for Migration, 50th Anniv. — A966

2001, July 5   *Perf. 12¾x12½*
1908 A966 22p blue & black   3.25 3.25

Thomas Alva Edison (1847-1931) A967

2001, July 12
1909 A967 22p multi   3.25 3.25

Laying of Foundation Stone for Montevideo Port, Cent. — A968

2001, July 18   *Perf. 12½x12¾*
1910 A968 11p multi   1.75 1.75

Fowl — A969

No. 1911: a, New Hampshire. b, Orpington-Buff. c, Araucanas. d, Leghorn-Light brown.
Illustration reduced.

2001, July 30   *Perf. 12*
1911 A969 11p Block of 4, #a-d   6.75 6.75

Moby Dick, by Herman Melville, 150th Anniv. — A970

2001, Aug. 2   *Perf. 12¾x12½*
1912 A970 22p multi   3.25 3.25

Bernardo González Pecotche (1901-63), Founder of Logosophy A971

2001, Aug. 7   *Perf. 12*
1913 A971 11p multi   1.75 1.75

First Concorde Flight, 25th Anniv. A972

2001, Aug. 10   *Perf. 12½x12¾*
1914 A972 22p multi   3.25 3.25

Rose Varieties — A973

No. 1915: a, Louis Philippe. b, Souvenir de Mme. Léonie Viennot. c, Kronenbourg. d, Lady Hillingdon.

2001, Aug. 16   *Perf. 12*
1915 A973 11p Block of 4, #a-d   6.75 6.75

Apiculture — A974

No. 1916: a, Apiculturists. b, Bee on flower.
Illustration reduced.

2001, Sept. 12
1916 A974 12p Horiz. pair, #a-b   3.50 3.50

Town of Dolores, Bicent. — A975

2001, Sept. 21   *Perf. 12¾x12½*
1917 A975 12p multi   1.75 1.75

Uruguay Philatelic Club, 75th Anniv. A976

Sun and inscription: No. 1918, 12p, "75 Años." No. 1919, 12p, "1er Presidente / Dr. Miguel A. Paez Formoso."

2001, Sept. 26   *Perf. 12½x12¾*
1918-1919 A976   Set of 2   3.50 3.50

America Issue - UNESCO World Heritage Sites — A977

Buildings from Historic Quarter of Colonia del Sacramento: a, 12p, Basilica del Santisimo. b, 24p, San Benito de Palermo Chapel.

2001, Sept. 28   *Perf. 12*
1920 A977   Horiz. pair, #a-b   5.25 5.25

Carlos Amoretti, 50th Anniv. as Artist A978

2001, Oct. 2   *Perf. 12½x12¾*
1921 A978 12p multi   1.75 1.75

Town of Sauce, 150th Anniv. — A979

2001, Oct. 12   *Perf. 12¾x12½*
1922 A979 12p multi   1.75 1.75

Uruguay - Japan Diplomatic Relations, 80th Anniv. A980

Perf. 12¼x12¾
2001, Sept. 24   *Litho*
1923 A980 24p multi   3.50 3.50

Prevention of Illegal Drug Use A981

2001, Oct. 16
1924 A981 12p multi   1.75 1.75

Year of Dialogue Among Civilizations A982

2001, Oct. 23 *Perf. 12¾x12¼*
1925 A982 24p multi 3.50 3.50

Honorary Committee for Fighting Cancer — A983

2001, Oct. 29
1926 A983 12p multi 1.75 1.75

Ultimas Noticias Newspaper, 20th Anniv. — A984

2001, Oct. 31
1927 A984 12p multi 1.75 1.75

Sauce Basketball Club, 50th Anniv. A985

2001, Nov. 9 *Perf. 12¼x12¾*
1928 A985 12p multi 1.75 1.75

Blood Donor's Day — A986

2001, Nov. 12 *Perf. 12¾x12¼*
1929 A986 12p multi 1.75 1.75

Juan Zorilla de San Martín (1855-1931), Writer — A987

2001, Nov. 13 *Perf. 12¼x12¾*
1930 A987 12p multi 1.75 1.75

Uruguayan Navy's Hydrographic Ship "Oyarvide" — A988

2001, Nov. 14
1931 A988 12p multi 1.75 1.75

Uruguayan Visit of Rotary Intl. President Richard King and Wife Cherie — A989

2001, Nov. 20 *Perf. 12¾x12¼*
1932 A989 24p multi 3.50 3.50

Peñarol Athletic Club, 110th Anniv. — A990

2001, Nov. 22 *Perf. 12*
1933 A990 12p multi 1.75 1.75

Julio Sosa (1926-64), Tango Singer — A991

2001, Nov. 26 *Perf. 12¾x12¼*
1934 A991 12p multi 1.75 1.75

José Nasazzi (1901-68), Soccer Player — A992

2001, Nov. 29
1935 A992 12p multi 1.75 1.75

Christmas — A993

Paintings of Adoration of the Shepherds, by: 12p, José Ribera. 24p, Anton Raphael Mengs.

2001, Dec. 6
1936-1937 A993 Set of 2 5.25 5.25

Church of San Carlos, Bicent. — A994

2001, Dec. 7
1938 A994 12p multi 1.75 1.75

National Museum of Visual Arts, 90th Anniv. — A995

2001, Dec. 12 *Perf. 12*
1939 A995 12p multi 1.75 1.75

State Insurance Bank, 90th Anniv. — A996

2001, Dec. 20 *Perf. 12¾x12¼*
1940 A996 12p multi 1.75 1.75

Guettarda Uruguensis — A997

2001, Dec. 21 *Perf. 12¼x12¾*
1941 A997 24p multi 3.50 3.50

St. Josemaría Escrivá de Balaguer (1902-75) — A998

Balaguer and quotes: a, "El trabajo es. . ." b, "Quieres de verdad. . ." c, "La santidad. . ." d, "Que busques. . ."
Illustration reduced.

2002, Jan. 9 *Perf. 12*
1942 A998 12p Block of 4, #a-d 7.00 7.00

Uruguayan Association of Directors of Carnivals and Folk Festivals, 50th Anniv. — A999

Feet of: a, Ringmaster. b, Clown. c, Acrobat.

2002, Mar. 8 **Litho.** *Perf. 12½*
Self-Adhesive
1943   Booklet pane of 3   3.25 3.25
a.-b.   A999 6p Either single   .80 .80
c.   A999 12p black   1.60 1.60
      Booklet, #1943   3.25

Christianity in Armenia, 1700th Anniv. A1000

2002, Apr. 23 *Perf. 12*
1944 A1000 12p multi 1.50 1.50

New Year 2003 (Year of the Horse) — A1001

2002, May 14 *Perf. 12¾x12¼*
1945 A1001 24p multi 3.00 3.00

2002 World Cup Soccer Championships, Japan and Korea — A1002

No. 1946: a, Flags, soccer ball, and field (38mm diameter). b, Soccer players, years of Uruguayan championships.
Illustration reduced.

2002, May 21 *Perf. 12¾*
1946 A1002 12p Horiz. pair, #a-b 2.75 2.75

See Argentina No. 2184, Brazil No. 2840, France No. 2891, Germany No. 2163 and Italy No. 2526.

Book Day — A1003

2002, May 24 *Perf. 12¾x12¼*
1947 A1003 12p multi 1.40 1.40

Inter-American Children's Institute, 75th Anniv. — A1004

2002, June 10 *Perf. 12¼x12¾*
1948 A1004 12p multi 1.40 1.40

Department of Tacuarembó, 165th Anniv. — A1005

2002, June 14
1949 A1005 12p multi   1.40 1.40

Cerro de Montevideo Lighthouse, Bicent. — A1006

Designs: 12p, Old lighthouse. 24p, New lighthouse, vert.

Perf. 12¼x12¾, 12¾x12¼
2002, June 24
1950-1951 A1006 Set of 2   3.75 3.75

Villa Constitución, 150th Anniv. — A1007

2002, July 11   **Perf. 12¼x12¾**
1952 A1007 12p multi   1.00 1.00

"We Are United" A1008

2002, July 17
1953 A1008 6p multi   .50 .50
Printed in sheets of 3 + label. Value $2.

Natural Uruguay A1009

2002, July 22   **Litho.**
1954 A1009 24p blue & orange   2.40 2.40

Montevideo Botanical Gardens, Cent. — A1010

No. 1955: a, Botanical Gardens building, Erythrina cristigalli. b, Rhodophiala bifida. c, Prof. Atilio Lombardo and Tillandsia arequitae. d, Heteropterys dumetorum.

2002, July 31   **Perf. 12**
1955   Horiz. strip of 4   4.25 4.25
   a.-d. A1010 12p Any single   1.00 1.00

Montevideo Wanderers Soccer Team, Cent. — A1011

2002, Aug. 1   **Perf. 12¾x12¼**
1956 A1011 12p black   1.10 1.10

Sportsmen — A1012

Designs: No. 1957, 12p, Lorenzo Fernández, soccer player. No. 1958, 12p, José Leandro Andrade, soccer player. No. 1959, 12p, Alvaro Gestido, soccer player. No. 1960, 12p, César L. Gallardo, fencer. No. 1961, 12p, Pedro Petrone, soccer player.

2002, Aug. 16   **Perf. 12¼x12¾**
1957-1961 A1012 Set of 5   5.25 5.25

Elvis Presley (1935-77) A1013

2002, Aug. 19   **Perf. 12¾x12¼**
1962 A1013 24p multi   2.10 2.10

Agustín Bisio (1894-1952), Poet — A1014

2002, Aug. 30   **Perf. 12¾x12¼**
Self-Adhesive
1963 A1014 12p multi   1.10 1.10

City of Artigas, 150th Anniv. — A1015

2002, Sept. 12   **Perf. 12¾x12¼**
Self-Adhesive
1964 A1015 12p multi   1.10 1.10

Uruguayan Cooperative Society of Bus Services, 65th Anniv. — A1016

2002, Sept. 16   **Perf. 12¼x12¾**
1965 A1016 12p multi   1.10 1.10

Psychoanalysis, Cent. — A1017

2002, Sept. 20   **Perf. 12**
1966 A1017 12p multi   1.10 1.10
24th Latin American Psychoanalysis Congress, Montevideo.

Horacio Arredondo (1888-1967), Historical Preservationist, and San Miguel Fort — A1018

2002, Sept. 20   **Perf. 12¼x12¾**
1967 A1018 12p multi   1.10 1.10

Paso del Rey Barracks Natl. Historic Monument — A1019

2002, Sept. 23   **Perf. 12**
1968 A1019 12p multi   1.10 1.10

Intl. Year of Ecotourism — A1020

2002, Sept. 24   **Litho.**
1969 A1020 12p multi   1.10 1.10

Uruguayan Postal Services, 175th Anniv. — A1021

Designs: No. 1970, Postal Services headquarters, Montevideo. No. 1971, Letter box.

2002, Oct. 9   **Perf. 12¾x12¼**
1970 A1021 12p multi   1.10 1.10

Souvenir Sheet
Imperf
1971 A1021 12p multi   1.10 1.10

First Equestrian Statue of Brig. Gen. Juan Antonio Lavalleja, Cent. — A1022

2002, Oct. 11   **Perf. 12¾x12¼**
1972 A1022 12p multi   1.10 1.10

America Issue - Youth, Education and Literacy A1023

"ANALFABETISMO" in: 12p, Word search puzzle. 24p, Bowl of alphabet soup.

2002, Oct. 16   **Perf. 12¼x12¾**
1973-1974 A1023 Set of 2   3.25 3.25

Christmas A1024

2002, Nov. 4   **Perf. 12¾x12¼**
1975 A1024 12p multi   1.10 1.10

Association of Uruguayan Pharmacies, 65th Anniv. — A1025

2002, Nov. 8   **Litho.**
1976 A1025 12p multi   1.10 1.10

Tannat Wine — A1026

2002, Nov. 13
1977 A1026 12p multi   1.10 1.10

Uruguayan Navy, 185th Anniv. — A1027

2002, Nov. 13   *Perf. 13½*
978 A1027 12p multi   1.10 1.10

National Organ and Tissue Bank, 25th Anniv. A1028

2002, Nov. 15
979 A1028 12p multi   1.10 1.10

Taxis in Uruguay, Cent. A1029

2002, Nov. 25   *Perf. 12¼x12¾*
980 A1029 12p multi   1.10 1.10

Brig. Gen. Manuel Oribe (1792-1857) A1030

2002, Nov. 28   *Perf. 12¾x12¼*
981 A1030 12p multi   1.10 1.10

George Harrison (1943-2001), Rock Musician A1031

2002, Nov. 29   *Perf. 13½*
982 A1031 24p multi   2.25 2.25

Pan-American Health Organization, Cent. — A1032

2002, Dec. 2
983 A1032 12p multi   1.10 1.10

Uruguayan Participation in U.N. Peace Keeping Missions, 50th Anniv. — A1033

2002, Dec. 6   *Perf. 12¼x12¾*
1984 A1033 12p multi   1.10 1.10

Alfredo Testoni (1919-2000), Artist — A1034

2002, Dec. 9   *Perf. 13½*
1985 A1034 12p multi   1.10 1.10

Mercosur A1035

Designs: 12p, Ship and coastline. 24p, Beach.

2002, Dec. 12
1986-1987 A1035   Set of 2   3.25 3.25

Battle of Ituzaingó, 175th Anniv. A1036

2002, Dec. 17   *Litho.*
1988 A1036 12p multi   1.10 1.10

Battle of Juncal, 175th Anniv. A1037

2002, Dec. 17
1989 A1037 12p multi   1.10 1.10

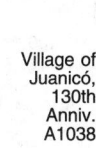

Village of Juanicó, 130th Anniv. A1038

2002, Dec. 23   *Perf. 12¼x12¾*
1990 A1038 12p multi   1.10 1.10

Uruguay on World Map A1039

2003, Jan. 17   *Litho.*   *Perf. 12¼x12¾*
1991 A1039 12p multi   .85 .85

Busqueda Weekly, 30th Anniv. A1040

2003, Jan. 29
1992 A1040 12p multi   .85 .85

Water Goddess Iemanja — A1041

2003, Jan. 29   *Perf. 12¾x12¼*
1993 A1041 12p multi   .85 .85

Uruguay - People's Republic of China Diplomatic Relations, 15th Anniv. — A1042

2003, Jan. 31   *Perf. 12*
1994 A1042 12p multi   .85 .85

New Year 2003 (Year of the Ram) — A1043

2003, Feb. 7   *Perf. 12¾x12¼*
1995 A1043 5p multi   .35 .35

Explorers A1044

Explorers and maps of their voyages: a, Christopher Columbus, 4th voyage, 1502. b, Juan Díaz de Solís, 1516. c, Sebastian Cabot, 1526-30. d, Hernando Arias de Saavedra, 1597-1618.

2003, Feb. 14   *Perf. 12*
1996   Horiz. strip of 4   3.50 3.50
a.-d.   A1044 12p Any single   .85 .85

Communications Services Regulatory Union, 2nd Anniv. — A1045

2003, Feb. 21   *Perf. 12¼x12¾*
1997 A1045 12p multi   .85 .85

Intl. Women's Day — A1046

2003, Mar. 7   *Perf. 12¾x12¼*
1998 A1046 12p multi   .85 .85

City of Treinta y Tres, 150th Anniv. A1047

2003, Mar. 10   *Perf. 12¼x12¾*
1999 A1047 12p multi   .85 .85

Butterflies — A1048

No. 2000: a, Heliconius erato. b, Junonia evarete. c, Dryadula phaetusa. d, Parides perrhebus.

2003, Mar. 18   *Perf. 12*
2000 A1048 12p Block of 4, #a-d   3.50 3.50

First Presidency of José Batlle y Ordóñez, Cent. — A1049

No. 2001 — Batlle y Ordóñez: a, Wearing overcoat. b, Wearing presidential sash. c, With head on hand. d, Wearing white jacket.

2003, Mar. 25   *Perf. 12*
2001   Horiz. strip of 4   3.50 3.50
a.-d.   A1049 12p Any single   .85 .85

Rural Women's Crafts A1050

No. 2002: a, Basket weaving. b, Knitting. c, Pottery making. d, Food canning. e, Jewelry making.

2003, Mar. 23   Litho.   Perf. 12
2002   Horiz. strip of 5   4.25 4.25
a.-e. A1050 12p Any single   .85   .85

Farruco's Chapel — A1051

2003, Apr. 4   Litho.   Perf. 12¾x12¼
2003 A1051 12p multi   .85   .85

Natural Foods A1052

2003, Apr. 9   Perf. 12¼x12¾
2004 A1052 12p multi   .85   .85

Cerros Azules Caiman Farm A1053

Serpentine Die Cut 11¼
2003, Apr. 10
Self-Adhesive
2005 A1053 12p multi   .85   .85

Memorial to 1972 Airplane Crash in the Andes — A1054

2003, Apr. 22   Perf. 12¾x12¼
2006 A1054 12p multi   .85   .85

Military Center — A1055

2003, May 21
2007 A1055 12p multi   .95   .95

May 18, 1811 Military Museum, 150th Anniv. A1056

2003, May 26   Perf. 12
2008 A1056 12p multi   .95   .95

Casa de Ximénes and Las Bóvedas, Montevideo Historical District — A1057

2003, May 30   Perf. 12¼
2009 A1057 14p multi   1.10 1.10

Wilson Ferreira Aldunate (1919-88), Politician — A1058

No. 2010: a, Brown background. b, Green background. c, Dark violet background, text at right. d, Light violet background, text at left.
Illustration reduced.

2003, June 16   Litho.   Perf. 12
2010 A1058 14p Block of 4, #a-d 4.25 4.25

Olympic Soccer Gold Medal, 75th Anniv. A1059

2003, June 18
2011 A1059 14p multi   1.10 1.10

Richard Anderson College, 70th Anniv. — A1060

2003, July 15
2012 A1060 14p multi   1.10 1.10

Santa Isabel del Paso de los Toros, Cent. — A1061

2003, July 17
2013 A1061 14p multi   1.10 1.10

National Association of Affiliates, 70th Anniv. — A1062

2003, July 24
2014 A1062 14p multi   1.00 1.00

Jesús María College, Carrasco, 50th Anniv. — A1063

2003, Aug. 4
2015 A1063 14p multi   1.00 1.00

Philatelic Academy of Uruguay, 25th Anniv. A1064

2003, Aug. 5
2016 A1064 14p multi   1.00 1.00

Palacio Heber A1065

2003, Aug. 14
2017 A1065 14p multi   1.10 1.10

Parva Domus Magna Quies, 125th Anniv. — A1066

2003, Aug. 15
2018 A1066 14p multi   1.10 1.10

Security Dept. Commission of Interior Ministry, 4th Anniv. — A1067

2003, Aug. 18
2019 A1067 14p multi   1.00 1.00

First International Victory of Uruguayan Soccer Team, Cent. — A1068

2003, Sept. 12   Perf. 12½x12¾
2020 A1068 14p multi   1.00 1.00

Lauro Ayestarán (1913-66), Musicologist — A1069

2003, Sept. 19   Perf. 12
2021 A1069 14p multi   1.10 1.10

Asociacion Española Primera de Socorros Mutuos Hospital, 150th Anniv. A1070

2003, Sept. 19   Perf. 12½x12¾
2022 A1070 14p multi   1.10 1.10

Dr. Manuel Quintela Clinical Hospital, 50th Anniv. A1071

2003, Sept. 23   Perf. 12
2023 A1071 14p multi   1.00 1.00

Society of Friends of Public Education, 135th Anniv. — A1072

2003, Sept. 24
2024 A1072 14p multi   1.00 1.00

Association of Uruguayan Newspaper Reporters, 45th Anniv. — A1073

2003, Sept. 29   Perf. 12½x12¾
2025 A1073 14p multi   1.00 1.00

Pres. Fructoso Rivera (c. 1788-1854) A1074

2003, Oct. 1
2026 A1074 14p multi   *Perf. 12*
                              1.00 1.00

Naval Club, 75th Anniv. A1075

2003, Oct. 1   *Perf. 12½x12¾*
2027 A1075 14p multi   1.00 1.00

Malos Pensamientos Radio Program — A1076

2003, Oct. 3
2028 A1076 14p multi   1.00 1.00

Successes in Intl. Events by Milton Wynants, Cyclist — A1077

2003, Oct. 7   *Perf. 12¾x12½*
2029 A1077 14p multi   1.00 1.00

Ente Nazionale Assistenza Sociale in Uruguay, 50th Anniv. — A1078

2003, Oct. 9   *Perf. 12½x12¾*
2030 A1078 14p multi   1.00 1.00

City of Cardona, Cent. — A1079

2003, Oct. 10   *Perf. 12*
2031 A1079 14p multi   1.00 1.00

Construction League of Uruguay, 84th Anniv. — A1080

2003, Oct. 14   *Perf. 12¾x12½*
2032 A1080 14p multi   1.00 1.00

María Tsakos Foundation, 25th Anniv. — A1081

2003, Oct. 15
2033 A1081 14p multi   1.00 1.00

America Issue - Flora and Fauna A1082

Designs: 14p, Prosopis affinis. 36p, Agouti paca paca.

2003, Oct. 22   *Perf. 12½x12¾*
2034-2035 A1082 Set of 2   3.50 3.50

Independence of Lebanon, 60th Anniv. — A1083

2003, Oct. 24
2036 A1083 14p olive grn & red 1.00 1.00

Souvenir Sheet

Masons in Uruguay, 147th Anniv. — A1084

2003, Oct. 29   *Perf. 12¾x12½*
2037 A1084 14p multi   1.00 1.00

Cacho Bochinche Television Show, 30th Anniv. A1085

2003, Oct. 29   *Perf. 12½x12¾*
2038 A1085 14p multi   1.00 1.00

Morenada, 50th Anniv. — A1086

2003, Oct. 29
2039 A1086 14p multi   1.00 1.00

Brig. Gen. Juan A. Lavalleja (c. 1786-1853) A1087

2003, Oct. 30   *Perf. 12*
2040 A1087 14p multi   1.00 1.00

Souvenir Sheet

Election of Pope John Paul II, 25th Anniv. — A1088

No. 1089 — Uruguayan flag and: a, Pope John Paul II, Vatican arms. b, Polish eagle, map of Latin America.

2003, Oct. 31
2041 A1088 12p Sheet of 2, #a-b 1.75 1.75
  Union of Latin American Polish Societies and Organizations, 10th anniv. (#2041b).

Souvenir Sheet

2006 World Cup Soccer Championships, Germany — A1089

No. 2042 — World Cup trophy and: a, Uruguayan flag, J. A. Schiaffino. b, German flag, Fritz Walter.

2003, Oct. 31
2042 A1089 12p Sheet of 2, #a-b 1.75 1.75

Christmas A1090

2003, Nov. 7   *Perf. 12¾x12½*
2043 A1090 14p multi   1.00 1.00

Italian Chamber of Commerce of Uruguay, 120th Anniv. A1091

2003, Nov. 10   *Perf. 12½x12¾*
2044 A1091 14p multi   1.00 1.00

Visit of Manuel Fraga Iribarne, President of Spanish Autonomous Community of Galicia — A1092

2003, Nov. 10
2045 A1092 14p multi   1.00 1.00

San Gregorio de Polanco, 150th Anniv. A1093

2003, Nov. 14
2046 A1093 14p multi   1.00 1.00

United Biblical Society, Bicent. A1094

2003, Nov. 24
2047 A1094 14p multi   1.00 1.00

R.O.U. Paysandu A1095

2003, Nov. 25   *Perf. 12*
2048 A1095 14p multi   1.00 1.00

University Culture Foundation, 35th Anniv. — A1096

2003, Nov. 28
2049 A1096 14p multi   1.00 1.00

Uruguayan Air Force, 50th Anniv. A1097

2003, Dec. 4
2050 A1097 14p multi   1.00 1.00

Visit of Mirko Tremaglia, Italian Minister for Italians Abroad — A1098

2003, Dec. 15
2051 A1098 14p multi   1.00 1.00

Mercosur A1099

Designs: 14p, Horn. 36p, Silver stirrup.

2003, Dec. 16
2052-2053 A1099 Set of 2   3.50 3.50

Powered Flight, Cent. A1100

2003, Dec. 19
2054 A1100 14p multi   1.00 1.00

Nos. 1378, 1382, 1458 and 1492 Surcharged in Black or Blue Violet

j

k

Methods and Perfs. as Before
2004   **Wmk. 332**
2055 A654(j) 1p on 1.20p
          #1492   .20 .20
2056 A639(j) 2p on 2.60p
          #1458 (BV)   .20 .20
2057 A589(k) 5p on 2500p
          #1382   .35 .35
2058 A589(k) 10p on 360p #1378 .70 .70
     Nos. 2055-2058 (4) 1.45 1.45

Issued: Nos. 2055-2056, 1/19; Nos. 2057-2058, 2/16. Obliterator on Nos. 2055 and 2056 covers the centesimos portion of the denomination.

Birds — A1101

No. 2060: a, Puffinius gravis. b, Macronectes halli. c, Daption capense. d, Diamedea melanophrys. Illustration reduced.

Unwmk.
2004, Jan. 22   Litho.   Perf. 12
2060 A1101 14p Block of 4, #a-d 4.00 4.00

Abitab, 10th Anniv. — A1103

Unwmk.
2004, Feb. 12   Litho.   Perf. 12
2062 A1103 14p multi   .95 .95

SEMI-POSTAL STAMPS

Indigent Old Man — SP1

Unwmk.
1930, Nov. 13   Engr.   Perf. 12
B1 SP1 1c + 1c dark violet   .20 .20
B2 SP1 2c + 2c deep green   .20 .20
B3 SP1 5c + 5c red   .30 .30
B4 SP1 8c + 8c gray violet   .30 .30
     Nos. B1-B4 (4)   1.00 1.00

The surtax on these stamps was for a fund to assist the aged.
For surcharge see No. 419.

| Catalogue values for unused stamps in this section, from this point to the end of the section, are for Never Hinged items. |

Dam, Child and Rising Sun — SP2

Wmk. 327
1959, Sept. 29   Litho.   Perf. 11½
B5 SP2 5c + 10c green & org   .20 .20
B6 SP2 10c + 10c dk bl & org   .20 .20
B7 SP2 1p + 10c purple & org   .40 .40
     Nos. B5-B7,CB1-CB2 (5)   1.35 1.35

National recovery. For surcharges see Nos. 727, Q100.

Souvenir Sheet

Taipei '96, Intl. Philatelic Exhibition — SP3

Illustration reduced.

Unwmk.
1996, Oct. 21   Litho.   Perf. 12
B8 SP3 7p +3p multi   4.00 4.00

Gen. Artigas Central Railway Station, Montevideo, Cent. — SP4

a, Baldwin, 1889. b, Hudswell Clarke, 1895. c, Luis Andreoni, engineer. d, Hawthorn Leslie, 1914. e, General Electric, 1954.

Perf. 12½
1997, July 15   Litho.   Unwmk.
B9 SP4 4p +1p, Strip of 5, #a.- e. 7.50 7.50

Diana, Princess of Wales (1961-97) — SP5

Designs: No. B10, In protective clothing. No. B11, In blue blouse. No. B12, In white.

1998, Jan. 15   Litho.   Perf. 12½
B10 SP5 2p +1p multi   1.25 1.25
B11 SP5 2p +1p multi   1.25 1.25

Souvenir Sheet
Perf. 12
B12 SP5 12p +3p multi   10.00 10.00

No. B12 contains one 35x50mm stamp.

AIR POST STAMPS

No. 91 Overprinted in Dark Blue, Red or Green

1921-22   Unwmk.   Perf. 14
C1 A38 25c bister brn (Bl)   12.00 10.00
  a.   Black overprint   550.00 550.00
C2 A38 25c bister brn (R)   4.50 3.50
  a.   Inverted overprint   65.00 65.00

C3 A38 25c bister brn (G)
          ('22)   4.50 3.50
     Nos. C1-C3 (3)   21.00 17.00

This overprint also exists in light yellow green.

No. C1a was not issued. Some authorities consider it an overprint color trial.

AP2

Wmk. 188
1924, Jan. 2   Litho.   Perf. 11½
C4 AP2 6c dark blue   2.50 2.50
C5 AP2 10c scarlet   3.50 3.00
C6 AP2 20c deep green   5.00 5.00
     Nos. C4-C6 (3)   11.00 10.50

Heron — AP3

1925, Aug. 24   Perf. 12½
Inscribed "MONTEVIDEO"
C7 AP3 14c blue & blk   22.50 14.00
Inscribed "FLORIDA"
C8 AP3 14c blue & blk   22.50 14.00

These stamps were used only on Aug. 25, 1925, the cent. of the Assembly of Florida, on letters intended to be carried by airplane between Montevideo and Florida, a town 60 miles north. The stamps were not delivered to the public but were affixed to the letters and canceled by post office clerks. Later uncanceled copies came on the market.

One authority believes Nos. C7-C8 served as registration stamps on these two attempted special flights.

Gaucho Cavalryman at Rincón AP4

1925, Sept. 24   Perf. 11
C9 AP4 45c blue green   8.00

Centenary of Battle of Rincon. Used only on Sept. 24. No. C9 was affixed and canceled by post office clerks.

Albatross — AP5

1926, Mar. 3   Wmk. 188   Imperf.
C10 AP5 6c dark blue   1.50 1.50
C11 AP5 10c vermilion   2.00 2.00
C12 AP5 20c blue green   2.50 2.50
C13 AP5 25c violet   4.00 4.00
     Nos. C10-C13 (4)   10.00 10.00

Excellent counterfeits exist.

1928, June 25   Perf. 11
C14 AP5 10c green   1.50 1.25
C15 AP5 20c orange   2.40 1.75
C16 AP5 30c indigo   2.40 1.75
C17 AP5 38c green   4.25 3.50
C18 AP5 40c yellow   4.75 3.50
C19 AP5 50c violet   5.25 4.25
C20 AP5 76c orange   10.50 9.00
C21 AP5 1p red   9.00 6.50
C22 AP5 1.14p indigo   24.00 21.00
C23 AP5 1.52p yellow   35.00 35.00

C24	AP5	1.90p violet	47.50	42.50
C25	AP5	3.80p red	125.00	90.00
		Nos. C14-C25 (12)	271.55	220.00

Counterfeits of No. C25 exist.

1929, Aug. 23 — **Unwmk.**

C26	AP5	4c olive brown	4.00	3.00

The design was redrawn for Nos. C14-C26. The numerals are narrower, "CENTS" is 1mm high instead of 2½mm and imprint letters touch the bottom frame line.

Pegasus
AP6

1929-43 — **Engr.** — **Perf. 12½**

Size: 34x23mm

C27	AP6	1c red lilac ('30)	.25	.25
C28	AP6	1c dk blue ('32)	.25	.25
C29	AP6	2c yellow ('30)	.25	.25
C30	AP6	2c olive grn ('32)	.25	.25
C31	AP6	4c Prus bl ('30)	.45	.35
C32	AP6	4c car rose ('32)	.45	.35
C33	AP6	6c dull vio ('30)	.45	.35
C34	AP6	6c red brn ('32)	.45	.35
C35	AP6	8c red orange	2.10	1.75
C36	AP6	8c gray ('30)	2.75	1.90
C36A	AP6	8c brt grn ('43)	.30	.30
C37	AP6	16c indigo	1.75	1.40
C38	AP6	16c rose ('30)	2.00	1.90
C39	AP6	24c claret	1.75	1.50
C40	AP6	24c brt vio ('30)	2.75	2.10
C41	AP6	30c bister	1.90	1.75
C42	AP6	30c dk grn ('30)	1.25	.60
C43	AP6	40c dk brown	3.50	3.00
C44	AP6	40c yel org ('30)	3.75	3.50
C45	AP6	60c blue green	3.00	2.10
C46	AP6	60c emer ('30)	5.25	4.25
C47	AP6	60c dp org ('31)	1.90	1.25
C48	AP6	80c ultra	5.50	4.75
C49	AP6	80c green ('30)	9.25	7.75
C50	AP6	90c light blue	5.50	4.25
C51	AP6	90c dk olive grn ('30)	9.25	7.75
C52	AP6	1p car rose ('30)	4.75	3.50
C53	AP6	1.20p olive grn	13.50	12.50
C54	AP6	1.20p dp car ('30)	19.00	17.00
C55	AP6	1.50p red brown	13.50	10.50
C56	AP6	1.50p blk brn ('30)	7.75	6.25
C57	AP6	3p deep red	21.00	17.50
C58	AP6	3p ultra ('30)	17.00	14.00
C59	AP6	4.50p black	40.00	30.00
C60	AP6	4.50p violet ('30)	26.00	21.00
C60A	AP6	10p dp ultra ('43)	11.00	7.75
		Nos. C27-C60A (36)	239.75	194.20

See Nos. C63-C82. For surcharges see Nos. C106-C112, C114.

Nos. 450, 452 Overprinted in Red

1934, Jan. 1 — **Perf. 11½**

C61	A130	17c ver, gray & vio	16.00	12.00
a.		Sheet of 6	125.00	
b.		Gray omitted	150.00	
c.		Double overprint	150.00	
C62	A130	36c red, blk & yel	16.00	12.00
a.		Sheet of 6	125.00	

7th Pan-American Conference, Montevideo.

Pegasus Type of 1929

1935 — **Engr.** — **Perf. 12½**

Size: 31½x21mm

C63	AP6	15c dull yellow	1.40	1.10
C64	AP6	22c brick red	.85	.70
C65	AP6	30c brown violet	1.40	1.10
C66	AP6	37c gray lilac	.70	.55
C67	AP6	40c rose lake	1.10	.70
C68	AP6	47c rose	2.25	2.00
C69	AP6	50c Prus blue	.70	.45
C70	AP6	52c dp ultra	2.25	2.00
C71	AP6	57c grnsh blue	1.10	1.00
C72	AP6	62c olive green	1.00	.45
C73	AP6	87c gray green	2.75	2.25
C74	AP6	1p olive	2.00	1.25
C75	AP6	1.12p brown red	2.00	1.25
C76	AP6	1.20p bister brn	8.25	7.00
C77	AP6	1.27p red brown	8.25	7.00
C78	AP6	1.62p rose	5.50	5.00
C79	AP6	2p brown rose	9.25	8.00

C80	AP6	2.12p dk slate grn	9.25	8.00
C81	AP6	3p dull blue	8.25	7.25
C82	AP6	5p orange	27.50	27.50
		Nos. C63-C82 (20)	95.75	84.55

Counterfeits exist.

Power Dam on
Black
River — AP7

Imprint: "Imp. Nacional" at center

1937-41 — **Litho.**

C83	AP7	20c lt green ('38)	3.25	2.50
C84	AP7	35c red brown	5.00	4.00
C85	AP7	62c blue grn ('38)	.55	.25
C86	AP7	68c yel org ('38)	1.25	.90
C86A	AP7	68c pale vio brn ('41)	1.10	.45
C87	AP7	75c violet	4.50	.85
C88	AP7	1p dp pink ('38)	1.75	1.10
C89	AP7	1.38p rose ('38)	15.00	12.50
C90	AP7	3p dk blue ('40)	10.50	7.75
		Nos. C83-C90 (9)	42.90	30.30

Imprint at left

C91	AP7	8c pale green ('39)	.35	.30
C92	AP7	20c lt green ('38)	1.25	.90

For surcharge and overprint see Nos. 545, C120.

Plane over
Sculptured
Oxcart — AP8

1939-44 — **Perf. 12½**

C93	AP8	20c slate	.30	.25
C94	AP8	20c lt violet ('43)	.50	.55
C95	AP8	20c blue ('44)	.40	.25
C96	AP8	35c red	.65	.50
C97	AP8	50c brown org	.65	.20
C98	AP8	75c deep pink	.70	.20
C99	AP8	1p dp blue ('40)	2.00	.35
C100	AP8	1.38p brt vio	3.50	1.40
C101	AP8	1.38p yel org ('44)	3.00	2.50
C102	AP8	2p blue	5.00	.90
a.		Perf. 11	4.75	.70
C103	AP8	5p rose lilac	6.50	2.50
C104	AP8	5p bl grn ('44)	8.50	3.50
C105	AP8	10p rose ('40)	52.50	37.50
		Nos. C93-C105 (13)	84.20	50.60

Counterfeits exist. They are perf 13, rather than 12½.
For surcharges see Nos. C116-C119.

Nos. C68,
C71, C75,
C73, C77-C78,
C80
Surcharged in
Red or Black

1944, Nov. 22

C106	AP6	40c on 47c	1.00	1.00
C107	AP6	40c on 57c (R)	1.00	1.00
C108	AP6	74c on 1.12p	1.00	1.00
C109	AP6	79c on 87c	2.00	2.00
C110	AP6	79c on 1.27p	3.00	3.00
C111	AP6	1.20p on 1.62p	2.00	2.00
C112	AP6	1.43p on 2.12p (R)	2.00	2.00
		Nos. C106-C112 (7)	12.00	12.00

Catalogue values for unused stamps in this section, from this point to the end of the section, are for Never Hinged items.

Legislature
Building
AP9

Unwmk.

1945, May 11 — **Engr.** — **Perf. 11**

C113	AP9	2p ultra	4.00	2.00

Type of 1929, Surcharged in Violet

1945, Aug. 14 — **Perf. 12½**

C114	AP6	44c on 75c brown	1.00	.50

Allied Nations' victory in Europe.

"La Eolo"
AP10

1945, Oct. 31 — **Perf. 11**

C115	AP10	8c green	2.00	1.00

Nos. C97 and C101 Surcharged in
Violet, Black or Blue

1945-46 — **Perf. 12½**

C116	AP8	14c on 50c (V) ('46)	1.00	.50
a.		Inverted surcharge	37.50	
C117	AP8	23c on 1.38p	1.00	.50
a.		Inverted surcharge	75.00	
C118	AP8	23c on 50c	1.00	.50
a.		Inverted surcharge	75.00	
C119	AP8	1p on 1.38p (Bl)	1.00	.50
a.		Inverted surcharge	75.00	
		Nos. C116-C119 (4)	4.00	2.00

Victory of the Allied Nations in WWII.

No. C85 Overprinted in Black

1946, Jan. 9

C120	AP7	62c blue green	2.00	1.00

Issued to commemorate the inauguration of the Black River Power Dam.

AP11

Black Overprint

1946-49 — **Litho.**

C121	AP11	8c car rose	.20	.20
a.		Inverted overprint		
C122	AP11	50c brown	.40	.20
a.		Double overprint	25.00	
C123	AP11	1p lt bl	.65	.25
C124	AP11	2p ol ('49)	3.50	2.00
C125	AP11	3p lil rose	4.50	3.00
C126	AP11	5p rose car	8.50	6.00
		Nos. C121-C126 (6)	17.75	11.65

Four-Motored
Plane — AP12

National
Airport — AP13

1947-49 — **Perf. 11½, 12½**

C129	AP12	3c org brn ('49)	.20	.20
C130	AP12	8c car rose ('49)	.20	.20
C131	AP12	14c ultra	.20	.20
C132	AP12	23c emerald	.20	.20
C133	AP13	1p car & brn ('49)	.95	.25
C134	AP13	3p ultra & brn ('49)	2.25	1.25
C135	AP13	5p grn & brn ('49)	8.00	4.00
C136	AP13	10p lil rose & brn	10.00	6.00
		Nos. C129-C136 (8)	22.00	12.30

Counterfeits exist, perf 11¼. Design size of genuine copies is 34½x24mm, while forgeries are 33½x23½mm.
See Nos. C145-C164. For surcharges see Nos. C206, Q94.

AP14

School of
Architecture,
University of
Uruguay
AP15

Black Overprint

1948, June 9 — **Perf. 12½**

C137	AP14	12c blue	.20	.20
C138	AP14	24c Prus grn	.30	.20
C139	AP14	36c slate blue	.45	.30
		Nos. C137-C139 (3)	.95	.70

1949, Dec. 7

Designs: 27c, Medical School. 31c, Engineering School. 36c, University.

C141	AP15	15c carmine	.20	.20
C142	AP15	27c chocolate	.20	.20
C143	AP15	31c dp ultra	.40	.20
C144	AP15	36c dull green	.60	.30
		Nos. C141-C144 (4)	1.40	.90

Founding of the University of Uruguay, cent.

Plane Type of 1947-49

1952-59 — **Unwmk.** — **Perf. 11, 12½**

C145	AP12	10c blk ('54)	.20	.20
C146	AP12	10c lt red ('58)	.20	.20
a.		Imperf., pair	30.00	
C147	AP12	15c org brn	.20	.20
a.		Vert. pair, imperf btwn.	42.50	
C148	AP12	20c lil rose ('54)	.25	.20
C149	AP12	21c purple	.30	.20
C150	AP12	27c yel grn ('57)	.30	.20
C151	AP12	31c chocolate	.45	.20
C152	AP12	36c ultra	.30	.20
C153	AP12	36c blk ('58)	.30	.20
C154	AP12	50c lt bl ('57)	.50	.35
C155	AP12	50c blk ('58)	.35	.20
C156	AP12	62c dl sl bl ('53)	.55	.35
C157	AP12	65c rose ('53)	.60	.35
C158	AP12	84c org ('59)	.45	.30
C159	AP12	1.08p vio brn	.85	.30
C160	AP12	2p Prus bl	1.40	.50
C161	AP12	3p red org	1.60	.65
C162	AP12	5p dk gray grn	3.25	1.50
C163	AP12	5p gray ('57)	2.00	1.00
C164	AP12	10p dp grn ('55)	8.25	4.50
		Nos. C145-C164 (20)	22.30	11.80

Planes and
Show
Emblem
AP16

Unwmk.

1956, Jan. 5   **Litho.**   *Perf. 11*
C166 AP16 20c ultra   .35   .35
C167 AP16 31c olive grn   .45   .25
C168 AP16 36c car rose   .70   .30
    Nos. C166-C168 (3)   1.50   .90

First Exposition of National Products.

Type of Regular Issue and

José
Batlle y
Ordonez
AP17

Designs: 10c, Full-face portrait without hand. 36c, Portrait facing right.

     Perf. 13½
1956, Dec. 15   **Wmk. 90**   **Photo.**
C169 A178 10c magenta   .30   .20
C170 A178 20c grnsh blk   .30   .20
C171 AP17 31c brown   .30   .30
C172 A178 36c bl grn   .60   .40
    Nos. C169-C172 (4)   1.50   1.10

Stamp of 1856 and
Stagecoach — AP18

1956, Dec. 15   **Litho.**
C173 AP18 20c grn, bl & pale yel   .45   .30
C174 AP18 31c brn, bl & lt bl   .55   .30
C175 AP18 36c dp claret & bl   .65   .30
    Nos. C173-C175 (3)   1.65   .90

1st postage stamps of Uruguay, cent.

Flags of 21
American
Nations — AP19

Men and Torch of
Freedom — AP20

    Perf. 11, 11½ (No. C177)
1958, June 19   **Unwmk.**
C176 AP19 23c blue & blk   .30   .20
C177 AP19 34c green & blk   .45   .20
C178 AP19 44c cerise & blk   .45   .30
    Nos. C176-C178 (3)   1.20   .70

Organization of American States, 10th anniv.

1958, Dec. 10   *Perf. 11*
C179 AP20 23c blk & blue   .25   .20
C180 AP20 34c blk & yel grn   .35   .20
C181 AP20 44c blk & org red   .65   .35
    Nos. C179-C181 (3)   1.25   .75

10th anniversary of the signing of the Universal Declaration of Human Rights.

"Flight" from
Monument to
Fallen
Aviators — AP21

1959   **Litho.**   *Perf. 11*
     Size: 22x37½mm
C182 AP21 3c bis brn & blk   .20   .20
C183 AP21 8c brt lil & blk   .20   .20
C184 AP21 38c black   .20   .20
C185 AP21 50c citron & blk   .20   .20

C186 AP21 60c vio & blk   .20   .20
C187 AP21 90c ol grn & blk   .25   .20
C188 AP21 1p blue & blk   .30   .20
C189 AP21 2p ocher & blk   1.00   .45
C190 AP21 3p grn & blk   1.25   .70
C191 AP21 5p vio brn & blk   1.75   1.25
C192 AP21 10p dp rose car &
          blk   5.50   3.75
    Nos. C182-C192 (11)   11.05   7.55

See Nos. C211-C222. For surcharge see No. Q97.

Alberto Santos-Dumont — AP22

1959, Feb. 13   **Wmk. 327**   *Perf. 11½*
C193 AP22 31c multi   .25   .20
C194 AP22 36c multi   .25   .20

Airplane flight of Alberto Santos-Dumont, Brazilian aeronaut, in 1906 in France.

Girl and
Waves
AP23

Designs: 38c, 60c, 1.05p, Compass and map of Punta del Este.

1959, Mar. 6   *Perf. 11½*
C195 AP23 10c ocher & lt bl   .20   .20
C196 AP23 38c grn & bis   .20   .20
C197 AP23 60c lilac & bister   .30   .20
C198 AP23 90c red org & grn   .40   .25
C199 AP23 1.05p blue & bister   .60   .45
    Nos. C195-C199 (5)   1.70   1.30

50th anniv. of Punta del Este, seaside resort.

Torch,
YMCA
Emblem
and
Chrismon
AP24

1959, Dec. 22   **Wmk. 327**   **Litho.**   *Perf. 11½*
C200 AP24 38c emer, blk & gray   .30   .25
C201 AP24 50c bl, blk & gray   .35   .20
C202 AP24 60c red, blk & gray   .45   .40
    Nos. C200-C202 (3)   1.10   .85

50th anniv. of the YMCA in Uruguay.

José Artigas and
George
Washington
AP25

Refugees and
WRY Emblem
AP26

1960, Mar. 2   *Perf. 11½x12*
C203 AP25 38c red & blk   .20   .20
C204 AP25 50c brt bl & blk   .25   .20
C205 AP25 60c dp grn & blk   .40   .20
    Nos. C203-C205 (3)   .85   .60

Pres. Eisenhower's visit to Uruguay, Feb. 1960.

No. C204 exists imperforate, but was not regularly issued in this form.

No. C150
Surcharged

1960, Apr. 8   **Unwmk.**   *Perf. 11*
C206 AP12 20c on 27c yel grn   .25   .20
   a.   Perf. 12½   .25   .20

1960, June 6   **Wmk. 332**
     Size: 24x35mm
C207 AP26 60c brt lil rose & blk   .35   .20

World Refugee Year, 7/1/59-6/30/60.

Type of Regular Issue, 1960
     Wmk. 332
1960, Nov. 4   **Litho.**   *Perf. 12*
C208 A186 38c bl & ol grn   .20   .20
C209 A186 50c bl & ver   .20   .20
C210 A186 60c bl & pur   .30   .20
    Nos. C208-C210 (3)   .70   .60

Type of 1959 Redrawn with Silhouette
of Airplane Added

1960-61   **Litho.**   *Perf. 12*
C211 AP21 3c blk & pale vio   .30   .20
C212 AP21 20c blk & crimson   .30   .20
C213 AP21 38c blk & pale bl   .30   .20
C214 AP21 50c blk & buff   .30   .20
C215 AP21 60c blk & dp grn   .40   .20
C216 AP21 90c blk & rose   .45   .20
C217 AP21 1p blk & gray   .60   .20
C218 AP21 2p blk & yel grn   .85   .20
C219 AP21 3p blk & red lil   1.10   .25
C220 AP21 5p blk & org ver   1.60   .50
C221 AP21 10p blk & yel   3.00   1.00
C222 AP21 20p blk & dk bl ('61)   5.75   2.25
    Nos. C211-C222 (12)   14.95   5.60

Pres.
Gronchi
and Flag
Colors
AP27

1961, Apr. 17   **Wmk. 332**   *Perf. 12*
C223 AP27 90c multi   .25   .20
C224 AP27 1.20p multi   .30   .25
C225 AP27 1.40p multi   .35   .35
    Nos. C223-C225 (3)   .90   .80

Visit of President Giovanni Gronchi of Italy to Uruguay, April, 1961.

Carrasco
National
Airport
AP28

1961, May 16   **Wmk. 332**   *Perf. 12*
     Building in Gray
C226 AP28 1p lt vio   .25   .20
C227 AP28 2p ol gray   .45   .20
C228 AP28 3p orange   .75   .40
C229 AP28 4p purple   .90   .45
C230 AP28 5p aqua   1.25   .60
C231 AP28 10p lt ultra   2.40   1.00
C232 AP28 20p maroon   3.75   2.00
    Nos. C226-C232 (7)   9.75   4.85

Type of Regular "CIES" Issue, 1961
1961, Aug. 3   **Litho.**   **Wmk. 332**
C233 A189 20c blk & org   .25   .20
C234 A189 45c blk & grn   .25   .20
C235 A189 50c blk & gray   .25   .20
C236 A189 90c blk & plum   .25   .20
C237 A189 1p blk & dp rose   .30   .20
C238 A189 1.40p blk & lt vio   .35   .20
C239 A189 2p blk & bister   .45   .20
C240 A189 3p blk & lt bl   .65   .30
C241 A189 4p blk & yellow   .90   .45
C242 A189 5p blk & blue   1.25   .55
C243 A189 10p blk & yel grn   2.00   1.00
C244 A189 20p blk & dp pink   4.50   2.10
    Nos. C233-C244 (12)   11.40   5.80

Swiss
Flag,
Plow,
Wheat
Sheaf
AP29

1962, Aug. 1   **Wmk. 332**   *Perf. 12*
C245 AP29 90c car, org & blk   .25   .2
C246 AP29 1.40p car, bl & blk   .35   .3

Cent. of the Swiss Settlement in Uruguay.

Red-crested
Cardinal — AP30

Birds: 45c, White-capped tanager, horiz. 90c, Vermilion flycatcher. 1.20p, Great kiskadee, horiz. 1.40p, Fork-tailed flycatcher.

1962, Dec. 5   **Litho.**   *Perf. 12*
C247 AP30 20c gray, blk & red   .20   .2
C248 AP30 45c multi   .35   .2
C249 AP30 90c crim rose, blk
          & lt brn   .75   .2
C250 AP30 1.20p lt bl, blk & yel   .60   .2
C251 AP30 1.40p blue & sepia   1.10   .2
    Nos. C247-C251 (5)   3.00   1.0

No frame on #C248, thin frame on #C251.
See #C258-C263. For surcharge see #C320.

Type of Regular UPAE Issue, 1963
1963, May 31   **Wmk. 332**   *Perf. 12*
C252 A195 45c bluish grn & blk   .20   .2
C253 A195 90c magenta & blk   .25   .2

Freedom from Hunger
Type of Regular Issue
1963, July 9   **Wmk. 332**   *Perf. 12*
C254 A196 90c red & yel   .25   .2
C255 A196 1.40p violet & yel   .35   .3

"Alferez
Campora"
AP31

1963, Aug. 16   **Litho.**
C256 AP31 90c dk grn & org   .30   .2
C257 AP31 1.40p ultra & yel   .50   .4

Voyage around the world by the Uruguayan sailing vessel "Alferez Campora," 1960-63.

Bird Type of 1962

Birds: 1p, Glossy cowbird (tordo). 2p, Yellow cardinal. 3p, Hooded siskin. 5p, Sayaca tanager. 10p, Blue and yellow tanager. 20p, Scarlet-headed marsh-bird. All horizontal.

1963, Nov. 15   **Wmk. 332**   *Perf. 12*
C258 AP30 1p vio bl, blk &
          brn org   .45   .2
C259 AP30 2p lt brn, blk &
          yel   1.00   .2
C260 AP30 3p yel, brn & blk   1.50   .4
C261 AP30 5p emer, bl grn &
          blk   2.40   .5
C262 AP30 10p multi   5.00   1.0
C263 AP30 20p gray, org & blk   10.50   5.5
    Nos. C258-C263 (6)   20.85   7.8

Frame on Nos. C260-C263.

Pres.
Charles de
Gaulle
AP32

2.40p, Flags of France and Uruguay.

1964, Oct. 9   Litho.   Perf. 12
C264 AP32 1.50p multi   .35 .20
C265 AP32 2.40p multi   .65 .35
    Charles de Gaulle, Pres. of France, Oct. 1964.

Submerged Statue of Ramses II — AP33

Design: 2p, Head of Ramses II.

1964, Oct. 30   Litho.   Wmk. 332
C266 AP33 1.30p multi   .30 .25
C267 AP33   2p bis, red brn & brt bl   .60 .45
  a.   Souv. sheet of 3, #713, C266-C267, imperf.   1.60 1.60
    UNESCO world campaign to save historic monuments in Nubia.

National Flag AP34

1965, Feb. 18   Wmk. 332   Perf. 12
C268 AP34 50p gray, dk bl & yel   5.25 3.00

Kennedy Type of Regular Issue
1965, Mar. 5   Wmk. 327   Perf. 11½
C269 A202 1.50p gold, lil & blk   .25 .25
C270 A202 2.40p gold, brt bl & blk   .35 .35

Issue of 1864, No. 23 — AP35

6c, 8c, 10c denominations of 1864 issue.

Wmk. 332
1965, Mar. 19   Litho.   Perf. 12
C271   Sheet of 10   1.60 1.60

"URUGUAY" at bottom
  a.   AP35 1p blue & black   .20 .20
  b.   AP35 1p brick red & black   .20 .20
  c.   AP35 1p green & black   .20 .20
  d.   AP35 1p ocher & black   .20 .20
  e.   AP35 1p carmine & black   .20 .20

"URUGUAY" at top
  f.   AP35 1p blue & black   .20 .20
  g.   AP35 1p brick red & black   .20 .20
  h.   AP35 1p green & black   .20 .20
  i.   AP35 1p ocher & black   .20 .20
  j.   AP35 1p carmine & black   .20 .20

    1st Rio de la Plata Stamp Show, sponsored jointly by the Argentine and Uruguayan philatelic associations, Montevideo, Mar. 19-28. No. C271 contains two horizontal rows of stamps and two rows of labels; Nos. C271a-C271e are in first row, Nos. C271f-C271j in second row. Adjacent labels in top and bottom rows.
    For overprint see No. C298.

National Arms — AP36

Artigas Monument AP37

1965, Apr. 30   Wmk. 332   Perf. 12
C272 AP36 20p multi   1.75 1.00

Type of Regular Issue and AP37.
    Designs: 1.50p, Artigas and wagontrain. 2.40p, Artigas quotation.

Perf. 11½x12, 12x11½
1965, May 17   Litho.   Wmk. 327
C273 AP37   1p multi   .20 .20
C274 A205 1.50p multi   .30 .25
C275 A205 2.40p multi   .45 .35
    Nos. C273-C275 (3)   .95 .80
    José Artigas (1764-1850), leader of the independence revolt against Spain.

Olympic Games Type of Regular Issue
    Designs: 1p, Boxing. 1.50p, Running. 2p, Fencing. 2.40p, Sculling. 3p, Pistol shooting. 20p, Olympic rings.

1965, Aug. 3   Litho.   Perf. 12x11½
C276 A206   1p red, gray & blk   .20 .20
C277 A206 1.50p emer, bl & blk   .20 .20
C278 A206   2p dk car, bl & blk   .30 .25
C279 A206 2.40p lt ultra, org & blk   .45 .30
C280 A206   3p lil, yel & blk   .60 .35
C281 A206   20p dk vio bl, pink & lt bl   .95 .70
    Nos. C276-C281 (6)   2.70 2.00

Souvenir Sheet
    Designs: 5p, Stamp of 1924, No. 284. 10p, Stamp of 1928, No. 389.

C282   Sheet of 2   1.60 1.60
  a.   5p buff, blue & black   .55 .55
  b.   10p blue, black & rose red   .80 .80
    18th Olympic Games, Tokyo, 10/10-25/64.

ITU Emblem and Satellite AP38

1966, Jan. 25   Wmk. 332   Perf. 12
C283 AP38 1p bl, bluish blk & ver   .25 .20
    Cent. of the ITU (in 1965).

Winston Churchill — AP39

1966, Apr. 29   Wmk. 332   Perf. 12
C284 AP39 2p car, brn & gold   .45 .20

Rio de Janeiro Type of Regular Issue
1966, June 9   Wmk. 332   Perf. 12
C285 A208 80c dp org & brn   .25 .20

International Cooperation Year Emblem AP40

1966, June 9   Litho.
C286 AP40 1p bluish grn & black   .25 .20
    UN International Cooperation Year.

President Zalman Shazar of Israel AP41

1966, June 21   Wmk. 327
C287 AP41 7p multi   .45 .25
    Visit of Pres. Zalman Shazar of Israel.

Crested Screamer — AP42

1966, July 7   Wmk. 327   Perf. 12
C288 AP42 100p bl, blk, red & gray   6.00 1.75

Jules Rimet Cup, Soccer Ball and Globe AP43

1966, July 11   Litho.
C289 AP43 10p dk pur, org & lil   .60 .25
    World Cup Soccer Championship, Wembley, England, July 11-30.

Bulls AP44

1966   Wmk. 327, 332 (10p)
C290 AP44   4p Hereford   .20 .20
C291 AP44   6p Holstein   .20 .20
C292 AP44 10p Shorthorn   .45 .25
C293 AP44 15p Aberdeen Angus   .75 .30
C294 AP44 20p Norman   1.40 .45
C295 AP44 30p Jersey   1.75 .75
C296 AP44 50p Charolais   3.00 1.25
    Nos. C290-C296 (7)   7.75 3.40
    Issued to publicize Uruguayan cattle. Issued: 4p, 50p, 8/13; 6p, 30p, 8/29; 10p, 15p, 20p, 9/26.

Boiso Lanza, Early Plane and Space Capsule AP45

1966, Oct. 14   Litho.   Perf. 12
C297 AP45 25p ultra, blk & lt bl   .75 .45
    Issued to honor Capt. Juan Manuel Boiso Lanza, pioneer of military aviation.

No. C271 Overprinted: "CENTENARIO DEL SELLO / ESCUDITO RESELLADO"
1966, Nov. 4   Wmk. 332
C298   Sheet of 10   1.60 1.60
"URUGUAY" at bottom
  a.-e.   AP35 1p each   .20 .20
"URUGUAY" at top
  f.-j.   AP35 1p each   .20 .20
    2nd Rio de la Plata Stamp Show, Buenos Aires, Apr. 1966, sponsored by the Argentine and Uruguayan philatelic associations, and for the cent. of Uruguay's 1st surcharged issue. The addition of black numerals makes the designs resemble the surcharged issue of 1866, Nos. 24-28.

    Labels in top row are overprinted "SEGUNDA MUESTRA 1966," in bottom row "SEGUNDAS JORNADAS 1966" and "CENTENARIO DEL SELLO / ESCUDITO RESELLADO" in both rows. One label each in top and bottom rows is overprinted "BUENOS AIRES / ABRIL 1966."

No. 613 Surcharged in Dark Blue

Perf. 12½x13
1966, Dec. 17   Engr.   Unwmk.
C299 A175 1p on 12c   .25 .20
    Philatelic Club of Uruguay, 40th anniv.

Dante Alighieri — AP46   Planetarium Projector — AP47

Wmk. 332
1966, Dec. 27   Litho.   Perf. 12
C300 AP46 50c sepia & bister   .25 .20
    Dante Alighieri (1265-1321), Italian poet.

1967, Jan. 13   Wmk. 332   Perf. 12
C301 AP47 5p dl bl & blk   .45 .25
    Montevideo Municipal Planetarium, 10th anniv.

Archbishop Makarios and Map of Cyprus AP48

1967, Feb. 14   Wmk. 332   Perf. 12
C302 AP48 6.60p rose lil & blk   .25 .20
    Visit of Archbishop Makarios, president of Cyprus, Oct. 21, 1966.

Dr. Albert Schweitzer Holding Fawn — AP49

1967, Mar. 31   Litho.   Wmk. 332
C303 AP49 6p grn, blk, brn & sal   .45 .45
    Albert Schweitzer (1875-1965), medical missionary.

Corriedale Ram AP50

    Various Rams: 4p, Ideal. 5p, Romney Marsh. 10p, Australian Merino.

1967, Apr. 5
C304 AP50 3p red org, blk & gray   1.10 .20
C305 AP50 4p emer, blk & gray   1.10 .20

C306 AP50   5p ultra, blk & gray   1.10   .20
C307 AP50   10p yel, blk & gray   1.10   .40
    Nos. C304-C307 (4)   4.40   1.00
    Uruguayan sheep raising.

Flag of Uruguay and Map of the Americas AP51

1967, Apr. 8
C308 AP51   10p dk gray, bl & gold   .35   .20
    Meeting of American Presidents, Punta del Este, Apr. 10-12.

Numeral Stamps of 1866, Nos. 30-31 AP52

Design: 6p, Nos. 32-33; diff. frame.

Wmk. 332
1967, May 10   **Litho.**   **Perf. 12**
C309 AP52   3p bl, yel grn & blk   .20   .20
    a.   Souvenir sheet of 4   .75   .75
C310 AP52   6p bis, dp rose & blk   .35   .25
    a.   Souvenir sheet of 4   1.75   1.75

    Cent. of the 1866 numeral issue. Nos. C309a-C310a each contain 4 stamps similar to Nos. C309 and C310 respectively (the arrangement of colors differs in the souvenir sheets).

Ansina, Portrait by Medardo Latorre — AP53

1967, May 17
C311 AP53   2p gray, dk bl & red   .25   .20
    Issued to honor Ansina, servant of Gen. José Artigas.

Plane Landing AP54

1967, May 30
C312 AP54   10p red, bl, blk & yel   .35   .25
    30th anniv. (in 1966) of PLUNA Airline.

Shooting for Basket — AP55

Basketball Game — AP56

Basketball Players in Action: No. C314, Driving (ball shoulder high). No. C315, About to pass (ball head high). No. C316, Ready to pass (ball held straight in front). No. C317, Dribbling with right hand.

1967, June 9
C313 AP55   5p multi   .25   .25
C314 AP55   5p multi   .25   .25
C315 AP55   5p multi   .25   .25
C316 AP55   5p multi   .25   .25
C317 AP55   5p multi   .25   .25
    a.   Strip of 5, Nos. C313-C317   1.25   1.25

Souvenir Sheet

C318 AP56   10p org, brt grn & blk   1.10   1.10
    5th World Basketball Championships, Montevideo, May 1967.
    For overprint see No. C349.

José Artigas, Manuel Belgrano, Flags of Uruguay and Argentina — AP57

Wmk. 332
1967, June 19   **Litho.**   **Imperf.**
C319 AP57   5p bl, grn & yel   .60   .60
    3rd Rio de la Plata Stamp Show, Montevideo, Uruguay, June 18-25.
    For surcharge see No. 859.

Nos. C248 and C252 Surcharged in Gold

1967, June 22   **Perf. 12**
C320 AP30   5.90p on 45c multi   .25   .20
C321 A195   5.90p on 45c multi   .25   .20

Don Quixote and Sancho Panza, Painted by Denry Torres — AP58

1967, July 10
C322 AP58   8p bister brn & brn   .30   .25
    Issued in honor of Miguel de Cervantes Saavedra (1547-1616), Spanish novelist.
    For surcharge see No. C356.

Stone Axe — AP59

Railroad Crossing AP60

    Designs: 15p, Headbreaker stones. 20p, Spearhead. 50p, Birdstone. 75p, Clay pot. 100p, Ornitholite (ritual sculpture), Balizas, horiz. 150p, Lasso weights (boleadores). 200p, Two spearheads.

1967-68   **Wmk. 332**   **Perf. 12**
C323 AP59   15p gray & blk   .20   .20
C324 AP59   20p gray & blk   .20   .20
C325 AP59   30p gray & lt gray   .45   .20
C326 AP59   50p gray & blk   .60   .20
C327 AP59   75p brn & blk   1.00   .35
C328 AP59   100p gray & blk   1.40   .60
C329 AP59   150p gray & blk
    ('68)   1.75   .60
C330 AP59   200p gray & blk
    ('68)   2.40   1.25
    Nos. C323-C330 (8)   8.00   3.60

1967, Dec. 4
C331 AP60   4p blk, yel & red   .25   .20
    10th Pan-American Highway Congress, Montevideo.

Lions Emblem and Map of South America — AP61

1967, Dec. 29
C332 AP61   5p pur, yel & emer   .30   .20
    50th anniversary of Lions International.

Boy Scout AP62

1968, Jan. 24   **Litho.**
C333 AP62   9p sepia & brick red   .40   .25
    Issued in memory of Robert Baden-Powell, founder of the Boy Scout organization.

Sun, UN Emblem and Transportation Means — AP63

1968, Feb. 29   **Wmk. 332**   **Perf. 12**
C334 AP63   10p gray, yel, lt & dk bl   .25   .20
    Issued for International Tourist Year.

Octopus AP64

    Marine Fauna: 20p, Silversides. 25p, Characin. 30p, Catfish, vert. 50p, Squid, vert.

1968   **Wmk. 332**   **Perf. 12**
C335 AP64   15p lt grn, bl & blk   .60   .20
C336 AP64   20p brn, grn & bl   .60   .20
C337 AP64   25p multi   .80   .20
C338 AP64   30p bl, grn & blk   .90   .30
C339 AP64   50p dp org, grn & dk bl   1.40   .45
    Nos. C335-C339 (5)   4.30   1.35
    Issued: 30p, 50p, 10/10; 15p, 20p, 25p, 11/5.

Navy Type of Regular Issue

    Designs: 4p, Naval Air Force. 6p, Naval arms. 10p, Signal flags, vert. 20p, Corsair (chartered by General Artigas).

1968, Nov. 12   **Litho.**
C340 A226   4p bl, blk & red   .20   .20
C341 A226   6p multi   .20   .20
C342 A226   10p lt ultra, red & yel   .20   .20
C343 A226   20p ultra & blk   .30   .20
    Nos. C340-C343 (4)   .90   .80

Rowing AP65

1969, Feb. 11   **Wmk. 332**   **Perf. 12**
C344 AP65   30p shown   .35   .20
C345 AP65   50p Running   .65   .30
C346 AP65   100p Soccer   1.00   .45
    Nos. C344-C346 (3)   2.00   .95
    19th Olympic Games, Mexico City, 10/12-27/68.

Bicycling Type of Regular Issue

    Designs: 20p, Bicyclist and globe, vert.

1969, Mar. 21   **Wmk. 332**   **Perf. 12**
C347 A229   20p bl, pur & yel   .30   .20

"EFIMEX 68" and Globe AP66

1969, Apr. 10   **Wmk. 332**   **Perf. 12**
C348 AP66   20p dk grn, red & bl   .30   .20
    EFIMEX '68, International Philatelic Exhibition, Mexico City, Nov. 1-9, 1968.

No. C318 Overprinted with Names of Participating Countries, Emblem, Bars, etc. and "CAMPEONATO MUNDIAL DE VOLEIBOL"

1969, Apr. 25

Souvenir Sheet

C349 AP56   10p org, brt grn & blk   .45   .45
    Issued to commemorate the World Volleyball Championships, Montevideo, Apr. 1969.

Book, Quill and Emblem — AP67

Automobile Club Emblem — AP68

1969, Sept. 16   Litho.   *Perf. 12*
C350 AP67 30p grn, org & blk   .45 .25
10th Congress of Latin American Notaries.

1969, Oct. 7   Wmk. 332   *Perf. 12*
C351 AP68 10p ultra & red   .25 .20
50th anniv. (in 1968) of the Uruguayan Automobile Club.

ILO Emblem
AP69

1969, Oct. 29   Litho.   *Perf. 12*
C352 AP69 30p dk bl grn & blk   .40 .25
50th anniv. of the ILO.

Exhibition Emblem — AP70

1969, Nov. 15   Wmk. 332   *Perf. 12*
C353 AP70 20p ultra, yel & grn   .30 .20
ABUEXPO 69 Philatelic Exhibition, San Pablo, Brazil, Nov. 15-23.

Rotary Emblem and Hemispheres AP71

1969, Dec. 6   *Perf. 12*
C354 AP71 20p ultra, bl & bis   .50 .25
South American Regional Rotary Conference and the 50th anniv. of the Montevideo Rotary Club.

Dr. Luis Morquio — AP72

1969, Dec. 22   Litho.   Wmk. 332
C355 AP72 20p org red & brn   .25 .20
Centenary of the birth of Dr. Luis Morquio, pediatrician.

No. C322 Surcharged "FELIZ AÑO 1970 / 6.00 / PESOS"

1969, Dec. 24
C356 AP58 6p on 8p bis brn & brn   .25 .20
Issued for New Year 1970.

Mahatma Gandhi and UNESCO Emblem AP73

1970, Jan. 26   Wmk. 332   *Perf. 12*
C357 AP73 100p lt bl & brn   3.00 .80
Mohandas K. Gandhi (1869-1948), leader in India's fight for independence.

Evaristo C. Ciganda — AP74   Giuseppe Garibaldi — AP75

1970, Mar. 10   Litho.
C358 AP74 6p brt grn & brn   .25 .20
Ciganda, author of the 1st law for teachers' pensions, birth cent.

1970, Apr. 7   Unwmk.   *Perf. 12*
C359 AP75 20p rose car & pink   .25 .20
Centenary of Garibaldi's command of foreign legionnaires in the Uruguayan Civil War.

Fur Seal AP76

Designs: 20p, Rhea, vert. 30p, Common tegu (lizard). 50p, Capybara. 100p, Mulita armadillo. 150p, Puma. 200p, Nutria.

1970-71   Wmk. 332   *Perf. 12*
C361 AP76 20p pur, emer & blk   .75 .20
C362 AP76 30p emer, yel & blk   .75 .25
C363 AP76 50p dl yel & brn   1.50 .45
C365 AP76 100p org, sep & blk   2.00 .65
C366 AP76 150p emer & brn   1.50 .75
C367 AP76 200p brt rose, brn & blk ('71)   3.75 1.90
C368 AP76 250p gray, bl & blk   4.75 2.00
Nos. C361-C368 (7)   15.00 6.20

Soccer and Mexican Flag AP77

1970, June 2   Litho.   *Perf. 12*
C369 AP77 50p multi   .60 .45
9th World Soccer Championships for the Jules Rimet Cup, Mexico City, 5/30-6/21.

"U N" and Laurel — AP78

1970, June 26   Wmk. 332   *Perf. 12*
C370 AP78 32p dk bl & gold   .50 .25
25th anniversary of the United Nations.

Eisenhower and US Flag — AP79

1970, July 14   Litho.
C371 AP79 30p gray, vio bl & red   .30 .25
Issued in memory of Gen. Dwight David Eisenhower, 34th Pres. of US (1890-1969).

Neil A. Armstrong Stepping onto Moon — AP80

1970, July 21
C372 AP80 200p multi   3.00 1.25
1st anniv. of man's 1st landing on the moon.

Flag of the "Immortals" — AP81

1970, Aug. 24   Wmk. 332   *Perf. 12*
C373 AP81 500p bl, blk & red   4.50 4.50
The 145th anniversary of the arrival of the 33 "Immortals," the patriots, who started the revolution for independence.

Congress Emblem with Map of South America AP82

1970, Sept. 16   Unwmk.   *Perf. 12*
C374 AP82 30p bl, dk bl & yel   .30 .25
Issued to publicize the 5th Pan-American Congress of Rheumatology, Punta del Este.

Souvenir Sheet

Types of First Air Post Issue — AP83

1970, Oct. 1   Wmk. 332   *Perf. 12½*
C375 AP83 Sheet of 3   1.90 1.90
a.   25p brown (Bl)   .60 .60
b.   25p brown (R)   .60 .60
c.   25p brown (G)   .60 .60

Stamp Day. #C375 contains 3 stamps similar to #C1-C3, but with denominations in pesos.

Flags of ALALC Countries — AP84

1970, Nov. 23   Litho.   *Perf. 12*
C376 AP84 22p multi   .30 .25
For the Latin-American Association for Free Trade (Asociación Latinoamericana de Libre Comercio).

Yellow Fever, by J. M. Blanes AP85

1971, June 8   Wmk. 332   *Perf. 12*
C377 AP85 50p blk, dk red brn & yel   .55 .30
Juan Manuel Blanes (1830-1901), painter.

Racial Equality, UN Emblem AP86

1971, June 28   Litho.
C378 AP86 27p blk, pink & bis   .35 .25
Intl. Year Against Racial Discrimination.

Congress Emblem with Maps of Americas AP87

1971, July 6   Wmk. 332   *Perf. 12*
C379 AP87 58p dl grn, blk & org   .45 .35
12th Pan-American Congress of Gastroenterology, Punta del Este, Dec. 5-10, 1971.

 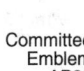

Committee Emblem AP88

1971, Nov. 29
C380 AP88 30p bl, blk & yel   .30 .25
Inter-governmental Committee for European Migration.

Llama and
Mountains
AP89

Munich Olympic
Games
Emblem — AP90

1971, Dec. 30
C381 AP89 37p multi   .45 .35

EXFILIMA '71, Third Inter-American Philatelic Exposition, Lima, Peru, Nov. 6-14.

1972, Feb. 1   Perf. 11½x12
Designs (Munich '72 Emblem and): 100p,
Torchbearer. 500p, Discobolus.

C382 AP90 50p blk, red & org   .25 .20
C383 AP90 100p multi   .45 .35
C384 AP90 500p multi   2.25 1.60
        Nos. C382-C384 (3)   2.95 2.15

20th Olympic Games, Munich, 8/26-9/11.

Retort and WHO
Emblem — AP91

Ship with Flags
Forming
Sails — AP92

1972, Feb. 22   Perf. 12
C385 AP91 27p multi   .25 .20

50th anniversary of the discovery of insulin
by Frederick G. Banting and Charles H. Best.

1972, Mar. 6   Wmk. 332
C386 AP92 37p multi   .25 .20

Stamp Day of the Americas.

1924 and 1928 Gold Medals,
Soccer — AP93

Design: 300p, Olympic flag, Motion and
Munich emblems, vert.

1972, June 12   Litho.   Perf. 12
C387 AP93 100p bl & multi   .45 .45
C388 AP93 300p multi   1.40 1.40

20th Olympic Games, Munich, 8/26-9/11.

Cross
AP94

1972, Aug. 10
C389 AP94 37p vio & gold   .25 .20

Dan A. Mitrione (1920-70), slain US official.

Interlocking
Squares and UN
Emblem — AP95

1972, Aug. 16
C390 AP95 30p gray & multi   .25 .20

3rd UN Conf. on Trade and Development
(UNCTAD III), Santiago, Chile, Apr.-May 1972.

Brazil's "Bull's-eye," 1843 — AP96

Wmk. 332
1972, Aug. 26   Litho.   Perf. 12
C391 AP96 50p grn, yel & bl   .25 .20

4th Inter-American Philatelic Exhibition,
EXFILBRA, Rio de Janeiro, Aug. 26-Sept. 2.

Map of South
America,
Compass
Rose — AP97

1972, Sept. 28
C392 AP97 37p multi   .30 .20

Uruguay's support for extending territorial
sovereignty 200 miles into the sea.

Adoration of the Kings and Shepherds,
by Rafael Perez Barradas — AP98

1972, Oct. 12
C393 AP98 20p lemon & multi + la-
          bel   .30 .25

Christmas 1972 and first biennial exhibition
of Uruguayan painting, 1970.

WPY
Emblem
AP99

Wmk. 332
1974, Aug. 20   Litho.   Perf. 12
C394 AP99 500p gray & red   .75 .60

World Population Year 1974.

Soccer, Olympics
and UPU
Emblems
AP100

Anniversaries and events: No. C398a, 17th
UPU Congress, Lausanne. No. C398b, World
Soccer Federation, 1st South American presi-
dent. No. C398c, 1976 Summer and Winter
Olympics, Innsbruck and Montreal.

1974, Aug. 30
C395 AP100 200p grn & multi   .65 .65
C396 AP100 300p org & multi   .65 .65
C397 AP100 500p multicolored   6.75 6.75
Souvenir Sheet
C398   Sheet of 3   70.00 70.00
a.-c.   AP100 500p any single   20.00 20.00

Centenary of Universal Postal Union.
Nos. C397-C398 had limited distribution.

Mexico
No. O1
and
Mexican
Coat of
Arms
AP101

Wmk. 332
1974, Oct. 15   Litho.   Perf. 12
C399 AP101 200p multi   .25 .20

EXFILMEX '74 5th Inter-American Philatelic
Exhibition, Mexico City, Oct. 26-Nov. 3.

Christmas Type of 1974

240p, Kings following star. 2500p, Virgin &
Child.

1974
C400 A315 240p multi   .30 .20
Miniature Sheet
C401 A315 2500p multi   3.00 3.00
Issued: 240p. Dec. 27; 2500p, Dec. 31.

Spain No. 1, Colors of Spain and
Uruguay — AP102

1975, Mar. 4
C402 AP102 400p multi   .35 .25

Espana 75, International Philatelic Exhibition, Madrid, Apr. 4-13.

Souvenir Sheet

Nos. C253, 893 and C402 — AP103

Wmk. 332
1975, Apr. 4   Litho.   Perf. 1?
C403 AP103 Sheet of 3   3.50 3.5?
  a.   1000p No. C253   1.10 1.1?
  b.   1000p No. 893   1.10 1.1?
  c.   1000p No. C402   1.10 1.1?

Espana 75 Intl. Phil. Exhib., Madrid, Apr. 4-
13.

1976 Summer &
Winter Olympics,
Innsbruck &
Montreal
AP104

1975, May 16   Perf. 1?
C404 AP104 400p shown   .60 .4?
C405 AP104 600p Flags,
             Olympic
             rings   .90 .7?

Souvenir Sheets
C406   Sheet of 2
  a.   AP104 500p Montreal emblem
  b.   AP104 1000p Innsbruck emblem
C407   Sheet of 2
  a.   AP104 500p Emblems, horiz.
  b.   AP104 1000p Flags, horiz.

Nos. C404-C407 had limited distribution.

Floor
Design for
Capitol,
Rome
AP105

1975, Aug. 15
C408 AP105 1p multi   .85 .8?

500th birth anniversary of Michelangelo
Buonarroti (1475-1564), Italian sculptor,
painter and architect.

Apollo-Soyuz Space Mission, USA &
Uruguay Independence — AP106

Anniversaries and events: 15c, Apollo-
Soyuz spacecraft. 20c, Apollo-Soyuz spacecraft. 25c, Artigas monument, vert. 30c,
George Washington, Pres. Artigas. No. C412,
Early Aircraft, vert. No. C413a, Apollo spacecraft, astronauts. No. C413b, US and Uruguayan Declarations of Independence. No.
C413c, Modern aircraft. No. C413d, UN Sec-
retaries General. No. C414c, Boiso Lanza, aviation pioneer. 1p, Flags of UN and Uruguay.

1975, Sept. 29
C409	AP106 10c multicolored	.75	.55
C410	AP106 15c multicolored	1.10	.75
C411	AP106 25c multicolored	1.25	.90
C412	AP106 50c multicolored	1.90	1.10
	Nos. C409-C412 (4)	5.00	3.30

Souvenir Sheets
C413	Sheet of 4	32.50	26.00
a.-d.	AP106 40c any single	6.00	6.00
C414	Sheet of 4	32.50	26.00
a.	AP106 20c multicolored	1.25	1.25
b.	AP106 30c multicolored	3.50	3.50
c.	AP106 50c multicolored	6.00	6.00
d.	AP106 1p multicolored	12.00	12.00

Nos. C409-C414 had limited distribution.

Sun, Uruguay No. C59 and other Stamps — AP108

Wmk. 332

1975, Oct. 13   Litho.   *Perf. 12*
C415	AP108 1p blk, gray & yel	2.00	1.00

Uruguayan Stamp Day.

Montreal Olympic Emblem and Argentina '78 — AP109

Flags of US and Uruguay — AP110

UPU and UPAE Emblems AP111

Wmk. 332

1975, Oct. 14   Litho.   *Perf. 11½*
C416	AP109 1p multi	1.40	.60
C417	AP110 1p multi	1.40	.60
C418	AP111 1p multi	1.40	.60
a.	Souvenir sheet of 3	14.00	14.00
	Nos. C416-C418 (3)	4.20	1.80

EXFILMO '75 and ESPAMER '75 Stamp Exhibitions, Montevideo, Oct. 10-19. No. C418a contains 3 stamps similar to Nos. C416-C418, 2p each.

Ocelot AP112

Orchid: #C416, Oncidium bifolium.

1976, Jan.   Litho.   *Perf. 12*
C419	AP112 50c vio bl & multi	.40	.30
C420	AP112 50c emer & multi	.40	.30

Souvenir Sheets

Olympics, Soccer, Telecommunications and UPU — AP113

1976, June 3   *Perf. 11½*
C422	Sheet of 3	42.50	42.50
a.	AP113 30c Soccer player	5.50	5.50
b.	AP113 70c Alexander Graham Bell	12.50	12.50
c.	AP113 1p UPU emblem, UN #5	18.00	18.00
C423	Sheet of 3	42.50	42.50
a.	AP113 40c Discus thrower	4.75	4.75
b.	AP113 60c Telephone, cent.	7.25	7.25
c.	AP113 2p UPU emblem, UN #11	24.00	24.00

Nos. C422-C423 had limited distribution.

Anniversaries and Events Type of 1976
Souvenir Sheets

20c, Frederick Passy, Henri Dunant. 35c, Nobel prize, 75th anniv. 40c, Viking spacecraft. 60c, 1976 Summer Olympics, Montreal. 75c, US space missions. 90c, 1976 Summer Olympics, diff.
World Cup Soccer Championships, Argentina: 1p, Uruguay, 1930 champions. 1.50p, Uruguay, 1950 champions.

1976, Nov. 12   *Perf. 12*
C424	Sheet of 4	30.00	30.00
a.	A355 20c multicolored	1.75	1.75
b.	A355 40c multicolored	3.50	3.50
c.	A355 60c multicolored	5.25	5.25
d.	A355 1.50p multicolored	13.50	13.50
C425	Sheet of 4	30.00	30.00
a.	A355 35c multicolored	2.75	2.75
b.	A355 75c multicolored	6.00	6.00
c.	A355 90c multicolored	7.25	7.25
d.	A355 1p multicolored	8.00	8.00

Nos. C424-C425 had limited distribution.

Nobel Prize Type of 1977
Souvenir Sheets

Anniversaries and events: 10c, World Cup Soccer Championships. 40c, Victor Hess, Nobel Prize in Physics. 60c, Max Plank, Nobel Prize in Physics. 80c, Graf Zeppelin, Concorde. 90c, Virgin and Child by Rubens. 1.20p, World Cup Soccer Championships, diff. 1.50p, Eduardo Bonilla, Count von Zeppelin. 2p, The Nativity by Rubens.

1977, July 21
C426	Sheet of 4	26.00	26.00
a.	A361 10c multicolored	.60	.60
b.	A361 60c multicolored	3.50	3.50
c.	A361 80c multicolored	4.75	4.75
d.	A361 2p multicolored	12.00	12.00
C427	Sheet of 4	26.00	26.00
a.	A361 40c multicolored	2.00	2.00
b.	A361 90c multicolored	4.50	4.50
c.	A361 1.20p multicolored	6.00	6.00
d.	A361 1.50p multicolored	7.50	7.50

Nos. C426-C427 had limited distribution.

Uruguay Natl. Postal System, 150th Anniv. AP114

1977, July 27
C428	AP114 8p multicolored	8.00	8.00

Souvenir Sheet
C429	AP114 10p multicolored	11.00	11.00

No. C428, imperf., was not valid for postage. Souvenir sheets sold in the package with No. C429 were not valid for postage.
For overprint see No. C435.

Paintings Type of 1978

Paintings: 1p, St. George Slaying Dragon by Durer. 1.25p, Duke of Lerma by Rubens. No. 432a, Madonna and Child by Durer. No. 432b, Holy Family by Rubens. No. 432c, Flight from Egypt by Francisco de Goya (1746-1828).

1978, June 13   *Perf. 12½*
C430	A374 1p brn & blk	2.75	2.75
C431	A374 1.25p blk & brn	3.00	3.00

Souvenir Sheet
C432	Sheet of 3	12.50	12.50
a.-c.	A374 1p any single	3.50	3.50

Nos. C430-C432 had limited distribution.

Souvenir Sheet

ICAO, 30th Anniv. and 1st Powered Flight, 75th Anniv. — AP115

Designs: a, Concorde, Dornier DO-x. b, Graf Zeppelin, Wright Brothers' Flyer. c, Space shuttle and De Pinedo's plane.

1978, June 13
C433	Sheet of 3	17.50	17.50
a.-c.	AP115 1p any single	5.00	5.00

No. C433 had limited distribution.

Souvenir Sheet

World Cup Soccer Championships, Argentina — AP116

1978, June 13   *Perf. 12*
C434	Sheet of 3	40.00	40.00
a.	AP116 50c multicolored	3.75	3.75
b.	AP116 1.50p multicolored	10.50	10.50
c.	AP116 2p multicolored	15.00	15.00

No. C434 had limited distribution.

No. C428 Overprinted in Black

1978, Aug. 28
C435	AP114 8p multicolored	4.75	2.50

No. C435 had limited distribution.

Madonna and Child Type of 1979

Various Madonna and Child etchings by Albrecht Dürer with Intl. Year of the Child emblem at: a, UL. b, UR.

Wmk. 332

1979, June 18   Litho.   *Perf. 12½*
C436	A390 1.50p Sheet of 2, #a-b	17.50	17.50

No. C436 had limited distribution.

Boiso Lanza, Wright Brothers AP117

75th anniv. of powered flight.

1979, June 18   *Perf. 12½*
C437	AP117 1.80p multicolored	2.25	1.10

No. C437 had limited distribution. Issued in sheet of 24 containing 6 blocks of 4r with margin around. See Nos. 1040-1042.

Souvenir Sheet

1982 World Cup Soccer Championships, Spain — AP118

1979, June 18   *Perf. 12*
C438	Sheet of 3	27.50	27.50
a.	AP118 50c Jules Rimet cup	1.90	1.90
b.	AP118 2.50p Uruguay flag	9.25	9.25
c.	AP118 3p Espana '82	11.50	11.50

No. C438 had limited distribution.

AIR POST SEMI-POSTAL STAMPS

Catalogue values for unused stamps in this section are for Never Hinged items.

Type of Semi-Postal Stamps, 1959
Wmk. 327

1959, Dec. 29   Litho.   *Perf. 11½*
CB1	SP2 38c + 10c brown & org	.25	.25
CB2	SP2 60c + 10c gray grn & org	.30	.30

Issued for national recovery.

SPECIAL DELIVERY STAMPS

No. 242 Overprinted MENSAJERÍAS

1921, Aug.   Unwmk.   *Perf. 11½*
E1	A97 2c fawn	.45	.20
a.	Double overprint	3.25	

Caduceus — SD1

Imprint: "IMP. NACIONAL."

1922, Dec. 2   Litho.   **Wmk. 188**
Size: 21x27mm
E2	SD1 2c light red	.25	.20

1924, Oct. 1
E3	SD1 2c pale ultra	.25	.20

1928   Unwmk.   *Perf. 11*
E4	SD1 2c light blue	.30	.20

Imprint: "IMPRA. NACIONAL."

1928-36   **Wmk. 188**
Size: 16½x19½mm.
E5   SD1   2c black, *green*   .20 .20
Unwmk.
E6   SD1   2c blue green ('29)   .20 .20
Perf. 11½, 12½
E7   SD1   2c blue ('36)   .20 .20
   Nos. E5-E7 (3)   .60 .60

1944, Oct. 23   **Perf. 12½**
E8   SD1   2c salmon pink   .20 .20

> **Catalogue values for unused stamps in this section, from this point to the end of the section, are for Never Hinged items.**

1947, Nov. 19
E9   SD1   2c red brown   .20 .20

No. E9 Surcharged with New Value
1957, Oct. 30
E10   SD1   5c on 2c red brown   .20 .20

LATE FEE STAMPS

Galleon and Modern Steamship — LF1

Wmk. Crossed Keys in Sheet
1936, May 18   **Litho.**   **Perf. 11**
I1   LF1   3c green   .20 .20
I2   LF1   5c violet   .20 .20
I3   LF1   6c blue green   .20 .20
I4   LF1   7c brown   .20 .20
I5   LF1   8c carmine   .35 .35
I6   LF1   12c deep blue   .50 .50
   Nos. I1-I6 (6)   1.65 1.65

POSTAGE DUE STAMPS

D1

1902   **Unwmk.**   **Engr.**   **Perf. 14 to 15**
Size: 21¼x18½mm
J1   D1   1c blue green   .30 .20
J2   D1   2c carmine   .35 .20
J3   D1   4c gray violet   .50 .20
J4   D1   10c dark blue   .75 .25
J5   D1   20c ocher   1.10 .60
   Nos. J1-J5 (5)   3.00 1.45

Surcharged in Red

1904
J6   D1   1c on 10c dk bl   .60 .60
   a.   Inverted surcharge   6.00 6.00

1913-15   **Litho.**   **Perf. 11½**
Size: 22½x20mm
J7   D1   1c lt grn   .35 .20
J8   D1   2c rose red   .35 .20
J9   D1   4c dl vio   .50 .20
J10   D1   6c dp brn   .60 .25
Size: 21¼x19mm
J11   D1   10c dl bl   .60 .20
   Nos. J7-J11 (5)   2.40 1.10

Imprint: "Imprenta Nacional"
1922
Size: 20x17mm
J12   D1   1c bl grn   .20 .20
J13   D1   2c red   .20 .20
J14   D1   3c red brn   .30 .25
J15   D1   4c brn vio   .20 .20

J16   D1   5c blue   .35 .20
J17   D1   10c gray grn   .40 .20
   Nos. J12-J17 (6)   1.65 1.25

1926-27   **Wmk. 188**   **Perf. 11**
Size: 20x17mm
J18   D1   1c bl grn ('27)   .20 .20
J19   D1   3c red brn ('27)   .30 .20
J20   D1   5c slate blue   .30 .20
J21   D1   6c light brown   .35 .30
   Nos. J18-J21 (4)   1.15 .90

1929   **Unwmk.**   **Perf. 10½, 11**
J22   D1   1c blue green   .20 .20
J23   D1   10c gray green   .25 .20

Figure of Value Redrawn
(Flat on sides)
1932   **Wmk. 188**
J24   D1   6c yel brn   .35 .25

Imprint: "Casa A. Barreiro Ramos S. A."
1935   **Unwmk.**   **Litho.**   **Perf. 12½**
Size: 20x17mm
J25   D1   4c violet   .30 .20
J26   D1   5c rose   .30 .20

Type of 1935
Imprint: "Imprenta Nacional" at right
1938
J27   D1   1c blue green   .20 .20
J28   D1   2c red brown   .20 .20
J29   D1   3c deep pink   .20 .20
J30   D1   4c light violet   .20 .20
J31   D1   5c blue   .20 .20
J32   D1   8c rose   .20 .20
   Nos. J27-J32 (6)   1.20 1.20

OFFICIAL STAMPS

Regular Issues Handstamped in Black, Red or Blue

Many double and inverted impressions exist of the handstamped overprints on Nos. O1-O83. Prices are the same as for normal stamps or slightly more.

On Stamps of 1877-79
1880-82   **Unwmk.**   **Rouletted 8**
O1   A9   1c red brown   4.00 3.50
O2   A10   5c green   3.00 2.50
O3   A11   20c bister   2.50 2.00
O4   A11   50c black   18.00 15.00
O5   A12   1p blue   20.00 16.00
   Nos. O1-O5 (5)   47.50 39.00

On No. 44
Rouletted 6
O6   A9   1c brown ('81)   4.00 3.50

On Nos. 43-43A
Rouletted 8
O7   A11   50c black (R)   15.00 14.00
O8   A12   1p blue (R)   22.50 20.00

On Nos. 45, 41, 37a
Perf. 12½
O9   A13   7c blue (R) ('81)   2.75 2.00
Rouletted 8
O10   A11   10c ver (Bl)   1.75 1.50
Perf. 13½
O11   A8b   15c yellow (Bl)   5.00 4.00

On Nos. 46-47
1883   **Perf. 12½**
O12   A14   1c green   6.00 5.00
O13   A14a   2c rose   5.00 5.00

On Nos. 50-51
Perf. 12½, 12x12½, 13
O14   A17   5c blue (R)   2.50 2.50
   a.   Imperf., pair   4.50
O15   A18   10c brown (Bl)   5.00 4.00
   a.   Imperf., pair   6.00

No. 48 Handstamped

1884   **Perf. 12½**
O16   A15   1c green   27.50 24.00

Overprinted Type "a" in Black
On Nos. 48-49
1884   **Perf. 12, 12x12½, 13**
O17   A15   1c green   27.50 24.00
O18   A16   2c red   10.00 8.00

On Nos. 53-56
Rouletted 8
O19   A11   1c on 10c ver   1.25 1.00
   a.   Small "1" (No. 53a)   5.00
Perf. 12½
O20   A14a   2c rose   4.00 4.00
O21   A22   5c ultra   4.00 4.00
O22   A23   5c blue   3.25 1.25
   Nos. O17-O22 (6)   50.00 42.25

On Stamps of 1884-88
1884-89   **Rouletted 8**
O23   A24   1c gray   8.00 3.50
O24   A24   1c green ('88)   1.50 .75
O25   A24   1c olive grn   2.00 1.00
O26   A24a   2c vermilion   .70 .40
O27   A24a   2c rose ('88)   1.40 .75
O28   A24b   5c slate blue   1.40 .75
O29   A24b   5c slate bl, *bl*   3.00 2.00
O30   A24b   5c violet ('88)   4.00 2.00
O31   A24b   5c lt blue ('89)   4.00 2.00
O32   A25   7c dk brown   2.00 1.00
O33   A25   7c orange ('89)   2.00 1.40
O34   A26   10c olive brn   1.25 .60
O35   A30   10c violet ('89)   10.00 6.00
O36   A27   20c red violet   2.00 1.00
O37   A27   20c bister brn ('89)   10.00 4.50
O38   A28   25c gray violet   3.50 2.50
O39   A28   25c vermilion ('89)   12.00 8.00
   Nos. O23-O39 (17)   68.75 38.15

The OFICIAL handstamp, type "a," was also applied to No. 73, the 5c violet with "Provisorio" overprint, but it was not regularly issued.

On No. 71
1887   **Rouletted 9**
O40   A29   10c lilac   4.00
   No. O40 was not regularly issued.

On Stamps of 1889-1899
Perf. 12½ to 15 and Compound
1890-1900
O41   A32   1c green   .50 .20
O43   A32   1c blue ('95)   1.10 1.10
O44   A33   2c rose   .50 .20
O45   A33   2c red brn ('95)   1.50 1.50
O46   A33   2c orange ('00)   .65 .30
O47   A34   5c deep blue   1.00 1.00
O48   A34   5c rose ('95)   2.00 2.00
O49   A35   7c bister brown   .75 .50
O50   A35   7c green ('95)   19.00
O51   A36   10c blue green   .75 .65
O52   A36   10c orange ('95)   19.00
O53   A37   20c orange   .75 .65
O54   A37   20c brown ('95)   19.00
O55   A38   25c red brown   .75 .65
O56   A38   25c ver ('95)   37.50
O57   A39   50c lt blue   3.50 3.50
O58   A39   50c lilac ('95)   4.00 4.00
O59   A40   1p lilac   7.00 5.00
O60   A40   1p lt blue ('95)   35.00 17.50
   Nos. O50, O52, O54, O56 and O60 were not regularly issued.

On No. 99
1891   **Rouletted 8**
O61   A24b   5c violet   1.00 1.00
   a.   "1391"   9.00

On Stamps of 1895-99
Perf. 12½ to 15 and Compound
1895-1900
O62   A51   1c bister   .20 .20
O63   A51   1c slate blue ('97)   .45 .25
O64   A52   2c blue   .20 .20
O65   A52   2c claret ('97)   .75 .50
O66   A53   5c red   .50 .35
O67   A53   5c green ('97)   .75 .45
O68   A53   5c grnsh blue ('00)   .75 .65
O69   A54   7c deep green   .35 .35
O70   A55   10c brown   .35 .35
O71   A56   20c green & blk   .50 .50
O72   A56   20c claret & blk ('97)   3.00 1.50
O73   A57   25c red brn & blk   .55 .55
O74   A57   25c pink & bl ('97)   3.00 1.50
O75   A58   50c blue & blk   .75 .75

O76   A58   50c grn & brn ('97)   4.00 1.5
O77   A59   1p org brn & blk   4.00 4.0
O78   A59   1p yel brn & bl ('97)   7.00 5.0
   a.   Inverted overprint
   Nos. O62-O78 (17)   27.10 18.6

On Nos. 133-135
1897, Sept.
O79   A62   1c brown vio & blk   1.00 1.0
O80   A63   5c pale bl & blk   1.25 1.0
O81   A64   10c lake & blk   1.25 .7
   Nos. O79-O81 (3)   3.50 2.7

On Nos. 136-137
Perf. 12½ to 15 and Compound
1897-1900
O82   A68   10c red   2.50 1.5
O83   A68   10c red lilac ('00)   1.25 1.2

Regular Issue of 1900-01 Overprinted
1901   **Perf. 14 to 1**
O84   A72   1c yellow green   .25 .2
O85   A75   2c vermilion   .30 .2
O86   A73   5c dull blue   .30 .2
O87   A76   7c brown orange   .40 .4
O88   A74   10c gray violet   .45 .4
O89   A37   20c lt blue   5.00 4.0
O90   A38   25c bister brown   .75 .6
O91   A40   1p deep green   9.00 6.0
   a.   Inverted overprint   12.50 8.
   Nos. O84-O91 (8)   16.45 12.1

Most of the used official stamps of 190 1928 have been punched with holes of variou shapes, in addition to the postal cancellation

Regular Issue of 1904-05 Overprinted
1905   **Perf. 11**
O92   A79   1c green   .25 .2
O93   A80   2c orange red   .25 .2
O94   A81   5c deep blue   .25 .2
O95   A82   10c dark violet   .50 .3
O96   A83   20c gray green   1.50 .9
   a.   Inverted overprint
O97   A84   25c olive bister   1.00 .6
   Nos. O92-O97 (6)   3.75 2.4

Regular Issues of 1904-07 Overprinted
1907, Mar.
O98   A79   1c green   .20 .2
O99   A86   5c deep blue   .20 .2
O100   A86   7c orange brown   .20 .2
O101   A82   10c dark violet   .20 .2
O102   A83   20c gray green   .30 .2
   a.   Inverted overprint   4.00
O103   A84   25c olive bister   .30 .3
O104   A86   50c rose   .60 .5
   Nos. O98-O104 (7)   2.00 1.8

Regular Issues of 1900-10 Overprinted

OFICIAL 1910

1910, July 15   **Perf. 14½ to 1**
O105   A75   2c vermilion   6.00 3.5
O106   A73   5c slate green   4.00 3.0
O107   A74   10c gray violet   2.00 1.2
O108   A37   20c grnsh blue   2.00 1.0
O109   A38   25c bister brown   3.00 2.0
Perf. 11½
O110   A86   50c rose   5.00 2.5
   a.   Inverted overprint   20.00 15.0
   Nos. O105-O110 (6)   22.00 13.2

Peace—O1

1911, Feb. 18   Litho.
O111	O1	2c red brown	.35	.20
O112	O1	5c dark blue	.35	.20
O113	O1	8c slate	.35	.20
O114	O1	20c gray brown	.50	.25
O115	O1	23c claret	.75	.35
O116	O1	50c orange	1.00	.60
O117	O1	1p red	3.00	1.00
	Nos. O111-O117 (7)		6.30	2.80

Regular Issue of
1912-15 Overprinted

1915, Sept. 16
O118	A90	2c carmine	.50	.35
O119	A90	5c dark blue	.50	.35
O120	A90	8c ultra	.50	.35
O121	A90	20c dark brown	1.10	.45
O122	A91	23c dark blue	3.00	2.50
O123	A91	50c orange	5.00	2.50
O124	A91	1p vermilion	8.00	4.00
	Nos. O118-O124 (7)		18.60	10.50

Regular Issue of 1919
Overprinted

1919, Dec. 25
O125	A95	2c red & black	.70	.20
a.	Inverted overprint		3.50	
O126	A95	5c ultra & blk	.90	.35
O127	A95	8c gray bl & lt brn	.90	.35
a.	Inverted overprint		3.50	
O128	A95	20c brown & blk	1.75	.60
O129	A95	23c green & brn	1.75	.60
O130	A95	50c brown & bl	2.50	1.25
O131	A95	1p dull red & bl	10.00	4.00
a.	Double overprint		15.00	
	Nos. O125-O131 (7)		18.50	7.35

Regular Issue of 1923
Overprinted

1924   Wmk. 189   Perf. 12½
O132	A100	2c violet	.20	.20
O133	A100	5c light blue	.20	.20
O134	A100	12c deep blue	.30	.20
O135	A100	20c buff	.35	.20
O136	A100	36c blue green	1.25	.90
O137	A100	50c orange	2.75	1.90
O138	A100	1p pink	6.00	4.00
O139	A100	2p lt green	12.00	10.00
	Nos. O132-O139 (8)		23.05	17.60

Same Overprint on Regular Issue of
1924

1926-27   Unwmk.   Imperf.
O140	A100	2c rose lilac	.35	.20
O141	A100	5c pale blue	.50	.20
O142	A100	8c pink ('27)	.55	.20
O143	A100	12c slate blue	.75	.20
O144	A100	20c brown	1.25	.35
O145	A100	36c dull rose	2.50	.75
	Nos. O140-O145 (6)		5.90	1.90

Regular Issue of 1924
Overprinted

1928   Perf. 12½
O146	A100	2c rose lilac	1.25	.75
O147	A100	8c pink	1.25	.30
O148	A100	10c turq blue	1.75	.30
	Nos. O146-O148 (3)		4.25	1.35

Since 1928, instead of official stamps, Uruguay has used envelopes with "S. O." printed on them, and stamps of many issues which are punched with various designs such as star or crescent.

NEWSPAPER STAMPS

No. 245 Surcharged

1922, June 1   Unwmk.   Perf. 11½
P1	A97	3c on 4c orange	.25	.25
a.	Inverted surcharge		6.00	6.00
b.	Double surcharge		2.50	2.50

Nos. 235-237
Surcharged

1924, June 1   Perf. 14½
P2	A96	3c on 2c car & blk	.30	.25
P3	A96	6c on 4c red org & bl	.30	.25
P4	A96	9c on 5c bl & brn	.30	.25
	Nos. P2-P4 (3)		.90	.75

Nos. 288, 291, 293 Overprinted or
Surcharged in Red:

          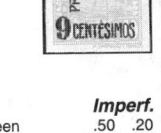

1926   Imperf.
P5	A100	3c gray green	.50	.20
a.	Double overprint		1.00	1.00
P6	A100	9c on 10c turq bl	.60	.35
a.	Double surcharge		1.00	1.00
P7	A100	15c light violet	.75	.45
	Nos. P5-P7 (3)		1.85	1.00

PARCEL POST STAMPS

Mercury — PP1

Imprint: "IMPRENTA NACIONAL"
Perf. 11½

1922, Jan. 15   Litho.   Unwmk.
Size: 20x29½mm
Inscribed "Exterior"
Q1	PP1	5c grn, *straw*	.20	.20
Q2	PP1	10c grn, *bl gray*	.30	.20
Q3	PP1	20c grn, *rose*	1.50	.45
Q4	PP1	30c grn, *grn*	1.40	.20
Q5	PP1	50c grn, *blue*	2.50	.20
Q6	PP1	1p grn, *org*	4.50	1.00
	Nos. Q1-Q6 (6)		10.40	2.25

Inscribed "Interior"
Q7	PP1	5c grn, *straw*	.20	.20
Q8	PP1	10c grn, *bl gray*	.20	.20
Q9	PP1	20c grn, *rose*	.65	.20
Q10	PP1	30c grn, *grn*	1.10	.20
Q11	PP1	50c grn, *blue*	1.50	.25
Q12	PP1	1p grn, *org*	5.00	1.00
	Nos. Q7-Q12 (6)		8.65	2.05

Imprint: "IMP. NACIONAL"
Inscribed "Exterior"

1926, Jan. 20   Perf. 11½
Q13	PP1	20c grn, *rose*	1.75	.50

Inscribed "Interior"
Perf. 11
Q14	PP1	5c grn, *yellow*	.30	.20
Q15	PP1	10c grn, *bl gray*	.35	.20
Q16	PP1	20c grn, *rose*	.90	.20
Q17	PP1	30c grn, *bl grn*	1.25	.25
	Nos. Q13-Q17 (5)		4.55	1.35

Inscribed "Exterior"

1926
Q18	PP1	5c blk, *straw*	.25	.20
Q19	PP1	10c blk, *bl gray*	.40	.20
Q20	PP1	20c blk, *rose*	1.10	.20

Inscribed "Interior"
Q21	PP1	5c blk, *straw*	.25	.20
Q22	PP1	10c blk, *bl gray*	.30	.20
Q23	PP1	20c blk, *rose*	.60	.20
Q24	PP1	30c blk, *bl grn*	1.10	.20
	Nos. Q18-Q24 (7)		4.00	1.40

PP2   PP3

Perf. 11, 11½
1927, Feb. 22   Wmk. 188
Q25	PP2	1c dp bl	.20	.20
Q26	PP2	2c lt grn	.20	.20
Q27	PP2	4c violet	.20	.20
Q28	PP2	5c red	.20	.20
Q29	PP2	10c dk brn	.25	.20
Q30	PP2	20c orange	.35	.20
	Nos. Q25-Q30 (6)		1.40	1.20

See Nos. Q35-Q38, Q51-Q54.

1928, Nov. 20   Perf. 11
Size: 15x20mm
Q31	PP3	5c blk, *straw*	.20	.20
Q32	PP3	10c blk, *gray blue*	.20	.20
Q33	PP3	20c blk, *rose*	.30	.20
Q34	PP3	30c blk, *green*	.50	.20
	Nos. Q31-Q34 (4)		1.20	.80

Type of 1927 Issue
1929-30   Unwmk.   Perf. 11, 12½
Q35	PP2	1c violet	.20	.20
Q36	PP2	1c ultra ('30)	.20	.20
Q37	PP2	2c bl grn ('30)	.20	.20
Q38	PP2	5c red ('30)	.20	.20
	Nos. Q35-Q38 (4)		.80	.80

Nos. Q35-Q38, and possibly later issues, occasionally show parts of a papermaker's watermark.

PP4

1929, July 27   Wmk. 188   Perf. 11
Q39	PP4	10c orange	.50	.50
Q40	PP4	15c slate blue	.50	.50
Q41	PP4	20c ol brn	.50	.50
Q42	PP4	25c rose red	1.00	.50
Q43	PP4	50c dark gray	2.00	1.00
Q44	PP4	75c violet	8.00	6.00
Q45	PP4	1p gray green	7.50	3.00
	Nos. Q39-Q45 (7)		20.00	12.00

For overprints see Nos. Q57-Q63.

Ship and   Numeral of
Train — PP5   Value — PP6

1938-39   Unwmk.   Perf. 12½
Q46	PP5	10c scarlet	.35	.20
Q47	PP5	20c dk bl	.50	.20
Q48	PP5	30c lt vio ('39)	.75	.20
Q49	PP5	50c green	1.10	.20
Q50	PP5	1p brn org	2.00	1.10
	Nos. Q46-Q50 (5)		4.70	1.90

See #Q70-Q73, Q80, Q88-Q90, Q92-Q93, Q95.

Type of 1927 Redrawn
1942-55?   Litho.   Perf. 12½
Q51	PP2	1c vio ('55)		
Q52	PP2	2c bl grn	.20	.20
Q54	PP2	5c lt red ('44)	.20	.20

The vertical and horizontal lines of the design have been strengthened, the "2"

redrawn, etc. No. Q51 has oval "O" in CENTESIMO, 2¼mm from frame line at right; No. Q35 has round "O" 1¾mm from frame line.

1943, Apr. 28   Engr.
Q55	PP6	1c dk car rose	.20	.20
Q56	PP6	2c grnsh blk	.20	.20

Parcel Post
Stamps of
1929
Overprinted in
Black

1943, Dec. 15   Wmk. 188   Perf. 11
Q57	PP4	10c orange	1.00	.50
Q58	PP4	15c slate blue	1.00	.50
Q59	PP4	20c olive brn	1.00	.50
Q60	PP4	25c rose red	1.50	1.00
Q61	PP4	50c dk gray	2.50	2.00
Q62	PP4	75c violet	5.00	4.00
Q63	PP4	1p gray grn	8.00	4.50
	Nos. Q57-Q63 (7)		20.00	13.00

> Catalogue values for unused stamps in this section, from this point to the end of the section, are for Never Hinged items.

Bank of the   University — PP8
Republic — PP7

Perf. 12½
1945, Sept. 5   Litho.   Unwmk.
Q64	PP7	1c green	.20	.20
Q65	PP8	2c brt vio	.20	.20

See Nos. Q77-Q79, Q84.

Custom   Type A141
House — PP9   Overprinted

1946, Dec. 11   Perf. 11½
Q66	PP9	5c yel brn & bl	.20	.20

Red Overprint
1946, Dec. 27   Perf. 12½
Q67	A141	1p light blue	.70	.20

See Nos. Q69, Q76.

Mail   Type A141
Coach — PP11   Overprinted

1946, Dec. 23
Q68	PP11	5p red & ol brn	12.00	5.00

Black Overprint
1947
Q69	A141	2c dull violet brn	.20	.20

See Nos. Q74-Q76.

Type of 1938
1947-52   Unwmk.   Perf. 12½
Q70	PP5	5c brown org ('52)	.20	.20
Q71	PP5	10c violet	.20	.20
Q72	PP5	20c vermilion	.25	.20
Q73	PP5	30c blue	.50	.20
	Nos. Q70-Q73 (4)		1.15	.80

Type of 1947
Black Overprint

1948-49
Q74　A141　1c rose lilac ('49)　　.20　.20
Q75　A141　5c ultra　　　　　　.20　.20
Q76　A141　5p rose carmine　　3.25 1.25
　　　Nos. Q74-Q76 (3)　　　　3.65 1.65

Types of 1945

1950
Q77　PP8　1c vermilion　　　　.20　.20
Q78　PP7　2c chalky blue　　　.20　.20

1952　　　　　　　　　　*Perf. 11*
Q79　PP7　10c blue green　　　.20　.20

Type of 1938-39

1954　　　　　　　　　　*Perf. 12½*
Q80　PP5　20c carmine　　　　.20　.20

Custom House — PP13

1p, State Railroad Administration Building.

1955　*Unwmk.*　*Litho.*　*Perf. 12½*
Q81　PP13　5c brown　　　　　.20　.20
Q82　PP13　1p light ultra　　2.00 1.50
　　See Nos. Q83, Q85-Q86, Q96. For surcharge see No. Q87.

Types of 1945 and 1955
Design: 20c, Solis Theater.

1956-57　　　　　　　　　*Perf. 11*
Q83　PP13　5c gray ('57)　　　.30　.20
Q84　PP7　10c lt olive grn　　.20　.20
Q85　PP13　20c yellow　　　　.20　.20
Q86　PP13　20c lt red brn ('57)　.20　.20
　　　Nos. Q83-Q86 (4)　　　　.90　.80

No. Q83 Surcharged with New Value in Red

1957
Q87　PP13　30c on 5c gray　　.20　.20

Type of 1938-39

1957-60　　*Wmk. 327*　　*Perf. 11*
Q88　PP5　20c lt blue ('59)　　.20　.20
　　　　　　Unwmk.
Q89　PP5　30c red lilac　　　　.20　.20
　　　　　　Perf. 12½
Q90　PP5　1p dk blue ('60)　　.25　.25
　　　Nos. Q88-Q90 (3)　　　　.65　.65
　　Nos. Q88 and Q93 are in slightly larger format-17¼x21mm instead of 16x19½mm.

National
Printing
Works
PP14

1960, Mar. 23　*Wmk. 327*　*Perf. 11*
Q91　PP14　30c yellow green　.20　.20

Type of 1938-39

1962-63　　*Wmk. 332*　　*Perf. 11*
Q92　PP5　50c slate green　　.20　.20
　　　　　　Perf. 10½
Q93　PP5　1p blue grn ('63)　　.40　.40

No. C158
Surcharged

1965　　*Unwmk.*　　　*Perf. 11*
Q94　AP12　5p on 84c orange　.30　.20
　For use on regular and air post parcels.

Types of 1938-55
1p, State Railroad Administration Building.

1966　　*Litho.*　　*Perf. 10½*
Q95　PP5　10c blue green　　.20　.20
　　　　　Wmk. 327
Q96　PP13　1p brown　　　　.20　.20

No. C184
Surcharged in Red

1966　　*Unwmk.*　　*Perf. 11*
Q97　AP21　1p on 38c black　.20　.20

Plane and
Bus — PP15

Design: 20p, Plane facing left and bus; "Encomiendas" on top.

　　　　Wmk. 332
1969, July 8　*Litho.*　*Perf. 12*
Q98　PP15　10p blk, crim & bl grn　.20　.20
Q99　PP15　20p bl, blk & yel　　.30　.20

Encomiendas
No. B7 Surcharged　　**$ 0.60**

1971, Feb. 3　*Wmk. 327*　*Perf. 11½*
Q100　SP2　60c on 1p + 10c　.60　.60

No. 761 Surcharged in Red

IMPUESTOS A ENCOMIENDAS $0.60

1971, Nov. 12　*Wmk. 332*　*Perf. 12*
Q101　A226　60c on 6p lt grn & blk　.25　.25

Nos. 770-771 Surcharged

1972, Nov. 6　　*Litho.*　　*Perf. 12*
Q102　A233　1p on 6p multi (#770)　.30　.30
Q103　A233　1p on 6p multi (#771)　.30　.30
　a.　Pair, #Q102-Q103　　　.60　.60
　　See note after No. 771.

Parcels and
Arrows
PP16

Old Mail
Truck
PP17

Designs: Early means of mail transport.

1974　*Wmk. 332*　*Litho.*　*Perf. 12*
Q104　PP16　75p shown　　　.20　.20
Q105　PP17　100p shown　　　.25　.25
Q106　PP17　150p Steam engine　.25　.25
Q107　PP17　300p Side-wheeler　.60　.45
Q108　PP17　500p Plane　　　1.00　.75
　　　Nos. Q104-Q108 (5)　　2.30 1.85
　Issue dates: 75p, Feb. 13; others, Mar. 6.

ADVANTAGE STOCKSHEETS

Designed with the collector in mind, Advantage stock sheets fit directly in your 2-post or 3-ring National or Specialty album. For unprecedented durability and flexibility choose Advantage Stocksheets. Choose from 1 to 8 pockets.
Sheets are sold in packages of 10.

- Stock sheets match album pages in every respect, including border, size, and color.
- Punched and drilled to fit perfectly in binder
- Available with 1 to 8 pockets. Ideal for storing minor varieties and collateral material. A great place to keep new issues until the next supplement is available.
- Provide the protection and durability of crystal clear acetate pockets on heavyweight pages.

NATIONAL BORDER

ITEM			RETAIL
AD11	1 Pocket	242mm	$15.99
AD12	2 Pockets	119mm	$15.99
AD13	3 Pockets	79mm	$15.99
AD14	4 Pockets	58mm	$15.99
AD15	5 Pockets	45mm	$15.99
AD16	6 Pockets	37mm	$15.99
AD17	7 Pockets	31mm	$15.99
AD18	8 Pockets	31mm	$15.99

SPECIALTY BORDER

AD21	1 Pocket	242mm	$15.99
AD22	2 Pockets	119mm	$15.99
AD23	3 Pockets	79mm	$15.99
AD24	4 Pockets	58mm	$15.99
AD25	5 Pockets	45mm	$15.99
AD26	6 Pockets	37mm	$15.99
AD27	7 Pockets	31mm	$15.99
AD28	8 Pockets	31mm S	$15.99

Available from your favorite stamp dealer or direct from:

SCOTT

1-800-572-6885
P.O. Box 828,
Sidney OH 45365
www.amosadvantage.com

AMOS
HOBBY PUBLISHING

UZBEKISTAN

ₑᵦuz-ˌbe-ki-'stan

LOCATION — Central Asia, bounded by Kazakhstan, Turkmenistan, Tajikistan, Afghanistan and Kyrgyzstan
GOVT. — Independent republic, member of the Commonwealth of Independent States
AREA — 172,741 sq. mi.
POP. — 25,155,064 (2001 est.)
CAPITAL — Tashkent (Toshkent)

With the breakup of the Soviet Union on Dec. 26, 1991, Uzbekistan and ten former Soviet republics established the Commonwealth of Independent States.

100 Kopecks = 1 Ruble
100 Tiyin = 1 Sum

Catalogue values for all unused stamps in this country are for Never Hinged items.

Princess Nadira (1792-1842) — A1

1992, May 7   Unwmk.   Photo.
1   A1   20k multicolored   .30   .30

Melitaea Acreina A2

1992, Aug. 31   Litho.   Perf. 12
2   A2   1r multicolored   .25   .25

Independence from Soviet Union, 1st Anniv. — A3

1992, Sept. 25   Photo.   Perf. 12
3   A3   1r multicolored   .25   .25

Khiva Mosque, 19th Cent. — A4

1992, Oct. 20   Perf. 11½
4   A4   50k multicolored   .20   .20

Samarkand — A5

1992, Oct. 28   Litho.   Perf. 13x13½
5   A5   10r multicolored   .40   .40

Winner of 1992 Aga Khan Award for Architecture.

Samovar, 19th Cent. — A6

1992, Nov. 20   Perf. 12x11½
6   A6   50k multicolored   .35   .35

Fauna A7

Designs: 1r, Teratoscincus scincus. No. 8, Naja oxiana. No. 9, Ondatra zibethica, vert. 3r, Pandion haliaetus, vert. 5r, Remiz pendulinus, vert. 10r, Dryomys nitedula, vert. 15r, Varanus griseus. 20r, Cervus elaphus baktrianus.

1993, Mar. 12   Litho.   Perf. 12
7   A7   1r multicolored   .20   .20
8   A7   2r multicolored   .20   .20
9   A7   2r multicolored   .20   .20
10   A7   3r multicolored   .20   .20
11   A7   10r multicolored   .20   .20
12   A7   10r multicolored   .35   .35
13   A7   15r multicolored   .55   .55
      Nos. 7-13 (7)   1.90   1.90

Souvenir Sheet
14   A7   20r multicolored   .75   .75

Russia Nos. 4596-4600, 5838, 5841-5843, 5984 Surcharged in Vio Bl, Brt Bl, Bl, Red, Blk and Grn

a

Methods and perfs as before
1993
15   A2765   2r on 1k (#5838,
               BB)   .30   .30
16   A2138   8r on 4k (#4599,
               Bl)   .25   .25
17   A2138   15r on 2k (#4597)   1.50   1.50
18   A2765   15r on 2k (#5984)   1.50   1.50
19   A2765   15r on 3k (#5839,
               R)   1.50   1.50
20   A2765   15r on 4k (#4520,
               V)   1.50   1.50
21   A2765   15r on 4k (#5840,
               R)   1.50   1.50
22   A2765   15r on 5k (#5841)   1.50   1.50
23   A2139   15r on 6k (#4600,
               R)   1.50   1.50
24   A2765   15r on 7k
               (#5985a, R)   1.50   1.50
25   A2765   15r on 10k
               (#5842)   1.50   1.50
26   A2765   15r on 15k
               (#5843, R)   1.50   1.50
27   A2138   20r on 4k (#4599,
               Bk)   .45   .45
28   A2139   30r on 3k (#4598,
               G)   .45   .45
28A   A2138   100r on 1k (#4596,
               R)   .65   .65

---

29   A2138   500r on 1k (#4596,
               Bl)   3.00   3.00
      Nos. 15-29 (16)   20.10 20.10

No. 18 exists imperf. Numbers have been reserved for additional stamps with uncertain status.

Flag and Coat of Arms — A8

Perf. 12x12½, 11½x12 (#33)
1993, June 10   Litho.
30   A8   8r multicolored   .20   .20
31   A8   15r multicolored   .20   .20
33   A8   50r multicolored   .60   .60
34   A8   100r multicolored   1.25   1.25
      Nos. 30-34 (4)   2.25   2.25

No. 33 is 19x26½mm.

Flowers — A9

1993, Sept. 10   Perf. 12
38   A9   20r Dianthus uzbekis-
            tanicus   .20   .20
39   A9   20r Colchicum kesselr-
            ingii   .20   .20
40   A9   25r Crocus alatavicus   .20   .20
41   A9   25r Salvia bucharica   .20   .20
42   A9   30r Tulipa kaufmanniana   .20   .20
43   A9   30r Tulipa greigii   .20   .20
      Nos. 38-43 (6)   1.20   1.20

Souvenir Sheet
44   A9   50r Tulip   .50   .50

Coat of Arms — A10

1994, July 2   Litho.   Perf. 12
45   A10   1t green   .20   .20
                         Perf. 11½x12
46   A10   75s claret   .25   .25

1995   Litho.   Perf. 14
47   A10   2s green   .20   .20
                    Size: 20x33mm
48   A10   3s carmine   .20   .20
49   A10   6s carmine   .40   .40
49A   A10   15s blue   .90   .90

Denomination Shown with Decimal
50   A10   3s carmine   .25   .25
51   A10   6s blue   .50   .50
      Nos. 45-51 (8)   2.90   2.90

Issued: 15s, 12/26; others, 4/18.
See Nos. 151A-154.

Statue of Tamerlane, Tashkent — A10a

1994, Sept. 1   Litho.   Perf. 12½x12
52   A10a   20t multicolored   .20   .20

Bakhouddin, 675th Anniv. — A11

1994, Aug. 1   Perf. 12½x12
55   A11   100s multi + label   .25   .25

Souvenir Sheet

President's Cup Intl. Tennis Tournament, Tashkent — A12

1994, June 3   Perf. 12x12½
56   A12   500s multicolored   .70   .70

Ulugh Beg (1394-1449), Astronomer — A13

30t, Portals of Samarkand. 35t, Portals of Bukhara. 40t, Globe, astrolabe. 45t, Statue. 60t, Portrait.

1994, Sept. 15   Litho.   Perf. 12x12½
57   A13   30t multi + label   .20   .20
58   A13   35t multi + label   .20   .20
59   A13   40t multi + label   .20   .20
60   A13   45t multi + label   .20   .20
      Nos. 57-60 (4)   .80   .80

Souvenir Sheet
61   A13   60t multicolored   .35   .35

Russia Nos. 4596, 5113, 5839, 5840, 5843, 5984 Surcharged in Red Violet or Red

b

Methods and perfs as before
1995, Jan.
61A   A2138(a)   2s on 1k
                  (#4596, R)   .80   .80
61B   A2765(a)   2s on 3k
                  (#5839, R)   .80   .80
61C   A2765(b)   200s on 2k
                  (#5984)   .80   .80
61D   A2765(b)   200s on 4k
                  (#5840)   .80   .80
61E   A2436(b)   200s on 5k
                  (#5113)   .80   .80
61F   A2765(b)   200s on 15k
                  (#5843)   .80   .80
      Nos. 61A-61F (6)   4.80   4.80

No. 61C exists imperf.

Souvenir Sheet

End of World War II, 50th Anniv. — A14

1995, May 8   Litho.   Perf. 12
62 A14 20s multicolored   1.60 1.60

Souvenir Sheet

UPU — A15

1995, Sept. 21
63 A15 20s multicolored   1.25 1.25

Capra Falconeri A16

1995, Aug. 15   Perf. 12½
64 A16 6s shown   .35 .35
65 A16 10s Three on mountain .50 .50
66 A16 10s Up close   .50 .50
67 A16 15s Lying down   .80 .80
    Nos. 64-67 (4)   2.15 2.15
World Wildlife Fund.

Intl. Tennis Tournament, Tashkent '95 — A17

1995, Aug. 25   Perf. 14
68 A17 10s multicolored   .65 .65

Silk Road Architecture A19

Designs: 6s, Mosque, 15th cent. No. 71, Blue-domed mosque, ruins, 15th cent. No. 72, Mosque with 4 minarets, 19th cent. No. 73, Cylindrical-style mosque, 19th cent. 20s, Map of mosque sites, camel, mosque.

1995, Aug. 28   Litho.   Perf. 12x12½
70 A19 6s multicolored   .35 .35
71 A19 10s multicolored   .50 .50
72 A19 10s multicolored   .50 .50
73 A19 15s multicolored   .75 .75
    Nos. 70-73 (4)   2.10 2.10
Souvenir Sheet
74 A19 20s multicolored   1.25 1.25

Folktales — A20

6s, Man wrestling with creature, woman spilling bowls. #76, Man looking at stork, nest of eggs. #77, Women watching man cut into watermelon full of gold coins. #78, Creature carrying woman. 15s, Man holding beads, parrot.

1995, Aug. 24
75 A20 6s multi + label   .35 .35
76 A20 10s multicolored   .60 .60
77 A20 10s multicolored   .60 .60
78 A20 10s multicolored   .60 .60
79 A20 15s multicolored   .75 .75
    Nos. 75-79 (5)   2.90 2.90

Moths A21

6s, Karanasa abramovi. #81, Colias romanovi. #82, Parnassius delphius. #83, Neohipparchia fatua. #84, Chasara staudingeri. #85, Colias wiskotti. 15s, Parnassius tianschanicus. 20s, Colias christophi.

1995, Oct. 10   Perf. 12½x12
80 A21 6s multicolored   .35 .35
81 A21 10s multicolored   .60 .60
82 A21 10s multicolored   .60 .60
83 A21 10s multicolored   .60 .60
84 A21 10s multicolored   .60 .60
85 A21 10s multicolored   .60 .60
86 A21 15s multicolored   .90 .90
    Nos. 80-86 (7)   4.25 4.25
Souvenir Sheet
87 A21 20s multicolored   1.25 1.25

Aircraft A22

1995, Oct. 10
88 A22 6s JIN-2   .35 .35
89 A22 10s IL-76   .60 .60
90 A22 10s KA-22   .60 .60
91 A22 10s AN-8   .60 .60
92 A22 10s AN-22   .60 .60
93 A22 10s AN-12   .60 .60
94 A22 15s IL-114   .90 .90
    Nos. 88-94 (7)   4.25 4.25
Souvenir Sheet
95 A22 20s like No. 94   1.25 1.25

Wildlife from Tashkent Zoo — A23

Designs: 6s, Camelus ferus. No. 97, Aegupius monachus. No. 98, Ursus arctos isabellinus. No. 99, Zebra. No. 100, Macaca mulatta. No. 101, Pelecanus crispus. 15s, Loxodonta africana. 20s, Capra falconeri.

1995, Nov. 30   Perf. 12x12½
96 A23 6s multicolored   .35 .35
97 A23 10s multicolored   .60 .60
98 A23 10s multicolored   .60 .60
99 A23 10s multicolored   .60 .60
100 A23 10s multicolored   .60 .60
101 A23 10s multicolored   .60 .60
102 A23 15s multicolored   .95 .95
    Nos. 96-102 (7)   4.30 4.30
Souvenir Sheet
103 A23 20s multicolored   1.40 1.40

Wild Animals A24

Designs: 10s, Ovis ammon bocharensis. No. 105, Ovis ammon severtzov. No. 106, Cervus elaphus bactrianus. No. 107, Capra sibirica. No. 108, Ovis ammon karelini. No. 109, Ovis ammon cycloceros. 20s, Saiga tatarica.
25s, Gazella subgutturosa.

1996, Feb. 16   Perf. 12½x12
104 A24 10s multicolored   .50 .50
105 A24 15s multicolored   .75 .75
106 A24 15s multicolored   .75 .75
107 A24 15s multicolored   .75 .75
108 A24 15s multicolored   .75 .75
109 A24 15s multicolored   .75 .75
110 A24 20s multicolored   1.00 1.00
    Nos. 104-110 (7)   5.25 5.25
Souvenir Sheet
111 A24 25s multicolored   1.40 1.40

Painting A25

1995, Oct.   Litho.   Perf. 12x12½
112 A25 15s multicolored   1.00 1.00

Souvenir Sheet

Save the Aral Sea — A26

a, 15s, Felis caracal. b, 15s, Salmo trutta aralensis. c, 20s, Hyaena hyaena. d, 20t, Pseudoscaphirynchus kaufmanni. e, 25t, Aspiolucius esocinus.

1996, May 15   Perf. 14
113 A26 Sheet of 5, #a.-e. 3.50 3.50

See Kazakhstan #145, Kyrgyzstan #107, Tadjikistan #91, Turkmenistan #52.

1996 Summer Olympic Games, Atlanta A27

1996, June 23   Litho.   Perf. 12½x1
114 A27 6s Soccer   .20 .2
115 A27 10s Equestrian event .35 .3
116 A27 15s Boxing   .50 .5
117 A27 20s Cycling   .70 .7
    Nos. 114-117 (4)   1.75 1.7

Souvenir Sheet

Tamerlane (1336-1405) — A28

1996, Aug. 31   Litho.   Perf. 14
118 A28 20s multicolored   2.10 2.1
a.   Inscribed "1336-1404," perf
      12x12½   4.50 4.5

Issued: No. 118a, 8/9/96.

Souvenir Sheet

Independence Day — A29

Illustration reduced.

1996, Aug. 27   Litho.   Perf. 12x12½
119 A29 20s multicolored   1.40 1.40

Tashkent Tennis Cup Championship A30

1996, Sept. 2   Litho.   Perf. 14
121 A30 12s green   .85 .85

A31

A32

1996, Sept. 18   Perf. 14
122 A31 15s Faijzulla Khodjaev   .85 .85

1996, Oct. 14   Litho.   Perf. 14
123 A32 15s black & buff   .85 .85
    Abdurauf Fitrat (1886-1996).

Futuristic Space Travel — A33

9s, Shuttle-type vehicle. #126, Vehicle in front of sun. #127, Sun's rays, vehicle traveling left. #128, Large vehicle, sun in distance. #129, Saucer-shaped vehicle landing on planet. 25s, Two men in cockpit.
30s, Two different space vehicles.

1997, Mar. 17
124	A33	9s multi, vert.	.35	.35
125	A33	15s shown	.55	.55
126	A33	15s multi	.55	.55
127	A33	15s multi	.55	.55
128	A33	15s multi, vert.	.55	.55
129	A33	15s multi, vert.	.55	.55
130	A33	25s multi, vert.	1.00	1.00
		Nos. 124-130 (7)	4.10	4.10

Souvenir Sheet
131	A33	30s multi, vert.	1.50	1.50

Fairy Tales A34

#132, Genie. #133, Bird. #134, Child holding mirror in front of couple. #135, Ape. #136, Face of creature, horse. #137, Large bird attacking deer. 30s, Two people kneeling before throne.
35s, Man on horse.

1997, Apr. 18
132	A34	15s multicolored	.60	.60
133	A34	15s multicolored	.60	.60
134	A34	20s multicolored	.80	.80
135	A34	20s multicolored	.80	.80
136	A34	25s multicolored	1.00	1.00
137	A34	25s multicolored	1.00	1.00
138	A34	30s multicolored	1.25	1.25
		Nos. 132-138 (7)	6.05	6.05

Souvenir Sheet
139	A34	35s multicolored	1.75	1.75

Abdulhamid Sulaymon, Birth Cent. — A35

1997, June 20
140	A35	6s lilac, black & gray	.25	.25

Pantera Pardus Tullianus A36

Designs: No. 142, Yawning. No. 143, Stretching. 25s, Walking on fallen tree. 30s, With mouth open.

1997, May 28
141	A36	9s multicolored	.35	.35
142	A36	15s multicolored	.65	.65
143	A36	15s multicolored	.65	.65
144	A36	25s multicolored	1.10	1.10
		Nos. 141-144 (4)	2.75	2.75

Souvenir Sheet
145	A36	30s multicolored	1.50	1.50

No. 145 contains one 30x40mm stamp.

Sites on Silk Road A37

In Bukhara: No. 146, Ancient citadel. No. 147, Tomb of Ismail Samani, vert.
In Khiva: No. 148, Minaret, vert. No. 149, Fortress wall with open door.
No. 150, Mosque, Bukhara. No. 151, Minaret, Khiva, diff., vert.

1997   Litho.   Perf. 14
146	A37	15s multicolored	.75	.75
147	A37	15s multicolored	.75	.75
148	A37	15s multicolored	.75	.75
149	A37	15s multicolored	.75	.75
		Nos. 146-149 (4)	3.00	3.00

Souvenir Sheets
150	A37	30s multicolored	1.50	1.50
151	A37	30s multicolored	1.50	1.50

Issued: Nos. 146-147, 150, 10/7; Nos. 148-149, 151, 10/8.

Arms Type of 1994 Redrawn
1998   Litho.   Perf. 14
Size: 14x22mm
151A	A10	2s green	.20	.20
152	A10	3s carmine	.20	.20
153	A10	6s green	.20	.20
153A	A10	12s green	.35	.35
153B	A10	15s red	.45	.45
154	A10	45s blue	1.25	1.25
		Nos. 151A-154 (6)	2.65	2.65

Nos. 152-154 have country name "O'ZBEKISTON" at top and "POCHTA 1998" at bottom.
#152, 153 exist dated 1999.
Issued: 6s, 2/25; 12s, 15s, 45s, 3/25; 2s, 4/16; 3s, 4/17.

Intl. Tennis Tournament, Tashkent A38

Emblem and: No. 155, President's Cup. No. 156, Tennis player. No. 157, Camel.

1997   Litho.   Perf. 14
155	A38	6s blue & grn	.75	.75
156	A38	6s blue & grn	.75	.75
157	A38	6s blue & grn	.75	.75
		Nos. 155-157 (3)	2.25	2.25

Automobiles — A39

a, 9s, Tico. b, 12s, Damas. c, 15s, Nexia.

1997, Sept. 19   Litho.   Perf. 14
158	A39	Block of 3, #a.-c. + label	2.25	2.25

Tennis Tournament A40

Sharq Taronlalari Intl. Music Festival A41

1998, Aug. 17   Litho.   Perf. 14
159	A40	15s multicolored	.65	.65

1998, July 15
160	A41	15s multicolored	.65	.65

Berdaq Monument A42

Kamoliddin Behzod, Poet A43

1998, Aug. 17
161	A42	15s blue & brown	.65	.65

1998, Aug. 17
162	A43	15s multicolored	.65	.65

Imam Al-Buxorily A44

Ahmad Al-Fargoni A45

1998, June 26
163	A44	15s multicolored	.65	.65

1998, June 26
164	A45	15s multicolored	.65	.65

Folktales A46

Designs: a, 8s, Woman holding baby. b, 10s, "Alpomish" over rainbow. c, 15s, Three men seated before fire. d, 15s, Man talking to man with sword. e, 18s, Man riding horse. f, 18s, Knight with longbow, squire with arrow. g, 20s, Swordmaker at work. h, 20s, Man fighting lion. i, 25s, Man, woman walking arm in arm.

1998, Nov. 27   Litho.   Perf. 14
165	A46	Sheet of 9, #a.-i.	3.25	3.25

No. 165 is a continuous design.

Arms Type of 1994 Redrawn
1999-2001   Litho.   Perf. 14
Size: 14x23mm
167	A10	5s blue green	.20	.20
168	A10	6s green	.20	.20
168A	A10	10s dk green	.20	.20
168B	A10	15s lt blue	.20	.20
168C	A10	17s dk blue	.20	.20
169	A10	30s blue	.20	.20
170	A10	40s rose	.20	.20
170A	A10	45s rose	.25	.25
a.		45s carmine, dated 2001	.20	.20
171	A10	60s rose car	.35	.35
		Nos. 167-171 (9)	2.00	2.00

Issued: 6s, 3/22/99. 5s, 60s, 1/17/01; 10s, 40s, 2/5/01. 15s, 17s, 30s, 45s, 12/5/00.
Nos. 167-171 have country name "O'ZBEKISTON" at top and "POCHTA" and year at bottom. Stamps issued in 2001 are inscribed "2000". No. 170 exists dated "2001." No. 168 is inscribed "6 so'm." No. 153 is inscribed "6-00."

Trains — A47

Locomotives: #172, OV steam, 1897-1917. #173, EA steam, 1931-35. 28s, FD steam, 1931-41. 36s, SO steam, 1934-52. #176, VL-22 electric. #177, KCh. 69s, TEP-6.

1999, May 11   Litho.   Perf. 14
172	A47	18s multicolored	.20	.20
173	A47	18s multicolored	.20	.20
174	A47	28s multicolored	.20	.20
175	A47	36s multicolored	.20	.20
176	A47	56s multicolored	.25	.25
177	A47	56s multicolored	.25	.25
178	A47	69s multicolored	.30	.30
		Nos. 172-178 (7)	1.60	1.60

A48

A49

Designs: 18s, Horse rearing.
No. 180, horiz.: a, 36s, Robed rider on horse. b, 28s, White horse. c, 69s, Jockey on race horse.
75s, Black horse, horiz.

1999, May 25
179	A48	18s multicolored	.20	.20
180	A48	Vert. strip of 3, #a.-c.	.60	.60

Souvenir Sheet
181	A48	75s multicolored	.35	.35

No. 180 printed in sheets of 8 stamps containing 2 strips and one each of Nos. 180a and 180c.

1999, June 8

Story of Badal Qorachi - #182: a, 18s, Woman, deer. b, 18s, Two archers on horses. c, 28s, Archer on horse. d, 36s, White giant. e, 56s, Black giant. f, 56s, Troll, cat, bones. g, Man, woman.
75s, Woman on sofa, demon, horiz.

182	A49	Sheet of 7, #a.-g. + label	1.40	1.40

Souvenir Sheet
183	A49	75s multicolored	.35	.35

A50   A51

Reptiles: No. 184, Trapelus sanguinolentus. No. 185, horiz.: a, 18s, Eremias arguta. b, 18s, Vipera ursinii. c, 28s, Phrynocephalus mystaceus. d, 36s, Agkistrodon halys. e, 56s, Eumeces schneideri. f, 69s, Vipera lebetina. 75s, Two lizards, horiz.

1999, June 22
184 A50 56s multicolored   .25   .25
185 A50 Sheet of 6, #a.-f.   1.10 1.10

Souvenir Sheet
186 A50 75s multicolored   .35   .35

1999, July 7
187 A51 45s light green & black   .20   .20
     UPU, 125th anniv.

A52

1999, July 21
188 A52 30s green & claret   .20   .20
Muhammadrizo Erniyozbek ogli-Ogahiy, poet.

A53

1999, Oct. 22   Litho.   Perf. 14x13¾
Birds of Prey: No. 189, Circaetus qallicus. No. 190, Falco tinnunculus. No. 191, Aquila chrysaetos. No. 192, Gyps fulvus. 36s, Falco cherrug. 56s, Gypaetus barbatus. 60s, Pandion haliaetus. 75s, Bird, hatchlings.

189 A53 15s multi   .20   .20
190 A53 15s multi   .20   .20
191 A53 18s multi   .20   .20
192 A53 18s multi   .20   .20
193 A53 36s multi   .20   .20
194 A53 56s multi   .25   .25
195 A53 60s multi   .30   .30
     Nos. 189-195 (7)   1.55 1.55

Souvenir Sheet
196 A53 75s multi   .35   .35

A54

A55

Soccer.

1999, Nov. 8
197 A54 15s Two players   .20   .20
198 A54 18s Two players, diff.   .20   .20
199 A54 28s Two players, diff.   .20   .20
200 A54 28s Player, goalie   .20   .20
201 A54 36s Player, goalie, diff.   .20   .20
202 A54 56s Two players, diff.   .25   .25
203 A54 69s Two players, diff.   .30   .30
     Nos. 197-203 (7)   1.55 1.55

Souvenir Sheet
Perf. 13¾x14
204 A54 75s Two players, horiz.   .35   .35

1999, Dec. 13   Litho.   Perf. 14x13¾
Prehistoric Animals: a, 28s, Meqaneura. b, 28s, Mesosaurus. c, 36s, Rhamphorhynchus. d, 36s, Styracosaurus albertensis. e, 56s, Trachodon annectens. f, 56s, Tarbosaurus bataar. g, 69s, Arsinoitherium. h, 75s, Phororhacos.

205 A55 Sheet of 8, #a.-h.   1.25 1.25

Uzbek National Circus — A56

28s, Woman and lion. # 207, 36s, Acrobat with bow and arrow. #208, 36s, Acrobat. #209, 56s, Clown on horse. #210, 56s, Two riders on horse. 69s, Wire walker.
100s, Woman, camels, llamas, horiz.

2000. Jan. 4   Perf. 14
206 A56 28s multi   .20   .20
207 A56 36s multi   .20   .20
208 A56 36s multi   .20   .20
209 A56 56s multi   .20   .20
210 A56 56s multi   .20   .20
211 A56 69s multi   .20   .20
     Nos. 206-211 (6)   1.20 1.20

Souvenir Sheet
212 A56 100s multi   .30   .30

Horses — A57

Designs: 69s, Horses pulling carriage. No. 214: a, 36s, Horse in dressage competition. b, 36s, Horse jumping fences. c, 56s, Horses in race. d, 56s, Horse jumping steeplechase fence. e, 75s, Horse with sulky. f, 75s, Race winner.

2000, Feb. 1
213 A57 69s multi   .20   .20

Sheet of 6
214 A57 #a.-f.   1.00 1.00

Ajiniyoz Qo'siboy, Poet — A58

2000, Mar. 31   Litho.   Perf. 14
215 A58 28s multi   .20   .20

Famous Uzbek Writers — A59

Designs: No. 216, 60s, Burhoniddin al Marg'inoliy. No. 217, 60s, Imam Abu mansur al-Moturidiy, horiz.

2000, Oct. 24
Stamp + label
216-217 A59 Set of 2   .80   .80

UN High Commissioner for Refugees, 50th Anniv. — A60

2000, Dec. 11
218 A60 125s multi + label   .80   .80

Bats
A61

Designs: 15s, Tadarida teniotis. 30s, Otonycteris hemrichi. 45s, Nyctalus lasiopterus, vert. 50s, Muotis frater, vert. 60s, Rhinolophus hipposideros, vert. 90s, Barbastella leucomelas, vert. 125s, Nyctalus noctula, vert. 160s, Unidentified bat, vert.

2001, Feb. 23   Perf. 13¾x14, 14x13¾
219-225 A61 Set of 7   2.40 2.40
Souvenir Sheet
226 A61 160s multi   .90   .90
     Dated 2000.

Native Costumes — A62

2001, Feb. 26   Perf. 14x13¾
227   Horiz. strip of 5 + label   2.10 2.10
  a. A62 45s multi   .25   .25
  b. A62 50s multi, diff.   .30   .30
  c. A62 60s multi, diff.   .35   .35
  d. A62 90s multi, diff.   .50   .50
  e. A62 125s multi, diff.   .80   .80
     Dated 2000.

Arms Type of 1994 Redrawn
2001-03   Litho.   Perf. 1
Size: 14x23mm
228 A10 15s emerald   .20   .2
229 A10 17s dull green   .20   .2
230 A10 20s dull green   .20   .2
231 A10 25s bright blue   .20   .2
232 A10 30s sky blue   .20   .2
232A A10 30s green   .20   .2
233 A10 33s gray blue   .20   .2
234 A10 45s red   .20   .2
235 A10 50s rose   .20   .2
236 A10 60s rose pink   .20   .2
237 A10 100s rose   .30   .3
     Nos. 228-237 (11)   2.30 2.3

     Issued: 15s, 17s, 25s, 33s, 50s, 60s, 100s 4/3; 20s, 30s, 4/11; 45s, 6/22.
     No. 237 exists dated "2003." No. 232A 5/26/03.

Ali Shir Nava'i (1441-1501), Poet — A63

2001, Apr. 11
238   Horiz. strip of 5 + label   1.40 1.40
  a. A63 60s Hayrat ul-abror   .20   .20
  b. A63 70s Farhod va Shirin   .20   .20
  c. A63 85s Layli va Majnun   .25   .25
  d. A63 90s Sab'ai sayyora   .25   .25
  e. A63 125s Saddi Iskandariy   .40   .40

World Environment Day — A64

2001, June 20
239 A64 100s multi   .30   .30

Avesto, 2700th Anniv. — A65

2001, June 20
240 A65 160s multi   .50   .50

Souvenir Sheet

Termiz, 2500th Anniv. — A66

2001, June 20
241 A66 175s multi   .55   .55

Souvenir Sheet

Independence, 10th Anniv. — A67

2001, June 20

| 242 | A67 | 175s multi | .55 | .55 |

Souvenir Sheet

Regional Communications
Cooperation — A68

2001, June 20

| 243 | A68 | 175s multi | .55 | .55 |

10th Anniv. of Independence Issue

Vertical Label

Horizontal
Label

Tourist
Hotel — A69

Monuments — A70

Inauguration of Pres. Islam
Karimov — A71

Pres.
Karimov at
United
Nations
A72

Pres.
Karimov at
Istanbul
Summit
A73

Hirmon
A74

Silk
Cocoons
A75

Fergana
Refinery
A76

Power
Station
A77

Daewoo
Auto
Factory
A78

Securities
Exchange
A79

Kamchik
Tunnel
A80

Pres.
Karimov
and US
Pres.
Clinton
A81

Pres.
Karimov
and
Russian
Pres.
Vladimir
Putin
A82

Pres.
Karimov
and
Japanese
Emperor
Akihito
A83

Pres.
Karimov
and
Chinese
Pres.
Jiang
Zemin
A84

Pres.
Karimov
and
German
Chancellor
Gerhard
Schröder
A85

Pres.
Karimov
and French
Pres.
Jacques
Chirac
A86

Pres.
Karimov
and British
Prime
Minister
John
Major
A87

Pres. Karimov and Iranian Pres. Ali
Mohammad Khatami — A88

Pres.
Karimov
and
Egyptian
Pres.
Hosni
Mubarak
A89

Pres.
Karimov
and Italian
Pres.
Carlos
Ciampi
A90

Pres.
Karimov
and Indian
Pres.
Kocheril
Narayanan
A91

Pres.
Karimov
and Pope
John Paul
II — A92

Textile
Workers
A93

Shurtan Gas
Complex — A94

Muborak
Refinery — A95

Oil Pipeline — A96

Solar
Collector
A97

Soldiers
with Flag
A98

Missiles
A99

Soldiers
Training
A100

Kurash
Sports
Complex
A101

New Year's Celebration — A102

Mother and
Child — A103

Wedding
A104

Bukhara
Refinery — A105

Nuclear Power
Plant — A106

A70 Designs: No. 245, Zahriddin Bobur Monument. No. 246, Amir Temur Monument. No. 247, Al-Motorudi Monument. No. 248, Al-Marginoniy Monument. No. 249, Jaloliddin Manguberdi Monument. No. 250, Al-Bukhoriy Monument. No. 273, Alisher Navoi Monument. No 274, Berdaq Monument. No. 284, Alpomish Monument. No. 288, Al-Fargoniy Monument.

2001 Litho. Perf. 14x13¾, 13¾x14
Stamp + Label with Same
Orientation

244	A69	60s multi	.20	.20
245	A70	60s multi	.20	.20
246	A70	70s multi	.20	.20
247	A70	75s multi	.20	.20
248	A70	75s multi	.20	.20
249	A70	85s multi	.25	.25
250	A70	90s multi	.25	.25
251	A71	90s multi	.25	.25
252	A72	90s multi	.25	.25
253	A73	90s multi	.25	.25
254	A74	90s multi	.25	.25
255	A75	90s multi	.25	.25
256	A76	90s multi	.25	.25
257	A77	90s multi	.25	.25
258	A78	90s multi	.25	.25
259	A79	90s multi	.25	.25
260	A80	90s multi	.25	.25
261	A81	95s multi	.30	.30
262	A82	95s multi	.30	.30
263	A83	95s multi	.30	.30
264	A84	95s multi	.30	.30
265	A85	95s multi	.30	.30
266	A86	95s multi	.30	.30
267	A87	95s multi	.30	.30
268	A88	95s multi	.30	.30
269	A89	95s multi	.30	.30
270	A90	95s multi	.30	.30
271	A91	95s multi	.30	.30
272	A92	95s multi	.30	.30
273	A70	115s multi	.35	.35
274	A70	115s multi	.35	.35
275	A93	115s multi	.35	.35
276	A94	115s multi	.35	.35
277	A95	115s multi	.35	.35
278	A96	115s multi	.35	.35
279	A97	115s multi	.35	.35
280	A98	115s multi	.35	.35
281	A99	115s multi	.35	.35
282	A100	115s multi	.35	.35
283	A101	115s multi	.35	.35
284	A70	125s multi	.35	.35
285	A102	125s multi	.35	.35
286	A103	125s multi	.35	.35
287	A104	125s multi	.35	.35
288	A70	160s multi	.45	.45
289	A105	160s multi	.45	.45
290	A106	160s multi	.45	.45
		Nos. 244-290 (47)	14.20	14.20

Nos. 244-290 were each printed in sheets of 2 stamps and 2 labels.

Uzbekistan Arms — A107

Uzbekistan Flag — A108

Motor
Vehicles
A109

Central Bank
Building — A110

Bank Association
Building — A111

Tashkent
Khokimiyat
Building
A112

Central
Trade
Center
Building
A113

Shurtan
Gas
Complex
A114

Shurtan
Gas
Complex
A115

Couple
with Baby
A116

Children
A117

Farm Equipment
A118

Airplanes
A119

Constitution
A120

Majlis Hall — A121

Gold
Ingots and
Coins
A122

Muruntay
Gold Mine
A123

Independence Day
Celebrations — A124

Independence Day
Celebrations — A125

A109 Designs: No. 292a, Nexia. No. 292b, Damas. No. 293a, Tico. No. 293b, Matiz.
A118 Designs: No. 298a, Case 2022 cotton picker. No. 298b, SHR-100 tractor.
A119 Designs: No. 299a, IL-76 MF cargo plane. No. 299b, IL-114-100 passenger plane.

291		Pair with central label	.50	.50
	a.	A107 90s multi	.25	.25
	b.	A108 90s multi	.25	.25
292		Pair with central label	.50	.50
	a.-b.	A109 90s Any single	.25	.25
293		Pair with central label	.50	.50
	a.-b.	A109 90s multi	.25	.25
294		Pair with central label	.50	.50
	a.	A110 90s multi	.25	.25
	b.	A111 90s multi	.25	.25
295		Pair with central label	.50	.50
	a.	A112 90s multi	.25	.25
	b.	A113 90s multi	.25	.25
296		Pair with central label	.80	.80
	a.	A114 115s multi	.35	.35
	b.	A115 115s multi	.35	.35
297		Pair with central label	.80	.80
	a.	A116 125s multi	.35	.35
	b.	A117 125s multi	.35	.35
298		Pair with central label	.90	.90
	a.-b.	A118 160s Any single	.45	.45
299		Pair with central label	.60	.60
	a.	A119 90s multi	.25	.25
	b.	A119 115s multi	.35	.35
300		Pair with central label	.55	.55
	a.	A120 115s multi	.35	.35
	b.	A121 60s multi	.20	.20
301		Pair with central label	.60	.60
	a.	A122 115s multi	.35	.35
	b.	A123 90s multi	.25	.25
302		Pair with central label	.60	.60
	a.	A124 125s multi	.35	.35
	b.	A125 90s multi	.25	.25
		Nos. 291-302 (12)	7.35	7.35

Nos. 291-302 printed in sheets of four stamps and two labels (two pairs).

Theater
A126

Theater
A127

Theater
A128

Medals — A129

Combine
A130

Combine
A131

Pres.
Karimov
and
Farmers
A132

Soldier
Taking
Oath
Before
Flag
A133

Man and
Soldier
Embracing
A134

Frontier
Guards
and Dog
A135

Athletes — A136

Soldiers in
Formation
A137

Diver
Training
A138

Decontamination Training — A139

Modern Architecture — A140

Armed Forces — A141

Archaeology — A142

High School — A143

Uzbekistan on World Map — A144

A129 Designs: No. 304a, Dostelik. No. 304b, I Darajali "Shon-Sharaf." No. 304c, II Darajali "Shon-Sharaf." No. 305a, I Darajali Sog'lom Avlod Uchun. No. 305b, II Darajali

Sog'lom Avlod Uchun. No. 305c, Mehnat Shuhrati. No. 306a, Jaloliddin Manguberdi. No. 306b, Buyuk Xizmatlari Uchun. No. 306c, El-Yurt Hurmati. No. 307a, Oltin Yildiz. No. 307b, Mustaqillik. No. 307c, Amir Temur.

A136 Designs: No. 310a, Muhammadqodir Abdullayev. No. 310b, Lina Cheryazova. No. 310c, Artur Grigoryan. No. 312a, 160s, Armen Bagdasarov. No. 312b, 160s, Rustam Qosimjonov. No. 312c, 115s, Otabek Kosimov. No. 312d, 115s, Iroda To'laganova. No. 312e, 100s, Dilshod Muxtorov. No. 312e, 115s, Oksana Chusovitina.

No. 313: a, Temuriylar Tarixi Muzeyi (Amir Temur Museum). b, Oqsaroy. c, Oliy Majlis. d, Motamsaro Ona (Monument to Grieving Mother). e, Shahidlar Xotirasi (Respect Monument). f, Interkontinental mehmonxonasi (Intercontinental Hotel). g, Milliy Bank (National Bank). h, Yunusobod Sport Majmuasi (Yunusobod Sport Complex).

No. 314: a, 60s, Infantrymen, tank. b, 70s, Airplane and crew. c, 80s, Helicopter and crew. d, 90s, Soldier directing tank with flags. e, 90s, Minesweeper. f, 115s, Soldiers in classroom. g, 160s, Tanks. h, 60s, Artillery.

No. 315: a, 75s, Pot. b, 75s, Artifact with arch. c, 75s, Artifact with hole at top and side. d, 80s, Anthropomorphic figure with arms. f, 80s, Buddha. g, 80s, Costumed figure. h, 80s, Disk. i, 80s, Anthropomorphic figure missing arm. j, 80s, Box. k, 80s, Face.

303		Strip of 3 + label	.75 .75
a.	A126	90s multi	.25 .25
b.	A127	90s multi	.25 .25
c.	A128	90s multi	.25 .25
304		Strip of 3 + label	1.40 1.40
a.-c.	A129	160s Any single	.45 .45
305		Strip of 3 + label	1.40 1.40
a.-c.	A129	160s Any single	.45 .45
306		Strip of 3 + label	1.40 1.40
a.-c.	A129	160s Any single	.45 .45
307		Strip of 3 + label	1.40 1.40
a.-c.	A129	160s Any single	.45 .45
308		Strip of 3 + label	1.40 1.40
a.	A130	160s multi	.45 .45
b.	A131	160s multi	.45 .45
c.	A132	160s multi	.45 .45
309		Strip of 3 + label	.80 .80
a.	A133	60s multi	.20 .20
b.	A134	80s multi	.25 .25
c.	A135	90s multi	.25 .25
310		Strip of 3 + label	1.25 1.25
a.	A136	160s multi	.45 .45
b.-c.	A136	115s Any single	.35 .35
311		Block of 3 + label	.80 .80
a.	A137	115s multi	.35 .35
b.	A138	80s multi	.25 .25
c.	A139	70s multi	.20 .20
		Nos. 303-311 (9)	10.60 10.60

Sheets

312	A136	Sheet of 6, #a-f, + 3 labels	2.25 2.25
313	A140	115s Sheet of 8, #a-h, + label	3.00 3.00
314	A141	Sheet of 8, #a-h, + label	2.25 2.25
315	A142	Sheet of 11, #a-k, + label	2.60 2.60

Souvenir Sheets

316	A143	160s multi	.45 .45
317	A144	175s multi	.50 .50

Labels have same orientation as stamps and are at left side of strips on Nos. 303-310, and at UR on No. 311. No. 312 contains three different labels.

Commonwealth of
Independent States,
10th Anniv. — A145

2001, Nov. 8   Perf. 13¾x14
318 A145 60s multi   20 .20

Artwork of Oral Tansiqboyev — A146

No. 319: a, 100s, Mening Qo'shig'im (My Song). b, 125s, Angren-Qo'qon Tog'yo'li (Angren-Kokand Mountain Road).
Illustration reduced.

2001, Nov. 8
319 A146 Pair, #a-b, with central label   .65 .65

Flowers — A147

Designs: 45s, Zygophyllum bucharicum. 50s, Viola hissarica. 60s, Bergenia hissarica. 70s, Eremurus hilariae. 85s, Salvia korolkowii. 90s, Lamyropappus schakaptaricus. 145s, Punica granatum.
175s, Undescribed flowers.

2002, May 10   Litho.   Perf. 14x13¾
320-326 A147   Set of 7   1.40 1.40
Souvenir Sheet
327 A147 175s multi   .45 .45

Hominids — A148

No. 328: a, 40s, Dryopithecus maior. b, 45s, Homo erectus modjokertensis. c, 50s, Pithecanthropus erectus. d, 60s, Australopithecus afarensis. e, 70s, Zinjanthropus boisei. f, 85s, Homo sapiens neanderthalensis. g, 90s, Sinanthropus pekinensis. h, 125s, Protanthropus heidelbergensis. i, 160s, Homo sapiens fossilis.

2002, May 10   Perf. 13¾x14
328 A148 Sheet of 9, #a-i, + 3 labels   1.75 1.75

Protection of Ozone
Layer — A149

2002, June 7   Litho.   Perf. 13¾x14
329 A149 40s multi   .20 .20

Souvenir Sheet

City of Shahrisabz, 2700th
Anniv. — A150

2002, June 14   Perf. 14
330 A150 30s multi   .20 .20

Uzbek Sports A151

Designs: 45s, Chavgon. 50s, Poyga. 60s, Kamandon otish. 70s, Qiz quvmoq. 85s, Ro'molcha olish. 90s, Kurash. 145s, Uloq. 175s, Ro'molcha olish, diff.

2002, July 26   **Perf. 13¾x14**
331-337 A151   Set of 7   1.25   1.25
Souvenir Sheet
338 A151   175s multi   .45   .45

Ancient Coins — A152

No. 339: a, 30s, Silver tetradrachm of Eucratides I c. 171-135 BC, obverse. b, 45s, As "a," reverse. c, 60s, Silver coin of Buxoro, obverse. d, 90s, As "c," reverse. e, 125s, Silver miri of Tamerlane, 1370-1405, obverse. f, 160s, As "e," reverse.
Illustration reduced.

2002, Aug. 1
339 A152   Block of 6, #a-f   1.25   1.25

City of Nukus, 70th Anniv. — A153

2002, Oct. 2
340 A153   100s multi   .25   .25

Iris Varieties — A154

Designs: 15s, Qoraqum. 30s, Solnechniy zaychik. 45s, Simfoniya. 50s, Chimyon. 60s, Ikar. 90s, Babye leto. 125s, Toshkent. 160s, Askiya.

2002, Oct. 2   **Perf. 14x13¾**
341-347 A154   Set of 7   1.00   1.00
Souvenir Sheet
348 A154   160s multi   .40   .40

Uzbekistan postal officials have declared the following items as "illegal:"
Sheets of eight stamps depicting Trains (4 different sheets with denominations of 56s, 75s, 95s and 125s);
Sheets of six stamps with various denominations depicting Birds (2 different), Animals, Year of the Snake, Chiroptera, Lizards, Chess;
Sheets of one label and five stamps with various denominations depicting Perissodactyla;
Souvenir sheets of one depicting Trains (8 different 36s sheets, 4 different 56s sheets, 2 different 75s sheets).

G'afur G'ulom (1903-66), Poet — A155

2003, May 4   **Litho.**   **Perf. 13¾x14**
349 A155   1000s brown   2.10   2.10

European Bank Annual Meeting Issue

Vertical Label

Horizontal Label

National Bank, Tashkent — A156

Kaltaminor Minaret, Khiva — A157

Aloqabank, Tashkent A158

Pres Karimov and European Bank for Reconstruction and Development Pres. Jean Lemierre — A159

Islamkhodja Minaret, Khiva — A160

East Gates, Khiva — A161

Samanid Museum, Bukhara — A162

Ark, Bukhara — A163

Women's Traditional Dress — A164

Women's Traditional Dress — A165

Women's Traditional Dress — A166

Women's Traditional Dress — A167

Women's Traditional Dress — A168

A157 Designs: 630s, Gumbazi Sayyidon Mausoleum, Shahrisabz. 920s, Go'ri Amir Mausoleum, Samarqand. 970s, Chorminor Madrasasi, Bukhara. 1330s, Registon, Samarqand, horiz.

2003, May 4   **Perf. 14x13¾, 13¾x14**
Stamp + Label with Same Orientation

350	A156	520s multi	1.10	1.10
351	A157	520s multi	1.10	1.10
352	A157	630s multi	1.25	1.25
353	A157	920s multi	1.90	1.90
354	A157	970s multi	2.00	2.00
355	A158	970s multi	2.00	2.00
356	A157	1330s multi	2.75	2.75
357	A159	1330s multi	2.75	2.75
358		Horiz. pair with central label	2.25	2.25
a.	A160	580s multi	1.10	1.10
b.	A161	520s multi	1.10	1.10
359		Horiz. pair with central label	3.75	3.75
a.	A162	1170s multi	2.40	2.40
b.	A163	630s multi	1.25	1.25
360		Horiz. strip of 5 with flanking label	4.75	4.75
a.	A164	240s multi	.50	.50
b.	A165	320s multi	.65	.65
c.	A166	520s multi	1.10	1.10
d.	A167	580s multi	1.10	1.10
e.	A168	630s multi	1.25	1.25

Types of 2001-02
Stamp + Label with Same Orientation

361	A110	520s multi	1.10	1.10
362	A111	580s multi	1.10	1.10
363		Horiz. pair with central label	2.25	2.25
a.	A74	170s multi	.35	.35
b.	A93	920s multi	1.90	1.90
364		Horiz. pair with central label	1.60	1.60
a.	A107	240s multi	.50	.50
b.	A108	520s multi	1.10	1.10
365		Horiz. pair with central label	1.75	1.75
a.	A114	630s multi	1.25	1.25
b.	A115	240s multi	.50	.50
366		Horiz. pair with central label	1.75	1.75
a.	A122	520s multi	1.10	1.10
b.	A123	320s multi	.65	.65
367		Horiz. pair with flanking label	2.25	2.25
a.	A152	520s Like #339a	1.10	1.10
b.	A152	520s Like #339b	1.10	1.10
368		Horiz. pair with flanking label	2.25	2.25
a.	A152	580s Like #339c	1.10	1.10
b.	A152	580s Like #339d	1.10	1.10
369		Horiz. pair with flanking label	2.50	2.50
a.	A152	630s Like #339e	1.25	1.25
b.	A152	630s Like #339f	1.25	1.25
370	A140	Sheet of 8 + central label	9.75	9.75
a.		520s Like #313a	1.10	1.10
b.		970s Like #313b	2.00	2.00
c.		580s Like #313c	1.10	1.10
d.		630s Like #313d	1.25	1.25
e.		320s Like #313e	.65	.65
f.		630s Like #313f	1.25	1.25
g.		920s Toshkent shahar hokimiyati (mayor's house)	1.90	1.90

h.	240s	Like #313h	.50	.50

Type of 2001 Redrawn

71	Horiz. pair with central label		3.25	3.25
a.	A109 630s Like #292a		1.25	1.25
b.	A109 970s Like #293b		2.00	2.00
	Nos. 350-371 (22)		55.15	55.15

Famous Men — A169

Designs: 125s, Komil Yormatov, film director. 500s, Jo'raxon Sultonov, singer.

2003, July 8   **Perf. 13¾x14**

372-373	A169	Set of 2	1.25	1.25

Birds — A170

Designs: No. 374, 100s, Ciconia ciconia asiatica. No. 375, 100s, Ciconia nigra. No. 376, 125s, Platalea leucorodia. No. 377, 125s, Phoenicopterus ruber.

2003, Sept. 17   **Perf. 14x13¾**

374-377	A170	Set of 4	1.00	1.00

Caps — A171

Designs: No. 378, 100s, Kula-tung. No. 379, 100s, Erkaklar do'ppisi. No. 380, 100s, Bayram do'ppisi. No. 381, 125s, Ayollar do'ppisi. No. 382, 125s, Ayollar taxya-do'ppisi. No. 383, 155s, Erkaklar do'ppisi, diff. No. 384, 155s, Bolalar bayram do'ppisi.

2003, Oct. 7

378-384	A171	Set of 7	1.75	1.75

Paintings — A172

No. 385: a, Tong. Onalik, by R. Ahmedov. b, Baxt, by S. Ayitbayev.

2003, Nov. 19

385	A172 970s Horiz. pair, #a-b	4.00	4.00

See Kazakhstan No.

Abuxoliq G'ijduvoniy, Bukhara, 900th Anniv. — A173

Illustration reduced.

2003, Nov. 28   **Perf. 13¾x14**

386	A173 125s multi + label	.30	.30

VANUATU
ˌvan-ˌwä-ˈtü

LOCATION — Island group in south Pacific Ocean northeast of New Caledonia
GOVT. — Republic
AREA — 5,700 sq. mi.
POP. — 189,036 (1999 est.)
CAPITAL — Port Vila

The Anglo-French condominium of New Hebrides (Vol. 4) became the independent state of Vanuatu July 30, 1980.

Hebrides franc Vatu (1981)

> Catalogue values for all unused stamps in this country are for Never Hinged items.

Erromango Is. and Kaori Tree — A44

Designs: 10fr, Archipelago and man making copra. 15fr, Espiritu Santo Island and cattle. 20fr, Efate Island and Post Office, Vila. 25fr, Malakula Island and headdresses. 30fr, Aoba and Maewo Islands and pig tusks. 35fr, Pentecost Island and land diving. 40fr, Tanna Island and Prophet John Frum's Red Cross. 50fr, Shepherd Island and canoe with sail. 70fr, Banks Island and dancers. 100fr, Ambrym Island and carvings. 200fr, Aneityum Island and decorated baskets. 500fr, Torres Islands and fishing with bow and arrow.

Wmk. 373

1980, July 30   **Litho.**   **Perf. 14**

280	A44	5fr multicolored	.20	.20
281	A44	10fr multicolored	.20	.20
282	A44	15fr multicolored	.35	.30
283	A44	20fr multicolored	.45	.40
284	A44	25fr multicolored	.55	.45
285	A44	30fr multicolored	.70	.60
286	A44	35fr multicolored	.80	.65
287	A44	40fr multicolored	.80	.75
288	A44	50fr multicolored	.85	.90
289	A44	70fr multicolored	1.60	1.25
290	A44	100fr multicolored	1.60	1.00
291	A44	200fr multicolored	1.75	1.75
292	A44	500fr multicolored	3.25	3.75
		Nos. 280-292 (13)	13.10	12.20

Inscribed in French
Unwmk.

280a	A44	5fr multicolored	.35	.20
281a	A44	10fr multicolored	.45	.20
282a	A44	15fr multicolored	.50	.30
283a	A44	20fr multicolored	.55	.35
284a	A44	25fr multicolored	.60	.40
285a	A44	30fr multicolored	.60	.50
286a	A44	35fr multicolored	.60	.60
287a	A44	40fr multicolored	.95	.70
288a	A44	50fr multicolored	1.10	.80
289a	A44	70fr multicolored	1.50	1.10
290a	A44	100fr multicolored	1.60	1.25
291a	A44	200fr multicolored	1.90	2.00
292a	A44	500fr multicolored	4.25	4.00
		Nos. 280a-292a (13)	15.00	12.40

Rotary Emblem — A52   Kiwanis Emblem — A53

1980, Sept. 16   **Wmk. 373**

293	A52	10fr Emblem, horiz.	.20	.20
294	A52	40fr shown	.65	.65

Inscribed in French
Unwmk.

293a	A52	10fr multicolored	.20	.20
294a	A52	40fr multicolored	.85	.85

75th anniv. of Rotary Intl. and 8th anniv. of Port Vila Rotary Club (40fr).

1980, Sept. 16   **Wmk. 373**

295	A53	10fr shown	.20	.20
296	A53	40fr Emblem, horiz.	.50	.50

Inscribed in French
Unwmk.

295a	A53	10fr multicolored	.25	.20
296a	A53	40fr multicolored	1.00	.85

New Zealand District Kiwanis Convention, Port Vila, Sept. 16-18.

Christmas A54

Erythrura Trichroa — A55

Paintings: 10fr, Virgin and Child, by Michael Pacher. 15fr, Virgin and Child, by Hans Memling. 30fr, Rest on the Flight to Egypt, by Adriaen van der Werff.

1980, Nov. 12   **Wmk. 373**

297	A54	10fr multicolored	.20	.20
298	A54	15fr multicolored	.25	.25
299	A54	30fr multicolored	.55	.55
		Nos. 297-299 (3)	1.00	1.00

1981, Feb. 18

300	A55	10fr shown	.35	.20
301	A55	20fr Chalcophaps indica	.65	.40
302	A55	30fr Pachycephala pectoralis	1.00	.65
303	A55	40fr Ptilinopus tannensis	1.25	.85
		Nos. 300-303 (4)	3.25	2.10

Duke of Edinburgh's 60th Birthday — A56

1981, June 10   **Perf. 14x14½**

304	A56	15v Tribesman, portrait	.20	.20
305	A56	25v Portrait	.30	.30
306	A56	35v Family	.45	.45
307	A56	45v shown	.60	.60
		Nos. 304-307 (4)	1.55	1.55

Common Design Types
pictured following the introduction.

Royal Wedding Issue
Common Design Type

1981, July 29

308	CD331	15v Bouquet	.25	.25
309	CD331	45v Charles	.55	.55
310	CD331	75v Couple	.80	.80
		Nos. 308-310 (3)	1.60	1.60

First Anniv. of Independence — A57

1981, July 19

311	A57	15v Map, flag, vert.	.20	.20
312	A57	25v Emblem	.20	.20
313	A57	45v Anthem	.45	.45
314	A57	75v Arms, vert.	.65	.65
		Nos. 311-314 (4)	1.50	1.50

Christmas A58

Designs: Children's drawings.

Wmk. 373

1981, Nov. 11   **Litho.**   **Perf. 14**

315	A58	15v Three kings	.20	.20
316	A58	25v Girl holding lamb, vert.	.30	.30
317	A58	35v Butterfly-angel	.40	.40
318	A58	45v Gift bearer, vert.	.60	.60
a.		Souvenir sheet, #315-318	1.75	1.75
		Nos. 315-318 (4)	1.50	1.50

Broadbills — A59

Orchids — A60

1982, Feb. 8   **Perf. 14½x14**

319	A59	15v shown	.40	.40
320	A59	20v Rainbow lorries	.55	.55
321	A59	25v Buff-bellied flycatchers	.70	.70
322	A59	45v Fantails	1.25	1.25
		Nos. 319-322 (4)	2.90	2.90

Perf. 14x13½, 13½x14

1982, June 15

323	A60	1v Flickengeria comata	.20	.50
324	A60	2v Calanthe triplicata	.20	.55
325	A60	10v Dendrobium sladei	.25	.30
326	A60	15v Dendrobium mohlianum	.30	.25
327	A60	20v Dendrobium macrophyllum	.35	.30
328	A60	25v Dendrobium purpureum	.40	.35
329	A60	30v Robiquetia mimus	.55	.40
330	A60	35v Dendrobium mooreanum	.65	.50
331	A60	45v Spathoglottis plicata	.70	.75
332	A60	50v Dendrobium seemannii	.75	.85
333	A60	75v Dendrobium conanthum	1.25	1.60
334	A60	100v Dendrobium macranthum	1.60	1.60
335	A60	200v Coelogyne lamellata	2.75	2.75
336	A60	500v Bulbophyllum longiscapum	6.50	6.75
		Nos. 323-336 (14)	16.45	17.45

Nos. 330-333, 336 horiz.
For surcharges see Nos. 383, 512, 551-554, 586-589A, B1.

Scouting Year A61

Wmk. 373

1982, Sept. 1   Litho.   Perf. 14
337	A61	15v Around campfire	.30	.30
338	A61	20v First aid	.35	.35
339	A61	25v Signal tower	.45	.45
340	A61	45v Building raft	.85	.85
341	A61	75v Scout sign	1.25	1.25
		Nos. 337-341 (5)	3.20	3.20

Christmas — A62

Details from Nativity painting. 35v, 45v horiz.

1982, Nov. 16
342	A62	15v multicolored	.30	.30
343	A62	25v multicolored	.40	.40
344	A62	35v multicolored	.60	.60
345	A62	45v multicolored	.80	.80
a.		Souvenir sheet of 4, #342-345	2.50	2.50
		Nos. 342-345 (4)	2.10	2.10

Hypolimnas Octocula A63

1983, Jan. 17   Perf. 14½
346	Pair	1.50	1.10
a.	A63 15v shown	.75	.55
b.	A63 15v Euploea sylvester	.75	.55
347	Pair	1.75	1.40
a.	A63 20v Polyura sacco	.90	.70
b.	A63 20v Papilio canopus	.90	.70
348	Pair	2.00	1.40
a.	A63 25v Parantica pumila	1.00	.70
b.	A63 25v Luthrodes cleotas	1.00	.70
	Nos. 346-348 (3)	5.25	3.90

A64

1983, Mar. 14   Perf. 13½x14
349	A64	15v Pres. Sokomanu	.20	.20
350	A64	20v Fisherman	.25	.25
351	A64	25v Herdsman, cattle	.30	.30
352	A64	75v Flags, map	.90	.90
		Nos. 349-352 (4)	1.65	1.65

Commonwealth Day. 20v, 75v inscribed in French.

Economic Zone — A65

a, Thunnus albacares. b, Map. c, Matthew Isld. d, Hunter Isld. e, Epinephelus morrhua, etelis carbunculus. f, Katsuwonus pelamis.

Perf. 14x13½
1983, May 23   Litho.   Wmk. 373
353		Sheet of 6	3.00	3.00
a.-f.	A65 25v multicolored	.50	.50

Manned Flight Bicentenary — A66

Balloons or Airships: 15v, Montgolfiere, 1783. 20v, J.A.C. Charles 1st hydrogen balloon, 1783. 25v, Blanchard & Jeffries 1st English Channel crossing, 1785. 35v, H. Giffard's 1st mechanically powered airship, 1852. 40v, Renard and Krebs' airship, 1884. 45v, Graf Zeppelin's 1st transworld flight, 1929.

1983, Aug. 4   Litho.   Perf. 14
354	A66	15v multi, vert.	.30	.30
355	A66	20v multi, vert.	.35	.35
356	A66	25v multi, vert.	.45	.45
357	A66	35v multi	.60	.60
358	A66	40v multi	.70	.70
359	A66	45v multi	.85	.85
		Nos. 354-359 (6)	3.25	3.25

For overprint see No. 372.

World Communications Year — A67

1983, Oct. 10   Litho.   Wmk. 373
360	A67	15v Mail transport, Bauerfield Airport	.25	.25
361	A67	20v Switchboard operator	.35	.35
362	A67	25v Telex operator	.50	.50
363	A67	45v Satellite earth station	.90	.90
a.		Souv. sheet of 4, #360-363 + 3 labels	2.25	2.25
		Nos. 360-363 (4)	2.00	2.00

No. 363a issued for WCY and 75th anniv. of New Hebrides stamps.

Local Fungi — A68

1984, Jan. 9   Litho.   Perf. 14
364	A68	15v Cymatoderma elegans, vert.	.75	.75
365	A68	25v Lignosus rhinoceros, vert.	.90	.90
366	A68	35v Stereum ostrea	1.25	1.25
367	A68	45v Ganoderma boninenze, vert.	1.60	1.60
		Nos. 364-367 (4)	4.50	4.50

Lloyd's List Issue
Common Design Type

1984, Apr. 30   Litho.   Perf. 14½x14
368	CD335	15v Port Vila	.30	.30
369	CD335	20v Induna	.45	.45
370	CD335	25v Air Vanuatu jet	.60	.60
371	CD335	45v Brahman Express	1.10	1.10
		Nos. 368-371 (4)	2.45	2.45

No. 359 Overprinted "UPU CONGRESS / HAMBURG"

1984, June 11   Wmk. 373   Perf. 14
372	A66	45v multicolored	.90	.90

Cattle A69

1984, July 3   Litho.   Perf. 14
373	A69	15v Charolais	.30	.30
374	A69	25v Charolais-Afrikaner	.45	.45
375	A69	45v Friesian	.85	.85
376	A69	75v Charolais-Brahman	1.40	1.40
		Nos. 373-376 (4)	3.00	3.00

Ausipex '84 — A70

Ships.

1984, Sept. 7
377	A70	25v Makambo	.65	.45
378	A70	45v Rockton	1.10	.80
379	A70	100v Waroonga	2.00	3.25
a.		Souvenir sheet of 3, #377-379	4.00	4.50
		Nos. 377-379 (3)	3.75	4.50

Christmas A71

1984, Nov. 19   Litho.   Wmk. 373
380	A71	25v Father Christmas, child in hospital	.45	.25
381	A71	45v Nativity	.80	.65
382	A71	75v Father Christmas, children	1.25	1.25
		Nos. 380-382 (3)	2.50	2.15

No. 323 Surcharged with 2 Black Bars

1985, Jan. 22   Litho.   Perf. 14x13½
383	A60	5v on 1v multi	.75	.50

Ceremonial Dance Costumes — A71a

Audubon Birth Bicent. — A72

1985, Jan. 22   Perf. 14
384	A71a	20v Ambrym Island	.30	.30
385	A71a	25v Pentecost Island	.40	.40
386	A71a	45v Women's Grade Ceremony, S.W. Malakula	.70	.70
387	A71a	75v Same, men's	1.00	1.00
		Nos. 384-387 (4)	2.40	2.40

Wmk. 373
1985, Mar. 26   Litho.   Perf. 14

Peregrine falcons.
388	A72	20v multicolored	.90	.50
389	A72	35v multicolored	1.10	.75
390	A72	45v multicolored	1.25	1.10
391	A72	100v multicolored	2.25	2.50
		Nos. 388-391 (4)	5.50	4.85

Queen Mother 85th Birthday
Common Design Type
Perf. 14½x14

1985, June 7   Wmk. 384
392	CD336	5v Wedding photo	.20	.20
393	CD336	20v 80th birthday celebration	.40	.40
394	CD336	35v At Ancona, Italy	.55	.55
395	CD336	55v Holding Prince Henry	.85	.85
		Nos. 392-395 (4)	2.00	2.00

Souvenir Sheet
396	CD336	100v At Covent Garden Opera	2.50	2.50

EXPO '85, Tsukuba — A73

35v, Mala naval patrol boat. 45v, Japanese fishing fleet, Port Vila. 55v, Mobile Force Band. 100v, Prime Minister Walter H. Lini.

1985, July 26   Wmk. 373   Perf. 14
397	A73	35v multicolored	.65	.45
398	A73	45v multicolored	.80	.65
399	A73	55v multicolored	.85	.75
400	A73	100v multicolored	1.00	1.50
a.		Souvenir sheet of 4, #397-400	4.00	4.00
		Nos. 397-400 (4)	3.30	3.25

Natl. independence, 5th anniv.

Intl. Youth Year A74

Children's drawings.

1985, Sept. 16   Wmk. 373   Perf. 14
401	A74	20v Alain Lagaliu	.50	.50
402	A74	30v Peter Obed	.55	.55
403	A74	50v Mary Estelle	.95	.95
404	A74	100v Abel M rani	1.50	1.50
		Nos. 401-404 (4)	3.50	3.50

Natl. and UN Flags, Map A75

1985, Sept. 24   Litho.   Perf. 14
405	A75	45v multicolored	.80	.70

Admission of Vanuatu to UN, 4th anniv.

Sea Slugs — A76

Scuba Diving — A77

1985, Nov. 11   Wmk. 373   Perf. 14½
406	A76	20v Chromodoris elisa bethina	.35	.35
407	A76	35v Halgerda aurantiomaculata	.65	.65
408	A76	55v Chromodoris kuniei	1.00	1.00
409	A76	100v Notodoris minor	1.75	1.75
		Nos. 406-409 (4)	3.75	3.75

Nos. 407-408 horiz. See Nos. 497-500.

1986, Jan. 22   Wmk. 384   Perf. 14
410	A77	30v shown	.75	.45
411	A77	35v Volcanic eruption	1.00	.50
412	A77	55v Land diving	1.00	.80
413	A77	100v Wind surfing	1.25	1.75
		Nos. 410-413 (4)	4.00	3.50

See No. 479.

Queen Elizabeth II 60th Birthday
Common Design Type

Designs: 20v, With Prince Charles and Princess Anne, 1951. 35v, At christening of Prince William, the Music Room, Buckingham Palace, 1982. 45v, State visit, 1985. 55v, State visit to Mexico, 1974. 100v, Visiting Crown Agents' offices, 1983.

1986, Apr. 21   Litho.   Perf. 14x14½

14	CD337	20v scar, blk & sil	.35	.35
15	CD337	35v ultra & multi	.60	.60
16	CD337	45v green & multi	.70	.70
17	CD337	55v violet & multi	.90	.90
18	CD337	100v multicolored	1.75	1.75
		Nos. 414-418 (5)	4.30	4.30

For overprints & surcharges see #465-469, B2-B6.

AMERIPEX '86 — A78

1986, May 19   Wmk. 373   Perf. 14

19	A78	45v SS President Coolidge	.80	.55
20	A78	55v As troop ship, 1942	.95	.70
21	A78	135v Site of sinking, 1942	1.75	1.75
a.		Souvenir sheet of 3, #419-421	4.25	3.75
		Nos. 419-421 (3)	3.50	3.00

Halley's Comet A79

1986, June 23   Wmk. 384   Perf. 14½

22	A79	30v Comet, deity statue	.90	.90
23	A79	45v Family sighting comet	1.10	1.10
24	A79	55v Comet over SW Pacific	1.25	1.25
25	A79	100v Edmond Halley, manuscript	1.75	1.75
		Nos. 422-425 (4)	5.00	5.00

Coral A80

1986, Oct. 27   Wmk. 373   Perf. 14

26	A80	20v Daisy	.45	.45
27	A80	45v Organ pipe	1.00	1.00
28	A80	55v Sea fan	1.25	1.25
29	A80	135v Soft	3.00	3.00
		Nos. 426-429 (4)	5.70	5.70

Intl. Peace Year A81

1986, Nov. 3   Litho.   Perf. 14

30	A81	30v Children of the world	.60	.60
31	A81	45v Child praying	.90	.90
32	A81	55v UN building, negotiators	1.10	1.10
33	A81	135v Peoples working in harmony	2.75	2.75
		Nos. 430-433 (4)	5.35	5.35

Automotives A82

1987, Jan. 22

34	A82	20v Datsun 240Z, 1969	.35	.35
35	A82	45v Model A Ford, 1927	.65	.65
36	A82	55v Unic, 1924-25	.75	.75
37	A82	135v Citroen DS19, 1975	1.75	1.75
		Nos. 434-437 (4)	3.50	3.50

IRHO Coconut Research Station, 25th Anniv. A83

1987, May 13   Perf. 14½x14

438	A83	35v Nursery	.55	.55
439	A83	45v Cocos nucifera tree	.80	.80
440	A83	100v Cocos nucifera fruit	1.40	1.40
441	A83	135v Station	1.75	1.75
		Nos. 438-441 (4)	4.50	4.50

Fish — A84

Perf. 14x14½

1987, July 15   Wmk. 384

442	A84	1v Cirrhitichthys aprinus	.20	.20
443	A84	5v Zanclus cornutus	.20	.20
444	A84	10v Canthigaster cinctus	.20	.20
445	A84	15v Amphiprion rubrocinctus	.25	.25
446	A84	20v Acanthurus lineatus	.35	.35
447	A84	30v Thalassoma hardwicki	.45	.45
448	A84	35v Anthias tuka	.50	.50
449	A84	40v Adioryx microstomus	.55	.55
450	A84	45v Balistoides conspicillum	.70	.70
451	A84	50v Xyrichtys taeniouris	.75	.75
452	A84	65v Hemitaurich-thys polyepis	.80	.80
453	A84	90v Pterois volitans	.90	.90
454	A84	100v Paracirrhites forsteri	1.60	1.60
455	A84	300v Balistapus undulatus	4.00	4.00
456	A84	500v Chaetodon ephippium	6.25	6.25
		Nos. 442-456 (15)	17.70	17.70

Insects A85

1987, Sept. 22   Wmk. 373   Perf. 14

457	A85	45v Xylotrupes gideon	.85	.85
458	A85	55v Phyllodes imperialis	1.00	1.00
459	A85	65v Cyphogaster	1.25	1.25
460	A85	100v Othreis fullonia	1.90	1.90
		Nos. 457-460 (4)	5.00	5.00

Christmas Carols — A86

1987, Nov. 10   Perf. 13½x14

461	A86	20v Away in a Manger	.40	.40
462	A86	45v Once in Royal David's City	.90	.90
463	A86	55v While Shepherds Watched Their Flocks	1.10	1.10
464	A86	65v We Three Kings of Orient Are	1.25	1.25
		Nos. 461-464 (4)	3.65	3.65

Nos. 414-418 Ovptd. in Silver:
"40TH WEDDING ANNIVERSARY"

Perf. 14x14½

1987, Dec. 9   Litho.   Wmk. 384

465	CD337	20v scar, blk & sil	.40	.40
466	CD337	35v ultra & multi	.50	.50
467	CD337	45v green & multi	.65	.65

468	CD337	55v violet & multi	.75	.75
469	CD337	100v multicolored	1.25	1.25
		Nos. 465-469 (5)	3.55	3.55

World Wildlife Fund — A87

Dugongs.

1988, Feb. 29   Perf. 13x13½

470	A87	5v Mother, calf	.85	.35
471	A87	10v Adult	1.40	.35
472	A87	20v Two adults	1.75	.90
473	A87	45v Herd	3.25	2.40
		Nos. 470-473 (4)	7.25	4.00

Australia Bicentennial A88

Burns Philip emblem, bicent. emblem and steamships.

1988, May 18   Wmk. 373   Perf. 12

474	A88	20v S.S. Tambo	.35	.35
475	A88	45v S.S. Induna	.75	.75
476	A88	55v S.S. Morinda	.90	.90
477	A88	65v S.S. Marsina	1.00	1.00
		Nos. 474-477 (4)	3.00	3.00

Capt. James Cook (1728-1779), Explorer — A89

Perf. 14 on 2 or 3 Sides

1988, July 29   Wmk. 384

478	A89	45v black & red	.80	.80

SYDPEX '88. No. 478 printed in panes of 10 plus 5 center labels picturing a map of Vanuatu, HMS Resolution, exhibition emblem, HMS Endeavour or a map of Australia.

Tourism Type of 1986
Souvenir Sheet
Wmk. 373

1988, Aug. 24   Litho.   Perf. 14

479		Sheet of 2	3.00	3.00
a.		A77 55v like No. 412	1.00	1.00
b.		A77 100v like No. 413	2.00	2.00

EXPO '88. Nos. 479a-479b are dated 1988 and "Vanuatu" is inscribed in violet blue.

1988 Summer Olympics, Seoul — A90

1988, Sept. 19   Perf. 13½x14

480	A90	20v Boxing	.25	.25
481	A90	45v Track events	.70	.70
482	A90	55v Signing Olympic agreement	.80	.80
483	A90	65v Soccer	1.00	1.00
		Nos. 480-483 (4)	2.75	2.75

Souvenir Sheet

484	A90	150v Tennis	3.00	3.00

Intl. Tennis Federation, 75th anniv. (150v).

Lloyds of London, 300th Anniv.
Common Design Type

Designs: 20v, Lloyds new building, 1988. 55v, Cargo ship Shirrabank, horiz. 65v, Adela, horiz. 145v, Excursion steamer General Slocum on fire in New York Harbor, 1904.

FAO — A91

Perf. 14½x14, 14x14½

1988, Nov. 14

489	A91	45v Tending crops	.85	.85
490	A91	55v Fishing, vert.	.90	.90
491	A91	65v Animal husbandry, vert.	1.00	1.00
492	A91	120v Produce market	1.25	1.25
		Nos. 489-492 (4)	4.00	4.00

1988, Oct. 25   Wmk. 384   Perf. 14

485	CD341	20v multicolored	.40	.40
486	CD341	55v multicolored	1.00	1.00
487	CD341	65v multicolored	1.10	1.10
488	CD341	145v multicolored	2.75	2.75
		Nos. 485-488 (4)	5.25	5.25

Christmas A92

Carols: 20v, Silent Night, Holy Night. 45v, Angels From the Realms of Glory. 65v, O Come All Ye Faithful. 155v, In That Poor Stable How Charming Jesus Lies.

1988, Dec. 1   Litho.   Perf. 14½x14

493	A92	20v multicolored	.40	.40
494	A92	45v multicolored	.60	.60
495	A92	65v multicolored	.75	.75
496	A92	155v multicolored	2.00	2.00
		Nos. 493-496 (4)	3.75	3.75

Marine Life Type of 1985

Shrimp.

1989, Feb. 1   Perf. 14

497	A76	20v Periclimenes brevicarpalis	.35	.35
498	A76	45v Lysmata grabhami	.80	.80
499	A76	65v Rhynchocinetes	1.10	1.10
500	A76	150v Stenopus hispidus	2.50	2.50
		Nos. 497-500 (4)	4.75	4.75

Economic & Social Commission for Asia and the Pacific (ESCAP) A93

Perf. 12x12½

1989, Apr. 5   Litho.   Wmk. 373

501	A93	20v Consolidated Catalina	.85	.85
502	A93	45v Douglas DC-3	1.25	1.25
503	A93	55v Embraer EMB110 Bandeirante	1.40	1.40
504	A93	200v Boeing 737-300	4.25	4.25
		Nos. 501-504 (4)	7.75	7.75

Inauguration of the Sydney-Noumea-Espiritu Santo Service, 1948 (20v).

PHILEXFRANCE '89 — A94

Exhibition emblem and: No. 505a, Porte de Versailles Hall Number 1. No. 505b, Eiffel Tower. No. 506, Revolt of French Troops, Nancy, 1790.

1989, July 5   Wmk. 373   Perf. 12

505	A94	Pair	4.75	4.75
a.-b.		100v any single	2.25	2.25

Souvenir Sheet
Perf. 14
Wmk. 384

506	A94	100v multicolored	2.00	2.00

French revolution, bicent.

Moon Landing, 20th Anniv.
Common Design Type

Apollo 17: 45v, Command module in space. 55v, Harrison Schmitt, Gene Cerman and Ron Evans. 65v, Mission emblem. 120v, Liftoff. 100v, Recovery of Apollo 11 crew after spashdown.

1989, July 20   Wmk. 384   Perf. 14
Size of Nos. 508-509: 29x29mm

507	CD342	45v multicolored	1.25	1.25
508	CD342	55v multicolored	1.25	1.25
509	CD342	65v multicolored	1.50	1.50
510	CD342	120v multicolored	2.50	2.50
		Nos. 507-510 (4)	6.50	6.50

Souvenir Sheet

511	CD342	100v multicolored	2.75	2.75

No. 324
Surcharged

Perf. 14x13½
1989, Oct. 18   Litho.   Wmk. 373

512	A60	100v on 2v multi	4.00	4.00

STAMPSHOW '89, Melbourne.

World Stamp Expo '89 — A95

Perf. 14x13½
1989, Nov. 6   Litho.   Wmk. 384

513	A95	65v New Hebrides #256	1.10	1.10

Souvenir Sheet

514		Sheet of 2	2.75	2.75
a.		A95 65v New Hebrides #254	1.10	1.10
b.		A95 100v The White House (detail)	1.60	1.60

A96

A97

Flora.

Perf. 12½x12
1990, Jan. 5   Wmk. 373

515	A96	45v Alocasia macrorrhiza	.75	.75
516	A96	55v Acacia spirorbis	.90	.90
517	A96	65v Metrosideros collina	1.10	1.10
518	A96	145v Hoya australis	2.50	2.50
		Nos. 515-518 (4)	5.25	5.25

1990, Apr. 30   Perf. 13x13½

Stamp World London '90 Exhibition emblem and simulated stamps or stamps on stamps: 45v, Kava (simulated stamps). 65v, Luganville.

P.O. exterior, interior (simulated stamps). 100v, Propeller plane, 19th cent. packet (simulated stamps). 150v, New Hebrides #187-188, first day cancellation. 200v, Great Britain #1, Vanuatu #281.

519	A97	45v multicolored	.75	.75
520	A97	65v multicolored	1.25	1.25
521	A97	100v multicolored	1.75	1.75
522	A97	200v multicolored	3.25	3.25
		Nos. 519-522 (4)	7.00	7.00

Souvenir Sheet

523	A97	150v multicolored	5.00	5.00

Penny Black, 150th anniv. No. 523 margin pictures first day cancel and cachet.

Independence, 10th Anniv. — A98

25v, Natl. Council of Women Emblem. 50v, Pres. Frederick Kalomuana Timakata. 55v, Preamble to Constitution. 65v, Vanuaaku Pati flag. 80v, Reserve Bank. 150v, Prime Minister Walter H. Lini.

1990, July 30   Perf. 14

524	A98	25v multicolored	.40	.40
525	A98	50v multicolored	.85	.85
526	A98	55v multicolored	1.00	1.00
527	A98	65v multicolored	1.10	1.10
528	A98	80v multicolored	1.40	1.40
		Nos. 524-528 (5)	4.75	4.75

Souvenir Sheet

529	A98	150v multi	4.00	4.00

Minature Sheet

Charles De Gaulle (1890-1970) — A99

Wmk. 373
1990, Nov. 22   Litho.   Perf. 14

530		Sheet, 2 ea #530c-530f + 2 labels	11.50	11.50
a.		A99 20v At Bayeux, after D-day landing	2.50	2.50
b.		A99 25v Alsace, 1945	2.50	2.50
c.		A99 30v Portrait	.90	.90
d.		A99 45v Spitfire, Biggin Hill, 1942	.95	.95
e.		A99 55v Casablanca, 1943	1.00	1.00
f.		A99 65v Day of Glory, Paris, 1944	1.10	1.10

Christmas — A100

1990, Dec. 5   Perf. 13

531		Strip of 5	4.25	4.25
a.		A100 25v Angel facing right	.45	.45
b.		A100 50v Shepherds	.70	.70
c.		A100 65v Nativity	.80	.80
d.		A100 70v The Three Kings	.85	.85
e.		A100 80v Angel facing left	.85	.85

Butterflies A101

Perf. 14x14½
1991, Jan. 9   Wmk. 384

532	A101	25v Parthenos sylvia	.50	.50
533	A101	55v Euploea leucostictos	1.00	1.00
534	A101	80v Lampides boeticus	1.40	1.40
535	A101	150v Danaus plexippus	2.60	2.60
		Nos. 532-535 (4)	5.50	5.50

Art Festival — A102

Phila Nippon '91 — A103

Wmk. 373
1991, May 2   Litho.   Perf. 13½

536	A102	25v Dance	.40	.40
537	A102	65v Weaving	1.10	1.10
538	A102	80v Carving	1.40	1.40
539	A102	150v Music	2.60	2.60
		Nos. 536-539 (4)	5.50	5.50

Elizabeth & Philip, Birthdays
Common Design Types

Wmk. 384
1991, June 17   Litho.   Perf. 14½

540	CD345	65v multicolored	1.00	1.00
541	CD346	70v multicolored	1.10	1.10
a.		Pair, #540-541 + label	2.10	2.10

Wmk. 373
1991, Nov. 15   Litho.   Perf. 14½

Birds: 50v, White-collared kingfisher. 55v, Green palm lorikeet. 80v, Scarlet robin. 100v, Pacific swallow. 150v, Reef heron.

542	A103	50v multicolored	.90	.90
543	A103	55v multicolored	.95	.95
544	A103	80v multicolored	1.40	1.40
545	A103	100v multicolored	1.75	1.75
		Nos. 542-545 (4)	5.00	5.00

Souvenir Sheet

546	A103	150v multicolored	2.75	2.75

Fight Against AIDS A104

Designs: 25v, Multiple partners, unsafe sex can spread AIDS. 65v, AIDS victim and care giver. 80v, AIDS kills, shark. 150v, Children's playground.

1991, Nov. 29   Wmk. 384   Perf. 14

547	A104	25v multicolored	.50	.50
548	A104	65v multicolored	.90	.90
549	A104	80v multicolored	1.10	1.10
550	A104	150v multicolored	2.00	2.00
		Nos. 547-550 (4)	4.50	4.50

Nos. 324-326 & 329 Surcharged

Perf. 14x13½
1991, June 12   Litho.   Wmk. 373

551	A60	20v on 2v #324	.35	.35
552	A60	60v on 10v #325	1.00	1.00
553	A60	70v on 15v #326	1.25	1.25
554	A60	80v on 30v #329	1.40	1.40
		Nos. 551-554 (4)	4.00	4.00

Queen Elizabeth II's Accession to the Throne, 40th Anniv.
Common Design Type

1992, Feb. 6   Wmk. 384   Perf. 1

555	CD349	20v multicolored	.30	.3
556	CD349	25v multicolored	.40	.4
557	CD349	60v multicolored	.80	.8
558	CD349	65v multicolored	.85	.8

Wmk. 373

559	CD349	70v multicolored	.90	.9
		Nos. 555-559 (5)	3.25	3.2

New Hebrides Participation in World War II — A105

Designs: 50v, Grumman F4F-4 Wildcat. 55v, Douglas SBD-3 Dauntless. 65v, Consolidated PBY-5A Catalina. 80v, USS Hornet. 200v, Vought-Sikorsky OS2U-3.

Perf. 13½x14
1992, May 22   Litho.   Wmk. 37½

560	A105	50v multicolored	1.25	1.2
561	A105	55v multicolored	1.25	1.2
562	A105	65v multicolored	1.50	1.5
563	A105	80v multicolored	2.00	2.0
		Nos. 560-563 (4)	6.00	6.0

Souvenir Sheet

564	A105	200v multicolored	6.00	6.0

World Columbian Stamp Expo, Chicago (No. 564).
See Nos. 590-594, 664-667.

Vanuatu's Membership in the World Meteorological Organization, 10th Anniv. — A106

Designs: 25v, Meteorological station, Por Vila. 60v, Cyclone near Vanuatu seen by Japanese satellite GMS 4. 80v, Weather char showing cyclone. 105v, Cyclone warning broadcast by radio.

1992, June 20   Perf. 1

565	A106	25v multicolored	.40	.4
566	A106	60v multicolored	1.00	1.0
567	A106	80v multicolored	1.25	1.2
568	A106	105v multicolored	1.40	1.4
		Nos. 565-568 (4)	4.05	4.0

1992 Melanesian Cup — A107

1992, July 20   Perf. 13½x14

569	A107	20v Soccer team, trophy	.45	.4
570	A107	65v Soccer players	1.25	1.2
571	A107	70v Men's track	1.40	1.4
572	A107	80v Women's track	1.50	1.5
		Nos. 569-572 (4)	4.60	4.6

1992 Summer Olympics, Barcelona (#571-572).
For surcharges see Nos. 621-622.

World Food Day — A108

Designs: 20v, "Breast is best." 70v, Central Hospital, Port Vila. 80v, "Give your children a healthy future." 150v, Nutritious food.

1992, Oct. 16   Wmk. 384   Perf. 14

573	A108	20v green & brown	.30	.30
574	A108	70v brown & green	.85	.85
575	A108	80v green & brown	1.00	1.00
576	A108	150v brown & green	1.60	1.60
		Nos. 573-576 (4)	3.75	3.75

Turtles A109

1992, Dec. 15   Perf. 14x14½

577	A109	55v Leatherback turtle	1.10	1.10
578	A109	65v Loggerhead turtle	1.25	1.25
579	A109	70v Hawksbill turtle	1.50	1.50
580	A109	80v Green turtle	2.00	2.00
		Nos. 577-580 (4)	5.85	5.85

Souvenir Sheet

581	A109	200v Green turtle hatchlings	4.25	4.25

Hibiscus — A110

Designs: 25v, Light pink hibiscus rosa-sinensis. 55v, Hibiscus tiliaceus. 80v, Red hibiscus rosa-sinensis. 150v, Dark pink hibiscus rosa-sinensis.

Wmk. 384

1993, Mar. 3   Litho.   Perf. 14

582	A110	25v multicolored	.45	.45
583	A110	55v multicolored	1.00	1.00
584	A110	80v multicolored	1.40	1.40
585	A110	150v multicolored	2.60	2.60
		Nos. 582-585 (4)	5.45	5.45

Nos. 331, 333-335 Surcharged

Perf. 13½x14, 14x13½

1993, Apr. 21   Litho.   Wmk. 373

586	A60	40v on 45v #331	.75	.75
587	A60	55v on 75v #333	1.00	1.00
588	A60	65v on 100v #334	1.10	1.10
589	A60	150v on 200v #335	2.75	2.75
		Nos. 586-589 (4)	5.60	5.60

Size and location of surcharge varies.

No. 326 Surcharged

1993, June 1

589A	A60	20v on 35v #326	.35	.35

World War II Type of 1992

20v, Grumman F6F-3 Hellcat. 55v, Lockheed P-38F Lightning. 65v, GrummanTBF-1 Avenger. 80v, USS Essex. 200v, Douglas C-47 Dakota.

1993, June 30   Perf. 13½

590	A105	20v multicolored	.35	.35
591	A105	55v multicolored	1.00	1.00
592	A105	65v multicolored	1.25	1.25
593	A105	80v multicolored	1.40	1.40
		Nos. 590-593 (4)	4.00	4.00

Souvenir Sheet

594	A105	200v multicolored	3.65	3.65

Island Scenes A111

Designs: 5v, Iririki Island, Port Vila. 10v, Iririki Island, yachts. 15v, Court House, Port Vila. 20v, Two girls, Pentecost Island. 25v, Women dancers, Tanna Island. 30v, Market, Port Vila. 45v, Man with canoe, Erakor Island, vert. 50v, Coconut trees, Champagne Beach. 55v, Coconut trees, North Efate Islands. 60v, Fish (Banks Group). 70v, Sea fan, Tongoa Island, vert. 75v, Espiritu Santo Island. 80v, Sailboat at sunset, Port Vila Bay, vert. 100v, Mele Waterfall, vert. 300v, Yasur Volcano, Tanna Island, vert. 500v, Erakor Island.

1993, July 7   Perf. 14x14½, 14½x14

595	A111	5v multicolored	.20	.20
596	A111	10v multicolored	.20	.20
597	A111	15v multicolored	.25	.25
598	A111	20v multicolored	.35	.35
599	A111	25v multicolored	.40	.40
600	A111	30v multicolored	.50	.50
601	A111	45v multicolored	.75	.75
602	A111	50v multicolored	.80	.80
603	A111	55v multicolored	.90	.90
604	A111	60v multicolored	1.00	1.00
605	A111	70v multicolored	1.10	1.10
606	A111	75v multicolored	1.25	1.25
607	A111	80v multicolored	1.25	1.25
608	A111	100v multicolored	1.60	1.60
609	A111	300v multicolored	4.75	4.75
610	A111	500v multicolored	8.00	8.00
		Nos. 595-610 (16)	23.30	23.30

For surcharges see Nos. 619-620, 742-745A.

Shells — A112

Wmk. 373

1993, Sept. 15   Litho.   Perf. 14½

611	A112	55v Trochus niloticus	.90	.90
612	A112	65v Lioconcha castrensis	1.10	1.10
613	A112	80v Turbo petholatus	1.40	1.40
614	A112	150v Pleuroploca trapezium	2.50	2.50
		Nos. 611-614 (4)	5.90	5.90

See Nos. 632-635, 654-657.

Louvre Museum, Bicent. A113

Paintings by De La Tour: 25v, St. Joseph the Carpenter. 55v, The Newborn. 80v, Adoration of the Shepherds (detail). 150v, Adoration of the Shepherds (entire).

Wmk. 373

1993, Nov. 10   Litho.   Perf. 14

615	A113	25v multicolored	.40	.40
616	A113	55v multicolored	.85	.85
617	A113	80v multicolored	1.25	1.25
618	A113	150v multicolored	2.50	2.50
		Nos. 615-618 (4)	5.00	5.00

Nos. 570, 572, 598, 600 Surcharged

1993, Dec. 6   Litho.   Wmk. 373
Perfs. as Before

619	A111	15v on 20v #598	.25	.25
620	A111	25v on 30v #600	.40	.40
621	A107	55v on 65v #570	.90	.90
622	A107	70v on 80v #572	1.10	1.10
		Nos. 619-622 (4)	2.65	2.65

Service Organizations A114

Intl. Year of the Family A115

Hong Kong '94: 25v, Kiwanis Intl., Charity Races, vert. 60v, Lions Intl. Twin Otter on mercy mission. 75v, Rotary Intl. fighting malaria, vert. 150v, Red Cross blood donar service. 200v, Emblems of service organizations.

Perf. 14x15, 15x14

1994, Feb. 18   Litho.   Wmk. 373

623	A114	25v multicolored	.40	.40
624	A114	60v multicolored	1.00	1.00
625	A114	75v multicolored	1.25	1.25
626	A114	150v multicolored	2.50	2.50
		Nos. 623-626 (4)	5.15	5.15

Souvenir Sheet

627	A114	200v multicolored	3.25	3.25

1994, Mar. 2   Perf. 14

628	A115	25v vio & rose brn	.40	.40
629	A115	60v ver & dk grn	1.00	1.00
630	A115	90v green & sepia	1.50	1.50
631	A115	150v brn & vio bl	2.50	2.50
		Nos. 628-631 (4)	5.40	5.40

Shell Type of 1993

1994, May 31   Litho.   Perf. 12

632	A112	60v Cyprea argus	1.00	1.00
633	A112	70v Conus marmoreus	1.25	1.25
634	A112	85v Lambis chiragra	1.50	1.50
635	A112	155v Chicoreus brunneus	2.75	2.75
		Nos. 632-635 (4)	6.50	6.50

Tourism — A116

Designs: a, 25v, Slit gong (drum), traditional hut. b, 75v, Volcano, boats. c, 90v, Sailboats, airplane, green palm lorikeet. d, 200v, Helicopter, woman with tray of fruit.

1994, July 27   Litho.   Perf. 13½

636	A116	Strip of 4, #a.-d.	6.75	6.75

Anemonefish — A117

1994, Aug. 16   Litho.   Perf. 12

637	A117	55v Pink	.95	.95
638	A117	70v Clark's	1.25	1.25
639	A117	80v Red & black	1.40	1.40
640	A117	140v Orange-fin	2.50	2.50
a.		Souvenir sheet of 1	2.50	2.50
		Nos. 637-640 (4)	6.10	6.10

Philakorea '94 (#640a).

ICAO, 50th Anniv. — A118

Designs: 25v, 1950 Qantas Catalina. 60v, 1956 Tai Douglas DC3. 75v, 1966 New Herbrides Airways Drover. 90v, 1994 Air Vanuatu Boeing 737.

1994, Dec. 7

641	A118	25v multicolored	.40	.40
642	A118	60v multicolored	1.00	1.00
643	A118	75v multicolored	1.25	1.25
644	A118	90v multicolored	1.50	1.50
		Nos. 641-644 (4)	4.15	4.15

Hibiscus A119

1995, Feb. 1   Litho.   Perf. 12

645	A119	25v The Path	.45	.45
646	A119	55v Old Frankie	1.10	1.10
647	A119	90v Fijian white	1.60	1.60
648	A119	200v Surf rider	3.50	3.50
		Nos. 645-648 (4)	6.65	6.65

Lizards A120

Designs: 25v, Emoia nigromarginata. 55v, Nactus multicarinatus. 70v, Lepidodactylus. 80v, Emoia caerulocauda. 140v, Emoia sanfordi.

1995, Apr. 12

649	A120	25v multicolored	.45	.45
650	A120	55v multicolored	1.00	1.00
651	A120	70v multicolored	1.25	1.25
652	A120	80v multicolored	1.40	1.40
653	A120	140v multicolored	2.50	2.50
		Nos. 649-653 (5)	6.60	6.60

Shell Type of 1993

1995, June 1

654	A112	25v Epitonium scalare	.45	.45
655	A112	55v Strombus latissimus	1.00	1.00
656	A112	90v Conus bullatus	1.60	1.60
657	A112	200v Pterynotus pinnatus	3.50	3.50
		Nos. 654-657 (4)	6.55	6.55

Anniversaries — A121

Designs: 25v, Girls wearing traditional head pieces. 55v, Stylized picture of natives dancing, vert. 60v, Children, doves, natl. flag, UN flag, vert. 75v, Embroidered tapestry of native, vert. 90v, Troops parading. 140v, Group in traditional ceremony.

Perf. 14x13½, 13½x14

1995, July 28   Litho.
658	A121	25v multicolored	.45	.45
659	A121	55v multicolored	1.00	1.00
660	A121	60v multicolored	1.10	1.10
661	A121	75v multicolored	1.40	1.40
662	A121	90v multicolored	1.60	1.60
663	A121	140v multicolored	2.50	2.50
a.		Souvenir sheet of 1	2.00	2.00
		Nos. 658-663 (6)	8.05	8.05

UN, 50th anniv. (#660). Singapore 95 (#663a). Others, independence, 15th anniv.

World War II Type of 1992

1995, Sept. 1   Litho.   Perf. 12½
664	A105	60v SB2C Helldiver	1.10	1.10
665	A105	70v Spitfire Mk VIII	1.25	1.25
666	A105	75v F4U-1A Corsair	1.25	1.25
667	A105	80v PV1 Ventura	1.40	1.40
		Nos. 664-667 (4)	5.00	5.00

Souvenir Sheet
Perf. 13½
667A	A105	140v Japanese surrender, USS Missouri	2.00	2.00

No. 667A for Singapore 95.

Artifacts — A122

Ambae money mat and: a, 25v, Rambaramp mortuary effigy, Malakula. b, 60v, Wusi pot, Espiritu Santo. c, 75v, Slit gong, Efate Island. d, 90v, Tapa cloth, Erromango Island. Nos. 668e, 668f, like No. 668d. Illustration reduced.

1995, Nov. 22   Litho.   Perf. 13½x13
668	A122	Strip of 4, #a.-d.	4.50	4.50
e.		90v Perf. 14	1.60	1.60
f.		Souvenir sheet, #668e	1.60	1.60

No. 668f, 9th Asian Intl. Philatelic Exhibition, Beijing.

Issued: Nos. 668e, 668f, Dec. 1995.
See No. 720.

Fishing
A123

1996, Feb. 1   Litho.   Perf. 14
669	A123	55v Cast net	1.00	1.00
670	A123	75v Reef	1.25	1.25
671	A123	80v Deep water, vert.	1.40	1.40
672	A123	140v Game, vert.	2.50	2.50
		Nos. 669-672 (4)	6.15	6.15

Flying
Foxes
A124

No. 673, Notopteris macdonaldi, facing left. No. 674, Pteropus anetianus, green leaves on tree, vert. No. 675, Pteropus anetianus, diff., vert. No. 676, Notopteris macdonaldi, diff. No. 677, vert: a, 90v, Pteropus tonganus. b, 140v, Pteropus tonganus, diff.

1996, Apr. 3   Litho.   Perf. 14
673	A124	25v multicolored	.55	.55
674	A124	25v multicolored	.55	.55
675	A124	25v multicolored	.55	.55
676	A124	25v multicolored	.55	.55
		Nos. 673-676 (4)	2.20	2.20

Souvenir Sheet
677	A124	Sheet of 2, #a.-b.	4.25	4.25

World Wildlife Fund (Nos. 673-676). 9th Asian Intl. Philatelic Exhibition (No. 677).

UNICEF, 50th Anniv. A125

Unwmk.
1996, June 5   Litho.   Perf. 14
678	A125	55v Immunizations	1.00	1.00
679	A125	60v Breast feeding	1.10	1.10

Radio, Cent. A126

60v, Airplane, radio signal. 75v, Radio Vanuatu. 80v, Guglielmo Marconi. 90v, Ship, radio signal.

1996, June 5   Perf. 14½
680	A126	60v multicolored	1.10	1.10
681	A126	75v multicolored	1.25	1.25
682	A126	80v multicolored	1.40	1.40
683	A126	90v multicolored	1.60	1.60
a.		Block of 4, #680-683	5.50	5.50

Modern Olympic Games, Cent. — A127

Designs: 25v, Marie Kapalu, Tawai Keiruan, Baptiste Firiam, Tava Kalo, 1996 athletes from Vanuatu. 70v, 1996 Athletes in training. 75v, 1950's Athletes. 200v, 1896 Athletes.

1996, July 17   Litho.   Perf. 14
684	A127	25v multicolored	.45	.45
685	A127	70v multicolored	1.25	1.25
686	A127	75v multicolored	1.25	1.25
687	A127	200v multicolored	3.50	3.50
		Nos. 684-687 (4)	6.45	6.45

Christmas
A128

Children of various races holding candles in front of churches: a, 25v, Presbyterian, Roman Catholic. b, 60v, Church of Christ. c, 75v, 7th Day Adventist, Apostolic. d, 90v, Anglican.

1996, Sept. 11   Litho.   Perf. 14
688	A128	Strip of 4, #a.-d.	4.50	4.50

No. 688 is a continuous design.

Hibiscus
A129

1996, Nov. 13   Litho.   Perf. 13½
689	A129	25v Lady Cilento	.45	.45
690	A129	60v Kinchen's Yellow	1.10	1.10
691	A129	90v D.J. O'Brien	1.60	1.60
692	A129	200v Cuban Variety	3.50	3.50
a.		Sheet of 2, #689, #692	4.10	4.10
		Nos. 689-692 (4)	6.65	6.65

Hong Kong '97. No. 692a issued 2/12/97.

Diving
A130

Designs: 70v, Coral Garden. 75v, Lady of the President Coolidge. 90v, "Boris," Queensland grouper. 140v, Wreck of the President Coolidge.

1997, Jan. 15   Litho.   Perf. 14½x14
693	A130	70v multicolored	1.25	1.25
694	A130	75v multicolored	1.25	1.25
695	A130	90v multicolored	1.60	1.60
696	A130	140v multicolored	2.40	2.40
a.		Souvenir sheet, #694, 696	3.75	3.75
b.		Souvenir sheet, #693-696	6.50	6.50
		Nos. 693-696 (4)	6.50	6.50

Pacific '97 (#696a).

Birds
A131

25v, Sharp-tailed sandpiper. 55v, Crested tern. 60v, Little pied cormorant. 75v, Brown booby. 80v, Reef heron. 90v, Red-tailed tropic bird.

1997, June 4   Litho.   Perf. 13½x14
697	A131	25v multi	.50	.50
698	A131	55v multi	1.00	1.00
699	A131	60v multi	1.10	1.10
700	A131	75v multi	1.40	1.40
701	A131	80v multi, vert.	1.40	1.40
702	A131	90v multi, vert.	1.60	1.60
		Nos. 697-702 (6)	7.00	7.00

Air Vanuatu, 10th Anniv. A132

Designs: 25v, Pilot at controls. 60v, Airplane being serviced, cargo loaded. 90v, Serving drinks to passengers. 200v, Passengers leaving plane upon arrival at Vanuatu.

1997, Apr. 2   Perf. 14½x14
703	A132	25v multicolored	.45	.45
704	A132	60v multicolored	1.10	1.10
705	A132	90v multicolored	1.60	1.60
706	A132	200v multicolored	3.50	3.50
		Nos. 703-706 (4)	6.65	6.65

No. 704 is 81x31mm.

Thomas A. Edison (1847-1931) — A133

Designs: 60v, Light bulb, Edison. 70v, Hydro dam, Santo. 200v, Port Vila by dusk.

1997, Aug. 27   Litho.   Perf. 12
707	A133	60v multicolored	1.10	1.10
708	A133	70v multicolored	1.25	1.25
709	A133	200v multicolored	3.50	3.50
a.		Block of 3, #707-709 + label	6.00	6.00

No. 709 is 80x30mm.

Fish — A134

Designs: 25v, Yellow-faced angelfish. 55v, Flame angelfish. 60v, Lemonpeel angelfish. 70v, Emperor angelfish. 140v, Multi-barred angelfish.

1997, Nov. 12   Litho.   Perf. 14x13
710	A134	25v multicolored	.45	.45
711	A134	55v multicolored	1.00	1.00
712	A134	60v multicolored	1.10	1.10
713	A134	70v multicolored	1.25	1.25
714	A134	140v multicolored	2.50	2.50
		Nos. 710-714 (5)	6.30	6.30

Architecture in Vanuatu A135

Designs: 30v, Fale-Espiritu Santo. 65v, Natl. Cultural Center. 80v, University of the South Pacific. 200v, Chief's Nakamal.

1998, Feb. 11   Litho.   Perf. 14½x1
715	A135	30v multicolored	.50	.50
716	A135	65v multicolored	1.10	1.10
717	A135	80v multicolored	1.25	1.25
718	A135	200v multicolored	3.25	3.25
		Nos. 715-718 (4)	6.10	6.10

Diana, Princess of Wales (1961-97)
Common Design Type

Various portraits: a, 75v. b, 85v. c, 145v.

1998, Mar. 31   Litho.   Perf. 14½x14
718A	CD355	95v multicolored	1.40	1.40

Sheet of 4
719	CD355	#a.-c., 718A	7.50	7.50

No. 719 sold for 400v + 50v, with surtax from international sales being donated to The Diana, Princess of Wales Memorial Fund and surtax from national sales being donated to designated local charity.

Artifacts Type of 1995

Tribal masks: a, 30v, South West Malakula. b, 65v, North Ambrym. c, 75v, Gana Island Banks. d, 85v, Uripiv Island, Malakula. e, 95v, Vao Island, Malakula, and Central South Pentecost.

1998, June 3   Litho.   Perf. 14½
720	A122	Strip of 5, #a.-e.	5.30	5.30

Butterflies — A136

30v, Danaus plexippus. 60v, Hypolimnas bolina. 65v, Eurema hecabe. 75v, Nymphalidae. 95v, Precis villida. 205v, Tirumala hamata.

1998, July 23   Litho.   Die Cut
Self-Adhesive
721	A136	30v multicolored	.45	.45
722	A136	60v multicolored	.90	.90
723	A136	65v multicolored	1.00	1.00
724	A136	75v multicolored	1.10	1.10
725	A136	95v multicolored	1.40	1.40
726	A136	205v multicolored	3.00	3.00
a.		Souvenir sheet of 1	3.00	3.00
		Nos. 721-726 (6)	7.85	7.85

Singpex '98 (#726a).

Volcanoes — A137

30v, Yasur, Tanna. 60v, Marum & Benbow, Ambrym. 75v, Gaua. 80v, Lopevi. 145v, Ambae.

1998, Oct. 23   Litho.   Perf. 15x14

728	A137	30v multicolored	.45	.45
729	A137	60v multicolored	.90	.90
730	A137	75v multicolored	1.10	1.10
731	A137	80v multicolored	1.10	1.10
732	A137	145v multicolored	2.25	2.25
		Nos. 728-732 (5)	5.80	5.80

Early Explorers A138

Explorer, ship: 34v, Pedro Fernandez de Quiros, San Pedro y Paulo, 1606. 73v, Louis-Antoine de Bougainville, Boudeuse, 1768. 84v, Capt. James Cook, HMS Resolution, 1774. 90v, Jean-Fancois de Galaup de la Perousse, Astrolabe, 1788. 96v, Jules Sebastien-Cesar Dumont d'Urville, Astrolabe, "1788."

1999, Feb. 17   Litho.   Perf. 14

733	A138	34v multicolored	.55	.55
734	A138	73v multicolored	1.25	1.25
735	A138	84v multicolored	1.40	1.40
a.		Souv. sheet, #733-735	3.25	3.25
736	A138	90v multicolored	1.40	1.40
737	A138	96v multicolored	1.50	1.50
a.		Souv. sheet, #734, 736-737	4.00	4.00
		Nos. 733-737 (5)	6.10	6.10

No. 735A was released for Australia '99 World Stamp Expo on 3/19/99; No. 737a for PhilexFrance 99.

Birds — A139

34v, Vanuatu kingfisher. 67v, Shining cuckoo. 73v, Peregrine falcon. 107v, Rainbow lorikeet.

1999, May 12   Litho.   Perf. 14

738	A139	34v multicolored	.55	.55
739	A139	67v multicolored	1.10	1.10
a.		Booklet, 5 #739	5.50	
740	A139	73v multicolored	1.25	1.25
741	A139	107v multicolored	1.75	1.75
a.		Sheet of 1	1.75	1.75
b.		Sheet of 1 with China 1999 emblem in margin	1.75	1.75
		Nos. 738-741 (4)	4.65	4.65

Issued: #741b, 8/18.

Nos. 601, 603-605, 608 Surcharged

Perf. 14½x14, 14x14½
1998-2000   Litho.

742	A111	1v on 100v #608	.20	.20
742A	A111	2v on 45v #601	.20	.20
743	A111	2v on 55v #603	.20	.20
744	A111	3v on 60v #604	.20	.20
744A	A111	3v on 75v #606	.20	.20
745	A111	4v on 45v #601	.20	.20
745A	A111	5v on 70v #605		
745B	A111	34v on 20v #598	.50	.50
745C	A111	67v on 300v #609	1.00	1.00
		Nos. 742-745C (8)	2.70	2.70

Issued: No. 742, No. 742A, 743, 744, 745, 745A, 12/18/98; No. 744A, 4/27/99; Nos. 745B, 745C, 2/17/00.

Ceremonial Dancers — A140

1v, Banks Islands. 2v, Small Nambas, Laman-Malakula. 3v, Small Nambas, Malakula. 5v, Smol Bag Theatre. 107v, South West Bay, Malakula. 200v, Big Nambas, Malakula. 500v, Pentacost.

1999, July 14   Perf. 14

746	A140	1v multicolored	.20	.20
747	A140	2v multicolored	.20	.20
748	A140	3v multicolored	.20	.20
749	A140	5v multicolored	.20	.20
750	A140	107v multicolored	1.60	1.60
751	A140	200v multicolored	3.25	3.25
752	A140	500v multicolored	7.75	7.75
		Nos. 746-752 (7)	13.40	13.40

Poisonous Fish — A141

Designs: 34v, Pterois antennata. 84v, Pterois antennata, diff. 90v, Pterois volitans. 96v, Pterois volitans, diff.

1999, Oct. 13   Litho.   Perf. 14¼

753	A141	34v multi	.55	.55
754	A141	84v multi	1.25	1.25
755	A141	90v multi	1.40	1.40
756	A141	96v multi	1.50	1.50
		Nos. 753-756 (4)	4.70	4.70

Millennium A142

Designs: a, 34v, Fish. b, 68v, Girl, land diver, vert. c, 84v, Fetish, vert. d, 90v, Bird, flowers. e, 96v, Man with conch shell.

1999, Dec. 1   Perf. 14½
757 A142 Sheet of 5, #a.-e.   6.00 6.00

Souvenir Sheet

Queen Mother, 100th Birthday — A143

a, 107v, As child. b, 100v, As old woman. Illustration reduced.

Litho. with Foil Application
2000, May 22   Perf. 13¼
758 A143 Sheet of 2, #a-b   3.00 3.00
The Stamp Show 2000, London.

Intelsat A144

Designs: 10v, Launch vehicle. 34v, Port Vila ground station. 100v, Intelsat 802 over Vaunatu. 225v, Intelsat and Tam Tam drum.

Litho. with Foil Application
2000, June 21   Die Cut Perf. 10
Self-Adhesive

| 759-762 | A144 | Set of 4 | 5.25 | 5.25 |
| 762a | | Souvenir sheet, #760, 762 | 3.75 | 3.75 |

World Stamp Expo 2000, Anaheim (#762a).

Independence, 20th Anniv., UN Peace Year — A145

Artwork: 34v, Abstract painting by Sero Kuautonga. 67v, Tapa cloth by Moses Pita. 73v, Tapestry by Juliet Pita. 84v, Natora wood carving by Emmannuel Watt. 90v, Watercolor by Joseph John.

2000, July 29   Litho.   Perf. 13¾x13¼
| 763-767 | A145 | Set of 5 | 5.00 | 5.00 |
| | | Booklet, 5 #764 | 5.00 | |

2000 Summer Olympics, Sydney — A146

Designs: 56v, Runner. 67v, Weight lifter. 90v, High jumper. 96v, Boxer.

2000, Sept. 15   Perf. 13¼x13
| 768-771 | A146 | Set of 4 | 4.50 | 4.50 |
| | | Booklet, 5 #769 | 5.00 | |

Dolphins — A147

34v, Common. 73v, Spotted. 84v, Spinner. 107v, Bottlenose.

2000, Nov. 30   Litho.   Perf. 12½
| 772-775 | A147 | Set of 4 | 4.25 | 4.25 |
| 775a | | Souvenir sheet, #774-775 | 2.60 | 2.60 |

Hong Kong 2001 Stamp Exhibition (#775a).

Birds — A148

Designs: 35v, Cardinal honeyeater. 60v, Vanuatu white-eye. 90v, Santo Mountain starling. 100v, Royal parrotfinch. 110v, Vanuatu Mountain honeyeater.

2001, Feb. 1   Litho.   Perf. 14
| 776-780 | A148 | Set of 5 | 5.50 | 5.50 |
| 780a | | Horiz. strip, #776-780 | 5.50 | 5.50 |

Exports — A149

Designs: 35v, Vanilla. 75v, Cacao. 90v, Coffee. 110v, Copra.

2001, Apr. 11   Perf. 13¼x13
781-784 A149 Set of 4   4.25 4.25

Whales A150

Designs: 60v, Sperm. 80v, Humpback, vert. 90v, Blue.

Perf. 14½x14¾, 14¾x14½
2001, July 18   Litho.
| 785-787 | A150 | Set of 3 | 3.25 | 3.25 |
| 787a | | Souvenir sheet, #785-787, perf. 14½ | 3.25 | 3.25 |

See New Caledonia No. 874.

Ceremonial Dancers Type of 1999

Designs: 35v, Snake dance, Banks Islands, horiz. 100v, Toka Dance, Tanna, horiz. 300v, Rom Dance, Ambryn, horiz. 1000v, Brasive Dance, Futuna, horiz.

2001, Sept. 12   Litho.   Perf. 13x13¼
788	A140	35v multi	.50	.50
789	A140	100v multi	1.40	1.40
790	A140	300v multi	4.25	4.25

Litho. With Foil Application
| 791 | A140 | 1000v multi | 14.00 | 14.00 |
| | | Nos. 788-791 (4) | 20.15 | 20.15 |

Sand Drawings — A151

Various sand drawings and: a, Four people on beach. b, Man standing in canoe in water. c, Man sitting on canoe, man rowing canoe. d, Canoe, shelter.

Perf. 12¾x13½
2001, Nov. 28   Litho.
792	A151	60v multi	.85	.85
792A	A151	90v multi	1.25	1.25
792B	A151	110v multi	1.50	1.50
792C	A151	135v multi	1.90	1.90
Cd.		Horiz. strip of 4 + central label	5.50	5.50

Intl. Year of
Ecotourism
A152

Designs: Nos. 793, 798a, 35v, Mount Yasur, Pentecost Island land diver, dancers. Nos. 794, 798b, 60v Dancers, man making kava. Nos. 795, 798c, 75v, Siri Falls, flowers, birds, vert. Nos. 796, 798d, 110v, Kayakers, scuba diver, vert. Nos. 797, 798e, 135v, Beach bungalows, tourists.

2002, Jan. 30   Litho.   Perf. 14
Stamps + Label

| 793-797 | A152 | Set of 5 | 5.75 | 5.75 |

Souvenir Sheet
Without Labels
Perf. 14½x14¾

| 798 | A152 | Sheet of 5, #a-e | 5.75 | 5.75 |

Nos. 793, 794, and 797 are 38x26mm and Nos. 795-796 are 26x38mm, while Nos. 798a, 798b, and 798e are 37x25mm and Nos. 798c-798d are 25x37mm.

Horses
A153

Designs: 35v, Working horses. 60v, Cattle roundup. 75v, Horse racing. 80v, Tourism and horses. 200v, Wild Tanna horse.

2002, Mar. 27   Perf. 14¾x14

799-803	A153	Set of 5	6.25	6.25
803a		Souvenir sheet of 1	2.75	2.75
803b		Souvenir sheet of 1 with Philakorea 2002 emblem	3.00	3.00

Issued: No. 803b, 7/31/02.

Soccer
A154

Designs: 35v, Children's soccer. 80v, Under 17 soccer. 110v, Women's soccer. 135v, International soccer.

2002, May 31   Litho.   Perf. 13¾

| 804-807 | A154 | Set of 4 | 5.50 | 5.50 |

Value is for stamps with surrounding selvage.

Reforestation — A155

No. 808: a, Girl with seedling of Artocarpus atilis. b, Boy and man planting seedling of Endospermum medullosum. c, Canoe carver with Gyrocarpus americanus log. d, Mother and child with Dracontomelon vitiense fruit.

Serpentine Die Cut
2002, July 31   Litho.
Self-Adhesive

808	Horiz. strip of 4		4.25	
a.	A155	35v multi	.50	.50
b.	A155	60v multi	.90	.90
c.	A155	90v multi	1.25	1.25
d.	A155	110v multi	1.60	1.60

Dugongs
A156

Designs: 35v, Pair nuzzling. 75v, Pair swimming. 80v, One swimming. 135v, One on ocean floor.

2002, Sept. 25   Litho.   Perf. 13¾

| 812-815 | A156 | Set of 4 | 4.75 | 4.75 |
| 815a | | Souvenir sheet, #814-815 | 3.25 | 3.25 |

Orchids — A157

Designs: 35v, Dendrobium gouldii. 60v, Dendrobium polysema. 90v, Dendrobium spectabile. 110v, Flickingeria comata.

2002, Nov. 27   Litho.   Perf. 13¼

| 816-819 | A157 | Set of 4 | 4.50 | 4.50 |

Year of
Cattle — A158

Cattle Breeds: 35v, Limousin. 80v, Charolais. 110v, Simmental. 135v, Red Brahman.

2003, Jan. 29   Perf. 13

| 820-823 | A158 | Set of 4 | 5.75 | 5.75 |

Pentecost
Island Land
Divers — A159

Designs: 35v, Diver on platform. 80v, Diver in air. 110v, Dancers, platform. 200v, Diver and platform (35x90mm).

2003, Mar. 26   Perf. 13¾x13¼

| 824-827 | A159 | Set of 4 | 6.75 | 6.75 |
| 827a | | Souvenir sheet of 1 | 3.25 | 3.25 |

Snorkeling
A160

Various people snorkeling: 35v, 80v, 90v, 110v, 135v. 80v and 90v are vert.

2003, May 28   Litho.   Perf. 13¾

| 828-832 | A160 | Set of 5 | 7.50 | 7.50 |
| 832a | | Souvenir sheet, #828-832, perf. 13¼ | 7.50 | 7.50 |

Natanggura
Palm — A161

Half of palm nut and: 35v, Man planting palm tree, carved dolphins. 80v, Man weaving thatch for roof, carved turtle. 90v, Carver, carved lizard. 135v, Carvers, carved fish.

2003, July 23   Perf. 13¾x13¼

| 833-836 | A161 | Set of 4 | 5.75 | 5.75 |

Opening of
Underwater Post
Office in May
2003 — A162

2003, Sept. 24   Perf. 13¾

| 837 | A162 | 90v multi | 1.60 | 1.60 |

Sea
Horses — A163

Designs: 60v, Hippocampus kuda. 90v, Hippocampus histrix. 200v, Hippocampus bargibanti.

2003, Sept. 24

| 838-840 | A163 | Set of 3 | 6.00 | 6.00 |
| 840a | | Souvenir sheet of 1 | 3.50 | 3.50 |

Moths
A164

Designs: 35v, Daphnis hypothous. 90v, Hippotion celerio. 110v, Euchromia creusa. 135v, Eudocima salaminia.

2003, Nov. 26   Perf. 13½

| 841-844 | A164 | Set of 4 | 6.50 | 6.50 |

Activities at
Underwater Post
Office — A165

Designs: 35v, Workers placing mail in bag. 80v, Swimmer placing mail in mail box. 110v, Swimmer at counter. 220v, Clerk at counter, swimmer near mail box.

2004, Jan. 30   Perf. 13¾x13

| 845-848 | A165 | Set of 4 | 8.25 | 8.2 |
| 848a | | Souvenir sheet of 1 | 4.00 | 4.0 |

2004 Hong Kong Stamp Expo (#848a).

Starfish
A166

Designs: 35v, Protoreaster nodulosus. 60v, Linckia laevigata. 90v, Fromia monilis. 250v, Echinaster callosus.

Serpentine Die Cut
2004, Apr. 28   Litho.
Self-Adhesive

| 849-852 | A166 | Set of 4 | 7.75 | 7.7 |

SEMI POSTAL STAMPS

Nos. 324 and 414-418 Surcharged
"Hurricane Relief Fund"
Wmk. 373 (No. B1), 384
Perf. 14x13½, 14x14½

1987, May 12   Litho.

B1	A60	20v +10v on 2v	.75	.75
B2	CD337	20v +10v	.75	.75
B3	CD337	35v +15v	1.25	1.25
B4	CD337	45v +20v	1.50	1.50
B5	CD337	55v +25v	2.75	2.75
B6	CD337	100v +50v	3.00	3.00
		Nos. B1-B6 (6)	10.00	10.00

Old value of #B1 obliterated by 2 horizontal bars. Surcharge indicated by text "Surcharge +10."

VATICAN CITY

ˈva-ti-kən ˈsi-tē

LOCATION — Western Italy, directly outside the western boundary of Rome
GOVT. — Independent state subject to certain political restrictions under a treaty with Italy
AREA — 108.7 acres
POP. — 870 (1999 est.)

100 Centesimi = 1 Lira
100 Cents = 1 Euro (2002)

Catalogue values for unused stamps in this country are for Never Hinged items, beginning with Scott 68 in the regular postage section, Scott C1 in the airpost section, Scott E3 in the special delivery section, and Scott J7 in the postage due section.

Watermarks

Wmk. 235 —   Wmk. 277 —
Crossed Keys   Winged Wheel

Papal Arms — A1

Pope Pius XI — A2

Unwmk.

1929, Aug. 1   Engr.   Perf. 14
Surface-Colored Paper
1	A1	5c dk brn & pink	.20	.25
2	A1	10c dk grn & lt grn	.25	.30
3	A1	20c violet & lilac	.55	.40
4	A1	25c dk bl & lt bl	.70	.45
5	A1	30c indigo & yellow	.80	.60
6	A1	50c ind & sal buff	1.25	.65
7	A1	75c brn car & gray	1.60	1.00

Photo.
White Paper
8	A2	80c carmine rose	1.25	.40
9	A2	1.25 l dark blue	2.00	.75
10	A2	2 l olive brown	3.75	1.40
11	A2	2.50 l red orange	3.25	2.50
12	A2	5 l dk green	3.75	8.50
13	A2	10 l olive blk	8.00	11.50
	Nos. 1-13,E1-E2 (15)		53.35	52.20
	Set, never hinged		150.00	

The stamps of Type A1 have, in this and subsequent issues, the words "POSTE VATI-CANE" in rows of colorless letters in the background.

For surcharges and overprints see Nos. 14, 5-40, 61-67, J1-J6, Q1-Q13.

No. 5 Surcharged in Red ≡ C. ≡ 25

1931, Oct. 1
14	A1	25c on 30c ind & yel	2.10	1.40
	Never hinged		6.75	

Arms of Pope Pius XI — A5

Vatican Palace and Obelisk — A6

Vatican Gardens — A7

Pope Pius XI A8

St. Peter's Basilica A9

1933, May 31   Engr.   Wmk. 235
19	A5	5c copper red	.20	.20
a.	Imperf., pair		250.00	275.00
20	A6	10c dk brn & blk	.20	.20
21	A6	12½c dp grn & blk	.20	.20
22	A6	20c orange & blk	.20	.20
a.	Vertical pair imperf. between and at bottom		250.00	250.00
23	A6	25c dk olive & blk	.20	.20
a.	Imperf., pair		150.00	175.00
24	A7	30c blk & dk brn	.20	.20
25	A7	50c viot & dk brn	.20	.20
26	A7	75c brn red & dk brn	.20	.20
27	A7	80c rose & dk brn	.20	.20
28	A8	1 l violet & blk	3.25	2.75
29	A8	1.25 l dk bl & blk	11.00	5.00
30	A8	2 l dk brn & blk	27.50	20.00
31	A8	2.75 l dk vio & blk	32.50	40.00
32	A8	5 l blk brn & dk	.20	.25
33	A9	10 l dk blue & dk grn	.20	.30
34	A9	20 l blk & dp grn	.25	.35
	Nos. 19-34,E3-E4 (18)		77.40	71.35
	Set, never hinged		210.00	

Nos. 8-13 Surcharged in Black ≡ 40 ≡

1934, June 16   Unwmk.
35	A2	40c on 80c	3.25	1.90
36	A2	1.30 l on 1.25 l	57.50	37.50
a.	Small figures "30" in "1.30"		10,000.	7,250.
	Never hinged		12,500.	
37	A2	2.05 l on 2 l	125.00	14.00
a.	No comma btwn. 2 & 0		275.00	20.00
	Never hinged		850.00	
38	A2	2.55 l on 2.50 l	82.50	150.00
a.	No comma btwn. 2 & 5		150.00	275.00
	Never hinged		475.00	
39	A2	3.05 l on 5 l	275.00	275.00
40	A2	3.70 l on 10 l	250.00	400.00
a.	No comma btwn. 3 & 7		793.25	878.40
	Nos. 35-40 (6)			
	Set, never hinged		2,300.	

A second printing of Nos. 36-40 was made in 1937. The 2.55 l and 3.05 l of the first printing and 1.30 l of the second printing sell for more.

The status of No. 40a has been questioned. The editors would like to examine an authenticated copy of this variety.

Forged surcharges of Nos. 35-40 are plentiful.

Tribonian Presenting Pandects to Justinian I A10

Pope Gregory IX Promulgating Decretals A11

1935, Feb. 1   Photo.
41	A10	5c red orange	1.25	.75
42	A10	10c purple	1.25	.75
43	A10	25c green	12.50	12.50
44	A11	75c rose red	45.00	27.50
45	A11	80c dark brown	35.00	21.00
46	A11	1.25 l dark blue	45.00	20.00
	Nos. 41-46 (6)		140.00	82.50
	Set, never hinged		500.00	

Intl. Juridical Congress, Rome, 1934.

Doves and Bell — A12

Allegory of Church and Bible — A13

St. John Bosco — A14

St. Francis de Sales — A15

1936, June 22
47	A12	5c blue green	.75	1.00
48	A13	10c black	.75	1.00
49	A12	25c yellow green	40.00	8.50
50	A13	50c rose violet	.75	1.00
51	A13	75c rose red	40.00	40.00
52	A14	80c orange brn	1.50	1.00
53	A15	1.25 l dark blue	2.00	2.00
54	A15	5 l dark brown	2.00	6.25
	Nos. 47-54 (8)		87.75	61.75
	Set, never hinged		300.00	

Catholic Press Conference, 1936.

Crypt of St. Cecilia in Catacombs of St. Calixtus A16

Basilica of Sts. Nereus and Achilleus in Catacombs of St. Domitilla A17

1938, Oct. 12   Perf. 14
55	A16	5c bister brown	.20	.20
56	A16	10c deep orange	.20	.20
57	A16	25c deep green	.25	.25
58	A17	75c deep rose	5.50	5.50
59	A17	80c violet	17.00	17.00
60	A17	1.25 l blue	22.50	22.50
	Nos. 55-60 (6)		45.65	45.65
	Set, never hinged		125.00	

Intl. Christian Archaeological Congress, Rome, 1938.

Interregnum Issue

Nos. 1-7 Overprinted in Black

1939, Feb. 20   Perf. 14
61	A1	5c dk brn & pink	27.50	6.00
62	A1	10c dk grn & lt grn	.30	.20
63	A1	20c violet & lilac	.30	.20
64	A1	25c dk bl & lt bl	3.00	3.50
65	A1	30c indigo & yellow	.60	.20
a.	Pair, one without ovpt.		1,300.	
66	A1	50c indigo & sal buff	.60	.20
67	A1	75c brn car & gray	.60	.20
	Nos. 61-67 (7)		32.90	10.50
	Set, never hinged		92.50	

> Catalogue values for unused stamps in this section, from this point to the end of the section, are for Never Hinged items.

Coronation of Pope Pius XII — A18

1939, June 2   Photo.
68	A18	25c green	2.25	.30
69	A18	75c rose red	.50	.45
70	A18	80c violet	6.25	3.00
71	A18	1.25 l deep blue	.50	.45
	Nos. 68-71 (4)		9.50	4.20

Coronation of Pope Pius XII, Mar. 12, 1939.

Vatican

Roman States #12-18

We Sell!

Large stock of top quality material at realistic prices.

Fresh original gum NH Reprints from original plates by Moens of Brussels, circa 1880's. Beautiful set! Reprints offered at less than 1% of cv! Imperf set #12-18 VF. Reprint set of 7 NH .... $9.00 Block of 4 NH .... $36.00 FREE set (single set) with any Vatican order over $75.00 - please request!

Free Price List

Year Units, Individual Sets NH & H Postal Stationery and specialized material. Western European country price lists also available.

Save 10%! **Vatican Complete mint NH 1958-2003** Buy a complete run of Year Sets and save 10%! Regularly $1103.00   **10% off**   **$992.50** (All normally issued stamps & S/S)

We Buy!

We buy all Vatican and Italian Area including quantity material to date. Top prices paid! *Especially needed:* Collections, rarities, covers, Zeppelin flights, errors and Europa!

Henry Gitner Philatelists, Inc.

Philately-The Quiet Excitement!

PO Box 3077-S, Middletown, NY 10940
Tel: 845-343-5151 Fax: 845-343-0068
Toll Free: 1-800-947-8267
E-mail: hgitner@hgitner.com
http://www.hgitner.com

Arms of Pope
Pius XII — A19

Pope Pius XII
A20   A21

Wmk. 235

1940, Mar. 12   Engr.   Perf. 14

72	A19	5c dark carmine	.20	.20
73	A20	1 l purple & blk	.20	.20
74	A21	1.25 l slate bl & blk	.20	.20
a.		Imperf., pair	450.00	500.00
75	A20	2 l dk brn & blk	1.40	.85
76	A21	2.75 l dk rose vio & blk	2.00	1.75
		Nos. 72-76 (5)	4.00	3.20

See #91-98. For surcharges see #102-109.

A22

A23

Picture of Jesus inscribed "I have Compassion on the Multitude."

1942, Sept. 1   Photo.   Unwmk.

77	A22	25c dk blue green	.20	.20
78	A22	80c chestnut brown	.20	.20
79	A22	1.25 l deep blue	.20	.20
		Nos. 77-79 (3)	.60	.60

See Nos. 84-86, 99-101.

1942, Jan. 16

Consecration of Archbishop Pacelli by Pope Benedict XV.

80	A23	25c myr grn & gray grn	.20	.20
81	A23	80c dk brn & yel grn	.20	.20
82	A23	1.25 l sapphire & vio bl	.20	.20
a.		Name and value panel omitted		
83	A23	5 l vio blk & gray blk	.20	.25
		Nos. 80-83 (4)	.80	.85

25th anniv. of the consecration of Msgr. Eugenio Pacelli (later Pope Pius XII) as Archbishop of Sardes.

Type of 1942
Inscribed MCMXLIII

1944, Jan. 31

84	A22	25c dk blue green	.20	.20
85	A22	80c chestnut brown	.20	.20
86	A22	1.25 l deep blue	.20	.20
		Nos. 84-86 (3)	.60	.60

Raphael
Sanzio — A24

Designs: 80c, Antonio da Sangallo. 1.25 l, Carlo Maratti. 10 l, Antonio Canova.

1944, Nov. 21   Wmk. 235   Photo.

87	A24	25c olive & green	.30	.20
88	A24	80c cl & rose vio	.60	.25
a.		Dbl. impression of center	750.00	
89	A24	1.25 l bl vio & dp bl	.60	.25
a.		Imperf., pair	650.00	900.
90	A24	10 l bister & ol brn	1.25	.90
		Nos. 87-90 (4)	2.75	1.45

400th anniv. of the Pontifical Academy of the Virtuosi of the Pantheon.

Types of 1940

1945, Mar. 5   Engr.   Unwmk.

91	A19	5c gray	.20	.20
a.		Imperf., pair	200.00	
92	A19	30c brown	.20	.20
a.		Imperf., pair	120.00	
93	A19	50c dark green	.20	.20
94	A21	1 l brown & blk	.20	.20
95	A21	1.50 l rose car & blk	.20	.20
a.		Imperf., pair	325.00	
96	A21	2.50 l dp ultra & blk	.20	.20
97	A20	5 l rose vio & blk	.20	.25
98	A20	20 l gray grn & blk	.25	.30
		Nos. 91-98,E5-E6 (10)	2.25	2.35

Nos. 91-96 exist in pairs imperf. between, some vertical, some horizontal. Value, each $150.

Pair imperf. vertically exist of 30c and 50c (value $50), and of 5 lire (value $90).

Type of 1942
Inscribed MCMXLIV

Wmk. 277

1945, Sept. 12   Photo.   Perf. 14

99	A22	1 l dk blue green	.20	.20
100	A22	3 l dk carmine	.20	.20
a.		Jesus image omitted	100.00	100.00
101	A22	5 l deep ultra	.20	.20
		Nos. 99-101 (3)	.60	.60

Nos. 99-101 exist in pairs imperf. between, both horizontal and vertical. Value, each $140. Pairs imperf. horizontally exist of 3 lire (value $50) and 5 lire (value $60).

Nos. 91 to 98 Surcharged with New
Values and Bars in Black or Blue

Two types of 25c on 30c:
I — Surcharge 16mm wide.
II — Surcharge 19mm wide.

Two types of 1 l on 50c:
I — Surcharge bars 5mm wide.
II — Bars 4mm wide.

1946, Jan. 9   Unwmk.   Perf. 14

102	A19	20c on 5c	.20	.20
103	A19	25c on 30c (I)	.20	.20
a.		Type II		
b.		Inverted surcharge (II)	350.00	350.00
104	A19	1 l on 50c (I)	.20	.20
a.		Type II	5.00	3.50
105	A21	1.50 l on 1 l (Bl)	.20	.20
a.		Double surcharge	175.00	
106	A21	3 l on 1.50 l	.20	.20
107	A21	5 l on 2.50 l	.40	.20
108	A20	10 l on 5 l	1.10	.55
109	A20	30 l on 20 l	3.25	1.50
		Nos. 102-109,E7-E8 (10)	14.25	6.75

Nos. 102, 105-109 exist in horizontal pairs, imperf. between. Value, each $150.
Vertical pairs imperf. between exist of Nos. 102, 106-107 (value, each $150) and of No. 104a (value $250).
Nos. 102, 104-108 exist in pairs imperf. vertically or horizontally, or both. Value $40 to $60.
Nos. 102-108 exist in pairs, one without surcharge. Value, Nos. 102-105, each $150; Nos. 106-108, each $200.

St. Vigilio
Cathedral,
Trent — A28

St. Angela
Merici — A29

Designs: 50c, St. Anthony Zaccaria. 75c, St. Ignatius of Loyola. 1 l, St. Cajetan Thiene. 1.50 l, St. John Fisher. 2 l, Christoforo Cardinal Madruzzi. 2.50 l, Reginald Cardinal Pole. 3 l, Marello Cardinal Cervini. 4 l, Giovanni Cardinal del Monte. 5 l, Emperor Charles V. 1 l, Pope Paul III.

Perf. 14, 14x13½

1946, Feb. 21   Photo.   Unwmk.

Centers in Dark Brown

110	A28	5c olive bister	.20	.20
111	A29	25c purple	.20	.20
112	A29	50c brown orange	.20	.20
113	A29	75c black	.20	.20
114	A29	1 l dk violet	.20	.20
115	A29	1.50 l red orange	.20	.20
116	A29	2 l yellow green	.20	.20
117	A29	2.50 l deep blue	.20	.20
118	A29	3 l brt carmine	.20	.20
119	A29	4 l ocher	.20	.20
120	A29	5 l brt ultra	.20	.20
121	A29	10 l dp rose car	.20	.20
		Nos. 110-121,E9-E10 (14)	2.80	2.80

Council of Trent (1545-63), 400th anniv.
Vertical pairs imperf. between exist of Nos. 110-111, 114, 116-117 (value, each $150); Nos. 113, 119 (value, each $100); Nos. 115, 118 (value, each $75).
Horizontal pairs imperf. between exist of #121 (value $200); #113, 117 (value $150).

Basilica of St.
Agnes — A40

Basilica of
the Holy
Cross in
Jerusalem
A41

Pope
Pius XII
A42

Basilicas: 3 l, St. Clement. 5 l, St. Prassede. 8 l, St. Mary in Cosmedin. 16 l, St. Sebastian. 25 l, St. Lawrence. 35 l, St. Paul. 40 l, St. Mary Major.

Perf. 14, 14x13½

1949, Mar. 7   Photo.   Wmk. 235

122	A40	1 l dark brown	.20	.20
123	A40	3 l violet	.20	.20
124	A40	5 l deep orange	.20	.20
a.		Perf. 14x13½	15.00	4.50
125	A40	8 l dp blue grn	.20	.20

Perf. 14, 13½x14

126	A41	13 l dull green	6.00	5.0
127	A41	16 l dk olive brn	.20	
a.		Perf. 14	.75	
128	A41	25 l car rose	4.75	.6
129	A41	35 l red violet	26.00	12.0
a.		Perf. 13½x14	55.00	8.
130	A41	40 l blue	.20	
a.		Perf. 13½x14	.25	.2

Engr.
Perf. 14

131	A42	100 l sepia	3.00	3.0
		Nos. 122-131,E11-E12 (12)	88.95	45.

All values come in two perfs except the 10 l.

Jesus Giving St.
Peter the Keys to
Heaven — A43

Cathedrals of St.
Peter, St. Paul, St.
John Lateran and
St. Mary
Major — A44

Pope Boniface VIII
Proclaiming Holy
Year in
1300 — A45

Pope Pius XII in
Ceremony of
Opening the Holy
Door — A46

Wmk. 277

1949, Dec 21   Photo.   Perf. 14

132	A43	5 l red brn & brn	.20	.20
133	A44	6 l ind & yel brn	.20	.20
134	A45	8 l ultra & dk grn	.75	.35
135	A46	10 l green & slate	.25	.25
136	A43	20 l dk grn & red brn	1.25	.25
137	A44	25 l sepia & dp blue	.60	.25
138	A45	30 l grnsh blk & rose lil	1.50	1.00
139	A46	60 l blk brn & brn rose	1.00	1.00
		Nos. 132-139 (8)	5.75	3.50

Holy Year, 1950.

Palatine Guard and
Statue of St.
Peter — A47

1950, Sept. 12

140	A47	25 l sepia	8.25	2.50
141	A47	35 l dark green	3.25	2.50
142	A47	55 l red brown	1.90	2.50
		Nos. 140-142 (3)	13.40	7.50

Centenary of the Palatine Guard.

Pope Pius XII
Making
Proclamation
A48

Crowd at the
Basilica of St.
Peter — A49

1951, May 8   **Unwmk.**
143 A48 25 l chocolate   8.50   .75
144 A49 55 l bright blue   3.50 10.50
    Proclamation of the Roman Catholic dogma
of the Assumption of the Virgin Mary, Nov. 1,
1950.

Pope
Pius X — A50

Pope
Pius X — A51

Perf. 14x13½
1951, June 3   **Photo.**   **Wmk. 235**
Background of Medallion in Gold
145 A50   6 l purple   .20   .20
146 A50 10 l Prus green   .20   .20
147 A51 60 l blue   5.50 5.50
148 A51 115 l brown   15.00 15.00
   Nos. 145-148 (4)   20.90 20.90

Council of
Chalcedon
A52

Pope Leo I Remonstrating with Attila
the Hun — A53

1951, Oct. 31   **Engr.**   **Perf. 14x13½**
149 A52   5 l dk gray green   .50   .25
  a.   Pair, imperf. horiz.   350.00
150 A53 25 l red brown   3.00 1.75
  a.   Horiz. pair, imperf. btwn.   700.00 700.00
151 A53 35 l carmine rose   8.00 3.00
152 A53 60 l deep blue   22.50 10.00
153 A53 100 l dark brown   30.00 25.00
   Nos. 149-153 (5)   64.00 40.00
   Council of Chalcedon, 1500th anniv.

**No. 126 Surcharged with New Value
and Bars in Carmine**
1952, Mar. 15   **Perf. 14**
154 A41 12 l on 13 l dull grn   1.75   1.00
  a.   Perf. 13½x14   1.75   1.00
  b.   Pair, one without surcharge   300.00 300.00

Roman States Stamp and
Stagecoach — A54

1952, June 9   **Engr.**   **Perf. 13**
155 A54 50 l sep & dp bl, cr   5.00 3.25
  a.   Souvenir sheet   140.00 100.00
   1st stamp of the Papal States, cent.
#155a contains 4 stamps similar to #155,
with papal insignia and inscription in purple.
Singles from the souvenir sheet differ slightly
from #155. The colors are closer to black and
blue, and the cream tone of the paper is visible
on the back.

St. Maria
Goretti — A55

St. Peter — A56

Perf. 13½x14
1953, Feb. 12   **Photo.**   **Wmk. 235**
156 A55 15 l dp brown & vio   4.25 2.00
157 A55 35 l dp rose & brn   3.25 2.00
   Martyrdom of St. Maria Goretti, 50th anniv.

Perf. 13½x13, 14
1953, Apr. 23   **Engr.**
   Designs: 5 l, Pius XII and Roman sepulcher. 10 l, St. Peter and Tomb of the Apostle.
12 l, Sylvester I and Constantine Basilica. 20 l,
Julius II and Bramante's plans. 25 l, Paul III
and the Apse. 35 l, Sixtus V and dome. 45 l,
Paul V and facade. 60 l, Urban VIII and the
canopy. 65 l, Alexander VII and colonnade.
100 l, Pius VI and the sacristy.
158 A56   3 l dk red brn & blk   .20   .20
159 A56   5 l slate & blk   .20   .20
160 A56 10 l dk green & blk   .20   .20
161 A56 12 l chestnut & blk   .20   .20
162 A56 20 l violet & blk   .20   .20
163 A56 25 l dk brown & blk   .20   .20
164 A56 35 l dk carmine & blk   .20   .20
165 A56 45 l olive brn & blk   .20   .20
166 A56 60 l dk blue & blk   .20   .20
167 A56 65 l car rose & blk   .20   .20
168 A56 100 l rose vio & blk   .20   .20
   Nos. 158-168,E13-E14 (13)   2.75 2.65

St. Clare of
Assisi — A57

Peter Lombard
Medal — A59

Virgin Mary
and St.
Bernard
A58

Unwmk.
1953, Aug. 12   **Photo.**   **Perf. 13**
169 A57 25 l aqua, yel brn &
        vio brn   2.00 1.00
170 A57 35 l brn red, yel brn &
        vio brn   14.00 9.00
   Death of St. Clare of Assisi, 700th anniv.

1953, Nov. 10
171 A58 20 l ol grn & dk vio
        brn   .75   .50
172 A58 60 l brt bl & ol grn   7.25 4.00
   Death of St. Bernard of Clairvaux, 800th
anniv.

1953, Dec. 29
173 A59 100 l lil rose, bl, dk
        grn & yel   32.50 20.00
   Peter Lombard, Bishop of Paris 1159.

Pope
Pius XI and
Vatican
City — A60

1954, Feb. 12   **Wmk. 235**
174 A60 25 l bl, red brn & cr   1.25 1.00
175 A60 60 l yel brn & dp bl   3.00 2.50
   Signing of the Lateran Pacts, 25th anniv.

Pope
Pius IX
A61

   Portraits: (At left) - 6 l, 20 l, Pope Pius IX. (At
right) — 4 l, 12 l, 35 l, Pope Pius XII.

1954, May 26   **Engr.**   **Perf. 13**
176 A61   3 l violet   .20   .20
177 A61   4 l carmine   .20   .20
178 A61   6 l plum   .20   .20
179 A61 12 l blue green   1.00   .20
180 A61 20 l red brown   .90   .85
181 A61 35 l ultra   2.25 2.25
   Nos. 176-181 (6)   4.75 3.90
   Marian Year; centenary of the dogma of the
Immaculate Conception.

St. Pius X — A62

1954, May 29   **Photo.**
**Colors (except background): Yellow
and Plum**
182 A62 10 l dark brown   .25   .25
183 A62 25 l violet   2.50 1.25
184 A62 35 l dk slate gray   4.25 2.50
   Nos. 182-184 (3)   7.00 4.00
   Canonization of Pope Pius X, May 20, 1954.
#182-184 exist imperf. Value, each pair
$800.

Basilica of
St. Francis
of Assisi
A63

1954, Oct. 1   **Photo.**   **Perf. 14**
185 A63 20 l dk vio gray & cr   2.00 1.75
186 A63 35 l dk brown & cream   1.50 1.40
   Consecration of the Basilica of St. Francis of
Assisi, 200th anniv.

St.
Augustine
A64

1954, Nov. 13
187 A64 35 l blue green   1.00 .90
188 A64 50 l redsh brown   1.90 1.75
   1600th birth anniv. of St. Augustine.

Madonna of the
Gate of Dawn,
Vilnius — A65

1954, Dec. 7
189 A65 20 l pink & multi   1.00   .75
190 A65 35 l blue & multi   7.50 3.75
191 A65 60 l multicolored   12.50 5.75
   Nos. 189-191 (3)   21.00 10.25
   Issued to mark the end of the Marian Year.

St. Boniface
and Fulda
Abbey
A66

1955, Apr. 28   **Engr.**   **Perf. 13**
192 A66 10 l grnsh gray   .20   .20
193 A66 35 l violet   .60   .60
  a.   Imperf., pair   100.00
194 A66 60 l brt blue green   .70   .70
   Nos. 192-194 (3)   1.50 1.50
   1200th death anniv. of St. Boniface.

Pope Sixtus II
and St.
Lawrence
A67

Pope
Nicholas V
A68

Wmk. 235
1955, June 27   **Photo.**   **Perf. 14**
195 A67 50 l carmine   3.75 2.00
196 A67 100 l deep blue   2.50 2.00
   Fra Angelico (1387-1455), painter. Design is
from a Fra Angelico fresco.

1955, Nov. 28
197 A68 20 l grnsh bl & ol brn   .20   .20
198 A68 35 l rose car & ol brn   .35   .25
199 A68 60 l yel grn & ol brn   .70   .35
   Nos. 197-199 (3)   1.25   .80
   Death of Pope Nicholas V, 500th anniv.

St. Bartholomew
and Church of
Grottaferrata
A69

Capt. Gaspar Roust
A70

1955, Dec. 29

200	A69	10 l brown & gray	.20	.20
201	A69	25 l car rose & gray	.80	.30
202	A69	100 l dk green & gray	2.00	1.50
		Nos. 200-202 (3)	3.00	2.00

900th death anniv. of St. Bartholomew, abbot of Grottaferrata.

1956, Apr. 27   Engr.   Perf. 13

6 l, 50 l, Guardsman. 10 l, 60 l, Two drummers.

203	A70	4 l dk carmine rose	.20	.20
204	A70	6 l deep orange	.20	.20
205	A70	10 l deep ultra	.20	.20
206	A70	35 l brown	.55	.40
207	A70	50 l violet	.75	.60
208	A70	60 l blue green	.85	.65
		Nos. 203-208 (6)	2.75	2.25

450th anniv. of the Swiss Papal Guard.

St. Rita of Cascia — A71

Pope Paul III Confirming Society of Jesus — A72

1956, May 19   Photo.   Perf. 14

209	A71	10 l gray green	.20	.20
210	A71	25 l olive brown	.60	.60
211	A71	35 l ultra	.45	.45
		Nos. 209-211 (3)	1.25	1.25

500th death anniv. of St. Rita of Cascia.

1956, July 31   Engr.   Perf. 13

212	A72	35 l dk red brown	.55	.55
213	A72	60 l blue gray	1.10	1.00

400th death anniv. of St. Ignatius of Loyola, founder of the Society of Jesus.

St. John of Capistrano A73

1956, Oct. 30   Perf. 14

214	A73	25 l slate blk & grn	2.25	1.25
215	A73	35 l dk brn car & brn	1.00	.75

5th cent. of the death of St. John of Capistrano, leader in the war against the Turks.

Black Madonna of Czestochowa — A74   St. Domenico Savio — A75

1956, Dec. 20

216	A74	35 l dk blue & blk	.25	.25
217	A74	60 l green & ultra	.60	.55
218	A74	100 l brn & dk car rose	1.00	.85
		Nos. 216-218 (3)	1.85	1.65

300th anniv. of the proclamation of the Madonna of Czestochowa as "Queen of Poland."

1957, Mar. 21   Wmk. 235   Perf. 13½

6 l, 60 l, Sts. Domenico Savio and John Bosco.

219	A75	4 l red brown	.20	.20
220	A75	6 l brt carmine	.20	.20
221	A75	25 l green	.20	.20
222	A75	60 l ultra	1.40	1.10
		Nos. 219-222 (4)	2.00	1.70

Death cent. of St. Domenico Savio.

Cardinal Capranica and College A76

Design: 10 l, 100 l, Pope Pius XII.

1957, June 27   Engr.   Perf. 13

223	A76	5 l dk carmine rose	.20	.20
224	A76	10 l pale brown	.20	.20
225	A76	35 l grnsh black	.20	.20
226	A76	100 l ultra	.50	.50
		Nos. 223-226 (4)	1.10	1.10

500th anniv. of Capranica College, oldest seminary in the world.

Pontifical Academy of Science A77

1957, Oct. 9   Photo.   Perf. 14

227	A77	35 l dk blue & green	.55	.55
228	A77	60 l brown & ultra	.80	.55

Pontifical Academy of Science, 20th anniv.

Mariazell A78

High Altar — A79

1957, Nov. 14   Engr.   Perf. 13½

229	A78	5 l green	.20	.20
230	A79	15 l slate	.20	.20
231	A78	60 l ultra	.70	.25
232	A79	100 l violet	.90	.85
		Nos. 229-232 (4)	2.00	1.50

Mariazell shrine, Austria, 800th anniv.

Apparition of the Virgin Mary — A80

Designs: 10 l, 35 l, Sick man and basilica. 15 l, 100 l, St. Bernadette.

Perf. 13x14

1958, Feb. 21   Wmk. 235

233	A80	5 l dark blue	.20	.20
234	A80	10 l blue green	.20	.20
235	A80	15 l reddish brown	.20	.20
236	A80	25 l rose carmine	.20	.20
237	A80	35 l gray brown	.20	.20
238	A80	100 l violet	1.20	1.20
		Nos. 233-238 (6)	1.20	1.20

Centenary of apparition of the Virgin Mary at Lourdes and the establishment of the shrine.

Pope Pius XII — A81   Statue of Pope Clement XIII by Canova — A82

60 l, 100 l, Vatican pavilion at Brussels fair.

1958, June 19   Engr.   Perf. 13

239	A81	35 l claret	.30	.25

Perf. 13x14

240	A81	60 l fawn	.55	.55
241	A81	100 l violet	1.75	1.25
242	A81	300 l ultra	1.40	1.10
a.		Souvenir sheet of 4, #239-242	20.00	15.00
		Nos. 239-242 (4)	4.00	3.15

Universal and Intl. Exposition, Brussels.

1958, July 2   Perf. 14

Statues: 10 l, Clement XIV. 35 l, Pius VI. 100 l, Pius VII.

243	A82	5 l brown	.20	.20
244	A82	10 l carmine rose	.20	.20
245	A82	35 l blue gray	.25	.25
246	A82	100 l dark blue	.85	.85
		Nos. 243-246 (4)	1.50	1.50

Antonio Canova (1757-1822), sculptor.

Interregnum Issue

St. Peter's Keys and Papal Chamberlain's Insignia — A83

Wmk. 235

1958, Oct. 21   Photo.   Perf. 14

247	A83	15 l brn blk, *yel*	1.40	1.00
248	A83	25 l brown black	.20	.20
249	A83	60 l brn blk, *pale vio*	.20	.20
		Nos. 247-249 (3)	1.80	1.40

Pope John XXIII — A84

Pope Pius XI — A85

Design: 35 l, 100 l, Coat of Arms.

1959, Apr. 2   Photo.   Perf. 14

250	A84	25 l car rose, bl & buff	.20	.20
251	A84	35 l multicolored	.20	.20
252	A84	60 l rose car, bl & ocher	.20	.20
253	A84	100 l multicolored	.20	.20
		Nos. 250-253 (4)	.80	.80

Coronation of Pope John XXIII, 11/4/58.

1959, May 25   Wmk. 235   Perf. 14

254	A85	30 l brown	.20	.20
255	A85	100 l violet blue	.20	.20

Lateran Pacts, 30th anniversary.

St. Lawrence A86

Radio Tower and Archangel Gabriel A87

Portraits of Saints: 25 l, Pope Sixtus II. 50 l, Agapitus. 60 l, Filicissimus. 100 l, Cyprianus. 300 l, Fructuosus.

1959, May 25

256	A86	15 l red, brn & yel	.25	.20
257	A86	25 l lilac, brn & yel	.25	.20
258	A86	50 l Prus bl, blk & yel	.25	.20
259	A86	60 l ol grn, brn & bis	.25	.20
260	A86	100 l maroon, brn & yel	.25	.20
261	A86	300 l bis brn & dk brn	.50	.35
		Nos. 256-261 (6)	1.75	1.35

Martyrs of Emperor Valerian's persecutions.

1959, Oct. 27   Photo.   Perf. 14

262	A87	25 l rose, org yel & dk brn	.20	.20
263	A87	60 l multicolored	.20	.20

2nd anniv. of the papal radio station, St. Maria di Galeria.

St. Casimir, Palace and Cathedral, Vilnius A88

1959, Dec. 14   Engr.   Wmk. 235

264	A88	50 l brown	.20	.20
265	A88	100 l dull green	.25	.20

500th anniv. (in 1958) of the birth of St. Casimir, patron saint of Lithuania.

Nativity by Raphael — A89

1959, Dec. 14   Engr.   Perf. 13½

266	A89	15 l dark gray	.20	.20
267	A89	25 l magenta	.20	.20
268	A89	60 l bright ultra	.20	.20
		Nos. 266-268 (3)	.60	.60

St. Antoninus — A90

Transept of Lateran Basilica — A91

25 l, 110 l, St. Antoninus preaching.

Perf. 13x14

1960, Feb. 29 — Wmk. 235

269	A90	15 l ultra	.20	.20
270	A90	25 l turquoise	.20	.20
271	A90	60 l brown	.30	.25
272	A90	110 l rose claret	.60	.35
		Nos. 269-272 (4)	1.30	1.00

5th cent. of death of St. Antoninus, bishop of Florence.

1960, Feb. 29 — Photo. — Perf. 14

273	A91	15 l brown	.20	.20
274	A91	60 l black	.40	.20

Roman Diocesan Synod, February, 1960.

Flight into Egypt by Fra Angelico — A92

Cardinal Sarto's Departure from Venice — A93

Designs: 10 l, 100 l, St. Peter Giving Alms to the Poor, by Masaccio. 25 l, 300 l, Madonna of Mercy, by Piero della Francesca.

1960, Apr. 7 — Wmk. 235 — Perf. 14

275	A92	5 l green	.20	.20
276	A92	10 l gray brown	.20	.20
277	A92	25 l deep carmine	.20	.20
278	A92	60 l lilac	.20	.20
279	A92	100 l ultra	1.90	1.50
280	A92	300 l Prus green	.65	.40
		Nos. 275-280 (6)	3.35	2.70

World Refugee Year, 7/1/59-6/30/60.

1960, Apr. 11 — Engr. — Perf. 13½

35 l, Pope John XXIII praying at coffin of Pope Pius X. 60 l, Body of Pope Pius X returning to Venice.

281	A93	15 l brown	.25	.25
282	A93	35 l rose carmine	.60	.60
283	A93	60 l Prus green	1.25	.85
		Nos. 281-283 (3)	2.10	1.70

Return of the body of Pope Pius X to Venice.

Feeding the Hungry A94

"Acts of Mercy," by Della Robbia: 10 l, Giving drink to the thirsty. 15 l, Clothing the naked. 20 l, Sheltering the homeless. 30 l, Visiting the sick. 35 l, Visiting prisoners. 40 l, Burying the dead. 70 l, Pope John XXIII.

1960, Nov. 8 — Photo. — Perf. 14
Centers in Brown

284	A94	5 l red brown	.20	.20
285	A94	10 l green	.20	.20
286	A94	15 l slate	.20	.20
287	A94	20 l rose carmine	.20	.20
288	A94	30 l violet blue	.20	.20
289	A94	35 l violet brown	.20	.20
290	A94	40 l red orange	.20	.20
291	A94	70 l ocher	.20	.20
		Nos. 284-291,E15-E16 (10)	2.00	2.00

Holy Family by Gerard van Honthorst A95

1960, Dec. 6 — Wmk. 235 — Perf. 14

292	A95	10 l slate grn & slate blk	.20	.20
293	A95	15 l sepia & ol blk	.20	.20
294	A95	70 l grnsh bl & dp bl	.30	.20
		Nos. 292-294 (3)	.70	.60

St. Vincent de Paul — A96

St. Meinrad — A97

Designs: 70 l, St. Louisa de Marillac. 100 l, St. Louisa and St. Vincent.

1960, Dec. 6

295	A96	40 l dull violet	.20	.20
296	A96	70 l dark gray	.30	.20
297	A96	100 l dk red brown	.70	.30
		Nos. 295-297 (3)	1.20	.70

Death of St. Vincent de Paul, 300th anniv.

1961, Feb. 28 — Perf. 14

Designs: 40 l, Statue of Our Lady of Einsiedeln. 100 l, Einsiedeln monastery, horiz.

298	A97	30 l dark gray	.45	.20
299	A97	40 l lt violet	1.50	.40
300	A97	100 l brown	1.50	.85
		Nos. 298-300 (3)	3.45	1.45

Death of St. Meinrad, 1,100th anniv.; Einsiedeln Abbey, Switzerland.

Pope Leo the Great Defying Attila — A98

1961, Apr. 6 — Wmk. 235 — Photo. — Perf. 14

301	A98	15 l rose brown	.20	.20
302	A98	70 l Prus green	.25	.25
303	A98	300 l brown black	1.75	.55
		Nos. 301-303 (3)	2.20	1.00

Death of Pope Leo the Great (St. Leo Magnus), 1,500th anniv. The design is from a marble bas-relief in St. Peter's Basilica.

St. Paul Arriving in Rome, 61 A.D. — A99

10 l, 30 l, Map showing St. Paul's journey to Rome. 20 l, 200 l, First Basilica of St. Paul, Rome.

1961, June 13 — Wmk. 235 — Perf. 14

304	A99	10 l Prus green	.20	.20
305	A99	15 l dl red brn & gray	.20	.20
306	A99	20 l red org & gray	.20	.20
307	A99	30 l blue	.20	.20
308	A99	75 l org brn & gray	.30	.30
309	A99	200 l blue & gray	1.60	1.10
		Nos. 304-309 (6)	2.70	2.20

Arrival of St. Paul in Rome, 1,900th anniv.

1861 and 1961 Mastheads A100

70 l, Editorial offices. 250 l, Rotary press.

1961, July 4

310	A100	40 l red brn & blk	.20	.20
311	A100	70 l blue & blk	.40	.30
312	A100	250 l yellow & blk	1.90	1.10
		Nos. 310-312 (3)	2.50	1.60

Centenary of L'Osservatore Romano, Vatican's newspaper.

St. Patrick's Purgatory, Lough Derg — A101

Arms of Roncalli Family — A102

10 l, 40 l, St. Patrick, marble sculpture.

Wmk. 235
1961, Oct. 6 — Photo. — Perf. 14

313	A101	10 l buff & slate grn	.20	.20
314	A101	15 l blue & sepia	.20	.20
315	A101	40 l yellow & bl grn	.25	.20
316	A101	150 l Prus bl & red brn	.70	.50
		Nos. 313-316 (4)	1.35	1.10

Death of St. Patrick, 1,500th anniv.

1961, Nov. 25

Designs: 25 l, Church at Sotto il Monte. 30 l, Santa Maria in Monte Santo, Rome. 40 l, Church of San Carlo al Corso, Rome (erroneously inscribed with name of Basilica of Sts. Ambrosius and Charles, Milan). 70 l, Altar, St. Peter's, Rome. 115 l, Pope John XXIII.

317	A102	10 l gray & red brn	.20	.20
318	A102	25 l ol bis & sl grn	.20	.20
319	A102	30 l vio bl & pale pur	.20	.20
320	A102	40 l lilac & dk blue	.20	.20
321	A102	70 l gray grn & org brn	.30	.20
322	A102	115 l choc & slate	.70	.45
		Nos. 317-322 (6)	1.80	1.45

80th birthday of Pope John XXIII.

"The Adoration" by Lucas Chen — A103

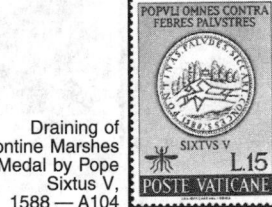

Draining of Pontine Marshes Medal by Pope Sixtus V, 1588 — A104

1961, Nov. 25
Center Multicolored

323	A103	15 l bluish green	.20	.20
324	A103	40 l gray	.20	.20
325	A103	70 l pale lilac	.30	.20
		Nos. 323-325 (3)	.70	.60

Christmas.

1962, Apr. 7 — Wmk. 235 — Perf. 14

40 l, 300 l, Map of Pontine Marshes showing 18th cent. drainage under Pope Pius VI.

326	A104	15 l dark violet	.20	.20
327	A104	40 l rose carmine	.20	.20
328	A104	70 l brown	.20	.20
329	A104	300 l dull green	.65	.40
		Nos. 326-329 (4)	1.25	1.00

WHO drive to eradicate malaria.

"The Good Shepherd" A105

Wheatfield (Luke 10:2) — A106

1962, June 2 — Photo.

330	A105	10 l lilac & black	.20	.20
331	A105	15 l blue & ocher	.20	.20
332	A105	70 l lt green & blk	.25	.30
333	A106	115 l fawn & ocher	1.25	1.10
334	A105	200 l brown & black	2.00	1.40
		Nos. 330-334 (5)	3.90	3.20

Issued to honor the priesthood and to stress its importance as a vocation.
"The Good Shepherd" is a fourth-century statue in the Lateran Museum, Rome.

St. Catherine of Siena — A107

Paulina M. Jaricot — A108

1962, June 12

335	A107	15 l brown	.20	.20
336	A107	60 l brt violet	.30	.25
337	A107	100 l blue	.60	.40
		Nos. 335-337 (3)	1.10	.85

Canonization of St. Catherine of Siena, 500th anniv. The portrait is from a fresco by Il Sodoma, Church of St. Dominic, Siena.

1962, July 5
Portrait Multicolored

338	A108	10 l pale violet	.20	.20
339	A108	50 l dull green	.20	.20
340	A108	150 l gray	.80	.50
		Nos. 338-340 (3)	1.20	.90

Paulina M. Jaricot (1799-1862), founder of the Society for the Propagation of the Faith.

Sts. Peter and Paul A109

Design: 40 l, 100 l, "The Invincible Cross," relief from sarcophagus.

Wmk. 235

1962, Sept. 25   **Photo.**   **Perf. 14**

341	A109	20 l lilac & brown	.20	.20
342	A109	40 l lt brown & blk	.20	.20
343	A109	70 l bluish grn & brn	.20	.20
344	A109	100 l sal pink & blk	.20	.20
		Nos. 341-344 (4)	.80	.80

6th Congress of Christian Archeology, Ravenna, Sept. 23-28.

"Faith" by Raphael — A110

Designs: 10 l, "Hope." 15 l, "Charity." 25 l, Arms of Pope John XXIII and emblems of the Four Evangelists. 30 l, Ecumenical Congress meeting in St. Peter's. 40 l, Pope John XXIII on throne. 60 l, Statue of St. Peter. 115 l, The Holy Ghost as a dove (symbolic design).

Photo.; Center Engr. on 30 l

1962, Oct. 30

345	A110	5 l brt blue & blk	.20	.20
346	A110	10 l green & blk	.20	.20
347	A110	15 l ver & sepia	.20	.20
348	A110	25 l ver & slate	.20	.20
349	A110	30 l lilac & blk	.20	.20
350	A110	40 l dk carmine & blk	.20	.20
351	A110	60 l dk grn & dp org	.20	.20
352	A110	115 l crimson	.20	.20
		Nos. 345-352 (8)	1.60	1.60

Vatican II, the 21st Ecumenical Council of the Roman Catholic Church, which opened Oct. 11, 1962. Nos. 345-347 show "the Three Theological Virtues" by Raphael.

Nativity Scene A111

Set in India, following a design by Marcus Toano.

1962, Dec. 4

Center Multicolored

353	A111	10 l gray	.20	.20
354	A111	15 l brown	.20	.20
355	A111	90 l dull green	.30	.20
		Nos. 353-355 (3)	.70	.60

Miracle of the Loaves and Fishes by Murillo — A112

Pope John XXIII — A113

Design: 40 l, 200 l, "The Miraculous Catch of Fishes" by Raphael.

Wmk. 235

1963, Mar. 21   **Photo.**   **Perf. 14**

356	A112	15 l brn & dk brn	.20	.20
357	A112	40 l rose red & blk	.20	.20
358	A112	100 l blue & dk brn	.20	.20
359	A112	200 l bl grn & blk	.20	.20
		Nos. 356-359 (4)	.80	.80

FAO "Freedom from Hunger" campaign.

1963, May 8

360	A113	15 l red brown	.20	.20
361	A113	160 l black	.40	.20

Awarding of the Balzan Peace Prize to Pope John XXIII.

Interregnum Issue

Keys of St. Peter and Papal Chamberlain's Insignia — A114

1963, June 15   **Wmk. 235**   **Perf. 14**

362	A114	10 l dk brown	.20	.20
363	A114	40 l dk brown, yel	.20	.20
364	A114	100 l dk brown, vio	.20	.20
		Nos. 362-364 (3)	.60	.60

Pope Paul VI — A115

St. Cyril — A116

Design: 40 l, 200 l, Arms of Pope Paul VI.

1963, Oct. 16   **Engr.**   **Perf. 13x14**

365	A115	15 l black	.20	.20
366	A115	40 l carmine	.20	.20
367	A115	115 l redsh brown	.20	.20
368	A115	200 l slate blue	.40	.25
		Nos. 365-368 (4)	1.00	.85

Coronation of Pope Paul VI, June 30, 1963.

Wmk. 235

1963, Nov. 22   **Photo.**   **Perf. 14**

Designs: 70 l, Map of Hungary, Moravia and Poland, 16th century. 150 l, St. Methodius.

369	A116	30 l violet black	.20	.20
370	A116	70 l brown	.30	.20
371	A116	150 l rose claret	.40	.20
		Nos. 369-371 (3)	.90	.60

1100th anniv. of the beginning of missionary work among the Slavs by Sts. Cyril and Methodius. The pictures of the saints are from 16th century frescoes in St. Clement's Basilica, Rome.

African Nativity Scene — A117

Church of the Holy Sepulcher, Jerusalem A118

1963, Nov. 22

372	A117	10 l brn & pale brn	.20	.20
373	A117	40 l ultra & brown	.20	.20
374	A117	100 l gray olive & brn	.25	.20
		Nos. 372-374 (3)	.65	.60

The design is after a sculpture by the Burundi artist Andreas Bukuru.

1964, Jan. 4   **Wmk. 235**   **Perf. 14**

15 l, Pope Paul VI. 25 l, Nativity Church, Bethlehem. 160 l, Well of the Virgin Mary, Nazareth.

375	A118	15 l black	.20	.20
376	A118	25 l rose brown	.20	.20
377	A118	70 l brown	.20	.20
378	A118	160 l ultra	.20	.20
		Nos. 375-378 (4)	.80	.80

Visit of Pope Paul VI to the Holy Land, Jan. 4-6.

St. Peter from Coptic Church at Wadi-es-Sebua, Sudan — A119

Design: 20 l, 200 l, Trajan's Kiosk, Philae.

1964, Mar. 10   **Photo.**

379	A119	10 l ultra & red brn	.20	.20
380	A119	20 l multicolored	.20	.20
381	A119	70 l gray & red brn	.20	.20
382	A119	200 l gray & multi	.20	.20
		Nos. 379-382 (4)	.80	.80

UNESCO world campaign to save historic monuments in Nubia.

Pietà by Michelangelo A120

Isaiah by Michelangelo A121

Designs: 15 l, 100 l, Pope Paul VI. 250 l, Head of Mary from Pietà.

1964, Apr. 22   **Wmk. 235**   **Perf. 14**

383	A120	15 l violet blue	.20	.20
384	A120	50 l dark brown	.20	.20
385	A120	100 l slate blue	.20	.20
386	A120	250 l chestnut	.20	.20
		Nos. 383-386 (4)	.80	.80

New York World's Fair, 1964-65.

1964, June 16   **Engr.**   **Perf. 13½x14**

387	A121	10 l Michelangelo, after Jacopino del Conte	.20	.20
388	A121	25 l Isaiah	.20	.20
389	A121	30 l Delphie Sibyl	.20	.20
390	A121	40 l Jeremiah	.20	.20
391	A121	150 l Joel	.20	.20
		Nos. 387-391 (5)	1.00	1.00

Michelangelo Buonarroti (1475-1564). Designs are from the Sistine Chapel.

The Good Samaritan A122

Perf. 14x13½

1964, Sept. 22   **Engr.**   **Wmk. 23**

392	A122	10 l red brown & red	.20	.2
393	A122	30 l dark blue & red	.20	.2
394	A122	300 l gray & red	.25	.6
		Nos. 392-394 (3)	.65	.6

Cent. (in 1963) of the founding of the In Red Cross.

Birthplace of Cardinal Nicolaus Cusanus A123

Design: 200 l, Cardinal's sepulcher, Churc of San Pietro in Vincoli, Rome.

1964, Nov. 16   **Wmk. 23**

395	A123	40 l dull blue grn	.20	.2
396	A123	200 l rose red	.30	.2

German cardinal Nicolaus Cusanus (Nico laus Krebs of Kues) (1401-1464).

Japanese Nativity Scene by Kimiko Koseki — A124

Pope Paul VI and Map of India and Southeast Asia — A125

1964, Nov. 16   **Photo.**   **Perf. 14**

397	A124	10 l multicolored	.20	.20
a.		Yellow omitted		
398	A124	15 l black & multi	.20	.20
399	A124	135 l bister & multi	.25	.20
		Nos. 397-399 (3)	.65	.60

1964, Dec. 2

Designs: 15 l, Pope Paul VI at prayer. 25 l, Eucharistic Congress altar, Bombay, horiz. 60 l, Gateway of India, Bombay, horiz.

400	A125	15 l dull violet	.20	.20
401	A125	25 l green	.20	.20
402	A125	60 l brown	.20	.20
403	A125	200 l dull violet	.20	.20
		Nos. 400-403 (4)	.80	.80

Trip of Pope Paul VI to India, Dec. 2-5, 1964.

Uganda Martyrs — A126

Dante by Raphael — A127

Various groups of Martyrs of Uganda.

Perf. 13½x14

1965, Mar. 16   Engr.   Wmk. 235
404	A126	15 l Prus green	.20	.20
405	A126	20 l brown	.20	.20
406	A126	30 l ultra	.20	.20
407	A126	75 l black	.20	.20
408	A126	100 l rose red	.20	.20
409	A126	160 l violet	.20	.20
		Nos. 404-409 (6)	1.20	1.20

Canonization of 22 African martyrs, 10/18/64.

Photogravure and Engraved
1965, May 18   Perf. 13½x14

Designs: 40 l, Dante and the 3 beasts at entrance to the Inferno. 70 l, Dante and Virgil at entrance to Purgatory. 200 l, Dante and Beatrice in Paradise. (40 l, 70 l, 200 l, by Botticelli.)

410	A127	10 l bis brn & dk brn	.20	.20
411	A127	40 l rose & dk brn	.20	.20
412	A127	70 l lt grn & dk brn	.20	.20
413	A127	200 l pale lil & dk brn	.20	.20
		Nos. 410-413 (4)	.80	.80

Birth of Dante Alighieri, 700th anniv.

St. Benedict by Perugino A128

Pope Paul VI Addressing UN Assembly A129

Design: 300 l, View of Monte Cassino.

1965, July 2   Photo.   Perf. 14
414	A128	40 l brown	.20	.20
415	A128	300 l dark green	.30	.20

Conferring of the title Patron Saint of Europe upon St. Benedict by Pope Paul VI; restoring of the Abbey of Monte Cassino.

1965, Oct. 4   Wmk. 235   Perf. 14

30 l, 150 l, UN Headquarters and olive branch.

416	A129	20 l brown	.20	.20
417	A129	30 l sapphire	.20	.20
418	A129	150 l olive green	.20	.20
419	A129	300 l rose violet	.25	.20
		Nos. 416-419 (4)	.85	.80

Visit of Pope Paul VI to the UN, NYC, Oct. 4.

Peruvian Nativity Scene A130

Cartographer A131

1965, Nov. 25   Engr.   Perf. 13½x14
420	A130	20 l rose claret	.20	.20
421	A130	40 l red brown	.20	.20
422	A130	200 l gray green	.20	.20
		Nos. 420-422 (3)	.60	.60

1966, Mar. 8   Photo.   Perf. 14

Designs: 5 l, Pope Paul VI. 10 l, Organist. 20 l, Painter. 30 l, Sculptor. 40 l, Bricklayer. 55 l, Printer. 75 l, Plowing farmer. 90 l, Blacksmith. 130 l, Scholar.

423	A131	5 l sepia	.20	.20
424	A131	10 l violet	.20	.20
425	A131	15 l brown	.20	.20
426	A131	20 l gray green	.20	.20
427	A131	30 l brown red	.20	.20
428	A131	40 l Prus green	.20	.20
429	A131	55 l dark blue	.20	.20
430	A131	75 l dk rose brown	.20	.20
431	A131	90 l carmine rose	.20	.20
432	A131	130 l black	.20	.20
		Nos. 423-432,E17-E18 (12)	2.40	2.40

The Pope's portrait is from a bas-relief by Enrico Manfrini; the arts and crafts designs

---

are bas-reliefs by Mario Rudelli from the chair in the Pope's private chapel.

King Mieszko I and Queen Dabrowka A132

Designs: 25 l, St. Adalbert (Wojciech) and Cathedrals of Wroclaw and Gniezno. 40 l, St. Stanislas, Skalka Church, Wawel Cathedral and Castle, Cracow. 50 l, Queen Jadwiga (Hedwig), Holy Gate with Our Lady of Mercy, Vilnius, and Jagellon University Library, Cracow. 150 l, Black Madonna of Czestochowa, cloister and church of Bright Mountain, Czestochowa, and St. John's Cathedral, Warsaw. 220 l, Pope Paul VI blessing students and farmers.

Perf. 14x13½
1966, May 3   Engr.   Wmk. 235
433	A132	15 l black	.20	.20
434	A132	25 l violet	.20	.20
435	A132	40 l brick red	.20	.20
436	A132	50 l claret	.20	.20
437	A132	150 l slate blue	.20	.20
438	A132	220 l brown	.20	.20
		Nos. 433-438 (6)	1.20	1.20

Millenium of Christianization of Poland.

Pope John XXIII Opening Vatican II Council A133

Nativity, Sculpture by Scorzelli A134

Designs: 15 l, Ancient Bible on ornate display stand. 55 l, Bishops celebrating Mass. 90 l, Pope Paul VI greeting Patriarch Athenagoras I. 100 l, Gold ring given to participating bishops. 130 l, Pope Paul VI carried in front of St. Peter's.

1966, Oct. 11   Photo.   Perf. 14
439	A133	10 l red & black	.20	.20
440	A133	15 l brown & green	.20	.20
441	A133	55 l blk & brt rose	.20	.20
442	A133	90 l slate grn & blk	.20	.20
443	A133	100 l green & ocher	.20	.20
444	A133	130 l orange brn & brn	.20	.20
		Nos. 439-444 (6)	1.20	1.20

Conclusion of Vatican II, the 21st Ecumenical Council of the Roman Catholic Church, Dec. 8, 1965.

1966, Nov. 24   Wmk. 235   Perf. 14
445	A134	20 l plum	.20	.20
446	A134	55 l slate green	.20	.20
447	A134	225 l yellow brown	.20	.20
		Nos. 445-447 (3)	.60	.60

St. Peter, Fresco, Catacombs, Rome — A135

Cross, People and Globe — A136

Designs: 20 l, St. Paul, fresco from Catacombs, Rome. 55 l, Sts. Peter and Paul, glass painting, Vatican Library. 90 l, Baldachin by Bernini, St. Peter's, Rome. 220 l, Interior of St. Paul's, Rome.

Perf. 13½x14
1967, June 15   Photo.   Unwmk.
448	A135	15 l multi	.20	.20
449	A135	20 l multi	.20	.20
450	A135	55 l multi	.20	.20

451	A135	90 l multi	.20	.20
452	A135	220 l multi	.20	.20
		Nos. 448-452 (5)	1.00	1.00

Martyrdom of the Apostles Peter and Paul, 1,900th anniv.

1967, Oct. 13   Wmk. 235   Perf. 14
453	A136	40 l carmine rose	.20	.20
454	A136	130 l brt blue	.20	.20

3rd Congress of Catholic Laymen, Rome, Oct. 11-18.

Sculpture of Shepherd Children of Fatima — A137

Nativity, 9th Century Painting on Wood — A138

Designs: 50 l, Basilica at Fatima. 200 l, Pope Paul VI praying before statue of Virgin of Fatima.

1967, Oct. 13   Perf. 13½x14
455	A137	30 l multi	.20	.20
456	A137	50 l multi	.20	.20
457	A137	200 l multi	.60	.60
		Nos. 455-457 (3)		

Apparition of the Virgin Mary to 3 shepherd children at Fatima, 50th anniv.

Christmas Issue
1967, Nov. 28   Photo.   Unwmk.
458	A138	25 l purple & multi	.20	.20
459	A138	55 l gray & multi	.20	.20
460	A138	180 l green & multi	.20	.20
		Nos. 458-460 (3)	.60	.60

Pope Paul VI — A139

Holy Infant of Prague — A140

Designs: 55 l, Monstrance from fresco by Raphael. 220 l, Map of South America.

1968, Aug. 22   Wmk. 235   Perf. 14
461	A139	25 l blk & dk red brn	.20	.20
462	A139	55 l blk, gray & ocher	.20	.20
463	A139	220 l blk, lt bl & sep	.20	.20
		Nos. 461-463 (3)	.60	.60

Visit of Pope Paul VI to the 39th Eucharistic Congress in Bogotá, Colombia, Aug. 22-25.

Engraved and Photogravure
1968, Nov. 28   Perf. 13½x14
464	A140	20 l plum & pink	.20	.20
465	A140	50 l vio & pale vio	.20	.20
466	A140	250 l dk bl & lt bluish gray	.20	.20
		Nos. 464-466 (3)	.60	.60

The Resurrection, by Fra Angelico de Fiesole — A141

Pope Paul VI with African Children — A142

Easter Issue
Perf. 13½x14
1969, Mar. 6   Engr.   Wmk. 235
467	A141	20 l dk carmine & buff	.20	.20
468	A141	90 l green & buff	.20	.20
469	A141	180 l ultra & buff	.20	.20
		Nos. 467-469 (3)	.60	.60

Common Design Types pictured following the introduction.

Europa Issue
Common Design Type
Perf. 13½x14
1969, Apr. 28   Photo.   Wmk. 235
Size: 36½x27mm
470	CD12	50 l gray & lt brn	.20	.20
471	CD12	90 l vermilion & lt brn	.20	.20
472	CD12	130 l olive & lt brn	.20	.20
		Nos. 470-472 (3)	.60	.60

Perf. 13½x14
1969, July 31   Photo.   Wmk. 235

Designs: 55 l, Pope Paul VI and African bishops. 250 l, Map of Africa with Kampala, olive branch and compass rose.

473	A142	25 l bister & brown	.20	.20
474	A142	55 l dk red & brown	.20	.20
475	A142	250 l multicolored	.20	.20
		Nos. 473-475 (3)	.60	.60

Visit of Pope Paul VI to Uganda, 7/31-8/2.

Pope Pius IX — A143

Mt. Fuji and EXPO '70 Emblem — A144

Designs: 50 l, Chrismon, emblem of St. Peter's Circle. 220 l, Pope Paul VI.

Perf. 13½x14
1969, Nov. 18   Engr.   Wmk. 235
476	A143	30 l red brown	.20	.20
477	A143	50 l dark gray	.20	.20
478	A143	220 l deep plum	.20	.20
		Nos. 476-478 (3)	.60	.60

Centenary of St. Peter's Circle, a lay society dedicated to prayer, action and sacrifice.

1970, Mar. 16   Photo.   Unwmk.

EXPO '70 Emblem and: 25 l, EXPO '70 emblem. 40 l, Osaka Castle. 55 l, Japanese

Virgin and Child, by Domoto in Osaka Cathedral. 90 l, Christian Pavilion.

479	A144	25 l gold, red & blk	.20	.20
480	A144	40 l red & multi	.20	.20
481	A144	55 l brown & multi	.20	.20
482	A144	90 l gold & multi	.20	.20
483	A144	110 l blue & multi	.20	.20
		Nos. 479-483 (5)	1.00	1.00

EXPO '70 Intl. Exhibition, Osaka, Japan, Mar. 15-Sept. 13.

Centenary Medal, Jesus Giving St. Peter the Keys — A145

Designs: 50 l, Coat of arms of Pope Pius IX. 180 l, Vatican I Council meeting in St. Peter's, obverse of centenary medal.

Engr. & Photo.; Photo. (50 l)

1970, Apr. 29   Perf. 13x14

484	A145	20 l orange & brown	.20	.20
485	A145	50 l multicolored	.20	.20
486	A145	180 l ver & brn	.30	.25
		Nos. 484-486 (3)	.70	.65

Centenary of the Vatican I Council.

Christ, by Simone Martini A146

25 l, Christ with Crown of Thorns, by Rogier van der Weyden. 50 l, Christ, by Albrecht Dürer. 90 l, Christ, by El Greco. 180 l, Pope Paul VI.

1970, May 29   Photo.   Perf. 14x13

487	A146	15 l gold & multi	.20	.20
488	A146	25 l gold & multi	.20	.20
489	A146	50 l gold & multi	.20	.20
490	A146	90 l gold & multi	.20	.20
491	A146	180 l gold & multi	.25	.20
		Nos. 487-491 (5)	1.05	1.00

Ordination of Pope Paul VI, 50th anniv.

Adam, by Michelangelo; UN Emblem — A147

Pope Paul VI — A148

UN Emblem and: 90 l, Eve, by Michelangelo. 220 l, Olive branch.

1970, Oct. 8   Photo.   Perf. 13x14

492	A147	20 l multi	.20	.20
493	A147	90 l multi	.20	.20
494	A147	220 l multi	.25	.20
		Nos. 492-494 (3)	.65	.60

25th anniversary of the United Nations.

1970, Nov. 26   Photo.   Unwmk.

Designs: 55 l, Holy Child of Cebu, Philippines. 100 l, Madonna and Child, by Georg Hamori, Darwin Cathedral, Australia. 130 l,

Cathedral of Manila. 220 l, Cathedral of Sydney.

495	A148	25 l multi	.20	.20
496	A148	55 l multi	.20	.20
497	A148	100 l multi	.20	.20
498	A148	130 l multi	.25	.20
499	A148	220 l multi	.25	.20
		Nos. 495-499 (5)	1.05	1.00

Visit of Pope Paul VI to the Far East, Oceania and Australia, Nov. 26-Dec. 5.

Angel Holding Lectern — A149

Madonna and Child by Francesco Ghissi — A150

Sculptures by Corrado Ruffini: 40 l, 130 l, Crucified Christ surrounded by doves. 50 l, like 20 l.

1971, Feb. 2   Perf. 13x14

500	A149	20 l multicolored	.20	.20
501	A149	40 l dp orange & multi	.20	.20
502	A149	50 l purple & multi	.20	.20
503	A149	130 l multicolored	.25	.20
		Nos. 500-503 (4)	.85	.80

Intl. year against racial discrimination.

1971, Mar. 26   Photo.   Perf. 14

Paintings: Madonna and Child, 40 l, by Sassetta (Stefano di Giovanni); 55 l, Carlo Crivelli; 90 l, by Carlo Maratta. 180 l, Holy Family, by Ghisberto Ceracchini.

504	A150	25 l gray & multi	.20	.20
505	A150	40 l gray & multi	.20	.20
506	A150	55 l gray & multi	.20	.20
507	A150	90 l gray & multi	.20	.20
508	A150	180 l gray & multi	.20	.20
		Nos. 504-508 (5)	1.00	1.00

St. Dominic, Sienese School — A151

St. Stephen, from Chasuble, 1031 — A152

Portraits of St. Dominic: 55 l, by Fra Angelico. 90 l, by Titian. 180 l, by El Greco.

1971, May 25   Unwmk.   Perf. 13x14

509	A151	25 l multi	.20	.20
510	A151	55 l multi	.20	.20
511	A151	90 l multi	.20	.20
512	A151	180 l multi	.25	.20
		Nos. 509-512 (4)	.85	.80

St. Dominic de Guzman (1170-1221), founder of the Dominican Order.

1971, Nov. 25

180 l, Madonna as Patroness of Hungary, 1511.

513	A152	50 l multi	.20	.20
514	A152	180 l black & yellow	.30	.20

Millenium of the birth of St. Stephen (975?-1038), king of Hungary.

Bramante A153

Designs: 25 l, Bramante's design for dome of St. Peter's. 130 l, Design for spiral staircase.

1972, Feb. 22   Engr.   Perf. 13½x14

515	A153	25 l dull yellow & blk	.20	.20
516	A153	90 l dull yellow & blk	.20	.20
517	A153	130 l dull yellow & blk	.25	.60
		Nos. 515-517 (3)	.65	.60

Bramante (real name Donato d'Agnolo; 1444-1514), architect.

St. Mark in Storm, 12th Century Mosaic — A154

Map of Venice, 1581 — A155

Design: 180 l, St. Mark's Basilica, Painting by Emilio Vangelli.

Unwmk.

1972, June 6   Photo.   Perf. 14

518	A154	25 l lt brown & multi	.20	.20
519	A155	Block of 4	1.00	.60
a.-d.		50 l, UL, UR, LL, LR, each	.25	.20
520	A154	180 l lt blue & multi	1.10	.65
a.		Souvenir sheet, #518-520	2.50	2.50
		Nos. 518-520 (3)	2.30	1.45

UNESCO campaign to save Venice.

Gospel of St. Matthew, 13th Century, French A156

Illuminated Initials from: 50 l, St. Luke's Gospel, Biblia dell'Aracoeli 13th century, French. 90 l, Second Epistle of St. John, 14th century, Bologna. 100 l, Apocalypse of St. John, 14th century, Bologna. 130 l, Book of Romans, 14th century, Central Italy.

1972, Oct. 11   Perf. 14x13½

521	A156	30 l multi	.20	.20
522	A156	50 l multi	.20	.20
523	A156	90 l multi	.20	.20
524	A156	100 l multi	.20	.20
525	A156	130 l multi	.35	.26
		Nos. 521-525 (5)	1.15	1.05

Intl. Book Year. Illustrations are from illuminated medieval manuscripts.

Luigi Orione A157

Design: 180 l, Lorenzo Perosi and musi from "Hallelujah."

1972, Nov. 28   Photo.   Perf. 14x13½

526	A157	50 l rose, lilac & blk	.20	.20
527	A157	180 l orange, grn & blk	.30	.20

Secular priests Luigi Orione (1872-1940) founder of CARITAS, Catholic welfare organization; and Lorenzo Perosi (1872-1956) composer.

Cardinal Bessarion A158

Eucharistic Congress Emblem — A159

40 l, Reading Bull of Union between the Greek and Latin Churches, 1439, from bronze door of St. Peter's. 130 l, Coat of arms from tomb, Basilica of Holy Apostles, Rome.

Perf. 13x14

1972, Nov. 28   Wmk. 235   Engr.

528	A158	40 l dull green	.20	.20
529	A158	90 l carmine	.25	.20
530	A158	130 l black	.20	.20
		Nos. 528-530 (3)	.65	.60

Johannes Cardinal Bessarion (1403?-1472), Latin Patriarch of Constantinople, who worked for union of the Greek and Latin Churches. Portrait by Cosimo Rosselli in Sistine Chapel.

1973, Feb. 27   Photo.   Unwmk.

Designs: 75 l, Head of Mary (Pietá), by Michelangelo. 300 l, Melbourne Cathedral.

531	A159	25 l violet & multi	.20	.20
532	A159	75 l olive & multi	.20	.20
533	A159	300 l multicolored	.50	.40
		Nos. 531-533 (3)	.90	.80

40th Intl. Eucharistic Congress, Melbourne, Australia, Feb. 18-25.

St. Teresa — A160

Copernicus A161

Designs: 25 l, St. Teresa's birthplace, Alençon. 220 l, Lisieux Basilica.

1973, May 23   Engr. & Photo.

534	A160	25 l	black & pink	.20	.20
535	A160	55 l	black & yellow	.20	.20
536	A160	220 l	black & lt blue	.40	.25
			Nos. 534-536 (3)	.80	.65

St. Teresa of Lisieux and of the Infant Jesus (1873-1897), Carmelite nun.

1973, June 19   Engr.   Perf. 14

Designs: 20 l, 100 l, View of Torun.

537	A161	20 l	dull green	.20	.20
538	A161	50 l	brown	.20	.20
539	A161	100 l	lilac	.20	.20
540	A161	130 l	dark blue	.30	.20
			Nos. 537-540 (4)	.90	.80

Nicolaus Copernicus (1473-1543), Polish astronomer.

St. Wenceslas A162

1973, Sept. 25   Photo.   Perf. 14

541	A162	20 l	shown	.20	.20
542	A162	90 l	Arms of Prague Diocese	.20	.20
543	A162	150 l	Spire of Prague Cathedral	.25	.20
544	A162	220 l	St. Adalbert	.35	.20
			Nos. 541-544 (4)	1.00	.80

Millenium of Prague Latin Episcopal See.

St. Nerses Shnorali — A163

25 l, Church of St. Hripsime. 90 l, Armenian khatchkar, a stele with cross and inscription.

Engr. & Litho.
**   Perf. 13x14**

545	A163	25 l	tan & dk brown	.20	.20
546	A163	90 l	lt violet & blk	.20	.20
547	A163	180 l	lt green & sepia	.35	.20
			Nos. 545-547 (3)	.75	.60

Armenian Patriarch St. Nerses Shnorali (1102-1173).

Noah's Ark, Rainbow and Dove (Mosaic) — A164

Design: 90 l, Lamb drinking from stream, and Tablets of the Law (mosaic).

1974, Apr. 23   Litho.   Perf. 13x14

548	A164	50 l	gold & multi	.20	.20
549	A164	90 l	gold & multi	.30	.20

Centenary of the Universal Postal Union.

"And There was Light" — A165

St. Thomas Aquinas Teaching — A166

Designs: 25 l, Noah's Ark, horiz. 50 l, The Annunciation. 90 l, Nativity (African). 180 l, Hands holding grain (Spanish inscription: The Lord feeds his people), horiz. Designs chosen through worldwide youth competition in connection with 1972 Intl. Book Year.

Perf. 13x14, 14x13

1974, Apr. 23   Photo.

550	A165	15 l	brown & multi	.20	.20
551	A165	25 l	yellow & multi	.20	.20
552	A165	50 l	blue & multi	.20	.20
553	A165	90 l	green & multi	.20	.20
554	A165	180 l	rose & multi	.25	.20
			Nos. 550-554 (5)	1.05	1.00

"The Bible: the Book of Books."

Engr. & Litho.
1974, June 18   Unwmk.   Perf. 13x14

Designs: 50 l, Students (left panel). 220 l, Students (right panel). Designs from a painting in the Convent of St. Mark in Florence, by an artist from the School of Fra Angelico.

Sizes: 50 l, 220 l, 20x36mm,
90 l, 26x36mm

555	A166	50 l	dk brown & gold	.20	.20
556	A166	90 l	dk brown & gold	.20	.20
557	A166	220 l	dk brown & gold	.40	.25
a.			Strip of 3, #555-557	.70	.55

St. Thomas Aquinas (1225-1274), scholastic philosopher.

St. Bonaventure A167

Woodcuts: 40 l, Civita Bagnoregio. 90 l, Tree of Life (13th century).

1974, Sept. 26   Photo.   Perf. 13x14

558	A167	40 l	gold & multi	.20	.20
559	A167	90 l	gold & multi	.25	.20
560	A167	220 l	gold & multi	.30	.20
			Nos. 558-560 (3)	.75	.60

St. Bonaventure (Giovanni di Fidanza; 1221-1274), scholastic philosopher.

Christ, St. Peter's Basilica — A168

Pope Paul VI Giving his Blessing — A169

Holy Year 1975: 10 l, Christus Victor, Sts. Peter and Paul. 30 l, Christ. 40 l, Cross surmounted by dove. 50 l, Christ enthroned. 55 l, St. Peter. 90 l, St. Paul. 100 l, St. Peter. 130 l, St. Paul. 220 l, Arms of Pope Paul VI. Designs of 10 l, 25 l, are from St. Peter's; 30 l, 40 l, from St. John Lateran; 50 l, 55 l, 90 l, from St. Mary Major; 100 l, 130 l, from St. Paul outside the Walls.

1974, Dec. 19   Photo.   Perf. 13x14

561	A168	10 l	multi	.20	.20
562	A168	25 l	multi	.20	.20
563	A168	30 l	multi	.20	.20
564	A168	40 l	multi	.20	.20
565	A168	50 l	multi	.20	.20
566	A168	55 l	multi	.20	.20
567	A168	90 l	multi	.20	.20
568	A168	100 l	multi	.20	.20
569	A168	130 l	multi	.20	.20
570	A169	220 l	multi	.25	.20
571	A169	250 l	multi	.30	.25
			Nos. 561-571 (11)	2.35	2.25

Pentecost, by El Greco — A170

1975, May 22   Engr.   Perf. 13x14

572	A170	300 l	car rose & orange	.60	.40

Fountain, St. Peter's Square — A171

Fountains of Rome: 40 l, Piazza St. Martha, Apse of St. Peter's. 50 l, Borgia Tower and St. Peter's. 90 l, Belvedere Courtyard. 100 l, Academy of Sciences. 200 l, Galleon.

Litho. & Engr.

1975, May 22   Perf. 14

573	A171	20 l	buff & blk	.20	.20
574	A171	40 l	pale violet & blk	.20	.20
575	A171	50 l	salmon & blk	.20	.20
576	A171	90 l	pale citron & blk	.20	.20
577	A171	100 l	pale green & blk	.20	.20
578	A171	200 l	pale blue & blk	.30	.25
			Nos. 573-578 (6)	1.30	1.25

European Architectural Heritage Year.

Miracle of Loaves and Fishes, Gilt Glass A172

Designs: 150 l, Painting of Christ, from Comodilla Catacomb. 200 l, Raising of Lazarus. All works from 4th century.

Perf. 14x13½

1975, Sept. 25   Photo.   Unwmk.

579	A172	30 l	multi	.20	.20
580	A172	150 l	brown & multi	.25	.20
581	A172	200 l	green & multi	.45	.30
			Nos. 579-581 (3)	.90	.70

9th Intl. Congress of Christian Archaeology.

Investiture of First Librarian Bartolomeo Sacchi by Pope Sixtus IV A173

Designs: 100 l, Pope Sixtus IV and books in old wooden press, from Latin Vatican Codex 2044, vert. 250 l, Pope Sixtus IV visiting Library, fresco in Hospital of the Holy Spirit. Design of 70 l is from fresco by Melozzo da Forli in Vatican Gallery.

Perf. 14x13½, 13½x14

1975, Sept. 25   Litho. & Engr.

582	A173	70 l	gray & lilac	.20	.20
583	A173	100 l	lt yellow & grn	.25	.20
584	A173	250 l	gray & red	.55	.30
			Nos. 582-584 (3)	1.00	.70

Founding of the Vatican Apostolic Library, 500th anniv.

Mt. Argentario Monastery A174

St. Paul of the Cross, by Giovanni Della Porta — A175

Design: 300 l, Basilica of Sts. John and Paul and burial chapel of Saint.

1975, Nov. 27   Photo.   Perf. 14x13½

585	A174	50 l	multi	.20	.20
586	A174	150 l	multi	.25	.20
587	A174	300 l	multi	.45	.25
			Nos. 585-587 (3)	.90	.65

Bicentenary of death of St. Paul of the Cross, founder of the Passionist religious order in 1737.

Praying Women, by Fra Angelico — A176

International Women's Year: 200 l, Seated women, by Fra Angelico.

1975, Nov. 27   Perf. 13½x14

588	A176	100 l	multi	.20	.20
589	A176	200 l	multi	.40	.25

Virgin and Child in Glory, by Titian A177

Design: 300 l, The Six Saints, by Titian. Designs from "The Madonna in Glory with the Child Jesus and Six Saints."

1976, May 13   Engr.   Perf. 14x13½

590	A177	100 l	rose magenta	.25	.20
591	A177	300 l	rose magenta	.50	.40
a.			Pair, #590-591	.75	.60

Titian (1477-1576), painter.

A178

A179

Designs: 150 l, Eucharist, wheat and globe. 200 l, Hands Holding Eucharist. 400 l, Hungry mankind reaching for the Eucharist.

1976, July 2   Photo.   Perf. 13½x14
592 A178 150 l gold, red & bl   .20 .20
593 A178 200 l gold & blue   .25 .25
594 A178 400 l gold, grn & brn   .40 .40
    Nos. 592-594 (3)   .85 .85

41st Intl. Eucharistic Congress, Philadelphia, PA, Aug. 1-8.

1976, Sept. 30 Photo.   Perf. 13½x14
Details from Transfiguration by Raphael: 30 l, Moses Holding Tablets. 40 l, Transfigured Christ. 50 l, Prophet Elijah with book. 100 l, Apostles John and Peter. 150 l, Group of women. 200 l, Landscape.

595 A179 30 l ocher & multi   .20 .20
596 A179 40 l red & multi   .20 .20
597 A179 50 l violet & multi   .20 .20
598 A179 100 l multicolored   .20 .20
599 A179 150 l green & multi   .25 .20
600 A179 200 l ocher & multi   .35 .25
    Nos. 595-600 (6)   1.40 1.25

St. John's Tower A180

Roman Views: 100 l, Fountain of the Sacrament. 120 l, Fountain at entrance to the gardens. 180 l, Basilica, Cupola of St. Peter's and Sacristy. 250 l, Borgia Tower and Sistine Chapel. 300 l, Apostolic Palace and Courtyard of St. Damasius.

Litho. & Engr.
1976, Nov. 23   Perf. 14
601 A180 50 l gray & black   .20 .20
602 A180 100 l salmon & dk brn   .20 .20
603 A180 120 l citron & dk grn   .20 .20
604 A180 180 l pale gray & blk   .20 .20
605 A180 250 l yellow & brn   .25 .20
606 A180 300 l pale lilac & mag   .30 .25
    Nos. 601-606 (6)   1.35 1.25

The Lord's Creatures A181

70 l, Brother Sun. 100 l, Sister Moon and Stars. 130 l, Sister Water. 170 l, Praise in infirmities and tribulations. 200 l, Praise for bodily death. Designs are illustrations by Duilio Cambellotti for "The Canticle of Brother Sun," by St. Francis.

1977, Mar. 10 Photo.   Perf. 14x13½
607 A181 50 l multi   .20 .20
608 A181 70 l multi   .20 .20
609 A181 100 l multi   .20 .20
610 A181 130 l multi   .20 .20

611 A181 170 l multi   .20 .20
612 A181 200 l multi   .25 .20
    Nos. 607-612 (6)   1.25 1.20
St. Francis of Assisi, 750th death anniv.

Sts. Peter and Paul A182

Design: 350 l, Pope Gregory XI and St. Catherine of Siena. Designs are after fresco by Giorgio Vasari.

1977, May 20   Engr.   Perf. 14
613 170 l black   .30 .20
614 350 l black   .50 .30
    a. A182 Pair, #613-614   .85 .60
Return of Pope Gregory XI from Avignon, 600th anniv.

Dormition of the Virgin — A183

1977, July 5   Photo.   Perf. 13½x14
Design: 400 l, Virgin Mary in Heaven. Both designs after miniatures in Latin manuscripts, Vatican Library.

615 A183 200 l multi   .30 .20
616 A183 400 l multi   .55 .30
    Feast of the Assumption.

The Nile Deity, Roman Sculpture — A184

Sculptures: 120 l, Head of Pericles. 130 l, Roman Couple Joining Hands. 150 l, Apollo Belvedere, head. 170 l, Laocoon, head. 350 l, Apollo Belvedere, torso.

1977, Sept. 29   Perf. 14x13½
617 A184 50 l multi   .20 .20
618 A184 120 l multi   .75 .20
619 A184 130 l multi   .20 .20
620 A184 150 l multi   .20 .20
621 A184 170 l multi   .20 .20
622 A184 350 l multi   .30 .30
    Nos. 617-622 (6)   1.30 1.30
Classical sculptures in Vatican Museums.

Creation of Man and Woman — A185

Designs: 70 l, Three youths in the furnace. 100 l, Adoration of the Kings. 130 l, Raising of Lazarus. 200 l, The Good Shepherd. 400 l, Chrismon, Cross, sleeping soldiers (Resurrection). Designs are bas-reliefs from Christian sarcophagi, 250-350 A.D., found in Roman excavations.

1977, Dec. 9   Photo.   Perf. 14x13½
623 A185 50 l multi   .20 .20
624 A185 70 l multi   .20 .20
625 A185 100 l multi   .20 .20
626 A185 130 l multi   .20 .20

627 A185 200 l multi   .20 .20
628 A185 400 l multi   .35 .25
    Nos. 623-628 (6)   1.35 1.25

Madonna with the Parrot and Rubens Self-portrait A186

1977, Dec. 9   Perf. 13½x14
629 A186 350 l multi   .50 .50
Peter Paul Rubens (1577-1640).

Pope Paul VI, by Lino Bianchi Barriviera A187

Design: 350 l, Christ's Face, by Pericle Fazzini and arms of Pope Paul VI.

1978, Mar. 9   Photo.   Perf. 14
630 A187 350 l multi   .50 .30
631 A187 400 l multi   .50 .40
80th birthday of Pope Paul VI.

Pope Pius IX (1792-1878) A188

Designs: 130 l, Arms of Pope Pius IX. 170 l, Seal of Pius IX, used to sign definition of Dogma of Immaculate Conception.

Litho. & Engr.
1978, May 9   Perf. 13x14
632 A188 130 l multi   .20 .20
633 A188 170 l multi   .30 .20
634 A188 200 l multi   .35 .20
    Nos. 632-634 (3)   .85 .60

Interregnum Issues

Keys of St. Peter and Papal Chamberlain's Insignia A189

A190

1978, Aug. 23 Photo.   Perf. 14
635 A189 120 l purple & lt green   .30 .20
636 A189 150 l purple & salmon   .35 .20
637 A189 250 l purple & yellow   .35 .20
    Nos. 635-637 (3)   1.00 .60

1978, Oct. 12 Photo.   Perf. 14
638 A190 120 l black & multi   .25 .20
639 A190 200 l black & multi   .25 .20
640 A190 250 l black & multi   .25 .20
    Nos. 638-640 (3)   .75 .60

Pope John Paul I Pope from Aug. 26 to Sept. 28, 1978 — A191

Pope John Paul I: 70 l, Sitting on his throne. 250 l, Walking in Vatican garden. 350 l, Giving blessing, horiz.

1978, Dec. 11   Perf. 13x14, 14x1
641 A191 70 l multi   .20 .2
642 A191 120 l multi   .25 .2
643 A191 250 l multi   .30 .3
644 A191 350 l multi   .40 .4
    Nos. 641-644 (4)   1.15 1.1

Arms of Pope John Paul II A192

Designs: 250 l, Pope John Paul II raising hand in blessing. 400 l, Jesus giving keys to St. Peter.

Litho. & Engr.
1979, Mar. 22   Perf. 14x1
645 A192 170 l black & multi   .25 .2
646 A192 250 l black & multi   .30 .3
647 A192 400 l black & multi   .55 .4
    Nos. 645-647 (3)   1.10 1.0
Inauguration of pontificate of Pope John Paul II.

Martyrdom of St. Stanislas A193

St. Basil the Great Instructing Monk A194

Designs: 150 l, St. Stanislas appearing to the people. 250 l, Gold reliquary, 1504, containing saint's head. 500 l, View of Cracow Cathedral.

1979, May 18 Photo.   Perf. 14
648 A193 120 l multi   .20 .20
649 A193 150 l multi   .20 .20
650 A193 250 l multi   .35 .30
651 A193 500 l multi   .75 .65
    Nos. 648-651 (4)   1.50 1.35
900th anniversary of martyrdom of St. Stanislas (1030-1079), patron saint of Poland.

Engr. & Photo.
1979, June 25   Perf. 13½x14
St. Basil the Great, 16th cent. of death:
520 l, St. Basil the Great visiting the sick.

652 A194 150 l multi   .20 .20
653 A194 520 l multi   .85 .70

Father Secchi, Solar Protuberance, Spectrum and Meteorograph — A195

Father Angelo Secchi (1818-1878), astronomer, solar protuberance, spectrum and: 220 l, Spectroscope. 300 l, Telescope.

Litho. & Engr.

1979, June 25   *Perf. 14x13½*
654	A195	180 l	multi	.25 .25
655	A195	220 l	multi	.35 .30
656	A195	300 l	multi	.40 .30
	Nos. 654-656 (3)			1.00 .85

Vatican City A196

Papal Arms and Portraits: 70 l, Pius XI. 120 l, Pius XII. 150 l, John XXIII. 170 l, Paul VI. 250 l, John Paul I. 450 l, John Paul II.

1979, Oct. 11   **Photo.**   *Perf. 14x13½*
657	A196	50 l	multi	.20 .20
658	A196	70 l	multi	.20 .20
659	A196	120 l	multi	.20 .20
660	A196	150 l	multi	.20 .20
661	A196	170 l	multi	.25 .25
662	A196	250 l	multi	.30 .30
663	A196	450 l	multi	.65 .50
	Nos. 657-663 (7)			2.00 1.85

Vatican City State, 50th anniversary.

Infant, by Andrea Della Robbia, IYC Emblem — A197

IYC Emblem and Della Robbia Bas Reliefs, Hospital of the Innocents, Florence.

Engr. & Photo.

1979, Nov. 27   *Perf. 13½x14*
664	A197	50 l	multi	.20 .20
665	A197	120 l	multi	.20 .20
666	A197	200 l	multi	.30 .30
667	A197	350 l	multi	.50 .40
	Nos. 664-667 (4)			1.20 1.00

International Year of the Child.

Abbot Desiderius Giving Codex to St. Benedict — A198

Illuminated Letters and Illustrations, Codices, Vatican Apostolic Library: 100 l, St. Benedict writing the Rule. 150 l, Page from the Rule. 220 l, Death of St. Benedict. 450 l, Montecassino (after painting by Paul Bril).

1980, Mar. 21   **Photo.**   *Perf. 14x13½*
668	A198	80 l	multi	.20 .20
669	A198	100 l	multi	.20 .20
670	A198	150 l	multi	.25 .25
671	A198	220 l	multi	.30 .30
672	A198	450 l	multi	.60 .55
	Nos. 668-672 (5)			1.55 1.50

St. Benedict of Nursia (patron saint of Europe), 1500th birth anniversary.

Bernini, Medallion Showing Baldacchino in St. Peter's — A199

Gian Lorenzo Bernini (1598-1680), Architect (Self-portrait and Medallion): 170 l, St. Peter's Square with third wing (never built). 250 l, Bronze chair, Doctors of the Church. 350 l, Apostolic Palace stairway.

1980, Oct. 16   **Litho.**   *Perf. 14x13½*
673	A199	80 l	multicolored	.20 .20
674	A199	170 l	multicolored	.25 .25
675	A199	250 l	multicolored	.35 .30
676	A199	350 l	multicolored	.55 .35
	Nos. 673-676 (4)			1.35 1.10

St. Albertus Magnus on Mission of Peace — A200

1980, Nov. 18   **Litho.**   *Perf. 13½x14*
677	A200	300 l	shown	.40 .30
678	A200	400 l	As bishop	.55 .40

St. Albertus Magnus, 700th death anniv.

Communion of the Saints — A201

1980, Nov. 18   *Perf. 14x13½*
679	A201	250 l	shown	.35 .25
680	A201	500 l	Christ and saints	.65 .60

Feast of All Saints.

Guglielmo Marconi and Pope Pius XI, Vatican Radio Emblem, Vatican Arms A202

Designs: 150 l, Microphone, Bible text. 200 l, St. Maria di Galeria Radio Center antenna, Archangel Gabriel statue. 600 l, Pope John Paul II.

1981, Feb. 12   **Photo.**   *Perf. 14x13½*
681	A202	100 l	shown	.20 .20
682	A202	150 l	multicolored	.25 .20
683	A202	200 l	multicolored	.30 .25
684	A202	600 l	multicolored	.80 .65
	Nos. 681-684 (4)			1.55 1.30

Vatican Radio, 50th anniversary.

Virgil Seated at Podium, Vergilius Romanus — A203

1981, Apr. 23   **Litho.**   *Perf. 14*
685	A203	350 l	multicolored	.75 .65
686	A203	600 l	multicolored	1.40 1.10

2000th birth anniversary of Virgil. Issued in sheets of 16 stamps plus 9 labels.

Congress Emblem A204

Congress Emblem and: 150 l, Virgin appearing to St. Bernadette. 200 l, Pilgrims going to Lourdes. 500 l, Bishop and pilgrims.

1981, June 22   **Photo.**
687	A204	80 l	multicolored	.20 .20
688	A204	150 l	multicolored	.20 .20
689	A204	200 l	multicolored	.30 .30
690	A204	500 l	multicolored	.60 .60
	Nos. 687-690 (4)			1.30 1.30

42nd Intl. Eucharistic Congress, Lourdes, France, July 16-23.

Intl. Year of the Disabled A205

1981, Sept. 29   **Photo.**   *Perf. 14x13½*
691	A205	600 l	multicolored	.90 .80

Jan van Ruusbroec, Flemish Mystic, 500th Birth Anniv. — A206

Litho. & Engr.

1981, Sept. 29   *Perf. 13½x14*
692	A206	200 l	shown	.35 .35
693	A206	300 l	Portrait	.45 .45

1980 Journeys of Pope John Paul II — A207

1981, Dec. 3   **Photo.**   *Perf. 13½x14½*
694	A207	50 l	Papal arms	.20 .20
695	A207	100 l	Map of Africa	.20 .20
696	A207	120 l	Crucifix	.20 .20
697	A207	150 l	Communion	.20 .20
698	A207	200 l	African bishop	.20 .20
699	A207	250 l	Visiting sick	.30 .30
700	A207	300 l	Notre Dame, France	.40 .40
701	A207	400 l	UNESCO speech	.50 .50
702	A207	600 l	Christ of the Andes, Brazil	.90 .90
703	A207	700 l	Cologne Cathedral, Germany	1.00 1.00
704	A207	900 l	John Paul II	1.10 1.10
	Nos. 694-704 (11)			5.20 5.20

700th Death Anniv. of St. Agnes of Prague — A208

Designs: 700 l, Handing order to Grand Master of the Crosiers of the Red Star. 900 l, Receiving letter from St. Clare.

1982, Feb. 16   **Photo.**   *Perf. 13½x14½*
705	A208	700 l	multicolored	1.00 1.00
706	A208	900 l	multicolored	1.10 1.10

Pueri Cantores A209   St. Teresa of Avila (1515-1582) A210

Luca Della Robbia (1400-1482), Sculptor: No. 708, Pueri Cantores, diff. No. 709, Virgin in Prayer (44x36mm).

Photo. & Engr.

1982, May 21   *Perf. 14*
707	A209	1000 l	multicolored	1.25 1.10
708	A209	1000 l	multicolored	1.25 1.10
709	A209	1000 l	multicolored	1.25 1.10
a.	Strip of 3, #707-709			4.00 3.50

1982, Sept. 23   **Photo.**

Sketches of St. Teresa by Riccardo Tommasi-Ferroni.
710	A210	200 l	multicolored	.25 .25
711	A210	600 l	multicolored	.80 .80
712	A210	1000 l	multicolored	1.25 1.25
	Nos. 710-712 (3)			2.30 2.30

Christmas A211

Nativity Bas-Reliefs: 300 l, Wit Stwosz, Church of the Virgin Mary, Cracow. 450 l, Enrico Manfrini.

Photo. & Engr.

1982, Nov. 23   *Perf. 14*
713	A211	300 l	multicolored	.45 .45
714	A211	450 l	multicolored	.65 .65

400th Anniv. of Gregorian Calendar — A212

Sculpture Details, Tomb of Pope Gregory XIII, Vatican Basilica.

1982, Nov. 23   **Engr.**   *Perf. 13½x14*
715	A212	200 l	Surveying the globe	.25 .25
716	A212	300 l	Receiving Edict of Reform	.40 .40
717	A212	700 l	Presenting edict	.90 .90
a.	Souvenir sheet of 3, #715-717			2.50 2.50
	Nos. 715-717 (3)			1.55 1.55

Souvenir Sheets

Greek Vase — A213

1983, Mar. 10   **Litho.**   *Perf. 13½x14*
718		Sheet of 6		3.25 2.00
a.	A213 100 l	shown		.20 .20
b.	A213 200 l	Italian vase		.35 .25
c.	A213 250 l	Female terra-cotta bust		.50 .30
d.	A213 300 l	Marcus Aurelius bust		.55 .35
e.	A213 350 l	Bird fresco		.65 .45
f.	A213 400 l	Pope Clement VIII vestment		.75 .45

1983, June 14   Litho.   *Perf. 13½x14*

719		Sheet of 6		3.50	3.50
a.	A213	100 l	Horse's head, Etruscan terra cotta	.20	.20
b.	A213	200 l	Horseman, Greek fragment	.25	.20
c.	A213	300 l	Male head, Etruscan	.30	.20
d.	A213	400 l	Apollo Belvedere head	.50	.25
e.	A213	500 l	Moses, Roman fresco	.55	.35
f.	A213	1000 l	Madonna and Child, by Bernardo Daddi	1.25	.70

1983, Nov. 10   Litho.   *Perf. 13½x14*

720		Sheet of 6		4.00	4.00
a.	A213	150 l	Greek cup, Oedipus and the Sphinx	.25	.20
b.	A213	200 l	Etruscan bronze statue of a child	.30	.20
c.	A213	350 l	Emperor Augustus marble statue	.40	.25
d.	A213	400 l	Good Shepherd marble statue	.55	.30
e.	A213	500 l	St. Nicholas Saving a ship by G. da Fabriano	.70	.40
f.	A213	1200 l	The Holy face by G. Rouault	1.50	1.00

Vatican Collection: The Papacy and Art - US 1983 exhibition, New York, Chicago, San Francisco.

Extraordinary Holy Year, 1983-84 (1950th Anniv. of Redemption) A214

Sketches by Giovanni Hajnal.

1983, Mar. 10   Photo. & Engr.

721	A214	300 l	Crucifixion	.45	.30
722	A214	350 l	Christ the Redeemer	.55	.40
723	A214	400 l	Pope	.45	.45
724	A214	2000 l	Holy Spirit	2.75	2.75
		Nos. 721-724 (4)		4.20	3.90

Theology, by Raphael (1483-1517) A215

St. Casimir of Lithuania (1458-1484) A217

Gregor Johann Mendel (1822-1884), Biologist — A216

Allegories, Room of the Segnatura.

1983, June 14

725	A215	50 l	shown	.20	.20
726	A215	400 l	Poetry	.60	.60
727	A215	500 l	Justice	.70	.70
728	A215	1200 l	Philosphy	1.75	1.75
		Nos. 725-728 (4)		3.25	3.25

Photo. & Engr.

1984, Feb. 28   *Perf. 14x13½*

Phases of pea plant hybridization.

729	A216	450 l	multicolored	.60	.45
730	A216	1500 l	multicolored	2.00	1.50

1984, Feb. 28   *Perf. 14*

731	A217	550 l	multicolored	.90	.55
732	A217	1200 l	multicolored	2.00	1.25

Pontifical Academy of Sciences — A218

1984, June 18   Litho. & Engr.

733	A218	150 l	shown	.25	.20
734	A218	450 l	Secret Archives	.65	.55
735	A218	550 l	Apostolic Library	.85	.65
736	A218	1500 l	Observatory	2.25	1.75
		Nos. 733-736 (4)		4.00	3.15

Papal Journeys A218a

1984-85   Photo.   *Perf. 13½x14½*

737	A218a	50 l	Pakistan	.20	.20
738	A218a	100 l	Philippines	.20	.20
739	A218a	150 l	Guam	.30	.20
740	A218a	250 l	Japan	.45	.30
741	A218a	300 l	Alaska	.55	.50
742	A218a	400 l	Africa	.80	.50
743	A218a	450 l	Portugal	.90	.60
a.		Bklt. pane, 4 ea #738, 741-743 + 4 labels ('85)		12.00	
744	A218a	550 l	Grt. Britain	1.10	.70
745	A218a	1000 l	Argentina	2.00	1.40
746	A218a	1500 l	Switzerland	3.00	1.90
747	A218a	2500 l	San Marino	4.00	3.25
748	A218a	4000 l	Spain	8.00	5.25
		Nos. 737-748 (12)		21.50	15.00

St. Damasus I (b. 304) A219

St. Damasus I and: 200 l, Sepulchre of Sts. Marcellinus and Peter. 500 l, Epigraph of St. Januarius. 2000 l, Basilica, Church of the Martyrs Simplicius, Faustinus and Beatrice.

1984, Nov. 27   Photo.   *Perf. 14x13½*

749	A219	200 l	multicolored	.35	.25
750	A219	500 l	multicolored	.90	.60
751	A219	2000 l	multicolored	3.75	2.25
		Nos. 749-751 (3)		5.00	3.10

St. Methodius (d. 885) — A220

St. Methodius and: 500 l, Madonna and Christ. 600 l, St. Cyril, carrying the body of St. Clement I. 1700 l, Sts. Benedict and Cyril, patrons of Europe.

Photo. & Engr.

1985, May 7   *Perf. 13½x14*

752	A220	500 l	multicolored	.90	.50
753	A220	600 l	multicolored	1.10	.60
754	A220	1700 l	multicolored	3.25	1.60
		Nos. 752-754 (3)		5.25	2.70

St. Thomas More (1477-1535) — A221

St. Thomas More (from a portrait by Hans Holbein) and: 250 l, map of British Isles. 400 l, Frontispiece of Utopia. 2000 l, Frontispiece of Domenico Regi's biography of More.

Litho. & Engr.

1985, May 7   *Perf. 14x13½*

755	A221	250 l	multicolored	.45	.45
756	A221	400 l	multicolored	.80	.40
757	A221	2000 l	multicolored	3.75	2.00
		Nos. 755-757 (3)		5.00	2.65

St. Gregory VII (c. 1020-85) A222

Designs: 150 l, Eagle from Byzantine door, St. Paul's Basilica, Rome. 450 l, St. Gregory blessing. 2500 l, Sarcophagus.

Perf. 13½x14, 14x13½

1985, June 18   Photo.

758	A222	150 l	multi, vert.	.25	.20
759	A222	450 l	multi, vert.	.75	.45
760	A222	2500 l	multicolored	4.00	2.50
		Nos. 758-760 (3)		5.00	3.15

43rd Intl. Eucharistic Congress — A223

Emblem, host, cross and: 100 l, Outline map of Africa. 400 l, Altar and Assembly of Bishops. 600 l, African chalice. 2300 l, African Christian family.

Photo. & Engr.

1985, June 18   *Perf. 13½x14*

761	A223	100 l	multicolored	.20	.20
762	A223	400 l	multicolored	.60	.40
763	A223	600 l	multicolored	.90	.55
764	A223	2300 l	multicolored	3.50	2.00
		Nos. 761-764 (4)		5.20	3.15

Concordat Agreement Ratification A224

1985, Oct. 15   Photo.   *Perf. 14x13½*

765	A224	400 l	Papal arms, map of Italy	.65	.35

Coaches A225

1985, Oct. 15   Litho. & Engr.

766	A225	450 l	dp lil rose & int bl	.75	.35
767	A225	1500 l	brt bl & dp lil rose	2.00	1.40
a.		Souvenir sheet of 2, #766-767, perf. 13½x12½		3.25	3.25

Italia '85.

Intl. Peace Year 1986 — A226

Biblical and gospel texts: 50 l, Isaiah 2:4. 350 l, Isaiah 52:7. 450 l, Matthew 5:9. 650 l, Luke 2:14. 2000 l, Message for World Peace speech of Pope John Paul II, Jan. 1, 1986.

1986, Apr. 14   Photo.   *Perf. 1*

768	A226	50 l	multicolored	.20	
769	A226	350 l	multicolored	.55	.3
770	A226	450 l	multicolored	.80	.4
771	A226	650 l	multicolored	1.10	.6
772	A226	2000 l	multicolored	3.50	2.0
		Nos. 768-772 (5)		6.15	3.5

Vatican City — A227

1986, Apr. 14   *Perf. 13½x14*

773	A227		Block of 6	6.75	3.00
a.-f.		550 l, any single		1.10	.50

UNESCO World Heritage Campaign. No. 773 has continuous design.

Patron Saints of the Sick — A228

Conversion of St. Augustine (354-430) in 387 — A230

Pontifical Academy of Sciences, 50th Anniv. A229

Designs: No. 774, St. Camillus de Lellis rescuing invalid during Tiber flood, by Pierre Subleyras (1699-1749). No. 775, St. John of God with invalids, by Gomez Moreno (1834-1918). 2000 l, Pope John Paul II visiting the sick.

Litho. & Engr.

1986, June 12   *Perf. 13½x14*

774	A228	700 l	multicolored	1.25	.60
775	A228	700 l	multicolored	1.25	.60
776	A228	2000 l	multicolored	3.50	1.90
		Nos. 774-776 (3)		6.00	3.10

Litho. & Engr.

1986, Oct. 2   *Perf. 14x13½*

School of Athens (details), by Raphael: 1500 l, Scribes. 2500 l, Students learning math.

777	A229	1500 l	multicolored	2.75	1.50
778	A229	2500 l	multicolored	4.25	2.50

1987, Apr. 7   Photo.   *Perf. 13½x14*

Religious art: 300 l, St. Augustine reading St. Paul's Epistles, fresco by Benozzo Gozzoli (1420-1498), Church of St. Augustine, San Gimignano. 400 l, Baptism of St. Augustine, painting by Bartolomeo di Gentile (1470-1534), Vatican Art Gallery. 500 l, Ecstasy of St. Augustine, fresco by Benozzo Gozzoli, Church of St. Augustine. 2200 l, St. Augustine, detail of Disputa del Sacramento, fresco by Raphael (1483-1520), Room of the Segnatura, Apostolic Palace.

779	A230	300 l	multicolored	.50	.30
780	A230	400 l	multicolored	.70	.45
781	A230	500 l	multicolored	.85	.50
782	A230	2200 l	multicolored	3.75	2.25
		Nos. 779-782 (4)		5.80	3.50

A231

Christianization
Anniversaries
A232

Seals: 700 l, Church of Riga, 1234-1269.
2400 l, Marian Basilica of the Assumption,
Aglona, 1780.

1987, June 2   Photo.   Perf. 13½x14

783	A231	700 l	multicolored	1.40 .95
784	A231	2400 l	multicolored	4.75 3.25

Christianization of Latvia, 800th anniv.

1987, June 2   Perf. 13½x14

Designs: 200 l, Christ, statue in the Lithuanian Chapel, Vatican Crypt. 700 l, Two Angels
and Our Lady Holding the Body of Christ, by a
Lithuanian artist. 3000 l, Lithuanian shrine.

785	A232	200 l	multicolored	.30 .25
786	A232	700 l	multicolored	1.10 .75
787	A232	3000 l	multicolored	4.50 3.00
	Nos. 785-787 (3)			5.90 4.00

Christianization of Lithuania, 600th anniv.

OLYMPHILEX '87,
Rome, Aug. 29-Sept.
9 — A233

Details of mosaic from the Baths of Cara-
calla: 400 l, Judge. 500 l, Athlete. 600 l, Athlete, diff. 2000 l, Athlete, diff.

Litho. & Engr.
1987, Aug. 29   Perf. 14

788	A233	400 l	multicolored	.65 .45
789	A233	500 l	multicolored	.85 .55
790	A233	600 l	multicolored	1.00 .65
791	A233	2000 l	multicolored	3.25 2.25
	Nos. 788-791 (4)			5.75 3.90

Souvenir Sheet

792	Sheet of 4 + 4 labels		5.75 5.75
a.	A233 400 l like No. 788		.65 .65
b.	A233 500 l like No. 789		.80 .80
c.	A233 600 l like No. 780		1.00 1.00
d.	A233 2000 l like No. 791		3.25 3.25

Stamps from souvenir sheet have a Greek
border in blue surrounding vignettes (pictured). Nos. 788-791 have single line border in
blue. No. 792 has 4 labels picturing the papal
arms, a goblet, a crown and the exhibition
emblem.

Inauguration of the Philatelic and
Numismatic Museum — A235

Designs: 400 l, Philatelic department, Vatican City, No. 1. 3500 l, Numismatic department, 1000-lire coin of 1986.

1987, Sept. 29   Photo.   Perf. 14x13½

793	A235	400 l	multicolored	.60 .45
794	A235	3500 l	multicolored	5.50 3.75

Journeys of
Pope John
Paul II,
1985-86
A236

Designs: 50 l, Venezuela, Peru, Ecuador
and Trinidad & Tobago, 1985. 250 l, The
Netherlands, Luxembourg, Belgium, 1985.
400 l, Togo, Ivory Coast, Cameroun, Central
Africa, Zaire, Kenya and Morocco, 1985. 500 l,
Liechtenstein, 1986. 4000 l, Bangladesh, Singapore, Fiji, New Zealand, Australia and Seychelles, 1986.

1987, Oct. 27   Photo.   Perf. 14x13½

795	A236	50 l	multicolored	.20 .20
796	A236	250 l	multicolored	.65 .45
797	A236	400 l	multicolored	1.10 .70
798	A236	500 l	multicolored	1.25 .85
799	A236	600 l	multicolored	1.60 1.00
800	A236	700 l	multicolored	1.90 1.25
801	A236	2500 l	multicolored	6.75 4.50
802	A236	4000 l	multicolored	11.00 7.25
	Nos. 795-802 (8)			24.45 16.20

A237

A238

Transfer of St. Nicholas Relics from Myra to
Bari, 900th anniv.: 500 l, Arrival of relics at
Bari. 700 l, Act of charity, three improverished
women. 3000 l, Miraculous rescue of ship.

1987, Dec. 3   Perf. 13½x14

803	A237	500 l	multicolored	2.00 1.25
804	A237	700 l	multicolored	3.00 2.00
805	A237	3000 l	multicolored	12.50 8.00
	Nos. 803-805 (3)			17.50 11.25

St. Nicholas of Bari (c. 270-352), bishop of
Myra. Legend of Santa Claus originated
because of his charitable works. Printed in
sheets of 8 + 16 se-tenant labels picturing
Santa Claus.

1988, Apr. 19   Photo.

Children and: 500 l, Sister of the Institute of
the Daughters of Mary Help of Christians.
1000 l, St. John Bosco. 2000 l, Salesian lay
brother. Printed in a continuous design.

806	Strip of 3		5.25 4.00
a.	A238 500 l multicolored		.70 .50
b.	A238 1000 l multicolored		1.50 1.00
c.	A238 2000 l multicolored		3.00 2.00

St. John Bosco (1815-1888), educator.

A239

A240

1988, June 16   Photo.   Perf. 13½x14

807	A239	50 l	Annunciation	.20 .20
808	A239	300 l	Nativity	.40 .25
809	A239	500 l	Pentecost	.65 .40
810	A239	750 l	Assumption	1.10 .60
811	A239	1000 l	Mother of the Church	1.40 .80
812	A239	2400 l	Refuge of Sinners	3.25 1.90
	Nos. 807-812 (6)			7.00 4.15

Marian Year, 1987-88.

1988, June 16

Baptism of the Rus' of Kiev, Millennium:
450 l, "Prince St. Vladimir the Great," from a
15th cent. icon. 650 l, Cathedral of St. Sophia,
Kiev. 2500 l, "Mother of God in Prayer," from a
mosaic at the cathedral.

813	A240	450 l	multicolored	.75 .45
814	A240	650 l	multicolored	1.00 .65
815	A240	2500 l	multicolored	3.75 2.25
	Nos. 813-815 (3)			5.50 3.35

Paintings by Paolo Veronese (1528-
1588) — A241

Designs: 550 l, Marriage of Cana (Madonna
and Christ) the Louvre, Paris. 650 l, Self-portrait of the Artist, Villa Barbaro of Maser, Tre-
viso. 3000 l, Marriage of Cana (woman and
two men).

Perf. 13½x14, 14x13½
1988, Sept. 29   Photo. & Engr.

816	A241	550 l	multicolored	.80 .45
817	A241	650 l	multi, horiz.	.95 .55
818	A241	3000 l	multicolored	4.25 2.50
	Nos. 816-818 (3)			6.00 3.50

Christmas
A242

Luke 2:14 and: 50 l, Angel facing LR. 400 l,
Angel facing UR. 500 l, Angel facing LL. 550 l,
Shepherds. 850 l, Nativity. 1500 l, Magi.

1988, Dec. 12   Photo.   Perf. 13½x14

819	A242	50 l	multicolored	.20 .20
820	A242	400 l	multicolored	.60 .30
821	A242	500 l	multicolored	.70 .35
822	A242	550 l	multicolored	.80 .40
823	A242	850 l	multicolored	1.25 .60
824	A242	1500 l	multicolored	2.25 1.00
	Nos. 819-824 (6)			5.80 2.85

Souvenir Sheet

825	Sheet of 6		5.75 5.75
a.	A242 50 l gold & multi		.20 .20
b.	A242 400 l gold & multi		.60 .30
c.	A242 500 l gold & multi		.70 .35
d.	A242 550 l gold & multi		.80 .40
e.	A242 850 l gold & multi		1.25 .60
f.	A242 1500 l gold & multi		2.25 1.00

No. 825 has continuous design.

Feast of the
Visitation, 600th
Anniv. — A243

Illuminations: 550 l, The Annunciation. 750 l,
The Visitation (Virgin and St. Elizabeth).
2500 l, Mary, Elizabeth and infants.

1989, May 5   Photo.   Perf. 13½x14

826	A243	550 l	multicolored	.80 .40
827	A243	750 l	multicolored	1.10 .55
828	A243	2500 l	multicolored	3.75 1.90
	Nos. 826-828 (3)			5.65 2.85

Souvenir Sheet

Gregorian Egyptian
Museum, 150th
Anniv. — A244

Designs: 400 l, Apis. 650 l, Isis and Apis
dicephalous bust. 750 l, Statue of the physician Ugiahorresne. 2400 l, Pharaoh
Mentuhotep.

Litho. & Engr.
1989, May 5   Perf. 14x13½

829	Sheet of 4		6.00 6.00
a.	A244 400 l multicolored		.55 .30
b.	A244 650 l multicolored		.90 .50
c.	A244 750 l multicolored		1.10 .55
d.	A244 2400 l multicolored		3.25 1.75

A245

A246

Birds from engravings by Eleazar Albin in
Histoire Naturelle des Oiseaux, 1750.

1989, June 13   Photo.   Perf. 12
Granite Paper

830	A245	100 l	Parrot	.20 .20
831	A245	150 l	Green wood-pecker	.20 .20
832	A245	200 l	Crested and common wrens	.25 .20
833	A245	350 l	Kingfisher	.45 .25
834	A245	500 l	Red grosbeak of Virginia	.65 .30
835	A245	700 l	Bullfinch	.90 .45
836	A245	1500 l	Lapwing plover	2.00 1.00
837	A245	3000 l	French teal	4.00 2.00
	Nos. 830-837 (8)			8.65 4.60

Photo. & Engr.
1989, Sept. 29   Perf. 13½x14

Symbols of the Eucharist.

838	A246	550 l	shown	.80 .40
839	A246	850 l	multi, diff.	1.25 .65
840	A246	1000 l	multi, diff.	1.50 .75
841	A246	2500 l	multi, diff.	3.75 1.90
	Nos. 838-841 (4)			7.30 3.70

44th Intl. Eucharistic Cong., Seoul, Oct. 5-8.

Ecclesiastical Hierarchy in the US,
Bicent. — A247

Designs: 450 l, Basilica of the Assumption
of the Blessed Virgin Mary, Baltimore. 1350 l,
John Carroll (1735-1815), 1st bishop of Baltimore and the US. 2400 l, Cathedral of Mary
Our Queen, Baltimore.

1989, Nov. 9	Photo.		Perf. 12	
842	A247	450 l multicolored	.65	.40
843	A247	1350 l multicolored	2.00	1.25
844	A247	2400 l multicolored	3.50	2.00
	Nos. 842-844 (3)		6.15	3.65

Papal
Journeys
1988
A248

Papal arms, Pope John Paul II and maps:
50 l, Uruguay, Bolivia, Peru and Paraguay,
May 7-19. 550 l, Austria, June 23-27. 800 l,
Zimbabwe, Botswana, Lesotho, Swaziland
and Mozambique, Sept. 10-19. 1000 l, France,
Oct. 8-11. 4000 l, Pastoral visits in Italy, 1978-
1988.

1989, Nov. 9			Perf. 14x13½	
845	A248	50 l multicolored	.20	.20
846	A248	550 l multicolored	.80	.50
847	A248	800 l multicolored	1.10	.70
848	A248	1000 l multicolored	1.50	.90
849	A248	4000 l multicolored	5.75	3.50
	Nos. 845-849 (5)		9.35	5.80

St. Angela Merici
(c. 1474-1540)
A249

Designs: 700 l, The vision of the mystical
stair, Prophecy of the Ursulines. 800 l, Evangelical counsel. 2800 l, Ursulines mission
continued.

1990, Apr. 5	Photo.		Perf. 13½x14	
850	A249	700 l multicolored	1.25	.80
851	A249	800 l multicolored	1.40	.95
852	A249	2800 l multicolored	4.75	3.25
	Nos. 850-852 (3)		7.40	5.00

Caritas Intl.,
40th Anniv.
A250

Designs: 450 l, Abraham. 650 l, Three visitors. 800 l, Abraham and Sarah. 2000 l, Three
visitors at Abraham's table.

1990, June 5	Photo.	Perf. 12x11½		
		Granite Paper		
853	A250	450 l multicolored	.75	.45
854	A250	650 l multicolored	1.10	.70
855	A250	800 l multicolored	1.25	.85
856	A250	2000 l multicolored	3.25	2.00
	Nos. 853-856 (4)		6.35	4.00

	Souvenir Sheet			
857		Sheet of 4	6.00	6.00
a.	A250 450 l like #853		.65	.50
b.	A250 650 l like #854		1.00	.65
c.	A250 800 l like #855		1.25	.85
d.	A250 2000 l like #856		3.00	2.00

Nos. 853-856 have a single line border in
gold. Nos. 857a-857d have no border line.

A251

A252

1990, June 5		Perf. 13½x14		
858	A251	300 l Ordination of St.		
		Willibrord	.50	.30
859	A251	700 l Stay in Antwerp	1.10	.70
860	A251	3000 l Leaving belong-		
		ings, death	4.75	3.25
	Nos. 858-860 (3)		6.35	4.25

1300th anniv. of ministry of St. Willibrord.

1990, Oct. 2

Diocese of Beijing-Nanking, 300th Anniv.:
500 l, Lake Beijing. 750 l, Church of the
Immaculate Conception, Beijing, 1650. 1500 l,
Lake Beijing, diff. 2000 l, Church of the
Redeemer, Beijing, 1703.

861	A252	500 l multicolored	.70	.45
862	A252	750 l multicolored	1.10	.70
863	A252	1500 l multicolored	2.25	1.40
864	A252	2000 l multicolored	2.75	1.90
	Nos. 861-864 (4)		6.80	4.45

Christmas
A253

Details from painting by Sebastiano
Mainardi.

1990, Nov. 27	Photo.		Perf. 13	
865	A253	50 l Choir of Angels	.20	.20
866	A253	200 l St. Joseph	.30	.30
867	A253	650 l Holy Child	1.10	1.10
868	A253	750 l Madonna	1.25	1.25
869	A253	2500 l Nativity scene,		
		vert.	4.00	4.00
	Nos. 865-869 (5)		6.85	6.85

Paintings of the
Sistine
Chapel — A254

Different details from lunettes: 50 l, 100 l,
Eleazar. 150 l, 250 l, Jacob. 350 l, 400 l,
Josiah. 500 l, 650 l, Asa. 800 l, 1000 l, Zerub-
babel. 2000 l, 3000 l, Azor.

1991, Apr. 9	Photo.		Perf. 11½	
		Granite Paper		
870	A254	50 l multicolored	.20	.20
871	A254	100 l multicolored	.20	.20
a.	Booklet pane of 6		.75	
872	A254	150 l multicolored	.20	.20
a.	Booklet pane of 6		1.25	
873	A254	250 l multicolored	.35	.35
874	A254	350 l multicolored	.45	.45
875	A254	400 l multicolored	.50	.50
876	A254	500 l multicolored	.70	.70
877	A254	650 l multicolored	.90	.90
a.	Booklet pane of 6		5.50	
878	A254	800 l multicolored	1.00	1.00
879	A254	1000 l multicolored	1.40	1.40
880	A254	2000 l multicolored	2.75	2.75
881	A254	3000 l multicolored	4.00	4.00
	Nos. 870-881 (12)		12.65	12.65

Encyclical
Rerum
Novarum,
Cent.
A255

Arms of Pope Leo XIII and: 600 l, Title page
of Encyclical. 750 l, Allegory of Church's interest in workers, employers. 3500 l, Pope Leo
XIII (1878-1903).

1991, May 23	Engr.		Perf. 14x13½	
882	A255	600 l blue & dk grn	.90	.90
883	A255	750 l sage grn & rose		
		car	1.10	1.10
884	A255	3500 l brt pur & dk bl	5.25	5.25
	Nos. 882-884 (3)		7.25	7.25

Vatican
Observatory,
Cent. — A256

Canonization
of
St. Bridget, 600th
Anniv. — A257

Designs: 750 l, Astrograph for making photographic sky map, 1891. 1000 l, Zeiss Double
Astrograph, Lake Castelgandolfo, 1935, horiz.
3000 l, New telescope, Vatican Observatory,
Mt. Graham, Arizona, 1991.

Perf. 11½x12, 12x11½				
1991, Oct. 1			Photo.	
		Granite Paper		
885	A256	750 l multicolored	1.10	1.10
886	A256	1000 l multicolored	1.50	1.50
887	A256	3000 l multicolored	4.50	4.50
	Nos. 885-887 (3)		7.10	7.10

1991, Oct. 1		Perf. 12½x13		

Designs: 1500 l, Receiving Madonna's revelations. 2000 l, Receiving Christ's revelations.

888	A257	1500 l multicolored	2.25	2.25
889	A257	2000 l multicolored	3.25	3.25

Journeys of Pope
John Paul II,
1990 — A258

Pope John Paul II and: 200 l, Cathedral of
Immaculate Conception, Ouagadougou,
Burkina Faso. 550 l, St. Vitus' Cathedral,
Prague. 750 l, Our Lady of Guadaloupe's
Basilica, Mexico. 1000 l, Ta' Pinu Sanctuary,
Gozo. 3500 l, Cathedral of Christ the King,
Gitega, Burundi.

	Litho. & Engr.			
1991, Nov. 11			Perf. 13½x14	
890	A258	200 l green & multi	.30	.30
891	A258	550 l org brn &		
		multi	.85	.85
892	A258	750 l claret & multi	1.10	1.10
893	A258	1500 l dk brn & multi	2.25	2.25
894	A258	3500 l grn bl & multi	5.50	5.50
	Nos. 890-894 (5)		10.00	10.00

West Africa, Jan. 25-Feb. 1 (200 l); Czecho-
slovakia, Apr. 21-22 (550 l); Mexico, Curacao,
May 6-14 (750 l); Malta, May 25-27 (1500 l);
Tanzania, Burundi, Rwanda, Ivory Coast,
Sept. 1-10 (3500 l).

A259

A260

Special Assembly for Europe of Synod of
Bishops: 300 l, Colonnade of St. Peter's Basilica. 500 l, St. Peter's Basilica and Square.
4000 l, Colonnade of St. Peter's Basilica,
Apostolic Palace.

1991, Nov. 11	Engr.		Perf. 12½x13	
895	A259	300 l olive & blk	.45	.45
896	A259	500 l olive & blk	.80	.80
897	A259	4000 l olive & blk	6.00	6.00
a.	Strip of 3, #895-897		8.00	8.00

No. 897a has continous design.

1992, Mar. 24	Photo.	Perf. 11½x12		

Discovery and Evangelization of America,
500th Anniv.: 500 l, Christopher Columbus.
600 l, Saint Peter Claver. 850 l, La Virgen de
los Reyes Catolicos. 1000 l, Bishop Bartolome
de las Casas. 2000 l, Father Junipero Serra.
Charts: 1500 l, New World. 2500 l, Old
World.

	Granite Paper			
898	A260	500 l multicolored	.75	.75
899	A260	600 l multicolored	.90	.90
900	A260	850 l multicolored	1.25	1.25
901	A260	1000 l multicolored	1.50	1.50
902	A260	2000 l multicolored	3.00	3.00
	Nos. 898-902 (5)		7.40	7.40

	Souvenir Sheet			
		Perf. 12		
903	A260	Sheet of 2	6.00	6.00
a.	1500 l multicolored		2.25	2.25
b.	2500 l multicolored		3.75	3.75

Piero Della
Francesca (d.
1492),
Painter — A261

Frescoes: 300 l, 750 l (detail), Our Lady of
Childbirth. 1000 l, 3000 l (detail), Resurrection.

1992, May 15	Photo.		Perf. 13½x14	
904	A261	300 l multicolored	.40	.40
905	A261	750 l multicolored	1.10	1.10
906	A261	1000 l multicolored	1.40	1.40
907	A261	3000 l multicolored	4.25	4.25
	Nos. 904-907 (4)		7.15	7.15

St. Giuseppe
Benedetto
Cottolengo (1786-
1842)
A262

1992, May 15		Perf. 11½x12		

St. Giuseppe Benedetto Cottolengo: 650 l,
Comforting the sick. 850 l, With Little House of
Divine Providence.

	Granite Paper			
908	A262	650 l multicolored	1.00	1.00
909	A262	850 l multicolored	1.40	1.40

850

A263

A264

Plants of the New World: a, Frumentum indicum. b, Solanum pomiferum. c, Opuntia. d, Cacaos, cacavifera. e, Solanum tuberosum, capsicum, mordens. f, Ananas sagitae folio.

1992, Sept. 15   Photo.   Perf. 11½x12
Granite Paper
910   Block of 6   7.50 7.50
a.-f. A263 850 l any single   1.25 1.25

1992, Oct. 12   Perf. 12½x13
911 A264 700 l multicolored   1.00 1.00

4th General Conference of the Latin American Episcopacy.

Christmas
A265

Mosaics from Basilica of St. Maria Maggiore, Rome: 600 l, The Annunciation. 700 l, Nativity. 1000 l, Adoration of the Magi. 1500 l, Presentation to the Temple.

1992, Nov. 24   Photo.   Perf. 11½
Granite Paper
912 A265 600 l multicolored   .90 .90
913 A265 700 l multicolored   1.00 1.00
914 A265 1000 l multicolored   1.40 1.40
915 A265 1500 l multicolored   2.10 2.10
        Nos. 912-915 (4)   5.40 5.40

St. Francis Healing Man from Ilerda, by Giotto di Bondone (1266-1337) — A266

1993, Jan. 9   Litho.   Perf. 13½x14
916 A266 1000 l multi + label   1.25 1.25
Prayer Meeting for Peace in Europe, Assisi.

Architecture of Vatican City and Rome — A267

Buildings: 200 l, St. Peter's Basilica, Vatican City. 300 l, St. John Lateran Basilica, Rome. 350 l, St. Mary Major's Basilica, Rome. 500 l, St. Paul's Basilica, Rome. 600 l, Apostolic Palace, Vatican. 700 l, Lateran Apostolic Palace, Rome. 850 l, Papal Palace, Castel Gandolfo.

1000 l, Chancery Palace, Rome. 2000 l, Palace of the Propagation of the Faith, Rome. 3000 l, St. Calixtus Palace, Rome.

1993, Mar. 23   Photo.   Perf. 12x11½
Granite Paper
917 A267 200 l multicolored   .25 .25
a.   Booklet pane of 4   1.10
918 A267 300 l multicolored   .40 .40
a.   Booklet pane of 4   1.60
919 A267 350 l multicolored   .50 .50
a.   Booklet pane of 4   2.00
920 A267 500 l multicolored   .65 .65
a.   Booklet pane of 4   2.75
921 A267 600 l multicolored   .80 .80
922 A267 700 l multicolored   .95 .95
923 A267 850 l multicolored   1.10 1.10
924 A267 1000 l multicolored   1.40 1.40
925 A267 2000 l multicolored   2.75 2.75
926 A267 3000 l multicolored   4.00 4.00
        Nos. 917-926 (10)   12.80 12.80

A268

Congress emblem, Vatican arms and: 500 l, Cross, grape vines. 700 l, Cross, hands breaking bread. 1500 l, Hands lifting chalice. 2500 l, Wheat, banner.

1993, May 22   Litho.   Perf. 14x13½
927 A268 500 l multicolored   .60 .60
928 A268 700 l multicolored   .90 .90
929 A268 1500 l multicolored   1.90 1.90
930 A268 2500 l multicolored   3.00 3.00
        Nos. 927-930 (4)   6.40 6.40

45th Intl. Eucharistic Congress, Seville.

A269

1993, May 22   Engr.   Perf. 13½x14
Traditio Legis Sarcophagus, St. Peter's Basilica: a, 200 l, Sacrifice of Isaac. b, 750 l, Apostle Peter receiving law from Jesus, Apostle Paul. c, 3000 l, Christ watching servant pouring water on Pilate's hands.
931 A269 Triptych, #a.-c.   5.00 5.00

Ascension Day, May 20.

Contemporary Art — A270

Europa: 750 l, Crucifixion, by Felice Casorati (1886-1963). 850 l, Rouen Cathedral, by Maurice Utrillo (1883-1955).

1993, Sept. 29   Photo.   Perf. 13
932 A270 750 l multicolored   .95 .95
933 A270 850 l multicolored   1.00 1.00

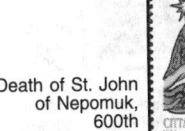

Death of St. John of Nepomuk, 600th Anniv. — A271

2000 l, Buildings in Prague, Charles Bridge.

1993, Sept. 29   Litho.   Perf. 13½x14
934 A271 1000 l multicolored   1.25 1.25
935 A271 2000 l multicolored   2.50 2.50

Travels of Pope John Paul II — A272

Visits to: 600 l, Senegal, Gambia, Guinea. 1000 l, Angola, St. Thomas and Prince. 5000 l, Dominican Republic.

1993, Nov. 23   Photo.   Perf. 12x11½
Granite Paper
936 A272 600 l multicolored   .70 .70
937 A272 1000 l multicolored   1.25 1.25
938 A272 5000 l multicolored   5.75 5.75
        Nos. 936-938 (3)   7.70 7.70

Hans Holbein the Younger (1497?-1543), Painter — A273

Details or entire paintings: 700 l, 1000 l, Madonna of Solothurn. 1500 l, Self-portrait.

1993, Nov. 23   Litho. & Engr.   Perf. 13½x14
939 A273 700 l multicolored   .85 .85
940 A273 1000 l multicolored   1.25 1.25
941 A273 1500 l multicolored   1.75 1.75
        Nos. 939-941 (3)   3.85 3.85

Synod of Bishops, Special Assembly for Africa A274

Designs: 850 l, Stylized crosier, dome with cross, vert. 1000 l, Crucifix, dome of St. Peter's Basilica, crosiers, African landscape.

Perf. 12½x13, 13x12½
1994, Apr. 8   Photo.
942 A274 850 l multicolored   1.10 1.10
943 A274 1000 l multicolored   1.25 1.25

The Restored Sistine Chapel — A275

Frescoes, by Michelangelo: Creation of the Sun and Moon: No. 944, Sun. No. 945, God pointing toward moon. Creation of Man: No. 946, Adam, No. 947, God. Original Sin: No. 948, Adam, Eve taking apple from serpent. No. 949, Adam, Eve forced from Garden of Eden. The Flood: No. 950, People on dry ground. No. 951, People on stone outcropping.
4000 l, Detail of Last Judgment, Christ and the Virgin.

1994, Apr. 8   Photo.   Perf. 11½
944 A275 350 l multicolored   .40 .40
945 A275 350 l multicolored   .40 .40
a.   A275 Pair, #944-945   .80 .80
946 A275 500 l multicolored   .60 .60
947 A275 500 l multicolored   .60 .60
a.   A275 Pair, #946-947   1.25 1.25
948 A275 1000 l multicolored   1.25 1.25
949 A275 1000 l multicolored   1.25 1.25
a.   A275 Pair, #948-949   2.50 2.50
950 A275 2000 l multicolored   2.50 2.50
951 A275 2000 l multicolored   2.50 2.50
a.   A275 Pair, 950-951   5.00 5.00
        Nos. 944-951 (8)   9.50 9.50

Souvenir Sheet
Perf. 12
952 A275 4000 l multicolored   5.00 5.00
No. 952 contains one 36x54mm stamp.

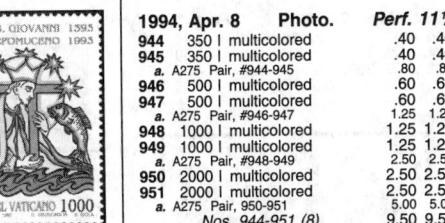

European Inventions, Discoveries — A276

Europa: 750 l, Progess from wheel to atom traced by white thread. 850 l, Galileo in center of solar system, scientific instruments.

1994, May 31   Litho.   Perf. 13x13½
953 A276 750 l multicolored   .95 .95
954 A276 850 l multicolored   1.10 1.10

Intl. Year of the Family — A277

Stained glass: 400 l, God creating man and woman. 750 l, Family under names of four Evangelists. 1000 l, Parents teaching son. 2000 l, Young man comforting elderly couple.

1994, May 31   Photo.   Perf. 13x14
955 A277 400 l multicolored   .50 .50
956 A277 750 l multicolored   .95 .95
957 A277 1000 l multicolored   1.25 1.25
958 A277 2000 l multicolored   2.50 2.50
        Nos. 955-958 (4)   5.20 5.20

Giovanni da Montecorvino (1247-1328), Missionary — A278

1994, Sept. 27   Litho.   Perf. 14
959 A278 1000 l multicolored   1.40 1.40
Evangelization of China, 700th anniv.

13th Intl. Convention of Christian Archaeology, Split, Croatia — A279

Mosaics from Euphrasian Basilica, Parentium, Croatia, 6th Cent.: 700 l, Bishop Euphrasius, Archdeacon Claudius, Claudius' son. 1500 l, Madonna and Child, two angels. 3000 l, Christ, Apostles Peter & Paul.

1994, Sept. 27   *Perf. 13x14*
960	A279	700 l	multicolored	1.00	1.00
961	A279	1500 l	multicolored	2.00	2.00
962	A279	3000 l	multicolored	4.25	4.25
		Nos. 960-962 (3)		7.25	7.25

Travels of Pope John Paul II — A280

Designs: 600 l, Benin, Uganda, Sudan. 700 l, Albania. 1000 l, Spain. 2000 l, Jamaica, Mexico, US. 3000 l, Lithuania, Latvia, Estonia.

1994, Nov. 18   *Perf. 13*
963	A280	600 l	multicolored	.85	.85
964	A280	700 l	multicolored	1.00	1.00
965	A280	1000 l	multicolored	1.40	1.40
966	A280	2000 l	multicolored	2.75	2.75
967	A280	3000 l	multicolored	4.25	4.25
		Nos. 963-967 (5)		10.25	10.25

Christmas
A281

The Nativity, by Il Tintoretto: 700 l, The Holy Family. No. 969, The Holy Family, two women. No. 970, Adoration of the shepherds.

1994, Nov. 18   **Photo.**   *Perf. 11½*
Granite Paper
968	A281	700 l	multicolored	1.00	1.00

Size: 45x27mm
969	A281	1000 l	multicolored	1.40	1.40
970	A281	1000 l	multicolored	1.40	1.40
a.		Pair, #969-970		2.80	2.80
		Nos. 968-970 (3)		3.80	3.80

Peace and Freedom
A282

1995, Mar. 25   **Photo.**   *Perf. 14x13*
971	A282	750 l	shown	.90	.90
972	A282	850 l	Hands clasp, dove	1.00	1.00

Europa.

Shrine of Loreto, 700th Anniv. — A283

Details of artworks from vaults of Sacristy: 600 l, St. Mark's, Angel with chalice, by Melozzo da Forli. 700 l, St. Mark's, Angel with lamb, by da Forli. 1500 l, 2500 l, St. John's, Music making angels, by Luca Signorelli. No. 977, Marble carving showing Holy House of Loreto.

1995, Mar. 25   *Perf. 11½*
973	A283	600 l	multicolored	.70	.70
974	A283	700 l	multicolored	.80	.80
975	A283	1500 l	multicolored	1.75	1.75
976	A283	2500 l	multicolored	3.00	3.00
		Nos. 973-976 (4)		6.25	6.25

Souvenir Sheet
977	A283	3000 l	multicolored	3.50	3.50

No. 977 contains one 36x36mm stamp.

Radio, Cent.
A284

Designs: 850 l, Guglielmo Marconi, transmitting equipment. 1000 l, Archangel Gabriel, Pope John Paul II, Marconi broadcasting station, Vatican City.

1995, June 8   **Photo.**   *Perf. 14*
978	A284	850 l	multicolored	1.00	1.00
979	A284	1000 l	multicolored	1.25	1.25

See Germany No. 1990, Ireland Nos. 973-974, San Marino Nos. 1336-1337.

A285

A286

European Nature Conservation Year (Scenes in Vatican Gardens & Castel Gandolfo: 200 l, Fountain of the Triton, arches of rhyncospernum jasminoides. 300 l, Avenue of roses, Palazzo Barberini. 400 l, Statue of Apollo Citaredo. 550 l, Ruins of Domitian's Villa, Avenue of roses. 750 l, Acer negundo, Viale dell'Osservatorio. 1500 l, Belvedere garden. 2000 l, Fountain of the Eagle, Quercus ilex. 3000 l, Avenue of cypresses, equestrian statue.

1995, June 8   *Perf. 12*
Granite Paper
980	A285	200 l	multicolored	.25	.25
981	A285	300 l	multicolored	.35	.35
a.		Booklet pane of 3		1.00	
982	A285	400 l	multicolored	.50	.50
a.		Booklet pane of 3		1.50	
983	A285	550 l	multicolored	.70	.70
a.		Booklet pane of 3		2.25	
984	A285	750 l	multicolored	.90	.90
a.		Booklet pane of 3		2.75	
		Complete booklet, #981a, 982a, 983a, 984a		7.50	
985	A285	1500 l	multicolored	1.90	1.90
986	A285	2000 l	multicolored	2.50	2.50
987	A285	3000 l	multicolored	3.75	3.75
		Nos. 980-987 (8)		10.85	10.85

1995, Oct. 3   **Photo.**   *Perf. 13½x13*
Paintings of peace, by Paolo Guiotto: 550 l, Small hearts flying from large heart. 750 l, Stylized faces. 850 l, Doves in flight. 1250 l, Lymph reaching to smallest branches. 2000 l, Explosion of colors, people.
988	A286	550 l	multicolored	.70	.70
989	A286	750 l	multicolored	.95	.95
990	A286	850 l	multicolored	1.10	1.10
991	A286	1250 l	multicolored	1.50	1.50
992	A286	2000 l	multicolored	2.50	2.50
		Nos. 988-992 (5)		6.75	6.75

UN, 50th anniv.

A287

A288

St. Anthony of Padua (1195-1231): 750 l, St. John of God (1495-1550). 3000 l, St. Philip Neri (1515-95).

Litho. & Engr.
1995, Oct. 3   *Perf. 13½x14*
993	A287	500 l	green & brown	.65	.65
994	A287	750 l	violet & green	.95	.95
995	A287	3000 l	magenta & black	3.75	3.75
		Nos. 993-995 (3)		5.35	5.35

1995, Nov. 20   **Photo.**   *Perf. 12x11½*
Scenes depicting life of Jesus Christ from illuminated manuscripts: 400 l, The Annunciation. 850 l, Nativity. 1250 l, Flight into Egypt. 2000 l, Jesus among the teachers.
Granite Paper
996	A288	400 l	multicolored	.50	.50
997	A288	850 l	multicolored	1.10	1.10
998	A288	1250 l	multicolored	1.60	1.60
999	A288	2000 l	multicolored	2.50	2.50
		Nos. 996-999 (4)		5.70	5.70

Towards the Holy Year 2000.

Travels of Pope John Paul II
A289

Designs: 1000 l, Giving greeting in Croatia, statue of Blessed Lady, Zagreb Cathedral. 2000 l, In Italy, lighthouse in Genoa, Orvieto Cathedral, Valley of Temples in Agrigento.

1995, Nov. 20   **Litho.**   *Perf. 14½x14*
1000	A289	1000 l	multicolored	1.25	1.25
1001	A289	2000 l	multicolored	2.50	2.50

Religious Anniversaries
A290

Designs: 1250 l, Angel holding crosses, Union of Brest-Litovsk, 400th anniv. 2000 l, Cross with branches, Latin episcopal mitre, Byzantine mitre, Union of Uzhorod, 350th anniv.

1996, Mar. 16   **Photo.**   *Perf. 13½x14*
1002	A290	1250 l	multicolored	1.60	1.60
1003	A290	2000 l	multicolored	2.50	2.50

A291

Marco Polo's Return from China, 700th Anniv. — A292

Designs from miniatures, Bodleian Library Oxford: 350 l, Marco Polo delivering Pope Gregory X's letter to Great Khan. 850 l, Great Khan dispensing alms to poor in Cambaluc. 1250 l, Marco Polo receiving golden book from Great Khan. 2500 l, Marco Polo in Persia listening to story of three Kings who go to Bethlehem to adore Jesus.

2000 l, Stylized portrait of Marco Polo drawn from first printed edition of "Il Milione." Illustration reduced.

1996, Mar. 15   *Perf. 11½*
Granite Paper
1004	A291	350 l	multicolored	.45	.45
1005	A291	850 l	multicolored	1.10	1.10
1006	A291	1250 l	multicolored	1.60	1.60
1007	A291	2500 l	multicolored	3.25	3.25
		Nos. 1004-1007 (4)		6.40	6.40

Souvenir Sheet
Perf. 12x11½
1008	A292	2000 l	black	2.50	2.50

A293

A294

Famous Women: 750 l, Gianna Baretta Molla (1922-62), physician. 850 l, Sister Edith Stein (1891-1942).

1996, May 7   **Engr.**   *Perf. 13x14*
1009	A293	750 l	blue	1.00	1.00
1010	A293	850 l	brown	1.10	1.10

1996, May 7   **Photo.**   *Perf. 13*
Modern Olympic Games, Cent.: a, Statue of athlete. b, Athlete's torso. c, Hand. d, Statue of athlete reaching upward. e, Hercules.
1011		Strip of 5		8.00	8.00
a.-e.	A294	1250 l	any single	1.60	1.60

Ordination of Pope John Paul II, 50th Anniv.
A295

Designs: 500 l, Wawel Cathedral, Krakow. 750 l, Pope John Paul II giving blessing. 1250 l, Basilica of St. John Lateran, Rome.

1996, Oct. 12   **Litho.**   *Perf. 14*
1012	A295	500 l	multicolored	.65	.65
1013	A295	750 l	multicolored	1.00	1.00
1014	A295	1250 l	multicolored	1.60	1.60
		Nos. 1012-1014 (3)		3.25	3.25

Life of Jesus Christ from Illuminated Manuscripts A296

Designs: 550 l, Baptism of Jesus at River Jordan. 850 l, Temptation in the desert. 1500 l, Cure of the leper. 2500 l, Jesus the teacher.

1996, Oct. 12 Photo. Perf. 12x11½

1015	A296	550 l	multicolored	.75 .75
1016	A296	850 l	multicolored	1.10 1.10
1017	A296	1500 l	multicolored	2.00 2.00
1018	A296	2500 l	multicolored	3.25 3.25
		Nos. 1015-1018 (4)		7.10 7.10

Christmas — A297

Nativity, by Murillo (1618-82).

1996, Nov. 20 Litho. Perf. 13½

1019	A297	750 l	multicolored	1.00 1.00

St. Celestine V (1215-96) A298

#1021, St. Alfonso Maria De'Liguori (1696-1787).

1996, Nov. 20 Perf. 13½x14

1020	A298	1250 l	multicolored	1.60 1.60
1021	A298	1250 l	multicolored	1.60 1.60

Travels of Pope John Paul II, 1995 A299

Designs: 250 l, Jan. 11-21, Philippines, Papua New Guinea, Australia, Sri Lanka. 500 l, May 20-22, Czech Republic, Poland. 750 l, June 3-4, Belgium. 1000 l, June 30-July 3, Slovakia. 2000 l, Sept. 14-20, Cameroun, South Africa, Kenya. 5000 l, Oct. 4-9, UN headquarters, NY, US.

1996, Nov. 20 Perf. 14x13½

1022	A299	250 l	blue & multi	.35 .35
1023	A299	500 l	blue green & multi	.65 .65
1024	A299	750 l	green & multi	1.00 1.00
1025	A299	1000 l	brown & multi	1.25 1.25
1026	A299	2000 l	gray & multi	2.50 2.50
1027	A299	5000 l	pink & multi	6.75 6.75
		Nos. 1022-1027 (6)		12.50 12.50

Papal Carriages and Automobiles A300

Designs: 50 l, Touring carriage. 100 l, Graham Paige. 300 l, Festive traveling carriage. 500 l, Citroen Lictoria VI. 750 l, Grand touring

carriage. 850 l, Mercedes Benz. 1000 l, Festive half carriage. 1250 l, Mercedes Benz 300SEL. 2000 l, Touring carriage, diff. 4000 l, Fiat "Pope mobile."

1997, Mar. 20 Photo. Perf. 12
Granite Paper

1028	A300	50 l	multicolored	.20 .20
1029	A300	100 l	multicolored	.20 .20
1030	A300	300 l	multicolored	.35 .35
1031	A300	500 l	multicolored	.60 .60
1032	A300	750 l	multicolored	.90 .90
1033	A300	850 l	multicolored	1.00 1.00
1034	A300	1000 l	multicolored	1.10 1.10
1035	A300	1250 l	multicolored	1.50 1.50
1036	A300	2000 l	multicolored	2.25 2.25
1037	A300	4000 l	multicolored	4.75 4.75
		Nos. 1028-1037 (10)		12.85 12.85

A301

A302

Swiss Guard: 750 l, Guard in traditional attire. 850 l, Guard in armor with sword in front of iron gate.

1997, Mar. 20 Litho. Perf. 13½

1038	A301	750 l	multicolored	.90 .90
1039	A301	850 l	multicolored	1.00 1.00
a.		Strip of 2 + 2 labels		1.90 1.90

Europa.

1997, Apr. 23 Engr. Perf. 14

1040	A302	850 l	deep violet	1.00 1.00

St. Adalbert (956-997). See Germany No. 1964, Poland No. 3337, Czech Republic No. 3012, Hungary No. 3569.

"Looking at the Classics," Museum Exhibition — A304

Pictures from texts of Latin and Greek classics: 500 l, Aristotle observing and describing various species from man to insect, from his "De Historia Animalium." 750 l, Bacchus riding dragon, from "Metamorphoses" by Ovid. 1250 l, General haranguing his soldiers, from "Iliad" by Homer. 2000 l, Hannibal leaving Canne, two horsemen, foot soldier, from "Ab Urbe Condita" by Titus Livius.

Masks from "Comedies," by Terrence: No. 1045: a, Man, woman. b, Two women. c, Two men.

1997, Apr. 23 Photo. Perf. 14

1041	A303	500 l	multicolored	.60 .60
1042	A303	750 l	multicolored	.90 .90
1043	A303	1250 l	multicolored	1.50 1.50
1044	A303	2000 l	multicolored	2.40 2.40
		Nos. 1041-1044 (4)		5.40 5.40

Perf. 13½

1045	A304	1000 l	Sheet of 3, #a.-c.	3.50 3.50

A305

A306

46th Intl. Eucharistic Congress, Wroclaw, Poland: 650 l, Elements of the Eucharist, chalice, consecrated Host, arms of Wroclaw. 1000 l, The Last Supper, fish, Congress emblem. 1250 l, Wroclaw Cathedral, sheaf of wheat, holy spirit descending on church. 2500 l, "IHS" symbol of Christ on cross, doves, world with two hands on it.

1997, May 27 Photo. Perf. 13

1046	A305	650 l	multicolored	.75 .75
1047	A305	1000 l	multicolored	1.10 1.10
1048	A305	1250 l	multicolored	1.40 1.40
1049	A305	2500 l	multicolored	2.75 2.75
		Nos. 1046-1049 (4)		6.00 6.00

1997, Sept. 15 Litho. Perf. 13x14

1050	A306	900 l	multicolored	1.00 1.00

Pope Paul VI (1897-1978).
No. 1050 was printed se-tenant with 4 labels.

St. Ambrose (d. 397) — A307

Towards the Holy Year 2000 — A308

1997, Sept. 15 Photo. Perf. 13x14

1051	A307	800 l	multicolored	.90 .90

1997, Sept. 15 Perf. 12

Illustrations of Christ's miracles: 400 l, Healing of paralyzed man. 800 l, Calming of the tempest. 1300 l, Multiplication of bread and fish. 3600 l, Peter's confession and conferment of primacy.

Granite Paper

1052	A308	400 l	multicolored	.45 .45
1053	A308	800 l	multicolored	.90 .90
1054	A308	1300 l	multicolored	1.90 1.90
1055	A308	3600 l	multicolored	4.25 4.25
		Nos. 1052-1055 (4)		7.50 7.50

1996 Travels of Pope John Paul II — A309

Designs: 400 l, Central & South America, Feb. 5-12. 900 l, Tunisia, Apr. 14. 1000 l, Slovenia , May 17-19. 1300 l, Germany, June 21-23. 2000 l, Hungary, Sept. 6-7. 4000 l, France, Sept. 19-22.

1997, Nov. 11 Litho. Perf. 14x13½

1056	A309	400 l	multicolored	.50 .50
1057	A309	900 l	multicolored	1.00 1.00
1058	A309	1000 l	multicolored	1.25 1.25
1059	A309	1300 l	multicolored	1.50 1.50
1060	A309	2000 l	multicolored	2.25 2.25
1061	A309	4000 l	multicolored	4.75 4.75
		Nos. 1056-1061 (6)		11.25 11.25

Christmas — A310

Detail from "The Nativity," by Benozzo Gozzoli (1420-97).

1997, Nov. 11 Photo. Perf. 14

1062	A310	800 l	multicolored	.95 .95

Feasts of Sts. Peter and Paul, June 29th — A311

1998, Mar. 24 Photo. Perf. 13

1063	A311	800 l	St. Peter	.90 .90
1064	A311	900 l	St. Paul	1.00 1.00

Europa.

The Popes of the Holy Years 1300-1525 A312

Designs: 200 l, Boniface VIII, 1300. 400 l, Clement VI, 1350. 500 l, Boniface IX, 1390, 1400. 700 l, Martin V, 1423. 800 l, Nicholas V, 1450. 900 l, Sixtus IV, 1475. 1300 l, Alexander VI, 1500. 3000 , Clement VII, 1525.

1998, Mar. 24 Litho. Perf. 14

1065	A312	200 l	multicolored	.25 .25
1066	A312	400 l	multicolored	.45 .45
1067	A312	500 l	multicolored	.60 .60
1068	A312	700 l	multicolored	.80 .80
1069	A312	800 l	multicolored	.90 .90
1070	A312	900 l	multicolored	1.00 1.00
1071	A312	1300 l	multicolored	1.50 1.50
1072	A312	3000 l	multicolored	3.50 3.50
		Nos. 1065-1072 (8)		9.00 9.00

Nos. 1065-1072 were each printed se-tenant with a label picturing the respective papal arms.
See Nos. 1095-1102, 1141-1150.

A313

A314

Litho. & Engr.
1998, May 19   *Perf. 13½x14*
1073 A313   900 l   Face on Shroud   1.00   1.00
1074 A313   2500 l   Cathedral of Turin   2.75   2.75

Exposition of the Shroud of Turin.

1998, May 19   Photo.   *Perf. 12*

Frescoes of Angels, by Melozzo da Forli (1438-94), Basilica of Sts. Apostles, Rome: Angels playing various musical instruments.

Granite Paper
1075 A314   450 l   multicolored   .60   .60
1076 A314   650 l   multicolored   .75   .75
1077 A314   800 l   multicolored   .90   .90
1078 A314   1000 l   multicolored   1.10   1.10
1079 A314   1300 l   multicolored   1.50   1.50
1080 A314   2000 l   multicolored   2.25   2.25
   Nos. 1075-1080 (6)   7.10   7.10

Towards Holy Year 2000
A315

Episodes from the Life of Christ: 500 l, Triumphal entry into Jerusalem. 800 l, Washing of the feet. 1300 l, The Last Supper. 3000 l, Crucifixion.

1998, May 19   *Perf. 12*
Granite Paper
1081 A315   500 l   multicolored   .60   .60
1082 A315   800 l   multicolored   .90   .90
1083 A315   1300 l   multicolored   1.50   1.50
1084 A315   3000 l   multicolored   3.25   3.25
   Nos. 1081-1084 (4)   6.25   6.25

Italia '98
A316

1998, Oct. 23   Photo.   *Perf. 14*
1085 A316   800 l   Pope John Paul II   1.00   1.00

The Good Shepherd — A317
Christian Sculptures — A318

1998, Oct. 25   *Perf. 12 Vert.*
Granite Paper
Booklet Stamp
1086 A317   900 l   multicolored   1.10   1.10
  a.   Booklet pane of 5   5.50
     Complete booklet, #1086a   5.50

Italia '98.

1998, Oct. 25   *Perf. 12*

Designs: a, 600 l, Peter's denial. b, 900 l, Praying woman. c, 1000 l, Christ and the Cyrenean. 2000 l, Christ with the Cross and Two Apostles.

Granite Paper
1087 A318   Sheet of 4, #a.-d.   5.50   5.50

Italia '98. Margin is embossed.

Christmas — A319

1998, Dec. 1   Litho.   *Perf. 14x13½*
1088 A319   800 l   multicolored   1.00   1.00

See Croatia No. 381.

1997 Travels of Pope John Paul II — A320

Designs: 300 l, Sarajevo, 4/12-13/97. 600 l, Prague, 4/25-27/97. 800 l, Beirut, 5/10-11/97. 900 l, Poland, 5/21-6/10/97. 1300 l, Paris, 8/21-24/97. 5000 l, Rio de Janeiro, 10/2-6/97.

1998, Dec. 1   *Perf. 12½*
1089 A320   300 l   brown   .35   .35
1090 A320   600 l   green   .70   .70
1091 A320   800 l   brown   1.00   1.00
1092 A320   900 l   violet blue   1.10   1.10
1093 A320   1300 l   org brn   1.60   1.60
1094 A320   5000 l   org brn   6.00   6.00
   Nos. 1089-1094 (6)   10.75   10.75

Popes of the Holy Years Type of 1998

Popes: 300 l, Julius III, 1550. 600 l, Gregory XIII, 1575. 800 l, Clement VII, 1600. 900 l, Urban VIII, 1625. 1000 l, Innocent X, 1650. 1300 l, Clement X, 1675. 1500 l, Innocent XII, 1700. 3000 l, Benedict XIII, 1725.

1999, Mar. 23   Litho.   *Perf. 14*
1095 A312   300 l   multicolored   .35   .35
1096 A312   600 l   multicolored   .65   .65
1097 A312   800 l   multicolored   .90   .90
1098 A312   900 l   multicolored   1.00   1.00
1099 A312   1000 l   multicolored   1.10   1.10
1100 A312   1300 l   multicolored   1.40   1.40
1101 A312   1500 l   multicolored   1.60   1.60
1102 A312   2000 l   multicolored   2.25   2.25
   Nos. 1095-1102 (8)   9.25   9.25

Nos. 1095-1102 were each printed se-tenant with a label picturing the respective papal arms.

Flowers from Vatican Gardens and Papal Villa, Castelgandolfo
A321

Europa: 800 l, John Paul II Rose. 900 l, Water lilies.

1999, Mar. 23   Litho.   *Perf. 12½x13*
1103 A321   800 l   multicolored   .90   .90
1104 A321   900 l   multicolored   1.00   1.00
  a.   Pair, #1103-1104 + label   1.90   1.90

Padre Pio de Pietrelcina (1887-1968) — A322

#1106: a, 1st church, San Giovanni Rotondo. b, New church, San Giovanni Rotondo. c, Like #1105.

1999, Apr. 27   Litho.   *Perf. 14x13*
1105 A322   800 l   multicolored   .90   .90
Souvenir Sheet
Perf. 13x13½
1106 A322   Sheet of 3   2.10   2.10
  a.   300 l multi, vert.   .35   .35
  b.   600 l multi, vert.   .70   .70
  c.   900 l multi   1.00   1.00

Nos. 1106a-1106b are 30x40mm, No. 1106c is 60x40mm.

A323

Holy Places in Palestine — A324

Nos. 1107-1111: 19th cent. watercolors, Pontifical Lateran University Library.
Map of Holy Land from "Geographia Blaviana," 17th cent - #1112: a, Mediterranean Sea, denomination, LL. b, Mediterranean Sea, denomination LR. c, Red Sea, Holy Land. d, Inscription indentifying map.

1999, May 25   Photo.   *Perf. 11½*
Granite Paper
1107 A323   200 l   Bethlehem   .20   .20
1108 A323   500 l   Nazareth   .55   .55
1109 A323   800 l   Lake of Tiberias   .85   .85
1110 A323   900 l   Jerusalem   1.00   1.00
1111 A323   1300 l   Mount Tabor   1.40   1.40
   Nos. 1107-1111 (5)   4.00   4.00
Perf. 12x11¾
1112 A324   1000 l   Sheet of 4, #a.-d.   4.25   4.25

Towards Holy Year 2000
A325

Events from life of Christ: 400 l, Deposition from the Cross. 700 l, Resurrection. 1300 l, Pentecost. 3000 l, Last Judgement.

1999, May 25   *Perf. 12x11¾*
Granite Paper
1113 A325   400 l   multicolored   .45   .45
1114 A325   700 l   multicolored   .75   .75
1115 A325   1300 l   multicolored   1.40   1.40
1116 A325   3000 l   multicolored   3.25   3.25
   Nos. 1113-1116 (4)   5.85   5.85

Kosovo 1999 — A326

1999, May 25   *Perf. 12¼*
Granite Paper
1117 A326   3600 l   black   4.00   4.00

Proceeds from sale of stamp benefits victims of the fighting in Kosovo.

1998 Travels of Pope John Paul II — A327

600 l, Cuba, June 21-26. 800 l, Nigeria, Mar. 21-23. 900 l, Austria, June 19-21. 1300 l, Croatia, Oct. 2-4. 2000 l, Italy, Oct. 20.

1999, Oct. 12   Litho.   *Perf. 14x13½*
1118 A327   600 l   multicolored   .70   .70
1119 A327   800 l   multicolored   .90   .90
1120 A327   900 l   multicolored   1.00   1.00
1121 A327   1300 l   multicolored   1.50   1.50
1122 A327   2000 l   multicolored   2.25   2.25
   Nos. 1118-1122 (5)   6.35   6.35

Council of Europe, 50th Anniv. — A328

1999, Oct. 12   Photo.   *Perf. 11¾*
Granite Paper
1123 A328   1200 l   multicolored   1.40   1.40

Christmas A329

The Birth of Christ, by Giovanni di Pietro: 500 l, Joseph (detail). 800 l, Christ (detail). 900 l, Mary (detail). 1200 l, Entire painting.

Perf. 13¼x12½
1999, Nov. 24   Litho.
1124 A329   500 l   multi   .50   .50
1125 A329   800 l   multi   .80   .80
1126 A329   900 l   multi   .90   .90
1127 A329   1200 l   multi   1.25   1.25
   Nos. 1124-1127 (4)   3.45   3.45

Opening of the Holy Door for Holy Year 2000
A330

Various panels of Holy Door. Stamps on No. 1136 lack white border.

1999, Nov. 24 Photo. *Perf. 11¾x12*

Granite Paper

1128	A330	200 l multi	.20	.20
1129	A330	300 l multi	.30	.30
1130	A330	400 l multi	.40	.40
1131	A330	500 l multi	.50	.50
1132	A330	600 l multi	.60	.60
1133	A330	800 l multi	.75	.75
1134	A330	1000 l multi	1.00	1.00
1135	A330	1200 l multi	1.25	1.25
		Nos. 1128-1135 (8)	5.00	5.00

Souvenir Sheet

1136		Sheet of 8, #a.-h.	5.25	5.25
a.	A330	200 l Like #1128	.20	.20
b.	A330	300 l Like #1129	.30	.30
c.	A330	400 l Like #1130	.40	.40
d.	A330	500 l Like #1131	.50	.50
e.	A330	600 l Like #1132	.60	.60
f.	A330	800 l Like #1133	.80	.80
g.	A330	1000 l Like #1134	1.00	1.00
h.	A330	1200 l Like #1135	1.25	1.25

Holy Year
2000 — A331

Designs: 800 l, St. Peter's Basilica. 1000 l, Basilica of St. John Lateran. 1200 l, Basilica of St. Mary Major. 2000 l, Basilica of St. Paul.

2000, Feb. 4 Photo. *Perf. 11¾*

Granite Paper

1137	A331	800 l multi	.75	.75
1138	A331	1000 l multi	1.00	1.00
1139	A331	1200 l multi	1.25	1.25
1140	A331	2000 l multi	2.00	2.00
		Nos. 1137-1140 (4)	5.00	5.00

Popes of the Holy Year Type of 1998

Designs: 300 l, Benedict XIV, 1750. 400 l, Pius VI, 1775. 500 l, Leo XII, 1825. 600 l, Pius IX, 1875. 700 l, Leo XIII, 1900. 800 l, Pius XI, 1925. 1200 l, Pius XII, 1950. 1500 l, Paul VI, 1975. No. 1149, John Paul II with miter, 2000. No. 1150, John Paul II with hand on chin, 2000.

2000, Feb. 4 Litho. *Perf. 13¾*

1141	A312	300 l multi + label	.30	.30
1142	A312	400 l multi + label	.40	.40
1143	A312	500 l multi + label	.50	.50
1144	A312	600 l multi + label	.60	.60
1145	A312	700 l multi + label	.70	.70
1146	A312	800 l multi + label	.75	.75
1147	A312	1200 l multi + label	1.25	1.25
1148	A312	1500 l multi + label	1.50	1.50
1149	A312	2000 l multi + label	2.00	2.00
		Nos. 1141-1149 (9)	8.00	8.00

Souvenir Sheet

1150	A312	2000 l multi	2.00	2.00

No. 1150 contains one label.

Christianity in Iceland, 1000th Anniv.
A332

2000, Feb. 4 *Perf. 13¼x13¾*

1151	A332	1500 l multi	1.50	1.50

See Iceland Nos. 900-901.

Europa, 2000
Common Design Type

2000, May 9 Litho. *Perf. 13¼x13*

1152	CD17	1200 l multi	1.25	1.25

Printed in sheets of 10, with left and right side selvage of Priority Mail etiquettes.

Pope John Paul II, 80th Birthday — A333

800 l, Pope. 1200 l, Black Madonna of Jasna Gora. 2000 l, Pope's silver cross.

2000, May 9 Engr. *Perf. 13x12¾*

1153	A333	800 l purple	.75	.75
1154	A333	1200 l dark blue	1.25	1.25
1155	A333	2000 l green	2.00	2.00
		Nos. 1153-1155 (3)	4.00	4.00

See Poland Nos. 3520-3522.

Restored Sistine Chapel Frescoes — A334

Designs: 500 l, The Calling of St. Peter and St. Andrew, by Domenico Ghirlandaio. 1000 l, The Trials of Moses, by Sandro Botticelli. 1500 l, The Donation of the Keys, by Pietro Perugino. 3000 l, The Worship of the Golden Calf, by Cosimo Rosselli.

Perf. 11½x11¾

2000, May 9 Photo. Blue Frame

Granite Paper

1156	A334	500 l multi	.50	.50
1157	A334	1000 l multi	1.00	1.00
1158	A334	1500 l multi	1.50	1.50
1159	A334	3000 l multi	3.00	3.00
		Nos. 1156-1159 (4)	6.00	6.00

20th World Youth Day — A335

Various photos of Pope John Paul II and youth.

Perf. 13¾x13¼

2000, June 19 Litho.

Color of Cross

1160	A335	800 l red	.80	.80
1161	A335	1000 l green	1.00	1.00
1162	A335	1200 l violet	1.10	1.10
1163	A335	1500 l orange	1.50	1.50

Booklet Stamp

Self-Adhesive

Serpentine Die Cut 12

1164	A335	1000 l green	1.00	1.00
a.		Booklet of 4 + 4 labels	4.00	
		Nos. 1160-1164 (5)	5.40	5.40

47th Intl. Eucharistic Congress
A336

2000, June 19 *Perf. 13x12½*

1165	A336	1200 l multi	1.10	1.10

Beatification of Pope John XXIII — A337

2000, Sept. 1 Photo. *Perf. 13¼x14*

1166	A337	1200 l multi	1.10	1.10

1999 Travels of Pope John Paul II — A338

#1167: a, Mexico, 1/22-28. b, Romania, 5/7-9. c, Poland, 6/17. d, Slovenia, 9/19. e, India and Georgia, 11/5-9.

2000, Sept. 1 *Perf. 11¾*

Granite Paper

1167		Horiz. strip of 5	4.50	4.50
a.-e.	A338	1000 l Any single	.90	.90

Christmas
A339

Frescoes in Basilica of St. Francis, Assisi, by Giotto: 800 l, Nativity. 1200 l, Infant Jesus. 1500 l, Mary. 2000 l, Joseph.

2000, Nov. 7 Photo. *Perf. 11¾x11½*

Granite Paper

1168-1171	A339	Set of 4	5.00	5.00

Sistine Chapel Restoration Type of 2000

Paintings: 800 l, The Baptism of Christ, by Pietro Perugino. 1200 l, The Passage of the Red Sea, by Biagio d'Antonio. 1500 l, The Punishment of Core, Datan and Abiron, by Sandro Botticelli. 4000 l, The Sermon on the Mount, by Cosimo Rosselli.

Perf. 11½x11¾

2001, Feb. 15 Photo.

Granite Paper

Red Frame

1172-1175	A334	Set of 4	7.00	7.00

Christian Conversion of Armenia, 1700th Anniv. — A340

Scenes from illuminated code of 1569: 1200 l, St. Gregory prepares to give King Tiridates human features. 1500 l, St. Gregory makes Agatangel write history of Armenians. 2000 l, St. Gregory and King Tiridates meet Emperor Constantine and Pope Sylvester I.

2001, Feb. 15 *Perf. 11¾*

Granite Paper

1176-1178	A340	Set of 3	4.50	4.50

Year of Dialogue Among Civilizations
A341

2001, May 22 Litho. *Perf. 14¼x14*

1179	A341	1500 l multi	1.40	1.40

Europa — A342

Designs: 800 l, Hands holding water above earth. 1200 l, Hand catching water.

2001, May 22 *Perf. 13½x13¼*

1180-1181	A342	Set of 2	1.75	1.75

Giuseppe Verdi (1813-1901), Composer
A343

Verdi and: 800 l, Score from Nabucco. 1500 l, Costumes from Aida. 2000 l, Scenery from Othello.

2001, May 22 *Perf. 13¼x14¼*

1182-1184	A343	Set of 3	3.75	3.75

2000 Travels of Pope John Paul II — A344

Designs: 500 l, Mount Sinai, Feb. 26. 800 l, Mount Nebo, Mar. 20. 1200 l, The Last Supper, Mar. 23. 1500 l, Holy Sepulchre, Mar. 26. 5000 l, Fatima, May 12. 3000 l, Western Wall.

2001, Sept. 25 Litho. *Perf. 13¼*

1185-1189	A344	Set of 5	8.50	8.50

Souvenir Sheet

Perf. 13¼x14

1190	A344	3000 l multi	2.75	2.75

No. 1190 contains one 35x26mm stamp.

Remission of Debts of Poor Countries
A345

Various panels by Carlo di Camerino: 200 l, 400 l, 800 l, 1000 l, 1500 l.

2001, Sept. 25 Photo. *Perf. 13*

1191-1195	A345	Set of 5	3.75	3.75

FILATELIA RIVA RENO
PAYING TOP PRICES • SERIOUS BUYER...
TRIESTE ZONE A – ZONE B
ITALY, SAN MARINO and VATICAN
Collections, Lots, Accumulations, Postal History & Covers
- A.M.G. - Italian Social Republic - Italian Offices Abroad

american philatelic society

borsa filatelica nazionale milano

BEFORE SELLING, ASK US!
Don't hesitate! Call or fax for our...top buying prices and quick payment in US funds!

feder. nazion. comm filatelici italiani-roma

philatelic traders' society

NEW ISSUE SERVICE!
• Special Conditions for Dealers •
Filatelia Riva Reno di Luciano Morselli
Via Galliera, 23 - 40121 Bologna - Italy
FAX +39-051-232180 • TEL +39-051-237480

verband des deutschen briefm. handels

american stamp dealers' association

VATICAN CITY SPECIALIST
We service everything for the Vatican collector.
We carry a complete line of...
• MINT AND CANCELED SETS
•FDCs • MAXIMUM CARDS • ACTAS
... for Past as well as New Issues.
We also carry Papal Trips commemorative cover sets
"Since 1912"
PENNY BLACK STAMP CO.
P.O. BOX 78 DEXTER, MI 48130
PH & FAX: 734-424-3043
email: pennyblack@earthlink.net
www.pennyblackstamp.com   VPS
★ Send for our complete pricelist ★

Giuseppe Toniolo Institute for Higher Studies, 80th Anniv. — A346

Litho. & Embossed
2001, Nov. 22   *Perf. 12¾*
1196 A346 1200 l red & blue   1.10 1.10

Etruscan Museum Gold Objects — A347

Designs: 800 l, Parade fibula. 1200 l, Earrings. 1500 l, Vulci fibula. 2000 l, Head of Medusa.

2001, Nov. 22   **Photo.**   *Perf. 13½*
1197-1200 A347   Set of 4   5.25 5.25

Christmas A348

Artwork by Egino G. Weinert: 800 l, The Annunciation. 1200 l, The Nativity. 1500 l, Adoration of the Magi.

2001, Nov. 22   **Litho.**   *Perf. 13x13¼*
1201-1203 A348   Set of 3   3.25 3.25
1202a   Booklet pane of 4 + 4 etiquettes   4.50
   Booklet, #1202a   4.50

100 Cents = 1 Euro (€)

Depictions of Virgin Mary in Vatican Basilica — A349

Designs: 8c, Our Lady of Women in Labor. 15c, Our Lady with People Praying. 23c, Our Lady at the Tomb of Pius XII. 31c, Our Lady of the Fever. 41c, Our Lady of the Slap. 52c, Mary Immaculate. 62c, Our Lady Help of Christians. 77c, Virgin of the Deesis. €1.03, L'Addolorata. €1.55, Presentation of Mary at the Temple.

2002, Mar. 12   **Litho.**   *Perf. 13¼x13*
1204	A349	8c multi	.20 .20
1205	A349	15c multi	.25 .25
1206	A349	23c multi	.40 .40
1207	A349	31c multi	.55 .55
1208	A349	41c multi	.75 .75
1209	A349	52c multi	.90 .90
1210	A349	62c multi	1.10 1.10
1211	A349	77c multi	1.40 1.40
1212	A349	€1.03 multi	1.90 1.90
1213	A349	€1.55 multi	2.75 2.75
		Nos. 1204-1213 (10)	10.20 10.20

Pontifical Ecclesiastical Academy, 300th Anniv. — A350

No. 1214: a, Pope Clement XI. b, Academy building (46x33mm). c, Pope John Paul II.

2002, Mar. 12   **Engr.**   *Perf. 13¼x13*
1214 A350   Horiz. strip of 3   4.25 4.25
a.-c.   77c Any single   1.40 1.40

Sistine Chapel Restoration Type of 2000

Designs: 26c, The Temptation of Christ, by Sandro Botticelli. 41c, The Last Supper, by Cosimo Rosselli. 77c, Moses' Journey in Egypt, by Pietro Perugino. €1.55, The Last Days of Moses, by Luca Signorelli.

Perf. 11½x11¾
2002, June 13   **Photo.**
Granite Paper
1215-1218 A334   Set of 4   5.75 5.75

Europa — A351

Christ and the Circus, by Aldo Carpi: 41c, Entire painting. 62c, Detail.

2002, June 13   *Perf. 13¼*
1219-1220 A351   Set of 2   2.00 2.00

Roman States Postage Stamps, 150th Anniv. — A352

Designs: 41c, Regina Viarum, Roman States #11. 52c, Cassian Way, Roman States #25. €1.03, Vatican walls, Vatican City #2. €1.55, St. Peter's Basilica.

2002, June 13   *Perf. 13x13¼*
1221-1223 A352   Set of 3   3.75 3.75
Souvenir Sheet
Perf.
1224 A352 €1.55 multi   3.00 3.00
No. 1224 contains one 31mm diameter stamp.

St. Leo IX (1002-54), Pope A353

Designs: 41c, Portrait. 62c, In procession, receiving papal miter. €1.29, Reading from scroll, as prisoner of Normans.

2002, Sept. 26   **Litho.**   *Perf. 13x13¼*
1225-1227 A353   Set of 3   4.75 4.75

Cimabue (1240-1302), Artist — A354

Designs: 26c, Crucifix. 62c, Jesus Christ. 77c, Virgin Mary. €1.03, St. John.

2002, Sept. 26   **Photo.**   *Perf. 13¼x14*
1228-1231 A354   Set of 4   5.25 5.25

Nativity, by Pseudo Ambrogio di Baldese — A355

2002, Nov. 21   **Photo.**   *Perf. 13*
1232 A355 41c multi   .85 .85
See New Zealand No. 1834.

2001 Travels of Pope John Paul II — A356

Designs: 41c, Greece, Syria and Malta, May 4-9. 62c, Ukraine, June 23-27. €1.55, Armenia and Kazakhstan, Sept. 22-27.

2002, Nov. 21   **Litho.**   *Perf. 13x13¼*
1233-1235 A356   Set of 3   5.25 5.25
1234a   Booklet pane, 4 #1234 + 4 etiquettes   5.00
   Booklet, #1234a   5.00

A357

Pontificate of John Paul II, 25th Anniv. — A358

No. 1236: a, Election as Pope, 1978. b, In Poland, 1979. c, In France, 1980. d, Assassination attempt, 1981. e, At Fatima, Portugal, 1982. f, Extraordinary Holy Year, 1983. g, At Quirinale Palace, Rome, 1984. h, World Youth Day, 1985. i, At synagogue, Rome, 1986. j, Pentecost vigil, 1987. k, At European Parliament, Strasbourg, France, 1988. l, Meeting with Mikhail Gorbachev, 1989. m, At Guinea-Bissau leper colony, 1990. n, At European Bishops' Synod, 1991. o, Publication of Catechism of the Catholic Church, 1992. p, Praying for the Balkans in Assisi, 1993. q, At Sistine Chapel, 1994. r, At UN Headquarters for 50th anniv. celebrations, 1995. s, In Germany, 1996. t, In Sarajevo, Bosnia & Herzegovina, 1997. u, In Cuba, 1998. v, Opening Holy Doors, 1999. w, World Youth Day, 2000. x, Closing Holy Doors, 2001. y, Addressing Italian Parliament, 2002.

2003, Mar. 20   **Litho.**   *Perf. 13x13¼*
1236   Sheet of 25   22.50 22.50
a.-y.   A357 41c Any single   .90 .90

Etched on Silver Foil
Die Cut Perf. 12½x13
Self-Adhesive

1237 A358 €2.58 Pope John
Paul II 5.50 5.50

Cancels can be easily removed from No. 1237.
See Poland Nos. 3668-3669.

Martyrdom of St. George, 1700th Anniv. A359

2003, May 6 Litho. & Engr. Perf. 13
1238 A359 62c multi 1.40 1.40

Europa — A360

Poster art for: 41c, 1975 Holy Year. 62c, Exhibition of Slav codices, incunabula and rare books at Sistine Hall, 1985.

2003, May 6 Litho. Perf. 13¼x13
1239-1240 A360 Set of 2 2.40 2.40

Masterpieces by Beato Angelico in Niccolina Chapel — A361

Designs: 41c, Diaconal Consecration of St. Lawrence. 62c, St. Stephen Preaching. 77c, Trial of St. Lawrence. €1.03, Stoning of St. Stephen.

2003, May 6 Photo. Perf. 13¼
1241-1244 A361 Set of 4 6.50 6.50

Beatification of Mother Teresa of Calcutta — A362

Perf. 13½x13¼
2003, Sept. 23 Litho.
1245 A362 41c multi + label .95 .95

Printed in sheets of 5 + 5 different labels.

19th Century Artists — A363

Designs: 41c, Blessed Are the Pure at Heart, by Paul Gauguin. 62c, The Pietà, by Vincent van Gogh.

Perf. 13¼x13½
2003, Sept. 23 Photo.
1246 A363 41c multi .95 .95
1247 A363 62c multi 1.50 1.50
a. Booklet pane of 4 + 4 etiquettes 6.00 —
Complete booklet, #1247a 6.00

Animals in Vatican Basilica Art A364

Designs: 21c, Dragon. 31c, Camel. 77c, Horse. €1.03, Leopard.

2003, Sept. 23
1248-1251 A364 Set of 4 5.50 5.50

Canonization of Josemaría Escrivá de Balaguer, Oct. 6, 2003 — A365

2003, Nov. 18 Litho. Perf. 14x13¼
1252 A365 41c multi 1.00 1.00

2002 Travels of Pope John Paul II — A366

Designs: 62c, Bulgaria and Azerbaijan, May 22-26. 77c, Canada, Guatemala and Mexico, July 23-Aug. 2. €2.07, Poland, Aug. 16-19.

2003, Nov. 18 Perf. 13x13¼
1253-1255 A366 Set of 3 8.50 8.50

Christmas A367

2003, Nov. 18
Stamp With White Border
1256 A367 41c multi 1.00 1.00
Souvenir Sheet
Stamp Without White Border
1257 A367 41c multi 1.00 1.00

Death of Pope Paul VI, 25th anniv. (#1257).

St. Pius V (1504-72) A368

Altarpiece by Grazio Cossoli in Chapel of the Rosary, Santa Croce di Bosco Marengo:

4c, Detail depicting St. Pius V and flag. €2, Entire altarpiece.

Litho. & Silk Screened
2004, Mar. 18 Perf. 13¼x13
1258-1259 A368 Set of 2 5.00 5.00

2003 Travels of Pope John Paul II — A369

Designs: 60c, Spain, May 3-4. 62c, Bosnia & Herzegovina, June 22. 80c, Croatia, June 5-9. €1.40, Slovakia, Sept. 11-14.

2004, Mar. 18 Litho.
1260-1263 A369 Set of 4 8.50 8.50

Papal Visits to Poland — A370

No. 1264, 45c: a, Pope with hand on chin. b, Pope praying. c, Pope carrying crucifix. d, Pope with crucifix against head.
No. 1265, 62c: a, Pope holding crucifix, diff. b, Pope with arm raised. c, Pope, wearing white, seated. d, Pope, wearing red cape, seated.

Litho. (Labels Litho. & Embossed)
2004, Mar. 18
Sheets of 4, #a-d, + 8 Labels
1264-1265 A370 Set of 2 10.50 10.50

SEMI-POSTAL STAMPS

Holy Year Issue

Cross and Orb
SP1 SP2

1933 Unwmk. Engr. Perf. 13x13½
B1 SP1 25c + 10c green 3.50 3.50
B2 SP1 75c + 15c scarlet 6.25 11.50
B3 SP2 80c + 20c red brown 22.50 16.00
B4 SP2 1.25 l + 25c ultra 7.00 12.00
Nos. B1-B4 (4) 39.25 43.00
Set, never hinged 100.00

AIR POST STAMPS

Catalogue values for unused stamps in this section are for Never Hinged items.

Statue of St. Peter AP1

Dove of Peace over Vatican AP2

Elijah's Ascent into Heaven AP3

Our Lady of Loreto and Angels Moving the Holy House AP4

Wmk. 235
1938, June 22 Engr. Perf. 14
C1 AP1 25c brown .20 .20
C2 AP2 50c green .20 .20
C3 AP3 75c lake .20 .20
C4 AP4 80c dark blue .20 .20
C5 AP1 1 l violet .45 .45
C6 AP2 2 l ultra 1.00 .60
C7 AP3 5 l slate blk 2.25 1.50
C8 AP4 10 l dk brown vio 2.25 1.90
Nos. C1-C8 (8) 6.75 5.25

Dove of Peace Above St. Peter's Basilica — AP5

House of Our Lady of Loreto — AP6

Birds Circling Cross — AP7

1947, Nov. 10 Photo.
C9 AP5 1 l rose red .20 .20
C10 AP6 4 l dark brown .20 .20
C11 AP5 5 l brt ultra .20 .20
C12 AP7 15 l brt purple .90 .50
C13 AP6 25 l dk blue green 3.50 .40
C14 AP7 50 l dk gray 5.00 1.50
C15 AP7 100 l red orange 25.00 2.00
Nos. C9-C15 (7) 35.00 5.00

Nos. C13-C15 exist imperf. Value, each pair $1,000.

Archangel Raphael and Young Tobias AP8

1948, Dec. 28 Engr. Perf. 14
C16 AP8 250 l sepia 25.00 10.00
C17 AP8 500 l ultra 450.00 275.00
Set, hinged 300.00

Angels and
Globe
AP9

1949, Dec. 3
C18 AP9 300 l ultra   20.00   5.00
C19 AP9 1000 l green   100.00 47.50
         Set, hinged   75.00

UPU, 75th anniversary.

Franciscus
Gratianus
AP10

Dome of St. Peter's
Cathedral
AP11

1951, Dec. 20   **Perf. 14x13**
C20 AP10 300 l deep plum   240.00 150.00
C21 AP10 500 l deep orange   35.00 17.50
         Set, hinged   175.00

Publication of unified canon laws, 800th anniv.

1953, Aug. 10   **Perf. 13**
C22 AP11 500 l chocolate   21.00   2.50
C23 AP11 1000 l brown   62.50 12.50
         Set, hinged   40.00

See Nos. C33-C34.

Archangel Gabriel
by Melozzo da
Forli — AP12

Obelisk of St.
John
Lateran — AP13

Archangel Gabriel: 10 l, 35 l, 100 l, Annunciation by Pietro Cavallini. 15 l, 50 l, 300 l, Annunciation by Leonardo da Vinci.

1956, Feb. 12   **Wmk. 235**
C24 AP12   5 l gray black   .20   .20
C25 AP12   10 l blue green   .20   .20
C26 AP12   15 l deep orange   .20   .20
C27 AP12   25 l dk car rose   .20   .20
C28 AP12   35 l carmine   .25   .20
C29 AP12   50 l olive brown   .20   .20
C30 AP12   60 l ultra   2.75 2.25
C31 AP12 100 l orange brown   .25   .20
C32 AP12 300 l deep violet   .50   .20
         Nos. C24-C32 (9)   4.70 3.85

Type of 1953

1958   **Perf. 13½**
C33 AP11 500 l grn & bl
              grn   7.50 4.00
  a.   Perf. 14   1,200. 700.00
C34 AP11 1000 l dp mag   .75   .75
  a.   Perf. 14   .75   .75

1959, Oct. 27 Engr.   Perf. 13½x14
Obelisks, Rome: 10 l, 60 l, St. Mary Major. 15 l, 100 l, St. Peter. 25 l, 200 l, Piazza del Popolo. 35 l, 500 l, Trinita dei Monti.

C35 AP13   5 l dull violet   .20   .20
C36 AP13   10 l blue green   .20   .20
C37 AP13   15 l dk brown   .20   .20
C38 AP13   25 l slate grn   .20   .20
C39 AP13   35 l ultra   .20   .20
C40 AP13   50 l yellow grn   .20   .20
C41 AP13   60 l rose carmine   .20   .20
C42 AP13 100 l bluish black   .20   .20
C43 AP13 200 l brown   .20   .20
C44 AP13 500 l orange brn   .30   .20
         Nos. C35-C44 (10)   2.10 2.00

Archangel Gabriel
by Filippo
Valle — AP14

Jet over St.
Peter's Cathedral
AP15

1962, Mar. 13   **Wmk. 235**
C45 AP14 1000 l brown   1.25   .75
C46 AP14 1500 l dark blue   1.75 1.25

1967, Mar. 7   Photo.   Perf. 14
Designs: 40 l, 200 l, Radio tower and statue of Archangel Gabriel (like A87). 90 l, 500 l, Aerial view of St. Peter's Square and Vatican City.

C47 AP15   20 l brt violet   .20   .20
C48 AP15   40 l black & pink   .20   .20
C49 AP15   90 l sl bl & dk gray   .20   .20
C50 AP15 100 l black & salmon   .20   .20
C51 AP15 200 l vio blk & gray   .20   .20
C52 AP15 500 l dk brn & lt brn   .25   .20
         Nos. C47-C52 (6)   1.25 1.20

Archangel Gabriel
by Fra
Angelico — AP16

1968, Mar. 12   Engr.   Perf. 13½x14
C53 AP16 1000 l dk car rose, cr 1.00   .75
C54 AP16 1500 l black, cr   1.75 1.50

St.
Matthew,
by Fra
Angelico
AP17

The Evangelists, by Fra Angelico from Niccolina Chapel: 300 l, St. Mark. 500 l, St. Luke. 1000 l, St. John.

Engr. & Photo.
Perf. 14x13½
1971, Sept. 30   **Unwmk.**
C55 AP17 200 l blk & pale grn   .20   .20
C56 AP17 300 l black & bister   .20   .20
C57 AP17 500 l black & salmon   .85   .60
C58 AP17 1000 l black & pale lil 1.00   .75
         Nos. C55-C58 (4)   2.25 1.75

AP18

AP19

Seraph, mosaic from St. Mark's Basilica, Venice.

Litho. & Engr.
1974, Feb. 21   **Perf. 13x14**
C59 AP18 2500 l multicolored   2.50 2.00

Litho. & Engr.
1976, Feb. 19   **Perf. 13x14**
Last Judgment, by Michelangelo: 500 l, Angel with trumpet. 1000 l, Ascending figures. 2500 l, Angels with trumpets.

C60 AP19 500 l sal, bl & brn   1.25 1.10
C61 AP19 1000 l sal, bl & brn   1.50 1.10
C62 AP19 2500 l sal, bl & brn   2.00 1.50
         Nos. C60-C62 (3)   4.75 3.70

Radio
Waves,
Antenna,
Papal
Arms
AP20

1978, July 11   Engr.   Perf. 14x13
C63 AP20 1000 l multicolored   1.00   .70
C64 AP20 2000 l multicolored   2.00 1.40
C65 AP20 3000 l multicolored   3.00 1.90
         Nos. C63-C65 (3)   6.00 4.00

10th World Telecommunications Day.

Pope John
Paul II
Shaking
Hands,
Arms of
Dominican
Republic
AP21

1980   Litho. & Engr.   Perf. 14x13½
C66 AP21 200 l shown   .25   .25
C67 AP21 300 l Mexico   .30   .30
C68 AP21 500 l Poland   .60   .60
C69 AP21 1000 l Ireland   1.10 1.10
C70 AP21 1500 l US   1.75 1.75
C71 AP21 2000 l UN   2.00 2.00
C72 AP21 3000 l with Dimitrios
              I, Turkey   3.50 3.50
         Nos. C66-C72 (7)   9.50 9.50

Issued: 3000 l, Sept. 18; others June 24.

World Communications Year — AP22

Designs: 2000 l, Moses Explaining The Law to the People by Luca Signarelli. 5000 l, Paul Preaching in Athens, Tapestry of Raphael design.

1983, Nov. 10   **Perf. 14**
C73 AP22 2000 l multicolored   3.00 3.00
C74 AP22 5000 l multicolored   6.75 6.75

Journeys
of Pope
John
Paul II,
1983-84
AP23

Designs: 350 l, Central America, the Caribbean, 1983. 450 l, Warsaw Cathedral, Our Lady of Czestochowa, Poland, 1983. 700 l, Statue of Our Lady, Lourdes, France, 1983. 1000 l, Mariazell Sanctuary, St. Stephen's Cathedral, Austria, 1983. 1500 l, Asia, the Pacific, 1984. 2000 l, Einsiedeln Basilica, St. Nicholas of Flue, Switzerland, 1984. 2500 l, Quebec's Notre Dame Cathedral, five crosses of the Jesuit martyrs, Canada, 1984. 5000 l, Saragossa, Spain, Dominican Republic and Puerto Rico, 1984.

1986, Nov. 20 Photo.   Perf. 14x13½
C75 AP23 350 l multicolored   .50   .50
C76 AP23 450 l multicolored   .65   .65
C77 AP23 700 l multicolored   1.00 1.00
C78 AP23 1000 l multicolored   1.50 1.50
C79 AP23 1500 l multicolored   2.25 2.25
C80 AP23 2000 l multicolored   3.25 3.25
C81 AP23 2500 l multicolored   4.00 4.00
C82 AP23 5000 l multicolored   8.00 8.00
         Nos. C75-C82 (8)   21.15 21.15

Papal Journeys Type of 1986

Designs: 450 l, Horseman, shepherdess, St. Peter's Basilica, Cathedral of Santiago in Chile, and the Sanctuary of Our Lady of Lujan, Argentina. 650 l, Youths and the Cathedral of Speyer, Federal Republic of Germany. 1000 l, St. Peter's Basilica, Altar of Gdansk, flowers and thorns. 2500 l, Crowd and American skyscrapers. 5000 l, Tepee at Fort Simpson, Canada, and American Indians.

1988, Oct. 27 Photo.   Perf. 14x13½
C83 AP23 450 l multicolored   .65   .65
C84 AP23 650 l multicolored   .95   .95
C85 AP23 1000 l multicolored   1.50 1.50
C86 AP23 2500 l multicolored   3.50 3.50
C87 AP23 5000 l multicolored   7.25 7.25
         Nos. C83-C87 (5)   13.85 13.85

Uruguay, Chile and Argentina, Mar. 30-Apr. 14, 1987 (450 l); Federal Republic of Germany, Apr. 30-May 4, 1987 (650 l); Poland, June 8-14, 1987 (1000 l); US, Sept. 10-19, 1987 (2500 l); and Canada, Sept. 20, 1987 (5000 l).

Journeys of
Pope John
Paul II, 1989
AP24

1990, Nov. 27   Photo.   Perf. 12
                  Granite Paper
C88 AP24 500 l Africa   .80   .80
C89 AP24 1000 l Scandinavia   1.60 1.60
C90 AP24 3000 l Santiago de
              Composte-
              la, Spain   5.00 5.00
C91 AP24 5000 l Asia   8.00 8.00
         Nos. C88-C91 (4)   15.40 15.40

Madagascar, Reunion, Zambia and Malawi, Apr. 28-May 6 (500 l); Norway, Iceland, Finland, Denmark and Sweden, June 1-10 (1000 l); Korea, Indonesia and Mauritius, Oct. 6-16 (5000 l).

Travels of
Pope John
Paul II,
1991
AP25

1992, Nov. 24   Photo.   Perf. 14
C92 AP25 500 l multicolored   .65   .65
C93 AP25 1000 l multicolored   1.40 1.40
C94 AP25 4000 l multicolored   5.25 5.25
C95 AP25 6000 l multicolored   8.00 8.00
         Nos. C92-C95 (4)   15.30 15.30

Portugal, May 10-13 (500 l); Poland, June 1-9 (1000 l); Poland, Hungary, Aug. 13-20 (4000 l); Brazil, Oct. 12-21 (6000 l).

SPECIAL DELIVERY STAMPS

Pius XI
SD1

Unwmk.

1929, Aug. 1   Photo.   Perf. 14

E1	SD1	2 l	carmine rose	14.00 11.50
E2	SD1	2.50 l	dark blue	12.00 12.00

For overprints see Nos. Q14-Q15.

Catalogue values for unused stamps in this section, from this point to the end of the section, are for Never Hinged items.

Aerial View of Vatican City SD2

1933   Wmk. 235   Engr.

E3	SD2	2 l	rose red & brn	.35 .35
E4	SD2	2.50 l	dp blue & brn	.35 .55

1945   Unwmk.

E5	SD2	3.50 l	dk car & ultra	.30 .30
E6	SD2	5 l	ultra & green	.30 .30

Nos. E5 and E6 Surcharged with New Values and Bars in Black

1946, Jan. 9

E7	SD2	6 l	on 3.50 l dk car & ultra	4.25 1.75
E8	SD2	12 l	on 5 l ultra & grn	4.25 1.75

Vertical pairs imperf. between exist of No. E7 (value $150) and No. E8 (value $200).

Bishop Matteo Giberti SD3

Design: 12 l, Gaspar Cardinal Contarini.

1946, Feb. 21   Photo.

Centers in Dark Brown

E9	SD3	6 l	dark green	.20 .20
E10	SD3	12 l	copper brown	.20 .20

See note after No. 121.
#E9-E10 exist imperf and part perf.

Basilica of St. Peter SD5

Design: 80 l, Basilica of St. John.

1949   Wmk. 235   Perf. 14

E11	SD5	40 l	slate gray	10.50 3.25
a.		Perf. 13½x14		21.00 7.50
E12	SD5	80 l	chestnut brown	37.50 20.00
a.		Perf. 13½x14		40.00 22.50

St. Peter and His Tomb — SD6

85 l, Pius XII and Roman sepulcher.

Perf. 13½x13, 14

1953, Apr. 23   Engr.

E13	SD6	50 l	blue grn & dk brn	.20 .20
E14	SD6	85 l	dp orange & dk brn	.35 .25

Arms of Pope John XXIII SD7

1960   Photo.   Perf. 14

E15	SD7	75 l	red & brown	.20 .20
E16	SD7	100 l	dk blue & brown	.20 .20

Pope Paul VI by Enrico Manfrini — SD8

Design: 150 l, Papal arms.

1966, Mar. 8   Wmk. 235   Perf. 14

E17	SD8	150 l	black brown	.20 .20
E18	SD8	180 l	brown	.20 .20

POSTAGE DUE STAMPS

Regular Issue of 1929 Overprinted in Black and Brown

1931   Unwmk.   Perf. 14

J1	A1	5c	dk brown & pink	.20 .20
a.		Double frame		
J2	A1	10c	dk grn & lt grn	.20 .20
a.		Frame omitted		675.00
J3	A1	20c	violet & lilac	5.75 2.00

Surcharged

J4	A1	40c	on 30c indigo & yel	1.50 4.00

Surcharged

J5	A2	60c	on 2 l olive brn	27.50 18.00
J6	A2	1.10 l	on 2.50 l red	3.75 16.00
		org		
		Nos. J1-J6 (6)		38.90 40.40
		Set, never hinged		100.00

In addition to the surcharges, #J4-J6 are overprinted with ornamental frame as on #J1-J3.

Catalogue values for unused stamps in this section, from this point to the end of the section, are for Never Hinged items.

Papal Arms
D1   D2

1945   Unwmk.   Typo.   Perf. 14

J7	D1	5c	black & yellow	.20 .20
J8	D1	20c	black & lilac	.20 .20
J9	D1	80c	black & salmon	.20 .20
J10	D1	1 l	black & green	.20 .20
J11	D1	4 l	black & blue	.20 .20
J12	D1	5 l	black & gray	.20 .20
a.		Imperf., pair		125.00 125.00
		Nos. J7-J12 (6)		1.20 1.20

A second type of Nos. J7-J12 exists, in which the colored lines of the background are thicker.

The 20c and 5 lire exist in horizontal pairs imperf. vertically. Value, each $100.
The 20c exists in horizontal pairs imperf. between. Value $275.

Perf. 13½x13

1954   Wmk. 235   Engr.

J13	D2	4 l	black & rose	.20 .20
J14	D2	6 l	black & green	.30 .30
J15	D2	10 l	black & yellow	.20 .20
J16	D2	20 l	black & blue	.45 .30
J17	D2	50 l	black & ol brn	.20 .20
J18	D2	70 l	black & red brn	.20 .20
		Nos. J13-J18 (6)		1.55 1.40

Papal Arms — D3

Photo. & Engr.

1968, May 28   Wmk. 235   Perf. 14

J19	D3	10 l	black, grysh bl	.20 .20
J20	D3	20 l	black, pale bl	.20 .20
J21	D3	50 l	black, pale lil rose	.20 .20
J22	D3	60 l	black, gray	.20 .20
J23	D3	100 l	black, dull yel	.20 .20
J24	D3	180 l	black, bluish lil	.20 .20
		Nos. J19-J24 (6)		1.20 1.20

PARCEL POST STAMPS

Regular Issue of 1929 Overprinted

1931   Unwmk.   Perf. 14

Q1	A1	5c	dk brown & pink	.40 .30
Q2	A1	10c	dk grn & lt grn	.40 .30
Q3	A1	20c	violet & lilac	4.75 5.50
Q4	A1	25c	dk bl & lt bl	6.25 4.25
Q5	A1	30c	indigo & yel	9.25 4.25
Q6	A1	50c	indigo & sal buff	9.25 4.25
Q7	A1	75c	brn car & gray	2.75 2.75

Overprinted

Q8	A2	80c	carmine rose	1.60 1.90
Q9	A2	1.25 l	dark blue	2.75 2.00
Q10	A2	2 l	olive brown	.55 .85
a.		Inverted overprint		325.00 475.00
Q11	A2	2.50 l	red orange	.55 .85
a.		Double overprint		225.00
b.		Inverted overprint		500.00
Q12	A2	5 l	dark green	.55 .85
Q13	A2	10 l	olive black	.55 .85
a.		Double overprint		325.00

Special Delivery Stamps of 1929 Overprinted Vertically

Q14	SD1	2 l	carmine rose	.55 .85
Q15	SD1	2.50 l	dark blue	.55 .85
		Nos. Q1-Q15 (15)		40.70 30.60
		Set, never hinged		95.00

ADVANTAGE STOCKSHEETS

Designed with the collector in mind, Advantage stock sheets fit directly in your 2-post or 3-ring National or Specialty album. For unprecedented durability and flexibility choose Advantage Stocksheets. Choose from 1 to 8 pockets.
Sheets are sold in packages of 10.

- Stock sheets match album pages in every respect, including border, size, and color.

- Punched and drilled to fit perfectly in binder.

- Available with 1 to 8 pockets.
  Ideal for storing minor varieties and collateral material. A great place to keep new issues until the next supplement is available.

- Provide the protection and durability of crystal clear acetate pockets on heavyweight pages.

NATIONAL BORDER

Item			Retail
AD11	1 Pocket	242mm	$15.99
AD12	2 Pockets	119mm	$15.99
AD13	3 Pockets	79mm	$15.99
AD14	4 Pockets	58mm	$15.99
AD15	5 Pockets	45mm	$15.99
AD16	6 Pockets	37mm	$15.99
AD17	7 Pockets	31mm	$15.99
AD18	8 Pockets	31mm	$15.99

SPECIALTY BORDER

AD21	1 Pocket	242mm	$15.99
AD22	2 Pockets	119mm	$15.99
AD23	3 Pockets	79mm	$15.99
AD24	4 Pockets	58mm	$15.99
AD25	5 Pockets	45mm	$15.99
AD26	6 Pockets	37mm	$15.99
AD27	7 Pockets	31mm	$15.99
AD28	8 Pockets	31mm S	$15.99

Available from your favorite stamp dealer or direct from:

SCOTT

1-800-572-6885
P.O. Box 828,
Sidney OH 45365
www.amosadvantage.com

AMOS
HOBBY PUBLISHING

VENEZUELA

ˌve-nə-ˈzwā-lə

LOCATION — Northern coast of South America, bordering on the Caribbean Sea
GOVT. — Republic
AREA — 352,143 sq. mi.
POP. — 23,203,466 (1999 est.)
CAPITAL — Caracas

100 Centavos = 8 Reales = 1 Peso
100 Centesimos = 1 Venezolano (1879)
100 Centimos = 1 Bolivar (1880)

Watermark

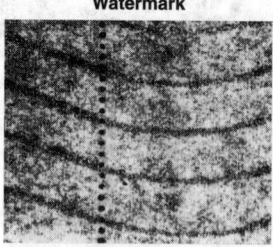

Wmk. 346

Catalogue values for unused stamps in this country are for Never Hinged items, beginning with Scott 743 in the regular postage section, Scott B2 in the semipostal section, Scott C709 in the airpost section, and Scott E1 in the special delivery section.

Coat of Arms — A1

Fine Impression
No Dividing Line Between Stamps
Unwmk.

1859, Jan. 1		**Litho.**		**Imperf.**
1	A1	½r yellow	19.00	8.00
a.		½r orange	22.50	9.00
b.		Greenish paper	225.00	
2	A1	1r blue	275.00	17.00
a.		Half used as ½r on cover		400.00
3	A1	2r red	35.00	12.00
a.		2r dull rose red	45.00	14.00
b.		Half used as 1r on cover		450.00
c.		Greenish paper	225.00	140.00
		Nos. 1-3 (3)	329.00	37.00

Coarse Impression

1859-62

Thick Paper

4	A1	½r orange ('61)	9.00	3.50
a.		½r yellow ('59)	450.00	25.00
b		½r olive yellow	750.00	35.00
c.		Bluish paper	575.00	
d.		½r dull rose (error)		
5	A1	1r blue ('62)	16.00	10.00
a.		1r pale blue	30.00	11.00
b.		1r dark blue	30.00	11.00
c.		Half used as ½r on cover		400.00
d.		Bluish paper	200.00	
6	A1	2r red ('62)	25.00	15.00
a.		2r dull rose	30.00	15.00
b.		Tête bêche pair	5,000.	3,500.
c.		Half used as 1r on cover		400.00
d.		Bluish paper	225.00	
		Nos. 4-6 (3)	50.00	28.50

In the fine impression, the background lines of the shield are more sharply drawn. In the coarse impression, the shading lines at each end of the scroll inscribed "LIBERTAD" are usually very heavy. Stamps of the coarse impression are closer together, and there is usually a dividing line between them.

Nos. 1-3 exist on thick paper and on bluish paper. Nos. 1-6 exist on pelure paper.

The greenish paper varieties (Nos. 1b and 3c) and the bluish paper varieties were not regularly issued.

Arms — A2

Eagle — A3

1862				**Litho.**
7	A2	¼c green	16.00	90.00
8	A2	½c dull lilac	25.00	160.00
a.		½c violet	35.00	175.00
9	A2	1c gray brown	35.00	190.00
		Nos. 7-9 (3)	76.00	440.00

Counterfeits are plentiful. Forged cancellations abound on Nos. 7-17.

1863-64

10	A3	½c pale red ('64)	45.00	110.00
a.		½c red	50.00	110.00
11	A3	1c slate ('64)	50.00	125.00
12	A3	½r orange	6.50	3.00
13	A3	1r blue	15.00	7.00
a.		1r pale blue	25.00	
b.		Half used as ½r on cover		400.00
14	A3	2r green	20.00	17.00
a.		2r deep yellow green	25.00	17.00
b.		Quarter used as ½r on cover		1,000.
c.		Half used as 1r on cover		450.00

Counterfeits exist.

Redrawn

1865

15	A3	½r orange	3.50	2.00
a.		½r yellow	3.50	4.00

The redrawn stamp has a broad "N" in "FEDERACION." "MEDIO REAL" and "FEDERACION" are in thin letters. There are 52 instead of 49 pearls in the circle.
The status of No. 15 has been questioned.

A4

Simón Bolívar — A5

1865-70

16	A4	½c yel grn ('67)	175.00	275.00
17	A4	1c bl grn ('67)	175.00	225.00
18	A4	½r brn vio (thin paper)	7.50	1.75
19	A4	½r lil rose ('70)	7.50	2.25
a.		½r brownish rose	7.50	2.75
b.		Tête bêche pair	110.00	150.00
20	A4	1r vermilion	35.00	13.00
a.		Half used as ½r on cover		200.00
21	A4	2r yellow	125.00	65.00
a.		Half used as 1r on cover		750.00
b.		Quarter used as ½r on cover		1,000.
		Nos. 16-21 (6)	525.00	582.00

This issue is known unofficially rouletted.
Postal forgeries exist of the ½r.
For overprints see Nos. 37-48.

Overprinted in Very Small Upright Letters "Bolivar Sucre Miranda dash> Decreto de 27 de Abril de 1870", or "Decreto de 27 de Junio 1870" in Slanting Letters

(The "Junio" overprint is continuously repeated, in four lines arranged in two pairs, with the second line of each pair inverted.)

Un	1	Siete	7
Dos	2	Nueve	9
Tres	3	Quince	15
Cuatro	4	Veinte	20
Cinco	5	Cincuenta	50

1871-76 **Litho.**

22	A5	1c yellow	.85	.30
a.		1c orange	1.40	.45
b.		1c brown orange ('76)	1.40	.30
c.		1c pale buff ('76)	1.40	.45
d.		Laid paper	3.00	.55
23	A5	2c yellow	1.40	.45
a.		2c orange	4.00	.45
b.		2c brown orange	3.50	.75
c.		2c pale buff ('76)	3.50	.45
d.		Laid paper	3.50	.55
e.		Frame inverted	4,000.	3,000.
24	A5	3c yellow	2.25	.55
a.		3c orange	3.00	1.40
b.		3c pale buff ('76)	5.50	1.75
25	A5	4c yellow	3.00	.55
a.		4c orange	4.50	1.25
b.		4c brown orange ('76)	4.50	1.25
c.		4c buff ('76)	4.50	1.25
26	A5	5c yellow	3.00	.55
a.		5c orange	3.00	.90
b.		5c pale buff ('76)	3.00	.90
c.		Laid paper	6.50	.90

27	A5	1r rose	3.00	.45
a.		1r pale rose	3.00	.45
b.		Laid paper	5.00	.90
c.		Half used as ½r on cover		1,800.
28	A5	2r rose	4.50	.80
a.		2r pale red	4.50	.80
b.		Laid paper	12.00	2.50
29	A5	3r rose	5.50	.80
a.		3r pale red	5.50	.80
30	A5	5r rose	5.50	1.00
a.		5r pale red	5.50	1.00
31	A5	7r rose	7.00	2.50
a.		7r pale red	7.00	2.50
32	A5	9r green	15.00	4.25
a.		9r olive green	15.00	6.00
33	A5	15r green	30.00	8.50
a.		15r gray green ('76)	30.00	8.50
b.		Frame inverted	8,000.	6,500.
34	A5	20r green	70.00	14.00
a.		Laid paper	110.00	35.00
35	A5	30r green	325.00	110.00
a.		30r gray green ('76)	600.00	160.00
b.		Double overprint		
36	A5	50r green	1,100.	300.00
a.		50r gray green ('76)		
		Nos. 22-34 (13)	151.00	34.70
		Nos. 22-35 (14)	476.00	144.70

These stamps were made available for postage and revenue by official decree, and were the only stamps sold for postage in Venezuela from Mar., 1871 to Aug., 1873.

Due to lack of canceling stamps, the majority of specimens were canceled with pen marks. Fiscal cancellations were also made with the pen. The values quoted are for pen-canceled copies.

Different settings were used for the different overprints. Stamps with the upright letters were issued in 1871. Those with the slanting letters in one double line were issued in 1872-73. Specimens with the slanting overprint in two double lines were issued starting in 1874 from several different settings, those of 1877-78 showing much coarser impressions of the design than the earlier issues. The 7r and 9r are not known with this overprint. Stamps on laid paper (1875) are from a separate setting.

Stamps and Types of 1866-67
Overprinted in Two Lines of Very Small Letters Repeated Continuously
Overprinted "Estampillas de Correo — Contrasena"

1873, July 1

37	A4	½r pale rose	60.00	11.00
a.		½r rose	60.00	11.00
b.		Inverted overprint	125.00	50.00
c.		Tête bêche pair	2,750.	2,000.
38	A4	1r vermilion	80.00	25.00
a.		Inverted overprint	400.00	175.00
b.		Half used as ½r on cover		550.00
39	A4	2r yellow	160.00	80.00
a.		Inverted overprint	400.00	175.00
b.		Half used as 1r on cover		12,000.
		Nos. 37-39 (3)	300.00	116.00

Overprinted
"Contrasena — Estampillas de Correo"

1873, Nov.

40	A4	1c gray lilac	25.00	27.50
a.		Inverted overprint	6.50	17.00
41	A4	2c green	110.00	75.00
a.		Inverted overprint	40.00	50.00
42	A4	½r rose	60.00	11.00
a.		Inverted overprint	30.00	4.00
b.		½r pink	60.00	11.00
43	A4	1r vermilion	70.00	19.00
a.		Inverted overprint	35.00	9.00
b.		Half used as ½r on cover		300.00
44	A4	2r yellow	275.00	125.00
a.		Inverted overprint	110.00	50.00
b.		Half used as 1r on cover		1,500.
		Nos. 40-44 (5)	540.00	257.50

Overprinted
"Contrasena — Estampilla de Correos"

1875

45	A4	½r rose	70.00	8.50
a.		Inverted overprint	125.00	25.00
b.		Double overprint	160.00	90.00
46	A4	1r vermilion	125.00	13.00
a.		Inverted overprint	200.00	80.00
b.		Tête bêche pair	3,500.	3,000.
c.		Half used as ½r on cover		250.00

Overprinted
"Estampillas de correo — Contrasena"

1876-77

47	A4	½r rose	65.00	7.50
a.		½r pink	65.00	7.50
b.		Inverted overprint	65.00	7.50
c.		Both lines of overprint read "Contrasena"	75.00	17.50
d.		Both lines of overprint read "Estampillas de correo"	75.00	17.50
e.		Double overprint	125.00	35.00
48	A4	1r vermilion ('77)	75.00	20.00
a.		Inverted overprint	85.00	24.00
b.		Tête bêche pair	2,250.	2,500.
c.		Half used as ½r on cover		250.00

On Nos. 47 and 48 "correo" has a small "c" instead of a capital. Nos. 45 and 46 have the overprint in slightly larger letters than the other stamps of the 1873-76 issues.

Simón Bolívar
A6　　　　　　　A7

Overprinted
"Decreto de 27 Junio 1870"
Twice, One Line Inverted

1879 **Imperf.**

49	A6	1c yellow	2.50	.20
a.		1c orange	3.50	.75
b.		1c olive yellow	4.00	1.00
50	A6	5c yellow	3.50	.50
a.		5c orange	2.50	.75
b.		Double overprint	20.00	10.00
51	A6	10c blue	5.00	.50
52	A6	30c blue	6.25	1.00
53	A6	50c blue	7.50	1.00
54	A6	90c blue	30.00	6.25
55	A7	1v rose red	65.00	8.75
56	A7	3v rose red	110.00	35.00
57	A7	5v rose red	190.00	65.00
		Nos. 49-57 (9)	419.75	118.20

In 1879 and the early part of 1880 there were no regular postage stamps in Venezuela and the stamps inscribed "Escuelas" were permitted to serve for postal as well as revenue purposes. Postally canceled copies are extremely scarce. Values quoted are for stamps with cancellations of banks or business houses or with pen cancellations. Copies with pen marks removed are sometimes offered as unused stamps, or may have fraudulent postal cancellations added.

Nos. 49-57 exist without overprint. These probably are revenue stamps.

A8

A9

1880 **Perf. 11**

58	A8	5c yellow	1.25	.20
a.		5c orange	1.25	.20
b.		Printed on both sides	150.00	85.00
59	A8	10c yellow	2.00	.20
a.		10c orange	2.00	.20
60	A8	25c yellow	1.75	.20
a.		25c orange	2.00	.35
b.		Printed on both sides	110.00	52.50
c.		Impression of 5c on back	175.00	90.00
61	A8	50c yellow	3.50	.30
a.		50c orange	4.00	.35
b.		Half used as 25c on cover		400.00
c.		Printed on both sides	150.00	90.00
d.		Impression of 25c on back	150.00	90.00
62	A9	1b pale blue	8.75	.75
63	A9	2b pale blue	14.00	.85
64	A9	5b pale blue	32.50	.75
a.		Half used as 2½b on cover		
65	A9	10b rose red	160.00	52.50
66	A9	20b rose red	1,000.	160.00
67	A9	25b rose red	4,250.	500.00
		Nos. 58-65 (8)	223.75	55.80

See note on used values below No. 57.

Bolívar — A10

1880 **Litho.** **Perf. 11**

Thick or Thin Paper

68	A10	5c blue	12.00	6.00
a.		Printed on both sides	225.00	140.00
69	A10	10c rose	17.00	10.00
a.		10c carmine	17.00	10.00
b.		Double impression	90.00	75.00
c.		Horiz. pair, imperf. btwn.	75.00	75.00
70	A10	10c scarlet	18.00	10.50
a.		Horiz. pair, imperf. btwn.	75.00	75.00
71	A10	25c yellow	12.00	6.00
b.		Thick paper	20.00	10.00
72	A10	50c brown	80.00	30.00
a.		50c deep brown	80.00	30.00
b.		Printed on both sides	225.00	140.00
73	A10	1b green	125.00	40.00
a.		Horiz. pair, imperf. btwn.	300.00	300.00
		Nos. 68-73 (6)	264.00	102.50

Nos. 68 to 73 were used for the payment of postage on letters to be sent abroad and the Escuelas stamps were then restricted to internal use.

Counterfeits of this issue exist in a great variety of shades as well as in wrong colors. They are on thick and thin paper, white or toned, and imperf. or perforated 11, 12 and compound. They are also found tête bêche. Counterfeits of Nos. 68 to 72 inclusive often have a diagonal line across the "S" of "CENTS" and a short line from the bottom of that letter to the frame below it. Originals of No. 73 show parts of a frame around "BOLIVAR."

Simón Bolívar
A11   A12

A13   A14

A15

1882, Aug. 1   Engr.   Perf. 12

74	A11	5c blue	.50	.25
75	A12	10c red brown	.60	.25
76	A13	25c yellow brown	.75	.25
a.		Printed on both sides	50.00	27.50
77	A14	50c green	1.40	.60
78	A15	1b violet	2.75	1.25
		Nos. 74-78 (5)	6.00	2.50

Nos. 75-78 exist imperf. Value, set $32.50.
See Nos. 88, 92-95. For surcharges and overprints see Nos. 100-103, 108-112.

A16   A17

A18   A19

A20   A21

A22   A23

1882-88

79	A16	5c blue green	.20	.20
80	A17	10c brown	.20	.20
81	A18	25c orange	.20	.20
82	A19	50c blue	.20	.20
83	A20	1b vermilion	.20	.20
84	A21	3b dull vio ('88)	.20	.20

85	A22	10b dark brn ('88)	.50	.50
86	A23	20b plum ('88)	.65	.65
		Nos. 79-86 (8)	2.35	2.35

By official decree, dated Apr. 14, 1882, stamps of types A11 to A15 were to be used for foreign postage and those of types A16 to A23 for inland correspondence and fiscal use.
Issue date: Nos. 79-83, Aug. 1.
See Nos. 87, 89-91, 96-99. For surcharges and overprints see Nos. 104-107, 114-122.

1887-88   Litho.   Perf. 11

87	A16	5c gray green	.25	.20
88	A13	25c yellow brown	42.50	15.00
89	A18	25c orange	.40	.35
90	A20	1b orange red ('88)	3.50	.75
		Nos. 87-90 (4)	46.65	16.30

Perf. 14

| 91 | A16 | 5c gray green | 70.00 | 22.50 |

Stamps of type A16, perf. 11 and 14, are from a new die with "ESCUELAS" in smaller letters. Stamps of the 1887-88 issue, perf. 12, and a 50c dark blue, perf. 11 or 12, are believed by experts to be from printer's waste.
Counterfeits of No. 91 have been made by perforating printers waste of No. 96.

Rouletted 8

92	A11	5c blue	30.00	15.00
93	A13	25c yel brown	12.00	7.50
94	A14	50c green	12.00	7.50
95	A15	1b purple	24.00	15.00
		Nos. 92-95 (4)	78.00	45.00

1887-88

96	A16	5c green	.20	.20
97	A18	25c orange	.20	.20
98	A19	50c dark blue	.40	.40
99	A21	3b purple ('88)	1.90	1.90
		Nos. 96-99 (4)	2.70	2.70

The so-called imperforate varieties of Nos. 92 to 99, and the pin perforated 50c dark blue, type A19, are believed to be from printer's waste.

Stamps of 1882-88 Handstamp Surcharged in Violet

1892   Perf. 12

100	A11	25c on 5c blue	40.00	40.00
101	A12	25c on 10c red brn	16.00	16.00
102	A13	1b on 25c yel brn	16.00	16.00
103	A14	1b on 50c green	20.00	20.00
		Nos. 100-103 (4)	92.00	92.00

See note after No. 107.

1892

104	A16	25c on 5c bl grn	10.00	6.00
105	A17	25c on 10c brown	10.00	6.00
106	A18	1b on 25c orange	12.50	7.00
107	A19	1b on 50c blue	17.50	7.00
		Nos. 104-107 (4)	50.00	26.00

Counterfeits of this surcharge abound.

Stamps of 1882-88 Overprinted in Red or Black:

1893

108	A11	5c blue (R)	.50	.20
a.		Inverted overprint	3.25	3.25
b.		Double overprint	16.00	16.00
109	A12	10c red brn (Bk)	.65	.65
a.		Inverted overprint	4.00	4.00
b.		Double overprint	16.00	16.00
110	A13	25c yel brn (R)	.50	.25
a.		Inverted overprint	5.25	5.25
b.		Double overprint	16.00	16.00
c.		25c yel brn (Bk)	250.00	250.00
111	A14	50c green (R)	.65	.40
a.		Inverted overprint	5.25	5.25
b.		Double overprint	27.50	27.50
112	A15	1b pur (R)	1.50	.60
a.		Inverted overprint	10.00	10.00
		Nos. 108-112 (5)	3.80	2.10

1893

114	A16	5c bl grn (R)	.20	.20
a.		Inverted overprint	3.25	3.25
b.		Double overprint	5.25	5.25
115	A17	10c brn (R)	.20	.20
a.		Inverted overprint	3.25	3.25
116	A18	25c org (R)	.20	.20
a.		Inverted overprint	3.25	3.25
117	A18	25c org (Bk)	2.25	2.00
a.		Inverted overprint	8.25	5.00
118	A19	50c blue (R)	.20	.20
a.		Inverted overprint	3.25	3.25
119	A20	1b ver (Bk)	.45	.25
a.		Inverted overprint	4.00	4.00
120	A21	3b dl vio (R)	.60	.30
a.		Double overprint	8.25	8.25
121	A22	10b dk brn (R)	1.75	1.50
a.		Double overprint	10.00	10.00
b.		Inverted overprint	20.00	20.00
122	A23	20b plum (Bk)	1.50	1.50
a.		Double overprint	10.00	20.00
b.		Inverted overprint	20.00	20.00
		Nos. 114-122 (9)	7.35	6.35

Counterfeits exist.

Simón Bolívar
A24   A25

1893   Engr.

123	A24	5c red brn	.60	.20
124	A24	10c blue	2.50	.60
125	A24	25c magenta	12.00	.35
126	A24	50c brn vio	2.50	.40
127	A24	1b green	3.25	.60
		Nos. 123-127 (5)	20.85	2.15

Many shades exist in this issue, but their values do not vary.

1893

128	A25	5c gray	.20	.20
129	A25	10c green	.20	.20
130	A25	25c blue	.20	.20
131	A25	50c orange	.20	.20
132	A25	1b red vio	.20	.20
133	A25	3b red	.35	.20
134	A25	10b dl vio	.65	.50
135	A25	20b red brn	2.00	1.75
		Nos. 128-135 (8)	4.00	3.45

By decree of Nov. 28, 1892, the stamps inscribed "Correos" were to be used for external postage and those inscribed "Instruccion" were for internal postage and revenue purposes.
For surcharge see No. 230.

After July 1, 1895, stamps inscribed "Escuelas" or "Instruccion" were no longer available for postage. Stamps of design A25 in shades different than those listed were printed after 1895.

Landing of Columbus
A26

1893   Perf. 12

| 136 | A26 | 25c magenta | 10.00 | .60 |

4th cent. of the discovery of the mainland of South America, also participation of Venezuela in the Intl. Exhib. at Chicago in 1893.

Map of Venezuela
A27

1896   Litho.

137	A27	5c yel grn	2.50	2.10
a.		5c apple green	2.50	2.10
138	A27	10c blue	3.25	2.25
139	A27	25c yellow	3.25	4.25
a.		25c orange	3.25	4.25
b.		Tête bêche pair	62.50	62.50
140	A27	50c rose red	42.50	21.00
a.		50c red	42.50	42.50
b.		Tête bêche pair	300.00	300.00
141	A27	1b violet	32.50	21.00
		Nos. 137-141 (5)	84.00	50.60

Gen. Francisco Antonio Gabriel de Miranda (1752-1816).

These stamps were in use from July 4 to Nov. 4, 1896. Later usage is known.
There are many forgeries of this issue. They include faked errors, imperforate stamps and many tête bêche. The paper of the originals is thin, white and semi-transparent. The gum is shiny and crackled. The paper of the reprints is often thick and opaque. The gum is usually dull, smooth, thin and only slightly adhesive.

Bolívar — A28

1899-1901   Engr.

142	A28	5c dk grn	.75	.20
143	A28	10c red	1.00	.25
144	A28	25c blue	1.25	.40
145	A28	50c gray blk	1.50	.75
146	A28	50c org ('01)	1.25	.40
147	A28	1b yel grn	25.00	12.50
149	A28	2b orange	300.00	190.00
		Nos. 142-147,149 (7)	330.75	204.50

Stamps of 1899 Overprinted in Black

1900

150	A28	5c dk grn	.75	.20
a.		Inverted overprint	4.00	4.00
151	A28	10c red	.75	.25
a.		Inverted overprint	5.25	5.25
b.		Double overprint	10.50	10.50
152	A28	25c blue	5.00	.75
a.		Inverted overprint	10.50	10.50
153	A28	50c gray blk	2.50	.40
a.		Inverted overprint	9.25	9.25
154	A28	1b yel grn	1.00	.50
a.		Double overprint	13.00	13.00
b.		Inverted overprint	9.25	9.25
155	A28	2b orange	1.75	1.25
a.		Inverted overprint	27.50	27.50
b.		Double overprint	32.50	32.50
		Nos. 150-155 (6)	11.75	3.35

Initials are those of R. T. Mendoza.
Counterfeit overprints exist, especially of inverted and doubled varieties.

Bolívar Type of 1899-1903 Overprinted

1900

156	A28	5c dk grn	150.00	150.00
157	A28	10c red	150.00	150.00
158	A28	25c blue	300.00	150.00
159	A28	50c yel orange	18.00	1.00
160	A28	1b slate	1.00	.75
a.		Without overprint	4,000.	
		Nos. 156-160 (5)	619.00	451.75

Overprinted

1900, Aug. 14

161	A28	5c green	5.00	.35
162	A28	10c red	4.00	.65
163	A28	25c blue	5.00	.60
		Nos. 161-163 (3)	14.00	1.60

Inverted Overprint

161a	A28	5c	8.00	5.25
162a	A28	10c	8.00	5.25
163a	A28	25c	10.00	5.25
		Nos. 161a-163a (3)	26.00	15.75

Overprint exists on each value without "Castro" or without "1900."

Type of 1893
Surcharged

1904, Jan.   **Perf. 12**
230 A25 5c on 50c green   .50   .40
   a.   "Vele"   18.00 18.00
   b.   Surcharge reading up   .75   .35
   c.   Double surcharge   18.00 18.00

Gen. José de   Pres. Cipriano
Sucre — A35   Castro — A37

1904-09   **Engr.**
231 A35 5c bl grn   .25   .20
232 A35 10c carmine   .30   .20
233 A35 15c violet   .55   .20
234 A35 25c dp ultra   4.00   .20
235 A35 50c plum   .55   .20
236 A35 1b plum   .60   .25
   Nos. 231-236 (6)   6.25 1.30

Issued: 15c, Dec. 1909; others, July 1, 1904.

1905, July 5   **Litho.**   **Perf. 11½**
245 A37 5c vermilion   3.00 3.00
   a.   5c carmine   4.50 4.50
246 A37 10c dark blue   4.75 4.00
247 A37 25c yellow   1.75 1.25
   Nos. 245-247 (3)   9.50 8.25

National Congress. Issued for interior postage only. Valid only for 90 days.
Various part-perforate varieties of Nos. 245-247 exist. Value, $15-$30.

Liberty — A38

1910, Apr. 19   **Engr.**   **Perf. 12**
249 A38 25c dark blue   11.00   .60

Centenary of national independence.

Francisco de   Rafael
Miranda   Urdaneta
A39   A40

Bolívar — A41

1911   **Litho.**   **Perf. 11½x12**
250 A39 5c dp grn   .30   .20
251 A39 10c carmine   .30   .20
252 A40 15c gray   4.00   .25
253 A40 25c dp bl   2.00   .40
   a.   Imperf., pair   40.00 50.00
254 A41 50c purple   2.50   .30
255 A41 1b yellow   2.50 1.25
   Nos. 250-255 (6)   11.60 2.60

The 50c with center in blue was never issued although copies were postmarked by favor.
The centers of Nos. 250-255 were separately printed and often vary in shade from the rest of the design. In a second printing of the 5c and 10c, the entire design was printed at one time.

Redrawn

1913
255A A40 15c gray   3.00 1.75
255B A40 25c deep blue   1.50   .50
255C A41 50c purple   1.50   .50
   Nos. 255A-255C (3)   6.00 2.75

The redrawn stamps have two berries instead of one at top of the left spray; a berry has been added over the "C" and "S" of "Centimos"; and the lowest leaf at the right is cut by the corner square.

Simón Bolívar
A42   A43

1914, July   **Engr.**   **Perf. 13½, 14, 15**
256 A42 5c yel grn   30.00   .45
257 A42 10c scarlet   27.50   .40
258 A42 25c dark blue   4.50   .20
   Nos. 256-258 (3)   62.00 1.05

Printed by the American Bank Note Co.

Different frames.

1915-23   **Perf. 12**
259 A43 5c green   3.25   .20
260 A43 10c vermilion   7.75   .40
261 A43 10c claret ('22)   7.75   .70
262 A43 15c dull ol grn   7.50   .45
263 A43 25c ultra   5.00   .20
   a.   25c blue   10.00   .50
264 A43 40c dull green   17.50 7.50
265 A43 50c dp violet   4.50   .50
266 A43 50c ultra ('23)   11.00 3.75
267 A43 75c lt blue   45.00 15.00
   a.   75c greenish blue   45.00 15.00
268 A43 1b dark gray   20.00 4.00
   Nos. 259-268 (10)   129.25 32.70

See Nos. 269-285. For surcharges see Nos. 307, 309-310.

Type of 1915-23 Issue
Printed by Waterlow & Sons, Ltd.
Re-engraved

1924-39   **Perf. 12½**
269 A43 5c orange brn   .40   .20
   a.   5c yellow brown   .40   .20
   b.   Horiz. pair, imperf. btwn.   25.00 40.00
270 A43 5c green ('39)   7.50   .80
271 A43 7½c yel grn ('39)   .75   .25
272 A43 10c dk green   .20   .20
273 A43 10c dk car ('39)   2.50   .20
274 A43 15c olive grn   1.50   .35
275 A43 15c brown ('27)   .25   .20
276 A43 25c ultra   1.50   .20
277 A43 25c red ('28)   .20   .20
   a.   Horiz. pair, imperf. btwn.   50.00 85.00
278 A43 40c dp blue ('25)   .40   .20
279 A43 40c slate bl ('39)   5.00   .75
280 A43 50c dk blue   .40   .20
281 A43 50c dk pur ('39)   6.00   .20
282 A43 1b black   .40   .20
283 A43 3b yel org ('25)   1.25   .70
284 A43 3b red org ('39)   10.00 3.25
285 A43 5b dull vio ('25)   12.00 6.50
   Nos. 269-285 (17)   50.25 15.10

Perf. 14
269c   A43   5c   5.25   1.25
272a   A43   10c   5.25   1.25
274a   A43   15c   6.50   2.00
276a   A43   25c   8.00   3.00
280a   A43   50c   26.00 11.00
282a   A43   1b   35.00 21.00
   Nos. 269c-282a (6)   86.00 39.50

The re-engraved stamps may readily be distinguished from the 1915 issue by the perforation and sometimes by the colors. The designs differ in many minor details which are too minute for illustration or description.

Bolívar
and Sucre
A44

Perf. 11½x12, 12
1924, Dec. 1   **Litho.**
286 A44 25c grayish blue   2.25   .40

Redrawn

286A A44 25c ultra   2.75   .65

Centenary of the Battle of Ayacucho.
The redrawn stamp has a whiter effect with less shading in the faces. Bolívar's ear is

clearly visible and the outline of his aquiline nose is broken.

A45   A46

Revenue Stamps Surcharged in Black or Red

1926   **Perf. 12, 12½**
287 A45 5c on 1b ol grn   .50   .25
   a.   Double surcharge   8.00 8.00
   b.   Pair, one without surcharge   12.00 12.00
   c.   Inverted surcharge   8.00 8.00
288 A46 25c on 5c dk brn (R)   .50   .30
   a.   Inverted surcharge   8.00 8.00
   b.   Double surcharge   8.00 8.00

View of Ciudad
Bolívar and
General J.V.
Gómez — A47

1928, July 21   **Litho.**   **Perf. 12**
289 A47 10c deep green   .65   .40
   a.   Imperf., pair   40.00

25th anniversary of the Battle of Ciudad Bolívar and the foundation of peace in Venezuela.

Simón Bolívar
A48   A49

1930, Dec. 9
290 A48 5c yellow   .75   .30
291 A48 10c dark blue   .75   .20
292 A48 25c rose red   .75   .20
   Nos. 290-292 (3)   2.25   .70

Imperf., Pairs
290a   A48   5c   5.25   5.25
291a   A48   10c   6.50   6.50
292a   A48   25c   10.50 10.50

Death centenary of Simón Bolívar (1783-1830), South American liberator.
Nos. 290-292 exist part-perforate, including pairs imperf. between, imperf. horiz., imperf. vert. Value range, $6-12.

Various Frames
Bluish Winchester Security Paper

1932-38   **Engr.**   **Perf. 12½**
293 A49 5c violet   .25   .20
294 A49 7½c dk green ('37)   .60   .25
295 A49 10c green   .35   .20
296 A49 15c yellow   .80   .20
297 A49 22½c dp car ('38)   2.00   .40
298 A49 25c red   .65   .20
299 A49 37½c ultra ('36)   2.50 1.25
300 A49 40c indigo   2.50   .20
301 A49 50c olive grn   2.50   .25
302 A49 1b lt blue   3.25   .55
303 A49 3b brown   25.00 10.00
304 A49 5b yellow brn   32.50 13.00
   Nos. 293-304 (12)   72.90 26.70

For surcharges see Nos. 308, 318-319, C223.

Arms of
Bolívar — A50

1933, July 24   **Litho.**   **Perf. 11**
306 A50 25c brown red   2.00 1.50
   a.   Imperf., pair   32.50 32.50

150th anniv. of the birth of Simón Bolívar. Valid only to Aug. 21.

1933

Stamps of 1924-32
Surcharged in
Black: (Blocks of
Surcharge in Color
of stamps)

1933
307 A43 7½c on 10c grn   .40   .20
   a.   Double surcharge   2.50 2.50
   b.   Inverted surcharge   3.25 3.25
308 A49 22½c on 25c (#298)   1.40   .70
309 A43 22½c on 25c (#277)   1.25 1.25
   a.   Double surcharge   10.00 10.00
310 A43 37½c on 40c dp bl   1.50   .75
   a.   Double surcharge   11.50 11.50
   b.   Inverted surcharge   8.25 8.25
   Nos. 307-310 (4)   4.55 2.90

Nurse and   River
Child — A51   Scene — A52

Gathering Cacao
Pods — A53

Cattle
Raising
A54

Plowing
A55

Perf. 11, 11½ or Compound
1937, July 1   **Litho.**
311 A51 5c deep violet   .40   .30
312 A52 10c dk slate grn   .40   .20
313 A53 15c yellow brn   .80   .40
314 A51 25c cerise   .80   .25
315 A54 50c yellow grn   5.00 3.25
316 A55 3b red orange   8.75 6.00
317 A51 5b lt brown   18.00 12.00
   Nos. 311-317 (7)   34.15 22.40

Nos. 311-317 exist imperforate. Value for set $75. Nos. 311-315 exist in pairs, imperf. between; value range, $20-$30.
For overprints and surcharges see Nos. 321-324, 345, 376-377, 380-384.

1937

No. 300
Surcharged in
Black

1937, July   **Perf. 12½**
318 A49 25c on 40c indigo   5.00   .65
   a.   Double surcharge   16.00 16.00
   b.   Inverted surcharge   13.00 13.00
   c.   Triple surcharge   32.50 32.50

1937

Surcharged

VALE POR 25

319 A49 25c on 40c indigo 325.00 275.00
  a. Double surcharge

A56

1937, Oct. 28 **Litho.** **Perf. 10½**
320 A56 25c blue 1.00 .40

Acquisition of the Port of La Guaira by the Government from the British Corporation, June 3, 1937. Exists imperf. See Nos. C64-C65.

A redrawn printing of No. 320, with top inscription beginning "Nacionalización . . ." was prepared but not issued. Value, $40.

For surcharge see No. 385.

Stamps of 1937
Overprinted in Black

RESELLADO
1937-1938

1937, Dec. 17 **Perf. 11, 11½**
321 A51 5c deep violet 5.00 2.00
322 A52 10c dk slate grn 1.50 .50
  a. Inverted overprint 13.00 13.00
323 A51 25c cerise 1.50 .50
  a. Inverted overprint 16.00 16.00
324 A55 3b red orange 375.00 225.00
  Nos. 321-324 (4) 383.00 228.00

Part-perforate pairs exist of Nos. 321-322 and 324. Value range, $12.50 to $125.

See Nos. C66-C78.

Gathering Coffee
Beans — A57

Simón
Bolívar — A58

Post Office,
Caracas — A59

1938 **Engr.** **Perf. 12**
325 A57 5c green .30 .20
326 A57 5c deep green .30 .20
327 A58 10c car rose .50 .20
328 A58 10c dp rose .50 .20
329 A59 15c dk violet 1.00 .20
330 A59 15c olive grn .65 .20
331 A58 25c lt blue .30 .20
332 A58 25c dk blue .30 .20
333 A58 37½c dk blue 6.00 2.50
334 A58 37½c lt blue 2.00 .65
335 A59 40c sepia 15.00 4.00
336 A59 40c black 12.50 4.00
337 A57 50c olive grn 20.00 4.00
338 A57 50c dull violet 7.00 .65
339 A58 1b dp brown 8.25 4.00
340 A58 1b black brown 12.50 1.00
341 A57 3b orange 70.00 26.00
342 A59 5b black 8.75 4.00
  Nos. 325-342 (18) 165.85 52.40

See Nos. 400 and 412.

1937

Teresa
Carreño — A60

Bolívar
Statue — A61

1938, June 12 **Perf. 11½x12**
343 A60 25c blue 4.00 .40

Teresa Carreno, Venezuelan pianist, whose remains were repatriated Feb. 14, 1938.
For surcharge see No. 386.

1938, July 24 **Perf. 12**
344 A61 25c dark blue 4.50 .40

"The Day of the Worker."
For surcharge see No. 387.

VALE
Type of 1937 **Bs. 0.40**
Surcharged in Black
1938

1938 **Litho.** **Perf. 11, 11½**
345 A51 40c on 5b lt brn 7.00 3.00
  a. Inverted surcharge 21.00 21.00

Gen. José I. Paz
Castillo, Postmaster of
Venezuela, 1859 — A62

1939, Apr. 19 **Engr.** **Perf. 12½**
348 A62 10c carmine 1.75 .40

80th anniv. of the first Venezuelan stamp.

View of
Ojeda
A63

1939, June 24 **Photo.**
349 A63 25c dull blue 7.75 .60

Founding of city of Ojeda.

Cristóbal
Mendoza
A64

Diego
Urbaneja
A65

1939, Oct. 14 **Engr.** **Perf. 13**
350 A64 5c green .40 .20
351 A64 10c dk car rose .40 .20
352 A64 15c olive 1.00 .25
353 A64 25c brt ultra .80 .20
354 A64 37½c dark blue 15.00 6.25
355 A64 50c lt olive grn 16.00 4.00
356 A64 1b dark brown 6.50 3.50
  Nos. 350-356 (7) 40.10 14.60

Mendoza (1772-1839), postmaster general.

1940-43 **Perf. 12**
357 A65 5c Prus green .45 .20
357A A65 7½c dk bl grn ('43) .65 .25
358 A65 15c olive .80 .25
359 A65 37½c deep blue 1.25 .60
360 A65 40c violet blue .95 .30
361 A65 50c violet 5.50 1.40
362 A65 1b dk violet brn 2.75 .75
363 A65 3b scarlet 8.00 3.25
  Nos. 357-363 (8) 20.35 7.00

See Nos. 399, 408, 410 and 411. For surcharges see Nos. 396, C226.

Battle of
Carabobo,
1821 — A67

1940, June 13
365 A67 25c blue 5.25 .45

Birth of General José Antonio Páez, 150th anniv.

"Crossing the
Andes" by Tito
Salas — A68

1940, June 13
366 A68 25c dark blue 5.25 .45

Death cent. of General Francisco Santander.

Monument and
Urn containing
Ashes of Simón
Bolívar — A69

Bed where Simón
Bolívar was
Born — A70

Designs: 15c, "Christening of Bolivar" by Tito Salas. 20c, Bolivar's birthplace, Caracas. 25c, "Bolivar on Horseback" by Salas. 30c, Patio of Bolivar House, Caracas. 37½c, Patio of Bolivar's Birthplace. 50c, "Rebellion of 1812" by Salas.

1940-41
367 A69 5c turq green .20 .20
368 A70 10c rose pink .20 .20
369 A69 15c olive .50 .20
370 A70 20c blue ('41) .85 .20
371 A69 25c lt blue .50 .20
372 A70 30c plum ('41) 1.25 .20
373 A70 37½c dk blue 2.50 .85
374 A70 50c purple 1.50 .40
  Nos. 367-374 (8) 7.50 2.45

110th anniv. of the death of Simón Bolívar. See #397, 398, 403, 405-407, 409. For surcharges see #375, 401-402, C224, C237-C238.

No. 371 Surcharged
In Black

1941
375 A69 20c on 25c lt blue .50 .20
  a. Inverted surcharge 10.00 10.00

Nos. 311-312
Overprinted in Black

1941 **Perf. 11½**
376 A51 5c deep violet 1.50 .45
  a. Double overprint 10.00 8.25
  b. Vert. pair, imperf. btwn. 14.00 14.00
  c. Inverted overprint 20.00 16.00
377 A52 10c dk slate grn .85 .25
  a. Double overprint 13.00 13.00

Symbols of
Industry
A77

Caracas
Cathedral
A78

1942, Dec. 17 **Litho.** **Perf. 12**
378 A77 10c scarlet .75 .20
  a. Imperf., pair 22.50 22.50

Grand Industrial Exposition, Caracas.

1943 **Engr.**
379 A78 10c rose carmine .60 .20

See No. 404.

Stamps of 1937
Overprinted in Black

Resellado
1943

1943 **Perf. 11, 11½**
380 A51 5c deep violet 12.00 7.50
381 A52 10c dk slate grn 4.50 3.00
382 A54 50c yellow green 6.00 3.50
383 A55 3b red orange 35.00 17.50
  Nos. 380-383 (4) 57.50 31.50

Issued for sale to philatelists & sold only in sets.

Stamps of 1937-38
Surcharged in Black

Habilitado
Vale
Bs. 0.20

1943 **Perf. 11½, 10½, 12**
384 A51 20c on 25c cerise 22.50 22.50
385 A56 20c on 25c blue 60.00 60.00
386 A60 20c on 25c dk blue 12.00 12.00
387 A61 20c on 25c dk blue 12.00 12.00
  a. Inverted surcharge 27.50 27.50
  Nos. 384-387 (4) 106.50 106.50

Issued for sale to philatelists & sold only in sets.

Souvenir Sheet

A79

1944, Aug. 22 **Litho.** **Perf. 12**
Flags in Red, Yellow, Blue & Black
388 A79 Sheet of 4 27.50 27.50
  a. 5c Prussian green 3.00 .80
  b. 10c rose 4.50 .80
  c. 20c ultramarine 4.50 1.75
  d. 1b rose lake 6.00 2.25

80th anniv. of Intl. Red Cross and 37th anniv. of Venezuela's joining.
No. 388 exists imperf. Value $60.

Antonio José de
Sucre — A80

1945, Mar. 3   Engr.   Unwmk.
389 A80 5c orange yellow   .85   .30
390 A80 10c dark blue   1.25   .60
391 A80 20c rose pink   1.50   .60
   Nos. 389-391,C206-C215 (13) 15.40 10.30

Birth of Antonio de Sucre, 150th anniv.

Andrés   Gen. Rafael
Bello — A81   Urdaneta — A82

1946, Aug. 24
392 A81 20c deep blue   .65   .35
393 A82 20c deep blue   .65   .35
   Nos. 392-393,C216-C217 (4) 3.50 1.10

80th anniversary of the death of Andrés
Bello (1780?-1865), educator and writer, and
the centenary of the death of Gen. Rafael
Urdaneta.

Allegory of the
Republic — A83

1946, Oct. 18   Litho.   Perf. 11½
394 A83 20c greenish blue   .60   .25
   Nos. 394,C218-C221 (5)   4.60 3.45

Anniversary of Revolution of October, 1945.
Exists imperf.

Anti-tuberculosis Institute,
Maracaibo — A84

1947, Jan. 12
395 A84 20c ultra & yellow   .60   .25
   Nos. 395,C228-C231 (5)   6.05 4.65

12th Pan-American Health Conf., Caracas,
Jan. 1947. Exists imperf. and part perf.

J. R. G.

No. 362 Surcharged   **CORRESO**
in Green   **Vale Bs. 0.15**
                          1946

396 A65 15c on 1b dk vio brn   .65   .25
 a.   Inverted surcharge   6.00 5.00
   Nos. 396,C223-C227 (6)   28.05 23.75

Types of 1938-40

1947   Engr.
397 A69 5c green   .20   .20
398 A70 30c black   .60   .40
399 A65 40c red violet   .40   .20
400 A59 5b deep orange   32.50 16.00
   Nos. 397-400 (4)   33.70 16.80

In 1947 a decree authorized the use
of 5c and 10c revenue stamps of the
above type for franking correspondence. Other denominations were also
used unofficially.
   For surcharges see Nos. 876-883.

Nos. 398 and 373
Surcharged in Red

1947   Unwmk.   Perf. 12
401 A70 5c on 30c black   .30   .20
 a.   Inverted surcharge   5.00 5.00
402 A70 5c on 37½c dk bl   .35   .20
 a.   Inverted surcharge   5.00 5.00

Types of 1938-43

1947-48
403 A69 5c brt ultra   .20   .20
404 A78 10c red   .20   .20
405 A69 15c rose car   .40   .20
406 A69 25c violet   .30   .20
407 A70 30c dk vio brn ('48)   .40   .20
408 A70 40c orange ('48)   .40   .20
409 A70 50c olive green   .65   .20
410 A65 1b deep blue   1.25   .20
411 A65 3b gray   2.50   .65
412 A59 5b chocolate   11.00 4.25
   Nos. 403-412 (10)   17.30 6.50

M. S.
Republica
de
Venezuela
A85

Imprint: "American Bank Note
Company"

1948-50   Engr.   Perf. 12
413 A85 5c blue   .20   .20
414 A85 7½c red org ('49)   .40   .25
 a.   Booklet pane of 20
415 A85 10c car rose   .30   .20
 a.   Booklet pane of 10
416 A85 15c gray ('50)   .30   .20
417 A85 20c sepia   .20   .20
418 A85 25c violet ('49)   .30   .20
419 A85 30c orange ('50)   2.25 1.10
420 A85 37½c brown ('49)   1.00   .80
421 A85 40c olive ('50)   1.50 1.00
422 A85 50c red violet ('49)   .40   .20
423 A85 1b gray green   1.00   .30
   Nos. 413-423 (11)   7.85 4.65

Grand Colombian Merchant Fleet. See Nos.
632-634, C256-C271, C554-C556. For
surcharges see Nos. 450-451.

Santos
Michelena — A86

Christopher
Columbus — A87

1949, Apr. 25   Perf. 12½
424 A86 5c ultra   .20   .20
425 A86 10c carmine   .35   .20
426 A86 20c sepia   1.40   .60
427 A86 1b green   4.75 2.75
   Nos. 424-427,C272-C277 (10) 12.70 6.55

Centenary of the death of Santos
Michelena, Finance Minister, and the 110th
anniversary of the Postal Convention of
Bogota.

1949-50   Engr.
428 A87 5c deep ultra   .25   .20
429 A87 10c carmine   1.00   .30
430 A87 20c dark brown   1.25   .40
431 A87 1b green   3.00 1.50
   Nos. 428-431,C278-C283 (10) 11.50 4.70

450th anniversary (in 1948) of Columbus'
discovery of the American mainland.
   Issued: 5c, 10c, 1949; 20c, 1b, Jan. 1950.

Arms of
Venezuela
A88

1948
432 A88 5c blue   1.25   .65
433 A88 10c red   1.50   .75

The 20c and 1b, type A88, and six similar air
post stamps were prepared but not issued.
Value, set of 8, about $125.

Gen. Francisco de
Miranda — A89

1950, Mar. 28   Unwmk.   Perf. 12
434 A89 5c blue   .20   .20
435 A89 10c green   .35   .20
436 A89 20c sepia   .70   .30
437 A89 1b rose carmine   3.25 1.50
   Nos. 434-437 (4)   4.50 2.20

Bicentenary of birth of General Francisco de
Miranda.

Map and   Alonso de
Population   Ojeda — A91
Chart — A90

1950, Sept. 1
438 A90 5c blue   .20   .20
439 A90 10c gray   .20   .20
440 A90 15c sepia   .20   .20
441 A90 25c green   .30   .20
442 A90 30c red   .40   .20
443 A90 50c violet   .80   .30
444 A90 1b red brown   2.00 1.00
   Nos. 438-444,C302-C310 (16) 8.90 5.70

8th National Census of the Americas.

1950, Dec. 18   Photo.   Perf. 11½
445 A91 5c deep blue   .20   .20
446 A91 10c deep red   .25   .20
447 A91 15c slate gray   .30   .20
448 A91 20c ultra   1.25   .50
449 A91 1b blue green   5.00 2.50
   Nos. 445-449 (5)   7.00 3.60
   Nos. 445-449,C316-C321 (11) 13.90 7.15

450th anniversary (in 1949) of the discovery
of the Gulf of Maracaibo.

Nos. 414 and 420 Surcharged in Black

1951   Unwmk.   Perf. 12
450 A85 5c on 7½c red org   .25   .20
451 A85 10c on 37½c brn   .25   .20
 a.   Inverted surcharge   16.00 16.00

Telegraph Stamps
Surcharged in
Black or Red

1951, June   Engr.
Grayish Security Paper
452 5c on 5c brown   .20   .20
453 10c on 10c green   .25   .20
454 20c on 1b blk (R)   .50   .20
455 25c on 25c carmine   .65   .25
456 30c on 2b ol grn (R)   .85   .65
   Nos. 452-456 (5)   2.45 1.50

The 5c and 10c surcharges include quotation marks on each line and values are
expressed "Bs. 0.05" etc.

Bolivar
Statue, New
York — A92

1951, July 13   Perf. 12
457 A92 5c green   .20   .20
458 A92 10c car rose   .40   .20
459 A92 20c ultra   .40   .20
460 A92 30c slate gray   .50   .25
461 A92 40c deep green   .70   .25
462 A92 50c red brown   1.50   .50
463 A92 1b gray black   4.75 2.50
   Nos. 457-463 (7)   8.45 4.10
   Nos. 457-463,C322-C329 (15) 14.20 7.45

Relocation of the equestrian statue of
Simon Bolivar in NYC, Apr. 19, 1951.

Arms of Carabobo
and
"Industry" — A93

1951   Unwmk.   Photo.   Perf. 11½
464 A93 5c green   .20   .20
465 A93 10c red   .20   .20
466 A93 15c brown   .25   .20
467 A93 20c ultra   .35   .20
468 A93 25c orange brn   .40   .20
469 A93 30c blue   .85   .35
470 A93 35c purple   3.25 2.75
   Nos. 464-470 (7)   5.50 4.10

Issue dates: 5c, 10c, Oct. 8; others, Oct. 29.

Arms of Zulia and "Industry"
471 A93 5c green   .20   .20
472 A93 10c red   .30   .20
473 A93 15c brown   .65   .30
474 A93 20c ultra   .85   .20
475 A93 50c brown org   5.25 3.75
476 A93 1b dp gray grn   1.75   .65
477 A93 5b rose violet   3.75 2.50
   Nos. 471-477 (7)   12.75 8.00

Issued: 5c, 10c, Sept. 8; others, Sept. 20.

Arms of Anzoategui and Globe
478 A93 5c green   .20   .20
479 A93 10c red   .20   .20
480 A93 15c brown   .65   .30
481 A93 20c ultra   1.10   .20
482 A93 40c red orange   2.25 1.10
483 A93 45c rose violet   6.75 3.75
484 A93 3b blue gray   2.50 1.25
   Nos. 478-484 (7)   13.65 7.45

Issue date: Nov. 9.

Arms of Caracas and Buildings
485 A93 5c green   .40   .20
486 A93 10c red   .50   .20
487 A93 15c brown   1.25   .30
488 A93 20c ultra   2.50   .30
489 A93 25c orange brn   3.75   .65
490 A93 30c blue   3.25   .75
491 A93 35c purple   32.50 19.00
   Nos. 485-491 (7)   44.15 21.40

Issued: 5c, 10c, June 20; others, Aug. 6.

**Arms of Tachira and Agricultural
Products**
492 A93 5c green   .20   .20
493 A93 10c red   .40   .20
494 A93 15c brown   .75   .25
495 A93 20c ultra   1.75   .45

496	A93 50c brown org	110.00	14.00
497	A93 1b dp gray grn	1.75	.65
498	A93 5b dull purple	4.50	2.50
	Nos. 492-498 (7)	119.35	18.25

Issue date: Aug. 9.

Arms of Venezuela and Statue of Simon Bolivar

499	A93 5c green	.30	.20
500	A93 10c red	.25	.20
501	A93 15c brown	2.25	.45
502	A93 20c ultra	2.25	.30
503	A93 25c orange brn	3.75	.85
504	A93 30c blue	3.75	.85
505	A93 35c purple	20.00	15.00
	Nos. 499-505 (7)	32.55	17.85

Issue date: Aug. 6.

1952
Arms of Miranda and Agricultural Products

506	A93 5c green	.20	.20
507	A93 10c red	.20	.20
508	A93 15c brown	.45	.20
509	A93 20c ultra	.50	.20
510	A93 25c orange brn	.65	.30
511	A93 30c blue	1.10	.50
512	A93 35c purple	6.50	4.50
	Nos. 506-512 (7)	9.60	6.10

Arms of Aragua and Stylized Farm

513	A93 5c green	.20	.20
514	A93 10c red	.20	.20
515	A93 15c brown	.40	.20
516	A93 20c ultra	.40	.20
517	A93 25c orange brn	.90	.25
518	A93 30c blue	.90	.40
519	A93 35c purple	5.00	3.75
	Nos. 513-519 (7)	8.00	5.20

Issue date: 20c, 30c, Mar. 24.

Arms of Lara, Agricultural Products and Rope

520	A93 5c green	.20	.20
521	A93 10c red	.20	.20
522	A93 15c brown	.30	.20
523	A93 20c ultra	.70	.20
524	A93 25c orange brn	.80	.50
525	A93 30c blue	1.50	.40
526	A93 35c purple	6.25	3.75
	Nos. 520-526 (7)	9.95	5.45

Issue date: 20c, 30c, Mar. 24.

Arms of Bolivar and Stylized Design

527	A93 5c green	.20	.20
528	A93 10c red	.20	.20
529	A93 15c brown	.30	.20
530	A93 20c ultra	.65	.20
531	A93 40c red orange	2.50	.85
532	A93 45c rose violet	6.50	4.50
533	A93 3b blue gray	3.00	2.00
	Nos. 527-533 (7)	13.35	8.15

Issue date: 20c, Mar. 24.

Arms of Sucre, Palms and Seascape

534	A93 5c green	.20	.20
535	A93 10c red	.20	.20
536	A93 15c brown	.75	.20
537	A93 20c ultra	.75	.20
538	A93 40c red orange	2.50	.65
539	A93 45c rose violet	9.00	5.50
540	A93 3b blue gray	2.25	1.50
	Nos. 534-540 (7)	15.65	8.45

Arms of Trujillo Surrounded by Stylized Tree

541	A93 5c green	.20	.20
542	A93 10c red	.20	.20
543	A93 15c brown	1.10	.20
544	A93 20c ultra	1.10	.20
545	A93 50c brown orange	6.25	3.00
546	A93 1b dp gray green	1.50	.55
547	A93 5b dull purple	3.75	1.90
	Nos. 541-547 (7)	14.10	6.30

1953-54
Map of Delta Amacuro and Ship

548	A93 5c green	.20	.20
549	A93 10c red	.20	.20
550	A93 15c brown	.30	.20
551	A93 20c ultra	.50	.20
552	A93 40c red orange	1.60	1.00
553	A93 45c rose violet	7.50	4.50
554	A93 3b blue gray	2.00	1.50
	Nos. 548-554 (7)	12.30	7.80

Arms of Falcon and Stylized Oil Refinery

555	A93 5c green	.20	.20
556	A93 10c red	.20	.20
557	A93 15c brown	.40	.20
558	A93 20c ultra	.40	.20
559	A93 50c brown orange	2.00	1.00
560	A93 1b dp gray grn	1.25	.80
561	A93 5b dull purple	3.75	2.00
	Nos. 555-561 (7)	8.20	4.60

Issue date: 20c, Feb. 13.

Arms of Guarico and Factory

562	A93 5c green	.20	.20
563	A93 10c red	.20	.20
564	A93 15c brown	.40	.20
565	A93 20c ultra	.45	.20
566	A93 40c red orange	2.25	1.40
567	A93 45c rose violet	5.50	2.75
568	A93 3b blue gray	2.25	1.25
	Nos. 562-568 (7)	11.25	6.20

Issue date: 20c, Feb. 13.

Arms of Merida and Church

569	A93 5c green	.20	.20
570	A93 10c red	.20	.20
571	A93 15c brown	.25	.20
572	A93 20c ultra	.65	.20
573	A93 50c brown orange	3.00	1.25
574	A93 1b dp gray green	.80	.55
575	A93 5b dull purple	3.00	1.60
	Nos. 569-575 (7)	8.10	4.20

Issue date: 20c, Feb. 2.

Arms of Monagas and Horses

576	A93 5c green	.20	.20
577	A93 10c red	.20	.20
578	A93 15c brown	.30	.20
579	A93 20c ultra	.45	.20
580	A93 40c red orange	2.00	.75
581	A93 45c rose violet	6.25	3.75
582	A93 3b blue gray	2.50	2.00
	Nos. 576-582 (7)	11.90	7.35

Arms of Portuguesa and Forest

583	A93 5c green	.20	.20
584	A93 10c red	.20	.20
585	A93 15c brown	.25	.20
586	A93 20c ultra	.50	.20
587	A93 50c brown org	2.75	1.75
588	A93 1b dp gray grn	.70	.30
589	A93 5b dull purple	3.00	2.00
	Nos. 583-589 (7)	7.60	4.85

Issue date: 5c, 10c, Feb. 2.

Map of Amazonas and Orchid

590	A93 5c green	.50	.20
591	A93 10c red	.50	.20
592	A93 15c brown	1.10	.20
593	A93 20c ultra	3.00	.30
594	A93 40c red orange	3.50	1.00
595	A93 45c rose violet	5.50	2.75
596	A93 3b blue gray	8.00	3.00
	Nos. 590-596 (7)	22.10	7.65

Issue date: Jan. 1954.

Arms of Apure, Horse and Bird

597	A93 5c green	.20	.20
598	A93 10c red	.20	.20
599	A93 15c brown	.35	.20
600	A93 20c ultra	1.75	.20
601	A93 50c brown org	2.25	1.75
602	A93 1b dp gray grn	.75	.65
603	A93 5b dull purple	4.50	2.50
	Nos. 597-603 (7)	10.00	5.70

Issue date: Jan. 1954.

Arms of Barinas, Cow and Horse

604	A93 5c green	.20	.20
605	A93 10c red	.20	.20
606	A93 15c brown	.25	.20
607	A93 20c ultra	1.75	.25
608	A93 50c brown org	2.00	1.25
609	A93 1b dp gray grn	.50	.25
610	A93 5b dull purple	4.50	2.25
	Nos. 604-610 (7)	9.40	4.60

Issue date: Jan. 1954.

Arms of Cojedes and Cattle

611	A93 5c green	.20	.20
612	A93 10c red	.20	.20
613	A93 15c brown	.20	.20
614	A93 20c ultra	.20	.20
615	A93 25c orange brown	.90	.25
616	A93 30c blue	1.40	.40
617	A93 35c purple	1.75	1.10
	Nos. 611-617 (7)	4.85	2.55

Issue date: Dec, 17, 1953.

Arms of Nueva Esparta and Fish

618	A93 5c green	.20	.20
619	A93 10c red	.20	.20
620	A93 15c brown	.45	.20
621	A93 20c ultra	.50	.20
622	A93 40c red orange	2.25	.85
623	A93 45c rose vio	5.50	3.25
624	A93 3b blue gray	2.50	1.75
	Nos. 618-624 (7)	11.60	6.65

Issue date: Jan. 1954.

Arms of Yaracuy and Tropical Foliage

625	A93 5c green	.40	.20
626	A93 10c red	.20	.20
627	A93 15c brown	.30	.20
628	A93 20c ultra	.45	.20
629	A93 25c orange brn	.65	.30
630	A93 30c blue	.75	.20
631	A93 35c purple	1.75	1.10
	Nos. 625-631 (7)	4.50	2.45
	Nos. 464-631 (168)	420.40	180.85

Issue date: Jan. 1954.
See Nos. C338-C553.

Ship Type of 1948-50, Redrawn Coil Stamps
Imprint: "Courvoisier S.A."

1952 Unwmk. Photo. Perf. 11½x12

632	A85 5c green	.65	.20
633	A85 10c car rose	1.10	.20
634	A85 15c gray	3.75	.20
	Nos. 632-634,C554-C556 (6)	9.50	1.20

Juan de Villegas and Cross of Father Yepez — A94

Virgin of Coromoto and Child — A95

1952, Sept. 14 Perf. 11½

635	A94 5c green	.20	.20
636	A94 10c red	.50	.20
637	A94 20c dk gray bl	.80	.25
638	A94 40c dp org	3.75	1.50
639	A94 50c brown	2.00	.85
640	A94 1b violet	3.75	1.00
	Nos. 635-640 (6)	11.00	4.00
	Nos. 635-640,C557-C564 (14)	20.65	8.90

Founding of the city of Barquisimeto by Juan de Villegas, 400th anniv.

1952-53 Perf. 11½x12
Size: 17x26mm

641	A95 1b rose pink	6.00	1.00

Size: 26½x41mm

642	A95 1b rose pink ('53)	4.50	1.00

Size: 36x55mm

643	A95 1b rose pink ('53)	2.00	.75
	Nos. 641-643 (3)	12.50	2.75

300th anniv. of the appearance of the Virgin Mary to a chief of the Coromoto Indians.
Issue date: No. 641, Oct. 6.

Telegraph Stamps Surcharged in Black or Red

Correos
Exposición Objetiva Nacional 1948 - 1952
5c.

1952, Nov. 24 Engr. Perf. 12
Grayish Security Paper

644	5c on 25c car	.25	.20
645	10c on 1b blk (R)	.25	.20

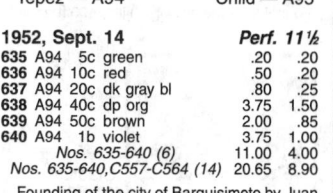

Surcharged

1952, Dec.

646	20c on 25c car	.30	.20
647	30c on 2b ol grn	1.90	1.25
648	40c on 1b blk (R)	.75	.40
649	50c on 3b red org	2.50	1.50
	Nos. 646-649 (4)	5.45	3.35

Post Office, Caracas — A96

Perf. 13x12½

1953-54 Unwmk. Photo.

650	A96 5c green	.20	.20
a.	Bklt. pane of 10		
651	A96 7½c brt green	.35	.25
652	A96 10c rose carmine	.25	.20
a.	Bklt. pane of 10		
653	A96 15c gray	.40	.20
654	A96 20c ultra	.25	.20
655	A96 25c magenta	.40	.20
656	A96 30c blue	1.90	.25

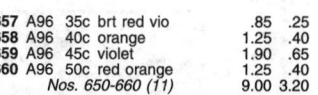

657	A96 35c brt red vio	.85	.25
658	A96 40c orange	1.25	.40
659	A96 45c violet	1.90	.65
660	A96 50c red orange	1.25	.40
	Nos. 650-660 (11)	9.00	3.20

Issued: 20c, 30c, 45c, 3/11; 7½c, 25c, 50c, 6/53; 5c, 10c, 2/54; 15c, 1954.
See Nos. C565-C575, C587-C589.

Type of 1953-54 Inscribed "Republica de Venezuela"

1955

661	A96 5c green	.20	.20
662	A96 10c rose car	.20	.20
663	A96 15c gray	.20	.20
664	A96 20c ultra	.25	.20
665	A96 30c blue	.65	.40
666	A96 35c brt red vio	.65	.20
667	A96 40c orange	1.00	.25
668	A96 45c violet	1.25	.50
	Nos. 661-668 (8)	4.40	2.15
	Nos. 661-668,C597-C606 (18)	10.80	5.40

Arms of Valencia and Industrial Scene — A97

Coat of Arms — A98

1955, Mar. 26 Engr. Perf. 12

669	A97 5c brt grn	.20	.20
670	A97 20c ultra	.40	.20
671	A97 25c reddish brn	.65	.20
672	A97 50c vermilion	1.00	.25
	Nos. 669-672,C590-C596 (11)	4.85	2.40

Founding of Valencia del Rey, 400th anniv.

1955, Dec. 9 Unwmk. Perf. 11½

673	A98 5c green	.30	.20
674	A98 20c ultra	1.00	.20
675	A98 25c rose car	.80	.20
676	A98 50c orange	1.00	.20
	Nos. 673-676,C607-C612 (10)	5.50	2.15

1st Postal Convention, Caracas, 2/9-15/54.

Book and Map of the Americas — A99

Simon Bolivar — A100

1956 Photo. Perf. 11½
Granite Paper

677	A99 5c lt grn & bluish grn	.20	.20
678	A99 10c lil rose & rose vio	.20	.20
679	A99 20c ultra & dk bl	.20	.20
680	A99 25c gray & lil gray	.25	.20
681	A99 30c lt bl & bl	.25	.20
682	A99 40c bis brn & brn	.30	.20
683	A99 50c ver & red brn	.65	.30
684	A99 1b lt pur & vio	1.00	.50
	Nos. 677-684 (8)	3.05	2.00
	Nos. 677-684,C629-C635 (15)	5.55	3.65

Book Festival of the Americas, 11/15-30/56.

Engraved, Center Embossed

1957-58 Unwmk. Perf. 13½

685	A100 5c brt bl grn	.20	.20
686	A100 10c red	.20	.20
687	A100 20c lt slate bl	.40	.20
688	A100 25c rose lake	.40	.20
689	A100 30c vio blue	.50	.20
690	A100 40c red orange	.75	.20
691	A100 50c orange yel	1.00	.50
	Nos. 685-691 (7)	3.45	1.70
	Nos. 685-691,C636-C642 (14)	7.30	3.40

150th anniv. of the Oath of Monte Sacro and the 125th anniv. of the death of Simon Bolivar (1783-1830).
Issued: 10c, 50c, 1958; others, 11/15/57.

Hotel Tamanaco, Caracas A101

1957-58   Engr.   Perf. 13
692 A101 5c green   .20 .20
693 A101 10c carmine   .20 .20
694 A101 15c black   .25 .20
695 A101 20c dark blue   .30 .20
696 A101 25c dp claret   .30 .20
697 A101 30c dp ultra   .50 .20
698 A101 35c purple   .30 .20
699 A101 40c orange   .40 .20
700 A101 45c rose violet   .50 .20
701 A101 50c yellow   .70 .25
702 A101 1b dk slate grn   1.00 .40
     Nos. 692-702 (11)   4.65 2.45
     Nos. 692-702,C643-C657 (26) 12.85 7.00

Issued: 5c, 10c, Oct. 10, 1957; others, 1958.
For surcharge see No. 878.

Main Post Office, Caracas — A102

1958, May 14   Litho.   Perf. 14
703 A102 5c emerald   .20 .20
704 A102 10c rose red   .20 .20
705 A102 15c gray   .20 .20
706 A102 20c lt bl   .20 .20
707 A102 35c red lilac   .20 .20
708 A102 45c brt vio   1.25 .85
709 A102 50c yellow   .30 .20
710 A102 1b lt ol grn   .75 .40
     Nos. 703-710 (8)   3.30 2.45
     Nos. 703-710,C658-C670 (21) 11.65 8.60

See Nos. 748-750, C658-C670, C786-C792.
For surcharges see Nos. 865, C807, C856-C861.

Main Post Office, Caracas A103

1958, Nov. 17   Engr.   Perf. 11½x12
711 A103 5c green   .25 .20
712 A103 10c rose red   .40 .20
713 A103 15c black   .50 .20
     Nos. 711-713,C671-C673 (6) 2.25 1.20

Arms of Merida — A104

1958, Oct. 9   Photo.   Perf. 14x13½
714 A104 5c green   .20 .20
715 A104 10c bright red   .20 .20
716 A104 15c greenish gray   .20 .20
717 A104 20c blue   .20 .20
718 A104 25c magenta   .40 .20
719 A104 30c violet   .20 .20
720 A104 35c light purple   .25 .20
721 A104 40c orange   .60 .20
722 A104 45c deep rose lilac   .30 .20
723 A104 50c bright yellow   .50 .20
724 A104 1b gray green   1.50 .50
     Nos. 714-724 (11)   4.55 2.50
     Nos. 714-724,C674-C689 (27) 12.85 7.15

400th anniversary of the founding of the city of Merida. For surcharge see No. 873.

Arms of Trujillo, Bolivar Monument and Trujillo Hotel — A105

1959, Nov. 17   Unwmk.   Perf. 14
725 A105 5c emerald   .20 .20
726 A105 10c rose   .20 .20
727 A105 15c gray   .20 .20
728 A105 20c blue   .20 .20
729 A105 25c brt pink   .25 .20
730 A105 30c lt ultra   .40 .20
731 A105 35c lt pur   .40 .20
732 A105 45c rose lilac   .50 .25
733 A105 50c yellow   .50 .20
734 A105 1b lt ol grn   1.25 .65
     Nos. 725-734 (10)   4.10 2.50
     Nos. 725-734,C690-C700 (21) 8.75 5.25

Founding of the city of Trujillo, 400th anniv.

Stadium A106

1959 Mar. 10   Litho.   Perf. 13½
735 A106 5c brt grn   .20 .20
736 A106 10c rose pink   .20 .20
737 A106 20c blue   .40 .20
738 A106 30c dk bl   .50 .20
739 A106 50c red lilac   .80 .20
     Nos. 735-739 (5)   2.10 1.00
     Nos. 735-739,C701-C705 (10) 3.70 2.25

8th Central American and Caribbean Games, Caracas, Nov. 29-Dec. 14, 1958.
#735-739 exist imperf. Value, pair $25.

Stamp of 1859, Mailman and José Ignacio Paz Castillo A107

Stamp of 1859 and: 50c, Mailman on horseback and Jacinto Gutierrez. 1b, Plane, train and Miguel Herrera.

1959, Sept. 15   Engr.   Perf. 13½x14
740 A107 25c org yel   .30 .20
741 A107 50c blue   .50 .20
742 A107 1b rose red   1.00 .40
     Nos. 740-742,C706-C708 (6) 3.45 1.70

Centenary of Venezuelan postage stamps.

> **Catalogue values for unused stamps in this section, from this point to the end of the section, are for Never Hinged items.**

Alexander von Humboldt — A108

Newspaper, 1808, and View of Caracas, 1958 — A109

1960, Feb. 9   Unwmk.   Perf. 13½
743 A108 5c grn & yel grn   .35 .25
744 A108 30c vio bl & vio   .95 .25
745 A108 40c org & brn org   1.25 .40
     Nos. 743-745,C709-C711 (6) 5.25 1.65

Centenary of the death of Alexander von Humboldt, German naturalist and geographer.

Post Office Type of 1958

1960, July   Litho.   Perf. 14
748 A102 25c yellow   .20 .20
749 A102 30c light blue   .25 .20
750 A102 40c fawn   .55 .20
     Nos. 748-750 (3)   1.00 .60

1960, June 6   Litho.   Perf. 14
751 A109 10c rose & blk   .40 .20
752 A109 20c lt blue & blk   .65 .20
753 A109 35c lilac & blk   1.00 .70
     Nos. 751-753,C712-C714 (6) 6.45 2.75

150th anniv. (in 1958) of the 1st Venezuelan newspaper, Gazeta de Caracas.

Agustin Codazzi A110

National Pantheon — A111

1960, June 15   Engr.   Unwmk.
754 A110 5c brt green   .20 .20
755 A110 15c gray   .65 .20
756 A110 20c blue   .50 .20
757 A110 45c purple   .65 .30
     Nos. 754-757,C715-C720 (10) 5.65 2.55

Centenary (in 1959) of the death of Agustin Codazzi, geographer.
For surcharges see Nos. 869, C884.

1960, May 9   Litho.
Pantheon in Bister
758 A111 5c emerald   .20 .20
759 A111 20c brt blue   .50 .20
760 A111 25c light olive   .80 .20
761 A111 30c dull blue   .95 .25
762 A111 40c fawn   1.40 .45
763 A111 45c lilac   1.25 .45
     Nos. 758-763 (6)   5.10 1.75
     Nos. 758-763,C721-C734 (20) 23.20 6.75

For surcharges see Nos. C894-C895.

Andres Eloy Blanco, Poet (1896-1955) A112

1960, May 21   Unwmk.   Perf. 14
Portrait in Black
764 A112 5c emerald   .25 .20
765 A112 30c dull blue   .30 .20
766 A112 50c yellow   .65 .25
     Nos. 764-766,C735-C737 (6) 4.10 1.45

For surcharge see No. C874.

Independence Meeting of April 19, 1810, Led by Miranda — A113

1960, Aug. 19   Litho.   Perf. 13½
Center Multicolored
767 A113 5c brt green   .50 .20
768 A113 20c blue   1.00 .25
769 A113 30c violet blue   1.40 .35
     Nos. 767-769,C738-C740 (6) 6.40 1.80

150th anniversary of Venezuela's Independence.
See Nos. 812-814, C804-C806. For surcharge see No. C893.

Drilling for Oil — A114

1960, Aug. 26   Engr.   Perf. 14
770 A114 5c grn & slate grn   1.75 .65
771 A114 10c dk car & brn   .65 .25
772 A114 15c gray & dull pur   .85 .30
     Nos. 770-772,C741-C743 (6) 5.60 2.10

Issued to publicize Venezuela's oil industry.

Luisa Cáceres de Arismendi A115

Unwmk.
1960, Oct. 21   Litho.   Perf. 14
Center Multicolored
773 A115 20c light blue   1.25 .35
774 A115 25c citron   1.00 .40
775 A115 30c dull blue   1.40 .50
     Nos. 773-774,C744-C746 (5) 6.70 2.35

Death of Luisa Càceres de Arismendi, 94th anniv.

José Antonio Anzoategui — A116

1960, Oct. 29   Engr.
776 A116 5c emerald & gray ol .30 .20
777 A116 15c ol gray & dl vio .45 .20
778 A116 20c blue & gray vio   .60 .20
     Nos. 776-778,C747-C749 (6) 3.20 1.50

140th anniversary (in 1959) of the death of General José Antonio Anzoategui.

Antonio José de Sucre — A117

Unwmk.
1960, Nov. 18   Litho.   Perf. 14
Center Multicolored
779 A117 10c deep rose   .40 .20
780 A117 15c gray brown   .50 .25
781 A117 20c blue   .70 .35
     Nos. 779-781,C750-C752 (6) 4.85 2.05

130th anniversary of the death of General Antonio José de Sucre.

Bolivar Peak, Merida — A118

Designs: 15c, Caroni Falls, Bolivar. 35c, Cuacharo caves, Monagas.

1960, Mar. 22   **Perf. 14**
782 A118 5c emerald & grn   1.00 1.00
783 A118 15c gray & dk gray   3.25 3.25
784 A118 35c rose lil & lil   2.75 2.75
   Nos. 782-784,C753-C755 (6) 12.70 12.70

Buildings and People — A119

1961   **Litho.**   **Unwmk.**
Building in Orange
785 A119 5c emerald   .20 .20
786 A119 10c carmine   .20 .20
787 A119 15c gray   .20 .20
788 A119 20c blue   .20 .20
789 A119 25c lt red brown   .25 .20
790 A119 30c dull blue   .20 .20
791 A119 35c red lilac   .35 .20
792 A119 40c fawn   .55 .25
793 A119 45c brt violet   .70 .30
794 A119 50c yellow   .55 .20
   Nos. 785-794 (10)   3.45 2.15

1960 national census. See #C756-C770. For surcharge see No. 866.

Rafael Maria Baralt — A120

Yellow-headed Parrot — A121

1961, Mar. 11   **Engr.**   **Perf. 14**
795 A120 5c grn & slate grn   .20 .20
796 A120 15c gray & dull red brn .40 .20
797 A120 35c rose lilac & lt vio .60 .20
   Nos. 795-797,C771-C773 (6) 3.55 1.60

Rafael Maria Baralt, statesman, death cent.

1961, Sept. 6   **Litho.**   **Perf. 14½**
798 A121 30c shown   .75 .40
799 A121 40c Snowy egret   1.10 .40
800 A121 50c Scarlet ibis   1.90 .70
   Nos. 798-800,C776-C778 (6) 6.40 3.30

Juan J. Aguerrevere — A122

1961, Oct. 21   **Unwmk.**   **Perf. 14**
801 A122 25c dark blue   .25 .20
 a. Souvenir sheet, imperf.   1.40 1.40

Centenary of the founding of the Engineering Society of Venezuela, Oct. 28, 1861.
No. 801a sold for 1b.
No. 801a exists with "Valor: Bs 1,00" omitted at lower left corner. Value, $7.

Battle of Carabobo, 1821 — A123

1961, Dec. 1   **Perf. 14**
Center Multicolored
802 A123 5c emerald & blk   .20 .20
803 A123 40c brown & blk   .60 .25
   Nos. 802-803,C779-C784 (8) 15.05 4.90

140th anniversary of Battle of Carabobo.

Oncidium Papilio Lindl. — A124

Orchids: 10c, Caularthron bilamellatum. 20c, Stanhopea Wardii Lodd. 25c, Catasetum pileatum. 30c, Masdevallia tovarensis. 35c, Epidendrum Stamfordianum Batem, horiz. 50c, Epidendrum atropurpureum Willd. 3b, Oncidium falcipetalum Lindl.

Perf. 14x13½, 13½x14
1962, May 30   **Litho.**   **Unwmk.**
Orchids in Natural Colors
804 A124 5c black & orange   .20   .20
805 A124 10c blk & brt grnsh
        bl   .20   .20
806 A124 20c black & yel grn   .50   .20
807 A124 25c black & lt blue   .70   .20
808 A124 30c black & olive   .80   .20
809 A124 35c black & yellow   .90   .25
810 A124 50c black & gray   1.00   .30
811 A124 3b black & vio   6.00 2.50
   Nos. 804-811 (8)   10.30 4.05
   Nos. 804-811,C794-C803 (18) 25.30 9.30

For surcharges see Nos. 872, C885-C887.

Independence Type of 1960
Signing Declaration of Independence.

1962, June 11   **Perf. 13½**
Center Multicolored
812 A113 5c emerald   .25 .20
813 A113 20c blue   .45 .20
814 A113 25c yellow   .70 .30
 a. Souv. sheet, #812-814, imperf 3.25 3.25
   Nos. 812-814,C804-C806 (6) 5.70 1.95

150th anniv. of the Venezuelan Declaration of Independence, July 5, 1811.
No. 814a sold for 1.50b.

Shot Put A125

1962, Nov. 30   **Litho.**   **Perf. 13x14**
815 A125 5c shown   .20 .20
816 A125 10c Soccer   .20 .20
817 A125 25c Swimming   .30 .20
 a. Souv. sheet, #815-817, imperf 2.75 2.75
   Nos. 815-817,C808-C810 (6) 3.20 1.80

1st Natl. Games, Caracas, 1961. The stamps are arranged so that two pale colored edges of each stamp join to make a border around blocks of four.
No. 817a sold for 1.40b.
For surcharge see No. C899.

Vermilion Cardinal — A126

Malaria Eradication Emblem, Mosquito and Map — A127

Birds: 10c, Great kiskadee. 20c, Glossy black thrush. 25c, Collared trogons. 30c, Swallow tanager. 40c, Long-tailed sylph. 3b, Black-necked stilt.

1962, Dec. 14   **Perf. 14x13½**
Birds in Natural Colors, Black Inscription
818 A126 5c brt yellow grn   .20 .20
819 A126 10c violet blue   .20 .20
820 A126 20c lilac rose   .40 .20
821 A126 25c dull brown   .50 .20
822 A126 30c lemon   .60 .20
823 A126 40c lilac   .80 .30
824 A126 3b fawn   5.00 3.00
   Nos. 818-824 (7)   7.70 4.30
   Nos. 818-824,C811-C818 (15) 22.40 10.60

For surcharges see Nos. 868, C880-C882.

Lithographed and Embossed
Perf. 13½x14
1962, Dec. 20   **Wmk. 346**
825 A127 50c brown & black   .65 .25

WHO drive to eradicate malaria. See Nos. C819-C819a.

White-tailed Deer A128

Designs: 10c, Collared peccary. 35c, Collared titi (monkey). 50c, Giant Brazilian otter. 1b, Puma. 3b, Capybara.

Perf. 13½x14
1963, Mar. 13   **Litho.**   **Unwmk.**
Multicolored Center; Black Inscriptions
826 A128 5c green   .20 .20
827 A128 10c orange   .20 .20
828 A128 35c red lilac   .25 .20
829 A128 50c blue   .55 .25
830 A128 1b rose brown   2.75 1.40
831 A128 3b yellow   5.50 3.50
   Nos. 826-831 (6)   9.45 5.75
   Nos. 826-831,C820-C825 (12) 23.75 11.00

For surcharges see #870-871, C888-C889.

Fisherman and Map of Venezuela A129

Cathedral of Bocono A130

1963, Mar. 21
832 A129 25c pink & ultra   .25 .20
   Nos. 832,C826-C827 (3) 1.30 .90

FAO "Freedom from Hunger" campaign.

1963, May 30   **Wmk. 346**
833 A130 50c brn, red & grn, buff .55 .20

400th anniversary of the founding of Bocono. See No. C828.

St. Peter's Basilica, Rome A131

1963, June 11   **Perf. 14x13½**
834 A131 35c dk bl, brn & buff   .45 .20
835 A131 45c dk grn, red brn &
        buff   .50 .20
   Nos. 834-835,C829-C830 (4) 3.15 1.10

Vatican II, the 21st Ecumenical Council of the Roman Catholic Church.

National Flag — A132

1963, July 29 **Unwmk.** **Perf. 14**
836 A132 30c gray, red, yel & bl .30 .20

Centenary of Venezuela's flag and coat of arms. See No. C831.

Lake Maracaibo Bridge — A133

Map, Soldier and Emblem — A134

Perf. 13½x14
1963, Aug. 24   **Wmk. 346**
837 A133 30c blue & brown   .35 .20
838 A133 35c bluish grn & brn .40 .20
839 A133 80c blue grn & brn   .85 .35
   Nos. 837-839,C832-C834 (6) 5.10 2.00

Opening of bridge over Lake Maracaibo. For surcharge see No. 875.

1963, Sept. 10   **Unwmk.**
840 A134 50c red, bl & grn, buff .50 .20

25th anniversary of the armed forces. See No. C835. For surcharge see No. C862.

Dag Hammarskjold and World Map — A135

Perf. 14x13½
1963, Sept. 25   **Unwmk.**
841 A135 25c dk bl, bl grn &
        ocher   .25 .20
842 A135 55c grn, grnsh bl &
        ocher   1.00 .30
   Nos. 841-842,C836-C837 (4) 3.45 1.45

"1st" anniv. of the death of Dag Hammarskjold, Secretary General of the UN, 1953-61.
See #C837a. For surcharges see #867, C875-C876.

Dr. Luis
Razetti — A136

Dr. Francisco A.
Risquez — A137

1963, Oct. 10   **Litho.**
843 A136 35c blue, ocher & brn   .45   .20
844 A136 45c mag, ocher & brn   .65   .20
   Nos. 843-844,C838-C839 (4)   4.00 1.75
Dr. Luis Razetti, physician, birth cent.

1963, Dec. 31   **Perf. 11½x12**
Design: 20c, Dr. Carlos J. Bello.
845 A137 15c multicolored   .20   .20
846 A137 20c multicolored   .30   .20
   Nos. 845-846,C840-C841 (4)   2.00 1.10
Cent. of the Intl. Red Cross.

Oil Field
Workers — A138

Pedro
Gual — A139

10c, Oil refinery. 15c Crane & building construction. 30c, Cactus, train & truck. 40c, Tractor.

1964, Feb. 5   **Litho.**   **Perf. 14x13½**
847 A138 5c multi   .20   .20
848 A138 10c multi   .20   .20
849 A138 15c multi   .25   .20
850 A138 30c multi   .45   .25
851 A138 40c multi   .50   .25
   Nos. 847-851 (5)   1.60 1.10
   Nos. 847-851,C842-C846 (10)   2.90 2.10
Department of Industrial Development, cent.

1964, Mar. 20   **Unwmk.**   **Perf. 14**
852 A139 40c lt olive green   .55   .20
853 A139 50c lt red brown   .70   .25
   Nos. 852-853,C847-C848 (4)   3.00 1.05
Pedro Gual (1784-1862), statesman.

Carlos
Arvelo — A140

1964, Apr. 17   **Engr.**   **Perf. 14x13½**
854 A140 1b dull bl & gray   1.40 .45
Centenary of the death of Dr. Carlos Arvelo (1784-1862), chief physician of Bolivar's revolutionary army, director of Caracas Hospital, rector of Central University and professor of pathology.
For surcharge see No. 874.

Foundry
Ladle and
Molds
A141

1964, May 22   **Perf. 14x13½**
855 A141 20c multicolored   .30   .20
856 A141 50c multicolored   .55   .20
   Nos. 855-856,C849-C850 (4)   3.00 1.15
Orinoco Steel Mills.

Romulo Gallegos,
Novelist, 80th
Birthday — A142

      Unwmk.
1964, Aug. 3   **Litho.**   **Perf. 12**
857 A142 5c dk & lt green   .20   .20
858 A142 10c bl & pale bl   .20   .20
859 A142 15c dk & lt red lil   .30   .20
   Nos. 857-859,C852-C854 (6)   2.35 1.25

Angel Falls,
Bolivar State
A143

Tourist Publicity: 10c, Tropical landscape, Sucre State. 15c, San Juan Peaks, Guarico. 30c, Net fishermen, Anzoategui. 40c, Mountaineer, Merida.

1964, Oct. 22   **Perf. 13½x14**
860 A143 5c multi   .20   .20
861 A143 10c multi   .20   .20
862 A143 15c multi   .20   .20
863 A143 30c multi   .40   .20
864 A143 40c multi   .60   .20
   Nos. 860-864 (5)   1.60 1.00

Issues of 1958-64
Surcharged in
Black, Dark Blue or
Lilac

1965
865 A102 5c on 1b (#710)   .40   .20
866 A119 10c on 45c (#793)   .20   .20
867 A135 15c on 55c (#842)   .20   .20
868 A126 20c on 3b (#824)   .20   .20
869 A110 25c on 45c (#757)
              (DB)   .20   .20
870 A128 25c on 1b (#830)   .25   .20
871 A128 25c on 3b (#831)   .30   .20
872 A124 25c on 3b (#811) (L)   .20   .20
873 A104 30c on 1b (#724)   .25   .20
874 A140 40c on 1b (#854)   .60   .20
875 A133 60c on 80c (#839)   .75   .25
   Nos. 865-875 (11)   3.55 2.25
Lines of surcharge arranged variously; old denomination obliterated with bars on Nos. 867, 870-872. See Nos. C856-C899.

Revenue Stamps
of 1947
Surcharged in
Red or Black

Imprint: "American Bank Note Co."
1965 Engr. Perf. 12, 13½ (No. 882)
876 R1 5c on 5c emerald   .20   .20
877 R1 5c on 20c red brn   .20   .20
878 R1 10c on 10c brn ol   .20   .20
879 R1 15c on 40c grn   .20   .20

---

880 R1 20c on 3b dk bl (R)   .30   .20
881 R1 25c on 5b vio bl (R)   .60   .25
882 R1 25c on 5b vio bl (R) (Imprint: "Bundesdruck-
     erei Berlin")   .30   .20
883 R1 60c on 3b dk bl (R)   .75   .25
   Nos. 876-883 (8)   2.75 1.70
Type R1 is illustrated above No. 401.

John F.
Kennedy
and
Alliance
for
Progress
Emblem
A144

1965, Aug. 20   **Photo.**   **Perf. 12x11½**
884 A144 20c gray   .35   .20
885 A144 40c bright lilac   .55   .20
   Nos. 884-885 (2)   .90   .40

Map of
Venezuela and
Guiana by
Codazzi,
1840 — A145

Maps of Venezuela and Guiana: 15c, by Juan M. Restrepo, 1827, horiz. 40c, by L. de Surville, 1778.

1965, Nov. 5   **Litho.**   **Perf. 13½**
886 A145 5c multi   .20   .20
887 A145 15c multi   .30   .20
888 A145 40c multi   .55   .20
  a. Souv. sheet, #886-888, imperf   6.00 6.00
   Nos. 886-888,C905-C907 (6)   2.65 1.30
Issued to publicize Venezuela's claim to part of British Guiana.
No. 888a sold for 85c.

Protesilaus
Leucones — A146

1966, Jan. 25 Litho. Perf. 13½x14
Various Butterflies in Natural Colors
      Black Inscriptions
889 A146 20c lt olive grn   .30   .20
890 A146 30c lt yellow grn   .45   .20
891 A146 50c yellow   .70   .25
   Nos. 889-891,C915-C917 (6)   4.55 1.85

Ship and
Map of
Atlantic
Ocean
A147

1966, Mar. 10   **Litho.**   **Perf. 13½x14**
892 A147 60c brown, bl & blk   1.40 .45
Bicentenary of the first maritime mail.

"El Carite" Dance — A148

Various Folk Dances

      Perf. 14x13½
1966, Apr. 5   **Litho.**   **Unwmk.**
893 A148 5c gray & multi   .20   .20
894 A148 10c orange & multi   .20   .20
895 A148 15c lemon & multi   .30   .20
896 A148 20c lilac & multi   .40   .20
897 A148 25c brt pink & multi   .55   .20
898 A148 35c yel grn & multi   .60   .20
   Nos. 893-898,C919-C924 (12)   9.00 3.60

Type of Air Post Stamps and

Arturo
Michelena,
Self-portrait
A149

Paintings: 1b, Penthesileia, battle scene. 1.05b, The Red Cloak.

    Perf. 12½x12, 12x12½
1966, May 12   **Litho.**   **Unwmk.**
899 A149 95c sepia & buff   .80   .60
900 AP74 1b multi   1.00   .60
901 AP74 1.05b multi   1.25   .60
   Nos. 899-901,C927-C929 (6)   6.30 3.30
Arturo Michelena (1863-1898), painter. Miniature sheets of 12 exist.

Construction
Worker and Map
of
Americas — A150

Designs: 20c, as 10c. 30c, 65c, Labor monument. 35c, Machinery worker and map of Venezuela. 50c, Automobile assembly line.

1966, July 6   **Perf. 14x13½**
902 A150 10c yellow & blk   .20   .20
903 A150 20c lt grnsh bl & blk   .25   .20
904 A150 30c lt blue & vio   .25   .20
905 A150 35c lemon & olive   .35   .20
906 A150 50c brt rose & claret   .50   .20
907 A150 65c salmon pink & brn   .65   .30
   Nos. 902-907 (6)   2.20 1.35
2nd Conference of Ministers of Labor of the Organization of American States.

Velvet
Cichlid
A151

1966, Aug. 31   **Litho.**   **Perf. 13½x14**
908 A151 15c shown   .25   .20
909 A151 25c Perch cichlid   .35   .20
910 A151 45c Piranha   .95   .30
   Nos. 908-910,C933-C935 (6)   5.75 1.90

Nativity — A152

Rubén
Dario — A154

Satellite, Radar, Globe, Plane and Ship A153

1966, Dec. 9   Litho.   *Perf. 13½x14*
911   A152   65c violet & blk   .80   .30
Christmas 1966.

1966, Dec. 28   *Perf. 13½x14*
912   A153   45c multi   .65   .25
Ministry of Communications, 30th anniv.

1967   Litho.
913   A154   70c gray bl & dk bl   1.00   .45
Rubén Dario (pen name of Felix Rubén Garcia Sarmiento, 1867-1916), Nicaraguan poet, newspaper correspondent and diplomat.

Old Building and Arms, University of Zulia A155

Perf. 13½x14
1967, Apr. 21   Litho.   Unwmk.
914   A155   80c gold, blk & car   1.00   .45
University of Zulia founding, 75th anniv.

Front Page and Printing Press — A156

1968, June 27   Photo.   *Perf. 14x13½*
915   A156   1.50b emer, blk & brn   1.50   .60
Newspaper Correo del Orinoco, 150th anniv.

Boll Weevil A157

Insect Pests: 20c, Corn borer, vert. 90c, Tobacco caterpillar.

Perf. 14x13½, 13½x14
1968, Aug. 30   Litho.
916   A157   20c multicolored   .30   .20
917   A157   75c olive & multi   1.10   .25
918   A157   90c multicolored   1.60   .35
    Nos. 916-918,C989-C991 (6)   4.25   1.40

Guayana Substation A158

Designs: 45c, Guaira River Dam, horiz. 50c, Macagua Dam and power plant, horiz. 80c, Guri River Dam and power plant.

1968, Nov. 8   Litho.
919   A158   15c fawn & multi   .20   .20
920   A158   45c dl yel & multi   .50   .20
921   A158   50c bl grn & multi   .75   .25
922   A158   80c blue & multi   1.10   .50
    Nos. 919-922 (4)   2.55   1.15
Electrification program.

House and Piggy Bank A159

1968, Dec. 6   Litho.   *Perf. 13½x14*
923   A159   45c blue & multi   .60   .25
National Savings System.

Nursery and Child Planting Tree A160

Designs: 15c, Child planting tree (vert.; this design used as emblem on entire issue). 30c, Waterfall, vert. 45c, Logging. 55c, Fields and village, vert. 75c, Palambra (fish).

Perf. 14x13½, 13½x14
1968, Dec. 19   Litho.
924   A160   15c multicolored   .25   .20
925   A160   20c multicolored   .25   .20
926   A160   30c multicolored   .30   .20
927   A160   45c multicolored   .45   .20
928   A160   55c multicolored   1.00   .30
929   A160   75c multicolored   .70   .20
    Nos. 924-929 (6)   2.95   1.30
    Nos. 924-929,C1000-C1005 (12)   7.05   3.05
Issued to publicize nature conservation.

Colorada Beach, Sucre A161

Designs: 45c, Church of St. Francis of Yare, Miranda. 90c, Stilt houses, Zulia.

1969, Jan. 24   *Perf. 13½x14*
930   A161   15c multicolored   .20   .20
931   A161   45c multicolored   .55   .20
932   A161   90c multicolored   .80   .50
    Nos. 930-932,C1006-C1008 (6)   2.55   1.50
Tourist publicity. For souvenir sheet see No. C1007a.

Bolivar Addressing Congress of Angostura — A162

1969, Feb. 15   Litho.   *Perf. 11*
933   A162   45c multicolored   .60   .25
Sesquicentennial of the Congress of Angostura (Ciudad Bolivar).

Martin Luther King, Jr. — A163

1969, Apr. 1   Litho.   *Perf. 13½*
934   A163   1b bl, red & dk brn   .90   .30
Rev. Dr. Martin Luther King, Jr. (1929-1968), American civil rights leader and recipient of the Nobel Peace Prize, 1964.

Tabebuia A164

Trees: 65c, Erythrina poeppigiana. 90c, Platymiscium.

1969, May 30   Litho.   *Perf. 13½x14*
935   A164   50c multicolored   .55   .20
936   A164   65c gray & multi   .75   .25
937   A164   90c pink & multi   1.10   .40
    Nos. 935-937,C1009-C1011 (6)   3.25   1.45
Issued to publicize nature conservation.

Still Life with Pheasant, by Rojas — A165

Paintings by Cristobal Rojas (1858-1890): 25c, On the Balcony, vert. 45c, The Christening. 50c, The Empty Place (family). 60c, The Tavern. 1b, Man's Arm, vert.

Perf. 14x13½, 13½x14
1969, June 27   Litho.   Unwmk.
    Size: 32x42mm, 42x32mm
938   A165   25c gold & multi   .25   .20
939   A165   35c gold & multi   .45   .20
940   A165   45c gold & multi   .75   .25
941   A165   50c gold & multi   .85   .30
942   A165   60c gold & multi   1.10   .35

     Perf. 11
    Size: 26x53mm
943   A165   1b gold & multi   1.60   .60
    Nos. 938-943 (6)   5.00   1.90

ILO Emblem A166

1969, July 28   *Perf. 13½*
944   A166   2.50b fawn & blk   2.00   1.25
50th anniv. of the ILO.

Charter and Coat of Arms A167

Industrial Complex A168

1969, Aug. 26   Litho.   *Perf. 13½*
945   A167   45c ultra & multi   .65   .25
946   A168   1b multicolored   1.00   .35
Industrial development.

House with Arcade, Carora — A169

Designs: 25c, Ruins of Pastora Church. 55c, Chapel of the Cross. 65c, House of Culture.

1969, Sept. 8   *Perf. 13x14½*
947   A169   20c multicolored   .20   .20
948   A169   25c multicolored   .30   .20
949   A169   55c multicolored   .75   .25
950   A169   65c multicolored   1.00   .35
    Nos. 947-950 (4)   2.25   1.00
400th anniversary of city of Carora.

Simon Bolivar in Madrid — A170

Designs: 10c, Bolivar's wedding, Madrid, 1802, horiz. 35c, Bolivar monument. Madrid.

Perf. 13½x14, 14x13½
1969, Oct. 28   Litho.
951   A170   10c multicolored   .20   .20
952   A170   15c brn red & blk   .30   .20
953   A170   35c multicolored   .40   .20
   a.   Souvenir sheet of 2   2.00   2.00
    Nos. 951-953 (3)   .90   .60
Bolivar's sojourn in Spain. No. 953a contains 2 imperf. stamps similar to Nos. 952-953 with simulated perforation. Sold for 75c.

"Birds in the Woods" — A171

Design: 45c, "Children in Summer Camp." Both designs are after children's paintings.

1969, Dec. 12   Litho.   *Perf. 12½*
954   A171   5c emerald & multi   .20   .20
955   A171   45c red & multi   .65   .30
Issued for Children's Day.

Map of Great Colombia A172

1969, Dec. 16   Litho.   Perf. 11½
956 A172 45c multicolored   .55 .20
150th anniversary of the founding of the State of Great Colombia.

St. Anthony's, Clarines A173

Churches: 30c, Church of the Conception, Caroni. 40c, St. Michael's, Burbusay. 45c, St. Anthony's, Maturin. 75c, St. Nicholas, Moruy. 1b, Coro Cathedral.

1970, Jan. 15   Perf. 14
957 A173 10c pink & multi   .20 .20
958 A173 30c emerald & multi   .25 .20
959 A173 40c yellow & multi   .55 .20
960 A173 45c gray bl & multi   .75 .25
 a.   Souvenir sheet of 1, imperf.   1.50 1.50
961 A173 75c yellow & multi   1.00 .35
962 A173 1b orange & multi   1.25 .45
      Nos. 957-962 (6)   4.00 1.65
Colonial architecture.
No. 960a sold for 75c.

A174

Design: Seven Hills of Valera.

1970, Feb. 13   Litho.   Perf. 13x14½
963 A174 95c multicolored   1.10 .35
Sesquicentennial of the city of Valera.

1970, July 29   Litho.   Perf. 14x13½
Flowers: 20c, Monochaetum Humboldtianum. 25c, Symbolanthus vasculosis. 45c, Cavedishia splendens. 1b, Befaria glauca.
964 A175 20c multicolored   .30 .20
965 A175 25c multicolored   .60 .20
966 A175 45c multicolored   .75 .30
967 A175 1b multicolored   1.10 .45
      Nos. 964-967,C1049-C1052 (8)   5.60 2.15

A175

Battle of Boyaca, by Martin Tovar y Tovar A176

1970, Aug. 7   Perf. 13½x14
968 A176 30c multicolored   .35 .20
150th anniversary of Battle of Boyaca.

Our Lady of Belén de San Mateo — A177

Designs: 35c, Pastoral Cross of Archbishop Silvestre Guevera y Lira, 1867. 40c, Our Lady of Valle. 90c, Virgin of Chiquinquira. 1b, Our Lady of Socorro de Valencia.

1970, Sept. 1   Perf. 14x13½
969 A177 35c gray & multi   .45 .20
970 A177 40c gray & multi   .55 .20
971 A177 60c gray & multi   .80 .30
 a.   Souvenir sheet of 1, imperf.   1.40 1.40
972 A177 90c gray & multi   .95 .40
973 A177 1b gray & multi   1.25 .50
      Nos. 969-973 (5)   4.00 1.60
The designs are from sculptures and paintings in various Venezuelan churches.
No. 971a sold for 75c.

Venezuela No. 22 and EXFILCA Emblem — A178

Designs: 20c, EXFILCA emblem and flags of participating nations, vert. 70c, Venezuela No. C13 and EXFILCA emblem, vert.

1970, Nov. 28   Litho.   Perf. 11
974 A178 20c yellow & multi   .30 .20
975 A178 25c dk blue & multi   .35 .20
976 A178 70c brown & multi   .75 .30
 a.   Souvenir sheet of 1, imperf.   1.40 1.40
      Nos. 974-976 (3)   1.40 .70
EXFILCA 70, 2nd Interamerican Philatelic Exhibition, Caracas, Nov. 27-Dec. 6. No. 976a is a hexagon with each side 50mm long. Sold for 85c.

Guardian Angel, by Juan Pedro Lopez — A179

1970, Dec. 1   Litho.   Perf. 14½x13½
977 A179 45c dull yellow & multi   .55 .25
Christmas 1970.

Jet and 1920 Plane A180

1970, Dec. 10   Perf. 13x14
978 A180 5c blue & multi   .25 .20
Venezuelan Air Force, 50th anniversary.

Question Mark Full of Citizens — A181

1971, Apr. 30   Litho.   Perf. 14x13½
Light Green, Red & Black
979 Block of 4   2.50 1.40
 a.   A181 30c frame L & T   .60 .25
 b.   A181 30c frame T & R   .60 .25
 c.   A181 30c frame L & B   .60 .25
 d.   A181 30c frame B & R   .60 .25
National Census, 1971. Sheet of 20 contains 5 No. 979 and 5 blocks of 4 labels. See No. C1054.

Battle of Carabobo A182

1971, June 21   Perf. 13½x14
980 A182 2b blue & multi   1.75 1.00
Sesquicentennial of Battle of Carabobo.

Map of Federal District — A183

State maps. 25c, 55c, 85c, 90c, vert.

1971   Litho.   Perf. 13½x14, 14x13½
981 A183 5c shown   .20 .20
982 A183 15c Monagas   .20 .20
983 A183 20c Nueva Esparta   .20 .20
984 A183 25c Portuguesa   .20 .20
985 A183 45c Sucre   .25 .20
986 A183 55c Tachira   .35 .20
987 A183 65c Trujillo   .45 .20
988 A183 75c Yaracuy   .55 .30
989 A183 85c Zulia   .70 .30
990 A183 90c Amazonas   1.25 .30
991 A183 1b Federal Dependencies   1.40 .55
      Nos. 981-991 (11)   5.75 2.85
      Nos. 981-991,C1035-C1048 (25)   14.65 6.85
Issued: 5c, 7/15; 15c, 20c, 8/16; 25c, 45c, 9/15; 55c, 65c, 10/15; 75c, 85c, 11/15; 90c, 1b, 12/15.

Madonna and Child A184

Luis Daniel Beauperthuy A185

Design: #993, Madonna & Jesus in manger.

1971, Dec. 1   Perf. 11
992 A184 25c multicolored   .30 .20
993 A184 25c multicolored   .30 .20
 a.   Pair, #992-993   .60 .50
Christmas 1971. Printed checkerwise.

1971, Dec. 10   Perf. 14x13½
994 A185 1b vio bl & multi   1.00 .50
Dr. Luis Daniel Beauperthuy, scientist.

Globe in Heart Shape — A186

Flags of Americas and Arms of Venezuela A187

1972, Apr. 7   Litho.   Perf. 14x13½
995 A186 1b red, ultra & blk   .75 .45
"Your heart is your health," World Health Day 1972.

1972, May 16   Litho.   Perf. 14x13½
Designs: 4b, Venezuelan flag. 5b, National anthem. 10b, Araguaney, national tree. 15b, Map, North and South America. All show flags of American nations in background.
996 A187 3b multicolored   3.50 1.00
997 A187 4b multicolored   3.75 1.75
998 A187 5b multicolored   4.25 2.25
999 A187 10b multicolored   8.50 3.00
1000 A187 15b multicolored   12.50 4.25
      Nos. 996-1000 (5)   32.50 12.25
"Venezuela in America."

Parque Central Complex A188

#1002, Front view ("Parque Central" on top). #1003, Side view ("Parque Central" at right).

1972, July 25   Perf. 11½
1001 A188 30c yellow & multi   .20 .20
1002 A188 30c blue & multi   .20 .20
1003 A188 30c red & multi   .20 .20
 a.   Strip of 3, #1001-1003   1.10 1.10
Completion of "Parque Central" middle-income housing project, Caracas.

Mahatma Gandhi — A189

1972, Oct. 2   Litho.   Perf. 13½x14
1004 A189 60c multicolored   .75 .40
103rd birthday of Mohandas K. Gandhi (1869-1948), leader in India's fight for independence, advocate of non-violence.

Children Playing Music — A190

Christmas: #1006, Children roller skating.

1972, Dec. 5   Litho.   Perf. 13½x14
1005 30c multicolored   .20 .20
1006 30c multicolored   .20 .20
 a.   A190 Pair, #1005-1006   .55 .55

Indigo
Snake
A191

Snake: 15c, South American chicken snake.
25c, Venezuelan lance-head. 30c, Coral
snake. 60c, Casabel rattlesnake. 1b, Boa
constrictor.

1972, Dec. 15   Litho.   Perf. 13½x14
1007	A191	10c	black & multi	.35	.20
1008	A191	15c	black & multi	.35	.20
1009	A191	25c	black & multi	.55	.20
1010	A191	30c	black & multi	.65	.20
1011	A191	60c	black & multi	1.00	.30
1012	A191	1b	black & multi	1.60	.45
	Nos. 1007-1012 (6)			4.50	1.55

Copernicus — A192

Sun — A193

Designs: 5c, Model of solarcentric system.
15c, Copernicus' book "De Revolutionibus."

1973, Feb. 19   Litho.   Perf. 13½x14
1013	5c multicolored	.20	.20
1014	10c multicolored	.25	.20
1015	15c multicolored	.35	.20
a.	A192 Strip of 3, #1013-1015	.90	.90

1973   Litho.   Perf. 13½
Designs: Planetary system.

Size: 26½x29mm
1016	A193	5c shown	.20	.20
1017	A193	5c Earth	.20	.20
1018	A193	20c Mars	.45	.20
1019	A193	20c Saturn	.30	.20
1020	A193	30c Asteroids	.35	.20
1021	A193	40c Neptune	.45	.20
1022	A193	50c Venus	.60	.30
1023	A193	60c Jupiter	.75	.35
1024	A193	75c Uranus	.90	.45
1025	A193	90c Pluto	1.10	.50
1026	A193	90c Moon	1.25	.60
1027	A193	1b Mercury	1.50	.75

Size: 27x55mm
Perf. 12
1028	A193	10c Orbits and Saturn	.20	.20
1029	A193	15c Sun, Mercury, Venus, Earth	.30	.20
1030	A193	15c Jupiter, Uranus, Neptune, Pluto	.35	.20
a.		Strip of 3, #1028-1030	.90	.90
		Nos. 1016-1030 (15)	8.90	4.75

10th anniversary of Humboldt Planetarium.
No. 1030a has continuous design showing
solar system.
Issue dates: Nos. 1016, 1018, 1021, 1023-
1025, Mar. 15; others Mar. 30.

OAS Emblem, Map of
Americas — A194

1973, Apr. 30   Litho.   Perf. 13½x14
1031	A194 60c multicolored	.45	.25

Organization of American States, 25th anniv.

José Antonio
Paez — A195

Street of the
Lancers, Puerto
Cabello — A196

Designs: 10c, Paez in uniform. 30c, Paez
and horse, from old print. 2b, Paez at Battle of
Centauro, horiz. 10c, 2b are after contemporary paintings.

1973   Perf. 14x13½, 13½x14
1032	A195	10c gold & multi	.20	.20
1033	A195	30c red, blk & gold	.25	.20
1034	A195	50c bl, vio bl & dk brn	.45	.25
1035	A196	1b multicolored	.90	.45
1036	A195	2b gold & multi	1.50	.90
		Nos. 1032-1036 (5)	3.30	2.00

Gen. José Antonio Paez (1790-1873),
leader in War of Independence, President of
Venezuela. The 1b for the sesquicentenary of
the fall of Puerto Cabello.
Issue dates: Nos. 1033-1034, May 6; Nos.
1032, 1036, June 13; No. 1035, Nov. 8.

José P. Padilla, Mariano Montilla,
Manuel Manrique — A197

1b, Naval battle. 2b, Line-up for naval battle.

1973, July 27   Litho.   Perf. 12½
1037	A197	50c multicolored	.35	.20
1038	A197	1b multicolored	.75	.35
1039	A197	2b multicolored	1.50	.75
		Nos. 1037-1039 (3)	2.60	1.30

150th anniv. of the Battle of Maracaibo.

Bishop Ramos de
Lora — A198

Plane, Ship,
Margarita
Island — A199

1973, Aug. 1   Photo.   Perf. 14x13½
1040	A198 75c gold & dk brn	.60	.25

Sesquicentennial of the birth of Ramos de
Lora (1722-1790), first Bishop of Merida de
Maracaibo and founder of the Colegio
Seminario, the forerunner of the University of
the Andes.

1973, Sept. 8   Litho.   Perf. 14x13½
1041	A199 5c multicolored	.20	.20

Establishment of Margarita Island as a free
port.

Map of Golden Road and
Waterfall — A200

Designs (Road Map and): 10c, Scarlet
macaw. 20c, Church ruins. 50c, 60c, Indian
mountain sanctuary. 90c, Colonial church. 1b,
Flags of Venezuela and Brazil.

1973, Oct. 1   Litho.   Perf. 13
1042	A200	5c black & multi	.20	.20
1043	A200	10c black & multi	.20	.20
1044	A200	20c black & multi	.30	.20
1045	A200	50c black & multi	.70	.25
1046	A200	60c black & multi	.70	.25
1047	A200	90c black & multi	.95	.30
1048	A200	1b black & multi	1.25	.45
		Nos. 1042-1048 (7)	4.30	1.85

Completion of the Golden Road from Santa
Elena de Uairen, Brazil, to El Dorado,
Venezuela.
Issued: 50c, 60c, Oct. 30; others Oct. 1.

Gen. Paez Dam
and Power
Station — A201

1973, Oct. 14   Perf. 14x13½
1049	A201 30c multicolored	.30	.20

Opening of the Gen. José Antonio Paez
Dam and Power Station.

Child on Slide — A202

Designs: No. 1051, Fairytale animals. No.
1052, Children's book. No. 1053, Children disembarking from plane for vacation.

1973, Dec. 4   Litho.   Perf. 12
1050	A202	10c multicolored	.25	.20
1051	A202	10c multicolored	.25	.20
1052	A202	10c multicolored	.25	.20
1053	A202	10c multicolored	.25	.20
		Nos. 1050-1053 (4)	1.00	.80

Children's Foundation Festival.

King Following Star — A203

Christmas: No. 1055, Two Kings.

1973, Dec. 5   Litho.   Perf. 14x13½
1054	30c multicolored	.35	.20
1055	30c multicolored	.35	.20
a.	A203 Pair, #1054-1055	.90	.90

Regional
Map of
Venezuela
A204

1973, Dec. 13   Perf. 13½x14
1056	A204 25c multicolored	.30	.20

Introduction of regionalization.

Handicraft
A205

Designs: 35c, Industrial park. 45c, Cog
wheels and chimney.

1973, Dec. 18   Perf. 14x13½
1057	A205	15c blue & multi	.20	.20
1058	A205	35c multicolored	.30	.20
1059	A205	45c yellow & multi	.50	.20
		Nos. 1057-1059 (3)	1.00	.60

Progress in Venezuela and jobs for the
handicapped.

Map of Carupano and
Revelers — A206

1974, Feb. 22   Perf. 13½x14
1060	A206 5c multicolored	.25	.20

10th anniversary of Carupano Carnival.

Congress
Emblem — A207

1974, May 20   Litho.   Perf. 13½
1061	A207 50c multicolored	.50	.20

9th Venezuelan Engineering Congress,
Maracaibo, May 19-25.

Waves
and
"M"
A208

Designs: Under-water photographs of deepsea fish and marine life.

1974, June 20   Litho.   Perf. 12½
1062	A208	15c multicolored	.40	.20
1063	A208	35c multicolored	.60	.20
1064	A208	75c multicolored	.75	.25
1065	A208	80c multicolored	.75	.35
		Nos. 1062-1065 (4)	2.50	1.00

3rd UN Conference on the Law of the Sea,
Caracas, June 20-Aug. 29.

Pupil and New School — A209

"Pay your Taxes" Campaign: 10c, 15c, 20c, like 5c. 25c, 30c, 35c, 40c, Suburban housing development. 45c, 50c, 55c, 60c, Highway and overpass. 65c, 70c, 75c, 80c, Playing field (sport). 85c, 90c, 95c, 1b, Operating room. All designs include Venezuelan coat of arms, coins and banknotes.

1974			Perf. 13½	
1066	A209	5c blue & multi	.20	.20
1067	A209	10c ultra & multi	.20	.20
1068	A209	15c violet & multi	.20	.20
1069	A209	20c lilac & multi	.20	.20
1070	A209	25c multicolored	.20	.20
1071	A209	30c multicolored	.40	.20
1072	A209	35c multicolored	.20	.20
1073	A209	40c olive & multi	.30	.20
1074	A209	45c multicolored	.30	.20
1075	A209	50c green & multi	.30	.20
1076	A209	55c multicolored	.55	.30
1077	A209	60c multicolored	.45	.20
1078	A209	65c bister & multi	1.00	.50
1079	A209	70c multicolored	.45	.20
1080	A209	75c multicolored	.50	.25
1081	A209	80c brown & multi	.50	.25
1082	A209	85c ver & multi	.50	.25
1083	A209	90c multicolored	.65	.25
1084	A209	95c multicolored	1.25	.65
1085	A209	1b multicolored	.65	.30
		Nos. 1066-1085 (20)	9.00	5.15

Bolivar at Battle of Junin A210

1974, Aug. 6　Litho.　Perf. 13½x14
1086 A210 2b multicolored　　1.50　.75
Sesquicentennial of the Battle of Junin.

Globe and UPU Emblem — A211

50c, Postrider, sailing ship, steamer and jet.

1974, Oct. 9　　　　Perf. 12
1087 A211 45c dk blue & multi　　.30　.20
1088 A211 50c black & multi　　.40　.20
Centenary of Universal Postal Union.

Rufino Blanco-Fombona — A212

Portraits of Blanco-Fombona and his books.

1974, Oct. 16	Litho.		Perf. 12½	
1089	A212	10c gray & multi	.20	.20
1090	A212	30c yellow & multi	.20	.20
1091	A212	45c multicolored	.30	.20
1092	A212	90c buff & multi	.50	.25
		Nos. 1089-1092 (4)	1.20	.85

Centenary of the birth of Rufino Blanco-Fombona (1874-1944), writer.

Children A213

1974, Nov. 29　Litho.　Perf. 13½
1093 A213 70c blue & multi　　.60　.25
Children's Foundation Festival.

General Sucre — A214

Globe with South American Map and Flags — A215

Battle of Ayacucho — A216

1b, Map of South America with battles marked.

1974, Dec. 9	Perf. 14x13½, 13½x14			
1094	A214	30c multicolored	.20	.20
1095	A215	50c multicolored	.30	.25
1096	A215	1b multicolored	.65	.30
1097	A216	2b multicolored	1.25	.65
		Nos. 1094-1097 (4)	2.40	1.40

Sesquicentennial of the Battle of Ayacucho.

Adoration of the Shepherds, by J. B. Mayno — A217

1974, Dec. 16　Photo.　Perf. 14x13½
1098　30c Shepherd　　　　.25　.20
1099　30c Madonna & Child　.25　.20
　a. A217 Pair, #1098-1099　.80　.80
Christmas 1974.

Road Building, 1905 and El Ciempies Overpass, 1972 — A219

Designs: 20c, 1b, Jesus Muñoz Tebar, first Minister of Public Works. 25c, Bridges on Caracas-La Guaira Road, 1912 and 1953. 40c, View of Caracas, 1874 and 1974. 70c, Tucacas Railroad Station, 1911, and projected terminal, 1974. 80c, Anatomical Institute, Caracas, 1911, and Social Security Hospital, 1969. 85c, Quininari River Bridge, 1804, and Orinoco River Bridge, 1967.

1974, Dec. 18	Litho.		Perf. 12½	
1100	A219	5c ultra & multi	.20	.20
1101	A219	20c ocher & blk	.25	.20
1102	A219	25c blue & multi	.30	.20
1103	A219	40c yellow & multi	.30	.20
1104	A219	70c green & multi	1.40	.25
1105	A219	80c multicolored	1.10	.30
1106	A219	85c orange & multi	1.50	.30
1107	A219	1b red & black	1.60	.50
		Nos. 1100-1107 (8)	6.65	2.15

Centenary of the Ministry of Public Works.

Women and IWY Emblem — A220

1975, Oct. 8　Litho.　Perf. 13½x14
1108 A220 90c multicolored　　.60　.35
International Women's Year.

Scout Emblem and Tents — A221

1975, Nov. 11　Litho.　Perf. 13½x14
1109 A221 20c multicolored　　.20　.20
1110 A221 80c multicolored　　.50　.25
14th World Boy Scout Jamboree, Lille-hammer, Norway, July 29-Aug. 7.

Adoration of the Shepherds — A222

1975, Dec. 5　Litho.　Perf. 13½x14
1111　30c multicolored　　　.20　.20
1112　30c multicolored　　　.20　.20
　a. A222 Pair, #1111-1112　.75　.75
Christmas 1975.

Bolivar's Tomb — A224

Design: 1.05b, National Pantheon.

1976, Feb. 2　Engr.　Perf. 14x13½
1113 A224　30c gray & ultra　　.20　.20
1114 A224　1.05b sepia & car　.50　.25
Centenary of National Pantheon.

Bolivia Flag Colors A225

1976, Mar. 22　Litho.　Perf. 13½
1115 A225 60c multicolored　　.35　.20
Sesquicentennial of Bolivia's independence.

Aerial Map Survey — A226

1976, Apr. 8　　　　Perf. 13½x12½
1116 A226 1b black & vio bl　　.50　.25
Natl. Cartographic Institute, 40th anniv.

Gen. Ribas' Signature A227

José Felix Ribas A228

1976, Apr. 26　Photo.　Perf. 12½x13
1117 A227 40c red & green　　.30　.20
**　　　　　　　　　　Perf. 13½**
1118 A228 55c multicolored　　.40　.20
Gen. José Felix Ribas (1775-1815), independence hero, birth bicentenary.

Musicians of the Chacao School, by Armandio Barrios — A229

Lamas's Colophon
A230

1976, May 13   Litho.   Perf. 13½
1119 A229 75c multicolored   .40   .25

Photo.   Perf. 12½x13
1120 A230 1.25b buff, red & gray   .70   .35
José Angel Lamas (1775-1814), composer, birth bicentenary.

Bolivar, by José Maria Espinoza — A231

1976   Engr.   Perf. 12
Size: 18x22½mm

1121 A231 5c green   .20   .20
1122 A231 10c lilac rose   .20   .20
1123 A231 15c brown   .20   .20
1124 A231 20c black   .20   .20
1125 A231 25c yellow   .20   .20
1126 A231 30c violet bl   .20   .20
1127 A231 45c dk purple   .20   .20
1128 A231 50c orange   .20   .20
1129 A231 65c blue   .25   .20
1130 A231 1b vermilion   .30   .25

Size: 26x32mm
Perf. 12x11½

1131 A231 2b gray   .65   .25
1132 A231 3b violet blue   .95   .40
1133 A231 4b yellow   1.25 .55
1134 A231 5b orange   1.50 .75
1135 A231 10b dull purple   3.50 1.40
1136 A231 15b blue   5.25 2.00
1137 A231 20b vermilion   6.50 2.75
     Nos. 1121-1137 (17)   21.75 10.15

Issued: 5c-1b, May 17; 2b-20b, July 15.

Coil Stamps
1978, May 22   Perf. 13½ Horiz.
Size: 18x22½mm

1138 A231 5c green   .20   .20
1139 A231 10c lilac rose   .20   .20
1140 A231 15c brown   .20   .20
1141 A231 20c black   .20   .20
1142 A231 25c yellow   .20   .20
1143 A231 30c violet blue   .20   .20
1144 A231 45c dk purple   .20   .20
1144A A231 50c orange   .25   .20
1144B A231 65c blue   .25   .20
1144C A231 1b vermilion   .40   .20
     Nos. 1138-1144C (10)   2.30 2.00

Black control number on back of every fifth stamp.

See Nos. 1305-1307, 1362-1366, 1401-1409, 1482, 1484, 1487, 1490. Compare with designs A405-A406.

Maze
A232

Central University
A233

Faculty Emblems
A234

1976, June 1   Litho.   Perf. 12½x13
1145 A232 30c multicolored   .20   .20
1146 A233 50c yel, org & blk   .25   .20
1147 A234 90c black & yellow   .55   .35
     Nos. 1145-1147 (3)   1.00 .75
Central University of Venezuela, 250th anniv.

"Unity" — A235

Washington, US Bicent. Emblem
A236

Designs: 45c, 1.25b, similar to 15c.

1976, June 29   Litho.   Perf. 12½
1148 A235 15c multicolored   .20   .20
1149 A235 45c multicolored   .25   .20
1150 A235 1.25b multicolored   .55   .35
     Nos. 1148-1150 (3)   1.00 .75
Amphictyonic Cong. of Panama, Sesqui.

1976, July 4   Engr.   Perf. 14
US Bicentennial Emblem and: No. 1152, Jefferson. No. 1153, Lincoln. No. 1154, F. D. Roosevelt. No. 1155, J. F. Kennedy.

1151 A236 1b red brn & blk   .60   .30
1152 A236 1b green & blk   .60   .30
1153 A236 1b purple & blk   .60   .30
1154 A236 1b blue & blk   .60   .30
1155 A236 1b olive & blk   .60   .30
     Nos. 1151-1155 (5)   3.00 1.50
American Bicentennial.

Valve — A237

Nativity, by Barbaro Rivas — A238

Computer drawings of valves & pipelines.

1976, Nov. 8   Photo.   Perf. 12⅓1x14
1156 A237 10c multicolored   .20   .20
1157 A237 30c multicolored   .20   .20
1158 A237 35c multicolored   .20   .20
1159 A237 40c multicolored   .20   .20
1160 A237 55c multicolored   .25   .20
1161 A237 90c multicolored   .45   .20
     Nos. 1156-1161 (6)   1.50 1.25
Nationalization of the oil industry.

1976, Dec. 1   Litho.   Perf. 13x14
1162 A238 30c multicolored   .35   .20
Christmas 1976.

Lithographed and Embossed
1976, Dec. 15   Perf. 14x13½
1163 A239 60c yellow & black   .35   .20
Declaration of Bogota (economic agreements of Andean countries), 10th anniv.

Coat of Arms of Barinas — A240

1977, May 25   Photo.   Perf. 12½x13
1164 A240 50c multicolored   .35   .20
400th anniv. of the founding of Barinas.

Crucified Christ, Patron Saint of La Grita — A241

1977, Aug. 6   Litho.   Perf. 13
1165 A241 30c multicolored   .25   .20
Founding of La Grita, 400th anniv. (in 1976).

Symbolic City — A242

1977, Aug. 26   Litho.   Perf. 13½
1166 A242 1b multicolored   .50   .25
450th anniversary of the founding of Coro.

Communications Symbols — A243

1977, Sept. 30   Litho.   Perf. 13½x14
1167 A243 85c multicolored   .50   .20
9th Interamerican Postal and Telecommunications Staff Congress, Caracas, Sept. 26-30.

Cable Connecting with TV, Telephone and Circuit Box — A244

1977, Oct. 12   Litho.   Perf. 14
1168 A244 95c multicolored   .50   .20
Inauguration of Columbus underwater cable linking Venezuela and the Canary Islands.

"Venezuela"
A245

Designs: "Venezuela" horizontal on 50c, 1.05b; reading up on 80c, 1.25b; reading down on 1.50b.

1977, Nov. 26   Photo.   Perf. 13½x13
1169 A245 30c brt yel & blk   .20   .20
1170 A245 50c dp org & blk   .25   .20
1171 A245 80c gray & blk   .45   .20
1172 A245 1.05b red & blk   .50   .20
1173 A245 1.25b yel & blk   .60   .20
1174 A245 1.50b gray & blk   .75   .25
     Nos. 1169-1174 (6)   2.75 1.25
Iron industry nationalization, 1st anniv.

Juan Pablo Duarte — A246

Nativity, Colonial Sculpture — A247

1977, Dec. 8   Engr.   Perf. 11x13
1175 A246 75c black & lilac   .50   .20
Duarte (1813-76), leader in liberation struggle.

1977, Dec. 15   Litho.   Perf. 13
1176 A247 30c green & multi   .25   .20
Christmas 1977.

OPEC Emblem — A248

1977, Dec. 20
1177 A248 1.05b brt & lt bl & blk .60   .20
50th Conference of Oil Producing and Exporting Countries, Caracas.

Bicyclist
A249

1978, Jan. 16   Litho.   Perf. 13½x13
1178 A249 5c Racing bicyclists   .20   .20
1179 A249 1.25b shown   .60   .20
World Bicycling Championships, San Cristobal, Tachira, Aug. 22-Sept. 4.

Profiles
A250

1978, Apr. 21   Litho.   Perf. 13½x14
1180 A250 70c blk, gray & lil   .35   .20
Language Day.
Issued in tete-beche pairs. Value $2.75.

Magnetic Computer Tape and Satellite
A251

1978, May 17   Litho.   Perf. 14
1184 A251 75c violet blue   .40   .20
10th World Telecommunications Day.

"1777-1977" — A252

Goya's Carlos
III as Computer
Print — A253

1978, June 23   Litho.   Perf. 12
1185 A252 30c multicolored   .20 .20
1186 A253 1b multicolored   .55 .20
200th anniversary of Venezuelan unification.

Bolivar Bicentenary

Juan Vicente Bolivar y Ponte, Father
of Simon Bolivar — A254

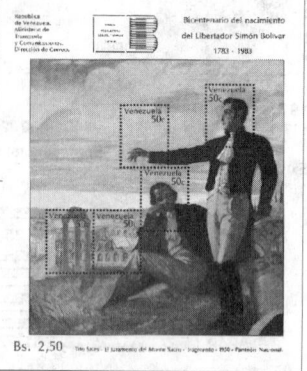

The Oath on Monte Sacro, Rome, by
Tito Salas — A255

Designs: 30c, Bolivar as infant in nurse-maid's arms (detail from design of No. 1189).
No. 1189, Baptism of the Liberator, by Tito
Salas, 1929.
Illustration A255 is reduced.

1978, July 24   Engr.   Perf. 12½
1187 A254 30c emerald & blk   .20 .20
1188 A254 1b multicolored   .55 .25

Souvenir Sheet
Litho.
Perf. 14
1189 A255   Sheet of 5   32.50 32.50
  a.   50c, single stamp   1.25 1.25

1978, Dec. 17   Engr.   Perf. 12½
Designs: 30c, Bolivar at 25. 1b, Simon Rodriguez. No. 1192, shown. (Bolivar's tutor).

1190 A254 30c multicolored   .20 .20
1191 A254 1b rose red & blk   .30 .20

Souvenir Sheet
Litho.
Perf. 14
1192 A255   Sheet of 5   16.00 16.00
  a.   50c, single stamp   .75   .75

Size of souvenir sheet stamps: 20x24mm.
Size of #1189: 154x130mm; #1192:
130x155mm.

1979, July 24   Engr.   Perf. 12½
Designs: 30c, Alexander Sabes Petion,
president of Haiti. 1b, Bolivar's signature.
No. 1195: a, Partial map of Jamaica, horiz.
b, Partial map of Jamaica, vert. c, Bolivar,
1816. d, Luis Brion. e, Petion.

1193 A254 30c org, vio & blk   .30 .20
1194 A254 1b red org & blk   .45 .20

Souvenir Sheet
Litho.
Perf. 14
1195 A255   Sheet of 5   3.25 3.25
  a.-e.   50c, any single   .30   .30
  Size of souvenir sheet stamps: 26x20,
20x26mm.

1979, Dec. 17   Engr.   Perf. 12½
Designs: 30c, Bolivar. 1b, Slave. No. 1198,
Freeing of the Slaves, by Tito Salas. (30c, 1b,
details from design of No. 1198.)

1196 A254 30c multicolored   .20 .20
1197 A254 1b multicolored   .30 .20

Souvenir Sheet
Litho.
Perf. 14
1198 A255   Sheet of 5   5.00 5.00
  a.   50c, single stamp   .90   .90

Simon Bolivar, birth centenary. Size of souvenir sheet stamps: 22x28mm.
See Nos. 1228-1230, 1264-1266, 1276-1284, 1294-1296, 1317-1322.

"T" and   Symbolic
"CTV" — A256   Design — A257

Designs: Different arrangement of letters "T"
and "CTV" for "Confederacion de Trabajeros
Venezolanos."

1978, Sept. 27 Photo. Perf. 13x13½
1199   Strip of 5   .65   .65
  a.-e. A256 30c, single stamp .20   .20
1200   Strip of 5   1.50 1.50
  a.-e. A256 95c, single stamp .25   .20
  Workers' Day.

1978, Oct. 3   Litho.   Perf. 14
1201 A257 50c dark brown   .50 .25
Rafael Rangel, physician and scientist, birth
cententary.

Drill Head,
Tachira Oil
Field
Map — A258

"P" as
Pipeline
A259

1978, Nov. 2   Litho.   Perf. 13½
1202 A258 30c multicolored   .25 .20
1203 A259 1.05b multicolored   .55 .25
Centenary of oil industry.

Star — A260

1978, Dec. 6   Litho.   Perf. 14
1204 A260 30c multicolored   .25 .20
Christmas 1978.

"P T" — A261

1979, Feb. 8   Litho.   Perf. 12½
1205 A261 75c black & red   .25 .20
Creation of Postal and Telegraph Institute.

"Dam Holding
Back Water"
A262

1979, Feb. 15   Photo.   Perf. 13½
1206 A262 2b silver, gray & blk   .65 .35
Guri Dam, 10th anniversary.

San Martin, by E. J. Maury — A263

60c, San Martin, by Mercedes. 70c, Monument, Guayaquil. 75c, San Martin's signature.

1979, Feb. 25   Perf. 12½x13
1207 A263 40c blue, blk & yel   .20 .20
1208 A263 60c blue, blk & yel   .25 .20
1209 A263 70c blue, blk & yel   .35 .20
1210 A263 75c blue, blk & yel   .35 .25
  Nos. 1207-1210 (4)   1.15 .85
José de San Martin (1778-1850), South
American liberator.

"Rotary" — A264

1979, Aug. 7   Litho.   Perf. 14x13½
1211 A264 85c gold & blk   .30 .20
Rotary Club of Caracas, 50th anniversary.

Our Lady of
Coromoto
Appearing to
Children
A265

Engraved and Lithographed
1979, Aug. 23   Perf. 13
1212 A265 55c black & dp org   .25 .20
Canonization of Our Lady of Coromoto, 25th
anniv.

London Residence, Coat of Arms,
Miranda — A266

1979, Oct. 23   Litho.   Perf. 14½x14
1213 A266 50c multicolored   .25 .20
Francisco de Miranda (1750-1816), Venezuelan independence fighter.

O'Leary,
Maps of
South
America
and
United
Kingdom
A267

1979, Nov. 6
1214 A267 30c multicolored   .25 .20
Daniel O'Leary (1801-1854), writer.

A268   A269

IYC Emblem and: 79c, Boy holding nest.
80c, Boys in water, bridge.

1979, Nov. 20   Litho.   Perf. 14½x14
1215 A268 70c lt blue & blk   .25 .20
1216 A268 80c multicolored   .30 .20
International Year of the Child.

1979, Dec. 1   Litho.   Perf. 13
1217 A269 30c multicolored   .25 .20
Christmas 1979.

Caudron
Bomber,
EXFILVE
Emblem
A270

EXFILVE Emblem and: No. 1219, Stearman
biplane. No. 1220, UH-1H helicopter. No.
1221, CF-5 jet fighter.

1979, Dec. 15   Perf. 11x11½
1218 A270 75c multicolored   .25 .20
1219 A270 75c multicolored   .25 .20
1220 A270 75c multicolored   .25 .20
1221 A270 75c multicolored   .25 .20
  a.   Block of 4, #1218-1221   1.25 .60
Venezuelan Air Force, 59th anniv.; EXFILVE
79, 3rd Natl. Philatelic Exhibition, Dec. 7-17.

IPOSTEL
Emblem,
World Map
A271

1979, Dec. 27   Perf. 11½
1222 A271 75c multicolored   .30 .20
Postal and Telegraph Institute, introduction
of new logo.

Queen Victoria, Hill — A272

1980, Feb. 13   Litho.   Perf. 12½
1223 A272 55c multicolored   .25 .20
  Sir Rowland Hill (1795-1879), originator of penny postage.

Dr. Augusto Pi Suner, Physiologist, Birth Centenary — A273

1980, Mar. 14   Litho.   Perf. 11½
1224 A273 80c multicolored   .30 .20

Spanish Seed Leaf — A274

Juan Lovera (1778-1841), Artist — A275

Lithographed and Engraved
1980, Mar. 27   Perf. 13
1225 A274 50c multicolored   .25 .20
  Pedro Loefling (1729-56), Swedish botanist.

1980, May 25   Litho.   Perf. 13½
1226 A275 60c blue & dp org   .20 .20
1227 A275 75c violet & org   .25 .20

  Bolivar Bicentenary Type of 1978

  30c, Signing of document. 1b, House of Congress. #1230, Angostura Congress, by Tito Salas.

1980, July 24   Engr.   Perf. 12½
1228 A254 30c multicolored   .20 .20
1229 A254 1b multicolored   .40 .20

Souvenir Sheet
Litho.
Perf. 14
1230 A255   Sheet of 5   3.25 3.25
  a.   50c, single stamp   .20 .20
  Simon Bolivar (1783-1830), revolutionary. Size of souvenir sheet stamps: 25x20mm, 20x25mm.

Dancing Girls, by Armando Reveron — A276

Bernardo O'Higgins — A277

1980, Aug. 17   Litho.   Perf. 13
1231 A276 50c shown   .20 .20
  Size: 25x40mm
1232 A276 65c Portrait   .45 .25
  Armando Reveron (1889-1955), artist.

Lithographed and Engraved
1980, Aug. 22   Perf. 13x14
1233 A277 85c multicolored   .60 .25
  Bernardo O'Higgins (1776-1842), Chilean soldier and statesman.

School Ship Simon Bolivar A278

Frigate Mariscal Sucre A279

Perf. 11½ (#1234), 11x11½
1980, Sept. 13   Litho.
1234 A278 1.50b shown   .80 .30
1235 A279 1.50b shown   .80 .30
1236 A279 1.50b Submarine Picua   .80 .30
1237 A279 1.50b Naval Academy   .80 .30
  Nos. 1234-1237 (4)   3.20 1.20
  "Picua" is misspelled on stamp.

Workers Holding OPEC Emblem A280

  20th Anniv. of OPEC (Organization of Petroleum Exporting Countries): #1239, Emblem.

1980, Sept. 14   Litho.   Perf. 12x11½
1238 A280 1.50b multicolored   .50 .25
1239 A280 1.50b multicolored   .50 .25

Death of Simon Bolivar A281

1980, Dec. 17   Litho.   Perf. 11x11½
1240 A281 2b multicolored   1.25 .40
  Simon Bolivar, 150th anniversary of death.

A282

A283

Lithographed and Engraved
1980, Dec. 17   Perf. 13x12½
1241 A282 2b multicolored   .70 .35
  Gen. José Antonio Sucre, 150th anniv. of death.

1980, Dec. 19   Litho.   Perf. 14x13½
1242 A283 1b Nativity by Rubens   .35 .25
  Christmas 1980.

Helen Keller's Initials (Written and Braille) — A284

Lithographed and Embossed
1981, Feb. 12   Perf. 12½
1243 A284 1.50b multicolored   .45 .25
  Helen Keller (1880-1968), blind and deaf writer and lecturer.

John Baptiste de la Salle — A285

San Felipe City, 250th Anniv. — A286

1981, May 15   Litho.   Perf. 11½x11
1244 A285 1.25b multicolored   .40 .20
  Christian Brothers' 300th anniv.

1981, May 1   Perf. 11½
1245 A286 3b multicolored   .75 .35

Municipal Theater of Caracas Centenary A287

1981, June 28   Litho.   Perf. 12
1246 A287 1.25b multicolored   1.40 .25

A288

A290

A289

1981, Sept. 15   Litho.   Perf. 11½
1247 A288 2b multicolored   .60 .20
  UPU membership centenary.

1981, Oct. 14   Litho.
1248 A289 1b multicolored   .30 .20
  11th natl. population and housing census.

1981, Dec. 3   Litho.   Perf. 11½
1249 A290 95c multicolored   .35 .20
  9th Bolivar Games, Barquismeto.

19th Cent. Bicycle A291

1981, Dec. 5   Photo.   Perf. 13x14
1250 A291 1b shown   .45 .30
1251 A291 1.05b Locomotive, 1926   .45 .30
1252 A291 1.25b Buick, 1937   .60 .30
1253 A291 1.50b Coach   .75 .35
  Nos. 1250-1253 (4)   2.25 1.25
  See Nos. 1289-1292, 1308-1311.

Christmas 1981 A292

1981, Dec. 21   Litho.   Perf. 11½
1254 A292 1b multicolored   .30 .20

50th Anniv. of Natural Science Society — A293

1982, Jan. 21   Perf. 11½
1255 A293 1b Mt. Autana   .30 .20
1256 A293 1.50b Sarisarinama   .45 .25
1257 A293 2b Guacharo Cave   .60 .30
  Nos. 1255-1257 (3)   1.35 .75

20th Anniv. of Constitution A294

1982, Jan. 28   Photo.   Perf. 13x13½
1258 A294 1.85b gold & blk   .60 .25

A295   A296

1982, Feb. 19   Litho.   Perf. 13½
1259 A295 3b multicolored   .90 .40
20th anniv. of agricultural reform.

1982, Mar. 12   Litho.   Perf. 13½
1260 A296 1b blue & dk blue   .30 .20
Jules Verne (1828-1905), science fiction writer.

Natl.
Anthem
Centenary
(1981)
A297

1982, Mar. 26   Perf. 11½
1261 A297 1b multicolored   .30 .20

1300th Anniv. of
Bulgaria
A298

6th Natl. 5-
Year Plan,
1981-85
A299

1982, June 2   Litho.   Perf. 13½
1262 A298 65c multicolored   .20 .20

1982, June 11
1263 A299 2b multicolored   .40 .20

Bolivar Types of 1978
1982, July 24   Engr.   Perf. 12½
1264 A254 30c Juan José
             Rondon   .20 .20
1265 A254 1b José Antonio
             Anzoategui   .20 .20

Souvenir Sheet
Litho.
Perf. 14
1266 A255   Sheet of 5   2.75 2.75
a.-e.   50c, any single   .20 .20

Single stamps of No. 1266 show details from Battle of Boyaca, by Martin Tovar y Tovar. Size of souvenir sheet stamps: 19x26mm, 26x19mm.

Cecilio Acosta
(1818-1881),
Writer — A299a

1982, Aug. 13   Litho.   Perf. 11½
1266F A299a 3b multicolored   .45 .25

Aloe
A300

1982, Oct. 14   Photo.   Perf. 13
1267 A300 1.05b shown   .50 .20
1268 A300 2.55b Tortoise   1.40 .20
1269 A300 2.75b Tara amarilla
             tree   1.50 .20
1270 A300 3b Guacharo bird   1.75 .25
     Nos. 1267-1270 (4)   5.15 .85

Andres Bello (1781-1865), Statesman
and Reformer — A301

1982, Nov. 20   Litho.   Perf. 12
1271 A301 1.05b multicolored   .35 .20
1272 A301 2.55b multicolored   .85 .30
1273 A301 2.75b multicolored   .85 .30
1274 A301 3b multicolored   1.10 .35
     Nos. 1271-1274 (4)   3.15 1.15

Christmas
1982 — A302

Design: Holy Family creche figures by Francisco J. Cardozo, 18th cent.

Photogravure and Engraved
1982, Dec. 7   Perf. 13½
1275 A302 1b multicolored   .20 .20

Bolivar Types of 1978
1982-83   Engr.   Perf. 12½
1276 A254 30c Victory Monu-
             ment, Carabobo   .20 .20
1277 A254 30c Monument to the
             Meeting plaque   .20 .20
1278 A254 30c Antonio de Sucre   .20 .20
1279 A254 1b Jose Antonio
             Paez   .35 .20
1280 A254 1b Sword hilt, 1824   .35 .20
1281 A254 1b Guayaquil Monu-
             ment   .35 .20
     Nos. 1276-1281 (6)   1.65 1.20

Souvenir Sheets
Litho.
Perf. 14
1282 A255   Sheet of 5   3.25 3.25
a.-e.   50c, any single   .20 .20
1283 A255   Sheet of 5   3.25 3.25
a.-e.   50c, any single   .20 .20
1284 A255   Sheet of 5   3.25 3.25
a.-e.   50c, any single   .20 .20

No. 1282: Battle of Carabobo by Martin Tovar y Tovar; No. 1283, Monument to the Meeting; No. 1284, Battle of Ayacucho, by Martin Tovar y Tovar.
Issue dates: Nos. 1276-1277, 1279, 1281-1283, Dec. 17; others, Apr. 18, 1983.

Gen. Jose Francisco
Bermudez — A303

Antonio
Nicolas
Briceno,
Liberation
Hero
A304

Perf. 13x13½, 15x14
1982, Dec. 23   Litho.
1285 A303 3b multicolored   1.10.30
1286 A304 3b multicolored   1.10.30

25th Anniv.
of 1958
Reforms
A305

1983, Jan. 23   Perf. 10½x10
1287 A305 3b multicolored   .65 .30

A306

1983, Mar. 20   Photo.   Perf. 13½x13
1288 A306 4b olive & red   .65 .30
25th anniv. of Judicial Police Technical Dept.

Transportation Type of 1981
Perf. 13½x14½
1983, Mar. 28   Photo.
1289 A291 75c Lincoln, 1923   .75 .30
1290 A291 80c Locomotive, 1889   .75 .30
1291 A291 85c Willys truck, 1927 .90 .30
1292 A291 95c Cleveland motor-
             cycle, 1920   .90 .30
     Nos. 1289-1292 (4)   3.30 1.20

A307

1983, May 17   Photo.   Perf. 13x12½
1293 A307 2.85b multicolored   .45 .30
World Communications Year.

Bolivar Type of 1978
Designs: 30c; Flags of Colombia, Peru, Chile, Venezuela, and Buenos Aires. 1b; Equestrian Statue of Bolivar.

Photo. & Engr. (#1294), Engr.
(#1295)
1983, July 25   Perf. 12½
1294 A254 30c multicolored   .20 .20
1295 A254 1b multicolored   .20 .20

Souvenir Sheet
Litho.
Perf. 14
1296 A255   Sheet of 5   3.25 3.25
a.-e.   50c, any single   .20 .20

Single stamps of No. 1296 show details of "The Liberator on the Silver Mountain of Potosi." Size of souvenir sheet stamps, 20x25mm.

9th Pan-American Games
A308   A309

Designs: #1303a, baseball. b, cycle wheel. c, boxing glove. d, soccer ball. e, target.

Lithographed and Engraved
1983, Aug. 25   Perf. 13
1297 A308 2b shown   .30 .20
1298 A308 2b Swimming   .30 .20
1299 A308 2.70b Cycling   .40 .30
1300 A308 2.70b Fencing   .40 .30
1301 A308 2.85b Runners   .45 .40
1302 A308 2.85b Weightlifting   .45 .40
     Nos. 1297-1302 (6)   2.30 1.80

Souvenir Sheet
1303   Sheet of 5   11.00 11.00
a.-e.   A309 1b, any single   11.00 11.00
#1303 for Copan '83. Size: 167x121mm.

25th Anniv. of
Cadafe (State
Electricity
Authority) — A310

1983, Oct. 27   Litho.   Perf. 14
1304 A310 3b multicolored   .90 .45

Bolivar Type of 1976
1983, Sept. 29   Engr.   Perf. 12
Size: 26x32mm
1305 A231 25b blue green   6.25 3.00
1306 A231 30b brown   7.50 3.75
1307 A231 50b brt rose lilac   11.50 6.25
     Nos. 1305-1307 (3)   25.25 13.00

Transportation Type of 1981
Various views of Caracas Metro.

1983, Dec.   Photo.   Perf. 13½x14½
1308 A291 55c multicolored   .45 .30
1309 A291 75c multicolored   .45 .30
1310 A291 95c multicolored   .45 .30
1311 A291 2b multicolored   1.10 .45
     Nos. 1308-1311 (4)   2.45 1.35

Christmas
1983
A311

1983, Dec. 1   Litho.   Perf. 13x14
1312 A311 1b Nativity   .20 .20

Scouting
Year
(1982)
A312

Lithographed and Engraved
1983, Dec. 14   Perf. 12½x13
1313 A312 2.25p Pitching tent   .40 .25
1314 A312 2.55b Planting tree   .40 .25
1315 A312 2.75b Mountain climb-
             ing   .45 .25
1316 A312 3b Camp site   .45 .25
     Nos. 1313-1316 (4)   1.70 1.00

Bolivar Type of 1976
Designs: No. 1317, Title page of "Opere de Raimondo Montecuccoli" (most valuable book in Caracas University Library). No. 1318, Pedro Gual, Congress of Panama delegate, 1826. No. 1319, Jose Maria Vargas (b. 1786), University of Caracas pres. No. 1320, José Faustino Sanchez Carrion, Congress of Panama delegate, 1826.

1984   Engr.   Perf. 12½
1317 A254 30c multicolored   .20 .20
1318 A254 30c multicolored   .20 .20
1319 A254 1b multicolored   .20 .20
1320 A254 1b multicolored   .20 .20
     Nos. 1317-1320 (4)   .80 .80

Souvenir Sheets
Litho.
Perf. 14

1321	A255	Sheet of 5	2.75	2.75
a.-e.		50c, any single	.20	.20
1322	A255	Sheet of 5	3.25	3.25
a.-e.		50c, any single	.20	.20

Single stamps of No. 1321 show details of Arts, Science and Education, fresco by Hector Poleo; 1322, Map of South America, 1829. Size of souvenir sheet stamps: 20x30mm; 27x20mm.
Issued: #1317, 1319, 1321, 1/19; others, 1/20.

Radio Waves — A313

Intelligentsia for Peace — A314

1984, Jan. 30   Litho.   Perf. 14x13
1323 A313 2.70b multicolored   .40 .20
Radio Club of Venezuela, 50th anniv.

1984, Jan. 31
1324	A314	1b Doves	.20	.20
1325	A314	2.70b Profile	.40	.20
1326	A314	2.85b Flower, head	.40	.20
		Nos. 1324-1326 (3)	1.00	.60

President Romulo Gallegos (1884-1969) A315

Gallegos: No. 1327, Portrait as a young man in formal dress. No. 1328, Portrait, 1948.

1984-85   Litho.   Perf. 11½
1327	A315	1.70b royal bl, dl bl, beige & blk	.40	.25
1328	A315	1.70b ocher, org brn & buff	.40	.25

Issued: #1327, 10/12/84; #1328, 1/18/85. See Nos. 1335-1336.

Pan-American Union of Engineering Associations, 18th Convention A316

1984, Oct. 28
1329 A316 2.55b pale buff, dk bl   .50 .20

Christmas 1984 A317

1984, Dec. 3
1330 A317 1b multicolored   .25 .20

Pope John Paul II, Statue of the Virgin of Caracas A318

1985, Jan. 26   Litho.   Perf. 12
1331 A318 1b multicolored   .80 .25
Papal visit, 1985.

Pascua City Bicent. A319

1985, Feb. 10
1332 A319 1.50b multicolored   .40 .25

Dr. Mario Briceno-Iragory (b. 1897), Historian — A320

1985, Oct.   Litho.   Perf. 12
1333 A320 1.25b silver & ver   .30 .20

Natl. St. Vincent de Paul Soc., Cent. — A321

1985, July
1334 A321 1b dk ol bis, ver & buff   .25 .20

Gallegos Memorial Type of 1984-85
Designs: Gallegos, diff.

1985, Aug. 8
1335	A315	1.70b gray grn, dk gray grn & dl gray grn	.30	.20
1336	A315	1.70b grn, sage grn & dl grn	.30	.20

Dated 1984.

Latin American Economic System, 10th Anniv. A322

1985, Aug. 15
1337 A322 4b black & red   1.40 .60

Miniature Sheet

Virgin Mary, Birth Bimillennium A323

Statues: a, Virgin of the Divine Shepherd. b, Chiquinquira Madonna. c, Coromoto Madonna. d, Valley Madonna. e, Virgin of Perpetual Succor. f, Virgin of Peace. g, Immaculate Conception Virgin. h, Soledad Madonna. i, Virgin of Consolation. j, Nieves Madonna.

1985, Sept. 9
1338		Sheet of 10	4.25	4.25
a.-j.	A323	1b, any single	.40	.20

OPEC, 25th Anniv. A324

1985, Sept. 13
1339 A324 6b multicolored   1.10 .60

Opening of the Museum of Contemporary Art, Caracas — A325

1985, Oct. 24   Perf. 13½
1340 A325 3b multicolored   .55 .30
Dated 1983.

UN, 40th Anniv. A326

1985, Nov. 15   Perf. 12
1341 A326 10b brt blue & ver   1.50 .90

Intl. Youth Year A327

1985, Nov. 26
1342 A327 1.50b multicolored   .30 .20

Christmas 1985 — A328

Nativity: a, Sheperds. b, Holy Family, Magi. Se-tenant in a continuous design.

1985, Dec. 2
1343	A328	Pair	1.25	1.25
a.-b.		2b, any single	.60	.20

Dr. Luis Maria Drago (b. 1859), Politician A329

1985, Dec. 20   Perf. 13½
1344 A329 2.70b tan, ver & sepia   .50 .35
Dated 1984.

Miniature Sheet

Natl. Oil Industry, 10th Anniv. A330

Designs: a, Industry emblem. b, Isla Oil Refinery. c, Bariven oil terminal. d, Pequiven refinery. e, Corpoven drilling rig. f, Maraven offshore rig. g, Intevep labs. h, Meneven refinery. i, Lagoven refinery. j, Emblem, early drilling rig.

1985, Dec. 13   Perf. 12
1345		Sheet of 10	7.50	7.50
a.-b.	A330	1b multi	.25	.20
c.-d.	A330	2b multi	.45	.20
e.-f.	A330	3b multi	.75	.25
g.-h.	A330	4b multi	.90	.30
i.-j.	A330	5b multi	1.10	.40

Simon Bolivar Memorial Coins — A331

1985, Dec. 18
1346	A331	2b multicolored	.35	.25
1347	A331	2.70b multicolored	.50	.30
1348	A331	3b multicolored	.55	.35
		Nos. 1346-1348 (3)	1.40	.90

Dated 1984.

Guayana Development Corp., 25th Anniv. — A332

1985, Dec. 27
1349	A332	2b Guayana City	.35	.25
1350	A332	3b Orinoco Steel Mill	.55	.35
1351	A332	5b Raul Leoni-Guri Hydro-electric Dam	.90	.60
		Nos. 1349-1351 (3)	1.80	1.20

Miniature Sheet

A333

Dr. Jose Vargas (1786-1854) — A334

Designs: No. 1352a, Handwriting and signature. b, Portrait, 1874, by Martin Tovar y Tovar. c, Statue, Palace of the Academies. d, Flags, EXFILBO '86 emblem. e, Vargas do Caracas Hospital. f, Frontispiece of lectures manual, 1842. g, Portrait, 1986, by Alirio Palacios. h, Gesneria vargasii. i, Bolivar-Vargas commemorative medal, 1955, 6th Natl. Medical Sciences Cong. j, Portrait, anonymous, 19th cent.
No. 1353a, Portrait, facing front. b, Portrait, facing left, Nos. 1352a, 1352d, 1352e, 1352h and 1352i have horizontal vignettes.

1986, Mar. 10   Litho.   Perf. 12
1352   Sheet of 10   7.75   7.75
a.-j.   A333 3b, any single   .65   .30

Souvenir Sheet
Imperf
1353   Sheet of 2   10.00   10.00
a.-b.   A334 15b, any single   4.50   .75

EXFILBO '86, Mar. 10-17, Caracas, 1st Bolivarian exhibition.

Youths Painting School Wall A335

1986, May 12   Perf. 12
1354   A335   3b shown   .50   .25
1355   A335   5b Repairing desk   .90   .25

Founding and maintenance of educational institutions.

Francisco Miranda's Work for American Liberation, Bicent. (1981) A336

Lithographed and Engraved
1986, Apr. 18   Perf. 13
1356   A336   1.05b multicolored   .20   .20

Dated 1983.

INDULAC, 45th Anniv. A337

1986, June 27   Litho.   Perf. 12
1357   A337   2.55b Milk trucks, vert.   .30   .20
1358   A337   2.70b Map, vert.   .35   .20
1359   A337   3.70b Milk processing plant   .40   .20
    Nos. 1357-1359 (3)   1.05   .60

Industria Lactea (INDULAC), Venezuelan milk processing company.

Miniature Sheet

Viasa Venezuelan Airlines, 25th Anniv. A338

a, Commemorative coin. b, Douglas DC-8 ascending. c, DC-8 taxiing. d, Boeing 747 in flight. e, DC-10 tails. f, Map of hemispheres. g, DC-10 taking off. h, Rear of DC-10 & DC8 on runway. i, DC-9 over mountains. j, Crew in cockpit.

1986, Aug. 11   Litho.   Perf. 12
1360   Sheet of 10   6.25   6.25
a.-e.   A338 3b, any single   .40   .25
f.-j.   A338 3.25b, any single   .45   .25

Miniature Sheet

Romulo Betancourt (1908-1981), President — A339

a, i, Portrait with natl. flag. b, j, Seated in armchair, smoking pipe. c, h, Wearing hat, text. d, f, Wearing sash of office. e, g, Reading.

1986, Sept. 28
1361   Sheet of 10   5.00   5.00
a.-e.   A339 2.70b, any single   .30   .20
f.-j.   A339 3b, any single   .35   .25

Redrawn Bolivar Type of 1976
1986, Sept. 29   Litho.   Perf. 12½
1362   A231   25c red   .35   .25
1363   A231   50c blue   .35   .25
1364   A231   75c pink   .35   .25
1365   A231   1b orange   .35   .25
1366   A231   2b brt yellow grn   .40   .25
    Nos. 1362-1366 (5)   1.80   1.25

Nos. 1362-1366 inscribed Armitano. For surcharges see Nos. 1453-1464.

Re-opening of Zulia University, 40th Anniv. — A340

1986, Sept. 29
1367   A340   2.70b shown   .30   .25
1368   A340   2.70b Library entrance   .30   .25
a.   Pair, #1367-1368   .60   .60

11th Congress of Architects, Engineers and Affiliated Professionals — A341

1986, Oct. 3
1369   A341   1.40b multicolored   .20   .20
1370   A341   1.55b multicolored   .20   .20
a.   Pair, #1369-1370   1.50   1.50

Fauna and Flora A342

1986, Sept. 12   Photo.   Perf. 13½
1371   A342   70c Priodontes maximus   .35   .35
1372   A342   85c Espeletia angustifolia   .35   .35
1373   A342   2.70b Crocodylus intermedius   .35   .35
1374   A342   3b Brownea grandiceps   .40   .35
    Nos. 1371-1374 (4)   1.45   1.40

Miniature Sheet

State Visit of Pope John Paul II — A343

1986, Oct. 22   Perf. 12
1375   Sheet of 10   4.25   4.25
a.   A343 1b Pope, mountains   .20   .20
b.   A343 2b Bridge   .30   .20
c.   A343 3b Kissing the ground   .40   .20
d.   A343 3b Statue of Our Lady   .40   .20
e.   A343 4b Crosier, buildings   .60   .20
f.   A343 5.25b Waterfall   .80   .25

#1375 contains 2 each #1375a-1375b, 1375e-1375f and one each #1375c-1375d.

Miniature Sheet

Children's Foundation, 20th Anniv. A344

Children's drawings: a, Three children. b, Hearts, children, birds. c, Child, animals. d, Animals, house. e, Landscape. f, Child, flowers on table. g, Child holding ball. h, Children, birds. i, Lighthouse, port. j, Butterfly in flight.

1986, Nov. 10
1376   Sheet of 10   4.00   4.00
a.-e.   A344 2.55b, any single   .35   .20
f.-j.   A344 2.70b, any single   .35   .20

Christmas — A345

Creche figures carved by Eliecer Alvarez.

1986, Nov. 10
1377   2b shown   .25   .20
1378   2b Virgin and child   .25   .20
a.   A345 Pair, #1377-1378   .50   .50

City Police, 25th Anniv. A346

Emblem and: a, Emergency medical aid, helicopter. b, Security at sporting event. c, Bar code. d, Cadets in front of police academy. e, Motorcycle police.

1986, Dec. 10
1379   Strip of 5   1.90   1.90
a.-e.   A346 2.70b, any single   .35   .25

Folk Art A347

Lithographed and Engraved
1987, Jan. 31   Perf. 13
1380   A347   2b Musical instrument   .30   .20
1381   A347   2b Fabric   .30   .20
1382   A347   3b Ceramic pot   .40   .20
1383   A347   3b Basket work   .40   .20
    Nos. 1380-1383 (4)   1.40   .80

Dated 1983. Nos. 1380, 1382 show Pre-Hispanic art.

Discovery of the Tubercle Bacillus by Robert Koch, Cent. (in 1982) A348

Lithographed and Engraved
1987, Feb. 27   Perf. 14x14½
1384   A348   2.55b multicolored   .55   .20

Dated 1983.

Miniature Sheet

Easter 1987 A349

Paintings and sculpture: a, Arrival of Jesus in Jerusalem. b, Christ at the Column. c, Jesus of Nazareth. d, The Descent. e, The Solitude. f, The Last Supper. g, Christ Suffering. h, The Crucifixion. i, Christ Entombed. j, The Resurrection.

1987, Apr. 2   Litho.   Perf. 12
1385   Sheet of 10   15.00   15.00
a.-e.   A349 2b, any single   1.00   .25
f.-j.   A349 2.25b, any single   1.10   .25

World Neurochemistry Congress — A350

3b, Bolivar and Bello, outdoor sculpture by Marisol Escobar. 4.25b, Retinal neurons.

1987, May 8   Litho.   Perf. 12
1386   A350   3b multicolored   .50   .20
1387   A350   4.25b multicolored   .60   .20
a.   Pair, #1386-1387   3.00   3.00

Miniature Sheet

Tourism A351

Hotels: a, f, Barquisimeto Hilton. b, g, Lake Hotel Intercontinental, Maracaibo. c, h, Macuto Sheraton, Caraballeda. d, i, Melia Caribe, Caraballeda. e, j, Melia, Puerto la Cruz.

1987, May 29   Litho.   Perf. 12
1388   Sheet of 10   5.50   5.50
a.-e.   A351 6b, any single   .50   .50
f.-j.   A351 6.50b, any single, diff.   .50   .25

Natl. Institute of Canalization, 35th Anniv. — A352

1987, June 25   Litho.   Perf. 12
1389   A352   2b Map of Amazon territory waterways   .20   .20

1390 A352 4.25b Apure and Bolivar
states waterways .35 .25
g. Pair, #1389-1390 .60 .60

Vincente Emilion Sojo (1887-1974),
Composer — A352a

2b, Academy of Fine Arts, Caracas. 4b, Sojos directing choir. 5b, Hymn to Bolivar score. 6b, Sojo, score on blackboard. 7b, Portrait, signature.

1987, July 1   Litho.   Perf. 12
1390A   Strip of 5   37.50 37.50
b. A352a 2b tan & sepia   1.25 1.25
c. A352a 4b tan & sepia   2.00 1.40
d. A352a 5b tan & sepia   2.00 1.40
e. A352a 6b tan & sepia   3.25 2.00
f. A352a 7b tan & sepia   4.00 2.00

Printed in sheets of 10 containing two strips of five, black control number (UR).

Simon
Bolivar
University,
20th Anniv.
A353

Designs: a, Bolivar statue by Roca Rey, 1973. b, Outdoor sculpture of solar panels by Alejandro Otero, 1972. c, Rectory, 1716. d, Laser. e, Owl, sculpture, 1973.

1987, July 9   Litho.   Perf. 12
1391   Strip of 5   11.00 11.00
a. A353 2b multicolored   1.00 .50
b. A353 3b multicolored   1.50 .50
c. A353 4b multicolored   2.00 .60
d. A353 5b multicolored   2.50 1.00
e. A353 6b multicolored   3.00 1.00

Miniature Sheet

Ministry of Transportation and
Communication — A354

Designs: a, Automobiles. b, Ship. c, Train, Cathedral. d, Letters, telegraph key. e, Communication towers. f, Highway. g, Airplane. h, Locomotive, rail caution signs. i, Satellite dish. j, Satellite in orbit.

1987, July 16
1392   Sheet of 10   6.25 6.25
a.-e. A354 2b any single   .20 .20
f.-j. A354 2.25b any single   .20 .20

Nos. 1392a and 1392f, 1392b and 1392g, 1392c and 1392h, 1392d and 1392i, 1392e and 1392j have continuous designs.

Miniature Sheet

Venezuela
Navigation
Company,
70th Anniv.
A355

Designs: a, Corporate headquarters. b, Fork lift. c, Ship's Superstructure. d, Engine room. e, The Zulia. f, The Guarico. g, Ship's officer on the bridge. h, Bow of supertanker. i, Loading dock. j, Map of sea routes.

1987, July 31   Litho.   Perf. 12
1393   Sheet of 10   6.25 6.25
a.-b. A355 2b, any single   .20 .20
c.-d. A355 3b, any single   .25 .20

e.-f. A355 4b, any single   .30 .20
g.-h. A355 5b, any single   .40 .20
i.-j. A355 6b, any single   .45 .25

Nos. 1393a, 1393c, 1393e, 1393g and 1393i in vertical strip; No. 1393b, 1393d, 1393f, 1393h and 1393j in vertical strip.

Miniature Sheet

Natl.
Guard, 50th
Anniv.
A356

a, f, Air-sea rescue. b, g, Traffic control. c, h, Environment and nature protection. d, i, Border control. e, j, Industrial security.

1987, Aug. 6
1394   Sheet of 10   40.00 40.00
a.-e. A356 2b, any single   1.25 .25
f.-j. A356 4b, any single   3.00 .50

Discovery
of America,
500th
Anniv. (in
1992)
A357

20th cent. paintings (details): 2b, Departure from Port of Palos, by Jacobo Borges. 7b, Discovery of America, by Tito Salas. 11.50b, El Padre de las Casas, Protector of the Indians, by Salas. 12b, Trading in Venezuela at the Time of the Conquest, by Salas. 12.50b, Defeat of Guaicaipuro, by Borges.

1987, Oct.   Litho.   Perf. 12
1395   Strip of 5   8.00 8.00
a. A357 2b multi   .20 .20
b. A357 7b multi   .60 .30
c. A357 11.50b multi   1.00 .45
d. A357 12b multi   1.10 .55
e. A357 12.50b multi   1.25 .55

Christmas
1987 — A358

Paintings and sculpture representing the Spanish Colonial School, 18th cent.: 2b, *The Annunciation,* by Juan Pedro Lopez (1724-1787). 3b, *Nativity,* by Jose Francisco Rodriguez (1767-1818). 5.50b, *Adoration of the Magi,* anonymous. 6b, *Flight into Egypt,* by Lopez.

1987, Nov. 17   Litho.   Perf. 12
1396   Block of 4   6.75 6.75
a. A358 2b multi   .25 .25
b. A358 3b multi   .30 .25
c. A358 5.50b multi   .50 .30
d. A358 6b multi   .60 .30

Miniature Sheet

Meeting of 8 Latin American
Presidents, 1st Anniv. — A360

1987, Nov. 23
1397   Sheet of 10   7.75 7.75
a. A359 2b multi   .20 .20
b. A359 6b multi   .60 .30
c. A359 7b multi   .70 .35
d. A359 11.50b multi   1.10 .55
e. A359 12b black   1.25 .60
f. A359 2b multi   .20 .20
g. A359 6b multi   .60 .30
h. A359 7b multi   .70 .35
i. A359 11.50b multi   1.10 .55
j. A359 12b multi   1.25 .60

1987, Nov. 26
1398 A360 6b multi   .60 .30

Pequiven
Petrochemical
Co., 10th
Anniv. — A361

1987, Dec. 1
1399   Strip of 5   7.75 7.75
a. A361 2b Plastics   .20 .20
b. A361 6b Refined oil products   .60 .30
c. A361 7b Fertilizers   .70 .30
d. A361 11.50b Installations   1.10 .55
e. A361 12b Expansion   1.25 .60

St. John
Bosco
(1815-88)
A362

Portrait of Bosco and: 2b, Map, children. 3b, National Church, Caracas. 4b, Vocational training (printer's apprentice). 5b, Church of Mary Auxiliadora. 6b, Missionary school (nun teaching children).

1987, Dec. 8
1400   Strip of 5   4.00 4.00
a. A362 2b multi   .20 .20
b. A362 3b multi   .30 .20
c. A362 4b multi   .40 .20
d. A362 5b multi   .45 .25
e. A362 6b multi   .60 .30

Redrawn Bolivar Type of 1976

1987, Dec. 31   Litho.   Perf. 12½
1401 A231 3b emerald grn   .30 .20
1402 A231 4b gray   .40 .20
1403 A231 5b vermilion   .45 .20
1404 A231 10b dark olive bister   .90 .25
1405 A231 15b rose claret   1.40 .35
1406 A231 20b bright blue   1.90 .45
1407 A231 25b olive bister   2.25 .55
1408 A231 30b dark violet   2.75 .70
1409 A231 50b carmine   4.75 1.25
Nos. 1401-1409 (9)   15.10 4.15

Nos. 1401-1409 inscribed Armitano.

29th Assembly of Inter-American
Development Bank Governors — A363

1988, Mar. 18   Litho.   Perf. 12
1410 A363 11.50b multi   1.00 .55

Miniature Sheet

Republic
Bank, 30th
Anniv.
A364

Bank functions and finance projects: a, Personal banking at branch. b, Capital for labor. c, Industrial projects. d, Financing technology. e, Exports and imports. f, Financing agriculture. g, Fishery credits. h, Dairy farming development. i, Construction projects. j, Tourism trade development.

1988, Apr. 11
1411   Sheet of 10   3.25 3.25
a.-e. A364 2b any single   .20 .20
f.-j. A364 6b any single   .45 .25

No. 1411 contains two strips of five.

Anti-Polio
Campaign
Day of
Victory,
May
25 — A365

Design: Polio victims pictured on bronze relief, Rotary and campaign emblems.

1988, May 20   Litho.   Perf. 12
1412 A365 11.50b multi   .90 .45

Carlos Eduardo Frias (1906-1986),
Founder of the Natl. Publicity
Industry — A366

1988, May 27   Litho.   Perf. 12
1414 A366   Pair   1.10 1.10
a.   4b multi   .35 .25
b.   10b multi   .75 .45

Publicity Industry, 50th anniv.

Venalum Natl.
Aluminum
Corp., 10th
Anniv. — A367

Designs: 2b, Factory interior. 6b, Electric smelter. 7b, Aluminum pipes. 11.50b, Aluminum blocks moved by crane. 12b, Soccer team, aluminum equipment on playing field.

1988, June 10
1415   Strip of 5   9.00 9.00
a. A367 2b multi   .30 .20
b. A367 6b multi   .80 .25
c. A367 7b multi   .90 .25
d. A367 11.50b multi   1.50 .55
e. A367 12b multi   1.50 .55

Nature Conservation — A368

Birds: 2b, Carduelis cucullata. 6b, Eudocimus ruber. 11.50b, Harpia harpyja.

12b, Phoenicopterus ruber ruber. 12.50b, Pauxi pauxi.

1988, June 17   Litho.   Perf. 12
1416	Strip of 5	4.25	4.25
a.	A368 2b multi	.25	.20
b.	A368 6b multi	.60	.25
c.	A368 11.50b multi	1.10	.45
d.	A368 12b multi	1.25	.40
e.	A368 12.50b multi	1.25	.45

Army Day — A369

Military uniforms: a, Simon Bolivar in dress uniform, 1828. b, Gen.-in-Chief Jose Antonio Paez in dress uniform, 1821. c, Liberation Army division gen., 1810. d, Brig. gen., 1820. e, Artillery corpsman, 1836. f, Alferez Regiment parade uniform, 1988. g, Division Gen. No. 1 dress uniform, 1988. h, Line Infantry Regiment, 1820. i, Promenade Infantry, 1820. j, Light Cavalry, 1820.

1988, June 20
1417	Sheet of 10	15.00	15.00
a., f.	A369 2b multi	.30	.20
b., g.	A369 6b multi	.75	.25
c., h.	A369 7b multi	.90	.25
d., i.	A369 11.50b multi	1.50	.45
e., j.	A369 12b multi	1.60	.45

Scabbard, Sword and Signature A370

Paintings by Tito Salas: 4.75b, The General's Wedding. 6b, Portrait. 7b, Battle of Valencia. 12b, Retreat from San Carlos.

1988, July 1   Litho.   Perf. 12
1418	Strip of 5	7.50	7.50
a.	A370 2b shown	.35	.25
b.	A370 4.75b multi	.65	.25
c.	A370 6b multi	.75	.25
d.	A370 7b multi	1.25	.30
e.	A370 12b multi	2.75	.45

General Rafael Urdaneta (b. 1788).

General Santiago Marino (b. 1788), by Martin Tovar y Tovar — A371

1988, July
1419	A371 4.75b multi	.45	.25

1988 Summer Olympics, Seoul — A372

1988, Aug. 2
1420	A372 12b multi	.90	.45

Electric Industry, Cent. A373

Buildings, 1888: 2b, 1st Office. 4.75b, Jaime Carrillo and electrical plant. 10b, Bolivar Plaza. 11.50b, Baralt Theater. 12.50b, Central Thermoelectric Plant, Ramon Lagoon, 1988.

1988, Oct. 25   Litho.   Perf. 12
1421	Strip of 5	6.50	6.50
a.	A373 2b multi	.20	.20
b.	A373 4.75b multi	.40	.20
c.	A373 10b multi	.80	.35
d.	A373 11.50b multi	.90	.45
e.	A373 12.50b multi	1.00	.45

Christmas — A374

Designs: 4b, Nativity (left side), by Tito Salas, 1936. 6b, Christ child, anonymous, 17th cent. 15b, Nativity (right side).

1988, Dec. 9
1422	4b multi	.30	.20
1423	6b multi	.45	.25
1424	15b multi	1.25	.60
a.	A374 Strip, #1423, 2 ea #1422, 1424	7.00	7.00

Miniature Sheet

Marian Year — A375

Icons: a, Our Lady of Copacabana, Bolivia. b, Our Lady of Chiquinquira, Colombia. c, Our Lady of Coromoto, Venezuela. d, Our Lady of the Clouds, Ecuador. e, Our Lady of Antigua, Panama. f, Our Lady of the Evangelization, Peru. g, Our Lady of Lujan, Argentina. h, Our Lady of Altagracia, Dominican Republic. i, Our Lady of Aparecida, Brazil. j, Our Lady of Guadalupe, Mexico.

1988, Aug. 15   Litho.   Perf. 12
1425	Sheet of 10	8.75	8.75
a.-e.	A375 4.75b any single	.35	.20
f.-j.	A375 6b any single	.40	.25

Juan Manuel Cagigal Observatory, Cent. — A376

Designs: 2b, Bardou refracting telescope. 4.75b, Universal theodolite AUZ-27. 6b, Bust of Cagigal. 11.50b, Boulton cupola and night sky over Caracas in September. 12b, Satellite photographing Hurricane Allen.

1989, Sept. 5
1426	Strip of 5	6.75	6.75
a.	A376 2b multicolored	.25	.25
b.	A376 4.75b multicolored	.45	.25
c.	A376 6b multicolored	.60	.30
d.	A376 11.50b multicolored	1.00	.50
e.	A376 12b multicolored	1.10	.60

Comptroller-General's Office, 50th Anniv. — A377

1988, Oct. 14   Litho.   Perf. 12
1427	A377 10b multi	.75	.40

Portrait of Founder Juan Pablo Rojas Paul, by Cristobal Rojas, 1890 — A378

1989, Oct. 21   Litho.   Perf. 12
1428	A378	6b Commemorative medal	.40	.25
1429	A378	6.50b shown	.45	.25
a.		Pair, #1428-1429	1.00	1.00

Natl. History Academy, cent.

Portrait of Ricardo A379

Paintings: No. 1430, Simon Bolivar and Dr. Mordechay Ricardo. No. 1430A, The Octagon. Nos. 1430-1430B printed in continuous design completing the painting The Liberator in Curacao, by John de Pool.

1989, Jan. 27   Litho.   Perf. 12
1430	A379	10b multi	.75	.40
1430A	A379	10b multi	.75	.40
1430B	A379	11.50b shown	1.10	.50
c.		Strip of 5, #1430B, 2 ea #1430-1430A	9.25	9.25

Convention with Holy See, 25th Anniv. — A380

Designs: a, Raul Leoni, constitutional president, 1964-69. b, Cardinal Quintero, archbishop of Caracas, 1960-80. c, Arms of Cardinal Lebrun, archbishop of Caracas since 1980. d, Arms of Luciano Storero, titular archbishop of Tigimma. e, Pope Paul VI.

1989, May 4   Litho.   Perf. 12
1431	Strip of 5	4.00	4.00
a.-b.	A380 4b any single	.30	.20
c.-d.	A380 12b any single	.85	.55
	A380 16b multi	1.10	.75

Bank of Venezuela, Cent. A381

Designs: a, Cocoa Harvest, by Tito Salas, 1946. b, Teaching a Boy How to Grow Coffee,

---

by Salas, 1946. c, Bank headquarters, Caracas. d, Archive of the Liberator, Caracas. e, Archive of the Liberator, Caracas. e, Aforestation campaign (seedling). f, Aforestation campaign (five youths planting seedlings). g, 50-Bolivar bank note (left side). h, 50 Bolivar bank note (right side). i, 500-Bolivar bank note (left side). j, 500-Bolivar bank note (right side).

1989, Aug. 1
1432	Sheet of 10	8.50	8.50
a.-f.	A381 4b any single	.25	.20
g.-j.	A381 8b any single	.60	.35

Nos. 1432g-1432h and 1432i-1432j printed in continuous designs.

America Issue — A382

UPAE emblem and pre-Columbian votive bisque artifacts: 6b, Vessel. 24b, Statue of a man.

1989
1433	A382 6b multicolored	.40	.25
1434	A382 24b multicolored	2.75	1.40
a.	Pair, #1433-1434	3.75	3.75

Christmas A383

a, Shepherds, sheep. b, Angel appears to 3 shepherds. c, Holy Family. 12b, Two witnesses. 15b, Adoration of the kings.

1989   Litho.   Perf. 12
1435	Strip of 5	11.50	11.50
a.	A383 5b shown	.40	.25
b.-c.	A383 6b any single	.45	.25
d.	A383 12b multicolored	1.00	.45
e.	A383 15b multicolored	1.10	.45

Miniature Sheets

Bank of Venezuela, 20th Anniv. — A384

Tree and arms: No. 1436: a, Tabebuia chrysantha, national. b, Ceiba pentandra, Federal District. c, Myrospermum frutescens, Anzoategui. d, Pithecellobium saman, Aragua. e, Cedrela odorata, Barinas. f, Diptenyx punctata, Bolivar. g, Licania pyrofolia, Apure. h, Sterculia apetala, Carabobo.

No. 1437: a, Tabebuia rosea, Cojedes. b, Prosopis juliflora, Falcon. c, Copernicia tectorum, Guarico. d, Erythrina poeppigiana, Merida. e, Brawnea leucantha, Miranda. f, Mauritia flexuosa, Monagas. g, Malpighia glabra, Lara. h, Guaicum officinale, Nueva Esparta.

No. 1438: a, Swietenia macrophylla, Portuguesa. b, Platymiscium diadelphum, Sucre. c, Prumnopitys montana de Laub, Tachira. d, Roystonea venezuelana, Yaracuy. e, Cocos nucifera, Zulia. f, Hevea benthamiana, Federal Territory of Amazonas. g, Erythrina fusca, Trujillo. h, Rhizophora mangle, Territory of the Amacuro Delta.

1990, June 27   Litho.   Perf. 12
1436	Sheet of 8 + 2 labels	15.00	15.00
a.-f.	A384 10b any single	.50	.25
g.	A384 40b multicolored	2.00	1.00
h.	A384 50b multicolored	2.50	1.25
1437	Sheet of 8 + 2 labels	15.00	15.00
a.-f.	A384 10b any single	.50	.25
g.	A384 40b multicolored	2.00	1.00
h.	A384 50b multicolored	2.50	1.25

438	Sheet of 8 + 2 labels	15.00	15.00
a.-f.	A384 10b any single	.50	
g.	A384 40b multicolored	2.00	1.00
h.	A384 50b multicolored	2.50	1.25

Central Bank of Venezuela, 50th Anniv. A385

Designs: a, Santa Capilla Headquarters, 1943. b, Headquarters, 1967. c, Left half of 500b Bank Note, 1940. d, Right half of 500b Bank Note, 1940. e, Sun of Peru decoration, 1825. f, Medals Ayacucho, 1824, Boyaca, 1820 and Liberators of Quito, 1822. g, Swords of Peru, 1825. h, Cross pendant, Bucaramanga, 1830. i, Medallion of George Washington, 1826. j, Portrait of Gen. O'Leary.

1990, Oct. 15

1439	Sheet of 10	10.50	10.50
a.-f.	A385 10b any single	.50	.30
g.-h.	A385 15b any single	.75	.35
i.	A385 40b multicolored	2.00	1.00
j.	A385 50b multicolored	2.50	1.25

University of Zulia, Cent. A386

Designs: a, Dr. Francisco Ochoa, founder. b, Dr. Jesus E. Lossada, President, 1946-47. c, Soil conservation. d, Developing alternative automotive fuels. e, Organ transplants.

1990, Sept. 18   Litho.   Perf. 12

1440	Strip of 5	8.00	8.00
a.-b.	A386 10b any single	.50	.30
c.-d.	A386 15b any single	.75	.35
e.	A386 20b multicolored	1.10	.55

Christmas A387

Paintings: a, St. Joseph and Child by Juan Pedro Lopez. b, The Nativity by Lopez. c, The Return from Egypt by Matheo Moreno. d, The Holy Family by unknown artist. e, The Nativity (oval painting) by Lopez.

1990, Nov. 25

1441	Strip of 5	7.50	7.50
a.-c.	A387 10b any single	.50	.30
d.-e.	A387 20b any single	1.10	.55

OPEC, 30th Anniv. — A388

a, Globe. b, Square emblem. c, Circular emblem. d, Diamond emblem. e, Flags.

1990, Dec. 21   Litho.   Perf. 12

1442	Strip of 5	5.50	5.50
a.-b.	A388 10b any single	.50	.30
c.	A388 20b multicolored	1.10	.55
d.	A388 30b multicolored	1.50	.75
e.	A388 40b multicolored	2.00	1.10

America Issue — A389

1990, Dec. 12   Litho.   Perf. 12

1443	A389 10b Lake dwelling	.50	.30
1444	A389 40b Coastline	2.00	1.00
a.	Pair, #1443-1444	4.00	4.00

Exfilve '90, Caracas — A389a

Designs: 40b, Bank of Venezuela 1000b note. 50b, Bank of Caracas 100b note.

1990, Nov. 16   Imperf.

1444B	A389a 40b multicolored	2.25	2.25
1444C	A389a 50b multicolored	2.75	2.75

No. 1444B, Bank of Venezuela, cent. No. 1444C, Bank of Caracas, cent.

St. Ignatius of Loyola (1491-1556) A390

Designs: a, Jesuit quarters, Caracas. b, Death mask. c, Statue by Francisco de Vergara, 18th century. d, Statue of Our Lady of Montserrat, 11th century.

1991, Apr. 12   Litho.   Perf. 12

1445	Strip of 4 + label	12.50	12.50
a.-b.	A390 12b any single	.55	.30
c.	A390 40b multicolored	2.00	.90
d.	A390 50b multicolored	2.25	1.10

Venezuelan-American Cultural Center, 50th Anniv. — A391

Designs: a, Elisa Elvira Zuloaga (1900-1980), painter & engraver. b, Gloria Stolk (1912-1979), writer. c, Caroline Lloyd (1924-1980), composer. d, Jules Waldman (1912-1990), publisher. e, William Coles (1908-1978), attorney.

1991, July 4   Litho.   Perf. 12

1446	Strip of 5	12.50	12.50
a.-c.	A391 12b any single	.55	.30
d.	A391 40b multicolored	2.00	1.00
e.	A391 50b multicolored	2.25	1.10

Miniature Sheet

Orchids — A392

Designs: No. 1447a, 12b, Acineta alticola. b, 12b, Brassavola nodosa. c, 12b, Brachionidium brevicaudatum. d, 12b, Bifrenaria maguirei. e, 12b, Odontoglossum spectatissimum. f, 12b, Catasetum macrocarpum. g, 40b, Mendocella jorisiana. h, 40b, Cochleanthes discolor. i, 50b, Maxillaria splendens. j, 50b, Pleurothallis dunstervillei. No. 1448, Cattleya violacea.

1991, Aug. 22   Litho.   Perf. 12

1447	A392	Sheet of 10, #a.-j.	15.00	15.00

Souvenir Sheet

1448	A392 50b multicolored	5.50	5.50

No. 1448 contains one 42x37mm stamp. No. 1447 exists imperf. Value $42.50. See Nos. 1499-1500, 1508-1509.

Democratic Action Party, 50th Anniv. — A393

Designs: a, People voting. b, Agricultural reform. c, Students and teachers. d, Nationalization of the petroleum industry.

1991, Sept. 13   Litho.   Perf. 12

1449	A393 12b Block of 4, #a.-d.	2.00	2.00

America Issue A394

1991, Oct. 24

1450	A394 12b Terepaima Chief	.45	.25
1451	A394 40b Paramaconi Chief	2.00	1.25
a.	Pair, #1450-1451	2.50	2.50

Children's Foundation, 25th Anniv. — A395

Children's drawings: a, 12b, Children in house. b, 12b, Playground. c, 12b, Carnival. d, 12b, Woman and girl walking by pond. e, 12b, Boy in hospital. f, 12b, Five children around tree. g, 40b, Two girls in colorful room. h, 40b, Classroom. i, 50b, Three children. j, 50b, Four children dancing.

1991, Oct. 31   Litho.   Perf. 12

1452	A395 Sheet of 10, #a.-j.	12.00	12.00

Nos. 1362-1364 Surcharged

1991   Litho.   Perf. 12½

1453	A231	5b on 25c red	.20	.20
1454	A231	5b on 75c pink	.20	.20
1455	A231	10b on 25c red	.40	.20
1456	A231	10b on 75c pink	.40	.20
1457	A231	12b on 50c blue	.50	.25
1458	A231	12b on 75c pink	.50	.25
1459	A231	20b on 50c blue	.80	.40
1460	A231	20b on 75c pink	.80	.40
1461	A231	40b on 50c blue	1.60	.80
1462	A231	40b on 75c pink	1.60	.80
1463	A231	50b on 50c blue	2.00	1.00
1464	A231	50b on 75c pink	2.00	1.00
	Nos. 1453-1464 (12)		11.00	5.70

Christmas A396

Children's art work: a, 10b, Wise men. b, 12b, Holy Family. c, 20b, Statues of Holy Family. d, 25b, Shepherds. e, 30b, Holy Family, cow, donkey.

1991, Nov. 14   Litho.   Perf. 12

1465	A396 Strip of 5, #a.-e.	6.75	6.75

866

VENEZUELA

Souvenir Sheet

Exfilve '91, Caracas — A397

1991, Nov. 29   Litho.   *Perf. 12*
1466   A397   50b   No. 136   2.10   2.10

Discovery of America, 500th Anniv. (in 1992) A398

a, 12b, Coat of arms of Columbus. b, 12b, Santa Maria. c, 12b, Map by Juan de la Cosa. d, 40b, Sighting land. e, 50b, Columbus with Queen Isabella and King Ferdinand II.

1991, Dec. 12   Litho.   *Perf. 12*
1468   A398   Strip of 5, #a.-e.   4.75   4.75

1992, Mar. 15

Designs: No. 1469a, 12b, Emblem for discovery of America Commission. b, 12b, Venezuelan pavillion, Expo '92. c, 12b, 15th century map of Spain. d, 12b, Portrait of Columbus, by Susy Dembo. e, 12b, Encounter, by Ivan Jose Rojas. f, 12b, 0x500 America, by Annella Armas. g, 40b, Imago-Mundi, by Alessandro Grechi. h, 40b, Long Journey, by Gloria Fiallo. i, 50b, Playa Dorado, by Carlos Riera. j, 50b, Irminaoro, by Erasmo Sanches Cedeno. No. 1470, Untitled work, by Mauricio Sanchez.

1469   A398   Sheet of 10, #a.-j.   12.00   12.00
1470   A398   50b multicolored   2.25   2.25

Expo '92, Seville. No. 1470 contains one 38x42mm stamp.

Protection of Nature — A399

Turtles: No. 1471a, Geochelone carbonaria, facing left. b, Geochelone carbonaria, facing right. c, Podocnemis expansa, facing left. d, Podocnemis expansa, swimming.

1992, June 12   Litho.   *Perf. 12*
1471   A399   12b Block of 4, #a.-d.   4.75   2.50
World Wildlife Fund.

Miniature Sheet

Beatification of Josemaria Escriva — A400

Designs: a, 18b, Teaching in Venezuela, 1975. b, 18b, Celebrating mass. c, 18b, Parents, Jose Escriva and Dolores Albas. d, 18b, Text with autograph. e, 18b, Kissing feet of Madonna. f, 18b, Commemorative medallion. g, 60b, With Pope Paul VI. h, 60b, At desk,

---

writing. i, 75b, Portrait. j, 75b, Portrait in St. Peter's Square, 1992.

1992, Oct. 2   Litho.   *Perf. 12*
1472   A400   Sheet of 10, #a.-j.   12.00   12.00

Electrification of Southern Regions A401

Designs: a, 12b, Roof of native hut. b, 12b, Transmission lines and towers. c, 12b, Horses running through pond. d, 40b, Workmen under tower. e, 50b, Baskets, crafts.

1992, July 15   Litho.   *Perf. 12*
1473   A401   Strip of 5, #a.-e.   2.75   2.75

Miniature Sheet

Artwork, by Mateo Manaure — A402

Color of background: a, 12b, Red. b, 12b, Red violet. c, 12b, Gray. d, 12b, Violet brown. e, 40b, Brown. f, 40b, Blue. g, 50b, Blue violet. h, 50b, Black.

1993, July 23
1474   A402   Sheet of 8, #a.-h. + 2 labels   6.00   6.00

Bank of Maracaibo, 110th anniv.

Discovery of America, 500th Anniv. — A403

Paintings: a, 18b, The Third Trip, by Elio Caldera. b, 60b, Descontextura, by Juan Pablo Nascimiento.

1992, Nov. 20   Litho.   *Perf. 12*
1476   A403   Pair, #a.-b.   2.40   2.40

Christmas A404

Artwork by Lucio Rivas: a, 18b, Adoration of the Shepherds. b, 75b, Adoration of the Magi.

100b, Flight into Egypt.

1992, Dec. 3   Litho.   *Perf. 12*
1477   A404   Pair, #a.-b.   2.75   2.75

Souvenir Sheet

1478   A404   100b multicolored   2.75   2.75

No. 1478 contains one 42x38mm stamp.

Redrawn Bolivar Type of 1976 and

A405   A406

Designs: 5b, Natl. Pantheon. 10b, Victory Monument, Carabobo. 20b, Jose Antonio Paez. 25b, Luisa Caceres de Arismendi. 35b, Ezequiel Zamora. 40b, Cristobal Mendoza. #1490, Central University. #1491, Jose Felix Ribas. #1494, Manuel Piar. 200b, Simon Bolivar.

1993-94   Litho.   *Perf. 12½*
Size: 18x22mm

1479	A405	1b silver	.25	.20
1480	A405	2b greenish blue	.25	.20
1482	A231	5b red	.25	.20
1484	A231	10b violet	.25	.20
1487	A231	20b olive green	.55	.25
1488	A405	25b red brown	.40	.30
1488A	A405	35b brt yel grn	.60	.40
1489	A405	40b lt blue	.65	.45
1490	A231	50b orange	1.40	.60
1491	A405	50b lilac rose	.90	.65
1493	A406	100b brown	2.75	1.40
1494	A405	100b dark blue	1.75	1.00
1496	A405	200b brown	3.50	2.00
		Nos. 1479-1496 (13)	13.50	7.85

Nos. 1479-1493 inscribed Armitano.
See Nos. 1548-1562.

Orchid Type of 1991
Miniature Sheet

Designs: a, 20b, Cattleya percivaliana. b, 20b, Anguloa ruckeri. c, 20b, Chondrorhyncha flaveola. d, 20b, Stenia pallida. e, 20b, Zygosepalum lindeniae. f, 20b, Maxillaria triloris. g, 80b, Stanhopea wardii. h, 80b, Oncidium papilio. i, 100b, Oncidium hastilabium. j, 100b, Sobralia cattleya. 150b, Polycycnis muscifera.

1993, Apr. 1   Litho.   *Perf. 12*
1499   A392   Sheet of 10, #a.-j.   13.00   13.00

Souvenir Sheet

1500   A392   150b multicolored   5.00   5.00

Miniature Sheet

Settlement of Tovar Colony, 150th Anniv. — A408

Designs: a, 24b, Woman. b, 24b, Children. c, 24b, Catholic Church, 1862. d, 24b, Statue of St. Martin of Tours, 1843. e, 24b, Fruits and vegetables. f, 24b, School, 1916. g, 80b, Home of founder, Augustin Codazzi, 1845. h, 80b, House of colony director, Alexander

---

Benitz, 1845. i, 100b, Breidenbach Mill, 1860. j, 100b, Parade.

1993, Apr. 12   Litho.   *Perf. 12*
1501   A408   Sheet of 10, #a.-j.   12.50   12.50

Miniature Sheet

19th Pan-American Railways Conference — A409

Designs: a, 24b, Tucacas steam locomotive. b, 24b, Halcon steam locomotive on Las Mostazas Bridge, 1894. c, 24b, Maracaibo locomotive. d, 24b, Tender, rail cars, Palo Grande Station. e, 24b, Fiat diesel locomotive, 1957. f, 24b, GP-9-L diesel locomotive, 1957. g, 80b, GP-15-L diesel locomotive, 1982. h, 80b, Metro subway train, Caracas. i, 100b, Electric locomotive. j, 100b, Passenger cars of electric train.

1993, May 25   Litho.   *Perf. 12*
1502   A409   Sheet of 10, #a.-j.   15.00   15.00

Nos. 1502c-1502d, 1502i-1502j are continuous designs.

A410   A411

World Day to Stop Smoking: a, 24b, Shown. b, 80b, "No smoking" emblem.

1993, May 27   Litho.   *Perf. 12½x12*
1503   A410   Pair, #a.-b.   2.75   2.75

1993, Oct. 7   Litho.   *Perf. 12*

America Issue: a, 24b, Amazona barbadensis. b, 80b, Ara macao.

1504   A411   Pair, #a.-b.   4.75   4.75

Miniature Sheets

Native Indians — A412   Christmas — A413

Designs: No. 1505a, 1b, Two Yanomami children with painted bodies, spear. b, 1b, Yanomami woman preparing food. c, 40b, Two Panare children performing in Katyayinto ceremony. d, 40b, Panare man with nose flute. e, 40b, Taurepan man in canoe. f, 40b, Taurepan girl weaving. g, 40b, Piaroa woman with infant. h, 40b, Piaroa dancers wearing war masks. i, 100b, Hoti man blowing flute. j, 100b, Hoti woman carrying baby, basket over back.
150b, Child blowing traditional whistle.

1993, Nov. 25 **Litho.** *Perf. 12*
1505 A412 Sheet of 10,
#a.-j. 9.25 9.25
Souvenir Sheet
1506 A412 150b multicolored 3.25 3.25

1993, Nov. 30
Nativity scene: a, f, 24b, Joseph. b, g, 24b, Madonna and Child. c, h, 24b, Shepherd boy, wise man holding gift, lambs. d, i, 80b, Wise man with hands folded, boy. e, j, 100b, Wise man presenting gift, boy with hands folded.
1507 A413 Sheet of 10, #a.-j. 10.50 10.50
Nos. 1507f-1507j are black, magenta & buff.

Orchid Type of 1991
Miniature Sheet

Designs: a, 35b, Chrysocycnis schlimii. b, 35b, Galeandra minax. c, 35b, Oncidium falcipetalum. d, 35b, Oncidium lanceanum. e, 40b, Sobralia violacea linden. f, 40b, Sobralia infundibuligera. g, 80b, Mendoncella burkei. h, 80b, Phragmipedium caudatum. i, 100b, Phragmipedium kaieteurum. j, 200b, Stanhopea grandiflora.
150b, Epidendrum elongatum.

1994, May 19 **Litho.** *Perf. 12*
1508 A392 Sheet of 10,
#a.-j. 15.00 15.00
Souvenir Sheet
1509 A392 150b multicolored 3.00 3.00
No. 1509 contains one 42x37mm stamp.

Miniature Sheet of 10

FEDECAMARAS (Federal Council of Production & Commerce Associations), 50th Anniv. — A414

a, 35b; f, 80b, Anniversary emblem. b, 35b; e, 80b, Luis Gonzalo Marturet (1914-64), 1st president. c, 35b; d, 80b, FEDECAMARAS emblem.

1994, July 17 **Litho.** *Perf. 12*
1510 A414 #c, f, 2 ea #a-b, d-e 9.75 9.75

Judicial
Service
A415

1994, Sept. 13 **Litho.** *Perf. 12*
1511 A415 100b multicolored 1.75 1.75

Miniature Sheet

Christmas
A416

Paintings: a, 35b, g, 80b, The Nativity, by follower of Jose Lorenzo de Alvarado. b, 35b, h, 80b, Birth of Christ, 19th cent. c, 35b, i, 80b, The Nativity, diff., by follower of Jose Lorenzo de Alvarado. d, 35b, j, 80b, Adoration of the Magi, 17th cent.. e, 35b, f, 80b, Birth of Christ, by School of Tocuyo.

1994, Dec. 1
1512 A416 Sheet of 10, #a.-j. 9.75 9.75

Miniature Sheet

Antonio Jose de Sucre (1795-1830) — A417

Designs: No. 1513a, 25b, Portrait. b, 25b, Dona Mariana Carcelen Y Larrea Marquesa de Solanda. c, 35b, Top of equestrian monument. d, 35b, Bottom of monument. e, 40b, Painting of Battle of Pichincha, mountains at top. f, 40b, Painting of Battle of Pichincha, battle scent. g, 80b, Painting of Battle of Ayacucho, soldiers on horseback. h, 80b, Painting of Battle of Ayacucho, dead soldiers. i, 100b, Painting of Surrender at Ayachucho, general signing document. j, 100b, Painting of Surrender at Ayachucho, seated general at right.
150b, Portion of mural, Carabobo, by Pedro Centeno Vallenilla.

1995, Feb. 2
1513 A417 Sheet of 10, #a.-j. 9.50 9.50
Souvenir Sheet
1514 A417 150b multicolored 2.50 2.50

Postal Transportation — A418

a, 35b, Post office van. b, 80b, Airplane.

1995, Mar. 22 **Litho.** *Perf. 12*
1515 A418 Pair, #a.-b. 2.10 2.10
No. 1515 issued in sheets of 10 stamps.

Miniature Sheet

St. Jean-Baptiste de La Salle (1651-1719), Educator — A419

Denomination LR: a, 100b, Portrait. b, 35b, Students with microscope, academic education. c, 35b, Soccer players, sports education. d, 35b, Scouts at camp, citizenship education. e, 80b, La Salle College, Caracas.
Denomination LL: f, like #1516e. g, like #1516d. h, like #1516b. i, like #1516c. j, like #1516a.

1995, May 15
1516 A419 Sheet of 10, #a.-j. 7.75 7.75

Miniature Sheet

Founding of
Salesian
Order,
Cent.
A420

Designs: a, 35b, St. John Bosco (1815-88), priest with child. b, 35b, Lonely child, Madonna and Child. c, 35b, Man running machine tool. d, 35b, Young men working with electronic instruments. e, 35b, Baseball game. f, 35b, Basketball game. g, 80b, People working in fields. h, 80b, Man looking at chili peppers. i, 100b, Young tribal natives receiving religious training. j, 100b, Tribal native.

1995, Apr. 26
1517 A420 Sheet of 10, #a.-j. 7.75 7.75

Miniature Sheet

Orchids
A421

Designs: a, 35b, Maxillaria guareimensis. b, 35b, Paphinia lindeniana. c, 50b, Catasetum longifolium. d, 50b, Anguloa clowesii. e, 35b, Coryanthes biflora. f, 35b, Catasetum pileatum. g, 80b, Maxillaria histrionica. h, 80b, Sobralia ruckeri. i, 35b, Mormodes convolutum. j, 35b, Huntleya lucida.
150b, Catasetum barbatum.

1995, May 31 **Litho.** *Perf. 12*
1518 A421 Sheet of 10, #a.-j. 8.00 8.00
Souvenir Sheet
1519 A421 150b multicolored 2.25 2.25
No. 1519 contains one 42x36mm stamp.
See #1534-1535, 1563-1564, 1587-1588.

CAF (Andes
Development
Corporation),
25th
Anniv. — A422

1995, June 7
1520 A422 80b multicolored 1.25 1.25

Miniature Sheet

Beatification
of Mother
Maria of San
Jose
A423

Designs: a, 35b, In formal habit. b, 35b, Pope John Paul II. c, 35b, As young woman distributing Bibles. d, 35b, Doing embroidery work. e, 35b, Statue of Madonna, altar. f, 35b, Kneeling in devotions. g, 80b, Walking with Sisters in hospital. h, 80b, With patient in hospital. i, 100b, Working with children. j, 100b, Helping person seated along road.

1995, July 2
1521 A423 Sheet of 10, #a.-j. 9.25 9.25
Nos. 1521a-1521b, 1521c-1521d, 1521e-1521f, 1521g-1521h, 1521i-1521j are each continuous designs.

UN, 50th Anniv. — A424

Designs: a, People from different countries unfurling UN flag. b, Emblem on UN flag.

1995, June 26
1522 A424 50b Pair, #a.-b. 3.00 3.00

Gen. José Gregorio Monagas (1795-1858), President, Liberator of the Slaves — A425

a, Portrait. b, Slave family with opened chains.

1995, July 26 **Litho.** *Perf. 12*
1523 A425 50b Pair, #a.-b. 1.40 1.40

Slave Rebellion, Bicent. — A426

Jose Leonardo Chirino and: a, Liberty leading the people (after Delacroix). b, Revolutionaries with weapons.

1995, Aug. 16
1524 A426 50b Pair, #a.-b. 1.50 1.50

Venezuelan
Red Cross,
Cent.
A427

Designs: a, 100b, Red Cross flag. b, 80b, Carlos J. Bello Hospital. c, 35b, Surgery scene. d, 35b, Rescue workers carrying victim. e, 35b, Care givers with child.

1995, Aug. 30
1525 A427 Strip of 5, #a.-e. 4.50 4.50

America
Issue
A428

Environmental protection: a, 35b, Trees, lake. b, 80b, Flowers, hillside.

1995, Sept. 13 **Litho.** *Perf. 12*
1526 A428 Pair, #a.-b. 2.00 2.00
No. 1526 was issued in sheets of 10 stamps.
No. 1526 exists in two types: the heavy border at top is above "America" only: the heavy line extends over the denomination. Values the same.

Miniature Sheet

Native
Aboriginals
A429

No. 1527: a, 25b, Kuana man seated on post. b, 25b, Kuana woman using stones to do laundry. c, 35b, Guahibo people, one playing flute. d, 35b, Guahibo shaman with child. e, 50b, Uruak man with tree branch. f, 50b, Uruak woman cooking. g, 80b, Warao woman spinning twine. h, 80b, Warao man, woman in boat. i, 100b, Bari men with bows, arrows. j, 100b, Bari man rubbing sticks to make fire. 150b, Young boy with bird.

1995, Oct. 18
1527 A429   Sheet of 10, #a.-j.   8.75 8.75

Souvenir Sheet
1528 A429 150b multicolored   2.40 2.40
See Nos. 1541-1542.

Miniature Sheet

Electricity in Caracas, Cent. A430

Designs: a, 35b, Ricardo Zuloaga, early pioneer. b, 35b, Early electric plant. c, 35b, Substation. d, 35b, 1908 Electric trams. e, 35b, Electric lampposts mandated by Congress, 1908. f, 35b, Lampposts, Bolivar Plaza. g, 80b, Electrical repairman. h, 80b, Lighted cross, Avila. i, 100b, Teresa Carreño Cultural Complex. j, 100b, Ricardo Zuloaga main generator plant.

1995, Nov. 6
1529 A430 Sheet of 10, #a.-j.   9.00 9.00

Miniature Sheet

Christmas A431

Designs: a, 35b, The Annunciation. b, 35b, Being turned away at the inn. c, 100b, Birth of Christ in the stable. d, 35b, Angel appearing to shepherds. e, 35b, Three Magi. f, 40b, Christmas pageant. g, 40b, Children skating. h, 100b, Christmas presents. i, 40b, Women preparing food for holidays. j, 40b, Children, mother preparing food for holidays.

1995, Nov. 15
1530 A431 Sheet of 10, #a.-j.   8.50 8.50
Nos. 1530f-1530g, and 1530i-1530j are each continuous designs.

Miniature Sheet

Petroleum Industries of South America (PDVSA), 20th Anniv. A432

a, 35b, PDVSA emblem, 7 petroleum company emblems. b, PDVSA emblem, 6 petroleum company emblems. c, 80b, Oil derrick. d, 80b, Refinery. e, 35b, Oil tanker crossing under bridge. f, 35b, Worker, orimulsion tanks. g, 35b, Two people examining carbon. h, 35b, Semi truck hauling petrochemicals. i, 35b, Filling station. j, 35b, Gas storage tanks.

1995, Dec. 13   Litho.   Perf. 12
1531 A432 Sheet of 10, #a.-j.   9.00 9.00

Miniature Sheet

Town of El Tocuyo, 450th Anniv. A433

Designs: a, 35b, City arms. b, 35b, Workers in sugar cane field. c, Church of Our Lady of Immaculate Conception. d, Statue of Madonna inside church. e, 35b, Ruins of Temple of Santa Domingo. f, 35b, House of Culture. g, 80b, Cactus, vegetation. h, 80b, Cactus up close. i, 100b, Dancers with swords. j, 100b, Man playing guitar.

1995, Dec. 5
1532 A433 Sheet of 10, #a.-j.   9.00 9.00

Miniature Sheet

Vist of Pope John Paul II — A434

Statues of various saints, Pope and: a, 25b, Children. b, 25b, Man, woman. c, 40b, Man, woman, baby. d, 40b, Elderly man. e, 50b, Woman, boy. f, 50b, Sick person. g, 60b, Man in prison. h, 60b, Working man. i, 100b, People of various career fields. j, 100b, Priests, nuns.
200b, Pope John Paul II holding crucifix.

1996, Jan. 26
1533 A434   Sheet of 10, #a.-j.   9.00 9.00

Souvenir Sheet
1533K A434 200b multicolored   2.50 2.50

Orchid Type of 1995

Designs: a, Epidendrum fimbriatum. b, Myoxanthus reymondii. c, Catasetum pileatum. d, Ponthieva maculata. e, Maxillaria triloris. f, Scaphosepalum breve. g, Cleistes rosea. h, Maxillaria sophronitis. i, Catasetum discolor. j, Oncidium ampliatum.
200b, Odontoglossum naevium.

1996, May 31   Litho.   Perf. 12
1534 A421 60b Sheet of 10, #a.-j.   7.25 7.25

Souvenir Sheet
1535 A421 200b multicolored   2.50 2.50

1996 Summer Olympic Games, Atlanta A435

Designs: a, Emblem of Olympic Committee. b, Swimmer. c, Boxer. d, Cyclist. e, Medal winners.

1996, June 28   Litho.   Perf. 12
1536 A435 130b Strip of 5, #a.-e.   6.50 6.50
No. 1536 was issued in a sheet of 10 stamps.

Use of Automation at Maiquetia Intl. Airport, 25th Anniv. A436

Designs: a, Symbol of automation. b, Map of airport flight routes. c, La Guaira Airdrome, 1929. d, Maiqueitia Airport, 1944. e, Simon Bolivar Airport, 1972. f, Interior view of terminal. g, Airport police, control tower. h, Airport firetruck. i, Airplane at terminal, Simon Bolivar Airport. j, Airplane on taxiway, Simon Bolivar Airport.

1996, Aug. 4
1537 A436 80b Sheet of 10, #a-j   8.50 8.50

America Issue A437

Traditional costumes: a, 60b, Women's. b, 130b, Men's.

1996, Sept. 10
1538 A437 Pair, #a.-b.   2.00 2.00
No. 1538 was issued in sheets of 10 stamps.

Mario Briceño-Iragorry (1897-1958) — A438

Portraits: a, As young man, Trujillo, 1913. b, At University of Mérida, 1919. c, As politician, 1944. d, As writer, 1947. e, As older man, Caracas, 1952.

1996, Sept. 24
1539 A438 80b Strip of 5, #a.-e.   4.25 4.25
No. 1539 was issued in sheets of 10 stamps.

Caracas Rotary Club, 70th Anniv. — A439

1996, Oct. 3
1540 A439 50b multicolored   .55 .55
No. 1540 was issued in sheets of 10.

Native Aboriginal Type of 1995

Designs: a, 80b, Yukpa boy working in garden. b, 80b, Paraujanos girl carrying fruit. c, 80b, Kinaroes man, woman bundling cattails. d, 80b, Motilon man with bananas. e, 80b, Chaque mother carrying infant on back. f, 100b, Guajiros man, young woman fixing hair. g, 100b, Mucuchi man carrying pack on back. h, 100b, Mape man with bow and arrow. i, 100b, Macoa working with grain, painted faces. j, 100b, Yaruros man weaving.
200b, Woman breastfeeding infant.

1996, Oct. 11
1541 A429   Sheet of 10, #a.-j.   9.75 9.75

Souvenir Sheet
1542 A429 200b multicolored   2.10 2.10

Souvenir Sheet

Taipei '96, Intl. Philatelic Exhibition — A440

1996, Oct. 21   Litho.   Perf. 12
1543 A440 200b Ara chloroptera   5.25 5.25

José Gregorio Hernández (1864-1908), Physician — A441

a, As young boy. b, As student, anatomy drawing. c, Praying, Madonna statue. d, Thinking of the needy. e, In research study. f, A professor of university. g, Comforting sick patient. h, Empty chair at academy. i, Vargas Hospital, statue, portrait of Hernández. j, Hospital named after Hernández, statue.
200b, Portrait of Hernández.

1996, Oct. 26   Litho.   Perf. 1.
1544 A441 60b Sheet of 10, #a.-j.   4.50 4.5●

Souvenir Sheet
1545 A441 200b multicolored   1.50 1.5●
No. 1545 contains one 42x36mm stamp.

Christmas A442

Designs: a, 60b, Child setting up Nativity scene. b, 60b, Three men with guitars, woman. c, 60b, Rooster, people making music. d, 60b, People with painted faces dancing, singing. e, 60b, Men, woman playing drums, instruments. f, 80b, Exchanging gifts of food. g, 80b, Family at table, looking at gift of food. h, 80b, Child in hammock, presents. i, 80b, Parading replica of infant Jesus. j, 80b, Kissing feet of Christ Child.

1996, Nov. 7
1546 A442 Sheet of 10, #a.-j.   4.25 4.25

Andrés Eloy Blanco (1896-1955), Politician, Writer A443

Designs: a, As adolescent. b, As Caracas city official, government building. c, With family. d, With democratic founders. e, As politician, building. f, As President of Constituent Assembly, building. g, As "Poet of Pueblo." h, Lincoln Memorial, as Chancellor of the Republic. i, Author of writings on Spain, sailing ship. j, Map of Spain, sailing ships, conquistador on horseback.

1997, Feb. 17   Litho.   Perf. 12
1547 A443 100b Sheet of 10, #a.-j.   6.25 6.25

Simon Bolivar (1783-1830) — A444

1997, Mar. 7   Litho.   Perf. 13½x13
1548	A444	15b olive	.20	.20
1549	A444	20b brown org	.20	.20
1550	A444	40b dark brown	.25	.25
1551	A444	50b rose claret	.30	.30
1552	A444	70b deep violet	.45	.45
1553	A444	90b deep blue	.60	.60
1554	A444	200b dp grn bl	1.25	1.25
1555	A444	300b dp bl grn	1.25	1.25
1556	A444	400b gray	1.60	1.60
1557	A444	500b pale sepia	2.00	2.00
1558	A444	600b pale brown	2.40	2.40
1559	A444	800b pale vio brn	3.25	3.25
1560	A444	900b slate blue	3.50	3.50

1561	A444	1000b dk org brn	4.00	4.00
1562	A444	2000b olive bister	8.00	8.00
		Nos. 1548-1562 (15)	29.25	29.25

Orchid Type of 1995

Designs: a, Phragmipedium lindleyanum. b, Zygosepalum labiosum. c, Acacallis cyanea. d, Maxillaria camaridii. e, Scuticaria steelei. f, Aspasia variegata. g, Comparettia falcata. h, Scapyglottis stellata. i, Maxillaria ruffescens. j, Vanilla pompona.
250b, Rodriguezia lanceolata.

1997, May 30   **Perf. 12**
1563 A421 165b Sheet of 10,
        #a.-j.   6.75 6.75
Souvenir Sheet
1564 A421 250b multicolored   1.00 1.00
No. 1564 contains one 42x37mm stamp.

Independence Conspiracy of Gual and España, Bicent. — A445

#1565, José María España, proclamation for independence being read. #1566, España under arrest. #1567, Manuel Gual, soldiers. #1568, Gual fleeing through door, sailing ship, standing on Trinidad. #1569, Revolutionary flag, sailing ship.

1997, July 16
1565	A445	165b multicolored	.55	.55
1566	A445	165b multicolored	.55	.55
a.		Pair, #1565-1566	1.10	1.10
1567	A445	165b multicolored	.55	.55
a.		Pair, #1566-1567	1.10	1.10
1568	A445	165b multicolored	.55	.55
a.		Pair, #1567-1568	1.10	1.10
1569	A445	165b multicolored	.55	.55
a.		Pair, #1565, 1569	1.10	1.10
b.		Pair, #1568-1569	1.10	1.10

Printed in sheet of 10 containing one each #1566a, 1567a, 1568a, 1569a-1569b.

Treaty of Tlatelolco Banning Use of Nuclear Weapons in Latin America, 30th Anniv. — A446

Various stylized designs representing devastation resulting from use of nuclear weapons: a.-e., White inscriptions. f.-j., Black inscriptions.

1997, July 31
1570 A446 140b Sheet of 10,
        #a.-j.   6.50 6.50

Stories for Children — A447

"The Rabbit and the Tiger:" a, Rabbit, tiger carrying satchel. b, Watching rat figure digging. c, Watching turtle on his back. d, Rabbit. e, Rat in net, rabbit. f, Tiger, house, rat. g, Bird, rat, rabbit, bee, beehive. h, Rabbit, turtle. i, Tiger with stick over shoulder. j, Tiger with mouth open, bees.
250b, Rabbit, tiger.

1997, Aug. 7
1571 A447 55b Sheet of 10,
        #a.-j.   2.75 2.75
Souvenir Sheet
1572 A447 250b multicolored   1.25 1.25
No. 1572 contains one 42x37mm stamp. The reverse of Nos. 1571a-1571j are each inscribed with parts of the childrens' story.

Unexpected Adventures of a Postman — A448

America Issue: 110p, Giving letter to woman with dog. 280p, With motor scooter in rain.

1997, Aug. 29   **Litho.**   **Perf. 12**
1573	A448	110p multicolored	.90	.90
1574	A448	280p multicolored	2.00	2.00
a.		Pair, #1573-1574	5.00	5.00

No. 1574a was issued in sheets of 10 stamps.

Villa of Anauco Villa, Bicent. A449

Designs: a, Inscription. b, Main entrance. c, Entrance corridor. d, Interior patio. e, Exterior corridor leading to kitchen. f, Kitchen. g, Stairs leading to balcony. h, Coach house. i, Stable. j, Outside stable, water trough.

1997, Sept. 23
1575 A449 110b Sheet of 10,
        #a.-j.   5.00 5.00

Independence in India, 50th Anniv. — A450

Designs: a, 165b, Jawaharlal Nehru. b, 200b, Sardar Patel, flag. c, 165b, Congressional building. d, 200b, Gandhi. e, 165b, Purification at the Ganges. f, 200b, Rabindranath Tagore. g, 165b, Motion picture industry. h, 200b, Traditional music. i, 165b, Insat-1B meteorological satellite. j, 200b, Use of modern technology.
250b, Minarets of Taj Majal.

1997, Oct. 2
1576 A450 Sheet of 10, #a.-j.   8.50 8.50
Souvenir Sheet
1577 A450 250b multicolored   1.60 1.60

Heinrich von Stephan (1831-97) A451

a, 110b, Portrait. b, 280b, UPU emblem.

1997, Oct. 9   **Litho.**   **Perf. 12**
1578 A451 Pair, #a.-b.   1.10 1.10

Wicker-work A452

No. 1579: a, Red basket, Ye'Kuana. b, With handles, Ye'Kuana. c, Round, Ye'Kuana. d, Tray, Panare. e, Backpack, Pemon. f, With carrying strap, Yanomami. g, Round (dk brown), diff., Ye'Kuana. h, Tray, Ye'Kuana. i, Oval tray, Panare. j, Wide mouth, Warao.
250b, Square box with lid, Ye'Kuana.

1997, Oct. 24   **Perf. 12**
1579 A452 140b Sheet of 10,
        #a.-j.   4.00 4.00
Souvenir Sheet
1580 A452 250b multicolored   .75 .75
No. 1580 contains one 42x37mm stamp.

Christmas A453

a, Annunciation. b, Mary, St. Elizabeth. c, No room at the inn. d, Nativity. e, Annunciation to shepherds. f, Adoration of the shepherds. g, Magi following star. h, Adoration of the Magi. i, Presentation of Christ child in temple. j, Flight into Egypt.

1997, Oct. 31
1581 A453 110b Sheet of 10,
        #a.-j.   5.00 5.00

7th Summit of Latin American Chiefs of State and Government, Isla de Margarita A454

a, 165b, j, 200b, Social justice. b, 165b, i, 200b, Free elections. c, 165b, h, 200b, Summit emblem. d, 165b, g, 200b, Truthful information. e, 165b, f, 200b, Human rights.

1997, Nov. 5
1582 A454 Sheet of 10, #a.-j.   5.00 5.00

Diocese of Zulia, Cent. A455

Churches: a, Convent. b, Church of St. Ann. c, Reliquary, Chiquinquira. d, Basilica of Chiquinquira and St. John of God. e, Church, Aranza. f, Cathedral, Maracaibo. g, Cathedral, Machiques. h, Archbishop's seal. i, Cathedral, Cabimas. j, Cathedral of the Virgin, San Carlos.

1997, Dec. 16
1583 A455 110b Sheet of 10,
        #a.-j.   3.00 3.00

Democracy in Venezuela, 40th Anniv. — A456

Designs: a, Commemorative emblem. b, Popular decision. c, Public education. d, Social development. e, Freedom of expression. f, Capital, constitution. g, Popular culture. h, Civil rights. i, Environmental protection. j, Social and civic participation.

1998, Feb. 19   **Litho.**   **Perf. 12**
1584 A456 110b Sheet of 10,
        #a.-j.   4.25 4.25

Discovery of Margarita Island, 500th Anniv. — A457

Map of Margarita Islands and: a, 200b, Angel Rock. b, 265b, Christopher Columbus, ship. c, 200b, Simon Bolivar. d, 200b, Pearl diver. e, 265b, Statue of the Virgin del Valle, church. f, 100b, Mending fish net, fishermen in boats. g, 200b, Gen. Santiago Marino. h, 100b, Petronila Mata, cannon. i, 200b, Gen. Juan Bautista Arismendi. j, 100b, Parrot.
250b, Women weeping at the Lagoon of Martyrs, horiz.

1998, Mar. 26   **Litho.**   **Perf. 12**
1585 A457 Sheet of 10, #a.-j.   6.25 6.25
Souvenir Sheet
1586 A457 250b multicolored   .85 .85
No. 1586 contains one 42x37mm stamp.

Orchid Type of 1995

a, Oncidium orthostates. b, Epidendrum praetervisum. c, Odontoglossum schilleranum. d, Bletia lansbergii. e, Caularthron bicornutum. f, Darwiniera bergoldii. g, Houlletia tigrina. h, Pleurothallis acuminata. i, Elleanthus lupulinus. j, Epidendrum ferrugineum.
250b, Pleurothallis immersa.

1998, May 29
1587 A421 185b Sheet of 10,
        #a.-j.   6.50 6.50
Souvenir Sheet
1588 A421 250b multicolored   .85 .85
No. 1588 contains one 42x37mm stamp.

Henri Pittier Natl. Park, 60th Anniv. — A458

Fauna: a, 140b, Crax pauxi. b, 150b, Spizaetus ornatus. c, 200b, Touit collaris. d, 200b, Trogon collaris. e, 350b, Cyanocorax yncas. f, 140b, Tersina viridis. g, 150b, Phyllomedusa trinitatis. h, 200b, Morpho peleides. i, 200b, Acrocinus longimanus. j, 350b, Dynastes hercules.

1998, July 17
1589 A453 Sheet of 10, #a.-j.   7.25 7.25

Comptroller General of the Republic,
60th Anniv. — A459

Designs: a, 140b, Gumersindo Torres Millet, founding Comptroller. b, 140b, Luis Antonio Pietri Yépez, first Comptroller of the democracy. c, 140b, View of capitol dome. d, 140b, Colors of flag (service to society). e, 200b, Simon Bolivar, coins. f, 200b, Various numbers on green background. g, 350b, Newspaper headlines (inform the public). h, 350b, Statue of justice (uphold law). i, 350b, Text of duties of the Comptroller General. j, 350b, Emblem, the 6th Assembly of the Latin American and Caribbean States Comptrollers.

1998, July 29
1590 A459 Sheet of 10, #a.-j.   8.25 8.25

Organization of the American States (OAS), 50th Anniv. — A460

a, 140b, Logo of the anniversary. b, 140b, OAS emblem. c, 350b, Flags forming double helix, US flag at center left. d, 150b, Deactivating land mine. e, 150b, Defending human rights. f, 200b, Simon Bolivar. g, 200b, Scroll, quill pen, inkwell. h, 350b, Flags forming double helix, Venezuelan flag at center right. i, 200b, Road sign with map of Americas. j, 200b, Mountain climbers.

1998, July 30
1591 A460 Sheet of 10, #a.-j.   7.25 7.25

Expo '98, Lisbon A461

Designs: a, 140b, Bird, turtle, crab. b, 140b, Fishermen throwing net from boat. c, 150b, Seashells, turtle. d, 150b, Fish. e, 200b, Marine life, denomination, UR. f, 200b, Marine life, denomination LR. g, 200b, Man riding through river on horse. h, 200b, Cattle in river, monkey. i, 350b, Two sea birds. j, 350b, Monkey, waterfall, flower.

1998, July 31
1592 A461 Sheet of 10, #a.-j.   7.25 7.25

18th Central American and Caribbean Games, Maracaibo A462

Figures: a, 150b, Running. b, 200b, Playing basketball. c, 150b, Bowling. d, 200b, Boxing. e, 150b, Cycling. f, 200b, Fencing. g, 150b, Performing gymnastics. h, 200b, Weight lifting. i, 150b, Swimming. j, 200b, Playing tennis.

1998, Aug. 4
1593 A462 Sheet of 10, #a.-j.   6.00 6.00

Discovery of Venezuela, 500th Anniv. — A463

Designs: a, 350b, Christopher Columbus. b, 200b, Juan de la Cosa (1460?-1510), map. c, 200b, Huts built on stilts in water. d, 150b, Women of three different races. e, 140b, 13th cent. artifact. f, 350b, Alonso de Ojeda (1465-1515), map. g, 200b, Detail of map of Jodocus Hondius. h, 200b, Modern city. i, 150b, Various people of modern Venezuela. j, 140b, Statues of Catholic king and queen.

1998, Aug. 10
1594 A463 Sheet of 10, #a.-j.   7.25 7.25

Landing of Christoper Columbus, and Exploration of Amerigo Vespucci, 500th Anniv. A464

1998, Aug. 12
1595 A464 400b multicolored   1.40 1.40
See Italy No. 2252.

Treaty of Amazon Cooperation, 20th Anniv. A465

Designs: a, Casiquiare River, denomination LR. b, Casiquiare River, denomination LL. c, Bactris gasipaes. d, Neblinaria celiae. e, Paracheidon axelrodi. f, Dendrobates leucomelas. g, Nocthocrax urumatum. h, Speothos venaticus. i, Cocuy mountain. j, Neblina Mountains.

1998, Aug. 20
1596 A465 200b Sheet of 10,
              #a.-j.   7.00 7.00

Children's Story — A466

Cockroach Martinez and Perez Rat: a, Cockroach. b, Burro. c, Parrot. d, Insects with camera, pad. e, Cat. f, Cockroach, pig. g, Goat. h, Cockroach, rat. i, Rat. j, Cockroach, bird.
350b, Cockroach.

1998, Aug. 21   Litho.   Perf. 12
1597 A466 130b Sheet of 10,
              #a.-j.   4.50 4.50
              Souvenir Sheet
1598 A466 350b multicolored   1.25 1.25

State of Israel, 50th Anniv. — A467

a, 350b, Menorah. b, 350b, Moses, Ten Commandments. c, 200b, Theodore Herzl. d, 200b, King David. e, 140b, Blowing of Shofar. f, 350b, Torah. g, 350b, Praying at Wailing Wall. h, 200b, David Ben Gurion. i, 200b, Knesset. j, 140b, Book Museum.

1998, Sept. 15
1599 A467 Sheet of 10, #a.-j.   6.00 6.00

              Souvenir Sheet

Comptroller General, 60th Anniv. — A468

1998, Sept.
1600 A468 480b multicolored   1.75 1.75

UPU, 125th Anniv. A469

a, 100b, Customer at window, clerks at left. b, 100b, Scanning bar code, woman at right. c, 100b, Electronic mail. d, 100b, Hybrid mail. e, 100b, Business mail. f, 300b, Like "a," clerks at right. g, 300b, Like "b," woman at left. h, 300b, Like "c," large monitor at right. i, 300b, Like "d," woman at right. j, 300b, Like "e," building with stacks at left.

1998, Sept. 29
1601 A469 Sheet of 10, #a.-j.   7.00 7.00

Legendary Caciques A470

a, Caruao. b, Manaure. c, Guacamayo. d, Tapiaracay. e, Mamacuri. f, Maniacuare. g, Mara. h, Chacao. i, Tamanaco. j, Tiuna.
500b, Indian.

1998, Oct. 9
1602 A470 420b Sheet of 10,
              #a.-j.   15.00 15.00
              Souvenir Sheet
1603 A470 500b multicolored   1.75 1.75

Evangelism in Venezuela, 500th Anniv. A471

No. 1604: a, 100b, Fr. Francisco de Córdoba, Fr. Juan Garcés. b, 100b, Fr. Matías Ruíz Blanco. c, 100b, Fr. Vincente de Requejada. d, 100b, Fr. José Gumilla. e, 100b, Fr. Antonio Gonzáles de Acuña. f, 300b, Fr. Pedro de Córdoba. g, 300b, Fr. Francisco de

Pamplona. h, 300b, Fr. Bartolomé Díaz. 300b, Fr. Filipe Salvador Gilij. j, 300b, Do Mariano Martí.
350b, Emblem of Papal Nuncio.

1998, Oct. 24   Litho.   Perf. 1
1604 A471 Sheet of 10, #a.-j.   5.50 5.5
              Souvenir Sheet
1605 A471 350b multicolored   1.00 1.0
No. 1605 contains one 42x37mm stamp.

Special Olympics, 30th Anniv. A472

180b: a, Carrying torch. b, Giving hug. c Soccer players. d, Girl holding small flag. e Girl performing gymnastics.
420b: f, Swimmer. g, Coach walking with athletes. h, Hitting volleyball. i, Participants cheering. j, Coach instructing girl in softball.

1998, Oct. 30   Litho.   Perf. 12
1606 A472 Sheet of 10, #a.-j.   10.50 10.5

Christmas A473

Children standing in front of windows — 180b: a, Girl holding sparkler. b, Boy holding artist's brush, ornament. c, Girl with kite. d, Boy with pinwheel. e, Girls playing musical instruments.
420b: f, Boy on wagon. g, Girl with yo-yo, doll. h, Boy with bell. i, Girl with spool and thread. j, Boy on skateboard.

1998, Nov. 4
1607 A473 Sheet of 10, #a.-j.   10.50 10.50

America Issue — A474

Famous women: a, 180b, Teresa de la Parra (1889-1936), writer. b, 420b, Teresa Carreño (1853-1917), pianist.

1998, Nov. 23
1608 A474 Pair, #a.-b.   2.25 2.25

William H. Phelps (1875-1965), Ornithologist A475

Portrait of Phelps and — 200b: a, Cephalopterus ornatus. b, Topaza pella. c, Grallaria excelsa phelpsi. d, Chrysolampis mosquitus. e, Tangara xanthogastra phelpsi.
300b: f, Radio transmitter. g, Mt. Phelps. h, Baseball and glove. i, Phelps Library. j, Cash register.

1998, Dec. 4
1609 A475 Sheet of 10, #a.-j.   8.75 8.75

Msgr. Jesús Manuel Jáuregui Moreno (1848-1905) A476

Designs: a, Portrait as younger man. b, Christ on the cross. c, Our Mother of Angels Church. d, Madonna and Child. e, Portrait as older man.

1999, Jan. 30   Litho.   Perf. 12
1610 A476 500b Strip of 5, #a.-e. 8.75 8.75

Holy Sacrament for the Consecration of the Republic of Venezuela, Cent. A477

No. 1612: a, Man, elderly woman. b, Priest. c, Ostensorium (top). d, Boy with basketball, girl. e, Man, woman holding baby. f, Lady doctor. g, Woman. h, Ostensorium (base). i, Soldier. j, Native man holding spear.
500b, Hands of priest holding the Host.

1999, June 16   Litho.   Perf. 12
1611 A477 250b Sheet of 10,
             #a.-j.   8.25 8.25
Souvenir Sheet
1612 A477 500b multicolored   1.60 1.60
No. 1612 contains one 42x37mm stamp.

Souvenir Sheet

Andino Parliament, 20th Anniv. — A478

1999   Litho.   Perf. 12
1613 A478 500b multi   1.50 1.50

Christmas A479

a, 500b, Betrothal of Joseph, Mary. b, 500b, Annunciation. c, 500b, Elizabeth, Mary. d, 500b, The search for lodging in Bethlehem. e, 500b, Birth of Jesus. f, 300b, Vision of the shepherds. g, 300b, Magi following star. h, 300b, Adoration of the Magi. i, 300b, Flight into Egypt. j, 300b, Slaughter of the innocents.

1999, Nov. 5   Perf. 12x12¼
1614 A479 Sheet of 10, #a.-j. 12.00 12.00

Souvenir Sheet

Expo 2000, Hanover — A480

Illustration reduced.

2000, July 8   Litho.   Perf. 12
1615 A480 650b multi   2.10 2.10

2nd Summit of Heads of State and Government of OPEC Countries — A481

No. 1616 — Sites in Venezuela: a, 300b, Angel Falls. b, 300b, Llanos, Cojedes. c, 300b, Quebrada Jaspe. d, 300b, Morichal Largo. e, 300b, Auyantepuy, Carrao River. f, 400b, Lake Maracaibo. g, 400b, Humboldt Peak. h, 400b, Mochima. i, 400b, Morichal Largo River. j, 400b, Auyantepuy, from Uruyen.
No. 1617, 550b: a, Saudi Arabia. b, Algeria. c, United Arab Emirates. d, Indonesia. e, Iraq. f, Iran. g, Kuwait. h, Libya. i, Nigeria. j, Qatar.

2000, Sept. 26   Litho.   Perf. 12
Sheets of 10, #a-j
1616-1617 A481 Set of 2   27.50 27.50

Christmas — A482

No. 1618: a, 300b, Angel and "Gloria." b, 300b, Angel and "a." c, 650b, Angel and "Dios." d, 300b, Angel and "en los." e, 300b, Angel and "Cielos." f, 300b, Shepherd and lamb. g, 550b, Joseph. h, 650b, Jesus. i, 550b, Mary. j, 300b, Woman with water jar.

2000, Nov. 29
1618 A482 Sheet of 10, #a-j 12.00 12.00

America Issue, A New Millennium Without Arms — A483

No. 1619: a, 300b, Finger in gun barrel. b, 650b, Man in heaven.

2000, Dec. 14
1619 A483 Vert. pair, #a-b   2.75 2.75

Educational Building and Endowment Foundation, 25th Anniv. — A484

No. 1620 — School buildings in: a, Caracas. b, Vargas State. c, Portuguesa State. d, Mérida State. e, Yaracuy State.

2001, May 9   Litho.   Perf. 12
1620   Horiz. strip of 5   4.75 4.75
a.-c. A484 300b Any single   .85   .85
d.-e. A484 400b Any single   1.10 1.10

Orchids — A485

No. 1621: a, 200b, Galeottia jorisiana. b, 200b, Lycaste longipetala. c, 300b, Coryanthes albertinae. d, 300b, Hexisea bidentata. e, 400b, Lycaste macrophylla. f, 400b, Masdevallia maculata. g, 550b, Ada aurantiaca. h, 550f, Kefersteinia graminea. i, 550b, Sobralia liliastrum. j, 550b, Gongora maculata.
650b, Masdevallia tovarensis.

2001, May 25
1621 A485 Sheet of 10, #a-j 11.50 11.50
Souvenir Sheet
1622 A485 650b multi   1.90 1.90

Blessed Josemaría Escrivá de Balaguer (1902-75), Founder of Opus Dei — A486

No. 1623: a, 300b, Portrait. b, 300b, Bell of Nuestra Senora de los Angeles Church. c, 300b, Figure of Infant Jesus. d, 300b, Escrivá with men. e, 300b, Escrivá with women. f, 550f, Escrivá receiving doctorate, 1972. g, 550b, Escrivá with children, 1975. h, 300b, Commemorative plaque, Caracas Cathedral. i, 550b, Color portrait. j, 300b, Beatification ceremony, St. Peter's Square, Vatican City.

2001, June 8
1623 A486 Sheet of 10, #a-j 11.50 11.50

Battle of Carabobo, 180th Anniv. A487

No. 1624: a, Thomas I. Ferriar. b, Bolívar in Buenavista, by Martín Tovar y Tovar. c, Quote by Simón Bolívar. d, Commemorative column. e, Pedro Camejo. f, José Antonio Páez, by Tovar y Tovar. g, Santiago Mariño, by Tovar y

Tovar. h, Simón Bolívar, by M. Eberstein. i, Manuel Cedeño, by Tito Salas. j, Ambrosio Plaza, by Salas.

2001, June 22
1624   Sheet of 10   14.00 14.00
a.-e. A487 400b Any single   1.10   1.10
f.-j. A487 600b Any single   1.60   1.60

Christmas — A488

Holy Family and angel with: a, 200b, Clarinet. b, 200b, Guitar. c, 220b, Lute. d, 220b, Trumpet. e, 280b, Violin. f, 280b, Harp. g, 400b, Bagpipes. h, 400b, Pan pipes. i, 500b, Drum. j, 500b, Stringed instrument.

2001, Nov. 30   Litho.   Perf. 12
1625 A488 Sheet of 10, #a-j 12.50 12.50

Navigational Signaling, 160th Anniv. — A489

Navigational aids: a, Margarita Aqueduct buoy. b, BNFA buoy. c, Punta Brava lighthouse. d, Punta Macolla lighthouse. e, Los Roques lighthouse. f, Isla Redonda lighthouse. g, Punta Faragoza lighthouse. h, Punta Ballena lighthouse. i, Punta Tigre lighthouse. j, Recalada de Güiria lighthouse.

2002, May 10   Litho.   Perf. 12
1626   Sheet of 10   9.75 9.75
a.-b. A489 300b Either single   .60   .60
c.-f. A489 450b Any single   .90   .90
g.-j. A489 500b Any single   1.00 1.00

Symbolic Incorporation of Guacaipuro into National Pantheon — A490

No. 1627: a, Tiaora and Caycape, sisters of Guacaipuro. b, Guacaipuro defeats Pedro de Miranda. c, Guacaipuro defeated by Juan Rodriguez Suárez. d, Killing in the gold mines. e, Death of Juan Rodriguez Suárez. f, Guacaipuro's escape from cabin fire. g, Death of Guacaipuro. h, Urquía, companion of Guacaipuro. i, Baruta, first son of Guacaipuro. j, Guacaipuro, Cacique of the Teques and Caracas people.

2002, Oct. 29   Litho.   Perf. 12
1627   Sheet of 10   5.00 5.00
a.   A490 200b multi   .30   .30
b-g. A490 300b any single   .45   .45
h.   A490 350b multi   .55   .55
i.   A490 400b multi   .60   .60
j.   A490 500b multi   .75   .75

Mission Robinson — A491

No. 1628: a, Toddler. b, Boy reading. c, Simón Bolívar and torch. d, Simón "Robinson" Rodriguez, Bolívar's teacher. e, Rodriguez and Eiffel Tower. f, Bolívar and flag. g, Bolívar and Rodriguez reading. h, Bolívar standing and Rodriguez seated. i, Rodriguez, men and women reading. j, Indians reading.

2003, Sept. 19   Litho.   Perf. 12x12¼

1628	A491	Sheet of 10	5.00	5.00
a.-d.		300b Any single	.35	.35
e.-f.		400b Either single	.50	.50
g.-j.		500b Any single	.65	.65

Agricultural, Fishery and Forestry
Fund (FONDAFA) — A492

No. 1629: a, Cattle drive. b, Farmer plowing field. c, Row of tractors. d, Farmer tending crops. e, Corn in field. f, Boats. g, Ear of corn. h, Farmer in tractor in field. i, Cacao pods. j, Cacao beans.

2003, Nov. 7   Perf. 12

1629	A492	Sheet of 10	4.50	4.50
a.-f.		300b Any single	.35	.35
g.-h.		400b Either single	.50	.50
i.-j.		500b Either single	.65	.65

Natl. Urban Transportation Fund
(FONTUR), 12th Anniv. — A494

No. 1631: a, Av. Uruguay, Lara. b, Carretera del Páramo, Merida. c, Av. Cumanan-Cumanacoa, Sucre. d, Carratera Santa Lucia, Barinas. e, Francissco Fajardo Expressway, Caracas. f, Students. g, Paraiso Tunnel, Caracas. h, VIVEX Module. i, Row of buses. j, Av. Cruz Paredes, Barinas.

2003, Dec. 18   Litho.   Perf. 14¼

1631	A494	Sheet of 10	5.25	5.25
a.-c.		300b Any single	.35	.35
d.-f.		400b Any single	.50	.50
g.-j.		500b Any single	.65	.65

Foundation for the Development of
Community and Municipal
Reconstruction (FUNDACOMUN),
42nd Anniv. — A496

No. 1633: a, Miranda. b, Trujillo. c, Mérida. d, Falcón. e, Vargas. f, Esparta. g, Caracas, denomination at left. h, Caracas, denomination at right. i, Barinas. j, Lara.

2004, Mar. 10   Litho.   Perf. 12

1633	A496	Sheet of 10	4.25	4.25
a.-c.		300b Any single	.30	.30
d.-f.		400b Any single	.45	.45
g.-j.		500b Any single	.50	.50

Barrio Adentro Mission — A497

No. 1634: a, Houses on hillside, people in doorway. b, Woman, house, ladder, people in alley. c, Woman, mother and child. d, Family, children. e, Boys playing baseball, boat. f, People near fence, man with cap. g, Man,

sand dunes. h, Man with guitar, cows. i, Mountain, woman, cross and statue. j, Indians, river.

2004, Mar. 24   Perf. 12

1634	A497	Sheet of 10	8.50	8.50
a.-b.		300b Either single	.30	.30
c.-f.		500b Any single	.50	.50
g.		750b multi	.80	.80
h.-i.		1500b Either single	1.60	1.60
j.		1700b multi	1.75	1.75

SEMI-POSTAL STAMPS

A 5c green stamp of the Cruzada Venezolana Sanitaria Social portraying Simon Bolivar was overprinted "EE. UU. DE VENEZUELA CORREOS" in 1937.
It is stated that 50,000 copies without control numbers on back were sold by post offices and 147,700 with control numbers on back were offered for sale by the Society at eight times face value.

Bolívar
Funeral
Carriage
SP1

Unwmk.
1942, Dec. 17   Engr.   Perf. 12
B1 SP1 20c + 5c blue   4.50 .50
Cent. of the arrival of Simón Bolívar's remains in Caracas. The surtax was used to erect a monument to his memory. See Nos. CB1-CB2.

Catalogue values for unused stamps in this section, from this point to the end of the section, are for Never Hinged items.

Red Cross
Nurse — SP2

1975, Dec. 15   Litho.   Perf. 14
B2 SP2 30c + 15c multi   .30 .20
B3 SP2 50c + 25c multi   .45 .30
Surtax for Venezuelan Red Cross.

Carmen América
Fernandez de
Leoni — SP3

Children in
Home — SP4

1976, June 7   Litho.   Perf. 13½
B4 SP3 30c + 15c multi   .25 .20
B5 SP4 50c + 25c multi   .45 .30
Surtax was for the Children's Foundation, founded by Carmen América Fernandez de Leoni in 1966.

Patient — SP5

1976, Dec. 8   Litho.   Perf. 1
B6 SP5 10c + 5c multi   .20 .2
B7 SP5 30c + 10c multi   .25 .2
Surtax was for Anti-tuberculosis Society.

AIR POST STAMPS

Air post stamps of 1930-42 perfo rated "GN" (Gobierno Nacional) were for official use.

Airplane and Map of Venezuela
AP1   AP2

1930		**Unwmk. Litho. Perf. 12**		
C1	AP1	5c bister brn	.20	.20
C2	AP1	10c yellow	.20	.20
a.		10c salmon	32.50	32.50
C3	AP1	15c gray	.20	.20
C4	AP1	25c lilac	.20	.20
C5	AP1	40c olive grn	.20	.20
a.		40c slate blue	40.00	
b.		40c slate green	40.00	
C6	AP1	75c dp red	.25	.20
C7	AP1	1b indigo	.40	.20
C8	AP1	1.20b blue grn	.60	.30
C9	AP1	1.70b dk blue	.75	.40
C10	AP1	1.90b blue grn	.75	.40
C11	AP1	2.10b blue	1.50	.60
C12	AP1	2.30b vermilion	1.50	.45
C13	AP1	2.50b dk blue	1.50	.45
C14	AP1	3.70b blue grn	1.50	1.00
C15	AP1	10b dull vio	4.50	2.25
C16	AP1	20b gray grn	7.00	4.25
		Nos. C1-C16 (16)	21.25	11.55

Nos. C1-C16 exist imperforate or partly per forated. See Nos. C119-C126.
Issued: 10b, June 8; 20b, June 16; others, Apr. 5.

Bluish Winchester Security Paper
1932, July 12		**Engr. Perf. 12½**		
C17	AP2	5c brown	.35	.20
C18	AP2	10c org yel	.35	.20
C19	AP2	15c gray lilac	.35	.20
C20	AP2	25c violet	.35	.20
C21	AP2	40c ol grn	.60	.20
C22	AP2	70c rose	.45	.20
C23	AP2	75c red org	.75	.20
C24	AP2	1b dk bl	.90	.20
C25	AP2	1.20b green	1.90	.65
C26	AP2	1.70b red brn	3.75	.45
C27	AP2	1.80b ultra	1.90	.30
C28	AP2	1.90b green	4.50	3.00
C29	AP2	1.95b blue	5.25	2.25
C30	AP2	2b blk brn	3.00	1.90
C31	AP2	2.10b blue	7.75	4.75
C32	AP2	2.30b red	3.00	1.90
C33	AP2	2.50b dk bl	4.50	1.10
C34	AP2	3b dk vio	4.50	.65
C35	AP2	3.70b emerald	6.25	4.75
C36	AP2	4b red org	4.50	1.10
C37	AP2	5b black	5.25	1.90
C38	AP2	8b dk car	10.50	3.75
C39	AP2	10b dk vio	21.00	6.25
C40	AP2	20b grnsh slate	42.00	17.00
		Nos. C17-C40 (24)	136.65	53.30

Pairs imperf. between exist of the 1b (value $150); the 25c and 4b (value $300 each).

Air Post Stamps of
1932 Surcharged
in Black

1937, June 4

C41	AP2	5c on 1.70b red brn	9.25	5.50
C42	AP2	10c on 3.70b emer	9.25	5.50
C43	AP2	15c on 4b red org	4.00	2.75
C44	AP2	25c on 5b blk	4.00	2.75
C45	AP2	1b on 8b dk car	3.25	2.75
C46	AP2	2b on 2.10b bl	25.00	18.00
		Nos. C41-C46 (6)	54.75	37.25

Various varieties of surcharge exist, including double and triple impressions. No. C43 exists in pair imperf. between; value $30 unused, $50 used.

Allegory of Flight AP3

Allegory of Flight AP4

National Pantheon at Caracas AP5

Airplane — AP6   AP7

Perf. 11, 11½ and Compound

1937, July 1   Litho.

C47	AP3	5c brn org	.25	.30
C48	AP4	10c org red	.25	.20
C49	AP5	15c gray blk	.50	.30
C50	AP6	25c dk vio	.55	.30
C51	AP4	40c yel grn	.90	.45
C52	AP5	70c red	.90	.30
C53	AP5	75c bister	2.10	1.10
C54	AP3	1b dk gray	1.25	.45
C55	AP4	1.20b pck grn	5.25	3.50
C56	AP3	1.80b dk ultra	2.50	1.60
C57	AP5	1.95b lt ultra	8.00	6.25
C58	AP6	2b chocolate	3.50	2.25
C59	AP4	2.50b gray bl	9.25	9.25
C60	AP4	3b lt vio	5.25	3.75
C61	AP6	3.70b rose red	9.25	12.50
C62	AP5	10b red vio	20.00	12.50
C63	AP3	20b gray	25.00	19.00
		Nos. C47-C63 (17)	94.70	74.00

All values except 3.70b exist imperf. and part-perf.

Counterfeits exist.

For overprints & surcharges see #C66-C78, C114-C118, C164-C167, C169-C172, C174-C180.

1937, Oct. 28   **Perf. 11**

C64	AP7	70c emerald	1.10	.50
C65	AP7	1.80b ultra	1.90	.80

Acquisition of the Port of La Guaira by the Government from the British Corporation, June 3, 1937. Exist imperf.

A redrawn printing of Nos. C64-C65, with lower inscription beginning "Nacionalización . . ." was prepared but not issued. Price, $40 each.

For overprints see Nos. C168, C173.

Air Post Stamps of 1937 Overprinted in Black

1937, Dec. 17   **Perf. 11, 11½**

C66	AP4	10c org red	.80	.50
a.		Inverted overprint	13.00	10.00

C67	AP6	25c dk vio	1.50	.75
C68	AP4	40c yel grn	1.75	1.10
C69	AP3	70c red	1.25	.75
a.		Inverted overprint	13.00	11.50
b.		Double overprint	20.00	16.00
C70	AP3	1b dk gray	1.75	1.10
a.		Inverted overprint	16.00	13.00
b.		Double overprint	13.00	
C71	AP4	1.20b pck grn	25.00	15.00
a.		Inverted overprint	65.00	
C72	AP3	1.80b dk ultra	4.75	1.90
C73	AP5	1.95b lt ultra	6.25	3.50
a.		Inverted overprint	50.00	30.00
C74	AP6	2b chocolate	40.00	19.00
a.		Inverted overprint	100.00	90.00
b.		Double overprint	82.50	82.50
C75	AP6	2.50b gray bl	40.00	15.00
a.		Inverted overprint	70.00	
b.		Inverted overprint	100.00	82.50
C76	AP4	3b lt vio	25.00	9.25
C77	AP5	10b red vio	57.50	30.00
C78	AP3	20b gray	65.00	37.50
a.		Double overprint	150.00	150.00
		Nos. C66-C78 (13)	270.55	135.35

Counterfeit overprints exist on #C77-C78.

View of La Guaira AP8

National Pantheon AP9

Oil Wells AP10

1938-39   **Engr.**   **Perf. 12**

C79	AP8	5c green	.75	.40
C80	AP8	5c dk grn	.20	.20
C81	AP9	10c car rose	1.10	.65
C82	AP9	10c scarlet	.20	.20
C83	AP8	12½c dull vio	.50	.45
C84	AP10	15c slate vio	2.50	1.00
C85	AP10	15c dk bl	.65	.20
C86	AP8	25c dk bl	2.50	.95
C87	AP10	25c bis brn	.25	.20
C88	AP10	30c vio ('39)	1.75	.20
C89	AP9	40c dk vio	2.75	.90
C90	AP9	40c redsh brn	2.10	.20
C91	AP8	45c Prus grn ('39)	.85	.20
C92	AP9	50c blue ('39)	1.00	.20
C93	AP10	70c car rose	.70	.25
C94	AP8	75c bis brn	5.00	1.75
C95	AP8	75c ol bis	1.10	.20
C96	AP10	90c red org ('39)	.80	.20
C97	AP9	1b ol & bis	5.75	2.10
C98	AP9	1b dk vio	1.00	.20
C99	AP10	1.20b orange	17.00	4.75
C100	AP10	1.20b green	1.75	.40
C101	AP8	1.80b ultra	1.75	.40
C102	AP9	1.90b black	4.25	2.25
C103	AP10	1.95b lt bl	3.50	2.00
C104	AP8	2b ol gray	37.50	13.00
C105	AP8	2b car rose	1.40	.55
C106	AP9	2.50b red brn	37.50	15.00
C107	AP9	2.50b orange	8.00	2.25
C108	AP10	3b lt grn	15.00	4.00
C109	AP10	3b ol gray	4.25	1.75
C110	AP8	3.70b gray blk	6.25	4.25
C111	AP10	5b red brn ('39)	6.25	1.75
C112	AP9	10b vio brn	16.00	1.90
C113	AP10	20b red org	45.00	20.00
		Nos. C79-C113 (35)	236.85	84.90

See Nos. C227a, C235-C236, C254-C255. For surcharge see No. C227.

1938, Apr. 15   **Perf. 11, 11½**

C114	AP3	5c on 1.80b	.60	.40
a.		Inverted surcharge	12.50	7.50
C115	AP6	10c on 2.50b	2.75	1.25
a.		Inverted surcharge	10.00	7.50
C116	AP6	15c on 2b	1.25	.90
C117	AP4	25c on 40c	1.50	1.25
C118	AP6	40c on 3.70b	2.75	2.50
		Nos. C114-C118 (5)	8.85	6.30

Plane & Map Type of 1930
White Paper; No Imprint

1938-39   **Engr.**   **Perf. 12½**

C119	AP1	5c dk grn ('39)	.25	.20
C120	AP1	10c org yel ('39)	.45	.20
C121	AP1	12½c rose vio ('39)	.90	.75
C122	AP1	15c dp bl	.75	.20
C123	AP1	25c brown	.90	.20
C124	AP1	40c olive ('39)	2.25	.35
C125	AP1	70c rose car ('39)	15.00	6.25
C126	AP1	1b dk bl ('39)	6.25	2.75
		Nos. C119-C126 (8)	26.75	10.90

Monument to Sucre — AP11

Monuments at Carabobo
AP12   AP13

1938, Dec. 23   **Perf. 13½**

C127	AP11	20c brn blk	.40	.25
C128	AP12	30c purple	.60	.25
C129	AP13	45c dk bl	.85	.20
C130	AP11	50c lt bl	.75	.20
C131	AP13	70c dk car	13.00	7.25
C132	AP12	90c red org	1.25	.50
C133	AP13	1.35b gray blk	1.50	.75
C134	AP11	1.40b slate gray	6.00	2.40
C135	AP12	2.25b green	3.00	1.75
		Nos. C127-C135 (9)	27.35	13.55

For surcharge see No. C198.

Simón Bolívar and Carabobo Monument AP14

1940, Mar. 30   **Perf. 12**

C136	AP14	15c blue	.45	.20
C137	AP14	20c olive bis	.45	.20
C138	AP14	25c red brn	1.90	.30
C139	AP14	40c blk brn	1.50	.20
C140	AP14	1b red lilac	3.50	.50
C141	AP14	2b rose car	7.75	1.10
		Nos. C136-C141 (6)	15.55	2.50

"The Founding of Grand Colombia" AP15

1940, June 13

C142	AP15	15c copper brown	.75	.35

Founding of the Pan American Union, 50th anniv.

Statue of Simón Bolívar, Caracas — AP16

1940-44

C143	AP16	5c dk grn ('42)	.20	.20
C144	AP16	10c scar ('42)	.20	.20
C145	AP16	12½c dull purple	.60	.25
C146	AP16	15c blue ('43)	.40	.20

C147	AP16	20c bis brn ('44)	.40	.20
C148	AP16	25c bis brn ('42)	.40	.20
C149	AP16	30c dp vio ('43)	.40	.20
C150	AP16	40c blk brn ('43)	.50	.20
C151	AP16	45c turq grn ('43)	.50	.20
C152	AP16	50c blue ('44)	.50	.20
C153	AP16	70c rose pink	1.50	.25
C154	AP16	75c ol bis ('43)	6.00	1.25
C155	AP16	90c red org ('43)	1.00	.25
C156	AP16	1b dp red lil ('42)	.50	.20
C157	AP16	1.20b dp yel grn ('43)	1.90	.60
C158	AP16	1.35b gray blk ('42)	8.00	3.75
C159	AP16	2b rose pink ('43)	1.50	.20
C160	AP16	3b ol blk ('43)	2.50	.60
C161	AP16	4b black	2.00	.60
C162	AP16	5b brown ('44)	16.00	6.25
		Nos. C143-162 (20)	45.00	16.00

See #C232-C234, C239-C253. For surcharges see #C225, C873.

Nos. C48, C50-C65 Overprinted

Perf. 11, 11½ & Compound

1943, Dec. 21

C164	AP4	10c orange red	1.00	.90
C165	AP6	25c dk violet	1.00	.90
C166	AP4	40c yellow grn	1.00	.90
C167	AP3	70c red	1.00	.90
C168	AP7	70c emerald	1.00	.90
C169	AP5	75c bister	1.00	.90
C170	AP3	1b dk gray	1.00	.90
C171	AP4	1.20b peacock grn	3.00	1.60
C172	AP3	1.80b dk ultra	3.00	1.60
C173	AP7	1.80b dk ultra	3.00	2.50
C174	AP5	1.95b lt ultra	4.00	3.25
C175	AP6	2b chocolate	4.00	3.25
C176	AP6	2.50b gray blue	3.00	3.25
C177	AP4	3b lt violet	4.00	3.25
C178	AP6	3.70b rose red	50.00	45.00
C179	AP5	10b red violet	10.00	10.00
C180	AP3	20b gray	25.00	20.00
		Nos. C164-C180 (17)	116.00	100.00
		Set, never hinged	175.00	

Issued for sale to philatelists. Nos. C164-C169 were sold only in sets.

Nearly all are known with invtd. ovpt.

Flags of Venezuela and the Red Cross — AP17

Baseball Players — AP18

1944, Aug. 22   **Litho.**   **Perf. 12**

Flags in red, yellow, blue and black

C181	AP17	5c gray green	.20	.20
C182	AP17	10c magenta	.20	.20
C183	AP17	20c brt blue	.25	.20
C184	AP17	30c violet bl	.30	.20
C185	AP17	40c chocolate	.40	.20
C186	AP17	45c apple green	1.25	.40
C187	AP17	90c orange	1.00	.40
C188	AP17	1b gray black	2.00	.40
		Nos. C181-C188 (8)	5.60	2.20
		Set, never hinged	6.25	

80th anniv. of the Intl. Red Cross and 37th anniv. of Venezuela's joining the organization. Nos. C181-C188 exist imperf. and part perf.

1944, Oct. 12

"AEREO" in dark carmine

C189	AP18	5c dull vio brn	.30	.20
C190	AP18	10c gray green	.50	.20
C191	AP18	20c ultra	.50	.25
C192	AP18	30c dull rose	1.00	.35
C193	AP18	45c rose violet	2.00	.55
C194	AP18	90c red orange	2.00	1.00
C195	AP18	1b dark gray	2.00	1.00

Nos. C51, C56, C58-C59, C61 Surcharged

1938
VALE CINCO CENTIMOS
(on img_9)

C196 AP18 1.20b yellow grn   7.50 6.50
C197 AP18 1.80b ocher   10.00 7.75
    Nos. C189-C197 (9)   25.80 17.80
    Set, never hinged   32.50

7th World Amateur Baseball Championship
Games, Caracas.
Nos. C189-C197 exist imperf., and all but 1b
exist part perf. Various errors of "AEREO"
overprint exist.

No. C134 Surcharged
in Black

1944, Nov. 17   **Perf. 13½**
C198 AP11 30c on 1.40b   .40   .40
  a.   Double surcharge   32.50 32.50
  b.   Inverted surcharge   12.50 12.50

Charles
Howarth — AP19

Antonio José
de
Sucre — AP20

1944, Dec. 21   Unwmk.   **Perf. 12**
C199 AP19 5c black   .20   .20
C200 AP19 10c purple   .20   .20
C201 AP19 20c sepia   .30   .30
C202 AP19 30c dull green   .35   .30
C203 AP19 1.20b bister   1.75 1.50
C204 AP19 1.80b deep ultra   4.00 3.00
C205 AP19 3.70b rose   3.00 3.00
    Nos. C199-C205 (7)   9.80 8.50
    Set, never hinged   12.50

Cent. of founding of 1st cooperative shop in
Rochdale, England, by Charles Howarth.
Nos. C199-C205 exist imperf. and part perf.

1945, Mar. 3   **Engr.**
C206 AP20 5c orange   .20   .20
C207 AP20 10c violet   .20   .20
C208 AP20 20c grnsh blk   .20   .20
C209 AP20 30c brt green   .20   .20
C210 AP20 40c olive   .50   .50
C211 AP20 45c black brn   .75   .50
C212 AP20 90c redsh brn   1.00 .50
C213 AP20 1b dp red lil   1.00 .50
C214 AP20 1.20b black   3.00 2.50
C215 AP20 2b yellow   4.75 3.50
    Nos. C206-C215 (10)   11.80 8.80
    Set, never hinged   14.50

150th birth anniv. of Antonio Jose de Sucre,
Grand Marshal of Ayacucho.

Type of 1946

1946, Aug. 24   **Perf. 12**
C216 A81 30c Bello   1.10 .20
C217 A82 30c Urdaneta   1.10 .20
    Set, never hinged   2.75

Nos. 297, 371, C152
and 362 Surcharged
in Black

1947, Jan.   **Perf. 12**
C223 A49 10c on 22½c dp car .20   .20
  a.   Inverted surcharge   4.00 4.00
C224 A69 15c on 25c lt bl   .30   .20
C225 AP16 20c on 50c blue   .30   .20
  a.   Inverted surcharge   5.00 5.00
C226 A65 70c on 1b dk vio brn .60 .40
  a.   Inverted surcharge   4.00 4.00

Type of 1938 Surcharged in Black

C227 AP10 20b on 20b org
           red   26.00 22.50
  a.   Surcharge omitted   85.00 40.00
    Nos. C223-C227 (5)   27.40 23.50
    Set, never hinged   35.00

"J. R. G." are the initials of "Junta Revolucionaria de Gobierno."
Also exist: 20c on #C143, 10c on #371.

Anti-tuberculosis
Institute,
Maracaibo — AP24

1947, Jan. 12   **Litho.**
Venezuela Shown on Map in Yellow
C228 AP24 15c dark blue   .40   .30
C229 AP24 20c dark brown   .40   .30
C230 AP24 30c violet   .40   .30
C231 AP24 1b carmine   4.25 3.50
    Nos. C228-C231 (4)   5.45 4.40
    Set, never hinged   6.25

12th Pan-American Health Conf., Caracas,
Jan. 1947.
Nos. C228-C231 exist imperf., part perf. and
with yellow omitted.

Types of 1938-40

1947, Mar. 17   **Engr.**
C232 AP16 75c orange   7.50 4.50
C233 AP16 1b brt ultra   .50   .20
C234 AP16 3b red brown   17.50 8.00
C235 AP10 5b scarlet   12.50 5.00
C236 AP9 10b violet   16.00 7.50
    Nos. C232-C236 (5)   54.00 25.20
    Set, never hinged   75.00

On Nos. C235 and C236 the numerals of
value are in color on a white table.

No. 370
Surcharged in
Black

1947, June 20
C237 A70 5c on 20c blue   .40   .20
C238 A70 10c on 20c blue   .40   .20
  a.   Inverted surcharge   5.00 5.00
    Set, never hinged   1.00

Types of 1938-44

1947-48   **Engr.**
C239 AP16 5c orange   .20   .20
C240 AP16 10c dk green   .20   .20
C241 AP16 12½ bister brn   .40   .20
C242 AP16 15c gray   .20   .20
C243 AP16 20c violet   .20   .20
C244 AP16 25c dull green   .20   .20
C245 AP16 30c brt ultra   .20   .20
C246 AP16 40c green ('48)   .20   .20
C247 AP16 45c vermilion   .40   .20
C248 AP16 50c red violet   .25   .20
C249 AP16 70c dk car   .80   .40
C250 AP16 75c purple ('48)   .40   .20
C251 AP16 90c black   .85   .25
C252 AP16 1.20b red brn ('48) .85 .45
C253 AP16 3b dp blue   1.00 .45

C254 AP10 5b olive grn   8.50 5.00
C255 AP9 10b yellow   7.00 4.00
    Nos. C239-C255 (17)   22.05 12.75
    Set, never hinged   30.00

On Nos. C254 and C255 the numerals of
value are in color on a white tablet.
Issue dates: 5c, 10c, Oct. 8. 15c, Dec. 2,
40c, 75c, 1.20b, May 10, 1948. Others, Oct.
27, 1947.

M. S. Republica de
Venezuela — AP25

Imprint: "American Bank Note
           Company"

1948-50   Unwmk.   **Perf. 12**
C256 AP25 5c red brown   .20   .20
C257 AP25 10c deep green   .20   .20
C258 AP25 15c brown   .20   .20
C259 AP25 20c violet brn   .20   .20
C260 AP25 25c brown black   .20   .20
C261 AP25 30c olive green   .20   .20
C262 AP25 45c blue green   .35   .25
C263 AP25 50c gray black   .50   .30
C264 AP25 70c orange   1.00 .30
C265 AP25 75c brt ultra   1.75 .45
C266 AP25 90c car lake   1.00 .90
C267 AP25 1b purple   1.25 .60
C268 AP25 2b gray   1.40 .90
C269 AP25 3b emerald   5.00 2.50
C270 AP25 4b deep blue   2.40 2.50
C271 AP25 5b orange red   10.00 4.25
    Nos. C256-C271 (16)   25.85 14.15

Issued to honor the Grand-Colombian
Merchant Fleet. See Nos. C554-C556.
Issued: 5c, 10c, 15c, 25c, 30c, 1b, 7/9/48;
45c, 75c, 5b, 5/11/50; others, 3/9/49.
For surcharges see Nos. C863-C864.

Santos
Michelena
AP26

1949, Apr. 25
C272 AP26 5c orange brn   .20   .20
C273 AP26 10c gray   .20   .20
C274 AP26 15c red orange   .35   .20
C275 AP26 25c dull green   .75   .35
C276 AP26 30c plum   .75   .35
C277 AP26 1b violet   3.75 1.50
    Nos. C272-C277 (6)   6.00 2.80

See note after No. 427.

Christopher
Columbus
AP27

1948-49   Unwmk.   **Perf. 12½**
C278 AP27 5c brown ('49)   .20   .20
C279 AP27 10c gray   .25   .20
C280 AP27 15c orange ('49)   .40   .20
C281 AP27 25c green ('49)   .75   .25
C282 AP27 30c red vio ('49) .90   .35
C283 AP27 1b violet ('49)   3.50 1.10
    Nos. C278-C283 (6)   6.00 2.30

See note after No. 431.

AP28   AP29

Symbols of global air mail.

1950   **Perf. 1.**
C284 AP28 5c red brown   .20   .2
C285 AP28 10c dk green   .20   .2
C286 AP28 15c olive brn   .20   .2
C287 AP28 25c dark gray   .30   .2
C288 AP28 30c olive grn   .45   .2
C289 AP28 50c black   .30   .2
C290 AP28 60c brt ultra   .90   .4
C291 AP28 90c carmine   1.25 .5
C292 AP28 1b purple   1.40 .3
    Nos. C284-C292 (9)   5.20 2.6

75th anniv. of the UPU.
Issue dates: 5c, Jan. 28. Others, Feb. 19.

1950, Aug. 25   Photo.   **Perf. 11**

Araguaney, Venezuelan national tree.

Foliage in Yellow
C293 AP29 5c orange brn   .20   .2
C294 AP29 10c blue grn   .20   .2
C295 AP29 15c deep plum   .45   .2
C296 AP29 25c dk gray grn   3.00 1.2
C297 AP29 30c red orange   3.25 1.6
C298 AP29 50c dark gray   1.75 .4
C299 AP29 60c deep blue   3.00 .8
C300 AP29 90c red   5.50 1.6
C301 AP29 1b rose violet   6.50 2.0
    Nos. C293-C301 (9)   23.85 8.25

Issued to publicize Forest Week, 1950.

Census Type of 1950

1950, Sept. 1   Engr.   **Perf. 12**
C302 A90 5c olive gray   .20   .2
C303 A90 10c green   .20   .2
C304 A90 15c olive green   .20   .2
C305 A90 25c gray   .30   .2
C306 A90 30c orange   .45   .25
C307 A90 50c lt brown   .30   .2
C308 A90 60c ultra   .30   .2
C309 A90 90c rose carmine   1.10 .45
C310 A90 1b violet   1.75 1.40
    Nos. C302-C310 (9)   4.80 3.40

Signing Act of Independence — AP31

1950, Nov. 17
C311 AP31 5c vermilion   .20   .20
C312 AP31 10c red brown   .20   .20
C313 AP31 15c violet   .35   .20
C314 AP31 30c brt blue   .55   .25
C315 AP31 1b green   3.00 1.40
    Nos. C311-C315 (5)   4.30 2.25

200th anniversary of the birth of Gen. Francisco de Miranda.

Alonso de Ojeda Type of 1950

1950, Dec. 18   Photo.   **Perf. 11½**
C316 A91 5c orange brn   .20   .20
C317 A91 10c cerise   .25   .20
C318 A91 15c black brn   .30   .20
C319 A91 25c violet   .55   .25
C320 A91 30c orange   1.10 .45
C321 A91 1b emerald   4.50 2.25
    Nos. C316-321 (6)   6.90 3.55

Bolivar Statue Type of 1951

1951, July 13   Engr.   **Perf. 12**
C322 A92 5c purple   .25   .20
C323 A92 10c dull green   .30   .20
C324 A92 20c olive gray   .30   .20
C325 A92 25c olive green   .35   .20
C326 A92 30c vermilion   .45   .20
C327 A92 40c lt brown   .45   .30
C328 A92 50c gray   1.40 .55
C329 A92 70c orange   2.25 1.40
    Nos. C322-C329 (8)   5.75 3.35

Queen Isabella
I — AP34

1951, Oct. 12   Photo.   **Perf. 11½**
C330 AP34 5c dk green & buff .30   .20
C331 AP34 10c dk red & cream .30   .20
C332 AP34 20c dp blue & gray .50   .20

333 AP34 30c dk blue & gray .50 .20
a. Souv. sheet of 4, #C330-C333 3.00 2.75
Nos. C330-C333 (4) 1.60 .80

500th anniv. of the birth of Queen Isabella I of Spain.

Bicycle Racecourse — AP35

1951, Dec. 18   Engr.   Perf. 12

C334 AP35 5c green .65 .20
C335 AP35 10c rose carmine .75 .20
C336 AP35 20c redsh brown .85 .25
C337 AP35 30c brown 1.10 .35
a. Souv. sheet, #C334-C337 11.00 11.00
Nos. C334-C337 (4) 3.35 1.00

3rd Bolivarian Games, Caracas, Dec. 1951.

Arms of Carabobo
and
"Industry" — AP36

1951   Photo.   Perf. 11½

C338 AP36 5c blue green .20 .20
C339 AP36 7½c gray grn .30 .30
C340 AP36 10c car rose .20 .20
C341 AP36 15c dark brown .25 .20
C342 AP36 20c gray blue .35 .20
C343 AP36 30c deep blue 1.25 .25
C344 AP36 45c magenta .55 .20
C345 AP36 60c olive brown 1.10 .55
C346 AP36 90c rose brown 3.00 1.75
Nos. C338-C346 (9) 7.20 3.90

Issue date: Oct. 29.

Arms of Zulia and "Industry"

C347 AP36 5c blue green .20 .20
C348 AP36 10c car rose .20 .20
C349 AP36 15c dark brown .40 .20
C350 AP36 30c deep blue 3.00 1.25
C351 AP36 60c olive brown 1.60 .40
C352 AP36 1.20b brown car 7.00 5.00
C353 AP36 3b blue gray 1.75 .75
C354 AP36 5b purple brn 3.00 2.00
C355 AP36 10b violet 5.00 4.00
Nos. C347-C355 (9) 22.15 14.00

Issued: 5b, 9/8; 5c, 3b, 10b, 10/8; others, 10/29.

Arms of Anzoategui

C356 AP36 5c blue green .20 .20
C357 AP36 10c car rose .20 .20
C358 AP36 15c dk brown .30 .20
C359 AP36 25c sepia .40 .20
C360 AP36 30c deep blue 1.10 .80
C361 AP36 50c henna brn 1.10 .40
C362 AP36 60c olive brn 1.60 .20
C363 AP36 1b purple 2.00 .80
C364 AP36 2b violet gray 3.75 1.75
Nos. C356-C364 (9) 10.65 4.80

Issue date: Nov. 9.

Arms of Caracas and Buildings

C365 AP36 5c blue green .20 .20
C366 AP36 7½c gray green 1.90 .75
C367 AP36 10c car rose .30 .20
C368 AP36 15c dk brown 4.50 .50
C369 AP36 20c gray blue 3.00 .50
C370 AP36 30c deep blue 5.00 1.00
C371 AP36 45c magenta 3.00 1.00
C372 AP36 60c olive brn 10.00 1.25
C373 AP36 90c rose brn 6.00 5.00
Nos. C365-C373 (9) 34.20 10.00

Issue date: Aug. 6.

Arms of Tachira and Agricultural Products

C374 AP36 5c blue green .20 .20
C375 AP36 10c car rose .20 .20
C376 AP36 15c dk brown .65 .20
C377 AP36 30c deep blue 9.00 1.10
C378 AP36 60c olive brn 7.00 1.10
C379 AP36 1.20b brown car 7.00 5.00
C380 AP36 3b blue gray 1.75 .90
C381 AP36 5b purple brn 4.00 2.00
C382 AP36 10b violet 5.75 4.00
Nos. C374-C382 (9) 35.55 14.70

Issue date: Aug. 9.

Arms of Venezuela and Bolivar Statue

C383 AP36 5c blue green .30 .20
C384 AP36 7½c gray grn .85 .65
C385 AP36 10c car rose .20 .20
C386 AP36 15c dk brown 2.00 .60
C387 AP36 20c gray blue 2.75 .50
C388 AP36 30c deep blue 5.00 1.10
C389 AP36 45c magenta 2.25 .45
C390 AP36 60c olive brn 11.00 2.25
C391 AP36 90c rose brn 7.00 5.00
Nos. C383-C391 (9) 31.35 11.00

Issue date: Aug. 6.

1952
Arms of Miranda and Agricultural Products

C392 AP36 5c blue green .20 .20
C393 AP36 7½c gray grn .30 .30
C394 AP36 10c car rose .20 .20
C395 AP36 15c dark brown .40 .20
C396 AP36 20c gray blue .65 .25
C397 AP36 30c deep blue 1.10 .40
C398 AP36 45c magenta .90 .20
C399 AP36 60c olive brn 2.25 .55
C400 AP36 90c rose brn 12.00 8.00
Nos. C392-C400 (9) 18.00 10.30

Issue date: 7½c, 15c, 20c, 30c, Mar. 24.

Arms of Aragua and Stylized Farm

C401 AP36 5c blue green .40 .20
C402 AP36 7½c gray grn .30 .20
C403 AP36 10c car rose .20 .20
C404 AP36 15c dk brown 1.00 .25
C405 AP36 20c gray blue .55 .20
C406 AP36 30c deep blue 1.60 .30
C407 AP36 45c magenta 1.40 .25
C408 AP36 60c olive brn 2.75 .40
C409 AP36 90c rose brn 14.00 8.00
Nos. C401-C409 (9) 22.20 10.15

Issue date: 7½c, 15c, 20c, 30c, Mar. 24.

Arms of Lara, Agricultural Products and Rope

C410 AP36 5c blue green .40 .20
C411 AP36 7½c gray grn .30 .30
C412 AP36 10c car rose .20 .20
C413 AP36 15c dk brown .65 .20
C414 AP36 20c gray blue .90 .20
C415 AP36 30c deep blue 2.25 .40
C416 AP36 45c magenta .90 .35
C417 AP36 60c olive brn 2.25 .65
C418 AP36 90c rose brn 13.00 10.00
Nos. C410-C418 (9) 20.85 12.50

Issue date: 7½c, 15c, 20c, Mar. 24.

Arms of Bolivar and Stylized Design

C419 AP36 5c blue green 3.00 .35
C420 AP36 10c car rose .20 .20
C421 AP36 15c dark brown .35 .20
C422 AP36 25c sepia .30 .20
C423 AP36 30c deep blue 1.75 .95
C424 AP36 50c henna brn 1.25 .40
C425 AP36 60c olive brn 2.25 .55
C426 AP36 1b purple 1.75 .40
C427 AP36 2b violet gray 3.75 1.75
Nos. C419-C427 (9) 14.60 5.00

Issue date: 15c, 30c, Mar. 24.

Arms of Sucre, Palms and Seascape

C428 AP36 5c blue green .30 .20
C429 AP36 10c car rose .20 .20
C430 AP36 15c dk brown .40 .20
C431 AP36 25c sepia 8.50 .20
C432 AP36 30c deep blue 2.75 .85
C433 AP36 50c henna brn 1.25 .30
C434 AP36 60c olive brn 1.60 .65
C435 AP36 1b purple 2.00 .50
C436 AP36 2b violet gray 4.50 2.25
Nos. C428-C436 (9) 21.50 5.35

Issue date: 15c, 30c, Mar. 24.

Arms of Trujillo Surrounded by Stylized Tree

C437 AP36 5c blue green 4.50 .35
C438 AP36 10c car rose .20 .20
C439 AP36 15c dk brown 1.10 .20
C440 AP36 30c deep blue 5.00 1.10
C441 AP36 60c olive brn 4.00 1.00
C442 AP36 1.20b rose red 3.75 2.40
C443 AP36 3b blue gray 1.60 1.00
C444 AP36 5b purple brn 3.75 1.75
C445 AP36 10b violet 6.00 4.00
Nos. C437-C445 (9) 29.90 12.00

Issue date: 5c, 30c, Mar. 24.

1953-54
Map of Delta Amacuro and Ship

C446 AP36 5c bl grn .30 .20
C447 AP36 10c car rose .20 .20
C448 AP36 15c dk brn .45 .20
C449 AP36 25c sepia .65 .30
C450 AP36 30c dp bl 2.25 .65
C451 AP36 50c hn brn 1.10 .30
C452 AP36 60c ol brn 1.75 .50
C453 AP36 1b purple 2.25 .75
C454 AP36 2b vio gray 3.75 2.75
Nos. C446-C454 (9) 12.70 5.85

Issue date: 15c, 30c, Feb. 13.

Arms of Falcon and Stylized Oil Refinery

C455 AP36 5c bl grn .50 .20
C456 AP36 10c car rose .20 .20
C457 AP36 15c dk brn .45 .20
C458 AP36 30c dp bl 3.75 .90
C459 AP36 60c ol brn 2.75 .65
C460 AP36 1.20b rose red 3.50 3.00
C461 AP36 3b bl gray 3.75 2.00
C462 AP36 5b pur brn 6.00 4.00
C463 AP36 10b violet 6.00 4.50
Nos. C455-C463 (9) 26.90 15.65

Issue date: 10c, 15c, 30c, Feb. 13.

Arms of Guarico and Factory

C464 AP36 5c blue grn .30 .20
C465 AP36 10c car rose .20 .20
C466 AP36 15c dk brn .45 .20
C467 AP36 25c sepia .65 .30
C468 AP36 30c dp bl 2.50 1.00
C469 AP36 50c hn brn 1.25 .45
C470 AP36 60c ol brn 1.50 .65
C471 AP36 1b purple 2.50 .65
C472 AP36 2b vio gray 3.75 2.00
Nos. C464-C472 (9) 13.10 5.65

Issue date: 15c, 30c, Feb. 13.

Arms of Merida and Church

C473 AP36 5c bl grn .25 .20
C474 AP36 10c car rose .20 .20
C475 AP36 15c dk brn .40 .20
C476 AP36 30c dp bl 3.75 .80
C477 AP36 60c ol brn 1.60 .40
C478 AP36 1.20b rose red 3.00 2.00
C479 AP36 3b bl gray 1.60 .80
C480 AP36 5b pur brn 3.75 2.00
C481 AP36 10b violet 5.00 3.25
Nos. C473-C481 (9) 19.55 9.85

Issue date: 10c, Feb. 2.

Arms of Monagas and Horses

C482 AP36 5c bl grn .25 .20
C483 AP36 10c car rose .20 .20
C484 AP36 15c dk brn .40 .20
C485 AP36 25c sepia .30 .20
C486 AP36 30c dp bl 3.00 .90
C487 AP36 50c hn brn 1.10 .40
C488 AP36 60c ol brn 1.40 .40
C489 AP36 1b purple 2.00 .55
C490 AP36 2b vio gray 3.75 1.60
Nos. C482-C490 (9) 11.40 4.65

Issue date: 10c, Feb. 2.

Arms of Portuguesa and Forest

C491 AP36 5c bl grn 1.10 .30
C492 AP36 10c car rose .20 .20
C493 AP36 15c dk brn .50 .20
C494 AP36 30c dp bl 3.50 1.50
C495 AP36 60c ol brn 2.50 .55
C496 AP36 1.20b rose red 6.25 3.75
C497 AP36 3b bl gray 2.00 1.00
C498 AP36 5b pur brn 3.75 2.00
C499 AP36 10b violet 5.50 4.50
Nos. C491-C499 (9) 25.30 14.00

Issue date: 5c, 10c, 30c, Feb. 2.

Map of Amazonas and Orchid

C500 AP36 5c bl grn .85 .20
C501 AP36 10c car rose .20 .20
C502 AP36 15c dk brn .85 .20
C503 AP36 25c sepia 1.75 .20
C504 AP36 30c dp bl 4.50 .45
C505 AP36 50c hn brn 3.50 .75
C506 AP36 60c ol brn 4.50 .75
C507 AP36 1b purple 17.50 2.50
C508 AP36 2b vio gray 7.00 3.00
Nos. C500-C508 (9) 40.65 8.25

Issue date: Jan. 1954

Arms of Apure, Horse and Bird

C509 AP36 5c bl grn .40 .20
C510 AP36 10c car rose .20 .20
C511 AP36 15c dk brn .40 .20
C512 AP36 30c dp bl 2.00 .80
C513 AP36 60c ol brn 1.90 .40
C514 AP36 1.20b brn car 3.00 2.00
C515 AP36 3b bl gray 1.90 .85
C516 AP36 5b pur brn 3.75 1.60
C517 AP36 10b violet 5.25 3.75
Nos. C509-C517 (9) 18.80 10.00

Issue date: Jan. 1954.

Arms of Barinas, Cow and Horse

C518 AP36 5c bl grn .20 .20
C519 AP36 10c car rose .20 .20
C520 AP36 15c dk brn .75 .20
C521 AP36 30c dp blue 2.50 1.00
C522 AP36 60c ol brn 2.50 .50
C523 AP36 1.20b brn car 3.50 1.90
C524 AP36 3b bl gray 2.25 1.00
C525 AP36 5b pur brn 3.75 1.25
C526 AP36 10b violet 5.50 4.00
Nos. C518-C526 (9) 21.15 10.25

Issue date: Jan. 1954.

Arms of Cojedes and Cattle

C527 AP36 5c bl grn 2.50 .40
C528 AP36 7½c gray grn .65 .40
C529 AP36 10c car rose .20 .20
C530 AP36 15c dk brn .20 .20
C531 AP36 20c gray bl .50 .20
C532 AP36 30c dp blue 3.50 .50
C533 AP36 45c mag 1.25 .30

Arms of Falcon and Stylized Oil Refinery (continued)

C534 AP36 60c ol brn 2.50 .45
C535 AP36 90c rose brn 3.00 1.75
Nos. C527-C535 (9) 14.30 4.40

Issue date: Dec.

Arms of Nueva Esparta and Fish

C536 AP36 5c bl grn .40 .20
C537 AP36 10c car rose .20 .20
C538 AP36 15c dk brn .65 .20
C539 AP36 25c sepia 1.10 .25
C540 AP36 30c dp bl 2.25 .50
C541 AP36 50c hn brn 2.25 .50
C542 AP36 60c ol brn 2.25 .30
C543 AP36 1b purple 3.25 .75
C544 AP36 2b vio gray 4.50 2.25
Nos. C536-C544 (9) 16.85 5.15

Issue date: Jan. 1954.

Arms of Yaracuy and Tropical Foliage

C545 AP36 5c bl grn .45 .20
C546 AP36 7½c gray grn 6.00 6.00
C547 AP36 10c car rose .20 .20
C548 AP36 15c dk brn .45 .20
C549 AP36 20c gray bl .85 .20
C550 AP36 30c dp bl 1.75 .50
C551 AP36 45c mag 1.25 .30
C552 AP36 60c ol brn 1.25 .50
C553 AP36 90c rose brn 3.50 2.50
Nos. C545-C553 (9) 15.70 10.60
Nos. C338-C553 (216) 504.55 218.00

Issue date: Jan. 1954.

Ship Type of 1948-50 Redrawn Coil Stamps
Imprint: "Courvoisier S.A."

1952   Unwmk.   Perf. 12x11½

C554 AP25 5c rose brn .85 .20
C555 AP25 10c org red 1.40 .20
C556 AP25 15c rose brn 1.75 .20
Nos. C554-C556 (3) 4.00 .60

Barquisimeto Type of 1952

1952, Sept. 14   Photo.   Perf. 11½

C557 A94 5c blue green .20 .20
C558 A94 10c car rose .20 .20
C559 A94 20c dk blue .30 .20
C560 A94 25c black brn .40 .20
C561 A94 30c ultra .55 .20
C562 A94 40c brown org 3.00 1.50
C563 A94 50c ol grn 1.00 .40
C564 A94 1b purple 4.00 2.00
Nos. C557-C564 (8) 9.65 4.90

Caracas Post Office Type of 1953-54

1953, Mar. 11   Perf. 12½

C565 A96 7½c yellow grn .20 .20
C566 A96 15c dp plum .20 .20
C567 A96 20c slate .20 .20
C568 A96 25c sepia .35 .20
C569 A96 40c plum .35 .20
C570 A96 45c rose vio .35 .20
C571 A96 50c red orange .55 .20
C572 A96 70c dk sl grn 1.10 .55
C573 A96 75c dp ultra 3.75 .80
C574 A96 90c brown org .90 .45
C575 A96 1b violet blue .90 .45
Nos. C565-C575 (11) 8.85 3.65

See Nos. C587-C589, C597-C606.

Simon
Rodriguez
AP39

Quotation from
Bolivar's
Manifesto of
1824
AP40

1954, Feb. 28   Perf. 11½

C576 AP39 5c blue green .25 .20
C577 AP39 10c car rose .35 .20
C578 AP39 20c gray blue .45 .20
C579 AP39 45c magenta .70 .25
C580 AP39 65c gray green 2.25 1.00
Nos. C576-C580 (5) 4.00 1.85

Centenary of the death of Simon Rodriguez, scholar and tutor of Bolivar.

1954, Mar. 1   Unwmk.

C581 AP40 15c blk & brn buff .20 .20
C582 AP40 25c dk red brn & gray .65 .20
C583 AP40 40c dk red brn & red org .45 .20
C584 AP40 65c black & blue 1.10 .60

C585 AP40 80c dk red brn & rose .85 .45
C586 AP40 1b pur & rose lil 1.75 .35
Nos. C581-C586 (6) 5.00 2.00

10th Inter-American Conf., Caracas, Mar. 1954.

P.O. Type of 1953
1954, Feb. **Photo.** **Perf. 12½**
C587 A96 5c orange .20 .20
C588 A96 30c red brown 1.90 1.00
C589 A96 60c bright red 1.90 1.25
Nos. C587-C589 (3) 4.00 2.45

Valencia Arms Type of 1955
1955, Mar. 26 **Engr.** **Perf. 12**
C590 A97 5c blue green .20 .20
C591 A97 10c rose pink .20 .20
C592 A97 20c ultra .20 .20
C593 A97 25c gray .20 .20
C594 A97 40c violet .45 .25
C595 A97 50c vermilion .45 .25
C596 A97 60c olive green .90 .25
Nos. C590-C596 (7) 2.60 1.55

P.O. Type of 1953 Inscribed: "Republica de Venezuela"
1955 **Photo.** **Perf. 12½**
C597 A96 5c orange .20 .20
C598 A96 10c olive brn .20 .20
C599 A96 15c deep plum .20 .20
C600 A96 20c slate .25 .20
C601 A96 30c red brn .25 .20
C602 A96 40c plum .75 .25
C603 A96 45c rose violet .75 .40
C604 A96 70c dk slate grn 1.90 .85
C605 A96 75c deep ultra 1.25 .50
C606 A96 90c brown org .65 .25
Nos. C597-C606 (10) 6.40 3.25

Caracas Arms Type of 1955
1955, Dec. 9 **Unwmk.** **Perf. 11½**
C607 A98 5c yellow org .20 .20
C608 A98 15c claret brn .20 .20
C609 A98 25c violet blk .20 .20
C610 A98 40c red .45 .20
C611 A98 50c red orange .45 .20
C612 A98 60c car rose .90 .35
Nos. C607-C612 (6) 2.40 1.35

University Hospital, Caracas AP43

5c, 10c, 15c, 70c, O'Leary School, Barinas. 25c, 30c, 80c, University Hospital, Caracas. 40c, 45c, 50c, 1b, Caracas-La Guaira Highway. 60c, 65c, 75c, 2b, Towers of Simon Bolivar Center.

1956-57 **Unwmk.** **Perf. 11½**
C613 AP43 5c orange .20 .20
C614 AP43 10c sepia .20 .20
C615 AP43 15c claret brown .20 .20
C616 AP43 20c dark blue .20 .20
C617 AP43 25c gray black .20 .20
C618 AP43 30c henna brown .25 .20
C619 AP43 40c bright crimson .35 .20
C620 AP43 45c brown violet .25 .20
C621 AP43 50c deep orange .45 .20
C622 AP43 60c olive green .45 .20
C623 AP43 65c bright blue .70 .20
C624 AP43 70c blue green .75 .25
C625 AP43 75c ultra .80 .35
C626 AP43 80c carmine rose .90 .20
C627 AP43 1b plum .55 .25
C628 AP43 2b dark car rose 1.10 .75
Nos. C613-C628 (16) 7.55 4.00

Issued: 20c, 40c, 45c, 50c, 1b, 11/5/56; others, 1957.

Book and Flags of American Nations — AP44

1956-57
Granite Paper
C629 AP44 5c orange & brn .20 .20
C630 AP44 10c brn & pale brn .20 .20
C631 AP44 20c blue & sapphire .20 .20
C632 AP44 25c gray vio & gray .25 .20
C633 AP44 40c rose red & pale pur .35 .20

C634 AP44 45c vio brn & gray brn .45 .20
C635 AP44 60c olive & gray ol .85 .45
Nos. C629-C635 (7) 2.50 1.65

Book Festival of the Americas, 11/15-30/56. Issued: 5c, 40c, 11/15; others, 2/7/57.

Bolivar Type of 1957-58
Engraved; Center Embossed
1957-58 **Unwmk.** **Perf. 13½**
C636 A100 5c orange .20 .20
C637 A100 10c olive gray .20 .20
C638 A100 20c blue .55 .20
C639 A100 25c gray black .60 .20
C640 A100 40c rose red .55 .20
C641 A100 45c rose lilac .65 .25
C642 A100 65c yellow brn 1.10 .45
Nos. C636-C642 (7) 3.85 1.70

Issued: 45c, 1958; others, Nov. 15, 1957.

Tamanaco Hotel Type of 1957-58
1957-58 **Engr.** **Perf. 13**
C643 A101 5c dull yellow .20 .20
C644 A101 10c brown .20 .20
C645 A101 15c chocolate .20 .20
C646 A101 20c gray blue .20 .20
C647 A101 25c sepia .20 .20
C648 A101 30c violet bl .20 .20
C649 A101 40c car rose .25 .20
C650 A101 45c claret .30 .20
C651 A101 50c red org .30 .20
C652 A101 60c yellow grn .55 .20
C653 A101 65c orange brn 1.50 .75
C654 A101 70c slate .80 .35
C655 A101 75c grnsh blue .90 .45
C656 A101 1b dk claret .90 .45
C657 A101 2b dk gray 1.50 .55
Nos. C643-C657 (15) 8.20 4.55

Issue dates: 5c, 10c, Oct. 10; others, 1958. For surcharge see No. C878.

Post Office Type of 1958
1958, May 14 **Litho.** **Perf. 14**
C658 A102 5c dp yellow .20 .20
C659 A102 10c brown .20 .20
C660 A102 15c red brn .20 .20
C661 A102 20c lt blue .20 .20
C662 A102 25c lt gray .20 .20
C663 A102 30c lt ultra .20 .20
C664 A102 40c brt yel grn .20 .20
C665 A102 50c red orange .20 .20
C666 A102 60c rose pink .20 .20
C667 A102 65c red .25 .20
C668 A102 90c violet .35 .20
C669 A102 1b lilac .45 .20
C670 A102 1.20b bister brn 5.50 3.75
Nos. C658-C670 (13) 8.35 6.15

See Nos. C786-C792. For surcharges see Nos. C856-C861.

Post Office Type of 1958
Coil Stamps
1958 **Engr.** **Perf. 11½x12**
C671 A103 5c deep yellow .25 .20
C672 A103 10c brown .35 .20
C673 A103 15c dark brown .50 .20
Nos. C671-C673 (3) 1.10 .60

Merida Type of 1958
1958, Oct. 9 **Photo.** **Perf. 13½**
C674 A104 5c orange yellow .20 .20
C675 A104 10c gray brown .20 .20
C676 A104 15c dull red brn .20 .20
C677 A104 20c chalky blue .20 .20
C678 A104 25c brown gray .25 .20
C679 A104 30c violet bl .25 .20
C680 A104 40c rose car .35 .20
C681 A104 45c brt lilac .35 .20
C682 A104 50c red orange .45 .25
C683 A104 60c lt olive grn .35 .20
C684 A104 65c hennna brn 1.10 .45
C685 A104 70c gray black .65 .35
C686 A104 75c brt grnsh bl 1.25 .65
C687 A104 80c brt vio bl .80 .35
C688 A104 90c blue green .80 .35
C689 A104 1b lilac .90 .45
Nos. C674-C689 (16) 8.30 4.65

Trujillo Type of 1959
1958, Nov. 17 **Photo.** **Perf. 14**
C690 A105 5c orange yel .20 .20
C691 A105 10c lt brown .20 .20
C692 A105 15c redsh brown .20 .20
C693 A105 20c lt blue .20 .20
C694 A105 25c pale gray .25 .20
C695 A105 30c lt vio blue .25 .20
C696 A105 40c brt yel grn .30 .20
C697 A105 50c red orange .30 .20
C698 A105 60c lilac rose .45 .25
C699 A105 65c vermilion 1.40 .65
C700 A105 1b lilac .90 .25
Nos. C690-C700 (11) 4.65 2.75

Emblem — AP45

1959, Mar. 10 **Litho.** **Perf. 13½**
C701 AP45 5c yellow .20 .20
C702 AP45 10c red brown .20 .20
C703 AP45 15c orange .25 .20
C704 AP45 30c gray .45 .30
C705 AP45 50c green .50 .35
Nos. C701-C705 (5) 1.60 1.25

8th Central American and Caribbean Games, Caracas, Nov. 29-Dec. 14, 1958. Exist imperf. Value, pair $25.

Stamp Centenary Type of 1959
Stamp of 1859 and: 25c, Mailman and José Ignacio Paz Castillo. 50c, Mailman on horseback and Jacinto Gutierrez. 1b, Plane, train and Miguel Herrera.

1959, Sept. 15 **Engr.** **Perf. 13½**
C706 A107 25c orange yel .30 .20
C707 A107 50c blue .45 .25
C708 A107 1b rose red .90 .45
Nos. C706-C708 (3) 1.65 .90

> Catalogue values for unused stamps in this section, from this point to the end of the section, are for Never Hinged items.

Alexander von Humboldt Type of 1960
1960, Feb. 9 **Unwmk.**
C709 A108 5c ocher & brn .35 .20
C710 A108 20c brt bl & turq bl .95 .20
C711 A108 40c ol & ol grn 1.40 .35
Nos. C709-C711 (3) 2.70 .75

Newspaper Type of 1960
1960, June 11 **Litho.** **Perf. 14**
C712 A109 5c yellow & blk 1.90 .80
C713 A109 15c lt red brn & blk 1.00 .30
C714 A109 65c salmon & blk 1.50 .55
Nos. C712-C714 (3) 4.40 1.65

Agustin Codazzi Type of 1960
1960, June 15 **Engr.**
C715 A110 5c yel org & brn .20 .20
C716 A110 10c brn & dk brn .20 .20
C717 A110 25c gray & blk .40 .20
C718 A110 30c vio bl & sl .55 .20
C719 A110 50c org brn & brn .90 .30
C720 A110 70c gray ol & ol gray 1.40 .55
Nos. C715-720 (6) 3.65 1.65

For surcharge see No. C884.

National Pantheon Type of 1960
1960, May 9 **Litho.**
Pantheon in Bister
C721 A111 5c dp bister .20 .20
C722 A111 10c red brown .25 .20
C723 A111 15c fawn .30 .20
C724 A111 20c lt blue .45 .20
C725 A111 25c gray 2.40 .25
C726 A111 30c lt vio bl 2.40 .40
C727 A111 40c brt yel grn .45 .20
C728 A111 45c lt violet .70 .20
C729 A111 60c deep pink .90 .30
C730 A111 65c salmon .90 .30
C731 A111 70c gray 1.25 .40
C732 A111 75c chalky blue 3.75 .70
C733 A111 80c lt ultra 1.90 .60
C734 A111 1.20b bister brn 2.25 .85
Nos. C721-C734 (14) 18.10 5.00

For surcharges see Nos. C894-C895.

Andres Eloy Blanco Type of 1960
1960, May 21 **Perf. 14**
Portrait in Black
C735 A112 20c blue .40 .20
C736 A112 75c grnsh blue 1.25 .30
C737 A112 90c brt violet 1.25 .30
Nos. C735-C737 (3) 2.90 .80

For surcharge see No. C874.

Independence Type of 1960
1960, Aug. 19 **Litho. Perf. 13½**
Center Multicolored
C738 A113 50c orange .85 .25
C739 A113 75c brt grnsh blue 1.25 .40
C740 A113 90c purple 1.40 .35
Nos. C738-C740 (3) 3.50 1.00

Oil Refinery AP46

Unwmk.
1960, Aug. 26 **Engr.** **Perf. 1**
C741 AP46 30c dk bl & sl bl .50 .2
C742 AP46 40c yel grn & ol .85 .3
C743 AP46 50c org & red brn 1.00 .4
Nos. C741-C743 (3) 2.35 .9

Issued to publicize Venezuela's oil industry.

Luisa Cáceres de Arismendi Type of 1960
1960, Oct. 21 **Litho.** **Perf. 1**
Center Multicolored
C744 A115 5c bister .95 .3
C745 A115 10c redsh brown 1.25 .5
C746 A115 60c rose carmine 2.25 .7
Nos. C744-C746 (3) 4.45 1.6

José Antonio Anzoategui Type of 1960
1960, Oct. 29 **Engr**
C747 A116 25c gray & brown .55 .2
C748 A116 40c yel grn & ol gray .55 .4
C749 A116 45c rose cl & dl pur .75 .3
Nos. C747-C749 (3) 1.85 .9

Antonio José de Sucre Type of 1960
Unwmk.
1960, Nov. 18 **Litho.** **Perf. 1**
Center Multicolored
C750 A117 25c gray .75 .30
C751 A117 30c violet blue 1.10 .40
C752 A117 50c brown orange 1.40 .55
Nos. C750-C752 (3) 3.25 1.25

Type of Regular Issue, 1960
Designs: 30c, Bolivar Peak. 50c, Caron Falls. 65c, Cuacharo caves.

1960, Mar. 22 **Perf. 14**
C753 A118 30c vio bl & blk bl 1.90 1.90
C754 A118 50c brn org & brn 1.90 1.90
C755 A118 65c red org & red brn 1.90 1.90
Nos. C753-C755 (3) 5.70 5.70

Cow's Head, Grain, Man and Child AP47

Arms of San Cristobal AP48

1961, Feb. 6 **Litho.** **Unwmk.**
Cow and Inscription in Black
C756 AP47 5c yellow .20 .20
C757 AP47 10c brown .20 .20
C758 AP47 15c redsh brn .20 .20
C759 AP47 20c dull blue .20 .20
C760 AP47 25c gray .20 .20
C761 AP47 30c violet bl .25 .20
C762 AP47 40c yellow grn .30 .20
C763 AP47 45c lilac .35 .20
C764 AP47 50c orange .40 .20
C765 AP47 60c cerise .45 .20
C766 AP47 65c red orange .60 .20
C767 AP47 70c gray .90 .30
C768 AP47 75c brt grnsh bl .85 .25
C769 AP47 80c brt violet .85 .20
C770 AP47 90c violet 1.25 .40
Nos. C756-C770 (15) 7.20 3.35

9th general census & 3rd agricultural census. Issued: 5-15c, 30c, 60-65c, 75-80c, 2/6; others, 4/6.
For surcharges see Nos. C865-C866.

Rafael Maria Baralt Type of 1961
1961, Mar. 11 **Engr.** **Perf. 14**
C771 A120 25c gray & sepia .65 .30
C772 A120 30c dk blue & vio .75 .30
C773 A120 40c yel grn & ol grn .95 .40
Nos. C771-C773 (3) 2.35 1.00

1961, Apr. 10   Litho.
Arms in Original Colors
C774	AP48	5c orange & blk	.20	.20
C775	AP48	55c yel grn & blk	.65	.25

400th anniversary of San Cristobal.
For surcharge see No. C879.

Bird Type of 1961
Birds: 5c, Troupial. 10c, Golden cock of the rock. 15c, Tropical mockingbird.

1961, Sept. 6   Unwmk.   Perf. 14½
C776	A121	5c multicolored	1.25	.85
C777	A121	10c multicolored	.60	.45
C778	A121	15c multicolored	.80	.50
		Nos. C776-C778 (3)	2.65	1.80

Charge, Battle of Carabobo — AP49

1961, Dec. 1   Litho.   Perf. 14
Center Multicolored
C779	AP49	50c black & ultra	.75	.20
C780	AP49	1.05b black & org	1.75	.50
C781	AP49	1.50b blk & lil rose	2.00	.10
C782	AP49	1.90b black & lilac	2.50	1.00
C783	AP49	2b black & gray	3.25	1.00
C784	AP49	3b black & grnsh bl	4.00	1.25
		Nos. C779-C784 (6)	14.25	4.45

140th anniversary of Battle of Carabobo.
For surcharges see Nos. C867-C870.

Arms of Cardinal Quintero AP50

Archbishop Rafael Arias Blanco — AP51

1962, Mar. 1   Unwmk.
C785	AP50	5c lilac rose	.25	.20
a.		Souv. sheet of 1, imperf.	1.90	1.90

1st Venezuelan Cardinal, José Humberto Quintero.
No. C785a, issued Mar. 23, sold for 1b.

Post Office Type of 1958
1962, Apr. 12   Litho.   Perf. 13½x14
C786	A102	35c citron	.25	.20
C787	A102	55c gray olive	.40	.20
C788	A102	70c bluish green	.65	.25
C789	A102	75c brown orange	.80	.20
C790	A102	80c fawn	.80	.30
C791	A102	85c deep rose	1.25	.45
C792	A102	95c lilac rose	.85	.40
		Nos. C786-C792 (7)	5.00	2.00

For surcharges see Nos. C856-C861.

1962, May 10   Perf. 10½
C793	AP51	75c red lilac	.80	.30

4th anniversary (in 1961) of the anti-communist pastoral letter of the Archbishop of Caracas, Rafael Arias Blanco.

Orchid Type of 1962
Orchids: 5c, Oncidium volvox. 20c, Cycnoches chlorochilon. 25c, Cattleya Gaskelliana. 30c, Epidendrum difforme, horiz. 40c, Catasetum callosum Lindl, horiz. 50c, Oncidium bicolor Lindl. 1b, Brassavola nodosa Lindl, horiz. 1.05b, Epidendrum lividum Lindl. 1.50b, Schomburgkia undulata Lindl. 2b, Oncidium zebrinum.

Perf. 14x13½, 13½x14
1962, May 30   Litho.   Unwmk.
Orchids in Natural Colors
C794	A124	5c blk & lt grn	.20	.20
C795	A124	20c black	.20	.20
C796	A124	25c black & fawn	.55	.20
C797	A124	30c black & pink	.50	.20
C798	A124	40c black & yel	.55	.20
C799	A124	50c black & lil	.75	.20
C800	A124	1b blk & pale rose	1.00	.35
C801	A124	1.05b blk & dp org	3.25	1.00
C802	A124	1.50b blk & pale vio	3.50	1.10
C803	A124	2b blk & org brn	4.50	1.60
		Nos. C794-C803 (10)	15.00	5.25

For surcharges see Nos. C885-C887.

Independence Type of 1960
Signing Declaration of Independence.

1962, June 11   Perf. 13½
Center Multicolored
C804	A113	55c olive	.60	.20
C805	A113	1.05b brt rose	2.10	.55
C806	A113	1.50b purple	1.60	.50
a.		Souv. sheet of 3, #C804-C806, imperf.	5.00	5.00
		Nos. C804-C806 (3)	4.30	1.25

No. C806a, issued Oct. 13, sold for 4.10b.
A buff cardboard folder exists with impressions of Nos. 812-814, C804-C806. Perforation is simulated. Sold for 5.60b. Value $3.
For surcharge see No. C893.

No. 710 Surcharged in Rose Carmine:
"BICENTENARIO DE UPATA 1762-1962 RESELLADO AEREO VALOR Bs. 2,00"

1962, July 7   Perf. 13½x14
C807	A102	2b on 1b lt ol grn	2.00	.90

Upata, a village in the state of Bolivar, 200th anniv.

National Games Type of 1962
Perf. 13x14
1962, Nov. 30   Unwmk.   Litho.
C808	A125	40c Bicycling	.40	.25
C809	A125	75c Baseball	.60	.30
C810	A125	85c Woman athlete	1.50	.65
a.		Souv. sheet of 3, #C808-C810 imperf.	3.00	3.00
		Nos. C808-C810 (3)	2.50	1.20

See note after No. 817.
No. C810a sold for 3b.
For surcharge see No. C899.

Bird Type of 1962
Birds: 5c, American kestrel. 20c, Black-bellied tree duck, horiz. 25c, Amazon kingfisher. 30c, Rufous-tailed chachalaca. 50c, Black-and-yellow troupial. 55c, White-naped nightjar. 2.30b, Red-crowned woodpecker. 2.50b, Black-moustached quail-dove.

1962, Dec. 14   Perf. 14x13½, 13½x14
Birds in Natural Colors; Black Inscription
C811	A126	5c car rose	.20	.20
C812	A126	20c brt blue	.50	.20
C813	A126	25c lt gray	.60	.20
C814	A126	30c lt olive	.65	.20
C815	A126	50c violet	1.00	.30
C816	A126	55c dp orange	1.75	.45
C817	A126	2.30b dl red brn	5.00	2.25
C818	A126	2.50b orange yel	5.00	2.50
		Nos. C811-C818 (8)	14.70	6.30

For surcharges see Nos. C880-C882.

Malaria Eradication Emblem, Mosquito and Map — AP52

Lithographed and Embossed
Perf. 13½x14
1962, Dec. 20   Wmk. 346
C819	AP52	30c green & blk	.55	.25
a.		Souv. sheet of 2, #825, C819, imperf.	3.00	3.00

WHO drive to eradicate malaria. No. C819a sold for 2b.

Animal Type of Regular Issue
5c, Spectacle bear, vert. 40c, Paca. 50c, Three-toed sloths. 55c, Great anteater. 1.50b, South American tapirs. 2b, Jaguar.

Perf. 14x13½, 13½x14
1963, Mar. 13   Litho.   Unwmk.
Multicolored Center; Black Inscriptions
C820	A128	5c yellow	.25	.20
C821	A128	40c brt green	.80	.25
C822	A128	50c lt violet	1.10	.30
C823	A128	55c brown olive	1.40	.40
C824	A128	1.50b gray	4.00	1.60
C825	A128	2b ultra	6.75	2.50
		Nos. C820-C825 (6)	14.30	5.25

For surcharges see Nos. C888-C889.

Freedom from Hunger Type of 1963
40c, Map, shepherd. 75c, Map, farmer.

1963, Mar. 21
C826	A129	40c lt yel grn & dl red	.45	.30
C827	A129	75c yellow & brown	.60	.40

Arms of Bocono — AP53

1963, May 30   Wmk. 346
C828	AP53	1b multicolored	1.40	.40

400th anniversary of the founding of Bocono.
For surcharge see No. C892.

Papal and Venezuelan Arms AP54

1963, June 11   Perf. 14x13½
Arms Multicolored
C829	AP54	80c light green	1.10	.30
C830	AP54	90c gray	1.10	.40

Vatican II, the 21st Ecumenical Council of the Roman Catholic Church.
For surcharges see Nos. C871-C872.

Arms of Venezuela — AP55

1963, July 29   Unwmk.   Perf. 14
C831	AP55	70c gray, red, yel & bl	.95	.40

Cent. of Venezuela's flag and coat of arms.
For surcharge see No. C883.

Lake Maracaibo Bridge AP56

Wmk. 346
1963, Aug. 24   Litho.   Perf. 14
C832	AP56	90c grn, brn & ocher	1.25	.40
C833	AP56	95c blue, brn & och	1.25	.45
C834	AP56	1b ultra, brn & och	1.00	.40
		Nos. C832-C834 (3)	3.50	1.25

Opening of bridge over Lake Maracaibo.
For surcharges see Nos. C897-C898.

Armed Forces Type of 1963
1963, Sept. 10   Unwmk.
C835	A134	1b red & bl, buff	1.60	.75

For surcharge see No. 862.

Hammarskjold Type of 1963
1963, Sept. 25   Unwmk.   Perf. 14
C836	A135	80c dk bl, lt ultra & ocher	.95	.40
C837	A135	90c dk bl, bl & ocher	1.25	.55
a.		Souv. sheet of 4, #841-842, C836-C837, imperf.	4.50	4.50

No. C837a sold for 3b.
For surcharges see Nos. C875-C876.

Dr. Luis Razetti, Physician, Birth Cent. — AP57

1963, Oct. 10   Engr.
C838	AP57	95c dk blue & mag	1.40	.60
C839	AP57	1.05b dk brn & grn	1.50	.75

For surcharges see Nos. C890-C891.

Red Cross Type of 1963
Designs: 40c, Sir Vincent K. Barrington. 75c, Red Cross nurse and child.

1963, Dec. 31   Litho.   Perf. 11½x12
C840	A137	40c multicolored	.55	.30
C841	A137	75c multicolored	.95	.40

Development Type of 1964
Designs: 5c, Loading cargo. 10c, Tractor and corn. 15c, Oil field workers. 20c, Oil refinery. 50c, Crane and building construction.

1964, Feb. 5   Unwmk.   Perf. 14x13½
C842	A138	5c multicolored	.20	.20
C843	A138	10c multicolored	.20	.20
C844	A138	15c multicolored	.20	.20
C845	A138	20c multicolored	.20	.20
C846	A138	50c multicolored	.50	.20
		Nos. 842-846 (5)	1.30	1.00

Cent. of the Dept. of Industrial Development and to publicize the Natl. Industrial Expo.

Pedro Gual Type of 1964
1964, Mar. 20   Perf. 14x13½
C847	A139	75c dull blue green	.75	.25
C848	A139	1b bright pink	1.00	.35

Blast Furnace and Map of Venezuela — AP58

Arms of Ciudad Bolivar — AP59

1964, May 22   Litho.   Perf. 13½x14
C849	AP58	80c multi	.90	.35
C850	AP58	1b multi	1.25	.40

Issued to publicize the Orinoco steel mills.

1964, May 22   Perf. 10½
C851	AP59	1b multi	1.25	.70

Bicentenary of Ciudad Bolivar.

AP60

AP61

1964, Aug. 3   Unwmk.   Perf. 11½
C852 AP60 30c bister brn & yel   .35 .20
C853 AP60 40c plum & pink   .55 .25
C854 AP60 50c brn & tan   .75 .25
  Nos. C852-C854 (3)   1.65 .65

80th birthday of novelist Romulo Gallegos.

1964, Nov. 11 Litho.   Perf. 14x13½
C855 AP61 1b orange & dk vio   1.10 .50

Eleanor Roosevelt and 15th anniv. (in 1963) of the Universal Declaration of Human Rights. For surcharge see No. C896.

Issues of 1947-64 Surcharged in Black, Dark Blue, Red, Carmine or Lilac with New Value and: "RESELLADO / VALOR"

1965
C856 A102 5c on 55c (#C787)   .20 .20
C857 A102 5c on 70c (#C788)   .20 .20
C858 A102 5c on 80c (#C790)   .20 .20
C859 A102 5c on 85c (#C791)   .20 .20
C860 A102 5c on 90c (#C668)   .20 .20
C861 A102 5c on 95c (#C792)   .20 .20
C862 A134 5c on 1b (#C835)   .40 .40
C863 AP25 10c on 3b (#C269) (C)   .20 .20
C864 AP25 10c on 4b (#C270) (C)   .50 .20
C865 AP47 10c on 70c (#C767) (C)   .25 .20
C866 AP47 10c on 90c (#C770) (C)   .25 .20
C867 AP49 10c on 1.05b (#C780)   .20 .20
C868 AP49 10c on 1.90b (#C782)   .40 .20
C869 AP49 10c on 2b (#C783)   .25 .20
C870 AP49 10c on 3b (#C784)   .25 .20
C871 AP54 10c on 80c (#C829)   .20 .20
C872 AP54 10c on 90c (#C830)   .20 .20
C873 AP16 15c on 3b (#C253)   .25 .20
C874 A112 15c on 90c (#C737)   .20 .20
C875 A135 15c on 80c (#C836)   .20 .20
C876 A135 15c on 90c (#C837)   .20 .20
C877 AP59 15c on 1b (#C851)   .25 .20
C878 A101 20c on 2b (#C657) (R)   .35 .20
C879 AP48 20c on 55c (#C775) (DB)   .25 .20
C880 A126 20c on 55c (#C816)   .25 .20
  a.   25c on 55c (#C816)   .40 .20
C881 A126 20c on 2.30b (#C817)   .25 .20
C882 A126 20c on 2.50b (#C818)   .40 .20
C883 AP55 20c on 70c (#C831)   .40 .20
C884 A110 25c on 70c (#C720) (DB)   .45 .20
C885 A124 25c on 1.05b (#C801) (L)   .25 .20
C886 A124 25c on 1.50b (#C802) (L)   .25 .20
C887 A124 25c on 2b (#C803) (L)   .40 .20
C888 A128 25c on 1.50b (#C824)   .40 .20
C889 A128 25c on 2b (#C825)   .40 .20
C890 AP57 25c on 95c (#C838)   .35 .20
C891 AP57 25c on 1.05b (#C839)   .40 .20
C892 AP53 30c on 1b (#C828)   .55 .20
C893 A113 40c on 1.05b (#C805) (DB)   .40 .20
C894 A111 50c on 65c (#C730) (DB)   .20 .20
C895 A111 50c on 1.20b (#C734) (DB)   .55 .20
C896 AP61 50c on 1b (#C855)   .25 .20
C897 AP56 60c on 90c (#C832)   .85 .30
C898 AP56 60c on 95c (#C833)   .65 .20
C899 A125 75c on 85c (#C810)   .75 .30
  Nos. C856-C899 (44)   14.50 9.00

Lines of surcharge arranged variously on Nos. C856-C899. Old denominations obliterated with bars on Nos. C862, C871-C873, C875-C877, C883, C885-C887, C889, C892, C896-C898. Vertical surcharge on Nos. C865-C866, C871-C872, C874, C878, C896.

Kennedy Type of 1965

1965, Aug. 20 Photo.   Perf. 12x11½
C900 A144 60c lt grnsh bl   .75 .30
C901 A144 80c red brn   .90 .35

Medical Federation Emblem — AP62

1965, Aug. 24 Litho.   Perf. 13½x14
C902 AP62 65c red org & blk   1.10 .55

20th anniversary of the founding of the Medical Federation of Venezuela.

Unisphere and Venezuela Pavilion AP63

1965, Aug. 31   Perf. 14x13½
C903 AP63 1b multi   1.00 .30

New York World's Fair, 1964-65.

Andrés Bello (1780?-1865), Educator and Writer — AP64

Perf. 14x13½
1965, Oct. 15 Litho.   Unwmk.
C904 AP64 80c dk brn & org   1.10 .55

Map Type of 1965

Maps of Venezuela and Guiana: 25c, Map of Venezuela and Guiana by J. Cruz Cano, 1775. 40c, Map stamp of 1896 (No. 140). 75c, Map by the Ministry of the Exterior, 1965 (all horiz.).

1965, Nov. 5   Perf. 13½
C905 A145 25c multi   .35 .20
C906 A145 40c multi   .50 .20
C907 A145 75c multi   .75 .30
  a.   Souv. sheet of 3, #C905-C907, imperf.   11.00 11.00
  Nos. C905-C907 (3)   1.60 .70

#C907a, issued June 7, 1966, sold for 1.65b.

ITU Emblem and Telegraph Poles AP65

1965, Nov. 19 Litho.   Perf. 13½x14
C908 AP65 75c blk & ol grn   .75 .30

Cent. of the ITU.

Simon Bolivar and Quotation AP66

1965, Dec. 9   Perf. 14x13½
C909 AP66 75c lt bl & dk brn   .75 .30

Sesquicentennial of Bolivar's Jamaica letter, Sept. 6, 1815.

Children Riding Magic Carpet and Three Kings on Camels — AP67

1965, Dec. 16   Perf. 13½x14
C910 AP67 70c yel & vio bl   1.10 .55

Children's Festival, 1965 (Christmas).

Fermin Toro — AP68

1965, Dec. 22   Perf. 14x13½
C911 AP68 1b blk & org   .90 .30

Death centenary of Fermin Toro (1808-1865), statesman and writer.

Winston Churchill — AP69

1965, Dec. 29   Perf. 14½x13
C912 AP69 1b lilac & blk   1.10 .40

Sir Winston Spencer Churchill (1874-1965), statesman and World War II leader.

ICY Emblem, Arms of Venezuela and UN Emblem AP70

1965, Dec. 30   Perf. 13½x14
C913 AP70 85c gold & vio blk   1.10 .40

International Cooperation Year, 1965.

OAS Emblem and Map of America — AP71

Farms of 1936 and 1966 — AP72

1965, Dec. 31   Perf. 14x13½
C914 AP71 50c bl, blk & gold   .90 .30

Organization of American States, 75th anniv.

Butterfly Type of 1966

1966, Jan. 25 Litho.   Perf. 13½x1
Various Butterflies in Natural Colors; Black Inscriptions
C915 A146 65c lilac   .75 .3
C916 A146 85c blue   1.10 .4
C917 A146 1b salmon pink   1.25 .5
  Nos. C915-C917 (3)   3.10 1.2

1966, Mar. 1   Perf. 14x13½
C918 AP72 55c blk, yel & emer   .80 .3

30th anniversary of the Ministry for Agriculture and Husbandry.

Dance Type of 1966

Various folk dances.

1966, Apr. 5 Litho.   Perf. 14
C919 A148 40c bl & multi   .75 .25
C920 A148 50c multi   .90 .30
C921 A148 60c vio & multi   .60 .20
C922 A148 70c multi   1.40 .40
C923 A148 80c red & multi   1.50 .50
C924 A148 90c ocher & multi   1.60 .60
  Nos. C919-C924 (6)   6.75 2.25

Title Page "Popule Meus" AP73

1966, Apr. 15   Perf. 13½x14
C925 AP73 55c yel grn, blk & bis   .55 .30
C926 AP73 95c dp mag, blk & bis   .75 .40

150th anniv. (in 1964) of the death of José Angel Lamas, composer of natl. anthem.

Circus Scene, by Michelena — AP74

Paintings by Michelena: 1b, Miranda in La Carraca. 1.05b, Charlotte Corday.

Perf. 12x12½
1966, May 12 Litho.   Unwmk.
C927 AP74 95c multi   .90 .50
C928 AP74 1b multi   1.10 .50
C929 AP74 1.05b multi   1.25 .50
  Nos. C927-C929 (3)   3.25 1.50

Cent. of the birth of Arturo Michelena (1863-1898), painter. Miniature sheets of 12 exist. See Nos. 900-901.

Abraham Lincoln — AP75

1966, May 31   Perf. 13½x14
C930 AP75 1b gray & blk   .90 .55

Dr. José Gregorio Hernandez AP76

1966, July 29 Litho.   Perf. 14x13½
C931 AP76 1b brt bl & vio bl   1.25 .40

Centenary (in 1964) of the birth of Dr. José Gregorio Hernandez, physician.

Dr. Manuel
Dagnino and
Hospital
AP77

1966, Aug. 16   Litho.   Perf. 13½x14
932 AP77 1b sl grn & yel grn   1.10   .40
Founding of Chiquinquira Hospital, cent.

Fish Type of 1966

Fish: 75c, Pearl headstander, vert. 90c, wordtail characine.   1b, Ramirez's dwarf chlid.

Perf. 14x13½, 13½x14
1966, Aug. 31
933 A151 75c multi   1.40   .40
934 A151 90c grn & multi   1.40   .40
935 A151 1b multi   1.40   .40
Nos. C933-C935 (3)   4.20   1.20

Rafael Arevalo
Gonzalez — AP78

Simon Bolivar,
1816 — AP79

1966, Sept. 13   Litho.   Perf. 13½x14
936 AP78 75c yel bis & blk   1.00   .40
Centenary of the birth of Rafael Arevalo
Gonzalez, journalist.

Imprint: "Bundesdruckerei Berlin
1966"

Bolivar Portraits: 25c, 30c, 35c, by José Gil e Castro, 1825. 40c, 50c, 60c, Anonymous painter, 1825. 80c, 1.20b, 4b, Anonymous painter, c. 1829.

1966
Multicolored Center
937 AP79 5c lem & blk   .20   .20
938 AP79 10c lt ol grn & blk   .20   .20
939 AP79 20c grn & blk   .20   .20
940 AP79 25c salmon & blk   .20   .20
941 AP79 30c pink & blk   .20   .20
942 AP79 35c dl rose & blk   .25   .20
943 AP79 40c bis brn & blk   .20   .20
944 AP79 50c org brn & blk   .35   .20
945 AP79 60c brn red & blk   .35   .20
946 AP79 80c brt bl & blk   .75   .30
947 AP79 1.20b dl bl & blk   1.10   .55
948 AP79 4b vio bl & blk   3.75   2.25
Nos. C937-C948 (12)   7.75   4.90
Issued to honor Simon Bolivar.
Issue dates: Nos. C937-C939, Aug. 15; Nos. C940-C942, Sept. 29; others, Oct. 14.
See Nos. C961-C972.

"Justice" — AP80

1966, Nov. 3   Litho.   Perf. 14x13½
949 AP80 50c pale lil & red lil   .75   .30
50th anniversary of the Academy of Political
and Social Sciences.

Angostura Bridge, Orinoco
River — AP81

1967, Jan. 6   Litho.   Perf. 13½x14
C950 AP81 40c multi   .30   .20
Issued to commemorate the opening of the
Angostura Bridge over the Orinoco River.

Pavilion of
Venezuela
AP82

1967, Apr. 28   Litho.   Perf. 11x13½
C951 AP82 1b multi   .90   .30
EXPO '67, International Exhibition, Montreal, Apr. 28-Oct. 27, 1967.

Statue of Chief
Guaicaipuro
AP83

Constellations over Caracas, 1567 and
1967 — AP84

Designs: 45c, Captain Francisco Fajardo. 55c, Diego de Losada, the Founder. 65c, Arms of Caracas. 90c, Map of Caracas, 1578. 1b, Market on Plaza Mayor, 1800.

1967   Litho.   Perf. 14x13½, 13½x14
C952 AP83 15c multi   .20   .20
C953 AP83 45c gold, car & brn   .35   .20
C954 AP83 55c multi   .45   .20
C955 AP84 60c blk, ultra & sil   .50   .20
C956 AP83 65c multi   .65   .25
C957 AP84 90c multi   .80   .30
C958 AP84 1b multi   .90   .35
Nos. C952-C958 (7)   3.85   1.70
400th anniv. of the founding of Caracas (1st
issue). See Nos. C977-C982 (2nd issue).
Two souvenir sheets each contain single
stamps similar to Nos. C952-C953, but with
simulated perforation. Sold for 1b each. Size:
80x119mm. Value $45 each.
Issued: 55c, 65c, July 28; others, July 12.

Gen. Francisco
Esteban
Gomez — AP85

Juan Vicente
González — AP86

1967, July 31   Litho.   Perf. 14x13½
C959 AP85 90c multi   .90   .40
150th anniversary, Battle of Matasiete.

1967, Oct. 18   Litho.   Perf. 14x13½
C960 AP86 80c ocher & blk   .90   .30
Centenary of the death (in 1866) of Juan
Vicente González, journalist.

Bolivar Type of 1966
Imprint: "Druck Bruder Rosenbaum.
Wien"

1967-68   Litho.   Perf. 13½x14
Multicolored Center
C961 AP79 5c lemon & blk   .20   .20
C962 AP79 10c lemon & blk   .20   .20
C963 AP79 20c grn & blk   .30   .20
C964 AP79 25c salmon & blk   .25   .20
C965 AP79 30c pink & blk   .30   .20
C966 AP79 35c dl rose & blk   .30   .20
C967 AP79 40c bis brn & blk   .50   .20
C968 AP79 50c org brn & blk   4.00   .30
C969 AP79 60c brn red & blk   1.75   .80
C970 AP79 80c brt bl & blk   1.00   .40
C971 AP79 1.20b dl bl & blk   1.50   .30
C972 AP79 4b vio bl & blk   4.00   1.60
Nos. C961-C972 (12)   14.30   4.80
Issue dates: 20c, 30c, 50c, Nov. 24; 5c, 25c,
40c, Feb. 5, 1968; others, Aug, 28, 1967.

Child with
Pinwheel
AP87

1967, Dec. 15   Litho.   Perf. 14x13½
C973 AP87 45c multi   .50   .20
C974 AP87 75c multi   .65   .25
C975 AP87 90c multi   .85   .30
Nos. C973-C975 (3)   2.00   .75
Children's Festival.

Madonna with
the Rosebush,
by Stephan
Lochner
AP88

1967, Dec. 19
C976 AP88 1b multi   1.25   .55
Christmas 1967.

Palace of the Academies,
Caracas — AP89

Views of Caracas: 50c, St. Theresa's
Church, vert. 70c, Federal Legislature. 75c,
University City. 85c, El Pulpo highways crossing. 2b, Avenida Libertador.

1967, Dec. 28   Perf. 13½x14, 14x13½
C977 AP89 10c multi   .20   .20
C978 AP89 50c lil & multi   .35   .20
C979 AP89 70c multi   .65   .20
C980 AP89 75c multi   .75   .25
C981 AP89 85c multi   .80   .30
C982 AP89 2b multi   2.25   .85
Nos. C977-C982 (6)   5.00   2.00
400th anniv. of Caracas (2nd issue).

Dr. José Manuel
Nuñez Ponte
(1870-1965),
Educator — AP90

1968, Mar. 8   Litho.   Perf. 14
C983 AP90 65c multi   .55   .25

De Miranda
and Printing
Press
AP91

Designs (Miranda Portraits and): 35c, Parliament, London. 45c, Arc de Triomphe, Paris. 70c, Portrait, vert. 80c, Portrait bust and Venezuelan flags, vert.

Perf. 13½x14, 14x13½
1968, June 20   Litho.
C984 AP91 20c yel brn, grn &
brn   .25   .20
C985 AP91 35c multi   .40   .20
C986 AP91 45c lt bl & multi   .75   .30
C987 AP91 70c multi   .90   .25
C988 AP91 80c multi   1.10   .40
Nos. C984-C988 (5)   3.40   1.35
General Francisco de Miranda (1750?-
1816), revolutionist, dictator of Venezuela.

Insect Type of 1968

Insect Pests: 5c, Red leaf-cutting ant, vert.
15c, Sugar cane beetle, vert. 20c, Leaf beetle.

Perf. 14x13½, 13½x14
1968, Aug. 30   Litho.
C989 A157 5c multi   .20   .20
C990 A157 15c multi   .45   .20
C991 A157 20c gray & multi   .60   .20
Nos. C989-C991 (3)   1.25   .60

Three
Keys — AP92

1968, Oct. 17   Litho.   Perf. 14x13½
C992 AP92 95c yel, vio & dk grn   .95   .35
Natl. Comptroller's Office, 30th anniv.

Fencing — AP93

Designs: 5c, Pistol shooting, vert. 15c, Running. 75c, Boxing. 5b, Sailing, vert.

Perf. 14x13½, 13½x14
1968, Nov. 6   Litho.   Unwmk.
C993 AP93 5c vio, bl & blk   .20   .20
C994 AP93 15c multi   .30   .20
C995 AP93 30c yel grn, dk grn
& blk   .45   .20

C996 AP93 75c multi .90 .30
C997 AP93 5b multi 4.50 1.60
   Nos. C993-C997 (5) 6.35 2.50

19th Olympic Games, Mexico City, 10/12-27.

Holy Family, by Francisco José de Lerma — AP94

Dancing Children and Stars — AP95

1968, Dec. 4   **Litho.**   **Perf. 14x13½**
C998 AP94 40c multi .55 .20

Christmas 1968.

1968, Dec. 13   **Litho.**   **Perf. 14x13½**
C999 AP95 80c vio & org .75 .30

Issued for the 5th Children's Festival.

Conservation Type of 1968

Designs: 15c, Marbled wood-quail, vert. 20c, Water birds, vert. 30c, Woodcarvings and tools, vert. 90c, Brown trout. 95c, Valley and road. 1b, Red-eyed vireo feeding young bronzed cowbird.

Perf. 13½x14, 14x13½
1968, Dec. 19   **Litho.**
C1000 A160 15c multi .25 .20
C1001 A160 20c multi .25 .20
C1002 A160 30c multi .35 .20
C1003 A160 90c multi .85 .30
C1004 A160 95c multi 1.40 .50
C1005 A160 1b multi 1.00 .35
   Nos. C1000-C1005 (6) 4.10 1.75

Tourist Type of 1969

Designs: 15c, Giant cactus and desert, Falcon. 30c, Hotel Humboldt, Federal District. 40c, Cable car and mountain peaks, Merida.

1969, Jan. 24   **Perf. 13½x14**
C1006 A161 15c multi .25 .20
C1007 A161 30c multi .25 .20
   a. Souv. sheet of 2, #931,
      C1007, imperf. 1.40 1.40
C1008 A161 40c multi .50 .20
   Nos. C1006-C1008 (3) 1.00 .60

Tree Type of 1969

Trees: 5c, Cassia grandis. 20c, Triplaris caracasana. 25c, Samanea saman.

1969, May 30   **Litho.**   **Perf. 13½x14**
C1009 A164 5c lt grn & multi .20 .20
C1010 A164 20c org & multi .30 .20
C1011 A164 25c lt vio & multi .35 .20
   Nos. C1009-C1011 (3) .85 .60

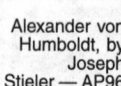

Alexander von Humboldt, by Joseph Stieler — AP96

Map of Maracaibo, 1562 — AP97

1969, Sept. 12   **Photo.**   **Perf. 14**
C1012 AP96 50c multi .60 .20

Alexander von Humboldt (1769-1859), naturalist and explorer.

Perf. 13½x13, 13x13½
1969, Sept. 30   **Litho.**

20c, Ambrosio Alfinger, Alfonso Pacheco, Pedro Maldonado, horiz. 40c, Maracaibo coat of arms. 70c, University Hospital. 75c, Monument to the Indian Mara. 1b, Baralt Square, horiz.

C1013 AP97 20c lil & multi .25 .20
C1014 AP97 25c org & multi .30 .20
C1015 AP97 40c multi .35 .20
C1016 AP97 70c grn & multi .75 .25
C1017 AP97 75c brn & multi .90 .30
C1018 AP97 1b multi 1.10 .40
   Nos. C1013-C1018 (6) 3.65 1.55

400th anniversary of Maracaibo.

Astronauts Neil A. Armstrong, Edwin E. Aldrin, Jr., Michael Collins and Moonscape AP98

1969, Nov. 18   **Litho.**   **Perf. 12½**
C1019 AP98 90c multi 1.25 .50
   a. Souv. sheet of 1, imperf. 1.90 1.90

See note after US No. C76.

Virgin with the Rosary, 17th Century AP99

Christmas: 80c, Holy Family, Caracas, 18th Cent.

1969, Dec. 1   **Litho.**   **Perf. 12½**
C1020 AP99 75c gold & multi .75 .30
C1021 AP99 80c gold & multi .90 .35
   a. Pair, #C1020-C1021 1.75 1.75

Simon Bolivar, 1819, by M. N. Bate — AP100

Bolivar Portraits: 45c, 55c, like 15c. 65c, 70c, 75c Drawing by Francois Roulin, 1828. 85c, 90c, 95c, Charcoal drawing by José Maria Espinoza, 1828. 1b, 1.50b, 2b, Drawing by Espinoza, 1830.

1970, Mar. 16   **Litho.**   **Perf. 14x13½**
C1022 AP100 15c multi .20 .20
C1023 AP100 45c bl & multi .40 .20
C1024 AP100 55c org & multi .55 .20
C1025 AP100 65c multi .55 .25

C1026 AP100 70c bl & multi .65 .35
C1027 AP100 75c org & multi .85 .35
C1028 AP100 85c multi .95 .35
C1029 AP100 90c bl & multi 1.00 .40
C1030 AP100 95c org & multi 1.10 .45
C1031 AP100 1b multi 1.10 .45
C1032 AP100 1.50b bl & multi 1.25 .50
C1033 AP100 2b multi 2.75 1.60
   Nos. C1022-C1033 (12) 11.35 5.30

Issued to honor Simon Bolivar (1783-1830), liberator and father of his country.

General Antonio Guzmán Blanco and Dr. Martin J. Sanabria AP101

1970, June 26   **Litho.**   **Perf. 13**
C1034 AP101 75c brt grn & multi .65 .30

Free obligatory elementary education, cent.

Map of Venezuela with Claim to Part of Guyana — AP102

State map and arms. 55c, 90c, vert.

Perf. 13½x14, 14x13½
1970-71   **Litho.**
C1035 AP102 5c shown .20 .20
C1036 AP102 15c Apure .20 .20
C1037 AP102 20c Aragua .25 .20
C1038 AP102 20c Anzoategui .30 .20
C1039 AP102 25c Barinas .30 .20
C1040 AP102 25c Bolivar .30 .20
C1041 AP102 45c Carabobo .50 .20
C1042 AP102 55c Cojedes .55 .20
C1043 AP102 65c Falcon .60 .20
C1044 AP102 75c Guárico .75 .25
C1045 AP102 85c Lara .90 .30
C1046 AP102 90c Mérida .90 .30
C1047 AP102 1b Miranda .90 .40
C1048 AP102 2b Delta
              Amacuro
              Territory 2.25 .95
   Nos. C1035-C1048 (14) 8.90 4.00

Issued: 5c, 7/15; 15c, #C1037, 1/18; #C1038-C1039, 2/15/71; #C1040, 45c, 3/15/71; 55c, 65c, 4/15; 75c, 85c, 5/15/71; 90c, 1b, 6/15/71; 2b, 7/15/71.

Flower Type of 1970

Flowers: 20c, Epidendrum secundum. 25c, Oyedaea verbesinoides. 45c, Heliconia villosa. 1b, Macleania nitida.

1970, July 29   **Litho.**   **Perf. 14x13½**
C1049 A175 20c multi .30 .20
C1050 A175 25c multi .35 .20
C1051 A175 45c multi .95 .25
C1052 A175 1b multi 1.25 .35
   Nos. C1049-C1052 (4) 2.85 1.00

Caracciolo Parra Olmedo AP104

1970, Nov. 16   **Photo.**   **Perf. 12½**
C1053 AP104 20c bl & multi .30 .20

Sesquicentennial of birth of Caracciolo Parra Olmedo (1819-1900), professor of law, rector of University of Merida.

Census Chart — AP105

1971, Apr. 30   **Litho.**   **Perf. 13½x**
C1054   Block of 4 4.50 2.?
   a. AP105 70c, frame L & T .80
   b. AP105 70c, frame T & R .80
   c. AP105 70c, frame L & B .80
   d. AP105 70c, frame B & R .80

See note after No. 979.

Cattleya Gaskelliana — AP106

Orchids: 20c, Cattleya percivaliana, ve 75c, Cattleya mossiae, vert. 90c, Cattleya vi lacea. 1b, Cattleya lawrenciana.

Perf. 14x13½, 13½x14
1971, Aug. 25
C1055 AP106 20c blk & multi .30 .?
C1056 AP106 25c blk & multi .35 .?
C1057 AP106 75c blk & multi .70 .?
C1058 AP106 90c blk & multi .80 .?
C1059 AP106 1b blk & multi .95 .?
   Nos. C1055-C1059 (5) 3.10 1.?

40th anniversary of Venezuelan Society Natural History. Issued in sheets of 5 stamp and one label with Society emblem in blu Value $20.

Draft of Constitution Superimposed on Capitol AP107

1971, Dec. 29   **Litho.**   **Perf. 13?**
C1060 AP107 90c multi .80 .4?

Anniversary of 1961 Constitution.

AIR POST SEMI-POSTAL STAMPS

King Vulture SPAP1

Unwmk.
1942, Dec. 17   **Engr.**   **Perf. 1?**
CB1 SPAP1 15c + 10c org brn 2.25 .6?
CB2 SPAP1 30c + 5c violet 2.25 .7?
   Set, never hinged 7.50

See note after No. B1.

SPECIAL DELIVERY STAMPS

Catalogue values for unused stamps in this section are for Never Hinged items.

SD1   SD2

Perf. 12½

1949, Mar. 9   Unwmk.   Engr.
1 SD1 30c red   .40 .20

Wmk. 116

1961, Apr. 7   Litho.   Perf. 13½
2 SD2 30c orange   .45 .20

REGISTRATION STAMPS

Bolívar — R1

1899, May   Unwmk.   Engr.   Perf. 12
F1 R1 25c yellow brown   2.50 1.90

No. F1 Overprinted like Nos. 150-155

1900
F2 R1 25c yellow brown   1.50 1.50
  a. Inverted overprint   22.50 22.50
  b. Double overprint   30.00 30.00

Counterfeit overprints exist, especially of the varieties.

OFFICIAL STAMPS

Coat of Arms
O1   O3

Lithographed, Center Engraved
1898, May 1   Unwmk.   Perf. 12
O1 O1 5c bl grn & blk   .40 .35
O2 O1 10c rose & blk   .80 .70
O3 O1 25c bl & blk   1.00 .90
O4 O1 50c yel & blk   1.90 1.75
O5 O1 1b vio & blk   1.90 1.75
    Nos. O1-O5 (5)   6.00 5.45

Nos. O4 and O5
Handstamp
Surcharged in
Magenta or Violet

1899, Nov.
O6 O1 5c on 50c yel &
        blk   3.50 3.25
O7 O1 5c on 1b vio & blk   14.00 12.50
O8 O1 25c on 50c yel &
        blk   14.00 12.50
O9 O1 25c on 1b vio & blk   8.50 7.75
    Nos. O6-O9 (4)   40.00 36.00

Inverted Surcharge
O6a O1 5c on 50c   12.50 12.50
O7a O1 5c on 1b   32.50 32.50
O8a O1 25c on 50c   27.50 27.50
O9a O1 25c on 1b   27.50 27.50
    Nos. O6a-O9a (4)   100.00 100.00

Nos. O6-O9 exist with double surcharge. Value each $18.50-$37.50.
Many of the magenta overprints have become violet. There are intermediate shades.
Counterfeit overprints exist.

1900   Litho., Center Engr.
O14 O3 5c bl grn & blk   .25 .25
O15 O3 10c rose & blk   .30 .30
O16 O3 25c bl & blk   .30 .30
O17 O3 50c yel & blk   .40 .35
O18 O3 1b dl vio & blk   .45 .50
    Nos. O14-O18 (5)   1.70 1.70

O4   No Stars Above
               Shield — O5

Imprint: "American Bank Note Co., N.Y."

1904, July   Engr.
O19 O4 5c emerald & blk   .20 .20
O20 O4 10c rose & blk   .40 .35
O21 O4 25c blue & blk   .40 .35
O22 O4 50c red brn & blk   2.50 2.25
    a. 50c claret & black   2.50 2.25
O23 O4 1b red brn & blk   1.25 1.10
    a. 1b claret & black   1.25 1.10
    Nos. O19-O23 (5)   4.75 4.25

1912   Lithographed in Caracas
O24 O5 5c grn & blk   .20 .20
O25 O5 10c car & blk   .20 .20
O26 O5 25c dk bl & blk   .20 .20
O27 O5 50c pur & blk   .25 .20
    a. Center double   19.00
O28 O5 1b yel & blk   .50 .45
    Nos. O24-O28 (5)   1.35 1.25

Perforated Initials

After 1925, Venezuela's official stamps consisted of regular postage stamps, some commemoratives and air post stamps of 1930-42 punched with "GN" (Gobierno Nacional) in large perforated initials.

LOCAL STAMPS FOR THE PORT OF CARUPANO

In 1902 Great Britain, Germany and Italy, seeking compensation for revolutionary damages, established a blockade of La Guaira and seized the custom house. Carúpano, a port near Trinidad, was isolated and issued the following provisionals. A treaty effected May 7, 1903, referred the dispute to the Hague Tribunal.

A1

A2

1902   Typeset   Imperf.
1 A1 5c purple, *orange*   19.00
2 A2 10c black, *orange*   30.00
  a. Tête bêche pair   82.50
3 A1 25c purple, *green*   25.00
4 A1 50c green, *yellow*   47.50
5 A1 1b blue, *rose*   60.00
    Nos. 1-5 (5)   181.50

A3

1902
6 A3 1b black, *yellow*   135.00
  a. Tête bêche pair

A4

1903   Handstamped
7 A4 5c carmine, *yellow*   19.00 19.00
8 A4 10c green, *yellow*   60.00 60.00
9 A4 25c green, *orange*   25.00 25.00
10 A4 50c blue, *rose*   25.00 25.00
11 A4 1b violet, *gray*   25.00 25.00
12 A4 2b carmine, *green*   25.00 25.00
13 A4 5b violet, *blue*   25.00 25.00
    Nos. 7-13 (7)   204.00 204.00

Dangerous counterfeits exist of Nos. 1-13.

LOCAL STAMPS FOR THE STATE OF GUAYANA

Correos da Venezuela.
ESTADO   5   CENTIMOS   5   GUAYANA
Revolutionary
Steamship
"Banrigh" — A1

FISCALIA DE INSTRUCCION PUBLICA
ESTADO GUAYANA
Control Mark

1903   Typo.   Perf. 12
1 A1 5c black, *gray*   19.00 19.00
2 A1 10c black, *orange*   47.50 47.50
3 A1 25c black, *pink*   19.00 19.00
4 A1 50c black, *blue*   30.00 30.00
5 A1 1b black, *straw*   25.00 25.00
    Nos. 1-5 (5)   140.50 140.50

Nos. 1-5 can be found with or without the illustrated control mark which covers four stamps.
Counterfeits include the 10c and 50c in red and are from different settings from the originals. They are on papers differing in colors from the originals. All 5c on granite paper are bogus.

CORREOS DE VENEZUELA
ESTADO   GUAYANA
LIBERTAD
10   CENTIMOS   10
Coat of
Arms
A2

1903
11 A2 5c black, *pink*   40.00
12 A2 10c black, *orange*   50.00
13 A2 25c black, *gray blue*   40.00
  a. 25c black, *blue*   40.00

---

14 A2 50c black, *straw*   40.00
15 A2 1b black, *gray*   30.00
    Nos. 11-15 (5)   200.00

Postally used examples are very scarce, and are specimens having 9 ornaments in horizontal borders. Nos. 11-15 pen canceled sell for same values as unused.
See note on controls after No. 5.
Counterfeits exist of Nos. 11-15. Stamps with 10 ornaments in horizontal borders are counterfeits.
Nos. 1-5, 11-15 were issued by a group of revolutionists and had a limited local use. The dates on the stamps commemorate the declaration of Venezuelan independence and a compact with Spain against Joseph Bonaparte.

VIET NAM

vē-'et-'näm

LOCATION — In eastern Indo-China
GOVT. — Kingdom
AREA — 123,949 sq. mi.
POP. — 77,311,210 (1999 est.)
CAPITAL — Hanoi

Viet Nam, which included the former French territories of Tonkin, Annam and Cochin China, became an Associated State of the French Union in 1949. The Communist Viet Minh obtained control of Northern Viet Nam in 1954, and the republic of South Viet Nam was established in October, 1955.

100 Cents (Xu) = 1 Piaster (Dong)

Catalogue values for unused stamps in this country are for Never Hinged items, beginning with Scott 27 in the regular postage section, Scott B2 in the semipostal section, Scott C1 in the airpost section, Scott J1 in the postage due section, and Scott M1 in the military section..

Bongour Falls, Dalat — A1

Emperor Bao-Dai — A2

Designs: 20c, 2pi, 10pi, Imperial palace, Hué. 30c, 15pi, Lake, Hanoi. 50c, 1pi, Temple, Saigon.

Perf. 13x13½, 13½x13
Unwmk.

			Photo.	
1951, June 6-Oct. 23				
1	A1	10c olive green	.20	.20
2	A1	20c deep plum	.20	.20
3	A1	30c blue	.30	.40
4	A1	50c red	.50	.20
5	A1	60c brown	.40	.20
6	A1	1pi chestnut brn	.40	.20
7	A2	1.20pi yellow brn	2.00	2.50
8	A1	2pi purple	.75	.20
9	A2	3pi dull blue	2.00	.20
10	A1	5pi green	2.50	.35
11	A1	10pi crimson	6.75	.45
12	A1	15pi red brown	37.50	3.00
13	A2	30pi blue green	22.50	3.50
		Nos. 1-13 (13)	76.00	11.60
		Set, never hinged	250.00	

Souvenir booklets exist comprising five gummed sheets of 1 containing Nos. 1, 2, 6, 9, 12, together with commemorative inscriptions. Value, $150.

Empress Nam-Phuong A3

Globe and Lightning Bolt A4

			Perf. 12½	
1952, Aug. 15				
14	A3	30c dk pur, yel & brn	.50	.30
15	A3	50c blue, yel & brn	1.00	.55
16	A3	1.50pi ol grn, yel & brn	2.00	.25
		Nos. 14-16 (3)	3.50	1.10
		Set, never hinged	8.00	

For surcharge see No. B1.

			Engr.	**Perf. 13**
1952, Aug. 24				
17	A4	1pi greenish blue	2.50	1.40
		Never hinged	4.75	

Viet Nam's admission to the ITU, 1st anniv.

Coastal Scene and UPU Emblem A5

1952, Sept. 12				
18	A5	5pi red brown	2.75	1.00
		Never hinged	4.00	

Viet Nam's admission to the UPU, 1st anniv.

Bao-Dai and Pagoda of Literature, Hanoi — A6

			Perf. 12	
1952, Nov. 10				
19	A6	1.50pi rose violet	2.50	.50
		Never hinged	3.50	

39th birthday of Emperor Bao-Dai.

Crown Prince Bao-Long in Annamite Costume — A7

70c, 80c, 100pi, Prince in Annamite costume. 90c, 20pi, 50pi, Prince in Western uniform.

			Perf. 13	
1954, June 15				
20	A7	40c aqua	.20	.20
21	A7	70c claret	.20	.20
22	A7	80c black brown	.20	.30
23	A7	90c dark green	.40	.80
24	A7	20pi rose pink	1.25	2.25
25	A7	50pi violet	3.75	6.25
26	A7	100pi blue violet	6.00	10.00
		Nos. 20-26 (7)	12.00	20.00
		Set, never hinged, brown gum	17.50	
		Set, never hinged, white gum	35.00	

SOUTH VIET NAM

(Republic of Viet Nam)

(Viet Nam Cong Hoa)

GOVT. — Republic
AREA — 66,280 sq. mi.
POP. — 19,600,000 (est. 1973)
CAPITAL — Saigon

Catalogue values for unused stamps in this section, from this point to the end of the section, are for Never Hinged items. Because of the tropical conditions, never hinged stamps must also be free of wrinkles, toning, and any other disturbance.

Mythological Turtle — A8

			Engr.	**Perf. 13**
1955, July 20		**Unwmk.**		
27	A8	30c claret	1.25	.20
28	A8	50c dark green	3.00	.75
29	A8	1.50pi bright blue	2.75	.30
		Nos. 27-29 (3)	7.00	1.25

Refugees on Raft — A9

1955, Oct. 11				
30	A9	70c crimson rose	.85	.20
31	A9	80c brown violet	2.50	.35
32	A9	10pi indigo	5.25	.50
33	A9	20pi vio, red brn & org	16.00	.75
34	A9	35pi dk bl, blk brn & yel	32.50	3.75
35	A9	100pi dk grn, brn vio & org	72.50	6.75
		Nos. 30-35 (6)	129.60	12.30

1st anniv. of the flight of the North Vietnamese.

No. 34 is inscribed "Chien-Dich-Huynh-Dê" (Operation Brotherhood) below design. See No. 54.

Post Office, Saigon — A10

Pres. Ngo Dinh Diem — A11

			Perf. 12	
1956, Jan. 10				
36	A10	60c bluish green	1.90	.25
37	A10	90c violet	3.50	.40
38	A10	3pi red brown	6.75	.60
		Nos. 36-38 (3)	12.15	1.25

5th anniv. of independent postal service.

		Engr.	**Perf. 13x13½**	
1956				
39	A11	20c orange ver	.30	.20
40	A11	30c rose lilac	.60	.20
41	A11	50c brt carmine	.30	.20
42	A11	1pi violet	.60	.20
43	A11	1.50pi violet	1.25	.20
44	A11	3pi black brown	1.25	.20
45	A11	4pi dark blue	1.90	.20
46	A11	5pi red brown	2.50	.20
47	A11	10pi blue	3.00	.25
48	A11	20pi gray black	7.75	.50
49	A11	35pi green	21.00	1.10
50	A11	100pi brown	45.00	4.25
		Nos. 39-50 (12)	85.45	7.70

Nos. 36-38 Overprinted

			Perf. 12	
1956, Aug. 6				
51	A10	60c bluish green	.75	.30
52	A10	90c violet	1.50	.30
53	A10	3pi red brown	2.25	.60
		Nos. 51-53 (3)	4.50	1.20

The overprint reads: "Government Post Office Building."

No. 34 with Black Bar over Inscription below Design

1956, Aug. 6				
54	A9	35pi dk bl, blk brn & yel	5.50	2.75

Bamboo — A12

Children — A13

			Litho.	**Perf. 13x13**
1956, Oct. 26				
55	A12	50c scarlet	.75	.2
56	A12	1.50pi rose violet	1.00	.2
57	A12	2pi brt green	1.25	.2
58	A12	4pi deep blue	3.25	.2
		Nos. 55-58 (4)	6.25	1.0

1st anniv. of the Republic.

			Engr.	**Perf. 13½x1**
1956, Nov. 7				
59	A13	1pi lilac rose	.50	.2
60	A13	2pi blue green	.75	.2
61	A13	6pi purple	1.25	.2
62	A13	35pi violet blue	7.00	1.2
		Nos. 59-62 (4)	9.50	1.8

"Operation Brotherhood."

Hunters on Elephants A14

Loading Cargo A15

Design: 90c, 2pi, 3pi, Mountain dwelling.

			Photo.	**Perf. 1**
1957, July 7				
63	A14	20c yellow grn & pur	.50	.2
64	A14	30c bister & dp mag	.60	.2
65	A14	90c yel grn & dk brn	.70	.2
66	A14	2pi green & ultra	.95	.2
67	A14	3pi blue vio & brn	1.25	.3
		Nos. 63-67 (5)	4.00	1.1

				Perf. 13½x1
1957, Oct. 21				
68	A15	20c rose violet	.20	.2
69	A15	40c lt olive grn	.20	.2
70	A15	50c lt carmine rose	.35	.2
71	A15	2pi ultra	1.10	.2
72	A15	3pi brt green	1.50	.2
		Nos. 68-72 (5)	3.35	1.0

9th Colombo Plan Conference, Saigon.

Torch, Map and Constitution A16

Farmers, Tractor and Village A17

			Litho.	**Perf. 13x13½**
1957, Oct. 26				
73	A16	50c black, green & sal	.20	.20
74	A16	80c black, brt bl & mag	.20	.20
75	A16	1pi black, bl grn & brt car	.35	.20
76	A16	4pi blk, ol grn & fawn	.50	.20
77	A16	5pi blk, grnsh bl & cit	.75	.20
78	A16	10pi black, ultra & rose	1.50	.48
		Nos. 73-78 (6)	3.50	1.48

Republic of South Viet Nam, 2nd anniv.

			Engr.	**Perf. 13½**
1958, July 7				
79	A17	50c yellow green	.30	.2
80	A17	1pi deep violet	.45	.2
81	A17	2pi ultra	.75	.2
82	A17	10pi brick red	1.75	.6
		Nos. 79-82 (4)	3.25	1.2

4th anniv. of the government of Ngo Dinh Diem.

Girl and Lantern — A18

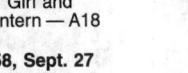

A19

1958, Sept. 27

83	A18	30c yellow	.30 .20
84	A18	50c dk carmine rose	.35 .20
85	A18	2pi dp carmine	.40 .20
86	A18	3pi blue green	.85 .20
87	A18	4pi lt olive green	1.40 .20
		Nos. 83-87 (5)	3.30 1.00

Children's Festival.

1958, Oct. 26 — Perf. 13½

88	A19	1pi dull red brown	.40 .20
89	A19	2pi bluish green	.50 .20
90	A19	4pi rose carmine	.75 .20
91	A19	5pi rose lilac	1.60 .35
		Nos. 88-91 (4)	3.25 .95

Issued for United Nations Day.

Most South Viet Nam stamps from 1958 onward exist imperforate in issued and trial colors, and also in small presentation sheets in issued colors.

UNESCO Building, Paris — A20

Torch and UN Emblem — A21

1958, Nov. 3 — Perf. 12½x13

92	A20	50c ultra	.30 .20
93	A20	2pi bright red	.40 .20
94	A20	3pi lilac rose	.80 .20
95	A20	6pi violet	1.25 .30
		Nos. 92-95 (4)	2.75 .90

UNESCO Headquarters in Paris opening, 11/3.

1958, Dec. 10 — Engr. — Perf. 13½

96	A21	50c dark blue	.20 .20
97	A21	1pi brown carmine	.25 .20
98	A21	4pi yellow green	.40 .20
99	A21	6pi rose violet	.85 .35
		Nos. 96-99 (4)	1.70 .95

Signing of the Universal Declaration of Human Rights, 10th anniv.

Cathedral of Hué — A22

Thien Mu Pagoda, Hué — A23

National Museum A24

50c, 2pi, Palace of Independence, Saigon.

1958-59 — Perf. 13½

100	A22	10c dk blue gray	.20 .20
101	A23	30c green ('59)	.60 .20
102	A24	40c dk green ('59)	.65 .20
103	A24	50c green ('59)	.65 .20
104	A24	2pi grnsh blue ('59)	2.00 .20
105	A23	4pi dull purple ('59)	2.25 .30
106	A24	5pi dk carmine ('59)	2.40 .30
107	A22	6pi orange brown	3.25 .40
		Nos. 100-107 (8)	12.00 2.00

Trung Sisters on Elephants A25

1959, Mar. 14 — Photo. — Perf. 13

108	A25	50c multicolored	.60 .20
109	A25	2pi ocher, grn & bl	1.25 .20
110	A25	3pi emerald, vio & bis	1.90 .20
111	A25	6pi multicolored	3.75 .40
		Nos. 108-111 (4)	7.50 1.00

Sisters Trung Trac and Trung Nhi who resisted a Chinese invasion in 40-44 A.D.

Symbols of Agrarian Reforms A26

1959, July 7 — Engr. — Perf. 13

112	A26	70c lilac rose	.30 .20
113	A26	2pi dk grn & Prus bl	.35 .20
114	A26	3pi olive	.60 .20
115	A26	6pi dark red & red	1.25 .35
		Nos. 112-115 (4)	2.50 .95

5th anniv. of Ngo Dinh Diem's presidency.

Diesel Engine and Map of North and South Viet Nam — A27

1959, Aug. 7

116	A27	1pi lt violet & grn	.70 .20
117	A27	2pi gray & green	.80 .20
118	A27	3pi grnsh bl & grn	1.10 .20
119	A27	4pi maroon & grn	1.90 .25
		Nos. 116-119 (4)	4.50 .85

Re-opening of the Saigon-Dongha Railroad.

Volunteer Road Workers A28

1959, Oct. 26

120	A28	1pi org brn, ultra & grn	.65 .20
121	A28	2pi violet, org & grn	.85 .20
122	A28	4pi dk bl, bl & bis	1.90 .30
123	A28	5pi bister, brn & ocher	2.10 .45
		Nos. 120-123 (4)	5.50 1.15

4th anniv. of the constitution, stressing communal development.

Boy Scout — A29

1959, Dec. — Engr. — Perf. 13

124	A29	3pi brt yellow grn	.35 .20
125	A29	4pi deep lilac rose	.90 .20
126	A29	8pi dk brn & lil rose	1.50 .35
127	A29	20pi Prus bl & bl grn	3.75 .90
		Nos. 124-127 (4)	6.50 1.45

National Boy Scout Jamboree.

Symbols of Family and Justice A30

1960

128	A30	20c emerald	.30 .20
129	A30	30c brt grnsh blue	.35 .20
130	A30	2pi orange & maroon	.85 .20
131	A30	6pi car & rose vio	3.00 .55
		Nos. 128-131 (4)	4.50 1.15

Issued to commemorate the family code.

Refugee Family and WRY Emblem A31

1960, Apr. 7 — Engr. — Perf. 13

132	A31	50c brt lilac rose	.25 .20
133	A31	3pi brt green	.45 .20
134	A31	4pi scarlet	.55 .25
135	A31	5pi dp violet blue	.75 .35
		Nos. 132-135 (4)	2.00 1.00

World Refugee Year, 7/1/59-6/30/60.

Henri Dunant — A32

1960, May 8

Cross in Carmine

136	A32	1pi dark blue	.45 .20
137	A32	3pi green	1.40 .20
138	A32	4pi crimson rose	1.40 .30
139	A32	6pi dp lilac rose	1.75 .45
		Nos. 136-139 (4)	5.00 1.15

Centenary (in 1959) of the Red Cross idea.

Model Farm A33

1960, July 7 — Perf. 13

140	A33	50c ultra	.35 .20
141	A33	1pi dark green	.45 .20
142	A33	3pi orange	.95 .25
143	A33	7pi bright pink	1.75 .35
		Nos. 140-143 (4)	3.50 1.00

Establishment of communal rice farming.

Girl With Basket of Rice and Rice Plant A34

1960, Nov. 21

144	A34	2pi emerald & green	.50 .20
145	A34	4pi blue & ultra	1.00 .30

Conf. of the UN FAO, Saigon, Nov. 1960.

Map and Flag of Viet Nam — A35

1960, Oct. 26 — Engr. — Perf. 13

146	A35	50c grnsh bl, car & yel	.40 .20
147	A35	1pi ultra, car & yel	.55 .20
148	A35	3pi purple, car & yel	.95 .20
149	A35	7pi yel grn, car & yel	1.60 .30
		Nos. 146-149 (4)	3.50 .90

Fifth anniversary of the Republic.

Agricultural Development Center, Tractor and Plow — A36

1961, Jan. 3 — Perf. 13

150	A36	50c red brown	.30 .20
151	A36	70c rose lilac	.55 .20
152	A36	80c rose red	.65 .20
153	A36	10pi bright pink	3.00 .40
		Nos. 150-153 (4)	4.50 1.00

Plant and Child — A37

Pres. Ngo Dinh Diem — A38

1961, Mar. 23 — Perf. 13

154	A37	70c light blue	.30 .20
155	A37	80c ultra	.40 .20
156	A37	4pi olive bister	.55 .20
157	A37	7pi grnsh bl & yel grn	1.25 .35
		Nos. 154-157 (4)	2.50 .95

Child protection.

1961, Apr. 29 — Perf. 13

158	A38	50c brt ultra	.55 .20
159	A38	1pi red	.95 .20
160	A38	2pi lilac rose	1.75 .20
161	A38	4pi brt violet	3.75 .20
		Nos. 158-161 (4)	7.00 .80

Second term of Pres. Ngo Dinh Diem.

Boy, Girl and Flaming Torch A39

1961, July 7 — Engr. — Perf. 13

162	A39	50c red	.20 .20
163	A39	70c bright pink	.35 .20
164	A39	80c ver & maroon	.45 .20
165	A39	8pi dp claret & mag	1.25 .40
		Nos. 162-165 (4)	2.25 1.00

Issued for Youth Day.

Saigon-Bien Hoa Highway Bridge — A40

1961, July 28

166	A40	50c yellow green	.35	.20
167	A40	1pi orange brown	.50	.20
168	A40	2pi dark blue	.75	.20
169	A40	5pi brt red lilac	1.40	.20
		Nos. 166-169 (4)	3.00	.80

Opening of Saigon-Bien Hoa Highway.

Alexandre de Rhodes A41

1961, Sept. 5

170	A41	50c rose carmine	.35	.20
171	A41	1pi claret	.50	.20
172	A41	3pi bister brown	.55	.20
173	A41	6pi emerald	1.60	.30
		Nos. 170-173 (4)	3.00	.90

Alexandre de Rhodes (1591-1660), Jesuit missionary who introduced Roman characters to express the Viet Nam language.

Young Man with Torch, Sage, Pagoda — A42

Temple Dedicated to Confucius — A43

1961, Oct. 26   Perf. 13

174	A42	50c orange ver	.30	.20
175	A42	1pi brt green	.55	.20
176	A42	3pi rose red	.65	.20
177	A42	8pi rose lilac & brn	2.00	.30
		Nos. 174-177 (4)	3.50	.90

Moral Rearmament of Youth Movement.

1961, Nov. 4   Engr.

178	A43	1pi brt green	.30	.20
179	A43	2pi rose red	.45	.20
180	A43	5pi olive	1.25	.25
		Nos. 178-180 (3)	2.00	.65

15th anniversary of UNESCO.

Earth Scraper Preparing Ground for Model Village — A44

Man Fighting Mosquito and Emblem — A45

1961, Dec. 11   Perf. 13

181	A44	50c dark green	1.00	.20
182	A44	1pi Prus bl & car lake	1.25	.20
183	A44	2pi olive grn & brn	1.75	.20
184	A44	10pi Prus blue	6.00	.35
		Nos. 181-184 (4)	10.00	.95

Agrarian reform program.

1962, Apr. 7   Perf. 13

185	A45	50c brt lilac rose	.30	.20
186	A45	1pi orange	.40	.20
187	A45	2pi emerald	.55	.20
188	A45	6pi ultra	1.25	.40
		Nos. 185-188 (4)	2.50	1.00

WHO drive to eradicate malaria.

Postal Check Center, Saigon — A46

Madonna of Vang — A47

1962, May 15   Engr.   Perf. 13

189	A46	70c dull green	.20	.20
190	A46	80c chocolate	.30	.20
191	A46	4pi lilac rose	.90	.20
192	A46	7pi rose red	2.10	.40
		Nos. 189-192 (4)	3.50	1.00

Inauguration of postal checking service.

1962, July 7

193	A47	50c violet & rose red	.25	.20
194	A47	1pi red brn & indigo	.35	.20
195	A47	2pi brown & rose car	.65	.20
196	A47	8pi green & dk blue	3.25	.25
		Nos. 193-196 (4)	4.50	.85

Catholic shrine of the Madonna of Vang.

Armed Guards and Village A48

1962, Oct. 26

197	A48	50c bright red	.35	.20
198	A48	1pi yellow green	.55	.20
199	A48	1.50pi lilac rose	.70	.20
200	A48	7pi ultra	1.90	.40
		Nos. 197-200 (4)	3.50	1.00

"Strategic village" defense system.

Gougah Waterfall, Dalat — A49

1963, Jan. 3

201	A49	60c orange red	.75	.20
202	A49	1pi bluish black	1.00	.20

62nd birthday of Pres. Ngo Dinh Diem; Spring Festival.

1963, Mar. 1   Engr.

203	A50	50c green	.20	.20
204	A50	1pi dk carmine rose	.30	.20
205	A50	3pi lilac rose	.40	.20
206	A50	8pi violet blue	1.10	.40
		Nos. 203-206 (4)	2.00	1.00

Issued for Women's Day.

Farm Woman with Grain A51

1963, Mar. 21   Perf. 13

207	A51	50c red	.30	.20
208	A51	1pi dk car rose	.35	.20
209	A51	3pi lilac rose	.50	.20
210	A51	5pi violet	.85	.30
		Nos. 207-210 (4)	2.00	.90

FAO "Freedom from Hunger" campaign.

Common Defense Emblem — A52

1963, July 7   Engr.   Perf. 13

211	A52	30c bister	.45	.20
212	A52	50c lilac rose	.55	.20
213	A52	3pi brt green	.85	.20
214	A52	8pi red	1.40	.25
		Nos. 211-214 (4)	3.25	.85

Common defense effort. The inscription says: "Personalism-Common Progress."

1963, Oct. 26   Perf. 13

215	A53	50c rose red	.25	.20
216	A53	1pi emerald	.40	.20
217	A53	4pi purple	.85	.25
218	A53	5pi orange	1.50	.55
		Nos. 215-218 (4)	3.00	1.20

The fighting soldiers of the Republic.

Centenary Emblem and Map — A54

1963, Nov. 17   Engr.
Cross in Deep Carmine

219	A54	50c Prus blue	.35	.20
220	A54	1pi deep carmine	.75	.20
221	A54	3pi orange yellow	1.00	.20
222	A54	6pi brown	2.40	.40
		Nos. 219-222 (4)	4.50	1.00

Centenary of International Red Cross.

Constitution and Scales — A55

1963, Dec. 10   Perf. 13

223	A55	70c orange	.20	.20
224	A55	1pi brt rose	.35	.20
225	A55	3pi green	.45	.20
226	A55	8pi ocher	1.10	.35
		Nos. 223-226 (4)	2.10	.95

15th anniv. of the Universal Declaration of Human Rights.

Danhim Hydroelectric Station — A56

1964, Jan. 15   Engr.

227	A56	40c rose red	.40	.20
228	A56	1pi bister brown	.40	.20
229	A56	3pi violet blue	.60	.20
230	A56	8pi olive green	1.10	.45
		Nos. 227-230 (4)	2.50	1.05

Inauguration of the Danhim Hydroelectric Station.

Atomic Reactor A57

1964, Feb. 3   Perf. 1

231	A57	80c olive	.40	
232	A57	1.50pi brown orange	.40	
233	A57	3pi chocolate	.85	
234	A57	7pi brt blue	1.10	.4
		Nos. 231-234 (4)	2.75	1.0

Peaceful uses of atomic energy.

Compass Rose, Barograph and UN Emblem — A58

South Vietnamese Gesturing to North Vietnamese; Map — A59

1964, Mar. 23   Engr

235	A58	50c bister	.20	.20
236	A58	1pi vermilion	.25	.20
237	A58	1.50pi rose claret	.35	.20
238	A58	10pi emerald	1.10	.40
		Nos. 235-238 (4)	1.90	1.00

4th World Meteorological Day, Mar. 23.

1964, July 20   Perf. 13

239	A59	30c dk grn, ultra & mar	1.10	.40
240	A59	50c dk car rose, yel & blk	1.10	.35
241	A59	1.50pi dk bl, dp org & blk	1.10	.35
		Nos. 239-241 (3)	3.30	.75

10th anniv. of the Day of National Grief, July 20, 1954, when the nation was divided into South and North Viet Nam.

Hatien Beach — A60

1964, Sept. 7   Engr.   Perf. 13½

242	A60	20c bright ultra	.25	.25
243	A60	3pi emerald	1.00	.30

Revolutionists and "Nov. 1" — A61

Designs: 80c, Soldier breaking chain. 3pi, Broken chain and date: "1-11 1963," vert.

1964, Nov. 1   Engr.   Perf. 13

244	A61	50c red lilac & indigo	.40	.20
245	A61	80c violet & red brn	.45	.20
246	A61	3pi dk blue & red	.85	.55
		Nos. 244-246 (3)	1.70	.95

Anniv. of November 1963 revolution.

Temple, Saigon A62

Designs: 1pi, Royal tombs, Hué. 1.50pi, Fishermen and sailboats at Phan-Thiet beach. 3pi, Temple, Gia-Dinh.

1964-66   Perf. 13

Size: 35½x26mm

247	A62	50c fawn, grn & dl vio	.55	.20
248	A62	1pi olive bis & ind	.85	.20
249	A62	1.50pi ol gray & dk sl grn	.80	.20

0 A62 3pi vio, dk sl grn & cl 1.60 .40
Nos. 247-250 (4) 3.80 1.00

Coil Stamp
Size: 23x17mm

0A A62 1pi ol bis & ind ('66) 6.00 3.50

Issue date: Nos. 247-250, Dec. 2, 1964.

Hung Vuong and Au Co with their Children A63

1965, Apr.   Engr.   Perf. 13
1 A63 3pi car lake & org red 1.25 .30
2 A63 100pi brown vio & vio 11.00 2.25

Mythological founders of Viet Nam, c. 2000 C.

ITU Emblem, Insulator and TV Mast — A64

Buddhist Wheel of Life and Flames — A65

1965, May 17   Engr.
3 A64 1pi olive, dp car & bister .45 .20
4 A64 3pi henna brn, car & lil 1.10 .30
ITU, centenary.

1965, May 15   Perf. 13
1.50pi, Wheel, lotus blossom and world map, horiz. 3pi, Wheel and Buddhist flag.

Inscribed: "Phat-Giao" (Buddhism)
5 A65 50c dark carmine 1.25 .20
6 A65 1.50pi dk blue & ocher 1.25 .20
7 A65 3pi org brn & dk brn 2.00 .35
Nos. 255-257 (3) 4.50 .75

Anniversary of Buddha's birth.

ICY Emblem and Women of Various Races — A66

Ixora — A67

1965, June 26
58 A66 50c bluish blk & bis .70 .20
59 A66 1pi dk brn & brn .70 .20
60 A66 1.50pi dark red & gray 1.10 .30
Nos. 258-260 (3) 2.50 .70

International Cooperation Year.

1965, Sept. 10   Engr.   Perf. 13
Flowers: 80c, Orchid. 1pi, Chrysanthemum. 1.50pi, Lotus, horiz. 3pi, Plum blossoms.

261 A67 70c grn, slate grn & red .25 .20
262 A67 80c dk brn, lil & sl grn .35 .20
263 A67 1pi dk blue & yellow .40 .20
264 A67 1.50pi sl grn, dl grn & gray .65 .20
265 A67 3pi slate grn & org 1.25 .30
Nos. 261-265 (5) 2.90 1.10

Student, Dormitory and Map of Thu Duc — A68

1965, Oct. 15   Perf. 13
266 A68 50c dark brown .20 .20
267 A68 1pi bright green .20 .20
268 A68 3pi crimson .50 .20
269 A68 7pi dark blue violet 1.40 .45
Nos. 266-269 (4) 2.30 1.05

Issued to publicize higher education.

Farm Boy and Girl, Pig and 4-T Emblem A69

4pi, Farm boy with chicken, village and 4-T flag.

1965, Nov. 25   Engr.   Perf. 13
270 A69 3pi emerald & dk red .65 .20
271 A69 4pi dull violet & plum .85 .25

10th anniv. of the 4-T Clubs and the National Congress of Young Farmers.

Basketball A70

Designs: 1pi, Javelin. 1.50pi, Hand holding torch, athletic couple. 10pi, Pole vault.

1965, Dec. 14   Engr.   Perf. 13
272 A70 50c dk car & brn org .40 .20
273 A70 1pi brn org & red brn .50 .20
274 A70 1.50pi brt green .75 .20
275 A70 10pi red lil & brn org 2.10 .50
Nos. 272-275 (4) 3.75 1.10

Radio Tower — A71

Loading Hook and Globe — A72

Radio tower, telephone dial, map of Viet Nam.

1966, Apr. 24   Engr.   Perf. 13
276 A71 3pi brt blue & brn .45 .20
277 A71 4pi purple, red & blk .55 .25

Saigon microwave station.

1966, June 22   Engr.   Perf. 13
278 A72 3pi gray & dk car rose .35 .20
279 A72 4pi olive & dk purple .45 .20
280 A72 6pi brt grn & dk blue .75 .30
Nos. 278-280 (3) 1.55 .70

Appreciation of the help given by the free world.

Hands Reaching for Persecuted Refugees A73

1966, July 20
281 A73 3pi brn, vio brn & olive .40 .20
282 A73 7pi claret, vio brn & dk pur .85 .20

Refugees from communist oppression.

Paper Soldiers, Votive Offering A74

Designs: 1.50pi, Man and woman making offerings. 3pi, Floating candles in paper boats. 5pi, Woman burning paper offerings.

1966, Aug. 30   Engr.   Perf. 13
283 A74 50c red, blk & bis brn .60 .20
284 A74 1.50pi brown, emer & grn 1.00 .20
285 A74 3pi rose red & lake 1.40 .20
286 A74 5pi org brn, bis & dk brn 2.00 .30
Nos. 283-286 (4) 5.00 .90

Wandering Souls Festival.

Oriental Two-string Violin A75

Vietnamese Instruments: 3pi, Woman playing 16-string guitar. 4pi, Musicians playing two-string guitars. 7pi, Woman and boy playing flutes.

1966   Engr.   Perf. 13
Size: 35½x26mm
287 A75 1pi brown red & brn .75 .20
288 A75 3pi rose lilac & pur .75 .20
289 A75 4pi rose brown & brn 1.25 .25
290 A75 7pi dp blue & vio bl 2.75 .40
Nos. 287-290 (4) 5.50 1.05

Coil Stamp
Size: 23x17mm
290A A75 3pi rose lil & pur 7.00 .50
b. Booklet pane of 5 70.00

Nos. 287-290 were issued Sept. 28. No. 290Ab contains two vertical strip of 5 with selvage at either end. These strips were also sold loose without booklet cover.

WHO Building, Geneva, and Flag — A76

Designs: 50c, WHO Building and emblem, horiz. 8pi, WHO flag and building.

1966, Oct. 12
291 A76 50c purple & carmine .20 .20
292 A76 1.50pi red brn, vio bl & blk .20 .20
293 A76 8pi grnsh bl, vio bl & brn 1.00 .50
Nos. 291-293 (3) 1.40 .90

Opening of WHO Headquarters, Geneva.

Hand Holding Spade, and Soldiers A77

Soldier and Workers — A78

Designs: 1.50pi, Flag, workers. 4pi, Soldier and cavalryman.

1966, Nov. 1   Engr.   Perf. 13
294 A77 80c dull brn & red brn .35 .20
295 A77 1.50pi car rose, yel & brn .70 .20
296 A78 3pi brown & slate grn .70 .20
297 A78 4pi lilac, black & brn 2.50 .30
Nos. 294-297 (4) 4.25 .90

3rd anniv. of the revolution against the government of Pres. Ngo Dinh Diem.

Symbolic Tree and UNESCO Emblem — A79

Designs: 3pi, Globe and olive branches. 7pi, Symbolic temple, horiz.

1966, Dec. 15   Engr.   Perf. 13
298 A79 1pi pink, brn & dk car .60 .20
299 A79 3pi dp bl, grn & brn org .60 .20
300 A79 7pi grnsh bl, dk bl & red 1.50 .35
Nos. 298-300 (3) 2.70 .75

20th anniv. of UNESCO.

Bitter Melon A80

1967, Jan. 12   Engr.   Perf. 13
301 A80 50c Cashew, vert. 1.00 .20
302 A80 1.50pi shown 1.50 .20
303 A80 3pi Sweetsop 1.75 .20
304 A80 20pi Areca nuts 4.25 .40
Nos. 301-304 (4) 8.50 1.00

Phan-Boi-Chau — A81

Designs: 20pi, Phan-Chau-Trinh portrait and addressing crowd.

1967, Mar. 24   Engr.   Perf. 13
305 A81 1pi mar, red brn & dk brn .25 .20
306 A81 20pi vio, slate grn & blk 1.25 .45

Issued to honor Vietnamese patriots.

Woman Carrying Produce A82

Labor Day: 1pi, Market scene. 3pi, Two-wheeled horse cart. 8pi, Farm scene with water buffalo.

1967, May 1   Engr.   Perf. 13
307 A82 50c vio bl, dk bl & ultra   .20   .20
308 A82   1pi sl grn & dull pur   .20   .20
309 A82   3pi dk carmine   .40   .40
310 A82   8pi brt car rose & pur   .85   .40
Nos. 307-310 (4)   1.65   1.00

Potter, Vases and Lamp — A83

Weavers and Potters A84

Designs: 1.50pi, Vase and basket. 35d, Bag and lacquerware.

1967, July 22   Engr.   Perf. 13
311 A83   50c red brn, grn & ul-tra   .20   .20
312 A83 1.50pi grnsh bl, car & blk   .40   .20
313 A84   3pi red, vio & org brn   1.00   .20
314 A83   35pi bis brn, blk & dk red   3.00   .60
Nos. 311-314 (4)   4.60   1.20

Issued to publicize Vietnamese handicrafts.

Wedding Procession A85

1967, Sept. 18   Engr.   Perf. 13
315 A85   3pi rose cl, dk vio & red   1.50   .25

Symbols of Stage, Music and Art — A86

Litho. & Engr.
1967, Oct. 27   Perf. 13
316 A86 10pi bl gray, blk & red   1.50   .20

Issued to publicize the Cultural Institute.

"Freedom and Justice" A87

Balloting A88

"Establishment of Democracy" — A89

1967, Nov. 1   Photo.
317 A87   4pi mag, brn & ocher   .75   .20
318 A88   5pi brown, yel & blk   1.00   .20
319 A89 30pi dl lil, indigo & red   2.75   .50
Nos. 317-319 (3)   4.50   .90

National Day; general elections.

Pagoda and Lions Emblem A90

1967, Dec. 5   Photo.   Perf. 13½x13
320 A90 3pi multicolored   1.50   .80

50th anniversary of Lions International.

Teacher with Pupils and Globe — A91

1967, Dec. 10   Perf. 13x13½
321 A91 3pi tan, blk, yel & car   1.50   .25

International Literacy Day, Sept. 8, 1967.

Tractor and Village — A92

Rural Construction Program: 9pi, Bulldozer and home building. 10pi, Wheelbarrow, tractor and new building. 20pi, Vietnamese and Americans working together.

1968, Jan. 26   Photo.   Perf. 13½
322 A92   1pi multicolored   .20   .20
323 A92   9pi lt blue & multi   .80   .20
324 A92 10pi multicolored   1.25   .25
325 A92 20pi yel, red lil & blk   1.65   .35
Nos. 322-325 (4)   3.90   1.00

WHO Emblem — A93

1968, Apr. 7   Photo.   Perf. 13½
326 A93 10pi gray grn, blk & yel   1.50   .80

WHO, 20th anniversary.

Flags of Viet Nam's Allies — A94

Designs: 1.50pi, Flags surrounding SEATO emblem. 3pi, Flags, handclasp, globe and map of Viet Nam. 50pi, Flags and handclasp.

1968, June 22   Photo.   Perf. 13½
327 A94   1pi multicolored   .60   .20
328 A94 1.50pi multicolored   1.25   .20
329 A94   3pi multicolored   2.40   .20
330 A94 50pi multicolored   7.75   .95
Nos. 327-330 (4)   12.00   1.55

Issued to honor Viet Nam's allies.

Three-wheeled Truck and Tractor — A95

Private Property Ownership: 80c, Farmer, city man and symbols of property. 2pi, Three-wheeled cart, taxi and farmers. 30pi, Taxi, three-wheeled cart and tractor in field.

Inscribed: "HUU-SAN-HOA CONG-NHAN VA NONG-DAN"

1968, Nov. 1   Photo.   Perf. 13½
331 A95   80c multicolored   .20   .20
332 A95   2pi steel blue & multi   .20   .20
333 A95 10pi orange brn & multi   .85   .35
334 A95 30pi gray blue & multi   2.75   1.00
Nos. 331-334 (4)   4.00   1.75

Human Rights Flame — A96

Men of Various Races — A97

1968, Dec. 10   Photo.   Perf. 13½
335 A96 10pi multicolored   .75   .25
336 A97 16pi purple & multi   1.50   .30

International Human Rights Year.

UNICEF Emblem, Mother and Child — A98

6pi, Children flying kite with UNICEF emblem.

1968, Dec. 11
337 A98   6pi multicolored   1.00   .25
338 A98 16pi multicolored   1.25   .40

Workers and Train — A99

1.50pi, 3pi, Crane, train, map of Viet Nam.

1968, Dec. 15
339 A99 1.50pi multicolored   .70
340 A99   3pi org, vio bl & grn   .85
341 A99   9pi multicolored   1.10
342 A99 20pi multicolored   2.00
Nos. 339-342 (4)   4.65

Reopening of Trans-Viet Nam Railroad.

Farm Woman — A100

Vietnamese Women: 1pi, Merchant. 3p Nurses, horiz. 20pi, Three ladies.

1969, Mar. 23   Engr.   Perf. 1.
343 A100 50c vio bl, lil & ocher   .20   .2
344 A100   1pi grn, bis & dk brn   .20   .2
345 A100   3pi brown, blk & bl   .30   .2
346 A100 20pi lilac & multi   1.40   .5
Nos. 343-346 (4)   2.10   1.1

Soldiers and Civilians A101

Family Welcoming Soldier A102

1969, June 1   Photo.   Perf. 13
347 A101   2pi multicolored   .20   .20
348 A102 50pi multicolored   2.25   .50

Pacification campaign.

Man Reading Constitution, Scales of Justice A103

Voters, Torch and Scales A104

1969, June 9
349 A103   1pi yel org, yel & blk   .20   .20
350 A104 20pi multicolored   2.50   .30

Constitutional democracy. Phrase on both stamps: "Democratic and Governed by Law."

Mobile Post Office — A105

Mobile Post Office: 3pi, Window service. 4pi, Child with letter. 20pi, Crowd at window and postmark: "15, 12, 67."

1969, July 10
351 A105   1pi multicolored   .20   .20
352 A105   3pi multicolored   .45   .20
353 A105   4pi multicolored   .55   .20
354 A105 20pi ocher & multi   1.10   .35
Nos. 351-354 (4)   2.30   .95

Installation of the first mobile post office in Viet Nam.

Mnong-gar Woman A106

1pi, Djarai woman. 50pi, Bahnar man.

1969, Aug. 29	**Photo.**		*Perf. 13*	
455	A106	1pi brt pink & multi	.75	.20
456	A106	6pi sky blue & multi	1.75	.20
457	A106	50pi gray & multi	7.50	.40
	Nos. 355-357 (3)		10.00	.80

Ethnic minorities in Viet Nam.

Civilians Becoming Soldiers A107

General Mobilization: 3pi, Bayonet training. 6pi, Guard duty. 10pi, Farewell.

1969, Sept. 20
Inscribed: "TONG BONG VIEN"

358	A107	1.50pi orange & multi	.75	.20
359	A107	3pi purple & multi	1.60	.20
360	A107	5pi blk, red & ocher	2.40	.20
361	A107	10pi pink & multi	3.25	.35
	Nos. 358-361 (4)		8.00	.95

ILO Emblem and Globe — A108

1969, Oct. 29	**Photo.**		*Perf. 13*	
362	A108	6pi blue grn, blk & gray	.55	.20
363	A108	20pi red, blk & gray	1.40	.20

ILO, 50th anniversary.

Pegu House Sparrow — A109

Birds: 6pi, Moluccan munia. 7pi, Great hornbill. 30pi, Old world tree sparrow.

1970, Jan. 15	**Photo.**		*Perf. 12½x14*	
364	A109	2pi blue & multi	.90	.25
365	A109	6pi orange & multi	2.00	.50
366	A109	7pi org brn & multi	3.00	.50
367	A109	30pi blue & multi	11.50	1.50
	Nos. 364-367 (4)		17.40	2.75

Burning House and Family — A110

Design: 20pi, Family fleeing burning house and physician examining child.

1970, Jan. 31	**Photo.**		*Perf. 13*	
368	A110	10pi multicolored	1.25	.20
369	A110	20pi multicolored	2.00	.25

Mau Than disaster, 1968.

Vietnamese Costumes — A111

Traditional Costumes: 1pi, Man, woman and priest, vert. 2pi, Seated woman with fan. 100pi, Man and woman.

Inscribed: "Y-PHUC CO TRUYEN"

1970, Mar. 13	**Photo.**		*Perf. 13*	
370	A111	1pi lt brown & multi	.20	.20
371	A111	2pi pink & multi	.20	.20
372	A111	3pi ultra & multi	.20	.20
373	A111	100pi multicolored	6.00	1.65
	Nos. 370-373 (4)		6.60	2.25

Issued for the Trung Sisters' Festival.

Building Workers, Pagodas and Bridge A112

Rebuilding of Hué: 20pi, Concrete mixers and scaffolds.

1970, June 10		**Litho. & Engr.**		
374	A112	6pi multicolored	.85	.20
375	A112	20pi rose lil, brn & bis	1.40	.40

Plower in Rice Field — A113

1970, Aug. 29			*Perf. 13*	
376	A113	6pi multicolored	.75	.20

"Land to the Tiller" agricultural reform program.

New Building and Scaffold A114

Construction Work — A115

1970, Sept. 15	**Engr.**		*Perf. 13*	
377	A114	8pi pale ol & brn org	.50	.20
378	A115	16pi brn, indigo & yel	1.00	.30

Reconstruction after 1968 Tet Offensive.

Productivity Year Emblem A116

1970, Oct. 3				
379	A116	10pi multicolored	.50	.20

Asian Productivity Year.

Nguyen-Dinh-Chieu — A117

Education Year Emblem — A118

1970, Nov. 16	**Engr.**		*Perf. 13½*	
380	A117	6pi dull vio, red & brn	.55	.20
381	A117	10pi grn, red & dk brn	.85	.20

Nguyen-Dinh-Chieu (1822-1888), poet.

Litho. & Engr.

1970, Nov. 30			*Perf. 13*	
382	A118	10pi pale brn, yel & blk	1.00	.30

International Education Year.

Parliament Building A119

1970, June 10		**Litho. & Engr.**		
	Design: 6pi, Senate Building.			

Design: 6pi, Senate Building.

1970, Dec.

383	A119	6pi lt bl, cit & dk brn	.40	.20
384	A119	10pi multicolored	.85	.20

6pi issued Dec. 8 for the 6th Cong.; 10pi issued Dec. 9 for the 9th General Assembly of the Asian Interparliamentary Union.

Dancers — A120

1971, Jan. 12

Designs: Various Vietnamese dancers and musicians. 6pi and 7pi horizontal.

385	A120	2pi ultra & multi	.45	.20
386	A120	6pi pale green & multi	1.25	.20
387	A120	7pi pink & multi	1.50	.20
388	A120	10pi brown org & multi	1.60	.25
	Nos. 385-388 (4)		4.80	.85

For surcharge see No. 500.

Farmers and Law — A121

Agrarian Reform Law: 3pi, Tractor and law, dated 26.3.1970. 16pi, Farmers, people rejoicing and law book.

1971, Mar. 26	**Engr.**		*Perf. 13*	
389	A121	2pi vio bl, dk brn & dl org	.20	.20
390	A121	3pi pale grn, brn & dk bl	.25	.20
391	A121	16pi multicolored	1.10	.20
	Nos. 389-391 (3)		1.55	.60

For surcharge see No. 482.

Courier on Horseback A122

Design: 6pi, Mounted courier with flag.

Engr. & Photo.

1971, June 6			*Perf. 13*	
392	A122	2pi violet & multi	.30	.20
393	A122	6pi tan & multi	1.25	.20

Postal history.

Military and Naval Operations on Vietnamese Coast — A123

1971, June 19				
394	A123	3pi multi + label	1.00	.25
395	A123	40pi multi + label	5.00	.65

Armed Forces Day.

Deer — A124

Rice Harvest A125

1971, Aug. 20		**Engr.**		
396	A124	9pi shown	.80	.20
397	A124	30pi Tiger	2.75	.35

Litho. & Engr.

1971, Sept. 28			*Perf. 13*	

30pi, Threshing and winnowing rice and rice plants. 40pi, Bundling and carrying rice.

398	A125	1pi multicolored	.20	.20
399	A125	30pi sal pink, dk pur & blk	1.65	.25
400	A125	40pi sepia, yel & grn	1.90	.30
	Nos. 398-400 (3)		3.75	.75

For surcharge see No. 496.

Inauguration of UPU Building, Bern — A126

1971, Nov. 9	**Engr.**		*Perf. 13*	
401	A126	20pi green & multi	1.10	.25

Fish — A127

Various Fish; 2pi vertical.

1971, Nov. 16		**Photo. & Engr.**		
402	A127	2pi multicolored	1.00	.20
403	A127	10pi violet & multi	2.00	.20
404	A127	100pi lilac & multi	15.00	1.50
	Nos. 402-404 (3)		18.00	1.90

Mailman and Woman on Water Buffalo A128

Rural Mail: 10pi, Bird carrying letter. 20pi, Mailman with bicycle delivering mail to villagers.

1971, Dec. 20   Engr.   Perf. 13
Inscribed: "PHAT TRIEN BUU-CHINH NONG THON"
405	A128	5pi multicolored	.30	.20
406	A128	10pi multicolored	.60	.20
407	A128	20pi multicolored	1.10	.30
		Nos. 405-407 (3)	2.00	.70

Trawler Fishermen, and Fish — A129

Publicity for Fishing Industry: 7pi, Net fishing from boat. 50d, Trawler with seine.

1972, Jan. 2   Engr.   Perf. 13
408	A129	4pi pink, blk & blue	.35	.20
409	A129	7pi lt blue, blk & red	.55	.20
410	A129	50pi multicolored	2.75	.60
		Nos. 408-410 (3)	3.65	1.00

King Quang Trung (1752-1792) — A130

1972, Jan. 28   Perf. 13½
411	A130	6pi red & multi	.75	.20
a.		Booklet pane of 10	65.00	
412	A130	20pi black & multi	2.00	.40

No. 411a is imperf. horizontally.

Road Workers A131

1972, Feb. 4
413	A131	3pi multicolored	.25	.20
414	A131	8pi multicolored	.85	.20

Community development.

Rice Farming A132

1972, Mar. 26   Engr.   Perf. 13½
415	A132	1pi shown	.20	.20
416	A132	10pi Wheat farming	1.40	.20

Farmers' Day.

Plane over Dalat — A133

1972, Apr. 18   Engr. & Photo.
417	A133	10pi shown	2.50	.25
418	A133	10pi over Ha-tien	2.50	.25
419	A133	10pi over Hue	2.50	.25
420	A133	10pi over Saigon	2.50	.25
a.		Block of 4, #417-420	10.00	2.00
421	A133	25pi like No. 417	4.75	.25
422	A133	25pi like No. 418	4.75	.25

423	A133	25pi like No. 419	4.75	.25
424	A133	25pi like No. 420	4.75	.25
a.		Block of 4, #421-424	21.00	3.50
		Nos. 417-424 (8)	29.00	2.00

20 years Air Viet Nam.

Scholar A134

20pi, Teacher, pupils. 50pi, Scholar, scroll.

1972, May 5   Engr. & Litho.
425	A134	5pi multicolored	.35	.20

Engr.
426	A134	20pi lt green & multi	1.50	.40
427	A134	50pi pink & multi	4.00	.60
		Nos. 425-427 (3)	5.85	1.20

Ancient letter writing art.

Armed Farmer — A135

6pi, Civilian rifleman & Self-defense Forces emblem, horiz. 20pi, Man, woman training with rifles.

1972, June 15   Engr. & Litho.   Perf. 13
428	A135	2pi brt rose & multi	1.25	.25
429	A135	6pi multicolored	2.00	.25
430	A135	20pi lt violet & multi	2.75	.25
		Nos. 428-430 (3)	6.00	.75

Civilian Self-defense Forces.

Hands Holding Safe — A136

1972, July 10
431	A136	10pi lt blue & multi	1.75	.20
432	A136	25pi lt green & multi	3.25	.40

Treasury Bonds campaign.

Frontier Guard — A137

Soldier Helping Wounded Man — A138

Designs: 10pi, 3 guards and horse, horiz. 40pi, Marching guards, horiz.

Engr. & Litho.
1972, Aug. 14   Perf. 13
433	A137	10pi olive & multi	.55	.20
434	A137	30pi buff & multi	1.40	.25
435	A137	40pi lt blue & multi	1.90	.45
		Nos. 433-435 (3)	3.85	.90

Historic frontier guards.

1972, Sept. 1
Designs: 16pi, Soldier on crutches and flowers. 100pi, Veterans' memorial, map and flag.
436	A138	9pi olive & multi	.75	.25
437	A138	16pi yellow & multi	1.00	.25
438	A138	100pi lt blue & multi	5.50	1.00
		Nos. 436-438 (3)	7.25	1.50

For surcharge see No. 483.

Tank, Memorial, Flag and Map — A139

Soldiers and Map of Viet Nam — A140

1972, Nov. 25   Litho.   Perf. 13
439	A139	5pi multicolored	8.00	.20
440	A140	10pi ultra & multi	12.00	.20

Victory at Binh-Long.

Book Year Emblem and Globe — A141

Designs: 4pi, Emblem, books circling globe. 5pi, Emblem, books and globe.

1972, Nov. 30
441	A141	2pi dp carmine & multi	.45	.20
442	A141	4pi blue & multi	.75	.20
443	A141	5pi yellow bister & multi	1.10	.20
		Nos. 441-443 (3)	2.30	.60

International Book Year.

Liberated Vietnamese Family — A142

Soldiers Raising Vietnamese Flag — A143

1973, Feb. 18   Litho.   Perf. 13
444	A142	10pi yellow & multi	2.00	.20

To celebrate the 200,000th returnee.

1973, Feb. 24   Litho.   Perf. 13
Design: 10pi, Victorious soldiers and map of demilitarized zone, horiz.
445	A143	3pi lilac & multi	1.00	.20
446	A143	10pi yellow grn & multi	1.50	.20

Victory at Quang Tri.

Satellite, Storm over Viet Nam — A144

1973, Mar. 23   Litho.   Perf. 12½x12
447	A144	1pi lt blue & multi	.80	.20

World Meteorological Day.
For surcharge see No. 497.

Farmers with Tractor, Symbol of Law — A145

Farmer Plowing with Water Buffalos A146

Pres. Thie Holding Agrarian Reform Law A147

1973, Mar. 26   Litho.   Perf. 12½x1
448	A145	2pi lt green & multi	2.00	.2
449	A146	5pi orange & multi	2.00	.2

Perf. 11
450	A147	10pi blue & multi	60.00	10.0
		Nos. 448-450 (3)	64.00	10.5

3rd anniv. of the agrarian reform law; 5-yea plan for rural development.
Value for No. 450 is for stamp with first da cancel. Commercially used copies are wor substantially more.
See No. 475.

INTERPOL Emblem and Headquarters A148

2pi, INTERPOL emblem. 25pi, INTERPO emblem, side view of Headquarters.

1973, Apr. 8   Litho.   Perf. 12½x1
451	A148	1pi olive & multi	.20	.2
452	A148	2pi yellow & multi	.20	.2
453	A148	25pi ocher, lilac & brn	2.75	.6
		Nos. 451-453 (3)	3.15	.6

Intl. Criminal Police Org., 50th anniv.
For surcharge see No. 498.

ITU Emblem and Waves A149

2pi, Globe and waves. 3pi, ITU emblem.

1973, May 17
454	A149	1pi dull blue & multi	.25	.2
455	A149	2pi brt blue & multi	.50	.2
456	A149	3pi orange & multi	.75	.2
		Nos. 454-456 (3)	1.50	.6

World Telecommunications Day.
For surcharge see No. 499.

Globe, Hand Holding House — A150

Men Building Pylon — A151

Design: 10pi, Fish in net, symbols of agricul ture, industry and transportation.

1973, Nov. 6   Litho.   Perf. 12x12
457	A150	8pi gray & multi	.70	.2
458	A150	10pi vio bl, blk & gray	.90	.2
459	A151	15pi blk, org & lil rose	1.40	.2
		Nos. 457-459 (3)	3.00	.6

National development.

For surcharge see No. 514.

Water Buffalos
A152

1973, Dec. 20   Litho.   Perf. 12½x12
460 A152 5pi shown   .70 .20
461 A152 10pi Water buffalo   1.00 .20

Human Rights
Flame, Three
Races
A153

Design: 100pi, Human Rights flame, scales
and people, vert.

1973, Dec. 29   Perf. 12½x12, 12x12½
462 A153 15pi ultra & multi   .75 .20
463 A153 100pi green & multi   2.25 .30

25th anniv. of Universal Declaration of
Human Rights.

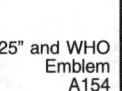

"25" and WHO
Emblem
A154

Design: 15pi, WHO emblem, diff.

1973, Dec. 31   Perf. 12½x12
464 A154 8pi orange, bl & brn   .60 .20
465 A154 15pi lt brn, bl & brt pink   .90 .20

25th anniversary of WHO.
For surcharge see No. 515.

Sampan
Ferry
A155

Design: 10pi, Sampan ferry (different).

1974, Jan. 13   Perf. 14x13½
466 A155 5pi lt blue & multi   1.25 .20
467 A155 10pi yellow grn & multi   1.75 .40

Sampan ferry women.

Soldiers of 7
Nations
A156

American War
Memorial
A157

Map of South Viet
Nam and Allied
Flags — A158

Design: No. 469, Soldiers and flags of South
Viet Nam, Korea, US, Australia New Zealand,
Thailand and Philippines. Same flags shown
on 8pi and 60pi.

1974, Jan. 28   Perf. 12½x12, 12x12½
468 A156 8pi multicolored   .40 .20
469 A156 15pi lt brown & multi   .85 .20
470 A157 15pi multicolored   .85 .20
471 A158 60pi multicolored   2.50 .20
        Nos. 468-471 (4)   4.60 .80

In honor of South Viet Nam's allies.
For surcharge see No. 516.

Trung Sisters
on Elephants
Fighting
Chinese
A159

1974, Feb. 27   Litho.   Perf. 12½x12
472 A159 8pi green, citron & blk   1.10 .20
473 A159 15pi dp orange & multi   1.40 .20
474 A159 80pi ultra, pink & blk   2.75 .20
        Nos. 472-474 (3)   5.25 .60

Trung Trac and Trung Nhi, queens of Viet
Nam, 39-43 A.D. Day of Vietnamese Women.

Pres. Thieu Type of 1973 and

Farmers
Going to
Work — A160

Woman Farmer
Holding
Rice — A161

1974, Mar. 26   Litho.   Perf. 14
475 A147 10pi blue & multi   .50 .20
Perf. 12½x12, 12x12½
476 A160 20pi yellow & multi   .50 .20
477 A161 70pi blue & multi   5.00 .50
        Nos. 475-477 (3)   6.00 .90

Agriculture Day. Size of No. 475 is
31x50mm, No. 450 is 34x54mm and printed
on thick paper. No. 475 has been extensively
redrawn and first line of inscription in bottom
panel changed to "26 THANG BA."

Value for No. 477 is for stamp with first day
cancel. Commercially used copies are worth
substantially more.

Hung
Vuong with
Bamboo
Tallies
A162

Flag
Inscribed:
Hung
Vuong,
Founder of
Kingdom
A163

1974, Apr. 2   Perf. 14x13½
478 A162 20pi yellow & multi   1.00 .30
479 A163 100pi olive & multi   3.50 .50

Hung Vuong, founder of Vietnamese nation
and of Hông-Bang Dynasty (2879-258 B.C.).

National
Library
A164

New National Library Building: 15pi, Library,
right facade and Phoenix.

1974, Apr. 14
480 A164 10pi orange, brn & blk   .65 .30
481 A164 15pi multicolored   .85 .40

Nos. 391 and 437 Surcharged with
New Value and Two Bars in Red

1974   **Perf. 13**
482 A121 25pi on 16pi multi   1.75 .35
483 A138 25pi on 16pi multi   1.75 .40

Memorial Tower,
Saigon — A165

Globe, Crane
Lifting
Crate — A167

Crane with
Flags, Globe
and Map of
Viet
Nam — A166

Perf. 12x12½, 12½x12
1974, June 22   **Litho.**
484 A165 10pi blue & multi   .60 .25
485 A166 20pi multicolored   1.40 .30
486 A167 60pi yellow & multi   4.50 .35
        Nos. 484-486 (3)   6.50 .90

International Aid Day.

Sun and
Views of
Saigon,
Dalat Hué
A168

Cau-Bong
Bridge,
Nha Trang
A169

Thien-Mu
Pagoda,
Hué — A170

1974, July 12   Perf. 14x13½, 13½x14
487 A168 5pi blue & multi   .95 .30
488 A169 10pi blue & multi   .95 .30
489 A170 15pi yellow & multi   1.50 .30
        Nos. 487-489 (3)   3.40 .90

Tourist publicity.

Rhynchostylis Gigantea — A171

Orchids: 20pi, Cypripedium caliosum, vert.
200pi, Dendrobium nobile.

1974, Aug. 18
490 A171 10pi blue & multi   .30 .20
491 A171 20pi yellow & multi   .35 .25
492 A171 200pi bister & multi   5.00 1.00
        Nos. 490-492 (3)   5.65 1.45

Hands Passing
Letter, UPU
Emblem
A172

UPU Emblem and
Woman — A173

UPU Cent.: 30pi, World map, bird, UPU
emblem.

Perf. 12½x12, 12x12½
1974, Oct. 9   **Litho.**
493 A172 20pi ultra & multi   .25 .20
494 A172 30pi orange & multi   .50 .25
495 A173 300pi gray & multi   3.25 1.00
        Nos. 493-495 (3)   4.00 1.45

Nos. 398, 447, 451, 454, 387
Surcharged with New Value and Two
Bars in Red

1974-75
496 A125 25pi on 1pi multi   6.25
497 A144 25pi on 1pi multi   6.25
498 A148 25pi on 1pi multi   6.25
499 A149 25pi on 1pi multi   9.00
500 A120 25pi on 7pi multi   9.00
        Nos. 496-500 (5)   36.75

Issued: #496, 498, 1/1/75; others, 11/18/74.

Hien Lam
Pavilion,
Hué
A174

Throne,
Imperial
Palace,
Hué
A175

Water
Pavilion,
Hué
A176

1975, Jan. 5   Litho.   Perf. 14x13½
501 A174 25pi multicolored   1.50 .25
502 A175 30pi multicolored   2.25 .25
503 A176 60pi multicolored   2.75 .50
        Nos. 501-503 (3)   6.50 1.00

Historic sites.

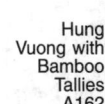

Symbol of Youth,
Children Holding
Flower — A177

Family and
Emblem
A178

1975, Jan. 14   Perf. 11½
504 A177 20pi blue & multi   3.50   .30

Perf. 12½x12
505 A178 70pi yellow & multi   3.50   .35
Intl. Conf. on Children & Natl. Development.

Unicorn Dance
A179

Boy Lighting Firecracker
A180

Bringing New Year Gifts and Wishes — A181

Perf. 14x13½, 13½x14
1975, Jan. 26   Litho.
506 A179 20pi multicolored   2.50   .25
507 A180 30pi blue & multi   3.00   .30
508 A181 100pi bister & multi   7.00   .50
    Nos. 506-508 (3)   12.50 1.05
Lunar New Year, Tet.

A182

A183

A184

Designs: 25pi, Military chief from play "San Hau." 40pi, Scene from "Tam Ha Nam Duong." 100pi, Warrior Luu-Kim-Dinn.

1975, Feb. 23
509 A182 25pi rose & multi   1.25   .30
510 A183 40pi lt green & mul-
            ti   2.00   .30
511 A184 100pi violet & multi   6.75   .50
    Nos. 509-511 (3)   10.00 1.10
National theater.

Produce, Map of Viet Nam, Ship — A185

Irrigation Project A186

1975, Mar. 26   Litho.   Perf. 12½x12
512 A185 10pi multicolored   1.75   .20
513 A186 50pi multicolored   5.25   .30
Agriculture Day; 5th anniv. of Agrarian Reform Law.

Nos. 457, 464, 468 Surcharged with New Value and Two Bars in Red
1975
514 A150 10pi on 8pi multi   12.00 2.00
515 A154 10pi on 8pi multi   8.00 1.00
516 A156 25pi on 8pi multi   8.00 1.50
    Nos. 514-516 (3)   28.00 4.50

In the 1980's a number of South Viet Nam stamps appeared on the market. These apparently had been printed before the collapse of the Republic but saw no postal use. These include, but are not limited to, sets of two for western electric and for rural electric, one each for history, library, New Year and cows, a set of three for transportation and a set of four for economic development.

SEMI-POSTAL STAMPS

Type of 1952 Surcharged in Carmine

+50c

Perf. 12x12½
1952, Nov. 10   Unwmk.
B1 A3 1.50pi + 50c bl, yel &
          brn   4.00 3.25
    Never hinged   10.00
The surtax was for the Red Cross.

> **Catalogue values for unused stamps in this section, from this point to the end of the section, are for Never Hinged items. Because of the tropical conditions, never hinged stamps must also be free wrinkles, toning, and any other disturbance.**

Sabers and Flag — SP1

1952, Dec. 21   Engr.   Perf. 13
B2 SP1 3.30pi + 1.70pi dp clar-
            et   1.50   .50
The surtax was for the Wounded Soldiers' Aid Organization.

X-ray Camera and Patient SP2

1960, Aug. 1   Perf. 13
B3 SP2 3pi + 50c bl grn & red   1.00   .60
The surtax was for the Anti-Tuberculosis Foundation.

AIR POST STAMPS

> **Catalogue values for unused stamps in this section, from this point to the end of the section, are for Never Hinged items. Because of the tropical conditions, never hinged stamps must also be free wrinkles, toning, and any other disturbance.**

AP1

AP2

Perf. 13½x12½
1952-53   Unwmk.   Photo.
C1 AP1 3.30pi dk brn red & pale
            yel grn   1.00   .50
C2 AP1 4pi brown & yellow   1.50   .25
C3 AP1 5.10pi dk vio bl & sal
            pink   1.50   .40
C4 AP2 6.30pi yellow & car   1.50   .50
    Nos. C1-C4 (4)   5.50 1.65
Issued: #C2, 11/24/53; others, 3/8/52.

Dragon AP3

Fish — AP4

1952, Sept. 3   Engr.   Perf. 13
C5 AP3 40c red   1.40   .35
C6 AP3 70c green   2.40   .50
C7 AP3 80c ultra   2.40   .50
C8 AP3 90c brown   2.40   .50
C9 AP4 3.70pi deep magenta   5.25   .75
    Nos. C5-C9 (5)   13.85 2.60
Nos. C5-C9 exist imperforate in a souvenir booklet. Value, $175.

South Viet Nam

Phoenix — AP5

1955, Sept. 7
C10 AP5 4pi violet & lil rose   2.75 .5

Crane Carrying Letter AP6

1960, Dec. 20.   Perf. 1.
C11 AP6 1pi olive   .60   .2
C12 AP6 4pi green & dk blue   1.50   .2
C13 AP6 5pi ocher & purple   1.75   .3
C14 AP6 10pi deep magenta   3.00   .7
    Nos. C11-C14 (4)   6.85 1.6

POSTAGE DUE STAMPS

> **Catalogue values for unused stamps in this section, from this point to the end of the section, are for Never Hinged items. Because of the tropical conditions, never hinged stamps must also be free wrinkles, toning, and any other disturbance.**

Temple Lion D1

Dragon D2

Perf. 13x13½
1952, June 16   Typo.   Unwmk.
J1 D1 10c red & green   .85   .20
J2 D1 20c green & yellow   1.10   .20
J3 D1 30c purple & orange   1.40   .20
J4 D1 40c dk grn & sal rose   1.90   .25
J5 D1 50c dp carmine & gray   2.50   .30
J6 D1 1pi blue & silver   4.25   .20
    Nos. J1-J6 (6)   12.00 1.35

South Viet Nam
1955-56
J7 D2 2pi red vio & org   .40   .20
J8 D2 3pi violet & grnsh bl   .55   .20
J9 D2 5pi violet & yellow   .60   .20
J10 D2 10pi dk green & car   .90   .20
J11 D2 20pi red & brt grn
           ('56)   2.00   .50
J12 D2 30pi brt grn & yel
           ('56)   3.00   .75
J13 D2 50pi dk red brn & yel
           ('56)   6.00 1.50
J14 D2 100pi pur & yel ('56)   12.00 3.50
    Nos. J7-J14 (8)   25.45 7.05
Nos. J11-J14 inscribed "BUU-CHINH" instead of "TIMBRE-TAXE."

Atlas Moth — D3

Design: 3pi, 5pi, 10pi, Three butterflies.

1968, Aug. 20 Photo. Perf. 13½x13
J15 D3 50c multicolored   1.25   .25
J16 D3 1pi multicolored   1.40   .25
J17 D3 2pi multicolored   2.75   .25
J18 D3 3pi multicolored   4.00   .25
J19 D3 5pi multicolored   6.75   .25
J20 D3 10pi multicolored   9.00   .25
    Nos. J15-J20 (6)   25.15 1.50

Nos. J15-J18 Surcharged with New
Value and Two Bars in Red

974, Oct. 1

21	D3	5pi on 3pi multi	.75
22	D3	10pi on 50c multi	.75
23	D3	40pi on 1pi multi	2.75
24	D3	60pi on 2pi multi	3.25
		Nos. J21-J24 (4)	7.50

MILITARY STAMPS

Catalogue values for unused
stamps in this section, from this
point to the end of the section, are
for Never Hinged items. Because
of the tropical conditions, never
hinged stamps must also be free of
wrinkles, toning, and any other
disturbance.

Soldier
Guarding
Village
M1

Rouletted 7½

1961, June		**Unwmk.**		**Litho.**
M1	M1	och, brn, dk grn & blk	4.00	1.00

1961, Sept.				**Typo.**
M2	M1	org yel, dk grn & brn	3.50	1.00

Bottom inscription on No. M1 is black, brown
on No. M2.

Battle and
Refugees
M2

1969, Feb. 22		**Litho.**		*Imperf.*
M3	M2	red & green		60.00
a.		Booklet pane of 10		600.00

NORTH VIET NAM

LOCATION — In eastern Indo-China
GOVT. — Republic
AREA — 61,293 sq. mi.
POP. — 18,800,000 (1968 est.)
CAPITAL — Hanoi

Beginning in 1946, the Communist
Viet Minh fought the French in a guerrilla war that ended with the French
defeat at Dien Bien Phu in 1954. In an
agreement signed in Geneva on July
21, 1954, Viet Nam was partitioned at
the 17th parallel. The government in
Hanoi controlled the north, and
engaged in another protracted military
campaign against American and South
Vietnamese forces that led to the official
reunification of the country under Communist control on July 2, 1976.

100 Cents (Xu) = 10 Hao = 1 Piaster
(Dong)

All stamps are without gum
unless otherwise indicated. Values
for stamps with gum are for Never
Hinged items.

Watermark

Wmk. 376 — "R de C"

VIET MINH ISSUES
Stamps and Types of Indo-China
Overprinted or Surcharged
**Printing Methods and Perfs as
Before**

1945-46   Without Gum
**No. 236 Overprinted
"VIET-NAM DAN-CHU CONG-HOA"**

1L1	A41	1pi yel grn (Yersin)	8.00

**Nos. 238-239 (Rhodes) Overprinted
"VIET-NAM DAN-CHU CONG-HOA"
with "VN" & "IXIXIXIXIX"
Obliterators**
Perf. 11 ½

1L2	A43	15c dk vio brn, perf.	
		11½	1.25
a.		Perf. 12	1.25
b.		Perf. 11½, green overprint	2.50
1L3	A43	30c org brn, perf.	
		11½	1.00
a.		Perf. 13½	2.00
b.		Perf. 12	15.00

**No. 242 Overprinted
"VIET-NAM DAN-CHU CONG-HOA"
with "VN" & "VN.VN" Obliterators**

1L4	A44	50c dl red (Athlete)	7.00

**No. 241 Overprinted
"VIET-NAM DAN-CHU CONG-HOA"
with "VN" & "XXXX" Obliterators**

1L5	A44	10c dk vio brn & yel	
		(Athlete)	18.00

**Nos. 218-222 (Petain) Overprinted
"VIET-NAM DAN-CHU CONG-HOA"
with "Buu-Chinh" and
Wavy Line Obliterators**

1L6	A32	3c olive brn, perf.	
		11½	1.75
a.		Perf. 12x14	5.00
b.		Perf. 14	15.00
1L7	A32	6c rose red	1.00
1L8	A32	10c dull grn (R)	5.00
1L9	A32	40c dk bl (R)	3.00
1L10	A32	40c slate bl (R)	3.00
		Nos. 1L6-1L10 (5)	13.75

**Nos. 245-246 and Type (Pavie)
Overprinted "VIET-NAM DAN-CHU
CONG-HOA" with "BUU-CHINH" and
Wavy Line & "VN" Obliterators**

1L11	A46	4c org yel	1.50
1L12	A46	10c dl grn	1.50
1L13	A46	20c dark red	1.25
		Nos. 1L11-1L13 (3)	4.25

**No. 165A Overprinted
"VIET-NAM DAN-CHU CONG-HOA"
with "BUU CHINH" and
Slanted Lines Obliterator**

1L14	A22	25c dk bl (Planting	
		Rice, R), top	
		line 18 mm	
		wide	60.00
a.		Top line 20 mm wide	80.00

Nos. 1L14-1L14a issued with gum.

**No. 232 (Courbet) Overprinted
"VIET-NAM DAN-CHU CONG-HOA
DOC-LAP TU-DO HANH-PHUC"**

1L15	A39	3c lt brn	1.00
1L16	A39	6c car rose	2.00

**No. 261 (Lagree) Overprinted
Vertically "VIET-NAM DAN-CHU
CONG-HOA DOC-LAP TU-DO
HANH-PHUC" with
"BUU-CHINH" & "III" Obliterator**

1L17	A52	40c brt bl	1.50

**Nos. 253-255 (Doumer) Overprinted
"VIET-NAM DOC-LAP TU-DO
HANH-PHUC BUU-CHINH"
with Wavy Line Obliterators**

1L18	A50	2c red vio	1.50
1L19	A50	4c lt brn	1.25
1L20	A50	10c yel grn	1.50
		Nos. 1L18-1L20 (3)	4.25

**Nos. 217, 256-258 (Petain, Charner)
Overprinted "VIET-NAM DOC-LAP
TU-DO HANH-PHUC BUU-CHINH"
with "VN" and
Wavy Line Obliterators**

1L21	A32	1c blk brn	2.00
1L22	A51	10c green	1.75
1L23	A51	20c brn red	1.75
1L24	A51	1pi pale yel grn	7.50
		Nos. 1L21-1L24 (4)	13.00

**No. 230 and Type (Genouilly)
Overprinted "VIET-NAM DOC-LAP
TU-DO HANH-PHUC BUU-CHINH"
with "X" Obliterator**

1L25	A37	5c dull brown	1.50
1L26	A37	6c carmine rose	5.00

**Nos. 210-212 (Sihanouk) Surcharged
with New Value & "X" Obliterators**

1L27	A28	5d on 1c red org	
		(Bl)	12.50
1L28	A28	10d on 6c violet (R)	15.00
1L29	A28	15d on 25c dp ultra	
		(R)	15.00
		Nos. 1L27-1L29 (3)	42.50

**Nos. 225-226 (Sihanouk) Surcharged
with New Value with Wavy Line
and Straight Line Obliterators**

1L30	A34	50xu on 1c brown	3.00
1L31	A35	2d on 6c car rose	20.00

**Nos. 213-214 (Elephant) Surcharged
with New Value, "VIET-NAM DAN-
CHU
CONG-HOA," Wavy Line and
Straight Line Obliterators**

1L32	A29	2d on 3c reddish brn	
		(G)	12.50
1L33	A29	4d on 6c crim (G)	12.50

**Nos. 247-248 (Pasquier) Surcharged
Vertically with New Value,
"VIET NAM DAN CHU CONG HOA,"
Wavy Line & "X" Obliterators**

1L34	A47	1d on 5c brn vio	4.00
1L35	A47	10d on 10c dl grn	6.50

**No. B30 Surcharged with New
Value,
"VIET-NAM DAN-CHU CONG-HOA,"
"Binh-si Bi-nan,"
Wavy Line Obliterator**

1L36	SP7	5d on 15c+60c brn	
		vio (Cathedral)	25.00

**Nos. 259-260 (Lagree) Surcharged
Vertically with New Value,
"VIET-NAM DAN CHU CONG HOA
BUU-CHINH,"
Wavy Line & "VN" Obliterators**

1L37	A52	30xu on 1c dl gray	
		brn (R)	1.75
1L38	A52	3d on 15c dl rose	
		vio	3.00

**Nos. 243-244 (La Grandiere)
Surcharged
with New Value, "VIET-NAM DAN
CHU CONG HOA BUU CHINH,"
Wavy Line Obliterator**

1L39	A45	1d on 5c dk brn (Bl)	12.50
1L40	A45	4d on 1c dull brn	3.00

**Surcharged with New Value,
"VIET-NAM Dan-chu Cong-hoa
BUU-CHINH,"
Wavy & Straight Line Obliterators**

1L41	A42	30xu on 15c brn vio	
		(Garnier, R)	2.50

**No. 242 (Garnier) Surcharged
with New Value, "VIET-NAM
DAN CHU CONG HOA BUU-CHINH,"
Wavy & Straight Line Obliterators**

1L42	A42	5d on 1c dull ol bis	5.00

**Nos. 249-252 (De Lanessan, Van
Vollenhoven)
Surcharged with New Value,
"VIET-NAM DAN CHU CONG
HOA BUU CHINH,"
Straight Line Obliterators**

1L43	A49	50xu on 1c dl gray	
		brn	3.00
1L44	A48	60xu on 1c ol brn	4.50
1L45	A48	1.60d on 10c green	14.00
1L46	A49	3d on 15c dl rose	
		vio (Bl)	4.50
		Nos. 1L43-1L46 (4)	26.00

**Nos. B30-B31 (Cathedral)
Surcharged with New Value,
"VIET-NAM DAN-CHU CONG-HOA
CUU-DOI,"
Wavy Line Obliterators**

1L47	SP7	2d on 15c+60c brn	
		vio	22.50
1L48	SP7	3d on 40c+1.10pi	
		blue	22.50

**No. 234 (Yersin) Surcharged
with Added Value,
"VIET-NAM DAN-CHU CONGHOA
Bao Anh,"
and Straight Line obliterators**

1L49	A41	+2d on 6c car rose	9.00

**No. 233 (Behaine) Surcharged
with Added Value, "VIET-NAM
DAN-CHU CONG-HOA Binh si bi
nan,"
Wavy Line, "V" & "N" Obliterators**

1L50	A40	+3d on 20c dull red	5.00

**No. 215 (Saigon Fair) Surcharged
with Added Value, "VIET-NAM
DAN CHU CONG HOA Chong nan
mu chu" & Wavy Line**

1L51	A30	+4d on 6c car rose	9.00

**No. 229 (Natl. Revolution)
Surcharged
with Added Value, "VIET-NAM
DAN-CHU CONGHOA Doi song
moi,"
and "X" Obliterator**

1L52	A36	+4d on 6c car rose	6.50

**Nos. 213-214 Surcharged
with Added Value, "VIET-NAM
DAN-CHU CONG-HOA Quoc-Phong"
and Wavy Line in Blue**

1L53	A29	+5d on 3c reddish	
		brown	17.50
1L54	A29	+10d on 6c crimson	17.50

**Nos. 216, 224 Surcharged with
"VIET-NAM DAN-CHU CONG-HOA
DAN-SINH" & Straight Lines**

1L55	A31	30xu +3d on 6c	
		(Nam-	
		Phuong)	3.75

Perf. 13½

1L56	A33	30xu +3d on 6c	
		(Bao-Dai)	3.75
a.		Perf. 12	50.00

Ho Chi Minh

1946	**Litho.**	**Unwmk.**	**Perf. 11½**

Without Gum

1L57	VM1	1h green	.50
1L58	VM1	3h rose	.50
1L59	VM1	9h yellow bister	.50

**With Added Inscription "+PHU THU
CUU-QUOC"**

1L60	VM1	4h +6h Prussian blue	1.50
1L61	VM1	6h +9h brown violet	1.50
		Nos. 1L57-1L61 (5)	4.50

1948　　Typo.　　*Perf. 7 Rough*
Thin, Rough, Brown Paper
1L62	VM2 2d brown	22.50
1L63	VM2 5d red	22.50

For surcharge and overprints see Nos. 50, O6-O7.

REPUBLIC OF NORTH VIET NAM

> From 1945-2002, all stamps are without gum unless otherwise indicated. Values for stamps with gum are for Never Hinged items.

> Many North Vietnamese stamps are roughly perforated, especially issues before 1958.

Ho Chi Minh, Map of Vietnam — A1

1951-55　Unwmk.　Litho.　*Imperf.*
1	A1 100d brown	10.00	4.00
a.	Perf. 11¼ ('55)	10.00	4.00
2	A1 100d green	10.00	4.00
a.	Perf. 11¼ ('55)	10.00	4.00

Perf. 11¼
3	A1 200d red	10.00	4.00
a.	Imperf. ('55)	10.00	4.00
	Nos. 1-3 (3)	30.00	12.00

Nos. 1-3 printed on thin semi-transparent paper.

Nos. 1-3 used values are for cto. Postally used copies are worth about 5 times these values.

Counterfeits exist.

For surcharges, see Nos. 9-14, 36-38, and note before No. J1.

WORLD THEMATIC & VIETNAM CAMBODIA LAOS INDO-CHINA

- Covers + FDC
- Imperf stamps
- Proofs
- Deluxe Sheet
- Errors
- Old Pictures
- Post Card

FREE LISTS, etc.

TRAN ROBERT

4 ETIENNE DOLET
92240 MALAKOFF
FRANCE

TEL & FAX 33147352713

Blacksmith — A2

1953-55　　　　　　*Perf. 11¼*
4	A2 100d violet	3.00	3.00
5	A2 500d brown	5.00	7.00

Issued: 100d, 6/53. 500d, 2/55.

Georgi Malenkov, Ho Chi Minh, Mao Tse-tung and Flags — A3

1954-55　　　　　　*Perf. 11¼*
6	A3 50d brown & red, brnish	10.00	15.00
7	A3 100d red	10.00	25.00
8	A3 100d yellow & red, brnish	10.00	20.00
	Nos. 6-8 (3)	30.00	60.00

Issued: 50d, 10/54; #7, 1/54; #8, 4/55.
No. 7 printed on thin, white paper.

Nos. 1-3 Surcharged in Red or Blue

1954, Oct.　　　　　*Imperf.*
9	A1 10d on 100d brown	10.00	20.00
10	A1 10d on 100d green	10.00	20.00

Perf. 11
11	A1 20d on 200d red (Bl)	10.00	30.00
	Nos. 9-11 (3)	30.00	70.00

Nos. 1-3 Surcharged in Black, Red or Blue

1954, Oct.　　　　　*Imperf.*
12	A1 10d on 100d brown (Bk, R or Bl)	15.00	25.00
13	A1 10d on 100d green (Bk, R or Bl)	15.00	25.00

Perf. 11
14	A1 20d on 200d red (Bk or Bl)	20.00	50.00
	Nos. 12-14 (3)	50.00	100.00

Nos. 9-14 exist with counterfeit surcharges, counterfeit surcharges on counterfeit stamps, and with fantasy surcharges.

Victory at Dien Bien Phu A4

1954-56　　　　　　*Perf. 11¼*
17	A4 10d red brn & yel brn	10.00	20.00
a.	Imperf	30.00	50.00
18	A4 50d red & org yel	10.00	20.00
a.	Imperf	30.00	50.00
19	A4 150d brown & blue	10.00	25.00
a.	Imperf	30.00	50.00
	Nos. 17-19 (3)	30.00	60.00

Issued: Imperfs, 10/54; others, 1956. See #O5.

Used values for Nos. 17-19 are for postally used copies. The 10d exists cto, perf or imperf. Value about 1/10 those shown above.

Liberation of Hanoi — A5

1955, Jan. 1　　　　*Perf. 11½*
20	A5 10d lt blue & bl	5.00	2.00
21	A5 50d dk grn & grn	5.00	2.00
22	A5 150d rose & brn red	10.00	4.00
	Nos. 20-22 (3)	20.00	8.00

Nos. 20-22 used values are for postally used copies. Cto copies are worth about $1 each.

Land Reform A6

1955-56　　　　　　*Perf. 11¼*
23	A6 5d lt green	10.00	5.00
24	A6 10d gray	10.00	5.00
25	A6 20d orange	10.00	5.00
26	A6 50d rose	10.00	5.00
27	A6 100d lt brown	20.00	20.00
	Nos. 23-27 (5)	60.00	40.00

Issued: 100d, 12/55; 20d, 50d, 2/56; others, 6/56. See Nos. O8-O9.

Return of Government to Hanoi — A7

1956, Mar. 1　　　　*Perf. 11¼*
28	A7 1000d violet	20.00	10.00
29	A7 1500d dk blue	20.00	10.00
30	A7 2000d turquoise	50.00	30.00
31	A7 3000d blue green	100.00	100.00
	Nos. 28-31 (4)	190.00	150.00

Counterfeits exist, often imperf and offered as proofs.

Re-opening of Hanoi-China Railroad — A8

1956, Mar. 1
32	A8 100d dark blue	20.00	10.00
33	A8 200d blue green	20.00	10.00
34	A8 300d violet	20.00	20.00
35	A8 500d lilac brown	20.00	40.00
	Nos. 32-35 (4)	80.00	80.00

Counterfeits exist, often imperf and offered as proofs.

Nos. 1-3 Surcharged

1954, Oct.　　　　　*Imperf.*
36	A1 10d on 100d brown	30.00	50.00
37	A1 10d on 100d green	30.00	50.00

Perf. 11
38	A1 20d on 200d red	30.00	50.00
	Nos. 36-38 (3)	90.00	150.00

Nos. 36-38 exist with counterfeit surcharges, counterfeit surcharges on counterfeit stamps, and with fantasy surcharges.

Tran Dang Ninh (1910-55), Guerrilla Leader A9

1956, July　　Litho.　　*Perf. 11*
39	A9 5d bl grn & pale grn	2.00	.3
40	A9 10d lilac & rose	2.00	.3
41	A9 20d gr brn & dk gray	3.00	.4
42	A9 100d dk blue pale bl	3.00	.4
	Nos. 39-42 (4)	10.00	1.4

Nos. 39-42 used values are for cto. Postal used value, set $14.

Mac Thi Buc (1927-51), Guerrilla Leader A10

1956, Nov. 3　　　　*Perf. 11*
43	A10 1000d rose & lilac rose	100.00	100.0
44	A10 2000d brown & bister	100.00	100.0
45	A10 4000d bl grn & green	150.00	100.0
46	A10 5000d ultra & lt blue	300.00	400.0
	Nos. 43-46 (4)	650.00	700.0

Nos. 43-46 used values are for postal used. Cto value, set $100.

Counterfeits exist, often imperf and offered as proofs.

Bai Thuong Dam — A11

1956-58　　　　　　*Perf. 11*
47	A11 100d vio bl & lil brn	5.00	1.0
a.	Perf 13	8.00	1.0
48	A11 200d lilac & gr grn	5.00	1.0
a.	Perf 13	8.00	1.0
49	A11 300d rose & lil brn	12.00	1.5
a.	Perf 13	10.00	1.0
	Nos. 47-49 (3)	22.00	3.5

Nos. 47-49 used values are for cto. Postal used copies are worth about 10 times thes values.

Issued: #47-49, 12/15/56; #47a-49a, 1958

No. 1L63 Surcharged

1956, Dec.　Typo.　　*Perf. 7 Roug*
50	VM2 50d on 5d dp red, brnish	30.00	50.0

Reprints and counterfeits exist.

Nam Dinh Textile Mill — A13

1957, Mar.　Litho.　　*Perf. 12*
51-53	A13 100d, 200d, 300d, set of 3	22.50	3.0
51a	Perf. 11½	2.00	1.0

Nos. 51-53 used values are for cto. Postal used value, set $15.

No. 51 also exists perf 11½x12½, impe and imperf by perf 11½.

Ho Chi Minh — A14

1957   *Perf. 12½*
54-57 A14 20d, 60d, 100d,
        300d, set of 4   20.00 8.50
    Issued: 20d, 60d, 12/13; others, 5/19.

Fourth World Trade Union Congress, Leipzig A15

1957, Aug. 1   *Perf. 12½*
58 A15 300d red violet   6.00 2.00
    See Nos. O17-O20.

Democratic Republic, 12th Anniv. A16

1957, Sept. 2   *Perf. 13*
59-60 A16 20d, 100d, set of 2   9.00 5.00

Presidents Voroshilov, Ho Chi Minh — A17

1957, Nov. 7   *Perf. 12½*
61-63 A17 100d, 500d, set of
        1000d, 3   37.50 30.00
    Russian revolution, 40th anniv.

Anti-illiteracy Campaign — A18

1958, Jan. 6   *Perf. 12½*
64-66 A18 50d, 150d, 1000d,
        set of 3   30.00 22.50

A19   A20

1958, Mar. 8
67-68 A19 150d, 500d, set of 2 26.00 22.50
    Physical education.

1958, May 1
69-70 A20 50d, 150d, set of 2   8.00 5.00
    May Day.

Fourth Intl. Congress of Democratic Women, Vienna A21

1958, May   *Typo.*
71 A21 150d blue   5.50 5.00

A22

A22a

    #72, 150d, #75, 2000d, Basket, lace & cup,
    vert. #73, 150d, #74, 1000d, Potter.
1958   *Litho.*
72-75 A22, A22a Set of 4   22.50 18.00
    Arts & Crafts Fair, Hanoi.
    Issued: Nos. 72, 75, 6/26; others, 8/19.

Building the Reunification Railway — A23

1958, July 20
76-77 A23 50d, 150d, set of 2   7.00 3.00

August Revolution, 13th Anniv. A24

1958, Aug. 19
78-79 A24 150d, 500d, set of 2 6.50 5.50

Resistance Movement in South Viet Nam, 13th Anniv. A25

1958, Sept. 23
80-81 A25 50d, 150d, set of 2 10.50 5.00

A26

1958, Oct.
82 A26 150d grnsh blue & blk   2.50 1.50
    Tran Hung Dao (1253-1300),

A27

1958, Nov. 7   *Engr.*   *Perf. 11½*
    Hanoi Engineering Plant.
83 A27 150d brown   2.50 1.00

Mutual Aid Teams — A28

1958, Nov. 7
84-85 A28 150d, 500d, set of 2 12.00 4.50

Ngoc Son Temple (Temple of Jade) — A29

1958, Dec. 1   *Photo.*   *Perf. 12*
86-87 A29 150d, 2000d, set of
                            2   32.50 11.00

Rattanware Cooperative A30

1958, Dec. 31
88 A30 150d greenish blue   2.25 .85

Ha Long Bay — A31

1959, Feb. 8
89-90 A31 150d, 350d, set of 2 6.00 3.00

Cam Pha Coal Mines — A32

1959, Mar. 3   *Engr.*   *Perf. 11½*
91 A32 150d blue   6.00 .60

Trung Sisters — A33

1959, Mar. 14   *Litho.*   *Perf. 11*
92-93 A33 5xu, 8xu, set of 2   5.00 3.50

World Peace Movement, 10th Anniv. — A34

1959, Apr. 15
94 A34 12xu purple, *rose*   2.50 .60

Xuan Quang Dam A35

1959, May 1
95-96 A35 6xu, 12xu, set of 2   8.50 1.50

Phu Loi Massacre A36

1959, May 15
97-98 A36 12xu, 20xu, set of 2 6.00 1.50

Hien Luong Bridge — A37

1959, July 20
99 A37 12xu black & carmine   3.00 1.50

Me Tri Radio Station — A38

1959, Aug. 10
100-101 A38 3xu, 12xu, set of 2 3.50 1.00

Sports A39

    Designs: 1xu, Shooting. 6xu, Swimming.
    12xu, Wrestling.

1959, Sept. 2
102-104 A39 Set of 3   6.50 2.50
    Size of No. 103 is 43x31mm.

People's Republic of China, 10th Anniv. — A40

1959, Oct. 1
105 A40 12xu multicolored   3.00   .40

Fruits — A41

Designs: 3xu, Coconuts. 12xu, Bananas. 30xu, Pineapple.

1959, Nov. 20
106-108 A41 Set of 3   8.00 3.50

People's Army, 15th Anniv. A42

1959, Dec. 22
109 A42 12xu multicolored   2.25 1.25

A43   A44

1960, Jan. 6
110-111 A43 2xu, 12xu, set of 2   4.50 2.50
Vietnamese Workers' Party, 30th Anniv.

1960, Jan. 6
Ethnic costumes: 2xu, Ede. 10xu, Meo. No. 114, 12xu, Tay. No. 115, 12xu, Thai.
112-115 A44 Set of 4   7.50 6.00

Census A45

Designs: 1xu, People. 12xu, Transmitting tower, dam, buildings, workers.

1960, Feb. 20
116-117 A45 Set of 2   3.50 2.50
No. 117 is 37x26mm.

Intl. Women's Day, 50th Anniv. A46

1960, Mar. 8
118 A46 12xu multicolored   1.75 1.50

A47   A48

1960, Apr. 5
119-120 A47 4xu, 12xu, set of 2   62.50 30.00
Hung Vuong Temple.

1960, Apr. 22
121-122 A48 5xu, 12xu, set of 2   5.50
121a   Souv. sheet of 1, olive brown
         & blue, imperf.   75.00
Lenin. No. 121a exists on brownish paper.

Election of National Assembly Delegates — A49

1960, May 3   *Perf. 11*
123 A49 12xu multicolored, *rose*   1.25 1.00

A50   A51

1960, May 8
124-125 A50 8xu, 12xu, set of 2   4.00   .75
Viet Nam Red Cross.

1960, May 19
Ho Chi Minh, 70th Birthday: Nos. 128, 130, Ho with children.
126 A51 4xu green & purple
127 A51 12xu pink & brown
128 A51 12xu multicolored
         Nos. 126-128 (3)   8.00 3.00
Souvenir Sheets
Imperf
129 A51 10xu yel bis & brn,
         rose   9.00
130 A51 10xu multicolored   8.00
         No. 128 is 25x39mm.

New Constitution A52

1960, July 7
131 A52 12xu lemon & gray   2.00 1.00

National Day, 15th Anniv. A53

1960, Sept. 2
132-133 A53 4xu, 12xu, set of 2   5.50 5.00

Development — A54

Designs: No. 134, Classroom. No. 135, Plowing. No. 136, Factory.

1960, Sept. 2
134-136 A54 12xu Set of 3   8.50

3rd Vietnamese Communist Party Congress — A55

1960, Sept. 4
137-138 A55 1xu, 12xu, set of 2   5.25 2.50

World Federation of Trade Unions, 15th Anniv. — A56

1960, Oct. 3
139 A56 12xu black & vermilion   5.00 4.50

Hanoi, 950th Anniv. A57

1960, Oct. 10   *Litho.*   *Perf. 11*
140-141 A57 8xu, 12xu, set of 2   7.50 3.00
141a   Souv. sheet of 1, imperf. 11.00 10.00
No. 141a exists on brownish paper.

15 Years' Achievements Exhibition — A58

1960, Oct. 20
142-143 A58 2xu, 12xu, set of 2   3.50 1.75

World Federation of Democratic Youth 15th Anniv. — A59

1960, Nov. 10
144 A59 12xu multicolored   2.75 2.5

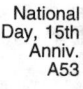

Trade Unions, 2nd Natl. Congress A60

1961, Feb. 10
145 A60 12xu multicolored, *rose* 2.00 1.0

Vietnamese Women's Union, 3rd Natl. Congress — A61

1961, Mar. 8   **Tinted Paper**
146-147 A61 6xu, 12xu, set of 2   4.50 1.5

Animals — A62   Ly Tu Trong — A63

Designs: 12xu, Rusa unicolor. 20xu, Helarctos malynus. 50xu, Elephas maximus. 1d, Hylobates leucogenys.

1961, Mar. 8
148-151 A62 Set of 4   22.50 10.00
         Imperf., #148-151   60.00 60.00

1961, Mar. 18
152-153 A63 2xu, 12xu, set of 2   2.75 1.50
Youth Labor Union, 3rd Congress.

Young Pioneers, 20th Anniv. — A64

1961, May 2
154-155 A64 1xu, 12xu, set of 2   4.75 2.50

Intl. Red Cross — A65

1961, May 8
156-157 A65 6xu, 12xu, set of 2   5.00 2.25

Intl. Children's Day — A66

1961, June 1   *Perf. 11*
158-159 A66 4xu, 12xu, set of 2   4.25 2.25

Yuri Gagarin's Space Flight A67

1961, June 15
160-161 A67 6xu, 12xu, set of 2   20.00 9.00
   Imperf., #160-161   20.00

Hanoi, Hue and Saigon A68

1961, July 20
162-163 A68 12xu, 3d, set of 2 22.50 17.00

A69   A70

1961, July 20
164-165 A69 12xu, 2d, set of 2   8.00 2.25
   Imperf., #164-165
Reunification campaign.

1961, Aug. 21
166-167 A70 6xu, 12xu, set of 2   5.00 2.00
Geological exploration.

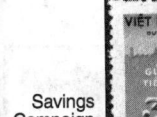

Savings Campaign A71

1961, Aug. 21
168-169 A71 3xu, 12xu, set of 2   5.00 1.50

Ancient Towers — A72

Gherman Titov's Space Flight — A73

Designs: 6xu, Thien Mu, Hue. 10xu, Pen Brush, Bac Ninh. No. 172, 12xu, Binh Son, Vinh Phuc. No. 173, 12xu, Cham, Phan Rang.

1961, Sept. 12
170-173 A72 Set of 4   7.50 3.00
   Imperf., #170-173   10.00

1961, Oct. 17
174-175 A73 6xu, 12xu, set of 2   6.00 3.00
   Imperf., #174-175   8.00

A74   A76

Port of Haiphong — A75

1961, Oct. 17
176 A74 12xu vermilion & black   3.00 2.00
22nd Communist Party Congress, Moscow.

1961, Nov. 7
177-178 A75 5xu, 12xu, set of 2   8.00 2.50

1961, Nov. 18   *Perf. 13½*
Musicians: No. 179, 12xu, Flutist. No. 180, 12xu, Cymbalist. 30xu, Dancer with fan. 50xu, Guitarist.

179-182 A76   Set of 4   12.00 11.00
   Imperf., #179-182   15.00
182a   Souvenir sheet, #179-182   50.00
   Stamps on No. 182a are se-tenant and perfed on outside edges of the strip of 4.

5th World Trade Union Congress, Moscow A77

1961, Dec. 4   *Perf. 11*
183 A77 12xu dp red lil & gray   2.00 .80

Natl. Resistance, 15th Anniv. A78

1961, Dec. 4
184-185 A78 4xu, 12xu, set of 2   2.25 2.00

Tet Holiday — A79

Designs: 6xu, Sow, piglets. 12xu, Poultry.

1962, Jan. 16   *Litho.*
186-187 A79 Set of 2   9.00 6.00

Tet Tree-Planting Festival — A80

1962, Jan. 16
188-189 A80 12xu, 40xu, set of 2 4.00

Crops — A81

Designs: 2xu, Camellia sinensis. 6xu, Illicium verum. No. 192, 12xu, Coffea arabica. No. 193, 12xu, Ricinus communis. 30xu, Rhus succedanea.

1962, Mar. 1
190-194 A81 Set of 5   15.00 6.00

Folk Dances — A82

Designs: No. 195, 12xu, Rong Chieng. No. 196, 12xu, Bamboo. 30xu, Hat. 50xu, Parasol.

1962, Mar. 20   Photo.   Perf. 11½x12
195-198 A82 Set of 4   13.50 4.00
   Imperf., #195-198   17.50
Souvenir Sheet
199 A82 30xu like #195   20.00

First Five Year Plan — A83

Designs: 1xu, Kim Lien Apartments, Hanoi. 3xu, State farm. 8xu, Natl. Institute of Hydraulics.

1962, Apr. 10   Litho.   Perf. 11
200-202 A83 Set of 3   3.00 3.00

A84   A85

Flowers: No. 203, 12xu, Hibiscus rosa sinensis. No. 204, 12xu, Plumeria acutifolia. 20xu, Chrysanthemum indicum. 30xu, Nelumbium nuciferum. 50xu, Ipomoea pulchella.

Perf. 12½x11½
1962, Apr. 10   *Photo.*
203-207 A84 Set of 5   22.50 10.00
   Imperf., #203-207   30.00
206a   Souvenir sheet of 1   12.00

1962, May 4   Litho.   Perf. 11
208 A85 12xu multicolored   3.00 3.00
3rd Natl. Heroes of Labor Congress.

Harrow A86

Dai Lai Lake A87

1962, May 25
209-210 A86-A87 6xu, 12xu, set of 2   4.00 4.00

Visit by Gherman Titov A88

Titov: 12xu, Waving at children. 20xu, Receiving medal from Ho Chi Minh. 30xu, Wearing space suit.

1962, June 12
211-213 A88 Set of 3   7.00 6.00
   Imperf., #211-213   7.00

Anti-Malaria Campaign A89

1962, July 9
214-216 A89 8xu, 12xu, 20xu, set of 3   7.50 3.00

War for Reunification — A90

1962, July 20
217 A90 12xu multicolored   2.50 1.25

Ba Be
Lake — A91

Design: No. 219, Ban Gioc Falls, vert.

1962, Aug. 14
218-219 A91 12xu Set of 2   3.50 3.00

A stamp picturing a weight lifter exists, but was not released.

King Quang Trung
(1752-92)
A92

Nguyen Trai
(1380-1442)
A93

1962, Sept. 16
220-221 A92 3xu, 12xu, set of 2   3.50 2.50

1962, Sept. 19
222-223 A93 3xu, 12xu, set of 2   3.50

Food Crops
A94

Designs: 1xu, Peanuts. 4xu, Beans. 6xu, Sweet potatoes. 12xu, Corn. 30xu, Cassava.

1962, Oct. 10
224-228 A94 Set of 5   9.00 4.00
    Imperf., #224-228

Animal
Husbandry
A95

Designs: 2xu, Feeding poultry. No. 230, 12xu, Feeding pigs. No. 231, 12xu, Cattle grazing. No. 232, 12xu, Tending water buffalo.

1962, Nov. 28
229-232 A95 Set of 4   7.00 3.50

A stamp commemorating the 45th anniversary of the Russian Revolution exists, but was not issued.

First Five
Year Plan
A96

#233, Evening classes. #234, Clearing land.

1962, Dec. 28
233-234 A96 12xu Set of 2   5.00 2.00

Flights of
Vostok 3
and
4 — A97

12xu, Pavel Popovich, Vostok 4. 20xu, Andrian Nikolayev, Vostok 3. 30xu, Rockets lifting-off, vert.

1962, Dec. 28   **Perf. 11**
235-237 A97 Set of 3   6.00 2.75
    Imperf., #235-237   10.00

Guerrilla
A98

Hoang Hoa Tham
(1846-1913)
A99

1963, Jan. 15
238-239 A98 5xu, 12xu, set of 2   2.75 1.50

1963, Feb. 10
240-241 A99 6xu, 12xu, set of 2   2.50 1.25

A100

First Five
Year Plan
A100a

Designs: No. 242, Fertilizing rice paddy. No. 243, Lam Thao superphosphate plant.

1963, Feb. 25
242-243 A100-A100a 12xu Set of
    2   3.50 1.50

Karl Marx — A101

1963, Mar. 14
244-245 A101 3xu, 12xu, set of 2   3.25 1.50
    Nos. 244-245 are printed on greenish and rose toned paper respectively.

Fidel Castro,
Vietnamese
Soldiers
A102

1963, Apr. 17
246 A102 12xu multicolored   1.50 .80

May
Day
A103

1963, May 8
247 A103 12xu multicolored   1.50 .80

A104

Intl. Red Cross,
Cent. — A105

Design: No. 249, Child, syringe.

1963, May 8
248 A104 12xu grn, blk & red
249 A104 12xu grn, red & blk
250 A105 20xu multicolored
    Nos. 248-250 (3)   6.00

Mars 1 Spacecraft — A106

6xu, 12xu (#252), Mars 1 approaching Mars. 12xu (#253), 20xu, Mars 1 entering orbit, vert.

1963, May 21
251-254 A106 Set of 4   7.00 5.00
    Imperf., #251-254   15.00

Fishing
Industry
A107

Designs: No. 255, Trawler, offshore fish. No. 256, Freshwater fish.

1963, July 3
255-256 A107 12xu Set of 2   8.50 5.00

Ho Chi Minh,
Nguyen Van
Hien — A108

1963, July 20
257 A108 12xu multicolored   2.50 1.75

Flights
of
Vostok
3, 4
A109

Designs: 12xu, Rockets in orbit. 20xu, Nikolayev. 30xu, Popovich.

1963, Aug. 11
258-260 A109 Set of 3   7.00 6.00
    Imperf., #258-260   13.00

First Five
Year Plan
for
Chemical
Industry
A110

Designs: 3xu, Viet Tri Insecticide Factory. 12xu, Viet Tri Chemical Factory.

1963, Aug. 11
261-262 A110 Set of 2   3.00 2.00

Fish
A111

Designs: No. 263, 12xu, Cyprinus carpio. No. 264, 12xu, Myloharyngodon piceus. No. 265, 12xu, Hypophthalmichthys molitrix. 20xu, Ophiocephalus caqua. 30xu, Tilapia mossambica.

1963, Sept. 10
263-267 A111 Set of 5   13.00 6.00
    Imperf., #263-267   17.00

A112

A113

Birds: #268, 12xu, Francolinus stephenson. #269, 12xu, Acridotheres cristatellus. #270, 12xu, Halcyon smyrneusis. 20xu, Diardigallus diardi, horiz. 30xu, Egretta. 40xu, Psittacula alexandri.

Perf. 11½x12, 12x11½
1963, Oct. 15   **Photo.**
268-273 A112 Set of 6   35.00 15.00
    Imperf., #268-273   45.00

Souvenir Sheet
274 A112 50xu Sheet of 1, like
    #272   85.00

1963, Oct. 20   Litho.   Perf. 11
275 A113 12xu multicolored   2.00 1.00
    World Federation of Trade Unions Congress for Viet Nam.

GANEFO
Games
A114

#276, 12xu, Swimming. #277, 12xu, Volleyball, vert. #278, 12xu, Soccer, vert. 30xu, High jump.

1963, Nov. 10
276-279 A114 Set of 4   4.00 4.00
    Imperf., #276-279   6.00

A115

A116

Flowers: 6xu, Rauwolfia verticillata. No. 281, 12xu, Sophora japonica. No. 282, 12xu,

Fibraurea tinctoria. No. 283, 12xu, Chenopodium ambrosioides. 20xu, Momordica cochinchinensis.

1963, Dec. 3
280-284 A115 Set of 5   5.00 2.50
  Imperf., #280-284   10.00

1963, Dec. 20
285 A116 12xu multicolored   2.50 1.00
  World Day for Viet Nam.

A117

First Five-Year Plan — A118

6xu, Molten cast iron. #287, 12xu, Thai Nguyen Steel & Iron Works. #288, 12xu, Power lines.

1964, Jan. 25   **Litho.**
286-288 A117-A118 Set of 3   4.50 1.75

Intl. Quiet Sun Year — A119

1964, Jan. 25
289-290 A119 12xu, 50xu, set
    of 2   5.00 3.00
  Imperf., #289-290   20.00

Flights of Vostok 5 and 6 A120

#291, 12xu, Rockets in orbit. #292, 12xu, Valery Bykovsky. 30xu, Valentina Tereshkova.

1964, Mar. 25
291-293 A120 Set of 3   6.00 5.00
  Imperf., #291-293   12.00

A stamp commemorating the anniversary of the founding of the People's Democratic Republic of Korea was printed but not issued.

A121   A122

Flowers: No. 294, 12xu, Persica vulgaris. No. 295, 12xu, Hibiscus mutabilis. No. 296, 12xu, Passiflora hispida. No. 297, 12xu, Saraca dives. 20xu, Michelia champaca. 30xu, Camellia amplexicaulis.

1964, Apr. 10   **Perf. 11½x12**
294-299 A121 Set of 6   13.00 5.00
  Imperf., #294-299   15.00

1964, Apr. 27   **Perf. 11**
  Costumes: 6xu, Peasant, 19th cent. No. 301, 12xu, Woman wearing large hat, 19th cent. No. 302, 12xu, Woman carrying hat.
300-302 A122 Set of 3   5.00 3.00

Battle of Dien Bien Phu, 10th Anniv. A123

Designs: 3xu, Artillery. 6xu, Machine gun emplacement. Nos. 305, 307c, Bomb disposal. Nos. 306, 307d, Farmer on tractor.

1964, May 7
303 A123   3xu red & black
304 A123   6xu blue & black
305 A123   12xu yel org & blk
306 A123   12xu red lilac & black
  Nos. 303-306
    (4)   6.50 5.00
  Imperf., #303-306   10.00

    Souvenir Sheet
      Imperf
307   Sheet of 4   12.50
 a.   A123 3xu orange & black
 b.   A123 6xu yellow green & black
 c.   A123 12xu red, black & orange
 d.   A123 12xu blue & black

Ham Rong Bridge — A124

1964, May 17
308 A124 12xu multicolored   1.75 .75

Wild Animals A125

Designs: No. 309, 12xu, Panthera tigris, vert. No. 310, 12xu, Pseudaxis axis, vert. No. 311, 12xu, Tapirus indicus. 20xu, Bubalus bubalis. 30xu, Rhinoceros bicornis. 40xu, Bibos banteng.

1964, June 2   **Perf. 10½**
309-314 A125 Set of 6   11.00 9.00
  Imperf., #309-314   14.00

Geneva Agreement on Viet Nam, 10th Anniv. A126

Intl. Labor Federation Committee United with People of South Viet Nam — A127

1964, July 20   **Perf. 11**
315-316 A126-A127 12xu Set of
    2   3.00 1.50

Nam Bac Ninh Pumping Station A128

1964, Aug. 25
317 A128 12xu blue gray & black   1.50 .70

Liberation of Hanoi, 10th Anniv. — A129

6xu, People cheering soldiers in truck. 12xu, Construction, hammerhead crane.

1964, Oct. 10
318-319 A129 Set of 2   3.50 2.50

Natl. Defense Games — A130

Designs: 5xu, Rowing. No. 321, 12xu, Parachuting, vert. No. 322, 12xu, Gliders, vert. No. 323, 12xu, Shooting.

1964, Oct. 18
320-323 A130 Set of 4   6.50 2.50

Fruits — A131

Designs: No. 324, 12xu, Mangifera indica. No. 325, 12xu, Guarcinia mangostana. No. 326, 12xu, Nephelium litchi. 20xu, Anona squamosa. 50xu, Citrus medica.

1964, Oct. 31 Photo.   **Perf. 11½x12**
324-328 A131 Set of 5   12.50 4.75
  Imperf., #324-328   15.00

World Solidarity Conference — A132

Designs: a, Ba Dinh Hall. b, Vietnamese soldier shaking hands with foreign people. c, Fist, planes, submarine.

1964, Nov. 25   **Litho.**   **Perf. 11**
329 A132 12xu Strip of 3, #a.-c.   4.50 3.00

People's Army, 20th Anniv. A133

Designs: No. 330, Soldiers, flag. No. 331a, Coast guards. No. 331b, Mounted border guards, vert.

1964, Dec. 22
330 A133 12xu multicolored
331 A133 12xu Pair, #a.-b.
  Nos. 330-331 (2)   5.00 1.25

Cuban Revolution, 6th Anniv. — A134

Designs: a, Vietnamese, Cuban flags. b, Cuban revolutionaries.

1965, Jan. 1
332 A134 12xu Pair, #a.-b.   4.50 3.00

Economic & Cultural Development of Mountain Region — A135

Designs: 2xu, 3xu, Women pollinating corn. 12xu, Girls walking to school.

1965, Jan. 1
333-335 A135 Set of 3   3.00 2.50
  Imperf., #333-335

A136

Vietnamese Worker's Party, 35th Anniv. — A137

Politicians: No. 336a, Le Hong Phong. b, Tran Phu. c, Hoang Van Thu. d, Ngo Gia Tu. e, Nguyen Van Cu.
No. 337a, Party flag. b, Worker, soldier.

1965   **Litho.**   **Perf. 11**
336 A136 6xu Strip of 5, #a.-e.
337 A137 12xu Pair, #a.-b.
  Nos. 336-337 (2)   5.00 4.75
  Issued: No. 336, 2/3; No. 337, 1/30.

Transportation Ministers Conference, Hanoi — A138

12xu, 30xu, Nguyen Van Troi, locomotive.

1965, Mar. 23
338-339 A138 Set of 2   7.00 2.00
  Imperf., #338-339

Vignette on No. 339 is mirror image of No. 338.

Flight of Voskhod 1 — A139

20xu, Cosmonauts Komarov, Feoktistov, Yegorov, rocket, globe. 1d, Cosmonauts, rocket.

1965, Mar. 30
340-341 A139 Set of 2   7.00 7.00
    Imperf., #340-341   11.00

Lenin, 95th
Birth Anniv.
A140

1965, Apr. 22   Litho.
342-343 A140 8xu, 12xu, set of 2 4.00

A141

1965, May 19
344-345 A141 6xu, 12xu, set of 2 2.50 1.90
    Ho Chi Minh, 75th birthday.

A142

1965, May 19
346 A142 12xu multicolored   2.50 2.00
    Afro-Asian Conference, 10th anniv.

Trade Union Conference,
Hanoi — A143

Designs: No. 347, Workers solidarity. No. 348, Soldiers, vert. No. 349, Naval battle.

1965, June 2
347-349 A143 12xu Set of 3   3.00

Wild Animals — A144

Designs: No. 350, 12xu, Martes flavigula. No. 351, 12xu, Chrotogale owstoni. No. 352, 12xu, Manis pentadactyla. No. 353, 12xu, Presbytis delacouri, vert. 20xu, Petaurista lylei, vert. 50xu, Nycticebus pygmaeus, vert.

1965, June 24   Photo.   *Perf. 12*
350-355 A144 Set of 6   17.00 5.50
    Imperf., #350-355   25.00

A145

A146

1965, July 1   *Perf. 11½x11*
356 A145 12xu multicolored   3.50 .40
6th Socialist Postal Ministers Conference.

1965, July 20   Litho.   *Perf. 11*
    Nguyen Van Troi (1940-64). Denominations: 12xu, 50xu, 4d.
357-359 A146 Set of 3   9.00 6.00

A147

Insects — A148

Designs: No. 360, 12xu, Tessaratoma papillosa. No. 361, 12xu, Rhynchocoris humeralis. No. 362, 12xu, Poeciliocoris latus. No. 363, 12xu, Tosena melanoptera. 20xu, Cicada. 30xu, Fulgora candelaria.

1965, July 24   Photo.
360-362 A147 Set of 3
363-365 A148 Set of 3
    Nos. 360-365 (6)   12.00 7.00
    Imperf., #360-365   15.00

August
Revolution,
20th Anniv.
A149

1965, Aug. 19   Litho.
366-367 A149 6xu, 12xu, set of 2 2.50 1.50

Crustaceans — A150

Designs: No. 368, 12xu, Penaeus indicus. No. 369, 12xu, Scylla serrata. No. 370, 12xu, Metapenaeus joyneri. No. 371, 12xu, Neptunus. 20xu, Palinurus japonicus. 50xu, Uca marionis.

1965, Aug. 19
368-373 A150 Set of 6   20.00 8.00
    Imperf., #368-373   20.00

500th US
Warplane Shot
Down — A151

1965, Aug. 30
374 A151 12xu gray green & lilac 7.00 5.50

A152

Completion of 1st
Five-Year
Plan — A153

#375, Foundry worker. #376, Electricity, irrigation. #377, Public health, education. #377, Students, children playing. #378, Factory worker. #379, Agricultural workers.

1965
375-377 A152 12xu Set of 3   3.50 1.75
378-380 A153 12xu Set of 3   3.50 1.75
    Imperf., #375-380

    Issued: #375-377, 9/2; #378-380, 12/25.

Nghe An, Ha Tinh Uprising, 35th
Anniv. — A154

1965, Sept. 12
381-382 A154 10xu, 12xu, set of
                            2   2.50 1.65
    Imperf., #381-382

Friendship Between Viet Nam,
People's Republic of China, 16th
Anniv. — A155

Designs: No. 383, Youth holding flags, Friendship Gate. No. 384, Children waving flags, walking through Gate, vert.

1965, Oct. 1
383-384 A155 12xu Set of 2   10.00 1.75

Flight of Voskhod 2 — A156

#385, 12xu, Konstantin Tsiolkovsky, Sputnik I. #386, 12xu, Voskhod 2, A. Leonov, P. Belyayev. #387, 50xu, Yuri Gagarin. #388, 50xu, Leonov walking in space.

1965, Oct. 5
385-388 A156 Set of 4   8.00 3.25
    Imperf., #385-388

A157

Norman R. Morrison, US anti-war demonstration.

1965, Nov. 22
389 A157 12xu black & red   2.50 1.25

1965, Nov. 25
    Nguyen Du (1765-1820), poet: No. 390, 12xu, Birthplace. No. 391, 12xu, Museum. 20xu, Volume of poems entitled Kieu. 1d, Scene from Kieu.

390-393 A158 Set of 4   6.00 5.00

A158

A159

Designs: No. 394, 12xu, Ho Chi Minh. No. 395, 12xu, Karl Marx. No. 396, 12xu, Lenin. 50xu, Frederich Engels.

Litho. & Engr. (#394), Litho.
1965, Nov. 28   **Perf. 11½**
394-397   A159   Set of 4   5.00   5.00

Nos. 395-397 have white border.

Butterflies
A160

#398, 12xu, Cethosia cyane. #399, 12xu, Zelides sarpedon. #400, 12xu, Cethosia. #401, 12xu, Apatura ambica. 20xu, Papilio paris. 30xu, Tros aristolochiae.

1965, Nov. 28   **Litho.**   **Perf. 11**
398-403   A160   Set of 6   21.00   6.50
    Imperf., #398-403   55.00

South Viet Nam Natl. Liberation Front, 5th Anniv. — A161

1965, Dec. 20
404   A161   12xu lilac   2.50   1.25
   Imperf.

1st General Elections, 20th Anniv. — A162

1966, Jan. 6
405   A162   12xu black & red   2.50   1.25

A163   A164

Orchids: No. 406, 12xu, Vanda teres. No. 407, 12xu, Dendrobium meschatum. No. 408, 12xu, Dendrobium nobile. No. 409, 12xu, Dendrobium crystallinum. 20xu, Vandopsis gigantea. 30xu, Dendrobium.

1966, Jan. 10   **Perf. 12**
406-411   A163   Set of 6   10.00   4.75
    Imperf., #406-411   20.00

1966, Jan. 18   **Perf. 11**
412   A164   12xu multicolored   2.50   1.00
   Imperf.

New Year 1966 (Year of the Horse).

Reptiles
A165

#413, 12xu, Physignathus cocincinus. #414, 12xu, Gekko gecko. #415, 12xu, Trionyx sinensis. #416, 12xu, Testudo elongata. 20xu, Varanus salvator. 40xu, Eretmochelys imbricata.

1966, Feb. 25   **Perf. 12x11½**
413-418   A165   Set of 6   10.00   5.00
    Imperf., #413-418   20.00

Natl.
Sports
A166

Designs: No. 419, Archery. No. 420, Wrestling. No. 421, Spear fighting.

1966, Mar. 25   **Perf. 11**
419-421   A166   12xu Set of 3   5.00   2.75

6xu, 12xu, 1d stamps for running, swimming and shooting were printed but not issued.

Youth Labor
Union, 35th
Anniv. — A167

1966, Mar. 26
422   A167   12xu multicolored   1.50   1.50

1000th US Warplane Shot
Down — A168

1966, Apr. 29
423   A168   12xu multicolored   7.50   4.00

May
Day — A169

1966, May 1
424   A169   6xu multicolored   1.50   .50

Defending Con Co Island — A170

1966, June 1
425   A170   12xu multicolored   2.50   1.50

A171

A172

1966, June 1
426   A171   12xu red & black   1.75   1.00
   Young Pioneers, 25th anniv.

1966, July 1
  Designs: 3xu, View of Yenan. 12xu, Ho Chi Minh, Mao Tse-Tung.
427-428   A172   Set of 2   7.00   1.50
    Imperf., #427-428

  Chinese Communist Party, 45th anniv.

A173

A174

  Luna 9: 12xu, Flight path to moon. 50xu, In lunar orbit.

1966, Aug. 5
429-430   A173   Set of 2   7.50   3.00
    Imperf., #429-430   8.50

1966, Oct. 10
431   A174   12xu multicolored   10.00   3.00
With Additional Inscription: "NGAY 14.10.1966"
431A   A174   12xu multicolored   15.00   3.75
    Imperf., #431-431A

  1500th US warplane shot down.

Victory in Dry Season
Campaign — A175

Designs: 1xu, 2xu (No. 433), Woman guerrilla carrying guns. 12xu (No. 434), Soldier escorting prisoners of war.

1966, Oct. 15
432-434   A175   Set of 3   3.25   1.65
    Imperf., #432-434

Vietnamese Women's Union, 20th
Anniv. — A176

1966, Oct. 20
435   A176   12xu orange & black   1.00   .70
   Imperf.

Birds
A177

Designs: No. 436, 12xu, Pitta moluccensis. No. 437, 12xu, Psarisomus dolhousiae. Nos. 438, 12xu, Alcedo atthis, vert. No. 439, 12xu, Oriolus chinensis, vert. 20xu, Upupa epops, vert. 30xu, Oriolus traillii.

1966, Oct. 31   **Perf. 12x12½, 12½x12**
436-441   A177   Set of 6   10.00   5.00
    Imperf., #436-441   25.00

GANEFO Asian
Games — A178

Designs: No. 442, Soccer. No. 443, Shooting. No. 444, Swimming. No. 445, Running.

1966, Nov. 25   **Perf. 11**
442-445   Set of 4   6.00   4.00
    Imperf., #442-445   9.00
443a   A178   12xu Pair, #442-443
445a   A178   30xu Pair, #444-445
    Nos. 443a,
    445a (4)   8.50

Ho Chi Minh's Appeal for Natl.
Resistance, 20th Anniv. — A179

Designs: No. 446, Flags, workers. No. 447, Soldiers, workers, ships.

1967, Jan. 30
446-447   A179   12xu Set of 2   2.00   1.75
    See Nos. 501-504.

Rice
Harvest
A180

1967, Jan. 30
448   A180   12xu multicolored   1.50   1.40

Bamboo
A181

#449, 12xu, Bambusa arundinaceu. #450,
12xu, Arundinaria rolleana. #451, 12xu,
Arundinaria racemosa. #452, 12xu, Bambusa
bingami. 30xu, Bambusa nutans. 50xu, Den-
drocalamus petellaris.

1967, Feb. 2   Perf. 12x11½
449-454 A181 Set of 6   9.00 7.25
    Imperf., #449-454   12.00

Wild Animals — A182

Designs: No. 455, 12xu, Cuon rutilans. No.
456, 12xu, Arctictis binturong. No. 457, 12xu,
Arctonyx collaris. 20xu, Viverra zibetha. 40xu,
Macaca speciosa. 50xu, Neofelis nebulosa.

1967, Mar. 26   Litho.   Perf. 12
455-460 A182 Set of 6   10.00 5.50
    Imperf., #455-460   13.00

2000th US
Aircraft Shot
Down — A183

1967, June 7   Perf. 11
461-462 A183 6xu, 12xu, set
              of 2   10.00 8.00

Fish
A184

#463, 12xu, Saurida filamentosa. #464,
12xu, Scomberomorus niphonius. #465, 12xu,
Haplogenys mucronatus. 20xu, Lethrinus
haematopterus. 30xu, Formio niger. 50xu,
Lutianus erythropterus.

1967, July 25   Perf. 12
463-468 A184 Set of 6   10.00 9.00
    Imperf., #463-468   13.00

A185   A186

Launch of 1st Chinese ballistic missile:
12xu, Missile, flag, agricultural scene. 30xu,
Missile, Gate of Heavenly Peace.

1967, July 25   Perf. 11
469-470 A185 Set of 2   7.50 3.00
    Imperf., #469-470

1967, Oct. 15
Russian October Revolution, 50th anniv.:
6xu, Lenin, revolutionary soldiers. No. 472a,
12xu, Lenin, armed mob. No. 472b, 12xu,
Lenin, Marx, Vietnamese soldiers. 20xu,
Cruiser Aurora.

471-473 A186 Set of 4   4.00 3.00
No. 472 is printed se-tenant.

2500th US Warplane Shot
Down — A187

Design: No. 475, Plane in flames, vert.

1967, Nov. 6
474-475 A187 12xu Set of 2   9.00 8.00

1st Chinese Hydrogen Bomb
Test — A188

Designs: 12xu, Atomic symbol, Gate of
Heavenly Peace. 20xu, Chinese lantern,
atomic symbol, dove.

1967, Nov. 20
476-477 A188 Set of 2   5.00 3.00
    Imperf., #476-477   32.50
No. 477 is 30x35mm.

A189

#478, 12xu, Rifle fire from trenches. #479,
12xu, Militia with captured US pilot. #480,
12xu, Factory anti-aircraft unit. #481, 12xu,
Naval anti- aircraft unit. 20xu, Aerial dog-fight.
30xu, Heavy anti-aircraft battery.

1967, Dec. 19   Perf. 12
478-483 A189 Set of 6   6.00 4.75

Chickens — A190

Designs: No. 484, 12xu, White spotted cock,
hen. No. 485, 12xu, Black hens. No. 486,
12xu, Bantam cock, hen. No. 487, 12xu, Bantam cock. 20xu, Fighting cocks. 30xu, Exotic
hen. 40xu, Hen, chicks from Ho region. 50xu,
Dong Cao's cock, hen.

1968, Feb. 29
484-491 A190 Set of 8   11.00 5.00
    Imperf., #484-491   17.50

Victories of 1966-67 — A191

No. 492: a, Soldier attacking US tank. b,
Gunner firing on US ships. c, Burning village.
d, Soldier firing mortar.
No. 493: a, Attacking US artillery. b, Escort-
ing US prisoners. c, Interrogating refugees. d,
Civilian demonstration.

1968, Mar. 5   Perf. 11
492-493 A191 12xu, 2 blocks of 4 6.00 6.00
    Imperf., #492-493

Maxim Gorki (1868-1936) — A192

1968, Mar. 5
494 A192 12xu brown & black   1.50 .80
    Imperf.

Roses — A193

Designs: No. 495, 12xu, Pale red. No. 496,
12xu, Orange. No. 497, 12xu, Pink. 20xu, Yellow, 30xu, Dark red. 40xu, Lilac.

1968, Apr. 25   Photo.   Perf. 11½x12
495-500 A193 Set of 6   12.00 12.00
    Imperf., #495-500   16.00

Ho Chi Minh's Appeal for Resistance
Type

Values and colors: No. 501, 6xu, greenish
blue and yellow. No. 502, 12xu, vermilion. No.
503, 12xu, bright blue. No. 504, 12xu, brownish lilac.

1968, Apr. 25   Litho.   Perf. 11
                  Size: 25x17mm
501-504 A179 6xu, 12xu Set of 4 6.00 3.00
    Imperf., #501-504

Ho Chi
Minh, Flag
A195

1968, May 19
505 A195 12xu brown & red   2.00 .50
    Imperf.

Karl
Marx — A196

1968, May 19
506 A196 12xu olive grn & blk 1.75 .25

3000th
US
Warplane
Shot
Down
A197

#507: a, 12xu, Anti-aircraft machine gun-
ners. b, 12xu, Women firing anti-aircraft gun.
#508: a, 40xu, Vietnamese plane shooting
down US plane. b, 40xu, Anti-aircraft missile.

1968, May 19
507-508 A197 Set of 2 pairs   14.00 10.00
    Imperf., #507-508

Handicrafts — A198

6xu, Rattan products. #510, 12xu, Ceramics. #511, 12xu, Bamboo products. 20xu, Ivory
carving. 30xu, Lacquerware. 40xu, Silverware.

1968, July 5   Perf. 12
509-514 A198 Set of 6   6.50 6.00
    Imperf., #509-514   15.00

Martial Arts
A199

Designs: No. 515, 12xu, Saber fencing. No.
516, 12xu, Stick fighting. No. 517, 12xu, Dagger fighting. 30xu, Unarmed combat. 40xu,
Chinese war sword fighting. 50xu, Duel with
swords, shields.

1968, Nov. 1
515-520 A199 Set of 6   10.00   9.00
   Imperf., #515-520   16.00

Architecture — A200

Designs: No. 521, 12xu, Khue Van tower, vert. No. 522, 12xu, Bell tower, Keo pagoda, vert. 20xu, Covered bridge, Thay pagoda. 30xu, One-pillar pagoda, Hanoi, vert. 40xu, Gateway, Ninh Phuc pagoda. 50xu, Tay Phuong pagoda.

1968, Nov. 5
521-526 A200 Set of 6   6.00   5.75
   Imperf., #521-526   10.00

Foreign Solidarity with Viet Nam — A201

#527, 12xu, Latin American guerrilla, vert. #528, 12xu, Cuban, Vietnamese militia. 20xu, Asian, African, Latin American soldiers, vert.

1968, Dec. 15   Wmk. 376   Perf. 12½
With Gum

527-529 A201 Set of 3   4.00 3.00

Scenes of War
A202

Artworks: No. 530, 12xu, Defending the mines. No. 531, 12xu, Plowman with rifle, vert. 30xu, Repairing railway track. 40xu, Wreckage of US aircraft.

1968, Dec. 15   Wmk. 376   Perf. 12½
With Gum

530-533 A202 Set of 4   4.00 3.75

Victories in South Viet Nam — A203

#534, 12xu, Tay Nguyen throwing grenade. #535, 12xu, Gun crews, Tri Thien. #536, 12xu, Nam Ngai shooting down US aircraft. 40xu, Insurgents, Tay Ninh, destroyed US armor. 50xu, Guerrillas preparing bamboo spike booby traps.

1969, Feb. 16   Unwmk.   Perf. 11½
534-538 A203 Set of 5   6.00 6.00

Timber Industry
A204

Designs: 6xu, Loading timber trucks. No. 540, 12xu, Log raft running rapids. No. 541,

12xu, Launch towing log raft. No. 542, 12xu, Elephant hauling timber. No. 543, 12xu, Forest protection. 20xu, Water buffalo hauling log. 30xu, Hauling logs by overhead cable.

1969, Apr. 10
539-545 A204 Set of 7   9.00 8.75
   Imperf., #539-545   15.00

Scenes of War — A205

Designs: No. 546, 12xu, Young guerrilla. No. 547, 12xu, Scout on patrol. 20xu, Female guerrilla, vert. 30xu, Halt at way station. 40xu, After a skirmish. 50xu, Liberated hamlet.

Perf. 12½x11½, 11½x12½
1969, July 20
546-551 A205 Set of 6   8.00 5.50
   Imperf., #546-551   15.00

Tet Offensive Battles — A206

Designs: 8xu, 12xu (No. 553), Ben Tre. No. 554, 12xu, Mortar crew, Khe Sanh, vert. No. 555, 12xu, Two soldiers, flag, Hue, vert. No. 556, 12xu, Soldier running toward US Embassy, Saigon, vert.

1969, July 31   Perf. 11
552-556 A206 Set of 5   3.50 2.25
   Imperf., #552-556

Liberation of Hanoi, 15th Anniv. A207

#557, Soldier with flamethrower. #558, Children constructing toy buildings.

1969, Oct. 10
557-558 A207 12xu Set of 2   3.50 1.75
   Imperf., #557-558

A208

A209

1969, Oct. 10
559 A208 12xu brn, blk & red   2.50 .80
   Imperf.

   Bertrand Russell Intl. War Crimes Tribunal, Stockholm and Roskilde.

1969, Nov. 20   Perf. 12

Fruits: No. 560, 12xu, Papaya. No. 561, 12xu, Grapefruit. 20xu, Tangerines. 30xu, Oranges. 40xu, Lychee nuts. 50xu, Persimmons.

560-565 A209 Set of 6   5.50 2.75
   Imperf., #560-565   8.50

Viet Nam Labor Party, 40th Anniv. — A210

Designs: No. 566, Nguyen Ai Quoc. No. 567, Ho Chi Minh. No. 568, Le Hong Phong. No. 569, Tran Phu. No. 570, Nguyen Van Cu.

1970, Feb. 3   Perf. 11
566-570 A210 12xu Set of 5   5.00 4.00
   Imperf., #566-570

   Nos. 568-570 are 40x25mm. Nos. 566-567 issued in vert. or horiz. se-tenant pairs. Nos. 568-570 issued in horizontal strips of 3.

Children's Activities — A211

Designs: No. 571, 12xu, Playing with toys. No. 572, 12xu, Three boys at kindergarten. No. 573, 20xu, Tending a garden. No. 574, 20xu, Tending water buffaloes. 30xu, Feeding chickens. 40xu, Piano, violin duet. 50xu, Flying model airplane. 60xu, Walking to school.

1970, Mar. 8   Perf. 12
571-578 A211 Set of 8   6.50 6.50

   For overprints see Nos. 2181-2188.

Lenin, Birth Centenary A212

Designs: 12xu, Making speech. 1d, Portrait.

1970, Apr. 22   Perf. 11
579-580 A212 Set of 2   4.00 3.75
   Imperf., #579-580

Shells A213

No. 581, 12xu, On con lon. No. 582, 12xu, Oc xa cu. 20xu, Oc tien. 1d, Oc tu va.

1970, Apr. 26   Perf. 12½x12
581-584 A213 Set of 4   6.50 6.00
   Imperf., #581-584   10.00

Ho Chi Minh — A214

12xu (#585, 588c, 588g), In 1930 (full face, no beard). 12xu (#586, 588b, 588f), In 1945 (facing right, beard). 2d, 6xu, (#587, 588a, 588e), In 1969 (full face, beard).

1970, May 19   Perf. 11
585-587 A214 Set of 3   4.75 4.50
   Imperf., #585-587
Souvenir Sheets of 3
Imperf

588   Types of #585-587, #a.-c.,   7.00
     orange background
588D   Types of #585-587, #e.-g.,   7.50
     pale lilac background

   Stamps in souvenir sheets have white backgrounds. The 6xu stamp is larger than the 2d stamp. Nos. 588a and 588e, 588c and 588g are different colors.

Vietcong Flag A215

1970, June 6
589 A215 12xu multicolored   1.50 .75

   Formation of Revolutionary Provisional Government of South Viet Nam, 1st anniv.

Fruits and Vegetables A216

#590, 12xu, Watermelon. #591, 12xu, Pumpkin. 20xu, Cucumber. 50xu, Zucchini. 1d, Melon.

1970, July 15   Perf. 12
590-594 A216 Set of 5   6.00 6.00
   Imperf., #590-594   13.00

Consumer Industries — A217

#595, Coal miners, truck. #596, Power linesman, vert. #597, Textile worker, soldier, vert. #598, Stoker, power plant, vert.

Perf. 12x11½, 11½x12
1970, Aug. 25   Litho. & Engr.
595-598 A217 12xu Set of 4   3.25 3.25

Agriculture
A218

1970, Aug. 25   Litho.   Perf. 11
599 A218 12xu multicolored   2.00   .75

Democratic Republic of Viet Nam, 25th
Anniv. — A219

Famous people: #600, 12xu, Vo Thi Sau facing firing squad. #601, 12xu, Nguyen Van Troi,
captors. #602, 12xu, Phan Din Giot attacking
pillbox. #603, 12xu, Ho Chi Minh. 20xu,
Nguyen Viet Xuan, troops in battle. 1d,
Nguyen Van Be attacking tank with mine.

1970, Sept. 2
600-605 A219 Set of 6   4.00 3.75
      Imperf., #600-605
            No. 603 is 41x28mm.

Indo-Chinese People's Summit
Conf. — A220

1970, Oct. 25
606 A220 12xu multicolored   2.50   .70
      Imperf.

Bananas
A221

Designs: No. 607, 12xu, Tay. No. 608, 12xu,
Tieu. 50xu, Ngu. 1d, Mat.

1970, Oct. 25   Perf. 12
607-610 A221 Set of 4   7.00 4.00
      Imperf., #607-610   10.00

Friedrich Engels — A222

1970, Nov. 28   Perf. 11
611-612 A222 12xu, 1d, set of 2   3.25 3.00

Snakes
A223

Designs: 12xu, Akistrodon ciatus. 20xu, Calliophis macclellandii. 50xu, Bungarus faciatus.
1d, Trimeresurus gramineus.

1970, Nov. 30 Photo. Perf. 12x11½
613-616 A223 Set of 4   6.00 5.00
      Imperf., #613-616   20.00

Natl. Liberation Front of South Viet
Nam, 10th Anniv. — A224

Design: 6xu, Mother and child, flag, vert.

1970, Dec. 20   Litho.   Perf. 11
617-618 A224 Set of 2   2.50 1.65
      Imperf., #617-618

Launching of 1st Chinese Satellite, 1st
Anniv. — A225

1971, Apr. 10
619-620 A225 12xu, 50xu Set of
                            2   5.00 2.00
      Imperf., #619-620

Ho Chi
Minh
A226

Denominations: 1xu, 3xu, 10xu, 12xu.

1971, May 19
621-624 A226 Set of 4   2.00 1.75
      Imperf., #621-624
624a   Souvenir sheet of 1, imperf.   6.00
   No. 624a contains one 52x52mm stamp.

Tay Son Uprising, Bicent. — A227

1971, June 1
625-626 A227 6xu, 12xu, set of 2 2.50 1.65
      Imperf., #625-626

Marx, Music for The
Internationale — A228

1971, June 20   Perf. 12½
627 A228 12xu org, blk & red   1.00   .75
      Imperf.
            Paris Commune, cent.

Hai
Thuong
Lan Ong,
Physician,
250th Birth
Anniv.
A229

1971, July 1
628-629 A229 12xu, 50xu Set of
                            2   3.50 2.00
      Imperf., #628-629

Statues from
Tay Phuong
Pagoda
A230

Designs: No. 630, 12xu, Vasumitri. No. 631,
12xu, Kapimala. No. 632, 12xu, Dhikaca. No.
633, 12xu, Sangkayasheta. 30xu, Bouddha
Nandi. 40xu, Rahulata. 50xu, Sangha Nandi.
1d, Cakyamuni.

1971, July 30 Photo.   Perf. 12
630-637 A230 Set of 8   11.00 11.00
      Imperf., #630-637   15.00

Ho Chi Minh
Working Youth
Union, 40th
Anniv.
A231

1971, Sept. 7   Litho.   Perf. 11
638 A231 12xu multicolored   1.50   .75
      Imperf.

Flight of Luna
16 — A232

Luna 16: No. 639a, 12xu, Return from
Moon. No. 639b, 12xu, Flight to Moon. 1d, On
Moon.

1971, Sept. 17
639-640 A232 Set of 3   4.00 3.50
      Imperf., #639-640   12.00
            No. 639 is setenant.

Flight
of
Luna
17
A233

Designs: No. 641, 12xu, Landing on Moon
vert. No. 642 12xu, On Moon. 1d, Lunakhod
crossing lunar crevasse.

1971, Oct. 15
641-643 A233 Set of 3   3.25 3.25
      Imperf., #641-643   16.00

Five Tigers
A234

Folk paintings: No. 644, 12xu, White tiger.
No. 645, 12xu, Red tiger. No. 646, 12xu, Yellow tiger. 40xu, Green tiger. 50xu, Black tiger.
1d, Five tigers.

1971, Nov. 25   Perf. 12
644-649 A234 Set of 6   10.00 6.00
      Imperf., #644-649   15.00
               Size: 90x119mm
                   Imperf
650 A234 1d multicolored   12.00

Chinese
Communist
Party, 50th
Anniv.
A235

1971, Dec. 1   Perf. 11
651 A235 12xu multicolored   1.50   .40

Mongolian
People's Republic,
50th
Anniv. — A236

1971, Dec. 25
652 A236 12xu multicolored   1.50   .40

Folk Engravings from Dong
Ho — A237

#653a, 12xu, Traditional wrestling. #653b,
12xu, Drum procession. #654a, 12xu, Gathering coconuts, vert. #654b, 12xu, Jealousy,
vert. 40xu, Wedding of mice. 50xu, Frog
school.

1972, Jan. 30
653-656 A237 Set of 6   10.00 9.00
      Imperf., #653-656   10.00
            No. 653 is tete-beche.
The 30xu in design of #654a is a proof.

3rd Natl. Trade Unions Congress A238

Designs: 1xu, Workers facing right. 12xu, Workers facing left.

1972, May 1
657-658 A238 Set of 2   2.00 1.25
    Imperf., #657-658

Natl. Resistance, 25th Anniv. — A239

Designs: No. 659, Munitions worker. No. 660, Soldier in battle. No. 661, Woman in paddy field. No. 662, Text of Ho Chi Minh's appeal.

1972, May 5
659-662 A239 12xu Set of 4   3.50 1.75
    Imperf., #659-662

Ho Chi Minh's Birthplace A240

Design: No. 664, Home in Hanoi.

1972, May 19
663-664 A240 12xu Set of 2   2.50 1.75
    Imperf., #663-664

A241

A242

1972, June 20
665-666 A241 12xu Set of 2   5.00 2.50
    Imperf., #665-666

3500th US warplane shot down. Added inscription on No. 666 reads "NGAY 20.4.1972."

1972, Aug. 15
Georgi Dimitrov (1882-1949), Bulgarian politician: No. 668, Dimitrov at Leipzig Court, 1933.

667-668 A242 12xu Set of 2   2.50 1.50
    Imperf., #667-668

Birds — A243

Designs: No. 669, 12xu, Lobivanellus indicus. No. 670, 12xu, Anas falcata. 30xu, Bubulcus ibis. 40xu, Gallicrex cinerea. 50xu, Prophyria porphyrio. 1d, Leptoptilos dubius.

1972, Oct. 12   *Perf. 12*
669-674 A243 Set of 6   10.00 8.00
    Imperf., #669-674   20.00

A244

A245

4000th US warplane shot down: No. 676, Gunner holding rocket.

1972, Oct. 19   *Perf. 11*
675-676 A244 12xu Set of 2   7.00 1.75
    Imperf., #675-676

1972, Dec. 1   *Perf. 12*
Tay Nguyen folk dances: #677, 12xu, Drum. #678, 12xu, Umbrella. #679, 12xu, Shield. 20xu, Horse. 30xu, Ca Dong. 40xu, Rice pounding. 50xu, Khaen. 1d, Cham rong.

677-684 A245 Set of 8   9.00 8.00
    Imperf., #677-684   10.00

Flight of Soyuz 11 A246

Designs: 12xu, Soyuz 11 docking with Salyut laboratory. 1d, Soyuz 11 cosmonauts.

1972, Dec. 30   *Perf. 11*
685-686 A246 Set of 2   3.00 2.75
    Imperf., #685-686   16.00

Wild Animals — A247

Designs: 12xu, Cuon alpinus. 30xu, Panthera pardus. 50xu, Felis bengalensis. 1d, Lutra lutra.

1973, Feb. 15   *Perf. 12½*
687-690 A247 Set of 4   7.00 5.00
    Imperf., #687-690   17.00

Copernicus A248

Copernicus and: No. 691a, 12xu, Armillary sphere. No. 691b, 12xu, Sun. 30xu, Signature, vert.

1973, Feb. 17   *Perf. 11*
691-692 A248 Set of 3   3.50 3.00
    Imperf., #691-692

Engravings on Ngoc Lu Bronze Drums — A249

Designs: No. 693, Drummers (Nha Danh Trong). No. 694, Pounding rice (Nha Gia Gao). No. 695, Dancers (Mua). No. 696, War canoe (Thuyen). No. 697, Birds (Chim, Thu).

1973, Apr. 12
693-697 A249 12xu Set of 5   4.00 4.00
    Imperf., #693-697

Wild Animals — A250

Designs: 12xu, Tragulus javanicus. 30xu, Capricornis sumatraensis. 50xu, Sus scrofa. 1d, Moschus moschiferus.

1973, May 25   *Perf. 12x12½*
698-701 A250 Set of 4   5.00 5.00
    Imperf., 698-701   9.00

Birds A251

#702, 12xu, Pycnonotus jocosus. #703, 12xu, Megalurus palustris. 20xu, Capsychus saularis. 40xu, Rhipidura albicollis. 50xu, Parus major. 1d, Zosterops japonica.

1973, July 15   *Perf. 12*
702-707 A251 Set of 6   7.00 4.00
    Imperf., 702-707   10.00

Disabled Soldiers
A252   A252a

Three Readiness Youth Movement A253

Designs: No. 710, Road building. No. 711, Open-air class. No. 712, On the march.

1973, Sept. 2
710-712 A253 12xu Set of 3   2.50 1.25
    Imperf., #710-712

Democratic People's Republic of Korea, 25th Anniv. — A254

1973, Sept. 9
713 A254 12xu multicolored   1.50 .40
    Imperf.

4181st US Warplane Shot Down A255

Designs: No. 714, 12xu, US B-52 hit by air attack. No. 715, 12xu, US B-52, fighter crashing over Haiphong Harbor. No. 716, 12xu, Anti-aircraft battery. 1d, Aircraft wreckage caught in fishing net.

1973, Oct. 10
714-717 A255 Set of 4   7.50 3.75
    Imperf., #714-717

Flowers — A256

6xu, 12xu (#719), Chrysanthemum (Cuc). #720, 12xu, Rose. #721, 12xu, Dahlia. #722, 12xu, Chrysanthemum (Bach mi). #723, 12xu, Chrysanthemum (Dai doa).

1974, Jan. 15
718-723 A256 Set of 6   40.00
    Imperf., #718-723   70.00

No. 718 may not have been officially released.

Elephants A257

#724, 12xu, Hauling logs. #725, 12xu, War elephant. 40xu, Setting logs in place. 50xu, Circus elephant. 1d, Carrying war supplies.

1974, Feb. 10   *Perf. 11½*
724-728 A257 Set of 5   7.50 7.00
    Imperf., #724-728   12.00

1973, July 27   *Perf. 11*
708-709 A252, A252a 12xu Set of 2   2.50
    Imperf., #708-709

Victory at Dien Bien Phu, 20th Anniv. — A258

Designs: a, Dien Bien Phu soldier's badge. b, Soldier waving victory flag.

1974, May 7   **Perf. 11**
729 A258 12xu Pair, #a.-b.   2.50 .70
    Imperf.

Three Responsibilities Women's Movement — A259

Designs: a, Armed worker, peasant. b, Female textile worker.

1974, June 1
730 A259 12xu Pair, #a.-b.   2.50 1.50
    Imperf.

A260

A261

Chrysanthemums: No. 731, 12xu, Brown. No. 732, 12xu, Yellow (Vang). 20xu, Ngoc Khong Tuoc. 30xu, White. 40xu, Kim. 50xu, Hong mi. 60xu, Gam. 1d, Lilac.

1974, June 20   **Perf. 12x12½**
731-738 A260   Set of 8   7.00 4.00
    Imperf., #731-738   11.00

1974, Aug. 15   **Perf. 11**
Industrial plants: No. 739, 12xu, Corchorus capsularis. No. 740, 12xu, Cyperus tojet jormis. 30xu, Morus alba.

739-741 A261   Set of 3   4.50 2.75
    Imperf., #739-741

Liberation of Hanoi, 20th Anniv. — A262

Designs: a, Woman laying bricks. b, Soldier holding child waving flag.

1974, Oct. 10
742 A262 12xu Pair, #a.-b.   2.50 .80

Solidarity with Chilean Revolution A263

Designs: No. 743, Pres. Salvador Allende, flag. No. 744, Pablo Neruda, poet.

1974, Oct. 15
743-744 A263 12xu Set of 2   2.50 .70
    Imperf., #743-744

Marine Life — A264

Designs: No. 745, 12xu, Rhizostoma. No. 746, 12xu, Loligo. 30xu, Haleotis. 40xu, Pteria martensii. 50xu, Sepia officinalis. 1d, Palinurus japonicus.

1974, Oct. 25   **Perf. 12½**
745-750 A264   Set of 6   7.00 2.50
    Imperf., #745-750   12.00

People's Republic of Albania, 30th Anniv. — A265

Designs: a, Natl. arms. b, Albanian, Vietnamese flags, women.

1974, Nov. 29   **Perf. 11**
752 A265 12xu Pair, #a.-b.   2.25 .75
    Imperf.

Paris Agreement on Vietnam, 2nd Anniv. — A266

Designs: No. 753, Intl. Conference on Viet Nam in session, 5-line inscription. No. 754, Signing of Paris Agreement, 4-line inscription.

1975, Jan. 27
753-754 A266 12xu Set of 2   2.50 .75
    Imperf.

Medicinal Plants — A267

Designs: No. 755, 12xu, Costus speciosus. No. 756, 12xu, Curcuma zedoaria. No. 757,

12xu, Rosa laevigata. 30xu, Erythrina indica. 40xu, Lilium brownii. 50xu, Hibiscus sagittifolius. 60xu, Papaver somniferum. 1d, Belamcanda chinensis.

1975, Feb. 2   **Perf. 11½x12**
755-762 A267   Set of 8   8.00 8.00
    Imperf., #755-762   12.50

Vietnamese Labor Party, 45th Anniv. — A268

Designs: No. 763, 12xu, Tran Phu. No. 764, 12xu, Le Hong Phong. No. 765, 12xu, Nguyen Van Cu. No. 766, 12xu, Ngo Gia Tu. 60xu, Ho Chi Minh in 1924, vert.

1975, Feb. 3   **Perf. 11**
763-767 A268   Set of 5   2.75 2.00
    Imperf., #763-767

A269

A270

Fruit: No. 768, 12xu, Achras sapota. No. 769, 12xu, Persica vulgaris. 20xu, Eugenia jambos. 30xu, Chrysophyllum cainito. 40xu, Lucuma mamosa. 50xu, Prunica granitum. 60xu, Durio ziberthinus. 1d, Prunus salicina.

1975, Apr. 25   **Perf. 12x12½**
768-775 A269   Set of 8   7.50 6.00
    Imperf., 768-775   12.00

1975, May 19   **Perf. 11**
776-777 A270 12xu, 60xu,   set of 2   3.50 1.25
    Imperf., #776-777   10.00

Ho Chi Minh, 85th birthday.

People's Republic of Poland, 30th Anniv. A271

1975, July 5
778-781 A271 1xu, 2xu, 3xu, 12xu, set of 4   3.00
    Imperf., #778-781

Flags A272

Natl. Arms — A273

Flag of North Viet Nam and: No. 782, Draped flag. No. 783, Flag with star & cresent. No. 784, DDR flag and handshake.

1975
782-785 A272-A273 12xu Set of 4   6.00
    Imperf., #782-784

People's Republic of China, 25th anniv. (#782), Republic of Algeria, 20th anniv. (#783), German Democratic Republic, 25th anniv. (#784), liberation of Hungary, 30th anniv. (#785).
    Issued: No. 782, 7/5. Nos. 783-785, 8/15.

Independence, 30th Anniv. — A274

#786, Flag. #787, Natl. arms. #788-789, Ho Chi Minh proclaiming independence.

1975, Sept. 2
786-788 A274 12xu Set of 3   3.50 1.25

Souvenir Sheet
Imperf
789   A274 20xu multicolored 15.00
    No. 789 contains one 45x30mm stamp.

Reptiles A275

#790, 12xu, Dermochelys coriacea. #791, 12xu, Physignathus cocincinus. 20xu, Hydrophis brookii. 30xu, Platysternum megacephalum. 40xu, Leiolepis belliana. 50xu, Python molurus. 60xu, Naja hannah. 1d, Draco maculatus.

1975, Nov. 25   **Perf. 12**
790-797 A275   Set of 8   8.00 7.00
    Imperf., #790-797   16.00

Butterflies — A276

#798, 12xu, Pathysa antiphates. #799, 12xu, Danaus plexippus. 20xu, Cynautocera papilionaria. 30xu, Maenas salaminia. 40xu, Papilio machaon. 50xu, Ixias pyrene. 60xu, Eusemia vetula. 1d, Eriboea.

1976, Jan. 6
798-805 A276   Set of 8   9.00 9.00
    Imperf., #798-805   10.00

    No. 799 misspelled "Danais."

Lan Hoang
Thao Orchid
A277

1976, Jan. 25   *Perf. 11*
806-807 A277 6xu, 12xu, set of 2 4.00 1.75
See Nos. 854-855.

Wild Animals
A278

#808, 12xu, Calloscciurus erythraeus. #809, 12xu, Paguma larvata. 20xu, Macaca mulatta. 30xu, Hystrix hodgsoni. 40xu, Nyctereutes procyonoides. 50xu, Selenarctos thibetanus. 60xu, Panthera pardus. 1d, Cynocephalus variegatus.

1976, Mar. 20   *Perf. 12*
808-815 A278 Set of 8   7.00 2.50
    Imperf., #808-815   10.00

1st
Elections
to Unified
Natl.
Assembly
A279

6xu (#816), Map, hand placing ballot in ballot box. 6xu (#817), 12xu, Map, voters.

1976, Apr. 10   *Perf. 11*
816-818 A279 Set of 3   3.50 1.25
    Imperf., #816-818
Size of Nos. 817-818 is 35x22mm.
Identical stamps inscribed "Mien Nam Viet Nam" are National Front issues. Same values.

Unified
Natl.
Assembly,
1st
Session
A280

Design: 12xu, Inscribed "Doc Lap Thong Nhat Chu Nghia Xa Hoi."

1976, June 24
819-820 A280 6xu, 12xu, set of 2 2.50 .80
Identical stamps inscribed "Mien Nam Viet Nam" are National Front issues. Same values.

A281

A282

1976, June 24   *Perf. 12x12½*
821 A281 12xu multicolored   1.50 .40
Reunification of Viet Nam.

1976, June 24   *Perf. 12*
Orchids: No. 822, 12xu, Habenaria rhodocheila. No. 823, 12xu, Dendrobium devonianum. 20xu, Dendrobium tortile. 30xu, Doritis pulcherrima. 40xu, Dendrobium farmeri. 50xu, Dendrobium aggregatum. 60xu, Eria pannea. 1d, Paphiopedilum concolor.

822-829 A282 Set of 8   8.00 2.00
    Imperf., #822-829   10.00

Socialist Republic of Viet Nam
AREA—128,000 sq. mi.
POP.—77,311,210 (1999 est.0
CAPITAL—Hanoi

Vietnamese Red Cross, 30th
Anniv. — A283

1976, July 27   *Perf. 11*
830 A283 12xu multicolored   2.50 .80
    Imperf.

Fish — A284

#831, 12xu, Lutjanus sebae. #832, 12xu, Dampieria melanotaenia. 20xu, Therapon theraps. 30xu, Amphirion bifasciatus. 40xu, Abudefduf sexfasciatus. 50xu, Heniochus acuminatus. 60xu, Amphirion macrostoma. 1d, Symphorus spilurus.

1976, Aug. 15   *Perf. 12*
831-838 A284 Set of 8   5.00 4.00
    Imperf., #831-838   7.00

Viet Nam
Worker's
Party, 4th
Natl.
Congress
A285

1976, Nov. 12   *Perf. 11*
839-844 A285 2, 3, 5, 10, 12,
    20xu, set of 6   3.50 2.50

Viet Nam Communist Party, 4th Natl.
Congress — A286

Designs: a, Agriculture, industry. b, Ho Chi Minh, worker, farmer, soldier, scientist.

Design size 24.5mmx35mm

1976, Dec. 10
845 A286 12xu Pair, #a.-b.   2.50 .80
    Imperf.
See Nos. 951-954.

Unification of Viet
Nam — A287

1976, Dec. 14
846-847 A287 6xu, 12xu, set of 2 2.50 .80
    Imperf., #846-847

General Offensive, 1975 — A288

Designs: 2xu, 50xu, Liberation of Buon Me Thuot. 3xu, 1d, Tanks liberating Da Nang. 6xu, 2d, Tank, soldiers liberating Presidential palace, Saigon.

1976, Dec. 14
848-853 A288 Set of 6   4.50 4.50

Lan Hoang Thao Orchid Type of 1976
Inscribed "VIET NAM" and "1976"

1976, Dec.   *Litho.*   *Perf. 11*
854-855 A277 6xu, 12xu Set of
    2   40.00 14.00

Dragonflies — A289

#856, 12xu, Ho. #857, 12xu, Bao. 20xu, Canh dom. 30xu, Nuong. 40xu, Suoi. 50xu, Canh vang. 60xu, Canh khoang. 1d, Canh den.

1977, Jan. 25   *Perf. 12*
856-863 A289 Set of 8   7.00 1.50
    Imperf., #856-863   16.00

A290

A291

Rare Birds: 12xu (#864), 60xu, Buceros bicornis. 12xu (#865), Ptilolaemus tickelli. 20xu, Berenicornis comatus. 30xu, Aceros undulatus. 40xu, Anthracoceros malabaricus. 50xu, Anthracoceros malayanus. 1d, Aceros nipalensis.

1977, Apr. 15
864-871 A290 Set of 8   6.00 2.75
    Imperf., #864-871   9.00

1977, Apr. 25   *Perf. 11*
Bronze drum and: 4xu, Thang Long Tower. 5xu, Map. 12xu, Lotus blossom. 50xu, Flag.
872-875 A291 Set of 4   4.50 2.00
    Imperf., #872-875
Natl. Assembly general elections, 1st anniv.

Beetles
A292

#876, 12xu, Black-spotted (Dom den). #877, 12xu, Yellow-spotted (Lang vang). 20xu, Veined (Van gach). 30xu, Green (Nhung xanh). 40xu, Green-spotted (Hoa xanh). 50xu, Black (Van den). 60xu, Leopard skin (Da bao). 1d, Nine-spotted (Chin cham).

1977, June 15   *Perf. 12½x12*
876-883 A292 Set of 8   7.00 1.75
    Imperf., #876-883   11.00

Wildflowers
A293

Designs: No. 884, 12xu, Thevetia peruviana. No. 885, 12xu, Broussonetia papvrifera. 20xu, Aleurites montana. 30xu, Cerbera manghes. 40xu, Cassia multijuga. 50xu, Cassia nodosa. 60xu, Hibiscus schizopetalus. 1d, Lagerstroesnia speciosa.

1977, Aug. 19   *Perf. 12x12½*
884-891 A293 Set of 8   5.00 1.75
    Imperf., #884-891   10.00

A294   A295

Dahlias: 6xu (#892), 12xu (#894), Pink. 6xu (#893), 12xu (#895), Orange.

1977, Sept. 10   *Perf. 11*
892-895 A294 Set of 4   3.75 1.75
See Nos. 921-924.

1977, Sept. 10

Children drawing map of unified Viet Nam. Denominations: 4xu, 5xu, 10xu, 12xu, 30xu each have different colored border.

896-900 A295 Set of 5   3.75 3.75

Goldfish
A296

Designs: No. 901, 12xu, Dong nai. No. 902, 12xu, Velvet (Hoa nhung). 20xu, Blue Chinese (Tau xanh). 30xu, Dragon-eyed (Mat bong). 40xu, Cam trang. 50xu, Five-colored (Ngu sac). 60xu, Dong nai. 1d, Thap cam.

1977, Oct. 20   *Perf. 12*
901-908 A296 Set of 8   7.50 2.00
Imperf., #901-908   10.00

A297

A298

Russian October Revolution, 60th anniv.: 12xu (No. 909, olive background), 12xu (No. 910, blue background), Ho Chi Minh, Lenin banner. 50xu, Mother holding child with flag. 1d, Workers, farmers, Moscow Kremlin, cruiser Aurora.

1977, Nov. 7
909-912 A297 Set of 4   3.00 2.50

1978, Jan. 25

Songbirds: 12xu, Gracula religiosa. No. 914, 20xu, Garrulax canorus. No. 915, 20xu, Streptopelia chinensis. 30xu, Linius schach. 40xu, Garrulax formosus. 50xu, Garrulax chinensis. 60xu, Acridotheres cristatellus. 1d, Garrulax yersini.

913-920 A298 Set of 8   6.00 1.75
Imperf., #913-920   12.00

Cultivated Flower Type of 1977

5xu, 10xu, Sunflower. 6xu, 12xu, Pansy.

1978, Mar. 20   *Perf. 11*
921-924 A294 Set of 4   3.50 2.00

Intl. Children's Day (June 1977) — A299

1978, Mar. 20
925 A299 12xu multicolored   1.75 .40

Sports
A300

#926, 12xu, Discus. #927, 12xu, Long jump. 20xu, Hurdles. 30xu, Hammer throw. 40xu, Shot put. 50xu, Javelin. 60xu, Running. 1d, High jump.

1978, Apr. 10   *Perf. 11½*
926-933 A300 Set of 8   4.50 2.00
Imperf., #926-933   10.00

A301

A302

4th Viet Nam Trade Union Cong.: #934, Trade Union emblem. #935, Ho Chi Minh, workers.

1978, May 1   *Perf. 11*
934-935 A301 10xu Set of 2   2.50 .80

1978, May 15

10xu, Ho Chi Minh conducting orchestra. 12xu, Ho Chi Minh's mausoleum, horiz.

936-937 A302 Set of 2   2.00 .80
No. 937 is 39x23mm.

Young Pioneers' Cultural Palace, Hanoi — A303

1978, May 29
938 A303 10xu multicolored   1.50 .40
Intl. Children's Day.

Sculptures from Tay Phuong Pagoda — A304

Designs: No. 939, 12xu, Sanakavasa. No. 940, 12xu, Parsva. No. 941, 12xu, Punyasas. No. 942, 20xu, Kumarata. No. 943, 20xu, Nagarjuna. 30xu, Yayata. 40xu, Cadiep. 50xu, Ananda. 60xu, Buddhamitra. 1d, Asvagmosa.

1978, July 1   *Perf. 12*
939-948 A304 Set of 10   7.00 3.00
Imperf., #939-948   20.00

Cuban Revolution, 25th Anniv. — A305

1978, July 20   *Perf. 11*
949-950 A305 6xu, 12xu Set of 2   2.50 .80

Types of 1976

6xu (No. 951), 12xu (No. 953), like #845a. 6xu (No. 952), 12xu (No. 952), like #845b.

Design size 18.5mmx23mm

1978, Aug. 15
951-954 A286 Set of 4   4.00 2.00

Space Exploration, 20th Anniv. — A306

#955, 12xu, Sputnik. #956, 12xu, Venus 1. 30xu, Spacecraft docking. 40xu, Molniya 1. 60xu, Soyuz. 2d, Cosmonauts Gubarev, Grechko.

1978, Aug. 28   *Perf. 12½x12*
955-960 A306 Set of 6   5.00 1.75
Imperf., #955-960   10.00

World Telecommunications Day — A307

Designs: a, Printed circuit. b, ITU emblem.

1978, Sept. 25   *Perf. 11*
962 A307 12xu Pair, #a.-b.   2.50 .80
Imperf.   15.00

20th Congress of Socialist Postal Ministers — A308

1978, Sept. 25
963 A308 12xu multicolored   1.50 .40

Chrysanthemums — A309

No. 964, 12xu, Tim. No. 965, 12xu, Kim tien 20xu, Hong. 30xu, Van tho. 40xu, Vang. 50xu, Thuy tim. 60xu, Vang mo. 1d, Nau do.

1978, Oct. 1   *Perf. 12*
964-971 A309 Set of 8   5.50 2.00
Imperf., #964-971   12.00

Dinosaurs
A310

Designs: No. 972, 12xu, Plesiosaurus. No. 973, 12xu, Brontosaurus. 20xu, Iguanodon. 30xu, Tyrannosaurus rex. 40xu, Stegosaurus. 50xu, Mosasaurus. 60xu, Triceratops. 1d, Pteranodon.

1979, Jan. 1   Litho.   *Perf. 11½*
972-979 A310 Set of 8   9.00 2.00
Imperf., #972-979   17.00

No. 977 misspelled "Mozasaurus."

A311

A312

1979, Jan. 1   *Perf. 11*
980 A311 12xu multicolored   1.50 .40
Imperf.

Socialist Republic of Cuba, 20th anniv.

1979, Feb. 1

Quang Trung's victory over the Chinese, 190th Anniv.: #981, Battle plan. #982, Quang Trung.

981-982 A312 12xu Set of 2   2.50 .80
   a.   Perf 12, #981-982

Albert Einstein, Physicist
A313

Designs: No. 983, 12xu, Einstein. No. 984, 60xu, Equation, sun, planets.

1979, Mar. 14
983-984 A313 12xu, 60xu, set of 2   3.00 1.50

Domestic Animals — A314

10xu, Ram. 12xu, Ox. 20xu, Ewe, lamb. 30xu, White water buffalo, vert. 40xu, Cow. 50xu, Goat. 60xu, Water buffalo, calf. 1d, Young goat, vert.

1979, Mar. 20 *Perf. 12*
985-992 A314 Set of 8   5.00 1.50
  Imperf., #985-992   7.00

Five Year Plan (1976-80) — A315

#993, 998, Map, emblem. #994, 999, Factory worker. #995, 1000, Peasant woman, tractor. #996, 1001, Soldier. #997, 1002, Man, atom, compass.

1979 *Perf. 11*
993-997   A315 6xu Set of 5
998-1002 A315 12xu Set of 5
1000a   *Perf. 12*
  Nos. 993-1002 (10)   10.00
  Issued: Nos. 993-997, 5/1. Nos. 998-1002, 6/1. Nos. 993, 996-1002 on toned paper.

Philaserdica '79, Intl. Stamp Exhibition, Sofia, Bulgaria A316

1979, May 27 *Perf. 12*
1003-1004 12xu, 30xu, set of 2 2.50 .80

Intl. Year of the Child — A317

2xu, Ho Chi Minh, children. 20xu, Nurse, mother, child. 50xu, Children with glider, painting supplies. 1d, Girls of different races.

1979, June 1 *Perf. 11*
1005-1008 A317 Set of 4   4.00 3.00

Ornamental Birds — A318

#1009, 12xu, Lophura diardi. #1010, 12xu, Tragopan temminckii. 20xu, Phasianus colchicus. 30xu, Lophura edwardsi. 40xu, Lophura nycthemera, vert. 50xu, Polyplectron germaini, vert. 60xu, Rheinartia ocellata, vert. 1d, Pavo muticus, vert.

1979, June 16 *Perf. 12*
1009-1016 A318 Set of 8   5.00 1.75
  Imperf., #1009-1016   10.00

Orchids A319

Designs: No. 1017, 12xu, Dendrobium heterocacpum. No. 1018, 12xu, Cymbidium hybridum. 20xu, Rhynchostylis gigantea. 30xu, Dendrobium mobile. 40xu, Aerides falcatum. 50xu, Paphiopedilum callosum. 60xu, Vanda teres. 1d, Dendrobium phalaenopsis.

1979, Aug. 10 *Perf. 12*
1017-1024 A319 Set of 8   6.50 1.75
  Imperf., #1017-1024   10.00

Cats A320

Designs: No. 1025, 12xu, Meo tam the. No. 1026, 12xu, Meo muop, vert. 20xu, Meo khoang, vert. 30xu, Meo dom van. 40xu, Meo muop dom, vert. 50xu, Meo vang, vert. 60xu, Meo xiem. 1d, Meo van am.

1979, Nov. 10
1025-1032 A320 Set of 8   5.00 3.00
  Imperf., #1025-1032   10.00

Vietnamese People's Army, 25th Anniv. — A321

a, People greeting soldiers. b, Frontier guards.

1979, Dec. 22 *Perf. 11*
1033 A321 12xu Pair, #a.-b.   .80 .80

Roses — A322

Designs: 1xu, 12xu (No. 1036), Red, pink roses. 2xu, 12xu (No. 1037), Single pink rose.

1980, Jan. 1
1034-1037 A322 Set of 4   5.00 2.00
  See Nos. 1084-1085.

Aquatic Flowers A323

#1038, 12xu, Nelumbium nuciferum. #1039, 12xu, Nymphala stellata. 20xu, Ipomola reptans. 30xu, Nymphoides indicum. 40xu, Jussiala repens. 50xu, Eichhornia crassipes. 60xu, Monochoria voginalis. 1d, Nelumbo nucifera.

1980, Jan. 15 *Perf. 12½*
1038-1045 A323 Set of 8   5.00 2.00
  Imperf., #1038-1045   9.00

Vietnamese Communist Party, 50th Anniv. — A324

Designs: No. 1046a, Ho Chi Minh proclaiming independence, 1945. No. 1046b, Peasants with banner, improvised weapons. No. 1047a, Map, soldiers, tanks storming palace. No. 1047b, Soldiers waving flag at Dien Bien Phu. 2d, Ho Chi Minh, soldiers and workers.

1980, Feb. 3 *Perf. 11*
1046 A324 12xu Pair, #a.-b.
1047 A324 20xu Pair, #a.-b.
1048 A324 2d multicolored
  Nos. 1046-1048 (5)   3.50 3.50

Lenin, 110th Anniv. of Birth A325

1980, Apr. 22 *Perf. 12*
1049-1051 A325 6xu, 12xu, 1d, set of 3   3.25 2.00

1980 Summer Olympics, Moscow — A326

#1052, 12xu, Hurdles. #1053, 12xu, Running. 20xu, Team handball. 30xu, Soccer. 40xu, Wrestling. 50xu, Gymnastics, horiz. 60xu, Swimming, horiz. 1d, Sailing, horiz.

1980, May 1 *Perf. 12x12½, 12½x12*
1052-1059 A326 Set of 8   5.00 1.50
  Imperf., #1052-1059   10.00

A327

A328

Ho Chi Minh, 90th anniv. of birth: 12xu, In 1924. 40xu, As president.

1980, May 19 *Perf. 11*
1060-1061 A327 Set of 2   2.00 1.25

1980, June 15
1062 A328 5xu multicolored   1.00 .40
  Intl. Children's Day.

Intercosmos '80, Soviet-Vietnamese Space Mission — A329

Designs: No. 1063, 12xu, Cosmonauts. No. 1064, 12xu, Soyuz 37 atop booster. 20xu, Soyuz 37. 40xu, Soyuz docking with Salyut space station. 1d, Soyuz firing retro-rockets. 2d, Parachute landing. 3d, Cosmonauts, Soyuz-Salyut station.

1980, July 24 *Perf. 12x12½*
1063-1068 A329 Set of 6   7.00 1.25
  Imperf., #1063-1068   7.50
Souvenir Sheet
1069 A329 3d multicolored   6.00
  Imperf.

Saltwater Fish — A330

Designs: No. 1070, 12xu, Rhincodon typus. No. 1071, 12xu, Galeocerdo cuvier. 20xu, Orectolobus japonicus. 30xu, Heterodontus zebra. 40xu, Dasyatis uarnak. 50xu, Pristis microdon. 60xu, Sphyrna lewini. 1d, Myliobatis tobijei.

1980, Aug. 1 *Perf. 12*
1070-1077 A330 Set of 8   5.00 1.75
  Imperf., #1070-1077   10.00

A331   A332

Post and Telecommunications Office, 35th Anniv.: 12xu, Ho Chi Minh reading newspaper. 20xu, Ho Chi Minh talking on telephone. 50xu, Kim Dong carrying bird in cage. 1d, Dish antenna.

1980, Aug. 15 *Litho.* *Perf. 12½*
1078-1081 A331 Set of 4   3.50 3.00

1980, Aug. 25 *Perf. 11, 12 (#1083)*
  Natl. Telecommunications Day: No. 1082, Telephone switchboard operator. No. 1083, Train, map.
1082-1083 A332 12xu Set of 2   2.00 1.60

Rose Type of 1980

No. 1084, Pink. No. 1085, Red and pink.

1980, Aug. 25   *Perf. 11*
Size: 20x24mm
1084-1085   A322   12xu   Set of 2   2.00   1.40
For surcharge see No. 1385.

Republic of
Vietnam, 35th
Anniv. — A333

Designs: No. 1086, 12xu, Ho Chi Minh. No. 1087, 12xu, Natl. arms. 40xu, Pac Bo Cave. 1d, Source of Lenin River, horiz.

1980, Sept. 2   *Perf. 12½*
1086-1089   A333   Set of 4   4.00   4.00

A334

1980, Sept. 20   *Perf. 12*
1090-1092   A334   Set of 3   3.75

Natl. emblems: 6xu, Arms. No. 1091, 12xu, Flag, horiz. No. 1092, 12xu, Anthem.

A335

1980, Oct. 6   *Perf. 11*
Nguyen Trai, 600th birth anniv.: 12xu, Nguyen Trai. 50xu, Books, horiz. 1d, Ho Chi Minh reading commemorative stele, Con Son.
1093-1095   A335   Set of 3   5.00   5.00
For surcharge see No. 1386.

A336

Natl. Women's Union, 50th Anniv.: #1096, Ho Chi Minh, women. #1097, Group of 4 women.

1980, Oct. 20
1096-1097   A336   12xu Set of 2   1.50   .80

A337

1980, Nov. 20   *Perf. 12½*
Flowers: No. 1098, 12xu, Ipomoea pulchella. No. 1099, 12xu, Biguoniaceae venusta. 20xu, Petunia hybrida. 30xu, Trapaeolum majus. 40xu, Thunbergia grandiflora. 50xu, Anlamanda cathartica. 60xu, Campsis radicans. 1d, Bougainivillaea spectabilis.
1098-1105   A337   Set of 8   5.50   1.40
     Imperf., #1098-1105   10.00

Ornamental Fish — A338

Designs: No. 1106, 12xu, Betta splendens. No. 1107, 12xu, Symphysodon aequifasciata. 20xu, Poecilobrycon eques. 30xu, Gyrinocheilus aymonieri. 40xu, Barbus tetrazona. 50xu, Pterophyllum eimekei. 60xu, Xiphophorus helleri. 1d, Trichopterus sumatranus.

1981, Jan. 15   *Perf. 12*
1106-1113   A338   Set of 8   5.50   5.50
     Imperf., #1106-1113   10.00

26th Soviet
Communist
Party Congress
A339

20xu, Rocket, book. 50xu, Young people, flag.

1981, Feb. 23   *Perf. 11*
1114-1115   A339   Set of 2   2.50   2.00

Animals from Cuc Phuona Natl.
Forest — A340

#1116, 12xu, Hylobates concolor. #1117, 12xu, Macaca speciosa. 20xu, Selenarctos thibetanus. 30xu, Cuon alpinus. 40xu, Sus scrofa. 50xu, Cervus unicolor. 60xu, Panthera pardus. 1d, Panthera tigris.

1981, Apr. 10   *Perf. 12½x12*
1116-1123   A340   Set of 8   8.00   1.75
     Imperf., #1116-1123   10.00

Doves
A341

#1124, 12xu, Treron sieboldi. #1125, 12xu, Ducula aenea, vert. 20xu, Streptopelia tranquebarica, vert. 30xu, Macropygia unchall, vert. 40xu, Ducula badia, vert. 50xu, Treron apicauda, 60xu, Chalcophaps indica. 1d, Seimun treron seimundi.

1981, June 5   *Perf. 12*
1124-1131   A341   Set of 8   5.00   4.00
     Imperf., #1124-1131   9.00

Nectar-sucking Birds — A342

Designs: No. 1132, 20xu, Aethypga siparaja. No. 1133, 20xu, Anthreptes singalensis. 30xu, Aethopyga saturata. 40xu, Aethopyga gouldiae. No. 1136, 50xu, Nectarinia chalcostetha. No. 1137, 50xu, Nectarinia hypogrammica. 60xu, Nectarinia sperata. 1d, Aethopyga nipalensis.

1981, Aug. 5   *Perf. 12½x12*
1132-1139   A342   Set of 8   5.00   1.75
     Imperf., #1132-1139   10.00

A343   A343a

1981, Aug. 5   *Perf. 11*
1140   A343   12xu Lotus flower   1.00

1981, Aug. 5
Design: Factory militiawoman.
1140A   A343a   12xu yel & multi   20.00
     See Nos. M30-M31.

A344   A345

Fruit: No. 1141, 20xu, Elaeagnus latifolia. No. 1142, 20xu, Fortunella japonica. 30xu, Nephelium lappaceum. 40xu, Averrhoa bilimbi. No. 1145, 50xu, Ziziphus mauritiana. No. 1146, 50xu, Fragaria vesca. 60xu, Bouea oppositifolia. 1d, Syzygium aqueum.

1981, Oct. 12   *Perf. 12*
1141-1148   A344   Set of 8   5.75   1.75
     Imperf., #1141-1148   10.00

1981, Nov. 15   *Perf. 11*
Planting trees: No. 1149, Ho Chi Minh. No. 1150, Three people.
1149-1150   A345   30xu Set of 2   1.75   1.00
     Tree planting festival.

Bulgaria,
1300th
Anniv.
A346

1981, Dec. 9   *Perf. 11*
1151-1153   A346   30xu, 50xu, 2d, set of 3   5.50   5.50

Wild Animals — A347

Designs: No. 1154, 30xu, Orangutan. No. 1155, 30xu, Bison bonasus. No. 1156, 40xu, Kangaroo. No. 1157, 40xu, Hippopotamus. No. 1158, 50xu, Rhinoceros sondaicus. No. 1159, 50xu, Giraffe. 60xu, Zebra. 1d, Lion.

1981, Dec. 9   *Perf. 12½x12*
1154-1161   A347   Set of 8   5.00   2.00
     Imperf., #1154-1161   9.00

A348

A349

World Food Day: 30xu, 50xu, Woman holding sheaf of rice. 2d, FAO emblem, horiz.

1982, Jan. 26   *Perf. 11*
1162-1164   A348   Set of 3   3.50

1982, Feb. 19
1165-1166   A349   50xu, 5d, set of 2   4.75   4.75
10th World Trade Unions Congress, Havana, Cuba.

5th Vietnamese Communist Party
Congress — A350

Designs: No. 1167, 30xu, Ho Chi Minh. No. 1168, 30xu, Hammer, sickle. No. 1169, 30xu, Worker, dam. 50xu, Women harvesting rice. 1d, Ho Chi Minh.

1982, Feb. 15
1167-1170   A350   Set of 4   4.00   2.00
     Imperf
     Size: 99x61 mm
1171   A350   1d multicolored   50.00

Bees &
Wasps
A351

Designs: No. 1172, 20xu, Ong bove. No. 1173, 20xu, Ong van xanh. 30xu, To vo nau. 40xu, Ong vang. No. 1176, 50xu, Ong dau nau. No. 1177, 50xu, To vo xanh. 60xu, Ong bau. 1d, Ong mat.

1982, Feb. 25   *Perf. 12*
1172-1179   A351   Set of 8   5.00   2.00
     Imperf., #1172-1179   10.00

Soccer
A352

#1180, 30xu, 3 players. #1181, 30xu, 2 players. #1182, 40xu, Striped background. #1183, 40xu, grass background. #1184, 50xu, Vertically striped background. #1185, 50xu, Horizonally striped background. 60xu, 1d, Various soccer scenes.

1982, Apr. 15
1180-1187 A352 Set of 8   5.00   2.00
    Imperf., #1180-1187   10.00

For overprints see Nos. 2142-2149.

A353   A354

Vietnamese Red Cross, 35th Anniv.: 1d, Red Cross emblem.

1982, May 15   *Perf. 11*
1188-1189 A353 Set of 2   2.50

1982, May 19   *Perf. 12*
  5th Natl. Women's Congress: No. 1191, Congress emblem, three women.

1190-1191 A354 12xu Set of 2   2.00

A355

A356

Birds of Prey: No. 1192, 30xu, Microhierax melanoleucos. No. 1193, 30xu, Falco tinnunculus. 40xu, Aviceda leuphotes. No. 1195, 50xu, Icthyophaga nana. No. 1196, 50xu, Milvus korschun. 60xu, Neohierax harmandi, horiz. No. 1198, 1d, Elanus caeruleus, horiz. No. 1199, 1d, Circaetus gallicus.

1982, June 1
1192-1199 A355 Set of 8   8.00   2.25
    Imperf., #1192-1199   12.00

1982, June 1   *Perf. 11*
1200-1201 A356 30xu, 3d, set of 2   5.00

  Georgi Dimitrov (1882-1949), Bulgarian Communist leader.

Dahlias
A357

  Designs (last word or two of Vietnamese inscription): No. 1202, 30xu, Da cam. No. 1203, 30xu, Do. 40xu, Canh se. No. 1205, 50xu, Do nhung. No. 1206, 50xu, Vang. 60xu, Do tuoi. No. 1208, 1d, Bien. No. 1209, 1d, Trang. Various flowers.

1982, July 15   *Perf. 12x12½*
1202-1209 A357 Set of 8   7.00   2.25
    Imperf., #1202-1209   12.00

1982 World Cup Soccer Championships, Spain — A358

  #1210, 50xu, Ball at bottom right. #1211, 50xu, Ball at right in air. #1212, 50xu, Ball at bottom center. #1213, 1d, 1 player. #1214, 1d, 3 players. 2d, 2 players.

1982, July 15   *Perf. 12x12½*
1210-1215 A358 Set of 6   8.00   8.00
    Imperf., #1210-1215   10.00

A359

1982, July 25   *Perf. 11*
1216 A359 30xu Natl. defense   1.50   .80
    See No. M32.

A360

1982, Aug. 15
1217 A360 30xu multicolored   1.50
  Cuban victory at Giron (Bay of Pigs), 20th anniv.

World Environment Day — A361

  #1219, Ho Chi Minh, children planting tree.

1982, Aug. 15
1218-1219 A361 30xu Set of 2   2.00

A362

A363

1982, Sept. 20
1220 A362 30xu multicolored   1.50   .80
  Rabindranath Tagore (1861-1941), poet.

1982, Sept. 25   *Perf. 12x12½*
  Insects: No. 1221, 30xu, Catacanthus incarnatus. No. 1222, 30xu, Sycanus falleni. 40xu, Nezara viridula. No. 1224, 50xu, Lohita grandis. No. 1225, 50xu, Helcomeria spinosa. 60xu, Chrysocoris stollii. No. 1227, 1d, Pterygamia srayi. No. 1228, 1d, Tiarodes ostentans.

1221-1228 A363 Set of 8   6.75   2.25
    Imperf., #1221-1228   11.50

Russian Revolution, 65th Anniv. — A364

  Design: No. 1230, Lenin, workers.

1982, Nov. 7   *Perf. 11*
1229-1230 A364 30xu Set of 2   1.75

9th South East Asian Games, New Delhi, India
A365

  #1231, 30xu, Table tennis. #1232, 30xu, Swimming. 1d, Wrestling. 2d, Shooting.

1982, Nov. 19
1231-1234 A365 Set of 4   5.50

Fish
A366

  Designs: No. 1235, 30xu, Samaris cristatus. No. 1236, 30xu, Tephrinectes sinensis. No. 1237, 40xu, Psettodes erumei. No. 1238, 40xu, Zebrias zebra. No. 1239, 50xu, Cynoglossus puncticeps. No. 1240, 50xu, Pardachirus pavoninus. 60xu, Brachirus orientalis. 1d, Psettina iijimae.

1982, Dec. 15   *Perf. 12*
1235-1242 A366 Set of 8   6.00   1.75
    Imperf., #1235-1242   10.00

Socialist Ideals — A367

  #1243, 30xu, Agriculture. #1244, 30xu, Industry. 1d, Natl. defense. 2d, Health & education.

1982, Dec. 25   *Perf. 11*
1243-1246 A367 Set of 4   5.50

Founding of Soviet Union, 60th Anniv.
A368

1982, Dec. 30
1247 A368 30xu multicolored   2.50   .80

Sampans
A369

  Designs: 30xu, Docked. 50xu, With striped sails. 1d, Sampans on Red River. 3d, With white sails. 5d, With patched sail. 10d, Fast sampan, horiz.

1983, Jan. 10   *Perf. 12½*
1248-1253 A369 Set of 6   7.50
    Imperf., #1248-1253   12.50

Locomotives — A370

  30xu, Class 231-300. 50xu, Class 230-000. 1d, Class 140-601. 2d, Class 241-000. 3d, Class 141-500. 5d, Class 150-000. 8d, Class 40-300.

1983, Feb. 20   *Perf. 13*
1254-1260 A370 Set of 7   7.50
    Imperf., #1254-1260   12.50

1st Manned Balloon Flight, Bicent.
A371

  Balloons: 30xu, Montgolfier. 50xu, Yellow. 1d, CA-11. 2d, Hot-air. 3d, Over harbor. 5d, Le Geant. 8d, Ascending. 10d, Montgolfier, diff.

1983, Mar. 25   Litho.   Perf. 12½
1261-1267 A371   Set of 7   8.00
          Imperf., #1261-1267   15.00
Souvenir Sheet
Perf. 13
1268 A371 10d Sheet of 1   4.00
No. 1268 contains one 32x40mm stamp.

Discovery of Tubercle Bacillus,
Cent. — A372

1983, Mar. 25   Perf. 11
1269 A372 5d multicolored   3.00

Laos-Cambodia-Viet Nam
Summit — A373

1983, Mar. 25
1270-1271 A373 50xu, 5d Set of
                              2   2.75

Cosmonauts — A374

Designs: 30xu, Gubarev, Remek. No. 1273,
50xu, Klimuk, Hermaszewski. No. 1274, 50xu,
Bykovsky, Jahn. No. 1275, 1d, Rukavishnikov,
Ivanov. No. 1276, 1d, Farcas, Kubasov. No.
1277, 2d, Mendez, Romanenko. No. 1278, 2d,
Gorbatko, Tuan. 5d, Dzhanibekov, Gurragcha.
8d, Popov, Prunariu. No. 1281, Gagarin.

1983, Apr. 1   Perf. 12½x12
1272-1280 A374   Set of 9   9.00
          Imperf., #1272-1280   14.00
Souvenir Sheet
1281 A374 10d multicolored   4.00
No. 1281 contains one 36x28mm stamp.

Reptiles
A375

Designs: No. 1282, 30xu, Teratolepis fasciata. No. 1283, 30xu, Chamaeleo jacksoni.
No. 1284, 50xu, Uromastyx acanthinurus. No.
1285, 80xu, Heloderma suspectum. 1d,
Cameleo menle. 2d, Amphibolurus barbatus.
5d, Chlamydosaurus kingi. 10d, Phrynosoma
coronatum.

1983, Apr. 5   Perf.
1282-1289 A375   Set of 8   7.50
          Imperf., #1282-1289   13.00

Raphael (1483-
1520),
Painter — A375a

Designs: 30xu, Virgin Mother Seated on
Chair. 50xu, Granduca, the Virgin Mother. 1d,
Sistine Madonna. 2d, Marriage of Maria. 3d,
The Gardener. 5d, Woman with Veil. 8d, 10d,
Self-Portrait.

1983, Apr. 30   Perf. 12½
1289A-1289G A375a Set of 7   6.00
Souvenir Sheet
Perf. 13
1289H A375a 10d multicolored   6.50

Chess
Pieces — A376

Designs: 30xu, Vietnamese pawns. 50xu,
Indian elephant. 1d, Scottish knight, bishop.
2d, Indian elephant, diff. 3d, Knight. 5d, Sailing
ship. 8d, Jester, elephant. 10d, Modern
pawns.

1983, May 9   Perf. 13
1290-1296 A376   Set of 7   7.00
          Imperf., #1290-1296   12.00
Souvenir Sheet
1297 A376 10d multicolored   6.00
No. 1297 contains one 28x36mm stamp.

Souvenir Sheet

TEMBAL '83 World Stamp Exhibition,
Basel — A377

1983, May 21   Perf. 13
1298 A377 10d multicolored   5.00 5.00

1984 Summer
Olympics, Los
Angeles
A378

Designs: 30xu, Long jump. 50xu, Running.
1d, Javelin. 2d, High jump, horiz. 3d, Hurdles,
horiz. 5d, Shot put. 8d, Pole vault. 10d,
Discus.

1983, June 13   Litho.   Perf. 13
1299-1305 A378   Set of 7
Souvenir Sheet
1306 A378 10d Sheet of 1
No. 1306 contains one 32x40mm stamp.
The issuance of this set has been
questioned.

Souvenir Sheet

Brasiliana '83, Rio de Janeiro — A379

1983, July 20   Perf. 13
1307 A379 10d Rhamphastos
                  toco   6.00 5.00

Butterflies
A380

Designs: No. 1308, 30xu, Leptocircus
meges. No. 1309, 30xu, Terias hecabe. No.
1310, 40xu, Zetides agamemnon. No. 1311,
40xu, Nyctalemon patroclus. No. 1312, 50xu,
Papilio chaon. No. 1313, 50xu, Precis almana.
60xu, Thauria lathyi. 1d, Kallima inachus.

1983, July 30   Litho.   Perf. 12
1308-1315 A380   Set of 8   5.00
          Imperf., #1308-1315   10.00

Souvenir Sheet

Bangkok '83 — A381

1983, Aug. 4   Perf. 13
1316 A381 10d multicolored   10.00 10.00

Karl Marx
(1818-1883)
A382

1983, Oct. 10   Perf. 11
1317-1318 A382 50xu, 10d, set
                         of 2 5.00
          Imperf., #1317-1318   50.00

Phu Dong Sports Festival — A383

1983, Oct. 10
1319-1320 A383 30xu, 1d, set of
                              2   2.00

World
Food Day
A384

Design: 50xu, Infant, fish. 4d, Family.

1983, Oct. 10   Perf. 12½
1321-1322 A384   Set of 2   2.50
          Imperf., #1321-1322   5.00

Mushrooms
A385

#1323, 50xu, Flammulina velutipes. #1324,
50xu, Pleurotus ostreatus. #1325, 50xu,
Cantharellus cibarius. #1326, 50xu, Coprinus
atramentarius. 1d, Volvariella volvacea. 2d,
Agaricus silvaticus. 5d, Morchella esculenta.
10d, Amanita caesarea.

1983, Oct. 10   Perf. 12x12½
1323-1330 A385   Set of 8   7.00 5.00
          Imperf., #1323-1330   11.00

For overprints see Nos. 2150-2157.

World Communications Year — A386

50xu, Letter carrier. 2d, Mail sorting room.
8d, Switchboard operators. #1334, 10d, Radio
operator, antenna. #1335, 10d, Telephone, letter, dish antenna, ship.

1983, Oct. 30   Perf. 12½
1331-1334 A386   Set of 4   4.50
Souvenir Sheet
Perf. 13
1335 A386 10d Sheet of 1   3.00

5th Natl. Trade Unions
Congress — A387

50xu, Woman with flowers, Vietnam-Soviet
Union Friendship Cultural Building. 2d, 30d,
Welder.

1983, Nov. 16   Perf. 11
1336-1338 A387   Set of 3   7.50

Water Birds
A388

Designs: No. 1339, 50xu, Ciconia nigra. No. 1340, 50xu, Ardea cinerea. No. 1341, 50xu, Ardea purpurea. No. 1342, 50xu, Ibis leucocephalus. 1d, Grus grus. 2d, Platalea minor. 5d, Nycticorax nycticorax. 10d, Anastomus oscitans.

1983, Nov. 20   **Perf. 12x12½**
1339-1346 A388   Set of 8   9.00 5.00
   Imperf., #1339-1346   14.00

No. 1343 inscribed "Grus grue."

World Peace Conference, Prague — A389

Designs: 50xu, Shown. 3d, 5d, 20d, Hands, globe, dove.

1984, Jan. 15   **Perf. 11**
1347-1350 A389   Set of 4   9.00

1984 Winter Olympics, Sarajevo, Yugoslavia — A390

#1351, 50xu, Cross-country skiing, vert. #1352, 50xu, Biathlon, vert. 1d, Speed skating, vert. 2d, Bobsled, vert. 3d, Hockey. 5d, Ski jumping. 6d, Slalom skiing. 10d, Pairs figure skating.

1984, Jan. 30   **Perf. 12½**
1351-1357 A390   Set of 7   6.00
   Imperf., #1351-1357   12.00
Souvenir Sheet
1358   A390 10d multicolored   4.00

No. 1358 contains one 40x32mm stamp.

Soviet Union-Vietnamese Projects, 1978-83 — A391

Designs: 20xu (No. 1359), 4d, Hoa Binh Hydro-electric project. 20xu (No. 1360), Vietnamese-Soviet Cultural Palace. 50xu, Thang Long Bridge.

1984, Jan. 31   **Perf. 11**
With Gum
1359-1362 A391   Set of 4   55.00

Endangered Animals — A392

Designs: No. 1363, 50xu, Felis marmorata. No. 1364, 50xu, Panthera tigris. No. 1365, 50xu, Panthera pardus. No. 1366, 1d, Hylobates lar. No. 1367, 1d, Nycticebus coucang. No. 1368, 2d, Elephas indicus. No. 1369, 2d, Bos gaurus.

1984, Feb. 26   **Perf. 12½x12**
1363-1369 A392   Set of 7   5.00
   Imperf., #1363-1369   14.00

A393

A394

Wildflowers: No. 1370, 50xu, Banhinia variegata. No. 1371, 50xu, Caesalpinia pulcherrima. 1d, Cassia fistula. 2d, Delonix regia. 3d, Artagotrys uncinatus. 5d, Corchorus olitorius. 8d, Banhinia grandiflora.

1984, Mar. 15   **Perf. 12x12½**
1370-1376 A393   Set of 7   6.50
   Imperf., #1370-1376   12.50
Souvenir Sheet
1377   A393 10d Delonix regia   3.75

Location of inscriptions differs on Nos. 1373, 1377.

1984, Mar. 28   **Perf. 13**
Orchids: No. 1378, 50xu, Cymbidium. No. 1379, 50xu, Brasse cattleya. 1d, Cattleya Dianx. 2d, Cymbidium, diff. 3d, Cymbidium hybridum. 5d, Phoenix winged orchids. 8d, Yellow Queen orchids.

1378-1384 A394   Set of 7   7.00
   Imperf., #1378-1384   10.00

Nos. 1085, 1093 Surcharged

a   b

1984, Apr. 25   **Perfs. as before**
1385   A322(a)   50xu on 12xu
       #1085   2.00
1386   A335(b)   50xu on 12xu
       #1093   2.00

Souvenir Sheet

Espana '84, Madrid — A395

1984, Apr. 27   **Perf. 12½**
1387   A395 10d Ciconia ciconia   4.50

Victory at Dien Bien Phu, 30th Anniv. A396

#1388, 50xu; #1395, 10d, Ho Chi Minh, generals, battle map. #1389, 50xu, Troops, truck. 1d, Civilians carrying provisions. 2d, Man-hauling artillery. 3d, Anti-aircraft battery. 5d, Troops attacking enemy base. 8d, Troops waving flag.

1984, May 7   **Perf. 12½**
1388-1394 A396   Set of 7   5.00
Souvenir Sheet
1395   A396 10d multicolored   4.00

Souvenir Sheet

UPU Congress, Hamburg '84 — A397

1984, June 19   **Perf. 13**
1396   A397 10d Junkers JU-52
     3M   4.50

Fish
A398

Designs: No. 1397, 30xu, Cypselurus spilopterus. No. 1398, 30xu, Ostracion cornutus. 50xu, Diodon hystrix. 80xu, Chelmon rostratus. 1d, Antennarius tridens. 2d, Pterois russelli. 5d, Mola mola. 10d, Minous monodactylus.

1984, June 25   **Litho.**   **Perf. 12**
1397-1404 A398   Set of 8   5.00
   Imperf., #1397-1404   10.00

Ornamental Fish — A399

Designs: No. 1405, 50xu, Trichogaster trichopterus. No. 1406, 50xu, Brachydanio rerio. 1d, Macropodus opercularis. 2d, Gymnocorymbus ternetzi. 3d, Hyphessobrycon serpae. 5d, Labeo bicolor. 8d, Batta splendens.

1984, June 29   **Perf. 12½**
1405-1411 A399   Set of 7   5.00
   Imperf., #1405-1411   10.00

Vietnamese Trade Union Movement, 55th Anniv. — A400

Designs: No. 1412a, 50xu, House at 15 Hang Non St., Hanoi, vert. No. 1412b, 50xu, Nguyen Duc Canh, vert. 1d, Striking workers. 2d, Ho Chi Minh visiting factory. 3d, Hanoi Mechanical Engineering plant. 5d, Intl. trade union movement.

1984, July 20   **Perf. 11**
1412-1416 A400   Set of 6   3.75
Souvenir Sheet
Imperf
1417   A400 2d like #1414   10.00

No. 1412 printed se-tenant. No. 1417 contains one 45x38mm stamp.

Rock Formations, Ha Long Bay — A401

#1418, 50xu, Hang-Bo Nau. #1419, 50xu, Nui Yen Ngua. #1420, 50xu, Hon Dua. #1421, 50xu, Hang Con Gai. #1422, 1d, Hon Coc. #1423, 1d, Hon Ga Choi. 2d, Hon Dinh Huong. 3d, Hon Su Tu. 5d, Hon Am. 8d, Nui Bai Tho.

1984, July 30   **Perf. 12½x12**
1418-1427 A401   Set of 10   7.00
   Imperf., #1418-1427   12.50

Dinosaurs — A402

#1428, 50xu, Styracosaurus. #1429, 50xu, Diplodocus. #1430, 1d, Corythosaurus. #1431, 1d, Rhamphyorhynchus. 2d, Seymouria. 3d, Allosaurus. 5d, Dimetrodon. 8d, Brachiosaurus.

1984, Aug. 30
1428-1435 A402   Set of 8   11.00
   Imperf., #1428-1435   15.00

Viet Nam-Laos-Cambodia Friendship — A403

1984, Aug. 30   **Perf. 11**
1436-1437 A403 50xu, 10d, set
             of 2 5.00

Souvenir Sheet

Ausipex '84, Melbourne,
Australia — A404

1984, Sept. 20   *Perf. 13*
1438 A404 10d Koala   10.00

Viet Nam-
Cambodia
Friendship
Agreement, 5th
Anniv. — A405

50xu, 3d, People, pagoda, statue. 50d,
Dancers.

1984, Sept. 30   *Perf. 11*
1439-1441 A405 Set of 3   10.00

Liberation
of Hanoi,
30th
Anniv.
A406

Designs: 50xu, Thang Long Bridge. 1d,
Khue Van Gateway. 2d, Ho Chi Minh
mausoleum.

1984, Oct. 5
1442-1444 A406 Set of 3   3.50

Vintage Automobiles — A407

#1445, 50xu, Vis-a-Vis, vert. #1446, 50xu,
Duc. 1d, Tonneau. 2d, Double phaeton. 3d,
Landaulet. 5d, Torpedo. 6d, Coupe de Ville.

1984, Oct. 30   *Perf. 12½x13, 13x12½*
1445-1451 A407   5.00
    Imperf., #1445-1451   11.50

Lenin (1870-
1924)
A408

Paintings of Lenin: 50xu, At his desk. 1d,
Standing with revolutionaries. 3d, Speaking at
factory. 5d, Meeting with farmers.

1984, Nov. 15   *Perf. 12x12½*
1452-1455 A408 Set of 4   3.50
    Imperf., #1452-1455   8.00

UNICEF
A409

Paintings: 30xu, Woman, soldiers. 50xu,
Mother, children. 1d, Miner, family. 3d, Young
girl, vert. 5d, Children playing on ground. 10d,
Women, child, vert.

1984, Dec. 7   *Perf. 12*
1456-1461 A409 Set of 6   5.50
    Imperf., #1456-1461   10.00

A410   A411

50xu, 30d. Frontier Forces, 25th anniv.

1984, Dec. 15   *Perf. 11*
1462-1463 A410 Set of 2   11.00
    Imperf., #1462-1463
    See No. M39.

1984, Dec.   *Perf. 12½x12*
Flora and Fauna: 20xu, Bubalus bubalis.
30xu, Felis marmorata. No. 1466, 50xu, Hibiscus rosa-sinensis. No. 1467, 50xu, Ailurus
fulgens. No. 1468, 50xu, Rosa centifolia. No.
1469, 50xu, Betta splendens. No. 1470, 1d,
Chrysanthemum sinense. No. 1471, 1d,
Nymphaea ampla. No. 1472, 1d, Pelecanus
onocrotalus. No. 1473, 1d, Panthera tigris. No.
1474, 2d, Nycticebus coucang. No. 1475, 2d,
Macaca fascicularis. No. 1476, 2d, Dalia coccinea. 5d, Gekko gecko. 10d, Rhytidoceros
bicornis.

1464-1478 A411 Set of 15   12.50
    Imperf., #1464-1478   15.00

No. 1466 inscribed "Hybiscus." No. 1470
inscribed "Chrysanthemun."

A412   A413

1985   *Perf. 11*
1479-1480 A412 3d, 5d, set of 2   2.25
    Imperf., #1479-1480   30.00
    New Year 1985 (Year of the Buffalo).
    Issued: 3d, 1/21; 5d, 4/30.

1985, Apr. 26   *Perf. 11*
1481 A413 2d Ho Chi Minh   .60
    Vietnamese Communist Party, 55th anniv.

Military
Victory in
South Viet
Nam, 10th
Anniv.
A414

Designs: 1d, Soldiers advancing forward.
2d, 10d, Ho Chi Minh, tank, soldiers. 4d, Construction worker. 5d, Map, women.

1985, Apr. 30   *Perf. 12½*
1482-1485 A414 Set of 4   3.00

Souvenir Sheet
Perf. 13
1486 A414 10d multicolored   3.75

Cactus
A415

Designs: No. 1487, 50xu, Echinocereus
knippelianus. No. 1488, 50xu, Lemaireocereus
thurberi. 1d, Notocactus haselbergii. 2d,
Parodia chrysacanthion. 3d, Pelecyphora
pseudopectinata. 5d, Rebutia frebrighii. 8d,
Lobivia aurea.

1985, Apr. 30   *Perf. 11½*
1487-1493 A415 Set of 7   5.75
    Imperf., #1487-1493   15.00

Vietnamese People's Army, 40th
Anniv. — A416

Designs: No. 1494, 50xu, Ho Chi Minh. No.
1495, 50xu, Taking oath on flag. 1d, Anti-aircraft missile. 2d, Soldiers, civilians working
together. 3d, Tank entering grounds of presidential palace, Saigon. 5d, Soldier demonstrating use of rifle. 8d, Officers, soldiers, map.
10d, Four soldiers representing branches of
military.

1985, May 6   *Perf. 12½*
1494-1500 A416   Set of 7   4.75

Souvenir Sheet
1501   A416 10d multicolored 2.75

A417

A418

End of World War II, 40th Anniv.: 1d, 10d,
Victory Monument. 2d, Vietnamese soldier.
4d, Dove, falling American eagle. 5d, Child,
doves.

1985, May 7   *Perf. 12x12½*
1502-1505 A417 Set of 4   3.25
    Imperf., #1502-1505   12.50

Souvenir Sheet
1506 A417 10d multicolored   3.25

1985, May 13   *Perf. 11*
Liberation of Haiphong, 30th anniv.: 2d,
Long Chau Lighthouse. 5d, An Duong Bridge,
horiz. 10d, To Hieu (1912-44), vert.

1507-1508 A418 Set of 2   1.75

Souvenir Sheet
Imperf
1509 A418 10d multicolored   2.75

Ho Chi Minh, 95th Birth
Anniv. — A419

Ho Chi Minh: 1d, At battlefield. 2d, Reading.
4d, 10d, Portrait, vert. 5d, Writing.

1985, May 19   *Perf. 12½*
1510-1513 A419 Set of 4   3.25

Souvenir Sheet
Perf. 13
1514 A419 10d multicolored   3.00
No. 1514 contains one 30x36mm stamp.

Motorcycles, Cent. — A420

Designs: No. 1515, 1d, 1895, Germany. No.
1516, 1d, 1898 tricycle, France. No. 1517, 2d,
1913 Harley-Davidson, US. No. 1518, 2d,
1918 Cleveland, US. 3d, 1935 Simplex, US.
4d, 1984 Minarelli, Italy. 6d, 1984 Honda,
Japan. 10d, 1984 Honda racing bike.

1985, June 28   *Perf. 13*
1515-1521 A420 Set of 7   4.75
    Imperf., #1515-1521   14.00

Souvenir Sheet
1522 A420 10d multicolored   3.25
No. 1522 contains one 32x40mm stamp.

Argentina '85, Buenos Aires — A421

Wild animals: No. 1523, 1d, Aptenodytes
pennati, vert. No. 1524, 1d, Dolichotis
patagonum, vert. No. 1525, 2d, Panthera
onca. No. 1526, 2d, Hydrochoerys capibara.
3d, Peterocnemia pennata, vert. 4d, Priodontes giganteus. 6d, Voltur gryphus. 10d,
Lama glama, horiz.

1985, July 5   *Perf. 12½*
1523-1529 A421 Set of 7   8.00
    Imperf., #1523-1529   16.00

Souvenir Sheet
With Gum
Perf. 13
1530 A421 10d multicolored   4.25
No. 1530 contains one 40x32mm stamp.

12th World
Youth and
Students
Festival,
Moscow
A422

No. 1531, 2d, Youth carrying flags, globe.
No. 1532, 2d, Workers, power transmission
lines. 4d, Lighthouse, coastal defense. 5d, Intl.
festival.

1985, July 27   *Perf. 12½*
1531-1534 A422   Set of 4   3.50
Imperf., #1531-1534   17.50
Souvenir Sheet
With Gum
Perf. 13
1535 A422 10d like #1531   2.75

Marine Life
A423

#1536, 30xu, Nadoa tuberculata. #1537, 30xu, Luidia maculata. #1538, 30xu, Stichopus chloronotus. #1539, 30xu, Holothuria monacaria. #1540, 40xu, Astropyga radiata. #1541, 40xu, Astropecten scoparius. #1542, 40xu, Linckia laevigata.

1985, July 30   *Perf. 12*
1536-1542 A423   Set of 7   7.00
Imperf., #1536-1542   19.00

Socialist
Republic of Viet
Nam, 40th
Anniv. — A424

Designs: 2d, Construction. 3d, Hands shaking, doves. 5d, Flag, military forces. No. 1567, 10d, Flag, Ho Chi Minh.

1985, Aug. 28   *Perf. 12½*
1543-1546 A424   Set of 4   4.50
Imperf., #1543-1546   17.50
Souvenir Sheet
Perf. 13
1547 A424 10d like #1543   4.00
No. 1547 contains one 32x40mm stamp.

Vietnamese Police Force, 40th
Anniv. — A425

1985, Aug. 30   *Perf. 11*
1548 A425 10d multicolored   3.50
See No. M41.

1st Natl.
Sports
Festival
A426

Designs: 5d, Gymnastics. 10d, Gymnastics, running, swimming.

1985, Aug. 30
1549-1550 A426   Set of 2   4.00

German Railways, 150th
Anniv. — A427

Various locomotives: #1551, 1d, Facing left. #1552, 1d, Facing right. #1553, 2d, Facing left. #1554, 2d, Facing right. 3d, 4d, 6d.

1985, Sept. 13   *Perf. 12½*
1551-1557 A427   Set of 7   5.75
Imperf., #1551-1557   10.00
Souvenir Sheet
With Gum
Perf. 13
1558 A427 10d multicolored   3.00
No. 1558 contains one 32x40mm stamp.

Vietnamese Geological Survey, 30th
Anniv. — A428

#1559, Drilling rigs. #1560, Aerial survey.

1985, Oct. 5   *Perf. 11*
1559-1560 A428 1d Set of 2   1.00

Italia '85
A429

Vintage Italian cars: No. 1561, 1d, 1922 Alfa Romeo. No. 1562, 1d, 1932 Bianchi Berlina. No. 1565, 3d, 1912 Itala. No. 1563, 2d, 1928 Isotta Fraschini. No. 1564, 2d, 1930 Bugatti. 4d, 1934 Lancia Augusta. 6d, 1927 Fiat Convertable (top up). 10d, 1927 Fiat Convertable (top down).

1985, Oct. 25   *Perf. 13*
1561-1567 A429   Set of 7   4.75
Imperf., #1561-1567   11.00
Souvenir Sheet
With Gum
1568 A429 10d multicolored   2.75
No. 1568 contains one 40x32mm stamp.

Whales
A430

Designs: No. 1569, 1d, Balaenoptera musculus. No. 1570, 1d, Balaena borealis. No. 1571, 2d, Orcinus orca. No. 1572, 2d, Delphinus. 3d, Megaptera boops. 4d, Balaenoptera physalus. 6d, Eubalaena glacialis.

1985, Nov. 15
1569-1575 A430   Set of 7   8.50
Imperf., #1569-1575   15.00

1988 World Cup Soccer
Championships, Mexico City — A431

Various soccer plays: No. 1576, 1d, From behind goal. No. 1577, 1d, Goalie from side. No. 1578, 2d, From behind goal. No. 1579, 2d, From in front of goal, vert. 3d, vert. 4d, vert. 6d, vert.

1985, Nov. 30
1576-1582 A431   Set of 7   5.00
Imperf., #1576-1582   10.00
Souvenir Sheet
Perf. 13
1583 A431 10d multicolored   3.00
No. 1583 contains one 40x32mm stamp.

People's
Democratic
Republic of
Laos, 10th
Anniv. — A432

a, Woman, dove. b, Woman dancing, natl. arms.

1985, Dec. 2   *Perf. 11*
1584 A432 1d Pair, #a.-b.   .75

Traditional Musical
Instruments — A433

#1585, 1d, Stone chimes. #1586, 1d, Large bronze drum. #1587, 2d, Flutes. #1588, 2d, Large red drum. 3d, Monochord. 4d, Moon-shaped lute. 6d, Vietnamese two-string violin.

1985, Dec. 5   *Perf. 12½x12*
1585-1591 A433   Set of 7   5.00

A434

A435

Socialist Republic of Viet Nam, 40th Anniv.: No. 1592, 10d, Industry. No. 1593, 10d, Agriculture. 20d, Public health. 30d, Education.

1985, Dec. 15   *Perf. 11*
1592-1595 A434   Set of 4   30.00

1986, Jan. 6   *Litho.*   *Perf. 11*
1596-1597 A435 50xu, 1d Set of
2   .75
1st Natl. Elections, 40th anniv.

A436

A437

1986, Jan. 6
1598 A436 1d multicolored   .50
UN 40th anniv.

1986, Feb. 24   *Perf. 12½*
Halley's Comet: No. 1599, 2d, Edmond Halley. No. 1600, 2d, Isaac Newton. 3d, Rocket, flags. 5d, Comet.
1599-1602 A437   Set of 4   3.50
Imperf., #1599-1602   9.00

A438

A439

Soviet Communist Party, 27th Congress: 50xu, Kremlin, map. 1d, Lenin banner.

1986, Feb. 25   *Perf. 11*
1603-1604 A438   Set of 2   .75

1986, Mar. 1
1605 A439 1d Map of Battle of
Xuong Giang   .50
Le Loi, 600th birth anniv.

1986 World
Cup Soccer
Championships,
Mexico
City — A440

Various soccer players in action: No. 1606, 1d, Viet Nam at left. No. 1607, 1d, Viet Nam at right. 2d, Viet Nam at left. No. 1609, 3d, Viet Nam at left. No. 1610, 3d, Viet Nam at right. No. 1611, 5d, Viet Nam at left. No. 1612, 5d, Viet Nam at right.

1986, Mar. 3   *Perf. 12½*
1606-1612 A440   Set of 7   4.00
Imperf., #1606-1612   9.00
Souvenir Sheet
Perf. 13
1613 A440 10d multicolored   3.00
No. 1613 contains one 40x32mm stamp.

1st Manned Space Flight, 25th Anniv. A441

#1614, 1d, Konstantin Tsiolkovsky. #1615, 1d, Rocket on transporter. 2d, Yuri Gagarin. #1617, 3d, Valentina Tereshkova, vert. #1618, 3d, Alexei Leonov. #1619, 5d, Apollo-Soyuz, crews. #1620, 5d, Soyuz, Salut space station. 10d, Cosmonauts, vert.

1986, Apr. 12   **Perf. 13**
1614-1620 A441 Set of 7   3.50
     Imperf., #1614-1620   10.00
Souvenir Sheet
1621 A441 10d multicolored   2.50
   No. 1621 contains one 32x40mm stamp.

Ernst Thalmann (1886-1944), German Politician — A442

1986, Apr. 16   **Perf. 11**
1622 A442 2d red & black   .90

May Day — A443

1986, May 1
1623-1624 A443 1d, 5d, set of 2   2.00

Vancouver Expo '86 — A444

Airplanes: No. 1625, 1d, Hawker Hart. No. 1626, 1d, Curtiss Jenny. 2d, PZL-P23. No. 1628, 3d, Yakovlev Yak-11. No. 1629, 3d, Fokker Dr.1. No. 1630, 5d, Boeing P-12 (1920). No. 1631, 5d, Nieuport-Delage NiD.29C1 (1929).

1986, May 12   **Perf. 13**
1625-1631 A444 Set of 7   4.00
     Imperf., #1625-1631   8.00

Dam-Strengthening Committee, 40th Anniv. — A445

1986, May 22   **Perf. 11**
1632 A445 1d carmine   .60

Bonsai — A446

Designs: No. 1633, 1d, Ficus glomerata. No. 1634, 1d, Ficus benjamina. 2d, Ulmus tonkinensis. No. 1636, 3d, Persica vulgaris. No. 1637, 3d, Streblus asper. No. 1638, 5d, Pinus khasya. No. 1639, 5d, Podocarpus macrophyllus. 10d, Serissa foetida, horiz.

1986, June 16   **Perf. 12x12½**
1633-1639 A446 Set of 7   5.00
     Imperf., #1633-1639   14.00
Souvenir Sheet
     Perf. 12½x12
1640 A446 10d multicolored   3.50

Domestic Cats — A447

Various cats (Background colors): No. 1641, 1d, blue green. No. 1642, 1d, red. 2d, blue. No. 1644, 3d, brown. No. 1645, 3d, blue. No. 1646, 5d, violet. No. 1647, 5d, red, vert.

   Perf. 13x12½, 12½x13
1986, June 16
1641-1647 A447 Set of 7   5.00
     Imperf., #1641-1647   11.00

Traditional Houses A448

Designs: No. 1648, 1d, Thai den. No. 1649, 1d, Nung. 2d, Thai trang. No. 1651, 3d, Tay. No. 1652, 3d, Hmong. No. 1653, 5d, Dao. No. 1654, 5d, Tay nguyen, vert.

   Perf. 12½x12, 12x12½
1986, June 20
1648-1654 A448 Set of 7   5.00
     Imperf., #1648-1654   12.50
Souvenir Sheet
     Perf. 12x12½
1655 A448 10d like #1654   3.50

Postal Service, 40th Anniv. — A449

Designs: No. 1656, 2d, Telecommunications. No. 1657, 2d, Map, letter carrier. 4d, Soldiers, Nguyen Thi Nghia. 5d, Dish antenna.

1986, Aug. 15   **Perf. 13**
1656-1659 A449 Set of 4   2.50
     Imperf., #1656-1659   15.00

A450

Birds: No. 1660, 1d, Merops apiaster. No. 1661, 1d, Cissa chinensis. 2d, Pteruthius erythropterus. No. 1663, 3d, Garrulax leucolophus. No. 1664, 3d, Psarisomus dalhousiae, horiz. No. 1665, 5d, Cyanopica cyanus, horiz. No. 1666, 5d, Motacilla alba. 10d, Copsychus malabaricus.

1986, Aug. 28   **Perf. 13**
1660-1666 A450 Set of 7   5.00
     Imperf., #1660-1666   11.50
Souvenir Sheet
     Perf. 12½
1667 A450 10d multicolored   4.25
   No. 1667 contains one 32x40mm stamp. Stockholmia '86.

A451

Domestic fowl: No. 1668, 1d, Plymouth Rock. No. 1669, 1d, Maleagris gallopavo. No. 1670, 2d, Ri. No. 1671, 2d, White Plymouth rock. No. 1672, 3d, Leghorn. No. 1673, 3d, Rhode Island red. No. 1674, 3d, Rhode ri. 5d, Gray Plymouth rock hen.

1986, Sept. 15   **Perf. 12x12½**
1668-1675 A451 Set of 8   5.50
     Imperf., #1668-1675   12.50

11th Intl. Trade Unions Congress — A452

1986, Sept. 16   **Perf. 12½**
1676 A452 1d blue & red   .50

Artifacts, Hung-Vuong Period — A453

Designs: No. 1677, 1d, Seated figure, vert. No. 1678, 1d, Knife hilt in form of female figure, vert. 2d, Bronze axe. No. 1680, 3d, Bronze axe, diff. No. 1681, 3d, Bronze bowl. No. 1682, 5d, Bronze pot (round). No. 1683, 5d, Bronze vase (open top).

1986, Oct. 15   **Perf. 12x12½, 12½x12**
1677-1683 A453 Set of 7   5.00
     Imperf., #1677-1683   11.00
Souvenir Sheet
     Perf. 12x12½
1684 A453 10d like #1677   3.50

Vietnamese Red Cross, 40th Anniv. — A454

1986, Oct. 20   **Perf. 12½**
1685 A454 3d rose & greenish blue   .85

Sailing Ships — A455

Various sail and oar-powered ships (sail colors): #1686, 1d, bl, grn, yel. #1687, 1d, org. 2d, yel. #1689, 3d, pur & red. #1690, 3d, bl. #1691, 5d, bl, brn, org. #1692, 5d, org.

   Perf. 12½x12, 12½x13 (#1688)
1986, Oct. 20
1686-1692 A455 Set of 7   4.25
   No. 1688 is 38x47mm.

Butterflies — A456

Designs: No. 1693, 1d, Catopsilia scylla. No. 1694, 1d, Euploea midamus. 2d, Appias nero. No. 1696, 3d, Danaus chrysippus. No. 1697, 3d, Papilio polytes stichius. No. 1698, 5d, Euploea diocletiana. No. 1699, 5d, Charaxes polyxena.

1986, Nov. 11   **Perf. 12½**
1693-1699 A456 Set of 7   4.75
     Imperf., #1693-1699   11.00
   No. 1696 misspelled "Danais."

Vietnamese Communist Party, 6th Congress — A457

1d, Construction projects. 2d, Natl. defense. 4d, Ho Chi Minh. 5d, Intl. cooperation.

1986, Nov. 20   **Perf. 11**
1700-1703 A457 Set of 4   3.50
1700a-1703a   Perf. 12½   25.00
1702b   Perf. 11x12½   15.00
Souvenir Sheet
     Imperf
1704 A457 10d like #1700   3.50

Insects A458

Designs: No. 1705, 1d, Poecilocoris nepalensis. No. 1706, 1d, Bombus americanorum. 2d, Romalea microptera. No. 1708, 3d, Chalcocoris rutilans. No. 1709, 3d, Chrysocoris sellatus. No. 1710, 5d, Paranthrene palmi. No. 1711, 5d, Crocisa crucifera. 10d, Anabrus simplex.

1986, Nov. 30   *Perf. 12½*
1705-1711 A458   Set of 7   4.50
    Imperf., #1705-1711   12.50
Souvenir Sheet
1712 A458   10d multicolored   4.00

No. 1712 contains one 32x40mm stamp.

Intl. Peace
Year — A459

1986, Dec. 7   *Perf. 11*
1713-1714 A459   1d, 3d, set of 2   1.25

Handicrafts — A460

Designs: No. 1715, 1d, Round dish. No. 1716, 1d, Rattan handbag. 2d, Rattan foot stool. No. 1718, 3d, Bamboo hand basket. No. 1719, 3d, Muong pannier. No. 1720, 5d, Rattan basket with shoulder straps. No. 1721, 5d, Rattan basket with lid. 10d, Tall rattan basket.

1986, Dec. 10   *Perf. 11½*
1715-1721 A460   Set of 7   5.00
    Imperf., #1715-1721   9.00
Souvenir Sheet
1722 A460   10d multicolored   3.50

A461

A462

1986, Dec. 18   *Perf. 11*
1723 A461   2d blue green & fawn   .90
Natl. Resistance, 40th anniv.

1986, Dec. 26   *Perf. 12x12½*
Endangered flora: No. 1724, 1d, Fokienia hodginsii. No. 1725, 1d, Amentotaxus yunnanensis. 2d, Pinus kwangtungensis. No. 1727, 3d, Taxus chinensis. No. 1728, 3d, Cupressus torulosa. No. 1729, 5d,

Ducampopinus krempfii. No. 1730, 5d, Tsuga yunnanensis. 10d, Abies nukiangensis.
1724-1730 A462   Set of 7   5.00
    Imperf., #1724-1730   12.00
Souvenir Sheet
1731 A462   10d multicolored   3.50

Elephants — A463

#1732, 1d, Two elephants. #1733, 1d, Female, calf. #1734, 3d, Elephant. #1735, 1d, Elephant facing, vert. #1736, 5d, Man riding elephant, vert. #1737, 5d, Four elephants.

1986, Dec. 30   *Perf. 12½*
1732-1737 A463   Set of 6   5.00
    Imperf., #1732-1737   13.50

No. 1737 is 68x27mm.

Vietnamese
Legends
A464

Designs: a, Son Tinh. b, My Nuong. c-e, Battle between Mountain Genie and Water Genie. f-h, Celebration.

1987, Jan. 20   *Perf. 12*
1738 A464   3d Strip of 8, #a.-h.   7.00
    Imperf.   13.50

New Year 1987
(Year of the
Cat) — A465

1987, Jan. 25   *Perf. 11*
1739 A465   3d red lilac   .50

Natl.
Events
A466

Ho Chi Minh and: 10d, August revolution, Aug. 19, 1945. 20d, Proclaiming independence, Sept. 9, 1945. 30d, Victory at Dien Bien Phu, July 7, 1954. 50d, Capture of Saigon, Apr. 30, 1975.

1987, Apr. 10   *Perf. 11*
1740-1743 A466   Set of 4   5.25

A467

A468

Champa art: 3d, Temple, Da Nang. 10d, Tower, Na Trang. 15d, Temple, Da Nang (side view). 20d, Dancing girl. 25d, Bust of woman. 30d, Girl playing flute. 40d, Dancing girl, diff.

1987, June 30   *Perf. 12x12½*
1744-1750 A467   Set of 7   5.50
    Imperf., #1744-1750   9.50
Souvenir Sheet
1751 A467   50d like #1749   4.00

1987, July 10   *Perf. 12½*
Various flowering cacti: 5d, 10d, 15d, 20d, 25d, 30d, 40d.
1752-1758 A468   Set of 7   4.00
Souvenir Sheet
Perf. 13
1759 A468   50d multicolored   3.00

Global Population Reaches 5
Billion — A469

1987, July 11   *Perf. 13*
1760 A469   5d multicolored   .50

World Wildlife
Fund — A470

Designs: No. 1761, 5d, Concolor gibbon. No. 1762, 5d, Douc monkeys. 15d, Black concolor gibbon. 40d, Douc monkey.

1987, July 15   *Perf. 12½*
1761-1764 A470   Set of 4   7.50
    Imperf., #1761-1764   20.00

A471

A472

Western high plateau costumes: 5d, Male Bana. No. 1766, 20d, Female Bana. No. 1767, 20d, Female Gia Rai. No. 1768, 30d, Male Gia Rai. No. 1769, 30d, Male Ede. 40d, Female Ede.

1987, July 25   *Perf. 12x12½*
1765-1770 A471   Set of 6   5.00
    Imperf., #1765-1770   10.00

1987, July 27   *Perf. 13*
1771 A472   5d multicolored   .50
Day of the Invalids, 40th anniv.

Postal
Trade
Union,
40th
Anniv.
A473

Designs: 5d, Letter carrier, jet, truck, train. 30d, Switchboard operator.

1987, Aug. 30
1772-1773 A473   Set of 2   1.75

A474

Paintings by Picasso: No. 1774, 3d, *The Three Musicians.* No. 1775, 20d, War. No. 1776, 20d, Peace. No. 1777, 30d, Child with Dove, vert. No. 1778, 30d, Portrait of Gertrude Stein, vert. 40d, Guernica. 50d, Child as Harlequin.

1987, Oct. 1   *Perf. 12½*
1774-1779 A474   Set of 6   3.75
    Imperf., #1774-1779   10.00
Souvenir Sheet
1780 A474   50d multicolored   3.75

No. 1779 is 44x27mm. No. 1780 contains one 40x32mm stamp.

Coral — A475

Designs: 5d, Epanouis. 10d, Acropora. 15d, Rhizopsammia. 20d, Acropora, diff. 25d, Alcyone, 30d, Corollum. 40d, Cristatella.

1987, Oct. 3   *Perf. 12x12½*
1781-1787 A475   Set of 7   5.75
    Imperf., #1781-1787   12.50

Intl. Year
for
Housing
for the
Homeless
A476

1987, Oct. 5   *Perf. 13*
1788 A476   5d greenish bl & blk   .50

Russian Revolution, 70th Anniv. — A477

Designs: 5d, 65d, Industry, agriculture. 20d, Lenin. 30d, Construction. 50d, Ho Chi Minh.

1987, Oct. 6   *Perf. 13*
1789-1792 A477   Set of 4   2.50
Souvenir Sheet
1793 A477   65d multicolored   3.25

Hafnia '87 A478

Seaplanes: 5d, PBY-5. 10d, LeO H-246. 15d, Dornier DO-18. 20d, Short Sunderland. 25d, Rohrbach Rostra. 30d, Chetverikov ARK-3. 40d, CANT Z-509. 50d, Curtiss H-16.

1987, Oct. 12   *Perf. 13*
1794-1800 A478   Set of 7   3.50
Souvenir Sheet
1801 A478   50d multicolored   2.50

No. 1801 contains one 40x32mm stamp.

Czechoslovakia-Viet Nam Friendship Agreement, 10th Anniv. — A479

10d, Handshake. 50d, Flags, buildings.

1987, Oct. 31
1802-1803 A479   Set of 2   2.75
   Imperf., 1802-1803   17.50

Viet Nam-Soviet Union Cooperation — A480

Designs: 5d, Industry. 50d, Buildings.

1987, Nov. 3
1804-1805 A480   Set of 2   2.75

Mushrooms A481

Designs: 5d, Polyporellus squamosus. 10d, Clitocybe geotropa. 15d, Tricholoma terreum. 20d, Russula aurata. 25d, Collybia fusipes. 30d, Cortinarius violaceus. 40d, Boletus aereus.

1987, Nov. 10   *Perf. 12½*
1806-1812 A481   Set of 7   5.00
   Imperf., #1806-1812   10.00

Peace A482

1987, Nov. 30   *Perf. 13*
1813 A482   10d multicolored   .75

Afro-Asian Solidarity Committee (AAPSO), 30th Anniv. — A483

10d, Hands, dove. 30d, Map, hands, vert.

1987, Nov. 30
1814-1815 A483   Set of 2   1.25
   Imperf., #1814-1815   20.00

Victory Over US Bombing Campaign, 15th Anniv. — A484

Designs: 10d, B-52 wreckage. 30d, Children with flowers, wreckage.

1987, Dec. 26
1816-1817 A484   Set of 2   1.25
   Imperf., #1816-1817   15.00

Productivity A485

Designs: 5d, Consumer goods. 20d, Agriculture. 30d, Export products.

1987, Dec. 30
1818-1820 A485   Set of 3   2.50

Hoang Sa, Truong Sa Islands A486

Designs: 10d, Ship, sailor. 100d, Maps.

1988, Jan. 19
1821-1822 A486   Set of 2   3.25

Roses — A487

Various roses: 5d, 10d, 15d, 20d, 25d, 30d, 40d.

1988, Jan. 20   *Perf. 12½*
1823-1829 A487   Set of 7   4.50
   Imperf., #1823-1829   10.00
Souvenir Sheet   *Perf. 13*
1830 A487   50d multicolored   3.00

Tropical Fish A488

Designs: 5d, Red betta splendens. 10d, Labeo bicolor. 15d, Puntis tetrazona. 20d, Brachydania albolineatus. 25d, Puntis conchonius. 30d, Betta splendens, diff. 40d, Botia lecontei.

1988, Jan. 20   *Perf. 13*
1831-1837 A488   Set of 7   5.00
   Imperf., #1831-1837   12.00

Intl. Red Cross, Red Crescent, 125th Anniv. — A489

1988, Feb. 17
1838 A489   10d multicolored   .60

Battle of Bach Dang, 700th Anniv. A490

80d, Fleet of ships. 200d, Battle scene.

1988, Apr. 8
1839-1840 A490   Set of 2   3.75

Tourism A491

5d, One-pillar pagoda. 10d, Bach Dang River. 15d, Thien Mu Tower, Hue. 20d, Hgu Hanh Mountain, Da Nang. 25d, Nha Trang beach. 30d, Pren Waterfalls. 40d, Market, Ben Thanh. 50d, Cleft Rocks, Quang Ninh.

1988, Apr. 20   *Perf. 12½x12*
1841-1847 A491   Set of 7   5.50   5.50
   Imperf., #1841-1847   10.00
Souvenir Sheet
1848 A491   50d multicolored   2.75

Water Lilies — A492

Designs: 5d, Nymphaea lotus. No. 1850, 10d, Nymphaea pubescens. No. 1851, 10d, Nymphaea nouchali. No. 1852, 20d,

---

Nymphaea rubra. No. 1853, 20d, Nymphaea gigantea. 30d, Nymphaea laydekeri. 50d, Nymphaea capensis.

1988, Apr. 20   *Perf. 12x12½*
1849-1855 A492   Set of 7   5.25
   Imperf., #1849-1855   12.50

Offshore Oil Drilling — A493

1988, Apr. 28   *Perf. 13*
1856 A493   1000d multicolored   7.50

A494

Parrots: No. 1857, 10d, Ara ararauna. No. 1858, 10d, Psittacula himalayana. No. 1859, 20d, Aprosmictus erythropterus. No. 1860, 20d, Ara chloroptera. No. 1861, 30d, Ara militaris. No. 1862, 30d, Psittacula alexandri. 50d, Loriculus vernalis. 80d, Ara chloroptera, diff.

1988, May 5   *Perf. 12x12½*
1857-1863 A494   Set of 7   5.00
   Imperf., #1857-1863   11.00
Souvenir Sheet
1864 A494   80d multicolored   3.50

A495   A496

Membership in Council of Mutual Economic Assistance, 10th Anniv.: 200d, Map. 300d, Headquarters building.

1988, May 29   *Perf. 13*
1865-1866 A495   Set of 2   4.50

1988, June 1
1867 A496   60d multicolored   1.00

Vaccinations against disease.

Problems of Peace and Socialism Magazine, 30th Anniv. — A497

1988, July 20
1868 A497   20d multicolored   .50

A498

A499

1988, Aug. 20
1869 A498 150d multicolored 1.50
Pres. Ton Duc Thang, birth cent.

1988, Aug. 28
6th Vietnamese Trade Union Congress: 50d, Emblem. 100d, Workers.
1870-1871 A499 Set of 2 1.75

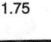

Children's Paintings A500

#1872, 10d, My Family. #1873, 10d, My House. #1874, 20d, Fishing. #1875, 20d, Flying Kites. #1876, 30d, Girl playing guitar, animals. #1877, 30d, Children in rain, vert. 50d, Girl holding dove, vert. 80d, Family, diff., vert.

Perf. 12½x12, 12x12½
1988, Sept. 25
1872-1878 A500 Set of 7 4.25 1.25
Imperf., #1872-1878 7.00
Souvenir Sheet
Perf. 12x12½
1879 A500 80d multicolored 3.75

Hydroelectric Plants — A501

Designs: 2000d, Tri An. 3000d, Hoa Binh.

1988, Sept. 27 **Perf. 13**
1880-1881 A501 Set of 2 11.00

A502   A503

1988, Nov. 3 **Perf. 13½x13**
1882 A502 50d multicolored .50
Viet Nam-USSR Friendship Agreement, 10th anniv.

1988, Dec. 27
Designs: 100d, Fidel Castro. 300d, Flags, Vietnamese, Cuban people.
1883-1884 A503 Set of 2 1.00
Cuban revolution, 30th anniv.

Wild Animals A504

Designs: No. 1885, 10d, Bos banteng. No. 1886, 10d, Bos gaurus. No. 1887, 20d, Axis porcinus. No. 1888, 20d, Tapirus indicus. No. 1889, 30d, Capricornis sumatrensis. No. 1890, 30d, Sus scrofa. 50d, Bubalus bubalus. 80d, Rhinoceros sodaicus.

1988, Dec. 30 **Perf. 12½**
1885-1891 A504 Set of 7 4.25
Imperf., #1885-1891 12.50
Souvenir Sheet
1892 A504 80d multicolored 3.00
Imperf. 13.00

Locomotives — A505

Designs: No. 1893, 20d, Kiha 80, Japan. No. 1894, 20d, LRC, Canada. No. 1895, 20d, Hitachi, Japan. No. 1896, 20d, BL-85, USSR. No. 1897, 30d, RC-1, Sweden. No. 1898, 30d, DR-1A, USSR. 50d, T3-136, USSR. 80d, SCNF Z6400.

1988, Dec. 30 **Perf. 13**
1893-1899 A505 Set of 7 4.50
Imperf., #1893-1899 12.50
Souvenir Sheet
1900 A505 80d multicolored 2.50
Imperf. 5.00
No. 1900 contains one 40x32mm stamp.

A506

A507

Fruits, vegetables: No. 1901, 10d, Lagenaria siceraria. No. 1902, 10d, Momordica charantia. No. 1903, 20d, Solanum melongena. No. 1904, 20d, Cucurbita moschata. No. 1905, 30d, Luffa cylindrica. No. 1906, 30d, Benincasa hispida. 50d, Lycopercicon esculentum.

1988, Dec. 30 **Perf. 12x12½**
1901-1907 A506 Set of 7 5.00
Imperf., #1901-1907 8.50

1988, Dec. 30 **Perf. 13**
Various project spacecraft: No. 1908, 10d, Mars. No. 1909, 10d, Moon. No. 1910, 20d, Saturn. No. 1911, 20d, Inter-planetary. No. 1912, 30d, Venus. No. 1913, 30d, Earth orbital

space station. 50d, Cosmos house. 80d, Lander docking with orbiter.
1908-1914 A507 Set of 7 3.50
Souvenir Sheet
1915 A507 80d multicolored 2.50
Cosmos Day.
No. 1915 contains one 32x40mm stamp.

Shells A508

Designs: No. 1916, 10d, Conus miles. No. 1917, 10d, Strombus lentiginosus. No. 1918, 20d, Nautilus. No. 1919, 20d, Bursa rana. No. 1920, 30d, Turbo petholatus. No. 1921, 30d, Oliva erythros. 50d, Mitra eriscopalis. 80d, Tonna tessellata.

1988, Dec. 30 **Perf. 12½x12**
1916-1922 A508 Set of 7 4.50
Imperf., #1916-1922 13.50
Souvenir Sheet
1923 A508 80d multicolored 3.50

India '89 — A509

Butterflies: No. 1924, 50d, Anaea echemus. No. 1925, 50d, Ascia monuste. No. 1926, 50d, Juniona evarete. No. 1927, 100d, Phoebis avellaneda. No. 1928, 100d, Eurema proterpia. 200d, Papilio palamedes. 300d, Danaus plexippus. 400d, Parides gundlachiamus.

1989, Jan. 7 **Perf. 12½**
1924-1930 A509 Set of 7 4.00
Imperf., #1924-1930 9.00
Souvenir Sheet
1931 A509 400d multicolored 2.50
No. 1931 contains one 40x32mm stamp. Nos. 1924-1930 printed with se-tenant label.

Natl. Day of Cambodia, 10th Anniv. — A510

Designs: 100d, Soldiers, women working in field. 500d, Viet Nam-Cambodia friendship.

1989, Jan. 7 **Perf. 13x13½**
1932-1933 A510 Set of 2 1.75
Imperf., #1932-1933 20.00

India '89 — A511

Designs: No. 1934, 100d, Science, technology. No. 1935, 100d, Agriculture, industry. 300d, Asoka pillar. 600d, Nehru (1889-1964).

1989, Jan. 20 **Perf. 13**
1934-1937 A511 Set of 4 3.00

Battle of Dong Da, Bicent. — A512

Designs: 100d, Festival. 1000d, Quang Trung defeating Qing invaders.

1989, Feb. 10 **Perf. 13**
1938-1939 A512 Set of 2 3.00

Inter-Parliamentary Union, Cent. — A513

Designs: 100d, Vietnamese membership, 10th anniv. 200d, Centennial emblem.

1989, Mar. 1
1940-1941 A513 Set of 2 1.10

Fishing Boats — A513a

Boats from: No. 1942, 10d, Quang Nam. No. 1943, 10d, Quang Tri. No. 1944, 20d, Thua Thien. No. 1945, 20d, Da Nang (sail furled). No. 1946, 30d, Da Nang (under sail). No. 1947, 30d, Quang Tri (under sail). 50d, Hue.

1989, Mar. 20 **Perf. 12½x12**
1942-1948 A513a Set of 7 5.00
Imperf., #1942-1948 10.00

Helicopters — A514

#1949, 10d, Kamov KA-26. #1950, 10d, Boeing Vertol 234. #1951, 20d, Mil MI-10(V10). #1952, 20d, MBB BO 105. #1953, 30d, Kawasaki Hughes 369HS. #1954, 30d, Bell 206B Jet Ranger. 50d, Mil MI-8. 80d, Puma SA330.

1989, Apr. 12 **Perf. 12½**
1949-1955 A514 Set of 7 4.00
Imperf., #1949-1955 10.00
Souvenir Sheet
1956 A514 80d multicolored 2.75
Imperf. 10.00
No. 1956 contains one 40x32mm stamp.

Bicycles A515

#1957, 10d, Bowden Spacelander. #1958, 10d, Rabasa Derbi. #1959, 20d, Huffy. #1960, 20d, Rabasa Derbi. #1961, 30d, VMX-PL. #1962, 30d, Premier. 50d, Columbia RX5.

1989, May 1   *Perf. 13*
1957-1963 A515 Set of 7   4.00
   Imperf., #1957-1963   10.00

Turtles — A516

No. 1964, 10d, Cuora trifasciata. No. 1965, 10d, Testudo elegans. No. 1966, 20d, Eretmochelys imbricata. No. 1967, 20d, Platysternon megacephalum. No. 1968, 30d, Dermochelys coriacea. No. 1969, 30d, Chelonia mydas. 50d, Caretta caretta. 80d, Caretta caretta, diff.

1989, May 1   *Perf. 12½*
1964-1970 A516 Set of 7   6.00
   Imperf., #1964-1970   11.50
Souvenir Sheet
1971 A516 80d multicolored   2.75
   Imperf.   10.00
Finlandia '88 (#1971).

Poisonous Snakes — A517

Designs: No. 1972, 10d, Trimeresurus popeorum. No. 1973, 10d, Trimeresurus mucrosquamatus. No. 1974, 20d, Bungarus fasciatus. No. 1975, 20d, Bungarus candidus. No. 1976, 30d, Calliophis maclellandii. No. 1977, 30d, Ancistrodon acutus. 50d, Ophiophagus hannah, vert.

1989, May 1
1972-1978 A517 Set of 7   5.75
   Imperf., #1972-1978   13.50

Pairs Figure Skating — A518

Various figure skaters: No. 1979, 10d, "Viet Nam" at left. No. 1980, 10d, "Viet Nam" at right. No. 1981, 20d, "Viet Nam" at left. No. 1982, 20d, "Viet Nam" at right, horiz. No. 1983, 30d, "Viet Nam" at left. No. 1984, 30d, "Viet Nam" at right, horiz. 50d, "Viet Nam" at left, horiz.

1989, May 29   *Perf. 13*
1979-1985 A518 Set of 7   3.50
   Imperf., #1979-1985   10.00
Souvenir Sheet
With Gum
1986 A518 80d multi, horiz.   2.75
No. 1986 contains one 40x32mm stamp.

 A519   A520

1989, June 5   *Perf. 13*
1987 A519 100d buff   .50
Post & Telecommunications.

1989, July 1   *Perf. 12*
Ceramics, Li-Tran Period: 50d, Pitcher. No. 1989, 100d, Bowl. No. 1990, 100d, Jug. 200d, Jug, diff. 300d, Vase.
1988-1992 A520 Set of 5   3.25
   Imperf., #1988-1992   6.00

Legend of Giong A521

Designs: 50d, Mother nursing infant. No. 1994, 100d, Giong meets imperial messenger. No. 1995, 100d, Giong riding iron horse, people following. 200d, Giong pulling up bamboo trees. 300d, Giong flying into sky.

1989, July 1   *Perf. 12½x12*
1993-1997 A521 Set of 5   3.50
   Imperf., #1993-1997   5.50

French Revolution, Bicent. — A522

Designs: 100d, Emblem. 500d, Liberty leading the people, after Delacroix.

1989, July 14   *Perf. 13½x13*
1998-1999 A522 Set of 2   1.40

PHILEXFRANCE '89 — A523

Paintings: No. 2000, 50d, Oath of the Tennis Court, by David. No. 2001, 50d, Capture of Louis XVI, horiz. No. 2002, 50d, Liberty, Equality, Fraternity, horiz. No. 2003, 100d, Storming the Bastille. No. 2004, 100d, Death of Marat, by David. 200d, Child and Rabbit, by Prud'hon. 300d, Slave Market, by Gerome, horiz. 400d, Liberty Leading the People, by Delacroix.

1989, July 14   *Perf. 13*
2000-2006 A523 Set of 7   5.00
   Imperf., #2000-2006   10.00
Souvenir Sheet
2007 A523 400d multicolored   2.75
No. 2007 contains one 33x44mm stamp.

1990 World Cup Soccer Championships, Italy — A524

Soccer plays: No. 2008, 50d, Dribbling. No. 2009, 50d, Tackling. No. 2010, 50d, Goalie. No. 2011, 100d, Dribbling, diff. No. 2012, 100d, Dribbling, diff., vert. 200d, Preparing to kick, vert. 300d, Heading ball, vert. 400d, Heading ball, diff., vert.

Perf. 13x12½, 12½x13
1989, Aug. 27
2008-2014 A524 Set of 7   3.75
   Imperf., #2008-2014   11.00
Souvenir Sheet
Perf. 13
2015 A524 400d multicolored   2.25
No. 2015 contains one 32x40mm stamp.

Dogs A525

#2016, 50d, Dachshund. #2017, 50d, Beagle. #2018, 50d, English setter, vert. #2019, 100d, German short-haired pointer, vert. #2020, 100d, Basset hounds. 200d, German sheperd, vert. 300d, Beagle, diff.

1989, Aug. 20   *Perf. 12½*
2016-2022 A525 Set of 7   4.00
   Imperf., #2016-2022   10.00
No. 2020 is 68x28mm.

Horses A526

#2023, 50d, Tennessee Walking. #2024, 50d, Appaloosa. #2025, 50d, Tersky. #2025, 100d, Kladruber. #2026, 100d, Welsh cob. 200d, Pinto. 300d, Pony and bridle.

1989, Sept. 23   *Perf. 13*
2023-2029 A526 Set of 7   4.00
   Imperf., #2023-2029   12.50
No. 2029 is 68x28mm.

Flowers — A527

No. 2030, 50d, Paphiopedilum siamense. No. 2031, 50d, Fuchsia fulgens. No. 2032, 100d, Hemerocallis fulva. No. 2033, 100d, Gloriosa superba. 200d, Strelitzia reginae. 300d, Iris.

1989, Sept. 23   *Perf. 12½*
2030-2035 A527 Set of 6   4.50 2.00
   Imperf., #2030-2035   9.00

German Democratic Republic, 40th Anniv. — A528

1989, Oct. 7   *Perf. 13*
2036 A528 200d multicolored   .60

Immunization Campaign — A529

#2037, Woman receiving vaccination. #2038, Child receiving oral vaccine. #2039, Clinic.

1989, Oct. 20
2037-2039 A529 100d Set of 3   1.00

Drawings of Everyday Life, 19th Cent. — A530

Designs: 50d, Assembling plow. No. 2041, 100d, Harrowing. No. 2042, 100d, Irrigating. 200d, Fertilizing. 300d, Harvesting.

1989, Oct. 28   *Perf. 12x12½*
2040-2044 A530 Set of 5   3.25 2.00
   Imperf., #2040-2044   5.50

Horse Paintings, by Xu Beihong (1895-1953) A531

Various horses: 100d, 200d, 300d, 500d horiz., 800d, 1000d, 1500d.

1989, Dec. 22   *Perf. 13*
2045-2051 A531 Set of 7   4.00
   Imperf., #2045-2051   9.00
Imperf
Size: 117x72mm
2052 A531 2000d multicolored   3.00
   Imperf.   11.00

Vietnamese Communist Party, 60th Anniv. — A532

Designs: 100d, Ho Chi Minh, tank. 500d, Workers, refinery, field.

1990, Feb. 3   *Litho.*   *Perf. 13*
2053-2054 A532 Set of 2   2.50
   Imperf., #2053-2054   4.50

Ducks — A533

a, 100d, Anas platyrhynchos hybrid. b, 300d, Anas penelope. c, 500d, Anas platyrhynchos. d, 1000d, Anas erythrorhyncha. e, 2000d, Anas platyrhynchos, diff. f, 3000d, Anas undulata.

1990, Feb. 15
2055 A533 Block of 6, #a.-f. 3.00

Trucks
A534

100d, Mack. 200d, Volvo F89. 300d, Tatra 915 S1. 500d, Hino KZ30000. 1000d, Iveco. 2000d, Leyland DAF Super Comet. 3000d, Kamaz 53212.

1990, Feb. 20
2056-2062 A534 Set of 7 4.00 1.50
    Imperf., #2056-2062 5.50

Architectural Sites, Hue — A535

#2063, 100d, Tu Duc's Mausoleum. #2064, 100d, Hien Nhon Arch. 200d, Ngo Mon Gate. 300d, Thien Mu Temple. 400d, Palace, gateway.

1990, Feb. 20   **Perf. 12½x12**
2063-2066 A535 Set of 4 2.00
Souvenir Sheet
2067 A535 400d multicolored 1.50

Goldfish — A536

1990, Apr. 10

London '90: 100d, Antonia Zarate, by Goya. 200d, Girl Holding a Paper Fan, by Renoir.

300d, Janet Grizel, by John Russell. 500d, Love Untieing the Belt of Beauty, by Sir Joshua Reynolds. 1000d, Portrait of a Woman, by George Romney. 2000d, Portrait of Madame Ginoux, by Van Gogh. 3000d, Woman in Blue, by Gainsborough. 3500d, Woman in a Straw Hat, by Van Gogh.

2074-2080 A537 Set of 7 3.00 1.00
    Imperf., #2074-2080 7.50
Souvenir Sheet
2081 A537 3500d multicolored 2.25 1.00

1990 World Cup Soccer
Championships, Italy — A538

Various soccer players in action: 100d, 200d, 300d, 500d, 1000d, 2000d, 3000d.

1990, Apr. 19
2082-2088 A538 Set of 7 3.00
Souvenir Sheet
2089 A538 3500d multicolored 2.00
No. 2089 contains one 32x40mm stamp.
For overprints see Nos. 2189-2196.

Cats — A539

Various cats: 100d, horiz., 200d, 300d, horiz., 500d, 1000d, horiz., 2000d, 3000d.

1990, May 5
2090-2096 A539 Set of 7 3.25
Souvenir Sheet
2097 A539 3500d multicolored 2.00
No. 2097 contains one 44x33mm stamp. Belgica '90 (#2097).

1990, May 15

Various dogs: 100d, 200d, 300d, 500d, 1000d, 2000d, 3000d.

Dogs — A540

2098-2104 A540 Set of 7 3.00
Souvenir Sheet
2105 A540 3500d Collies 2.00
New Zealand '90.

Ho Chi Minh
(1890-1969)
A541

Ho Chi Minh and: 100d, Lenin. 300d, Soldiers waving flag. 500d, Hand holding rifle, dove. 1000d, Map. 2000d, Child, dove. 3000d, Stylized globe. 3500d, Flag.

1990, May 17   **Perf. 13**
2106-2111 A541 Set of 6 3.00
    Imperf., #2106-2111 5.00
Souvenir Sheet
    Perf. 12½x13
2112 A541 3500d multicolored 1.50
No. 2112 contains one 33x44mm stamp.

Dinosaurs — A542

100d, Gorgosaurus. 500d, Ceratosaurus. 1000d, Ankylosaurus. 2000d, Ankylosaurus, diff. 3000d, Edaphosaurus.

1990, June 1   **Perf. 13**
2113-2117 A542 Set of 5 5.25 2.25

Columbus' Discovery of America,
500th Anniv. — A543

Designs: 50d, Fleet. No. 2119, 100d, Columbus presenting gifts to natives. No. 2120, 100d, Columbus, priest at Rabida. No. 2121, 100d, Columbus at Court of Ferdinand, Isabella. No. 2122, 200d, Map of Caribbean. No. 2123, 200d, Columbus, arms. 300d, Map of Atlantic. 500d, Teotihuacan pot.

1990, June 10   **Perf. 12½**
2118-2124 A543 Set of 7 5.00
Souvenir Sheet
2125 A543 500d multicolored 2.00
No. 2125 contains one 40x32mm stamp.
For overprints see Nos. 2313-2320.

Sailing
Ships
A544

Designs: 100d, Viking longship. 500d, Caravel. No. 2128, 1000d, Carrack, 14th-15th cent. No. 2129, 1000d, Flit. No. 2130, 1000d, Carrack, 15th cent., vert. 2000d, Galleon, vert. 3000d, Galleon, diff. 4200d, Egyptian barge.

1990, June 10   **Perf. 13**
2126-2132 A544 Set of 7 3.50
    Imperf., #2126-2132 9.00
Souvenir Sheet
    Perf. 13x12½
2133 A544 4200d multicolored 1.75
No. 2133 contains one 44x33mm stamp.

11th Asian
Games,
Beijing — A545

Designs: 100d, High jump. 200d, Basketball. 300d, Table tennis. 500d, Volleyball. 1000d, Rhythmic gymnastics. 2000d, Tennis. 3000d, Judo. 3500d, Hurdles.

1990, June 20   **Perf. 13**
2134-2140 A545 Set of 7 3.00 2.00
    Imperf., #2134-2140 6.50
Souvenir Sheet
    Perf. 12½x13
2141 A545 3500d multicolored 1.50
No. 2141 contains one 33x44mm stamp.

Nos. 1180-1187 Ovptd. in Red, Green
and Black

1990, June 22   **Perf. 12**
2142-2149 A352 Set of 8 2.75
1990 World Cup Soccer Championships, Italy.

Nos. 1323-1330 Ovptd. in Black and
Red

1990, June 22   **Perf. 12x12½**
2150-2157 A385 Set of 8 4.50
Tourism.

Modern
Ships
A546

100d, Freighter. 300d, Container ship. 500d, Cruise ship. 1000d, Liquified natural gas tanker. 2000d, Ro-Ro ship. 3000d, Ferry.

1990, July 20   **Perf. 13**
2158-2163 A546 Set of 6 3.00
    Imperf., #2158-2163 7.50

Post & Telecommunications Dept.,
45th Anniv. — A547

Designs: 100d, Dove, ship, plane. 1000d, Satellite antenna.

1990, Aug. 15   **Perf. 13x13½**
2164-2165 A547 Set of 2 .50
    Imperf., #2164-2165 2.75

Socialist Republic of
Viet Nam, 45th
Anniv. — A548

Designs: 100d, Flag, construction projects. 500d, Map, tank, soldiers. 1000d, "VI," ship, communications network. 3000d, Workers, oil rigs. 3500d, Ho Chi Minh.

Paintings
A537

100d, Bulging-eyed, horiz. 300d, Telescopic-eyed, horiz. 500d, Red-headed, horiz. 1000d, Double-tailed. 2000d, Rainbow. 3000d, Comet.

1990, Mar. 20   **Perf. 13**
2068-2073 A536 Set of 6 3.50 1.00
    Imperf., #2068-2073 7.00

1990, Sept. 1
2166-2169 A548 Set of 4   *Perf. 13*
     1.75
     Imperf., #2166-2169   4.00

Souvenir Sheet
Perf. 12½x13

2170 A548 3500d multicolored   1.50

No. 2170 contains one 33x44mm stamp. Sixth Vietnamese Communist Party Congress (#2168).

Airships
A549

Designs: 100d, Henry Gifford, 1871. 200d, Lebandy, 1910. 300d, Graf Zeppelin. 500d, R-101, 1930. 1000d, Soviet, 1936. 2000d, Tissandier, 1883. 3000d, US Navy. 3500d, "Zodiac," 1931.

1990, Sept. 10   *Perf. 12½*
2171-2177 A549 Set of 7   3.00

Souvenir Sheet

2178 A549 3500d multicolored   1.50 1.00

No. 2178 contains one 40x32mm stamp. Helvetia '90, Stamp World London '90.

Fable of Thach
Sanh — A550

Designs: a, 100d, Thach Sanh carrying bundles of wood. b, 300d, Ly Thong. c, 500d, Thach Sanh killing python. d, 1000d, Thach Sanh shooting arrow at eagle. e, 2000d, Thach Sanh in prison. f, 3000d, Thach Sanh, princess.

1990, Sept. 20   *Perf. 13*
2179 A550 Block of 6, #a.-f.   2.75
     Imperf.   6.00

Asian-Pacific Postal Training Center, 20th Anniv. — A551

1990, Sept. 25
2180 A551 150d multicolored   .20

Nos. 571-578 Ovptd. with Red Cross in Red and "FOR THE FUTURE GENERATION" in various Languages in Black

Language: No. 2181, 12xu, Japanese. No. 2182, 12xu, Italian. No. 2183, 20xu, German. No. 2184, 20xu, Vietnamese. 30xu, English. 40xu, Russian. 50xu, French. 60xu, Spanish.

1990, Sept. 25   *Perf. 12*
2181-2188 A211 Set of 8   3.25

Position of overprint varies. Use of these stamps at stated face value is unlikely.

Nos. 2082-2089 Ovptd.

1990, Sept. 25   *Perf. 13*
2189-2195 A538 Set of 7   3.00

Souvenir Sheet

2196 A538 3500d multicolored   2.00

Vietnamese Women's Federation, 60th Anniv. — A552

Designs: 100d, Woman carrying rifle. 500d, Women working in field, laboratory.

1990, Oct. 10
2197-2198 A552 Set of 2   .50
     Imperf., #2197-2198   1.00

Correggio (1494-1534), Painter — A553

Various paintings of the Madonna and Child: No. 2199, 50xu, shown. No. 2200, 50xu, diff. 1d, 2d, 3d, 5d, 6d.

1990, Nov. 13   *Perf. 12½*
2199-2205 A553 Set of 7   3.75

Souvenir Sheet

2206 A553 10d multicolored   3.00

No. 2206 contains one 32x40mm stamp. Dated "1984." Use of these stamps at stated face value is unlikely.

Protection of Forests — A554

Designs: 200d, Water conservation, healthy forest. 1000d, SOS, prevent forest fires.

1990, Nov. 15   *Perf. 13*
2207-2208 A554 Set of 2   .75

A555

A555a

Poisonous mushrooms: 200d, Amanita pantherina. 300d, Amanita phalloides. 1000d,

---

Amanita virosa. 1500d, Amanita muscaria. 2000d, Russula emetica. 3000d, Boletus satanas.

1991, Jan. 21
2209-2214 A555 Set of 6   3.50
     Imperf., #2209-2214   7.00

1991, Jan. 31

1992 Summer Olympics, Barcelona: 200d, Sailing. 300d, Boxing. 400d, Cycling. 1000d, High jump. 2000d, Equestrian. No. 2220, 3000d, Judo. No. 2221, 3000d, Wrestling, horiz. 5000d, Soccer, horiz.

2215-2221 A555a Set of 7   4.50
     Imperf., #2215-2221   7.00

Souvenir Sheet

2222 A555a 5000d multicolored   2.25
     Imperf., #2222   5.00

No. 2222 contains one 44x33mm stamp.

Nguyen Binh Khiem (1491-1585), Writer — A556

1991, Feb. 15
2223 A556 200d multicolored   1.25
     Imperf.   2.00

Discovery of America, 500th Anniv. — A557

Sailing ships: 200d, Marisiliana. No. 2225, 400d, Venetian. No. 2226, 400d, Cromster, vert. No. 2227, 2000d, Nina. No. 2228, 2000d, Pinta. 3000d, Howker, vert. 5000d, Santa Maria.
6500d, Portrait of Columbus.

1991, Feb. 22
2224-2230 A557 Set of 7   5.00
     Imperf., #2224-2230   6.00

Souvenir Sheet

2231 A557 6500d multicolored   4.00
     Imperf.   6.00

Golden Heart Charity — A558

Women wearing traditional costumes: 200d, 500d, 1000d, 5000d.

1991, Feb. 26
2232-2235 A558 Set of 4   3.00
     Imperf., #2232-2235   5.00

Sharks
A559

Designs: 200d, Carcharhinus melanopterus. 300d, Carcharhinus amblyrhynchos. 400d, Triakis semifasciata. 1000d, Sphyrna mokarran. 2000d, Triaenodon abesus. No. 2241, 3000d, Carcharias laurus. No. 2242, 3000d, Carcharhinus leucas.

1991, Apr. 6
2236-2242 A559 Set of 7   4.00
     Imperf., #2236-2242   7.50

Endangered Birds — A560

World Wildlife Fund: 200d, Grus vipio. 300d, Grus antigone chick, vert. 400d, Grus japonensis, vert. 1000d, Grus antigone, adults, vert. 2000d, Grus nigricollis, vert. No. 2248, 3000d, Balearica regulorum, vert. No. 2249, 3000d, Bugeranus leucogerranus.

1991, Apr. 20
2243-2249 A560 Set of 7   5.00
     Imperf., #2243-2249   6.00

Shellfish
A561

Designs: 200d, 1000d, 2000d, Palinurus, all diff. 300d, Alpheus bellulus. 400d, Periclemenes brevicarpalis. No. 2255, 3000d, Astacus. No. 2256, 3000d, Palinurus, diff.

1991, Apr. 20
2250-2256 A561 Set of 7   4.00
     Imperf., #2250-2256   7.00

Young Pioneers, 50th Anniv. — A562

Designs: 200d, shown. 400d, UN Convention on Children's Rights.

1991, May 15
2257-2258 A562 Set of 2   2.00
     Imperf., #2257-2258   4.00

Rally Cars
A563

#2259, 400d, Lada. #2260, 400d, Nissan. 500d, Ford Sierra RS Cosworth. 1000d, Suzuki. 2000d, Mazda 323 4WD. #2264, 3000d, Lancia. #2265, 3000d, Peugeot. 5000d, Peugeot 405.

1991, May 24
2259-2265 A563 Set of 7   4.00
     Imperf., #2259-2265   5.00

Souvenir Sheet

2266 A563 5000d multicolored   2.50
     Imperf.   5.00

No. 2266 contains one 44x33mm stamp.

Locomotives — A564

#2267, 400d, Puffing Billy, 1811, vert. #2268, 400d, Fusee, 1829, vert. 500d, Stevens, 1825. 1000d, Crampton #80, 1852. 2000d, Locomotion, 1825. #2272, 3000d, Saint-Lo, 1844. #2273, 3000d, Coutances, 1855. 5000d, Atlantic, 1843.

1991, May 25
2267-2273 A564 Set of 7   5.00
   Imperf., #2267-2273   8.00
   Souvenir Sheet
2274 A564 5000d multicolored   3.00
   Imperf.   6.00

No. 2274 contains one 33x44mm stamp.

Frogs
A565

World Wildlife Fund: 200d, Dendrobates leucomelas. 400d, Rana esculenta. 500d, Mantella aurantiaca. 1000d, Dendrobates tinctorius. 2000d, Hyla halowelli. No. 2280, 3000d, Agalychnis callidryas. No. 2281, 3000d, Hyla aurea.

1991, June 12
2275-2281 A565 Set of 7   6.00
   Imperf., #2275-2281   6.00

7th Vietnamese
Communist
Party Congress
A566

Designs: 200d, Ho Chi Minh, buildings. 300d, Workers. 400d, Mother, children.

1991, June
2282-2284 A566 Set of 3   2.25
   Imperf., #2282-2284   4.50

Vietnamese
Communist
Party, 60th
Anniv. — A566a

1991, June 24 Litho. **Perf. 13**
2284A A566a 100d red   1.25

1992
Winter
Olympics,
Albertville
A567

Designs: 200d, Speed skating. 300d, Free- style skiing, vert. 400d, Bobsled. 1000d, Biathlon. 2000d, Slalom skiing. No. 2290, 3000d, Cross-country skiing, vert. No. 2291, 3000d, Ice dancing, vert. 5000d, Hockey, vert.

1991, July 15
2285-2291 A567 Set of 7   3.50
   Imperf., #2285-2291   4.00
   Souvenir Sheet
2292 A567 5000d multicolored   2.50
   Imperf.   4.00

No. 2292 contains one 33x44mm stamp.

Prehistoric Animals — A568

Designs: a, 200d, Arsinoitherium zitteli. b, 500d, Elephas primigenius. c, 1000d, Baluchitherium. d, 2000d, Deinotherium giganteum. e, 3000d, Brontops. f, 3000d, Uinatherium.

1991, July 26
2293 A568 Block of 6, #a.-f.   4.50

A569

Golden Heart Charity: 200d, Eye, folded hands. 3000d, Tennis player in wheelchair.

1991, July 27
2294-2295 A569 Set of 2   1.25

1991, Aug. 20

Chess pieces: 200d, Pawn. 300d, Knight. 1000d, Rook. 2000d, Queen. No. 2300, 3000d, Bishop. No. 2301, 3000d, King. 5000d, Pawn, Knight, King.

2296-2301 A570 Set of 6   4.25
   Imperf., #2296-2301   5.00
   Souvenir Sheet
2302 A570 5000d multicolored   2.50
   Imperf.   5.00

No. 2302 contains one 33x44mm stamp.

PHILANIPPON '91 — A571

Butterflies: 200d, Attacus atlas. 400d, Morpho cypris. 500d, Troides rotschildi. No. 2306, 1000d, Papilio demetrius. No. 2307, 1000d, Vanessa atalanta. 3000d, Papilio weiskei. 5000d, Apatura ilia substituta. 5500d, Heliconius melpomene.

1991, Aug. 29
2303-2309 A571 Set of 7   4.50
   Imperf., #2303-2309   5.00
   Souvenir Sheet
2310 A571 5500d multicolored   2.50
   Imperf.   5.00

No. 2310 contains one 44x33mm stamp.

Post and Telecommunications
Research Institute, 25th
Anniv. — A572

1991, Aug.
2311 A572 200d multicolored   1.25
   Imperf.   2.00
   Souvenir Sheet
2312 A572 3500d Communica-
      tions network,
      horiz.   2.50
   Imperf.   5.00

No. 2312 contains one 44x33mm stamp.

Nos. 2118-2125 Ovptd. in Red

1992, Jan. 15   **Perf. 12½**
2313-2319 A543 Set of 7   6.50
   Souvenir Sheet
2320 A543 500d multicolored   4.00

7th Vietnamese
Communist Party
Congress
A574

200d, Workers, industry, agriculture, atomic energy symbol. 2000d, Map of Asia, hands clasped.

1992, Feb. 3 Litho. **Perf. 13**
2322-2323 A574 Set of 2   1.00

1992 Winter Olympics,
Albertville — A575

Designs: 200d, Biathlon. 2000d, Hockey. 4000d, Slalom skiing. 5000d, Pairs figure skating. 6000d, Downhill skiing.

1992, Feb. 5
2324-2328 A575 Set of 5   4.50

Columbus' Discovery of America,
500th Anniv. — A576

Designs: a, 4000d, Columbus, flag. b, 6000d, Columbus, natives. c, 8000d, Aboard ship. d, 3000d, Two sailing ships. e, 400d, Columbus' fleet setting sail. 11,000d, Columbus with Ferdinand and Isabella.

1992, Feb. 12
2329 A576 #a.-f. + label   5.00
   Imperf
   Size: 102x70mm
2330 A576 11,000d multicolored 5.00

Airplanes — A577

Designs: 400d, Tupelov TU-154M. 500d, Concorde. 1000d, Airbus A-320. 3000d, Airbus A340-300. 4000d, Boeing Dash 8-400. 5000d, Boeing 747-200. 6000d, McDonnell-Douglas MD-11CF.

1992, Mar. 6   **Perf. 13**
2331-2337 A577 Set of 7   5.00

A578

Intl. Decade for Natural Disaster Reduction: 400d, Storm system, weather forecasting equipment. 4000d, Man taking water depth readings.

1992, Mar. 23
2338-2339 A578 Set of 2   1.00

1992, Mar. 28

1992 Summer Olympics, Barcelona: 400d, Archery. 600d, Volleyball. 1000d, Wrestling. 3000d, Fencing. 4000d, Running. 5000d, Weight lifting. 6000d, Field hockey. 10,000d, Basketball.

A579

2340-2346 A579 Set of 7   4.50
   Souvenir Sheet
2347 A579 10,000d multicolored 3.00

No. 2347 contains one 32x43mm stamp.

Motorcycles — A580

Designs: 400d, 5000d, Suzuki 500F. 500d, Honda CBR 600F. 1000d, Honda HRC 500F. 3000d, Kawasaki 250F, vert. 4000d, Suzuki RM 250F. vert. 6000d, BMW 1000F. 10,000d, Suzuki RM 250F, diff.

1992, Apr. 8
2348-2354 A580   Set of 7   5.00
Souvenir Sheet
2355 A580 10,000d multicolored   4.50
No. 2355 contains one 33x44mm stamp.

Intl. Space Year A581

400d, Space shuttle launch, vert. 500d, Launch of shuttle Columbia, vert. 3000d, Columbia in space. 4000d, Space station, shuttle Hermes. 5000d, Shuttle Hermes. 6000d, Astronauts, Hubble space telescope, vert.

1992, Apr. 12
2356-2361 A581   Set of 6   5.00

Saigon Post Office, Cent. A582

200d, Main entrance. 10,000d, Facade.

1992, Apr. 30   *Perf. 13*
2362 A582 200d multicolored   1.00
Souvenir Sheet
                                    Perf. 13½
2363 A582 10,000d multicolored   2.50
No. 2363 contains one 43x32mm stamp.

European Cup Soccer Championships A583

Various soccer players in action: 200d, 2000d, 4000d, 5000d, 6000d.

1992, May 14   *Perf. 13*
2364-2368 A583   Set of 5   5.00
Souvenir Sheet
2369 A583 9000d multicolored   4.00
No. 2369 contains one 44x33mm stamp.

Spanish Paintings A584

Designs: 400d, Portrait of a Girl, by Zurbaran. 500d, Woman with a Jug, by Murillo. 1000d, Portrait of Maria Aprickaia, by Velazquez. 3000d, Holy Family with St. Katherine, by de Ribera. 4000d, Madonna and Child with Saints Agnes and Thekla, by El Greco. 5000d, Woman with a Jug, by Goya, horiz. 6000d, The Naked Maja, by Goya, horiz. 10,000d, Three Women, by Picasso, horiz.

1992, May 30
2370-2376 A584   Set of 7   5.00
Souvenir Sheet
2377 A584 10,000d multicolored   4.00
No. 2377 contains one 44x33mm stamp. Expo '92, Seville (#2377).

UN Conference on Environmental Protection, 20th Anniv. — A585

Designs: 200d, Clean, polluted water. 4000d, Graph comparing current development pattern with environmentally safe pattern.

1992, June 1
2378-2379 A585   Set of 2   1.00

A586   Flowers — A587

Lighthouses: 200d, Cu Lao Xanh. 3000d, Can Gio. 5000d, Vung Tau. 6000d, Long Chau.

1992, June 14   *Perf. 13½x13*
2380-2383 A586   Set of 4   4.50
Genoa '92.

1992, June 28   *Perf. 13*
Designs: 200d, Citrus maxima. 2000d, Nerium indicum. 4000d, Ixora coccinea. 5000d, Cananga oborata. 6000d, Cassia surattensis.
2384-2388 A587   Set of 5   4.00

Birds — A588

Rodents — A589

Designs: 200d, Ducula spilorrhoa. 2000d, Petrophassa ferruginea. 4000d, Columba livia. 5000d, Lopholaimus antareticus. 6000d, Streptopelia senegalensis, horiz.

1992, July 3
2389-2393 A588   Set of 5   4.50

1992, July 26
Designs: 200d, 500d, Cavia porcellus, horiz. 3000d, Hystrix indica, horiz. 4000d, Gerbillus gerbillus. 5000d, Petaurista petaurista. 6000d, Oryctolagus cuniculus.
2394-2399 A589   Set of 6   5.00

Disabled Soldiers Day, 45th Anniv. A590

1992, July 27
2400 A590 200d multicolored   .50

3rd Phu Dong Games A591

1992, Aug. 1
2401 A591 200d multicolored   .50

Betta Splendens — A592

Various fish: 200d, 500d, 3000d, 4000d, 5000d, 6000d.

1992, Aug. 15
2402-2407 A592   Set of 6   5.00

Intl. Planned Parenthood Federation, 40th Anniv. — A593

Designs: 200d, Map showing member's locations, vert. 4000d, Anniv. emblem, map.

1992, Oct. 1
2408-2409 A593   Set of 2   1.00

Hanoi Medical School, 90th Anniv. A594

Designs: 200d, Medical students. 5000d, Alexandre Yersin, school.

1992, Nov. 20
2410-2411 A594   Set of 2   1.25

SOS Children's Villages — A595

Designs: 200d, Adult sheltering child. 5000d, Women, children inside house.

1992, Dec. 22
2412-2413 A595   Set of 2   1.50

17th Southeast Asian Games, Singapore — A596

1993, Jan. 1
2414 A596 200d multicolored   .50

Bees A597

Designs: 200d, Apis dorsata. 800d, Apis koschevnikovi. 1000d, Apis laboriosa. 2000d, Apis cerana japonica. 5000d, Apis cerana cerana. 10,000d, Apis mellifera, vert.

1993, Jan. 15
2415-2420 A597   Set of 6   5.00

Fable of Tam Cam — A598

Designs: 200d, Returning from river. 800d, Vision of old man by goldfish pool. 1000d, With unsold rice at market. 3000d, Trying on slipper for prince. 4000d, Rising from lotus flower. 10,000d, Royal couple.

1993, Jan. 18
2421-2426 A598   Set of 6   4.50

New Year 1993 (Year of the Rooster) A599

200d, 5000d, Rooster, hen and chicks.

1993, Jan. 20
2427-2428 A599   Set of 2   2.50

Medicinal Plants
A600

Designs: 200d, Atractylodes macrocephala. No. 2430, 1000d, Lonicera japonica. No. 2431, 1000d, Quisqualis indica. 3000d, Rehmannia glutinosa. 12,000d, Gardenia jasminoides.

1993, Feb. 27
2429-2433 A600 Set of 5   4.00

Communications
A601

200d, Map, communications equipment. 2500d, Map, Hong Kong-Sri Racha Cable route.

1993, Mar. 1
2434-2435 A601 Set of 2   .75

Asian Animals
A602

200d, Ailuropoda melanoleuca. 800d, Panthera tigris. 1000d, Elephas maximus. 3000d, Rhinoceros unicornis. 4000d, Hylobates leucogenys. #2441, 10,000d, Neofelis nebulosa. #2442, 10,000d, Bos sauveli.

1993, Mar. 10
2436-2441 A602 Set of 6   4.50
Souvenir Sheet
Perf. 13½
2442 A602 10,000d multicolored   2.50

1994 World Cup Soccer Championships, U.S. — A603

Various soccer players in action.

1993, Mar. 30   *Perf. 13*
2443-2445 A603 200d, 1500d, 7000d, set of 3   2.00

Transportation — A604

Designs: 200d, Wheelbarrow. 800d, Buffalo cart. 1000d, Rickshaw, top up. 2000d, Rickshaw with passenger. 5000d, Rickshaw, top down. 10,000d, Horse-drawn carriage.

1993, Apr. 6
2446-2451 A604 Set of 6   4.50

500Kv Electricity Lines — A605

1993, May 1
2452-2453 300d, 400d, set of 2   .60

Polska '93 — A606

Paintings: 200d, Sunflowers, by Van Gogh. No. 2455, 1000d, Young Woman, by Mogidliani. No. 2456, 1000d, Couple in Forest, by Rousseau. 5000d, Harlequin with Family, by Picasso. No. 2458, 10,000d, Female Model, by Matisse, horiz. No. 2459, 10,000d, Portrait of Dr. Gachet, by Van Gogh.

1993, May 7   *Perf. 13*
2454-2458 A606 Set of 5   2.50
Souvenir Sheet
Perf. 12½
2459 A606 10,000d multicolored   2.50
No. 2459 contains one 32x43mm stamp.

Da Lat, Cent.
A607

Orchids: 400d, Paphiopedilum hirsutissimum. No. 2461, 1000d, Paphiopedilum malipoense. No. 2462, 1000d, Paphiopedilum gratrixianum. 12,000d, Paphiopedilum hennisianum.

1993, June 15   *Perf. 13*
2460-2463 A607 Set of 4   3.50

Asian Architecture — A608

Landmark buildings from: 400d, Thailand, vert. 800d, Indonesia, vert. 1000d, Singapore, vert. No. 2467, 2000d, Malaysia. No. 2468, 2000d, Cambodia. 6000d, Laos. 8000d, Brunei.
10,000d, Thai Binh, Viet Nam, vert.

1993, July 10   *Litho.*
2464-2470 A608 Set of 7   4.75
Souvenir Sheet
Perf. 14x13½
2471 A608 10,000d multicolored   2.50 2.50

7th Trade Union Congress — A608a

Designs: 400d, Industry, communications. 5000d, Hand holding hammer, doves, flowers.

1993, July 28   *Litho.*   *Perf. 13*
2471A-2471B   A608a Set of 2   1.25

Crabs
A609

Designs: 400d, Scylla serrata. 800d, Portunus sanguinotentus. 1000d, Charybdis bimaculata. 2000d, Paralithodes brevipes. 5000d, Portunus pelagicus. 10,000d, Lithodes turritus.

1993, July 30
2472-2477 A609 Set of 6   4.50

Stamp Day
A610

5000d, Hand holding stamped envelope.

1993, Aug. 15
2478-2479 A610 Set of 2   1.25

Miniature Sheet

Tennis — A611

Women tennis players: a, 400d. c, 1000d. Male tennis players: b, 1000d. d, 12,000d.

1993, Sept. 20
2480 A611 #a.-d. + 2 labels   3.50

A613

A614

Costumes: 400d, Lo Lo. 800d, Thai. 1000d, Dao Do. 2000d, H'mong. 5000d, Kho Mu. No. 2488, 10,000d, Kinh.
No. 2489, 10,000d, Precious gem stones.

1993, Oct. 1   *Perf. 13*
2483-2488 A613 Set of 6   2.50
Souvenir Sheet
Perf. 13½
2489 A613 10,000d multicolored   2.50

Bangkok '93. Issued: Nos. 2483-2488, 10/1/93. No. 2489, 10/10/93.
No. 2489 contains one 43x32mm stamp.

1994, Jan. 1

New Year 1994 (Year of the Dog): Various dogs.

2490-2491 A614 400d, 6000d, set of 2   1.75
Imperf., #2490-2491   4.00

Flowers
A615

#2492, 400d, Prunus persica. #2493, 400d, Chrysanthemum morifolium. #2494, 400d, Rosa chinensis. 15,000d, Delonix regia.

1994
2492-2495 A615 Set of 4   4.50

Issued: #2492, 1/4; 15,000d, 4/3; #2493, 7/30; #2494, 10/10.

Chess
A616

Designs: 400d, Anatoly Karpov. 1000d, Gary Kasparov. 2000d, Bobby Fischer. 4000d, Emanuel Lasker. No. 2500, 10,000d, Jose Capablanca.
No. 2501, 10,000d, King.

1994, Jan. 20
2496-2500 A616 Set of 5   4.50
Imperf., #2496-2500   8.00
Souvenir Sheet
2501 A616 10,000d multicolored   2.75
Imperf.   4.75

Hong Kong '94 — A617

Festivals: 400d, Hoi Lim. 800d, Cham. 1000d, Tay Nguyen. 12,000d, Nam Bo.

1994, Feb. 18
2502-2505 A617 Set of 4   4.00
Imperf., #2502-2505   6.75

A618

A619

Various opera masks: 400d, 500d, 2000d, 3000d, 4000d, 7000d.

1994, Mar. 15
2506-2511　A618　Set of 6　　　4.75
　　Imperf., #2506-2511　　　　8.50

1994, Mar. 30
Various gladiolus hybridus: 400d, 2000d, 5000d, 8000d.
2512-2515　A619　Set of 4　　　3.75
　　Imperf., #2512-2515　　　　6.75

Japanese Paintings — A620

Paintings by: 400d, Utamaro. 500d, Harunobu. 1000d, Hokusai. 2000d, Hiroshige. 3000d, Hokusai, diff. 4000d, Utamaro, diff. 8000d, Choki.

1994, Apr. 9
2516-2522　A620　Set of 7　　　5.25
　　Imperf., #2516-2522　　　　9.25

Insects — A621

Designs: 400d, Cicindela aurulenta. 1000d, Harmonia octomaculata. 6000d, Cicindela tennipes. 7000d, Collyris.

1994, Apr. 20
2523-2526　A621　Set of 4　　　3.75
　　Imperf., #2523-2526　　　　5.50

Victory at Dien Bien Phu, 40th Anniv.
A622

Designs: 400d, Soldiers dragging equipment. 3000d, Celebration.

1994, Apr.
2527-2528　A622　Set of 2　　　.90
　　Imperf., #2527-2528　　　　1.25

Newspaper "Young Pioneers," 40th Anniv.
A623

1994, May 15　　　　Perf. 13x13½
2529　A623　400d　red & black　.45

Crocodiles — A625

Designs: 400d, Crocodylus porosus. 600d, Alligator mississippiensis. 2000d, Crocodylus niloticus. 3000d, Alligator sinensis. 4000d, Caiman yacare. 9000d, Crocodylus johnsoni. 10,000d, Caiman crocodilus.

1994, June 1　　　　　Perf. 13x13½
2532-2537　A625　Set of 6　　　5.00
　　Imperf., #2532-2537　　　　7.50
Souvenir Sheet
Perf. 13½
2538　A625　10,000d multicolored　2.75
　　Imperf.　　　　　　　　　4.00
No. 2538 contains one 43x32mm stamp.

1994 World Cup Soccer Championships, US — A626

Various soccer players in action: 400d, 600d, 1000d, 2000d, 3000d, 11,000d.

1994, June 15　　　　　Perf. 13
2539-2544　A626　Set of 6　　　4.75
　　Imperf., #2539-2544　　　　8.25
Souvenir Sheet
Perf. 13½
2545　A626　10,000d multicolored　2.75
　　Imperf.　　　　　　　　　4.75
No. 2545 contains one 32x43mm stamp.

Yersin's Discovery of Plague Bacillus, Cent.
A627

1994, June　　　　　Perf. 13x13½
2546　A627　400d multicolored　.45

UPU, 120th Anniv.
A629

Designs: 400d, UPU emblem, "120." 5000d, World map. 10,000d, UPU emblem, "P," vert.

1994, Aug. 1　　　　　Perf. 13
2551-2552　A629　Set of 2　　　1.40
Souvenir Sheet
Perf. 14x13½
2553　A629　10,000d multicolored　2.75

PHILAKOREA '94 — A630

Birds: 400d, Numenius arquata. 600d, Oceanites oceanicus. 1000d, Fregata minor. 2000d, Morus capensis. 3000d, Lunda cirrhata. 11,000d, Larus belcheri. 10,000d, Collocalia fuciphaga.

1994, Aug. 16　　　　Perf. 13x13½
2554-2559　A630　Set of 6　　　4.75
Souvenir Sheet
Perf. 13½
2560　A630　10,000d multicolored　2.75
No. 2560 contains one 43x32mm stamp.

A631

A632

Bamboo: 400d, Bambusa blumeana. 1000d, Phyllostachys aurea. 2000d, Bambusa vulgaris. 4000d, Tetragonocalamus quadrangularis. 10,000d, Bambusa venticosa.

1994, Aug. 17　　　　Perf. 13½x13
2561-2565　A631　Set of 5　　　4.50
Singpex '94.

1994, Sept. 20　　　Perf. 13x13½
Various bridges: 400d, 900d, 8000d.
2566-2568　A632　Set of 3　　　2.25

Children's Future
A634

Designs: 400d+100d, Boy helping girl in wheelchair with kite. 2000d, Children dancing, vert.

1994, Oct. 2　Litho.　　Perf. 13
2572-2573　A634　Set of 2　　　.80

A636

A637

People's Army, 50th Anniv.: 400d, People in formation. 1000d, Soldiers, battle map. 2000d,

---

Ho Chi Minh, child. 4000d, Anti-aircraft battery.

1994, Dec. 22
2576-2579　A636　Set of 4　　　2.00

1994, June 25　　　　　Perf. 13
Intl. Olympic Committee, Cent.: 400d, Flags. 6000d, Pierre de Coubertin.
2580-2581　A637　Set of 2　　　1.90

ICAO, 50th Anniv.
A638

Jets: 400d, In flight. 3000d, On ground.

1994, Dec. 7
2582-2583　A638　Set of 2　　　.90

Trams
A639

Designs: 400d, With overhead conductor. 900d, Paris tram. 8000d, Philadelphia mail.

1994, Oct. 10　Litho.　Perf. 13x13½
2584-2586　A639　Set of 3　　　2.00

Liberation of Hanoi, 40th Anniv.
A640

Designs: 400d, Greeting soldiers. 2000d, Workers, students, modern technology.

1994, Oct. 10
2587-2588　A640　Set of 2　　　.55

New Year 1995 (Year of the Boar)
A641

Stylized boars: 400d, Adult, five young. 8000d, One eating.

1995, Jan. 2　Litho.　　Perf. 13
2589-2590　A641　Set of 2　　　1.90

A642

A643

Birds: No. 2591, 400d, Pluvialis apricaria, horiz. No. 2592, 400d, Philetairus socius, horiz. No. 2593, 400d, Oxyruncus cristatus, horiz. No. 2594, 400d, Pandion haliaetus. No. 2595, 5000d, Cariama cristata.

1995, Jan. 20 *Perf. 13x13½, 13½x13*
2591-2595 A642 Set of 5   1.50

A number has been reserved for a souvenir sheet with this set.

1995, Feb. 1   *Perf. 13*

Traditional women's attire: 400d, Young women, bicycle. 3000d, Bride. 5000d, Girl in formal dress holding hat.

2597-2599 A643 Set of 3   1.90

Vietstampex '95 — A644

Owls — A645

1995, Feb. 18
2600 A644 5500d multicolored   1.25

1995, Mar. 1   *Perf. 13½x13*

Designs: 400d, Ketupa zeylonensis. 1000d, Strix aluco. 2000d, Strix nebulosa. 5000d, Strix seloputo. 10,000d, Otus leucotis. 12,500d, Tyto alba.

2601-2605 A645 Set of 5   3.75

Souvenir Sheet
Perf. 14x13½

2606 A645 12,500d multicolored   2.25
      Imperf.   4.25

Fish A646

Designs: 400d, Pomacanthus arcuatus. 1000d, Rhinecanthus rectangulus. 2000d, Pygoplites diacanthus. 4000d, Pomacanthus ciliaris. 5000d, Balistes vetula. 9000d, Balistes conspicillum.

1995, Mar. 20   *Perf. 13*
2607-2612 A646 Set of 6   4.25

Lenin, 125th Birth Anniv. — A647

1995, Apr. 22   *Litho.*   *Perf. 13*
2613 A647 400d red & black   .25

End of World War II, 50th Anniv. A648

1995, May 2   *Litho.*   *Perf. 13*
2614 A648 400d multicolored   .35

A649

A650

1996 Summer Olympics, Atlanta: 400d, Hammer throw. 3000d, Cycling. 4000d, Running. 10,000d, Pole vault. 12,500d, Basketball.

1995, Apr. 5   *Litho.*   *Perf. 13*
2615-2618 A649 Set of 4   3.75

Souvenir Sheet

2619 A649 12,500d multicolored   2.75

1995, May 5

Various balloons: 500d, 1000d, 2000d, 3000d, 4000d, 5000d, 7000d.

2620-2626 A650 Set of 7   5.00

Finlandia '95, Intl. Philatelic Exhibition, Helsinki.

Miniature Sheets

Tapirus Indicus — A651

No. 2627a, 400d, With young. b, 1000d, Facing left. c, 2000d, Walking right. d, 4000d, Mouth open, left.
No. 2528a, 4000d, Facing right. b, 4000d, Eating leaves. c, 5000d, In water. d, 6000d, Head protruding out of water.

1995, Apr. 25
2627 A651 Sheet of 4, #a.-d.   2.50
2628 A651 Sheet of 4, #a.-d.   4.25

World Wildlife Fund (#2627).

Miniature Sheet

Parachutes — A652

No. 2629: a, 400d, One parachutist descending from sky. b, 2000d, Two descending. c, 3000d, One about to touch ground. d, 9000d, Three men on ground with open parachute.

1995, May 24
2629 A652 Sheet of 4, #a.-d.   3.25

Rhododendrons — A653

Designs: 400d, Fleuryi. 1000d, Sulphoreum. 2000d, Sinofalconeri. 3000d, Lyi. 5000d, Ovatum. 9000d, Tanastylum.

1995, June 30
2630-2635 A653 Set of 6   4.50

Miniature Sheet

Native Folktale — A654

a, 400d, Brothers and their parents. b, 1000d, Mother saying farewell to her departing sons. c, 3000d, One brother is transformed into a statue. d, 10,000d, Both brothers transformed into statues.

1995, July 20   *Litho.*   *Perf. 13*
2636 A654 Sheet of 4, #a.-d.   3.25

A655

A656

400d, Statue of a woman holding child. 3000d, Three women of different races, emblem, horiz.

1995, Aug. 5
2637-2638 A655 Set of 2   .80

Women's Federation of Viet Nam: 65th anniv. (#2637), 1995 Intl. Women's Conf., Beijing (#2638).

1995, July 26
2639 A656 400d multicolored   .25

Admission to Assoc. of Southeast Asian Nations (ASEAN).

Natl. Day — A657

#2640, 400d, Ho Chi Minh, people waving flags, dove of peace. #2641, 400d, Ho Chi Minh holding child. #2642, 1000d, Communist symbol, bridge, electrical wire, building. #2643, 1000d, Ho Chi Minh, silhouettes of soldiers, building with flags flying. #2644, 2000d, Soldiers, natl. flag. #2645, 2000d, Antenna, satellite dish, van, olive branch, people on motorcycles.

1995, Aug. 14
2640-2645 A657 Set of 6   1.50

Viet Nam Labor Party, 65th anniv. (No. 2640). Ho Chi Minh, 105th birth anniv. (No. 2641). Evacuation of French troops from North Viet Nam, 40th anniv. (No. 2642). End of war in Viet Nam, 20th anniv. (No. 2643). Natl. army, 50th anniv. (No. 2644). Post and Telecommunications Service, 50th anniv. (No. 2645).

Sir Rowland Hill (1795-1879) A658

Design: 4000d, Hill, "penny black."

1995, Aug. 15
2646 A658 4000d multicolored   .95

Natl. Sports Games — A659

1995, Aug. 30
2647 A659 400d multicolored   .25

Singapore '95 — A660

Orchids: 400d, Paphiopedilum druryi. 2000d, Dendrobium orcraceum. 3000d, Vanda. 4000d, Cattelya. 5000d, Paphiopedilum hirsutissimum. 6000d, Christenosia vietnamica haeger.
12,500d, Angraecum sesquipedale.

1995, Sept. 1
2648-2653 A660 Set of 6   5.25
Souvenir Sheet
2654 A660 12,500d multicolored   2.75
No. 2654 contains one 32x43mm stamp.

Asian Sites — A661

Designs: 400d, Buildings, monuments, tombs, Hue, Viet Nam. 3000d, Walkway over water, Trung Quoc. 4000d, Temple, Macao. 5000d, Kowloon, Hong Kong. 6000d, Pagoda, Dai Bac.

1995, Sept. 6
2655-2659 A661 Set of 5   4.25

UN, 50th Anniv. A662

1995, Oct. 10
2660 A662 2000d multicolored   .45

Total Solar Eclipse, Oct. 10, 1995 A663

1995, Dec. 23   Litho.   **Perf. 13**
2661 A663 400d multicolored   .35

Paintings of Women A664

Designs: 400d, Woman in white dress, flowers, by To Ngoc Van (1906-54) (4-1). 2000d, Washing hair, by Tran Van Can (1906-94) (4-2). 6000d, Standing beside vase of flowers, by To Ngoc Van (4-3). 8000d, Two women, by Tran Van Can (4-4).

1995, Nov. 15   Litho.   **Perf. 13**
2662-2665 A664 Set of 4   3.75

New Year 1996 (Year of the Rat) — A665

Stylized rats: 400d, One carrying fan, one riding horse. 8000d, Four carrying one in palanquin.
13,000d, Marching in parade, carrying banner.

1996, Jan. 2   Litho.   **Perf. 13**
2666 A665   400d multicolored   .20
2667 A665   8000d multicolored   1.75
Souvenir Sheet
2668 A665 13,000d multi, vert.   2.75
No. 2668 contains one 32x43mm stamp.

Dinosaurs — A666

Designs: 400d, Tsintaosaurus. 1000d, Archaeopteryx. 2000d, Psittacosaurus. 3000d, Hypsilophodon. 13,000d, Parasaurolophus.

1996, Mar. 6
2669-2673 A666 Set of 5   4.50

Kingfishers A667

Designs: 400d, Halcyon smyrnensis. 1000d, Megaceryle alcyon. 2000d, Alcedo Atthis. 4000d, Halcyon coromanda. 12,000d, Ceryle rudis.

1996, Mar. 11
2674-2678 A667 Set of 5   4.50

Flowers A668

Various flowers: No. 2679, 400d, brown (5-1). No. 2680, 400d, claret (5-2). No. 2681, 400d, green (5-3). No. 2682, 400d, blue (5-4). No. 2683, 5000d, red (5-5), vert.

Perf. 13x13½, 13½x13
1996, Jan. 10   Litho.
2679-2683 A668 Set of 5   1.25

8th Vietnamese Communist Party Congress — A669

Designs: 400d, Ho Chi Minh (2-1). 3000d, Stylized dove, satellite dish, electrical towers, hammer & sickle, building, olive branch (2-2).

1996, Feb. 3   **Perf. 13**
2684-2685 A669 Set of 2   .75

Asian Sites — A670

Monuments and statues in: 400d, Hanoi. 2000d, Thailand. 3000d, Bhubanesvar, India. 4000d, Kyoto, Japan. 10,000d, Borobudur, Java.

1996, Feb. 10   Litho.   **Perf. 13**
2686-2690 A670 Set of 5   4.50
See Nos. 2773-2777.

Statues — A671

Various statues of men in traditional costumes of early warriors: 400d, 600d, 1000d, 2000d, 3000d, 5000d, 6000d, 8000d.

1996   Litho.   **Perf. 13½x13**
2691-2698 A671 Set of 8   5.50

Central Committee, 50th Anniv. — A672

1996, May 22   **Perf. 13**
2699 A672 400d multicolored   .25

UNICEF, 50th Anniv. A673

Designs: 400d, Children of different races, cultures. 7000d, Plant, emblem, water droplets containing representations of education, drinking water, medicine, food.

1996, May 15
2700-2701 A673 Set of 2   1.75

Red Cross of Viet Nam, 50th Anniv. A674

1996, May 8   **Perf. 13½**
2702 A674 3000d Quotation, Ho Chi Minh   .75

A675

Traditional Musical Instruments: a, 400d, Mandolin. b, 3000d, Bow and string instrument. c, 4000d, Square-shaped guitar-like instrument. d, 9000d, Zither.

1996, Apr. 24   **Perf. 13½x13**
2703 A675 Sheet of 4, #a.-d.   3.50
China '96 Intl. Philatelic Exhibition.

A676

1996, May 20   **Perf. 13**
Insects: 400d, Cincindela japonica. 500d, Calodema wallacei. 1000d, Mylabris oculata. 4000d, Chrysochroa buqueti. 5000d, Ophioniea nigrofasciata. 12,000d, Carabus tauricus.
2704-2709 A676 Set of 6   5.00

1996 Summer Olympic Games, Atlanta A677

Designs: 2000d, Soccer. 4000d, Sailing. 5000d, Field hockey.

1996, July 8
2710-2712 A677 Set of 3   2.75

Euro '96, European Soccer Championships, Great Britain — A678

Designs: a, 400d, Net, goalie. b, 8000d, Player making shot on goal.

1996, June 1
2713 A678 Pair, #a.-b.   2.00
No. 2713 is a continuous design.

Aircraft A679

400d, Airbus A320. 1000d, AN-72. 2000d, MD-11F. 6000d, RJ-85. 10,000d, B747-400F. 13,000d, Space shuttle carried by Boeing 747.

1996, June 1
2714-2718 A679 Set of 5   4.50
Souvenir Sheet
Perf. 13½
2719 A679 13,000d multicolored   2.75

Stamp Day
A680

1996, Aug. 15   **Perf. 13**
2720 A680 400d No. 1L57 (1-1)   .25

Paintings by Nguyen Sáng (1923-88) A681

400d, Woman, vase of flowers (2-1). 8000d, Soldiers returning from battle (2-2).
1996, Sept. 10   **Perf. 13**
2721-2722 A681 Set of 2   2.00

Hue School, Cent. — A682

400d, Women walking beside entrance (2-1). 3000d, View of portals, building (2-2).
1996, Sept. 5
2723-2724 A682 Set of 2   .75

Mushrooms A683

Designs: 400d, Aleuria aurantia. 500d, Morchella conica. 1000d, Anthurus archeri. 4000d, Laetiporus serlphureus. 5000d, Filoboletus manipularis. 12,000d, Tremiscus helvelloides.
1996, Aug. 26   Litho.   **Perf. 13**
2725-2730 A683 Set of 6   5.25

Wild Animals — A684

Designs: a, 400d, Pygathrix nemacus. b, 2000d, Panthera tigris. c, 4000d, Rhinoceros sondaicus. d, 10,000d, Balearica regulorum.
1996, Oct. 10   Litho.   **Perf. 13**
2731 A684 Sheet of 4, #a.-d.   3.75
Taipei '96.

Campaign Promoting Iodized Salt — A685

1996, Nov. 2   Litho.   **Perf. 13**
2732 A685 400d multicolored   .40

Natl. Liberation Movement, 50th Anniv. — A686

1996, Dec. 19
2733 A686 400d multicolored   .40

Fruit — A687

Designs: No. 2734, Hylocereus undatus. No. 2735, Durio zibethinus. No. 2736, Persea americana. No. 2737, Garcinia mangostana. No. 2738, Nephelium lappaceum.
1997, Jan. 2   **Perf. 13x13½**
2734-2738 A687 400d Set of 5   .75

New Year 1997 (Year of the Ox) — A688

Stylized oxen: 400d, Adult, calf. 8000d, Adult.
1997, Jan. 8   Litho.   **Perf. 13**
2739-2740 A688 Set of 2   2.00

8th Vietnamese Communist Party Congress — A689

1997, Feb. 3
2741 A689 400d multicolored   .40

Goldfish A690

Various carassius auratus: 400d, 1000d, 5000d, 7000d, 8000d.
1997, Feb. 5
2742-2746 A690 Set of 5   4.00

Souvenir Sheet
Perf. 13½x14
2747 A690 14,000d multicolored   3.00
No. 2747 contains one 43x32mm stamp. Hong Kong '97 (#2747).

Sculptures from Ly Dynasty — A691

Designs: 400d, Serpents in round figure, vert. 1000d, Dragon head, vert. 3000d, People playing instruments. 5000d, Gargoyle. 10,000d, Dragon-head bowl.
1997, Mar. 5
2748-2752 A691 Set of 5   4.50

Scenes — A692

Designs: 400d, Lake, people in park, Hà Tay. 5000d, Footbridge over river, Lai Chau. 7000d, Houses, fog, trees, Lào Cai.
1997, Mar. 20
2753-2755 A692 Set of 3   3.00

Huynh Thuc Khang (1876-1947) A693

1997, Apr. 21   Litho.   **Perf. 13½x13**
2756 A693 400d multi   .35

1997, Apr. 27   **Perf. 13**
1000d, Tennis. 6000d, Shooting.
2757-2758 A694 Set of 2   1.60

Disabled People in Sports — A694

Wild Animals A695

400d, Chrotogale owstoni. 3000d, Lutra lutra. 4000d, Callosciurus erythraeus. 10,000d, Felis bangalensis.
1997, May 2
2759-2762 A695 Set of 4   3.75

A696

1997, May 19
2763 A696 400d Women's Union   .35

A697

1997, Apr. 15   Litho.   **Perf. 13**
Lilium longiflorum ?(Lilies): 400d, Red. 1000d, White. 5000d, Pink & white. 10,000d, Orange.
2764-2767 A697 Set of 4   3.50

PACIFIC 97 — A698

Suspension bridges: 400d, Golden Gate, San Francisco. 5000d, Raippaluoto. 10,000d, Seto.
1997, May 12
2768-2770 A698 Set of 3   3.25

Children A699

400d, UN Convention on the Rights of the Child. 5000d, Breast milk is better.
1997, June 1   Litho.   **Perf. 13**
With Gum
2771-2772 A699 Set of 2   1.25 1.25

Asian Sites Type of 1996
Designs: 400d, Pagoda, Hanoi, Viet Nam. 1000d, Ruins of Persepolis, Iran. 3000d, Statue of woman, Iraq. 5000d, Sacred Rock, Kyaikto, Burma. 10,000d, Statue of Buddha lying down, Sr. Lanka.
1997, June 20   Litho.   **Perf. 13**
2773-2777 A670 Set of 5   4.25

Women's Costumes A700

Various costumes: 400d, Woman holding umbrella, San Chay. 2000d, Woman sewing, wearing jacket tied with sash, Dao quain trang. 5000d, Woman pumping water from well provided by UNICEF, Phù Lá. 10,000d, Woman holding hands in air, Kho Me.

1997, July 8
2778-2781 A700 Set of 4   3.75

A701

A702

1997, July 11
2782 A701 400d multicolored   .35
Prevention of AIDS.

1997, Aug. 8 Litho. *Perf. 13*
2783 A702 400d multicolored   .35
ASEAN, 30th anniv.

Monument to War Martyrs & Invalids, 50th Anniv. — A703

1997, July 25
2784 A703 400d multicolored   .35

Hibiscus — A704

a, 1000d, Hibiscus rosa sinensis. b, 3000d, Hibiscus schizopetalus. c, 5000d, Hibiscus syriacus (pink). d, 9000d, Hibiscus syriacus (yellow).

1997, Aug. 1
2785 A704 Sheet of 4, #a.-d.   3.75

A705

A706

1997, Aug. 26 Litho. *Perf. 13*
2786 A705 400d multicolored   .35
Post and Telecommunications Union, 50th anniv.

1997, Sept. 4
Sea horses: 400d, 1000d, Hippocampus (diff.). 3000d, Hippocampus guttulatus. 5000d, Hippocampus kelloggi. 6000d, Hippocampus japonicus. 7000d, Hippocampus hippocampus.

2787-2792 A706 Set of 6   4.75

19th Southeast Asian Games — A707

1997, Oct. 11 Litho. *Perf. 13*
2793 A707 5000d multicolored   1.25

Handicrafts A708

Designs: No. 2794, 400d, Lamp. No. 2795, 400d, Two baskets. No. 2796, 400d, Swan-shaped basket. No. 2797, 400d, Deer-shaped basket. 2000d, Basket with handle.

1998, Jan. 1 Litho. *Perf. 13*
2794-2798 A708 Set of 5   1.10

7th Francophone Summit, Hanoi — A709

1997, Sept. 24 Litho. *Perf. 13½x13*
2799 A709 5000d multicolored   2.25

Birds A710

400d, Syrmaticus ellioti. 3000d, Lophura diardi. 5000d, Phasianus cholchicus. 6000d, Chrysolophus amherstiae. 8000d, Polyplectron germaini.
14,000d, Lophura imperialis.

1997, Oct. 15 *Perf. 13*
2800-2804 A710 Set of 5   4.75
Souvenir Sheet
Perf. 13½
2805 A710 14,000d multicolored   2.75
No. 2805 contains one 43x30mm stamp.

New Year 1998 (Year of the Tiger) A711

Stylized tigers: 400d, Adult with young. 8000d, Adult.

1998, Jan. 5 *Perf. 13*
2806-2807 A711 Set of 2   1.75

Sites in Vietnam A712

Designs: No. 2808, 400d, Rocks, lake, Ninh Thuan. No. 2809, 400d, Lake, cavern, Quang Binh. 10,000d, Village of Quang Nam.

1998, Feb. 2
2808-2810 A712 Set of 3   2.10

Communist Manifesto, 150th Anniv. — A713

1998, Feb. 3
2811 A713 400d multicolored   .35

Bonsai A714

#2812, 400d, Limonia acidissima. #2813, 400d, Deeringia polysperma. #2814, 400d, Pinus merkusii, vert. 4000d, Barringtonia acutangula, vert. 6000d, Ficus elastica, vert. 10,000d, Wrightia religiosa, vert.
No. 2818, Adenium obesum.

1998, Mar. 2
2812-2817 A714 Set of 6   4.25

Souvenir Sheet
Perf. 13½
2818 A714 14,000d multicolored   2.60
No. 2818 contains one 43x32mm stamp.

Tet Offensive, 30th Anniv. — A715

1998, Jan. 30 Litho. *Perf. 1*
2819 A715 400d multicolored   .40

Opera — A716

Designs: a, 400d, Thi kính bi oan. b, 1000d, Thi mâu lên chúa. c, 2000d, Thi mâu-gia nô. d, 4000d, Thi me dôp-Xa trúong. e, 6000d, Thi kính bi phat va. f, 9000d, Thi kính xin sua.

1998, Apr. 20
2820 A716 Sheet of 6, #a.-f.   4.50

Raptors A717

Designs: No. 2821, 400d, Pernis apivorus. No. 2822, 400d, Spizaetus ornatus. No. 2823, 400d, Accipiter gentilis. 3000d, Buteo buteo. 5000d, Circus melanoleucas. 12,000d, Haliaeetus albicilla.

1998, May 4 Litho. *Perf. 13*
2821-2826 A717 Set of 6   4.10

Ho Chi Minh City (Saigon), 300th Anniv. — A718

400d, Tank, natl. flag, Ho Chi Minh as young man, building. 5000d, Monument to Ho Chi Minh, symbols of industry, communications, and transportation.

1998, Apr. 30
2827-2828 A718 Set of 2   1.10

Orchids A719

Designs: 400d, Paphiopedilum appletoni-num. 6000d, Paphiopedilum helenae.

1998, May 18 Litho. **Perf. 13½**
2829-2830 A719 Set of 2 1.40

Children's Paintings A720

UNICEF: 400d, Children, mother in front of home. 5000d, Children on playground.

1998, June 1 **Perf. 13**
2831-2832 A720 Set of 2 1.25

1998 World Cup Soccer Championships, France — A721

Various soccer plays: 400d, 5000d, 7000d.

1998, June 10
2833-2835 A721 Set of 3 2.50

Sculptures of the Tran Dynasty A722

Ornate designs: No. 2836, 400d, Serpent. No. 2837, 400d, Two people. 1000d, Shown. 8000d, Person. 9000d, Face.

1998, June 15 Litho. **Perf. 13**
2836-2840 A722 Set of 5 3.50 3.50

A723

1998, July 13
2841 A723 2000d multicolored .70 .70

Stamp Day — A725

1998, Aug. 15
2843 A725 400d Bell's telephone .35 .35

Ton Duc Thang (1888-1980) A726

1998, Aug. 20
2844 A726 400d multicolored .35 .35

Moths A727

Designs: No. 2845, 400d, Antheraea helferi. No. 2846, 400d, Attacus atlas. 4000d, Argema mittrei, vert. 10,000d, Argema maenas, vert.

1998, Aug. 22
2845-2848 A727 Set of 4 3.25 3.25

Paintings by Te Bach Thach (Qi Baishi; 1863-1957) A728

Various paintings: 400d, Dragonfly & Lotus. 1000d, Chrysanthemum, Cock & Hens. 2000d, Shrimps, 1948. 4000d, Crabs. 6000d, Lotus & Mandarin Ducks. 9000d, Shrimps, 1949.

1998, Sept. 16
2849-2854 A728 Set of 6 4.25 4.25

Legend of the Lake A729

Designs: No. 2855, Turtle with sword leading boat. No. 2856, Lake.

1998, Oct. 10
2855-2856 A729 400d Set of 2 .70 .70

Le Thanh Tong (1442-1497) — A730

1998, Oct. 12
2857 A730 400d multicolored .35 .35

Souvenir Sheet

Italia '98, Intl. Philatelic Exhibition — A731

Milan Cathedral. Illustration reduced.

1998, Oct. 6 **Perf. 13½**
2858 A731 16,000d multicolored 3.25 3.00

8th Trade Union Congress A732

1998, Oct. 15 Litho. **Perf. 13**
2859 A732 400d multicolored .35 .35

Quy Nhon City, 396th Anniv., Binh Dinh Province, Cent. — A733

1998, Oct. 20
2860 A733 400d multicolored .35 .35

Buoi-Chu Van An Secondary School, 90th Anniv. — A734

Designs: 400d, Students outside school. 5000d, Students listening to speaker.

1998, Nov. 20
2861-2862 A734 Set of 2 1.25 1.25

6th ASEAN Congress, Hanoi — A735

1998, Dec. Litho. **Perf. 13**
2863 A735 1000d multicolored .45 .45

Cuban Revolution, 40th Anniv. (in 1999) — A736

1998, Dec. Litho. **Perf. 13**
2864 A736 400d multicolored .30 .30

A737

Paintings: 400d, Birds, tree, flowers (Spring). 1000d, Flowers, ducks (Summer). 3000d, Flowers, rooster (Fall). 12,000d, Tree, flowers, deer & fawn (Winter).

1999, Jan. 4 Litho. **Perf. 13½x13**
2865-2868 A737 Set of 4 3.00 3.00

A738

New Year 1999 (Year of the Cat): 400d, Cat holding tree branch. 8000d, Two cats. 13,000d, Kittens, ball.

1999, Jan. 6 **Perf. 13½**
2869-2870 A738 Set of 2 1.75 1.75
Souvenir Sheet
2871 A738 13,000d multicolored 2.50 2.50

No. 2871 contains one 32x43mm stamp.

Kites — A739

400d, Large bird with long tail. 5000d, Crescent-shaped. 7000d, Bird with long legs.

1999 Litho. **Perf. 13½x13**
2872-2874 A739 Set of 3 2.25 2.25

Australia '99, World Stamp Expo A740

Various sailing vessels: #2875, 400d, (4-1). #2876, 400d, (4-2). 7000d, (4-3). 9000d, (4-4).

1999, Mar. 10 Litho. **Perf. 13**
2875-2878 A740 Set of 4 3.00 3.00

Intl. Year of the Ocean A724

1998, Aug. 1 Litho. **Perf. 13**
2842 A724 400d multicolored .35 .35

Medicinal Plants A741

Designs: No. 2879, 400d, Kaempferia galanga. No. 2880, 400d, Tacca chantrieri, vert. No. 2881, Alpinia galanga, vert. 6000d, Typhonium trilobatum, vert. 13,000d, Asarum maximum, vert.

1999, Mar. 15
2879-2883 A741 Set of 5   3.75 3.75

Opera Masks A742

Various masks: 400d (6-1). 1000d (6-2). 2000d (6-3). 5000d (6-4). 6000d (6-5). 10,000d (6-6).

1999, Apr. 16   *Perf. 13½*
2884-2889 A742 Set of 6   4.25 4.25

IBRA'99, World Philatelic Exhibition, Nuremberg A743

Octopuses: No. 2890, 400d, Octopus gibertianus. No. 2891, 400d, Philonexis catenulata. 4000d, Paroctopus yendol. 12,000d, Octopus vulgaris.

1999, Apr. 20
2890-2893 A743 Set of 4   3.00 3.00

Landscape Paintings of Southern Viet Nam — A744

#2894, 400d, Sun over lake, Cà Mau. #2895, 400d, Rocks protruding out of water, Kien Giang. 12,000d, Traditional huts, Bac Lieu.

1999, May 4   *Perf. 13*
2894-2896 A744 Set of 3   2.25 2.25

Asia-Pacific Telecommunity, 20th Anniv. — A745

1999, May 10 Litho.   *Perf. 13x13¼*
2897 A745 400d multi   .50 .50

Woodpeckers A746

Designs: 400d, Chrysocolaptes lucidus. 1000d, Picumnus innominatus. 3000d, Picus rabieri. 13,000d, Blythipicus pyrrhotis.

1999, May 18   Litho.   *Perf. 13*
2898-2901 A746 Set of 4   3.00 3.00

UNICEF A747

Designs: 400d, Girl, hand. 5000d, Boy carrying factory.

1999, June 1   Litho.   *Perf. 13*
2902-2903 A747 Set of 2   1.00 1.00

Architecture of Late 19th and Early 20th Centuries — A748

Designs: No. 2904, 400d, Government Office Building, Hanoi (3-1). No. 2905, 400d, History Museum, Ho Chi Minh City (3-2). 12,000d, Duc Ba Cathedral (3-3). 15,000d, Theater, Hanoi.

1999, June 10   *Perf. 13*
2904-2906 A748 Set of 3   2.25 2.25
Souvenir Sheet
Perf. 13½x14
2907 A748 15,000d multi   2.75 2.75
   PhilexFrance '99 (No. 2907). No. 2907 contains one 44x32mm stamp.

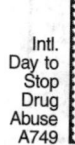

Intl. Day to Stop Drug Abuse A749

1999, June 24   Litho.   *Perf. 13*
2908 A749 400d multicolored   .35 .35

Da Rang Bridge, Phu Yen A750

1999, July 1   Litho.   *Perf. 13*
2909 A750 400d multi   .40 .40

Le Dynasty Sculptures — A751

Designs: No. 2910, 1000d, Man Against Tiger (5-1). No. 2911, 1000d, Phoenix (5-2). 3000d, Playing Chess, vert. (5-3). 7000d, Hostler, vert. (5-4). 9000d, Dragon (5-5).

1999, July 1
2910-2914 A751 Set of 5   3.75 3.75

Birth of World's Six Billionth Person — A752

1999, Aug. 2
2915 A752 400d multi   .35 .35

Chinese Landscapes — A753

Designs: 400d, Park, Beijing (4-1). 2000d, Scenic overlook, Anhwei (4-2). 3000d, Park, Shandong, (4-3). 10,000d, Park, Beijing, diff. (4-4).
   14,000d, Great Wall of China.

1999, Aug. 16   *Perf. 13*
2916-2919 A753 Set of 4   3.00 3.00
Souvenir Sheet
Perf. 13½x14
2920 A753 14,000d multi   2.50 2.50
   China 1999 World Philatelic Exhibition (No. 2920). No. 2920 contains one 43x32mm stamp.

Boat Races A754

Races from regions: 400d, North (3-1). 2000d, Central (3-2). 10,000d, South (3-3).

1999, Sept. 10   *Perf. 13*
2921-2923 A754 Set of 3   2.25 2.25

Women's Costumes A755

Various costumes. #2924, 400d (3-1). #2925, 400d (3-2). #2926, 12,000d (3-3).

1999, Sept. 10
2924-2926 A755 Set of 3   2.25 2.25

Buffalo Fighting Festivals A756

Fighting buffaloes: 400d, (2-1). 5000d, (2-2).

1999, Sept. 15
2927-2928 A756 Set of 2   1.00 1.00

Ngo Quyen (898-944), General — A757

1999, Oct. 21
2929 A757 400d multi   .35 .35

Nguyen Van Sieu (1799-1872), Teacher, Writer — A758

1999, Nov. 2   Litho.   *Perf. 13*
2930 A758 400d multi   .35 .35

Tran Xuan Soan (1849-1923), Anticolonial Leader — A759

1999, Nov. 24
2931 A759 400d multi   .35 .35

United Nations Development Program — A760

Designs: 400d, Mother and child, farmer, fisherman. 8000d, Villagers, buildings.

1999, Dec. 3
2932-2933 A760 Set of 2   1.75 1.75

Viet Nam in the 20th Century — A761

Designs; No. 2934, 400d, Founding of Viet Nam Communist Party (6-1). No. 2935, 400d, Ho Chi Minh's declaration of country's independence (6-2). No. 2936, 1000d, Conquest

of South Viet Nam (6-3). No. 2937, 1000d,
People, dam, high tension wire tower, atom (6-
4). 8000d, People, satellite, satellite dish, dam,
high tension wire tower (6-5). 12,000d, Organizations Viet Nam belongs to (6-6).

2000, Jan. 1 Litho. Perf. 13
With Gum
2934-2939 A761 Set of 6 3.75 3.75
2939a Sheet, #2934-2939, without 4.00 4.00
gum

New Year 2000 (Year of the Dragon) A762

Dragon: 400d, Facing right (2-1). 8000d,
Facing right (2-2).

2000, Jan. 3 Perf. 13½
With Gum
2940-2941 A762 Set of 2 1.75 1.75

Intl. Year of Culture and Peace A763

2000, Jan. 18 With Gum
2942 A763 400d multi .35 .35

Viet Nam Communist Party, 70th Anniv. — A764

#2943, Ho Chi Minh (1890-1969), Pres. (8-
1). #2944, Tran Phu (1904-31), 1st Gen. Sec.
(8-2). #2945, Le Hong Phong (1902-42), Gen.
Sec. (8-3). #2946, Ha Huy Tap (1902-41),
Gen. Sec. (8-4). #2947, Nguyen Van Cu
(1912-41), Gen. Sec. (8-5). #2948, Truong
Chinh (1907-88), Gen. Sec. (8-6). #2949, Le
Duan (1907-86), Gen. Sec. (8-7). #2950,
Nguyen Van Linh (1915-98), Gen. Sec. (8-8).

2000, Feb. 2 Perf. 13
With Gum
2943-2950 A764 400d Set of 8 1.10 1.10

Cockfighting — A765

Postures: No. 2951, 400d, Song long cuoc
(4-1). No. 2952, 400d, Long vu da dao (4-2).
7000d, Song long phuong hoang (4-3). 9000d,
Nhan o giap chien (4-4).

2000, Feb. 8 Litho. Perf. 13
2951-2954 A765 Set of 4 3.00 3.00
Imperf., #2951-2954 5.75

Bangkok 2000 Stamp Exhibition A766

Palanquins: 400d, Imperial court roofed palanquin (3-1). 7000d, Palanquin without roof (3-
2). 8000d, Roofed palanquin (3-3).
15,000d, Palanquin in procession.

2000, Mar. 10 With Gum
2955-2957 A766 Set of 3 2.75 2.75
Souvenir Sheet
2958 A766 15,000d multi 2.75 2.75

Legend of Lac Long Quan and Au Co — A767

Designs: No. 2959, 400d, Lang Long Quan
and Au Co marry (6-1). No. 2960, 400d, Au
Co, gives birth to 100 sons (6-2). 500d, Au Co
takes 50 children to forest (6-3). 3000d, Lac
Long Quan takes 50 children to sea (6-4).
4000d, Eldest son, Hung Vuong ascends to
throne (6-5). 11,000d, Vietnamese ethnic
groups as descendents (6-6).

2000, Apr. 4 Perf. 13½
2959-2964 A767 Set of 6 3.25 3.25

Souvenir Sheet

The Stamp Show 2000, London — A768

No. 2965 — Fire engines: a, 400d, Iveco
Magirus, Germany. b, 1000d, Hino, Japan. c,
5000d, ZIL 103E, Russia. d, 12,000d, FPS.32
Camiva, France.
Illustration reduced.

2000, May 15 Perf. 13
2965 A768 Sheet of 4, #a-d 3.00 3.00

Worldwide Fund for Nature A769

Pseudoryx nghetinhensis: No. 2966, 400d,
Head, vine (4-1). No. 2967, 400d, In grass (4-
2). 5000d, Near pond (4-3). 10,000d, Head,
mountains (4-4).

2000, May 18 Perf. 13½
With Gum
2966-2969 A769 Set of 4 2.75 2.75
2969a Sheet, 2 each #2966-2969 5.50 5.50

Ho Chi Minh (1890-1969) A770

2000, May 19 Perf. 13
With Gum
2970 A770 400d multi .35 .35

World Stamp Expo 2000, Anaheim A771

Water puppets: No. 2971, 400d, Chu teu (6-
1). No. 2972, 400d, Fairy (6-2). No. 2973,
400d, Man plowing field (6-3). 3000d, Female
peasant (6-4). 9000d, Drummer (6-5).
11,000d, Fisherman (6-6).

2000, June 28 Perf. 13½
2971-2976 A771 Set of 6 4.00 4.00

50th Vietnam Youth Volunteers' Day — A772

2000, July 15 Perf. 13
With Gum
2977 A772 400d multi .35 .35

Phu Dong Natl. Youth Sports Festival A773

2000, July 20 With Gum
2978 A773 400d multi .35 .35

Fish A774

Designs: No. 2979, 400d, Cephalopholis
miniatus (6-1). No. 2980, 400d, Pomacanthus
imperator (6-2). No. 2981, 400d, Epinephelus
merra (6-3). 4000d, Zancius cornutus, vert. (6-
4). 6000d, Chaetodon ephippium, vert. (6-5).
12,000d, Heniochus acuminatus, vert. (6-6).
15,000d, Chaetodon lunula.

2000, Aug. 7 Perf. 13
2979-2984 A774 Set of 6 4.00 4.00
Souvenir Sheet
Perf. 13½x13¾
2985 A774 15,000d multi 2.75 2.75

Post and Telegraph Dept., 55th Anniv. A775

2000, Aug. 15 Perf. 13
With Gum
2986 A775 400d multi .35 .35

People's Police, 50th Anniv. A776

Designs: 400d, Ho Chi Minh, five policemen.
2000d, Policeman checking documents, vert.

2000, Aug. 19 Litho. Perf. 13
With Gum
2987-2988 A776 Set of 2 .55 .55

Gen. Nguyen Tri Phuong, 200th Anniv. of Birth — A777

2000, Aug. 31 Perf. 13½
With Gum
2989 A777 400d multi .25 .25

UN Right of the Child Conference, 10th Anniv. — A778

Emblem and: 400d, Boy and girl. 5000d,
Five children, vert.

2000, Sept. 8 Perf. 13
2990-2991 A778 Set of 2 1.25 1.25

2000 Summer Olympics, Sydney — A779

Designs: 400d, Running. 6000d, Shooting.
7000d, Taekwondo, vert.

2000, Sept. 15
2992-2994 A779 Set of 3 2.25 2.25

Gen. Tran Hung Dao, 700th Anniv. of Death. — A780

2000, Sept. 17 With Gum
2995 A780 400d multi .25 .25

Birds — A781

Designs: No. 2996, 400d, Leiothrix
argentauris. No. 2997, 400d, Pitta ellioti. No.
2998, 400d, Pomatorinus ferruginosus. 5000d,

Dicrurus paradiceus, vert. 7000d, Mela-nochlora sultanea, vert. 10,000d, Stachyris striolata, vert.

2000, Sept. 28   **Perf. 13½**
2996-3001   A781   Set of 6   4.00 4.00
   Souvenir Sheet
      Perf. 13½x13¾
3002   A781   15,000d Trena puella   2.75 2.75

No. 3002 contains one 42x31mm stamp. España 2000 Intl. Philatelic Exhibition (No. 3002).

Vietnam Philately Association, 40th Anniv. — A782

2000, Oct. 6   **Perf. 13**
      With Gum
3003   A782   400d No. 820   .25   .25

Farmer's Association, 70th Anniv. — A783

2000, Oct. 14   **With Gum**
3004   A783   400d multi   .25   .25

Women's Union, 70th Anniv. A784

2000, Oct. 14   **With Gum**
3005   A784   400d multi   .25   .25

Hanoi, 990th Anniv. A785

Designs: 400d, Building, and Ly Thai To, founder of Hanoi. 3000d, Temple, two people, monuments. 10,000d, Peasants with goods, building.
15,000d, People and doves.

2000, Oct. 15   **Perf. 13**
3006-3008   A785   Set of 3   2.25 2.25
   Souvenir Sheet
      Perf. 13½x13¾
3009   A785   15,000d multi   2.75 2.75

Bats — A786

Designs: No. 3010, 400d, Scotmanes ornatus. No. 3011, 400d, Pteropus lylei. 2000d, Rhinolophus paradoxolophus. 6000d,

Eonycteris spelaea. 11,000d, Cynopterus sphinx.

2000, Oct. 16   **Perf. 13**
3010-3014   A786   Set of 5   3.25 3.25

Fatherland Front, 70th Anniv. — A787

2000, Oct. 18   **With Gum**
3015   A787   400d multi   .25   .25

6th Natl. Emulation Congress A788

Designs: 400d, People at work. 3000d, Symbols of industry, vert.

2000, Nov. 10   **With Gum**
3016-3017   A788   Set of 2   .90   .90

Flowers A789

Designs: 400d, Oxyspora sp. 5000d, Melanstoma villosa, vert.

2000, Nov. 15   **Perf. 13½**
      With Gum
3018-3019   A789   Set of 2   1.00 1.00

Hon Khoai Uprising, 60th Anniv. A790

2000, Dec. 13   **Perf. 13**
      With Gum
3020   A790   400d multi   .25   .25

Advent of New Millennium A791

2001, Jan. 1   **With Gum**
3021   A791   400d multi   .25   .25

New Year 2001 (Year of the Snake) A792

Snake and: 400d, Pink flowers. 8000d, Yellow flowers.

2001, Jan. 1   **Perf. 13½**
      With Gum
3022-3023   A792   Set of 2   1.60 1.60

Hong Kong 2001 Stamp Exhibition — A793

Fish: 400d, Toxotes microlepis. 800d, Cosmocheilus harmandi. 2000d, Anguilla bicolor pacifica. 3000d, Chitala ornata. 7000d, Megalops cyprinoides. 8000d, Probarbus jullieni.

2001, Jan. 18   Litho.   **Perf. 13**
3024-3029   A793   Set of 6   3.50 3.50

Nobel Prize, Cent. A794

2001, Jan. 27   **Perf. 13½**
      With Gum
3030   A794   400d multi   .35   .35

Four Seasons — A795

No. 3031: a, 400d, Peach blossoms and birds (spring). b, 800d, Cotton rose and pheasant (summer). c, 4000d, Chrysanthemum and phoenix (autumn). d, 10,000d, Pine tree and cranes (winter).

2001, Feb. 1   **Perf. 13¼x13**
      With Gum
3031   A795   Sheet of 4, #a-d   2.40 2.40

Wild Fruits — A796

Designs: No. 3032, 400d, Rubus cochinchinensis. No. 3033, 400d, Rhizophora mucronata. No. 3034, 400d, Podocarpus neriifolius. No. 3035, 400d, Magnolia pumila. 15,000d, Taxus chinensis.

2001, Feb. 8   **Perf. 13½**
      With Gum
3032-3036   A796   Set of 5   2.60 2.60

Landscapes — A797

Designs: No. 3037, 400d, Co Tien Mountain (3-1). No. 3038, 400d, Dong Pagoda, Yen Tu

Mountain (3-2). 10,000d, King Dinh Temple (3-3).

2001, Feb. 23   **Perf. 1**
3037-3039   A797   Set of 3   2.00 2.0

Nhan Dan Newspaper, 50th Anniv. — A798

2001, Mar. 11   **With Gum**
3040   A798   400d multi   .35   .3

Rubies Found in Tan Huong A799

Designs: 400d, 1960-gram ruby. 6000d, 2160-gram "Viet Nam Star."

2001, Mar. 20   **With Gum**
3041-3042   A799   Set of 2   1.10 1.10

Ho Chi Minh Youth Union, 70th Anniv. — A800

2001, Mar. 26   Litho.   **Perf. 13**
      With Gum
3043   A800   400d multi   .35   .35

9th Communist Party Congress — A801

Designs: 400d, Ho Chi Minh, flag, map (2-1). 3000d, Hammer and sickle, Ngoc Lu bronze drum head, symbols of technology, vert (2-2).

2001, Apr. 18   **With Gum**
3044-3045   A801   Set of 2   .55   .55

Fauna in Cat Tien Natl. Park — A802

Designs: 400d, Arborophila davidi (4-1). 800d, Stichophthalma uemurai (4-2). 3000d, Rhinoceros sondaicus (4-3). 5000d, Crocodylus siamensis (4-4).

2001, Apr. 30   **Perf. 13½**
3046-3049   A802   Set of 4   2.00 2.00

Mushrooms
A803

Designs: No. 3050, 400d, Phallus indusiatus (7-1). No. 3051, 400d, Aseroe arachnoidea (7-2). No. 3052, 400d, Phallus tenuis (7-3). 2000d, Phallus impudicus (7-4). 5000d, Phallus rugulosus (7-5). 6000d, Simblum periphragmoides (7-6). 7000d, Mutinus bambusinus (7-7).

2001, May 2   Set of 7   4.00 4.00
3050-3056 A803
A number has been reserved for a souvenir sheet for this set.

Mushrooms Type of 2001

Design: 13,000d,   Pseudocolus schellenbergiae.

2001, May 2   Litho.   **Perf. 13½x13¾**
3057 A803 13,000d multi   2.25 2.25
No. 3057 contains one 42x31mm stamp.

Ho Chi Minh Young Pioneer's League, 60th Anniv. — A804

2001, May 15   Litho.   **Perf. 13**
With Gum
3058 A804 400d multi   .35 .35

Viet Minh Front, 60th Anniv. A805

2001, May 19   **With Gum**
3059 A805 400d multi   .35 .35

Campaign Against Smoking — A806

2001, May 30   **Perf. 13¼x13½**
With Gum
3060 A806 800d multi   .45 .45

Children A807

Designs: 400d, Two children, UNICEF emblem. 5000d, Five children, UN emblem.

2001, June 1   **Perf. 13½**
3061-3062 A807   Set of 2   .90 .90
Children's safety day (#3061); UN Special Session on Children, Washington, DC (#3062).

Diesel Locomotives — A808

Designs: No. 3063, 400d, D18E (6-1). No. 3064, 400d, D4H (6-2). 800d, D11H (6-3). 2000d, D5H (6-4). 6000d, D9E (6-5). 7000d, D12E (6-6).

2001, June 5   **Perf. 13**
3063-3068 A808   Set of 6   3.00 3.00
Souvenir Sheet
Perf. 13½x13¾
3069 A808 13,000d D11H, diff.   2.25 2.25
No. 3069 contains one 43x32mm stamp.

Orchids
A809

Designs: No. 3070, 800d, Vanda sp. (6-1). No. 3071, 800d, Dendrobium lowianum (6-2). No. 3072, 800d, Phajus wallichii (6-3). No. 3073, 800d, Habenaria medioflexa (6-4). No. 3074, 800d, Arundina graminifolia, vert. (6-5). 12,000d, Calanthe clavata, vert. (6-6).

Perf. 13½x13¼, 13¼x13½
2001, July 5
With Gum
3070-3075 A809   Set of 6   2.60 2.60

Phila Nippon '01 — A810

Butterflies: No. 3076, 800d, Troides aeacus (6-1). No. 3077, 800d, Inachis io (6-2). No. 3078, 800d, Ancyluris formosissima (6-3). 5000d, Cymothoe sanguris (6-4). 7000d, Taenaris selene (6-5). 10,000d, Trogonoptera brookiana (6-6).
13,000d, Atrophaneura horishanus, vert.

2001, July 16   **Perf. 13½x13¼**
3076-3081 A810   Set of 6   4.00 4.00
Souvenir Sheet
Perf. 13¾x13½
3082 A810 13,000d multi   2.25 2.25
No. 3082 contains one 32x42mm stamp.

2002 World Cup Soccer Championships, Japan and Korea — A811

No. 3083: a, 800d, Player with red shirt. b, 3000d, Player with white shirt.

2001, July 24   **Perf. 13**
With Gum
3083 A811   Horiz. pair, #a-b   .65 .65

Musical Instruments — A812

Designs: No. 3084, 800d, Ho gáo (6-1). No. 3085, 800d, Kenh (6-2). No. 3086, 800d, Dàn tú, vert. (6-3). 2000d, Dàn t'rung, vert. (6-4). 6000d, Trong kinang, vert . (6-5). 9000d, Tính tau, vert. (6-6).

Perf. 13x13¼, 13¼x13
2001, Aug. 4   Set of 6   2.60 2.60
3084-3089 A812

Year of Dialogue Among Civilizations — A813

2001, Oct. 9   Litho.   **Perf. 13¼x13½**
With Gum
3090 A813 800d multi   .35 .35

Tran Huy Lieu (1901-69), Writer — A814

2001, Nov. 5   **Perf. 13x12¾**
With Gum
3091 A814 800d multi   .35 .35

Nam Cao (1917-51), Writer A815

2001, Nov. 30   **Perf. 13x13¼**
With Gum
3092 A815 800d multi   .35 .35

A816   A817

2001   **Perf. 13½**
With Gum
3093 A816   800d multi   .20 .20
3094 A817   3000d multi   .50 .50

New Year 2002 (Year of the Horse) A818

Horse facing: 800d, Right. 8000d, Left. 14,000d, Horse galloping.

2002, Jan. 2   **Perf. 13½**
With Gum
3095-3096 A818   Set of 2   1.40 1.40
Souvenir Sheet
Perf. 13½x13¼
3097 A818 14,000d multi   2.25 2.25
No. 3097 contains one 42x31mm stamp.

Opera Costumes A819

Designs: No. 3098, 1000d, Giáp Tuong Nam (6-1). No. 3099, 1000d, Giáp Tuong Nu (6-2). 2000d, Giáp Tuong Phan Dien (6-3). 3000d, Long Chan (6-4). 5000d, Giáp Tuong Phien (6-5). 9000d, Lung Xiem Quan Giáp (6-6).

2002, Jan. 15   **Perf. 13**
3098-3103 A819   Set of 6   3.25 3.25

Vo Thi Sáu, Heroine, 50th Anniv. of Death A820

2002, Jan. 23   **Perf. 13x13¼**
3104 A820 1000d multi   .25 .25

Program Implementation of 9th Communist Party Congress A821

Designs: 800d, Map, satellite, buildings, dam, power lines, bridge, computer keyboard (2-1). 3000d, Flag, building, doves, people (2-2).

2002, Feb. 1   **Perf. 13¼x13**
With Gum
3105-3106 A821   Set of 2   .90 .90

Cacti — A822

Designs: No. 3107, 1000d, Echinocereus albatus (5-1). No. 3108, 1000d, Echinocereus delaetii (5-2). No. 3109, 1000d, Cylindropuntia bigelowii (5-3). 5000d, Echinocereus triglochidatus (5-4). 10,000d, Epiphyllum truncatum (5-5).

2002, Feb. 18   **Perf. 13¼x13½**
3107-3111 A822   Set of 5   3.00 3.00

Victor Hugo (1802-85), French Writer A823

2002, Feb. 26   **Perf. 13x13¼**
With Gum
3112 A823 1000d multi   .30   .30

A824

2002   **Litho.**   **Perf. 13x13¼**
With Gum
3113 A824 800d multi   .35   .35

Birds — A825

Designs: 600d, Actinodura sodangorum (6-1). No. 3115, 800d, Garrulax ngoclinhensis (6-2). No. 3116, 800d, Garrulax pectoralis (6-3). No. 3117, 800d, Pomatorhinus hypoleucos (6-4). 5000d, Minla ignotincta (6-5). 8000d, Minla cyanouroptera (6-6).

2002, Mar. 15   **Litho.**   **Perf. 13½**
With Gum
3114-3119 A825   Set of 6   2.40 2.40

Landscapes
A826

Designs: No. 3120, 800d, Ganh Son, Binh Thuan (3-1). No. 3121, 800d, Dawn over Tung Estuary, Quang Tri (3-2). 10,000d, Sa Huynh Harbor, Quang Ngai (3-3).

2002, Mar. 15   **With Gum**
3120-3122 A826   Set of 3   1.75 1.75

Primates — A827

Designs: 600d, Trachypithecus poliocephalus (8-1). 800d, Trachypithecus delacouri (8-2). 1000d, Rhinopithecus avunculus (8-3). 2000d, Pygathrix cinerea (8-4). 4000d, Nomascus concolor (8-5). 5000d, Trachypithecus laotum hatinhensis (8-6). 7000d, Trachypithecus phayrei (8-7). 9000d, Pygathrix nemaeus (8-8).

2002, Apr. 10
3123-3130 A827   Set of 8   4.50 4.50
3130a   Souvenir sheet, #3123-3130 + label   4.50 4.50

Bui Thi Xuan, 200th Anniv. of Death — A828

2002, Apr. 13   **Perf. 13**
With Gum
3131 A828 1000d multi   .20   .20

Souvenir Sheet

2002 World Cup Soccer Championships, Japan and Korea — A829

Color of player or players: a, 1000d, Blue. b, 2000d, Red. c, 5000d, Red violet. d, 7000d, Green.

2002, June 1   **Litho.**
With Gum
3132 A829   Sheet of 4, #a-d   2.40 2.40

Flowers — A830

Designs: 600d, Paphiopedilum concolor (7-1). 800d, Sterculia lanceolata (7-2). 1000d, Schefflera alongensis (7-3). 2000d, Hibiscus tiliaceus (7-4). 3000d, Mussaenda glabra (7-5). 5000d, Boniodendron parviflorum (7-6). 9000d, Bauhinia ornata.

2002, June 5
3133-3139 A830   Set of 7   3.25 3.25

Chau Van Liem, Communist Party Leader, Cent. of Birth — A831

2002, June 28   **Litho.**   **Perf. 13**
With Gum
3140 A831 800d multi   .35   .35

Stamp Day — A832

2002, July 1   **Perf. 13x12¾**
With Gum
3141 A832 800d multi + label   .35   .35

Soft-shell Turtles
A834

Designs: 800d, Pelochelys bibroni (4-1). 2000d, Pelodiscus sinensis. 5000d, Palea steindachneri. 9000d, Trionyx cartilagineus.

2002, July 15   **Litho.**   **Perf. 13½**
3143-3146 A834   Set of 4   2.60 2.60
3146a   Souvenir sheet, 2 each #3143-3146   5.25 5.25

Viet Nam — Laos Diplomatic Relations, 40th Anniv. A835

2002, July 18   **Perf. 13**
With Gum
3147 A835 800d multi   .35   .35

Civil Aircraft A836

Designs: 800d, Super King Air B200 in air (4-1). 2000d, Fokker 70 (4-2). 3000d, ATR-72 (4-3). 8000d, Boeing 767-300 (4-4). 14,000d, Super King Air B200 on ground.

2002, Aug. 1   **Perf. 13**
With Gum
3148-3151 A836   Set of 4   2.25 2.25
Souvenir Sheet
Perf. 13½x13¾
3152 A836 14,000d multi   2.25 2.25

Autumn Festival Lanterns A837

Designs: No. 3153, 800d, Den Ong Sao (4-1). No. 3154, 800d, Den Ong Su (4-2). 2000d, Den Con Tho Om Trang (4-3). 7000d, Den Xep (4-4).

2002, Aug. 16   **Perf. 13½**
With Gum
3153-3156 A837   Set of 4   1.50 1.50

Viet Nam Posts and Telecommunications Trade Union, 55th Anniv. — A838

2002, Aug. 23   **Perf. 13**
With Gum
3157 A838 800d multi   .35   .35

Bridges — A839

Designs: No. 3158, 800d, Cau Long Bien (4-1). No. 3159, 800d, Cau Song Han (4-2). 2000d, Cau Truong Tien (4-3). 10,000d, Cau My Thuan (4-4).

2002, Sept. 27   **Perf. 13x13½**
With Gum
3158-3161 A839   Set of 4   2.00 2.00

Communist Party's Ideology and Culture Commission, 72nd Anniv. — A840

2002, Oct. 10   **Perf. 13**
With Gum
3162 A840 800d multi   .35   .35

Hanoi Medical University, Cent. A841

2002, Nov. 15   **With Gum**
3163 A841 800d multi   .35   .35

Teachers' Day — A842

2002, Nov. 20   **With Gum**
3164 A842 800d multi   .35   .35

New Year 2003 (Year of the Ram) — A843

Various goats with background colors of: 800d, Rose pink (2-1). 8000d, Orange (2-2).

2002, Dec. 15   **Perf. 13½**
With Gum
3165-3166 A843   Set of 2   1.25 1.25

Viet Nam — South Korea Diplomatic Relations, 10th Anniv. — A844

Pagoda from: No. 3167, 800d, Viet Nam (2-1). No. 3168, 800d, South Korea (2-2).

...002, Dec. 21   **Perf. 13**
With Gum
...167-3168 A844 Set of 2   .65 .65

Starting with the 2003 issues, stamps
re gummed unless otherwise
dicated.

Landscapes — A845

Designs: 800d, Rung Cao Su, Bình Phuoc
3-1). 3000d, Ao Bà Om, Trà Vinh (3-2).
000d, Mot nhanh song Rach Gam-Xoài Mút,
Tien Giang (3-3).

2003, Feb. 1   **Litho.**   **Perf. 13**
3169-3171 A845 Set of 3   1.40 1.40

Viet Nam Culture
Program, 60th
Anniv. — A846

2003, Feb. 3
3172 A846 800d multi   .30 .30

Viet Nam Cinema Association, 50th
Anniv. — A847

2003, Mar. 1
3173 A847 1000d multi   .30 .30

Khanh
Hoa
Province,
350th
Anniv.
A848

2003, Mar. 25
3174 A848 800d multi   .30 .30

Cycle Rickshaws
A849

Cycle rickshaws from: 800d, Hanoi. 3000d,
Ho Chi Minh City. 8000d, Haiphong.

2003, Apr. 1
3175-3177 A849 Set of 3   1.60 1.60

Adventures of the
Cricket — A850

2003, May 1   **Perf. 13¼x13½**
3178   Horiz. strip of 6   2.60 2.60
   a. A850 800d Toi là út. . . (6-1)   .20 .20
   b. A850 1000d Chang bao. . . (6-2)   .20 .20
   c. A850 2000d Toi an han. . . (6-3)   .25 .25
   d. A850 3000d Toi và Trui. . . (6-4)   .40 .40
   e. A850 5000d Mot ngày. . . (6-5)   .65 .65
   f. A850 8000d Tu nay the. . . (6-6)   1.00 1.00

Animals in
Ba Vi
National
Park — A851

Designs: No. 3179, 800d, Manis
pentadactyla (4-1). No. 3180, 800d, Petaurista
petaurista (4-2). 5000d, Selenarctos
thibetanus (4-3). 10,000d, Capricornis sumatraensis (4-4).

2003, June 5   **Perf. 13½**
3179-3182 A851 Set of 4   2.25 2.25

22nd South
East Asian
Games, Viet
Nam — A852

Designs: 800d, Soccer (4-1). 2000d, Hurdles (4-2). 3000d, Kayaking (4-3). 7000d,
Wrestling (4-4).
10,000d, Games emblem, mascot, stadium.

2003, July 1   **Perf. 13**
3183-3186 A852 Set of 4   1.75 1.75
Souvenir Sheet
Perf. 13½x13¾
3187 A852 10,000d multi   1.25 1.25

Ninth Congress
of Viet Nam
Federation of
Trade
Unions — A853

2003, July 28   **Perf. 13**
3188 A853 800d multi   .30 .30

Camellias — A854

Designs: 800d, Camellia petelotii (4-1).
1000d, Camellia rubriflora (4-2). 5000d,

Camellia vietnamensis (4-3). 6000d, Camellia
gilberti (4-4).

2003, Sept. 1   **Perf. 13½**
3189-3192 A854 Set of 4   1.75 1.75
Bangkok 2003 World Philatelic Exhibition.

Orchids
A855

Designs: 800d, Paphiopedilum dianthum (2-
1). 8000d, Pleione bulbocodioides (2-2).

2003, Oct. 1   **Perf. 13**
3193-3194 A855 Set of 2   1.10 1.10

Asian
Elephants
A856

Designs: 800d, Elephant with trunk
extended (4-1). 1000d, Elephants and riders
(4-2). 2000d, Elephant with trunk down (4-3).
8000d, Two elephants (4-4)

2003, Oct. 1   **Perf. 13½**
3195-3198 A856 Set of 4   1.50 1.50
3198a   Miniature sheet, 2 each   3.00 3.00
    #3195-3198

My Son World Heritage Site — A857

Various ruins: 800d, (3-1). 3000d, (3-2).
8000d (3-3).
10,000d, Temple (43x32mm).
Illustration reduced.

2003, Dec. 1   **Perf. 13x13¼**
3199-3201 A857 Set of 3   1.50 1.50
Souvenir Sheet
Perf. 13½x13¾
3202 A857 10,000d multi   1.25 1.25

New Year
2004 (Year
of the
Monkey)
A858

Monkeys and: 800d, Apple tree (2-1).
8000d, Palm leaf (2-2).

2003, Dec. 1   **Perf. 13½**
3203-3204 A858 Set of 2   1.10 1.10

Ngo Gia Tu (1908-
35), Leader of 1926
Strike — A859

2003, Dec. 30   **Perf. 13¼x13**
3205 A859 800d multi   .30 .30

Congratulations
A860

Designs: 800d, Flowers (2-1). 8000d, Bird
with envelope (2-2).

2004, Jan. 1   **Perf. 13 Syncopated**
3206-3207 A860 Set of 2   1.10 1.10

Shells
A861

Designs: 800d, Murex trocheli (3-1). 3000d,
Murex haustellum (3-2). 8000d, Chicoreus
ramosus (3-3).

2004, Feb. 1   **Perf. 13**
3208-3210 A861 Set of 3   1.50 1.50

SEMI-POSTAL STAMPS

World Communications Year — SP1

#B1, Hands holding envelope with ITU
emblem. #B2, Satellite dish antenna.

    Unwmk.
1983, Nov. 1   **Litho.**   **Perf. 11**
B1-   SP1 50xu +10xu Set of 2
B2   3.75

AIR POST STAMP

AP1

    Unwmk.
1959, Nov. 20   **Litho.**   **Perf. 11**
C1 AP1 20xu blue & black   8.00 6.00

POSTAGE DUE STAMPS

Nos. 1-4 exist with handstamps of
"TT" in a diamond. It is unclear to the
editors if these stamps were used.

D1

D2

1955   **Typo.**   **Perf. 11½**
J14 D1   50d brown & yellow   12.00 7.00

1958, Dec. 1   Litho.   Perf. 12½
J15 D2   10d purple & red
J16 D2   20d orange & aqua
J17 D2   100d gray blue & red
J18 D2   300d olive grn & red
    Nos. J15-J18 (4)   12.50 12.00

MILITARY STAMPS

M1

Perf. 12½
1958, May 1   Litho.   Unwmk.
M1 M1 multicolored   8.50 5.00

Invalids in
Field
Paddy
M2

1959-60   Litho.   Perf. 11
M2 M2 org brn & brown
M3 M2 grey blue & olive
    Nos. M2-M3 (2)   7.50 3.00
Issued: No. M2, 3/14/59; No. M3, 7/27/60.

Soldier, Train — M3

1959, July 1
M4 M3 bluish green   4.50 1.75

Frontier
Guard — M4

1961, Jan. 3
M5 M4 multicolored   10.00 6.50

Naval
Patrol
M5

1962, June 15
M6 M5 multicolored   4.50 2.50

Military Medal,
Invalid's
Badge — M6

1963, Sept. 10
M7 M6 12xu multicolored   4.00 3.50

Rifleman
M7

1964, Aug.
M8 M7 multicolored   5.00 4.00

Rifleman Jumping
Wall — M8

1965
M9   M8 red & black
M10 M8 yellow green & black
    Nos. M9-M10 (2)   5.00 3.50
Issued: No. M9, 7/1; No. M10, 12/25.

Soldier,
Guerrilla
Woman
M9

1966-67
M11 M9 greenish blue & vio bl 5.00 4.00
Redrawn with two boats at right
M12 M9 olive & brown bl   11.00 9.00
Issued: #M11, Sept. 25, 1966; #M12, 1967.

Badge of
People's
Army — M10

1967, Oct. 7
M13 M10 multicolored   2.50 1.00

M11

M12

1968, Nov. 10
M14 M11 lilac   3.00 .80

1969, Nov. 15
M15 M12 red & brown red   2.50 1.25

M13

1971, Apr. 27
M16 M13 yellow, brown & red 3.00 1.25

Nguyen
Van Be
M14

Design: No. M18, Nguyen Viet Xuan.

1971, Oct. 30   Perf. 11
M17 M14 multicolored   2.25 1.10
             Perf. 12½
M18 M14 black, pink & buff   2.25 1.10

M15

M16

1973, Dec. 20   Perf. 11
M20 M15 blue, black & buff
  a.   Perf. 12½
M22 M16 olive, red & black
  a.   Perf. 12½
    Nos. M20, M22 (2)   4.50 3.00

Disabled
Veteran in
Factory
M17

No. M24, Invalid's Badge, open book, vert.

1976, July 27
M23-M24 M17 Set of 2   3.50 1.75

Soldier,
Map — M18

Pilot — M19

1976, Oct. 21
M25 M18 red & black   2.00

1978
No. M27, Tank driver. No. M28, Seaman.
M26-M28 M19 Set of 3   5.00 2.0
Issued: No. M26, 6/3; others, 10/10.

M20

Designs: a, Pilot. b, Badge of People's
Army.

1979, Dec. 22
M29 M20 Vertical pair, #a.-b.   1.75

Types A343a, A359 and

Ho Chi
Minh — M21

#M30, Factory militiawoman. #M31, Soldier,
woman pointing. #M32, Militiawoman.

1981, Aug. 5
M30 A343a salmon & multi
M31 A343a green & multi
M32 A359   blue & multi
M33 M21   blue & tan
    Nos. M30-M33 (4)   4.50 2.25
Size of No. M32: 13x18mm.

M22

1982, Nov. 9
M34 M22 pink & greenish blue 1.50 1.00

M23

1983, Apr. 30
M35 M23 multicolored   2.25 1.10

Victory at Dien Bien Phu, 30th Anniv. M24

984, May 5   **Litho.**
137 M24 multicolored   1.25

Disabled Soldier Teaching Class — M25

1984, Nov. 10
M38 M25   tan & brown   1.25

Frontier Forces Type of 1984

1984, Dec. 15
M39 A410   multicolored   1.00

M26

1984, Dec. 22
M40 M26   multicolored   2.50

Policemen and Women M27

1985, Aug. 30
M41 M27   multicolored   1.00

M28

1986, Oct. 1
M42 M28   olive brown & black   1.50   .75

M29

1987, Sept. 23
M43 M29   carmine and tan   2.00   1.00

OFFICIAL STAMPS

Harvesting Rice — O1

Denominations in grams or kilograms of rice. Dated 1952.

     Perf. 11¼
1953, July   **Litho.**   **Unwmk.**
O1   O1   600g rose   5.50   2.50
O2   O1   1kg ol brown   6.00   4.00
O3   O1   2kg orange   8.50   6.50
O4   O1   5kg gray   15.00   12.00
   Nos. O1-O4 (4)   35.00   25.00

Dien Bien Phu Type of 1954

1954-56   **Perf. 11**
O5   A4   600g sepia & ocher   10.00   7.00
   No. O5 exists perf 6 and also imperf.
   Issued: #O5, 10/54; perf 6, 12/54; imperf, 1956.

Nos. 1L62-1L63 Overprinted

1955   **Typo.**   **Perf. 7 Rough**
O6-O7   VM2   100g on 2d, 100g
            on 5d, set
            of 2   210.00

Land Reform Type of 1955-56
Inscribed "SU VU" Above Value

1955   **Litho.**   **Perf. 11**
O8-O9   A6   40d, 80d, set of 2   22.50   19.00

Cu Chinh Lan (1930-1952) O3

Denominations: 20d, 80d, 100d, 500d, 1000d, 2000d, 3000d.

1956, June   **Litho.**   **Perf. 11½**
O10-O16   O3   Set of 7   190.00   175.00

4th World Trade Union Congress Type of 1957
Inscribed "SU VU" Above Value

1957, Aug. 1   **Perf. 12½**
O17-O20   A15   20d, 40d, 80d,
             100d, set of 4   16.00   13.00

One-Pillar Pagoda — O4

1957-58
O21   O4   150d green and brown
O22   O4   150d orange and slate
     Nos. O21-O22 (2)   17.50   7.50
   Nos. O21-O22 exist with and without imprint and designer's name. Issued: No. O21, 12/22/57; No. O22, 3/12/58.

Craft Fair, Hanoi — O5

1958, May 30
O23-O24   O5   150d, 200d, set of
            2   4.00   3.00

1st World Congress of Young Workers, Prague — O6

1958, June 26
O25   O6   150d lt olive green & red   2.50   1.25

Soldier, Factory, Crops — O7

1958, Aug. 19
O26-O28   O7   50, 150, 200d, set
            of 3   6.00   4.00

Opening of New Hanoi Stadium O8

1958, Dec. 31
O29-O32   O8   10d, 20d, 80d,
            150d, set of 4   6.00   3.00

Planting Rice — O9

1962, Sept. 1   **Perf. 11**
O33-O35   O9   3, 6, 12xu, set of 3   3.00   2.50

Rural Mail Service O10

1966, July 1   **Perf. 11**
O36-O37   O10   3xu, 6xu, set of 2   3.00   2.50

ADVANTAGE STOCKSHEETS

Designed with the collector in mind, Advantage stock sheets fit directly in your 2-post or 3-ring National or Specialty album. For unprecedented durability and flexibility choose Advantage Stocksheets. Choose from 1 to 8 pockets. **Sheets are sold in packages of 10.**

- Stock sheets match album pages in every respect, including border, size, and color.
- Punched and drilled to fit perfectly in binder.
- Available with 1 to 8 pockets. Ideal for storing minor varieties and collateral material. A great place to keep new issues until the next supplement is available.
- Provide the protection and durability of crystal clear acetate pockets on heavyweight pages.

NATIONAL BORDER

Item			Retail
AD11	1 Pocket	242mm	$15.99
AD12	2 Pockets	119mm	$15.99
AD13	3 Pockets	79mm	$15.99
AD14	4 Pockets	58mm	$15.99
AD15	5 Pockets	45mm	$15.99
AD16	6 Pockets	37mm	$15.99
AD17	7 Pockets	31mm	$15.99
AD18	8 Pockets	31mm	$15.99

SPECIALTY BORDER

AD21	1 Pocket	242mm	$15.99
AD22	2 Pockets	119mm	$15.99
AD23	3 Pockets	79mm	$15.99
AD24	4 Pockets	58mm	$15.99
AD25	5 Pockets	45mm	$15.99
AD26	6 Pockets	37mm	$15.99
AD27	7 Pockets	31mm	$15.99
AD28	8 Pockets	31mm S	$15.99

Available from your favorite stamp dealer or direct from:

SCOTT

1-800-572-6885
P.O. Box 828,
Sidney OH 45365
www.amosadvantage.com

AMOS
HOBBY PUBLISHING

VIRGIN ISLANDS

ˈvər-jən ˈī-lənds

LOCATION — West Indies, southeast of Puerto Rico
GOVT. — British colony
AREA — 59 sq. mi.
POP. — 19,107 (1997)
CAPITAL — Road Town

The British Virgin Islands constituted one of the presidencies of the former Leeward Islands colony until it became a colony itself in 1956. For many years stamps of Leeward Islands were used concurrently.

The Virgin Islands group is divided between Great Britain and the United States. See Danish West Indies.

12 Pence = 1 Shilling
20 Shillings = 1 Pound
100 Cents = 1 Dollar (1951)
100 Cents = 1 US Dollar (1962)

Catalogue values for unused stamps in this country are for Never Hinged items, beginning with Scott 88 in the regular postage section and Scott O1 in the officials section.

Values for unused stamps are for examples with original gum as defined in the catalogue introduction. However, Nos. 1-2c are valued without gum as the vast majority of examples are found thus.

Virgin and Lamps — A1

St. Ursula — A2

A3

A4

1866   Litho.   Unwmk.   Perf. 12
Toned or White Paper

1	A1	1p green	45.00	60.00
a.		Toned paper	45.00	60.00
c.		Perf. 15x12, toned paper	4,250.	6,500.
2	A3	6p rose	55.00	90.00
a.		Large "V" in "VIRGIN"	275.00	375.00
b.		White paper	90.00	100.00
c.		As "a," white paper	375.00	475.00

Copies offered as No. 1c frequently have forged perfs.

1867-70   Perf. 15

3	A1	1p blue grn ('70)	65.00	75.00
4	A1	1p yel grn ('68)	80.00	75.00
a.		Toned paper	85.00	75.00
5	A2	4p lake, buff	40.00	55.00
a.		4p lake, rose	50.00	70.00
6	A3	6p rose	475.00	475.00
a.		Toned paper ('68)	225.00	275.00
7	A4	1sh rose & blk	140.00	175.00
a.		Toned paper	140.00	200.00
b.		Double lined frame	200.00	275.00
c.		As "b," bluish paper	200.00	275.00

Colored Margins

8	A4	1sh rose & blk	47.50	55.00
a.		White paper	47.50	55.00
b.		Bluish paper	750.00	900.
c.		Central figure omitted	75,000.	
		Nos. 3-8 (6)	847.50	910.00

Copies of No. 8c have perfs. trimmed on one or two sides.

1878   Wmk. 1   Perf. 14

9	A1	1p green	70.00	80.00

See #16-17, 19-20. For surcharge see #18.

Queen Victoria — A5

1880   Typo.

10	A5	1p green	65.00	80.00
11	A5	2½p red brown	90.00	120.00

1883-84   Wmk. 2

12	A5	½p yellow	80.00	80.00
13	A5	½p green	3.50	7.50
a.		Imperf., pair	1,750.	
14	A5	1p rose	22.50	22.50
15	A5	2½p ultra ('84)	2.75	9.00
		Nos. 12-15 (4)	108.75	119.00

No. 13a probably is a plate proof.

1887   Litho.

16	A2	4p brick red	40.00	60.00
a.		4p brown red	40.00	65.00
17	A3	6p violet	15.00	45.00

No. 8 Handstamp Surcharged in Violet

1888   Unwmk.   Perf. 15

18	A4	4p on 1sh dp rose & blk, toned paper	110.00	140.00
a.		Double surcharge	9,000.	
b.		Inverted surcharge	45,000.	
c.		White paper	140.00	175.00

1889   Wmk. 2   Perf. 14

19	A1	1p carmine	2.00	5.00
20	A4	1sh brown	47.50	70.00
a.		1sh black brown	75.00	100.00

St. Ursula with Sheaf of Lilies
A7

Edward VII
A8

1899   Engr.

21	A7	½p yellow grn	.75	.50
a.		"PFNNY"	80.00	125.00
b.		"F" without cross bar	80.00	125.00
c.		Horiz. pair, imperf. between	7,000.	
22	A7	1p red	2.50	2.50
23	A7	2½p ultra	10.50	5.00
24	A7	4p chocolate	3.50	12.00
a.		"PENCF"	700.	1,100.
25	A7	6p dark violet	4.00	4.50
26	A7	7p slate green	6.25	8.00
27	A7	1sh ocher	20.00	27.50
28	A7	5sh dark blue	62.50	70.00
		Nos. 21-28 (8)	110.00	130.00

1904   Typo.   Wmk. 3

29	A8	½p violet & bl grn	.70	.55
30	A8	1p violet & scar	1.50	.45
31	A8	2p violet & bis	4.50	4.00
32	A8	2½p violet & ultra	1.60	1.75
33	A8	3p violet & blk	2.75	2.50
34	A8	6p violet & brn	2.50	2.50
35	A8	1sh green & scar	2.50	4.50
36	A8	2sh6p green & blk	18.00	42.50
37	A8	5sh green & ultra	42.50	62.50
		Nos. 29-37 (9)	76.55	121.25

Numerals of 2p, 3p, 1sh and 2sh6p of type A8 are in color on plain tablet.

George V
A9

Colony Seal
A10

Die I

For description of dies I and II see back of this volume.

1913
Ordinary Paper

38	A9	½p green	.60	2.25
39	A9	1p scarlet	2.25	7.25
a.		1p carmine red	45.00	25.00
40	A9	2p gray	1.90	15.00
41	A9	2½p ultra	2.50	5.75

Chalky Paper

42	A9	3p vio, yel	1.75	4.00
43	A9	6p dl vio & red vio	2.75	6.25
44	A9	1sh blk, green	3.50	5.75
45	A9	2sh6p blk & red, bl	27.50	32.50
46	A9	5sh grn & red, yel	37.50	75.00
		Nos. 38-46 (9)	80.25	153.75

Numerals of 2p, 3p, 1sh and 2sh6p of type A9 are in color on plain tablet.

1921   Wmk. 4
Die II

47	A9	½p green	1.60	15.00
48	A9	1p carmine	1.25	12.50

For overprints see Nos. MR1-MR2.

1922   Wmk. 3

49	A10	3p violet, yel	.90	8.50
50	A10	1sh black, emerald	.85	8.50
51	A10	2sh6p blk & red, bl	4.25	7.00
52	A10	5sh grn & red, yel	25.00	52.50
		Nos. 49-52 (4)	31.00	76.50

1922-28   Wmk. 4

53	A10	½p green	.90	2.10
54	A10	1p rose red	.65	.40
55	A10	1p violet ('27)	1.00	2.75
56	A10	1½p rose red ('27)	1.60	2.00
57	A10	1½p fawn ('28)	1.90	1.50
58	A10	2p gray	.65	4.25
59	A10	2½p ultra	1.60	11.00
60	A10	2½p orange ('23)	1.25	1.25
61	A10	3p dl vio, yel ('28)	2.10	7.75
62	A10	5p dl lil & ol grn	5.25	35.00
63	A10	6p dl vio & red vio	1.25	5.00
a.		6p brown lilac & red violet	.85	3.50
64	A10	1sh blk, emer ('28)	2.75	9.00
65	A10	2sh6p blk & red, bl ('28)	20.00	37.50
66	A10	5sh grn & red, yel ('23)	20.00	55.00
		Nos. 53-66 (14)	60.90	174.50

The ½, 1, 2 and 2½p are on ordinary paper, the others on chalky.

Common Design Types pictured following the introduction.

Silver Jubilee Issue
Common Design Type

1935, May 6   Engr.   Perf. 11x12

69	CD301	1p car & dk blue	.50	1.75
70	CD301	1½p black & ultra	.50	1.75
71	CD301	2½p ultra & brn	1.00	1.75
72	CD301	1sh brn vio & ind	6.50	7.25
		Nos. 69-72 (4)	8.50	12.50
		Set, never hinged	14.00	

Coronation Issue
Common Design Type

1937, May 12   Perf. 11x11½

73	CD302	1p dark carmine	.20	.50
74	CD302	1½p brown	.20	1.50
75	CD302	2½p deep ultra	.35	.50
		Nos. 73-75 (3)	.75	2.50
		Set, never hinged	1.10	

King George VI and Seal of the Colony — A11

1938-47   Photo.   Perf. 14

76	A11	½p green	.20	.20
77	A11	1p scarlet	.20	.20
78	A11	1½p red brown	.35	.50
79	A11	2p gray	.25	.40
80	A11	2½p ultra	.35	.75
81	A11	3p orange	.25	.50
82	A11	6p deep violet	.90	.40
83	A11	1sh olive bister	1.00	.45
84	A11	2sh6p sepia	7.50	3.50
85	A11	5sh rose lake	10.00	4.50

86	A11	10sh brt blue ('47)	5.00	9.7
87	A11	£1 gray blk ('47)	8.00	16.0
		Nos. 76-87 (12)	34.00	37.
		Set, never hinged	50.00	

Catalogue values for unused stamps in this section, from this point to the end of the section, are for Never Hinged items.

Peace Issue
Common Design Type

1946, Nov. 1   Engr.   Wmk.

88	CD303	1½p red brown	.20	.2
89	CD303	3p orange	.20	.2

Silver Wedding Issue
Common Design Types

1949, Jan. 3   Photo.   Perf. 14x14

90	CD304	2½p brt ultra	.25	.2

Engr.; Name Typo.
Perf. 11½x11

91	CD305	£1 gray black	12.00	12.50

UPU Issue
Common Design Types
Engr.; Name Typo. on Nos. 93 & 94

1949, Oct. 10   Perf. 13½, 11x11½

92	CD306	2½p ultra	.40	.40
93	CD307	3p deep orange	1.00	1.6
94	CD308	6p red lilac	.65	.40
95	CD309	1sh olive	.65	.40
		Nos. 92-95 (4)	2.70	2.8

University Issue
Common Design Types

1951   Engr.   Perf. 14x14½

96	CD310	3c red brn & gray blk	.25	.25
97	CD311	12c purple & black	.85	.85

Map of the Islands
A12

1951, Apr. 2   Wmk. 4   Perf. 14½x14

98	A12	6c red orange	.25	.25
99	A12	12c purple	.35	.35
100	A12	24c olive grn	.50	.55
101	A12	$1.20 carmine	1.90	1.50
		Nos. 98-101 (4)	3.00	2.65

Restoration of the Legislative Council, 1950.

Sombrero Lighthouse — A13

Map of Jost van Dyke — A14

Designs: 3c, Sheep. 4c, Map, Anegada. 5c, Cattle. 8c, Map, Virgin Gorda. 12c, Map, Tortola. 24c, Badge of the Presidency. 60c, Dead Man's Chest. $1.20, Sir Francis Drake Channel. $2.40, Road Town. $4.80, Map, Virgin Islands.

1952, Apr. 15   Perf. 12½x13, 13x12½

102	A13	1c gray black	.25	.65
103	A14	2c deep green	.55	.20
104	A14	3c choc & gray blk	.30	.50
105	A14	4c red	.45	.65
106	A14	5c gray blk & rose lake	.90	.30
107	A14	8c ultra	.55	.55
108	A14	12c purple	1.00	.65
109	A13	24c dk brown	1.10	.20
110	A14	60c blue & ol grn	1.75	7.00
111	A14	$1.20 ultra & blk	4.00	7.50
112	A14	$2.40 hn brn & dk grn	8.50	8.25
113	A14	$4.80 rose car & bl	14.00	9.00
		Nos. 102-113 (12)	33.35	35.45

Coronation Issue
Common Design Type
1953, June 2   Perf. 13½x14
14 CD312 2c dk green & blk   .25 .40

Map of Tortola — A15

Brown Pelican A16

Designs: 1c, Virgin Islands sloop. 2c, Nelthrop Red Poll bull. 3c, Road Harbor. 4c, Mountain travel. 5c, St. Ursula. 8c, Beach scene. 12c, Boat launching. 24c, White Cedar Tree. 60c, Skipjack tuna. $1.20, Treasury Square. $4.80, Magnificent frigatebird.

Perf. 13x12½
1956, Nov. 1   Engr.   Wmk. 4
115	A15	½c claret & blk	.30	.20
116	A15	1c dk bl & grnsh bl	1.25	.70
117	A15	2c black & ver	.25	.20
118	A15	3c olive & brt bl	.25	.30
119	A15	4c blue grn & brn	.30	.30
120	A15	5c gray	.35	.20
121	A15	8c dp ultra & org	.50	.40
122	A15	12c car & brt ultra	1.75	.70
123	A15	24c dull red & grn	.80	.60
124	A15	60c yel org & dk bl	6.50	7.50
125	A15	$1.20 car & yel grn	1.75	6.75

Perf. 12x11½
126	A16	$2.40 vio brn & dl yel	25.00	12.50
127	A16	$4.80 grnsh bl & dk brn	26.00	12.50
Nos. 115-127 (13)		65.00	42.85

Types of 1956 Surcharged   **2¢**

Perf. 13x12½
1962, Dec. 10   Wmk. 314
128	A15	1c on ½c	.20	.20
129	A15	2c on 1c	.75	.20
130	A15	3c on 2c	.20	.20
131	A15	4c on 3c	.20	.20
132	A15	5c on 4c	.20	.20
133	A15	8c on 8c	.25	.25
134	A15	10c on 12c	.30	.30
135	A15	12c on 24c	.40	.40
136	A15	25c on 60c	2.00	.80
137	A15	70c on $1.20	.45	2.00

Perf. 12x11½
138	A16	$1.40 on $2.40	7.50	4.75
139	A16	$2.80 on $4.80	7.50	9.25
Nos. 128-139 (12)		19.95	18.75

Freedom from Hunger Issue
Common Design Type
1963, June 4   Photo.   Perf. 14x14½
140 CD314 25c lilac   .50 .50

Red Cross Centenary Issue
Common Design Type
     Wmk. 314
1963, Sept. 2   Litho.   Perf. 13
141 CD315 2c black & red   .20 .20
142 CD315 25c ultra & red   .90 .90

Shakespeare Issue
Common Design Type
1964, Apr. 23   Photo.   Perf. 14x14½
143 CD316 10c ultramarine   .25 .25

Bonito — A17

Map of Tortola Island — A18

2c, Seaplane at Soper's Hole. 3c, Brown pelican. 4c, Dead Man's Chest (mountain). 5c, The Baths, Virgin Gorda. 6c, Fallen Jerusalem Island. 8c, Road Harbor. 10c, Map of Virgin Islands. 12c, Ferry service, Tortola—St. Thomas. 15c, The Towers. 25c, Plane at Beef Island Airfield. $1, Virgin Gorda Island. $1.40, Yachts, Tortola. $2.80, Badge.

Perf. 13x12½
1964, Nov. 2   Engr.   Wmk. 314
144	A17	1c gray ol & dk bl	.20	1.10
145	A17	2c rose red & ol	.20	.25
146	A17	3c grnsh bl & sep	2.25	1.10
147	A17	4c carmine & blk	.60	1.10
148	A17	5c green & blk	.50	1.10
149	A17	6c orange & blk	.20	.75
150	A17	8c pink & blk	.20	.50
151	A17	10c lt violet & mar	.85	.25
152	A17	12c vio bl & Prus grn	1.50	1.50
153	A17	15c gray & yel grn	.25	1.60
154	A17	25c pur & yel grn	8.25	1.50

Perf. 13x13½
Size: 27x30½mm
155	A18	70c bister brn & blk	2.75	3.50
156	A18	$1 red brn & yel grn	2.25	1.50
157	A18	$1.40 pink & blue	15.00	7.00

Perf. 11½x12
Size: 27x37mm
158	A18	$2.80 rose lilac & blk	15.00	7.25
Nos. 144-158 (15)		50.00	30.00

For surcharges & overprints see Nos. 173-175, 190-191.

ITU Issue
Common Design Type
Perf. 11x11½
1965, May 17   Litho.   Wmk. 314
159 CD317 4c yellow & bl grn   .20 .20
160 CD317 25c blue & org yel   .80 .80

Intl. Cooperation Year Issue
Common Design Type
1965, Oct. 25   Wmk. 314   Perf. 14½
161 CD318 1c blue grn & cl   .20 .20
162 CD318 25c lt violet & grn   .65 .65

Churchill Memorial Issue
Common Design Type
1966, Jan. 24   Photo.   Perf. 14
Design in Black, Gold and Carmine Rose
163 CD319 1c brt blue   .20 .20
164 CD319 2c green   .20 .20
165 CD319 10c brown   .40 .40
166 CD319 25c violet   1.00 1.00
Nos. 163-166 (4)   1.80 1.80

Royal Visit Issue
Common Design Type
1966, Feb. 22   Litho.   Perf. 11x12
167 CD320 4c violet blue   .20 .20
168 CD320 70c dk car rose   2.25 2.25

Stamps of 1866 — A19

Designs: 5c, R.M.S. Atrato, 1866. 25c, Beechcraft mail plane on Beef Island Airfield and 6p stamp (No. 2). 60c, Landing mail at Road Town, 1866, and 1p stamp (No. 1).

Perf. 12½x13
1966, Apr. 25   Wmk. 314
169 A19 5c grn, yel, red & blk   .20 .20
170 A19 10c yel, grn, red, blk & rose   .20 .20
171 A19 25c lt grn, bl, red, blk & rose   .50 .50
172 A19 60c bl, red, blk, & grn   1.00 1.00
Nos. 169-172 (4)   1.90 1.90
Centenary of Virgin Islands postage stamps.

Nos. 155, 157-158 Surcharged with New Value and Two Bars
Perf. 13x12½, 11½x12
1966, Sept. 15   Engr.   Wmk. 314
173 A18 50c on 70c   1.75 1.25
174 A18 $1.50 on $1.40   3.75 2.75
175 A18 $3 on $2.80   3.75 4.00
Nos. 173-175 (3)   9.25 8.00

UNESCO Anniversary Issue
Common Design Type
1966, Dec. 1   Litho.   Perf. 14
176 CD323 2c "Education"   .20 .20
177 CD323 12c "Science"   .25 .25
178 CD323 60c "Culture"   .70 .70
Nos. 176-178 (3)   1.15 1.15

Map and Seal of Virgin Islands A20

Wmk. 314
1967, Apr. 18   Photo.   Perf. 14½
179 A20 2c gold, grn & org   .20 .20
180 A20 10c gold, rose red, grn & org   .25 .25
181 A20 25c gold, red brn, grn & org   .25 .25
182 A20 $1 gold, bl, grn & org   .85 .85
Nos. 179-182 (4)   1.55 1.55
Introduction of new constitution.

Map of Virgin Islands, Bermuda and C.S. Mercury — A21

10c, Communications center, Chalwell, Virgin Islands. 50c, Cable ship Mercury.

1967, Sept. 14   Wmk. 314   Perf. 14½
183 A21 4c green & multi   .20 .20
184 A21 10c dp plum & multi   .20 .20
185 A21 50c bister & multi   .45 .45
Nos. 183-185 (3)   .85 .85
Completion of the Bermuda-Tortola, Virgin Islands, telephone link.

Blue Marlin A22

Designs: 10c, Sergeant fish (cobia). 25c, Peto fish (Wahoo). 40c, Fishing boat, map of Virgin Islands and fishing records.

Perf. 12½x12
1968, Jan. 2   Photo.   Wmk. 314
186 A22 2c multicolored   .20 .20
187 A22 10c multicolored   .25 .25
188 A22 25c multicolored   .50 .50
189 A22 40c multicolored   .80 .80
Nos. 186-189 (4)   1.75 1.75
Game fishing in Virgin Islands waters.

Nos. 151 and 154 Overprinted: "1968 / INTERNATIONAL / YEAR FOR / HUMAN RIGHTS"
1968, July 1   Engr.   Perf. 13x12½
190 A17 10c lt violet & maroon   .20 .20
191 A17 25c purple & green   .30 .30

Martin Luther King, Bible and Sword A23

1968, Oct. 15   Litho.   Perf. 14
192 A23 4c dl org, vio & blk   .25 .25
193 A23 25c dl org, gray grn & blk   .35 .50
Martin Luther King, Jr. (1929-68), American civil rights leader.

DHC-6 Twin Otter A24

Designs: 10c, Hawker Siddeley 748. 25c, Hawker Siddeley Heron. $1, Badge from cap of Royal Engineers.

1968, Dec. 16   Unwmk.   Perf. 14
194 A24 2c brn red & multi   .20 .60
195 A24 10c grnsh bl, blk & red   .20 .20
196 A24 25c ultra, lt bl, org & blk   .40 .20
197 A24 $1 green & multi   1.60 2.00
Nos. 194-197 (4)   2.40 3.00
Opening of enlarged Beef Island Airport.

Long John Silver and Jim Hawkins — A25

Tourist and Rock Grouper — A26

Scenes from Treasure Island: 10c, Jim's escape from the pirates, horiz. 40c, The fight with Israel Hands. $1, Treasure trove, horiz.

Perf. 13½x13, 13x13½
1969, Mar. 18   Photo.   Wmk. 314
198 A25 4c dp car & multi   .40 .20
199 A25 10c multicolored   .45 .25
200 A25 40c ultra & multi   .55 .65
201 A25 $1 black & multi   1.10 2.00
Nos. 198-201 (4)   2.50 3.10
Robert Louis Stevenson (1850-94). The Virgin Islands were used as the setting for "Treasure Island."

1969, Oct. 20   Litho.   Perf. 12½
Tourist Publicity: 10c, Yachts in Road Harbor, Tortola, horiz. 20c, Tourists on beach in Virgin Gorda National Park, horiz. $1, Pipe organ cactus and woman tourist.
202 A26 2c multicolored   .20 .55
203 A26 10c multicolored   .20 .20
204 A26 20c multicolored   .35 .25
205 A26 $1 multicolored   1.75 2.00
Nos. 202-205 (4)   2.50 3.00

Carib
Canoe
A27

Ships: 1c, Santa Maria. 2c, H.M.S. Elizabeth Bonaventure. 3c, Dutch buccaneer, 1660.
4c, Thetis (1827 merchant ship). 5c, Henry
Morgan's ship. 6c, Frigate Boreas. 8c,
Schooner L'Eclair, 1804. 10c, H.M.S. Formidable. 12c, H.M.S. Nymph burning. 15c,
Packet Windsor Castle fighting French privateer. 25c, Frigate Astrea, 1808. 50c, H.M.S.
Rhone. $1, Tortola sloop. $2, H.M.S. Frob-
isher. $3, Booker Line Viking (cargo ship). $5,
Hydrofoil Sun Arrow.

Wmk. 314 Sideways

			1970, Feb. 16		*Perf. 14½*
206	A27	½c brn & ocher		.20	.20
207	A27	1c bl, lt grn & vio		.20	.20
208	A27	2c red brn, org & gray		.20	.20
209	A27	3c ver, bl & brn		.20	.20
210	A27	4c brn, bl & vio bl		.20	.20
211	A27	5c grn, pink & blk		.20	.20
212	A27	6c lil, grn & blk		.20	.20
213	A27	8c lt ol, yel & brn		.25	.25
214	A27	10c ocher, bl & brn		.30	.30
215	A27	12c sep, yel & dp cl		.45	.45
216	A27	15c org, grnsh bl & brn		.40	.40
217	A27	25c bl, grnsh gray & pur		.60	.60
218	A27	50c rose car, lt grn & brn		1.25	1.25
219	A27	$1 brn, sal pink & dk grn		2.50	2.50
220	A27	$2 gray & yel		5.00	5.00
221	A27	$3 brn, ol bis & dk bl		7.75	7.75
222	A27	$5 lil & gray		12.50	12.50
		Nos. 206-222 (17)		32.40	32.40

For overprints see Nos. 235-236.

			1973, Oct. 17	Wmk. 314 Upright	
206a	A27	½c		.85	5.75
209a	A27	3c		2.00	2.25
210a	A27	4c		2.00	4.25
211a	A27	5c		2.00	2.10
214a	A27	10c		2.40	2.40
215a	A27	12c		3.25	3.25
		Nos. 206a-215a (6)		12.50	20.00

Wmk. 314 Sideways

			1974, Nov. 11		*Perf. 13½*
207a	A27	1c		1.25	1.90
214b	A27	10c		2.25	2.10
215b	A27	12c		2.25	3.00
216a	A27	15c		3.25	3.00
		Nos. 207a-216a (4)		9.00	10.00

"A Tale
of Two
Cities,"
by
Dickens
A28

Charles Dickens: 10c, "Oliver Twist." 25c,
"Great Expectations."

		1970, May 4	Litho.		*Perf. 14½*
223	A28	5c blk, gray & pink		.20	.20
224	A28	10c blk, pale yel grn & blue		.40	.35
225	A28	25c blk, yel & lt yel grn		.65	.95
		Nos. 223-225 (3)		1.25	1.50

Hospital
Visitor
A29

10c, Girl Scouts receiving 1st aid training at
lake side. 25c, Red Cross & Virgin Islands
coat of arms.

		1970, Aug. 10	Wmk. 314		*Perf. 14*
226	A29	4c multicolored		.20	.20
227	A29	10c multicolored		.30	.20
228	A29	25c multicolored		.75	.70
		Nos. 226-228 (3)		1.25	1.10

Centenary of British Red Cross.

Mary Read — A30

Pirates: 10c, George Lowther. 30c, Edward
Teach (Blackbeard). 60c, Henry Morgan.

		1970, Nov. 16	Wmk. 314		*Perf. 14*
229	A30	½c dp rose & multi		.20	.20
230	A30	10c blue grn & multi		.40	.40
231	A30	30c ultra & multi		1.00	1.00
232	A30	60c multicolored		1.40	1.40
		Nos. 229-232 (4)		3.00	3.00

Children
Spelling
out
"UNICEF"
A31

		1971, Dec. 13			
233	A31	15c tan & multi		.20	.20
234	A31	30c lt blue & multi		.50	.50

25th anniv. of UNICEF.

Nos. 210 and 217 Dated "1972" and
Overprinted: "VISIT OF / H.R.H. / THE
/ PRINCESS MARGARET"

		1972, Mar. 7			*Perf. 14½*
235	A27	4c multicolored		.20	.20
236	A27	25c multicolored		.30	.40

Seaman,
1800 — A32

10c, Boatswain, 1787-1807. 30c, Captain,
1795-1812. 60c, Admiral in full dress uniform,
1787-95.

		1972, Mar. 17			*Perf. 14x13½*
237	A32	½c yellow & multi		.20	.20
238	A32	10c brt pink & multi		.40	.40
239	A32	30c orange & multi		1.10	1.10
240	A32	60c blue & multi		2.50	2.50
		Nos. 237-240 (4)		4.20	4.20

INTERPEX, 14th Intl. Stamp Exhib., NYC,
Mar. 17-19.

Silver Wedding Issue, 1972
Common Design Type

Design: Queen Elizabeth II, Prince Philip,
sailfish and "Sir Winston Churchill" yacht.

		1972, Nov. 24	Photo.		*Perf. 14x14½*
241	CD324	15c ultra & multi		.35	.35
242	CD324	25c Prus blue & multi		.35	.35

Allison
Tuna
A33

		1972, Dec. 12	Litho.		*Perf. 13½x14*
243	A33	½c Wahoo		.20	.20
244	A33	½c Blue marlin		.20	.20
a.		Horiz. or vert. pair, #243-244		.20	.20
245	A33	15c shown		.40	.40
246	A33	25c White marlin		.60	.60
247	A33	50c Sailfish		1.10	1.10

248	A33	$1 Dolphin		2.50	2.50
a.		Souvenir sheet of 6, #243-248		8.50	8.50
		Nos. 243-248 (6)		5.00	5.00

Game fish.

Lettsom House and Medal — A34

Themes from Quaker History: ½c, Dr. John
Coakley Lettsom, vert. 15c, Dr. William Thornton, vert. 30c, US Capitol, Washington, DC,
and Dr. Thornton who designed it. $1, Library
Hall, Philadelphia, and William Penn.

		1973, Mar. 9	Litho.		*Perf. 13½*
249	A34	½c rose & multi		.20	.20
250	A34	10c multicolored		.20	.20
251	A34	15c multicolored		.30	.30
252	A34	30c ultra & multi		.60	.60
253	A34	$1 multicolored		1.90	1.90
		Nos. 249-253 (5)		3.20	3.20

INTERPEX, 15th Intl. Phil. Exhib., NYC,
Mar. 9-11.

Hummingbirds on 1c Coin — A35

Coins and Beach Scenes: 5c, Zenaida
doves. 10c, Kingfisher. 25c, Mangrove cuck-
oos. 50c, Brown pelicans. $1, Magnificent frig-
ate birds.

		1973, June 30	Wmk. 314		*Perf. 14½*
254	A35	1c orange & multi		.20	.35
255	A35	5c lt blue & multi		.60	.20
256	A35	10c pale ultra & multi		.85	.20
257	A35	25c yellow & multi		1.10	.20
258	A35	50c lt violet & multi		1.25	1.25
259	A35	$1 ultra & multi		1.50	2.50
		Nos. 254-259 (6)		5.50	4.70

New Virgin Islands coinage.

Princess Anne's Wedding Issue
Common Design Type

		1973, Nov. 16	Wmk. 314		*Perf. 14*
260	CD325	5c citron & multi		.20	.20
261	CD325	50c blue grn & multi		.80	.80

Virgin and Child,   Arms of French
by Bernardino   Minesweeper
Pintoricchio   Canopus
A36   A37

Christmas (Paintings of the Virgin and Child
by): 3c, Lorenzo Credi. 25c, Carlo Crivelli. 50c,
Bernardino Luini.

		1973, Dec. 7			*Perf. 14x14½*
262	A36	½c lt green & multi		.20	.20
263	A36	3c rose & multi		.20	.20
264	A36	25c ocher & multi		.50	.50
265	A36	50c lt blue & multi		.95	.95
		Nos. 262-265 (4)		1.85	1.85

		1974, Mar. 22	Wmk. 314		*Perf. 14*
266	A37	5c shown		.20	.20
267	A37	18c USS Saginaw		.40	.40
268	A37	25c HMS Rothesay		.50	.50
269	A37	50c HMCS Ottawa		1.00	1.00
a.		Souvenir sheet of 4, #266-269		3.00	3.00
		Nos. 266-269 (4)		2.10	2.10

INTERPEX Phil. Exhib., NYC, Mar. 22-24.

Famous
Explorers — A38

		1974, Aug. 19			*Perf. 14*
270	A38	5c Columbus		.25	.2
271	A38	10c Sir Walter Raleigh		.35	.3
272	A38	25c Sir Martin Frobisher		.40	.4
273	A38	40c Sir Francis Drake		.75	.7
a.		Souvenir sheet of 4, #270-273		2.00	2.0
		Nos. 270-273 (4)		1.75	1.7

Sea
Shells
A39

		1974, Sept. 30			*Perf. 13x13½*
274	A39	5c Trumpet triton		.40	.40
275	A39	18c West Indian murex		.85	.85
276	A39	25c Bleeding tooth		1.00	1.00
277	A39	75c Virgin Island latirus		2.50	2.50
a.		Souvenir sheet of 4, #274-277		5.75	5.75
		Nos. 274-277 (4)		4.75	4.75

St. Mary, Aldermanbury,
London, — A40

Design: 50c, St. Mary, Fulton, Missouri.

		1974, Nov. 30	Wmk. 373		*Perf. 14*
278	A40	10c multicolored		.20	.20
279	A40	50c multicolored		.50	.50
a.		Souvenir sheet of 2, #278-279		1.00	1.00

Sir Winston Churchill (1874-1965).

Figurehead from
"Boreas" — A41

Figureheads: 18c, The Golden Hind. 40c,
Crowned lion from the "Superb." 85c, Warrior,
from the "Formidable."

					Perf. 13½x13
		1975, Mar. 14		Wmk. 314	
280	A41	5c multicolored		.20	.20
281	A41	18c multicolored		.45	.45
282	A41	40c multicolored		.60	.60
283	A41	85c multicolored		1.25	1.25
a.		Souv. sheet of 4, #280-283, perf. 14		3.25	3.25
		Nos. 280-283 (4)		2.50	2.50

INTERPEX, 17th Phil. Exhib., NYC, Mar.
14-16.

Rock
Beauty
A42

Designs: Fish.

1975 · Wmk. 373 · Perf. 14

284	A42	½c shown	.20	.20
285	A42	1c Squirrelfish	.50	.50
286	A42	3c Queen trigger-fish	1.25	1.25
287	A42	5c Blue angelfish	.35	.35
288	A42	8c Stoplight parrotfish	.35	.35
289	A42	10c Queen angelfish	.35	.35
290	A42	12c Nassau grouper	.50	.50
291	A42	13c Blue tang	.50	.50
292	A42	15c Sergeant major	.50	.50
293	A42	18c Jewfish	.90	.90
294	A42	20c Bluehead wrasse	.70	.70
295	A42	25c Gray angelfish	1.25	1.25
296	A42	60c Glasseye snapper	1.50	1.50
297	A42	$1 Blue chromis	2.10	2.10
298	A42	$2.50 French angelfish	3.50	3.50
299	A42	$3 Queen parrotfish	4.50	4.50
300	A42	$5 Four-eye butterflyfish	5.00	5.00
		Nos. 284-300 (17)	23.95	23.95

Issue dates: $5, Aug. 15. Others, June 16. ½c, 5c, 8c, 10c, 12c, 13c, 15c, 20c reissued dated "1977."

St. Georges Parish School A43

Designs: 25c, Legislative Council Building. 40c, Mace and gavel of Legislative Council. 75c, Scroll with dates of historical events.

1975, Nov. 27 · Litho. · Wmk. 373

301	A43	5c ultra & multi	.20	.20
302	A43	25c green & multi	.40	.40
303	A43	40c ocher & multi	.50	.50
304	A43	75c ultra & multi	.65	.65
		Nos. 301-304 (4)	1.75	1.75

Restoration of Legislative Council, 25th anniv.

Copper Mine Point A44

Historic Sites: 18c, Dr. Thornton's Ruin, Pleasant Valley. 50c, Callwood distillery. 75c, The Dungeon.

1976, Mar. 12 · Litho. · Perf. 14½

305	A44	5c red & multi	.20	.20
306	A44	18c red & multi	.35	.35
307	A44	50c red & multi	.70	.70
308	A44	75c red & multi	1.00	1.00
		Nos. 305-308 (4)	2.25	2.25

Massachusetts Brig Hazard — A45

Designs: 22c, American Privateer Spy. 40c, Continental Navy Frigate Raleigh. 75c, Frigate Alliance and HMS Trepasy.

1976, May 29 · Wmk. 373 · Perf. 14

309	A45	8c multicolored	.30	.20
310	A45	22c multicolored	.70	.50
311	A45	40c multicolored	1.25	1.00
312	A45	75c multicolored	2.50	1.75
a.		Souvenir sheet of 4, #309-312	6.00	6.00
		Nos. 309-312 (4)	4.75	3.45

American Bicentennial.

Government House, Tortola — A46

Designs: 15c, Government House, St. Croix, vert. 30c, Flags of US and British Virgin Islands, vert. 75c, Arms of British and US Virgin Islands.

1976, Oct. 29 · Litho. · Perf. 14

313	A46	8c green & multi	.20	.20
314	A46	15c green & multi	.20	.20
315	A46	30c green & multi	.35	.35
316	A46	75c green & multi	.75	.75
		Nos. 313-316 (4)	1.50	1.50

US and British Virgin Islands Friendship Day, 5th anniversary.

Holy Bible — A47

8c, Queen visiting Agricultural Station, Tortola, 1966. 60c, Presentation of Holy Bible.

1977, Feb. 7 · Perf. 14x13½

317	A47	8c silver & multi	.20	.20
318	A47	30c silver & multi	.30	.30
319	A47	60c silver & multi	.50	.50
		Nos. 317-319 (3)	1.00	1.00

25th anniv. of the reign of Elizabeth II. For overprints see Nos. 324-326.

Virgin Islands Chart, 1739 — A48

18th Century Maps of Virgin Islands: 22c, 1758. 30c, 1775. 75c, 1779.

1977, June 12 · Wmk. 373 · Perf. 13½

320	A48	8c multicolored	.25	.20
321	A48	22c multicolored	.55	.45
322	A48	30c multicolored	.70	.60
323	A48	75c multicolored	1.50	1.50
		Nos. 320-323 (4)	3.00	2.75

Type of 1977 Inscribed: "ROYAL VISIT"

Designs: 5c, Queen visiting Agricultural Station, Tortola, 1966. 25c, Holy Bible. 50c, Presentation of Holy Bible.

1977, Oct. 26 · Litho. · Perf. 14x13½

324	A47	5c yel brn & multi	.20	.20
325	A47	25c dk blue & multi	.30	.30
326	A47	50c purple & multi	.50	.50
		Nos. 324-326 (3)	1.00	1.00

Caribbean visit of Queen Elizabeth II.

Divers Checking Equipment — A49

Tourist publicity: 5c, Cup coral inside bow of "Rhone." 8c, Sponge growing on superstructure of "Rhone." 22c, Sponge and cup coral.

30c, Scuba diver searching for sponges in cave. 75c, Marine life.

1977, Dec. 15 · Wmk. 373 · Perf. 13½

327	A49	½c multicolored	.20	.20
328	A49	5c multicolored	.20	.20
329	A49	8c multicolored	.20	.20
330	A49	22c multicolored	.50	.50
331	A49	30c multicolored	.65	.65
332	A49	75c multicolored	1.10	1.10
		Nos. 327-332 (6)	2.85	2.85

Corals A50

1978, Feb. 10 · Perf. 14

333	A50	8c Fire	.30	.30
334	A50	15c Staghorn	.40	.40
335	A50	40c Brain	.80	.80
336	A50	75c Elkhorn	1.75	1.75
		Nos. 333-336 (4)	3.25	3.25

Elizabeth II Coronation Anniversary Issue
Common Design Types
Souvenir Sheet

1978, June 2 · Unwmk. · Perf. 15

337		Sheet of 6	2.75	2.75
a.		CD326 50c Falcon of the Plantagenets	.40	.40
b.		CD327 50c Elizabeth II	.40	.40
c.		CD328 50c Iguana	.40	.40

No. 337 contains 2 se-tenant strips of Nos. 337a-337c, separated by horizontal gutter.

Lignum Vitae A51

Flowering Trees: 22c, Ginger thomas. 40c, Dog almond. 75c, White cedar.

1978, Sept. 4 · Litho. · Perf. 13x13½

338	A51	8c multicolored	.35	.35
339	A51	22c multicolored	.55	.55
340	A51	40c multicolored	.75	.75
341	A51	75c multicolored	1.10	1.10
a.		Souvenir sheet of 4, #338-341	2.75	2.75
		Nos. 338-341 (4)	2.75	2.75

Eurema Lisa A52

Butterflies: 22c, Dione vanillae. 30c, Heliconius charitonius. 75c, Hemiargus hanno.

1978, Dec. 4 · Wmk. 373 · Perf. 14

342	A52	5c multicolored	.20	.20
343	A52	22c multicolored	.80	.65
a.		Sheet of 9, 6 #342, 3 #343	3.75	3.75
344	A52	30c multicolored	1.00	.90
345	A52	75c multicolored	2.50	2.25
		Nos. 342-345 (4)	4.50	4.00

Spiny Lobsters A53

Conservation: 15c, Iguana, vert. 22c, Hawksbill turtle. 75c, Black coral, vert.

1979, Feb. 10 · Litho.

346	A53	5c multicolored	.20	.20
347	A53	15c multicolored	.40	.40
348	A53	22c multicolored	.65	.65
349	A53	75c multicolored	1.50	1.50
a.		Souvenir sheet of 4, #346-349	3.00	3.00
		Nos. 346-349 (4)	2.75	2.75

Strawberry Cactus — A54

West Indies Girl and Church — A55

Native Cacti: 5c, Snowy cactus. 13c, Barrel cactus. 22c, Tree cactus. 30c, Prickly pear. 75c, Dildo cactus.

1979, May 7 · Wmk. 373 · Perf. 14

350	A54	½c multicolored	.20	.20
351	A54	5c multicolored	.25	.25
352	A54	13c multicolored	.40	.40
353	A54	22c multicolored	.50	.50
354	A54	30c multicolored	.60	.60
355	A54	75c multicolored	.80	.80
		Nos. 350-355 (6)	2.75	2.75

1979, July 9 · Perf. 14x14½

Children and IYC Emblem: 10c, African boy and dancers. 13c, Asian girl and children playing. 22c, European girl and bicycle.

356	A55	5c multicolored	.20	.20
357	A55	10c multicolored	.20	.20
358	A55	13c multicolored	.20	.20
359	A55	$1 multicolored	.50	.50
a.		Souvenir sheet of 4, #356-359	1.40	1.40
		Nos. 356-359 (4)	1.10	1.10

International Year of the Child.

No. 118 — A56

Pencil Urchin — A57

Rowland Hill's Signature and: 13c, Virgin Islands No. 11, horiz. 75c, Unissued Great Britain 2d stamp, 1910, horiz. $1, Virgin Islands No. 8c.

1979, Oct. 1 · Photo. · Perf. 13½

360	A56	5c multicolored	.20	.20
361	A56	13c multicolored	.20	.20
362	A56	75c multicolored	.85	.85
		Nos. 360-362 (3)	1.25	1.25

Souvenir Sheet

363	A56	$1 multicolored	1.00	1.00

Sir Rowland Hill (1795-1879), originator of penny postage. For overprints see Nos. 389-390.

1979-80 · Litho. · Perf. 14

364	A57	½c Calcified algae	.20	.20
365	A57	1c Purple-tipped sea anemone	.20	.20
366	A57	3c Starfish	.20	.20
367	A57	5c shown	.20	.20
368	A57	8c Triton's trumpet	.20	.20
369	A57	10c Christmas tree worms	.20	.20

370	A57	13c Flamingo tongue snails	.25	.25
371	A57	15c Spider crab	.30	.30
372	A57	18c Sea squirts	.30	.30
373	A57	20c Tree tulip	.35	.35
374	A57	25c Rooster tail conch	.45	.45
375	A57	30c Fighting conch	.55	.55
376	A57	60c Mangrove crab	1.10	1.10
377	A57	$1 Coral polyps	1.75	1.75
378	A57	$2.50 Peppermint shrimp	4.50	4.50
379	A57	$3 West Indian murex	5.25	5.25
380	A57	$5 Carpet anemone	9.00	9.00
		Nos. 364-380 (17)	25.00	25.00

Issued: 5, 8, 10, 15, 20, 25c, $2.50, $3, 12/17; others, 4/1/80.
Nos. 367-368, 370-371, 373, 375 reissued inscribed 1982.
For overprints see Nos. O1-O15.

Rotary Athletic Meet, Tortola, Emblem A58

1980, Mar. 3   Litho.   Perf. 13½x14

381	A58	8c shown	.20	.20
382	A58	22c Paul P. Harris	.25	.25
383	A58	60c Mount Sage National Park	.55	.55
384	A58	$1 Anniversary emblem	1.00	1.00
a.		Souvenir sheet of 4, #381-384	2.50	2.50
		Nos. 381-384 (4)	2.00	2.00

Rotary International, 75th anniv.

Brown Booby, London 1980 Emblem A59

1980, May 6   Wmk. 373   Perf. 14

385	A59	20c shown	.35	.35
386	A59	25c Magnificent frigatebird	.45	.45
387	A59	50c White-tailed tropic bird	.70	.70
388	A59	75c Brown pelican	.95	.95
a.		Souvenir sheet of 4, #385-388	3.00	3.00
		Nos. 385-388 (4)	2.45	2.45

London 80 Intl. Stamp Exhib., May 6-14.

Nos. 361-362 Overprinted:
"CARIBBEAN
COMMONWEALTH
PARLIAMENTARY
ASSOCIATION
MEETING
TORTOLA 11-19 JULY 1980"

1980, July 7   Photo.   Perf. 13½

389	A56	13c multicolored	.20	.20
390	A56	75c multicolored	.80	.80

Sir Francis Drake — A60

1980, Sept. 26   Litho.   Perf. 14½

391	A60	8c shown	.40	.40
392	A60	15c Queen Elizabeth I	.60	.60
393	A60	30c Drake knighted	.75	.75
394	A60	75c Golden Hinde	1.50	1.50
a.		Souvenir sheet of 4, #391-394	3.50	3.50
		Nos. 391-394 (4)	3.25	3.25

400th anniv. of circumnavigation of the world.

Jost Van Dyke A61

British Virgin Islands

1980, Dec. 1   Wmk. 373   Perf. 14

395	A61	2c shown	.20	.20
396	A61	5c Peter Island	.20	.20
397	A61	13c Virgin Gorda	.20	.20
398	A61	22c Anegada	.30	.30
399	A61	30c Norman Island	.35	.35
400	A61	$1 Tortola	1.00	1.00
a.		Souvenir sheet of 1	1.50	1.50
		Nos. 395-400 (6)	2.25	2.25

Dancing Lady — A62

1981, Mar. 3   Litho.   Perf. 11

401	A62	5c shown	.30	.30
402	A62	20c Love in the mist	.35	.35
403	A62	22c Red pineapple	.35	.35
404	A62	75c Dutchman's pipe	.90	.90
405	A62	$1 Maiden apple	1.10	1.10
		Nos. 401-405 (5)	3.00	3.00

Royal Wedding Issue
Common Design Type

1981, July 22   Litho.   Perf. 14

406	CD331	10c Bouquet	.20	.20
407	CD331	35c Charles, Queen Mother	.45	.45
408	CD331	$1.25 Couple	1.50	1.50
		Nos. 406-408 (3)	2.15	2.15

#406-408 each se-tenant with decorative label.

Duke of Edinburgh's Awards, 25th Anniv. — A63

1981, Sept. 16   Wmk. 373   Perf. 14

409	A63	10c Stamp collecting	.20	.20
410	A63	15c Running	.25	.25
411	A63	50c Camping	.85	.85
412	A63	$1 Duke of Edinburgh	1.60	1.60
		Nos. 409-412 (4)	2.90	2.90

Intl. Year of the Disabled A64

1981, Oct. 19   Litho.   Perf. 14

413	A64	15c Children	.30	.30
414	A64	20c Fort Charlotte Children's Center	.40	.40
415	A64	30c Playing music	.60	.60
416	A64	$1 Center, diff.	2.00	2.00
		Nos. 413-416 (4)	3.30	3.30

A65   A66

Virgin and Child (Christmas): Details from Adoration of the Shepherds, by Rubens. 50c, horiz.

1981, Nov. 30   Litho.   Perf. 14

417	A65	5c multicolored	.20	.20
418	A65	15c multicolored	.25	.25
419	A65	30c multicolored	.50	.50
420	A65	$1 multicolored	2.00	2.00
		Nos. 417-420 (4)	2.95	2.95

Souvenir Sheet

421	A65	50c multicolored	1.00	1.00

1982, Apr. 15   Litho.   Perf. 14x14½

Hummingbirds on local flora.

422	A66	15c Green-throated carib, erythrina	.35	.35
423	A66	30c Same, bougainvillea	.70	.70
424	A66	35c Antillean crested hummingbird, granadilla passiflora	.80	.80
425	A66	$1.25 Same, hibiscus	2.75	2.75
		Nos. 422-425 (4)	4.60	4.60

10th Anniv. of Lions Club of Tortola — A67

1982, May 3   Perf. 13½x14

426	A67	10c Helping disabled	.20	.20
427	A67	20c Headquarters	.35	.35
428	A67	30c Map	.50	.50
429	A67	$1.50 Emblem	2.50	2.50
a.		Souvenir sheet of 4, #426-429	3.75	3.75
		Nos. 426-429 (4)	3.55	3.55

Princess Diana Issue
Common Design Type

1982, July 1   Litho.   Perf. 14

430	CD333	10c Arms	.20	.20
431	CD333	35c Diana	.55	.55
432	CD333	50c Wedding	.75	.75
433	CD333	$1.50 Portrait	2.50	2.50
		Nos. 430-433 (4)	4.00	4.00

10th Anniv. of Air BVI (Natl. Airline) A68

1982, Sept. 10   Wmk. 373   Perf. 14

434	A68	10c Douglas DC-3	.20	.20
435	A68	15c Britten-Norman Islander	.30	.30
436	A68	60c Hawker-Siddeley	1.25	1.25
437	A68	75c Planes	1.50	1.50
		Nos. 434-437 (4)	3.25	3.25

Scouting Year A69

1982, Nov. 18

438	A69	8c Emblem, Flag raising	.20	.20
439	A69	20c Cub scout, nature study	.40	.40
440	A69	50c Kayak, sea scout	1.00	1.00

441	A69	$1 Camp Brownsea Is., Baden-Powell	2.00	2.00
		Nos. 438-441 (4)	3.60	3.60

Commonwealth Day — A70

1983, Mar. 14   Perf. 13½x14

442	A70	10c Legislature in session	.20	.20
443	A70	30c Wind surfing	.50	.50
444	A70	35c Globe	.60	.60
445	A70	75c Flags	1.25	1.25
		Nos. 442-445 (4)	2.55	2.55

Nursing Week A71

1983, May 9   Litho.   Perf. 14½

446	A71	10c Florence Nightingale (1820-1910), vert.	.20	.20
447	A71	30c Nurse, assistant, vert.	.55	.55
448	A71	60c Public health	1.10	1.10
449	A71	75c Peebles Hospital	1.40	1.40
		Nos. 446-449 (4)	3.25	3.25

Boat Building A72

1983, July 25   Perf. 14

450	A72	15c First stage	.30	.30
451	A72	25c 2nd stage	.50	.50
452	A72	50c Launching	1.00	1.00
453	A72	$1 First voyage	1.90	1.90
a.		Souvenir sheet of 4, #450-453	4.00	4.00
		Nos. 450-453 (4)	3.70	3.70

Manned Flight Bicentenary — A73

1983, Sept. 15   Wmk. 373   Perf. 14

454	A73	10c Grumman Goose	.20	.20
455	A73	30c De Havilland Heron	.50	.50
456	A73	60c EMB Bandeirante	1.00	1.00
457	A73	$1.25 Hawker-Siddeley 748	2.00	2.00
		Nos. 454-457 (4)	3.70	3.70

Christmas — A74

Raphael Paintings.

1983, Nov. 7   Litho.   Perf. 14½

458	A74	8c Madonna & Child with Infant Baptist	.20	.20
459	A74	15c La Belle Jardiniere	.30	.30
460	A74	50c Madonna del Granduca	.95	.95
461	A74	$1 Terranuova Madonna	1.90	1.90
a.		Souvenir sheet of 4, #458-461	3.50	3.50
		Nos. 458-461 (4)	3.35	3.35

World Chess Federation, 60th
Anniv. — A75

984, Feb. 20   Litho.   Perf. 14

62	A75	10c Local tournament	.30	.30
63	A75	35c Chess pieces, vert.	1.00	1.00
64	A75	75c 1980 Olympiad, Winning board, vert.	2.25	2.25
465	A75	$1 Gold medal	3.25	3.25
		Nos. 462-465 (4)	6.80	6.80

Lloyd's List Issue
Common Design Type

984, Apr. 16   Litho.   Perf. 14½x14

466	CD335	15c Port Purcell, Tortola	.30	.30
467	CD335	25c Boeing 747	.50	.50
468	CD335	50c Shipwreck of RMS Rhone	1.00	1.00
469	CD335	$1 Booker Viking	2.00	2.00
		Nos. 466-469 (4)	3.80	3.80

Souvenir Sheet

UPU Congress — A76

1984, May 16   Wmk. 373   Perf. 14

470	A76	$1 Emblem, jet, mailboat	2.00	2.00

1984
Summer
Olympics
A77

1984, July 3

471	A77	15c Runners	.35	.35
472	A77	15c Runner	.35	.35
a.		Pair, #471-472	.70	.70
473	A77	20c Wind surfers	.45	.45
474	A77	20c Wind surfer	.45	.45
a.		Pair, #473-474	.90	.90
475	A77	30c Yachts	.70	.70
476	A77	30c Yacht	.70	.70
a.		Pair, #475-476	1.40	1.40
		Nos. 471-476 (6)	3.00	3.00

Souvenir Sheet

477	A77	$1 Torch bearer, vert.	2.00	2.00

Festival (Slavery Abolition
Sesquicentennial) — A78

Designs: No. 478: a, Steel band. b, Calypso
dancers. c, Dancers (men). d, Woman in traditional dress. e, Parade float.
No. 479 (Sail color of boat(s) in foreground):
a, Green & white. b, Red & white, white, purple & white. c, white, yellow & white, blue &
white. d, Yellow, red & white. e, Purple &
white, white.
Nos. 478 and 479 each in continuous
design.

1984, Aug. 14   Perf. 13½x14

478		Strip of 5, Parade	.95	.95
a.-e.		A78 10c, any single	.20	.20
479		Strip of 5, Regatta	2.75	2.75
a.-e.		A78 30c, any single	.55	.55

Local
Boats
A79

1984, Nov. 15   Wmk. 373   Perf. 13

480	A79	10c Sloop	.25	.25
481	A79	35c Fishing boat	.80	.80
482	A79	60c Schooner	1.50	1.50
483	A79	75c Cargo boat	1.75	1.75
a.		Souvenir sheet of 4, #480-483	3.75	3.75
		Nos. 480-483 (4)	4.30	4.30

Four stamps picturing Michael Jackson were printed. The designs were not
acceptable to the Virgin Islands so they
were not issued. A number of copies
had been distributed in advance for
publicity purposes.

New
Coinage
A80

1985, Jan. 15   Litho.   Perf. 14½

484	A80	1c Hawksbill Turtle	.20	.20
485	A80	5c Bonito	.20	.20
486	A80	10c Great Barricuda	.20	.20
487	A80	25c Blue Marlin	.50	.50
488	A80	50c Dolphin	1.00	1.00
489	A80	$1 Spotfin Butterfly Fish	2.00	2.00
a.		Miniature sheet of 6, #484-489	4.00	4.00
		Nos. 484-489 (6)	4.10	4.10

Birds — A81

1985, July 3   Wmk. 373   Perf. 14

490	A81	1c Boatswain bird	.20	.20
491	A81	2c Night gaulin	.20	.20
492	A81	5c Rain bird	.20	.20
493	A81	8c Mockingbird	.20	.20
494	A81	10c Chinchary	.25	.25
495	A81	12c Wild pigeon	.30	.30
496	A81	15c Bittlin	.35	.35
497	A81	18c Blach witch	.40	.40
498	A81	20c Pond shakey	.45	.45
499	A81	25c Killy-killy	.55	.55
500	A81	30c Thrushie	.70	.70
501	A81	35c Marmi dove	.80	.80
502	A81	40c Little gaulin	.95	.95
503	A81	50c Ground dove	1.10	1.10
504	A81	60c Blue gaulin	1.40	1.40
505	A81	$1 Pimleco	2.25	2.25
506	A81	$2 White booby	4.75	4.75
507	A81	$3 Cow bird	6.75	6.75
508	A81	$5 Turtle dove	11.50	11.50
		Nos. 490-508 (19)	33.30	33.30

For overprints see Nos. O16-O34.

1987, Oct. 28   Wmk. 384

494a	A81	10c	.30	.30
496a	A81	15c	.45	.45
498a	A81	20c	.60	.60
499a	A81	25c	.75	.75
501a	A81	35c	1.00	1.00
505a	A81	$1	3.00	3.00
507a	A81	$3	9.00	9.00
		Nos. 494a-507a (7)	15.10	15.10

Queen Mother,
85th
Birthday — A82

Audubon Birth
Bicent. — A83

Portraits.

1985, Aug. 26   Litho.   Perf. 12½

509	A82	10c Facing right	.20	.20
510	A82	10c Facing left	.20	.20
511	A82	25c Facing right	.45	.45
512	A82	25c Facing left	.45	.45
513	A82	50c Facing right	.90	.90
514	A82	50c Facing forward	.90	.90
515	A82	75c Facing right	1.25	1.25
516	A82	75c Facing forward	1.25	1.25
		Nos. 509-516 (8)	5.60	5.60

Souvenir Sheets

1985-86   Litho.   Perf. 13x12½

517		Sheet of 2	3.50	3.50
a.-b.		A82 $1 dull grn & multi	1.75	1.75
518		Sheet of 2	3.50	3.50
a.-b.		A82 $1 orange & multi	1.60	1.60
519		Sheet of 2	8.50	8.50
a.-b.		A82 $2.50 dl yel & multi	4.25	4.25

Issued: #517, 12/18/85; #518-519, 2/18/86.
For overprints see Nos. 528-531.

1985, Dec. 17   Perf. 15

520	A83	5c Seaside sparrow	.20	.20
521	A83	30c Passenger pigeon	.60	.60
522	A83	50c Yellow-breasted chat	1.00	1.00
523	A83	$1 American kestrel	2.00	2.00
		Nos. 520-523 (4)	3.80	3.80

Cruise
Ships
A84

1986, Jan. 27

524	A84	35c Flying Cloud	.65	.65
525	A84	50c Newport Clipper	.95	.95
526	A84	75c Cunard Countess	1.40	1.40
527	A84	$1 Sea Goddess	1.90	1.90
		Nos. 524-527 (4)	4.90	4.90

Nos. 511-512, 515-516 Ovptd. "MIAMI
/ B.V.I. / INAUGURAL FLIGHT"

1986, Apr. 17   Litho.   Perf. 12½

528	A82	25c on No. 511	.50	.50
529	A82	25c on No. 512	.50	.50
530	A82	75c on No. 515	1.50	1.50
531	A82	75c on No. 516	1.50	1.50
		Nos. 528-531 (4)	4.00	4.00

Queen Elizabeth II, 60th
Birthday — A85

Perf. 13x12½, 12½x13

1986, Apr. 21   Litho.

532	A85	12c Portrait, 1958	.20	.20
533	A85	35c Maundy service	.55	.55
534	A85	$1.50 Contemporary photograph	2.25	2.25

535	A85	$2 Canberra, 1982, vert.	3.00	3.00
		Nos. 532-535 (4)	6.00	6.00

Souvenir Sheet

536	A85	$3 Contemporary photograph, diff.	6.00	6.00

Stamps with blue ribbons and frames omitted were from stock sold when the printer was
liquidated.

Wedding of Prince Andrew and Sarah
Ferguson — A86

1986, July 23   Perf. 12½

537	A86	35c Couple, vert.	.55	.55
538	A86	35c Sarah, vert.	.55	.55
539	A86	$1 Andrew	1.60	1.60
540	A86	$1 Sarah, diff.	1.60	1.60
		Nos. 537-540 (4)	4.30	4.30

Stamps of the same denomination exist se-
tenant.
Nos. 537-540 Overprinted "Congratulations
to T.R.H. The Duke & Duchess of York" were
not issued.

Traditional Rum Production — A87

1986, July 30   Perf. 14

541	A87	12c Harvesting sugar cane	.30	.30
542	A87	40c Grinding	1.10	1.10
543	A87	60c Distillery	1.65	1.65
544	A87	$1 Transport	2.75	2.75
		Nos. 541-544 (4)	5.80	5.80

Souvenir Sheet

545	A87	$2 Up Spirits ceremony, 19th cent.	5.50	5.50

Souvenir Sheet

Wedding of Prince Andrew and Sarah
Ferguson — A88

1986, Oct. 15   Litho.   Perf. 13x12½

546	A88	$4 multicolored	7.50	6.00

Cable-Laying Ships — A89

1986, Oct. 15   Wmk. 380   Perf. 12½

547	A89	35c Sentinel	.70	.70
548	A89	35c Retriever	.70	.70
a.		Pair, #547-548	1.40	1.40
549	A89	60c Cable Enterprise	1.25	1.25
550	A89	60c Mercury	1.25	1.25
a.		Pair, #549-550	2.50	2.50
551	A89	75c Recorder	1.50	1.50
552	A89	75c Pacific Guardian	1.50	1.50
a.		Pair, #551-552	3.00	3.00

553	A89	$1 Great Eastern	2.00	2.00
554	A89	$1 Cable Venture	2.00	2.00
a.		Pair, #553-554	4.00	4.00
		Nos. 547-554 (8)	10.90	10.90

Souvenir Sheets

555		Sheet of 2	1.40	1.40
a.-b.	A89 40c, like #547-548		.70	.70
556		Sheet of 2	1.75	1.75
a.-b.	A89 50c, like #549-550		.90	.90
557		Sheet of 2	2.75	2.75
a.-b.	A89 80c, like #551-552		1.40	1.40
558		Sheet of 2	5.25	5.25
a.-b.	A89 $1.50, like #553-554		2.50	2.50

Cable and wireless in the islands, 20th anniv.

Souvenir Sheets

Statue of Liberty, Cent. — A90

Various views of the statue.

1986, Dec. 15   Litho.   Perf. 14

559	A90	50c multicolored	.95	.95
560	A90	75c multicolored	1.60	1.60
561	A90	90c multicolored	1.75	1.75
562	A90	$1 multicolored	2.00	2.00
563	A90	$1.25 multicolored	2.50	2.50
564	A90	$1.50 multicolored	3.00	3.00
565	A90	$1.75 multicolored	3.50	3.50
566	A90	$2 multicolored	3.75	3.75
567	A90	$2.50 multicolored	5.00	5.00
		Nos. 559-567 (9)	24.05	24.05

A91

Shipwrecks — A92

1987, Apr. 15   Perf. 14

572	A91	12c Spanish galleon, 18th cent.	.35	.35
573	A91	35c HMS Astrea, 1808	1.00	1.00
574	A91	75c RMS Rhone, 1867	2.00	2.00
575	A91	$1.50 SS Rocus, 1929	4.25	4.25
		Nos. 572-575 (4)	7.60	7.60

Souvenir Sheet

| 576 | A92 | $2.50 Brig Volvart, 1918 | 7.00 | 7.00 |

Natl. Flags, Outline Maps — A93

Botanical Gardens — A94

1987, May 28

577	A93	10c Montserrat	.20	.20
578	A93	15c Grenada	.30	.30
579	A93	20c Dominica	.40	.40
580	A93	25c St. Kitts-Nevis	.50	.50
581	A93	35c St. Vincent and Grenadines	.65	.65
582	A93	50c Virgin Isls.	.95	.95
583	A93	75c Antigua & Barbuda	1.40	1.40
584	A93	$1 St. Lucia	1.90	1.90
		Nos. 577-584 (8)	6.30	6.30

11th Meeting of the Organization of Eastern Caribbean States.

1987, Aug. 12   Wmk. 384

585	A94	12c Spider lily	.25	.25
586	A94	35c Barrel cactus	.75	.75
587	A94	$1 Wild plantain	2.00	2.00
588	A94	$1.50 Little butterfly orchid	3.00	3.00
		Nos. 585-588 (4)	6.00	6.00

Souvenir Sheet

| 589 | A94 | $2.50 White cedar | 5.00 | 5.00 |

Postal Service Bicent. A95

Designs: 10c, 18th Cent. packet, #7 canceled "A13." 20c, Map of the islands, #22 canceled "A91." 35c, Tortola Post Office and Customs House, and #5 canceled "Tortola De 20 61." $1.50, Mail plane and #154 canceled "Road town No 2 64 Tortola W.I." $2.50, Late 19th cent. steam packet and #10 canceled "A Tortola Ap 12 70."

1987, Dec. 17   Litho.   Perf. 14½

590	A95	10c multicolored	.30	.30
591	A95	20c multicolored	.55	.55
592	A95	35c multicolored	1.00	1.00
593	A95	$1.50 multicolored	4.25	4.25
		Nos. 590-593 (4)	6.10	6.10

Souvenir Sheet

| 594 | A95 | $2.50 multicolored | 5.00 | 5.00 |

Paintings by Titian — A96

10c, Salome, 1512. 12c, Man with the Glove, c. 1520-22. 20c, Fabrizio Salvaresio, 1558. 25c, Daughter of Roberto Strozzi, 1542. 40c, Pope Julius II. 50c, Bishop Ludovico Beccadelli, 1552. 60c, Philip II. $1, Empress Isabella of Portugal, 1548. #603, Emperor Charles V at Muhlberg, 1548. #604, Pope Paul III & His Grandsons, 1546.

Perf. 13½x14

1988, Aug. 11   Unwmk.

595	A96	10c multicolored	.20	.20
596	A96	12c multicolored	.25	.25
597	A96	20c multicolored	.40	.40
598	A96	25c multicolored	.50	.50
599	A96	40c multicolored	.80	.80
600	A96	50c multicolored	1.00	1.00
601	A96	60c multicolored	1.25	1.25
602	A96	$1 multicolored	2.00	2.00
		Nos. 595-602 (8)	6.40	6.40

Souvenir Sheet

| 603 | A96 | $2 multicolored | 4.00 | 4.00 |
| 604 | A96 | $2 multicolored | 4.00 | 4.00 |

1st Annual Open Chess Tournament — A97

35c, Pawn & Transporter aircraft over Sir Francis Drake Channel. $1, King & Jose Raul Capablanca (1888-1942), Cuban chess master and world champion from 1921-27. $2, Match scene.

1988, Aug. 25   Unwmk.   Perf. 14

| 605 | A97 | 35c multicolored | .70 | .70 |
| 606 | A97 | $1 multicolored | 2.00 | 2.00 |

Souvenir Sheet

| 607 | A97 | $2 multicolored | 4.00 | 4.00 |

1988 Summer Olympics, Seoul A98

1988, Sept. 8

608	A98	12c Hurdling	.25	.25
609	A98	20c Windsurfing	.40	.40
610	A98	75c Basketball	1.50	1.50
611	A98	$1 Tennis	2.00	2.00
		Nos. 608-611 (4)	4.15	4.15

Souvenir Sheet

| 612 | A98 | $2 Running | 4.00 | 4.00 |

Intl. Red Cross, 125th Anniv. A99

Safety warnings and steps in administering cardiopulmonary resuscitation (CPR): 12c, "Don't swim alone." 30c, "No swimming during electrical storms." 60c, "Don't eat before swimming." $1, "Proper equipment for boating." No. 617a, Turn victim on back. No. 617b, Position victim's chin so breathing passages are not blocked. No. 617c, Mouth-to-mouth resuscitation. No. 617d, Chest compressions. Nos. 617a-617d vert.

1988, Sept. 26

613	A99	12c multicolored	.25	.25
614	A99	30c multicolored	.60	.60
615	A99	60c multicolored	1.25	1.25
616	A99	$1 multicolored	2.00	2.00
		Nos. 613-616 (4)	4.10	4.10

Souvenir Sheet

| 617 | | Sheet of 4 | 4.00 | 4.00 |
| a.-d. | A99 50c any single | | 1.00 | 1.00 |

#617a-617d has a continuous design.

Visit of Princess Alexandra — A100

World Wildlife Fund — A101

Various photographs of the princess.

1988, Nov. 9   Litho.   Perf. 14

| 618 | A100 | 40c shown | .80 | .80 |
| 619 | A100 | $1.50 multi, diff. | 3.00 | 3.00 |

Souvenir Sheet

| 620 | A100 | $2 multi, diff. | 4.00 | 4.00 |

1988, Nov. 15

Brown pelicans, *Pelecanus Occidentalis.*

621	A101	10c Pelican in flight	.20	
622	A101	12c Perched	.25	
623	A101	15c Close-up of head	.30	
624	A101	35c Swallowing fish	.70	
		Nos. 621-624 (4)	1.45	1.4

Reptiles, Marine Mammals and Birds — A102

20c, Anegada rock iguana. 40c, Virgin gorda dwarf gecko. 60c, Hawksbill turtle. $1 Humpback whale. #629, Northern shoveler, American widgeon & ring-necked ducks. #630, Trunk turtle.

1988, Nov. 15

625	A102	20c multicolored	.40	.4
626	A102	40c multicolored	.80	.8
627	A102	60c multicolored	1.25	1.2
628	A102	$1 multicolored	2.00	2.0
		Nos. 625-628 (4)	4.45	4.4

Souvenir Sheets

| 629 | A102 | $2 multicolored | 4.00 | 4.00 |
| 630 | A102 | $2 multicolored | 4.00 | 4.00 |

Spring Regatta A103

Various yachts.

1989, Apr. 7   Litho.   Perf. 14

631	A103	12c multi, diff., vert.	.25	.25
632	A103	40c shown	.80	.80
633	A103	75c multi, diff., vert.	1.50	1.50
634	A103	$1 multi, diff.	2.00	2.00
		Nos. 631-634 (4)	4.55	4.55

Souvenir Sheet

| 635 | A103 | $2 multi, diff., vert. | 4.00 | 4.00 |

Pre-Columbian Societies and Their Customs — A104

1989, May 18

636	A104	10c Hammock	.20	.20
637	A104	20c Making a fire	.40	.40
638	A104	25c Carvers	.50	.50
639	A104	$1.50 Arawak family	3.00	3.00
		Nos. 636-639 (4)	4.10	4.10

Souvenir Sheet

| 640 | A104 | $2 Ritual | 4.00 | 4.00 |

Discovery of America 500th anniv. (in 1992).

1st Moon Landing, 20th Anniv. A105

Highlights of the Apollo 11 mission: 15c, Lunar surface, mission emblem. 30c, Buzz Aldrin conducting solar wind experiment. 65c, Raising American flag. $1, Recovery of crew after splashdown. $2, Portrait of crew.

1989, Sept. 28 — Litho. — Perf. 14

641	A105	15c multicolored	.30	.30
642	A105	30c multicolored	.60	.60
643	A105	65c multicolored	1.25	1.25
644	A105	$1 multicolored	2.00	2.00
		Nos. 641-644 (4)	4.15	4.15

Souvenir Sheet
Perf. 13½x14

645	A105	$2 multicolored	4.00	4.00

No. 645 contains one 37x46mm stamp.

Methodist Church, 200th Anniv. A106

Designs: 12c, Black Harry, Nathaniel Gilbert preaching. 25c, Book symbolizing role of the church in education. 35c, East End Methodist Church, 1810. $1.25, John Wesley, modern youth choir. $2, Thomas Coke.

1989, Oct. 24 — Perf. 14

646	A106	12c multicolored	.25	.25
647	A106	25c multicolored	.50	.50
648	A106	35c multicolored	.75	.75
649	A106	$1.25 multicolored	2.50	2.50
		Nos. 646-649 (4)	4.00	4.00

Souvenir Sheet

650	A106	$2 multicolored	4.00	4.00

1990 World Cup Soccer Championships, Italy — A107

Various athletes.

1989, Nov. 6

651	A107	5c shown	.20	.20
652	A107	10c multi, diff.	.20	.20
653	A107	20c multi, diff.	.40	.40
654	A107	$1.75 multi, diff.	3.50	3.50
		Nos. 651-654 (4)	4.30	4.30

Souvenir Sheet

655	A107	$2 Natl. team	4.00	4.00

Princess Alexandra, Sunset House — A108

Royal Yacht Britannia — A109

b, Princess Margaret, Government House. c, Hon. Angus Ogilvy, Little Dix Bay Hotel. d, Princess Diana & her children, Necker Island Resort.

1990, May 3 — Litho. — Perf. 14

656		Min. sheet of 4	4.00	4.00
a.-d.		A108 50c any single	1.00	1.00

Souvenir Sheet

657	A109	$2 multicolored	4.00	4.00

Stamp World London '90.

Audubon's Shearwater — A110

1990, May 15

658	A110	5c shown	.20	.20
659	A110	12c Red-necked pigeon	.25	.25
660	A110	20c Common gallinule	.40	.40
661	A110	25c Green heron	.50	.50
662	A110	40c Yellow warbler	.80	.80
663	A110	60c Smooth-billed ani	1.25	1.25
664	A110	$1 Antillean crested hummingbird	2.00	2.00
665	A110	$1.25 Black-faced grassquit	2.50	2.50
		Nos. 658-665 (8)	7.90	7.90

Souvenir Sheets

666	A110	$2 Egg of royal tern	4.00	4.00
667	A110	$2 Egg of red-billed tropicbird	4.00	4.00

Blue Tang A111

1990, June 18

668	A111	10c shown	.20	.20
669	A111	35c Glasseye	.70	.70
670	A111	50c Slippery Dick	1.00	1.00
671	A111	$1 Porkfish	2.00	2.00
		Nos. 668-671 (4)	3.90	3.90

Souvenir Sheet

672	A111	$2 Yellowtail snapper	4.00	4.00

A112

A113

1990, Aug. 30 — Litho. — Perf. 14

673	A112	12c multicolored	.25	.25
674	A112	25c multi, diff.	.50	.50
675	A112	60c multi, diff.	1.25	1.25
676	A112	$1 multi, diff.	2.00	2.00
		Nos. 673-676 (4)	4.00	4.00

Souvenir Sheet

677	A112	$2 multi, diff.	4.00	4.00

Queen Mother, 90th birthday.

1990, Dec. 10 — Litho. — Perf. 14

Various soccer players.

678	A113	12c multicolored	.25	.25
679	A113	20c multi, diff.	.40	.40
680	A113	50c multi, diff.	1.00	1.00
681	A113	$1.25 multi, diff.	2.50	2.50
		Nos. 678-681 (4)	4.15	4.15

Souvenir Sheet

682	A113	$2 multi, diff.	4.00	4.00

World Cup Soccer Championships, Italy.

1992 Summer Olympics, Barcelona A114

1990, Dec. 20 — Litho. — Perf. 14

683	A114	12c Judo	.25	.25
684	A114	40c Yachting	.80	.80
685	A114	60c Hurdles	1.25	1.25
686	A114	$1 Show jumping	2.00	2.00
		Nos. 683-686 (4)	4.30	4.30

Souvenir Sheet

687	A114	$2 Windsurfing	4.00	4.00

Copper Mine Ruins A115

1991, Mar. 1 — Litho. — Perf. 14

688	A115	10c Cyanthea arborea, vert.	.20	.20
689	A115	25c shown	.50	.50
690	A115	35c Mt. Healthy windmill ruin, vert.	.70	.70
691	A115	$2 Baths, Virgin Gorda	4.00	4.00
		Nos. 688-691 (4)	5.40	5.40

National Park Trust.

Flowers — A116

Butterflies — A117

1991-92 — Litho. — Perf. 14

692	A116	1c Haiti Haiti	.20	.20
693	A116	2c Lobster claw	.20	.20
694	A116	5c Frangipani	.20	.20
695	A116	10c Autograph tree	.20	.20
696	A116	12c Yellow allamanda	.25	.25
697	A116	15c Lantana	.30	.30
698	A116	20c Jerusalem thorn	.40	.40
699	A116	25c Turk's cap	.50	.50
700	A116	30c Swamp immortelle	.60	.60
701	A116	35c White cedar	.70	.70
702	A116	40c Mahoe tree	.80	.80
703	A116	45c Pinguin	.90	.90
704	A116	50c Christmas orchid	1.00	1.00
705	A116	70c Lignum vitae	1.40	1.40
706	A116	$1 African tulip tree	2.00	2.00
707	A116	$2 Beach morning glory	4.00	4.00
708	A116	$3 Organ pipe cactus	6.00	6.00
709	A116	$5 Tall ground orchid	10.00	10.00
710	A116	$10 Ground orchid	20.00	20.00
		Nos. 692-710 (19)	49.65	49.65

Nos. 695, 701, 703 exist dated "1995."
The 70c, $1 and $2 exist perf 12, the $3 prerf 12½. These were issued in Aug. 1995.
Issued: $10, 5/92; others, 5/1/91.
For overprints see Nos. O37-O51.

1991, June 28 — Litho. — Perf. 14

711	A117	5c Cloudless sulphur	.20	.20
712	A117	10c Flambeau	.20	.20
713	A117	15c Caribbean buckeye	.30	.30
714	A117	20c Gulf fritillary	.40	.40
715	A117	25c Polydamus swallowtail	.50	.50
716	A117	30c Little sulphur	.60	.60
717	A117	35c Zebra	.70	.70
718	A117	$1.50 Malachite	3.00	3.00
		Nos. 711-718 (8)	5.90	5.90

Souvenir Sheets

719	A117	$2 Monarch, horiz.	4.00	4.00
720	A117	$2 Red rim, horiz.	4.00	4.00

Voyages of Discovery A118

Ships of explorers: 12c, Ferdinand Magellan, 1519-1521. 50c, Rene-Robert de la Salle, 1682. 75c, John Cabot, 1497-1498. $1, Jacques Cartier, 1534. $2, Columbus' ship, 1493 woodcut, vert.

1991, Sept. 20 — Litho. — Perf. 14

721	A118	12c multicolored	.25	.25
722	A118	50c multicolored	1.00	1.00
723	A118	75c multicolored	1.50	1.50
724	A118	$1 multicolored	2.00	2.00
		Nos. 721-724 (4)	4.75	4.75

Souvenir Sheet

725	A118	$2 multicolored	4.00	4.00

Vincent Van Gogh (1853-1890), Painter — A119

Paintings: 15c, Cottage with Decrepit Barn and Stooping Woman. 30c, Paul Gauguin's Armchair, vert. 75c, Breton Women. $1, Vase with Red Gladioli, vert. $2, The Dance Hall in Arles (detail).

1991, Nov. 1 — Perf. 13

726	A119	15c multicolored	.30	.30
727	A119	30c multicolored	.60	.60
728	A119	75c multicolored	1.50	1.50
729	A119	$1 multicolored	2.00	2.00
		Nos. 726-729 (4)	4.40	4.40

Souvenir Sheet

730	A119	$2 multicolored	4.00	4.00

Christmas A120

Entire paintings or details by Quinten Massys: 15c, The Virgin and Child Enthroned. 30c, The Virgin and Child Enthroned, diff. 60c, The Adoration of the Magi. $1, Virgin in Adoration. No. 735, The Virgin Standing with Angels. No. 736, The Adoration of the Magi.

1991, Dec. 12 — Litho. — Perf. 12

731	A120	15c multicolored	.30	.30
732	A120	30c multicolored	.60	.60
733	A120	60c multicolored	1.20	1.20
734	A120	$1 multicolored	2.00	2.00
		Nos. 731-734 (4)	4.10	4.10

Souvenir Sheets
Perf. 14½

735	A120	$2 multicolored	4.00	4.00
736	A120	$2 multicolored	4.00	4.00

Mushrooms — A121

1992, Jan. 15   *Perf. 14*
737 A121 12c Agaricus bisporus, vert.   .25   .25
738 A121 30c Lentinus edodes   .60   .60
739 A121 45c Hyrocybe acutoconica, vert.   .90   .90
740 A121 $1 Gymnopilus chrysopellus   2.00   2.00
   Nos. 737-740 (4)   3.75   3.75

Souvenir Sheet
741 A121 $2 Pleurotus ostreatus   4.00   4.00

Queen Elizabeth II's Accession to the Throne, 40th Anniv.
Common Design Type

1992, Feb. 6   Litho.   *Perf. 14*
742 CD348 12c multicolored   .25   .25
743 CD348 45c multicolored   .90   .90
744 CD348 60c multicolored   1.20   1.20
745 CD348 $1 multicolored   2.00   2.00
   Nos. 742-745 (4)   4.35   4.35

Souvenir Sheet
746 CD348 $2 multicolored   4.00   4.00

Discovery of America, 500th Anniv. A122

10c, Queen Isabella. 15c, Columbus' fleet. 20c, Columbus' second coat of arms. 30c, Landing Monument on Watling Island, Columbus' signature. 45c, Columbus. 50c, Flag of Ferdinand & Isabella, Columbus landing on Watling Island. 70c, Convent at La Rabida. $1.50, Replica of Santa Maria at New York World's Fair, 1964-65. #755, Columbus' 2nd fleet. #756, Map.

1992, May 26   Litho.   *Perf. 14*
747 A122 10c multi, vert.   .20   .20
748 A122 15c multi   .30   .30
749 A122 20c multi   .40   .40
750 A122 30c multi   .60   .60
751 A122 45c multi, vert.   .90   .90
752 A122 50c multi   1.00   1.00
753 A122 70c multi, vert.   1.40   1.40
754 A122 $1.50 multi   3.00   3.00
   Nos. 747-754 (8)   7.80   7.80

Souvenir Sheet
755 A122 $2 multicolored   4.00   4.00
756 A122 $2 multicolored   4.00   4.00

1992 Summer Olympics, Barcelona — A123

1992, Aug.   Litho.   *Perf. 14*
757 A123 15c Basketball   .30   .30
758 A123 30c Tennis   .60   .60
759 A123 60c Volleyball   1.25   1.25
760 A123 $1 Soccer   2.00   2.00
   Nos. 757-760 (4)   4.15   4.15

Souvenir Sheet
761 A123 $2 Olympic flame   4.00   4.00

Ministerial Government, 25th Anniv. — A124

Designs: 12c, Social progress and development. 15c, Map of Virgin Islands. 45c, Administration complex. $1.30, International finance.

1993, Apr.   Litho.   *Perf. 14*
762 A124 12c multicolored   .25   .25
763 A124 15c multicolored   .30   .30
764 A124 45c multicolored   .85   .85
765 A124 $1.30 multicolored   2.60   2.60
   Nos. 762-765 (4)   4.00   4.00

Tourism A125

15c, Swimming from anchored yacht. 30c, Sailboat. 60c, Scuba diver in pink wetsuit. $1, Snorkelers, anchored boat.
#770: a, Trimaran, vert. b, Scuba diver, vert.

1993, Apr.   Litho.   *Perf. 14*
766 A125 15c multi   .30   .30
767 A125 30c multi, vert.   .60   .60
768 A125 60c multi   1.25   1.25
769 A125 $1 multi, vert.   2.00   2.00
   Nos. 766-769 (4)   4.15   4.15

Souvenir Sheet
770 A125 $1 Sheet of 2, #a.-b.   4.00   4.00

Miniature Sheet

Coronation of Queen Elizabeth II, 40th Anniv. A126

No. 771: a, 12c, Official coronation photograph. b, 45c, Dove atop Rod of Equity and Mercy. c, 60c, Royal family. d, $1, Recent color photo.

1993, June 2   Litho.   *Perf. 13½x14*
771 A126 Sheet, 2 each #a.-d.   8.75   8.75
A souvenir sheet containing a $2 stamp was not an authorized issue.

Discovery of Virgin Islands, 500th Anniv. A127

3c, Ferdinand and Isabella supporting Columbus. 12c, Departure of Columbus. 15c, Departure of second voyage. 25c, Arms, flag of British Virgin Islands. 30c, Columbus, Santa Maria. 45c, Columbus' second fleet at sea. 60c, Rowing ashore. $1, Landing of Columbus. #781, Natives watching ships. #782, Columbus, two ships of his fleet.

1993, Sept. 24   Litho.   *Perf. 14*
773 A127 3c multicolored   .20   .20
774 A127 12c multicolored   .25   .25
775 A127 15c multicolored   .30   .30
776 A127 25c multicolored   .50   .50
777 A127 30c multicolored   .60   .60
778 A127 45c multicolored   .90   .90
779 A127 60c multicolored   1.25   1.25
780 A127 $1 multicolored   2.00   2.00
   Nos. 773-780 (8)   6.00   6.00

Souvenir Sheets
781 A127 $2 multicolored   4.00   4.00
782 A127 $2 multicolored   4.00   4.00

Secondary Education and Library Services, 50th Anniv. — A128

Designs: 5c, Historical documents. 10c, Sporting activities. 15c, Stanley W. Nibbs, educator, vert. 20c, Bookmobile. 30c, Norwell E. Harrigan, educator, vert. 35c, Public library's annual summer program. 70c, Text. $1, High school.

Perf. 14x13½, 13½x14

1993, Dec.   Litho.
783 A128 5c multicolored   .20   .20
784 A128 10c multicolored   .20   .20
785 A128 15c multicolored   .30   .30
786 A128 20c multicolored   .40   .40
787 A128 30c multicolored   .55   .55
788 A128 35c multicolored   .65   .65
789 A128 70c multicolored   1.25   1.25
790 A128 $1 multicolored   1.90   1.90
   Nos. 783-790 (8)   5.45   5.45

Anegada Ground Iguana — A129

5c, Crawling right. 10c, Head up to right. 15c, View from behind. 45c, Head up to left. $2, Head.

1994, Jan.   Litho.   *Perf. 14*
791 A129 5c multicolored   .20   .20
792 A129 10c multicolored   .20   .20
793 A129 15c multicolored   .25   .25
794 A129 45c multicolored   .85   .85
   Nos. 791-794 (4)   1.50   1.50

Souvenir Sheet
795 A129 $2 multicolored   3.75   3.75

World Wildlife Fund.

Rotary Club of Virgin Islands, 25th Anniv. A130

Designs: 15c, Disaster relief airlift. 45c, Kids, Sea "Kats." 50c, Donated hospital equipment. 90c, Paul P. Harris (1868-1947), founder of Rotary Intl.

1994, June 3   Litho.   *Perf. 14*
796 A130 15c multicolored   .30   .30
797 A130 45c multicolored   .85   .85
798 A130 50c multicolored   .95   .95
799 A130 90c multicolored   1.65   1.65
   Nos. 796-799 (4)   3.75   3.75

Miniature Sheet of 6

First Manned Moon Landing, 25th Anniv. A131

Designs: No. 800a, Anniversary emblem. b, Lunar landing training vehicle. c, Apollo 11 liftoff, July 16, 1969. d, Lunar module Eagle in flight. e, Moon landing site approached by Eagle. f, 1st step on Moon, July 20, 1969. No. 801, Mission patch, crew signatures.

1994, Sept. 30   Litho.   *Perf. 14*
800 A131 50c #a.-f.   6.00   6.00

Souvenir Sheet
801 A131 $2 multicolored   4.00   4.00

A132   A133

Previous champions: 15c, Argentina, 1978. 35c, Italy, 1982. 50c, Argentina, 1986. $1.30, W. Germany, 1990.
$2, US flag, World Cup trophy, horiz.

1994, Dec. 16   Litho.   *Perf. 14*
802 A132 15c multicolored   .30   .30
803 A132 35c multicolored   .70   .70
804 A132 50c multicolored   1.00   1.00
805 A132 $1.30 multicolored   2.50   2.50
   Nos. 802-805 (4)   4.50   4.50

Souvenir Sheet
806 A132 $2 multicolored   4.00   4.00

1994 World Cup Soccer Championships, US.

UN, 50th Anniv.
Common Design Type

Designs: 15c, Peugeot P4 all-purpose light vehicle. 30c, Foden medium tanker. 45c, Sisu all-terrain vehicle. $2, Westland Lynx AH7 helicopter.

Wmk. 373
1995, Oct. 24   Litho.   *Perf. 14*
807 CD353 15c multicolored   .30   .30
808 CD353 30c multicolored   .60   .60
809 CD353 45c multicolored   .90   .90
810 CD353 $2 multicolored   4.00   4.00
   Nos. 807-810 (4)   5.80   5.80

Wmk. 373
1995, Nov. 15   Litho.   *Perf. 13*

Anegada Flamingos.
811 A133 15c Juveniles   .30   .30
812 A133 20c Adults   .45   .45
813 A133 60c Adult feeding   1.25   1.25
814 A133 $1.45 Adult feeding chick   3.00   3.00
   Nos. 811-814 (4)   5.00   5.00

Souvenir Sheet
815 A133 $2 Chicks   4.00   4.00

Christmas — A134

Children's paintings: 12c, House with palm trees. 50c, Santa in boat. 70c, Red house, Christmas tree, presents. $1.30, Dove of peace.

Wmk. 384
1995, Dec. 1   Litho.   *Perf. 14*
816 A134 12c multicolored   .25   .25
817 A134 50c multicolored   1.00   1.00
818 A134 70c multicolored   1.40   1.40
819 A134 $1.30 multicolored   2.50   2.50
   Nos. 816-819 (4)   5.15   5.15

Island Scenes A135

Designs: 15c, Seine fishing. 35c, Sandy Spit, Jost Van Dyke. 90c, Map of Jost Van Dyke. $1.50, Foxy's wooden boat regatta.

Perf. 13½x13
1996, Feb. 14   Litho.   **Wmk. 373**
820 A135 15c multicolored   .30   .30
821 A135 35c multicolored   .70   .70
822 A135 90c multicolored   1.75   1.75
823 A135 $1.50 multicolored   3.00   3.00
   Nos. 820-823 (4)   5.75   5.75

See Nos. 892-896.'

Queen Elizabeth II, 70th Birthday
Common Design Type

Queen in various attire, scenes of Virgin Islands: 10c, Government House, Tortola. 30c, Legislative Council Chambers. 45c, Road Harbor. $1.50, Map of Virgin Islands.
$2, Wearing royal crown.

Perf. 13½x14

			1996, Apr. 22	Litho.	Wmk. 373
824	CD354	10c multicolored		.20	.20
825	CD354	30c multicolored		.60	.60
826	CD354	45c multicolored		.90	.90
827	CD354	$1.50 multicolored		3.00	3.00
		Nos. 824-827 (4)		4.70	4.70

Souvenir Sheet
Perf. 13x13½

828	CD354	$2 multicolored	4.00	4.00

Modern Olympic Games, Cent. A136

Wmk. 373

			1996, May 22	Litho.	Perf. 13
829	A136	20c Hurdles		.40	.40
830	A136	35c Volleyball		.70	.70
831	A136	50c Swimming		1.00	1.00
832	A136	$1 Sailing		2.00	2.00
		Nos. 829-832 (4)		4.10	4.10

CAPEX '96 A137

Vintage automobiles: 15c, 1934 Mercedes-Benz 500KA Cabriolet. 40c, 1934 Citroen 12. 60c, 1932 Cadillac V-8 Sport Phaeton. $1.35, 1934 Rolls Royce Phantom II.
$2, 1932 Ford Sport Coupe.

Wmk. 373

			1996, June 8	Litho.	Perf. 13½
833	A137	15c multicolored		.30	.30
834	A137	40c multicolored		.70	.70
835	A137	60c multicolored		1.25	1.25
836	A137	$1.35 multicolored		2.75	2.75
		Nos. 833-836 (4)		5.00	5.00

Souvenir Sheet

837	A137	$2 multicolored	4.00	4.00

UNICEF, 50th Anniv. A138

Goals of UNICEF for the year 2000: 10c, Educate the child. 15c, Children first. 30c, Children have rights. 45c, No more polio.

Perf. 14x14½

			1996, Sept. 16	Litho.	Wmk. 373
838	A138	10c multicolored		.20	.20
839	A138	15c multicolored		.30	.30
840	A138	30c multicolored		.60	.60
841	A138	45c multicolored		.90	.90
		Nos. 838-841 (4)		2.00	2.00

Girl Guiding in Virgin Islands, 25th Anniv. — A139

Designs: 10c, Rainbows, arts and crafts. 15c, Brownies, community service. 30c, Guides, campfire. 45c, Rangers, H.M. Queen's birthday parade. $2, Lady Baden-Powell, world chief guide.

Wmk. 373

			1996, Dec. 30	Litho.	Perf. 13½
842	A139	10c multicolored		.20	.20
843	A139	15c multicolored		.30	.30
844	A139	30c multicolored		.60	.60
845	A139	45c multicolored		.90	.90
846	A139	$2 multicolored		4.00	4.00
		Nos. 842-846 (5)		6.00	6.00

Game Fish A140

Wmk. 384

			1997, Jan. 6		Perf. 14
847	A140	1c Mackerel		.20	.20
848	A140	10c Wahoo		.20	.20
849	A140	15c Barracuda		.30	.30
850	A140	20c Tarpon		.40	.40
851	A140	25c Tiger shark		.50	.50
852	A140	35c Sailfish		.70	.70
853	A140	40c Dolphin		.80	.80
854	A140	50c Blackfin tuna		1.00	1.00
855	A140	60c Yellowfin tuna		1.25	1.25
856	A140	75c Kingfish		1.50	1.50
857	A140	$1.50 White marlin		3.00	3.00
a.		Souvenir sheet of 1, wmk. 373		3.00	3.00
858	A140	$1.85 Amberjack		3.75	3.75
859	A140	$2 Bonito		4.00	4.00
860	A140	$5 Bonefish		10.00	10.00
861	A140	$10 Blue marlin		20.00	20.00
		Nos. 847-861 (15)		47.60	47.60

No. 857a, Hong Kong '97.

Queen Elizabeth II and Prince Philip, 50th Wedding Anniv. — A141

#862, Prince with horse. #863, Queen Elizabeth II. #864, Queen riding in open carriage. #865, Prince Philip. #866, Queen holding hat down, Prince. #867, Prince Charles on polo pony.
$2, Queen, Prince riding in open carriage, horiz.

Wmk. 373

			1997, July 10	Litho.	Perf. 13
862		30c multicolored		.60	.60
863		30c multicolored		.60	.60
a.		A141 Pair, #862-863		1.20	1.20
864		45c multicolored		.90	.90
865		45c multicolored		.90	.90
a.		A141 Pair, #864-865		1.80	1.80
866		70c multicolored		1.40	1.40
867		70c multicolored		1.40	1.40
a.		A141 Pair, #866-867		2.80	2.80
		Nos. 862-867 (6)		5.80	5.80

Souvenir Sheet

868	A141	$2 multicolored	4.00	4.00

Crabs A142

Wmk. 373

			1997, Sept. 11	Litho.	Perf. 13
869	A142	12c Fiddler		.25	.25
870	A142	15c Coral		.30	.30
871	A142	35c Blue		.70	.70
872	A142	$1 Giant hermit		2.00	2.00
		Nos. 869-872 (4)		3.25	3.25

Souvenir Sheet

873	A142	$2 Arrow	4.00	4.00

Orchids A143

Designs: a, 20c, Psychilis macconnelliae. b, 50c, Tolumnia prionochila. c, 60c, Tetramicra canaliculata. d, 75c, Liparis elata.
$2, Dendrobium crumenatum, vert.

Wmk. 373

			1997, Nov. 26	Litho.	Perf. 14
874	A143	Strip of 4, #a.-d.		4.00	4.00

Souvenir Sheet

875	A143	$2 multicolored	4.00	4.00

World Voyage of Sir Francis Drake A144

Portions of map and: No. 876: a, Francis Drake. b, Drake Coat of Arms. c, Queen Elizabeth I. d, Christopher & Marigold. e, Golden Hinde. f, Swan. g, Cacafuego. h, Elizabeth. i, Maria. j, Drake's Astrolabe. k, Golden Hinde beakhead. l, 16th cent. compass rose.
$2, Modern ship named, "Sir Francis Drake."

			1997, Dec. 13		Perf. 14½
876	A144	40c Sheet of 12, #a.-l.		9.50	9.50

Souvenir Sheet

877	A144	$2 multicolored	4.00	4.00

Diana, Princess of Wales (1961-97)
Common Design Type

Portraits: a, 15c. b, 45c. c, 70c. d, $1.

Perf. 14½x14

			1998, Mar. 31	Litho.	Wmk. 373
878	CD355	Sheet of 4, #a.-d.		5.00	5.00

No. 878 sold for $2.30 + 20c, with surtax from international sales being donated to the Princess Diana Memorial Fund and surtax from national sales being donated to designated local charity.

Royal Air Force, 80th Anniv.
Common Design Type of 1993 Reinscribed

Designs: 20c, Fairey IIIF. 35c, Supermarine Scapa. 50c, Westland Sea King HAR3. $1.50, BAe Harrier GR7.
No. 883: a, Curtiss H.12 Large America. b, Curtiss JN-4A. c, Bell Airacobra. d, Boulton-Paul Defiant.

Perf. 13½x14

			1998, Apr. 1	Litho.	Wmk. 373
879	CD350	20c multicolored		.40	.40
880	CD350	35c multicolored		.70	.70
881	CD350	50c multicolored		1.00	1.00
882	CD350	$1.50 multicolored		3.00	3.00
		Nos. 879-882 (4)		5.10	5.10

Souvenir Sheet

883	CD350	75c Sheet of 4, #a.-d.	6.00	6.00

Marine Life — A145

Designs: 15c, Fingerprint cyphoma. 30c, Long spined sea urchin. 45c, Split crown feather duster worm. $1, Upside down jelly. $2, Giant anemone.

			1998, May 20	Wmk. 384	Perf. 14½
884	A145	15c multicolored		.30	.30
885	A145	30c multicolored		.60	.60
886	A145	45c multicolored		.90	.90
887	A145	$1 multicolored		2.00	2.00
		Nos. 884-887 (4)		3.80	3.80

Souvenir Sheet

888	A145	$2 multicolored	4.00	4.00

No. 888 is a continuous design.

Childrens' Art Festival A146

Wmk. 373

			1998, Aug. 25	Litho.	Perf. 14
889	A146	30c Girl in yellow & red, vert.		.60	.60
890	A146	45c Dancer, vert.		.90	.90
891	A146	$1.30 shown		2.75	2.75
		Nos. 889-891 (3)		4.25	4.25

Island Scenes Type of 1996

Designs: 12c, Salt pond. 30c, Shipwreck, HMS Rhone. 70c, Traditional house. $1.45, Salt Island.
$2, Gathering salt.

			1998, Oct. 28		
892	A135	12c multicolored		.25	.25
893	A135	30c multicolored		.60	.60
894	A135	70c multicolored		1.40	1.40
895	A135	$1.45 multicolored		3.00	3.00
		Nos. 892-895 (4)		5.25	5.25

Souvenir Sheet

896	A135	$2 multicolored	4.00	4.00

Anniversaries and Events — A147

5c, Classes in computer training, woodworking, electronics. 15c, Students playing musical instruments. 30c, Chapel, Mona Campus, Jamaica. 45c, Plaque on wall, university crest. 50c, Dr. John Coakley Lettsom, map of Little Jost Van Dyke island. $1, Crest of the Medical Society of London, building.

Wmk. 384

			1998, Dec. 14	Litho.	Perf. 14
897	A147	5c multicolored		.20	.20
898	A147	15c multicolored		.30	.30
899	A147	30c multicolored		.65	.65
900	A147	45c multicolored		.85	.85
901	A147	50c multicolored		1.00	1.00
902	A147	$1 multicolored		2.00	2.00
		Nos. 897-902 (6)		5.00	5.00

Comprehensive education in Virgin Islands, 30th anniv. (#897-898). University of West Indies, 50th anniv. (#899-900). Founding of the Medical Society of London by Dr. John Coakley Lettsom, 225th anniv. (#901-902).

Lizards A148

Designs: 5c, Rock iguana. 35c, Pygmy gecko. 60c, Slippery back skink. $1.50, Wood slave gecko.
No. 907: a, Doctor lizard. b, Yellow-bellied lizard. c, Man lizard. d, Ground lizard.

Perf. 14½x14

			1999, Apr. 30	Litho.	Wmk. 373
903	A148	5c multicolored		.20	.20
904	A148	35c multicolored		.70	.70
905	A148	60c multicolored		1.25	1.25
906	A148	$1.50 multicolored		3.00	3.00
		Nos. 903-906 (4)		5.15	5.15

Sheet of 4

907	A148	75c #a.-d.	6.00	6.00

Wedding of Prince Edward and Sophie Rhys-Jones
Common Design Type

Perf. 13¾x14

			1999, June 15	Litho.	Wmk. 384
908	CD356	20c Separate portraits		.40	.40
909	CD356	$3 Couple		6.00	6.00

1st Manned Moon Landing, 30th Anniv.
Common Design Type

Designs: 10c, Apollo 11 on launch pad. 40c, Second stage fires. 50c, Artist's rendition of Apollo 11 on moon. $2, Astronauts transfer to lunar module.
$2.50, Looking at earth from moon.

Perf. 14x13¾

1999, July 20	**Litho.**		**Wmk. 384**	
910	CD357	10c multicolored	.20	.20
911	CD357	40c multicolored	.80	.80
912	CD357	50c multicolored	1.00	1.00
913	CD357	$2 multicolored	4.00	4.00
	Nos. 910-913 (4)		6.00	6.00

Souvenir Sheet
Perf. 14

914	CD357	$2.50 multicolored	5.00	5.00

No. 914 contains one 40mm circular stamp.

Shells — A149

Designs: 25c, Measle cowrie. 35c, West Indian top shell. 75c, Zigzag scallop. $1, West Indian fighting conch.
No. 919: a, 5c, Sunrise tellin. b, 10c, King helmet. c, 25c, Like No. 915. d, 35c, Like No. 916. e, 75c, Like No. 917. f, $1, Like No. 918.

Wmk. 373

1999, Nov. 1	**Litho.**		*Perf. 14¼*	
915	A149	25c multi	.50	.50
916	A149	35c multi	.75	.75
917	A149	75c multi	1.50	1.50
918	A149	$1 multi	2.00	2.00
919	A149	Strip of 6, #a.-f.	5.00	5.00
	Nos. 915-919 (5)		9.75	9.75

Vignette extends to the top perforations on Nos. 915-918, but does not on stamps from No. 919.

Christmas A150

Churches: 20c, Zion Hill Methodist. 35c, Fat Hogs Bay Seventh Day Adventist. 50c, Ruins of Kingstown St. Philip's Anglican. $1, Road Town St. William's Catholic.

Perf. 13¼x13

1999, Dec. 16	**Litho.**		**Wmk. 373**	
920	A150	20c multi	.40	.40
921	A150	35c multi	.70	.70
922	A150	50c multi	1.00	1.00
923	A150	$1 multi	2.00	2.00
	Nos. 920-923 (4)		4.10	4.10

British Monarchs — A151

Illustration reduced.
a, Henry VII. b, Lady Jane Grey. c, Charles I. d, William III. e, George III. f, Edward VII.

Wmk. 373

2000, Feb. 29	**Litho.**		*Perf. 14*	
924	A151	60c Sheet of 6, #a.-f.	7.25	7.25

The Stamp Show 2000, London.

Prince William, 18th Birthday
Common Design Type

William: 20c, As toddler, on chest. 40c, As toddler, standing. 50c, With ski cap & goggles. 60c, Wearing suits & striped shirts. $1, Wearing sweater & bow tie.

Perf. 14¼x13¾, 13¾x14¼

2000, June 21	**Litho.**		**Wmk. 373**	

Stamps With White Border

925	CD359	20c multi	.40	.40
926	CD359	40c multi, vert.	.80	.80
927	CD359	50c multi, vert.	1.00	1.00
928	CD359	$1 multi	2.00	2.00
	Nos. 925-928 (4)		4.20	4.20

Souvenir Sheet
Stamps Without White Border
Perf. 14¼

929		Sheet of 5	5.50	5.50
a.	CD359	20c multi	.40	.40
b.	CD359	40c multi	.80	.80
c.	CD359	50c multi	1.00	1.00
d.	CD359	60c multi	1.25	1.25
e.	CD359	$1 multi	2.00	2.00

Queen Mother, 100th Birthday — A152

Various photos. Frame color: 15c, Lilac. 35c, Light green. 70c, Pink. $1.50, Light blue.

Wmk. 373

2000, Aug. 4	**Litho.**		*Perf. 13¾*	
930-933	A152	Set of 4	5.50	5.50

Flowering Plants and Trees — A153

10c, Red hibiscus. 15c, Pink oleander. 35c, Yellow bell. 50c, Yellow & white frangipani. 75c, Flamboyant. $2, Bougainvillea.

2000, Sept. 7			*Perf. 13½x13¾*	
934-939	A153	Set of 6	7.75	7.75

Millennium — A154

Virgin Islands history: 5c, Site of Emancipation Proclamation. 20c Nurse Mary Louise Davies. 30c, Cheyney University, US, founded by Richard Humphries. 45c, Enid Leona Scatliffe, former chief education officer. 50c, H. Lavity Stoutt Community College. $1 Sir J. Olva Georges.
$2, Victoria Cross of Pvt. Samuel Hodge, vert.

Wmk. 373

2000, Nov. 16	**Litho.**		*Perf. 14*	
940-945	A154	Set of 6	5.00	5.00

Souvenir Sheet

946	A154	$2 multi	4.00	4.00

Restoration of the Legislative Council, 50th Anniv. — A155

Virgin Islands Councilmen: 10c, Dr. Q. William Osbourne & Arnando Scatliffe. 15c, H. Robinson O'Neal & A. Austin Henley. 20c, Wilfred W. Smith & John C. Brudenell-Bruce. 35c, Howard R. Penn & I. G. Fonseca. 50c, Carlton L. de Castro & Theodolph H. Faulkner. 60c, Willard W. Wheatley. $1, H. Lavity Stoutt.

2000, Nov. 22				
947-953	A155	Set of 7	5.75	5.75

Souvenir Sheet

New Year 2001 (Year of the Snake) — A156

No. 954: a, 50c, White-crowned dove. b, 50c, Bar-tailed cuckoo dove. Illustration reduced.

2001, Feb. 1			*Perf. 14½*	
954	A156	Sheet of 2, #a-b	2.00	2.00

Hong Kong 2001 Stamp Exhibition.

Visiting Royal Navy Ships A157

Designs: 35c, HMS Wistaria, 1923-30. 50c, HMS Dundee, 1934-35. 60c, HMS Eurydice, 1787. 75c, HMS Pegasus, 1787. $1, HMS Astrea, 1807. $1.50 HM Yacht Britannia, 1966.

Wmk. 373

2001, Sept. 28	**Litho.**		*Perf. 14*	
955-960	A157	Set of 6	9.50	9.50

Nobel Prizes, Cent. — A158

Nobel laureates: 10c, Fridtjof Nansen, Peace, 1922. 20c, Albert Einstein, Physics, 1921. 25c, Sir Arthur Lewis, Economics, 1979. 40c, Saint-John Perse, Literature, 1960. 70c, Mother Teresa, Peace, 1979. $2, Christian Lous Lange, Peace, 1921.

2001, Oct. 5				
961-966	A158	Set of 6	7.50	7.50

Reign Of Queen Elizabeth II, 50th Anniv. Issue
Common Design Type

Designs: Nos. 967, 971a, 15c, Princess Elizabeth in uniform. Nos. 968, 971b, 50c, In 1977. Nos. 969, 971c, 60c, Holding flowers. Nos. 970, 971d, 75c, In 1996. No. 971e, $1, 1955 portrait by Annigoni (38x50mm).

Perf. 14¼x14½, 13¾ (#971e)

2002, Feb. 6	**Litho.**		**Wmk. 373**	

With Gold Frames

967-970	CD360	Set of 4	4.00	4.00

Souvenir Sheet
Without Gold Frames

971	CD360	Sheet of 5, #a-e	6.00	6.00

Reptiles in Guinness Book Of World Records A159

Designs: 5c, Estuarine crocodile. 20c, Reticulated python. 30c, Komodo dragon. 40c, Boa constrictor. $1, Dwarf caiman. $2, Sphaerodactylus parthenopion.
$1.50, Head of Sphaerodactylus parthenopion.

Perf. 13¼x13

2002, June 10	**Litho.**		**Wmk. 373**	
972-977	A159	Set of 6	8.00	8.00

977a		Sheet of 6, #972-977	8.00	8

Souvenir Sheet

978	A159	$1.50 multi	3.00	3.

Queen Mother Elizabeth (1900-200
Common Design Type

Designs: 20c, Wearing tiara (black an white photograph). 60c, Wearing dark blu hat. Nos. 981, 983a, $2, Wearing hat (bla and white photograph). Nos. 982, 983b, $ Wearing pink hat.

Perf. 13¾x14¼

2002, Aug. 5	**Litho.**		**Wmk. 37**	

With Purple Frames

979-982	CD361	Set of 4	11.50	11.5

Souvenir Sheet
Without Purple Frames
Perf. 14½x14¼

983	CD361	Sheet of 2, #a-b	10.00	10.

Royal Navy Ships A160

Designs: 20c, HMS Invincible and HMS Argo. 35c, HMS Boreas and HMS Solebay. 50c, HMS Coventry. $3, HMS Argyll.

Wmk. 373

2002, Aug. 30	**Litho.**		*Perf. 14*	
984-987	A160	Set of 4	8.25	8.2

Island Scenes Type of 1996

Designs: 5c, Spring Bay. 40c, Devils Bay. 60c, The Baths. 75c, St. Thomas Bay. $1, Savannah and Pond Bay. $2, Trunk Bay.

2002, Sept. 13				
988-993	A135	Set of 6	9.75	9.75

West Indian Whistling Duck — A161

Designs: Nos. 994, 998a, 10c, Duckling and eggs. Nos. 995, 998b, 35c, Duck standing on rock, vert. Nos. 996, 998c, 40c, Duck in water, vert. Nos. 997, 998d, 70c, Two ducks. No. 998e, $2, Duck's head.

Perf. 14¼x13¾, 13¾x14¼

2002, Dec.	**Litho.**		**Wmk. 373**	

Stamps With Brown Border

994-997	A161	Set of 4	3.25	3.25

Souvenir Sheet
Stamps Without Brown Border
Perf. 14¼x14½ (Horiz. stamps), 14½ (Vert. stamps)

998	A161	Sheet of 5, #a-e	7.25	7.25

Birdlife International.

Anniversaries and Events — A162

No. 999, 10c: a, Sprinters. b, Cyclists.
No. 1000, 35c: a, Laser class sailboats. b, Women's long jump.
No. 1001, 50c: a, Bareboat class sailboats. b, Racing Cruiser class sailboats.
No. 1002, $1.35: a, Carlos and Esme Downing, founders of Island Sun newspaper. b, Island Sun newspaper and emblem.
Illustration reduced.

Wmk. 373

2003, Mar. 13	**Litho.**		*Perf. 13½*	

Horiz. pairs, #a-b

999-1002	A162	Set of 4	9.25	9.25

2002 Commonwealth Games (#999); Admission to Olympic Games, 20th anniv. (#1000); Spring Regatta, 30th anniv. (#1001); Island Sun newspaper, 40th anniv. (#1002).

Head of Queen Elizabeth II
Common Design Type
Wmk. 373

2003, June 2	Litho.	Perf. 13¾
1003 CD362 $5 multi	10.00	10.00

Coronation of Queen Elizabeth II, 50th Anniv.
Common Design Type

Designs: Nos. 1004, 1006a, 15c, Queen in gown. Nos. 1005, 1006b, $5, Royal Family on Buckingham Palace balcony.

Perf. 14¼x14½		
2003, June 2	Litho.	Wmk. 373

Vignettes Framed, Red Background
| 1004-1005 CD363 Set of 2 | 10.50 | 10.50 |

Souvenir Sheet
Vignettes Without Frame, Purple Panel
| 1006 CD363 Sheet of 2, #a-b | 10.50 | 10.50 |

Prince William, 21st Birthday
Common Design Type

Designs: 50c, William in polo uniform at right. $2, William on polo pony at left.

Wmk. 373

2003, June 21	Litho.	Perf. 14¼

With Gray Frames
| 1007 CD364 50c multi | 1.00 | 1.00 |
| 1008 CD364 $2 multi | 4.00 | 4.00 |

Without Gray Frames
1009	Horiz. pair	5.00	5.00
a.	CD364 50c multi	1.00	1.00
b.	CD364 $2 multi	4.00	4.00
	Nos. 1007-1009 (3)	10.00	10.00

Powered Flight, Cent. — A163

Designs: 15c, Douglas DC-4. 20c, Boeing Stearman "Kaydet." 35c, B-25 J Mitchell. 40c, F-4B Phantom. 70c, CH-47 Chinook helicopter. $2, AH-64 Apache helicopter. Illustration reduced.

Perf. 13¼x13¾		
2003, Nov. 15	Litho.	Wmk. 373

Stamp + Label
| 1010-1015 A163 Set of 6 | 7.75 | 7.75 |

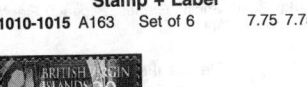

Christmas — A164

Details from Arrival of the English Ambassadors, by Vittore Carpaccio: 20c, Men standing near railing and pillar. 40c, Men, ships in background. $2.50, Seated man.
No. 1019a (36x36mm), Kneeling man delivering message.

Perf. 13¾x13½		
2003, Dec. 15	Litho.	Wmk. 373
1016-1018 A164 Set of 3	6.25	6.25

Souvenir Sheet
| 1019 A164 | Sheet, #1016-1018, 1019a | 8.25 | 8.25 |
| a. | $1 multi, perf. 13½x13¼ | 2.00 | 2.00 |

WAR TAX STAMPS

Regular Issue of 1913 Overprinted

1916-17	Wmk. 3	Perf. 14
	Die I	
MR1 A9 1p scarlet	.25	2.00
a.	1p carmine	1.00	3.50
MR2 A9 3p violet, yellow	1.50	6.00

OFFICIAL STAMPS

Catalogue values for unused stamps in this section are for Never Hinged items.

Nos. 365-368, 370-380 Overprinted "OFFICIAL" in Silver

1985, July	Litho.	Perf. 14
O1 A57 1c multi	.25	.50
O2 A57 3c multi	.30	.50
O3 A57 5c multi	.30	.40
O4 A57 8c multi	.40	.40
O5 A57 13c multi	.50	.40
O6 A57 15c multi	.50	.40
O7 A57 18c multi	.75	.60
O8 A57 20c multi	.75	.60
O9 A57 25c multi	.90	.75
O10 A57 30c multi	1.25	.90
O11 A57 60c multi	1.75	1.75
O12 A57 $1 multi	2.75	2.75
O13 A57 $2.50 multi	5.00	5.00
O14 A57 $3 multi	7.50	7.50
O15 A57 $5 multi	10.00	10.00
Nos. O1-O15 (15)	32.90	32.45

Nos. 364-380 overprinted in gold and Nos. 364, 369 overprinted in silver exist but were not issued by the Virgin Islands.

Nos. 490-508 Ovptd. "OFFICIAL"

1986	Litho.	Perf. 14
O16 A81 1c multicolored	.20	.20
O17 A81 2c multicolored	.20	.20
O18 A81 5c multicolored	.20	.20
O19 A81 8c multicolored	.20	.20
O20 A81 10c multicolored	.20	.20
O21 A81 12c multicolored	.25	.25
O22 A81 15c multicolored	.30	.30
O23 A81 18c multicolored	.35	.35
O24 A81 20c multicolored	.40	.40
O25 A81 25c multicolored	.50	.50
O26 A81 30c multicolored	.60	.60
O27 A81 35c multicolored	.70	.70
O28 A81 40c multicolored	.80	.80
O29 A81 50c multicolored	.90	.90
O30 A81 60c multicolored	1.00	1.00
O31 A81 $1 multicolored	1.75	1.75
O32 A81 $2 multicolored	3.50	3.50
O33 A81 $3 multicolored	5.25	5.25
O34 A81 $5 multicolored	9.00	9.00
Nos. O16-O34 (19)	26.30	26.30

Issue: 1, 5, 10, 15, 20-35c, $5, 7/3; others, 1/28.

Nos. 694-695, 698, 701-706, 708 Ovptd. "OFFICIAL"

1991, Sept.	Litho.	Perf. 14
O37 A116 5c multicolored	.20	.20
O38 A116 10c multicolored	.20	.20
O41 A116 20c multicolored	.40	.40
O44 A116 35c multicolored	.70	.70
O45 A116 40c multicolored	.80	.80
O46 A116 45c multicolored	.90	.90
O47 A116 50c multicolored	1.00	1.00
O48 A116 70c multicolored	1.40	1.40
O49 A116 $1 multicolored	2.00	2.00
O51 A116 $3 multicolored	6.00	6.00
Nos. O37-O51 (10)	13.60	13.60

Ovpt. on Nos. O37-O51 is 19mm long.
Used values are for c-t-o copies.
Nos. O37-O38, O41, O44-O49, O51 were not available unused until mid-1992.
This set was never used in the Virgin Islands.

Nos. 694-695, 698, 700-706, 708 Ovptd. "OFFICIAL"

1992	Litho.	Perf. 14
O55 A116 5c multicolored	.20	.20
O56 A116 10c multicolored	.20	.20
O59 A116 20c multicolored	.40	.40
O61 A116 30c multicolored	.60	.60
O62 A116 35c multicolored	.70	.70
O63 A116 40c multicolored	.80	.80
O64 A116 45c multicolored	.90	.90
O65 A116 50c multicolored	1.00	1.00

O66 A116 70c multicolored	1.40	1.40
O67 A116 $1 multicolored	2.00	2.00
O69 A116 $3 multicolored	6.00	6.00
Nos. O55-O69 (11)	14.20	14.20

Ovpt. on Nos. O55-O56, O59, O61-O67, O69 is 15½mm long.

WALLIS AND FUTUNA ISLANDS

'wä-ləs and fə-'tü-nə

'i-ləndz

LOCATION — Group of islands in the South Pacific Ocean, northeast of Fiji
GOVT. — French Overseas Territory
AREA — 106 sq. mi.
POP. — 15,129 (1999 est.)
CAPITAL — Mata-Utu, Wallis Island

100 Centimes = 1 Franc

Catalogue values for unused stamps in this country are for Never Hinged items, beginning with Scott 127 in the regular postage section, Scott B9 in the semipostal section, Scott C1 in the airpost section, and Scott J37 in the postage due section.

New Caledonia Stamps of 1905-28 Overprinted in Black or Red

1920-28	Unwmk.	Perf. 14x13½
1 A16 1c black, green	.20	.20
a.	Double overprint	85.00	
2 A16 2c red brown	.20	.20
3 A16 4c blue, org	.25	.25
4 A16 5c green	.25	.25
5 A16 5c dull blue ('22)	.20	.20
6 A16 10c rose	.40	.40
7 A16 10c green ('22)	.45	.45
8 A16 10c red, pink ('25)	1.40	1.40
9 A16 15c violet	.65	.65
10 A17 20c gray brown	.65	.65
11 A17 25c blue, grn	1.00	1.00
12 A17 25c red, yel ('22)	.55	.55
13 A17 30c brown, org	1.10	1.10
14 A17 30c dp rose ('22)	.85	.85
15 A17 30c red orange ('25)	.55	.55
16 A17 30c lt green ('27)	1.60	1.60
17 A17 35c black, yel (R)	.65	.65
18 A17 40c rose, grn	.75	.75
19 A17 45c violet brn, pnksh	1.00	1.00
20 A17 50c red, org	1.00	1.00
21 A17 50c dark blue ('22)	1.10	1.10
22 A17 50c dark gray ('25)	1.40	1.40
23 A17 65c deep blue ('28)	4.00	4.00
24 A17 75c olive green	1.40	1.40

Overprinted

25 A18 1fr blue, yel grn	3.00	3.00
a.	Triple overprint	125.00	
26 A18 1.10fr orange brn ('28)	4.00	4.00
27 A18 2fr carmine, bl	4.75	4.75
28 A18 5fr black, org (R)	9.50	9.50
Nos. 1-28 (28)	42.85	42.85

No. 9 Surcharged New Value and Bars in Various Colors

1922
29 A16 0.01c on 15c violet (Bk)	.55	.55
30 A16 0.02c on 15c violet (Bl)	.55	.55
31 A16 0.04c on 15c violet (G)	.55	.55
32 A16 0.05c on 15c violet (R)	.55	.55
Nos. 29-32 (4)	2.20	2.20

Stamps and Types of 1920 Surcharged with New Values and Bars in Black or Red

1924-27			
33 A18 25c on 2fr car, bl		.75	.75
34 A18 25c on 5fr black, org		.75	.75
35 A17 65c on 40c rose red, grn ('25)		1.10	1.10
36 A17 85c on 75c ol grn ('25)		1.00	1.00
37 A17 90c on 75c dp rose ('27)		1.50	1.50
38 A18 1.25fr on 1fr dp bl (R; '26)		.75	.75
39 A18 1.50fr on 1fr dp bl, bl ('27)		3.00	3.00
a.	Double overprint		175.00	
b.	Surcharge omitted		210.00	
40 A18 3fr on 5fr red vio ('27)		5.00	5.00
a.	Surcharge omitted		210.00	
b.	Double surcharge		200.00	
41 A18 10fr on 5fr ol, lav ('27)		22.50	22.50
42 A18 20fr on 5fr vio rose, yel ('27)		29.00	29.00
Nos. 33-42 (10)		65.35	65.35

New Caledonia Stamps and Types of 1928-40 Overprinted as in 1920

1930-40	Perf. 13½, 14x13, 14x13½	
43 A19 1c brn vio & indigo	.20	.20
a.	Double overprint	110.00	
44 A19 2c dk brn & yel grn	.20	.20
45 A19 3c brn vio & ind ('40)	.20	.20
46 A19 4c org & Prus grn	.20	.20
47 A19 5c Prus bl & dp ol	.20	.20
48 A19 10c gray lil & dk brn	.20	.20
49 A19 15c yel brn & dp bl	.20	.20
50 A19 20c brn red & dk brn	.40	.40
51 A19 25c dk grn & dk brn	.75	.75
52 A20 30c gray grn & bl grn	.75	.75
53 A20 35c Prus grn & dk grn ('38)	.75	.75
a.	Without overprint	125.00	
54 A20 40c brt red & olive	.75	.75
55 A20 45c dp bl & red org	.75	.75
56 A20 45c bl grn & dl grn ('40)	.60	.60
57 A20 50c violet & brn	.75	.75
58 A20 55c bl vio & rose red ('38)	1.60	1.60
59 A20 60c vio bl & car ('40)	.20	.20
60 A20 65c org bl & brn	1.40	1.40
61 A20 70c dp rose & brn ('38)	.80	.80
62 A20 75c Prus bl & ol gray	2.10	2.10
63 A20 80c dk cl & grn ('38)	.80	.80
64 A20 85c green & brown	2.50	2.50
65 A20 90c dp red & brt red	1.60	1.60
66 A20 90c ol grn & rose red ('39)	.75	.75
67 A21 1fr dp ol & sal red	2.50	2.50
68 A21 1fr rose red & dk car ('38)	1.60	1.60
69 A21 1fr brn red & grn ('40)	.20	.20
70 A21 1.10fr dp grn & brn	22.50	22.50
71 A21 1.25fr brn red & grn ('33)	2.25	2.25
72 A21 1.25fr rose red & dk car ('39)	.60	.60
73 A21 1.40fr dk bl & red org ('40)	.75	.75
74 A21 1.50fr dp bl & bl	.80	.80
75 A21 1.60fr dp grn & brn ('40)	1.00	1.00
76 A21 1.75fr dk bl & red org ('40)	9.00	9.00
77 A21 1.75fr vio bl ('38)	1.60	1.60
78 A21 2fr red org & brn	1.25	1.25
79 A21 2.25fr vio bl ('39)	1.25	1.25
80 A21 2.50fr brn & lt brn ('40)	1.25	1.25
81 A21 3fr magenta & brn	1.25	1.25
82 A21 5fr dk bl & brn	1.60	1.60
83 A21 10fr vio & brn, pnksh	2.25	2.25
84 A21 20fr red & brn, yel	3.25	3.25
Nos. 43-84 (42)	73.55	73.55

For overprints see Nos. 94-126.

For types A19 and A21 of New Caledonia, with "RF," overprinted as above, see Nos. 126A-126F.

Common Design Types pictured following the introduction.

Colonial Exposition Issue
Common Design Types

1931, Apr. 13   Engr.   Perf. 12½
Name of Country Typo. in Black

85	CD70	40c deep green	6.00	6.00
86	CD71	50c violet	6.00	6.00
87	CD72	90c red orange	6.00	6.00
88	CD73	1.50fr dull blue	6.00	6.00
	Nos. 85-88 (4)		24.00	24.00

Colonial Arts Exhibition Issue
Common Design Type
Souvenir Sheet

1937   Imperf.

| 89 | CD78 | 3fr red violet | 17.50 | 22.50 |

New York World's Fair Issue
Common Design Type

1939, May 10   Engr.   Perf. 12½x12

| 90 | CD82 | 1.25fr carmine lake | 2.00 | 2.00 |
| 91 | CD82 | 2.25fr ultramarine | 2.00 | 2.00 |

Petain Issue
New Caledonia Nos. 216A-216B
Overprinted "WALLIS ET FUTUNA" in Lilac or Red

1941   Engr.   Perf. 12½x12

| 92 | A21a | 1fr bluish green (L) | .85 | |
| 93 | A21a | 2.50fr dark blue (R) | .85 | |

Nos. 92-93 were issued by the Vichy government in France, but were not placed on sale in Wallis & Futuna.
For surcharges, see Nos. B8A-B8B.

Nos. 43-69, 71, 74, 77-78, 80-84 with Additional Overprint in Black

1941-43   Perf. 14x13½

94	A19	1c	2.00	2.00
95	A19	2c	2.00	2.00
96	A19	3c	55.00	55.00
97	A19	4c	2.50	2.50
98	A19	5c	2.50	2.50
99	A19	10c	2.50	2.50
100	A19	15c	2.50	2.50
101	A19	20c	3.50	3.50
102	A19	25c	3.50	3.50
103	A20	30c	3.50	3.50
104	A20	35c	2.50	2.50
105	A20	40c	3.00	3.00
106	A20	45c #55	3.00	3.00
107	A20	45c #56	65.00	65.00
108	A20	50c	2.50	2.50
109	A20	55c	55.00	55.00
110	A20	60c	2.50	2.50
111	A20	65c	2.50	2.50
112	A20	70c	2.50	2.50
113	A20	75c	3.50	3.50
114	A20	80c	2.50	2.50
115	A20	85c	3.00	3.00
116	A20	90c #65	2.50	2.50
117	A21	1fr #68	3.00	3.00
118	A21	1.25fr #71	3.00	3.00
119	A21	1.50fr	2.50	2.50
120	A21	1.75fr #77	2.50	2.50
121	A21	2fr	3.00	3.00
122	A21	2.50fr	100.00	100.00
123	A21	3fr	2.50	2.50
124	A21	5fr	5.75	5.75
125	A21	10fr	40.00	40.00
126	A21	20fr	60.00	60.00
	Nos. 94-126 (33)		451.75	451.75

Types of New Caledonia Without "RF" overprinted as in 1920

1944

126A	A19	10c gray lil & dk brn	.75	
126B	A19	15c yel brn & dp bl	.85	
126C	A21	1fr brn red & grn	1.25	
126D	A21	1.50fr blue	1.40	

126E	A21	10fr vio & brn, pnksh	1.40	
126F	A21	20fr red & brn, yel	1.50	
	Nos. 126A-126F (6)		7.15	

Nos. 126a-126F were issued by the Vichy government in France, but were not placed on sale in Wallis & Futuna.

Catalogue values for unused stamps in this section, from this point to the end of the section, are for Never Hinged items.

Ivi Poo, Bone Carving in Tiki Design — A1

1944   Unwmk.   Photo.   Perf. 11½x12

127	A1	5c lt brown	.20	.20
128	A1	10c dp gray blue	.20	.20
129	A1	25c emerald	.20	.20
130	A1	30c dull orange	.20	.20
131	A1	40c dk slate grn	.65	.65
132	A1	80c brown red	.65	.65
133	A1	1fr red violet	.20	.20
134	A1	1.50fr red	.20	.20
135	A1	2fr gray black	.35	.35
136	A1	2.50fr brt ultra	.45	.45
137	A1	4fr dark purple	.65	.65
138	A1	5fr lemon yellow	.80	.80
139	A1	10fr chocolate	1.00	1.00
140	A1	20fr deep green	1.00	1.00
	Nos. 127-140 (14)		6.75	6.75

Nos. 127, 129 and 136 Surcharged with New Values and Bars in Black or Carmine

1946

141	A1	50c on 5c lt brown	.45	.45
142	A1	60c on 5c lt brown	.55	.55
143	A1	70c on 5c lt brown	.55	.55
144	A1	1.20fr on 5c lt brown	.55	.55
145	A1	2.40fr on 25c emerald	.65	.65
146	A1	3fr on 25c emerald	.65	.65
147	A1	4.50fr on 25c emerald	1.25	1.25
148	A1	15fr on 2.50fr (C)	1.25	1.25
	Nos. 141-148 (8)		5.90	5.90

Military Medal Issue
Common Design Type
Engraved and Typographed

1952, Dec. 1   Perf. 13

| 149 | CD101 | 2fr multicolored | 4.50 | 4.50 |

Wallis Islander A2

Unwmk.

1957, June 11   Engr.   Perf. 13

| 150 | A2 | 3fr dk purple & lil rose | .85 | .85 |
| 151 | A2 | 9fr bl, dl lil & vio brn | 1.60 | 1.60 |

Imperforates
Most Wallis and Futuna stamps from 1957 onward exist imperforate in issued and trial colors, and also in small presentation sheets in issued colors.

Flower Issue
Common Design Type
Design: 5fr, Montrouziera, horiz.

1958, Aug. 4   Photo.   Perf. 12½x12

| 152 | CD104 | 5fr multicolored | 2.50 | 1.50 |

Human Rights Issue
Common Design Type

1958, Dec. 10   Engr.   Perf. 13

| 153 | CD105 | 17fr brt bl & dk bl | 3.00 | 3.00 |

Women Making Tapa Cloth — A3

Kava Ceremony A4

17fr, Dancers. 19fr, Dancers with paddles.

1960, Sept. 19   Engr.   Perf. 13

154	A3	5fr dk brown, grn & org brn	.85	.85
155	A4	7fr dk brown & Prus grn	1.00	1.00
156	A4	17fr ultra, claret & grn	1.75	1.75
157	A3	19fr claret & slate	1.75	1.75
	Nos. 154-157 (4)		5.35	5.35

Map of South Pacific — A4a

1962, July 18   Photo.   Perf. 13x12

| 158 | A4a | 16fr multicolored | 3.00 | 3.00 |

5th South Pacific Conf., Pago Pago, 1962.

Sea Shells — A5

1962-63   Engr.   Perf. 13
Size: 22x36mm

159	A5	25c Triton	.60	.60
160	A5	1fr Mitra episcopalis	.60	.60
161	A5	2fr Cypraecassis rufa	.80	.80
162	A5	4fr Murex tenuspina	2.00	2.00
163	A5	10fr Oliva erythrostoma	5.00	5.00
164	A5	20fr Cyprae tigris	7.25	7.25
	Nos. 159-164,C18 (7)		24.25	23.25

Red Cross Centenary Issue
Common Design Type

1963, Sept. 2   Unwmk.   Perf. 13

| 165 | CD113 | 12fr red lil, gray & car | 2.50 | 2.50 |

Human Rights Issue
Common Design Type

1963, Dec. 10   Engr.

| 166 | CD117 | 29fr dk red & ocher | 5.50 | 5.50 |

Philatec Issue
Common Design Type

1964, Apr. 15   Unwmk.   Perf. 13

| 167 | CD118 | 9fr dk sl grn, grn & red | 2.50 | 2.50 |

Queen Amelia and Ship "Queen Amelia" A6

1965, Feb. 15   Photo.   Perf. 12½x13

| 168 | A6 | 11fr multicolored | 5.50 | 5.50 |

WHO Anniversary Issue
Common Design Type

1968, May 4   Engr.   Perf. 1

| 169 | CD126 | 17fr bl grn, org & lil | 4.50 | 4.5 |

Human Rights Year Issue
Common Design Type

1968, Aug. 10   Engr.   Perf.

| 170 | CD127 | 19fr dk pur, org brn & brt mag | 2.75 | 2.7 |

Outrigger Canoe A7

1969, Apr. 30   Photo.   Perf. 1

| 171 | A7 | 1fr multicolored | .80 | .8 |
| | Nos. 171,C31-C35 (6) | | 27.30 | 14.3 |

ILO Issue
Common Design Type

1969, Nov. 24   Engr.   Perf. 1

| 172 | CD131 | 9fr orange, brn & bl | 2.25 | 2.2 |

UPU Headquarters Issue
Common Design Type

1970, May 20   Engr.   Perf. 1

| 173 | CD133 | 21fr lil rose, ind & ol bis | 2.75 | 2.7 |

No. 157 Surcharged with New Value and Two Bars

1971   Engr.   Perf. 1

| 174 | A3 | 12fr on 19fr | 1.25 | 1.2 |

Weight Lifting — A8

1971, Oct. 25

175	A8	24fr shown	4.00	4.0
176	A8	36fr Basketball	5.00	5.0
	Nos. 175-176,C37-C38 (4)		18.50	14.5

4th South Pacific Games, Papeete, French Polynesia, Sept. 8-19.

De Gaulle Issue
Common Design Type
Designs: 30fr, Gen. de Gaulle, 1940. 70f Pres. de Gaulle, 1970.

1971, Nov. 9   Engr.   Perf. 1

| 177 | CD134 | 30fr blue & black | 6.50 | 4.5 |
| 178 | CD134 | 70fr blue & black | 10.00 | 7.2 |

Child's Outrigger Canoe A9

Designs: 16fr, Children's canoe race. 18f Outrigger racing canoe.

1972, Oct. 16   Photo.   Perf. 13x12
Size: 35½x26½mm

179	A9	14fr dk green & multi	7.25	3.0
180	A9	16fr dk plum & multi	7.25	3.0
181	A9	18fr blue & multi	11.00	4.0
	Nos. 179-181,C41 (4)		55.50	28.0

Outrigger sailing canoes.

Rhinoceros Beetle A10

Insects: 25fr, Cosmopolites sordidus (beetle). 35fr, Ophideres fullonica (moth). 45fr, Dragonfly.

1974, July 29   Photo.   Perf. 13

182	A10	15fr ol & multi	2.50	2.00
183	A10	25fr ol & multi	3.50	3.00
184	A10	35fr gray bl & multi	5.00	4.00
185	A10	45fr multicolored	7.25	6.00
	Nos. 182-185 (4)		18.25	15.00

Georges Pompidou (1911-74), Pres. of France — A11

1975, Dec. 1   Engr.   Perf. 13

186	A11	50fr ultra & slate	5.00	4.00

Battle of Yorktown and George Washington — A12

American Bicentennial: 47fr, Virginia Cape Battle and Lafayette.

1976, June 28   Engr.   Perf. 13

187	A12	19fr blue, red & olive	2.00	1.25
188	A12	47fr blue, red & maroon	3.50	3.00

For overprints see Nos. 205-206.

Conus Ammiralis — A13

Sea Shells: 23fr, Cyprae assellus. 43fr, Turbo petholatus. 61fr, Mitra papalis.

1976, Oct. 1   Engr.   Perf. 13

189	A13	20fr multicolored	2.00	1.25
190	A13	23fr multicolored	2.00	1.25
191	A13	43fr multicolored	4.50	3.00
192	A13	61fr ultra & multi	6.50	4.00
	Nos. 189-192 (4)		15.00	9.50

Father Chanel and Poi Church — A14

32fr, Father Chanel and map of islands.

1977, Apr. 28   Litho.   Perf. 12

193	A14	22fr multicolored	1.25	1.10
194	A14	32fr multicolored	1.75	1.50

Return of the ashes of Father Chanel, missionary.

Bowl, Mortar and Pestle A15

Handicrafts: 25fr, Wooden bowls and leather bag. 33fr, Wooden comb, club, and boat model. 45fr, War clubs, Futuna. 69fr, Lances.

1977, Sept. 26   Litho.   Perf. 12½

195	A15	12fr multicolored	.80	.55
196	A15	25fr multicolored	1.50	.75
197	A15	33fr multicolored	1.75	1.00
198	A15	45fr multicolored	2.25	1.25
199	A15	69fr multicolored	3.00	2.50
	Nos. 195-199 (5)		9.30	6.05

Post Office, Mata Utu — A16

50fr, Sia Hospital, Mata Utu. 57fr, Administration Buildings, Mata Utu. 63fr, St. Joseph's Church, Sigave. 120fr, Royal Palace, Mara Utu.

1977, Dec. 12   Litho.   Perf. 13

200	A16	27fr multicolored	1.25	1.00
201	A16	50fr multicolored	2.00	1.25
202	A16	57fr multicolored	2.00	1.25
203	A16	63fr multicolored	2.50	2.00
204	A16	120fr multicolored	6.50	3.25
	Nos. 200-204 (5)		14.25	8.75

Nos. 187-188 Overprinted: "JAMES COOK / Bicentenaire de la / découverte des Iles / Hawaii 1778-1978"

1978, Jan. 20   Engr.   Perf. 13

205	A12	19fr multicolored	2.50	2.00
206	A12	47fr multicolored	5.00	3.00

Bicentenary of the arrival of Capt. Cook in the Hawaiian Islands.

Cruiser Triomphant — A17

Warships: 200fr, Destroyers Cap des Palmes and Chevreuil. 280fr, Cruiser Savorgnan de Brazza.

1978, June 18   Photo.   Perf. 13x12½

207	A17	150fr multicolored	7.00	4.50
208	A17	200fr multicolored	10.00	6.50
209	A17	280fr multicolored	13.50	9.00
	Nos. 207-209 (3)		30.50	20.00

Free French warships serving in the Pacific, 1940-1944.

Solanum Seaforthianum — A18

Flowers: 24fr, Cassia alata. 29fr, Gloriosa superba. 36fr, Hymenocallis littoralis.

1978, July 11   Photo.   Perf. 13

210	A18	16fr multicolored	1.00	.60
211	A18	24fr multicolored	1.10	.70
212	A18	29fr multicolored	1.50	1.00
213	A18	36fr multicolored	2.50	1.25
	Nos. 210-213 (4)		6.10	3.55

Gray Egret — A19

Birds: 18fr, Red-footed booby. 28fr, Brown booby. 35fr, White tern.

1978, Sept. 5   Photo.   Perf. 13

214	A19	17fr multicolored	.95	.60
215	A19	18fr multicolored	1.25	.75
216	A19	28fr multicolored	1.60	1.00
217	A19	35fr multicolored	2.25	1.25
	Nos. 214-217 (4)		6.05	3.60

Traditional Patterns — A20

Designs: 55fr, Corpus Christi procession. 59fr, Chief's honor guard.

1978, Oct. 3

218	A20	53fr multicolored	2.00	1.25
219	A20	55fr multicolored	2.75	1.50
220	A20	59fr multicolored	3.00	1.75
	Nos. 218-220 (3)		7.75	4.50

Human Rights Flame A21

1978, Dec. 10   Litho.   Perf. 12½

221	A21	44fr multicolored	1.25	.75
222	A21	56fr multicolored	1.75	1.00

30th anniversary of Universal Declaration of Human Rights.

Fishing Boat — A22

Designs: 30fr, Weighing young tuna. 34fr, Stocking young tunas. 38fr, Measuring tuna. 40fr, Angler catching tuna. 48fr, Adult tuna.

1979, Mar. 19   Litho.   Perf. 12

223	A22	10fr multicolored	.55	.25
224	A22	30fr multicolored	1.00	.45
225	A22	34fr multicolored	1.25	.60
226	A22	38fr multicolored	1.60	.75
227	A22	40fr multicolored	2.10	1.00
228	A22	48fr multicolored	2.50	1.50
a.	Souv. sheet of 6, #223-228 + 3 labels		18.00	18.00
	Nos. 223-228 (6)		9.00	4.55

Tuna tagging by South Pacific Commission. For surcharge see No. 261.

Boy with Raft and IYC Emblem — A23

Design: 58fr, Girl on horseback.

1979, Apr. 9   Photo.   Perf. 13

229	A23	52fr multicolored	1.40	.90
230	A23	58fr multicolored	1.75	1.10

International Year of the Child.

Bombax Ellipticum — A24

64fr, Callophyllum. 76fr, Pandanus odoratissimus.

1979, Apr. 23   Litho.   Perf. 13

231	A24	50fr multicolored	1.10	.75
232	A24	64fr multicolored	1.90	.90
233	A24	76fr multicolored	2.00	1.10
	Nos. 231-233 (3)		5.00	2.75

Green and Withered Landscapes — A25

1979, May 28   Photo.   Perf. 13

234	A25	22fr multicolored	1.10	.60

Anti-alcoholism campaign.

Flowers — A26

1979, July 16   Photo.   Perf. 12½x13

235	A26	20fr Crinum	.60	.30
236	A26	42fr Passiflora	1.40	.70
237	A26	62fr Canna indica	2.00	1.00
	Nos. 235-237 (3)		4.00	2.00

See Nos. 279-281.

Swimming — A27

1979, Aug. 27　　Engr.　　Perf. 13
238 A27 31fr shown　　　　1.50 1.00
239 A27 39fr High jump　　　2.00 1.25
6th South Pacific Games, Suva, Fiji, Aug. 27-Sept. 8.

Flower Necklaces — A28

Design: 140fr, Coral necklaces.

1979, Aug. 27　　　　　　Litho.
240 A28 110fr multicolored　　3.00 1.75
241 A28 140fr multicolored　　3.75 2.25

Trees and Birds, by Sutita — A29

Paintings by Local Artists: 65fr, Birds and Mountain, by M. A. Pilioko, vert. 78fr, Festival Procession, by Sutita.

1979, Oct. 8　　Perf. 13x12½, 12½x13
242 A29 27fr multicolored　　1.00 .50
243 A29 65fr multicolored　　1.60 .90
244 A29 78fr multicolored　　2.50 1.25
　　Nos. 242-244 (3)　　　5.10 2.65

Marine Mantis A30

Marine Life: 23fr, Hexabranchus sanguineus. 25fr, Spondylus barbatus. 43fr, Gorgon coral. 45fr, Linckia laevigata. 63fr, Tridacna squamosa.

1979, Nov. 5　　Photo.　　Perf. 13x12½
245 A30 15fr multicolored　　.75 .40
246 A30 23fr multicolored　　1.00 .50
247 A30 25fr multicolored　　1.25 .60
248 A30 43fr multicolored　　1.50 .75
249 A30 45fr multicolored　　1.75 .80
250 A30 63fr multicolored　　2.50 1.25
　　Nos. 245-250 (6)　　8.75 4.30

See #294-297. For surcharge see #272.

Transportation Type of 1979

1980, Feb. 29　　Litho.　　Perf. 13
251 AP32 1fr like No. C87　　.20 .20
252 AP32 3fr like No. C88　　.20 .20
253 AP32 5fr like No. C89　　.20 .20
　　Nos. 251-253 (3)　　　.60 .60

Radio Station and Tower — A31

1980, Apr. 21　　Litho.　　Perf. 13
254 A31 47fr multicolored　　1.60 1.00
Radio station FR3, 1st anniversary.

Jesus Laid in the Tomb, by Maurice Denis — A32

1980, Apr. 28　　　　Perf. 13x12½
255 A32 25fr multicolored　　1.00 .65
Easter 1980.

Gnathodentex Mossambicus — A33

1980, Aug. 25　　Litho.　　Perf. 12½x13
256 A33 23fr shown　　　　1.00 .65
257 A33 27fr Pristipomoides fi-
　　　　　lamentosus　　　1.25 .75
258 A33 32fr Etelis carbuncu-
　　　　　lus　　　　　　1.90 1.00
259 A33 51fr Cephalopholis
　　　　　wallisi　　　　2.50 1.75
260 A33 59fr Aphareus rutilans　3.00 2.00
a.　Vert. strip of 5, Nos. 256-260　10.00 10.00

No. 228 Surcharged:

1980, Sept. 29　　Litho.　　Perf. 12
261 A22 50fr on 48fr multi　　2.00 1.25
Sydpex 80 Philatelic Exhibition, Sydney.

13th World Telecommunications Day — A34

1981, May 17　　Litho.　　Perf. 12½
262 A34 49fr multicolored　　1.25 .85

Pierre Curie and Laboratory Equipment — A35

1981, May 25　　Litho.　　Perf. 13
263 A35 56fr multicolored　　1.50 1.00
Pierre Curie (1859-1906), discoverer of radioactivity.

Conus Textile A36

Designs: Marine life.

1981, June 22　　　　Perf. 12½x13
264 A36 28fr Favites　　　.80 .50
265 A36 30fr Cyanophycees　　.90 .50
266 A36 31fr Ceratium vultur　1.10 .50
267 A36 35fr Amphiprion frenatus　1.50 .50
268 A36 40fr shown　　　1.75 .75
269 A36 55fr Comatule　　2.25 1.00
a.　Vert. strip of 6, Nos. 264-269　9.00 9.00
No. 269a is from sheet of 24.

60th Anniv. of Anti-tuberculin Vaccine (Developed by Calmette and Guerin) — A37

1981, July 28　　Litho.　　Perf. 13
270 A37 27fr multicolored　　1.00 .60

Intl. Year of the Disabled — A38

1981, Aug. 17
271 A38 42fr multicolored　　1.25 .80

No. 245 Surcharged in Red

1981, Sept.　　Photo.　　Perf. 13x12½
272 A30 5fr on 15fr multi　　.45 .25

Thomas Edison (1847-1931) and his Phonograph, 1878 — A39

1981, Sept. 5　　Engr.　　Perf. 13
273 A39 59fr multicolored　　2.50 1.25

Battle of Yorktown, 1781 (American Revolution) — A40

1981, Oct. 19　　Engr.　　Perf. 13
274 A40 66fr Admiral de Grasse　1.75 1.25
275 A40 74fr Sea battle, vert.　2.25 1.75

200-Mile Zone Surveillance — A41

1981, Dec. 4　　Litho.　　Perf. 1
276 A41 60fr Patrol boat Diep-
　　　　　poise　　　　1.25 1.0
277 A41 85fr Protet　　　2.50 1.7

TB Bacillus Centenary — A42

1982, Mar. 24　　Litho.　　Perf. 1.
278 A42 45fr multicolored　　3.00 1.0

Flower Type of 1979 in Changed Colors

1982, May 3　　Photo.　　Perf. 12½x1.
279 A26 1fr like No. 235　　.20 .2
280 A26 2fr like No. 236　　.25 .2
281 A26 3fr like No. 237　　.25 .2
　　Nos. 279-281 (3)　　.70 .6

PHILEXFRANCE '82 Intl. Stamp Exhibition, Paris, June 11-21 — A43

1982, May 12　　Engr.　　Perf. 13
282 A43 140fr No. 25　　2.50 1.75

Acanthe Phippium A44

Orchids and rubiaceae (83fr).

1982, May 24　　Litho.　　Perf. 12½x13
283 A44 34fr shown　　　.80 .65
284 A44 68fr Acanthe phippium,
　　　　　diff.　　　　1.50 1.10
285 A44 70fr Spathoglottis pacifi-
　　　　　ca　　　　　1.75 1.25
286 A44 83fr Mussaenda
　　　　　raiateensis　2.10 1.50
　　Nos. 283-286 (4)　　6.15 4.50

Scouting Year A45

1982, June 21　　　　Perf. 12½
287 A45 80fr Baden-Powell　1.50 1.10

Cypraea Talpa A46

Porcelaines shells.

1982, June 28　　　　Perf. 12½x13
288 A46 10fr shown　　　.30 .20
289 A46 15fr Cypraea vitellus　.70 .30
290 A46 25fr Cypraea argus　.85 .50
291 A46 27fr Cypraea carneola　1.10 .75
292 A46 40fr Cypraea mappa　1.40 1.10
293 A46 50fr Cypraea tigris　1.75 1.25
　　Nos. 288-293 (6)　　6.10 4.10

Marine Life Type of 1979

1982, Oct. 1   Photo.   Perf. 13x12½

294	A30	32fr Gorgones milithea	.85	.30
295	A30	35fr Linckia laevigata	.85	.50
296	A30	46fr Hexabranchus sanguineus	1.40	.80
297	A30	63fr Spondylus barbatus	1.90	1.25
		Nos. 294-297 (4)	5.00	2.85

St. Teresa of Jesus of Avila (1515-1582) — A48

1982, Nov. 8   Engr.   Perf. 13

298 A48 31fr multicolored   .90 .55

See No. 315.

Traditional House A49

1983, Jan. 20   Litho.   Perf. 13

299 A49 19fr multicolored   .60 .35

Gustave Eiffel (1832-1923), Architect — A50

1983, Feb. 14   Engr.   Perf. 13

300 A50 97fr multicolored   2.50 1.50

A51

1983, June 28   Engr.   Perf. 13

301 A51 92fr Thai dancer, 19th cent.   2.00 1.25

BANGKOK '83 Intl. Stamp Show, Aug. 4-13.

1983, Aug. 25   Litho.   Perf. 13x13½

302 A52 20fr multicolored   .40 .20

World Communications Year.

A52

Cone Shells A53

1983-84   Litho.   Perf. 13½x13

303	A53	10fr Conus tulipa	.30	.20
304	A53	17fr Conus capitaneus	.50	.30
305	A53	21fr Conus virgo	.50	.30
306	A53	22fr Strombus lentiginosus	.40	.30
307	A53	25fr Lambis chiragra	.50	.30
308	A53	35fr Strombus dentatus	.80	.35
309	A53	39fr Conus vitulinus	.90	.45
310	A53	43fr Lambis scorpius	1.25	.50
311	A53	49fr Strombus aurisdianae	1.40	.90
312	A53	52fr Conus marmoreus	1.25	.90
313	A53	65fr Conus leopardus	1.40	1.00
314	A53	76fr Lambis crocata	2.00	1.25
		Nos. 303-314 (12)	11.20	6.75

Issued: 22, 25, 35, 43, 49, 76fr, 3/23/84; others, 10/14/83.

No. 298 Redrawn with Espana '84 Emblem

1984, Apr. 27   Engr.   Perf. 13

315 A48 70fr multicolored   1.50 .85

Denis Diderot (1713-1784), Philosopher A54

1984, May 11

316 A54 100fr Portrait, encyclopedia title page   2.00 1.25

Nature Protection (Whale) A55

1984, June 5   Litho.   Perf. 13x12½

317 A55 90fr Orcina orca   2.75 1.25

4th Pacific Arts Festival — A56

1984, Nov. 30   Litho.   Perf. 13

318 A56 160fr Islanders   3.00 2.00

Lapita Pottery — A57

Ethno-Archaeological Museum: Excavation site, reconstructed ceramic bowl.

1985, Jan. 16   Litho.   Perf. 13

319 A57 53fr multicolored   1.00 .65

Seashells A58

1985, Feb. 11

320	A58	2fr Nautilus pompilius	.20	.20
321	A58	3fr Murex bruneus	.20	.20
322	A58	41fr Casmaria erinaceus	.75	.35
323	A58	47fr Conus vexillum	1.00	.45
324	A58	56fr Harpa harpa	1.50	.50
325	A58	71fr Murex ramosus	1.75	.85
		Nos. 320-325 (6)	5.40	2.55

Victor Hugo, Author (1802-1885) A59

1985, Mar. 7   Engr.

326 A59 89fr multicolored   2.00 1.25

Bat — A60

1985, Apr. 29   Litho.

327 A60 38fr multicolored   2.00 .75

Intl. Youth Year — A61

1985, May 20   Litho.   Perf. 12½x13

328 A61 64fr Children   1.00 .75

UN, 40th Anniv. — A61a

1985, July 12   Engr.   Perf. 13

328A A61a 49fr Prus grn, dk ultra & red   1.00 .65

Pierre de Ronsard (1524-1585), Poet — A62

1985, Sept. 16   Engr.   Perf. 13

329 A62 170fr brt bl, sep & brn   3.50 2.50

Dr. Albert Schweitzer — A63

1985, Nov. 22   Engr.   Perf. 13

330 A63 50fr blk, dk red lil & org brn   1.40 .95

World Food Day — A64

1986, Jan. 23   Litho.   Perf. 12½x13

331 A64 39fr Breadfruit   1.00 .55

Flamboyants — A65

1986, Feb. 13   Perf. 13x12½

332 A65 38fr multicolored   1.75 .60

Seashells A66

1986, Apr. 24   Litho.   Perf. 13½x13

333	A66	4fr Lambis truncata	.20	.20
334	A66	5fr Charonia tritonis	.20	.20
335	A66	10fr Oliva miniacea	.35	.20
336	A66	18fr Distorsio anus	.55	.45
337	A66	25fr Mitra mitra	.85	.55
338	A66	107fr Conus distans	2.75	1.50
		Nos. 333-338 (6)	4.90	3.10

Also exists in se-tenant strips of 6 from sheet of 24.

1986 World Cup Soccer Championships, Mexico — A67

1986, May 20   Perf. 13x12½

339 A67 95fr multicolored   2.00 1.25

UNICEF.

Discovery of Horn Islands, 370th Anniv. — A68

No. 340: a, 8fr, William Schouten, ship. b, 9fr, Jacob LeMaire, ship. c, 155fr, Map of Alo & Alofi.

1986, June 19 **Engr.** **Perf. 13**
340 A68 Strip of 3, #a.-c. 4.00 3.00

James Watt (1736-1819), Inventor, and Steam Engine — A69

1986, July 11
341 A69 74fr blk & dk red 2.10 1.10

La Lorientaise Patrol Boat — A70

7fr, 120fr vertical.

1986, Aug. 7
342 A70 6fr shown .40 .25
343 A70 7fr Commandant Blaison .40 .25
344 A70 120fr Balny escort ship 4.00 2.00
   Nos. 342-344 (3) 4.80 2.50

Rose Laurel — A71

1986, Oct. 2 **Litho.** **Perf. 13x12½**
345 A71 97fr multi 2.25 1.40

Virgin and Child, by Sandro Botticelli A72

1986, Dec. 12 **Litho.** **Perf. 12½x13**
346 A72 250fr multicolored 5.00 3.00

Christmas.

Butterflies — A73

1987, Apr. 2 **Litho.** **Perf. 12½**
347 A73 2fr Papilio montrouzieri .20 .20
348 A73 42fr Belenois java 1.25 .60
349 A73 46fr Delias ellipsis 1.40 .60
350 A73 50fr Danaus pumila 1.60 .75
351 A73 52fr Luthrodes cleotas 2.00 .85
352 A73 59fr Precis villida 2.25 1.00
   Nos. 347-352 (6) 8.70 4.00

World Wrestling Championships — A74

1987, May 26 **Litho.** **Perf. 12½**
353 A74 97fr multi 2.00 1.00

For overprint see No. 360.

Seashells A75

1987, June 24 **Litho.** **Perf. 13**
354 A75 3fr Cymatium pileare .25 .20
355 A75 4fr Conus textile .30 .20
356 A75 28fr Cypraea mauritiana .70 .35
357 A75 44fr Bursa bubo 1.00 .50
358 A75 48fr Cypraea testudinaria 1.00 .60
359 A75 78fr Cypraecassis rufa 1.75 1.10
   Nos. 354-359 (6) 5.00 2.95

Also exists in se-tenant strips of 6 from sheet of 24.

No. 353 Overprinted

1987, Aug. 29 **Litho.** **Perf. 12½**
360 A74 97fr multicolored 2.50 1.25

OLYMPHILEX '87, Rome.

Bust of a Girl, by Auguste Rodin (1840-1917) A76

1987, Sept. 15 **Engr.** **Perf. 13**
361 A76 150fr plum 4.25 2.00

See No. 390.

World Post Day — A77

1987, Oct. 9 **Litho.** **Perf. 13**
362 A77 116fr multicolored 2.50 1.25

Birds — A78

1987, Oct. 28 **Perf. 13x12½**
363 A78 6fr Anas superciliosa .20 .20
364 A78 19fr Pluvialis dominica .50 .20
365 A78 47fr Gallicolumba stairi 1.25 .50
366 A78 56fr Arenaria interpres 1.60 .85
367 A78 64fr Rallus philippensis 1.75 .85
368 A78 68fr Limosa lapponica 2.25 1.00
   Nos. 363-368 (6) 7.55 3.60

Francis Carco (1886-1958), Painter — A79

Design: Carco and views of the Moulin de la Galette and Place du Tertre, Paris.

1988, Jan. 29 **Litho.** **Perf. 13**
369 A79 40fr multicolored 1.00 .50

Jean-Francois de Galaup (1741-c.1788), Comte de La Perouse, Explorer — A80

Design: Ships L'Astrolabe and La Boussole, portrait of La Perouse.

1988, Mar. 21 **Engr.** **Perf. 13**
370 A80 70fr org brn, dark blue & olive grn 2.75 1.25

Intl. Red Cross and Red Crescent Organizations, 125th Annivs. — A81

1988, July 4 **Engr.** **Perf. 13**
371 A81 30fr blk, dark red & brt blue grn 2.00 1.00

1988 Summer Olympics, Seoul — A82

1988, Sept. 1 **Engr.** **Perf. 13**
372 A82 11fr Javelin .35 .35
373 A82 20fr Women's volleyball .65 .45
374 A82 60fr Windsurfing 1.40 1.00
375 A82 80fr Yachting 1.75 1.25
   a. Souv. sheet of 4, #372-375 + 2 labels, gutter between 5.50 5.50
   Nos. 372-375 (4) 4.15 3.05

Intl. Maritime Organization Emblem and Packet Escorteur F727 — A83

1989, Jan. 26 **Litho.** **Perf. 13**
376 A83 26fr multi 1.00 .50

Jean Renoir (1894-1979), Film Director, and Scene from The Grand Illusion — A84

1989, Feb. 16 **Engr.** **Perf. 13**
377 A84 24fr brt lil rose, dark vio brn & brt org .85 .55

Antoine Becquerel (1788-1878), Physicist — A85

Perf. 13x12½
1988, Nov. 9 **Engr.** **Unwmk.**
378 A85 18fr blk & dark ultra .55 .35

Futuna Hydroelectric Plant — A86

Wmk. 385
1989, Apr. 13 **Litho.** **Perf. 13½**
379 A86 25fr multi .75 .35

A87

A88

Unwmk.
1988, Oct. 26 Litho. *Perf. 13*
380 A87 17fr multi .70 .35
World Post Day.

1989, May 17 *Perf. 12½x13*
381 A88 21fr multi .85 .35
World Telecommunications Day.

Fresco
A89

1989, June 8 *Perf. 12½*
382 A89 22fr multi .75 .35

PHILEXFRANCE '89 — A90

Declaration of Human Rights and
Citizenship, Bicent. — A91

1989, July 7 Litho. *Perf. 13*
383 A90 29fr multi .55 .25
384 A91 900fr multi 16.00 12.50
 a. Souv. sheet of 2, #383-384 +
 label 22.50 22.50
No. 384 is airmail. No. 384a sold for 1000fr.

World Cycling Championships — A92

1989, Sept. 14 Engr. *Perf. 13*
385 A92 10fr blk, red brn & emer .60 .45

World Post Day — A93

Unwmk.
1989, Oct. 18 Litho. *Perf. 13*
386 A93 27fr multicolored .75 .35

Landscape — A94

1989, Nov. 23 Litho. *Perf. 13*
387 A94 23fr multicolored .75 .35

Star of
Bethlehem
A95

1990, Jan. 9 Litho. *Perf. 12½*
388 A95 44fr multicolored 1.00 .65

Fossilized
Tortoise
A96

1990, Feb. 15 Litho. *Perf. 12½x13*
389 A96 48fr multicolored 2.25 1.10

Sculpture by
Auguste Rodin
(1840-1917)
A97

1990, Mar. 15 Engr. *Perf. 13*
390 A97 200fr royal blue 5.00 2.75

1990 World Cup Soccer
Championships, Italy — A98

1990, Apr. 16 Litho.
391 A98 59fr multicolored 1.25 .70

Orchids
A99

1990, May 17 Litho. *Perf. 12½*
392 A99 78fr multicolored 2.50 1.25
Mother's Day

Phaeton — A100

1990, July 16 *Perf. 13*
393 A100 300fr multicolored 8.00 4.00
394 A100 600fr Island 17.50 8.00

Moana II — A101

1990, Aug. 16 Engr. *Perf. 13*
395 A101 40fr shown 1.10 .60
396 A101 50fr Moana III 1.75 .75

Native Huts
A102

1990, Sept. 17 Litho. *Perf. 13x12½*
397 A102 28fr multicolored .90 .45

Stamp Day
A103

1990, Oct. 16 Litho. *Perf. 12½*
398 A103 97fr multicolored 2.50 1.50

Wallis Island
Pirogue — A104

1990, Nov. 16 Litho. *Perf. 13x12½*
399 A104 46fr multicolored 1.50 .60

Best Wishes — A105

1990, Dec. 17 Litho. *Perf. 13x12½*
400 A105 100fr multicolored 2.50 1.25

Patrol Boat La Glorieuse — A106

1991 Engr. *Perf. 13*
401 A106 42fr La Moqueuse 1.10 .55
402 A106 52fr shown 1.40 .70
Issue dates: 42fr, Jan. 7; 52fr, Mar. 4.

A107

1991, Feb. 4 Litho. *Perf. 13*
403 A107 7fr Breadfruit picker .30 .25
404 A107 54fr Taro planter 1.50 .70
405 A107 62fr Spear fisherman 1.60 .75
406 A107 72fr Native warrior 1.90 .90
407 A107 90fr Kailao dancer 2.75 1.25
 a. Souv. sheet of 5, #403-407 9.00 9.00
 Nos. 403-407 (5) 8.05 3.85
Issued: 7fr, 9/2; 54fr, 5/13; 62fr, 4/1; 72fr,
2/4; 90fr, 11/4.
No. 407a sold for 300fr.

Doctors
Without
Borders,
20th Anniv.
A108

1991, Feb. 18 Litho. *Perf. 13½*
408 A108 55fr multicolored 1.40 .65

Ultralight Aircraft — A108a

1991, June 24
409 A108a 85fr multicolored 2.10 1.00

Portrait of Jean by Auguste Renoir
(1841-1919) — A109

1991, July 8 Photo. *Perf. 12½x13*
410 A109 400fr multicolored 10.00 5.50
Litho.
Die Cut
Self-Adhesive
411 A109 400fr multicolored 10.00 5.50

Overseas Territorial Status, 30th
Anniv. — A110

1991, July 29　　Litho.　　*Perf. 13*
412　A110　102fr multicolored　　2.50　1.25

Feast of the Assumption — A111

1991, Aug. 15　　　*Perf. 13x12½*
413　A111　30fr multicolored　　.65　.35

Amnesty
Intl., 30th
Anniv.
A113

1991, Oct. 7　　　*Perf. 13x12½*
414　A113　140fr bl, vio & yel　　3.25　1.75

Central Bank for Economic
Cooperation, 50th Anniv. — A114

1991, Dec. 2　　Litho.　　*Perf. 13*
415　A114　10fr multicolored　　.35　.30

Flowers
A115

1fr, Monette allamanda cathartica. 4fr,
Hibiscus rosa sinensis. 80fr, Ninuphar.

1991, Dec. 2　*Perf. 12½x13, 13x12½*
416　A115　1fr multi　　　　.25　.20
417　A115　4fr multi, vert.　　.25　.20
418　A115　80fr multi　　　　1.60　1.00
　　　Nos. 416-418 (3)　　　2.10　1.40

Christmas — A116

1991, Dec. 16　　Litho.　　*Perf. 13*
419　A116　60fr multicolored　　1.50　.75

Maritime Surveillance — A117

1992, Jan. 20　　Litho.　　*Perf. 13*
420　A117　48fr multicolored　　1.25　.65

1992 Winter Olympics,
Albertville — A118

1992, Feb. 17　　Litho.　　*Perf. 13*
421　A118　150fr multicolored　　3.50　2.00

Canada '92, Intl. Philatelic Exposition,
Montreal — A119

Illustration reduced.

1992, Mar. 25　　Engr.　　*Perf. 13*
422　A119　35fr blk, violet & red　　1.00　.50

1992 Summer Olympics,
Barcelona — A120

1992, Apr. 15　　Engr.　　*Perf. 13*
423　A120　106fr bl grn, grn & bl　　2.50　1.25

Granada '92, Intl. Philatelic
Exposition — A121

Illustration reduced.

1992, Apr. 17　　Engr.　　*Perf. 12½x12*
424　A121　100fr multicolored　　2.75　1.40

Expo '92, Seville — A122

1992, Apr. 20　　　*Perf. 13*
425　A122　200fr bl grn, ol & red
　　　　　brn　　　　　4.50　2.25

Chaetodon Ephippium — A123

Designs: 22fr, Chaetodon auriga. 23fr, Heniochus monoceros. 24fr, Pygoplites diacanthus. 25fr, Chaetodontoplus conspicillatus.
26fr, Chaetodon unimaculatus. 27fr, Siganus
punctatus. 35fr, Zebrasoma veliferum. 45fr,
Paracanthurus hepatus. 53fr, Siganus
vulpinus.

1992-93　　　Litho.　　*Perf. 13*
426　A123　21fr multicolored　　.60　.30
427　A123　22fr multicolored　　.65　.35
428　A123　23fr multicolored　　.65　.35
429　A123　24fr multicolored　　.70　.35
430　A123　25fr multicolored　　.70　.35
431　A123　26fr multicolored　　.70　.35
432　A123　27fr multicolored　　.70　.35
433　A123　35fr multicolored　　.85　.40
434　A123　45fr multicolored　　1.10　.60
435　A123　53fr multicolored　　1.40　.70
　　　Nos. 426-435 (10)　　8.05　4.10
　　Issued: 21fr, 26fr, 5/18; 22fr, 7/27; 25fr,
7/27; 23fr, 24fr, 9/14; 35fr, 45fr, 6/21/93; 27fr,
53fr, 9/6/93.

Natives
A125

a, 3 warriors. b, 2 warriors. c, Warrior, 2
boats. d, 2 spear fisherman. e, 3 fisherman.

1992, June 15　　Litho.　　*Perf. 12*
436　A125　70fr Strip of 5, #a.-e.　　9.00　4.75
　f.　　Souvenir sheet of 5, #a.-e.　11.50　5.25
#436 has continuous design. #436f sold for
450fr.

Support
Ship, "La
Garonne"
A126

1992, Oct. 12　　Litho.　　*Perf. 12*
437　A126　20fr multicolored　　.65　.35

L'Idylle D'Ixelles,
by Auguste
Rodin (1840-
1917)
A127

1992, Nov. 17　　Engr.　　*Perf. 13*
438　A127　300fr lilac & dk blue　　8.00　4.00

Miribilis
Jalapa
A128

1992, Dec. 7　　Litho.　　*Perf. 12½*
439　A128　200fr multicolored　　5.00　2.50

Maritime Forces of the Pacific — A129

1993, Jan. 27　　Litho.　　*Perf. 13x12½*
440　A129　130fr multicolored　　2.50　1.50

School
Art — A130

1993, Feb. 22　　Litho.　　*Perf. 12*
441　A130　56fr multicolored　　1.40　.65
　　　See Nos. 451-452.

Birds
A131

Designs: 50fr, Rallus philippensis swindellsi.
60fr, Porphyrio porphyrio. 110fr, Ptilinopus
greyi.

1993, Mar. 20　　　*Perf. 13½*
442　A131　50fr multicolored　　1.40　.75
443　A131　60fr multicolored　　1.60　.85
444　A131　110fr multicolored　　3.25　1.75
　　　Nos. 442-444 (3)　　6.25　3.35

Mother's
Day
A132

1993, May 30　　Litho.　　*Perf. 12½*
445　A132　95fr Hibiscus　　2.25　1.25
446　A132　120fr Siale　　2.75　1.75

Admiral Antoine d'Entrecasteaux
(1737-1793), French
Navigator — A133

1993, July 12　　Engr.　　*Perf. 13*
447　A133　170fr grn bl, red brn &
　　　　　blk　　　　　3.75　1.90

Taipei '93 — A134

1993, Aug. 14 Litho. Perf. 13x12½
448 A134 435fr multicolored 12.00 6.00

Churches — A135

1993, Aug. 15 Perf. 13
449 A135 30fr Tepa, Wallis .65 .40
450 A135 30fr Vilamalia, Futuna .65 .40

School Art Type of 1993
1993 Litho. Perf. 13x13½, 13½x13
451 A130 28fr Stylized trees .60 .30
452 A130 52fr Family, vert. 1.10 .55
Issue dates: 28fr, Oct. 18. 52fr, Nov. 8.

Christmas
A136

1993, Dec, 6 Perf. 13
453 A136 80fr multicolored 1.75 1.00

Traditional
Arts and
Crafts
Exhibition
A137

1994, Mar. 24 Litho. Perf. 12½
454 A137 80fr multicolored 1.75 1.00

Liberation of Paris, 50th
Anniv. — A138

1994, Apr. 21 Engr. Perf. 13
455 A138 110fr black, blue & red 3.00 1.75

Satellite Communications — A139

1994, June 23 Litho.
456 A139 10fr multicolored 1.10 .25

1994 World Cup Soccer
Championships, U.S. — A140

1994, June 23
457 A140 105fr multicolored 2.25 1.50

Princesses
Ouveennes,
1903 — A141

1994, July 21 Engr. Perf. 13
458 A141 90fr blue grn, blk & red 2.50 1.25

Symbols of Playing Cards
Suits — A142

1994, Aug. 25 Litho. Perf. 13
459 A142 40fr multicolored 1.00 .50

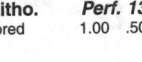
Ultra-Light Aircraft — A143

1994, Aug. 25
460 A143 5fr multicolored 1.00 .25

Coconut — A144

1994, Oct. 13 Litho. Perf. 13
461 A144 36fr multicolored 1.00 .55

Parrots
A145

1994, Nov. 17 Litho. Perf. 13x13½
462 A145 62fr multicolored 2.00 1.10

Grand Lodge of France, Cent. — A146

1994, Nov. 24 Engr. Perf. 13
463 A146 250fr multicolored 6.50 3.50

Preparing Traditional Meal — A147

1995, Jan. 25 Litho. Perf. 13
464 A147 80fr multicolored 2.40 1.25

Aerial View
of Islands
A148

1995, Feb. 21 Perf. 13x13½, 13½x13
465 A148 85fr Nukulaelae 2.00 1.25
466 A148 90fr Nukufetau, vert. 2.25 1.40
467 A148 100fr Nukufotu,
Nukuloa 2.75 1.50
Nos. 465-467 (3) 7.00 4.15

Mua
College — A149

1995, Apr. 11 Perf. 12
468 A149 35fr multicolored 1.10 .60

UN, 50th Anniv. — A150

Illustration reduced.

1995, June 26 Litho. Perf. 13½
469 A150 55fr multicolored 1.50 .80

10th South Pacific Games — A151

1995, Aug. 1 Litho. Perf. 13
470 A151 70fr multicolored 1.90 1.00

Local
Plants — A152

1995, Oct. 24 Litho. Perf. 13½x13
471 A152 20fr Breadfruit tree .50 .25
472 A152 60fr Tarot 1.50 .75
473 A152 65fr Kava 2.00 .80
Nos. 471-473 (3) 4.00 1.80
See Nos. 478-481, 484-485.

Tapa — A153

1995, Dec. 12 Litho. Perf. 13
474 A153 25fr Native life, vert. .65 .35
475 A153 26fr Fish, sea shells .65 .35

Mothers from the
Islands — A154

1996, Jan. 14 Litho. Perf. 13½x13
476 A154 80fr multicolored 2.00 1.10

Golf
A155

1996, Jan. 24 Perf. 13
477 A155 95fr multicolored 3.50 1.40

Local Plant Type of 1995
1996 Litho. Perf. 13½x13
478 A152 27fr Cananga odorata .60 .30
479 A152 28fr Mahoaa .75 .40
480 A152 45fr Hibiscus 1.00 .60
481 A152 52fr Ufi 1.25 .70
Nos. 478-481 (4) 3.60 2.00
Issued: #479, 481, 3/14; #478, 480, 6/20.

Sanglants Swamp — A156

1996, June 26   **Perf. 13**
482 A156 53fr multicolored   1.10   .55

Chess — A157

1996, July 17
483 A157 110fr multicolored   2.75 1.50

Plant Type of 1995
Designs: 30fr, 48fr, Calladium.

1996, Sept. 17   **Litho.**   **Perf. 13½x13**
      Background Color
484 A152 30fr blue green   .65   .30
485 A152 48fr lilac   1.10   .60

Francoise Perroton,
Missionary — A158

1996, Oct. 25   **Perf. 13**
486 A158 50fr multicolored   1.25   .65

UNICEF,
50th Anniv.
A159

1996, Dec. 4   **Litho.**   **Perf. 13**
487 A159 25fr multicolored
               .55   .30

CPS, 50th
Anniv.
A160

1997, Feb. 6   **Litho.**   **Perf. 13**
488 A160 7fr multicolored   .20   .20

Royal
Standards
A161

1997, Feb. 14 Litho. Perf. 13x13½
489 A161 56fr King Lavelua   1.10   .55
490 A161 60fr King Tuiagaifo   1.25   .60
491 A161 70fr King Tuisigave   1.40   .65
    Nos. 489-491 (3)   3.75 1.80

Brasseur de
Kava — A162

1997, Apr. 17   **Perf. 13½x13**
492 A162 170fr multicolored   3.50 1.75

Island
Scenes
A163

Designs: 10fr, Old man telling stories to children seated around campfire. 36fr, Braiding
mat, vert. 40fr, Preparing "Kai'umu" (feast).

Perf. 13x13½, 13½x13
1997, May 20   **Litho.**
493 A163 10fr multicolored   .20   .20
494 A163 36fr multicolored   .80   .50
495 A163 40fr multicolored   .90   .60
    Nos. 493-495 (3)   1.90 1.30

Green
Lagoon
Turtles
A164

1997, June 18   **Perf. 13x13½**
496 A164 62fr Crawling ashore   1.50   .75
497 A164 80fr Swimming   1.90 1.00

Festival of Avignon — A165

1997, July 31   **Litho.**   **Perf. 13**
498 A165 160fr multicolored   3.50 1.75

Berlin
Handicapped
Sports
Festival — A166

1997, Aug. 12
499 A166 35fr multicolored   .80   .45

D'Uvéa Karate Club — A167

Illustration reduced.
1997, Oct. 15   **Litho.**   **Perf. 13x13½**
500 A167 24fr multicolored   .50   .25

Fight Against
AIDS — A168

1997, Dec. 1   **Litho.**   **Perf. 13**
501 A168 5fr multicolored   .40   .20

Christmas — A169

1997, Dec. 24
502 A169 85fr Nativity   1.90 1.00

Preparation of UMU — A170

1998, Jan. 26
503 A170 800fr multicolored   16.00 8.00

Orchids — A171

70fr, Vanda T.M.A.. 85fr, Cattleya bow bells.
90fr, Arachnis. 105fr, Cattleya.

1998, Feb. 18   **Litho.**   **Perf. 13**
504 A171 70fr multi, vert.   1.40   .60
505 A171 85fr multi   1.75   .75
506 A171 90fr multi, vert.   1.75   .85
507 A171 105fr multi   2.10   .95
    Nos. 504-507 (4)   7.00 3.15

Telecom 2000 — A172

1998, Mar. 24   **Litho.**   **Perf. 13**
508 A172 7fr multicolored   .30   .20

Fishing — A173

Designs: 50fr, Fisherman casting net into
lagoon. 52fr, Fisherman sorting catch.

1998, May 26   **Litho.**   **Perf. 13**
509 A173 50fr multicolored   1.00   .45
510 A173 52fr multicolored   1.00   .50

1998 World Cup Soccer
Championships, France — A174

1998, June 10
511 A174 80fr multicolored   1.60   .70

Insects
A175

1998, July 21   **Litho.**   **Perf. 13x13½**
512 A175 36fr Dragonfly   .75   .30
513 A175 40fr Cicada   .80   .35

Coral — A176

Various corals: a, 4fr. b, 5fr. c, 10fr. d, 15fr.

1998   **Litho.**   **Perf. 13x13½**
514 A176 Strip of 4, #a.-d.   1.00 1.00

52nd Autumn Philatelic Salon — A177

1998, Nov. 5   **Litho.**   **Perf. 13½**
515 A177 175fr multicolored   3.50 2.00

World Fight Against AIDS
A178

1998, Dec. 1   **Perf. 13**
516 A178 62fr multicolored   1.25   .60

Islet of Nuku Taakimoa
A179

1999, Mar. 22   **Litho.**   **Perf. 13**
517 A179 130fr multicolored   2.75 1.50

Souvenir Sheet

Lagoon Life — A180

a, 20fr, Various fish. b, 855fr, Fish, diver.

1999, May 17   **Litho.**   **Perf. 13**
518 A180 Sheet of 2, #a.-b.   17.50 17.50

PhilexFrance '99, World Philatelic Exhibition — A181

1999, July 2   **Litho.**   **Perf. 13**
519 A181 200fr multicolored   4.00 2.00

French Senate, Bicent. — A182

1999, Sept. 20   **Engr.**   **Perf. 13**
520 A182 125fr multi   2.50 1.10

Territorial Assembly Building — A183

1999, Aug. 23   **Litho.**
521 A183 17fr multi   .40   .20

Pandanus
A184

1999, Oct. 18
522 A184 25fr multi   .50   .20

Man Making Canoe
A185

1999, Nov. 8
523 A185 55fr multi   1.10   .60

French Postage Stamps, 150th Anniv. — A186

1999, Dec. 1
524 A186 65fr Wallis & Futuna #86   1.40   .75

Millennium — A187

2000, Jan. 1   **Litho.**   **Perf. 13**
525 A187 350fr multi   7.00 4.00

Mata'utu Cathedral
A188

2000, Apr. 28   **Photo.**   **Perf. 13x13¼**
526 A188 300fr multi   6.00 3.25

Patrol Boat "La Glorieuse" — A189

2000, June 5   **Engr.**   **Perf. 13x12¾**
527 A189 155fr multi   3.25 1.50

Sosefo Papilio Makape, First Senator — A190

2000, June 19   **Perf. 12¾x13**
528 A190 115fr multi   2.25 1.10

Overseas Broadcasting Institute — A191

2000, July 3   **Perf. 13x12½**
529 A191 200fr multi   4.00 2.25

Taro Cultivation
A192

2000, July 27   **Litho.**   **Perf. 13**
530 A192 275fr multi   5.50 2.75

Souvenir Sheet

2000 Summer Olympics, Sydney — A193

Traditional games, 85fr: a, Spear throwing. b, Sailing. c, Rowing. d, Volleyball.

2000, Sept. 15   **Perf. 13**
531 A193   #a-d + 2 labels   7.00 4.00

8th Pacific Arts Festival
A194

2000, Oct. 23   **Perf. 13x13¼**
532 A194 330fr multi   6.50 3.25

Fish — A195

No. 533: a, Coryphaena hippurus. b, Caranx melanpygyus. c, Thunnus albacares.

2000, Nov. 9   **Litho.**   **Perf. 13**
533   Vert. strip of 3 + 2 labels   9.25 9.25
  a.-c. A195 115fr Any single   2.25   .85

Canonization of St. Marcellin Champagnat, 1st Anniv. — A196

2000, Nov. 13
534 A196 380fr multi   7.50 3.50

Talietumu Archaeological Site — A197

2000, Dec. 1   **Perf. 13x13½**
535 A197 205fr multi   4.00 2.00

Christmas
A198

2000, Dec. 25   **Perf. 13**
536 A198 225fr multi   4.50 2.25

Ship "Jacques Cartier" — A199

2001, Feb. 26   **Engr.**   **Perf. 13**
537 A199 225fr multi   4.50 2.00

Campaign Against Alcoholism
A200

2001, Mar. 14   **Litho.**   **Perf. 13¼x13**
538 A200 75fr multi   1.50   .75

Souvenir Sheet

Tapas — A201

Tapa with: a, Large diamond, shells, map of islands. b, Triangles and diamonds. c, Scenes of native life, fish, shells, boat. d, Overlapping ovals.

2001, Apr. 14   *Perf. 13*
539 A201 90fr Sheet of 4, #a-d, + 2 labels   7.25 7.25

Children's Drawings of Flowers — A202

2001, May 31
540   Horiz. strip of 4   6.00 6.00
   a.   A202 50fr multi   1.00 .50
   b.   A202 55fr multi   1.10 .55
   c.   A202 95fr multi   1.90 .95
   d.   A202 100fr multi   2.00 1.00

Territorial Status, 40th Anniv. A203

2001, July 29   Litho.   *Perf. 13*
541 A203 165fr multi   3.25 1.25

Installation of Mediator, 1st Anniv. A204

2001, Sept. 26
542 A204 800fr multi   16.00 8.00

Year of Dialogue Among Civilizations A205

2001, Oct. 9
543 A205 390fr multi   8.00 4.00

5th Autumn Salon — A206

Birds: a, Dacula pacifica. b, Vini australis. c, Tyto alba.

2001, Nov. 8
544   Vert. strip of 3 + 2 labels   9.00 4.50
   a.-c.   A206 150fr Any single   3.00 1.50

Children's Drawings of Fruit A207

No. 545, 65fr: a, Custard apple (pomme canelle). b, Breadfruit (fruit de pain).
No. 546, 65fr: a, Pineapple. b, Mango.

2001, Aug. 22   Litho.   *Perf. 13*
     Vert. Pairs, #a-b
545-546 A207   Set of 2 pairs   5.25 2.75

Tomb of Futuna King Fakavelikele — A208

2001, Dec. 28   Litho.   *Perf. 13*
547   A208 325fr multi   6.50 3.25

Finemui-Teesi College — A209

2002, Jan. 29   *Perf. 13x13½*
548 A209 115fr multi   2.25 1.10

Intl. Women's Day — A210

2002, Mar. 5   Litho.   *Perf. 13*
549 A210 800fr Queen Aloisia   16.00 8.00

Arms of Bishop Pompallier A211

2002, Apr. 19   Engr.   *Perf. 13¼*
550 A211 500fr multi   10.00 5.00

Uvea Firefighters A212

    Serpentine Die Cut
2002, Apr. 28   *Photo.*
     Self-Adhesive
551 A212 85fr multi   1.75 .80

2002 World Cup Soccer Championships, Japan and Korea — A213

2002, May 31   Litho.   *Perf. 13*
552 A213 65fr multi   1.25 .60

World Environment Day — A214

2002, June 5   *Perf. 13x13½*
553 A214 330fr multi   6.50 3.25

Traditional Buildings A215

Designs: No. 554, 50fr, Building with overhanging roof. No. 555, 50fr, Open-air shelter, vert. No. 556, 55fr, Building with two entryways. No. 557, 55fr, Building with ladder to roof, vert.

2002, Aug. 9   Engr.   *Perf. 13¼*
554-557 A215   Set of 4   4.25 2.00

Discovery of the Horn Islands, 1616 A216

No. 558: a, Jacob Lemaire and compass rose. b, Map of Futuna and Alofi Islands. c, William Schouten and ship.

2002, Aug. 30   Litho.   *Perf. 13x13¼*
558   Horiz. strip of 3   7.50 3.75
   a.-c.   A216 125fr any single   2.50 1.25
   d.   Souvenir sheet, #558   7.50 7.50

Landscapes A217

No. 559: a, Utua Bay. b, Liku Bay. c, Kingfisher at Vele. d, Aka'Aka Bay.

2002, Sept. 20
559   Horiz. strip of 4   8.75 8.75
   a.   A217 95fr multi   1.90 .95
   b.   A217 100fr multi   2.00 1.00
   c.   A217 105fr multi   2.10 1.00
   d.   A217 135fr multi   2.75 1.40

Enygrus Bibroni — A218

2002, Oct. 28   Litho.   *Perf. 13¼x13*
560 A218 75fr multi   1.50 .75

Fish A219

No. 561: a, Dendrochirus biocellatus. b, Discordipina griessingeri. c, Antennacius nummifer. d, Novaculichthys taeniourus.

2002, Nov. 7   *Perf. 13x13¼*
561   Vert. strip of 4 + 3 labels   9.00 9.00
   a.-d.   A219 110fr Any single   2.25 1.10

Best Wishes A220

2002, Dec. 5
562 A220 140fr multi   2.75 1.40

Last Avro Lancaster Flight to Wallis, 40th Anniv. A221

2003, Jan. 26   *Perf. 13*
563 A221 135fr multi   2.75 1.40

St. Valentine's Day — A222

2003, Feb. 14   *Perf. 13*
564 A222 85fr multi   1.75 .85

Introduction of the Euro, 1st Anniv. A223

2003, Feb. 17   *Perf. 12½x12¾*
565 A223 125fr multi   2.50 1.25

Values are for examples with surrounding selvage.

Postal Art — A225

Various designs.

2003, Mar. 31   Litho.   *Perf. 13*
567   Horiz. strip of 5   1.75 .85
a.   A225 5fr multi   .20 .20
b.   A225 10fr multi   .20 .20
c.   A225 15fr multi   .25 .20
d.   A225 20fr multi   .35 .20
e.   A225 40fr multi   .75 .35

Coral Reefs A226

Various views.

2003, Apr. 10   *Perf. 13x13¼*
568   Horiz. strip of 4   7.75 4.00
a.   A226 95fr multi   1.75 .85
b.   A226 105fr multi   1.90 .95
c.   A226 110fr multi   2.00 1.00
d.   A226 115fr multi   2.10 1.10

St. Pierre Chanel (1803-41), Martyred Missionary A227

2003, Apr. 28   Engr.   *Perf. 12¼*
569 A227 130fr multi   2.60 1.25

2003 Census — A228

2003, June 12   Litho.   *Perf. 13*
570 A228 55fr multi   1.10 .55

Pacific Legends A229

Legend of the Coconut Palm: 30fr, Eel. 50fr, Coconut palms, split coconut. 60fr, Split and whole coconuts. 70fr, Coconut palms and clouds.

2003, July 28   Litho.   *Perf. 13x13¼*
571   Horiz. strip of 4   4.00 2.00
a.   A229 30fr multi   .60 .30
b.   A229 50fr multi   .95 .45
c.   A229 60fr multi   1.10 .55
d.   A229 70fr multi   1.25 .60
e.   Souvenir sheet, #571a-571d   4.00 2.00

Still Life with Maori Statuette, by Paul Gauguin (1848-1903) A230

No. 573a: Study of Heads of Tahitian Women, by Gauguin.

2003   *Perf. 13*
572 A230 100fr multi   2.00 1.00

Souvenir Sheet
573   Sheet, #572, 573a   4.00 2.00
a.   A230 100fr multi   2.00 1.00
Issued: No. 572, 7/31; No. 573, 8/20. See New Caledonia No. 929.

Futuna Waterfalls — A231

2003, Aug. 6   *Perf. 13¼x13*
574 A231 115fr multi   2.25 1.10

Frigate Le Nivose A232

2003, Sept. 15   Engr.   *Perf. 13¼*
575 A232 325fr multi   6.25 6.25

Bishop Alexandre Poncet (1884-1973) A233

2003, Sept. 18   Engr.   *Perf. 13¼*
576 A233 205fr multi   4.00 2.00

Arms of Bishop Pierre Bataillon (1810-77) — A234

2003, Oct. 1   Litho.   *Perf. 13¼*
577 A234 500fr multi   9.75 9.75

2003 Rugby World Cup, Australia A235

2003, Oct. 10   *Perf. 13*
578 A235 65fr multi   1.25 1.25

Parinari Insularum A236

2003, Nov. 6   Litho.   *Perf. 13¼x13*
579 A236 250fr multi   5.00 5.00

Goddess Havea Hikule'o — A237

2004, Jan. 8
580 A237 85fr multi   1.90 1.90

People in Canoe A238

2004, Jan. 13   *Perf. 13*
581 A238 75fr multi   1.60 1.60

SEMI-POSTAL STAMPS

French Revolution Issue
Common Design Type
Unwmk.
1939, July 5   Photo.   *Perf. 13*
Name and Value Typo. in Black

B1	CD83	45c + 25c green	9.50	*14.00*
B2	CD83	70c + 30c brown	9.50	*14.00*
B3	CD83	90c + 35c red org	9.50	*14.00*
B4	CD83	1.25fr + 1fr rose pink	9.50	*14.00*
B5	CD83	2.25fr + 2fr blue	9.50	*14.00*
	Nos. B1-B5 (5)		47.50	*70.00*
	Set, never hinged		75.00	

New Caledonia Nos. B10 and B12 Overprinted "WALLIS ET FUTUNA" in Blue or Red, and Common Design Type
1941   Photo.   *Perf. 13½*

B6	SP2	1fr + 1fr red	.90
B7	CD86	1.50fr + 3fr maroon	.90
B8	SP3	2.50fr + 1fr dark blue	.90
	Nos. B6-B8 (3)		2.70
	Set, never hinged		4.75

Nos. B6-B8 were issued by the Vichy government in France, but were not placed on sale in Wallis & Futuna.

Nos. 92-93 Surcharged in Black or Red

1944   Engr.   *Perf. 12x12½*

B8A		50c + 1.50fr on 2.50fr deep blue (R)	.90
B8B		+ 2.50fr on 1fr green	.90

Colonial Development Fund.
Nos. B8A-B8B were issued by the Vichy government in France, but were not placed on sale in Wallis & Futuna.

> **Catalogue values for unused stamps in this section, from this point to the end of the section, are for Never Hinged items.**

Red Cross Issue
Common Design Type
1944   Photo.   *Perf. 14½x14*
B9   CD90 5fr + 20fr red orange   2.00 *2.00*

The surtax was for the French Red Cross and national relief.

AIR POST STAMPS

> **Catalogue values for unused stamps in this section are for Never Hinged items.**

Victory Issue
Common Design Type
Perf. 12½
1946, May 8   Unwmk.   Engr.
C1   CD92 8fr dark violet   1.25 1.25

Chad to Rhine Issue
Common Design Types
1946

C2	CD93	5fr dark violet	.80	.80
C3	CD94	10fr dk slate grn	.95	.95
C4	CD95	15fr violet brn	.95	.95
C5	CD96	20fr brt ultra	1.25	1.25
C6	CD97	25fr brown orange	1.50	1.50
C7	CD98	50fr carmine	2.00	2.00
	Nos. C2-C7 (6)		7.45	7.45

Types of New Caledonia Air Post Stamps of 1948, Overprinted in Blue:

1949, July 4   Perf. 13x12½, 12½x13
C8 AP2 50fr yel & rose red   5.00 5.00
C9 AP3 100fr yel & red brn   8.50 8.50
The overprint on No. C9 is in three lines.

UPU Issue
Common Design Type
1949, July 4   Engr.   Perf. 13
C10 CD99 10fr multicolored   6.00 5.50

Liberation Issue
Common Design Type
1954, June 6
C11 CD102 3fr sepia & vio brn   6.00 5.25

Father Louis Marie Chanel — AP1

1955, Nov. 21   Unwmk.   Perf. 13
C12 AP1 14fr dk grn, grnsh bl &
          ind   2.00 1.10
Issued in honor of Father Chanel, martyred missionary to the Islands.

View of Mata-Utu, Queen Amelia and Msgr. Bataillon — AP2

33fr, Map of islands and sailing ship.

1960, Sept. 19   Engr.   Perf. 13
C13 AP2 21fr blue, brn & grn   3.00 4.00
C14 AP2 33fr ultra, choc & bl grn 5.00 4.50

Shell Diver — AP3

1962, Sept. 20   Unwmk.   Perf. 13
C16 AP3 100fr bl, grn & dk red
          brn   15.00 11.00

Telstar Issue
Common Design Type
1962, Dec. 5
C17 CD111 12fr dk pur, mar & bl 2.50 2.50

Sea Shell Type of Regular Issue
1963, Apr. 1   Engr.
          Size: 26x47mm
C18 A5 50fr Harpa ventricosa   8.00 7.00

Javelin Thrower — AP4

1964, Oct. 10   Engr.   Perf. 13
C19 AP4 31fr emer, ver & vio
          brn   16.00 10.00
18th Olympic Games, Tokyo, Oct. 10-25.

ITU Issue
Common Design Type
1965, May 17   Unwmk.   Perf. 13
C20 CD120 50fr multicolored   15.00 11.00

Mata-Utu Wharf — AP5

1965, Nov. 26   Engr.   Perf. 13
C21 AP5 27fr brt bl, sl grn & red
          brn   4.50 3.00

French Satellite A-1 Issue
Common Design Type
Designs: 7fr, Diamant rocket and launching installations. 10fr, A-1 satellite.
1966, Jan. 17   Engr.   Perf. 13
C22 CD121 7fr crim, red & car
            lake   2.75 2.25
C23 CD121 10fr car lake, red &
            crim   2.75 2.25
a.   Strip of 2, #C22-C23 + label 6.50 6.50

French Satellite D-1 Issue
Common Design Type
1966, June 2   Engr.   Perf. 13
C24 CD122 10fr lake, bl grn &
            red   2.50 2.50

WHO Headquarters, Geneva, and Emblem — AP6

1966, July 5   Photo.   Perf. 12½x13
C25 AP6 30fr org, maroon & bl   2.75 2.50
New WHO Headquarters, Geneva.

Girl and Boy Reading; UNESCO Emblem — AP7

1966, Nov. 4   Engr.   Perf. 13
C26 AP7 50fr green, org & choc 4.00 3.25
20th anniv. of UNESCO.

Athlete and Pattern AP8

Design: 38fr, Woman ballplayer and pattern.
1966, Dec. 8   Engr.   Perf. 13x12½
C27 AP8 32fr bl, dp car & blk   3.50 2.25
C28 AP8 38fr emer & brt pink   4.00 2.75
2nd South Pacific Games, Nouméa, 12/8-18.

Samuel Wallis' Ship and Coast of Wallis Island — AP9

1967, Dec. 16   Photo.   Perf. 13
C29 AP9 12fr multicolored   5.50 3.75
Bicentenary of the discovery of Wallis Island.

Concorde Issue
Common Design Type
1969, Apr. 17   Engr.   Perf. 13
C30 CD129 20fr black & plum   10.00 7.50

Man Climbing Coconut Palm — AP10

32fr, Horseback rider. 38fr, Men making wooden stools. 50fr, Spear fisherman & man holding basket with fish. 100fr, Women sorting coconuts.

1969, Apr. 30   Photo.   Perf. 13
C31 AP10 20fr multi   2.00 1.00
C32 AP10 32fr multi   3.50 2.00
C33 AP10 38fr multi   4.00 2.00
C34 AP10 50fr multi   6.00 3.25
C35 AP10 100fr multi   11.00 5.25
     Nos. C31-C35 (5)   26.50 13.50

No. C14 Surcharged with New Value and Three Bars
1971   Engr.   Perf. 13
C36 AP2 21fr on 33fr multi   3.50 3.00

Pole Vault — AP11

1971, Oct. 25   Engr.   Perf. 13
C37 AP11 48fr shown   4.00 2.00
C38 AP11 54fr Archery   5.50 3.50
4th South Pacific Games, Papeete, French Polynesia, Sept. 8-19.

South Pacific Commission Headquarters, Noumea — AP12

1972, Feb. 5   Photo.   Perf. 13
C39 AP12 44fr blue & multi   4.25 2.75
South Pacific Commission, 25th anniv.

Round House and Festival Emblem — AP13

1972, May 15   Engr.   Perf. 13
C40 AP13 60fr dp car, grn & pur 6.00 3.50
South Pacific Festival of Arts, Fiji, May 6-20.

Canoe Type of Regular Issue
Design: 200fr, Outrigger sailing canoe race and island woman.

1972, Oct. 16   Photo.   Perf. 13x12½
          Size: 47½x28mm
C41 A9 200fr multicolored   30.00 18.00

La Pérouse and "La Boussole" — AP14

Explorers and their Ships: 28fr, Samuel Wallis and "Dolphin." 40fr, Dumont D'Urville and "Astrolabe." 72fr, Bougainville and "La Boudeuse."

1973, July 20   Engr.   Perf. 13
C42 AP14 22fr brn, slate & car 8.00 4.25
C43 AP14 28fr sl grn, dl red &
           bl   8.50 4.25
C44 AP14 40fr brn, ind & ultra 11.00 6.50
C45 AP14 72fr brown, bl & pur 13.00 8.50
     Nos. C42-C45 (4)   40.50 23.50

Charles de Gaulle — AP15

1973, Nov. 9   Engr.   Perf. 13
C46 AP15 107fr brn org & dk
           brn   12.00 4.50
Pres. Charles de Gaulle (1890-1970).

Red Jasmine AP16

Designs: Flowers from Wallis.

1973, Dec. 6   Photo.   Perf. 13

C47	AP16	12fr shown	1.00 .70
C48	AP16	17fr Hibiscus tiliaceus	1.50 1.25
C49	AP16	19fr Phaeomeria magnifica	2.00 1.25
C50	AP16	21fr Hibiscus rosa sinensis	2.50 1.40
C51	AP16	23fr Allamanda cathartica	3.50 1.90
C52	AP16	27fr Barringtonia	4.00 2.00
C53	AP16	39fr Flowers in vase	5.50 3.75
		Nos. C47-C53 (7)	20.00 12.25

UPU Emblem and Symbolic Design — AP17

1974, Oct. 9   Engr.   Perf. 13

C54 AP17 51fr multicolored   5.50 3.50

Centenary of Universal Postal Union.

Holy Family, Primitive Painting AP18

1974, Dec. 9   Photo.   Perf. 13

C55 AP18 150fr multi   11.00 7.25

Christmas 1974.

Tapa Cloth — AP19

Tapa Cloth: 24fr, Village scene. 36fr, Fish & marine life. 80fr, Marine life, map of islands, village scene.

1975, Feb. 3   Photo.   Perf. 13

C56	AP19	3fr multicolored	.60 .50
C57	AP19	24fr multicolored	1.50 1.10
C58	AP19	36fr multicolored	3.00 1.60
C59	AP19	80fr multicolored	6.25 4.00
		Nos. C56-C59 (4)	11.35 7.20

DC-7 in Flight — AP20

Volleyball AP21

1975, Aug. 13   Engr.   Perf. 13

C60 AP20 100fr multicolored   5.00 4.00

First regular air service between Nouméa, New Caledonia, and Wallis.

1975, Nov. 10   Photo.   Perf. 13

C61	AP21	26fr shown	1.50 .80
C62	AP21	44fr Soccer	2.00 1.25
C63	AP21	56fr Javelin	3.50 2.00
C64	AP21	105fr Spear fishing	7.25 4.50
		Nos. C61-C64 (4)	14.25 8.55

5th South Pacific Games, Guam, Aug. 1-10.

Lalolalo Lake, Wallis — AP22

Landscapes: 29fr, Vasavasa, Futuna. 41fr, Sigave Bay, Futuna. 68fr, Gahi Bay, Wallis.

1975, Dec. 1   Litho.   Perf. 13

C65	AP22	10fr grn & multi	1.00 .65
C66	AP22	29fr grn & multi	2.00 1.25
C67	AP22	41fr grn & multi	3.00 1.75
C68	AP22	68fr grn & multi	4.00 2.50
		Nos. C65-C68 (4)	10.00 6.15

Concorde, Eiffel Tower and Sugar Loaf Mountain — AP23

1976, Jan. 21   Engr.   Perf. 13

C69 AP23 250fr multi   20.00 13.50

1st commercial flight of supersonic jet Concorde from Paris to Rio, Jan. 21. For overprint see No. C73.

Hammer Throw and Stadium — AP24

39fr, Diving, Stadium and maple leaf.

1976, Aug. 2   Engr.   Perf. 13

C70	AP24	31fr multi	2.25 1.50
C71	AP24	39fr multi	3.25 2.40

21st Olympic Games, Montreal, Canada, July 17-Aug. 1.

De Gaulle Memorial AP25

Photogravure and Embossed

1977, June 18   Perf. 13

C72 AP25 100fr gold & multi   7.00 5.50

5th anniversary of dedication of De Gaulle Memorial at Colombey-les-Deux-Eglises.

No. C69 Overprinted in Dark Brown: "PARIS NEW-YORK / 22.11.77 / 1er VOL COMMERCIAL"

1977, Nov. 22   Engr.   Perf. 13

C73 AP23 250fr multicolored   16.00 12.00

Concorde, 1st commercial flight, Paris-NY.

Balistes Niger — AP26

Fish: 35fr, Amphiprion akindynos. 49fr, Pomacanthus imperator. 51fr, Zanclus cornutus.

1978, Jan. 31   Litho.   Perf. 13

C74	AP26	26fr multi	1.00 .65
C75	AP26	35fr multi	1.50 1.00
C76	AP26	49fr multi	2.50 1.50
C77	AP26	51fr multi	3.00 1.75
		Nos. C74-C77 (4)	8.00 4.90

Map of Wallis and Uvea Islands — AP27

300fr, Map of Futuna and Alofi Islands, horz.

1978, Mar. 7   Engr.

C78	AP27	300fr vio bl & grnsh bl	12.00 8.50
C79	AP27	500fr multi	16.00 12.50

Father Bataillon, Churches on Wallis and Futuna Islands — AP28

72fr, Monsignor Pompallier, map of Wallis, Futuna and Alofi Islands, outrigger canoe.

1978, Apr. 28   Litho.   Perf. 13x12½

C80	AP28	60fr multi	1.75 1.00
C81	AP28	72fr multi	2.25 1.40

First French missionaries on Wallis and Futuna Islands.

ITU Emblem — AP29

1978, May 17   Litho.   Perf. 13

C82 AP29 66fr multi   2.50 1.40

10th World Telecommunications Day.

Nativity and Longhouse — AP30

1978, Dec. 4   Photo.   Perf. 13

C83 AP30 160fr multi   6.50 4.00

Christmas 1978.

Popes Paul VI, John Paul I, St. Peter's, Rome — AP31

37fr, Pope Paul VI. 41fr, Pope John Paul I.

Perf. 12½x13, 13x12½

1979, Jan. 31   Litho.

C84	AP31	37fr multi, vert.	1.40 .65
C85	AP31	41fr multi, vert.	1.60 .90
C86	AP31	105fr multi	3.75 2.00
		Nos. C84-C86 (3)	6.75 3.55

In memory of Popes Paul VI and John Paul I.

Monoplane of UTA Airlines AP32

68fr, Freighter Muana. 80fr, Hihifo Airport.

1979, Feb. 28   Perf. 13x12½

C87	AP32	46fr multi	1.25 .75
C88	AP32	68fr multi	1.50 1.00
C89	AP32	80fr multi	2.25 1.40
		Nos. C87-C89 (3)	5.00 3.15

Inter-Island transportation. See Nos. 251-253.

France No. 67 and Eole Weather Satellite — AP33

70fr, Hibiscus & stamp similar to #25. 90fr, Rowland Hill & Penny Black. 100fr, Birds, Kano School, Japan 17th cent. & Japan #9.

1979, May 7   Photo.   Perf. 13

C90	AP33	5fr multi	.50	.30
C91	AP33	70fr multi, vert.	2.50	1.25
C92	AP33	90fr multi	3.00	1.75
C93	AP33	100fr multi	4.00	2.50
		Nos. C90-C93 (4)	10.00	5.80

Sir Rowland Hill (1795-1879), originator of penny postage.

Cross of Lorraine and People — AP34

1979, June 18   Engr.   Perf. 13

C94 AP34 33fr multi   1.75 1.25

Map of Islands, Arms of France AP35

1979, July 19   Photo.   Perf. 13

C95 AP35 47fr multi   2.00 1.40

Visit of Pres. Valery Giscard d'Estaing of France.

Capt. Cook, Ships and Island — AP36

1979, July 28

C96 AP36 130fr multi   5.00 3.00

Capt. James Cook (1728-1779).

Telecom Emblem, Satellite, Receiving Station — AP37

1979, Sept. 20   Litho.   Perf. 13

C97 AP37 120fr multi   3.50 2.50

3rd World Telecommunications Exhibition, Geneva, Sept. 20-26.

Virgin of the Crescent Moon, by Albrecht Durer AP38

1979, Dec. 17   Engr.   Perf. 13

C98 AP38 180fr red & blk   6.50 4.50

Christmas 1979. See No. C163.

Rotary International, 75th Anniversary — AP39

1980, Feb. 29   Litho.   Perf. 13

C99 AP39 86fr multi   4.00 2.50

Rochambeau and Troops, US Flag, 1780 — AP40

1980, May 27   Engr.   Perf. 13

C100 AP40 102fr multi   4.00 2.50

Rochambeau's landing at Newport, RI (American Revolution), bicentenary.

National Day, 10th Anniversary — AP41

1980, July 15   Litho.   Perf. 13

C101 AP41 71fr multi   1.50 1.00

Transatlantic Airmail Flight, 50th Anniversary — AP42

1980, Sept. 22   Engr.   Perf. 13

C102 AP42 122fr multi   3.25 2.50

Fleming, Penicillin Bacilli — AP43

1980, Oct. 20

C103 AP43 101fr multi   2.75 1.75

Alexander Fleming (1881-1955), discoverer of penicillin, 25th death anniversary.

Charles De Gaulle, 10th Anniversary of Death — AP44

1980, Nov. 9   Engr.   Perf. 13

C104 AP44 200fr sep & dk ol grn   6.50 5.00

Virgin and Child with St. Catherine, by Lorenzo Lotto — AP45

1980, Dec. 20   Litho.   Perf. 13x12½

C105 AP45 150fr multi   3.50 2.50

Christmas 1980.

Alan B. Shepard and Spacecraft AP46

20th Anniv. of Space Flight: 44fr, Yuri Gagarin.

1981, May 11   Litho.   Perf. 13

C106	AP46	37fr multi	1.00	.50
C107	AP46	44fr multi	1.25	.60

Vase of Flowers, by Paul Cezanne (1839-1906) — AP47

Design: 135fr, Harlequin, by Pablo Picasso.

1981, Oct. 22   Litho.   Perf. 12½x13

C108	AP47	53fr multi	1.75	1.00
C109	AP47	135fr multi	3.50	2.10

Espana '82 World Cup Soccer — AP48

1981-82   Engr.   Perf. 13

C110	AP48	120fr blk, brn & grn	2.50	1.50
C110A	AP48	120fr lil, brn & ol grn	2.75	2.00

Issued: #C110, 11/16/81; #C110A,5/13/82. For overprint see No. C115.

Christmas 1981 — AP49

1981, Dec. 21   Litho.   Perf. 12½

C111 AP49 180fr multi   4.50 3.00

Tapestry, by Pilioho Aloi AP50

1982, Feb. 22   Litho.   Perf. 12½x13

C112 AP50 100fr multi   4.50 2.50

Boats at Colioure, by George Braque (1882-1963) — AP51

1982, Apr. 13   Litho.   Perf. 12½x13

C113 AP51 300fr multi   6.50 4.00

Alberto Santos-Dumont (1873-1932), Aviation Pioneer — AP52

1982, July 24

C114 AP52 95fr multi   2.50 1.75

No. C110 Overprinted with Winner's Name in Blue

1982, Aug. 26 **Engr.** *Perf. 13*
C115 AP48 120fr multi 2.75 2.00
Italy's victory in 1982 World Cup.

French Overseas Possessions Week, Sept. 18-25 — AP53

1982, Sept. 17 **Litho.**
C116 AP53 105fr Beach 2.00 1.40

Day of the Blind — AP54

1982, Oct. 18 **Engr.**
C117 AP54 130fr red & blue 2.50 1.60

Christmas 1982 AP55

Adoration of the Virgin, by Correggio.

1982, Dec. 20 **Litho.** *Perf. 12½x13*
C118 AP55 170fr multi 3.50 2.00

Wind Surfing (1984 Olympic Event) — AP56

1983, Mar. 4 **Litho.** *Perf. 13*
C119 AP56 270fr multi 5.50 3.00

World UPU Day — AP57

1983, Mar. 30 **Litho.** *Perf. 13*
C120 AP57 100fr multi 2.00 1.25

Manned Flight Bicentenary AP58

1983, Apr. 25 **Litho.** *Perf. 13*
C121 AP58 205fr Montgolfiere 4.25 2.50

Cat, 1926, by Foujita (d. 1968) AP59

1983, May 20 **Litho.** *Perf. 12½x13*
C122 AP59 102fr multi 3.75 2.00

Pre-Olympic Year — AP60

1983, July 5 **Engr.** *Perf. 13*
C123 AP60 250fr Javelin 4.50 3.00

Alfred Nobel (1833-1896) — AP61

1983, Aug. 1 **Engr.** *Perf. 13*
C124 AP61 150fr multi 2.75 1.60

Nicephore Niepce (1765-1833), Photography Pioneer — AP62

1983, Sept. 20 **Engr.** *Perf. 13*
C125 AP62 75fr dk grn & rose vio 1.75 1.25

Raphael (1483-1520), 500th Birth Anniv. — AP63

1983, Nov. 10 **Litho.** *Perf. 12½x13*
C126 AP63 167fr The Triumph of Galatea 3.50 2.00

Pandanus AP64

1983, Nov. 30 **Litho.** *Perf. 13*
C127 AP64 137fr multi 2.75 2.00

Christmas 1983 AP65

1983, Dec. 22 **Litho.** *Perf. 12½x13*
C128 AP65 200fr Sistine Madonna, by Raphael 3.75 2.50

Steamer Commandant Bory — AP66

1984, Jan. 9 *Perf. 13*
C129 AP66 67fr multi 1.50 1.00

1984 Summer Olympics — AP67

1984, Feb. 3 **Litho.** *Perf. 13*
C130 AP67 85fr Weight lifting 1.75 1.00

Frangipani Blossoms AP68

1984, Feb. 28 *Perf. 12½*
C131 AP68 130fr multi 2.75 1.40

Easter 1984 AP69

1984, Apr. 17 **Litho.** *Perf. 12½x13*
C132 AP69 190fr Descent from the Cross 3.75 2.25

Homage to Jean Cocteau AP70

1984, June 30 **Litho.** *Perf. 13*
C133 AP70 150fr Portrait 3.25 2.00

Soano Hoatau Tiki Sculpture AP71

1984, July 26
C134 AP71 175fr multi 3.50 2.50

Portrait of Alice, by Modigliani (1884-1920) AP72

1984, Aug. 20
C135 AP72 140fr multi 3.00 2.00

Ausipex '84 — AP73

1984, Sept. 21 **Litho.** *Perf. 12½x13*
C136 AP73 180fr Pilioko Tapestry 3.75 2.00
Se-tenant with label showing exhibition emblem.

Local Dances, by Jean
Michon — AP74

1984, Oct. 11   Photo.   Perf. 13
C137 AP74 110fr multi   3.50 2.00

Altar
AP75

1984, Nov. 5   Litho.   Perf. 13x12½
C138 AP75 52fr Mount Lulu Chap-
el   1.50 .90

Christmas 1984 — AP76

1984, Dec. 21   Litho.   Perf. 13x12½
C139 AP76 260fr Tropical Nativity 5.50 3.00

Pilioko Tapestry — AP77

1985, Apr. 3   Litho.   Perf. 13x12½
C140 AP77 500fr multi   9.50 5.00

The Post in
1926, by
Utrillo
AP78

1985, June 17   Litho.   Perf. 12½x13
C141 AP78 200fr multi   4.00 2.50

Wallis Island Pirogue — AP79

1985, Aug. 9   Perf. 13
C142 AP79 350fr multi   7.00 3.50

Ship Jacques
Cartier — AP80

1985, Oct. 2   Engr.   Perf. 13x13½
C143 AP80 51fr Prus bl, brt bl &
dk bl   1.25 .80

Portrait of a
Young
Woman, by
Patrice
Nielly
AP81

1985, Oct. 28   Litho.   Perf. 12½x13
C144 AP81 245fr multi
5.00 3.00

Nativity, by
Jean
Michon
AP82

1985, Dec. 19   Litho.   Perf. 12½x13
C145 AP82 330fr multi   6.50 4.00

Halley's Comet — AP83

1986, Mar. 6   Litho.   Perf. 13
C146 AP83 100fr multi   2.50 1.40

Cure of Ars, Birth
Bicent. — AP84

1986, Mar. 28   Litho.   Perf. 12½x13
C147 AP84 200fr multi   4.00 3.00

French Overseas Territory Status, 25th
Anniv. — AP85

1986, July 29   Engr.   Perf. 13
C148 AP85 90fr Queen Amelia   1.75 1.00
C149 AP85 137fr July 30 Law,
Journal of the
Republic   2.75 1.50
  a.   Strip of 2, #C148-C149 + label 5.00 4.00
  Queen Amelia's request to France for pro-
tection, cent.

World Post Day — AP86

1986, Oct. 9   Litho.   Perf. 13
C150 AP86 270fr multi   5.25 3.00

Statue of Liberty,
Cent. — AP87

1986, Oct. 31   Engr.
C151 AP87 205fr multi   6.25 3.50

Poi Basilica, 1st
Anniv. — AP88

1987, Apr. 30   Litho.   Perf. 13
C152 AP88 230fr Fr. Chanel, ba-
silica   4.50 2.50

Telstar Transmitting to Pleumeur-
Bodou, France — AP89

1987, May 17   Engr.   Perf. 13
C153 AP89 200fr gray, brt bl &
brn org   4.50 2.50
  World Communications Day, 25th anniv. of
Telstar.

Piccard,
Bathyscaphe
Trieste and
Stratospheric
Balloon — AP90

1987, Aug. 21   Engr.   Perf. 13
C154 AP90 135fr brt ol grn, dk bl
& brt bl   3.00 2.00
  Auguste Piccard (1884-1962), physicist.

Arrival of First Missionary, 150th
Anniv. — AP91

  Design: 260fr, Monsignor Bataillon's arrival
in 1837, ship and the islands.

1987, Nov. 8   Engr.   Perf. 13
C155 AP91 260fr brt blue, blk &
blue grn   5.50 3.50

Christmas 1987 — AP92

1987, Dec. 15   Litho.   Perf. 13x12½
C156 AP92 300fr multi   6.50 3.50

Garros and Bleriot Aircraft — AP93

1988, Feb. 18   Engr.   Perf. 13
C157 AP93 600fr multi   13.00 7.50
  Roland Garros (1888-1918), aviator and
tennis player.

Self-portrait
with Lace
Cravat, by
Maurice
Quentin de
La Tour
(1704-88)
AP94

1988, Apr. 8   Litho.
C158 AP94 500fr multi   11.00 6.50

World Telecommunications
Day — AP95

1988, May 5   Litho.   *Perf. 12½x13*
C159 AP95 100fr multi   2.00 1.25

South Pacific Episcopal
Conference — AP96

1988, June 1   Litho.   *Perf. 13*
C160 AP96 90fr Map, bishop   2.10 1.25

Christmas — AP97

Unwmk.
1988, Dec. 15   Litho.   *Perf. 13*
C161 AP97 400fr multi   8.50 5.00

Royal
Throne — AP98

1989, Mar. 11
C162 AP98 700fr multi   14.50 7.50

The Virgin of the Crescent Moon Type
of 1979

1989, Dec. 21   Engr.   *Perf. 13½x13*
C163 AP38 800fr plum   16.00 8.50
Christmas 1989.

Clement Ader (1841-1926), Aviation
Pioneer — AP100

1990, June 9   Engr.   *Perf. 13*
C164 AP100 56fr multicolored   1.60 .90
First anniversary of Wallis-Tahiti air link.

Gen. Charles de Gaulle (1890-
1979) — AP101

1990, Nov. 22   *Perf. 12½x13*
C165 AP101 1000fr multi   24.00 14.00

Father Louis Marie Chanel, 150th
Death Anniv. — AP102

1991, Apr. 28   Litho.   *Perf. 13*
C166 AP102 235fr multicolored   6.00 3.25

French Open Tennis Championships,
Cent. — AP103

Illustration reduced.

1991, May 24   Engr.   *Perf. 13x12½*
C167 AP103 250fr blk, grn & org   6.00 4.00

Wolfgang
Amadeus
Mozart,
Death
Bicent.
AP104

1991, Sept. 23   Engr.   *Perf. 13*
C168 AP104 500fr multicolored   12.50 7.00

World Columbian Stamp Expo '92,
Chicago — AP105

1992, May 22   Litho.   *Perf. 13x12½*
C169 AP105 100fr multicolored   2.75 1.75

1992, July 15   *Perf. 13*
C170 AP105 800fr multicolored   20.00 11.00
Genoa '92.

First French Republic,
Bicent. — AP106

1992, Aug. 17   Engr.   *Perf. 13*
C171 AP106 350fr blk, bl & red   9.00 6.00

Louvre Museum, Bicent. — AP107

1993, Apr. 12   Engr.   *Perf. 13*
C172 AP107 315fr blue, dk blue
                        & red   7.50 4.00

Nicolaus Copernicus, Heliocentric
Solar System — AP108

1993, May 7   Engr.   *Perf. 13*
C173 AP108 600fr multicolored   13.50 7.50
Polska '93.

Second Year of First French Republic,
Bicent. — AP109

1993, Sept. 22   Engr.   *Perf. 13*
C174 AP109 400fr bl, blk & red   8.00 5.00

Wallis Island Landscape — AP110

1994, Jan. 26   Litho.   *Perf. 13*
C175 AP110 400fr multicolored   8.50 4.50

Hong Kong '94 — AP111

1994, Feb. 18   Litho.   *Perf. 14x13½*
C176 AP111 700fr multicolored   15.00 9.00

South Pacific Geography
Day — AP112

1994, May 4   Litho.   *Perf. 13*
C177 AP112 85fr multicolored   2.25 1.25
See New Caledonia No. C259.

European Stamp
Salon,
Paris — AP113

1994, Sept. 22   Litho.   *Perf. 13*
C178 AP113 300fr multicolored   9.00 4.50

Antoine de Saint-Exupery (1900-44),
Aviator, Author — AP114

1994, Oct. 27   Engr.   *Perf. 13*
C179 AP114 800fr multicolored   15.00 10.00

Christmas
AP115

1994, Dec. 15   Litho.   *Perf. 13*
C180 AP115 150fr multicolored   4.00 2.50

Louis Pasteur (1822-95) — AP116

1995, Mar. 25   Litho.   *Perf. 13*
C181 AP116 350fr multicolored   9.00 3.50

AP117

AP118

1995, Apr. 19   *Perf. 13½x13*
C182 AP117 115fr multicolored   3.00 1.25
University Teacher's Training Institute of the
Pacific. See French Polynesia No. 656.

1995, May 17   *Perf. 13*
C183 AP118 200fr Painting of
            Cocoa Nuts   5.25 3.00

Intl. Youth Year, 10th Anniv. — AP119

1995, July 25   **Litho.**   *Perf. 13*
C184 AP119 450fr multicolored   11.00 6.00

Singapore '95 — AP120

1995, Aug. 24   **Litho.**   *Perf. 13*
C185 AP120 500fr multicolored   12.50 5.00

Motion Pictures, Cent. — AP121

Lumiere Brothers, film strip. Illustration
reduced.

1995, Sept. 19
C186 AP121 600fr multicolored   15.00 6.00

Charles de Gaulle (1890-
1970) — AP122

1995, Nov. 14   **Engr.**   *Perf. 13*
C187 AP122 315fr multicolored   8.00 4.00

7th Va'a (Outrigger Canoe) World
Championship, Noumea, New
Caledonia — AP123

1996, Apr. 24   **Litho.**   *Perf. 13*
C188 AP123 240fr multicolored   5.00 3.00

Sisia
College — AP124

1996, May 22   **Litho.**   *Perf. 13½x13*
C189 AP124 235fr multicolored   5.00 2.75

Radio, Cent. — AP125

1996, July 25   **Engr.**   *Perf. 13*
C190 AP125 550fr multicolored   12.00 6.00

Modern Olympic Games,
Cent. — AP126

1996, Aug. 20   **Engr.**   *Perf. 13*
C191 AP126 1000fr blk & dk bl   22.50 15.00

50th
Autumn
Stamp
Salon
AP127

1996, Oct. 24   **Litho.**   *Perf. 13*
C192 AP127 175fr multicolored   4.00 2.50

Campaign
to Control
Alcoholism
AP128

1996, Nov. 19   *Perf. 13x13½*
C193 AP128 260fr multicolored   5.25 2.75

Natl. Center for
Scientific
Research
AP129

1997, Mar. 14   **Litho.**   *Perf. 13*
C194 AP129 400fr Lapita pottery   8.00 4.50

HIHIFO Air Service — AP130

1997, July 8   **Litho.**   *Perf. 13*
C195 AP130 130fr multicolored   2.50 1.25

Sundown Over
the
Lagoon — AP131

1997, Sept. 22   **Litho.**   *Perf. 13½x13*
C196 AP131 300fr multicolored   6.00 3.50

51st Autumn Stamp Salon — AP132

350fr, #C194, 492, 497, 486, C184, C185,
475, C192, C188, 464, 493.
1000fr, Hemispheres, #486, 475, 464,
C185, C175, 493, C184, 492, C192, 497,
C188, C194, Winged Victory of Samothrace.

1997, Nov. 6   **Litho.**   *Perf. 13*
C197 AP132 350fr multi   7.00 3.50
                       Imperf
C198 AP132 1000fr multi   20.00 20.00

Marshal Jacques Leclerc (1902-
47) — AP133

1997, Nov. 28   **Litho.**   *Perf. 13*
C199 AP133 800fr multicolored   16.00 9.00

Alphonse Daudet (1840-97),
Writer — AP134

1997, Dec. 16   **Litho.**   *Perf. 13*
C200 AP134 710fr multicolored   14.50 7.50

Alofi Beach — AP135

1998, Apr. 21   **Litho.**   *Perf. 13*
C201 AP135 315fr multicolored   6.25 3.25

Cricket
AP136

1998, Sept. 22   **Litho.**   *Perf. 13x13½*
C202 AP136 106fr multicolored   2.75 1.00

Paul Gauguin (1848-1903) — AP137

1998, Oct. 27   **Litho.**   *Perf. 13*
C203 AP137 700fr multicolored   14.00 6.75

Garden of Happiness — AP138

1998, Nov. 17
C204 AP138 460fr multicolored   9.25 4.50

Polynesian
Dancing
AP139

1998, Dec. 15   **Litho.**   *Perf. 13*
C205 AP139 250fr multicolored   5.00 2.50

Kava Porter
AP140

1999, Jan. 18
C206 AP140 600fr multicolored 12.00 6.00

Shells
AP141

95fr, Epitonium scalare. 100fr, Cassis cornuta. 110fr, Charonia tritonis. 115fr, Lambis lambis.

1999, Feb. 15
C207	AP141	95fr multi, vert.	1.90 .95
C208	AP141	100fr multi, vert.	2.00 1.00
C209	AP141	110fr multi	2.25 1.10
C210	AP141	115fr multi	2.25 1.10
		Nos. C207-C210 (4)	8.40 4.15

Finemui — AP142

Illustration reduced.

1999, Apr. 19   Engr.   Perf. 12¾
C211 AP142 900fr multicolored 18.00 8.75

Birds of
Nuku Fotu
AP143

a, 10fr, Airgrettes. b, 20fr, Audubon's. c, 26fr, Fregates. d, 54fr, Paille en queue.

1999, June 14 Litho. Perf. 13x13¾
C212 AP143 Strip of 4, #a.-d. 2.25 2.25

Wind Song — AP144

1999, Nov. 22   Engr.   Perf. 13
C213 AP144 325fr multi 6.50 2.90

Sunrise
Over a
Lagoon
AP145

1999, Dec. 20   Litho.
C214 AP145 500fr multi 10.00 4.25

First Transport Flight to Futuna, 30th
Anniv. — AP146

2000, Aug. 24 Litho. Perf. 13
C215 AP146 350fr multi 7.00 2.75

AIR POST SEMI-POSTAL STAMPS

New Caledonia Nos. CB2-CB3
overprinted "ILES WALLIS ET
FUTUNA"

1942, June 22   Engr.   Perf. 13
CB1	SPAP1	1.50fr + 3.50fr green	1.50
CB2	SPAP1	2fr + 6fr yellow brown	1.50

Native children's welfare fund.
Nos. CB1-CB2 were issued by the Vichy government in France, but were not placed on sale in Wallis & Futuna.

Colonial Education Fund
New Caledonia No. CB4 Common
Design Type overprinted "ILES
WALLIS ET FUTUNA"

1942, June 22
CB3	CD86a	1.20fr + 1.80fr blue & red	1.50

No. CB3 was issued by the Vichy government in France, but was not placed on sale in Wallis & Futuna.

POSTAGE DUE STAMPS

Postage Due Stamps
of New Caledonia,
1906, Overprinted in
Black or Red

ILES WALLIS et FUTUNA

1920   Unwmk.   Perf. 13½x14
J1	D2	5c ultra, *azure*	.65 .65
J2	D2	10c brn, *buff*	.75 .75
J3	D2	15c grn, *grnsh*	.75 .75
J4	D2	20c blk, *yel* (R)	1.00 1.00
a.		Double overprint	125.00
J5	D2	30c carmine rose	1.00 1.00
J6	D2	50c ultra, *straw*	1.60 1.60
J7	D2	60c olive, *azure*	2.00 2.00
a.		Double overprint	92.50
J8	D2	1fr grn, *cream*	2.50 2.50
		Nos. J1-J8 (8)	10.25 10.25

Type of 1920 Issue Surcharged

2ⁱ

1927
J9	D2	2fr on 1fr brt vio	12.00 12.00
J10	D2	3fr on 1fr org brn	12.00 12.00

Postage Due Stamps of New
Caledonia, 1928, Overprinted as in
1920

1930
J11	D3	2c sl bl & dp brn	.20 .20
J12	D3	4c brn red & bl grn	.20 .20
J13	D3	5c red org & bl blk	.20 .20
J14	D3	10c mag & Prus bl	.20 .20
J15	D3	15c dl grn & scar	.20 .20
J16	D3	20c maroon & ol grn	.55 .55
J17	D3	25c bis brn & sl bl	.55 .55
J18	D3	30c bl grn & ol grn	1.00 1.00
J19	D3	50c lt brn & dk red	.60 .60
J20	D3	60c mag & brt rose	1.00 1.00
J21	D3	1fr dl bl & Prus grn	1.00 1.00
J22	D3	2fr dk red & ol grn	1.00 1.00
J23	D3	3fr vio & brn	1.00 1.00
		Nos. J11-J23 (13)	7.70 7.70

Postage Due Stamps of **FRANCE LIBRE**
1930 with Additional
Overprint in Black

1943
J24	D3	2c sl bl & dp brn	25.00 25.00
J25	D3	4c brn red & bl grn	25.00 25.00
J26	D3	5c red org & bl blk	25.00 25.00
J27	D3	10c mag & Prus bl	25.00 25.00
J28	D3	15c dl grn & scar	26.00 26.00
J29	D3	20c mar & ol grn	26.00 26.00
J30	D3	25c bis brn & sl bl	26.00 26.00
J31	D3	30c bl grn & ol grn	26.00 26.00
J32	D3	50c lt brn & dk red	26.00 26.00
J33	D3	60c mag & brt rose	26.00 26.00
J34	D3	1fr dl bl & Prus grn	27.50 27.50
J35	D3	2fr dk red & ol grn	27.50 27.50
J36	D3	3fr violet & brn	27.50 27.50
		Nos. J24-J36 (13)	338.50 338.50

> **Catalogue values for unused stamps in this section, from this point to the end of the section, are for Never Hinged items.**

Thalassoma Lunare — D1

Fish: 1fr, Zanclus cornutus, vert. 5fr, Amphiprion percula.

Perf. 13x13½
			Unwmk.
1963, Apr. 1		**Typo.**	
J37	D1	1fr yel org, bl & blk	.50 .50
J38	D1	3fr red, grnsh bl & grn	1.25 *1.60*
J39	D1	5fr org, bluish grn & blk	2.00 *2.25*
		Nos. J37-J39 (3)	3.75 4.35

WESTERN UKRAINE

'wes-tərn yü-'krān

LOCATION — In Eastern Central Europe

GOVT. — A former short-lived independent State

A provisional government was established in 1918 in the eastern part of Austria-Hungary but the area later came under Polish administration.

100 Shahiv (Sotykiv) = 1 Hryvnia
100 Heller = 1 Krone

> **Forgeries of almost all Western Ukraine stamps are plentiful.**
> Used values are for stamps canceled to order.

Kolomyya Issue

Укр. Н. Р.

Austria Nos. 168,
145, 147, 149
Surcharged

5

1918, Dec. 12   Unwmk.   Perf. 12½
1	A42	5sh on 15h dl red	75.00 100.00
2	A37	10sh on 3h vio	75.00 100.00
3	A37	10sh on 6h dp org	*850.00 700.00*
4	A37	10sh on 12h lt bl	*850.00 700.00*
		Nos. 1-4 (4)	1,850. 1,600.

No. 1 exists with surcharge inverted. All inverted surcharges on Nos. 2-4 are forgeries. Double surcharges are forgeries.

Lviv Issue

Austria Nos. 145-146,
148, 169 Overprinted

1918
5	A37	3h bright violet	50.00 200.00
6	A37	5h light green	40.00 150.00
7	A37	10h magenta	40.00 150.00
8	A42	20h dark green	40.00 150.00
		Nos. 5-8 (4)	170.00 650.00

Nos. 5-8 exist with surcharge inverted and in tete beche pairs. Red or green overprints are proofs.
These stamps, the first Western Ukraine issue, were used in Lviv for only two days, November 20 and 21. After the fall of the city they were used in Khodoriv, Stanislav and Kolomyya.
Forgeries exist.

Stanislav Issue

**Пошта
Укр.Н.Рєн.**

Austrian Stamps of
1916-18 Surcharged
in Shahiv (shown)
and Hryvnia
Currency

			warie
			＊ ＊

1919, Mar. 18
11	A37	3sh brt violet	15.00 20.00
12	A37	5sh lt green	15.00 20.00
13	A37	6sh deep org	30.00 50.00
14	A37	10sh magenta	22.50 35.00
15	A37	12sh lt blue	22.50 35.00
16	A42	15sh dull red	22.50 35.00
17	A42	20sh dp green	22.50 35.00
18	A42	30sh dull violet	150.00 225.00
19	A39	40sh olive green	22.50 35.00
20	A39	50sh dark green	22.50 35.00
21	A39	60sh deep blue	22.50 35.00
22	A39	80sh orange brn	22.50 35.00
23	A39	1hr car, *yel*	32.50 40.00
24	A40	2hr lt blue	35.00 45.00
25	A40	3hr car rose	45.00 60.00
a.		3hr claret	2,500. 2,750.
26	A40	4hr yel grn	45.00 60.00
a.		4hr deep green	200.00 250.00
27	A40	10hr deep violet	550.00 750.00
		Nos. 11-26 (16)	547.50 800.00
		Nos. 11-27 (17)	1,097. 1,550.

The overprint exists inverted on 12sh and 80sh, double on 12sh and 10hr.
The 25sh, type A42, with this overprint is considered bogus.

1919
		Granite Paper	
28	A40	3hr carmine rose	35.00 45.00

**Same Surcharged on Austrian
Military Semipostal Stamps of 1918**
Perf. 12½x13
31	MSP7	10sh gray green	77.50 92.50
32	MSP8	20sh magenta	60.00 72.50
33	MSP7	45sh blue	45.00 55.00
		Nos. 28-33 (4)	217.50 265.00

The overprint exists inverted on Nos. 31-33, double on Nos. 31-32.

**Same Surcharge on Austrian
Military Stamps of 1917**
Perf. 12½
34	M3	1sh grnsh blue	650.00 650.00
35	M3	2sh red orange	65.00 65.00
36	M3	3sh olive gray	140.00 150.00
37	M3	5sh olive grn	225.00 225.00
38	M3	6sh violet	125.00 140.00
39	M3	10sh org brn	750.00 650.00
40	M3	12sh blue	450.00 500.00
41	M3	15sh brt rose	450.00 500.00
42	M3	20sh red brown	10.50 11.50
43	M3	25sh ultra	2,750. 3,250.
44	M3	30sh slate	750.00 900.00
45	M3	40sh olive bis	650.00 650.00
46	M3	50sh deep green	6.50 6.50
47	M3	60sh car rose	600.00 600.00
48	M3	80sh dull blue	40.00 40.00

49	M3	90sh dk vio	800.00	650.00
50	M4	2hr rose, *straw*	11.00	15.00
51	M4	3hr blue, *grn*	20.00	22.50
52	M4	4hr rose, *grn*	20.00	22.50
53	M4	10hr dl violet, *gray*		

The overprint exists double on 2sh, 3sh, 20sh, 50sh, 3hr and 4hr; inverted on 2sh, 12sh, 15sh, 50sh, 80sh, 2hr, 3hr and 4hr.

Same Surcharge on Austrian Postage Due Stamps of 1916

54	D5	1hr ultra	100.00	150.00
55	D5	5hr ultra	*1,000.*	*1,500.*

Surcharged on Austrian Postage Due Stamps of 1917 with two bars over "PORTO"

57	A38	15sh on 36h vio	300.00	400.00
58	A38	50sh on 42h choc		
			5,000.	5,000.

Shahiv is in two parts in the overprint looking like "wa" and "rib."

Same Surcharge on Postage Due Stamps of Bosnia, 1904

1919, May 5

61	D1	1sh blk, red & yel	30.00	20.00
62	D1	2sh blk, red & yel	7.50	11.00
63	D1	3sh blk, red & yel	7.50	11.00
64	D1	4sh blk, red & yel	75.00	75.00
65	D1	5sh blk, red & yel	2,750.	3,000.
66	D1	6sh blk, red & yel	150.00	140.00
67	D1	7sh blk, red & yel	15.00	14.00
68	D1	8sh blk, red & yel	15.00	20.00
69	D1	10sh blk, red & yel	850.00	1,100.
70	D1	15sh blk, red & yel	325.00	325.00
71	D1	20sh blk, red & yel	5,250.	5,000.
72	D1	50sh blk, red & yel	140.00	140.00

Two types of surcharge on No. 61: Shahiv in singular (wara) and in plural (warib). Value the same.

The overprint exists inverted on #61, 64, 66-68. Double, triple and sideways overprints exist. Some values exist perf 12½x13.

A2

Black Surcharge on Austrian Military Stamps of 1917-18.

1919, May

75	A2	2hr on 2k rose, *straw*	10.00	9.00
76	A2	3hr on 2k rose, *straw*	10.00	10.00
77	A2	3hr on 3k grn, *blue*	70.00	110.00
78	A2	4hr on 2k rose, *straw*	7.00	10.00
79	A2	4hr on 4k rose, *grn*	1,000.	1,500.
80	A2	5hr on 2k rose, *straw*	10.00	10.00
	a.	Inverted surch.	250.00	
81	A2	10hr on 50h dp grn (Austria type M3)	12.00	27.50

Austrian Stamps of 1916-18 Overprinted

1919, May

85	A37	3h brt violet	.50	1.00
86	A37	5h light green	.50	1.00
87	A37	6h deep orange	.50	1.00
88	A37	10h magenta	.50	1.00
89	A37	12h light blue	.50	1.00
90	A42	15h dull red	.50	1.00
91	A42	20h deep green	.50	1.00
92	A42	25h blue	.50	1.00
93	A42	30h dull vio	.50	1.00
94	A39	40h olive green	.75	1.10
95	A39	50h dark green	.75	1.10
96	A39	60h deep blue	.75	1.10
97	A39	80h orange brn	1.00	1.25
98	A39	90h red violet	1.00	1.50
99	A39	1k car, *yel*	1.25	3.75
100	A40	2k light blue	2.00	5.50
101	A40	3k carmine rose	2.50	5.75
102	A40	4k yellow grn	10.00	12.50
103	A40	10k deep violet	15.00	37.50
		Nos. 85-103 (19)	39.50	80.05

The four letters in the overprint are the initials of Ukrainian words equivalent to "Western Ukrainian National (or Peoples) Republic." The country was formed from the eastern part of Galicia, formerly a province of the Austro-Hungarian Empire.
Forged cancellations abound.

REGISTRATION STAMPS

Kolomyya Issue

RS1

Without Gum

1918-19   Unwmk.   Typeset   *Imperf.*

F1	RS1	30sot blk, *rose*	175.00	150.00
F2	RS1	50sot blk, *dp rose* ('19)	100.00	*125.00*

Forgeries exist.

OCCUPATION STAMPS

Romanian Occupation of Pokutia

Austrian Stamps Surcharged in Dark Blue Black

1919   Unwmk.   Perf. 12½
On Stamps of 1916-18

N3	A37	40h on 5h lt grn	3.00	4.00
N10	A39	1k 20h on 50h dk grn	4.00	5.00
N11	A39	1k 20h on 60h dp bl	8.00	10.00
N14	A39	1k 20h on 1k car, *yel*	16.00	18.00

On Stamps of 1917-18

N15	A42	60h on 15h dl red	5.00	6.00
N16	A42	60h on 20h dp grn	2.00	2.50
N17	A42	60h on 25h blue	11.00	12.00
N18	A42	60h on 30h dl vio	10.00	11.00

Surcharge in colors other than dark blue black are bogus or proofs. Surcharges on other stamps are bogus.

POSTAGE DUE STAMPS

Austrian Postage Due Stamps Surcharged like Regular Issues

1919   Unwmk.   Perf. 12½
On Stamps of 1916

NJ1	D4	40h on 5h rose red	
NJ5	D4	1k 20h on 25h rose red	
NJ6	D4	1k 20h on 30h rose red	

On Stamp of 1917

NJ13	A38	1k 20h on 50h on 42h choc	

WEST IRIAN

'west ˌir-ē-'än

(Irian Barat)

(West New Guinea)

LOCATION — Western half of New Guinea, southwest Pacific Ocean
GOVT. — Province of Indonesia
AREA — 162,927 sq. mi.
POP. — 923,440 (1973)
CAPITAL — Djajapura (formerly Hollandia)

The former Netherlands New Guinea became a territory under the administration of the United Nations Temporary Executive Authority on Oct. 1, 1962.

The territory came under Indonesian administration on May 1, 1963.

100 Cents = 1 Gulden
100 Sen = 1 Rupiah
(1 rupiah = 1 former Netherlands New Guinea gulden)

> Catalogue values for all unused stamps in this country are for Never Hinged items.

Netherlands New Guinea Stamps of 1950-60 Overprinted

Type 2 Overprint
Perf. 12½x12, 12½x13½

1962-63   Photo.   Unwmk.

1a	A4	1c vermilion & yel	.20	.20
2a	A1	2c deep orange	.25	.20
3a	A4	5c choc & yel	.25	.20
4a	A5	7c org red, bl & brn vio		
			.25	.20
5a	A4	10c aqua & red brn	.25	.20
6a	A5	12c grn, bl & brn vio	.25	.20
7a	A4	15c dp yel & red brn	.50	.25
8a	A5	17c brn vio & bl	.60	.35
9a	A4	20c lt bl grn & red brn	.60	.35
10a	A6	25c red	.35	.30
11a	A6	30c deep blue	.80	.35
12a	A6	40c deep orange	.80	.35
13a	A6	45c dark olive	1.40	.75
14a	A6	55c slate blue	1.25	.55
15a	A6	80c dl gray vio	5.75	5.75
16a	A6	85c dk vio brn	3.00	3.00
17a	A6	1g plum	3.50	1.90

Engr.

18a	A3	2g reddish brn	9.75	13.00
19a	A3	5g green	6.00	3.50
		Nos. 1a-19a (19)	35.75	31.60

The overprint exists in four types:
1) Size 17½mm. Applied locally and sold in 1962 in West New Guinea. Top of "N" is slightly lower than the "U," and the base of the "T" is straight, or nearly so. This set sells for about $10 more than Nos. 1a-19a.
2) Size 17½mm. Applied in the Netherlands and sold in 1963 by the UN in New York. Top of the "N" is slightly higher than the "U," and the base of the "T" is concave. This is the set listed above.
3) Size 14mm. Exists on eight values.
4) Size 19mm. Exists on 1c and 10c.
Types 3 and 4 were applied in West New Guinea and it is doubtful whether they were regularly issued.
See the *U.S. Specialized Catalogue* for complete listings and values of the UNTEA overprints.

West Irian
Indonesia Nos. 454, 456, 494-501, 387, 390, 392 and 393 Surcharged or Overprinted: "IRIAN BARAT"
Perf. 12½x13½

1963, May 1   Photo.   Unwmk.

20	A63	1s on 70s org ver	.20	.20
21	A63	2s on 90s yel grn	.20	.20

Perf. 12x12½

22	A76	5s gray	.20	.20
23	A76	6s on 20s ocher	.20	.20
24	A76	7s on 50s dp bl	.20	.20
25	A76	10s red brn	.20	.20
26	A76	15s plum	.20	.20
27	A76	25s brt bl grn	.20	.20
28	A76	30s on 75s scar	.20	.25
29	A76	40s on 1.15r plum	.20	.30

Perf. 12½x12

30	A55	1r purple	.45	.55
31	A55	2r green	.80	.90
32	A55	3r dk bl	1.40	1.50
33	A55	5r brown	2.25	3.00
		Nos. 20-33 (14)	6.90	8.10

"Indonesia's Flag from Sabang to Merauke" — A1

20s, 50s, Parachutist landing in New Guinea. 60s, 75s, Bird of paradise and map of New Guinea.

1963, May 1

34	A1	12s org brn, blk & red	.20	.20
35	A1	17s org brn, blk & red	.20	.20
36	A1	20s multi	.20	.20
37	A1	50s multi	.20	.25
38	A1	60s multi	.20	.60
39	A1	75s multi	.25	1.00
		Nos. 34-39 (6)	1.25	2.45

Liberation of West New Guinea.

Maniltoa Gemmipara — A2

15s, Dendrobium lancifolium (orchid). 30s, Gardenia gjellerupii. 40s, Maniltoa flower. 50s, Phalanger. 75s, Cassowary. 1r, Kangaroo. 3r, Crowned pigeons.

1968, Aug. 17   Photo.   Perf. 12½x12

40	A2	5s dl grn & vio blk	.40	.40
41	A2	15s emer & dk pur	.75	.75
42	A2	30s org & dp grn	1.25	1.25
43	A2	40s lemon & brt pur	1.25	1.25
44	A2	50s rose car & blk	1.25	1.25
45	A2	75s dl bl & blk	1.60	1.60
46	A2	1r brn org & blk	3.50	3.50
47	A2	3r apple grn & blk	6.00	6.00
		Nos. 40-47 (8)	16.00	16.00

Man, Map of Indonesia and Torches — A3

1968, Aug. 17

48	A3	10s ultra & gold	2.50	1.75
49	A3	25s crimson & gold	4.00	2.50

Issued to publicize the pledge of the people of West Irian to remain unified and integrated with the Republic of Indonesia.

Carving, Mother and Child — A4 | Black-capped Lory — A5

West Irian Wood Carvings: 6s, Shield with 3 human figures. 7s, Child atop filigree carving. 10s, Drum. 25s, Seated man. 30s, Drum (3-tiered base). 50s, Carved bamboo. 75s, Man-shaped ornament. 1r, Shield. 2r, Seated man (hands raised).

1970   Photo.   Perf. 12½x12

50	A4	5s multi	.30	.30
51	A4	6s multi	.30	.30
52	A4	7s multi	.30	1.25
53	A4	10s multi	.30	1.25
54	A4	25s multi	.30	.30
55	A4	30s multi	.50	.30
56	A4	50s multi	.60	.30
57	A4	75s multi	.60	.30
58	A4	1r multi	.75	.30
59	A4	2r multi	1.00	.70
		Nos. 50-59 (10)	4.95	5.30

Issued: #50-54, 4/30; #55-59, 4/15.

1970, Oct. 26 Photo. Perf. 12x12½

60	A5	5r shown	1.25 2.25
61	A5	10r Bird of paradise	1.25 4.50

POSTAGE DUE STAMPS

Type of Indonesia Overprinted: "IRIAN BARAT"

Perf. 13½x12½

1963, May 1 Litho. Unwmk.

J1	D8	1s light brown	.20 .30
J2	D8	5s light gray olive	.20 .30
J3	D8	10s light blue	.20 .30
J4	D8	25s gray	.20 .60
J5	D8	40s salmon	.20 .80
J6	D8	100s bister	.25 1.50
		Nos. J1-J6 (6)	1.25 3.80

Type of Indonesia Dated "1968" and Overprinted: "IRIAN BARAT"

1968 Photo. Perf. 13½x12½

J7	D9	1s blue & lt grn	.20 .40
J8	D9	5s grn & pink	.20 .40
J9	D9	10s red & gray	.20 .40
J10	D9	25s grn & yel	.20 .40
J11	D9	40s vio brn & pale grn	.50 .75
J12	D9	100s org & bister	1.00 1.50
		Nos. J7-J12 (6)	2.30 3.85

STOCKSHEETS

HAGNER STYLE STOCK SHEETS

Hagner-style stock pages offer convenience and flexibility. Pages are produced on thick, archival-quality paper with acetate pockets glued from the bottom of each pocket. They're ideal for the topical collector who may require various page styles to store a complete collection.

- Black background makes beautiful stamp presentation.
- Pockets use pull away/snap back principle.
- Made from archival-quality heavyweight paper that offers unprecedented protection and clarity.
- Multi-hole punch fits most binder types.
- Available in 9 different page formats.
  8½" x 11" size accomodates every size stamp.

Sold in packages of 10.

Available with pockets on one side or both sides.

"D" in item number denotes two-sided page.

1 POCKET — 242 mm

ITEM	RETAIL
S1	$10.99
S1D	$15.99

2 POCKET — 119 mm

ITEM	RETAIL
S2	$10.99
S2D	$15.99

3 POCKET — 79 mm

ITEM	RETAIL
S3	$10.99
S3D	$15.99

4 POCKET — 58 mm

ITEM	RETAIL
S4	$10.99
S4D	$15.99

5 POCKET — 45 mm

ITEM	RETAIL
S5	$10.99
S5D	$15.99

6 POCKET — 37 mm

ITEM	RETAIL
S6	$10.99
S6D	$15.99

7 POCKET — 31 mm

ITEM	RETAIL
S7	$10.99
S7D	$15.99

8 POCKET — 27 mm

ITEM	RETAIL
S8	$10.99
S8D	$15.99

MULTI-POCKETS — 36 mm, 67 mm, 139 mm

ITEM	RETAIL
S9	$10.99
S9D	$15.99

SCOTT

1-800-572-6885
P.O. Box 828, Sidney OH 45365-0828
www.amosadvantage.com

AMOS
HOBBY PUBLISHING

Publishers of *Coin World, Linn's Stamp News* and *Scott Publishing Co.*

YEMEN

ˈye-mən

LOCATION — Arabian Peninsula, south of Saudi Arabia and bordering on the Red Sea
GOVT. — Republic
AREA — 204,000 sq. mi. (est.)
POP. — 16,942,230 (1999 est.)
CAPITAL — Sana'a (San'a)

40 Bogaches = 1 Imadi
40 Bogaches = 1 Riyal (1962)
100 Fils = 1 Riyal (1978)

The Yemen Arab Republic and the People's Republic of Yemen planned a 30-month unification process scheduled for completion by November 1992. While government ministries merged, both currencies remained valid. A civil war in 1994 delayed the merger.

> **Catalogue values for unused stamps in this country are for Never Hinged items, beginning with Scott 44 in the regular postage section, Scott C1 in the air-post section.**

Watermarks

Wmk. 127 —
Quatrefoils

Wmk. 258 —
Arabic
Characters and
Y G Multiple

Wmk. 277 — Winged Wheel

For Domestic Postage

A1

Crossed Daggers and Arabic Inscriptions — A2

1926   Unwmk.   Typo.   Imperf.
Laid Paper
Without Gum

1	A1	2½b black	40.00	40.00
2	A1	2½b black, *orange*	40.00	40.00
3	A2	5b black	40.00	40.00
		Nos. 1-3 (3)	120.00	120.00

No. 2 is known rouletted 7½ or 9.
Type A1 differs from A2 primarily in the inscription in the left dagger blade.
All come on wove paper.

For Foreign and Domestic Postage

Arabic Inscriptions
A3   A4

1930-31   Wmk. 127   Perf. 14

7	A3	½b orange ('31)	.20	.20
8	A3	1b green	.35	.30
9	A3	1b yellow grn ('31)	.20	.20
10	A3	2b olive grn	.50	.40
11	A3	2b olive brn ('31)	.30	.30
12	A3	3b dull vio ('31)	.40	.35
13	A3	4b red	.95	.70
14	A3	4b deep rose ('31)	.55	.40
15	A3	5b slate gray ('31)	.70	.50
16	A4	6b dull blue	1.50	1.25
17	A4	6b dp ultra ('31)	.95	.70
18	A4	8b lilac rose ('31)	1.10	.75
19	A4	10b lt brown	2.40	2.00
20	A4	10b brn org ('31)	1.40	1.00
21	A4	20b yel grn ('31)	4.50	3.25
22	A4	1i red brn & lt bl	13.00	8.75
23	A4	1i lil rose & yel grn ('31)	11.00	8.50
		Nos. 7-23 (17)	40.00	30.00

Some values exist imperforate.
For surcharges and overprints see Nos. 30, 59-62, 166-167, 169-171, 174-176.

Flags of Saudi Arabia, Yemen and Iraq — A5

1939   Litho.   Wmk. 258   Perf. 12½

24	A5	4b dl rose & ultra	.80	.80
25	A5	6b slate bl & ultra	.80	.80
26	A5	10b fawn & ultra	1.40	1.40
27	A5	14b olive & ultra	2.25	2.25
28	A5	20b yel grn & ultra	3.25	3.25
29	A5	1i claret & ultra	6.50	6.50
		Nos. 24-29 (6)	15.00	15.00

2nd anniv. of the Arab Alliance. Nos. 24-29 exist imperforate.
For overprints see Nos. C29-C29D.

No. 7 Handstamped in Black

Three types of surcharge:
a. 11½x16mm
b. 13-13½x15½mm
c. 12x16mm
Values of surcharged stamps are for ordinary copies. Clear, legible surcharges command a premium.

1939   Wmk. 127   Perf. 14

30	A3	4b on ½b orange	10.00	10.00

See Nos. 44-48, 59-67, 82, 86-87.

A6

A7

1940   Wmk. 258   Litho.   Perf. 12½

31	A6	½b ocher & ultra	.30	.25
32	A6	1b lt grn & rose red	.30	.25
33	A6	2b bis brn & vio	.35	.25
34	A6	3b dl vio & ultra	.35	.25
35	A6	4b rose & yel grn	.35	.25
36	A6	5b dk gray grn & bis brn	.45	.25
37	A7	6b ultra & lt org	.55	.25
38	A7	8b claret & dull bl	.75	.40
39	A7	10b brn org & yel grn	.85	.55
40	A7	14b gray grn & vio	1.10	.75
41	A7	18b emerald & blk	1.75	1.40
42	A7	20b yel ol & cerise	2.40	1.75
43	A7	1i vio rose, yel grn & brn red	5.50	3.50
		Nos. 31-43 (13)	15.00	10.10
		Set, never hinged	20.00	

No. 36 was used as a 4b stamp in 1957.
For surcharges see Nos. 44-47.

> **Catalogue values for unused stamps in this section, from this point to the end of the section, are for Never Hinged items.**

Nos. 31-34, 36 Handstamped Type "b" in Black

1946-51   Perf. 12½

44	A6	4b on ½b ('51)	3.50	1.75
45	A6	4b on 1b ('49)	2.50	2.50
46	A6	4b on 2b ('49)	2.50	2.50
47	A6	4b on 3b ('49)	2.50	2.50

1945-48   Handstamp Type "a"

44a	A6	4b on ½b	3.50	2.00
45a	A6	4b on 1b ('48)	4.00	1.75
46a	A6	4b on 2b ('48)	3.00	1.50
47a	A6	4b on 3b ('48)	3.50	1.75
48	A6	4b on 5b ('46)	3.50	1.75

Forged surcharges exist.

A8

1946

Frames in Emerald

49	A8	4b black	1.50	.85
50	A8	6b lilac rose	2.25	1.50
51	A8	10b ultra	3.25	1.90
52	A8	14b olive green	5.50	3.25
		Nos. 49-52 (4)	12.50	7.50

Opening of Mutawakkili Hospital. Exist imperforate.
For overprints see Nos. 168, 172-173.

Mocha Coffee Tree — A9   Palace, San'a — A10

1947-58   Unwmk.   Engr.   Perf. 12½

53	A9	½b yellow brown	.25	.20
54	A9	1b purple	.70	.40
55	A9	2b ultra	1.40	.90
56	A10	4b red	2.25	1.25
57	A10	5b gray blue	2.50	1.50
58	A9	6b yellow green ('58)	3.50	2.00
		Nos. 53-58 (6)	10.60	6.25

No. 58 was printed in 1947 but not officially issued until June, 1958.

Additional values, prepared but not issued, were 10b, 20b and 1i, with views of palaces superimposed on flag, and palace square. These were looted from government storehouses during the 1948 revolution and a number of copies later reached collectors.
For surcharges see Nos. 63-65.

Admission of Yemen to the U.N.
Ten postage, 5 airmail and 5 postage due stamps for the Admission of Yemen to the UN were not officially issued. Pictured on some of the stamps were Truman, Roosevelt, Churchill and the Statue of Liberty.

Nos. 9, 11, 12 and 15 Handstamped Type "a" in Black

1949   Wmk. 127   Perf. 14

59	A3	4b on 1b yellow grn	2.00	1.25
60	A3	4b on 2b olive brn	12.50	6.25
61	A3	4b on 3b dull vio	2.00	1.50
62	A3	4b on 5b slate gray	2.00	1.50

Handstamped type "b" are bogus.

Nos. 53-55 Handstamped Type "b" and "a"

1949   Unwmk.   Perf. 12½

63	A9(b)	4b on ½b yel brn	2.00	2.00
64	A9(a)	4b on 1b purple	2.00	2.00
a.		Handstamp type "b"	2.00	2.00
65	A9(a)	4b on 2b ultra	4.00	3.75
a.		Handstamp type "b"	4.00	
b.		Handstamp 13x15mm		

Nos. J1-J2 Handstamped Type "b" in Black

1953   Wmk. 258

66	D1	4b on 1b org & yel grn	7.50	6.00
67	D1	4b on 2b org & yel grn	7.50	6.00
a.		Handstamp type "c"		
		Nos. 59-67 (9)	41.50	30.25

Three minor types of this handstamped 4b surcharge exist. Types "a" and "b" exist inverted, double or horizontal.
Forged surcharges exist.

Parade Ground, San'a — A13

Mosque, San'a A14

Designs: 5b, Flag of Yemen. 6b, Flag & eagle. 8b, Mocha coffee branch. 14b, Walled city of San'a. 20b, 1i, Ta'iz & its citadel.

1951   Wmk. 277   Photo.   Perf. 14

68	A13	1b dark brown	.30	.20
69	A13	2b red brown	.60	.20
70	A13	3b lilac rose	.75	.35
71	A14	5b blue & red	1.25	.60
72	A13	6b dk pur & red	1.40	.65
73	A13	8b dk bl & gray grn	1.50	.75
74	A14	10b rose lilac	1.25	.85
75	A14	14b blue green	2.25	1.00
76	A14	20b rose red	3.25	1.75
77	A14	1i violet	7.50	3.00
		Nos. 68-77 (10)	20.05	9.35
		Nos. 68-77,C3-C9 (17)	44.70	17.70

No. 71 was used as a 4b stamp in 1956. For surcharges see Nos. 82, 86-87.

Palace of the Rock, Wadi Dhahr — A15

Design: 20b, Walls of Ibb.

Engraved and Photogravure
1952   Unwmk.   Perf. 14½, Imperf.
78 A15 12b choc, bl & dl grn   6.00   6.00
79 A15 20b dp car, bl & brn   9.00   9.00
  Nos. 78-79,C10-C11 (4)   35.00 35.00

Flag and View of San'a (Palace in Background) — A16

1952
80 A16 1i red brn, car & gray   18.00 18.00

4th anniv. of the accession of King Ahmed, Feb. 18, 1948. See Nos. 81, C12-C13.

Palace in Foreground
1952
81 A16 30b red brn, car & dk grn 11.00 11.00

Victory of Mar. 13, 1948. See No. C13.

No. 69 Handstamped Type "b" in Black
1951 (?)   Wmk. 277   Perf. 14
82 A13 4b on 2b red brown   5.00   3.00

Forged surcharges exist. See Nos. 86-87.

King Ahmed I

Leaning Minaret, Mosque of Ta'iz — A17

Yemen Gate, San'a — A18

1954   Photo.   Unwmk.
83 A17 4b deep orange   1.25   .40
84 A17 6b deep blue   2.00   .60
85 A17 8b deep blue green   2.50   1.50
  Nos. 83-85,C14-C16 (6)   19.50   6.65

Accession of King Ahmed I, 5th anniv.

Nos. 68 and 70 Handstamped Type "b" in Black
1955   Wmk. 277   Perf. 14
86 A13 4b on 1b dk brown   5.00   4.00
  a. Handstamp type "c"   12.50 10.00
87 A13 4b on 3b lilac rose 7.50   6.00

1956-57   Wmk. 277   Perf. 14
87A A18 1b lt brown   1.00   .75
87B A18 5b blue green   1.25   .75
87C A18 10b dark blue ('57) 1.50   .85
  Nos. 87A-87C (3)   3.75   2.35

Nos. 87A-87C were prepared for official use, but issued for regular postage. The 1b

---

and 5b were used as 4b stamps. A 20b and 1-imadi of type A18 were not issued.

Arab Postal Union Issue

Globe — A19

Perf. 13½x13
1957-58   Wmk. 195   Photo.
88 A19 4b yellow brown   1.00   .90
89 A19 6b green ('58)   1.40   1.10
90 A19 16b violet ('58)   2.00   1.50
  Nos. 88-90 (3)   4.40   3.50

Arab Postal Union founding, July 1, 1954.

Telecommunications Issue

Globe, Radio and Telegraph A20

1959, Mar.   Wmk. 318   Perf. 13x13½
91 A20 4b vermilion   1.75   1.25

Arab Union of Telecommunications.

United Arab States Issue

Flags of UAR and Yemen A21

1959, Mar. 13
92 A21 1b dl red brn & blk .35   .25
93 A21 2b dk blue & blk   .45   .35
94 A21 4b sl grn, car & blk .65   .50
  Nos. 92-94,C17-C19 (6)   6.55   5.05

First anniversary of United Arab States.

Arab League Center Issue

Arab League Center, Cairo A22

Perf. 13x13½
1960, Mar. 22   Wmk. 328
95 A22 4b dull green & blk .90   .90

Opening of the Arab League Center and the Arab Postal Museum in Cairo.

Refugees Pointing to Map of Palestine A23

1960, Apr. 7   Photo.
96 A23 4b brown   1.10   .75
97 A23 6b yellow green   1.75   1.25

World Refugee Year, 7/1/59-6/30/60.
In 1961 a souvenir sheet was issued containing a 4b gray and 6b sepia in type A18, imperf. Black marginal inscription, "YEMEN 1960," repeated in Arabic. Size: 103x85mm. Value $42.50.

Torch and Olympic Rings A24

1960, Dec.   Unwmk.   Perf. 14x14½
98   A24 2b black & lil rose   .55   .35
99   A24 4b black & yellow   .85   .50
100 A24 6b black & orange   1.20   .75
101 A24 8b brn blk & bl grn   2.10   1.40
102 A24 20b dk bl, org & vio 5.00   3.00
  Nos. 98-102 (5)   9.70   6.00

17th Olympic Games, Rome, 8/25-9/11.
An imperf. souvenir sheet exists, containing one copy of No. 99. Size: 100x60mm. Value $90.

UN Emblem Breaking Chains — A25

1961   Unwmk.   Perf. 14x14½
103 A25 1b violet   .35   .25
104 A25 2b green   .40   .30
105 A25 3b grnsh blue   .50   .35
106 A25 4b brt ultra   .55   .40
107 A25 6b brt lilac   .70   .50
108 A25 14b rose brown 1.00   .60
109 A25 20b brown   2.00   1.60
  Nos. 103-109 (7)   5.50   4.00

15th anniversary (in 1960) of UN.
An imperf. souvenir sheet exists, containing one copy of No. 106. Blue marginal inscription. Size: 100x60mm. Value $25.
For overprints see Nos. 137-143.

Cranes and Ship, Hodeida A26

1961, June   Litho.   Perf. 13x13½
110 A26 4b multicolored   .85   .40
111 A26 6b multicolored   1.40   .75
112 A26 16b multicolored 2.75   1.60
  Nos. 110-112 (3)   5.00   2.75

Opening of deepwater port at Hodeida.
An imperf. souvenir sheet exists, containing one each of Nos. 110-112. Size: 160x130mm. Value $5.75.
For overprints see Nos. 177, 180.

Alabaster Funerary Mask — A27

Imam's New Palace, San'a — A28

Designs (ancient sculptures from Marib, Sheba): 2b, Horned animal's head, symbolizing Moon God (limestone). 4b, Bronze head of an Emperor 1st or 2nd century. 8b, Statue of Emperor Dhamar Ali. 10b, Statue of a child, 2nd or 3rd century (alabaster). 12b, Stairs in court of Temple of the Moon God. 20b, Alabaster relief, boy riding monster. 1i, Woman with grapes, relief.

1961, Oct. 14   Photo.   Perf. 11½
Granite Paper
113 A27 1b salmon, blk & gray   .35   .20
114 A27 2b purple & gray   .60   .20
115 A27 4b pale brn, gray & blk   .80   .20
116 A27 8b brt pink & blk   1.00   .20
117 A27 10b yellow & blk   1.00   .35
118 A27 12b lt vio bl & blk   .85   .50

---

119 A27 20b gray & blk   2.40   .60
120 A27 1i gray ol & blk   5.00   1.25
  Nos. 113-120,C20-C21 (10)   16.90   5.20

For overprints see Nos. 144-145, 147, 151, 153, 156-158, C24, C25.

1961, Nov. 15   Unwmk.
8b, Side view of Imam's palace, San'a, horiz. 10b, Palace of the Rock (Dar al-Hajar).
121 A28 4b black & lt bl grn   .35   .20
122 A28 8b blk, brt pink & grn   .75   .45
123 A28 10b black, sal & grn   .85   .50
  Nos. 121-123,C22-C23 (5)   3.90   1.95

Exist imperf.
For overprints see #148, 152, 154, C24A, C25A.

Hodeida-San'a Road — A29

1961, Dec. 25   Litho.   Perf. 13½x13
124 A29 4b multicolored   .75   .20
125 A29 6b multicolored   .90   .40
126 A29 8b multicolored   1.50   .50
  Nos. 124-126 (3)   3.15   1.10

Opening of the Hodeida-San'a highway. A miniature sheet exists containing one each of Nos. 124-126, imperf. Size: 159x129mm. Value $7.
For overprints see Nos. 178-179.

Trajan's Kiosk, Philae, Nubia — A30

1962, Mar. 1   Photo.   Perf. 11x11½
127 A30 4b dk red brown   3.50   1.00
128 A30 6b blue green   6.25   2.00

Issued to publicize UNESCO's help in safeguarding the monuments of Nubia.
A souvenir sheet exists, containing one each of #127-128, imperf. Size: 100x88½mm. Value $12.50.

Arab League Building, Cairo, and Emblem — A31

1962, Mar. 22   Perf. 13½x13
129 A31 4b dark green   .70   .25
130 A31 6b deep ultra   .85   .40

Arab League Week, Mar. 22-28.
A souvenir sheet exists, containing one each of Nos. 129-130, imperf. Size: 94x80mm. Value $3.50.
For overprints see Nos. 164-165.

Nurses, Mother and Child — A32

Malaria Eradication Emblem — A33

Designs: 4b, Nurse weighing child. 6b, Vaccination. 10b, Weighing infant.

1962, June 20   Unwmk.   Perf. 11½
131	A32	2b multicolored	.60	.25
132	A32	4b multicolored	.85	.30
133	A32	6b multicolored	1.00	.40
134	A32	10b multicolored	1.75	.50
		Nos. 131-134 (4)	4.20	1.45

Issued for Child Welfare.
For overprints see Nos. 146, 149-150, 155.

1962, July 20   Perf. 13½x13
135	A33	4b black & dp org	.70	.25
136	A33	6b dk brown & grn	1.00	.40

WHO drive to eradicate malaria. An imperf. souvenir sheet contains one each of Nos. 135-136. Size: 95x79mm. Value $15.
No. 136 has laurel leaves added and inscription rearranged.
For overprints see Nos. 189-190.

Nos. 103-109 Overprinted

1962 Photo. Unwmk.   Perf. 14x14½
137	A25	1b violet	1.50	1.50
138	A25	2b green	1.50	1.50
139	A25	3b greenish blue	1.50	1.50
140	A25	4b brt ultra	1.50	1.50
141	A25	6b brt lilac	1.50	1.50
142	A25	14b rose brown	1.50	1.50
143	A25	20b brown	1.50	1.50
		Nos. 137-143 (7)	10.50	10.50

Nos. 113-123 and 131-134 Ovptd. in Dark Green or Dark Red

a

b

1963, Jan. 1   Perf. 11½
144	A27 (a)	1b No. 113 (G)	.20	.20
145	A27 (a)	2b No. 114	.20	.20
146	A32 (b)	2b No. 131	.40	.40
147	A27 (a)	4b No. 115 (G)	.40	.40
148	A28 (a)	4b No. 121	.55	.55
149	A32 (b)	4b No. 132 (G)	.55	.55
150	A32 (b)	6b No. 133	.70	.70
151	A27 (a)	8b No. 116	.70	.70
152	A28 (b)	8b No. 122 (G)	1.00	1.00
153	A27 (a)	10b No. 117	1.00	1.00
154	A28 (a)	10b No. 123	1.75	1.75
155	A32 (b)	10b No. 134 (G)	1.75	1.75
156	A27 (a)	12b No. 118	1.40	1.40
157	A27 (a)	20b No. 119	2.00	2.00
158	A27 (a)	1i No. 120	5.50	5.50
		Nos. 144-158 (15)	18.10	18.10

For overprints see Nos. C24-C25A.

Proclamation of the Republic
A34

UN Freedom From Hunger Campaign
A35

1963, Mar. 15   Perf. 11x11½
159	A34	4b shown	.55	.55
160	A34	6b Flag, tank	.85	.85

See Nos. C26-C28.

1963, Mar. 21   Perf. 11½x11, 11x11½
162	A35	4b Milk cow, horiz.	.90	
163	A35	6b shown	1.25	

An imperf. souvenir sheet of 2 exists containing one each Nos. 162-163.
For overprints see Nos. 219-220.

Nos. 129-130 Ovptd. in Dark Red

1963, Sept. 1   Perf. 13½x13
164	A31	4b dark green	7.00	7.00
165	A31	6b deep ultra	7.00	7.00

Nos. 15-16, 18-23, 50-52 Ovptd. in Black

a

b

1963, Sept. 1
166	A3 (a)	5b No. 15	1.40	1.40
167	A4 (a)	6b No. 16	1.75	1.75
168	A8 (b)	6b No. 50	1.75	1.75
169	A4 (a)	8b No. 18	2.00	2.00
170	A4 (a)	10b No. 19	2.50	2.50
171	A8 (b)	10b No. 20	2.50	2.50
172	A8 (b)	10b No. 51	2.50	2.50
173	A8 (b)	14b No. 52	7.00	7.00
174	A4 (a)	20b No. 21	2.75	2.75
175	A4 (a)	1i No. 22	7.00	7.00
176	A4 (a)	1i No. 23	5.25	5.25
		Nos. 166-176 (11)	36.40	36.40

Nos. 111-112 and 125-126 Ovptd. in Black

Perf. 13x13½, 13½x13
1963, Sept. 1   Litho.   Unwmk.
177	A26	6b No. 111	1.75	1.75
178	A29	6b No. 125	1.75	1.75
179	A29	10b No. 126	2.50	2.50
180	A26	16b No. 112	2.50	2.50

On Nos. 178-179 the bars eliminate old inscription with text of overprint positioned below and to the right of them, on Nos. 177 and 180, the text is slightly left below the bars.
Imperf. souvenir sheets of 2 exist containing Nos. 177 and 180 or Nos. 178-179.

1st Anniv. of the Revolution — A36

Perf. 11½x11, 11x11½
1963, Sept. 26   Photo.
186	A36	2b Flag, torch, candle, vert.	.35	.30
187	A36	4b shown	.55	.45
188	A36	6b Flag, grain, chain, vert.	.90	.70

Imperf. souvenir sheets of 3 exist containing one each Nos. 186-188.

Red Cross Centenary. Set of six. ¼, ⅓, ½, 4, 8, 20b. Imperf. souv. sheet of two, 4, 8b. Oct. Nos. 6301-6307.

Nos. 135-136 Ovptd. in Black

1963, Nov. 25   Perf. 13½x13
189	A33	4b black & dp orange	3.00	3.00
190	A33	6b dk brown & green	4.00	4.00

UN Declaration of Human Rights, 15th Anniv. — A37

1963, Dec. 10   Perf. 13½
191	A37	4b orange & dk brn vio	.55	.55
192	A37	6b blue grn & blk	.75	.75

An imperf. souvenir sheet of 2 exists containing one each Nos. 191-192.

1964
Olympic Sports. Set of eight, ¼, ⅓, ½, 1, 1½b, airmail 4, 20b, 1r. Imperf. souv. sheet, 4b. Mar. 30. Nos. 6401-6409.

Bagel Spinning and Weaving Factory Inauguration — A38

1964, Apr. 10   Perf. 11x11½, 11½x11
193	A38	2b Factory, bobbin, spool, cloth	.30	.20
194	A38	4b Loom machine	.40	.30
195	A38	6b Factory, spool, bolt of cloth	.55	.35
196	A38	16b shown	1.50	1.40

Nos. 193-195 vert. An imperf. souvenir sheet of one exists containing No. 195.
No. 196 is air mail.

Hodeida Airport Inauguration — A39

1964, Apr. 30   Perf. 11½x11
197	A39	4b Runway	.40	.35
198	A39	6b Runway, terminal	.55	.50
199	A39	10b Aircraft, terminal, ship at sea	.75	.55

An imperf. souvenir sheet of one exists containing No. 199.

New York World's Fair. Set of seven, ¼, ⅓, ½, 1, 4b, airmail 16, 20b. Imperf. souv. sheet, 20b. May 10. Nos. 6410-6417.
Summer Olympics, Tokyo. Set of nine, ¼, ⅓, ½, 1, 1½b, airmail, 4, 6, 12, 20b, Imperf. souv. sheet, 20b. June 1. Nos. 6418-6427.
Boy Scouts. Set of nine, ¼, ⅓, ½, 1, 1½b, airmail, 4, 6, 16, 20b. Two souvenir sheets, 16b, perf.; 20b, imperf. June 20. Nos. 6428-6438.
Animals. Set of eleven, ¼, ⅓, ½, 1, 1½b, airmail, 4, 12, 20b, postage due, 4, 12, 20b. Aug. 15. Nos. 6439-6449.
Flowers. Set of eight, ¼, ⅓, ½, 1, 1½b, airmail, 4, 12, 20b. Sept. 1. Nos. 6450-6457.

San'a Intl. Airport Inauguration — A40

1964, Oct. 1
200	A40	1b shown	.35	.35
201	A40	2b Terminal, runway, aircraft	.35	.35
202	A40	4b like 2b	.35	.35
203	A40	8b like 1b	.70	.70

An imperf. souvenir sheet of two exists containing one each Nos. 202 and C30.
See No. C30.

Arab Postal Union, 10th Anniv.
A41

2nd Arab Summit Conference
A42

1964, Oct. 15   Perf. 13½
204	A41	4b multicolored	.75	.65

See No. C31.

1964, Nov. 30
205	A42	4b shown	.75	.65
206	A42	6b Conference emblem, map	1.00	.80

An imperf. souvenir sheet of 2 exists containing one each Nos. 205-206.
For overprints see Nos. 221-222.

2nd Anniv. of
the Revolution
A43

Deir Yassin
Massacre
A44

1964, Dec. 30
207 A43 2b Torch, map .35 .30
208 A43 4b Revolutionary .70 .50
209 A43 6b Flag, 2 candles, map .70 .50

An imperf. souvenir sheet of one exists containing No. 209.

1965
Birds. Set of eleven, ¼, ½, ¾, 1, 1½, 4b, airmail, 6, 8, 12, 20b, 1r. Imperf. souv. sheet, 20b. Jan. 30. Nos. 6501-6512.

1965, Apr. 30   **Perf. 11x11½**
210 A44 4b red lil & deep blue .80 .60

See No. C32.

Intl. Telecommunications Union (ITU),
Cent. — A45

1965, May 17 **Perf. 11x11½, 11½x11**
211 A45 4b red & pale blue, vert. .75 .40
212 A45 6b org brn & grn 1.00 .55

A souvenir sheet of 1 exists containing #212.

Burning
of Algiers
Library,
3rd Anniv.
A46

1965, July 7   **Perf. 11½x11**
214 A46 4b sepia, red & grn .75 .50

See No. C33.

3rd Anniv. of the Revolution — A47

1965, Sept. 26
215 A47 4b Tractor, corn, grain .75 .50
216 A47 6b Tractor, tower, buildings 1.00 .55

An imperf. souvenir sheet of one exists containing No. 216.

Intl. Cooperation
Year — A48

1965, Oct. 15   **Perf. 11x11**
217 A48 4b shown .80 .60
218 A48 6b UN building, New York 1.10 .65

An imperf. souvenir sheet of one exists containing No. 218.

John F. Kennedy Memorial. Set of eight, 3x¼, ⅓, ½, 4b, airmail, 8, 12b. Two imperf. souv. sheets, 4, 8b. Nov. 29. Nos. 6513-6522.
Space Exploration. Set of eight, 3x¼, ⅓, ½b, airmail, 4, 8, 16b. Imperf. souv. sheet, 16b. Dec. 29. Nos. 6523-6531.

Nos. 162-163 Overprinted in Black

a

b

1966, Jan. 15 Perf. 11½x11, 11x11½
219 A35 4b sal rose & golden
    (a)   brn 1.00 .75
220 A35 6b brt pur & yel
    (b) 1.75 1.00

An imperf. souvenir sheet of two exists containing Nos. 219-220.

Communications. Set of eight, 3x¼, ⅓, ½b, airmail, 4, 6, 20b. Imperf. airmail souv. sheet, 20b. Jan. 29. Nos. 6601-6609.
Animals issue of 1965 overprinted in black or red "Prevention of Cruelty to Animals" in English and Arabic. Set of eleven. Souv. sheet, 20b. Mar. 5. Nos. 6610-6621.

Nos. 205-206
Ovptd. in Red or
Black

1966, Mar. 20   **Perf. 13½**
221 A42 4b dark green (R) .75 .50
222 A42 6b orange brown .85 .55

An imperf. souvenir sheet of two exists containing Nos. 221-222 ovptd. in bright pink (4b) or black (6b) with additional inscription at bottom "CASABLANCA / 1965."

Builders of World Peace. Set of nine, 3x¼, ⅓, ½, 4b, airmail, 6, 10, 12b. Two imperf. souvenir sheets, 4, 8b. Mar. 25. Nos. 6622-6632.
Domestic Animals. Set of six, 3x¼, ⅓, ½, 4b. Imperf. souv. sheet, 22b. May 5. Nos. 6633-6639.
Space Exploration issue of 1965 overprinted "Luna IX / 3 February 1966" in English and Arabic. Set of eight. Imperf. souvenir sheet. Nos. 6640-6648.
World Cup Soccer Championship. Set of eight, 3x¼, ⅓, ½b, airmail, 4, 5, 20b. Imperf. souvenir sheet, 20b. May 29. Nos. 6649-6657.

Traffic Day — A49

1966, June 30   **Perf. 11x11½**
223 A49 4b green & ver .75 .50
224 A49 6b green & ver .85 .55

Space Exploration issue of 1965 overprinted "Surveyor 1 / 2 June 1966" in English and Arabic. Set of five, 3x1b on ¼b, 3b on ½b, 4b on ½b. Aug. 15. Nos. 6658-6662.
Revolution, 4th Anniv. Set of three, 2, 4, 6b. Imperf. souv. sheet of 2; 4, 6b. Sept. Nos. 6663-6666.
World's Fair issue of 1964 overprinted "1965 Sana'a." Set of seven. Imperf. souvenir sheet. Nos. 6667-6674.
WHO Headquarters Inauguration. Set of six, 3x¼b, airmail, 4, 8, 16b. Imperf. souvenir sheet, 16b. Nov. 1. Nos. 6675-6681.
Gemini 6-7. Set of eight, 3x¼, ⅓, ½, 2b, airmail, 8, 12b. Imperf. souvenir sheet, 12b. Dec. 1. Nos. 6682-6690.
Gemini 6-7 issue overprinted in red "Gemini IX / Cernan-Stafford / June 1966" in English and Arabic. Set of eight. Imperf. souvenir sheet. Dec. 25. Nos. 6691-6699.

1967
Fruit. Set of thirteen, 3x¼, ⅓, ½, 2, 4b, airmail, 6, 8, 10b, postage due, 6, 8, 10b. Feb. 10. Nos. 6701-6713.

Arab
League,
25th
Anniv.
A56

1970, Oct. 5   Photo.   Perf. 11½x11
276 A56 5b org, grn & dark pur .35 —
277 A56 7b blue, grn & brn .75 —
278 A56 16b dark olive grn, grn &
          chalky blue 1.75 —

An imperf souvenir sheet of one exists containing No. 278.

UN, 25th
Anniv.
A60

1971, Apr. 4   Photo.   Perf. 11½x11
282 A60 5b dark olive grn, grn
          & dark vio .55 .45
283 A60 7b blue, grn & dark
          blue .90 .75

Souvenir Sheet
Imperf
284 A60 16b multicolored 2.00 1.50

10th anniv. of
Revolution
A80

1972, Nov. 25   Photo.   Perf. 13
301 A80 7b lt blue, blk & multi .65 .50
302 A80 10b gray, blk & multi 1.00 .65
    Nos. 301-302,C40 (3) 6.65 4.65

For surcharge see No. 318.

25th Anniv. of
WHO — A81

1972, Dec. 1   **Litho.**
303 A81 2b lt yel grn & multi .50 .35
304 A81 21b sky blue & multi 1.40 1.20
305 A81 37b red lilac & multi 2.25 2.00
    Nos. 303-305 (3) 4.15 3.55

For surcharge see No. 341A.

Burning of Al-Aqsa Mosque, 2nd
Anniv. — A82

1972, Jan. 1   **Photo.**   **Perf. 13½**
306 A82 7b lt bl, blk & multi 1.50 .60
307 A82 18b lt bl, blk & multi 2.50 1.10
    Nos. 306-307,C41 (3) 6.00 3.10

For surcharges see Nos. 319, 341.

25th Anniv. of UNICEF — A83

1973, Jan. 15   Photo.   Perf. 13
308 A83 7b lt bl, blk & multi 1.00 .65
309 A83 10b lt bl, blk & multi 1.50 .80
    Nos. 308-309,C42 (3) 4.25 2.95

For surcharge see No. C46.

UPU Cent. — A84

10th World
Hunger
Program
A85

1974, Nov. 20   Photo.   Perf. 14
310 A84 10b multicolored .75 .40
311 A84 30b multicolored 2.25 1.50
312 A84 60b multicolored 3.25 1.90
    Nos. 310-312 (3) 6.25 3.80

For surcharge see No. 341B.

1975, Feb. 5   Litho.   Perf. 13½
313 A85 10b multicolored   .25 .25
314 A85 30b multicolored   .70 .70
315 A85 63b multicolored   1.25 1.25
    Nos. 313-315 (3)   2.20 2.20

12th Anniv.
of Revolution
A86

1975, Sept. 25
316 A86 25f Janad Mosque   .50 .35
317 A86 75f Althawra Hospital 1.00 .65

Nos. 301, 306 surcharged in Black
with New Values and Bars

1975, Nov. 15   Photo.   Perf. 13½
318 A80 75f on 7b   2.00 2.00
319 A82 278f on 7b   3.50 1.25
    Nos. 318-319,C46-C48 (5) 17.75 11.40

Telephone   Coffee Bean
Cent. — A87   Branch — A88

1976, Mar. 10   Litho.   Perf. 14½
320 A87 25f brt pink & blk   .65 .65
321 A87 75f lt grn & blk   2.00 2.00
322 A87 160f lt bl & blk   3.25 3.25
    a. Souvenir sheet of 1   4.00 4.00
        Nos. 320-322 (3)   5.90 5.90

No. 322a exists both perf. and imperf.

1976, Apr. 25   Perf. 14
323 A88 1f dull lilac   .20 .20
324 A88 3f pale gray   .20 .20
325 A88 5f lt bl grn   .20 .20
326 A88 10f bis brn   .20 .20
327 A88 25f golden brn   .25 .25
328 A88 50f brt plum   .40 .40
329 A88 75f dull pink   .70 .60

Size: 22x30mm
Perf. 14½
330 A88 1r sky blue   1.25 .70
331 A88 1.50r red lilac   1.90 1.40
332 A88 2r light grn   2.25 1.40
333 A88 5r yel org   5.00 3.00
    Nos. 323-333 (11)   12.55 8.55

For surcharges see Nos. 403-407, 592.

2nd Anniv. of
Reformation
Movement — A89

1976, June 13 Photo. Perf. 12x12½
334 A89 75f Industrial Park 1.50 1.50
335 A89 135f Forestry   2.50 2.50

Souvenir Sheet
336 A89 135f Forestry   5.00 5.00

No. 336 contains one stamp (32x47mm).

14th Anniv. of
Revolution — A90

3rd Anniv. of
Correction
Movement — A91

Designs: 25f, Natl. Institute of Public Administration. 75f, Housing and population census.
160f, Sanaa University emblem.

1976, Sept. 26 Photo. Perf. 12x12½
337 A90 25f buff & multi   .60 .60
338 A90 75f yel bis & multi 1.60 1.60
339 A90 160f pale grn & multi 3.00 3.00
    Nos. 337-339 (3)   5.20 5.20

Souvenir Sheet
340 A90 160f pale grn & multi 5.00 5.00

No. 340 contains one stamp (33x49mm).

No. 306 Surcharged in Black with New
Value and Bars

1976
341 A82 75f on 7b   1.00 .65

160F

Nos. 304, 312
Surcharged in
Black or Red

1976   Photo.   Perf. 14
341A A81 75f on 21b (R)
341B A84 160f on 40b

Size and location of surcharge varies.

1977   Photo.   Perf. 14
342 A91 25f Dish antenna   .45 .30
343 A91 75f Computer, techni-
          cian   1.25 .65
    a. Miniature sheet of 1   4.00 4.00

15th Anniv. of September
Revolution — A92

1977   Photo.   Perf. 13½
344 A92 25f Sa'ada-San'a Road .45 .35
345 A92 75f Television, Trans-
          mitting tower   1.25 .85
346 A92 160f like 25f   2.50 2.00
    a. Souvenir sheet of 1   5.00 5.00
        Nos. 344-346 (3)   4.20 3.20

25th Anniv. of   Pres. Hamdi — A94
Arab Postal
Union — A93

1978   Perf. 14
347 A93 25f lt yel grn & multi .90 .75
348 A93 60f bis & multi   2.25 1.60
    a. Miniature sheet of 1   5.00 4.50

1978   Perf. 11½
349 A94 25f dk grn & blk   .35 .35
350 A94 75f ultra & blk   1.25 1.10
351 A94 160f brn & blk   2.50 1.90
    a. Miniature sheet of 1 15.00 6.50
        Nos. 349-351 (3)   4.10 3.35

30th
Anniv.
of
ICAO
(1977)
A95

1979, Nov. 15 Photo. Perf. 13½
352 A95 75f multi   1.90 1.00
353 A95 135f multi   3.00 1.60
    a. Miniature sheet of 1   5.00 4.50

Book, World Map, Arab
Achievements — A96

1979, Dec. 1   Perf. 14
354 A96 25f multi   .60 .35
355 A96 75f multi   1.50 1.00
    a. Souvenir sheet of 1   3.75 3.25

A97

A98

1980, Jan. 1
356 A97 75f multi   1.75 1.00
357 A97 135f multi, horiz.   2.75 1.60
    a. Miniature sheet of 1   5.00 4.50

12th World Telecommunications Day, May
17, 1979.

1980   Photo.   Perf. 14
Dome of the Rock.
358 A98 5f brt bl & multi   .50 .35
359 A98 10f yel & multi   1.00 .65

Palestinian fighters and their families.

Argentina World Cup — A99

World Cup emblem and various players.

1980, Mar. 30
360 A99 25f gold & multi   .40 .40
361 A99 30f gold & multi   .40 .30
362 A99 35f gold & multi   .50 .40
363 A99 50f gold & multi   .70 .50
    Nos. 360-363,C49-C52 (8)   6.55 4.80

Issued in sheets of 8.

International Year of the Child — A100

1980, Apr. 1   Perf. 13½
364 A100 25f Girl, bird   1.60 .50
365 A100 50f Girl, bird, diff. 2.25 .80
366 A100 75f Boy, butterfly,
           flower   2.40 1.25
    Nos. 364-366,C53-C55 (6) 16.75 6.80

Issued in sheets of 6.

World Scouting Jamboree — A101

1980, May 1   Perf. 13½x14
367 A101 25f Fishing   .60 .30
368 A101 35f Troup, aircraft 1.40 .50
369 A101 40f Mounted bugler,
           flag   1.40 .50
370 A101 50f Telescope, night
           sky   1.50 .65
    Nos. 367-370,C56-C58 (7) 13.05 5.35

Issued in sheets of 6.

Argentina 1978 World Cup
Winners — A102

World cup emblem and various soccer
players.

1980, June 1   Perf. 14
371 A102 25f gold & multi   .45 .25
372 A102 30f gold & multi   .60 .30
373 A102 35f gold & multi   .60 .40
374 A102 50f gold & multi   .90 .40
    Nos. 371-374,C59-C62 (8)   8.05 4.35

Hegira, 1500th Anniv. — A102A

Designs: 160f, Outside view.

1980, July 1   Perf. 13½
375 A102a 25f blk & multi   .30 .20
376 A102a 75f car rose & multi .90 .60
377 A102a 160f blk & multi   1.90 .75
    a. Miniature sheet of 1   4.00 4.00
        Nos. 375-377 (3)   3.10 1.55

17th Anniv. of September Revolution A103

A104

1980, Sept. 26   *Perf. 13½*
378 A103 25f multi   .35   .25
379 A104 75f multi   1.10   .65

Souvenir Sheet
380   100f multi   3.75   3.75

No. 380 contains one stamp combining designs A103 and A104 (42x34mm).

Al Aqsa Mosque A105

Mosques: 25f, Al-Rawda entrance. 100f, Al-Nabwi. 160f, Al-Haram.

1980, Nov. 6   **Photo.**   *Perf. 13½*
381 A105 25f multi   .25   .20
382 A105 75f multi   .60   .50
383 A105 100f multi   1.50   .65
384 A105 160f multi   2.00   1.00
    Nos. 381-384 (4)   4.35   2.35

Souvenir Sheet
385   160f multi   6.00   3.25

Islamic Postal Systems Week and Hegira. No. 385 contains one stamp (109x47mm) combining designs of Nos. 382-384.

Intl. Palestinian Solidarity Day — A106

1980, Nov. 29
386 A106 25f lt bl & multi   .40   .25
387 A106 75f ver & multi   1.10   .90
    Inscribed 1979.

9th Arab Archaeological Conference — A107

1981, Mar. 1   *Perf. 13½*
388 A107 75f Al Aamiriya
    Mosque   1.10   .60
389 A107 125f Al Hadi Mosque   1.75   .85
  a.   Souvenir sheet of 2, #388-389   3.25   3.25

1980 World Tourism Conference, Manila A108

1981, Apr. 1
390 A108 25f shown   .20   .20
391 A108 75f Mosque, houses   .60   .30
392 A108 100f Columns, horiz.   .80   .45
393 A108 135f Bridge   1.10   .60
394 A108 160f Vuiew of San'a,
     horiz.   1.40   .60
  a.   Miniature sheet of 1   4.50   4.50
    Nos. 390-394 (5)   4.10   2.15

Sir Rowland Hill (1795-1879), Postage Stamp Inventor — A109

1981, Sept. 15   **Litho.**   *Perf. 14*
395 A109 25f Portrait, UPU
     emblem   .60
396 A109 30f Emblem, stamp
     of 1963   .70
397 A109 50f Portrait, stamps   1.00
398 A109 75f Portrait, globe,
     jet   1.60
399 A109 100f Portrait, stamp
     collection   2.25
400 A109 150f Jets, No. 322   4.00
    Nos. 395-400 (6)   10.15

Souvenir Sheets
401 A109 200f Portrait, vert.   7.50

Imperf
402 A109 200f Portrait, diff.   7.50
    Nos. 398-402 are airmail.

Nos. 323-327 Surcharged

1981
403 A88 125f on 1f   1.00
404 A88 150f on 3f   1.25
405 A88 325f on 5f   2.75
406 A88 350f on 10f   3.25
407 A88 375f on 25f   3.50
    Nos. 403-407 (5)   11.75

20th Anniv. of Yemen Airways — A110

1983, Apr. 1   **Litho.**   *Perf. 14*
408 A110 75f yel & multi   .50   .50
409 A110 125f red & multi   .80   .80
410 A110 325f bl & multi   2.00   2.00
    Nos. 408-410 (3)   3.30   3.30

Folk Costumes — A111

1983, May 1
411 A111 50f Woman carrying
     waterjar   2.00
412 A111 50f Women, sheep   2.00
413 A111 50f Man, donkeys   2.00
414 A111 50f Man in town
     square   2.00
415 A111 75f Women, child,
     well   3.00
416 A111 75f Scholar   3.00
417 A111 75f Woman on
     beach   3.00
418 A111 75f Camel-drawn
     plow   3.00
    Nos. 411-418 (8)   20.00

Souvenir Sheets
419 A111 200f Woman   8.00

Imperf
420 A111 200f Man   8.00
    #411-414 vert. #415-420 are airmail.

Sept. 26th Revolution, 20th Anniv. (1982) — A112

1983, Sept. 26   **Litho.**   *Perf. 14*
421 A112 100f Communications
422 A112 150f Literacy
423 A112 325f Educational develop-
     ment
  a.   Souvenir sheet of 2, #422, 423
424 A112 400f Independence

World Communications Year — A113

1983, Dec. 15
425 A113 150f lt bl & multi
426 A113 325f lt grn & multi
  a.   Souvenir sheet of 1

Sept. 26 Revolution, 21st Anniv. — A114

1984, Apr. 1   **Litho.**   *Perf. 14*
427 A114 100f shown
428 A114 150f Fist, statue
429 A114 325f Gate, tank
  a.   Souvenir sheet of 1

Israel Aggression Day — A115

1984, Sept. 7
430 A115 150f multi   1.50
431 A115 325f multi   4.00

Size: 91x120mm
Imperf
432 A115 325f multi   25.00
    Nos. 430-432 (3)   30.50

Sept. 26 Revolution, 22nd Anniv. — A116

1985, Oct. 1
433 A116 50f Triumphal Arch
434 A116 150f San'a Castle walls
435 A116 325f Stadium, Govt. Palace,
     San'a
  a.   Souvenir sheet of 1

Intl. Anti-Apartheid Year (1978) — A117

1985, Jan. 1
436 A117 150f dp ver & multi
437 A117 325f grn & multi
  a.   Souvenir sheet of 1

Intl. Civil Aviation Org., 40th Anniv. A118

1985, Sept. 20
438 A118 25f multi
439 A118 50f multi
440 A118 150f multi
441 A118 325f multi
  a.   Souvenir sheet of 1

Arabsat Satellite, 1st Anniv. A119

1986, Apr. 15   **Litho.**   *Perf. 14*
442 A119 150f multi   2.50
443 A119 325f multi   5.50
  a.   Souvenir sheet of 1   8.50

World Telecommunications, 120th
Anniv. — A120

1986, May 1
444 A120 150f multi ... 2.50
445 A120 325f multi ... 5.25
a. Souvenir sheet of 1 ... 9.00

General People's Conference, 2nd
Anniv. — A121

1986, May 1
446 A121 150f multi ... 2.50
447 A121 325f multi ... 4.50
a. Souvenir sheet of 1 ... 6.00

A122

A123

1986, July 1
448 A122 150f multi ... 2.50
449 A122 325f multi ... 4.50
a. Souvenir sheet of 1 ... 6.00
15th Islamic Foreign Ministers' Conference,
San'a, Dec. 18-22, 1984.

1986, Oct. 1
450 A123 150f multi ... 2.50
451 A123 325f multi ... 4.50
a. Souvenir sheet of 1 ... 6.00
UN 40th anniv.

Arab
League,
39th
Anniv.
A124

1986, Nov. 15
452 A124 150f multi ... 2.50
453 A124 325f multi ... 4.50

Natl. Arms
A125

1987, Sept. 26   Litho.   Perf. 14
454 A125 100f multi ... .90
455 A125 150f multi ... 1.25
456 A125 425f multi ... 3.75
a. Souvenir sheet of 1 ... 4.00
457 A125 450f multi ... 4.00
Sept. 26th Revolution, 25th anniv.
For surcharge see No. 593.

Intl. Youth
Year (1985)
A126

1987, Oct. 15   Perf. 13x13½
458 A126 150f multi
459 A126 425f multi
a. Souvenir sheet of 1
For surcharge see No. C150.

Drilling of
the
Republic's
First Oil
Well, 1984
A127

1987, Nov. 1   Perf. 14
460 A127 150f Oil derrick
461 A127 425f Derrick, refinery
a. Souvenir sheet of 1
For surcharge see No. C151.

General
Population
and
Housing
Census,
1986
A128

1987, Dec. 1
462 A128 150f multi ... 2.50
463 A128 425f multi ... 4.50
a. Souvenir sheet of 1 ... 5.50
For surcharge see No. C152.

1986 World Cup Soccer
Championships, Mexico — A129

Designs: 100f, 150f, Match scenes, vert.
425f, Match scene and Pique, character
trademark.

1988, Jan. 1   Litho.   Perf. 14
464 A129 100f multi
465 A129 150f multi, diff.
466 A129 425f multi
a. Souvenir sheet of 1
For surcharge see No. C153.

17th Scouting
Conference,
San'a — A130

1988, Mar. 1   Litho.   Perf. 14
467 A130 25f Skin diving
468 A130 30f Table tennis
469 A130 40f Tennis
470 A130 50f Two scouts, flag
471 A130 60f Volleyball
472 A130 100f Tug-of-war

473 A130 150f Basketball
474 A130 425f Archery
Souvenir Sheet
475 A130 425f Scout, emblem,
hand sign
For surcharge see No. C154.

San'a Preservation — A131

1988, May 1   Litho.   Perf. 14
476 A131 25f multicolored
477 A131 50f multicolored
478 A131 100f multicolored
479 A131 150f multicolored
480 A131 425f multicolored
a. Souvenir sheet of 1
For surcharge see No. 594.

Battle of
Hattin,
800th
Anniv. in
1987
A132

1988   Litho.   Perf. 14
482 A132 150f multicolored
483 A132 425f multicolored
a. Souvenir sheet
For surcharge see No. C155.

Arab Telecommunication Day,
1987 — A133

1988
484 A133 100f multicolored
485 A133 150f multicolored
486 A133 425f multicolored
a. Souvenir sheet
For surcharge see No. C156.

A134

Sept. 26
Revolution, 26th
Anniv. — A134a

1989, Sept. 30
487 A134 300f multicolored
488 A134 375f multicolored
489 A134a 850f multicolored
490 A134a 900f multicolored
A souvenir sheet containing one #488 exists.
For surcharges see Nos. 595, 605.

A135

October 14
Revolution, 25th
Anniv. — A135a

1989, Oct. 14
491 A135 300f multicolored
492 A135 375f multicolored
493 A135a 850f multicolored
494 A135a 900f multicolored
A souvenir sheet containing one #492 exists.
For surcharges see Nos. 596, 606.

1988
Summer
Olympics,
Seoul
A136

Game emblem and various events: 300f,
Table tennis, basketball, track, boxing. 375f,
Soccer game. 850f, Soccer, judo, vert. 900f,
Torch bearer.

1989, Nov. 10   Litho.   Perf. 13x13½
495 A136 300f multicolored
496 A136 375f multicolored
a. Souvenir sheet
497 A136 850f multicolored
498 A136 900f multicolored
For surcharges see Nos. 597, 607.

Palestinian
Uprising
A137

1989, Dec. 9   Perf. 13x13½, 13½x13
499 A137 300f shown
500 A137 375f Flag raising, vert.
a. Souvenir sheet of 1
501 A137 850f Burning barri-
cades
502 A137 900f Man waving flag,
vert.
For surcharges see Nos. 598, 608.

Arab Cooperation Council — A138

1990, Feb. 16   Litho.   Perf. 13x13½
504 A138 300f multicolored
505 A138 375f multicolored
a. Souvenir sheet
506 A138 850f multicolored
507 A138 900f multicolored
For surcharges see Nos. 599, 609.

First Exported Oil — A139

1990, Mar. 15   *Perf. 14*
508 A139 300f multicolored
509 A139 375f multicolored
  a. Souvenir sheet
510 A139 850f multi, diff.
511 A139 900f like 850f

For surcharges see Nos. 600, 610.

Arab Scout Movement, 75th Anniv. A140

1990, June 15   Litho.   *Perf. 13x13½*
512 A140 300f Scouts holding globe
513 A140 375f like No. 512
  a. Souvenir sheet of 1
514 A140 850f Oil rig, scouts, globe
515 A140 900f like No. 514

For surcharges see Nos. 601, 611.

Arab Board for Medical Specializations, 10th Anniv. — A141

1990, Apr. 15   Photo.   *Perf. 13½x13*
516 A141 300f brt grn & multi
517 A141 375f lt bl & multi
  a. Sheet of 1, perf. 12½
518 A141 850f lt org & multi
519 A141 900f lt vio & multi

For surcharges see Nos. 602, 612.

Immunization Campaign — A142

300f, 375f, Mother feeding infant, vert.

1990, May 15   *Perf. 13½x13, 13x13½*
520 A142 300f lt bl & multi
521 A142 375f lt org & multi
  a. Sheet of 1, perf. 12½
522 A142 850f lt bl grn & multi
523 A142 900f lt lake & multi

No. 521a contains one 26x37mm stamp.
For surcharges see Nos. 603, C157.

UN Development Program, 40th Anniv. — A144

1990, Oct. 24   Litho.   *Perf. 12*
532 A144 150f multicolored

For surcharge see No. 622.

Ducks A145

1990, Sept. 18   Litho.   *Perf. 12*
533 A145 10f Pintail swimming
534 A145 20f Wigeon
535 A145 25f Ruddy shelduck
536 A145 40f Gadwall
537 A145 75f Shelduck, male
538 A145 150f Shoveler
539 A145 600f Teal

Souvenir Sheet
540 A145 460f Pintail in flight
For surcharge see No. 623.

Moths and Butterflies A146

1990, Nov. 3   *Perf. 12½x12*
541 A146 5f Dirphia multicolor
542 A146 20f Automeris io
543 A146 25f Papilio machaon
544 A146 40f Bhutanitis lidderdalii
545 A146 55f Prepona demophon muson
546 A146 75f Agarista agricola
547 A146 700f Attacus edwardsii

Souvenir Sheet
Perf. 12x12½
548 A146 460f Daphnis nerii, vert.

Prehistoric Animals A147

Perf. 12x12½, 12½x12
1990, Nov. 27
549 A147 5f Protembolotherium, vert.
550 A147 10f Diatryma, vert.
551 A147 35f Mammuthus
552 A147 40f Edaphosaurus
553 A147 55f Dimorphodon
554 A147 75f Phororhacos
555 A147 700f Ichthyosaurus, vert.

Size: 61x90mm
Imperf
556 A147 460f Tyrannosaurus, vert.

A148

A149
Various domestic cats.

1990, Dec. 26   *Perf. 12x12½*
557 A148 5f multicolored
558 A148 15f multicolored
559 A148 35f multicolored
560 A148 55f multicolored
561 A148 60f multicolored
562 A148 150f multicolored
563 A148 600f multicolored

Size: 70x90mm
Imperf
564 A148 460f multicolored

1991, Mar. 18   Litho.   *Perf. 12x12½*
Mushrooms.
565 A149 50f Boletus aestivalis
566 A149 60f Suillus luteus
567 A149 80f Gyromitra esculenta
568 A149 100f Leccinum scabrum
569 A149 130f Amanita muscaria
570 A149 200f Boletus erythropus
571 A149 300f Leccinum testaceoscabrum

Size: 70x90mm
Imperf
572 A149 460f Stropharia aeruginosa

Unified Yemen Republic, 1st Anniv. A150

Designs: 300f, 375f, Eagle crest. 850f, 900f, Hand holding flag, map, sun.

1991, May 22   *Perf. 13x13½*
573 A150 300f pink & multi
574 A150 375f grn bl multi
  a. Sheet of 1, perf. 12½
575 A150 850f lt bl & multi
576 A150 900f bl grn & multi

No. 574a contains one 37x27mm stamp.
For surcharges see #604, 613, 624, 627.

Unity Agreement Signed Nov. 30, 1989 — A151

Designs: 300f, 375f, 850f, Fist, flag, map.

1991, May 22   *Perf. 13½x13*
577 A151 225f multicolored
578 A151 300f multicolored
579 A151 375f multicolored
  a. Sheet of 1, perf. 12½
580 A151 650f multicolored
581 A151 850f multicolored

No. 579a contains one 27x37mm stamp.
For surcharges see #614, 617-619, 625.

World Anti-Smoking Day — A153

Designs: 300f, 375f, 850f, Man facing skull smoking cigarette.

1991, May 31   *Perf. 13x13½*
582 A153 225f multicolored
583 A153 300f multicolored
584 A153 375f multicolored
  a. Sheet of 1, perf. 12½
585 A153 650f multicolored
586 A153 850f multicolored

No. 584a contains one 36x26mm stamp.
For surcharges see Nos. 615, 620, 626.

United Nations, 45th Anniv. A154

1991, June 26   *Perf. 13x13½*
587 A154 5f multicolored
588 A154 8f multicolored
589 A154 10f multicolored
590 A154 12f multicolored

Souvenir Sheet
Perf. 12½
591 A154 6f multicolored

No. 591 contains one 37x28mm stamp.

Nos. 329, 456, 480, 489-490, 493-494, 497-498, 501-502, 506-507, 510-511, 514-515, 518-519, 523, 575-576, 581 & 586 Surcharged, "Rials" Spelled Out

1993, Jan. 1   *Perfs., Etc. as Before*
592 A88 5r on 75f #329
593 A125 8r on 425f #456
594 A131 8r on 425f #480
595 A134a 10r on 900f #490
596 A135a 10r on 900f #494
597 A136 10r on 900f #498
598 A137 10r on 900f #502
599 A138 10r on 900f #507
600 A139 10r on 900f #511
601 A140 10r on 900f #515
602 A141 10r on 900f #519
603 A142 10r on 900f #523
604 A150 10r on 900f #576
605 A134a 12r on 850f #489
606 A135a 12r on 850f #493
607 A136 12r on 850f #497
608 A137 12r on 850f #501
609 A138 12r on 850f #506
610 A139 12r on 850f #510
611 A140 12r on 850f #514
612 A141 12r on 850f #518
613 A150 12r on 850f #575
614 A151 12r on 850f #581
615 A153 12r on 850f #586

Size and location of surcharge varies.

Yemen (PDR) Nos. 441, 443, 447, and Yemen Nos. 577-578, 583 Surcharged Type a or

c
50
R.Y

1993   *Perfs., Etc. as Before*
616 A139(a) 50r on 500f #447
617 A151(a) 50r on 225f #577
618 A151(c) 50r on 225f #577
  a. Pair, #617-618
619 A151(a) 100r on 300f #578
620 A153(a) 100r on 300f #583
621 A139(a) 200r on 5f #441
  a. 3-Line surcharge
621B A139(a) 200r on 20f #443

Size and location of surcharge varies.

Yemen Republic Nos. 532, 538, 573-574, 579, & 584 Surcharged

a
50
R

1993, Sept. 1   *Perfs., Etc. as Before*
622 A144(a) 50r on 150f #532
623 A145(a) 50r on 150f #538
624 A150(a) 50r on 375f #574
625 A151(a) 50r on 375f #579
626 A153(a) 50r on 375f #584
627 A150(a) 100r on 300f #573

Size and location of surcharge varies.
No. 623 exists with a surcharge similar to surcharge "c."

Yemen People's Democratic Republic
Nos. 75, 84B, 204, 208, 216, 232,
235, 244, 267, 335-336, 347, 425,
436-437, 439 & Types Surcharged
Type a and:

b

1993, Sept. 1   Perfs., Etc. as Before

628	A25(a)	8r on 100f #84B
629	A63(a)	8r on 110f #204
630	A64(a)	8r on 110f #208
631	A66(a)	8r on 110f #216
632	A72(a)	8r on 110f #232
633	A74(a)	8r on 110f #235
634	A76(a)	8r on 110f #244
635	A86(a)	8r on 110f #267
636	A105(a)	100r on 2d #347
637	A137(a)	100r on 300f #439
638	A24(a)	200r on 5f #75
639	(b)	200r on 15f
640	A105(b)	200r on 15f #335
641	(b)	200r on 20f
642	A105(b)	200r on 20f #336
643	A131(a)	200r on 20f #425
644	A134(a)	200r on 75f #436
645	A135(a)	200r on 250f #437

Size and location of surcharge varies.
No. 582 exists with a 50r type "b" surcharge.
No. 636 exists with a surcharge similar to
surcharge "c."
Nos. 639, 641 without surcharge have not
been listed in the Scott Catalogue.

Yemen Unity,
4th
Anniv. — A155

Various views of govt. building, San'a.

1994, Sept. 27   Litho.   Perf. 13½x14

646	A155	3r multicolored
647	A155	5r multicolored
648	A155	8r multicolored
649	A155	20r multicolored

Souvenir Sheet

650	A155	20r multi, diff.

1994 World Cup
Soccer
Championships,
US — A156

2r, Player in yellow shirt dribbling ball, vert.
6r, Player in striped shirt dribbling, vert. 10r,
Goal keeper. No. 654, Heading ball, vert.
No. 655, Tackling.

1994, Oct. 1   Perf. 14x13½, 13½x14

651	A156	2r multicolored
652	A156	6r multicolored
653	A156	10r multicolored
654	A156	12r multicolored

Souvenir Sheet

655	A156	12r multicolored

World Day of   FAO, 50th Anniv.
Environmental   A158
Protection
A157

Perf. 14x13½, 13½x14

1995, Oct. 15   Litho.

656	A157	15r Arabian leopard
657	A157	20r Caracal lynx
658	A157	30r Guinea fowl, horiz.

Souvenir Sheet

659	A157	50r Partridge, horiz.

1995, Oct. 16   Perf. 14x13½

Emblem, field, hand holding: 10r, Plant. 25r,
Seed. 30r, Fish. 50r, Grain.

660	A158	10r violet & multi
661	A158	25r claret & multi
662	A158	30r light blue & multi

Souvenir Sheet

663	A158	50r dark blue & multi

A159   A160

UN, 50th anniv.: Various views of Aden
Dam.

1995, Oct. 24   Perf. 14x13½, 13½x14

664	A159	10r multi
665	A159	20r multi
666	A159	25r multi, horiz.

Souvenir Sheet

667	A159	50r multi, horiz.

Perf. 14x13½, 13½x14

1995, Nov. 29

Naseem Hamed Kashmem, world boxing
champion: 10r, With champion belts. 20r, Up
close. 25r, Boxing opponent, horiz. 30r, Holding up arm as winner, trainer.
50r, Boxing opponent, diff., horiz.

668	A160	10r multicolored
669	A160	20r multicolored
670	A160	25r multicolored
671	A160	30r multicolored

Souvenir Sheet

672	A160	50r multicolored

Souvenir Sheet

CHINA '96, 9th Asian Intl. Philatelic
Exhibition — A161

Illustration reduced.

1996, May 18   Litho.   Perf. 11½
673 A161 80r Shanghai

1996 Summer
Olympic
Games,
Atlanta — A162

1996, July 19   Perf. 14x13½, 13½x14

674	A162	20r Wrestling, vert.
675	A162	50r High jump
676	A162	60r Running, vert.
677	A162	70r Gymnastics, vert.
678	A162	100r Judo, vert.

Souvenir Sheet

679	A162	150r Javelin, vert.

Landmarks
A163

10r, 70r, 250r, Popular Heritage Museum,
Seiyoan. 15r, 40r, 60r, 500r, Rock Palace,
Wadi Dhahr, vert. 20r, 100r, 200r, Old Sana'a
City. 30r, 50r, 150r, 300r, Al-Mohdhar Minaret,
Tarim, vert.

Perf. 13½x14, 14x13½

1996, Sept. 26   Litho.

680	A163	10r org yel & multi
681	A163	15r grn yel & multi
682	A163	20r lt blue & multi
683	A163	30r blue & multi
684	A163	40r salmon & multi
685	A163	50r green & multi
686	A163	60r lilac & multi
687	A163	70r violet & multi
688	A163	100r yellow & multi
689	A163	150r orange & multi
690	A163	200r rose & multi
691	A163	250r gray & multi
692	A163	300r red & multi
693	A163	500r yellow & multi

Birds — A164

Designs: 20r, Tyto alba. 50r, Alectoris
philbyi. 60r, Gypaetus barbatus. 70r, Alectoris
melanocephala. 100r, Chlamydotis undulata.
150r, Ixobrychus minutus, vert.

1996, Oct. 14   Litho.   Perf. 13½x14

694	A164	20r multicolored
695	A164	50r multicolored
696	A164	60r multicolored
697	A164	70r multicolored
698	A164	100r multicolored

Souvenir Sheet
Perf. 14x13½

699	A164	150r multicolored

Rare Plants in
Yemen — A165

Designs: 20r, Parodia masii. 50r, Notocatus
cristata. 60r, Adenium obesum socotranum.
70r, Dracaena cinnabari. 100r, Mammillaria
erythrosperma.
150r, Parodia maasii, diff.

1996, Nov. 30   Perf. 13½x14

700	A165	20r multicolored
701	A165	50r multicolored
702	A165	60r multicolored
703	A165	70r multicolored
704	A165	100r multicolored

Souvenir Sheet

705	A165	150r multicolored

A166

A167

Fish: 20r, Heniochus acuminatus. 50r, 150r,
Cheilinus undulatus. 60r, Zebrasoma
xanthurum. 70r, Pomacanthus imperator.
100r, Pomacanthus vanthometopon.

1996, Nov. 30

706	A166	20r multicolored
707	A166	50r multicolored
708	A166	60r multicolored
709	A166	70r multicolored
710	A166	100r multicolored

Souvenir Sheet

711	A166	150r multicolored

1996, Dec. 11   Perf. 14x13½

UNICEF, 50th Anniv.: 20r, Children with
books. 50r, Girls clapping hands. 60r, Mother,
child. 70r, Mother, three children.
150r, Child making jewelry, horiz.

712	A167	20r multicolored
713	A167	50r multicolored
714	A167	60r multicolored
715	A167	70r multicolored

Souvenir Sheet
Perf. 13½x14

716	A167	150r multicolored

1998 World Cup Soccer
Championships, France — A168

Various soccer plays.

1998, June 10   Litho.   Perf. 13x13½

717	A168	10r multicolored
718	A168	15r multicolored
719	A168	35r multicolored
720	A168	65r multicolored
721	A168	75r multicolored
a.		Souvenir sheet, #717-721

Birds
A169

Designs: 10r, Ardeotis arabs. 15r, Neophron
percnopterus. 35r, Coracias abyssinicus. 65r,
Cinnyricinclus leucogaster. 75r, Melierax
metabates.

1998, Sept. 26   Litho.   Perf. 13

722-726	A169	Set of 5	4.25 4.25
726a		Sheet of 5, #722-726	4.25 4.25

Universal
Declaration
of Human
Rights,
50th Anniv.
A170

15r, Hands in air. 35r, Hands clasped in
handshake. 100r, Hands reaching out.

1998, Oct. 12

727-729	A170	Set of 3	3.25 3.25
729a		Sheet of 3, #727-729	3.25 3.25

First
General
Conference
of Yemeni
Immigrants
(in 1999)
A171

Emblem &: 60r, Dhows. 90r, Fort, camel.

2000, May 16   Litho.   Perf. 14½x14

730-731	A171	Set of 2	2.00 2.00
731a		Souvenir sheet, #730-731	2.00 2.00

Tenth National Day — A172

Background colors: 30r, Light green. 50r, Rose lilac. 70r, Light blue. 150r, Orange.

2000, May 22 — *Perf. 14x14½*
732-734 A172 Set of 3 — 1.60 1.60
Souvenir Sheet
735 A172 150r multi — 1.60 1.60

Plants of Socotra — A173

Designs: 30r, Euphorbia abdalkuri. 70r, Dendrosicyos socotranus. 80r, Caralluma socotrana. 120r, Dracaena cinnabari. 300r, Exacum affine.

2000, July 15
736-739 A173 Set of 4 — 4.00 4.00
Souvenir Sheet
740 A173 300r multi — 4.00 4.00

2000 Summer Olympics, Sydney — A174

Designs: 50r, Judo. 70r, Runner. 80r, Hurdler. 100r, Shooting. 300r, Tennis.

2000, Sept. 15
741-744 A174 Set of 4 — 4.00 4.00
Souvenir Sheet
745 A174 300r multi — 4.00 4.00

Antiquities — A175

Designs: 30r, Stone idols, 3000 B.C. 70r, Statue of Ma'adi Karib, 800 B.C. 100r, Horned griffin, Royal Palace of Shabwa, 300. 120r, Statue of King of Awsan Yasduq Eil, 100 B.C. 320r, Stele with bull's head, 100 B.C., horiz.

2002, June 15 Litho. *Perf. 13x12¾*
746-749 A175 Set of 4 — 4.25 4.25
Souvenir Sheet
Imperf
750 A175 320r multi — 4.25 4.25
No. 750 contains one 41x26mm stamp.

2002 World Cup Soccer Championships, Japan and Korea — A176

Soccer players with background colors of: 30r, Bister, vert. 70r, Green. 100r, Blue, vert. 120r, Red brown, vert. No. 755: a, Player's foot and ball. b, World Cup trophy.

2002, May 31 *Perf. 13x12¾, 12¾x13*
751-754 A176 Set of 4 — 4.25 4.25
Souvenir Sheet
Perf.
755 A176 160r Sheet of 2, #a-b — 4.25 4.25
No. 755 contains two 28mm diameter stamps.

Scouting in Yemen, 75th Anniv. A177

Designs: 30r, Scout escorting man across street. 60r, Scout digging. 70r, Scouts in rowboat. 160r, Scout saluting, vert.

2002, Apr. 30 *Perf. 12¾x13*
756-758 A177 Set of 3 — 2.10 2.10
Souvenir Sheet
Perf. 13x13¼
759 A177 160r multi — 2.10 2.10
No. 759 contains one 16x26mm stamp.

Palestinian Intifada — A178

Designs: 30r, Frightened child. 60r, Bleeding child. 90r, Dome of the Rock, horiz.

2002, Apr. 27 *Perf. 13x12¾*
760-761 A178 Set of 2 — 1.25 1.25
Imperf
Size: 111x78mm
762 A178 90r multi — 1.25 1.25

Poets — A179   Revolution, 40th Anniv. — A180

Designs: Nos. 763, 30r, 765, 60r, 767a, 70r, Hussain Al-Muhdhar (1931-2000). Nos. 764, 30r, 766, 60r, 767b, 70r, Abdullah Al-Baradony (1929-99).

2002, June 30 Litho. *Perf. 13x12¾*
763-766 A179 Set of 4 — 2.25 2.25
Souvenir Sheet
Perf. 13x13¼
767 A179 70r Sheet of 2, #a-b — 1.75 1.75
No. 767 contains two 16x28mm stamps.

2002, Sept. 26 *Perf. 13x12¾*
Background colors: 30r, Dull green. 60r, Rose. 90r, Lilac.
768-769 A180 Set of 2 — 1.10 1.10
Imperf
Size: 110x76mm
770 A180 90r multi — 1.10 1.10

World Under-17 Soccer Championships, Finland — A181

Various soccer players with background color of: 30r, Red violet. 50r, Golden brown. 70r, Blue. 100r, Green. 250r, Soccer team and stadium

2003, Aug. 13 Litho. *Perf. 12¾x13*
771-774 A181 Set of 4 — 3.00 3.00
Imperf
Size: 109x74mm
775 A181 250r multi — 3.00 3.00

Antiquities — A182

Various sculptures with background colors of: 20r, Pale yellow. 40r, Lilac. 50r, Light green. 150r, Pink. 260r, Black, horiz.

2003, Sept. 26 *Perf. 13x12¾*
776-779 A182 Set of 4 — 3.00 3.00
Souvenir Sheet
Perf. 12¾x13
780 A182 260r multi — 3.00 3.00

Traditional Women's Clothing — A183

Various women with panel colors of: 30r, Purple. 60r, Yellow green. 70r, Dark green. 100r, Red violet. 150r, Brown. 410r, Purple background, horiz.

2003, Oct. 14 *Perf. 13x12¾*
781-785 A183 Set of 5 — 4.75 4.75
Souvenir Sheet
Perf. 12¾x13
786 A183 410r multi — 4.75 4.75

Children's Art — A184

Designs: 20r, Girl with flower on globe, vert. 30r, Dove over buildings, vert. 40r, Dove holding swing, vert. 50r, Children in field. 60r, Animals in field. 70r, Street and park.

2003, Oct. 15 *Perf. 13x12¾, 12¾x13*
787-792 A184 Set of 6 — 3.00 3.00

Sana'a, 2004 Arabic Cultural Capital — A185

Various buildings with frame colors of: 30r, White. 50r, Purple. 70r, Black. 100r, Dark brown. 150r Red brown. 400r, Buildings, horiz.

2003, Nov. 30 *Perf. 13x12¾*
793-797 A185 Set of 5 — 4.50 4.50
Souvenir Sheet
Perf. 12¾x13
798 A185 400r multi — 4.50 4.50

AIR POST STAMPS

Catalogue values for unused stamps in this section are for Never Hinged items.

Plane over San'a — AP1

1947 Unwmk. Engr. *Perf. 12½*
C1 AP1 10b bright blue — 6.00 2.00
C2 AP1 20b olive green — 10.00 2.50

Views Type of Regular Issue

6b, 8b, View of San'a. 10b, Mocha coffee branch. 12b, Palace of the Rock, Wadi Dhahr. 16b, Palace, Ta'iz. 20b, 1i, Parade Ground, San'a.

1951 Wmk. 277 Photo. *Perf. 14*
C3 A14 6b blue — 1.40 .50
C4 A14 8b dark brown — 1.75 .60
C5 A14 10b dark green — 2.25 1.40
C6 A13 12b dark blue — 2.50 .80
C7 A14 16b lilac rose — 3.00 .80
C8 A13 20b orange brown — 3.75 1.25
C9 A13 1i dark red — 10.00 3.00
Nos. C3-C9 (7) — 24.65 8.35

Nos. C3 and C4 were used provisionally in 1957 for registry and foreign ordinary mail.

Type of Regular Issue

Designs: 12b, Palace of the Rock, Wadi Dhahr. 20b, Walls of Ibb.

Engraved and Photogravure
1952 Unwmk. *Perf. 14½*
C10 A15 12b grnsh blk, bl & brn — 10.00 10.00
C11 A15 20b indigo, bl & brn — 10.00 10.00

Flag-and-View Type
1952
C12 A16 1i dk brn, car & brt ultra — 18.00 18.00

Palace in Foreground
1952
C13 A16 30b yel grn, car & gray — 11.00 11.00

Leaning Minaret, Mosque of Ta'iz — AP6

1954 Photo. *Perf. 14*
C14 AP6 10b scarlet — 3.25 .90
C15 AP6 12b dull blue — 4.00 1.25
C16 AP6 20b olive bister — 6.50 2.00
Nos. C14-C16 (3) — 13.75 4.15

Accession of King Ahmed I, 5th anniv.

Type of Regular Issue

1959   **Wmk. 318**   *Perf. 13x13½*

C17	A21	6b orange & blk	1.00	.70
C18	A21	10b red & blk	1.60	1.25
C19	A21	16b brt violet & red	2.50	2.00
		Nos. C17-C19 (3)	5.10	3.95

Antiquities of Marib Type

Designs: 6b, Columns, Temple of the Moon God. 16b, Control tower and spillway of 2,700-year-old dam of Marib.

Perf. 11½

1961, Oct. 14   **Unwmk.**   **Photo.**

C20	A27	6b lt bl grn & blk	1.00	.20
C21	A27	16b lt blue & blk	2.75	.60

For overprints see Nos. C24, C25.

Buildings Type

6b, Bab al-Yemen, main gate of San'a, horiz. 16b, Palace of the Rock (Dar al-Hajar).

1961, Nov. 15

C22	A28	6b blk, lt bl & grn	.55	.20
C23	A28	16b blk, rose & grn	1.40	.60

For overprints see Nos. C24A, C25A.

Nos. C20-C23 Ovptd. Like Nos. 144-158 in Dark Red or Black

Perf. 11½

1963, Jan. 1   **Photo.**   **Unwmk.**

C24	A27 (a)	6b No. C20	.70	.70
C24A	A28 (b)	6b No. C22	.85	.85
C25	A27 (a)	16b No. C21	1.75	1.75
C25A	A28 (a)	16b No. C23 (B)	2.75	2.75

Proclamation of the Republic Type

1963, Mar. 15   *Perf. 11x11½, 11½x11*

C26	A34	8b Bayonette, torch	1.50	1.50
C27	A34	10b Jet, torch, tank	2.00	2.00
C28	A34	16b Flag, chain, torch	2.75	2.75
		Nos. C27-C28 horiz.		

Nos. 25-29 Ovptd. in Black

Wmk. 258

1963, Sept. 1   **Litho.**   *Perf. 12½*

C29	A5	6b slate blue & ultra	1.50	1.50
C29A	A5	10b fawn & ultra	1.90	1.90
C29B	A5	14b olive & ultra	2.25	2.25
C29C	A5	20b yel grn & ultra	3.00	3.00
C29D	A5	1i claret & ultra	6.50	6.50
		Nos. C29-C29D (5)	15.15	15.15

Astronauts. Set of five airmail, ¼, ⅓, ½, 4, 20b. Airmail imperf. souvenir sheet, 20b. Dec. 5. Nos. 63C01-63C06. Value, set $11, souvenir $9.

1964

Astronauts issue of 1963 overprinted in black or red brown "John F. Kennedy / 1917 / 1963" in English or Arabic. Set of five airmail. May 5. Nos. 64C01-64C05.

San'a Intl. Airport Type

Perf. 11½x11

1964, Oct. 1   **Photo.**   **Unwmk.**

C30	A40	6b Sun, buildings, aircraft	.70	.70

See note after No. 203.

APU 10th Anniv. Type

1964, Oct. 15   *Perf. 13½*

C31	A41	6b blue grn & blk	1.00	.80

An imperf. souvenir sheet of one exists containing No. C31. Value $3.

Deir Yassin Massacre Type

1965, Apr. 30   *Perf. 11x11½*

C32	A44	6b ver & brt org	1.00

Library Type

1965, July 7   *Perf. 11½x11*

C33	A46	6b sepia, red & int blue	.85	.55

An imperf. souvenir sheet of one exists containing No. C33. Value $2.50.

1966

Butterflies. Set of four airmail, 6, 8, 10, 16b. May 5. Nos. 66C01-66C04.

Lenin's Birth Centenary AP7

1970, Aug. 15   **Litho.**   *Perf. 12x12½*

C34	AP7	6b Public speech	1.40	1.10
C35	AP7	16b Meeting with Arab delegates	3.00	1.90

8th Anniv. of the Revolution — AP8

1971, Jan. 24   *Perf. 13*

C36	AP8	5b Country estate	.75	
C37	AP8	7b Workers	1.10	
C38	AP8	16b Handshake, flag, flowers, open book	1.50	
		Nos. C36-C38 (3)	3.35	

A souv. sheet of 1 exists containing No. C38. Value $5.

Revolution Type

1972, Nov. 25   **Photo.**   *Perf. 13*

C40	A80	21b lilac, blk & multi	5.00	3.50

Al-Aqsa Mosque Type

1973, Jan. 1   **Photo.**   *Perf. 13½*

C41	A82	24b lt bl, blk & multi	2.00	1.40
a.		Min. sheet of 1, imperf.		

UNICEF Type

1973, Jan. 15   **Photo.**   *Perf. 13*

C42	A83	18b lt bl, blk & multi	1.75	1.50
a.		Min. sheet of 1, imperf.	3.25	2.50

For surcharge see No. C46.

11th Anniv. of Revolution AP10

1973, Sept. 26   **Photo.**   *Perf. 14*

C43	AP10	7b Bank	.50	.35
C44	AP10	10b Cement factory	.65	.55
C45	AP10	18b Hospital	1.50	1.10
		Nos. C43-C45 (3)	2.65	2.00

For surcharges see Nos. C47-C48.

Nos. C42, C43, C45 Surcharged in Black with New Value and Bars

1975, Nov. 15

C46	A83	75f on 18b lt bl, blk & multi	2.50	2.50
C46A	A80	75f on 21b #C40 (R)	—	—
C47	AP10	90f on 7b multi	5.50	2.75
C48	AP10	120f on 18b multi	4.25	4.25
a.		Overprinted in red		

Argentina 1978 World Cup Type

World cup emblem and various soccer players.

1980, Mar. 30   **Photo.**   *Perf. 14*

C49	A99	60f gold & multi	.80	.60
C50	A99	75f gold & multi	1.00	.70
C51	A99	80f gold & multi	1.25	.90
C52	A99	100f gold & multi	1.50	1.00
		Nos. C49-C52 (4)	4.55	3.20

Two 225f souvenir sheets exist.

IYC Type

1980, Apr. 1   *Perf. 13½*

C53	A100	80f Girl, bird	3.00	1.25
C54	A100	100f Boy, butterfly, flower	3.00	1.25
C55	A100	150f Boy, butterfly, flower, diff.	4.50	1.75
		Nos. C53-C55 (3)	10.50	4.25

Two 200f souvenir sheets exist.

Scouting Type of 1980

1980, May 1   **Photo.**   *Perf. 13½x14*

C56	A101	60f Bicycling	2.00	.80
C57	A101	75f Fencing	2.40	1.10
C58	A101	120f Butterfly catching	3.75	1.50
		Nos. C56-C58 (3)	8.15	3.40

Two 300f souvenir sheets exist.

Argentina 1978 Winners' Type

World cup emblem and various soccer players.

1980, June 1   **Photo.**   *Perf. 14*

C59	A102	60f gold & multi	1.00	.50
C60	A102	75f gold & multi	1.40	.65
C61	A102	80f gold & multi	1.50	.75
C62	A102	100f gold & multi	1.60	1.10
		Nos. C59-C62 (4)	5.50	3.00

Two 225f souvenir sheets exist.

19th Anniv. of Sept. 26th Revolution (1981) — AP11

1982, Jan. 25   **Litho.**   *Perf. 14*

C63	AP11	75f Map	.45	.25
C64	AP11	125f Map in sunset	.70	.40
C65	AP11	325f Dove in natl. colors	2.00	1.25
a.		Souvenir sheet of 1	5.00	5.00
C66	AP11	400f Jets	2.25	1.40
		Nos. C63-C66 (4)	5.40	3.30

Al-Hasan Ibn Al-Hamadani, Writer — AP12

1982, Feb. 1

C67	AP12	125f green & multi	1.25	.60
C68	AP12	325f blue & multi	2.75	1.40

Souvenir Sheet

C69	AP12	375f multi	3.50	3.50

No. C69 contains one stamp (36x46mm). For surcharge see No. C138.

World Food Day — AP13

Designs: No. C76a, Eggplants. No. C76b, Tomatoes. No. C76c, Beets, peas. No. C76d, Cauliflower, carrots. No. C77a, Dove. No. C77b, Water birds. No. C77c, Fish. No. C77d, Geese.

1982, Mar. 1   **Litho.**   *Perf. 14*

C70	AP13	25f Rabbits	.50
C71	AP13	50f Rooster, Hens	1.00
C72	AP13	60f Turkeys	1.25
C73	AP13	75f Sheep	1.50
C74	AP13	100f Cattle	2.00
C75	AP13	125f Deer	2.50
		Nos. C70-C75 (6)	8.75

Souvenir Sheets

76		Sheet of 4	2.00
a.-d.	AP13	100f, any single	.50
77		Sheet of 4	2.50
a.-d.	AP13	125f, any single	.60

For surcharges see Nos. C139, C144.

1980 Summer Olympics, Moscow AP14

1982, Apr. 1

C78	AP14	25f Gymnastics	
C79	AP14	50f Pole vault	
C80	AP14	60f Javelin	
C81	AP14	75f Running	
C82	AP14	100f Basketball	
C83	AP14	125f Soccer	

Two souvenir sheets of 4 exist: 100f, picturing boxing, wrestling, canoeing, swimming, and 125f, picturing weight lifting, discus, long jump, fencing.
For surcharges see Nos. C140, C145.

Aviation — AP15

Various space and aircraft.

1982, May 21

C86	AP15	25f multi	
C87	AP15	50f multi	
C88	AP15	60f multi	
C89	AP15	75f multi	
C90	AP15	100f multi	
C91	AP15	125f multi	

Two souvenir sheets of 4 exist, 100f and 125f, picturing various aircraft and satellites.
For surcharges see Nos. C141, C146.

Intl. Year of the Disabled — AP16

Designs: Nos. C94-C99, Diff. flowers.
No. C100a, Emblem, natl. flag. b, Emblem on globe. c, Natl. colors, UN emblems. d, Disabled man, gifts, nurse.
No. C101a, Flags, globe and nurse. b, UN emblems, natl. flag. c, Emblem, disabled man. d, UN emblem, nurse.

1982, June 1

C94	AP16	25f	multi
C95	AP16	50f	multi
C96	AP16	60f	multi
C97	AP16	75f	multi
C98	AP16	100f	multi
C99	AP16	125f	multi

Souvenir Sheets

C100		Sheet of 4
a.-d.	AP16 100f, any single	
C101		Sheet of 4
a.-d.	AP16 125f, any single	

For surcharge see No. C147.

Telecommunications Progress — AP17

Designs: 25f, FNRR communication center. 50f, Dish receivers, satellite, globe. 60f, Broadcast towers, dish receivers. 75f, Receivers, birds over plain. 100f, Receivers, satellite, telegraph key. No. C107, Receivers, passenger jet, Earth.
No. C108a, Receivers, Earth. b, Earth, television, flag and camera. c, Computer. d, Skyscraper, Earth, telephone.
No. C109a, Receivers, satellite, ship. b, Communication center, bolts of energy, receivers. c, Receivers, jet, ship, train, car, carriage. d, Radar.

1982, July 1   Litho.   Perf. 14

C102	AP17	25f	multi
C103	AP17	50f	multi
C104	AP17	60f	multi
C105	AP17	75f	multi
C106	AP17	100f	multi
C107	AP17	125f	multi

Souvenir Sheets

C108		Sheet of 4
a.-d.	AP17 100f any single	
C109		Sheet of 4
a.-d.	AP17 100f any single	

For surcharges see Nos. C142, C148.

TB Bacillus Centenary — AP18

1982   Litho.   Perf. 14

C110	AP18	25f	multi
C111	AP18	50f	multi
C112	AP18	60f	multi
C113	AP18	75f	multi
C114	AP18	100f	multi
C115	AP18	125f	multi

Souvenir Sheets

C116		Sheet of 4, Fruit
a.	AP18 100f, any single	
C117		Sheet of 4, Flowers
a.	AP18 125f, any single	

For surcharges see Nos. C143, C149.

1982 World Cup Soccer Championships, Spain — AP19

Various soccer plays.

1982, Sept. 1   Perf. 14

C118	AP19	25f	multi
C119	AP19	50f	multi
C120	AP19	60f	multi
C121	AP19	75f	multi
C122	AP19	100f	multi
C123	AP19	125f	multi

Palestinian Children's Day — AP20

1982, Oct. 20

C126	AP20	75f	Boy
C127	AP20	125f	Girl
C128	AP20	325f	Boy and girl
a.			Souvenir sheet of 1

Arab Postal Union, 30th Anniv. — AP21

1982, Dec. 1

C129	AP21	75f	yellow & multi
C130	AP21	125f	green & multi
C131	AP21	325f	magenta & multi
a.			Souvenir sheet of 1

1984 Summer Olympics, Los Angeles — AP22

1984, Nov. 15

C132	AP22	20f	Wrestling
C133	AP22	30f	Boxing
C134	AP22	40f	Running
C135	AP22	60f	Hurdling
C136	AP22	150f	Pole vault
C137	AP22	325f	Javelin throw

Two souvenir sheets of four 75f stamps exist picturing water sports, gymnastics, weightlifting, shot put and discus throwing.

No. C67 Surcharged

Nos. 459, 461, 463, 466, 474, 483, 486, 522, C73, C75, C81, C83, C89, C91, C97, C105, C107, C113 & C115 Surcharged with New Value and "AIR MAIL"

1993, Jan. 1   Perfs, etc. as Before

C138	AP12	3r on 125f #C67
C139	AP13	3r on 125f #C75
C140	AP14	3r on 125f #C83
C141	AP15	3r on 125f #C91
C142	AP17	3r on 125f #C107
C143	AP18	3r on 125f #C115
C144	AP13	5r on 75f #C73
C145	AP14	5r on 75f #C81
C146	AP15	5r on 75f #C89
C147	AP16	5r on 75f #C97
C148	AP17	5r on 75f #C105
C149	AP18	5r on 75f #C113
C150	A126	8r on 425f #459
C151	A127	8r on 425f #461
C152	A128	8r on 425f #463
C153	A129	8r on 425f #466
C154	A130	8r on 425f #474
C155	A132	8r on 425f #483
C156	A133	8r on 425f #486
C157	A142	12r on 850f #522

Size and location of surcharge varies.

POSTAGE DUE STAMPS

D1

1942   Litho.   Wmk. 258   Perf. 12½

J1	D1	1b	org & yel grn	.20	.20
J2	D1	2b	org & yel grn	.25	.25
J3	D1	4b	org & yel grn	.45	.45
J4	D1	6b	org & brt ultra	.55	.55
J5	D1	8b	org & brt ultra	.80	.80
J6	D1	10b	org & brt ultra	1.00	1.00
J7	D1	12b	org & brt ultra	1.50	1.50
J8	D1	20b	org & brt ultra	3.00	3.00
		Nos. J1-J8 (8)		7.75	7.75

Yemen had no postage due system. Nos. J1-J8 were used for regular postage. See Nos. 66-67 for surcharges.

YEMEN, PEOPLE'S DEMOCRATIC REPUBLIC OF

'pē-pəls ri-'pə-blik of 'ye-mən

LOCATION — Southern Arabia
GOVT. — Republic
AREA — 111,074 sq. mi.
POP. — 2,030,000 (est. 1981)
CAPITAL — Aden

The People's Republic of Southern Yemen was proclaimed Nov. 30, 1967, when the Federation of South Arabia achieved independence. It consisted of the former British colony of Aden and the protectorates. The name was changed to People's Democratic Republic of Yemen on Nov. 30, 1970. See South Arabia.
The Yemen Arab Republic and the People's Republic of Yemen planned a 30-month unification process scheduled for completion by November 1992. While government ministries merged, both currencies remained valid. A civil war in 1994 delayed the merger.

1,000 Fils = 1 Dinar

> **Catalogue values for all unused stamps in this country are for Never Hinged items.**

People's Republic of Southern Yemen
South Arabia Nos. 3-16 Overprinted in Red or Blue

جمهورية اليمن الجنوبية الشعبية

Nos. 1-10

PEOPLE'S REPUBLIC OF SOUTHERN YEMEN

جمهورية اليمن الجنوبية الشعبية

PEOPLE'S REPUBLIC OF SOUTHERN YEMEN
Nos. 11-14

Perf. 14½x14

1968, Apr. 1   Photo.   Unwmk.

1	A1	5f	blue	.20	.20
2	A1	10f	lt vio bl	.20	.20
3	A1	15f	bl grn	.20	.20
4	A1	20f	green	.20	.20
5	A1	25f	org brn (B)	.20	.20
6	A1	30f	lemon	.20	.20
7	A1	35f	red brn (B)	.25	.20
8	A1	50f	rose red (B)	.35	.25
9	A1	65f	lt yel grn	.45	.30
10	A1	75f	rose car (B)	.60	.40
11	A2	100f	multi (B)	.90	.50
12	A2	250f	multi	1.75	1.00
13	A2	500f	multi (B)	3.25	2.00
14	A2	1d	vio & multi	8.25	5.00
		Nos. 1-14 (14)		17.00	10.85

Globe and Flag A1

Designs: 15f, Revolutionist with broken chain and flames, vert. 50f, Aden Harbor. 100f, Cotton picking.

1968, May 25   Litho.   Perf. 13x12½

15	A1	10f	multi	.20	.20
16	A1	15f	multi	.20	.20
17	A1	50f	multi	.30	.30
18	A1	100f	multi	.65	.65
		Nos. 15-19 (5)		1.65	1.65

Independence Day, Nov. 30, 1967.

Girl Scouts at Campfire A2

Designs: 25f, Three Girl Scouts, vert. 50f, Three Girl Scout leaders.

Perf. 13½

1968, Sept. 21   Litho.   Unwmk.

19	A2	10f	ultra & sepia	.30	.30
20	A2	25f	org brn & Prus bl	.40	.40
21	A2	50f	yel, bl & brn	.80	.80
		Nos. 19-21 (3)		1.50	1.50

Girl Scout movement in Southern Yemen, established 1966 (in Aden).

Revolutionary — A3

"Freedom-Socialism-Unity" A4

King of Ausan, Alabaster Statue A5

Design: 30f, Radfan Mountains where first revolutionary fell.

1968, Oct. 14   **Unwmk.**   *Perf. 13*
22	A3	20f brn & lt bl	.25	.25
23	A3	30f grn & brn	.35	.35
24	A4	100f ver & yel	.90	.90
		Nos. 22-24 (3)	1.50	1.50

Revolution Day (revolution of Oct. 14, 1963).

1968, Dec. 28   **Litho.**   *Perf. 13*

Antiquities of Southern Yemen: 35f, African-type sculpture of a man. 50f, Winged bull, Assyrian-type bas-relief, horiz. 65f, Bull's head (Moon God), alabaster plaque, 230 B.C., horiz.

25	A5	5f olive & bister	.20	.20
26	A5	35f maroon & lt bl	.30	.30
27	A5	50f bister & blue	.65	.65
28	A5	65f grnsh bl & lilac	.85	.85
		Nos. 25-28 (4)	2.00	2.00

A6

A7

Martyr Monument, Steamer Point, Aden.

1969, Feb. 11   **Litho.**   *Perf. 13*
29	A6	15f yellow & multi	.20	.20
30	A6	35f emerald & multi	.20	.20
31	A6	100f orange & multi	.60	.60
		Nos. 29-31 (3)	1.00	1.00

Issued for Martyr Day.

1969, June 1   **Litho.**   *Perf. 13*

Albert Thomas Monument, Geneva, and ILO emblem.

32	A7	10f brt grn, blk & lt brn	.25	.25
33	A7	35f car rose, blk & lt brn	.75	.75

50th anniv. of the ILO, and to honor founder Albert Thomas.

Classroom — A8

1969, Sept. 8   **Litho.**   *Perf. 13*
34	A8	35f orange & multi	.40	.40
35	A8	100f yellow & multi	1.10	1.10

International Literacy Day, Sept. 8.

Mahatma Gandhi — A9

1969, Sept. 27   **Litho.**   *Perf. 13*
36	A9	35f lt ultra & vio brn	1.10	.40

Mohandas K. Gandhi (1869-1948), leader in India's fight for independence.

Family A10

1969, Oct. 1
37	A10	25f lt grn & multi	.50	.40
38	A10	75f car rose & multi	1.00	.60

Issued for Family Day.

UN Headquarters, NYC — A11

1969, Oct. 24   *Perf. 13*
39	A11	20f rose red & multi	.40	.20
40	A11	65f emer & multi	.85	.40

Issued for United Nations Day.

Map and Flag of Southern Yemen — A12

40f, 50f, Tractors, flag (agricultural progress).

1969, Nov. 30   **Litho.**   **Unwmk.**

Size: 41x24½mm
41	A12	15f multi	.20	.20
42	A12	35f multi	.40	.20

Size: 37x37mm
43	A12	40f blue & multi	.45	.25
44	A12	50f brown & multi	.70	.35
		Nos. 41-44 (4)	1.75	1.00

Second anniversary of independence.

Map of Arab League Countries, Flag and Emblem — A13

1970, Mar. 22   **Unwmk.**   *Perf. 13*
45	A13	35f lt bl & multi	.75	.25

25th anniversary of the Arab League.

Lenin — A14   Fighter — A15

1970, Apr. 22   **Litho.**   *Perf. 13*
46	A14	75f multi	1.25	.50

Lenin (1870-1924), Russian communist leader.

1970, May 15

Designs: 35f, Underground soldier and plane destroyed on ground. 50f, Fighting people hailing Arab liberation flag, horiz.

47	A15	15f grn, red & blk	.20	.20
48	A15	35f grn, bl, red & blk	.40	.35
49	A15	50f grn, blk & red	.55	.45
		Nos. 47-49 (3)	1.15	1.00

Issued for Palestine Day.

UPU Headquarters, Bern — A16

1970, May 22   **Litho.**   *Perf. 13*
50	A16	15f org & brt grn	.40	.20
51	A16	65f yel & car rose	.85	.40

New UPU Headquarters in Bern.

Yemeni Costume — A17

Regional Costumes: 15f, 20f, Women's costumes. 50f, Three men of Aden.

1970, July 2   **Litho.**   *Perf. 13*
52	A17	10f yel & multi	.25	.20
53	A17	15f lt lil & multi	.25	.20
54	A17	20f lt bl & multi	.40	.20
55	A17	50f multi	.85	.30
		Nos. 52-55 (4)	1.75	.90

Camel and Calf — A18

Designs: 25f, Goats. 35f, Arabian oryx. 65f, Socotra dwarf cows.

1970, Aug. 31   **Litho.**   *Perf. 13*
56	A18	15f dk brn & multi	.25	.20
57	A18	25f car rose & multi	.45	.30
58	A18	35f ultra & multi	.90	.60
59	A18	65f brt grn & multi	1.40	.90
		Nos. 56-59 (4)	3.00	2.00

A19

35f, Natl. Front Organization Headquarters. 50f, Farm worker, 1970, battle scene, 1963.

1970, Oct. 14   **Litho.**   *Perf. 13*

Size: 41½x29½mm
60	A19	25f multi	.35	.20

Size: 56½x27mm
61	A19	35f multi	.45	.30

Size: 41x24½mm
62	A19	50f multi	.70	.40
		Nos. 60-62 (3)	1.50	.90

7th anniversary of Oct. 14 Revolution.

UN Headquarters, Emblem — A20

1970, Oct. 24   **Litho.**   *Perf. 13*
63	A20	10f org & bl	.40	.20
64	A20	65f brt pink & bl	.85	.45

25th anniversary of the United Nations.

People's Democratic Republic of Yemen

Temples at Philae — A21

1971, Feb. 1   **Litho.**   *Perf. 13½x13*
65	A21	5f violet & multi	.20	.20
66	A21	35f blue & multi	.40	.25
67	A21	65f green & multi	.95	.55
		Nos. 65-67 (3)	1.55	1.00

UNESCO campaign to save the monuments in Nubia.

Scales, Book and Sword A22

1971, Mar. 1   *Perf. 13x12½*
68	A22	10f brt pink & multi	.20	.20
69	A22	15f brt grn & multi	.20	.20
70	A22	35f lt ultra & multi	.30	.30
71	A22	50f rose & multi	.40	.40
		Nos. 68-71 (4)	1.10	1.10

First Constitution, 1971.

Men of 3 Races, Human Rights Emblem A23

1971, Mar. 21
72	A23	20f lt bl & multi	.20	.20
73	A23	35f grn & multi	.40	.40
74	A23	75f lt vio & multi	.65	.65
		Nos. 72-74 (3)	1.25	1.25

Intl. year against racial discrimination.

Map and Flag — A24

"Brothers' Blood" Tree, Socotra Island — A25

1971-77		Litho.	Perf. 13½	
75	A24	5f yel & multi	.20	.20
76	A24	10f grn & multi	.20	.20
77	A24	15f yel & multi	.20	.20
78	A24	20f org & multi	.20	.20
79	A24	25f bl & multi	.20	.20
80	A24	35f red org & multi	.25	.20
81	A24	41f vio & multi	.35	.20
82	A24	50f yel grn & multi	.50	.30
82A	A24	60f red & multi	1.00	.40
83	A24	65f pale vio & multi	.65	.45
84	A24	80f org brn & multi	.75	.55
84A	A24	90f ol & multi	1.00	.50
		Perf. 13		
84B	A25	110f brn & multi	1.50	.65
85	A25	125f ultra & multi	1.25	1.10
86	A25	250f org & multi	2.25	1.40
87	A25	500f multi	4.50	2.75
88	A25	1d grn & multi	10.00	6.00
		Nos. 75-88 (17)	25.00	15.50

Issued: #82A, 84A-84B, 10/17/77; others, 4/1/71.
See Nos. 332-333. For surcharges see Yemen Nos. 628, 638.

Machine Gun and Map A26

Arms with Wrench and Cogwheel A27

Designs: 45f, Woman fighter and flame, horiz. 50f, Fighter, factories and rainbow.

1971, June 9		Litho.	Perf. 12½x13	
89	A26	15f multi	.20	.20
90	A26	45f green & multi	.50	.30
91	A26	50f multi	.80	.50
		Nos. 89-91 (3)	1.50	1.00

Armed revolution in the Arabian Gulf.

1971, June 22

25f, Torch, factories, symbols. 65f, Windmill.

92	A27	15f blue & multi	.25	.20
93	A27	25f multi	.75	.55
94	A27	65f multi	1.25	.75
		Nos. 92-94 (3)	2.25	1.55

2nd anniversary of the revolution of June 22, 1969 (Corrective Move).
A 20f picturing a fighter holding rifle and flag, with flag colors transposed, was withdrawn on day of issue.

Revolutionary Emblem — A28

40f, Map of southern Arabia & flag of republic.

1971, Sept. 26.

95	A28	10f yellow & multi	.20	.20
96	A28	40f lt grn & multi	.60	.40

9th anniv. of the revolution of Sept. 26.

Gamal Abdel Nasser — A29

UNICEF Emblem, Children of the World — A30

1971, Sept. 28		Litho.	Perf. 12½x13	
97	A29	65f multi	.80	.50

1st anniv. of the death of Gamal Abdel Nasser (1918-1970), President of Egypt.

1971, Dec. 11			Perf. 13x13½	
98	A30	15f org, car & blk	.20	.20
99	A30	40f lt ultra, car & blk	.30	.25
100	A30	50f yel grn, car & blk	.50	.40
		Nos. 98-100 (3)	1.00	.85

25th anniv. of UNICEF.

Pigeons A31

Birds: 40f, Partridge. 65f, Partridge and guinea fowl. 100f, European kite.

1971, Dec. 22			Perf. 13½x13	
101	A31	5f bl, blk & car	.25	.20
102	A31	40f salmon & multi	.90	.50
103	A31	65f brt grn, blk & car	2.10	.75
104	A31	100f yel, blk & car	3.50	1.50
		Nos. 101-104 (4)	6.75	2.95

Dhow under Construction A32

Design: 80f, Dhow under sail, vert.

1972, Feb. 15		Perf. 13½x13, 13x13½		
105	A32	25f bl, brn & yel	.40	.25
106	A32	80f lt bl & multi	1.25	.90

Band — A33

Designs: 25f, 40f, 80f, Various folk dances.

1972, Apr. 8		Litho.	Perf. 13	
107	A33	10f lt grn & multi	.20	.20
108	A33	25f org & multi	.30	.20
109	A33	40f red & multi	.60	.35
110	A33	80f blue & multi	1.10	.75
		Nos. 107-110 (4)	2.20	1.55

Palestinian Fighter and Barbed Wire — A34

1972, May 15

111	A34	5f emerald & multi	.25	.20
112	A34	20f blue & multi	.50	.30
113	A34	65f org ver & multi	1.25	.75
		Nos. 111-113 (3)	2.00	1.25

Struggle for Palestine liberation.

Policemen on Parade A35

Design: 80f, Militia women on parade.

1972, June 20		Litho.	Perf. 13½	
114	A35	25f lt bl & multi	.30	.20
115	A35	80f bl grn & multi	1.25	.75
a.		Souv. sheet of 2, #114-115	4.25	4.25

Police Day. No. 115a sold for 150f.

Start of Bicycle Race A36

15f Parade of young women. 40f, Yemeni Guides & Scouts on parade. 80f, Acrobats, vert.

1972, July 20		Litho.	Perf. 13½	
116	A36	10f lt bl & multi	.25	.20
117	A36	15f multi	.25	.20
118	A36	40f buff & multi	.50	.35
119	A36	80f lt ultra & multi	1.25	.50
		Nos. 116-119 (4)	2.25	1.25

Turtle A37

1972, Sept. 2		Litho.	Perf. 13	
120	A37	15f Shown	.45	.20
121	A37	40f Sailfish	.60	.35
122	A37	65f Kingfish	.75	.45
123	A37	125f Spiny lobster	1.50	.80
		Nos. 120-123 (4)	3.30	1.80

Book Year Emblem A38

1972, Sept. 9				
124	A38	40f red, ultra & yel	.55	.35
125	A38	65f org, ultra & yel	.85	.60

International Book Year 1972.

Farm Couple and Fields A39

1972, Nov. 23		Litho.	Perf. 13	
126	A39	10f orange & multi	.20	.20
127	A39	25f rose lilac & multi	.45	.30
128	A39	40f red & multi	.75	.50
		Nos. 126-128 (3)	1.40	1.00

Lands Day, publicizing land reforms.

Militia — A40

20f, Soldier guarding village. 65f, Industrial, agricultural and educational progress, vert.

1972, Dec. 2		Litho.	Perf. 13	
129	A40	5f multi	.20	.20
130	A40	20f multi	.20	.20
131	A40	65f multi	.45	.45
a.		Souv. sheet of 3, #129-131, imperf.	1.75	1.75
		Nos. 129-131 (3)	.85	.85

5th anniversary of independence.

Census Chart A41

1973, Apr. 3		Litho.	Perf. 12½x13½	
132	A41	25f org, emer & ol	.20	.20
133	A41	40f rose, bl & vio	.35	.35

Population census 1973.

WHO Emblem and "25" — A42

1973, Apr. 7		Perf. 14x12½, 12½x14		
134	A42	5f "25" and WHO emblem, vert	.20	.20
135	A42	20f Shown	.20	.20
136	A42	125f "25" and WHO emblem	.60	.60
		Nos. 134-136 (3)	1.00	1.00

25th anniv. of the WHO.

Elephant Bay A43

Tourist Publicity: 20f, Taweels Tanks Reservoir, vert. 25f, Shibam Town. 100f, Al-Mohdar Mosque, Tarim.

1973, June 9		Litho.	Perf. 13	
137	A43	20f multi	.20	.20
138	A43	25f multi	.20	.20
139	A43	40f multi	.30	.30
140	A43	100f multi	.55	.55
		Nos. 137-140 (4)	1.25	1.25

Office Buildings and Slum,
Aden — A44

Design: 80f, Intersection, Aden, vert.

1973, Aug. 4   Litho.   Perf. 13
141	A44	20f multi	.20	.20
142	A44	80f multi	.50	.50

Nationalization of buildings.

Army
Unit
A45

People's Army: 20f, Four marching soldiers.
40f, Sailors on parade. 80f, Tanks.

1973, Sept. 1
143	A45	10f multi	.20	.20
144	A45	20f multi	.20	.20
145	A45	40f multi	.30	.30
146	A45	80f multi	.50	.50
		Nos. 143-146 (4)	1.20	1.20

FAO
Emblem,
Loading
Food
A46

Design: 80f, Workers and grain sacks.

1973, Dec. 19   Litho.   Perf. 13
147	A46	20f blue & multi	.20	.20
148	A46	80f blue & multi	.50	.50

World Food Program, 10th anniversary.

Letter and
UPU
Emblem
A47

UPU Emblem
and Yemeni
Flag — A48

Map of Yemen,
UPU
Emblem — A49

UPU cent.: 20f, "100" formed by people,
and UPU emblem.

1974, Oct. 9   Litho.   Perf. 12½x13½
149	A47	5f multi	.20	.20
150	A47	20f multi	.20	.20
151	A48	40f multi	.35	.35
152	A49	125f multi	.60	.60
		Nos. 149-152 (4)	1.35	1.35

Irrigation System — A50

Progress in Agriculture: 20f, Bulldozer
pushing soil. 100f, Tractors plowing field.

1974   Litho.   Perf. 13
153	A50	10f multi	.20	.20
154	A50	20f multi	.20	.20
155	A50	50f multi	.50	.50
		Nos. 153-155 (3)	.90	.90

Lathe
Operator — A51

Industrial progress: 40f, Printers. 80f,
Women textile workers, horiz.

1975, May 1   Litho.   Perf. 13
156	A51	10f multi	.20	.20
157	A51	40f multi	.30	.30
158	A51	80f multi	.50	.50
		Nos. 156-158 (3)	1.00	1.00

Yemeni
Woman — A52

Designs: Various women's costumes.

1975, Nov. 15   Litho.   Perf. 11½x12
159	A52	5f blk & ocher	.20	.20
160	A52	10f blk & vio	.20	.20
161	A52	15f blk & olive	.20	.20
162	A52	25f blk & rose lil	.25	.25
163	A52	40f blk & Prus bl	.40	.40
164	A52	50f blk & org brn	.60	.60
		Nos. 159-164 (6)	1.85	1.85

Women
Factory
Workers,
IWY
Emblem
A53

1975, Dec. 30   Litho.   Perf. 12x11½
165	A53	40f blk & salmon	.25	.25
166	A53	50f blk & yel grn	.40	.40

International Women's Year 1975.

Soccer Player
and
Field — A54

Designs: Different scenes from soccer.

1976, Apr. 1   Litho.   Perf. 11½x12
167	A54	5f lt bl & brn	.20	.20
168	A54	40f yel & green	.30	.30
169	A54	80f salmon & vio	.50	.50
		Nos. 167-169 (3)	1.00	1.00

Rocket Take-off
from
Moon — A55

15f, Alexander Satalov. 40f, Lunokhod on
moon, horiz. 65f, Valentina Tereshkova,
rocket.

Perf. 11½x12, 12x11½
1976, Apr. 17   Litho.
170	A55	10f multi	.20	.20
171	A55	15f multi	.20	.20
172	A55	40f multi	.40	.40
173	A55	65f multi	.55	.55
		Nos. 170-173 (4)	1.35	1.35

Soviet cosmonauts and space program.

Traffic
Policemen
A56

1977, Apr. 16   Litho.   Perf. 14
174	A56	25f red & blk	.30	.30
175	A56	60f yel & blk	.60	.60
176	A56	75f grn & blk	.75	.75
177	A56	110f dp bl & blk	1.00	1.00
		Nos. 174-177 (4)	2.65	2.65

Traffic change to right side of road.

APU
Emblem — A57

1977, Apr. 12   Litho.   Perf. 13½
178	A57	20f lt bl & multi	.20	.20
179	A57	60f gray & multi	.40	.40
180	A57	70f lt grn & multi	.50	.50
181	A57	90f bl grn & multi	.55	.55
		Nos. 178-181 (4)	1.65	1.65

Arab Postal Union, 25th anniversary.

Congress
Decree
and Red
Star
A58

Designs: 25f, Pres. Salim Rubi'a Ali, Council members Ali Nasser Muhamed and Abdul
Farta Ismail. 65f, Women's militia on parade.
95f, Aerial view of textile mill.

1977, May   Photo.   Perf. 13
182	A58	25f grn, gold & dk brn	.20	.20
183	A58	35f red, gold & lt bl	.25	.25
184	A58	65f bl, gold & lil	.40	.40
185	A58	95f org, gold & grn	.45	.45
		Nos. 182-185 (4)	1.30	1.30

Unification Congress, 1st anniversary.

Afrivoluta
Pringlei
A59

Shells: 60f, Festilyria duponti, vert. 110f,
Conus splendidulus. 180f, Cypraea
4broderipii.

1977, July 16   Litho.   Perf. 13½
186	A59	60f multi	.40	.30
187	A59	90f multi	.60	.35
188	A59	110f multi	1.00	.60
189	A59	180f multi	1.40	1.00
		Nos. 186-189 (4)	3.40	2.20

Emblem and
Flag — A60

Designs: 20f, Man with broken chain. 90f,
Pipeline, agriculture and industry. 110f, Flag,
symbolic tree and hands holding tools.

1977, Nov. 30   Litho.   Perf. 13½
190	A60	5f blk & multi	.20	.20
191	A60	20f blk & multi	.20	.20
192	A60	90f blk & multi	.30	.20
193	A60	110f blk & multi	.50	.25
		Nos. 190-193 (4)	1.20	.85

10th anniversary of independence.

Dome of
the Rock
A61

1978, May 15   Perf. 12
194	A61	5f multi	.65	.35

Palestinian fighters & families. See #264A.

Congress
Emblem and
"CUBA" — A62

Designs: 60f, Congress emblem. 90f, Festival emblem as flower. 110f, Festival emblem,
dove, young man and woman.

1978, June 22   Litho.   Perf. 14
195	A62	5f multi	.20	.20
196	A62	60f multi	.55	.35
197	A62	90f multi	.70	.40
198	A62	110f multi	.90	.60
		Nos. 195-198 (4)	2.35	1.55

11th World Youth Festival, Havana.

Silver Ornaments — A63

Designs: Various silver ornaments.

1978, July 22   Litho.   Perf. 13½
199	A63	10f blk & multi	.20	.20
200	A63	15f blk & multi	.20	.20
201	A63	20f blk & multi	.20	.20
202	A63	60f blk & multi	.20	.20
203	A63	90f blk & multi	.40	.25
204	A63	110f blk & multi	.50	.30
		Nos. 199-204 (6)	1.70	1.35

For surcharge see Yemen No. 629.

Yemeni Musical Instruments — A64

1978, Aug. 26   Perf. 14
205	A64	35f Almarfaai	.20	.20
206	A64	60f Almizmar	.25	.20
207	A64	90f Alqnboos	.30	.20
208	A64	110f Simsimiya	.50	.30
		Nos. 205-208 (4)	1.25	.90

For surcharge see Yemen No. 630.

"V" for Vanguard A65

Man with Palm, Factories — A66

1978, Oct. 11   Litho.   Perf. 14
209	A65	5f multi	.20	.20
210	A65	20f multi	.20	.20
211	A65	60f multi	.25	.20
212	A65	180f multi	.50	.30
		Nos. 209-212 (4)	1.15	.90

1st Conf. of Vanguard Party, Oct. 11-13.

1978, Oct. 14

Designs: 10f, Palm branches, broken chains, horiz. 60f, Candle and "15." 110f, Woman and man with rifle, "15."

213	A66	10f multi	.20	.20
214	A66	35f multi	.20	.20
215	A66	60f multi	.40	.20
216	A66	110f multi	.70	.40
		Nos. 213-216 (4)	1.50	1.00

15th Revolution Day.
For surcharge see Yemen No. 631.

Child, Map of Arabia and IYC Emblem — A67

1979, Mar. 20   Litho.   Perf. 13½
217	A67	15f multi	.20	.20
218	A67	20f multi	.20	.20
219	A67	60f multi	.25	.20
220	A67	90f multi	.35	.20
		Nos. 217-220 (4)	1.00	.80

International Year of the Child.

Sickle, Star, Tractor, Wheat and Dove — A68

Designs: 35f, Pylon, star, compass, wheat and hammer. 60f, Students, worker and clock. 90f, Woman with raised arms, doves and star.

1979, June 22   Litho.   Perf. 14
221	A68	20f multi	.20	.20
222	A68	35f multi	.20	.20
223	A68	60f multi	.25	.20
224	A68	90f multi	.35	.20
		Nos. 221-224 (4)	1.00	.80

Corrective Move, 10th anniversary.

Yemen #52, Hill A69

Hill and: 110f, Yemen #56. 250f, Aden #12.

1979, Aug. 27   Litho.   Perf. 14
225	A69	90f multi	.30	.20
226	A69	110f multi	.40	.25

Souvenir Sheet
227	A69	250f multi	1.00	1.00

Sir Rowland Hill (1795-1879), originator of penny postage.

Book, World Map, Arab Achievements — A70

1979, Sept. 26   Litho.   Perf. 14
228	A70	60f multi	.25	.20

Party Emblem — A71

Cassia Adenesis — A72

1979, Oct. 13   Perf. 14½x14
229	A71	60f multi	.25	.20

Yemeni Socialist Party, 1st anniversary.

1979, Nov. 30   Litho.   Perf. 13½

Flowers: 90f, Nerium oleander. 110f, Calligonum comosum. 180f, Adenium obesium.

230	A72	20f multi	.20	.20
231	A72	90f multi	.65	.35
232	A72	110f multi	1.00	.50
233	A72	180f multi	1.25	.65
		Nos. 230-233 (4)	3.10	1.70

For surcharge see Yemen No. 632.

First Anniv. of Iranian Revolution — A73

1980, Feb. 12   Litho.   Perf. 13½
234	A73	60f multi	.25	.25

Dido A74

1980, Mar. 5   Litho.   Perf. 13½
235	A74	110f shown	.65	.30
236	A74	180f Anglia	.90	.40
237	A74	250f India	1.25	.50
		Nos. 235-237 (3)	2.80	1.20

For surcharge see Yemen No. 633.

Basket Maker, London 1980 Emblem — A75

1980, May 6   Litho.   Perf. 14
238	A75	60f shown	.20	.20
239	A75	90f Hubble bubble pipe maker	.30	.20
240	A75	110f Weaver	.40	.25
241	A75	250f Potter	.90	.50
		Nos. 238-241 (4)	1.80	1.15

London 1980 Intl. Stamp Exhib., May 6-14.

Hemprich's Skink — A76

1980, May 8   Litho.   Perf. 14
242	A76	20f shown	.20	.20
243	A76	35f Mole viper	.30	.20
244	A76	110f Carter's day gecko	.75	.30
245	A76	180f Cobra	1.25	.60
		Nos. 242-245 (4)	2.50	1.30

For surcharge see Yemen No. 634.

Misha and Olympic Emblem — A77

Farmers Armed — A78

1980, July 19   Litho.   Perf. 12½x12
246	A77	110f multi	.50	.30

For overprint see No. 287.

1980, Oct. 17   Perf. 13½
247	A78	50f Armed farmers working, horiz.	.30	.20
248	A78	90f shown	.45	.30
249	A78	110f Sickle (wheat) and fist	.60	.40
		Nos. 247-249 (3)	1.35	.90

10th anniversary of farmers' uprising.

110th Birth Anniversary of Lenin — A79

1980, Nov. 7   Litho.   Perf. 12
250	A79	35f multi	.20	.20

Douglas DC-3 — A80

1981, Mar. 11   Litho.   Perf. 13½
251	A80	60f shown	.20	.20
252	A80	90f Boeing 707	.40	.20
253	A80	250f DHC Dash 7	1.00	.50
		Nos. 251-253 (3)	1.60	.90

Democratic Yemen Airlines, 10th anniv.

Ras Boradli Earth Satellite Station A82

1981, June 22   Litho.   Perf. 12
257	A82	60f multi	.40	.30

Conocarpus Lancifolius — A83

Supreme People's Council, 10th Anniv. — A84

1981, Aug. 1   Litho.   Perf. 12
258	A83	90f shown	.30	.20
259	A83	180f Ficus vasta	.70	.40
260	A83	250f Maerua crassifolia	1.00	.65
		Nos. 258-260 (3)	2.00	1.25

1981, Aug. 18   Litho.   Perf. 15x14½
261	A84	180f multi	.65	.40

Desert Fox — A85

1981, Sept. 26   Litho.   Perf. 14½
262 A85 50f shown   .30 .20
263 A85 90f South Arabian
                leopard   .60 .30
264 A85 250f Ibex   1.40 .75
         Nos. 262-264 (3)   2.30 1.25

No. 194 Redrawn
1981, Oct. 15   Litho.   Perf. 12
Size: 25x27mm
264A A61 5f multi   .20 .20
         Denomination in upper right.

Tephrosia
Apollinea — A86

1981, Nov. 30   Litho.   Perf. 13½
265 A86 50f shown   .20 .20
266 A86 90f Citrullus colo-
                cynthis   .30 .20
267 A86 110f Aloe sqarrosa   .40 .20
268 A86 250f Lawsonia inermis 1.00 .60
         Nos. 265-268 (4)   1.90 1.20
For surcharge see Yemen No. 635.

Intl. Year
of the
Disabled
A87

1981, Dec. 12   Litho.   Perf. 14½
269 A87 50f multi   .20 .20
270 A87 100f multi   .40 .20
271 A87 150f multi   .60 .40
         Nos. 269-271 (3)   1.20 .80

TB Bacillus Centenary — A88

1982, Mar. 24   Litho.   Perf. 14½
272 A88 50f multi   .30 .20

30th
Anniv. of
Arab
Postal
Union
A89

1982, Apr. 12   Litho.   Perf. 14
273 A89 100f multi   .50 .30

1982
World Cup
A90

Designs: Various soccer players.
1982, June 13   Litho.   Perf. 14
274 A90 50f multi   .25 .20
275 A90 100f multi   .50 .30
276 A90 150f multi   .70 .45
277 A90 200f multi   1.00 .60
  a. Souv. sheet of 4, #274-277 2.50 1.50
         Nos. 274-277 (4)   2.45 1.55
For overprints see Nos. 281-284.

60th
Anniv.
of USSR
A93

1982, Dec. 22   Litho.   Perf. 12½x12
280 A93 50f Flags, arms   .50 .35

Nos. 274-277, 277a Ovptd. with
Emblem and "WORLD CUP /
WINNERS / 1982 / 1st ITALY / 2nd W-
GERMANY / 3rd POLAND / 4th
FRANCE" in Blue

1982, Dec. 30   Litho.   Perf. 14
281 A90 50f multi   .20 .20
282 A90 100f multi   .40 .40
283 A90 150f multi   .60 .60
284 A90 200f multi   .70 .70
  a. Souvenir sheet of 4, #281-284 2.00 2.00
         Nos. 281-284 (4)   1.90 1.90

Palestinian
Solidarity
A94

1983, Apr. 10   Perf. 13½x14½
285 A94 50f Yasser Arafat   .20 .20
286 A94 100f Arafat, Dome of the
                Rock   .40 .40
  a. Souvenir sheet of 1, imperf. .50 .50

No. 246 Ovptd. with TEMBAL '83
Emblem in Yellow
1983, May 21   Perf. 12½x12
287 A77 110f multi   .40 .40

World Communications Year — A95

Designs: 50f, Correspondent, postrider,
ship. 100f, Postman, coach, telegraph. No.
290, Telephones, bus. 200f, Telecommunications. No. 292, Montage.

1983, June 10   Perf. 13x13½
288 A95 50f blk & brt bl   .20 .20
289 A95 100f multi   .40 .40
290 A95 150f multi   .60 .60
291 A95 200f multi   .70 .70
         Nos. 288-291 (4)   1.90 1.90
         Souvenir Sheet
292 A95 150f multi   1.50 1.50

Pablo Picasso (1881-1973),
Painter — A96

Paintings: No. 293, The Poor Family, 1903.
No. 294, Woman with Crow. No. 295a, The
Gourmet. No. 295b, Woman with Child on
Beach. No. 295c, Sitting Beggar. No. 296,
The Solar Family, horiz.

1983, July 25   Perf. 14
293 A96 50f multi   .20 .20
294 A96 100f multi   .40 .40
         Souvenir Sheets
295   Sheet of 3   3.50 3.50
  a. A96 50f multi   .50 .50
  b. A96 100f multi   1.25 1.25
  c. A96 150f multi   1.75 1.75
296 A96 150f multi   8.00 8.00

23rd Pre-Olympics Games,
1984 — A97

1983, July 30
297 A97 25f Show jumping   .20 .20
298 A97 50f Show jumping, diff. .20 .20
299 A97 100f Three-day event   .40 .40
         Nos. 297-299 (3)   .80 .80
         Souvenir Sheets
300   Sheet of 4   5.00 5.00
  a. A97 20f Bay, vert.   1.00 1.00
  b. A97 40f Gray, vert.   1.00 1.00
  c. A97 60f Bay, diff., vert. 1.25 1.25
  d. A97 80f Arabian   1.75 1.75
301 A97 200f Show jumping, diff.,
                vert.   6.75 6.75

Locomotives — A98

1983, Aug. 24   Perf. 14½x15
302 A98 25f P8 steam engine,
                1905   .20 .20
303 A98 50f 880 steam, 1915   .20 .20
304 A98 100f GT 2-4-4, 1923   .40 .40
         Nos. 302-304 (3)   .80 .80
         Souvenir Sheets
305   Sheet of 3   9.00 9.00
  a. A98 40f D51 steam, 1936   2.25 2.25
  b. A98 60f 45 Series, 1937   2.25 2.25
  c. A98 100f PT 47, 1948   4.50 4.50
306 A98 200f P36, 1950   9.00 9.00

Natl.
Revolution,
20th Anniv.
A100

1983, Oct. 15   Litho.   Perf. 13½x13
312 A100 50f shown   .20 .20
313 A100 100f Flag, freedom fighter .40 .40

1st Manned
Flight,
Bicent. — A101

Balloons: 100f, La Montgolfiere prototype.
No. 316a, Lunardi's. No. 316b, Charles and
Robert's. No. 316c, Wiseman's. No. 316d,
Blanchard and Jeffries's. 200f, Five-balloon
craft.

1983, Oct. 25   Perf. 14
314 A101 50f shown   .20 .20
315 A101 100f multi   .40 .40
         Souvenir Sheets
316   Sheet of 4   6.75 6.75
  a. A101 20f multi   1.50 1.50
  b. A101 40f multi   1.50 1.50
  c. A101 60f multi   1.50 1.50
  d. A101 80f multi   2.25 2.25
317 A101 200f multi   8.00 8.00

1984
Winter
Olympics,
Sarajevo
A102

1983, Dec. 28   Litho.   Perf. 14
318 A102 50f Men's downhill
                skiing   .20 .20
319 A102 100f Two-man bobsled .40 .40
         Souvenir Sheets
320   Sheet of 2   6.50 6.50
  a. A102 40f Ski jumping   3.25 3.25
  b. A102 60f Figure skating   3.25 3.25
321 A102 200f Ice hockey   6.50 6.50

1984 Summer Olympics, Los
Angeles — A103

1984, Jan. 24
322 A103 25f Fencing   .20 .20
323 A103 50f Fencing, diff.   .20 .20
324 A103 100f Fencing, diff.   .40 .40
         Nos. 322-324 (3)   .80 .80
         Souvenir Sheets
325   Sheet of 4   5.00 5.00
  a. A103 20f Gymnastics   1.25 1.25
  b. A103 40f Water polo   1.25 1.25
  c. A103 60f Wrestling   1.25 1.25
  d. A103 80f Show jumping   1.25 1.25
326 A103 200f Show jumping,
                diff.   5.00 5.00

Nos. 83 and 84B Surcharged with
Black Squares
1984, May 26   Litho.   Perf. 13½, 13
332 A24 50f on 65f multi
333 A25 100f on 110f multi

Fish — A105

1984, Nov. 25   Litho.   Perf. 11½

334	A105	10f Abalistes stellaris	.20 .20
335	A105	15f Caranx speciocus	.20 .20
336	A105	20f Pomadasys maculatus	.20 .20
337	A105	25f Chaetodon fasciatus	.20 .20
338	A105	35f Pomacanthus imperator	.20 .20
339	A105	50f Rastrelliger kanagurta	.20 .20
340	A105	100f Euthynnus affinis	.40 .40
341	A105	150f Heniochus acuminatus	.60 .60
342	A105	200f Pomacanthus maculosus	.80 .80
343	A105	250f Pterois russellii	1.00 1.00
344	A105	400f Argyrops spinifer	1.60 1.60
345	A105	500f Dasyatis uarnak	2.00 2.00
346	A105	1d Epinephalus chlorostigma	3.75 3.75
347	A105	2d Drepane longimana	8.00 8.00
		Nos. 334-347 (14)	19.35 19.35

For surcharges see Yemen Nos. 636, 640, 642.

Natl. Literacy Campaign A106

1985, Feb. 27   Perf. 12

350	A106	50f Girls writing	.20 .20
351	A106	100f Hand, fountain pen, vert.	.40 .40

Victory Parade, Red Square, Moscow, 1945 — A107

12th World Youth and Students Festival — A108

1985, May 9   Perf. 12x12½

352 A107 100f multi   .40 .40

Defeat of Nazi Germany, end of World War II, 40th anniv.

1985, Aug. 3   Perf. 12

353	A108	50f Emblem	.20 .20
354	A108	100f Hand holding emblem	.40 .40

UNESCO World Heritage Campaign — A109

Natl. Socialist Party, 3rd Gen. Cong. — A110

1985, Aug. 29

355	A109	50f Shibam city	.20 .20
356	A109	50f Close-up of buildings	.20 .20
357	A109	100f Windows	.40 .40
358	A109	100f Door	.40 .40
		Nos. 355-358 (4)	1.20 1.20

Nos. 355-357 horiz.

1985, Oct. 10

359	A110	25f Energy	.20 .20
360	A110	50f Industry	.20 .20
361	A110	100f Agriculture	.40 .40
		Nos. 359-361 (3)	.80 .80

UN Child Survival Campaign — A111

World Food Day — A112

1985, Nov. 28

362	A111	50f Mother feeding child	.20 .20
363	A111	50f Holding child	.20 .20
364	A111	100f Feeding child, diff.	.40 .40
365	A111	100f Breastfeeding	.40 .40
		Nos. 362-365 (4)	1.20 1.20

1986, Jan. 30

366	A112	20f Almihdar Mosque, Aden	.20 .20
367	A112	180f Palm trees	1.00 1.00

UN Food and Agriculture Org., 40th anniv.

Lenin, Red Square, Moscow A113

1986, Feb. 25   Perf. 12x12½

368	A113	75f multi	.45 .45
369	A113	250f multi	1.50 1.50

27th Soviet Communist Party Cong., Moscow.

Costumes Worn at the 1984 Brides Dance Festival — A114

Designs: No. 370, Bride wearing red and green costume, face markings. No. 371, Violet costume. No. 372, Veiled bride. No. 373, Unveiled bride. No. 374, Groom holding dagger. No. 375, Groom holding rifle.

1986, Feb. 27

370	A114	50f multi	.30 .30
371	A114	50f multi	.30 .30
372	A114	50f multi	.30 .30
373	A114	100f multi	.60 .60
374	A114	100f multi	.60 .60
375	A114	100f multi	.60 .60
		Nos. 370-375 (6)	2.70 2.70

Revolution Martyrs A115

1986, Oct. 15   Litho.   Perf. 12

376	A115	75f Abdul Fattah Ismail	.45 .45
377	A115	75f Ali Shayaa Hadi	.45 .45
378	A115	75f Saleh Musleh Kasim	.45 .45
379	A115	75f Ali Ahmed N. Antar	.45 .45
		Nos. 376-379 (4)	1.80 1.80

UN Child Survival Campaign A116

Infant Immunization Program.

1987, Apr. 7   Litho.   Perf. 12

380	A116	20f Immunizing pregnant woman	.20 .20
381	A116	75f Immunizing infant	.45 .45
382	A116	140f Oral immunization	.85 .85
383	A116	150f Infant, girl, pregnant woman	.90 .90
		Nos. 380-383 (4)	2.40 2.40

1st Socialist Party General Conference — A117

1987, July 30   Litho.   Perf. 12

384	A117	75fr multi	.45 .45
385	A117	150fr multi	.90 .90

October Revolution, Russia, 70th Anniv. — A118

Monuments, Ancient City of Shabwa — A119

1987, Nov. 7   Litho.   Perf. 12½x12

386 A118 250f multi   1.50 1.50

1987, Nov. 18   Perf. 12

387	A119	25f Royal palace and court	.20 .20
388	A119	75f Palace, diff.	.45 .45
389	A119	140f Winged lion bas-relief on stone	.85 .85
390	A119	150f The Moon, legend on bronze tablet	.90 .90
		Nos. 387-390 (4)	2.40 2.40

Nos. 387-388 horiz.

Natl. Independence, 20th Anniv. — A120

Designs: 5f, Students walking to school. 75f, Family, apartments. 140f, Workers, oil derrick, thermal plant. 150f, Workers, soldier, Workers' Party headquarters.

1987, Nov. 29   Perf. 12x12½

391	A120	25f multi	.20 .20
392	A120	75f multi	.45 .45
393	A120	140f multi	.85 .85
394	A120	150f multi	.90 .90
		Nos. 391-394 (4)	2.40 2.40

September 26th Revolution, 25th Anniv. A121

WHO, 40th Anniv. A122

1988, Feb. 27   Litho.   Perf. 13

395 A121 75f Revolution monument, San'a   .45 .45

1988, Apr. 7   Litho.   Perf. 12

396	A122	40f Sanitary public water supply, vert.	.25 .25
397	A122	75f No smoking	.45 .45
398	A122	140f Child immunization	.85 .85
399	A122	250f Health care for all by the year 2000	1.55 1.55
		Nos. 396-399 (4)	3.10 3.10

1988 Summer Olympics, Seoul A125

1988, Sept. 17   Litho.   Perf. 12x12½

406	A125	40f Weight lifting	.25 .25
407	A125	75f Running	.45 .45
408	A125	140f Boxing	.85 .85
409	A125	150f Soccer	.90 .90
		Nos. 406-409 (4)	2.45 2.45

1st Freedom Fighter Killed at the Liberation Front, Radfan Mountains A126

Perf. 12½x12, 12x12½

1988, Oct. 12   Litho.

410	A126	25f Freedom fighters, flag, vert.	.20 .20
411	A126	75f shown	.45 .45
412	A126	300f Anniv. emblem, vert.	1.90 1.90
		Nos. 410-412 (3)	2.55 2.55

October 14th Revolution, 25th anniv.

Indigenous Birds A127

1988, Nov. 5   Perf. 12x12½, 12½x12
413	A127	40f Treron waalia	.25	.25
414	A127	50f Coracias caudatus lorti, vert.	.30	.30
415	A127	75f Upupa epops, vert.	.45	.45
416	A127	250f Chlamydotis undulata macqueenii	1.55	1.55
		Nos. 413-416 (4)	2.55	2.55

Handicrafts — A128

Designs: 25f, Incense brazier. 75f, Cage-shaped dress form. 150f, Shell and wicker lidded basket. 250f, Wicker basket.

1988, Nov. 29 Litho.   Perf. 12½x12
417	A128	25f multi	.20	.20
418	A128	75f multi	.45	.45
419	A128	150f multi	.90	.90
420	A128	250f multi	1.55	1.55
		Nos. 417-420 (4)	3.10	3.10

Aden Harbor and Yemen Port Authority, Cent. A129

1988, Dec. 5   Perf. 12x12½
421	A129	75f Old harbor facility	.65	.65
422	A129	300f New facility	2.75	2.75

Preservation of San'a City, a Site on the UNESCO World Heritage List — A130

1988, Dec. 15 Perf. 12x12½, 12½x12
423	A130	75f shown	.45	.45
424	A130	250f City view, diff., vert.	1.55	1.55

World Wildlife Fund — A131

1989, May 18 Litho.   Perf. 12½x12
425	A131	20f Sand cat	.20	.20
426	A131	25f Cat's head	.20	.20
427	A131	50f Fennec fox	.30	.30
428	A131	75f Fox's head	.45	.45
		Nos. 425-428 (4)	1.15	1.15

For surcharge see Yemen No. 643.

Military Forces — A132

Abdul Fattah Ismail — A133

Developments of the corrective movement.

1989, Aug. 15   Perf. 12x12½
429	A132	25f shown	.20	.20
430	A132	35f Industry	.25	.25
431	A132	40f Agriculture	.25	.25
		Nos. 429-431 (3)	.70	.70

June 22 Corrective Movement, 20th anniv.

1989, Aug. 28
432	A133	75f multi	.45	.45
433	A133	150f multi	.90	.90

50th Birthday of Abdul Fattah Ismail, 1st secretary-general of the natl. Socialist Party.

Ali Anter Yemeni Pioneer Organization, 15th Anniv. — A134

Perf. 12x12½, 12½x12
1989, Sept. 29   Litho.
434	A134	10f Drawing by Abeer Anwer	.20	.20
435	A134	25f Girl in pioneer uniform	.20	.20
436	A134	75f Parade, Aden	.45	.45
		Nos. 434-436 (3)	.85	.85

Nos. 434-435 vert.
For surcharge see Yemen No. 644.

Nehru and the Taj Mahal — A135

1989, Nov. 14   Photo.   Perf. 14
437	A135	250f blk & golden brn	1.50	1.50

Jawaharlal Nehru, 1st prime minister of independent India.
For surcharge see Yemen No. 645.

Seventy-Day Siege of San'a, 1967-68 — A136

Coffee Plant — A137

1989, Oct. 25   Litho.   Perf. 12x12½
438	A136	150f multicolored	.90	.90

1989, Dec. 20
439	A137	300f multicolored	1.75	1.75

For surcharge see Yemen No. 637.

Seera Rock, Aden, and the Arc de Triomphe, Paris A138

1989, Dec. 29   Litho.   Perf. 12½x12
440	A138	250f multicolored	1.50	1.50

French Revolution, bicent.

World Cup Soccer Championships, Italy — A139

Character trademark, soccer plays and flags of participants: 5f, US, Belgium, 1930. 10f, Switzerland, Holland, 1934. 20f, Italy, France, 1938. 35f, Sweden, Spain, 1950. 50f, Federal Republic of Germany, Austria, 1954. Brazil, England, 1958. 500f, Russia, Uruguay, 1962. No. 448, Soccer game.

1990, Apr. 30   Litho.   Perf. 12½x12
441	A139	5f multicolored	.20	.20
442	A139	10f multicolored	.20	.20
443	A139	20f multicolored	.20	.20
444	A139	35f multicolored	.25	.25
445	A139	50f multicolored	.30	.30
446	A139	60f multicolored	.35	.35
447	A139	500f multicolored	3.00	3.00
		Nos. 441-447 (7)	4.50	4.50

Souvenir Sheet
448	A139	340f multicolored	2.00	2.00

For surcharges see Yemen Nos. 616, 621-621B.

ADVANTAGE STOCKSHEETS

Designed with the collector in mind, Advantage stock sheets fit directly in your 2-post or 3-ring National or Specialty album. For unprecedented durability and flexibility choose Advantage Stocksheets. Choose from 1 to 8 pockets.
Sheets are sold in packages of 10.

- Stock sheets match album pages in every respect, including border, size, and color.

- Punched and drilled to fit perfectly in binder.

- Available with 1 to 8 pockets. Ideal for storing minor varieties and collateral material. A great place to keep new issues until the next supplement is available.

- Provide the protection and durability of crystal clear acetate pockets on heavyweight pages.

NATIONAL BORDER
ITEM			RETAIL
AD11	1 Pocket	242mm	$15.99
AD12	2 Pockets	119mm	$15.99
AD13	3 Pockets	79mm	$15.99
AD14	4 Pockets	58mm	$15.99
AD15	5 Pockets	45mm	$15.99
AD16	6 Pockets	37mm	$15.99
AD17	7 Pockets	31mm	$15.99
AD18	8 Pockets	31mm	$15.99

SPECIALTY BORDER
AD21	1 Pocket	242mm	$15.99
AD22	2 Pockets	119mm	$15.99
AD23	3 Pockets	79mm	$15.99
AD24	4 Pockets	58mm	$15.99
AD25	5 Pockets	45mm	$15.99
AD26	6 Pockets	37mm	$15.99
AD27	7 Pockets	31mm	$15.99
AD28	8 Pockets	31mm S	$15.99

Available from your favorite stamp dealer or direct from:

SCOTT

1-800-572-6885
P.O. Box 828,
Sidney OH 45365
www.amosadvantage.com

AMOS HOBBY PUBLISHING

YUGOSLAVIA

yü-gō-'slä-vē-ə

LOCATION — Southern Europe, bordering on the Adriatic Sea
GOVT. — Republic
AREA — 39,500 sq. mi. (est)
POP. — 11,206,847 (1999 est.)
CAPITAL — Belgrade

On December 1, 1918, Bosnia and Herzegovina, Croatia, Dalmatia, Montenegro, Serbia and Slovenia united to form a kingdom which was later called Yugoslavia. A republic was proclaimed November 29, 1945. Other listings may be found under all.

100 Heller = 1 Krone (Bosnia & Herzegovina)
100 Filler = 1 Krone (Croatia-Slavonia)
100 Paras = 1 Dinar (General Issues)

Catalogue values for unused stamps in this country are for Never Hinged items, beginning with Scott 410 in the regular postage section, Scott C50 in the airpost section, Scott F1 in the registered letter section, Scott J67 in the postage due section, Scott RA1 in the postal tax section, and Scott RAJ1 in the postal tax due section.

Counterfeits exist of most of the 1918-19 overprints for Bosnia and Herzegovina, Croatia-Slavonia and Slovenia.

BOSNIA AND HERZEGOVINA

Stamps of Bosnia and Herzegovina, 1910, Overprinted or Surcharged in Black or Red

a

b

c

1918		Unwmk.		Perf. 12½
1L1	A4(a)	3h olive green	.40	.70
1L2	A4(b)	5h dk grn (R)	.20	.20
1L3	A4(a)	10h carmine	.20	.20
1L4	A4(a)	20h dk brn (R)	.20	.20
1L5	A4(a)	25h deep blue (R)	.20	.20
1L6	A4(b)	30h green	.20	.20
1L7	A4(b)	40h orange	.20	.20
1L8	A4(b)	45h brown red	.20	.20
1L9	A4(b)	50h dull violet	.20	.20
1L10	A4(b)	60h on 50h dl vio	.20	.20
1L11	A4(b)	80h on 6h org brown	.20	.30
1L12	A4(a)	90h on 35h myr green	.20	.20
1L13	A5(c)	2k gray green	.20	.35
1L14	A4(b)	3k on 3h ol grn	.80	1.25

1L15	A5(c)	4k on 1k mar	1.40	1.90
1L16	A4(b)	10k on 2h vio	2.25	2.50
		Nos. 1L1-1L16 (16)	7.25	9.00

Inverted and double overprints and assorted varieties exist on the stamps for Bosnia and Herzegovina.

Bosnian Girl — A1

1918		Typo.	Perf. 11½
1L17	A1	2h ultramarine	.20	.20
1L18	A1	6h violet	.55	1.90
1L19	A1	10h rose	.20	.20
1L20	A1	20h green	.20	.20
		Nos. 1L17-1L20 (4)	1.15	2.90

Imperforate stamps of this type (A1) are newspaper stamps of Bosnia.
See Nos. 1L21-1L22, 1L43-1L45.

Bosnia and Herzegovina Nos. P1-P2
(Nos. 1L17-1L18, Imperf.) Surcharged

1918			Imperf.
1L21	A1	3h on 2h ultra	.20	.20
a.		Double surcharge		14.00
1L22	A1	5h on 6h violet	.20	.20
a.		Double surcharge		14.00

Stamps of Bosnia and Herzegovina, 1906-17, Overprinted or Surcharged in Black or Red:

d   e

f

1919			Perf. 12½
1L25	A23(d)	3h claret	.20	.50
1L26	A23(e)	5h green	.20	.20
1L27	A23(e)	10h on 6h dark gray	.20	.20
1L28	A24(d)	20h on 35h myr green	.20	.20
1L29	A23(e)	25h ultra	.20	.20
1L30	A23(d)	30h orange red	.45	.90
1L31	A24(d)	45h olive brn	.35	.45
1L32	A27(d)	45h on 80h org brown	.20	.20
a.		Perf. 11½	3.25	4.00
1L33	A24(e)	50h slate blue	20.00	24.00
1L34	A24(e)	50h on 72h dk blue (R)	.20	.20
1L35	A24(d)	60h brown violet	.20	.20
1L36	A27(d)	80h orange brown	.20	.25
a.		Perf. 11½	24.00	30.00
1L37	A27(d)	90h dark violet	.20	.20
a.		Perf. 11½	2.25	2.75
1L38	A5(f)	2k gray green	.20	.25
a.		Imperf.	27.50	
b.		Perf. 9½	4.50	5.00
1L39	A26(d)	3k car, green	.80	.90
1L40	A28(d)	4k car, green	1.75	2.50
1L41	A26(d)	5k dk vio, gray	1.75	2.75
1L42	A28(e)	10k dk vio, gray	2.00	2.75
		Nos. 1L25-1L42 (18)	29.30	36.85

Nos. 1L32, 1L36, 1L37, 1L40 and 1L42 have no bars in the overprint.
Nos. 1L25 to 1L42 exist with inverted overprint or surcharge.

Bosnia and Herzegovina Nos. P2-P4
(Nos. 1L18-1L20, Imperf.) Surcharged

1920			Imperf.
1L43	A1	2h on 6h violet	50.00	70.00
1L44	A1	2h on 10h rose	20.00	40.00
1L45	A1	2h on 20h green	1.10	2.75
		Nos. 1L43-1L45 (3)	71.10	112.75

SEMI-POSTAL STAMPS ISSUES FOR BOSNIA AND HERZEGOVINA

Leading Blind Soldier — SP1   Wounded Soldier — SP2

Semi-Postal Stamps of Bosnia and Herzegovina, 1918 Overprinted

1918		Unwmk.	Perf. 12½, 13
1LB1	SP1	10h greenish bl	.65	1.00
a.		Overprinted as No. 1LB2	27.50	37.50
1LB2	SP2	15h red brown	1.75	1.75
a.		Overprinted as No. 1LB1	27.50	37.50

Bosnian Semi-Postal Stamps of 1916 Overprinted like No. 1LB2

1LB3	SP1	5h green	125.00	140.00
a.		Overprinted as No. 1LB1	240.00	300.00
1LB4	SP2	10h magenta	75.00	95.00
		Nos. 1LB1-1LB4 (4)	202.40	237.75

Inverted and double overprints exist on Nos. 1LB1-1LB4.

Mail Wagon SP3

Bridge at Mostar SP4

Scene near Sarajevo — SP5

Regular Issue of Bosnia, 1906 Surcharged in Black

1919				
1LB5	SP3	10h + 10h on 40h org red	1.75	1.90
1LB6	SP4	20h + 10h on 20h dk brown	.60	.60
1LB7	SP5	45h + 15h on 1k mar	2.50	2.75
		Nos. 1LB5-1LB7 (3)	4.85	5.25

Nos. 1LB5-1LB7 exist with surcharge inverted. Value each $7.50.

SPECIAL DELIVERY STAMPS ISSUES FOR BOSNIA AND HERZEGOVINA

Lightning
SD1   SD2
Bosnian Special Delivery Stamps Overprinted in Black

1918		Unwmk.	Perf. 12½, 13
1LE1	SD1	2h vermilion	4.75	5.00
a.		Inverted overprint	32.50	
b.		Overprinted as No. 1LE2	30.00	35.00
1LE2	SD2	5h deep green	1.40	1.50
a.		Inverted overprint	18.00	
b.		Overprinted as No. 1LE1	30.00	35.00

POSTAGE DUE STAMPS ISSUES FOR BOSNIA AND HERZEGOVINA

Postage Due Stamps of Bosnia and Herzegovina, 1916, Overprinted in Black or Red:

a   b

1918		Unwmk.	Perf. 12½, 13
1LJ1	D2 (a)	2h red	.20	.20
1LJ2	D2 (b)	4h red	.25	.65
1LJ3	D2 (a)	5h red	.20	.20
1LJ4	D2 (b)	6h red	.30	.40
1LJ5	D2 (a)	10h red	.20	.20
1LJ6	D2 (b)	15h red	4.00	4.75
1LJ7	D2 (a)	20h red	.20	.20
1LJ8	D2 (b)	25h red	.25	.70
1LJ9	D2 (b)	30h red	.25	.70
1LJ10	D2 (a)	40h red	.20	.20
1LJ11	D2 (a)	50h red	.50	.80

c   d

1LJ12	D2 (c)	1k dark blue (R)	.25	.20
1LJ13	D2 (d)	3k dark blue (R)	.20	.20
		Nos. 1LJ1-1LJ13 (13)	7.00	9.45

Nos. 1LJ1-1LJ13 exist with overprint double or inverted. Value $3 to $7.
Nos. 1LJ1-1LJ11 exist with type "b" overprint instead of type "a," and vice versa. Value, each $10.

Stamps of Bosnia and Herzegovina, 1900-04, Surcharged

e   f

1919				
1LJ14	A2 (e)	2h on 35h blue	.25	1.10
1LJ15	A2 (e)	5h on 45h grnsh bl	.40	.85
1LJ16	A2 (f)	10h on 10 red	.20	.20
1LJ17	A2 (e)	15h on 40h org	.20	.80
1LJ18	A2 (f)	20h on 5h green	.20	.20
1LJ19	A2 (e)	25h on 20h pink	.20	.50
1LJ20	A2 (f)	30h on 30h bis brn	.20	.45
1LJ21	A2 (e)	1k on 50h red lil	.20	.20
1LJ22	A2 (e)	3k on 25h blue	.20	.30

Postage Due Stamps of Bosnia and Herzegovina, 1904 Surcharged:

g   h

1LJ23	D1 (g)	40h on 6h blk, red & yel		.20	.20
1LJ24	D1 (h)	50h on 8h blk, red & yel		.20	.20
1LJ25	D1 (h)	200h blk, red & grn		2.50	2.50
1LJ26	D1 (h)	4k on 7h blk, red & yel		.20	.30
	Nos. 1LJ14-1LJ26 (13)			5.15	7.80

Nos. 1LJ14-1LJ26 exist with overprint double or inverted. Value, $3 to $6.

CROATIA-SLAVONIA

Stamps of Hungary Overprinted in Blue

A1

1918   **Wmk. 137**   **Perf. 15**

On Stamps of 1913

2L1	A1	6f olive green	1.10	2.00
2L2	A1	50f lake, *blue*	.85	1.75

A2   A3

On Stamps of 1916

2L3	A2	10f violet	20.00	27.50
2L4	A3	15f red	20.00	27.50

A4

On Hungary Nos. 106-107
White Numerals

2L4A	A4	10f rose	240.00	300.00
2L5	A4	15f violet	22.50	27.50
a.		*Inverted overprint*		125.00

On Stamps of 1916-18
Colored Numerals

2L6	A4	2f brown orange	.20	.20
2L7	A4	3f red lilac	.20	.20
2L8	A4	5f green	.20	.20
2L9	A4	6f greenish blue	.20	.25
2L10	A4	10f rose red	1.60	2.75
2L11	A4	15f violet	.20	.20
2L12	A4	20f gray brown	.20	.30
2L13	A4	25f dull blue	.20	.20
2L14	A4	35f blue	.20	.20
2L15	A4	40f olive green	.20	.45

The overprints and surcharges for Croatia-Slavonia exist inverted, double, double inverted, in wrong colors, on wrong stamps, on back, in pairs with one lacking overprint, etc.

A5

A6

2L16	A5	50f red vio & lilac	.20	.20
2L17	A5	75f brt bl & pale bl	.20	.25
2L18	A5	80f grn & pale grn	.20	.20
2L19	A6	1k red brown & cl	.20	.20
2L20	A6	2k olive brn & bis	.20	.20
2L21	A6	3k dark vio & ind	.40	1.00
2L22	A6	5k dk brn & lt brn	2.00	4.00
2L23	A6	10k vio brn & vio	7.50	14.00

Stamps of Hungary Overprinted in Blue, Black or Red

A7   A8

2L24	A7	10f scarlet (Bl)	.20	.20
2L25	A7	20f dark brown (Bk)	.20	.20
2L26	A7	25f deep blue (R)	.80	2.50
2L27	A8	40f olive green (Bl)	.20	.20
	Nos. 2L6-2L27 (22)		15.70	28.10

Many other stamps of the 1913-18 issues of Hungary, the Semi-Postal Stamps of 1915-16 and Postage Due Stamps were surreptitiously overprinted but were never sold through the post office.

Freedom of Croatia-Slavonia — A9

1918   **Unwmk.**   **Litho.**   **Perf. 11½**

2L28	A9	10f rose	1.00	1.00
2L29	A9	20f violet	1.25	1.25
2L30	A9	25f blue	2.50	2.50
2L31	A9	45f greenish blk	24.00	24.00
	Nos. 2L28-2L31 (4)		28.75	28.75

Independence of Croatia, Slavonia and Dalmatia.

#2L28-2L31 exist imperforate, but were not officially issued in this condition.

Excellent counterfeits of #2L28-2L31 exist.

Allegory of Freedom   Youth with Standard
A10   A11

Falcon, Symbol of Liberty — A12

1919   **Perf. 11½**

2L32	A10	2f brn orange	.20	.20
2L33	A10	3f violet	.20	.20
2L34	A10	5f green	.20	.20
2L35	A11	10f red	.20	.20
2L36	A11	20f black brown	.20	.20
2L37	A11	25f deep blue	.20	.20
2L38	A11	45f dark ol grn	.20	.20
2L39	A12	1k carmine rose	.20	.20
2L40	A12	3k dark violet	.35	.35
2L41	A12	5k deep brown	.85	.70
	Nos. 2L32-2L41 (10)		2.80	2.65

Perf. 12½

2L32a	A10	2f	1.25	1.25
2L33a	A10	3f	1.25	1.25
2L34a	A10	5f	40.00	52.50
2L35a	A11	10f	.35	.35
2L36a	A11	20f	.30	.25
	Nos. 2L32a-2L36a (5)		43.15	55.60

#2L32-2L41 exist imperf. Value, set $25.

SEMI-POSTAL STAMPS ISSUES FOR CROATIA-SLAVONIA

SP1   SP2

SP3

1918   **Wmk. 137**   **Perf. 15**

2LB1	SP1	10f + 2f rose red	.30	2.75
2LB2	SP2	15f + 2f dull violet	.20	.40
2LB3	SP3	40f + 2f brn carmine	.20	.85
	Nos. 2LB1-2LB3 (3)		.70	4.00

SPECIAL DELIVERY STAMP ISSUE FOR CROATIA-SLAVONIA

SD1

Hungary No. E1 Overprinted in Black

1918   **Wmk. 137**   **Perf. 15**

2LE1	SD1	2f gray green & red	.20	.20

POSTAGE DUE STAMPS ISSUES FOR CROATIA-SLAVONIA

D1

Postage Due Stamps of Hungary Overprinted in Blue

1918   **Wmk. Crown (136)**   **Perf. 15**

2LJ1	D1	50f green & blk	175.00	175.00

Wmk. Double Cross (137)

2LJ2	D1	1f green & red	6.25	6.25
a.		*Inverted overprint*	22.50	22.50
2LJ3	D1	2f green & red	.75	.75
2LJ4	D1	10f green & red	.55	.55
2LJ5	D1	12f green & red	25.00	25.00
2LJ6	D1	15f green & red	.45	.45
2LJ7	D1	20f green & red	.45	.45
2LJ8	D1	30f green & red	1.10	1.10
2LJ9	D1	50f green & blk	7.75	7.75
	Nos. 2LJ2-2LJ9 (8)		42.30	42.30

NEWSPAPER STAMPS ISSUES FOR CROATIA-SLAVONIA

N1   N2

Hungary No. P8 Overprinted in Black

1918   **Wmk. 137**   **Imperf.**

2LP1	N1	(2f) orange	.20	.30

1919   **Litho.**   **Unwmk.**

2LP2	N2	2f yellow	.20	.50

SLOVENIA

Chain Breaker
A1   A2

3, 5, 10, 15f: Chain on right wrist is short, extending only about half way to the frame.

10f: Numerals are 8½mm high.

20, 25, 30, 40f: Distant mountains show faintly between legs of male figure.

40f: Numerals 7mm high. The upright strokes of the "4" extend to the same height; the "0" is 3mm wide.

1919   **Unwmk.**   **Perf. 11½**
Lithographed at Ljubljana
Fine Impression

3L1	A1	3f violet	.20	.20
3L2	A1	5f green	.20	.20
3L3	A1	10f carmine rose	.20	.20
3L4	A1	15f blue	.20	.20
3L5	A2	20f brown	.20	.20
3L6	A2	25f blue	.20	.20
3L7	A2	30f lilac rose	.20	.20
3L8	A2	40f bister	.20	.20
	Nos. 3L1-3L8 (8)		1.60	1.60

Various stamps of this series exist imperforate and part perforate. Many shades exist.

See Nos. 3L9-3L17, 3L24-3L28. For surcharges see Nos. 3LJ15-3LJ32.

Allegories of Freedom
A3   A4

King Peter I — A5

3, 5, 15f: The chain on the right wrist touches the bottom tablet.

10f: Numerals are 7½mm high.

15f: Curled end of loin cloth appears above letter "H" in the bottom tablet.

20, 25, 30, 40f: The outlines of the mountains have been redrawn and they are more distinct than on the lithographed stamps.

40f: Numerals 8mm high. The left slanting stroke of the "4" extends much higher than the main vertical stroke. The "0" is 2½mm wide and encloses a much narrower space than on the lithographed stamp.

1919-20   **Perf. 11½**
Typographed at Ljubljana and Vienna
Coarse Impression

3L9	A1	3f violet	.20	.20
3L10	A1	5f green	.20	.20
3L11	A1	10f red	.20	.20
3L12	A1	15f blue	.20	.20
3L13	A2	20f brown	.20	.20
3L14	A2	25f blue	.20	.20
3L15	A2	30f carmine rose	.20	.20
3L16	A2	30f dp red	2.75	.90
3L17	A2	40f orange	.25	.20
3L18	A3	50f green	.30	.20
a.		*50f dark green*	.30	.20
b.		*50f olive green*	3.50	1.10
3L19	A3	60f dark blue	.50	.20
a.		*60f violet blue*	.85	.20
3L20	A4	1k vermilion	.30	.20
a.		*1k red orange*	.45	.20
3L21	A4	2k blue	.30	.20
a.		*2k dull ultramarine*	.90	.20

3L22	A5	5k brown lake	.45	.20
a.		5k lake	12.00	1.60
b.		5k dull red	.60	.20
3L23	A5	10k deep ultra	2.75	.90
		Nos. 3L9-3L23 (15)	9.00	4.40

Nos. 3L9-3L23 exist imperf, set $90. Many of the series exist part perforate. Many shades exist of lower values. See Nos. 3L29-3L32, 3L40-3L41.

Serrate Roulette 13½

3L24	A1	5f light grn	.20	.20
3L25	A1	10f carmine	.20	.20
3L26	A1	15f slate blue	.20	.20
3L27	A2	20f dark brown	.30	.20
a.		Serrate x straight roul.	.55	.20
3L28	A2	30f car rose	.20	.20
a.		Serrate x straight roul.	.60	.20
3L29	A3	50f green	.30	.20
3L30	A3	60f dark blue	.45	.20
a.		60f violet blue	2.25	1.10
3L31	A4	1k vermilion	.65	.20
a.		1k rose red	.60	.20
3L32	A4	2k blue	13.00	1.50
		Nos. 3L24-3L32 (9)	15.50	3.10

Roulette x Perf. 11½

3L24a	A1	5f	125.00	140.00
3L25a	A1	10f	45.00	47.50
3L26a	A1	15f	140.00	150.00
3L28b	A2	30f	45.00	47.50
3L29a	A3	50f	5.25	4.00
3L30b	A3	60f	45.00	47.50
3L31b	A4	1k	45.00	47.50

Thick Wove Paper

1920   Litho.   Perf. 11½

3L40	A5	15k gray green	4.00	5.25
3L41	A5	20k dull violet	1.00	2.00

On Nos. 3L40-3L41 the horizontal lines have been removed from the value tablets. They are printed over a background of pale brown wavy lines.

Chain Breaker A7

Freedom A8

King Peter I — A9

Dinar Values:
Type I — Size: 21x30½mm.
Type II — Size: 22x32½mm.

Thin to Thick Wove Paper

1920   Serrate Roulette 13½

3L42	A7	5p olive green	.20	.20
3L43	A7	10p green	.20	.20
3L44	A7	15p brown	.20	.20
3L45	A7	20p carmine	.75	1.00
3L46	A7	25p chocolate	.30	.30
3L47	A8	40p dark violet	.20	.20
3L48	A8	45p yellow	.20	.20
3L49	A8	50p dark blue	.20	.20
3L50	A8	60p red brown	.20	.20
3L51	A9	1d dark brown (I)	.20	.20

Perf. 11½

3L52	A9	2d gray vio (II)	.20	.20
3L53	A9	4d grnsh black (I)	.30	.30
3L54	A9	6d olive brn (II)	.20	.25
3L55	A9	10d brown red (II)	.30	.35
		Nos. 3L42-3L55 (14)	3.65	4.00

The 2d and 6d have a background of pale red wavy lines, the 10d of gray lines. Counterfeits exist of No. 3L45.

POSTAGE DUE STAMPS ISSUES FOR SLOVENIA

D1

1919   Litho.   Unwmk.   Perf. 11½
Ljubljana Print
Numerals 9½mm high

3LJ1	D1	5f carmine	.20	.20
3LJ2	D1	10f carmine	.20	.20
3LJ3	D1	20f carmine	.20	.20
3LJ4	D1	50f carmine	.20	.20

Nos. 3LJ1-3LJ4 were also printed in scarlet and dark red.

Numerals 8mm high

3LJ5	D1	1k dark blue	.45	.30
3LJ6	D1	5k dark blue	.65	.50
3LJ7	D1	10k dark blue	.90	.75
		Nos. 3LJ1-3LJ7 (7)	2.80	2.35

1920
Vienna Print
Numerals 11 to 12 mm high

3LJ8	D1	5f red	.20	.20
3LJ9	D1	10f red	.20	.20
3LJ10	D1	20f red	.20	.20
3LJ11	D1	50f red	1.25	.85

Numerals 7mm high

3LJ12	D1	1k Prussian blue	1.10	.70
a.		1k dark blue	5.00	4.50
3LJ13	D1	5k Prussian blue	1.60	1.25
a.		5k dark blue	8.00	6.75
3LJ14	D1	10k Prussian blue	3.75	3.25
a.		10k dark blue	14.00	15.00
		Nos. 3LJ8-3LJ14 (7)	8.30	6.65

Nos. 3LJ8-3LJ14 exist imperf. Value, set $40.

No. 3L4 Surcharged in Red

1920   Perf. 11½
On Litho. Stamps

3LJ15	A1	5p on 15f blue	.20	.20
3LJ16	A1	10p on 15f blue	.60	.60
3LJ17	A1	20p on 15f blue	.20	.20
3LJ18	A1	50p on 15f blue	.20	.20
		Nos. 3LJ15-3LJ18 (4)	1.20	1.20

Nos. 3L7, 3L12, 3L26, 3L28, 3L28a Surcharged in Dark Blue

3LJ19	A2	1d on 30f lil rose	.20	.20
3LJ20	A2	3d on 30f lil rose	.20	.20
3LJ21	A2	8d on 30f lil rose	1.10	.60
		Nos. 3LJ19-3LJ21 (3)	1.50	1.00

On Typographed Stamps
Perf. 11½

3LJ22	A1	5p on 15f pale bl	12.00	2.50
3LJ23	A1	10p on 15f pale bl	27.50	22.50
3LJ24	A1	20p on 15f pale bl	11.00	4.00
3LJ25	A1	50p on 15f pale bl	6.00	7.00
		Nos. 3LJ22-3LJ25 (4)	56.50	36.00

Serrate Roulette 13½

3LJ26	A1	5p on 15f slate bl	2.75	.50
3LJ27	A1	10p on 15f slate bl	8.50	3.25
3LJ28	A1	20p on 15f slate bl	2.75	.50
3LJ29	A1	50p on 15f slate bl	2.75	.50
3LJ30	A2	1d on 30f dp rose	2.75	.65
a.		Serrate x straight roulette	7.00	4.50
3LJ31	A2	3d on 30f dp rose	5.75	1.75
a.		Serrate x straight roulette		5.50
3LJ32	A2	8d on 30f dp rose	95.00	6.50
		Nos. 3LJ26-3LJ32 (7)	120.25	13.65

The para surcharges were printed in sheets of 100, ten horizontal rows of ten. There were: 5p three rows, 10p one row, 20p three rows,

50p three rows. The dinar surcharges were in a setting of 50, arranged in vertical rows of five. There were: 1d five rows, 3d three rows, 8d two rows.

NEWSPAPER STAMPS ISSUES FOR SLOVENIA

Eros — N1

2 4 6 10

1919   Unwmk.   Litho.   Imperf.
Ljubljana Print

3LP1	N1	2f gray	.20	.20
3LP2	N1	4f gray	.20	.20
3LP3	N1	6f gray	3.25	4.00
3LP4	N1	10f gray	.20	.20
3LP5	N1	30f gray	.20	.20
		Nos. 3LP1-3LP5 (5)	4.05	4.80

See Nos. 3LP6-3LP13. For surcharges see Nos. 3LP14-3LP23, 4LB1-4LB5.

2 4 6 10

1920
Vienna Print

3LP6	N1	2f gray	.20	.20
3LP7	N1	4f gray	6.50	10.00
3LP8	N1	6f gray	1.75	2.75
3LP9	N1	10f gray	14.00	21.00
3LP10	N1	2f blue	.20	.30
3LP11	N1	4f blue	.20	.20
3LP12	N1	6f blue	90.00	110.00
3LP13	N1	10f blue	.20	.20
		Nos. 3LP6-3LP13 (8)	113.05	144.65

Nos. 3LP1, 3LP10 Surcharged:

a   b

On Ljubljana Print

3LP14	N1	(a)	2p on 2f gray	.25	.40
3LP15	N1	(a)	4p on 2f gray	.25	.40
3LP16	N1	(a)	6p on 2f gray	.40	.65
3LP17	N1	(b)	10p on 2f gray	.65	.80
3LP18	N1	(b)	30p on 2f gray	.65	.85

On Vienna Print

3LP19	N1	(a)	2p on 2f blue	.20	.20
3LP20	N1	(a)	4p on 2f blue	.20	.20
3LP21	N1	(a)	6p on 2f blue	.20	.20
3LP22	N1	(b)	10p on 2f blue	.20	.20
3LP23	N1	(b)	30p on 2f blue	.20	.25
			Nos. 3LP14-3LP23 (10)	3.20	4.15

The five surcharges were arranged in a setting of 100, in horizontal rows of ten. There were: 2p three rows, 4p three rows, 6p two rows, 10p one row and 30p one row. The sheets were perforated 11½ horizontally between the groups of the different values.

SEMI-POSTAL STAMPS ISSUE FOR CARINTHIA PLEBISCITE

SP1

Nos. 3LP2, 3LP1 Surcharged With Various Designs in Dark Red

1920

4LB1	SP1	5p on 4f gray	.20	.20
4LB2	SP1	15p on 4f gray	.20	.20
4LB3	SP1	25p on 4f gray	.20	.20
4LB4	SP1	45p on 2f gray	.20	.20
4LB5	SP1	50p on 2f gray	.20	.20
4LB6	SP1	2d on 2f gray	1.25	1.60
		Nos. 4LB1-4LB6 (6)	2.25	2.60

Nos. 4LB1 to 4LB6 have a different surcharge on each stamp but each includes the letters "K.G.C.A." which signify Carinthian Governmental Commission, Zone A.
Sold at three times face value for the benefit of the Plebiscite Propaganda Fund.

GENERAL ISSUES

For Use throughout the Kingdom

King Alexander — A1

King Peter I — A2

Unwmk.

1921, Jan. 16   Engr.   Perf. 12

1	A1	2p olive brown	.20	.20
2	A1	5p deep green	.20	.20
3	A1	10p carmine	.20	.20
4	A1	15p violet	.20	.20
5	A1	20p black	.20	.20
6	A1	25p dark blue	.20	.20
7	A1	50p olive green	.20	.20
8	A1	60p vermilion	.20	.20
9	A1	75p purple	.20	.20
10	A2	1d orange	.20	.20
11	A2	2d olive bister	.25	.20
12	A2	4d dark green	.40	.20
13	A2	5d carmine rose	2.00	.20
14	A2	10d red brown	4.00	.55
		Nos. 1-14 (14)	8.65	3.15

Exist imperf. Value, set $22.50.
For surcharge see No. 27.

Nos. B1-B3 Surcharged in Black, Brown, Green or Blue:

a

b

1922-24

15	SP1(a)	1d on 10p	.20	.20
16	SP2(b)	1d on 15p ('24)	.20	.20
17	SP3(a)	1d on 25p (Br)	.20	.20
18	SP2(b)	3d on 15p (G)	.80	.20
a.		Blue surcharge	1.90	.20
19	SP2(b)	8d on 15p (G)	1.40	.20
a.		Double surcharge	32.50	30.00
b.		9d on 15p (error)	100.00	
20	SP2(b)	20d on 15p	6.50	1.00
21	SP2(b)	30d on 15p (Bl)	13.50	2.50
		Nos. 15-21 (7)	22.80	4.50

A3

1923, Jan. 23   Engr.

22	A3	1d red brown	.65	.20
23	A3	5d carmine	3.25	.20
24	A3	8d violet	6.25	.20
25	A3	20d green	16.00	.75
26	A3	30d red orange	42.50	2.00
		Nos. 22-26 (5)	68.65	3.40

For surcharge see No. 28.

Nos. 8 and 24
Surcharged in Black
or Blue

1924, Feb. 18
27 A1 20p on 60p ver .25 .20
28 A3 5d on 8d violet (Bl) 4.75 .60

The color of the surcharge on No. 28 varies, including blue, blue black, greenish black and black.

A4   A5

1924, July 1   **Perf. 14**
29 A4 20p black .90 .20
30 A4 50p dark brown .90 .20
31 A4 1d carmine .35 .20
32 A4 2d myrtle green .75 .20
33 A4 3d ultramarine .60 .20
34 A4 5d orange brown 2.50 .20
35 A5 10d dark violet 8.50 .20
36 A5 15d olive green 5.00 .20
37 A5 20d vermilion 4.50 .20
38 A5 30d dark green 4.50 1.10
      Nos. 29-38 (10) 28.50 2.90

No. 33 Surcharged

1925, June 5
39 A4 25p on 3d ultramarine .20 .20
40 A4 50p on 3d ultramarine .20 .20

King Alexander
A6   A7

1926-27   **Typo.**   **Perf. 13**
41 A6 25p deep green .20 .20
42 A6 50p olive brown .20 .20
43 A6 1d scarlet .30 .20
44 A6 2d slate black .30 .20
45 A6 3d slate blue .40 .20
46 A6 4d red orange 2.00 .20
47 A6 5d violet 1.50 .20
48 A6 8d black brown 3.75 .20
49 A6 10d olive brown 3.50 .20
50 A6 15d brown ('27) 6.75 .20
51 A6 20d dark vio ('27) 8.25 .20
52 A6 30d orange ('27) 25.00 .45
      Nos. 41-52 (12) 52.15 2.65

For overprints and surcharges see Nos. 53-62, 87-101, B5-B16.

Semi-Postal Stamps of 1926
Overprinted over the Red Surcharge

1928, July
53 A6 1d scarlet 1.25 .20
   a. Surcharge "0.50" inverted
54 A6 2d black 4.00 .20
55 A6 3d deep blue 3.00 .35
56 A6 4d red orange 9.25 .40
57 A6 5d bright vio 3.00 .20
58 A6 8d black brown 4.50 .65

---

59 A6 10d olive brown 6.00 .20
60 A6 15d brown 35.00 2.00
61 A6 20d violet 18.00 2.00
62 A6 30d orange 40.00 4.00
      Nos. 53-62 (10) 124.00 10.20

With Imprint at Foot

1931-34   **Perf. 12½**
63 A7 25p black .70 .20
64 A7 50p green .60 .20
65 A7 75p slate green .20 .20
66 A7 1d red .65 .20
67 A7 1.50d pink .30 .20
68 A7 1.75d dp rose ('34) .55 .35
69 A7 3d slate blue 3.50 .20
70 A7 3.50d ultra ('34) 1.10 .25
71 A7 4d deep orange 2.00 .20
72 A7 5d purple 2.00 .20
73 A7 10d dark olive 5.50 .20
74 A7 15d deep brown 5.50 .20
75 A7 20d dark violet 9.25 .20
76 A7 30d rose 6.00 .45
      Nos. 63-76 (14) 37.85 3.25

Type of 1931 Issue
Without Imprint at Foot

1932-33
77 A7 25p black .20 .20
78 A7 50p green .30 .20
79 A7 1d red .65 .20
80 A7 3d slate bl ('33) 1.60 .20
81 A7 4d deep org ('33) 3.50 .20
82 A7 5d purple ('33) 5.25 .20
83 A7 10d dk olive ('33) 17.00 .20
84 A7 15d deep brn ('33) 21.00 .20
85 A7 20d dark vio ('33) 32.50 .20
86 A7 30d rose ('33) 37.50 .35
      Nos. 77-86 (10) 119.50 2.15

See Nos. 102-115.

ЈУГОСЛАВИЈА

Nos. 41 to 52
Overprinted

JUGOSLAVIJA

1933, Sept. 5   **Perf. 13**
87 A6 25p deep green .20 .20
88 A6 50p olive brown .20 .20
89 A6 1d scarlet .40 .20
90 A6 2d slate black 1.75 .70
91 A6 3d slate blue 1.60 .20
92 A6 4d red orange 1.10 .20
93 A6 5d violet 1.60 .20
94 A6 8d black brown 4.75 1.00
95 A6 10d olive brown 6.75 .20
96 A6 15d brown 8.25 1.75
97 A6 20d dark violet 15.00 .50
98 A6 30d orange 13.00 .65
      Nos. 87-98 (12) 54.60 6.00

Semi-Postal Stamps of 1926
Overprinted like Nos. 87 to 98 and
Four Bars over the Red Surcharge of
1926

1933, Sept. 5
99 A6 25p green .50 .20
100 A6 50p olive brown .60 .20
101 A6 1d scarlet 1.25 .40
      Nos. 99-101 (3) 2.35 .80

Nos. 99-101 exist with double impression of bars. Value, each $5.50 unused, $4.50 used.

King Alexander Memorial Issue
Type of 1931-34 Issues
Borders in Black

1934, Oct. 17
102 A7 25p black .20 .20
103 A7 50p green .20 .20
104 A7 75p slate green .20 .20
105 A7 1d red .20 .20
106 A7 1.50d pink .20 .20
107 A7 1.75d deep rose .20 .20
108 A7 3d slate blue .20 .20
109 A7 3.50d ultramarine .25 .20
110 A7 4d deep orange .40 .20
111 A7 5d purple .45 .20
112 A7 10d dark olive 1.90 .20
113 A7 15d deep brown 3.25 .20
114 A7 20d dark violet 5.00 .20
115 A7 30d rose 3.25 .20
      Nos. 102-115 (14) 15.90 2.80

Cyrillic Characters
Latin and Cyrillic inscriptions are transposed within some sets. In some sets some stamps are inscribed in Latin, others in Cyrillic. This will be mentioned only if it is necessary to identify otherwise identical stamps.

King Peter II — A10

1935-36   **Perf. 13x12½**
116 A10 25p brown black .20 .20
117 A10 50p yel orange .20 .20
118 A10 75p turq green .20 .20
119 A10 1d brown red .20 .20
120 A10 1.50d scarlet .20 .20
121 A10 1.75d cerise .20 .20
122 A10 2d magenta ('36) .20 .20
123 A10 3d brn orange .20 .20
124 A10 3.50d ultramarine .20 .20
125 A10 4d yellow grn .75 .20
126 A10 4d slate blue ('36) .20 .20
127 A10 10d bright vio .35 .20
128 A10 15d brown .60 .20
129 A10 20d bright blue 2.25 .20
130 A10 30d rose pink 1.50 .20
      Nos. 116-130 (15) 7.45 3.00

For overprints see Nos. N12, 14, N29.

King   Nikola
Alexander — A11   Tesla — A12

1935, Oct. 9   **Perf. 12½x11½, 11½**
131 A11 75p turq green .20 .20
132 A11 1.50d scarlet .20 .20
133 A11 1.75d dark brown .70 1.00
134 A11 3.50d ultramarine .70 1.00
135 A11 7.50d rose carmine .70 1.00
      Nos. 131-135 (5) 2.50 3.40

Death of King Alexander, 1st anniv.

1936, May 28   **Litho.**   **Perf. 12½x11½**
136 A12 75p yel grn & dk brn .20 .20
137 A12 1.75d dull blue & indigo .25 .20

80th birthday of Nikola Tesla (1856-1943), electrical inventor.

Memorial   Coats of Arms of
Church,   Yugoslavia, Greece,
Oplenac — A13   Romania and
              Turkey — A14

1937, July 1
138 A13 3d Prussian grn .60 .20
   a. Perf. 12½ 7.25 5.00
139 A13 4d dark blue .60 .20

"Little Entente," 16th anniversary.

Perf. 11, 11½, 12½
1937, Oct. 29   **Photo.**
140 A14 3d peacock grn .35 .20
141 A14 4d ultramarine .45 .30

Balkan Entente.

King Peter II — A16

1939-40   **Typo.**   **Perf. 12½**
142 A16 25p black ('40) .20 .20
143 A16 50p orange ('40) .20 .20
144 A16 1d yellow grn .20 .20
145 A16 1.50d red .20 .20
146 A16 2d dp mag ('40) .20 .20
147 A16 3d dull red brn .20 .20
148 A16 4d ultra .20 .20
148A A16 5d dk blue ('40) .20 .20
148B A16 5.50d dk vio brn ('40) .20 .20

---

149 A16 6d slate blue .40 .20
150 A16 8d sepia .40 .20
151 A16 12d bright vio .70 .20
152 A16 16d dull violet 1.00 .20
153 A16 20d blue ('40) 1.00 .20
154 A16 30d brt pink ('40) 2.25 .30
      Nos. 142-154 (15) 7.55 3.10

For overprints and surcharges see Nos. N1-N11, N13, N15-N28, N30-N35, Croatia 1-25.

Arms of Yugoslavia, Greece, Romania
and Turkey

A17   A18

1940, June 1
155 A17 3d ultramarine .65 .35
156 A18 3d ultramarine .65 .35
   a. Pair, #155-156 2.50 2.50
157 A17 4d dark blue .65 .35
158 A18 4d dark blue .65 .35
   a. Pair, #157-158 2.50 2.50
      Nos. 155-158 (4) 2.60 1.40

Balkan Entente.

Bridge at
Obod
A19

1940, Sept. 29   **Litho.**
159 A19 5.50d slate grn & dull grn 1.50 1.75

Zagreb Phil. Exhib.; 500th anniv. of Johann Gutenberg's invention of printing. The first press in the Yugoslav area was located at Obod in 1493.

Issues for Federal Republic
Types of Serbia, 1942-43, Surcharged
in Green or Vermilion

1944, Dec.   **Unwmk.**   **Perf. 11½**
Overprinted with Pale Green
Network
159A OS4 5d (3d + 2d) rose pink .20 .20
159B OS4 10d (7d + 3d) dk sl grn (V) .20 .25

Similar Surcharge on Serbia Nos.
2N37-2N39

1945, Jan. 24   **Without Network**
159C OS4 5d (3d + 2d) rose pink .20 .20
159D OS4 10d (7d + 3d) dk sl grn (V) .20 .25
159E OS4 25d (4d + 21d) ultra (Bk) .20 .25
      Nos. 159C-159E (3) .60 .75

Marshal Tito
(Josip
Broz) — A20

Prohor Pcinski
Monastery — A21

1945   Photo.   Perf. 12½
160 A20 25p bright bl grn .25 .20
161 A20 50p deep green .25 .20
162 A20 1d crimson rose 2.50 .20
163 A20 2d dark car rose .25 .20
164 A20 4d deep blue .50 .20
165 A20 5d deep green .20 .40
166 A20 6d dark purple .40 .20
167 A20 9d orange brown .80 .20
168 A20 10d deep rose .20 .40
169 A20 20d orange 4.00 1.50
170 A20 25d dark purple .20 .20
171 A20 30d deep blue .20 .70
Nos. 160-171 (12) 9.75 4.60

1945, Aug. 2   Typo.   Perf. 11½
172 A21 2d red .60 .20
Formation of the Popular Antifascist Chamber of Deputies of Macedonia, Aug. 2, 1944.

Partisans A22 A23

Marshal Tito — A24   City of Jajce — A25

Partisan Girl and Flag — A26

1945, Oct. 10   Litho.   Perf. 12½
173 A22 50p olive gray .20 .20
174 A22 1d blue green .20 .20
175 A23 1.50d orange brown .20 .20
176 A24 2d scarlet .20 .20
177 A25 3d red brown .65 .20
178 A24 4d dark blue .20 .20
179 A25 5d dark yel grn .65 .20
180 A26 6d black .25 .20
181 A26 9d deep plum .25 .20
182 A23 12d ultramarine .40 .20
183 A22 16d blue .40 .20
184 A23 20d orange ver 1.00 .20
Nos. 173-184 (12) 4.60 2.40

See Nos. 211-214. For surcharges and overprints see Nos. 202-203, 273-292, 286-289, Istria 42, 44, 46, 48, 50, Trieste 5-14.

"Labor" and "Agriculture" A27 A28

1945, Nov. 29   Photo.   Perf. 12
185 A27 2d brn carmine 3.00 3.00
186 A28 2d brn carmine 3.00 3.00
187 A27 4d deep blue 3.00 3.00
188 A28 4d deep blue 3.00 3.00
189 A27 6d dk slate grn 3.00 3.00
190 A28 6d dk slate grn 3.00 3.00
191 A27 9d red orange 3.00 3.00
192 A28 9d red orange 3.00 3.00
193 A27 16d bright ultra 3.00 3.00
194 A28 16d bright ultra 3.00 3.00
195 A27 20d dark brown 3.00 3.00
a. Souv. sheet of 2, #191, 195, perf. 11½ 8.00 8.00
196 A28 20d dark brown 3.00 3.00
a. Souv. sheet of 2, #192, 196, perf. 11½ 8.00 8.00
Nos. 185-196 (12) 36.00 36.00
Se-tenant pairs, #185-196 (6) 60.00 60.00
Constitution for the Democratic Federation of Yugoslavia, Nov. 29, 1945.

Parade of Armed Forces — A31   Svetozar Markovic — A32

1946, May 9   Unwmk.   Perf. 12½
199 A31 1.50d org yel & red .30 .20
200 A31 2.50d cerise & red .45 .25
201 A31 5d blue & red 1.25 .90
Nos. 199-201 (3) 2.00 1.35
Victory over fascism, 1st anniv.

Type of 1945 Surcharged with New Values in Black
1946, Apr. 1
202 A26 2.50d on 6d bright red .90 .20
203 A26 8d on 9d orange .95 .20

1946, Sept. 22
204 A32 1.50d blue green .75 .35
205 A32 2.50d dp red lilac .85 .50
Markovic, Serbian socialist, birth cent.

People's Theater, Sofia A33

Sigismund Monument, Warsaw — A35

Designs: 1d, Prague. 2½d, Victory Monument, Belgrade. 5d, Spassky Tower, Kremlin.

1946, Dec. 8   Litho.   Perf. 11½
206 A33 ½d dk brn & yel brn .20 .20
207 A33 1d grnsh blk & emer .20 .20
208 A35 1½d dk car rose & rose .20 .20
209 A35 2½d hn brn & brn org .20 .20
210 A35 5d dark bl & blue .30 .20
Nos. 206-210 (5) 1.10 1.00
Pan-Slavic Congress, Belgrade, Dec. 1946.

Types of 1945
1947, Jan. 15   Litho.   Perf. 12½
211 A26 2.50d red orange .35 .20
212 A25 3d dull red .35 .20
213 A25 5d dark blue 1.10 .20
214 A26 8d orange .90 .20
Nos. 211-214 (4) 2.70 .80

Gorski Vijenac — A38   Peter P. Nyegosh — A39

1947, June 8   Typo.
215 A38 1.50d Prus grn & blk .20 .20
216 A39 2.50d ol bis & dk car .25 .20
217 A38 5d blue & black .25 .20
Nos. 215-217 (3) .70 .60
Centenary of the Montenegrin national epic "Gorski Vijenac" (Wreath of Mountains) by Nyegosh.

Girls' Physical Training Classes — A40

Girl Runner — A41

Physical Culture Parade A42

1947, June 15   Litho.   Perf. 11
218 A40 1.50d brown .20 .20
219 A41 2.50d red .25 .25
220 A42 4d violet blue .40 .35
Nos. 218-220 (3) .85 .80
Natl. sports meet, Belgrade, 6/15-22/47.

Map and Star — A43

1947, Sept. 16   Typo.
231 A43 2.50d dp car & dark bl .20 .20
232 A43 5d org brn & dk grn .20 .20
Annexation of Julian Province.

Music and One-string Gusle A44

Vuk Karadzic — A45

1947, Sept. 27   Perf. 11½x12, 12½
233 A44 1.50d green .25 .25
234 A45 2.50d orange red .25 .25
235 A44 5d violet blue .25 .25
Nos. 233-235 (3) .75 .75
Centenary of Serbian literature.

Symbols of Industry and Agriculture, Map and Flag — A46

Danube River Scene — A47

1948, Apr. 8   Litho.   Perf. 12½
236 A46 1.50d grn, bl & salmon .20 .20
237 A46 2.50d red brn, bl & salmon .20 .20
238 A46 5d dk bl, bl & salmon .20 .20
Nos. 236-238 (3) .60 .60
International Fair, Zagreb, May 8-17.

1948, July 30   Unwmk.
239 A47 2d green 2.25 2.25
240 A47 3d carmine 2.25 2.25
241 A47 5d blue 2.25 2.25
242 A47 10d brown orange 2.25 2.25
Nos. 239-242 (4) 9.00 9.00
Danube Conference, Belgrade.

Marchers with Party Flag — A48

Laurent Kosir — A49

1948, July 21   Perf. 11½, 12½
243 A48 2d dark green .20 .20
244 A48 3d dark red .25 .20
245 A48 10d dark blue vio .35 .20
Nos. 243-245 (3) .80 .60
5th Congress of the Communist Party in Yugoslavia, July 21, 1948.

1948, Aug. 21   Perf. 12½
246 A49 3d claret .20 .20
247 A49 5d blue .20 .20
248 A49 10d red orange .20 .20
249 A49 12d dull green .20 .20
Nos. 246-249 (4) .80 .80
80th death anniv. of Laurent Kosir, recognized by Yugoslavia as inventor of the postage stamp.

Arms of Bosnia and Herzegovina A50

Arms of Yugoslavia A51

1948, Nov. 29   Perf. 12½, 12x11½
Arms of Yugoslav Peoples Republics
250 A50 3d green .30 .30
251 A50 3d rose lil (Macedonia) .30 .30
252 A50 3d gray bl (Serbia) .30 .30
253 A50 3d gray (Montenegro) .30 .30
254 A50 3d rose (Croatia) .30 .30
255 A50 3d orange (Slovenia) .30 .30
256 A51 10d deep carmine 1.40 1.40
Nos. 250-256 (7) 3.20 3.20
The Cyrillic and Latin inscriptions are transposed on Nos. 252, 253 and 255.

Franc
Presern — A52

1949, Feb. 8   Photo.   Perf. 11½
257	A52	3d dark blue	.30	.20
258	A52	5d brown orange	.30	.20
259	A52	10d olive black	.30	.20
		Nos. 257-259 (3)	.90	.60

Death cent. of Franc Presern, poet.

Ski Jump,
Planica
A53

Ski Jumper
A54

Perf. 12½x11½
1949, Mar. 20   Litho.
260	A53	10d magenta	.75	.55
261	A54	12d slate gray	.75	.55

Intl. Ski Championships, Planica, Mar. 13-20.

Soldiers — A55

Farmers — A56

Arms and Flags
of Macedonia
and
Yugoslavia — A57

1949, Aug. 2   Perf. 12½
262	A55	3d carmine rose	.20	.20
263	A56	5d dull blue	.20	.20
264	A57	12d red brown	2.00	2.75
		Nos. 262-264 (3)	2.40	3.15

Liberation of Macedonia, 5th anniv.
It is reported that No. 264 was not sold to
the public at post offices.
For overprints see Nos. C30-C32.

Postal
Communications
A58

UPU, 75th anniversary: 5d, Plane, locomotive and stagecoach, horiz.

1949, Sept. 8   Unwmk.
265	A58	3d red	1.10	1.10
266	A58	5d blue	.25	.25
267	A58	12d brown	.25	.25
		Nos. 265-267 (3)	1.60	1.60

For overprints see Trieste Nos. 15-16.

Locomotives
A60

1949, Dec. 15   Photo.
269	A60	2d Early steam	.85	.20
270	A60	3d Modern steam	.90	.20
271	A60	5d Diesel	2.50	.25
272	A60	10d Electric	8.75	5.50
		Nos. 269-272 (4)	13.00	6.15

Centenary of Yugoslav railroads.
For overprints see Trieste Nos. 17-20.

Official Stamps
Nos. O7 and O8
Surcharged:

1949   Typo.
272A	O1	3d on 8d chocolate	.20	.20
272B	O1	3d on 12d violet	.20	.20

Stamps of 1945 and 1947 Overprinted
or Surcharged in Black:

a   b

c   d

1949   Litho.
273	A22 (a)	50p olive gray	.20	.20
274	A22 (a)	1d blue green	.20	.20
275	A24 (b)	2d scarlet	.20	.20
276	A26 (c)	3d on 8d orange	.20	.20
277	A25 (d)	3d dull red	.20	.20
278	A25 (d)	5d dark blue	.20	.20
279	A23 (a)	10d on 20d org ver	.25	.20
280	A23 (a)	12d ultramarine	.35	.20
281	A22 (a)	16d blue	.60	.20
282	A23 (a)	20d orange ver	.45	.20
		Nos. 273-282 (10)	2.85	2.00

On No. 279 the surcharge includes a rule
below "JUGOSLAVIJA" and "D 10" with two
bars over "20D."
See Nos. 286-289.

Surveying for
Highway
A61

Bridge, Map
and
Automobile
A62

Highway
Completion
Symbolized
A63

1950, Jan. 16   Photo.   Perf. 12½
283	A61	2d blue green	.35	.35
284	A62	3d rose brown	.20	.20
285	A63	5d violet blue	.80	.80
		Nos. 283-285 (3)	1.35	1.35

Completion of Belgrade-Zagreb highway,
Dec. 1949.

Types of 1945 Overprinted in Black

1950   Unwmk.   Perf. 12½
286	A22 (a)	1d brownish org	.20	.20
287	A24 (b)	2d blue green	.20	.20
288	A25 (d)	3d rose pink	.20	.20
289	A25 (d)	5d blue	.25	.20
		Nos. 286-289 (4)	.85	.80

Marshal
Tito — A64

Child
Eating — A65

1950, Apr. 30   Engr.
290	A64	3d red	.70	.30
291	A64	5d dull blue	.70	.30
292	A64	10d brown	4.50	3.25
293	A64	12d olive black	1.25	.70
		Nos. 290-293 (4)	7.15	4.55

Labor Day, May 1.

1950, June 1   Photo.
294	A65	3d brown red	.25	.20

Issued to publicize Children's Day, June 1.

Boy and Model
Plane — A66

Map and Chess
Symbols — A67

Designs: 3d, Glider aloft. 5d, Parachutists.
10d, Aviatrix. 20d, Glider on field.

1950, July 2   Engr.
295	A66	2d dark green	.65	.30
296	A66	3d brown red	.65	.30
297	A66	5d violet	.65	.30
298	A66	10d chocolate	.65	.30
299	A66	20d ultramarine	5.50	4.00
		Nos. 295-299 (5)	8.10	5.20

Third Aviation Meet, July 2-11.

1950, Aug. 20   Photo.   Perf. 11½

3d, Rook and ribbon. 5d, Globe and chess
board. 10d, Allegory of international chess.
20d, View of Dubrovnik, knight and ribbon.
300	A67	2d red brn & rose brown	.45	.35
301	A67	3d blk brn, gray brn & dl yellow	.45	.35
302	A67	5d dk grn, bl & buff	.75	.45
303	A67	10d cl, bl & org yel	1.10	.60
304	A67	20d dk bl, bl & org yellow	7.75	5.00
		Nos. 300-304 (5)	10.50	6.75

Intl. Chess Matches, Dubrovnik, Aug. 1950.

Electrification
A68

Coal and Logs for
Export
A69

Designs: 50p, Metallurgy. 2d, Agriculture.
3d, Construction. 5d, Fishing. 7d, Mining.
10d, Fruitgrowing. 12d, Lumbering. 16d,
Gathering sunflowers. 20d, Livestock raising.
30d, Book manufacture. 50d, Loading ship.

1950-51   Unwmk.   Engr.   Perf. 12½
305	A68	50p dk brn ('51)	.20	.20
306	A68	1d blue green	.20	.20
307	A68	2d orange	.20	.20
308	A68	3d rose red	.20	.20
309	A68	5d ultramarine	.30	.20
310	A68	7d gray	.30	.20
311	A68	10d chocolate	.50	.20
312	A68	12d vio brn ('51)	1.25	.20
313	A68	16d vio bl ('51)	1.75	.30
314	A68	20d ol grn ('51)	1.75	.25
314A	A68	30d red brn ('51)	3.50	1.00
315	A68	50d violet ('51)	21.00	12.00
		Nos. 305-315 (12)	31.15	15.15

See Nos. 343-354, 378-384A. For overprints see Trieste Nos. 68-75, 90-92.

1950, Sept. 23   Photo.
316	A69	3d red brown	.30	.20

Zagreb International Fair, 1950.

Early Sailing
Vessel
"Dubrovnik"
A70

Partisans with
Flag — A71

Designs: 3d, Partisans in boat. 5d, Loading
freighter. 10d, Transatlantic ship "Zagreb."
12d, Sailboats. 20d, Naval gun and ship.

1950, Nov. 29
317	A70	2d brown violet	.20	.20
318	A70	3d orange brown	.20	.20
319	A70	5d dull green	.20	.20
320	A70	10d chalky blue	.30	.20
321	A70	12d dark blue	.70	.30
322	A70	20d red brown	2.00	1.10
		Nos. 317-322 (6)	3.60	2.20

Yugoslav navy.

1951, Mar. 27   Engr.
323	A71	3d red & red brn	2.75	1.50

Yugoslavia's resistance to Nazi Germany,
10th anniv.

Stane
Rozman
A72

5d, Post-boy during Slovene insurrection.

1951, Apr. 27   Photo.
324	A72	3d brown red	.35	.25
325	A72	5d dark blue	.60	.40

Slovene insurrection, 10th anniv.

Children
Painting
A73

1951, June 3
326 A73 3d red .60 .20
Issued to publicize Children's Day, June 3.

Zika
Jovanovich — A74

Serbian
Revolutionists
A75

1951, July 7
327 A74 3d brown red .45 .25
328 A75 5d deep blue .70 .40
Serbian insurrection, 10th anniv.

Sava Kovacevich
A76

Kovacevich
Leading
Revolutionists
A77

1951, July 13
329 A76 3d rose pink .70 .25
330 A77 5d light blue 1.00 .40
Montenegrin insurrection, 10th anniv.

Monument to
Marko Oreskovich
A78

1951, July 27
331 A78 3d shown .45 .25
332 A78 5d Monument to wounded .70 .40
Croatian insurrection, 10th anniv.

Sium
Bolaj — A79

Revolutionists
A80

1951, July 27
333 A79 3d rose brown .35 .20
334 A80 5d blue .75 .40
Revolution in Bosnia and Herzegovina, 10th
anniv.

Primoz
Trubar — A81

National
Handicrafts — A82

12d, Marko Marulic. 20d, Tsar Stefan
Duschan.

1951, Sept. 9 Engr.
335 A81 10d slate gray .40 .25
336 A81 12d brown orange .40 .25
337 A81 20d violet 2.50 2.00
Nos. 335-337 (3) 3.30 2.50
Yugoslav cultural anniversaries.
For overprints see Trieste Nos. 40-41.

1951, Sept. 15 Litho. Perf. 11½
338 A82 3d multicolored 1.75 .45
Zagreb International Fair, 1951.

Mirce
Acev — A83

Monument at
Skopje
A84

1951, Oct. 11
339 A83 3d deep plum .55 .30
340 A84 5d indigo 1.10 .65
Macedonian insurrection, 10th anniv.

Soldier and
Emblem — A85

Peter P.
Nyegosh — A86

1951, Dec. 22 Photo. Perf. 12½
341 A85 15d deep carmine .45 .20
Army Day. See No. C54.

1951, Nov. 29 Engr.
342 A86 15d deep claret 2.00 .55
Death centenary of Nyegosh. See note
after No. 217.

Types of 1950-51

1951-52 Engr.
Designs: 15d, Gathering sunflowers. 25d,
Agriculture. 35d, Construction. 75d, Lumber-
ing. 100d, Metallurgy.

343 A68 1d gray ('52) .20 .20
344 A68 2d rose car ('52) .25 .20
345 A68 5d orange ('52) 1.25 .20
346 A68 10d emerald ('52) 4.75 .20
347 A68 15d rose car ('52) 10.50 1.50
348 A68 20d purple 2.25 .20
349 A68 25d yel brn ('52) 7.00 .20
350 A68 30d blue 1.25 .20
351 A68 35d red brn ('52) 1.60 .20
352 A68 50d greenish bl 1.25 .20
353 A68 75d purple ('52) 1.90 .20
354 A68 100d sepia ('52) 3.00 .25
Nos. 343-354 (12) 35.20 3.75
No. 349 exists with and without printer's
inscriptions at bottom, with stamps differing
slightly.

Marshal Tito
A87 A88

1952, May 25 Photo. Perf. 11½
355 A87 15d shown .50 .45
356 A88 28d shown 1.10 .90
357 A87 50d Tito facing left 8.50 7.75
Nos. 355-357 (3) 10.10 9.10
60th birthday of Marshal Tito

Child with
Ball — A89

1952, June 1 Litho. Perf. 12½
358 A89 15d bright rose 3.50 1.00
Issued to publicize Children's Day, June 1.
For overprint see Trieste No. 60.

Girl
Gymnast — A90

Split,
Dalmatia — A91

1952, July 10 Perf. 12½
359 A90 5d shown .50 .35
360 A90 10d Runner .50 .35
361 A90 15d Swimmer .50 .35
362 A90 28d Boxer .50 .35
363 A90 50d Basketball 4.00 2.00
364 A90 100d Soccer 8.50 6.25
Nos. 359-364 (6) 14.50 9.65
15th Olympic Games, Helsinki, 1952.
Nos. 359-364 exist imperf. Value $250.
For overprints see Trieste Nos. 51-56.

1952, Sept. 10 Litho.
365 A91 15d shown 1.10 1.10
366 A91 28d Naval scene 1.75 1.75
367 A91 50d St. Stefan 6.75 6.75
Nos. 365-367 (3) 9.60 9.60
Yugoslav navy, 10th anniv.
For overprints see Trieste Nos. 57-59.

Belgrade,
16th
Century
A92

1952, Sept. 14 Engr. Perf. 11½
368 A92 15d violet brn 6.00 5.00
1st Yugoslav Phil. Exhib., Sept. 14-20. Sold
only at the exhibition.

Marching
Workers and
Congress
Flag — A93

1952, Nov. 2 Perf. 11½
369 A93 15d red brown 1.25 1.10
370 A93 15d dark vio blue 1.25 1.10
371 A93 15d dark brown 1.25 1.10
372 A93 15d blue green 1.25 1.10
Nos. 369-372 (4) 5.00 4.40
6th Yugoslav Communist Party Congress,
Zagreb.
For overprints see Trieste Nos. 61-64.

Nikola
Tesla — A94

Woman Pouring
Water — A95

1953, Jan. 7 Unwmk.
373 A94 15d brown carmine .65 .20
374 A94 30d chalky blue 2.00 .35
Death of Nikola Tesla, 10th anniv.
For overprints see Trieste Nos. 66-67.

1953, Mar. 24 Litho. Perf. 11½
Designs: 30d, Hands holding two birds.
50d, Woman holding Urn.

375 A95 15d dk olive green .90 .30
376 A95 30d chalky blue .90 .30
377 A95 50d henna brown 6.00 1.60
Nos. 375-377 (3) 7.80 2.20
Issued to honor the United Nations.
See Nos. RA19 and RAJ16. For overprints
see Trieste Nos. 76-78.

Types of 1950-52

1953-55   **Litho.**   *Perf. 12½*

8d, Mining. 17d, Livestock raising.

378	A68	1d dull gray	.70	.20
379	A68	2d carmine	2.50	.20
380	A68	5d orange	3.50	.20
381	A68	8d blue	2.50	.20
382	A68	10d yellow green	5.50	.20
383	A68	12d lt vio brown	25.00	.20
384	A68	15d rose red	11.00	.20
384A	A68	17d vio brn ('55)	2.00	.20
		Nos. 378-384A (8)	52.70	1.60

For overprints see Trieste Nos. 68-75, 90-92.

Automobile Climbing Mt. Lovcen — A96

30d, Motorcycle & auto at Opatija. 50d, Racers leaving Belgrade. 70d, Auto near Mt. Triglav.

1953, May 10   **Photo.**   *Perf. 12½*

385	A96	15d sal & dp plum	.20	.20
386	A96	30d bl & dark blue	.30	.20
387	A96	50d ocher & choc	.45	.20
388	A96	70d lt grn & ol grn	1.90	.40
		Nos. 385-388 (4)	2.85	1.00

Intl. Automobile & Motorcycle Races, 1953.

President Tito — A97   Star and Flag-encircled Globe — A98

1953, June 28   **Engr.**   **Unwmk.**

389 A97 50d deep purple   4.25 1.25

Marshal Tito's election to the presidency, Jan. 14, 1953.
For overprint see Trieste No. 83.

1953, July 25   **Engr.; Star Typo.**

390 A98 15d gray & green   2.50 2.00

38th Esperanto Cong., Zagreb, 7/25-8/1.
For overprint see Trieste No. 84.

Macedonian Revolutionary A99   Nicolas Karev A100

1953, Aug. 2   **Litho.**

391	A99	15d dark red brown	.85	.65
392	A100	30d dull green	3.00	1.75

Macedonian Insurection of 1903, 50th anniv.

Family — A101

Branko Radicevic — A102

1953, Sept. 6   **Photo.**

393 A101 15d deep green   10.00 2.50

Liberation of Istria and the Slovene coast, 10th anniv.
For overprint see Trieste No. 85.

1953, Oct. 1   **Engr.**

394 A102 15d lilac   4.25 1.50

10th death anniv. of Branko Radicevic, poet.
For overprint see Trieste No. 86.

View of Jajce — A103

Designs: 30d, First meeting place. 50d, Marshal Tito addressing Assembly.

1953, Nov. 29   *Perf. 12½x12*

395	A103	5d dark green	1.40	.70
396	A103	30d rose car	1.90	1.10
397	A103	50d dark brown	7.75	7.00
		Nos. 395-397 (3)	11.05	8.80

2nd Assembly of the Natl. Republic of Yugoslavia, 10th anniv.
For overprints see Trieste Nos. 87-89.

Wildlife A104

Lammergeier A105

1954, June 30   **Photo.**   *Perf. 11½*

398	A104	2d Ground squirrel	.25	.20
399	A104	5d Lynx	.25	.20
400	A104	10d Red deer	.25	.20
401	A104	15d Brown bear	.35	.20
402	A104	17d Chamois	.35	.20
403	A104	25d White pelican	.60	.40
404	A105	30d shown	.60	.40
405	A105	35d Black beetle	.60	.40
406	A105	50d Bush cricket	5.00	3.25
407	A105	65d Adriatic lizard	10.00	5.00
408	A105	70d Salamander	9.00	5.00
409	A105	100d Trout	15.00	15.00
		Nos. 398-409 (12)	42.25	30.45

See Nos. 497-505. For overprints see Trieste Nos. 93-104.

> Catalogue values for unused stamps in this section, from this point to the end of the section, are for Never Hinged items.

Ljubljana, 17th Century A106

1954, July 29   **Engr.**

410 A106 15d multicolored   11.00 10.50

2nd Yugoslav Phil. Exhib., July 29-Aug. 8. Sold for 50d, which included admission to the exhibition.

Revolutionary Flag — A107

Engr. & Typo.

1954, Oct. 3   *Perf. 12½*

411	A107	15d shown	1.60	.45
412	A107	30d Cannon	2.25	.80
413	A107	50d Revolutionary seal	5.00	1.10
414	A107	70d Karageorge	32.50	15.00
		Nos. 411-414 (4)	41.35	17.35

1st Serbian insurrection, 150th anniv.
For overprints see Trieste Nos. 105-108.

Vatroslav Lisinski — A108

30d, Andrea Kacic-Miosic. 50d, Jure Vega. 70d, Jovan Jovanovic-Zmaj. 100d, Philip Visnic.

1954, Dec. 25   **Engr.**

415	A108	15d dark green	2.75	1.00
416	A108	30d chocolate	2.75	1.60
417	A108	50d dp claret	3.75	3.00
418	A108	70d indigo	7.50	7.00
419	A108	100d purple	19.00	19.00
		Nos. 415-419 (5)	35.75	31.60

Scene from "Robinja" — A109

"A Midsummer Night's Dream" A110

1955   **Photo.**   *Perf. 12x11½, 12½*
Glazed Paper

420	A109	15d brown lake	1.00	.55
421	A110	30d dark blue	3.50	1.60

Festival at Dubrovnik.

Dragon Emblem of Ljubljana — A111

1955   **Engr.**   *Perf. 12½*

422 A111 15d dk grn & brn   3.00 .95

1st Intl. Exhib. of Graphic Arts, Ljubljana, July 3-Sept. 3.

Symbol of Sign Language — A112   Hops — A113

1955, Aug. 23

423 A112 15d rose lake   1.75 .45

2nd World Congress of Deaf Mutes, Zagreb, Aug. 23-27.

1955, Sept. 24   **Photo.**   *Perf. 11½*

Medicinal Plants.

424	A113	5d shown	.20	.20
425	A113	10d Tobacco	.20	.20
426	A113	15d Poppy	.20	.20
427	A113	17d Linden	.20	.20
428	A113	25d Chamomile	.20	.20
429	A113	30d Salvia	.40	.20
430	A113	50d Dog rose	5.25	1.50
431	A113	70d Gentian	6.50	1.90
432	A113	100d Adonis	12.00	2.50
		Nos. 424-432 (9)	25.15	7.10

"Peace" Statue, New York — A114

Woman and Dove — A115

1955, Oct. 24   **Litho.**   *Perf. 12½*

433 A114 30d lt bl & blk   1.75 1.10

United Nations, 10th anniversary.

1955, Nov. 29   **Engr.**

434 A115 15d dull violet   .65 .20

10th anniv. of the "New Yugoslavia."

St. Donat, Zadar — A116

Cornice, Cathedral at Sibenik A117

Yugoslav Art: 10d, Relief of a King, Split. 15d, Griffin, Studenica Monastery. 20d, Figures, Trogir Cathedral. 25d, Fresco, Sopocani Monastery. 30d, Tombstone, Radimlje. 40d, Ciborium, Kotor Cathedral. 50d, St. Martin from Tryptich, Dubrovnik. 70d, Figure, Belec Church. 100d, Rihard Jakopic, self-portrait. 200d, "Peace" Statue, New York.

1956, Mar. 24   Photo.   Perf. 11½

435	A116	5d blue vio	.25 .20
436	A116	10d slate grn	.25 .20
437	A116	15d olive brn	.25 .20
438	A116	20d brown car	.25 .20
439	A116	25d black brn	.25 .20
440	A116	30d dp claret	.25 .20
441	A117	35d olive grn	.60 .20
442	A117	40d red brown	1.00 .30
443	A116	50d olive brn	1.50 .40
444	A116	70d dk green	5.50 4.00
445	A116	100d dark pur	19.00 12.00
446	A116	200d deep blue	45.00 19.00
		Nos. 435-446 (12)	74.10 37.10

13th Century Tower, Zagreb A118

1956, Apr. 20   Engr.   Perf. 11½
Chalky Paper

447 A118 15d vio brn, bis brn & gray   .40 .20
 a. Miniature sheet of 4   4.50 1.60

3rd Yugoslavia Phil. Exhib. (JUFIZ III), Zagreb, May 20-27. No. 447a was sold at the exhibition, tipped into a folder, for 75 dinars. See No. C56.

Induction Motor — A119

Perf. 11½x12½

1956, July 10   Photo.

448	A119	10d shown	.25 .20
449	A119	15d Transformer	.30 .20
450	A119	30d Electronic controls	.55 .25
451	A119	50d Nikola Tesla	1.90 1.00
		Nos. 448-451 (4)	3.00 1.65

Birth cent. of Nikola Tesla, inventor.

Sea Horse — A120

Paper Nautilus A121

Designs: 20d, European rock lobster. 25d, "Sea Prince." 30d, Sea perch. 35d, Red mullet. 50d, Scorpion fish. 70d, Wrasse. 100d, Dory.

1956, Sept. 10   Perf. 11½
Granite Paper
Animals in Natural Colors

452	A120	10d bright grn	.20 .20
453	A121	15d ultra & blk	.20 .20
454	A121	20d deep blue	.20 .20
455	A121	25d violet blue	.30 .20
456	A121	30d brt grnsh bl	.35 .20
457	A121	35d dk bl green	.70 .20
458	A121	50d indigo	2.75 .80
459	A121	70d slate grn	4.50 1.40
460	A121	100d dark blue	12.00 4.00
		Nos. 452-460 (9)	21.20 7.40

Runner A122

Centaury — A123

Designs: 15d, Paddling kayak. 20d, Skiing. 30d, Swimming. 35d, Soccer. 50d, Water polo. 70d, Table tennis. 100d, Sharpshooting.

1956, Oct. 24   Litho.   Perf. 12½
Design and Inscription in Bister

461	A122	10d dk carmine	.20 .20
462	A122	15d dark blue	.20 .20
463	A122	20d ultramarine	.20 .20
464	A122	30d olive grn	.20 .20
465	A122	35d dark brown	.25 .20
466	A122	50d green	.65 .20
467	A122	70d brn violet	2.00 1.10
468	A122	100d dark red	4.75 2.25
		Nos. 461-468 (8)	8.45 4.55

16th Olympic Games, Melbourne, 11/22-12/8.

1957, May 25   Photo.   Perf. 11½

Medicinal Plants: 15d, Belladonna. 20d, Autumn crocus. 25d, Marsh mallow. 30d, Valerian. 35d, Woolly Foxglove. 50d, Aspidium. 70d, Green Winged Orchid. 100d, Pyrethrum.

Granite Paper
Flowers in Natural Colors

469	A123	10d dk bl & grn	.20 .20
470	A123	15d violet	.20 .20
471	A123	20d lt ol grn & brn	.20 .20
472	A123	25d dp cl & dk bl	.30 .20
473	A123	30d lil rose & claret	.55 .20
474	A123	35d dk gray & dl pur	.90 .20
475	A123	50d dp grn & choc	1.50 .45
476	A123	70d pale brn & grn	2.75 1.00
477	A123	100d gray & brown	8.50 1.90
		Nos. 469-477 (9)	15.10 4.55

See #538-546, 597-605, 689-694, 772-777.

Hand Holding Factory A124

1957, June 25   Engr.   Perf. 12½
478 A124 15d dark car rose   .35 .20
479 A124 30d violet blue   1.40 .35

Congress of Workers' Councils, Belgrade, June 25.

2nd Gymnastic Meet, Zagreb, July 10-14 — A125

Various gymnastic positions.

1957, July 1   Photo.

480	A125	10d ol grn & blk	.20 .20
481	A125	15d brn red & blk	.20 .20
482	A125	30d Prus bl & blk	.50 .20
483	A125	50d brn & black	2.25 1.25
		Nos. 480-483 (4)	3.15 1.85

Montenegro A126

Natl. Costumes: 15d, Macedonia. 30d, Croatia. 50d, Serbia. 70d, Bosnia and Herzegovina. 100d, Slovenia. 50d, 70d, 100d vert.

1957, Sept. 24   Typo.   Perf. 12½
Background in Bister Brown

484	A126	10d dk brn, ultra & red	.20 .20
485	A126	15d dk brn, blk & red	.20 .20
486	A126	30d dk brn, grn & red	.20 .20
487	A126	50d dk brn & green	.50 .20
488	A126	70d dk brn & black	.65 .40
489	A126	100d dk brn, grn & red	3.25 1.90
		Nos. 484-489 (6)	5.00 3.10

Revolutionists A127

Simon Gregorcic — A128

Lithographed and Engraved
1957, Nov. 7   Perf. 11½x12½
490 A127 15d ocher & red   .55 .40

Russian Revolution, 40th anniv.

1957, Dec. 3   Engr.   Perf. 12½

Famous Yugoslavs: 30d, Anton Linhart, dramatist and historian. 50d, Oton Kucera, physicist. 70d, Stevan Mokranjac, composer. 100d, Jovan Sterija Popovic, writer

491	A128	15d sepia	.45 .20
492	A128	30d indigo	.60 .20
493	A128	50d reddish brn	1.25 .20
494	A128	70d dl violet	9.00 2.50
495	A128	100d olive grn	15.00 13.00
		Nos. 491-495 (5)	26.30 16.10

"Young Man on Fire" — A129

Stylized Bird — A130

1958, Apr. 22   Photo.
496 A129 15d deep plum   .35 .20

Union of Yugoslav Communists, 7th congress, Ljubljana, Apr. 22.

Types of 1954

Game birds.

1958, May 25   Perf. 11½
Granite Paper
Birds in Natural Colors

497	A104	10d Mallard	.20 .20
498	A104	15d Capercaillie	.20 .20
499	A104	20d Ring-necked pheasant	.20 .20
500	A105	25d Coot	.20 .20
501	A104	30d Water rail	.30 .20
502	A105	35d Great bustard	.50 .20
503	A104	50d Rock partridge	2.00 .70
504	A104	70d Woodcock	3.50 1.75
505	A105	100d Eurasian crane	7.50 4.00
		Nos. 497-505 (9)	14.60 7.65

1958, June 14   Engr.   Perf. 12½
506 A130 15d bluish black   .50 .25

Opening of Postal Museum, Belgrade.

Flag and Laurel A131

1958, July 1   Unwmk.
507 A131 15d brn carmine   .40 .20

15th anniv. of victory over Germans at Sutjeska, Bosnia.

Onufrio Well, Dubrovnik A132

1958, Aug. 10   Litho.   Perf. 12½
508 A132 15d black & brn   .55 .30

Marin Drzic, dramatist, 450th birth anniv.

Sisak Steel Works — A133

Titograd Hotel and Open-Air Theater — A134

Industrial Progress Designs: 2d, Crude oil production. 5d, Shipbuilding. 10d, Sisak steel works. 15d, Jablanica hydroelectric works. 17d, Lumber industry. 25d, Overpass, Zagreb-Ljubljana highway. 30d, Litostroy turbine factory. 35d, Lukavac coke plant. 50d, Bridge at Skopje. 70d, Railroad station, Sarajevo. 100d, Triple bridge, Ljubljana. 200d, Mestrovic station, Zagreb. 500d, Parliament, Belgrade.

1958   Typo.   Perf. 12½ Horiz.
509 A133 10d green   7.75 3.50
510 A133 15d orange ver   7.75 3.50

Engr. Perf. 12½

511	A133	2d olive	.20	.20
512	A133	5d brown red	.20	.20
513	A133	10d green	.20	.20
514	A133	15d orange ver	.20	.20
515	A133	17d deep claret	.20	.20
516	A133	25d slate	.20	.20
517	A133	30d blue black	.20	.20
518	A133	35d rose red	.20	.20
519	A134	40d car rose	.25	.20
520	A134	50d bright bl	.30	.20
521	A134	70d orange ver	.45	.20
522	A134	100d green	2.25	.20
523	A134	200d red brown	2.00	.20
524	A134	500d intense bl	3.75	.30
		Nos. 511-524 (14)	10.60	2.90

Nos. 509-510 are coil stamps.
See #555-562, 627-645, 786-789, 830-840.

Ocean
Exploration
A135

1958, Oct. 24 Unwmk.
525 A135 15d brown violet .50 .25
Intl. Geophysical Year, 1957-58. See #C58.

White and
Black Hands
Holding
Scales
A136

1958, Dec. 10 Perf. 12½
526 A136 30d steel blue .55 .30
Universal Declaration of Human Rights,
10th anniv.

Dubrovnik
A137

Red
Flags — A138

Tourist attractions: #528, Bled. #529, Postojna grotto. #530, Ohrid. #531, Opatija. #532, Plitvice National Park. #533, Split. #534, Sveti Stefan. #535, Exhibition Hall, Belgrade.

1959, Feb. 16 Litho. Perf. 12½

527	A137	10d crim rose & cit	.20	.20
528	A137	10d lt grn & lt vio bl	.20	.20
529	A137	15d grnsh bl & pur	.20	.20
530	A137	15d grn & bright bl	.20	.20
531	A137	20d lt grn & grnsh bl	.20	.20
532	A137	20d ol bis & brt grn	.20	.20
533	A137	30d yel org & purple	.70	.20
534	A137	30d lt vio bl & gray ol	.70	.20
535	A137	70d gray & grnsh bl	2.25	1.10
		Nos. 527-535 (9)	4.85	2.70

Nos. 527, 530, 532 and 534 are inscribed in
Cyrillic characters. See #650-658, 695-700.

1959, Apr. 20 Unwmk. Perf. 12½
536 A138 20d multicolored .25 .20
Yugoslav Communist Party, 40th anniv.

Dubrovnik,
15th
Century
A139

1959, May 24 Engr. Perf. 11½
537 A139 20d yel grn, dk grn &
bl .85 .75
4th Yugoslavia Phil. Exhib. (JUFIZ IV),
Dubrovnik.

Type of 1957

Medicinal Plants: 10d, Lavender. 15d, Black Alder. 20d, Scopolia. 25d, Monkshood. 30d, Bilberry. 35d, Juniper. 50d, Primrose. 70d, Pomegranate. 100d, Jimson weed.

1959, May 25 Photo.
Granite Paper
Flowers in Natural Colors

538	A123	10d lt bl & dk blue	.20	.20
539	A123	15d brt yel & car	.20	.20
540	A123	20d dk ol bis & mar	.20	.20
541	A123	25d ap grn & dk pur	.20	.20
542	A123	30d pink & dk bl	.20	.20
543	A123	35d bis brn & vio bl	.40	.20
544	A123	50d brn & green	.95	.25
545	A123	70d yel & ocher	1.25	.45
546	A123	100d lt brn & brn	2.50	1.10
		Nos. 538-546 (9)	6.10	3.00

Tug of
War — A140

Sports: 15d, High jump and runners. 20d, Ring and parallel bar exercises. 35d, Women gymnasts. 40d, Sailors doing gymnastics. 55d, Field ball and basketball. 80d, Swimming. 100d, Festival emblem, vert.

1959, June 26 Litho. Perf. 12½

547	A140	10d dk sl grn & ocher	.20	.20
548	A140	15d vio bl & sepia	.20	.20
549	A140	20d ol bis & dl lil	.20	.20
550	A140	35d deep cl & gray	.20	.20
551	A140	40d violet & gray	.20	.20
552	A140	55d sl grn & ol bis	.20	.20
553	A140	80d indigo & olive	.75	.35
554	A140	100d pur & bister	1.75	1.00
		Nos. 547-554 (8)	3.70	2.55

Physical Culture Festival.

Types of 1958; Designs as before

Designs: 8d, Lumber industry. 15d, Overpass, Zagreb-Ljubljana highway. 20d, Jablanica hydroelectric works. 40d, Titograd Hotel. 55d, Bridge at Skopje. 80d, Railroad Station, Sarajevo.

1959 Typo. Perf. 12½ Horizontally
555 A133 15d green 2.50 1.10
556 A133 20d orange ver 3.00 1.10

		Engr.	Perf. 12½	
557	A133	8d deep claret	.25	.20
558	A133	15d green	.35	.20
559	A133	20d orange ver	.60	.20
560	A134	40d bright blue	1.40	.20
561	A134	55d carmine rose	2.25	.20
562	A134	80d orange ver	3.75	.20
		Nos. 557-562 (6)	8.60	1.20

Nos. 555-556 are coil stamps.

Fair
Emblem — A141

Athletics — A142

1959, Sept. 5 Litho. Unwmk.
563 A141 20d lt vio bl & blk .55 .20
50th International Fair at Zagreb.

1960, Apr. 25 Perf. 12½

564	A142	15d shown	.20	.20
565	A142	20d Swimming	.20	.20
566	A142	30d Skiing	.20	.20
567	A142	35d Wrestling	.20	.20
568	A142	40d Bicycling	.20	.20
569	A142	55d Yachting	.25	.20
570	A142	80d Horseback riding	.55	.35
571	A142	100d Fencing	.70	.45
		Nos. 564-571 (8)	2.50	2.00

17th Olympic Games.

Hedgehog
A143

1960, May 25 Photo. Perf. 12x11½
Animals in Natural Colors

572	A143	15d shown	.20	.20
573	A143	20d Red squirrel	.20	.20
574	A143	25d Pine marten	.20	.20
575	A143	30d Hare	.20	.20
576	A143	35d Red fox	.20	.20
577	A143	40d Badger	.20	.20
578	A143	55d Wolf	.40	.25
579	A143	80d Roe deer	.65	.35
580	A143	100d Wild boar	1.40	1.00
		Nos. 572-580 (9)	3.65	2.80

See Nos. 663-671.

Lenin, 90th Birth
Anniv. — A144

1960, June 22 Engr. Perf. 12½
581 A144 20d dk grn & slate grn .20 .20

Atomic
Accelerator
A145

1960, Aug. 23 Unwmk.
582 A145 15d shown .20 .20
583 A145 20d Generator .20 .20
584 A145 40d Nuclear reactor .30 .20
Nos. 582-584 (3) .70 .60
Nuclear energy exposition, Belgrade.

Serbian National
Theater, Novi
Sad — A146

Ivan Cankar,
Writer — A147

Designs: 20d, Woman from Croatian play. 40d, Edward Rusijan and early plane. 55d, Symbolic hand holding fruit. 80d, Atom and UN emblem.

1960, Oct. 24 Perf. 12½

585	A146	15d gray black	.20	.20
586	A146	20d brown	.20	.20
587	A146	40d dark gray blue	.20	.20
588	A146	55d dull claret	.20	.20
589	A146	80d dark green	.30	.20
		Nos. 585-589 (5)	1.10	1.00

Serbian Natl. Theater, Novi Sad, cent. (#585); Croatian Natl. Theater, Zagreb, cent. (#586); 1st flight in Yugoslavia, 50th anniv. (#587); 15th anniv. of the Yugoslav Republic (#588); UN, 15th anniv. (#589).

1960, Dec. 24 Engr. Perf. 12½

Famous Yugoslavs: 20d, Silvije Strahimir Kranjcevic, poet. 40d, Paja Jovanovic, painter. 55d, Dura Jaksic, writer and painter. 80d, Mihajlo Pupin, electro-technician. 100d, Rudjer Boscovich, mathematician.

590	A147	15d dark green	.20	.20
591	A147	20d henna brown	.20	.20
592	A147	40d olive bister	.20	.20
593	A147	55d magenta	.20	.20
594	A147	80d dark blue	.30	.20
595	A147	100d Prussian bl	.60	.30
		Nos. 590-595 (6)	1.70	1.30

International Atomic
Energy
Commission
Emblem
A148

Victims'
Monument,
Kragujevac
A149

Engr. & Litho.
1961, May 15 Perf. 12½
596 A148 25d multicolored .25 .20
Intl. Nuclear Electronic Conf., Belgrade.

Flower Type of 1957

Medicinal plants: 10d, Yellow foxglove. 15d, Marjoram. 20d, Hyssop. 25d, Scarlet haw. 40d, Rose mallow. 50d, Soapwort. 60d, Clary. 80d, Blackthorn. 100d, Marigold.

1961, May 25 Photo. Perf. 11½
Granite Paper
Flowers in Natural Colors

597	A123	10d lt bl & grnsh bl	.20	.20
598	A123	15d gray & chnt	.20	.20
599	A123	20d buff & green	.20	.20
600	A123	25d lt vio & vio	.20	.20
601	A123	40d lt ultra & ultra	.35	.20
602	A123	50d lt bl & blue	.35	.25
603	A123	60d beige & dk car rose	.50	.25
604	A123	80d lt grn & green	.60	.40
605	A123	100d redsh brn & choc	1.75	.95
		Nos. 597-605 (9)	4.35	2.85

1961, July 3 Perf. 12x12½

Monuments: 15d, Stevan Filipovic, Valjevo. 20d, Relief from Insurrection, Bozansko Grahovo. 60d, Victory, Nova Gradiska. 100d, Marshal Tito, Titovo Uzice.

Granite Paper
Gold Frames and Inscriptions

606	A149	15d crimson & brn	.20	.20
607	A149	20d brn & ol bis	.20	.20
608	A149	25d bl grn & gray olive	.20	.20
609	A149	60d violet	.25	.20
610	A149	100d indigo & black	.55	.40
		Nos. 606-610 (5)	1.40	1.20

Souvenir Sheet
Imperf
611 A149 500d indigo & black 60.00 60.00

Natl. Insurrection, 20th anniv.

Men of Five Races A150

National Assembly Building, Belgrade — A151

1961, Sept. 1		**Litho.**	**Perf. 11½**	
613	A150	25d brown	.20	.20

Engr.

614 A151 50d blue green .20 .20
Nos. 613-614,C59-C60 (4) 3.80 2.65

Miniature Sheet
Imperf
615 A150 1000d claret 12.00 12.00

Conference of Non-aligned Nations, Belgrade, Sept. 1961.

St. Clement, 14th Century Wood Sculpture — A152

1961, Sept. 10		**Engr.**	**Perf. 12½**	
616	A152	25d sepia & olive	.25	.20

12th Intl. Congress for Byzantine Studies.

Serbian Women A153

Regional Costumes: 25d, Montenegro. 30d, Bosnia and Herzegovina. 50d, Macedonia. 65d, Croatia. 100d, Slovenia.

1961, Nov. 28			**Litho.**	
617	A153	15d beige, brn & red	.20	.20
618	A153	25d beige, red brn & black	.20	.20
619	A153	30d beige, brn & dk red	.20	.20
620	A153	50d multicolored	.20	.20
621	A153	65d brn, red & yel	.30	.20
622	A153	100d multicolored	.90	.25
	Nos. 617-622 (6)		2.00	1.25

Luka Vukalovic — A154

Hands with Flower and Rifle — A155

1961, Dec. 15			**Engr.**	
623	A154	25d slate blue	.20	.20

Centenary of Herzegovina insurrection.

1961, Dec. 22				
624	A155	25d red & vio blue	.20	.20

20th anniversary of Yugoslav army.

Miladinov Brothers A156

1961, Dec. 25			**Litho.**	
625	A156	25d buff & claret	.20	.20

Centenary of Macedonian folksong "Koder;" Dimitri and Konstantin Miladinov, brothers who collected and published folksongs. Monument is at Struga.

Types of 1958; Designs as Before

Designs: 5d, Shipbuilding. 8d, Lumber industry. 10d, Sisak steel works. 15d, Overpass. 20d, Jablanica hydroelectric works. 25d, Cable factory, Svetozarevo. 30d, Litostroy turbine factory. 40d, Lukavac coke plant. 50d, Zenica steel works. 65d, Sevojno copper works. 100d, Crude oil production. 150d, Titograd hotel. 200d, Bridge, Skoplje. 300d, Railroad station, Sarajevo. 500d, Triple bridge, Ljubljana. 1000d, Mestrovic station, Zagreb. 2000d, Parliament, Belgrade.

1961-62		**Typo.**	**Perf. 12½ Horiz.**	
627	A133	10d dark red brn	4.00	.55
628	A133	15d emerald	7.00	.30
		Engr.	**Perf. 12½**	
629	A133	5d dull orange	.20	.20
630	A133	8d gray	.20	.20
631	A133	10d dk red brn	.20	.20
632	A133	15d emerald	.20	.20
633	A133	20d violet blue	.20	.20
634	A133	25d vermilion	.20	.20
635	A133	30d red brown	.20	.20
636	A133	40d dp cl ('62)	.20	.20
637	A133	50d gray blue	.25	.20
638	A133	65d green	.20	.20
639	A133	100d yel olive	1.75	.20
640	A134	150d carmine ('62)	.40	.20
641	A134	200d slate grn ('62)	.40	.20
642	A134	300d olive ('62)	.90	.20
643	A134	500d dull violet	.90	.20
644	A134	1000d bister brn	2.00	.20
645	A134	2000d claret	4.50	.30
	Nos. 629-645 (17)		12.90	3.50

Nos. 627-628 are coil stamps. For surcharges see Nos. 786, 789.

Isis of Kalabsha — A157

Joy of Motherhood by Frano Krsinic — A158

Design: 50d, Ramses II, Abu Simbel.

1962, Apr. 7		**Engr.**	**Perf. 12½**	
646	A157	25d grnsh blk, cream	.20	.20
647	A157	50d brown, buff	.35	.20

15th anniv. (in 1961) of UNESCO.

1962, Apr. 7				
648	A158	50d black, cream	.30	.20

15th anniv. (in 1961) of UNICEF.

Anopheles Mosquito — A159

1962, Apr. 7			**Unwmk.**	
649	A159	50d black, gray	.30	.20

WHO drive to eradicate malaria.

Scenic Type of 1959

Tourist attractions: #650, Portoroz. #651, Jajce. #652, Zadar. #653, Popova Sapka. #654, Hvar. #655, Bay of Kotor. #656, Danube, Iron Gate. #657, Rab. #658, Zagreb.

1962, Apr. 24			**Litho.**	
650	A137	15d ol & chlky bl	.20	.20
651	A137	15d blue grn & bis	.20	.20
652	A137	25d blue & red brn	.20	.20
653	A137	25d dk bl & pale bl	.20	.20
654	A137	30d blue & brn org	.20	.20
655	A137	30d gray & chlky bl	.20	.20
656	A137	50d ol & grnsh bl	.45	.20
657	A137	50d blue & olive	.45	.20
658	A137	100d dk grn & gray bl	2.00	.40
	Nos. 650-658 (9)		4.10	2.00

#651, 653, 655-656 are inscribed in Cyrillic.

Marshal Tito, by Augustincic A160

Pole Vault — A161

Design: 50d, 200d, Sideview of bust by Antun Augustincic.

1962, May 25		**Engr.**	**Perf. 12½**	
659	A160	25d dark green	.20	.20
660	A160	50d dark brown	.20	.20
661	A160	100d dark blue	.45	.30
662	A160	200d greenish blk	1.75	.90
a.	Souv. sheet of 4, #659-662, imperf.		12.00	12.00
	Nos. 659-662 (4)		2.60	

70th birthday of Pres. Tito (Josip Broz).

Animal Type of 1960

Designs: 15d, Crested newt. 20d, Fire salamander. 25d, Yellow-bellied toad. 30d, Pond frog. 50d, Pond turtle. 65d, Lizard. 100d, Emerald lizard. 150d, Leopard snake. 200d, European viper (adder).

1962, June 8		**Photo.**	**Perf. 12x11½**	
Animals in Natural Colors				
663	A143	15d green	.20	.20
664	A143	20d purple	.20	.20
665	A143	25d chocolate	.20	.20
666	A143	30d violet blue	.20	.20
667	A143	50d dark red	.20	.20
668	A143	65d bright grn	.20	.20
669	A143	100d black	.35	.30
670	A143	150d brown	.95	.95
671	A143	200d car rose	2.25	1.25
	Nos. 663-671 (9)		4.75	3.70

1962, July 10	**Litho.**	**Perf. 12½**	

Sports: 25d, Woman discus thrower, horiz. 30d, Long distance runners. 50d, Javelin thrower, horiz. 65d, Shot put. 100d, Women runners, horiz. 150d, Hop, step and jump. 200d, High jump, horiz.

Athletes in Black
672	A161	15d blue	.20	.20
673	A161	25d magenta	.20	.20
674	A161	30d emerald	.20	.20
675	A161	50d red	.20	.20
676	A161	65d vio blue	.20	.20
677	A161	100d green	.40	.20
678	A161	150d orange	.45	.30
679	A161	200d orange brn	.95	.60
	Nos. 672-679 (8)		2.80	2.10

7th European Athletic Championships, Belgrade, Sept. 12-16. See No. C61.

Child at Play — A162

		Litho. & Engr.		
1962, Oct. 1			**Perf. 12½**	
680	A162	25d red & black	.30	.20

Issued for Children's Week.

Gold Mask, Trebeniste, 5th Century B.C. — A163

Bathing the Infant Christ, Fresco, Decani Monastery — A164

Yugoslav Art Treasures: 25d, Horseman and bird, bronze vase (5th cent. B.C.). 50d, God Kairos, marble relief. 65d, "The Pigeons of Nerezi," fresco (12th cent.). 150d, Archangel Gabriel, icon (14th cent.).

1962, Nov. 28			**Photo.**	
681	A163	25d Prus bl, blk & gold	.20	.20
682	A163	30d gold, saph & blk	.20	.20
683	A164	50d dk grn, brn & gold	.20	.20
684	A164	65d multicolored	.35	.20
685	A164	100d multicolored	.45	.60
686	A163	150d multicolored	1.90	1.10
	Nos. 681-686 (6)		3.30	2.50

Parched Earth and Wheat — A165

Dr. Andrija Mohorovicic and UN Emblem — A166

1963, Mar. 21   **Engr.**   **Perf. 12½**
687 A165 50d dark brn, *tan*   .25 .20

FAO "Freedom from Hunger" campaign.

1963, Mar. 23   **Unwmk.**
688 A166 50d dk blue, *gray*   .25 .20

UN 3rd World Meteorological Day, Mar. 23. Dr. Mohorovicic (1857-1936) was director of the Zagreb meteorological observatory.

Flower Type of 1957

Medicinal Plants: 15d, Lily of the valley. 25d, Iris. 30d, Bistort. 50d, Henbane. 65d, St. John's wort. 100d, Caraway.

1963, May 25   **Photo.**   **Perf. 11½**
Granite Paper
Flowers in Natural Colors
689	A123	15d gray grn & grn	.20	.20
690	A123	25d lt bl, ultra & pur	.20	.20
691	A123	30d gray & black	.20	.20
692	A123	50d redsh brn & red brn	.20	.20
693	A123	65d pale brn & brn	.30	.20
694	A123	100d slate & blk	.90	.35
		Nos. 689-694 (6)	2.00	1.35

Scenic Type of 1959

Tourist attractions: 15d, Pula. 25d, Vrnjacka Banja. 30d, Crikvenica. 50d, Korcula. 65d, Durmitor mountain. 100d, Ljubljana.

1963, June 6   **Litho.**   **Perf. 12½**
695	A137	15d multicolored	.20	.20
696	A137	25d multicolored	.20	.20
697	A137	30d multicolored	.20	.20
698	A137	50d multicolored	.20	.20
699	A137	65d multicolored	.20	.20
700	A137	100d multicolored	.85	.25
		Nos. 695-700 (6)	1.85	1.25

Partisans on the March, by Djordje Andrejevic-Kun — A167

Sutjeska (Gorge) — A168

Design: No. 702A, As 15d, but inscribed "Vis 1944-1964." 50d, Partisans in battle.

Engr. & Litho.; Litho. (No. 702)
1963-64   **Perf. 12½, 11½**
701	A167	15d gray & dk sl grn	.20	.20
702	A168	25d dark slate grn	.20	.20
702A	A167	25d gray & dark car rose	.20	.20
703	A167	50d tan & purple	.20	.20
		Nos. 701-703 (4)	.80	.80

20th anniv. of the Partisan Battle of Sutjeska (Nos. 701, 702-703); 20th anniv. of the arrival of the Yugoslav General Staff on the island of Vis (No. 702A).
Issued: #702A, 7/27/64; others, 7/3/63.

Gymnast on Vaulting Horse — A169

Mother, by Ivan Mestrovic A170

1963, July 6   **Litho.**   **Perf. 12½**
704	A169	25d shown	.20	.20
705	A169	50d Parallel bars	.20	.20
706	A169	100d Rings	.35	.35
		Nos. 704-706 (3)	.75	.75

5th Gymnastics Europa Prize.

1963, Sept. 28   **Engr.**
Sculptures by Mestrovic (1883-1962): 50d, "Reminiscences" (woman). 65d, Head of Kraljevic Marko. 100d, Indian on Horseback.
707	A170	25d brown, *buff*	.20	.20
708	A170	50d sl green, *grnsh*	.20	.20
709	A170	65d grnsh blk, *grysh*	.70	.30
710	A170	100d black, *grayish*	1.00	.60
		Nos. 707-710 (4)	2.10	1.30

Children with Toys — A171

1963, Oct. 5   **Litho.**
711 A171 25d multicolored   .35 .20

Issued for Children's Week.

Soldier with Gun and Flag — A172

Litho. & Engr.
1963, Oct. 20   **Perf. 12½**
712 A172 25d ver, tan & gold   .20 .20

Yugoslavian Democratic Federation, 20th anniv.

Relief from Tombstone, Herzegovina A173

Dositej Obradovic A174

Art through the centuries: 30d, Horseback trio, Split Cathedral. 50d, King & queen on horseback, Beram Church, Istria. 65d, Archangel Michael, Dominican monastery, Dubrovnik. 100d, Man pouring water, fountain, Ljubljana. 150d, Archbishop Eufrasie, mosaic, Porec Basilica, Istria.

1963, Nov. 29   **Photo.**
713	A173	25d multi	.20	.20
714	A173	30d multi, horiz.	.20	.20
715	A173	50d multi, horiz.	.20	.20
716	A173	65d multi	.25	.20
717	A173	100d multi	.25	.20
718	A173	150d multi	.95	.60
		Nos. 713-718 (6)	2.00	1.60

Issued for the Day of the Republic.

1963, Dec. 10   **Engr.**
Famous Yugoslavians: 30d, Vuk Stefanovic Karadzic, reformer of Serbian language. 50d, Franc Miklosic, Slovenian philologist. 65d, Ljudevit Gaj, reformer of Croatian language. 100d, Peter Petrovich Nyegosh, Montenegrin prince, bishop and poet.
Variously Toned Paper
719	A174	25d black	.20	.20
720	A174	30d black	.20	.20
721	A174	50d black	.20	.20
722	A174	65d black	.40	.20
723	A174	100d black	.65	.50
		Nos. 719-723 (5)	1.65	1.30

Vanessa Io — A175

Fireman Rescuing Child — A176

Butterflies & Moths: 30d, Vanessa antiopa. 40d, Daphnis nerii. 50d, Parnassius apollo. 150d, Saturnia pyri. 200d, Papilio machaon.

1964, May 25   **Photo.**   **Perf. 12½**
724	A175	25d multicolored	.20	.20
725	A175	30d multicolored	.20	.20
726	A175	40d multicolored	.20	.20
727	A175	50d multicolored	.20	.20
728	A175	150d multicolored	.40	.30
729	A175	200d multicolored	.65	.40
		Nos. 724-729 (6)	1.85	1.50

1964, June 14   **Litho.**
730 A176 25d red & black   .25 .20

Centenary of voluntary firemen.

Runner A177

1964, July 1   **Unwmk.**   **Perf. 12½**
731	A177	25d shown	.20	.20
732	A177	30d Boxing	.20	.20
733	A177	40d Rowing	.20	.20
734	A177	50d Basketball	.20	.20
735	A177	150d Soccer	.35	.20
736	A177	200d Water polo	.60	.35
		Nos. 731-736 (6)	1.75	1.35

18th Olympic Games, Tokyo, Oct. 10-25.

UN Flag over Scaffolding A178

25d, Upheaval of the earth & scaffolding.

1964, July 26   **Engr.**
737	A178	25d red brown	.20	.20
738	A178	50d blue	.20	.20

Earthquake at Skopje; 1st anniv.

Serbian Women — A179

Friedrich Engels — A180

Regional Costumes: 30d, Slovenia. 40d, Bosnia and Herzegovina. 50d, Croatia. 150d, Macedonia. 200d, Montenegro.

1964, Aug. 5   **Litho.**
Costumes Multicolored
740	A179	25d violet & brn	.20	.20
741	A179	30d slate & green	.20	.20
742	A179	40d redsh brn & blk	.20	.20
743	A179	50d blue & black	.20	.20
744	A179	150d dl grn & sepia	.40	.20
745	A179	200d tan, red & brn	.50	.45
		Nos. 740-745 (6)	1.70	1.45

Litho. & Engr.
1964, Sept. 27   **Perf. 11½**
746	A180	25d shown	.20	.20
747	A180	50d Karl Marx	.20	.20

1st Socialist Intl., London, Sept. 28, 1864.

Children at Play — A181

1964, Oct. 4   **Litho.**   **Perf. 12½**
748 A181 25d ver, pink & gray grn   .35 .20

Issued for Children's Week.

The Victor by Ivan Mestrovic — A182

1964, Oct. 20   **Engr.**   **Perf. 11½**
749 A182 25d gold & blk, *pnksh*   .20 .20

Liberation of Belgrade, 20th anniv.

Initial from Evangel of Hilandar — A183

Hand, "Liberty and Equality" — A184

Art through the centuries: 30d, Initial from Evangel of Miroslav (musician). 40d, Detail from Cetigne octavo, 1494 (saint with scroll). 50d, Miniature from Evangel of Trogir, 13th cent. (female saint). 150d, Miniature from Hrovoe Missal, 15th cent. (knight on horseback). 200d, Miniature from 14th cent. manuscript (symbolic fight), horiz.

Perf. 11½x12, 12x11½
1964, Nov. 29   Photo.   Unwmk.

750	A183	25d multicolored	.20 .20
751	A183	30d multicolored	.20 .20
752	A183	40d multicolored	.20 .20
753	A183	50d multicolored	.20 .20
754	A183	150d multicolored	.35 .20
755	A183	200d multicolored	.70 .40
		Nos. 750-755 (6)	1.85 1.40

Issued for Day of the Republic.

1964, Dec. 7   *Perf. 12*

50d, Dove over factory, "Peace and Socialism." 100d, Smokestacks, "Building Socialism."

756	A184	25d multicolored	.20 .20
757	A184	50d multicolored	.20 .20
758	A184	100d multicolored	.40 .25
		Nos. 756-758 (3)	.80 .65

Yugoslav Communist League, 8th congress.

Table Tennis Player — A185

Titograd — A186

1965, Apr. 15   Litho.   *Perf. 12½*
759	A185	50d shown	.20 .20
760	A185	150d Player at left	.40 .25

28th Table Tennis Championships, Ljubljana, Apr. 15-25.

1965, May 8   Engr.
761	A186	25d shown	.20 .20
762	A186	30d Skopje	.20 .20
763	A186	40d Sarajevo	.20 .20
764	A186	50d Ljubljana	.20 .20
765	A186	150d Zagreb	.30 .20
766	A186	200d Belgrade	.65 .40
		Nos. 761-766 (6)	1.75 1.40

Liberation of Yugoslavia from the Nazis, 20th anniv.

Young Pioneer — A187

ITU Emblem and Television Tower — A188

1965, May 10   Litho. & Engr.
767	A187	25d blk & tan, *buff*	.20 .20

Young Pioneer Games "20 Years of Freedom."

1965, May 17   Engr.
768	A188	50d dark blue	.20 .20

ITU, centenary.

Iron Gate, Danube — A189

Arms of Yugoslavia and Romania and Djerdap Dam — A190

50d, Iron Gate hydroelectric plant and dam.

1965, May 20   Litho.   *Perf. 12½x12*
769	A189	25d (30b) lt bl & grn	.20 .20
770	A189	50d (55b) lt bl & dk red	.25 .20

Miniature Sheet
Perf. 13½x13
771	A190	Sheet of 4	2.50 2.50
a.		100d multicolored	.35 .35
b.		150d multicolored	.70 .70

Nos. 769-771 were issued simultaneously by Yugoslavia and Romania to commemorate the start of the construction of the Iron Gate hydroelectric plant. Nos. 769-770 were valid for postage in both countries.

No. 771 contains one each of Nos. 771a, 771b and Romania Nos. 1747a and 1747b. Only Nos. 771a and 771b were valid in Yugoslavia. Sold for 500d.

See Romania Nos. 1745-1747.

Flower Type of 1957

Medicinal Plants: 25d, Milfoil. 30d, Rosemary. 40d, Inula. 50d, Belladonna. 150d, Mint. 200d, Foxglove.

1965, May 25   Photo.   *Perf. 11½*
Granite Paper
Flowers in Natural Colors
772	A123	25d deep carmine	.20 .20
773	A123	30d olive bister	.20 .20
774	A123	40d red brown	.20 .20
775	A123	50d dark blue	.20 .20
776	A123	150d violet blue	.35 .20
777	A123	200d purple	.85 .60
		Nos. 772-777 (6)	2.00 1.60

Intl. Cooperation Year Emblem A191

1965, June 26   Litho.   *Perf. 12½*
778	A191	50d dk bl & dull bl	.20 .20

Sibenik — A192

Cat — A193

1965, July 6   Unwmk.   *Perf. 12½*
779	A192	25d Rogaska Slatina	.20 .20
780	A192	30d shown	.20 .20
781	A192	40d Prespa Lake	.20 .20
782	A192	50d Prizren	.20 .20
783	A192	150d Scutari	.30 .20
784	A192	200d Sarajevo	.60 .55
		Nos. 779-784 (6)	1.70 1.55

1965, Oct. 3   Litho.   *Perf. 12½*
785	A193	30d maroon & brt yel	.45 .20

Issued for Children's Week.

Nos. 630 and 634 Surcharged in Maroon and Type of 1958

Designs: 20d, Jablanica hydroelectric works. 30d, Litostroy turbine factory.

1965   Engr.   *Perf. 12½*
786	A133	5d on 8d gray	.60 .20
787	A133	20d emerald	.50 .20
788	A133	30d red orange	.80 .20
789	A133	50d on 25d vermilion	.60 .20
		Nos. 786-789 (4)	2.50 .80

Branislav Nusic — A194

Marshal Tito — A195

Famous Yugoslavs: 50d, Antun Gustav Matos, poet. 60d, Ivan Mazuranic, writer. 85d, Fran Levstik, writer. 200d, Josif Pancic, physician and botanist. 500d, Dimitrije Tucovic, political writer.

1965, Nov. 28   Engr.
Variously Toned Paper
790	A194	30d dull red	.20 .20
791	A194	50d indigo	.20 .20
792	A194	60d brown	.20 .20
793	A194	85d dark blue	.20 .20
794	A194	200d dk olive grn	.20 .20
795	A194	500d deep claret	.60 .45
		Nos. 790-795 (6)	1.60 1.45

1966, Feb. 4   Litho.   *Perf. 12½*
796	A195	20p bluish grn	.40 .20
797	A195	30p rose pink	.55 .20

Rowing A196

30p, Long jump. 50p, Ice hockey. 3d, Hockey sticks, puck. 5d, Oars, scull.

1966, Mar. 1   Engr.
798	A196	30p dk car rose	.20 .20
799	A196	50p dk purple	.20 .20
800	A196	1d gray green	.20 .20
801	A196	3d dk red brn	.35 .20
802	A196	5d dark blue	.65 .50
		Nos. 798-802 (5)	1.60 1.30

25th Balkan Games; World ice hockey championship; 2nd rowing championships.

"T" from 15th Century Psalter — A197

Radio Amateurs' Emblem — A198

Art through the Centuries (Initials from Medieval Manuscripts): 50p, Cyrillic "V," Divosh Evangel, 14th cent. 60p, "R," Gregorius I, Libri moralium, 12th cent. 85p, Cyrillic "P," Miroslav Evangel, 12th cent. 2d, Cyrillic "B," Radomir Evangel, 13th cent. 5d, "F," Passional, 11th cent.

1966, Apr. 25   Photo.   *Perf. 12*
803	A197	30p multicolored	.20 .20
804	A197	50p multicolored	.20 .20
805	A197	60p multicolored	.20 .20
806	A197	85p multicolored	.30 .20
807	A197	2d multicolored	.30 .20
808	A197	5d multicolored	.65 .60
		Nos. 803-808 (6)	1.75 1.60

1966, May 23   Engr.   *Perf. 12½x12*
809	A198	85p dark blue	.20 .20

Union of Yugoslav Radio Amateurs, 20th anniv.; Intl. Congress of Radio Amateurs, Opatija, 5/23-28.

Stag Beetle — A199

Serbia No. 2, 1866 — A200

Beetles: 50p, Floral beetle. 60p, Oil beetle. 85p, Ladybird. 2d, Rosalia alpina. 5d, Aquatic beetle.

1966, May 25   Photo.   *Perf. 12x12½*
810	A199	30p gray, blk & bis	.20 .20
811	A199	50p gray, emer & blk	.20 .20
812	A199	60p bluish blk, sl grn & gray	.20 .20
813	A199	85p dl org, dp org & black	.20 .20
814	A199	2d gray, ultra & blk	.25 .20
815	A199	5d tan, brn & blk	.40 .40
		Nos. 810-815 (6)	1.45 1.40

1966, June 25   Litho. & Engr.   *Perf. 12½*
816	A200	30p shown	.20 .20
817	A200	50p No. 3	.20 .20
818	A200	60p No. 4	.20 .20
819	A200	85p No. 5	.20 .20
820	A200	2d No. 6	.45 .35
		Nos. 816-820 (5)	1.25 1.15

Souvenir Sheet
Imperf
821	A200	10d No. 1	2.00 2.00

Serbia's first postage stamps, cent.

Leather Shield with Farmer, Soldier and Woman — A201

Bishop Strossmayer and Franjo Racki — A202

1966, July 2   *Perf. 12½*
822	A201	20p pale grn, gold & red brown	.20 .20
823	A201	30p buff, gold & dp mag	.20 .20
824	A201	85p lt gray, gold & Prus bl	.20 .20
825	A201	2d lt bl, gold & vio	.25 .20
		Nos. 822-825 (4)	.85 .85

25th anniversary of National Revolution.

1966, July 15
826	A202	30p dl ol, blk & buff	.20 .20

Centenary of Academy of Arts and Sciences, founded by Bishop Josip Juraj Strossmayer with Racki as first president.

Mostar Bridge, Neretva River — A203

1966, Sept. 24   Engr.   Perf. 12½
827 A203 30p rose claret   1.75 .25
400th anniversary of Mostar Bridge.

Medieval View of Sibenik A204

1966, Sept. 24
828 A204 30p deep plum   .25 .20
900th anniversary of Sibenik.

Girl A205   Shipbuilding A206

1966, Oct. 2   Litho.
829 A205 30p ultra, org, red & blk   .70 .20
Issued for Children's Week.

1966   Engr.   Perf. 12½
Designs: 10p, Sisak steel works. 15p, Overpass. 20p, Jablonica hydroelectric works. 30p, Litostroy turbine factory. 40p, Lukavac coke factory. 50p, Zenica steel works. 60p, Cable factory, Svetozarevo. 65p, Sevojno copper works. 85p, Lumber industry. 1d, Crude oil production.

830 A206   5p dull orange   .20 .20
831 A206 10p brown   .20 .20
832 A206 15p vio blue   .20 .20
833 A206 20p emerald   .30 .20
834 A206 30p vermilion   1.10 .20
835 A206 40p dp claret   .20 .20
836 A206 50p gray blue   .25 .20
837 A206 60p red brown   .25 .20
838 A206 65p green   .35 .20
839 A206 85p dl purple   .55 .20
840 A206   1d yel olive   .80 .20
       Nos. 830-840 (11)   4.40 2.20

Issued: 5, 15p, 6/10; 10, 40, 50p, 6/8; 20, 30p, 4/28; 60, 65, 85p, 5/12; 1d, 6/18.
For surcharge see No. 1322.

UNESCO Emblem — A207   Santa Claus — A208

1966, Nov. 4   Litho.
841 A207 85p violet blue   .20 .20
20th anniversary of UNESCO.

1966, Nov. 25   Litho.   Perf. 12½
Designs: 15p, Stylized winter landscape. 30p, Stylized Christmas tree.

842 A208 15p org & dk bl   .20 .20
843 A208 20p org & purple   .20 .20
844 A208 30p org & sl grn   .20 .20

1966, Dec. 23   Photo.   Perf. 12½
845 A208 15p gold & dk bl   .30 .20
846 A208 20p gold & red   .30 .20
847 A208 30p gold & green   .30 .20
       Nos. 842-847 (6)   1.50 1.20

Nos. 842-847 issued for New Year, 1967.

Wolf's Head Coin of Durad I, 1373 — A209

Medieval Coins: 50p, ½d of King Stefan, c. 1461 (arms of Bosnia). 60d, Dinar of Serbia (portrait of Durad Brankovic). 85p, Dinar of Ljubljana, c. 1250 (heraldic eagle). 2d, Dinar of Split, c. 1403-1413 (shield with arms of Duke Hrvoje Vukcic). 5d, Dinar of Emperor Stefan Dusan, c. 1346-1355 (Emperor on horseback).

1966, Nov. 28   Photo.
Coins in Silver, Gray and Black
848 A209 30p ver & blk   .20 .20
849 A209 50p ultra & blk   .20 .20
850 A209 60p magenta & blk   .20 .20
851 A209 85p violet & blk   .20 .20
852 A209   2d dk ol bis & blk   .20 .20
853 A209   5d brt grn & blk   .55 .35
       Nos. 848-853 (6)   1.55 1.35

Medicinal Plants — A210   Marshal Tito — A211

1967, May 25   Photo.   Perf. 11½
Granite Paper
854 A210 30p Arnica   .20 .20
855 A210 50p Flax   .20 .20
856 A210 85p Oleander   .20 .20
857 A210 1.20d Gentian   .20 .20
858 A210   3d Laurel   .20 .20
859 A210   5d African rue   .50 .30
       Nos. 854-859 (6)   1.50 1.30

Youth Day, May 25.

1967, May 25   Engr.   Perf. 12½
Size: 20x27½mm
860 A211   5p orange   .20 .20
861 A211 10p dk red brown   .20 .20
862 A211 15p dk vio blue   .20 .20
863 A211 20p green   .20 .20
864 A211 30p vermilion   .20 .20
865 A211 40p black   .20 .20
866 A211 50p Prussian grn   .20 .20
867 A211 60p lilac   .20 .20
868 A211 85p deep blue   .20 .20
869 A211   1d plum   .20 .20
       Nos. 860-869 (10)   2.00 2.00

75th birthday of Pres. Tito. Sheets of 15.
Nos. 860-869 were reissued in 1967 with slight differences including thinner paper and slightly darker shades.
See #924-939. For surcharge see #1414.

Coil Stamps
1968-69   Photo.   Perf. 12½ Horiz.
869A A211 20p green   .30 .20
869B A211 30p vermilion   .40 .20
869C A211 50p vermilion ('69)   .30 .20
       Nos. 869A-869C (3)   1.00 .60

EXPO Emblem, Sputnik 1 and Explorer 1 — A212   ITY Emblem, St. Tripun's Church, Kotor — A213

Spacecraft: 50p, Tiros, Telstar and Molniya. 85p, Luna 9 and lunar satellite. 1.20d, Mariner 4, and Venus 3. 3d, Vostok, Gemini and Agena Rocket. 5d, Astronaut walking in space.

1967, June 26   Photo.   Perf. 11½
870 A212 30p ultra & multi   .20 .20
871 A212 50p yel & multi   .20 .20
872 A212 85p slate & multi   .20 .20
873 A212 1.20d multicolored   .20 .20
874 A212   3d vio & multi   .20 .20
875 A212   5d blue & multi   .35 .35
       Nos. 870-875 (6)   1.35 1.35

EXPO '67, Montreal, Apr. 28-Oct. 27; 18th Congress of the Intl. Astronautical Federation, Belgrade.

1967, July 17   Engr.
Designs (ITY Emblem and): 50p, Municipal Building, Maribor. 85p, Cathedral, Trogir. 1.20d, Fortress gate, Nis. 3d, Drina Bridge, Visegrad. 5d, Daut-pasha's Bath, Skopje.

876 A213 30p slate bl & lt ol   .20 .20
877 A213 50p brn & dl vio   .20 .20
878 A213 85p dk bl & dp claret   .20 .20
879 A213 1.20d dp claret & brn   .20 .20
880 A213   3d brn & slate grn   .35 .20
881 A213   5d slate grn & brn   .50 .45
       Nos. 876-881 (6)   1.65 1.45

Issued for International Tourist Year, 1967.

Partridge — A214

1967, Sept. 22   Photo.   Perf. 14
882 A214 30p shown   .20 .20
883 A214 50p Pike   .20 .20
884 A214 1.20d Red deer   .20 .20
885 A214   5d Peregrine falcon   .75 .70
       Nos. 882-885 (4)   1.35 1.30

Intl. Fishing and Hunting Exposition and Fair, Novi Sad.

Congress Emblem with Sputnik 1 A215

Litho. & Engr.
1967, Sept. 25   Perf. 12½
886 A215 85p dk bl, lt bl & gold   .20 .20
18th Congress of the Intl. Astronautical Federation, Belgrade, Sept. 25-30.

Old Theater and Castle, Ljubljana — A216

Child's Drawing: Winter Scene — A217

1967, Sept. 29   Engr.   Perf. 12½
887 A216 30p sepia & dk grn   .20 .20
Centenary of Slovene National Theater.

1967, Oct. 2   Litho.
888 A217 30p multicolored   .50 .20
International Children's Week, Oct. 2-8.

Lenin by Mestrovic A218   4-Leaf Clover A219

1967, Nov. 7   Engr.   Perf. 12½
889 A218 30p dark purple   .20 .20
890 A218 85p olive gray   .25 .20
Souvenir Sheet
Imperf
891 A218 10d magenta   3.75 3.00
Russian October Revolution, 50th anniv.

1967, Nov. 15   Photo.   Perf. 14
30p, Chimney sweep. 50p, Horseshoe & flower.

Dated "1968"
892 A219 20p shown   .20 .20
893 A219 30p Chimney sweep   .20 .20
894 A219 50p Horseshoe, flower   .60 .60
       Nos. 892-894 (3)   .60 .60

New Year 1968. See Nos. 957-959.

The Young Sultana, by Vlaho Bucovac — A220

Paintings: 85p, The Watchtower, by Dura Jaksic. 2d, Visit to the Family, by Josip Petkovsek. 3d, The Cock Fight, by Paja Jovanovic. 5d, "Spring" (woman and children), by Ivana Kobilca.

Perf. 11½x12, 12x11½
1967, Nov. 28   Engr. & Litho.
895 A220 85p multi, vert.   .20 .20
896 A220   1d multi   .20 .20
897 A220   2d multi   .30 .25
898 A220   3d multi   .40 .40
899 A220   5d multi, vert.   .75 .70
       Nos. 895-899 (5)   1.85 1.75

Issued for the Day of the Republic, Nov. 29.
See Nos. 942-946, 995-1000.

Ski Jump — A221

Annunciation A222

Sport: 1d, Figure skating pair. 2d, Downhill skiing. 5d, Ice hockey.

1968, Feb. 5   Engr.   Perf. 12½
900 A221 50p dk bl & dk pur   .20 .20
901 A221   1d brn & sl green   .20 .20
902 A221   2d sl grn & lake   .20 .25
903 A221   5d sl grn & dk bl   .70 .35
       Nos. 900-903 (4)   1.30 1.00

10th Winter Olympic Games, Grenoble, France, Feb. 6-18.

1968, Apr. 20   Photo.   Perf. 13½

Medieval Icons: 50p, Madonna, St. George's Church, Prizren. 1.50d, St. Sava and St. Simeon. 2d, Christ's descent into hell, Ohrid. 3d, Crucifixion, St. Clement's Church, Ohrid. 5d, Madonna, Church of Our Lady of the Bell Tower, Split.

906	A222	50p gold & multi	.20	.20
907	A222	1d gold & multi	.20	.20
908	A222	1.50d gold & multi	.20	.20
909	A222	2d gold & multi	.35	.25
910	A222	3d gold & multi	.50	.40
911	A222	5d gold & multi	1.10	1.00
		Nos. 906-911 (6)	2.55	2.25

European Bullfinch — A223   800-meter Race for Women — A224

Finches: 1d, Goldfinch. 1.50d, Chaffinch. 2d, European greenfinch. 3d, Red crossbill. 5d, Hawfinch.

1968, May 25   Photo.   Perf. 11½
Birds in Natural Colors

912	A223	50p bister	.20	.20
913	A223	1d rose lake	.20	.20
914	A223	1.50d gray blue	.20	.20
915	A223	2d deep orange	.25	.20
916	A223	3d olive green	.45	.20
917	A223	5d pale violet	.70	.45
		Nos. 912-917 (6)	2.00	1.45

Issued for Youth Day.

Litho. & Engr.
1968, June 28   Perf. 12½

1d, Basketball. 1.50d, Gymnast on vaulting horse. 2d, Rowing. 3d, Water polo. 5d, Wrestling.

918	A224	50p dk brn & dk red brown	.20	.20
919	A224	1d Prus bl & blk	.20	.20
920	A224	1.50d slate & dk brn	.20	.20
921	A224	2d bis & sl grn	.20	.20
922	A224	3d blk brn & ind	.25	.20
923	A224	5d dk grn & vio blk	.50	.45
		Nos. 918-923 (6)	1.55	1.45

19th Olympic Games, Mexico City, 10/12-27.

Tito Type of 1967

1968-72   Engr.   Perf. 12½
Size: 20x27½mm

924	A211	20p dark blue	.20	.20
925	A211	25p lake	.20	.20
926	A211	30p green	.20	.20
927	A211	50p vermilion	.20	.20
928	A211	70p black	.30	.20
929	A211	75p slate grn	.40	.20
930	A211	80p olive	.40	.20
930A	A211	80p red org ('72)	.35	.20
931	A211	90p olive	.30	.20
932	A211	1.20d dark blue	.50	.20
932A	A211	1.20d sl grn ('72)	.40	.20
933	A211	1.25d deep blue	.45	.20
934	A211	1.50d slate grn	.40	.20

Size: 20x30½mm

935	A211	2d sepia	.60	.20
936	A211	2.50d Prussian grn	1.60	.20
937	A211	5d deep plum	1.40	.20
938	A211	10d violet blk	3.00	.35
939	A211	20d bluish black	4.25	.45
		Nos. 924-939 (18)	15.15	4.00

The shading of the background of Nos. 924-939 has been changed from the 1967 issue to intensify the contrast around the portrait.

Cannon and Laurel Wreath — A225

Mother Nursing Twins, Fresco by Jan of Kastav — A226

1968, Aug. 2   Photo.   Perf. 12½
940   A225   50p org brn & gold   .20 .20

65th anniversary of the Ilinden uprising.

1968, Sept. 9   Litho.
941   A226   50p black & multi   .20 .20

Annexation of Istria and the Slovene Coast to Yugoslavia, 25th anniv.

Painting Type of 1967

Paintings: 1d, Lake Klansko, by Marko Pernhart. 1.50d, Bavarian Landscape, by Milan Popovic. 2d, Porta Terraferma, Zadar, by Ferdo Quiquerez. 3d, Mt. Triglav seen from Bohinj, by Anton Karinger. 5d, Studenica Monastery, by Djordje Krstic.

Engr. & Litho.
1968, Oct. 3   Perf. 14x13½

942	A220	1d gold & multi	.20	.20
943	A220	1.50d gold & multi	.20	.20
944	A220	2d gold & multi	.20	.20
945	A220	3d gold & multi	.30	.20
946	A220	5d gold & multi	.80	.70
		Nos. 942-946 (5)	1.70	1.50

Aleksa Santic (1868-1924), Poet — A227

"Going for a Walk" — A228

1968, Oct. 5   Engr.   Perf. 12½
947   A227   50p dark blue   .20 .20

1968, Oct. 6   Litho.
948   A228   50p multicolored   .20 .20

Issued for Children's Week.

Karl Marx (1818-1883), by N. Mitric — A229

Old Theater and Belgrade Castle — A230

1968, Oct. 11   Engr.
949   A229   50d dk car rose   .20 .20

1968, Nov. 22   Engr.   Perf. 12½
950   A230   50p ol brn & sl grn   .20 .20

Serbian National Theater, Belgrade, cent.

Hasan Brkic — A231

The Family, by J. Soldatovic A232

Portraits: 75p, Ivan Milutinovic. 1.25d, Rade Koncar. 2d, Kuzman Josifovski. 2.50d, Tone Tomsic. 5d, Mosa Pijade.

1968, Nov. 28   Engr.   Perf. 12½

951	A231	50p violet black	.20	.20
952	A231	75p black	.20	.20
953	A231	1.25d red brown	.25	.20
a.		Souv. sheet, 2 ea #951-953	12.50	12.50
954	A231	2d bluish black	.30	.20
955	A231	2.50d slate green	.50	.25
956	A231	5d claret	1.10	.75
a.		Souv. sheet, 2 ea #954-956	12.50	12.50
		Nos. 951-956 (6)	2.55	1.80

2nd Assembly of the National Republic of Yugoslavia, 25th anniv.

Type of New Year's Issue, 1967

1968, Nov. 25   Photo.   Perf. 14
Dated "1969"

957	A219	20p Four-leaf clover	.20	.20
958	A219	30p Chimney sweep	.20	.20
959	A219	50p Horseshoe, flower	.20	.20
		Nos. 957-959 (3)	.60	.60

Issued for New Year 1969.

1968, Dec. 10   Engr.   Perf. 12½
960   A232   1.25d dark blue   .25 .20

International Human Rights Year.

ILO Emblem — A233

Dove, Hammer and Sickle Emblem — A234

Litho. & Engr.
1969, Jan. 27   Perf. 12½
961   A233   1.25d red & black   .25 .20

ILO, 50th anniv.

Engr. & Photo.
1969, Mar. 11   Perf. 12½

75p, Graffiti "TITO" & 5-pointed star. 1.25d, 5-pointed crystal. 10d, Marshal Tito in 1943.

962	A234	50p black & red	.20	.20
963	A234	75p ol bis & blk	.20	.20
964	A234	1.25d red & black	.25	.20
		Nos. 962-964 (3)	.65	.60

Souvenir Sheet

964A		Sheet of 9	5.50	5.50
b.		A234 10d brown, engr.	3.00	3.00

Communist Federation of Yugoslavia, 50th anniv.; 9th party congress.
#964A contains 4 #962, 2 each #963-964, 964b.

St. Nikita, from Manasija Monastery A235

Frescoes from Monasteries: 75p, Apostles, Zakopani. 1.25d, Crucifixion, Studenica. 2d, Wedding at Cana, Kalenic. 3d, Angel at the Grave, Milseva. 5d, Pietá, Nerezi.

1969, Apr. 7   Photo.   Perf. 13½

965	A235	50p gold & multi	.20	.20
966	A235	75p gold & multi	.20	.20
967	A235	1.25d gold & multi	.20	.20
968	A235	2d gold & multi	.20	.20
969	A235	3d gold & multi	.45	.45
970	A235	5d gold & multi	1.25	.90
		Nos. 965-970 (6)	2.50	2.15

Roman Memorial and View of Ptuj A236

1969, Apr. 23   Engr.   Perf. 11½
971   A236   50p violet brown   .20 .20

1900th anniv. of Ptuj, the Roman Petovio. Issued in sheets of 9 (3x3).

Vasil Glavinov — A237   Thin-leafed Peony — A238

1969, May 8   Perf. 12x12½
972   A237   50p ocher & rose lilac   .20 .20

Vasil Glavinov, Macedonian socialist, birth cent.. Issued in sheets of 9 (3x3).

1969, May 25   Photo.   Perf. 11½

Medicinal Plants: 75p, Coltsfoot. 1.25d, Primrose. 2d, Hellebore. 2.50d, Violets. 5d, Anemones.

Flowers in Natural Colors

973	A238	50p yellow brn	.20	.20
974	A238	75p dull purple	.20	.20
975	A238	1.25d blue	.20	.20
976	A238	2d brown	.20	.20
977	A238	2.50d plum	.25	.20
978	A238	5d green	.80	.60
		Nos. 973-978 (6)	1.85	1.60

See Nos. 1056-1061, 1140-1145.

Eber, by Vasa Ivankovic — A239

Paintings of Sailing Ships: 1.25d, Tare, by Franasovic. 1.50d, Brig Sela, by Vasa Ivankovic. 2.50d, Dubrovnik galleon, 16th century. 3.25d, Madre Mimbelli, by Antoine Roux. 5d, The Virgin Saving Seamen from Disaster, 16th century ikon.

1969, July 10   Photo.   Perf. 11½

979	A239	50p gold & multi	.20	.20
980	A239	1.25d gold & multi	.20	.20
981	A239	1.50d gold & multi	.20	.20
982	A239	2.50d gold & multi	.35	.25

983 A239 3.25d gold & multi .65 .45
984 A239 5d gold & multi 1.40 1.00
    Nos. 979-984 (6) 3.00 2.30

Dubrovnik Summer Festival, 20th anniv.

11th World Games for the Deaf, Belgrade, Aug. 9-16 — A240

1969, Aug. 9   **Engr.**   *Perf. 12½*
985 A240 1.25d dp claret & dl vio .40 .20

Lipice Horse A241

Horses: 75p, Bosnian mountain horse. 3.25d, Ljutomer trotter. 5d, Half-breed.

1969, Sept. 26   **Photo.**   *Perf. 11½*
986 A241 75p multicolored .20 .20
987 A241 1.25d olive & multi .20 .20
988 A241 3.25d brn & multi .25 .20
989 A241 5d multicolored .60 .60
    Nos. 986-989 (4) 1.25 1.20

Zagreb Veterinary College, 50th anniv.

Children and Birds, by Tanja Vucanik, 13 years A242

1969, Oct. 5   **Litho.**   *Perf. 12½*
990 A242 50p org, blk & gray .20 .20

Issued for Children's Week.

Arms of Belgrade — A243

Josip Smodlaka A244

Arms: #992, Skopje (bridge & mountain). #993, Titograd (bridge & fortifications).

1969   **Litho.**   *Perf. 12½*
991 A243 50p gold & multi .20 .20
992 A243 50p gold & multi .20 .20
993 A243 50p gold & multi .20 .20
    Nos. 991-993 (3) .60 .60

Liberation of capitals of the Federated Republics, 25th anniv. See Nos. 1017-1020.

1969, Nov. 9   **Engr.**
994 A244 50p dark blue .20 .20

Smodlaka (1869-1956), leader in Yugoslavia's fight for independence.

Painting Type of 1967

Paintings of Nudes: 50p, The Little Gypsy with the Rose, by Nikola Martinoski. 1.25d, Girl on a Red Chair, by Sava Sumanovic. 1.50d, Woman Combing her Hair, by Marin

Tartaglia. 2.50d, Olympia, by Miroslav Kraljevic. 3.25d, The Bather, by Jovan Bijelic. 5d, Woman on a Couch, by Matej Sternen.

Photo. & Engr.
1969, Nov. 29   *Perf. 13½*
995 A220 50p multi, vert. .20 .20
996 A220 1.25d multi, vert. .35 .20
997 A220 1.50d multi, vert. .45 .20
998 A220 2.50d multi, vert. .55 .50
999 A220 3.25d multi, vert. 1.10 .90
1000 A220 5d multi 2.00 2.00
    Nos. 995-1000 (6) 4.65 4.00

University of Ljubljana, 50th Anniv. A245

1969, Dec. 9   **Engr.**   *Perf. 11½*
1001 A245 50p slate grn .20 .20

Seal of Zagreb University A246

Jovan Cvijic, Geographer A247

Photo. & Engr.
1969, Dec. 17   *Perf. 12½*
1002 A246 50p gold, bl & brn .20 .20

University of Zagreb, 300th anniv.

Common Design Types pictured following the introduction.

Europa Issue, 1969
Common Design Type

1969, Dec. 20   **Photo.**   *Perf. 11½*
1003 CD12 1.25d grnsh gray, buff & brn 2.00 2.00
1004 CD12 3.25d rose lil, gray & dk bl 6.75 6.75

Yugoslavia's admission to CEPT.

1970, Feb. 16   **Engr.**   *Perf. 12½*
Famous Yugoslavs: 1.25d, Dr. Andrija Stampar, hygienist. 1.50d, Joakim Krcovski, author. 2.50d, Marko Miljanov, Montenegrin patriot-hero. 3.25d, Vaca Pelagic, socialist. 5d, Oton Zupancic, Slovenian poet.

1005 A247 50p reddish brn .20 .20
1006 A247 1.25d brnsh black .20 .20
1007 A247 1.50d lilac .20 .20
1008 A247 2.50d slate grn .25 .20
1009 A247 3.25d reddish brn .25 .20
1010 A247 5d blue vio .50 .40
    Nos. 1005-1010 (6) 1.60 1.40

Punishment of Dirce, Pulj — A248

Mosaics from the 1st-4th Centuries: 1.25d, Cerberus, Bitola, horiz. 1.50d, Angel of the Annunciation, Porec. 2.50d, Hunters, Gamzigard. 3.25d, Bull and cherry tree, horiz. 5d, Virgin and Child enthroned, Porec.

1970, Mar. 16   **Photo.**   *Perf. 13½*
1011 A248 50p gold & multi .20 .20
1012 A248 1.25d gold & multi .20 .20
1013 A248 1.50d gold & multi .20 .20
1014 A248 2.50d gold & multi .30 .25
1015 A248 3.25d gold & multi .55 .35
1016 A248 5d gold & multi 1.00 1.00
    Nos. 1011-1016 (6) 2.45 2.20

Arms Type of 1969

#1017, Sarajevo (arcade). #1018, Zagreb (castle). #1019, Ljubljana (dragon and tower). #1020a, Yugoslavia (embossed coat of arms.)

1970   **Litho.**   *Perf. 12½*
1017 A243 50p gold & multi .20 .20
1018 A243 50p gold & multi .20 .20
1019 A243 50p gold & multi .20 .20
    Nos. 1017-1019 (3) .60 .60
    Souvenir Sheet
1020   Sheet of 7 4.25 4.25
  a.   A243 12d gold & black 2.00 2.00

Liberation of Yugoslavia, 25th anniv. No. 1020 contains Nos. 991-993, 1017-1019, 1020a + 2 labels.
Issued: #1017, Apr. 6; #1018, May 8; #1019, May 9; #1020, May 15.

Lenin (1870-1924), by S. Stojanovic A249

Basketball A250

Design: 1.25d, Lenin sculpture facing left.

1970, Apr. 22   **Engr.**
1021 A249 50p rose lilac .20 .20
1022 A249 1.25d blue gray .20 .20

1970, Apr. 25
1023 A250 1.25d plum .25 .20

6th World Basketball Championships, Ljubljana, May 10-23.

Europa Issue, 1970
Common Design Type

1970, May 4   **Photo.**   *Perf. 11½*
    Size: 32½x23mm
1024 CD13 1.25d lt bl, dk bl & lt grnsh bl .20 .20
1025 CD13 3.25d rose lil, plum & gray .55 .55

Istrian Shorthaired Hound A251

Yugoslav Breeds of Dogs: 1.25d, Yugoslav tricolor hound. 1.50d, Istrian hard-haired hound. 2.50d, Balkan hound. 3.25d, Dalmatian. 5d, Shara mountain dog.

1970, May 25   **Photo.**   *Perf. 11½*
    Granite Paper
1026 A251 50p tan & multi .20 .20
1027 A251 1.25d olive & multi .20 .20
1028 A251 1.50d violet & multi .20 .20
1029 A251 2.50d slate & multi .25 .20
1030 A251 3.25d multi .45 .20
1031 A251 5d multi .70 .60
    Nos. 1026-1031 (6) 2.00 1.60

Telegraph Circuit — A252

Stylized Gymnast — A254

Bird — A253

1970, June 20   **Litho.**   *Perf. 12½*
1032 A252 50p henna brn, gold & blk .20 .20

Telegraph service in Montenegro, cent.

1970, Oct. 5
1033 A253 50p multicolored .20 .20

Issued for Children's Week, Oct. 5-11.

1970, Oct. 22   **Engr.**
1034 A254 1.25d car & slate .20 .20

17th World Gymnastics Championships, Ljubljana, Oct. 22-27.

UN Emblem and Hand Holding Dove, by Makoto A255

1970, Oct. 24   **Litho. & Engr.**   *Perf. 11½*
1035 A255 1.25d dk brn, blk & gold .25 .20

25th anniversary of the United Nations.

Ascension, by Teodor D. Kracum A256

Baroque Paintings: 75p, Abraham's Sacrifice, by Federiko Benkovic. 1.25d, Holy Family, by Francisek Jelovsek. 2.50d, Jacob's Ladder, by Hristofor Zefarovic. 3.25d, Baptism of Christ, by unknown Serbian painter. 5.75d, The Coronation of Mary, by Tripo Kokolja.

Engr. & Photo.

1970, Nov. 28   *Perf. 13½x14*

1036	A256	50p gold & multi	.20	.20
1037	A256	75p gold & multi	.20	.20
1038	A256	1.25d gold & multi	.20	.20
1039	A256	2.50d gold & multi	.20	.20
1040	A256	3.25d gold & multi	.45	.20
1041	A256	5.75d gold & multi	.75	.70
		Nos. 1036-1041 (6)	2.00	1.70

Alpine Rhododendron — A257

European Nature Protection Year emblem and: 3.25d, Bearded vulture.

1970, Dec. 14   **Photo.**   *Perf. 11½*

1042	A257	1.25d multi	2.25	2.25
1043	A257	3.25d multi	7.25	6.25

Sheets of 9.

Frano Supilo — A258

British, French, Canadian, Italian Satellites A259

Litho. & Engr.

1971, Jan. 25   *Perf. 12½*

1044	A258	50p black & buff	.20	.20

Supilo (1870-1917), Croat leader for independence from Austria-Hungary. Sheets of 9.

1971, Feb. 8   **Photo.**   *Perf. 13½*

75p, Satellite. 1.25d, Automated moon exploration. 2.50d, Various spacecraft. 3.25d, 1st experimental space station. 5.75d, Astronauts on moon.

1045	A259	50p multi	.20	.20
1046	A259	75p multi	.20	.20
1047	A259	1.25d multi	.30	.20
1048	A259	2.50d multi, horiz.	.70	.45
1049	A259	3.25d multi, horiz.	.95	.85
1050	A259	5.75d multi, horiz.	2.25	2.00
		Nos. 1045-1050 (6)	4.60	3.90

"Space in the service of science." Sheets of 9.

Proclamation of the Commune, Town Hall, Paris — A260

Litho. & Engr.

1971, Mar. 18   *Perf. 11½*

1051	A260	1.25d bis brn & gray brn	.20	.20

Centenary of the Paris Commune.

Europa Issue, 1971
Common Design Type

1971, May 4   **Photo.**   *Perf. 11½*
Size: 33x23mm

1052	CD14	1.50d Prus bl, pale grn & dk bl	.20	.20
1053	CD14	4d mag, pink & dk mag	.50	.50

Circles — A261

Prince Lazar, Fresco, Lazarica Church — A262

1971, May 5   *Perf. 13½*

1054	A261	50p shown	.40	.20
1055	A261	1.25d 20 circles	1.10	.60

2nd Congress of Managers of Autonomous States.

Flower Type of 1969

Medicinal Plants: 50p, Common mallow. 1.50d, Common buckthorn. 2d, Water lily. 2.50d, Poppy. 4d, Wild chicory. 6d, Physalis.

1971, May 25   **Photo.**   *Perf. 11½*
Flowers in Natural Colors

1056	A238	50p lt ultra	.20	.20
1057	A238	1.50d olive bis	.20	.20
1058	A238	2d dull blue	.20	.20
1059	A238	2.50d dark car	.30	.20
1060	A238	4d dp bister	.40	.25
1061	A238	6d org brown	.70	.60
		Nos. 1056-1061 (6)	2.00	1.65

1971, June 28   **Photo.**   *Perf. 13½*

1062	A262	50p gray & multi	.20	.20

600th anniversary of founding of Krusevac by Prince Lazar Hrebeljanovic (1329-1389).

View of Krk — A263

Views: 5p, Krusevac. 10p, Castle & church, Gradacac. 20p, Church & bridge, Bohinj. 35p, Shore & mountains, Omis. 40p, Peje. 50p, Memorial column, Krusevac. 60p, Logar Valley. 75p, Bridge & church, Bohinj. 80p, Church, Piran. 1d, Street, Bitolj. 1.20d, Minaret, Pocitelj. 1.25d, 1.50d, Gate tower, Hercegnovi. 2d, Cathedral & City Hall Square, Novi Sad. 2.50d, Crna River.

1971-73   **Engr.**   *Perf. 13*

1063	A263	5p orange ('73)	.20	.20
1064	A263	10p brown ('72)	.20	.20
1065	A263	20p vio blk ('73)	.20	.20
1066	A263	30p ol gray ('72)	.20	.20
a.		30p green	.85	.20
1067	A263	35p brn car ('73)	.20	.20
1068	A263	40p black ('72)	.20	.20
1069	A263	50p vermilion	1.25	.20
1070	A263	50p green ('72)	.20	.20
1071	A263	60p purple ('72)	.20	.20
1072	A263	75p slate green	.20	.20
1073	A263	80p rose red ('72)	1.25	.20
1073A	A263	1d violet brn	1.25	.45
1073B	A263	1.20d sl grn ('72)	1.60	.20
1073C	A263	1.25d deep blue	.90	.20
1073D	A263	1.50d bluish blk ('73)	.25	.20
1073E	A263	2d blue ('72)	.85	.20
1073F	A263	2.50d dl pur ('73)	.85	.20
		Nos. 1063-1073F (17)	10.00	3.65

Issued with and without fluorescent bars.

See type A323. See Nos. 1482-1486, 1599-1600, 1602-1603, 1717. For surcharges see Nos. 1413, 1711-1712, 1765-1766, 1769.

Emperor Constantine, 4th Century — A264

UNICEF Emblem, Children in Balloon — A265

Tourist Issue

Antique Bronzes excavated in Yugoslavia: 1.50d, Boy with fish. 2d, Hercules, replica after Lysippus. 2.50d, Satyr. 4d, Head of Aphrodite. 6d, Citizen of Emona, 1st century tomb.

1971, Sept. 20   **Photo.**   *Perf. 13½*

1074	A264	50p rose & multi	.20	.20
1075	A264	1.50d multicolored	.20	.20
1076	A264	2d multicolored	.20	.20
1077	A264	2.50d lem & multi	.25	.20
1078	A264	4d ocher & multi	.40	.25
1079	A264	6d multicolored	.75	.60
		Nos. 1074-1079 (6)	2.00	1.65

Sheets of 9.

1971, Oct. 4   **Litho.**   *Perf. 13x13½*

1080	A265	50p multicolored	.25	.20

Children's Week, Oct. 3-10.

Woman in Serbian Costume, by Katarina Ivanovic A266

Portraits, 19th Century: 1.50d, The Merchant Ivanisevic, by Anastasije Bocaric. 2d, Ana Kresic, by Vjekoslav Karas. 2.50d, Pavle Jagodic, by Konstantin Danil. 4r, Luiza Pesjakova, by Mihael Stroj. 6d, Old Man and view of Ljubljana, by Matevz Langus.

Engraved and Photogravure

1971, Nov. 29   *Perf. 13½x14*

1081	A266	50p gold & multi	.20	.20
1082	A266	1.50d gold & multi	.20	.20
1083	A266	2d gold & multi	.20	.20
1084	A266	2.50d gold & multi	.25	.20
1085	A266	4d gold & multi	.40	.30
1086	A266	6d gold & multi	.90	.80
		Nos. 1081-1086 (6)	2.15	1.90

See Nos. 1120-1125.

Letter with Postal Code, Map of Yugoslavia — A267

Damjan Gruev (1871-1906), Macedonian Revolutionist A268

1971, Dec. 15   **Photo.**   *Perf. 13½x14*

1087	A267	50p ultra & multi	.20	.20

Introduction of postal code system.

1971, Dec. 22   **Engr.**   *Perf. 12½*

1088	A268	50p dark blue	.20	.20

11th Winter Olympic Games, Sapporo, Japan, Feb. 3-13 A269

Engr. & Typo.

1972, Feb. 3   *Perf. 11½*

1089	A269	1.25d Speed skating	.80	.50
1090	A269	6d Slalom	3.25	2.10

Sheets of 9.

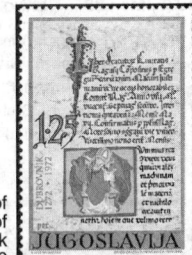

First Page of Statute of Dubrovnik A270

Lithographed and Engraved

1972, Mar. 15   *Perf. 13½*

1091	A270	1.25d gold & multi	.25	.20

700th anniversary of the Statute of Dubrovnik, a legal code given by Prince Marko Justiniani.

Ski Jump Track, Planica — A271

Water Polo and Olympic Rings — A272

1972, Mar. 21   *Perf. 11½*

1092	A271	1.25d blk, lt bl & grn	.25	.20

World Ski Jump Championships, Planica, Mar. 22-26.

1972, Apr. 17   **Litho.**   *Perf. 12½x12*

1093	A272	50p shown	.20	.20
1094	A272	1.25d Basketball	.20	.20
1095	A272	2.50d Butterfly stroke	.20	.20
1096	A272	3.25d Boxing	.30	.20
1097	A272	5d Running	.50	.25
1098	A272	6.50d Yachting	1.00	.65
		Nos. 1093-1098 (6)	2.40	1.70

20th Olympic Games, Munich, Aug. 26-Sept. 10. Sheets of 9.

Europa Issue 1972
Common Design Type

1972, May 4   **Photo.**   *Perf. 11½*
1100	CD15	1.50d bl, grn & yel	.60	.60
1101	CD15	5d brt rose, mag & org	.90	.80

Wall Creeper — A275

Marshal Tito, by Bozidar Jakac — A276

Birds: 1.25d, Little bustard. 2.50d, Red-billed chough. 3.25d, Spoonbill. 5d, Eagle owl. 6.50d, Rock ptarmigan.

1972, May 8
Birds in Natural Colors
1102	A275	50p gray violet	.20	.20
1103	A275	1.25d ocher	.20	.20
1104	A275	2.50d gray olive	.20	.20
1105	A275	3.25d light plum	.35	.20
1106	A275	5d red brown	.60	.30
1107	A275	6.50d violet	1.25	.80
		Nos. 1102-1107 (6)	2.80	1.90

Nature protection.

1972, May 25   **Litho.**   *Perf. 12½*
1108	A276	50p cream & dk brn	.20	.20
1109	A276	1.25d gray & indigo	.50	.25

Souvenir Sheet
Imperf
1110	A276	10d gray & blk brn	2.75	2.75

80th birthday of Pres. Tito. Sheets of 9. No. 1110 printed in blocks of 4.

First Locomotive Built in Serbia, 1882 — A277

5d, Modern Yugoslavian electric locomotive.

1972, June 12   **Photo.**   *Perf. 11½*
1111	A277	1.50d multicolored	.20	.20
1112	A277	5d multicolored	.70	.25

Intl. Railroad Union, 50th anniv.

Glider A278

1972, July 8   **Photo.**   *Perf. 12½*
1113	A278	2d bl gray, gold & blk	.20	.20

13th World Gliding Championships, Vrsac Airport, July 9-23. Sheets of 9.

Pawn on Chessboard — A279

6d, Chessboard, emblems of King and Queen.

1972, Sept. 18   *Perf. 11½*
1114	A279	1.50d multi	.20	.20
1115	A279	6d multi	.80	.70

20th Men's and 5th Women's Chess Olympiad, Skopje, Sept.-Oct. Sheets of 9.

Boy on Rocking Horse — A280

1972, Oct. 2   **Litho.**   *Perf. 12½*
1116	A280	80p org & multi	.20	.20

Children's Week, Oct. 2-8.

Goce Delchev — A281

1972, Oct. 16   *Perf. 13*
1117	A281	80p yel grn & blk	.20	.20

Delchev (1872-1903), Macedonian freedom fighter.

Grga Martic, by Ivan Mestrovic A282

1972, Nov. 3   *Perf. 12½*
1118	A282	80p red, yel grn & blk	.20	.20

Brother Grga Martic (1822-1905), Franciscan administrator, educator and poet.

Serbian National Library, Belgrade A283

1972, Nov. 25   **Engr.**   *Perf. 11½x12*
1119	A283	50p chocolate	.20	.20

140th anniversary of the Serbian National Library and opening of new building.

Painting Type of 1971

Still-Life Paintings: 50p, by Milos Tenkovic, horiz. 1.25d, by Jozef Pekovsek. 2.50d, by Katarina Jovanovic, horiz. 3.25d, by Konstantin Danil, horiz. 5d, by Nikola Masic. 6.50d, by Celestin Medovic, horiz.

Perf. 14x13½, 13½x14

1972, Nov. 28   **Engr. & Photo.**
1120	A266	50p gold & multi	.20	.20
1121	A266	1.25d gold & multi	.20	.20
1122	A266	2.50d gold & multi	.20	.20
1123	A266	3.25d gold & multi	.30	.20
1124	A266	5d gold & multi	.40	.30
1125	A266	6.50d gold & multi	.70	.50
		Nos. 1120-1125 (6)	2.00	1.60

Battle of Stubica, by Krsto Hegedusic — A284

6d, Battle of Krsko, by Gojmir Anton Kos.

1973, Jan. 29   **Photo.**   *Perf. 11½*
1126	A284	2d gold & multi	.30	.20
1127	A284	6d gold & multi	1.25	.70

Croatian-Slovenian Rebellion, 400th anniv. (2d); Beginning of the peasant rebellions in Slovenia, 500th anniv. (6d). Sheets of 9.

Radoje Domanovic (1873-1908), Serbian Writer — A285

1973, Feb. 3   **Litho.**   *Perf. 12½*
1128	A285	80p tan & brn	.40	.20

Sheets of 9.

Skofja Loka A286

1973, Feb. 15   *Perf. 11½*
1129	A286	80p brown & buff	.30	.20

Millennium of the founding of Skofja Loka. Sheets of 9.

Novi Sad, by Peter Demetrovic — A287

Old Engravings: 1.25d, Zagreb, by Josef Szeman. 2.50d, Kotor, by Pierre Mortier. 3.25d, Belgrade, by Mancini. 5d, Split, by Louis-Francois Cassas. 6.50d, Kranj, by Matthaus Merian.

Engraved and Photogravure
1973, Mar. 15   *Perf. 13½*
1130	A287	50p gold, buff & blk	.20	.20
1131	A287	1.25d gold, gray & black	.20	.20
1132	A287	2.50d gold & blk	.20	.20
1133	A287	3.25d gold & blk	.20	.20
1134	A287	5d gold, buff & blk	.35	.30
1135	A287	6.50d gold & blk	.50	.45
		Nos. 1130-1135 (6)	1.65	1.55

Championship Poster A288

1973, Apr. 5   **Litho.**   *Perf. 13½x13*
1136	A288	2d multicolored	.35	.20

32nd Intl. Table Tennis Championships, Sarajevo, Apr. 5-15. Sheets of 9.

Europa Issue, 1973
Common Design Type

1973, Apr. 30   **Photo.**   *Perf. 11½*
Size: 32½x23mm
1138	CD16	2d dk bl, lil & lt grn	.35	.30
1139	CD16	5.50d pur, cit & sal pink	1.40	1.25

Sheets of 9.

Flower Type of 1969

Medicinal Plants: 80p, Birthwort. 2d, Globe thistles. 3d, Olive branch. 4d, Corydalis. 5d, Mistletoe. 6d, Comfrey.

1973, May 25   **Photo.**   *Perf. 11½*
Flowers in Natural Colors
1140	A238	80p orange & grn	.20	.20
1141	A238	2d dl bl & blue	.20	.20
1142	A238	3d olive & blk	.25	.20
1143	A238	4d yel grn & grn	.40	.25
1144	A238	5d org & sepia	.60	.40
1145	A238	6d lilac & grn	1.10	.75
		Nos. 1140-1145 (6)	2.75	2.00

Anton Jansa (1734-1773), Teacher, Apiculturist and Bee — A291

1973, Aug. 25   **Engr.**   *Perf. 12½*
1147	A291	80p black	.20	.20

Sheets of 9.

Championship Badge A292

1973, Sept. 1   **Litho.**   *Perf. 13½x13*
1148	A292	2d multicolored	.30	.20

World water sport championships (swimming, water polo, water jumps, figure swimming), Belgrade, Sept. 1-9. Sheets of 9.

"Greeting the Sun," by Ivan Vucovic A293

Post Horn — A294

1973, Oct. 1   *Perf. 12½*
1149	A293	80p multicolored	.35	.20

Children's Week, Oct. 1-7. Sheets of 9.

Coil Stamps
1973-77   **Photo.**   *Perf. 14½x14*
1150	A294	30p brown	.20	.20
1151	A294	50p gray blue	.20	.20
1152	A294	80p rose red ('74)	.20	.20
1153	A294	1d yel grn ('77)	.20	.20
1154	A294	1.20d pink ('74)	.30	.20
1155	A294	1.50d rose ('77)	.20	.20
		Nos. 1150-1155 (6)	1.30	1.20

Juraj Dalmatinac, Sculptor, Architect, 500th Anniv. of Death — A295

1973, Oct. 8   **Litho.**   *Perf. 12½*
1158	A295	80p grnsh gray & ol blk	.20	.20

Sheets of 9.

Nadezda Petrovic (1873-1915), Self-Portrait — A296

Lithographed and Engraved
1973, Oct. 12   **Perf. 11½**
1159 A296 2d gold & multi   .30   .20
Sheets of 9.

Interior, by Marko Celebonovic — A297

Paintings of Interiors by Yugoslav artists: 2d, St. Duja, by Emanuel Vidovic. 3d, Room with Slovak Woman, by Marino Tartaglia. 4d, Painter with Easel, by Miljenko Stancic. 5d, Studio, by Milan Konjovic. 6d, Tavern in Stara Loka, by France Slana.

1973, Oct. 20   **Photo.**   **Perf. 13½**
1160 A297 80p gold & multi   .20   .20
1161 A297 2d gold & multi   .20   .20
1162 A297 3d gold & multi   .20   .20
1163 A297 4d gold & multi   .20   .20
1164 A297 5d gold & multi   .35   .25
1165 A297 6d gold & multi   .45   .40
    Nos. 1160-1165 (6)   1.60   1.45
Sheets of 9.

Dragojlo Dudic — A298

Lithographed and Engraved
1973, Nov. 29   **Perf. 12½**
      Gray and Indigo
1166 A298 80p shown   .20   .20
1167 A298 80p Strahil Pindzur   .20   .20
1168 A298 80p Boris Kidric   .20   .20
1169 A298 80p Radoje Dakic   .20   .20
      Gray and Plum
1170 A298 2d Josip Mazar-
         Sosa   .25   .25
1171 A298 2d Zarko Zrenjanin   .25   .25
1172 A298 2d Emin Duraku   .25   .25
1173 A298 2d Ivan-Lola Ribar   .25   .25
   a.   Sheet of 8, #1166-1173   1.50   1.50

Republic Day, Nov. 29, honoring national heroes who perished during WWII.

Memorial, by O. Boljka, Ljubljana A299   Winged Globe, by D. Dzamonja, at Podgaric A300

Sculptures: 4.50d, Tower by D. Dzamonja, at Kozara. 5d, Memorial, by B. Grabulovski, at Belcista. 10d, Abstract, by M. Zivkovic, at Sutjeska. 50d, Stone "V," by Zivkovic, at Kragujevac.

1974   **Engr.**   **Perf. 12½**
1174 A299 3d slate grn   1.10   .20
1175 A299 4.50d brn lake   1.75   .20
1176 A299 5d dark vio   1.75   .20
   b.   Perf. 13½   5.00
1177 A300 10d slate grn   2.10   .35
1178 A300 20d dull pur   2.50   .45
1179 A300 50d indigo   5.50   1.40
    Nos. 1174-1179 (6)   14.70   2.80

1978-82   **Litho.**
1176a A299 5d   1.90   .20
1177a A300 10d ('81)   1.90   .45
1178a A300 20d ('81)   2.75   .45
1179a A300 50d ('82)   3.00   .75
    Nos. 1176a-1179a (4)   9.55   1.85

Metric Measure A301

1974, Jan. 10   **Litho.**   **Perf. 13**
1180 A301 80p plum & multi   .20   .20
Centenary of introduction of metric system.

European Ice Skating Championships, Jan. 29-Feb. 2, Zagreb — A302

1974, Jan. 29
1181 A302 2d multicolored   .65   .25

Diligence, 1874 A303

Litho. & Engr.
1974, Feb. 25   **Perf. 11½**
1182 A303 80p shown   .20   .20
1183 A303 2d New UPU head-
         quarters   .20   .20
1184 A303 8d Jet plane   .75   .50
    Nos. 1182-1184 (3)   1.15   .90
Centenary of the Universal Postal Union.

Montenegro No. 1 — A304

Litho. & Engr.
1974, Mar. 11   **Perf. 13**
1185 A304 80p shown   .20   .20
1186 A304 6d Montenegro No. 7   .40   .20
Centenary of first Montenegrin postage stamps.

Marshal Tito — A305   Lenin, by Nandor Glid — A306

1974   **Litho.**   **Perf. 13**
1193 A305 50p green   .20   .20
   a.   Perf. 13x12½
1196 A305 80p vermilion   .20   .20
1198 A305 1.20d slate green   .25   .20
1201 A305 2d gray blue   .25   .20
   a.   Perf. 13x12½   .50
    Nos. 1193-1201 (4)   .90   .80

Issued with and without fluorescence.
For surcharge see No. 1415.

1974, Apr. 20   **Litho.**   **Perf. 13**
1204 A306 2d blk & silver   .25   .20
50th death anniv. of Lenin.

Lepenski Vir Statue, c. 4950 B.C. — A307

Europa: 6d, Widow & Child, by Ivan Mestrovic.

1974, Apr. 29   **Photo.**   **Perf. 11½**
1205 A307 2d multicolored   .40   .40
1206 A307 6d multicolored   1.60   1.60

Great Tit — A308   Congress Poster — A309

1974, May 25   **Photo.**   **Perf. 11½**
1207 A308 80p shown   .20   .20
1208 A308 2d Rose   .55   .20
1209 A308 6d Cabbage butterfly   1.40   1.10
    Nos. 1207-1209 (3)   2.15   1.50
Youth Day. Issued in sheets of 9.

1974, May 27   **Litho.**   **Perf. 11½**
1210 A309 80p gold & multi   .20   .20
1211 A309 2d silver & multi   .20   .20
1212 A309 6d ocher & multi   .40   .40
    Nos. 1210-1212 (3)   .80   .80
10th Congress of Yugoslav League of Communists, Belgrade, May 27-30.

Radar Ground Station, Ivanjica — A311

Games Emblem and Soccer Cup — A312

1974, June 7   **Engr.**   **Perf. 13**
1214 A311 80p shown   .20   .20
1215 A311 6d Intelsat IV   1.10   .50
Opening of first satellite ground station in Yugoslavia at Ivanjica. Sheets of 9.

1974, June 13   **Litho.**   **Perf. 13**
1216 A312 4.50d vio bl & multi   1.25   .90
World Cup Soccer Championship, Munich, June 13-July 7. Sheets of 9.

Klek Mountain, Edelweiss, Mountaineers' Emblem — A313

1974, June 15
1217 A313 2d grn & multi   .20   .20
Mountaineering in Yugoslavia, cent. Sheets of 9.

Children's Dance, by Jano Knjazovic — A314

Paintings: 2d, "Crucified Rooster," by Ivan Generalic, vert. 5d, Laundresses, by Ivan Lackovic, vert. 8d, Dance, by Janko Brasic.

1974, Sept. 9   **Photo.**   **Perf. 11½**
1218 A314 80p multi   .20   .20
1219 A314 2d multi   .20   .20
1220 A314 5d multi   .60   .45
1221 A314 8d multi   1.90   .75
    Nos. 1218-1221 (4)   2.90   1.60
Yugoslav primitive art.

Cock and Flower, by Kaca Milinojsin A315

Designs (Children's Paintings): 3.20d, Girl and Boy, by Ewa Medrzecka, vert. 5d, Cat and Kitten, by Jelena Anastasijevic.

1974, Oct. 7   **Litho.**   **Perf. 13**
1222 A315 1.20d multi   .20   .20
1223 A315 3.20d multi   .20   .20
1224 A315 5d multi   .70   .20
    Nos. 1222-1224 (3)   1.10   .60
Children's Week, Oct. 1-7, and Joy of Europe meeting in Belgrade. Sheets of 9.

Library and Primoz Trubar Statue A316

1974, Oct. 21   **Engr.**   **Perf. 13**
1225 A316 1.20d black   .20   .20
Natl. University Library, Ljubljana, 200th anniv.

White Peonies, by Petar Dobrovic
A317

Paintings of Flowers by Yugoslav artists: 2d, Carnations, by Vilko Gecan. 3d, Flowers, still-life, by Milan Konjovic. 4d, White Vase, by Sava Sumanovic. 5d, Larkspur, by Stane Kregar. 8d, Roses, by Petar Lubarda.

1974, Nov. 28   Photo.   Perf. 11½

1226	A317	80p gold & multi	.20	.20
1227	A317	2d gold & multi	.20	.20
1228	A317	3d gold & multi	.20	.20
1229	A317	4d gold & multi	.30	.20
1230	A317	5d gold & multi	.45	.20
1231	A317	8d gold & multi	.85	.35
	Nos. 1226-1231 (6)		2.20	1.35

Sheets of 9.

Title Page and View of Belgrade
A318

1975, Jan. 8   Litho.   Perf. 13

1232	A318	1.20d citron	.20	.20
a.	Perf. 12½			

Sesquicentennial of the first publication of Matica Srpska, literary journal.

Map of Europe and Dove — A319

Svetozar Markovic, by Stevan Bodnarov
A321

Gold-plated Bronze Earring
A320

1975, Jan. 30   Perf. 12x11½

1233	A319	3.20d bl & multi	.55	.25
1234	A319	8d multi	1.75	.90

Interparliamentary Union for European Cooperation and Security, 2nd Conference, Belgrade, Jan. 31-Feb. 6.

1975, Feb. 25   Photo.   Perf. 14x13

Antique jewelry in Yugoslav museums: 2.10d, Silver bracelet, 18th cent. 3.20d, Silver gilt belt buckle, 18th cent. 5d, Silver ring with Nike cameo, 14th cent. 6d, Silver necklace, 17th cent. 8d, Bronze gilt bracelet, 14th cent.

1235	A320	1.20d multi	.20	.20
1236	A320	2.10d multi	.20	.20
1237	A320	3.20d multi	.20	.20
1238	A320	5d multi	.35	.25

1239	A320	6d multi	.65	.40
1240	A320	8d multi	.80	.75
	Nos. 1235-1240 (6)		2.40	2.00

1975, Feb. 26   Engr.   Perf. 13

1241	A321	1.20d blue blk	.20	.20

Markovic (1846-1875), writer and poet.

Fettered Woman, by Frano Krsinic
A322

Street, Ohrid — A323

1975, Mar. 8   Photo.   Perf. 14½x14

1242	A322	3.20d gold & sepia	.30	.20

International Women's Year.

1975-77   Litho.   Perf. 13

Views: 25p, Budva. 75p, City Hall, Rijeka (Fiume). Nos. 1245, 1246, Street, Ohrid. 1.50d, Church, Bihac. 2.10d, Street and fountain, Hvar. 3.20d, Skofja Loka. 3.40d, Main Square, Vranje. 4.90d, Mosque, Perast.

No Inscription at Bottom

1243	A323	25p carmine ('76)	.20	.20
1244	A323	75p purple ('76)	.20	.20
1245	A323	1d dull purple	.25	.20
1246	A323	1d dl grn ('76)	.20	.20
a.	Perf. 13x12½		.20	
1247	A323	1.50d rose red ('76)	.30	.20
a.	Perf. 13x12½		10.00	
1248	A323	2.10d gray green	.50	.20
1249	A323	3.20d dull blue	.70	.20
1250	A323	3.40d gray grn ('77)	.30	.20
a.	Perf. 13x12½		1.00	
1251	A323	4.90d dl bl ('76)	.55	.20
	Nos. 1243-1251 (9)		3.20	1.80

See Nos. 1487-1491, 1598, 1601, 1603A, 1713, 1718-1719. For surcharges see Nos. 1382-1383, 1481, 1502, 1545, 1550, 1594-1597A, 1764, 1767-1768, 1770-1771, 1964, 1973.

Europa Issue 1975

Still Life with Eggs, by Mosa Pijade
A325

Painting: 8d, Three Graces, by Ivan Radovic.

1975, Apr. 28

1252	A325	3.20d gold & multi	.20	.20
1253	A325	8d gold & multi	.60	.60

Srem Front Fighters' Monument, by Dusan Dzamonja
A326

1975, May 9   Litho.   Perf. 13½

1254	A326	3.20d red & multi	.30	.20

Victory over Fascism in WWII; liberation of Yugoslavia, 30th anniv.

Garland Flower — A327

Kayak — A328

1975, May 24   Photo.   Perf. 14x14½

1255	A327	1.20d shown	.20	.20
1256	A327	2.10d Garden balsam	.20	.20
1257	A327	3.20d Rose mallow	.20	.20
1258	A327	5d Geranium	.40	.25
1259	A327	6d Crocus	.55	.30
1260	A327	8d Oleander	.85	.60
	Nos. 1255-1260 (6)		2.40	1.75

Youth Day.

1975, June 20   Litho.   Perf. 13½

1261	A328	3.20d grnsh bl & multi	.25	.20

9th World Championship of Wild Water Racing, Radika River, June 24-25, and 14th World Championship of Canoe-Slalom, Treska River, June 28-29.

Ambush, Herzegovinian Insurgents, by Ferdo Quiquerez — A329

1975, July 9   Photo.   Perf. 13½x14½

1262	A329	1.20d gold & multi	.20	.20

Bosnian & Herzegovinian Uprising, cent.

Stjepan Mitrov Ljubisa (1824-1878)
A330

Yugoslav writers: 2.10d, Ivan Prijatelj (1875-1937). 3.20d, Jakov Ignjatovic (1824-1889). 5d, Dragojla Jarnevic (1824-1889). 6d, Svetozar Corovic (1875-1919). 8d, Ivana Brlic-Mazuranic (1874-1938).

1975, Sept. 16   Litho.   Perf. 13

1263	A330	1.20d brick red & blk	.20	.20
1264	A330	2.10d dl grn & blk	.20	.20
1265	A330	3.20d dl bis & blk	.20	.20
1266	A330	5d brn org & blk	.35	.20
1267	A330	6d yel grn & blk	.40	.20
1268	A330	8d Prus bl & blk	.50	.30
	Nos. 1263-1268 (6)		1.85	1.30

"Joy of Europe" Children's Meeting, Oct. 2-7, Belgrade
A331

Children's drawings.

1975, Oct. 1   Litho.   Perf. 13½

1269	A331	3.20d Young Lion	.35	.20
1270	A331	6d Baby Carriage	1.60	.65

Peace Dove
A332

1975, Oct. 10

1271	A332	3.20d multi	.20	.20
1272	A332	8d multi	.75	.45

European Security and Cooperation Conference, Helsinki, July 30-Aug. 1.

Red Cross, "100", Map of Yugoslavia
A333

8d, Red Cross, people seeking help.

1975, Nov. 1   Litho.   Perf. 13½x13

1273	A333	1.20d red & multi	.20	.20
1274	A333	8d red & multi	.45	.30

Centenary of Red Cross in Yugoslavia.

Soup Kitchen, by Dorde Andrejevic-Kun
A334

Social paintings by 20th century Yugoslav artists: 2.10d, People at the Door, by Vinko Grdan. 3.20d, Drunks in Coach, by Marijan Detoni, horiz. 5d, Workers' Lunch, by Tone Kralj, horiz. 6d, Water Wheel, by Lazar Licenoski. 8d, The Hanging, by Krsto Hegedusic.

Perf. 14½x13½, 13½x14½

1975, Nov. 28   Photo.

1275	A334	1.20d gold & multi	.20	.20
1276	A334	2.10d gold & multi	.20	.20
1277	A334	3.20d gold & multi	.20	.20
1278	A334	5d gold & multi	.20	.20
1279	A334	6d gold & multi	.30	.25
1280	A334	8d gold & multi	.55	.55
	Nos. 1275-1280 (6)		1.65	1.60

Sheets of 9.

Diocletian's Palace, 304 A.D. — A335

3.20d, House of Ohrid, 19th cent., vert. 8d, Gracanica Monastery, Kosovo, 1321.

1975, Dec. 10   Engr.   Perf. 13½

1281	A335	1.20d dark brown	.20	.20
1282	A335	3.20d bluish black	.30	.20
1283	A335	8d dk vio brown	.80	.35
	Nos. 1281-1283 (3)		1.30	.75

European Architectural Heritage Year 1975. Sheets of 9.

12th Winter Olympic Games, Feb. 4-15, Innsbruck, Austria
A336

1976, Feb. 4   Engr.   Perf. 13½

1284	A336	3.20d Ski jump	.20	.20
1285	A336	8d Pair figure skating	.70	.40

Red Flag — A337

1976, Feb. 14   Litho.
1286 A337 1.20d red & multi   .20 .20
"Red Flag" workers demonstration, Kragujevac, Feb. 15, 1876.

Svetozar Miletic (1826-1901), Lawyer, Founder of United Serbian Youth — A338

1976, Feb. 23   Perf. 13½x13
1287 A338 1.20d grnsh gray & dl grn   .20 .20

Borislav "Bora" Stankovic, (1876-1927), Writer A339

1976, Mar. 31   Litho.   Perf. 13½x13
1288 A339 1.20d lem, ol & mar   .20 .20
Sheets of 9.

Europa Issue 1976

King Matthias, by Jakob Pogorelec, 1931 — A340

1976, Apr. 26   Photo.   Perf. 11½
1289 A340 3.20d shown   .20 .20
1290 A340 8d Bowl, 14th cent   .30 .30

Ivan Cankar (1876-1918), Slovenian Writer A341

1976, May 8   Litho.   Perf. 13½x13
1291 A341 1.20d orange & plum   .20 .20

Train on Viaduct in Bosnia A342

Design: 8d, Train on viaduct in Montenegro.

1976, May 15   Engr.   Perf. 13½
1292 A342 3.20d deep magenta   .20 .20
1293 A342 8d deep blue   .55 .25
Inauguration of the Belgrade-Bar railroad.

Hawker Dragonfly A343

Fresh-water Fauna: 2.10d, Winkle. 3.20d, Rudd. 5d, Green frog. 6d, Ferruginous duck. 8d, Muskrat.

1976, May 25   Litho.
1294 A343 1.20d yel & multi   .20 .20
1295 A343 2.10d bl & multi   .20 .20
1296 A343 3.20d vio & multi   .20 .20
1297 A343 5d multicolored   .40 .30
1298 A343 6d multicolored   .45 .40
1299 A343 8d multicolored   .75 .50
Nos. 1294-1299 (6)   2.20 1.80
Youth Day.

Vladimir Nazor, Croatian Writer, Birth Cent. — A344

1976, May 29   Perf. 13
1300 A344 1.20d pale lil & dl bl   .20 .20

Battle of Vucji Dol, 1876 A345

1976, June 16   Litho.   Perf. 13
1301 A345 1.20d gold, brn & buff   .20 .20
Liberation of Montenegro from Turkey, cent.

Serbian Pitcher A346

Water Pitchers: 2.10d, Slovenia. 3.20d, Bosnia-Herzegovina. 5d, Vojvodina 6d, Macedonia. 8d, Kosovo.

1976, June 22   Photo.   Perf. 14x13
1302 A346 1.20d dk car & multi   .20 .20
1303 A346 2.10d olive & multi   .20 .20
1304 A346 3.20d red & multi   .20 .20
1305 A346 5d brown & multi   .30 .20
1306 A346 6d dk grn & multi   .40 .30
1307 A346 8d dk bl & multi   .85 .35
Nos. 1302-1307 (6)   2.15 1.45

Tesla Monument, Belgrade, and Niagara Falls — A347

1976, July 10   Engr.   Perf. 13
1308 A347 5d slate grn & indigo   .50 .20
Nikola Tesla (1856-1943), electrical engineer and inventor. Sheets of 9.

21st Olympic Games, July 17-Aug. 1, Montreal, Canada, A348

1976, July 17
1309 A348 1.20d Long jump   .20 .20
1310 A348 3.20d Team handball   .20 .20
1311 A348 5d Target shooting   .25 .20
1312 A348 8d Single scull rowing   .45 .25
Nos. 1309-1312 (4)   1.10 .85
Sheets of 9.

World Map and Peace Dove A349

1976, Aug. 16   Litho.   Perf. 13
1313 A349 4.90d multi   .30 .20
5th Summit Conference of Non-Aligned Countries, Colombo, Sri Lanka, Aug. 9-19. Sheets of 9.

Children's Train — A350

Children's drawings: 4.90d, Navy Day (submarine).

1976, Oct. 2   Litho.   Perf. 13
1314 A350 4.90d multi   .35 .20
1315 A350 8d multi   .90 .35
"Joy of Europe" Children's Meeting, Belgrade, Oct. 2-7.

Herzegovinian Fugitives, by Uros Predic — A351

Historical paintings by 19th-20th century Yugoslav painters: 1.20d, Battle of the Montenegrins, by Djura Jaksic. 2.10d, Nikola S. Zrinjski at Siget, by Oton Ivekovic, vert. 5d, Uprising at Razlovci, by Borko Lazeski. 6d, Enthroning of Slovenian Duke at Gospovetsko Field, by Anton Gojmir Kos. 8d, Break-through at Solun Front, by Veljko Stanojevic.

Perf. 13½x12½, 12½x13½
1976, Nov. 29   Photo.
1316 A351 1.20d gold & multi   .20 .20
1317 A351 2.10d gold & multi   .20 .20
1318 A351 3.20d gold & multi   .20 .20
1319 A351 5d gold & multi   .25 .25
1320 A351 6d gold & multi   .45 .35
1321 A351 8d gold & multi   .55 .50
Nos. 1316-1321 (6)   1.85 1.70
Sheets of 9.

No. 839 Surcharged with New Value and 3 Bars in Rose

1976, Dec. 8   Engr.   Perf. 12½
1322 A206 1d on 85p dl pur   .20 .20

Mateja Nenadovic A352

Rajko Zinzifov — A353

1977, Feb. 4   Photo.   Perf. 13½x14
1323 A352 4.90d multicolored   .30 .20
Prota Mateja Nenadovic (1777-1854), Serbian Duke, archbishop and writer.

1977, Feb. 10   Litho.   Perf. 13x13½
1324 A353 1.50d brn & sepia   .20 .20
Rajko Zinzifov (1839-1877), writer.

Phlox — A354   Alojz Kraigher — A356

Croatian Music Institute, Zagreb, 150th Anniv. A355

Flowers: 3.40d, Lily. 4.90d, Bleeding heart. 6d, Zinnia. 8d, Spreading marigold. 10d, Horseshoe geranium.

1977, Mar. 8   Perf. 13½x13
1325 A354 1.50d multi   .20 .20
1326 A354 3.40d multi   .25 .20
1327 A354 4.90d multi   .30 .20
1328 A354 6d multi   .35 .20
1329 A354 8d multi   .55 .20
1330 A354 10d multi   .90 .55
Nos. 1325-1330 (6)   2.55 1.55

1977, Apr. 4   Engr.   Perf. 13
1331 A355 4.90d bl & sepia   .30 .20

1977, Apr. 11   Litho.   Perf. 13½
1332 A356 1.50d lemon & brn   .20 .20
Kraigher (1877-1959), Slovenian writer.

Boka Kotorska, by Milo Milunovic A357

10d, Zagorje in November, by Ljubo Babie.

1977, May 4   Photo.   Perf. 11½
1333 A357 4.90d gold & multi   .20 .20
1334 A357 10d gold & multi   .55 .55
Europa. Issued in sheets of 9.

Marshal Tito, by Omer Mujadzic A358

Mountain Range and Gentian — A359

1977, May 25   *Perf. 11½x12*
1335 A358 1.50d gold & multi   .20   .20
1336 A358 4.90d gold & multi   .30   .25
1337 A358 8d gold & multi   .60   .40
   Nos. 1335-1337 (3)   1.10   .85
85th birthday of Pres. Tito. Sheets of 9.

1977, June 6   *Litho.*   *Perf. 13x13½*
Design: 10d, Plitvice Lakes Falls, trees, robin and environmental protection emblem.
1338 A359 4.90d multicolored   .30   .20
1339 A359 10d multicolored   .70   .50
World Environment Day.

Petar Kocic (1877-1916), Writer A360

1977, June 15   *Perf. 13½*
1340 A360 1.50d pale grn & brn   .20 .20

Map of Europe and Peace Dove A361

1977, June 15   *Litho.*   *Perf. 13½*
1341 A361 4.90d multi   .90   .90
1342 A361 10d multi   3.75   3.75
Security and Cooperation Conference, Belgrade, June 15.

Child on Float — A362

Children's drawings: 10d, Fruit picking.

1977, Oct. 3   *Litho.*   *Perf. 13½*
1343 A362 4.90d multi   .35   .20
1344 A362 10d multi   .90   .40
"Joy of Europe" Children's Meeting.

Sava Congress Center, Belgrade A363

1977, Oct. 4   *Litho.*   *Perf. 13½*
1345 A363 4.90d bl & multi   .55   .40
1346 A363 10d car & multi   4.00   3.00
European Security and Cooperation Conference, Belgrade.

Exhibition Emblem — A364

1977, Oct. 20   *Litho.*   *Perf. 13½*
1347 A364 4.90d gold & multi   .30   .20
Balkanfila 1977, 6th Intl. Phil. Exhib. of Balkan Countries, Belgrade, Oct. 24-30.

Double Flute and Shepherd A365

Landscape and Musician: 3.40d, 4.90d, 6d, Various string instruments. 8d, Bagpipes. 10d, Panpipes.

1977, Oct. 25   *Engr.*   *Perf. 13½*
1348 A365 1.50d och & red brn   .20   .20
1349 A365 3.40d green & brn   .20   .20
1350 A365 4.90d dk brn & yel   .25   .20
1351 A365 6d bl & red brn   .40   .20
1352 A365 8d brick red & sep   .60   .20
1353 A365 10d sl grn & bis   .90   .25
   Nos. 1348-1353 (6)   2.55   1.25
Musical instruments from Belgrade Ethnographical Museum.

Ivan Vavpotic, Self-portrait A366

Self-portraits of Yugoslav artists: 3.40d, Mihailo Vukotic. 4.90d, Kosta Hakman. 6d, Miroslav Kraljevic. 8d, Nikola Martinovski. 10d, Milena Pavlovic-Barili.

    Perf. 13½x12½
1977, Nov. 26   *Photo.*
1354 A366 1.50d gold & multi   .20   .20
1355 A366 3.40d gold & multi   .20   .20
1356 A366 4.90d gold & multi   .20   .20
1357 A366 6d gold & multi   .30   .20
1358 A366 8d gold & multi   .45   .20
1359 A366 10d gold & multi   .65   .65
   Nos. 1354-1359 (6)   2.00   1.65

Festival of Testaccio, by Klovic — A367

Julija Klovic, by El Greco — A368

1978, Jan. 14   *Photo.*   *Perf. 13½*
1360 A367 4.90d multicolored   .20   .20
1361 A368 10d multicolored   .35   .30
Julija Klovic (1498-1578), Croat miniaturist.

Stampless Cover, Banaviste to Kubin, 1869 — A369

Designs: 3.40d, Mailbox. 4.90d, Ericsson telephone, 1900. 10d, Morse telegraph, 1844.

1978, Jan. 28   *Perf. 13x14*
1362 A369 1.50d multicolored   .20   .20
1363 A369 3.40d multicolored   .20   .20
1364 A369 4.90d multicolored   .25   .20
1365 A369 10d multicolored   .50   .40
   Nos. 1362-1365 (4)   1.15   1.00
Post Office Museum, Belgrade.

Battle of Pirot A370

1978, Feb. 20   *Litho.*   *Perf. 13½*
1366 A370 1.50d gold, blk & sl grn   .20 .20
Centenary of Serbo-Turkish War.

Airplanes A371

1978, Apr. 24   *Litho.*   *Perf. 13½*
1367 A371 1.50d S-49A, 1949   .20   .20
1368 A371 3.40d Galeb, 1961   .25   .20
1369 A371 4.90d Utva-75, 1976   .35   .20
1370 A371 10d Orao, 1974   .95   .40
   Nos. 1367-1370 (4)   1.75   1.00
Aeronautical Day.

Europa Issue

View of Golubac A372

1978, May 3   *Photo.*   *Perf. 11½*
1371 A372 4.90d shown   .20   .20
1372 A372 10d St. Naum Monastery, Ohrid   .80   .80

Boxing Glove A373

Honeybee A374

1978, May 5   *Litho.*   *Perf. 13½*
1373 A373 4.90d multicolored   .35   .20
Amateur Boxing Championships.

1978, May 25   *Photo.*   *Perf. 11½*
Bees of Yugoslavia: 3.40d, Halictus scabiosae. 4.90d, Blue carpenter bee. 10d, Large earth bumblebee.
1374 A374 1.50d multi   .20   .20
1375 A374 3.40d multi   .25   .20
1376 A374 4.90d multi   .40   .25
1377 A374 10d multi   .95   .70
   Nos. 1374-1377 (4)   1.80   1.35

Filip Filipovic (1878-1938), Radovan Radovic (1878-1906), Revolutionaries — A375

1978, June 19   *Litho.*   *Perf. 13½*
1378 A375 1.50d dk pur & dl ol   .20 .20

Marshal Tito — A376

Congress Emblem — A377

1978, June 20
1379 A376 2d red & multi   .20   .20
1380 A377 4.90d red & multi   .45   .20

    Souvenir Sheet
    Imperf
1381 A376 15d red & multi   3.75   2.60
11th Congress of Yugoslav League of Communists, Belgrade, June 20-23.

Nos. 1246, 1248 Surcharged with New Value and Two Bars in Brown

1978   *Litho.*   *Perf. 13*
1382 A323 2d on 1d   .25   .20
1383 A323 3.40d on 2.10d   .25   .20
Issue dates: #1382, July 17; #1383, Aug. 1.

Conference Emblem over Belgrade — A378

Championship Emblem — A379

1978, July 25   Photo.   Perf. 13½
1384 A378 4.90d bl & lt blue   .20 .20
Conference of Foreign Ministers of Nonaligned Countries, Belgrade, July 25-29.

1978, Aug. 10   Litho.   Perf. 13½x13
1385 A379 4.90d multicolored   .30 .20
14th Kayak and Canoe Still Water Championships, Lake Sava, Aug. 10-14.

Mt. Triglav, North Rock — A380

Black Lake, Mt. Durmitor A381

1978, Aug. 26   Photo.   Perf. 14
1386 A380 2d multicolored   .20 .20
Bicentenary of first ascent of Mt. Triglav by Slovenian climbers.

1978, Sept. 20
1387 A381 4.90d shown   .25 .20
1388 A381 10d Tara River   .55 .30
Protection of the environment.

Night Sky A382

1978, Sept. 30   Litho.   Perf. 13x12½
1389 A382 4.90d bl blk, blk & gold   .20 .20
29th Congress of International Astronautical Federation, Dubrovnik, Oct. 1-8.

People in Forest A383

Children's drawings: 10d, Family around pond.

1978, Oct. 2   Perf. 13½x13
1390 A383 4.90d multi   .35 .20
1391 A383 10d multi   .80 .45
"Joy of Europe" Children's Meeting.

Seal on Insurrection Declaration A384

1978, Oct. 5   Perf. 13½
1392 A384 2d gold, brn & blk   .20 .20
Centenary of Kresna uprising.

Teachers' Training Institute, Sombor, Bicent. A385

1978, Oct. 16
1393 A385 2d multicolored   .20 .20

Croatian Red Cross, Cent. A386

1978, Oct. 21
1394 A386 2d lt bl, blk & red   .20 .20

Metallic Sculpture XXII, by Dusan Dzamonja A387

Modern Sculptures: 3.40d, Circulation in Space I, by Vojin Bakic, vert. 4.90d, Tectonic Octopode, by Olga Jevric, vert. 10d, Tree of Life, by Drago Trsar.

Perf. 13½x13, 13x13½
1978, Nov. 4   Litho.
1395 A387 2d multicolored   .20 .20
1396 A387 3.40d multicolored   .20 .20
1397 A387 4.90d multicolored   .25 .20
1398 A387 10d multicolored   .65 .40
Nos. 1395-1398 (4)   1.30 1.00

Crossing of Neretva Pass, by Ismet Mujezinovic A388

1978, Nov. 10   Litho.   Perf. 13
1399 A388 2d multicolored   .20 .20
35th anniversary of Battle of Neretva.

Workers Leaving Factory, by Marijan Detoni — A389

Larch Cone — A390

Engravings: 3.40d, Workers, by Maksim Sedej. 4.90d, Lumberjacks, by Daniel Ozmo. 6d, Meal Break, by Pivo Karamatijevic. 10d, Hanged Man and Raped Woman, by Djordje Andrejevic Kun.

1978, Nov. 28   Photo.   Perf. 14x13½
1400 A389 2d gold, blk & buff   .20 .20
1401 A389 3.40d gold & black   .20 .20
1402 A389 4.90d gold, yel & blk   .30 .20
1403 A389 6d gold, buff & blk   .40 .25
1404 A389 10d gold, cr & blk   .70 .50
Nos. 1400-1404 (5)   1.80 1.35
Republic day.

1978, Dec. 11   Photo.   Perf. 13x12½
1405 A390 1.50d shown   .20 .20
1406 A390 1.50d Red squirrel   .20 .20
1407 A390 2d Sycamore leaves   .25 .20
1408 A390 2d Red deer   .25 .20
a. Bklt. pane of 8   1.25
1409 A390 3.40d Alder leaves   .35 .20
1410 A390 3.40d Partridge   .35 .20
1411 A390 4.90d Oak leaves   .45 .20
1412 A390 4.90d Grouse   .45 .20
a. Bklt. pane of 8   3.25
Nos. 1405-1412 (8)   2.50 1.60
New Year 1979. Nos. 1405-1412 printed se-tenant in sheets of 25.
No. 1408a contains 4 each of Nos. 1407-1408; No. 1412a 2 each of Nos. 1409-1412, with background colors changed.

Nos. 1064, 868, 1198 Surcharged with New Value and Bars

1978   Engr.; Litho.   Perf. 12½, 13½
1413 A263 35p on 10p brown   .20 .20
1414 A211 60p on 85p dp bl   .20 .20
1415 A305 80p on 1.20d sl grn   .20 .20
Nos. 1413-1415 (3)   .60 .60

First Masthead of Politika A391

1979, Jan. 25   Litho.   Perf. 13½
1416 A391 2d gold & black   .20 .20
Politika daily newspaper, 75th anniv.

Red Flags and Emblem A392

Child and IYC Emblem A393

1979, Feb. 15
1417 A392 2d red & gold   .20 .20
11th Meeting of Self-managers, Kragujevac, Feb. 15-16.

1979, Mar. 1   Photo.   Perf. 11½x12
1418 A393 4.90d gold vio & bl   .45 .30
International Year of the Child.

Sabre, Mace, Koran Pouch A394

Old Weapons: 3.40d, Pistol and ramrod, Montenegro. 4.90d, Short carbine and powder horn, Slovenia and Croatia. 10d, Oriental rifle and cartridge pouch.

1979, Mar. 26   Photo.   Perf. 14
1419 A394 2d multicolored   .20 .20
1420 A394 3.40d multicolored   .20 .20
1421 A394 4.90d multicolored   .20 .20
1422 A394 10d multicolored   .40 .40
Nos. 1419-1422 (4)   1.00 1.00

5-Pointed Star, Hammer and Sickle — A395

1979, Apr. 20   Photo.   Perf. 13½
1423 A395 2d multicolored   .20 .20
1424 A395 4.90d multicolored   .35 .20
Communist and Communist Youth Leagues, 60th anniversary.

Cyril and Methodius University and Emblem A396

1979, Apr. 24   Litho.
1425 A396 2d multicolored   .20 .20
Sts. Cyril and Methodius University, Skopje, 30th anniv.

19th Century Belgrade, by C. Goebel A397

Europa: 10d, Postilion and Ljubljana, 17th century, by Jan van der Heyden.

1979, Apr. 30   Photo.   Perf. 11½
1426 A397 4.90d multicolored   .20 .20
1427 A397 10d multicolored   .55 .55

Blue Sow Thistles A398

Milutin Milankovic, by Paja Jovanovic A399

Flowers: 3.40d, Anemones. 4.90d, Astragalus. 10d, Alpine trifolium.

1979, May 25   Photo.   Perf. 13½
1428 A398 2d multicolored   .20 .20
1429 A398 3.40d multicolored   .20 .20
1430 A398 4.90d multicolored   .30 .20
1431 A398 10d multicolored   .65 .30
Nos. 1428-1431 (4)   1.35 .90

1979, May 28
1432 A399 4.90d multi   .35 .20
Milutin Milankovic (1879-1958), scientist.

Kosta Abrasevic (1879-1898), Poet — A400

1979, May 29   Litho.   Perf. 13½x13
1433 A400 2d org, blk & gray   .20 .20

Eight-Oared Shell A401

1979, Aug. 28   Litho.   Perf. 13
1434 A401 4.90d multicolored   .40 .25
9th World Rowing Championship, Lake Bled.

8th Mediterranean Games, Sept. 15-
29, Split — A402

1979, Sept. 10
1435	A402	2d Games Emblem	.20	.20
1436	A402	4.90d Mascot	.30	.20
1437	A402	10d Map, Flags	.60	.30
		Nos. 1435-1437 (3)	1.10	.70

Seal, 15th
Century
A403

1979, Sept. 14   Perf. 12½
1438	A403	2d multicolored	.20 .20

Zagreb Postal Service, 450th anniversary.

Lake
Palic — A404

Environment Protection: 10d, Lakefront,
Prokletije Mountains.

1979, Sept. 20 Photo. Perf. 14x13½
1439	A404	4.90d multicolored	.35	.20
1440	A404	10d multicolored	.65	.40

Bank and
Fund
Emblems
A405

Engr. & Photo.
1979, Oct. 1   Perf. 13½
1441	A405	4.90d multicolored	.40	.20
1442	A405	10d multicolored	.80	.40

Meeting of the World Bank and International
Monetary Fund, Belgrade, Oct. 2-5.

"Joy of
Europe"
A406

Children's drawings.

1979, Oct. 2   Litho.
1443	A406	4.90d shown	.40	.20
1444	A406	10d Child in yard	.85	.45

Mihailo Pupin
(1854-1935),
Physicist,
Inventor — A407

1979, Oct. 9   Perf. 13x13½
1445	A407	4.90d multicolored	.40 .20

Marko Cepenkov
A408

Radovan Portal,
Trogir Cathedral
A410

Pristina
University,
10th
Anniversary
A409

1979, Nov. 15 Litho. Perf. 13½
1446	A408	2d multicolored	.20 .20

Cepenkov (1829-1920), Macedonian
folklorist.

1979, Nov. 17
1447	A409	2d multicolored	.20 .20

1979, Nov. 28   Photo.
Romanesque Sculptures: 3.40d, Choir stall,
Cathedral of Split. 4.90d, Triforium, Church of
the Resurrection, Decani. 6d, Buvina Portal,
Cathedral of Split. 10d, Western portal,
Church of Our Lady, Studenica.

1448	A410	2d multi	.20	.20
1449	A410	3.40d multi	.25	.20
1450	A410	4.90d multi	.30	.20
1451	A410	6d multi	.35	.20
1452	A410	10d multi	.70	.30
		Nos. 1448-1452 (5)	1.80	1.10

Sarajevo
University,
30th
Anniversary
A411

1979, Dec. 1   Litho.
1453	A411	2d multicolored	.20 .20

Duro Dakovic and Nikola Hecimovic,
Communist Revolutionaries, 50th
Death Annivs. — A412

1979, Dec. 10
1454	A412	2d multicolored	.20 .20

Sidewheeler Deligrad, 1862-
1914 — A413

1979, Dec. 14
1455	A413	4.90d shown	.85	.85
1456	A413	10d Sidewheeler		
		Serbia, 1917-72	1.90	1.90

Danube Conference.

Milton
Manaki and
Camera
A414

Edward Kardelj, by
Zdenko Kalin — A415

1980, Jan. 21 Litho. Perf. 13½
1457	A414	2d deep bister & plum	.20 .20

Manaki (1880-1964), photographer and doc-
umentary film maker.

1980, Jan. 26
1458	A415	2d multicolored	.20 .20

Kardelj (1910-1979), labor movement leader.

No. 1458 Overprinted in Red

1980, Jan. 26
1459	A415	2d multicolored	.25 .20

Ploce renamed Kardeljevo.

13th Winter
Olympic
Games, Feb.
12-24, Lake
Placid,
NY — A416

1980, Feb. 13
1460	A416	4.90d Speed skating	.35	.25
1461	A416	10d Cross-country skiing	.90	.50

University of
Belgrade,
75th
Anniversary
A417

1980, Feb. 27
1462	A417	2d multicolored	.20 .20

22nd
Summer
Olympic
Games, July
19-Aug. 3,
Moscow
A418

1980, Apr. 21
1463	A418	2d Fencing	.20	.20
1464	A418	3.40d Bicycling	.25	.25
1465	A418	4.90d Field hockey	.35	.35
1466	A418	10d Archery	.75	.75
		Nos. 1463-1466 (4)	1.55	1.55

Marshal Tito,
by Antun
Augustincic
A419

Europa: 13d, Tito, by Djordje Prudnikov.

1980, Apr. 28 Photo. Perf. 11½
Granite Paper
1467	A419	4.90d multi	.25	.25
1468	A419	13d multi	1.75	1.75

Marshal Tito,
by Bozidar
Jakac — A420

1980, May 4 Litho. Perf. 13½
1469	A420	2.50d purplish blk	.20	.20
a.		Perf. 10½	.40	.35
1470	A420	4.90d gray black	3.00	3.00

Marshal Tito (1892-1980) memorial. Issued
in sheets of 8 plus label.

Sava Kovacevic (1905-1943),
Revolutionary — A421

1980, May 11 Litho. Perf. 13½
1471	A421	2.50d multicolored	.20 .20

Wood
Baton and
Letter
A422

1980, May 14
1472	A422	2d multicolored	.20 .20

1st Tito Youth Relay Race, 35th anniv.

Flying
Gunard — A423

Emperor Trajan
Decius Coin, 3rd
Cent. — A424

1980, May 24 Photo. Perf. 12
1473	A423	2d shown	.20	.20
1474	A423	3.40d Loggerhead tur-tle	.40	.20
1475	A423	4.90d Sea swallow	.35	.25
1476	A423	10d Dolphin	.65	.50
		Nos. 1473-1476 (4)	1.60	1.15

1980, June 10

3rd Century Roman Coins (Illyrian Emperors): 3.40d, Aurelianus. 4.90d, Probus. 10d, Diocletianus.

1477	A424	2d multicolored	.20	.20
1478	A424	3.40d multicolored	.25	.20
1479	A424	4.90d multicolored	.30	.20
1480	A424	10d multicolored	.60	.40
		Nos. 1477-1480 (4)	1.35	1.00

No. 1247 Surcharged with New Value and Bars

1980, June 17   **Perf. 13½**

1481	A323	2.50d on 1.50d	.20	.20

Types of 1971-77

Views: 5p, Krusevac. 10p, Gradacac. 30p, Krk. 35p, Omis. 40p, Pec. 2.50d, Kragujevac. 3.50d, Vrsac. 5.60d, Travnik. 8d, Dubrovnik.

Perf. 13½, 13½x12½ (#1487)

1980-81

1482	A263	5p deep orange	.20	.20
1483	A263	10p brown	.25	.20
1483A	A263	20p purple ('78)	.20	.20
1484	A263	30p olive gray	.20	.20
1485	A263	35p brown red	.20	.20
1486	A263	40p gray	.20	.20
1487	A323	2.50d rose red	.20	.20
1488	A323	2.50d bl gray ('81)	.20	.20
1489	A323	3.50d red org ('81)	.30	.20
1490	A323	5.60d gray grn ('81)	.40	.20
1491	A323	8d gray ('81)	.50	.20
		Nos. 1482-1491 (11)	2.85	2.20

No. 1483A has all three numerals in denomination the same size. On No. 1065 "20" is taller than first "0."

Perf. 13x12½

1482a	A263	5p
1485a	A263	35p
1487a	A323	2.50d
1488a	A323	2.50d
1489a	A323	3.50d
1490a	A323	5.60d
1491a	A323	8d

400th Anniversary of Lipica Stud Farm → A425

1980, June 25

1493	A425	2.50d black	.25	.20

A426

A427

1980, June 27   **Perf. 13½**

1494	A426	2.50d magenta & red	.25	.20

Tito, Basic Law of Self-management, 30th anniv.

1980, June 28   **Perf. 13**

1495	A427	2.50d light green	.25	.20

University of Novi Sad, 20th anniv.

Mljet National Park — A428

Minerals — A429

1980, Sept. 5   **Photo.**   **Perf. 14**

1496	A428	4.90d shown	.25	.20
1497	A428	13d Galicica Natl. Park	.65	.40

European Nature Protection Year.

1980, Sept. 10   **Litho.**   **Perf. 13½**

1498	A429	2.50d Pyrrhotine	.20	.20
1499	A429	3.40d Dolomite	.20	.20
1500	A429	4.90d Sphalerite	.30	.20
1501	A429	13d Wulfenite	.65	.40
		Nos. 1498-1501 (4)	1.35	1.00

No. 1244 Surcharged with New Value and Bars

1980, Oct. 15   **Litho.**   **Perf. 13**

1502	A323	5d on 75p purple	.35	.20

View of Kotor, UNESCO Emblem A430

1980, Sept. 23   **Perf. 13½**

1503	A430	4.90d multicolored	.30	.20

21st UNESCO General Conf., Belgrade,

Children in Garden A431

Joy of Europe Children's Festival: 13d, 3 faces.

1980, Oct. 2   **Perf. 13½x13**

1504	A431	4.90d multi	.35	.25
1505	A431	13d multi	.90	.50

Dove over Madrid Meeting Hall — A432

Lithographed and Engraved

1980, Nov. 11   **Perf. 13½**

1506	A432	4.90d dk grn & bl grn	.30	.25
1507	A432	13d dk brn & yel brown	1.25	.75

European Security Conference, Madrid.

Federal Flag of Yugoslavia A433

Republic Day: Socialist Republic flags. Nos. 1508-1515 se-tenant. No. 1511 has Latin letters.

1980, Nov. 28   **Litho.**   **Perf. 12½**

1508	A433	2.50d Bosnia & Herzegovina	.20	.20
1509	A433	2.50d Croatia	.20	.20
1510	A433	2.50d shown	.20	.20
1511	A433	2.50d Yugoslavia	.20	.20
1512	A433	2.50d Macedonia	.20	.20
1513	A433	2.50d Montenegro	.20	.20
1514	A433	2.50d Serbia	.20	.20
1515	A433	2.50d Slovenia	.20	.20
		Nos. 1508-1515 (8)	1.60	1.60

Woman with Straw Hat — A434

Paintings: 3.40d, Atelier No. 1, by Gabriel Stupica. 4.90d, To the Glory of the Sutjeska Fighters, by Ismet Mujezinovic. 8d, Serenity, by Marino Tartaglia. 13d, Complaint, by Milos Vuskovic.

1980, Dec. 16   **Perf. 13½**

1516	A434	2.50d multi	.20	.20
1517	A434	3.40d multi	.20	.20
1518	A434	4.90d multi	.25	.20
1519	A434	8d multi, vert.	.35	.30
1520	A434	13d multi, vert.	.60	.45
		Nos. 1516-1520 (5)	1.60	1.35

Ivan Ribar (1881-1968), Politician — A435

1981, Jan. 21   **Litho.**   **Perf. 13½**

1521	A435	2.50d rose red & blk	.20	.20

Cementusa Hand Bomb A436

Partisan Weapons: 5.60d, Rifle. 8d, 52-mm Cannon. 13d, Man-powered tank.

1981, Feb. 16

1522	A436	3.50d brick red & blk	.20	.20
1523	A436	5.60d grn & blk	.25	.20
1524	A436	8d bis brn & blk	.35	.20
1525	A436	13d rose vio & blk	.55	.30
		Nos. 1522-1525 (4)	1.35	.90

Monastery of the Virgin, Eleousa, 900th Anniversary A437

1981, Mar. 3

1526	A437	3.50d multicolored	.20	.20

36th World Table Tennis Championship, Novi Sad, Apr. 14-26 — A438

1981, Apr. 14   **Litho.**   **Perf. 13½**

1527	A438	8d multicolored	.40	.25

Europa Issue

Wedding in Herzegovina, by Nikola Arsenovic A439

Paintings by Nikola Arsenovic (1823-85): 13d, Witnesses at a Wedding.

1981, May 5   **Photo.**   **Perf. 12**
Granite Paper

1528	A439	8d multicolored	.25	.20
1529	A439	13d multicolored	.50	.35

Dimitrije Tucovic and Slavija Square, Belgrade A440

1981, May 13   **Litho.**   **Perf. 13½**

1530	A440	3.50d bl vio & red	.20	.20

Tucovic (1881-1914), Socialist leader.

Marshal Tito, by Milivoje Unkovic — A441

1981, May 25   **Photo.**   **Perf. 11½x12**
Granite Paper

1531	A441	3.50d gold & dk brn	.75	.75

Marshal Tito's 89th birth anniversary.

Sunflower A442

3rd Autonomous Enterprises Cong. A443

1981, May 28   **Photo.**   **Perf. 11½**
Granite Paper

1532	A442	3.05d shown	.20	.20
1533	A442	5.60d Hops	.20	.20
1534	A442	8d Corn	.30	.25
1535	A442	13d Wheat	.55	.35
		Nos. 1532-1535 (4)	1.25	1.00

1981, June 16   **Litho.**   **Perf. 13½**

1536	A443	3.50d multicolored	.20	.20

Djordje Petrov (1864-1921), Macedonian Revolutionary A444

1981, June 22

1537	A444	3.50d bister & black	.20	.20

National Insurrection, 40th Anniv. A445

1981, July 4   **Perf. 12½**

1538	A445	3.50d red org & tan	.20	.20
1539	A445	8d red org & tan	.35	.20

Souvenir Sheet
Imperf

1540	A445	30d Lenin monument	1.50	1.25

800th Anniv. of Varazdin — A446

1981, Aug. 20　　Litho.　　Perf. 13½
1541　A446　3.50d multicolored　　　.20 .20

Parliament Building, Belgrade — A447

1981, Sept. 1
1542　A447　8d red & blue　　　.35 .30

Belgrade Conference of Non-Aligned Countries, 20th anniv.

Serbian Printing Office, 150th Anniv. A448

1981, Sept. 15
1543　A448　3.50d pale rose & dk bl　.20 .20

Fran Levstik (1831-1887), Writer A449

1981, Sept. 28　　　Perf. 12x11½
1544　A449　3.50d dl red & gray　　.20 .20

No. 1251 Surcharged with New Value and Bars

1981, Oct.　　　　　Perf. 13
1545　A323　5d on 4.90d dl bl　　.35 .20
　a.　　Perf. 13x12½　　　　　.75

Joy of Europe Children's Festival A450

1981, Oct. 2
1546　A450　8d Barnyard　　　.30 .30
1547　A450　13d Skiers　　　　.60 .40

125th Anniv. of European Danube Commission — A451

1981, Oct. 28　　Litho.　　Perf. 13½
1548　A451　8d Tugboat Karlovac　.30 .30
1549　A451　13d Train hauling boat, Sip Canal　　　　.60 .40

No. 1250a Surcharged with New Value and Bars

1981, Oct. 9　　Litho.　　Perf. 13x12½
1550　A323　3.50d on 3.40d gray grn　.40 .20
　a.　　on #1250

Savings Bank of Yugoslavia, 60th Anniv. — A452　　Intl. Inventions Conference — A453

1981, Oct. 31　　　Perf. 11½x12
1551　A452　3.50d multicolored　　.20 .20

1981, Nov. 4　　　Perf. 13½
1552　A453　8d red & gold　　　.30 .30

Nature Protection — A454

1981, Nov. 14
1553　A454　8d Plant, Ruguvo Ravine　　　　　.35 .35
1554　A454　13d Lynx, Prokletjie Mountains　　　.50 .50

August Senoa (1838-1881), Writer — A455

1981, Dec. 12　　　Perf. 11½x12
1555　A455　3.50d dl gray vio & gldn brn　　　　　.20 .20

Still Life with a Fish, by Jovan Bijelic (1886-1964) — A456

Paintings of Animals: 5.60d, Raven, by Milo Milunovic (1897-1967). 8d, Bird on Blue Background, by Marko Celebonovic (b. 1902). 10d, Horses, by Peter Lubarda (1907-1974). 13d, Sheep, by Nikola Masic (1852-1902).

1981, Dec. 29　　Photo.　　Perf. 13½
1556　A456　3.50d multi　　　.20 .20
1557　A456　5.60d multi　　　.20 .20
1558　A456　8d multi　　　　.25 .25
1559　A456　10d multi　　　.35 .35
1560　A456　13d multi　　　.45 .45
　　　Nos. 1556-1560 (5)　1.45 1.45

40th Anniv. of Foca Regulations A457

1982, Jan. 14　　Litho.　　Perf. 13½
1561　A457　3.50d Mosa Pijade　.20 .20

60th Anniv. of Communist Newspaper Borba A458

1982, Feb. 19　　　　　　Litho.
1562　A458　3.50d red & blk　　.20 .20

500th Anniv. of City of Cetinje — A459

1982, Mar. 10
1563　A459　3.50d dull red brn　　.20 .20

Capt. Ivo Visin (1806-1868), Boka Kotorska's Map — A460

1982, May 5　　Photo.　　Perf. 11½
1564　A460　8d shown　　　.25 .25
1565　A460　15d Ship Splendido　.40 .40

Europa, 1st Yugoslavian circumnavigation, 1852-1859.

Male House Sparrow A461

1982, May 24　　Litho.　　Perf. 13½
1566　A461　3.50d shown　　　.20 .20
1567　A461　5.60d Female house sparrow　　　.25 .25
1568　A461　8d Male field sparrow　　　　.40 .40
1569　A461　15d Female field sparrow　　　.70 .70
　　　Nos. 1566-1569 (4)　1.55 1.55

See Nos. 1687-1690.

90th Birth Anniv. of Marshal Tito — A462

1982, May 25　Photo.　Perf. 11½x12
Granite Paper
1570　A462　3.50d multicolored　.20 .20

1982 World Cup — A463

Designs: Soccer ball in various positions.

1982, June 12　　　　Perf. 11½
Granite Paper
1571　　　Sheet of 4　　　1.25 1.25
　a.　A463　3.50d multicolored　.20 .20
　b.　A463　5.60d multicolored　.20 .20
　c.　A463　8d multicolored　　.30 .30
　d.　A463　15d multicolored　.55 .55

12th Congress of Yugoslavian Communists' League, Belgrade, June 26-29 A464

1982 June 26　　Litho.　　Perf. 13½
1572　A464　3.50d orange & red　.20 .20
1573　A464　8d gray & red　　.25 .25

Souvenir Sheet
Perf. 12½
1574　　　Sheet of 2　　　1.25 1.25
　a.　A464　10d like 3.50d　　.40 .40
　b.　A464　20d like 8d　　　.80 .80

Dura Jaksic (1832-1878), Writer, Painter A465

1982, July 27　　Litho.　　Perf. 14
1575　A465　3.50d Self-portrait　.20 .20

1982 World Championships Held in Yugoslavia — A466

1982, July 30　　　Perf. 13½
1576　A466　8d Gymnastics　　.25 .25
1577　A466　8d Kayak　　　.25 .25
1578　A466　8d Weightlifting　.25 .25
　　　Nos. 1576-1578 (3)　.75 .75

Ivan Zajc (1832-1914), Composer and Conductor A467

1982, Aug. 3
1579　A467　4d brown　　　.20 .20

Breguet XIX and Potez XXV A468

1982, Sept. 1　　Litho.　　Perf. 13½
1580　A468　4d shown　　　.20 .20
1581　A468　6.10d Super Galeb G-4　　　　　.20 .20
1582　A468　8.80d Armed boat　.35 .35
1583　A468　15d Rocket gun boat　　　　.50 .50
　　　Nos. 1580-1583 (4)　1.25 1.25

40th anniv. of Air Force/Anti-aircraft Defense and Navy.

Spruce Branch, Tara Natl. Park A469

1982, Sept. 3
1584 A469 8.80d shown .35 .35
1585 A469 15d Mediterranean
monk seal,
Kornati .55 .55

14th Joy of Europe Children's Festival — A470

1982, Oct. 2
1586 A470 8.80d Traffic .30 .30
1587 A470 15d In the Bath .45 .45

Small Onofrio's Fountain, 15th Cent. A471

1982, Oct. 23
1588 A471 8.80d multi .25 .25
16th Universal Federation of Travel Agents' Assoc. Cong., Dubrovnik, Oct. 24-30.

600th Anniv. of Hercegnovi A472

1982, Oct. 28
1589 A472 4d multicolored .20 .20

14th Winter Olympic Games, Sarajevo, Feb. 8-19, 1984 — A473

1982, Nov. 20   *Perf. 12½*
1590 A473 4d Bridge, Miljacka
River .20 .20
1591 A473 6.10d Minaret,
Mosque .20 .20
1592 A473 8.80d Evangelical
Church .30 .30
1593 A473 15d Street .45 .45
Nos. 1590-1593 (4) 1.15 1.15

Nos. 1488a and 1489a Surcharged In Red, Blue, Black or Red Violet with Two Bars or Shield

1982-83   Litho.   *Perf. 13x12½*
1594 A323 30p on 2.50d (R) .20 .20
1595 A323 50p on 2.50d (Bl) .20 .20
1596 A323 60p on 2.50d ('83) .20 .20
1597 A323 1d on 3.50d .20 .20
1597A A323 2d on 2.50d (RV) .20 .20
Nos. 1594-1597A (5) 1.00 1.00

Perf. 13
1594a A323 30p on #1488
1595a A323 50p on #1488
1596a A323 60p on #1488
1597b A323 1d on #1489

Types of 1971-77

Designs: 3d, Skofja Loka. 4d, Pocitelj. 5d, Osijek. 6.10d, like 2.10d. 8.80d, Hercegnovi. 10d, Sarajevo. 16.50d, Ohrid.

1982-83   Litho.   *Perf. 13x12½*
1598 A323 3d gray bl .20 .20
1599 A263 4d red org .20 .20
1600 A263 5d grnsh bl ('83) .20 .20
1601 A323 6.10d olive grn .30 .30
1602 A263 8.80d gray .50 .20

Perf. 13½
1603 A263 10d red lil ('83) .50 .20
1603A A323 16.50d dl bl ('83) .80 .25
Nos. 1598-1603A (7) 2.70 1.45

Type styles of Nos. 1600, 1603-1603A differ somewhat from illustrations.

Perf. 13
1598a A323 3d
1599a A323 4d
1600a A323 5d
1601a A323 6.10d
1602a A323 8.80d
1603b A323 10d
1603c A323 16.50d

40th Anniv. of Anti-Fascist Council A474

1982, Nov. 26   *Perf. 13½*
1604 A474 4d Bihac, 1942 .20 .20

The Manuscript, by Janez Bernik (b. 1933) — A475

4d, Prophet on Golden Background, by Joze Ciuha (b. 1924). 6.10d, Journey to the West, by Andrej Jemec (b. 1934). 8.80d, Black Comb with Red Band, by Riko Debenjak (b. 1908). 15d, The Vitrine, by Adriana Maraz (b. 1931).

1982, Nov. 27
1605 A475 4d multi, vert. .20 .20
1606 A475 6.10d multi, vert. .20 .20
1607 A475 8.80d multi, vert. .25 .20
1608 A475 10d multi .25 .20
1609 A475 15d multi .40 .30
Nos. 1605-1609 (5) 1.30 1.10

Uros Predic (1857-1953), Painter — A476

Union of Pioneers, 40th Anniv. — A477

1982, Dec. 7
1610 A476 4d multicolored .20 .20

1982, Dec. 27   *Perf. 12*
1611 A477 4d multicolored .20 .20

Articles from Museum of Applied Art, Belgrade A478

Designs: 4d, Lead pitcher, Gnjilane, 16th cent. 6.10d, Silver-plated jug, Macedonia, 18th cent. 8.80d, Goblet, 16th cent., Dalmatia. 15d, Mortar, 15th cent., Kotor.

1983, Feb. 19
1612 A478 4d multicolored .20 .20
1613 A478 6.10d multicolored .20 .20
1614 A478 8.80d multicolored .20 .20
1615 A478 15d multicolored .40 .30
Nos. 1612-1615 (4) 1.00 .90

Mount Jalovec — A479

Serbian Telephone Service Centenary — A480

1983, Feb. 26
1616 A479 4d blue & lt bl .20 .20
Slovenian Mountaineering Soc., 90th anniv.

1983, Mar. 15
1617 A480 3d Ericsson phone .20 .20

25th Anniv. of Intl. Org. for Maritime Navigation (OMI) — A481

1983, Mar. 17   *Perf. 13½x14*
1618 A481 8.80d multi .30 .30

Edible Mushrooms A482

1983, Mar. 21   *Perf. 14*
1619 A482 4d Agaricus
campestris .20 .20
1620 A482 6.10d Morchella vulgaris .20 .20
1621 A482 8.80d Boletus edulis .25 .25
1622 A482 15d Cantharellus
cibarius .35 .35
Nos. 1619-1622 (4) 1.00 1.00

Rijeka Railway, 110th Anniv. — A483

Boro and Ramiz Monument, Landovica A484

1983, Apr. 5
1623 A483 4d Steam engine series
401 .20 .20
1624 A483 23.70d on 8.80d Thyris-
tor locomotive
442 .35 .35
No. 1624 not issued without surcharge.

1983, Apr. 10
1625 A484 4d multi .20 .20
Boro Vukmirovic and Ramiz Sadiku, revolutionary martyrs, 40th death anniv.

Ivo Andric (1892-1975), Poet, 1961 Nobel Prize Winner A485

1983, May 5   Photo.   *Perf. 11½*   Granite Paper
1626 A485 8.80d Medal, Travnik
Chronicle text .20 .20
1627 A485 20d Portrait, Bridge,
Drina River .40 .35
Europa.

50th Intl. Agricultural Fair, Novi Sad — A486

1983, May 13   Litho.   *Perf. 14*
1628 A486 4d Combine harvester .20 .20

40th Anniv. of Battle of Sutjeska A487

1983, May 14   *Perf. 12½*
1629 A487 3d Assault, by Pivo
Karamatijevic .20 .20

A488

A489

1983, May 25   *Perf. 13½*
1630 A488 4d Tito, Parliament .20 .20
a.   Perf. 12½
30th anniv. of election of Pres. Tito.

1983, May 27
1631 A489 4d First mail and
passenger car .20 .20
1632 A489 16.50d Mountain road,
Kotor .40 .20
80th anniv. of automobile service in Montenegro.

A490

A491

1983, June 5   *Perf. 14*
1633 A490 23.70d multi .60 .30
UN Conference on Trade and Development, 6th session, Belgrade, June 6-30.

1983, June 7   *Perf. 12½*
1634 A491 4d Engraving by
Valvasor .20 .20
Town of Pazin millenium.

Triumphal Arch, Titograd A492

1983, June 9 — Perf. 12½
1635 A492 100d Memorial to F. Filipovic, Valjevo, vert. 2.25 1.10
  a. Perf. 13x13½
1636 A492 200d shown 4.50 2.25
  a. Perf. 13½x13

Skopje Earthquake, 20th Anniv. — A493

1983, July 26 — Litho. — Perf. 12½
1637 A493 23.70d deep magenta .55 .25
  a. Perf. 13½

For surcharge, see No. 1715.

Sculpture by Ivan Mestrovic A494

Joy of Europe A496

European Nature Protection — A495

1983, Aug. 15
1638 A494 6d multicolored .20 .20

1983, Sept. 10 — Litho. — Perf. 13
16.50d, Gentian, Kopaonik National Park. 23.70d, Chamois, Perucica Gorge.
1639 A495 16.50d multi .30 .20
1640 A495 23.70d multi .55 .25

See Nos. 1685-1686.

1983, Oct. 3 — Litho. — Perf. 13½
Children's Paintings: 16.50d, Bride and Bridegroom by Verna Paunkonik. 23.70d, Andres and his Mother by Marta Lopez-Ibor.
1641 A496 16.50d multi .35 .20
1642 A496 23.70d multi .45 .25

A497   A498

1983, Oct. 17 — Litho. — Perf. 12½
1643 A497 5d multicolored .20 .20

Kragujevac High School sesquicentenary.

1983, Oct. 17 — Litho. — Perf. 13½
1644 A498 5d multicolored .20 .20

Timok Uprising centenary.

14th Winter Olympic Games, Sarajevo, Feb. 8-19, 1984 A499

1983, Nov. 25 — Engr. — Perf. 13½
1645 A499 4d Ski jump .20 .20
1646 A499 4d Slalom .20 .20
1647 A499 16.50d Bobsledding .40 .20

1648 A499 16.50d Downhill skiing .40 .20
1649 A499 23.70d Speed skating .60 .30
1650 A499 23.70d Hockey .60 .30
  Nos. 1645-1650 (6) 2.40 1.40

Souvenir Sheet
Imperf
1651 A499 50d Emblem 1.40 .60

Jovan Jovanovic Zmaj (1833-1904), Poet, Neven Masthead A500

1983, Nov. 24 — Litho. — Perf. 12½
1652 A500 5d multicolored .20 .20

Peasant Wedding, by Pieter Brueghel A501

Paintings: No. 1654, Susanna with the Old Men, No. 1655, Allegory of Wisdom and Strength, by Paolo Veronese (1528-1588). No. 1656, Virgin Mary from Salamanca, by Robert Campin (1375-1444). No. 1657, St. Ann with Madonna and Jesus, by Albrecht Dürer (1471-1528).

1983, Nov. 26 — Perf. 14
1653 A501 4d multi .20 .20
1654 A501 16.50d multi .40 .20
1655 A501 16.50d multi .40 .20
1656 A501 23.70d multi .50 .25
1657 A501 23.70d multi .50 .25
  Nos. 1653-1657 (5) 2.00 1.10

View of Jajce — A502

Koco Racin (1908-1943), Writer — A504

World Communications Year — A503

1983, Nov. 28 — Perf. 13x12½
1658 A502 5d multicolored .20 .20
Souvenir Sheet
Imperf
1659 A502 30d Tito 1.25 .60

40th anniv. of Second Session of the Antifascist Council of the Natl. Liberation of Yugoslavia, Jajce, Nov. 29-30.

1983, Dec. 10 — Perf. 13½
1660 A503 23.70d multi .50 .25

1983, Dec. 22
1661 A504 5d multicolored .20 .20

Politika Front Page, Oct. 28, 1944 — A505

1984, Jan. 25 — Litho. — Perf. 12½
1662 A505 5d red & black .20 .20

80th anniv. of Politika newspaper and 40th anniv. in Yugoslavia.

Veljko Petrovic (1884-1967), Poet — A506

1984, Feb. 4 — Litho. — Perf. 13½
1663 A506 5d multicolored .20 .20

1984 Winter Olympics A507

1984, Feb. 8
1664 A507 4d Biathlon .20 .20
1665 A507 4d Giant slalom .20 .20
1666 A507 5d Bobsledding .20 .20
1667 A507 5d Slalom .20 .20
1668 A507 16.50d Speed skating .40 .20
1669 A507 16.50d Hockey .40 .20
1670 A507 23.70d Ski jumping .60 .30
1671 A507 23.70d Downhill skiing .60 .30
  Nos. 1664-1671 (8) 2.80 1.80

Souvenir Sheets
Imperf
1672 A507 50d Flame, rings 1.40 .70
1673 A507 100d Flame, map 2.75 1.40

Natl. Heroines A508

Designs: a, Marija Bursac (1902-43). b, Jelena Cetkovic (1916-43). c, Nada Dimic (1923-42). d, Elpida Karamandi (1920-42). e, Toncka Cec Olga (1896-1943). f, Spasenija Babovic Cana (1907-77). g, Jovanka Radivojevic Kica (1922-43). h, Sonja Marinkovic (1916-41).

1984, Mar. 8 — Litho. — Perf. 14
1674 Sheet of 8 + label 1.00 .75
  a.-h. A508 5d any single .20 .20

Slovenia Monetary Institute, 40th Anniv. A509

1984, Mar. 12 — Perf. 12½
1675 A509 5d Bond, note .20 .20

Railroad Service in Serbia (Belgrade-Nis) Centenary — A510

1984, Apr. 9 — Perf. 13
1676 A510 5d Train, Central Belgrade Station .20 .20

Jure Franko, Giant Slalom Silver Medalist, 1984 — A511

1984, Apr. 28
1677 A511 23.70d multi .60 .35

Yugoslavia's first Winter Olympic medalist.

Europa (1959-84) A512

1984, Apr. 30 — Perf. 13½
1678 A512 23.70d multi .30 .25
1679 A512 50d multi .80 .50

1984 Summer Olympics, Los Angeles A513

1984, May 14
1680 A513 5d Basketball .20 .20
1681 A513 16.50d Diving .35 .20
1682 A513 23.70d Equestrian .45 .20
1683 A513 50d Running 1.10 .50
  Nos. 1680-1683 (4) 2.10 1.10

Marshal Tito — A514

1984, May 25 — Perf. 13
1684 A514 5d brown red .20 .20

Nature Type of 1983
Designs: 26d, Centaurea gloriosa (flower), Biokovo Mountain Park. 40d, Anophthalmus (insect), Pekel Cave, Savinja Valley.

1984, June 11 — Litho. — Perf. 13½
1685 A495 26d multicolored .30 .20
1686 A495 40d multicolored .50 .20

Bird Type of 1982
1984, June 28
1687 A461 4d Great black-backed gull .20 .20
1688 A461 5d Black-headed gull .20 .20
1689 A461 16.50d Herring gull .25 .20
1690 A461 40d Common tern .35 .20
  Nos. 1687-1690 (4) 1.00 .80

19th Cent. Cradles A515

1984, Sept. 1 — Litho. — Perf. 12½
1691 A515 4d Bosnia & Herzegovina .20 .20
1692 A515 5d Montenegro .20 .20
1693 A515 26d Macedonia .25 .20
1694 A515 40d Serbia .35 .20
  Nos. 1691-1694 (4) 1.00 .80

Olive Tree, Mirovica A516

1984, Sept. 1
1695 A516 5d multi .20 .20

Joy of Europe — A517

Map, Concentric Waves — A519

City of Virovitica, 750th Anniv. A518

Children's Drawings.

1984, Oct. 2   Litho.   Perf. 14
1696 A517 26d Traditional costumes .30 .20
1697 A517 40d Girl with doll carriage .50 .20

1984, Oct. 4   Perf. 13½
1698 A518 5d Engraving, 17th
cent. .20 .20

1984, Oct. 10
1699 A519 6d Prus bl & brt grn .20 .20
Radio and telegraph service in Montenegro, 80th anniv.

Veterans Conference A520

1984, Oct. 18
1700 A520 26d multicolored .30 .20
1701 A520 40d multicolored .50 .20
Conf. of Veterans on Security, Disarmament & Cooperation in Europe, Belgrade, 10/18-20.

Liberation of Belgrade, 40th Anniv. — A521

Miloje Milojevic (1884-1946), Composer A522

1984, Oct. 20
1702 A521 6d "40," arms .20 .20

1984, Oct. 27
1703 A522 6d Portrait, score .20 .20

Medals Events, 1984 Summer Olympics A522a

Designs: a, Wrestling. b, Running. c, Field hockey. d, Shot put. e, Soccer. f, Basketball. g, Netball. h, Rowing.

1984, Nov. 14   Litho.   Perf. 13½
1704 Sheet of 8 2.75 2.50
a.-h. A522a 26d any single .30 .25

The Tahitians, by Gauguin — A523

Paintings by Foreign Artists in Yugoslav Museums: 6d, Portrait of Madame Tatichek, by Ferdinand Waldmuller (1793-1865). No. 1706, The Bathers, by Renoir (1841-1919). No. 1707, At the Window, by Henri Matisse (1869-1954). 40d, Ballerinas, by Edgar Degas (1834-1917).

Perf. 13½x14, 14x13½
1984, Nov. 15
1705 A523 6d multi, vert. .20 .20
1706 A523 26d multi, vert. .35 .30
1707 A523 26d multi, vert. .35 .20
1708 A523 38d multi .50 .30
1709 A523 40d multi .60 .30
Nos. 1705-1709 (5) 2.00 1.30

Nova Macedonia Newspaper, 40th Anniv. A523a

1984, Nov. 29   Perf. 13½
1710 A523a 6d 1st & recent editions .20 .20

Nos. 1602, 1599 and 1637 Surcharged with Three Bars in Red Brown or Black, Types of 1975 and

Exhibition Center, Zagreb A524

Bird, Jet, Landscape A525

Designs: 6d, Kikinda. 26d, Korcula. 38d, Maribor. 70d, Trumpeter monument, riverside buildings in Zagreb. 1000d, bird, tail of jet on airfield.

Perf. 13½x12½, 13 (#1713, 1717),
12½ (#1715)
1984-86   **Litho.**
1711 A263 2d on 8.80d .20 .20
 a. on #1602a
1712 A263 6d on 4d (RBr) .20 .20
 a. on #1599a
1713 A323 6d lt red brn .20 .20
 a. Perf. 13x12½
1715 A493 20d on 23.70d .20 .20
1717 A263 26d dp ultra .25 .20
 a. Perf. 13x12½
1718 A323 38d dp lil rose .30 .20
 a. Perf. 13
1719 A323 70d brt ultra
('85) .30 .25
 b. Perf. 13
Perf. 14
1719A A524 100d brt org yel &
vio .50 .30
Perf. 12½
1720 A525 500d redsh brn &
multi ('85) 2.50 1.75
1721 A525 1000d org brn &
multi ('85) 5.00 3.50
 a. Perf. 13½
Nos. 1711-1721 (10) 9.65 7.00
Type styles for Nos. 1717-1718 differ some-what from illustration.

Museum Exhibits - Fossils A526

1985, Feb. 4   Litho.   Perf. 12½
1722 A526 5d Aturia aturi .20 .20
1723 A526 6d Pachyophis
woodwardi .20 .20
1724 A526 33d Chaetodon
hoeferi .20 .20
1725 A526 60d Homo sapiens
neanderthalen-
sis .40 .20
Nos. 1722-1725 (4) 1.00 .80

40th Anniv., Monument Protection A527

1985, Feb. 20   Litho.   Perf. 12½
1726 A527 6d Hopovo church .20 .20

Ski Jumping at Planica, 50th Anniv. A528

European Nature Conservation A529

1985, Mar. 15   Litho.   Perf. 13½
1727 A528 6d Three herons in
flight .20 .20

1985, Mar. 30   Perf. 14
1728 A529 42d Pandion haliaetus .35 .20
1729 A529 60d Upupa epops .50 .20
Audubon birth bicentenary, European Infor-mation Center for Nature Protection.

A530

A531

Fresco of St. Methodius, St. Naum Monas-tery, Ohrid.

1985, Apr. 6   Litho.   Perf. 11½x12
1730 A530 10d multicolored .20 .20
St. Methodius (d. 885), archbishop of Pan-nonia and Moravia.

1985, Apr. 16   Litho.   Perf. 12½
1731 A531 6d Clasped hands .20 .20
Osimo Agreements, 10th anniv. Yugoslavia-Italy political and economic cooperation.

Josip Slavenski (1896-1955), Composer A532

Europa: 60d, Portrait, block flute, darabukka. 80d, Balkanophonia score, signature.

1985, Apr. 29   Perf. 14
1732 A532 60d multi .70 .70
1733 A532 80d multi .70 .70

Joachim Vujic, by Dimitrije Avramovic (1815-1855) A533

1985, May 8   Perf. 12x11½
1734 A533 10d multi .20 .20
Joachim Vujic Theater, Kragujevac, 150th anniv.

Liberation from German Occupation Forces, 40th Anniv. — A534

1985, May 9   Perf. 13½
1735 A534 10d shown .20 .20
1736 A534 10d Order of Natl. Liberation .20 .20

Franjo Kluz (1912-1944), Rudi Cajevac (1911-1942), Breguet-19 Fighter — A535

1985, May 21   Perf. 13x12½
1737 A535 10d multi .20 .20
Air Force Day.

Pres. Tito (1892-1980)
A536

Cres-Losinj Municipal Tourism Bureau, Cent. — A537

1985, May 25   *Perf. 13½*
1738 A536 10d Portrait   .20 .20

1985, June 12
1739 A537 10d Map, town arms, villa   .20 .20

UN 40th Anniv. — A538   Rowing — A539

1985, June 26   Litho.   *Perf. 12½*
1740 A538 70d Emblem, rainbow   .55 .25

1985, June 29   Litho.   *Perf. 13½*
1741 A539 70d multicolored   .55 .25

Souvenir Sheet
1742 A539 100d Course map, arms .75 .35

Intl. European-Danube Rowing Regatta, 30th anniv.

Nautical Tourism — A540

1985, July 1   Litho.
1743 A540 8d Sailboat   .20 .20
1744 A540 10d Windsurfing   .20 .20
1745 A540 50d Sailboat, diff.   .35 .20
1746 A540 70d Sailboat, diff.   .45 .25
   Nos. 1743-1746 (4)   1.20 .85

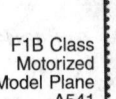

F1B Class Motorized Model Plane A541

1985, Aug. 10   Litho.   *Perf. 12½x13*
1747 A541 70d multicolored   .45 .35

Free Flight World Championships, Livno, Aug. 12-18.

Algae — A542

1985, Sept. 20   *Perf. 14*
1748 A542 8d Corallina official-is   .20 .20
1749 A542 10d Desmarestia viridis   .20 .20
1750 A542 50d Fucus vesiculosus   .30 .20
1751 A542 70d Padina pavonia   .40 .30
   Nos. 1748-1751 (4)   1.10 .90

Intl. Federation of Stomatologists, 73rd Congress, Belgrade, Sept. 21-28 — A543

1985, Sept. 21   *Perf. 12x11½*
1752 A543 70d multicolored   .45 .30

Children's Drawings A544

Designs: 50d, Children in a Horse-drawn Cart, by Branka Lukic, age 14, Yugoslavia. 70d, Children in Field, by Suzanne Straathof, age 9, Netherlands.

1985, Oct. 2   *Perf. 14*
1753 A544 50d multicolored   .30 .20
1754 A544 70d multicolored   .40 .30

Croatian Natl. Theater, Zagreb, 125th Anniv. A545

1985, Nov. 23   *Perf. 12½*
1755 A545 10d Facade detail   .20 .20

Miladin Popovic   Natl. Coat of Arms
A546   A547

1985, Nov. 26   *Perf. 11½x12*
1756 A546 10d Portrait   .20 .20

Popovic (1910-1945), revolutionary.

1985, Nov. 28   *Perf. 13½*
1757 A547 10d multicolored   .20 .20

Souvenir Sheet
Imperf
1758 A547 100d multicolored   .65 .45

Socialist Federal Republic of Yugoslavia, 40th anniv. No. 1758 contains one stamp 18x27mm.

Royal Procession, by Iromie Wijewardena, Sri Lanka — A548

Paintings from the Art Gallery of Non-aligned Countries, Titograd: 10d, Return from Hunting, by Mama Cangare, Mali. No. 1761, Drum of Coca, by Agnes Ovando Sanz De Franck, Bolivia. No. 1762, The Cock, by Mariano Rodriguez, Cuba. 70d, Three Women, by Quamrul Hassan, Bangladesh.

1985, Dec. 2   *Perf. 14*
1759 A548 8d multicolored   .20 .20
1760 A548 10d multicolored   .20 .20
1761 A548 50d multicolored   .30 .20
1762 A548 50d multicolored   .30 .20
1763 A548 70d multicolored   .40 .30
   Nos. 1759-1763 (5)   1.40 1.10

Nos. 1243, 1482, 1485a, 1490, 1491, 1713a, 1717a, 1603A and 1718 Surcharged in Light Red Brown, Brown or Dark Brown

1985-86   Litho.   *Perf. 13½, 13½x12½*
1764 A323 1d on 25p (B)   .20 .20
1765 A263 2d on 5p (DB)   .20 .20
   a.   on #1482a
1766 A263 3d on 35p (DB)   .20 .20
   a.   on #1485a
1767 A323 4d on 5.60d (B)   .20 .20
   b.   on #1490
1767A A323 5d on 8d (B)   .20 .20
   c.   on #1491a
1768 A323 8d on 6d   .20 .20
   a.   on #1713
1769 A263 20d on 26d   .20 .20
   a.   on #1717
1770 A323 50d on 16.50d (B)   .40 .30
   a.   on #1603c
1771 A323 70d on 38d   .55 .40
   Nos. 1764-1771 (9)   2.35 2.10

Issued: #1767A, 3/17/86; others, 12/85.

Natl. Automobile Assoc., 40th Anniv. A549

1986, Feb. 25   *Perf. 12½*
1772 A549 10d Car   .20 .20
1773 A549 70d Helicopter   .40 .30

Tara River, Montenegro A550

1986, Mar. 3   *Perf. 14*
1774 A550 100d Canyon   .55 .40
1775 A550 150d Bridge   .95 .60

European nature protection. Sheets of 9.

Studenica Monastery, 800th Anniv. — A551

1986, Mar. 15   *Perf. 13½*
1776 A551 10d Chapel of Our Lady   .20 .20

A552

Various soccer plays.

1986, Apr. 5   Litho.   *Perf. 14*
1777 A552 70d multi   .35 .25
1778 A552 150d multi   .75 .55

1986 World Cup Soccer Championships, Mexico.

Arrival of St. Clement in Ohrid, 1100th Anniv. A553

1986, Apr. 12   *Perf. 12½*
1779 A553 10d Township model   .20 .20

Europa Issue

Brain, Mushroom Cloud — A554

1986, Apr. 28   *Perf. 14*
1780 A554 100d shown   .50 .35
1781 A554 200d Injured deer   .90 .70

European Men's Senior Judo Championships, Belgrade, May 8-11 — A555

1986, May 7   *Perf. 12½*
1782 A555 70d multi   .35 .25

Natl. Costumes   Yachts, Moscenika A556   Draga Bay A557

a, Slovenia. b, Vojvodina. c, Croatia. d, Macedonia. e, Serbia. f, Montenegro. g, Kosovo. h, Bosnia & Herzegovina.

1986, May 22   Litho.   *Perf. 12x13*
Booklet Stamps
1783   Bklt. pane of 8   2.25
   a.-h.   A556 50d any single   .25 .20

1986, May 23   *Perf. 14*
1784 A557 50d multi   .25 .20
1785 A557 80d multi, diff.   .40 .20

Souvenir Sheet
Imperf
1786 A557 100d multi   .55 .50

European Sailing Championships, Croatia, May 29-June 7, Flying Dutchman Class. No. 1786 contains one stamp 22x28mm.

Marshal Tito — A557a

1986, May 24   *Perf. 13x12½*
1787 A557a 10d multicolored   .20 .20

Moths and Butterflies A558

1986, May 26   *Perf. 14*
1788 A558 10d Eudia pavonia   .20 .20
1789 A558 20d Inachis io   .20 .20
1790 A558 50d Parnassius apollo   .20 .20
1791 A558 100d Apatura iris   .50 .20
   Nos. 1788-1791 (4)   1.10 .80

Ancient Manuscripts A558a

Designs: 10d, Evangelical, 18th cent. 20d, Leontijevo Evangelical, 16th cent. 50d, Astrological, Mesopotamia, 15th cent. 100d, Hebrew Haggadah, Spain, 14th cent.

1986, June 12   Litho.   *Perf. 14*
1792 A558a 10d multicolored   .20 .20
1793 A558a 20d multicolored   .20 .20
1794 A558a 50d multicolored   .30 .20
1795 A558a 100d multicolored   .60 .30
   Nos. 1792-1795 (4)   1.30 .90

A559

A560

Designs: 20d, Postman on motorcycle. 30d, Postman, resident. 40d, Forklift, mail pallets. 50d, Mail train. 60d, Man posting letters in mailbox. 93d, Open envelope and greetings telegram form. 100d, Postman, mail van. No. 1803, Computer operator facing right. No. 1804, 140d, Computer operator facing left. 120d, Woman sending love letter. 200d, Freighter in high seas. 500d, Postal employee sorting mail. 1000d, Woman at telephone station. 2000d, Aircraft, hemispheres on world map. 30d, 60d, 93d, 106d, 120d, 140d, 500d, 1000d vert.

Perf. 13½, 12½x13½ (20d, 40d, 50d), 14 (100d)

1986-88   Litho.
1796 A559 20d brt pink   .20 .20
   a. Perf. 13
1797 A559 30d lt brn vio   .20 .20
   a. Perf. 13x12½
1798 A559 40d brt red   .25 .20
   a. Perf. 13
1799 A559 50d violet   .30 .20
   a. Perf. 13
1800 A559 60d lt sage grn   .25 .20
1801 A559 93d ultra   .25 .20
1802 A559 100d dl magenta   .65 .30
1803 A559 106d rose red   .30 .20
1804 A559 106d brn org   .20 .20
1805 A559 120d dull blue grn   .20 .20

1806 A559 140d dull rose   .20 .20
1807 A559 200d greenish bl   1.25 .60
   a. Perf. 12½
   b. Perf. 12½x13½
1808 A559 500d deep blue & beige   .75 .35
1809 A559 500d chalky blue & yel   .60 .25
1810 A559 1000d vio & blue grn   1.10 .60
   b. Perf. 12½
1810A A560 2000d brt blue, red & brt vio   2.25 1.10
    & brt vio   2.25 1.10
   Nos. 1796-1810A (16)   8.95 5.20

   Size of No. 1802: 19½x18mm.

Issued: 20d, 3/17; 50d, 200d, 6/4; 40d, 7/17; 100d, 6/12; 30d, 7/26; 60d, 6/5/87; #1803, 12/10/87; 93d, 12/16/87; #1804, 1/22/88; #1808, 4/29/88; 1000d, 7/21/88; 20d, 140d, 2000d, #1809, 9/5/88.

See Nos. 1935-1945, 2004-2007, 2013-2015, 2021. For surcharges see Nos. 1877, 1912-1913, 1947-1948, 1972, 1974-1975, 2017, 2019, 2048-2051, 2053.

13th Communist Federations Congress (SKJ) A561

1986, June 25   *Perf. 12½*
1811 A561 10d shown   .20 .20
1812 A561 20d Star   .20 .20

Souvenir Sheet
Imperf
1813 A561 100d Tito   .50 .25

Trubar, Abecedarian Manuscript Title Page A562

1986, June 28   Litho.   *Perf. 12½x13*
1814 A562 20d multi   .20 .20

Primoz Trubar (1508-1568), Slovenian philologist and religious reformer.

Serbian Natl. Theater, Novi Sad, 125th Anniv. — A563

1986, July 28   *Perf. 14*
1815 A563 40d Thalia   .20 .20

Rugovo Dance, Kosovo Province — A564

1986, Sept. 10
1816 A564 40d multi   .20 .20

1987 Universiade Games, Zagreb, July 8-19 — A565

1986, Sept. 22   *Perf. 13½*
1817 A565 30d Volleyball   .20 .20
1818 A565 40d Canoeing   .20 .20
1819 A565 100d Gymnastics   .45 .20
1820 A565 150d Fencing   .65 .30
   Nos. 1817-1820 (4)   1.50 .90

18th Joy of Europe Youth Conference A566

Children's drawings: 100d, Dove, by Tanja Faletic, 14. 150d, Buildings, by Johanna Kraus, 12, DDR.

1986, Oct. 2   *Perf. 14*
1821 A566 100d multicolored   .45 .20
1822 A566 150d multicolored   .70 .30

Rotary Switching Apparatus, Village of Bled — A567

1986, Oct. 4   *Perf. 13½*
1823 A567 40d multicolored   .20 .20

Telephone exchanges connected with automatic switching equipment, 50th anniv.

INTERPOL 55th General Assembly, Belgrade, Oct. 6-13 — A568

Intl. Brigades, 50th Anniv. — A569

1986, Oct. 6   *Perf. 14*
1824 A568 150d multicolored   .65 .30

1986, Oct. 21   *Perf. 13½*
1825 A569 40d multicolored   .20 .20

Intl. Peace Year — A570

1986, Nov. 20
1826 A570 150d multicolored   .65 .30

Serbian Academy of the Arts and Sciences, Cent. A571

1986, Nov. 1   Photo.   *Perf. 13½*
1827 A571 40d multicolored   .20 .20

Paintings by Foreign Artists in the Museum of Contemporary Art, Skopje — A572

No. 1828, Still Life, by Frantisek Muzika, Czechoslovakia. #1829, Disturbance, by Rafael Canogar, England. #1830, Iol, by Victor Vasarely, France. #1831, Portrait, by Bernard Buffet, France. #1832, Woman's Head, by Pablo Picasso, Spain.

1986, Dec. 10   Litho.   *Perf. 14*
1828 A572 30d multi   .20 .20
1829 A572 40d multi   .20 .20
1830 A572 100d multi, vert.   .55 .25
1831 A572 100d multi, vert.   .55 .25
1832 A572 150d multi, vert.   .75 .40
   Nos. 1828-1832 (5)   2.25 1.30

Wildlife Conservation A573

30d, Lutra lutra. 40d, Ovis musimon. 100d, Cervus elaphus. 150d, Ursus arctos.

1987, Jan. 22   Litho.   *Perf. 13½x14*
1833   Strip of 4 + label   1.10 .65
   a. A573 30d multi   .20 .20
   b. A573 40d multi   .20 .20
   c. A573 100d multi   .30 .20
   d. A573 150d multi   .50 .30

Label pictures nature reserve.

Rudjer Boscovich (1711-1787), Scientist, and Solar Eclipse over Brera Observatory, Italy — A574

1987, Feb. 13   *Perf. 14*
1834 A574 150d multicolored   .65 .30

European Nature Protection — A575

1987 World Alpine Skiing Championships, Crans Montana — A576

1987, Mar. 9
1835 A575 150d shown   .60   .30
1836 A575 400d Triglav glacial
                   lake   1.40   .75

1987, Mar. 20   Litho.   *Perf. 14*
1837 A576 200d multicolored   .75   .40
   No. 1837 printed in sheets of 8 plus center
label.

Natl.
Civil
Aviation,
60th
Anniv.
A577

1987, Mar. 20   *Perf. 14*
1838 A577 150d POTEZ-29   .60   .30
1839 A577 400d DC-10   1.60   .80
   Each printed in sheets of 8 plus center label.

Kole
Nedelkovski
(1912-1941),
Poet,
Revolutionary
A578

1987, Apr. 2   *Perf. 13½*
1840 A578 40d multicolored   .20   .20

Liberation of
Montenegro
from Turkey,
125th Anniv.
A579

1987, Apr. 16   *Perf. 13½*
1841 A579 40d Battle flags, folk
                   guitar   .20   .20

Slovenian Communist Party, Cebine,
50th Anniv. — A580

1987, Apr. 18   *Perf. 14*
1842 A580 40d multicolored   .20   .20

Europa Issue

Tito Bridge,
Krk — A581

1987, Apr. 30   Litho.   *Perf. 14*
1843 A581 200d shown   .70   .45
1844 A581 400d Bridges over ca-
                   nal   1.00   .75

Fruit
Trees — A582

Tito, 1930, by Mosa
Pijade — A583

1987, May 15   Litho.   *Perf. 14*
1845 A582 60d Almond   .20   .20
1846 A582 150d Pear   .30   .20
1847 A582 200d Apple   .50   .25
1848 A582 400d Plum   1.00   .50
       Nos. 1845-1848 (4)   2.00 1.15

1987, May 25
1849 A583 60d multi   .20   .20
   50th anniv. of Tito's assumption of Yugoslavian communist party leadership.

Vuk Stefanovik Karadzic (1787-1864),
Linguist and Historian — A584

   60d, Bust by Petar Ubavkic, his Trsic resi-
dence & Vienna. 200d, Portrait by Uros
Knezevic, & alphabet from Karadzic's Serbian
Dictionary, 1818.

1987, June 10
1850 A584 60d multi   .20   .20
1851 A584 200d multi   .50   .25

Zrenjanin
Postal
Service,
250th Anniv.
A585

1987, June 22   *Perf. 13½*
1852 A585 60d multi   .20   .20

UNIVERSIADE
'87, Zagreb, July
8-19 — A586

1987, July 8   Litho.   *Perf. 13½*
1853 A586 60d Hurdling   .20   .20
1854 A586 150d Basketball   .30   .20
1855 A586 200d Balance beam   .40   .25
1856 A586 400d Swimming   .90   .45
       Nos. 1853-1856 (4)   1.80 1.10
   Each printed in sheets of eight plus label.

Fire Fighting
A587

Monument, Anindol
Park,
Samobor — A588

1987, July 20   *Perf. 14*
1857 A587 60d Canadair CL-215
                   spraying forest   .20   .20
1858 A587 200d Fire boat   .45   .25
   Each printed in sheets of eight plus label.

1987, Aug. 1   *Perf. 13½*
1859 A588 60d multi   .20   .20
   Communist Party of Croatia, 50th anniv.

Sabac High
School, 150th
Anniv.
A589

1987, Sept. 10   Litho.   *Perf. 13½*
1860 A589 80d multi   .20   .20

Exhibition
Emblem,
Balkan
Peninsula,
Flowers
A590

**XI FILATELISTIČKA IZLOŽBA
BALKANSKIH ZEMALJA**

NOVI SAD · JUGOSLAVIJA

Clock Tower, Petrovaradin Fortress
and Novi Sad — A591

1987, Sept. 19   *Perf. 14*
1861 A590 250d multi   .50   .25
Souvenir Sheet
Imperf
1862 A591 400d multi   .90   .80
   BALKANFILA XI, Novi Sad, Sept. 19-26.

19th Joy of Europe
Conference
A592

Bridges
A593

   Children's drawings: 250d, Girls in forest, by
Bedic Aranka, Juguoslavia. 400d, Scarecrow,
by Schaffer Ingeborg, Austria.

1987, Oct. 2   Litho.   *Perf. 14*
1863 A592 250d multi   .65   .30
1864 A592 400d multi   1.00   .50
   Printed in sheets of nine.

1987, Oct. 15
1865 A593 80d Arslanagica,
                   Trebinje, 16th
                   cent.   .20   .20
1866 A593 250d Terzija, Djakovica,
                   15th cent.   .70   .35

Ship, Dunav-
Tisa Channel
A594

1987, Oct. 20   *Perf. 13½*
1867 A594 80d multi   .20   .20
   City of Titov Vrbas, 600th anniv.

Astronomical and Meteorological
Observatory, Belgrade, Cent. — A595

1987, Nov. 21   *Perf. 14*
1868 A595 80d multi   .20   .20

St. Luke the
Evangelist, by
Raphael
A596

   Paintings by foreign artists in national museums: 200d, Infanta Maria Theresa, by Velazquez. 250d, Nicholas Rubens, Painter's Son
by Rubens. 400d, Louis Laure Sennegon,
Painter's Niece, by Jean-Baptiste-Camille
Corot (1796-1875).

1987, Nov. 28
1869 A596 80d shown   .20   .20
1870 A596 200d multi   .45   .25
1871 A596 250d multi   .55   .35
1872 A596 400d multi   .90   .55
       Nos. 1869-1872 (4)   2.10 1.35

Traditional
Competitions
A597

   80d, Bull fighting. 200d, Ljubicevo Horse
Games. 250d, Moresca game. 400d, Sinj iron
ring.

1987, Dec. 10
1873 A597 80d multi   .20   .20
1874 A597 200d multi   .40   .20
1875 A597 250d multi   .55   .20
1876 A597 400d multi   .85   .40
       Nos. 1873-1876 (4)   2.00 1.10

No. 1800 Surcharged

1987, Sept. 22   *Perf. 13*
1877 A559 80d on 60d sg grn   .20   .20

Vinodol Codex, City of Vinodolski, Coat of Arms — A598

1988, Jan. 6   **Litho.**   *Perf. 14*
1878 A598 100d multi   .25 .20
Vinodol Codex, 700th anniv.

Intl. Women's Golden Fox Skiing Championships, 25th Anniv. — A599

1988, Jan. 30
1879 A599 350d Slalom, emblem, Mirobor City   .85 .40
Printed in sheets of eight plus center label.

World Wildlife Fund — A600

Brown bears (Ursus arctos).

1988, Feb. 1
1880 A600 70d Cub   .20 .20
1881 A600 80d Cubs   .25 .20
1882 A600 200d Adult, head   .55 .25
1883 A600 350d Adult   1.00 .50
   Nos. 1880-1883 (4)   2.00 1.15

1988 Winter Olympics, Calgary — A601

1988, Feb. 13   *Perf. 14x13½*
1884 A601 350d Slalom   .85 .40
1885 A601 1200d Ice hockey   3.00 1.50
Each printed in sheets of 8 plus center label.

Souvenir Sheet

Map of Europe Highlighting Balkan Nations — A602

1988, Feb. 24   **Litho.**   **Imperf.**
1886 A602 1500d multi   3.00 3.00
Congress of Foreign Affairs Ministers of the Balkan Countries, Belgrade, Feb. 24-26.

1988 Summer Olympics, Seoul — A603

South Korean Landscape — A604

1988, Mar. 21   *Perf. 14x13½*
1887 A603 106d Basketball   .20 .20
1888 A603 450d High jump   .90 .45
1889 A603 500d Pommel horse   1.00 .50
1890 A603 1200d Boxing   2.40 1.25
   Nos. 1887-1890 (4)   4.50 2.40

Souvenir Sheet
Imperf
1891 A604 1500d multi   2.75 2.75
Nos. 1887-1890 printed in sheets of 8 plus center label.

Europa Issue

Telecommunications — A605

1988, Apr. 30   **Litho.**   *Perf. 13½x14*
1892 A605 450d shown   .45 .30
1893 A605 1200d Transportation   1.25 .80

Sea Shells — A606

1988, May 14
1894 A606 106d Gibbula magus   .20 .20
1895 A606 550d Pecten jacobaeus   .75 .35
1896 A606 600d Tonna galea   .80 .40
1897 A606 1000d Argonauta argo   1.25 .65
   Nos. 1894-1897 (4)   3.00 1.60

Trial of Tito and Five Comrades, 60th Anniv. — A607

1988, May 25
1898 A607 106d black & brn   .20 .20

Palace of Princess Ljubica of Serbia, 1st University Building A608

1988, June 14   **Litho.**   *Perf. 13½*
1899 A608 106d multi   .20 .20
Belgrade University, 150th anniv.

Flowers — A609

Esperanto, Cent. — A610

1988, July 2   *Perf. 14*
1900 A609 600d Phelypaea boissieri   .60 .30
1901 A609 1000d Campanula formanekiana   1.00 .50
Council of Europe.

1988, July 14   *Perf. 13½*
1902 A610 600d dull vio & ol grn   .60 .30
Printed in sheets of 8 plus center label.

Cargo Ships — A611

Map of the Danube Basin — A612

1988, Aug. 18   **Litho.**   *Perf. 14*
1903 A611 1000d multi   .80 .40

Souvenir Sheet
Imperf
1904 A612 2000d multi   1.50 1.50
Danube Conference, 40th anniv.

13th European Junior Basketball Championships, Aug. 21-28 — A613

1988, Aug. 20   *Perf. 14*
1905 A613 600d multi   .50 .25

1st Horse Race in Belgrade, 125th Anniv. — A614

1988, Aug. 27
1906 A614 140d Thoroughbred racing   .20 .20
1907 A614 600d Steeplechase   .40 .20
1908 A614 1000d Harness racing   .70 .35
   Nos. 1906-1908 (3)   1.30 .75

Museum of Bosnia and Herzegovina, Sarajevo, Cent. A615

1988, Sept. 10   *Perf. 13½*
1909 A615 140d Museum, Bosnian bellflower   .20 .20

Anti-Cancer and AIDS Campaigns A616

1988, Sept. 24   *Perf. 14*
1910 A616 140d Arm, lobster claw .20 .20
1911 A616 1000d Blood, scream   .80 .40

Nos. 1801 and 1804 Surcharged

1988, July   **Litho.**   *Perf. 13½*
1912 A559 120d on 93d ultra   .20 .20
1913 A559 140d on 106d brn org   .20 .20

Joy of Europe Youth Conference A617

Portraits of girls by: 1000d, P. Ranosovic. 1100d, Renoir.

1988, Oct. 1   **Litho.**   *Perf. 14*
1914 A617 1000d multi   .80 .40
1915 A617 1100d multi   .85 .45
See Nos. 1987-1988.

Slovenski Academy, 50th Anniv. — A618

1988, Oct. 13   **Litho.**   *Perf. 14*
1916 A618 200d multi   .20 .20

Museum Exhibits and Places of Origin A618a

200d, Wood bassinet, traditional wedding (Galicka). #1918, Embroidery, man and woman wearing folk costumes of Vojvodina.

#1919, Scimitar, flintlock, man & woman wearing folk costumes of Kotor (Bokelji). 1100d, Masks (Kurenti).

1988, Oct. 18
1917	A618a	200d multi, vert.	.20	.20
1918	A618a	1000d shown	.65	.35
1919	A618a	1000d multi, vert.	.65	.35
1920	A618a	1100d multi	.75	.40
	Nos. 1917-1920 (4)		2.25	1.30

Woman with Lyre, 4th Cent. B.C. — A618b

Grecian terra cotta figurines: #1922, Eros & Psyche, 2nd cent. BC. #1923, Seated woman, 3rd cent. BC. 1100d, Woman by Stele, 3rd cent. BC.

1988, Oct. 28
1921	A618b	200d multi	.20	.20
1922	A618b	1000d multi	.45	.20
1923	A618b	1000d multi	.45	.20
1924	A618b	1100d multi	.50	.25
	Nos. 1921-1924 (4)		1.60	.85

Peter II (1813-1851), Prince Bishop and Poet — A618c

Portraits and: 200d, Cetinje Monastery and frontispiece of his principal work. 1000d, Njegos Mausoleum.

1988, Nov. 1
1925	A618c	200d multi	.20	.20
1926	A618c	1000d multi	.80	.40

Postal Service Types of 1986 and

Telephone Receiver and Telephone Card — A619

Bird, Posthorn, Simulated Stamp — A620

Propeller Plane, Two Arrows and Map — A621

Designs: 170d, 300d, Flower, envelope, mailbox and simulated stamp. 220d, PTT emblem on simulated stamp, mail coach. 800d, Postman on motorcycle. No. 1941, Postman, resident. No. 1942, Mail train. No. 1943, Envelopes, satellite dish. No. 1944, Earth, telecommunications satellite. 100,000d, Bird, open envelope, flower. 170d, 220d, 300d, 2000d, 5000d, No. 1941 vert.

1988-89 | **Litho.** | | **Perf. 13½**
1935	A559	170d dl grn	.20	.20
1936	A559	220d brn org	.20	.20
1937	A559	300d ver	.20	.20
1938	A559	800d brt ultra	.20	.20
1939	A619	2000d multi	.20	.20
1940	A620	5000d dk red & ultra	1.00	.50
1941	A559	10,000d org & brt lil	.35	.20
1942	A559	20,000d lt ol grn & lt red brn	.35	.35

Perf. 13½
1943	A560	10,000d multi	2.00	1.40
1944	A560	20,000d multi	1.50	1.00
1944A	A621	50,000d org & dl bl	1.60	.75
1945	A560	100,000d org & dl grn	1.60	1.00
	Nos. 1935-1945 (12)		9.40	6.20

Perf. 12½
1937a	A559	300d	.20	.20
1938a	A559	800d	.20	.20
1939a	A619	2000d	.20	.20
1940a	A620	5000d	1.00	.50
1941a	A559	10,000d	.20	.20
	Nos. 1937a-1941a (4)		1.60	1.10

Issued: 1988 - 170d, 11/17; 220d, 12/6; 1989 - 300d, 5/11; 800d, 2000d, 7/20; 5000d, 1/20; #1941, 11/28; #1942, 12/8; #1943, 3/20; #1944, 7/19; 50,000d, 11/8; 100,000d, 12/4.
See Nos. 2008-2009, 2017, 2052. For surcharges see Nos. 1972, 1974, 2048.

Yugoslavia, 70th Anniv. — A622

1988, Dec. 1 | **Litho.** | **Perf. 14**
1946 A622 200d Krsmanovic Hall, Belgrade .20 .20

Nos. 1805-1806 Surcharged

1988 | **Litho.** | **Perf. 13½**
1947 A559 170d on 120d .20 .20
1948 A559 220d on 140d .20 .20
Issued: #1947, Dec. 21; #1948, Dec. 15.

Miniature Sheet

Victory of Yugoslavian Athletes at the 1988 Summer Olympics, Seoul — A623

Medals and events: a, Women's air pistol. b, Team handball. c, Table tennis. d, Wrestling. e, Double sculls. f, Basketball. g, Water polo. h, Boxing.

1988, Dec. 31 | **Litho.** | **Perf. 14**
1949 Sheet of 8 + label 1.75 1.40
a.-h. A623 500d any single .20 .20

Ivan Gundulic (1589-1638), Poet — A624

1989, Jan. 7 | **Perf. 13½**
1950 A624 220d multi .20 .20

World Wildlife Fund — A625

Ducks.

1989, Feb. 23 | **Litho.** | **Perf. 14**
1951 Strip of 4 + label 4.00 3.00
a. A625 300d Anas platyrhynchos .20 .20
b. A625 2100d Anas crecca 1.25 .60
c. A625 2200d Anas acuta 1.25 .60
d. A625 2200d Anas clypeata 1.25 .65
Printed in sheets of 20+5 labels. Label pictures WWF emblem.

Publication of The Glory of the Duchy of Kranjska, by Johann Valvasor (1641-1693), 300th Anniv. A626

1989, Mar. 10 | **Perf. 13½**
1952 A626 300d Portrait .20 .20

Flowering Plants — A627

1989, Mar. 20 | **Perf. 14**
1953	A627	300d Bulbocodium vernum	.20	.20
1954	A627	2100d Nymphaea alba	.95	.45
1955	A627	2200d Fritillaria degeniana, vert.	1.00	.50
1956	A627	3000d Orchis simia, vert.	1.40	.70
	Nos. 1953-1956 (4)		3.55	1.85

6th World Air-Gun Championships, Sarajevo, Apr. 27-30 — A628

1989, Apr. 26
1957 A628 3000d multi 1.50 .75

Europa 1989 — A629

1989, Apr. 29
1958 A629 3000d shown .75 .60
1959 A629 6000d Marbles 1.75 1.25

15th European Trophy for Natl. Athletic Club Champions, Belgrade, June 3-4 — A630

1989, June 1 | **Litho.** | **Perf. 13½**
1960 A630 4000d Pole vault .50 .25
Printed in sheets of 8+label picturing flags of participating nations.

Yugoslavia Motorcycle Grand Prix, Rijeka, June 9-11 — A631

Various race scenes.

1989, June 9 | **Perf. 14**
1961 A631 500d multi .20 .20
1962 A631 4000d multi .60 .30

Souvenir Sheet
Perf. 14x13½
1963 A631 6000d multi .90 .45
No. 1963 contains one 54x35 stamp.

No. 1246 Surcharged
1989, Apr. 6 | **Litho.** | **Perf. 13**
1964 A323 100d on 1d dull grn .20 .20
a. Perf. 13x12½ .70

Tito — A632

1989, May 25 | **Perf. 13½x14**
1965 A632 300d multi .20 .20

Early Adriatic Ships A633

a, Ancient Greek galley. b, Roman galley. c, Crusade galleon, 13th cent. d, Nava of Dubrovnik, 16th cent. e, French ship, 17th cent. f, Vessels, 18th cent. 3000d, View of Dubrovnik seaport, called Ragusa in Italian, from a 17th cent. engraving.

1989, June 10 | **Perf. 13½**
1966 Block of 6 .90 .45
a.-f. A633 1000d any single .20 .20
Souvenir Sheet
1967 A633 3000d multi .45 .20
No. 1967 contains one 75x32mm stamp. Nos. 1966-1967 printed se-tenant and sold folded in booklet cover.

26th European Basketball Championships — A634

Map of Europe, basketball and flags of: No. 1968, France, Yugoslavia, Greece, Bulgaria. No. 1969, Netherlands, Italy, Russia, Spain.

1989, June 20 | **Litho.** | **Perf. 13½x14**
1968 A634 2000d multi .25 .20
1969 A634 2000d multi .25 .20
Nos. 1968-1969 exist with setenant label.

Defeat of the Serbians at the Battle of Kosovo, 1389 — A635

1989, June 28
1970 A635 500d multi .20 .20

Danilovgrad Library, Cent. A636

1989, July 15　Litho.　Perf. 13½
1971 A636 500d multi　　.20　.20

Nos. 1797, 1719, 1935, 1936
Surcharged

1989
1972 A559 400d on 30d lt brn vio　.20　.20
1973 A323 700d on 70d brt ultra　.20　.20
1974 A559 700d on 170d dull green　.20　.20
1975 A559 700d on 220d brn org　.20　.20
　Nos. 1972-1975 (4)　　.80　.80

Issued: #1975, 7/19; #1974, 8/10; #1972, 8/23; #1973, 12/13.

Kulin Ban Charter, 800th Anniv. A638

1989, Aug. 29　Litho.　Perf. 14
1976 A638 500d multi　　.20　.20

World Rowing Championships A639

1989, Sept. 2　　Perf. 13½
1977 A639 10,000d multi　　.75　.35

Interparliamentary Union, Cent. — A640

Architecture: No. 1978, Parliament, London (emblem at R). No. 1979, Notre Dame Cathedral (emblem at L).

1989, Sept. 4　　Perf. 13½x14
1978 A640 10,000d multi　　.65　.30
1979 A640 10,000d multi　　.65　.30

A641

View of Belgrade and Maps
BEOGRAD '89 — A642

Architecture & antiquities of exhibition host cities: #1980, Belgrade '61, Cairo '64. #1981, Lusaka '70, Algiers '73. #1982, Colombo '76, Havana '79. #1983, New Delhi '83, Harare '76.

1989, Sept. 4
1980 A641 10,000d multi　　.65　.30
1981 A641 10,000d multi　　.65　.30
1982 A641 10,000d multi　　.65　.30
1983 A641 10,000d multi　　.65　.30
　Nos. 1980-1983 (4)　　2.60　1.20

Souvenir Sheet
Perf. 14
1984 A642 20,000d multi　　1.50　1.50

European Nature Protection A643

8000d, Paeonia officinalis, Brezovica-Jazinac Lake. 10,000d, Paeonia corallina, Mirusa Canyon.

1989, Sept. 11　　Perf. 14
1985 A643 8000d multi　　.45　.20
1986 A643 10,000d multi　　.55　.25

Joy of Europe Type of 1988
Portraits of children: No. 1987, Child with Lamb, by Jovan Popovic. No. 1988, Girl Feeding Dog, by Albert Cuyp (1620-1691).

1989, Oct. 2　Litho.　Perf. 14
1987 A617 10,000d multi　　.60　.30
1988 A617 10,000d multi　　.60　.30

Karpos Uprising, 300th Anniv. — A644

1989, Oct. 20　Litho.　Perf. 13½
1989 A644 1200d ver & dark brn　.20　.20

No. 1833c, Cancellation, Quill Pen, Wax Seals and Seal Device on Parchment A645

1989, Oct. 31　　Perf. 14
1990 A645 1200d multicolored　.20　.20

Stamp Day.

Museum Exhibits A646

1989, Nov. 2
1991 A646 1200d Pack-saddle maker　.20　.20
1992 A646 14,000d Cooper　.60　.30
1993 A646 15,000d Winegrower　.65　.35
1994 A646 30,000d Weaver　1.40　.70
　Nos. 1991-1994 (4)　　2.85　1.55

Religious Paintings — A647

2100d, Apostle Matthew, vert. 21,000d, St. Barbara, vert. 30,000d, The Fourth Day of Creation. 50,000d, The Fifth Day of Creation.

1989, Nov. 28　Litho.　Perf. 14
1997 A647 2100d multicolored　.20　.20
1998 A647 21,000d multicolored　.65　.30
1999 A647 30,000d multicolored　.90　.45
2000 A647 50,000d multicolored　1.50　.75
　Nos. 1997-2000 (4)　　3.25　1.70

A648

League of Communists 14th Congress — A649

1990, Jan. 20　Litho.　Perf. 13½x14
2001 A648 10,000d Star　　.20　.20
2002 A648 50,000d Computer　.75　.35

Souvenir Sheet
Imperf
2003 A649 100,000d Star, diff.　1.50　1.50

Postal Service Types of 1986-88
10p, Man posting letters in mailbox. 20p, Postal employee sorting mail. 30p, Postman, resident. 40p, Woman at telephone station. 1d, Mail train. 2d, Ship & envelope. 3d, Flower, mailbox, envelope & simulated stamp. 5d, Airplane, letters, map of Europe. 10d, Bird, open envelope, flower. 20d, Woman at telephone station.

10p, 20p, 30p, 40p, 3d, 5d vert.

1990-92　　Perf. 12½
2004 A559 10p br yel grn & vio　.20　.20
2005 A559 20p red vio & org　.20　.20
2006 A559 30p org & yel grn　.20　.20
2007 A559 40p blue grn & red vio　.20　.20
2008 A620 50p pur & blue grn　.20　.20

2009 A619 60p red org & brt vio　.20　.20
2013 A559 1d rose lil & greenish bl　.20　.20
2014 A559 2d red lil & blue　.25　.20
2015 A559 3d org & dl blue　.50　.25
2017 A619 5d ultra & grnsh blue　.50　.30
2019 A559 10d red org & vio bl　1.75　.90
Perf. 13½
2021 A559 20d car rose & org　.30　.20
　Nos. 2004-2019 (11)　　4.40　3.05

Issued: 10p, 20p, 2/9; 30p, 40p, 1/24; 50p, 1/29; 60p, 2/6; 2d, 2/14; 3d, 2/22; 5d, 1/31; 1d, 5/24; 10d, 6/12; 20d, 1/27/92.
For surcharges see Nos. 2049-2053, 2168-2178.
This is an expanding set. Numbers will change if necessary.

1990
2006a　Perf. 13½　　.20　.20
2007a　Perf. 13½　　.20　.20
2008a　Perf. 13½　　.20　.20
2013a　Perf. 13½　　1.60　1.25
2014a　Perf. 13½　　.35　.30
2015a　Perf. 13½　　2.00　1.75
2017a　Perf. 13½　　1.00　.85
2019a　Perf. 13½　　4.00　4.00
　Nos. 2006a-2019a (8)　9.55　8.75

Anti-smoking Campaign A650

1990, Jan. 31　Litho.　Perf. 13½x13
2034 A650 10d gry & yel brn　1.75　.85

Protected Fish — A651

1990, Feb. 15　　Perf. 13½
2035　Strip of 4 + label　5.25　2.75
　a. A651 1d Esox lucius　.20　.20
　b. A651 5d Silurus glanis　.85　.40
　c. A651 10d Lota lota　1.60　.80
　d. A651 15d Perca fluviatilis　2.50　1.25

Zabljak Fortress, Illuminated Manuscript, Coat of Arms — A652

1990, Mar. 9　　Perf. 14x13½
2036 A652 50p multicolored　.20　.20

Enthronement of Djuradj Crnojevic, 500th anniv.

ITU, 125th Anniv. A653

1990, Mar. 23
2037 A653 6.50d Telegrapher, computer　1.10　.55

1990 World Cup
Soccer
Championships,
Italy — A654

1990, Apr. 16
2038	A654	6.50d shown	1.10	.55
2039	A654	10d multi, diff.	1.60	.80

Europa
1990 — A655

Post offices: 6.50d, PTT Central, Skopje.
10d, Telecommunications Central, Belgrade.

1990, Apr. 23   **Perf. 13½x14**
2040	A655	6.50d multicolored	1.25	.55
2041	A655	10d multicolored	2.00	.80

A656

A657

1990, Apr. 30   **Litho.**   **Perf. 13½**
2042	A656	6.50d multicolored	1.25	.60

Labor Day, cent.

No. 2043 exists with setenant label.

1990, May 5   **Perf. 14x13½**

Eurovision Song Contest: 10d, Conductor,
musical score.

2043	A657	6.50d multicolored	1.25	.60
2044	A657	10d multicolored	1.75	.90

Tennis — A658

1990, May 15   **Litho.**   **Perf. 14**
2045	A658	6.50d multicolored	1.25	.60
2046	A658	10d multicolored	1.90	.95

Tito — A659

1990, May 25   **Perf. 13½x14**
2047	A659	50p multicolored	.20	.20

Nos. 1938, 2005-2007 Surcharged

1990   **Litho.**   **Perf. 13½**
2048	A559	50p on 800d #1938	.20	.20

           Perf. 12½
2049	A559	50p on 20p red vio & org	.20	.20
2050	A559	1d on 30p org & yel grn	.20	.20
2051	A559	2d on 40p bl grn & red vio, I	.40	.20
a.		Type II, perf. 13½	.40	.20
b.		Type I, perf. 13½		
		Nos. 2048-2051 (4)	1.00	.80

Type II surcharge has 3 instead of 2 bars
obliterating old value, new denomination is at
bottom of stamp.
Issued: #2048, 5/24; #2049, 9/18; #2050,
8/8.
This is an expanding set. Numbers will
change if necessary.

Nos. 2004, 2009 Surcharged

10

5 ══   ══

1991   **Litho.**   **Perf. 12½**
2052	A619	5d on 60p	.20	.20
2053	A559	10d on 10p	.20	.20

Issued: #2052, Dec. 7; #2053, Dec. 12.

Public
Postal
Service
in
Serbia,
150th
Anniv.
A660

1990, May 25
2056	A660	50p multicolored	.20	.20

Pigeons
A661

1990, June 8   **Perf. 13½**
2057	A661	50p multicolored	.20	.20
2058	A661	5d multicolored	.80	.40
2059	A661	6.50d multi, vert.	1.10	.55
2060	A661	10d multi, vert.	1.60	.75
		Nos. 2057-2060 (4)	3.70	1.90

Mercury Mine
at Idrija, 500th
Anniv. — A662

Designs: 6.50d, Miners at work, ca. 1490.

1990, June 22   **Perf. 13½x14**
2061	A662	50p multicolored	.20	.20
2062	A662	6.50d multicolored	1.10	.55

Newspaper
"Vjesnik," 50th
Anniv. — A663

1990, June 23   **Perf. 13½**
2063	A663	60p multicolored	.20	.20

Serbian Migration, 300th
Anniv. — A664

1990, Sept. 20   **Perf. 14**
2064	A664	1d shown	.20	.20
2065	A664	6.50d Caravan	1.25	.60

European Track & Field
Championships, Split — A665

1990, Aug. 27   **Perf. 13½**
2067	A665	1d Start of race	.20	.20
2068	A665	6.50d Runners' feet	1.10	.55

         Souvenir Sheet
2069	A665	10d Runners	1.75	.90

No. 2069 contains one 54x35mm stamp. A
50p exists but no information on its postal category is available.

Joy of Europe
A666

Paintings: 6.50d, Children by I. Kobilca. 10d,
William III of Orange as a Child by A. Hanne-
man, vert.

1990, Oct. 2   **Litho.**   **Perf. 14**
2070	A666	6.50d multicolored	1.00	.50
2071	A666	10d multicolored	1.75	.80

Souvenir Sheets

29th Chess
Olympics, Novi
Sad — A667

1990, Oct. 2   **Perf. 11½**
         Granite Paper
2072		Sheet of 4	4.50	4.50
a.	A667	1d shown	.20	.20
b.	A667	5d Rook, bishop, knight	1.00	1.00
c.	A667	6.50d King, bishop, knght, pawn	1.25	1.25
d.	A667	10d Chess pieces	2.00	2.00

           Imperf
2073		Sheet of 4	4.50	4.50
a.	A667	1d like No. 2072a	.20	.20
b.	A667	5d like No. 2072b	1.00	1.00
c.	A667	6.50d like No. 2072c	1.25	1.25
d.	A667	10d like No. 2072d	2.00	2.00

No. 2073 has blue margin inscriptions.
Emblems on Nos. 2072a-2072d are in silver,
those on Nos. 2073a-2073d are in gold.

Stamp
Day
A668

1990, Oct. 2   **Perf. 14**
2074	A668	2d multicolored	.40	.20

150th anniv. of the Penny Black.

Environmental
Protection
A669

1990, Nov. 16   **Litho.**   **Perf. 14**
2075	A669	6.50d Vransko Lake	1.25	1.25
2076	A669	10d Gyps fulvus	1.75	1.75

Frescoes — A670

Designs: 2d, King Milutin, Monastery of Our
Lady, Ljeviska. 5d, Saint Sava, Mileseva
Monastery. 6.50d, Saint Elias, Moraca Monas-
tery. 10d, Jesus Christ, Sopocani Monastery.

1990, Nov. 28
2077	A670	2d multicolored	.35	.35
2078	A670	5d multicolored	.80	.80
2079	A670	6.50d multicolored	1.10	1.10
2080	A670	10d multicolored	1.75	1.75
		Nos. 2077-2080 (4)	4.00	4.00

Dr. Bozo
Milanovic
(1890-1980),
Religious
and Political
Leader
A671

1990, Dec. 20   **Litho.**   **Perf. 13½**
2081	A671	2d multicolored	.35	.35

Religious
Carvings
A672

Designs: 2d, Christ in the temple. 5d, Nativity scene. 6.50d, Flight from Egypt, horiz. 10d,
Entry into Jerusalem, horiz.

1990, Dec. 24   **Perf. 13½x14, 14x13½**
2082	A672	2d gld, brn, & blk	.35	.35
2083	A672	5d gld, brn, & blk	.90	.90
2084	A672	6.50d gld, brn, & blk	1.10	1.10
2085	A672	10d gld, brn, & blk	1.90	1.90
		Nos. 2082-2085 (4)	4.25	4.25

Protected
Birds — A673

1991, Jan. 31   **Litho.**   **Perf. 14x13½**
2086		Strip of 4 + label	4.50	4.50
a.	A673	2d Vanellus vanellus	.35	.35
b.	A673	5d Lanius senator	.95	.95
c.	A673	6.50d Grus grus	1.25	1.25
d.	A673	10d Mergus merganser	1.90	1.90

1991, Feb. 20
2087	A674	2d Crocus kosaninii	.30	.30
2088	A674	6d Crocus scardicus	.90	.90
2089	A674	7.50d Crocus rujanesis	1.10	1.10
2090	A674	15d Crocus adamii	2.40	2.40
		Nos. 2087-2090 (4)	4.70	4.70

Bishop Josip J. Strossmayer (1815-1905), Founder of Academy of Arts and Sciences A675

1991, Mar. 4   Litho.   Perf. 13½x14
2091	A675	2d multicolored	.30	.30

Academy of Arts and Sciences, 125th Anniv.

Wolfgang Amadeus Mozart, Composer A676

1991, Mar. 20   Perf. 14
2092	A676	7.50d multicolored	1.00	1.00

Otto Lilienthal's First Glider Flight, Cent. — A677

Designs: 7.50d, Edvard Rusjan (1886-1911), pilot, aircraft designer. 15d, Otto Lilienthal (1848-1896), aviation pioneer.

1991, Apr. 1
2093	A677	7.50d multicolored	.90	.90
2094	A677	15d multicolored	1.90	1.90

Printed in sheets of 8 plus label.

Lhotse I, Himalayas, South Face First Climbed by Tomo Cesen, 1990 — A678

1991, Apr. 24   Perf. 14x13½
2095	A678	7.50d multicolored	.75	.75

Europa A679

Designs: 7.50d, Telecommunications satellite. 15d, Satellite, antenna, telephone.

1991, May 6   Perf. 14
2096	A679	7.50d multicolored	1.00	.60
2097	A679	15d multicolored	2.00	1.25

Franciscan Monastery, Trsat, 700th Anniv. — A680

1991, May 10   Litho.   Perf. 13½x14
2098	A680	3.50d multicolored	.40	.40

Governments of Danube River Region Conf., Belgrade — A681

15d, Danube River shipping. 20d, Course of Danube, landmarks, regional animals.

1991, May 15   Perf. 13½
2099	A681	7.50d multicolored	.65	.65
2100	A681	15d multicolored	1.10	1.10

Souvenir Sheet
2101	A681	20d multicolored	1.75	1.75

No. 2101 contains one 55x35mm stamp.

Opening of Karavanke Tunnel — A682

Designs: 4.50d, Passage Over Karavanke by J. Valvasor, 17th century. 11d, Entrance to new Karavanke Tunnel.

1991, June 1   Perf. 14x13½
2102	A682	4.50d multicolored	.35	.35
2103	A682	11d multicolored	.90	.90

Basketball, Cent. — A683

1991, June 15   Perf. 13½x14
2104	A683	11d shown	.95	.95
2105	A683	15d Nets, "100"	1.25	1.25

Yugoslavian Insurrection, 50th Anniv. — A684   Tin Ujevic (1891-1955), Writer — A685

Designs: 4.50d, Partisan Memorial Medal, 1941. 11d, Medal for Courage.

1991, July 4   Litho.   Perf. 14
2106	A684	4.50d multicolored	.35	.35
2107	A684	11d multicolored	.90	.90

Yugoslav Natl. Army, 50th Anniv.

1991, July 5   Perf. 13½
2108	A685	4.50d multicolored	.40	.40

Jacobus Gallus (1550-1591), Composer A686

1991, July 18
2109	A686	11d multicolored	.80	.80

Lighthouses of Adriatic and Danube — A687

Designs: a, Savudrija, 1818. b, Sveti Ivan na pucini, 1853. c, Porer, 1833. d, Stoncica, 1865. e, Olipa, c. 1842. f, Glavat, 1884. g, Veli rat, 1849. h, Vir, 1881. i, Tajerske sestrice, 1876. j, Razanj, 1875. k, Derdap-Danube. l, Tamis-Danube.

1991, July 25   Litho.   Perf. 13½
2110	A687	10d Bklt. pane of 12, #a.-l.	10.50	10.50

Sremski Karlovci High School, Bicent. — A688

1991, Sept. 12   Litho.   Perf. 14
2111	A688	4.50d multicolored	.40	.40

European Nature Protection A689

1991, Sept. 24   Perf. 13½x14
2112	A689	11d Palingenia longicauda	.95	.95
2113	A689	15d Phalacrocorax pygmaeus	1.25	1.25

A690

A691

1991, Sept. 28   Perf. 14
2114	A690	4.50d multicolored	.40	.40

Town of Subotica, 600th anniv.

1991, Oct. 2
Paintings: 15d, Little Dubravka, by Jovan Bijelic (1886-1964). 30d, Little Girl with a Cat by Mary Cassatt (1845-1926).
2115	A691	15d multicolored	1.10	1.10
2116	A691	30d multicolored	2.25	2.25

Joy of Europe.

33rd Intl. Apicultural Congress, APIMONDIA '91 — A692

1991, Sept. 28   Litho.   Perf. 13½x14
2117	A692	11d multicolored	.75	.75

Stamp Day, Monument to Prince Michael Obrenovich, Serbia #1 — A693

1991, Oct. 31   Perf. 14
2118	A693	4.50d multicolored	.40	.40

First Serbia Postage Stamps, 125th Anniv.

Museum Exhibits A694

Flags and medals: 20d, Vucjido battle flag, medal for courage. 30d, Grahovac battle flag and medal. 40d, Montenegrin state flag, medal for bravery. 50d, Montenegrin court flag, medal of Petrovich Nyegosh Dynasty.

1991, Nov. 28   Perf. 13½x14
2119	A694	20d multicolored	.65	.65
2120	A694	30d multicolored	1.00	1.00
2121	A694	40d multicolored	1.40	1.40
2122	A694	50d multicolored	1.75	1.75
		Nos. 2119-2122 (4)	4.80	4.80

Illustrations from Ancient Manuscripts A695

Designs: 20d, Angel carrying Sun around Earth, 17th cent. 30d, Celnica Gospel, menology for April, 14th cent. 40d, Angel from the Annunciation, 13th cent. 50d, Mary Magdalene, 12th cent.

1991, Dec. 12
2123	A695	20d multicolored	.65	.65
2124	A695	30d multicolored	1.00	1.00
2125	A695	40d multicolored	1.40	1.40
2126	A695	50d multicolored	1.75	1.75
		Nos. 2123-2126 (4)	4.80	4.80

Gotse Deltchev (1872-1903), Macedonian Revolutionary A696

1992, Jan. 29   Litho.   Perf. 13½
2127 A696 5d multicolored   .20   .20

Red Star, European and World Soccer Champions A697

1992, Jan. 29   Litho.   Perf. 14x13½
2128 A697 17d multicolored   .25   .20

A698   A699

1992, Feb. 8   Perf. 14x13½
2129 A698 80d Ski jumping   1.10   .55
2130 A698 100d Freestyle skiing   1.40   .70
1992 Winter Olympics, Albertville.

1992, Mar. 10   Litho.   Perf. 14
Protected Animals: a, 50d, Lepus europaeus. b, 60d, Pteromys volans. c, 80d, Dryomys nitedula. d, 100d, Cricetus cricetus.
2131 A699 Strip of 4, #a.-d. + label   3.75   1.90

Madonna and Child, 14th century, Pec — A700

1992, Mar. 14   Perf. 13½x14
2132 A700 80d multicolored   1.00   .50
Promotion of Breastfeeding.

Ski Association of Montenegro — A701

1992, Mar. 25   Perf. 14x13½
2133 A701 8d multicolored   .20   .20
Skiing in Montenegro, cent.

1860 Fountain, Belgrade — A702

A702a

A702b

A702c

A702d

A702e

A702f

A702g

A702h

A702i

A702j

5d, Griffins, 14th cent. #2136, #2139, Fisherman Fountain, Belgrade. #2138, like #2137. 300d, Kalemegdan Fountain, Belgrade. 500d, Fountain, Sremski Karlovci. #2142, Symbols of Miroslav-Evangelium, 12th cent. 3000d, Fountain, Studenica. 5000d, Fountain, Oplenzu. 10,000d, 500,000d, Health spa, Vrnjacka Banja. 50,000d, Envelopes over map of Europe. #2147, Airplane. #2148, Health spa, Bukovacka Banja.

1992-93   Litho.   Perf. 13½
2135 A702a   5d brn & olive   .30   .20
2136 A702   50d dk bl & lt bl   .30   .25
2137 A702   50d violet   .20   .20
2138 A702   100d lil rose & pink   .20   .20
2139 A702   100d dk grn & lt grn   .20   .20
2140 A702b   300d brn & red brn   .25   .20
2141 A702c   500d dk ol & pale org   .25   .20
2142 A702d   (A) red, 18x22mm   .50   .25
2143 A702e   3000d red brn   .25   .20
 a.   Perf. 12½   2.00   2.00
2144 A702f   5000d vio & yel brn   .25   .20
2145 A702g   10,000d vio bl & grn bl   .25   .20
2146 A702h   50,000d gray & gray bl   .30   .20
2147 A702i   100,000d red & bl   .50   .25
 a.   Perf. 12½   .50   .50
2148 A702j   100,000d brn red & brn   .30   .20
2149 A702g   500,000d bl & vio   .50   .25
 Nos. 2135-2149 (15)   4.55   3.20

Issued: #2137, 4/1/92; #2139, 5/6/92; 5d, 11/24/92; #2136, 12/15/92; #2138, 12/22/92; 300d, 12/3/92; 500d, 1/14/93; #2142, 4/5/93; #2143, 4/23/93; 5000d, 3/18/93; 10,000d, 11/9/93; 50,000d, 6/10/93; 100,000d, 6/28/93; 100,000d, 12/6/93; 500,000d, 8/10/93.
No. 2142 was valued at 3000d on day of issue.
See No. 2386. For surcharges see Nos. 2220A-2220I, 2253-2254.
This is an expanding set. Numbers may change.

Sinking of the Titanic, 80th Anniv. — A703

1992, Apr. 14   Perf. 14
2152 A703 150d multicolored   1.25   .80

Expo '92, Seville A704

1992, Apr. 20
2153 A704 150d multicolored   1.25   .80

Discovery of America, 500th Anniv. — A705

1992, May 5   Litho.   Perf. 13½x14
2154 A705 300d Columbus, ship   2.00   1.25
2155 A705 500d Columbus' fleet   3.25   2.10

Souvenir Sheet
Perf. 14x13½
2156 A705 1200d Ships in port   7.50   7.50
Europa. No. 2156 contains one 54x34mm stamp.

1992 Summer Olympics, Barcelona — A706

1992, May 20   Perf. 14x13½
2157 A706 500d Pistol shooting   1.40   .70
2158 A706 500d Water polo   1.40   .70
2159 A706 500d Tennis   1.40   .70
2160 A706 500d Handball   1.40   .70
 Nos. 2157-2160 (4)   5.60   2.80

European Soccer Championships — A707

Various soccer plays.

1992, June 1   Perf. 13½
2161 A707 1000d shown   2.25   1.10
2162 A707 1000d multicolored   2.25   1.10

Domestic Cats — A708

Designs: No. 2163, Red Persian. No. 2164, White Persian. No. 2165, Yellow tabby. No. 2166, British blue short-hair.

1992, June 25   Litho.   Perf. 13½x14
Background Color
Cyrillic Letters
2163 A708 1000d blue   1.25   .80
2164 A708 1000d purple   1.25   .80
Latin Letters
2165 A708 1000d dark purple   1.25   .80
2166 A708 1000d brown   1.25   .80
 Nos. 2163-2166 (4)   5.00   3.20

Steam Locomotives A709

Designs: a, JDZ 162. b, JDZ 151. c, JDZ 73. d, JDZ 83. e, JDZ 16. f, Prince Nicholas' coach.

1992, July 3   Litho.   Perf. 14
2167 A709 1000d Booklet pane of 6, #a.-f.   12.00   10.00

Nos. 2005-2006, 2007a, 2008, 2013a, 2014a, 2015a, 2017a Surcharged

1992   Perfs., Etc. as Before
2168 A559   2d on 30p #2006   .20   .20
2169 A559   5d on 20p #2005   .20   .20
2170 A559   5d on 40p #2007a   .20   .20
2171 A620   10d on 50p #2008   .20   .20
2172 A621   10d on 5d #2017a   .20   .20
2173 A559   20d on 1d #2013a   .40   .25
2174 A621   20d on 5d like #2017,yel, bl & grn bl   .40   .25
2175 A559   50d on 2d #2014a   1.00   .70
2176 A559   100d on 3d #2015a   2.10   1.40
 Nos. 2168-2176 (9)   4.90   3.60

Issued: #2168, 2170, 10/26; #2169, 9/12; #2171, 9/17; #2172, 10/29; #2173, 2175-2176, 8/6; #2174, 11/9.

World Chess Champions A710

1992, Sept. 14   Litho.   Perf. 14
2177 A710 500d Bobby Fischer   1.90   1.25
2178 A710 500d Boris Spassky   1.90   1.25

Telephone Service in Vojvodina, Cent. A711

1892 Telephone, buildings of Novi Sad, Subotica and Zrenjanin.

1992, Oct. 1
2179 A711 10d multicolored   1.00   .70

Stamp Day A712

Design: Montenegro #7, musician.

1992, Oct. 2
2180 A712 50d multicolored   1.50 1.00

European
Art — A713

Protection of
Nature — A714

Europa: No. 2181, Ballet Dancer, by Edgar Degas (1834-1917). No. 2182, Painting of young man, by V. Knezevic.

1992, Oct. 2
2181 A713 500d multicolored   1.90 1.25
2182 A713 500d multicolored   1.90 1.25

1992, Nov. 14   *Perf. 13½*
2183 A714 500d Tetrao urogallus   3.25 2.00
2184 A714 500d Pelecanus
            onocrotalus   3.25 2.00

Serbian
Writers
Assoc.,
Cent. — A715

1992, Nov. 20   *Perf. 14*
2185 A715 100d multicolored   1.00 .70

Traditional Architecture — A716

Designs: No. 2186, Ancient hut, Zlatibor region. No. 2187, Round house, Morava region. No. 2188, House, on stone cliff, Metohija region. No. 2189, Large estate house, Vojvodina region.

1992, Dec. 12
2186 A716 500d multicolored   1.10 .75
2187 A716 500d multicolored   1.10 .75
2188 A716 500d multicolored   1.10 .75
2189 A716 500d multicolored   1.10 .75
    Nos. 2186-2189 (4)   4.40 3.00

Icons, Mosaics — A717

#2190, St. Petka, St. Petka Church, Belgrade. #2191, St. Vasilije-Ostronoski, St. Vasilije-Ostronoski Church, Montenegro. #2192, Mosaic of Simeon Nemanja with model of Blessed Virgin Church, Studenica. #2193,

Mosaic of St. Lazar with model of Ravanica Monastery.

1992, Dec. 15
2190 A717 500d multi   1.40 1.00
2191 A717 500d multi   1.40 1.00
2192 A717 500d multi, vert.   1.40 1.00
2193 A717 500d multi, vert.   1.40 1.00
    Nos. 2190-2193 (4)   5.60 4.00

Aviation in
Yugoslavia,
80th
Anniv. — A718

1992, Dec. 24
2194 A718 500d Bleriot XI   1.25 .80

Diocletian's
Reformation of
the Roman
Empire, 1700th
Anniv. — A719

Design: Detail of Roman fresco.

1993, Jan. 28   Litho.   Perf. 13½
2195 A719 1500d multicolored   1.25 .80

State
Museum,
Cetinje,
Cent. — A720

1993, Feb. 12   *Perf. 14*
2196 A720 2500d multicolored   1.25 .80

Marine
Life — A721

Designs: a, Acipenser sturio. b, Scorpaena scrofa. c, Xiphias gladius. d, Tursiops truncatus.

1993, Mar. 20   *Perf. 13½*
2197 A721 10,000d Strip of 4,
            #a.-d. + la-
            bel   4.75 4.00

Serbian
Money — A722

#2198, Ancient document, 10 para coins. #2199, 5 dinar banknotes, 5 dinar coins.

1993, Mar. 30
2198 A722 10,000d multicolored   1.75 1.10
2199 A722 10,000d multicolored   1.75 1.10

Restablishment of Serbian monetary system, 125th anniv. (No. 2198). Restoring dinars as Serbian currency, 120th anniv. (No. 2199).

Famous
People
A723

Designs: No. 2200, Milos Crnjanski (1893-1977), writer, journalist. No. 2201, Nicola Tesla (1856-1943), physicist. No. 2202, Mihailo Petrovic (1868-1943), mathematician. No. 2203, Aleksa Santic (1868-1924), poet.

1993, Apr. 1
2200 A723 40,000d multicolored   1.40 1.00
2201 A723 40,000d multicolored   1.40 1.00
2202 A723 40,000d multicolored   1.40 1.00
2203 A723 40,000d multicolored   1.40 1.00
    Nos. 2200-2203 (4)   5.60 4.00

Joy of
Europe — A724

Contemporary
Art — A725

Children's paintings: No. 2204, Girl holding flowers, children, dove, by M. Markovski. No. 2205, Angels, birds, by J. Rugovac.

1993, Apr. 5
2204 A724 50,000d multicolored   1.75 1.10
2205 A724 50,000d multicolored   1.75 1.10

1993, May 5
Europa: No. 2206, Nude with a Mirror, by M. Milunovic. No. 2207, Composition, by M.P. Barili.

2206 A725 95,000d multicolored   2.25 2.00
2207 A725 95,000d multicolored   2.25 2.00

A726

A727

A728

A729

A730

Ancient Fortresses: No. 2208, Sutorina, Montenegro. No. 2209, Kalemegdan, Belgrade. No. 2210, Medun, Montenegro. No. 2211, Petrovaradin, near Novi Sad. No. 2212, Bar, Montenegro. No. 2213, Golubac.

1993, July 9
Booklet Stamps
2208 A726 900,000d multicolored   1.25 .80
2209 A727 900,000d multicolored   1.25 .80
2210 A728 900,000d multicolored   1.25 .80
2211 A729 900,000d multicolored   1.25 .80
2212 A730 900,000d multicolored   1.25 .80
2213 A730 900,000d multicolored   1.25 .80
  a.   Booklet pane, #2208-2213   7.50
        Complete booklet, #2213a   7.50

Flowers
A731

Colors of various flowers in vases: No. 2214, Yellow, white. No. 2215, Orange, red. No. 2216, Purple, pink, white. No. 2217, Mixed.

1993, July 10   *Perf. 14*
2214 A731 1,000,000d multi   1.25 .80
2215 A731 1,000,000d multi   1.25 .80
2216 A731 1,000,000d multi   1.25 .80
2217 A731 1,000,000d multi   1.25 .80
    Nos. 2214-2217 (4)   5.00 3.20

Electrification
of Serbia,
Cent.
A732

1993, July 28   *Perf. 13½*
2218 A732 2,500,000d multi   1.00 .70

Protection of
Nature
A733

Designs: No. 2219, Garrulus glandarius. No. 2220, Oriolus oriolus.

1993, Sept. 30
2219 A733 3,000,000d multi   3.00 2.00
2220 A733 3,000,000d multi   3.00 2.00

Nos. 2147a, 2135, 2144, 2136 and
2140 Surcharged

No. 2143 Surcharged

1993   *Perfs., Etc. as Before*
2220A A702i   10d on 100,000d   .20   .20
2220C A702a   50d on 5d   .20   .20
2220D A702f   100d on 5000d   .20   .20
2220E A702   500d on 50d   .20   .20
2220F A702e   1000d on 3000d   .20   .20
2220H A702b   10,000d on 300d   .60   .40
2220I A702a   50,000d on 5d   3.00   2.00
     Nos. 2220A-2220I (7)   4.60   3.40

Issued: 50,000d, 11/9/93; others, 10/18/93.
Size and location of surcharge varies.

Cooperation on the Danube
River — A735

Designs: No. 2221, Ships on river. No.
2222, Ship going down river. 20,000d, Map
showing location of Danube River.
Illustration reduced (A735).

1993, Oct. 20   *Perf. 14*
2221 A734 15,000d multicolored   1.40   1.00
2222 A734 15,000d multicolored   1.40   1.00
     Souvenir Sheet
2223 A735 20,000d multicolored   2.50   1.75

Post Office in
Jagodina,
150th Anniv.
A736

1993, Oct. 30   *Perf. 13½*
2224 A736 12,000d multicolored   1.50   1.00
     Stamp Day.

Joy of
Europe — A737

Icons in
Monasteries
A738

Paintings: No. 2225, Boy with Cat, by Sava
Sumanovic (1896-1942). No. 2226, Circus
Rider, by Georges Rouault (1871-1958).

1993, Nov. 26
2225 A737 2,000,000d multi   1.75   1.10
2226 A737 2,000,000d multi   1.75   1.10

1993, Dec. 15
Designs: No. 2227, The Annunciation,
Mileseva. No. 2228, Nativity, Studenica. No.
2229, Madonna and Child, Bogorodica
Ljeviska. No. 2230, Flight into Egypt, Oplenac.
2227 A738 400,000,000d multi   .95   .60
2228 A738 400,000,000d multi   .95   .60
2229 A738 400,000,000d multi   .95   .60
2230 A738 400,000,000d multi   .95   .60
     Nos. 2227-2230 (4)   3.80   2.40

Traditional
Houses — A739

Publication of
Oktoechos, 500th
Anniv. — A740

#2231, A-frame huts, Savardak, horiz.
#2232, Watchtower. #2233, Stone house on
edge of river. #2234, Crmnicka house, Bar,
horiz.

1993, Dec. 31
2231 A739 50d multicolored   .95   .60
2232 A739 50d multicolored   .95   .60
2233 A739 50d multicolored   .95   .60
2234 A739 50d multicolored   .95   .60
     Nos. 2231-2234 (4)   3.80   2.40

1994, Jan. 17   **Litho.**   *Perf. 13½*
2235 A740 1000d Text   .90   .60
2236 A740 1000d Liturgists   .90   .60

Raptors
A741

Designs: a, Neophron percnopterus. b,
Falco cherrug. c, Buteo rufinus. d, Falco
naumanni.

1994, Feb. 7
2237 A741 80p Strip of 4, #a.-d.
      + label   7.50   7.50

Intl. Mimosa
Festival, Herceg-
Novi
A742

1994, Feb. 28
2238 A742 80p multicolored   1.50   1.00

Natl.
Museum,
Belgrade,
150th Anniv.
A743

Design: No. 2240, National Theater, Belgrade, 125th anniv., portrait of Prince Milos
Obrenovic.

1994, Mar. 19
2239 A743 80p multicolored   1.40   1.00
2240 A743 80p multicolored   1.40   1.00

1994 Winter Olympics,
Lillehammer — A744

a, Speed skater. b. Olympic rings, flame. c,
Skier.

1994, Apr. 11
2241 A744 60p Strip of 3, #a.-c.   3.75   3.75

Europa
A745

Map of flight route and: 60p, Kodron C61,
automobile. 1.80d, Kodron C61 in air over
Belgrade.

1994, May 5
2242 A745   60p multicolored   1.75   1.10
2243 A745 1.80d multicolored   2.75   1.60

First night flight Paris-Belgrade-Bucharest-
Istanbul, piloted by Louis Guidon, 1923.

Burning
of
Relics
of Holy
Sava,
400th
Anniv.
A746

1994, May 10   *Perf. 14*
2244 A746 60p multicolored   1.75   1.10

1994 World Cup Soccer
Championships, U.S. — A747

60p, Three players with arms raised in victory. 1d, Three players down on ground.

1994, June 10   *Perf. 13½*
2245 A747 60p multicolored   1.40   1.00
2246 A747   1d multicolored   2.40   1.60

A748

A749

1994, July 8
2247 A748 60p Basset hound   1.10   .75
2248 A748 60p Maltese   1.10   .75
2249 A748 60p Welsh terrier   1.10   .75
2250 A748   1d Husky   1.90   1.25
     Nos. 2247-2250 (4)   5.20   3.50

1994, July 20
2251 A749 60p multicolored   1.50   1.00

Assembly of Eastern Orthodox Christian
nations.

Protecting the
Ecology of
Montenegro
A750

1994, July 28
2252 A750 50p Tcherna Gora
         Park   1.75   1.10

Nos. 2148, 2145
Surcharged

1994, July 15   *Perf. 13½*
2253 A702j 10p on 100,000d   .25   .20
2254 A702g 50p on 10,000d   1.25   .80

A751

A752

Monasteries: 1p, Moraca, 13th cent. 5p,
Gracanica, 14th cent. 10p, Ostrog. No. 2258-
2259, Lazarica, 14th cent. 50p, Studenica,
12th cent. 1d, Sopocani, 13th cent.

1994   **Litho.**   *Perf. 13½*
2255 A751   1p bister & purple   .20   .20
2256 A751   5p yel brn & blue   .20   .20
2257 A751   10p magenta & slate   .20   .20
2258 A751   20p lil rose & pale vio   .40   .25
2259 A751   20p pale car & gray   .40   .25
2260 A751   50p deep pur & mag   1.00   .70
2261 A751   1d blue & org brown   2.10   1.40
     Nos. 2255-2261 (7)   4.50   3.20

UNESCO (#2260-2261).
Issued: 1p, 5p, #2258, 1d, 8/15; #2259,
9/10; 10p, 50p, 11/10.
Nos. 2262-2271 are unassigned.
For surcharge, see Serbia No. 195.

1994, Sept. 10
2272 A752 50p multicolored   1.25   .80

St. Arsenius Seminary, Sremski Karlovci,
bicent.

Protection of Nature A753

Designs: 1d, Fishing pier, Reka Bojana. 1.50d, Lake, Belgrade.

1994, Sept. 20
2273 A753	1d multicolored	2.25	1.50
2274 A753	1.50d multicolored	3.50	2.10

Painting by U. Knezevic — A754

Sailing Ships in Bottles — A755

1994, Oct. 5   *Perf. 14*
2275 A754	1d multicolored	2.00	1.40

Joy of Europe.

1994, Oct. 27   *Perf. 13½*

a, Revenge, 1585. b, Grand yacht, 1678. c, Santa Maria, 15th cent. d, Nava, 15th cent. e, Mayflower, 1615. f, Carrack, 14th cent.

2276 A755	50p Bklt. pane of 6, #a.-f.	6.00	5.50
	Complete booklet, #2276	6.00	

Stamp Day — A756

Drawings on Gravestones A757

1994, Oct. 31
2277 A756	50p multicolored	2.00	1.40

1994, Nov. 25

#2278, Man holding umbrella, purse. #2279, 2 men. #2280, Cemetery, stone with man on horse, inscriptions. #2281, Fence, 2 gravestones, cross, man.

2278 A757	50p multicolored	1.10	.75
2279 A757	50p multicolored	1.10	.75
2280 A757	50p multicolored	1.10	.75
2281 A757	50p multicolored	1.10	.75
	Nos. 2278-2281 (4)	4.40	3.00

Religious Art — A758

#2282, The Annunciation, by D. Bacevic. #2283, Adoration of the Magi, by N. Neskovic. #2284, Madonna and Child, by T.N. Cesljar. #2285, St. John Baptizing Christ, by T. Kracun.

1994, Dec. 15
2282 A758	60p multicolored	1.25	.80
2283 A758	60p multicolored	1.25	.80
2284 A758	60p multicolored	1.25	.80
2285 A758	60p multicolored	1.25	.80
	Nos. 2282-2285 (4)	5.00	3.20

Natl. Symbols A759

1995, Jan. 26   Litho.   *Perf. 13½*
2286 A759	1d Flag	1.50	1.00
2287 A759	1d Arms	1.50	1.00

Sheets of 8

World Chess Champions A760

#2288: a, Wilhelm Steinitz (1836-1900), Austria. b, Silhouettes of chessman. c, Emmanuel Lasker (1868-1941), Germany. d, Knight. e, Chessman, row of pawns at top. f, José Raúl Capablanca (1888-1942), Cuba. g, Chessman, rook at left. h, Alexander Alekhine (1892-1946), Russia.
#2289: a, Max Euwe, Netherlands. b, Board, pawn in center. c, Mikhail M. Botvinik, Soviet Union. d, Board, queen in middle. e, Board, bishop, knight. f, Vassili Smyslov, Soviet Union. g, Silhouette of knight, rook queen, chessboard. h, Mikhail N. Tal, Soviet Union.

1995
2288 A760	60p #a.-h. + label	6.25	6.00
2289 A760	60p #a.-h. + label	6.25	6.00

Issued: No. 2288, 2/28; No. 2289, 9/1.

Red Star Army Sport Club, 50th Anniv. A761

1995, Mar. 4
2290 A761	60p bl, red & bister	1.75	1.10

Protection of Nature A762

a, Salamandra salamandra. b, Triturus alpestris. c, Rana graeca. d, Pelobates syriacus balcanicus.

1995, Mar. 23
2291 A762	60p Strip of 4, #a.-d. + label	6.75	6.00

A763

A764

1995, Apr. 20
2292 A763	60p multicolored	1.75	1.10

Radnicki Soccer Club, Belgrade, 75th anniv.

1995, May 6

Europa: 60p, Eagle, mountains. 1.90d, Girl on tricycle, elderly man, woman on park bench, horiz.

2293 A764	60p multicolored	1.60	1.10
2294 A764	1.90d multicolored	2.40	1.60

A765

1995, May 9
2295 A765	60p multicolored	1.50	1.00

End of World War II, 50th anniv.

A766

1995, May 28
2296 A766	60p multicolored	1.75	1.10

Opening of Vukov-Denkmal Subway Station, Belgrade.

Draba Bertiscea A767

a, shown. b, Plants, diff. c, Flowers, mountain. d, Plants on rock, stems at right.

1995, June 12
2297 A767	60p Strip of 4, #a.-d. + label	4.50	4.00

European Nature Protection A768

Designs: 60p, Eremophila alpestris balcanica. 1.90d, Rhinolophus blasii.

1995, July 10
2298 A768	60p multicolored	1.10	.65
2299 A768	1.90d multicolored	3.50	2.10

Slovakian Folk Festival, by Zuzka Medvedova (1897-1985), Painter — A769

1995, Aug. 3
2300 A769	60p multicolored	1.50	1.00

Volleyball, Cent. — A770

Church of St. Luke, Kotor, 800th Anniv. — A771

1995, Sept. 10
2301 A770	90d multicolored	1.50	1.00

1995, Sept. 20
2302 A771	80p multicolored	1.50	1.00

Motion Pictures, Cent. A772

Designs: 1.10d, Newsreel showing coronation of King Peter II. 2.20d, Auguste and Louis Jean Lumière, film projector.

1995, Oct. 3
2303 A772	1.10d dk brn, lt red brn	1.25	.80
2304 A772	2.20d dk brn, lt red brn	2.25	1.50

Army Sports Club "Partisan," 50th Anniv. — A773

1995, Oct. 4
2305 A773	80p multi + label	1.50	1.00

UN, 50th Anniv. — A774

Stamp
Day — A775

1995, Oct. 24
2306 A774 1.10d multicolored　　1.50 1.00

1995, Oct. 31
2307 A775 1.10d multicolored　　1.50 1.00

Joy of
Europe — A776

Paintings: 1.10d, Young boy by Milos
Tenkovic. 2.20d, Young girl by Pierre Bonnard.

1995, Nov. 26
2308 A776 1.10d multicolored　　1.25 .80
2309 A776 2.20d multicolored　　2.25 1.50
　　　　　　Children's Day.

Souvenir Sheet

JUFIZ VIII, Natl. Philatelic Exhibition,
Budva — A777

Design: Montenegro #37, Serbia #6.

1995, Dec. 13　　　　　　**Perf. 14**
2310 A777 2.50d Sheet of 1 + la-
　　　　　　bel　　　　　1.50 1.00

Christmas
A778

Contemporary religious paintings: No. 2311,
Flight into Egypt, by Z. Halupova. No. 2312,
Nativity, by D. Milojevic, vert. No. 2313, Out-
door Christmas scene, by M. Rasic, vert. No.
2314, Indoor traditional Christmas scene, by J.
Brasic.

1995, Dec. 26　　　　　　**Perf. 13½**
2311 A778 1.10d multicolored　　.60 .40
2312 A778 1.10d multicolored　　.60 .40
2313 A778 2.20d multicolored　　1.10 .75
2314 A778 2.20d multicolored　　1.10 .75
　　　Nos. 2311-2314 (4)　　3.40 2.30

Airplanes
A779

1995, Dec. 26
2315 A779 1.10d Saric No. 1　　.60 .40
2316 A779 1.10d Douglas DC-3　.60 .40
2317 A779 2.20d Fizir FN　　　1.10 .75
2318 A779 2.20d Caravelle　　　1.10 .75
　　　Nos. 2315-2318 (4)　　3.40 2.30

Battle of
Mojkovac, 80th
Anniv. — A780

Design: Montenegrins on mountain.

1996, Jan. 6
2319 A780 1.10d multicolored　　.45 .30

Birth of Sava
Sumanovic,
Cent.
A781

Design: 1927 Painting, "Drink Boat."

1996, Jan. 22
2320 A781 1.10d multicolored　　.45 .30

A782　　　　　　　A783

Insects: a, Pyrgomorphela serbica. b,
Calosoma sycopanta. c, Formica rufa. d,
Ascalaphus macaronius.

1996, Feb. 15
2321 A782 2.20d Strip of 4, #a.-
　　　　　　d. + label　　2.75 2.50
　　　　Protection of nature.

1996, Feb. 29　　**Litho.**　　**Perf. 12½**
　　　　Churches.

2322 A783　5d Ljeviska　　　1.60 .95
2323 A783 10d Zica　　　　　3.25 2.00
2324 A783 20d Decani　　　　6.50 4.00
　　　Nos. 2322-2324 (3)　　11.35 6.95

Chess Champions — A784

Designs: a, Tigran Petrosian, Soviet Union.
b, Chess pieces, sundial, chess board. c,
Boris Spassky, Soviet Union. d, Chess pieces,
board, clock showing two time zones. e, Garry
Kasparov, Soviet Union. f, Chess pieces, hand
holding hour glass. g, Bobby Fischer, US. h,
Chess pieces, six clocks. i, Anatoly Karpov,
Soviet Union.

1996, Mar. 15　　**Litho.**　　**Perf. 13½**
2325 A784 1.50d Sheet of 9, #a.-
　　　　　　i.　　　　　6.25 6.00

Olympic
Games,
Cent.
A786

1.50d, Discus throwers. 2.50d, Runners.

　　　　　　Perf. 13½x13¼
1996, Mar. 30　　　　　　**Litho.**
2326 A786 1.50d multi　　　　.55 .45
2327 A786 2.50d multi　　　　1.00 1.00

1996
Summer
Olympics,
Atlanta —
A787

1996, Apr. 12
2328 A787 1.50d shown　　　1.00 .75
2329 A787 1.50d Basketball　1.00 .75
2330 A787 1.50d Handball　　1.00 .75
2331 A787 1.50d Volleyball　1.00 .75
2332 A787 1.50d Shooting　　1.00 .75
2333 A787 1.50d Water polo　1.00 .75
　　　Nos. 2328-2333 (6)　　6.00 4.50

1996 Summer Olympic Games,
Atlanta — A787a

1996, Apr. 12　　**Litho.**　　**Perf. 13**
2334 A787 5d Sheet of 1 + label　2.00 1.50

Stamp
Day — A788

1996, Apr. 30　　**Litho.**　　**Perf. 13½**
2335 A788 1.50d Railway mail
　　　　　　car　　　　.65 .50

Famous Women
Writers — A789

Europa: 2.50d, Isidora Sekulic (1877-1958).
5d, Desanka Maksimovic (1898-1993).

1996, May 7　　**Litho.**　　**Perf. 13½**
2336 A789 2.50d multicolored　1.10 .65
2337 A789　5d multicolored　2.40 1.60

Serbian Red
Cross, 120th
Anniv.
A790

Architectural
Education in
Yugoslavia, 150th
Anniv. — A791

1996, May 8
2338 A790 1.50d Dr. Vladan
　　　　　　Djordjevic　　.75 .60

1996, June 1　　**Litho.**　　**Perf. 13½**
2339 A791 1.50d multicolored　.65 .50

Birds — A792

1996, June 28
2340 A792 2.50d Platalea
　　　　　　leucorodia　　.85 .65
2341 A792　5d Plegadis
　　　　　　falcinellus　1.75 1.25

Prince Peter I
Petrovic at
Battle of
Martinici,
1796 — A793

Design: 2.50d, Prince's Guard at Battle of
Kruse (1796), by Valerio, vert.

1996, July 22
2342 A793 1.50d multicolored　.65 .50
2343 A793 2.50d multicolored　1.00 .75

Horse
Racing,
Ljubicevo
A794

1996, Sept. 2　　**Litho.**　　**Perf. 13½**
2344 A794 1.50d shown　　　.70 .55
2345 A794 2.50d 3 horses racing 1.25 1.00

Fauna
A795

Designs: a, 1.50d, Probosciger aterrimus. b,
2.50d, Goura scheepmakeri. c, 1.50d, Equus
burchelli. d, 2.50d, Panthera tigris.

1996, Sept. 25
2346 A795　Strip of 4, #a.-d. +
　　　　　　label　　　3.75 3.50
　　　　Belgrade Zoo, 60th anniv.

Children's
Day — A796

1996, Oct. 2
2347 A796 1.50d multicolored　.70 .55
2348 A796 2.50d Bird　　　　1.25 1.00

Medalists, 1996 Summer Olympic Games
A797

Designs: No. 2349, Shooting, bronze. No. 2350, Shooting, gold. No. 2351, Volleyball, bronze. No. 2352, Basketball, silver.

1996, Oct. 31   Litho.   Perf. 13½
2349	A797	2.50d multicolored	.60	.50
2350	A797	2.50d multicolored	.60	.50
2351	A797	2.50d multicolored	.60	.50
2352	A797	2.50d multicolored	.60	.50
	Nos. 2349-2352 (4)		2.40	2.00

Savings Accounts, 75th Anniv. — A798

1996, Oct. 31   Litho.   Perf. 13½
2353	A798	1.50d multicolored	.65	.55

Soccer in Yugoslavia, Cent. — A799

Archaeological Finds — A800

1996, Nov. 8   Litho.   Perf. 13½
2354	A799	1.50d multicolored	.60	.50

1996, Nov. 25

Sculptures: No. 2355, God of Autumn. No. 2356, Mother with child. No. 2357, Head of woman. No. 2358, Redheaded goddess.

2355	A800	1.50d multicolored	.60	.50
2356	A800	1.50d multicolored	.60	.50
2357	A800	2.50d multicolored	1.00	.75
2358	A800	2.50d multicolored	1.00	.75
	Nos. 2355-2358 (4)		3.20	2.50

A801

A802

Christmas (Paintings): No. 2359, Annunciation. No. 2360, Mother of God with Christ. No. 2361, Birth of Christ. No. 2362, Palm Sunday.

1996, Dec. 10
2359	A801	1.50d multicolored	.60	.50
2360	A801	1.50d multicolored	.60	.50
2361	A801	2.50d multicolored	1.00	.75
2362	A801	2.50d multicolored	1.00	.75
	Nos. 2359-2362 (4)		3.20	2.50

1997, Jan. 24   Litho.   Perf. 13½
2363	A802	1.50d multicolored	.35	.25

Radomir Putnik Voivode, 150th birth anniv.

25th Intl. Film Festival, Belgrade
A803

1997, Jan. 31
2364	A803	1.50d multicolored	.35	.25

Protected Birds — A804

Designs: No. 2365, Dendrocopos major. No. 2366, Nucifraga caryocatactes. No. 2367, Parus cristatus. No. 2368, Erithacus rubecula.

1997, Feb. 21
2365	A804	1.50d multicolored	.35	.25
2366	A804	2.50d multicolored	.55	.40
2367	A804	1.50d multicolored	.35	.25
2368	A804	2.50d multicolored	.55	.40
a.	Strip of 4, #2365-2368 + label		1.90	1.75

A805

A806

1997, Mar. 17   Litho.   Perf. 13
2369	A805	1.50d multicolored	.50	.40

St. Achilleus Church, 700th Anniv.

1997, Apr. 3   Perf. 13½

Design: Prince Peter I Petrovic (1747-1830), Bishop of Montenegro.

2370	A806	1.50d multicolored	.50	.40

A807

A808

1997, Apr. 19
2371	A807	2.50d multicolored	.85	.70

10th Belgrade Marathon.

1997, Apr. 22   Litho.   Perf. 13½
2372	A808	2.50d multicolored	.90	.75

Serbian Medical Assoc., 125th anniv.

Air Mail Being Loaded at Night
A809

1997, May 3
2373	A809	2.50d multicolored	.90	.75

Stamp Day.

Tennis Tournaments in Yugoslavia — A810

Stylized designs: No. 2374, Player, large racket overhead, Budva. No. 2375, Player with ball flying from racket, Belgrade. No. 2376, Player with racket out in front, Novi Sad.

1997, May 8
2374	A810	2.50d multi + label	.90	.75
2375	A810	2.50d multi + label	.90	.75
2376	A810	2.50d multi + label	.90	.75
	Nos. 2374-2376 (3)		2.70	2.25

Stories and Legends
A811

Europa: 2.50d, Shackled Bach Chelik surrounded by creatures. 6d, Bach Chelik in chains, prince fighting with him, princess, castle.

1997, May 30   Perf. 11½
2377	A811	2.50d multicolored	.90	.75
2378	A811	6d multicolored	2.10	1.60

Each issued in sheets of 8 + label.

Nature Protection
A812

1997, June 5
2379	A812	2.50d	Cerambyx cerdo	.90	.75
2380	A812	6d	Quercus robur	2.10	1.60

Stanislav Binicki (1872-1947)
A813

Printing of Gorski Vijenac, 150th Anniv. — A814

1997, June 7   Perf. 13½
2381	A813	2.50d multicolored	.90	.75

1997, June 7   Perf. 13½
2382	A814	2.50d multicolored	.90	.75

Flowers — A815

Designs: a, 1.50d, Pelargonium grandiflorum. b, 2.50d, Saintpaulia ionantha. c, 1.50d, Hydrangea macrophylla. d, 2.50d, Oncidium varicosum.

1997, Sept. 10   Litho.   Perf. 13
2383	A815	Strip of 4, #a.-d. + label	2.75	2.50

Souvenir Sheet

JUFIZ IX, 9th Natl. Philatelic Exhibition — A816

Design: Sculpture, by Dragomir Arambasic, in front of art gallery. Illustration reduced.

1997, Sept. 10   Perf. 14
2384	A816	5d multicolored	1.75	1.40

A817

A818

1997, Sept. 24   Perf. 13½x14
2385	A817	2.50d multicolored	.85	.70

Serbian Chemical Society, cent.

Type of 1993

1997, Oct. 2   *Perf. 14*
          Size: 18x18mm
2386 A702d (A) like #2142   .20 .20

1997, Oct. 2

Joy of Europe children's art works: 2.50d, 5d, Busts of people formed from collage of various food products.

2387 A818 2.50d multicolored   .85 .70
2388 A818   5d multicolored   1.75 1.40

"May Assembly in Sremski Karlivoci," by Pavle Simic — A819

1997, Oct. 10   *Litho.*   *Perf. 14*
2389 A819 2.50d multicolored   .95 .75
Matica Srpska Gallery, 150th anniv.

A820

A821

Museum exhibits: No. 2390, Two-headed statuette. No. 2391, Parade helmet. No. 2392, Terra cotta statuette. No. 2393, Virgin icon.

1997, Nov. 12
2390 A820 1.50d multicolored   .50 .40
2391 A820 1.50d multicolored   .50 .40
2392 A820 2.50d multicolored   .85 .65
2393 A820 2.50d multicolored   .85 .65
          Nos. 2390-2393 (4)   2.70 2.10

1997, Dec. 2   *Perf. 11½*

Icons (Chelandari Serbian Monastery, Mount Athos): No. 2394, Christ. No. 2395, Madonna and Child, 12th cent. No. 2396, Madonna and Child, 13th cent. No. 2397, 3-handed Madonna.

Granite Paper
2394 A821 1.50d multicolored   .50 .40
2395 A821 1.50d multicolored   .50 .40
2396 A821 2.50d multicolored   .85 .65
2397 A821 2.50d multicolored   .85 .65
          Nos. 2394-2397 (4)   2.70 2.10

A822

A823

1998, Jan. 20   *Litho.*   *Perf. 13½*
2398 A822 1.50d Savina   .55 .45
2399 A822 2.50d Donji Brceli   .95 .75
Monasteries of Montenegro.

1998, Feb. 6   *Perf. 14*
2400 A823 2.50d Figure skater   .95 .75
2401 A823   6d Skier   2.25 1.75
1998 Winter Olympic Games, Nagano.

Horses
A824

Designs: a, 1.50d, Two running. b, 2.50d, Arabian up close. c, 1.50d, Thoroughbred. d, 2.50d, Thoroughbred running on race track.

1998, Feb. 26   *Litho.*   *Perf. 12x11½*
2402 A824 Strip of 4, #a.-d. +
               label   3.00 2.50

Intl. Women's Day
A825

1998, Mar. 7   *Perf. 13½*
2403 A825 2.50d multicolored   .95 .75

Yugoslav Airlines Assoc., 50th Anniv. A826

1998, Apr. 24
2404 A826 2.50d multicolored   .95 .75

Europa — A827

Paintings: 6d, "Dressing the Bride," by Paja Jovanovic (1859-1957). 9d, "Bishop's Congratulations," by Pero Pocek (1878-1963).

1998, May 4   *Litho.*   *Perf. 12*
          Granite Paper
2405 A827   6d multicolored   1.10 .90
2406 A827   9d on 2.50d, multi   1.75 1.40
No. 2406 was not issued without the silver surcharge.

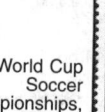

1998 World Cup Soccer Championships, France — A828

1998, May 15   *Litho.*   *Perf. 13½*
2407 A828   6d shown   1.25 1.25
2408 A828   9d Soccer players,
                   diff.   1.75 1.75

Souvenir Sheet

Danube Commission, 50th Anniv. — A829

Illustration reduced.

1998, May 19   *Perf. 14*
2409 A829 9d multicolored   1.75 1.75

Famous People of Serbia — A831

a, Djura Jaksic (1832-78), poet, painter. b, Nadezda Petrovic (1873-1915), painter. c, Radoje Domanovic (1873-1908), writer. d, Vasilije Mokranjac (1923-1984), composer. e, Streten Stojanovic (1898-1960), sculptor. f, Milan Konjovic (1898-1993), painter. g, Desanka Maksimovic (1898-1993), poet. h, Ivan Tabakovic (1898-1977), painter.

1998, June 30   *Litho.*   *Perf. 12*
          Granite Paper
          Sheet of 8
2412 A831 1.50d #a.-h. + label   2.25 2.25

Souvenir Sheet

Yugoslavia, Winner of World Basketball Championships — A832

1998, Aug. 21   *Perf. 13½*
2413 A832 10d multicolored   2.00 2.00

Protected Animals — A833

a, 2d, Martes martes. b, 2d, Anthropoides virgo. c, 5d, Lynx lynx. d, 5d, Loxia curvirostra.

1998, Sept. 2
2414 A833 Strip of 4, #a.-d. +
               label   2.75 2.75

Development of the Railway — A837

Trains: a, 1847. b, 1900. c, 1920. d, 1930. e, Diesel locomotive. f, 1990.

1998, Nov. 3   *Litho.*   *Perf. 13½*
2420 A837 2.50d Booklet pane of
               6, #a.-f.   3.00 3.00
          Complete booklet, #2420   3.25

Paintings of Sailing Ships, Maritime Museum, Kotor A838

#2421, Veracruz, 1873. #2422, Pierino, 1883. #2423, Draghetto, 1865. #2424, Group of ships.

1998, Nov. 11   *Perf. 12*
          Granite Paper
2421 A838 2d multicolored   .40 .30
2422 A838 2d multicolored   .40 .30
2423 A838 5d multicolored   1.00 .80
2424 A838 5d multicolored   1.00 .80
          Nos. 2421-2424 (4)   2.80 2.20

Chelandari Monastery, 800th Anniv. — A839

Views of monastery: No. 2425, Looking from center of complex, two trees. No. 2426, Group of taller buildings. No. 2427, Aerial view. No. 2428, Looking across group of buildings, crosses on turrets.

1998, Dec. 9   *Perf. 14*
2425 A839 2d multicolored   .40 .30
2426 A839 2d multicolored   .40 .30
2427 A839 5d multicolored   1.00 .80
2428 A839 5d multicolored   1.00 .80
          Nos. 2425-2428 (4)   2.80 2.20

Third Meeting of Southeast European Postal Ministers
A840

1998, Dec. 17   Litho.   Perf. 14
2429 A840 5d multicolored   1.00   .80

Souvenir Sheet

Yugoslavia, Silver Medalists at 1998 World Volleyball Championships — A841

Illustration reduced.

1998, Dec. 19   Perf. 13½
2430 A841 10d multicolored   2.00 1.60

Post and Telecommunications Museum, Belgrade, 75th Anniv. — A842

#2431, Postrider. #No. 2432, Antique telegraph equipment, museum building.

1998, Dec. 21   Engr.
2431 A842 5d olive brown & slate 1.00 .80
2432 A842 5d red & brown   1.00 .80

Serbian Monasteries
A843

1999, Jan. 14   Litho.   Perf. 13¾
2433 A843 2d Visoki Decani   .40   .30
2434 A843 5d Grachanica   1.00   .80

Farm Animals
A844

Designs: a, 2d, Pigs. b, 6d, Goat. c, 2d, Oxen. d, 6d, Long-horn sheep.

1999, Feb. 5   Litho.   Perf. 13½
2435 A844 Strip of 4, #a.-d. +
           label   3.25 3.00

A845

A846

1999, Feb. 24   Litho.   Perf. 13¼
2436 A845 6d Scouting   1.10   .90

1999, Mar.
2437 A846 6d brown & buff   1.10   .90
Yugoslav Bar Association, 70th anniv.

Target
A847   A848

1999   Perf. 12¼x12½
2438 A847 (A) black   .40   .30
2439 A848 (A) black & red   .40   .30
Nos. 2438-2439 sold for 2.04d when issued.

World Table Tennis Championships, Belgrade — A849

1999, Apr.   Perf. 13¼
Player colors
2440 A849 6d blue & red   1.10   .90
2441 A849 6d green & red   1.10   .90

A850

A851

Europa, National Parks and Reserves: 6d, Falcon, trees, mountains, Kopaonik Natl. Park. 15d, Flowers, mountains, Lovcen Natl. Park.

1999, May 5   Photo.   Perf. 11¾
Granite Paper
2442 A850 6d multicolored   3.00 2.00
2443 A850 15d multicolored 5.00 3.50
Each printed in shheets of 8 + 1 central label.

1999, May   Perf. 11¾x12
Nature protection.
2444 A851 6d Shovel, spider
           web   1.10   .90
2445 A851 15d Thumb squeezing
           earth   2.75 2.00

Mushrooms
A852

Designs: a, Amanita virosa. b, Amanita pantherina. c, Hypholoma fasciculare. d, Ramaria pallida.

1999, June 18 Litho. Perf. 11¾x12
Granite Paper
2446 A852 6d Strip of 4, #a.-d., +
           central label   5.00 4.50
Central labels differ on sheet.

Famous Montenegrins — A853

Designs: a, Stjepan Mitrov Ljubisa (1824-78). b, Marko Milanov (1833-1901). c, Pero Pocek (1878-1963). d, Risto Stijovic (1894-1974). e, Milo Milunovic (1897-1967). f, Petar Lubarda (1907-74). g, Vuko Radovic (1911-96). h, Mihailo Lalic (1914-92).

1999, June 30   Perf. 13¼
2447 A853 2d Sheet of 8, #a.-h.,
           + central label   2.75 2.50

UPU, 125th Anniv.
A854

1999, Sept. 15   Perf. 13¼
2448 A854 6d shown   1.00   .80
2449 A854 12d Envelopes cir-
           cling globe   2.00 1.60

Joy of Europe Children's Drawings
A855

1999, Oct. 1   Perf. 13¾
2450 A855 6d Lion   1.10   .90
2451 A855 15d Family, vert. 2.75 2.00

Frédéric Chopin (1810-49), Composer
A856

1999, Oct. 15   Perf. 13¼
2452 A856 10d multi   1.75 1.40

No. 2438, Mastheads of "Filatelista"
A857

1999, Oct. 18
2453 A857 10d multi   1.75 1.40
Stamp Day.

A858

Bridges Destroyed by NATO Air Strikes
A859

Bridges: #2454, Varadinski. #2455, Ostruznica. #2456, Murino. #2457, Grdelica. #2458, Bistrica. #2459, Zezeljev.

1999, Oct. 29   Perf. 13¾
2454 A858 2d shown   .30   .25
2455 A859 2d shown   .30   .25
2456 A859 2d multi   .30   .25
2457 A859 6d multi   1.00   .75
2458 A859 6d multi   1.00   .75
2459 A859 6d multi   1.00   .75
   Nos. 2454-2459 (6)   3.90 3.00

Millennium
A860

a, 6d, Roman altars, statue of Jupiter. b, 6d, Sculpture of Emperor Trajan and army leaders, mosaic, lamp, lead mirror. c, 6d, Mosaic of Dionysius, arch. d, 6d, Hagia Sophia, mosaic of Madonna and Child, Emperor Constantine. e, 6d, Large cross, candle, fibula, pot. f, 6d, Church, boats, manuscript. g, 15d, Nativity and crucifixion of Christ, boats, farmers.

1999, Nov. 19
2460 A860 Booklet pane of 7,
           #a.-g., + 2 labels 9.00 8.00
   Complete booklet, #2460   9.00
   Size of #2460g: 105x55mm.

A861

Bomb Damage
A862

#2461, Bolnice. #2462, Telecommunications complex. #2463, Refinery. #2464, Bolnice, diff. #2465, Telecommunications complex, diff. #2466, Television complex.

1999, Nov. 27		**Litho.**	**Perf. 13¾**	
2461	A861	2d shown	.30	.25
2462	A862	2d shown	.30	.25
2463	A862	2d multi	.30	.25
2464	A862	6d multi	1.00	.75
2465	A862	6d multi	1.00	.75
2466	A862	6d multi	1.00	.75
	Nos. 2461-2466 (6)		3.90	3.00

A863

Frescoes of Poganovo Monastery,
500th Anniv. — A864

Design A863 has Latin letters, A864 has Cyrillic letters.

1999, Dec. 23				
2467	A863	6d shown	1.00	.75
2468	A864	6d shown	1.00	.75
2469	A863	6d Fresco, diff.	1.00	.75
2470	A864	6d Fresco, diff.	1.00	.75
	Nos. 2467-2470 (4)		4.00	3.00

A865

Gold Prospectors in Pec River — A866

Design A865 has Latin letters, A866 has Cyrillic letters.

1999, Dec. 30				
2471	A865	6d shown	1.00	.75
2472	A866	6d shown	1.00	.75
2473	A865	6d Prospectors, diff.	1.00	.75
2474	A866	6d Prospectors, diff.	1.00	.75
	Nos. 2471-2474 (4)		4.00	3.00

Krusedol Monastery
A867

2000, Jan. 13			**Perf. 13¼**	
2475	A867	10d shown	1.75	1.40
2476	A867	10d Rakovac Monastery	1.75	1.40

Yugoslavian Archives, 50th Anniv.
A868

2000, Jan. 21				
2477	A868	10d multi	15.00	15.00

Butterflies — A869

No. 2478: a, Nymphalis antiopa. b, Parnalius polyxena. c, Limenitis populi. d, Melanargia galathea.

2000, Feb. 25		**Litho.**	**Perf. 13¾**	
2478		Horiz. strip of 4 + central label	7.50	7.50
a.-d.	A869	10d Any single	1.75	1.75

Worldwide Fund for Nature
A870

Perdix perdix: a, Pair in snow. b, Pair facing right. c, Bird on nest. d, Pair, one facing left.

2000, Mar. 14		**Litho.**	**Perf. 12x11¾**	
2479	A870	10d Strip of 4, #a.-d., + central label	6.75	5.00

Damage from NATO Airstrikes
A871

Various destroyed buildings. Colors: 10d, Blue. 20d, Brown.

2000, Mar. 24		**Engr.**	**Perf. 13¼**	
2480-2481	A871	Set of 2	2.50	2.00

Souvenir Sheet

JUFIZ X Philatelic Exhibition,
Belgrade — A872

Illustration reduced.

2000, May 2			**Litho.**	
2482	A872	15d multi	30.00	30.00

Nature Protection
A873

Designs: No. 2483, 30d, Feeding chicks by hand. No. 2484, 30d, Map of Europe in tree's leaves, vert.

Perf. 12x11¾, 11¾x12				
2000, May 4			**Litho.**	
2483-2484	A873	Set of 2	9.00	7.50

Europa — A874

"2000" and: No. 2485, 30d, Astronaut on moon. No. 2486, 30d, Star and mountains.

2000, May 9			**Perf. 11¾x12**	
2485-2486	A874	Set of 2	9.00	7.50

European Soccer Championships
A875

Inscriptions in: No. 2487, 30d, Cyrillic letters. No. 2488, 30d, Latin letters.

2000, May 20		**Litho.**	**Perf. 13¾**	
2487-2488	A875	Set of 2	9.00	7.50

Postal Services in Serbia, 160th Anniv. — A876

2000, June 7		**Litho.**	**Perf. 13¾**	
2489	A876	10d multi	1.60	1.25

2000 Summer Olympics, Sydney — A877

Map of Australia and: 6d, Kangaroo. 12d, Emu. 24d, Koala and soccer ball. 30d, Parrot.

2000, June 28				
2490-2493	A877	Set of 4	12.00	9.00

Stamp Day — A878

2000, Sept. 26			**Perf. 13¼**	
2494	A878	10d multi	1.60	1.25

"Joy of Europe"
A879

Children's art: 30d, Cows. 40d, Cranes, vert.

2000, Oct. 2				
2495-2496	A879	Set of 2	12.00	9.00

World Teachers' Day — A880

2000, Oct. 5				
2497	A880	10d multi	1.60	1.25

13th Apiarists Congress
A881

2000, Oct. 6				
2498	A881	10d multi	1.60	1.25

Medals Won at 2000 Summer Olympics
A882

Designs: No. 2499, 20d, Water polo (bronze). No. 2500, 20d, Shooting (silver). 30d, Volleyball, vert.

2000, Oct. 23			**Perf. 13¾**	
2499-2500	A882	Set of 2	6.75	5.00
Souvenir Sheet				
2501	A882	30d multi	10.00	10.00

No. 2501 contains one 35x46mm stamp.

Millennium
A883

No. 2502: a, Ships. b, Papermaking. c, Galileo and telescopes. d, Steam locomotive and steamship. e, Nikola Tesla, invention of the telephone. f, Astronaut, outer space settlement. g, Ships, airplanes, balloons, horses.

2000, Nov. 2		**Litho.**	**Perf. 13¾**	
2502		Booklet pane of 7 + 2 labels	3.50	
a.-f.	A883	12d Any single	.35	.35
g.	A883	40d multi	1.25	1.25
	Booklet, #2502		3.50	

Size of No. 2502g: 105x55mm.

Nativity Fresco, Pec — A884

2000, Nov. 7		**Litho.**	**Perf. 13¾**	
2503	A884	A multi	.60	.30

No. 2503 sold for 3.56d on day of issue.

Serb Clothing From the 1900s — A885

Designs: 6d, Vest, Jagodina. 12d, Dresses, Metochija. 24d, Blouse, Pec. 30d, Vest, Kupres.

2000, Dec. 7
2504-2507 A885   Set of 4   12.00 9.00

Montenegrin Religious Art — A886

Designs: 6d, Madonna and Child, 1573-74. 12d, Nativity, 1666-67. 24d, St. Luke, 1672-73. 30d, Madonna and Child, 1642.

2000, Dec. 19
2508-2511 A886   Set of 4   12.00 9.00

A887

A887a

2000, Dec. 29   Litho.   Perf. 13¾
2512 A887   6d multi   1.00 .75
2513 A887a 12d multi   2.10 1.10
Resumption of Yugoslavia's membership in Organization for Security and Cooperation in Europe (#2512), and United Nations (#2513).

Vatoped Monastery, Mount Athos, Greece A888

Esfigmen Monastery, Mount Athos, Greece A889

2001, Jan. 26   Litho.   Perf. 13¼
2514 A888 10d multi   .30 .30
2515 A889 27d multi   .85 .85

Matica Srpska, 175th Anniv. — A890

2001, Feb. 16   Perf. 13¾
2516 A890 15d multi   .45 .45

Animals — A891

No. 2517: a, Felis leo. b, Ursus maritimus. c, Macaca fuscata. d, Spheniscus humboldti.

2001, Feb. 23
2517   Horiz. strip of 4 + central label   2.25 2.25
a. A891 6d multi   .20 .20
b. A891 12d multi   .35 .35
c. A891 24d multi   .75 .75
d. A891 30d multi   .95 .95

Women's World Chess Champions — A892

No. 2518: a, Vera Menchik (1927-44). b, Lyudmila Rudenko (1950-53). c, Yelisavyeta Bykova (1953-56, 1958-62). d, Olga Rubtsova (1956-58). e, Nona Gaprindashvili (1962-78). f, Maia Chiburdanidze (1978-91). g, Zsuzsa Polgar (1996-99). h, Xie Jun (1991-96, 1999-2000).

2001, Mar. 8   Perf. 13¼
2518 A892 10d Sheet of 8, #a-h, + label   2.50 2.50

Famous Men — A893

Designs: 50d, Stevan Mokranjac (1856-1914), composer. 100d, Nikola Tesla (1856-1943), inventor.

2001, Mar. 19   Perf. 13¾
2519-2520 A893   Set of 2   4.75 4.75

Flowers A894

No. 2521: a, Hibiscus syriacus. b, Nerium oleander. c, Lapageria rosea. d, Sorbus aucuparia.

2001, Apr. 13   Perf. 12x11¾
2521   Horiz. strip of 4 + central label   2.25 2.25
a. A894 6d multi   .20 .20
b. A894 12d multi   .40 .40
c. A894 24d multi   .75 .75
d. A894 30d multi   .90 .90

Europa — A895

Designs: 30d, Vratna River. 45d, Jerme Canyon.

2001, May 4   Perf. 11¾x12
2522-2523 A895   Set of 2   2.25 2.25

Serbian Mountaineering Association, Cent. — A896

2001, June 8   Perf. 13¼
2524 A896 15d multi   .45 .45

Nature Protection A897

Designs: 30d, Bird on branch, Lake Ludasko. 45d, Stork flying above Begej River.

2001, June 22   Perf. 12x11¾
2525-2526 A897   Set of 2   2.25 2.25

14th Cent. Book Illumination A898

2001, July 2   Perf. 13¼
2527 A898 E multi   .85 .85
Sold for 28.70d on day of issue.

Souvenir Sheet

Yugoslavian Victory in European Water Polo Championships — A899

2001, July 5   Perf. 13¾
2528 A899 30d multi   .85 .85

Souvenir Sheet

Serbiafila XII Stamp Exhibition — A900

2001, Sept. 8
2529 A900 30d multi   .90 .90

Solar Energy — A901

2001, Sept. 19   Perf. 13¼
2530 A901 15d multi   .45 .45

Danube Commission A902

Designs: 30d, Ships, hands raising bridge. 45d, Ship, hand, clock.

2001, Sept. 20   Perf. 13¾
2531-2532 A902   Set of 2   2.25 2.25

Joy of Europe — A903

Paintings: 30d, Child, by Marko Chelebonovic. 45d, Girl Under a Fruit Tree, by Beta Vukanovic.

2001, Oct. 2   Perf. 13¼
2533-2534 A903   Set of 2   2.25 2.25

Yugoslavian Victories in European Sports Championships A904

Designs: No. 2535, 30d, Men's basketball. No. 2536, 30d, Men's volleyball.

2001, Oct. 1
2535-2536 A904   Set of 2   1.90 1.90

Intl. Federation of Philately (FIP), 75th Anniv. A905

2001, Oct. 24
2537 A905 15d multi   .45 .45
Stamp Day.

Minerals
A906

2001, Nov. 2   *Perf. 13¾*
2538   Horiz. strip of 4 + cen-
              tral label   2.25 2.25
  a.   A906 7d Antimonite   .20   .20
  b.   A906 14d Calcite   .40   .40
  c.   A906 26.20d Quartz   .80   .80
  d.   A906 28.70d Calcite and galenite .85   .85

Pljevlja
Gymnasium,
Cent. — A907

2001, Nov. 18   *Perf. 13¼*
2539 A907 15d multi   .45   .45

Public
Telephone
Booths in
Serbia,
Cent. — A908

2001, Nov. 20
2540 A908 15d multi   .45   .45

Christmas
A910

Paintings of the Birth of Jesus Christ: 7d,
14d, 26.20d, 28.70d.

2001, Dec. 1   *Perf. 13¾*
2541-2544 A910   Set of 4   2.25 2.25

Junior World Ice Hockey
Championships, Belgrade — A911

2002, Jan. 5   *Perf. 13¼*
2545 A911 14d multi   .45   .45

2002 Winter
Olympics, Salt
Lake
City — A912

Designs: 28.70d, Skier. 50d, Four-man bobsled, vert.

2002, Jan. 25   *Perf. 13¼*
2546-2547 A912   Set of 2   2.40 2.40

Jovan Karamata
(1902-67),
Mathematician
A913

2002, Feb. 1
2548 A913 14d multi   .45   .45

Birds — A914

No. 2549: a, Saxicola torquata. b, Saxicola
rubetra. c, Parus caeruleus. d, Turdus
philomelos.

2002, Feb. 22
2549   Horiz. strip of 4 + cen-
              tral label   2.25 2.25
  a.   A914 7d multi   .20   .20
  b.   A914 14d multi   .40   .40
  c.   A914 26.20d multi   .80   .80
  d.   A914 28.70d multi   .85   .85

Easter — A915

Designs: 7d, Crucifixion, fresco from
Studenica Monastery, 1208. 14d, King Milu-
tin's Veil, 1300. 26.20d, Christ's Descent to
Hell, silverwork, 1540. 28.70d, Easter egg,
Pec Patriarchy, 1980.

2002, Mar. 7   *Perf. 13¾*
2550-2553 A915   Set of 4   2.25 2.25

Bunjevac
Women's
Clothing — A916

Woman with: 7d, White blouse. 28.70d,
Kerchief.

2002, Mar. 29   *Perf. 13¼*
2554-2555 A916   Set of 2   1.00 1.00

Zarko Tomic-
Sremac (b. 1900),
World War II
Hero — A917

2002, Apr. 15
2556 A917 14d multi   .45   .45

Danube
Fish — A918

No. 2557: a, Rutilus rutilus. b, Acipenser
ruthenus. c, Huso huso. d, Stizostedion
lucioperca.

2002, Apr. 25   **Litho.**   *Perf. 13¼*
2557   Horiz. strip of 4 + central
              label   2.25 2.25
  a.   A918 7d multi   .20   .20
  b.   A918 14d multi   .40   .40
  c.   A918 26.20d multi   .80   .80
  d.   A918 28.70d multi   .85   .85

Europa
A919

Designs: 28.70d, Trapeze artists. 50d, Tiger
trainer.

2002, May 3   *Perf. 13¾*
2558-2559 A919   Set of 2   2.40 2.40

Europa Type of 2002
Souvenir Sheet

Design: 45d, Trained horse act.

2002, May 3   **Litho.**   *Perf. 13¾*
2560 A919 45d multi   1.40 1.40
No. 2560 contains one 46x35mm stamp.

Civil Aviation
in
Yugoslavia,
75th Anniv.
A920

Designs: 7d, Potez-29. 28.70d, Boeing 737-
300.

Perf. 13¼ Syncopated
2002, June 17   **Litho.**
2561-2562 A920   Set of 2   1.25 1.25

Types of 1993 and 2001
2002, July 25   **Litho.**   *Perf. 12½*
Size: 19x21mm (#2563)
2563 A702d A blue   .25   .25

Perf. 13¼
"E" in Green
2564 A898 E multi   1.00 1.00
    Nos. 2563-2564 were intended for use in
Montenegro and were sold there for 13c and
52c in euro currency respectively. The stamps
were valid for use in the Serbian section of
Yugoslavia.

European
Nature
Protection
A921

Designs: 28.70d, Tara National Park. 50d,
Golija Nature Park.

Perf. 13¼ Syncopated
2002, June 28   **Litho.**
2565-2566 A921   Set of 2   2.60 2.60

Mills — A922

Designs: 7d, Windmill, Melenci. 28.70d,
Water mill, Lyuberada.

2002, Sept. 14
2567-2568 A922   Set of 2   1.25 1.25

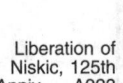

Liberation of
Niskic, 125th
Anniv. — A923

2002, Sept. 18   *Perf. 13¾*
2569 A923 14d multi   .45   .45

Souvenir Sheet

Victory in 2002 World Basketball
Championships — A924

2002, Sept. 20
2570 A924 30d multi   1.00 1.00

Souvenir Sheet

JUFIZ XI Philatelic Exhibition — A925

2002, Sept. 23
2571 A925 30d multi   1.00 1.00

Joy of
Europe — A926

Children's art: 28.70d, Boat. 50d, Bird.

2002, Oct. 2
2572-2573 A926   Set of 2   2.60 2.60

Moraca
Monastery,
750th
Anniv. — A927

2002, Oct. 10
2574 A927 16d multi   .55   .55

Types of Nos. 2255 and 2256
Surcharged in Black or Violet

2002 Perfs, etc., as Before
2575 A751 50p on 5p #2256
multi .20 .20
2576 A702g 10d on 10,000d
#2145 .35 .35
2577 A751 12d on 1p #2255
multi (V) .40 .40
Nos. 2575-2577 (3) .95 .95

Issued: No. 2575, 10/17; No. 2576, 11/28; No. 2577, 12/19.

Intl. Federation of Stamp Dealers Associations, 50th Anniv. — A928

2002, Oct. 24 Litho. Perf. 13¾
2578 A928 16d multi .55 .55

Serbian Folk Costumes — A929

Paintings of costumes by Olga Benson in Ethnographic Institute of Serbian Academy of Sciences and Arts: a, Man, Kusadak. b, Woman with red headdress, Belgrade. c, Man, Novo Selo. d, Woman in profile, Belgrade.

2002, Nov. 8 Perf. 13¾
2579 Horiz. strip of 4, + central label 3.25 3.25
a. A929 16d multi .55 .55
b. A929 24d multi .80 .80
c. A929 26.20d multi .90 .90
d. A929 28.70d multi .95 .95

Christmas A930

Religious art: 12d, Nativity, Stavronikita Monastery, Mount Athos, Greece, 1546. 16d, Nativity, Chilandari Monastery, Mount Athos, Greece, c. 1618. 26.20d, Nativity, Tretyakov Gallery, Moscow, 15th cent. 28.70d, Adoration of the Magi, by Sandro Botticelli.

2002, Dec. 2
2580-2583 A930 Set of 4 2.75 2.75

Abandoned Dogs — A931

Various dogs.

2003, Jan. 31 Perf. 13¾
2584 Horiz. strip of 4, + central label 3.25 3.25
a. A931 16d multi .55 .55
b. A931 24d multi .80 .80
c. A931 26.20d multi .90 .90
d. A931 28.70d multi .95 .95

Yugoslavia became Serbia & Montenegro on Feb. 4, 2003. See Serbia & Montenegro for subsequent issues.

SEMI-POSTAL STAMPS

Giving Succor to Wounded SP1

Wounded Soldier SP2

Symbolical of National Unity — SP3

Unwmk.
1921, Jan. 30 Engr. Perf. 12
B1 SP1 10p carmine .20 .20
B2 SP2 15p violet brown .20 .20
B3 SP3 25p light blue .20 .20
Nos. B1-B3 (3) .60 .60

Nos. B1-B3 were sold at double face value, the excess being for the benefit of invalid soldiers.
For surcharges see Nos. 15-21.

U. R. I.

This overprint was applied to 500,000 copies of No. B1 in 1923 and they were given to the Society for Wounded Invalids (Uprava Ratnih Invalida) which sold them for 2d apiece. These overprinted stamps had no franking power, but some were used through ignorance.

Regular Issue of 1926-27 Surcharged in Dark Red

1926, Nov. 1 Perf. 13
B5 A6 25p + 25p green .20 .20
B6 A6 50p + 50p olive brn .20 .20
B7 A6 1d + 50p scarlet .20 .20
B8 A6 2d + 50p black .60 .20
B9 A6 3d + 50p slate blue .50 .20
B10 A6 4d + 50p red org 1.40 .20
B11 A6 5d + 50p brt vio .75 .20
B12 A6 8d + 50p black brn 1.90 .60
B13 A6 10d + 1d olive brn 1.75 .60
B14 A6 15d + 1d brown 5.00 1.00
B15 A6 20d + 1d dark vio 4.50 .75
B16 A6 30d + 1d orange 15.00 1.90
a. Double surcharge
Nos. B5-B16 (12) 32.00 6.25

The surtax on these stamps was intended for a fund for relief of sufferers from floods.
For overprints see Nos. 99-101.

Cathedral at Duvno SP4

King Tomislav SP6

Kings Tomislav and Alexander SP5

Perf. 12½, 11½x12
1929, Nov. 1 Typo.
B17 SP4 50p (+ 50p) olive green .20 .20
B18 SP5 1d (+ 50p) red .20 .20
B19 SP6 3d (+ 1d) blue 1.25 1.10
Nos. B17-B19 (3) 1.65 1.50

Millenary of the Croatian kingdom. The surtax was used to create a War Memorial Cemetery in France and to erect a monument to Serbian soldiers who died there.

View of Dobropolje SP7

War Memorial — SP8

View of Kajmaktchalan SP9

1931, Apr. 1 Perf. 12½, 11½
B20 SP7 50p + 50p blue grn .20 .20
B21 SP8 1d + 1d scarlet .20 .20
B22 SP9 3d + 3d deep blue .20 .20
Nos. B20-B22 (3) .60 .60

The surtax was added to a fund for a War Memorial to Serbian soldiers who died in France during World War I.

SP10

SP12

SP11

Black Overprint
1931, Nov. 1 Perf. 12½, 11½x12
B23 SP10 50p (+ 50p) olive grn .20 .20
B24 SP11 1d (+ 50p) red .20 .20
B25 SP12 3d (+ 1d) blue .20 .20
Nos. B23-B25 (3) .60 .60

Surtax for War Memorial fund.

Rower on Danube at Smederevo SP13

Bled Lake SP14

Danube near Belgrade SP15

View of Split Harbor SP16

Zagreb Cathedral — SP17

Prince Peter — SP18

1932, Sept. 2 Litho. Perf. 11½
B26 SP13 75p + 50p dl grn & lt blue .40 1.00
B27 SP14 1d + ½d scar & lt blue .40 1.10
B28 SP15 1½d + ½d rose & green .40 1.10
B29 SP16 3d + 1d bl & lt bl .80 2.00
B30 SP17 4d + 1d red org & lt blue 4.00 10.00
B31 SP18 5d + 1d dl vio & lilac 4.00 8.50
Nos. B26-B31 (6) 10.00 23.70

European Rowing Championship Races, Belgrade.

King Alexander SP19

Prince Peter SP20

1933, May 25 Typo. Perf. 12½
B32 SP19 50p + 25p black 3.50 5.25
B33 SP19 75p + 25p yel grn 3.50 5.25
B34 SP19 1.50d + 50p rose 3.50 5.25
B35 SP19 3d + 1d bl vio 3.50 5.25
B36 SP19 4p + 1d dk grn 3.50 5.25
B37 SP19 5d + 1d orange 3.50 5.25
Nos. B32-B37 (6) 21.00 31.50

11th Intl. Congress of P.E.N. (Poets, Editors and Novelists) Clubs, Dubrovnik, May 25-27.
The labels at the foot of the stamps are printed in either Cyrillic or Latin letters and each bears the amount of a premium for the benefit of the local P.E.N. Club at Dubrovnik.

1933, June 28
B38 SP20 75p + 25p slate grn .20 .25
B39 SP20 1½d + ½d deep red .20 .25

60th anniv. meeting of the National Sokols (Sports Associations) at Ljubljana, July 1.

Eagle
Soaring
over City
SP22

Athlete and
Eagle
SP23

1934, June 1   **Perf. 12½**
B40 SP22   75p + 25p green   1.75 1.10
B41 SP22   1.50d + 50p car   3.50 1.60
B42 SP22   1.75d + 25p brown   5.50 2.25
  Nos. B40-B42 (3)   10.75 4.95

20th anniversary of Sokols of Sarajevo.

1934, June 1
B43 SP23   75p + 25p Prus grn   1.60 .90
B44 SP23   1.50d + 50p car   3.50 1.75
B45 SP23   1.75d + 25p choc   5.50 2.50
  Nos. B43-B45 (3)   10.60 5.15

60th anniversary of Sokols of Zagreb.

Mother and Children
SP24   SP25

Perf. 12½x11½
1935, Dec. 25   **Photo.**
B46 SP24 1.50d + 1d dk brn &
           brown   .70   .55
  a.   Perf. 11½   11.50 11.50
B47 SP25 3.50d + 1.50d bright
           ultra & bl   1.25 1.00

The surtax was for "Winter Help."

Queen
Mother Marie
SP26

Prince Regent
Paul
SP27

1936, May 3   **Litho.**
B48 SP26   75p + 25p grnsh bl   .40   .40
B49 SP26   1.50d + 50p rose pink   .45   .45
B50 SP26   1.75d + 75p brown   .65   .65
B51 SP26   3.50d + 1d brt bl   .50   .50
  Nos. B48-B51 (4)   2.00 2.00

1936, Sept. 20   **Typo.**
B52 SP27   75p + 50p turq grn &
             red   .20 4.50
B53 SP27   1.50d + 50p cer & red   .20 3.00

Surtax for the Red Cross.

Princes Tomislav and Andrej
SP28   SP29

Perf. 11½x12½, 12½x11½
1937, May 1
B54 SP28   25p + 25p red brn   .20   .25
B55 SP28   75p + 75p emerald   .20   .30
B56 SP29   1.50d + 1d org red   .25   .35
B57 SP29   2d + 1d magenta   .25   .35
  Nos. B54-B57 (4)   .90   1.25

Souvenir Sheet

National Costumes — SP30

1937, Sept. 12   **Perf. 14**
B57A SP30 Sheet of 4   1.75 2.75
  b.   1d blue green   .25   .35
  c.   1.50d bright violet   .25   .35
  d.   2d rose red   .25   .35
  e.   4d dark blue   .25   .35

1st Yugoslavian Phil. Exhib., Belgrade. Sold
only at the exhibition post office at 15d each.

SP31   SP32

Perf. 11½x12½, 12½x11½
1938, May 1   **Photo.**
B58 SP31   50p + 50p dark brn   .25   .30
B59 SP32   1d + 1d dk green   .30   .35
B60 SP31   1.50d + 1.50d scar   .35   .40
B61 SP32   2d + 2d magenta   .40   .45
  Nos. B58-B61 (4)   1.30 1.50

Surtax for the benefit of Child Welfare.
For overprints see Nos. B75-B78.

Bridge and Anti-
aircraft
Lights — SP33

1938, May 28   **Perf. 11½x12½**
B62 SP33   1d + 50p dk grn   .20   .25
B63 SP33   1.50d + 1d scarlet   .35   .40
  a.   Perf. 11½   17.50 17.50
B64 SP33   2d + 1d rose vio   .45   .50
  a.   Perf. 11½   16.00 16.00
B65 SP33   3d + 1.50d dp bl   .50   .60
  Nos. B62-B65 (4)   1.50 1.75

Intl. Aeronautical Exhib., Belgrade.

Cliff at Demir-Kapiya — SP34

Modern
Hospital
SP35

Runner Carrying
Torch — SP36

Alexander
I — SP37

Perf. 11½x12½, 12½x11½
1938, Aug. 1
B66 SP34   1d + 1d slate grn &
             dp grn   .45   .55
B67 SP35   1.50d + 1.50d scar   .60   .75
B68 SP36   2d + 2d claret & dp
             rose   .75   .85
B69 SP37   3d + 3d dp bl   .75   .85
  Nos. B66-B69 (4)   2.55 3.00

The surtax was to raise funds to build a
hospital for railway employees.

Runner
SP38

Shot-Putter
SP41

Hurdlers
SP39

Pole
Vaulter
SP40

1938, Sept. 11
B70 SP38   50p + 50p org brn   .70   .70
B71 SP39   1d + 1d sl grn & dp
             grn   .90   .90
B72 SP40   1.50d + 1.50d rose &
             dk mag   .90   .90
B73 SP41   2d + 2d dk blue   1.40 1.40
  Nos. B70-B73 (4)   3.90 3.90

Ninth Balkan Games.

Stamps of 1938 Overprinted in Black

a   b

1938, Oct. 1
B75 SP31(a)   50p + 50p dk brn   .35   .35
B76 SP32(b)   1d + 1d dk grn   .35   .35
B77 SP31(a)   1.50d + 1.50d scar   .35   .35
B78 SP32(b)   2d + 2d mag   .50   .50
  Nos. B75-B78 (4)   1.55 1.55

Surtax for the benefit of Child Welfare.

Postriders
SP43

1d+1d, Rural mail delivery. 1.50d+1.50d,
Mail train. 2d+2d, Mail bus. 4d+4d, Mail plane.

1939, Mar. 15   **Photo.**   **Perf. 11½**
B79 SP43 50p + 50p buff, bis &
             brown   .40   .50
B80 SP43 1d + 1d sl grn & dp
             green   .55   .75
B81 SP43 1.50d + 1.50d red, cop
             red & brn car   .60   .90
B82 SP43 2d + 2d dp plum &
             rose lilac   .70   1.25
B83 SP43 4d + 4d ind & sl bl   1.25 1.60
  Nos. B79-B83 (5)   3.50 5.00

Centenary of the present postal system in
Yugoslavia. The surtax was used for the Railway Benevolent Association.
The Cyrillic and Latin inscriptions are transposed on Nos. B82 and B83.

Child Eating
SP48

Children at
Seashore — SP49

Children in
Crib — SP51

Boy
Planing
Board
SP50

1939, May 1   **Perf. 12½**
B84 SP48 1d + 1d blk & dp
             bl green   1.25 1.40
B85 SP49 1.50d + 1.50d org
             brn & sal   .55   1.25
  a.   Perf. 11½   40.00 22.50
B86 SP50 2d + 2d mar &
             vio rose   1.10 1.40
B87 SP51 4d + 4d ind &
             royal blue   1.40 1.90
  Nos. B84-B87 (4)   4.30 5.95

The surtax was for the benefit of Child
Welfare.

Czar Lazar of
Serbia — SP52

Milosh
Obilich — SP53

1939, June 28 — *Perf. 11½*
B88 SP52 1d + 1d sl grn & bl grn .55 .70
B89 SP53 1.50d + 1.50d mar & brt car .55 .70
Battle of Kosovo, 550th anniversary.

Training Ship "Jadran" SP54

Designs: 1d+50p, Steamship "King Alexander." 1.50d+1d, Freighter "Triglan." 2d+1.50d, Cruiser "Dubrovnik."

1939, Sept. 6 — *Engr.*
B90 SP54 50p + 50p brn org .60 .70
B91 SP54 1d + 50p dull grn .80 .95
B92 SP54 1.50d + 1d dp rose .70 .80
B93 SP54 2d + 1.50d dark bl .80 1.10
Nos. B90-B93 (4) 2.90 3.55
Yugoslav Navy and Merchant Marine. The surtax aided a Marine Museum.

Motorcycle and Sidecar — SP58

Motorcycle SP60

Racing Car SP59

Racing Car SP61

1939, Sept. 3 — *Photo.*
B94 SP58 50p + 50p multi .55 .60
B95 SP59 1d + 1d multi .60 .70
B96 SP60 1.50d + 1.50d multi .70 .85
B97 SP61 2d + 2d multi 1.25 1.50
Nos. B94-B97 (4) 3.10 3.65
Automobile and Motorcycle Races, Belgrade. The surtax was for the Race Organization and the State Treasury.

Unknown Soldier Memorial SP62

1939, Oct. 9 — *Perf. 12½*
B98 SP62 1d + 50p sl grn & green .60 .85
B99 SP62 1.50d + 1d red & rose red .70 .90

B100 SP62 2d + 1.50d dp cl & vio rose .85 1.00
B101 SP62 3d + 2d dp bl & bl .85 1.00
Nos. B98-B101 (4) 3.00 3.75
Assassination of King Alexander, 5th anniv. The surtax was used to aid World War I invalids.

Postman Delivering Mail — SP64

Postman Emptying Mail Box — SP65

Parcel Post Delivery Wagon SP66

Parcel Post SP67

Repairing Telephone Wires — SP68

1940, Jan. 1
B102 SP64 50p + 50p brn & deep org .50 .55
B103 SP65 1d + 1d sl grn & blue grn .55 .70
B104 SP66 1.50d + 1.50d red brn & scar .70 .85
B105 SP67 2d + 2d dl vio & red lilac .85 1.40
B106 SP68 4d + 4d sl bl & bl 1.40 1.75
Nos. B102-B106 (5) 4.00 5.25
The surtax was used for the employees of the Postal System in Belgrade.

Croats' Arrival at Adriatic in 640 SP69

King Tomislav — SP70

Death of Matija Gubec — SP71

Anton and Stjepan Radic SP72

Map of Yugoslavia SP73

1940, Mar. 1 — *Typo. — Perf. 11½*
B107 SP69 50p + 50p brn org .25 .30
B108 SP70 1d + 1d green .25 .30
B109 SP71 1.50d + 1.50d brt red .30 .30
B110 SP72 2d + 2d dk cerise .35 .45
B111 SP73 4d + 2d dark blue .40 .50
Nos. B107-B111 (5) 1.55 1.85
The surtax was used for the benefit of postal employees in Zagreb.

Children Playing in Snow SP74

Children at Seashore — SP75

1940, May 1 — *Photo. — Perf. 11½, 12½*
B112 SP74 50p + 50p brn org & org yellow .25 .30
B113 SP75 1d + 1d sl grn & dk green .30 .40
B114 SP74 1.50d + 1.50d brn red & scarlet .25 .30
B115 SP75 2d + 2d mar & vio rose .35 .45
Nos. B112-B115 (4) 1.15 1.45
The surtax was for Child Welfare.

Nos. C11-C14 Surcharged in Carmine

Perf. 11½x12½, 12½x11½
1940, Dec. 23
B116 AP6 50p + 50p on 5d .30 .30
B117 AP7 1d + 1d on 10d .30 .30
B118 AP8 1.50d + 1.50d on 20d .35 .45
B119 AP9 2d + 2d on 30d .35 .45
Nos. B116-B119 (4) 1.30 1.50
The surtax was used to fight tuberculosis. For surcharges see Nos. NB1-NB4.

St. Peter's Cemetery, Ljubljana — SP76

Croatian, Serbian and Slovenian SP77

Chapel at Kajmaktchalan SP78

Memorial at Brezje SP79

1941, Jan. 1 — *Perf. 12½*
B120 SP76 50p + 50p gray grn & yel green .30 .35
B121 SP77 1d + 1d brn car & dl rose .30 .35
B122 SP78 1.50d + 1.50d myr grn & bl green .30 .45
B123 SP79 2d + 2d gray bl & pale lilac .40 .55
Nos. B120-B123 (4) 1.30 1.70
Surtax for the Ljubljana War Veterans Assoc.

Kamenita Gate, Zagreb — SP80

13th Century Cathedral, Zagreb — SP81

1941, Mar. 16 — *Engr. — Perf. 11½*
B124 SP80 1.50d + 1.50d choc .40 .80
B125 SP81 4d + 3d blue blk .40 .80
2nd Philatelic Exhibition of Croatia, at Zagreb, Mar. 16-27.
Nos. B124-B125 exist perf. 9½ on right side. Value, each $25.

1941, Apr.
B126 SP80 1.50d + 1.50d bl black 8.50 9.50
B127 SP81 4d + 3d choc 8.50 9.50
Regional philatelic exhibition at Slavonski Brod. Nos. B126-B127 with gold overprint, "Nezavisna Drzava Hrvatska," are Croatia Nos. B1-B2.
Nos. B126-B127 exist perf. 9½ on right side. Value, each $55 unused, $70 used.

Issues for Federal Republic

Carrying Wounded Soldier — SP82

Child — SP83

1945, Sept. 15   Typo.   Perf. 11½
B131 SP82 1d + 4d deep ultra   .70   .70
B132 SP83 2d + 6d scarlet   .70   .70

The surtax was for the Red Cross.

Russia, Yugoslavia Flags SP84

1945, Oct. 20   Photo.   Unwmk.
B133 SP84 2d + 5d multi   .80   .80

Liberation of Belgrade, 1st anniv.

Communications Symbols — SP85

1946, May 10   Perf. 12½
B134 SP85 1.50d + 1d emer   2.75   2.50
B135 SP85 2.50d + 1.50d car rose   2.75   2.50
B136 SP85 5d + 2d gray bl   2.75   2.50
B137 SP85 8d + 3.50d dl brn   2.75   2.50
    Nos. B134-B137 (4)   11.00 10.00

1st PTT Congress since liberation, May 10.

Flag and Young Laborers SP86

Handstand on Horizontal Bar SP87

1946, Aug. 1   Litho.
Flag in Red or Carmine and Deep or Dark Blue
B138 SP86 50p + 50p brn & buff   2.25   1.40
B139 SP86 1.50d + 1d dk grn & lt green   2.25   1.40
B140 SP86 2.50d + 2d rose vio & rose lilac   2.25   1.40
B141 SP86 5d + 3d gray bl & blue   2.25   1.40
    Nos. B138-B141 (4)   9.00   5.60

The surtax aided railroad reconstruction carried out by Yugoslav youths.

1947, Sept. 5   Perf. 11½
B142 SP87 1.50d + 50p dark grn   .20   .20
B143 SP87 2.50d + 50p carmine   .20   .20
B144 SP87 4d + 50p brt blue   .20   .20
    Nos. B142-B144 (3)   .60   .60

1947 Balkan Games, Sept. 5-7, Ljubljana.

Young Railway Laborers SP88

1947, Sept. 25   Typo.   Perf. 11½x12
B145 SP88 1d + 50p orange   .20   .20
B146 SP88 1.50d + 1d yel green   .20   .20
B147 SP88 2.50d + 1.50d car lake   .20   .20
B148 SP88 5d + 2d deep blue   .20   .20
    Nos. B145-B148 (4)   .80   .80

The surtax was for youth brigades employed in the construction of the Samac-Sarajevo railway.

Symbolizing Protection of "B.C.G." Vaccine SP89

Dying Serpent SP91

"Illness" and "Recovery" SP90

1948, Apr. 1   Litho.   Perf. 12½
B149 SP89 1.50d + 1d sl blk & red   .20   .20
B150 SP90 2.50d + 2d grnsh gray, ol blk & red   .20   .20
B151 SP91 5d + 3d dk bl & car   .20   .20
    Nos. B149-B151 (3)   .60   .60

Fight against tuberculosis. The surtax was for the Yugoslav Red Cross.

Juro Danicic SP92

Shot Put — SP93

Portraits: 2.50d+1d, Franjo Racki. 4d+2d, Josip J. Strossmayer.

1948, July 28   Perf. 11
B152 SP92 1.50d + 50p blk green   .25   .20
B153 SP92 2.50d + 1d dark red   .25   .20
B154 SP92 4d + 2d dark blue   .25   .20
    Nos. B152-B154 (3)   .75   .60

Yugoslav Academy of Arts and Sciences, Zagreb, 80th anniv. The surtax was for the Academy.

1948, Sept. 10   Perf. 12½
B155 SP93 2d + 1d shown   .25   .35
B156 SP93 3d + 1d Hurdles   .25   .35
B157 SP93 5d + 2d Pole vault   .25   .35
    Nos. B155-B157 (3)   .75   1.05

Balkan and Central Europe Games, 1948. On sale 4 days.

AIR POST STAMPS

Dubrovnik AP1

Lake Bled AP2

Falls of Jaice — AP3

Church at Oplenac — AP4

Bridge at Mostar — AP5

Perf. 12½
1934, June 15   Typo.   Unwmk.
C1 AP1 50p violet brown   .20   .20
C2 AP2 1d green   .20   .20
C3 AP3 2d rose red   .45   .20
C4 AP4 3d ultramarine   .50   .25
C5 AP5 10d vermilion   1.50   1.40
    Nos. C1-C5 (5)   2.85   2.25

King Alexander Memorial Issue

1935, Jan. 1
Border in Black
C6 AP4 3d ultramarine   1.50   1.25

St. Naum Convent — AP6

Sarajevo AP8

Port of Rab — AP7

Ljubljana AP9

Perf. 12½, 11½x12½, 12½x11½
1937, Sept. 12   Photo.
C7 AP6 50p brown   .20   .20
C8 AP7 1d yellow grn   .20   .20
C9 AP8 2d blue gray   .20   .20
C10 AP9 2.50d rose red   .20   .20
C11 AP6 5d brn violet   .20   .20
C12 AP7 10d brown lake   .20   .20
C13 AP8 20d dark green   .35   .35
C14 AP9 30d ultramarine   .70   .70
    Nos. C7-C14 (8)   2.25   2.25

For surcharges see Nos. B116-B119, NB1-NB4, NC1-NC8.

Cathedral of Zagreb AP10

Bridge at Belgrade AP11

1940, Aug. 15   Litho.   Perf. 12½
C15 AP10 40d Prus grn & pale green   .95   1.40
C16 AP11 50d slate bl & gray bl   1.10   1.40

For overprints see Nos. NC9-NC10.

Issues for Federal Republic

Plane over Terrace of Kalimegdan, Belgrade AP12

Plane over Dubrovnik AP13

1947, Apr. 21   Typo.   Perf. 11½
Cyrillic Inscription at Top
C17 AP12 50p ol gray & brn vio   .20   .20
C18 AP13 1d mag & ol gray   .20   .20
C19 AP12 2d blue & black   .20   .20
C20 AP13 5d green & gray   .30   .20
C21 AP12 10d olive bis & choc   .35   .20
C22 AP13 20d ultra & olive   .75   .35

Roman Inscription at Top
C23 AP12 50p ol gray & brn vio   .20   .20
C24 AP13 1d mag & ol gray   .20   .20
C25 AP12 2d blue & black   .20   .20
C26 AP13 5d green & gray   .30   .20
C27 AP12 10d olive bis & choc   .35   .20
C28 AP13 20d ultra & olive   .75   .35
    Nos. C17-C28 (12)   4.00   2.70

Sheets of each denomination contain alternately stamps with Cyrillic or Roman inscription at top. Value, 6 se-tenant pairs, $35.

Laurent Kosir and Birthplace AP14

1948, Aug. 27   Engr.
C29 AP14 15d red violet   1.00   .80

Kosir, recognized by Yugoslavia as inventor of the postage stamp, 80th death anniv. Issued in sheets of 25 stamps and 25 labels.

Nos. 262 to 264 Overprinted in Blue or Carmine

1949, Aug. 25   Unwmk.   Perf. 12½
C30 A55 3d carmine rose   1.10   2.50
C31 A56 5d dull blue (C)   1.10   2.50
C32 A57 12d red brown   1.10   2.50
    Nos. C30-C32 (3)   3.30   7.50

Liberation of Macedonia, 5th anniv. It is reported that No. C32 was not sold to the public at the post office.

Souvenir Sheet

Electric Train AP15

Perf. 11½x12½

1949, Dec. 15   **Photo.**
C33 AP15 10d lilac rose   35.00 19.00
   a.   Imperf.   35.00 19.00
   Centenary of Yugoslav railroads.
For overprint see Trieste No. C17.

Iron Gate, Derdap AP16

Belgrade AP17

   Designs: 2d, Cascades, Plitvice. 3d, Carolina. 6d, Roman bridge, Mostar. 10d, Ohrid. 20d, Gulf of Kotor. 30d, Dubrovnik. 50d, Bled.

Perf. 12½

1951, June 16   **Unwmk.**   **Engr.**
C34 AP16   1d deep org   .20   .20
C35 AP16   2d dk green   .20   .20
C36 AP16   3d dark red   .20   .20
C37 AP16   6d ultra   3.00   3.50
C38 AP16   10d dark brn   .25   .20
C39 AP16   20d grnsh blk   .30   .20
C40 AP16   30d dp claret   .50   .20
C41 AP16   50d dk purple   .90   .20
C42 AP17 100d dk gray bl   16.00   2.50
   Nos. C34-C42 (9)   21.55   7.40

Souvenir Sheet
Imperf

C43 AP17 100d red brn   65.00 65.00
   See Nos. C50-C53. For overprints see Nos. C44, C49, Trieste C22-C32.

Roman Bridge Type of 1951
Overprinted "ZEFIZ 1951" in Carmine
1951, June 16   **Perf. 12½**
C44 AP16 6d dark green   .80   .70
   Nos. C43-C44 were issued for Zagreb Philatelic Exhibition, June 16-26.

View on Mt. Kapaonik AP18

Plane and Parachutists AP19

Perf. 12½
1951, July   **Unwmk.**   **Photo.**
C45 AP18   3d shown   .90   .65
C46 AP18   5d Mt. Triglav   .90   .65
C47 AP18 20d Mt. Kalnik   32.50 27.50
   Nos. C45-C47 (3)   34.30 28.80
   Intl. Union of Mountaineers, 12th Assembly, Bled, July 13-18.

1951, Aug. 16   **Engr.**
C48 AP19 6d carmine   2.25 1.10

Type of 1951 Overprinted in Carmine

C49 AP16 50d blue   32.50 25.00
   First World Parachute Championship, Bled, Aug. 16-20.

> **Catalogue values for unused stamps in this section, from this point to the end of the section, are for Never Hinged items.**

Types of 1951
   Designs: 5d, Cascades, Plitvice. 100d, Carniola. 200d, Roman bridge, Mostar.

1951-52
C50 AP16   5d yel brn ('52)   .20   .20
C51 AP16 100d green   .65   .20
C52 AP16 200d deep car ('52)   1.00   .30
C53 AP17 500d blue vio ('52)   2.25   .65
   Nos. C50-C53 (4)   4.10 1.35

Marshal Tito, Tank, Factory and Planes AP20

1951, Dec. 22   **Unwmk.**
C54 AP20 150d deep blue   5.25 3.50
   Army Day, Dec. 22; 10th anniv. of the formation of the 1st military unit of "New" Yugoslavia.

Star and Flag-encircled Globe — AP21

1953, July 30   **Engr.**
C55 AP21 300d bl & grn   160.00 160.00
   38th Esperanto Congress, Zagreb, 7/25-8/1.
For overprint see Trieste No. C21.

13th Century Tower, Zagreb AP22

1956, May 20   **Perf. 11½**
Chalky Paper
C56 AP22 30d gray, vio bl & org   1.60   .90
   Yugoslav Intl. Phil. Exhib., JUFIZ III, Zagreb, May 20-27.

Workers and Cogwheel — AP23

Moon and Earth with Satellites — AP24

1956, June 15   **Photo.**
Glossy Paper
C57 AP23 30d car rose & blk   1.60 1.60
   10th anniversary of technical education.

1958, Oct. 24   **Engr.**   **Perf. 12½**
C58 AP24 300d dark blue   4.75 2.00
   Intl. Geophysical Year, 1957-58.

Types of Regular Issue, 1961
1961, Sept. 1   **Perf. 11½**
C59 A150 250d dark purple   .90   .50
C60 A151 500d violet blue   2.50 1.75

Type of Athletic Regular Issue, 1962
Souvenir Sheet
   Design: Army Stadium, Belgrade.

1962, Sept. 12   **Litho.**   **Imperf.**
C61 A161 600d vio & blk   3.25 2.50
   7th European Athletic Championships, Belgrade, Sept. 12-16.

REGISTERED LETTER STAMP

> **Catalogue values for unused stamps in this section are for Never Hinged items.**

RL1

1993, June 28   **Litho.**   **Perf. 12½**
F1   RL1 (R) ultra   .50
   No. F1 was valued at 11,000d on day of issue.
For surcharge, see Serbia No. 194.

Type of 1993
2002, July 25   **Litho.**   **Perf. 12½**
F2   RL1 R red   .75   .75
   No. F2 was intended for use in Montenegro and was sold there for 39c in euro currency. The stamp was valid for use in the Serbian section of Yugoslavia.

POSTAGE DUE STAMPS

King Alexander — D1

1921   **Typo.**   **Unwmk.**   **Perf. 11½**
Red or Black Surcharge
J1   D1 10p on 5p green (R)   .20   .20
J2   D1 30p on 5p green (Bk)   .20   .20

D2

D3

1921-22   **Typo.**   **Perf. 11½**
J3   D2 10p rose   .20   .20
J4   D2 30p yellow green   .20   .20
J5   D2 50p violet   .30   .20
J6   D2   1d brown   .35   .20
J7   D2   2d blue   .35   .20
J8   D3   5d orange   7.50   .40
J9   D3 10d violet brown   9.25   .45
   a.   Cliche of 10p in sheet of 10d   75.00 100.00
J10   D3 25d pink   30.00   2.00
J11   D3 50d green   27.50   1.60
   Nos. J3-J11 (9)   75.65   5.45

1924   **Perf. 9, 10½, 11½**
J12   D3 10p rose red   .20   .20
J13   D3 30p yellow green   .45   .35
J14   D3 50p violet   .20   .20
J15   D3   1d brown   .35   .20
J16   D3   2d deep blue   .55   .20
J17   D3   5d orange   9.25   .20
J18   D3 10d violet brown   21.00   .20
J19   D3 25d pink   42.50   1.00
J20   D3 50d green   57.50   .85
   Nos. J12-J20 (9)   132.00 3.40

Nos. J19-J20 Surcharged

1928
J21   D3 10d on 25d pink   3.25   .25
J22   D3 10d on 50d green   3.25   .25
   a.   Inverted surcharge   30.00 18.00
   A second type of "1" in surcharge has flag projecting horizontally. Value, each $15 unused, $3 used.

Coat of Arms — D4

Numeral of Value — D5

1931   **Typo.**   **Perf. 12½**
With Imprint at Foot
J23   D4 50p violet   1.10   .20
J24   D4   1d deep magenta   2.00   .20
J25   D4   2d deep blue   5.00   .20
J26   D4   5d orange   2.00   .20
J27   D4 10d chocolate   6.75   .70
   Nos. J23-J27 (5)   16.85 1.50
   For overprints see Nos. NJ1-NJ13, Croatia 26-29, J1-J5.

1932
Without Imprint at Foot
J28   D4 50p violet   .20   .20
J29   D4   1d deep magenta   .20   .20
J30   D4   2d deep blue   .20   .20
J31   D4   5d orange   .20   .20
J32   D4 10d chocolate   .20   .20
   Nos. J28-J32 (5)   1.00 1.00

1933   **Perf. 9, 10½, 11½**
Overprint in Green, Blue or Maroon
J33   D5 50p vio (G)   .20   .20
J34   D5   1d brown (Bl)   .20   .20
   a.   Perf. 10½   3.25   .85
J35   D5   2d blue (M)   .35   .20
   a.   Perf. 10½   1.60   .50
J36   D5   5d orange (Bl)   1.25   .20
J37   D5 10d violet brn (Bl)   6.00 1.00
   Nos. J33-J37 (5)   8.00 1.80

Issues for Federal Republic

Redrawn Type OD5,
German Occupation
of Serbia,
Overprinted in Black

1945		Unwmk.	Perf. 12½
J37A	OD5	10d red	.35 .35
J37B	OD5	20d ultramarine	.35 .35

In the redrawn design the eagle is replaced
by a colorless tablet.

Coat of Arms — D6　　　　Torches and Star — D7

1945　　Litho.　　Perf. 12½
Numerals in Black

J38	D6	2d brown violet	.20	.25
J39	D6	3d violet	.20	.25
J40	D6	5d green	.20	.25
J41	D6	7d orange brown	.20	.25
J42	D6	10d rose lilac	.20	.25
J43	D6	20d blue	.20	.25
J44	D6	30d light bl grn	.20	.35
J45	D6	40d rose red	.20	.35

Numerals in Color of Stamp

J46	D6	1d blue green	.20	.20
J47	D6	1.50d blue	.20	.20
J48	D6	2d vermilion	.20	.20
J49	D6	3d violet brown	.20	.20
J50	D6	4d rose violet	.20	.20
		Nos. J38-J50 (13)	2.60	3.20

For overprints see Nos. J64-J66.

1946-47		Typo.	Unwmk.
J51	D7	50p dp orange ('47)	.20 .20
J52	D7	1d orange	.20 .20
J53	D7	2d dark blue	.20 .20
J54	D7	3d yellow green	.20 .20
J55	D7	5d bright purple	.25 .20
J56	D7	7d crimson	.25 .20
J57	D7	10d brt pink ('47)	.50 .20
J58	D7	20d rose lake ('47)	.65 .20
		Nos. J51-J58 (8)	2.40 1.60

See Nos. J67-J79. For overprints see Trieste Nos. J1-J5, J11-J18.

Nos. J47, J49 and
J50 Overprinted in
Black

1950			Litho.
J64	D6	1.50d blue	.20 .20
J65	D6	3d violet brown	.20 .20
J66	D6	4d rose violet	.20 .20
		Nos. J64-J66 (3)	.60 .60

**Catalogue values for unused
stamps in this section, from this
point to the end of the section, are
for Never Hinged items.**

Type of 1946-47

1951-52		Typo.	Perf. 12½
J67	D7	1d brown ('52)	.20 .20
J68	D7	2d emerald	.20 .20
J69	D7	5d blue	.35 .20
J70	D7	10d scarlet	1.75 .20
J71	D7	20d purple	1.75 .20
J72	D7	30d org yel ('52)	3.00 .20
J73	D7	50d ultramarine	6.50 .25
J74	D7	100d dp plum ('52)	6.75 .45
		Nos. J67-J74 (8)	20.50 1.90

For overprints see Istria Nos. J20-J24, Trieste J11-J18.

1962		Litho.	Perf. 12½
J75	D7	10d red orange	2.50 .20
J76	D7	20d purple	2.50 .20
J77	D7	30d orange	3.75 .20

J78	D7	50d ultramarine	9.50 .50
J79	D7	100d rose lake	7.75 .70
		Nos. J75-J79 (5)	26.00 1.80

OFFICIAL STAMPS

Issues for Federal Republic

Arms of the
Federated
People's
Republic — O1

Perf. 12½

1946, Nov. 1		Unwmk.	Typo.
O1	O1	50p orange	.20 .20
O2	O1	1d blue green	.20 .20
O3	O1	1.50d olive green	.20 .20
O4	O1	2.50d red	.20 .20
O5	O1	4d yellow brown	.35 .20
O6	O1	5d deep blue	.45 .20
O7	O1	8d chocolate	.80 .20
O8	O1	12d violet	.95 .25
		Nos. O1-O8 (8)	3.35 1.65

For surcharges see Nos. 272A-272B, Istria
43, 45, 47, 49, 51.

POSTAL TAX STAMPS

**Catalogue values for unused
stamps in this section are for
Never Hinged items.**

The tax was for the Red Cross or The
Olympic Fund unless otherwise noted.

Red Cross
Emblem
PT1

Dr. Vladen
Djordjevic
PT2

Unwmk.

1933, Sept. 17		Litho.	Perf. 13
RA1	PT1	50p dark blue & red	.30 .20

Obligatory on inland letters during Red
Cross Week, Sept. 17-23.
See No. RAJ1.

1936, Sept. 20		Typo.	Perf. 12
RA2	PT2	50p brn blk & red	.35 .20

Obligatory on inland letters during Red
Cross Week, Sept. 20-26.

Aiding the
Wounded
PT3

1938, Sept. 18		Litho.	Perf. 12½
RA3	PT3	50p dk bl, red, yel & grn	.35 .20

1940, Sept. 15			Redrawn
RA4	PT3	50p slate blue & red	1.10 .20

The inscription at the upper right of this
stamp and the numerals of value are in
smaller characters.
Obligatory on all letters during the second
week of September.

Issues for Federal Republic

Ruined
Dwellings — PT4　　Red Cross
Nurse — PT5

1947, Jan. 1		Litho.	Perf. 12½
RA5	PT4	50p brn & scarlet	.20 .20

See No. RAJ2. For overprints see Trieste
Nos. RA1, RAJ1.

1948, Oct. 1			
RA6	PT5	50p dk vio bl & red	.20 .20

See No. RAJ3.

Nurse and
Child — PT6　　Nurse Holding
Book — PT7

1949, Nov. 5			
RA7	PT6	50p red & brown	.20 .20

See No. RAJ4. For overprints see Trieste
Nos. RA2, RAJ2.

1950, Oct. 1			
RA8	PT7	50p dark green & red	.20 .20

Obligatory Oct. 1-8, 1950.
See No. RAJ6.

Hands Raising
Red Cross
Flag — PT8　　Nurse — PT9

1951, Oct. 7			
RA9	PT8	50p vio bl & red	.20 .20

Obligatory Oct. 7-14.
For overprints see Trieste Nos. RA3, RAJ3.

1952, Oct. 5		Photo.	Perf. 12½
RA10	PT9	50p gray & carmine	.20 .20

For overprint see Trieste No. RA4.

Child Receiving
Blood
Transfusion
PT10　　Youths Carrying
Flags
PT11

1953, Oct. 25			Litho.
RA11	PT10	2d red vio & red	.20 .20

See No. RAJ8. For overprints see Trieste
Nos. RA5, RAJ5.

1954, Nov. 1			
RA12	PT11	2d gray grn & red	.20 .20

See Nos. RAJ9.

Infant — PT11a

1954, Oct. 4			
RA12A	PT11a	2d brn & salmon	.60 1.25

The tax was for Children's Week.

Girl
PT12　　Nurse Opening
Window
PT13

1955, Oct. 2		Unwmk.	Perf. 12½
RA13	PT12	2d dull red	.20 .20

The tax was for child welfare.
See No. RAJ10.

1955, Oct. 31			
RA14	PT13	2d vio blk & red	.20 .20

See No. RAJ11.

Ruins in the
Snow — PT14　　Children and
Goose — PT15

1956, May 6			Perf. 12½
RA15	PT14	2d sepia & red	.20 .20

See No. RAJ12.

1956, Sept. 30			
RA16	PT15	2d gray green	.20 .20

The tax was for child welfare.
See No. RAJ13.

Plane over
Temporary
Shelter — PT16

1957, May 5			Litho.
RA17	PT16	2d lt bl, blk & car	.20 .20

See No. RAJ14.

Girl and Boy
Pioneers
PT17

1957, Sept. 30		Unwmk.	Perf. 12½
RA18	PT17	2d rose & gray	.20 .20

Children's Week. Obligatory Oct. 2-6.
See No. RAJ15.

Redrawn Type of Regular Issue, 1953
1958, May 4			Perf. 12½x12
RA19	A95	2d multicolored	.20 .20

On No. RA19 the UN emblem has been left
out, Cyrillic inscriptions at left added, country
name in Latin letters.

Playing
Children — PT18

Helping Hand
and
Family — PT19

1958, Oct. 5   Litho.   *Perf. 12½*
RA20 PT18 2d brt yel & black   .20 .20
   Children's Week, Oct. 5-11.

1959, May 3
RA21 PT19 2d blue vio & red   .20 .20
   Red Cross centenary. Obligatory May 3-9.
   See No. RAJ18.

Blackboard,
Flower and
Fish — PT20

"Reconstruction"
PT21

1959, Oct. 5   Unwmk.
RA22 PT20 2d ocher & Prus grn   .20 .20
   Children's Week. Obligatory on domestic
mail, Oct. 5-11.
   See No. RAJ19.

1960, May 8   *Perf. 12½*
RA23 PT21 2d slate & red   .20 .20
   Obligatory May 8-14. See No. RAJ20.

Girl and
Toys — PT22

Blood Donor
Symbolism
PT23

1960, Oct. 2   Litho.   *Perf. 12½*
RA24 PT22 2d red   .20 .20
   Issued for Children's Week. Obligatory on
domestic mail Oct. 2-8.

See No. RAJ21.

1961, May 7
RA25 PT23 2d multicolored   .20 .20
   Obligatory May 7-13. Exists imperf. Value
$12.50.
   See No. RAJ22.

Bird Holding
Flower
PT24

1961, Oct. 1
RA26 PT24 2d orange & violet   .20 .20
   Children's Week. Obligatory on domestic
mail, Oct. 1-7.
   See No. RAJ23.

Bandages and Symbols of Home,
Industry, Weather, Transportation, Fire
and Flood — PT25

1962, Apr. 30   *Perf. 12½*
RA27 PT25 5d red brn, gray & red   .20 .20
   Obligatory on domestic mail May 6-12.
   See No. RAJ24.

Centenary
Emblem — PT26

Parachute Drop of
Supplies,
Yugoslav
Flag — PT27

1963, May 5   Unwmk.   *Perf. 12½*
RA28 PT26 5d dl yel, red & gray   .20 .20
   Intl. Red Cross, centenary. Obligatory on all
domestic mail during Red Cross Week, May 5-
11.
   See No. RAJ25.

1964, Apr. 27   Litho.
RA29 PT27 5d blue, rose & dk bl   .20 .20
   Obligatory on domestic mail, May 3-9.

Children in
Circle — PT28

1965, May 2   Litho.   *Perf. 12½*
RA30 PT28 5d tan & red   .20 .20
   Obligatory on domestic mail, May 2-8.

Arrows
PT29

1966, Apr. 28   Litho.   *Perf. 12½*
RA31 PT29 5p gray & multi   .20 .20
   Obligatory on domestic mail, May 1-7.

Crosses and
Flower
PT30

1967, Apr. 28   Litho.   *Perf. 12½*
RA32 PT30 5p vio, red & yel grn   .20 .20

Honeycomb and
Red
Cross — PT31

1968, Apr. 30   Litho.   *Perf. 12*
RA33 PT31 5p multicolored   .20 .20
   Obligatory on all domestic mail May 5-11.

Aztec Calendar
Stone and
Olympic
Rings — PT32

1968, Oct. 12   *Perf. 12½*
RA34 PT32 10p black & multi   .20 .20

Red Cross,
Hands and
Globe — PT33

Globe, Olympic
Torch and
Rings — PT34

1969, May 18   Litho.   *Perf. 12*
RA35 PT33 20p red org, dl red &
           blk   .20 .20

1969, Nov. 24   Litho.   *Perf. 11*
RA36 PT34 10p gold & multi   .20 .20
   Yugoslav Olympic Committee, 50th anniv.

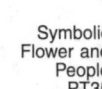

Symbolic
Flower and
People
PT35

1970, Apr. 27   Litho.   *Perf. 13*
RA37 PT35 20p vio bl, org & red   .20 .20

Olympic
Flag — PT36

Red Cross
Encircling
Globe
PT37

Olympic Rings
and Disk — PT38

1970, June 10   Litho.   *Perf. 13x13½*
RA38 PT36 10p multicolored   .20 .20

1971, Apr. 26   Litho.   *Perf. 12½*
RA39 PT37 20p blue, yel & red   .20 .20

1971, June 15   Litho.   *Perf. 12½*
RA40 PT38 10p blue & black   .20 .20

Red Cross
and
Hemispheres
PT39

1972, Apr. 27   *Perf. 13½x13*
RA41 PT39 20p red & multi   .20 .20

Olympic Rings,
TV Tower, Munich
and Sapporo
Emblems — PT40

1972, May   *Perf. 13x13½*
RA42 PT40 10p ultra & multi   .20 .20

Red Cross,
Crescent and Lion
Emblems — PT41

Globe and Olympic Rings — PT42

1973, Apr. 24   **Litho.**   **Perf. 13x13½**
RA43 PT41 20p blue & multi   .20 .20

1973, June 1   **Litho.**   **Perf. 13x13½**
RA44 PT42 10p multicolored   .20 .20

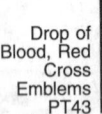

Drop of Blood, Red Cross Emblems PT43

1974, Apr. 25   **Litho.**   **Perf. 13**
RA45 PT43 20p red & multi   .20 .20

Olympic Rings PT44

1974, June 1   **Litho.**   **Perf. 13**
RA46 PT44 10p blue & multi   .20 .20

Red Cross, Hands PT45

1975, Apr. 23   **Photo.**   **Perf. 11½**
RA47 PT45 20p blue, car & blk   .20 .20

Olympic Rings — PT46

1975, June 2   **Litho.**   **Perf. 13½**
RA48 PT46 10p multicolored   .20 .20

Ruin and Clock — PT47

1975, July 26   **Litho.**   **Perf. 13x13½**
RA49 PT47 30p blk & dk bl   .20 .20
   Solidarity Week, July 26-Aug. 1. See Nos. RA61-RA62.

Red Crescent, Red Cross, Red Lion — PT48

1976, May 8   **Photo.**   **Perf. 12½x13**
RA50 PT48 20p multicolored   .85 .50

1984 Olympics PT49

1976, July 26   **Litho.**   **Perf. 13½**
RA51 PT49 10p intense blue   .30 .20

Fight Tuberculosis, Red Cross — PT50

1977, Sept. 14   **Photo.**
RA52 PT50 50p multicolored   5.25 5.25
RA53 PT50 1d multicolored   .80 .80

1984 Olympics PT51

1977, Dec. 17   **Perf. 13½x13**
RA54 PT51 10p multicolored   .22 .20

   Postal Tax Stamps for use in a particular republic or republics fall beyond the scope of this catalogue and are not listed. These stamps, issued since 1977, were not intended for nationwide use. Some of these issues have designs which are similar to stamps used nationwide, most notably those using variations of the Ruin and Clock (PT47) design. Most others show the Red Cross or the Tuberculosis Cross.

Red Crescent, Red Cross, Red Lion — PT52

1978, May 7   **Litho.**   **Perf. 13½**
RA55 PT52 20p on 1d bl & red   .70 .35
RA56 PT52 1d blue & red   .30 .20

1984 Olympics PT53

1978, Sept.
RA57 PT53 30p multicolored   .30 .25

8th Mediterranean Games, Split, Sept. 15-29 — PT54

1979, Mar. 1   **Photo.**   **Perf. 13½x13**
RA58 PT54 1d violet   .25 .25
RA59 PT54 1d greenish blue   .25 .25

Red Cross Week PT55

1979, May 6   **Perf. 13½**
RA60 PT55 1d multicolored   .25 .25

Ruin and Clock Type of 1975 Inscribed "1.-7.VI"

1979, June 1
RA61 PT47 30p blk & intense bl   .30 .20
     Solidarity Week.

Ruin and Clock Type of 1975 Inscribed "1.-7.VI"

1980, June 1   **Litho.**   **Perf. 13x13½**
RA62 PT47 1d black & blue   .25 .25
     Solidarity Week, June 1-7.

Olympic Week — PT57

1979, Oct. 15   **Photo.**   **Perf. 14**
RA63 PT57 30p blue & red   .25 .25

Sculpture, Red Cross — PT58

Olympic Week — PT59

1980, May 4   **Litho.**   **Perf. 13½**
RA64 PT58 1d multicolored   .30 .30

1980, Oct. 20   **Perf. 14**
RA65 PT59 50p multicolored   .25 .25

SPENS '81, Novi Sad — PT60

1980, Dec. 20   **Perf. 13½**
RA66 PT60 1d multicolored   .20 .20

Red Cross — PT61

Fight Tuberculosis, Red Cross — PT62

1981, May 4   **Photo.**
RA67 PT61 1d multicolored   .20 .20

1981, Sept. 14
RA68 PT62 1d multicolored   .20 .20

Handshake PT63

Robert Koch PT64

Fight Tuberculosis, Red Cross — PT65

1982, May   **Litho.**   **Perf. 13**
RA69 PT63 1d black & red   .20 .20

1983, Sept. 18   **Litho.**   **Perf. 13**
RA70 PT64 1d multicolored   .20 .20
     For surcharge see No. RA76.

1983, Sept. 14   **Litho.**   **Perf. 13½**
RA71 PT65 1d bluish grn, blk & red .20 .20
RA72 PT65 2d bluish grn, blk & red .20 .20

1984 Winter Olympics, Sarajevo PT66

1983, Oct. 20   **Litho.**   **Perf. 12½**
RA73 PT66 2d greenish blue   .20 .20

PLANICA 50 — PT67

1985, Apr. 1   **Photo.**   **Perf. 14**
RA74 PT67 2d brt ultra & blue   .20 .20

Ruin, Clock and Red
Cross — PT68

1987, June 1   Litho.   Perf. 10
RA75 PT68 30d multicolored   .20 .20
   Solidarity Week, June 1-7.

No. RA70 Surcharged in Silver

1988, Sept. 14   Litho.   Perf. 13
RA76 PT64 12d on 1d multi   .20 .20

Intl. Red Cross, 125th
Anniv. — PT69

1989, May 8   Litho.   Perf. 12x11
Without Gum
RA77 PT69 20d bl, sil & red   .20 .20
RA78 PT69 80d bl, sil & red   .20 .20
RA79 PT69 150d bl, sil & red   .20 .20
RA80 PT69 160d bl, sil & red   .20 .20
   Nos. RA77-RA80 (4)   .80 .80
   Souvenir folders with perf. or imperf. minia-
ture sheets of 4 sold for 3200d.

Ruin, Clock   Building, Clock
and Red   and Red
Cross — PT70   Cross — PT71

1989, June 1   Perf. 10
Without Gum
RA81 PT70 250d red & silver   .20 .20
   Roulette 10
RA82 PT71 400d brt bl gray & red   .20 .20
   Souvenir folders with perf. or imperf. minia-
ture sheets containing one 45x65mm stamp
like RA81 sold for 3200d.

Fight TB, Red   Red
Cross — PT72   Cross — PT73

1989, Sept. 14   Rough Perf. 10½
Without Gum
RA83 PT72 20d black & red   .20 .20
RA84 PT72 200d black & red   .20 .20
RA85 PT72 250d black & red   .20 .20
RA86 PT72 400d black & red   .20 .20
RA87 PT72 650d black & red   .20 .20
   Nos. RA83-RA87 (5)   1.00 1.00

1990, May 8   Perf. 13½
Without Gum
RA88 PT73 10p green & red   .20 .20
RA89 PT73 20p green & red   .20 .20
RA90 PT73 30p green & red   .20 .20
   Nos. RA88-RA90 (3)   .60 .60

Flowers — PT74

Macedonian Red
Cross, 45th
Anniv. — PT75

1990, May 8   Perf. 10
Without Gum
RA91 PT74 20p shown   .20 .20
RA92 PT74 20p multi, diff.   .20 .20
RA93 PT75 20p multicolored   .20 .20
   a.   Block of 3 + label, #RA91-
        RA93   .45 .45
   Souvenir folders with perf. or imperf. minia-
ture sheets of 3 + label sold for 4d.

PT76   PT77

1990, Sept. 14   Litho.   Perf. 10
Without Gum
RA94 PT76 20p blue, org & red   .20 .20
RA95 PT76 25p blue, yel & red   .20 .20
RA96 PT76 50p blue, yel & red   .35 .20
   Nos. RA94-RA96 (3)   .75 .60
   Fight tuberculosis, Red Cross.

1991, Sept. 14   Litho.   Perf. 12½
Without Gum
RA97 PT77 1.20d dk bl, yel & red   .70 .35
RA98 PT77 2.50d multicolored
   Required on mail 9/14-21/91.

PT78   PT79

1994, May 8   Litho.   Perf. 13½
RA99 PT78 10p multicolored
   No. RA99 was required on mail 5/8-15/94.

1994, Sept. 14   Litho.   Perf. 13x13½
RA100 PT79 10p multicolored
   No. RA100 was required on mail 9/14-21/94.

PT80   PT81

1995, May 8   Litho.   Perf. 13½x13
RA101 PT80 10p multicolored
   No. RA101 was required on mail 5/8-15/95.

1995, Sept. 9   Litho.   Perf. 13½x13
RA102 PT81 10p Wilhelm Rönt-
gen
   Fight Tuberculosis. No. RA102 was required
on mail 9/9-14/95.

PT82   PT83

1996, May 8   Litho.   Perf. 12x12½
RA103 PT82 15p multicolored
   No. RA103 was required on mail 5/8-15/96.

1996, Sept.   Litho.   Perf. 12x12½
RA104 PT83 20p multicolored

PT84

1997, May 8   Litho.   Perf. 13
RA105 PT84 20p multicolored
   No. RA105 was required on mail 5/8-15/97.

Milutin Rankovic (1880-
1967), Artist — PT85

1997, Sept. 14   Litho.   Perf. 14
RA106 PT85 20p multicolored
   Fight Tuberculosis. No. RA106 was required
on mail 9/14-21/97.

PT86

1998, May 8   Litho.   Perf. 13¾
RA107 PT86 20p multicolored
   No. RA107 was required on mail 5/8-15/98.

Red Cross — PT87

1999, May 8   Litho.   Perf. 13¾
RA108 PT87 1d multi
   No. RA108 was required on mail 5/8-5/15/99.

Red Cross — PT88

1999, Sept. 14
RA109 PT88 1d multi
   No. RA109 was required on mail 9/14-
9/21/99.

POSTAL TAX DUE STAMPS

Catalogue values for unused
stamps in this section are for
Never Hinged items.

The tax of Nos. RAJ1-RAJ9, RAJ11-
RAJ12, RAJ14 and RAJ18 was for the
Red Cross.

Inscribed "PORTO."

Type of Postal Tax Stamp, 1933
1933   Unwmk.   Litho.   Perf. 13
RAJ1 PT1 50p dull grn & red   .80 .20

Type of Postal Tax Stamp, 1947
1947   Perf. 12½
RAJ2 PT4 50p blue grn & scar   .75 .20
   For surcharge see Trieste No. RAJ1.

Type of Postal Tax Stamp, 1948
1948
RAJ3 PT5 50p dark grn & red   .75 .20

Type of Postal Tax Stamp, 1949
1949
RAJ4 PT6 50p red & violet   1.10 .20
   For overprint see Trieste No. RAJ2.

Cross and Map   Red Cross
of Yugoslavia   PTD3
PTD2

1950   Unwmk.   Perf. 12½
RAJ5 PTD2 50p red brown & red   .40 .20

Type of Postal Tax Stamp, 1951
1951
RAJ6 PT8 50p emerald & red   .50 .20
   For overprint see Trieste No. RAJ3.

1952   Unwmk.   Photo.   Perf. 12½
RAJ7 PTD3 50p gray & car   .60 .20
   For overprint see Trieste No. RAJ4.

Types of Postal Tax Stamps, 1953-57
1953-57   Litho.
RAJ8 PT10 2d yel brown & red   .80 .20
RAJ9 PT11 2d lilac & red ('54)   .80 .20
RAJ10 PT12 2d yel grn ('55)   .70 .20
RAJ11 PT13 2d dk vio brn & red
   ('55)   .90 .20
RAJ12 PT14 2d blue grn & red
   ('56)   .35 .20
RAJ13 PT15 2d violet brn ('56)   .70 .20
RAJ14 PT16 2d gray, blk & car
   ('57)   .65 .20
RAJ15 PT17 2d lt bl, bis & grn
   ('57)   .50 .20
   Nos. RAJ8-RAJ15 (8)   5.40 1.60
For overprints see Trieste Nos. RAJ5-RAJ5.

Redrawn Type of Regular Issue, 1953
1958   Perf. 12½x12
RAJ16 A95 2d multicolored   .35 .20

Child With Toy — PTD4

1958   Litho.   Perf. 12½
RAJ17 PTD4 2d lt ultra & blk   .30 .20
Issued for Children's Week, Oct. 5-11.

Type of Postal Tax Stamp, 1959
1959
RAJ18 PT19 2d yel org & red   .30 .20

Type of Postal Tax Stamp, 1959
Design: Tree, cock and wheat.
1959
RAJ19 PT20 2d ocher & mar   .40 .20

Type of Postal Tax Stamp, 1960
1960
RAJ20 PT21 2d vio brn & red   .50 .20

Type of Postal Tax Stamp, 1960
Design: Boy, tools and ball.
1960
RAJ21 PT22 2d Prussian blue   .45 .20

Type of Postal Tax Stamp, 1961
1961, May 7
RAJ22 PT23 2d multicolored   .55 .20

Type of Postal Tax Stamp, 1961
1961, Oct. 1
RAJ23 PT24 2d apple grn & brn   .30 .20

Type of Postal Tax Stamp, 1962
1962, Apr. 30
RAJ24 PT25 5d brn red, bl & red   .25 .20

Type of Postal Tax Stamp, 1963
1963, May 5
RAJ25 PT26 5d red org, red & gray   .30 .20

OFFICES ABROAD

King Peter II — A1

1943   Unwmk.   Typo.   Perf. 12½
1K1 A1 2d dark blue   .20 4.00
1K2 A1 3d slate   .20 4.00
1K3 A1 5d carmine   .20 4.00
1K4 A1 10d black   .20 4.00
   Nos. 1K1-1K4 (4)   .80 16.00
For surcharges see Nos. 1KB1-1KB4.

V. Vodnik — A2   Peter Nyegosh — A3

3d, Ljudovit Gaj. 4d, Vuk Stefanovic Karadzic. 5d, Bishop Joseph Strossmayer. 10d, Karageorge.

1943, Dec. 1   Engr.   Perf. 12½x13
1K5 A2 1d red org & black   .30 8.25
1K6 A3 2d yel green & blk   .35 8.50
1K7 A2 3d dp ultra & blk   .35 8.75
1K8 A3 4d dk pur & brn blk   .40 9.25
1K9 A2 5d brn vio & brn blk   .40 9.75
1K10 A3 10d brn & brown blk   .45 10.00
   Nos. 1K5-1K10 (6)   2.25 54.50

Souvenir Sheet
Perf. 13½
Center in Black

1K11 Sheet of 6, #1K5-1K10   6.75

25th anniv. of the Union of Liberated Yugoslavia. Valid on ships of the Yugoslav Navy and Mercantile Marine.
Nos. 1K5-1K10 overprinted diagonally "1945" in London were not issued. In 1950, they were sold by the Yugoslav Government without postal validity. Later they appeared with the additional overprint of the outline of a plane at upper left in carmine or black.

OFFICES ABROAD SEMI-POSTAL STAMPS

Nos. 1K1-1K4 Surcharged in Orange or Black

1943   Unwmk.   Perf. 12½
1KB1 A1 2d + 12.50d dk bl   .65 8.25
1KB2 A1 3d + 12.50d slate   .65 8.25
1KB3 A1 5d + 12.50d car (Bk)   .65 8.25
1KB4 A1 10d + 12.50d black   .65 8.25
   Nos. 1KB1-1KB4 (4)   2.60 33.00
The surtax was for the Red Cross.

LJUBLJANA
(Lubiana, Laibach)
Italian Occupation

Under Italian occupation in 1941, the western half of Slovenia was known as the Province of Ljubljana (Lubiana to the Italians, Laibach to the Germans) and a quisling administration was set up under the profascist General Rupnik.

100 Centesimi = 1 Lira

Yugoslavia Nos. 127, 128, 142-154 Overprinted in Black

1941   Unwmk.   Perf. 12½, 13x12½
N1 A16 25p black   .75 1.00
N2 A16 50p orange   .75 1.00
N3 A16 1d yellow grn   .75 1.00
N4 A16 1.50d red   .75 1.00
N5 A16 2d dp magenta   .75 1.00
N6 A16 3d dl red brn   .75 1.00
N7 A16 4d ultra   .75 1.00
N8 A16 5d dark blue   .75 1.00
N9 A16 5.50d dk vio brn   .75 1.00
N10 A16 6d slate blue   1.00 1.50
N11 A16 8d sepia   1.00 1.50
N12 A10 10d bright vio   1.00 1.50
N13 A16 12d brt violet   2.00 2.50
N14 A10 15d brown   110.00 140.00
N15 A16 16d dl violet   2.00 2.50
N16 A16 20d blue   5.00 6.50
N17 A16 30d brt pink   20.00 27.50
   Nos. N1-N17 (17)   148.75 192.50

Yugoslavia Nos. 127, 142-154 Overprinted in Black

N18 A16 25p black   .60 .50
N19 A16 50p orange   .60 .50
N20 A16 1d yellow grn   .60 .50
N21 A16 1.50d red   .60 .50
N22 A16 2d dp magenta   .60 .50
N23 A16 3d dl red brn   .60 .50
N24 A16 4d ultra   .60 .50
N25 A16 5d dark blue   .60 .50
N26 A16 5.50d dk vio brn   .60 .50
N27 A16 6d slate blue   .60 .50
N28 A16 8d sepia   .60 .50
N29 A10 10d brt violet   1.25 1.00

N30 A16 12d bright vio   .60 .50
N31 A16 16d dl violet   1.25 1.00
N32 A16 20d blue   5.00 4.50
N33 A16 30d brt pink   35.00 32.50

Yugoslavia Nos. 145, 148 Surcharged in Black

N34 A16 50p on 1.50d red   .50 .60
N35 A16 1d on 4d ultra   .50 .60
   Nos. N18-N35 (18)   50.70 46.20

German Occupation
Stamps of Italy, 1929-42, Overprinted or Surcharged in Blue, Carmine, Black or Green

a   b

c

1944   Wmk. 140   Perf. 14
N36 A90(a) 5c ol brown   .20 1.25
N37 A92(b) 10c dark brn   .20 1.25
N38 A93(a) 15c sl grn (C)   .20 1.25
N39 A91(b) 20c rose red   .20 1.25
N40 A94(a) 25c dp grn (C)   .20 1.25
N41 A95(b) 30c ol brown   .20 1.25
N42 A95(b) 35c dp bl (C)   .20 1.25
N43 A95(b) 50c purple (C)   .20 2.00
N44 A94(a) 75c rose red   .20 2.75
N45 A91(b) 1 l deep vio   .20 2.75
N46 A94(a) 1.25 l dp bl (C)   .20 1.60
N47 A92(b) 1.75 l red org   .85 8.50
N48 A93(a) 2 l car lake   .20 2.00
N49 A90(c) 2.55 l on 5c ol brn (Bk)   .50 4.00
N50 A94(a) 5 l on 25c dp grn   .40 4.00
N51 A93(b) 10 l purple   2.75 16.00
N52 A91(a) 20 l on 20c rose red (G)   2.75 16.00
N53 A93(b) 25 l on 2 l car lake (G)   2.75 27.50
N54 A92(a) 50 l on 1.75 l red org (C)   6.50 50.00
   Nos. N36-N54 (19)   18.90 145.85

Krizna Jama — A1

Cerknica Lake — A2

Designs: 20c, Railroad Bridge, Borovnica. 25c, Landscape near Ljubljana. 50c, Church, Ribnica. 75c, View, Ljubljana. 1 l, Old Castle, Ljubljana. 1.25 l, Kocevje (Gottschee). 1.50 l, Borovnica Falls. 2 l, Castle, Konstanjevnica. 2.50 l, Castle, Turjak. 3 l, Castle, Zuzemperk. 5 l, View of Krk. 10 l, View of Otolac. 20 l, Farm, Carniola. 30 l, Castle and church, Tabor.

Perf. 10½x11½, 11½x10½
1945   Photo.   Unwmk.
N55 A1 5c black   .25 .75
N56 A2 10c red orange   .25 .75
N57 A2 20c brn carmine   .25 .75
N58 A2 25c dk sl green   .25 .75
N59 A1 50c deep violet   .25 .75
N60 A2 75c vermilion   .25 .75
N61 A2 1 l dark ol grn   .25 .75

N62 A1 1.25 l dark blue   .25 .75
N63 A1 1.50 l olive black   .25 .75
N64 A2 2 l ultramarine   .40 1.10
N65 A2 2.50 l brown   .40 1.10
N66 A1 3 l brt red vio   .75 2.25
N67 A1 5 l dk red brn   .75 2.25
N68 A2 10 l slate green   1.50 5.25
N69 A2 20 l sapphire   4.00 20.00
N70 A1 30 l rose pink   40.00 150.00
   Nos. N55-N70 (16)   52.05 188.70

SEMI-POSTAL STAMPS
Italian Occupation
Yugoslavia Nos. B116-B119 with Additional Overprint in Black

R.Commissariato
Civile
Territori Sloveni
occupati
LUBIANA

◆◆◆◆◆◆◆◆◆◆◆◆◆◆

Perf. 11½x12½, 12½x11½
1941   Unwmk.
NB1 AP6 50p + 50p on 5d   7.50 9.75
NB2 AP7 1d + 1d on 10d   7.50 9.75
NB3 AP8 1.50d + 1.50d on 20d   7.50 9.75
NB4 AP9 2d + 2d on 30d   7.50 9.75
   Nos. NB1-NB4 (4)   30.00 39.00

German Occupation
Italy Nos. E14 and E15 Surcharged in Red:

1944   Wmk. 140
NB5 SD4 1.25 l + 50 l green   12.50 125.00
NB6 SD4 2.50 l + 50 l dp org   12.50 125.00
The surtax aided the Red Cross.

Same, Surcharged in Blue or Green:

NB7 SD4 1.25 l + 50 l grn (B)   12.50 125.00
NB8 SD4 2.50 l + 50 l dp org   12.50 125.00
   Nos. NB5-NB8 (4)   50.00 500.00

The surtax aided the Homeless Relief Fund.
The German and Slovenian inscriptions in the surcharges are transposed on Nos. NB6 and NB8.

Italy Nos. C12-C14, C16-C18 Surcharged "DEN WAISEN," "SIROTAM," Heraldic Eagle and Surtax in Blue or Red

1944   Wmk. 140
NB9 AP4 25c + 10 l dk grn   6.00 40.00
NB10 AP3 50c + 10 l ol brn   6.00 40.00
NB11 AP5 75c + 20 l org brn   6.00 40.00
NB12 AP5 1 l + 20 l purple   6.00 40.00
NB13 AP6 2 l + 20 l dp bl   6.00 40.00
   (R)
NB14 AP3 5 l + 20 l dk grn   6.00 40.00
   Nos. NB9-NB14 (6)   36.00 240.00

The surcharge aided orphans.

Same, Surcharged "WINTERHILFE," "ZIMSKA POMOC," Heraldic Eagle and Surtax in Blue or Red
NB15 AP4 25c + 10 l dk grn   6.00 40.00
NB16 AP3 50c + 10 l ol brn   6.00 40.00
NB17 AP5 75c + 20 l org brn   6.00 40.00
NB18 AP5 1 l + 20 l purple   6.00 40.00
NB19 AP6 2 l + 20 l dp bl   6.00 40.00
   (R)
NB20 AP3 5 l + 20 l dk grn   6.00 40.00
   Nos. NB15-NB20 (6)   36.00 240.00

The surcharge was for winter relief.

AIR POST STAMPS

Italian Occupation

Yugoslavia Nos. C7-C16 Ovptd. like
Nos. NB1-NB4

Perf. 12½, 12½x11½, 11½x12½

			1941	Unwmk.	
NC1	AP6	50p brown		.40	.85
NC2	AP7	1d yel grn		.40	.85
NC3	AP8	2d bl gray		.55	1.10
NC4	AP9	2.50d rose red		.55	1.10
NC5	AP6	5d brn vio		1.00	1.75
NC6	AP7	10d brn lake		1.00	1.75
NC7	AP8	20d dark grn		8.25	10.00
NC8	AP9	30d ultra		37.50	22.50
NC9	AP10	40d Prus grn & pale grn		110.00	70.00
NC10	AP11	50d sl bl & gray bl		75.00	45.00
a.		Inverted overprint		200.00	
		Nos. NC1-NC10 (10)		234.65	154.90

German Occupation

Italy Nos. C12-C14, C16-C19
Overprinted Types "a" and "b" in
Carmine, Green or Blue

			1944	Wmk. 140	Perf. 14
NC11	AP4(a)	25c dk grn (C)		1.10	6.25
NC12	AP3(b)	50c ol brn (C)		4.25	30.00
NC13	AP5(a)	75c org brn (G)		1.25	8.75
NC14	AP5(b)	1 l pur (C)		5.25	24.00
NC15	AP6(a)	2 l db brn (Bl)		3.00	20.00
NC16	AP3(b)	5 l dk grn (C)		3.00	24.00
NC17	AP3(a)	10 l dp car (G)		2.25	32.50
		Nos. NC11-NC17 (7)		20.10	145.50

AIR POST SPECIAL DELIVERY STAMP

German Occupation

Italy #CE3 Ovptd. Type "b" in Blue

			1944	Wmk. 140	Perf. 14
NCE1	APSD2	2 l gray blk		3.75	15.00

SPECIAL DELIVERY STAMP

German Occupation

Italy #E14 Ovptd. Type "b" in Green

			1944	Wmk. 140	Perf. 14
NE1	SD4	1.25 l green		1.00	5.00

POSTAGE DUE STAMPS

Italian Occupation

Yugoslavia Nos. J28-J32 Overprinted
in Black Like Nos. N1-N17

			1941	Unwmk.	Perf. 12½
NJ1	D4	50p violet		.40	.65
NJ2	D4	1d rose		.40	.65
NJ3	D4	2d deep blue		.40	.65
NJ4	D4	5d orange		4.50	5.50
NJ5	D4	10d chocolate		4.50	5.50
		Nos. NJ1-NJ5 (5)		10.20	12.95

Same Overprinted in Black

NJ6	D4	50p violet		.20	.25
NJ7	D4	1d rose		.20	.25
NJ8	D4	2d deep blue		.40	.75
NJ9	D4	5d orange		22.50	30.00
NJ10	D4	10d chocolate		8.00	10.00
		Nos. NJ6-NJ10 (5)		31.30	41.25

Same Overprinted in Black

R. Commissariato Civile Territori Sloveni occupati LUBIANA

NJ11	D4	50p violet		.25	.50
NJ12	D4	1d rose		.50	.70
NJ13	D4	2d deep blue		9.25	11.50
		Nos. NJ11-NJ13 (3)		10.00	12.70

German Occupation

Postage Due Stamps of Italy, 1934,
Overprinted or Surcharged in Various
Colors

d   e

f   g

			1944	Wmk. 140	Perf. 14
NJ14	D6(d)	5c brown (Br)		1.25	13.00
NJ15	D6(e)	10c blue (Bl)		1.25	13.00
NJ16	D6(d)	20c rose red (R)		.20	.55
NJ17	D6(e)	25c green (G)		.20	.55
NJ18	D6(f)	30c on 50c vio (Bk)		.20	.55
NJ19	D6(g)	40c on 5c brn (Bl)		.20	.55
NJ20	D6(d)	50c violet (V)		.20	.55
NJ21	D7(e)	1 l red orange (R)		1.25	6.50
NJ22	D7(d)	2 l green (Bl)		1.25	6.50
		Nos. NJ14-NJ22 (9)		6.00	41.75

Fiume-Kupa Zone
Italian Occupation

Four issues of 1941-42 consist of
overprints on Yugoslav stamps of 1939-
41: (a.) 14 stamps overprinted "ZONA
OCCUPATO FIUMANO KUPA" and
"ZOFK ZOFK ZOFK." (b.) 3 stamps
overprinted as illustrated. (c.) 1 stamp
surcharged "MEMENTO AVDERE
SEMPER." "L1," etc. (d.) 3 stamps
overprinted in arch: "Pro Maternite e
Infanzia."

ISSUES FOR ISTRIA AND THE SLOVENE COAST (ZONE B)

Grapes — A1

Olive Branch — A2

Sailboat, Pola — A3

Designs: 50c, Donkey. Nos. 25-26, Ruined
home. 2 l, Duino Castle. 5 l, Birthplace of
Vladimir Gortan. 10 l, Plowing. Nos. 33-34,
Tuna. 30 l, Viaduct at Solkan, Soca River.

Perf. 11½, 12, 10½x11½

			1945-46		Photo.
23	A1	25c dark green		.85	1.00
24	A1	50c red brown		.20	.20
25	A1	1 l green		.20	.20
26	A1	1 l red		.20	.20
27	A2	1.50 l olive brown		.20	.20
28	A2	2 l dk Prus grn		.20	.20
29	A3	4 l red		.20	.20
30	A3	4 l bright blue		.30	.40
31	A3	5 l gray black		.20	.20
32	A3	10 l brown		.20	.20
33	A3	20 l blue		1.60	.85
34	A3	20 l dark violet		4.50	4.00
35	A3	30 l magenta		1.25	.60
		Nos. 23-35 (13)		10.10	8.45

The first (Ljubljana) printing is perf.
10½x11½ and consists of Nos. 23-24, 26-28,
30-32, 34-35. The second (Zagreb) printing is
perf. 12 and consists of Nos. 23-25, 27-29, 31-
33, 35. The third (Belgrade) printing is perf.
11½ and consists of Nos. 25, 28, 40-41.
See Nos. 40-41. For surcharges see Nos.
36-37, J1-J19.

Nos. 33 and 35 Surcharged with New
Values and Bars in Black

			1946	Unwmk.	Perf. 11½
36	A3	1 l on 20 l blue		.70	.35
37	A3	2 l on 30 l magenta		.65	.35

Types of 1945

Design: 3 l, Duino Castle

1946, Nov. 30

40	A2	3 l crimson		.20	.20
41	A3	6 l ultra		.20	.20

Types of Yugoslavia and of Official
Stamps of 1946 Surcharged in Black

On A26

On O1

			1947	Unwmk.	Perf. 12½
42	A26	1 l on 9d lilac rose		.20	.20
43	O1	1.50 l on 50p blue		.20	.20
44	A26	2 l on 9d lilac rose		.20	.20
45	O1	3 l on 50p blue		.20	.20
46	A26	5 l on 9d lilac rose		.20	.20
47	O1	6 l on 50p blue		.20	.20
48	A26	10 l on 9d lilac rose		.20	.20
49	O1	15 l on 50p blue		.20	.20
50	A26	35 l on 9d lilac rose		.20	.20
51	O1	50 l on 50p blue		.20	.20
		Nos. 42-51 (10)		2.00	2.00

POSTAGE DUE STAMPS

Nos. 23, 24 34
and 35
Surcharged in
Black

			1945	Unwmk.	Perf. 10½x11½
J1	A3	50c on 20 l dk vio		.50	1.25
J2	A1	1 l on 25c dk grn		2.75	3.50
J3	A3	2 l on 30 l magenta		.40	1.00
J4	A1	4 l on 50c red brn		.30	.20
J5	A1	8 l on 50c red brn		.25	.20
J6	A1	10 l on 50c red brn		3.00	1.60
J7	A1	20 l on 50c red brn		3.00	1.60
		Nos. J1-J7 (7)		10.20	9.35

Nos. 25 and 35
Surcharged in
Black

			1945		Perf. 12
J8	A1	1 l on 1 l green		.20	.20
J9	A1	2 l on 1 l green		.20	.20
J10	A1	4 l on 1 l green		.25	.20
J11	A3	10 l on 30 l magenta		.55	.40
J12	A3	20 l on 30 l magenta		3.00	1.50
J13	A3	30 l on 30 l magenta		3.00	1.50
		Nos. J8-J13 (6)		7.20	4.00

The surcharges are arranged to fit the
designs of the stamps.

No. 23
Surcharged in
Black

			1946		
J14	A1	1 l on 25c dark green		.60	.70
J15	A1	2 l on 25c dark green		.85	1.00
J16	A1	4 l on 25c dark green		1.00	1.10

No. 33 Surcharged in Black

J17	A3	10 l on 20 l blue		3.00	.50
J18	A3	20 l on 20 l blue		5.50	4.00
J19	A3	30 l on 20 l blue		6.75	5.00
		Nos. J14-J19 (6)		17.70	12.30

Type of Yugoslavia
Postage Due Stamps,
1946, Surcharged in
Black

			1947		
J20	D7	1 l on 1d brt blue grn		.20	.20
J21	D7	2 l on 1d brt blue grn		.20	.20
J22	D7	6 l on 1d brt blue grn		.20	.20
J23	D7	10 l on 1d brt blue grn		.20	.20
J24	D7	30 l on 1d brt blue grn		.30	.40
		Nos. J20-J24 (5)		1.10	1.20

TRIESTE, ZONE A
See listing under Italy, Vol. 3.

TRIESTE

A free territory (1947-1954) on the
Adriatic Sea between Italy and Yugoslavia. In 1954 the territory was divided,
Italy acquiring the northern section and
seaport, Yugoslavia the southern section (Zone B).

> Catalogue values for all unused
> stamps in this country are for
> Never Hinged items.

ZONE B

Issued by the Yugoslav Military Government

100 Centesimi = 1 Lira
100 Paras = 1 Dinar (1949)

See Istria and the Slovene Coast (Zone B)
for preceding issues of 1945-47.

Stylized Gymnast
and Arms of
Trieste — A1

1948 Unwmk. Litho. Perf. 10½x11
Inscriptions in:

1	A1	100 l Italian	2.50	1.75
2	A1	100 l Croatian	2.50	1.75
3	A1	100 l Slovene	2.50	1.75
a.		Strip of 3, #1-3	12.50	17.50
		Nos. 1-3 (3)	7.50	5.25

May Day.

Clasped Hands, Hammer and Sickle — A2

1949   Photo.   Perf. 11½x12½

4	A2	10 l grnsh blk & ol grn	.50	.40

Labor Day, May 1, 1949. "V.U.J.A. S.T.T." are the initials of "Vojna Uprava Jugoslovenske Armije, Slobodna Teritorija Trsta" (Military Administration Yugoslav Army, Free Territory of Trieste).

Stamps of Yugoslavia, 1945-47 Overprinted in Carmine or Ultramarine

1949, Aug. 15   Perf. 12½

5	A22	50p ol gray	.25	.25
6	A22	1d bl grn	.25	.25
7	A24	2d scar (U)	.25	.25
8	A25	3d dl red (U)	.25	.25
9	A24	4d dk bl	.50	.35
10	A25	5d dk bl	.50	.35
11	A26	9d rose vio (U)	1.25	.75
12	A23	12d ultra	3.00	2.00
13	A22	16d blue	3.75	2.50
14	A23	20d org ver (U)	5.00	3.00
		Nos. 5-14 (10)	15.00	9.95

The letters of the overprint are set closer and in one line on Nos. 7 and 9.

Yugoslavia Nos. 266 and 267 Overprinted in Carmine

Burelage in Color of Stamp
1949

15	A58	5d blue	7.50	6.50
16	A58	12d brown	7.50	6.50

75th anniv. of the UPU.

Yugoslavia, Nos. 269 to 272, Overprinted in **VUJA - STT** Carmine

1950

17	A60	2d bl grn	1.00	.60
18	A60	3d car rose	1.25	.75
19	A60	5d blue	1.75	1.00
20	A60	10d dp org	4.75	3.25
		Nos. 17-20 (4)	8.75	5.60

Workers Carrying Tools and Flag — A3

Peasant on Ass — A4

1950, May 1   Photo.

21	A3	3d violet	.50	.40
22	A3	10d carmine	.75	.50

Labor Day, May 1, 1950.

1950   Unwmk.   Perf. 12½

Designs: 1d, Cockerel. 2d, Goose. 3d, Bees and honeycomb. 5d, Oxen. 10d, Turkey. 15d, Goats. 20d, Silkworms.

23	A4	50p dk gray	.20	.20
24	A4	1d brn car	.20	.20
25	A4	2d dp bl	.20	.20
26	A4	3d org brn	.30	.20
27	A4	5d aqua	1.00	.20
28	A4	10d brown	1.40	.20
29	A4	15d violet	6.75	4.00
30	A4	20d dk grn	2.50	1.50
		Nos. 23-30 (8)	12.55	6.70

1951

31	A4	1d orange brown	.35	.20
32	A4	3d rose brown	.50	.20

Worker A5

1951, May 1

33	A5	3d dark red	.55	.40
34	A5	10d brown olive	.95	.60

Labor Day.

Pietro Paolo Vergerio — A7

Bicycle Race — A8

1951, Oct. 21   Litho.

37	A7	5d blue	.65	.50
38	A7	10d claret	.65	.50
39	A7	20d sepia	.65	.50
		Nos. 37-39 (3)	1.95	1.50

Types of Yugoslavia, 1951, Overprinted "STT VUJA"
1951, Nov.

40	A81	10d brn org (V)	.90	.60
41	A81	12d grnsh blk (C)	.90	.60

1952   Photo.

42	A8	5d shown	.20	.20
43	A8	10d Soccer	.20	.20
44	A8	15d Rowing	.20	.20
45	A8	28d Sailing	.70	.50
46	A8	50d Volleyball	1.50	.85
47	A8	100d Diving	4.00	2.50
		Nos. 42-47 (6)	6.80	4.45

Marshal Tito
A9   A10

1952, May 25   Perf. 11½

48	A9	15d dk brn	1.75	1.00
49	A10	28d red brn	2.25	2.00
50	A9	50d dk gray grn	2.75	2.00
		Nos. 48-50 (3)	6.75	5.00

60th birthday of Marshal Tito.

Types of Yugoslavia 1952 Overprinted in Carmine "STT VUJNA"
1952, July 26   Perf. 12½

51	A90	5d dk brn & sal, cr	.65	.40
52	A90	10d dk grn & grn	.65	.40
53	A90	15d dk brn & bl, lil	.65	.40
54	A90	28d dk brn & buff, cr	1.50	1.00
55	A90	50d dk brn & buff, yel	6.00	4.00
56	A90	100d ind & lil, pink	13.50	10.00
		Nos. 51-56 (6)	22.95	16.20

15th Olympic Games, Helsinki, 1952. Nos. 52, 54, 56 inscribed in Cyrillic characters. The added "N" in "VUJNA" stands for "Narodna" (Peoples"). See note after No. 4. Nos. 51-56 exist imperf. Value of set, $375.

Yugoslavia Nos. 365 to 367 Overprinted in Carmine "STT VUJNA"
1952, Sept. 13

57	A91	15d deep claret	.55	.55
58	A91	28d dark brown	.75	.75
59	A91	50d gray	3.00	3.00
		Nos. 57-59 (3)	4.30	4.30

Formation of the Yugoslav navy, 10th anniv.

Yugoslavia No. 358 Overprinted "STT VUJA" in Blue
1952, June 22

60	A89	15d bright rose	.90	.95

Children's Week.

Yugoslavia Nos. 369-372 Overprinted "VUJNA STT" in Blue or Carmine
1952, Nov. 4

61	A93	15d red brn (Bl)	.50	.75
62	A93	15d dk vio bl	.50	.75
63	A93	15d dk brn	.50	.75
64	A93	15d ol grn	.50	.75
		Nos. 61-64 (4)	2.00	3.00

Issued to publicize the 6th Yugoslavia Communist Party Congress, Zagreb, 1952.

Anchovies and Starfish — A11

1952 Unwmk. Photo. Perf. 11x11½

65	A11	15d red brown	1.25	1.60
a.		Souvenir sheet, imperf.	8.75	15.00

Capodistria Phil. Exhib., Nov. 29-Dec. 7. No. 65a contains a 50d dark blue green stamp. Sold for 85d.

Stamps or Types of Yugoslavia Overprinted "STT VUJNA" in Various Colors
1953, Feb. 3   Perf. 12½

66	A94	15d brn carmine (Bl)	.30	.40
67	A94	30d chalky blue (R)	.85	.55

10th anniv. of the death of Nikola Tesla.

1953

68	A68	1d gray	2.25	2.50
69	A68	2d car (V)	.45	.50
70	A68	3d rose red (R)	.45	.50
71	A68	5d orange	.45	.50
72	A68	10d emerald (G)	.45	.50
73	A68	15d rose red (V)	.90	1.10
74	A68	30d blue (Bl)	1.90	2.00
75	A68	50d grnsh bl (Bl)	3.50	4.00
		Nos. 68-75 (8)	10.35	11.60

Nos. 69, 71 and 73 are lithographed. See Nos. 90-92.

1953, Apr. 21   Perf. 11½

76	A95	15d dk ol grn (O)	.35	.40
77	A95	30d chalky blue (O)	.35	.40
78	A95	50d henna brown	1.10	1.10
		Nos. 76-78 (3)	1.80	1.90

Issued in honor of the United Nations.

Automobile Climbing Mt. Lovcen — A12

Various automobiles and motorcycles.

1953, June 2   Perf. 12½

79	A12	15d ocher & choc	.35	.20
80	A12	30d lt bl grn & ol grn	.35	.45
81	A12	50d salmon & dp plum	.35	.75
82	A12	70d bl & dk bl	.70	.75
		Nos. 79-82 (4)	1.75	1.75

Intl. Automobile and Motorcycle Races, 1953.

Stamps or Types of Yugoslavia Overprinted "STT VUJNA" in Various Colors
1953, July 8   Engr.

83	A97	50d grnsh gray (C)	1.90	1.50

Tito's election to the presidency, 1/14/53.

1953, July 31

84	A98	15d gray & grn (C)	2.00	1.90

38th Esperanto Cong., Zagreb, July 25-Aug. 1, 1953. See No. C21.

1953, Sept. 5

85	A101	15d blue (C)	3.25	2.25

Liberation of Istria & the Slovene coast, 10th anniv.

1953, Oct. 3

86	A102	15d gray	1.40	1.40

Cent. of the death of Branko Radicevic, poet.

1953, Nov. 29   Perf. 12½x12

87	A103	15d gray vio (V)	.45	.40
88	A103	30d claret (Br)	.65	.55
89	A103	50d dl bl grn (Dk Bl)	1.00	.95
		Nos. 87-89 (3)	2.10	1.90

10th anniv. of the 1st republican legislative assembly of Yugoslavia.

1954, Mar. 5   Perf. 12½

90	A68	5d org (V)	.50	.40
91	A68	10d yel grn (C)	.35	.40
92	A68	15d rose red (G)	.50	.40
		Nos. 90-92 (3)	1.35	1.10

Overprinted in Carmine
1954   Photo.   Perf. 11½

93	A104	2d red brn, sl & cr	.20	.25
94	A104	5d gray & dk yel brn	.20	.25
95	A104	10d ol grn & dk org brn	.20	.25
96	A104	15d dp bl grn & dk org brn	.20	.25
97	A104	17d gray brn, dk brn & cr	.20	.25
98	A104	25d bis, gray bl & org yel	.20	.25
99	A105	30d lil & dk brn	.20	.25
100	A105	35d rose vio & bl blk	.30	.50
101	A105	50d yel grn & vio blk	.45	.75
102	A105	65d org brn & gray blk	2.25	3.50
103	A105	70d bl & org brn	4.50	7.50
104	A105	100d brt bl & blk brn	15.00	25.00
		Nos. 93-104 (12)	23.90	39.00

Overprinted in Various Colors
1954, Oct. 8   Perf. 12½

105	A107	15d mar, red, ocher & dk bl (Bk)	.35	.35
106	A107	30d dk bl, grn, sal buff & choc (G)	.35	.35
107	A107	50d brn, bis & red (G)	.55	.55
108	A107	70d dk grn, gray grn & choc (R)	1.40	1.25
		Nos. 105-108 (4)	2.65	2.50

150th anniv. of the 1st Serbian insurrection.

AIR POST STAMPS

AP1

Perf. 12½x11½
1948, Oct. 17   Photo.   Unwmk.

C1	AP1	25 l gray	.75	.75
C2	AP1	50 l orange	.75	.75

Economic Exhib. at Capodistria, Oct. 17-24.

Fishermen — AP2

Farmer and Pack Mule — AP3

Mew over Chimneys AP4

1949, June 1 — **Perf. 11½**
C3	AP2	1 l grnsh bl	.20	.20
C4	AP3	2 l red brn	.20	.20
C5	AP2	5 l blue	.20	.20
C6	AP3	10 l purple	1.25	.85
C7	AP2	25 l brown	1.60	.90
C8	AP3	50 l ol grn	1.60	.90
C9	AP4	100 l dk vio brn	2.25	1.50
		Nos. C3-C9 (7)	7.30	4.75

Italian inscriptions on Nos. C5 and C6, Croatian on No. C7, Slavonic on No. C8.
Nos. C3-C4 exist imperf. Value, each $135.

Nos. C3-C9 Surcharged "DIN," or New Value and "DIN" in Various Colors
1949, Nov. 5
C10	AP2	1d on 1 l (Bk)	.20	.20
C11	AP3	2d on 2 l (Br)	.20	.20
C12	AP3	5d on 5 l (Bl)	.20	.20
C13	AP3	10d on 10 l (V)	.45	.40
C14	AP3	15d on 25 l (Br)	4.75	4.50
C15	AP3	20d on 50 l (Gr)	1.60	1.50
C16	AP4	30d on 100 l (Bk)	1.60	1.50
		Nos. C10-C16 (7)	9.00	8.50

On Nos. C14 and C15 the original value is obliterated by a framed block, on No. C16 by four parallel lines.

Yugoslavia No. C33 Overprinted in Carmine and Lilac Rose Network

VUJA - STT

Souvenir Sheet
1950 — **Perf. 11½x12½**
C17	AP15	10d lilac rose	50.00	57.50
a.		Imperf.	50.00	57.50

Main Square, Capodístria — AP5
Lighthouse, Pirano — AP6

Design: 25d, Hotel, Portorose.

1952 Unwmk. Photo. — **Perf. 12½**
C18	AP5	5d brown	7.50	7.00
C19	AP6	15d brt bl	4.75	5.50
C20	AP5	25d green	4.75	5.50
		Nos. C18-C20 (3)	17.00	18.00

75th anniv. (in 1949) of the UPU.

Type of Yugoslavia, 1953 Overprinted "STT VUJNA" in Carmine
1953, July 31
C21	AP21	300d vio & grn	190.00	160.00

38th Esperanto Cong., Zagreb, 7/25-8/1. Sheets of 12 (12,000 stamps) and sheets of 8 (3,000 stamps in light violet and green).
A private red overprint was applied marginally to 250 sheets of 8: "Esperantski Kongres — 38 — a Universala Kongreso de Esperanto — Congresso del Esperanto."

Air Post Stamps of Yugoslavia in New Colors Overprinted "STT VUJNA" in Various Colors
1954 — **Engr.**
C22	AP16	1d dp pur gray	.20	.20
C23	AP16	2d brt grn (G)	.20	.20
C24	AP16	3d red brn (Br)	.20	.20
C25	AP16	5d chocolate	.20	.20
C26	AP16	10d bl grn	.20	.20
C27	AP16	20d brn (Br)	.25	.40
C28	AP16	30d blue	.25	.40
C29	AP16	50d olive blk	.40	.55
C30	AP16	100d scar (R)	1.10	1.50
C31	AP16	200d dk bl vio (Bl)	2.75	3.75

Perf. 11x11½
32	AP17	500d orange (Br)	8.50	12.00
		Nos. C22-C32 (11)	14.25	19.60

POSTAGE DUE STAMPS

Yugoslavia Nos. J51 to J55 Overprinted "S T T VUJA" in Two Lines in Ultramarine or Carmine
1949 Unwmk. — **Perf. 12½**
J1	D7	50p dp org	.55	.55
J2	D7	1d orange	.55	.55
J3	D7	2d dk bl (C)	.55	.55
J4	D7	3d yel grn (C)	.55	.55
J5	D7	5d brt pur (C)	1.10	1.10
		Nos. J1-J5 (5)	3.30	3.30

Croakers D1

Anchovies D2

1950 — **Photo.**
J6	D1	50p brn org	.20	.20
J7	D1	1d dp ol grn	.90	.95
J8	D2	2d dk grnsh bl	.90	.95
J9	D2	3d dk vio bl	.90	.95
J10	D2	5d plum	4.50	4.25
		Nos. J6-J10 (5)	7.40	7.30

Yugoslavia Nos. J67-J74 Overprinted "STT VUJNA" in Blue or Carmine
1952
J11	D7	1d brown (Bl)	.20	.20
J12	D7	2d emerald	.20	.20
J13	D7	5d blue	.20	.20
J14	D7	10d scar (Bl)	.20	.20
J15	D7	20d purple	.20	.20
J16	D7	30d org yel (Bl)	.20	.20
J17	D7	50d ultra	.20	.20
J18	D7	100d dp plum (Bl)	3.00	4.50
		Nos. J11-J18 (8)	4.40	5.90

POSTAL TAX STAMPS

Yugoslavia No. RA5 Surcharged in Blue

1948 Unwmk. — **Perf. 12½**
RA1	PT4	2 l on 50p brn & scar	6.50	10.00

Obligatory on all mail from May 22-30.

Yugoslavia No. RA7 Overprinted "VUJA STT" in Black
1950, July 3
RA2	PT6	50p red & brn	.35	.40

Yugoslavia No. RA9 Overprinted "STT VUJA" in Black
1951
RA3	PT8	50p vio bl & red	6.50	10.00

Yugoslavia No. RA10 Overprinted "STT VUJNA" in Carmine
1952
RA4	PT9	50p gray & carmine	.20	.20

Type of Yugoslavia, 1953, Overprinted "STT VUJNA" in Blue
1953
RA5	PT10	2d org brn & red	.20	.30

The tax of Nos. RA1-RA5 was for the Red Cross.

POSTAL TAX DUE STAMPS

Yugoslavia No. RAJ2 Surcharged Like No. RA1 in Scarlet
1948 Unwmk. — **Perf. 12½**
RAJ1	PT4	2 l on 50p bl grn & scar	100.00	140.00

Yugoslavia No. RAJ4 Overprinted "VUJA STT" in Black
1950, July 3
RAJ2	PT6	50p red & vio	.85	1.25

Yugoslavia No. RAJ6 Overprinted "STT VUJA" in Black
1951
RAJ3	PT8	50p emer & red	85.00	110.00

Yugoslavia No. RAJ7 Overprinted "STT VUJNA" in Carmine
1952
RAJ4	PTD3	50p gray & car	.50	.60

Type of Yugoslavia, 1953, Overprinted "STT VUJNA" in Blue
1953
RAJ5	PT10	2d lilac rose & red	.50	.60

ZAIRE

zä-'ir

(Congo Democratic Republic)

LOCATION — Central Africa
GOVT. — Republic
AREA — 905,365 sq. mi.
POP. — 50,481,305 (1999 est.)
CAPITAL — Kinshasa

Congo Democratic Republic changed its name to Republic of the Zaire in November 1971. Issues before that date are listed in Vol. 2 under Congo Democratic Republic.

100 Sengi = 1 Li-Kuta
100 Ma-Kuta = 1 Zaire
100 Centimes = 1 Franc (July 1998)

Catalogue values for all unused stamps in this country are for Never Hinged items.

UNICEF Emblem, Child Care — A143

UNICEF Emblem and: 14k, Map of Africa showing Zaire. 17k, Boy in African village.

Perf. 14x13½
1971, Dec. 18 — **Unwmk.**
750	A143	4k gold & multi	.40	.20
751	A143	14k lt bl, gold, red & grn	1.10	.65
752	A143	17k gold & multi	1.50	.60
		Nos. 750-752 (3)	3.00	1.45

25th anniv. of UNICEF. For surcharge see No. 1327.

Pres. Mobutu, MPR Emblem A144

1972 Photo. — **Perf. 11½**
753	A144	4k multi	1.75	1.40
754	A144	14k multi	1.75	1.40
755	A144	22k multi	1.75	1.40
		Nos. 753-755 (3)	5.25	4.20

5th anniv. of the People's Revolutionary Movement (MPR). For surcharge see #1308.

Zaire Arms — A145

Pres. Joseph D. Mobutu — A146

1972 Litho. — **Perf. 14**
756	A145	10s red org & blk	.20	.20
757	A145	40s brt bl & multi	.20	.20
758	A145	50s citron & multi	.20	.20

Perf. 13
759	A146	1k sky bl & multi	.20	.20
760	A146	2k org & multi	.20	.20
761	A146	3k multi	.20	.20
762	A146	4k emer & multi	.20	.20
763	A146	5k multi	.20	.20
764	A146	6k multi	.20	.20
765	A146	8k cit & multi	.20	.20
766	A146	9k multi	.20	.20
767	A146	10k lt lil & multi	.25	.20
768	A146	14k multi	.35	.25
769	A146	17k multi	.40	.30
770	A146	20k yel & multi	.45	.35
771	A146	50k multi	1.60	.70
772	A146	100k fawn & multi	2.75	1.50
		Nos. 756-772 (17)	8.00	5.50

For surcharges and overprints see Nos. 860, 1328, O1-O11.

Same, Denominations in Zaires
1973, Feb. 21
773	A146	0.01z sky bl & multi	.20	.20
774	A146	0.02z org & multi	.20	.20
775	A146	0.03z multi	.20	.20
776	A146	0.04z multi	.20	.20
777	A146	0.10z multi	.25	.20
778	A146	0.14z multi	.35	.30
		Nos. 773-778 (6)	1.40	1.30

Inga Dam A147

1973, Jan. 25 Litho. — **Perf. 13½**
790	A147	0.04z multi	.20	.20
791	A147	0.14z pink & multi	.30	.25
792	A147	0.18z yel & multi	.50	.40
		Nos. 790-792 (3)	1.00	.85

Completion of first section of Inga Dam Nov. 24, 1972.

World Map A148

1973, June 23 Photo. — **Perf. 12½x12**
793	A148	0.04z lil & multi	.20	.20
794	A148	0.07z multi	.30	.20
795	A148	0.18z multi	.75	.35
		Nos. 793-795 (3)	1.25	.75

3rd Intl. Fair at Kinshasa, June 23-July 8.
The dark brown ink of the inscription was applied by a thermographic process and varnished, producing a shiny, raised effect.

Hand and
INTERPOL
Emblem — A149

1973, Sept. 28   Litho.   Perf. 12½
796 A149 0.06z multi .40 .20
797 A149 0.14z multi .85 .40

50th anniversary of International Criminal
Police Organization.

Leopard
with Soccer
Ball on
Globe
A150

1974, July 17   Photo.   Perf. 11½x12
798 A150 1k multi .20 .20
799 A150 2k multi .25 .20
800 A150 3k multi .40 .20
801 A150 4k multi .50 .20
802 A150 5k multi .60 .20
803 A150 14k multi 1.50 .45
    Nos. 798-803 (6) 3.45 1.45

World Cup Soccer Championship, Munich,
June 13-July 7.

Foreman-Ali
Fight — A151

1974, Nov. 9   Litho.   Perf. 12x12½
804 A151 1k multi .20 .20
805 A151 4k multi .20 .20
806 A151 6k multi .30 .20
807 A151 14k multi .60 .20
808 A151 20k multi .80 .30
    Nos. 804-808 (5) 2.10 1.10

World Heavyweight Boxing Championship
match between George Foreman and Muhammad Ali, Kinshasa, Oct. 30 (postponed from
Sept. 25).

Same, Type of
1974,
Denominations
in Zaires and
Inscribed in
Various Colors

1975, Aug.   Litho.   Perf. 12x12½
809 A151 0.01z multi (R) .20 .20
810 A151 0.04z multi (Br) .20 .20
811 A151 0.06z multi (Bk) .20 .20
812 A151 0.14z multi (G) .30 .25
813 A151 0.20z multi (Bk) .55 .40
    Nos. 809-813 (5) 1.45 1.25

Judge,
Lawyers,
IWY
Emblem
A152

1975, Dec.   Photo.   Perf. 11½
814 A152 1k dull blk & multi .20 .20
815 A152 2k dp rose & multi .25 .20
816 A152 4k dull grn & multi .50 .20
817 A152 14k violet & multi 1.25 .55
    Nos. 814-817 (4) 2.20 1.15

International Women's Year 1975.

Waterfall — A153

Okapis
A154

1975   Photo.   Perf. 11½
818 A153 1k multicolored .20 .20
819 A153 2k lt blue & multi .30 .20
820 A153 3k multicolored .45 .25
821 A153 4k salmon & multi .65 .30
822 A153 5k green & multi .65 .40
    Nos. 818-822 (5) 2.25 1.35

12th General Assembly of the Intl. Union for
Nature Preservation (U.I.C.N.), Kinshasa,
Sept. 1975.

1975
823 A154 1k blue & multi .20 .20
824 A154 2k yellow grn & multi .20 .20
825 A154 3k brown red & multi .20 .20
826 A154 4k green & multi .30 .30
827 A154 5k yellow & multi .35 .35
    Nos. 823-827 (5) 1.25 1.25

Virunga National Park, 50th anniversary.

Siderma
Maluku
Industry
A155

Designs: 1k, Sozacom apartment building,
vert. 3k, Matadi flour mill, vert. 4k, Women
parachutists. 8k, Pres. Mobutu visiting Chair-
man Mao, vert. 10k, Soldiers working along
the Salongo. 14k, Pres. Mobutu addressing
UN Gen. Assembly, Oct. 1974. 15k, Celebrating crowd.

1975
828 A155 1k ocher & multi .20 .20
829 A155 2k yel grn & multi .20 .20
830 A155 3k multi .20 .20
831 A155 4k multi .30 .20
832 A155 8k dk brn & multi .55 .25
833 A155 10k sep & multi .65 .35
834 A155 14k bl & multi .90 .45
835 A155 15k org & multi 1.10 .55
    Nos. 828-835 (8) 4.10 2.40

10th anniversary of new government.

Tshokwe
Mask — A156

Map of Zaire, UPU
Emblem — A157

Designs: 2k, 4k, Seated woman, Pende. 7k,
like 5k. 10k, 14k, Antelope mask, Suku. 15k,
18k, Kneeling woman, Kongo. 20k, 25k, Kuba
mask.

1977, Jan. 8   Photo.   Perf. 11½
836 A156 2k multi .20 .20
837 A156 4k multi .20 .20
838 A156 5k gray & multi .20 .20

839 A156 7k multi .20 .20
840 A156 10k multi .25 .20
841 A156 14k multi .35 .20
842 A156 15k multi .40 .20
843 A156 18k multi .45 .25
844 A156 20k multi .95 .30
845 A156 25k vio & multi 1.00 .40
    Nos. 836-845 (10) 4.20 2.35

Wood carving and masks of Zaire.

1977, Apr.   Litho.   Perf. 13½
846 A157 1k org & multi .20 .20
847 A157 4k dk bl & multi .20 .55
848 A157 7k ol grn & multi .75 .20
849 A157 50k brn & multi 3.25 2.40
    Nos. 846-849 (4) 4.40 3.35

Cent. of UPU (in 1974).

Congo Stamps of 1968-1971
Surcharged with New Value, Bars and
"REPUBLIQUE DU ZAIRE"

1977
850 A126 1k on 10s (#642) .20 .20
851 A122 2k on 9.6k (#618) .20 .20
852 A140 10k on 10s (#735) .25 .20
853 A134 25k on 10s (#703) .65 .45
854 A127 40k on 9.6k (#652) 1.10 .70
855 A135 48k on 10s (#713) 1.40 .90
    Nos. 850-855 (6) 3.80 2.65

Congo Nos. 644, 643, 635, 746
Surcharged with New Value, Bars and
"REPUBLIQUE DU ZAIRE" in Black or
Carmine, Zaire No. 757 Surcharged

1977
856 A126 5k on 30s .20 .20
857 A126 10k on 15s (C) .20 .20
858 A124 20k on 9.60k .50 .20
859 A141 30k on 12k .95 .35
860 A145 100k on 40s (C) 2.75 1.50
    Nos. 856-860 (5) 4.60 2.45
    Nos. 850-860 (11) 8.40 5.10

Souvenir Sheet

Adoration of the Kings, by
Rubens — A158

1977, Dec. 19   Photo.   Perf. 13½
861 A158 5z multi 24.00 22.50

Christmas 1977.

Pantodon
Buchholzi
A159

Soccer Game,
Argentina-France
A160

Fish: 70s, Aphyosemion striatum. 55, Cte-
nopoma fasciolatum. 8k, Malapterurus elec-
tricus. 10k, Hemichromis bimaculatus. 30k,
Marcusenius isidori. 40k, Synodontis nigriven-
tris. 48k, Julidochromis ornatus. 100k,
Nothobranchius brieni. 250k, Micralestes
interruptus.

1978, Jan. 23   Litho.   Perf. 14
862 A159 30s multi .20 .20
863 A159 70s multi .20 .20
864 A159 5k multi .20 .20
865 A159 8k multi .20 .20
866 A159 10k multi .20 .20
867 A159 30k multi .70 .40
868 A159 40k multi .95 .50
869 A159 48k multi 1.10 .70
870 A159 100k multi 3.25 1.40
    Nos. 862-870 (9) 7.00 4.00

Souvenir Sheet
    Perf. 13½
871 A159 250k multi 5.50 5.50

No. 871 contains one 46x35mm stamp. For
surcharges see Nos. 1294, 1311.

1978, Aug. 7   Litho.   Perf. 12½

Various Soccer Games and Jules Rimet
Cup: 3k, Austria-Brazil. 7k, Scotland-Iran. 9k,
Netherlands-Peru. 10k, Hungary-Italy. 20k,
Fed. Rep. of Germany-Mexico. 50k, Tunisia-
Poland. 100k, Spain-Sweden. 500k, Rimet
Cup, Games' emblem and cartoon of soccer
player, horiz.

872 A160 1k multi .20 .20
873 A160 3k multi .20 .20
874 A160 7k multi .20 .20
875 A160 9k multi .20 .20
876 A160 10k multi .30 .20
877 A160 20k multi .50 .20
878 A160 50k multi .85 .50
879 A160 100k multi 1.65 1.00
    Nos. 872-879 (8) 3.80 2.70

Souvenir Sheets
880 A160 500k blue & multi 11.00 8.50
881 A160 500k red & multi 11.00 8.50

11th World Cup Soccer Championship,
Argentina, June 1-25. Nos. 880-881 contain
one stamp each (47x36mm). Stamp of No.
880 has blue frameline. Stamp of No. 881 has
red frame line.
For surcharge see No. 1259.

Mama
Mobutu — A161

Pres. Joseph D.
Mobutu — A162

1978, Oct. 23   Photo.   Perf. 12
882 A161 8k multi .20 .20

Mama Mobutu (1941-77), wife of Pres.
Mobutu.

Frame Color
1978   Photo.   Perf. 12
    Granite Paper
883 A162 2k blue .20 .20
884 A162 5k bister .20 .20
885 A162 6k Prussian blue .20 .20
886 A162 8k red brown .20 .20
887 A162 10k emerald .20 .20
888 A162 25k red .20 .20
889 A162 48k purple .50 .30
890 A162 1z green .95 .70
    Nos. 883-890 (8) 2.65 2.20

See Nos. 1053, 1055-1056. For surcharges
see Nos. 1313, 1333-1336.

Souvenir Sheet

Elizabeth II in Westminster Abbey — A163

1978, Dec. 11   Photo.   Perf. 13½
891 A163 5z multi   10.50 10.50
Coronation of Queen Elizabeth II, 25th anniv.

Souvenir Sheet

Albrecht Dürer, Self-portrait — A164

1978, Dec. 18   Perf. 13
892 A164 5z multi   10.50 10.50
Albrecht Dürer (1471-1528), German painter and engraver.

Leonardo da Vinci and his Drawings — A165

History of Aviation: 70s, Planes of Wright Brothers, 1905, and Santos Dumont, 1906. 1k, Bleriot XI, 1909, and Farman F-60, 1909. 5k, Junkers G-38, 1929, and Spirit of St. Louis, 1927. 8k, Sikorsky S-42B, 1934 and Macchi-Castoldi MC-72, 1934. 10k, Boeing 707, 1960, and Fokker F-VII, 1935. 50k, Apollo XI, 1969, and Concorde, 1976. 75k, Helicopter and Douglas DC-10, 1971. 5z, Giffard's balloon, 1852, and Hindenburg LZ 129, 1936.

1978, Dec. 28   Litho.   Perf. 13
893 A165 30s multi   .20   .20
894 A165 70s multi   .20   .20
895 A165 1k multi   .20   .20
896 A165 5k multi   .20   .20
897 A165 8k multi   .20   .20
898 A165 10k multi   .20   .20
899 A165 50k multi   1.25   .95
900 A165 75k multi   1.50   1.10
     Nos. 893-900 (8)   3.95   3.25

Souvenir Sheet
Perf. 11½
901 A165 5z multi   11.00 11.00
For overprint and surcharges see Nos. 993, 1173-1181, 1291, 1295.

Pres. Mobutu, Map of Zaire, N'tombe Dancer — A166

Pres. Mobutu & Map: 3k, Bird. 4k, Elephant. 10k, Diamond and cotton boll. 14k, Hand holding torch. 17k, Leopard's head and Victoria Regia lily. 25k, Finzia waterfall. 50k, Wagenia fishermen.

1979, Feb.   Litho.   Perf. 14x13½
902 A166 1k multicolored   .20   .20
903 A166 3k multicolored   .20   .20
904 A166 4k multicolored   .20   .20
905 A166 10k multicolored   .20   .20
  a.   Souvenir sheet of 4, #902-905   1.75   1.25
906 A166 14k multicolored   .20   .20
907 A166 17k multicolored   .30   .20
908 A166 25k multicolored   .45   .30
909 A166 50k multicolored   .90   .65
  a.   Souvenir sheet of 4, #906-909   10.00   7.00
     Nos. 902-909 (8)   2.65   2.15
Zaire (Congo) River expedition.

Phylloporus Ampliporus A167

Mushrooms: 5k, Engleromyces goetzei. 8k, Scutellinia virungae.   10k, Pycnoporus sanguineus. 30k, Cantharellus miniatescens. 40k, Lactarius phlebonemus. 48k, Phallus indusiatus. 100k, Ramaria moelleriana.

1979, Mar.   Photo.   Perf. 13½x13
910 A167 30s multicolored   .20   .20
911 A167 5k multicolored   .20   .20
912 A167 8k multicolored   .25   .20
913 A167 10k multicolored   .35   .20
914 A167 30k multicolored   1.10   .60
915 A167 40k multicolored   1.25   .90
916 A167 48k multicolored   1.65   1.10
917 A167 100k multicolored   3.00   2.25
     Nos. 910-917 (8)   8.00   5.65
For surcharges see Nos. 1296, 1298, 1312, 1361-1362, 1365-1366, 1368-1369, 1372, 1375.

Souvenir Sheets

Pope John XXIII (1881-1963) A168

Popes: No. 919, Paul VI (1897-1978). No. 920, John Paul I (1912-78).

1979, June 25   Litho.   Perf. 11½
918 A168 250k multi   2.75   1.50
919 A168 250k multi   2.75   1.50
920 A168 250k multi   2.75   1.50
     Nos. 918-920 (3)   8.25   4.50

Boy Beating Drum — A169

IYC Emblem on Map of Zaire and: 10k, 20k, Girl, diff. 50k, Boy. 100k, Boys. 300k, Mother and child. 10z, Mother and children, horiz.

1979, July 23   Litho.   Perf. 12½
921 A169 5k multi   .20   .20
922 A169 10k multi   .20   .20
923 A169 20k multi   .25   .20
924 A169 50k multi   .60   .35
925 A169 100k multi   1.25   .70
926 A169 300k multi   3.50   1.65
     Nos. 921-926 (6)   6.00   3.30

Souvenir Sheet
927 A169 10z multi   12.00   9.25
International Year of the Child.
For surcharges see Nos. 997, 999, 1299, 1306.

Globe and Drummer A170

1979, July 23
928 A170 1k multi   .20   .20
929 A170 9k multi   .20   .20
930 A170 90k multi   .60   .40
931 A170 100k multi   .65   .45
     Nos. 928-931 (4)   1.65   1.25

Souvenir Sheet
932 A170 500k multi   4.75   2.75
6th International Fair, Kinshasa. No. 932 contains one 52x31mm stamp.
For overprint & surcharge see #996, 1320.

Globe and School Desk — A171

1979, Dec. 24   Litho.   Perf. 13
933 A171 10k multi   .20   .20
Intl. Bureau of Education, Geneva, 50th anniv.

Adoration of the Kings, by Memling — A172

1979, Dec. 24   Imperf.
934 A172 5z multi   5.00   2.50
Christmas 1979.

"Puffing Billy," 1814, Gt. Britain A173

1980, Jan. 14   Litho.   Perf. 13½x13
935 A173 50s shown   .20   .20
936 A173 1.50k Buddicom No. 33, 1843, France .20   .20
937 A173 5k "Elephant," 1835, Belgium   .20   .20
938 A173 8k No. 601, 1906, Zaire   .20   .20
939 A173 50k "Slieve Gullion 440," Ireland .35   .20

---

940 A173 75k "Black Elephant," Germany   .50   .35
941 A173 2z Type 1-15, Zaire   1.00   .85
942 A173 5z "Golden State," US   2.50   2.00
     Nos. 935-942 (8)   5.15   4.20

Souvenir Sheet
943 A173 10z Type E.D.75, Zaire   7.50   5.50
For overprints and surcharges see Nos. 991-992, 994, 1325.

Hill, Belgian Congo No. 257 A174

1980, Jan. 28   Perf. 13½x14
944 A174 2k No. 5   .20   .20
945 A174 4k No. 13   .20   .20
946 A174 10k No. 24   .20   .20
947 A174 20k No. 38   .30   .20
948 A174 40k No. 111   .30   .20
949 A174 150k No. B29   .90   .60
950 A174 200k No. 198   1.10   .75
951 A174 250k shown   1.40   .90
     Nos. 944-951 (8)   4.50   3.25

Souvenir Sheet
952 A174 10z No. 198   6.50   5.00
Sir Rowland Hill (1795-1879), originator of penny postage.
For overprint and surcharge see Nos. 998, 1329.

Albert Einstein (1879-1955), Theoretical Physicist A175

1980, Feb. 18   Perf. 13
953 A175 40s multi   .20   .20
954 A175 2k multi   .20   .20
955 A175 4k multi   .20   .20
956 A175 15k multi   .20   .20
957 A175 50k multi   .40   .20
958 A175 300k multi   1.50   .75
     Nos. 953-958 (6)   2.70   1.80

Souvenir Sheet
959 A175 5z multi, diff.   4.50   2.50
For surcharges see Nos. 1285, 1290, 1304.

Salvation Army Brass Players — A176

50s, Booth Memorial Hospital, NYC. 4.50k, Commissioner George Railton sailing for US mission. 10k, Mobile dispensary, Masina. 20k, Gen. Evangeline Booth, officer holding infant, vert. 75k, Outdoor well-baby clinic. 1.50z, Disaster relief. 2z, Parade, vert. 10z, Gen. & Mrs. Arnold Brown.

1980, Mar. 3   Perf. 11
960 A176 50s multi   .20   .20
961 A176 4.50k multi   .20   .20
962 A176 10k multi   .20   .20
963 A176 20k multi   .20   .20
964 A176 40k multi   .35   .20
965 A176 75k multi   .55   .25
966 A176 1.50z multi   1.10   .55
967 A176 2z multi   1.60   .80
     Nos. 960-967 (8)   4.40   2.60

Souvenir Sheet
968 A176 10z multi   7.50   5.00
Salvation Army cent. in US. No. 968 contains one 53x38mm stamp and 2 labels.

Souvenir Sheets

Visite de Sa Sainteté le Pape Jean Paul II
au Zaïre — Mai 1980

Pope John Paul II — A177

1980, May 2 Litho. Perf. 11½
969 A177 10z multi 5.00 3.50
Visit of Pope John Paul II to Zaire, May.

Baia Castle, by Antonio Pitloo — A178

1980, May 5
970 A178 10z multi 5.50 3.00
20th International Philatelic Exhibition, Europa '80, Naples, Apr. 26-May 4.

A179

Perf. 12½x13, 13x12½
1980, May 24 Litho.
971 A179 50k Woman, line-
drawing .20 .20
972 A179 100k Plutiarch .40 .30
973 A179 500k Kneeling man,
sculpture, vert. 2.00 1.40
a. Souvenir sheet of 3 2.60 1.90
Nos. 971-973 (3) 2.60 1.90
Rotary Intl., 75th anniv. No. 973a contains 3 stamps similar to Nos. 971-973, size: 55x35, 35x55mm. Exists imperf.
For surcharge see No. 1313.

Tropical Fish — A180

1980, Oct. 20 Litho. Perf. 14x13½
974 A180 1k Chaetodon collaris .20 .20
975 A180 5k Zebrasoma ve-
liferum .20 .20
976 A180 10k Euxiphipops
xanthometapon .20 .20
977 A180 20k Pomacanthus
annularis .20 .20
978 A180 50k Centropyge
oriculus .25 .20

---

979 A180 150k Oxymona-
canthus
longirostris .65 .40
980 A180 200k Balistoides niger .85 .50
981 A180 250k Rhinecanthus
aculeatus 1.10 .65
Nos. 974-981 (8) 3.65 2.55
Souvenir Sheet
981A A180 5z Baliste ondule 2.75 1.25
For surcharge see No. 1307.

Exhibition Emblem, Congo
#365 — A181

1980, Dec. 6 Litho. Perf. 13
982 Block of 4 1.75 1.40
a. A181 1z, UR shown .40 .30
b. A181 1z, UL Belgium #511 .40 .30
c. A181 1z, UR like #982b .40 .30
d. A181 1z, UL like #982a .40 .30
983 Block of 4 3.50 2.25
a. A181 2z, UR Congo #432 .85 .55
b. A181 2z, UL Belgium # B835 .85 .55
c. A181 2z, UR like #983b .85 .55
d. A181 2z, UL like #983a .85 .55
984 Block of 4 5.25 3.50
a. A181 3z, UR Zaire #755 1.25 .80
b. A181 3z, UL Belgium # B878 1.25 .80
c. A181 3z, UR like #984b 1.25 .80
d. A181 3z, UL like #984a 1.25 .80
985 Block of 4 7.25 4.50
a. A181 4z, UR Congo #572 1.60 1.00
b. A181 4z, UL Belgium # B996 1.60 1.00
c. A181 4z, UR like #985b 1.60 1.00
d. A181 4z, UL like #985a 1.60 1.00
Nos. 982-985 (4) 17.75 11.65
PHIBELZA, Belgium-Zaire Phil. Exhib. #982-985 can be collected as strips of 4.
For surcharge see No. 1342.

Map of
Africa,
King
Leopold I
A182

Belgian independence sesquicentennial: 75k, Stanley expedition, Leopold II. 100k, Colonial troops, Albert I. 270k, 145k, protected animals, Leopold III. Visit of King Baudouin and Queen Fabiola.

1980, Dec. 13 Photo. Perf. 14
986 A182 10k multi .20 .20
987 A182 75k multi .55 .30
988 A182 100k multi .65 .35
989 A182 145k multi .90 .55
990 A182 270k multi 1.60 .90
Nos. 986-990 (5) 3.90 2.30
For surcharges see Nos. 1326, 1331, 1345, 1357, 1408-1412, 1426.

Nos. 935, 936, 898, 939, 900, 931, 925, 951, Overprinted in Red, Silver or Black: 20e Anniversaire-Independence / 1960-1980

1980, Dec. 13 Litho.
991 A173 50s multi .20 .20
992 A173 1.50k multi .20 .20
993 A165 10k multi .20 .20
994 A173 50k multi .30 .20
995 A165 75k multi .40 .20
996 A170 100k multi (S) .55 .35
997 A169 1z on 5z on 100k
multi (B) .65 .35
998 A174 250k multi 1.40 .80
999 A169 5z on 100k multi (B) 2.75 1.50
Nos. 991-999 (9) 6.65 4.00
20th anniversary of independence. For surcharges see Nos. 1300, 1316.

Nativity
A183

1980, Dec. 24 Perf. 13
1000 A183 10k Shepherds and
angels .20 .20
1001 A183 75k Flight into Egypt .50 .30
1002 A183 80k Three kings .50 .30
1003 A183 145k shown .80 .50
Nos. 1000-1003 (4) 2.00 1.30
Souvenir Sheet
1004 A183 10z Church, nativity 4.00 3.00
Christmas 1980. No. 1004 contains one 49x33mm stamp. Exists imperf. For surcharges see Nos. 1301, 1317-1318.

Postal Clerk
Sorting Mail,
by Norman
Rockwell
A184

Designs: Saturday Evening Post covers by Norman Rockwell.

1981, Apr. 27 Litho. Perf. 14
1005 A184 10k multi .20 .20
1006 A184 20k multi .20 .20
1007 A184 50k multi .30 .20
1008 A184 80k multi .50 .30
1009 A184 100k multi .55 .35
1010 A184 125k multi .65 .40
1011 A184 175k multi .95 .55
1012 A184 200k multi 1.10 .60
Nos. 1005-1012 (8) 4.45 2.80
For surcharges see Nos. 1262, 1265, 1269, 1275, 1281, 1354.

First
Anniv.
of Visit
of Pope
John
Paul II
A185

Scenes of Pope's visit. 50k, 500k, vert.

1981, May 2 Perf. 13
1013 A185 5k multi .20 .20
1014 A185 10k multi .20 .20
1015 A185 50k multi .25 .20
1016 A185 100k multi .50 .20
1017 A185 500k multi 2.50 1.40
1018 A185 800k multi 4.00 2.25
Nos. 1013-1018 (6) 7.65 4.50
For surcharges see #1190-1194, 1292, 1302, 1343.

Soccer
Players — A186

Designs: Soccer scenes.

1981, July 6 Litho. Perf. 12½
1019 A186 2k multi .20 .20
1020 A186 10k multi .20 .20
1021 A186 25k multi .20 .20
1022 A186 90k multi .30 .25
1023 A186 2z multi .60 .40
1024 A186 3z multi .90 .60
1025 A186 6z multi 1.75 1.10
1026 A186 8z multi 2.75 2.00
Nos. 1019-1026 (8) 6.90 4.95
Souvenir Sheet
1027 Sheet of 2 3.75 3.00
a. A186 5z like #1019 1.75 1.00
b. A186 5z like #1025 1.75 1.00
ESPANA '82 World Cup Soccer Championship. For surcharges see Nos. 1287, 1303, 1309, 1321.

Intl. Year of the Disabled — A187

1981, Nov. 2 Litho. Perf. 14x14½
1028 A187 2k Archer .20 .20
1029 A187 5k Ear, sound
waves .20 .20
1030 A187 10k Amputee .20 .20
1031 A187 18k Cane braille,
sunglasses .20 .20
1032 A187 50k Boy with leg
braces .20 .20
1033 A187 150k Sign language .30 .25
1034 A187 500k Hands .90 .75
1035 A187 800k Dove 1.60 1.40
Nos. 1028-1035 (8) 3.80 3.40
For surcharges see Nos. 1288, 1293, 1305, 1314.

Souvenir Sheet

Birth Sesqui. of Heinrich von Stephan, UPU Founder — A188

Photogravure and Engraved
1981, Dec. 21 Perf. 11½x12
1036 A188 15z purple 4.75 3.00

Christmas
1981 — A189

1981, Dec. 21 Litho. Perf. 14
Designs: 25k, 1z, 1.50z, 3z, 5z, Various children. 10z, Holy Family, horiz.

1037 A189 25k multi .20 .20
1038 A189 1z multi .40 .20
1039 A189 1.50z multi .50 .25
1040 A189 3z multi 1.00 .50
1041 A189 5z multi 1.75 .90
Nos. 1037-1041 (5) 3.85 2.05
Souvenir Sheet
1042 A189 10z multi 3.50 3.00

13th World Telecommunications Day
(1981) — A190

Designs: Symbols of communications and health care delivery.

1982, Feb. 8   Litho.   Perf. 13
1043	A190	1k purple	.20	.20
1044	A190	25k multi	.20	.20
1045	A190	90k multi	.25	.20
1046	A190	1z multi	.25	.20
1047	A190	1.70z multi	.40	.30
1048	A190	3z multi	.75	.55
1049	A190	4.50z multi	1.10	.75
1050	A190	5z multi	1.25	.85
	Nos. 1043-1050 (8)		4.40	3.25

For surcharges see Nos. 1270, 1282.

Pres. Mobutu Type of 1978
Frame Color

1982   Photo.   Perf. 12
Granite Paper
1053	A162	50k purple	.20	.20
1055	A162	2z bister	.25	.20
1056	A162	5z Prussian blue	1.25	.75
	Nos. 1053-1056 (3)		1.70	1.15

20th Anniv. of African Postal Union (1981) — A191

1982, Mar. 8   Litho.   Perf. 13
1057	A191	1z yel grn & gold	.30	.20

For surcharges see Nos. 1348, 1352.

1982 World Cup A192

Designs: Flags and players of finalists.

1982
1058	A192	2k multi	.20	.20
1059	A192	8k multi	.20	.20
1060	A192	25k multi	.20	.20
1061	A192	50k multi	.20	.20
1062	A192	90k multi	.20	.20
1063	A192	1z multi	.35	.20
1064	A192	1.45z multi	.40	.25
1065	A192	1.70z multi	.55	.30
1066	A192	3z multi	.80	.55
1067	A192	3.50z multi	1.10	.60
1068	A192	5z multi	1.60	.85
1069	A192	6z multi	1.90	1.10
	Nos. 1058-1069 (12)		7.70	4.85

Souvenir Sheet
1070	A192	10z multi	4.50	3.00

Issued: #1058-1069, July 6; #1070, Sept. 21.
For surcharges see #1289, 1315, 1322, 1344, 1435 and footnote after #1336.

9th Conference of Heads of State of Africa and France, Kinshasa, Oct. — A193

1982, Oct. 8   Litho.   Perf. 13
1071	A193	75k multi	.20	.20
1072	A193	90k multi	.20	.20
1073	A193	1z multi	.20	.20
1074	A193	1.50z multi	.20	.20
1075	A193	3z multi	.40	.30
1076	A193	5z multi	.60	.50
1077	A193	8z multi	1.00	.80
	Nos. 1071-1077 (7)		2.80	2.40

For surcharges see Nos. 1268, 1271, 1280, 1283, 1347, 1351.

Animals from Virunga Natl. Park — A194

1982, Nov. 5
1078	A194	1z Lions	.20	.20
1079	A194	1.70z Buffalo	.55	.35
1080	A194	3.50z Elephants	1.25	.75
1081	A194	6.50z Antelope	2.00	1.25
1082	A194	8z Hippopota-mus	3.00	1.75
1083	A194	10z Monkeys	3.50	2.00
1084	A194	10z Leopard	3.50	2.00
a.	Pair, #1083-1084 + label		7.50	6.50
	Nos. 1078-1084 (7)		14.00	8.30

#1084a has continuous design.
For surcharge see No. 1430.

Scouting Year — A195

1982, Nov. 29   Photo.   Perf. 11½
Granite Paper
1085	A195	90k Camp	.20	.20
1086	A195	1.70z Campfire	.45	.35
1087	A195	3z Scout	.75	.60
1088	A195	5z First aid	1.60	1.10
1089	A195	8z Flag signals	3.00	1.90
	Nos. 1085-1089 (5)		6.00	4.15

Souvenir Sheet
1090	A195	10z Baden-Powell	3.75	3.00

For surcharges see Nos. 1207-1214.

Local Birds — A196

1982, Dec. 6   Litho.   Perf. 13
1091	A196	25k Quelea quelea	.20	.20
1092	A196	50k Ceyx picta	.20	.20
1093	A196	90k Tauraco persa	.40	.20
1094	A196	1.50z Charadrius tricollaris	.45	.30
1095	A196	1.70k Cursorius tem-minckii	.50	.30
1096	A196	2z Campethera bennettii	.65	.40
1097	A196	3z Podiceps ruficollis	.95	.55
1098	A196	3.50z Kaupifalco monogram-micus	1.10	.60
1099	A196	5z Limnocorax flavirostris	1.60	.85
1100	A196	8z White-headed vulture	2.50	1.50
	Nos. 1091-1100 (10)		8.55	5.10

All except 3.50z, 8z horiz.
For surcharges see Nos. 1263, 1266, 1272, 1276, 1278, 1284, 1425, 1432, 1438, 1440.

Souvenir Sheet

Christmas — A197

1982, Dec. 20   Photo.   Perf. 13½
1101	A197	15z Adoration of the Magi, by van der Goes	5.50	4.50

Quartz A198

1983, Feb. 13   Photo.   Perf. 11½
Granite Paper
1102	A198	2k Malachite, vert.	.20	.20
1103	A198	45k shown	.25	.20
1104	A198	75k Gold	.25	.20
1105	A198	1z Uraninite	.40	.20
1106	A198	1.50z Bournonite, vert.	.55	.30
1107	A198	3z Cassiterite	1.10	.55
1108	A198	6z Dioptase, vert.	2.25	1.10
1109	A198	8z Cuprite, vert.	2.75	1.60
	Nos. 1102-1109 (8)		7.75	4.35

Souvenir Sheet
1110	A198	10z Diamonds	4.50	4.50

For surcharges see Nos. 1324, 1330, 1332, 1346.

TB Bacillus Centenary — A199

1983, Feb. 21   Litho.   Perf. 13
1111	A199	80k multi	.25	.20
1112	A199	1.20z multi	.40	.20
1113	A199	3.60z multi	1.25	.60
1114	A199	9.60z multi	3.25	1.60
	Nos. 1111-1114 (4)		5.15	2.60

For surcharges see Nos. 1319, 1356, 1358, 1360, 1433, 1436, 1441.

Kinshasa Monuments — A200

1983, Apr. 25
1115	A200	50k Zaire Diplo-mat, vert.	.20	.20
1116	A200	1z Echo of Zaire	.35	.20
1117	A200	1.50z Messengers, vert.	.50	.25
1118	A200	3z Shield of Revolution, vert.	1.00	.50
1119	A200	5z Weeping Wo-man	1.60	.80
1120	A200	10z Militant, vert.	3.50	1.60
	Nos. 1115-1120 (6)		7.15	3.55

For surcharges see Nos. 1267, 1279, 1349-1350.

ITU Plenipotentiaries Conference, Nairobi, Sept. 1982 — A201

Various satellites, dish antennae and maps.

1983, June 13   Litho.   Perf. 13
1121	A201	2k multi	.20	.20
1122	A201	4k multi	.20	.20
1123	A201	25k multi	.20	.20
1124	A201	1.20z multi	.40	.20
1125	A201	2.05z multi	.65	.35
1126	A201	3.60z multi	1.25	.60
1127	A201	6z multi	2.00	1.00
1128	A201	8z multi	2.50	1.40
	Nos. 1121-1128 (8)		7.40	4.15

For surcharges see Nos. 1260-1261, 1264, 1273-1274, 1277, 1355, 1359, 1429, 1434, 1437, 1439, 1442.

Christmas 1983 — A202

Raphael Paintings; No. 1129: a, Virgin and Child. b, Holy Family. c, Esterhazy Madonna. d, Sistine Madonna. No. 1130: a, La Belle Jardiniere. b, Virgin of Alba. c, Holy Family, diff. d, Virgin and Child, diff.

1983, Dec. 26   Photo.   Perf. 13½x13
1129		Sheet of 4	3.50	3.50
a.-d.	A202 10z, any single		.85	.85
1130		Sheet of 4	5.25	5.25
a.-d.	A202 15z, any single		1.25	1.25

Garamba Park — A203

1984, Apr. 2   Litho.   Perf. 13
1131	A203	10k Darby's Eland	.20	.20
1132	A203	15k Eagles	.20	.20
1133	A203	3z Servals	.20	.20
1134	A203	10z White rhi-noceros	.75	.75
1135	A203	15z Lions	1.10	1.10
1136	A203	37.50z Warthogs	2.75	2.75
1137	A203	40z Koris bus-tards	3.00	3.00
1138	A203	40z Crowned cranes	3.00	3.00
a.	Pair, #1137-1138 + label		6.00	6.00
	Nos. 1131-1138 (8)		11.20	11.20

Nos. 1137-1138 are narrower, 49x34mm, with continuous design.
For surcharge see No. 1428.

World Communications Year — A204

Designs: 10k, Computer operator, Congo River ferry. 15k, Communications satellite. 8.50z, Engineer, Congo River Bridge. 10z, Satellite, ground receiving station. 15z, TV camerawoman filming crowed crane. 37.50z, Satellite, dish antennas. 80z, Switchboard operator, bus.

1984, May 14   Litho.   Perf. 13x12½
1139	A204	10k multi	.20	.20
1140	A204	15k multi	.20	.20
1141	A204	8.50z multi	.60	.60
1142	A204	10z multi	.65	.65
1143	A204	15z multi	1.00	1.00
1144	A204	37.50z multi	2.50	2.50
1145	A204	80z multi	5.50	5.50
	Nos. 1139-1145 (7)		10.65	10.65

Hypericum Revolutum A205

Local flowers: 15k, Borreria dibrachiata. 3z, Disa erubescens. 8.50z, Scaevola plumieri. 10z, Clerodendron thompsonii. 15z, Thumbergia erecta. 37.50z, Impatiens niamniamensis. 100z, Canarina emini.

1984, May 28 Photo. Perf. 14x13½

1146	A205	10k multi	.20	.20
1147	A205	15k multi	.20	.20
1148	A205	3z multi	.20	.20
1149	A205	8.50z multi	.70	.70
1150	A205	10z multi	.75	.75
1151	A205	15z multi	1.10	1.10
1152	A205	37.50z multi	2.75	2.75
1153	A205	100z multi	7.75	7.75
	Nos. 1146-1153 (8)		13.65	13.65

1984 Summer Olympics A206

Manned Flight Bicent. — A207

1984, June 5 Litho. Perf. 13

1154	A206	2z Basketball	.20	.20
1155	A206	3z Equestrian	.25	.25
1156	A206	10z Running	.75	.75
1157	A206	15z Long jump	1.10	1.10
1158	A206	20z Soccer	1.50	1.50
	Nos. 1154-1158 (5)		3.80	3.80

Souvenir Sheet
Perf. 11½

1159	A206	50z Kayak	4.00	4.00

No. 1159 contains one 31x49mm stamp. For surcharge see No. 1427.

1984, June 28 Litho. Perf. 14

10k, Montgolfiere, 1783. 15k, Charles & Robert, 1783. 3z, Gustave, 1783. 5z, Santos-Dumont III, 1899. 10z, Stratospheric balloon, 1934. 15z, Zeppelin LZ-129, 1936. 37.50z, Double Eagle II, 1978. 80z, Hot air balloons.

1160	A207	10k multi	.20	.20
1161	A207	15k multi	.20	.20
1162	A207	3z multi	.20	.20
1163	A207	5z multi	.40	.40
1164	A207	10z multi	.75	.75
1165	A207	15z multi	1.10	1.10
1166	A207	37.50z multi	2.75	2.75
1167	A207	80z multi	6.00	6.00
	Nos. 1160-1167 (8)		11.60	11.60

For surcharges see Nos. 1413-1420.

Okapi — A208

1984, Oct. 15 Litho. Perf. 13

1168	A208	2z Grazing	.20	.20
1169	A208	3z Resting	.25	.20
1170	A208	8z Mother and young	.75	.55
1171	A208	10z In water	1.25	1.00
	Nos. 1168-1171 (4)		2.45	1.95

Souvenir Sheet
Perf. 11½

1172	A208	50z like 10z	3.25	3.25

World Wildlife Fund. No. 1172 contains one 36x51mm stamp, margin continues the design of the 10z without emblem.

Nos. 893, 896, 894-895, 898, 897, 900, 899 Ovptd. with Black Bar, Silver Emblem and Surcharged on Stamp and Margin: 60e ANNIVERSAIRE/1re LIASON AERIENNE/BRUXELLES-KINSHASAL/PAR EDMOND THIEFFRY in 3 or 5 Lines

1985, Feb. 19 Perf. 13, 11½

1173	A165	2.50z on 30s multi	.20	.20
1174	A165	5z on 5k multi	.40	.40
1175	A165	6z on 70s multi	.40	.40
1176	A165	7.50z on 1k multi	.60	.60
1177	A165	8.50z on 10k multi	.60	.60
1178	A165	10z on 8k multi	.75	.75
1179	A165	12.50z on 75k multi	.95	.95
1180	A165	30z on 50k multi	2.25	2.25
	Nos. 1173-1180 (8)		6.15	6.15

Souvenir Sheet

1181	A165	50z on 5z multi	11.50	11.50

OLYMPHILEX '85, Lausanne — A209

1985, Apr. 19 Perf. 13

1182	A209	1z Swimming	.20	.20
1183	A209	2z Soccer, vert.	.20	.20
1184	A209	3z Boxing	.20	.20
1185	A209	4z Basketball, vert.	.25	.25
1186	A209	5z Equestrian	.40	.40
1187	A209	10z Volleyball, vert.	.75	.75
1188	A209	15z Running	1.25	1.25
1189	A209	30z Cycling, vert.	2.50	2.50
	Nos. 1182-1189 (8)		5.75	5.75

Nos. 1013-1018, 969 Ovptd. and Surcharged with 1 or 2 Gold Bars and "AOUT 1985" in Gold or Black

1985, Aug. 15 Perf. 13, 11½

1190	A185	2z on 5k	.20	.20
1191	A185	3z on 50k	.25	.25
1192	A185	5z on 50k	.40	.40
1192A	A185	10z on 100k	.80	.80
1192B	A185	15z on 500k	1.25	1.25
1193	A185	40z on 800k	3.50	3.50
	Nos. 1190-1193 (6)		6.40	6.40

Souvenir Sheet

1194	A177	50z on 10z (B)	4.50	4.50

Second visit of Pope John Paul II.

Audubon Birth Bicent. — A210

Illustrations of North American bird species by John Audubon.

1985, Oct. 1 Perf. 13

1195	A210	5z Great egret	.25	.25
1196	A210	10z Yellow-beaked duck	.50	.50
1197	A210	15z Small heron	.75	.75
1198	A210	25z White-fronted duck	1.25	1.25
	Nos. 1195-1198 (4)		2.75	2.75

For surcharges see Nos. 1421-1424.

Natl. Independence, 25th Anniv. — A211

1985, Oct. 23 Photo. Perf. 12
Granite Paper

1200	A211	5z multi	.25	.25
1201	A211	10z multi	.45	.45
1202	A211	15z multi	.70	.70
1203	A211	20z multi	1.10	1.10
	Nos. 1200-1203 (4)		2.50	2.50

Souvenir Sheet
Perf. 11½

1204	A211	50z multi	2.00	2.00

UN, 40th Anniv. A212

1985, Nov. 26

1205	A212	10z Flags, vert.	.50	.50
1206	A212	50z Emblem, UN building	2.50	2.50

Nos. 1087-1088, 1085-1086, 1089-1090 Surcharged

1985, Dec. 2 Perf. 11½
Granite Paper

1207	A195	3z on 3z multi	.20	.20
1208	A195	5z on 5z multi	.25	.25
1209	A195	7z on 90k multi	.30	.30
1210	A195	10z on 90k multi	.50	.50
1211	A195	15z on 1.70z multi	.75	.75
1212	A195	20z on 8z multi	.95	.95
1213	A195	50z on 90k multi	2.50	2.50
	Nos. 1207-1213 (7)		5.45	5.45

Souvenir Sheet

1214	A195	50z on 10z multi	2.50	2.50

Intl. Youth Year.

Souvenir Sheet

Virgin and Child, by Titian — A213

Photogravure and Engraved
1985, Dec. 23 Perf. 13½

1215	A213	100z brown	4.50	4.50

Christmas 1985.

Natl. Transit Authority, 50th Anniv. — A214

1985, Dec. 31 Perf. 13

1216	A214	7z Kokolo mail ship	.25	.25
1217	A214	10z Steam locomotive	.40	.40
1218	A214	15z Luebo ferry	.55	.55
1219	A214	50z Stanley locomotive	1.90	1.90
	Nos. 1216-1219 (4)		3.10	3.10

Postage Stamp, Cent. A215

Stamps on stamps: 7z, Belgian Congo No. 30. 15z, Belgian Congo No. B28. 20z, Belgian Congo No. 226. 25z, Zaire No. 1059. 40z, Zaire No. 1152. 50z, Zaire No. 883 and Belgium No. 1094.

1986, Feb. 23 Perf. 13

1220	A215	7z multi	.35	.35
1221	A215	15z multi	.75	.75
1222	A215	20z multi	1.00	1.00
1223	A215	25z multi	1.25	1.25
1224	A215	40z multi	2.00	2.00
	Nos. 1220-1224 (5)		5.35	5.35

Souvenir Sheet
Perf. 11½

1225	A215	50z multi	2.50	2.50

No. 1225 contains one 50x35mm stamp.

Beatification of Sister Anuarite Nengapeta, Aug. 15, 1985 — A216

1986, Feb. 21 Litho. Perf. 13

1226	A216	10z Pope John Paul II	.35	.35
1227	A216	15z Sr. Anuarite	.55	.55
1228	A216	25z Both portraits	.90	.90
	Nos. 1226-1228 (3)		1.80	1.80

Souvenir Sheet
Imperf

1229	A216	100z Both portraits, triangular	3.75	3.75

Nos. 1226-1227 vert. No. 1229 contains one quadrilateral stamp, size: 30x36x60mm. For surcharges see Nos. 1370-1371, 1373, 1376-1377.

Congo Stamp Cent. — A217

1986, Feb. 22 Litho. Perf. 13

1230	A217	25z Belgian Congo No. 3	1.00	1.00

See Belgium No. 1236.

Indigenous Reptiles A218

1987, Feb. 11   Litho.   Perf. 13
1231 A218 2z Dasypeltis scaber   .20 .20
1232 A218 5z Agama agama   .20 .20
1233 A218 10z Python regius   .25 .25
1234 A218 15z Chamaeleo dilepis   .45 .45
1235 A218 25z Dendroaspis jamesoni   .65 .65
1236 A218 50z Naja nigricolis   1.25 1.25
    Nos. 1231-1236 (6)   3.00 3.00

Christmas
1987 — A219

Paintings (details) by Fra Angelico: 50z, Virgin and Child, center panel of the Triptych of Cortona, 1435. 100z, The Nativity. 120z, Virgin and Child with Angels and Four Saints, Fiesole Retable. 180z, Virgin and Child with Six Saints, Annalena Retable.

1987, Dec. 24   Litho.   Perf. 13
1237 A219 50z multi   .75 .75
1238 A219 100z multi   1.50 1.50
1239 A219 120z multi   1.90 1.90
1240 A219 180z multi   2.80 2.80
    Nos. 1237-1240 (4)   6.95 6.95

French Revolution, Bicent. — A220

Designs: 50z, Declaration of the Rights of Man and Citizen. 100z, Abstract art. 120z, Globe showing Africa, South America.

1989   Litho.   Perf. 13½x14½
1241 A220 40z multicolored   .45 .45
1242 A220 50z multicolored   .55 .55
1243 A220 100z multicolored   1.10 1.10
1244 A220 120z multicolored   1.40 1.40
    Nos. 1241-1244 (4)   3.50 3.50

REGIDESCO, 50th Anniv. — A221

1989
1245 A221 40z Administration bldg.   .40 .40
1246 A221 50z Modern factory   .50 .50
1247 A221 75z Water works   .75 .75
1248 A221 120z Woman drawing water   1.25 1.25
    Nos. 1245-1248 (4)   2.90 2.90

Fight Against AIDS — A222

Designs: 40z, Bowman firing arrow through SIDA. 80z, "SIDA" on Leopard. 150z, World map with AIDS symbols.

1989
1249 A222 30z multicolored   .50 .50
1250 A222 40z multicolored   .65 .65
1251 A222 80z multicolored   1.40 1.40
    Nos. 1249-1251 (3)   2.55 2.55

Souvenir Sheet
Perf. 14
1252 A222 150z multicolored   2.50 2.50

Tourist Attractions — A223

1990   Litho.   Perf. 13½x14½
1253 A223 40z Waterfalls of Venus   .55 .55
1254 A223 60z Rural village   .85 .85
1255 A223 100z Kivu Lake   1.40 1.40
1256 A223 120z Niyara Gongo Volcano   1.75 1.75
    Nos. 1253-1256 (4)   4.55 4.55

Souvenir Sheet
Perf. 14½
1257 A223 300z Kisantu Botanical Gardens, vert.   4.25 4.25

Souvenir Sheet

Christmas — A224

Illustration reduced.

1990   Litho.   Perf. 14
1258 A224 500z multicolored   3.40 3.40

Various 1971-1983 Stamps Surcharged in Gold

1990   Perfs., Etc. as Before
1259 A160 20z on 20k #877   .40 .40
1260 A201 40z on 2k #1121   .40 .40
1261 A201 40z on 4k #1122   .40 .40
1262 A184 40z on 10k #1005   .40 .40
1263 A196 40z on 25k #1091   .40 .40
1264 A201 40z on 25k #1123   .40 .40
1265 A184 40z on 50k #1007   .40 .40
1266 A196 40z on 50k #1092   .40 .40
1267 A200 40z on 50k #1115   .40 .40
1268 A193 40z on 75k #1071   .40 .40
1269 A184 40z on 80k #1008   .40 .40
1270 A190 40z on 90k #1045   .40 .40
1271 A193 40z on 90k #1072   .40 .40
1272 A196 40z on 90k #1093   .40 .40
1273 A201 80z on 2k #1121   .80 .80
1274 A201 80z on 4k #1122   .80 .80
1275 A184 80z on 10k #1005   .80 .80
1276 A196 80z on 25k #1091   .80 .80
1277 A201 80z on 25k #1123   .80 .80
1278 A196 80z on 50k #1092   .80 .80
1279 A200 80z on 50k #1115   .80 .80
1280 A193 80z on 75k #1071   .80 .80
1281 A184 80z on 80k #1008   .80 .80
1282 A190 80z on 90k #1045   .80 .80
1283 A193 80z on 90k #1072   .80 .80
1284 A196 80z on 90k #1093   .80 .80
1285 A175 100z on 40s #953   1.00 1.00
1287 A186 100z on 2k #1019   1.00 1.00
1288 A187 100z on 2k #1028   1.00 1.00
1289 A192 100z on 2k #1058   1.00 1.00
1290 A175 100z on 4k #955   1.00 1.00
1291 A165 100z on 5k #896   1.00 1.00
1292 A185 100z on 5k #1013   1.00 1.00
1293 A187 100z on 5k #1029   1.00 1.00
1294 A159 100z on 8k #865   1.00 1.00
1295 A165 100z on 8k #897   1.00 1.00
1296 A167 100z on 8k #912   3.00 3.00
1298 A167 100z on 10k #913   1.00 1.00
1299 A169 100z on 10k #922   1.00 1.00
1300 A165 100z on 10k #993   5.00 5.00
1301 A183 100z on 10k #1000   5.00 5.00
1302 A185 100z on 10k #1014   1.00 1.00
1303 A186 100z on 10k #1020   1.00 1.00
1304 A175 100z on 15k #956   1.00 1.00
1305 A187 100z on 18k #1031   1.00 1.00
1306 A169 100z on 20k #923   1.00 1.00
1307 A180 100z on 20k #977   1.00 1.00
1308 A144 100z on 22k #755   1.00 1.00
1309 A186 100z on 25k #1021   1.00 1.00
1311 A159 100z on 48k #869   1.00 1.00
1312 A167 100z on 48k #916   3.00 3.00
1313 A179 100z on 50k #971   1.00 1.00
1314 A187 100z on 50k #1032   1.00 1.00
1315 A192 100z on 50k #1061   1.00 1.00
1316 A165 100z on 75k #995   1.00 1.00
1317 A183 100z on 75k #1001   1.00 1.00
1318 A183 100z on 80k #1002   2.00 2.00
1319 A199 100z on 80k #1111   1.00 1.00
1320 A170 100z on 90k #930   1.00 1.00
1321 A186 100z on 90k #1022   1.00 1.00
1322 A192 100z on 90k #1062   .40 .40
1324 A198 300z on 2k #1102   3.00 3.00
1325 A173 300z on 8k #938   3.00 3.00
1326 A182 300z on 10k #986   3.00 3.00
1327 A143 300z on 14k #751   3.00 3.00
1328 A146 300z on 17k #769   3.00 3.00
1329 A174 300z on 20k #947   3.00 3.00
1330 A198 300z on 45k #1103   3.00 3.00
1331 A182 300z on 75k #987   3.00 3.00
1332 A198 300z on 75k #1104   3.00 3.00
1333 A162 500z on 8k #886   5.00 5.00
1334 A162 500z on 10k #887   2.00 2.00
1335 A162 500z on 25k #888   2.00 2.00
1336 A162 500z on 48k #889   2.00 2.00
    Nos. 1259-1336 (74)   100.60 100.60

Size and location of surcharge varies. Some surcharges show "z" before numeral.
100z on #1060 was surcharged in error.
Numbers have been reserved for additional values in this set.

Various 1980-1983 Stamps Surcharged

1991   Perfs., Etc., as Before
1342 A181 1000z on 1z #982a-982d   1.40 1.40
1343 A185 1000z on 100k #1016   .35 .35
1344 A192 1000z on 1z #1063   .35 .35
1345 A182 2000z on 100k #988   .70 .70
1346 A198 2000z on 1z #1105   .70 .70
1347 A193 2500z on 1z #1073   .80 .80
1348 A191 3000z on 1z #1057   1.10 1.10
1349 A200 4000z on 1z #1116   1.40 1.40
1350 A200 5000z on 1z #1116   1.60 1.60
1351 A193 10,000z on 1z #1073   3.25 3.25
1352 A191 15,000z on 1z #1057   5.00 5.00
    Nos. 1342-1352 (11)   16.65 16.65

Size and location of surcharge varies.

The editors have received from a collector mint stamps bearing the surcharges shown below. There is conflicting data as to the validity of these surcharges, and anyone with information on them is asked to contact the new issues editor.

12-6-92
6° ANNIVERSAIRE DE OFFICE NATIONAL DU TOUR.SME

  1.000.000 Z

12-3-92
INAUGURATION STATION POMPAGE

600.000 Z.

Du 8 au 15-6-92
2° Conférence Addis - Abeba
Virus VIH 1 - et VIH 2
EN AFRIQUE

10.000.000 Z

 5.000.000 Z

Conférence Nationale Souveraine
3 mars - 4 decembre
1991 - 1992

Nos. 989, 1010, 1112, 1124
Surcharged

1992, Aug. 18   *Perfs., Etc. as Before*
1354	A184	50th z on 125k		
		#1010	.20	.20
1355	A201	100th z on 1.20z		
		#1124	.40	.40
1356	A199	150th z on 1.20z		
		#1112	.60	.60
1357	A182	200th z on 145k #989	.75	.75
1358	A199	250th z on 1.20z		
		#1112	.95	.95
1359	A201	300th z on 1.20z		
		#1124	1.10	1.10
1360	A199	500th z on 1.20z		
		#1112	2.00	2.00
	Nos. 1354-1360 (7)		6.00	6.00

Size and location of surcharge varies. Numbers have been reserved for additional values in this set.

#1361-1366

#1368-1374

1993, Oct. 29   **Photo.**   *Perf. 13½x13*
1361	A167	500th z on 30s #910	.20	.20
1362	A167	500th z on 5k #911	.20	.20
1365	A167	750th z on 8k #912	.30	.30
1366	A167	750th z on 10k #913	.30	.30
1368	A167	1 mil z on 30k #914	.40	.40
1369	A167	1 mil z on 40k #915	.40	.40
1370	A167	5 mil z on 48k #916	2.00	2.00
1371	A167	10 mil z on 100k		
		#917	4.00	4.00
	Nos. 1361-1371 (8)		7.80	7.80

Nos. 1226-1229 Surcharged in Black or Red (#1374)

1993, Oct. 29   **Litho.**   *Perf. 13*
1373	A216	3 mil z on 10z		
		#1226		
1374	A216	3 mil z on 10z	1.25	1.25
		#1226		
1375	A216	5 mil z on 15z		
		#1227	2.00	2.00
1376	A216	10 mil z on 25z		
		#1228	4.00	4.00

Souvenir Sheet
1377	A216	10 mil z on 100z		
		#1229	4.00	4.00

Size and location of surcharge varies.

Natl. Game Parks, 50th Anniv. A225

1993   **Litho.**   *Perf. 13*
1403	A225	30k Cape eland	.20	.20
1404	A225	50k Elephants	.20	.20
1405	A225	1.50z Giant eland	.35	.35
1406	A225	3.50z White rhinoceros	.75	.75
1407	A225	5z Bongo	1.10	1.10
	Nos. 1403-1407 (5)		2.60	2.60

For surcharge see No. 1431.

Nos. 986-900 Surcharged

1994, Apr. 23   **Photo.**   *Perf. 14*
1408	A182	30k on 10k	.20	.20
1409	A182	50k on 75k	.40	.40
1410	A182	1.50z on 100k	1.10	1.10
1411	A182	3.50z on 145k	2.75	2.75
1412	A182	5z on 270k	3.75	3.75
	Nos. 1408-1412 (5)		8.20	8.20

Nos. 1160-1167 Surcharged

1994, Apr. 23   **Litho.**   *Perf. 14*
1413	A207	30k on 10k	.20	.20
1414	A207	50k on 15k	.40	.40
1415	A207	1.50z on 3z	1.10	1.10
1416	A207	2.50z on 5z	1.90	1.90
1417	A207	3.50z on 10z	2.75	2.75
1418	A207	5z on 15z	3.75	3.75
1419	A207	7.50z on 37.50z	5.75	5.75
1420	A207	10z on 80z	7.75	7.75
	Nos. 1413-1420 (8)		23.60	23.60

Nos. 1195-1198 Surcharged

1994, Apr. 23   **Litho.**   *Perf. 13*
1421	A210	50k on 5z	.30	.30
1422	A210	1.50z on 10z	.90	.90
1423	A210	3.50z on 15z	2.00	2.00
1424	A210	5z on 25z	3.00	3.00
	Nos. 1421-1424 (4)		6.20	6.20

Nos. 990, 1079, 1094, 1097, 1113, 1125-1126, 1133, 1155, & 1404
Surcharged in Gold

1994, Aug. 31   *Perfs., Etc. as Before*
1425	A196	20z on 3z #1097	.20	.20
1426	A182	40z on 270k #990	.20	.20
1427	A206	45z on 3z #1155	.20	.20
1428	A203	50z on 3z #1133	.20	.20
1429	A201	100z on 2.05z #1125	.30	.30
1430	A194	150z on 1.70z #1079	.40	.40
1431	A225	200z on 50k #1404	.55	.55
1432	A196	250z on 1.50z #1094	.70	.70

1433	A199	300z on 3.60z #1113	.85	.85
1434	A201	500z on 3.60z #1126	1.40	1.40
	Nos. 1425-1434 (10)		5.00	5.00

Size and location of surcharge varies.

Nos. 1067, 1094, 1113, 1125-1126
Surcharged in Gold

100NZ

1000 NZ

1996   *Perfs., Etc. as Before*
1435	A192	100z on 3.50z	
		#1067	
1436	A199	500z on 3.60z	
		#1113	
1437	A201	1000z on 2.05z	
		#1125	
1438	A196	2500z on 1.50z	
		#1094	
1439	A201	5000z on 3.60z	
		#1126	
1440	A196	6000z on 1.50z	
		#1094	
1441	A199	15,000z on 3.60z	
		#1113	
1442	A201	25,000z on 3.60z	
		#1126	

1996 Summer Olympic Games, Atlanta A226

1996, July 29   **Litho.**   *Perf. 11½*
1444	A226	1000z Equestrian	
1445	A226	12,500z Boxing	
1446	A226	25,000z Table tennis	
1447	A226	35,000z Basketball, vert.	
1448	A226	50,000z Tennis	

Insects & Spiders A227

No. 1449: a, Lasius niger. b, Calopterygides. c, Peucetia. d, Sphecides.

1996   **Litho.**   *Perf. 13½*
Sheet of 4
1449	A227	15,000z #a.-d.	4.50	4.50

Minerals A228

No. 1450: a, Uraninite. b, Malachite. c, Ruby. d, Diamond.
No. 1452, Uranotile, cuprosklodowskite, horiz.

1996

Sheet of 4
1450	A228	40,000z #a.-d.	12.00	12.00

Souvenir Sheet
1452	A228	105,000z multicolored	7.75	7.75

A number has been reserved for an additional sheet with this set.

Raptors A229

No. 1453: a, Congo eagle. b, Crowned eagle. c, Melierax metabates. d, Urotriorchis macrourus.

1996

Sheet of 4
1453	A229	50,000z #a.-d.	15.00	15.00

Butterflies A230

a, Cymothoe sangaris. b, Colotis zoe. c, Physcaeneura leda. d, Charaxes candiope.

1996

Sheet of 4
1454	A230	70,000z #a.-d.	20.00	20.00

The validity of Nos. 1455-1481 and other stamps from the same time period has been questioned. The editors are attempting to find out more about these stamps.

1998 World Cup Soccer Championships, France — A231

Numbers on players: No. 1455, #12. No. 1456, none. No. 1457, #7. No. 1458, #3. #1459a-1459d: like #1455-1458, but with part of World Cup Trophy behind each player. #1459: a, British player. b, Brazilian player.

1996
1455-1458	A231	35,000z Set of 4	9.00	9.00

Souvenir Sheets of 2 & 4
1459	A231	10,500z #a.-b.	1.25	1.25
1460	A231	35,000z #a.-d.	9.00	9.00

No. 1459 contains 2 42x39mm stamps. See Nos. 1467-1476.

World Wildlife Fund A236

Pan Paniscus: a, With young. b, Two in trees. c, Holding vines. d, Head.

1997

Block of 4

1466 A236 20,000z #a.-d.   4.50 4.50

1998 World Cup Soccer Championships Type of 1996

African soccer players: No. 1467, Soccer ball at his right. No. 1468, Ball at head. No. 1469, Yellow uniform. No. 1470, Ball on knee. German soccer players, soccer ball on stamp at: No. 1471, UR. No. 1472, LL. No. 1473, LR. No. 1474, UL.

Nos. 1475a-1475d, 1476a-1476d are like Nos. 1467-1474 but with part of World Cup Trophy behind each player.

1996		**Litho.**	**Perf. 13½**
1467-1470	A231	20,000z Set of 4	5.00 5.00
1471-1474	A231	50,000z Set of 4	12.25 12.25

Souvenir Sheets of 4

1475	A231	20,000z #a.-d.	5.00 5.00
1476	A231	50,000z #a.-d.	12.25 12.25

Boy Scouts and Lions Intl. Clubs A232

Diceros bicornis: No. 1477: a, Walking forward. b, Walking left, left leg up. c, Facing left. d, Holding head up.

Panthera leo: No. 1478: a, Cubs. b, Adult male. c, Adult male facing forward, mouth open. d, Adult female on fallen tree.

Loxodonta africana: No. 1479: a, Walking right, trunk in air. b, Reaching up to tree limb with trunk. c, Walking right, trunk down. d, Mother with calf.

105,000z, Hippopotamus amphibus.

1997		**Litho.**	**Perf. 13x13½**

Sheets of 4

1477	A232	40,000z #a.-d.	9.50 9.50
1478	A232	50,000z #a.-d.	11.75 11.75
1479	A232	70,000z #a.-d.	19.00 19.00

Souvenir Sheet

1480 A232 105,000z multi   6.25 6.25

Boy Scouts (#1477, 1479-1480). Lions Intl. Clubs (#1478).

Jacqueline Kennedy Onassis (1929-94) A233

Various portraits.

1997		**Litho.**	**Perf. 13½**
1481	A233	15,000z Sheet of 9, #a.-i.	7.00 7.00

No. 1481 also exists imperf.

Stamps from this country are now being released under the previous name, "Republique Democratique du Congo," or Congo Democratic Republic, despite the resumption of civil war. We will continue to list these stamps under the country's name of Zaire until the situation is resolved.

Diana, Princess of Wales (1961-97) — A234

Mother Teresa (1910-97) — A235

Portraits — #1482: a, Wearing tiara. b, In white jacket. c, In white hat. d, In polka dotted dress. e, Scarf around neck. f, Low cut evening dress.

No. 1483: a, Wearing tiara. b, Hand under chin. c, Leaning chin on both hands. d, One-shoulder-covered outfit.

No. 1484: a, Red & black dress. b, White jacket, pearls. c, Profile view. d, Wearing tiara.

No. 1485, In black evening dress. No. 1486, Holding flowers.

1998, Aug. 6		**Litho.**	**Perf. 14**

Sheet of 6

1482 A234 50,000z #a.-f.   4.50 4.50

Sheets of 4

1483	A234	100,000z #a.-d.	5.75 5.75
1484	A234	125,000z #a.-d.	7.25 7.25

Souvenir Sheets

1485-1486 A234 400,000z each 5.75 5.75

1998, Aug. 6

1487 A235 50,000z shown   .75 .75

Souvenir Sheet

1488 A235 325,000z Portrait, diff. 4.75 4.75

No. 1487 was issued in sheets of 6.

100 Centimes = 1 Franc (1998)

Native Dwelling — A236

Arms — A237

Inauguration of Pres. Laurent Kabila — A238

Designs: 1.25fr, Troops and civilians in Kinshasa. 3fr, Flag, crowd, Pres. Kabila breaking chain with sword, horiz.

2.50fr, Gun, arrow, handshake, tractor. 3.50fr, Pres. Kabila.

1999, May 12		**Litho.**	**Perf. 14**
1489	A236	25c multi	.25 .25
1490	A236	50c multi	.55 .55
1491	A238	75c multi	.80 .80
1492	A238	1.25fr multi	1.40 1.40
1493	A238	3fr multi	3.25 3.25
		Nos. 1489-1493 (5)	6.25 6.25

Souvenir Sheets

1494	A238	2.50fr multi	2.60 2.60
1495	A238	3.50fr multi	3.75 3.75

Conquest of Kinshasa by troops of Laurent Kabila, 2nd anniv.

Chinese Zodiac Animals — A239

No. 1496: a, Rat. b, Ox. c, Tiger. d, Rabbit. e, Dragon. f, Snake. g, Horse. h, Ram. i, Monkey. j, Cock. k, Dog. l, Boar.

1999, Aug. 20			**Perf. 13¼x13½**
1496	A239	78c Sheet of 12, #a-l	4.25 4.25

A240

A241

A242

A243

Outlaws of the Marsh — A244

No. 1497 — Sheet with text starting with "The historical novel. . .": a, 1.45fr, Men fighting. b, 1.50fr, Man uprooting tree. c, 1.60fr, Man with sword in snowstorm. d, 1.70fr, Man with sword, other men at bridge. e, 1.80fr, Three men at table.

No. 1498 — Sheet with text starting with "The main theme. . .": a, 1.45fr, Men and baskets. b, 1.50fr, Man threatening another man with sword. c, 1.60fr, Man attacking tiger. d, 1.70fr, People watching men in martial arts battle. e, 1.80fr, Battling horsemen.

No. 1499 - Sheet with text starting with "The common people. . .": a, 1.45fr, Men fighting in boat. b, 1.50fr, Man with sword fighting man with hatchets. c, 1.60fr, Men near fortified wall. d, 1.70fr, Men fighting on cobblestone street. e, 1.80fr, Archer on horseback at doorway.

No. 1500 — Sheet with text starting with "Today, it is thought. . .": a, 1.45fr, Man seated and other man standing near table. b, 1.50fr, Man setting fire to building. c, 1.60fr, Man in room. d, 1.70fr, Man lifting another man in a battle. e, 1.80fr, Man holding torn scroll.

1999, Aug. 20			**Perf. 13¼**

Sheets of 5, #a-e

1497-1500 A240 Set of 4 14.50 14.50

Souvenir Sheets

Perf. 13¼x13½

1501	A241	10fr multi	4.50 4.50
1502	A242	10fr multi	4.50 4.50
1503	A243	10fr multi	4.50 4.50
1504	A244	10fr multi	4.50 4.50

A245

A246

African Flora and Fauna — A247

Designs: 1fr, Telophorus quadricolor. 1.50fr, Panthera pardus. No. 1507, 2fr, Colotis protomedia. No. 1508, 2fr, Kobus vardoni. No. 1509, 3fr, Canarina abyssinica. No. 1510, 3fr, Smutsia temminckii. 7.80fr, Lion.

No. 1512: a, Okapi. b, Bird, rainbow, waterfalls. c, Giraffe, rainbow, waterfalls. d, Giraffe, waterfall mist. e, Mandrill. f, Chimpanzee. g, Leopard. h, Butterflies. i, Hippopotamus. j, Bird in water. k, Flowers. l, Antelope.

No. 1513: a, Sun. b, Pieris citrina. c, Merops apiaster. d, Lanius collurio. e, Ploceus cucullatus. f, Charaxes pelias. g, Charaxes eupale. h, Giraffa camelopardalis. i, Galago moholi. j, Strelitzia reginae. k, Gazella thomsoni. l, Upupa epops.

No. 1514, 10fr, Taurotragus oryx. No. 1515, 10fr, Hippopotamus amphibus.

No. 1516, 10fr, Warthog.

Perf. 14, 14¼x14¾ (#1511), 14¼x14 (#1516)

2000, Feb. 28			
1505-1510	A245	Set of 6	5.50 5.50
1511	A246	7.80fr multi	3.50 3.50
1512	A247	1fr Sheet of 12, #a-l	5.50 5.50
1513	A245	1.50fr Sheet of 12, #a-l	8.00 8.00

Souvenir Sheets

1514-1515	A245	Set of 2	9.00 9.00
1516	A247	10fr multi	4.50 4.50

No. 1516 contains one 42x57mm.

Wild Felines and Canines — A248

No. 1517, 1.50fr: a, Felis bengalensis. b, Felis aurata. c, Felis caracal. d, Felis conocolor. e, Felis nigripes. f, Panthera leo. g, Neofelis nebulosa. h, Felis wiedii. i, Acinonyx jubatus. j, Felis pardina. k, Felis yagouaroundi. l, Felis serval.

No. 1518, 2fr: a, Canis mesomelas. b, Otocyon megalotis. c, Speothos venaticus. d, Canis latrans. e, Cuon alpinus. f, Fennecus zerda. g, Urocyon cinereoargenteus. h, Canis lupus. i, Vulpes macrotis. j, Chrysocyon brachyurus. k, Nyctereutes procyonoides. l, Vulpes vulpes.

No. 1519, 10fr, Panthera pardus. No. 1520, 10fr, Alopex lagopus.

2000, Feb. 28   *Perf. 14*
Sheets of 12, #a-l

1517-1518	A248	Set of 2	19.00	19.00

Souvenir Sheets

1519-1520	A248	Set of 2	9.00	9.00

Millennium A249

2000, June 10

1521		Horiz. strip of 3	13.00	13.00
a.	A249	4.50fr multi	2.00	2.00
b.	A249	9fr multi	4.00	4.00
c.	A249	15fr multi	7.00	7.00

Printed in sheets containing two strips.

A250   A251

Birds A252

Designs: No. 1522, 3fr, Alopochen aegyptiacus. No. 1523, 3fr, Ardeola ibis. No. 1524, 4.50fr, Oena capensis. No. 1525, 4.50fr, Lybius torquatus. No. 1526, 9fr, Falco tinnunculus. No. 1527, 9fr, Corythaelo cristata.

No. 1528, 8.50fr, Psephotus chrysopterygius chrysopterygius. 8fr, Amazona aestiva. No. 1530, 8.50fr, Are nobilis cumanensis. No. 1531, 9fr, Agapornis roseicollis.

No. 1532, 8.50fr, Lophornis ornata. No. 1533, 9fr, Polytrus guauvunibi.

No. 1534, 9fr: a, Euplectes orix. b, Euplectes ardens. c, Oriolus auratus. d, Plocens cucullatus. e, Amandava subflava. f, Nectarina senegalensis.

No. 1535, 9fr: a, Haleyon malimbicus. b, Tachymarptis melba. c, Haliaeetus vocifer. d, Ardea purpurea. e, Balaeniceps rex. f, Balearica regulorum.

No. 1536: a, Ertoxeres aquila. b, Aglaiolepus kinde. c, Archilochus calobris. d, Trochlus polytaus. e, Chaliostigna herrani. f, Ensifera. g, Chrysolampus mosquitus. h, Phorethornus syrmatophorus. i, Calypre hetervare.

No. 1537, 5fr: a, Eos squamata squamata. b, Aratinga guarouba. c, Aratinga aurea. d, Psuedeos fuscata. e, Agapornis fischeri. f, Aratinga nana nana. g, Aratinga mitrata. h,

Trichoglossus haematodus rubitorquis. i, Cacatua galerita galerita.

No. 1538, 5fr: a, Ara macao. b, Neophema elegans. c, Loriculus vernalis. d, Aratinga solstitialis. e, Pionites melancephala. f, Bolborhynchus lineola. g, Ara severa. h, Psephotus chrysopterygius dissimilis. i, Ara militaris.

No. 1539, 15fr, Actophilornis africanus, horiz. No. 1540, 20fr, Ceryle rudis, horiz.

No. 1541, 15fr, Opopsitta diophthalma. No. 1542, 15fr, Ara ararrauna, horiz.

No. 1543, 15fr, Coeligena torgoata. No. 1544, 20fr, Campylopterus hemileicurus.

2000, Aug. 16   *Perf. 14*

1522-1527	A250	Set of 6	15.00	15.00
1528-1531	A251	Set of 4	13.50	13.50
1532-1533	A252	Set of 2	7.75	7.75

Sheets of 6, #a-f

1534-1535	A250	Set of 2	47.50	47.50
1536	A252	4.50fr Sheet of 9, #a-i	18.00	18.00

Sheets of 9, #a-i

1537-1538	A251	Set of 2	40.00	40.00

Souvenir Sheets

1539-1540	A250	Set of 2	16.00	16.00
1541-1542	A251	Set of 2	13.50	13.50
1543-1544	A252	Set of 2	16.00	16.00

Surcharges on Unissued Stamps A253

Designs: 10fr on 70,000z, Colotis zoe. 15fr on 25,000z, Bulbophyllum falcatum. 35fr on 15,000z, Sphecides. 50fr on 35,000z, Termitomyces aurantiacus.

2000   **Litho.**   *Perf. 13¼*

1545	A253	10fr on 70,000z multi	—	—
1546	A253	15fr on 25,000z multi	—	—
1548	A253	35fr on 15,000z multi	—	—
1550	A253	50fr on 35,000z multi	—	—

Location of surcharges varies. All surcharged stamps have white margins. Five additional surcharges exist. The editors would like to examine any examples.

A254

Trains — A255

Designs: 1fr, Missouri-Kansas-Texas Line locomotive. 2fr, Spremberg steam locomotive. No. 1556, 3fr, King Class, Great Western Railway. No. 1557, 3fr, Crocodile locomotive. 5fr, Inner-city trains, Great Britain. 6fr, Big Boy, Union Pacific.

No. 1560, 4.50fr: a, Class SU, 2-6-2, Russia. b, Prussian locomotive. c, Zimbabwe locomotive. d, Hunslet 2-8-2, Peru. e, London, Midland & Scottish Railway locomotive. f, London Northeastern Railway locomotive.

No. 1561, 8fr: a, Denver & Rio Grande Western Railroad locomotive. b, Mikado 2-8-2, Louisville & Nashville. c, Mogul, Rio Grande. d, New York Central Railway locomotive. e, Sumpter Valley Railway steam locomotive. f, Three-truck Shay No. 7.

No. 1562, 9.50fr: a, Compagnie du Nord locomotive, France. b, Union Pacific locomotive. c, Great Northern Railway locomotive. d, Liverpool & Manchester Railway locomotive. e, Patentee 2-2-2, London & Birmingham. f, Puffing Billy.

No. 1563, 10fr: a, Chicago, Rock Island & Pacific Railway locomotive. b, Powhattan Arrow, Norfolk & Western. c, Class S-1, New York Central Hudson River Railway. d, Reading Railroad locomotive. e, Great Bear, Great Western Railway. f, Bi-polar, Chicago, Milwaukee, St. Paul & Pacific Railway.

No. 1564, 5fr: a, Beyer-Garratt 50 4-8-2+2-8-4 locomotive. b, Locomotive Express 4-6-2. c, 780CV electric locomotive. d, Electric locomotive on curve. e, Class 2-10-0 Locomotive 56001. f, Electric locomotive on straight track. g, Class 2-8-4 Locomotive 284. h, Class G 6/6 electric locomotive.

No. 1565, 8.50fr: a, Class B-B electric locomotive AE4/4. b, Class EX, Paris-Lyon-Mediterranean. c, Big Boy. d, Tourist car. e, Class 4-8-4 GS-4. f, Class 46 electric locomotive. g, Class-4-6-0 County. h, Class DA Diesel-electric locomotive.

No. 1566, 15fr, New York Central & Hudson River Railway locomotive. No. 1567, 20fr, Mohawk & Hudson Railroad locomotive. No. 1568, 20fr, Broadway Limited, Pennsylvania Railroad. No. 1569, 20fr, Trans-Europe Express.

No. 1570, 20fr, Deltic electric locomotive, Great Britain. No. 1571, 20fr, Diesel-electric locomotive, Canada Pacific.

2001, Jan. 15   **Litho.**   *Perf. 14*

1554-1559	A254	Set of 6	—	—

Sheets of 6, #a-f

1560-1563	A254	Set of 4	—	—

Sheets of 8, #a-h

1564-1565	A255	Set of 2	—	—

Souvenir Sheets

1566-1569	A254	Set of 4	—	—
1570-1571	A255	Set of 2	—	—

Ships A256

Designs: 2.50fr, Clipper. 5fr, Arab bum. 20fr, Flemish galley. 21.70fr, Trabaccolo, vert. 30fr, Dutch galliot. 45.80fr, Japanese coaster.

No. 1578, 10fr: a, Trireme. b, Roman caudicaria. c, 13th cent. warship. d, Byzantine galley. e, Lateneer. f, 14th century cog. g, Arab dhow. h, Hanseatic cog. i, Portuguese galley.

No. 1579, 10fr: a, Egyptian sailing ship. b, Egyptian rowing craft. c, Egyptian seagoing ship. d, Greek galley. e, Etruscan merchantman f, Etruscan fishing skiff. g, Greek merchantman. h, Minoan passenger ship. i, Roman harbor boat.

No. 1580, 10fr: a, Flemish galleon. b, English galleon. c, Carrack. d, Chinese war galley. e, Venetian galley. f, Polacre. g, Hemmena. h, Venetian bragozzo. i, Schooner.

No. 1581, 25fr, Viking drakkar. No. 1582, 25fr, Portuguese caravel, vert. No. 1583, 25fr, HMS Endeavour, vert.

2001, June 22   *Perf. 14*

1572-1577	A256	Set of 6	—	—

Sheets of 9, #a-i

1578-1580	A256	Set of 3	—	—

Souvenir Sheets
Perf. 13¾

1581-1583	A256	Set of 3	—	—

No. 1581 contains one 50x38mm stamp; Nos. 1582-1583 each contain one 38x50mm stamp.

History of Aviation — A257

No. 1584: a, Montgolfier balloon (36x61mm). b, Boxkite and Tiger Moth airplanes (36x61mm). c, Gladiator. d, Eurofighter. e, Mosquito. f, Chipmunk.

No. 1585: a, Blackburn and Spartan Arrow airplanes (36x61mm). b, Tiger Moth. c, Lightning. d, Vulcan B2. e, Tornado.

No. 1586, 25fr, Fox Moth and Avro 540K airplanes. No. 1587, 25fr, Avro 504K and Fox Moth airplanes.

2001, June 22   *Perf. 14¼*

1584	A257	10fr Sheet of 6, #a-f	—	—
1585	A257	10fr Sheet of 6, #1584a, 1585a-1585e	—	—

Souvenir Sheets
Perf. 14¼x14½

1586-1587	A257	Set of 2	—	—

First Zeppelin Flight, Cent. — A258

No. 1588: a, LZ-6. b, LZ-7. c, US Navy airship Akron. c, Lindstrand HS-110 Pittsburgh Tribune-Review airship.

No. 1589, 100fr, LZ-130 Graf Zeppelin II. No. 1590, 100fr, LZ-1.

2001, June 22   *Perf. 14*

1588	A258	60fr Sheet of 4, #a-d	—	—

Souvenir Sheets

1589-1590	A258	Set of 2	—	—

Butterflies — A259

Designs: 5fr, Striped policeman. 21.70fr, Brown-veined white. 45fr, Common dotted border. 45.80fr, Cabbage. 50fr, African migrant. 51.80fr, Mocker swallowtail.

No. 1597, 6fr, horiz.: a, Common grass blue. b, Golden tiger. c, Palla. d, Blue diadem. e, African giant swallowtail. f, African leaf. g, Gold-banded forester. h, Small harvester.

No. 1598, 6fr, horiz.: a, Guinea fowl. b, Forest queen. c, Sweet potato acraea. d, Wanderer. e, Evening brown. f, African ringlet. g, Plain tiger. h, Monarch.

No. 1599, 8fr, horiz.: a, Broad-bordered grass yellow. b, Crimson tip. c, Orange-banded protea. d, Azure hairstreak. e, Marshall's false monarch. f, Blue swallowtail. g, Figtree blue. h, Grass jewel.

No. 1600, 25fr, Long-tailed blue, horiz. No. 1601, 25fr, Chief, horiz. No. 1602, 25fr, Large spotted acraea, horiz.

2001, June 22

1591-1596	A259	Set of 6	—	—

Sheets of 8, #a-h

1597-1599	A259	Set of 3	—	—

Souvenir Sheets

1600-1602	A259	Set of 3	—	—

Flowers and Insects — A260

Designs; 20fr, Aconite, Brazilian frog-hopper. 21.70fr, Larkspur, Mexican cicada. 25fr, Blue orchid, dragonfly. 45.80fr, Spotted blossom orchid, buck moth.

No. 1607, 10fr, horiz.: a, Rein orchids, tiger moth. b, Ivy, Siamese wasp. c, Pink lady's slipper, goat weed emperor. d, Gletscher-petersbart, velvet ant. e, Licorice, viceroy butterfly. f, Grass pink, aphid. g, Ranunculus, spider wasp. h, Clamshell orchid, tropical bee. i, Bog orchids, mayfly.

No. 1608, 10fr, horiz.: a, Common lantana, red-spotted purple butterfly. b, Deep purple lilac, zebra swallowtail. c, Mt. Fujiyama, ruddy copper butterfly. d, Pinafore pink, red admiral butterfly. e, Argemone mexicana, purple hairstreak butterfly. f, Soapwort, sulphur butterfly. g, Lungwort, Buckeye butterfly. h, Wild thyme, pipevine swallowtail. i, Loeselia mexicana, banded purple butterfly.

No. 1609, 10fr, horiz.: a, Cymbidium Stanley Fouraker Highlander, scarlet tiger moth. b, Cymbidium Sparkle "Ruby Lips," Sumatran carpenter bee. c, Dendrobium Sussex, ant lion. d, Cymbidium Vieux Rose Loch Lomond, nachahmend butterfly. e, Cymbidium, cicada-killer wasp. f, Dendrobium Mousmee, spechosoma wasp. g, Arachnis flos-aeris, green lacewing. h, Paphiopedilum, seven-spot ladybug. i, Eulophia quartiniana, damselfly.

No. 1610, 25fr, Jolly Jocker pansy, monarch butterfly, horiz. No. 1611, 25fr, Pink peony, wasp (inscribed erroneously like No. 1610), horiz. No. 1612, 25fr, Plumbago capensis, honey bee, horiz.

2001, June 22   **Perf. 14**
1603-1606 A260   Set of 4

Sheets of 9, #a-i
Perf. 14¼x14½
1607-1609 A260   Set of 3

Souvenir Sheets
1610-1612 A260   Set of 3

Nos. 1607-1609 each contain nine 37x30mm stamps; Nos. 1610-1612 each contain one 50x37mm stamp.

Tintin in
Africa — A261

Designs: 190fr, Tintin with hand above eyes. 461fr, Tintin in car with dog and native.

2001, Dec. 31   **Photo.**   **Perf. 11½**
1613 A261 190fr multi   1.25 1.25

Souvenir Sheet
1614 A261 461fr multi   3.00 3.00

No. 1614 contains one 48x38mm stamp. See Belgium Nos. 1875-1876.

OFFICIAL STAMPS

Nos. 756-772
Overprinted

1975   **Litho.**   **Perf. 14**
O1 A145 10s red org & blk   .20   .20
O2 A145 40s multi   .20   .20
O3 A145 50s multi   .20   .20

Perf. 13
O4   A146 1k multi   .20   .20
O5   A146 2k multi   .20   .20
O6   A146 3k multi   .20   .20
O7   A146 4k multi   .25   .20
O8   A146 5k multi   .25   .20
O9   A146 6k multi   .30   .20
O10 A146 8k multi   .40   .20
O11 A146 9k multi   .40   .20
O12 A146 10k multi   .45   .20
O13 A146 14k multi   .65   .25
O14 A146 17k multi   .75   .30
O15 A146 20k multi   .75   .30
O16 A146 50k multi   1.90   .75
O17 A146 100k multi   6.25 2.75
         Nos. O1-O17 (17)   13.55 6.75

"SP" are the initials of "Service Public."

ZAMBEZIA

zam-ˈbē-zē-ə

LOCATION — A former district of the Mozambique Province in Portuguese East Africa
GOVT. — Part of the Portuguese East Africa Colony

The districts of Quelimane and Tete were created from Zambezia. Eventually stamps of Mozambique came into use. See Quelimane and Tete.

1000 Reis = 1 Milreis

King Carlos
     A1   A2
Perf. 11½, 12½, 13½

1894   **Typo.**   **Unwmk.**
1   A1   5r yellow   .25   .25
2   A1   10r red violet   .75   .45
3   A1   15r chocolate   1.00   .65
 a.   Perf. 12½   27.50 19.00
4   A1   20r lavender   1.00   .65
5   A1   25r blue green   2.00   1.25
 a.   Perf. 11½
6   A1   50r lt blue   2.00   1.25
7   A1   75r carmine   4.50   3.25
 a.   Perf. 11½   50.00 35.00
8   A1   80r yellow grn   4.00   2.50
9   A1   100r brown, buff   3.00   1.75
10 A1   150r car, rose   6.00   3.00
11 A1   200r dk blue, bl   6.00   3.00
 a.   Perf. 11½   200.00 150.00
 b.   Perf. 13½   32.50 24.00
12 A1   300r dk bl, salmon 10.00   4.50
 a.   Perf. 11½   25.00 20.00
         Nos. 1-12 (12)   40.50 22.50

For surcharges and overprints see Nos. 36-47, 73-74, 77-81, 84-88.

1898-1903   **Perf. 11½**
Name and Value in Black or Red (500r)
13 A2   2½r gray   .45   .45
14 A2   5r orange   .45   .45
15 A2   10r lt green   .75   .50
16 A2   15r brown   1.25   1.00
17 A2   15r gray grn ('03) 1.60 1.40
18 A2   20r gray violet   1.25   1.00
19 A2   25r sea green   1.25   1.00
20 A2   25r carmine ('03) 1.00   .85
21 A2   50r blue   1.25   1.10
22 A2   50r brown ('03)   2.75   2.25
23 A2   65r dull bl ('03) 8.00   5.50
24 A2   75r rose   10.00   5.25
25 A2   75r lilac ('03)   3.25   2.75
26 A2   80r violet   5.00   3.00
27 A2   100r dk bl, bl   2.00   2.00
28 A2   115r org brn, pink
                 ('03)   10.00   7.25
29 A2   130r brn, straw ('03) 10.00 7.25
30 A2   150r brn, buff   6.00   3.50
31 A2   200r red vio, pnksh 6.00 3.50
32 A2   300r dk bl, rose 8.00   3.50
33 A2   400r dull bl, straw
                 ('03)   10.00   8.50
34 A2   500r blk, bl ('01) 12.00 6.75
35 A2   700r vio, yelsh ('01) 15.00 8.75
         Nos. 13-35 (23) 117.25 77.50

For surcharges and overprints see Nos. 49-68, 72, 82-83, 93-107.

Stamps of 1894
Surcharged

1902   **Perf. 11½, 12½**
36 A1   65r on 10r red vio 9.00 7.00
37 A1   65r on 15r choc   9.00 7.00
38 A1   65r on 20r lav   9.00 7.00
39 A1   65r on 300r bl, sal 9.00 7.00
40 A1   115r on 5r yel   9.00 7.00
41 A1   115r on 25r bl grn 9.00 7.00
42 A1   115r on 80r yel grn 9.00 7.00
43 A1   130r on 75r car   7.00 7.00
44 A1   130r on 150r car, rose 5.25 5.25
45 A1   400r on 50r lt bl   2.00 3.25
46 A1   400r on 100r brn, buff 2.00 3.50
47 A1   400r on 200r bl, bl 2.00 3.50

Same Surcharge on No. P1
48 N1   130r on 2½r brn   9.00 7.00
         Nos. 36-48 (13)   90.25 78.50

Stamps of 1898
Overprinted

1902   **Perf. 11½**
49 A2   15r brown   2.00   1.40
50 A2   25r sea green   2.00   1.40
51 A2   50r blue   2.00   1.40
52 A2   75r rose   6.00   3.75
         Nos. 49-52 (4)   12.00   7.95

No. 23 Surcharged in
Black

1905
53 A2   50r on 65r dull blue 5.75 4.00

Stamps of 1898-1903
Overprinted in
Carmine or Green

1911
54 A2   2½r gray   .35   .20
55 A2   5r orange   .35   .20
56 A2   10r light green   .40   .25
 a.   Inverted overprint   15.00 12.50
57 A2   15r gray green   .40   .25
58 A2   20r gray violet   .50   .30
59 A2   25r carmine (G)   1.50   .50
60 A2   50r brown   .40   .35
61 A2   75r lilac   1.25   .90
62 A2   100r dk bl, bl   1.25   .90
63 A2   115r org brn, pink 1.25   .90
64 A2   130r brown, straw 1.25   .90
65 A2   200r red vio, pnksh 1.25   .90
66 A2   400r dull bl, straw 2.10 1.10
67 A2   500r blk & red, bl 2.10 1.10
68 A2   700r violet, yelsh 2.25 1.50
         Nos. 54-68 (15) 16.60 10.25

Stamps of 1902-05
Overprinted in
Carmine or Green

1914
Without Gum
72 A2   50r on 65r dl bl 1,200. 800.00
73 A1   115r on 5r yellow 1.25   1.50
74 A1   115r on 25r bl grn 1.25 1.50
75 A1   115r on 80r yel grn 1.25 1.50
76 N1   130r on 2½r brn (G) 1.25 1.50
 a.   Carmine overprint   22.50 22.50
77 A1   130r on 75r car   1.75   1.50
 a.   Perf. 12½   5.50   7.00
78 A1   130r on 150r car,
                 rose   1.75   1.50
79 A1   400r on 50r lt bl 2.50   3.00
 a.   Perf. 12½   11.00 11.00
80 A1   400r on 100r brn,
                 buff   2.50   2.50
81 A1   400r on 200r bl, bl 2.50 2.50
On Nos. 51-52
82 A2   50r blue   1.50   1.50
83 A2   75r rose   1.50   1.50
         Nos. 73-83 (11) 19.00 20.00

Preceding Issues
Overprinted in
Carmine

1915
On Provisional Issue of 1902
84 A1   115r on 5r yellow .85   .45
85 A1   115r on 25r bl grn .85   .45
86 A1   115r on 80r lt grn .85   .45
87 A1   130r on 75r carmine .85   .45
 a.   Perf. 12½   4.50   2.25
88 A1   130r on 150r car, rose .85 .45
92 N1   130r on 2½r (down) .85   .45
On Nos. 51, 53
93 A2   50r blue   .85   .50
 a.   "Republica" inverted 15.00 15.00
94 A2   50r on 65r dull bl 3.50   4.50
         Nos. 84-94 (8)   9.45   7.70

Stamps of 1898-1903
Overprinted Locally
in Carmine

1917
Without Gum
95   A2   2½r gray   1.50   3.00
96   A2   5r orange   7.00   6.50
97   A2   10r light green   7.00   6.00
98   A2   15r gray green   6.50   6.50
99   A2   20r gray violet   7.25   6.50
100 A2   25r sea green   13.50 15.00
101 A2   100r blue, blue   4.00   2.75
102 A2   115r org brn, pink 4.00 2.75
103 A2   130r brown, straw 4.00   2.75
104 A2   200r red vio, pnksh 4.00 2.75
105 A2   400r dull bl, straw 4.50 3.50
106 A2   500r blk & red, bl 5.50 3.75
107 A2   700r vio, yelsh   9.00   5.25
         Nos. 95-107 (13) 77.75 67.00

NEWSPAPER STAMP

N1

1894 **Unwmk.** **Typo.** **Perf. 12½**
P1 N1 2½r brown   .60   .35

For overprints and surcharges see Nos. 76, 92.

ZAMBIA

'zam-bē-ə

LOCATION — Southern Africa
GOVT. — Republic
AREA — 290,586 sq. mi.
POP. — 9,663,535 (1999 est.)
CAPITAL — Lusaka

The former British protectorate of Northern Rhodesia became an independent republic Oct. 24, 1964, taking the name Zambia. See Northern Rhodesia; see Rhodesia and Nyasaland.

12 Pence = 1 Shilling
20 Shillings = 1 Pound
100 Ngwee = 1 Kwacha (1968)

Catalogue values for all unused stamps in this country are for Never Hinged items.

Pres. Kenneth D. Kaunda, Victoria Falls — A1

College of Further Education, Lusaka — A2

Perf. 14½x14, 14x14½

1964, Oct. 24   Photo.   Unwmk.
1	A1	3p shown	.20	.20
2	A2	6p shown	.30	.20
3	A1	1sh3p Barotse dancer	.40	.30
		Nos. 1-3 (3)	.90	.70

Zambia's independence, Oct. 24, 1964.

Farmer and Silo A3

X-Ray Technician A4

Designs: 2p, Chinyau dancer. 3p, Woman picking cotton. 4p, Angoni bull. 6p, Communications by drum and teletype. 9p, Redwood blossoms and factory. 1sh, Night fishing on Lake Tanganyika. 1sh3p, Woman tobacco worker. 2sh, Tonga basket maker and child. 2sh6p, Elephants in Luangwa Valley Game Reserve. 5sh, Child and school. 10sh, Copper mining. £1, Makishi dancer.

1964, Oct. 24   Photo.   Perf. 14½
Size: 23x19mm, 19x23mm
4	A3	½p emerald, blk & red	.20	.25
5	A4	1p ultra, blk & brn	.20	.20
6	A4	2p orange, brn & red	.20	.20
7	A4	3p red & black	.20	.20
8	A3	4p orange & black	.20	.20

Perf. 13½x14½, 14½x13½
Size: 32x23mm, 23x32mm
9	A3	6p Prus grn, brn & org	.20	.20
10	A3	9p ultra, brn & dk car rose	.20	.20
11	A3	1sh blue, bis & blk	.20	.20
12	A4	1sh3p dk bl, ver, blk & yel	.25	.20
13	A4	2sh org, blk, brn & ultra	.30	.20
14	A3	2sh6p org yel & blk	.75	.40
15	A4	5sh emerald, blk & yel	1.10	.55
16	A3	10sh orange & blk	3.50	2.50
17	A4	£1 red, blk, brn & blk	2.50	3.00
		Nos. 4-17 (14)	10.00	8.50

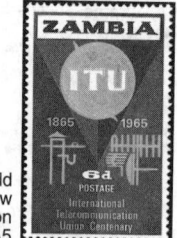

ITU Emblem, Old and New Communication Equipment — A5

1965, July 26   Photo.   Perf. 14
18	A5	6p brt lilac & gold	.20	.20
19	A5	2sh6p gray & gold	.80	1.00

Cent. of the ITU.

ICY Emblem A6

1965, July 26   Perf. 14
20	A6	3p grnsh blue & gold	.20	.20
21	A6	1sh3p ultra & gold	.50	.40

International Cooperation Year, 1965.

Pres. Kaunda and State House, Lusaka — A7

Clematopsis — A8

Designs: 6p, Fireworks over Independence Stadium. 2sh6p, Tithonia diversifolia.

Perf. 13½x14½

1965, Oct. 18   Unwmk.
22	A7	3p multicolored	.20	.20
23	A7	6p ind, yel & brt pink	.20	.20

Perf. 14
24	A8	1sh3p pink, yel & brn	.20	.20
25	A8	2sh6p brt grn, dp org & brn	.40	.40
		Nos. 22-25 (4)	1.00	1.00

1st anniv. of independence, Oct. 24.

Inauguration of WHO Headquarters, Geneva — A9

1966, May 18   Perf. 14
26	A9	3p rose brn, brt bl & gold	.20	.20
27	A9	1sh3p vio bl, brt bl & gold	.60	.50

University of Zambia — A10

1966, July 12   Photo.   Perf. 14
28	A10	3p brt green & gold	.20	.20
29	A10	1sh3p brt purple & gold	.25	.20

University of Zambia opening, Mar. 17.

National Assembly Building — A11

1967, May 2   Unwmk.   Perf. 14
30	A11	3p slate & bronze	.20	.20
31	A11	6p yellow grn & bronze	.20	.20

Completion of National Assembly Building.

Lusaka Airport — A12

1967, Oct. 2   Photo.   Perf. 13½x14½
32	A12	6p vio blue & bronze	.20	.20
33	A12	2sh6p brown & bronze	.70	.70

Opening of Lusaka International Airport.

Symbols of Agriculture A13

Radio, Telephone and Television — A14

Designs: 4p, Emblem of Zambia Youth Service. 1sh, Map showing locations of Zambia coalfields. 1sh6p, Map showing Zambia-Tanzania Road.

Perf. 14½x13½, 13½x14½

1967, Oct. 23
34	A14	4p gray, red & gold	.20	.20
35	A13	6p lt vio bl, gold & blk	.20	.20
36	A14	9p dull blue, sil & blk	.25	.25
37	A14	1sh gold, red, blk & vio bl	.50	.20
38	A13	1sh6p bl grn, ultra, gold & blk	.75	1.00
		Nos. 34-38 (5)	1.90	1.85

Issued to publicize National Development.

Lusaka Cathedral — A15

Baobab Tree — A16

Designs: 3n, Zambia Airways plane. 5n, National Museum, Livingstone. 8n, Vimbuza dancer. 10n, Woman tobacco picker. 15n, Nudaurelia zambesina butterfly. 20n, Crowned cranes. 25n, Angoni warrior. 50n, Chokwe dancer. 1k, Railroad bridge, Kafue River. 2k, Eland.

Perf. 13½x14½, 14½x13½

1968, Jan. 16   Photo.
Size: 26x22mm, 22x26mm
39	A15	1n bronze & multi	.20	.20
a.		Booklet pane of 6	.20	
b.		Booklet pane of 4	.20	
40	A16	2n bronze & multi	.20	.20
41	A15	3n bronze & multi	.20	.20
a.		Booklet pane of 6	.60	
b.		Booklet pane of 4	.40	
42	A16	5n sepia & bronze	.20	.20
43	A16	8n bronze & multi	.20	.20
44	A16	10n bronze & multi	.25	.20

Size: 32x26mm, 26x32mm
45	A15	15n bronze & multi	.35	.20
46	A16	20n bronze & multi	.50	.20
47	A16	25n bronze & multi	.55	.20
48	A16	50n bronze, org & blk	1.25	.25
49	A15	1k dk blue & brnz	2.00	.30
50	A15	2k copper & blk	5.00	.75
		Nos. 39-50 (12)	10.90	3.10

Used values of Nos. 48-50 are for canceled-to-order stamps. Postally used copies sell for more.

Map of Zambia, Arrow Pointing to Ndola — A17

Perf. 14½x14

1968, June 29   Photo.   Unwmk.
51	A17	15n brt green & gold	.25	.25

Zambia Trade Fair at Ndola.

Children and Human Rights Flame — A18

WHO Emblem A19

Children A20

Photogravure; Gold Impressed

1968, Oct. 23   Perf. 14½x14
52	A18	3n ultra, dk bl & gold	.20	.20
53	A19	10n brt violet & gold	.20	.20
54	A20	25n brt blue, blk & gold	.50	.50
		Nos. 52-54 (3)	.90	.90

Intl. Human Rights Year; 20th anniv. of WHO; 21st anniv. of UNICEF (25n).

Copper Miner — A21

Map of Africa with Zambia — A22

Design: 25n, Worker poling furnace, horiz.

Perf. 14½x13½

1969, June 18   Photo.
55	A21	3n dp violet & copper	.25	.20
56	A21	25n yellow, blk & copper	1.25	1.00

50th anniv. of the ILO.

Perf. 13½x14, 14x13½

1969, Oct. 23   **Photo.**

10n, Waterbucks, Kafue National Park, horiz. 15n, Golden perch, Kasaba Bay, horiz. 25n, Carmine bee-eater, Luangwa Valley.

57	A22	5n ultra, yel & copper	.20	.20
58	A22	10n copper & multi	.25	.20
59	A22	15n copper & multi	.50	.30
60	A22	25n copper & multi	1.25	1.00
		Nos. 57-60 (4)	2.20	1.70

International Year of African Tourism.

Nimbus III Weather Satellite — A23

1970, Mar. 23   **Litho.**   **Perf. 13x11**

61	A23	15n multicolored	.30	.50

Issued for World Meteorological Day.

"Clean Water" — A24

Designs: 15n, "Nutrition" (infant on scale). 25n, Children's immunization and Edward Jenner, M.D.

1970, July 4   **Litho.**   **Perf. 13x12½**

62	A24	3n multicolored	.20	.20
63	A24	15n multicolored	.50	.50
64	A24	25n multicolored	.85	.85
		Nos. 62-64 (3)	1.55	1.55

Issued to publicize preventive medicine and the "Under Five" children's clinics.

Mural by Gabriel Ellison A25

1970, Sept. 8   **Litho.**   **Perf. 14x14½**

65	A25	15n multicolored	.35	.35

Opening of the Conf. of Non-Aligned Nations in Mulungushi Hall (decorated with murals by Mrs. Ellison) in Zambia.

Ceremonial Axe — A26

Traditional Crafts: 5n, Clay pipe bowl with antelope head. 15n, Makishi mask, vert. 25n, The Kuomboka Ceremony (dancers and ceremonial boat).

1970, Nov. 30   **Litho.**   **Perf. 14x14½**
Size: 34x25mm

66	A26	3n dp lil rose & multi	.20	.20
67	A26	5n dp org, blk & sepia	.20	.20

Perf. 13x13½
Size: 30x45½mm

68	A26	15n dp lil rose & multi	.45	.45

Perf. 12½
Size: 71½x23½mm

69	A26	25n violet, blue & multi	.75	.75
a.		Souvenir sheet of 4, #66-69	8.50	8.50
		Nos. 66-69 (4)	1.60	1.60

Dag Hammarskjold and UN General Assembly — A27

Hammarskjold and: 10n, Downed plane. 15n, Dove with olive branch. 25n, Plaque and flowers.

1971, Sept. 18   **Perf. 13½**

70	A27	4n brown & multi	.20	.20
71	A27	10n yellow grn & multi	.20	.20
72	A27	15n blue & multi	.30	.30
73	A27	25n plum & multi	.45	.45
		Nos. 70-73 (4)	1.15	1.15

10th anniv. of the death of Dag Hammarskjold, (1905-61) Secretary-General of the UN, near Ndola, Zambia.

Red-Breasted Bream — A28

1971, Dec. 10

74	A28	4n shown	.20	.20
75	A28	10n Green-headed bream	.60	.50
76	A28	15n Tiger fish	1.50	.75
		Nos. 74-76 (3)	2.30	1.45

Christmas.

Cheetah — A29

Soil Conservation A30

1972, Mar. 15   **Perf. 13½x14**

77	A29	4n shown	.30	.20
78	A29	10n Lechue	.70	.55

Perf. 14x13½

79	A30	15n Cape porcupine	1.10	.85
80	A30	25n Elephant	2.75	1.40
		Nos. 77-80 (4)	4.85	3.00

Conservation Year.

1972, June 30   **Litho.**   **Perf. 14x13½**
Size: 18½x45mm

81	A30	4n shown	.25	.25
82	A30	10n Forest conservation	.75	.75

Perf. 13½x14

83	A29	15n Water conservation (river view)	1.10	1.10
84	A29	25n Woman in corn field	1.90	1.90
		Nos. 81-84 (4)	4.00	4.00

Souvenir Sheet

85		Sheet of 4	10.00	12.50
a.		A30 10n Giraffe and zebra	1.40	
b.		A30 10n Rhinoceros	1.40	

c.		A30 10n Hippopotamus and deer	1.40	
d.		A30 10n Lion	1.40	

Conservation Year. Stamp size: 27x50mm.

1972, Sept. 22   **Perf. 13½x14**

Designs: All horizontal.
Size: 48x35mm

86	A30	4n Zambian flowers	.90	.50
87	A30	10n Citrus swallowtails and roses	1.60	1.40
88	A30	15n Bee	3.00	2.00
89	A30	25n Locusts in corn field	4.50	3.00
		Nos. 86-89 (4)	10.00	6.90

Conservation Year.

Mary and Joseph Going to Bethlehem — A31

1972, Dec. 1   **Litho.**   **Perf. 14**

90	A31	4n shown	.20	.20
91	A31	9n Holy Family	.25	.25
92	A31	15n Adoration of the shepherds	.40	.40
93	A31	25n Kings following the star	.75	.75
		Nos. 90-93 (4)	1.60	1.60

Christmas.

Broken Hill Man A32

Designs: 4n, Oudenodon and rubidgea (artist's conception; vert.). 10n, Zambiasaurus. 15n, Skull of Luangwa Drysdalli. 25n, Glossoptoris (seed).

Perf. 14x13½, 14

1973, Feb. 1   **Litho.**
Size: 29x45mm

94	A32	4n org ver & multi	.65	.30

Size: 37½x21mm

95	A32	9n org ver & multi	1.00	.65
96	A32	10n apple grn & multi	1.10	.85
97	A32	15n lilac & multi	1.50	1.10
98	A32	25n orange brn & multi	2.75	2.75
		Nos. 94-98 (5)	7.00	5.65

Fossils from Luangwa area (except 9n), over 200 million years old.

Meeting of Stanley and Livingstone at Ujiji — A33

4n, Livingstone, the missionary. 9n, Livingstone at Victoria Falls. 10n, Livingstone stopping slave traders. 15n, Livingstone, the physician. 25n, Portrait & tree in Chitumbu, marking burial place of heart.

1973, May 1   **Perf. 13x13½**

99	A33	3n multicolored	.20	.20
100	A33	4n multicolored	.30	.30
101	A33	9n multicolored	.60	.60
102	A33	10n multicolored	.75	.75
103	A33	15n multicolored	1.10	1.10
104	A33	25n multicolored	1.75	1.75
		Nos. 99-104 (6)	4.70	4.70

Dr. David Livingstone (1813-73), medical missionary and explorer.

Parliamentary Mace — A34

1973, Sept. 24   **Litho.**   **Perf. 13½x14**

105	A34	9n tan & multi	.70	.70
106	A34	15n gray & multi	1.40	1.40
107	A34	25n brt green & multi	1.90	1.90
		Nos. 105-107 (3)	4.00	4.00

Third Commonwealth Conference of Speakers and Presiding Officers, Lusaka.

Vaccination — A35

WHO Emblem and: 4n, Mother washing infant, vert. 9n, Nurse weighing infant, vert. 15n, Child eating cereal and fruit.

1973, Oct. 16   **Litho.**   **Perf. 14**

108	A35	4n blue & multi	60.00	25.00
109	A35	9n orange & multi	.30	.30
110	A35	10n brt grn & multi	.40	.40
111	A35	15n violet & multi	.50	.50
		Nos. 108-111 (4)	61.20	26.20

WHO, 25th anniv.

A36

A37

Birth of the Second Republic: 4n, UNIP flag. 9n, United National Independence Party Headquarters, Lusaka. 10n, Army band. 15n, Women dancing and singing. 25n, President's parliamentary chair.

1973, Dec. 13   **Litho.**   **Perf. 14x13½**

112	A36	4n multicolored	17.50	7.50
113	A36	9n multicolored	.25	.25
114	A36	10n multicolored	.30	.30
115	A36	15n multicolored	.45	.45
116	A37	25n multicolored	.75	.75
		Nos. 112-116 (5)	19.25	9.25

Pres. Kaunda and his Home During Struggle for Independence — A38

4n, Pres. Kaunda at Mulungushi. 15n, Pres. Kaunda holding torch of freedom.

1974, Apr. 28   Litho.   Perf. 14½x14

117	A38	4n multi, vert.	.70 .70
118	A38	9n multi	.90 .90
119	A38	15n multi	1.40 1.40
		Nos. 117-119 (3)	3.00 3.00

50th birthday of Pres. Kenneth Kaunda.

Nakambla Sugar Estate — A39

Designs: 4n, Local market. 9n, Kapiri glass factory. 10n, Kafue hydroelectric plant. 15n, Kafue Bridge. 25n, Conference of Non-aligned Nations, Lusaka, 1970.

1974, Oct. 24   Litho.   Perf. 13½x14

120	A39	3n multicolored	.20 .20
121	A39	4n multicolored	.20 .20
122	A39	9n multicolored	.40 .40
123	A39	10n multicolored	.50 .50
124	A39	15n multicolored	.70 .70
125	A39	25n multicolored	1.10 1.10
		Nos. 120-125 (6)	3.10 3.10

Souvenir Sheet

126		Sheet of 4	7.00 7.00
a.	A39	15n Academic education	1.50
b.	A39	15n Teacher Training College	1.50
c.	A39	15n Technical education	1.50
d.	A39	15n University of Zambia	1.50

10th anniversary of indepencence.

Mobile Post Office — A40

UPU Emblem and: 9n, Rural mail service by Zambia Airways. 10n, Modern Post Office, Chipata. 15n, Ndola Postal Training Center.

1974, Nov. 15

127	A40	4n multicolored	.20 .20
128	A40	9n multicolored	.25 .20
129	A40	10n multicolored	.30 .20
130	A40	15n multicolored	.45 .30
		Nos. 127-130 (4)	1.20 .90

Centenary of Universal Postal Union.

Radar by Day A41

1974, Dec. 16

131	A41	4n shown	.25 .20
132	A41	9n Radar by night	.50 .40
133	A41	15n Radar at dawn	1.00 .70
134	A41	25n Radar station	1.75 1.25
		Nos. 131-134 (4)	3.50 2.55

Inauguration of Mwembeshi Earth Station, Oct. 21, 1974.

Rhinoceros and Calf — A42

Peanut Harvest — A43

1975, Jan. 3   Litho.   Perf. 13½x14

135	A42	1n shown	.45
136	A42	2n Guinea fowl	.45 .35
137	A42	3n Zambian dancers	.20 .35
138	A42	4n Fish eagle	.60 .20
139	A42	5n Bridge, Victoria Falls	.75 .45
140	A42	8n Sitatunga	.75 .35
141	A42	9n Elephant, Kasaba Bay Resort	.75 .20
142	A42	10n Giant pangolin	.20 .20

Perf. 13

143	A43	15n Zambezi River source, Monument	.25 .20
144	A43	20n shown	.75 .65
145	A43	25n Tobacco field	1.10 .20
146	A43	50n Flying doctor service	1.75 1.25
147	A43	1k Lady Ross's touraco	3.25 1.25
148	A43	2k Village scene	2.75 4.00
		Nos. 135-148 (14)	14.00 10.00

For surcharges see #188-191, 319, 371.

Map of Namibia (South-West Africa) — A44

1975, Aug. 26   Litho.   Perf. 14x13½

149	A44	4n green & dk green	.20 .20
150	A44	9n dk blue & gray bl	.25 .25
151	A44	15n yellow & orange	.35 .40
152	A44	25n orange & dp orange	.45 .70
		Nos. 149-152 (4)	1.25 1.55

Namibia Day.

Sprinkler Irrigation — A45

Designs: 9n, Sprinkler irrigation over rows of vegetables. 15n, Furrow irrigation.

1975, Dec. 16   Litho.   Perf. 13

153	A45	4n multicolored	.20 .20
154	A45	9p multicolored	.50 .50
155	A45	15n multicolored	.80 .80
		Nos. 153-155 (3)	1.50 1.50

Intl. Commission on Irrigation and Drainage, 25th anniv.

Julbernardia Paniculata — A46

Trees of Zambia: 4n, Sycamore fig. 9n, Baikiaea plurijuga. 10n, Colophospermum. 15n, Uapaca kirkiana. 25n, Pterocarpus angolensis.

1976, Mar. 22   Litho.   Perf. 13

156	A46	3n multicolored	.25 .25
157	A46	4n multicolored	.25 .25
158	A46	9n multicolored	.40 .40

159	A46	10n multicolored	.40 .40
160	A46	15n multicolored	.65 .65
161	A46	25n multicolored	.80 .80
		Nos. 156-161 (6)	2.75 2.75

World Forestry Day, Mar. 21.

TAZARA Passenger Train — A47

9n, Train carrying copper. 10n, Clearing the bush. #164, Train carrying heavy machinery. #166b, Track laying. 20n, Reinforcing railroad track. #165, Train carrying various goods. #166d, Completed tracks.

1976, Dec. 10   Litho.   Perf. 13

162	A47	4n multicolored	.20 .20
163	A47	9n multicolored	.45 .45
164	A47	15n multicolored	.80 .80
165	A47	25n multicolored	1.40 1.40
		Nos. 162-165 (4)	2.85 2.85

Souvenir Sheet

Perf. 13½x14

166		Sheet of 4	4.00 4.00
a.	A47	10n multicolored	.40 .28
b.	A47	15n multicolored	.60 .45
c.	A47	20n multicolored	.70 .50
d.	A47	25n multicolored	1.00 .65

Completion of Tanzania-Zambia Railroad.

Kayowe Dance — A48

1977, Jan. 18   Litho.   Perf. 13½x14

167	A48	4n shown	.20 .20
168	A48	9n Lilombola dance	.25 .20
169	A48	15n Initiation ceremony	.45 .40
170	A48	25n Munkhwele dance	.75 .50
		Nos. 167-170 (4)	1.65 1.30

2nd World Black and African Festival, Lagos, Nigeria, Jan. 15-Feb. 12.

Grimwood's Longclaw — A49

Birds of Zambia: 9n, Shelley's sunbird. 10n, Black-cheeked lovebird. 15n, Locust finch. 20n, White-chested tinkerbird. 25n, Chaplin's barbet.

1977, July 1   Litho.   Perf. 14½

171	A49	4n multicolored	.35 .20
172	A49	9n multicolored	.60 .45
173	A49	10n multicolored	.70 .45
174	A49	15n multicolored	.95 1.40
175	A49	20n multicolored	1.50 1.50
176	A49	25n multicolored	1.90 2.00
		Nos. 171-176 (6)	6.00 6.00

Children Playing with Blocks A50

Designs: 9n, Women of various races dancing in circle. 15n, Black and white girls with young bird.

1977, Oct. 20   Litho.   Perf. 14x14½

177	A50	4n multicolored	.20 .20
178	A50	9n multicolored	.20 .20
179	A50	15n multicolored	.35 .35
		Nos. 177-179 (3)	.75 .75

Combat racism and racial discrimination.

"Glory to God in the Highest" A51

Christmas: 9n, Nativity. 10n, Three Kings and camel. 15n, Presentation at the Temple.

1977, Dec. 20   Litho.   Perf. 14

180	A51	4n multicolored	.20 .20
181	A51	9n multicolored	.20 .20
182	A51	10n multicolored	.20 .20
183	A51	15n multicolored	.30 .30
		Nos. 180-183 (4)	.90 .90

Elephant and Road Check A52

Designs: 18n, Waterbuck and Kafue River boat patrol. 28n, Warthog and helicopter surveillance of National Parks. 32n, Cheetah and armed wildlife guards in Parks and Game Management Areas.

1978, Aug. 1   Litho.   Perf. 14x14½

184	A52	8n multicolored	.25 .25
185	A52	18n multicolored	.50 .50
186	A52	28n multicolored	.85 .85
187	A52	32n multicolored	.90 .90
		Nos. 184-187 (4)	2.50 2.50

Anti-poaching Campaign of Zambia Wildlife Conservation Society, Aug. 1978.

Nos. 141, 137, 145 and 143 Surcharged with New Value and 2 Bars

1979, Mar. 15   Perf. 13½x14, 13

188	A42	8n on 9n multi	.60 .20
189	A42	10n on 3n multi	.20 .20
190	A43	18n on 25n multi	.20 .20
191	A43	28n on 15n multi	.20 .20
		Nos. 188-191 (4)	1.20 .80

Kayowe Dance A53

Designs: 32n, Kutambala dance. 42n, Chitwansombo drummers. 58n, Lilombola dance.

1979, Aug. 1

192	A53	18n multicolored	.35 .35
193	A53	32n multicolored	.50 .50
194	A53	42n multicolored	.50 .50
195	A53	58n multicolored	.65 .65
		Nos. 192-195 (4)	2.00 2.00

Commonwealth Summit Conf., Lusaka, Aug. 1-9.

"Why the Zebra is Hornless" — A54

Children's Stories: 18n, Kalulu and the Tug of War. 42n, How the Tortoise got his Shell. 58n, Kalulu and the Lion.

1979, Sept. 21   Litho.   Perf. 14

196	A54	18n multicolored	.30	.20
197	A54	32n multicolored	.45	.55
198	A54	42n multicolored	.55	.75
199	A54	58n multicolored	.70	1.00
a.		Souvenir sheet of 4, #196-199	3.00	3.00
		Nos. 196-199 (4)	2.00	2.50

International Year of the Child.

Girls of
Different
Races
Holding
Emblem
A55

Anti-Apartheid Year (1978): 32n, Boys and
toy car. 42n, Infants and butterfly. 58n, Children and microscope.

1979, Nov. 16   Litho.   Perf. 14½x15

200	A55	18n multicolored	.25	.25
201	A55	32n multicolored	.45	.45
202	A55	42n multicolored	.65	.65
203	A55	58n multicolored	.90	.90
		Nos. 200-203 (4)	2.25	2.25

Hill,
Zambia
No. 13
A56

Hill and: 32n, Mailman & bicycle. 42n, No.
Rhodesia #75. 58n, Mailman & oxcart.

1979, Dec. 20   Litho.   Perf. 14½

204	A56	18n multicolored	.40	.25
205	A56	32n multicolored	.50	.50
206	A56	42n multicolored	.50	.65
207	A56	58n multicolored	.60	1.10
a.		Souvenir sheet of 4, #204-207	2.50	2.75
		Nos. 204-207 (4)	2.00	2.50

Sir Rowland Hill (1795-1879), originator of
penny postage.

Nos. 204-207a Overprinted "LONDON
1980"

1980, Mar 6   Litho.   Perf. 15

208	A56	18n multicolored	.30	.40
209	A56	32n multicolored	.40	.55
210	A56	42n multicolored	.50	.70
211	A56	58n multicolored	.80	.85
a.		Souvenir sheet of 4	3.00	3.00
		Nos. 208-211 (4)	2.00	2.50

London 80 Intl. Stamp Exhib., May 6-14.

Anniverary Emblem on Map of
Zambia — A57

1980, June 18   Litho.   Perf. 14

212	A57	8n multicolored	.20	.20
213	A57	32n multicolored	.60	.60
214	A57	42n multicolored	.75	.75
215	A57	58n multicolored	.95	.95
a.		Souvenir sheet of 4, #212-215	2.75	2.75
		Nos. 212-215 (4)	2.50	2.50

Rotary International, 75th anniversary.

Running
A58

1980, July 19   Litho.   Perf. 13

216	A58	18n shown	.35	.35
217	A58	32n Boxing	.60	.60
218	A58	42n Soccer	.70	.70
219	A58	58n Swimming	1.10	1.10
a.		Souvenir sheet of 4, #216-219	3.00	3.00
		Nos. 216-219 (4)	2.75	2.75

22nd Summer Olympic Games, Moscow,
July 19-Aug. 3.

Zaddach's Forester — A59

1980, Sept. 22

220	A59	18n shown	.35	.20
221	A59	32n Northern highflier	.55	.45
222	A59	42n Zambezi skipper	.85	.95
223	A59	58n Modest blue	1.25	1.90
a.		Souvenir sheet of 4, #220-223	4.25	4.25
		Nos. 220-223 (4)	3.00	3.50

Coat of
Arms — A60

A61

1980, Sept. 27   Litho.   Perf. 14½

224	A60	18n multicolored	.30	.25
225	A60	32n multicolored	.50	.55
226	A60	42n multicolored	.60	.70
227	A60	58n multicolored	.85	1.25
		Nos. 224-227 (4)	2.25	2.75

26th Commonwealth Parliamentary Association Conference, Lusaka.

1980, Oct.   Litho.   Perf. 14

Nativity and St. Francis of Assisi (stained
glass window), Ndola Church.

228	A61	8n multicolored	.20	.20
229	A61	28n multicolored	.50	.70
230	A61	32n multicolored	.50	.70
231	A61	42n multicolored	.80	.90
		Nos. 228-231 (4)	2.00	2.50

Christmas and 50th anniv. of Catholic
Church in Copperbelt (central Zambia).

Trichilia
Emetica
Seed
Pods,
Musikili
A62

Designs: Seed Pods.

1981, Mar. 21   Litho.   Perf. 14

232	A62	8n shown	.20	.20
233	A62	18n Afzelia quanzensis, Mupapa	.40	.40
234	A62	28n Erythrina abyssinica, Mulunguti	.45	.65
235	A62	32n Combretum collinum, Mulama	.45	1.00
		Nos. 232-235 (4)	1.50	2.25

World Forestry Day.

ITU
Emblem — A63

Mask
Maker — A64

Designs: 18n, 32n, WHO emblem.

1981, May 15   Litho.   Perf. 14½

236	A63	8n multicolored	.50	.50
237	A63	18n multicolored	.65	.65
238	A63	28n multicolored	.75	.75
239	A63	32n multicolored	.85	.85
		Nos. 236-239 (4)	2.75	2.75

13th World Telecommunications Day (8n,
28n).

1981-83

240	A64	1n shown	.20	.20
241	A64	2n Blacksmiths	.20	.20
242	A64	5n Potter	.20	.20
243	A64	8n Straw basket fishing	.20	.20
244	A64	10n Roof thatching	.20	.20
244A	A64	12n Picking mushrooms ('83)	3.25	2.50
245	A64	18n Millet grinding	.40	.20
246	A64	28n Royal Barge paddler	.60	.20
247	A64	30n Makishi tightrope dancer	.60	.20
248	A64	35n Tonga-ila granary, house	.65	.20
249	A64	42n Cattle herding	.65	1.10

Perf. 14
Size: 37x25mm

250	A64	50n Traditional healer	.65	.20
251	A64	75n Carrying water jugs ('83)	.65	.80
252	A64	1k Grinding corn ('83)	.65	.80
253	A64	2k Woman smoking pipe	.65	.80
		Nos. 240-253 (15)	9.75	8.00

For surcharges see Nos. 358, 372, 499-506,
596.

Kankobele — A65

Banded
Ironstone — A66

Designs: Traditional musical instruments.

1981, Sept. 30   Litho.   Perf. 14½

254	A65	8n shown	.55	.20
255	A65	18n Inshingili	.65	.55
256	A65	28n Ilimba	.90	1.25
257	A65	32n Bango	.90	1.50
		Nos. 254-257 (4)	3.00	3.50

1982, Jan. 5   Litho.   Perf. 14

258	A66	8n shown	1.00	.20
259	A66	18n Cobaltocalcite	2.25	.80
260	A66	28n Amazonite	2.75	2.25
261	A66	32n Tourmaline	3.00	2.75
262	A66	42n Uranium ore	3.50	4.00
		Nos. 258-262 (5)	12.50	10.00

1982, July 1   Litho.   Perf. 14

263	A66	8n Bornite	1.00	1.00
264	A66	18n Chalcopyrite	2.50	2.50
265	A66	28n Malachite	2.75	2.75
266	A66	32n Azurite	2.75	2.75
267	A66	42n Vanadinite	3.50	3.50
		Nos. 263-267 (5)	12.50	12.50

Scouting
Year
A67

1982, Mar. 30   Litho.   Perf. 14

268	A67	8n Scouts, flag	.35	.35
269	A67	18n Baden-Powell	.70	.70
270	A67	28n Horned buffalo, patrol pennat	.70	.70
271	A67	1k Eagle, conservation badge	2.25	2.25
a.		Souvenir sheet of 4, #268-271	4.00	4.00
		Nos. 268-271 (4)	4.00	4.00

Drilling Rig,
1926
A68

Steam locomotives.

1983, Jan. 26   Perf. 14x14½

272	A68	8n shown	.50	.25
273	A68	18n Class B6, 1910	.75	.75
274	A68	28n Borsig engine, 1925	1.25	2.00
275	A68	32n 7th class, 1900	1.50	2.25
		Nos. 272-275 (4)	4.00	5.25

Commonwealth Day — A68a

1983, Mar. 10   Litho.   Perf. 14

276	A68a	12n Cotton picking	.20	.20
277	A68a	18n Miners	.30	.20
278	A68a	28n Ritual pot, dancers	.25	.35
279	A68a	1k Victoria Falls, purple-crested lorie	2.50	3.25
		Nos. 276-279 (4)	3.25	4.00

Local
Flowers — A69

1983, May 26   Litho.   Perf. 14

280	A69	12n Eulophia cucullata	.20	.20
281	A69	28n Kigelia africana	.50	.50
282	A69	35n Protea gaguedi	.60	.60
283	A69	50n Leonotis nepotifolia	.85	.85
a.		Souvenir sheet of 4, #280-283, perf. 12x12½	2.25	2.25
		Nos. 280-283 (4)	2.15	2.15

Thornicroft's Giraffes — A70

1983, July 21   Litho.   Perf. 14

284	A70	12n shown	.75	.75
285	A70	28n Cookson's wildebeest	1.00	1.00
286	A70	35n Black lechwe	1.25	1.25
287	A70	1k Yellow-backed duiker	2.50	2.50
		Nos. 284-287 (4)	5.50	5.50

Tiger Fish
A71

1983, Sept. 29   Litho.   Perf. 14
288 A71 12n shown   .45   .20
289 A71 28n Silver Barbel   .75   .50
290 A71 35n Spotted Squeaker   .85   1.40
291 A71 38n Red Breasted
            Bream   .95   1.40
        Nos. 288-291 (4)   3.00   3.50
        For surcharge see No. 597.

Christmas — A72

1983, Dec. 12   Litho.   Perf. 14x14½
292 A72 12n Annunciation   .20   .20
293 A72 28n Shepherds   .35   .30
294 A72 35n Three Kings   .45   .75
295 A72 38n Flight into Egypt   .50   1.00
        Nos. 292-295 (4)   1.50   2.25

40th Anniv.
of Intl. Civil
Aviation
Org. — A73

1984, Jan. 26   Litho.   Perf. 14
296 A73 12n Boeing 737, 1983   .20   .20
297 A73 28n Beaver, 1954   .35   .35
298 A73 35n Short Solent Flying
            Boat, 1948   .45   .45
299 A73 1k DH-66, 1931   1.25   1.25
        Nos. 296-299 (4)   2.25   2.25

60th
Birthday of
Pres.
Kaunda
A74

Perf. 14½x14, 14x14½
1984, Apr. 28   Litho.
300 A74 12n Receiving greetings   .40   .40
301 A74 28n Swearing in, 1983,
            vert.   .60   .60
302 A74 60n Planting cherry tree   1.10   1.10
303 A74 1k Opening Natl. As-
            sembly, vert.   1.40   1.40
        Nos. 300-303 (4)   3.50   3.50

1984 Summer
Olympics — A75

1984, July 18   Litho.   Perf. 14
304 A75 12n Soccer   .20   .20
305 A75 28n Running   .45   .45
306 A75 35n Hurdles   .55   .55
307 A75 50n Boxing   .80   .80
        Nos. 304-307 (4)   2.00   2.00

Reptiles
A76

1984, Sept. 5   Litho.   Perf. 14
308 A76 12n Gabon viper   .30   .30
309 A76 28n Chameleon   .65   .65
310 A76 35n Nile crocodile   .80   .80
311 A76 1k Blue-headed agama   1.75   1.75
   a.   Souvenir sheet of 4, #308-311 4.00   4.00
        Nos. 308-311 (4)   3.50   3.50

20th Anniv. of Independence — A77

1984, Oct. 22   Litho.   Perf. 14
312 A77 12n Pres. Kaunda,
            Mulungushi Rock   .25   .25
313 A77 28n Freedom Statue   .40   .40
314 A77 1k Produce   1.25   1.25
        Nos. 312-314 (3)   1.90   1.90

Local Mushrooms
A78

1984, Dec. 12   Litho.   Perf. 14x14½
315 A78 12n Amanita flammeola   1.25   1.25
316 A78 28n Amanita zambiana   1.50   1.50
317 A78 32n Termitomyces letes-
            tui   2.25   2.25
318 A78 75n Cantharellus
            miniatescens   3.75   3.75
        Nos. 315-318 (4)   8.75   8.75
        For surcharge see No. 600.

**No. 146 Surcharged with New Value
and Two Bars**

1985, Mar. 5   Litho.   Perf. 13½
319 A43 5k on 50n multi   2.25   2.25

Primates
A79

1985, Apr. 25   Litho.   Perf. 14
320 A79 12n Chacma baboon   .70   .70
321 A79 20n Moloney's monkey   .90   .90
322 A79 45n Blue monkey   1.90   1.90
323 A79 1k Vervet monkey   3.00   3.00
        Nos. 320-323 (4)   6.50   6.50
        For surcharge see No. 604.

SADCC,
5th Anniv.
A80

1985, July 9   Litho.   Perf. 14
324 A80 20n Map   .75   .75
325 A80 45n Mining   1.90   1.90
326 A80 1k Mulungushi Hall   2.10   2.10
        Nos. 324-326 (3)   4.75   4.75

Southern African Development Coordination
Conference.
        For surcharge see No. 605.

Queen
Mother,
85th
Birthday
— A81

25n, Portrait in blue, age 80. 45n, Queen
Consort at Clarence House, 1963. 55n, With
Elizabeth II and Princess Margaret. 5k, With
royal family, christening of Prince Henry, 1984.

1985, Aug. 2
327 A81 25n multi, vert.   .20   .20
328 A81 45n multi, vert.   .20   .20
329 A81 55n multi   .20   .20
330 A81 5k multi   1.40   1.40
        Nos. 327-330 (4)   2.00   2.00

For surcharges see Nos. 401, 406, 410,
414, 595, 606, 611.

National Anniversaries — A81a

#330A, Pres. Kenneth Kaunda, Mulungushi
Rock. #330B, Kaunda, agricultural products.
#330C, Freedom statue, flags.

Die Cut Perf. 10
1985, Oct. 23   Embossed
330A-
330C   A81a 5k gold   3.50   6.25

United National Independence Party, 26th
anniv. (No. 330A); Independence, 20th anniv.
(Nos. 330B-330C).

Postal and Telecommunications Corp.,
10th Anniv. — A82

1985, Dec. 12   Perf. 13½x13
331 A82 20n Lusaka P.O., 1958   .60   .60
332 A82 45n Livingstone P.O.,
            1950   .90   .90
333 A82 55n Kalomo P.O., 1902   1.00   1.00
334 A82 5k Transcontinental
            Telegraph, 1900   3.25   3.25
        Nos. 331-334 (4)   5.75   5.75
        For surcharges see Nos. 590-593.

UN, 40th
Anniv. — A83

1985, Dec. 19   Perf. 14
335 A83 20n Boy in cornfield   .40   .40
336 A83 45n Mining   .70   .70
337 A83 1k Pres. Kaunda, 1970   1.25   1.25
338 A83 2k Charter signing,
            1945   1.90   1.90
        Nos. 335-338 (4)   4.25   4.25
        For surcharges see #594, 607.

Beetles
A84

1986, Mar. 20
339 A84 35n Mylabris tricolor   .20   .20
340 A84 1k Phasgonocnema
            melananthe   .30   .30
341 A84 1.70k Amarodes pas-
            serinii   .50   .50
342 A84 5k Ranzania petersiana   1.50   1.50
        Nos. 339-342 (4)   2.50   2.50
        For surcharges see #609, 612.

┌──────────────────────────────────────┐
│ Common Design Types   │
│ pictured following the introduction. │
└──────────────────────────────────────┘

Queen Elizabeth II 60th Birthday
Common Design Type

Designs: 35n, At the Flower Ball, Savoy
Hotel, London, 1951. 1.25k, With Prince
Andrew at Lusaka Airport, Commonwealth
Conf., 1979. 1.70k, With Dr. Kaunda observing natl. anthem. 1.95k, Wearing Queen Mary
tiara, state visit to Luxembourg, 1976. 5k, Visiting Crown Agents' offices, 1983.

1986, Apr. 21   Wmk. 384   Perf. 14
343 CD337 35n scar, blk & sil   .25   .25
344 CD337 1.25k ultra & multi   .35   .35
345 CD337 1.70k grn, blk & sil   .40   .40
346 CD337 1.95k vio & multi   .40   .40
347 CD337 5k rose vio & multi   .60   .60
        Nos. 343-347 (5)   2.00   2.00

For surcharges see Nos. 402, 405, 407,
411, 415.

Royal Wedding Issue, 1986
Common Design Type

Designs: 1.70k, Sarah Ferguson kissing
Prince Andrew. 5k, Andrew in informal dress.

1986, July 23   Litho.   Perf. 14
348 CD338 1.70k multicolored   .35   .35
349 CD338 5k multicolored   .90   .90

1986 World Cup
Soccer
Championships,
Mexico — A85

Various soccer plays.

1986, June 27   Litho.   Perf. 14½
350 A85 35n multicolored   .75   .75
351 A85 1.25k multicolored   2.00   2.00
352 A85 1.70k multicolored   2.25   2.25
353 A85 5k multicolored   3.50   3.50
        Nos. 350-353 (4)   8.50   8.50

For surcharges see Nos. 403, 408, 412, 416.

Halley's
Comet
A86

Designs: 1.25k, Edmond Halley (1656-
1742), by Henry Pegram. 1.70k, Giotto space
probe approaching comet. 2k, Youth, astronomer. 5k, Halley's map of the southern
constellations.

1986, July 4
354 A86 1.25k multicolored   .90   .90
355 A86 1.70k multicolored   1.10   1.10
356 A86 2k multicolored   1.50   1.50
357 A86 5k multicolored   3.25   3.25
        Nos. 354-357 (4)   6.75   6.75

For surcharges see Nos. 404, 409, 413, 417.

#244A Surchd. in Light Red Brown
1986, July   Litho.   Perf. 14½
358 A64 20n on 12n multi   .20   .20

Christmas
A87

Children's drawings.

1986, Dec. 15   Litho.   Perf. 14
359 A87   35n Nativity   .35 .35
360 A87 1.25k Magi   1.25 1.25
361 A87 1.60k Nativity   1.40 1.40
362 A87   5k Angel, house, tree   3.00 3.00
    Nos. 359-362 (4)   6.00 6.00

For surcharges see #602, 608.

Tazara
Railroad,
10th
Anniv.
A88

Locomotive traveling various railway lines.

1986, Dec. 22
363 A88   35n Overpass,
            Kasama   .30 .30
364 A88 1.25k Tunnel 21 vicinity   .45 .45
365 A88 1.70k Tunnels 6-7   .50 .50
366 A88   5k Mpika Station
            grade separation   1.00 1.00
    Nos. 363-366 (4)   2.25 2.25

University
of Zambia
A89

Designs: 35n, Pres. Kaunda shaking council
member's hand. 1.25k, University crest, vert.
1.60k, University statue. 5k, Kaunda laying
university building cornerstone, vert.

1987, Jan. 27   Litho.   Perf. 14
367 A89   35n multicolored   .35 .35
368 A89 1.25k multicolored   .75 .75
369 A89 1.60k multicolored   .90 .90
370 A89   5k multicolored   3.00 3.00
    Nos. 367-370 (4)   5.00 5.00

Nos. 137, 243 Surcharged in Black or
Blue

1987   Perf. 13½x14
371 A42   10n on 3n multi   .20 .20
        Perf. 14½
372 A64   25n on 8n multi (Bl)   .20 .20

Municipal
Arms — A90

Birds — A91

1987, Mar. 26   Perf. 14
373 A90   35n Kitwe   .20 .20
374 A90 1.25k Ndola   .25 .25
375 A90 1.70k Lusaka   .30 .30
376 A90   20k Livingstone   3.00 3.00
    Nos. 373-376 (4)   3.75 3.75

For surcharge see No. 603.

1987-88   Perf. 11x13
    Size: 20x25½mm
377 A91   25n Long-toed fluff tail   2.00 2.00
378 A91   30n Miombo pied bar-
            bet   .20 .20
379 A91   35n Black-and-rufous
            swallow   2.00 2.00

    Size: 25x38½mm
        Perf. 14
380 A91   50n Slaty egret   .20 .20
381 A91   1k Bradfield's hornbill   2.00 2.00
382 A91 1.25k Margaret's batis   2.00 2.00
383 A91 1.60k Red-and-blue sun-
            bird   2.00 2.00
384 A91 1.70k Boehm's bee-eat-
            er   2.25 2.25
385 A91 1.95k Gorgeous bush
            shrike   2.25 2.25
386 A91   2k Shoebill   .30 .30
387 A91   5k Taita falcon   2.75 2.75

        Surcharged

    Size: 20x25½mm
        Perf. 11x13
388 A91   20n on 1n Yellow
            swamp warbler   .25 .25
389 A91   75n on 2n Olive-
            flanked robin   .25 .25
390 A91 1.65k on 2k #378   .25 .25
    Size: 25x38½mm
        Perf. 14
391 A91   10k on 50n #380   .90 .90
392 A91   20k on 2k #386   1.40 1.40
    Nos. 377-392 (16)   21.00 21.00

Issued: #377, 379, 381-385, 387, 9/14/87;
#391-392, 3/10/88; others 10/8/87.
Nos. 388-389 not issued without overprint.
See Nos. 433-435, 527-547. For surcharges
see Nos. 490, 492-498.

Look-out Tree, Livingstone — A92

1987, June 30   Perf. 14
393 A92   35n shown   .30 .30
394 A92 1.25k Rafting, Zambezi
            River   .35 .35
395 A92 1.70k Walking safari,
            Luangwa Valley   1.60 1.60
396 A92   10k White pelicans   6.00 6.00
    Nos. 393-396 (4)   8.25 8.25

Zambia
Airways,
20th
Anniv.
A93

1987, Sept. 21
397 A93   35n De Havilland
            Beaver   .60 .60
398 A93 1.70k DC-10   1.40 1.40
399 A93   5k DC-3   3.50 3.50
400 A93   10k Boeing 707   5.50 5.50
    Nos. 397-400 (4)   11.00 11.00

Issues of 1985-86 Surcharged in Gold
or Black

1987, Sept. 14   Perfs. as Before
401 A81   3k on 25n #327   .90 .90
        (G)   .90 .90
402 CD337   3k on 35n #343   .70 .70
403 A85   3k on 35n #350   .90 .90
404 A86   3k on 1.25k #354   1.60 1.60
        (G)   1.60 1.60
405 CD337   4k on 1.25k #344   .85 .85
406 A81   6k on 45n #328   1.60 1.60
407 CD337   6k on 1.70k #345   1.25 1.25
408 A85   6k on 1.25k #351   1.60 1.60
409 A86   6k on 1.70k #355   2.50 2.50
        (G)   2.50 2.50
410 A81   10k on 55n #329   2.25 2.25
        (G)   2.25 2.25
411 CD337   10k on 1.95k #346   2.10 2.10
412 A85   10k on 1.70k #352   2.25 2.25
413 A86   10k on 2k #356   4.25 4.25
        (G)   4.25 4.25
414 A81   20k on 5k #330   4.50 4.50
        (G)   4.50 4.50
415 CD337   20k on 5k #347   4.50 4.50
416 A85   20k on 5k #353   4.50 4.50

417 A86   20k on 5k #357   7.75 7.75
        (G)   44.00 44.00
    Nos. 401-417 (17)   44.00 44.00

World
Food
Day — A94

Cattle.

1987, Oct. 1   Perf. 14½x15
418 A94   35n Friesian-Holstein   .20 .20
419 A94 1.25k Simmental   .40 .40
420 A94 1.70k Sussex   .40 .40
421 A94   20k Brahma   2.00 2.00
    Nos. 418-421 (4)   3.00 3.00

Traditional
Heritage — A95

Zambian people.

1987, Oct. 20   Perf. 13x12½
422 A95   35n Mpoloto Ne
            Mikobango   .25 .25
423 A95 1.25k Zintaka   .40 .40
424 A95 1.70k Mufuluhi   .60 .60
425 A95   10k Ntebwe   1.75 1.75
426 A95   20k Kubangwa Aa
            Mbulunga   3.00 3.00
    Nos. 422-426 (5)   6.00 6.00

World Wildlife
Fund — A96

Wild Cats — A97

1987, Dec. 21   Litho.   Perf. 14
427 A96   50n Black lechwe
            drinking water   .75 .75
428 A96   2k Adults and young,
            horiz.   1.75 1.75
429 A96 2.50k Running, horiz.   1.75 1.75
430 A96   10k Male, diff.   4.75 4.75
    Nos. 427-430 (4)   9.00 9.00

        Souvenir Sheets
431 A97   20k Cheetah   5.00 5.00
432 A97   20k Caracal   5.00 5.00

        Bird Type of 1987
1987   Litho.   Perf. 11x13
433 A91   5n Black-tailed cisticola   .20 .20
434 A91   10n White-winged star-
            ling   .20 .20
435 A91   40n Wattled crane   .20 .20
    Nos. 433-435 (3)   .60 .60

For surcharge see No. 491.

Intl. Fund for Agricultural Development
(IFAD), 10th Anniv. — A98

1988, Apr. 2   Perf. 14
436 A98   50n Cassava crop   .20 .20
437 A98 2.50k Net fishing   .65 .65
438 A98 2.85k Cattle breeding   .75 .75
439 A98   10k Coffee picking   2.50 2.50
    Nos. 436-439 (4)   4.10 4.10

A99

A100

1988, Sept. 12   Litho.   Perf. 12½
440 A99   50n Breast-feeding   .20 .20
441 A99   2k Growth monitoring   .55 .55
442 A99 2.85k Immunization   .75 .75
443 A99   10k Oral rehydration   2.50 2.50
    Nos. 440-443 (4)   4.00 4.00

UN child survival campaign.

1988, Oct. 10   Litho.   Perf. 12½x13
444 A100   50n Asbestos cement   .20 .20
445 A100 2.35k Textiles   .60 .60
446 A100 2.50k Tea   .70 .70
447 A100   10k Poultry   2.50 2.50
    Nos. 444-447 (4)   4.00 4.00

Preferential Trade Area Fair.

Intl. Red Cross and Red Crescent
Organizations, 125th Anniv. — A101

1988, Oct. 20   Perf. 14
448 A101   50n Famine relief   .20 .20
449 A101 2.50k Giving first aid   .60 .60
450 A101 2.85k Teaching first aid   .70 .70
451 A101   10k Jean-Henri Du-
            nant   2.60 2.60
    Nos. 448-451 (4)   4.10 4.10

Endangered Species — A102

1988, Dec. 5   Litho.   Perf. 14
452 A102   50n Aardvark   .20 .20
453 A102   2k Pangolin   .50 .50
454 A102 2.85k Wild dog   .75 .75
455 A102   20k Black rhinoceros   5.25 5.25
    Nos. 452-455 (4)   6.70 6.70

1988 Summer Olympics, Seoul A103

1988, Dec. 30   Litho.   Perf. 14

456	A103	50n Boxing	.20	.20
457	A103	2k Running	.50	.50
458	A103	2.50k Hurdling	.65	.65
459	A103	20k Soccer	5.25	5.25
		Nos. 456-459 (4)	6.60	6.60

Souvenir Sheets

460	A103	30k Tennis	6.50	6.50
461	A103	30k Martial arts	6.50	6.50

Frogs and Toads A104

1989, Jan. 25   Litho.   Perf. 12½

462	A104	50n Red toad	.20	.20
463	A104	2.50k Puddle frog	.50	.50
464	A104	2.85k Marbled reed frog	.60	.60
465	A104	10k Young reed frogs	2.00	2.00
		Nos. 462-465 (4)	3.30	3.30

Bats A105

1989, Mar. 22   Litho.   Perf. 12½x13

466	A105	50n Common slit-faced	.20	.20
467	A105	2.50k Little free-tailed	.50	.50
468	A105	2.85k Hildebrandt's horseshoe	.60	.60
469	A105	10k Peters' epauletted fruit	2.00	2.00
		Nos. 466-469 (4)	3.30	3.30

A106   A107

1989, May 2   Litho.   Perf. 12½

470	A106	50n Map of Zambia	.20	.20
471	A106	6.85k Peace dove	1.40	1.40
472	A106	7.85k Papal arms	1.60	1.60
473	A106	10k Victoria Falls	2.00	2.00
		Nos. 470-473 (4)	5.20	5.20

State visit of Pope John Paul II, May 2-4. For surcharges see #614, 616.

1989, July 26   Litho.   Perf. 14½x15

Edible wild fruits.

474	A107	50n Parinari curatellifolia	.20	.20
475	A107	6.50k Uapaca kirkiana	1.25	1.25
476	A107	6.85k Ficus capensis	1.40	1.40
477	A107	10k Borassus aethiopum	2.00	2.00
		Nos. 474-477 (4)	4.85	4.85

For surcharges see #613, 615.

Grasshoppers — A108

1989, Nov. 8   Litho.   Perf. 14x13½

478	A108	70n Phamphagid	.20	.20
479	A108	10.40k Pyrgomorphid	1.25	1.25
480	A108	12.50k Brown katydid	1.50	1.50
481	A108	15k Bush locust	1.85	1.85
		Nos. 478-481 (4)	4.80	4.80

No. 480 misspelled "Catydid."

Christmas — A109

Flowers.

1989, Dec. 6   Litho.   Perf. 14½

482	A109	70n Fireball	.20	.20
483	A109	10.40k Flame lily	1.25	1.25
484	A109	12.50k Foxglove lily	1.40	1.40
485	A109	20k Vlei lily	2.30	2.30
		Nos. 482-485 (4)	5.15	5.15

Stamp World London '90 A110

Designs: 1.20k, Lusaka Main P.O., van, mailman, bicycle. 19.50k, Zambia #220. 20.50k, Rhodesia and Nyasaland #164A, No. Rhodesia #1. 50k, Great Britain #1, Maltese Cross cancel in red.

Unwmk.

1990, May 2   Litho.   Perf. 14

486	A110	1.20k multicolored	.20	.20
487	A110	19.50k multicolored	1.00	1.00
488	A110	20.50k multicolored	1.10	1.10
489	A110	50k multicolored	2.75	2.75
		Nos. 486-489 (4)	5.05	5.05

Nos. 379, 381-387, 433 Surcharged

1989, July 1   Perf. 11x13

490	A91	70n on 35n #379	.20	.20
491	A91	3k on 5n #433	.20	.20

Size: 25x38½mm

Perf. 14

492	A91	8k on 1.25k #382	.40	.40
493	A91	9.90k on 1.70k #384	.50	.50
494	A91	10.40k on 1.60k #383	.50	.50
495	A91	12.50k on 1k #381	.60	.60
496	A91	15k on 1.95k #385	.75	.75
497	A91	20k on 2k #386	1.00	1.00
498	A91	20.35k on 5k #387	1.05	1.05
		Nos. 490-498 (9)	5.20	5.20

Nos. 242, 244-245, 247-248 251, 253 Surcharged in Black, Orange Brown, Red Brown, or Violet

a   b

1989   Perf. 14½

		Size: 22x26mm		
499	A64(a)	1.20k on 35n #248 (OB)	.20	.20
500	A64(b)	3.75k on 5n #242	.20	.20
501	A64(b)	8.11k on 10n #244	.40	.40
502	A64(b)	9k on 30n #247	.45	.45
		Size: 37x25mm		
		Perf. 14		
503	A64(b)	10k on 75n #251	.50	.50
504	A64(c)	18.50k on 2k #253	.90	.90
		Size: 22x26mm		
		Perf. 14½		
505	A64(a)	19.50k on 12n #244A (RB)	.95	.95
506	A64(a)	20.50k on 18n #245 (V)	1.00	1.00
		Nos. 499-506 (8)	4.60	4.60

Issued: #500-504, 7/1; others, 11/1.

World Cup Soccer Championships, Italy — A111

Soccer players in various positions.

1990, July 7   Litho.   Perf. 14

507	A111	1.20k multicolored	.20	.20
508	A111	18.50k multicolored	.90	.90
509	A111	19.50k multicolored	1.00	1.00
510	A111	20.50k multicolored	1.10	1.10
		Nos. 507-510 (4)	3.20	3.20

Souvenir Sheet

510A	A111	50k multicolored	2.50	2.50

Southern African Development Coordination Conf. (SADCC), 10th Anniv. — A112

Map of SADCC members and: 1.20k, Truck. 19.50k, Telecommunications. 20.50k, Regional cooperation. 50k, Coal transport by cable car.

1990, July 23   Litho.   Perf. 12½

511	A112	1.20k multicolored	.20	.20
512	A112	19.50k multicolored	1.00	1.00
513	A112	20.50k multicolored	1.10	1.10
514	A112	50k multicolored	2.50	2.50
		Nos. 511-514 (4)	4.80	4.80

Independence, 26th Anniv. — A113

1990, Oct. 23   Litho.   Perf. 14

515	A113	1.20k Agriculture	.20	.20
516	A113	19.50k Shoe factory	1.00	1.00
517	A113	20.50k Satellite communications	1.10	1.10
518	A113	50k Mother and child statue	2.50	2.50
		Nos. 515-518 (4)	4.80	4.80

Small Carnivores — A114

1990, Nov. 12

519	A114	1.20k Genet	.20	.20
520	A114	18.50k Civet	1.40	1.40
521	A114	19.50k Serval	1.50	1.50
522	A114	20.50k African wild cat	1.60	1.60
		Nos. 519-522 (4)	4.70	4.70

Intl. Literacy Year — A115   Soy Beans — A116

Children's stories.

1991, Jan. 11   Litho.   Perf. 14

523	A115	1.20k Bird and the Snake	.20	.20
524	A115	18.50k Hare and the Leopard	.90	.90
525	A115	19.50k Mouse and Lion	1.00	1.00
526	A115	20.50k Hare and the Hippo	1.10	1.10
		Nos. 523-526 (4)	3.20	3.20

Bird Type of 1987

1990-91   Litho.   Perf. 11x13

527	A91	10n Livingstone's flycatcher	.20	.20
528	A91	15n Bar-winged weaver	.20	.20
529	A91	30n Purple-throated cuckoo shrike	.20	.20
530	A91	50n Red-billed helmet shrike	.20	.20
531	A91	50n like #527	.20	.20
532	A91	1k like #528	.20	.20
533	A91	1.20k Western bronze-naped pigeon	.20	.20
534	A91	2k like #529	.20	.20
535	A91	3k like #530	.20	.20
536	A91	5k like #533	.20	.20
		Size: 25x38½mm		
		Perf. 14		
537	A91	15k Corn crake	.60	.60
538	A91	20k Dickinson's grey kestrel	.80	.80
539	A91	20.50k like #538	.85	.85
540	A91	50k Denham's bustard	2.00	2.00
		Nos. 527-540 (14)	6.25	6.25

Issued: #533, 1k, 2k, 3k, 5k, 20k, 5/7/91; others, 10/30.

1991, June 28   Litho.   Perf. 13½

548	A116	1k Woman cooking	.20	.20
549	A116	2k Soy bean seed	.20	.20
550	A116	5k Woman feeding child	.20	.20
551	A116	20k Malnourished, healthy children	.80	.80
552	A116	50k Pres. Kaunda, child	2.00	2.00
		Nos. 548-552 (5)	3.40	3.40

United Church of Zambia / Rotary Foundation Project.

St. Ignatius of Loyola (1491-1556), Founder of Jesuit Order — A117

1k, Chilubula Church near Kasama. 2k, Chikuni Church near Monze. 20k, Bishop Joseph Du Pont.

1991, July 18 Litho. Perf. 13½
553 A117 1k multicolored .20 .20
554 A117 2k multicolored .20 .20
555 A117 20k multicolored .80 .80
556 A117 50k shown 2.00 2.00
Nos. 553-556 (4) 3.20 3.20

Flowering
Trees
A118

1991, Nov. 29 Litho. Perf. 13½
557 A118 1k Baobab .20 .20
558 A118 2k Dichrostachys
cinerea .20 .20
559 A118 10k Sterospermum
kunthianum .40 .40
560 A118 30k Azanza garckeana 1.20 1.20
Nos. 557-560 (4) 2.00 2.00

**Queen Elizabeth II's Accession to
the Throne, 40th Anniv.**
Common Design Type
Perf. 14x13½

1992, Feb. 2 Litho. Wmk. 373
561 CD349 4k multicolored .20 .20
562 CD349 32k multicolored 1.25 1.25
563 CD349 35k multicolored 1.40 1.40
564 CD349 38k multicolored 1.50 1.50
565 CD349 50k multicolored 2.00 2.00
Nos. 561-565 (5) 6.35 6.35

For surcharges see Nos. 690-692.

Orchids — A119

Masks — A120

Perf. 13x13½

1992, Feb. 28 Unwmk.
566 A119 1k Disa hamatopetala .20 .20
567 A119 2k Eulophia paivae-
ana .20 .20
568 A119 5k Eulophia quartiniana .20 .20
569 A119 20k Aerangis verdickii .80 .80
Nos. 566-569 (4) 1.40 1.40

1992, Mar. 10
570 A120 1k Kasinja .20 .20
571 A120 2k Chizaluke .20 .20
572 A120 10k Mwanapweu .40 .40
573 A120 30k Maliya 1.20 1.20
Nos. 570-573 (4) 2.00 2.00

Antelopes
A121

1992, Sept. 14 Litho. Perf. 14
574 A121 4k Bushbuck .20 .20
575 A121 40k Eland .40 .40
576 A121 45k Roan antelope .50 .50
577 A121 100k Sable antelope 1.00 1.00
Nos. 574-577 (4) 2.10 2.10

Airmail
Services,
75th
Anniv.
A122

1992, Nov. 24 Litho. Perf. 14
578 A122 4k DH66 Hercules .20 .20
579 A122 40k VC10 .40 .40
580 A122 45k C Class flying
boat .45 .45
581 A122 100k DC10 1.00 1.00
Nos. 578-581 (4) 2.05 2.05

1992 Summer
Olympics,
Barcelona — A123

1992, Dec. 28
582 A123 10k 400-meter hurdles .20 .20
583 A123 40k Boxing .40 .40
584 A123 80k Judo .80 .80
585 A123 100k Cycling 1.00 1.00
Nos. 582-585 (4) 2.40 2.40

Christmas — A124

1992, Dec. 23 Litho. Perf. 14
586 A124 10k Wise men .20 .20
587 A124 80k Nativity scene .80 .80
588 A124 90k Angels singing .90 .90
589 A124 100k Angel, shepherds 1.00 1.00
a. Souvenir sheet of 4, #586-589 3.00 3.00
Nos. 586-589 (4) 2.90 2.90

For surcharges see Nos. 658-659.

K2

Nos. 331-334 Surcharged

━━━━

1991, Mar. 4 Litho. Perf. 13½x13
590 A82 2k on 20n #331
591 A82 2k on 45n #332
592 A82 2k on 55n #333
593 A82 2k on 5k #334

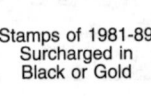

Stamps of 1981-89
Surcharged in
Black or Gold

Perfs. as Before

1991, July 5 Litho.
594 A83 2k on 20n #335
595 A81 2k on 25n #327 (G)
596 A64 2k on 28n #246
597 A71 2k on 28n #289
600 A78 2k on 32n #317
602 A87 2k on 35n #359
603 A90 2k on 35n #373
604 A79 2k on 45n #322
605 A80 2k on 45n #325
606 A81 2k on 45n #328
607 A83 2k on 45n #336
608 A87 2k on 1.60k #361
609 A84 2k on 1.70k #341

---

611 A81 2k on 5k #330
612 A84 2k on 5k #342
613 A107 2k on 6.50k #475
614 A106 2k on 6.85k #471
615 A107 2k on 6.85k #476
616 A106 2k on 7.85k #472

Numbers have been reserved for additional
surcharges in this set.

Waterfalls
A125

1993, Sept. 30 Litho. Perf. 13½
617 A125 50k Nkundalila .20 .20
618 A125 200k Chishimba .80 .80
619 A125 250k Chipoma 1.00 1.00
620 A125 300k Lumangwe 1.25 1.25
Nos. 617-620 (4) 3.25 3.25

Healthy
Hearts — A126

1993, Oct. 20 Litho. Perf. 14½
621 A126 O Runner .20 .20
622 A126 P Heart .30 .30

No. 621 sold for 50k and No. 622 sold for
80k on date of issue.

Sunbirds
A127

Designs: 20k, Bronze. 50k, Violet-backed.
No. 625, Marico. No. 626, Eastern double-collared. 100k, Scarlet-chested. 150k, Banner-
man's blue-headed. 200k, Oustalet's.
250k, Red and blue. 300k, Olive. 350k, Green-
headed. 400k, Scarlet tufted malachite. 500k,
Yellow-bellied. 800k, Copper. 1000k, Orange-
tufted. 1500k, Black. 2000k, Green-throated.

1993, May 30 Litho. Perf. 13
623 A127 20k multicolored .20 .20
624 A127 50k multicolored .20 .20
625 A127 O multicolored .20 .20
626 A127 P multicolored .30 .30
627 A127 100k multicolored .35 .35
628 A127 150k multicolored .55 .55
629 A127 200k multicolored .65 .65
630 A127 250k multicolored .80 .80
631 A127 300k multicolored 1.00 1.00
632 A127 350k multicolored 1.25 1.25
633 A127 400k multicolored 1.40 1.40
634 A127 500k multicolored 1.60 1.60
635 A127 800k multicolored 2.75 2.75
636 A127 1000k multicolored 3.50 3.50
637 A127 1500k multicolored 5.25 5.25
638 A127 2000k multicolored 7.00 7.00
Nos. 623-638 (16) 27.00 27.00

Nos. 625 sold for 50k and 626 sold for 80k
on date of issue.

Snakes — A128

1994, Sept. 28 Litho. Perf. 14
639 A128 50k Tiger snake .20 .20
640 A128 200k Egyptian cobra .60 .60
641 A128 300k African python .90 .90
642 A128 500k Green mamba 1.50 1.50
Nos. 639-642 (4) 3.20 3.20

ILO, 75th
Anniv.
A129

1995, Apr. 3 Litho. Perf. 14
643 A129 100k Road rehabilitation .30 .30
644 A129 450k Block making 1.40 1.40

For surcharge see No. 781A.

Christmas Angels — A130

1995, Aug. 29 Perf. 14½x14
645 A130 100k shown .30 .30
646 A130 300k With animals .90 .90
647 A130 450k Blowing horn,
birds 1.40 1.40
648 A130 500k Playing drum 1.50 1.50
Nos. 645-648 (4) 4.10 4.10

UN, 50th
Anniv.
A131

1995, Dec. 30 Litho. Perf. 11½
Granite Paper
649 A131 700k multicolored 1.50 1.50

Natl. Monuments
A132

Designs: 100k, David Livingstone. 300k,
Mbereshi Mission. 450k, Von Lettow-Vorbeck.
500k, Niamkolo Church.

1996, Feb. 21 Litho. Perf. 14
650 A132 100k multicolored .20 .20
651 A132 300k multicolored .65 .65
652 A132 450k multicolored .95 .95
653 A132 500k multicolored 1.10 1.10
Nos. 650-653 (4) 2.90 2.90

World
Wildlife
Fund
A133

Designs: 200k, Saddle-billed stork. 300k,
Black-cheeked lovebird. 500k, Two black-
cheeked lovebirds. 900k, Saddle-billed stork
with young.

1996, Nov. 27 Litho. Perf. 14x14½
654 A133 200k multicolored .30 .30
655 A133 300k multicolored .45 .45
656 A133 500k multicolored .75 .75
657 A133 900k multicolored 1.40 1.40
Nos. 654-657 (4) 2.90 2.90

Nos. 587-588 Surcharged

1996 Litho. *Perf. 14*
658 A124 (O) on 90k #588 .85 .85
659 A124 900k on 80k #587 1.50 1.50

No. 658 was valued at 500k on day of issue.
Size and location of surcharge varies.

New Year 1997 (Year of the Ox) — A134

Disney characters posing for portrait in Chinese scene, vert.: #660: a, Clarabelle seated. b, Holding scroll. c, Playing musical instrument. d, On bicycle. e, Minnie, Mickey, Clarabelle. f, Holding mirror.
No. 661: a, 250k, Faces of Minnie, Mickey, Clarabelle Cow. b, 400k, Clarabelle seated. c, 500k, Clarabelle standing. d, 600k, Mickey, Clarabelle, Minnie dressed in Chinese outfits. e, 750k, Minnie, Clarabelle, Mickey dancing. f, 1000k, Clarabelle with parasol.

1997, Jan. 28 Litho. *Perf. 14x13½*
660 A134 500k Sheet of 6, #a.-f. 5.00 5.00
661 A134 Sheet of 6, #a.-f. 6.00 6.00

No. 660 contains six 35x61mm stamps.

Endangered Species — A135

Species of the world: No. 662: a, Spider monkey. b, Manatee. c, Jaguar. d, Puerto Rican parrot. d, Green sea turtle. e, Harpy eagle.
Species of Africa: No. 663a, Black rhinoceros. b, Leopard. c, Champanzee. d, Zebra (Grants). e, Mountain gorilla. f, African elephant.
No. 664, Lion (African). No. 665, Margay cat.

1997, Feb. 12 *Perf. 14*
662 A135 500k Sheet of 6, #a.-f. 5.00 5.00
663 A135 1000k Sheet of 6, #a.-f. 10.00 10.00

Souvenir Sheets
664-665 A135 3000k each 5.00 5.00

Deng Xiaoping (1904-97) — A136

Various portraits of Deng Xiaoping and: 800k, Flags, map of Hong Kong. 1000k, Flag, Hong Kong harbor. 2000k, Hong Kong at night, countdown clock. 2500k, World map with China highlighted.

1997, May 26 Litho. *Perf. 14*
666 A136 800k multicolored 1.40 1.40
667 A136 1000k multicolored 1.75 1.75

Souvenir Sheets
668 A136 2000k multicolored 3.25 3.25
669 A136 2500k multicolored 4.25 4.25

Nos. 666-667 were issued in sheets of 3 each. No. 669 contains one 72x47mm stamp.

Trains — A137   A138

Locomotives: 200k, Suburban tank, Eastern Railway, France. 300k, Streamlined express, Belgian Natl. Railways. 500k, "Mountain" type express, Union Pacific Railraod. 900k, 2-8-2 "Mikado," Kenya & Uganda Railway. 1000k, 4-6-0 "Royal Scot," LM & S Railway. 1500k, 4-6-0 "Lord Nelson" type, Southern Railway.
No. 676: a, Express, German State Railways. b, Express, "Duke of Abercorn," NCC (LMSR), Ireland. c, Heavy freight tank, Netherlands Railways. d, Express, Austrian Federal Railways. e, "Governor" class, Gold Coast Railways. f, 4-8-4 Express, Canadian Natl. Railways.
No. 677, Diesel-electric passenger, Royal Siamese State Railways. No. 678, "Pacific" type, South African Railways.

1997, June 2
670-675 A137 Set of 6 7.25 7.25
676 A137 500k Sheet of 6, #a.-f. 5.00 5.00

Souvenir Sheets
677-678 A137 3000k each 5.00 5.00

1997, Aug. 8 Litho. *Perf. 14*
Butterflies and Moths: 300k, No. 683a, Gaudy commodore. 500k, No. 683b, African moon moth. 700k, No. 683c, Emperor moth. No. 682, 900k, Emperor swallowtail.

679-682 A138 Set of 4 4.00 4.00
683 A138 900k Sheet of 4, #a.-c., #682 6.00 6.00

Queen Elizabeth II and Prince Philip, 50th Wedding Anniv. A139

No. 684: a, Queen Elizabeth II. b, Royal arms. c, Queen wearing crown, Prince in uniform. d, Queen, Prince riding in open carriage. e, Buckingham Palace. f, Prince waving.
3200k, Queen, Prince waving from balcony.

1997, Aug. 26 Litho. *Perf. 14*
684 A139 500k Sheet of 6, #a.-f. 4.50 4.50

Souvenir Sheet
685 A139 3200k multicolored 5.00 5.00

Paul P. Harris (1868-1947), Founder of Rotary, Intl. — A140

1000k, First Rotarians, Silvester Schiele, Harris, Hiram Shorey, Gus Loehr, portrait of Harris.
3200k, Zambian interactors with retirees.

1997, Aug. 27
686 A140 1000k multicolored 1.50 1.50
Souvenir Sheet
687 A140 3200k multicolored 5.00 5.00

Heinrich von Stephan (1831-97), Founder of UPU A141

Portrait of Von Stephan and: #688a, World Postal Congress, Berne, 1874. #688b, UPU emblem. #688c, Savannah, paddle steamer, 1819.
3200k, Von Stephan, Prussian postilion, 1715.

1997, Aug. 28
688 A141 1000k Sheet of 3, #a.-c. 4.50 4.50
Souvenir Sheet
689 A141 3200k multicolored 5.00 5.00

Nos. 562-564 Surcharged

1997, Sept. 19 Litho. *Perf. 14x13½*
690 CD349 500k on 35k .75 .75
691 CD349 (O) on 32k .90 .90
692 CD349 900k on 38k 1.25 1.25
Nos. 690-692 (3) 2.90 2.90

No. 691 was valued at 600k on day of issue.

Owls — A142

300k, #697b, Verreaux's eagle owl. 500k, #697c, Pel's fishing owl. 700k, #697a, Barn owl. #696, Spotted eagle owl.

1997, Dec. 18 Litho. *Perf. 14*
693 A142 300k multicolored .50 .50
694 A142 500k multicolored .85 .85
695 A142 700k multicolored 1.25 1.25
696 A142 900k multicolored 1.50 1.50
Nos. 693-696 (4) 4.10 4.10
Sheet of 4
697 A142 900k #a.-c., #696 6.00 6.00

Christmas A143

Entire paintings or details, sculpture: No. 698, 50k, Winged Victory of Samothrace. No. 699, 50k, Ognissanti Madonna, by Giotto. No. 700, 100k, Angel, by Antonio Pollaiuolo. No. 701, 100k, Angel of the Annunciation, by Jacopo da Pontormo. No. 702, 500k, No. 703, 1000k, The Virgin and Child Enthroned Among Angels and Saints, by Benozzo Gozzoli.
No. 704, All of the Rebel Angels, detail, by Rubens. No. 705, The Resurrection of the Dead, by Joseph Christian.

1997, Dec. 18 Litho. *Perf. 14*
698-703 A143 Set of 6 2.75 2.75
Souvenir Sheets
704-705 A143 3200k each 5.00 5.00

No. 704 incorrectly inscribed "The Virgin and Child Enthroned Among Angels and Saints, by Bonozzo Gozzoli."

Diana, Princess of Wales (1961-97) — A144

Various portraits with color of sheet margin: No. 706, Pale green. No. 707, Pale yellow. No. 708, Touching hand of blind man (in sheet margin). No. 709, With Barbara Bush (in sheet margin).

1997
706 A144 500k Sheet of 6, #a.-f. 4.50 4.50
707 A144 700k Sheet of 6, #a.-f. 6.50 6.50
Souvenir Sheets
708-709 A144 2500k each 4.00 4.00

PAPU (Pan African Postal Union), 18th Anniv. A145

Designs: 500k, Kobus leche kafuensis. (O), Dove carrying letter over map. 900k, Emblem of dove carrying letter.

1998 *Perf. 14½*
710 A145 500k multicolored .75 .75
711 A145 (O) multicolored .95 .95
712 A145 900k multicolored 1.25 1.25
Nos. 710-712 (3) 2.95 2.95

No. 711 was valued at 600k on day of issue.

Mahatma Gandhi (1869-1948) — A146

Portraits of Gandhi: 250k, As law student in London, 1888. 500k, With Nehru, 1946. No. 715, (O), In front of Red Fort, New Delhi. 900k, At prayer.
2000k, Gandhi at 2nd Round Table Conference, London, 1931.

1998, Jan. 30 Litho. *Perf. 13½*
713-716 A146 Set of 4 3.25 3.25
Souvenir Sheet
717 A146 2000k multicolored 3.00 3.00

No. 715 was valued at 600k on day of issue. Nos. 713, 715-717 are vert.

Flowers — A147

Designs: No. 718, Lantana camara. No. 719, Clusia rosea. No. 720, Nymphaea hybrids. No. 721, Portulaca grandiflora.
No. 722: a, Hibiscus rosa-sinensis. b, Plumeria. c, Erythrina variegata. d, Bauhinia blakeana. e, Carissa grandiflora. f, Cordia sebestena. g, Couroupita guianensis. h, Eustoma grandiflorum. i, Passiflora.

3200k, Strelitzia reginae, horiz.

998, Feb. 27   Litho.   Perf. 14
18-721 A147 500k Set of 4   3.25 3.25
'22 A147 500k Sheet of 9, #a.-i.   7.50 7.50

Souvenir Sheet
'23 A147 3200k multicolored   5.25 5.25

New Year
1998
(Year of
the Tiger)
A148

Chinese symbols and stylized tigers: No. 724: a, Looking right. b, Looking left. c, Facing forward, denomination UL. d, Facing forward, denomination UR.
1500k, Tiger, symbols on both sides.

1998   Litho.   Perf. 14
724 A148 700k Set of 4, #a.-
d.   4.00 4.00

Souvenir Sheet
725 A148 1500k multicolored   2.10 2.10

Sites of
India
A149

Designs: a, Taj Mahal, Agra. b, Gateway to India, Calcutta. c, Great Imambara Mosque, Lucknow.

1998
726 A149 900k Sheet of 3, #a.-c.   3.75 3.75

Art
of
India
A150

No. 727: a, Ragmala, School of Mewar, 17th cent. b, Babar Nama, Mogul School, 16th cent. c, Hamza Nama, Mogul School, 16th cent. d, Meghamallar, School of Mewar, 16th cent.
2500k, Hindola Raga, School of Deccan, 17th-18th cent.

1998
727 A150 700k Sheet of 4, #a.-
d.   4.00 4.00

Souvenir Sheet
728 A150 2500k multicolored   3.50 3.50

1998 World Cup Soccer
Championships, France — A151

No. 729: a, Albert, Belgium. b, Bebeto, Brazil. c, Beckenbauer, W. Germany. d, Littbarski, W. Germany. e, Juninho, Brazil. f, Lineker, England. g, Lato, Poland. h, McCoist, Scotland.
No. 730: a, Maier, W. Germany, 1974. b, Bellini, Brazil, 1958. c, Kempes, Argentina, 1978. d, Nazassi, Uruguay, 1930. e, Pele, Brazil, 1970. f, Beckenbauer, W. Germany, 1974. g, Combi, Italy, 1934. h, Zoff, Italy, 1982.

No. 731: a, Keane, Rep. of Ireland. b, Seaman, England. c, Like #729b. d, Futre, Portugal. e, Ravanelli, Italy. f, Weah, Liberia. g, Bergkamp, Holland. h, Raduciolu, Romania.
No. 732, Juninho, Brazil. No. 733, Romario, Brazil, horiz. No. 734, McCoist, Scotland, horiz.

1998, Apr. 17   Perf. 13½x14, 14x13½
Sheets of 8 + Label
729 A151 450k #a.-h.   5.25 5.25
730-731 A151 500k #a.-h., each   5.75 5.75

Souvenir Sheets
732-734 A151 3200k each   4.50 4.50

Parrots — A152

No. 735: a, Rainbow lorikeet. b, Budgerigar, blossom-headed parakeet. c, Blue-yellow macaw. d, Blue-crowned parrot. e, Golden conure. f, Sulphur-crested cockatoo.
No. 736: a, Ara ararauna. b, Ara chloropterd. c, Pale-headed rosellas. d, Northern rosella. e, Gang-gang cockatoo. f, Palm cockatoo.
No. 737, Mulda parakeet. No. 738, Major Mitchell cockatoo, horiz.

1998, June 1   Litho.   Perf. 14
735 A152 500k Sheet of 6, #a.-
f.   4.25 4.25
736 A152 1000k Sheet of 6, #a.-
f.   8.50 8.50

Souvenir Shets
737-738 A152 3200k each   4.75 4.75

Mushrooms — A153

No. 739, 250k, Red-tufted wood tricholoma. No. 740, 250k, Chlorophyllum molybdites. No. 741, 450k, Stuntz's psilocybe. No. 742, 450k, Lepista sordida. No. 743, 500k, Lepiota. No. 744, 500k, Rosy gomphidius. No. 745, 900k, Cantharellus cybrina. No. 746, 900k, Olive-capped boletus. No. 747, 1000k, Showy volvaria. No. 748, 1000k, Sooty brown waxy cap.
No. 749: a, Leller's boletus. b, Short-stemmed russula. c, Anise-scented clitocybe. d, Dung roundhead. e, Oak-loving collybia. f, Wine-red strophania.
No. 750: a, Flat-topped mushroom. b, Alice Eastwood's boletus. c, Pitted milky cap. d, Short-stemmed slippery jask. e, Rose-red russula. f, Zeller's tricholoma.
No. 751, Honey mushroom. No. 752, Velvet-stemmed flammulina.

1998, July 1
739-748 A153 Set of 10   8.00 8.00
Sheets of 6
749-750 A153 900k #a.-f., each   7.75 7.75
Souvenir Sheets
751-752 A153 3200k each   4.50 4.50
Nos. 749-752 are continuous designs.

Traditional
Stories — A154

No. 755: a, like #753. b, like #754.

1998, Dec. 2   Litho.   Perf. 14
753 A154 300k Luchela nganga   .45   .45

754 A154 500k Kasuli   .70   .70

Souvenir Sheet
755 A154 2000k Sheet of 2, #a.-
b.   4.25 4.25

Christmas.

Orchids
A155

Designs, vert.: No. 756, 100k, Paphiopedilum callosum. No. 757, 100k, Phaius tankervilleae. No. 758, 500k, Paphiopedilum fairrieanum. No. 759, 500k, Barkeria lindleyana. No. 760, 1000k, Laelia flava. No. 761, 1000k, Masdervallia unifloria, masdervallia angulifera.
No. 762: a, Acacallis cyanea. b, Miltoniopsis phalaenopsis. c, Dendrobium bellatulum. d, Polystachya campyloglossa. e, Pleione bulbocodioides. f, Rhynchostylis gigantea. g, Cattleya lawrenceana. h, Sopbrolaelia. i, Laelia tenebrosa.
No. 763: a, Acacallis cyanea, diff. b, Epidendrum gastropodium. c, Laelia rubescens. d, Paphiopedilum dayanum. e, Laelia lobata. f, Dendrobium crepidatum. g, Cattleya nobilior. h, Dendrobium johnsoniae. i, Trichopilia fragrans.
No. 764, Cattleya maxima, vert. No. 765, Cattleya violacea.

1998, Dec. 23
756-761 A155 Set of 6   3.50 3.50
Sheets of 9
762-763 A155 900k #a.-i., each   8.75 8.75
Souvenir Sheets
764-765 A155 4000k each   4.50 4.50

Classic
Cars
A156

Designs: 300k, Ferrari Daytona 365 GTB/4. 500k, Austin Healey Sprite. 900k, Gordon Keeble. 1000k, Alvis TD.
No. 770: a, Mercedes-Benz 300Sl. b, Chevrolet Corvair. c, AC Cobra 427. d, Aston Martin DB5. e, BMW 2002 Turbo. f, Cadillac Eldorado Brougham.
No. 771: a, Mercedes-Benz 280SE 3.5. b, Aston Martin DB2. c, Volkswagen Beetle. d, Lancia Aurelia B20 GT. e, Lamborghini 350 GT. f, Cisitalia 202 Coupe.
No. 771G: h, 1995 Ferrari 750 Pinnafarina. i, 1997 Federrari 312T2/77. j, 1983 Ferrari 208 Turbo. k, 1962 Ferrari Dino 268 SP. l, 1994 Ferrari F355 Berlinetta. m, Ferrari 250 GTE Coupe 2+2 California.
No. 772, Citroen Light 15. No. 773, Austin Healey MKII 3000.

1998, Dec. 23
766-769 A156 Set of 4   3.00 3.00
Sheets of 6, #a-f
770-771G A156 900k Set of 3   17.50 17.50
Souvenir Sheets
772-773 A156 4000k each   4.50 4.50

New Year
1999
(Year of
the
Rabbit)
A157

Various rabbits, denomination at - #774: a, LL. b, LR. c, LL (scratching). d, LR (nose near ground).
2000k, Rabbit, vert.

1999, Jan. 4
774 A157 700k Sheet of 4, #a.-
d.   3.00 3.00
Souvenir Sheet
775 A157 2000k multicolored   2.25 2.25

Trains
A158

Locomotives: No. 776, (0), U20C Diesel electric, 1967. No. 777, 800k, 7th Class No. 70, 1900. No. 778, 800k, 15A Class Beyer-Garrat No. 401, 1950. No. 779, 900k, HP diesel electric, 1966. No. 780, 900k, 20th Class No. 708, 1954.
4000k, 7th Class No. 955, 1892.

1999, Feb. 1   Litho.   Perf. 14½
776-780 A158 Set of 5   4.50 4.50
Souvenir Sheet
781 A158 4000k multicolored   4.50 4.50
No. 776 was valued at 600k on day of issue.

No. 643 Surcharged

Methods and Perfs as Before
1999, June 1
781A A129 500k on 100k multi

Queen Mother (b. 1900) — A159

No. 782: a, With Princess Elizabeth, 1936. b, Lady of the Garter. c, With Prince Andrew, 1960. d, At Ascot.
5000k, Wedding photograph, 1923.

1999, Sept. 1   Perf. 14
782 A159 2000k Sheet of 4, #a.-
d., + label   6.75 6.75
Souvenir Sheet
Perf. 13¾
783 A159 5000k multicolored   4.25 4.25
No. 783 contains one 38x51mm stamp.

Dinosaurs
A160

Designs: 50k, Dimetrodon. 100k, Deinonychus. 500k, Protoceratops. 900k, Heterodontosaurus. 1000k, Oviraptor. 1800k, Psittacosaurus.
No. 790: a, Stegosaurus. b, Triceratops. c, Brontosaurus. d, Gallimimus. e, Saurolophus. f, Lambeosaurus. g, Centrosaurus. h, Edmontonia. i, Parasaurolophus.
No. 791, a, Ceratosaurus. b, Daspletosaurus. c, Baryonyx. d, Ornitholestes. e, Troodon. f, Coelophysis. g, Tyrannosaurus. h, Allosaurus. i, Compsognathus.
No. 792, Saltasaurus, vert. No. 793, Stygimoloch, vert.

1999, Sept. 27   Litho.   Perf. 14
784-789 A160 Set of 6   3.75 3.75
Sheets of 9
790-791 A160 900k #a.-i., each   6.75 6.75
Souvenir Sheets
792-793 A160 4000k each   3.50 3.50

Johann Wolfgang von Goethe (1749-
1832), German Poet — A161

No. 794: a, A drinking party in Amerbach's
cellar. b, Goethe and Friedrich von Schiller. c,
Faust falls in love with Margaret.
5000k, Angel.

1999, Oct. 4　　**Litho.**　　*Perf. 14*
794 A161 2000k Sheet of 3, #a.-
c.　　　　4.25 4.25

Souvenir Sheet
795 A161 5000k org brn & brn　3.75 3.75

A162

A163

Cats: 50k, White Devon Rex. 100k, Red
Persian. 500k, Chartreux. 900k, Brown tabby
Maine Coon.
No. 800, horiz.: a, Tortie point Himalayan. b,
Blue mackerel tabby Scottish Fold. c, Choco-
late lynx point Balinese. d, Havana Brown. e,
Seal point Ragdoll. f, Silver shaded Persian.
No. 801, horiz.: a, Red spotted tabby Exotic
Shorthair. b, Blue tortie smoke Persian. c,
Brown classic tabby longhaired Scottish Fold.
d, Spotted tabby American Bobtail. e, Silver
spotted tabby Ocicat. f, Blue British Shorthair.
No. 802, Silver tabby longhair Persian,
horiz. No. 803, Tabby point Siamese.

1999, Oct. 18
796-799 A162　Set of 4　　1.10 1.10
Sheets of 6, #a.-f.
800-801 A162 1000k each　　4.25 4.25
Souvenir Sheets
802-803 A162 4000k each　　3.00 3.00

1999, Oct. 18
Dogs: 100k, Welsh corgi. 500k, Shetland
sheepdog. 900k, Italian greyhound. 1000k,
Tibetan spaniel.
No. 808, horiz.: a, Dalmatian. b, Shetland
sheepdogs. c, Bearded collie. d, Eskimo. e,
Basenji. f, Saluki.
No. 809, horiz.: a, Norwegian elkhound. b,
Flat-coated retriever. c, St. Bernard. d, Basset
hound, Pembroke Welsh corgi. e, Pembroke
Welsh corgi, Pointer. f, Petit Basset Griffon
Vendeen.
No. 810, Whippet. No. 811, Rottweiler.

804-807 A163　Set of 4　　1.75 1.75
Sheets of 6, #a.-f.
808-809 A163 1000k each　　4.25 4.25
Souvenir Sheets
810-811 A163 4000k each　　3.00 3.00

11th Intl. Conference on AIDS in
Africa, Lusaka — A164

Designs: 500k, Emblem, waterfalls. 900k,
Emblem, close-up view of waterfalls.

1999, Oct. 20
812-813 A164　Set of 2　　1.00 1.00

Paintings by
Zhang Daqian
(1899-1983)
A165

No. 814: a, Water Lily in the Rain. b, Ching-
hai Tribal Girl and a Black Hound. c, Taking a
Nap. d, Monkey and Old Tree. e, Bird and Tree
of Chin-Chang Mountain. f, Watching Waterfalls. g, On the Way to Switzerland and Austria. h, A Boat Brings the Wine. i, Brown Landscape. j, Nice Autumn.
No. 815: a, 1000k, White Water Lily, horiz.
b, 2000k, Cloudy Waterfalls and Summer
Mountain, horiz.

1999, Oct. 21　　　　*Perf. 13*
814 A165 500k Sheet of 10,
#a.-j.　　　3.75 3.75
815 A165　Sheet of 2, #a.-b.　2.10 2.10
China 1999 World Philatelic Exhibition,
22nd UPU Congress, Beijing. #815 contains
two 52x39mm stamps.

A166

Flora &
Fauna
A167

Designs: 50k, Leatherback turtle. 100k,
American kestrel. No. 818, 500k, Great blue
heron. 900k, Mesene phareus. 1000k, Laelio-
cattleya. 1800k, Papilio cresphontes.
No. 822, Cairn's birdwing. No. 823, Pintail.
No. 824, Rose. No. 825, Gray tree frog.
No. 826: a, White-tailed tropicbird. b, Sooty
tern. c, Laughing gull. d, Black skimmer. e,
Brown pelican. f, Bottle-nosed dolphin. g,
Common dolphin. h, Man in sailboat. i, Blue
tang. j, Southern stingray. k, Hammerhead
shark. l, Mako shark.
No. 827: a, Heliconia. b, Purple-throated
Carib. c, St. Vincent parrot. d, Bananaquit. e,
prepona meander. f, Unidentified butterfly. g,
Hawksbill turtle. h, Black-necked stilt. i,
Banded butterflyfish. j, Porkfish. k, Seahorse.
l, Chain moray eel.
No. 828: a, Baltimore oriole. b, Chipmunk. c,
Blue jay. d, Monarch butterfly. e, Gray heron. f,
Mallard. g, Canadian otter. h, American lotus.
i, Fowler's toad. j, Bluegill sunfish. k, Rainbow
trout. l, Terrapin.
No. 829, Amazona guildingii. No. 830, Bot-
tle-nosed dolphin, diff. No. 831, Fuchsia. No.
832, Red-banded pereute.

1999, Oct. 27
816-821 A166　Set of 6　　3.25 3.25
822-825 A167　500k Set of 4　1.40 1.40
Sheets of 12, #a.-l.
826-827 A166 700k each　　6.00 6.00
828　　A167 700k multi　　6.00 6.00

Souvenir Sheets
829-830 A166 4000k each　　3.00 3.00
831-832 A167 4000k each　　3.00 3.00

IBRA '99 — A168

Trains: 1000k, Crampton. 3200k, Post standard 2-8-4 tank locomotive.
Illustration reduced.

1999　　　　*Perf. 14x14¾*
833-834 A168　Set of 2　　3.00 3.00

Souvenir Sheets

PhilexFrance '99 — A169

#835, Paris-Orleans Railway 4-4-0. #836,
paris, Lyon & Mediterranean Railway 2-4-2.

1999　　　　*Perf. 14¼*
835-836 A169 5000k each　　3.75 3.75

Wedding of Prince
Edward and
Sophie Rhys-
Jones
A170

No. 837: a, 500k, Sophie. b, 900k, Couple.
c, 100k, Edward.
3000k, Couple kissing.

1999　　　　*Perf. 14*
837 A170　Sheet of 3, #a.-c.　1.75 1.75
Souvenir Sheet
838 A170 3000k multi　　　2.10 2.10

Birds — A171

Designs: 50k, Blacksmith plover. 100k,
Sacred ibis. 200k, Purple gallinule. 250k, Purple heron. 300k, Glossy ibis. 400k, Marabou
stork. 450k, African spoonbill. 500k, African
finfoot. O, No. 847, Knot-billed duck. 600k,
Darter. 700k, African skimmer. 800k, Spur-
winged goose. 900k, Hammerkop. 1000k,
White pelican. 1500k, Black-winged stilt.
2000k, Black-crowned night heron.

1999, Dec. 20　Litho.　Perf. 14½x15
839-854 A171　Set of 16　　7.00 7.00
No. 847 sold for 500k on day of issue.
Design size of No. 847 is 30 ½mm wide. See
Nos. 927-930.

Flowers
A172

Various flowers making up a photomosaic of
Princess Diana.

1999, Dec. 31　　　　*Perf. 13¾*
855 A172 1000k Sheet of 8,
#a.-h.　　　6.25 6.25

Millennium
A173

Highlights of 1950-2000: a, Venice Biennale
shows Jackson Pollock and Abstract Expres-
sionism. b, James Watson and Francis Crick
piece together the structure of DNA. c,
Edmund Hillary reaches the summit of Mount
Everest. d, Jonas Salk's polio vaccine. e,
Ghana achieves independence. f, Yuri
Gagarin becomes 1st man in space. g, Rachel
Carson and the beginning of the environmen-
tal movement. h, Indira Gandhi becomes
Prime Minister of India. i, 1st successful heart
transplant. j, Apollo 11 lands on moon. k,
Microprocessor developed. l, Richard Nixon
visits People's Republic of China. m, Qin Shi
Huang Mausoleum discovered. n, Stephen
Hawking proposes new ideas about the uni-
verse and black holes. o, Margaret Thatcher
elected 1st female Prime Minister of Great
Britain. p, Mikhail Gorbachev becomes leader
of Soviet Union. q, Fall of the Berlin Wall. r,
Nelson Mandela elected Pres. of South Africa.

2000, Feb. 7　　　*Perf. 12¾x12½*
856 A173 500k Sheet of 18, #a.-
r., + label　　6.25 6.25

Butterflies
A174

400k, Papilio antimachus. 450k, Amauris
niavius. 500k, Charaxes smaragdalis. 800k,
Charaxes zelica. 900k, Cymothoe confusa.
1000k, #862, Labobunea ansorgei.
No. 863: a, Palla ussheri. b, Euphaedra
aureola. c, Graphium cyrnus nuscyrus. d,
Salamis cacta. e, Salamis parhassus. f,
Charaxes pelias.
No. 864: a, Large Spotted Acraea. b, Palla
(orange wings). c, Palla (blue wings). d, Gold-
banded Forester (white wings). e, Figtree blue.
f, Gold-banded Forester (pink wings).
No. 865: a, Colotis ione. b, Charaxes
acraeoides. c, Euphaedra edwardsi. d, Colotis
phisadia. e, Charaxes lydiae. f, Euphaedra
eupaulus.
No. 866: a, Papilio zalmoxis. b, Amauris
niavius. c, Salamis cytora. d, Salamis temora.
e, Charaxes eupale. f, Cymothoe hypatha.
No. 867, Euphaedra ceres. No. 868,
Cymothoe fumana. No. 869, Euphaedra spati-
osa. No. 870, Euryphene gambiae.

2000, Feb. 8　　　　*Perf. 14*
857-862 A174　Set of 6　　2.75 2.75
Sheets of 6, #a.-f.
863-864 A174 1000k each　　4.25 4.25
865-866 A174 1500k each　　6.25 6.25
Souvenir Sheets
867-870 A174 5000k each　　3.50 3.50

No. 650
Surcharged

Method and Perf. as Before
2000, Apr. 11
670A A132 700k on 100k multi

Orchids — A175

Illustration reduced.
No. 871: a, Paphiopedilum sioux. b, Phalaenopsis amabilis hybrid. c, Thelymitza ixioides. d, Phalaenopsis schilleriana.
No. 872: a, Miltoniopsis pansy orchid. b, Paphiopedilum venustum. c, Odontoglossum grande. d, Vanda sanderiana alba. e, Phalaenopsis violacea. f, Pleione alishan.
No. 873: a, Cyrtorchis arcuata. b, Cymbioiella rhodochila. c, Unidentified orchid. d, Eulophia quartiana. e, Augraecum montanum. f, Polystacha vulcanica.
No. 874, vert.: a, Catasetum splendens. b, Miltonia spectabilis. c, Stenia pallida. d, Cozacias spatulata. e, Eriopsis sceptzum. f, Paphinia cristata.
No. 875, Cattleya hybrid. No. 876, Brachycorythis kalbreyeri.

2000, May 16   Litho.   Perf. 14
871 A175 1500k Sheet of 4,
         #a.-d.   4.00 4.00
Sheets of 6, #a.-f.
872-874 A175 1500k each   6.00 6.00
Souvenir Sheets
875-876 A175 6000k each   4.00 4.00
The Stamp Show 2000, London.

Popes — A176

No. 877: a, Liberius, 352-66. b, Linus, 67-76. c, Lucius I, 253-54. d, Marcellinus, 296-304. e, Mark, 336. f, Pius I, 140-155.
No. 878: a, Simplicius, 468-83. b, Siricius, 384-99. c, Stephen I, 254-57. d, Urban I, 222-30. e, Zephyrinus, 199-217. f, Zosimus, 417-18.
No. 879, Silverius, 536-37. No. 880, Vigilius, 537-55.
Illustration reduced.

2000, July 7   Litho.   Perf. 13¾
Sheets of 6, #a-f
877-878 A176 1500k Set of 2 11.00 11.00
Souvenir Sheets
879-880 A176 5000k Set of 2   6.00 6.00

Birds — A177

400k, Great Indian hornbill. 500k, Cockatiel. 600k, Amazonian umbrellabird. 1000k, Unidentified bird. 2000k, Rainbow lorikeet.
No. 886: a, Green aracari. b, Eclectus parrot. c, Crimson topaz. d, King bird of paradise. e, keel-billed toucan. f, Australian king parrot. g, Sailboat. h, Hyacinth macaw.
No. 887: a, Resplendent quetzal. b, Carmine bee-eater. c, Wattled false sunbird. d, Palm trees. e, Sulphur-crested cockatoo. f, Great blue turaco. g, Crimson rosella. h, Malabar pied hornbill.
No. 888: a, Yellow-crowned amazon. b, Green turaco. c, Butterfly and palm trees. d, Plate-billed mountain toucan. e, Scarlet macaw. f, Blue and yellow macaw. g, Guianan cock of the rock. h, Palm cockatoo.
No. 889, Red-crested pochard. No. 890, Toco toucan, horiz. No. 891, Blue and yellow macaw, horiz.

2000, Sept. 8   Perf. 14
881-885 A177 Set of 5   2.75 2.75
Sheets of 8, #a-h
886-888 A177 1500k Set of 3 21.00 21.00
Souvenir Sheets
889-891 A177 5000k Set of 3   9.00 9.00

Birds — A178

Designs: 700k, Red-backed shrike. 800k, Golden pipet. No. 894, 1200k, Orange-breasted sunbird. No. 895, 1400k, Eurasian goldfinch. 1500k, Red-crested turaco. 3000k, Carmine bee-eater.
No. 898, 1000k: a, Gouldian finch. b, Parrot finch. c, Purple grenadier. d, Red bishop. e, Red-crested cardinal. f, Spectacled monarch. g, Crimson chat. h, Necklaced laughing thrush. i, Chestnut-backed jewel babbler.
No. 899, 1200k: a, Lovely cotinga. b, Andean cock-of-the-rock. c, Orange-bellied leafbird. d, Pin-tailed manakin. e, Pin-tailed broadbill. f, Rufous motmot. g, American goldfinch. h, Double-barred finch. i, Golden-breasted starling.
No. 900, 1400k: a, Campo oriole. b, Hooded warbler. c, Purple honeycreeper. d, Blue-faced honeyeater. e, Scarlet tanager. f, Green-headed tanager. g, Blue-breasted fairy wren. h, Banded pitta. i, Wire-tailed manakin.
No. 901, 5000k, Pin-tailed sandgrouse. No. 902, 5000k, Black bustard.

2000, Sept. 8   Litho.   Perf. 14
892-897 A178 Set of 6   4.75 4.75
Sheets of 9, #a-i
898-900 A178 Set of 3   18.00 18.00
Souvenir Sheets
901-902 A178 Set of 2   5.75 5.75

African
Creation
Legends
A179

Designs: Nos. 903, 906a, 600k, Creation in Clay. Nos. 904, 906b, 1000k, The Chameleon

---

and the Lizard. Nos. 905, 906c, 1400k, Why the Stones Do Not Die.

Perf. 14¼x14½
2000, Nov. 10   Litho.
903-905 A179   Set of 3   1.40 1.40
906 A179   Horiz. strip of 3, #a-c 1.40 1.40
Souvenir Sheet
No Frame Around Stamp
907 A179 3500k The Rooster in
                the Sky   1.60 1.60
No. 906 issued in sheets of 9 stamps.

Common
Market for
Eastern and
Southern
Africa
A180

Designs: 600k, Map of member nations. 700k, Truck crossing border. 1000k, Exchange of money and sale of goods at border.

2000
908-910 A180   Set of 3   1.10 1.10

Nos. 713-714 Surcharged

2000   Method and Perf. as Before
911 A146 1200k on 250k multi
912 A146 1500k on 500k multi

UN High
Commissioner
for Refugees,
50th
Anniv. — A181

Designs: 700k, Children receiving food. 1500k, Woman carrying child.

Perf. 13¾x14¼
2001, Mar. 13   Litho.
915-916 A181   Set of 2   1.40 1.40

A182

Animals — A183

Designs: 500k, African buffalo. 1000k, Cheetah, vert. No. 919, 2000k, Female elephant. 3200k, Ruffed lemur, vert.
No. 921, 2000k: a, Crimson-breasted shrike. b, Common bee-eater. c, Blue monkey. d, Chimpanzee. e, Bush baby. f, Genet.
No. 922, 2000k, horiz.: a, Defassa waterbuck. b, Crowned crane. c, Red hartebeest. d, Pygmy hippopotamus. e, White rhinoceros. f, Giant forest hog.
No. 923, 2000k, horiz.: a, Three adult, one young impala. c, Four adult impalas. d, Warthog. e, Two lions. f, Four lions.
No. 924, 6000k, Bull elephant. No. 925, 6000k, Black rhinoceros. No. 926, 6000k, Zebras, vert.

Perf. 13¼x13½, 13½x13¼
2001, Mar. 30
917-920 A182   Set of 4   4.00 4.00
Sheets of 6, #a-f
921-923 A183   Set of 3   22.50 22.50
Souvenir Sheets
924-926 A182   Set of 3   11.00 11.00

Bird Type of 1999
Designs: No. 927, O, Knob-billed duck. No. 928, A, Blacksmith plover. No. 929, B, Sacred ibis. No. 930, C, Purple gallinule.

Perf. 14½x14¾
2001, Mar. 19   Litho.
927-930 A171   Set of 4   3.00 3.00

Nos. 927-930 each sold for 700k, 1200k, 1400k, and 1500k respectively on day of issue. No. 927 is dated "2000" and has a design width of 31 ½mm. No. 847 has no date and has a design width of 30½mm.

Total Solar
Eclipse, June
21 — A184

Eclipse and: 1000k, Woman. 1500k, Bird. 1700k, Lizard. 1800k, Elephant and man. 2200k, Man.

2001, June 1   Litho.   Perf. 13¾
931-935 A184   Set of 5   4.50 4.50

Phila Nippon '01, Japan — A185

Designs: No. 936, 500k, Senya Nakamura as Toknatsu, by Kiyomasu Torii I. No. 937, 500k, Kantaro Sanjo II and Monosuke Ichikawa I, by Okumura Masanobu, 1720. No. 938, 1000k, Kantaro Sanjo and Monosuke Ichikawa, by Masanobu, c. 1730. No. 939, 1000k, Standing Figure of a Woman, by Kiyomasu Torii I. 1500k, Ono no Komachi, by Masanobu. 1800k, Dog Bringing a Love Letter, by Shigenaga.

No. 942, 3200k: a, Matsue Nakamura as a Cat Woman, by Shunsho. b, Kantaro Sanjo With Branch of Bamboo, by Kiyomasu Torii I. c, Kinsaku Yamashika I as Peddler, by Kiyomasu Torii I. d, Portrait of an Actor, by Shunsho.

No. 943, 3200k: a, Kumetaro Nakamura I, by Shunsho. b, Actor in Female Role, by Kiyomasu Torii I. c, Kikunojo Segawa Leaning on Sugoroku Board, by Kiyomasu Torii I. d, Gennosuke Ichikawa as a Wakashu, by Kiyomasu Torii I.

No. 944, 6000k, Akashi of the Tamaya, by Ryukoku Hishikawa. No. 945, 6000k, Events of Year in the Floating World, by Moroshige, horiz.

2001, July 4 — **Perf. 14**
936-941 A185 Set of 6   3.50 3.50
Sheets of 4, #a-d
942-943 A185 Set of 2   14.00 14.00
Souvenir Sheets
944-945 A185 Set of 2   6.50 6.50

SOS Children's Village A186

2001, July 30
946 A186 2500k multi   1.40 1.40

Royal Navy Submarines, Cent. — A187

No. 947, horiz.: a, HMS Tabard. b, HMS Opossum. c, HMS Unicorn. d, HMS Churchill. e, HMS Victorious. f, HMS Triumph.
6000k, Lieutenant Commander Malcolm David Wanklyn.

2001, July 30
947 A187 2000k Sheet of 6, #a-f   6.75 6.75
Souvenir Sheet
948 A187 6000k multi   3.50 3.50

Giuseppe Verdi (1813-1901), Opera Composer — A188

No. 949 — Actors in Falstaff : a, Benjamin Luxon (without hat). b, Luxon (with hat). c, Paul Plishka. d, Anne Collin.
8000k, Falstaff.

2001, July 30
949 A188 4000k Sheet of 4, #a-d   9.00 9.00
Souvenir Sheet
950 A188 8000k multi   4.50 4.50

Monet Paintings — A189

No. 951, horiz.: a, The Promenade at Argenteuil. b, View of the Argenteuil Plain from the Sannois Hills. c, The Seine at Argenteuil. d, The Basin at Argenteuil.
6000k, Rouen Cathedral Portal, Overcast Weather.

2001, July 30 — **Perf. 13¾**
951 A189 1500k Sheet of 4, #a-d   3.50 3.50
Souvenir Sheet
952 A189 6000k multi   3.50 3.50

Queen Victoria (1819-1901) — A191

No. 955: a, As child. b, Wearing black dress. c, With child. d, With Prince Albert. e, Wearing crown and red sash. f, Wearing red dress.
7000k, Portrait.

2001, July 30 — **Perf. 14**
955 A191 2000k Sheet of 6, #a-f   6.75 6.75
Souvenir Sheet
956 A191 7000k multi   4.00 4.00

Queen Elizabeth II, 75th Birthday — A192

No. 957: a, As infant. b, As child. c, As child, in garden. d, Wearing hat.
8000k, Wearing green and black hat.

2001, July 30
957 A192 4000k Sheet of 4, #a-d   9.00 9.00
Souvenir Sheet
958 A192 8000k multi   4.50 4.50
No. 957 contains four 28x42mm stamps.

First Zeppelin Flight, Cent. — A193

No. 959: a, LZ-1. b, Parseval PL25. c, LZ-3. d, Baldwin. e, LZ-129. f, Norge Nobile N1.
No. 960, 700k, Graf Zeppelin, vert.

2001, July 30
959 A193 2000k Sheet of 6, #a-f   6.75 6.75
Souvenir Sheet
960 A173 700k multi   .40 .40
No. 960 contains one 38x51mm stamp.

Pres. F. J. T. Chiluba — A194

Chiluba: 1000k, Recieving Master's degree. 1500k, Signing forms. 1700k, With arm raised, horiz.
6000k, Receiving Master's degree, diff.

2001 — **Litho.** — **Perf. 14**
961-963 A194 Set of 3   2.25 2.25
Souvenir Sheet
964 A194 6000k multi   3.00 3.00

Nobel Prizes, Cent. (in 2001) — A195

No. 965, 2000k — Peace laureates: a, Norman E. Borlaug, 1970. b, Lester B. Pearson, 1957. c, Intl. Red Cross, 1944. d, Anwar Sadat, 1978. e, Georges Pire, 1958. f, Linus Pauling, 1962.
No. 966, 2000k — Literature laureates: a, Isaac Bashevis Singer, 1978. b, Gao Xingjian, 2000. c, Claude Simon, 1985. d, Naguib Mahfouz, 1988. e, Camilo Jose Cela, 1989. f, Czeslaw Milosz, 1980.
No. 967, 2000k — Literature laureates: a, Seamus Heaney, 1995. b, Toni Morrison, 1993. c, Günter Grass, 1999. d, Wislawa Szymborska, 1996. e, Dario Fo, 1997. f, José Saramago, 1998.
No. 968, 6000k, George C. Marshall, Peace, 1953. No. 969, 6000k, Gerard Debreu, Economics, 1983. No. 970, 6000k, Robert W. Fogel, Economics, 1993.

2002, Feb. 11 — **Litho.** — **Perf. 14**
Sheets of 6, #a-f
965-967 A195 Set of 3   16.00 16.00
Souvenir Sheets
968-970 A195 Set of 3   8.25 8.25

Souvenir Sheet

New Year 2002 (Year of the Horse) — A196

2002, Feb. 18 — **Perf. 13¼**
971 A196 5000k multi   2.40 2.40

2002 World Cup Soccer
Championships, Japan and
Korea — A197

No. 972, 2000k: a, Poster from 1954 World
Cup, Switzerland. b, Stanly Matthews and
English flag. c, Scottish player and flag. d, Belgian player and flag. e, Player and Daejon
World Cup Stadium, Korea, horiz.
No. 973, 2000k: a, Ferenc Puskas and Hungarian flag. b, Poster from 1962 World Cup,
Chile. c, Spanish player and flag. d, English
player and flag. e, Player and Jeonju World
Cup Stadium, Korea, horiz.
No. 974, 8000k, Bryan Robson's goal
against France, 1982. No. 975, 8000k,
Salenko's fifth goal against Cameroon, 1994,
horiz.

2002, Feb. 26		Perf. 14	
Sheets of 5, #a-e			
972-973 A197	Set of 2	8.75	8.75
Souvenir Sheets			
974-975 A197	Set of 2	7.00	7.00

Size of Nos. 972a-972d, 973a-973d:
28x42mm.

United We
Stand — A198

2002, Feb.		Perf. 13½x13¼	
976 A198	3200k multi	1.40	1.40

Issued in sheets of 4.

Reign of Queen Elizabeth, 50th
Anniv. — A199

No. 977: a, Wearing blue and white hat. b,
Without hat. c, Wearing scarf. d, Wearing
tiara.
7500k, With Prince Philip.

2002, July 15	Litho.	Perf. 14¼	
977 A199	3200k Sheet of 4, #a-d	5.75	5.75
Souvenir Sheet			
978 A199	7500k multi	3.50	3.50

2002
Winter
Olympics,
Salt Lake
City
A200

Designs: 1000k, Ice hockey. 3200k, Cross-country skiing.

2002, July 30		Perf. 13¼x13¾	
979-980 A200	Set of 2	1.90	1.90

20th World Scout Jamboree,
Thailand — A201

No. 981, horiz.: a, Troop hiking. b, Knot
tying. c, Archery. d, Fire making.
8000k, Camping.

2002, July 30		Perf. 14	
981 A201	3200k Sheet of 4, #a-d	5.75	5.75
Souvenir Sheet			
982 A201	8000k multi	3.50	3.50

Intl. Year of Mountains — A202

No. 983: a, Mt. Whitney, US. b, Mt. Aconcagua, Argentina and Chile. c, Mt. Mönch, Switzerland. d, Mt. Ararat, Turkey.
9000k, Mt. Everest, Nepal and China.

2002, July 30			
983 A202	1500k Sheet of 4, #a-d	2.75	2.75
Souvenir Sheet			
984 A202	9000k multi	4.00	4.00

Birds — A203

Designs: 700k, Bee-eater. 1200k, Blue-cheeked bee-eater. 1400k, Boehm's bee-eater.
1500k, Little bee-eater.

2002, Aug. 12			
985-988 A203	Set of 4	2.10	2.10

Flowers, Butterflies and
Mushrooms — A204

No. 989, 2500k — Flowers: a, Camel's foot.
b, Christmas bells. c, Impala lily. d, Everlasting. e, Anomatheca grandiflora. f, Soldier lily.
No. 990, 2500k — Butterflies: a, False monarch. b, Golden piper. c, Blue pansy. d, Christmas tree acraea. e, Grass yellow. f, Gold-spotted sylph.
No. 991, 2500k — Mushrooms: a, Copper
trumpet. b, King bolete. c, Death cap. d, Fly
agaric. e, Chanterelle. f, Deadly fiber cap.
No. 992, 8000k, Arum lily. No. 993, 8000k,
African monarch butterfly. No. 994, 8000k,
Stump brittle-head mushrooms.

2002, Sept. 9		Litho.	
Sheets of 6, #a-f			
989-991 A204	Set of 3	20.00	20.00
Souvenir Sheets			
992-994 A204	Set of 3	11.00	11.00

No. 645 Surcharged

Methods & Perfs as Before

2002, July 1			
998 A130	1000k on 100k #645	—	—

Numbers have been reserved for three additional surcharges. The editors would like to
examine any examples.

Coronation of Queen Elizabeth II, 50th
Anniv. — A205

No. 999: a, Wearing crown and pearl necklace. b, Wearing tiara and jeweled necklace. c,
Wearing pink and black hat.
10,000k, Wearing flowered dress and hat.

2003, May 19	Litho.	Perf. 14	
999 A205	5000k Sheet of 3, #a-c	6.25	6.25
Souvenir Sheet			
1000 A205	10,000k multi	4.25	4.25

Prince William, 21st Birthday — A206

No. 1001: a, Wearing bow tie. b, Wearing
blue shirt and tie. c, Wearing yellow and black
sports shirt.
10,000k, Wearing sweater.

2003, May 19			
1001 A206	5000k Sheet of 3, #a-c	6.25	6.25
Souvenir Sheet			
1002 A206	10,000k multi	4.25	4.25

Nos. 654-657 Surcharged

Nos. 639-642
Surcharged

Nos. 617-
620
Surcharged

Nos. 650-653
Surcharged

Nos. 710-
712
Surcharged

Methods & Perfs. as Before
2003, June 26

1003	A133	1000k on 200k #654	.45	.45
1004	A133	1000k on 300k #655	.45	.45
1005	A133	1000k on 500k #656	.45	.45
1006	A133	1000k on 900k #657	.45	.45
1007	A128	1700k on 50k #639	.70	.70
1008	A128	1700k on 200k #640	.70	.70
1009	A128	1700k on 300k #641	.70	.70
1010	A128	1700k on 500k #642	.70	.70
1011	A125	1800k on 50k #617	.75	.75
1012	A125	1800k on 200k #618	.75	.75
1013	A125	1800k on 250k #619	.75	.75
1014	A125	1800k on 300k #620	.75	.75
1015	A132	2200k on 100k #650	.90	.90
1016	A132	2200k on 300k #651	.90	.90
1017	A132	2200k on 450k #652	.90	.90
1018	A132	2200k on 500k #653	.90	.90
1019	A145	2500k on 500k #710	1.00	1.00
1020	A145	2500k on (O) #711	1.00	1.00
1021	A145	2500k on 900k #712	1.00	1.00
		Nos. 1003-1021 (19)	14.20	14.20

Location of surcharges vary on Nos. 1019-1021.

Miniature Sheet

New Year 2003 (Year of the Ram) — A207

No. 1022 - Background colors: a, Green. b, Blue violet. c, Maroon. d, Purple.

2003, July 30   **Litho.**   **Perf. 13¼**

1022	A207	3200k Sheet of 4, #a-d	5.50	5.50

Intl. Year of Fresh Water — A208

No. 1023: a, Cabora Bassa Dam. b, Lake Kariba. c, Mana Pools National Park. 10,000k, Victoria Falls.

2003, July 30   **Perf. 13½x13¼**

1023	A208	5000k Sheet of 3, #a-c	6.50	6.50

Souvenir Sheet

1024	A208	10,000k multi	4.25	4.25

Powered Flight, Cent. — A209

No. 1025: a, Avro 547A. b, Avro 504O with floats. c, Avro 584 Avrocet. d, Avro 504M. 10,000k, Avro 621 Tutor Replica.

2003, July 30   **Perf. 14**

1025	A209	4000k Sheet of 4, #a-d	6.75	6.75

Souvenir Sheet

1026	A209	9000k multi	4.00	4.00

Bird Type of 2002

Designs: 1000k, White-fronted bee-eaters. 1200k, Little bee-eaters. 1500k, Blue-cheeked bee-eater. 1800k, Boehn's bee-eater.

2003, Dec. 26   **Perf. 13¼**
Size: 25x20mm

1027-1030	A203	Set of 4	2.50	2.50

POSTAGE DUE STAMPS

Type of Northern Rhodesia
Perf. 12½

1964, Oct. 24   **Litho.**   **Unwmk.**

J1	D1	1p orange	.20	.20
J2	D1	2p dark blue	.20	.20
J3	D1	3p rose claret	.25	.25
J4	D1	4p violet blue	.35	.35
J5	D1	6p purple	.50	.50
J6	D1	1sh emerald	1.50	1.50
		Nos. J1-J6 (6)	3.00	3.00

ZANZIBAR

ˈzan-zə-ˌbär

LOCATION — Group of islands about twenty miles off the coast of Tanganyika in East Africa
GOVT. — Republic
AREA — 1,044 sq. mi. (approx.)
POP. — 354,360 (est. 1967)
CAPITAL — Zanzibar

Before 1895, unoverprinted stamps of India were used in Zanzibar.

Zanzibar was a British protectorate until Dec. 10, 1963, when it became independent. After a revolt in January, 1964, a republic was established. Zanzibar joined Tanganyika Apr. 26, 1964, to form the United Republic of Tanganyika and Zanzibar (later renamed Tanzania). See Tanzania.

12 Pies = 1 Anna
16 Annas = 1 Rupee
100 Cents = 1 Rupee (1908)
100 Cents = 1 Shilling (1935)

Catalogue values for unused stamps in this country are for Never Hinged items, beginning with Scott 201 in the regular postage section and Scott J18 in the postage due section.

Watermarks

Wmk. 47 — Multiple Rosette

Wmk. 71 — Rosette

Stamps of British India Overprinted

On Stamps of 1882-95

1895   **Wmk. Star (39)**   **Perf. 14**
Blue Overprint

1	A17	½a green	10,500.	3,000.
2	A19	1a violet brown	2,000.	575.
a.		"Zanzibar"		6,000.

1895-96
Black Overprint

3	A17	½a green	3.00	2.50
a.		"Zanibar"	800.00	550.00
b.		"Zanibar"	850.00	1,250.
c.		"Zapzibar"		
4	A19	1a violet brn	3.25	2.50
a.		"Zanibar"		
b.		"Zanibar"	1,100.	1,250.
5	A20	1a6p bister brn	3.50	2.50
a.		"Zanibar"	2,250.	750.00
b.		"Zanibar"	1,400.	
c.		"Zanibar"	1,000.	1,150.
d.		"Zapzibar"		
6	A21	2a ultra	4.00	3.50
a.		"Zanibar"	2,500.	1,250.
b.		"Zanibar"	3,000.	1,500.
c.		"Zapzibar"		
d.		Double overprint	250.00	
7	A28	2a6p green	5.00	3.75
a.		"Zanibar"	2,750.	1,250.
b.		"Zanibar"	425.00	750.00
c.		"Zapzibar"		
d.		"Zanipar"	900.00	
8	A22	3a orange	8.00	7.00
a.		"Zanibar"	600.00	1,250.
b.		"Zanibar"	3,250.	3,500.
9	A23	4a olive grn	14.00	10.00
a.		"Zanibar"	4,500.	3,000.
10	A25	8a red vio	10.00	15.00
a.		"Zanibar"	4,500.	4,500.
11	A26	12a vio, *red*	12.50	7.50
a.		"Zanibar"	4,500.	3,000.
12	A27	1r gray	80.00	70.00
a.		"Zanibar"	4,000.	3,500.
13	A29	1r car rose & grn	7.50	20.00
a.		Vertical overprint	400.00	
14	A30	2r brn & rose	40.00	60.00
a.		"Zanibar"	5,000.	4,500.
b.		Inverted "r"	3,500.	3,500.
c.		Pair, one without overprint		
15	A30	3r grn & brn	40.00	50.00
a.		"Zanibar"	5,000.	
b.		Inverted "r"	3,250.	3,500.
16	A30	5r vio & blue	37.50	60.00
a.		"Zanibar"	5,000.	
b.		Inverted "r"	2,750.	3,500.
c.		Dbl. ovpt., one invtd.	750.00	

On Stamp of 1873-76
Wmk. Elephant's Head (38)

17	A14	6a bister	14.00	10.00
a.		"Zanzibar"	5,000.	3,000.
b.		"Zanzibarr"	3,500.	3,000.
c.		"Zanziba"	550.00	1,000.
d.		"Zapzibar"		
e.		Double overprint		
		Nos. 3-17 (15)	282.25	324.25

Nos. 4-6 Surcharged:

a   b

c   d

e   2 f

1896   **Wmk. Star (39)**
Black Surcharge

18	(a)	2½a on 1a	175.00	100.0
19	(b)	2½a on 1a	400.00	350.0
20	(c)	2½a on 1a	200.00	150.0

Red Surcharge

21	(a)	2½a on 1a	250.00	400.00
22	(b)	2½a on 1a	600.00	600.00
23	(c)	2½a on 1a	250.00	500.00
24	(a)	2½a on 1a6p	60.00	125.00
a.		"Zanzibar"	1,600.	1,000.
b.		"Zanzibar"	2,000.	1,500.
24C	(b)	2½a on 1a6p	175.00	500.00
25	(c)	2½a on 1a6p	150.00	200.00
26	(d)	2½a on 1a6p	150.00	80.00
27	(e)	2½a on 1a6p	375.00	450.00
27A	(f)	2½a on 1a6p	7,000.	4,000.
28	(a)	2½a on 2a	110.00	250.00
28A	(b)	2½a on 2a	160.00	350.00
29	(c)	2½a on 2a	100.00	250.00
30	(d)	2½a on 2a	65.00	35.00
31	(e)	2½a on 2a	200.00	125.00
31A	(f)	2½a on 2a	3,500.	1,250.

Certain type varieties are found in the word "Zanzibar" on Nos. 1 to 31A viz: Inverted "q" for "b," broken "p" for "n," "i" without dot, small second "z" and tall second "z." These varieties are found on all values from ½a to 1r inclusive and the tall "z" is also found on the 2r, 3r and 5r.

Stamps of British East Africa, 1896, Overprinted in Black or Red

1896   **Wmk. Crown and C A (2)**

32	A8	½a yellow grn	27.50	15.00
33	A8	1a carmine	24.00	15.00
34	A8	2½a dk blue (R)	70.00	40.00
35	A8	4½a orange	40.00	45.00
36	A8	5a dark ocher	45.00	25.00
37	A8	7½a lilac	30.00	40.00
		Nos. 32-37 (6)	236.50	180.00

Sultan Seyyid Hamed-bin-Thwain

A2   A3

1896, Sept. 20   **Engr.**   **Wmk. 71**

38	A2	½a yel grn & red	3.00	1.25
39	A2	1a indigo & red	1.10	1.25
40	A2	2a red brn & red	1.50	.60
41	A2	2½a ultra & red	7.50	1.00
42	A2	3a slate & red	6.00	3.50
43	A2	4a dk green & red	4.00	2.50
44	A2	4½a orange & red	2.75	3.50
45	A2	5a bister & red	2.50	2.00
a.		Half used as 2½a on cover		2,750.
46	A2	7½a lilac & red	2.10	2.00
47	A2	8a ol gray & red	8.00	2.00
48	A3	1r ultra & red	8.50	8.00
49	A3	2r green & red	20.00	8.50
50	A3	3r violet & red	17.00	8.50
51	A3	4r lake & red	14.00	12.00
52	A3	5r blk brn & red	19.00	12.00
		Nos. 38-52 (15)	116.95	72.60

No. 43 Surcharged in Red

1897

53	A2	(a) 2½a on 4a	60.00	40.00
54	A2	(b) 2½a on 4a	200.00	125.00
55	A2	(c) 2½a on 4a	75.00	45.00
		Nos. 53-55 (3)	335.00	210.00

1898   **Engr.**   **Wmk. 47**

56	A2	½a yel grn & red	1.25	.30
57	A2	1a indigo & red	.90	.50
58	A2	2a red brn & red	2.50	.70
58A	A2	2½a ultra & red	1.25	.30
59	A2	3a slate & red	4.00	.60
60	A2	4a dk grn & red	2.00	.90
60A	A2	4½a orange & red	4.50	.60
61	A2	5a bister & red	10.00	1.60

No.	Type	Description	Unused	Used
61A	A2	7½a lilac & red	3.75	2.50
61B	A2	8a ol gray & red	7.00	2.00
		Nos. 56-61B (10)	37.15	10.00

Sultan Seyyid Hamoud-bin-Mahommed-bin-Said
A4   A5

1899-1901

No.	Type	Description	Unused	Used
62	A4	½a yel grn & red	1.50	.50
63	A4	1a indigo & red	3.50	.25
64	A4	1a car & red ('01)	1.50	.25
65	A4	2a red brn & red	1.75	.45
66	A4	2½a ultra & red	1.50	.55
67	A4	3a slate & red	1.50	1.90
68	A4	4a dk green & red	2.50	1.10
69	A4	4½a orange & red	7.00	1.90
70	A4	4½a ind & red ('01)	10.00	10.00
71	A4	5a bister & red	2.25	1.10
72	A4	7½a lilac & red	2.50	3.25
73	A4	8a ol gray & red	2.50	3.75

Wmk. 71

No.	Type	Description	Unused	Used
74	A5	1r ultra & red	16.00	12.50
75	A5	2r green & red	16.00	15.00
76	A5	3r violet & red	25.00	30.00
77	A5	4r lilac rose & red	37.50	42.50
78	A5	5r gray brown & red	42.50	50.00
		Nos. 62-78 (17)	175.00	175.00

For surcharges see Nos. 94-98.

Monogram of Sultan Ali bin Hamoud
A6   A7

1904, June 8   Typo.   Wmk. 47

No.	Type	Description	Unused	Used
79	A6	½a emerald	1.00	.75
80	A6	1a rose red	1.00	.20
81	A6	2a bister brown	1.00	.40
82	A6	2½a ultra	2.00	.30
83	A6	3a gray	2.00	1.90
84	A6	4a blue green	2.00	1.40
85	A6	4½a black	2.50	2.10
86	A6	5a ocher	2.75	1.10
87	A6	7½a violet	3.50	6.00
88	A6	8a olive green	3.25	2.10
89	A7	1r ultra & red	17.50	8.75
90	A7	2r green & red	15.00	30.00
91	A7	3r violet & red	35.00	62.50
92	A7	4r magenta & red	40.00	75.00
93	A7	5r olive & red	42.50	82.50
		Nos. 79-93 (15)	171.00	275.00

Nos. 69-70, 72-73 Surcharged in Black or Lake:

1904

No.	Type	Description	Unused	Used
94	A4 (g)	1a on 4½a	1.25	2.75
95	A4 (g)	1a on 4½a (L)	3.75	12.00
96	A4 (h)	2a on 4a (L)	12.00	13.00
97	A4 (i)	2½a on 7½a	11.00	14.00
a.		"Hlaf"	10,000	
98	A4 (i)	2½a on 8a	12.50	22.50
a.		"Hlaf"	9,500.	5,000.
		Nos. 94-98 (5)	40.50	64.25

Sultan Ali bin Hamoud
A8   A9

A10

Palace of the Sultan — A11

1908-09   Engr.   Wmk. 47

No.	Type	Description	Unused	Used
99	A8	1c gray ('09)	1.50	.25
100	A8	3c yellow grn	3.00	.20
101	A8	6c carmine	5.75	.20
102	A8	10c org brn ('09)	1.60	1.75
103	A8	12c violet	8.25	2.10
104	A9	15c ultra	6.50	.35
105	A9	25c brown	2.40	.90
106	A9	50c dp green	4.00	3.25
107	A9	75c slate ('09)	7.00	10.50
108	A10	1r yellow green	20.00	10.50
109	A10	2r violet	14.50	12.50
110	A10	3r yellow brown	18.00	42.20
111	A10	4r red	35.00	67.50
112	A10	5r blue	32.50	47.50
113	A11	10r brn & dk grn	100.00	200.00
114	A11	20r yel grn & blk	200.00	400.00
115	A11	30r dk brn & blk	250.00	500.00
116	A11	40r org brn & blk	400.00	
117	A11	50r lilac & blk	350.00	
118	A11	100r blue & blk	700.00	
119	A11	200r black & brn	1,100.	
		Nos. 99-112 (14)	160.00	199.70

It is probable that Nos. 118 and 119 were used only for fiscal purposes.

Sultan Khalifa bin Harub — A12

Dhow — A13

Dhow — A14

1913   Perf. 14

No.	Type	Description	Unused	Used
120	A12	1c gray	.20	.20
121	A12	3c yellow grn	.30	.20
122	A12	6c carmine	.80	.20
123	A12	10c brown	.70	.80
124	A12	12c violet	.65	.20
125	A12	15c ultra	.90	.35
126	A12	25c black brn	.70	.45
127	A12	50c dk green	2.00	2.75
128	A12	75c dk gray	1.50	1.50
129	A13	1r yellow grn	3.00	4.00
130	A13	2r dk violet	7.00	18.00
131	A13	3r orange	10.00	25.00
132	A13	4r red	17.50	45.00
133	A13	5r blue	25.00	27.50
134	A14	10r brown & grn	60.00	100.00
135	A14	20r yel grn & blk	85.00	175.00
136	A14	30r dk brn & blk	100.00	250.00
137	A14	40r orange & blk	200.00	350.00
138	A14	50r dull vio & blk	225.00	350.00
139	A14	100r blue & blk	350.00	350.00
140	A14	200r black & brn	700.00	700.00
		Nos. 120-134 (15)	130.25	226.15

1914-22   Wmk. 3

No.	Type	Description	Unused	Used
141	A12	1c gray	.20	.25
142	A12	3c yellow grn	.70	.20
143	A12	6c carmine	.70	.20
144	A12	8c vio, yel ('22)	.65	2.25
145	A12	10c dk grn, yel ('22)	.50	.40
146	A12	15c ultra	.75	2.50
148	A12	50c dark green	4.00	4.50
149	A12	75c deep gray	2.50	17.00
150	A13	1r yellow grn	4.00	2.50
151	A13	2r dark violet	13.00	22.50
152	A13	3r brown org	14.00	60.00
153	A13	4r red	15.00	45.00
154	A13	5r blue	60.00	175.00
155	A14	10r brown & grn	120.00	339.30
		Nos. 141-155 (14)		

1921-29   Wmk. 4

No.	Type	Description	Unused	Used
156	A12	1c gray	.20	7.00
157	A12	3c yellow grn	.20	2.00
158	A12	3c orange ('22)	.20	.20
159	A12	4c green ('22)	.40	.40
160	A12	6c carmine	.30	.40
161	A12	6c vio, bl ('22)	.50	.20
162	A12	10c lt brown	.70	5.00
163	A12	12c violet	.50	.35
164	A12	12c carmine ('22)	.50	.50
165	A12	15c ultra	.70	4.50
166	A12	20c dk blue ('22)	.75	.70
167	A12	25c black brn	.85	6.50
168	A12	50c blue green	1.00	1.50
169	A12	75c dark gray	2.00	30.00
170	A13	1r yellow grn	2.00	1.60
171	A13	2r dk violet	2.00	5.00
172	A13	3r ocher	3.50	6.00
173	A13	4r red	8.00	25.00
174	A13	5r blue	13.00	45.00
175	A14	10r brown & grn	45.00	125.00
176	A14	20r green & blk	110.00	200.00
177	A14	30r dk brn & blk ('29)	150.00	300.00
		Nos. 156-175 (20)	82.30	266.85

Sultan Khalifa bin Harub ("CENTS" with Serifs) — A15

1926-27

No.	Type	Description	Unused	Used
184	A15	1c brown	.20	.20
185	A15	3c yellow org	.20	.20
186	A15	4c deep green	.25	.25
187	A15	6c dark violet	.35	.20
188	A15	8c slate	.75	1.60
189	A15	10c olive green	.60	.25
190	A15	12c deep red	1.25	.20
191	A15	20c ultra	.60	.25
192	A15	25c violet, yel	3.00	1.00
193	A15	50c claret	.80	.40
194	A15	75c olive brown	5.25	7.00
		Nos. 184-194 (11)	13.25	11.55

> **Catalogue values for unused stamps in this section, from this point to the end of the section, are for Never Hinged items.**

"CENTS" without Serifs — A16

Dhow — A17

Dhow — A18

1936   Perf. 14

No.	Type	Description	Unused	Used
201	A16	5c deep green	.20	.20
202	A16	10c black	.20	.20
203	A16	15c carmine	.30	.20
204	A16	20c brown org	.40	.20
205	A16	25c violet, yel	.50	.30
206	A16	30c ultra	.60	.35
207	A16	40c black brown	.60	.45
208	A16	50c claret	.90	.65
209	A17	1sh yellow grn	1.25	.65
210	A17	2sh dark violet	2.00	.95
211	A17	5sh red	6.75	4.50
212	A17	7.50sh blue	9.00	9.00
213	A18	10sh brn & grn	10.00	7.50
		Nos. 201-213 (13)	32.70	25.10

For overprints see Nos. 222-223.

A19

A20

1936, Dec. 9

No.	Type	Description	Unused	Used
214	A19	10c olive grn & blk	.75	.30
215	A19	20c red violet & blk	2.25	.50
216	A19	30c deep ultra & blk	5.50	.75
217	A19	50c red orange & blk	6.50	2.00
		Nos. 214-217 (4)	15.00	3.55

Reign of Sultan Khalifa bin Harub, 25th anniv.

Perf. 14
1944, Nov. 20   Engr.   Wmk. 4

Dhow & Map Showing Zanzibar & Muscat.

No.	Type	Description	Unused	Used
218	A20	10c violet blue	.50	1.00
219	A20	20c brown orange	.50	1.25
220	A20	50c Prus green	.50	.25
221	A20	1sh dull purple	.50	.35
		Nos. 218-221 (4)	2.00	2.85

200th anniv. of the Al Busaid Dynasty.

Nos. 202 and 206 Overprinted in Red

1946, Nov. 11

No.	Type	Description	Unused	Used
222	A16	10c black	.20	.20
223	A16	30c ultra	.30	.30

Victory of the Allied Nations in WW II.

Common Design Types pictured following the introduction.

Silver Wedding Issue
Common Design Types
1949, Jan. 10   Photo.   Perf. 14x14½

No.	Type	Description	Unused	Used
224	CD304	20c orange	.60	.60

Engraved; Name Typographed
Perf. 11½x11

No.	Type	Description	Unused	Used
225	CD305	10sh light brown	15.00	22.50

UPU Issue
Common Design Types
Engr.; Name Typo. on 30c, 50c
Perf. 13½, 11x11½
1949, Oct. 10   Wmk. 4

No.	Type	Description	Unused	Used
226	CD306	20c red orange	.30	1.00
227	CD307	30c indigo	1.10	.50
228	CD308	50c red lilac	1.25	1.00
229	CD309	1sh blue green	1.25	2.00
		Nos. 226-229 (4)	3.90	4.50

Sultan Khalifa bin Harub — A21

Seyyid
Khalifa
Schools
A22

Perf. 12x12½, 13x12½

1952, Aug. 26			Engr.	
230	A21	5c black	.20	.20
231	A21	10c red orange	.20	.20
232	A21	15c green	.30	.20
233	A21	20c carmine	.30	.20
234	A21	25c plum	.50	.25
235	A21	30c blue green	.25	.25
236	A21	35c ultra	.25	.40
237	A21	40c chocolate	.25	.50
238	A21	50c purple	.65	.45
239	A22	1sh choc & bl grn	.25	.60
240	A22	2sh claret & ultra	1.25	1.40
241	A22	5sh carmine & blk	1.25	2.50
242	A22	7.50sh emer & gray	15.00	13.50
243	A22	10sh gray blk & rose red	8.00	5.50
		Nos. 230-243 (14)	28.65	26.15

Sultan Khalifa bin
Harub — A23

1954, Aug. 26			Perf. 12½x12	
244	A23	15c green	.20	.20
245	A23	20c scarlet	.20	.20
246	A23	30c ultra	.25	.25
247	A23	50c purple	.40	.40
248	A23	1.25sh brown orange	.95	.95
		Nos. 244-248 (5)	2.00	2.00

The frames differ on Nos. 245 and 247. Sultan Khalifa bin Harub, 75th birth anniv.

Cloves — A24

Sultan's
Barge — A26

Dhows
A25

Malindi Minaret
Mosque — A27

Kibweni
Palace — A28

Sultan Khalifa bin Harub and: 25c, 35c, and 50c Map showing location of Zanzibar. 1sh, 2sh, Dimbani Mosque.

**Perf. 11½ (A24), 11x11½ (A25),
14x13½ (A26), 13½x14 (A27),
13x13½ (A28)**

1957, Aug. 26			Engr.	Wmk. 314
249	A24	5c dull grn & org	.20	.20
250	A24	10c rose car & brt grn	.20	.20
251	A25	15c dk brn & grn	.20	.20
252	A26	20c ultra	.20	.20
253	A26	25c blk & brn org	.20	.20
254	A25	30c int blk & rose car	.20	.20
255	A26	35c brt grn & ind	.20	.20

256	A27	40c int blk & redsh brn		
257	A26	50c dull grn & bl	.20	.20
258	A27	1sh int blk & brt car	.30	.25
259	A25	1.25sh rose car & dk grn	.40	.30
260	A27	2sh dull grn & org	.55	.45
261	A25	5sh ultra	.75	.65
262	A28	7.50sh green	1.60	1.25
263	A28	10sh rose carmine	2.75	5.75
		Nos. 249-263 (15)	3.75	3.25
			11.70	13.50

Sultan Seyyid
Abdulla bin
Khalifa — A29

Designs as before with portrait of Sultan Seyyid Abdulla bin Khalifa.

**Perf. 11½ (A29), 11x11½ (A25),
14x13½ (A26), 13½x14 (A27)**

1961, Oct. 17			Engr.	Wmk. 314
264	A29	5c dull grn & org	.20	.20
265	A29	10c rose car & brt grn	.20	.20
266	A25	15c dk brn & grn	.20	.20
267	A26	20c ultra	.20	.20
268	A26	25c blk & brn org	.20	.20
269	A25	30c int blk & rose car	.20	.20
270	A26	35c brt grn & indigo	.20	.20
271	A27	40c int blk & redsh brn	.20	.20
272	A26	50c dull grn & bl	.20	.20
273	A27	1sh int blk & brt car	.30	.25
274	A25	1.25sh rose car & dk grn	.60	.60
275	A27	2sh dull grn & org	.65	.65

		Perf. 13x13½		
276	A28	5sh ultra	1.25	1.10
277	A28	7.50sh green	2.75	2.75
278	A28	10sh rose carmine	3.25	3.25
279	A28	20sh dk brown	8.00	8.00
		Nos. 264-279 (16)	18.60	18.40

For overprints see Nos. 285-300.

Freedom from Hunger Issue

Common Design Type with Portrait of
Sultan Seyyid Abdulla bin Khalifa

1963, June 4			Photo.	Perf. 14x14½
280	CD314	1.30sh sepia	.55	.55

Independent State

Sultan Seyyid
Jamshid bin
Abdulla and
Zanzibar
Clove — A30

Designs: 50c, "To Prosperity," arch and sun. 1.30sh, "Religious Tolerance," composite view of churches and mosques, horiz. 2.50sh, "Towards the Light," Mangapwani Cave.

Perf. 12½

1963, Dec. 10			Photo.	Unwmk.
281	A30	30c multicolored	.20	.20
282	A30	50c multicolored	.30	.30
283	A30	1.30sh multicolored	.40	.40
284	A30	2.50sh multicolored	.65	.65
		Nos. 281-284 (4)	1.55	1.55

Zanzibar's independence, Dec. 10, 1963. For overprints see Nos. 301-304.

Republic

Nos. 264-279
Overprinted

1964, Feb. 28			As Before	
285	A29	5c dull grn & org	.20	.20
286	A29	10c rose car & brt grn	.20	.20
287	A25	15c dk brn & grn	.20	.20
288	A26	20c ultra	.20	.20
289	A25	25c blk & brn org	.20	.20
290	A25	30c int blk & rose car	.20	.20

291	A26	35c brt grn & ind	.20	.20
292	A27	40c int blk & redsh brn	.20	.20
293	A26	50c dull grn & blue	.20	.20
294	A27	1sh int blk & brt car	.20	.20
295	A25	1.25sh rose car & dk grn	.20	.20
296	A27	2sh dull grn & org	.35	.35
297	A25	5sh ultra	1.00	1.00
298	A28	7.50sh green	1.50	1.50
299	A28	10sh rose carmine	1.90	1.90
300	A28	20sh dark brown	3.50	3.50
		Nos. 285-300 (16)	10.45	10.45

The overprint was applied in England. It is in 2 lines on 40c and 1sh to 20sh. "Jamhuri" means "republic."

Overprint Handstamped

285a	A29	5c	.25	.25
286a	A29	10c	.25	.25
287a	A25	15c	.25	.25
288a	A26	20c	.25	.25
289a	A25	25c	.25	.25
290a	A25	30c	.25	.25
291a	A26	35c	.25	.25
292a	A27	40c	.25	.25
293a	A26	50c	.25	.25
294a	A27	1sh	.25	.25
295a	A25	1.25sh	.30	.30
296a	A27	2sh	1.50	1.50
297a	A25	5sh	3.50	3.50
298a	A28	7.50sh	6.00	6.00
299a	A28	10sh	6.50	6.50
300a	A28	20sh	8.00	8.00
		Nos. 285a-300a (16)	28.30	28.30

This overprint was applied locally. It has one line of serifed letters. These are found diagonal, vertical, horizontal, double and inverted. See Nos. 301a-304b. Other stamps with this overprint, including postage dues, were unofficial.

Nos. 281-284
Overprinted

1964, Feb. 28			As Before	
301	A30	30c multi	.20	.20
302	A30	50c multi	.30	.30
303	A30	1.30sh multi	.45	.45
304	A30	2.50sh multi	.75	.75
a.		Green omitted	60.00	
		Nos. 301-304 (4)	1.70	1.70

One-line overprint on 1.30sh.

Overprint Handstamped

301a	A30	30c	.20	.20
302a	A30	50c	.30	.30
303a	A30	1.30sh	.45	.45
304b	A30	2.50sh	.75	.75
		Nos. 301a-304b (4)	1.70	1.70

See note after No. 300a.

Moorish Arch, Ax,
Sword and
Spear — A31

Designs: 10c, 20c, Arch and arrow piercing chain. 25c, 40c, Man with rifle. 30c, 50c, Man breaking chain. 1sh, Man, flag and sun. 1.30sh, Hands breaking chain and cloves, horiz. 2sh, Hands waving flag, horiz. 5sh, Map of Zanzibar and Pemba and flag, horiz. 10sh, Flag and map of Zanzibar and Pemba. 20sh, Flag of Zanzibar, horiz

Perf. 13x13½, 13½x13

1964, June 21			Litho.	Unwmk.
305	A31	5c multicolored	.20	.20
306	A31	10c multicolored	.20	.20
307	A31	15c multicolored	.20	.20
308	A31	20c multicolored	.20	.20
309	A31	25c multicolored	.20	.20
310	A31	30c multicolored	.20	.20
311	A31	40c multicolored	.20	.20
312	A31	50c multicolored	.20	.20
313	A31	1sh multicolored	.25	.25
314	A31	1.30sh multicolored	.30	.30
315	A31	2sh multicolored	.50	.50
316	A31	5sh multicolored	1.10	1.10
317	A31	10sh multicolored	2.00	2.00
318	A31	20sh multicolored	4.25	4.25
		Nos. 305-318 (14)	10.00	10.00

Soldier and
Maps of
Zanzibar and
Pemba
A32

Reconstruction
A33

Perf. 13½x13, 13x13½

1965, Jan. 12			Unwmk.	
319	A32	20c green & yel grn	.20	.20
320	A33	30c dk brn & ocher	.20	.20
321	A32	1.30sh vio blue & blue	.30	.30
322	A33	2.50sh purple & rose	.55	.55
		Nos. 319-322 (4)	1.25	1.25

First anniversary of the revolution.

Zanzibar and Tanzania

Rice
Planting
A34

Design: 30c, 1.30sh, Hands holding rice.

Perf. 13x12½

1965, Oct. 17			Litho.	Unwmk.
323	A34	20c blue & blk brn	.20	.20
324	A34	30c brt pink & blk brn	.20	.20
325	A34	1.30sh org & blk brn	.30	.30
326	A34	2.50sh emer & blk brn	.60	.60
		Nos. 323-326 (4)	1.30	1.30

Issued to publicize agricultural development.

Symbols of
Trade,
Agriculture,
Industry and
Education
A35

Pres. Abeid Amani
Karume and Vice-
Pres. Abdulla
Kassim Hanga
A36

Designs: 50c, 2.50sh, Soldier and sunburst.

1966, Jan. 12 Litho. Perf. 12½x13

327	A35	20c ultra, red & gray	.20	.20
328	A35	50c black & yel	.20	.20
329	A35	1.30sh multicolored	.35	.35
330	A35	2.50sh black & org	.55	.55
		Nos. 327-330 (4)	1.30	1.30

2nd anniv. of the revolution of Jan. 12, 1964.

1966, Apr. 26 Photo. Perf. 13½x13

Design: 50c, 1.30sh, Flag, laurel and hands holding Flame of the Union (inscribed: Jamhuri Tanzania Zanzibar).

331	A36	30c multicolored	.20	.20
332	A36	50c multicolored	.20	.20
333	A36	1.30sh multicolored	.30	.30
334	A36	2.50sh multicolored	.55	.55
		Nos. 331-334 (4)	1.25	1.25

Union of Tanganyika and Zanzibar, 2nd anniv.

Logging A37

10c, 1sh, Clove trees & man. 15c, 40c, Cabinetmaker. 20c, 5sh, Lumumba College & book. 25c, 1.30sh, Farmer & tractor. 30c, 2sh, Volunteer farm workers. 50c, 10sh, Street scene, vert.

Perf. 13x12½, 12½x13

1966, June 5 Litho.

335	A37	5c lemon & vio brn	.20	.20
336	A37	10c brt grn & vio brn	.20	.20
337	A37	15c vio brn & bl	.20	.20
338	A37	20c vio bl & org	.20	.20
339	A37	25c vio brn & yel	.20	.20
340	A37	30c vio brn & dl yel	.20	.20
341	A37	40c vio brn & rose	.20	.20
342	A37	50c green & yel	.20	.20
343	A37	1sh ultra & vio brn	.25	.25
344	A37	1.30sh lt bl grn & vio brn	.35	.35
345	A37	2sh brt grn & vio brn	.45	.45
346	A37	5sh ver & gray	1.25	1.25
347	A37	10sh red brn & yel	2.50	2.50
348	A37	20sh brt pink & vio brn	5.00	5.00
		Nos. 335-348 (14)	11.40	11.40

Symbols of Education — A38

1966, Sept. 25 Perf. 13½x13

349	A38	50c blue, blk & org	.20	.20
350	A38	1.30sh blue, blk & yel grn	.30	.30
351	A38	2.50sh blue, blk & pink	.50	.50
		Nos. 349-351 (3)	1.00	1.00

Introduction of free education.

People and Flag A39

Design: 50c, 1.30sh, Vice-President Abdulla Kassim Hanga, flag and crowd, vert.

Perf. 14x14½, 14½x14

1967, Feb. 5 Litho. Unwmk.

352	A39	30c multicolored	.20	.20
353	A39	50c multicolored	.20	.20
354	A39	1.30sh multicolored	.30	.30
355	A39	2.50sh multicolored	.55	.55
		Nos. 352-355 (4)	1.25	1.25

10th anniversary of Afro-Shirazi Party.

Volunteer Workers A40

Perf. 12½x12

1967, Aug. 20 Photo. Unwmk.

| 356 | A40 | 1.30sh multicolored | .30 | .30 |
| 357 | A40 | 2.50sh multicolored | .55 | .55 |

Volunteer (Young) Workers Brigade.
All Zanzibar stamps were withdrawn July 1, 1968, and replaced with current Kenya, Uganda and Tanzania stamps.

POSTAGE DUE STAMPS

D1

1931 Rouletted 10 Typeset Unwmk. Thin Paper Without Gum

J1	D1	1c blk, orange	7.50	
J2	D1	2c blk, orange	2.25	
J3	D1	3c blk, orange	3.00	
J3A	D1	6c blk, orange		
J4	D1	9c blk, orange	2.00	
J4A	D1	12c blk, orange		
J4B	D1	12c blk, green	1,250.	500.00
J5	D1	15c blk, orange	2.00	6.50
J6	D1	18c blk, orange	8.00	
a.		18c black, salmon	4.00	
J7	D1	20c blk, orange	4.00	
J8	D1	21c blk, orange	2.75	
J8A	D1	25c blk, orange		
J8B	D1	25c blk, magenta	1,750.	
J9	D1	31c blk, orange	8.00	
J10	D1	50c blk, orange	20.00	
J11	D1	75c blk, orange	50.00	

The variety "cent.s" occurs once on each sheet of Nos. J3 to J11 inclusive.

D2

1931-33 Rouletted 5 Thick Paper

J12	D2	2c blk, salmon	3.00	
J13	D2	3c blk, rose	2.75	
J14	D2	6c blk, yellow	2.75	
J15	D2	12c blk, blue	4.00	
J16	D2	25c blk, pink	9.00	
J17	D2	25c blk, dull violet	7.50	
		Nos. J12-J17 (6)	29.00	

Catalogue values for unused stamps in this section, from this point to the end of the section, are for Never Hinged items.

D3

1936 Typo. Wmk. 4 Perf. 14

J18	D3	5c violet	1.75	5.50
J19	D3	10c carmine	1.75	2.50
J20	D3	20c green	1.25	3.50
J21	D3	30c brown	4.25	12.50
J22	D3	40c ultra	4.25	19.00
J23	D3	1sh gray	4.25	22.00
		Nos. J18-J23 (6)	17.50	65.00

Chalky paper was introduced in 1956 for the 5c, 30c, 40c, 1sh, and in 1962 for the 10c, 20c. See note after No. 300a.

ZIMBABWE

zim-'bä-bwē

LOCATION — Southeastern Africa, bordered by Zambia, Mozambique, South Africa, and Botswana
GOVT. — Republic
AREA — 150,872 sq. mi.
POP. — 11,163,160 (1999 est.)
CAPITAL — Harare

Formerly Rhodesia, the Republic of Zimbabwe was established April 18, 1980.

100 Cents = 1 Dollar

Catalogue values for all unused stamps in this country are for Never Hinged items.

Morganite A69   Black Rhinoceros A70

Odzani Falls — A71

Perf. 14½, 14½x14 (A70)

1980 Litho.

414	A69	1c shown	.20	.25
415	A69	3c Amethyst	.30	.25
416	A69	4c Garnet	.30	.20
417	A69	5c Citrine	.30	.20
418	A69	7c Blue topaz	.30	.20
419	A70	9c shown	.20	.20
420	A70	11c Lion	.20	.20
421	A70	13c Warthog	.20	.20
422	A70	15c Giraffe	.20	.20
423	A70	17c Zebra	.20	.20
424	A71	21c shown	.20	.20
425	A71	25c Goba Falls	.25	.25
426	A71	30c Inyangombe Falls	.30	.40
426A	A71	40c Bundi Falls	5.50	3.75
427	A71	$1 Bridal Veil Falls	.40	1.60
428	A71	$2 Victoria Falls	.70	3.00
		Nos. 414-428 (16)	9.75	11.30

Rotary International, 75th Anniversary — A72

1980, June 18 Perf. 14½

429	A72	4c multicolored	.20	.20
430	A72	13c multicolored	.20	.30
431	A72	21c multicolored	.25	.50
432	A72	25c multicolored	.35	.75
a.		Souvenir sheet of 4, #429-432	1.40	1.40
		Nos. 429-432 (4)	1.00	1.75

Olympic Rings A73

1980, July 19

| 433 | A73 | 17c multicolored | .30 | .35 |

22nd Summer Olympic Games, Moscow, July 19-Aug. 3.

Gatooma Post Office, 1912 A74

Post Offices: 7c, Salisbury, 1912. 9c, Umtali, 1901. 17c, Bulawayo, 1895.

1980 Litho. Perf. 14½

434	A74	5c multicolored	.20	.20
435	A74	7c multicolored	.20	.20
436	A74	9c multicolored	.20	.20
437	A74	17c multicolored	.25	.25
a.		Souvenir sheet of 4, #434-437	1.00	1.25
		Nos. 434-437 (4)	.85	.85

Post Office Savings Bank, 75th anniv.

Intl. Year of the Disabled — A75   Natl. Tree Day — A76

Designs: Various disabilities. Nos. 438-441 form a continuous design.

1981, Sept. 23 Litho. Perf. 14½

438	A75	5c multicolored	.20	.20
439	A75	7c multicolored	.20	.20
440	A75	11c multicolored	.20	.20
441	A75	17c multicolored	.25	.25
		Nos. 438-441 (4)	.85	.85

1981, Dec. 4

442	A76	5c Msasa	.20	.20
443	A76	7c Mopane	.20	.20
444	A76	21c Flat-crowned acacia	.70	.70
445	A76	30c Pod mahogany	.90	.90
		Nos. 442-445 (4)	2.00	2.00

Rock Paintings A77

Designs: 9c, Khoisan figures, Gwamgwadza Cave. 11c, Kudus, human figures, Epworth Mission. 17c, Diana's Vow, Rusape. 21c, Giraffes, Gwamgwadza Cave. 25c, Warthog, Mucheka Cave. 30c, Hunters, Shinzwini Shelter.

1982, Mar. 17 Litho. Perf. 14½

446	A77	9c multicolored	.60	.60
447	A77	11c multicolored	.75	.75
448	A77	17c multicolored	1.00	1.00
449	A77	21c multicolored	1.50	1.50
450	A77	25c multicolored	1.50	1.50
451	A77	30c multicolored	2.25	2.25
		Nos. 446-451 (6)	7.60	7.60

Scouting Year — A78

1982, July 21

452	A78	9c Emblem	.35	.35
453	A78	11c Campfire	.40	.40
454	A78	21c Map reading	.75	.75
455	A78	30c Baden Powell	1.00	1.00
		Nos. 452-455 (4)	2.50	2.50

TB
Bacillus
Centenary
A79

1982, Nov. 17 Perf. 14½
456 A79 11c Koch 1.00 1.25
457 A79 30c Scientist examining
slide 2.00 2.25

Commonwealth Day — A80

Sculptures: 9c, Wing Woman, by Henry Mudzengerere, vert. 11c, Telling Secrets, by Joseph Ndandarika. 30c, Hornbill Man, by John Takawira. $1, The Chief, by Nicholas Mukomberanwa, vert.

1983, Mar. 14 Perf. 14½
458 A80 9c multicolored .20 .20
459 A80 11c multicolored .20 .20
460 A80 30c multicolored .30 .35
461 A80 $1 multicolored .80 1.50
Nos. 458-461 (4) 1.50 2.25

World Plowing Contest, May — A81

No. 463, mechanized plowing.

1983, May 13 Litho. Perf. 14½
462 A81 Pair .70 .70
a.-b. 21c, any single .35 .35
463 A81 Pair .90 .90
a.-b. 30c, any single .45 .45

World Communications Year — A82

Means of communication and transportation. Nos. 464-467 vert.

1983, Oct. 12 Litho. Perf. 14½
464 A82 9c Mailman .20 .20
465 A82 11c Signaling airplane .25 .25
466 A82 15c Telephone operators .40 .40
467 A82 17c Reading newspapers .50 .50
468 A82 21c Truck on highway .60 .60
469 A82 30c Train .90 .90
Nos. 464-469 (6) 2.85 2.85

Zimbabwe Intl.
Trade Fair,
Bulawayo, May 5-
13 — A83

1984, Apr. 11 Litho. Perf. 14½
470 A83 9c shown .20 .20
471 A83 11c Globe .20 .20
472 A83 30c Emblem .50 .50
Nos. 470-472 (3) .90 .90

1984
Summer
Olympics
A84

Children's Drawings.

1984, July 18 Litho. Perf. 14½
473 A84 11c Bicycling .25 .20
474 A84 21c Swimming .50 .50
475 A84 30c Running .80 .80
476 A84 40c Hurdles 1.10 1.75
Nos. 473-476 (4) 2.65 3.25

Heroes'
Day
A85

1984, Aug. 8 Litho. Perf. 14½
477 A85 9c Heroes .20 .20
478 A85 11c Monument, vert. .25 .25
479 A85 17c Statue, vert. .45 .45
480 A85 30c Bas-relief .75 .75
Nos. 477-480 (4) 1.65 1.65

Fish Eagle — A86

1984, Oct. 10 Litho. Perf. 14½
481 A86 9c shown .60 .60
482 A86 11c Long crested eagle .65 .65
483 A86 13c Bateleur .75 .75
484 A86 17c Black eagle 1.00 1.00
485 A86 21c Martial eagle 1.25 1.25
486 A86 30c African hawk eagle 1.75 1.75
Nos. 481-486 (6) 6.00 6.00

Superheat Engine No. 86,
Mashonaland Railways, 1918 — A87

Steam locomotives: 11c, Engine No. 190, North British Locomotive Co., 1926. 17c, Engine No. 424, Beyer Peacock & Co., 1950. Engine No. 726, Beyer Peacock & Co., 1957.

1985, May 15 Litho.
487 A87 9c multicolored .80 .80
488 A87 11c multicolored 1.10 1.10
489 A87 17c multicolored 1.75 1.75
490 A87 30c multicolored 3.00 3.00
Nos. 487-490 (4) 6.65 6.65

INTELSAT V
A88

57c, Mazowe Earth Satellite Station.

Perf. 14½x14, 14½
1985, July 8 Litho.
491 A88 26c multicolored 1.75 2.00

Size: 62x23mm
492 A88 57c multicolored 3.50 4.00

Zimbabwe Bird
and
Tobacco — A89

Agriculture and industry.

Perf. 14¾x14½
1985, Aug. 21 Litho.
493 A89 1c shown .20 .20
a. Perf 14¼x13¾ — —
494 A89 3c Corn .20 .20
a. Perf 14¼x13¾ — —
495 A89 4c Cotton .20 .20
a. Perf 14¼x13¾ — —
496 A89 5c Tea .30 .20
497 A89 10c Cattle .30 .20
a. Perf 14¼x13¾ — —
498 A89 11c Birchenough
Bridge .80 .20
499 A89 12c Stamp mill 1.25 .20
500 A89 13c Gold production 2.40 .20
501 A89 15c Coal mining 1.75 .20
a. Perf 14¼x13¾ — —
502 A89 17c Amethyst mining 2.40 .30
503 A89 57c Electric train 2.40 .30
504 A89 20c Kariba Dam 1.60 .20
a. Perf 14¼x13¾ — —
505 A89 23c Elephants 2.50 .30
506 A89 25c Zambezi River
sunset .65 .30
507 A89 26c Baobab tree .65 .25
508 A89 30c Great Zimbabwe
ruins .80 .30
509 A89 35c Folk dancing .65 .30
510 A89 45c Crushing corn .80 .45
511 A89 57c Wood carving .80 .70
512 A89 $1 Mbira drum 1.25 .90
513 A89 $2 Mule-drawn
scotch cart 2.10 3.00
514 A89 $5 Natl. coat of arms 4.00 5.00
Nos. 493-514 (22) 28.00 14.10

Natl.
Archives,
50th
Anniv.
A90

Designs: 12c, Gatsi Rusere (c. 1589-1623), ruler of Mashonaland and Zambezi area; mutapa, 17th cent. 18c, Lobengula, ruler of Ndebele State (1870-94), sketch by E. A. Maund, 1889; 1888 Moffat Treaty and elephant seal. 26c, Archives exhibition hall. 35c, Archives building.

1985, Sept. 18 Perf. 14½
515 A90 12c multicolored .20 .20
516 A90 18c multicolored .25 .25
517 A90 26c multicolored .35 .35
518 A90 35c multicolored .50 .50
Nos. 515-518 (4) 1.30 1.30

UN
Decade
for
Women
A91

1985, Nov. 13
519 A91 10c Computer operator .50 .50
520 A91 17c Nurse, child .75 .75
521 A91 26c Engineer 1.25 1.25
Nos. 519-521 (3) 2.50 2.50

Harare Conference Center — A92

1986, Jan. 29 Litho. Perf. 14½
523 A92 26c Facade .90 .90
524 A92 35c Interior 1.60 1.60

Southern African Development
Coordination Conference — A93

1986, Apr. 1 Perf. 14½
525 A93 12c Grain elevators .45 .45
526 A93 18c Rhinoceros 2.40 2.40
527 A93 26c Map, jet 2.40 2.40
528 A93 35c Map, flags 2.75 2.75
Nos. 525-528 (4) 8.00 8.00

Moths — A94

1986, June 18 Litho. Perf. 14½x14
529 A94 12c Jackson's emperor 1.50 1.50
530 A94 18c Oleander hawk 2.00 2.00
531 A94 26c Zaddach's emperor 2.50 2.50
532 A94 35c Southern marbled
emperor 3.00 3.00
Nos. 529-532 (4) 9.00 9.00

8th Non-
aligned
Summit
Conference
A95

1986, Aug. 28 Litho. Perf. 14½x14
533 A95 26c Victoria Falls 2.50 2.50

Size: 66x26mm
Perf. 14½
534 A95 $1 Great Zimbabwe
Enclosure 5.50 5.50

Motoring
Cent.
A96

1986, Oct. 8 Perf. 14½
535 A96 10c Sopwith, 1921 .60 .60
536 A96 12c Gladiator, 1902 .60 .60
537 A96 17c Douglas, 1920 .90 .90
538 A96 26c Ford Model-A, 1930 1.40 1.40
539 A96 35c Schacht, 1909 1.75 1.75
540 A96 40c Benz Velocipede,
1886 1.75 1.75
Nos. 535-540 (6) 7.00 7.00

A97   A98

UN Child Survival Campaign: a, Growth monitoring. b, Breast-feeding. c, Oral rehydration. d, Immunization.

1987, Feb. 11 Litho. Perf. 14x14½
541 Block of 4 6.50 6.50
a.-d. A97 12c any single 1.50 1.50

1987, Apr. 15 — Perf. 14½
Indigenous owls.

542	A98	12c Barred	2.00	2.00
543	A98	18c Pearl-spotted	2.50	2.50
544	A98	26c White-faced	3.00	3.00
545	A98	35c Scops	4.50	4.50
		Nos. 542-545 (4)	12.00	12.00

Natl. Girl Guides Movement, 75th Anniv. — A99

1987, June 24
546	A99	15c Commitment	.70	.70
547	A99	23c Adventure	.90	.90
548	A99	35c Service	1.00	1.00
549	A99	$1 Intl. friendship	2.40	2.40
		Nos. 546-549 (4)	5.00	5.00

Duikers and Population Maps — A100

1987, Oct. 7 — Perf. 14½x14
550	A100	15c Common gray	.80	.80
551	A100	23c Zebra	.95	.95
552	A100	25c Yellow-backed	.95	.95
553	A100	30c Blue	1.10	1.10
554	A100	35c Jentink's	1.10	1.10
555	A100	38c Red	1.10	1.10
		Nos. 550-555 (6)	6.00	6.00

Insects A101

1988, Jan. 12 — Litho. — Perf. 14½
556	A101	15c Praying mantis	.80	.20
557	A101	23c Scarab beetle	.95	.30
558	A101	35c Short-horned grasshopper	1.25	1.00
559	A101	45c Giant shield bug	1.50	2.50
		Nos. 556-559 (4)	4.50	4.00

Natl. Gallery of Art, 30th Anniv. — A102

Aloes and Succulents A103

Sculpture and paintings: 15c, Cockerel, by Arthur Azevedo. 23c, Changeling, by Bernard Matemera. 30c, Spirit Python, by Henry Munyaradzi. 35c, Spirit Bird Carrying People, by Thomas Mukarobgwa, horiz. 38c, The Song of the Shepherd Boy, by George Nene, horiz. 45c, War Victim, by Joseph Muzondo, horiz.

Perf. 14x14½, 14½x14
1988, Apr. 14 — Litho.
560	A102	15c multicolored	.20	.20
561	A102	23c multicolored	.25	.25
562	A102	30c multicolored	.35	.35
563	A102	35c multicolored	.45	.45

564	A102	38c multicolored	.45	.45
565	A102	45c multicolored	.55	.55
		Nos. 560-565 (6)	2.25	2.25

1988, July 14 — Perf. 14½
566	A103	15c Aloe cameronii bondana	.25	.25
567	A103	23c Orbeopsis caudata	.45	.45
568	A103	25c Euphorbia wildii	.45	.45
569	A103	30c Euphorbia fortissima	.50	.50
570	A103	35c Aloe aculeata	.50	.50
571	A103	38c Huernia zebrina	.60	.60
		Nos. 566-571 (6)	2.75	2.75

A104

1988, Oct. 6 — Litho. — Perf. 14½x14
572	A104	15c White-faced duck	.70	.20
573	A104	23c Pygmy goose	.80	.30
574	A104	30c Hottentot teal	.90	.90
575	A104	35c Knob-billed duck	1.00	1.00
576	A104	38c White-backed duck	1.10	1.10
577	A104	45c Maccoa	1.50	2.00
		Nos. 572-577 (6)	6.00	5.50

Geckos A105

1989, Jan. 10 — Litho. — Perf. 14½
578	A105	15c O'Shaughnessy's banded	.75	.75
579	A105	23c Tiger rock	.85	.85
580	A105	35c Tasman's	1.40	1.40
581	A105	45c Bibron's	1.50	1.50
		Nos. 578-581 (4)	4.50	4.50

Wildflowers A106

1989, Apr. 12 — Litho. — Perf. 14½
582	A106	15c Spotted-leaved arum-lily	.40	.40
583	A106	23c Grassland vlei-lily	.50	.50
584	A106	30c Manica protea	.50	.50
585	A106	35c Flame lily	.60	.60
586	A106	38c Poppy hibiscus	.65	.65
587	A106	45c Blue sesbania	.75	.75
		Nos. 582-587 (6)	3.40	3.40

Fish A107

1989, July 12 — Litho. — Perf. 14½
588	A107	15c Red-breasted bream	.65	.20
589	A107	23c Chessa	.85	.20
590	A107	30c Eastern bottle-nose	.95	.75
591	A107	35c Vundu	.95	.75
592	A107	38c Largemouth black bass	1.10	1.10
593	A107	45c Tiger fish	1.50	1.75
		Nos. 588-593 (6)	6.00	4.75

See Nos. 696-701.

Endangered Species A108

1989 — Litho. — Perf. 14½x14
594	A108	15c Black rhinoceros	1.25	1.25
595	A108	23c Cheetah	1.40	1.40
596	A108	30c Wild dog	1.50	1.50
597	A108	35c Pangolin	1.50	1.50
598	A108	38c Brown hyena	1.60	1.60
599	A108	45c Roan antelope	1.75	1.75
		Nos. 594-599 (6)	9.00	9.00

Achievements, 1980-1990 A109

1990, Apr. 17 — Litho. — Perf. 14½x14
600	A109	15c Unity accord	.40	.20
601	A109	23c Conference center	.45	.20
602	A109	30c Education	.50	.50
603	A109	35c Satellite dish	.60	.60
604	A109	38c Sports stadium	.60	.60
605	A109	45c Agriculture	.95	1.50
		Nos. 600-605 (6)	3.50	3.60

City of Harare, Cent. A110

1990, July 11 — Litho. — Perf. 14½
606	A110	15c Runhare house, 1986	.40	.40
607	A110	23c Market hall, 1894	.55	.55
608	A110	30c Charter house, 1959	.60	.60
609	A110	35c Supreme Court, 1927	.65	.65
610	A110	38c Standard Chartered Bank, 1911	.65	.65
611	A110	45c Town house, 1933	.90	.90
		Nos. 606-611 (6)	3.75	3.75

36th Commonwealth Parliamentary Conf. — A111

1990, Sept. 17
612	A111	35c Speaker's mace	.50	.50
613	A111	$1 Speaker's chair	1.75	1.75

Animals — A112

Hand Crafts — A113

Transportation — A114

Perf. 14, 14¾x14½ (#615, 617, 619), 14½x14 (#620-625), 14¼ (#626)
1990, Jan. 2 — Litho.
614	A112	1c Tiger fish	.20	.20
a.		Perf 14¾x14½	—	—
615	A112	2c Helmeted guineafowl	.35	.35
a.		Perf 14¾x14½	—	—
616	A112	3c Scrub hare	.20	.20
a.		Perf 14¾x14½	—	—
617	A112	4c Pangolin	.20	.20
a.		Perf 14¾x14½	—	—
618	A112	5c Greater kudu	.30	.30
619	A112	9c Black rhinoceros	.90	.90
a.		Perf 14	—	—
620	A113	15c Head rest	.20	.20
621	A113	20c Hand axe	.20	.20
622	A113	23c Gourd, water pot	.20	.20
623	A113	25c Snuff box	.20	.20
624	A113	26c Winnowing basket	.25	.25
625	A113	30c Grinding stone	.25	.25
626	A113	33c Riding bicycles	.55	.55
627	A114	35c Buses	.90	.90
628	A114	38c Train	.90	.90
629	A114	45c Motorcycle, trailer	.90	.90
630	A114	$1 Jet	1.40	1.40
631	A114	$2 Tractor-trailer truck	1.40	1.40
		Nos. 614-631 (18)	9.50	9.50

Animals A115

A116

1991, Jan. 15 — Litho. — Perf. 14½x14
632	A115	15c Small-spotted genet	.85	.85
633	A115	23c Red squirrel	.90	.90
634	A115	35c Night ape	1.25	1.25
635	A115	45c Bat-eared fox	1.75	1.75
		Nos. 632-635 (4)	4.75	4.75

1991, Apr. 16 — Litho. — Perf. 14½
Traditional musical instruments.

636	A116	15c Hosho	.45	.20
637	A116	23c Mbira	.50	.20
638	A116	30c Ngororombe	.55	.55
639	A116	35c Chipendani	.70	.70
640	A116	38c Marimba	.70	.70
641	A116	45c Ngoma	.85	1.10
		Nos. 636-641 (6)	3.75	3.45

Wild Fruits — A117

A118

1991, July 17   Litho.   Perf. 14x14½
642 A117 20c Snot-apple   .55   .55
643 A117 39c Marula   .65   .65
644 A117 51c Mobola plum   .70   .70
645 A117 60c Water berry   .80   .80
646 A117 65c Northern dwaba
              berry   .85   .85
647 A117 77c Mahobohobo   .95   .95
      Nos. 642-647 (6)   4.50 4.50

See Nos. 870-875.

1991, Oct. 16   Litho.   Perf. 14½
648 A118 20c Bridal Veil Falls   .60   .60
649 A118 39c Conference Em-
              blem   .60   .60
650 A118 51c Chinhoyi Caves   .75   .75
651 A118 60c Kariba Dam Wall   .85   .85
652 A118 65c Victoria Falls   .95   .95
653 A118 77c Balancing Rocks   1.00 1.00
      Nos. 648-653 (6)   4.75 4.75

Commonwealth Heads of Government
meeting, Harare.

Wild Cats
A119

1992, Jan. 8   Litho.   Perf. 14½
654 A119 20c Lion   .75   .20
655 A119 39c Leopard   1.10   .55
656 A119 60c Cheetah   1.75 1.75
657 A119 77c Serval   2.40 2.25
      Nos. 654-657 (4)   6.00 4.75

Mushrooms
A120

Birds — A121

Designs: 20c, Amanita zambiana. 39c,
Boletus edulis. 51c, Termitomyces. 60c,
Cantharellus densifolius. 65c, Cantharellus
longisporus. 77c, Cantharellus cibarius.

1992, Apr. 8   Litho.   Perf. 14x14½
658 A120 20c multicolored   .65   .65
659 A120 39c multicolored   .90   .90
660 A120 51c multicolored   1.00 1.00
661 A120 60c multicolored   1.10 1.10
662 A120 65c multicolored   1.25 1.25
663 A120 77c multicolored   1.60 1.60
      Nos. 658-663 (6)   6.50 6.50

1992, July 17   Litho.   Perf. 14½
664 A121 25c Blackeyed bulbul   .65   .65
665 A121 59c Fiscal shrike   .90   .90
666 A121 77c Forktailed dron-
              go   1.00 1.00
667 A121 90c Cardinal wood-
              pecker   1.10 1.10
668 A121 98c Yellowbilled
              hornbill   1.10 1.10
669 A121 $1.16 Crested francolin 1.25 1.25
      Nos. 664-669 (6)   6.00 6.00

Butterflies
A122

1992, Oct. 15   Litho.   Perf. 14½x14
670 A122 25c Foxy charaxes   .75   .75
671 A122 59c Orange & lem-
              on   1.40 1.40

672 A122 77c Emperor swal-
              lowtail   1.60 1.60
673 A122 90c Blue pansy   1.90 1.90
674 A122 98c African mon-
              arch   2.10 2.10
675 A122 $1.16 Gaudy com-
              modore   2.25 2.25
      Nos. 670-675 (6)   10.00 10.00

Minerals
A123

Owls — A124

1993, Jan. 12   Litho.   Perf. 14½x14
676 A123 25c Autunite   .20   .20
677 A123 59c Chromite   .30   .30
678 A123 77c Azurite   .35   .35
679 A123 90c Coal   .40   .40
680 A123 98c Gold   .45   .45
681 A123 $1.16 Emerald   .55   .55
      Nos. 676-681 (6)   2.25 2.25

1993, Apr. 6   Litho.   Perf. 14½
682 A124 25c Wood owl   .20   .20
683 A124 59c Pels fishing owl   .25   .25
684 A124 90c Spotted eagle
              owl   .35   .35
685 A124 $1.16 Giant eagle owl   .45   .45
      Nos. 682-685 (4)   1.25 1.25

Household
Pottery
A125

Orchids — A126

1993, July 13   Litho.   Perf. 14½x14
686 A125 25c Hadyana   .20   .20
687 A125 59c Chirongo   .25   .25
688 A125 77c Mbiya   .30   .30
689 A125 90c Pfuko   .35   .35
690 A125 98c Tsaya   .40   .40
691 A125 $1.16 Gate   .45   .45
      Nos. 686-691 (6)   1.95 1.95

1993, Oct. 12   Litho.   Perf. 14½
692 A126 35c Polystachya den-
              drobiflora   .20   .20
693 A126 $1 Diaphananthe
              subsimplex   .40   .40
694 A126 $1.50 Ansellia gigantea   .60   .60
695 A126 $1.95 Vanilla polyepis   .75   .75
      Nos. 692-695 (4)   1.95 1.95

Fish Type of 1989

1994, Jan. 20   Litho.   Perf. 14½
696 A107 35c Hunyani salmon   .20   .20
697 A107 $1 Barbel   .40   .40
698 A107 $1.30 Rainbow trout   .50   .50
699 A107 $1.50 Mottled eel   .60   .60
700 A107 $1.65 Mirror carp   .65   .65
701 A107 $1.95 Robustus bream   .75   .75
      Nos. 696-701 (6)   3.10 3.10

City of
Bulawayo,
Cent.
A127

1994, Apr. 5   Litho.   Perf. 14½
702 A127 35c City Hall   .20   .20
703 A127 80c Cresta Churchill
              Hotel   .20   .20
704 A127 $1.15 High Court   .30   .30
705 A127 $1.75 Douslin House   .40   .40
706 A127 $1.95 Goldfields Build-
              ing   .50   .50
707 A127 $2.30 Parkade Centre   .55   .55
      Nos. 702-707 (6)   2.15 2.15

Export
Flowers — A128   Christmas — A129

1994, July 12   Litho.   Perf. 14½
708 A128 35c Strelitzia   .20   .20
709 A128 80c Protea   .20   .20
710 A128 $1.15 Phlox   .30   .30
711 A128 $1.75 Chrysanthemum   .45   .45
712 A128 $1.95 Lillum   .50   .50
713 A128 $2.30 Rose   .60   .60
      Nos. 708-713 (6)   2.25 2.25

1994, Oct. 11   Litho.   Perf. 14½
Designs: 35c, Archangel Gabriel, Virgin
Mary. 80c, Mary, Joseph on way to Bethlehem. $1.15, Nativity scene. $1.75, Angel
pointing way to shepherds. $1.95, Magi follow-
ing star. $2.30, Madonna and child.

714 A129 35c multicolored   .20   .20
715 A129 80c multicolored   .20   .20
716 A129 $1.15 multicolored   .30   .30
717 A129 $1.75 multicolored   .40   .40
718 A129 $1.95 multicolored   .50   .50
719 A129 $2.30 multicolored   .55   .55
      Nos. 714-719 (6)   2.15 2.15

A130

1995-96   Litho.   Perf. 14
720 A130 1c Corn   .20   .20
721 A130 2c Sugar cane   .20   .20
722 A130 3c Sunflowers   .20   .20
723 A130 4c Sorghum   .20   .20
724 A130 5c Mine workers   .20   .20
725 A130 10c Underground
              mining   .20   .20
726 A130 20c Coal mining   .20   .20
727 A130 30c Chrome smelting   .20   .20
728 A130 40c Opencast mining   .20   .20
728A A130 45c Underground
              drilling   .20   .20
729 A130 50c Gold smelting   .20   .20
730 A130 70c Boggie Clock
              Tower   .20   .20
731 A130 80c Masvingo
              Watchtower   .20   .20
732 A130 $1 Hanging tree   .25   .25
733 A130 $2 Cecil House   .50   .50
734 A130 $5 The Toposcope   1.25 1.25
735 A130 $10 Paper House   2.50 2.50
      Nos. 720-735 (17)   7.10 7.10

Issued: 45c, 6/3/96; others, 1/17/95.

Insects
A131

6th All Africa
Games,
Harare — A132

1995, Apr. 4   Litho.   Perf. 14
736 A131 35c Spider-hunting
              wasp   .20   .20
737 A131 $1.15 Emperor dragon-
              fly   .30   .3
738 A131 $1.75 Foxy charaxes   .40   .4
739 A131 $2.30 Antlion   .55   .5
      Nos. 736-739 (4)   1.45 1.45

1995, July 11   Litho.   Perf. 14x14½
740 A132 35c Soccer   .20   .20
741 A132 80c Track   .20   .20
742 A132 $1.15 Boxing   .30   .30
743 A132 $1.75 Swimming   .40   .40
744 A132 $1.95 Field hockey   .45   .45
745 A132 $2.30 Volleyball   .55   .55
      Nos. 740-745 (6)   2.10 2.10

UN, 50th
Anniv. — A133

1995, Oct. 17   Litho.   Perf. 14½
746 A133 35c Health   .20   .20
747 A133 $1.15 Environment   .30   .30
748 A133 $1.75 Food distribution   .40   .40
749 A133 $2.30 Education   .55   .55
      Nos. 746-749 (4)   1.45 1.45

Flowering
Trees — A134

1996, Jan. 24   Litho.   Perf. 14½
750 A134 45c Fernandoa   .20   .20
751 A134 $1 Round leaf
              mukwa   .20   .20
752 A134 $1.50 Luckybean tree   .30   .30
753 A134 $2.20 Winter cassia   .45   .45
754 A134 $2.50 Sausage tree   .55   .55
755 A134 $3 Sweet thorn   .65   .65
      Nos. 750-755 (6)   2.35 2.35

Dams of
Zimbabwe
A135

1996, Apr. 9   Litho.   Perf. 14½
756 A135 45c Mazvikadei   .20   .20
757 A135 $1.50 Mutirikwi   .30   .30
758 A135 $2.20 Ncema   .45   .45
759 A135 $3 Odzani   .60   .60
      Nos. 756-759 (4)   1.55 1.55

Scenic
Views
A136

Designs: 45c, Matusadonha Natl. Park.
$1.50, Juliasdale Rocky Outcrops. $2.20,
Honde Valley. $3, Finger Rocks, Morgenster
Mission.

1996, July 18   Litho.   Perf. 14½

760	A136	45c multicolored	.20	.20
761	A136	$1.50 multicolored	.30	.30
762	A136	$2.20 multicolored	.45	.45
763	A136	$3 multicolored	.60	.60
		Nos. 760-763 (4)	1.55	1.55

Wood Carvings
A137

1996, Oct. 15   Litho.   Perf. 14½

764	A137	45c Frog	.20	.20
765	A137	$1.50 Tortoise	.30	.30
766	A137	$1.70 Kudu	.35	.35
767	A137	$2.20 Chimpanzee	.45	.45
768	A137	$2.50 Porcupine	.50	.50
769	A137	$3 Rhinoceros	.60	.60
		Nos. 764-769 (6)	2.40	2.40

Cattle
A138

1997, Jan. 7   Litho.   Perf. 14½

770	A138	45c Mashona cow	.20	.20
771	A138	$1.50 Tuli cow	.30	.30
772	A138	$2.20 Nkoni bull	.40	.40
773	A138	$3 Brahman bull	.55	.55
		Nos. 770-773 (4)	1.45	1.45

Convention on Intl. Trade in Endangered Species of Flora and Fauna (CITES) — A139

1997, Apr. 15   Litho.   Perf. 14½

774	A139	45c Cycad	.20	.20
775	A139	$1.50 Peregrine falcon	.25	.25
776	A139	$1.70 Pangolin	.30	.30
777	A139	$2.20 Black rhinoceros	.40	.40
778	A139	$2.50 Elephant	.45	.45
779	A139	$3 Python	.55	.55
		Nos. 774-779 (6)	2.15	2.15

Aspects of Rural Life
A140

1997, July 22   Litho.   Perf. 14½

780	A140	65c Carving	.20	.20
781	A140	$1 Winnowing	.20	.20
782	A140	$2.40 Dancing	.40	.40
783	A140	$2.50 Plowing	.45	.45
784	A140	$3.10 Stamping	.55	.55
785	A140	$4.20 Fetching water	.75	.75
		Nos. 780-785 (6)	2.55	2.55

Zimbabwe Railway, Cent.
A141

1997, Oct. 28   Litho.   Perf. 14½

786	A141	65c Passenger coach	.20	.20
787	A141	$1 12th Class, No. 257	.20	.20
788	A141	$2.40 16A Class, No. 605	.35	.35
789	A141	$2.50 El 1, No. 4107	.35	.35
790	A141	$3.10 Jack Tar	.45	.45
791	A141	$4.20 DE 2, No. 1211	.60	.60
		Nos. 786-791 (6)	2.15	2.15

Wildlife
A142

1998, Jan. 20   Litho.   Perf. 14½

792	A142	65c Aardwolf	.20	.20
793	A142	$2.40 Large gray mongoose	.25	.25
794	A142	$3.10 Clawless otter	.35	.35
795	A142	$4.20 Antbear (Aardvark)	.45	.45
		Nos. 792-795 (4)	1.25	1.25

Apiculture
A143

Designs: $1.20, Honeybee on flower. $4.10, Queen, worker, drone. $4.70, Queen, retinue. $5.60, Rural beekeeper. $7.40, Commercial beekeepers. $9.90, Products of the hive.

1998, Apr. 14   Litho.   Perf. 14

796	A143	$1.20 multicolored	.20	.20
797	A143	$4.10 multicolored	.50	.50
798	A143	$4.70 multicolored	.60	.60
799	A143	$5.60 multicolored	.70	.70
800	A143	$7.40 multicolored	.90	.90
801	A143	$9.90 multicolored	1.20	1.20
		Nos. 796-801 (6)	4.10	4.10

Fossils
A144

1998, July 21   Litho.   Perf. 14½

802	A144	$1.20 Fossil fish	.20	.20
803	A144	$5.60 Allosaurus footprints	.60	.60
804	A144	$7.40 Massospondylus	.80	.80
805	A144	$9.90 Fossil wood	1.10	1.10
		Nos. 802-805 (4)	2.70	2.70

Birds — A145

Designs: $1.20, Yellow-bellied sunbird. $4.10, Lesser blue-eared starling. $4.70, Greyhooded kingfisher. $5.60, Mombo gray tit. $7.40, Chirinda apalis. $9.90, Swynnerton's robin.

1998, Oct. 20   Litho.   Perf. 14

806	A145	$1.20 multicolored	.20	.20
807	A145	$4.10 multicolored	.25	.25
808	A145	$4.70 multicolored	.30	.30
809	A145	$5.60 multicolored	.35	.35
810	A145	$7.40 multicolored	.45	.45
811	A145	$9.90 multicolored	.60	.60
		Nos. 806-811 (6)	2.15	2.15

UPU, 125th Anniv. — A146

$1.20, Counter services at Post Office and Philatelic Bureau. $5.60, Postman delivering mail on bicycle. $7.40, 19th cent. runner, EMS, PTC delivery today. $9.90, Harare Central Sorting Office.

1999, Jan. 19   Litho.   Perf. 14

812	A146	$1.20 multicolored	.20	.20
813	A146	$5.60 multicolored	.25	.25
814	A146	$7.40 multicolored	.35	.35
815	A146	$9.90 multicolored	.45	.45
		Nos. 812-815 (4)	1.25	1.25

A147

Wild cats of Zimbabwe.

1999, Mar. 16   Litho.   Perf. 14

816	A147	$1.20 Serval	.20	.20
817	A147	$5.60 Cheetah	.30	.30
818	A147	$7.40 Caracal	.40	.40
819	A147	$9.90 Leopard	.55	.55
		Nos. 816-819 (4)	1.45	1.45

A148

1999, June 8   Litho.   Perf. 14¼

Owls.

820	A148	$1.20 Cape eagle owl	.20	.20
821	A148	$5.60 Grass owl	.30	.30
822	A148	$7.40 Barn owl	.40	.40
823	A148	$9.90 Marsh owl	.50	.50
		Nos. 820-823 (4)	1.40	1.40

Tourist Activities
A149

1999, Aug. 10   Litho.   Perf. 14¼x14

824	A149	$2 Canoeing	.20	.20
825	A149	$6.70 Rock climbing	.35	.35
826	A149	$7.70 Microlighting	.40	.40
827	A149	$9.10 White water rafting	.50	.50
828	A149	$12 Scenic view	.65	.65
829	A149	$16 Viewing game	.90	.90
		Nos. 824-829 (6)	3.00	3.00

A150   A151

Christmas: $2, Christmas time - Family time. $6.70, Christmas tree in Africa. $7.70, Joy to you this Christmas. $9.10, Christmas time - Flame lily time. $12, Glory to God & Peace on Earth. $16, The House of Christmas.

1999, Oct. 12   Litho.   Perf. 14x14¼

830	A150	$2 multi	.20	.20
831	A150	$6.70 multi	.35	.35
832	A150	$7.70 multi	.40	.40
833	A150	$9.10 multi	.50	.50
834	A150	$12 multi	.65	.65
835	A150	$16 multi	.90	.90
		Nos. 830-835 (6)	3.00	3.00

2000, Jan. 25   Litho.   Perf. 14¾

Designs: 1c, Nyala. 10c, Construction. 30c, Timber. 50c, Tobacco auction floors. 70c, Harare Central Sorting Office. 80c, New international airport, Harare. $1, Westgate Shopping Complex. $2, Nile crocodile. $3, Pungwe water project. $4, Zebra. $5, Mining. $7,

National University of Science and Technology. $10, Ostrich. $15, Cape parrot. $20, Leather products. $30, Lilac-breasted roller. $50, Victoria Falls. $100, Tokwe Mukorsi Dam.

836	A151	1c multi	.20	.20
837	A151	10c multi	.20	.20
838	A151	30c multi	.20	.20
839	A151	50c multi	.20	.20
840	A151	70c multi	.20	.20
841	A151	80c multi	.20	.20
842	A151	$1 multi	.20	.20
843	A151	$2 multi	.20	.20
844	A151	$3 multi	.20	.20
845	A151	$4 multi	.20	.20
846	A151	$5 multi	.25	.25
847	A151	$7 multi	.35	.35
848	A151	$10 multi	.55	.55
849	A151	$15 multi	.80	.80
850	A151	$20 multi	1.00	1.00
851	A151	$30 multi	1.60	1.60
852	A151	$50 multi	2.60	2.60
853	A151	$100 multi	5.25	5.25
		Nos. 836-853 (18)	14.40	14.40

Sports — A152

2000, Apr. 25   Litho.   Perf. 14

854	A152	$2 Basketball	.20	.20
855	A152	$6.70 Lawn tennis	.35	.35
856	A152	$7.70 Netball	.45	.45
857	A152	$9.10 Weight lifting	.50	.50
858	A152	$12 Taekwondo	.65	.65
859	A152	$16 Diving	.90	.90
		Nos. 854-859 (6)	3.05	3.05

Dr. Joshua Nkomo (1917-99), Vice-President
A153

Designs: $2, $12, Wearing suit. $9.10, $16, Wearing headdress.

2000, June 27   Litho.   Perf. 14x14¼
Background Color

860	A153	$2 blue	.20	.20
861	A153	$9.10 green	.50	.50
862	A153	$12 red	.65	.65
863	A153	$16 orange	.85	.85
		Nos. 860-863 (4)	2.20	2.20

Organizations Combatting Disease
A154

Designs: $2, Ministry of Health. $6.70, Rehabilitation and Prevention of Tuberculosis (RAPT). $7.70, New Start centers. $9.10, Riders for Health. $12, Natl. Aids Coordination Program (NACP). $16, Rotary Intl.

2000, July 18   Litho.   Perf. 14¼x14

864	A154	$2 multi	.20	.20
865	A154	$6.70 multi	.35	.35
866	A154	$7.70 multi	.40	.40
867	A154	$9.10 multi	.50	.50
868	A154	$12 multi	.65	.65
869	A154	$16 multi	.85	.85
		Nos. 864-869 (6)	2.95	2.95

Wild Fruits Type of 1991

$2, Masawu. $6.70, Spiny monkey orange. $7.70, Bird plum. $9.10, Shakama plum. $12, Wild medlar. $16, Wild custard apple.

2000, Oct. 24   Litho.   Perf. 14x14½

870-875	A117	Set of 6	2.00	2.00

Aviation
A155

Designs: $8, Boeing 737-200. $12, BAe Hawk MK 60. $14, Hawker Hunter FGA-9. $16, Cessna/Reims F-337. $21, Aerospatiale Alouette III helicopter. $28, Boeing 767-200ER.

2001, Jan. 31   Litho.   *Perf. 14¼*
876-881 A155   Set of 6   3.75   3.75

Total Solar Eclipse, June 21, 2001 — A156

Designs: $8, Solar prominences. $21, Eclipse path over Africa. $28, Eclipse phases (62x24mm).

Perf. 14¼x14, 14½ ($28)
2001, Apr. 24   Litho.
882-884 A156   Set of 3   2.00   2.00

Folklore — A157

Designs: $8, The Hare Who Rode Horseback. $12, The Hippo Who Lost His Hair. $13, The Lion Who Was Saved by a Mouse. $16, The Bush Fowl Who Wakes the Sun. $21, The Chameleon Who Came Too Late. $28, The Tortoise Who Collected Wisdom.

2001, July 24   Litho.   *Perf. 14x14¼*
885-890 A157   Set of 6   3.50   3.50
    a.   Souvenir sheet, #885-890   3.50   3.50

Heroes' Acre — A158

Designs: $8, Main entrance gate. $16, Statue of the Unknown Soldier. $21, General view. $28, Aerial view.

2001, Aug. 7   Litho.   *Perf. 14¼x14*
891-894 A158   Set of 4   2.60   2.60

Year of Dialogue Among Civilizations
A159

Winning stamp design entry in: $8, National competition (Three Faces, by Nation Mandla Mguni). $21, International competition.

2001, Oct. 16   Litho.   *Perf. 14¼*
895-896 A159   Set of 2   1.10   1.10

Butterflies
A160

Designs: $12, Large blue charaxes. $20, Painted lady. $25, Yellow pansy. $30, Gold-banded forester. $35, Sapphire. $45, Clear-spotted acrea.

2001, Dec. 6   Litho.   *Perf. 14¼x14*
897-902 A160   Set of 6   6.00   6.00
902a   Souvenir sheet, #897-902   6.00   6.00

Craftsmanship
A161

Designs: $12, Knitting and crocheting. $20, Art and design. $25, Basket making. $30, Pottery. $35, Wood carving. $45, Sculpture.

2002, Jan. 22
903-908 A161   Set of 6   6.00   6.00

Gemstones
A162

Designs: $12, Agate. $25, Aquamarine. $35, Diamond. $45, Emerald.

2002, Apr. 23   Litho.   *Perf. 14¼x14*
909-912 A162   Set of 4   4.25   4.25

Childline
A163

Children's art: $12, Children embracing. $25, Girl on phone. $35, Teddy bear. $45, Arm with phone receiver.

2002, June 4   Litho.   *Perf. 14¼x14*
913-916 A163   Set of 4   4.25   4.25

First Lady Sally Mugabe (1931-92) — A164

Various portraits: $20, $50, $70, $90.

2002, Aug. 6   *Perf. 14x14¼*
917-920 A164   Set of 4   8.25   8.25

Children's Stamp Design Contest Winners
A165

Designs: $20, Mail runner and bicycle at post office, by Agreement Ngwenya. $70, Mail runner and airplane, by Kudzai Chikomo.

2002, Oct. 8   Litho.   *Perf. 14¼*
921-922 A165   Set of 2   3.25   3.25

Wild Flowers
A166

Designs: $20, Dissotis princeps. $35, Leonotis nepetifolia. $40, Hibiscus vitifolius. $50, Boophane disticha. $70, Pycnostachys urticifolia. $90, Gloriosa superba.

2002, Oct. 22   *Perf. 14¼x14*
923-928 A166   Set of 6   11.00   11.00
928a   Souvenir sheet, #923-928   11.00   11.00

History Society of Zimbabwe, 50th Anniv. — A167

Map of Zimbabwe and: $30, Society emblem. $80, Hourglass, books, diploma. $110, People listening to speaker. $140, Old building.

2003, Jan. 28   Litho.   *Perf. 14x14¼*
929-932 A167   Set of 4   .90   .90

Harare Intl. Festival of the Arts — A168

Designs: $30, Festival emblem. $80, Emblem and flower. $110, Eye and flowers. $140, Emblem and flowers.

2003, Apr. 22   Litho.   *Perf. 14x14¼*
933-936 A168   Set of 4   .90   .90

Type of 2000

Designs: ($100), Bateleur eagle. $500, Goliath heron. $1000, White rhinoceros. $5000, Cheetah.

2003, June 24   Litho.   *Perf. 14¾*
937 A151   ($100) multi   .25   .25
938 A151 $500 multi   1.25   1.25
939 A151 $1000 multi   2.50   2.50
940 A151 $5000 multi   12.50   12.50
    Nos. 937-940 (4)   16.50   16.50

Spiders
A169

Designs: $150, Baboon spider. $200, Rain spider. $600, Black widow spider. $900, Wolf spider. $1250, Violin spider. $1600, Wall spider.

2003, July 30   *Perf. 14¼*
941-946 A169   Set of 6   11.50   11.50
946a   Souvenir sheet, #941-946   11.50   11.50

Women Empowerment
A170

Woman in cap and gown with: $300, Globe, hoe and briefcase. $2100, Traditional woman.

2003, Oct. 14   Litho.   *Perf. 14½*
947-948 A170   Set of 2   6.00   6.00

Endangered Medicinal Herbs — A171

Designs: $200, Wild verbena. $500, Pimpernel. $1000, African arrowroot. $3000, Bird pepper. $4200, Wild garlic. $5400, Cleome.

2003, Oct. 28   *Perf. 14x14½*
949-954 A171   Set of 6   7.00   7.00

Environmental Awareness
A172

Designs: $500, Environment Africa. $3000, Sondela. $4200, Water Africa. $5400, Tree Africa.

2004, Feb. 17   Litho.   *Perf. 14x14¼*
955-958 A172   Set of 4   6.75   6.75

Medals — A173

Designs: $1500, Zimbabwe Independence Medal. $9000, Bronze Cross of Zimbabwe. $13,000, Silver Cross of Zimbabwe. $16,500, Gold Cross of Zimbabwe.

2004, Apr. 6   Litho.   *Perf. 14¼*
959-962 A173   Set of 4   18.00   18.00

POSTAGE DUE STAMPS

D1   D2

1981   Litho.   *Perf. 14½*
J20 D1   1c emerald   .20   .20
J21 D1   2c ultramarine   .20   .20
J22 D1   5c lilac   .25   .25
J23 D1   6c yellow   .35   .35
J24 D1   10c red   .75   .75
    Nos. J20-J24 (5)   1.75   1.75
For surcharge see No. J30.

1985, Aug. 21   Litho.   *Perf. 14½*
J25 D2   1c pale orange   .20   .20
J26 D2   2c lilac rose   .20   .20
J27 D2   6c light green   .20   .20
J28 D2   10c tan   .20   .20
J29 D2   13c bright blue   .20   .20
    Nos. J25-J29 (5)   1.00   1.00

No. J24
Surcharged

1990, Jan. 2   Litho.   Perf. 14½

J30	D1	25c on 10c #J24	10.00	10.00

D3   D4

1995, Jan. 17   Litho.   Perf. 14½

J31	D3	1c yellow	.20	.20
J32	D3	2c yellow orange	.20	.20
J33	D3	5c rose lilac	.20	.20
J34	D3	10c pale blue	.20	.20
J35	D3	25c violet	.20	.20
J36	D3	40c green	.20	.20
J37	D3	60c orange	.20	.20
J38	D3	$1 brown	.30	.30
		Nos. J31-J38 (8)	1.70	1.70

2000, Jan. 25   Litho.   Perf. 14½

Bird sculpture.

J39	D4	1c blk, lt grn & grn	.20	.20
J40	D4	10c blk, lt blue & blue	.20	.20
J41	D4	50c blk, lt brn & brn	.20	.20
J42	D4	$1 blk, pink & red	.20	.20
J43	D4	$2 blk, lt yel & yel	.20	.20
J44	D4	$5 blk, lil & red vio	.25	.25
J45	D4	$10 blk, lt ver & ver	.55	.55
		Nos. J39-J45 (7)	1.80	1.80

ZULULAND

ˈzü-ₒlü-ˌland

LOCATION — Northeastern part of Natal, South Africa
GOVT. — British Colony, 1887-1897
AREA — 10,427 sq. mi.
POP. — 230,000 (estimated 1900)
CAPITAL — Eshowe

12 Pence = 1 Shilling
20 Shillings = 1 Pound

Stamps of Great Britain
Overprinted

1888-93   Wmk. 30   Perf. 14

1	A54	½p vermilion	3.50	3.00
2	A40	1p violet	29.00	4.50
3	A56	2p green & red	14.00	27.50
4	A57	2½p vio, bl ('91)	22.50	22.50
5	A58	3p violet, yel	29.00	25.00
6	A59	4p green & brn	50.00	65.00
7	A61	5p lil & bl ('93)	100.00	150.00
8	A62	6p vio, rose	15.00	20.00
9	A63	9p blue & lil ('92)	97.50	100.00
10	A65	1sh green ('92)	125.00	150.00

Wmk. 31

11	A51	5sh rose ('92)	600.00	700.00
		Nos. 1-10 (10)	485.50	567.50

Natal No. 66
Overprinted

1888-94   Wmk. 2

12	A14	½p green, no period	26.00	45.00
a.		Period after "Zululand"	62.50	85.00
b.		As "a," double overprint	1,600.	1,750.
c.		As "a," invtd. overprint	1,400.	
d.		As "a," pair, one without ovpt.	6,250.	
e.		As No. 12, double overprint	1,600.	1,750.

Natal No. 71 Ovptd. Like Nos. 1-11

13	A11	6p violet ('94)	62.50	62.50

A1   A2

1891

14	A1	1p lilac	3.50	3.50

By proclamation of the Governor of Zululand, dated June 27th, 1891, No. 14 was declared to be a postage stamp.

1894-96   Typo.

15	A2	½p lilac & grn	3.75	5.00
16	A2	1p lilac & rose	5.75	2.00
17	A2	2½p lilac & blue	16.00	9.75
18	A2	3p lilac & brn	9.25	4.00
19	A2	6p lilac & blk	22.50	22.50
20	A2	1sh green	45.00	45.00
21	A2	2sh6p grn & blk ('96)	85.00	97.50
22	A2	4sh grn & car rose	125.00	175.00
23	A2	£1 violet, red	550.00	625.00
24	A2	£5 vio & blk, red	5,250.	1,750.
		Nos. 15-23 (9)	862.25	985.75

Numerals of #19-24 are in color on plain tablet.
Purple or violet cancellations are not necessarily revenue cancels.

Zululand was annexed to Natal in Dec. 1897 and separate stamps were discontinued June 30, 1898.

OTTLIGHTS

How Good is the new Ott Light Executive Desk Organizer?
"It's so good, you can't have it back!"

That was the reaction we got when we asked Jim Kloetzel, Editor of the Scott Standard Postage Stamp Catalogue to test the new Ott Light Executive Desk Organizer out for a week, Jim put the light to test examining stamps and using it to review the fine print of the Catalogue pages!

OTT LITE EXECUTIVE DESK ORGANIZER LAMP

The Ott Lite Executive Desk Organizer Lamp features a 13-watt lamp that effectively brings natural daylight indoors. The light from this lamp reduces eye strain and is especially useful when looking at colors, which appear undistorted in the natural light. The lampshade can be adjusted from left to right or up and down, and the lamp arm can be adjusted forward and backward. A convenient data port on the back of the lamp can be connected via the included phone cord to a wall phone jack. Using a second phone cord a laptop computer, modem or telephone can be connected via the data port on the front of the lamp base directly below the on/off switch. This attractive and functional lamp will make an excellent addition to any stamp or coin den.

Item	Retail
ACC193	$89.99

OTT TRUE COLOR LIGHT WITH SWIVEL BASE

View the true colors and intricate details of your favorite stamps with this versatile, compact lamp that features full spectrum lighting.

This technologically advanced tabletop lamp provides bright, glare free illumination while reducing eye strain.

Made specifically for taking the guesswork out of your color matching problems. The sturdy, convenient fold-up design features an adjustable light head so you can put light where you need it. It's the closest thing to daylight without the sunshine.

Item	Retail
ACC191	$84.95

SCOTT

P.O. Box 828, Sidney OH 45365-0828
1-800-572-6885
www.amosadvantage.com

AMOS
HOBBY PUBLISHING

Publishers of
Coin World, Linn's Stamp News, Scott Publishing Co.

1086

scott**mounts**

For stamp presentation unequaled in beauty and clarity, insist on ScottMounts. Made of 100% inert polystyrol foil, ScottMounts protect your stamps from the harmful effects of dust and moisture. Available in your choice of clear or black backs, ScottMounts are center-split across the back for easy insertion of stamps and feature crystal clear mount faces. Double layers of gum assure stay-put bonding on the album page. Discover the quality and value ScottMounts have to offer. ScottMounts are available from your favorite stamp dealer or direct from:

Discover the quality and value ScottMounts have to offer.
For a complete list of ScottMount sizes call or write Scott Publishing Co.

SCOTT

Scott Publishing Co.
1-800-572-6885
P.O. Box 828 Sidney OH 45365-0828
www.amosadvantage.com

Publishers of:
Coin World, Linn's Stamp News and Scott Publishing Co.

AMOS
HOBBY PUBLISHING

Vol. 6 Number Additions, Deletions & Changes

Number in 2004 Catalogue	Number in 2005 Catalogue

Solomon Islands

new	930a
936	deleted

South Africa

1291	1293
1292	1291
1293	1294
1294	1292

Spain

new	605A-605F
new	605G
7LC12	7LC12a
7LC13	7LC13a
new	7LC14a
new	7LC15a
7LC14	7LC16a
7LC15	7LC12
1LC16	7LC13
7LC17	7LC14
7LC18	7LC15
7LC19	7LC16
new	7LC17
new	7LC17a
7LC20	7LC18
7LC21	7LC19
7LC22	7LC20
7LC23	7LC21
new	7LC22
7LE4	deleted
new	9LC4a
new	9LC6a
new	9LC11a
new	9LC12a
new	9LC15a
new	9LC18a
new	10L20a-c
new	10L21a-c
new	10L22a-c
new	10L23a-c
new	11L1a
new	11L5a
new	11L9a
11L12	11L12a
11L12a	11L12b
new	11L12
new	11LB12

Sudan

436A	446

Sweden

5b	deleted

Syria

1474	1472
1472	1473
1473	1474

Tahiti

1B	deleted
new	1B

Tannu Tuva

new	37
new	38
37	39
38	44
new	45-123a
new	C1-C18

Yemen

new	C46A

Zambia

910A	911
911	912

Illustrated Identifier

This section pictures stamps or parts of stamp designs that will help identify postage stamps that do not have English words on them.

Many of the symbols that identify stamps of countries are shown here as well as typical examples of their stamps.

See the Index and Identifier on the previous pages for stamps with inscriptions such as "sen," "posta," "Baja Porto," "Helvetia," "K.S.A.," etc.

Linn's Stamp Identifier is now available. The 144 pages include more 2,000 inscriptions and over 500 large stamp illustrations. Available from Linn's Stamp News, P.O. Box 29, Sidney, OH 45365-0029.

1. HEADS, PICTURES AND NUMERALS

GREAT BRITAIN

Great Britain stamps never show the country name, but, except for postage dues, show a picture of the reigning monarch.

Victoria

Edward VII　　George V　　Edward VIII

George VI

Elizabeth II

Some George VI and Elizabeth II stamps are surcharged in annas, new paisa or rupees. These are listed under Oman.

Silhouette (sometimes facing right, generally at the top of stamp)

The silhouette indicates this is a British stamp. It is not a U.S. stamp.

VICTORIA

Queen Victoria

INDIA

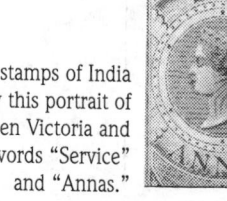

Other stamps of India show this portrait of Queen Victoria and the words "Service" and "Annas."

AUSTRIA

YUGOSLAVIA

(Also BOSNIA & HERZEGOVINA if imperf.)

BOSNIA & HERZEGOVINA

Denominations also appear in top corners instead of bottom corners.

HUNGARY

Another stamp has posthorn facing left

BRAZIL

AUSTRALIA

Kangaroo and Emu

GERMANY

Mecklenburg-Vorpommern

SWITZERLAND

PALAU

2. ORIENTAL INSCRIPTIONS

CHINA

Any stamp with this one character is from China (Imperial, Republic or People's Republic).
This character appears in a four-character overprint on stamps of Manchukuo. These stamps are local provisionals, which are unlisted. Other overprinted Manchukuo stamps show this character, but have more than four characters in the overprints. These are listed in People's Republic of China.

Some Chinese stamps show the Sun.

Most stamps of Republic of China show this series of characters.

Stamps with the China character and this character are from People's Republic of China.

Calligraphic form of People's Republic of China

(一)	(二)	(三)	(四)	(五)	(六)
I	II	III	IV	V	VI
(七)	(八)	(九)	(十)	(一十)	(二十)
VII	VIII	IX	X	XI	XII

Chinese stamps without China character

REPUBLIC OF CHINA

PEOPLE'S REPUBLIC OF CHINA

Mao Tse-tung

MANCHUKUO

Temple   Emperor Pu-Yi

The first 3 characters are common to
many Manchukuo stamps.

The last 3 characters are common
to other Manchukuo stamps.

Orchid Crest

Manchukuo
stamp with-
out these
elements

JAPAN

Chrysanthemum Crest   Country Name

Japanese stamps without these elements

The number of characters in the center and the
design of dragons on the sides will vary.

RYUKYU ISLANDS

Country Name

PHILIPPINES
(Japanese Occupation)

Country Name

NORTH BORNEO
(Japanese Occupation)

Indicates Japanese   Country
Occupation   Name

MALAYA
(Japanese Occupation)

Indicates Japanese Occupation   Country Name

BURMA
(Japanese Occupation)

Indicates Japanese Occupation   Country Name

Other Burma Japanese Occupation stamps
without these elements

Burmese Script

KOREA

These two characters, in any order, are common to stamps from the Republic of Korea (South Korea) or of the People's Democratic Republic of Korea (North Korea).

This series of four characters can be found on the stamps of both Koreas. Most stamps of the Democratic People's Republic of Korea (North Korea) have just this inscription.

Indicates Republic of Korea (South Korea)

South Korean postage stamps issed after 1952 do not show currency expressed in Latin letters. Stamps wiith "HW," "HWAN," "WON," "WN," "W" or "W" with two lines through it, if not illustrated in listings of stamps before this date, are revenues. North Korean postage stamps do not have currency expressed in Latin letters.

Yin Yang appears on some stamps.

THAILAND

Country Name

King Chulalongkorn

King Prajadhipok and
Chao P'ya Chakri

3. CENTRAL AND EASTERN ASIAN INSCRIPTIONS

INDIA - FEUDATORY STATES

Alwar   **Bhor**

Bundi

Similar stamps come with different designs in corners and differently drawn daggers (at center of circle).

Dhar   **Faridkot**

Hyderabad

Similar stamps exist with straight line frame around stamp, and also with different central design which is inscribed "Postage" or "Post & Receipt."

Indore   **Jhalawar**

A similar stamp has the central figure in an oval.

Nandgaon

Nowanuggur

Poonch

Similar stamps exist in various sizes

Rajpeepla   Soruth

BANGLADESH

বাংলাদেশ

Country Name

NEPAL

Similar stamps are smaller, have squares in upper corners and have five or nine characters in central bottom panel.

TANNU TUVA   ISRAEL

GEORGIA

This inscription is found on other pictorial stamps.

Country Name

ARMENIA

The four characters are found somewhere on pictorial stamps. On some stamps only the middle two are found.

---

4. AFRICAN INSCRIPTIONS

ETHIOPIA

---

5. ARABIC INSCRIPTIONS

AFGHANISTAN

Many early Afghanistan stamps show Tiger's head, many of these have ornaments protruding from outer ring, others show inscriptions in black.

Arabic Script

Mosque Gate & Crossed Cannons
The four characters are found somewhere
on pictorial stamps. On some stamps only
the middle two are found.

BAHRAIN

EGYPT

Postage

INDIA - FEUDATORY STATES

Jammu & Kashmir

Text and thickness of
ovals vary. Some stamps
have flower devices
in corners.

India-Hyderabad

IRAN

Country Name

Royal Crown

Lion with Sword

Symbol

IRAQ

JORDAN

LEBANON

Similar types have
denominations at top and
slightly different design.

LIBYA

Country Name in various styles

Other Libya stamps show Eagle and Shield (head
facing either direction) or Red, White and Black
Shield (with or without eagle in center).

Without Country Name

SAUDI ARABIA

PAKISTAN

Mohammed V

Mustafa Kemal

Tughra (Central design)

PAKISTAN - BAHAWALPUR

Country Name in top panel, star and crescent

TURKEY

Star & Crescent is a device found on many Turkish stamps, but is also found on stamps from other Arabic areas (see Pakistan-Bahawalpur)

Plane, Star and Crescent

Palm Tree and Swords

SYRIA

TURKEY IN ASIA

THRACE   YEMEN

Tughra (similar tughras can be found on stamps of Turkey in Asia, Afghanistan and Saudi Arabia)

Other Turkey in Asia pictorials show
star & crescent.
Other stamps show tughra shown under Turkey.

6. GREEK INSCRIPTIONS

GREECE

Country Name in various styles
(Some Crete stamps overprinted with the
Greece country name are listed in Crete.)

Lepta

Drachma   Drachmas   Lepton
Abbreviated Country Name

Other forms of Country Name

No country name

CRETE

Country Name

These words are on
other stamps

Grosion

Crete stamps with a surcharge that have the
year "1922" are listed under Greece.

EPIRUS   IONIAN IS.

Country Name

7. CYRILLIC INSCRIPTIONS

RUSSIA

Postage Stamp

Imperial Eagle

Postage in various styles

Abbreviation   Abbreviation   Russia
for Kopeck   for Ruble

Abbreviation for Russian Soviet
Federated Socialist Republic
RSFSR stamps were overprinted (see below)

Abbreviation for Union of Soviet
Socialist Republics

This item is footnoted in Latvia

RUSSIA - Army of the North

"OKCA"

RUSSIA - Wenden

RUSSIAN OFFICES IN THE TURKISH EMPIRE

These letters appear on other stamps of the Russian offices.

The unoverprinted version of this stamp and a similar stamp were overprinted by various countries (see below).

ARMENIA

BELARUS

FAR EASTERN REPUBLIC

Country Name

SOUTH RUSSIA

Country Name

FINLAND

Circles and Dots on stamps similar to Imperial Russia issues

BATUM

Forms of Country Name

TRANSCAUCASIAN FEDERATED REPUBLICS

 Abbreviation for Country Name

KAZAKHSTAN

Country Name

KYRGYZSTAN

КЫРГЫЗСТАН

КЫРГЫЗСТАН Country Name

ROMANIA

TADJIKISTAN

Country Name & Abbreviation

UKRAINE

Country Name in various forms

The trident appears on many stamps, usually as an overprint.   Abbreviation for Ukrainian Soviet Socialist Republic

WESTERN UKRAINE

Abbreviation for Country Name

AZERBAIJAN

AZƏRBAYCAN

AZƏRBAYCAN Country Name

Abbreviation for Azerbaijan Soviet Socialist Republic

MONTENEGRO

ЦРНА ГОРА

Country Name in various forms

Abbreviation for country name

No country name (A similar Montenegro stamp without country name has same vignette.)

SERBIA

СРБИЈА

Country Name in various forms

Abbreviation for country name

No country name

SERBIA & MONTENEGRO

YUGOSLAVIA

Showing country name

No Country Name

MACEDONIA

Country Name

Different form of Country Name

BOSNIA & HERZEGOVINA
(Serb Administration)

РЕПУБЛИКА СРПСКА

Country Name

РЕПУБЛИКЕ СРПСКЕ

Different form of Country Name

No Country Name

BULGARIA

Country Name   Postage

Stotinka

Stotinki (plural)   Abbreviation for
Stotinki

Country Name in various forms and styles

НР България

No country name

  Abbreviation for
Lev, leva

MONGOLIA

ШУУДАН   тегрег

Country name in   Tugrik in Cyrillic
one word

Country name in
two words

Mung in Cyrillic

No Country Name

Mung
in Mongolian

Tugrik
in Mongolian

Arms

scott**mounts**

For stamp presentation unequaled in beauty and clarity, insist on ScottMounts. Made of 100% inert polystyrol foil, ScottMounts protect your stamps from the harmful effects of dust and moisture. Available in your choice of clear or black backs, ScottMounts are center-split across the back for easy insertion of stamps and feature crystal clear mount faces. Double layers of gum assure stay-put bonding on the album page. Discover the quality and value ScottMounts have to offer. ScottMounts are available from your favorite stamp dealer or direct from:

Discover the quality and value ScottMounts have to offer.
For a complete list of ScottMount sizes call or write Scott Publishing Co.

SCOTT

Scott Publishing Co.
1-800-572-6885
P.O. Box 828 Sidney OH 45365-0828
www.amosadvantage.com

Publishers of:
Coin World, Linn's Stamp News and Scott Publishing Co.

AMOS
HOBBY PUBLISHING

INDEX AND IDENTIFIER

All page numbers shown are those in this Volume 6.

Postage stamps that do not have English words on them are shown in the Identifier which begins on page 1087.

S C O T T   P U B L I S H I N G   C O .

Specialty Series

Scott Publishing Co. produces album pages for more than 120 countries.
Scott Specialty pages are renowned for their quality and detail.
There are spaces for every major variety of postage stamp
within each country or specialty area.

Each space is identified by Scott number and many of the spaces are illustrated.
Pages are printed on one side only on chemically neutral paper
that will not harm your stamps.

Scott Specialty series pages are sold as page units only.
Binders and slipcases are sold separately.

For more information on the entire line of Scott products visit your favorite stamp dealer
or go online at:

www.amosadvantage.com

P.O. Box 828, Sidney OH 45365-0828
1-800-572-6885

AMOS
HOBBY PUBLISHING

LOOKING UP LISTINGS IN THE CATALOGUE HAS NEVER BEEN EASIER WITH

Scott Catalogue Tabs

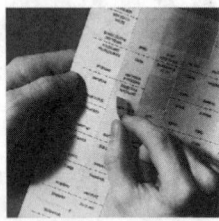

1. Select the country name or specialty area from the sheet.

2. Affix a portion of the tab to the appropriate page. Fold tab in half at dotted line.

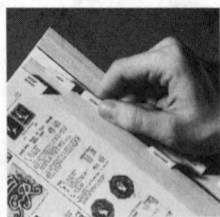

3. Use the tabs to reference catalogue listings. Blank tabs also included.

Tabs available for each Volume of the Scott Catalogue

ITEM	DESCRIPTION	RETAIL
CT1	Tabs Volume 1 *U.S. & Countries A - B*	$2.95
CT2	Tabs Volume 2 *Countries C - F*	$2.95
CT3	Tabs Volume 3 *Countries G - I*	$2.95
CT4	Tabs Volume 4 *Countries J - O*	$2.95
CT5	Tabs Volume 5 *Countries P - Slovenia*	$2.95
CT6	Tabs Volume 6 *Countries Solomon Islands - Z*	$2.95
CLGT6	Tabs *U.S. Specialized*	$2.95
CLGTC	Tabs Classic Specialized	$2.95

Catalogue Tabs are available from your favorite stamp dealer or direct from

SCOTT

1-800-572-6885
P.O. Box 828, Sidney OH 45365
www.amosadvantage.com

AMOS
HOBBY PUBLISHING

scott**mounts**

For stamp presentation unequaled in beauty and clarity, insist on ScottMounts. Made of 100% inert poly-styrol foil, ScottMounts protect your stamps from the harmful effects of dust and moisture. Available in your choice of clear or black backs, ScottMounts are center-split across the back for easy insertion of stamps and feature crystal clear mount faces. Double layers of gum assure stay-put bonding on the album page. Discover the quality and value ScottMounts have to offer. ScottMounts are available from your favorite stamp dealer or direct from:

Discover the quality and value ScottMounts have to offer.
For a complete list of ScottMount sizes call or write Scott Publishing Co.

SCOTT

Scott Publishing Co.
1-800-572-6885
P.O. Box 828 Sidney OH 45365-0828
www.amosadvantage.com

Publishers of:
Coin World, Linn's Stamp News and Scott Publishing Co.

AMOS
HOBBY PUBLISHING

2005
VOLUME 6
DEALER DIRECTORY
YELLOW PAGE LISTINGS

This section of your Scott Catalogue contains advertisements to help you conveniently find what you need, when you need it...!

REMEMBER OUR WEBSITE:

www.ASDAonline.com

It's the most helpful place on the WEB for the philatelist—packed with aids and resources from the more than 700 ASDA member dealers. Want to enjoy your hobby more?

Here's How:

• **Send an SASE to us now for the complete list of our members** by specialty and location.

• **Visit the ASDA's main website** where you'll not only find a complete list of all of our members, but lots of exciting and helpful information.

• **Selling your stamps?** Send SASE for our free brochure with lots of important tips for selling your collection.

• **BE SURE TO LOOK FOR THE FAMILIAR ASDA SYMBOL.** Dealer members who display our logo adhere to a rigid Code of Conduct.

American Stamp Dealers Association, Inc. SM

Established 1914

3-S School Street
Glen Cove NY 11542
Ph: (516) 759-7000 • Fax: 759-7014
www.asdaonline.com
E-mail: asda@erols.com

DEALERS: Become a Member!
Contact us for our special Member Kit.

Accessories

BROOKLYN GALLERY COIN & STAMP
8725 4th Avenue
Brooklyn, NY 11209
718-745-5701
718-745-2775 Fax
Email: info@brooklyngallery.com
Web: www.brooklyngallery.com

Appraisals

COLONIAL STAMP COMPANY
5757 Wilshire Blvd. PH #8
Los Angeles, CA 90036
323-933-9435
323-939-9930 Fax
Email: gwh225@aol.com
Web: www.colonialstamps.com

CONNEXUS
P.O. Box 819
Snow Camp, NC 27349
919-663-2267
Email:
throopbrown@stampsandstones
.com

Approvals-Personalized WW & US

THE KEEPING ROOM
P.O. Box 257
Trumbull, CT 06611
203-372-8436

Asia

MICHAEL ROGERS, INC.
660 Fairbanks Avenue
Suite 4
Winter Park, FL 32789
407-644-2290 or 800-843-3751
407-645-4434 Fax
Email: mrogersinc@aol.com
Web:
www.michaelrogersinc.com

Auctions

COLONIAL STAMP COMPANY
5757 Wilshire Blvd. PH #8
Los Angeles, CA 90036
323-933-9435
323-939-9930 Fax
Email: gwh225@aol.com
Web: www.colonialstamps.com

DANIEL F. KELLEHER CO., INC.
20 Walnut Street
Suite 213
Wellesley, MA 02481
781-235-0990
781-235-0945 Fax

JACQUES C. SCHIFF, JR., INC.
195 Main Street
Ridgefield Park, NJ 07660
201-641-5566
From NYC: 212-662-2777
201-641-5705 Fax

R. MARESCH & SON LTD.
5th Floor - 6075 Yonge Street
Toronto, Ontario M2M 3W2
CANADA
416-363-7777
416-363-6511 Fax
Web: www.maresch.com

THE STAMP CENTER/DUTCH COUNTRY AUCTIONS
4115 Concord Pike
Wilmington, DE 19803
302-478-8740
302-478-8779 Fax
Email: scdca@dol.net
Web: www.thestampcenter.com

Auctions - Public

ALAN BLAIR STAMPS/AUCTIONS
5405 Lakeside Ave.
Suite 1
Richmond, VA 23228
800-689-5602 Phone/Fax
Email: alanblair@prodigy.net

Austria

JOSEPH EDER
P.O. Box 185529
Hamden, CT 06518
203-281-0742
203-230-2410 Fax
Email: j.eder@worldnet.att.net
Web: www.ederstamps.com

Booklets-Worldwide

HENRY GITNER PHILATEL-ISTS, INC.
P.O. Box 3077-S
Middletown, NY 10940
845-343-5151 or 800-947-8267
845-343-0068 Fax
Email: hgitner@hgitner.com
Web: www.hgitner.com

Auctions

Schiff Auctions

Buyers, Auctioneers & Appraisers of U.S. & Worldwide Stamps & Covers

We have been catering to the individual buyer and seller since 1947. Let us put our **57 years** of experience to work for you when selling your stamps, covers or your collection. Whether you prefer consigning to public auction or selling outright, call us first. Describe your material before sending. Please include your address and telephone numbers.

CATALOG SUBSCRIPTIONS	N. AMERICA	OVERSEAS
1 Year Catalogs & Prices Realized	$10.00	$18.00
1 Year Catalog Only	$7.50	$15.00
1 Catalog with Prices Realized	$1.50	$2.50
1 Catalog Only	$1.00	$1.50

JACQUES C. SCHIFF, JR., INC.

195 Main St., Ridgefield Park, NJ 07660 USA
Telephone 201-641-5566 from NYC 662-2777
FAX 201-641-5705

OFFICIAL AUCTIONEERS:
AMERIPEX 1986.
WORLD STAMP EXPO 1989.
WORLD COLUMBIAN STAMP EXPO 1992.
AMERICAN PHILATELIC SOCIETY 2000-2003

QUALIFIED AUCTIONEER

British Commonwealth

EMPIRE STAMP CO.
P.O. Box 8337
Calabasa, CA 91372-8337
800-616-7278 or 818-225-1181
818-225-1182 Fax
Email: info@empirestamps.com
Web: www.empirestamps.com

JAY'S STAMP CO.
Box 28484
Dept. S
Philadelphia, PA 19149-0184
215-743-0207 Phone/Fax
Email: jasc@comcast.net
Web: www.jaysco.com

British Commonwealth

METROPOLITAN STAMP CO., INC.
P.O. Box 657
Park Ridge, IL 60068-0657
815-439-0142
815-439-0143 Fax
Email: metrostamp@aol.com

STATESIDE STAMPS
P.O. Box 1036
Evart, MI 49631
231-734-9943
Email: sreedy@netonecom.net
Web: www.statesidestamps.com

THE BRITISH COMMONWEALTH
O·F N·A·T·I·O·N·S

We are active buyers and sellers of stamps and postal history of all areas of pre-1960 British Commonwealth, including individual items, collections or estates. Want lists from all reigns are accepted with references.

L. W. Martin, Jr.

CROWN COLONY STAMPS
P.O. Box 1198
BELLAIRE, TEXAS 77402
PH. (713) 781-6563 • FAX (713) 789-9998
E-mail: lwm@crowncolony.com

"VISIT OUR BOOTH AT MOST MAJOR SHOWS"

British Commonwealth

VICTORIA STAMP CO.
P.O. Box 745
Ridgewood, NJ 07451
201-652-7283
201-612-0024 Fax
Email:
VictoriaStampCo@aol.com
Web:
www.VictoriaStampCo.com

WWW.WORLDSTAMPS.COM
242 West Saddle River Road
Upper Saddle River, NJ 07458
201-236-8122
201-236-8133 Fax
by mail:
Frank Geiger Philatelists
Email: info@WorldStamps.com
Web: www.WorldStamps.com

Central America

GUY SHAW
P.O. Box 10025
Bakersfield, CA 93389
661-834-7135 Phone/Fax
Email: guyshaw@guyshaw.com
Web: www.guyshaw.com

China

MICHAEL ROGERS, INC.
660 Fairbanks Avenue
Suite 4
Winter Park, FL 32789
407-644-2290 or 800-843-3751
407-645-4434 Fax
Email: mrogersinc@aol.com
Web:
www.michaelrogersinc.com

Collections

DR. ROBERT FRIEDMAN & SONS
2029 West 75th Street
Woodridge, IL 60517
800-588-8100
630-985-1588 Fax
Email:
drbobstamps@starband.net
Web:
www.drbobfriedmanstamps.com

Ducks

MICHAEL JAFFE
P.O. Box 61484
Vancouver, WA 98666
360-695-6161 or 800-782-6770
360-695-1616 Fax
Email:
mjaffe@brookmanstamps.com
Web:
www.brookmanstamps.com

Europe-Western

STATESIDE STAMPS
P.O. Box 1036
Evart, MI 49631
231-734-9943
Email: sreedy@netonecom.net
Web: www.statesidestamps.com

France

JOSEPH EDER
P.O. Box 185529
Hamden, CT 06518
203-281-0742
203-230-2410 Fax
Email: j.eder@worldnet.att.com
Web: www.ederstamps.com

STATESIDE STAMPS
P.O. Box 1036
Evart, MI 49631
231-734-9943
Email: sreedy@netonecom.net
Web: www.statesidestamps.com

France & Colonies

STATESIDE STAMPS
P.O. Box 1036
Evart, MI 49631
231-734-9943
Email: sreedy@netonecom.net
Web: www.statesidestamps.com

German Colonies

COLONIAL STAMP COMPANY
$1 million photo price list,
$5.00
(refundable against purchase)
5757 Wilshire Blvd. PH #8
Los Angeles, CA 90036
323-933-9435
323-939-9930 Fax
Email: gwh225@aol.com
Web: www.colonialstamps.com

JOSEPH EDER
P.O. Box 185529
Hamden, CT 06518
203-281-0742
203-230-2410 Fax
Email: j.eder@worldnet.att.net
Web: www.ederstamps.com

German Occupation

JOSEPH EDER
P.O. Box 185529
Hamden, CT 06518
203-281-0742
203-230-2410 Fax
Email: j.eder@worldnet.att.net
Web: www.ederstamps.com

Germany

JOSEPH EDER
P.O. Box 185529
Hamden, CT 06518
203-281-0742
203-230-2410 Fax
Email: j.eder@worldnet.att.net
Web: www.ederstamps.com

STATESIDE STAMPS
P.O. Box 1036
Evart, MI 49631
231-734-9943
Email: sreedy@netonecom.net
Web: www.statesidestamps.com

Germany-Third Reich

JOSEPH EDER
P.O. Box 185529
Hamden, CT 06518
203-281-0742
203-230-2410 Fax
Email: j.eder@worldnet.att.net
Web: www.ederstamps.com

British Commonwealth

Aron R. Halberstam Philatelists, Ltd.

POB 150168, Van Brunt Station
Brooklyn, NY 11215-0168, USA
Tel: 718-788-3978 Fax: 718-965-3099
Toll Free: 800-343-1303
E-mail: arh@aronrhalberstam.com

British Commonwealth
Pre-1960

Call or write to request our free Price List, or send us your Want Lists.
We are also eager buyers of better Commonwealth singles or sets and collections. Let us know what you have to offer.

Accepted on all orders.   Member

Visit our Website: www.aronrhalberstam.com

The British Empire
(A-Z 1840-1935 Mint & Used)
The Largest & Most Valuable Stock in America.

Want Lists (per Scott or S. G.) prompt expert service, 30 volumes in all price ranges, stocked individually so you can acquire exactly those you need on approval or per quotations (references appreciated). For decades we have had the great pleasure of working closely with our clients in the formation of many fine private or international exhibition standard collections. I will be pleased to place our expertise at your disposal.

British Empire Public Auctions
Please request a complimentary copy

George W. Holschauer

COLONIAL STAMP CO.
5757 WILSHIRE BLVD., PH #8
LOS ANGELES, CA 90036
Ph. (323) 933-9435 • Fax (323) 939-9930
www.colonialstamps.com

CCNY, CSDA, IFSDA,
INTERNATIONAL
SOCIETY OF APPRAISERS

British Commonwealth

BRITISH EMPIRE EXCLUSIVELY

Request a catalogue for our next Public Auction. Please specify your interests.

Want lists invited from serious collectors of the BRITISH EMPIRE. References please.

Selling? Ask us about consigning *your* collection to a future sale.

Victoria Stamp Co.

PHOEBE A. MacGILLIVARY
P.O. BOX 745, RIDGEWOOD, NJ 07451
PHONE 201-652-7283 • FAX 201-612-0024
www.VictoriaStampCo.com
Email: VictoriaStampCo@aol.com

Insurance

COLLECTIBLES INSURANCE AGENCY
P.O. Box 1200 SSC
Westminster, MD 21158
888-837-9537
410-876-9233 Fax
Email:
info@insurecollectibles.com
Web: www.collectinsure.com

Italy

LO GIUDICE'S ITALY STAMPS & COVERS
2513 S. Gessner Road, S.353
Houston, TX 77063-2007
713-975-7401
713-975-7789 Fax

Japan

MICHAEL ROGERS, INC.
660 Fairbanks Avenue
Suite 4
Winter Park, FL 32789
407-644-2290 or 800-843-3751
407-645-4434 Fax
Email: mrogersinc@aol.com
Web:
www.michaelrogersinc.com

Korea

MICHAEL ROGERS, INC.
660 Fairbanks Avenue
Suite 4
Winter Park, FL 32789
407-644-2290 or 800-843-3751
407-645-4434 Fax
Email: mrogersinc@aol.com
Web:
www.michaelrogersinc.com

Latin America

GUY SHAW
P.O. Box 10025
Bakersfield, CA 93389
661-834-7135 Phone/Fax
Email: guyshaw@guyshaw.com
Web: www.guyshaw.com

STATESIDE STAMPS
P.O. Box 1036
Evart, MI 49631
231-734-9943
Email: sreedy@netonecom.net
Web: www.statesidestamps.com

New Issues

DAVIDSON'S STAMP SERVICE
P.O. Box 36355
Indianapolis, IN 46236-0355
317-826-2620
Email: davidson@in.net
Web: www.newstampissues.com

Manchukuo

MICHAEL ROGERS, INC.
660 Fairbanks Avenue
Suite 4
Winter Park, FL 32789
407-644-2290 or 800-843-3751
407-645-4434 Fax
Email: mrogersinc@aol.com
Web:
www.michaelrogersinc.com

Mexico

AMEEN STAMPS
8831 Long Point Road
Suite 204
Houston, TX 77055
713-468-0644
713-468-2420 Fax
Email: rameen@ev1.net or
rameen03@sbcglobal.net

New Issues - Retail

BOMBAY PHILATELIC INC.
P.O. Box 480009
Delray Beach, FL 33448
561-499-7990
561-499-7553 Fax
Email:
sales@bombaystamps.com
Web: www.bombaystamps.com

New Issues-Wholesale

BOMBAY PHILATELIC INC.
P.O. Box 480009
Delray Beach, FL 33448
561-499-7990
561-499-7553 Fax
Email:
sales@bombaystamps.com
Web: www.bombaystamps.com

Publications-Collector

THE AMERICAN PHILATELIST
Dept. TZ
100 Match Factory Place
Bellefonte, PA 16823-1367
814-237-3803
814-237-6128 Fax
Email: apsinfo@stamps.org
Web: www.stamps.org

New Issues

Extensive Coverage - New Issues from the Entire World
NEW ISSUE SERVICE
Remember Our Specialty:
All Topicals and New Issues
Want Lists for Older Issues Serviced
Top Prices Paid for Collections & Accumulations
MONTHLY NEW ISSUE LIST WITH ILLUSTRATIONS
AVAILABLE AT www.stampcenter.com
COUNTY STAMP CENTER
CALL TOLL FREE 1-800-245-7597
FAX (410) 757-5800 email:alex@stampcenter.com
P.O. Box 3373, Annapolis, MD 21403
Ebay ID: stampcenter_md
ebay PowerSeller

Scandinavia

STATESIDE STAMPS
P.O. Box 1036
Evart, MI 49631
231-734-9943
Email: sreedy@netonecom.net
Web: www.statesidestamps.com

WWW.WORLDSTAMPS.COM
242 West Saddle River Road
Upper Saddle River, NJ 07458
201-236-8122
201-236-8133 Fax
by mail:
Frank Geiger Philatelists
Email: info@WorldStamps.com
Web: www.WorldStamps.com

Scandinavia-Year Sets

WALLACE STAMPS
Box 82
Port Washington, NY 11050
516-883-5578

Somaliland Protectorate

COLONIAL STAMP COMPANY
5757 Wilshire Blvd. PH #8
Los Angeles, CA 90036
323-933-9435
323-939-9930 Fax
Email: gwh225@aol.com
Web: www.colonialstamps.com

South Africa

COLONIAL STAMP COMPANY
5757 Wilshire Blvd. PH #8
Los Angeles, CA 90036
323-933-9435
323-939-9930 Fax
Email: gwh225@aol.com
Web: www.colonialstamps.com

South America

GUY SHAW
P.O. Box 10025
Bakersfield, CA 93389
661-834-7135 Phone/Fax
Email: guyshaw@guyshaw.com
Web: www.guyshaw.com

WWW.WORLDSTAMPS.COM
242 West Saddle River Road
Upper Saddle River, NJ 07458
201-236-8122
201-236-8133 Fax
by mail:
Frank Geiger Philatelists
Email: info@WorldStamps.com
Web: www.WorldStamps.com

South West Africa

COLONIAL STAMP COMPANY
5757 Wilshire Blvd. PH #8
Los Angeles, CA 90036
323-933-9435
323-939-9930 Fax
Email: gwh225@aol.com
Web: www.colonialstamps.com

Spain

WWW.WORLDSTAMPS.COM
242 West Saddle River Road
Upper Saddle River, NJ 07458
201-236-8122
201-236-8133 Fax
by mail:
Frank Geiger Philatelists
Email: info@WorldStamps.com
Web: www.WorldStamps.com

Sri Lanka

COLONIAL STAMP COMPANY
5757 Wilshire Blvd. PH #8
Los Angeles, CA 90036
323-933-9435
323-939-9930 Fax
Email: gwh225@aol.com
Web: www.colonialstamps.com

STAMP STORES

California

BROSIUS STAMP & COIN
2105 Main Street
Santa Monica, CA 90405
310-396-7480
310-396-7455 Fax

COLONIAL STAMP CO./BRITISH EMPIRE SPECIALIST
5757 Wilshire Blvd. PH #8 (by appt.)
Los Angeles, CA 90036
323-933-9435
323-939-9930 Fax
Email: gwh225@aol.com
Web: www.colonialstamps.com

FISCHER-WOLK PHILATELICS
24771 "G" Alicia Parkway
Laguna Hills, CA 92653
949-837-2932
Email:
fischerwolk@earthlink.net

NATICK STAMPS & HOBBIES
405 S. Myrtle Avenue
Monrovia, CA 91016
626-305-7333
Email: natickco@earthlink.net

STANLEY M. PILLER & ASSOCIATES
3351 Grand Avenue
Oakland, CA 94610
510-465-8290
510-465-7121 Fax
Email: stmpdlr@aol.com
Web: www.smpiller.com

Colorado

ACKLEY'S STAMPS
3230 N. Stone Ave.
Colorado Springs, CO 80907
719-633-1153
Email: ackl9@aol.com

SHOWCASE STAMPS
3865 Wadsworth
Wheat Ridge, CO 80033
303-425-9252
Email: kbeiner@colbi.net
Web:
www.showcasestamps.com

Connecticut

MILLER'S STAMP SHOP
41 New London Turnpike
Uncasville, CT 06382
860-848-0468 or 800-67-STAMP
860-848-1926 Fax
Email: millstamps@aol.com
Web: www.millerstamps.com

SILVER CITY COIN & STAMP
41 Colony Street
Meriden, CT 06451
203-235-7634
203-237-4915 Fax

STAMP STORES

Florida

CORBIN STAMP & COIN, INC.
108 West Robertson Street
Brandon, FL 33511
813-651-3266

R.D.C. STAMPS
7381 SW 24th Street
Miami, FL 33155-1402
305-264-4213
305-262-2919 Fax
Email: rdcstamps@aol.com

SUN COAST STAMP CO.
3231 Gulf Gate Drive
Suite 102
Sarasota, FL 34231
941-921-9761 or 800-927-3351
941-921-1762 Fax
Email:
email@suncoaststamp.com
Web: www.stampfinder.com

WINTER PARK STAMP SHOP
Ranch Mall (17-92)
325 S. Orlando Ave.
Suite 1-2
Winter Park, FL 32789-3608
407-628-1120 or 800-845-1819
407-628-0091 Fax
Email:
stamps@winterparkstampshop.com
Web:
www.winterparkstampshop.com

Georgia

STAMPS UNLIMITED OF GEORGIA
133 Carnegie Way
Room 250
Atlanta, GA 30303
404-688-9161

Illinois

DON CLARK'S STAMPS & COINS
937 1/2 W. Galena Blvd.
Aurora, IL 60506
630-896-4606

DR. ROBERT FRIEDMAN & SONS
2029 West 75th Street
Woodridge, IL 60517
800-588-8100
630-985-1588 Fax
Email:
drbobstamps@starband.net
Web:
www.drbobfriedmanstamps.com

Indiana

KNIGHT STAMP & COIN CO.
237 Main Street
Hobart, IN 46342
219-942-4341 or 800-634-2646
Email: knight@knightcoin.com
Web: www.knightcoin.com

Kentucky

COLLECTORS STAMPS LTD.
4012 Dupont Circle #313
Louisville, KY 40207
502-897-9045
Email: csl@aye.net

Massachusetts

KAPPY'S COINS & STAMPS
534 Washington Street
Norwood, MA 02062
781-762-5552
781-762-3292 Fax
Email: kappyscoins@aol.com

Maryland

BALTIMORE COIN & STAMP EXCHANGE
10194 Baltimore National Pike
Unit 104
Ellicott City, MD 21042
410-418-8282
410-418-4813 Fax

BULLDOG STAMP COMPANY
4641 Montgomery Avenue
Bethesda, MD 20814
301-654-1138

Michigan

THE MOUSE AND SUCH
696 N. Mill Street
Plymouth, MI 48170
734-454-1515
734-454-9812 Fax
Email:
weluvstamps@hotmail.com

New Jersey

AALLSTAMPS
38 N. Main Street
P.O. Box 249
Milltown, NJ 08850
732-247-1093
732-247-1094 Fax
Email: mail@aallstamps.com
Web: www.aallstamps.com

BERGEN STAMPS & COLLECTIBLES
717 American Legion Drive
Teaneck, NJ 07666
201-836-8987

RON RITZER STAMPS INC.
Millburn Mall
2933 Vauxhall Road
Vauxhall, NJ 07088
908-687-0007
908-687-0795 Fax
Email:
ritzerstamps@earthlink.net

TRENTON STAMP & COIN CO.
Thomas DeLuca
Store: Forest Glen Plaza
1804 Route 33
Hamilton Square, NJ 08690
Mail: P.O. Box 8574
Trenton, NJ 08650
800-446-8664
609-587-8664 Fax
Email: TOMD4TSC@aol.com

New York

CHAMPION STAMP CO., INC.
432 West 54th Street
New York, NY 10019
212-489-8130
212-581-8130 Fax
Email:
championstamp@aol.com
Web: www.championstamp.com

Ohio

FEDERAL COIN & STAMP EXCHANGE
P.O. Box 14579
401 Euclid Ave.
Suite 45
Cleveland, OH 44114
216-861-1160
216-861-5960 Fax

HILLTOP STAMP SERVICE
Richard A. Peterson
P.O. Box 626
Wooster, OH 44691
330-262-8907 or 330-262-5378
Email: hilltop@bright.net

Ohio

THE LINK STAMP CO.
3461 E. Livingston Avenue
Columbus, OH 43227
614-237-4125 Phone/Fax
800-546-5726 Phone/Fax

Pennsylvania

PHILLY STAMP & COIN CO., INC.
1804 Chestnut Street
Philadelphia, PA 19103
215-563-7341
215-563-7382 Fax
Email: phillysc@netreach.net
Web:
www.phillystampandcoin.com

Tennessee

HERRON HILL, INC.
5007 Black Road
Suite 140
Memphis, TN 38117
901-683-9644

Virginia

KENNEDY'S STAMPS & COINS
7059 Brookfield Plaza
Springfield, VA 22150
703-569-7300
703-569-7644 Fax
Email: kennedy@patriot.net

LATHEROW & CO., INC.
5054 Lee Hwy.
Arlington, VA 22207
703-538-2727 or 800-647-4624
703-538-5210 Fax

Washington

TACOMA MALL BLVD. COIN & STAMP
5225 Tacoma Mall Blvd. E101
Tacoma, WA 98409
253-472-9632
253-472-8948 Fax
Email:
kfeldman01@sprynet.com

Straits Settlements

COLONIAL STAMP COMPANY
5757 Wilshire Blvd. PH #8
Los Angeles, CA 90036
323-933-9435
323-939-9930 Fax
Email: gwh225@aol.com
Web: www.colonialstamps.com

Sudan

COLONIAL STAMP COMPANY
5757 Wilshire Blvd. PH #8
Los Angeles, CA 90036
323-933-9435
323-939-9930 Fax
Email: gwh225@aol.com
Web: www.colonialstamps.com

Switzerland

FEDERAL COIN & STAMP EXCHANGE
P.O. Box 14579
401 Euclid Ave.
Suite 45
Cleveland, OH 44114
216-861-1160
216-861-5960 Fax

Togo

COLONIAL STAMP COMPANY
5757 Wilshire Blvd. PH #8
Los Angeles, CA 90036
323-933-9435
323-939-9930 Fax
Email: gwh225@aol.com
Web: www.colonialstamps.com

Tonga

COLONIAL STAMP COMPANY
5757 Wilshire Blvd. PH #8
Los Angeles, CA 90036
323-933-9435
323-939-9930 Fax
Email: gwh225@aol.com
Web: www.colonialstamps.com

Topicals

KISHOR MEHTA
10 Rattlesnake Road,
Brampton,
Ontario - L6R 1P6
CANADA
905-792-9658
905-457-0618 fax

Topicals

TOPICALS- ALL TOPICS

For many years (first as Filatelia Pampa) we have been a leader in this field. ANY sub-topic is Not Strange for us!

VERY LARGE WORLDWIDE STOCK
... including varieties, cancels, covers, etc.

WANT LISTS WELCOME
... any Catalogue #, any main language.

ERCOLE GLORIA - Gregorio Zuskis
Piazza Pio XI 1, 20123 Milan, ITALY
TEL. +39.2804106 • FAX +39.02864217
WWW.ercolegloria.it • E-MAIL: info@ercolegloria.it

Topicals-Columbus

MR. COLUMBUS
Box 1492
Fennville, MI 49408
269-543-4755
Email: columbus@accn.org

Topicals-Miscellaneous

BOMBAY PHILATELIC INC.
P.O. Box 480009
Delray Beach, FL 33448
561-499-7990
561-499-7553 Fax
Email:
sales@bombaystamps.com
Web: www.bombaystamps.com

Transvaal

COLONIAL STAMP COMPANY
5757 Wilshire Blvd. PH #8
Los Angeles, CA 90036
323-933-9435
323-939-9930 Fax
Email: gwh225@aol.com
Web: www.colonialstamps.com

Trinidad

COLONIAL STAMP COMPANY
5757 Wilshire Blvd. PH #8
Los Angeles, CA 90036
323-933-9435
323-939-9930 Fax
Email: gwh225@aol.com
Web: www.colonialstamps.com

Turkey

WWW.WORLDSTAMPS.COM
242 West Saddle River Road
Upper Saddle River, NJ 07458
201-236-8122
201-236-8133 Fax
by mail:
Frank Geiger Philatelists
Email: info@WorldStamps.com
Web: www.WorldStamps.com

Turks & Caicos Islands

COLONIAL STAMP COMPANY
5757 Wilshire Blvd. PH #8
Los Angeles, CA 90036
323-933-9435
323-939-9930 Fax
Email: gwh225@aol.com
Web: www.colonialstamps.com

Uganda

COLONIAL STAMP COMPANY
5757 Wilshire Blvd. PH #8
Los Angeles, CA 90036
323-933-9435
323-939-9930 Fax
Email: gwh225@aol.com
Web: www.colonialstamps.com

Ukraine

MR. VAL ZABIJAKA
P.O. Box 3711
Silver Spring, MD 20918
301-593-5316 Phone/Fax
Email: bnm123@erols.com

United States

BROOKMAN STAMP CO.
P.O. Box 90
Vancouver, WA 98666
360-695-1391 or 800-545-4871
360-695-1616 Fax
Email:
dave@brookmanstamps.com
Web:
www.brookmanstamps.com

U.S.-Mint Sheets

METROPOLITAN STAMP CO., INC.
P.O. Box 657
Park Ridge, IL 60068-0657
815-439-0142
815-439-0143 Fax
Email: metrostamp@aol.com

Want Lists

BROOKMAN INTERNATIONAL
P.O. Box 450
Vancouver, WA 98666
360-695-1391 or 800-545-4871
360-695-1616 Fax
Email:
dave@brookmanstamps.com

CHARLES P. SCHWARTZ
P.O. Box 165
Mora, MN 55051
320-679-4705
Email: charlesp@ecenet.com

Want Lists-British Empire 1840-1935 German Cols./Offices

COLONIAL STAMP COMPANY
5757 Wilshire Blvd. PH #8
Los Angeles, CA 90036
323-933-9435
323-939-9930 Fax
Email: gwh225@aol.com
Web: www.colonialstamps.com

Wanted-Worldwide Collections

THE STAMP CENTER/DUTCH COUNTRY AUCTIONS
4115 Concord Pike
Wilmington, DE 19803
302-478-8740
302-478-8779 Fax
Email: scdca@dol.net
Web: www.thestampcenter.com

Wanted-U.S. Collections

THE STAMP CENTER/DUTCH COUNTRY AUCTIONS
4115 Concord Pike
Wilmington, DE 19803
302-478-8740
302-478-8779 Fax
Email: scdca@dol.net
Web: www.thestampcenter.com

Wholesale FDC's

HENRY GITNER PHILATEL-ISTS, INC.
P.O. Box 3077-S
Middletown, NY 10940
845-343-5151 or 800-947-8267
845-343-0068 Fax
Email: hgitner@hgitner.com
Web: www.hgitner.com

Worldwide-Collections

DR. ROBERT FRIEDMAN & SONS
2029 West 75th Street
Woodridge, IL 60517
800-588-8100
630-985-1588 Fax
Email:
drbobstamps@starband.net
Web:
www.drbobfriedmanstamps.com

Worldwide-Price Lists

STATESIDE STAMPS
P.O. Box 1036
Evart, MI 49631
231-734-9943
Email: sreedy@netonecom.net
Web: www.statesidestamps.com

Worldwide-Year Sets

BOMBAY PHILATELIC INC.
P.O. Box 480009
Delray Beach, FL 33448
561-499-7990
561-499-7553 Fax
Email:
sales@bombaystamps.com
Web: www.bombaystamps.com

WALLACE STAMPS
Box 82
Port Washington, NY 11050
516-883-5578

WWW.WORLDSTAMPS.COM
242 West Saddle River Road
Upper Saddle River, NJ 07458
201-236-8122
201-236-8133 Fax
by mail:
Frank Geiger Philatelists
Email: info@WorldStamps.com
Web: www.WorldStamps.com

Yugoslavia

WWW.WORLDSTAMPS.COM
242 West Saddle River Road
Upper Saddle River, NJ 07458
201-236-8122
201-236-8133 Fax
by mail:
Frank Geiger Philatelists
Email: info@WorldStamps.com
Web: www.WorldStamps.com

SCOTT PUBLISHING CO.

Specialty Series

Scott Publishing Co. produces album pages for more than 120 countries.
Scott Specialty pages are renowned for their quality and detail.
There are spaces for every major variety of postage stamp
within each country or specialty area.

Each space is identified by Scott number and many of the spaces are illustrated.
Pages are printed on one side only on chemically neutral paper
that will not harm your stamps.

Scott Specialty series pages are sold as page units only.
Binders and slipcases are sold separately.

For more information on the entire line of Scott products visit your favorite stamp dealer
or go online at:
www.amosadvantage.com

P.O. Box 828, Sidney OH 45365-0828
1-800-572-6885

AMOS
HOBBY PUBLISHING